## Sample Hospital Listing:

**ANYTOWN, Universal County**

☒ **ANYTOWN HOSPITAL & CLINICS (777777)**, (Formerly Anytown Area
Community Hospital and Clinic), 100 South Main Street, Zip 12345–6789;
tel. 123/456–7890 **A**9 10 ] ①
**F**10 12 23 24 29 30 31 37 39 49 51 55 57 64 65 66 68 70 71 72 77
78 83 87 88 91 96 97 106 107 110 111 113 124 **P**1 2 3 **S** Universal ⑦
County Health System ② ③
Primary Contact: Ann M. Generic, Chief Executive Officer
COO: Ann M. Generic
CFO: Michael M. Generic
CMO: Peterl Van Generic, President Medical Staff ④
CHR: Jerry Generic, Human Resources Director
Web address: www.website.org
**Control:** Other not–for–profit (including NFP Corporation) **Service:** General ⑤
Medical and surgical

**Staffed Beds:** 25 **Admissions:** 892 **Census:** 9 **Outpatient Visits:** 44014
**Births:** 51 **Total Expense ($000):** 19210 **Payroll Expense ($000):** 5864
**Personnel:** 182
⑥

**ANYTOWN, Universal County**

☒ **ANYTOWN HOSPITAL & CLINICS (777777)**, (Formerly Anytown Area
Community Hospital and Clinic), 100 South Main Street, Zip 12345–6789;
tel. 123/456–7890 **A**9 10

① = Approval Codes
② = Physician Codes
③ = Health Care System Name
④ = Titles of Chief Administrators
⑤ = Control and Service Classifications
⑥ = Utilization Data
⑦ = Facility Codes

---

**Hospital, Medicare Provider Number, Address, Telephone, Approval, Facility, and Physician Codes, Health Care System**

★ American Hospital Association (AHA) membership
◻ The Joint Commission accreditation
◊ DNV Healthcare Inc. accreditation
◯ Healthcare Facilities Accreditation Program
△ Commission on Accreditation of Rehabilitation Facilities (CARF) accreditation

---

## ① Approval Codes

*Reported by the approving bodies specified, as of the dates noted.*

**1** Accreditation under the hospital program of The Joint Commission (May 2013).
**2** Cancer program approved by American College of Surgeons (March 2013).
**†3** Approval to participate in residency training, by the Accreditation Council for Graduate Medical Education (April 2013).
**†5** Medical school affiliation, reported to the American Medical Association (April 2013).
**6** Hospital–controlled professional nursing school, reported by National League for Nursing.
**7** Accreditation by Commission on Accreditation of Rehabilitation Facilities (March 2013).

**8** Member of Council of Teaching Hospitals of the Association of American Medical Colleges (February 2013).
**9** Hospitals contracting or participating in a Plan, reported by the Blue Cross and Blue Shield Association (April 2013).
**10** Certified for participation in the Health Insurance for the Aged (Medicare) Program by the Centers for Medicare and Medical Services (February 2013).
**11** Healthcare Facilities Accreditation Program (May 2013).

**12** Internship approved by American Osteopathic Association (April 2013).
**13** Residency approved by American Osteopathic Association (April 2013).
**18** Critical Access Hospitals (May 2013).
**19** Rural Referral Center (May 2013).
**20** Sole Community Provider (May 2013).
**21** Accreditation by DNV Healthcare Inc. (May 2013).

**Nonreporting** indicates that the 2012 Annual Survey questionnaire for the hospital was not received prior to publication.

## ② Physician Codes

*Actually available within, and reported by the institution; for definitions, see page A12.*

**(Alphabetical/Numerical Order)**

**1** Closed physician–hospital organization (PHO)
**2** Equity model
**3** Foundation

**4** Group practice without walls
**5** Independent practice association (IPA)
**6** Integrated salary model

**7** Management service organization (MSO)
**8** Open physician–hospital organization (PHO)

## ③ Health Care System Name

*The inclusion of the letter "S" (1) indicates that the hospital belongs to a health care system and (2) identifies the specific system to which the hospital belongs.*

## ④ Titles of Chief Administrators

## ⑤ Control and Service Classification

*For a list of control and service classifications, see page A13.*

**Control–**The type of organization that is responsible for establishing policy for overall operation of the hospital.

**Service–**The type of service the hospital provides to the majority of admissions.

## ⑥ Utilization Data

*Definitions are based on the American Hospital Association's Hospital Administration Terminology. In completing the survey, hospitals were requested to report data for a full year, in accord with their fiscal year, ending in 2012.*

**Beds–**Number of beds regularly maintained (set up and staffed for use) for inpatients as of the close of the reporting period. Excludes newborn bassinets.

**Admissions–**Number of patients accepted for inpatient service during a 12–month period; does not include newborn.

**Census–**Average number of inpatients receiving care each day during the 12–month reporting period; does not include newborn.

**Outpatient Visits–**A visit by a patient who is not lodged in the hospital while receiving medical, dental, or other services. Each appearance of an outpatient in each unit constitutes one visit regardless of the number of diagnostic and/or therapeutic treatments that a patient receives.

**Births–**Number of infants born in the hospital and accepted for service in a newborn infant bassinet during a 12–month period; excludes stillbirths.

**Expense:** Expense for a 12–month period; both total expense and payroll components are shown. Payroll expenses include all salaries and wages.

**Personnel:** Represents personnel situations as they existed at the end of the reporting period; includes full-time equivalents of part–time personnel. Full–time equivalents were calculated on the basis that two part–time persons equal one full–time person.

---

†Data from the Graduate Medical Education Database, Copyright 2013, American Medical Association, Chicago, Illinois.

# Sample Hospital Listing:

**ANYTOWN, Universal County**

⊠ **ANYTOWN HOSPITAL & CLINICS (777777)**, (Formerly Anytown Area Community Hospital and Clinic), 100 South Main Street, Zip 12345–6789; tel. 123/456–7890 **A9** 10  ] ①

**F**10 12 23 24 29 30 31 37 39 49 51 55 57 64 65 66 68 70 71 72 77 78 83 87 88 91 96 97 106 107 110 111 113 124 **P**1 2 3 **S** Universal County Health System ] ⑦  ② ③

Primary Contact: Ann M. Generic, Chief Executive Officer
COO: Ann M. Generic
CFO: Michael M. Generic
CMO: Peterl Van Generic, President Medical Staff  ④
CHR: Jerry Generic, Human Resources Director
Web address: www.website.org
**Control:** Other not–for–profit (including NFP Corporation) **Service:** General Medical and surgical ] ⑤

**Staffed Beds:** 25 **Admissions:** 892 **Census:** 9 **Outpatient Visits:** 44014 **Births:** 51 **Total Expense ($000):** 19210 **Payroll Expense ($000):** 5864 **Personnel:** 182  ⑥

**ANYTOWN, Universal County**

⊠ **ANYTOWN HOSPITAL & CLINICS (777777)**, (Formerly Anytown Area Community Hospital and Clinic), 100 South Main Street, Zip 12345–6789; tel. 123/456–7890 **A9** 10

① = **Approval Codes**
② = **Physician Codes**
③ = **Health Care System Name**
④ = **Titles of Chief Administrators**
⑤ = **Control and Service Classifications**
⑥ = **Utilization Data**
⑦ = **Facility Codes**

---

**Hospital, Medicare Provider Number, Address, Telephone, Approval, Facility, and Physician Codes, Health Care System**

★ American Hospital Association (AHA) membership
□ The Joint Commission accreditation
◇ DNV Healthcare Inc. accreditation
○ Healthcare Facilities Accreditation Program
△ Commission on Accreditation of Rehabilitation Facilities (CARF) accreditation

---

## ⑦ Facility Codes

*Provided directly by the hospital; for definitions, see page A6.*

### (Numerical Order)

1. Acute long-term care
2. Adult day care program
3. Airborne infection isolation room
4. Alcoholism-drug abuse or dependency inpatient unit
5. Alcoholism-drug abuse or dependency outpatient unit
6. Alzheimer center
7. Ambulance services
8. Ambulatory surgery center
9. Arthritis treatment center
10. Assisted living
11. Auxiliary
12. Bariatric/weight control services
13. Birthing room-LDR room-LDRP room
14. Blood donor center
15. Breast cancer screening/mammograms
16. Burn care services
17. Cardiac intensive care
18. Adult cardiology services
19. Pediatric cardiology services
20. Adult diagnostic catheterization
21. Pediatric diagnostic catheterization
22. Adult interventional cardiac catheterization
23. Pediatric diagnostic catheterization
24. Adult cardiac surgery
25. Pediatric cardiac surgery
26. Adult cardiac electrophysiology
27. Pediatric cardiac electrophysiology
28. Cardiac rehabilitation
29. Case management
30. Chaplaincy/pastoral care services
31. Chemotherapy
32. Children's wellness program
33. Chiropractic services
34. Community health education
35. Community outreach
36. Complementary and alternative medicine services
37. Computer assisted orthopedic surgery (CAOS)
38. Crisis prevention
39. Dental services
40. Emergency department
41. Pediatric emergency department
42. Satellite emergency department
43. Trauma center (certified)
44. Enabling services
45. Optical colonoscopy
46. Endoscopic ultrasound
47. Ablation of Barrett's esophagus
48. Esophageal impedance study

49. Endoscopic retrograde cholangiopancreatography (ERCP)
50. Enrollment assistance services
51. Extracorporeal shock wave lithotripter (ESWL)
52. Fertility clinic
53. Fitness center
54. Freestanding outpatient care center
55. Genetic testing/counseling
56. Geriatric services
57. Health fair
58. Health research
59. Health screenings
60. Hemodialysis
61. HIV–AIDS services
62. Home health services
63. Hospice program
64. Hospital–based outpatient care center services
65. Immunization program
66. Indigent care clinic
67. Intermediate nursing care
68. Linguistic/translation services
69. Meals on wheels
70. Medical surgical intensive care services
71. Mobile health services
72. Neonatal intensive care
73. Neonatal intermediate care
74. Neurological services
75. Nutrition programs
76. Obstetrics
77. Occupational health services
78. Oncology services
79. Orthopedic services
80. Other special care
81. Outpatient surgery
82. Pain management program
83. Inpatient palliative care unit
84. Palliative care program
85. Patient controlled analgesia (PCA)
86. Patient education center
87. Patient representative services
88. Pediatric intensive care services
89. Pediatric medical–surgical care
90. Physical rehabilitation inpatient services
91. Assistive technology center
92. Electrodiagnostic services
93. Physical rehabilitation outpatient services
94. Prosthetic and orthotic services
95. Robot-assisted walking therapy
96. Simulated rehabilitation environment
97. Primary care department
98. Psychiatric care
99. Psychiatric child–adolescent services
100. Psychiatric consultation–liaison services

101. Psychiatric education services
102. Psychiatric emergency services
103. Psychiatric geriatric services
104. Psychiatric outpatient services
105. Psychiatric partial hospitalization services
106. Psychiatric residential treatment
107. CT scanner
108. Diagnostic radioisotope facility
109. Electron beam computed tomography (EBCT)
110. Full–field digital mammography (FFDM)
111. Magnetic resonance imaging (MRI)
112. Intraoperative magnetic resonance imaging
113. Magnetoencephalography (MEG)
114. Multi–slice spiral computed tomography (MSCT) (<64 slice CT)
115. Multi–slice spiral computed tomography (64 + slice CT)
116. Positron emission tomography (PET)
117. Positron emission tomography/CT (PET/CT)
118. Single photon emission computerized tomography (SPECT)
119. Ultrasound
120. Image–guided radiation therapy (IGRT)
121. Intensity–modulated radiation therapy (IMRT)
122. Proton beam therapy
123. Shaped beam radiation therapy
124. Stereotactic radiosurgery
125. Retirement housing
126. Robotic surgery
127. Rural health clinic
128. Skilled nursing care
129. Sleep center
130. Social work services
131. Sports medicine
132. Support groups
133. Swing bed services
134. Teen outreach services
135. Tobacco treatment/cessation program
136. Bone marrow transplant services
137. Heart transplant
138. Kidney transplant
139. Liver transplant
140. Lung transplant
141. Tissue transplant
142. Other transplant
143. Transportation to health services
144. Urgent care center
145. Virtual colonoscopy
146. Volunteer services department
147. Women's health center/services
148. Wound management services

# AHA Guide® to the Health Care Field

## 2014 Edition

AHA Members $237
Nonmembers $360
AHA Item Number 010014
Telephone ORDERS 1–800–AHA–2626


ISSN 0094–8969
ISBN–13: 978–0–87258–919–3

3 1502 00772 1531

# Contents

† List supplied by The Joint Commission

# Acknowledgements and Advisements

## Acknowledgements

The AHA Guide® to the Health Care Field is published annually by Health Forum LLC, an affiliate of the American Hospital Association. Contributions are made by Information Systems and Technology, Member Relations, Office of the President, Office of the Secretary, Printing Services Group, AHA Resource Center and the following participants:

| | |
|---|---|
| Grant Denton | Mary Krzywicki |
| DeAnn Ellis | Andrea Liebig |
| Joan Finn | Denise Loggins |
| Deanna Frazier | Jennifer Pagan |
| Tan Harris | Steve Reczynski |
| Stella Hines | Christine Remedios |
| Clisby Jackson | Elaine Singh |
| Danny Jackson | Susan Sheffey |
| Kimberly Jackson | Courtney Spousta |
| Peter Kralovec | Judy Williams |

Health Forum LLC acknowledges the cooperation given by many professional groups and government agencies in the health care field, particularly the following: American College of Surgeons; American Medical Association; Blue Cross and Blue Shield Association; Council of Teaching Hospitals of the Association of American Medical Colleges; The Joint Commission; DNV Healthcare Inc.; National League for Nursing Accrediting Commission; Commission on Accreditation of Rehabilitation Facilities; American Osteopathic Association, Centers for Medicare & Medicaid Services; and various offices within the U.S. Department of Health and Human Services.

## Advisements

The data published here should be used with the following advisements: The data is based on replies to an annual survey that seeks a variety of information, not all of which is published in this book. The information gathered by the survey includes specific services, but not all of each hospital's services. Therefore, the data does not reflect an exhaustive list of all services offered by all hospitals. For information on the availability of additional data and products, please contact Health Forum LLC at 800/821–2039, or visit our web site.

Health Forum LLC does not assume responsibility for the accuracy of information voluntarily reported by the individual institutions surveyed. **The purpose of this publication is to provide basic data reflecting the delivery of health care in the United States and associated areas, and is not to serve as an official and all inclusive list of services offered by individual hospitals. The information reflected is based on data collected as of May 31, 2013.**

## An Introduction to *AHA Guide*®

Welcome, and thank you for purchasing the 2014 edition of *AHA Guide*®. This section is designed to aid you in using the book. While the primary focus of *AHA Guide* is on hospitals, it also contains information on other areas of the health care field, divided across its three major sections:

A. Hospitals
B. Health care systems, networks, and alliances
C. Health care organizations, agencies, and other health care providers

The information contained within this publication was compiled using AHA membership, and the AHA Annual Survey of Hospitals. *AHA Guide* is the leading hospital directory and represents hospitals with or without AHA membership.

Additional information contained in the front of AHA Guide includes:

- A section by section table of contents
- Recognition of the source of data in the *Acknowledgements and Advisements* section
- Information on AHA's history as well as a listing of our awards in *AHA Offices, Officers, Historical Data, and Awards*

## Getting Started: The AHA Guide Code Chart

Open the front cover and *AHA Guide* begins with the *2014 AHA Guide Code Chart*. This two page section (front and back) explains how to find and understand the most important elements of each hospital's listing. The chart is specially perforated and is meant to be extracted and used alongside Section A as a resource. The information found on these pages is repeated in the first section, so don't worry about removing the chart.

The *Code Chart* is a very useful tool to have when reading. It allows new users to become familiar with the data, and it aids returning users in understanding the new design and layout of *AHA Guide*. At the top of the chart, there is a sample listing. If you have used this publication before, you will notice the new columnar listing of all hospital entries by city. The city and county names are highlighted in gray, and all hospitals within the city follow. After the hospital name, you will find the address, telephone number, approval, facility and service codes, and health care systems to which the hospital belongs. Following this are the chief administrators and classifications for the hospital. Utilization data for the hospital is found in the box at the bottom of each hospital's entry in *AHA Guide*.

The chart further demonstrates how to understand these important elements:

1. **Approval codes** refer to certifications held by a hospital; they represent information supplied by various national approving and reporting bodies. For example, code A–3 indicates accreditation under one of the programs of the Accreditation Council for Graduate Medical Education, evidence that the hospital has been approved for participation in residency training.
2. **Physician codes** represent the different types of arrangements the hospital participates in with its physicians. In this section, code P-1 signifies a closed physician-hospital organization.
3. **Health Care System names** reference specific health care system headquarters to which the hospital belongs. The presence of a system name indicates that the hospital is a member. If no names are listed, the hospital does not belong to a system.
4. **Titles of Chief Administrators** including the Chief Executive Officer and, when available, other C-Suite officers such as the Chief Financial Officer, Chief Information Officer, Chief Medical Officer, Chief Operating Officer, and Chief Human Resources Officer.
5. **Classification** refers to two items in *AHA Guide*. **Control** classification indicates the organization that operates the hospital, and

**2014 AHA Guide Code Chart**

Sample Hospital Listing:

© 2013 AHA Guide

## 2. Physician Codes (P)

## 1. Approval Codes (A)  ## 7. Facility Codes (F)  ## 3. System Codes (S)

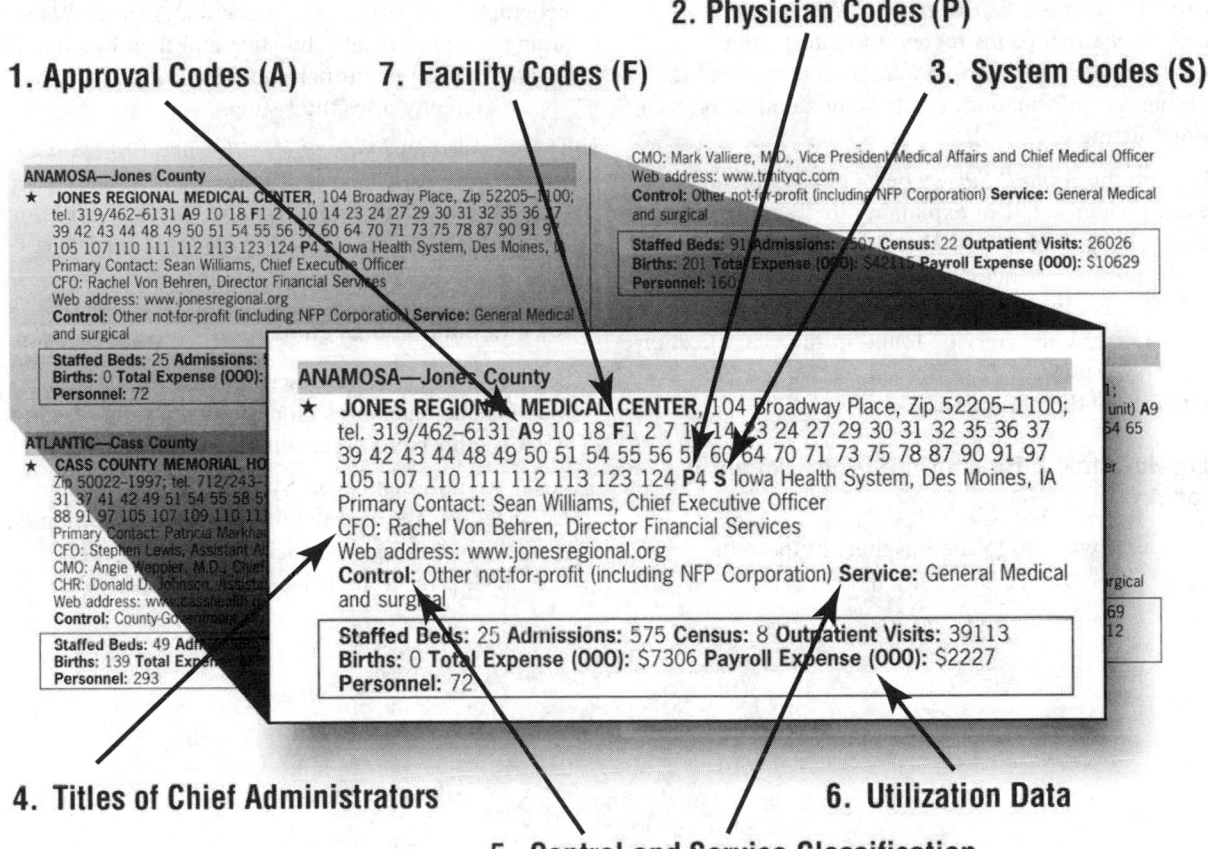

## 4. Titles of Chief Administrators

## 6. Utilization Data

## 5. Control and Service Classification

**Service** classification refers to the type of service the hospital offers. Previously, this section utilized numerical codes corresponding with a literal value, but the new design of *AHA Guide* bypasses the codes and instead displays the literal classifications for control and service.

- **Control:** In this section, organizations are divided among nonfederal government hospitals, nongovernment not-for-profit hospitals, investor owned for-profit hospitals, and federal government hospitals.
- **Service:** This section displays the primary type of service that a hospital offers. The most common value is general hospital. Among the other services listed in this section are specialties such as psychiatric hospitals or children's hospitals.

6. **Utilization Data** contains the statistics related to the day-to-day and cumulative operation of the hospital. The information included in this section consists of:
- **Beds:** Number of beds regularly maintained.
- **Admissions:** Amount of patients accepted for inpatient services over a 12-month period.

- **Census:** Average number of patients receiving care each day.
- **Outpatient Visits:** Amount of visits by patients not lodged in the hospital while receiving care.
- **Births:** Number of infants born in the hospital and accepted for service in a newborn infant bassinet.
- **Expense:** Includes all expenses (including payroll) that the hospital had over the 12-month period.
- **Personnel:** Represents personnel situations as they existed at the end of the reporting period. In this area, full time equivalency is calculated on the basis that two part-time persons equal one full-time person.

7. **Facility codes** provide a description of the specific services offered by a hospital. Code F-14, for instance, indicates that the hospital contains a Blood Donor Center.

### How To Use This Book

Section A begins with the *AHA Guide Hospital Listing Requirements*. This explains the requisite accreditations or characteristics a hospital must meet to be included in *AHA Guide*.

After this there is *An Explanation of the Hospital Listings*. These two pages review the information included in the Code Chart and are a vital resource in identifying the information, symbols, and codes for each hospital's listing.

Next up are the *Annual Survey* definitions, which go into even greater detail in explaining the facility and physician codes. Please note that these are arranged alphabetically and numerically to correspond with the code chart. Also included here are the definitions of the terms for Control and Service found in the Classification section. The listings of *Hospitals in the United States, by State* follow the definitions.

## Finding Hospitals & Health Care Professionals in Section A

There are two ways to locate hospitals in the print version of *AHA Guide*. One is by the hospital's geographic classification. In Section A, hospitals are arranged alphabetically by state and then by city. The second method is through the *Hospital Index* that appears directly after the listings.

There is also an *Index of Health Care Professionals* which begins after the first index that lists key people from hospitals and health systems. Look for fold out tabs and tabs on the sides of pages that mark the indices.

## AHA Membership Organizations

Section A ends with a description of the AHA Membership categories along with a listing of various AHA Membership organizations.

For more information on Systems, Networks, and Alliances, please read the introduction to Section B. Health organizations, agencies, and providers are described, prior to their listing, at the start of Section C.

# AHA Offices, Officers, and Historical Data

**Chicago:** 155 N. Wacker Drive, Chicago, IL 60606; tel. 312/422–3000

**Washington:** 325 Seventh Street, N.W., Suite 700, Washington, DC 20004; tel. 202/638–1100

**Chairman of the Board of Trustees:** James H. Hinton, Presbyterian Healthcare Services, P.O. Box 26666, Albuquerque, NM 87125
**Chairman–Elect of the Board of Trustees:** Jonathan B. Perlin, MD, HCA, One Park Plaza, 1–4W, Nashville, TN 37203

**Immediate Past Chairman of the Board of Trustees:** Benjamin K. Chu, MD, Kaiser Foundation Health Plan and Hospital, 393 E. Walnut Street, Pasadena, CA 91188
**President & CEO:** Richard J. Umbdenstock, 325 Seventh Street, N.W., Suite 700, Washington, DC 20004

**Senior Vice President and Secretary:** Michael P. Guerin, 155 N. Wacker Drive, Chicago, IL 60606
**Senior Vice President and Treasurer:** John Evans, 155 N. Wacker Drive, Chicago, IL 60606

## Past Presidents/Chairs†

| | | | | | |
|---|---|---|---|---|---|
| 1899 | ★James S. Knowles | 1938 | ★Robert E. Neff | 1977 | ★John M. Stagl |
| 1900 | ★James S. Knowles | 1939 | ★G. Harvey Agnew, M.D. | 1978 | ★Samuel J. Tibbitts |
| 1901 | ★Charles S. Howell | 1940 | ★Fred G. Carter, M.D. | 1979 | W. Daniel Barker |
| 1902 | ★J. T. Duryea | 1941 | ★B. W. Black, M.D. | 1980 | ★Sister Irene Kraus |
| 1903 | ★John Fehrenbatch | 1942 | ★Basil C. MacLean, M.D. | 1981 | ★Bernard J. Lachner |
| 1904 | ★Daniel D. Test | 1943 | ★James A. Hamilton | 1982 | ★Stanley R. Nelson |
| 1905 | ★George H. M. Rowe, M.D. | 1944 | ★Frank J. Walter | 1983 | Elbert E. Gilbertson |
| 1906 | ★George P. Ludlam | 1945 | ★Donald C. Smelzer, M.D. | 1984 | Thomas R. Matherlee |
| 1907 | ★Renwick R. Ross, M.D. | 1946 | ★Peter D. Ward, M.D. | 1985 | ★Jack A. Skarupa |
| 1908 | ★Sigismund S. Goldwater, M.D. | 1947 | ★John H. Hayes | 1986 | Scott S. Parker |
| 1909 | ★John M. Peters, M.D. | 1948 | ★Graham L. Davis | 1987 | Donald C. Wegmiller |
| 1910 | ★H. B. Howard, M.D. | 1949 | ★Joseph G. Norby | 1988 | Eugene W. Arnett |
| 1911 | ★W. L. Babcock, M.D. | 1950 | ★John N. Hatfield | 1989 | Edward J. Connors |
| 1912 | ★Henry M. Hurd, M.D. | 1951 | ★Charles F. Wilinsky, M.D. | 1990 | David A. Reed |
| 1913 | ★F. A. Washburn, M.D. | 1952 | ★Anthony J. J. Rourke, M.D. | 1991 | C. Thomas Smith |
| 1914 | ★Thomas Howell, M.D. | 1953 | ★Edwin L. Crosby, M.D. | 1992 | D. Kirk Oglesby, Jr. |
| 1915 | ★William O. Mann, M.D. | 1954 | ★Ritz E. Heerman | 1993 | Larry L. Mathis |
| 1916 | ★Winford H. Smith, M.D. | 1955 | ★Frank R. Bradley | 1994 | Carolyn C. Roberts |
| 1917 | ★Robert J. Wilson, M.D. | 1956 | ★Ray E. Brown | 1995 | Gail L. Warden |
| 1918 | ★A. B. Ancker, M.D. | 1957 | ★Albert W. Snoke, M.D. | 1996 | Gordon M. Sprenger |
| 1919 | ★A. R. Warner, M.D. | 1958 | ★Tol Terrell | 1997 | Reginald M. Ballantyne III |
| 1920 | ★Joseph B. Howland, M.D. | 1959 | ★Ray Amberg | 1998 | John G. King |
| 1921 | ★Louis B. Baldwin, M.D. | 1960 | ★Russell A. Nelson, M.D. | 1999 | Fred L. Brown |
| 1922 | ★George O'Hanlon, M.D. | 1961 | ★Frank S. Groner | 2000 | ★Carolyn Boone Lewis |
| 1923 | ★Asa S. Bacon | 1962 | ★Jack Masur, M.D. | 2001 | Gary A. Mecklenburg |
| 1924 | ★Malcolm T. MacEachern, M.D. | 1963 | ★T. Stewart Hamilton, M.D. | 2002 | Sr. Mary Roch Rocklage, RSM |
| 1925 | ★E. S. Gilmore | 1964 | ★Stanley A. Ferguson | 2003 | Dennis R. Barry |
| 1926 | ★Arthur C. Bachmeyer, M.D. | 1965 | ★Clarence E. Wonnacott | 2004 | David L. Bernd |
| 1927 | ★R. G. Brodrick, M.D. | 1966 | ★Philip D. Bonnet, M.D. | 2005 | George F. Lynn |
| 1928 | ★Joseph C. Doane, M.D. | 1967 | ★George E. Cartmill | **January–April 2006** | Richard J. Umbdenstock |
| 1929 | ★Louis H. Burlingham, M.D. | 1968 | ★David B. Wilson, M.D. | **April–December 2006** | George F. Lynn |
| 1930 | ★Christopher G. Parnall, M.D. | 1969 | ★George William Graham, M.D. | 2007 | Kevin E. Lofton |
| 1931 | ★Lewis A. Sexton, M.D. | 1970 | ★Mark Berke | 2008 | William D. Petasnick |
| 1932 | ★Paul H. Fesler | 1971 | ★Jack A. L. Hahn | 2009 | Thomas M. Priselac |
| 1933 | ★George F. Stephens, M.D. | 1972 | ★Stephen M. Morris | 2010 | Richard P. de Filippi |
| 1934 | ★Nathaniel W. Faxon, M.D. | 1973 | ★John W. Kauffman | 2011 | John W. Bluford |
| 1935 | ★Robert Jolly | 1974 | ★Horace M. Cardwell | 2012 | Teri G. Fontenot |
| 1936 | ★Robin C. Buerki, M.D. | 1975 | Wade Mountz | 2013 | Benjamin K. Chu, MD |
| 1937 | ★Claude W. Munger, M.D. | 1976 | H. Robert Cathcart | | |

## Chief Executive Officers

| | | | | | |
|---|---|---|---|---|---|
| 1917–18 | ★William H. Walsh, M.D. | 1943–54 | ★George Bugbee | 1986–91 | Carol M. McCarthy, Ph.D., J.D. |
| 1919–24 | ★Andrew Robert Warner, M.D. | 1954–72 | ★Edwin L. Crosby, M.D. | 1991 | Jack W. Owen (acting) |
| 1925–27 | ★William H. Walsh, M.D. | 1972 | Madison B. Brown, M.D. (acting) | 1991–2007 | Richard J. Davidson |
| 1928–42 | ★Bert W. Caldwell, M.D. | 1972–86 | J. Alexander McMahon | 2007 | Richard J. Umbdenstock (current) |

## Distinguished Service Award

The award recognizes significant lifetime contributions and service to health care institutions and associations.

| | | | | | |
|---|---|---|---|---|---|
| 1934 | Matthew O. Foley | 1964 | Russell A. Nelson, M.D. | 1990 | John W. Colloton |
| 1939 | Malcolm T. MacEachern, M.D. | 1965 | Albert W. Snoke, M.D. | 1991 | Carol M. McCarthy, Ph.D., J.D. |
| 1940 | Sigismund S. Goldwater, M.D. | 1966 | Frank S. Groner | 1992 | David H. Hitt |
| 1941 | Frederic A. Washburn, M.D. | 1967 | Rev. John J. Flanagan, S.J. | 1993 | Edward J. Connors |
| 1942 | Winford H. Smith, M.D. | 1968 | Stanley W. Martin | | Jack W. Owen |
| 1943 | Arthur C. Bachmeyer, M.D. | 1969 | T. Stewart Hamilton, M.D. | 1994 | George Adams |
| 1944 | Rt. Rev. Msgr. Maurice F. Griffin, LL.D. | 1970 | Charles Patteson Cardwell, Jr. | 1995 | Scott S. Parker |
| 1945 | Asa S. Bacon | 1971 | Mark Berke | 1996 | John A. Russell |
| 1946 | George F. Stephens, M.D. | 1972 | Stanley A. Ferguson | 1997 | D. Kirk Oglesby, Jr. |
| 1947 | Robin C. Buerki, M.D. | 1973 | Jack A. L. Hahn | 1998 | Henry B. Betts, M.D. |
| 1948 | James A. Hamilton | 1974 | George William Graham, M.D. | 1999 | Mitchell T. Rabkin, M.D. |
| 1949 | Claude W. Munger, M.D. | 1975 | George E. Cartmill | 2000 | Gail L. Warden |
| 1950 | Nathaniel W. Faxon, M.D. | 1976 | D. O. McClusky, Jr. | 2001 | Gordon M. Sprenger |
| 1951 | Bert W. Caldwell, M.D. | 1977 | Boone Powell | 2002 | Carolyn Boone Lewis |
| 1952 | Fred G. Carter, M.D. | 1978 | Richard J. Stull | 2003 | C. Thomas Smith |
| 1953 | Basil C. MacLean, M.D. | 1979 | Horace M. Cardwell | 2004 | Michael C. Waters |
| 1954 | George Bugbee | 1980 | Donald W. Cordes | 2005 | John G. King |
| 1955 | Joseph G. Norby | 1981 | Sister Mary Brigh Cassidy | 2006 | Gary A. Mecklenburg |
| 1956 | Charles F. Wilinsky, M.D. | 1982 | R. Zach Thomas, Jr. | | Sr. Mary Roch Rocklage, RSM |
| 1957 | John H. Hayes | 1983 | H. Robert Cathcart | 2007 | Richard J. Davidson |
| 1958 | John N. Hatfield | 1984 | Matthew F. McNulty, Jr., Sc.D. | 2008 | Fred L. Brown |
| 1959 | Edwin L. Crosby, M.D. | 1985 | J. Alexander McMahon | 2009 | George F. Lynn |
| 1960 | Oliver G. Pratt | 1986 | Sister Irene Kraus | 2010 | James J. Mongan, M.D. |
| 1961 | E. M. Bluestone, M.D. | 1987 | W. Daniel Barker | 2011 | Thomas C. Royer, M.D. |
| 1962 | Mother Loretto Bernard, S.C., R.N. | 1988 | Elbert E. Gilbertson | 2012 | Karen Davis, Ph.D. |
| 1963 | Ray E. Brown | 1989 | Donald G. Shropshire | 2013 | Thomas C. Dolan, Ph.D., FACHE |

★Deceased
†On June 3, 1972, the House of Delegates changed the title of the chief elected officer to chairman of the Board of Trustees, and the title of president was conferred on the chief executive officer of the Association.

# Award of Honor

Awarded to individuals, organizations, or groups to recognize an exemplary contribution to the health and well being of the people through leadership on a major health policy or social initiative.

| | | | | | |
|---|---|---|---|---|---|
| 1966 | Senator Lister Hill | | Mothers Against Drunk Driving (MADD) | 2006 | Jordan J. Cohen, M.D. |
| 1967 | Emory W. Morris, D.D.S. | 1997 | Paul B. Batalden, M.D. | | James W. Varnum |
| 1971 | Special Committee on Provision of Health | | Habitat for Humanity International | 2007 | Edward A. Eckenhoff |
| | Services (staff also) | 1998 | John E. Curley, Jr. | | Stanley F. Hupfeld |
| 1982 | Walter J. McNemey | | National Civic League | 2008 | Regina M. Benjamin, MD, MBA |
| 1989 | Ruth M. Rothstein | 1999 | Joseph Cardinal Bernardin, Literacy | | Alfred G. Stubblefield |
| 1990 | Joyce C. Clifford, R.N. | | Volunteers of America | 2009 | The Center to Advance Palliative Care |
| 1991 | Haynes Rice | 2000 | Institute for Safe Medication Practices | | Paul B. Hofmann, Dr.PH |
| 1992 | Donald W. Dunn | 2001 | Dennis R. Barry | 2010 | Jack Bovender |
| | Ira M. Lane, Jr. | 2002 | Donald M. Berwick, M.D. | 2011 | Cary Medical Center, Caribou, ME |
| 1993 | Elliott C. Roberts, Sr. | 2003 | Steven A. Schroeder, M.D. | 2012 | Ronald McDonald House Charities |
| | William A. Spencer, M.D. | | Dan S. Wilford | | The Schwartz Center for Compassionate |
| 1994 | Robert A. Derzon | 2004 | Ron J. Anderson, M.D. | | Healthcare |
| 1995 | Russell G. Mawby, Ph.D. | | Johnson & Johnson | 2013 | George C. Halvorson |
| | John K. Springer | 2005 | Sr. Mary Jean Ryan | | Reach Out and Read |
| 1996 | Stephen J. Hegarty | | | | |

# Justin Ford Kimball Innovators Award

Recognition to individuals or organizations that have made outstanding, innovative contributions to health care financing and/or delivery that improves access or coordination of care.

| | | | | | |
|---|---|---|---|---|---|
| 1958 | E. A. van Steenwyk | 1973 | Herman M. Somers | 1994 | Donald A. Brennan |
| 1959 | George A. Newbury | 1974 | William H. Ford, Ph.D. | 1995 | E. George Middleton, Jr. |
| 1960 | C. Rufus Rorem, Ph.D. | 1975 | Earl H. Kammer | | Glenn R. Mitchell |
| 1961 | James E. Stuart | 1976 | J. Ed McConnell | 1997 | Harvey Pettry |
| 1962 | Frank Van Dyk | 1978 | Edwin R. Werner | | D. David Sniff |
| 1963 | William S. McNary | 1979 | Robert M. Cunningham, Jr. | 1998 | Montana Health Research and Education |
| 1964 | Frank S. Groner | 1981 | Maurice J. Norby | | Foundation |
| 1965 | J. Douglas Colman | 1982 | Robert E. Rinehimer | 1999 | Kenneth W. Kizer, M.D. |
| 1967 | Walter J. McNemey | 1983 | John B. Morgan, Jr. | 2002 | David M. Lawrence, M.D. |
| 1968 | John W. Paynter | 1984 | Joseph F. Duplinsky | 2003 | Lowell C. Kruse |
| 1970 | Edwin L. Crosby, M.D. | 1985 | David W. Stewart | 2006 | Spencer Foreman, M.D. |
| 1971 | H. Charles Abbott | 1988 | Ernest W. Saward, M.D. | 2009 | On Lok |
| 1972 | John R. Mannix | 1990 | James A. Vohs | 2012 | Thomas S. Nesbitt, M.D. |
| | | 1993 | John C. Lewin, M.D. | | |

# Board of Trustees Award

Individuals or groups who have made substantial and noteworthy contributions to the work of the American Hospital Association.

| | | | | | |
|---|---|---|---|---|---|
| 1959 | Joseph V. Friel | | Samuel J. Tibbitts | 1999 | Sister Carol Keehan |
| | John H. Hayes | 1981 | Vernon A. Knutson | | C. Edward McCauley |
| 1960 | Duncan D. Sutphen, Jr. | | John E. Sullivan | | Stephen Rogness |
| 1963 | Eleanor C. Lambertsen, R.N., Ed.D. | 1982 | John Bigelow | 2000 | Dennis May |
| 1964 | John R. Mannix | | Robert W. O'Leary | 2001 | Spencer C. Johnson |
| 1965 | Albert G. Hahn | | Jack W. Owen | | Michael M. Mitchel |
| | Maurice J. Norby | 1984 | Howard J. Berman | 2002 | Victor L. Campbell |
| 1966 | Madison B. Brown, M.D. | | O. Ray Hurst | | Joseph A. Parker |
| | Kenneth Williamson | | James R. Neely | 2003 | J. Richard Gaintner, M.D. |
| 1967 | Alanson W. Wilcox | 1985 | James E. Ferguson | | Donald A. Wilson |
| 1968 | E. Dwight Barnett, M.D. | | Cleveland Rodgers | 2004 | Richard L. Clarke |
| 1969 | Vane M. Hoge, M.D. | 1986 | Rex N. Olsen | | Thelma Traut |
| | Joseph H. McNinch, M.D. | 1987 | Michael Lesparre | 2005 | Merrill Gappmayer |
| 1972 | David F. Drake, Ph.D. | 1988 | Barbara A. Donaho, R.N. | | Leo Greenawalt |
| | Paul W. Earle | 1989 | Walter H. MacDonald | 2006 | Robert L. Harman |
| | Michael Lesparre | | Donald R. Newkirk | | Kenneth G. Stella |
| | Andrew Pattullo | 1990 | William T. Robinson | 2007 | Deborah Freund, Ph.D. |
| 1973 | Tilden Cummings | 1992 | Jack C. Bills | | Michael D. Stephens |
| | Edmond J. Lanigan | | Anne Hall Davis | 2008 | James R. Castle |
| 1974 | James E. Hague | 1993 | Theodore C. Eickhoff, M.D. | 2009 | Richard M. Knapp, Ph.D. |
| | Sister Marybelle | | Stephen W. Gamble | 2010 | Fred Hessler |
| 1975 | Helen T. Yast | | Yoshi Honkawa | | John G. O'Brien |
| 1976 | Boynton P. Livingston | 1994 | Roger M. Busfield, Jr., Ph.D. | 2011 | Carolyn F. Scanlan |
| | James Ludlam | 1995 | Stephen E. Dorn | | Charlotte S. Yeh, MD |
| | Helen McGuire | | William L. Yates | 2012 | Larry S. Gage |
| 1979 | Newton J. Jacobson | 1996 | Leigh E. Morris | | Larry McAndrews |
| | Edward W. Weimer | | John Quigley | 2013 | Jeffrey D. Selberg |
| 1980 | Robert B. Hunter, M.D. | 1998 | John D. Leech | | |

# Citation for Meritorious Service

| | | | | | |
|---|---|---|---|---|---|
| 1968 | F. R. Knautz | | Gordon McLachlan | 1983 | David M. Kinzer |
| | Sister Conrad Mary, R.N. | 1977 | Theodore Cooper, M.D. | 1984 | Donald L. Custis, M.D. |
| 1971 | Hospital Council of Southern California | 1979 | Norman D. Burkett | 1985 | John A. D. Cooper, M.D. |
| 1972 | College of Misericordia, Dallas, PA | | John L. Quigley | | Imperial Council of the Ancient Arabic Order |
| 1973 | Madison B. Brown, M.D. | | William M. Whelan | | of the Nobles of the Mystic Shrine for North |
| | Samuel J. Tibbitts | 1980 | Sister Grace Marie Hiltz | | America |
| 1975 | Kenneth B. Babcock, M.D. | | Leo J. Gehrig, M.D. | 1986 | Howard F. Cook |
| | Sister Mary Maurita Sengelaube | 1981 | Richard Davi | 1987 | David H. Hitt |
| 1976 | Chaiker Abbis | | Pearl S. Fryar | | Lucile Packard |
| | Susan Jenkins | 1982 | Jorge Brull Nater | | |

This citation is no longer awarded

# AHA NOVA Awards

This award honors effective, collaborative programs focused on improving community health status.

## 1994
**Health Partners of Philadelphia (PA):** Albert Einstein Medical Center, Episcopal Hospital, Frankford Hospital, Medical College of Pennsylvania Hospital, St. Christopher's Hospital for Children, Temple University Hospital

**Decker Family Development Center:** Children's Hospital Medical Center of Akron (OH)
**Denver (CO) School–Based Clinics:** The Children's Hospital
**Basic Health Plan:** Dominican Network; Mount Carmel Hospital, Colville, WA; St. Joseph's

Hospital, Chewelah, WA; and Holy Family Hospital, Spokane, WA
**HealthLink:** Lakes Region General Hospital, Laconia, NH

## 1995
**Bladen Community Care Network:** Bladen County Hospital, Elizabethtown, NC
**Building a Healthier Community:** Community–Kimball Health Care System, Toms River, NJ

**Injury Prevention Program:** Harlem Hospital Center, New York City, NY
**The Community Ministries & Outreach Program:** Reaching Out to Our Vickery/Meadow

Neighborhood: Presbyterian Healthcare System, Dallas, TX
**"CHOICES":** Shriners Hospitals for Crippled Children, Tampa, FL

## 1996
**Lincoln and Sunnyslope:** John C. Lincoln Hospital and Health Center, Sunnyslope, AZ
**Growing into Life Task Force:** Aiken (SC) Regional Medical Centers

**People Caring for People:** Beatrice (NE) Community Hospital and Health Center
**Injury Prevention Center of the Greater Dayton (OH) Area:** The Children's Medical Center, Good

Samaritan Hospital and Health Center, Grandview Hospital, Kettering Memorial Hospital, Miami Valley Hospital, and St. Elizabeth Medical Center
**Family Road:** Hutzel Hospital, Detroit, MI

## 1997
**Health Promotion Schools of Excellence Program:** Alliant Health System and Kosair Children's Hospital, Louisville, KY
**Health, Outreach, Prevention, and Education (HOPE):** Health First Holmes Regional Medical Center, Melbourne, FL

**Healthy Community Initiative:** Roper Care Alliance, Charleston, SC
**Obstetrical Care and Prenatal Counseling Program:** St. Alexius Medical Center, Bismarck, ND
**HIV/AIDS Neighborhood Service Program:** Yale–New Haven Hospital, New Haven, CT

## 1998
**Partners for a Healthier Community:** Evergreen Community Health Care, Group Health Cooperative of Puget Sound, Overlake Hospital Medical Center, Providence Health System/Medalia HealthCare, Seattle, WA
**Glenwood–Lyndale Community Clinic:** Hennepin County Medical Center, Minneapolis, MN

**Greater Dallas (TX) Injury Prevention Center:** Parkland Health & Hospital System, Children's Medical Center of Dallas, Baylor Health Care System, Methodist Hospitals of Dallas, and Presbyterian Healthcare System
**Network of Trust:** Phoebe Putney Memorial Hospital, Albany, GA

**The Lauderdale Court:** A Community Partnership: St. Joseph Hospital and Health Centers, Memphis, TN

## 1999
**Making a Case for Community Health:** Middletown (OH) Regional Hospital
**The Family Resource Center:** Mount Carmel Medical Center, Pittsburgh, KS

**The Health Neighborhood Project:** St. Patrick Hospital, Missoula, MT
**Kids for Health:** Washington Regional Medical Center, Fayetteville, AR

**Children's Village:** Yakima Memorial Hospital, Yakima, WA

## 2000
**Community Healthcare Network:** Columbus (GA) Regional Healthcare System
**Pasadena County Asthma Project:** Huntington Memorial Hospital, Pasadena, CA

**Ashe County Health Council "Health Carolinias Task Force":** Ashe Memorial Hospital, Jefferson, NC
**Caritas–Connection Project:** St. Mary's Hospital, Passaic, NJ

**Correctional Health Care Program:** Baystate Health System, Springfield, MA

## 2001
**J.C. Lewis Health Center:** Memorial Health and St. Joseph's Candler Health System, Savannah, GA
**Project C.A.R.E.:** Mercy Medical Center, Canton, OH

**TeenHealthFX.com:** Atlantic Health System, Florham Park, NJ

**Vista ElderCARE:** Vista Health, Waukegan, IL

**Western Village Enterprise School:** INTEGRIS Health, Oklahoma City, OK

## 2002
**Chester Community Connections:** Crozer–Keystone Health System, Springfield, PA
**The Hope Street Family Center:** California Hospital Medical Center, Los Angeles, CA
**Mobile Health Outreach Ministry:** St. Vincent's Health System, Jacksonville, FL

**Operation Access:** Kaiser Foundation Hospitals, Oakland; Sutter Health, Sacramento; San Francisco General Hospital, San Francisco; St. Rose Hospital, Hayward; and Santa Rosa Memorial Hospital, Santa Rosa, CA

**Wilmington Health Access for Teens:** New Hanover Health Network, Wilmington, NC

## 2003
**C.O.A.C.H. for Kids:** Cedars–Sinai Medical Center, Los Angeles, CA
**Community Action Network:** Trinity Regional Medical Center, Fort Dodge, IA

**Hearts N' Health:** Glendale Adventist Medical Center, Glendale, CA
**Saint Joseph Health Center:** Saint Joseph Regional Medical Center, South Bend, IN

**St. Mary Medical Center Bensalem Ministries:** St. Mary Medical Center, Langhorne, PA

## 2004
**Better Beginnings:** Brockton Hospital, Brockton, MA
**Buffalo County Community Health Partners:** Good Samaritan Health Systems, Kearney, NE

**Quad City Health Initiative:** Genesis Health System, Davenport, IA and Trinity Regional Health System, Rock Island, IL
**Quality of Life in the Truckee Meadows:** Washoe Health System, Reno, NV

**Solano Coalition for Better Health, Inc.:** NorthBay Healthcare Group, Fairfield, CA; Sutter Solano Medical Center, Vallejo, CA; and Kaiser Permanente, Martinez, CA

## 2005
**Children's Health Connection:** McKay-Dee Hospital Center, Ogden, UT
**Palmetto Health's Vision Health Initiative:** Palmetto Health, Columbia, SC

**Project Dulce, Whittier Institute for Diabetes:** Scripps Health, San Diego, CA
**Toledo/Lucas County CareNet:** Mercy Health Partners, ProMedica Health System, and Medical

University of Ohio, all of Toledo, OH and St. Luke's Hospital, Maumee, OH
**Volunteer Health Advisor (VHA) Program:** Cambridge Health Alliance, Cambridge, MA

## 2006

**Healthy Learners, Columbia, SC:** Allendale County Hospital, Fairfax, SC; McLeod Medical Center–Dillon, Dillon, SC; Sisters of Charity Providence Hospitals, Columbia, SC; and Self Regional Healthcare, Greenwood, SC

**Primary Care Access Network (PCAN):** Health Central, Ocoee, FL; Florida Hospital, Winter Park, FL; and Orlando Regional Healthcare, Orlando, FL
**ProHealth Care Community Health Outreach Initiative:** ProHealth Care, Waukesha, WI

**St. Joseph Mobile Health Services:** Saint Joseph HealthCare Inc., Lexington, KY
**Yonkers Childhood Health Initiative:** St. John's Riverside, Yonkers, NY

## 2007

**Medical-Legal Partnership for Children:** Boston Medical Center, Boston, MA
**NOW (Nutritional Options for Wellness) Program:** Spectrum Health, Grand Rapids, MI

**Richland Care:** Palmetto Health, Columbia, SC
**Trauma Nurses Talk Tough:** Legacy Health System, Portland, OR

**UMass Memorial Medical Center Healthy Youth Development Initiative:** UMass Memorial Health Care, Worcester, MA
**Youth Health Partnership-Patee Market Youth Dental Clinic:** Heartland Health, St. Joseph, MO

## 2008

**Partnership for Community Health:** California Pacific Medical Center, San Francisco, CA
**Every Child Succeeds:** Cincinnati Children's Hospital Medical Center, Cincinnati, OH

**Memorial Hermann Health Centers for Schools:** Memorial Hermann, Houston, TX
**Nutrition Center of Maine:** Saint Mary's Health System, Lewiston, ME

*ENERGIZE!* **Pediatric Diabetes Intervention Program:** WakeMed Health & Hospitals, Raleigh, NC

## 2009

**Lighten Up 4 Life:** Mission Health System, Asheville, NC
**Project BRIEF:** Jacobi Medical Center and North Central Bronx Hospital, Bronx, NY

**Really Awesome Health (RAH) and Wholesome Routines:** Duke Raleigh Hospital, Raleigh, NC
**Student Success Jobs Program:** Brigham and Women's Hospital, Boston, MA

**Taos First Steps Program:** Holy Cross Hospital, Taos, NM

## 2010

**Community-Based Alternatives to the Emergency Room:** Lee Memorial Health System, Fort Meyers, FL
**Health-e-Access Telemedicine:** University of Rochester Medical Center, Rochester, NY

**Healthy Futures:** Munson Healthcare System, Traverse City, MI
**Healthy San Francisco:** San Francisco General Hospital, University of California Medical Center, Chinese Hospital, California Pacific Medical Center,

Saint Francis Memorial Hospital, St. Mary's Medical Center, and Kaiser Permanente, San Francisco, CA
**Pediatric Asthma Program:** Sinai Health System, Chicago, IL

## 2011

**Emergency Department Consistent Care Program:** Providence St. Peter Hospital, Olympia, WA
**Integrated Community Nursing Program at Parkview Health:** Parkview Health, Fort Wayne, IN

**Milwaukee Health Care Partnership:** Aurora Health Care, Children's Hospital & Health System, Inc., Columbia St. Mary's, and Froedtert Health, all of Milwaukee, WI, and Wheaton Franciscan Healthcare, Glendale, WI

**The Diabetes Collaborative:** Northwestern Memorial Hospital, Chicago, IL
**Rochester Youth Violence Partnership:** University of Rochester Medical Center and Rochester General Health System, Rochester, NY

## 2012

**The Beth Embraces Wellness: An Integrated Approach to Prevention in the Community:** Newark Beth Israel Medical Center and Children's Hospital of New Jersey, Newark, NJ

**CARE Network:** St. Joseph Health Queen of the Valley Medical Center, Napa, CA
**Fitness in the City:** Boston Children's Hospital, Boston, MA

**Puff City:** Henry Ford Health System, Detroit, MI
**Rural Health Initiative:** Shawano Medical Center of ThedaCare, Shawano, WI

## 2013

**Bangor Beacon Community:** EMHS, Brewer, ME and St. Joseph Healthcare, Bangor, ME
**Chippewa Health Improvement Partnership (CHIP):** St. Joseph's Hospital, Chippewa Falls, WI

**Core Health Program of Healthier Communities:** Spectrum Health, Grand Rapids, MI
**Free Preventive Screenings Program:** Good Samaritan Hospital, Vincennes, IN

**Hope Clinic and Pharmacy:** Ephraim McDowell Health, Danville, KY

# The Carolyn Boone Lewis Living the Vision Award

Organizations and individuals living AHA's vision of a society of healthy communities where all individuals reach their highest potential for health.

| | | | | | |
|---|---|---|---|---|---|
| 1998 | Memorial Healthcare System, Hollywood, FL Baptist Health System, Montgomery, AL | 2001 2002 | Salina Regional Health Center, Salina, KS Health Improvement Collaborative of Greater Cincinnati, Cincinnati, OH | 2005 | Fairbanks Memorial Hospital, Fairbanks, AK Boston Medical Center, Boston, MA |
| 1999 | Robert A. DeVries, Battle Creek, MI Memorial Health System, South Bend, IN | 2003 2004 | Franklin Memorial Hospital, Farmington, ME Jamaica Hospital Medical Center, Jamaica, New York | 2010 2011 | Lehigh Valley Health Network, Allentown, PA Alaska Native Tribal Health Consortium, Anchorage, AK |
| 2000 | Rockingham Memorial Hospital, Harrisonburg, VA | | | 2013 | St. Joseph's Hospital Health Center, Syracuse, NY |

# Circle of Life Award

This award celebrates innovation in palliative and end-of-life care.

## 2000

Improving Care through the End of Life, Franciscan Health System, Gig Harbor, WA

The Hospice of The Florida Suncoast, Largo, FL

Louisiana State Penitentiary Hospice Program, Angola, LA

## 2001

Department of Pain Medicine and Palliative Care, Beth Israel Medical Center, New York, NY

Palliative CareCenter & Hospice of the North Shore, Evanston , IL

St. Joseph's Manor, Trumbull, CT

## 2002

Children's Program of San Diego Hospice and Children's Hospital and Health Center of San Diego, San Diego, CA

Hospice of the Bluegrass, Lexington, KY
Project Safe Conduct, Hospice of the Western Reserve and Ireland Cancer Center, Cleveland, OH

**Special Circle of Life Award** Population–based Palliative Care Research Network (PoPCRN), Denver, CO

## 2003

Hospice & Palliative CareCenter, Winston–Salem, NC

Providence Health System, Portland, OR

University of California Davis Health System, Sacramento, CA

## 2004

Hope Hospice and Palliative Care, Fort Myers, FL

St. Mary's Healthcare System for Children, Bayside, NY

University of Texas M.D. Anderson Cancer Center Palliative Care, Houston, TX

**2005**

High Point Regional Health System, High Point, NC | Palliative and End-of-life Care Program, Hoag Memorial Hospital Presbyterian, Newport Beach, CA | Thomas Palliative Care Unit, VCU Massey Cancer Center, Richmond, VA

**2006**

Continuum Hospice Care, New York, NY | Mercy Supportive Care, St. Joseph Mercy Oakland, Pontiac, MI | Transitions and Life Choices, Fairview Health Services, Minneapolis, MN

**2007**

UCSF Palliative Care Program, San Francisco, CA | Covenant Hospice, Pensacola, FL | Woodwell: A Program of Presbyterian SeniorCare and Family Hospice and Palliative Care, Oakmont, PA

**2008**

Children's Hospitals and Clinics of Minnesota, Pain and Palliative Care Program, Minneapolis, MN | Haven Hospice, Gainesville, FL | The Pediatric Advanced Care Team, The Children's Hospital of Philadelphia, Philadelphia, PA

**2009**

Four Seasons, Flat Rock, NC | Oregon Health and Science University Palliative Medicine & Comfort Care Program, Portland, OR | Wishard Health Services Palliative Care Program, Indianapolis, IN

**2010**

Department of Veteran Affairs, VA New York/New Jersey Healthcare Network, Brooklyn, NY | Kansas City Hospice & Palliative Care, Kansas City, MO | Snohomish Palliative Partnership, Everett, WA

**2011**

The Center for Hospice & Palliative Care, Cheektowaga, NY | Gilchrist Hospice Care, Hunt Valley, MD | St. John Providence Health System, Detroit, MI

**2012**

Haslinger Family Pediatric Palliative Care Center, Akron Children's Hospital, Akron, OH | Calvary Hospital, Bronx, NY | Sharp HealthCare, San Diego, CA

**2013**

The Denver Hospice and Optio Health Services, Denver, CO | Hertzberg Palliative Care Institute at the Mount Sinai Medical Center, New York, NY | UnityPoint Health, Iowa and Illinois

# The American Hospital Association–McKesson Quest for Quality Prize

Honoring Leadership and Innovation in Patient Care Quality, Safety, and Commitment

**2002**

Missouri Baptist Medical Center, St. Louis, MO | **Finalist:** Fairview Hospital, Greater, Barrington, MA | **Finalist:** Minnesota Children's Hospital and Clinics, Minneapolis, MN

**2003**

Abington Memorial Hospital, Abington, PA | **Finalist:** Beaumont Hospitals, Royal Oak, MI | **Finalist:** University of Wisconsin Hospital and Clinics, Madison, WI

**2004**

Sentara Norfolk General Hospital, Norfolk, VA | **Finalist:** The Johns Hopkins Hospital, Baltimore, MD | **Finalist:** Mary Lanning Memorial Hospital, Hastings, NE

**2005**

North Mississippi Medical Center, Tupelo, MS | **Finalist:** El Camino Hospital, Mountain View, CA | **Finalist:** NewYork-Presbyterian Hospital, New York, NY

**2006**

Cincinnati Children's Hospital Medical Center, Cincinnati, OH

**2007**

Columbus Regional Hospital, Columbus, IN | **Finalist:** Cedars-Sinai Medical Center, Los Angeles, CA | **Finalist:** INTEGRIS Baptist Medical Center, Oklahoma City, OK

**2008**

Munson Medical Center, Traverse City, MI | **Finalist:** University of Michigan Hospitals & Health Centers, Ann Arbor, MI

**2009**

Bronson Methodist Hospital, Kalamazoo, MI | **Finalist:** Beth Israel Deaconess Medical Center, Boston, MA

**2010**

McLeod Regional Medical Center, Florence, SC | **Finalist:** Henry Ford Hospital, Detroit, MI

**2011**

Memorial Regional Hospital, Hollywood, FL | **Finalist:** AtlantiCare Regional Medical Center, Atlantic City, NJ | **Finalist:** Northwestern Memorial Hospital, Chicago, IL

**2012**

University Hospitals Case Medical Center, Cleveland, OH | **Finalist:** Lincoln Medical and Mental Health Center, Bronx, NY | **Finalist:** University of North Carolina Hospitals, Chapel Hill, NC and Life Choices, Fairview Health Services, Minneapolis, MN

**2013**

Beth Israel Deaconess Medical Center, Boston, MA | **Finalist:** Franklin Woods Community Hospital, Johnson City, TN

# Foster G. McGaw Prize

Honors health delivery organizations that have demonstrated exceptional commitment to community service.

| | | |
|---|---|---|
| **1986** | Lutheran Medical Center, Brooklyn, NY | |
| **1987** | Copley Hospital, Morrisville, VT | |
| | Mount Sinai Hospital, Hartford, CT | |
| **1988** | MetroHealth System, Cleveland, OH | |
| **1989** | Greater Southeast Healthcare System, Washington, DC | |
| **1990** | Mount Zion Medical Center of The University of California-San Francisco, San Francisco, CA | |
| **1991** | Franklin Regional Hospital, Franklin, NH | |
| **1992** | Mount Sinai Hospital Medical Center of Chicago, Chicago, IL | |
| **1993** | The Cambridge Hospital, Cambridge, MA | |

| | |
|---|---|
| **1994** | Parkland Memorial Hospital, Dallas, TX |
| **1995** | Our Lady of Lourdes Medical Center, Camden, NJ |
| **1996** | St. Mary's Hospital, Rochester, NY |
| **1997** | Bladen County Hospital Rural Health Network, Elizabethtown, NC |
| **1998** | Allina Health System, Minneapolis, MN |
| **1999** | LAC+USC Healthcare Network, Los Angeles, CA |
| **2000** | Kaweah Delta Health Care District, Visalia, CA |
| **2001** | Memorial Hospital of South Bend, South Bend, IN |
| **2002** | John C. Lincoln Health Network, Phoenix, AZ |

| | |
|---|---|
| **2003** | Phoebe Putney Memorial Hospital, Albany, GA |
| **2004** | Henry Ford Health System, Detroit, MI |
| **2005** | Venice Family Clinic, Venice, CA |
| **2006** | Memorial Healthcare System, Hollywood, FL |
| **2007** | Harborview Medical Center, Seattle, WA |
| **2008** | St. Mary's Health System, Lewiston, ME |
| **2009** | Heartland Health, St. Joseph, MO |
| **2010** | Allegiance Health, Jackson, MI |
| **2011** | Mt. Ascutney Hospital and Health Center, Windsor, VT |
| **2012** | St. Joseph's/Candler Health System, Savannah, GA |

An institution may be listed by the American Hospital Association if it is accredited as a hospital by The Joint Commission, American Osteopathic Association, DNV Healthcare accredited, or Medicare certified as a provider of acute service under Title 18 of the Social Security Act. Membership in the American Hospital Association is not a prerequisite.

If none of the four conditions mentioned above are satisfied, an insititution licensed as a hospital by the appropriate state agency may be registered by AHA as a hospital by meeting the following alernative requirements:

**Function:** The primary function of the institution is to provide patient services, diagnostic and therapeutic, for particular or general medical conditions.

1. The institution shall maintain at least six inpatient beds, which shall be continuously available for the care of patients who are nonrelated and who stay on the average in excess of 24 hours per admission.
2. The institution shall be constructed, equipped, and maintained to ensure the health and safety of patients and to provide uncrowded, sanitary facilities for the treatment of patients.

3. There shall be an identifiable governing authority legally and morally responsible for the conduct of the hospital.
4. There shall be a chief executive to whom the governing authority delegates the continuous responsibility for the operation of the hospital in accordance with established policy.
5. There shall be an organized medical staff of fully licensed physicians* that may include other licensed individuals permitted by law and by the hospital to provide patient care services independently in the hospital. The medical staff shall be accountable to the governing authority for maintaining proper standards of medical care, and it shall be governed by bylaws adopted by said staff and approved by the governing authority.
6. Each patient shall be admitted on the authority of a member of the medical staff who has been granted the privilege to admit patients to inpatient services in accordance with state law and criteria for standards of medical care established by the individual medical staff. Each patient's general medical condition is the responsibility of a qualified physician member of the medical staff. When nonphysician members of

the medical staff are granted privileges to admit patients, provision is made for prompt medical evaluation of these patients by a qualified physician. Any graduate of a foreign medical school who is permitted to assume responsibilities for patient care shall possess a valid license to practice medicine, or shall be certified by the Educational Commission for Foreign Medical Graduates, or shall have qualified for and have successfully completed an academic year of supervised clinical training under the direction of a medical school approved by the Liaison Committee on GAT Medical Education.
7. Registered nurse supervision and other nursing services are continuous.
8. A current and complete medical record shall be maintained by the institution for each patient and shall be available for reference.
9. Pharmacy service shall be maintained in the institution and shall be supervised by a registered pharmacist.
10. The institution shall provide patients with food service that meets their nutritional and therapeutic requirements; special diets shall also be available.

---

* Physician–Term used to describe an individual with an M.D. or D.O. degree who is fully licensed to practice medicine in all its phases.

‡ The completed records in general shall contain at least the following: the patient's identifying data and consent forms, medical history, record of physical examination, physicians' progress notes, operative notes, nurses' notes, routine x–ray and laboratory reports, doctors' orders, and final diagnosis.

## Types of Hospitals

In addition to meeting these 10 general requirements, hospitals are listed as one of four types of hospitals: general, special, rehabilitation and chronic disease, or psychiatric. The following definitions of function by type of hospital and special requirements are:

### General

The primary function of the institution is to provide patient services, diagnostic and therapeutic, for a variety of medical conditions. A general hospital also shall provide:

- diagnostic x–ray services with facilities and staff for a variety of procedures
- clinical laboratory service with facilities and staff for a variety of procedures and with anatomical pathology services regularly and conveniently available
- operating room service with facilities and staff.

### Special

The primary function of the institution is to provide diagnostic and treatment services for patients who have specified medical conditions, both surgical and nonsurgical. A special hospital also shall provide:

- such diagnostic and treatment services as may be determined by the Executive Committee of the Board of Trustees of the American Hospital Association to

be appropriate for the specified medical conditions for which medical services are provided shall be maintained in the institution with suitable facilities and staff. If such conditions do not normally require diagnostic x–ray service, laboratory service, or operating room service, and if any such services are therefore not maintained in the institution, there shall be written arrangements to make them available to patients requiring them.

- clinical laboratory services capable of providing tissue diagnosis when offering pregancy termination services.

### Rehabilitation and Chronic Disease

The primary function of the institution is to provide diagnostic and treatment services to handicapped or disabled individuals requiring restorative and adjustive services. A rehabilitation and chronic disease hospital also shall provide:

- arrangements for diagnostic x–ray services, as required, on a regular and conveniently available basis
- arrangements for clinical laboratory service, as required on a regular and conveniently available basis
- arrangements for operating room service, as required, on a regular and conveniently available basis
- a physical therapy service with suitable facilities and staff in the institution
- an occupational therapy service with suitable facilities and staff in the institution

- arrangements for psychological and social work services on a regular and conveniently available basis
- arrangements for educational and vocational services on a regular and conveniently available basis
- written arrangements with a general hospital for the transfer of patients who require medical, obstetrical, or surgical services not available in the institution.

### Psychiatric

The primary function of the institution is to provide diagnostic and treatment services for patients who have psychiatric–related illnesses. A psychiatric hospital also shall provide:

- arrangements for clinical laboratory service, as required, on a regular and conveniently available basis
- arrangements for diagnostic x–ray services, as required on a regular and conveniently available basis
- psychiatric, psychological, and social work service with facilities and staff in the institution
- arrangements for electroencephalograph services, as required, on a regular and conveniently available basis.
- written arrangements with a general hospital for the transfer of patients who require medical, obstetrical, or surgical services not available in the institution.

The American Hospital Association may, at the sole discretion of the Executive Committee of the Board of Trustees, grant, deny, or withdraw the listing of an institution.

---

\* Physician–Term used to describe an individual with an M.D. or D.O. degree who is fully licensed to practice medicine in all its phases.

‡ The completed records in general shall contain at least the following: the patient's identifying data and consent forms, medical history, record of physical examination, physicians' progress notes, operative notes, nurses' notes, routine x–ray and laboratory reports, doctors' orders, and final diagnosis.

---

# Explanation of Hospital Listings

## Sample Hospital Listing:

**ANYTOWN, Universal County**

⊠ **ANYTOWN HOSPITAL & CLINICS (777777)**, (Formerly Anytown Area Community Hospital and Clinic), 100 South Main Street, Zip 12345–6789; tel. 123/456–7890 **A9** 10  ]  ①

**F**10 12 23 24 29 30 31 37 39 49 51 55 57 64 65 66 68 70 71 72 77 78 83 87 88 91 96 97 106 107 110 111 113 124 **P1** 2 3 **S** Universal County Health System   ⑦ ② ③
Primary Contact: Ann M. Generic, Chief Executive Officer
COO: Ann M. Generic
CFO: Michael M. Generic
CMO: Peterl Van Generic, President Medical Staff   ④
CHR: Jerry Generic, Human Resources Director
Web address: www.website.org
**Control:** Other not–for–profit (including NFP Corporation) **Service:** General Medical and surgical   ⑤

**Staffed Beds:** 25 **Admissions:** 892 **Census:** 9 **Outpatient Visits:** 44014
**Births:** 51 **Total Expense ($000):** 19210 **Payroll Expense ($000):** 5864
**Personnel:** 182   ⑥

---

**ANYTOWN, Universal County**

⊠ **ANYTOWN HOSPITAL & CLINICS (777777)**, (Formerly Anytown Area Community Hospital and Clinic), 100 South Main Street, Zip 12345–6789; tel. 123/456–7890 **A9** 10

① = Approval Codes
② = Physician Codes
③ = Health Care System Name
④ = Titles of Chief Administrators
⑤ = Control and Service Classifications
⑥ = Utilization Data
⑦ = Facility Codes

---

| Hospital, Medicare Provider Number, Address, Telephone, Approval, Facility, and Physician Codes, Health Care System |
|---|
| ★ American Hospital Association (AHA) membership  ○ Healthcare Facilities Accreditation Program |
| □ The Joint Commission accreditation   ◇ DNV Healthcare Inc. accreditation   △ Commission on Accreditation of Rehabilitation Facilities (CARF) accreditation |

---

## ① Approval Codes

*Reported by the approving bodies specified, as of the dates noted.*

1 Accreditation under the hospital program of The Joint Commission (May 2013).
2 Cancer program approved by American College of Surgeons (March 2013).
†3 Approval to participate in residency training, by the Accreditation Council for Graduate Medical Education (April 2013).
†5 Medical school affiliation, reported to the American Medical Association (April 2013).
6 Hospital–controlled professional nursing school, reported by National League for Nursing.
7 Accreditation by Commission on Accreditation of Rehabilitation Facilities (March 2013).

8 Member of Council of Teaching Hospitals of the Association of American Medical Colleges (February 2013).
9 Hospitals contracting or participating in a Plan, reported by the Blue Cross and Blue Shield Association (April 2013).
10 Certified for participation in the Health Insurance for the Aged (Medicare) Program by the Centers for Medicare and Medical Services (February 2013).
11 Healthcare Facilities Accreditation Program (May 2013).

12 Internship approved by American Osteopathic Association (April 2013).
13 Residency approved by American Osteopathic Association (April 2013).
18 Critical Access Hospitals (May 2013).
19 Rural Referral Center (May 2013).
20 Sole Community Provider (May 2013).
21 Accreditation by DNV Healthcare Inc. (May 2013).

**Nonreporting** indicates that the 2012 Annual Survey questionnaire for the hospital was not received prior to publication.

## ② Physician Codes

*Actually available within, and reported by the institution; for definitions, see page A12.*

**(Alphabetical/Numerical Order)**

1 Closed physician–hospital organization (PHO)
2 Equity model
3 Foundation

4 Group practice without walls
5 Independent practice association (IPA)
6 Integrated salary model

7 Management service organization (MSO)
8 Open physician–hospital organization (PHO)

## ③ Health Care System Name

*The inclusion of the letter "S" (1) indicates that the hospital belongs to a health care system and (2) identifies the specific system to which the hospital belongs.*

## ④ Titles of Chief Administrators

## ⑤ Control and Service Classification

*For a list of control and service classifications, see page A13.*

**Control–**The type of organization that is responsible for establishing policy for overall operation of the hospital.

**Service–**The type of service the hospital provides to the majority of admissions.

## ⑥ Utilization Data

*Definitions are based on the American Hospital Association's Hospital Administration Terminology. In completing the survey, hospitals were requested to report data for a full year, in accord with their fiscal year, ending in 2012.*

**Beds–**Number of beds regularly maintained (set up and staffed for use) for inpatients as of the close of the reporting period. Excludes newborn bassinets.

**Admissions–**Number of patients accepted for inpatient service during a 12–month period; does not include newborn.

**Census–**Average number of inpatients receiving care each day during the 12–month reporting period; does not include newborn.

**Outpatient Visits–**A visit by a patient who is not lodged in the hospital while receiving medical, dental, or other services. Each appearance of an outpatient in each unit constitutes one visit regardless of the number of diagnostic and/or therapeutic treatments that a patient receives.

**Births–**Number of infants born in the hospital and accepted for service in a newborn infant bassinet during a 12–month period; excludes stillbirths.

**Expense:** Expense for a 12–month period; both total expense and payroll components are shown. Payroll expenses include all salaries and wages.

**Personnel:** Represents personnel situations as they existed at the end of the reporting period; includes full-time equivalents of part–time personnel. Full–time equivalents were calculated on the basis that two part–time persons equal one full–time person.

---

†Data from the Graduate Medical Education Database, Copyright 2012, American Medical Association, Chicago, Illinois.

## Sample Hospital Listing:

**ANYTOWN, Universal County**

⊞ **ANYTOWN HOSPITAL & CLINICS (777777)**, (Formerly Anytown Area Community Hospital and Clinic), 100 South Main Street, Zip 12345–6789; tel. 123/456–7890 **A**9 10  ] ①
**F**10 12 23 24 29 30 31 37 39 49 51 55 57 64 65 66 68 70 71 72 77 78 83 87 88 91 96 97 106 107 110 111 113 124 **P**1 2 3 **S** Universal ⑦
County Health System ② ③
Primary Contact: Ann M. Generic, Chief Executive Officer
COO: Ann M. Generic
CFO: Michael M. Generic ④
CMO: Peterl Van Generic, President Medical Staff
CHR: Jerry Generic, Human Resources Director
Web address: www.website.org
**Control:** Other not–for–profit (including NFP Corporation) **Service:** General ⑤
Medical and surgical

**Staffed Beds:** 25 **Admissions:** 892 **Census:** 9 **Outpatient Visits:** 44014
**Births:** 51 **Total Expense ($000):** 19210 **Payroll Expense ($000):** 5864 ⑥
**Personnel:** 182

**ANYTOWN, Universal County**

⊞ **ANYTOWN HOSPITAL & CLINICS (777777)**, (Formerly Anytown Area Community Hospital and Clinic), 100 South Main Street, Zip 12345–6789; tel. 123/456–7890 **A**9 10

① = **Approval Codes**
② = **Physician Codes**
③ = **Health Care System Name**
④ = **Titles of Chief Administrators**
⑤ = **Control and Service Classifications**
⑥ = **Utilization Data**
⑦ = **Facility Codes**

---

**Hospital, Medicare Provider Number, Address, Telephone, Approval, Facility, and Physician Codes, Health Care System**

★ American Hospital Association (AHA) membership
□ The Joint Commission accreditation
◇ DNV Healthcare Inc. accreditation
○ Healthcare Facilities Accreditation Program
△ Commission on Accreditation of Rehabilitation Facilities (CARF) accreditation

---

## ⑦ Facility Codes

*Provided directly by the hospital; for definitions, see page A6.*

### (Numerical Order)

1. Acute long-term care
2. Adult day care program
3. Airborne infection isolation room
4. Alcoholism-drug abuse or dependency inpatient unit
5. Alcoholism-drug abuse or dependency outpatient unit
6. Alzheimer center
7. Ambulance services
8. Ambulatory surgery center
9. Arthritis treatment center
10. Assisted living
11. Auxiliary
12. Bariatric/weight control services
13. Birthing room-LDR room-LDRP room
14. Blood donor center
15. Breast cancer screening/mammograms
16. Burn care services
17. Cardiac intensive care
18. Adult cardiology services
19. Pediatric cardiology services
20. Adult diagnostic catheterization
21. Pediatric diagnostic catheterization
22. Adult interventional cardiac catheterization
23. Pediatric diagnostic catheterization
24. Adult cardiac surgery
25. Pediatric cardiac surgery
26. Adult cardiac electrophysiology
27. Pediatric cardiac electrophysiology
28. Cardiac rehabilitation
29. Case management
30. Chaplaincy/pastoral care services
31. Chemotherapy
32. Children's wellness program
33. Chiropractic services
34. Community health education
35. Community outreach
36. Complementary and alternative medicine services
37. Computer assisted orthopedic surgery (CAOS)
38. Crisis prevention
39. Dental services
40. Emergency department
41. Pediatric emergency department
42. Satellite emergency department
43. Trauma center (certified)
44. Enabling services
45. Optical colonoscopy
46. Endoscopic ultrasound
47. Ablation of Barrett's esophagus
48. Esophageal impedance study

49. Endoscopic retrograde cholangiopancreatography (ERCP)
50. Enrollment assistance services
51. Extracorporeal shock wave lithotripter (ESWL)
52. Fertility clinic
53. Fitness center
54. Freestanding outpatient care center
55. Genetic testing/counseling
56. Geriatric services
57. Health fair
58. Health research
59. Health screenings
60. Hemodialysis
61. HIV–AIDS services
62. Home health services
63. Hospice program
64. Hospital–based outpatient care center services
65. Immunization program
66. Indigent care clinic
67. Intermediate nursing care
68. Linguistic/translation services
69. Meals on wheels
70. Medical surgical intensive care services
71. Mobile health services
72. Neonatal intensive care
73. Neonatal intermediate care
74. Neurological services
75. Nutrition programs
76. Obstetrics
77. Occupational health services
78. Oncology services
79. Orthopedic services
80. Other special care
81. Outpatient surgery
82. Pain management program
83. Inpatient palliative care unit
84. Palliative care program
85. Patient controlled analgesia (PCA)
86. Patient education center
87. Patient representative services
88. Pediatric intensive care services
89. Pediatric medical–surgical care
90. Physical rehabilitation inpatient services
91. Assistive technology center
92. Electrodiagnostic services
93. Physical rehabilitation outpatient services
94. Prosthetic and orthotic services
95. Robot-assisted walking therapy
96. Simulated rehabilitation environment
97. Primary care department
98. Psychiatric care
99. Psychiatric child–adolescent services
100. Psychiatric consultation–liaison services

101. Psychiatric education services
102. Psychiatric emergency services
103. Psychiatric geriatric services
104. Psychiatric outpatient services
105. Psychiatric partial hospitalization services
106. Psychiatric residential treatment
107. CT scanner
108. Diagnostic radioisotope facility
109. Electron beam computed tomography (EBCT)
110. Full–field digital mammography (FFDM)
111. Magnetic resonance imaging (MRI)
112. Intraoperative magnetic resonance imaging
113. Magnetoencephalography (MEG)
114. Multi–slice spiral computed tomography (MSCT) (<64 slice CT)
115. Multi–slice spiral computed tomography (64 + slice CT)
116. Positron emission tomography (PET)
117. Positron emission tomography/CT (PET/CT)
118. Single photon emission computerized tomography (SPECT)
119. Ultrasound
120. Image–guided radiation therapy (IGRT)
121. Intensity–modulated radiation therapy (IMRT)
122. Proton beam therapy
123. Shaped beam radiation therapy
124. Stereotactic radiosurgery
125. Retirement housing
126. Robotic surgery
127. Rural health clinic
128. Skilled nursing care
129. Sleep center
130. Social work services
131. Sports medicine
132. Support groups
133. Swing bed services
134. Teen outreach services
135. Tobacco treatment/cessation program
136. Bone marrow transplant services
137. Heart transplant
138. Kidney transplant
139. Liver transplant
140. Lung transplant
141. Tissue transplant
142. Other transplant
143. Transportation to health services
144. Urgent care center
145. Virtual colonoscopy
146. Volunteer services department
147. Women's health center/services
148. Wound management services

# Annual Survey

Each year, an annual survey of hospitals is conducted by the American Hospital Association through its Health Forum affiliate.

The facilities and services found below are provided by the hospital. For data products reflecting the services provided by a hospital through its health care system, or network or through a formal arrangement with another provider contact Health Forum at 800/821–2039, or visit www.healthforum.com.

The AHA Guide to the Health Care Field does not include all data collected from the 2012 Annual Survey. Requests for purchasing other Annual Survey data should be directed to Health Forum LLC, an affiliate of the American Hospital Association, 155 N. Wacker Drive, Chicago, IL 60606, 800/821–2039.

## Definitions of Facility Codes

1. **Acute long–term care.** Provides specialized acute hospital care to medically complex patients who are critically ill, have multisystem complications and/or failure, and require hospitalization averaging 25 days, in a facility offering specialized treatment programs and therapeutic intervention on a 24–hour/7 day a week basis.

2. **Adult day care program.** Program providing supervision, medical and psychological care, and social activities for older adults who live at home or in another family setting, but cannot be alone or prefer to be with others during the day. May include intake assessment, health monitoring, occupational therapy, personal care, noon meal, and transportation services.

3. **Airborne infection isolation room.** A single–occupancy room for patient care where environmental factors are controlled in an effort to minimize the transmission of those infectious agents, usually spread person to person by droplet nuclei associated with coughing and inhalation. Such rooms typically have specific ventilation requirements for controlled ventilation, air pressure and filtration.

4. **Alcoholism–drug abuse or dependency inpatient unit.** Provides diagnosis and therapeutic services to patients with alcoholism or other drug dependencies. Includes care for inpatient/residential treatment for patients whose course of treatment involves more intensive care than provided in an outpatient setting or where patient requires supervised withdrawal.

5. **Alcoholism–drug abuse or dependency outpatient unit.** Organized hospital services that provide medical care and/or rehabilitative treatment services to outpatients for whom the primary diagnosis is alcoholism or other chemical dependency.

6. **Alzheimer center.** Facility that offers care to persons with Alzheimer's disease and their families through an integrated program of clinical services, research, and education.

7. **Ambulance services.** Provision of ambulance services to the ill and injured who require medical attention on a scheduled or unscheduled basis.

8. **Ambulatory surgery center.** Facility that provides care to patients requiring surgery who are admitted and discharged on the same day. Ambulatory surgery centers are distinct from same day surgical units within the hospital outpatient departments for purposes of Medicare payments.

9. **Arthritis treatment center.** Specifically equipped and staffed center for the diagnosis and treatment of arthritis and other joint disorders.

10. **Assisted living.** A special combination of housing, supportive services, personalized assistance and health care designed to respond to the individual needs of those who need help in activities of daily living and instrumental activities of daily living. Supportive services are available, 24 hours a day, to meet scheduled and unscheduled needs, in a way that promotes maximum independence and dignity for each resident and encourages the involvement of a resident's family, neighbor and friends.

11. **Auxiliary.** A volunteer community organization formed to assist the hospital in carrying out its purpose and to serve as a link between the institution and the community.

12. **Bariatric/weight control services.** Bariatrics is the medical practice of weight reduction.

13. **Birthing room–LDR room–LDRP room.** A single room–type of maternity care with a more homelike setting for families than the traditional three–room unit (labor/delivery/recovery) with a separate postpartum area. A birthing room combines labor and delivery in one room. An LDR room accommodates three stages in the birthing process—labor, delivery, and recovery. An LDRP room accommodates all four stages of the birth process—labor, delivery, recovery and postpartum.

14. **Blood donor center.** A facility that performs, or is responsible for the collection, processing, testing or distribution of blood and components.

15. **Breast cancer screening/mammograms.** Mammography screening–the use of breast x–ray to detect unsuspected breast cancer in asymptomatic women. Diagnostic mammography–the x–ray imaging of breast tissue in symptomatic women who are considered to have a substantial likelihood of having breast cancer already.

16. **Burn care services.** Provides care to severely burned patients. Severely burned patients are those with any of the following: 1. Second–degree burns of more than 25% total body surface area for adults or 20% total body surface area for children; 2. Third–degree burns of more than 10% total body surface area; 3. Any severe burns of the hands, face, eyes, ears or feet or; 4. All inhalation injuries, electrical burns, complicated burn injuries involving fractures and other major traumas, and all other poor risk factors.

17. **Cardiac intensive care.** Provides patient care of a more specialized

nature than the usual medical and surgical care, on the basis of physicians' orders and approved nursing care plans. The unit is staffed with specially trained nursing personnel and contains monitoring and specialized support or treatment equipment for patients who, because of heart seizure, open–heart surgery, or other life–threatening conditions, require intensified, comprehensive observation and care. May include myocardial infarction, pulmonary care, and heart transplant units.

18. **Adult cardiology services.** An organized clinical service offering diagnostic and interventional procedures to manage the full range of adult heart conditions.

19. **Pediatric cardiology services.**

20. **Adult diagnostic catheterization.** (also called coronary angiography or coronary arteriography) is used to assist in diagnosing complex heart conditions. Cardiac angiography involves the insertion of a tiny catheter up into the artery in the groin then carefully threading the catheter up into the aorta where the coronary arteries originate. Once the catheter is in place, a dye is injected which allows the cardiologist to see the size, shape and distribution of the coronary arteries. These images are used to diagnose heart disease and to determine, among other things, whether or not surgery is indicated.

21. **Pediatric diagnostic catheterization.** (also called coronary angiography or coronary arteriography) is used to assist in diagnosing complex heart conditions. Cardiac angiography involves the insertion of a tiny catheter up into the artery in the groin then carefully threading the catheter up into the aorta where the coronary arteries originate. Once the catheter is in place, a dye is injected which allows the cardiologist to see the size, shape and distribution of the coronary arteries. These images are used to diagnose heart disease and to determine, among other things, whether or not surgery is indicated.

22. **Adult interventional cardiac catheterization.** Nonsurgical procedure that utilizes the same basic principles as diagnostic cathetereization and then uses advanced the techniques to improve the heart's function. It can be less invasive alternative to heart surgery.

23. **Pediatric diagnostic catheterization.** Nonsurgical

procedure that utilizes the same basic principles as diagnostic cathetereization and then uses advanced the techniques to improve the heart's function. It can be less invasive alternative to heart surgery.

24. **Adult cardiac surgery.** Includes minimally invasive procedures that include surgery done with only a small incision or no incision at all, such as through a laparoscope or an endoscope and more invasive major surgical procedures that include open chest and open heart surgery.

25. **Pediatric cardiac surgery.** Includes minimally invasive procedures that include surgery done with only a small incision or no incision at all, such as through a laparoscope or an endoscope and more invasive major surgical procedures that include open chest and open heart surgery defibrillator implantation and follow-up.

26. **Adult cardiac electrophysiology.** Evaluation and management of patients with complex rhythm or conduction abnormalities, including diagnostic testing, treatment of arrhythmias by catheter ablation or drug therapy, and pacemaker/ defibrillator implantation and follow-up.

27. **Pediatric cardiac electrophysiology.**

28. **Cardiac rehabilitation.** A medically supervised program to help heart patients recover quickly and improve their overall physical and mental functioning. The goal is to reduce risk of another cardiac event or to keep an already present heart condition from getting worse. Cardiac rehabilitation programs include: counseling to patients, an exercise program, helping patients modify risk factors such as smoking and high blood pressure, providing vocational guidance to enable the patient to return to work, supplying information on physical limitations and lending emotional support.

29. **Case management.** A system of assessment, treatment planning, referral and follow–up that ensures the provision of comprehensive and continuous services and the coordination of payment and reimbursement for care.

30. **Chaplaincy/pastoral care services.** A service ministering religious activities and providing pastoral counseling to patients, their families,

and staff of a health care organization.

31. **Chemotherapy.** An organized program for the treatment of cancer by the use of drugs or chemicals.

32. **Children's wellness program.** A program that encourages improved health status and a healthful lifestyle of children through health education, exercise, nutrition and health promotion.

33. **Chiropractic services.** An organized clinical service including spinal manipulation or adjustment and related diagnostic and therapeutic services.

34. **Community health education.** Education that provides health information to individuals and populations as well as support for personal, family and community health decisions with the objective of improving health status.

35. **Community outreach.** A program that systematically interacts with the community to identify those in need of services, alerting persons and their families to the availability of services, locating needed services, and enabling persons to enter the service delivery system.

36. **Complementary and alternative medicine services.** Organized hospital services or formal arrangements to providers that provide care or treatment not based solely on traditional western allopathic medical teachings as instructed in most U.S. medical schools. Includes any of the following; acupuncture, chiropractic, homeopathy, osteopathy, diet and lifestyle changes, herbal medicine, massage therapy, etc.

37. **Computer assisted orthopedic surgery (CAOS).** Orthopedic surgery using computer technology, enabling three–dimensional graphic models to visualize a patient's anatomy.

38. **Crisis prevention** Services provided in order to promote physical and mental well being and the early identification of disease and ill health prior to the onset and recognition of symptoms so as to permit early treatment.

39. **Dental services.** An organized dental service, not necessarily involving special facilities, that provides dental or oral services to inpatients or outpatients.

40. **Emergency department.** Hospital facilities for the provision of

unscheduled outpatient services to patients whose conditions require immediate care. Must be staffed 24 hours a day.

41. **Pediatric emergency department.** Hospital facilities for the provision of unscheduled outpatient services to patients whose conditions require immediate care.

42. **Satellite emergency department.** A facility owned and operated by the hospital but physically separate from the hospital for the provision of unscheduled outpatient services to patients whose conditions require.

43. **Trauma center (certified).** A facility certified to provide emergency and specialized intensive care to critically ill and injured patients.

44. **Enabling services.** A program that is designed to help the patient access health care services by offering any of the following linguistic services, transportation services, and/or referrals to local social services agencies.

45. **Optical colonoscopy.** An examination of the interior of the colon using a long, flexible, lighted tube with a small built-in camera.

46. **Endoscopic ultrasound.** Specially designed endoscope that incorporates an ultrasound transducer used to obtain detailed images of organs in the chest and abdomen. The endoscope can be passed through the mouth or the anus. When combined with needle biopsy the procedure can assist in diagnosis and staging of cancer.

47. **Ablation of Barrett's esophagus.** Premalignant condition that can lead to adenocarcinoma of the esophagus. The non surgical ablation of the premalignant tissue in Barrett's esophagus by the application of thermal energy or light through an endoscope passed from the mouth into the esophagus.

48. **Esophageal impedance study.** A test in which a catheter is placed through the nose into the esophagus to measure whether gas or liquids are passing from the stomach into the esophagus and causing symptoms.

49. **Endoscopic retrograde cholangiopancreatography (ERCP).** A procedure in which a catheter is introduced through an endoscope into the bile ducts and pancreatic ducts. Injection of contrast materials permits detailed x–ray of these structures. The procedure is used diagnostically as

well as therapeutically to relieve obstruction or remove stones

50. **Enrollment assistance services.** A program that provides enrollment assistance for patients who are potentially eligible for public health insurance programs such as Medicaid, State Children's Health Insurance, or local/state indigent care programs. The specific services offered could include explanation of benefits, assist applicants in completing the application and locating all relevant documents, conduct eligibilty interviews, and/or forward applications and documentation to state/local social service or health agency.

51. **Extracorporeal shock wave lithotripter (ESWL).** A medical device used for treating stones in the kidney or urethra. The device disintegrates kidney stones noninvasively through the transmission of acoustic shock waves directed at the stones.

52. **Fertility clinic.** A specialized program set in an infertility center that provides counseling and education as well as advanced reproductive techniques such as: injectable therapy, reproductive surgeries, treatment for endometriosis, male factor infertility, tubal reversals, in vitro fertilization (IVF), donor eggs, and other such services to help patients achieve successful pregnancies.

53. **Fitness center.** Provides exercise, testing, or evaluation programs and fitness activities to the community and hospital employees.

54. **Freestanding outpatient care center.** A facility owned and operated by the hospital, but physically separate from the hospital, that provides various medical treatments on an outpatient basis only. In addition to treating minor illnesses or injuries, the center will stabilize seriously ill or injured patients before transporting them to a hospital. Laboratory and radiology services are usually available.

55. **Genetic testing/counseling** A service equipped with adequate laboratory facilities and directed by a qualified physician to advise parents and prospective parents on potential problems in cases of genetic defects. A genetic test is the analysis of human DNA, RNA, chromosomes, proteins, and certain metabolites in order to detect heritable disease–related genotypes, mutations,

phenotypes, or karyotypes for clinical purposes. Genetic tests can have diverse purposes, including the diagnosis of genetic diseases in newborns, children, and adults; the identification of future health risks; the prediction of drug responses; and the assessment of risks to future children.

56. **Geriatric services.** The branch of medicine dealing with the physiology of aging and the diagnosis and treatment of disease affecting the aged. Services could include: Adult day care program; Alzheimer's diagnostic–assessment services; Comprehensive geriatric assessment; Emergency response system; Geriatric acute care unit; and/or Geriatric clinics.

57. **Health fair.** Community health education events that focus on the prevention of disease and promotion of health through such activities as audiovisual exhibits and free diagnostic services.

58. **Health research.** Organized hospital research program in any of the following areas: basic research, clinical research, community health research, and/or research on innovative health care delivery.

59. **Health screenings.** A preliminary procedure, such as a test or examination to detect the most characteristic sign or signs of a disorder that may require further investigation.

60. **Hemodialysis.** Provision of equipment and personnel for the treatment of renal insufficiency on an inpatient or outpatient basis.

61. **HIV–AIDS services.** Services may include one or more of the following: HIV–AIDS unit (special unit or team designated and equipped specifically for diagnosis, treatment, continuing care planning, and counseling services for HIV–AIDS patients and their families.) General inpatient care for HIV–AIDS (inpatient diagnosis and treatment for human immunodeficiency virus and acquired immunodeficiency syndrome patients, but dedicated unit is not available.) Specialized outpatient program for HIV–AIDS (special outpatient program providing diagnostic, treatment, continuing care planning, and counseling for HIV–AIDS patients and their families.)

62. **Home health services.** Service providing nursing, therapy, and

health–related homemaker or social services in the patient's home.

63. **Hospice program.** A program providing palliative care, chiefly medical relief of pain and supportive services, addressing the emotional, social, financial, and legal needs of terminally ill patients and their families. Care can be provided in a variety of settings, both inpatient and at home.

64. **Hospital–based outpatient care center services.** Organized hospital health care services offered by appointment on an ambulatory basis. Services may include outpatient surgery, examination, diagnosis, and treatment of a variety of medical conditions on a nonemergency basis, and laboratory and other diagnostic testing as ordered by staff or outside physician referral.

65. **Immunization program.** Program that plans, coordinates and conducts immunization services in the community.

66. **Indigent care clinic.** Health care services for uninsured and underinsured persons where care is free of charge or charged on a sliding scale. This would include "free clinics" staffed by volunteer practitioners, but could also be staffed by employees with sponsoring health care organizations subsidizing the cost of service.

67. **Intermediate nursing care.** Provides health–related services (skilled nursing care and social services) to residents with a variety of physical conditions or functional disabilities. These residents do not require the care provided by a hospital or skilled nursing facility, but do need supervision and support services.

68. **Linguistic/translation services.** Services provided by the hospital designed to make health care more accessible to non–English speaking patients and their physicians.

69. **Meals on wheels.** A hospital sponsored program which delivers meals to people, usually the elderly, who are unable to prepare their own meals. Low cost, nutritional meals are delivered to individuals' homes on a regular basis.

70. **Medical surgical intensive care services.** Provides patient care of a more intensive nature than the usual medical and surgical care, on the basis of physicians' orders and approved nursing care plans. These units are staffed with specially trained nursing personnel and contain monitoring and specialized support equipment of patients who, because of shock, trauma, or other life–threatening conditions, require intensified, comprehensive observation and care. Includes mixed intensive care units.

71. **Mobile health services.** Vans and other vehicles used to deliver primary care services.

72. **Neonatal intensive care.** A unit that must be separate from the newborn nursery providing intensive care to all sick infants including those with the very lowest birth weights (less that 1500 grams). NICU has potential for providing mechanical ventilation, neonatal surgery, and special care for the sickest infants born in the hospital or transferred from another institution. A full–time neonatologist serves as director of the NICU.

73. **Neonatal intermediate care.** A unit that must be separate from the normal newborn nursery and that provides intermediate and/or recovery care and some specialized services, including immediate resuscitation, intravenous therapy, and capacity for prolonged oxygen therapy and monitoring.

74. **Neurological services.** Services provided by the hospital dealing with the operative and nonoperative management of disorders of the central, peripheral, and autonomic nervous system.

75. **Nutrition programs.** Those services within a health care facility which are designed to provide inexpensive, nutritionally sound meals to patients.

76. **Obstetrics.** Levels should be designated: (1) unit provides services for uncomplicated maternity and newborn cases; (2) unit provides services for uncomplicated cases, the majority of complicated problems, and special neonatal services; and (3) unit provides services for all serious illnesses and abnormalities and is supervised by a full–time maternal/fetal specialist.

77. **Occupational health services.** Includes services designed to protect the safety of employees from hazards in the work environment.

78. **Oncology services.** Inpatient and outpatient services for patients with cancer, including comprehensive care, support and guidance in addition to patient education and preventiion, chemotherapy, counseling, and other treatment methods.

79. **Orthopedic services.** Services provided for the prevention or correction of injuries or disorders of the skeletal system and associated muscles, joints, and ligaments.

80. **Other special care.** Provides care to patients requiring care more intensive than that provided in the acute area, yet not sufficiently intensive to require admission to an intensive care unit. Patients admitted to the area are usually transferred here from an intensive care unit once their condition has improved. These units are sometimes referred to as definitive observation, step–down, or progressive care units.

81. **Outpatient surgery.** Scheduled surgical services provided to patients who do not remain in the hospital overnight. The surgery may be performed in operating suites also used for inpatient surgery, specially designated surgical suites for outpatient surgery, or procedure rooms within an outpatient care facility.

82. **Pain management program.** A hospital wide formalized program that includes staff education for the management of chronic and acute pain based on guidelines and protocols like those developed by the agency for Health Care Policy Research, etc.

83. **Inpatient palliative care unit.** An inpatient palliative care ward is a physically discreet, inpatient nursing unit where the focus is palliative care. The patient care focus is on symptom relief for complex patients who may be continuing to undergo primary treatment. Care is delivered by palliative medicine specialists.

84. **Palliative care program.** An organized program providing specialized medical care, drugs or therapies for the management of acute or chronic pain and/or the control of symptoms adminstered by specially trained physicians and other clinicians; and supportive care services, such as counseling on advanced directives, spiritual care, and social services, to patients with advanced disease and their families.

85. **Patient controlled analgesia (PCA).** Patient Controlled Analgesia (PCA) is intravenously administered pain medicine under the patient's control. The patient has a button on the end of a cord than can be pushed at will, whenever more pain medicine is desired. This button will only deliver more pain medicine at pre–

determined intervals, as programmed by the doctor's order.

86. **Patient education center.** Written goals and objectives for the patient and/or family related to therapeutic regimens, medical procedures, and self care.

87. **Patient representative services.** Organized hospital services providing personnel through whom patients and staff can seek solutions to institutional problems affecting the delivery of high–quality care and services.

88. **Pediatric intensive care services.** Provides care to pediatric patients that is of a more intensive nature than that usually provided to pediatric patients. The unit is staffed with specially trained personnel and contains monitoring and specialized support equipment for treatment of patients who, because of shock, trauma, or other life–threatening conditions, require intensified, comprehensive observation and care.

89. **Pediatric medical–surgical care.** Provides acute care to pediatric patients on the basis of physicians' orders and approved nursing care plans.

90. **Physical rehabilitation inpatient services.** Provides care encompassing a comprehensive array of restoration services for the disabled and all support services necessary to help patients attain their maximum functional capacity.

91. **Assistive technology center.** A program providing access to specialized hardware and software with adaptations allowing individuals greater independence with mobility, dexterity, or increased communication options.

92. **Electrodiagnostic services.** Diagnostic testing services for nerve and muscle function including services such as nerve conduction studies and needle electromyography.

93. **Physical rehabilitation outpatient services.** Outpatient program providing medical, health–related, therapy, social, and/or vocational services to help disabled persons attain or retain their maximum functional capacity.

94. **Prosthetic and orthotic services.** Services providing comprehensive prosthetic and orthotic evaluation, fitting, and training.

95. **Robot-assisted walking therapy.** A form of physical therapy that uses a robotic device to assist patients who are relearning how to walk.

96. **Simulated rehabilitation environment.** Rehabilitation focused on retraining functional skills in a contextually appropriate environment (simulated home and community settings) or in a traditional setting (gymnasium) using motor learning principles.

97. **Primary care department.** A unit or clinic within the hospital that provides primary care services (e.g. general pediatric care, general internal medicine, family practice and gynecology) through hospital–salaried medical and or nursing staff, focusing on evaluating and diagnosing medical problems and providing medical treatment on an outpatient basis.

98. **Psychiatric care.** Provides acute or long–term care to emotionally disturbed patients, including patients admitted for diagnosis and those admitted for treatment of psychiatric problems, on the basis of physicians' orders and approved nursing care plans. Long–term care may include intensive supervision to the chronically mentally ill, mentally disordered, or other mentally incompetent persons.

99. **Psychiatric child–adolescent services.** Provides care to emotionally disturbed children and adolescents, including those admitted for diagnosis and those admitted for treatment.

100. **Psychiatric consultation–liaison services.** Provides organized psychiatric consultation/liaison services to nonpsychiatric hospital staff and/or department on psychological aspects of medical care that may be generic or specific to individual patients.

101. **Psychiatric education services.** Provides psychiatric educational services to community agencies and workers such as schools, police, courts, public health nurses, welfare agencies, clergy and so forth. The purpose is to expand the mental health knowledge and competence of personnel not working in the mental health field and to promote good mental health through improved understanding, attitudes, and behavioral patterns.

102. **Psychiatric emergency services.** Services or facilities available on a 24–hour basis to provide immediate unscheduled outpatient care, diagnosis, evaluation, crisis intervention, and assistance to persons suffering acute emotional or mental distress.

103. **Psychiatric geriatric services.** Provides care to emotionally disturbed elderly patients, including those admitted for diagnosis and those admitted for treatment.

104. **Psychiatric outpatient services.** Provides medical care, including diagnosis and treatment of psychiatric outpatients.

105. **Psychiatric partial hospitalization services.** Organized hospital services of intensive day/evening outpatient services of three hours or more duration, distinguished from other outpatient visits of one hour.

106. **Psychiatric residential treatment.**

107. **CT scanner.** Computed tomographic scanner for head and whole body scans.

108. **Diagnostic radioisotope facility.** The use of radioactive isotopes (Radiopharmaceutical) as tracers or indicators to detect an abnormal condition or disease.

109. **Electron beam computed tomography (EBCT).** A high tech computed tomography scan used to detect coronary artery disease by measuring coronary calcifications. This imaging procedure uses electron beams which are magnetically steered to produce a visual of the coronary artery and the images are produced faster than conventional CT scans.

110. **Full–field digital mammography (FFDM).** Combines the x–ray generators and tubes used in analog screen–film mammography (SFM) with a detector plate that converts the x–rays into a digital signal.

111. **Magnetic resonance imaging (MRI).** The use of a uniform magnetic field and radio frequencies to study tissue and structure of the body. This procedure enables the visualization of biochemical activity of the cell in vivo without the use of ionizing radiation, radioisotopic substances, or high–frequency sound.

112. **Intraoperative magnetic resonance imaging.** An integrated surgery system which provides an MRI system in an operating room. The system allows for immediate evaluation of the degree to tumor resection while the patient is undergoing a surgical resection. Intraoperative MRI exists when a MRI (low–field or high–field) is placed in the operating theater and is

used during surgical resection without moving the patient from the operating room to the diagnostic imaging suite.

113. **Magnetoencephalography (MEG).** A noninvasive neurophysiological measurement tool used to study magnetic fields generated by neuronal activity of the brain. MEG provides direct information about the dynamics of evoked and spontaneous neural activity and the location of their sources in the brain. The primary uses of MEG include assisting surgeons in localizing the source of epilepsy, sensory mapping and the study of brain function. When it is combined with structural imaging, it is known as magnetic source imaging (MSI).

114. **Multi–slice spiral computed tomography (MSCT) (<64 slice CT).** A specialized computed tomography procedure that provides three–dimensional processing and allows narrower and multiple slices with increased spatial resolution and faster scanning times as compared to a regular computed tomography scan.

115. **Multi–slice spiral computed tomography (64 + slice CT).** Involves the acquisition of volumetric tomographic x–ray absorption data expressed in Hounsfield units using multiple rows of detectors. 64+ systems reconstruct the equivalent of 64 or greater slices to cover the imaged volume.

116. **Positron emission tomography (PET).** A nuclear medicine imaging technology which uses radioactive (positron emitting) isotopes created in a cyclotron or generator and computers to produce composite pictures of the brain and heart at work. PET scanning produces sectional images depicting metabolic activity or blood flow rather than anatomy.

117. **Positron emission tomography/CT (PET/CT).** Provides metabolic functional information for the monitoring of chemotherapy, radiotherapy and surgical planning.

118. **Single photon emission computerized tomography (SPECT).** A nuclear medicine imaging technology that combines existing technology of gamma camera imaging with computed tomographic imaging technology to provide a more precise and clear image.

119. **Ultrasound.** The use of acoustic waves above the range of 20,000

cycles per second to visualize internal body structures.

120. **Image–guided radiation therapy (IGRT).** Automated system for image–guided radiation therapy that enables clinicians to obtain high–resolution x–ray images to pinpoint tumor sites, adjust patient positioning when necessary, and complete a treatment, all within the standard treatment time slot, allowing for more effective cancer treatments.

121. **Intensity–modulated radiation Therapy (IMRT).** A type of three–dimensional radiation therapy, which improves the targeting of treatment delivery in a way that is likely to decrease damage to normal tissues and allows varying intensities diagnosis of genetic diseases in newborns, children, and adults; the identification of future health risks; the prediction of drug responses; and the assessment of risks to future children.

122. **Proton beam therapy.** A form of radiation therapy which administers proton beams. While producing the same biologic effects as x–ray beams, the energy distribution of protons differs from conventional x–ray beams in that they can be more precisely focused in tissue volumes in a three–dimensional pattern resulting in less surrounding tissue damage than conventional radiation therapy permitting administration of higher doses.

123. **Shaped beam radiation therapy.** A precise, non–invasive treatment that involves targeting beams of radiation that mirror the exact size and shape of a tumor at a specific area of a tumor to shrink or destroy cancerous cells. This procedure delivers a therapeutic dose of radiation that conforms precisely to the shape of the tumor, thus minimizing the risk to nearby tissues.

124. **Stereotactic radiosurgery.** Stereotactic radiosurgery (SRS) is a radiotherapy modality that delivers a high dosage of radiation to a discrete treatment area in as few as one treatment session. Includes gamma knife, cyberknife, etc.

125. **Retirement housing.** A facility which provides social activities to senior citizens, usually retired persons, who do not require health care but some short–term skilled nursing care may be provided. A retirement center may furnish housing and may also have acute hospital and long–term care facilities, or it may

arrange for acute and long term care through affiliated institutions.

126. **Robotic surgery.** The use of mechanical guidance devices to remotely manipulate surgical instrumentation.

127. **Rural health clinic.** A clinic located in a rural, medically under-served area in the United States that has a separate reimbursement structure from the standard medical office under the Medicare and Medicaid programs.

128. **Skilled nursing care.** Provides non–acute medical and skilled nursing care services, therapy, and social services under the supervision of a licensed registered nurse on a 24–hour basis.

129. **Sleep center.** Specially equipped and staffed center for the diagnosis and treatment of sleep disorders.

130. **Social work services.** Services may include one or more of the following: Organized social work services (services that are properly directed and sufficiently staffed by qualified individuals who provide assistance and counseling to patients and their families in dealing with social, emotional, and environmental problems associated with illness or disability, often in the context of financial or discharge planning coordination.) Outpatient social work services (social work services provided in ambulatory care areas.) Emergency department social work services (social work services provided to emergency department patients by social workers dedicated to the emergency department or on call.)

131. **Sports medicine.** Provision of diagnostic screening and assessment and clinical and rehabilitation services for the prevention and treatment of sports–related injuries.

132. **Support groups.** A hospital sponsored program which allows a group of individuals with the same or similar problems who meet periodically to share experiences, problems, and solutions, in order to support each other.

133. **Swing bed services.** A hospital bed that can be used to provide either acute or long–term care depending on community or patients needs. To be eligible a hospital must have a Medicare provider agreement in place, have fewer than 100 beds, be located in a rural area, not have a 24 hour nursing service waiver in effect, have not been terminated from the

program in the prior two years, and meet various service conditions.

134. **Teen outreach services.** A program focusing on the teenager which encourages an improved health status and a healthful lifestyle including physical, emotional, mental, social, spiritual and economic health through education, exercise, nutrition and health promotion.

135. **Tobacco treatment/cessation program.** Organized hospital services with the purpose of ending tobacco-use habits of patients addicted to tobacco/nicotine.

136.–142. **Transplant services.** The branch of medicine that transfers an organ or tissue from one person to another or from one body part to another to replace a diseased structure or to restore function or to change appearance. Services could include: Bone marrow transplant program (**136. Bone marrow**); heart (**137. Heart transplant**), kidney (**138. Kidney transplant**), liver (**139. Liver transplant**) lung (**140. Lung transplant**), tissue (**141. Tissue**

transplant**). Please include heart/lung or other multi– transplant surgeries in other (**142. Other Transplant**).

143. **Transportation to health services.** A long–term care support service designed to assist the mobility of the elderly. Some programs offer improved financial access by offering reduced rates and barrier–free buses or vans with ramps and lifts to assist the elderly or handicapped; others offer subsidies for public transport systems or operate mini–bus services exclusively for use by senior citizens.

144. **Urgent care center.** A facility that provides care and treatment for problems that are not life–threatening but require attention over the short term. These units function like emergency rooms but are separate from hospitals with which they may have backup affiliation arrangements.

145. **Virtual colonoscopy.** Noninvasive screening procedure used to visualize, analyze and detect cancerous or potentially cancerous polyps in the colon.

146. **Volunteer services department.** An organized hospital department responsible for coordinating the services of volunteers working within the institution.

147. **Women's center.** An area set aside for coordinated education and treatment services specifically for and promoted by women as provided by this special unit. Services may or may not include obstetrics but include a range of services other than OB.

148. **Wound management services.** Services for patients with chronic wounds and non–healing wounds often resulting from diabetes, poor circulation, improper seating and immunocompromising conditions. The goals are to progress chronic wounds through stages of healing, reduce and eliminate infections, increase physical function to minimize complications from current wounds and prevent future chronic wounds. Wound management services are provided on an inpatient or outpatient basis, depending on the intensity of service needed.

# Definitions of Physician Codes

1. **Closed physician–hospital organization (PHO).** A PHO that restricts physician membership to those practitioners who meet criteria for cost effectiveness and/or high quality.

2. **Equity model.** Allows established practitioners to become shareholders in a professional corporation in exchange for tangible and intangible assets of their existing practices.

3. **Foundation.** A corporation, organized either as a hospital affiliate or subsidiary, which purchases both the tangible and intangible assets of one or more medical group practices. Physicians remain in a separate corporate entity but sign a professional services agreement with the foundation.

4. **Group practice without walls.** Hospital sponsors the formation of, or

provides capital to physicians to establish, a 'quasi' group to share administrative expenses while remaining independent practitioners.

5. **Independent practice association (IPA).** A legal entity that hold managed care contracts. The IPA then contracts with physicians, usually in solo practice, to provide care either on a fee–for–services or capitated basis. The purpose of an IPA is to assist solo physicians in obtaining managed care contracts.

6. **Integrated salary model.** Physicians are salaried by the hospital or another entity of a health system to provide medical services for primary care and specialty care.

7. **Management services organization (MSO).** A corporation, owned by the

hospital or a physician/hospital joint venture, that provides management services to one or more medical group practices. The MSO purchases the tangible assets of the practices and leases them back as part of a full–service management agreement, under which the MSO employs all non–physician staff and provides all supplies/administrative systems for a fee.

8. **Open physician–hospital organization (PHO).** A joint venture between the hospital and all members of the medical staff who wish to participate. The PHO can act as a unified agent in managed care contracting, own a managed care plan, own and operate ambulatory care centers or ancillary services projects, or provide administrative services to physician members.

# Control and Service Classifications

## Control

### Government, nonfederal
State
County
City
City–county
Hospital district or authority

### Nongovernment not–for–profit
Church operated
Other

### Investor–owned (for–profit)
Individual
Partnership
Corporation

### Government, federal
Air Force
Army
Navy
Public Health Service other than 47
Veterans Affairs

Federal other than 41–45, 47–48
Public Health Service Indian Service
Department of Justice

### Osteopathic
Church operated
Other not–for–profit
Other
Individual for–profit
Partnership for–profit
Corporation for–profit

## Service

General medical and surgical
Hospital unit of an institution
  (prison hospital, college infirmary, etc.)
Hospital unit within an institution for the
  mentally retarded
Surgical
Psychiatric
Tuberculosis and other respiratory
  diseases
Cancer
Heart

Obstetrics and gynecology
Eye, ear, nose, and throat
Rehabilitation
Orthopedic
Chronic disease
Other specialty
Children's general
Children's hospital unit of an institution
Children's psychiatric
Children's tuberculosis and other
  respiratory diseases
Children's eye, ear, nose, and throat

Children's rehabilitation
Children's orthopedic
Children's chronic disease
Children's other specialty
Institution for mental retardation
Long–Term Acute Care
Alcoholism and other chemical
  dependency
Children's Long–Term Acute Care
Children's Cancer
Children's Heart

# Notes

# Notes

# Notes

# Notes

# U.S. Hospitals by State

# ALABAMA

## ALABASTER—Shelby County

☐ **NOLAND HOSPITAL SHELBY (012013)**, 1000 First Street North, 3rd Floor, Zip 35007–8703; tel. 205/620–8641 **A**1 9 10 **F**1 148 **S** Noland Health Services, Inc., Birmingham, AL
Primary Contact: Andrew Tatnall, Administrator
Web address: www.nolandhospitals.com/nhs.html
**Control:** Other not–for–profit (including NFP Corporation) **Service:** Long–Term Acute Care hospital

**Staffed Beds:** 52 **Admissions:** 133 **Census:** 9 **Outpatient Visits:** 0 **Births:** 0 **Total Expense ($000):** 3530 **Payroll Expense ($000):** 1465

☐ **SHELBY BAPTIST MEDICAL CENTER (010016)**, 1000 First Street North, Zip 35007–8703; tel. 205/620–8100 **A**1 2 9 10 **F**3 8 11 12 13 15 17 18 20 22 24 26 28 29 30 31 34 35 40 43 45 47 48 49 50 57 59 60 64 67 70 72 74 75 76 77 79 81 82 85 87 93 94 107 108 110 111 114 115 118 119 124 126 129 130 131 132 146 147 148 **S** Baptist Health System, Birmingham, AL
Primary Contact: David C. Wilson, President and Chief Executive Officer
CFO: Jennifer Pittman, Chief Financial Officer
CMO: David Cleveland, M.D., Chief Medical Officer
CIO: Mike Nighman, Facility Coordinator Information Systems
CHR: Cindy Nicholson, Director Human Resources
CNO: Martha Seahorn, R.N., Chief Nurse Office
Web address: www.bhsala.com/shelby/Home.aspx
**Control:** Church–operated, Nongovernment, not–for profit **Service:** General Medical and Surgical

**Staffed Beds:** 206 **Admissions:** 10631 **Census:** 138 **Outpatient Visits:** 125298 **Births:** 1138 **Total Expense ($000):** 144347 **Payroll Expense ($000):** 51161 **Personnel:** 897

## ALEXANDER CITY—Tallapoosa County

☒ **RUSSELL MEDICAL CENTER (010065)**, 3316 Highway 280, Zip 35010–3369, Mailing Address: P.O. Box 939, Zip 35011–0939; tel. 256/329–7100 **A**1 9 10 19 **F**3 11 13 15 18 20 22 28 29 30 31 32 34 35 36 40 43 45 49 50 51 53 57 59 60 64 67 75 76 77 78 79 80 81 85 87 89 93 96 107 108 110 111 114 115 116 117 118 119 121 123 129 130 131 132 143 144 146 147
Primary Contact: Lother E. Peace, III, President and Chief Executive Officer
CFO: Timothy J. Thornton, Chief Financial Officer
CMO: John James, M.D., Chief of Staff
CIO: Tommy Spraggins, Director Information Services
CHR: Mary Shockley, Director Human Resources
CNO: Tanya Johnson, R.N., Director of Nursing
Web address: www.russellmedcenter.com
**Control:** Other not–for–profit (including NFP Corporation) **Service:** General Medical and Surgical

**Staffed Beds:** 69 **Admissions:** 3245 **Census:** 29 **Outpatient Visits:** 98675 **Births:** 475 **Total Expense ($000):** 78550 **Payroll Expense ($000):** 23582 **Personnel:** 452

## ANDALUSIA—Covington County

☒ **ANDALUSIA REGIONAL HOSPITAL (010036)**, 849 South Three Notch Street, Zip 36420–5325, Mailing Address: P.O. Box 760, Zip 36420–1214; tel. 334/222–8466 **A**1 9 10 **F**3 8 13 15 29 30 34 35 40 43 45 46 51 57 59 60 64 65 68 69 74 75 76 77 79 80 81 82 85 87 89 93 107 108 110 111 114 116 117 119 129 131 133 135 146 147 148 **P**6 **S** LifePoint Hospitals, Inc., Brentwood, TN
Primary Contact: Rebecca Brewer, FACHE, Interim Chief Executive Officer
COO: Melissa Davis, Chief Operating Officer
CFO: Shirley M. Smith, Chief Financial Officer
CIO: Matthew Perry, Director Information Systems
CHR: Kaci Daughtry, Director Human Resources
Web address: www.andalusiaregionalhospital.com
**Control:** Corporation, Investor–owned, for–profit **Service:** General Medical and Surgical

**Staffed Beds:** 88 **Admissions:** 3081 **Census:** 28 **Outpatient Visits:** 49935 **Births:** 423 **Total Expense ($000):** 27313 **Payroll Expense ($000):** 11391 **Personnel:** 229

## ANNISTON—Calhoun County

☐ **NOLAND HOSPITAL ANNISTON (012011)**, 400 East 10th Street, 4th Floor, Zip 36207–4716; tel. 256/741–6141 **A**1 9 10 **F**1 3 29 148 **S** Noland Health Services, Inc., Birmingham, AL
Primary Contact: Bill Mitchell, Administrator
Web address: www.nolandhealth.com
**Control:** Other not–for–profit (including NFP Corporation) **Service:** Long–Term Acute Care hospital

**Staffed Beds:** 38 **Admissions:** 338 **Census:** 23 **Outpatient Visits:** 0 **Births:** 0 **Total Expense ($000):** 9169 **Payroll Expense ($000):** 2969 **Personnel:** 51

☒ **NORTHEAST ALABAMA REGIONAL MEDICAL CENTER (010078)**, 400 East Tenth Street, Zip 36207–4716, Mailing Address: P.O. Box 2208, Zip 36202–2208; tel. 256/235–5121 **A**1 2 9 10 **F**3 8 11 12 13 15 17 18 20 22 24 28 29 30 31 34 35 40 43 44 45 46 47 48 49 50 51 53 54 56 57 59 60 61 64 68 70 74 76 77 78 79 81 82 85 86 87 89 98 102 103 104 105 107 108 111 114 115 116 117 119 120 121 123 126 129 130 132 135 146 147 148 **P**6
Primary Contact: J. David McCormack, President and Chief Executive Officer
COO: Joe Weaver, Chief Operating Officer and Vice President Operations
CFO: Louis A. Bass, Vice President Finance
CMO: David Zinn, M.D., Vice President Medical Affairs
CIO: Pete Furlow, Director Information Technology Services
CHR: Michael S. Simms, Sr., Vice President Human Resources
CNO: Nisha Madhavan, R.N., Chief Nursing Officer and Vice President Patient Services
Web address: www.rmccares.org
**Control:** Hospital district or authority, Government, nonfederal **Service:** General Medical and Surgical

**Staffed Beds:** 276 **Admissions:** 13503 **Census:** 170 **Outpatient Visits:** 104950 **Births:** 1382 **Total Expense ($000):** 146970 **Payroll Expense ($000):** 53957 **Personnel:** 1211

☐ **STRINGFELLOW MEMORIAL HOSPITAL (010038)**, 301 East 18th Street, Zip 36207–3952; tel. 256/235–8900, (Nonreporting) **A**1 9 10 **S** Health Management Associates, Naples, FL
Primary Contact: Bryan McCauley, Chief Executive Officer
CIO: Peggy Henderson, Director Health Information
CHR: Tamatha Johnson, Director Human Resources
Web address: www.stringfellowhealth.com
**Control:** Corporation, Investor–owned, for–profit **Service:** General Medical and Surgical

**Staffed Beds:** 75

## ASHLAND—Clay County

★ **CLAY COUNTY HOSPITAL (010073)**, 83825 Highway 9, Zip 36251–7981, Mailing Address: P.O. Box 1270, Zip 36251–1270; tel. 256/354–2131, (Total facility includes 83 beds in nursing home–type unit) **A**9 10 **F**3 4 10 11 15 29 30 34 35 40 45 49 50 53 57 59 62 63 64 68 70 75 77 79 81 85 87 89 90 91 93 96 100 107 108 114 119 128 129 130 132 133 135 145 146 148 **P**3
Primary Contact: Linda U. Jordan, Administrator
COO: Linda U. Jordan, Administrator
CFO: Kerry W. Tomlin, Associate Administrator
CMO: George L. Beale, M.D., Director Medical Staff
CIO: Sherri Mulder, Director Information Technology
CHR: Linda T. Smith, Director Human Resources
CNO: Tommie Ann Fisher, R.N., Director of Nursing
Web address: www.claycountyhospital.com
**Control:** Hospital district or authority, Government, nonfederal **Service:** General Medical and Surgical

**Staffed Beds:** 124 **Admissions:** 1522 **Census:** 92 **Outpatient Visits:** 21127 **Births:** 0

---

**Hospital, Medicare Provider Number, Address, Telephone, Approval, Facility, and Physician Codes, Health Care System**

★ American Hospital Association (AHA) membership
☐ The Joint Commission accreditation
◇ DNV Healthcare Inc. accreditation
○ Healthcare Facilities Accreditation Program
△ Commission on Accreditation of Rehabilitation Facilities (CARF) accreditation

## ATHENS—Limestone County

☐ **ATHENS–LIMESTONE HOSPITAL (010079)**, 700 West Market Street,
Zip 35611–2457, Mailing Address: P.O. Box 999, Zip 35612–0999;
tel. 256/233–9292 **A**1 9 10 **F**1 3 4 7 8 11 13 15 16 17 28 29 34 35 40 45
46 50 51 53 54 56 57 58 59 64 67 68 70 72 73 75 76 77 79 80 81 84 85
86 87 88 89 90 93 98 107 108 111 119 128 129 130 131 132 135 143
144 146
Primary Contact: Kelli Powers, Chief Executive Officer
COO: Randy Comer, Chief Operating Officer
CFO: Randy Comer, Chief Financial Officer
CMO: Jon Bignault, M.D., Chief of Staff
CIO: Kim Hoback, Supervisor Information Systems
CHR: Rachel Frey, Director Human Resources
CNO: Jan Lenz, Chief Nursing Officer
Web address: www.athenslimestonehospital.com
**Control:** Hospital district or authority, Government, nonfederal **Service:** General
Medical and Surgical

**Staffed Beds:** 101 **Admissions:** 3975 **Census:** 40 **Outpatient Visits:** 119747
**Births:** 448 **Total Expense ($000):** 44484 **Payroll Expense ($000):** 25525
**Personnel:** 635

## ATMORE—Escambia County

★ **ATMORE COMMUNITY HOSPITAL (010169)**, 401 Medical Park Drive,
Zip 36502–3091; tel. 251/368–2500 **A**9 10 **F**3 11 12 15 18 29 30 34 35 40
41 43 56 57 59 64 65 70 75 77 79 81 85 89 93 107 108 114 128 133 144
148 **S** Baptist Health Care Corporation, Pensacola, FL
Primary Contact: A. William Perkins, Interim Administrator
Web address: www.ebaptisthealthcare.org/AtmoreCommunityHospital/
**Control:** Other not–for–profit (including NFP Corporation) **Service:** General
Medical and Surgical

**Staffed Beds:** 49 **Admissions:** 1510 **Census:** 17 **Outpatient Visits:** 36235
**Births:** 0 **Total Expense ($000):** 11873 **Payroll Expense ($000):** 7939
**Personnel:** 146

## BAY MINETTE—Baldwin County

**NORTH BALDWIN INFIRMARY (010129)**, 1815 Hand Avenue,
Zip 36507–4110, Mailing Address: P.O. Box 1409, Zip 36507–1409;
tel. 251/937–5521, (Nonreporting) **A**9 10 **S** Infirmary Health System, Mobile, AL
Primary Contact: Ormand P. Thompson, Administrator
CFO: J. Patrick Murphy, Chief Financial Officer
Web address: www.mobileinfirmary.org
**Control:** Other not–for–profit (including NFP Corporation) **Service:** General
Medical and Surgical

**Staffed Beds:** 35

## BESSEMER—Jefferson County

☐ **MEDICAL WEST (010114)**, 995 Ninth Avenue S.W., Zip 35022–4527;
tel. 205/481–7000 **A**1 9 10 **F**3 11 13 15 18 29 30 31 34 40 43 45 49 50 57
59 60 64 68 70 74 75 76 77 78 79 80 81 82 85 86 90 92 93 94 96 98 100
101 102 103 104 107 108 110 111 114 115 118 119 129 130 132 143 146
147 148 **P**6 **S** UAB Health System, Birmingham, AL
Primary Contact: Keith Pennington, President and Chief Executive Officer
CFO: Brandon H. Slocum, Senior Vice President and Chief Financial Officer
CMO: David Denney, M.D., President Medical Staff
CIO: Bob Duckworth, Director Information Systems
CHR: Gannon Davis, Director Human Resources
Web address: www.medicalwesthospital.org
**Control:** Hospital district or authority, Government, nonfederal **Service:** General
Medical and Surgical

**Staffed Beds:** 236 **Admissions:** 7751 **Census:** 103 **Outpatient Visits:**
185677 **Births:** 0 **Personnel:** 936

## BIRMINGHAM—Jefferson County

☒ **BIRMINGHAM VETERANS AFFAIRS MEDICAL CENTER**, (Formerly Veterans
Affairs Medical Center), 700 South 19th Street, Zip 35233–1927;
tel. 205/933–8101 **A**1 2 3 5 8 **F**3 4 5 8 12 17 18 20 22 24 26 28 29 30 31
34 35 38 39 40 43 44 45 47 50 54 56 57 58 59 60 61 62 63 64 65 68 70
74 75 77 78 79 81 82 83 84 85 87 90 92 93 94 96 97 98 100 101 102 103
104 106 107 108 109 111 112 113 114 115 116 117 118 119 120 124 127
129 130 132 135 143 146 147 148 **S** Department of Veterans Affairs,
Washington, DC
Primary Contact: Phyllis Smith, Acting Director
COO: Cynthia Cleveland, Ph.D., Acting Associate Director
COO: Phyllis Smith, Associate Director
CFO: Mary S. Mitchell, Chief Resource Management Services
CMO: Michael Thornsberry, M.D., Chief of Staff
CIO: Harald Carlisle, Acting Chief Information Officer
CIO: William Greer, Chief Information Officer
CHR: Jacqueline Caron, Chief Human Resources
CNO: Gregory S. Eagerton, Ph.D., Associate Director for Patient Care
Services/Nurse Executive
Web address: www.birmingham.va.gov/
**Control:** Veterans Affairs, Government, federal **Service:** General Medical and
Surgical

**Staffed Beds:** 151 **Admissions:** 6504 **Census:** 108 **Outpatient Visits:**
724517 **Births:** 0 **Total Expense ($000):** 398541 **Payroll Expense ($000):**
148931 **Personnel:** 2127

☒ **BROOKWOOD MEDICAL CENTER (010139)**, 2010 Brookwood Medical Center
Drive, Zip 35209–6875; tel. 205/877–1000 **A**1 2 3 5 10 **F**3 11 12 13 15 17
18 20 22 24 26 28 29 30 31 34 38 40 43 45 56 57 59 60 64 68 70 72 74
75 76 78 79 81 82 85 86 87 90 92 98 100 101 102 103 104 105 107 108
109 110 111 114 115 116 117 119 120 121 122 123 124 126 130 132 135
146 147 148 **S** TENET Healthcare Corporation, Dallas, TX
Primary Contact: Garry L. Gause, President and Chief Executive Officer
COO: Brenda H. Traweek, R.N., Chief Operating Officer
CFO: Doug Carter, Chief Financial Officer
CMO: Bradley Dennis, M.D., Chief Medical Officer
CIO: Manuel Price, Director Information Systems
CHR: Ronnelle Stewart, SPHR, Chief Human Resources Officer
Web address: www.bwmc.com
**Control:** Corporation, Investor–owned, for–profit **Service:** General Medical and
Surgical

**Staffed Beds:** 631 **Admissions:** 27363 **Census:** 367 **Outpatient Visits:**
124263 **Births:** 4014 **Total Expense ($000):** 252027 **Payroll Expense
($000):** 124948 **Personnel:** 1893

☒ **HEALTHSOUTH LAKESHORE REHABILITATION HOSPITAL (013025)**, 3800
Ridgeway Drive, Zip 35209–5599; tel. 205/868–2000 **A**1 9 10 **F**3 29 75 77 86
87 90 91 93 94 95 96 130 132 148 **P**8 **S** HEALTHSOUTH Corporation,
Birmingham, AL
Primary Contact: Heath Phillips, Administrator and Chief Executive Officer
CFO: Tammy Young, Controller
CMO: Paula Stewart, M.D., Medical Director
CHR: John Estis, Director Human Resources
Web address: www.healthsouthlakeshorerehab.com
**Control:** Corporation, Investor–owned, for–profit **Service:** Rehabilitation

**Staffed Beds:** 100 **Admissions:** 2550 **Census:** 89 **Outpatient Visits:** 13161
**Births:** 0 **Total Expense ($000):** 27711 **Payroll Expense ($000):** 15708
**Personnel:** 325

☐ **HILL CREST BEHAVIORAL HEALTH SERVICES (014000)**, 6869 Fifth Avenue
South, Zip 35212–1866; tel. 205/833–9000, (Nonreporting) **A**1 9 10 **S** Universal
Health Services, Inc., King of Prussia, PA
Primary Contact: Steve McCabe, Chief Executive Officer
CFO: Mark Teske, Chief Financial Officer
Web address: www.hillcrestbhs.com
**Control:** Corporation, Investor–owned, for–profit **Service:** Psychiatric

**Staffed Beds:** 94

☐ **NOLAND HOSPITAL BIRMINGHAM (012009)**, 50 Medical Park East Drive, 8th
Floor, Zip 35235; tel. 205/808–5100 **A**1 9 10 **F**1 148 **S** Noland Health Services,
Inc., Birmingham, AL
Primary Contact: Laura S. Wills, Administrator
Web address: www.nolandhealth.com
**Control:** Other not–for–profit (including NFP Corporation) **Service:** Long–Term
Acute Care hospital

**Staffed Beds:** 45 **Admissions:** 327 **Census:** 25 **Outpatient Visits:** 0 **Births:**
0 **Total Expense ($000):** 10012 **Payroll Expense ($000):** 3877 **Personnel:**
56

☐ **PRINCETON BAPTIST MEDICAL CENTER (010103)**, 701 Princeton Avenue S.W., Zip 35211–1303; tel. 205/783–3000 **A**1 2 3 5 9 10 **F**3 11 12 13 15 17 18 20 22 24 26 28 29 30 31 34 35 40 43 45 47 48 49 50 56 57 58 59 64 67 70 72 74 75 76 78 79 81 82 83 84 85 87 91 92 93 94 98 103 107 108 110 111 114 115 117 118 119 120 121 123 124 126 129 130 131 132 146 147 148 **S** Baptist Health System, Birmingham, AL
Primary Contact: Betsy Postlethwait, President
CFO: Gene Taylor, Chief Financial Officer
CMO: David Russakoff, M.D., Chief Medical Officer
Web address: www.bhsala.com
**Control:** Church–operated, Nongovernment, not–for profit **Service:** General Medical and Surgical

**Staffed Beds:** 295 **Admissions:** 13701 **Census:** 220 **Outpatient Visits:** 161194 **Births:** 368 **Total Expense ($000):** 192652 **Payroll Expense ($000):** 76783 **Personnel:** 1363

☒ **SELECT SPECIALTY HOSPITAL–BIRMINGHAM (012008)**, 800 Montclair Road, 9th Floor, Zip 35213–1908; tel. 205/599–4600, (Nonreporting) **A**1 9 10 **S** Select Medical Corporation, Mechanicsburg, PA
Primary Contact: Andrea White, Chief Executive Officer
CMO: Allan Goldstein, M.D., Medical Director and Chief of Staff
Web address: www.selectspecialtyhospitals.com/company/locations/birmingham.aspx
**Control:** Corporation, Investor–owned, for–profit **Service:** Long–Term Acute Care hospital

**Staffed Beds:** 38

☒ **ST. VINCENT'S BIRMINGHAM (010056)**, 810 St. Vincent's Drive, Zip 35205–1695, Mailing Address: P.O. Box 12407, Zip 35202–2407; tel. 205/939–7000 **A**1 2 3 5 9 10 **F**3 11 13 15 17 18 20 22 24 26 28 29 30 31 34 35 36 37 40 43 45 50 53 54 57 58 59 60 62 65 66 68 70 72 74 75 76 77 78 79 81 82 84 85 86 87 93 97 107 108 110 111 114 115 119 120 121 123 126 129 130 131 135 146 147 148 **P**7 8 **S** Ascension Health, Saint Louis, MO
Primary Contact: Andy Davis, President
COO: Andy Davis, Chief Operating Officer
CFO: Wilma Newton, Executive Vice President and Chief Financial Officer
CMO: Gregory L. James, D.O., Chief Medical Officer
CIO: Timothy Stellheimer, Vice President and Chief Information Officer
CHR: Michelle Galipeau, Director Human Resources
Web address: www.stvhs.com
**Control:** Other not–for–profit (including NFP Corporation) **Service:** General Medical and Surgical

**Staffed Beds:** 409 **Admissions:** 20258 **Census:** 250 **Outpatient Visits:** 193068 **Births:** 3151 **Total Expense ($000):** 332262 **Payroll Expense ($000):** 93961 **Personnel:** 1848

☒ **ST. VINCENT'S EAST (010011)**, 50 Medical Park East Drive, Zip 35235–9987; tel. 205/838–3000 **A**1 2 3 5 9 10 **F**3 11 12 13 17 18 20 22 24 26 28 29 30 31 34 35 40 42 43 44 45 48 49 50 51 53 54 57 58 59 60 64 65 70 72 74 76 77 78 79 81 85 86 87 90 93 94 96 97 98 100 101 102 103 104 105 107 108 111 114 119 121 123 126 129 130 131 132 135 146 **P**7 8 **S** Ascension Health, Saint Louis, MO
Primary Contact: Sean Tinney, FACHE, President and Chief Operating Officer
CFO: Jan DiCesare, Vice President Financial Operations
CMO: Adeeb Thomas, M.D., Vice President Medical Affairs
CIO: Beverly Golightly, Director Information Technology
CHR: Carol Maietta, Vice President Human Resources and Chief Learning Officer
CNO: Cynthia T. Williams, R.N., Interim Chief Nursing Officer
Web address: www.stvhs.com
**Control:** Other not–for–profit (including NFP Corporation) **Service:** General Medical and Surgical

**Staffed Beds:** 336 **Admissions:** 14499 **Census:** 205 **Outpatient Visits:** 130771 **Births:** 729 **Total Expense ($000):** 197921 **Payroll Expense ($000):** 65428 **Personnel:** 1099

☒ **THE CHILDREN'S HOSPITAL OF ALABAMA (013300)**, 1600 Seventh Avenue South, Zip 35233–1785; tel. 205/638–9100 **A**1 3 5 9 10 **F**3 7 8 11 12 16 17 19 21 23 25 27 29 30 31 32 34 35 38 39 40 41 43 46 48 49 50 54 55 57 58 59 60 61 64 65 68 72 74 75 77 78 79 80 81 82 84 85 86 87 88 89 92 93 94 97 98 99 100 101 102 104 107 111 114 115 116 117 118 119 129 130 131 132 134 135 136 142 143 144 146
Primary Contact: Wm. Michael Warren, Jr., Chief Executive Officer
COO: Tom Shufflebarger, Chief Operating Officer
CFO: Dawn Walton, Chief Financial Officer
CMO: Crayton A. Fargason, M.D., Medical Director
CIO: Mike McDevitt, Chief Information Officer
CHR: Douglas B. Dean, Chief Human Resources Officer
CNO: Deb Wesley, MSN, Chief Nursing Officer
Web address: www.childrensal.org
**Control:** Other not–for–profit (including NFP Corporation) **Service:** Children's general

**Staffed Beds:** 350 **Admissions:** 13636 **Census:** 223 **Outpatient Visits:** 670029 **Total Expense ($000):** 532802 **Payroll Expense ($000):** 205929 **Personnel:** 3529

☒ **TRINITY MEDICAL CENTER (010104)**, 800 Montclair Road, Zip 35213–1984; tel. 205/592–1000 **A**1 2 3 5 9 10 **F**3 11 12 13 15 17 18 20 22 24 26 28 29 30 31 34 35 36 40 43 45 46 47 48 49 50 51 53 54 57 58 59 64 70 72 73 74 75 76 77 78 79 81 82 84 85 90 93 96 98 99 102 103 106 107 108 109 110 111 114 115 116 117 118 119 120 122 124 126 129 130 131 132 135 146 147 148 **S** Community Health Systems, Inc., Franklin, TN
Primary Contact: Keith Granger, President and Chief Executive Officer
COO: Sean T. Dardeau, Chief Operating Officer
CFO: Julie Soekoro, Chief Financial Officer
CMO: Hugh O'Shields, M.D., President Medical Staff
CIO: Tim Townes, Director Information Systems
CHR: Joel R. Windham, Director Human Resources
CNO: Andy Romine, Chief Nursing Officer
Web address: www.bhsala.com
**Control:** Corporation, Investor–owned, for–profit **Service:** General Medical and Surgical

**Staffed Beds:** 379 **Admissions:** 13376 **Census:** 205 **Outpatient Visits:** 298880 **Births:** 594 **Total Expense ($000):** 219671 **Payroll Expense ($000):** 83627 **Personnel:** 1516

**UAB HIGHLANDS** See University of Alabama Hospital

☒ **UNIVERSITY OF ALABAMA HOSPITAL (010033)**, 619 19th Street South, Zip 35249–1900; tel. 205/934–4011, (Includes UAB HIGHLANDS, 1201 11th Avenue South, Zip 35205–5299; tel. 205/930–7000; Anthony Patterson, Chief Operating Officer), (Nonreporting) **A**1 2 3 5 8 9 10 **S** UAB Health System, Birmingham, AL
Primary Contact: Anthony Patterson, Interim Chief Executive Officer
COO: Reid F. Jones, Chief Operating Officer
CFO: Mary Beth Briscoe, Chief Financial Officer
CMO: Cynthia Brumfield, M.D., Chief of Staff
CIO: Joan Hicks, Chief Information Officer
CHR: Alesia Jones, Interim Chief Human Resources Officer
Web address: www.health.uab.edu
**Control:** State–Government, nonfederal **Service:** General Medical and Surgical

**Staffed Beds:** 1062

**VETERANS AFFAIRS MEDICAL CENTER** See Birmingham Veterans Affairs Medical Center

### BOAZ—Marshall County

☒ **MARSHALL MEDICAL CENTER SOUTH (010005)**, U.S. Highway 431 North, Zip 35957–0999, Mailing Address: P.O. Box 758, Zip 35957–0758; tel. 256/593–8310 **A**1 9 10 19 **F**3 7 8 11 12 13 15 18 20 22 28 29 31 32 34 35 37 40 43 45 46 50 53 54 57 59 64 68 70 74 75 76 78 79 81 85 86 87 93 100 107 108 110 111 114 117 119 121 123 129 130 131 132 135 141 145 146 147 148 **S** Marshall Health System, Guntersville, AL
Primary Contact: John D. Anderson, FACHE, Administrator
CFO: Kathy Nelson, Chief Financial Officer
Web address: www.mmcenters.com//index.php/facilities/marshall_south
**Control:** Hospital district or authority, Government, nonfederal **Service:** General Medical and Surgical

**Staffed Beds:** 114 **Admissions:** 5071 **Census:** 47 **Outpatient Visits:** 207598 **Births:** 719 **Total Expense ($000):** 75653 **Payroll Expense ($000):** 33309 **Personnel:** 518

---

**Hospital, Medicare Provider Number, Address, Telephone, Approval, Facility, and Physician Codes, Health Care System**

★ American Hospital Association (AHA) membership
☐ The Joint Commission accreditation
◇ DNV Healthcare Inc. accreditation
○ Healthcare Facilities Accreditation Program
△ Commission on Accreditation of Rehabilitation Facilities (CARF) accreditation

**AL**

## BREWTON—Escambia County

☐ **D. W. MCMILLAN MEMORIAL HOSPITAL (010099)**, 1301 Belleville Avenue, Zip 36426–1306, Mailing Address: P.O. Box 908, Zip 36427–0908; tel. 251/867–8061 **A**1 9 10 **F**3 7 11 13 15 31 34 35 40 45 57 59 62 64 70 75 76 78 79 81 85 86 89 93 100 107 108 111 114 119 127 129 130 131 132 133 135 143 146 **P**6
Primary Contact: Christopher B. Griffin, Chief Executive Officer
CFO: Richard Owens, Chief Financial Officer
CIO: Ian Vickery, Director Information Technology
CHR: Autherine Davis, Director Human Resources
CNO: Bob Ellis, Director of Nursing
Web address: www.dwmmh.org
**Control:** Hospital district or authority, Government, nonfederal **Service:** General Medical and Surgical

Staffed Beds: 49 **Admissions:** 2333 **Census:** 23 **Outpatient Visits:** 49232
**Births:** 277 **Total Expense ($000):** 26724 **Payroll Expense ($000):** 11066
**Personnel:** 229

## BUTLER—Choctaw County

★ **CHOCTAW GENERAL HOSPITAL (011304)**, (Critical Access Hospital), 401 Vanity Fair Avenue, Zip 36904–3032; tel. 205/459–9100, (Data for 301 days) **A**9 10 18 **F**3 13 29 30 34 35 40 41 87 91 93 103 104 107 111 119 133 146 148 **S** Rush Health Systems, Meridian, MS
Primary Contact: J. W. Cowan, Administrator
Web address: www.choctawgeneral.com/cgh/
**Control:** Other not–for–profit (including NFP Corporation) **Service:** Other specialty

Staffed Beds: 25 **Admissions:** 275 **Census:** 7 **Outpatient Visits:** 6126
**Births:** 0 **Total Expense ($000):** 9160 **Payroll Expense ($000):** 2589
**Personnel:** 69

## CAMDEN—Wilcox County

**J. PAUL JONES HOSPITAL (010102)**, 317 McWilliams Avenue, Zip 36726–1610; tel. 334/682–4131, (Nonreporting) **A**9 10 20
Primary Contact: Elizabeth M. Kennedy, Administrator
CMO: Willie White, M.D., Director Medical Staff
CIO: Jill Smith, Administrative Coordinator
CHR: Jill Smith, Administrative Coordinator
**Control:** City–County, Government, nonfederal **Service:** General Medical and Surgical

Staffed Beds: 21

## CARROLLTON—Pickens County

**PICKENS COUNTY MEDICAL CENTER (010109)**, 241 Robert K. Wilson Drive, Zip 35447, Mailing Address: P.O. Box 478, Zip 35447–0478; tel. 205/367–8111, (Nonreporting) **A**9 10 20
Primary Contact: Wayne McElroy, Administrator
CFO: Janice Winters, Controller
CMO: William R. Brooke, M.D., President Medical Staff
CHR: Dottie Wilson, Director Human Resources
Web address: www.dchsystem.com
**Control:** County–Government, nonfederal **Service:** General Medical and Surgical

Staffed Beds: 52

## CENTRE—Cherokee County

⊠ **CHEROKEE MEDICAL CENTER (010022)**, 400 Northwood Drive, Zip 35960–1023; tel. 256/927–5531 **A**1 9 10 **F**3 11 15 29 30 35 40 43 45 48 57 59 64 70 75 77 81 85 87 92 93 96 107 108 111 114 119 127 129 130 131 133 146 **P**6 **S** Community Health Systems, Inc., Franklin, TN
Primary Contact: Patrick Trammell, Chief Executive Officer
CFO: Zac Allen, CPA, Chief Financial Officer
CHR: Marlene Benefield, Director Human Resources
Web address: www.cherokeemedicalcenter.com
**Control:** Corporation, Investor–owned, for–profit **Service:** General Medical and Surgical

Staffed Beds: 45 **Admissions:** 866 **Census:** 10 **Outpatient Visits:** 20268
**Births:** 0 **Total Expense ($000):** 16355 **Payroll Expense ($000):** 5319
**Personnel:** 147

## CENTREVILLE—Bibb County

**BIBB MEDICAL CENTER (010058)**, 208 Pierson Avenue, Zip 35042–2918; tel. 205/926–4881 **A**9 10 **F**3 11 15 29 35 40 50 57 59 62 64 81 93 107 119 125 127 130 133 144 146 **P**6
Primary Contact: Joseph Marchant, Administrator
CFO: Heather Desmond, Chief Financial Officer
CMO: John Meigs, Jr., M.D., Chief of Staff
CHR: Kim Hayes, Director Human Resources
Web address: www.bibbmedicalcenter.com
**Control:** County–Government, nonfederal **Service:** General Medical and Surgical

Staffed Beds: 20 **Admissions:** 253 **Census:** 3 **Outpatient Visits:** 41981
**Births:** 0 **Total Expense ($000):** 15493 **Payroll Expense ($000):** 7787
**Personnel:** 190

## CHATOM—Washington County

★ **WASHINGTON COUNTY HOSPITAL AND NURSING HOME (011300)**, 14600 St. Stephens Avenue, Zip 36518–9998, Mailing Address: P.O. Box 1299, Zip 36518–1299; tel. 251/847–2223 **A**9 10 18 **F**15 29 34 40 57 59 64 89 107 114 119 128 133 148 **P**6
Primary Contact: Douglas Tanner, Chief Executive Officer
CFO: Alyson Overstreet, Chief Financial Officer
CMO: Steve Donald, M.D., Chief of Staff
CIO: Brady Wright, Information Technology Network Administrator
CHR: Linda Randolph, Director Personnel Services
CNO: Lamar Cooley, R.N., Director of Nursing
Web address: www.wchnh.org
**Control:** County–Government, nonfederal **Service:** General Medical and Surgical

Staffed Beds: 22 **Admissions:** 551 **Census:** 5 **Outpatient Visits:** 11200
**Births:** 0 **Total Expense ($000):** 6640 **Payroll Expense ($000):** 2703
**Personnel:** 74

## CULLMAN—Cullman County

☐ **CULLMAN REGIONAL MEDICAL CENTER (010035)**, 1912 Alabama Highway 157, Zip 35055, Mailing Address: P.O. Box 1108, Zip 35056–1108; tel. 256/737–2000 **A**1 9 10 19 **F**3 7 11 12 13 15 18 20 22 26 28 29 30 34 35 37 40 43 45 46 49 50 51 53 57 59 62 63 64 68 70 74 75 76 77 79 81 82 83 84 85 86 87 89 93 97 107 108 110 111 114 118 119 121 129 130 131 132 134 135 146 147 148
Primary Contact: James Weidner, President
COO: Jete Edmisson, Chief Operating Officer and Chief Financial Officer
CFO: Jete Edmisson, Chief Operating Officer and Chief Financial Officer
CMO: John Morris, M.D., Chief of Staff
CIO: Nancy Zavatchen, Director Information Technology
CHR: Toni Geddings, Director Human Resources
Web address: www.crmchospital.com
**Control:** Other not–for–profit (including NFP Corporation) **Service:** General Medical and Surgical

Staffed Beds: 115 **Admissions:** 7127 **Census:** 69 **Outpatient Visits:** 98728
**Births:** 870 **Total Expense ($000):** 74953 **Payroll Expense ($000):** 37388
**Personnel:** 869

## DADEVILLE—Tallapoosa County

**LAKE MARTIN COMMUNITY HOSPITAL (010052)**, 201 Mariarden Road, Zip 36853–6251, Mailing Address: P.O. Box 629, Zip 36853–0629; tel. 256/825–7821, (Nonreporting) **A**9 10
Primary Contact: Michael D. Bruce, Chief Executive Officer
CHR: Karen Treadwell, Director Human Resources
Web address: www.lakemartincommunityhospital.com
**Control:** Partnership, Investor–owned, for–profit **Service:** General Medical and Surgical

Staffed Beds: 28

## DAPHNE—Baldwin County

**EASTPOINTE HOSPITAL (014017)**, 7400 Roper Lane, Zip 36526–5274; tel. 251/378–6500, (Nonreporting) **A**9 10 **S** AltaPointe Health Systems, Mobile, AL
Primary Contact: Jarett Crum, Administrator
Web address: www.altapointe.org/eastpointe.php
**Control:** Corporation, Investor–owned, for–profit **Service:** Psychiatric

Staffed Beds: 18

## DECATUR—Morgan County

☐ **DECATUR GENERAL HOSPITAL (010085)**, 1201 Seventh Street S.E., Zip 35601–3303, Mailing Address: P.O. Box 2239, Zip 35609–2239; tel. 256/341–2000, (Includes DECATUR GENERAL HOSPITAL–WEST, 2205 Beltline Road S.W., Zip 35601–3687, Mailing Address: P.O. Box 2240, Zip 35609–2240; tel. 256/306–4000), (Nonreporting) **A**1 2 5 9 10
Primary Contact: Dean A. Griffin, President and Chief Executive Officer
CFO: Kim Shrewsbury, Vice President and Chief Financial Officer
CMO: Allen J. Schmidt, M.D., President, Medical Staff
CIO: Mark Megehee, Vice President and Chief Information Officer
CNO: Anita Walden, Vice President and Chief Nursing Officer
Web address: www.decaturgeneral.org
**Control:** Hospital district or authority, Government, nonfederal **Service:** General Medical and Surgical

Staffed Beds: 203

*Many Facility Codes have changed. Please refer to the AHA Guide Code Chart.*
© 2013 AHA Guide

☐ **DECATUR MORGAN HOSPITAL (010054)**, 1874 Beltline Road S.W., Zip 35601–5509, Mailing Address: P.O. Box 2239, Zip 35609–2239; tel. 256/350–2211, (Nonreporting) **A**1 5 9 10 **S** Huntsville Hospital Health System, Huntsville, AL
Primary Contact: Nathaniel Richardson, Jr., President
COO: Wayne Bowman, Interim Chief Nursing Officer
CFO: Danny Crowe, Chief Financial Officer
CMO: Cara Hoffman, M.D., Chief of Staff
CIO: Doyle Haynes, Director Information Systems
CHR: Don Zamora, Director Human Resources
Web address: www.parkwaymedicalcenter.com
**Control:** Corporation, Investor–owned, for–profit **Service:** General Medical and Surgical

**Staffed Beds:** 120

☐ **NORTH ALABAMA REGIONAL HOSPITAL (014009)**, 4218 Highway 31 South, Zip 35603–5039; tel. 256/560–2200, (Nonreporting) **A**1 10
Primary Contact: J. Randall Phillips, FACHE, Chief Executive Officer
CFO: Roger Kalonick, Business Manager
CMO: Duard Bok, M.D., Clinical Director
CIO: Ronald J. Thomas, Coordinator Information Systems
CHR: Gregory Ethridge, Manager Personnel
Web address: www.narh.mh.alabama.gov
**Control:** State–Government, nonfederal **Service:** Psychiatric

**Staffed Beds:** 74

**PARKWAY MEDICAL CENTER** See Decatur Morgan Hospital

## DEMOPOLIS—Marengo County

☐ **BRYAN W. WHITFIELD MEMORIAL HOSPITAL (010112)**, 105 U.S. Highway 80 East, Zip 36732–3616, Mailing Address: P.O. Box 890, Zip 36732–0890; tel. 334/289–4000, (Nonreporting) **A**1 9 10 20
Primary Contact: Michael D. Marshall, Administrator and Chief Executive Officer
CFO: Arthur D. Evans, Assistant Administrator
CHR: Danny Smith, Director Human Resources
Web address: www.bwwmh.com
**Control:** Hospital district or authority, Government, nonfederal **Service:** General Medical and Surgical

**Staffed Beds:** 99

## DOTHAN—Houston County

☒ **FLOWERS HOSPITAL (010055)**, 4370 West Main Street, Zip 36305–4000, Mailing Address: P.O. Box 6907, Zip 36302–6907; tel. 334/793–5000 **A**1 2 9 10 **F**1 3 4 12 13 15 16 17 18 20 22 24 26 28 29 31 34 35 40 46 48 49 50 51 56 57 59 60 61 64 67 68 70 74 75 76 77 78 79 80 81 82 85 86 87 89 90 92 93 97 98 107 108 110 111 114 115 116 117 118 119 126 128 129 132 134 135 146 147 148 **P**6 **S** Community Health Systems, Inc., Franklin, TN
Primary Contact: Suzanne Woods, President and Chief Executive Officer
CFO: Talana Bell, Chief Financial Officer
CHR: Scott H. Givens, Director Human Resources
CNO: Dan L. Cumbie, Chief Nursing Officer
Web address: www.flowershospital.com
**Control:** Corporation, Investor–owned, for–profit **Service:** General Medical and Surgical

**Staffed Beds:** 235 **Admissions:** 12058 **Census:** 150 **Outpatient Visits:** 161878 **Births:** 1280 **Total Expense ($000):** 178286 **Payroll Expense ($000):** 62079 **Personnel:** 1238

☒ **HEALTHSOUTH REHABILITATION HOSPITAL (013030)**, 1736 East Main Street, Zip 36301–3040, Mailing Address: P.O. Box 6708, Zip 36302–6708; tel. 334/712–6333 **A**1 9 10 **F**28 29 34 35 56 57 59 64 74 75 77 79 90 91 93 95 96 130 132 **P**5 **S** HEALTHSOUTH Corporation, Birmingham, AL
Primary Contact: Margaret A. Futch, Chief Executive Officer
CFO: Heath Watson, Controller
CMO: Stephen L. Chastain, M.D., Medical Director
CHR: Lydia Christion, Director Human Resources
Web address: www.healthsouthdothan.com
**Control:** Corporation, Investor–owned, for–profit **Service:** Rehabilitation

**Staffed Beds:** 39 **Admissions:** 1083 **Census:** 37 **Outpatient Visits:** 2314 **Births:** 0 **Total Expense ($000):** 9558 **Payroll Expense ($000):** 5385 **Personnel:** 136

☐ **LAUREL OAKS BEHAVIORAL HEALTH CENTER (014013)**, 700 East Cottonwood Road, Zip 36301–3644; tel. 334/794–7373 **A**1 9 10 **F**98 99 106 **S** Universal Health Services, Inc., King of Prussia, PA
Primary Contact: Derek Johnson, Chief Executive Officer
CMO: Nelson Handol, M.D., Medical Director
CHR: Lorrie Evans, Director Human Resources
Web address: www.laureloaksbhc.com
**Control:** Corporation, Investor–owned, for–profit **Service:** Children's hospital psychiatric

**Staffed Beds:** 38 **Admissions:** 945 **Census:** 31 **Outpatient Visits:** 0 **Births:** 0 **Total Expense ($000):** 11646 **Payroll Expense ($000):** 7128 **Personnel:** 262

☐ **NOLAND HOSPITAL DOTHAN (012010)**, 1108 Ross Clark Circle, 4th Floor, Zip 36301–3022; tel. 334/699–4300 **A**1 9 10 **F**1 148 **S** Noland Health Services, Inc., Birmingham, AL
Primary Contact: Kaye Burke, Administrator
Web address: www.nolandhealth.com
**Control:** Other not–for–profit (including NFP Corporation) **Service:** Long–Term Acute Care hospital

**Staffed Beds:** 35 **Admissions:** 310 **Census:** 25 **Outpatient Visits:** 0 **Births:** 0 **Total Expense ($000):** 9346 **Payroll Expense ($000):** 4044

☒ **SOUTHEAST ALABAMA MEDICAL CENTER (010001)**, 1108 Ross Clark Circle, Zip 36301–3024, Mailing Address: P.O. Box 6987, Zip 36302–6987; tel. 334/793–8111 **A**1 2 9 10 **F**3 8 12 13 15 18 20 22 24 26 28 29 30 31 32 34 35 37 40 43 44 45 49 50 51 53 56 57 59 60 62 63 64 68 70 71 74 75 76 77 78 79 81 82 85 86 87 89 93 94 98 100 101 102 103 104 105 107 108 110 111 114 115 116 117 118 119 120 121 123 124 126 129 130 132 135 146 147 148 **P**6
Primary Contact: Ronald S. Owen, FACHE, Chief Executive Officer
COO: Charles C. Brannen, Senior Vice President and Chief Operating Officer
CFO: Derek Miller, Senior Vice President and Chief Financial Officer
CMO: Charles Harkness, D.O., Vice President Medical Affairs
CHR: Peggy Sease, Vice President Human Resources
CNO: Diane Buntyn, MSN, Vice President Patient Care Services
Web address: www.samc.org
**Control:** Hospital district or authority, Government, nonfederal **Service:** General Medical and Surgical

**Staffed Beds:** 420 **Admissions:** 17887 **Census:** 239 **Outpatient Visits:** 129599 **Births:** 1642 **Total Expense ($000):** 267962 **Payroll Expense ($000):** 116739 **Personnel:** 2272

## ENTERPRISE—Coffee County

☒ **MEDICAL CENTER ENTERPRISE (010049)**, 400 North Edwards Street, Zip 36330–2510; tel. 334/347–0584 **A**1 9 10 **F**3 13 15 29 34 40 45 57 59 70 76 79 81 85 93 107 110 111 114 118 119 130 131 **S** Community Health Systems, Inc., Franklin, TN
Primary Contact: Richard Ellis, Chief Executive Officer
CFO: Greg McGilvray, Chief Financial Officer
CHR: Toni Kaminski, Director Human Resources
Web address: www.mcehospital.com
**Control:** Corporation, Investor–owned, for–profit **Service:** General Medical and Surgical

**Staffed Beds:** 117 **Admissions:** 4082 **Census:** 33 **Outpatient Visits:** 33796 **Births:** 827 **Total Expense ($000):** 40003

## EUFAULA—Barbour County

**MEDICAL CENTER BARBOUR (010069)**, 820 West Washington Street, Zip 36027–1899; tel. 334/688–7000 **A**9 10 20 **F**3 11 15 29 30 34 35 40 45 46 50 57 59 64 68 70 81 85 98 103 107 119 127 133 135 146
Primary Contact: Ralph H. Clark, Jr., FACHE, Chief Executive Officer
CFO: Debbie Norton, Chief Financial Officer
CHR: Cindy Griffin, Director Human Resources
CNO: Kathy Wilder, R.N., Chief Clinical Officer
Web address: www.medctrbarbour.org
**Control:** Hospital district or authority, Government, nonfederal **Service:** General Medical and Surgical

**Staffed Beds:** 47 **Admissions:** 1665 **Census:** 24 **Outpatient Visits:** 33378 **Total Expense ($000):** 15559 **Payroll Expense ($000):** 7258 **Personnel:** 198

## EUTAW—Greene County

★ **GREENE COUNTY HOSPITAL (010051)**, 509 Wilson Avenue, Zip 35462–1099; tel. 205/372–3388, (Nonreporting) **A**9 10
Primary Contact: Mark Chustz, Administrator
**Control:** County–Government, nonfederal **Service:** General Medical and Surgical

**Staffed Beds:** 20

---

**Hospital, Medicare Provider Number, Address, Telephone, Approval, Facility, and Physician Codes, Health Care System**

★ American Hospital Association (AHA) membership
☐ The Joint Commission accreditation
◇ DNV Healthcare Inc. accreditation
○ Healthcare Facilities Accreditation Program
△ Commission on Accreditation of Rehabilitation Facilities (CARF) accreditation

## EVERGREEN—Conecuh County

**EVERGREEN MEDICAL CENTER (010148)**, 101 Crestview Avenue, Zip 36401–3333, Mailing Address: P.O. Box 706, Zip 36401–0706; tel. 251/578–2480, (Nonreporting) **A**9 10 **S** Gilliard Health Services, Montgomery, AL
Primary Contact: William G. McKenzie, Interim Administrator
CFO: Sharon Jones, Chief Financial Officer
CMO: William Farmer, M.D., Chief of Staff
Web address: www.evergreenmedical.org
**Control:** Partnership, Investor–owned, for–profit **Service:** General Medical and Surgical

**Staffed Beds:** 42

## FAIRHOPE—Baldwin County

☐ **THOMAS HOSPITAL (010100)**, 750 Morphy Avenue, Zip 36532–1812, Mailing Address: P.O. Drawer 929, Zip 36533–0929; tel. 251/928–2375, (Nonreporting) **A**1 9 10 19 **S** Infirmary Health System, Mobile, AL
Primary Contact: William J. McLaughlin, Administrator
COO: Douglas Garner, Vice President
CFO: Patrick Murphy, Vice President Finance
CMO: Michael McBrearty, M.D., Vice President Medical Affairs
Web address: www.thomashospital.com
**Control:** Other not–for–profit (including NFP Corporation) **Service:** General Medical and Surgical

**Staffed Beds:** 136

## FAYETTE—Fayette County

☐ **FAYETTE MEDICAL CENTER (010045)**, 1653 Temple Avenue North, Zip 35555–1314, Mailing Address: P.O. Drawer 710, Zip 35555–0710; tel. 205/932–5966, (Nonreporting) **A**1 9 10 **S** DCH Health System, Tuscaloosa, AL
Primary Contact: Barry S. Cochran, FACHE, Administrator
CFO: Jeff Huff, Assistant Administrator Finance
CHR: Cindy Bohon, Director Human Resources
Web address: www.dchsystem.com
**Control:** Hospital district or authority, Government, nonfederal **Service:** General Medical and Surgical

**Staffed Beds:** 167

## FLORALA—Covington County

**FLORALA MEMORIAL HOSPITAL (010066)**, 24273 Fifth Avenue, Zip 36442–3523, Mailing Address: P.O. Box 189, Zip 36442–0189; tel. 334/858–3287 **A**9 10 **F**1 4 16 17 40 64 67 70 72 73 76 80 88 89 90 98 107 119 128
Primary Contact: Doreen Brock, Chief Operating Officer
Web address: www.floralahospital.org
**Control:** Corporation, Investor–owned, for–profit **Service:** General Medical and Surgical

**Staffed Beds:** 23 **Admissions:** 235 **Census:** 2 **Outpatient Visits:** 2710 **Births:** 0

## FLORENCE—Lauderdale County

☐ **ELIZA COFFEE MEMORIAL HOSPITAL (010006)**, 205 Marengo Street, Zip 35630–6033, Mailing Address: P.O. Box 818, Zip 35631–0818; tel. 256/768–9191, (Nonreporting) **A**1 9 10 **S** RegionalCare Hospital Partners, Brentwood, TN
Primary Contact: Russell Pigg, Chief Executive Officer
COO: Bryan Lee, Chief Operating Officer
Web address: www.chgroup.org
**Control:** Hospital district or authority, Government, nonfederal **Service:** General Medical and Surgical

**Staffed Beds:** 278

## FOLEY—Baldwin County

✠ **SOUTH BALDWIN REGIONAL MEDICAL CENTER (010083)**, 1613 North McKenzie Street, Zip 36535–2299; tel. 251/949–3400 **A**1 9 10 19 **F**3 12 13 15 18 20 28 29 30 31 34 35 38 40 43 45 49 50 51 54 57 59 60 62 64 65 68 70 75 76 77 79 81 82 85 86 87 93 107 108 110 111 114 116 117 118 119 130 131 132 133 134 135 144 146 147 148 **S** Community Health Systems, Inc., Franklin, TN
Primary Contact: Keith Newton, Chief Executive Officer
CMO: Karl Hakmiller, M.D., Chief Medical Officer
CIO: Lucas Phillips, Director Information Technology
CHR: Pam Brunson, Director Human Resources
Web address: www.southbaldwinrmc.com
**Control:** Corporation, Investor–owned, for–profit **Service:** General Medical and Surgical

**Staffed Beds:** 112 **Admissions:** 6175 **Census:** 69 **Outpatient Visits:** 137008 **Births:** 551 **Total Expense ($000):** 70158 **Personnel:** 661

## FORT PAYNE—Dekalb County

✠ **DEKALB REGIONAL MEDICAL CENTER (010012)**, 200 Medical Center Drive, Zip 35968–3458, Mailing Address: P.O. Box 680778, Zip 35968–1608; tel. 256/845–3150 **A**1 9 10 20 **F**3 8 12 13 15 18 20 22 26 28 29 35 40 43 45 46 53 56 57 59 70 74 75 76 79 81 82 87 98 103 107 108 110 111 114 119 129 146 147 **S** Community Health Systems, Inc., Franklin, TN
Primary Contact: Corey Ewing, Chief Executive Officer
COO: Jay Hinesley, Assistant Chief Executive Officer
CFO: Hugh Tobin, Chief Financial Officer
CMO: Jeff Thompson, M.D., Chief of Staff
CIO: Anthony Sherlin, Director Information Systems
CHR: Diane McMichen, Director Human Resources
CNO: Marquita Bailey, Chief Nursing Officer
Web address: www.dekalbregional.com
**Control:** Corporation, Investor–owned, for–profit **Service:** General Medical and Surgical

**Staffed Beds:** 121 **Admissions:** 4287 **Census:** 47 **Outpatient Visits:** 59611 **Births:** 714 **Total Expense ($000):** 36188 **Payroll Expense ($000):** 18039 **Personnel:** 400

## GADSDEN—Etowah County

✠ **GADSDEN REGIONAL MEDICAL CENTER (010040)**, 1007 Goodyear Avenue, Zip 35903–1195; tel. 256/494–4000 **A**1 2 9 10 **F**3 11 13 15 18 20 21 22 24 28 29 30 31 34 35 40 43 49 50 51 57 59 60 64 68 70 73 74 76 77 78 79 80 81 85 93 98 102 103 105 107 108 111 112 113 114 115 119 121 129 130 132 146 147 148 **S** Community Health Systems, Inc., Franklin, TN
Primary Contact: Stephen G. Pennington, Chief Executive Officer
COO: Paul Theriot, Chief Operating Officer
CFO: Michael Cotton, Chief Financial Officer
CMO: William Haller, III, M.D., Chief of Staff
CIO: Glenn Phillips, Director Information Systems
CHR: Gale H. Sanders, Director
CNO: Donna Nicholson, Chief Nursing Officer
Web address: www.gadsdenregional.com
**Control:** Corporation, Investor–owned, for–profit **Service:** General Medical and Surgical

**Staffed Beds:** 299 **Admissions:** 13001 **Census:** 190 **Outpatient Visits:** 97814 **Births:** 1114 **Total Expense ($000):** 153470 **Payroll Expense ($000):** 52609 **Personnel:** 1075

✠ **HEALTHSOUTH REHABILITATION OF GADSDEN (013032)**, 801 Goodyear Avenue, Zip 35903–1133; tel. 256/439–5000, (Nonreporting) **A**1 9 10 **S** HEALTHSOUTH Corporation, Birmingham, AL
Primary Contact: Michael W. Thompson, Chief Executive Officer
COO: Michael W. Thompson, Chief Executive Officer
CFO: Lori Norman, Chief Financial Officer
CMO: Catherine Harding, M.D., Medical Director
CIO: Lori Norman, Chief Financial Officer
CHR: Heather Blevins, Director Human Resources
Web address: www.healthsouth.com
**Control:** Corporation, Investor–owned, for–profit **Service:** Rehabilitation

**Staffed Beds:** 44

☐ **MOUNTAIN VIEW HOSPITAL (014006)**, 3001 Scenic Highway, Zip 35904–3047, Mailing Address: P.O. Box 8406, Zip 35902–8406; tel. 256/546–9265 **A**1 9 10 **F**2 54 98 99 102 104 105 130 132 **P**6
Primary Contact: G. Michael Shehi, M.D., Interim Chief Executive Officer
COO: Sara Romano, R.N., Vice President
CFO: Mary Jensen, Controller
CMO: G. Michael Shehi, M.D., Medical Director
CHR: Dave Jensen, Director Human Resources, Performance Improvement and Risk Management
Web address: www.mtnviewhospital.com
**Control:** Individual, Investor–owned, for–profit **Service:** Psychiatric

**Staffed Beds:** 108 **Admissions:** 1312 **Census:** 31 **Outpatient Visits:** 22841 **Births:** 0 **Total Expense ($000):** 12492 **Payroll Expense ($000):** 7104 **Personnel:** 171

☐ **RIVERVIEW REGIONAL MEDICAL CENTER (010046)**, 600 South Third Street, Zip 35901–5399; tel. 256/543–5200 **A**1 9 10 **F**5 8 12 15 17 18 20 22 24 26 29 30 34 37 40 41 45 46 47 48 49 50 51 56 57 59 60 68 69 70 74 75 77 79 81 85 87 91 92 93 94 97 103 107 108 109 110 111 114 115 118 119 120 126 129 130 146 148 **S** Health Management Associates, Naples, FL
Primary Contact: James H. Edmondson, Chief Executive Officer
CIO: Jay Terrell, Manager Management Information Systems
CHR: Dana Simpson, Manager Human Resources
Web address: www.riverviewregional.com
**Control:** Corporation, Investor–owned, for–profit **Service:** General Medical and Surgical

**Staffed Beds:** 250 **Admissions:** 6135 **Census:** 103 **Outpatient Visits:** 43201 **Births:** 0 **Total Expense ($000):** 83838 **Payroll Expense ($000):** 24646 **Personnel:** 618

*Many Facility Codes have changed. Please refer to the AHA Guide Code Chart.*

© 2013 AHA Guide

## GENEVA—Geneva County

★ **WIREGRASS MEDICAL CENTER (010062)**, 1200 West Maple Avenue, Zip 36340–1694; tel. 334/684–3655, (Nonreporting) **A**9 10
Primary Contact: James F. Heitzenrater, FACHE, Chief Executive Officer
CFO: Gloria McGowan, Chief Financial Officer
CIO: Tom Garske, Director Information Systems
CHR: Pam Phillips, Chief Human Resource Officer
CNO: Craig Cassady, Director of Nursing
Web address: www.alaweb.com/~tgarske
**Control:** Hospital district or authority, Government, nonfederal **Service:** General Medical and Surgical

Staffed Beds: 167

## GEORGIANA—Butler County

**GEORGIANA HOSPITAL (010047)**, 515 Miranda Street, Zip 36033–4519, Mailing Address: P.O. Box 548, Zip 36033–0548; tel. 334/376–2205, (Nonreporting) **A**9 10
Primary Contact: Harry Cole, Jr., Administrator
**Control:** Partnership, Investor–owned, for–profit **Service:** General Medical and Surgical

Staffed Beds: 22

## GREENSBORO—Hale County

**HALE COUNTY HOSPITAL (010095)**, 508 Green Street, Zip 36744–2316; tel. 334/624–3024, (Nonreporting) **A**9 10
Primary Contact: Thomas O. Lackey, Administrator
Web address: www.halecountyhospital.com
**Control:** Hospital district or authority, Government, nonfederal **Service:** General Medical and Surgical

Staffed Beds: 20

## GREENVILLE—Butler County

⊠ **L. V. STABLER MEMORIAL HOSPITAL (010150)**, 29 L. V. Stabler Drive, Zip 36037–3800; tel. 334/382–2671, (Nonreporting) **A**1 5 9 10 **S** Community Health Systems, Inc., Franklin, TN
Primary Contact: Connie Nicholas, Interim Chief Executive Officer
COO: Connie Nicholas, Interim Chief Executive Officer
CFO: Vann Windham, Chief Financial Officer
CMO: Norman F. McGowin, III, M.D., Chief of Staff
CHR: Robert Foster, Director Human Resources
CNO: Kimberli Weaver, Chief Nursing Officer
Web address: www.lvstabler.com
**Control:** Corporation, Investor–owned, for–profit **Service:** General Medical and Surgical

Staffed Beds: 61

## GROVE HILL—Clarke County

★ **GROVE HILL MEMORIAL HOSPITAL (010091)**, 295 South Jackson Street, Zip 36451–3231, Mailing Address: P.O. Box 935, Zip 36451–0935; tel. 251/275–3191, (Nonreporting) **A**9 10
Primary Contact: Wes Nall, Administrator
CFO: Elaine Averett, Chief Financial Officer
CMO: David Hubbs, M.D., Chief Medical Staff
CHR: Emily Steadham, Administrative Assistant Human Resources and Public Relations
Web address: www.grovehillmemorial.org
**Control:** City–Government, nonfederal **Service:** General Medical and Surgical

Staffed Beds: 33

## GUNTERSVILLE—Marshall County

⊠ **MARSHALL MEDICAL CENTER NORTH (010010)**, 8000 Alabama Highway 69, Zip 35976; tel. 256/753–8000 **A**1 5 9 10 **F**3 7 8 11 12 13 15 26 28 29 32 34 35 37 38 40 43 45 49 50 51 53 54 57 59 64 68 70 74 75 76 79 81 82 85 86 87 93 99 100 102 103 104 107 108 110 111 114 119 130 131 132 133 135 141 146 147 **S** Marshall Health System, Guntersville, AL
Primary Contact: Cheryl M. Hays, FACHE, Administrator
COO: Cheryl M. Hays, FACHE, Administrator
CFO: Kathy Nelson, Chief Financial Officer
CIO: Kim Bunch, Director Information Technology
CHR: Jeff Stone, Director Human Resources
CNO: Kathy Woodruff, R.N., Chief Nursing Officer
Web address: www.mmcenters.com
**Control:** Hospital district or authority, Government, nonfederal **Service:** General Medical and Surgical

Staffed Beds: 90 Admissions: 4196 Census: 49 Outpatient Visits: 133886 Births: 299 Total Expense ($000): 56887 Payroll Expense ($000): 25160 Personnel: 341

## HALEYVILLE—Winston County

⊠ **LAKELAND COMMUNITY HOSPITAL (010125)**, Highway 195 East, Zip 35565–9536, Mailing Address: P.O. Box 780, Zip 35565–0780; tel. 205/486–5213, (Nonreporting) **A**1 9 10 20 **S** LifePoint Hospitals, Inc., Brentwood, TN
Primary Contact: James P. Jeansonne, Chief Executive Officer
CFO: Penny Westmoreland, Chief Financial Officer
Web address: www.lifepointhospitals.com/serving–communities/community/lakeland–community–hospital/
**Control:** Corporation, Investor–owned, for–profit **Service:** General Medical and Surgical

Staffed Beds: 56

## HAMILTON—Marion County

⊠ **NORTH MISSISSIPPI MEDICAL CENTER–HAMILTON (010044)**, 1256 Military Street South, Zip 35570–5003; tel. 205/921–6200, (Nonreporting) **A**1 9 10 **S** North Mississippi Health Services, Inc., Tupelo, MS
Primary Contact: Donald J. Jones, FACHE, Administrator
CMO: Jeff Hager, M.D., President Medical Staff
CHR: Anne Lawler, Director Human Resources
CNO: Tanya Brasher, Director of Nursing
Web address: www.nmhs.net
**Control:** Other not–for–profit (including NFP Corporation) **Service:** General Medical and Surgical

Staffed Beds: 36

## HUNTSVILLE—Madison County

**BEHAVIORAL HEALTHCARE CENTER AT HUNTSVILLE (014018)**, 5315 Millennium Drive N.W., Zip 35806–2458; tel. 256/964–6700, (Nonreporting) **S** Tennessee Health Management, Parsons, TN
Primary Contact: Mike Maxwell, Administrator
**Control:** Corporation, Investor–owned, for–profit **Service:** Psychiatric

Staffed Beds: 20

⊠ **CRESTWOOD MEDICAL CENTER (010131)**, One Hospital Drive, Zip 35801–3403; tel. 256/429–4000 **A**1 5 9 10 **F**3 5 11 12 13 15 17 18 22 29 30 31 34 35 40 43 45 47 49 51 56 57 59 60 64 65 68 70 72 74 75 76 77 78 79 80 81 85 86 87 89 93 97 98 99 100 101 102 103 104 105 107 108 110 111 114 115 119 126 129 130 131 132 146 147 148 **S** Community Health Systems, Inc., Franklin, TN
Primary Contact: Pamela Hudson, M.D., Chief Executive Officer
COO: Bobby Ginn, Chief Operating Officer
CHR: Lynn Dingo, Director Human Resources
Web address: www.crestwoodmedcenter.com
**Control:** Corporation, Investor–owned, for–profit **Service:** General Medical and Surgical

Staffed Beds: 150 Admissions: 9584 Census: 100 Outpatient Visits: 108912 Births: 708 Total Expense ($000): 139826 Payroll Expense ($000): 47356 Personnel: 971

⊠ **HEALTHSOUTH REHABILITATION HOSPITAL OF NORTH ALABAMA (013029)**, 107 Governors Drive S.W., Zip 35801–4326; tel. 256/535–2300, (Nonreporting) **A**1 9 10 **S** HEALTHSOUTH Corporation, Birmingham, AL
Primary Contact: Douglas H. Beverly, Chief Executive Officer
Web address: www.healthsouthhuntsville.com
**Control:** Corporation, Investor–owned, for–profit **Service:** Rehabilitation

Staffed Beds: 70

☐ **HUNTSVILLE HOSPITAL (010039)**, 101 Sivley Road S.W., Zip 35801–4470; tel. 256/265–1000, (Includes HUNTSVILLE HOSPITAL FOR WOMEN AND CHILDREN, 911 Big Cove Road S.E., Zip 35801–3784; tel. 256/265–1000) **A**1 2 3 5 10 **F**5 7 8 12 13 14 15 17 18 19 20 21 22 23 24 25 26 28 29 30 31 35 37 38 39 40 41 43 48 49 50 51 53 54 56 57 59 60 64 68 70 71 72 73 76 78 79 80 81 82 84 88 89 93 96 98 99 100 101 102 103 104 105 107 108 109 110 111 114 115 116 117 118 119 126 129 130 131 142 144 145 146 147 148 **S** Huntsville Hospital Health System, Huntsville, AL
Primary Contact: David S. Spillers, Chief Executive Officer
COO: Jeff Samz, Chief Operating Officer
CFO: Lonnie D. Younger, Chief Financial Officer
CMO: Robert Chappell, M.D., Chief Medical Officer and Chief Quality Officer
CIO: Rick Corn, Chief Information Officer
CHR: Andrea P. Rosler, Vice President Human Resources
Web address: www.huntsvillehospital.org
**Control:** Hospital district or authority, Government, nonfederal **Service:** General Medical and Surgical

Staffed Beds: 835 Admissions: 42447 Census: 567 Outpatient Visits: 718549 Births: 5121 Total Expense ($000): 695259 Payroll Expense ($000): 271139 Personnel: 5782

---

**Hospital, Medicare Provider Number, Address, Telephone, Approval, Facility, and Physician Codes, Health Care System**

★ American Hospital Association (AHA) membership
☐ The Joint Commission accreditation
◇ DNV Healthcare Inc. accreditation
○ Healthcare Facilities Accreditation Program
△ Commission on Accreditation of Rehabilitation Facilities (CARF) accreditation

### JACKSON—Clarke County

**JACKSON MEDICAL CENTER (010128)**, 220 Hospital Drive, Zip 36545–2459, Mailing Address: P.O. Box 428, Zip 36545–0428; tel. 251/246–9021, (Nonreporting) **A**9 10 **S** Gilliard Health Services, Montgomery, AL
Primary Contact: Amy Gibson, Chief Executive Officer
COO: Jennifer M. Ryland, R.N., Chief Administrative Officer
CFO: Amy Gibson, Chief Executive Officer
CHR: Kathy Jones, Director Human Resources
Web address: www.jacksonmedicalcenter.org
**Control:** Partnership, Investor–owned, for–profit **Service:** General Medical and Surgical

**Staffed Beds: 26**

### JACKSONVILLE—Calhoun County

☐ **JACKSONVILLE MEDICAL CENTER (010146)**, 1701 Pelham Road South, Zip 36265–3399, Mailing Address: P.O. Box 999, Zip 36265–0999; tel. 256/435–4970 **A**1 9 10 **F**3 4 11 13 15 29 30 34 35 40 45 48 50 51 56 57 59 64 65 68 69 76 79 81 82 85 93 98 103 107 108 111 114 119 120 129 135 146 **P**6
Primary Contact: David P. Steitz, Interim Chief Executive Officer
COO: Jean Ann McMurray, R.N., Chief Nursing Officer
CFO: Tammy Cobb, Chief Financial Officer
CMO: James R. Yates, M.D., Chief of Staff
CIO: Richard Maust, Chief Information Officer
CHR: Doug Scott, Director Human Resources
Web address: www.jmchealth.com
**Control:** Corporation, Investor–owned, for–profit **Service:** General Medical and Surgical

**Staffed Beds: 69 Admissions: 1921 Census: 25 Outpatient Visits: 52317 Births: 340 Total Expense ($000): 27647 Payroll Expense ($000): 11079 Personnel: 217**

### JASPER—Walker County

☐ **WALKER BAPTIST MEDICAL CENTER (010089)**, 3400 Highway 78 East, Zip 35501–8907, Mailing Address: P.O. Box 3547, Zip 35502–3547; tel. 205/387–4000 **A**1 9 10 **F**3 8 11 13 15 18 20 22 26 29 30 31 34 35 40 41 43 45 47 49 50 56 57 59 64 67 68 70 75 76 77 78 79 81 82 85 87 94 96 97 98 100 101 102 103 104 107 108 110 111 115 119 126 130 132 146 147 148 **S** Baptist Health System, Birmingham, AL
Primary Contact: Robert Phillips, Administrator
CFO: John Langlois, Chief Financial Officer
CIO: Kenny Horton, Director Information Systems
CHR: Pat Morrow, Director Human Resources
CNO: Robbie Hindman, Vice President Patient Care Services and Chief Nursing Officer
Web address: www.bhsala.com/home_walker.cfm?id=41
**Control:** Church–operated, Nongovernment, not–for profit **Service:** General Medical and Surgical

**Staffed Beds: 236 Admissions: 7220 Census: 92 Outpatient Visits: 81140 Births: 750 Total Expense ($000): 87008 Payroll Expense ($000): 28477 Personnel: 591**

### LUVERNE—Crenshaw County

☐ **BEACON CHILDREN'S HOSPITAL (014015)**, 150 Hospital Drive, Zip 36049; tel. 334/335–5040, (Nonreporting) **A**1 9 10
Primary Contact: Carol Crowson, Administrator
Web address: www.beaconchildrenshospital.com
**Control:** Other not–for–profit (including NFP Corporation) **Service:** Psychiatric

**Staffed Beds: 24**

**CRENSHAW COMMUNITY HOSPITAL (010008)**, 101 Hospital Circle, Zip 36049–7344; tel. 334/335–3374, (Nonreporting) **A**9 10
Primary Contact: Bradley Eisemann, Administrator
COO: Victoria Lawrenson, Chief Operating Officer
CMO: Charles Tompkins, M.D., Chief of Staff
CHR: Patricia Jarry, Manager Human Resources
**Control:** Corporation, Investor–owned, for–profit **Service:** General Medical and Surgical

**Staffed Beds: 49**

### MADISON—Madison County

**BRADFORD HEALTH SERVICES AT HUNTSVILLE**, 1600 Browns Ferry Road, Zip 35758–9601, Mailing Address: P.O. Box 1488, Zip 35758–0176; tel. 256/461–7272, (Nonreporting) **S** Bradford Health Services, Birmingham, AL
Primary Contact: Bob Hinds, Executive Director
Web address: www.bradfordhealth.com
**Control:** Corporation, Investor–owned, for–profit **Service:** Alcoholism and other chemical dependency

**Staffed Beds: 84**

**MADISON HOSPITAL**, 8375 Highway 72 West, Zip 35758–9573; tel. 256/265–2012, (Data for 124 days) **F**13 29 34 37 40 45 50 64 70 76 81 107 111 119 146 147 **S** Huntsville Hospital Health System, Huntsville, AL
Primary Contact: Mary Lynne Wright, R.N., President
Web address: www.madisonalhospital.org/
**Control:** Hospital district or authority, Government, nonfederal **Service:** General Medical and Surgical

**Staffed Beds: 43 Admissions: 293 Census: 9 Outpatient Visits: 17174 Births: 14 Total Expense ($000): 16920 Payroll Expense ($000): 6860 Personnel: 297**

### MOBILE—Mobile County

**BAYPOINTE BEHAVIORAL HEALTH (014014)**, 5800 Southland Drive, Zip 36693–3313; tel. 251/661–0153, (Nonreporting) **A**9 10 **S** AltaPointe Health Systems, Mobile, AL
Primary Contact: Heather Joseph, Administrator
Web address: www.altapointe.org
**Control:** Corporation, Investor–owned, for–profit **Service:** Psychiatric

**Staffed Beds: 60**

☐ **INFIRMARY LONG TERM ACUTE CARE HOSPITAL (012006)**, 5 Mobile Infirmary Circle, Zip 36607–3513; tel. 251/660–5239, (Nonreporting) **A**1 9 10 **S** Infirmary Health System, Mobile, AL
Primary Contact: Susanne Marmande, Administrator
Web address: www.theinfirmary.com/
**Control:** Other not–for–profit (including NFP Corporation) **Service:** Long–Term Acute Care hospital

**Staffed Beds: 191**

☐ △ **MOBILE INFIRMARY MEDICAL CENTER (010113)**, 5 Mobile Infirmary Drive North, Zip 36607–3513, Mailing Address: P.O. Box 2144, Zip 36652–2144; tel. 251/435–2400, (Includes ROTARY REHABILITATION HOSPITAL, 5 Mobile Infirmary Circle, Zip 36607, Mailing Address: P.O. Box 2144, Zip 36652; tel. 334/431–3400), (Nonreporting) **A**1 2 3 5 7 9 10 **S** Infirmary Health System, Mobile, AL
Primary Contact: Joe Strough, Administrator
CFO: Joe Denton, Executive Vice President and Chief Financial Officer
CIO: Eddy Stephens, Vice President Information Technology
CHR: Sheila Young, Vice President Human Resources
Web address: www.mobileinfirmary.org
**Control:** Other not–for–profit (including NFP Corporation) **Service:** General Medical and Surgical

**Staffed Beds: 526**

✇ **PROVIDENCE HOSPITAL (010090)**, 6801 Airport Boulevard, Zip 36608–3785, Mailing Address: P.O. Box 850429, Zip 36685–0429; tel. 251/633–1000 **A**1 2 3 5 9 10 **F**3 11 13 15 17 18 20 22 24 26 28 29 30 31 34 35 40 44 45 49 50 51 53 54 57 58 59 60 61 64 65 68 70 73 74 75 76 77 78 79 80 81 82 83 84 85 86 87 89 92 93 96 102 107 108 110 111 114 115 117 119 120 121 124 126 129 130 131 132 135 146 148 **P**5 6 **S** Ascension Health, Saint Louis, MO
Primary Contact: Clark P. Christianson, President and Chief Executive Officer
COO: Todd S. Kennedy, Executive Vice President and Chief Operating Officer
CFO: C. Susan Cornejo, Senior Vice President Finance and Chief Financial Officer
CMO: William M. Lightfoot, M.D., Vice President Medical Services
CHR: Kathy Ross, Chief Information Officer
CHR: H. Jaquita Tucker, Executive Director Human Resources
CNO: Ann Doss, Interim Vice President and Chief Nursing Officer
Web address: www.providencehospital.org
**Control:** Church–operated, Nongovernment, not–for profit **Service:** General Medical and Surgical

**Staffed Beds: 349 Admissions: 13934 Census: 194 Outpatient Visits: 155305 Births: 1805 Total Expense ($000): 198638 Payroll Expense ($000): 68648 Personnel: 1662**

**ROTARY REHABILITATION HOSPITAL** See Mobile Infirmary Medical Center

☐ **SPRINGHILL MEMORIAL HOSPITAL (010144)**, 3719 Dauphin Street, Zip 36608–1798, Mailing Address: P.O. Box 8246, Zip 36689–0246; tel. 251/344–9630 **A**1 9 10 **F**11 13 15 17 18 20 22 24 26 28 29 30 31 34 40 46 47 49 50 51 57 60 70 74 75 76 77 78 79 81 82 85 86 87 88 89 93 107 110 111 115 118 119 126 127 129 130 132 146 147 148
Primary Contact: Jeffery M. St. Clair, President and Chief Executive Officer
COO: Jeffery M. St Clair, President and Chief Executive Officer
CFO: Randy Sucher, Executive Vice President
CIO: Mark Kilborn, Director Information Systems
CHR: Daniela Batchelor, Director Human Resources
Web address: www.springhillmemorial.com
**Control:** Corporation, Investor–owned, for–profit **Service:** General Medical and Surgical

**Staffed Beds: 193 Admissions: 8295 Census: 116 Outpatient Visits: 156796 Births: 637 Total Expense ($000): 127578 Payroll Expense ($000): 40832 Personnel: 1002**

*Many Facility Codes have changed. Please refer to the AHA Guide Code Chart.*

© 2013 AHA Guide

✠ **UNIVERSITY OF SOUTH ALABAMA CHILDREN'S AND WOMEN'S HOSPITAL (013301)**, (Childrens and Womens), 1700 Center Street, Zip 36604–3301; tel. 251/415–1000 **A**1 3 5 9 10 **F**3 7 11 13 15 21 27 29 30 31 40 48 49 52 55 58 59 64 72 73 74 75 76 77 78 79 81 85 86 87 88 89 93 107 111 114 119 130 143 146 147 **S** University of South Alabama Hospitals, Mobile, AL
Primary Contact: Owen Bailey, Administrator
CFO: William B. Bush, CPA, Chief Financial Officer
CIO: David Blough, Chief Information Officer
CHR: Janice Rehm, Manager Human Resources
CNO: Carol Druckenmiller, R.N., Assistant Administrator and Chief Nursing Officer
Web address: www.usahealthsystem.com/usacwh
**Control:** State–Government, nonfederal **Service:** Other specialty

Staffed Beds: **198** Admissions: **9272** Census: **168** Outpatient Visits: **60523** Births: **2666** Total Expense ($000): **110912** Payroll Expense ($000): **49758** Personnel: **1063**

✠ **UNIVERSITY OF SOUTH ALABAMA MEDICAL CENTER (010087)**, 2451 Fillingim Street, Zip 36617–2293; tel. 251/471–7000 **A**1 2 3 5 8 9 10 **F**3 11 16 17 18 20 22 24 26 29 31 34 40 43 46 49 57 58 59 60 61 64 70 74 78 79 81 85 87 107 108 111 114 115 119 130 146 148 **S** University of South Alabama Hospitals, Mobile, AL
Primary Contact: A. Elizabeth Anderson, Administrator
CFO: William B. Bush, CPA, Chief Financial Officer
CHR: Anita Shirah, Director Human Resources
Web address: www.usahealthsystem.com/usamc
**Control:** State–Government, nonfederal **Service:** General Medical and Surgical

Staffed Beds: **132** Admissions: **6686** Census: **111** Outpatient Visits: **46368** Births: **2** Total Expense ($000): **148453** Payroll Expense ($000): **71926** Personnel: **1224**

### MONROEVILLE—Monroe County

✠ **MONROE COUNTY HOSPITAL (010120)**, 2016 South Alabama Avenue, Zip 36460–3044, Mailing Address: P.O. Box 886, Zip 36461–0886; tel. 251/575–3111, (Nonreporting) **A**1 9 10 20
Primary Contact: Thomas J. Stone, FACHE, Chief Executive Officer
CFO: Michael Vaughn, Chief Financial Officer
CMO: Alexander Nettles, M.D., Chief of Staff
CIO: Lee Falkenberry, Director Information Systems
CHR: Tara Nowling, Director Human Resources
CNO: Barbara Harned, R.N., Chief Nursing Officer
Web address: www.mchcare.com
**Control:** Hospital district or authority, Government, nonfederal **Service:** General Medical and Surgical

Staffed Beds: **62**

### MONTGOMERY—Montgomery County

✠ **BAPTIST MEDICAL CENTER EAST (010149)**, 400 Taylor Road, Zip 36117–3512, Mailing Address: P.O. Box 241267, Zip 36124–1267; tel. 334/277–8330 **A**1 9 10 **F**3 11 12 13 15 29 30 34 35 40 44 45 47 49 50 56 57 63 64 68 70 72 73 75 76 77 79 81 82 85 86 89 90 93 94 107 108 111 114 115 119 126 129 130 132 135 146 147 **S** Baptist Health, Montgomery, AL
Primary Contact: Jeff Rains, Administrator and Chief Executive Officer
COO: Robin Barca, Chief Operating Officer
CFO: Katrina Belt, Chief Financial Officer
CIO: Wanda Sims, Chief Information Officer
CHR: Kay Bennett, Vice President Human Resources
Web address: www.baptistfirst.org
**Control:** Hospital district or authority, Government, nonfederal **Service:** General Medical and Surgical

Staffed Beds: **182** Admissions: **10186** Census: **116** Outpatient Visits: **86720** Births: **3301** Total Expense ($000): **96839** Payroll Expense ($000): **36960** Personnel: **728**

✠ **BAPTIST MEDICAL CENTER SOUTH (010023)**, 2105 East South Boulevard, Zip 36116–2409, Mailing Address: Box 11010, Zip 36111–0010; tel. 334/288–2100 **A**1 3 5 9 10 **F**3 5 11 12 13 15 17 18 20 22 24 26 28 29 30 31 34 35 40 44 45 47 49 50 56 57 58 59 60 61 63 64 68 70 72 74 75 76 78 79 81 82 84 85 86 87 89 90 93 94 98 100 101 102 103 104 105 107 108 110 111 113 114 118 119 126 129 130 131 132 135 146 147 148 **S** Baptist Health, Montgomery, AL
Primary Contact: Robin Barca, Chief Executive Officer
COO: Robin Barca, Chief Executive Officer
CFO: Lisa Goodlett, Chief Financial Officer
CMO: Donovan Kendrick, M.D., Chief of Staff
CIO: Wanda Sims, Chief Information Officer
CHR: Kay Bennett, System Director Human Resources
CNO: Teresa Parker, Vice President and Chief Nursing Officer
Web address: www.baptistfirst.org
**Control:** Hospital district or authority, Government, nonfederal **Service:** General Medical and Surgical

Staffed Beds: **386** Admissions: **18335** Census: **246** Outpatient Visits: **162688** Births: **807** Total Expense ($000): **275674** Payroll Expense ($000): **83841** Personnel: **1792**

✠ **CENTRAL ALABAMA VETERANS HEALTH CARE SYSTEM**, 215 Perry Hill Road, Zip 36109–3798; tel. 334/272–4670, (Includes MONTGOMERY DIVISION, 215 Perry Hill Road, tel. 334/272–4670; TUSKEGEE DIVISION, 2400 Hospital Road, Tuskegee, Zip 36083–5001; tel. 334/727–0550), (Total facility includes 100 beds in nursing home–type unit) **A**1 3 **F**3 4 5 29 30 35 38 39 40 45 50 53 56 59 63 64 65 68 70 75 77 80 81 82 83 84 86 87 90 91 93 94 97 98 100 101 102 104 105 106 107 108 111 114 115 116 117 119 128 130 132 135 143 146 147 148 **S** Department of Veterans Affairs, Washington, DC
Primary Contact: James R. Talton, MS, FACHE, Director
CFO: Brenda Schmitz, Manager Finance
CMO: N. Rao Chava, M.D., Director
CHR: Linda King, Chief Human Resources Management Service
Web address: www.centralalabama.va.gov/
**Control:** Veterans Affairs, Government, federal **Service:** General Medical and Surgical

Staffed Beds: **261** Admissions: **2420** Census: **189** Outpatient Visits: **395684** Births: **0** Total Expense ($000): **232229** Payroll Expense ($000): **104378** Personnel: **1572**

✠ **HEALTHSOUTH REHABILITATION HOSPITAL OF MONTGOMERY (013028)**, 4465 Narrow Lane Road, Zip 36116–2900; tel. 334/284–7700 **A**1 9 10 **F**3 9 28 29 34 35 54 56 57 59 64 74 75 77 86 90 93 95 130 131 132 143 146 148 **P**5 **S** HEALTHSOUTH Corporation, Birmingham, AL
Primary Contact: Linda Wade, Chief Executive Officer
CFO: Heath Watson, Controller
CMO: Jeffrey Eng, M.D., Medical Director
CIO: Diane Davis, Manager Business Office
CHR: Kim McDaniel, Director Human Resources
Web address: www.healthsouthmontgomery.com
**Control:** Corporation, Investor–owned, for–profit **Service:** Rehabilitation

Staffed Beds: **70** Admissions: **1700** Census: **58** Outpatient Visits: **4957** Births: **0** Total Expense ($000): **16666** Payroll Expense ($000): **9945** Personnel: **217**

✠ **JACKSON HOSPITAL AND CLINIC (010024)**, 1725 Pine Street, Zip 36106–1117; tel. 334/293–8000 **A**1 9 10 **F**13 15 17 18 20 22 24 26 29 30 31 34 40 45 46 49 57 59 64 68 70 74 76 77 78 79 81 82 84 85 86 87 89 93 107 108 111 114 116 117 118 119 126 130 131 135 146 147 **P**6
Primary Contact: Joe B. Riley, President and Chief Executive Officer
CIO: Richard E. Caldwell, Vice President Support Services
CNO: Sharon A. Goodison, R.N., Chief Nursing Officer
Web address: www.jackson.org
**Control:** Other not–for–profit (including NFP Corporation) **Service:** General Medical and Surgical

Staffed Beds: **251** Admissions: **13282** Census: **168** Outpatient Visits: **52755** Births: **1322** Total Expense ($000): **162274** Payroll Expense ($000): **61200** Personnel: **1335**

**LONG TERM CARE HOSPITAL** See Noland Hospital Montgomery

**MONTGOMERY DIVISION** See Central Alabama Veterans Health Care System

☐ **NOLAND HOSPITAL MONTGOMERY (012007)**, 1725 Pine Street, 5 North, Zip 36106–1109; tel. 334/240–0532 **A**1 9 10 **F**1 148 **S** Noland Health Services, Inc., Birmingham, AL
Primary Contact: Susan E. Legg, Interim Administrator
Web address: www.nolandhealth.com
**Control:** Other not–for–profit (including NFP Corporation) **Service:** Long–Term Acute Care hospital

Staffed Beds: **65** Admissions: **380** Census: **25** Outpatient Visits: **0** Births: **0** Total Expense ($000): **10243** Payroll Expense ($000): **4213**

---

**Hospital, Medicare Provider Number, Address, Telephone, Approval, Facility, and Physician Codes, Health Care System**

★ American Hospital Association (AHA) membership
☐ The Joint Commission accreditation
◇ DNV Healthcare Inc. accreditation
○ Healthcare Facilities Accreditation Program
△ Commission on Accreditation of Rehabilitation Facilities (CARF) accreditation

**AL**

## MOULTON—Lawrence County

☐ **LAWRENCE MEDICAL CENTER (010059)**, 202 Hospital Street, Zip 35650–1218, Mailing Address: P.O. Box 39, Zip 35650–0039; tel. 256/974–2200, (Nonreporting) **A**1 9 10
Primary Contact: Kyle Buchanan, Chief Executive Officer
CFO: Jim Crawford, Chief Financial Officer
CIO: Jeremy Duncan, Director Information Systems
CHR: Diane K. Secor, Director Human Resources
Web address: www.lawrencemedicalcenter.com
**Control:** County–Government, nonfederal **Service:** General Medical and Surgical

Staffed Beds: 53

## MUSCLE SHOALS—Colbert County

☐ **SHOALS HOSPITAL (010157)**, 201 Avalon Avenue, Zip 35661–2805, Mailing Address: P.O. Box 3359, Zip 35662–3359; tel. 256/386–1600, (Nonreporting) **A**1 9 10 **S** RegionalCare Hospital Partners, Brentwood, TN
Primary Contact: C. Ross Berry, Chief Executive Officer
Web address: www.shoalshospital.com
**Control:** Hospital district or authority, Government, nonfederal **Service:** General Medical and Surgical

Staffed Beds: 137

## NORTHPORT—Tuscaloosa County

☐ **NORTHPORT MEDICAL CENTER (010145)**, 2700 Hospital Drive, Zip 35476–3360; tel. 205/333–4500, (Nonreporting) **A**1 5 **S** DCH Health System, Tuscaloosa, AL
Primary Contact: Luke Standeffer, Administrator
CFO: Jon Kramer, Controller and Assistant Administrator
CMO: David Rice, M.D., Vice President Medical Affairs
CIO: Kim Ligon, Director Information Services
CHR: Beth Francis, Vice President Human Resources
Web address: www.dchsystem.com
**Control:** Hospital district or authority, Government, nonfederal **Service:** General Medical and Surgical

Staffed Beds: 196

## ONEONTA—Blount County

⊞ **ST. VINCENT'S BLOUNT (010050)**, 150 Gilbreath, Zip 35121–2827, Mailing Address: P.O. Box 1000, Zip 35121–0013; tel. 205/274–3000 **A**1 9 10 **F**3 11 15 18 29 30 35 36 37 40 42 43 45 57 59 64 65 70 75 77 79 81 82 85 93 97 107 108 110 119 135 **P**7 8 **S** Ascension Health, Saint Louis, MO
Primary Contact: Evan Ray, President
CFO: David Cauble, Chief Financial Officer
CMO: David R. Wilson, M.D., Chief of Staff
CIO: Timothy Stettheimer, Regional Chief Information Officer
CHR: Carol Maietta, Vice President and Talent Resource Officer Human Resources and Learning
CNO: Paula McCullough, VP Patient Care Services
Web address: www.stvhs.com
**Control:** Other not–for–profit (including NFP Corporation) **Service:** General Medical and Surgical

Staffed Beds: 40 Admissions: 1232 Census: 14 Outpatient Visits: 36832 Births: 0 Total Expense ($000): 11132 Payroll Expense ($000): 6265 Personnel: 138

## OPELIKA—Lee County

⊞ **EAST ALABAMA MEDICAL CENTER (010029)**, 2000 Pepperell Parkway, Zip 36801–5452; tel. 334/749–3411, (Total facility includes 113 beds in nursing home–type unit) **A**1 2 9 10 19 **F**3 7 10 11 13 15 17 18 20 22 24 26 28 29 30 31 32 34 40 43 45 50 51 53 54 56 57 58 59 60 61 64 68 70 74 75 76 77 78 79 81 82 84 85 86 89 93 98 99 100 102 103 104 107 108 110 111 114 115 117 118 119 120 121 123 125 126 128 129 130 131 132 135 146 148 **P**6
Primary Contact: Terry W. Andrus, President
COO: Laura D. Grill, R.N., Executive Vice President and Administrator
CFO: Sam Price, Executive Vice President Finance/Chief Financial Officer
CMO: Michael Lisenby, M.D., Vice President and Chief Medical Officer
CIO: Tommy Chittom, Vice President Information Services
CHR: Susan Johnston, Director Human Resources
Web address: www.eamc.org
**Control:** Hospital district or authority, Government, nonfederal **Service:** General Medical and Surgical

Staffed Beds: 371 Admissions: 13959 Census: 263 Outpatient Visits: 124643 Births: 1567 Total Expense ($000): 237519 Payroll Expense ($000): 93241 Personnel: 2454

## OPP—Covington County

★ **MIZELL MEMORIAL HOSPITAL (010007)**, 702 Main Street, Zip 36467–1626, Mailing Address: P.O. Box 1010, Zip 36467–1010; tel. 334/493–3541, (Nonreporting) **A**9 10
Primary Contact: Jana Wyatt, Chief Executive Officer
CFO: Amy Bess, Chief Financial Officer
CMO: Wheeler Gunnels, M.D., Medical Director
CIO: Elizabeth Cook, Chief Information Officer
CHR: Dianne Morrison, Director Human Resources
Web address: www.mizellmh.com
**Control:** Other not–for–profit (including NFP Corporation) **Service:** General Medical and Surgical

Staffed Beds: 58

## OZARK—Dale County

**DALE MEDICAL CENTER (010021)**, 126 Hospital Avenue, Zip 36360–2080; tel. 334/774–2601, (Nonreporting) **A**9 10
Primary Contact: Vernon Johnson, Administrator
CFO: Brad Hull, Chief Financial Officer
CMO: Steve Brandt, M.D., Chief of Staff
CHR: Sheila Dunn, Assistant Administrator Human Resources
Web address: www.dalemedical.org
**Control:** Corporation, Investor–owned, for–profit **Service:** General Medical and Surgical

Staffed Beds: 75

## PELL CITY—St. Clair County

⊞ **ST. VINCENT'S ST. CLAIR (010130)**, 7063 Veterans Parkway, Zip 35125–1499; tel. 205/338–3301 **A**1 9 10 **F**3 11 15 29 30 34 35 40 42 43 50 57 59 64 66 68 70 74 75 77 78 79 81 86 87 93 107 111 119 130 133 135 143 146 148 **P**7 8 **S** Ascension Health, Saint Louis, MO
Primary Contact: Evan Ray, President
CFO: Imelda Roberson, Director Finance
CHR: Tamara Barr, Human Resources Generalist
Web address: www.stvhs.com
**Control:** Other not–for–profit (including NFP Corporation) **Service:** General Medical and Surgical

Staffed Beds: 46 Admissions: 1582 Census: 17 Outpatient Visits: 38376 Births: 0 Total Expense ($000): 12277 Payroll Expense ($000): 7677 Personnel: 172

## PHENIX CITY—Russell County

**JACK HUGHSTON MEMORIAL HOSPITAL (010168)**, 4401 Riverchase Drive, Zip 36867–7483; tel. 334/732–3000 **A**9 10 **F**3 29 40 45 70 79 81 107 114 115 119
Primary Contact: Mark A. Baker, Chief Executive Officer
COO: Divya Matai, Chief Operating Officer and Chief Financial Officer
CFO: Divya Matai, Chief Operating Officer and Chief Financial Officer
CMO: Lamar Carden, M.D., Chief Medical Officer
CHR: Lana Thomas–Folds, System Director Human Resources
Web address: www.jackhughstonmemorialhospital.com
**Control:** Corporation, Investor–owned, for–profit **Service:** General Medical and Surgical

Staffed Beds: 35 Admissions: 2576 Census: 22 Outpatient Visits: 23475 Births: 0 Total Expense ($000): 45328 Payroll Expense ($000): 12582 Personnel: 287

⊞ **REGIONAL REHABILITATION HOSPITAL (013033)**, 3715 Highway 280/431 North, Zip 36867; tel. 334/732–2200 **A**1 9 10 **F**3 29 30 90 93 95 132 **S** HEALTHSOUTH Corporation, Birmingham, AL
Primary Contact: Jill Jordan, Chief Executive Officer
CFO: Bobby Edmondson, Controller
CIO: Jacki Cuevas, Director Health Information Services
CHR: Cindy Glynn, Director Human Resources
CNO: Brandy Cook, Chief Nursing Officer
Web address: www.regionalrehabhospital.com
**Control:** Partnership, Investor–owned, for–profit **Service:** Rehabilitation

Staffed Beds: 48 Admissions: 1035 Census: 43 Outpatient Visits: 4039 Births: 0 Total Expense ($000): 13667 Payroll Expense ($000): 7390 Personnel: 147

*Many Facility Codes have changed. Please refer to the AHA Guide Code Chart.*
© 2013 AHA Guide

## PRATTVILLE—Autauga County

⊠ **PRATTVILLE BAPTIST HOSPITAL (010108)**, 124 South Memorial Drive, Zip 36067–3619, Mailing Address: P.O. Box 681630, Zip 36068–1638; tel. 334/365–0651 **A**1 9 10 **F**3 11 12 15 29 30 34 35 40 44 45 50 56 57 59 63 64 68 70 75 81 82 84 85 86 87 107 111 114 129 132 146 **S** Baptist Health, Montgomery, AL
Primary Contact: Ginger Henry, Chief Executive Officer
CFO: LaDonna McDaniel, Financial Manager
CIO: B. Blaine Brown, Vice President and General Counsel
CHR: Renee Drayton, Chief Human Resources
Web address: www.baptistfirst.org/facilities/prattville–baptist–hospital/default.aspx
**Control:** Hospital district or authority, Government, nonfederal **Service:** General Medical and Surgical

**Staffed Beds:** 56 **Admissions:** 2015 **Census:** 19 **Outpatient Visits:** 58940 **Births:** 0 **Total Expense ($000):** 28309 **Payroll Expense ($000):** 9133 **Personnel:** 186

## RED BAY—Franklin County

★ **RED BAY HOSPITAL (011302)**, 211 Hospital Road, Zip 35582–3858, Mailing Address: P.O. Box 490, Zip 35582–0490; tel. 256/356–9532 **A**9 10 18 **F**15 29 30 34 39 40 45 53 56 57 59 64 65 75 81 86 93 107 111 119 128 131 133 135 143
Primary Contact: Glen M. Jones, Administrator
CFO: Samuel A. Strickland, Chief Financial Officer
CHR: Pam Bryant, Director Human Resources
Web address: www.redbayhospital.com
**Control:** Hospital district or authority, Government, nonfederal **Service:** General Medical and Surgical

**Staffed Beds:** 25 **Admissions:** 338 **Census:** 7 **Outpatient Visits:** 11989 **Total Expense ($000):** 6841 **Payroll Expense ($000):** 2676 **Personnel:** 77

## RUSSELLVILLE—Franklin County

⊠ **RUSSELLVILLE HOSPITAL (010158)**, 15155 Highway 43, Zip 35653–1975, Mailing Address: P.O. Box 1089, Zip 35653–1089; tel. 256/332–1611, (Nonreporting) **A**1 9 10 **S** LifePoint Hospitals, Inc., Brentwood, TN
Primary Contact: Christine R. Stewart, FACHE, Chief Executive Officer
CFO: Penny Westmoreland, Chief Financial Officer
CHR: Stephen Proctor, Director of Human Resources/Risk
CNO: Belinda Johnson, R.N., Chief Nursing Officer/Chief Clinical Officer
Web address: www.russellvillehospital.com
**Control:** Partnership, Investor–owned, for–profit **Service:** General Medical and Surgical

**Staffed Beds:** 92

## SCOTTSBORO—Jackson County

☐ **HIGHLANDS MEDICAL CENTER (010061)**, 380 Woods Cove Road, Zip 35768–2428, Mailing Address: P.O. Box 1050, Zip 35768–1050; tel. 256/259–4444, (Nonreporting) **A**1 5 9 10 20
Primary Contact: Kim Bryant, Chief Executive Officer
CFO: Dan Newell, Chief Financial Officer
CIO: Doug Newby, Chief Information Officer
CHR: Susanna S. Sivley, Chief Personnel Officer
Web address: www.highlandsmedcenter.com
**Control:** Hospital district or authority, Government, nonfederal **Service:** General Medical and Surgical

**Staffed Beds:** 92

## SELMA—Dallas County

⊠ **VAUGHAN REGIONAL MEDICAL CENTER (010118)**, 1015 Medical Center Parkway, Zip 36701–6352; tel. 334/418–4100 **A**1 3 5 9 10 20 **F**8 11 13 15 17 20 29 30 34 40 45 51 53 60 70 74 76 79 81 89 93 107 108 110 111 114 115 118 119 120 127 129 130 131 146 **S** LifePoint Hospitals, Inc., Brentwood, TN
Primary Contact: David R. Sirk, Chief Executive Officer
COO: Debbie Pace, Chief Operating Officer
CFO: Randy Rogers, Chief Financial Officer
CMO: Mark LeQuire, M.D., Chief of Staff
CHR: Dionne Williams, Director Human Resources
CNO: Verno Davidson, R.N., Chief Nursing Officer
Web address: www.vaughanregional.com
**Control:** Corporation, Investor–owned, for–profit **Service:** General Medical and Surgical

**Staffed Beds:** 149 **Admissions:** 7141 **Census:** 59 **Outpatient Visits:** 68730 **Births:** 677 **Total Expense ($000):** 55216 **Payroll Expense ($000):** 20439 **Personnel:** 467

## SHEFFIELD—Colbert County

⊠ **HELEN KELLER HOSPITAL (010019)**, 1300 South Montgomery Avenue, Zip 35660–6334, Mailing Address: P.O. Box 610, Zip 35660–0610; tel. 256/386–4196 **A**1 9 10 **F**13 15 20 28 29 30 31 32 34 35 36 40 45 47 49 53 59 60 64 65 74 75 76 77 78 79 81 82 83 84 85 86 87 89 93 94 107 108 110 111 114 115 116 117 118 119 126 129 130 131 144 146 148
Primary Contact: W. Douglas Arnold, President and Chief Executive Officer
COO: Paul Storey, Chief Operating Officer
CFO: Morris S. Strickland, Chief Financial Officer
CHR: Pam Bryant, Director Human Resources
Web address: www.helenkeller.com
**Control:** Hospital district or authority, Government, nonfederal **Service:** General Medical and Surgical

**Staffed Beds:** 159 **Admissions:** 7032 **Census:** 74 **Outpatient Visits:** 103548 **Births:** 1019 **Total Expense ($000):** 83662 **Payroll Expense ($000):** 29451 **Personnel:** 756

## SYLACAUGA—Talladega County

☐ **COOSA VALLEY MEDICAL CENTER (010164)**, 315 West Hickory Street, Zip 35150–2996; tel. 256/401–4000, (Nonreporting) **A**1 9 10
Primary Contact: Glenn C. Sisk, President
CFO: Janice Brown, Chief Financial Officer
CIO: Sandra Murchison, Director Medical Records
CHR: Christy Knowles, Chief Human Resources Officer
Web address: www.cvhealth.net
**Control:** Other not–for–profit (including NFP Corporation) **Service:** General Medical and Surgical

**Staffed Beds:** 101

## TALLADEGA—Talladega County

☐ **CITIZENS BAPTIST MEDICAL CENTER (010101)**, 604 Stone Avenue, Zip 35160–2217, Mailing Address: P.O. Box 978, Zip 35161–0978; tel. 256/362–8111 **A**1 9 10 19 **F**3 11 13 15 29 30 34 35 40 49 50 53 57 59 60 62 64 65 67 70 74 75 76 79 81 82 86 93 98 103 107 108 110 111 112 114 118 119 129 131 132 135 146 148 **S** Baptist Health System, Birmingham, AL
Primary Contact: Joel Taylor, Administrator
CFO: John Langlois, Vice President Finance
CHR: Sandra Willis, Manager Human Resources
Web address: www.bhsala.com/home_citizens.cfm?id=38
**Control:** Church–operated, Nongovernment, not–for profit **Service:** General Medical and Surgical

**Staffed Beds:** 116 **Admissions:** 3039 **Census:** 31 **Outpatient Visits:** 47977 **Births:** 333 **Total Expense ($000):** 33574 **Payroll Expense ($000):** 15415 **Personnel:** 315

## TALLASSEE—Elmore County

★ **COMMUNITY HOSPITAL (010034)**, 805 Friendship Road, Zip 36078–1234; tel. 334/283–6541, (Nonreporting) **A**9 10
Primary Contact: Jennie R. Rhinehart, Administrator and Chief Executive Officer
Web address: www.chal.org
**Control:** Other not–for–profit (including NFP Corporation) **Service:** General Medical and Surgical

**Staffed Beds:** 69

## TROY—Pike County

☐ **TROY REGIONAL MEDICAL CENTER (010126)**, 1330 Highway 231 South, Zip 36081–3058; tel. 334/670–5000, (Nonreporting) **A**1 9 10
Primary Contact: Teresa G. Grimes, Chief Executive Officer
CFO: Janet Smith, Chief Financial Officer
CIO: Brian Blackmon, Director Information Systems
CHR: Lori Austin, Director Human Resources
Web address: www.troymedicalcenter.com
**Control:** Corporation, Investor–owned, for–profit **Service:** General Medical and Surgical

**Staffed Beds:** 78

## TUSCALOOSA—Tuscaloosa County

☐ **BRYCE HOSPITAL (014007)**, 200 University Boulevard, Zip 35401–1294; tel. 205/759–0799, (Nonreporting) **A**1 3 5 10
Primary Contact: Roxanna Bender, Interim Administrator
CFO: Wendell Summerville, Chief Financial Officer
CMO: Cynthia Moore Sledge, M.D., Medical Director
CIO: Ronene Howell, Director Health Information Management
CHR: Jim Elliott, Director Human Resources
**Control:** State–Government, nonfederal **Service:** Psychiatric

**Staffed Beds:** 820

---

**Hospital, Medicare Provider Number, Address, Telephone, Approval, Facility, and Physician Codes, Health Care System**

★ American Hospital Association (AHA) membership
☐ The Joint Commission accreditation
◇ DNV Healthcare Inc. accreditation
○ Healthcare Facilities Accreditation Program
△ Commission on Accreditation of Rehabilitation Facilities (CARF) accreditation

☐ **DCH REGIONAL MEDICAL CENTER (010092)**, 809 University Boulevard East, Zip 35401–2029; tel. 205/759–7111 **A**1 2 3 5 9 10 **F**3 11 12 13 15 17 18 20 22 24 26 28 29 30 31 35 38 40 43 45 48 49 50 51 57 59 60 61 62 64 66 68 70 72 74 75 76 77 78 79 81 82 86 87 88 89 90 94 98 100 101 102 103 104 105 106 107 108 110 111 114 115 116 117 118 119 121 126 129 130 132 146 147 148 **P**8 **S** DCH Health System, Tuscaloosa, AL
Primary Contact: William H. Cassels, Administrator
CFO: John W. Winfrey, Vice President Finance and Chief Financial Officer
CMO: Kenneth Aldridge, M.D., Vice President Medical Affairs
CIO: Kim Ligon, Director Information Services
CHR: Beth Francis, Vice President Human Resources
Web address: www.dchsystem.com
**Control:** Hospital district or authority, Government, nonfederal **Service:** General Medical and Surgical

**Staffed Beds:** 622 **Admissions:** 32454 **Census:** 444 **Outpatient Visits:** 410770 **Births:** 3311 **Total Expense ($000):** 358379 **Payroll Expense ($000):** 192471 **Personnel:** 3751

☐ **MARY S HARPER GERIATRIC PSYCHIATRY CENTER (014012)**, 200 University Boulevard, Zip 35401–1250; tel. 205/759–0900, (Nonreporting) **A**1 10
Primary Contact: Beverly White, MS, Facility Director
CFO: Sarah Mitchell, Director Finance
CMO: Robin Barton Lariscy, M.D., Medical Director
CIO: Sarah Mitchell, Director Finance
CHR: Jim Elliott, Director Human Resources
Web address: www.mh.alabama.gov
**Control:** Corporation, Investor–owned, for–profit **Service:** Psychiatric

**Staffed Beds:** 96

☐ **NOLAND HOSPITAL TUSCALOOSA (012012)**, 809 University Boulevard E, 4th Floor, Zip 35401–2029; tel. 205/759–7241 **A**1 9 10 **F**1 148 **S** Noland Health Services, Inc., Birmingham, AL
Primary Contact: Dale Jones, Administrator
Web address: www.nolandhealth.com
**Control:** Other not–for–profit (including NFP Corporation) **Service:** Long–Term Acute Care hospital

**Staffed Beds:** 32 **Admissions:** 295 **Census:** 23 **Outpatient Visits:** 0 **Births:** 0 **Total Expense ($000):** 9089 **Payroll Expense ($000):** 3356

☐ **TAYLOR HARDIN SECURE MEDICAL FACILITY (014011)**, 1301 Jack Warner Parkway, Zip 35404–1060; tel. 205/556–7060, (Nonreporting) **A**1 10
Primary Contact: Shelia Taylor, Director
Web address: www.mh.alabama.gov/
**Control:** Corporation, Investor–owned, for–profit **Service:** Psychiatric

**Staffed Beds:** 114

☒ △ **TUSCALOOSA VETERANS AFFAIRS MEDICAL CENTER**, (Formerly Veterans Affairs Medical Center), 3701 Loop Road East, Zip 35404–5015; tel. 205/554–2000, (Total facility includes 198 beds in nursing home–type unit) **A**1 7 **F**3 4 5 11 29 30 35 36 39 50 53 54 56 57 58 59 63 64 66 68 71 74 75 77 83 84 86 87 90 91 92 93 94 96 97 98 101 103 104 105 106 107 127 128 130 132 135 143 146 147 148 **P**6 **S** Department of Veterans Affairs, Washington, DC
Primary Contact: Maria Andrews, MS, Director
COO: Gary D. Trende, FACHE, Associate Director
CFO: Angelia Stevenson, Manager Finance
CMO: Mark Nissenbaum, M.D., Chief of Staff
CHR: Janice Hardy, Chief Human Resources Management
Web address: www.tuscaloosa.va.gov
**Control:** Veterans Affairs, Government, federal **Service:** Psychiatric

**Staffed Beds:** 366 **Admissions:** 1082 **Census:** 261 **Outpatient Visits:** 205612 **Births:** 0

**TUSKEGEE—Macon County**

**TUSKEGEE DIVISION** See Central Alabama Veterans Health Care System, Montgomery

**UNION SPRINGS—Bullock County**

**BULLOCK COUNTY HOSPITAL (010110)**, 102 West Conecuh Avenue, Zip 36089–1303; tel. 334/738–2140, (Nonreporting) **A**9 10 20
Primary Contact: Jacques Jarry, Administrator
COO: Victoria Lawrenson, Chief Operating Officer
CFO: Allen J. Gamble, Comptroller
CMO: Maria Bernardo, M.D., Chief of Staff
CIO: Tony Lang, Chief Information Officer
**Control:** Corporation, Investor–owned, for–profit **Service:** General Medical and Surgical

**Staffed Beds:** 41

**VALLEY—Chambers County**

☐ **LANIER HEALTH SERVICES (010025)**, 4800 48th Street, Zip 36854–3666; tel. 334/756–9180, (Total facility includes 103 beds in nursing home–type unit) **A**1 9 10 19 **F**3 11 13 15 18 20 22 28 29 30 34 40 41 43 45 46 47 48 49 57 59 62 64 68 70 74 76 77 79 81 85 86 87 89 93 100 102 107 108 110 111 115 118 119 124 128 129 130 132 133 135 146 147
Primary Contact: Doug Dewberry, Chief Executive Officer and Administrator
CFO: Tommy Lane, Chief Financial Officer
CMO: Krishna K. Reddy, M.D., President Medical Staff
CIO: Kurt Leroy, Manager Information Management
CHR: Clara Pitts, Director Human Resources
Web address: www.lanierhospital.com
**Control:** Other not–for–profit (including NFP Corporation) **Service:** General Medical and Surgical

**Staffed Beds:** 173 **Admissions:** 2976 **Census:** 139 **Outpatient Visits:** 51715 **Births:** 380 **Total Expense ($000):** 52282 **Payroll Expense ($000):** 19418 **Personnel:** 369

**WARRIOR—Jefferson County**

**BRADFORD HEALTH SERVICES AT WARRIOR LODGE**, 1189 Allbritt Road, Zip 35180, Mailing Address: P.O. Box 129, Zip 35180–0129; tel. 205/647–1945, (Nonreporting) **S** Bradford Health Services, Birmingham, AL
Primary Contact: Roy M. Ramsey, Executive Director
Web address: www.bradfordhealth.com
**Control:** Corporation, Investor–owned, for–profit **Service:** Alcoholism and other chemical dependency

**Staffed Beds:** 100

**WEDOWEE—Randolph County**

**WEDOWEE HOSPITAL (010032)**, 209 North Main Street, Zip 36278–7428, Mailing Address: P.O. Box 307, Zip 36278–0307; tel. 256/357–2111, (Nonreporting) **A**9 10
Primary Contact: Richard Daniel, Administrator
Web address: www.wedoweehospital.org
**Control:** County–Government, nonfederal **Service:** General Medical and Surgical

**Staffed Beds:** 26

**WETUMPKA—Elmore County**

**ELMORE COMMUNITY HOSPITAL (010097)**, 500 Hospital Drive, Zip 36092–1625, Mailing Address: P.O. Box 130, Zip 36092–0003; tel. 334/567–4311, (Nonreporting) **A**9 10
Primary Contact: Gordon Faulk, Administrator
CFO: Mike Bruce, Chief Financial Officer
CHR: Cindy Futral, Director Human Resources
Web address: www.elmorehospital.com/
**Control:** Partnership, Investor–owned, for–profit **Service:** General Medical and Surgical

**Staffed Beds:** 49

**WINFIELD—Marion County**

☒ **NORTHWEST MEDICAL CENTER (010086)**, 1530 U.S. Highway 43, Zip 35594–5056; tel. 205/487–7000, (Nonreporting) **A**1 9 10 **S** LifePoint Hospitals, Inc., Brentwood, TN
Primary Contact: Scott Williams, Chief Executive Officer
CFO: James Gory, Chief Financial Officer
CMO: Gary Fowler, M.D., Chief of Staff Family Practice
CHR: Kelly Hagy, Director Human Resources and Professional Affairs
Web address: www.northwestmedcenter.com
**Control:** Corporation, Investor–owned, for–profit **Service:** General Medical and Surgical

**Staffed Beds:** 76

**YORK—Sumter County**

**HILL HOSPITAL OF SUMTER COUNTY (010138)**, 751 Derby Drive, Zip 36925–2121; tel. 205/392–5263, (Nonreporting) **A**9 10
Primary Contact: Mark W. Caton, Interim Administrator
CFO: Joyce Wedgeworth, Financial Clerk
CMO: Gary Walton, M.D., Chief Medical Officer
CHR: Annette Billingsley, Director Human Resources
**Control:** Other not–for–profit (including NFP Corporation) **Service:** General Medical and Surgical

**Staffed Beds:** 33

*Many Facility Codes have changed. Please refer to the AHA Guide Code Chart.*

© 2013 AHA Guide

# ALASKA

## ANCHORAGE—Anchorage Division

⊠ **ALASKA NATIVE MEDICAL CENTER (020026)**, 4315 Diplomacy Drive,
Zip 99508–5926; tel. 907/563–2662, (Nonreporting) **A**1 3 5 10
Primary Contact: Katherine Gottlieb, Chief Executive Officer
CFO: Gregory Burkel, Chief Financial Officer
CHR: Sonya Conant, Senior Director Human Resources
Web address: www.anmc.org
**Control:** Other not–for–profit (including NFP Corporation) **Service:** General
Medical and Surgical

**Staffed Beds:** 146

☐ **ALASKA PSYCHIATRIC INSTITUTE (024002)**, 3700 Piper Street,
Zip 99508–4677; tel. 907/269–7100 **A**1 10 **F**29 59 75 87 98 99 100 101 103
130 132 135 **P**1
Primary Contact: Ron Hale, Chief Executive Officer
CFO: Tina Williams, Chief Financial Officer
CMO: Jenny Love, M.D., Medical Director
CIO: Stephen Schneider, Manager Information Services
CHR: Annalisa Haynie, Administrative Assistant III
Web address: www.hss.state.ak.us/dbh/API/
**Control:** State–Government, nonfederal **Service:** Psychiatric

**Staffed Beds:** 80 **Admissions:** 1630 **Census:** 60 **Outpatient Visits:** 0 **Births:**
0 **Total Expense ($000):** 31692 **Payroll Expense ($000):** 15225
**Personnel:** 265

⊠ **ALASKA REGIONAL HOSPITAL (020017)**, 2801 Debarr Road,
Zip 99508–2997, Mailing Address: P.O. Box 143889, Zip 99514–3889;
tel. 907/264–1754, (Nonreporting) **A**1 2 9 10 **S** HCA, Nashville, TN
Primary Contact: Annie Holt, FACHE, Chief Executive Officer
CFO: Paul G. Morris, Chief Financial Officer
CMO: Norman Wilder, M.D., Vice President Medical Affairs
CIO: Michael Richardson, Director Information Services
CHR: Tammy Kaminski, Director Human Resources
Web address: www.alaskaregional.com
**Control:** Corporation, Investor–owned, for–profit **Service:** General Medical and
Surgical

**Staffed Beds:** 132

⊠ **NORTH STAR BEHAVIORAL HEALTH SYSTEM (024001)**, 2530 DeBarr Circle,
Zip 99508–2948; tel. 907/258–7575, (Includes NORTH STAR BEHAVIORAL
HEALTH, 1650 South Bragaw, Zip 99508–3467; tel. 907/258–7575) **A**1 5 9 10
**F**98 99 106 130 **P**8 **S** Universal Health Services, Inc., King of Prussia, PA
Primary Contact: Andrew Mayo, Chief Executive Officer and Managing Director
CFO: Michele Fissori, Chief Financial Officer
CMO: Ruth Dukoff, M.D., Medical Director
CIO: Terry Thompson, Director Information Services
CHR: Jana Durr, Director Human Resources
Web address: www.northstarbehavioral.com
**Control:** Corporation, Investor–owned, for–profit **Service:** Children's hospital
psychiatric

**Staffed Beds:** 200 **Admissions:** 1166 **Census:** 177 **Outpatient Visits:** 0
**Births:** 0 **Total Expense ($000):** 29201 **Payroll Expense ($000):** 16466
**Personnel:** 290

⊠ **PROVIDENCE ALASKA MEDICAL CENTER (020001)**, 3200 Providence Drive,
Zip 99508–4615, Mailing Address: P.O. Box 196604, Zip 99519–6604;
tel. 907/562–2211, (Includes CHILDREN'S HOSPITAL AT PROVIDENCE, 3200
Providence Drive, Zip 99508; tel. 907/212–3130) **A**1 2 9 10 **F**3 5 11 12 13
15 16 17 18 19 20 21 22 23 24 26 27 28 29 30 31 34 37 38 40 45 46 49
50 51 53 55 57 58 59 60 62 63 64 65 68 70 72 73 74 75 76 77 78 79 80
81 82 84 85 86 87 88 89 90 91 92 93 98 99 100 101 102 103 104 107 108
111 114 115 118 119 121 123 124 126 129 130 131 132 135 145 146 148
**P**6 8 **S** Providence Health & Services, Renton, WA
Primary Contact: Bruce Lamoureux, Vice President and Chief Executive Officer
CFO: Anthony Dorsch, Chief Financial Officer
CMO: Roy Davis, M.D., Chief Medical Officer
CIO: Stephanie Morton, Chief Information Officer
CHR: Scott Jungwirth, Chief Human Resources Officer
Web address: www.providence.org/alaska/pamc/default.htm
**Control:** Church–operated, Nongovernment, not–for profit **Service:** General
Medical and Surgical

**Staffed Beds:** 371 **Admissions:** 17322 **Census:** 250 **Outpatient Visits:**
249676 **Births:** 2763 **Total Expense ($000):** 511803 **Payroll Expense
($000):** 182685 **Personnel:** 2377

⊠ **ST. ELIAS SPECIALTY HOSPITAL (022001)**, 4800 Cordova Street,
Zip 99503–7218; tel. 907/561–3333, (Nonreporting) **A**1 9 10
Primary Contact: Sharon H. Kurz, Ph.D., Chief Executive Officer
Web address: www.st–eliashospital.com
**Control:** Other not–for–profit (including NFP Corporation) **Service:** Long–Term
Acute Care hospital

**Staffed Beds:** 45

## BARROW—North Slope Division

⊠ **SAMUEL SIMMONDS MEMORIAL HOSPITAL (021312)**, 1296 Agvik Street,
Zip 99723, Mailing Address: P.O. Box 29, Zip 99723–0029; tel. 907/852–4611,
(Nonreporting) **A**1 9 10 18
Primary Contact: Jeffrey Prater, Chief Executive Officer
CNO: Donna Patterson, Director of Nursing
Web address: www.arcticslope.org
**Control:** Other not–for–profit (including NFP Corporation) **Service:** General
Medical and Surgical

**Staffed Beds:** 14

## BETHEL—Bethel Division

⊠ **YUKON–KUSKOKWIM DELTA REGIONAL HOSPITAL (020018)**, 700 Chief
Eddie Hoffman Highway, Zip 99559–3000, Mailing Address: P.O. Box 528,
Zip 99559–0528; tel. 907/543–6300, (Nonreporting) **A**1 10
Primary Contact: Gene Peltola, President and Chief Executive Officer
CFO: Vanetta Van Cleave, Chief Financial Officer
CIO: William Pearch, Chief Information Officer
Web address: www.ykhc.org
**Control:** Other not–for–profit (including NFP Corporation) **Service:** General
Medical and Surgical

**Staffed Beds:** 37

## CORDOVA—Valdez–Cordova Division

★ **CORDOVA COMMUNITY MEDICAL CENTER (021307)**, 602 Chase Avenue,
Zip 99574, Mailing Address: P.O. Box 160, Zip 99574–0160;
tel. 907/424–8000, (Total facility includes 10 beds in nursing home–type unit) **A**9
10 18 **F**7 40 64 69 77 119 127 128 133
Primary Contact: Theresa Carte, Ph.D., Administrator and Chief Executive Officer
CFO: Mary Staab, Director Finance
CMO: Murray Buttner, M.D., Medical Director
CIO: Kim Dunn, Attorney–at–Law
CHR: Mary Staab, Director Finance
Web address: www.cdvcmc.com
**Control:** City–Government, nonfederal **Service:** Long–Term Acute Care hospital

**Staffed Beds:** 23 **Admissions:** 151 **Census:** 9 **Outpatient Visits:** 5802
**Births:** 0 **Total Expense ($000):** 7251 **Payroll Expense ($000):** 2981
**Personnel:** 71

## DILLINGHAM—Dillingham Division

⊠ **BRISTOL BAY AREA HEALTH CORPORATION (021309)**, 6000 Kanakanak
Road, Zip 99576, Mailing Address: P.O. Box 130, Zip 99576–0130;
tel. 907/842–5201, (Nonreporting) **A**1 5 9 10 18
Primary Contact: Robert J. Clark, President and Chief Executive Officer
COO: Lorraine M. Jewett, Vice President and Chief Operating Officer
CFO: Tom Berner, Vice President and Chief Financial Officer
CMO: Arnold Loera, M.D., Vice President and Medical Director
Web address: www.bbahc.org
**Control:** Other not–for–profit (including NFP Corporation) **Service:** General
Medical and Surgical

**Staffed Beds:** 14

---

Hospital, Medicare Provider Number, Address, Telephone, Approval, Facility, and Physician Codes, Health Care System

★ American Hospital Association (AHA) membership
☐ The Joint Commission accreditation
◇ DNV Healthcare Inc. accreditation
○ Healthcare Facilities Accreditation Program
△ Commission on Accreditation of Rehabilitation Facilities (CARF) accreditation

**AK**

## ELMENDORF AFB—Anchorage Division

⊠ **U. S. AIR FORCE REGIONAL HOSPITAL**, 5955 Zeamer Avenue,
Zip 99506–3702; tel. 907/580–3006, (Nonreporting) **A**1 5 **S** Department of the
Air Force, Washington, DC
Primary Contact: Colonel Thomas Harrell, Commander
COO: Colonel Rebecca Seese, Chief Operating Officer
CFO: Major Felicia Burks, Chief Financial Officer
CMO: Colonel Marriner Oldham, M.D., Chief Medical Officer
CIO: Major Phillip Oliphant, Chief Information Officer
CHR: Mark Clark, Human Resources Liaison
Web address: www.elmendorf.af.mil/
**Control:** Air Force, Government, federal **Service:** General Medical and Surgical

Staffed Beds: 64

## FAIRBANKS—Fairbanks North Star Division

⊠ **FAIRBANKS MEMORIAL HOSPITAL (020012)**, 1650 Cowles Street,
Zip 99701–5998; tel. 907/452–8181, (Total facility includes 90 beds in nursing
home–type unit) **A**1 2 9 10 **F**11 13 15 18 20 22 28 29 30 31 34 35 40 45 50
51 62 63 64 67 70 76 79 81 82 85 86 87 89 93 98 102 107 108 110 111
114 115 119 121 128 129 130 132 146 147 148 **S** Banner Health,
Phoenix, AZ
Primary Contact: Michael K. Powers, FACHE, Chief Executive Officer
CFO: Jim Lynch, Chief Financial Officer
CMO: Randy McGregor, M.D., Medical Director
CIO: Carl J. Kegley, System Director Information Technology
Web address: www.bannerhealth.com/locations/alaska/fairbanks+memorial+
Hospital
**Control:** Other not–for–profit (including NFP Corporation) **Service:** General
Medical and Surgical

Staffed Beds: 217 Admissions: 5384 Census: 129 Outpatient Visits:
385461 Births: 1111 Total Expense ($000): 211618 Payroll Expense
($000): 84816 Personnel: 1079

## FORT WAINWRIGHT—Fairbanks North Star Division

⊠ **BASSETT ARMY COMMUNITY HOSPITAL**, 1060 Gaffney Road, Box 7400,
Zip 99703–5001, Mailing Address: 1060 Gaffney Road, Box 7440,
Zip 99703–5001; tel. 907/361–5172, (Nonreporting) **A**1 **S** Department of the
Army, Office of the Surgeon General, Falls Church, VA
Primary Contact: John McNally, Deputy Commander Administration
CFO: Major Doug Stratton, Chief Resource Management Division
CMO: Colonel Leo Bennett, M.D., Deputy Commander Clinical Services
CIO: Michele Krause, Chief Information Management Officer
CHR: Terri Morefield, Deputy Chief Human Resources Division
Web address: www.alaska.amedd.army.mil
**Control:** Army, Government, federal **Service:** General Medical and Surgical

Staffed Beds: 24

## HOMER—Kenai Peninsula Division

★ **SOUTH PENINSULA HOSPITAL (021313)**, 4300 Bartlett Street,
Zip 99603–7000, (Total facility includes 28 beds in nursing
home–type unit) **A**9 10 18 **F**3 11 13 15 29 30 31 34 35 40 45 50 51 56 59 62
64 67 68 70 75 76 77 78 79 81 85 87 93 94 97 107 110 111 115 119 128
129 130 133 146 148 **P**8
Primary Contact: Robert F. Letson, FACHE, Chief Executive Officer
CFO: Lori Meyer, Interim Chief Financial Officer
CMO: Kenneth Hahn, M.D., Chief of Staff
CIO: Jim Bartilson, Manager Information Systems
CHR: Cindy H. Brinkerhoff, Director Human Resources
CNO: Shara Sutherlin, R.N., Director Patient Care Services
Web address: www.sphosp.com
**Control:** Hospital district or authority, Government, nonfederal **Service:** General
Medical and Surgical

Staffed Beds: 50 Admissions: 823 Census: 33 Outpatient Visits: 30697
Births: 128 Total Expense ($000): 40781 Payroll Expense ($000): 16622
Personnel: 217

## JUNEAU—Juneau Division

⊠ **BARTLETT REGIONAL HOSPITAL (020008)**, 3260 Hospital Drive,
Zip 99801–7808; tel. 907/796–8900 **A**1 9 10 20 **F**5 13 17 28 29 31 34 40
57 59 76 81 85 86 93 104 107 108 110 111 114 115 119 129 130 135 148
Primary Contact: Christine K. Harff, Chief Executive Officer
CFO: Ken Brough, Chief Financial Officer
CMO: Richard Welling, M.D., Chief of Staff
CIO: Doug Halstead, Manager Information Systems
CHR: Kyla Allred, Manager Human Resources
Web address: www.bartletthospital.org
**Control:** City–Government, nonfederal **Service:** General Medical and Surgical

Staffed Beds: 45 Admissions: 1378 Census: 14 Outpatient Visits: 31178
Births: 333 Total Expense ($000): 82498 Payroll Expense ($000): 26579
Personnel: 373

## KETCHIKAN—Ketchikan Gateway Division

⊠ **PEACEHEALTH KETCHIKAN MEDICAL CENTER (021311)**, 3100 Tongass
Avenue, Zip 99901–5746; tel. 907/225–5171, (Total facility includes 29 beds in
nursing home–type unit) **A**1 9 10 18 **F**15 18 30 31 34 35 40 45 46 53 57 59
62 63 64 65 68 75 76 77 79 81 84 85 93 94 100 104 107 108 110 111 114
119 128 129 130 131 146 147 148 **P**6 **S** PeaceHealth, Vancouver, WA
Primary Contact: Patrick J. Branco, Chief Executive Officer
CFO: Ken Tonjes, Chief Financial Officer
CMO: Peter Rice, M.D., Medical Director
CIO: Tim Walker, Manager Information Services
CHR: Lanetta Lundberg, Vice President Culture and People
Web address: www.peacehealth.org
**Control:** Other not–for–profit (including NFP Corporation) **Service:** General
Medical and Surgical

Staffed Beds: 54 Admissions: 1416 Census: 31 Outpatient Visits: 34764
Births: 252 Total Expense ($000): 59110 Payroll Expense ($000): 27277
Personnel: 390

## KODIAK—Kodiak Island Division

⊠ **PROVIDENCE KODIAK ISLAND MEDICAL CENTER (021306)**, 1915 East
Rezanof Drive, Zip 99615–6602; tel. 907/486–3281, (Total facility includes 19
beds in nursing home–type unit) **A**1 9 10 18 **F**3 11 12 13 15 29 30 31 32 34
35 38 40 44 45 46 50 59 62 64 66 67 68 70 75 76 77 78 79 81 84 85 87
90 92 93 98 99 100 101 102 103 104 105 107 110 111 114 119 128 129
130 132 133 146 148 **S** Providence Health & Services, Renton, WA
Primary Contact: Donald J. Rush, Chief Executive Officer
CFO: Timothy Hocum, Chief Financial Officer
CMO: Paul Zimmer, M.D., Chief of Staff
CIO: Fritz Ferrante, Manager Information Services
CHR: Brenda Zawacki, Manager Human Resources
CNO: LeeAnn Horn, Chief Nurse Executive
Web address: www.providence.org
**Control:** Other not–for–profit (including NFP Corporation) **Service:** General
Medical and Surgical

Staffed Beds: 25 Admissions: 869 Census: 26 Outpatient Visits: 20986
Births: 209 Total Expense ($000): 34764

## KOTZEBUE—Northwest Arctic Division

☐ **MANIILAQ HEALTH CENTER (021310)**, 436 5th Avenue, Zip 99752–0043,
Mailing Address: P.O. Box 43, Zip 99752–0043; tel. 907/442–7344,
(Nonreporting) **A**1 5 9 10 18
Primary Contact: Robert Ottone, Administrator
COO: Ian Erlich, President and Chief Executive Officer
CFO: Lucy Nelson, Director Finance
CMO: Ellen Elmore, M.D., Director Medical Services
CIO: Eugene Smith, Chief Information Officer
CHR: Deborah White, Director Human Resources
Web address: www.maniilaq.org
**Control:** Other not–for–profit (including NFP Corporation) **Service:** General
Medical and Surgical

Staffed Beds: 17

## NOME—Nome Division

⊠ **NORTON SOUND REGIONAL HOSPITAL (021308)**, Bering Straits, Zip 99762,
Mailing Address: P.O. Box 966, Zip 99762–0966; tel. 907/443–3311,
(Nonreporting) **A**1 5 9 10 18
Primary Contact: Angela Gorn, Vice President
COO: Roy Agloinga, Chief Administrative Officer
CFO: Cynthia Brandt, Interim Chief Financial Officer
CMO: David Head, M.D., Chief Medical Staff
CIO: Dan Bailey, Director Information Systems
CHR: Tiffany Martinson, Director Human Resources
Web address: www.nortonsoundhealth.org
**Control:** Other not–for–profit (including NFP Corporation) **Service:** General
Medical and Surgical

Staffed Beds: 36

## PALMER—Matanuska–Susitna Division

⊠ **MAT–SU REGIONAL MEDICAL CENTER (020006)**, 2500 South Woodworth
Loop, Zip 99645–8984, Mailing Address: P.O. Box 1687, Zip 99645–1687;
tel. 907/861–6000 **A**1 9 10 20 **F**3 8 13 15 18 19 20 22 26 28 29 30 31 34
35 40 45 47 50 51 54 57 59 64 65 68 70 74 75 76 77 78 79 81 85 86 87
93 97 107 108 110 111 114 115 119 126 128 129 130 132 133 135 144
146 148 **P**5 **S** Community Health Systems, Inc., Franklin, TN
Primary Contact: John R. Lee, Chief Executive Officer
CFO: Scott Bailey, Chief Financial Officer
CMO: Christopher Sahlstrom, M.D., Chief of Staff
CIO: Bryan Meurer, Director Information Systems
CHR: Cathy Babuscio, Director Human Resources
CNO: Emily Stevens, Chief Nursing Officer
Web address: www.matsuregional.com
**Control:** Partnership, Investor–owned, for–profit **Service:** General Medical and
Surgical

Staffed Beds: 74 Admissions: 4660 Census: 44 Outpatient Visits: 89293
Births: 789 Total Expense ($000): 96670 Payroll Expense ($000): 43220
Personnel: 580

*Many Facility Codes have changed. Please refer to the AHA Guide Code Chart.*

© 2013 AHA Guide

## PETERSBURG—Wrangell–Petersburg Division

★ **PETERSBURG MEDICAL CENTER (021304)**, 103 Fram Street, Zip 99833,
Mailing Address: Box 589, Zip 99833–0589; tel. 907/772–4291, (Nonreporting)
**A**9 10 18
Primary Contact: Elizabeth Woodyard, R.N., MSN, Chief Executive Officer
CFO: Leon Walsh, Chief Financial Officer
CHR: Cynthia Newman, Manager Human Resources
CNO: Jennifer Bryner, Chief Nursing Officer
Web address: www.pmc–health.com/
**Control:** City–Government, nonfederal **Service:** General Medical and Surgical

| Staffed Beds: 27 |
| --- |

## SEWARD—Kenai Peninsula Division

★ **PROVIDENCE SEWARD MEDICAL CENTER (021302)**, 417 First Avenue,
Zip 99664, Mailing Address: P.O. Box 365, Zip 99664–0365;
tel. 907/224–5205, (Nonreporting) **A**9 10 18 **S** Providence Health & Services,
Renton, WA
Primary Contact: Christopher Bolton, Administrator
Web address: www.providence.org
**Control:** Church–operated, Nongovernment, not–for profit **Service:** General
Medical and Surgical

| Staffed Beds: 6 |
| --- |

## SITKA—Sitka Division

⊠ **SEARHC MT. EDGECUMBE HOSPITAL (020027)**, 222 Tongass Drive,
Zip 99835–9416; tel. 907/966–2411, (Nonreporting) **A**1 5 9 10
Primary Contact: Martin Grasmeder, M.D., Administrator
CFO: David Edwards, Chief Financial Officer
CMO: Martin Grasmeder, M.D., Medical Director
CIO: Bob Cita, Director Information Services
CHR: Melanie Millhorn, Director Human Resources
Web address: www.searhc.org
**Control:** Other not–for–profit (including NFP Corporation) **Service:** General
Medical and Surgical

| Staffed Beds: 27 |
| --- |

★ **SITKA COMMUNITY HOSPITAL (021303)**, 209 Moller Avenue,
Zip 99835–7142; tel. 907/747–3241, (Nonreporting) **A**9 10 18
Primary Contact: Hugh R. Hallgren, Chief Executive Officer
CFO: Lee W. Bennett, Chief Financial Officer
CHR: Kelley Fink, Coordinator Human Resources
Web address: www.sitkahospital.org
**Control:** City–Government, nonfederal **Service:** General Medical and Surgical

| Staffed Beds: 27 |
| --- |

## SOLDOTNA—Kenai Peninsula Division

⊠ **CENTRAL PENINSULA GENERAL HOSPITAL (020024)**, 250 Hospital Place,
Zip 99669–6999; tel. 907/714–4404, (Nonreporting) **A**1 9 10 20
Primary Contact: Richard Davis, Chief Executive Officer
COO: Matt Dammeyer, Ph.D., Chief Operating Officer
CFO: Shaun Keef, Chief Financial Officer
CMO: Gregg Motonaga, M.D., Chief of Staff
CIO: Bryan Downs, Director Information Systems
CHR: John Dodd, Vice President Human Resources
Web address: www.cpgh.org
**Control:** Other not–for–profit (including NFP Corporation) **Service:** General
Medical and Surgical

| Staffed Beds: 117 |
| --- |

## VALDEZ—Valdez–Cordova Division

★ **PROVIDENCE VALDEZ MEDICAL CENTER (021301)**, 911 Meals Avenue,
Zip 99686–0550, Mailing Address: P.O. Box 550, Zip 99686–0550;
tel. 907/835–2249, (Total facility includes 10 beds in nursing home–type unit) **A**9
10 18 **F**3 5 8 13 17 18 19 29 30 31 32 34 35 38 40 43 44 45 50 57 59 64
65 67 68 70 76 77 81 82 91 93 96 98 99 102 103 104 107 114 119 129
130 133 148 **P**6 **S** Providence Health & Services, Renton, WA
Primary Contact: Sean McCallister, Administrator
CFO: Jeremy O'Neil, Manager Finance
CMO: John Cullen, M.D., Chief of Staff and Medical Director Long Term Care
CHR: Maureen Radotich, Director Human Resources
Web address: www.providence.org/alaska
**Control:** City–Government, nonfederal **Service:** General Medical and Surgical

| Staffed Beds: 21 **Admissions:** 191 **Census:** 13 **Outpatient Visits:** 10083 **Births:** 41 **Total Expense ($000):** 11721 **Payroll Expense ($000):** 5335 **Personnel:** 121 |
| --- |

## WRANGELL—Wrangell–Petersburg Division

★ **WRANGELL MEDICAL CENTER (021305)**, First Avenue & Bennett Street,
Zip 99929, Mailing Address: P.O. Box 1081, Zip 99929–1081;
tel. 907/874–7000, (Total facility includes 12 beds in nursing home–type unit) **A**9
10 18 **F**11 15 34 35 40 45 50 57 59 64 65 67 68 75 93 97 102 107 119
130 133
Primary Contact: Marla I. Sanger, R.N., Interim Chief Executive Officer
CFO: Olinda White, Chief Financial Officer
CIO: Cathy Gross, Director Health Information Management Systems
Web address: www.wrangellmedicalcenter.com
**Control:** City–County, Government, nonfederal **Service:** Long–Term Acute Care
hospital

| Staffed Beds: 22 **Admissions:** 177 **Census:** 4 **Outpatient Visits:** 10000 **Births:** 0 **Total Expense ($000):** 10199 **Payroll Expense ($000):** 4317 **Personnel:** 58 |
| --- |

---

**Hospital, Medicare Provider Number, Address, Telephone, Approval, Facility, and Physician Codes, Health Care System**

★ American Hospital Association (AHA) membership
☐ The Joint Commission accreditation          ◇ DNV Healthcare Inc. accreditation
○ Healthcare Facilities Accreditation Program
△ Commission on Accreditation of Rehabilitation Facilities (CARF) accreditation

## ARIZONA

### APACHE JUNCTION—Pinal County

**BANNER GOLDFIELD MEDICAL CENTER**, (Formerly Apache Junction Hospital), 2050 West Southern Avenue, Zip 85120–7305; tel. 480/733–3300, **S** Banner Health, Phoenix, AZ
Primary Contact: Julie Nunley, R.N., Chief Executive Officer
Web address: www.bannerhealth.com/Locations/Arizona/Banner+Goldfield+Medical+Center/_Welcome+to+Banner+Goldfield.htm
**Control:** Other not–for–profit (including NFP Corporation) **Service:** General Medical and Surgical

**Staffed Beds:** 30

### BENSON—Cochise County

**BENSON HOSPITAL (031301)**, 450 South Ocotillo Street, Zip 85602–6403, Mailing Address: P.O. Box 2290, Zip 85602–2290; tel. 520/586–2261, (Nonreporting) **A**9 10 18
Primary Contact: Ronald A. McKinnon, Chief Executive Officer
CFO: Denise Hurtado, Chief Financial Officer
Web address: www.bensonhospital.org
**Control:** Hospital district or authority, Government, nonfederal **Service:** General Medical and Surgical

**Staffed Beds:** 22

### BISBEE—Cochise County

★ **COPPER QUEEN COMMUNITY HOSPITAL (031312)**, 101 Cole Avenue, Zip 85603–1399; tel. 520/432–5383 **A**9 10 18 **F**3 11 15 18 30 40 43 45 46 62 74 75 77 81 85 107 110 114 119 130 133 135 147
Primary Contact: James J. Dickson, Administrator and Chief Executive Officer
COO: Lisa Cummings, Director Outpatient Services
CFO: Diane C. Moore, Chief Financial Officer
CMO: Jose Romo, M.D., Chief of Staff
CIO: David Chmura, Manager Management Information Systems
CHR: Virginia Martinez, Manager Human Resources
CNO: Linda Morin, Director of Nursing
Web address: www.cqch.org
**Control:** Other not–for–profit (including NFP Corporation) **Service:** General Medical and Surgical

**Staffed Beds:** 14 **Admissions:** 432 **Census:** 5 **Outpatient Visits:** 113740
**Births:** 0 **Total Expense ($000):** 18557 **Payroll Expense ($000):** 10282
**Personnel:** 169

### BULLHEAD CITY—Mohave County

⊞ **WESTERN ARIZONA REGIONAL MEDICAL CENTER (030101)**, 2735 Silver Creek Road, Zip 86442–8303; tel. 928/763–2273, (Nonreporting) **A**1 9 10 19 **S** Community Health Systems, Inc., Franklin, TN
Primary Contact: Alex Villa, Chief Executive Officer
Web address: www.warmc.com
**Control:** Corporation, Investor–owned, for–profit **Service:** General Medical and Surgical

**Staffed Beds:** 139

### CASA GRANDE—Pinal County

⊞ ◇ **CASA GRANDE REGIONAL MEDICAL CENTER (030016)**, 1800 East Florence Boulevard, Zip 85122–5399; tel. 520/381–6300 **A**1 9 10 21 **F**11 13 15 18 20 22 28 29 30 31 34 40 45 46 49 50 57 59 60 68 70 74 75 76 78 79 81 85 87 89 93 98 103 107 108 110 111 112 115 116 117 118 119 129 130 132 144 146 147 148
Primary Contact: Rona Curphy, President and Chief Executive Officer
CFO: Karen Francis, Chief Financial Officer
CMO: Richard Stubbs, M.D., Vice President Medical Affairs
CIO: Walter Chisenski, Director Information Technology
CHR: Carol D'Souza, Director Human Resources
CNO: Cheryse Austin, Vice President Patient Care Services and Chief Nursing Officer
Web address: www.casagrandehospital.com
**Control:** Other not–for–profit (including NFP Corporation) **Service:** General Medical and Surgical

**Staffed Beds:** 187 **Admissions:** 8309 **Census:** 91 **Outpatient Visits:** 108634
**Births:** 776 **Total Expense ($000):** 132623 **Payroll Expense ($000):** 48564
**Personnel:** 769

### CHANDLER—Maricopa County

☐ **ARIZONA ORTHOPEDIC SURGICAL HOSPITAL (030112)**, 2905 West Warner Road, Zip 85224–1674; tel. 480/603–9000 **A**1 9 10 **F**8 29 64 79 81 85 111 **S** United Surgical Partners International, Addison, TX
Primary Contact: Duane Scholer, Chief Executive Officer
Web address: www.azosh.com
**Control:** Corporation, Investor–owned, for–profit **Service:** Orthopedic

**Staffed Beds:** 24 **Admissions:** 724 **Census:** 5 **Outpatient Visits:** 3186
**Births:** 0 **Total Expense ($000):** 23375 **Payroll Expense ($000):** 5373
**Personnel:** 85

⊞ **CHANDLER REGIONAL MEDICAL CENTER (030036)**, 1955 West Frye Road, Zip 85224–6282; tel. 480/728–3000 **A**1 9 10 **F**3 11 12 13 15 17 18 20 22 24 26 28 29 30 31 34 35 40 45 46 47 48 49 50 51 54 57 58 59 60 63 65 68 70 71 72 73 74 75 76 78 79 81 82 84 85 86 87 93 96 107 108 110 111 114 115 119 126 130 131 132 135 143 144 146 147 148 **P**6 **S** Dignity Health, San Francisco, CA
Primary Contact: Tim Bricker, President and Chief Executive Officer
COO: Peter Menor, Vice President Operations
CFO: Mark Kem, Vice President Finance and Chief Financial Officer
CMO: Terry J. Happel, M.D., Vice President and Chief Medical Officer
CHR: Renea Brunke, Vice President Human Resources
CNO: Peg Smith, Vice President and Chief Nursing Officer
Web address: www.chandlerregional.com
**Control:** Other not–for–profit (including NFP Corporation) **Service:** General Medical and Surgical

**Staffed Beds:** 243 **Admissions:** 17521 **Census:** 188 **Outpatient Visits:** 118555 **Births:** 3580 **Total Expense ($000):** 290602 **Payroll Expense ($000):** 118823 **Personnel:** 1703

### CHINLE—Apache County

⊞ **CHINLE COMPREHENSIVE HEALTH CARE FACILITY (030084)**, Highway 191, Zip 86503, Mailing Address: P.O. Drawer PH, Zip 86503–8000; tel. 928/674–7011, (Nonreporting) **A**1 9 10 **S** U. S. Indian Health Service, Rockville, MD
Primary Contact: Ronald Tso, Chief Executive Officer
COO: Shirley Lewis
CFO: Philene Tyler, Chief Finance Officer
CMO: Kevin Rand, M.D., Clinical Director
CIO: Perry Francis, Supervisory Information Technology Specialist
CHR: Darlene J. Silverhatband, Supervisory Human Resource Specialist
CNO: Patricia Gorman, Chief Nurse Executive
Web address: www.ihs.gov
**Control:** PHS, Indian Service, Government, federal **Service:** General Medical and Surgical

**Staffed Beds:** 60

### COTTONWOOD—Yavapai County

★ ◇ **VERDE VALLEY MEDICAL CENTER (030007)**, 269 South Candy Lane, Zip 86326–4170; tel. 928/639–6000 **A**9 10 13 20 21 **F**3 8 11 13 15 18 20 22 28 29 30 31 32 34 35 36 40 44 46 47 48 49 50 53 57 59 60 62 64 68 70 74 75 77 78 79 81 82 85 86 87 93 98 100 101 103 106 107 108 110 111 114 115 117 118 119 120 121 123 129 130 131 132 135 143 145 146 147 148 **S** Northern Arizona Healthcare, Flagstaff, AZ
Primary Contact: Barbara Dember, Interim President and Chief Executive Officer
CFO: Gregory Kuzma, Vice President and Chief Financial Officer
CMO: Harry Alberti, M.D., Chief Medical Officer and Vice President Medical Affairs
CIO: Marilynn Black, Chief Information Officer
CHR: Lori L. Jackson, Director Human Resources
CNO: Jennifer Brewer, R.N., Chief Nursing Officer and Vice President Nursing Services
Web address: www.nahealth.com
**Control:** Other not–for–profit (including NFP Corporation) **Service:** General Medical and Surgical

**Staffed Beds:** 110 **Admissions:** 4510 **Census:** 50 **Outpatient Visits:** 75737
**Births:** 514 **Total Expense ($000):** 142439 **Payroll Expense ($000):** 61224
**Personnel:** 767

*Many Facility Codes have changed. Please refer to the AHA Guide Code Chart.*  © 2013 AHA Guide

## DOUGLAS—Cochise County

**SOUTHEAST ARIZONA MEDICAL CENTER (031303)**, 2174 Oak Avenue, Zip 85607–6003; tel. 520/364–7931, (Nonreporting) **A**9 10 18
Primary Contact: Annie Benson, Chief Executive Officer
CFO: Alvin Chilton, Chief Financial Officer
CMO: Christopher Spooner, M.D., Chief of Staff
CIO: Ann Bliss, Manager Computer Services
CHR: Roberta Berry, Manager Human Resources
Web address: www.samcdouglas.org
**Control:** Other not–for–profit (including NFP Corporation) **Service:** General Medical and Surgical

| Staffed Beds: 25 |
|---|

## FLAGSTAFF—Coconino County

★ ◇ **FLAGSTAFF MEDICAL CENTER (030023)**, 1200 North Beaver Street, Zip 86001–3118; tel. 928/779–3366 **A**9 10 21 **F**3 5 7 11 12 13 15 17 18 20 22 24 26 28 29 30 31 32 34 35 36 37 40 43 45 49 50 53 54 57 58 59 60 61 64 68 70 72 74 75 77 78 79 81 82 84 85 86 87 88 90 93 98 99 100 101 102 103 104 105 107 108 111 114 115 116 117 118 119 120 121 123 126 130 131 132 135 145 146 147 148 **S** Northern Arizona Healthcare, Flagstaff, AZ
Primary Contact: William T. Bradel, President
COO: William T. Bradel, President
CFO: Gregory Kuzma, Vice President and Chief Financial Officer
CMO: Steven Lewis, M.D., Senior Vice President and Chief Medical Officer
CIO: John Schofield, Chief Information Officer
CHR: Patricia Crofford, Vice President Human Resources
Web address: www.flagstaffmedicalcenter.com
**Control:** Other not–for–profit (including NFP Corporation) **Service:** General Medical and Surgical

| Staffed Beds: 267 Admissions: 13565 Census: 159 Outpatient Visits: 141702 Births: 1244 Total Expense ($000): 318311 Payroll Expense ($000): 122596 Personnel: 1689 |
|---|

☐ **GUIDANCE CENTER (034023)**, 2187 North Vickey Street, Zip 86004–6121; tel. 928/527–1899, (Nonreporting) **A**1 10
Primary Contact: Karissa Nisted, Interim Chief Executive Officer
Web address: www.tgcaz.org
**Control:** Other not–for–profit (including NFP Corporation) **Service:** Psychiatric

| Staffed Beds: 10 |
|---|

## FLORENCE—Pinal County

◇ **FLORENCE HOSPITAL AT ANTHEM (030132)**, 4545 North Hunt Highway, Zip 85132–6937; tel. 520/868–3333, (Nonreporting) **A**10 21
Primary Contact: David S. Wanger, Chief Executive Officer
Web address: www.florencehospital.org
**Control:** Partnership, Investor–owned, for–profit **Service:** General Medical and Surgical

| Staffed Beds: 36 |
|---|

## FORT DEFIANCE—Apache County

★ **FORT DEFIANCE INDIAN HEALTH SERVICE HOSPITAL (030071)**, Zip 86504; tel. 928/729–8014, (Nonreporting) **A**10 **S** U. S. Indian Health Service, Rockville, MD
Primary Contact: Leland Leonard, M.D., Administrator
COO: Laverne Miles, Chief Operating Officer
CFO: Daniel E. Johnson, Chief Financial Officer
CMO: David Downing, M.D., Chief Medical Officer
CIO: Virgil Chavez, Chief Information Officer
CHR: Vivian Santistevan, Chief Human Resources
Web address: www.ihs.gov
**Control:** PHS, Indian Service, Government, federal **Service:** General Medical and Surgical

| Staffed Beds: 52 |
|---|

## FORT MOHAVE—Mohave County

☒ **VALLEY VIEW MEDICAL CENTER (030117)**, 5330 South Highway 95, Zip 86426–9225; tel. 928/788–2273, (Nonreporting) **A**1 9 10 **S** LifePoint Hospitals, Inc., Brentwood, TN
Primary Contact: Richard G. Carter, Chief Executive Officer
CHR: Susan L. Scharles, Director Human Resources
CNO: Natasha Compton, Chief Nursing Officer
Web address: www.valleyviewmedicalcenter.net
**Control:** Corporation, Investor–owned, for–profit **Service:** Other specialty

| Staffed Beds: 66 |
|---|

## GANADO—Apache County

☒ **SAGE MEMORIAL HOSPITAL (031309)**, Highway 264, Zip 86505, Mailing Address: P.O. Box 457, Zip 86505–0457; tel. 928/755–4500, (Nonreporting) **A**1 9 10 18
Primary Contact: Ahmad Razaghi, Chief Executive Officer
COO: Tim Cousens, On–Site Administrator
CFO: Charity L. Askie, Director Finance
CMO: Sara Valladolid, M.D., Medical Director
CIO: Wayne White, Director Computer Services
CHR: Perphelia Fowler, Manager Human Resources
Web address: www.sagememorial.org
**Control:** Other not–for–profit (including NFP Corporation) **Service:** General Medical and Surgical

| Staffed Beds: 25 |
|---|

## GILBERT—Maricopa County

☒ **BANNER GATEWAY MEDICAL CENTER (030122)**, 1900 North Higley Road, Zip 85234–1604; tel. 480/543–2000 **A**1 9 10 **F**3 11 12 13 15 18 28 29 30 31 34 35 36 40 45 46 47 48 49 50 55 59 60 64 65 68 70 73 74 75 76 78 79 81 82 84 85 86 87 107 108 110 111 113 114 115 116 118 119 120 121 123 124 126 130 132 135 146 147 148 **S** Banner Health, Phoenix, AZ
Primary Contact: Todd S. Werner, Chief Executive Officer
CFO: Claire Agnew, Chief Financial Officer
CMO: David Edwards, M.D., Chief Medical Officer
CHR: Amber R. Kovacs, Chief Human Resources Officer
Web address: www.bannerhealth.com/Locations/Arizona/Banner+Gateway+Medical+Center/
**Control:** Other not–for–profit (including NFP Corporation) **Service:** General Medical and Surgical

| Staffed Beds: 177 Admissions: 14129 Census: 124 Outpatient Visits: 172526 Births: 4226 Total Expense ($000): 216938 Payroll Expense ($000): 69928 Personnel: 1216 |
|---|

**GILBERT HOSPITAL (030120)**, 5656 South Power Road, Zip 85295–8487; tel. 480/984–2000, (Nonreporting) **A**9 10
Primary Contact: David S. Wanger, Chief Executive Officer
CFO: Randy Calvert, Chief Financial Officer
CMO: Timothy Johns, M.D., Chief Medical Officer and Board President
CIO: Michelle Cianfrani, Director Information Technology
CHR: David S. Wanger, Chief Executive Officer
Web address: www.gilberter.com
**Control:** Corporation, Investor–owned, for–profit **Service:** General Medical and Surgical

| Staffed Beds: 19 |
|---|

☒ **MERCY GILBERT MEDICAL CENTER (030119)**, 3555 South Val Vista Road, Zip 85297–7323; tel. 480/728–8000 **A**1 9 10 **F**3 8 11 13 15 18 20 22 26 28 29 30 31 32 34 35 37 38 40 41 42 44 45 46 47 49 50 57 58 59 60 63 64 65 66 68 70 73 74 75 76 77 78 79 81 82 83 84 85 86 87 96 99 100 101 102 103 107 108 110 111 114 115 119 129 130 132 135 144 145 146 148 **P**6 **S** Dignity Health, San Francisco, CA
Primary Contact: Tim Bricker, President and Chief Executive Officer
CFO: Mark Kern, Vice President Finance and Chief Financial Officer
CMO: Terry J. Happel, M.D., Vice President and Chief Medical Officer
CIO: Bob Campbell, Vice President Business Development and Chief Strategy Officer
CHR: Renea Brunke, Vice President Human Resources
Web address: www.mercygilbert.org
**Control:** Church–operated, Nongovernment, not–for profit **Service:** General Medical and Surgical

| Staffed Beds: 212 Admissions: 13109 Census: 131 Outpatient Visits: 92241 Births: 2651 Total Expense ($000): 243524 Payroll Expense ($000): 79641 Personnel: 1087 |
|---|

## GLENDALE—Maricopa County

☒ **ARROWHEAD HOSPITAL (030094)**, 18701 North 67th Avenue, Zip 85308–7100; tel. 623/561–1000, (Nonreporting) **A**1 9 10 **S** Vanguard Health Systems, Nashville, TN
Primary Contact: Frank L. Molinaro, Chief Executive Officer
CFO: Joel Snook, Chief Financial Officer
CMO: Patrick Smith, M.D., Chief Medical Officer
CHR: Sharon M. Chadwick, Director Human Resources
Web address: www.arrowheadhospital.com
**Control:** Corporation, Investor–owned, for–profit **Service:** General Medical and Surgical

| Staffed Beds: 234 |
|---|

---

**Hospital, Medicare Provider Number, Address, Telephone, Approval, Facility, and Physician Codes, Health Care System**

★ American Hospital Association (AHA) membership
☐ The Joint Commission accreditation
◇ DNV Healthcare Inc. accreditation
○ Healthcare Facilities Accreditation Program
△ Commission on Accreditation of Rehabilitation Facilities (CARF) accreditation

**AZ**

☐ **AURORA PHOENIX HOSPITAL (034024)**, (Formerly Aurora Behavioral Health System–Glendale), 6015 West Peoria Avenue, Zip 85302–1213; tel. 623/344–4400, (Nonreporting) **A**1 9 10 **S** Aurora Behavioral Health Care, Corona, CA
Primary Contact: Bruce Waldo, Chief Executive Officer
CFO: Dino Quarante, Chief Financial Officer
CMO: Martin Newman, M.D., Chief Medical Officer
CHR: Vicki Thomsen, Director Human Resources
CNO: Ryan McKenzie, R.N., Director of Nursing
Web address: www.aurorabehavioral.com
**Control:** Corporation, Investor–owned, for–profit **Service:** Psychiatric

**Staffed Beds: 80**

⊠ **BANNER THUNDERBIRD MEDICAL CENTER (030089)**, 5555 West Thunderbird Road, Zip 85306–4696; tel. 602/865–5555, (Includes BANNER BEHAVIORAL HEALTH CENTER–THUNDERBIRD CAMPUS, 5555 West Thunderbird Road, Zip 85306; tel. 602/588–5555) **A**1 9 10 **F**3 5 13 15 17 18 20 22 23 24 25 26 27 28 29 30 31 34 35 36 37 38 40 41 43 45 46 47 49 50 51 55 58 59 60 64 68 70 72 74 75 76 78 79 81 82 85 86 87 88 89 92 93 98 99 102 103 104 107 108 109 110 111 114 115 117 118 119 120 121 123 124 126 129 130 132 134 135 146 147 148 **S** Banner Health, Phoenix, AZ
Primary Contact: Thomas C. Dickson, Chief Executive Officer
CFO: Richard Miller, Administrator Finance
CMO: Kathryn Perkins, M.D., Chief Medical Officer
CHR: Laura Witt, Administrator Human Resources
Web address: www.bannerhealth.com/Locations/Arizona/Banner+Thunderbird+Medical+Center/
**Control:** Other not–for–profit (including NFP Corporation) **Service:** General Medical and Surgical

**Staffed Beds: 504 Admissions: 33380 Census: 369 Outpatient Visits:** 332548 **Births:** 4996 **Total Expense ($000):** 391541 **Payroll Expense ($000):** 147641 **Personnel:** 2541

⊠ **HEALTHSOUTH VALLEY OF THE SUN REHABILITATION HOSPITAL (033032)**, 13460 North 67th Avenue, Zip 85304–1042; tel. 623/878–8800, (Nonreporting) **A**1 9 10 **S** HEALTHSOUTH Corporation, Birmingham, AL
Primary Contact: Beth Bacher, Chief Executive Officer
CFO: Kathryn Haney, Chief Financial Officer
CFO: Kathryn Haney, Controller
CMO: Michael Kravetz, M.D., Medical Director
CHR: Danette Garcia, Director Human Resources
CNO: Beth Mooney, R.N., Chief Nursing Officer
Web address: www.healthsouthvalleyofthesun.com
**Control:** Corporation, Investor–owned, for–profit **Service:** Rehabilitation

**Staffed Beds: 75**

### GLOBE—Gila County

★ **COBRE VALLEY REGIONAL MEDICAL CENTER (031314)**, 5880 South Hospital Drive, Zip 85501–9454; tel. 928/425–3261 **A**9 10 18 **F**3 11 12 13 15 18 29 30 34 35 40 43 45 46 49 51 57 59 70 74 75 76 78 79 81 82 87 92 93 97 107 108 111 115 118 119 127 128 129 130 133 135 146 147 **P**5 **S** HealthTech Management Services, Franklin, TN
Primary Contact: Neal Jensen, Chief Executive Officer
CFO: James R. Childers, Chief Financial Officer
CIO: Sharon Bennett, Manager Information Systems
CHR: Rita Murphy, Director Human Resources
Web address: www.cvrmc.org
**Control:** Other not–for–profit (including NFP Corporation) **Service:** General Medical and Surgical

**Staffed Beds: 25 Admissions: 1714 Census: 16 Outpatient Visits:** 50070 **Births:** 304 **Total Expense ($000):** 34759 **Payroll Expense ($000):** 17123 **Personnel:** 238

### GOODYEAR—Maricopa County

⊠ **WEST VALLEY HOSPITAL (030110)**, 13677 West McDowell Road, Zip 85395–2635; tel. 623/882–1500, (Nonreporting) **A**1 9 10 **S** Vanguard Health Systems, Nashville, TN
Primary Contact: Jo Adkins, Chief Executive Officer
CFO: Richard Franco, Chief Financial Officer
CMO: Ron Kenneth, M.D., Chief Medical Officer
CHR: Deborah L. Rosenburg, Director Human Resources
Web address: www.wvhospital.com
**Control:** Corporation, Investor–owned, for–profit **Service:** General Medical and Surgical

**Staffed Beds: 106**

☐ **WESTERN REGIONAL MEDICAL CENTER (030127)**, 14200 West Fillmore Street, Zip 85338–3005; tel. 623/207–3000, (Nonreporting) **A**1 **S** Cancer Treatment Centers of America, Schaumburg, IL
Primary Contact: David Veillette, President and Chief Executive Officer
Web address: www.cancercenter.com/western–hospital.cfm
**Control:** Corporation, Investor–owned, for–profit **Service:** Cancer

**Staffed Beds: 24**

### KEAMS CANYON—Navajo County

⊠ **HOPI HEALTH CARE CENTER (031305)**, Zip 86034; Mailing Address: Polacca, tel. 928/737–6000, (Nonreporting) **A**1 10 18 **S** U. S. Indian Health Service, Rockville, MD
Primary Contact: De Alva Honahnie, Chief Executive Officer
CFO: Dorothy Sulu, Chief Financial Officer
CMO: Darren Vicenti, M.D., Clinical Director
CIO: Adrian Tom, Supervisor Management Information Systems
Web address: www.ihs.gov/index.asp
**Control:** PHS, Indian Service, Government, federal **Service:** General Medical and Surgical

**Staffed Beds: 6**

### KINGMAN—Mohave County

⊠ ◇ **KINGMAN REGIONAL MEDICAL CENTER (030055)**, 3269 Stockton Hill Road, Zip 86409–3691; tel. 928/757–2101 **A**1 9 10 13 21 **F**3 11 13 15 17 18 22 24 28 29 30 31 34 35 40 42 43 49 51 53 57 59 60 62 63 64 70 74 75 76 77 78 79 81 82 84 85 86 87 89 90 93 97 104 105 107 108 110 111 114 115 116 117 118 119 121 123 127 129 130 132 135 143 144 146 147 148 **P**6 7
Primary Contact: Brian Turney, Chief Executive Officer
COO: Ryan Kennedy, Chief Operating Officer
CFO: Timothy D. Blanchard, Chief Financial Officer
CMO: Deborah Bennett, D.O., Chief Medical Officer
CIO: Robert (Bob) Sarnecki, Chief Information Officer
CHR: Heather N. Crowl, Chief Human Resources Officer
CNO: Kimberly Miyauchi, R.N., Chief Nursing Officer
Web address: www.azkrmc.com
**Control:** Hospital district or authority, Government, nonfederal **Service:** General Medical and Surgical

**Staffed Beds: 180 Admissions: 8493 Census: 111 Outpatient Visits:** 367402 **Births:** 593 **Total Expense ($000):** 206521 **Payroll Expense ($000):** 91081 **Personnel:** 1506

### LAKE HAVASU CITY—Mohave County

⊠ **HAVASU REGIONAL MEDICAL CENTER (030069)**, 101 Civic Center Lane, Zip 86403–5683; tel. 928/855–8185, (Nonreporting) **A**1 9 10 **S** LifePoint Hospitals, Inc., Brentwood, TN
Primary Contact: F. Dana Ellerbe, Chief Executive Officer
CFO: Christopher Flores, Chief Financial Officer
CMO: Michael Rosen, M.D., Chief Medical Officer
CIO: Linda Toy, Director Information Systems
CHR: Sheena Benson, Director Human Resources
CNO: Julie Bowman, Chief Nursing Officer
Web address: www.havasuregional.com
**Control:** Corporation, Investor–owned, for–profit **Service:** General Medical and Surgical

**Staffed Beds: 138**

### LAKESIDE—Navajo County

☐ **CCC AT PINEVIEW HOSPITAL (034027)**, 1920 West Commerce Drive, Zip 85929; tel. 928/368–4110, (Nonreporting) **A**1 9 10
Primary Contact: Michelle Witt, Administrator
Web address: www.ccc–az.org
**Control:** Other not–for–profit (including NFP Corporation) **Service:** Psychiatric

**Staffed Beds: 16**

### MESA—Maricopa County

☐ **ARIZONA SPINE AND JOINT HOSPITAL (030107)**, 4620 East Baseline Road, Zip 85206–4624; tel. 480/832–4770, (Nonreporting) **A**1 9 10 **S** National Surgical Hospitals, Chicago, IL
Primary Contact: Chris Hill, Chief Executive Officer
CFO: Brian Ebright, Chief Financial Officer
CHR: Lisa Garrett, Director Human Resources
Web address: www.azspineandjoint.com
**Control:** Corporation, Investor–owned, for–profit **Service:** Orthopedic

**Staffed Beds: 23**

⊠ **BANNER BAYWOOD MEDICAL CENTER (030088)**, 6644 East Baywood Avenue, Zip 85206–1797; tel. 480/321–2000 **A**1 9 10 **F**3 11 13 15 29 30 31 34 35 36 37 40 43 44 45 46 48 49 50 51 56 57 58 59 60 61 64 68 70 74 75 76 77 78 79 80 81 85 86 87 90 91 92 102 107 108 110 111 114 115 116 117 118 119 126 129 130 132 135 146 147 148 **P**8 **S** Banner Health, Phoenix, AZ
Primary Contact: Laura Robertson, R.N., Chief Executive Officer
CFO: Stanley Adams, Chief Financial Officer
CMO: Larry Spratling, M.D., Chief Medical Officer
CHR: Justina M. Uzzell, Chief Human Resources Officer
Web address: www.bannerhealth.com/locations/Arizona/banner+baywood+medical+center
**Control:** Other not–for–profit (including NFP Corporation) **Service:** General Medical and Surgical

**Staffed Beds: 340 Admissions: 20037 Census: 231 Outpatient Visits:** 255177 **Births:** 770 **Total Expense ($000):** 225537 **Payroll Expense ($000):** 88104 **Personnel:** 1452

*Many Facility Codes have changed. Please refer to the AHA Guide Code Chart.*

⊠ **BANNER DESERT MEDICAL CENTER (030065)**, 1400 South Dobson Road, Zip 85202–4707; tel. 480/412–3000, (Includes CARDON CHILDREN'S MEDICAL CENTER, 1400 South Dobson Road, tel. 480/412–3000; Rhonda Anderson, R.N., FACHE, Chief Executive Officer; SAMARITAN BEHAVIORAL HEALTH CENTER–DESERT SAMARITAN MEDICAL CENTER, 2225 West Southern Avenue, Zip 85202; tel. 602/464–4000) **A**1 3 5 9 10 **F**3 11 13 15 18 19 20 22 24 26 27 28 29 30 31 32 34 35 36 38 40 41 43 45 46 47 48 49 50 51 58 59 60 61 64 68 70 72 74 75 76 78 79 81 82 84 85 86 87 88 89 92 93 96 107 108 109 111 114 116 117 118 119 120 121 122 123 124 126 129 130 132 135 144 146 147 148 **S** Banner Health, Phoenix, AZ
Primary Contact: Robert Gould, Chief Executive Officer
CFO: Clifford Loader, Chief Financial Officer
CMO: Marjorie Bessel, M.D., Chief Medical Officer
CIO: Stacey Hinkle, Director Information Technology
CHR: Kevin McVeigh, Chief Human Resources Officer
Web address: www.bannerhealth.com/Locations/Arizona/Banner+Desert+Medical+Center
**Control:** Other not–for–profit (including NFP Corporation) **Service:** General Medical and Surgical

**Staffed Beds:** 549 **Admissions:** 34961 **Census:** 380 **Outpatient Visits:** 387047 **Births:** 4937 **Total Expense ($000):** 467518 **Payroll Expense ($000):** 169635 **Personnel:** 2816

⊠ **BANNER HEART HOSPITAL (030105)**, 6750 East Baywood Avenue, Zip 85206–1749; tel. 480/854–5000 **A**1 9 10 **F**3 17 18 20 22 24 26 28 29 30 34 35 50 58 68 75 81 82 86 87 102 119 126 130 132 135 146 147 148 **S** Banner Health, Phoenix, AZ
Primary Contact: Laura Robertson, R.N., Chief Executive Officer
CFO: Stanley Adams, Chief Financial Officer
CMO: Mark Starling, M.D., Chief Medical Officer
CIO: Michael S. Warden, Senior Vice President and Chief Information Officer
CHR: Justina M. Uzzell, Chief People Resources Officer
Web address: www.bannerhealth.com/Locations/Arizona/Banner+Heart+Hospital/
**Control:** Other not–for–profit (including NFP Corporation) **Service:** Heart

**Staffed Beds:** 111 **Admissions:** 5823 **Census:** 59 **Births:** 0 **Total Expense ($000):** 95567 **Payroll Expense ($000):** 26837 **Personnel:** 363

**CARDON CHILDREN'S MEDICAL CENTER** See Banner Desert Medical Center

⊠ **HEALTHSOUTH EAST VALLEY REHABILITATION HOSPITAL (033037)**, 5652 East Baseline Road, Zip 85206–4713; tel. 480/567–0350, (Nonreporting) **A**1 9 10 **S** HEALTHSOUTH Corporation, Birmingham, AL
Web address: www.healthsoutheastvalley.com
**Control:** Corporation, Investor–owned, for–profit **Service:** Rehabilitation

**Staffed Beds:** 40

◇ **MOUNTAIN VISTA MEDICAL CENTER (030121)**, 1301 South Crismon Road, Zip 85209–3767; tel. 480/358–6100, (Nonreporting) **A**9 10 21 **S** IASIS Healthcare, Franklin, TN
Primary Contact: Anthony Marinello, Chief Executive Officer
CNO: Bill Southwick, R.N., Chief Nursing Officer
Web address: www.mvmedicalcenter.com
**Control:** Corporation, Investor–owned, for–profit **Service:** General Medical and Surgical

**Staffed Beds:** 172

**PROMISE HOSPITAL OF PHOENIX (032006)**, 433 East 6th Street, Zip 85203–7104; tel. 480/427–3000, (Nonreporting) **A**10 **S** Promise Healthcare, Boca Raton, FL
Primary Contact: Scott Floden, Chief Executive Officer
COO: Wendy Larson, Chief Clinical Officer
CFO: Theo Clark, Director Financial Services
CMO: Syed Shahryar, M.D., Medical Director
CHR: Christie Brea, Manager Human Resources
Web address: www.promise-phoenix.com
**Control:** Corporation, Investor–owned, for–profit **Service:** Long–Term Acute Care hospital

**Staffed Beds:** 40

**RESTORA HOSPITAL OF MESA (032007)**, (Formerly Trillium Specialty Hospital–East Valley), 215 South Power Road, Zip 85206–5235; tel. 480/985–6992, (Total facility includes 60 beds in nursing home–type unit) (Data for 186 days) **A**10 **F**1 3 29 50 77 85 87 96 128 130 148 **S** Restora Healthcare, Alpharetta, GA
Primary Contact: Judith Schiros, Chief Executive Officer
Web address: www.restorahealthcare.com
**Control:** Partnership, Investor–owned, for–profit **Service:** Long–Term Acute Care hospital

**Staffed Beds:** 120 **Admissions:** 627 **Census:** 118 **Outpatient Visits:** 0 **Births:** 0 **Total Expense ($000):** 11746 **Payroll Expense ($000):** 4219 **Personnel:** 139

**SAMARITAN BEHAVIORAL HEALTH CENTER–DESERT SAMARITAN MEDICAL CENTER** See Banner Desert Medical Center

### NOGALES—Santa Cruz County

⊠ **CARONDELET HOLY CROSS HOSPITAL (031313)**, 1171 West Target Range Road, Zip 85621–2415; tel. 520/285–3000, (Total facility includes 31 beds in nursing home–type unit) **A**1 9 10 18 **F**11 13 29 30 32 35 40 50 51 56 57 59 60 63 64 68 70 75 76 77 79 81 84 86 87 89 93 102 107 111 119 128 130 132 133 134 135 146 **S** Ascension Health, Saint Louis, MO
Primary Contact: Debbie Knapheide, MSN, Site Administrator, Chief Nursing Officer and Chief Operating Officer
COO: Debbie Knapheide, MSN, Site Administrator, Chief Nursing Officer and Chief Operating Officer
CFO: Alan Strauss, Chief Financial Officer
CMO: Roy Farrell, M.D., Chief Medical Officer
CHR: Daisy Jenkins, Vice President Human Resources
CNO: Debbie Knapheide, MSN, Site Administrator, Chief Nursing Officer and Chief Operating Officer
Web address: www.carondelet.org
**Control:** Church–operated, Nongovernment, not–for profit **Service:** General Medical and Surgical

**Staffed Beds:** 56 **Admissions:** 1464 **Census:** 21 **Outpatient Visits:** 35721 **Births:** 692 **Total Expense ($000):** 24077 **Payroll Expense ($000):** 9462 **Personnel:** 147

### ORO VALLEY—Pima County

⊠ **ORO VALLEY HOSPITAL (030114)**, 1551 East Tangerine Road, Zip 85755–6213; tel. 520/901–3500, (Nonreporting) **A**1 9 10 **S** Community Health Systems, Inc., Franklin, TN
Primary Contact: Jae Dale, Chief Executive Officer
CFO: Mark Hoffman, Chief Financial Officer
CMO: Paul Bejarino, M.D., Chief of Staff
Web address: www.nmcorovalley.com
**Control:** Corporation, Investor–owned, for–profit **Service:** General Medical and Surgical

**Staffed Beds:** 144

### PAGE—Coconino County

⊠ **PAGE HOSPITAL (031304)**, 501 North Navajo Drive, Zip 86040, Mailing Address: P.O. Box 1447, Zip 86040–1447; tel. 928/645–2424 **A**1 9 10 18 **F**3 8 11 13 15 29 30 31 34 35 36 39 40 43 45 57 59 64 68 75 76 77 79 81 82 85 86 87 93 107 111 114 119 129 130 133 135 146 148 **S** Banner Health, Phoenix, AZ
Primary Contact: Sandy Haryasz, R.N., Chief Executive Officer
Web address: www.bannerhealth.com/Locations/Arizona/Page+Hospital
**Control:** Other not–for–profit (including NFP Corporation) **Service:** General Medical and Surgical

**Staffed Beds:** 25 **Admissions:** 495 **Census:** 3 **Outpatient Visits:** 36479 **Births:** 221 **Total Expense ($000):** 14495 **Payroll Expense ($000):** 5997 **Personnel:** 88

### PARKER—La Paz County

○ **LA PAZ REGIONAL HOSPITAL (030067)**, 1200 West Mohave Road, Zip 85344–6349; tel. 928/669–9201 **A**9 10 11 20 **F**3 11 15 18 20 22 26 28 29 34 35 39 40 43 45 46 51 53 56 57 59 64 65 70 75 79 81 85 86 87 90 92 93 97 107 110 111 115 127 130 135 144 146 148
Primary Contact: M. Victoria Clark, Chief Executive Officer
CFO: James Ehasz, Chief Financial Officer
CMO: Melinda Astran, M.D., Chief of Staff
CHR: Regina M. Martinez, Director Human Resources
Web address: www.lapazhospital.org
**Control:** Other not–for–profit (including NFP Corporation) **Service:** General Medical and Surgical

**Staffed Beds:** 25 **Admissions:** 608 **Census:** 6 **Outpatient Visits:** 28781 **Births:** 0 **Total Expense ($000):** 21753 **Payroll Expense ($000):** 8183 **Personnel:** 178

⊠ **U. S. PUBLIC HEALTH SERVICE INDIAN HOSPITAL (031307)**, 12033 Agency Road, Zip 85344–7718; tel. 928/669–2137, (Nonreporting) **A**1 9 10 18 **S** U. S. Indian Health Service, Rockville, MD
Primary Contact: Dee Hutchison, Chief Executive Officer
CFO: Robin Tahbo, Financial Management Officer
CMO: Laurence Norick, M.D., Clinical Director
CIO: JayLynn Saavedra, Chief Information Officer
Web address: www.ihs.gov
**Control:** Public Health Service, Government, federal **Service:** General Medical and Surgical

**Staffed Beds:** 20

---

**Hospital, Medicare Provider Number, Address, Telephone, Approval, Facility, and Physician Codes, Health Care System**

★ American Hospital Association (AHA) membership
□ The Joint Commission accreditation
◇ DNV Healthcare Inc. accreditation
○ Healthcare Facilities Accreditation Program
△ Commission on Accreditation of Rehabilitation Facilities (CARF) accreditation

**AZ**

### PAYSON—Gila County

⊞ **PAYSON REGIONAL MEDICAL CENTER (030033)**, 807 South Ponderosa Street, Zip 85541–5599; tel. 928/474–3222, (Nonreporting) **A**1 9 10 20 **S** Community Health Systems, Inc., Franklin, TN
Primary Contact: R. Chris Wolf, Chief Executive Officer
CFO: Peter Finelli, Chief Financial Officer
CMO: John Vandruff, M.D., Chief of Staff
CIO: Ross Skinner, Director Information Systems
CHR: Shawn M. Thomas, Director Human Resources
Web address: www.paysonhospital.com
**Control:** Corporation, Investor–owned, for–profit **Service:** General Medical and Surgical

Staffed Beds: 44

### PEORIA—Maricopa County

**KINDRED HOSPITAL ARIZONA–NORTHWEST PHOENIX** See Kindred Hospital Arizona–Phoenix, Phoenix

### PHOENIX—Maricopa County

☐ **ARIZONA STATE HOSPITAL (034021)**, 2500 East Van Buren Street, Zip 85008–6079; tel. 602/244–1331 **A**1 10 **F**3 29 30 39 53 57 59 65 68 75 77 94 98 130 135 143 **P**6
Primary Contact: Ann M. Froio, Interim Chief Executive Officer
COO: Donna Noriega, Chief Operating Officer
CFO: Donna Noriega, Chief Operating Officer
CMO: Steve Dingle, M.D., Chief Medical Officer
CIO: Bruce Randolph, Chief Information Technology
CHR: Jeanine Decker, Manager Human Resources
Web address: www.hs.state.az.us
**Control:** State–Government, nonfederal **Service:** Psychiatric

Staffed Beds: 338 Admissions: 75 Census: 237 Outpatient Visits: 0 Births: 0 Total Expense ($000): 54856 Payroll Expense ($000): 27862 Personnel: 459

⊞ **BANNER ESTRELLA MEDICAL CENTER (030115)**, 9201 West Thomas Road, Zip 85037–3332; tel. 623/327–4000 **A**1 9 10 **F**3 12 17 18 20 22 24 26 28 29 30 31 34 35 36 40 43 46 48 49 50 51 59 60 68 70 72 74 75 76 78 79 81 82 85 86 87 92 107 108 111 114 115 118 119 126 130 132 135 144 146 148 **S** Banner Health, Phoenix, AZ
Primary Contact: Debra J. Krmpotic, R.N., Chief Executive Officer
COO: Gary Foster, R.N., Assistant Administrator
CFO: Patty Rhoden, Chief Financial Officer
CMO: Kenneth Welch, M.D., Chief Medical Officer
CHR: Dina Steinberg, Chief People Resources Officer
CNO: Nancy Adamson, R.N., Chief Nursing Officer
Web address: www.bannerhealth.com/Locations/Arizona/Banner+Estrella+Medical+Center/
**Control:** Other not–for–profit (including NFP Corporation) **Service:** General Medical and Surgical

Staffed Beds: 214 Admissions: 17883 Census: 164 Outpatient Visits: 212479 Births: 3972 Total Expense ($000): 196624 Payroll Expense ($000): 79044 Personnel: 1308

⊞ **BANNER GOOD SAMARITAN MEDICAL CENTER (030002)**, 1111 East McDowell Road, Zip 85006–2666, Mailing Address: P.O. Box 2989, Zip 85062–2989; tel. 602/239–2000 **A**1 2 3 5 8 9 10 **F**3 11 13 15 17 18 20 22 24 26 28 29 30 31 34 35 36 37 38 40 43 45 46 47 48 49 50 51 52 53 55 56 58 59 60 61 64 65 66 68 70 72 74 75 76 78 79 81 82 83 84 85 86 87 90 91 92 93 94 96 97 98 100 101 102 103 104 105 107 108 109 110 111 114 115 116 117 118 119 120 121 123 124 126 130 131 132 135 138 139 141 142 146 147 148 **S** Banner Health, Phoenix, AZ
Primary Contact: Steve Narang, M.D., Chief Executive Officer
CFO: Kathy Kotin, Chief Financial Officer
CMO: Paul Stander, M.D., Chief Medical Officer
CIO: Michael S. Warden, Senior Vice President Information Technology
CHR: Michael Fleming, Chief People Officer
Web address: www.bannerhealth.com/Locations/Arizona/Banner+Good+Samaritan+Medical+Center
**Control:** Other not–for–profit (including NFP Corporation) **Service:** General Medical and Surgical

Staffed Beds: 653 Admissions: 34432 Census: 454 Outpatient Visits: 399803 Births: 5455 Total Expense ($000): 602338 Payroll Expense ($000): 221818 Personnel: 3354

**HAVEN SENIOR HORIZONS (034020)**, 1201 South 7th Avenue, Suite 200, Zip 85007–4076; tel. 623/236–2000, (Nonreporting) **A**10 **S** Haven Behavioral Healthcare, Nashville, TN
Primary Contact: Kathy Shaw, Chief Executive Officer
CHR: Erin McEldowney, Manager Human Resources
CNO: Char Ralstin, Director of Nursing
Web address: www.havenbehavioral.com
**Control:** Corporation, Investor–owned, for–profit **Service:** Psychiatric

Staffed Beds: 30

★ ○ **JOHN C. LINCOLN DEER VALLEY HOSPITAL (030092)**, 19829 North 27th Avenue, Zip 85027–4002; tel. 623/879–6100 **A**9 10 11 **F**3 8 15 17 18 20 22 24 26 28 29 31 34 35 40 41 43 45 46 49 50 54 55 57 58 59 60 64 70 74 75 77 78 79 81 85 87 89 92 107 108 111 114 115 118 119 126 130 132 145 146 147 148 **S** John C. Lincoln Health Network, Phoenix, AZ
Primary Contact: John L. Harrington, Jr., FACHE, Chief Executive Officer
CFO: David Lamparter, Senior Vice President and Chief Financial Officer
CMO: Mary Ann Turley, D.O., Medical Director
CHR: Frank L. Cummins, Vice President Human Resources
CNO: Jessica Rivas, R.N., Vice President and Chief Nursing Officer
Web address: www.jcl.com
**Control:** Other not–for–profit (including NFP Corporation) **Service:** General Medical and Surgical

Staffed Beds: 204 Admissions: 12899 Census: 126 Outpatient Visits: 126506 Births: 0 Total Expense ($000): 181482 Payroll Expense ($000): 68730 Personnel: 1146

★ **JOHN C. LINCOLN NORTH MOUNTAIN HOSPITAL (030014)**, 250 East Dunlap Avenue, Zip 85020–2825; tel. 602/943–2381 **A**9 10 **F**3 11 15 17 18 20 22 24 26 28 29 30 31 34 37 40 43 45 46 47 49 50 53 54 57 58 59 60 64 68 70 74 75 77 78 79 81 85 92 107 108 111 114 115 118 119 126 130 132 135 145 146 147 148 **S** John C. Lincoln Health Network, Phoenix, AZ
Primary Contact: Bruce Pearson, FACHE, Chief Executive Officer
CFO: David Lamparter, Senior Vice President and Chief Financial Officer
CMO: Christopher Shearer, M.D., Chief Medical Officer
CIO: Robert Slepin, Vice President and Chief Information Officer
CHR: Frank L. Cummins, Vice President Human Resources
CNO: Margaret Elizabeth Griffin, Vice Prsident and Chief Nursing Officer
Web address: www.jcl.com
**Control:** Other not–for–profit (including NFP Corporation) **Service:** General Medical and Surgical

Staffed Beds: 262 Admissions: 16625 Census: 197 Outpatient Visits: 105352 Births: 0 Total Expense ($000): 263876 Payroll Expense ($000): 95220 Personnel: 1896

⊞ **KINDRED HOSPITAL ARIZONA–PHOENIX (032000)**, 40 East Indianola Avenue, Zip 85012–2059; tel. 602/280–7000, (Includes KINDRED HOSPITAL ARIZONA–NORTHWEST PHOENIX, 13216 North Plaza Del Rio Boulevard, Peoria, Zip 85381–4907; tel. 623/974–5463; Karen Shammas, Chief Executive Officer), (Nonreporting) **A**1 10 **S** Kindred Healthcare, Louisville, KY
Primary Contact: Heidi Miller, Chief Executive Officer
Web address: www.khphoenix.com/
**Control:** Corporation, Investor–owned, for–profit **Service:** Long–Term Acute Care hospital

Staffed Beds: 58

**LOS NINOS HOSPITAL (033301)**, 2303 East Thomas Road, Zip 85016–7827; tel. 602/954–7311, (Nonreporting) **A**10
Primary Contact: William Timmons, Chief Executive Officer
Web address: www.losninoshospital.com
**Control:** Other not–for–profit (including NFP Corporation) **Service:** Children's other specialty

Staffed Beds: 15

★ ◇ **MARICOPA INTEGRATED HEALTH SYSTEM (030022)**, 2601 East Roosevelt Street, Zip 85008–4956; tel. 602/344–5011, (Includes ARIZONA CHILDREN'S CENTER, 2601 East Roosevelt Street, Zip 85008–4973; tel. 602/344–5051), (Nonreporting) **A**3 5 8 9 10 21
Primary Contact: Betsey Bayless, President and Chief Executive Officer
COO: William F. Vanaskie, Executive Vice President and Chief Operating Officer
CMO: Robert Fromm, M.D., Senior Vice President and Chief Medical Officer
CIO: Dave Kempson, Chief Information Officer
CHR: Marshall Jones, Senior Vice President Human Resources
Web address: www.mihs.org
**Control:** County–Government, nonfederal **Service:** General Medical and Surgical

Staffed Beds: 578

⊞ **MARYVALE HOSPITAL MEDICAL CENTER (030001)**, 5102 West Campbell Avenue, Zip 85031–1799; tel. 623/848–5000 **A**1 9 10 **F**3 13 18 20 22 26 29 34 35 40 45 49 59 68 70 73 74 75 76 81 85 86 107 108 111 130 146 **S** Vanguard Health Systems, Nashville, TN
Primary Contact: Crystal Hamilton, R.N., Chief Executive Officer
CFO: Julie Hastings–Smith, Chief Financial Officer
CHR: Erin Gonzalez, Director Human Resources and Education
CNO: Scott Morey, Chief Nursing Officer
Web address: www.maryvalehospital.com
**Control:** Corporation, Investor–owned, for–profit **Service:** General Medical and Surgical

Staffed Beds: 100 Admissions: 5684 Census: 53 Outpatient Visits: 53064 Total Expense ($000): 52143 Payroll Expense ($000): 29036 Personnel: 402

*Many Facility Codes have changed. Please refer to the AHA Guide Code Chart.*
© 2013 AIIA Guide

**AZ**

☒ **MAYO CLINIC HOSPITAL (030103)**, 5777 East Mayo Boulevard, Zip 85054–4502; tel. 480/515–6296 **A**1 2 3 5 8 9 10 **F**3 6 8 9 12 15 17 18 20 22 24 26 28 29 30 31 34 35 36 37 39 40 45 46 47 48 49 50 51 54 55 56 58 59 60 61 64 68 70 74 75 77 78 79 80 81 82 84 85 86 87 90 92 93 96 97 100 103 104 107 108 110 111 112 114 115 116 117 118 119 120 121 123 124 126 129 130 131 132 135 136 137 138 139 141 142 145 146 147 148 **P**6 **S** Mayo Clinic Health System, Rochester, MN
Primary Contact: Ann M. Meyers, Chief Executive Officer
COO: Kevin Paige, Chief Operations Officer
CFO: Jeffrey R. Froisland, Chief Financial Officer
CMO: Jeff T. Mueller, M.D., Medical Director
CIO: John Cranmer, Chief Information Officer
CHR: Jamie Schmitgen, Chair Human Resources
CNO: Teresa Connolly, MSN, Chief Nursing Officer
Web address: www.mayoclinic.org/arizona/
**Control:** Other not–for–profit (including NFP Corporation) **Service:** General Medical and Surgical

**Staffed Beds:** 268 **Admissions:** 12351 **Census:** 183 **Outpatient Visits:** 44032 **Births:** 0 **Total Expense ($000):** 400006 **Payroll Expense ($000):** 122860 **Personnel:** 3698

☐ **OASIS HOSPITAL (030131)**, 750 North 40th Street, Zip 85008–6486; tel. 602/797–7700, (Nonreporting) **A**1 9 10
Primary Contact: James Flinn, JD, FACHE, Chief Executive Officer
Web address: www.oasishospital.com
**Control:** Partnership, Investor–owned, for–profit **Service:** Orthopedic

**Staffed Beds:** 64

☒ **PARADISE VALLEY HOSPITAL (030083)**, 3929 East Bell Road, Zip 85032–2196; tel. 602/923–5000, (Nonreporting) **A**1 9 10 **S** Vanguard Health Systems, Nashville, TN
Primary Contact: David Tupponce, M.D., Interim Chief Executive Officer
COO: Sue Piarulli, Administrative Director Operations
CFO: Denise Chamberlain, Chief Financial Officer
CMO: David Tupponce, M.D., Chief Medical Officer
CHR: Michelle Wilkerson, Director Human Resources
CNO: Chris McConaughy, Chief Nursing Officer
Web address: www.paradisevalleyhospital.com
**Control:** Corporation, Investor–owned, for–profit **Service:** General Medical and Surgical

**Staffed Beds:** 142

☒ **PHOENIX BAPTIST HOSPITAL (030030)**, 2000 West Bethany Home Road, Zip 85015–2443; tel. 602/249–0212, (Includes ARIZONA HEART HOSPITAL, 1930 East Thomas Road, Zip 85016; tel. 602/532–1000; Jeffrey A. Ashin, Chief Executive Officer), (Nonreporting) **A**1 3 5 9 10 **S** Vanguard Health Systems, Nashville, TN
Primary Contact: Wayne Gillis, Interim Chief Executive Officer
COO: Wayne Gillis, Chief Operating Officer
CFO: Alan Germany, Chief Financial Officer
CMO: William Ellert, M.D., Chief Medical Officer
CHR: Julia Doucette, Director Human Resources
Web address: www.phoenixbaptisthospital.com
**Control:** Corporation, Investor–owned, for–profit **Service:** General Medical and Surgical

**Staffed Beds:** 215

☒ **PHOENIX CHILDREN'S HOSPITAL (033302)**, 1919 East Thomas Road, Zip 85016–7710; tel. 602/546–1000 **A**1 3 5 9 10 **F**3 8 11 15 17 19 21 23 25 27 29 30 31 32 34 35 37 38 39 40 41 42 43 44 46 48 49 50 54 55 57 58 59 60 61 64 65 66 68 71 72 73 74 75 77 78 79 81 82 84 85 86 87 88 89 91 92 93 94 96 97 98 99 100 101 102 104 105 107 108 111 113 114 115 116 117 118 119 129 130 131 132 134 136 138 144 146 148 **P**6
Primary Contact: Robert L. Meyer, President and Chief Executive Officer
COO: Betsy Kuzas, Executive Vice President and Chief Operating Officer
CFO: Craig L. McKnight, Senior Vice President and Chief Financial Officer
CMO: Murray Pollack, M.D., Vice President and Chief Medical Officer
CIO: David Higginson, Senior Vice President and Chief Information Officer
CHR: Thomas Diederich, Senior Vice President Human Resources
CNO: Pam Carlson, Senior Vice President and Chief Nursing Officer
Web address: www.phoenixchildrens.com
**Control:** Other not–for–profit (including NFP Corporation) **Service:** Children's general

**Staffed Beds:** 391 **Admissions:** 13834 **Census:** 239 **Outpatient Visits:** 197280 **Births:** 0 **Total Expense ($000):** 640551 **Payroll Expense ($000):** 246065 **Personnel:** 2964

☒ △ **PHOENIX VETERANS AFFAIRS HEALTH CARE SYSTEM**, 650 East Indian School Road, Zip 85012–1892; tel. 602/277–5551, (Nonreporting) **A**1 2 3 7 9 **S** Department of Veterans Affairs, Washington, DC
Primary Contact: Sharon M. Helman, Director
CFO: Christine Hollingsworth, Chief Financial Officer
CMO: Raymond Chung, M.D., Chief of Staff
Web address: www.phoenix.va.gov/
**Control:** Veterans Affairs, Government, federal **Service:** General Medical and Surgical

**Staffed Beds:** 197

☒ **SELECT SPECIALTY HOSPITAL–PHOENIX (032001)**, 350 West Thomas Road, 3rd Floor Main, Zip 85013–4409; tel. 602/406–6802, (Nonreporting) **A**1 10 **S** Select Medical Corporation, Mechanicsburg, PA
Primary Contact: Sharon Anthony, Chief Executive Officer
Web address: www.selectspecialtyhospitals.com/company/locations/phoenix.aspx
**Control:** Corporation, Investor–owned, for–profit **Service:** Long–Term Acute Care hospital

**Staffed Beds:** 48

**SELECT SPECIALTY HOSPITAL–PHOENIX DOWNTOWN** See Select Specialty Hospital–Scottsdale, Scottsdale

☒ △ **ST. JOSEPH'S HOSPITAL AND MEDICAL CENTER (030024)**, 350 West Thomas Road, Zip 85013–4496, Mailing Address: P.O. Box 2071, Zip 85001–2071; tel. 602/406–3000, (Includes CHILDREN'S HEALTH CENTER, 350 West Thomas Road, Zip 85013–4409) **A**1 2 3 5 7 8 9 10 **F**3 6 11 13 15 17 18 20 22 24 26 28 29 30 31 34 35 39 40 43 45 46 47 48 49 51 53 55 56 57 58 59 64 66 68 70 71 72 73 74 75 76 77 78 79 81 82 84 85 86 87 90 91 92 93 96 97 100 102 103 104 107 108 110 111 112 114 115 117 118 119 121 123 124 126 130 131 132 134 135 137 140 141 146 147 148 **P**5 6 **S** Dignity Health, San Francisco, CA
Primary Contact: Patty White, R.N., MS, President
CFO: John Peters, Chief Financial Officer
CHR: Maureen Sterbach, Vice President Human Resources
Web address: www.stjosephs–phx.org
**Control:** Church–operated, Nongovernment, not–for profit **Service:** General Medical and Surgical

**Staffed Beds:** 592 **Admissions:** 33563 **Census:** 426 **Outpatient Visits:** 436456 **Births:** 4646 **Total Expense ($000):** 884793 **Payroll Expense ($000):** 359267 **Personnel:** 4673

☐ ◇ **ST. LUKE'S BEHAVIORAL HEALTH CENTER (034013)**, 1800 East Van Buren, Zip 85006–3742; tel. 602/251–8546, (Nonreporting) **A**1 9 10 21 **S** IASIS Healthcare, Franklin, TN
Primary Contact: Gregory L. Jahn, R.N., Chief Executive Officer
CFO: Ruby Majhail, Chief Financial Officer
CMO: Mario Tafur, M.D., Chief of Staff
CIO: Chris Ulrey, Director Management Information Systems
CHR: Amy M. Howell, Director Human Resources
Web address: www.iasishealthcare.com
**Control:** Corporation, Investor–owned, for–profit **Service:** Psychiatric

**Staffed Beds:** 85

★ ◇ **ST. LUKE'S MEDICAL CENTER (030037)**, 1800 East Van Buren Street, Zip 85006–3742; tel. 602/251–8100, (Includes TEMPE ST. LUKE'S HOSPITAL, 1500 South Mill Avenue, Tempe, Zip 85281–6699; tel. 480/784–5510; Dale Larson, Administrator), (Nonreporting) **A**9 10 21 **S** IASIS Healthcare, Franklin, TN
Primary Contact: Edward W. Myers, Chief Executive Officer
CFO: Ken Walsh, Chief Financial Officer
CHR: Trinise Thompson, Director Human Resources
Web address: www.stlukesmedcenter.com
**Control:** Corporation, Investor–owned, for–profit **Service:** General Medical and Surgical

**Staffed Beds:** 225

☐ **SURGICAL SPECIALTY HOSPITAL OF ARIZONA (030108)**, 6501 North 19th Avenue, Zip 85015–1646; tel. 602/795–6020 **A**1 9 10 **F**12 29 45 49 70 81 107 111 114 119 **P**2
Primary Contact: William J. Comer, Chief Executive Officer
CFO: Greg Brink, Chief Financial Officer
CMO: Christopher A. Yeung, M.D., Chief of Staff
CHR: Deby Tooker, Director Human Resources
CNO: Karen Bonamase, R.N., Chief Nursing Officer
Web address: www.sshaz.com
**Control:** Corporation, Investor–owned, for–profit **Service:** Surgical

**Staffed Beds:** 33 **Admissions:** 1414 **Census:** 6 **Outpatient Visits:** 3017 **Births:** 0 **Total Expense ($000):** 15133 **Payroll Expense ($000):** 5999 **Personnel:** 114

---

**Hospital, Medicare Provider Number, Address, Telephone, Approval, Facility, and Physician Codes, Health Care System**

★ American Hospital Association (AHA) membership
☐ The Joint Commission accreditation    ◇ DNV Healthcare Inc. accreditation
○ Healthcare Facilities Accreditation Program
△ Commission on Accreditation of Rehabilitation Facilities (CARF) accreditation

**AZ**

⊠ **U. S. PUBLIC HEALTH SERVICE PHOENIX INDIAN MEDICAL CENTER (030078)**, 4212 North 16th Street, Zip 85016–5389; tel. 602/263–1200, (Nonreporting) **A**1 5 9 10 **S** U. S. Indian Health Service, Rockville, MD
Primary Contact: John Molina, Chief Executive Officer
CFO: Geraldine Harney, Chief Financial Officer
CMO: Dave Civic, M.D., Associate Director Clinical Services
CIO: Vina Montour, Director Information Technology
CHR: Betty Weston, Chief Human Resources Officer
Web address: www.ihs.gov
**Control:** PHS, Indian Service, Government, federal **Service:** General Medical and Surgical

| Staffed Beds: 127 |

☐ **VALLEY HOSPITAL PHOENIX (034026)**, 3550 East Pinchot Avenue, Zip 85018–7434; tel. 602/957–4000, (Nonreporting) **A**1 9 10 **S** Universal Health Services, Inc., King of Prussia, PA
Primary Contact: Michelle David, Interim Chief Executive Officer
Web address: www.valleyhospital–phoenix.com
**Control:** Corporation, Investor–owned, for–profit **Service:** Psychiatric

| Staffed Beds: 122 |

**PRESCOTT—Yavapai County**

⊠ **NORTHERN ARIZONA VETERANS AFFAIRS HEALTH CARE SYSTEM**, 500 Highway 89 North, Zip 86313–5000; tel. 928/445–4860, (Nonreporting) **A**1 9 **S** Department of Veterans Affairs, Washington, DC
Primary Contact: Donna K. Jacobs, FACHE, Director
COO: James Belmont, Associate Director
CFO: Ame Callahan, Acting Manager Resource Management Service
CMO: A. Panneer Selvam, M.D., Chief of Staff
CIO: Scott McCrimmon, Manager Information Technology
CHR: Jane Lewerke, Manager Human Resources
CNO: Marianne Locke, R.N., Associate Director Patient Care Services
Web address: www.prescott.va.gov/
**Control:** Veterans Affairs, Government, federal **Service:** General Medical and Surgical

| Staffed Beds: 137 |

★ **YAVAPAI REGIONAL MEDICAL CENTER (030012)**, 1003 Willow Creek Road, Zip 86301–1668; tel. 928/445–2700 **A**9 10 **F**8 11 13 14 15 17 18 20 22 24 28 29 30 31 32 34 35 40 42 45 46 50 53 54 57 59 60 64 68 70 74 75 77 79 81 82 84 85 86 87 93 107 108 111 114 116 117 118 119 130 131 132 135 143 146 147 148 **P**5 7
Primary Contact: Timothy Barnett, President and Chief Executive Officer
COO: Larry P. Burns, Jr., Chief Operating Officer
CFO: Brian Hoefle, Chief Financial Officer
CMO: Joseph Goldberger, M.D., Chief Medical Officer
CIO: Randy Rahman, Chief Information Officer
CHR: Mark Timm, Director Human Resources
CNO: Diane Drexler, R.N., Chief Nursing Officer
Web address: www.yrmc.org
**Control:** Other not–for–profit (including NFP Corporation) **Service:** General Medical and Surgical

| Staffed Beds: 134 Admissions: 7024 Census: 70 Outpatient Visits: 76976 Births: 0 Total Expense ($000): 162407 Payroll Expense ($000): 70805 Personnel: 1066 |

**PRESCOTT VALLEY—Yavapai County**

☐ **MOUNTAIN VALLEY REGIONAL REHABILITATION HOSPITAL (033036)**, 3700 North Windsong Drive, Zip 86314–1253; tel. 928/759–8800, (Nonreporting) **A**1 9 10 **S** Ernest Health, Inc., Albuquerque, NM
Primary Contact: Judy Baum, Chief Executive Officer
Web address: www.mvrrh.ernesthealth.com
**Control:** Corporation, Investor–owned, for–profit **Service:** Rehabilitation

| Staffed Beds: 16 |

**WINDHAVEN PSYCHIATRIC HOSPITAL (034025)**, 3347 North Windsong Drive, Zip 86314–2283; tel. 928/445–5211, (Nonreporting) **A**9 10
Primary Contact: Larry D. Green, Jr., Chief Executive Officer
CFO: Doug Oliver, Chief Financial Officer
CMO: Lisa Parsons, M.D., Chief Medical Officer
CHR: Pamela Pierce, Chief Human Resource
Web address: www.wygc.org
**Control:** Other not–for–profit (including NFP Corporation) **Service:** Psychiatric

| Staffed Beds: 16 |

★ **YAVAPAI REGIONAL MEDICAL CENTER – EAST (030118)**, 7700 East Florentine Road, Zip 86314–2245; tel. 928/445–2700 **A**9 10 **F**8 11 13 14 15 20 24 28 29 30 31 34 35 36 40 42 45 46 50 53 54 57 59 60 64 68 70 73 74 75 76 77 78 79 81 82 84 85 86 87 89 93 107 108 111 114 116 117 118 119 130 131 132 135 143 146 147 148 **P**7
Primary Contact: Timothy Barnett, Chief Executive Officer
COO: John Amos, COO East Campus
CFO: Brian Hoefle, Chief Financial Officer
CMO: Joseph Goldberger, M.D., Chief Medical Officer
CIO: Randy Rahman, Chief Information Officer
CHR: Mark Timm, Director Human Resouces
CNO: Diane Drexler, R.N., Chief Nursing Officer
Web address: www.yrmc.org
**Control:** Other not–for–profit (including NFP Corporation) **Service:** General Medical and Surgical

| Staffed Beds: 72 Admissions: 4278 Census: 25 Outpatient Visits: 47690 Births: 932 Total Expense ($000): 43558 Payroll Expense ($000): 23953 Personnel: 377 |

**SACATON—Pinal County**

⊠ **HUHUKAM MEMORIAL HOSPITAL (031308)**, 483 West Seed Farm Road, Zip 85147, Mailing Address: P.O. Box 38, Zip 85147–0001; tel. 602/528–1200, (Nonreporting) **A**1 9 10 18
Primary Contact: Amish Purohit, Chief Executive Officer
COO: Pamela Thompson, Chief Operations Officer
CFO: Elisa Banigan, Chief Financial Officer
CMO: Noel Habib, M.D., Chief Medical Officer
CHR: Michael Freeman, Director Human Resources
Web address: www.grhc.org
**Control:** Other not–for–profit (including NFP Corporation) **Service:** General Medical and Surgical

| Staffed Beds: 15 |

**SAFFORD—Graham County**

★ **MT. GRAHAM REGIONAL MEDICAL CENTER (030068)**, 1600 20th Avenue, Zip 85546–4097; tel. 928/348–4000 **A**9 10 20 **F**3 11 13 15 29 31 34 35 40 45 46 53 54 57 58 59 62 63 64 65 68 70 75 76 78 79 81 83 84 85 87 93 107 108 110 111 115 116 119 129 130 132 133 134 135 141 146 **P**5
Primary Contact: Pat O'Brien, Interim Chief Executive Officer
CFO: Keith Bryce, Chief Financial Officer
CIO: Keith Bryce, Chief Financial Officer
CHR: Wick Lewis, Vice President Human Resources and Clinic Management
Web address: www.mtgraham.org
**Control:** Other not–for–profit (including NFP Corporation) **Service:** General Medical and Surgical

| Staffed Beds: 49 Admissions: 1806 Census: 18 Outpatient Visits: 71926 Births: 518 Total Expense ($000): 52143 Payroll Expense ($000): 24352 Personnel: 410 |

**SAN CARLOS—Gila County**

⊠ **U. S. PUBLIC HEALTH SERVICE INDIAN HOSPITAL (030077)**, Zip 85550; tel. 928/475–2371, (Nonreporting) **A**1 10 **S** U. S. Indian Health Service, Rockville, MD
Primary Contact: Robert Harry, M.D., Chief Executive Officer
CFO: Vivie Hosteenez, Chief Financial Officer
CMO: Karen Health, M.D., Clinical Director
CIO: Lois Sprengeler Wesley, Director Quality Management
CHR: Shirley M. Boni, Administrative Officer
Web address: www.ihs.gov
**Control:** PHS, Indian Service, Government, federal **Service:** General Medical and Surgical

| Staffed Beds: 8 |

**SAN TAN VALLEY—Pinal County**

⊠ **BANNER IRONWOOD MEDICAL CENTER (030130)**, 37000 North Gantzel Road, Zip 85140–7303; tel. 480/394–4000 **A**1 9 10 **F**18 29 30 34 35 40 43 45 50 59 68 70 74 75 76 78 79 80 81 82 85 86 87 107 108 111 115 119 130 132 135 136 146 **S** Banner Health, Phoenix, AZ
Primary Contact: Julie Nunley, R.N., Chief Executive Officer
CFO: Lori Linder, Chief Financial Officer
CMO: Michael O'Connor, M.D., Chief Medical Officer
CHR: Nancy M. English, CHief Human Resources Officer
CNO: Cathy Townsend, Chief Nursing Officer
Web address: www.bannerhealth.com/Locations/Arizona/Banner+Ironwood/
**Control:** Other not–for–profit (including NFP Corporation) **Service:** General Medical and Surgical

| Staffed Beds: 53 Admissions: 2391 Census: 17 Outpatient Visits: 45885 Births: 892 Total Expense ($000): 53416 Payroll Expense ($000): 16214 Personnel: 277 |

*Many Facility Codes have changed. Please refer to the AHA Guide Code Chart.* © 2013 AHA Guide

**SCOTTSDALE—Maricopa County**

☒ **BANNER BEHAVIORAL HEALTH HOSPITAL – SCOTTSDALE (034004)**, 7575
East Earll Drive, Zip 85251–6915; tel. 480/941–7500 **A**1 9 10 **F**4 5 29 30 34
35 38 50 56 64 65 68 75 82 86 87 98 99 100 101 102 103 104 105 106
119 130 132 134 135 146 **P**5 **S** Banner Health, Phoenix, AZ
Primary Contact: Cherie Martin, R.N., MSN, FACHE, Chief Executive Officer
CFO: Michael A. Cimino, Jr., Chief Financial Officer
CMO: Clifford Zeller, M.D., Chief Medical Officer
CHR: Kevin McVeigh, Interim Chief Human Resources Officer
CNO: Cherri Anderson, Chief Nursing Officer
Web address: www.bannerhealth.com/Locations/Arizona/Banner+Behavioral+
Health
**Control:** Other not–for–profit (including NFP Corporation) **Service:** Psychiatric

**Staffed Beds:** 94 **Admissions:** 3987 **Census:** 83 **Outpatient Visits:** 27904
**Births:** 0 **Total Expense ($000):** 28964 **Payroll Expense ($000):** 16205
**Personnel:** 291

☒ **HEALTHSOUTH SCOTTSDALE REHABILITATION HOSPITAL (033025)**, 9630
East Shea Boulevard, Zip 85260–6267; tel. 480/551–5400, (Nonreporting) **A**1 9
10 **S** HEALTHSOUTH Corporation, Birmingham, AL
Primary Contact: Timothy T. Poore, Chief Executive Officer
CFO: Lisa Barrick, Controller
CMO: Keith W. Cunningham, M.D., Medical Director
CHR: Mary Beth Giczi, Director Human Resources
CNO: Diane M. Caruso, MSN, Chief Nursing Officer
Web address: www.healthsouthscottsdale.com
**Control:** Corporation, Investor–owned, for–profit **Service:** Rehabilitation

**Staffed Beds:** 60

★ ◇ **SCOTTSDALE HEALTHCARE SHEA MEDICAL CENTER (030087)**, 9003
East Shea Boulevard, Zip 85260–6771; tel. 480/323–3000, (Nonreporting) **A**2 3
5 9 10 21 **S** Scottsdale Healthcare, Scottsdale, AZ
Primary Contact: Peggy J. Reiley, Ph.D., MS, R.N., Senior Vice President and
Chief Clinical Officer
CFO: Todd La Porte, Senior Vice President and Chief Financial Officer
CMO: James Burke, M.D., Senior Vice President and Chief Medical Officer
CIO: James R. Cramer, Vice President and Chief Information Officer
CHR: Carol Henderson, Senior Vice President and Chief Talent Officer
Web address: www.shc.org
**Control:** Other not–for–profit (including NFP Corporation) **Service:** General
Medical and Surgical

**Staffed Beds:** 409

★ ◇ **SCOTTSDALE HEALTHCARE THOMPSON PEAK HOSPITAL (030123)**,
7400 East Thompson Peak Parkway, Zip 85255–4109; tel. 480/324–7000,
(Nonreporting) **A**9 10 21 **S** Scottsdale Healthcare, Scottsdale, AZ
Primary Contact: Kimberly Post, R.N., Vice President and Administrator
CFO: Todd La Porte, Chief Financial Officer
CMO: James Burke, M.D., Senior Vice President and Chief Medical Officer
CIO: James R. Cramer, Chief Information Officer
CHR: Carol Henderson, Vice President Human Resources
Web address: www.shc.org
**Control:** Other not–for–profit (including NFP Corporation) **Service:** General
Medical and Surgical

**Staffed Beds:** 64

★ ◇ **SCOTTSDALE HEALTHCARE–OSBORN MEDICAL CENTER (030038)**,
7400 East Osborn Road, Zip 85251–6403; tel. 480/882–4000, (Nonreporting)
**A**2 3 5 8 9 10 21 **S** Scottsdale Healthcare, Scottsdale, AZ
Primary Contact: Gary E. Baker, Senior Vice President and Administrator
CFO: Todd La Porte, Senior Vice President and Chief Financial Officer
CMO: James Burke, M.D., Senior Vice President and Chief Medical Officer
CIO: James R. Cramer, Vice President and Chief Information Officer
CHR: Carol Henderson, Vice President Human Resources
Web address: www.shc.org
**Control:** Other not–for–profit (including NFP Corporation) **Service:** General
Medical and Surgical

**Staffed Beds:** 347

☒ **SELECT SPECIALTY HOSPITAL–SCOTTSDALE (032005)**, 7400 East Osborn
Road, 3 West, Zip 85251–6432; tel. 480/882–4360, (Includes SELECT
SPECIALTY HOSPITAL–PHOENIX DOWNTOWN, 1012 East Wiletta Street, 4th Floor,
Phoenix, Zip 85006; tel. 602/239–6134; Sharon Anthony, Market Administrator),
(Nonreporting) **A**1 10 **S** Select Medical Corporation, Mechanicsburg, PA
Primary Contact: Anthony Martino, Chief Executive Officer
Web address: www.selectspecialtyhospitals.com/company/locations/scottsdale.
aspx
**Control:** Corporation, Investor–owned, for–profit **Service:** Long–Term Acute Care
hospital

**Staffed Beds:** 62

**SELLS—Pima County**

☒ **U. S. PUBLIC HEALTH SERVICE INDIAN HOSPITAL–SELLS (030074)**,
Zip 85634; tel. 520/383–7251, (Nonreporting) **A**1 9 10 **S** U. S. Indian Health
Service, Rockville, MD
Primary Contact: Priscilla Whitethorne, Chief Executive Officer
COO: Diane Shanley, Deputy Service Unit Director
CFO: Vivian Draper, Chief Financial Officer
CMO: Peter Ziegler, M.D., Acting Chief Medical Officer
CIO: Karen Wade, Chief Information Officer
CNO: Donna Hobbs, Nurse Executive
Web address: www.ihs.gov
**Control:** PHS, Indian Service, Government, federal **Service:** General Medical and
Surgical

**Staffed Beds:** 12

**SHOW LOW—Navajo County**

★ **SUMMIT HEALTHCARE REGIONAL MEDICAL CENTER (030062)**, 2200 East
Show Low Lake Road, Zip 85901–7800; tel. 928/537–4375, (Nonreporting) **A**9
10 20
Primary Contact: Ronald L. McArthur, Chief Executive Officer
COO: Doug Gilchrist, Chief Operating Officer
CFO: Kurt Loveless, Chief Financial Officer
CMO: Jeffrey Northup, D.O., Chief Medical Officer
CIO: Kent McQuillan, Chief Information Officer
CHR: Connie Kakavas, Chief Human Resources Officer
CNO: Cynthia Ebert, R.N., Chief Nursing Officer
Web address: www.summithealthcare.net
**Control:** Other not–for–profit (including NFP Corporation) **Service:** General
Medical and Surgical

**Staffed Beds:** 89

**SIERRA VISTA—Cochise County**

☒ **SIERRA VISTA REGIONAL HEALTH CENTER (030043)**, 300 El Camino Real,
Zip 85635–2899; tel. 520/417–3003 **A**1 9 10 13 20 **F**3 11 13 15 18 20 22
27 28 29 30 34 35 40 41 45 46 48 49 50 51 57 60 63 64 70 73 75 76 77
79 81 82 85 86 89 93 107 111 114 115 118 119 127 130 145 146 148
**S** RegionalCare Hospital Partners, Brentwood, TN
Primary Contact: Margaret Hepburn, MS, R.N., President and Chief Executive
Officer
CFO: Bruce J. Norton, Senior Vice President and Chief Financial Officer
CMO: Jaya Maddur, M.D., Chief of Staff
CIO: Bruce J. Norton, Senior Vice President and Chief Financial Officer
CHR: Marie Wurth, Vice President Human Resources and Public Relations Officer
Web address: www.svrhc.org
**Control:** Other not–for–profit (including NFP Corporation) **Service:** General
Medical and Surgical

**Staffed Beds:** 83 **Admissions:** 4868 **Census:** 42 **Outpatient Visits:** 90057
**Births:** 1042 **Total Expense ($000):** 90784 **Payroll Expense ($000):** 36148
**Personnel:** 632

**SPRINGERVILLE—Apache County**

**WHITE MOUNTAIN REGIONAL MEDICAL CENTER (031315)**, 118 South
Mountain Avenue, Zip 85938–5104; tel. 928/333–4368, (Nonreporting) **A**9
10 18
Primary Contact: James Robertson, Chief Executive Officer
CFO: James Hamblin, Chief Financial Officer
CMO: Scott Hamblin, M.D., President Medical Staff
Web address: www.wmrmc.com
**Control:** Other not–for–profit (including NFP Corporation) **Service:** General
Medical and Surgical

**Staffed Beds:** 20

---

**Hospital, Medicare Provider Number, Address, Telephone, Approval, Facility, and Physician Codes, Health Care System**

★ American Hospital Association (AHA) membership
☐ The Joint Commission accreditation
◇ DNV Healthcare Inc. accreditation
○ Healthcare Facilities Accreditation Program
△ Commission on Accreditation of Rehabilitation Facilities (CARF) accreditation

AZ

## SUN CITY—Maricopa County

☒ **BANNER BOSWELL MEDICAL CENTER (030061)**, 10401 West Thunderbird Boulevard, Zip 85351–3004, Mailing Address: P.O. Box 1690, Zip 85372–1690; tel. 623/832–4000, (Total facility includes 71 beds in nursing home–type unit) **A**1 2 9 10 **F**3 11 15 29 30 31 34 35 36 37 40 43 45 46 50 51 56 58 59 60 61 64 68 70 74 75 78 79 81 82 85 86 87 90 91 92 100 102 104 107 108 110 111 114 115 116 119 126 128 129 130 132 135 146 147 148 **S** Banner Health, Phoenix, AZ
Primary Contact: David Cheney, Chief Executive Officer
CFO: Jeremy Williams, Chief Financial Officer
CMO: Jason Krupp, M.D., Chief Medical Officer
Web address: www.bannerhealth.com/Locations/Arizona/Banner+Boswell+Medical+Center
**Control:** Other not–for–profit (including NFP Corporation) **Service:** General Medical and Surgical

**Staffed Beds:** 454 **Admissions:** 22254 **Census:** 296 **Outpatient Visits:** 242510 **Births:** 0 **Total Expense ($000):** 269249 **Payroll Expense ($000):** 106946 **Personnel:** 1717

**RESTORA HOSPITAL OF SUN CITY (032008)**, (Formerly Trillium Specialty Hospital–West Valley), 13818 North Thunderbird Boulevard, Zip 85351–2574; tel. 623/977–1325, (Total facility includes 60 beds in nursing home–type unit) (Data for 186 days) **A**10 **F**1 3 29 50 77 85 87 128 130 148 **S** Restora Healthcare, Alpharetta, GA
Primary Contact: Gregory Sassman, Interim Chief Executive Officer
Web address: www.restorahealthcare.com
**Control:** Individual, Investor–owned, for–profit **Service:** Long–Term Acute Care hospital

**Staffed Beds:** 120 **Admissions:** 533 **Census:** 100 **Outpatient Visits:** 0 **Births:** 0 **Total Expense ($000):** 9382 **Payroll Expense ($000):** 3719 **Personnel:** 147

## SUN CITY WEST—Maricopa County

☒ **BANNER DEL E. WEBB MEDICAL CENTER (030093)**, 14502 West Meeker Boulevard, Zip 85375–5299, Mailing Address: P.O. Box 5169, Zip 85376–5169; tel. 623/214–4000 **A**1 9 10 **F**3 5 11 13 15 17 20 22 26 28 29 30 31 34 35 37 40 45 49 50 51 53 56 59 60 64 68 70 73 74 75 76 78 79 81 82 83 84 85 86 87 90 91 92 93 94 96 98 100 101 102 103 104 105 107 108 111 114 115 118 119 126 130 131 132 135 146 147 148 **P**1 8 **S** Banner Health, Phoenix, AZ
Primary Contact: Debbie Flores, Chief Executive Officer
CMO: Michel Dagher, D.O., Vice President and Chief Medical Officer
CIO: David Runt, Chief Information Officer
Web address: www.bannerhealth.com/Locations/Arizona/Banner+Del+Webb+Medical+Center/
**Control:** Other not–for–profit (including NFP Corporation) **Service:** General Medical and Surgical

**Staffed Beds:** 373 **Admissions:** 19553 **Census:** 218 **Outpatient Visits:** 106102 **Births:** 1714 **Total Expense ($000):** 226479 **Payroll Expense ($000):** 88330 **Personnel:** 1493

## TEMPE—Maricopa County

☐ **AURORA TEMPE HOSPITAL (034028)**, 6350 Maple Street, Zip 85283–2857; tel. 480/345–5400, (Nonreporting) **A**1 9 10 **S** Aurora Behavioral Health Care, Corona, CA
Primary Contact: Bruce Waldo, Chief Executive Officer
**Control:** Partnership, Investor–owned, for–profit **Service:** Psychiatric

**Staffed Beds:** 70

## TUBA CITY—Coconino County

☒ **TUBA CITY REGIONAL HEALTH CARE CORPORATION (030073)**, 167 Main Street, Zip 86045–0611, Mailing Address: P.O. Box 600, Zip 86045–0600; tel. 928/283–2501 **A**1 3 9 10 **F**3 5 8 9 11 13 14 15 18 26 27 28 29 30 31 32 34 35 36 38 39 40 41 42 43 44 45 46 47 48 50 52 53 54 55 56 57 58 59 60 61 62 63 64 65 66 68 70 71 74 75 76 77 79 80 81 82 83 84 85 86 87 89 90 91 92 93 94 95 96 97 99 100 101 102 103 104 107 108 110 111 114 115 119 120 124 126 127 128 130 131 132 133 134 135 141 142 143 144 145 146 147 148 **P**6 7
Primary Contact: Joseph T. Engelken, Chief Executive Officer
COO: Lynette Bonar, Chief Support Services
CFO: Clifford Lee Olsson, Chief Financial Officer
CMO: Alan Spacone, M.D., Chief Medical Officer
CHR: John S. Pemberton, Director Human Resources
Web address: www.tchealth.org
**Control:** Other not–for–profit (including NFP Corporation) **Service:** General Medical and Surgical

**Staffed Beds:** 73 **Admissions:** 3641 **Census:** 37 **Outpatient Visits:** 733346 **Births:** 454 **Total Expense ($000):** 136775 **Payroll Expense ($000):** 69716 **Personnel:** 1020

## TUCSON—Pima County

☒ **CARONDELET ST. JOSEPH'S HOSPITAL (030011)**, 350 North Wilmot Road, Zip 85711–2678; tel. 520/296–3211 **A**1 9 10 **F**3 5 11 12 13 15 17 18 20 22 28 29 30 34 38 40 44 45 46 47 49 50 57 59 60 61 63 64 68 69 70 72 74 75 76 77 78 79 81 82 83 84 87 90 93 98 100 101 102 103 104 105 107 108 110 111 114 115 118 119 126 129 130 131 132 133 135 145 146 147 148 **S** Ascension Health, Saint Louis, MO
Primary Contact: Tony Fonze, President and Chief Executive Officer
CFO: Alan Strauss, Chief Financial Officer
CMO: Donald Denmark, M.D., Chief Medical Officer
CHR: Daisy Jenkins, Vice President Human Resources
Web address: www.carondelet.org
**Control:** Church–operated, Nongovernment, not–for profit **Service:** General Medical and Surgical

**Staffed Beds:** 449 **Admissions:** 17973 **Census:** 227 **Outpatient Visits:** 149196 **Births:** 2709 **Total Expense ($000):** 250315 **Payroll Expense ($000):** 88475 **Personnel:** 1448

☒ **CARONDELET ST. MARY'S HOSPITAL (030010)**, 1601 West St. Mary's Road, Zip 85745–2682; tel. 520/872–3000 **A**1 3 9 10 **F**3 5 11 12 15 16 17 20 22 29 30 31 34 38 40 44 47 49 50 51 56 57 59 60 61 63 64 68 70 74 77 78 79 81 82 83 84 87 90 93 98 100 101 102 103 104 105 107 108 110 111 114 115 116 118 119 126 129 130 132 133 135 145 146 148 **S** Ascension Health, Saint Louis, MO
Primary Contact: Amy Beiter, M.D., President and Chief Executive Officer
COO: Roberta B. Kaemmerling, MSN, Chief Operating Officer and Chief Nursing Officer
CFO: Deb Mohesky, Chief Financial Officer
CHR: Daisy Jenkins, Vice President Human Resources
Web address: www.carondelet.org
**Control:** Church–operated, Nongovernment, not–for profit **Service:** General Medical and Surgical

**Staffed Beds:** 429 **Admissions:** 12318 **Census:** 161 **Outpatient Visits:** 192281 **Births:** 0 **Total Expense ($000):** 193710 **Payroll Expense ($000):** 70829 **Personnel:** 1158

☐ **CORNERSTONE HOSPITAL OF SOUTHEAST ARIZONA (032004)**, 7220 East Rosewood Drive, Zip 85710–1350; tel. 520/546–4595, (Nonreporting) **A**1 10 **S** Cornerstone Healthcare Group, Dallas, TX
Primary Contact: Mindy S. Moore, Chief Executive Officer
CFO: Chad Deardorff, Group Chief Financial Officer
CMO: Paul Simon, M.D., Medical Director
CIO: Adam Davis, Director Information Technology
CHR: Isabel Dominguez, Director Human Resources and Payroll
Web address: www.chghospitals.com
**Control:** Corporation, Investor–owned, for–profit **Service:** Long–Term Acute Care hospital

**Staffed Beds:** 54

☒ **HEALTHSOUTH REHABILITATION HOSPITAL OF SOUTHERN ARIZONA (033029)**, 1921 West Hospital Drive, Zip 85704–7806; tel. 520/742–2800 **A**1 9 10 **F**3 29 34 59 64 69 90 93 95 96 130 131 132 143 148 **S** HEALTHSOUTH Corporation, Birmingham, AL
Primary Contact: Robert C. Honeycutt, FACHE, Chief Executive Officer
CFO: David Krogen, Controller
CMO: Susan Bulen, M.D., Medical Director
CHR: Maria Elena McElroy, Vice President Human Resources
Web address: www.healthsouthsouthernarizona.com
**Control:** Corporation, Investor–owned, for–profit **Service:** Rehabilitation

**Staffed Beds:** 60 **Admissions:** 1192 **Census:** 41 **Outpatient Visits:** 8577 **Births:** 0 **Total Expense ($000):** 16653 **Payroll Expense ($000):** 8739 **Personnel:** 145

☒ **HEALTHSOUTH REHABILITATION INSTITUTE OF TUCSON (033028)**, 2650 North Wyatt Drive, Zip 85712–6108; tel. 520/325–1300 **A**1 9 10 **F**29 34 35 62 90 93 96 130 132 **S** HEALTHSOUTH Corporation, Birmingham, AL
Primary Contact: Jeffrey Christensen, Chief Executive Officer
CFO: Mary Donovan, Controller
CMO: Jon Larson, M.D., Medical Director
CHR: Dawn Mosier, Director Human Resources
Web address: www.rehabinstituteoftucson.com
**Control:** Corporation, Investor–owned, for–profit **Service:** Rehabilitation

**Staffed Beds:** 80 **Admissions:** 1482 **Census:** 53 **Outpatient Visits:** 0 **Births:** 0 **Total Expense ($000):** 18991 **Payroll Expense ($000):** 10596 **Personnel:** 179

☒ **KINDRED HOSPITAL–TUCSON (032002)**, 355 North Wilmot Road, Zip 85711–2601; tel. 520/584–4500, (Nonreporting) **A**1 10 **S** Kindred Healthcare, Louisville, KY
Primary Contact: Marc Lemon, Chief Executive Officer
COO: Kathleen D. Kobbes Adams, R.N., Chief Clinical Officer
CFO: M. Troy Carpenter, Chief Financial Officer
CMO: Sunil Natrajan, M.D., Medical Director
Web address: www.khtucson.com
**Control:** Corporation, Investor–owned, for–profit **Service:** Long–Term Acute Care hospital

**Staffed Beds:** 51

*Many Facility Codes have changed. Please refer to the AHA Guide Code Chart.* © 2013 AHA Guide

☒ **NORTHWEST MEDICAL CENTER (030085)**, 6200 North La Cholla Boulevard, Zip 85741–3599; tel. 520/742–9000, (Nonreporting) **A**1 3 5 9 10 **S** Community Health Systems, Inc., Franklin, TN
Primary Contact: Kevin Stockton, Chief Executive Officer
COO: Veronica Knudson, Chief Operating Officer
CFO: Ronald Patrick, Chief Financial Officer
CMO: Abram Aguilar, M.D., Chief Medical Officer
CIO: David Bullock, Director Information Services
CHR: John Zubiena, Chief Human Resources Officer
CNO: Karen Stubbs, Chief Nursing Officer
Web address: www.northwestmedicalcenter.com
**Control:** Corporation, Investor–owned, for–profit **Service:** General Medical and Surgical

| |
|---|
| **Staffed Beds:** 270 |

**PALO VERDE MENTAL HEALTH SERVICES** See TMC Healthcare

☐ **SIERRA TUCSON**, 39580 South Lago Del Oro Parkway, Zip 85739–9637; tel. 520/624–4000 **A**1 5 **F**4 29 33 35 36 53 75 80 82 98 106 118 135 **P**6
Primary Contact: Stephen P. Fahey, Executive Director
COO: David E. Anderson, Ph.D., Chief Operating Officer
CFO: Loree Thompson, CPA, Chief Financial Officer
CMO: Michael E. Scott, M.D., Director Medical Services
CHR: Bertha Kenny, Director Human Resources
Web address: www.sierratucson.com
**Control:** Corporation, Investor–owned, for–profit **Service:** Psychiatric

| |
|---|
| **Staffed Beds:** 139 **Admissions:** 1065 **Census:** 88 **Outpatient Visits:** 0 **Births:** 0 **Total Expense ($000):** 37881 **Payroll Expense ($000):** 12737 **Personnel:** 228 |

☐ **SONORA BEHAVIORAL HEALTH HOSPITAL (034022)**, 6050 North Corona Road, Zip 85704–1096; tel. 520/469–8700 **A**1 3 9 10 **F**5 29 98 99 100 103 104 143 **P**5 **S** Acadia Healthcare Company, Inc., Franklin, TN
Primary Contact: Brian Gill, Chief Executive Officer
**Control:** Corporation, Investor–owned, for–profit **Service:** Psychiatric

| |
|---|
| **Staffed Beds:** 70 **Admissions:** 2450 **Census:** 49 **Outpatient Visits:** 3278 **Births:** 0 **Total Expense ($000):** 13522 **Payroll Expense ($000):** 9314 **Personnel:** 151 |

☒ △ **SOUTHERN ARIZONA VETERANS AFFAIRS HEALTH CARE SYSTEM**, 3601 South 6th Avenue, Zip 85723–0002; tel. 520/792–1450, (Nonreporting) **A**1 3 5 7 9 **S** Department of Veterans Affairs, Washington, DC
Primary Contact: Jonathan H. Gardner, FACHE, Director
CFO: Larry Korn, Manager Finance
CMO: Jayendra H. Shah, M.D., Chief Medical Officer
CIO: John Walston, Chief Information Officer
CHR: Patrice Craig, Manager Human Resources
Web address: www.tucson.va.gov
**Control:** Veterans Affairs, Government, federal **Service:** General Medical and Surgical

| |
|---|
| **Staffed Beds:** 285 |

★ **TMC HEALTHCARE (030006)**, 5301 East Grant Road, Zip 85712–2874; tel. 520/327–5461, (Includes PALO VERDE MENTAL HEALTH SERVICES, 2695 North Craycroft, Zip 85712–2244, Mailing Address: P.O. Box 40030, Zip 85717–0030; tel. 520/324–4340; TMC FOR CHILDREN, 5301 East Grant Road, Zip 85712–2805; tel. 520/327–5461) **A**3 5 8 9 10 **F**3 8 11 13 15 17 18 19 20 22 24 26 28 29 30 31 34 35 40 41 42 45 46 47 48 49 50 54 56 57 59 63 64 68 72 74 75 76 77 78 79 81 82 84 85 86 87 88 89 96 97 98 100 102 104 107 108 109 110 111 114 115 119 124 126 129 130 132 146 147 148 **P**4 7
Primary Contact: Judy F. Rich, President and Chief Executive Officer
COO: Linda Wojtowicz, R.N., Senior Vice President and Chief Operations Officer
CFO: Stephen Bush, Chief Financial Officer
CMO: Palmer Evans, M.D., Chief Medical Officer
CIO: Frank Marini, Vice President and Chief Information Officer
Web address: www.tmcaz.com
**Control:** Other not–for–profit (including NFP Corporation) **Service:** General Medical and Surgical

| |
|---|
| **Staffed Beds:** 584 **Admissions:** 31990 **Census:** 364 **Outpatient Visits:** 150259 **Births:** 5588 **Total Expense ($000):** 414712 **Payroll Expense ($000):** 168841 **Personnel:** 2915 |

☐ **UNIVERSITY OF ARIZONA MEDICAL CENTER – SOUTH CAMPUS (030111)**, 2800 East Ajo Way, Zip 85713–6289; tel. 520/874–2000 **A**1 5 6 9 10 **F**3 11 12 15 18 20 22 26 29 30 34 35 36 38 40 43 44 50 51 54 55 56 57 58 59 61 64 65 68 70 74 75 77 79 81 82 85 87 93 97 98 100 101 102 103 104 107 110 111 114 115 119 127 130 131 135 145 146 147 148 **P**4
Primary Contact: Sarah Frost, Administrator
CFO: Timothy Kares, Chief Financial Officer
CMO: John Kettelle, M.D., Vice President Operations and Medical Director
CIO: Kevin Christiansen, Director Information Technology
CHR: Tere LeBarron, Vice President Planning and Integration
Web address: www.uph.org
**Control:** Other not–for–profit (including NFP Corporation) **Service:** General Medical and Surgical

| |
|---|
| **Staffed Beds:** 161 **Admissions:** 7283 **Census:** 102 **Outpatient Visits:** 197657 **Births:** 0 **Total Expense ($000):** 135422 **Payroll Expense ($000):** 47917 **Personnel:** 1038 |

☒ **UNIVERSITY OF ARIZONA MEDICAL CENTER – UNIVERSITY CAMPUS (030064)**, 1501 North Campbell Avenue, Zip 85724–5128; tel. 520/694–0111, (Includes DIAMOND CHILDREN'S HOSPITAL, 1501 North Campbell Avenue, Zip 85724–0001; tel. 520/694–0111) **A**1 3 5 8 9 10 **F**3 8 11 12 13 17 18 19 20 21 22 23 24 25 26 27 28 29 30 31 32 34 35 36 37 38 40 41 42 43 44 45 46 47 48 49 50 52 53 54 57 58 59 60 61 62 64 67 68 69 70 72 74 75 76 77 78 79 81 84 85 86 87 88 89 92 93 97 99 100 101 102 103 107 108 111 114 115 116 117 118 119 120 121 123 124 126 130 132 135 136 137 138 139 140 141 142 145 146 147 148 **P**4 6
Primary Contact: Karen Mlawsky, Interim President and Chief Executive Officer
CIO: Shirley Gabriel, Chief Information Officer
CHR: John Marques, Vice President Human Resources
Web address: www.umcarizona.org
**Control:** Other not–for–profit (including NFP Corporation) **Service:** General Medical and Surgical

| |
|---|
| **Staffed Beds:** 463 **Admissions:** 25329 **Census:** 369 **Outpatient Visits:** 463234 **Births:** 1928 **Total Expense ($000):** 644884 **Payroll Expense ($000):** 216971 **Personnel:** 4187 |

**WHITERIVER—Navajo County**

☐ **U. S. PUBLIC HEALTH SERVICE INDIAN HOSPITAL–WHITERIVER (030113)**, 200 West Hospital Drive, Zip 85941–0860, Mailing Address: State Route 73, Box 860, Zip 85941–0860; tel. 928/338–4911, (Nonreporting) **A**1 10 **S** U. S. Indian Health Service, Rockville, MD
Primary Contact: Michelle Martinez, Interim Chief Executive Officer
CFO: Desdemona Leslie, Finance Officer
CMO: David Yost, M.D., Clinical Director
CIO: Russell Barker, Chief Information Officer
Web address: www.ihs.gov
**Control:** PHS, Indian Service, Government, federal **Service:** General Medical and Surgical

| |
|---|
| **Staffed Beds:** 35 |

**WICKENBURG—Maricopa County**

★ **WICKENBURG COMMUNITY HOSPITAL (031300)**, 520 Rose Lane, Zip 85390–1447; tel. 928/684–5421 **A**9 10 18 **F**11 15 34 40 53 57 59 63 65 90 93 107 110 111 115 117 119 127 133 146 148 **P**6
Primary Contact: James Tavary, Chief Executive Officer
CFO: Ron Smith, Chief Financial Officer
CMO: Dennis Barraco, D.O., Medical Director
CIO: Michael McKay, Manager Information Systems
CHR: Bill Horn, Director Human Resources
CNO: Linda Brockwell, R.N., Chief Nursing Officer
Web address: www.wickenburgcommunityhospital.com
**Control:** Other not–for–profit (including NFP Corporation) **Service:** General Medical and Surgical

| |
|---|
| **Staffed Beds:** 19 **Admissions:** 458 **Census:** 5 **Births:** 0 **Total Expense ($000):** 18819 **Payroll Expense ($000):** 8363 |

**WILLCOX—Cochise County**

★ **NORTHERN COCHISE COMMUNITY HOSPITAL (031302)**, 901 West Rex Allen Drive, Zip 85643–1009; tel. 520/384–3541, (Nonreporting) **A**9 10 18
Primary Contact: Roland Knox, Chief Executive Officer
COO: John Hilton, Operations Officer
CFO: Darcy Robertson, Financial Officer
CMO: Hisham Hamam, M.D., Chief of Staff
CHR: John Hilton, Director Human Resources
CNO: Laurel Kibler, Nursing Officer
Web address: www.ncch.com
**Control:** Hospital district or authority, Government, nonfederal **Service:** General Medical and Surgical

| |
|---|
| **Staffed Beds:** 48 |

---

**Hospital, Medicare Provider Number, Address, Telephone, Approval, Facility, and Physician Codes, Health Care System**

★ American Hospital Association (AHA) membership
☐ The Joint Commission accreditation
◇ DNV Healthcare Inc. accreditation
○ Healthcare Facilities Accreditation Program
△ Commission on Accreditation of Rehabilitation Facilities (CARF) accreditation

## WINSLOW—Navajo County

★ **LITTLE COLORADO MEDICAL CENTER (031311)**, 1501 Williamson Avenue,
Zip 86047–2797; tel. 928/289–4691, (Nonreporting) **A**9 10 18
Primary Contact: Jeffrey J. Hamblen, Chief Executive Officer
CFO: Randy Glassman, Chief Financial Officer
CMO: Perry Mitchell, M.D., Chief of Staff
CHR: Nina L. Ferguson, Director Human Resources
Web address: www.lcmcwmh.org
**Control:** Other not–for–profit (including NFP Corporation) **Service:** General
Medical and Surgical

**Staffed Beds:** 25

## YUMA—Yuma County

★ **YUMA REGIONAL MEDICAL CENTER (030013)**, 2400 South Avenue A,
Zip 85364–7170; tel. 928/344–2000 **A**9 10 **F**3 8 11 12 13 15 18 20 22 24
26 28 29 30 31 32 34 35 38 39 40 41 45 46 47 48 49 50 54 56 57 58 59
64 65 68 70 72 74 75 76 77 78 79 81 82 83 84 85 86 87 89 94 97 100
107 108 109 110 111 114 115 116 117 118 119 120 121 122 123 124 130
132 146 147 148 **P**7
Primary Contact: Pat Walz, President and Chief Executive Officer
CFO: Tony Struck, Chief Financial Officer
CMO: Carl Myers, M.D., Vice President Medical Affairs and Chief Medical Officer
CIO: Gene Shaw, Chief Information Officer
CHR: Sharon R. Gardner, Vice President Human Resources
CNO: Brenda Hall, R.N., Vice President Patient Care Services
Web address: www.yumaregional.org
**Control:** Other not–for–profit (including NFP Corporation) **Service:** General
Medical and Surgical

**Staffed Beds:** 369 **Admissions:** 15614 **Census:** 185 **Outpatient Visits:**
168801 **Births:** 3365 **Total Expense ($000):** 306237 **Payroll Expense
($000):** 118859 **Personnel:** 1715

✠ **YUMA REHABILITATION HOSPITAL (033034)**, 901 West 24th Street,
Zip 85364–6384; tel. 928/726–5000, (Nonreporting) **A**1 9 10 **S** HEALTHSOUTH
Corporation, Birmingham, AL
Primary Contact: Joshua Bowie, Chief Executive Officer
CFO: Larry Barclift, Chief Financial Officer
CMO: Rinely Aguiar–Olsen, M.D., Medical Director
CHR: Linda Woen, Director Human Resources
Web address: www.yumarehabhospital.com
**Control:** Corporation, Investor–owned, for–profit **Service:** Rehabilitation

**Staffed Beds:** 41

*Many Facility Codes have changed. Please refer to the AHA Guide Code Chart.*

AR

# ARKANSAS

## ARKADELPHIA—Clark County

⊠ **BAPTIST HEALTH MEDICAL CENTER–ARKADELPHIA (041321)**, 3050 Twin
Rivers Drive, Zip 71923–4299; tel. 870/245–2622 **A**1 9 10 18 **F**3 7 11 13 15
28 29 30 40 43 57 59 61 62 63 65 68 69 70 76 81 93 107 110 111 114
119 129 130 133 135 146 **S** Baptist Health, Little Rock, AR
Primary Contact: John Bowen, Assistant Vice President and Administrator
COO: Greg Stubblefield, Vice President and Administrator
CFO: Robert C. Roberts, Vice President and Chief Financial Officer
CMO: Guy Gardner, M.D., Chief Medical Officer
CIO: David House, Vice President and Chief Information Officer
CHR: Anthony Kendall, Vice President Human Resources
Web address: www.baptist–health.com/locations/accesspoint.
aspx?accessPointID=187
**Control:** Other not–for–profit (including NFP Corporation) **Service:** General
Medical and Surgical

**Staffed Beds: 25 Admissions:** 1327 **Census:** 12 **Outpatient Visits:** 24995
**Total Expense ($000):** 19348 **Personnel:** 173

## ASHDOWN—Little River County

★ **LITTLE RIVER MEMORIAL HOSPITAL (041320)**, 451 West Locke Street,
Zip 71822–3325; tel. 870/898–5011, (Nonreporting) **A**9 10 18
Primary Contact: James Dowell, Administrator and Chief Executive Officer
CFO: Barbra Crow, Chief Financial Officer
CHR: Gina Strickland, Administrative Assistant and Director Human Resources
**Control:** County–Government, nonfederal **Service:** General Medical and Surgical

**Staffed Beds: 25**

## BARLING—Sebastian County

☐ **VISTA HEALTH OF FORT SMITH (044006)**, 10301 Mayo Drive,
Zip 72923–1660; tel. 479/494–5700, (Nonreporting) **A**1 9 10
Primary Contact: Holli Baker, Chief Executive Officer
Web address: www.vistahealthfs.com
**Control:** Corporation, Investor–owned, for–profit **Service:** Psychiatric

**Staffed Beds: 57**

## BATESVILLE—Independence County

★ △ **WHITE RIVER MEDICAL CENTER (040119)**, 1710 Harrison Street,
Zip 72501–7303, Mailing Address: P.O. Box 2197, Zip 72503–2197;
tel. 870/262–1200, (Total facility includes 12 beds in nursing home–type unit) **A**7
9 10 **F**3 8 11 12 13 15 17 20 22 28 29 30 31 34 35 38 40 43 44 50 51 56
57 59 60 64 68 70 72 74 75 76 77 78 79 81 82 85 86 87 90 93 98 99 100
101 103 104 107 108 110 111 114 115 117 119 121 126 127 128 129 130
131 132 135 144 146 147 148 **P**6 **S** White River Health System, Batesville, AR
Primary Contact: Gary Bebow, FACHE, Administrator and Chief Executive Officer
COO: Tammy Gavin, Assistant Administrator and Chief Operating Officer
CFO: Jana Richardson, Chief Financial Officer
CMO: Tom Cummins, M.D., Director Hospitalist Program
CIO: Gary Paxson, Chief Information Officer
CHR: Gary McDonald, Assistant Administrator Human Resources
CNO: Dede Strecker, Chief Nursing Officer
Web address: www.whiteriverhealthsystem.com
**Control:** Other not–for–profit (including NFP Corporation) **Service:** General
Medical and Surgical

**Staffed Beds:** 209 **Admissions:** 8312 **Census:** 118 **Outpatient Visits:**
205588 **Births:** 749 **Total Expense ($000):** 149687 **Payroll Expense**
**($000):** 56628 **Personnel:** 1160

## BENTON—Saline County

☐ **RIVENDELL BEHAVIORAL HEALTH SERVICES OF ARKANSAS (044007)**, 100
Rivendell Drive, Zip 72019–9100; tel. 501/316–1255 **A**1 9 10 **F**29 38 59 75 98
99 100 101 102 105 106 130 132 **P**5 **S** Universal Health Services, Inc., King of
Prussia, PA
Primary Contact: Duane Runyan, Chief Executive Officer and Managing Director
CFO: Mike Rainbolt, Chief Financial Officer
Web address: www.rivendellofarkansas.com
**Control:** Corporation, Investor–owned, for–profit **Service:** Psychiatric

**Staffed Beds:** 77 **Admissions:** 2265 **Census:** 67 **Outpatient Visits:** 26
**Births:** 0 **Total Expense ($000):** 11373 **Payroll Expense ($000):** 5594
**Personnel:** 123

## SALINE MEMORIAL HOSPITAL (040084), 1 Medical Park Drive,

★ **SALINE MEMORIAL HOSPITAL (040084)**, 1 Medical Park Drive,
Zip 72015–3354; tel. 501/776–6000, (Nonreporting) **A**9 10
Primary Contact: Bob Trautman, Chief Executive Officer
CFO: Larry Don Alford, Chief Financial Officer
CIO: Shawn Shuffield, Executive Director Information Services
CHR: Carol Matthews, Director Human Resources
Web address: www.salinememorial.org
**Control:** Other not–for–profit (including NFP Corporation) **Service:** General
Medical and Surgical

**Staffed Beds: 124**

## BERRYVILLE—Carroll County

⊠ **MERCY HOSPITAL BERRYVILLE (041329)**, 214 Carter Street,
Zip 72616–4303; tel. 870/423–3355 **A**1 9 10 18 **F**3 11 15 28 29 30 31 34
35 40 43 45 46 48 50 57 59 61 64 68 75 77 78 79 81 85 93 107 108 114
119 129 130 131 132 133 146 148 **S** Mercy Health, Chesterfield, MO
Primary Contact: Kristy Estrem, FACHE, President
CFO: Sharon Ash, Vice President Finance
CFO: Sherry Clouse Day, Vice President Finance
CFO: Taya Flippo, Director
CHR: Taya James, Director
CNO: Michele Gann, Vice President Patient Services
Web address: www.mercy.net/berryvillear
**Control:** Church–operated, Nongovernment, not–for profit **Service:** General
Medical and Surgical

**Staffed Beds: 25 Admissions:** 781 **Census:** 7 **Outpatient Visits:** 22455
**Births:** 0 **Total Expense ($000):** 21427 **Payroll Expense ($000):** 7969
**Personnel:** 156

## BLYTHEVILLE—Mississippi County

☐ **GREAT RIVER MEDICAL CENTER (040069)**, 1520 North Division Street,
Zip 72315–1448, Mailing Address: P.O. Box 108, Zip 72316–0108;
tel. 870/838–7300 **A**1 9 10 **F**11 13 15 28 29 34 40 45 46 53 57 59 64 68
70 75 76 79 81 82 89 93 97 107 108 111 114 119 120 130 135 146 147
**P**7 **S** Mississippi County Hospital System, Blytheville, AR
Primary Contact: Ralph E. Beaty, Chief Executive Officer
COO: Chris Raymer, R.N., Chief Operating Officer and Chief Nursing Officer
CFO: Phil Norris, Chief Financial Officer
CMO: Jeffrey Hall, M.D., Chief of Staff
CHR: Cheri Blurton, Director Human Resources
**Control:** County–Government, nonfederal **Service:** General Medical and Surgical

**Staffed Beds:** 73 **Admissions:** 1965 **Census:** 14 **Outpatient Visits:** 29717
**Births:** 394 **Total Expense ($000):** 17143 **Payroll Expense ($000):** 8373
**Personnel:** 246

## BOONEVILLE—Logan County

**BOONEVILLE COMMUNITY HOSPITAL (041318)**, 880 West Main Street,
Zip 72927–3443, Mailing Address: P.O. Box 290, Zip 72927–0290;
tel. 479/675–2800 **A**9 10 18 **F**3 8 11 14 15 18 26 27 29 30 34 40 41 43 45
57 59 62 65 68 81 87 92 97 107 127 133 146
Primary Contact: David Hill, President and Chief Executive Officer
CMO: William Daniel, M.D., Chief Medical Officer
CIO: Aaron Albright, Chief Information Officer
CHR: Doris Whitaker, Vice President Human Resources
Web address: www.boonevillehospital.com
**Control:** Other not–for–profit (including NFP Corporation) **Service:** General
Medical and Surgical

**Staffed Beds: 25 Admissions:** 482 **Census:** 4 **Outpatient Visits:** 14563
**Births:** 0 **Total Expense ($000):** 10106 **Payroll Expense ($000):** 3868
**Personnel:** 112

## CALICO ROCK— County

**COMMUNITY MEDICAL CENTER OF IZARD COUNTY (041306)**, 61 Grasse
Street, Zip 72519, Mailing Address: P.O. Box 438, Zip 72519–0438;
tel. 870/297–3726, (Nonreporting) **A**9 10 18
Primary Contact: Ted Topolewski, Administrator
CMO: Bethany Knight, M.D., Chief of Staff
Web address: www.cmcofic.org
**Control:** Other not–for–profit (including NFP Corporation) **Service:** General
Medical and Surgical

**Staffed Beds: 25**

---

**Hospital, Medicare Provider Number, Address, Telephone, Approval, Facility, and Physician Codes, Health Care System**

★ American Hospital Association (AHA) membership
☐ The Joint Commission accreditation ◇ DNV Healthcare Inc. accreditation
○ Healthcare Facilities Accreditation Program
△ Commission on Accreditation of Rehabilitation Facilities (CARF) accreditation

AR

### CAMDEN—Ouachita County

✠ **OUACHITA COUNTY MEDICAL CENTER (040050)**, 638 California Avenue S.W., Zip 71701–4699, Mailing Address: P.O. Box 797, Zip 71711–0797; tel. 870/836–1000 **A**1 9 10 20 **F**3 4 5 7 8 11 13 15 29 31 34 40 41 42 43 46 48 49 56 57 59 62 63 64 65 68 69 70 75 76 77 78 81 85 87 89 93 98 100 102 103 107 108 111 114 115 119 127 129 130 132 133 135 146 148 **P**8
Primary Contact: Peggy Abbott, President and Chief Executive Officer
CFO: Robert Anders, Chief Financial Officer
CIO: Walter Silliman, Chief Information Officer
CHR: Mary Bridges, Director Human Resources
CNO: Diane Isaacs, Director of Nursing
Web address: www.ouachitamedcenter.com
**Control:** Other not–for–profit (including NFP Corporation) **Service:** General Medical and Surgical

**Staffed Beds:** 65 **Admissions:** 2314 **Census:** 24 **Outpatient Visits:** 26583 **Births:** 233 **Total Expense ($000):** 32646 **Payroll Expense ($000):** 15087 **Personnel:** 455

**OUACHITA MEDICAL CENTER** See Ouachita County Medical Center

### CLARKSVILLE—Johnson County

★ **JOHNSON REGIONAL MEDICAL CENTER (040002)**, 1100 East Poplar Street, Zip 72830–4419, Mailing Address: P.O. Box 738, Zip 72830–0738; tel. 479/754–5454 **A**5 9 10 **F**3 7 11 13 15 29 34 35 40 43 45 50 56 57 59 62 64 68 70 75 76 77 79 81 85 90 91 92 93 96 98 103 104 107 108 110 111 114 118 119 129 130 132 147 148
Primary Contact: Larry Morse, Chief Executive Officer and Administrator
COO: Larry Morse, Chief Executive Officer and Administrator
CFO: Edward Anderson, Chief Financial Officer
CIO: Deb Bjorgum, Manager Data Processing
CHR: Maribel Baker, Director Human Resources
CNO: Terri Stumbaugh, R.N., Director Patient Care Services
Web address: www.jrmc.com
**Control:** Other not–for–profit (including NFP Corporation) **Service:** General Medical and Surgical

**Staffed Beds:** 80 **Admissions:** 2884 **Census:** 32 **Outpatient Visits:** 38993 **Births:** 530 **Total Expense ($000):** 31670 **Payroll Expense ($000):** 14145 **Personnel:** 344

### CLINTON—Van Buren County

★ **OZARK HEALTH MEDICAL CENTER (041313)**, Highway 65 South, Zip 72031–9045, Mailing Address: P.O. Box 206, Zip 72031–0206; tel. 501/745–7000, (Nonreporting) **A**10 18
Primary Contact: David Deaton, Chief Executive Officer
CFO: Rhonda Shipp, Chief Financial Officer
CMO: Steve Schoettle, M.D., Chief Medical Staff
CIO: Kathy Fugitt, Chief Information Officer
CHR: Lisa Swofford, Director Administrative Services
Web address: www.ozarkhealthinc.com
**Control:** Other not–for–profit (including NFP Corporation) **Service:** General Medical and Surgical

**Staffed Beds:** 143

### CONWAY—Faulkner County

✠ **CONWAY REGIONAL MEDICAL CENTER (040029)**, 2302 College Avenue, Zip 72034–6297; tel. 501/329–3831 **A**1 9 10 **F**3 8 11 13 15 17 18 20 22 24 28 29 30 31 35 40 43 45 49 50 51 53 56 57 59 60 62 64 70 74 75 76 77 78 79 81 84 85 87 89 93 103 107 108 110 111 115 117 119 120 127 130 131 132 146 147 148 **P**8
Primary Contact: James M. Lambert, FACHE, President and Chief Executive Officer
COO: Alan Finley, Chief Operating Officer
CFO: Steven P. Rose, Chief Financial Officer
CMO: Keith Bell, M.D., Chief of Staff
CHR: Richard Tyler, Corporate Director Human Resources
CNO: Jacquelyn Wilkerson, R.N., Chief Nursing Officer
Web address: www.conwayregional.org
**Control:** Other not–for–profit (including NFP Corporation) **Service:** General Medical and Surgical

**Staffed Beds:** 154 **Admissions:** 8282 **Census:** 90 **Outpatient Visits:** 102362 **Births:** 1836 **Total Expense ($000):** 131861 **Payroll Expense ($000):** 49051 **Personnel:** 1031

**CONWAY REGIONAL REHAB HOSPITAL (043033)**, 2210 Robinson Street, Zip 72034–4943; tel. 501/932–3500, (Nonreporting) **A**9 10
Primary Contact: Sherry Gann, Administrator
Web address: www.conwayregional.org
**Control:** Partnership, Investor–owned, for–profit **Service:** Rehabilitation

**Staffed Beds:** 24

### CROSSETT—Ashley County

★ **ASHLEY COUNTY MEDICAL CENTER (041323)**, 1015 Unity Road, Zip 71635–9443, Mailing Address: P.O. Box 400, Zip 71635–0400; tel. 870/364–4111 **A**9 10 18 **F**3 11 13 15 18 29 30 31 34 35 40 45 50 53 56 57 59 62 64 68 70 75 76 77 78 79 81 85 93 98 100 103 104 105 107 108 110 111 115 119 127 129 130 132 133 148
Primary Contact: Phillip K. Gilmore, FACHE, Chief Executive Officer
CFO: Bill Couch, Chief Financial Officer
CMO: Steve Lynn, M.D., Chief of Staff
CIO: Dan Austin, Manager Data Processing
CHR: Shirley White, Director Human Resources
CNO: Emily Bendinelli, Interim Director of Nurses
Web address: www.acmconline.org
**Control:** Other not–for–profit (including NFP Corporation) **Service:** General Medical and Surgical

**Staffed Beds:** 33 **Admissions:** 971 **Census:** 13 **Outpatient Visits:** 73052 **Births:** 144 **Total Expense ($000):** 24472 **Payroll Expense ($000):** 10597 **Personnel:** 198

### DANVILLE—Yell County

★ **CHAMBERS MEMORIAL HOSPITAL (040011)**, Highway 10 at Detroit, Zip 72833, Mailing Address: P.O. Box 639, Zip 72833–0639; tel. 479/495–2241 **A**9 10 20 **F**3 11 29 35 40 43 57 62 81 93 107 114 119 128 130 133
Primary Contact: Michael Scott Peek, Chief Executive Officer
CMO: Philip Tippin, M.D., Chief of Staff
CIO: Amber Bottoms, Director Medical Records
CHR: Stacey Lane, Executive Assistant Human Resources
CNO: Joeann Bowerman, Director of Nursing Services
Web address: www.chambershospital.com
**Control:** Other not–for–profit (including NFP Corporation) **Service:** General Medical and Surgical

**Staffed Beds:** 41 **Admissions:** 2113 **Census:** 18 **Outpatient Visits:** 23848 **Births:** 0 **Total Expense ($000):** 17012 **Payroll Expense ($000):** 7503 **Personnel:** 184

### DARDANELLE—Yell County

**RIVER VALLEY MEDICAL CENTER (041302)**, 200 North Third Street, Zip 72834–3802, Mailing Address: P.O. Box 578, Zip 72834–0578; tel. 479/229–4677 **A**9 10 18 **F**3 29 40 45 56 57 59 64 65 68 75 81 93 98 103 107 128 129 133 148 **S** Allegiance Health Management, Shreveport, LA
Primary Contact: Christopher L. Bariola, Chief Executive Officer
CMO: William P. Scott, M.D., Chief of Staff
CHR: Kathy Hastin, Administrative Assistant Human Resources
**Control:** Corporation, Investor–owned, for–profit **Service:** General Medical and Surgical

**Staffed Beds:** 35 **Admissions:** 598 **Census:** 13 **Outpatient Visits:** 13633 **Births:** 0 **Total Expense ($000):** 11272 **Payroll Expense ($000):** 4705

### DE QUEEN—Sevier County

**DE QUEEN MEDICAL CENTER (041319)**, 1306 Collin Raye Drive, Zip 71832–2502; tel. 870/584–4111, (Nonreporting) **A**9 10 18
Primary Contact: Jeremy Icenhower, Administrator and Chief Executive Officer
CMO: Darrin Green, M.D., Medical Director
CHR: Teresa Hodges, Assistant Administrator
Web address: www.dequeenhospital.com
**Control:** Corporation, Investor–owned, for–profit **Service:** General Medical and Surgical

**Staffed Beds:** 35

### DE WITT—Arkansas County

★ **DEWITT HOSPITAL (041314)**, Highway 1 and Madison Street, Zip 72042–9481, Mailing Address: P.O. Box 32, Zip 72042–0032; tel. 870/946–3571, (Nonreporting) **A**9 10 18
Primary Contact: Darren Caldwell, Chief Executive Officer
CMO: Stan Burleson, M.D., Chief Medical Staff
CIO: Jonathan Fuchs, Chief Information Officer
CHR: Hannah Hackney, Director Accounting and Human Resources
CNO: Rosie Killion, R.N., Chief Nursing Officer
Web address: www.dhnh.org
**Control:** Other not–for–profit (including NFP Corporation) **Service:** General Medical and Surgical

**Staffed Beds:** 85

*Many Facility Codes have changed. Please refer to the AHA Guide Code Chart.* © 2013 AHA Guide

**DUMAS—Desha County**

**DELTA MEMORIAL HOSPITAL (041326)**, 811 South Highway 65, Zip 71639–3006, Mailing Address: P.O. Box 887, Zip 71639–0887; tel. 870/382–4303 **A**9 10 18 **F**3 11 13 15 29 34 35 40 43 45 50 55 57 59 62 76 81 93 97 107 114 119 120 127 130 133 135 148 **P**6
Primary Contact: Cris Bolin, Chief Executive Officer
CFO: Cris Bolin, Chief Executive Officer
CMO: Thomas Lewellen, D.O., Chief of Staff
CIO: Chris McTigrit, Manager Information Technology
CHR: Doris Fortenberry, Coordinator Human Resources
Web address: www.deltamem.org
**Control:** Other not–for–profit (including NFP Corporation) **Service:** General Medical and Surgical

Staffed Beds: 25 Admissions: 1015 Census: 8 Outpatient Visits: 35187 Births: 108 Total Expense ($000): 16875 Payroll Expense ($000): 6865 Personnel: 202

**EL DORADO—Union County**

⊞ **MEDICAL CENTER OF SOUTH ARKANSAS (040088)**, 700 West Grove Street, Zip 71730–4416, Mailing Address: P.O. Box 1998, Zip 71731–1998; tel. 870/863–2000 **A**1 9 10 **F**3 11 13 15 17 18 20 22 24 26 28 29 31 34 35 40 45 56 57 59 64 70 73 74 75 76 78 79 80 81 82 85 89 90 93 107 108 110 111 114 115 119 130 146 147 148 **P**7 8 **S** Community Health Systems, Inc., Franklin, TN
Primary Contact: Kyle Swift, Chief Executive Officer
COO: Kevin Decker, Assistant Chief Executive Officer
CFO: Mark Henke, Chief Financial Officer
CMO: Ken Gati, M.D., Chief of Staff
CIO: Rachel Scriber, Director of Marketing & Public Relations
CHR: LaKeitha Davis, Director Human Resources
CNO: Keitha Griffith, Chief Nursing Officer
Web address: www.themedcenter.net
**Control:** Corporation, Investor–owned, for–profit **Service:** General Medical and Surgical

Staffed Beds: 116 Admissions: 5135 Census: 46 Outpatient Visits: 56684 Births: 639 Total Expense ($000): 64245 Payroll Expense ($000): 23191 Personnel: 512

**EUREKA SPRINGS—Carroll County**

★ **EUREKA SPRINGS HOSPITAL (041304)**, 24 Norris Street, Zip 72632–3541; tel. 479/253–7400 **A**9 10 18 **F**3 11 15 29 30 34 35 40 44 45 50 57 59 64 75 77 81 85 86 87 90 93 104 107 119 128 130 131 132 133 143 146 148 **S** Allegiance Health Management, Shreveport, LA
Primary Contact: Christopher L. Bariola, Chief Executive Officer
CFO: Sondra Wear, Director Financial Services
CMO: Gregory Kresse, M.D., Chairman Medical Staff
CHR: Jodi Smith, Administrative Assistant Human Resources
Web address: www.eurekaspringshospital.com
**Control:** Corporation, Investor–owned, for–profit **Service:** General Medical and Surgical

Staffed Beds: 15 Admissions: 357 Census: 6 Outpatient Visits: 6096 Births: 0 Total Expense ($000): 6995 Payroll Expense ($000): 2650 Personnel: 76

**FAYETTEVILLE—Washington County**

⊞ **HEALTHSOUTH REHABILITATION HOSPITAL (043032)**, 153 East Monte Painter Drive, Zip 72703–4002; tel. 479/444–2200 **A**1 9 10 **F**3 29 34 57 59 64 75 77 79 90 91 92 93 94 95 96 **P**8 **S** HEALTHSOUTH Corporation, Birmingham, AL
Primary Contact: Jack C. Mitchell, FACHE, Chief Executive Officer
CFO: Robbi Hudson, Chief Financial Officer
CMO: Marty Hurlbut, M.D., Medical Director
CHR: Missy Cole, Director Human Resources
CNO: Miriam Irvin, CNO
Web address: www.healthsouthfayetteville.com
**Control:** Corporation, Investor–owned, for–profit **Service:** Rehabilitation

Staffed Beds: 60 Admissions: 1209 Census: 41 Outpatient Visits: 6821 Births: 0 Total Expense ($000): 12092 Payroll Expense ($000): 6720 Personnel: 140

○ **PHYSICIANS' SPECIALTY HOSPITAL (040152)**, 3875 North Parkview Drive, Zip 72703; tel. 479/571–7070, (Nonreporting) **A**9 10 11
Primary Contact: Russ Greene, Chief Executive Officer
Web address: www.pshfay.com
**Control:** Partnership, Investor–owned, for–profit **Service:** Surgical

Staffed Beds: 21

⊞ **REGENCY HOSPITAL OF NORTHWEST ARKANSAS (042009)**, 1125 North College Avenue, Zip 72703–1908; tel. 479/713–7000, (Includes REGENCY HOSPITAL OF NORTHWEST ARKANSAS – SPRINGDALE, 609 West Maple Avenue, 6th Floor, Springdale, Zip 72764; tel. 479/757–2600; Jerry Alexander, Chief Excutive Officer) **A**1 9 10 **F**1 3 29 68 75 77 85 86 87 130 148 **S** Select Medical Corporation, Mechanicsburg, PA
Primary Contact: Jerry Alexander, Chief Executive Officer
COO: Ruth Jones, Chief Operating Officer
CMO: Gary Templeton, M.D., Medical Director
CHR: Melissa Ross–Cole, Director Human Resources
Web address: www.regencyhospital.com
**Control:** Corporation, Investor–owned, for–profit **Service:** Long–Term Acute Care hospital

Staffed Beds: 50 Admissions: 427 Census: 28 Outpatient Visits: 0 Births: 0 Total Expense ($000): 16647 Payroll Expense ($000): 6002 Personnel: 118

☐ **SPRINGWOODS BEHAVIORAL HEALTH HOSPITAL (044019)**, 1955 West Truckers Drive, Zip 72704–5637; tel. 479/973–6000 **A**1 9 10 **F**5 34 38 56 57 98 99 100 101 102 103 104 105 106 130 132 134 **P**6
Primary Contact: Lee Christenson, Chief Executive Officer
Web address: www.springwoodsbehavioral.com
**Control:** Corporation, Investor–owned, for–profit **Service:** Psychiatric

Staffed Beds: 80 Admissions: 2160 Census: 57 Outpatient Visits: 1900 Births: 0

⊞ **VETERANS HEALTH CARE SYSTEM OF THE OZARKS**, 1100 North College Avenue, Zip 72703–1944; tel. 479/443–4301, (Nonreporting) **A**1 2 5 **S** Department of Veterans Affairs, Washington, DC
Primary Contact: Mark A. Enderele, M.D., Director
COO: Doris B. Cassidy, Associate Director
CMO: Bonnie Baker, M.D., Chief Medical Services
CIO: Michael Gracie, Chief Information Officer
CHR: Kathryn L. Barker, Chief Human Resources Management
Web address: www.fayettevillear.va.gov
**Control:** Veterans Affairs, Government, federal **Service:** General Medical and Surgical

Staffed Beds: 72

☐ **VISTA HEALTH (044004)**, 4253 North Crossover Road, Zip 72703–4596; tel. 479/521–5731 **A**1 9 10 **F**87 98 99 100 101 102 103 104 106 130 132 **P**6
Primary Contact: Connie Borengasser, Chief Executive Officer
CFO: Johnny Lancaster, Chief Financial Officer
CMO: Norman Snyder, M.D., Medical Director
CIO: Margaret Brown, Director Medical Records
CHR: Sandy Stout, Director Human Resources
CNO: Angela Klinikowski, Director of Nursing
Web address: www.vistahealthservices.com
**Control:** Corporation, Investor–owned, for–profit **Service:** Psychiatric

Staffed Beds: 92 Admissions: 2091 Census: 80 Outpatient Visits: 107834 Births: 0 Total Expense ($000): 22339 Payroll Expense ($000): 13948 Personnel: 276

⊞ **WASHINGTON REGIONAL MEDICAL CENTER (040004)**, 3215 North Hills Boulevard, Zip 72703–4424; tel. 479/463–1000 **A**1 9 10 **F**3 9 11 12 13 14 17 18 20 22 24 26 28 29 30 31 32 34 35 39 40 43 45 46 47 48 49 50 51 53 54 56 57 58 59 60 61 62 63 64 65 68 70 72 73 74 75 76 77 78 79 81 82 84 85 86 87 92 93 97 100 102 107 108 110 111 114 115 118 119 125 126 129 130 131 132 135 146 147 148 **P**8
Primary Contact: William L. Bradley, President and Chief Executive Officer
CFO: Dan Eckels, Chief Financial Officer
CMO: David Ratcliff, M.D., Chief Medical Affairs
CIO: Becky Magee, Chief Information Officer
CHR: Steve Percival, Director Human Resources
CNO: Claudia Williams, R.N., CNO
Web address: www.wregional.com
**Control:** Other not–for–profit (including NFP Corporation) **Service:** General Medical and Surgical

Staffed Beds: 270 Admissions: 12474 Census: 134 Outpatient Visits: 159077 Births: 1207 Total Expense ($000): 194260 Payroll Expense ($000): 72157 Personnel: 1821

**AR**

---

**Hospital, Medicare Provider Number, Address, Telephone, Approval, Facility, and Physician Codes, Health Care System**

★ American Hospital Association (AHA) membership
☐ The Joint Commission accreditation
◇ DNV Healthcare Inc. accreditation
○ Healthcare Facilities Accreditation Program
△ Commission on Accreditation of Rehabilitation Facilities (CARF) accreditation

**FORDYCE—Dallas County**

★ **DALLAS COUNTY MEDICAL CENTER (041317)**, 201 Clifton Street, Zip 71742–3099; tel. 870/352–6300, (Nonreporting) **A**9 10 18
Primary Contact: John R. Tucker, FACHE, Administrator and Chief Executive Officer
CFO: Billie Launius, Director Business Finance
CMO: Michael Payne, M.D., Chief of Staff
CHR: Audrey Allen, Coordinator Benefits
Web address: www.dallascountymedicalcenter.com
**Control:** County–Government, nonfederal **Service:** General Medical and Surgical

Staffed Beds: 25

**FORREST CITY—St. Francis County**

✉ **FORREST CITY MEDICAL CENTER (040019)**, 1601 Newcastle Road, Zip 72335–2218; tel. 870/261–0000, (Nonreporting) **A**1 9 10 20 **S** Community Health Systems, Inc., Franklin, TN
Primary Contact: Kevin Decker, Interim Chief Executive Officer
CFO: Stephen Doherty, Chief Financial Officer
CMO: Brandy Davis, M.D., Chief of Staff
CIO: Scott Miller, Director Information Services
CHR: Sherry McLaughlin, Director Human Resources
CNO: Rhonda Nelson, Chief Nursing Officer
Web address: www.forrestcitymedicalcenter.com
**Control:** Corporation, Investor–owned, for–profit **Service:** General Medical and Surgical

Staffed Beds: 70

**FORT SMITH—Sebastian County**

✉ **ADVANCE CARE HOSPITAL OF FORT SMITH (042008)**, 7301 Rogers Avenue, 4th Floor, Zip 72903–4100; tel. 479/314–4900 **A**1 9 10 **F**1 3 29 30 68 75 77 82 84 85 91 130 148 **S** Dubuis Health System, Houston, TX
Primary Contact: Keith Rogers, Interim Administrator
CFO: Paul Veillon, CPA, Chief Financial Officer
Web address: www.dubuis.org/AdvanceCareHospitalofFortSmith
**Control:** Church–operated, Nongovernment, not–for profit **Service:** Long–Term Acute Care hospital

Staffed Beds: 25 Admissions: 248 Census: 19 Outpatient Visits: 0 Births: 0 Total Expense ($000): 8263 Payroll Expense ($000): 3231 Personnel: 59

✉ **HEALTHSOUTH REHABILITATION HOSPITAL OF FORT SMITH (043028)**, 1401 South J Street, Zip 72901–5155; tel. 479/785–3300 **A**1 9 10 **F**28 29 34 35 77 90 91 93 94 95 96 129 131 132 **S** HEALTHSOUTH Corporation, Birmingham, AL
Primary Contact: Ryan Cassedy, Chief Executive Officer
CFO: Brenda Forbes, Controller
CMO: Cygnet Schroeder, D.O., Medical Director
CIO: Donna England, Director Medical Records
CHR: S. Janette Daniels, Director Human Resources
CNO: Jacqueline Floyd, Chief Nursing Officer
Web address: www.healthsouthfortsmith.com
**Control:** Corporation, Investor–owned, for–profit **Service:** Rehabilitation

Staffed Beds: 60 Admissions: 1243 Census: 39 Outpatient Visits: 6170 Births: 0 Total Expense ($000): 12336 Payroll Expense ($000): 7045

✉ △ **MERCY HOSPITAL FORT SMITH (040062)**, 7301 Rogers Avenue, Zip 72903–4189, Mailing Address: P.O. Box 17000, Zip 72917–7000; tel. 479/314–6000 **A**1 2 5 7 9 10 **F**3 11 12 13 15 17 18 20 22 24 26 28 29 30 31 32 34 35 40 42 43 44 49 53 57 58 59 61 62 63 64 65 68 70 71 72 73 74 75 76 77 78 79 81 82 83 84 85 86 87 89 90 93 96 102 107 108 110 111 114 115 119 120 121 123 124 126 129 130 135 143 146 147 148 **P**6 8 **S** Mercy Health, Chesterfield, MO
Primary Contact: Ryan Gehrig, President
COO: Brent Hubbard, Chief Operating Officer
CFO: Greta Wilcher, Senior Vice President and Chief Financial Officer
CHR: Tim Murphy, Vice President, Human Resources
Web address: www.stedwardmercy.com
**Control:** Church–operated, Nongovernment, not–for profit **Service:** General Medical and Surgical

Staffed Beds: 383 Admissions: 13809 Census: 200 Outpatient Visits: 228098 Births: 2354 Total Expense ($000): 221851 Payroll Expense ($000): 66903 Personnel: 1509

✉ **SELECT SPECIALTY HOSPITAL–FORT SMITH (042006)**, 1001 Towson Avenue, 6 Central, Zip 72901–4921; tel. 479/441–3960 **A**1 9 10 **F**1 3 29 34 45 46 56 57 74 75 78 79 94 148 **S** Select Medical Corporation, Mechanicsburg, PA
Primary Contact: Cindy McLain, Chief Executive Officer
Web address: www.selectspecialtyhospitals.com/company/locations/fortsmith.aspx
**Control:** Corporation, Investor–owned, for–profit **Service:** Long–Term Acute Care hospital

Staffed Beds: 34 Admissions: 419 Census: 29 Outpatient Visits: 0 Births: 0 Total Expense ($000): 12768 Payroll Expense ($000): 4180 Personnel: 77

☐ **SPARKS REGIONAL MEDICAL CENTER (040055)**, 100 Towson Avenue, Zip 72901–2632, Mailing Address: P.O. Box 17006, Zip 72917–7006; tel. 479/441–4000 **A**1 5 6 9 10 **F**3 8 12 13 15 17 18 20 22 24 26 28 29 30 31 34 35 40 45 46 47 48 49 50 51 53 54 56 58 59 60 62 64 67 70 72 74 75 76 77 78 79 81 82 85 86 87 89 93 97 98 103 107 108 110 111 112 114 115 117 119 120 121 122 124 126 127 129 130 144 146 147 148 **P**8 **S** Health Management Associates, Naples, FL
Primary Contact: Gary J. Blan, FACHE, Market Chief Executive Officer
COO: Jeremy Drinkwitz, Chief Operating Officer
CFO: Richard Boone, Chief Financial Officer
CMO: Katherine Irish–Clardy, M.D., Chief Medical Officer
CIO: Tom Sallis, Director Information Systems
CHR: Robert Freeman, Director Human Resources
CNO: Cindy Slaydon, Chief Nursing Executive
Web address: www.sparks.org
**Control:** Individual, Investor–owned, for–profit **Service:** General Medical and Surgical

Staffed Beds: 303 Admissions: 15736 Census: 211 Outpatient Visits: 162742 Births: 1168 Total Expense ($000): 197159 Payroll Expense ($000): 65172 Personnel: 1620

**GRAVETTE—Benton County**

**OZARKS COMMUNITY HOSPITAL (041331)**, 1101 Jackson Street S.W., Zip 72736–9121; tel. 479/787–5291 **A**9 10 18 **F**29 40 44 45 54 56 57 59 65 75 82 85 87 89 93 96 103 104 107 111 114 119 128 129 130 133 143 **P**6
Primary Contact: Paul Taylor, Administrator
Web address: www.ochonline.com/
**Control:** Corporation, Investor–owned, for–profit **Service:** General Medical and Surgical

Staffed Beds: 15 Admissions: 611 Census: 6 Outpatient Visits: 11788 Births: 0 Total Expense ($000): 11638 Payroll Expense ($000): 5321 Personnel: 153

**HARRISON—Boone County**

★ **NORTH ARKANSAS REGIONAL MEDICAL CENTER (040017)**, 620 North Main Street, Zip 72601–2911; tel. 870/414–4000 **A**9 10 **F**3 7 8 11 13 14 15 17 18 28 29 30 31 34 35 40 41 48 50 51 53 56 57 59 62 63 64 65 68 70 75 76 77 78 79 81 85 86 87 89 92 93 97 103 107 108 110 111 114 115 116 118 119 120 121 123 127 129 130 131 132 146 147 148 **P**8
Primary Contact: Vincent Leist, President and Chief Executive Officer
COO: Richard McBryde, Senior Vice President and Chief Operating Officer
CFO: Debbie Henry, Vice President Financial Services
CIO: Kent Kimes, Director Information Systems
CHR: Linda Dickey Melton, Vice President Human Resources
Web address: www.narmc.com
**Control:** Other not–for–profit (including NFP Corporation) **Service:** General Medical and Surgical

Staffed Beds: 122 Admissions: 4368 Census: 39 Outpatient Visits: 127489 Births: 761 Total Expense ($000): 71581 Payroll Expense ($000): 31022 Personnel: 663

**HEBER SPRINGS—Cleburne County**

✉ **BAPTIST HEALTH MEDICAL CENTER–HEBER SPRINGS (041312)**, 1800 Bypass Road, Zip 72543–9135; tel. 501/887–3000 **A**1 9 10 18 **F**3 8 11 15 28 29 30 31 34 35 36 40 43 45 48 50 57 59 64 68 74 75 77 78 79 81 85 93 102 107 110 111 115 117 119 127 129 131 132 133 134 135 143 146 **S** Baptist Health, Little Rock, AR
Primary Contact: Edward L. Lacy, FACHE, Vice President and Administrator
Web address: www.baptist–health.com/maps–directions/bhmc–heber–springs
**Control:** Other not–for–profit (including NFP Corporation) **Service:** General Medical and Surgical

Staffed Beds: 25 Admissions: 802 Census: 7 Outpatient Visits: 30660 Births: 0 Total Expense ($000): 18474 Payroll Expense ($000): 7003 Personnel: 154

**HELENA—Phillips County**

✉ **HELENA REGIONAL MEDICAL CENTER (040085)**, 1801 Martin Luther King Drive, Zip 72342, Mailing Address: P.O. Box 788, Zip 72342–0788; tel. 870/338–5800, (Nonreporting) **A**1 9 10 20 **S** Community Health Systems, Inc., Franklin, TN
Primary Contact: Buddy Daniels, Chief Executive Officer
CFO: Amy Rice, Chief Financial Officer
CIO: Robert White, Director Information Technology
CHR: Juril Fonzie, Director Human Resources
CNO: Shanna Pryor, R.N., Chief Nursing Officer
Web address: www.helenarmc.com
**Control:** Corporation, Investor–owned, for–profit **Service:** General Medical and Surgical

Staffed Beds: 100

**HOPE—Hempstead County**

**WADLEY REGIONAL MEDICAL CENTER AT HOPE** See

**AR**

## HOT SPRINGS—Garland County

☐ △ **NATIONAL PARK MEDICAL CENTER (040078)**, 1910 Malvern Avenue, Zip 71901–7799; tel. 501/321–1000 **A**1 7 9 10 19 **F**3 11 13 15 17 18 20 22 24 28 29 30 31 34 35 40 45 46 47 49 56 57 59 62 64 70 73 74 75 76 78 79 81 85 87 89 90 93 98 103 109 110 111 114 119 124 128 129 130 131 132 143 146 147 148 **P**1 **S** Capella Healthcare, Franklin, TN
Primary Contact: Jerry D. Mabry, FACHE, Chief Executive Officer
COO: Brian Bell, Associate Administrator and Chief Operating Officer
CFO: Robbie Pettey, Chief Financial Officer
CMO: David Desoto, M.D., Chief of Staff
CIO: Thomas Elmore, Director Information System
CHR: Sandra Culliver, Director Human Resources
Web address: www.nationalparkmedical.com
**Control:** Corporation, Investor–owned, for–profit **Service:** General Medical and Surgical

**Staffed Beds:** 191 **Admissions:** 6325 **Census:** 91 **Outpatient Visits:** 53335 **Births:** 601 **Total Expense ($000):** 66978 **Payroll Expense ($000):** 25386 **Personnel:** 649

## HOT SPRINGS NATIONAL PARK—Garland County

☒ **ADVANCE CARE HOSPITAL (042004)**, 300 Werner Street, 3rd Floor East, Zip 71913–6406; tel. 501/609–4300 **A**1 9 10 **F**1 3 29 30 45 68 77 79 85 87 118 130 135 148 **P**5 **S** Dubuis Health System, Houston, TX
Primary Contact: Keith Rogers, Administrator
CFO: Paul Veillon, CPA, Chief Financial Officer
CIO: David Cook, Manager Information Systems
CHR: Pearl Mohnkern, Vice President Human Resources
Web address: www.dubuis.org/AdvanceCareHospitalofHotSprings
**Control:** Church–operated, Nongovernment, not–for profit **Service:** Long–Term Acute Care hospital

**Staffed Beds:** 26 **Admissions:** 169 **Census:** 13 **Outpatient Visits:** 0 **Births:** 0 **Total Expense ($000):** 5880 **Payroll Expense ($000):** 2274 **Personnel:** 51

★ **LEVI HOSPITAL (040132)**, 300 Prospect Avenue, Zip 71901–4097; tel. 501/624–1281 **A**9 10 **F**40 57 59 64 93 98 102 103 104 130 131 132
Primary Contact: Patrick G. McCabe, Jr., FACHE, President and Chief Executive Officer
CFO: Charles Oswalt, Vice President and Chief Financial Officer
CMO: P. Ross Bandy, M.D., Chief Medical Officer and Chief of Staff
CIO: Charles Oswalt, Vice President, CFO and Compliane Officer
CHR: Susan Kramer, Director of Human Resources
CNO: Steven Boyd, R.N., Nurse Executive
Web address: www.levihospital.com
**Control:** Other not–for–profit (including NFP Corporation) **Service:** Psychiatric

**Staffed Beds:** 49 **Admissions:** 1470 **Census:** 24 **Outpatient Visits:** 14298 **Births:** 0 **Total Expense ($000):** 8007 **Payroll Expense ($000):** 4685 **Personnel:** 114

☒ **MERCY HOSPITAL HOT SPRINGS (040026)**, 300 Werner Street, Zip 71913–6406, Mailing Address: P.O. Box 29001, Zip 71903–9001; tel. 501/622–1000, (Includes HEALTHPARK HOSPITAL, 1636 Higdon Ferry Road, Zip 71913; tel. 501/520–2000), (Nonreporting) **A**1 2 9 10 **S** Mercy Health, Chesterfield, MO
Primary Contact: Kim Day, Interim President
COO: Andrew Runge, Chief Operating Officer
CFO: Sarah Bradey, Vice President Finance
CIO: Bill Perry, Director Information Systems
CHR: Jed M. Liuzza, Vice President Human Resources
Web address: www.saintjosephs.com
**Control:** Church–operated, Nongovernment, not–for profit **Service:** General Medical and Surgical

**Staffed Beds:** 282

## JACKSONVILLE—Pulaski County

**ALLEGIANCE SPECIALTY HOSPITAL OF LITTLE ROCK** See Cornerstone Hospital of North Little Rock

**CORNERSTONE HOSPITAL OF NORTH LITTLE ROCK (042010)**, (Formerly Allegiance Specialty Hospital of Little Rock), 1400 Braden Street, Zip 72076–3721; tel. 501/985–7026, (Nonreporting) **A**9 10 **S** Cornerstone Healthcare Group, Dallas, TX
Primary Contact: Paul E. Qualls, Jr., Interim Chief Executive Officer
CHR: Jennifer Rowen, Director Human Resources
CNO: Diane Cook, Chief Nursing Officer
Web address: www.chghospitals.com/littlerock/
**Control:** Corporation, Investor–owned, for–profit **Service:** Long–Term Acute Care hospital

**Staffed Beds:** 40

★ **NORTH METRO MEDICAL CENTER (040074)**, 1400 West Braden Street, Zip 72076–3788; tel. 501/985–7000, (Nonreporting) **A**9 10 **S** Allegiance Health Management, Shreveport, LA
Primary Contact: Cindy Stafford, Chief Executive Officer
CFO: Lynn Muller, Chief Financial Officer
CMO: Ann Layton, M.D., Chief of Staff
CHR: Jane Rockwell, Director Support Services
Web address: www.northmetromed.com
**Control:** Other not–for–profit (including NFP Corporation) **Service:** General Medical and Surgical

**Staffed Beds:** 76

## JONESBORO—Craighead County

☒ **HEALTHSOUTH REHABILITATION HOSPITAL OF JONESBORO (043029)**, 1201 Fleming Avenue, Zip 72401–4311, Mailing Address: P.O. Box 1680, Zip 72403–1680; tel. 870/932–0440, (Nonreporting) **A**1 9 10 **S** HEALTHSOUTH Corporation, Birmingham, AL
Primary Contact: Donna Harris, Chief Executive Officer
CFO: Allan Jones, Controller
CMO: Terence Braden, III, D.O., Medical Director
CHR: Tammy Barley, Director Human Resources
CHR: Tammy Barley, Manager Human Resources
Web address: www.healthsouthjonesboro.com
**Control:** Corporation, Investor–owned, for–profit **Service:** Rehabilitation

**Staffed Beds:** 67

☒ **NEA BAPTIST MEMORIAL HOSPITAL (040118)**, 3024 Stadium Boulevard, Zip 72401–7415; tel. 870/972–7000 **A**1 9 10 **F**3 11 12 13 17 18 20 22 24 28 29 30 31 34 39 40 45 46 48 49 57 59 60 74 75 76 77 78 79 81 82 84 85 86 87 93 107 108 111 115 118 119 124 130 135 146 148 **P**8 **S** Baptist Memorial Health Care Corporation, Memphis, TN
Primary Contact: Brad Parsons, Administrator and Chief Executive Officer
CFO: David Webb, Chief Financial Officer
CMO: Stephen Woodruff, M.D., Chief Medical Officer
CHR: James Keller, Director Human Resources
Web address: www.neabaptist.com
**Control:** Other not–for–profit (including NFP Corporation) **Service:** General Medical and Surgical

**Staffed Beds:** 100 **Admissions:** 6308 **Census:** 67 **Outpatient Visits:** 44192 **Births:** 743 **Total Expense ($000):** 86461 **Payroll Expense ($000):** 29125 **Personnel:** 630

☒ **ST. BERNARDS MEDICAL CENTER (040020)**, 225 East Jackson Avenue, Zip 72401–3119; tel. 870/972–4429, (Total facility includes 26 beds in nursing home–type unit) **A**1 9 10 19 **F**2 3 5 11 12 13 15 17 18 20 22 24 26 28 29 30 31 32 34 35 37 38 40 43 45 46 48 49 50 51 53 54 55 56 57 58 59 60 61 62 63 64 68 69 70 71 72 74 75 76 77 78 79 81 82 84 85 86 87 89 92 93 96 98 99 100 101 102 103 104 105 107 108 110 111 114 115 116 117 119 120 121 123 124 126 128 129 130 131 132 135 136 141 144 145 146 147 148 **P**6 8
Primary Contact: Chris B. Barber, FACHE, President and Chief Executive Officer
COO: Michael K. Givens, FACHE, Administrator
CFO: Harry Hutchison, Vice President Fiscal Services
CMO: David Pyle, M.D., Vice President Medical Affairs
CIO: Charles Pigg, Chief Information Officer
CHR: Jacque Hurd, Vice President Human Resources
CNO: Brenda Million, R.N., Vice President and Chief Nursing Officer
Web address: www.stbernards.info
**Control:** Church–operated, Nongovernment, not–for profit **Service:** General Medical and Surgical

**Staffed Beds:** 380 **Admissions:** 17474 **Census:** 210 **Outpatient Visits:** 223321 **Births:** 1336 **Total Expense ($000):** 233276 **Payroll Expense ($000):** 78110 **Personnel:** 1992

**SURGICAL HOSPITAL OF JONESBORO**, 909 Enterprise Drive, Zip 72401–9201; tel. 870/336–1100, (Nonreporting)
Primary Contact: Nate Miller, Chief Executive Officer
CFO: Carla Harral, Chief Financial Officer
CMO: Jason Brandt, M.D., Medical Director
CHR: Angie Stover, Administrative Assistant
Web address: www.tshj.com
**Control:** Corporation, Investor–owned, for–profit **Service:** Surgical

**Staffed Beds:** 12

---

**Hospital, Medicare Provider Number, Address, Telephone, Approval, Facility, and Physician Codes, Health Care System**

★ American Hospital Association (AHA) membership
☐ The Joint Commission accreditation
◇ DNV Healthcare Inc. accreditation
○ Healthcare Facilities Accreditation Program
△ Commission on Accreditation of Rehabilitation Facilities (CARF) accreditation

**AR**

## LAKE VILLAGE—Chicot County

★ **CHICOT MEMORIAL MEDICAL CENTER (041328)**, 2729 Highway 65 and 82 South, Zip 71653; tel. 870/265–5351 **A**9 10 18 **F**3 7 11 13 15 18 29 34 35 36 40 43 45 53 57 59 62 64 71 75 76 77 81 85 87 93 107 111 114 119 130 132 133 146 148
Primary Contact: David Mantz, Chief Executive Officer
CFO: Vicki Allen, Chief Financial Officer
CMO: Michael Bradley Mayfield, M.D., Chief of Staff
CIO: David Andrews, Manager Information Systems
CHR: Bobbie Ivey, Director Human Resources
CNO: Eric Selby, R.N., Chief Nursing Officer
Web address: www.chicotmemorial.com
**Control:** Other not–for–profit (including NFP Corporation) **Service:** General Medical and Surgical

> **Staffed Beds:** 25 **Admissions:** 1164 **Census:** 13 **Outpatient Visits:** 14953 **Births:** 110 **Total Expense ($000):** 15180 **Payroll Expense ($000):** 7458 **Personnel:** 153

**SOUTHEAST REHABILITATION HOSPITAL (043034)**, 2729–A Highway 65 and 82 South, Zip 71653; tel. 870/265–4333, (Nonreporting) **A**10
Primary Contact: Stacy Noble, Administrator
Web address: www.lakevillageclinic.com/SErehabhosp.html
**Control:** Partnership, Investor–owned, for–profit **Service:** Rehabilitation

> **Staffed Beds:** 15

## LITTLE ROCK—Pulaski County

⊠ **ARKANSAS CHILDREN'S HOSPITAL (043300)**, 1 Children's Way, Zip 72202–3500; tel. 501/364–1100 **A**1 3 5 8 9 10 **F**3 7 8 9 11 12 16 17 19 21 23 25 27 28 29 30 31 32 34 35 38 39 40 41 43 45 46 48 50 53 55 57 58 59 60 61 64 68 71 72 74 75 77 78 79 81 82 84 85 86 87 88 89 91 93 94 97 99 100 102 107 108 111 114 115 116 117 118 119 126 129 130 131 132 135 136 137 138 143 146 **P**1
Primary Contact: Marcella Doderer, President and Chief Executive Officer
COO: David Berry, Senior Vice President and Chief Operating Officer
CFO: Gena Wingfield, Senior Vice President and Chief Financial Officer
CMO: W. Robert Morrow, M.D., Senior Vice President and Medical Director
CIO: Darrell Leonhardt, Senior Vice President Information Systems
CHR: Andree Trosclair, Vice President Human Resources
CNO: Lori J. Brown, MSN, Senior Vice President and Chief Nursing Officer
Web address: www.archildrens.org
**Control:** Other not–for–profit (including NFP Corporation) **Service:** Children's general

> **Staffed Beds:** 306 **Admissions:** 14493 **Census:** 217 **Outpatient Visits:** 332470 **Births:** 0 **Total Expense ($000):** 453378 **Payroll Expense ($000):** 194211 **Personnel:** 3401

☐ **ARKANSAS HEART HOSPITAL (040134)**, 1701 South Shackleford Road, Zip 72211–4335; tel. 501/219–7000, (Nonreporting) **A**1 3 5 9 10
Primary Contact: Bruce Murphy, M.D., President and Chief Executive Officer
CHR: Brent Davis, Human Resources Team Leader
Web address: www.arheart.com
**Control:** Partnership, Investor–owned, for–profit **Service:** Heart

> **Staffed Beds:** 112

☐ **ARKANSAS STATE HOSPITAL (044011)**, 305 South Palm Street, Zip 72205–5432; tel. 501/686–9000 **A**1 3 5 9 10 **F**3 29 30 53 98 99 103 143 **P**6
Primary Contact: Steve Henson, Interim Chief Executive Officer
CFO: Jo Ann McDade, Assistant Administrator Finance
CMO: Albert Kittrell, M.D., Medical Director
CIO: Linda Jackson, Director Management Information Systems
CHR: Tracy Pearsall, Director Human Resources
Web address: www.state.ar.us/dhs/dmhs
**Control:** State–Government, nonfederal **Service:** Psychiatric

> **Staffed Beds:** 222 **Admissions:** 574 **Census:** 209 **Outpatient Visits:** 0 **Births:** 0 **Total Expense ($000):** 51609 **Payroll Expense ($000):** 25736

★ **BAPTIST HEALTH EXTENDED CARE HOSPITAL (042012)**, 9601 Interstate 630, Exit 7, 10th Floor, Zip 72205–7202; tel. 501/202–1070 **A**9 10 **F**1 3 29 31 77 87 130 148 **S** Baptist Health, Little Rock, AR
Primary Contact: Mike Perkins, Vice President and Administrator
CFO: Robert C. Roberts, Vice President
CIO: David House, Vice President
CHR: Anthony Kendall, Vice President Human Resources
CNO: Diane Smith, Chief Nursing Officer
Web address: www.baptist–health.com/maps–directions/bh_extended_care/default.aspx
**Control:** Other not–for–profit (including NFP Corporation) **Service:** Long–Term Acute Care hospital

> **Staffed Beds:** 37 **Admissions:** 278 **Census:** 23 **Outpatient Visits:** 0 **Births:** 0 **Total Expense ($000):** 10827 **Payroll Expense ($000):** 4836 **Personnel:** 86

⊠ **BAPTIST HEALTH MEDICAL CENTER–LITTLE ROCK (040114)**, 9601 Interstate 630, Exit 7, Zip 72205–7299; tel. 501/202–2000 **A**1 3 5 6 9 10 **F**3 4 5 7 8 11 12 13 15 17 18 20 22 24 26 28 29 30 31 32 34 35 36 37 38 40 43 44 45 49 50 54 56 57 58 59 64 65 67 68 70 72 73 74 75 76 77 78 79 81 82 85 86 87 89 93 98 99 100 101 102 103 104 107 108 110 111 114 118 119 126 128 129 130 131 132 134 135 137 138 143 144 146 147 148 **S** Baptist Health, Little Rock, AR
Primary Contact: Greg Crain, FACHE, Vice President and Administrator
CFO: Robert C. Roberts, Senior Vice President Financial Services
CMO: Anthony Bennett, M.D., Chief Clinical Affairs
CIO: David House, Vice President and Chief Information Officer
CHR: Anthony Kendall, Vice President Human Resources
CNO: Jill Massiet, R.N., Vice President Patient Care
Web address: www.baptist–health.org/maps–directions/bhmc–lr
**Control:** Other not–for–profit (including NFP Corporation) **Service:** General Medical and Surgical

> **Staffed Beds:** 687 **Admissions:** 25769 **Census:** 448 **Outpatient Visits:** 81173 **Births:** 3245 **Total Expense ($000):** 428290 **Payroll Expense ($000):** 145618 **Personnel:** 2614

⊠ △ **BAPTIST HEALTH REHABILITATION INSTITUTE (043026)**, 9601 Interstate 630, Exit 7, Zip 72205–7202; tel. 501/202–7000 **A**1 3 5 7 9 10 **F**11 29 30 35 50 53 64 75 79 87 90 91 93 95 96 130 132 143 146 **P**8 **S** Baptist Health, Little Rock, AR
Primary Contact: Lee Gentry, FACHE, Vice President and Administrator
CFO: Robert C. Roberts, Senior Vice President
CIO: David House, Vice President and Chief Information Officer
CHR: Anthony Kendall, Vice President Human Resources
Web address: www.baptist–health.com/locations/accesspoint.aspx?accessPointID=202
**Control:** Other not–for–profit (including NFP Corporation) **Service:** Rehabilitation

> **Staffed Beds:** 100 **Admissions:** 1787 **Census:** 59 **Outpatient Visits:** 134848 **Births:** 0 **Total Expense ($000):** 31801 **Payroll Expense ($000):** 15438 **Personnel:** 257

⊠ △ **CENTRAL ARKANSAS VETERANS HEALTHCARE SYSTEM**, 4300 West Seventh Street, Zip 72205–5484; tel. 501/257–1000, (Includes NORTH LITTLE ROCK DIVISION, 2200 Fort Roots Drive, North Little Rock, Zip 72114–1706; tel. 501/661–1202), (Total facility includes 152 beds in nursing home–type unit) **A**1 2 3 5 7 8 **F**2 3 5 6 15 17 18 20 22 26 28 29 30 31 34 35 38 39 40 45 46 48 49 50 56 57 58 59 60 61 62 64 65 68 70 74 75 77 78 79 80 81 82 83 84 85 86 87 90 91 92 93 94 96 97 98 100 101 102 103 104 105 106 107 108 110 111 114 115 118 119 127 128 129 130 132 135 143 144 145 146 147 148 **P**1 6 **S** Department of Veterans Affairs, Washington, DC
Primary Contact: Michael R. Winn, Director
CFO: Debby Felton, Chief Financial Officer
CMO: Nicholas P. Lang, M.D., Chief of Staff
CIO: Jim Hall, Acting Chief Information Officer
CHR: Daniel Peterson, Chief Human Resource Management Service
Web address: www.littlerock.va.gov/
**Control:** Veterans Affairs, Government, federal **Service:** General Medical and Surgical

> **Staffed Beds:** 551 **Admissions:** 11440 **Census:** 326 **Outpatient Visits:** 807148 **Births:** 0 **Total Expense ($000):** 581462 **Payroll Expense ($000):** 238366 **Personnel:** 3398

☐ **PINNACLE POINTE HOSPITAL (044013)**, 11501 Financial Center Parkway, Zip 72211–3715; tel. 501/223–3322 **A**1 9 10 **F**29 34 98 99 100 101 102 104 106 130 **S** Universal Health Services, Inc., King of Prussia, PA
Primary Contact: Thomas Stormanns, Chief Executive Officer
CMO: David Streett, M.D., Medical Director
CHR: James L. Howe, Chief Employee Relations
Web address: www.pinnaclepointehospital.com
**Control:** Corporation, Investor–owned, for–profit **Service:** Children's hospital psychiatric

> **Staffed Beds:** 124 **Admissions:** 2582 **Census:** 103 **Outpatient Visits:** 348588 **Births:** 0 **Total Expense ($000):** 21436 **Payroll Expense ($000):** 12962 **Personnel:** 172

⊠ **SELECT SPECIALTY HOSPITAL–LITTLE ROCK (042000)**, 2 St. Vincent Circle, 6th Floor, Zip 72205; tel. 501/661–4198 **A**1 9 10 **F**1 3 29 74 75 77 78 79 82 85 86 91 97 100 130 148 **S** Select Medical Corporation, Mechanicsburg, PA
Primary Contact: Barry Ewy, Chief Executive Officer
Web address: www.selectspecialtyhospitals.com/company/locations/littlerock.aspx
**Control:** Corporation, Investor–owned, for–profit **Service:** Long–Term Acute Care hospital

> **Staffed Beds:** 43 **Admissions:** 406 **Census:** 32 **Outpatient Visits:** 0 **Births:** 0 **Total Expense ($000):** 15713 **Payroll Expense ($000):** 5758 **Personnel:** 136

*Many Facility Codes have changed. Please refer to the AHA Guide Code Chart.* © 2013 AHA Guide

⊠ **ST. VINCENT INFIRMARY MEDICAL CENTER (040007)**, Two St. Vincent Circle, Zip 72205–5499; tel. 501/552–3000, (Includes ST. VINCENT DOCTORS HOSPITAL, 6101 West Capitol, Zip 72205–5331; tel. 501/552–6000) **A**1 3 9 10 **F**3 11 13 17 18 20 22 24 26 28 29 30 31 34 35 37 40 43 44 45 50 51 53 54 56 57 59 60 61 64 70 72 74 75 76 77 78 79 81 82 84 85 86 87 91 92 93 97 98 107 108 109 110 111 114 115 116 117 118 119 124 126 129 130 132 135 143 146 147 148 **P**1 **S** Catholic Health Initiatives, Englewood, CO
Primary Contact: Peter D. Banko, FACHE, President and Chief Executive Officer
COO: Bob Lyons, Senior Vice President and Chief Operating Officer
CFO: Matthew Cox, Senior Vice President and Chief Financial Officer
CMO: James Tanner, M.D., Vice President and Chief Medical Officer
CIO: David Peterson, Regional Chief Information Officer
CHR: Darrick Paul, Vice President and Chief People Officer
Web address: www.stvincenthealth.com
**Control:** Church–operated, Nongovernment, not–for profit **Service:** General Medical and Surgical

**Staffed Beds:** 447 **Admissions:** 20393 **Census:** 282 **Outpatient Visits:** 121189 **Births:** 1654 **Total Expense ($000):** 319262 **Payroll Expense ($000):** 121924 **Personnel:** 2121

⊠ **UAMS MEDICAL CENTER (040016)**, 4301 West Markham Street, Zip 72205–7102; tel. 501/686–7000 **A**1 3 5 8 9 10 13 **F**3 11 12 13 14 15 17 18 20 22 24 26 29 30 31 40 43 44 45 46 47 48 49 50 53 54 55 56 57 58 59 60 61 64 68 70 72 73 74 75 76 77 78 79 80 81 82 84 85 86 87 91 92 93 94 96 97 98 99 100 101 102 103 104 107 108 110 111 114 115 118 119 126 129 130 131 132 136 138 139 141 142 145 146 147 **P**6
Primary Contact: Roxane A. Townsend, M.D., Chief Executive Officer
COO: Melissa Fontaine, Chief Operating Officer
CFO: William Bowes, Chief Financial Officer
CMO: Nicholas P. Lang, M.D., Chief Medical Officer
CIO: David L. Miller, Chief Information Officer
CHR: Hosea Long, Director Human Resources
CNO: Mary Helen Forrest, R.N., Chief Nursing Officer
Web address: www.uams.edu/medcenter
**Control:** State–Government, nonfederal **Service:** General Medical and Surgical

**Staffed Beds:** 438 **Admissions:** 21544 **Census:** 371 **Outpatient Visits:** 427905 **Births:** 2653 **Total Expense ($000):** 572141 **Payroll Expense ($000):** 183317 **Personnel:** 3649

**MAGNOLIA—Columbia County**

★ **MAGNOLIA REGIONAL MEDICAL CENTER (040067)**, 101 Hospital Drive, Zip 71753–2415, Mailing Address: P.O. Box 629, Zip 71754–0629; tel. 870/235–3000 **A**9 10 20 **F**3 15 29 31 34 35 40 43 57 59 62 64 70 75 76 77 81 86 87 91 93 97 107 108 110 111 115 119 129 130 132 133 146 147 148 **S** CHRISTUS Health, Irving, TX
Primary Contact: Margaret M. West, MS, Chief Executive Officer
CMO: John Alexander, Jr., M.D., Chief of Staff
CHR: Shawnee Hicks, Director Human Resources
Web address: www.magnoliahospital.org
**Control:** City–Government, nonfederal **Service:** General Medical and Surgical

**Staffed Beds:** 49 **Admissions:** 1650 **Census:** 16 **Outpatient Visits:** 39705 **Births:** 236 **Total Expense ($000):** 20738 **Personnel:** 241

**MALVERN—Hot Spring County**

★ **H.S.C. MEDICAL CENTER (040076)**, 1001 Schneider Drive, Zip 72104–4828; tel. 501/332–1000 **A**9 10 **F**3 11 15 17 18 29 34 40 43 45 57 59 62 70 75 81 98 106 107 110 111 115 119 129 130 146 148
Primary Contact: Sheila Williams, Chief Executive Officer
CHR: Kelli Hopkins, Director Human Resources
Web address: www.hscmc.org
**Control:** Other not–for–profit (including NFP Corporation) **Service:** General Medical and Surgical

**Staffed Beds:** 72 **Admissions:** 1846 **Census:** 19 **Outpatient Visits:** 28907 **Births:** 0 **Total Expense ($000):** 19564 **Payroll Expense ($000):** 9703 **Personnel:** 300

**MAUMELLE—Pulaski County**

☐ **METHODIST BEHAVIORAL HOSPITAL OF ARKANSAS (044017)**, 1601 Murphy Drive, Zip 72113–6187; tel. 501/803–3388 **A**1 9 10 **F**30 32 38 50 54 64 75 86 87 98 99 102 104 106 130 **P**1
Primary Contact: Andy Altom, Chief Executive Officer
Web address: www.umch.org
**Control:** Other not–for–profit (including NFP Corporation) **Service:** Children's hospital psychiatric

**Staffed Beds:** 60 **Admissions:** 938 **Census:** 51 **Outpatient Visits:** 106837 **Births:** 0 **Total Expense ($000):** 16641 **Payroll Expense ($000):** 8058 **Personnel:** 107

**MCGEHEE—Desha County**

★ **MCGEHEE–DESHA COUNTY HOSPITAL (041308)**, 900 South Third, Zip 71654–2562, Mailing Address: P.O. Box 351, Zip 71654–0351; tel. 870/222–5600 **A**9 10 18 **F**3 11 29 40 45 57 59 62 64 68 81 107 111 119 132 133 135 146 148
Primary Contact: John E. Heard, Chief Executive Officer
CFO: Teresa Morgan, Chief Financial Officer
CMO: James Young, M.D., Chief of Staff
CIO: Shaun Perry, Chief Information Officer
CHR: Judy A. Sass, Chief Human Resources Officer
CNO: Sarah Calvert, Chief Nursing Officer
**Control:** Other not–for–profit (including NFP Corporation) **Service:** General Medical and Surgical

**Staffed Beds:** 25 **Admissions:** 306 **Census:** 3 **Outpatient Visits:** 33900 **Births:** 0 **Total Expense ($000):** 8825 **Payroll Expense ($000):** 4182 **Personnel:** 105

**MENA—Polk County**

★ **MENA REGIONAL HEALTH SYSTEM (040015)**, 311 North Morrow Street, Zip 71953–2516; tel. 479/394–6100 **A**9 10 20 **F**3 11 13 15 29 30 31 32 34 35 40 43 45 49 50 54 56 57 59 64 68 70 75 76 77 78 79 81 86 87 90 91 93 96 98 100 101 103 104 107 108 111 114 115 118 119 129 130 131 133 144 146 147 **P**8
Primary Contact: Tim Bowen, Chief Executive Officer
COO: Richard A. Billingsley, MSN, Chief Operating Officer and Chief Nursing Officer
CFO: Paul Rogers, Chief Financial Officer
CMO: Patrick Fox, M.D., Chief of Staff
CIO: John Roberts, Director Information Systems
CHR: Mary Ellen Winters, Director Human Resources
Web address: www.menaregional.com
**Control:** City–Government, nonfederal **Service:** General Medical and Surgical

**Staffed Beds:** 35 **Admissions:** 1718 **Census:** 24

**MONTICELLO—Drew County**

**DREW MEMORIAL HOSPITAL (040051)**, 778 Scogin Drive, Zip 71655–5729; tel. 870/367–2411, (Nonreporting) **A**9 10 20
Primary Contact: Michael G. Layfield, Chief Executive Officer
CFO: Shannon Clark, Chief Financial Officer
CMO: Jeffery Reinhart, M.D., Chief of Staff
CIO: Rusty Bryant, Director Information Technology
CHR: Keith Van Dee, Director Human Resources
CNO: Linda Orrell, Interim Chief Nursing Officer
Web address: www.drewmemorial.org
**Control:** County–Government, nonfederal **Service:** General Medical and Surgical

**Staffed Beds:** 49

**MORRILTON—Conway County**

★ **ST. VINCENT MORRILTON (041324)**, 4 Hospital Drive, Zip 72110–4510; tel. 501/977–2300 **A**9 10 18 **F**2 3 11 15 17 28 29 30 34 35 40 50 56 57 59 62 64 77 79 81 85 87 93 107 111 114 119 127 130 131 132 133 135 143 146 **P**6 **S** Catholic Health Initiatives, Englewood, CO
Primary Contact: Leslie Arnold, Chief Executive Officer
COO: Bob Lyons, Chief Operating Officer
CFO: Amanda George, Assistant Controller
CMO: Charles Howard, M.D., Chief of Staff
CHR: Tammy Smith, Director Human Resources
Web address: www.stanthonysmorrilton.com/
**Control:** Church–operated, Nongovernment, not–for profit **Service:** General Medical and Surgical

**Staffed Beds:** 25 **Admissions:** 832 **Census:** 9 **Outpatient Visits:** 30357 **Births:** 0 **Total Expense ($000):** 15215 **Payroll Expense ($000):** 6775 **Personnel:** 144

---

**Hospital, Medicare Provider Number, Address, Telephone, Approval, Facility, and Physician Codes, Health Care System**

★ American Hospital Association (AHA) membership
☐ The Joint Commission accreditation
◇ DNV Healthcare Inc. accreditation
○ Healthcare Facilities Accreditation Program
△ Commission on Accreditation of Rehabilitation Facilities (CARF) accreditation

### MOUNTAIN HOME—Baxter County

★ △ **BAXTER REGIONAL MEDICAL CENTER (040027)**, 624 Hospital Drive, Zip 72653–2955; tel. 870/508–1000 **A**7 9 10 **F**7 11 13 15 17 18 20 22 24 28 29 30 31 40 41 43 45 46 47 49 53 57 59 62 63 64 70 71 76 77 78 79 81 82 84 85 86 87 90 93 98 103 104 107 108 111 114 115 119 124 126 127 129 130 132 135 146 147 148 **P**6 8
Primary Contact: Ron Peterson, FACHE, President and Chief Executive Officer
COO: Rudy Darling, Chief Operating Officer
CFO: Ivan Holleman, Chief Financial Officer
CHR: Karen Adams, Vice President Human Resources
CNO: Cathleen Hamel, MS, Vice President and Chief Nursing Officer
Web address: www.baxterregional.org
**Control:** Other not–for–profit (including NFP Corporation) **Service:** General Medical and Surgical

**Staffed Beds: 209 Admissions: 9984 Census: 113 Outpatient Visits: 97754 Births: 614 Total Expense ($000): 156080 Payroll Expense ($000): 61111 Personnel: 1257**

### MOUNTAIN VIEW—Stone County

★ **STONE COUNTY MEDICAL CENTER (041310)**, 2106 East Main Street, Zip 72560–6439, Mailing Address: P.O. Box 510, Zip 72560–0510; tel. 870/269–4361 **A**9 10 18 **F**3 8 11 15 29 34 35 40 43 57 59 64 79 81 91 93 107 111 114 119 128 133 146 147 148 **S** White River Health System, Batesville, AR
Primary Contact: Renie Taylor, Administrator
CFO: Gary L. Britten, Chief Financial Officer
CFO: Jana Richardson, Interim Chief Financial Officer
CIO: Ken Poole, Coordinator Information Systems
CHR: Gary McDonald, Assistant Administrator Human Resources
CNO: Diana Sheldon, CNO
Web address: www.whiteriverhealthsystem.com
**Control:** Other not–for–profit (including NFP Corporation) **Service:** General Medical and Surgical

**Staffed Beds: 25 Admissions: 893 Census: 10 Outpatient Visits: 20037 Births: 2 Total Expense ($000): 15728 Payroll Expense ($000): 6623 Personnel: 132**

### NASHVILLE—Howard County

★ **HOWARD MEMORIAL HOSPITAL (041311)**, 130 Medical Circle, Zip 71852–8606; tel. 870/845–4400 **A**9 10 18 **F**3 11 15 29 30 34 35 39 40 43 45 50 57 64 65 70 77 81 85 87 93 102 107 108 110 119 133 146
Primary Contact: Debra J. Wright, R.N., Chief Executive Officer
CFO: William J. Craig, Chief Financial Officer
CMO: John Hearnsberger, M.D., Chief of Staff
CIO: Nathan Hale, Director Information Management
CHR: Gayla Lacefield, Director Human Resources
CNO: Angie Hanson, R.N., Chief Nursing Officer
Web address: www.howardmemorial.com
**Control:** Other not–for–profit (including NFP Corporation) **Service:** General Medical and Surgical

**Staffed Beds: 20 Admissions: 703 Census: 7 Outpatient Visits: 25679 Births: 0 Total Expense ($000): 12532 Payroll Expense ($000): 5570 Personnel: 128**

### NEWPORT—Jackson County

✠ **HARRIS HOSPITAL (040080)**, 1205 McLain Street, Zip 72112–3533; tel. 870/523–8911 **A**1 9 10 20 **F**3 11 13 15 17 18 19 29 30 34 35 38 40 43 50 56 57 59 64 65 70 73 75 76 77 79 81 85 87 89 93 98 102 103 105 107 111 114 119 133 135 146 147 **P**6 **S** Community Health Systems, Inc., Franklin, TN
Primary Contact: Robert Rupp, Chief Executive Officer
CFO: Misty Gates, Chief Financial Officer
CMO: Karen Jones, M.D., Chief of Staff
CHR: Margaret Gates, Chief Human Resources
CNO: Judy Haney, Chief Nursing Officer
Web address: www.harrishospital.com
**Control:** Corporation, Investor–owned, for–profit **Service:** General Medical and Surgical

**Staffed Beds: 104 Admissions: 2275 Census: 23 Outpatient Visits: 32147 Births: 373 Total Expense ($000): 23315 Payroll Expense ($000): 9904 Personnel: 213**

### NORTH LITTLE ROCK—Pulaski County

**CENTRAL ARKANSAS VETERANS HEALTHCARE SYSTEM, NORTH LITTLE ROCK DIVISION** See Central Arkansas Veterans Healthcare System, Little Rock

---

☐ **ARKANSAS SURGICAL HOSPITAL (040147)**, 5201 North Shore Drive, Zip 72118–5312; tel. 501/748–8000 **A**1 9 10 **F**3 29 35 40 74 75 79 81 82 85 87 107 111 114 119 131 146
Primary Contact: Carrie Helm, Chief Executive Officer
CFO: Charles Powell, Chief Financial Officer
CMO: Kenneth A. Martin, M.D., Chief of Staff
CIO: Scott Davis, Manager Information Technology
CHR: Tina Albright, Vice President Human Resources and Consumer Advocacy
Web address: www.ArkSurgicalHospital.com
**Control:** Corporation, Investor–owned, for–profit **Service:** General Medical and Surgical

**Staffed Beds: 51 Admissions: 3745 Census: 22 Outpatient Visits: 18969 Births: 0 Total Expense ($000): 46571 Payroll Expense ($000): 12046 Personnel: 252**

✠ △ **BAPTIST HEALTH MEDICAL CENTER – NORTH LITTLE ROCK (040036)**, 3333 Springhill Drive, Zip 72117–2922; tel. 501/202–3000 **A**1 3 7 9 10 **F**3 8 11 13 15 17 18 20 22 24 26 28 29 30 31 37 38 40 43 45 46 47 49 50 53 54 56 59 60 64 65 70 73 74 75 76 77 78 79 81 85 86 87 89 90 93 94 97 107 108 111 114 116 117 119 124 126 129 130 132 135 143 144 146 147 148 **S** Baptist Health, Little Rock, AR
Primary Contact: Harrison M. Dean, FACHE, Senior Vice President and Administrator
CFO: Robert C. Roberts, Senior Vice President Financial Services
CMO: Guy Gardner, M.D., Chief Medical Affairs
CIO: David House, Vice President and Chief Information Officer
CHR: Anthony Kendall, Vice President Human Resources
Web address: www.baptist–health.com/locations/accesspoint.aspx?accessPointID=190
**Control:** Other not–for–profit (including NFP Corporation) **Service:** General Medical and Surgical

**Staffed Beds: 220 Admissions: 12048 Census: 128 Outpatient Visits: 119552 Births: 1485 Total Expense ($000): 162737 Payroll Expense ($000): 57574 Personnel: 1074**

☐ **THE BRIDGEWAY (044005)**, 21 Bridgeway Road, Zip 72113–9516; tel. 501/771–1500 **A**1 9 10 **F**4 5 98 99 104 105 106 **P**5 **S** Universal Health Services, Inc., King of Prussia, PA
Primary Contact: Barry Pipkin, Chief Executive Officer
COO: Jason Miller, Chief Operating Officer
CFO: Fred Woods, Chief Financial Officer
CMO: Philip L. Mizell, M.D., Medical Director
CHR: Neely Robison, Director Human Resources
CNO: Sherrie James, R.N., Director of Nursing
Web address: www.thebridgeway.com
**Control:** Corporation, Investor–owned, for–profit **Service:** Psychiatric

**Staffed Beds: 103 Admissions: 4068 Census: 84 Outpatient Visits: 11027 Births: 0 Total Expense ($000): 17346 Payroll Expense ($000): 8100 Personnel: 154**

### OSCEOLA—Mississippi County

☐ **SOUTH MISSISSIPPI COUNTY REGIONAL MEDICAL CENTER (041316)**, 611 West Lee Avenue, Zip 72370–3001, Mailing Address: P.O. Box 607, Zip 72370–0607; tel. 870/563–7000 **A**1 9 10 18 **F**29 40 50 57 59 68 75 81 93 107 114 130 133 146 **S** Mississippi County Hospital System, Blytheville, AR
Primary Contact: Ralph E. Beaty, Chief Executive Officer
COO: Chris Raymer, R.N., Interim Chief Operating Officer
CFO: Paul Zuidema, Chief Financial Officer
CMO: Sherita Willis, M.D., Chief of Staff
Web address: www.mchealthsystem.com
**Control:** County–Government, nonfederal **Service:** General Medical and Surgical

**Staffed Beds: 25 Admissions: 590 Census: 7 Outpatient Visits: 11592 Births: 0 Total Expense ($000): 8192 Payroll Expense ($000): 3901 Personnel: 75**

### OZARK—Franklin County

★ **MERCY HOSPITAL OZARK (041303)**, 801 West River Street, Zip 72949–3000; tel. 479/667–4138 **A**9 10 18 **F**3 28 34 35 40 43 45 57 59 64 68 81 85 107 119 133 **S** Mercy Health, Chesterfield, MO
Primary Contact: Michael K. Smith, R.N., Regional Administrator
CMO: John Lachowsky, M.D., Chief Medical Officer
CIO: Tiana Bolduc, Chief Information Officer
Web address: www.mercy.net/northwestarar/practice/mercy-hospital-ozark
**Control:** Church–operated, Nongovernment, not–for profit **Service:** General Medical and Surgical

**Staffed Beds: 25 Admissions: 386 Census: 4 Outpatient Visits: 12587 Births: 0 Total Expense ($000): 9444 Payroll Expense ($000): 2141 Personnel: 58**

## PARAGOULD—Greene County

☒ △ **ARKANSAS METHODIST MEDICAL CENTER (040039)**, 900 West Kingshighway, Zip 72450–5942, Mailing Address: P.O. Box 339, Zip 72451–0339; tel. 870/239–7000 **A**1 7 9 10 19 **F**3 7 10 11 13 15 18 20 22 28 29 32 34 35 39 40 43 45 49 50 51 53 54 57 59 62 64 68 70 75 76 78 79 81 85 86 87 89 90 93 107 108 111 114 119 125 129 130 131 132 133 135 146 147 148 **P**6 8
Primary Contact: Barry L. Davis, FACHE, President and Chief Executive Officer
CFO: Brad Bloemer, Vice President Finance and Chief Financial Officer
CMO: Frank Schefano, M.D., Chief of Staff
CIO: Mardy Holmes, Director Information Technology
CHR: Dennis Cooper, Director Human Resources
CNO: Debra Vassar, Chief Nursing Officer
Web address: www.arkansasmethodist.org
**Control:** Other not–for–profit (including NFP Corporation) **Service:** General Medical and Surgical

**Staffed Beds:** 125 **Admissions:** 4854 **Census:** 61 **Outpatient Visits:** 117232 **Births:** 568 **Total Expense ($000):** 63682 **Payroll Expense ($000):** 26663 **Personnel:** 580

## PARIS—Logan County

★ **MERCY HOSPITAL PARIS (041300)**, 500 East Academy, Zip 72855–4099; tel. 479/963–6101 **A**9 10 18 **F**3 35 40 43 45 57 59 64 68 81 85 107 119 133 **S** Mercy Health, Chesterfield, MO
Primary Contact: Sharon Sorey, R.N., Regional Administrator
Web address: www.stedwardmercy.com
**Control:** Church–operated, Nongovernment, not–for profit **Service:** General Medical and Surgical

**Staffed Beds:** 16 **Admissions:** 196 **Census:** 3 **Outpatient Visits:** 13104 **Births:** 0 **Total Expense ($000):** 6889 **Payroll Expense ($000):** 1760 **Personnel:** 47

## PIGGOTT—Clay County

★ **PIGGOTT COMMUNITY HOSPITAL (041330)**, 1206 Gordon Duckworth Drive, Zip 72454–1911; tel. 870/598–3881 **A**9 10 18 **F**7 15 18 29 34 35 40 43 57 59 62 64 77 81 93 107 111 114 119 127 129 130 133 143 146 148
Primary Contact: James L. Magee, Executive Director
CFO: Linda Ort, Chief Financial Officer
Web address: www.piggottcommunityhospital.com
**Control:** City–Government, nonfederal **Service:** General Medical and Surgical

**Staffed Beds:** 25 **Admissions:** 653 **Census:** 7 **Outpatient Visits:** 29194 **Births:** 0 **Total Expense ($000):** 14559 **Payroll Expense ($000):** 7443 **Personnel:** 208

## PINE BLUFF—Jefferson County

**ARKANSAS DEPARTMENT OF CORRECTION HOSPITAL**, 7500 Correctional Circle, Zip 71603–1438; tel. 870/267–6999, (Nonreporting) **A**3 5
Primary Contact: Roland Anderson, M.D., Medical Director
**Control:** State–Government, nonfederal **Service:** Hospital unit of an institution (prison hospital, college infimary, etc.)

**Staffed Beds:** 27

☒ △ **JEFFERSON REGIONAL MEDICAL CENTER (040071)**, 1600 West 40th Avenue, Zip 71603–6301; tel. 870/541–7100 **A**1 3 5 6 7 9 10 20 **F**3 11 13 15 17 18 20 22 24 28 29 30 31 34 35 40 43 45 46 48 49 50 51 53 54 56 57 59 60 61 64 65 70 72 73 74 75 76 77 78 79 81 85 86 87 89 90 96 97 98 100 101 102 103 107 108 110 111 114 115 116 118 119 124 128 130 131 132 135 143 144 145 146 147 148 **P**7
Primary Contact: Walter E. Johnson, Jr., President and Chief Executive Officer
COO: Brian N. Thomas, Senior Vice President and Chief Operating Officer
CFO: Bryan G. Jackson, Vice President and Chief Financial Officer
CMO: Doug Coleman, M.D., Chief of Staff
CIO: Patrick Neece, Chief Information Officer
CHR: M Daryl Scott, Assistant Vice President
CNO: Louise Hickman, R.N., Vice President of Patient Care Services
Web address: www.jrmc.org
**Control:** Other not–for–profit (including NFP Corporation) **Service:** General Medical and Surgical

**Staffed Beds:** 333 **Admissions:** 9660 **Census:** 147 **Outpatient Visits:** 170640 **Births:** 1023 **Total Expense ($000):** 173555 **Payroll Expense ($000):** 74926 **Personnel:** 1551

## POCAHONTAS—Randolph County

**FIVE RIVERS MEDICAL CENTER (040047)**, 2801 Medical Center Drive, Zip 72455–9497; tel. 870/892–6000 **A**9 10 20 **F**3 11 15 18 20 29 40 43 45 47 57 59 62 70 81 85 93 98 103 107 111 113 115 119 130 133 146 148
Primary Contact: Luther J. Lewis, FACHE, Chief Executive Officer
CFO: Joey Radcliff, Chief Financial Officer
CHR: Alvin Taylor, Chief Human Resources
CNO: Mandy Dollins, R.N., Chief Nursing Officer
Web address: www.fiverivermedicalcenter.com
**Control:** Other not–for–profit (including NFP Corporation) **Service:** General Medical and Surgical

**Staffed Beds:** 46 **Admissions:** 916 **Census:** 15 **Outpatient Visits:** 17948 **Births:** 0 **Total Expense ($000):** 14442 **Payroll Expense ($000):** 8122 **Personnel:** 172

## ROGERS—Benton County

☒ **MERCY HOSPITAL ROGERS (040010)**, 2710 Rife Medical Lane, Zip 72758–1452; tel. 479/338–8000 **A**1 9 10 **F**3 8 11 13 15 18 20 22 24 28 29 30 40 43 45 46 49 57 59 62 64 70 72 75 76 77 79 81 82 84 86 87 89 93 107 108 110 111 115 118 119 129 130 131 132 135 146 148 **P**6 **S** Mercy Health, Chesterfield, MO
Primary Contact: Scott Street, President and Chief Executive Officer
CFO: Benny Stover, Vice President Finance
CMO: Cynthia Wilson, M.D., Chief of Staff
CHR: Rick Barclay, Vice President Support Services
Web address: www.mercyhealthnwa.smhs.com
**Control:** Church–operated, Nongovernment, not–for profit **Service:** General Medical and Surgical

**Staffed Beds:** 141 **Admissions:** 8655 **Census:** 78 **Outpatient Visits:** 171469 **Births:** 1318 **Total Expense ($000):** 128847 **Payroll Expense ($000):** 38983 **Personnel:** 768

## RUSSELLVILLE—Pope County

☐ **SAINT MARY'S REGIONAL MEDICAL CENTER (040041)**, 1808 West Main Street, Zip 72801–2724; tel. 479/968–2841 **A**1 9 10 19 **F**3 11 13 15 18 20 22 29 31 34 35 40 43 45 50 51 53 54 56 57 59 62 64 68 70 74 75 76 78 79 81 85 86 87 89 90 93 98 107 108 109 110 111 114 118 119 121 123 127 129 130 131 132 146 147 148 **S** Capella Healthcare, Franklin, TN
Primary Contact: Donald J. Frederic, FACHE, Chief Executive Officer
COO: Mike McCoy, Chief Operating Officer
CFO: Wendell VanEs, Chief Financial Officer
CMO: Chris Horan, M.D., Chief of Staff
CHR: Connie Gragg, Director Human Resources
Web address: www.saintmarysregional.com
**Control:** Corporation, Investor–owned, for–profit **Service:** General Medical and Surgical

**Staffed Beds:** 151 **Admissions:** 5794 **Census:** 66 **Outpatient Visits:** 73575 **Births:** 912 **Total Expense ($000):** 68402 **Payroll Expense ($000):** 22742 **Personnel:** 505

## SALEM—Fulton County

★ **FULTON COUNTY HOSPITAL (041322)**, 679 North Main Street, Zip 72576–9451, Mailing Address: P.O. Box 517, Zip 72576–0517; tel. 870/895–2691 **A**9 10 18 **F**7 28 29 34 35 40 45 57 59 107 119 133 146
Primary Contact: Marion A. Thompson, FACHE, Administrator and Chief Executive Officer
Web address: www.fultoncountyhospital.org
**Control:** County–Government, nonfederal **Service:** General Medical and Surgical

**Staffed Beds:** 25 **Admissions:** 742 **Census:** 11 **Outpatient Visits:** 48397 **Births:** 0

## SEARCY—White County

**ADVANCED CARE HOSPITAL OF WHITE COUNTY (042011)**, 1200 South Main Street, Zip 72143–7321; tel. 501/278–3155, (Nonreporting) **A**9 10
Primary Contact: Terri L. Parsons, Administrator
Web address: www.achwc.org
**Control:** Other not–for–profit (including NFP Corporation) **Service:** Long–Term Acute Care hospital

**Staffed Beds:** 27

**AR**

---

**Hospital, Medicare Provider Number, Address, Telephone, Approval, Facility, and Physician Codes, Health Care System**

★ American Hospital Association (AHA) membership
☐ The Joint Commission accreditation
◇ DNV Healthcare Inc. accreditation
○ Healthcare Facilities Accreditation Program
△ Commission on Accreditation of Rehabilitation Facilities (CARF) accreditation

**AR**

★ **WHITE COUNTY MEDICAL CENTER (040014)**, 3214 East Race Avenue, Zip 72143–4847; tel. 501/268–6121, (Includes CENTRAL ARKANSAS HOSPITAL, 1200 South Main Street, Zip 72143–7397; tel. 501/278–3100) **A**9 10 **F**1 3 11 12 13 17 18 20 22 24 28 29 30 31 34 35 39 40 43 45 51 54 57 59 61 62 64 68 70 74 75 76 77 78 79 81 86 87 89 90 93 98 100 102 103 105 107 108 111 115 119 126 129 130 131 132 134 135 145 146 147 148 **P**2 6
Primary Contact: Raymond W. Montgomery, II, FACHE, President and Chief Executive Officer
CFO: Stuart Hill, Vice President and Treasurer
CMO: Scott Dicus, M.D., Chief of Staff
CIO: Kevin Hoofman, Director Management Information
CHR: Pamela G. Williams, Director Human Resources
Web address: www.wcmc.org
**Control:** Other not–for–profit (including NFP Corporation) **Service:** General Medical and Surgical

> **Staffed Beds:** 286 **Admissions:** 12620 **Census:** 153 **Outpatient Visits:** 91139 **Births:** 1207 **Total Expense ($000):** 207424 **Payroll Expense ($000):** 75874 **Personnel:** 1377

**SHERWOOD—Pulaski County**

★ **ST. VINCENT MEDICAL CENTER–NORTH (040137)**, 2215 Wildwood Avenue, Zip 72120–5089; tel. 501/552–7100 **A**9 10 **F**3 11 15 18 20 22 26 29 35 40 43 45 46 47 50 64 70 74 79 81 85 87 107 108 110 111 115 119 146 **S** Catholic Health Initiatives, Englewood, CO
Primary Contact: David R. Fox, President
CMO: David Hall, M.D., Senior Vice President and Chief Medical Officer
CIO: Tommye Billing, Vice President and Chief Information Officer
CHR: Margaret Nixon, Director Human Resources
Web address: www.stvincenthealth.com
**Control:** Church–operated, Nongovernment, not–for profit **Service:** General Medical and Surgical

> **Staffed Beds:** 58 **Admissions:** 1980 **Census:** 21 **Outpatient Visits:** 30017 **Births:** 0 **Total Expense ($000):** 34768 **Payroll Expense ($000):** 8370 **Personnel:** 182

⊞ **ST. VINCENT REHABILITATION HOSPITAL (043031)**, 2201 Wildwood Avenue, Zip 72120–5074, Mailing Address: P.O. Box 6930, Zip 72124–6930; tel. 501/834–1800, (Nonreporting) **A**1 9 10 **S** HEALTHSOUTH Corporation, Birmingham, AL
Primary Contact: Lisa Watson, Chief Executive Officer
CFO: Pat Robinson, Manager Accounting
CMO: Sean Foley, M.D., Medical Director
CHR: Sandra Pearson, Manager Human Resources
Web address: www.stvincenthealth.com/svrehabhospital/index.html
**Control:** Partnership, Investor–owned, for–profit **Service:** Rehabilitation

> **Staffed Beds:** 71

**SILOAM SPRINGS—Benton County**

⊞ **SILOAM SPRINGS MEMORIAL HOSPITAL (040001)**, 205 East Jefferson Street, Zip 72761–3697; tel. 479/524–4141, (Nonreporting) **A**1 9 10 **S** Community Health Systems, Inc., Franklin, TN
Primary Contact: Kevin J. Clement, Chief Executive Officer
CFO: James E. Little, Chief Financial Officer
CMO: Hunt Cooper, M.D., Chief of Staff
CHR: Carmen Burasco, Director Human Resources
Web address: www.ssrh.net/Pages/home.aspx
**Control:** Corporation, Investor–owned, for–profit **Service:** General Medical and Surgical

> **Staffed Beds:** 43

**SPRINGDALE—Washington County**

⊞ **NORTHWEST MEDICAL CENTER (040022)**, 609 West Maple Avenue, Zip 72764–5394, Mailing Address: P.O. Box 47, Zip 72765–0047; tel. 501/751–5711, (Includes NORTHWEST MEDICAL CENTER – BENTONVILLE, 3000 Medical Center Parkway, Bentonville, Zip 72712; tel. 479/553–1000; Tripp Smith, Chief Operating Officer; WILLOW CREEK WOMEN'S HOSPITAL, 4301 Greathouse Springs Road, Johnson, Zip 72741–0544, Mailing Address: P.O. Box 544, Zip 72741–0544; tel. 479/684–3000; Debbie A. Crandall, Administrative Director), (Nonreporting) **A**1 3 9 10 **S** Community Health Systems, Inc., Franklin, TN
Primary Contact: Daniel E. McKay, Chief Executive Officer
CFO: Steve Flader, Chief Financial Officer
CMO: Robert Petrino, M.D., Chief of Staff
CIO: Paul DeMay, Chief Information Officer
Web address: www.northwesthealth.com
**Control:** Corporation, Investor–owned, for–profit **Service:** General Medical and Surgical

> **Staffed Beds:** 358

**STUTTGART—Arkansas County**

★ **BAPTIST HEALTH MEDICAL CENTER–STUTTGART (040072)**, North Buerkle Road, Zip 72160–3420, Mailing Address: P.O. Box 1905, Zip 72160–1905; tel. 870/673–3511 **A**9 10 **F**3 11 13 15 18 28 29 30 34 35 39 40 43 53 57 59 64 68 70 75 76 78 79 81 85 87 93 97 107 110 111 114 119 127 128 129 130 133 135 146 148 **S** Baptist Health, Little Rock, AR
Primary Contact: Terry L. Amstutz, FACHE, Vice President and Administrator
CMO: Raymond Kirk Coker, M.D., Chief of Staff
CIO: Warren Horton, Information Technologist
Web address: www.baptist–health.org/maps–directions/bhmc–stuttgart/default.aspx
**Control:** Other not–for–profit (including NFP Corporation) **Service:** General Medical and Surgical

> **Staffed Beds:** 49 **Admissions:** 1611 **Census:** 16 **Outpatient Visits:** 24254 **Births:** 209 **Total Expense ($000):** 24331 **Payroll Expense ($000):** 9176 **Personnel:** 225

**TEXARKANA—Miller County**

☐ **VISTA HEALTH TEXARKANA (044020)**, 701 Arkansas Boulevard, Zip 71854–2105; tel. 870/772–5028, (Nonreporting) **A**1 9 10
Primary Contact: Lucinda DeBruce, R.N., MS, Chief Executive Officer
Web address: www.vistahealthservices.com
**Control:** Corporation, Investor–owned, for–profit **Service:** Psychiatric

> **Staffed Beds:** 62

**VAN BUREN—Crawford County**

☐ **SUMMIT MEDICAL CENTER (040018)**, East Main and South 20th Streets, Zip 72956–5715, Mailing Address: P.O. Box 409, Zip 72957–0409; tel. 479/474–3401 **A**1 9 10 **F**3 11 15 29 30 34 40 43 45 50 51 56 57 59 64 65 68 70 74 75 77 78 79 81 82 85 86 87 93 100 107 108 110 111 114 119 130 131 132 135 144 146 148 **P**6 **S** Health Management Associates, Naples, FL
Primary Contact: Gary J. Blan, FACHE, Market Chief Executive Officer
CHR: James Ford, Director Human Resources
CNO: Shelly L. Weilenman, R.N., Administrator and Chief Nursing Executive
Web address: www.summitmedicalcenter.net
**Control:** Corporation, Investor–owned, for–profit **Service:** General Medical and Surgical

> **Staffed Beds:** 103 **Admissions:** 1678 **Census:** 15 **Outpatient Visits:** 37602 **Births:** 0 **Total Expense ($000):** 20549 **Payroll Expense ($000):** 8107 **Personnel:** 166

**WALDRON—Scott County**

★ **MERCY HOSPITAL WALDRON (041305)**, 1341 West 6th Street, Zip 72958–7642; tel. 479/637–4135 **A**9 10 18 **F**3 35 40 43 45 57 59 64 65 68 81 85 107 119 127 133 **S** Mercy Health, Chesterfield, MO
Primary Contact: Dorothy O'Bar, R.N., Regional Administrator
CFO: Greta Wilcher, Senior Vice President and Chief Financial Officer
Web address: www.stedwardmercy.com
**Control:** Church–operated, Nongovernment, not–for profit **Service:** General Medical and Surgical

> **Staffed Beds:** 24 **Admissions:** 445 **Census:** 4 **Outpatient Visits:** 29747 **Births:** 0 **Total Expense ($000):** 9916 **Payroll Expense ($000):** 2188 **Personnel:** 43

**WALNUT RIDGE—Lawrence County**

⊞ **LAWRENCE MEMORIAL HOSPITAL (041309)**, 1309 West Main, Zip 72476–1430, Mailing Address: P.O. Box 839, Zip 72476–0839; tel. 870/886–1200, (Includes LAWRENCE HALL NURSING HOME ), (Nonreporting) **A**1 9 10 18
Primary Contact: George S. Fray, Interim Administrator
CFO: Vanessa Wagner, Chief Financial Officer
CHR: Sherri Brown, Director Human Resources
CNO: Rosalind Casillas, Director of Nursing
Web address: www.lawrencehealth.net
**Control:** County–Government, nonfederal **Service:** General Medical and Surgical

> **Staffed Beds:** 194

**WARREN—Bradley County**

★ **BRADLEY COUNTY MEDICAL CENTER (041327)**, 404 South Bradley Street, Zip 71671–3493; tel. 870/226–3731 **A**9 10 18 **F**3 11 13 15 29 30 40 56 57 62 63 76 81 93 98 103 104 107 111 114 118 119 129 130 132 133 135 **P**8
Primary Contact: Brandon Gorman, Interim Chief Executive Officer
CFO: Brandon Gorman, Controller
CMO: Joe H. Wharton, M.D., Chief of Staff
CHR: Debra Marshall, Director Human Resources
CNO: Paulette Tolefree, Chief Nursing Officer
Web address: www.bradleycountymedicalcenter.com
**Control:** Other not–for–profit (including NFP Corporation) **Service:** General Medical and Surgical

> **Staffed Beds:** 35 **Admissions:** 1481 **Census:** 15 **Outpatient Visits:** 57195 **Births:** 114 **Total Expense ($000):** 15569 **Payroll Expense ($000):** 8243 **Personnel:** 201

*Many Facility Codes have changed. Please refer to the AHA Guide Code Chart.*  © 2013 AHA Guide

**WEST MEMPHIS—Crittenden County**

☐ **CRITTENDEN REGIONAL HOSPITAL (040042)**, 200 Tyler Avenue,
Zip 72301–4223, Mailing Address: P.O. Box 2248, Zip 72303–2248;
tel. 870/735–1500, (Nonreporting) **A**1 9 10
Primary Contact: Eugene Cashman, III, Chief Executive Officer
COO: Justin Vernon, Chief Operating Officer
CFO: Paul Rogers, Chief Financial Officer
Web address: www.crittendenregional.org/
**Control:** Other not–for–profit (including NFP Corporation) **Service:** General
Medical and Surgical

**Staffed Beds:** 142

**WYNNE—Cross County**

☒ **CROSSRIDGE COMMUNITY HOSPITAL (041307)**, 310 South Falls Boulevard,
Zip 72396–3013, Mailing Address: P.O. Box 590, Zip 72396–0590;
tel. 870/238–3300 **A**1 9 10 18 **F**3 11 15 28 34 35 40 43 50 57 59 62 64 68
69 75 77 81 93 107 111 114 119 130 133 135 146
Primary Contact: Gary R. Sparks, Administrator
COO: Bryan Mattes, Associate Administrator
CFO: Janice Morris, Accountant
CIO: Gail Copeland, Director Management Information Systems
CHR: Bertha Ragle, Director Personnel
CNO: Amelia Davis, Director of Nursing
**Control:** Church–operated, Nongovernment, not–for profit **Service:** General
Medical and Surgical

**Staffed Beds:** 15 **Admissions:** 626 **Census:** 6 **Outpatient Visits:** 17461
**Births:** 0 **Total Expense ($000):** 13054 **Payroll Expense ($000):** 5338
**Personnel:** 136

**Hospital, Medicare Provider Number, Address, Telephone, Approval, Facility, and Physician Codes, Health Care System**

★ American Hospital Association (AHA) membership
☐ The Joint Commission accreditation     ◇ DNV Healthcare Inc. accreditation
○ Healthcare Facilities Accreditation Program
△ Commission on Accreditation of Rehabilitation Facilities (CARF) accreditation

# CALIFORNIA

## ALAMEDA—Alameda County

☒ **ALAMEDA HOSPITAL (050211)**, 2070 Clinton Avenue, Zip 94501–4397; tel. 510/522–3700, (Nonreporting) **A**1 9 10
Primary Contact: Deborah E. Stebbins, FACHE, Chief Executive Officer
CFO: Robert C. Anderson, Interim Chief Financial Officer
CMO: Aika Sharma, M.D., President Medical Staff
CIO: Robert Lundy–Paine, Director Information Systems
CHR: Phyllis Weiss, Director Human Resources
Web address: www.alamedahospital.org
**Control:** Hospital district or authority, Government, nonfederal **Service:** General Medical and Surgical

Staffed Beds: 126

## ALHAMBRA—Los Angeles County

☐ **ALHAMBRA HOSPITAL MEDICAL CENTER (050281)**, 100 South Raymond Avenue, Zip 91801–3199, Mailing Address: P.O. Box 510, Zip 91802–2510; tel. 626/570–1606 **A**1 9 10 **F**3 18 29 31 34 35 40 49 51 57 59 60 65 68 70 74 77 78 79 80 81 82 85 87 90 93 94 97 107 114 119 128 130 143 146 **S** AHMC & Healthcare, Inc., Alhambra, CA
Primary Contact: Iris Lai, Chief Executive Officer
CFO: Linda Marsh, Vice President Financial Services and Chief Financial Officer
CIO: Johnson Legaspi, Director Information Systems
CHR: Elizabeth Sabandit, Director Human Resources
Web address: www.alhambrahospital.com
**Control:** Partnership, Investor–owned, for–profit **Service:** General Medical and Surgical

Staffed Beds: 144 Admissions: 4038 Census: 81 Outpatient Visits: 23544
Births: 0

## ALTURAS—Modoc County

**MODOC MEDICAL CENTER (051330)**, 228 West Mcdowell Avenue, Zip 96101–3934; tel. 530/233–5131, (Nonreporting) **A**9 10 18
Primary Contact: Walter G. Beck, Chief Executive Officer
CMO: Ed Richert, M.D., Chief of Staff
CHR: Diane Hagelthorn, Human Resources Generalist
Web address: www.modocmedicalcenter.com
**Control:** County–Government, nonfederal **Service:** General Medical and Surgical

Staffed Beds: 87

## ANAHEIM—Orange County

☐ **ANAHEIM REGIONAL MEDICAL CENTER (050226)**, 1111 West La Palma Avenue, Zip 92801–2881; tel. 714/774–1450, (Nonreporting) **A**1 2 9 10 **S** AHMC & Healthcare, Inc., Alhambra, CA
Primary Contact: Donald A. Lorack, Jr., Chief Executive Officer
COO: Deborah G. Webber, Chief Operating Officer
CFO: Frederick J. Drewette, Chief Financial Officer
CMO: Amitabh Prakash, M.D., Chief Medical Officer
CIO: Jeff DesRoches, Manager Information Systems
CHR: Kathy Doi, Executive Director Human Resources
CNO: Martha Dispoto, R.N., Chief Nursing Officer
Web address: www.anaheimregionalmc.com
**Control:** Other not–for–profit (including NFP Corporation) **Service:** General Medical and Surgical

Staffed Beds: 223

☒ **KAISER PERMANENTE ANAHEIM MEDICAL CENTER (050609)**, (Formerly Anaheim Medical Center), 3430 East La Palma Avenue, Zip 92806–2020; tel. 714/644–2000, (Includes ORANGE COUNTY IRVINE MEDICAL CENTER, 6640 Alton Parkway, Irvine, Zip 92618; tel. 949/932–5000) **A**1 3 5 10 **F**3 13 14 15 17 18 19 20 29 30 31 35 37 40 44 45 46 47 48 49 50 59 61 62 63 64 65 68 70 72 74 75 76 78 79 80 81 82 84 85 87 89 92 93 100 107 108 111 114 119 130 135 143 146 148 **S** Kaiser Foundation Hospitals, Oakland, CA
Primary Contact: Julie K. Miller–Phipps, Senior Vice President and Executive Director
COO: Margie Harrier, Medical Center Chief Operations Officer
CFO: Melvin J. Benner, Assistant Administrator Finance
CMO: Nancy Gin, M.D., Area Associate Medical Director
CIO: Donald M. Carren, Information Technology Leader
CHR: Jocelyn A. Herrera, Director Human Resources
Web address: www.kp.org
**Control:** Other not–for–profit (including NFP Corporation) **Service:** General Medical and Surgical

Staffed Beds: 436 Admissions: 22521 Census: 256 Outpatient Visits:
293469 Births: 5380 Personnel: 2430

☐ **WEST ANAHEIM MEDICAL CENTER (050426)**, 3033 West Orange Avenue, Zip 92804–3156; tel. 714/827–3000, (Nonreporting) **A**1 5 10 **S** Prime Healthcare Services, Ontario, CA
Primary Contact: Virgis Narbutas, Chief Executive Officer
CFO: Alan H. Smith, Chief Financial Officer
CMO: Hassan Alkhouli, M.D., Chief Medical Officer
CIO: Adam Morquecho, Director Information Technology
CHR: Stephanie Sioson, Director Human Resources
CNO: Virginia Edward, R.N., Administrator and Chief Nursing Officer
Web address: www.westanaheimmedctr.com
**Control:** Partnership, Investor–owned, for–profit **Service:** General Medical and Surgical

Staffed Beds: 219

☐ **WESTERN MEDICAL CENTER ANAHEIM (050744)**, 1025 South Anaheim Boulevard, Zip 92805–5806; tel. 714/533–6220, (Nonreporting) **A**1 9 10 **S** Integrated Healthcare, Santa Ana, CA
Primary Contact: Dennis M. Knox, Chief Executive Officer
CMO: Harmohinder Gogia, M.D., Chief Medical Officer
CIO: Nova Stewart, Chief Information Officer
Web address: www.westernmedanaheim.com
**Control:** Corporation, Investor–owned, for–profit **Service:** General Medical and Surgical

Staffed Beds: 181

## ANTIOCH—Contra Costa County

☒ **KAISER PERMANENTE ANTIOCH MEDICAL CENTER (050760)**, (Formerly Antioch Medical Center), 4501 Sand Creek Road, Zip 94531–8687; tel. 925/813–6500 **A**1 10 **F**3 5 9 13 15 29 30 31 32 34 35 36 38 40 45 49 50 54 56 57 59 60 61 63 64 65 68 70 72 74 75 76 77 78 79 81 82 83 84 85 86 87 91 92 93 94 96 97 99 100 101 102 103 104 107 108 109 110 111 112 115 116 119 130 132 134 135 141 144 146 147 148 **S** Kaiser Foundation Hospitals, Oakland, CA
Primary Contact: Colleen McKeown, Senior Vice President
COO: Tim F. Daly, Chief Operating Officer
CNO: Linda Krystof, Chief Nursing Officer
Web address: www.https://health.kaiserpermanente.org/wps/portal/facility/100382
**Control:** Other not–for–profit (including NFP Corporation) **Service:** General Medical and Surgical

Staffed Beds: 150 Admissions: 7764 Census: 77 Births: 1451 Personnel: 1326

☒ **SUTTER DELTA MEDICAL CENTER (050523)**, 3901 Lone Tree Way, Zip 94509–6253; tel. 925/779–7200 **A**1 9 10 **F**3 11 13 15 20 22 26 29 30 31 34 35 40 41 47 50 51 57 59 60 65 66 68 70 72 74 76 77 78 79 81 82 84 85 89 93 96 107 108 110 114 115 119 130 135 146 147 148 **S** Sutter Health, Sacramento, CA
Primary Contact: Gary D. Rapaport, Chief Executive Officer
COO: Susan C. Bumatay, R.N., Assistant Administrator
CFO: Julie Peterson, Chief Financial Officer
CMO: Bobby Glickman, M.D., Chief of Staff
CIO: Kathy Frederickson, Information Systems Site Lead
CHR: Christine Green, Administrative Director Human Resources
CNO: Dori Stevens, Chief Nursing Officer
Web address: www.sutterdelta.org
**Control:** Other not–for–profit (including NFP Corporation) **Service:** General Medical and Surgical

Staffed Beds: 136 Admissions: 8176 Census: 82 Outpatient Visits: 82151
Births: 988 Total Expense ($000): 158960 Payroll Expense ($000): 57723
Personnel: 676

**APPLE VALLEY—San Bernardino County**

★ ○ **ST. JOSEPH HEALTH ST. MARY (050300)**, (Formerly St. Mary Medical Center), 18300 Highway 18, Zip 92307–2206, Mailing Address: P.O. Box 7025, Zip 92307–0725; tel. 760/242–2311 **A**2 9 10 11 **F**8 11 13 15 18 20 22 24 26 28 29 30 34 35 40 45 46 50 57 59 60 64 65 68 70 71 72 75 76 77 78 79 81 82 83 84 85 86 87 89 93 107 108 111 115 119 126 127 130 132 135 143 146 148 **P**3 5 **S** St. Joseph Health, Irvine, CA
Primary Contact: Alan H. Garrett, Chief Executive Officer
COO: David O'Brien, M.D., Senior Vice President, COO
CFO: Pitt Calkin, Interim Chief Financial Officer
CMO: James Kyle, M.D., Vice President Medical Affairs
CIO: Doug Kleine, IT Director
CHR: Stephen Eckberg, Vice President Human Resources
CNO: Marilyn Drone, R.N., Vice President, CNO
Web address: www.stmaryapplevalley.com/
**Control:** Church–operated, Nongovernment, not–for profit **Service:** General Medical and Surgical

**Staffed Beds:** 204 **Admissions:** 16923 **Census:** 178 **Outpatient Visits:** 147998 **Births:** 2729 **Total Expense ($000):** 260574 **Payroll Expense ($000):** 93324 **Personnel:** 1520

**ARCADIA—Los Angeles County**

✉ **METHODIST HOSPITAL OF SOUTHERN CALIFORNIA (050238)**, 300 West Huntington Drive, Zip 91007–3473, Mailing Address: P.O. Box 60016, Zip 91066–6016; tel. 626/898–8000, (Total facility includes 26 beds in nursing home–type unit) **A**1 2 9 10 **F**1 3 12 13 14 15 17 18 20 22 24 26 28 29 30 31 34 35 37 38 40 45 46 48 49 50 51 55 56 57 58 59 60 64 65 68 70 72 74 75 76 77 78 79 81 82 84 85 86 87 90 92 94 100 102 107 108 111 114 115 117 119 120 121 123 130 132 135 146 147 148
Primary Contact: Dan F. Ausman, President and Chief Executive Officer
COO: Steven A. Sisto, Senior Vice President and Chief Operating Officer
CFO: William E. Grigg, Senior Vice President and Chief Financial Officer
CHR: William Budzinski, Vice President Human Resources
Web address: www.methodisthospital.org
**Control:** Other not–for–profit (including NFP Corporation) **Service:** General Medical and Surgical

**Staffed Beds:** 310 **Admissions:** 16684 **Census:** 215 **Outpatient Visits:** 60624 **Births:** 1831 **Total Expense ($000):** 278420 **Payroll Expense ($000):** 114882 **Personnel:** 1542

**ARCATA—Humboldt County**

○ **MAD RIVER COMMUNITY HOSPITAL (050028)**, 3800 Janes Road, Zip 95521–4788, Mailing Address: P.O. Box 1115, Zip 95518–1115; tel. 707/822–3621, (Nonreporting) **A**9 10 11
Primary Contact: Douglas A. Shaw, Chief Executive Officer
COO: Steve Engle, Chief Operations Officer
CFO: Michael Young, Chief Financial Officer
CMO: Gary Garcia, M.D., Chief of Staff
CIO: Steve Engle, Chief Operations Officer
CHR: Michele Bisgrove, Manager Human Resources
Web address: www.madriverhospital.com
**Control:** Corporation, Investor–owned, for–profit **Service:** General Medical and Surgical

**Staffed Beds:** 68

**ARROYO GRANDE—San Luis Obispo County**

✉ **ARROYO GRANDE COMMUNITY HOSPITAL (050016)**, 345 South Halcyon Road, Zip 93420–3899; tel. 805/489–4261, (Total facility includes 14 beds in nursing home–type unit) **A**1 2 9 10 **F**8 11 15 29 30 34 35 37 39 40 50 51 54 57 59 64 68 70 75 77 78 79 81 84 87 90 93 94 96 100 107 108 109 110 111 114 117 118 119 129 130 132 146 148 **S** Dignity Health, San Francisco, CA
Primary Contact: Kenneth Dalebout, Administrator and Chief Executive Officer
CHR: Ami Padilla, Director Human Resources
Web address: www.arroyograndehospital.org
**Control:** Other not–for–profit (including NFP Corporation) **Service:** General Medical and Surgical

**Staffed Beds:** 67 **Admissions:** 3041 **Census:** 37 **Outpatient Visits:** 63128 **Births:** 0 **Total Expense ($000):** 66431 **Payroll Expense ($000):** 24505 **Personnel:** 280

**ATASCADERO—San Luis Obispo County**

☐ **ATASCADERO STATE HOSPITAL**, 10333 El Camino Real, Zip 93422–5808, Mailing Address: P.O. Box 7001, Zip 93423–7001; tel. 805/468–2000 **A**1 **F**34 39 53 57 59 75 77 82 86 87 98 103 130 132 144 146 **P**1
Primary Contact: Linda Persons, Executive Director
Web address: www.dmh.ca.gov/statehospitals/atascadero
**Control:** State–Government, nonfederal **Service:** Psychiatric

**Staffed Beds:** 1275 **Admissions:** 1153 **Census:** 1047 **Births:** 0 **Total Expense ($000):** 149559 **Payroll Expense ($000):** 97286 **Personnel:** 1932

**AUBURN—Placer County**

✉ **SUTTER AUBURN FAITH HOSPITAL (050498)**, 11815 Education Street, Zip 95602–2410; tel. 530/888–4500 **A**1 2 9 10 **F**3 8 11 12 15 17 18 20 28 29 30 31 34 35 37 39 40 44 45 47 49 50 54 58 59 62 63 64 68 70 74 75 78 79 81 85 86 87 92 93 107 108 110 111 114 119 130 132 135 145 146 147 148 **S** Sutter Health, Sacramento, CA
Primary Contact: Mitchell J. Hanna, Chief Executive Officer
CFO: Gary Hubschman, Administrative Director Finance
CMO: John Mesic, M.D., Chief Medical Officer
CIO: Tom Ream, Regional Chief Information Officer
CHR: Lynda Dasaro, Director Human Resources
CNO: Virgie Galindo, Chief Nurse Executive
Web address: www.sutterhealth.org
**Control:** Other not–for–profit (including NFP Corporation) **Service:** General Medical and Surgical

**Staffed Beds:** 75 **Admissions:** 3979 **Census:** 35 **Outpatient Visits:** 83783 **Births:** 0 **Total Expense ($000):** 103062 **Payroll Expense ($000):** 33250 **Personnel:** 402

**AVALON—Los Angeles County**

★ **CATALINA ISLAND MEDICAL CENTER (051307)**, 100 Falls Canyon Road, Zip 90704, Mailing Address: P.O. Box 1563, Zip 90704–1563; tel. 310/510–0700, (Total facility includes 4 beds in nursing home–type unit) **A**9 10 18 **F**3 11 29 34 36 40 50 57 64 65 66 75 93 96 107 113 119 127 128 130 133 146
Primary Contact: John P. Friel, Chief Executive Officer
CFO: John Lovrich, Chief Financial Officer
CMO: Monte Mellon, M.D., Chief of Staff
CIO: Richard Kleinman, R.N., Manager Medical Informatics
CHR: Krista Steuter, Director Human Resources
CNO: Nancy Mattis, Chief Patient Care Services
Web address: www.catalinaislandmedicalcenter.org
**Control:** Other not–for–profit (including NFP Corporation) **Service:** General Medical and Surgical

**Staffed Beds:** 12 **Admissions:** 30 **Census:** 6 **Outpatient Visits:** 12701 **Births:** 0 **Total Expense ($000):** 6828 **Payroll Expense ($000):** 2710 **Personnel:** 49

**BAKERSFIELD—Kern County**

☐ **BAKERSFIELD HEART HOSPITAL (050724)**, 3001 Sillect Avenue, Zip 93308–6337; tel. 661/316–6000, (Nonreporting) **A**1 10
Primary Contact: Randall H. Rolfe, President
Web address: www.bakersfieldhearthospital.com
**Control:** Partnership, Investor–owned, for–profit **Service:** Heart

**Staffed Beds:** 47

✉ **BAKERSFIELD MEMORIAL HOSPITAL (050036)**, 420 34th Street, Zip 93301–2237; tel. 661/327–1792, (Nonreporting) **A**1 9 10 **S** Dignity Health, San Francisco, CA
Primary Contact: Jon Van Boening, President and Chief Executive Officer and Senior Vice President Operations Dignity Health Central Va
COO: Bruce Peters, Vice President and Chief Operating Officer
CFO: Jesica Hanson, Vice President and Chief Financial Officer
CMO: Rodney Mark Root, D.O., Vice President Medical Affairs
CHR: Sheri Comaianni, Vice President Human Resources
Web address: www.bakersfieldmemorial.org
**Control:** Other not–for–profit (including NFP Corporation) **Service:** General Medical and Surgical

**Staffed Beds:** 406

---

**Hospital, Medicare Provider Number, Address, Telephone, Approval, Facility, and Physician Codes, Health Care System**

★ American Hospital Association (AHA) membership
☐ The Joint Commission accreditation
◇ DNV Healthcare Inc. accreditation
○ Healthcare Facilities Accreditation Program
△ Commission on Accreditation of Rehabilitation Facilities (CARF) accreditation

☐ **GOOD SAMARITAN HOSPITAL (050257)**, 901 Olive Drive, Zip 93308–4144,
Mailing Address: P.O. Box 85002, Zip 93380–5002; tel. 661/399–4461,
(Nonreporting) **A**1 9 10
Primary Contact: Tim Kollars, Chief Executive Officer
COO: Noel Cabezzas, Chief Operating Officer
CFO: Vicki Nguyen, Chief Financial Officer
CMO: Ronnie Claiborne, M.D., Chief Medical Officer
CIO: Anand Manohara, Associate Administrator
CHR: Milissa Newton, Supervisor Human Resources
**Control:** Partnership, Investor–owned, for–profit **Service:** General Medical and
Surgical

**Staffed Beds:** 120

☒ **HEALTHSOUTH BAKERSFIELD REHABILITATION HOSPITAL (053031)**, 5001
Commerce Drive, Zip 93309–0689; tel. 661/323–5500 **A**1 9 10 **F**3 28 29 35
59 64 77 82 90 91 92 93 95 96 148 **S** HEALTHSOUTH Corporation,
Birmingham, AL
Primary Contact: Sandra Hegland, Chief Executive Officer
CFO: Robert Mosesian, Controller
CMO: Chris Yoon, M.D., Medical Director
CIO: Tara DeMontgorency, Director Business Development
CHR: Tami Holden, Director Human Resources
Web address: www.healthsouthbakersfield.com
**Control:** Corporation, Investor–owned, for–profit **Service:** Rehabilitation

**Staffed Beds:** 66 **Admissions:** 1648 **Census:** 55 **Outpatient Visits:** 7555
**Total Expense ($000):** 18711 **Payroll Expense ($000):** 11330 **Personnel:**
185

☐ **KERN MEDICAL CENTER (050315)**, 1700 Mount Vernon Avenue,
Zip 93306–4018; tel. 661/326–2000 **A**1 2 3 5 8 9 10 **F**2 3 11 15 20 29 31
34 40 44 45 49 50 51 54 57 58 59 61 62 64 66 68 70 72 73 74 75 76 78
79 81 85 87 89 92 93 94 97 98 106 107 108 111 114 115 119 130 146
147 **P**6
Primary Contact: Paul J. Hensler, Chief Executive Officer
CMO: Eugene Kercher, M.D., Chief Medical Officer
CIO: Bill Fawns, Interim Manager Information Systems
CHR: Steve O'Connor, Manager Human Resources
Web address: www.kernmedicalcenter.com
**Control:** County–Government, nonfederal **Service:** General Medical and Surgical

**Staffed Beds:** 188 **Admissions:** 9377 **Census:** 142 **Outpatient Visits:**
120259 **Births:** 3133 **Total Expense ($000):** 279548 **Payroll Expense
($000):** 121309 **Personnel:** 1813

☒ **MERCY HOSPITALS OF BAKERSFIELD (050295)**, 2215 Truxtun Avenue,
Zip 93301–3698, Mailing Address: P.O. Box 119, Zip 93302–0119;
tel. 661/632–5000, (Includes MERCY SOUTHWEST HOSPITAL, 400 Old River
Road, Zip 93311; tel. 661/663–6000) **A**1 2 9 10 **F**11 12 13 15 29 30 34 35
40 50 57 59 60 62 64 70 72 74 75 76 78 79 81 82 84 86 87 93 107 111
114 118 119 121 123 130 131 146 147 148 **S** Dignity Health, San
Francisco, CA
Primary Contact: Russell V. Judd, President
COO: Jeremy Zoch, Chief Operating Officer
CFO: Rodney Winegarner, Chief Financial Officer
CIO: Jeff Vague, Regional Manager Information Systems
CHR: Jay King, Vice President Human Resources
Web address: www.mercybakersfield.org
**Control:** Church–operated, Nongovernment, not–for profit **Service:** General
Medical and Surgical

**Staffed Beds:** 222 **Admissions:** 12982 **Census:** 148 **Outpatient Visits:**
130007 **Births:** 2376 **Total Expense ($000):** 254634 **Payroll Expense
($000):** 110652 **Personnel:** 1159

☒ **SAN JOAQUIN COMMUNITY HOSPITAL (050455)**, 2615 Chester Avenue,
Zip 93301–2014, Mailing Address: P.O. Box 2615, Zip 93303–2615;
tel. 661/395–3000 **A**1 9 10 **F**3 11 12 13 15 16 18 20 22 24 26 28 29 30 31
34 35 40 47 49 57 59 62 64 65 70 71 72 74 75 76 77 78 79 81 84 85 86
91 94 107 108 110 111 113 114 115 116 117 118 119 126 130 132 146
**P**7 **S** Adventist Health, Roseville, CA
Primary Contact: Doug Duffield, Interim President and Chief Executive Officer
CFO: Brent Soper, Chief Financial Officer
CHR: Marlene Kreidler, Executive Director Human Resources
Web address: www.sanjoaquinhospital.org
**Control:** Church–operated, Nongovernment, not–for profit **Service:** General
Medical and Surgical

**Staffed Beds:** 255 **Admissions:** 19658 **Census:** 206 **Outpatient Visits:**
79685 **Births:** 2802 **Total Expense ($000):** 308399 **Payroll Expense
($000):** 121082 **Personnel:** 1959

## BALDWIN PARK—Los Angeles County

☒ **KAISER PERMANENTE BALDWIN PARK MEDICAL CENTER (050723)**,
(Formerly Baldwin Park Medical Center), 1011 Baldwin Park Boulevard,
Zip 91706–5806; tel. 626/851–1011 **A**1 10 **F**3 8 13 15 18 29 30 31 34 35
40 41 44 56 57 58 59 60 61 62 63 64 65 68 70 72 74 75 76 77 78 79 81
82 84 85 86 87 93 94 107 111 119 130 146 147 148 **S** Kaiser Foundation
Hospitals, Oakland, CA
Primary Contact: Margaret H. Pierce, Executive Director
CFO: Rebecca Wheeler, Director Finance
CMO: John Bigley, M.D., Medical Director
CIO: Linda C. Salazar, Information Technology Leader
CHR: Leesa Malcom, Director Human Resources
Web address: www.kp.org
**Control:** Other not–for–profit (including NFP Corporation) **Service:** General
Medical and Surgical

**Staffed Beds:** 254 **Admissions:** 12688 **Census:** 120 **Outpatient Visits:**
235938 **Births:** 2820

★ ○ **KINDRED HOSPITAL–BALDWIN PARK (052045)**, 14148 East Francisquito
Avenue, Zip 91706–6120; tel. 626/388–2700 **A**9 10 11 **F**1 29 45 60 84 107
111 119 130 148 **S** Kindred Healthcare, Louisville, KY
Primary Contact: Swenda Moreh, Chief Executive Officer
COO: Dina Garrow, Chief Nursing Officer and Chief Operating Officer
CIO: Glenn P. Requierme, Director Information Technology
CHR: Antoinette Bibal, Director Human Resources
Web address: www.khbaldwinpark.com
**Control:** Corporation, Investor–owned, for–profit **Service:** Long–Term Acute Care
hospital

**Staffed Beds:** 72 **Admissions:** 865 **Census:** 68 **Outpatient Visits:** 0 **Births:**
0 **Total Expense ($000):** 29712 **Payroll Expense ($000):** 16638
**Personnel:** 244

## BANNING—Riverside County

☒ **SAN GORGONIO MEMORIAL HOSPITAL (050054)**, 600 North Highland
Springs Avenue, Zip 92220–3046; tel. 951/845–1121 **A**1 9 10 **F**3 8 11 13 15
18 28 29 30 34 35 40 45 56 57 64 79 81 82 93 104 107 110 115 119 130
146 147 148
Primary Contact: Mark S. Turner, Chief Executive Officer
CFO: David Recupero, Chief Financial Officer
CMO: Richard Sheldon, M.D., Vice President Medical Affairs
CIO: Linda Palmer, Coordinator Medical Records
CHR: Lynn M. Gomez, Executive Director Human Resources
CNO: Pat Brown, R.N., Chief Nursing Officer
Web address: www.sgmh.org
**Control:** Hospital district or authority, Government, nonfederal **Service:** General
Medical and Surgical

**Staffed Beds:** 77 **Admissions:** 3279 **Census:** 37 **Outpatient Visits:** 40568
**Births:** 481 **Total Expense ($000):** 49112 **Payroll Expense ($000):** 22537
**Personnel:** 279

## BARSTOW—San Bernardino County

☒ **BARSTOW COMMUNITY HOSPITAL (050298)**, 555 South Seventh Avenue,
Zip 92311–3043; tel. 760/256–1761 **A**1 9 10 20 **F**3 8 11 13 15 29 35 40 70
76 79 81 107 108 111 114 119 **P**8 **S** Community Health Systems, Inc.,
Franklin, TN
Primary Contact: S. Sean Fowler, Chief Executive Officer
CFO: Carrie Howell, Chief Financial Officer
CIO: Ian Riggall, Manager Data Processing
CHR: Vickie Hendricks, Director Human Resources
Web address: www.barstowhospital.com
**Control:** Corporation, Investor–owned, for–profit **Service:** General Medical and
Surgical

**Staffed Beds:** 30 **Admissions:** 2578 **Census:** 20 **Outpatient Visits:** 34364
**Births:** 323 **Total Expense ($000):** 37678 **Payroll Expense ($000):** 17013

## BERKELEY—Alameda County

☒ △ **ALTA BATES SUMMIT MEDICAL CENTER (050305)**, 2450 Ashby Avenue,
Zip 94705–2067; tel. 510/204–4444, (Includes ALTA BATES MEDICAL
CENTER–HERRICK CAMPUS, 2001 Dwight Way, Zip 94704; tel. 510/204–4444),
(Total facility includes 33 beds in nursing home–type unit) **A**1 3 5 7 9 10 **F**3 5 8
11 13 15 17 18 20 22 26 28 29 30 31 34 35 36 40 46 47 49 55 56 57 58
59 60 61 64 68 70 72 74 75 76 77 78 79 81 82 84 85 87 90 93 98 99 100
103 104 105 107 108 110 114 119 120 121 123 124 128 130 132 135 136
146 147 148 **S** Sutter Health, Sacramento, CA
Primary Contact: Charles Prosper, Chief Executive Officer
CFO: Robert Petrina, Chief Financial Officer
CMO: John Gentile, M.D., Vice President Medical Affairs
Web address: www.altabates.com
**Control:** Other not–for–profit (including NFP Corporation) **Service:** General
Medical and Surgical

**Staffed Beds:** 527 **Admissions:** 19911 **Census:** 300 **Outpatient Visits:**
148805 **Births:** 7269 **Total Expense ($000):** 618955 **Payroll Expense
($000):** 182001 **Personnel:** 1804

## BIG BEAR LAKE—San Bernardino County

★ **BEAR VALLEY COMMUNITY HOSPITAL (050618)**, 41870 Garstin Drive, Zip 92315, Mailing Address: P.O. Box 1649, Zip 92315–1649; tel. 909/866–6501, (Nonreporting) **A**9 10 20
Primary Contact: Raymond T. Hino, FACHE, Chief Executive Officer
COO: Scott Rogers, Chief Operating Officer
CFO: Rudy Shutta, Chief Financial Officer
CMO: Kurt Frauenpreis, M.D., Chief Medical Staff
CIO: Cindy Venuto, Public Information Officer
CHR: Karen Mathieu, Director Human Resources
CNO: Mary Norman, R.N., Chief Nursing Officer
Web address: www.bvchd.com
**Control:** Hospital district or authority, Government, nonfederal **Service:** General Medical and Surgical

| Staffed Beds: 30 |
| --- |

## BISHOP—Inyo County

⊞ **NORTHERN INYO HOSPITAL (051324)**, 150 Pioneer Lane, Zip 93514–2599; tel. 760/873–5811 **A**1 9 10 18 **F**3 11 13 15 31 34 40 45 46 47 64 68 70 76 77 79 81 85 89 93 107 108 111 115 119 124 127 130 133
Primary Contact: John Halfen, Administrator, Chief Executive Officer and Chief Financial Officer
CFO: John Halfen, Administrator, Chief Executive Officer and Chief Financial Officer
CMO: Charlotte Helvie, M.D., Chief of Staff
CIO: Adam Taylor, Manager Information Technology
CHR: Georgan L. Stottlemyre, Director Human Resources
Web address: www.nih.org
**Control:** Hospital district or authority, Government, nonfederal **Service:** General Medical and Surgical

| Staffed Beds: 25 Admissions: 846 Census: 7 Outpatient Visits: 65747 Births: 125 Total Expense ($000): 54913 Payroll Expense ($000): 20406 Personnel: 319 |
| --- |

## BLYTHE—Riverside County

☐ **PALO VERDE HOSPITAL (050423)**, 250 North First Street, Zip 92225–1702; tel. 760/922–4115, (Nonreporting) **A**1 9 10 20
Primary Contact: Peter Klune, Chief Executive Officer
CFO: Dennis E. Rutherford, Chief Financial Officer
CMO: Mohommad Bahktavar, M.D., Chief of Staff
CIO: James C. Mayes, Manager Information Technology and Chief Security Officer
CHR: Rebecca Morse, Chief Human Resources Officer
CNO: Tara Barth, Chief Nursing Officer
Web address: www.paloverdehospital.org
**Control:** Hospital district or authority, Government, nonfederal **Service:** General Medical and Surgical

| Staffed Beds: 20 |
| --- |

## BRAWLEY—Imperial County

☐ ◇ **PIONEERS MEMORIAL HEALTHCARE DISTRICT (050342)**, 207 West Legion Road, Zip 92227–7780; tel. 760/351–3333 **A**1 9 10 21 **F**3 11 13 15 18 29 30 31 34 35 40 43 45 49 51 53 54 57 59 64 65 70 73 74 75 76 77 78 79 81 82 85 86 89 93 97 107 108 110 111 114 115 118 119 127 130 144 146 147 148
Primary Contact: Larry Lewis, Chief Executive Officer
COO: Stephen J. Campbell, Chief Operating Officer
CFO: Daniel W. Smith, Chief Financial Officer
CMO: Travis Calvin, Jr., M.D., Chief of Staff
CIO: Doug Darby, Director Information Systems
CHR: Robert Honaker, Associate Administrator and Chief Human Resources Officer
Web address: www.pmhd.org
**Control:** Hospital district or authority, Government, nonfederal **Service:** General Medical and Surgical

| Staffed Beds: 107 Admissions: 6210 Census: 55 Outpatient Visits: 100308 Births: 1726 Total Expense ($000): 98996 Payroll Expense ($000): 38212 Personnel: 692 |
| --- |

## BREA—Orange County

⊞ **KINDRED HOSPITAL–BREA (052039)**, 875 North Brea Boulevard, Zip 92821–2699; tel. 714/529–6842, (Nonreporting) **A**1 9 10 **S** Kindred Healthcare, Louisville, KY
Primary Contact: Diane Zeoli, Chief Executive Officer
COO: Denise Jenkins, Chief Clinical Officer
CFO: John Browne, Assistant Administrator Finance
CMO: Jyotika Wali, M.D., Chief of Staff
Web address: www.kindredhospitalbrea.com/
**Control:** Corporation, Investor–owned, for–profit **Service:** Long–Term Acute Care hospital

| Staffed Beds: 48 |
| --- |

## BURBANK—Los Angeles County

⊞ △ **PROVIDENCE SAINT JOSEPH MEDICAL CENTER (050235)**, 501 South Buena Vista Street, Zip 91505–4866; tel. 818/843–5111 **A**1 2 7 9 10 **F**3 11 12 13 14 15 17 18 20 21 22 24 26 28 29 30 31 34 35 36 40 44 45 46 50 53 54 56 57 58 59 62 63 64 68 70 72 74 75 76 77 78 79 81 82 83 84 86 87 90 93 107 108 110 111 114 116 117 118 119 121 126 128 130 132 134 143 144 146 147 148 **S** Providence Health & Services, Renton, WA
Primary Contact: Michael A. Rembis, FACHE, Chief Executive Officer
CFO: Dave Mast, Chief Financial Officer
CMO: Myron Berdischewsky, M.D., Chief Medical Officer
CIO: Douglas Jones, Interim Chief Information Officer
CHR: John Saavedra, Service Area Director Human Resources
Web address: www.providence.org
**Control:** Church–operated, Nongovernment, not–for profit **Service:** General Medical and Surgical

| Staffed Beds: 446 Admissions: 18260 Census: 230 Outpatient Visits: 348901 Births: 2449 Total Expense ($000): 371995 Payroll Expense ($000): 151680 Personnel: 1850 |
| --- |

## BURLINGAME—San Mateo County

⊞ **MILLS–PENINSULA HEALTH SERVICES (050007)**, 1501 Trousdale Drive, Zip 94010–3282; tel. 650/696–5400, (Includes MILLS HOSPITAL, 100 South San Mateo Drive, San Mateo, Zip 94401; tel. 415/696–4400; PENINSULA HOSPITAL, 1783 El Camino Real, Zip 94010–3205; tel. 650/696–5400), (Total facility includes 137 beds in nursing home–type unit) **A**1 9 10 **F**2 3 4 5 6 9 11 12 13 15 17 18 20 22 24 26 28 29 30 31 34 35 36 38 40 46 47 48 49 51 53 54 56 57 59 60 64 65 66 68 72 75 76 77 78 79 81 84 85 86 87 89 90 91 93 97 98 99 100 101 102 103 104 105 107 108 109 110 111 112 114 115 116 117 118 119 120 121 122 123 124 128 129 130 132 135 143 146 147 **S** Sutter Health, Sacramento, CA
Primary Contact: Robert W. Merwin, Chief Executive Officer
CFO: Iftikhar Hussain, Chief Financial Officer
CMO: Michael K. Wood, M.D., Chief Medical Officer
CIO: Michael Reandeau, Chief Information Officer
CHR: Debbie Goodin, Vice President Human Resources
Web address: www.mills–peninsula.org
**Control:** Other not–for–profit (including NFP Corporation) **Service:** General Medical and Surgical

| Staffed Beds: 393 Admissions: 14678 Census: 238 Outpatient Visits: 329164 Births: 1882 Total Expense ($000): 491617 Payroll Expense ($000): 143725 Personnel: 1593 |
| --- |

## CAMARILLO—Ventura County

⊞ **ST. JOHN'S PLEASANT VALLEY HOSPITAL (050616)**, 2309 Antonio Avenue, Zip 93010–1414; tel. 805/389–5800, (Nonreporting) **A**1 9 10 **S** Dignity Health, San Francisco, CA
Primary Contact: Laurie Eberst, R.N., President and Chief Executive Officer and Senior Vice President Operations Dignity Health Southern C
COO: Kim A. Wilson, R.N., Chief Operating Officer
CFO: Robert D. Wardwell, Chief Financial Officer
CMO: Eugene Fussell, M.D., Chief Medical Officer
CIO: Jeff Perry, Director Information Technology
CHR: Ed Gonzales, Vice PResident Human Resources
CNO: Raye Burkhardt, Chief Nursing Officer
Web address: www.stjohnshealth.org
**Control:** Other not–for–profit (including NFP Corporation) **Service:** General Medical and Surgical

| Staffed Beds: 127 |
| --- |

## CAMP PENDLETON—San Diego County

⊞ **NAVAL HOSPITAL CAMP PENDLETON**, (Formerly Naval Hospital), Santa Margarita Road, Building H100, Zip 92055–5191, Mailing Address: P.O. Box 555191, Zip 92055–5191; tel. 760/725–1304, (Nonreporting) **A**1 3 5 **S** Bureau of Medicine and Surgery, Department of the Navy, Washington, DC
Primary Contact: Commander Alan Christian
CFO: Commander Gordon Blighton, Director Resource Management
CMO: Lynn Bailey, M.D., Director Primary Care and Medical Services
CIO: Gabe Vallido, Chief Information Officer
CHR: Lieutenant Jet Ramos, Head Staff Administration
Web address: www.cpen.med.navy.mil/
**Control:** Navy, Government, federal **Service:** General Medical and Surgical

| Staffed Beds: 72 |
| --- |

## CANOGA PARK—Los Angeles County, See Los Angeles

---

**Hospital, Medicare Provider Number, Address, Telephone, Approval, Facility, and Physician Codes, Health Care System**

★ American Hospital Association (AHA) membership
☐ The Joint Commission accreditation
◇ DNV Healthcare Inc. accreditation
○ Healthcare Facilities Accreditation Program
△ Commission on Accreditation of Rehabilitation Facilities (CARF) accreditation

## CARMICHAEL—Sacramento County

✠ **MERCY SAN JUAN MEDICAL CENTER (050516)**, 6501 Coyle Avenue, Zip 95608–0306, Mailing Address: P.O. Box 479, Zip 95609–0479; tel. 916/537–5000, (Nonreporting) **A**1 2 3 5 9 10 **S** Dignity Health, San Francisco, CA
Primary Contact: Brian K. Ivie, President
COO: Paul R. Luehrs, Chief Operating Officer
CFO: Robert Pascuzzi, Chief Financial Officer
CMO: Mark Owens, M.D., Vice President Medical Affairs
CHR: Donna Utley, Vice President Human Resources
Web address: www.mercysanjuan.org
**Control:** Church–operated, Nongovernment, not–for profit **Service:** General Medical and Surgical

| Staffed Beds: 359 |
|---|

## CASTRO VALLEY—Alameda County

✠ **EDEN MEDICAL CENTER (050488)**, 20103 Lake Chabot Road, Zip 94546–5305; tel. 510/537–1234, (Includes SAN LEANDRO HOSPITAL, 13855 East 14th Street, San Leandro, Zip 94578–2600; tel. 510/357–6500; Ronnie Bayduza, Administrator) **A**1 2 9 10 **F**3 11 13 15 17 29 30 31 34 35 38 40 43 49 50 51 53 56 57 58 59 60 64 65 68 70 72 74 75 76 77 78 79 81 84 85 87 89 90 93 98 100 102 107 108 110 111 114 116 117 118 119 124 130 132 135 143 144 145 146 147 148 **S** Sutter Health, Sacramento, CA
Primary Contact: George Bischalaney, President and Chief Executive Officer
Web address: www.edenmedcenter.org
**Control:** Other not–for–profit (including NFP Corporation) **Service:** General Medical and Surgical

| Staffed Beds: 199 Admissions: 9117 Census: 102 Outpatient Visits: 56931 Births: 1173 Total Expense ($000): 366041 Payroll Expense ($000): 137244 Personnel: 853 |
|---|

## CEDARVILLE—Modoc County

**SURPRISE VALLEY HEALTHCARE DISTRICT (051308)**, 741 North Main Street, Zip 96104, Mailing Address: P.O. Box 246, Zip 96104–0246; tel. 530/279–6111, (Nonreporting) **A**9 10 18
Primary Contact: Kelley Gentry, Chief Executive Officer
CFO: Renae Sweet, Chief Financial Officer
CMO: Chuck Colas, M.D., Medical Director
CHR: William Bostic, Administrative Assistant Human Resources
Web address: www.svhospital.org/
**Control:** Hospital district or authority, Government, nonfederal **Service:** General Medical and Surgical

| Staffed Beds: 4 |
|---|

## CERRITOS—Los Angeles County

☐ **COLLEGE HOSPITAL (054055)**, 10802 College Place, Zip 90703–1579; tel. 562/924–9581, (Nonreporting) **A**1 9 10 **S** College Health Enterprises, Santa Fe Springs, CA
Primary Contact: Stephen Witt, President and Chief Executive Officer
CFO: Roderick Bell, Chief Financial Officer
CHR: Holly Risha, Administrative Director Human Resources
Web address: www.collegehospitals.com
**Control:** Corporation, Investor–owned, for–profit **Service:** Psychiatric

| Staffed Beds: 157 |
|---|

## CHESTER—Plumas County

★ **SENECA HEALTHCARE DISTRICT (051327)**, 130 Brentwood Drive, Zip 96020–0737, Mailing Address: P.O. Box 737, Zip 96020–0737; tel. 530/258–2151, (Total facility includes 16 beds in nursing home–type unit) **A**9 10 18 **F**34 35 40 46 54 57 59 65 66 68 75 79 81 82 85 93 97 107 108 111 114 119 127 128 131 133 135 146 148
Primary Contact: Linda S. Wagner, MSN, Chief Executive Officer
CMO: Steen Jensen, M.D., Chief of Staff
CHR: Marie Stuersel, Director Human Resources
Web address: www.senecahospital.org
**Control:** Hospital district or authority, Government, nonfederal **Service:** General Medical and Surgical

| Staffed Beds: 26 Admissions: 211 Census: 16 Outpatient Visits: 31225 Births: 0 Personnel: 107 |
|---|

## CHICO—Butte County

✠ **ENLOE MEDICAL CENTER (050039)**, 1531 Esplanade, Zip 95926–3386; tel. 530/332–7300, (Includes ENLOE MEDICAL CENTER–COHASSET, 560 Cohasset Road, Zip 95926; tel. 530/332–7300), (Nonreporting) **A**1 9 10
Primary Contact: Michael C. Wiltermood, President and Chief Executive Officer
CMO: Forrest Olson, M.D., Chief Medical Officer
CHR: Carol Linscheid, Vice President Human Resources
Web address: www.enloe.org
**Control:** Other not–for–profit (including NFP Corporation) **Service:** General Medical and Surgical

| Staffed Beds: 265 |
|---|

## CHINO—San Bernardino County

○ **CANYON RIDGE HOSPITAL (054111)**, 5353 G Street, Zip 91710–5250; tel. 909/590–3700, (Nonreporting) **A**9 10 11 **S** Universal Health Services, Inc., King of Prussia, PA
Primary Contact: Jeff McDonald, Chief Executive Officer
CFO: Burt Harris, Chief Financial Officer
CMO: Mir Ali–Khan, M.D., Medical Director
CIO: Maria Patterson, Manager Health Information Management
CHR: Ericca Lopez, Director Human Resources
Web address: www.canyonridgehospital.com
**Control:** Corporation, Investor–owned, for–profit **Service:** Psychiatric

| Staffed Beds: 106 |
|---|

○ **CHINO VALLEY MEDICAL CENTER (050586)**, 5451 Walnut Avenue, Zip 91710–2672; tel. 909/464–8600, (Nonreporting) **A**10 11 12 13 **S** Prime Healthcare Services, Ontario, CA
Primary Contact: James M. Lally, D.O., President and Chief Medical Officer
CFO: Gregory Brentano, Chief Financial Officer
CIO: Vic Mahan, Chief Information Officer
CHR: Arti Dhuper, Regional Director Human Resources
Web address: www.cvmc.com
**Control:** Corporation, Investor–owned, for–profit **Service:** General Medical and Surgical

| Staffed Beds: 112 |
|---|

## CHULA VISTA—San Diego County

**SCRIPPS MERCY HOSPITAL CHULA VISTA** See Scripps Mercy Hospital, San Diego

✠ **SHARP CHULA VISTA MEDICAL CENTER (050222)**, 751 Medical Center Court, Zip 91911–6699, Mailing Address: P.O. Box 1297, Zip 91912–1297; tel. 619/502–5800, (Total facility includes 100 beds in nursing home–type unit) **A**1 2 9 10 **F**8 11 12 13 15 18 20 22 24 26 28 29 30 31 34 35 40 46 47 49 51 53 54 57 59 60 64 65 70 72 75 76 77 78 79 81 82 85 86 87 93 94 107 108 111 114 115 118 119 120 121 123 126 128 130 132 143 146 147 148 **P**5 **S** Sharp HealthCare, San Diego, CA
Primary Contact: Pablo Velez, Chief Executive Officer
CMO: Francisco Anguiano, M.D., Chief of Staff
CHR: Zoe Gardner, Manager Human Resources
Web address: www.sharp.com
**Control:** Other not–for–profit (including NFP Corporation) **Service:** General Medical and Surgical

| Staffed Beds: 343 Admissions: 15211 Census: 289 Outpatient Visits: 97262 Births: 2868 Total Expense ($000): 294066 Payroll Expense ($000): 122117 Personnel: 1481 |
|---|

## CLEARLAKE—Lake County

✠ **ST. HELENA HOSPITAL CLEAR LAKE (051317)**, (Formerly St. Helena Hospital Clearlake), 15630 18th Avenue, Zip 95422–9336, Mailing Address: P.O. Box 6710, Zip 95422; tel. 707/994–6486, (Nonreporting) **A**1 9 10 18 **S** Adventist Health, Roseville, CA
Primary Contact: Terry Newmyer, President and Chief Executive Officer
COO: David Santos, Chief Operating Officer (VP Operations)
CFO: Buck McDonald, Chief Financial Officer
CMO: Marc Shapiro, M.D., Chief Medical Officer
CIO: Joshua Cowan, Chief Information Officer
CHR: Wendi Fox, Human Resources Administrative Director
CNO: Joan Rogers, R.N., Chief Nursing Officer
Web address: www.adventisthealth.org
**Control:** Church–operated, Nongovernment, not–for profit **Service:** General Medical and Surgical

| Staffed Beds: 25 |
|---|

## CLOVIS—Fresno County

☐ **CLOVIS COMMUNITY MEDICAL CENTER (050492)**, 2755 Herndon Avenue, Zip 93611–6800; tel. 559/324–4000, (Nonreporting) **A**1 9 10 **S** Community Medical Centers, Fresno, CA
Primary Contact: Craig Castro, Chief Executive Officer
COO: Craig Waggoner, Chief Operating Officer
CFO: Tracy Kiritani, Vice President and Chief Financial Officer
CIO: George Vasquez, Chief Technology Officer
CHR: Ginny Burdick, Senior Vice President and Chief Human Resources Officer
Web address: www.communitymedical.org
**Control:** Other not–for–profit (including NFP Corporation) **Service:** General Medical and Surgical

| Staffed Beds: 109 |
|---|

CA

*Many Facility Codes have changed. Please refer to the AHA Guide Code Chart.*   © 2013 AHA Guide

## COALINGA—Fresno County

**COALINGA REGIONAL MEDICAL CENTER (050397)**, 1191 Phelps Avenue, Zip 93210–9609; tel. 559/935–6400, (Total facility includes 99 beds in nursing home–type unit) **A**9 10 20 **F**15 32 35 40 41 50 57 59 65 66 68 89 90 93 102 107 110 115 119 127 128 130 143 148
Primary Contact: Sharon A. Spurgeon, Chief Executive Officer
CFO: Sandra Earls, Chief Financial Officer
CMO: Lymar Bik, M.D., Medical Director
CIO: Rachael Diaz, Systems Operator
CHR: Amber Stiglianese, Manager Human Resources
CNO: Betty Hull, R.N., Director Patient Services
Web address: www.coalingamedicalcenter.com
**Control:** Hospital district or authority, Government, nonfederal **Service:** General Medical and Surgical

| | |
|---|---|
| **Staffed Beds:** 123 **Admissions:** 521 **Census:** 75 **Outpatient Visits:** 26699 **Births:** 0 **Total Expense ($000):** 22613 **Payroll Expense ($000):** 9587 **Personnel:** 215 | |

## COLTON—San Bernardino County

○ **ARROWHEAD REGIONAL MEDICAL CENTER (050245)**, 400 North Pepper Avenue, Zip 92324–1819; tel. 909/580–1000 **A**2 3 5 9 10 11 12 13 **F**3 8 13 15 16 18 20 22 28 29 30 31 32 34 35 36 39 40 43 45 47 49 50 51 52 54 55 56 57 60 64 66 68 70 71 72 74 75 76 77 78 79 81 82 84 85 86 87 89 92 93 97 98 100 101 102 106 107 108 110 111 114 115 118 119 120 121 130 132 135 146 147 148 **P**5
Primary Contact: Patrick A. Petre, Administrator
COO: Maureen A. Malone, Chief Operating Officer
CFO: Frank Arambula, Chief Financial Officer
CMO: Dev GnanaDev, M.D., Medical Director
CIO: Felix Ekpo, Interim Manager Information Systems
CHR: Victor Tordesillas, Director Human Resources
CNO: Michelle Sayre, R.N., Chief Nursing Officer
Web address: www.arrowheadmedcenter.org
**Control:** County–Government, nonfederal **Service:** General Medical and Surgical

| | |
|---|---|
| **Staffed Beds:** 436 **Admissions:** 24424 **Census:** 320 **Outpatient Visits:** 364945 **Births:** 2768 **Total Expense ($000):** 566131 **Payroll Expense ($000):** 160113 **Personnel:** 2683 | |

## COLUSA—Colusa County

⊠ **COLUSA REGIONAL MEDICAL CENTER (050434)**, 199 East Webster Street, Zip 95932–2954, Mailing Address: P.O. Box 331, Zip 95932–0331; tel. 530/458–5821, (Total facility includes 6 beds in nursing home–type unit) **A**1 9 10 20 **F**29 30 35 40 53 54 57 59 62 64 65 68 70 75 76 77 81 84 85 107 119 128 129 130 133 144 146
Primary Contact: Katherine Hughes, R.N., Interim Chief Operating Officer
CFO: Terry Deak, Chief Financial Officer
CMO: Samuel Medrano, M.D., Chief of Staff
CIO: Rachel Betke–Mena, Director Health Information Management
CHR: Dierdre Athenais, Director Human Resources
Web address: www.colusamedicalcenter.org
**Control:** Other not–for–profit (including NFP Corporation) **Service:** General Medical and Surgical

| | |
|---|---|
| **Staffed Beds:** 30 **Admissions:** 994 **Census:** 11 **Outpatient Visits:** 51756 **Births:** 165 **Total Expense ($000):** 19901 **Payroll Expense ($000):** 8982 **Personnel:** 154 | |

## CONCORD—Contra Costa County

⊠ **JOHN MUIR BEHAVIORAL HEALTH CENTER (054131)**, 2740 Grant Street, Zip 94520–2265; tel. 925/674–4100, (Nonreporting) **A**1 9 10 **S** John Muir Health, Walnut Creek, CA
Primary Contact: Elizabeth Stallings, Chief Operating Officer
COO: Elizabeth Stallings, Chief Operating Officer
CFO: Michael Moody, Senior Vice President and Chief Financial Officer
CMO: Nagui Achamallah, M.D., Chief of Staff
CIO: Eric Saff, Senior Vice President and Chief Information Officer
CHR: Alice A. Villanueva, Senior Vice President Human Resources
Web address: www.johnmuirhealth.com
**Control:** Other not–for–profit (including NFP Corporation) **Service:** Psychiatric

| | |
|---|---|
| **Staffed Beds:** 70 | |

⊠ **JOHN MUIR MEDICAL CENTER, CONCORD (050496)**, 2540 East Street, Zip 94520–1906; tel. 925/682–8200 **A**1 9 10 **F**3 12 15 17 18 20 22 24 26 28 29 30 31 34 37 40 44 45 46 47 48 49 50 54 56 57 58 59 64 70 74 75 78 79 80 81 82 84 85 86 87 93 107 108 110 114 115 118 119 120 121 123 126 130 132 135 141 143 145 146 148 **P**3 5 **S** John Muir Health, Walnut Creek, CA
Primary Contact: Michael S. Thomas, President and Chief Administrative Officer
COO: Michael S. Thomas, President and Chief Administrative Officer
CFO: Michael Moody, Chief Financial Officer
CMO: Hartwell Lin, M.D., Chief of Staff
CIO: Jim Wesley, Interim Senior Vice President and Chief Information Officer
CHR: Alice A. Villanueva, Vice President Human Resources
CNO: Donna Brackley, Senior Vice President Patient Care Services
Web address: www.johnmuirhealth.com
**Control:** Other not–for–profit (including NFP Corporation) **Service:** General Medical and Surgical

| | |
|---|---|
| **Staffed Beds:** 182 **Admissions:** 9583 **Census:** 119 **Outpatient Visits:** 186720 **Births:** 0 **Total Expense ($000):** 354214 **Payroll Expense ($000):** 143328 **Personnel:** 1128 | |

## CORCORAN—Kings County

★ **CORCORAN DISTRICT HOSPITAL (050349)**, 1310 Hanna Avenue, Zip 93212–2314, Mailing Address: P.O. Box 758, Zip 93212–0758; tel. 559/992–5051, (Nonreporting) **A**9 10
Primary Contact: Vonnie Nunes, Interim Chief Executive Officer
CIO: Eva Pierce, Chief Information Officer
CHR: Jose Romero, Director Human Resources
Web address: www.corcoranhospital.org
**Control:** Hospital district or authority, Government, nonfederal **Service:** General Medical and Surgical

| | |
|---|---|
| **Staffed Beds:** 20 | |

## CORONA—Riverside County

☐ **CORONA REGIONAL MEDICAL CENTER (050329)**, 800 South Main Street, Zip 92882–3420; tel. 951/737–4343, (Includes CORONA REGIONAL MEDICAL CENTER–REHABILITATION, 730 Magnolia Avenue, Zip 92879; tel. 951/736–7200), (Nonreporting) **A**1 9 10 **S** Universal Health Services, Inc., King of Prussia, PA
Primary Contact: Kevan Metcalfe, Chief Executive Officer
CFO: Becky Cheng, Chief Financial Officer
CMO: Michael Molinari, M.D., Chief of Staff
CIO: Tura Heckler, Director Information Systems
CHR: Ruth Battles, Administrative Director Human Resources
Web address: www.coronaregional.com
**Control:** Corporation, Investor–owned, for–profit **Service:** General Medical and Surgical

| | |
|---|---|
| **Staffed Beds:** 240 | |

## CORONADO—San Diego County

⊠ **SHARP CORONADO HOSPITAL AND HEALTHCARE CENTER (050234)**, 250 Prospect Place, Zip 92118–1999; tel. 619/522–3600, (Total facility includes 108 beds in nursing home–type unit) **A**1 9 10 **F**3 11 15 29 30 34 35 36 37 39 40 43 45 51 53 57 59 60 64 65 68 69 70 74 75 77 79 81 85 86 87 93 104 107 111 114 119 120 126 128 130 135 146 148 **S** Sharp HealthCare, San Diego, CA
Primary Contact: Susan Stone, R.N., Ph.D., Senior Vice President and Chief Executive Officer
COO: Tony Guerra, Chief Financial Officer and Chief Operating Officer
CFO: Tony Guerra, Chief Financial Officer and Chief Operating Officer
CHR: George Holtz, Manager Human Resources
Web address: www.sharp.com
**Control:** Other not–for–profit (including NFP Corporation) **Service:** General Medical and Surgical

| | |
|---|---|
| **Staffed Beds:** 154 **Admissions:** 2963 **Census:** 122 **Outpatient Visits:** 56654 **Births:** 0 **Total Expense ($000):** 78453 **Payroll Expense ($000):** 35121 **Personnel:** 436 | |

## COSTA MESA—Orange County

☐ **COLLEGE HOSPITAL COSTA MESA (050543)**, 301 Victoria Street, Zip 92627–7131; tel. 949/642–2734, (Nonreporting) **A**1 9 10 **S** College Health Enterprises, Santa Fe Springs, CA
Primary Contact: Susan L. Taylor, Chief Executive Officer
CFO: Dale Bracy, Chief Financial Officer
CMO: Craig A. Ross, M.D., Chief of Staff
CIO: Red Ladiana, Manager Information Systems
CHR: Sharon DuBruyne, Administrative Director Support Service and Human Resources
Web address: www.collegehospitals.com/cosHome
**Control:** Corporation, Investor–owned, for–profit **Service:** Psychiatric

| | |
|---|---|
| **Staffed Beds:** 122 | |

---

**Hospital, Medicare Provider Number, Address, Telephone, Approval, Facility, and Physician Codes, Health Care System**

★ American Hospital Association (AHA) membership
☐ The Joint Commission accreditation
◇ DNV Healthcare Inc. accreditation
○ Healthcare Facilities Accreditation Program
△ Commission on Accreditation of Rehabilitation Facilities (CARF) accreditation

### COVINA—Los Angeles County

☐ **AURORA CHARTER OAK HOSPITAL (054069)**, 1161 East Covina Boulevard, Zip 91724–1599; tel. 626/966–1632, (Nonreporting) **A**1 9 10 **S** Aurora Behavioral Health Care, Corona, CA
Primary Contact: Todd A. Smith, Chief Executive Officer
COO: Sheila Cordova, Director Clinical Services and Chief Operating Officer
CFO: Cory Delello, Chief Financial Officer
CMO: Adib Bitar, M.D., Medical Director
CHR: Christine de la Paz, Director Human Resources
Web address: www.aurorabehavioral.com
**Control:** Corporation, Investor–owned, for–profit **Service:** Psychiatric

**Staffed Beds:** 95

**CITRUS VALLEY MEDICAL CENTER (050382)**, 210 West San Bernadino Road, Zip 91723–1515, Mailing Address: P.O. Box 6108, Zip 91722–5108; tel. 626/331–7331, (Includes CITRUS VALLEY MEDICAL CENTER–INTER–COMMUNITY CAMPUS, 210 West San Bernardino Road, Mailing Address: P.O. Box 6108, Zip 91722–5108; tel. 626/331–7331; CITRUS VALLEY MEDICAL CENTER–QUEEN OF THE VALLEY CAMPUS, 1115 South Sunset Avenue, West Covina, Zip 91790–3940, Mailing Address: P.O. Box 1980, Zip 91793–1980; tel. 626/962–4011) **A**9 10 **F**3 7 8 11 13 15 17 18 20 22 24 25 26 27 28 29 30 31 32 34 35 40 41 44 45 46 47 49 50 51 55 56 57 59 64 65 68 69 70 71 72 74 75 76 77 78 79 80 81 82 83 84 85 86 87 89 90 92 93 96 98 102 103 105 107 108 110 114 115 118 119 120 121 124 126 128 129 130 131 132 135 143 146 147 148 **S** Citrus Valley Health Partners, Covina, CA
Primary Contact: Robert H. Curry, President and Chief Executive Officer
COO: Elvia Foulke, Executive Vice President Healthcare Delivery and Chief Operating Officer
CFO: Lois Conyers, Senior Vice President and Chief Financial Officer
CMO: Richard Gisi, M.D., Chief Medical Officer
CIO: David McCobb, Chief Information Officer
CHR: Lisa Foust, Senior Vice President Human Resources
Web address: www.cvhp.org
**Control:** Other not–for–profit (including NFP Corporation) **Service:** General Medical and Surgical

**Staffed Beds:** 343 **Admissions:** 26452 **Census:** 303 **Outpatient Visits:** 161393 **Births:** 4234 **Total Expense ($000):** 343681 **Payroll Expense ($000):** 119498 **Personnel:** 2101

### CRESCENT CITY—Del Norte County

⊠ **SUTTER COAST HOSPITAL (050417)**, 800 East Washington Boulevard, Zip 95531–8359; tel. 707/464–8511 **A**1 9 10 20 **F**3 8 11 13 15 29 30 34 35 40 43 45 50 51 54 57 59 62 68 70 75 76 79 81 82 84 85 87 93 97 107 108 110 114 118 119 127 130 132 135 144 146 148 **S** Sutter Health, Sacramento, CA
Primary Contact: Linda Horn, Interim Chief Executive Officer
CFO: Judi Swartout, Chief Financial Officer
Web address: www.sutterhealth.org
**Control:** Other not–for–profit (including NFP Corporation) **Service:** General Medical and Surgical

**Staffed Beds:** 49 **Admissions:** 2204 **Census:** 19 **Outpatient Visits:** 42947 **Births:** 332 **Total Expense ($000):** 67446 **Payroll Expense ($000):** 22317 **Personnel:** 394

### CULVER CITY—Los Angeles County

◇ **BROTMAN MEDICAL CENTER (050752)**, 3828 Delmas Terrace, Zip 90232–6806; tel. 310/836–7000, (Nonreporting) **A**9 10 21
Primary Contact: Barbara Schneider, R.N., Chief Executive Officer
COO: Diane Rafferty, Chief Operating Officer
CFO: Vincent Rubin, Chief Financial Officer
CMO: Martha Sonnenberg, M.D., Chief of Staff
CIO: Carrie Bonar, Chief Information Officer
CHR: Betty J. Harris, Director Human Resources
Web address: www.brotmanmedicalcenter.com
**Control:** Corporation, Investor–owned, for–profit **Service:** General Medical and Surgical

**Staffed Beds:** 232

### DALY CITY—San Mateo County

⊠ **SETON MEDICAL CENTER (050289)**, 1900 Sullivan Avenue, Zip 94015–2229; tel. 650/992–4000, (Nonreporting) **A**1 2 9 10 **S** Daughters of Charity Health System, Los Altos Hills, CA
Primary Contact: Joanne E. Allen, President and Chief Executive Officer
COO: Stephanie Mearns, Vice President Patient Care Services and Chief Nurse Executive
CFO: Richard Wood, Chief Financial Officer
CMO: David Goldschmid, M.D., President Medical Staff
CIO: David Kerrins, Vice President Informatics, Information Technology and Chief Informatics Officer
CHR: Patricia White, Vice President Human Resources
Web address: www.setonmedicalcenter.org
**Control:** Church–operated, Nongovernment, not–for profit **Service:** General Medical and Surgical

**Staffed Beds:** 429

### DAVIS—Yolo County

⊠ **SUTTER DAVIS HOSPITAL (050537)**, 2000 Sutter Place, Zip 95616–6201, Mailing Address: P.O. Box 1617, Zip 95617–1617; tel. 530/756–6440 **A**1 3 5 9 10 **F**3 8 11 13 15 29 31 40 47 48 49 57 70 75 76 78 79 81 85 86 107 108 114 118 119 124 146 **S** Sutter Health, Sacramento, CA
Primary Contact: Janet Wagner, R.N., Chief Executive Officer
CFO: Richard SooHoo, Chief Financial Officer
CMO: Daniel Kennedy, M.D., Chief of Staff
CHR: Eva Hilliard, Director Human Resources
CNO: Tracy Needham, Director of Nursing
Web address: www.sutterhealth.org
**Control:** Other not–for–profit (including NFP Corporation) **Service:** General Medical and Surgical

**Staffed Beds:** 48 **Admissions:** 3357 **Census:** 24 **Outpatient Visits:** 40285 **Births:** 1346 **Total Expense ($000):** 77665 **Payroll Expense ($000):** 25173 **Personnel:** 288

### DELANO—Kern County

○ **DELANO REGIONAL MEDICAL CENTER (050608)**, 1401 Garces Highway, Zip 93215–3690, Mailing Address: P.O. Box 460, Zip 93216–0460; tel. 661/725–4800, (Nonreporting) **A**9 10 11
Primary Contact: Bahram Ghaffari, Executive Director and Chief Financial Officer
CFO: Bahram Ghaffari, Executive Director and Chief Financial Officer
CIO: Sandy Bakich, Director Information Management
CHR: Del Garbanzos, Director Human Resources
Web address: www.drmc.com
**Control:** Other not–for–profit (including NFP Corporation) **Service:** General Medical and Surgical

**Staffed Beds:** 100

### DOWNEY—Los Angeles County

☐ ◇ **DOWNEY REGIONAL MEDICAL CENTER (050393)**, 11500 Brookshire Avenue, Zip 90241–4917; tel. 562/904–5000, (Nonreporting) **A**1 9 10 12 13 21
Primary Contact: Kenneth Strople, President and Chief Executive Officer
COO: Robert Fuller, Executive Vice President and Chief Operating Officer
CFO: Ed King, Chief Financial Officer
CIO: Nick Pappas, Chief Information Officer
CHR: Carole Everhart, Administrative Director Human Resources
CNO: Heather Conwell, Chief Nursing Officer
Web address: www.drmci.org
**Control:** Other not–for–profit (including NFP Corporation) **Service:** General Medical and Surgical

**Staffed Beds:** 181

★ ◇ **KAISER PERMANENTE DOWNEY MEDICAL CENTER (050139)**, 9333 Imperial Highway, Zip 90242–2812; tel. 562/657–9000 **A**10 21 **F**3 8 13 15 18 19 29 30 31 35 38 40 45 46 49 51 58 60 64 65 68 70 72 74 75 76 78 79 81 82 83 84 85 87 88 89 92 100 107 110 111 114 115 119 126 130 132 146 148 **S** Kaiser Foundation Hospitals, Oakland, CA
Primary Contact: E. Jane Finley, Senior Vice President and Executive Director
COO: Jim Branchick, R.N., Chief Operating Officer
CNO: Patricia J. Clausen, R.N., Chief Nurse Executive
Web address: www.kaiserpermanente.org
**Control:** Other not–for–profit (including NFP Corporation) **Service:** General Medical and Surgical

**Staffed Beds:** 342 **Admissions:** 16741 **Census:** 210 **Outpatient Visits:** 158861 **Births:** 3175 **Personnel:** 3063

☐ △ **RANCHO LOS AMIGOS NATIONAL REHABILITATION CENTER (050717)**, 7601 East Imperial Highway, Zip 90242–3496; tel. 562/401–7022, (Nonreporting) **A**1 3 5 7 9 10 **S** Los Angeles County–Department of Health Services, Los Angeles, CA
Primary Contact: Jorge Orozco, Chief Executive Officer
COO: Benjamin Ovando, Chief Operations Officer
CFO: Robin Bayus, Chief Financial Officer
CMO: Mindy Aisen, M.D., Chief Medical Officer
CIO: Betty Romeo, Chief Information Officer
CHR: Melinda Fonseca, Associate Director Human Resources
CNO: Michelle Sterling, R.N., Acting Chief Nursing Officer
Web address: www.rancho.org
**Control:** County–Government, nonfederal **Service:** Rehabilitation

**Staffed Beds:** 207

CA

## DUARTE—Los Angeles County

☒ **CITY OF HOPE'S HELFORD CLINICAL RESEARCH HOSPITAL (050146)**, 1500 East Duarte Road, Zip 91010–3012; tel. 626/256–4673 **A**1 2 3 5 8 9 10 **F**3 8 11 14 15 18 26 29 30 31 32 34 35 36 38 44 45 46 47 49 50 55 56 57 58 59 61 63 64 68 70 74 75 77 78 79 80 81 82 84 85 86 87 88 89 92 93 96 99 100 101 102 103 104 107 108 110 111 114 115 116 117 118 119 120 121 123 124 126 130 132 134 135 136 141 142 144 145 146 147 148 **P**3
Primary Contact: Michael A. Friedman, M.D., President and Chief Executive Officer
COO: Marty Sargeant, Chief Operating Officer
CFO: Gary F. Conner, Chief Financial Officer
CMO: Alexandra Levine, M.D., Chief Medical Officer
CIO: Paul Conocenti, Chief Information Officer
CHR: Stephanie Neuvirth, Chief Human Resource and Diversity Officer
Web address: www.cityofhope.org
**Control:** Other not–for–profit (including NFP Corporation) **Service:** Cancer

**Staffed Beds:** 185 **Admissions:** 6187 **Census:** 163 **Outpatient Visits:** 177877 **Total Expense ($000):** 632727 **Payroll Expense ($000):** 219505 **Personnel:** 2895

## EL CENTRO—Imperial County

☒ **EL CENTRO REGIONAL MEDICAL CENTER (050045)**, 1415 Ross Avenue, Zip 92243–4398; tel. 760/339–7100 **A**1 9 10 **F**3 11 13 14 15 18 29 30 31 34 40 43 45 46 47 48 49 50 51 54 57 59 60 64 66 70 72 74 75 76 78 79 81 82 85 86 87 89 93 107 108 111 114 115 119 124 126 127 130 132 141 143 145 146 147 148 **P**5
Primary Contact: David R. Green, Administrator and Chief Executive Officer
COO: Tomas Virgen, R.N., Chief Operating Officer
CFO: Kathleen Farmer, Assistant Administrator Finance and Chief Financial Officer
CIO: John Gaede, Director Information Systems
CHR: Bill Moore, Chief Human Resources
Web address: www.ecrmc.org
**Control:** City–Government, nonfederal **Service:** General Medical and Surgical

**Staffed Beds:** 165 **Admissions:** 6658 **Census:** 71 **Outpatient Visits:** 199294 **Births:** 1736 **Total Expense ($000):** 121061 **Payroll Expense ($000):** 44053 **Personnel:** 820

## ELDRIDGE—Sonoma County

**SONOMA DEVELOPMENTAL CENTER (050547)**, 15000 Arnold Drive, Zip 95431–8900, Mailing Address: P.O. Box 1493, Zip 95431–1493; tel. 707/938–6000, (Nonreporting) **A**10
Primary Contact: James E. Rogers, Executive Director
COO: Karen Clark, Director Administrative Services
CMO: Judith Bjorndal, M.D., Medical Director
CIO: Karen Litzenberg, Public Information Officer
CHR: Roy J. Johnson, Director Human Resources
Web address: www.dds.ca.gov/sonoma
**Control:** State–Government, nonfederal **Service:** Institution for mental retardation

**Staffed Beds:** 546

## ENCINITAS—San Diego County

☒ △ **SCRIPPS MEMORIAL HOSPITAL–ENCINITAS (050503)**, 354 Santa Fe Drive, Zip 92024–5182, Mailing Address: P.O. Box 230817, Zip 92023–0817; tel. 760/633–6501 **A**1 2 7 9 10 **F**3 8 11 13 14 15 18 20 26 28 29 30 31 34 35 40 44 49 54 57 58 59 64 65 68 70 74 75 76 77 78 79 81 82 84 85 86 87 90 91 92 93 94 96 102 107 108 111 114 115 119 130 132 146 148 **P**3 5 **S** Scripps Health, San Diego, CA
Primary Contact: Carl J. Etter, Chief Eecutive, Senior Vice President
COO: Rebecca Cofinas, Vice President and Chief Operating Executive Operations
CFO: Sharon Creal, Vice President Financial Operations
CHR: Cara Williams, Director Human Resources
Web address: www.scripps.org
**Control:** Other not–for–profit (including NFP Corporation) **Service:** General Medical and Surgical

**Staffed Beds:** 158 **Admissions:** 9294 **Census:** 112 **Outpatient Visits:** 69674 **Births:** 1500 **Total Expense ($000):** 211595 **Payroll Expense ($000):** 83524 **Personnel:** 1052

## ENCINO—Los Angeles County, See Los Angeles

## ESCONDIDO—San Diego County

☒ △ **PALOMAR MEDICAL CENTER (050115)**, 2185 West Citracado Parkway, Zip 92029–4159; tel. 760/739–3000, (Total facility includes 96 beds in nursing home type unit) **A**1 7 9 10 **F**3 11 12 13 15 17 18 20 22 24 28 29 30 31 40 42 43 45 46 47 50 51 64 68 70 74 75 76 77 78 79 81 84 85 86 87 90 93 96 97 98 100 102 103 104 105 107 108 111 112 114 115 119 120 121 123 124 126 128 129 130 131 146 147 **P**4 5 **S** Palomar Health, Escondido, CA
Primary Contact: Gerald E. Bracht, Chief Administrative Officer
COO: Gerald E. Bracht, Chief Administrative Officer
CFO: Robert Hemker, Chief Financial Officer
CMO: Duane Buringrud, M.D., Chief Medical and Quality Officer
CIO: Paul Peabody, Chief Information Officer
CHR: Brenda C. Turner, Chief Human Resources Officer
Web address: www.pph.org
**Control:** Hospital district or authority, Government, nonfederal **Service:** General Medical and Surgical

**Staffed Beds:** 368 **Admissions:** 20011 **Census:** 310 **Outpatient Visits:** 128039 **Births:** 3575 **Total Expense ($000):** 339401 **Payroll Expense ($000):** 139177 **Personnel:** 1594

## EUREKA—Humboldt County

**SEMPERVIRENS PSYCHIATRIC HEALTH FACILITY (054124)**, 720 Wood Street, Zip 95501–4413; tel. 707/268–2900, (Nonreporting) **A**10
Primary Contact: Phillip Crandall, Director
Web address: www.https://co.humboldt.ca.us/hhs/mhb/
**Control:** County–Government, nonfederal **Service:** Psychiatric

**Staffed Beds:** 16

☒ ○ **ST. JOSEPH HOSPITAL (050006)**, 2700 Dolbeer Street, Zip 95501–4799; tel. 707/445–8121, (Includes GENERAL HOSPITAL, 2200 Harrison Avenue, Zip 95501–3299; tel. 707/445–5111) **A**1 2 9 10 11 19 **F**3 8 11 12 13 15 17 18 20 22 24 26 28 29 30 31 35 40 45 46 47 48 49 53 54 62 63 64 68 70 72 75 76 77 78 79 81 82 84 85 86 87 89 90 93 96 107 108 110 111 114 115 117 118 119 120 121 123 124 129 130 144 146 148 **P**5 **S** St. Joseph Health, Irvine, CA
Primary Contact: David O'Brien, M.D., Interim President and Chief Executive Officer
CFO: Andrew Rybolt, Chief Financial Officer
CMO: Scott Sageman, M.D., Vice President and Chief Medical Officer
CIO: Wendy Thorpe, Area Director Information Systems
CHR: Linda Cook, Vice President Human Resources
CNO: Carol Reeder, R.N., Chief Nursing Officer
Web address: www.stjosepheureka.org
**Control:** Church–operated, Nongovernment, not–for profit **Service:** General Medical and Surgical

**Staffed Beds:** 138 **Admissions:** 6318 **Census:** 78 **Outpatient Visits:** 183189 **Births:** 628 **Total Expense ($000):** 183419 **Payroll Expense ($000):** 54118 **Personnel:** 973

## FAIRFIELD—Solano County

☒ **NORTHBAY MEDICAL CENTER (050367)**, 1200 B. Gale Wilson Boulevard, Zip 94533–3552; tel. 707/646–5000, (Includes NORTHBAY VACAVALLEY HOSPITAL, 1000 Nut Tree Road, Vacaville, Zip 95687–4100; tel. 707/624–7000) **A**1 2 5 9 10 **F**2 3 6 8 11 13 17 18 19 20 22 24 26 28 29 30 31 32 35 36 40ᵉ 41 43 44 49 50 51 54 56 59 62 63 64 65 70 72 73 74 75 76 77 78 79 80 81 82 84 85 87 89 92 93 94 96 97 104 107 114 115 118 119 121 130 132 146 147 148 **P**3
Primary Contact: Deborah Sugiyama, President
CFO: Arthur E. DeNio, Vice President and Chief Financial Officer
CMO: Mitesh Patel, M.D., Vice President Medical Affairs
CIO: Paul Alcala, Vice President and Chief Information Officer
CHR: Ken McCollum, Vice President, Human Resources
Web address: www.northbay.org
**Control:** Other not–for–profit (including NFP Corporation) **Service:** General Medical and Surgical

**Staffed Beds:** 157 **Admissions:** 8732 **Census:** 95 **Outpatient Visits:** 215272 **Births:** 1333 **Total Expense ($000):** 331703 **Payroll Expense ($000):** 147917 **Personnel:** 1290

---

**Hospital, Medicare Provider Number, Address, Telephone, Approval, Facility, and Physician Codes, Health Care System**

★ American Hospital Association (AHA) membership
☐ The Joint Commission accreditation
◇ DNV Healthcare Inc. accreditation
○ Healthcare Facilities Accreditation Program
△ Commission on Accreditation of Rehabilitation Facilities (CARF) accreditation

**FALL RIVER MILLS—Shasta County**

★ **MAYERS MEMORIAL HOSPITAL DISTRICT (051305)**, 43563 Highway 299 East, Zip 96028–0459, Mailing Address: P.O. Box 459, Zip 96028–0459; tel. 530/336–5511, (Total facility includes 87 beds in nursing home–type unit) **A**9 10 18 **F**13 40 45 56 57 59 63 64 76 81 85 93 107 114 119 128 130 132 133 146
Primary Contact: Matthew Rees, Chief Executive Officer
CMO: Chris Camarata, M.D., Chief of Staff
CIO: Martha Lucero, Director Special Projects
CHR: Paul McCoy, Director Human Resources
CNO: Sherry Wilson, R.N., Chief Nursing Officer Long Term Care
Web address: www.mayersmemorial.com
**Control:** Hospital district or authority, Government, nonfederal **Service:** General Medical and Surgical

| | |
|---|---|
| **Staffed Beds:** 109 **Admissions:** 458 **Census:** 103 **Outpatient Visits:** 19012 **Births:** 65 **Total Expense ($000):** 20906 **Payroll Expense ($000):** 8025 **Personnel:** 173 | |

**FALLBROOK—San Diego County**

⊞ **FALLBROOK HOSPITAL (050435)**, 624 East Elder Street, Zip 92028–3099; tel. 760/728–1191, (Nonreporting) **A**1 9 10 20 **S** Community Health Systems, Inc., Franklin, TN
Primary Contact: Kirkpatrick Conley, Chief Executive Officer
Web address: www.fallbrookhospital.com
**Control:** Hospital district or authority, Government, nonfederal **Service:** General Medical and Surgical

| |
|---|
| **Staffed Beds:** 86 |

**FOLSOM—Sacramento County**

⊞ **KINDRED HOSPITAL–SACRAMENTO (052033)**, 330 Montrose Drive, Zip 95630–2720; tel. 916/351–9151, (Nonreporting) **A**1 9 10 **S** Kindred Healthcare, Louisville, KY
Primary Contact: Janet Biedron, R.N., Chief Executive Officer
CFO: Bruce MacNeill, Chief Financial Officer
CMO: Alan Cubre, M.D., Medical Director
CHR: Michael G. Fanselau, District Director Human Resources
Web address: www.kindredsacramento.com/
**Control:** Corporation, Investor–owned, for–profit **Service:** Long–Term Acute Care hospital

| |
|---|
| **Staffed Beds:** 34 |

⊞ **MERCY HOSPITAL OF FOLSOM (050414)**, 1650 Creekside Drive, Zip 95630–3405; tel. 916/983–7400 **A**1 5 9 10 **F**3 8 11 13 29 30 34 35 36 39 40 43 49 57 59 60 64 66 68 70 74 75 76 77 79 81 82 84 85 86 93 107 108 114 115 118 119 130 132 146 147 148 **P**4 5 **S** Dignity Health, San Francisco, CA
Primary Contact: Michael R. Ricks, President
CFO: Robin Rogness, Vice President and Chief Financial Officer
CHR: Amy Mantell, Vice President Human Resources
Web address: www.mercyfolsom.org
**Control:** Church–operated, Nongovernment, not–for profit **Service:** General Medical and Surgical

| | |
|---|---|
| **Staffed Beds:** 106 **Admissions:** 5755 **Census:** 52 **Outpatient Visits:** 45338 **Births:** 908 **Total Expense ($000):** 136264 **Payroll Expense ($000):** 57203 **Personnel:** 510 | |

**FONTANA—San Bernardino County**

⊞ **KAISER PERMANENTE FONTANA MEDICAL CENTER (050140)**, (Formerly Fontana Medical Center), 9961 Sierra Avenue, Zip 92335–6720; tel. 909/427–5000 **A**1 3 5 10 **F**3 4 8 13 15 17 18 20 28 29 30 31 35 40 41 44 45 46 48 49 50 57 58 60 62 63 64 65 68 70 72 73 74 75 76 77 78 79 81 82 84 85 86 87 88 89 100 102 107 108 111 114 115 117 119 130 132 135 141 145 146 148 **S** Kaiser Foundation Hospitals, Oakland, CA
Primary Contact: Greg Christian, Executive Director
CFO: Donald P. Bernard, Chief Financial Officer
CMO: David Quam, M.D., Area Medical Director
CIO: Jennifer Resch–Silvestri, Director Public Affairs
CHR: Kimberly Labiaga, Human Resources Leader
Web address: www.kaiserpermanente.org
**Control:** Other not–for–profit (including NFP Corporation) **Service:** General Medical and Surgical

| | |
|---|---|
| **Staffed Beds:** 390 **Admissions:** 26503 **Census:** 314 **Outpatient Visits:** 151586 **Births:** 5214 **Personnel:** 4638 | |

**FORT BRAGG—Mendocino County**

⊞ **MENDOCINO COAST DISTRICT HOSPITAL (051325)**, 700 River Drive, Zip 95437–5495; tel. 707/961–1234, (Nonreporting) **A**1 9 10 18
Primary Contact: Wayne Allen, Interim Chief Executive Officer
CFO: Wayne Allen, Chief Financial Officer
CMO: John Kermen, D.O., Chief Medical Staff
CIO: Jeff Edwards, Manager Information Services
CHR: Scott Kidd, Director Human Resources
CNO: Bonnie Kittner, R.N., Chief Nursing Officer
Web address: www.mcdh.org
**Control:** Hospital district or authority, Government, nonfederal **Service:** General Medical and Surgical

| |
|---|
| **Staffed Beds:** 25 |

**FORT IRWIN—San Bernardino County**

⊞ **WEED ARMY COMMUNITY HOSPITAL**, Inner Loop Road and 4th Street, Building 166, Zip 92310–5065, Mailing Address: P.O. Box 105109, Zip 92310–5109; tel. 760/380–3108, (Nonreporting) **A**1 **S** Department of the Army, Office of the Surgeon General, Falls Church, VA
Primary Contact: Colonel Cheryl Taylor–Whitehead, Commander
CIO: Michael Haenelt, Chief Information Management
Web address: www.irwin.amedd.army.mil
**Control:** Army, Government, federal **Service:** General Medical and Surgical

| |
|---|
| **Staffed Beds:** 27 |

**FORTUNA—Humboldt County**

⊞ **REDWOOD MEMORIAL HOSPITAL (051318)**, 3300 Renner Drive, Zip 95540–3198; tel. 707/725–3361 **A**1 2 9 10 18 **F**3 11 13 15 17 18 29 30 34 35 39 40 45 50 53 56 57 59 63 64 68 70 75 76 77 79 81 82 84 85 86 88 89 93 107 110 114 119 130 131 132 133 146 **P**5 **S** St. Joseph Health, Irvine, CA
Primary Contact: David O'Brien, M.D., Interim President and Chief Executive Officer
COO: Joseph J. Rogers, Vice President and Chief Operating Officer
CFO: Andrew Rybolt, Vice President and Chief Financial Officer
CHR: Bob Sampson, Vice President Human Resources
Web address: www.redwoodmemorial.org/
**Control:** Church–operated, Nongovernment, not–for profit **Service:** General Medical and Surgical

| | |
|---|---|
| **Staffed Beds:** 25 **Admissions:** 1537 **Census:** 15 **Outpatient Visits:** 45391 **Births:** 348 **Total Expense ($000):** 39445 **Payroll Expense ($000):** 13483 **Personnel:** 170 | |

**FOUNTAIN VALLEY—Orange County**

⊞ **FOUNTAIN VALLEY REGIONAL HOSPITAL AND MEDICAL CENTER (050570)**, 17100 Euclid Street, Zip 92708–4043; tel. 714/966–7200, (Nonreporting) **A**1 2 5 9 10 **S** TENET Healthcare Corporation, Dallas, TX
Primary Contact: Debbie Walsh, MSN, Chief Executive Officer
COO: Paul M. Czajka, Chief Operating Officer
CFO: Cari Welsh, Interim Chief Financial Officer
CFO: Jon Zilkow, Chief Financial Officer
CMO: Sara Myla, M.D., Chief of Staff
CIO: Edwin Del Los Santos, Director Information Systems
CHR: Tim Howard, Chief Human Resources Officer
CNO: Mary Botticella, R.N., Chief Nursing Officer
Web address: www.fountainvalleyhospital.com
**Control:** Corporation, Investor–owned, for–profit **Service:** General Medical and Surgical

| |
|---|
| **Staffed Beds:** 400 |

⊞ **ORANGE COAST MEMORIAL MEDICAL CENTER (050678)**, 9920 Talbert Avenue, Zip 92708–5153; tel. 714/378–7000 **A**1 2 9 10 **F**3 11 12 13 15 18 20 22 24 26 28 29 30 31 34 35 38 40 44 45 46 49 50 51 53 55 56 57 58 59 64 65 68 70 72 74 75 76 77 78 79 81 82 84 85 86 87 93 107 108 110 111 114 116 117 119 124 126 130 131 132 135 143 145 146 147 **P**3 5 **S** MemorialCare, Fountain Valley, CA
Primary Contact: Marcia Manker, Chief Executive Officer
COO: Emily Randle, Vice President Operations
CFO: Steve McNamara, Chief Financial Officer
CIO: Scott Raymond, Director Information Systems
CHR: Lorraine Booth, Executive Director Human Resources
Web address: www.memorialcare.org
**Control:** Other not–for–profit (including NFP Corporation) **Service:** General Medical and Surgical

| | |
|---|---|
| **Staffed Beds:** 218 **Admissions:** 12874 **Census:** 125 **Outpatient Visits:** 67744 **Births:** 1711 **Total Expense ($000):** 230757 **Payroll Expense ($000):** 70328 **Personnel:** 1012 | |

*Many Facility Codes have changed. Please refer to the AHA Guide Code Chart.*

**CA**

**FREMONT—Alameda County**

☐ **FREMONT HOSPITAL (054110)**, 39001 Sundale Drive, Zip 94538–2005; tel. 510/796–1100 **A**1 9 10 **F**5 29 30 98 99 100 101 102 103 104 105 130 **S** Universal Health Services, Inc., King of Prussia, PA
Primary Contact: John C. Cooper, Chief Executive Officer
CMO: Travis Svensson, M.D., Medical Director
CHR: Mark Chatman, Director Human Resources
Web address: www.fremonthospital.com
**Control:** Corporation, Investor–owned, for–profit **Service:** Psychiatric

| | |
|---|---|
| **Staffed Beds:** 96 **Admissions:** 3968 **Census:** 87 **Outpatient Visits:** 12766 **Births:** 0 **Total Expense ($000):** 33744 **Payroll Expense ($000):** 13395 **Personnel:** 186 | |

☒ **WASHINGTON HOSPITAL HEALTHCARE SYSTEM (050195)**, 2000 Mowry Avenue, Zip 94538–1746; tel. 510/797–1111 **A**1 2 9 10 **F**3 8 13 15 17 18 20 22 24 26 28 29 30 31 34 35 36 37 38 39 40 45 49 50 55 57 58 59 60 65 70 71 74 75 76 77 78 79 81 84 85 86 87 89 93 102 107 108 110 115 118 119 120 121 124 126 130 132 133 144 146 147 148 **P**3 5 7
Primary Contact: Nancy D. Farber, Chief Executive Officer
COO: Edward J. Fayen, Associate Administrator Operations and Support
CFO: Chris Henry, Associate Administrator and Chief Financial Officer
CMO: Albert Brooks, M.D., Chief Medical Staff Services
CIO: Robert Thorwald, Chief Information Officer
CHR: Bryant Welch, Chief Human Resources
CNO: Stephanie Williams, R.N., Chief Nursing Officer
Web address: www.whhs.com
**Control:** Hospital district or authority, Government, nonfederal **Service:** General Medical and Surgical

| | |
|---|---|
| **Staffed Beds:** 269 **Admissions:** 12682 **Census:** 178 **Outpatient Visits:** 346536 **Births:** 1929 **Total Expense ($000):** 482941 **Payroll Expense ($000):** 203027 **Personnel:** 1573 | |

**FRENCH CAMP—San Joaquin County**

☐ **SAN JOAQUIN GENERAL HOSPITAL (050167)**, 500 West Hospital Road, Zip 95231–9693, Mailing Address: P.O. Box 1020, Stockton, Zip 95201–3120; tel. 209/468–6000 **A**1 3 5 10 **F**3 11 13 15 20 29 30 31 32 34 35 39 40 45 49 50 54 56 59 60 61 64 65 66 68 70 72 74 75 76 77 78 79 81 82 85 87 89 93 97 100 107 108 115 119 129 130 143 146 147
Primary Contact: David K. Culberson, Chief Executive Officer
CFO: Ron Kreutner, Chief Financial Officer
CMO: Jerry Royer, M.D., Chief Medical Officer
CIO: Don Johnston, Chief Information Officer
CHR: Patricia Wright, Personal Analyst
Web address: www.sjgeneralhospital.com/
**Control:** County–Government, nonfederal **Service:** General Medical and Surgical

| | |
|---|---|
| **Staffed Beds:** 110 **Admissions:** 8765 **Census:** 110 **Outpatient Visits:** 116161 **Births:** 2067 **Total Expense ($000):** 172810 **Payroll Expense ($000):** 84012 **Personnel:** 1257 | |

**FRESNO—Fresno County**

**COMMUNITY BEHAVIORAL HEALTH CENTER**, 7171 North Cedar Avenue, Zip 93720–3311; tel. 559/449–8000, (Nonreporting) **A**9 **S** Community Medical Centers, Fresno, CA
Primary Contact: Dawan Utecht, Chief Executive Officer
COO: Patrick W. Rafferty, Executive Vice President and Chief Operating Officer
CFO: Stephen Walter, Senior Vice President and Chief Financial Officer
CMO: Tom Utecht, M.D., Senior Vice President and Chief Quality Officer
CIO: George Vasquez, Vice President Information Services
CHR: Ginny Burdick, Vice President Human Resources
Web address: www.communitymedical.org
**Control:** Corporation, Investor–owned, for–profit **Service:** Psychiatric

| | |
|---|---|
| **Staffed Beds:** 60 | |

☐ **COMMUNITY REGIONAL MEDICAL CENTER (050060)**, 2823 Fresno Street, Zip 93721–1324; tel. 559/459–6000, (Total facility includes 106 beds in nursing home–type unit) **A**1 2 5 8 9 10 **F**3 7 11 13 15 16 17 18 20 22 24 26 29 30 31 34 35 37 39 40 43 44 45 46 47 48 49 50 51 54 55 56 57 58 59 60 61 62 64 65 66 68 70 72 74 75 76 77 78 79 81 82 84 85 86 87 89 90 93 97 98 100 101 102 103 104 105 106 107 108 109 110 111 112 113 114 115 118 119 120 121 122 124 126 128 130 132 135 143 145 146 147 148 **P**5
**S** Community Medical Centers, Fresno, CA
Primary Contact: John M. Chubb, Chief Executive Officer
COO: Patrick W. Rafferty, Executive Vice President and Chief Operating Officer
CFO: Stephen Walter, Senior Vice President and Chief Financial Officer
CMO: Tom Utecht, M.D., Chief Quality Officer
CIO: Craig Castro, Chief Information Officer
CHR: Ginny Burdick, Vice President Human Resources
Web address: www.communitymedical.org
**Control:** Other not–for–profit (including NFP Corporation) **Service:** General Medical and Surgical

| | |
|---|---|
| **Staffed Beds:** 793 **Admissions:** 37758 **Census:** 619 **Outpatient Visits:** 336308 **Births:** 6260 **Total Expense ($000):** 807023 **Payroll Expense ($000):** 290200 **Personnel:** 3744 | |

☐ **FRESNO HEART AND SURGICAL HOSPITAL (050732)**, 15 East Audubon Drive, Zip 93720–1542; tel. 559/433–8000, (Nonreporting) **A**1 9 10
Primary Contact: Wanda Holderman, Chief Executive Officer
CFO: Jon Edwards, Executive Director Finance
CMO: Keith Boone, M.D., Medical Director
CIO: Jonathon Anderson, Director Information Technology and Telecommunications
CHR: Lynn M. Horton, Executive Director Human Resources
Web address: www.fresnoheartandsurgical.org
**Control:** Corporation, Investor–owned, for–profit **Service:** Heart

| | |
|---|---|
| **Staffed Beds:** 60 | |

☐ **FRESNO SURGICAL HOSPITAL (050708)**, 6125 North Fresno Street, Zip 93710–5207; tel. 559/431–8000, (Nonreporting) **A**1 9 10
Primary Contact: Kristine Kassahn, Chief Executive Officer
CFO: Bruce Cecil, Chief Financial Officer
CMO: Bruce Witmer, M.D., Medical Director
CHR: Laura Patillo, Manager Human Resources
Web address: www.fresnosurgicalhospital.com
**Control:** Partnership, Investor–owned, for–profit **Service:** General Medical and Surgical

| | |
|---|---|
| **Staffed Beds:** 29 | |

☒ **KAISER PERMANENTE FRESNO MEDICAL CENTER (050710)**, (Formerly Fresno Medical Center), 7300 North Fresno Street, Zip 93720–2941; tel. 559/448–4500 **A**1 10 **F**3 4 8 12 13 15 17 29 30 31 33 40 45 46 47 48 49 51 53 59 63 64 68 70 72 73 74 76 77 78 79 81 82 83 84 85 86 87 88 89 90 93 96 97 98 102 107 108 110 111 114 116 117 118 119 124 128 130 135 144 146 148 **S** Kaiser Foundation Hospitals, Oakland, CA
Primary Contact: Jeffrey A. Collins, Senior Vice President and Area Manager
CFO: Richard Alves, Chief Financial Officer
CMO: Varouj Altebarmakian, M.D., Physician in Chief
CIO: Brad Bain, Information Systems Leader
Web address: www.kaiserpermanente.org
**Control:** Other not–for–profit (including NFP Corporation) **Service:** General Medical and Surgical

| | |
|---|---|
| **Staffed Beds:** 169 **Admissions:** 7246 **Census:** 69 | |

☒ **SAINT AGNES MEDICAL CENTER (050093)**, 1303 East Herndon Avenue, Zip 93720–3309; tel. 559/450–3000 **A**1 2 9 10 **F**3 8 11 13 15 17 18 20 22 24 26 28 29 30 31 34 35 37 40 44 45 46 47 49 50 51 56 57 58 59 64 66 70 74 75 76 77 78 79 81 82 84 85 86 87 107 108 110 111 112 113 114 115 116 117 118 119 120 121 123 124 126 130 132 146 147 148 **P**5 8
**S** Trinity Health, Livonia, MI
Primary Contact: Nancy Hollingsworth, R.N., MSN, President and Chief Executive Officer
COO: Mark T. Bateman, Interim Chief Operating Officer
CFO: Christine Sarrico, Chief Financial Officer
CMO: Stephen Soldo, M.D., Chief Medical Officer
CIO: Irfan Ali, Director Information Services
CHR: Stacy Vaillancourt, Vice President Marketing, Communications, Advocacy and Human Resources
Web address: www.samc.com
**Control:** Church–operated, Nongovernment, not–for profit **Service:** General Medical and Surgical

| | |
|---|---|
| **Staffed Beds:** 436 **Admissions:** 24946 **Census:** 277 **Outpatient Visits:** 296878 **Births:** 4281 **Total Expense ($000):** 397442 **Payroll Expense ($000):** 162720 **Personnel:** 2047 | |

CA

---

**Hospital, Medicare Provider Number, Address, Telephone, Approval, Facility, and Physician Codes, Health Care System**

★ American Hospital Association (AHA) membership
☐ The Joint Commission accreditation
◇ DNV Healthcare Inc. accreditation
○ Healthcare Facilities Accreditation Program
△ Commission on Accreditation of Rehabilitation Facilities (CARF) accreditation

☐ △ **SAN JOAQUIN VALLEY REHABILITATION HOSPITAL (053032)**, 7173 North Sharon Avenue, Zip 93720–3329; tel. 559/436–3600, (Nonreporting) **A**1 7 9 10 **S** Vibra Healthcare, Mechanicsburg, PA
Primary Contact: Mary Jo Jacobson, Chief Executive Officer
CFO: Margaret Casarez, Chief Financial Officer
CMO: Michael Azevedo, M.D., Medical Director
CIO: Christi Rolff, Director Business Development
CHR: Jennifer Morrow, Director Human Resources
Web address: www.sjvrehab.com
**Control:** Corporation, Investor–owned, for–profit **Service:** Rehabilitation

Staffed Beds: 40

☒ **VETERANS AFFAIRS CENTRAL CALIFORNIA HEALTH CARE SYSTEM**, 2615 East Clinton Avenue, Zip 93703–2223; tel. 559/225–6100, (Total facility includes 60 beds in nursing home–type unit) **A**1 3 5 **F**3 4 5 8 9 11 26 28 29 30 31 34 35 38 39 40 42 44 45 46 47 48 49 50 51 53 54 56 57 58 59 60 61 62 63 64 65 66 68 70 74 75 77 78 79 81 82 83 84 85 86 87 91 92 93 94 97 98 100 101 102 103 104 105 106 107 111 114 115 119 120 127 128 129 130 132 133 135 137 143 144 145 146 147 148 **S** Department of Veterans Affairs, Washington, DC
Primary Contact: Joanne Krumberger, R.N., FACHE, Director
CFO: Matthew Whetton, Chief Business Administration
CMO: Wessel Meyer, M.D., Chief of Staff
CIO: William Harris, Chief Information Resources Management
CHR: Sandra Stein, Chief Human Resources Management
Web address: www.fresno.va.gov/
**Control:** Veterans Affairs, Government, federal **Service:** General Medical and Surgical

Staffed Beds: 117 Admissions: 4048 Census: 82 Births: 0

### FULLERTON—Orange County

☒ △ **ST. JUDE MEDICAL CENTER (050168)**, 101 East Valencia Mesa Drive, Zip 92835–3809; tel. 714/992–3000 **A**1 2 5 7 9 10 **F**2 3 8 9 11 13 15 18 20 22 24 26 28 29 30 31 32 34 35 36 39 40 43 44 45 46 47 48 49 50 51 53 54 55 56 57 58 59 60 61 62 63 64 65 66 68 70 71 72 74 75 76 77 78 79 81 82 83 84 85 86 87 90 91 92 93 95 96 97 100 107 108 109 110 111 114 115 116 117 118 119 120 121 123 124 126 128 129 130 131 132 134 135 143 146 147 148 **P**3 5 **S** St. Joseph Health, Irvine, CA
Primary Contact: Lee Penrose, President and Chief Executive Officer
COO: Brian Helleland, Executive Vice President and Chief Operating Officer
CFO: Ed Salvador, Chief Financial Officer
CIO: Ryan Olsen, Vice President of Operations
CHR: Mark Jablonski, Senior Vice President Human Resources
CNO: Linda Jenkins, R.N., Vice President Patient Care Services
Web address: www.stjudemedicalcenter.org
**Control:** Church–operated, Nongovernment, not–for profit **Service:** General Medical and Surgical

Staffed Beds: 372 Admissions: 15249 Census: 206 Outpatient Visits: 470081 Births: 2058 Total Expense ($000): 420656 Payroll Expense ($000): 147174 Personnel: 2125

### GARBERVILLE—Humboldt County

☐ **JEROLD PHELPS COMMUNITY HOSPITAL (051309)**, 733 Cedar Street, Zip 95542–3201; tel. 707/923–3921, (Nonreporting) **A**9 10 18
Primary Contact: Harry Jasper, Administrator
COO: Kent Scown, Director Operations and Information Services
CFO: Mike Nagle, Director Financial Services
CMO: Mark H. Phelps, M.D., Chief of Staff and Medical Director
CIO: Kent Scown, Director Operations and Information Services
CHR: Linda Feretto, Director Human Resources
Web address: www.shchd.org
**Control:** Hospital district or authority, Government, nonfederal **Service:** General Medical and Surgical

Staffed Beds: 16

### GARDEN GROVE—Orange County

☐ **GARDEN GROVE HOSPITAL AND MEDICAL CENTER (050230)**, 12601 Garden Grove Boulevard, Zip 92843–1908; tel. 714/537–5160, (Nonreporting) **A**1 9 10 **S** Prime Healthcare Services, Ontario, CA
Primary Contact: Virgis Narbutas, Chief Executive Officer
CFO: Alan H. Smith, Chief Financial Officer
CMO: Hassan Alkhouli, M.D., Chief Medical Officer
CIO: Adam Morquecho, Director Information Systems
CHR: Stephanie Sioson, Director Human Resources
CNO: Sofia Abrina, Administrator and Chief Nursing Officer
Web address: www.gardengrovehospital.com
**Control:** Corporation, Investor–owned, for–profit **Service:** General Medical and Surgical

Staffed Beds: 74

### GARDENA—Los Angeles County

★ ○ **KINDRED HOSPITAL OF SOUTH BAY (052050)**, 1246 West 155th Street, Zip 90247–4011; tel. 310/323–5330, (Nonreporting) **A**9 10 11 **S** Kindred Healthcare, Louisville, KY
Primary Contact: Kevin Chavez, Chief Executive Officer
COO: Michael Grubb, Chief Operating Officer and Chief Financial Officer
CFO: Michael Grubb, Chief Operating Officer and Chief Financial Officer
CHR: Michelle Parra, Director Human Resources
Web address: www.khsouthbay.com/
**Control:** Corporation, Investor–owned, for–profit **Service:** Long–Term Acute Care hospital

Staffed Beds: 84

☐ **MEMORIAL HOSPITAL OF GARDENA (050468)**, 1145 West Redondo Beach Boulevard, Zip 90247–3528; tel. 310/532–4200, (Nonreporting) **A**1 9 10 **S** Avanti Hospitals, El Segundo, CA
Primary Contact: Araceli Lonergan, Chief Executive Officer
CFO: Daniel R. Heckathorne, Chief Financial Officer
CMO: Nosratian Farshao, M.D., Chief Medical Staff
CIO: Earle Johnson, Chief Information Officer
CHR: Matthew Kempiak, Director Human Resources and Administrative Services
CNO: Glenda Luce, Chief Nursing Officer
Web address: www.mhglax.com/
**Control:** Corporation, Investor–owned, for–profit **Service:** General Medical and Surgical

Staffed Beds: 172

**VISTA HOSPITAL OF SOUTH BAY** See Kindred Hospital of South Bay

### GILROY—Santa Clara County

☒ **SAINT LOUISE REGIONAL HOSPITAL (050688)**, 9400 No Name Uno, Zip 95020–3528; tel. 408/848–2000, (Nonreporting) **A**1 9 10 **S** Daughters of Charity Health System, Los Altos Hills, CA
Primary Contact: Carol Furgurson, Acting Chief Administrative Officer
COO: Carol Furgurson, Chief Operating Officer
CFO: Nicole Thomson, Chief Financial Officer
CIO: Dick Hutsell, Vice President Information Technology Services
CHR: Lin Velasquez, Vice President Human Resources
CNO: Marilyn Gerrior, R.N., Chief Nursing Executive
Web address: www.dochs.org
**Control:** Church–operated, Nongovernment, not–for profit **Service:** General Medical and Surgical

Staffed Beds: 93

### GLENDALE—Los Angeles County

☒ **GLENDALE ADVENTIST MEDICAL CENTER (050239)**, 1509 Wilson Terrace, Zip 91206–4007; tel. 818/409–8000 **A**1 2 3 5 9 10 **F**3 5 8 12 13 15 17 18 20 22 24 26 29 30 31 34 35 37 40 47 48 49 51 53 58 59 62 64 68 70 72 74 75 76 77 78 79 81 82 87 90 92 93 96 98 102 104 105 106 107 108 110 111 114 115 118 119 121 124 126 129 130 131 132 135 146 147 148 **S** Adventist Health, Roseville, CA
Primary Contact: Kevin A. Roberts, FACHE, President and Chief Executive Officer
COO: Warren Tetz, Senior Vice President and Chief Operating Officer
CFO: Kelly Turner, Senior Vice President Finance and Chief Financial Officer
CMO: Simon Keushkerian, M.D., Chief of Staff
CIO: Sharon Correa, Associate Vice President
CHR: Susan Crabtree, Director Human Resources
CNO: Judy Blair, Senior Vice President Clincial Services and Chief Nursing Officer
Web address: www.glendaleadventist.com
**Control:** Church–operated, Nongovernment, not–for profit **Service:** General Medical and Surgical

Staffed Beds: 462 Admissions: 19720 Census: 290 Outpatient Visits: 282700 Births: 2497 Total Expense ($000): 380660 Payroll Expense ($000): 140724 Personnel: 1940

☒ **GLENDALE MEMORIAL HOSPITAL AND HEALTH CENTER (050058)**, 1420 South Central Avenue, Zip 91204–2508; tel. 818/502–1900, (Nonreporting) **A**1 9 10 **S** Dignity Health, San Francisco, CA
Primary Contact: Jack Ivie, President
COO: Matthew S. Gerlach, Vice President and Chief Operating Officer
CFO: Robert Allen, Vice President and Chief Financial Officer
CIO: David Gibbons, Chief Information Officer
CHR: Sandra Davis Houston, Vice President Human Resources and Organizational Development
CNO: Claire H. Hanks, R.N., Vice President and Chief Nursing Officer
Web address: www.glendalememorial.com
**Control:** Other not–for–profit (including NFP Corporation) **Service:** General Medical and Surgical

Staffed Beds: 334

◇ **VERDUGO HILLS HOSPITAL (050124)**, 1812 Verdugo Boulevard, Zip 91208–1409; tel. 818/790–7100, (Nonreporting) **A**9 10 21
Primary Contact: Leonard LaBella, President and Chief Executive Officer
CFO: Cindy Trousdale, Chief Financial Officer
CHR: Paul Celuch, Vice President Human Resources and Support Services
Web address: www.verdugohillshospital.org
**Control:** Other not–for–profit (including NFP Corporation) **Service:** General Medical and Surgical

**Staffed Beds:** 114

### GLENDORA—Los Angeles County

○ **EAST VALLEY HOSPITAL MEDICAL CENTER (050205)**, 150 West Route 66, Zip 91740–6207; tel. 626/852–5000, (Nonreporting) **A**9 10 11
Primary Contact: C. Joseph Chang, President and Chief Executive Officer
CIO: Wayne Giddings, Manager Management Information Systems
CHR: Kim Bui, Director Human Resources
**Control:** Other not–for–profit (including NFP Corporation) **Service:** General Medical and Surgical

**Staffed Beds:** 118

⊞ **FOOTHILL PRESBYTERIAN HOSPITAL (050597)**, 250 South Grand Avenue, Zip 91741–4218; tel. 626/963–8411 **A**1 9 10 **F**3 7 11 13 17 18 29 30 31 34 35 40 41 44 45 49 50 51 60 64 68 70 74 75 76 77 78 79 81 85 86 87 107 108 114 119 130 131 143 146 **S** Citrus Valley Health Partners, Covina, CA
Primary Contact: Robert H. Curry, President and Chief Executive Officer
COO: Elvia Foulke, Executive Vice President and Chief Operating Officer
CFO: Lois Conyers, Senior Vice President and Chief Financial Officer
CMO: John DiMare, M.D., Medical Director
CIO: David McCobb, Chief Information Officer
CHR: Lisa Foust, Senior Vice President Human Resources
Web address: www.cvhp.org/Our_Facilities/Foothill_Presbyterian.aspx
**Control:** Other not–for–profit (including NFP Corporation) **Service:** General Medical and Surgical

**Staffed Beds:** 75 **Admissions:** 5123 **Census:** 49 **Outpatient Visits:** 56020 **Births:** 909 **Total Expense ($000):** 68771 **Payroll Expense ($000):** 27350 **Personnel:** 343

### GRANADA HILLS—Los Angeles County, See Los Angeles

### GRASS VALLEY—Nevada County

⊞ **SIERRA NEVADA MEMORIAL HOSPITAL (050150)**, 155 Glasson Way, Zip 95945–5723, Mailing Address: P.O. Box 1029, Zip 95945–1029; tel. 530/274–6000, (Nonreporting) **A**1 2 9 10 19 **S** Dignity Health, San Francisco, CA
Primary Contact: Katherine Medeiros, President and Chief Executive Officer
COO: Mary L. Gish, R.N., Vice President and Chief Nursing Officer
CFO: Carolyn Canady, Chief Financial Officer
CMO: Frank Lang, Jr., M.D., Chief of Medicine
CHR: Annalise O'Connor, Director Human Resources
Web address: www.snmh.org
**Control:** Other not–for–profit (including NFP Corporation) **Service:** General Medical and Surgical

**Staffed Beds:** 121

### GREENBRAE—Marin County

⊞ **MARIN GENERAL HOSPITAL (050360)**, 250 Bon Air Road, Zip 94904–1784, Mailing Address: P.O. Box 8010, San Rafael, Zip 94912–8010; tel. 415/925–7000, (Nonreporting) **A**1 10
Primary Contact: Lee Domanico, Chief Executive Officer
CFO: David W. Cox, Chief Financial Officer
CMO: Joel Sklar, M.D., Chief Medical Officer
CIO: Somayaji Bulusu, Chief Information Officer
CHR: Theresa Gianfortune, Chief Human Resources Officer
Web address: www.maringeneral.org
**Control:** Hospital district or authority, Government, nonfederal **Service:** General Medical and Surgical

**Staffed Beds:** 235

### GRIDLEY—Butte County

◇ **BIGGS–GRIDLEY MEMORIAL HOSPITAL (051311)**, 240 Spruce Street, Zip 95948–2216, Mailing Address: P.O. Box 97, Zip 95948–0097; tel. 530/846–5671, (Total facility includes 21 beds in nursing home–type unit) **A**9 10 18 21 **F**11 15 18 29 30 34 35 36 40 45 49 50 54 59 64 65 68 70 71 75 77 79 81 93 97 107 110 111 114 119 128 130 133 146 148
Primary Contact: Wade Sturgeon, Chief Executive Officer and Chief Financial Officer
COO: Ryan Quist, Administrative Assistant
CFO: Kevin Woodward, Chief Financial Officer
CMO: Henry Starkes, M.D., Medical Director
CIO: Ryan Quist, Administrative Assistant
Web address: www.bgmh.us.com/
**Control:** Other not–for–profit (including NFP Corporation) **Service:** General Medical and Surgical

**Staffed Beds:** 45 **Admissions:** 689 **Census:** 27 **Outpatient Visits:** 57162 **Births:** 0 **Total Expense ($000):** 22490 **Payroll Expense ($000):** 9347 **Personnel:** 186

### HANFORD—Kings County

⊞ **ADVENTIST MEDICAL CENTER – HANFORD (050121)**, (Formerly Hanford Community Medical Center), 115 Mall Drive, Zip 93230–3513; tel. 559/582–9000, (Includes ADVENTIST MEDICAL CENTER–SELMA, 1141 Rose Avenue, Selma, Zip 93662–3241; tel. 559/891–1000; Richard L. Rawson, President and Chief Executive Officer), (Nonreporting) **A**1 10 **S** Adventist Health, Roseville, CA
Primary Contact: Wayne Ferch, President and Chief Executive Officer
CIO: Michael Aubry, Director Information Systems
Web address: www.adventisthealthcv.com/hospital_newhanfordhospital.aspx
**Control:** Church–operated, Nongovernment, not–for profit **Service:** General Medical and Surgical

**Staffed Beds:** 94

⊞ **CENTRAL VALLEY GENERAL HOSPITAL (050196)**, 1025 North Douty Street, Zip 93230–3722, Mailing Address: P.O. Box 480, Zip 93232–0480; tel. 559/583–2100, (Nonreporting) **A**1 9 10 **S** Adventist Health, Roseville, CA
Primary Contact: Wayne Ferch, President and Chief Executive Officer
Web address: www.hanfordhealth.com
**Control:** Corporation, Investor–owned, for–profit **Service:** General Medical and Surgical

**Staffed Beds:** 30

### HARBOR CITY—Los Angeles County, See Los Angeles

### HAWAIIAN GARDENS—Los Angeles County

◇ **TRI–CITY REGIONAL MEDICAL CENTER (050575)**, 21530 South Pioneer Boulevard, Zip 90716–2608; tel. 562/860–0401 **A**9 10 21 **F**3 12 15 17 29 34 35 40 57 64 70 81 93 107 110 111 114 119 126 130 143 148
Primary Contact: Clifford Shiepe, President and Chief Executive Officer
COO: James Sherman, Executive Director Hospital Operations
CFO: Paul Brydon, Chief Financial Officer
CMO: Derek Dobalian, M.D., Chief of Staff
CIO: Anthony Carrasco, Director Information Systems
CHR: James Sherman, Executive Director Hospital Operations
CNO: Juliet Miranda, Chief Nursing Officer
Web address: www.tri-cityrmc.org
**Control:** Other not–for–profit (including NFP Corporation) **Service:** General Medical and Surgical

**Staffed Beds:** 107 **Admissions:** 2877 **Census:** 36 **Outpatient Visits:** 13177 **Total Expense ($000):** 63647 **Payroll Expense ($000):** 17350 **Personnel:** 321

### HAYWARD—Alameda County

⊞ **KAISER PERMANENTE HAYWARD MEDICAL CENTER (050512)**, (Formerly Hayward Medical Center), 27400 Hesperian Boulevard, Zip 94545–4235; tel. 510/784–4000, (Includes FREMONT MEDICAL CENTER, 39400 Paseo Padre Parkway, Fremont, Zip 94538–2310; tel. 510/248–3000; Denise Vincenzi, Administrator), (Nonreporting) **A**1 3 5 10 **S** Kaiser Foundation Hospitals, Oakland, CA
Primary Contact: Debbie Hemker, Interim Chief Executive Officer
COO: Debbie Hemker, Chief Operating Officer
Web address: www.kaiserpermanente.org
**Control:** Other not–for–profit (including NFP Corporation) **Service:** General Medical and Surgical

**Staffed Beds:** 208

---

**Hospital, Medicare Provider Number, Address, Telephone, Approval, Facility, and Physician Codes, Health Care System**

★ American Hospital Association (AHA) membership
☐ The Joint Commission accreditation
◇ DNV Healthcare Inc. accreditation
○ Healthcare Facilities Accreditation Program
△ Commission on Accreditation of Rehabilitation Facilities (CARF) accreditation

**CA**

☐ **ST. ROSE HOSPITAL (050002)**, 27200 Calaroga Avenue, Zip 94545–4383; tel. 510/264–4000 **A**1 2 9 10 **F**3 11 12 13 14 15 17 18 20 22 29 30 31 35 40 44 46 70 76
Primary Contact: Lex Reddy, Chief Executive Officer
CFO: Michael Taylor, Vice President Financial Services and Chief Financial Officer
CMO: Charles S. Feldstein, M.D., Vice President Medical Affairs
CHR: John Davini, Vice President
Web address: www.srhca.org
**Control:** Other not–for–profit (including NFP Corporation) **Service:** General Medical and Surgical

Staffed Beds: 150 Admissions: 6696 Census: 82 Births: 983

**HEALDSBURG—Sonoma County**

◇ **HEALDSBURG DISTRICT HOSPITAL (051321)**, 1375 University Avenue, Zip 95448–3382; tel. 707/431–6500, (Nonreporting) **A**9 10 18 21
Primary Contact: Nancy Schmid, Chief Executive Officer
COO: Janet Kiely, R.N., Chief Operating Officer and Chief Nursing Officer
CFO: Dan Hull, Chief Financial Officer
CMO: Paul Marguglio, M.D., Chief of Staff
CIO: Gary Crossan, Director Information Systems
CHR: George Protos, Director Human Resources
Web address: www.nschd.org
**Control:** Hospital district or authority, Government, nonfederal **Service:** General Medical and Surgical

Staffed Beds: 24

**HEMET—Riverside County**

☐ **HEMET VALLEY MEDICAL CENTER (050390)**, 1117 East Devonshire Avenue, Zip 92543–3083; tel. 951/652–2811, (Nonreporting) **A**1 9 10 **S** Physicians for Healthy Hospitals, Hemet, CA
Primary Contact: Joel Bergenfeld, Chief Executive Officer
CFO: John R. Collins, Chief Financial Officer
CHR: Michele Bird, Chief Human Resources Officer
CNO: Elizabeth C. Gardner, R.N., Chief Nursing Officer
Web address: www.valleyhealthsystem.com
**Control:** Hospital district or authority, Government, nonfederal **Service:** General Medical and Surgical

Staffed Beds: 159

**HOLLISTER—San Benito County**

☒ **HAZEL HAWKINS MEMORIAL HOSPITAL (050296)**, 911 Sunset Drive, Zip 95023–5695; tel. 831/637–5711, (Includes WILLIAM AND INEZ MABIE SKILLED NURSING FACILITY, 911 Sunset Drive, Zip 95023; tel. 408/637–5711), (Nonreporting) **A**1 9 10
Primary Contact: Ken Underwood, Chief Executive Officer
CFO: Mark Robinson, Associate Administrator and Chief Financial Officer
CIO: Julio Gil, Manager Information Services
CHR: Ysidro Gallardo, Associate Administrator Human Resources
Web address: www.hazelhawkins.com
**Control:** Hospital district or authority, Government, nonfederal **Service:** General Medical and Surgical

Staffed Beds: 113

**HOLLYWOOD—Los Angeles County, See Los Angeles**

**HUNTINGTON BEACH—Orange County**

☐ **HUNTINGTON BEACH HOSPITAL (050526)**, 17772 Beach Boulevard, Zip 92647–6819; tel. 714/843–5000, (Nonreporting) **A**1 10 **S** Prime Healthcare Services, Ontario, CA
Primary Contact: Virgis Narbutas, Chief Executive Officer
CFO: Alan H. Smith, Chief Financial Officer
CMO: Hassan Alkhouli, M.D., Medical Director
CIO: Adam Morquecho, Director Information Technology
CHR: Stephanie Sioson, Director Human Resources
CNO: Sofia Abrina, Administrator and Chief Nursing Officer
Web address: www.hbhospital.com
**Control:** Partnership, Investor–owned, for–profit **Service:** General Medical and Surgical

Staffed Beds: 130

**HUNTINGTON PARK—Los Angeles County**

○ **COMMUNITY HOSPITAL OF HUNTINGTON PARK (050091)**, 2623 East Slauson Avenue, Zip 90255–2926; tel. 323/583–1931 **A**10 11 **F**3 29 40 41 49 70 79 81 89 107 108 119 130 148 **S** Avanti Hospitals, El Segundo, CA
Primary Contact: Hector Hernandez, M.D., Chief Executive Officer
CFO: Steve K. Lopez, Chief Financial Officer
Web address: www.chhplax.com
**Control:** Corporation, Investor–owned, for–profit **Service:** General Medical and Surgical

Staffed Beds: 81 Admissions: 3895 Census: 30 Outpatient Visits: 29982 Births: 0 Personnel: 271

**INDIO—Riverside County**

☒ **JOHN F. KENNEDY MEMORIAL HOSPITAL (050534)**, 47111 Monroe Street, Zip 92201–6739; tel. 760/347–6191 **A**1 9 10 **F**3 8 13 18 20 29 30 31 34 35 37 40 46 47 48 49 50 54 56 57 59 68 70 72 74 76 77 78 79 81 85 87 89 97 107 108 111 118 119 126 130 131 133 135 146 148 **S** TENET Healthcare Corporation, Dallas, TX
Primary Contact: Gary Honts, Interim Chief Executive Officer
COO: Parrish Scarboro, Chief Operating Officer
CHR: Bill Peterson, Director Human Resources
Web address: www.jfkmemorialhosp.com
**Control:** Corporation, Investor–owned, for–profit **Service:** General Medical and Surgical

Staffed Beds: 119 Admissions: 8755 Census: 75 Outpatient Visits: 55166 Births: 2352 Total Expense ($000): 107388 Payroll Expense ($000): 51514 Personnel: 557

**INGLEWOOD—Los Angeles County**

☐ **CENTINELA HOSPITAL MEDICAL CENTER (050739)**, 555 East Hardy Street, Zip 90301–4011, Mailing Address: P.O. Box 720, Zip 90312–6720; tel. 310/673–4660, (Nonreporting) **A**1 10 **S** Prime Healthcare Services, Ontario, CA
Primary Contact: Linda Bradley, Chief Executive Officer
CFO: Mark Overeem, Chief Financial Officer
CMO: Etie Moghissi, M.D., Chief Medical Staff
CIO: Vicky Morgan, Director Information Services
CHR: Margaret Morgan, Director Human Resources
Web address: www.centinelamed.com
**Control:** Corporation, Investor–owned, for–profit **Service:** General Medical and Surgical

Staffed Beds: 369

**IRVINE—Orange County**

◇ **HOAG ORTHOPEDIC INSTITUTE (050769)**, 16250 Sand Canyon Avenue, Zip 92618–3714; tel. 949/517–3149, (Nonreporting) **A**5 21
Primary Contact: Deressa Reid, Interim Chief Executive Officer
Web address: www.hoag.org/Locations/Pages/HoagHospOrthoInstitute.aspx
**Control:** Other not–for–profit (including NFP Corporation) **Service:** Orthopedic

Staffed Beds: 20

**ORANGE COUNTY IRVINE MEDICAL CENTER** See Anaheim Medical Center, Anaheim

**JACKSON—Amador County**

☒ **SUTTER AMADOR HOSPITAL (050014)**, 200 Mission Boulevard, Zip 95642–2564; tel. 209/223–7500 **A**1 5 9 10 **F**29 34 35 40 46 47 54 59 64 65 70 75 76 77 78 79 81 85 87 107 108 110 111 115 119 129 130 132 146 148 **S** Sutter Health, Sacramento, CA
Primary Contact: Anne Platt, Chief Executive Officer
CFO: Brett Moore, CPA, Assistant Administrator Finance
CMO: Darrel K. Kerr, M.D., Chief of Staff
CIO: Tony Jackson, Director Information Technology
CHR: Beverly Revels, Director Human Resources
CNO: Nikki Allen, Patient Care Executive
Web address: www.sutteramador.org
**Control:** Other not–for–profit (including NFP Corporation) **Service:** General Medical and Surgical

Staffed Beds: 42 Admissions: 2369 Census: 22 Outpatient Visits: 49307 Births: 354 Total Expense ($000): 60293 Payroll Expense ($000): 19868 Personnel: 225

**JOSHUA TREE—San Bernardino County**

☒ **HI–DESERT MEDICAL CENTER (050279)**, 6601 White Feather Road, Zip 92252–6607; tel. 760/366–3711, (Total facility includes 120 beds in nursing home–type unit) **A**1 9 10 20 **F**3 8 11 13 15 18 29 30 34 35 40 45 46 50 54 57 59 62 63 64 65 66 68 70 71 74 76 77 79 81 82 93 94 97 104 107 108 111 115 119 127 130 135 146 148 **P**5
Primary Contact: Lionel K. Chadwick, Chief Executive Officer
COO: Jackie Combs, Chief Operating and Nursing Officer
CFO: Robert C. Tyk, Chief Financial Officer
CMO: Andre Kasko, D.O., Chief Medical Staff
CIO: Dan McClure, Chief Information Officer
CHR: Barbara Staresinic, Director Human Resources
Web address: www.hdmc.org
**Control:** Hospital district or authority, Government, nonfederal **Service:** General Medical and Surgical

Staffed Beds: 179 Admissions: 3854 Census: 138 Outpatient Visits: 113891 Births: 391 Total Expense ($000): 61830 Payroll Expense ($000): 26368 Personnel: 433

**CA**

## KENTFIELD—Marin County

☒ **KENTFIELD REHABILITATION AND SPECIALTY HOSPITAL (052043)**, 1125 Sir Francis Drake Boulevard, Zip 94904–1418; tel. 415/456–9680, (Nonreporting) **A**1 9 10 **S** Vibra Healthcare, Mechanicsburg, PA
Primary Contact: Ann Gors, Chief Executive Officer
CFO: Stephanie Lawrence, Chief Financial Officer
CMO: Curtis Roebken, M.D., Chief Medical Staff
CHR: Julene English, Director Human Resources
Web address: www.kentfieldrehab.com
**Control:** Corporation, Investor–owned, for–profit **Service:** Long–Term Acute Care hospital

**Staffed Beds:** 52

## KING CITY—Monterey County

☐ **GEORGE L. MEE MEMORIAL HOSPITAL (050189)**, 300 Canal Street, Zip 93930–3431; tel. 831/385–6000, (Nonreporting) **A**1 5 9 10 20
Primary Contact: Lex Smith, Chief Executive Officer
CFO: Gary L. Wangsmo, Chief Financial Officer
CMO: Schindelheim Roy, M.D., Chief of Staff
CIO: Mike McNamara, Chief Information Officer
CHR: Karen Wong, Chief Human Resources Officer
Web address: www.meememorial.com
**Control:** Other not–for–profit (including NFP Corporation) **Service:** General Medical and Surgical

**Staffed Beds:** 119

## LA JOLLA—San Diego County

☒ **SCRIPPS GREEN HOSPITAL (050424)**, 10666 North Torrey Pines Road, Zip 92037–1093; tel. 858/455–9100 **A**1 2 8 9 10 **F**3 8 11 12 14 15 17 18 20 22 24 26 28 29 30 31 34 35 36 37 44 45 46 47 49 50 51 54 57 58 59 61 64 68 70 74 75 77 78 79 80 81 82 84 85 86 87 93 107 108 110 111 113 114 115 118 119 120 121 123 124 126 130 131 132 136 138 139 141 142 146 148 **P**3 **S** Scripps Health, San Diego, CA
Primary Contact: Robin Brown, Chief Executive, Senior Vice President
CMO: Brent Eastman, M.D., Chief Medical Officer
CHR: Victor Buzachero, Corporate Senior Vice President for Innovation, Human Resources and Performance Management
Web address: www.scrippshealth.org
**Control:** Other not–for–profit (including NFP Corporation) **Service:** General Medical and Surgical

**Staffed Beds:** 173 **Admissions:** 10763 **Census:** 105 **Outpatient Visits:** 84559 **Births:** 0 **Total Expense ($000):** 296338 **Payroll Expense ($000):** 96067 **Personnel:** 1299

☒ **SCRIPPS MEMORIAL HOSPITAL–LA JOLLA (050324)**, 9888 Genesee Avenue, Zip 92037–1200, Mailing Address: P.O. Box 28, Zip 92038–0028; tel. 858/626–4123 **A**1 2 3 5 9 10 **F**3 4 5 8 11 12 13 14 15 17 18 20 22 24 26 28 29 30 31 34 35 40 43 44 45 46 48 49 53 54 57 58 59 64 65 68 70 74 75 76 77 78 79 81 82 84 85 86 87 91 92 93 94 99 100 101 102 103 104 107 108 110 111 114 115 116 117 118 119 121 123 124 126 130 132 141 142 145 146 147 148 **P**5 **S** Scripps Health, San Diego, CA
Primary Contact: Gary G. Fybel, Chief Executive, Senior Vice President
COO: Cindy Steckel, Vice President Chief Nurse and Operations Executive
CFO: Linda Honaker, Vice President Financial Operations
CMO: Brent Eastman, M.D., Chief Medical Officer
CHR: Sandra Hughes, Executive Director Human Resources
CNO: Cindy Steckel, Vice President Chief Nurse and Operations Executive
Web address: www.scripps.org/locations/hospitals__scripps–memorial–hospital–la–jolla
**Control:** Other not–for–profit (including NFP Corporation) **Service:** General Medical and Surgical

**Staffed Beds:** 302 **Admissions:** 17102 **Census:** 208 **Outpatient Visits:** 98939 **Births:** 3996 **Total Expense ($000):** 429709 **Payroll Expense ($000):** 155916 **Personnel:** 2018

## LA MESA—San Diego County

☐ **ALVARADO PARKWAY INSTITUTE BEHAVIORAL HEALTH SYSTEM (054075)**, 7050 Parkway Drive, Zip 91942–1535; tel. 619/465–4411, (Nonreporting) **A**1 9 10
Primary Contact: Patrick C. Ziemer, Chief Executive Officer
COO: Megan Montgomery, Chief Operating Officer
CFO: Chad Engbrecht, Chief Financial Officer
CMO: Bonnie Asada, Director of Nursing
CMO: Saleem Ishaque, Executive Medical Director
Web address: www.apibhs.com
**Control:** Partnership, Investor–owned, for–profit **Service:** Psychiatric

**Staffed Beds:** 66

☒ △ **SHARP GROSSMONT HOSPITAL (050026)**, 5555 Grossmont Center Drive, Zip 91942–3019, Mailing Address: P.O. Box 158, Zip 91944–0158; tel. 619/740–6000, (Total facility includes 30 beds in nursing home–type unit) **A**1 2 7 9 10 **F**3 8 11 13 15 17 18 20 22 24 26 28 29 30 31 34 35 36 38 39 40 43 44 45 49 50 51 54 56 57 58 59 60 61 62 63 64 65 68 70 72 74 75 76 77 78 79 80 81 82 83 84 85 86 87 90 93 94 96 98 100 101 102 103 107 108 111 114 115 116 117 118 119 121 123 124 126 128 129 130 132 135 141 143 145 146 147 148 **P**5 **S** Sharp HealthCare, San Diego, CA
Primary Contact: Michele T. Tarbet, R.N., Chief Executive Officer
COO: Maryann Cone, Chief Operating Officer
CFO: Kari Cornicelli, Chief Financial Officer
CMO: Michael Murphy, M.D., Chief Medical Officer
CIO: William T. Spooner, Senior Vice President and Chief Information Officer
CHR: Ruth Shannon, Director Human Resources
CNO: Janet Hanley, Chief Nursing Officer
Web address: www.sharp.com
**Control:** Other not–for–profit (including NFP Corporation) **Service:** General Medical and Surgical

**Staffed Beds:** 521 **Admissions:** 29561 **Census:** 331 **Outpatient Visits:** 300198 **Births:** 3510 **Total Expense ($000):** 551119 **Payroll Expense ($000):** 224345 **Personnel:** 2647

## LA MIRADA—Los Angeles County

☒ **KINDRED HOSPITAL–LA MIRADA (052038)**, 14900 East Imperial Highway, Zip 90638–2172; tel. 562/944–1900, (Includes KINDRED HOSPITAL SAN GABRIEL VALLEY, 845 North Lark Ellen Avenue, West Covina, Zip 91791–1069; tel. 626/339–5451; April Myers, Chief Executive Officer; KINDRED HOSPITAL SANTA ANA, 1901 North College Avenue, Santa Ana, Zip 92706–2334; tel. 714/564–7800), (Nonreporting) **A**1 9 10 **S** Kindred Healthcare, Louisville, KY
Primary Contact: April Myers, Administrator
COO: Jude Sullivan, Chief Clinical Officer
CFO: Nancy V. Wilson, Chief Financial Officer
CMO: Prakash Chandra Patel, M.D., Chief of Staff
CHR: Kristen Martinez, Coordinator Human Resources
Web address: www.kindredlamirada.com/
**Control:** Corporation, Investor–owned, for–profit **Service:** Long–Term Acute Care hospital

**Staffed Beds:** 216

## LA PALMA—Orange County

☐ **LA PALMA INTERCOMMUNITY HOSPITAL (050580)**, 7901 Walker Street, Zip 90623–1722; tel. 714/670–7400, (Nonreporting) **A**1 10 **S** Prime Healthcare Services, Ontario, CA
Primary Contact: Virgis Narbutas, Chief Executive Officer
CFO: Alan H. Smith, Chief Financial Officer
CMO: Sami Shoukair, M.D., Chief Medical Officer
CIO: Adam Morquecho, Director Information Technology
CHR: Stephanie Sioson, Director Human Resources
CNO: Margo Perusse, Administrator and Chief Nursing Officer
Web address: www.lapalmaintercommunityhospital.com
**Control:** Other not–for–profit (including NFP Corporation) **Service:** General Medical and Surgical

**Staffed Beds:** 141

## LAGUNA HILLS—Orange County

☒ **SADDLEBACK MEMORIAL MEDICAL CENTER (050603)**, 24451 Health Center Drive, Zip 92653–3689; tel. 949/837–4500, (Includes SADDLEBACK MEMORIAL MEDICAL CENTER – SAN CLEMENTE CAMPUS, 654 Camino De Los Mares, San Clemente, Zip 92673–2827; tel. 949/496–1122) **A**1 2 5 9 10 **F**3 11 12 13 14 15 18 20 22 24 26 28 29 30 31 34 35 36 38 40 44 45 49 50 51 53 54 55 56 57 58 59 62 63 64 65 68 70 72 74 75 76 77 78 79 81 82 84 85 86 87 93 94 96 100 107 108 110 111 114 115 118 119 120 121 123 126 130 132 135 141 142 143 145 146 147 148 **P**3 5 7 **S** MemorialCare, Fountain Valley, CA
Primary Contact: Steve Geidt, Chief Executive Officer
COO: Cheryl Jacob, Chief Operating Officer
CFO: Adolfo Chanez, Vice President Finance and Chief Financial Officer
CMO: Ronald Saltzman, M.D., Chief of Staff
CIO: J. Scott Joslyn, Senior Vice President and Chief Information Officer
CHR: Ron Salzberg, Executive Director Human Resources
Web address: www.memorialcare.org
**Control:** Other not–for–profit (including NFP Corporation) **Service:** General Medical and Surgical

**Staffed Beds:** 313 **Admissions:** 15924 **Census:** 179 **Outpatient Visits:** 283144 **Births:** 2648 **Total Expense ($000):** 335484 **Payroll Expense ($000):** 120671 **Personnel:** 1752

---

**Hospital, Medicare Provider Number, Address, Telephone, Approval, Facility, and Physician Codes, Health Care System**

★ American Hospital Association (AHA) membership
☐ The Joint Commission accreditation          ◇ DNV Healthcare Inc. accreditation
◯ Healthcare Facilities Accreditation Program
△ Commission on Accreditation of Rehabilitation Facilities (CARF) accreditation

## LAKE ARROWHEAD—San Bernardino County

✠ **SAN BERNARDINO MOUNTAINS COMMUNITY HOSPITAL DISTRICT (051312)**, 29101 Hospital Road, Zip 92352–9706, Mailing Address: P.O. Box 70, Zip 92352–0070; tel. 909/336–3651, (Total facility includes 20 beds in nursing home–type unit) **A**1 9 10 18 **F**11 29 30 31 34 35 39 40 45 50 57 64 65 66 68 69 71 75 79 81 85 86 87 99 104 107 114 119 127 128 130 133 146 148
Primary Contact: Charles Harrison, Chief Executive Officer
COO: Susan Lowell, Chief Operating Officer and Chief Nursing Officer
CFO: Yvonne Waggener, Chief Financial Officer
CMO: Lawrence Walker, M.D., Chief of Staff
CIO: Trace Kateley, Manager Information Systems
CHR: Julie Atwood, Director Human Resources
Web address: www.mchcares.com
**Control:** Hospital district or authority, Government, nonfederal **Service:** General Medical and Surgical

**Staffed Beds:** 37 **Admissions:** 388 **Census:** 22 **Outpatient Visits:** 29855 **Births:** 0 **Total Expense ($000):** 16166 **Payroll Expense ($000):** 7190

## LAKE ISABELLA—Kern County

**KERN VALLEY HEALTHCARE DISTRICT (051314)**, 6412 Laurel Avenue, Zip 93240–9529, Mailing Address: P.O. Box 1628, Zip 93240–1628; tel. 760/379–2681, (Total facility includes 74 beds in nursing home–type unit) **A**9 10 18 **F**11 29 30 34 35 40 45 57 59 64 70 77 81 93 103 107 114 119 127 128 130 133 146
Primary Contact: Timothy McGlew, Chief Executive Officer
CFO: Chester Beedle, Chief Financial Officer
CMO: Gary A. Finstad, M.D., Chief of Staff
CIO: Dena Griffith, Manager Information Systems
CHR: Debra Hoffman, Manager Human Resources
Web address: www.kvhd.org
**Control:** Hospital district or authority, Government, nonfederal **Service:** Long–Term Acute Care hospital

**Staffed Beds:** 99 **Admissions:** 752 **Census:** 63 **Outpatient Visits:** 23107 **Births:** 3 **Total Expense ($000):** 21281 **Payroll Expense ($000):** 9008 **Personnel:** 178

## LAKEPORT—Lake County

✠ **SUTTER LAKESIDE HOSPITAL (051329)**, 5176 Hill Road East, Zip 95453–6300; tel. 707/262–5000 **A**1 9 10 18 **F**3 8 11 13 15 18 29 30 34 35 40 43 45 46 51 54 56 57 59 60 61 64 65 66 68 70 71 75 76 77 79 81 85 86 87 91 93 97 107 109 110 111 114 116 118 119 127 130 131 133 135 146 147 148 **S** Sutter Health, Sacramento, CA
Primary Contact: Siri Nelson, Chief Administrative Officer
CFO: Krista Touros, Assistant Administrator Finance
CMO: Diane Pege, M.D., Vice President Medical Affairs
CIO: Jack Buell, Director Information Services
CHR: Richard Abbate, Director Human Resources
CNO: Teresa L. Wallace, Chief Nurse Executive
Web address: www.sutterlakeside.org
**Control:** Other not–for–profit (including NFP Corporation) **Service:** General Medical and Surgical

**Staffed Beds:** 25 **Admissions:** 2078 **Census:** 19 **Outpatient Visits:** 81265 **Births:** 337 **Total Expense ($000):** 66321 **Payroll Expense ($000):** 22362 **Personnel:** 269

## LAKEWOOD—Los Angeles County

✠ **LAKEWOOD REGIONAL MEDICAL CENTER (050581)**, 3700 East South Street, Zip 90712–1498, Mailing Address: P.O. Box 6070, Zip 90714–6070; tel. 562/531–2550 **A**1 9 10 **F**3 11 15 17 18 20 22 24 26 29 30 34 35 38 40 45 49 50 51 57 59 64 68 70 74 75 77 81 85 87 93 107 108 109 111 115 118 119 120 130 132 143 146 148 **S** TENET Healthcare Corporation, Dallas, TX
Primary Contact: B. Joseph Badalian, President and Chief Executive Officer
COO: Nathaniel Malcolm, Chief Operating Officer
CFO: Mary Beth Formby, Chief Financial Officer
CMO: Ronald L. Kaufman, M.D., Chief Medical Officer
CIO: Pat Pierce, Director Information Systems
CHR: Mary Okuhara, Director Human Resources
CNO: Terri Newton, Chief Nursing Officer
Web address: www.lakewoodregional.com
**Control:** Corporation, Investor–owned, for–profit **Service:** General Medical and Surgical

**Staffed Beds:** 153 **Admissions:** 8207 **Census:** 97 **Outpatient Visits:** 56642 **Births:** 0 **Total Expense ($000):** 129301 **Payroll Expense ($000):** 57445 **Personnel:** 707

## LANCASTER—Los Angeles County

✠ **ANTELOPE VALLEY HOSPITAL (050056)**, 1600 West Avenue J, Zip 93534–2894; tel. 661/949–5000, (Nonreporting) **A**1 9 10
Primary Contact: Pamela Hinson, Interim Administrator
CFO: Cheryl Tong, Chief Financial Officer
CMO: Doddanna Krishna, M.D., Chief of Staff
CIO: Humberto Quintanar, Chief Information Officer
CHR: Marie Reed, Director Human Resources
CNO: Marcey Jorgenson, Chief Nursing Officer
Web address: www.avhospital.org
**Control:** Hospital district or authority, Government, nonfederal **Service:** General Medical and Surgical

**Staffed Beds:** 368

## LEMOORE—Kings County

✠ **NAVAL HOSPITAL**, 937 Franklin Avenue, Zip 93246–5004; tel. 559/998–4481, (Nonreporting) **A**1 **S** Bureau of Medicine and Surgery, Department of the Navy, Washington, DC
CFO: Thomas M. Brui, Director Resource Management
CMO: Scott Cota, M.D., Director Medical Services
CIO: Victor Dela Torre, Command Legal Officer
CHR: Billy Newman, Department Head
Web address: www.med.navy.mil/sites/nhlem/Pages/index.aspx
**Control:** Navy, Government, federal **Service:** General Medical and Surgical

**Staffed Beds:** 16

## LIVERMORE—Alameda County

**VALLEY MEMORIAL** See ValleyCare Medical Center, Pleasanton

**VETERANS AFFAIRS PALO ALTO HEALTH CARE SYSTEM, LIVERMORE DIVISION** See Veterans Affairs Palo Alto Health Care System, Palo Alto

## LODI—San Joaquin County

✠ **LODI MEMORIAL HOSPITAL (050336)**, 975 South Fairmont Avenue, Zip 95240–5179, Mailing Address: P.O. Box 3004, Zip 95241–1908; tel. 209/334–3411, (Includes LODI MEMORIAL HOSPITAL WEST, 800 South Lower Sacramento Road, Zip 95242; tel. 209/333–0211), (Nonreporting) **A**1 9 10
Primary Contact: Joseph P. Harrington, President and Chief Executive Officer
COO: Mark Sey, Vice President and Chief Administrative Officer
CHR: Mark T. Wallace, Director Human Resources
Web address: www.lodihealth.org
**Control:** Other not–for–profit (including NFP Corporation) **Service:** General Medical and Surgical

**Staffed Beds:** 214

## LOMA LINDA—San Bernardino County

**LOMA LINDA UNIVERSITY HEART & SURGICAL HOSPITAL** See Loma Linda University Medical Center

✠ △ **LOMA LINDA UNIVERSITY MEDICAL CENTER (050327)**, 11234 Anderson Street, Zip 92354–2804, Mailing Address: P.O. Box 2000, Zip 92354–0200; tel. 909/558–4000, (Includes LOMA LINDA UNIVERSITY CHILDREN'S HOSPITAL, 11234 Anderson Street, tel. 909/558–8000; LOMA LINDA UNIVERSITY EAST CAMPUS HOSPITAL, 25333 Barton Road, Zip 92354–3053; tel. 909/558–6000; LOMA LINDA UNIVERSITY HEART & SURGICAL HOSPITAL, 26780 Barton Road, Zip 92354; tel. 909/583–2900) **A**1 2 3 5 7 8 9 10 **F**2 3 8 11 12 13 15 17 18 19 20 21 22 23 24 25 26 27 28 29 30 31 32 34 35 37 40 41 43 45 46 47 48 49 50 54 57 59 60 62 64 65 68 70 72 74 75 76 77 78 79 81 82 84 85 87 88 89 90 91 92 93 94 107 108 110 111 112 114 115 116 117 118 119 120 121 122 123 124 126 129 130 132 134 136 137 138 139 141 142 143 144 146 147 148 **P**3 **S** Loma Linda University Adventist Health Sciences Center, Loma Linda, CA
Primary Contact: Ruthita J. Fike, Chief Executive Officer
COO: Ruthita J. Fike, Chief Executive Officer
CFO: Steve Mohr, Senior Vice President Finance and Chief Financial Officer
CMO: Daniel Giang, M.D., Vice President for Medical Administration
CIO: Mark Zirkelbach, Chief Information Officer
CHR: Lizette Norton, Associate Vice President Human Resources Management
Web address: www.llumc.edu
**Control:** Other not–for–profit (including NFP Corporation) **Service:** General Medical and Surgical

**Staffed Beds:** 825 **Admissions:** 28735 **Census:** 542 **Outpatient Visits:** 698687 **Births:** 2827 **Total Expense ($000):** 1107814 **Payroll Expense ($000):** 400543 **Personnel:** 7441

*Many Facility Codes have changed. Please refer to the AHA Guide Code Chart.* © 2013 AHA Guide

**CA**

⊠ △ **VETERANS AFFAIRS LOMA LINDA HEALTHCARE SYSTEM,** (Formerly Jerry L. Pettis Memorial Veterans Medical Center), 11201 Benton Street, Zip 92357–1000; tel. 909/825–7084, (Total facility includes 108 beds in nursing home–type unit) **A**1 2 3 5 7 8 **F**2 3 5 8 12 15 17 18 20 22 26 28 29 30 31 33 35 36 38 39 40 45 46 47 48 49 50 51 55 56 57 58 59 60 61 62 63 64 65 68 70 74 75 77 78 79 81 82 84 85 86 87 90 92 93 94 97 98 100 102 103 104 107 108 110 111 114 115 117 118 119 127 128 129 130 132 135 143 145 146 147 148 **S** Department of Veterans Affairs, Washington, DC
Primary Contact: Donald F. Moore, Director
COO: Shane Elliott, Associate Director Administration
CFO: Ron Pitts, Chief Financial Officer
CMO: Dwight Evans, M.D., Chief of Staff
CIO: Doug Wirthgen, Facility Chief Information Officer
CHR: Eugene Wylie, Chief Human Resources Officer
CNO: Anne Gillespie, R.N., Associate Director Patient Care and Nursing Services
Web address: www.lomalinda.va.gov
**Control:** Veterans Affairs, Government, federal **Service:** General Medical and Surgical

**Staffed Beds:** 270 **Admissions:** 8390 **Census:** 189 **Outpatient Visits:** 718881 **Total Expense ($000):** 539373

### LOMPOC—Santa Barbara County

⊠ **LOMPOC VALLEY MEDICAL CENTER (050110),** 1515 East Ocean Avenue, Zip 93436–7092, Mailing Address: P.O. Box 1058, Zip 93438–1058; tel. 805/737–3300, (Nonreporting) **A**1 9 10
Primary Contact: James J. Raggio, Chief Executive Officer
COO: Naishadh Buch, Director Pharmacy and Chief Operating Officer
CFO: Robert M. Baden, Chief Financial Officer
CMO: Cecilia Ramos, M.D., Chief of Staff
CIO: Jim White, Chief Information Officer
CHR: Edwin R. Braxton, Director Human Resources
Web address: www.lompocvmc.com
**Control:** Hospital district or authority, Government, nonfederal **Service:** General Medical and Surgical

**Staffed Beds:** 60

### LONE PINE—Inyo County

★ **SOUTHERN INYO HEALTHCARE DISTRICT (051302),** 501 East Locust Street, Zip 93545–1009, Mailing Address: P.O. Box 1009, Zip 93545–1009; tel. 760/876–5501, (Nonreporting) **A**9 10 18
Primary Contact: Lee Barron, Chief Executive Officer
CFO: Lee Barron, Chief Executive Officer
CIO: Patricia M. Murray, Information Officer
CHR: Ashley Williams, Manager Human Resources
Web address: www.sihd.org
**Control:** Hospital district or authority, Government, nonfederal **Service:** General Medical and Surgical

**Staffed Beds:** 37

### LONG BEACH—Los Angeles County

☐ **COMMUNITY HOSPITAL OF LONG BEACH (050727),** 1720 Termino Avenue, Zip 90804–2180; tel. 562/498–1000 **A**1 9 10 **F**3 11 12 14 18 26 28 29 30 31 34 35 38 40 45 46 50 54 56 57 59 64 65 68 70 71 75 77 78 79 81 82 85 86 87 93 98 100 101 102 107 108 111 114 119 130 132 135 146 148 **S** MemorialCare, Fountain Valley, CA
Primary Contact: Diana Hendel, PharmD, Chief Executive Officer
COO: Diane DeWalsche, R.N., Chief Operating Officer
CMO: Dennis Parmer, M.D., Chief Medical Staff
CIO: Rob Klingseis, Manager Information Systems
CHR: Valene J. Martin, Administrative Director Human Resources
Web address: www.chlb.org
**Control:** Other not–for–profit (including NFP Corporation) **Service:** General Medical and Surgical

**Staffed Beds:** 148 **Admissions:** 4060 **Census:** 49 **Outpatient Visits:** 23977 **Births:** 0 **Total Expense ($000):** 49631 **Payroll Expense ($000):** 21900 **Personnel:** 375

⊠ △ **LONG BEACH MEMORIAL MEDICAL CENTER (050485),** 2801 Atlantic Avenue, Zip 90806–1701, Mailing Address: P.O. Box 1428, Zip 90801–1428; tel. 562/933–2000 **A**1 2 3 5 7 8 9 10 **F**3 9 11 12 14 15 17 18 20 22 24 26 28 29 30 31 34 35 36 37 38 39 40 43 44 45 47 48 49 50 52 53 55 56 57 58 59 61 63 64 65 68 70 74 75 77 78 79 81 82 84 85 86 87 90 93 96 97 100 101 107 108 110 111 114 115 116 117 119 120 121 123 124 126 129 130 131 132 135 141 142 143 144 146 147 148 **P**3 4 5 **S** MemorialCare, Fountain Valley, CA
Primary Contact: Diana Hendel, PharmD, Chief Executive Officer
COO: Tamra Kaplan, Chief Operating Officer
CFO: John Bishop, Chief Financial Officer
CMO: Susan Melvin, D.O., Chief Medical Officer
CIO: Danny Asaoka, Executive Director Information Systems
CHR: Myra Gregorian, Vice President Human Resources
CNO: Judith A. Fix, R.N., Senior Vice President and Chief Nursing Officer
Web address: www.memorialcare.org/LongBeach
**Control:** Other not–for–profit (including NFP Corporation) **Service:** General Medical and Surgical

**Staffed Beds:** 420 **Admissions:** 22398 **Census:** 286 **Outpatient Visits:** 105389 **Births:** 0 **Total Expense ($000):** 444971 **Payroll Expense ($000):** 147857 **Personnel:** 3340

☐ **MILLER CHILDREN'S HOSPITAL (053309),** 2801 Atlantic Avenue, Zip 90806–1701; tel. 562/933–5437 **A**1 9 10 **F**3 11 12 13 14 15 19 21 23 25 27 29 30 31 32 34 35 36 37 38 40 41 43 44 45 47 48 49 50 52 53 54 55 57 58 59 61 64 65 66 68 72 74 75 76 77 78 79 81 82 84 85 86 87 88 89 93 96 97 99 100 101 102 107 108 111 114 115 116 117 119 120 121 123 124 126 129 130 132 134 135 141 142 143 144 146 147 148 **P**5 **S** MemorialCare, Fountain Valley, CA
Primary Contact: Diana Hendel, PharmD, Chief Executive Officer
Web address: www.memorialcare.org
**Control:** Other not–for–profit (including NFP Corporation) **Service:** Children's general

**Staffed Beds:** 383 **Admissions:** 14602 **Census:** 213 **Outpatient Visits:** 91849 **Births:** 5333 **Total Expense ($000):** 397560 **Payroll Expense ($000):** 134952 **Personnel:** 1220

◇ **PACIFIC HOSPITAL OF LONG BEACH (050277),** 2776 Pacific Avenue, Zip 90806–2699, Mailing Address: P.O. Box 1268, Zip 90801–1268; tel. 562/595–1911, (Nonreporting) **A**9 10 12 13 21
Primary Contact: Michael D. Drobot, Chief Executive Officer
COO: Jennifer Ensminger, Chief Operating Officer
CFO: Jim Canedo, Chief Financial Officer
CMO: Luke Watson, M.D., Chief of Staff
CIO: Rohan Corea, Director Healthcare Information Technology
CHR: Ann Mattia Schiller, Vice President Human Resources
CNO: Kathryn McLaughlin, Vice President and Chief Nursing Officer
Web address: www.phlb.org
**Control:** Other not–for–profit (including NFP Corporation) **Service:** General Medical and Surgical

**Staffed Beds:** 157

⊠ **ST. MARY MEDICAL CENTER (050191),** 1050 Linden Avenue, Zip 90813–3321, Mailing Address: P.O. Box 887, Zip 90801–0887; tel. 562/491–9000 **A**1 2 3 5 9 10 **F**3 8 11 12 13 15 17 18 20 22 24 26 28 29 30 31 32 34 35 36 39 40 43 44 47 49 50 55 56 57 58 59 60 61 64 65 66 69 70 71 72 74 75 76 77 78 79 81 82 84 85 87 89 90 93 96 107 108 110 111 114 115 118 119 123 125 130 132 134 135 141 142 143 144 146 147 **P**5 **S** Dignity Health, San Francisco, CA
Primary Contact: Thomas A. Salerno, President and Chief Executive Officer
COO: Gail Daly, Chief Operating Officer
CMO: Stanley Goldberg, M.D., Chief of Staff
CIO: Robert Erndt, Site Manager
CHR: Bob Bokern, Director Human Resources
Web address: www.stmarymedicalcenter.org
**Control:** Other not–for–profit (including NFP Corporation) **Service:** General Medical and Surgical

**Staffed Beds:** 165 **Admissions:** 11202 **Census:** 144 **Outpatient Visits:** 233439 **Births:** 2832 **Total Expense ($000):** 262197 **Payroll Expense ($000):** 100171 **Personnel:** 1282

CA

---

**Hospital, Medicare Provider Number, Address, Telephone, Approval, Facility, and Physician Codes, Health Care System**

★ American Hospital Association (AHA) membership
☐ The Joint Commission accreditation
◇ DNV Healthcare Inc. accreditation
○ Healthcare Facilities Accreditation Program
△ Commission on Accreditation of Rehabilitation Facilities (CARF) accreditation

**CA**

✚ △ **VETERANS AFFAIRS LONG BEACH HEALTHCARE SYSTEM**, 5901 East 7th Street, Zip 90822–5201; tel. 562/826–8000 **A**1 2 3 5 7 8 **F**2 3 5 8 14 15 17 18 20 22 28 29 30 31 33 34 35 36 38 39 40 44 45 46 47 48 49 50 51 54 56 57 58 59 60 61 62 63 64 65 68 70 71 74 75 77 78 79 80 81 82 84 85 86 87 90 91 92 93 94 97 98 100 101 102 103 104 107 108 110 111 114 117 118 119 120 121 126 127 128 129 130 131 132 135 143 146 147 148 **P**1 **S** Department of Veterans Affairs, Washington, DC
Primary Contact: Isabel Duff, MS, Director
COO: Anthony DeFrancesco, Associate Director
CFO: Michael J. Rupert, Chief Financial Officer
CMO: Sandor Szabo, M.D., Chief of Staff
CIO: Rodney Sagmit, Chief Information Management
CHR: Mary E. McCartan, Manager Human Resources
Web address: www.longbeach.va.gov/
**Control:** Veterans Affairs, Government, federal **Service:** General Medical and Surgical

| |
|---|
| **Staffed Beds:** 356 **Admissions:** 7300 **Census:** 167 **Outpatient Visits:** 638008 **Births:** 0 **Total Expense ($000):** 205160 **Payroll Expense ($000):** 161674 |

### LOS ALAMITOS—Orange County

✚ **LOS ALAMITOS MEDICAL CENTER (050551)**, 3751 Katella Avenue, Zip 90720–3164; tel. 562/598–1311 **A**1 9 10 **F**3 8 11 13 15 17 18 20 22 28 29 31 34 35 40 41 44 45 49 50 51 54 55 56 57 59 64 65 66 68 70 75 76 77 78 79 81 82 85 86 87 98 103 107 108 109 110 111 112 114 115 116 117 119 120 121 124 130 132 142 143 146 148 **P**2 3 5 **S** TENET Healthcare Corporation, Dallas, TX
Primary Contact: Michele Finney, Chief Executive Officer
CFO: Dave Vickers, Chief Financial Officer
CIO: Sally Andrada, Chief Information Officer
CHR: Angie Driscoll, Director Human Resources
Web address: www.losalamitosmedctr.com
**Control:** Corporation, Investor–owned, for–profit **Service:** General Medical and Surgical

| |
|---|
| **Staffed Beds:** 167 **Admissions:** 9761 **Census:** 117 **Outpatient Visits:** 88249 **Births:** 1400 **Total Expense ($000):** 142069 **Payroll Expense ($000):** 70084 **Personnel:** 905 |

### LOS ANGELES—Los Angeles County

**(Mailing Addresses - Canoga Park, Encino, Granada Hills, Harbor City, Hollywood, Mission Hills, North Hollywood, Northridge, Panorama City, San Pedro, Sepulveda, Sherman Oaks, Sun Valley, Sylmar, Tarzana, Van Nuys, West Hills, West Los Angeles, Woodland Hills)**

✚ **BARLOW RESPIRATORY HOSPITAL (052031)**, 2000 Stadium Way, Zip 90026–2696; tel. 213/250–4200, (Nonreporting) **A**1 9 10
Primary Contact: Margaret W. Crane, Chief Executive Officer
COO: Mary B. Oelman, R.N., Chief Operating Officer and Chief Clinical Officer
CFO: Edward Engesser, Chief Financial Officer and Chief Information Officer
CMO: David Nelson, M.D., Medical Director
CIO: Edward Engesser, Chief Financial Officer and Chief Information Officer
CHR: Jeannine Coatsworth, Vice President Human Resources
Web address: www.barlow2000.org
**Control:** Other not–for–profit (including NFP Corporation) **Service:** Long–Term Acute Care hospital

| |
|---|
| **Staffed Beds:** 92 |

✚ **CALIFORNIA HOSPITAL MEDICAL CENTER (050149)**, 1401 South Grand Avenue, Zip 90015–3010; tel. 213/748–2411, (Total facility includes 31 beds in nursing home–type unit) **A**1 3 5 9 10 **F**1 3 4 11 16 17 29 30 31 34 35 40 43 45 49 51 53 57 59 64 67 70 72 73 76 78 79 81 84 88 89 90 98 102 107 108 111 114 119 121 128 130 132 135 143 146 147 **S** Dignity Health, San Francisco, CA
Primary Contact: Craig G. Myers, President
CFO: Robert Allen, Chief Financial Officer
CMO: Bruce A. Greenfield, M.D., Chief of Staff
CIO: Rich Patla, Director Information Technology
CHR: Sandra Davis Houston, Vice President Human Resources
Web address: www.chmcla.org
**Control:** Other not–for–profit (including NFP Corporation) **Service:** General Medical and Surgical

| |
|---|
| **Staffed Beds:** 318 **Admissions:** 16816 **Census:** 185 **Outpatient Visits:** 66252 **Births:** 4285 **Total Expense ($000):** 305978 **Payroll Expense ($000):** 124076 **Personnel:** 1470 |

✚ △ **CEDARS–SINAI MEDICAL CENTER (050625)**, 8700 Beverly Boulevard, Zip 90048–1865; Mailing Address: Box 48750, Zip 90048–0750; tel. 310/423–5000 **A**1 2 3 5 7 8 9 10 **F**3 5 6 8 9 11 12 13 14 15 17 18 19 20 21 22 23 24 25 26 27 28 30 31 32 33 34 35 36 37 38 39 40 43 44 45 46 47 48 49 50 51 52 53 54 55 56 57 58 59 60 61 64 65 66 68 69 70 71 72 74 75 76 77 78 79 81 82 83 84 85 86 87 88 89 90 91 92 93 96 97 99 100 101 102 103 104 105 106 107 108 109 110 111 112 113 114 115 116 117 118 119 120 121 122 123 124 126 130 131 132 133 134 135 136 137 138 139 140 141 142 145 146 147 148 **P**3 5 8
Primary Contact: Thomas M. Priselac, President and Chief Executive Officer
COO: Mark R. Gavens, Senior Vice President Clinical Care Services and Chief Operating Officer
CFO: Edward M. Prunchunas, Senior Vice President and Chief Financial Officer
CMO: Michael L. Langberg, M.D., Senior Vice President Medical Affairs and Chief Medical Officer
CIO: Darren Dworkin, Senior Vice President and Chief Information Officer
CHR: Jeanne Flores, Senior Vice President Human Resources and Organizational Development
Web address: www.cedars–sinai.edu
**Control:** Other not–for–profit (including NFP Corporation) **Service:** General Medical and Surgical

| |
|---|
| **Staffed Beds:** 865 **Admissions:** 49240 **Census:** 698 **Outpatient Visits:** 694923 **Births:** 6615 **Total Expense ($000):** 2321552 **Payroll Expense ($000):** 902711 **Personnel:** 10439 |

✚ **CHILDREN'S HOSPITAL LOS ANGELES (053302)**, 4650 Sunset Boulevard, Zip 90027–6062, Mailing Address: P.O. Box 27980, Zip 90027–0980; tel. 323/660–2450 **A**1 3 5 9 10 **F**3 5 8 14 17 19 21 23 25 27 29 30 31 32 34 35 36 38 39 40 41 43 44 45 46 49 50 51 54 55 57 58 59 60 61 64 68 70 71 72 74 75 77 78 79 80 81 82 84 85 86 87 88 89 90 93 99 100 104 107 108 111 114 115 116 117 118 119 120 121 129 130 131 132 134 135 136 137 138 141 146 148
Primary Contact: Richard D. Cordova, President and Chief Executive Officer
COO: Rodney Hanners, Senior Vice President and Chief Operating Officer
CFO: Lannie Tonnu, Senior Vice President and Chief Financial Officer
CMO: Brent Polk, M.D., Chair Department of Pediatrics and Vice President Academic Affairs
CIO: Marty Miller, Vice President and Chief Information Officer
CHR: Hugo Santos, Vice President Human Resources
CNO: Mary Dee Hacker, R.N., Vice President, Patient Care Services and Chief Nursing Officer
Web address: www.chla.org
**Control:** Other not–for–profit (including NFP Corporation) **Service:** Children's general

| |
|---|
| **Staffed Beds:** 327 **Admissions:** 12629 **Census:** 259 **Outpatient Visits:** 281281 **Births:** 0 **Total Expense ($000):** 591905 **Payroll Expense ($000):** 278506 **Personnel:** 4677 |

☐ **EAST LOS ANGELES DOCTORS HOSPITAL (050641)**, 4060 East Whittier Boulevard, Zip 90023–2526; tel. 323/268–5514 **A**1 9 10 **F**1 3 7 8 13 17 29 30 35 40 41 76 79 80 81 82 89 91 107 119 130 **S** Avanti Hospitals, El Segundo, CA
Primary Contact: Hector Hernandez, M.D., Chief Executive Officer
CFO: Daniel R. Heckathorne, Regional Chief Financial Officer
CMO: Kamlesh Dhawan, M.D., Chief of Staff
CIO: Earle Johnson, Chief Information Officer
CHR: Rob Taylor, Corporate Director Human Resources
CNO: Carmelo James, Chief Nursing Officer
Web address: www.elalax.com
**Control:** Partnership, Investor–owned, for–profit **Service:** General Medical and Surgical

| |
|---|
| **Staffed Beds:** 127 **Admissions:** 4131 **Census:** 73 **Outpatient Visits:** 19807 **Births:** 844 **Total Expense ($000):** 90437 **Payroll Expense ($000):** 25199 |

☐ **ENCINO HOSPITAL MEDICAL CENTER (050158)**, 16237 Ventura Boulevard, Encino, Zip 91436–2201; tel. 818/995–5000, (Total facility includes 26 beds in nursing home–type unit) **A**1 10 **F**17 29 35 38 40 49 51 57 70 75 77 78 79 81 98 103 107 118 119 128 130 146 **S** Prime Healthcare Services, Ontario, CA
Primary Contact: Bockhi Park, Chief Executive Officer
CFO: Kanner Tillman, Chief Financial Officer
CMO: Muhammad Anwar, M.D., Chief Medical Officer
CIO: Edward Barrera, Director Communications
CHR: Barbara Back, Manager Human Resources
CNO: Vilma L. Dinham, R.N., Chief Nursing Officer
Web address: www.encinomed.com
**Control:** Other not–for–profit (including NFP Corporation) **Service:** General Medical and Surgical

| |
|---|
| **Staffed Beds:** 66 **Admissions:** 1837 **Census:** 42 **Outpatient Visits:** 9993 **Births:** 0 **Total Expense ($000):** 26352 **Payroll Expense ($000):** 20028 **Personnel:** 268 |

○ **GATEWAYS HOSPITAL AND MENTAL HEALTH CENTER (054028)**, 1891 Effie Street, Zip 90026–1711; tel. 323/644–2000 **A**10 11 **F**29 35 77 98 99 100 101 104 106 130 **P**6
Primary Contact: Mara Pelsman, Chief Executive Officer
COO: Jeff Emery, Chief Financial Officer and Chief Operating Officer
CFO: Jeff Emery, Chief Financial Officer and Chief Operating Officer
CMO: Mark Hantoot, M.D., Medical Director
CIO: Jeff Emery, Chief Financial Officer and Chief Operating Officer
CHR: Melanie Van Heusen, Director Human Resources
Web address: www.gatewayshospital.org
**Control:** Other not–for–profit (including NFP Corporation) **Service:** Psychiatric

**Staffed Beds:** 55 **Admissions:** 992 **Census:** 35 **Outpatient Visits:** 121304
**Births:** 0 **Total Expense ($000):** 26331 **Payroll Expense ($000):** 13974
**Personnel:** 336

**GENERAL HOSPITAL** See LAC/University of Southern California Medical Center

□ △ **GOOD SAMARITAN HOSPITAL (050471)**, 1225 Wilshire Boulevard, Zip 90017–1901; tel. 213/977–2121 **A**1 2 3 5 7 9 10 **F**3 7 8 9 11 13 14 15 17 18 20 22 24 26 28 29 30 31 34 35 36 37 40 43 45 46 47 48 49 50 51 53 56 57 58 59 60 61 64 65 68 70 72 74 76 77 78 79 81 85 86 87 93 107 108 110 111 114 115 117 118 119 120 121 123 124 126 130 132 143 144 145 146 148 **P**5 7
Primary Contact: Andrew B. Leeka, President and Chief Executive Officer
CFO: Alan Ino, Chief Financial Officer
CMO: Andrew Fishmann, M.D., Chairman, Medical Staff
CIO: Dean Campbell, Vice President Information Services and Chief Information Officer
CHR: Lexie Schuster, Vice President Human Resources
CNO: Margaret Pfeiffer, R.N., Vice President Patient Care Services
Web address: www.goodsam.org
**Control:** Other not–for–profit (including NFP Corporation) **Service:** General Medical and Surgical

**Staffed Beds:** 374 **Admissions:** 13988 **Census:** 168 **Outpatient Visits:** 88622 **Births:** 4178 **Total Expense ($000):** 289255 **Payroll Expense ($000):** 111534 **Personnel:** 1297

◇ **HOLLYWOOD COMMUNITY HOSPITAL (050135)**, 6245 De Longpre Avenue, Zip 90028–9001; tel. 323/462–2271, (Includes HOLLYWOOD COMMUNITY HOSPITAL OF VAN NUYS, 14433 Emelita Street, Van Nuys, Zip 91401; tel. 818/787–1511), (Nonreporting) **A**10 21 **S** Alta Healthcare System, Los Angeles, CA
Primary Contact: Bruce P. Grimshaw, Chief Executive Officer
Web address: www.hollywoodcommunityhospital.org/
**Control:** Corporation, Investor–owned, for–profit **Service:** General Medical and Surgical

**Staffed Beds:** 45

**HOLLYWOOD COMMUNITY HOSPITAL OF VAN NUYS** See Hollywood Community Hospital

⊠ **HOLLYWOOD PRESBYTERIAN MEDICAL CENTER (050063)**, 1300 North Vermont Avenue, Zip 90027–6005; tel. 323/913–4914 **A**1 2 9 10 **F**3 15 17 18 20 22 24 26 29 30 31 34 35 40 46 49 55 57 58 59 61 64 65 68 70 72 74 75 76 77 78 79 80 81 82 84 85 87 89 90 92 93 96 107 108 111 114 119 120 130 132 146 148 **P**3 5 6
Primary Contact: Kenneth I. Rivers, President and Chief Executive Officer
CFO: Allen Stefanek, Chief Financial Officer
CMO: Robert Chesne, M.D., Chief Medical Officer
CIO: Steve Giles, Chief Information Officer
CHR: Norma Braun, Vice President Human Resources
CNO: Kathy Wojno, R.N., Chief Nursing Officer
Web address: www.hollywoodpresbyterian.com
**Control:** Partnership, Investor–owned, for–profit **Service:** General Medical and Surgical

**Staffed Beds:** 434 **Admissions:** 16175 **Census:** 252 **Outpatient Visits:** 57204 **Births:** 4053 **Payroll Expense ($000):** 96330

**KAISER FOUNDATION MENTAL HEALTH CENTER** See Kaiser Permanente Los Angeles Medical Center

⊠ **KAISER PERMANENTE LOS ANGELES MEDICAL CENTER (050138)**, (Formerly Los Angeles Medical Center), 4867 Sunset Boulevard, Zip 90027–5969; tel. 323/783–4011, (Includes KAISER FOUNDATION MENTAL HEALTH CENTER, 765 West College Street, Zip 90012; tel. 213/580–7200) **A**1 3 5 8 10 **F**3 8 13 15 17 18 19 20 21 22 23 24 25 26 27 28 29 30 31 35 36 38 40 44 45 46 47 49 50 51 54 56 57 60 61 62 63 64 65 66 68 70 72 73 74 75 76 78 79 80 81 82 83 84 85 86 87 88 89 97 98 99 100 101 102 103 104 105 106 107 108 109 111 113 114 115 118 119 120 121 122 123 124 126 132 144 146 147 148 **P**6 **S** Kaiser Foundation Hospitals, Oakland, CA
Primary Contact: Mark E. Costa, Executive Director
COO: Alice H. Issai, Chief Operating Officer
CFO: Prasanna Mohanty, Assistant Administrator Finance
CMO: Donald H. Marcus, M.D., Medical Director
CHR: Paul J. Martin, Director Human Resources
Web address: www.kaiserpermanente.org
**Control:** Other not–for–profit (including NFP Corporation) **Service:** General Medical and Surgical

**Staffed Beds:** 464 **Admissions:** 23369 **Census:** 330 **Outpatient Visits:** 2294985 **Births:** 2507 **Personnel:** 6178

⊠ **KAISER PERMANENTE PANORAMA CITY MEDICAL CENTER (050137)**, (Formerly Panorama City Medical Center), 13652 Cantara Street, Panorama City, Zip 91402–5497; tel. 818/375–2000 **A**1 3 5 10 **F**3 6 13 14 15 18 29 30 31 32 34 35 38 40 44 45 46 47 48 49 50 52 54 55 56 57 59 60 61 62 63 64 65 68 70 72 74 75 76 77 78 79 81 82 83 84 85 86 87 93 97 102 104 107 108 110 111 119 130 131 132 134 135 144 146 147 148 **S** Kaiser Foundation Hospitals, Oakland, CA
Primary Contact: Dennis C. Benton, Administrator and Executive Director
COO: Barbara C. Zelinski, Chief Operating Officer
CFO: Mechi R. Caballero, Assistant Administrator
CMO: Mary L. Wilson, M.D., Area Medical Director
CHR: Carole L. Erken, Human Resources Leader
Web address: www.kaiserpermanente.org
**Control:** Other not–for–profit (including NFP Corporation) **Service:** General Medical and Surgical

**Staffed Beds:** 154 **Admissions:** 14172 **Census:** 129 **Births:** 2098

⊠ **KAISER PERMANENTE SOUTH BAY MEDICAL CENTER (050411)**, (Formerly South Bay Medical Center), 25825 South Vermont Avenue, Harbor City, Zip 90710–3599; tel. 310/325–5111 **A**1 10 **F**3 12 13 15 17 29 30 31 34 35 40 44 45 46 47 48 49 50 57 54 56 57 60 61 64 65 68 70 72 74 75 76 78 79 81 82 84 85 86 87 89 94 100 107 108 111 114 116 117 118 119 130 135 143 146 147 148 **P**6 **S** Kaiser Foundation Hospitals, Oakland, CA
Primary Contact: Lesley A. Wille, Administrator and Executive Director
Web address: www.kaiserpermanente.org
**Control:** Other not–for–profit (including NFP Corporation) **Service:** General Medical and Surgical

**Staffed Beds:** 231 **Admissions:** 13448 **Census:** 132 **Outpatient Visits:** 67492 **Births:** 2163 **Personnel:** 970

⊠ **KAISER PERMANENTE WEST LOS ANGELES MEDICAL CENTER (050561)**, (Formerly West Los Angeles Medical Center), 6041 Cadillac Avenue, Zip 90034–1702; tel. 323/857–2201, (Nonreporting) **A**1 3 5 10 **S** Kaiser Foundation Hospitals, Oakland, CA
Primary Contact: Georgina R. Garcia, Executive Director
CFO: Alice H. Issai, Business Strategy and Finance Leader
CMO: Fred Alexander, M.D., Medical Director
CIO: Gregory M. Sincock, Information Technology Leader
Web address: www.kaiserpermanente.org
**Control:** Other not–for–profit (including NFP Corporation) **Service:** General Medical and Surgical

**Staffed Beds:** 172

⊠ **KAISER PERMANENTE WOODLAND HILLS MEDICAL CENTER (050677)**, (Formerly Woodland Hills Medical Center), 5601 DeSoto Avenue, Woodland Hills, Zip 91367–6701; tel. 818/719–2000 **A**1 3 5 10 **F**3 13 14 15 17 18 29 30 31 34 40 41 45 48 49 50 51 55 56 57 60 61 64 65 68 70 72 73 74 75 76 77 78 79 80 81 82 84 85 86 87 88 89 92 93 100 102 103 107 108 111 116 119 124 126 130 132 141 143 144 146 147 148 **P**6 **S** Kaiser Foundation Hospitals, Oakland, CA
Primary Contact: Michael C. Carter, Executive Director
COO: Richard Trogman, FACHE, Chief Operating Officer
CFO: Marilou Cheung, Assistant Administrator Finance
CMO: Shirley Suda, M.D., Area Medical Director
CIO: David Snow, Area Information Officer
CHR: Cathy Cousineau, Director Human Resources
CNO: Nancy Tankel, R.N., Chief Nurse Executive
Web address: www.kaiserpermanente.org
**Control:** Other not–for–profit (including NFP Corporation) **Service:** General Medical and Surgical

**Staffed Beds:** 175 **Admissions:** 10956 **Census:** 121 **Outpatient Visits:** 45036 **Births:** 1578 **Personnel:** 1477

**CA**

---

**Hospital, Medicare Provider Number, Address, Telephone, Approval, Facility, and Physician Codes, Health Care System**

★ American Hospital Association (AHA) membership
□ The Joint Commission accreditation
◇ DNV Healthcare Inc. accreditation
○ Healthcare Facilities Accreditation Program
△ Commission on Accreditation of Rehabilitation Facilities (CARF) accreditation

✠ **KECK HOSPITAL OF USC (050696)**, 1500 San Pablo Street, Zip 90033–5313; tel. 323/442–8500 **A**1 3 5 8 9 10 **F**3 6 12 15 17 18 20 22 24 26 29 30 31 34 35 37 39 44 45 46 47 48 49 50 51 53 54 55 56 57 58 59 60 61 64 65 68 70 74 75 77 78 79 81 82 83 84 85 86 87 91 92 93 94 96 97 98 100 101 103 104 105 106 107 108 110 111 112 114 115 116 117 118 119 120 121 123 124 126 129 130 131 132 136 137 138 139 140 141 142 145 146 147 148
Primary Contact: Scott Evans, PharmD, Chief Executive Officer
CFO: Jonathan Spees, Chief Financial Officer
CMO: Donald Larsen, M.D., Chief Medical Officer
CIO: Mark Amey, Chief Information Officer
CHR: Matthew McElrath, Chief Human Resources Officer
Web address: www.keckhospitalofusc.org
**Control:** Other not–for–profit (including NFP Corporation) **Service:** General Medical and Surgical

**Staffed Beds: 250 Admissions: 10260 Census: 208 Outpatient Visits: 185342 Births: 0 Total Expense ($000): 584389 Payroll Expense ($000): 211575 Personnel: 3123**

**KEDREN COMMUNITY MENTAL HEALTH CENTER (054083)**, 4211 South Avalon Boulevard, Zip 90011–5622; tel. 323/233–0425, (Nonreporting) **A**10
Primary Contact: John H. Griffith, President & Chief Executive Officer
COO: Madeline Valencerina, Chief Operating Officer
CFO: Rizwan A. Uraizee, Chief Financial Officer
CMO: Frank L. Williams, Executive Vice President/ Medical Director
CNO: Essie Adams, Director of Nursing
Web address: www.kedrenmentalhealth.com
**Control:** Other not–for–profit (including NFP Corporation) **Service:** Psychiatric

**Staffed Beds: 66**

✠ **KINDRED HOSPITAL–LOS ANGELES (052032)**, 5525 West Slauson Avenue, Zip 90056–1067; tel. 310/642–0325, (Nonreporting) **A**1 9 10 **S** Kindred Healthcare, Louisville, KY
Primary Contact: Phillip R. Wolfe, Administrator
CFO: Charles Natcher, Chief Financial Officer
Web address: www.kindredhospitalla.com/
**Control:** Corporation, Investor–owned, for–profit **Service:** Long–Term Acute Care hospital

**Staffed Beds: 81**

☐ **LAC–OLIVE VIEW–UCLA MEDICAL CENTER (050040)**, 14445 Olive View Drive, Sylmar, Zip 91342–1437; tel. 818/364–1555, (Nonreporting) **A**1 3 5 10 **S** Los Angeles County–Department of Health Services, Los Angeles, CA
Primary Contact: Carolyn F. Rhee, Chief Executive Officer
COO: Ernest Espinoza, Interim Chief Operating Officer
CFO: Anthony Gray, Chief Financial Officer
CMO: William Loos, M.D., Chief Medical Officer
CIO: Melvin Brewster, Chief Information Officer
CHR: Thomas Beggane, Manager Human Resources
Web address: www.ladhs.org
**Control:** County–Government, nonfederal **Service:** General Medical and Surgical

**Staffed Beds: 275**

☐ **LAC/UNIVERSITY OF SOUTHERN CALIFORNIA MEDICAL CENTER (050373)**, 1200 North State Street, Zip 90033–1029; tel. 323/226–2622, (Includes GENERAL HOSPITAL, 1200 North State Street, Zip 90033; WOMEN'S AND CHILDREN'S HOSPITAL, 1240 North Mission Road, Zip 90033), (Nonreporting) **A**1 2 3 5 8 9 10 **S** Los Angeles County–Department of Health Services, Los Angeles, CA
Primary Contact: Christina Ghaly, M.D., Interim Chief Executive Officer
COO: Henry Ornelas, Chief Operating Officer
CFO: Mark Corbet, Interim Chief Financial Officer
CMO: Stephanie Hall, M.D., Chief Medical Officer
CIO: Oscar Austelli, Chief Information Officer
Web address: www.lacusc.org
**Control:** County–Government, nonfederal **Service:** General Medical and Surgical

**Staffed Beds: 633**

☐ ◇ **LOS ANGELES COMMUNITY HOSPITAL (050663)**, 4081 East Olympic Boulevard, Zip 90023–3330; tel. 323/267–0477, (Includes LOS ANGELES COMMUNITY HOSPITAL OF NORWALK, 13222 Bloomfield Avenue, Norwalk, Zip 90650; tel. 562/863–4763), (Nonreporting) **A**1 10 21 **S** Alta Healthcare System, Los Angeles, CA
Primary Contact: Omar Ramirez, Chief Executive Officer
CFO: Johnnette Chong, Chief Financial Officer
**Control:** Corporation, Investor–owned, for–profit **Service:** General Medical and Surgical

**Staffed Beds: 180**

**LOS ANGELES COUNTY CENTRAL JAIL HOSPITAL**, 441 Bauchet Street, Zip 90012–2906; tel. 213/473–6100, (Nonreporting)
Primary Contact: Tom Flaherty, Assistant Administrator
**Control:** County–Government, nonfederal **Service:** Hospital unit of an institution (prison hospital, college infimary, etc.)

**Staffed Beds: 190**

☐ **MIRACLE MILE MEDICAL CENTER (050751)**, 6000 San Vicente Boulevard, Zip 90036–4404; tel. 323/930–1040, (Nonreporting) **A**1 9 10
Primary Contact: Jack Lahidjani, Chief Executive Officer
COO: Liz Cheever, Associate Administrator
CMO: Gil Tepper, M.D., Chief of Staff
CIO: Dipak Reddy, Director Information Technology
CHR: Liz Cheever, Associate Administrator
Web address: www.miraclemilemedicalcenter.com
**Control:** Individual, Investor–owned, for–profit **Service:** General Medical and Surgical

**Staffed Beds: 17**

☐ **MISSION COMMUNITY HOSPITAL (050704)**, 14850 Roscoe Boulevard, Panorama City, Zip 91402–4618; tel. 818/787–2222, (Nonreporting) **A**1 9 10
Primary Contact: James Theiring, Interim Chief Executive Officer
CFO: John Holder, Chief Financial Officer
CMO: Robert Thompson, M.D., Chief of Staff
CIO: Andre Henderson, Director Information Systems
CHR: Paul Williams, Director Human Resources
Web address: www.mchonline.org
**Control:** Other not–for–profit (including NFP Corporation) **Service:** General Medical and Surgical

**Staffed Beds: 115**

**MOTION PICTURE AND TELEVISION FUND HOSPITAL AND RESIDENTIAL SERVICES (050552)**, 23388 Mulholland Drive, Woodland Hills, Zip 91364–2733; tel. 818/876–1888, (Nonreporting) **A**9 10
Primary Contact: Bob Beitcher, Interim Chief Executive Officer
COO: Seth Ellis, Chief Operating Officer
CFO: Frank Guarrera, Executive Vice President and Chief Financial Officer
CHR: Jan Zlotowicz, Vice President Human Resources
Web address: www.mptvfund.org
**Control:** Other not–for–profit (including NFP Corporation) **Service:** General Medical and Surgical

**Staffed Beds: 20**

✠ △ **NORTHRIDGE HOSPITAL MEDICAL CENTER–ROSCOE BOULEVARD CAMPUS (050116)**, 18300 Roscoe Boulevard, Northridge, Zip 91325–4167; tel. 818/885–8500 **A**1 2 3 5 7 9 10 **F**2 3 5 8 11 12 13 14 15 17 18 20 22 24 26 28 29 30 31 34 35 38 40 41 43 48 49 56 57 58 59 60 61 64 68 70 72 74 75 76 77 78 79 81 82 84 85 86 87 88 89 90 93 97 98 99 100 101 102 103 104 105 107 108 110 111 114 117 118 119 121 124 126 129 130 132 134 146 147 148 **S** Dignity Health, San Francisco, CA
Primary Contact: Saliba Salo, President
COO: Saliba Salo, President
CHR: George Leisher, Vice President Human Resources
Web address: www.northridgehospital.org
**Control:** Other not–for–profit (including NFP Corporation) **Service:** General Medical and Surgical

**Staffed Beds: 371 Admissions: 17117 Census: 213 Outpatient Visits: 60618 Births: 1912 Total Expense ($000): 362198 Payroll Expense ($000): 152067 Personnel: 1797**

◇ **OLYMPIA MEDICAL CENTER (050742)**, 5900 West Olympic Boulevard, Zip 90036–4671; tel. 310/657–5900 **A**9 10 21 **F**3 6 8 15 17 29 31 34 35 40 45 46 47 49 56 57 58 59 64 70 74 75 77 78 79 81 82 85 86 87 93 100 103 104 107 111 115 119 130 131 132 143 146
Primary Contact: John A. Calderone, Ph.D., Chief Executive Officer
CFO: Babur Ozkan, Chief Financial Officer
CMO: James Peace, M.D., Chief of Staff
CIO: Fritz Campbell, Director Information Systems
CHR: Judy Synder, Director Human Resources
CNO: Karen Knueven, Chief Nursing Officer
Web address: www.olympiamc.com
**Control:** Partnership, Investor–owned, for–profit **Service:** General Medical and Surgical

**Staffed Beds: 204 Admissions: 6017 Census: 82 Outpatient Visits: 38604 Births: 0 Total Expense ($000): 98546 Payroll Expense ($000): 46346 Personnel: 564**

☐ △ **PACIFIC ALLIANCE MEDICAL CENTER (050018)**, 531 West College Street, Zip 90012–2315; tel. 213/624–8411, (Nonreporting) **A**1 7 9 10
Primary Contact: John R. Edwards, Administrator and Chief Executive Officer
CFO: Allan Shubin, Chief Financial Officer
CIO: John D. Brown, Director Information Systems
Web address: www.pamc.net
**Control:** Partnership, Investor–owned, for–profit **Service:** General Medical and Surgical

**Staffed Beds: 138**

*Many Facility Codes have changed. Please refer to the AHA Guide Code Chart.*
© 2013 AHA Guide

☐ **PACIFICA HOSPITAL OF THE VALLEY (050378)**, 9449 San Fernando Road, Sun Valley, Zip 91352–1421; tel. 818/767–3310, (Nonreporting) **A**1 9 10
Primary Contact: Ayman Mousa, R.N., Ph.D., Chief Executive Officer
CFO: Lawrence Tyrrell, Chief Financial Officer
CMO: Joseph Fipe, M.D., Chief Medical Officer
CIO: Mubashir Hashmi, Chief Information Officer
CHR: Patti Alonzo, Manager Human Resources
Web address: www.pacificahospital.com
**Control:** Corporation, Investor–owned, for–profit **Service:** General Medical and Surgical

**Staffed Beds:** 231

**PROMISE HOSPITAL OF EAST LOS ANGELES (052046)**, 443 South Soto Street, Zip 90033–4398; tel. 323/261–1181, (Nonreporting) **A**9 10 **S** Promise Healthcare, Boca Raton, FL
Primary Contact: Steve Popkin, Chief Executive Officer
Web address: www.promiseeastla.com
**Control:** Corporation, Investor–owned, for–profit **Service:** Long–Term Acute Care hospital

**Staffed Beds:** 36

☒ △ **PROVIDENCE HOLY CROSS MEDICAL CENTER (050278)**, 15031 Rinaldi Street, Mission Hills, Zip 91345–1207; tel. 818/365–8051, (Total facility includes 48 beds in nursing home–type unit) **A**1 2 7 9 10 **F**3 11 13 15 17 18 20 22 24 26 28 29 30 31 32 34 35 40 43 44 45 50 54 57 59 64 68 70 73 75 76 77 78 79 81 82 84 86 90 93 96 107 108 110 111 114 115 116 117 118 119 128 130 132 134 135 146 147 148 **S** Providence Health & Services, Renton, WA
Primary Contact: Bernard Klein, M.D., Chief Executive Officer
CFO: Dave Mast, Chief Financial Officer
CIO: Douglas Jones, Regional Chief Information Officer
CHR: Lori Curry, Regional Chief Human Resources Officer
CNO: Ann Dechairo–Marino, R.N., Chief Nursing Officer
Web address: www.https://california.providence.org/holy–cross/Pages/default. aspx
**Control:** Church–operated, Nongovernment, not–for profit **Service:** General Medical and Surgical

**Staffed Beds:** 254 **Admissions:** 18321 **Census:** 255

☒ △ **PROVIDENCE LITTLE COMPANY OF MARY MEDICAL CENTER SAN PEDRO (050078)**, 1300 West Seventh Street, San Pedro, Zip 90732–3505; tel. 310/832–3311 **A**1 7 9 10 **F**2 3 4 5 11 13 14 15 18 29 30 31 32 34 35 40 44 45 49 50 51 57 59 60 66 68 70 71 74 75 76 77 78 79 81 82 85 86 87 90 92 93 94 96 98 100 101 102 103 104 105 107 108 110 111 114 119 120 123 128 130 132 133 135 145 146 **S** Providence Health & Services, Renton, WA
Primary Contact: Nancy Carlson, Chief Executive
COO: Carlos W. Priestley, Chief Operating Officer
CFO: Elizabeth Zuanich, Chief Financial Officer
CMO: Herbert Webb, M.D., Chief Medical Officer
CIO: Rachel Sanchez, Director Information Systems
CHR: Andreas Viggers, Director Human Resources
CNO: Mary Jane Jones, R.N., Chief Nursing Officer
Web address: www.https://california.providence.org/san–pedro
**Control:** Other not–for–profit (including NFP Corporation) **Service:** General Medical and Surgical

**Staffed Beds:** 327 **Admissions:** 7474 **Census:** 202 **Outpatient Visits:** 71136 **Births:** 717 **Total Expense ($000):** 172685 **Payroll Expense ($000):** 66806 **Personnel:** 767

☒ **PROVIDENCE TARZANA MEDICAL CENTER (050761)**, 18321 Clark Street, Tarzana, Zip 91356–3521; tel. 818/881–0800 **A**1 9 10 **F**11 13 14 15 17 18 20 22 24 26 28 29 30 31 34 35 37 39 40 41 46 47 49 51 56 57 59 60 63 65 70 72 74 75 76 77 78 79 81 82 83 84 85 87 89 93 107 108 110 111 114 115 116 117 118 119 130 132 135 146 147 148 **S** Providence Health & Services, Renton, WA
Primary Contact: Gerald B. Clute, Chief Executive Officer
CFO: Nick Lymberopoulos, Chief Financial Officer
CMO: Glenn Irani, M.D., Chief Medical Officer
CIO: Craig Witmer, Chief Information Officer
CHR: Jo Lewis, Director Human Resources
Web address: www.providence.org/tarzana
**Control:** Other not–for–profit (including NFP Corporation) **Service:** General Medical and Surgical

**Staffed Beds:** 245 **Admissions:** 15012 **Census:** 198 **Outpatient Visits:** 35135 **Births:** 2341

☒ **RONALD REAGAN UNIVERSITY OF CALIFORNIA LOS ANGELES MEDICAL CENTER (050262)**, 757 Westwood Plaza, Zip 90095–8358; tel. 310/825–9111, (Includes MATTEL CHILDREN'S HOSPITAL, 10833 Le Conte Avenue, Zip 90024; tel. 310/825–9111) **A**1 3 5 8 9 10 **F**3 6 7 8 9 11 12 13 14 15 17 18 19 20 21 22 23 24 25 26 27 28 29 30 31 32 34 35 36 40 41 43 44 45 46 47 48 49 50 51 52 54 55 56 57 58 59 61 62 64 65 66 68 70 71 72 74 75 76 77 78 79 81 82 83 84 85 86 87 88 89 90 92 93 94 96 97 102 107 108 110 111 112 113 114 115 116 117 118 119 120 121 123 124 126 129 130 131 132 136 137 138 139 140 141 142 143 145 146 147 148 **P**6 **S** University of California–Systemwide Administration, Oakland, CA
Primary Contact: David Feinberg, M.D., Chief Executive Officer
CFO: Paul Staton, Chief Financial Officer
CMO: J. Thomas Rosenthal, M.D., Chief Medical Officer
CIO: Virginia McFerran, Chief Information Officer
CHR: Mark Speare, Senior Associate Director Human Resources
Web address: www.uclahealth.org
**Control:** State–Government, nonfederal **Service:** General Medical and Surgical

**Staffed Beds:** 466 **Admissions:** 23508 **Census:** 448 **Outpatient Visits:** 804874 **Births:** 2185 **Total Expense ($000):** 1327240 **Payroll Expense ($000):** 517750 **Personnel:** 7227

○ **SHERMAN OAKS HOSPITAL (050755)**, 4929 Van Nuys Boulevard, Sherman Oaks, Zip 91403–1702; tel. 818/981–7111 **A**10 11 **F**17 20 29 31 34 35 38 40 56 57 59 61 64 70 75 77 78 79 81 82 85 98 103 104 105 107 108 118 119 130 131 132 146 148 **S** Prime Healthcare Services, Ontario, CA
Primary Contact: Bockhi Park, Chief Executive Officer
CFO: Daniel Leon, Chief Financial Officer
CMO: Michael Malamed, M.D., Chief of Staff
Web address: www.shermanoakshospital.com
**Control:** Other not–for–profit (including NFP Corporation) **Service:** General Medical and Surgical

**Staffed Beds:** 77 **Admissions:** 4114 **Census:** 53 **Outpatient Visits:** 25688 **Births:** 0 **Total Expense ($000):** 35938 **Payroll Expense ($000):** 23129 **Personnel:** 513

☒ **SHRINERS HOSPITALS FOR CHILDREN–LOS ANGELES (053310)**, 3160 Geneva Street, Zip 90020–1199; tel. 213/388–3151, (Nonreporting) **A**1 3 5 9 10 **S** Shriners Hospitals for Children, Tampa, FL
Primary Contact: Janet Sanders, R.N., Interim Administrator
CFO: David Burkitt, Director Fiscal Services
CMO: Hugh Watts, M.D., Chief of Staff
CIO: Mark Garrett, Chief Information Officer
CHR: Rashawn Woods, Director Human Resources
Web address: www.shrinershospitalsforchildren.org/Hospitals/Locations/Losangeles.aspx
**Control:** Other not–for–profit (including NFP Corporation) **Service:** Children's rehabilitation

**Staffed Beds:** 30

☐ **SILVER LAKE MEDICAL CENTER (050763)**, 1711 West Temple Street, Zip 90026–5421; tel. 213/989–6100, (Includes SILVER LAKE MEDICAL CENTER–INGLESIDE HOSPITAL, 7500 East Hellman Avenue, Rosemead, Zip 91770; tel. 626/288–1160), (Nonreporting) **A**1 10 **S** Success Healthcare, Boca Raton, FL
Primary Contact: Brent A. Cope, Chief Executive Officer
CFO: John Cowles, Chief Financial Officer
CMO: Louis Acosta, M.D., Chief of Staff
CIO: Scott Musack, Chief Information Officer
CHR: Sylvia Cloud, Director Human Resources
Web address: www.silverlakemc.com
**Control:** Corporation, Investor–owned, for–profit **Service:** General Medical and Surgical

**Staffed Beds:** 150

**CA**

---

**Hospital, Medicare Provider Number, Address, Telephone, Approval, Facility, and Physician Codes, Health Care System**

★ American Hospital Association (AHA) membership
☐ The Joint Commission accreditation　　◇ DNV Healthcare Inc. accreditation

○ Healthcare Facilities Accreditation Program
△ Commission on Accreditation of Rehabilitation Facilities (CARF) accreditation

☒ **ST. VINCENT MEDICAL CENTER (050502)**, 2131 West Third Street, Zip 90057–1901, Mailing Address: P.O. Box 57992, Zip 90057–0992; tel. 213/484–7111, (Total facility includes 27 beds in nursing home–type unit) **A**1 2 9 10 **F**8 11 15 18 20 22 24 26 29 30 31 34 35 40 45 47 49 50 54 57 58 59 60 63 64 65 68 69 71 74 75 77 78 79 81 82 85 87 91 93 96 107 108 110 111 118 119 120 121 125 130 136 138 142 143 146 148 **S** Daughters of Charity Health System, Los Altos Hills, CA
Primary Contact: Catherine Fickes, R.N., President and Chief Executive Officer
COO: Douglas V. Kleam, Vice President and Chief Operating Officer
CFO: Michael Garko, Chief Financial Officer
CMO: Ronald Fishbach, M.D., Chief of Staff
CIO: Dan Robbins, Information Technology and Account Executive
CHR: Christine Carson, Vice President Human Resources
CNO: Kim Deese, R.N., Vice President/CNO
Web address: www.stvincentmedicalcenter.com
**Control:** Church–operated, Nongovernment, not–for profit **Service:** General Medical and Surgical

**Staffed Beds:** 271 **Admissions:** 7992 **Census:** 133 **Outpatient Visits:** 89040 **Births:** 0 **Total Expense ($000):** 229127 **Payroll Expense ($000):** 73129 **Personnel:** 1066

☒ **STEWART & LYNDA RESNICK NEUROPSYCHIATRIC HOSPITAL AT UCLA (054009)**, 760 Westwood Plaza, Zip 90095–8353; tel. 310/825–9989 **A**1 3 5 9 10 **F**1 3 4 5 6 16 17 29 30 35 40 42 43 55 56 64 67 68 70 72 73 76 77 80 86 87 88 89 90 98 99 100 101 102 103 104 105 128 130 132 134 147 **P**1 **S** University of California–Systemwide Administration, Oakland, CA
Primary Contact: Thomas Strouse, M.D., Medical Director
COO: Ruth Irwin, Associate Director Clinical Operations
CHR: Cindy Cohen, Director Human Resources
Web address: www.semel.ucla.edu/resnick
**Control:** State–Government, nonfederal **Service:** Psychiatric

**Staffed Beds:** 74 **Admissions:** 2064 **Census:** 68 **Outpatient Visits:** 15881 **Births:** 0 **Total Expense ($000):** 48162 **Payroll Expense ($000):** 29823 **Personnel:** 315

☐ **TEMPLE COMMUNITY HOSPITAL (050111)**, 235 North Hoover Street, Zip 90004–3672; tel. 213/382–7252, (Nonreporting) **A**1 9 10
Primary Contact: Herbert G. Needman, President and Chief Executive Officer
CFO: John Skelton, Director Finance
CMO: Assa Weinberg, M.D., Chief of Staff
CIO: Diane Adams, Director Business Services
CHR: Leslie Beasley, Director Human Resources
Web address: www.templecommunityhospital.com
**Control:** Corporation, Investor–owned, for–profit **Service:** General Medical and Surgical

**Staffed Beds:** 130

☒ **UNIVERSITY OF SOUTHERN CALIFORNIA–NORRIS CANCER HOSPITAL (050660)**, 1441 Eastlake Avenue, Zip 90089–0112; tel. 323/865–3000 **A**1 2 3 5 9 10 **F**3 6 15 18 20 22 24 26 29 30 31 34 35 37 39 44 45 46 47 48 49 50 51 53 54 55 56 57 58 59 60 61 64 65 68 70 74 75 77 78 79 81 82 84 85 86 87 91 92 93 94 96 97 100 101 103 104 105 107 108 110 111 112 114 115 116 117 118 119 120 121 123 124 126 129 130 131 132 135 136 137 138 139 140 141 142 145 146 147 148
Primary Contact: Scott Evans, PharmD, Chief Executive Officer
CMO: Alexandra Levine, M.D., Medical Director
CIO: David Wueste, Director Information Services
Web address: www.uscnorriscancerhospital.org
**Control:** Other not–for–profit (including NFP Corporation) **Service:** General Medical and Surgical

**Staffed Beds:** 30 **Admissions:** 1 **Census:** 1 **Outpatient Visits:** 79468 **Births:** 0 **Total Expense ($000):** 93163 **Payroll Expense ($000):** 23129 **Personnel:** 415

☒ ◇ **VALLEY PRESBYTERIAN HOSPITAL (050126)**, 15107 Vanowen Street, Van Nuys, Zip 91405–4598; tel. 818/782–6600 **A**1 9 10 21 **F**3 13 18 20 22 24 28 29 31 34 35 40 44 45 46 49 50 53 57 59 64 65 70 72 74 75 76 77 78 79 81 85 86 87 88 89 90 96 107 108 109 114 115 119 122 123 130 145 146 147 148 **P**5
Primary Contact: Gustavo A. Valdespino, President and Chief Executive Officer
COO: Gayathri S. Jith, M.P.H., Vice President Operations
CFO: William Wilson, Interim Chief Financial Officer
CIO: George Styer, Director Information Systems
CHR: Norma Resneder, Senior Vice President Human Resources and Organizational Development
CNO: Michelle Ann Quigley, MS, Vice President and Chief Nursing Officer
Web address: www.valleypres.org
**Control:** Other not–for–profit (including NFP Corporation) **Service:** General Medical and Surgical

**Staffed Beds:** 350 **Admissions:** 15827 **Census:** 189 **Outpatient Visits:** 107747 **Births:** 4266 **Total Expense ($000):** 301876 **Payroll Expense ($000):** 110329 **Personnel:** 1457

★ △ **VETERANS AFFAIRS GREATER LOS ANGELES HEALTHCARE SYSTEM**, 11301 Wilshire Boulevard, Zip 90073–1003; tel. 310/478–3711, (Nonreporting) **A**5 7 8 **S** Department of Veterans Affairs, Washington, DC
Primary Contact: Donna M. Beiter, R.N., MSN, Director
COO: Lynn Carrier, Associate Director Administration and Support
CFO: Olivia Ortiz–Bitner, Acting Chief Financial Officer
CMO: Dennis Schaberg, M.D., Chief Medicine
CIO: Eugene Archey, Chief Information Technology
CHR: Harold Goings, Chief Human Resources
Web address: www.losangeles.va.gov/
**Control:** Veterans Affairs, Government, federal **Service:** General Medical and Surgical

**Staffed Beds:** 1087

☒ **WEST HILLS HOSPITAL AND MEDICAL CENTER (050481)**, 7300 Medical Center Drive, West Hills, Zip 91307–1902; tel. 818/676–4000, (Nonreporting) **A**1 9 10 **S** HCA, Nashville, TN
Primary Contact: Douglas Long, President and Chief Executive Officer
COO: Omar Chughtai, Vice President and Chief Operating Officer
CFO: Tony Lopez, Vice President and Chief Financial Officer
CMO: Ron Chitayat, M.D., Chief Medical Staff
CIO: Tony Lopez, Chief Financial Officer
CHR: Edward Battista, Vice President Human Resources
CNO: Janet Brooks, R.N., Vice President and Chief Nursing Officer
Web address: www.westhillshospital.com
**Control:** Corporation, Investor–owned, for–profit **Service:** General Medical and Surgical

**Staffed Beds:** 293

☒ **WHITE MEMORIAL MEDICAL CENTER (050103)**, 1720 Cesar Chavez Avenue, Zip 90033–2414; tel. 323/268–5000 **A**1 2 3 5 9 10 **F**3 8 11 13 15 17 18 19 20 22 24 26 27 28 29 30 31 34 35 40 45 46 47 48 49 50 51 53 57 58 59 64 68 70 72 74 75 76 78 79 81 82 84 85 86 87 88 89 90 91 92 93 96 98 99 102 103 107 108 109 110 111 114 115 116 117 118 119 120 121 123 128 130 131 132 146 147 148 **S** Adventist Health, Roseville, CA
Primary Contact: Beth D. Zachary, President and Chief Executive Officer
CFO: John Raffoul, Senior Vice President Finance
CIO: Ralf Weissenberger, Director Information Systems
CHR: Natasha Milatovich, Association Vice President Human Resources
Web address: www.whitememorial.com
**Control:** Church–operated, Nongovernment, not–for profit **Service:** General Medical and Surgical

**Staffed Beds:** 280 **Admissions:** 21169 **Census:** 267 **Outpatient Visits:** 55110 **Births:** 3886 **Total Expense ($000):** 325126 **Payroll Expense ($000):** 124585 **Personnel:** 1698

**WOMEN'S AND CHILDREN'S HOSPITAL** See LAC/University of Southern California Medical Center

### LOS BANOS—Merced County

☒ **MEMORIAL HOSPITAL LOS BANOS (050528)**, 520 West I Street, Zip 93635–3419; tel. 209/826–0591 **A**1 9 10 20 **F**3 11 13 15 18 29 30 31 34 35 40 45 46 49 50 54 57 59 60 64 66 68 70 74 75 76 77 78 79 81 82 85 93 107 108 110 111 115 119 124 127 130 132 135 146 **S** Sutter Health, Sacramento, CA
Primary Contact: Richard S. Liszewski, Chief Executive Officer
CFO: Timothy J. Noakes, Chief Financial Officer
CHR: Shawn Garcia, Manager Human Resources
CNO: Barbara Medeiros, R.N., Chief Nurse Executive
Web address: www.memoriallosbanos.org/
**Control:** Other not–for–profit (including NFP Corporation) **Service:** General Medical and Surgical

**Staffed Beds:** 46 **Admissions:** 1361 **Census:** 10 **Outpatient Visits:** 54007 **Births:** 716 **Total Expense ($000):** 45626 **Payroll Expense ($000):** 13744 **Personnel:** 211

### LYNWOOD—Los Angeles County

☒ **ST. FRANCIS MEDICAL CENTER (050104)**, 3630 East Imperial Highway, Zip 90262–2636; tel. 310/900–8900, (Nonreporting) **A**1 9 10 **S** Daughters of Charity Health System, Los Altos Hills, CA
Primary Contact: Gerald T. Kozai, President
CFO: Jesse Guevara, Senior Vice President and Chief Financial Officer
CIO: Marsha Chan, PharmD, Chief Quality Officer
CHR: Laura Kato, Vice President Human Resources
Web address: www.dochs.org
**Control:** Church–operated, Nongovernment, not–for profit **Service:** General Medical and Surgical

**Staffed Beds:** 323

**CA**

*Many Facility Codes have changed. Please refer to the AHA Guide Code Chart.*
© 2013 AHA Guide

**CA**

## MADERA—Madera County

□ △ **CHILDREN'S HOSPITAL CENTRAL CALIFORNIA (053300)**, 9300 Valley Children's Place, Zip 93636–8762; tel. 559/353–3000 **A**1 3 5 7 9 10 **F**3 8 9 11 19 21 23 25 27 28 29 30 31 32 34 35 36 38 40 41 44 46 48 50 54 55 57 58 59 60 61 62 64 65 68 72 74 75 77 78 79 81 82 84 85 86 87 88 89 90 93 94 97 107 108 111 114 115 119 127 129 130 131 132 143 146 147 148
Primary Contact: Todd Suntrapak, President and Chief Executive Officer
COO: Todd Suntrapak, President and Chief Executive Officer
CFO: Michele Waldron, Vice President and Chief Financial Officer
CMO: David Christensen, M.D., Vice President Medical Affairs and Chief Medical Officer
CHR: Marta Boyer, Vice President Human Resources
Web address: www.childrenscentralcal.org
**Control:** Other not–for–profit (including NFP Corporation) **Service:** Children's general

**Staffed Beds:** 340 **Admissions:** 12772 **Census:** 218 **Outpatient Visits:** 215247 **Births:** 0 **Total Expense ($000):** 410634 **Payroll Expense ($000):** 162589 **Personnel:** 1931

○ **MADERA COMMUNITY HOSPITAL (050568)**, 1250 East Almond Avenue, Zip 93637–5696, Mailing Address: P.O. Box 1328, Zip 93639–1328; tel. 559/675–5501 **A**9 10 11 19 **F**3 13 29 30 34 35 40 45 46 47 48 49 54 59 62 64 70 75 76 77 79 81 82 107 108 110 111 114 119 127 132 146 147 148 **P**5
Primary Contact: John W. Frye, Jr., Chief Executive Officer
CFO: Mark Foote, Chief Financial Officer
CIO: Arthur Haggerty, Director Information Systems
CHR: Christine M. Watts–Johnson, Assistant Vice President
Web address: www.maderahospital.org
**Control:** Other not–for–profit (including NFP Corporation) **Service:** General Medical and Surgical

**Staffed Beds:** 106 **Admissions:** 4916 **Census:** 60 **Outpatient Visits:** 161829 **Births:** 1703 **Total Expense ($000):** 87103 **Payroll Expense ($000):** 36135 **Personnel:** 759

## MAMMOTH LAKES—Mono County

◇ **MAMMOTH HOSPITAL (051303)**, 85 Sierra Park Road, Zip 93546–2073, Mailing Address: P.O. Box 660, Zip 93546–0660; tel. 760/934–3311 **A**9 10 18 21 **F**3 11 13 15 18 29 31 34 35 39 40 45 46 50 53 57 59 64 65 68 70 74 75 76 77 78 79 81 82 85 93 97 99 104 107 110 111 114 119 127 131 132 146 147
Primary Contact: Gary Myers, Interim Chief Executive Officer
COO: Glen Halverson, Chief Operating Officer
CFO: Melanie Van Winkle, Chief Financial Officer
CMO: Audrey Pauly, M.D., Chief of Staff
CIO: Mark Lind, Director Information Systems
CHR: Jeff Byberg, Manager Human Resources
CNO: Kathleen Alo, R.N., Chief Nursing Officer
Web address: www.mammothhospital.com
**Control:** Hospital district or authority, Government, nonfederal **Service:** General Medical and Surgical

**Staffed Beds:** 17 **Admissions:** 627 **Census:** 4 **Outpatient Visits:** 9525 **Births:** 103 **Total Expense ($000):** 35016 **Payroll Expense ($000):** 16893 **Personnel:** 264

## MANTECA—San Joaquin County

⊠ **DOCTORS HOSPITAL OF MANTECA (050118)**, 1205 East North Street, Zip 95336–4900; tel. 209/823–3111 **A**1 9 10 **F**3 11 12 13 15 29 31 34 35 40 45 49 50 51 75 76 78 79 81 85 89 102 107 108 110 111 115 116 117 118 119 130 132 146 147 148 **S** TENET Healthcare Corporation, Dallas, TX
Primary Contact: Nicholas R. Tejeda, FACHE, Chief Executive Officer
COO: Carmen Silva, R.N., Chief Operating Officer
CFO: Tracy Roman, Chief Financial Officer
CHR: Traci Holzer, Chief Human Resources Officer
CNO: Patricia Pidge Gooch, Chief Nursing Officer
Web address: www.doctorsmanteca.com
**Control:** Corporation, Investor–owned, for–profit **Service:** General Medical and Surgical

**Staffed Beds:** 73 **Admissions:** 3906 **Census:** 42 **Outpatient Visits:** 58069 **Births:** 716 **Total Expense ($000):** 50712 **Payroll Expense ($000):** 33534 **Personnel:** 364

⊠ **KAISER PERMANENTE MANTECA MEDICAL CENTER (050748)**, (Formerly Manteca Medical Center), 1777 West Yosemite Avenue, Zip 95337–5187; tel. 209/825–3500, (Includes MODESTO MEDICAL CENTER, 4601 Dale Road, Modesto, Zip 95356–9718; tel. 209/735–5000; Corwin N. Harper, Administrator) **A**1 10 **F**1 3 4 13 15 16 17 20 29 30 31 39 40 50 64 67 70 72 73 74 75 76 77 78 79 80 81 82 84 85 86 87 88 89 90 93 100 107 108 110 111 114 115 119 128 130 146 148 **P**3 **S** Kaiser Foundation Hospitals, Oakland, CA
Primary Contact: Corwin N. Harper, Senior Vice President and Area Manager
COO: Corwin N. Harper, Senior Vice President and Area Manager
CFO: Debra L. Brown, Area Financial Officer
CMO: Moses D. Elam, M.D., Physician–in–Chief
CIO: Tom J. Osteen, Director Area Technology
CHR: Pat McKeldin, Human Resource Business Partner
Web address: www.kaiserpermanente.org
**Control:** Other not–for–profit (including NFP Corporation) **Service:** General Medical and Surgical

**Staffed Beds:** 184 **Admissions:** 8687 **Census:** 82 **Births:** 227 **Personnel:** 1784

## MARINA DEL REY—Los Angeles County

□ **MARINA DEL REY HOSPITAL (050740)**, 4650 Lincoln Boulevard, Zip 90292–6360; tel. 310/823–8911, (Nonreporting) **A**1 9 10
Primary Contact: Fred Hunter, R.N., Chief Executive Officer
COO: Phyllis Buchart, Chief Operating Officer
CFO: Stephen A. Hargett, Senior Vice President and Chief Financial Officer
Web address: www.marinahospital.com
**Control:** Corporation, Investor–owned, for–profit **Service:** General Medical and Surgical

**Staffed Beds:** 90

## MARIPOSA—Mariposa County

★ **JOHN C. FREMONT HEALTHCARE DISTRICT (051304)**, 5189 Hospital Road, Zip 95338–9524, Mailing Address: P.O. Box 216, Zip 95338–0216; tel. 209/966–3631, (Nonreporting) **A**9 10 18
Primary Contact: David L. Hill, Chief Executive Officer
CFO: Tish Miller, Chief Financial Officer
CMO: Kenneth Smith, M.D., Chief of Staff
CIO: Joanne Eskra, Supervisor Data and Information Technology
CHR: Dawn Yesitis, Director Human Resources
CNO: Karen Gulbenkian, R.N., Director Patient Care Services
Web address: www.jcfhospital.com
**Control:** Hospital district or authority, Government, nonfederal **Service:** General Medical and Surgical

**Staffed Beds:** 34

## MARTINEZ—Contra Costa County

□ **CONTRA COSTA REGIONAL MEDICAL CENTER (050276)**, 2500 Alhambra Avenue, Zip 94553–3156; tel. 925/370–5000 **A**1 2 10 **F**3 11 13 15 18 30 31 36 39 40 41 44 45 49 50 51 52 54 56 58 59 61 62 64 65 66 68 70 71 72 73 74 75 76 77 78 79 81 82 84 85 86 87 92 93 96 97 98 100 102 103 104 107 108 109 110 111 114 119 130 132 143 146 147 148 **P**6
Primary Contact: Anna M. Roth, Chief Executive Officer
CFO: Patrick Godley, Chief Financial Officer
Web address: www.cchealth.org/medical_center/
**Control:** County–Government, nonfederal **Service:** General Medical and Surgical

**Staffed Beds:** 113 **Admissions:** 8850 **Census:** 114 **Outpatient Visits:** 457975 **Births:** 1963 **Total Expense ($000):** 435273 **Payroll Expense ($000):** 148948 **Personnel:** 1761

## MARYSVILLE—Yuba County

⊠ **FREMONT–RIDEOUT HEALTH GROUP (050133)**, 726 Fourth Street, Zip 95901–5600; tel. 530/749–4300, (Includes FREMONT MEDICAL CENTER, 970 Plumas Street, Yuba City, Zip 95991–4087; tel. 530/751–4000), (Nonreporting) **A**1 2 9 10
Primary Contact: Theresa Hamilton, Chief Executive Officer
CMO: Robert Plass, M.D., Chief Medical Officer
CIO: Tarun Ghosh, Chief Information Officer
CHR: Tresha Moreland, Vice President Human Resources
Web address: www.frhg.org
**Control:** Other not–for–profit (including NFP Corporation) **Service:** General Medical and Surgical

**Staffed Beds:** 212

---

**Hospital, Medicare Provider Number, Address, Telephone, Approval, Facility, and Physician Codes, Health Care System**

★ American Hospital Association (AHA) membership
□ The Joint Commission accreditation
◇ DNV Healthcare Inc. accreditation
○ Healthcare Facilities Accreditation Program
△ Commission on Accreditation of Rehabilitation Facilities (CARF) accreditation

**CA**

## MENLO PARK—San Mateo County

✠ **MENLO PARK SURGICAL HOSPITAL (050754)**, 570 Willow Road,
Zip 94025–2617; tel. 650/324–8500 **A**1 5 9 10 **F**3 35 64 79 81 85 **S** Sutter
Health, Sacramento, CA
Primary Contact: Kathleen Palange, R.N., Chief Executive Officer
CMO: Andrew Gutow, M.D., Medical Director
Web address: www.pamf.org/mpsh
**Control:** Other not–for–profit (including NFP Corporation) **Service:** General
Medical and Surgical

**Staffed Beds:** 12 **Admissions:** 308 **Census:** 1 **Outpatient Visits:** 2682
**Births:** 0 **Total Expense ($000):** 11953 **Payroll Expense ($000):** 3961
**Personnel:** 40

## MERCED—Merced County

✠ **MERCY MEDICAL CENTER MERCED (050444)**, 333 Mercy Avenue,
Zip 95340–8319; tel. 209/564–5000, (Includes MERCY MEDICAL CENTER
MERCED–COMMUNITY CAMPUS, 301 East 13th Street, Zip 95340–6211;
tel. 209/385–7000; MERCY MEDICAL CENTER MERCED–DOMINICAN CAMPUS,
2740 M Street, Zip 95340–2880; tel. 209/384–6444; David S. Dunham,
President) **A**1 3 5 9 10 19 **F**3 13 15 18 20 26 28 29 30 34 35 39 40 41 45
49 50 57 59 62 64 65 66 68 74 75 76 77 79 81 84 85 86 87 93 96 97 107
108 110 111 115 119 127 130 132 146 148 **P**3 **S** Dignity Health, San
Francisco, CA
Primary Contact: David S. Dunham, President
CFO: Doreen Hartmann, Vice President and Chief Financial Officer
CMO: Robert Streeter, M.D., Vice President Medical Affairs
CIO: Noel Lee, Administrative Director and Chief Information Officer
CHR: Joe Lombardi, Vice President Human Resources
Web address: www.mercymercedcares.org
**Control:** Church–operated, Nongovernment, not–for profit **Service:** General
Medical and Surgical

**Staffed Beds:** 186 **Admissions:** 11061 **Census:** 122 **Outpatient Visits:**
199340 **Births:** 2830 **Total Expense ($000):** 238968 **Payroll Expense
($000):** 90717 **Personnel:** 1137

## MISSION HILLS—Los Angeles County, See Los Angeles

## MISSION VIEJO—Orange County

☐ **CHILDREN'S HOSPITAL AT MISSION (053306)**, 27700 Medical Center Road,
Zip 92691–6426; tel. 949/364–1400 **A**1 9 10 **F**3 11 36 72 74 79 81 85 88
89 146
Primary Contact: Kimberly C. Cripe, President and Chief Executive Officer
COO: Debra Mathias, Chief Operating Officer
CFO: Kerri Ruppert Schiller, Senior Vice President and Chief Financial Officer
CMO: Maria Minon, M.D., Vice President Medical Affairs and Chief Medical Officer
CIO: Mark Headland, Chief Information Officer
CHR: Susan M. Burrows, Vice President Human Resources
CNO: Louise White, R.N., Vice President Patient Care Services and Chief Nursing
Officer
Web address: www.choc.org
**Control:** Other not–for–profit (including NFP Corporation) **Service:** Children's
general

**Staffed Beds:** 48 **Admissions:** 1856 **Census:** 21 **Outpatient Visits:** 24795
**Births:** 0 **Total Expense ($000):** 49814 **Payroll Expense ($000):** 8059
**Personnel:** 90

✠ △ **MISSION HOSPITAL (050567)**, 27700 Medical Center Road,
Zip 92691–6426; tel. 949/364–1400, (Includes MISSION HOSPITAL LAGUNA
BEACH, 31872 Coast Highway, Laguna Beach, Zip 92651–6775;
tel. 949/499–1311) **A**1 2 7 9 10 **F**3 4 5 8 11 13 14 15 17 18 20 22 24 26 28
29 30 31 34 35 36 40 43 44 45 46 47 48 49 50 53 54 57 58 59 64 65 66
68 70 74 75 76 77 78 79 80 81 82 84 85 86 87 90 92 93 96 98 100 101
104 105 107 108 110 111 114 115 116 117 118 119 120 121 123 126 129
130 131 132 134 135 141 143 145 146 147 148 **P**3 **S** St. Joseph Health,
Irvine, CA
Primary Contact: Kenneth McFarland, President and Chief Executive Officer
COO: Markie Cowley, Executive Vice President and Chief Operating Officer
CMO: Dennis Haghighat, M.D., Vice President Medical Affairs
CIO: Cindy Emerson, Director Information Services
Web address: www.mission4health.com
**Control:** Church–operated, Nongovernment, not–for profit **Service:** General
Medical and Surgical

**Staffed Beds:** 249 **Admissions:** 21345 **Census:** 250 **Outpatient Visits:**
181402 **Births:** 2992 **Total Expense ($000):** 432419 **Payroll Expense
($000):** 145162 **Personnel:** 1912

## MODESTO—Stanislaus County

✠ **DOCTORS MEDICAL CENTER (050464)**, 1441 Florida Avenue,
Zip 95350–4418, Mailing Address: P.O. Box 4138, Zip 95352–4138;
tel. 209/578–1211 **A**1 2 9 10 **F**3 13 17 18 20 22 24 26 28 29 31 35 40 41
43 45 46 48 49 50 51 55 57 59 60 65 70 72 74 75 76 77 78 79 80 81 85
89 98 102 103 107 108 109 110 111 112 113 114 115 116 117 118 119
126 130 132 146 147 **P**4 **S** TENET Healthcare Corporation, Dallas, TX
Primary Contact: Warren J. Kirk, Chief Executive Officer
COO: Mike King, Chief Operating Officer
CFO: Greg Berry, Chief Financial Officer
CMO: Eric Ramos, M.D., Chief Medical Officer
CIO: Debbie Fuller, Director Health Information Systems and Chief Information
Officer
CHR: Michele West, Director Human Resources
Web address: www.dmc–modesto.com
**Control:** Corporation, Investor–owned, for–profit **Service:** General Medical and
Surgical

**Staffed Beds:** 455 **Admissions:** 22879 **Census:** 313 **Outpatient Visits:**
171761 **Births:** 3771 **Total Expense ($000):** 386912 **Payroll Expense
($000):** 175069 **Personnel:** 1940

**KAISER PERMANENTE MODESTO MEDICAL CENTER** See Kaiser Permanente
Manteca Medical Center, Manteca

✠ **MEMORIAL MEDICAL CENTER (050557)**, 1700 Coffee Road,
Zip 95355–2869, Mailing Address: P.O. Box 942, Zip 95353–0942;
tel. 209/526–4500, (Includes MEMORIAL MEDICAL CENTER, 1700 Coffee Road,
Zip 95355, Mailing Address: Box 942, Zip 95353; tel. 209/526–4500) **A**1 2 9
10 **F**8 11 12 13 15 17 18 20 22 24 28 29 30 31 34 35 40 43 57 59 60 62
70 73 74 75 76 77 78 79 81 82 85 86 89 107 108 111 114 115 118 119
120 121 124 130 146 148 **S** Sutter Health, Sacramento, CA
Primary Contact: Daryn J. Kumar, Chief Executive Officer
COO: Steve Mitchell, Chief Operating Officer
CFO: Eric Dalton, Chief Financial Officer
CIO: Patrick Anderson, Chief Information Officer
CHR: Paula Rafala, Director, Human Resources
CNO: Sandra Proctor, R.N., Chief Nurse Executive
Web address: www.memorialmedicalcenter.org
**Control:** Other not–for–profit (including NFP Corporation) **Service:** General
Medical and Surgical

**Staffed Beds:** 427 **Admissions:** 18465 **Census:** 237 **Outpatient Visits:**
132125 **Births:** 2001 **Total Expense ($000):** 501555 **Payroll Expense
($000):** 163886 **Personnel:** 2349

**STANISLAUS SURGICAL HOSPITAL (050726)**, 1421 Oakdale Road,
Zip 95355–3356; tel. 209/572–2700, (Nonreporting) **A**5 9 10
Primary Contact: Douglas V. Johnson, Chief Executive Officer
CMO: Harvey Palitz, M.D., Chief of Staff
CHR: Laura Boyles, Director Human Resources
Web address: www.stanislaussurgical.com
**Control:** Individual, Investor–owned, for–profit **Service:** General Medical and
Surgical

**Staffed Beds:** 23

## MONROVIA—Los Angeles County

○ **MONROVIA MEMORIAL HOSPITAL (052054)**, 323 South Heliotrope Avenue,
Zip 91016–2914; tel. 626/408–9800, (Nonreporting) **A**9 10 11
Primary Contact: Ron Kupferstein, Chief Executive Officer
Web address: www.monroviamemorial.com
**Control:** Partnership, Investor–owned, for–profit **Service:** Long–Term Acute Care
hospital

**Staffed Beds:** 49

## MONTCLAIR—San Bernardino County

☐ **MONTCLAIR HOSPITAL MEDICAL CENTER (050758)**, 5000 San Bernardino
Street, Zip 91763–2326; tel. 909/625–5411, (Nonreporting) **A**1 10 **S** Prime
Healthcare Services, Ontario, CA
Primary Contact: Gregory Brentano, Chief Executive Officer
Web address: www.montclair–hospital.com
**Control:** Corporation, Investor–owned, for–profit **Service:** General Medical and
Surgical

**Staffed Beds:** 102

## MONTEBELLO—Los Angeles County

◇ **BEVERLY HOSPITAL (050350)**, 309 West Beverly Boulevard, Zip 90640–4308;
tel. 323/726–1222, (Nonreporting) **A**9 10 21
Primary Contact: Gary V. Kiff, President and Chief Executive Officer
COO: Alice Cheng, Chief Operating Officer and Senior Vice President
CFO: Narci Egan, Vice President and Chief Financial Officer
CIO: Ronnie O. Cobarrubias, Director Information Systems
Web address: www.beverly.org
**Control:** Other not–for–profit (including NFP Corporation) **Service:** General
Medical and Surgical

**Staffed Beds:** 102

*Many Facility Codes have changed. Please refer to the AHA Guide Code Chart.*   © 2013 AHA Guide

## MONTEREY—Monterey County

✠ **COMMUNITY HOSPITAL OF THE MONTEREY PENINSULA (050145)**, 23625 Holman Highway, Zip 93940–5902, Mailing Address: Box 'HH', Zip 93942–6032; tel. 831/624–5311, (Total facility includes 28 beds in nursing home–type unit) **A**1 2 9 10 **F**3 5 11 12 13 14 15 17 18 20 22 24 26 28 29 30 31 34 35 37 40 44 45 46 47 48 49 50 51 53 54 57 58 59 60 61 62 63 64 68 70 73 74 75 76 77 78 79 81 82 84 85 86 87 89 91 92 93 94 96 98 99 100 101 102 103 104 105 107 108 109 110 111 114 115 116 117 118 119 120 121 123 124 128 129 130 132 134 135 145 146 148
Primary Contact: Steven J. Packer, M.D., President and Chief Executive Officer
CFO: Laura Zehm, Vice President and Chief Financial Officer
CMO: Anthony D. Chavis, M.D., Vice President Medical Affairs and Patient Safety Officer
CIO: Tom McNamara, Director Information Technology
CHR: Joanne Webster, Director Human Resources
Web address: www.chomp.org
**Control:** Other not–for–profit (including NFP Corporation) **Service:** General Medical and Surgical

**Staffed Beds:** 235 **Admissions:** 12130 **Census:** 162 **Outpatient Visits:** 283181 **Births:** 1182 **Total Expense ($000):** 402096 **Payroll Expense ($000):** 139483 **Personnel:** 1591

## MONTEREY PARK—Los Angeles County

☐ **GARFIELD MEDICAL CENTER (050737)**, 525 North Garfield Avenue, Zip 91754–1205; tel. 626/573–2222 **A**1 9 10 12 13 **F**3 11 13 15 17 18 20 22 24 26 28 29 31 34 35 40 44 45 49 50 56 57 59 60 64 68 70 72 74 75 76 77 78 79 81 82 85 86 87 90 91 92 93 107 108 119 130 132 143 146 147 148 **P**5 **S** AHMC & Healthcare, Inc., Alhambra, CA
Primary Contact: David J. Batista, Chief Executive Officer
COO: David J. Batista, Chief Operating Officer
CFO: Steve Maekawa, Chief Financial Officer
CMO: Terry Lee, M.D., Chief of Staff
CIO: Ann Curnutt, Director Information Systems
CHR: Rebecca R. Ricartti, Interim Director Human Resources
CNO: Shirley Tang, R.N., Chief Nursing Officer
Web address: www.garfieldmedicalcenter.com
**Control:** Partnership, Investor–owned, for–profit **Service:** General Medical and Surgical

**Staffed Beds:** 210 **Admissions:** 12734 **Census:** 148 **Outpatient Visits:** 31355 **Births:** 4560 **Personnel:** 1070

☐ **MONTEREY PARK HOSPITAL (050736)**, 900 South Atlantic Boulevard, Zip 91754–4780; tel. 626/570–9000 **A**1 9 10 **F**3 15 29 34 35 40 49 50 57 59 60 70 75 76 81 86 87 89 107 113 114 119 130 142 143 146 **S** AHMC & Healthcare, Inc., Alhambra, CA
Primary Contact: Philip A. Cohen, Chief Executive Officer
COO: Ericka Smith, Chief Operating Officer
CFO: Daniel Song, Chief Financial Officer
CMO: Shawn Adhami, M.D., Chief of Staff
CIO: Ann Curnutt, Director Information Systems
CHR: Margaret Ettenheim, Director Human Resources
CNO: Evelyn Ku, Chief Nursing Officer
Web address: www.montereyparkhosp.com
**Control:** Partnership, Investor–owned, for–profit **Service:** General Medical and Surgical

**Staffed Beds:** 101 **Admissions:** 5115 **Census:** 47 **Outpatient Visits:** 19557 **Births:** 1582 **Total Expense ($000):** 72776 **Payroll Expense ($000):** 20265 **Personnel:** 348

## MORENO VALLEY—Riverside County

✠ **KAISER PERMANENTE MORENO VALLEY MEDICAL CENTER (050765)**, (Formerly Moreno Valley Community Hospital), 27300 Iris Avenue, Zip 92555–4800; tel. 951/243–0811 **A**1 10 **F**3 13 17 29 30 35 40 44 45 46 49 50 59 60 64 65 68 70 75 76 77 79 81 85 87 97 100 102 107 108 109 111 115 119 130 135 146 148 **S** Kaiser Foundation Hospitals, Oakland, CA
Primary Contact: Corey A. Seale, Administrator
CFO: Michael Garko, Chief Financial Officer
**Control:** Other not–for–profit (including NFP Corporation) **Service:** General Medical and Surgical

**Staffed Beds:** 71 **Admissions:** 3920 **Census:** 33 **Outpatient Visits:** 34286 **Births:** 964 **Personnel:** 255

✠ **RIVERSIDE COUNTY REGIONAL MEDICAL CENTER (050292)**, 26520 Cactus Avenue, Zip 92555–3911; tel. 951/486–4000 **A**1 3 5 10 12 13 **F**3 8 11 13 15 29 30 31 32 35 39 40 43 44 46 47 49 50 56 57 58 59 64 65 66 68 70 71 72 74 75 76 77 78 79 81 82 85 87 88 89 93 94 97 98 99 100 101 102 103 104 107 108 111 114 118 119 130 135 143 146 147 148
Primary Contact: Douglas D. Bagley, Chief Executive Officer
COO: Ellie Bennett, Chief Operating Officer
CFO: David Runke, Chief Financial Officer
CMO: Arnold Tabuenca, M.D., Medical Director
Web address: www.rcrmc.org
**Control:** County–Government, nonfederal **Service:** General Medical and Surgical

**Staffed Beds:** 415 **Admissions:** 21900 **Census:** 320 **Outpatient Visits:** 250279 **Births:** 2331 **Total Expense ($000):** 414420 **Payroll Expense ($000):** 175846 **Personnel:** 2558

## MOUNT SHASTA—Siskiyou County

✠ **MERCY MEDICAL CENTER MOUNT SHASTA (051319)**, 914 Pine Street, Zip 96067–2143; tel. 530/926–6111 **A**1 9 10 18 **F**3 11 13 15 29 30 35 40 43 50 53 56 57 59 62 63 64 68 70 75 76 77 79 81 82 84 93 107 108 110 111 114 118 119 121 127 130 131 132 133 143 146 148 **S** Dignity Health, San Francisco, CA
Primary Contact: Kenneth E. S. Platou, President
CFO: Tim Panks, Chief Financial Officer
CMO: Jill Schenk, M.D., Chief of Staff
CHR: Gary Blevins, Director Human Resources
Web address: www.mercymtshasta.org
**Control:** Other not–for–profit (including NFP Corporation) **Service:** General Medical and Surgical

**Staffed Beds:** 33 **Admissions:** 1105 **Census:** 7 **Outpatient Visits:** 47384 **Births:** 164 **Total Expense ($000):** 45160 **Payroll Expense ($000):** 19554 **Personnel:** 207

## MOUNTAIN VIEW—Santa Clara County

✠ **EL CAMINO HOSPITAL (050308)**, 2500 Grant Road, Zip 94040–4302, Mailing Address: P.O. Box 7025, Zip 94039–7025; tel. 650/940–7000, (Includes EL CAMINO HOSPITAL LOS GATOS, 815 Pollard Road, Los Gatos, Zip 95032–1438; tel. 408/378–6131) **A**1 9 10 **F**3 8 11 12 13 15 17 18 20 22 24 28 29 30 31 34 35 36 38 40 46 50 51 53 54 55 56 57 58 59 60 64 65 68 70 72 74 75 76 77 78 79 81 82 83 84 86 87 89 90 93 98 101 102 103 104 105 107 108 110 111 112 114 115 117 118 119 120 121 123 124 126 129 130 132 133 135 143 145 146 147
Primary Contact: Tomi S. Ryba, President and Chief Executive Officer
COO: Mike Zdeblick, Chief Operating Officer
CFO: Michael King, Chief Financial Officer
CMO: Eric Pifer, M.D., Chief Medical Officer
CIO: Greg Walton, Chief Information Officer
CHR: Charlene Gliniecki, Vice President Human Resources
Web address: www.elcaminohospital.org
**Control:** Hospital district or authority, Government, nonfederal **Service:** General Medical and Surgical

**Staffed Beds:** 420 **Admissions:** 18202 **Census:** 219 **Outpatient Visits:** 241244 **Births:** 4679 **Total Expense ($000):** 579237 **Payroll Expense ($000):** 204641 **Personnel:** 1753

## MURRIETA—Riverside County

☐ **LOMA LINDA UNIVERSITY MEDICAL CENTER–MURRIETA (050770)**, 28062 Baxter Road, Zip 92563–1401; tel. 951/290–4000, (Nonreporting) **A**1 9 10 **S** Loma Linda University Adventist Health Sciences Center, Loma Linda, CA
Primary Contact: Richard L. Rawson, Chief Executive Officer
COO: Richard M. Tibbits, Vice President and Chief Operating Officer
CFO: James Uli, Chief Financial Officer
CMO: Jeff Conner, M.D., Chief Medical Staff
Web address: www.llumcmurrieta.org
**Control:** Other not–for–profit (including NFP Corporation) **Service:** General Medical and Surgical

**Staffed Beds:** 106

---

**Hospital, Medicare Provider Number, Address, Telephone, Approval, Facility, and Physician Codes, Health Care System**

★ American Hospital Association (AHA) membership
☐ The Joint Commission accreditation
◇ DNV Healthcare Inc. accreditation
○ Healthcare Facilities Accreditation Program
△ Commission on Accreditation of Rehabilitation Facilities (CARF) accreditation

**CA**

☐ **SOUTHWEST HEALTHCARE SYSTEM (050701)**, 25500 Medical Center Drive, Zip 92562–5965; tel. 951/696–6000, (Includes INLAND VALLEY MEDICAL CENTER, 36485 Inland Valley Drive, Wildomar, Zip 92595–9700; tel. 951/677–1111; Gino Patrizio, Chief Executive Officer and Managing Director; RANCHO SPRINGS MEDICAL CENTER, 25500 Medical Center Drive, tel. 951/696–6000), (Nonreporting) **A**1 9 10 **S** Universal Health Services, Inc., King of Prussia, PA
Primary Contact: Bradley D. Neet, FACHE, Chief Executive Officer
COO: Jared Giles, Chief Operating Officer
CFO: Barry Thorfinnson, Chief Financial Officer
CMO: Timothy Killeen, M.D., Chief of Staff
CIO: Tura Heckler, Director Information Services
CHR: Laura Culbertson, Director Human Resources
CNO: Melissa Burns, Chief Nursing Officer
Web address: www.swhealthcaresystem.com/
**Control:** Corporation, Investor–owned, for-profit **Service:** General Medical and Surgical

**Staffed Beds:** 252

### NAPA—Napa County

☐ **NAPA STATE HOSPITAL (054122)**, 2100 Napa–Vallejo Highway, Zip 94558–6293; tel. 707/253–5000 **A**1 3 5 10 **F**30 39 53 56 59 61 67 68 77 86 98 103 128 130 132 135 146 **P**6
Primary Contact: Dolly Matteucci, Interim Executive Director
COO: Dolly Matteucci, Interim Executive Director
Web address: www.dmh.ca.gov
**Control:** State–Government, nonfederal **Service:** Psychiatric

**Staffed Beds:** 1229 **Admissions:** 690 **Census:** 1166 **Outpatient Visits:** 0 **Births:** 0 **Total Expense ($000):** 261305 **Payroll Expense ($000):** 165000 **Personnel:** 2181

⊠ **QUEEN OF THE VALLEY MEDICAL CENTER (050009)**, 1000 Trancas Street, Zip 94558–2906, Mailing Address: P.O. Box 2340, Zip 94558–0688; tel. 707/252–4411 **A**1 2 9 10 **F**3 8 11 13 15 17 18 20 22 24 26 28 29 30 31 32 34 35 39 40 43 44 45 46 47 48 49 50 51 53 57 59 60 61 64 68 70 72 74 75 76 77 78 79 81 82 84 85 86 87 89 90 91 92 93 97 102 107 108 110 111 114 115 116 117 118 119 120 121 123 124 126 130 132 135 146 148 **S** St. Joseph Health, Irvine, CA
Primary Contact: Walt Mickens, President and Chief Executive Officer
CFO: Donald Miller, Vice President and Chief Financial Officer
CMO: Vincent Morgese, M.D., Vice President Medical Affairs
CHR: Ron Scott, Vice President Human Resources
Web address: www.thequeen.org
**Control:** Church–operated, Nongovernment, not–for profit **Service:** General Medical and Surgical

**Staffed Beds:** 174 **Admissions:** 7911 **Census:** 102 **Outpatient Visits:** 206634 **Births:** 831 **Total Expense ($000):** 250933 **Payroll Expense ($000):** 89544 **Personnel:** 1081

### NATIONAL CITY—San Diego County

☐ △ **PARADISE VALLEY HOSPITAL (050024)**, 2400 East Fourth Street, Zip 91950–2099; tel. 619/470–4321, (Includes BAYVIEW BEHAVIORAL HEALTH CAMPUS, 330 Moss Street, Chula Vista, Zip 91911–2005; tel. 619/426–6311; George Lewis, Executive Director), (Nonreporting) **A**1 7 9 10 **S** Prime Healthcare Services, Ontario, CA
Primary Contact: Luis Leon, Regional Chief Executive Officer
CFO: Janet L. Caceres, Chief Financial Officer
CMO: Genaro Fernandez, M.D., Chief of Staff
CIO: Amanda Kaems, Manager Information Systems
CHR: Lorraine Villegas, Manager Human Resources
Web address: www.paradisevalleyhospital.org
**Control:** Corporation, Investor–owned, for-profit **Service:** General Medical and Surgical

**Staffed Beds:** 205

### NEEDLES—San Bernardino County

**COLORADO RIVER MEDICAL CENTER (051323)**, 1401 Bailey Avenue, Zip 92363–3103; tel. 760/326–4531, (Nonreporting) **A**9 10 18
Primary Contact: Mark H. Uffer, Chief Executive Officer
CIO: Ron Chieffo, Chief Information Officer
**Control:** City–Government, nonfederal **Service:** General Medical and Surgical

**Staffed Beds:** 25

### NEWPORT BEACH—Orange County

★ ◇ **HOAG MEMORIAL HOSPITAL PRESBYTERIAN (050224)**, One Hoag Drive, Zip 92663–4120, Mailing Address: P.O. Box 6100, Zip 92658–6100; tel. 949/764–4624, (Includes HOAG HOSPITAL IRVINE, 16200 Sand Canyon Avenue, Irvine, Zip 92618–3714; tel. 949/764–8240) **A**9 10 21 **F**3 4 5 11 13 14 15 17 18 20 22 24 26 28 29 30 31 34 35 36 37 40 44 45 46 47 48 49 50 51 54 55 57 58 59 60 64 68 70 71 72 74 75 76 77 78 79 81 82 84 85 86 87 92 93 96 100 102 103 107 108 110 111 114 115 116 117 118 119 120 121 123 124 126 129 130 132 135 141 143 145 146 147 148 **P**5
Primary Contact: Robert Braithwaite, President and Chief Executive Officer
COO: Robert Braithwaite, President and Chief Operating Officer
CFO: Jennifer C. Mitzner, Senior Vice President Finance and Chief Financial Officer
CMO: Jack Cox, M.D., Senior Vice President and Chief Quality Officer
CIO: Tim Moore, R.N., Senior Vice President and Chief Information Officer
CHR: Jan L. Blue, Vice President Human Resources
CNO: Richard A. Martin, MSN, Senior Vice President and Chief Nursing Officer
Web address: www.hoaghospital.org
**Control:** Other not–for–profit (including NFP Corporation) **Service:** General Medical and Surgical

**Staffed Beds:** 482 **Admissions:** 24519 **Census:** 297 **Outpatient Visits:** 371645 **Births:** 5992 **Total Expense ($000):** 784848 **Payroll Expense ($000):** 251713 **Personnel:** 3879

**NEWPORT BAY HOSPITAL (054135)**, 1501 East 16th Street, Zip 92663–5924; tel. 949/650–9750 **A**10 **F**35 98 100 101 103 130 148
Primary Contact: James E. Parkhurst, President and Chief Executive Officer
COO: Garry Hardwick, R.N., Chief Operating Officer
CFO: Rocky Gentner, Chief Financial Officer
CMO: Jason Kellogg, M.D., Chief of Staff
CIO: Nina Swenson, Director Business Services
CHR: Phyllis Parkhurst, Vice President Support Services
Web address: www.newportbayhospital.com
**Control:** Corporation, Investor–owned, for-profit **Service:** Psychiatric

**Staffed Beds:** 34 **Admissions:** 829 **Census:** 30 **Outpatient Visits:** 0 **Births:** 0

### NORTH HOLLYWOOD—Los Angeles County, See Los Angeles

### NORTHRIDGE—Los Angeles County, See Los Angeles

### NORWALK—Los Angeles County

☐ **COAST PLAZA HOSPITAL (050771)**, 13100 Studebaker Road, Zip 90650–2531; tel. 562/868–3751, (Nonreporting) **A**1 10 **S** Avanti Hospitals, El Segundo, CA
Primary Contact: John J. Ferrelli, Chief Executive Officer
CFO: Mihi Lee, Chief Financial Officer
CMO: Galal S. Gough, M.D., Chief of Staff
CIO: Linda K. Roman, Administrator
Web address: www.coastplaza.com
**Control:** Partnership, Investor–owned, for-profit **Service:** General Medical and Surgical

**Staffed Beds:** 123

**LOS ANGELES COMMUNITY HOSPITAL OF NORWALK** See Los Angeles Community Hospital, Los Angeles

☐ **METROPOLITAN STATE HOSPITAL (054133)**, 11401 Bloomfield Avenue, Zip 90650–2015; tel. 562/863–7011, (Nonreporting) **A**1 10
Primary Contact: Michael Barsom, M.D., Executive Director
CFO: Maybelle Manlangit, Senior Accounting Officer
CIO: Paul Mello, Manager Data Processing
CHR: Eddie Park, Acting Director Human Resources
Web address: www.dmh.ca.gov
**Control:** State–Government, nonfederal **Service:** Psychiatric

**Staffed Beds:** 657

### NOVATO—Marin County

⊠ **NOVATO COMMUNITY HOSPITAL (050131)**, 180 Rowland Way, Zip 94945–5009, Mailing Address: P.O. Box 1108, Zip 94948–1108; tel. 415/209–1300 **A**1 9 10 **F**3 15 18 26 29 30 31 34 40 45 49 50 51 54 56 59 64 68 70 74 75 77 78 79 81 84 85 87 93 107 108 111 115 119 130 131 132 134 143 144 146 148 **S** Sutter Health, Sacramento, CA
Primary Contact: Brian Alexander, Chief Administrative Officer
CMO: Barbara Nylund, M.D., Chief of Staff
CIO: Kathryn Graham, Director Communications and Community Relations
CHR: Diana G. Johnson, Acting Chief Human Resources Officer
Web address: www.novatocommunity.sutterhealth.org
**Control:** Other not–for–profit (including NFP Corporation) **Service:** General Medical and Surgical

**Staffed Beds:** 40 **Admissions:** 1603 **Census:** 15 **Outpatient Visits:** 98170 **Births:** 0 **Total Expense ($000):** 62759 **Payroll Expense ($000):** 19645 **Personnel:** 303

*Many Facility Codes have changed. Please refer to the AHA Guide Code Chart.* © 2013 AHA Guide

**OAKDALE—Stanislaus County**

☒ **OAK VALLEY HOSPITAL DISTRICT (050067)**, 350 South Oak Street, Zip 95361–3519; tel. 209/847–3011, (Nonreporting) **A**1 5 9 10 **S** Dignity Health, San Francisco, CA
Primary Contact: John McCormick, Chief Executive Officer
CMO: Krystyna Belski, M.D., Chief of Staff
CIO: Sherry Peral, Manager Information Systems
CHR: Kim Bukhari, Manager Human Resources
Web address: www.oakvalleycares.org
**Control:** Church–operated, Nongovernment, not–for profit **Service:** General Medical and Surgical

**Staffed Beds:** 150

**OAKLAND—Alameda County**

☒ **ALAMEDA COUNTY MEDICAL CENTER (050320)**, 1411 East 31st Street, Zip 94602–1018; tel. 510/437–4800, (Includes ALAMEDA COUNTY MEDICAL CENTER–FAIRMONT CAMPUS, 15400 Foothill Boulevard, San Leandro, Zip 94578–1009; tel. 510/895–4200), (Nonreporting) **A**1 3 5 10
Primary Contact: Wright L. Lassiter, III, Chief Executive Officer
COO: Bill Manns, Chief Operating Officer
CFO: Marion Schales, Chief Financial Officer
CMO: Sang–ick Chang, M.D., Chief Medical Officer
CIO: Mark Zielazinski, Chief Information Officer
CHR: Jeanette L. Louden Corbett, Chief Human Resources Officer
Web address: www.acmedctr.org
**Control:** Hospital district or authority, Government, nonfederal **Service:** General Medical and Surgical

**Staffed Beds:** 387

☒ **ALTA BATES SUMMIT MEDICAL CENTER – SUMMIT CAMPUS (050043)**, 350 Hawthorne Avenue, Zip 94609–3100; tel. 510/655–4000, (Total facility includes 71 beds in nursing home–type unit) **A**1 2 9 10 **F**3 8 11 12 15 17 18 20 22 24 26 29 30 31 34 35 36 40 46 47 49 56 57 58 59 60 61 64 68 70 74 75 77 78 79 81 82 84 85 86 87 97 107 108 114 119 120 121 122 123 126 128 130 135 136 146 148 **S** Sutter Health, Sacramento, CA
Primary Contact: Charles Prosper, Chief Executive Officer
CFO: Robert Petrina, Chief Financial Officer
CMO: John Gentile, M.D., Vice President Medical Affairs
CHR: Mark Beiting, Vice President Human Resources
Web address: www.altabatessummit.com
**Control:** Other not–for–profit (including NFP Corporation) **Service:** General Medical and Surgical

**Staffed Beds:** 414 **Admissions:** 12055 **Census:** 204 **Outpatient Visits:** 120776 **Births:** 0 **Total Expense ($000):** 399918 **Payroll Expense ($000):** 150518 **Personnel:** 1719

☐ **CHILDREN'S HOSPITAL AND RESEARCH CENTER AT OAKLAND (053301)**, 747 52nd Street, Zip 94609–1809; tel. 510/428–3000 **A**1 3 5 9 10 **F**3 11 19 21 23 25 29 30 31 32 33 34 35 36 38 40 43 45 46 48 50 54 55 57 58 59 61 64 65 66 68 72 74 75 77 78 79 81 82 83 84 86 87 88 90 93 97 99 100 101 102 104 107 108 111 114 118 119 127 129 130 131 132 134 136 143 146 148 **P**3 5
Primary Contact: Bertram Lubin, M.D., President and Chief Executive Officer
CFO: Doug Myers, Senior Vice President and Chief Financial Officer
CIO: Don Livsey, Vice President and Chief Information Officer
Web address: www.childrenshospitaloakland.org
**Control:** Other not–for–profit (including NFP Corporation) **Service:** Children's general

**Staffed Beds:** 190 **Admissions:** 10183 **Census:** 138 **Outpatient Visits:** 230686 **Births:** 0 **Total Expense ($000):** 457665 **Payroll Expense ($000):** 180451

☒ **KAISER PERMANENTE OAKLAND MEDICAL CENTER (050075)**, (Formerly Oakland Medical Center), 280 West MacArthur Boulevard, Zip 94611–5693; tel. 510/752–1000, (Includes RICHMOND MEDICAL CENTER, 901 Nevin Avenue, Richmond, Zip 94801–2555; tel. 510/307–1500) **A**1 3 5 8 10 **F**3 7 11 12 13 15 18 19 29 30 31 34 35 36 38 40 41 44 45 46 49 50 51 55 56 57 58 59 60 61 62 63 64 65 68 70 72 74 75 76 77 78 79 80 81 82 83 84 85 86 87 88 89 93 94 97 99 100 107 110 111 112 115 119 129 130 131 132 135 144 146 147 148 **S** Kaiser Foundation Hospitals, Oakland, CA
Primary Contact: Nathaniel L. Oubre, Jr., Senior Vice President and Area Manager
CFO: Dennis Morris, Area Finance Officer
CMO: John Loftus, M.D., Chief of Staff
CIO: Johnny Law, Area Information Officer
CHR: Rick Mead, Human Resources Leader
CNO: Charlene Boyer, Chief Nursing Officer
Web address: www.kaiserpermanente.org
**Control:** Other not–for–profit (including NFP Corporation) **Service:** General Medical and Surgical

**Staffed Beds:** 267 **Admissions:** 14765 **Census:** 185 **Outpatient Visits:** 635309 **Births:** 2263 **Personnel:** 2731

☐ **TELECARE HERITAGE PSYCHIATRIC HEALTH CENTER (054146)**, 2633 East 27th Street, Zip 94601–1912; tel. 510/535–5115, (Nonreporting) **A**1 9 10
Primary Contact: Linda Reese, Administrator
Web address: www.tbhcare.com/
**Control:** Partnership, Investor–owned, for–profit **Service:** Psychiatric

**Staffed Beds:** 26

**OCEANSIDE—San Diego County**

☒ **TRI-CITY MEDICAL CENTER (050128)**, 4002 Vista Way, Zip 92056–4506; tel. 760/724–8411 **A**1 2 3 5 9 10 **F**3 11 13 14 15 17 18 20 22 24 26 28 29 30 31 34 35 38 40 45 46 47 49 50 51 53 57 58 59 62 63 64 65 67 68 72 74 75 76 77 78 79 81 82 84 85 86 87 90 93 96 100 101 102 103 104 105 107 108 110 111 114 115 117 118 119 126 130 132 133 135 143 146 147 148
Primary Contact: Larry B. Anderson, Chief Executive Officer
COO: Casey Fatch, Chief Operating Officer
CFO: Alex Yu, Chief Financial Officer
CIO: Mark Facuri, Director Information Systems
Web address: www.tricitymed.org
**Control:** Hospital district or authority, Government, nonfederal **Service:** General Medical and Surgical

**Staffed Beds:** 330 **Admissions:** 16480 **Census:** 189 **Outpatient Visits:** 206170 **Births:** 2749 **Personnel:** 1668

**ONTARIO—San Bernardino County**

☒ **KINDRED HOSPITAL–ONTARIO (052037)**, 550 North Monterey Avenue, Zip 91764–3399; tel. 909/391–0333, (Nonreporting) **A**1 9 10 **S** Kindred Healthcare, Louisville, KY
Primary Contact: Robin Rapp, MS, R.N., Chief Executive Officer
CFO: Omar Oregel, Controller
CMO: Marc Lynch, D.O., Chief of Staff
CHR: Laurel Scharber, Administrative Assistant and Coordinator Human Resources
CNO: Holly Ramos, R.N., Chief Clinical Officer
Web address: www.khontario.com/
**Control:** Corporation, Investor–owned, for–profit **Service:** Long–Term Acute Care hospital

**Staffed Beds:** 91

**ORANGE—Orange County**

☐ **CHAPMAN MEDICAL CENTER (050745)**, 2601 East Chapman Avenue, Zip 92869–3206; tel. 714/633–0011, (Nonreporting) **A**1 9 10 **S** Integrated Healthcare, Santa Ana, CA
Primary Contact: Don Kreitz, Chief Executive Officer
COO: Ada Yeh, R.N., Chief Operating Officer and Chief Nursing Officer
CFO: Ray Rivas, Chief Financial Officer
CMO: Steven Duckor, M.D., Chief of Staff
CIO: Nova Stewart, Chief Information Officer
CHR: JoAnne Suehs, Manager Human Resources
Web address: www.chapmanmedicalcenter.com
**Control:** Corporation, Investor–owned, for–profit **Service:** General Medical and Surgical

**Staffed Beds:** 100

☐ **CHILDREN'S HOSPITAL OF ORANGE COUNTY (053304)**, 455 South Main Street, Zip 92868–3835, Mailing Address: PO Box 5700, Zip 92863–5700; tel. 714/997–3000 **A**1 3 5 9 10 **F**3 14 17 19 21 23 25 27 29 30 31 32 34 35 50 55 57 58 59 61 64 65 66 68 71 72 74 75 77 78 79 81 85 86 87 88 89 91 92 93 97 104 126 129 130 132 134 136 146 **P**5
Primary Contact: Kimberly C. Cripe, President and Chief Executive Officer
COO: Debra Mathias, Chief Operating Officer
CFO: Kerri Ruppert Schiller, Senior Vice President and Chief Financial Officer
CMO: Maria Minon, M.D., Vice President Medical Affairs and Chief Medical Officer
CIO: Mark Headland, Chief Information Officer
CHR: Susan M. Burrows, Vice President Human Resources
CNO: Louise White, R.N., Vice President Patient Care Services and Chief Nursing Officer
Web address: www.choc.org
**Control:** Other not–for–profit (including NFP Corporation) **Service:** Children's general

**Staffed Beds:** 238 **Admissions:** 11487 **Census:** 162 **Outpatient Visits:** 206139 **Total Expense ($000):** 504959 **Payroll Expense ($000):** 127333 **Personnel:** 2115

---

**Hospital, Medicare Provider Number, Address, Telephone, Approval, Facility, and Physician Codes, Health Care System**

★ American Hospital Association (AHA) membership
☐ The Joint Commission accreditation
◇ DNV Healthcare Inc. accreditation
○ Healthcare Facilities Accreditation Program
△ Commission on Accreditation of Rehabilitation Facilities (CARF) accreditation

CA

☐ **HEALTHBRIDGE CHILDRENS REHABILITATION HOSPITAL (053308)**, 393 South Tustin Street, Zip 92866–2501; tel. 714/289–2400 **A**1 9 10 **F**1 3 4 16 17 29 64 65 67 70 72 73 75 77 80 88 89 90 93 98 128 130 132 146 148 **S** Nexus Health Systems, Houston, TX
Primary Contact: Allan G. Komarek, Ph.D., Chief Executive Officer and Administrator
Web address: www.HealthBridgeOrange.com
**Control:** Partnership, Investor–owned, for–profit **Service:** Children's rehabilitation

**Staffed Beds:** 27 **Admissions:** 121 **Census:** 21 **Outpatient Visits:** 6089 **Births:** 0 **Total Expense ($000):** 8385 **Payroll Expense ($000):** 5497 **Personnel:** 116

**CA**

⊠ **ST. JOSEPH HOSPITAL (050069)**, 1100 West Stewart Drive, Zip 92868–3849, Mailing Address: P.O. Box 5600, Zip 92863–5600; tel. 714/633–9111 **A**1 2 5 9 10 **F**3 5 8 12 13 14 15 17 18 19 20 21 22 23 24 25 26 27 28 29 30 31 34 35 37 39 40 41 45 46 47 48 49 51 52 53 54 55 57 58 59 60 64 65 66 68 69 70 71 74 75 76 77 78 79 80 81 82 84 85 86 87 91 92 93 98 100 102 104 105 107 108 109 110 111 113 114 115 116 117 118 119 120 121 123 124 126 129 130 131 132 135 138 141 146 147 148 **P**3 5 **S** St. Joseph Health, Irvine, CA
Primary Contact: Steven C. Moreau, President and Chief Executive Officer
CFO: Tina Mycroft, Vice President and Chief Financial Officer
CMO: Raymond Casciari, M.D., Chief Medical Officer
CIO: Tina Mycroft, Vice President and Chief Financial Officer
CHR: Mary P. Leahy, Vice President Human Resources
Web address: www.sjo.org
**Control:** Other not–for–profit (including NFP Corporation) **Service:** General Medical and Surgical

**Staffed Beds:** 392 **Admissions:** 20306 **Census:** 216 **Outpatient Visits:** 292279 **Births:** 4823 **Total Expense ($000):** 620598 **Payroll Expense ($000):** 203394 **Personnel:** 3085

⊠ **UNIVERSITY OF CALIFORNIA, IRVINE HEALTHCARE (050348)**, 101 The City Drive, Zip 92868–3298; tel. 714/456–6011 **A**1 2 3 5 8 9 10 **F**3 6 9 11 12 13 14 15 16 17 18 19 20 21 22 24 26 28 29 30 31 32 34 35 36 37 39 40 41 43 44 45 46 47 48 49 50 51 54 55 56 57 58 59 60 61 64 65 66 68 70 71 72 74 75 76 77 78 79 80 81 82 84 85 86 87 90 91 92 93 94 96 97 98 99 100 101 102 103 104 105 107 108 110 111 112 114 115 116 117 118 119 120 121 123 124 126 130 132 134 135 138 141 142 145 146 147 148 **P**6 **S** University of California–Systemwide Administration, Oakland, CA
Primary Contact: Terry A. Belmont, Chief Executive Officer
COO: Alice H. Issai, Chief Operating Officer
CFO: Morris J. Frieling, Chief Financial Officer
CMO: Bill Barron, M.D., Chief Medical Officer
CIO: Jim Murry, Chief Information Officer
CHR: Julie Molleston, Executive Director Human Resources and Customer Services
CNO: Karen A. Grimley, R.N., Chief Nursing Officer
Web address: www.ucihealth.com
**Control:** State–Government, nonfederal **Service:** General Medical and Surgical

**Staffed Beds:** 388 **Admissions:** 17787 **Census:** 294 **Outpatient Visits:** 519145 **Births:** 1399 **Total Expense ($000):** 676911 **Payroll Expense ($000):** 297077 **Personnel:** 4170

### OROVILLE—Butte County

**OROVILLE HOSPITAL (050030)**, 2767 Olive Highway, Zip 95966–6118; tel. 530/533–8500, (Total facility includes 20 beds in nursing home–type unit) **A**9 10 **F**3 11 13 15 18 26 28 29 30 31 32 33 34 35 38 39 40 41 43 44 45 46 47 49 50 51 54 56 57 59 60 61 62 64 65 66 68 70 74 75 76 78 79 81 82 84 85 86 87 93 94 96 97 107 108 110 111 115 116 117 118 119 126 127 128 129 130 132 144 146 147 148
Primary Contact: Robert J. Wentz, President and Chief Executive Officer
COO: Scott Chapple, Chief Operating Officer
CFO: Ashok Khanchandani, Chief Financial Officer
CMO: Mark T. Heinrich, D.O., President Medical Staff
CIO: Denise LeFevre, Chief Information Officer
CHR: Scott Chapple, Chief Operating Officer
Web address: www.orovillehospital.com
**Control:** Other not–for–profit (including NFP Corporation) **Service:** General Medical and Surgical

**Staffed Beds:** 133 **Admissions:** 10170 **Census:** 109 **Outpatient Visits:** 282831 **Births:** 407 **Total Expense ($000):** 169491 **Payroll Expense ($000):** 72110 **Personnel:** 1090

### OXNARD—Ventura County

⊠ **ST. JOHN'S REGIONAL MEDICAL CENTER (050082)**, 1600 North Rose Avenue, Zip 93030–3723; tel. 805/988–2500, (Nonreporting) **A**1 9 10 **S** Dignity Health, San Francisco, CA
Primary Contact: Laurie Eberst, R.N., President and Chief Executive Officer
COO: Kim A. Wilson, R.N., Chief Operating Officer
CFO: Robert D. Wardwell, Chief Financial Officer
CMO: Eugene Fussell, M.D., Chief Medical Officer
CIO: Jeff Perry, Director Information Technology
CHR: Ed Gonzales, Vice President Human Resources
CNO: Gudrun Moll, R.N., Chief Nursing Officer
Web address: www.stjohnshealth.org
**Control:** Other not–for–profit (including NFP Corporation) **Service:** General Medical and Surgical

**Staffed Beds:** 161

### PALM SPRINGS—Riverside County

⊠ **DESERT REGIONAL MEDICAL CENTER (050243)**, 1150 North Indian Canyon Drive, Zip 92262–4872, Mailing Address: P.O. Box 2739, Zip 92263–2739; tel. 760/323–6511, (Total facility includes 30 beds in nursing home–type unit) **A**1 2 9 10 **F**3 12 13 14 15 17 18 20 22 24 26 28 29 30 31 34 35 40 43 45 46 47 48 49 51 52 53 54 55 57 58 59 60 64 65 68 70 72 74 75 76 77 78 79 81 82 83 84 85 86 87 89 90 92 93 94 100 102 107 108 109 110 111 114 115 116 117 119 120 124 126 128 130 131 132 146 147 148 **S** TENET Healthcare Corporation, Dallas, TX
Primary Contact: Carolyn W. Caldwell, Chief Executive Officer
COO: Ken Wheat, Chief Operating Officer
CFO: Richard Phillips, Chief Financial Officer
CNO: Mary Anne McCrea, Chief Nursing Officer
Web address: www.desertmedctr.com
**Control:** Individual, Investor–owned, for–profit **Service:** General Medical and Surgical

**Staffed Beds:** 387 **Admissions:** 18347 **Census:** 211 **Outpatient Visits:** 154205 **Total Expense ($000):** 280800 **Payroll Expense ($000):** 135596 **Personnel:** 1567

### PALMDALE—Los Angeles County

☐ **PALMDALE REGIONAL MEDICAL CENTER (050204)**, 38600 Medical Center Drive, Zip 93551–4483; tel. 661/382–5000 **A**1 9 10 **F**3 8 11 12 18 20 24 26 29 30 40 45 46 47 49 50 51 64 68 70 74 77 79 81 85 87 93 107 108 111 114 115 119 130 141 146 148 **S** Universal Health Services, Inc., King of Prussia, PA
Primary Contact: Richard Allen, Interim Chief Executive Officer
COO: Karen Faulis, Chief Operating Officer
CFO: Kurt Broten, Chief Financial Officer
CIO: Roy Singleton, Director Computer Information Systems
CHR: Karen Hickling, Director Human Resources
CNO: Pat McClendon, MSN, Chief Nursing Officer
Web address: www.palmdaleregional.com
**Control:** Corporation, Investor–owned, for–profit **Service:** General Medical and Surgical

**Staffed Beds:** 157 **Admissions:** 8191 **Census:** 96 **Outpatient Visits:** 72049 **Births:** 0 **Total Expense ($000):** 105571 **Payroll Expense ($000):** 48585 **Personnel:** 630

### PALO ALTO—Santa Clara County

⊠ **LUCILE SALTER PACKARD CHILDREN'S HOSPITAL AT STANFORD (053305)**, 725 Welch Road, Zip 94304–1601; tel. 650/497–8000 **A**1 3 5 9 10 **F**3 7 11 12 13 15 17 19 25 27 28 29 30 31 32 34 35 36 38 43 44 45 46 47 48 49 50 54 55 57 58 59 60 61 62 64 65 66 68 71 72 73 74 75 76 77 78 79 80 81 82 84 85 86 87 88 89 91 92 93 96 97 99 100 101 104 107 111 115 119 124 126 129 130 131 132 134 136 137 138 139 140 141 142 144 145 146 148 **P**3 **S** Stanford Health Care, Palo Alto, CA
Primary Contact: Christopher G. Dawes, President and Chief Executive Officer
COO: Susan Flanagan, Chief Operating Officer
CFO: Timothy W. Carmack, Chief Financial Officer
CMO: Kenneth Cox, M.D., Chief Medical Officer
CIO: James McCaughey, Chief Strategy Officer
CHR: Greg Souza, Vice President Human Resources
Web address: www.lpch.org
**Control:** Other not–for–profit (including NFP Corporation) **Service:** Children's general

**Staffed Beds:** 302 **Admissions:** 12681 **Census:** 218 **Outpatient Visits:** 153815 **Births:** 4176 **Total Expense ($000):** 769831 **Payroll Expense ($000):** 251307 **Personnel:** 2627

*Many Facility Codes have changed. Please refer to the AHA Guide Code Chart.*   © 2013 AHA Guide

✠ **STANFORD HOSPITAL AND CLINICS (050441)**, 1520 Page Mill Road, Zip 94304–1125; tel. 650/723–4000, (Nonreporting) **A**1 3 5 8 9 10 **S** Stanford Health Care, Palo Alto, CA
Primary Contact: Amir Dan Rubin, President and Chief Executive Officer
COO: Margaret Vosburgh, Chief Operating Officer
CFO: Daniel Morrissette, Chief Financial Officer
CMO: Norman Rizk, M.D., Interim Chief Medical Officer
CIO: Pravene Nath, Interim Chief Information Officer
CNO: Nancy Lee, R.N., Vice President Patient Care Services and Chief Nursing Officer
Web address: www.stanfordhospital.com/
**Control:** Other not–for–profit (including NFP Corporation) **Service:** General Medical and Surgical

| **Staffed Beds:** 477 |
|---|

✠ **VETERANS AFFAIRS PALO ALTO HEALTH CARE SYSTEM**, 3801 Miranda Avenue, Zip 94304–1207; tel. 650/493–5000, (Includes PALO ALTO DIVISION, 3801 Miranda Avenue, tel. 650/493–5000; VETERANS AFFAIRS PALO ALTO HEALTH CARE SYSTEM, LIVERMORE DIVISION, 4951 Arroyo Road, tel. 510/447–2560) **A**1 2 3 5 7 8 **F**1 2 3 4 5 6 9 10 11 12 14 15 20 22 24 26 28 29 30 31 34 35 36 38 39 40 43 44 45 46 47 48 49 50 51 53 54 56 57 58 59 60 61 62 63 64 65 66 70 71 74 75 77 78 79 80 81 82 83 84 85 86 87 90 91 93 94 95 96 97 98 100 101 102 103 104 105 106 107 108 111 114 115 116 117 118 119 126 127 129 130 132 135 137 143 144 146 147 148 **S** Department of Veterans Affairs, Washington, DC
Primary Contact: Elizabeth Joyce Freeman, Director
CFO: Mel Niese, Chief Fiscal Service
CMO: Lawrence Leung, M.D., Chief of Staff
CIO: Doug Wirthgen, Chief Information Officer
CHR: Lori Peery, Chief Human Resource Management Services
Web address: www.paloalto.va.gov/
**Control:** Veterans Affairs, Government, federal **Service:** General Medical and Surgical

| **Staffed Beds:** 808 **Admissions:** 5674 **Census:** 397 **Births:** 0 |
|---|

### PANORAMA CITY—Los Angeles County, See Los Angeles

### PARADISE—Butte County

✠ **FEATHER RIVER HOSPITAL (050225)**, 5974 Pentz Road, Zip 95969–5509; tel. 530/877–9361, (Nonreporting) **A**1 2 9 10 **S** Adventist Health, Roseville, CA
Primary Contact: Kevin R. Erich, President and Chief Executive Officer
CFO: Dan Gordon, Chief Financial Officer
CMO: Anthony Nasr, M.D., Chief Medical Staff
CIO: Dan Gordon, Chief Financial Officer
CHR: Denton Gruzensky, Director Human Resources
Web address: www.frhosp.org
**Control:** Church–operated, Nongovernment, not–for profit **Service:** General Medical and Surgical

| **Staffed Beds:** 86 |
|---|

### PARAMOUNT—Los Angeles County

☐ **PROMISE HOSPITAL OF EAST LOS ANGELES, SUBURBAN MEDICAL CENTER CAMPUS**, 16453 South Colorado Avenue, Zip 90723–5011; tel. 562/531–3110, (Nonreporting) **A**1 9 **S** Promise Healthcare, Boca Raton, FL
Primary Contact: Steve Popkin, Chief Executive Officer
COO: Cynthia Duque, R.N., Chief Operating Officer
CMO: Mojtaba Sabahi, M.D., Chief of Staff
CIO: Jim Wilson, Vice President Information Technology
CHR: Sylvia Munoz, Director Human Resources
Web address: www.promiseeastla.com
**Control:** Corporation, Investor–owned, for–profit **Service:** General Medical and Surgical

| **Staffed Beds:** 182 |
|---|

### PASADENA—Los Angeles County

☐ **AURORA LAS ENCINAS HOSPITAL (054078)**, 2900 East Del Mar Boulevard, Zip 91107–4399; tel. 626/795–9901, (Nonreporting) **A**1 9 10 **S** Aurora Behavioral Health Care, Corona, CA
Primary Contact: Gerard Conway, Chief Executive Officer
COO: Steven Hytry, Chief Operating Officer
CFO: Tim Sides, Chief Financial Officer
CMO: Daniel Suzuki, M.D., Medical Director
CIO: Eric Kim, Chief Information Officer
CHR: Veronica Herrera, Director Human Resources
Web address: www.lasencinashospital.com
**Control:** Corporation, Investor–owned, for–profit **Service:** Psychiatric

| **Staffed Beds:** 138 |
|---|

✠ **HUNTINGTON MEMORIAL HOSPITAL (050438)**, 100 West California Boulevard, Zip 91105–3097, Mailing Address: P.O. Box 7013, Zip 91109–7013; tel. 626/397–5000 **A**1 2 3 5 9 10 **F**3 4 5 8 11 12 13 14 15 18 20 22 24 26 28 29 30 31 34 35 37 40 41 43 44 45 46 47 48 49 50 51 53 56 58 59 60 61 63 64 65 66 68 70 72 74 75 76 77 78 79 81 82 84 86 87 88 89 90 92 93 97 98 100 101 102 103 104 105 106 107 108 111 114 115 118 119 120 121 123 126 129 130 132 146 147 148 **P**3 5 7
Primary Contact: Stephen A. Ralph, President and Chief Executive Officer
COO: James S. Noble, Executive Vice President, Chief Operating Officer and Chief Financial Officer
CFO: James S. Noble, Executive Vice President, Chief Operating Officer and Chief Financial Officer
CMO: Paula Verrette, M.D., Vice President Quality and Performance Improvement and Chief Medical Officer
CIO: Debbie Tafoya, Vice President and Chief Information Officer
CHR: Debbie Ortega, Chief Human Resource Officer and Vice President Administrative Services
CNO: Bonnie Kass, Chief Nursing Officer and Vice President Patient Care and Support Services
Web address: www.huntingtonhospital.com
**Control:** Other not–for–profit (including NFP Corporation) **Service:** General Medical and Surgical

| **Staffed Beds:** 552 **Admissions:** 26152 **Census:** 327 **Outpatient Visits:** 149988 **Births:** 3386 **Total Expense ($000):** 515355 **Payroll Expense ($000):** 185340 **Personnel:** 3217 |
|---|

### PATTON—San Bernardino County

☐ **PATTON STATE HOSPITAL**, 3102 East Highland Avenue, Zip 92369–7813; tel. 909/425–7000 **A**1 **F**3 29 30 39 53 57 58 59 61 65 74 75 77 86 87 98 100 101 103 130 132 135 143 146 **P**1
Primary Contact: Octavio C. Luna, Executive Director
CFO: Kathleen Gamble, Fiscal Officer
CMO: George Christison, M.D., Medical Director
CIO: Cindy Barrett, Administrative Assistant
CHR: Nancy Varela, Director Human Resources
Web address: www.dmh.cahwnet.gov/statehospitals/patton
**Control:** State–Government, nonfederal **Service:** Psychiatric

| **Staffed Beds:** 1527 **Admissions:** 1031 **Census:** 1502 **Births:** 0 |
|---|

### PERRIS—Riverside County

★ ○ **KINDRED HOSPITAL OF RIVERSIDE (052052)**, 2224 Medical Center Drive, Zip 92571–2638; tel. 951/436–3535 **A**9 10 11 **F**3 29 39 45 48 49 50 56 74 75 77 84 85 87 92 94 103 107 108 119 130 148 **S** Kindred Healthcare, Louisville, KY
Primary Contact: James Linhares, Administrator
COO: Bennie Montgomery, R.N., Chief Nursing Officer and Chief Operations Officer
CFO: Paul Smith, Chief Financial Officer
Web address: www.khriverside.com
**Control:** Corporation, Investor–owned, for–profit **Service:** Long–Term Acute Care hospital

| **Staffed Beds:** 40 **Admissions:** 451 **Census:** 33 **Outpatient Visits:** 0 **Births:** 0 **Total Expense ($000):** 19788 **Payroll Expense ($000):** 9812 **Personnel:** 172 |
|---|

### PETALUMA—Sonoma County

✠ **PETALUMA VALLEY HOSPITAL (050136)**, 400 North McDowell Boulevard, Zip 94954–2369; tel. 707/778–1111 **A**1 9 10 **F**3 11 13 15 29 30 34 35 40 44 45 46 49 50 51 57 60 63 64 68 69 70 75 76 77 78 79 81 82 84 85 86 87 92 93 97 107 108 110 111 115 119 130 146 148 **S** St. Joseph Health, Irvine, CA
Primary Contact: Todd Salnas, President and Chief Executive Officer
COO: David Ziolkowski, Chief Operating Officer
CFO: Mich Riccioni, Chief Financial Officer
CMO: Gary Greensweig, D.O., Chief Medical Officer
CIO: Patrick Wylie, Director Information Systems
CHR: Debra Miller, Senior Vice President Human Resources
Web address: www.stjosephhealth.org/About–Us/Facilities/Petaluma–Valley–Hospital.aspx
**Control:** Other not–for–profit (including NFP Corporation) **Service:** General Medical and Surgical

| **Staffed Beds:** 28 **Admissions:** 2792 **Census:** 26 **Outpatient Visits:** 59026 **Births:** 423 **Total Expense ($000):** 84541 **Payroll Expense ($000):** 29749 **Personnel:** 332 |
|---|

**CA**

---

**Hospital, Medicare Provider Number, Address, Telephone, Approval, Facility, and Physician Codes, Health Care System**

★ American Hospital Association (AHA) membership
☐ The Joint Commission accreditation
◇ DNV Healthcare Inc. accreditation
○ Healthcare Facilities Accreditation Program
△ Commission on Accreditation of Rehabilitation Facilities (CARF) accreditation

© 2013 AHA Guide          *Many Facility Codes have changed. Please refer to the AHA Guide Code Chart.*          Hospitals **A79**

## PLACENTIA—Orange County

☒ **PLACENTIA–LINDA HOSPITAL (050589)**, 1301 North Rose Drive, Zip 92870–3899; tel. 714/993–2000 **A**1 9 10 **F**3 11 12 15 17 29 30 31 34 40 45 46 47 48 49 57 59 65 70 75 79 81 82 85 87 93 107 108 111 118 119 130 131 132 135 145 146 148 **P**5 **S** TENET Healthcare Corporation, Dallas, TX
Primary Contact: Kent G. Clayton, President and Chief Executive Officer
COO: Pat Swaller, R.N., Chief Operating Officer
CFO: Kristi Liberatore, Chief Financial Officer
CMO: David Petreccia, M.D., Physician Advisor
CIO: Freddie T. Sanchez, Director Information Systems
CHR: Diane Worthington, Director Human Resources
CNO: Judy Chabot, R.N., Chief Nursing Officer
Web address: www.placentialinda.com
**Control:** Corporation, Investor–owned, for–profit **Service:** General Medical and Surgical

**Staffed Beds:** 114 **Admissions:** 3653 **Census:** 33 **Outpatient Visits:** 49778 **Births:** 1 **Total Expense ($000):** 61450 **Payroll Expense ($000):** 28107 **Personnel:** 395

## PLACERVILLE—El Dorado County

☒ **MARSHALL MEDICAL CENTER (050254)**, 1100 Marshall Way, Zip 95667–6599; tel. 530/622–1441, (Nonreporting) **A**1 2 9 10
Primary Contact: James Whipple, Administrator and Chief Executive Officer
CFO: Laurie Eldridge, Chief Financial Officer
CMO: Rene Orona, M.D., Chief of Staff
CIO: Mike Jones, Director Information Services
CHR: Scott Comer, Director Administrative Services
Web address: www.marshallmedical.org
**Control:** Other not–for–profit (including NFP Corporation) **Service:** General Medical and Surgical

**Staffed Beds:** 105

## PLEASANTON—Alameda County

☒ **VALLEYCARE MEDICAL CENTER (050283)**, 5555 West Las Positas Boulevard, Zip 94588–4000; tel. 925/847–3000, (Includes VALLEY MEMORIAL, 1111 East Stanley Boulevard, Livermore, Zip 94550–4115; tel. 925/447–7000), (Total facility includes 26 beds in nursing home–type unit) **A**1 2 9 10 **F**3 8 11 12 13 15 17 18 20 22 24 26 28 29 30 31 32 34 35 40 45 46 48 49 50 53 54 56 57 59 64 65 69 70 71 73 74 75 76 77 78 79 81 84 85 86 87 89 93 96 98 103 107 108 110 111 114 119 128 129 130 131 132 133 144 145 146 147 148 **P**3
Primary Contact: Marcy L. Feit, President and Chief Executive Officer
COO: Cindy Noonan, Chief Operating Officer
CFO: Ken Jensen, Chief Financial Officer
CMO: Dat Nguyen, M.D., Chief of Staff
CIO: Bob Woods, Chief Information Officer
CHR: Chris Faber, Human Resources Analyst
Web address: www.valleycare.com
**Control:** Other not–for–profit (including NFP Corporation) **Service:** General Medical and Surgical

**Staffed Beds:** 207 **Admissions:** 7956 **Census:** 118 **Outpatient Visits:** 182892 **Births:** 1273 **Total Expense ($000):** 231102 **Payroll Expense ($000):** 104298 **Personnel:** 1138

## POMONA—Los Angeles County

☒ △ **CASA COLINA HOSPITAL FOR REHABILITATIVE MEDICINE (053027)**, 255 East Bonita Avenue, Zip 91767–1923, Mailing Address: P.O. Box 6001, Zip 91769–6001; tel. 909/596–7733, (Nonreporting) **A**1 7 9 10
Primary Contact: Felice L. Loverso, Ph.D., President and Chief Executive Officer
CFO: David Morony, Chief Financial Officer
CMO: Christopher Chalian, M.D., Medical Director
CIO: Ross Lesins, Chief Information Officer
CHR: Karen Du Pont, Chief Human Resource Officer
CNO: Kathryn Johnson, Chief Nursing Officer
Web address: www.casacolina.org
**Control:** Other not–for–profit (including NFP Corporation) **Service:** Rehabilitation

**Staffed Beds:** 68

**LANTERMAN DEVELOPMENTAL CENTER (050545)**, 3530 Pomona Boulevard, Zip 91768–3238, Mailing Address: P.O. Box 100, Zip 91769–0100; tel. 909/444–7200, (Nonreporting) **A**10
Primary Contact: Cheryl Bright, Executive Director
COO: Ignacio Pina, Director Administrative Services
CFO: Rosie Flores–Ramirez, Director Fiscal Services
CMO: Hao Nguyen, M.D., Medical Director
CIO: George Oliva, Associate Information Systems Analyst
CHR: Mark Kaufman, Director Human Resources
Web address: www.dds.ca.gov
**Control:** State–Government, nonfederal **Service:** Hospital unit within an institution for the mentally retarded

**Staffed Beds:** 481

☒ **POMONA VALLEY HOSPITAL MEDICAL CENTER (050231)**, 1798 North Garey Avenue, Zip 91767–2918; tel. 909/865–9500 **A**1 2 3 5 10 **F**3 11 13 15 17 18 20 22 24 26 28 29 30 31 34 35 40 45 47 49 50 51 53 54 55 57 58 59 60 61 63 64 68 69 70 72 74 75 76 77 78 79 81 84 85 89 92 93 107 108 110 111 114 115 116 117 118 119 120 121 123 124 126 129 130 131 132 135 144 145 146 147 148 **P**7
Primary Contact: Richard E. Yochum, President and Chief Executive Officer
COO: Kurt Weinmeister, Executive Vice President and Chief Operating Officer
CFO: Michael Nelson, Executive Vice President and Chief Financial Officer
CMO: Kenneth Nakamoto, M.D., Vice President Medical Affairs
CIO: Kent Hoyos, Chief Information Officer
CHR: Ray Inge, Vice President Human Resources
Web address: www.pvhmc.org
**Control:** Other not–for–profit (including NFP Corporation) **Service:** General Medical and Surgical

**Staffed Beds:** 415 **Admissions:** 20958 **Census:** 275 **Outpatient Visits:** 479629 **Births:** 6842 **Total Expense ($000):** 449878 **Payroll Expense ($000):** 212366 **Personnel:** 2672

## PORTERVILLE—Tulare County

**PORTERVILLE DEVELOPMENTAL CENTER (050546)**, (Development Disabilities), 26501 Avenue 140, Zip 93257–9109, Mailing Address: P.O. Box 2000, Zip 93258–2000; tel. 559/782–2222 **A**10 **F**3 29 39 57 65 67 77 119 128
Primary Contact: Theresa Billeci, Executive Director
COO: Larry Harris, Director Administrative Services
CFO: Karen Warren, Fiscal Officer
CMO: Rajachandran Srinivasan, M.D., Medical Director
CIO: Vincent Chandler, Director Information Services
CHR: Roger Wright, Director Human Resources
Web address: www.pdc.dds.ca.gov/
**Control:** State–Government, nonfederal **Service:** Other specialty

**Staffed Beds:** 753 **Admissions:** 893 **Census:** 89 **Outpatient Visits:** 0 **Births:** 0 **Total Expense ($000):** 161523 **Payroll Expense ($000):** 85837

☐ **SIERRA VIEW DISTRICT HOSPITAL (050261)**, 465 West Putnam Avenue, Zip 93257–3320; tel. 559/784–1110, (Total facility includes 35 beds in nursing home–type unit) **A**1 9 10 **F**3 13 15 29 30 31 34 35 40 45 47 49 54 57 59 60 65 68 70 75 76 78 79 81 85 87 89 93 107 108 110 111 115 119 121 123 130 132 135 146 147 148
Primary Contact: Joseph A. Stewart, President and Chief Executive Officer
CFO: Douglas Dickson, Senior Vice President Finance
CHR: Sharon Brown, Director Human Resources
Web address: www.sierra–view.com
**Control:** Hospital district or authority, Government, nonfederal **Service:** General Medical and Surgical

**Staffed Beds:** 151 **Admissions:** 7216 **Census:** 111 **Outpatient Visits:** 156924 **Births:** 1839 **Total Expense ($000):** 125897 **Payroll Expense ($000):** 50162

## PORTOLA—Plumas County

★ **EASTERN PLUMAS HEALTH CARE DISTRICT (051300)**, 500 First Avenue, Zip 96122–9406; tel. 530/832–6500, (Nonreporting) **A**9 10 18
Primary Contact: Thomas P. Hayes, Chief Executive Officer
COO: Teresa L. Whitfield, MS, Director Quality and Outcomes
CFO: Jeri Nelson, Chief Financial Officer
CMO: Eric Bugna, M.D., Chief of Staff
CHR: Cathy Conant, Chief Human Resources and Personnel
Web address: www.ephc.org
**Control:** Hospital district or authority, Government, nonfederal **Service:** General Medical and Surgical

**Staffed Beds:** 75

## POWAY—San Diego County

☒ **POMERADO HOSPITAL (050636)**, 15615 Pomerado Road, Zip 92064–2460; tel. 858/613–4000, (Total facility includes 129 beds in nursing home–type unit) **A**1 9 10 **F**3 11 12 13 14 18 20 29 30 31 34 35 36 40 45 46 47 50 51 54 55 56 57 58 59 62 64 65 67 68 70 72 74 75 76 77 78 79 81 82 84 85 87 97 98 100 101 102 103 107 110 111 119 120 128 130 131 132 133 143 144 146 147 148 **P**3 **S** Palomar Health, Escondido, CA
Primary Contact: David A. Tam, M.D., FACHE, Chief Administrative Officer
CFO: Robert Hemker, Chief Financial Officer
CIO: Steven Tanaka, Chief Information Officer
CHR: Brenda C. Turner, Chief Human Resources Officer
Web address: www.pph.org
**Control:** Hospital district or authority, Government, nonfederal **Service:** General Medical and Surgical

**Staffed Beds:** 236 **Admissions:** 6900 **Census:** 183 **Outpatient Visits:** 70139 **Total Expense ($000):** 149051 **Payroll Expense ($000):** 58660 **Personnel:** 637

*Many Facility Codes have changed. Please refer to the AHA Guide Code Chart.*

**CA**

**QUINCY—Plumas County**

☐ **PLUMAS DISTRICT HOSPITAL (051326)**, 1065 Bucks Lake Road,
Zip 95971–9599; tel. 530/283–2121 **A**1 9 10 18 **F**3 7 13 15 18 19 30 32 39
40 45 57 61 64 68 75 79 81 82 85 107 111 114 119 127
Primary Contact: Douglas L. Lafferty, Chief Executive Officer
CMO: Vincent Frantz, M.D., Chief of Staff
CIO: Brenda Compton, Manager Information Technology
CHR: Denise Harding, Director Human Resources
Web address: www.pdh.org
**Control:** Hospital district or authority, Government, nonfederal **Service:** General
Medical and Surgical

| | |
|---|---|
| **Staffed Beds:** 25 **Admissions:** 426 **Census:** 3 **Outpatient Visits:** 93923 **Births:** 72 **Total Expense ($000):** 19577 **Payroll Expense ($000):** 8945 **Personnel:** 164 | |

**RANCHO CUCAMONGA—San Bernardino County**

★ ○ **KINDRED HOSPITAL RANCHO (052049)**, 10841 White Oak Avenue,
Zip 91730–3811; tel. 909/581–6400 **A**9 10 11 **F**3 29 30 34 35 45 46 60 64
68 70 74 75 77 79 81 82 84 85 87 107 111 119 130 148 **S** Kindred
Healthcare, Louisville, KY
Primary Contact: Jody Knox, Administrator
Web address: www.khrancho.com
**Control:** Corporation, Investor–owned, for–profit **Service:** Long–Term Acute Care
hospital

| |
|---|
| **Staffed Beds:** 55 **Admissions:** 752 **Census:** 50 **Births:** 0 |

**RANCHO MIRAGE—Riverside County**

☒ △ **EISENHOWER MEDICAL CENTER (050573)**, 39000 Bob Hope Drive,
Zip 92270–3221; tel. 760/340–3911 **A**1 2 5 7 9 10 **F**2 3 9 11 12 15 17 18
20 22 24 26 28 29 30 31 34 35 37 40 41 45 47 49 50 53 54 56 57 58 59
60 61 64 65 68 70 74 75 77 78 79 81 82 84 85 86 87 89 90 93 96 97 98
100 101 102 103 107 108 109 110 111 112 114 115 116 117 119 120 121
123 124 126 129 130 131 132 135 144 145 146 147 148 **P**3
Primary Contact: G. Aubrey Serfling, President and Chief Executive Officer
COO: Martin Massiello, Senior Vice President and Chief Operating Officer
CFO: Kimberly Osborne, Vice President and Chief Financial Officer
CMO: Quinten VanderWerf, M.D., Chief Medical Officer
CIO: David Perez, Chief Information Officer
CHR: Liz Guignier, Vice President Human Resources
Web address: www.emc.org
**Control:** Other not–for–profit (including NFP Corporation) **Service:** General
Medical and Surgical

| |
|---|
| **Staffed Beds:** 380 **Admissions:** 18432 **Census:** 218 **Outpatient Visits:** 467850 **Births:** 0 **Total Expense ($000):** 479745 **Payroll Expense ($000):** 146268 **Personnel:** 2136 |

**RED BLUFF—Tehama County**

☒ **ST. ELIZABETH COMMUNITY HOSPITAL (050042)**, 2550 Sister Mary
Columba Drive, Zip 96080–4397; tel. 530/529–8000 **A**1 9 10 20 **F**3 7 8 11 13
15 29 30 32 34 35 40 43 45 51 54 57 62 63 64 68 70 75 76 81 82 84 85
89 93 107 108 110 111 114 119 130 131 132 133 145 146 148 **P**3
**S** Dignity Health, San Francisco, CA
Primary Contact: G. Todd Smith, President
CFO: Tim Panks, Chief Financial Officer
CMO: James DeSoto, M.D., Vice President Medical Affairs
CIO: Henry Niessink, Senior Manager Information Technology Systems
CHR: Dena Platz, Director Human Resources
Web address: www.mercy.org
**Control:** Church–operated, Nongovernment, not–for profit **Service:** General
Medical and Surgical

| |
|---|
| **Staffed Beds:** 65 **Admissions:** 3026 **Census:** 22 **Outpatient Visits:** 67804 **Births:** 719 **Total Expense ($000):** 74113 **Payroll Expense ($000):** 33729 **Personnel:** 375 |

**REDDING—Shasta County**

☒ **MERCY MEDICAL CENTER REDDING (050280)**, 2175 Rosaline Avenue,
Zip 96001–2549, Mailing Address: P.O. Box 496009, Zip 96049–6009;
tel. 530/225–6000 **A**1 2 3 5 9 10 **F**2 3 7 11 13 15 17 18 20 22 24 28 29 30
31 34 35 37 40 43 45 46 47 48 49 50 54 57 59 61 62 63 64 66 68 70 72
75 76 77 78 79 81 82 84 85 89 91 97 107 108 111 114 115 118 119 126
130 132 135 143 144 145 146 147 148 **S** Dignity Health, San Francisco, CA
Primary Contact: Mark Korth, Chief Executive Officer and Senior Vice President
Operations Dignity Health North State Service Area
COO: Patrick Varga, Chief Operating Officer
CFO: Tim Panks, Regional Vice President Finance and Chief Financial Officer
CMO: James DeSoto, M.D., Vice President Medical Affairs
CIO: Henry Niessink, Regional Director Information Technology Services
CHR: Steve Hosler, Vice President Human Resources
CNO: Andrea Kofl, R.N., Vice President Patient Care and Chief Nursing Executive
Web address: www.mercy.org
**Control:** Church–operated, Nongovernment, not–for profit **Service:** General
Medical and Surgical

| |
|---|
| **Staffed Beds:** 260 **Admissions:** 13372 **Census:** 150 **Outpatient Visits:** 136707 **Births:** 1975 **Total Expense ($000):** 347715 **Payroll Expense ($000):** 129069 **Personnel:** 1422 |

**PATIENTS' HOSPITAL OF REDDING (050697)**, 2900 Eureka Way,
Zip 96001–0220; tel. 530/225–8700 **A**9 10 **F**81 82 85
Primary Contact: Shari Lejsek, Administrator
CMO: James Tate, M.D., Chief of Staff
CIO: Kim Cameron, Manager Health Information Services
CHR: Traci Montgomery, Manager Human Resources
Web address: www.patientshospital.com
**Control:** Individual, Investor–owned, for–profit **Service:** Surgical

| |
|---|
| **Staffed Beds:** 10 **Admissions:** 242 **Census:** 1 **Outpatient Visits:** 2120 **Births:** 0 **Personnel:** 64 |

☒ **SHASTA REGIONAL MEDICAL CENTER (050764)**, 1100 Butte Street,
Zip 96001–0853, Mailing Address: P.O. Box 496072, Zip 96049–6072;
tel. 530/244–5400 **A**1 5 9 10 **F**3 11 17 18 20 22 24 26 28 29 30 34 40 43
45 49 50 51 57 59 65 70 74 75 77 79 81 84 85 86 89 107 108 111 115
119 132 146 148 **S** Prime Healthcare Services, Ontario, CA
Primary Contact: Randall Hempling, Chief Executive Officer
CFO: Sandra Bowen, Chief Financial Officer
CMO: Marcia McCampbell, M.D., Chief Medical Officer
CIO: Tony VanBoekel, Director Information Systems
CHR: Terry Jaqua, Director Human Resources
Web address: www.shastaregional.com
**Control:** Corporation, Investor–owned, for–profit **Service:** General Medical and
Surgical

| |
|---|
| **Staffed Beds:** 120 **Admissions:** 7258 **Census:** 80 **Outpatient Visits:** 58065 **Births:** 0 **Total Expense ($000):** 137909 **Payroll Expense ($000):** 39361 **Personnel:** 696 |

☐ **VIBRA HOSPITAL OF NORTHERN CALIFORNIA (052047)**, 2801 Eureka Way,
Zip 96001–0222; tel. 530/246–9000, (Total facility includes 32 beds in nursing
home–type unit) **A**1 9 10 **F**1 29 30 64 77 93 119 128 130 148 **S** Vibra
Healthcare, Mechanicsburg, PA
Primary Contact: Chris Jones, Chief Executive Officer
COO: Lisa Stevens, Chief Clinical Officer and Chief Operating Officer
CFO: Rebecca Andrews, Chief Financial Officer
CMO: Nanda Kumar, M.D., Chief of Staff
CIO: Mark Cardenas, Director Plant Operations
CHR: Wendy Tempest, Director Human Resources
Web address: www.norcalrehab.com
**Control:** Corporation, Investor–owned, for–profit **Service:** Long–Term Acute Care
hospital

| |
|---|
| **Staffed Beds:** 88 **Admissions:** 1199 **Census:** 73 **Outpatient Visits:** 3961 **Births:** 0 **Total Expense ($000):** 31316 **Payroll Expense ($000):** 15536 **Personnel:** 236 |

**REDLANDS—San Bernardino County**

☒ **LOMA LINDA UNIVERSITY BEHAVIORAL MEDICINE CENTER (054093)**,
1710 Barton Road, Zip 92373–5304; tel. 909/558–9200, (Nonreporting) **A**1 5 9
10 **S** Loma Linda University Adventist Health Sciences Center, Loma Linda, CA
Primary Contact: Jill Pollock, Administrator
COO: Ruthita J. Fike, Chief Executive Officer
CFO: Steve Mohr, Senior Vice President Finance and Chief Financial Officer
CMO: William Murdoch, M.D., Medical Director
CIO: Mark Zirkelback, Chief Information Officer
CHR: Mark Hubbard, Vice President Risk Management
Web address: www.llu.edu
**Control:** Other not–for–profit (including NFP Corporation) **Service:** Psychiatric

| |
|---|
| **Staffed Beds:** 89 |

⌧ **REDLANDS COMMUNITY HOSPITAL (050272)**, 350 Terracina Boulevard, Zip 92373–4897, Mailing Address: P.O. Box 3391, Zip 92373–0742; tel. 909/335–5500, (Nonreporting) **A**1 9 10
Primary Contact: James R. Holmes, President and Chief Executive Officer
Web address: www.redlandshospital.org
**Control:** Other not–for–profit (including NFP Corporation) **Service:** General Medical and Surgical

**Staffed Beds:** 189

### REDWOOD CITY—San Mateo County

⌧ **KAISER PERMANENTE REDWOOD CITY MEDICAL CENTER (050541)**, (Formerly Redwood City Medical Center), 1150 Veterans Boulevard, Zip 94063–2037; tel. 650/299–2000 **A**1 3 5 10 **F**3 8 13 15 18 20 22 26 28 29 30 31 32 34 35 36 40 45 49 50 51 53 54 55 56 57 58 59 64 65 68 70 73 74 75 76 77 78 79 80 81 82 84 85 86 87 91 92 93 94 95 96 97 99 100 101 103 104 107 108 110 111 114 115 119 129 130 131 132 134 135 146 147 148 **P**6 **S** Kaiser Foundation Hospitals, Oakland, CA
Primary Contact: Frank T. Beirne, Senior Vice President and Area Manager
COO: Maureen O'Brien, Chief Operating Officer
CIO: Angel Shew, Director Area Technology
CHR: Sharon Barncord, Business Partner Human Resources
Web address: www.kaiserpermanente.org
**Control:** Other not–for–profit (including NFP Corporation) **Service:** General Medical and Surgical

**Staffed Beds:** 213 **Admissions:** 7454 **Census:** 84 **Outpatient Visits:** 332065 **Births:** 1433 **Personnel:** 1476

⌧ **SEQUOIA HOSPITAL (050197)**, 170 Alameda De Las Pulgas, Zip 94062–2799; tel. 650/369–5811 **A**1 9 10 **F**11 12 13 15 18 20 22 24 26 28 29 30 31 32 34 35 37 40 45 46 49 50 53 57 59 60 64 68 70 74 75 76 77 78 79 81 84 86 87 92 93 94 107 108 110 111 114 115 118 119 120 121 123 126 129 130 132 135 146 147 148 **P**3 **S** Dignity Health, San Francisco, CA
Primary Contact: Glenna L. Vaskelis, CPA, President and Administrator and Senior Vice President Operations Dignity Health Bay Area Service Are
CFO: Gratia Barton, Chief Financial Officer
CMO: Christopher Dunn, M.D., Vice President Medical Affairs
CIO: Gracie O'Brien, Chief Information Officer
CHR: Linde Cheema, Vice President Human Resources
Web address: www.sequoiahospital.org
**Control:** Other not–for–profit (including NFP Corporation) **Service:** General Medical and Surgical

**Staffed Beds:** 128 **Admissions:** 6978 **Census:** 72 **Outpatient Visits:** 115314 **Births:** 1627 **Total Expense ($000):** 219485 **Payroll Expense ($000):** 87208 **Personnel:** 698

### REEDLEY—Fresno County

★ ◇ **ADVENTIST MEDICAL CENTER–REEDLEY (050192)**, 372 West Cypress Avenue, Zip 93654–2199; tel. 559/638–8155, (Nonreporting) **A**9 10 21 **S** Adventist Health, Roseville, CA
Primary Contact: Wayne Ferch, President and Chief Executive Officer
CFO: Teresa Jacques, Interim Chief Financial Officer
CMO: Todd Spencer, M.D., Chief Medical Staff
CIO: Valerie Alvarez, Executive Assistant
CHR: Ramona Alvarado, Interim Manager Human Resources
Web address: www.skdh.org
**Control:** Hospital district or authority, Government, nonfederal **Service:** General Medical and Surgical

**Staffed Beds:** 44

### RESEDA—Los Angeles County

☐ **JOYCE EISENBERG–KEEFER MEDICAL CENTER (054147)**, 7150 Tampa Avenue, Zip 91335–3700; tel. 818/774–3000, (Nonreporting) **A**1 10
Primary Contact: Ilana Grossman, Administrator
CNO: Haya Berci, Executive Director of Nursing
Web address: www.jha.org
**Control:** Other not–for–profit (including NFP Corporation) **Service:** Psychiatric

**Staffed Beds:** 10

### RICHMOND—Contra Costa County

**RICHMOND MEDICAL CENTER** See Oakland Medical Center, Oakland

### RIDGECREST—Kern County

★ ◇ **RIDGECREST REGIONAL HOSPITAL (050448)**, 1081 North China Lake Boulevard, Zip 93555–3130; tel. 760/446–3551, (Total facility includes 26 beds in nursing home–type unit) (Data for 334 days) **A**9 10 20 21 **F**8 11 13 18 19 28 29 30 32 34 35 40 50 57 59 62 63 64 66 70 75 76 77 79 81 84 89 93 97 104 107 108 110 111 114 115 119 127 128 129 130 144 146 147 148
Primary Contact: James A. Suver, FACHE, Chief Executive Officer
CFO: Lois Johnson, Administrator Fiscal Services
CMO: Victoria Schauf, M.D., Chief of Staff
CIO: Randy Ferguson, Chief Information Officer
CHR: Dave Shary, Administrator Human Resources
Web address: www.rrh.org
**Control:** Other not–for–profit (including NFP Corporation) **Service:** General Medical and Surgical

**Staffed Beds:** 51 **Admissions:** 1991 **Census:** 22 **Outpatient Visits:** 44244 **Births:** 436 **Total Expense ($000):** 69341 **Payroll Expense ($000):** 25385 **Personnel:** 503

### RIVERSIDE—Riverside County

⌧ **KAISER PERMANENTE RIVERSIDE MEDICAL CENTER (050686)**, (Formerly Riverside Medical Center), 10800 Magnolia Avenue, Zip 92505–3000; tel. 951/353–2000 **A**1 3 5 10 **F**3 13 15 17 28 29 30 31 35 40 44 45 46 48 49 50 51 59 60 62 63 64 65 68 70 72 74 75 76 77 78 79 81 82 84 85 86 87 89 92 93 97 100 102 107 108 109 110 111 114 115 117 118 119 130 144 146 147 148 **S** Kaiser Foundation Hospitals, Oakland, CA
Primary Contact: Vita M. Willett, Administrator and Executive Director
CFO: Lorna Curtis, Chief Financial Officer
CMO: Richard Rajatatnam, M.D., Area Medical Director
CIO: Alfred T. Velasquez, Area Information Officer
CHR: Wendy Sander, Director Human Resources
CNO: Kim E. Hadden, R.N., Chief Nurse Executive
Web address: www.kaiserpermanente.org
**Control:** Other not–for–profit (including NFP Corporation) **Service:** General Medical and Surgical

**Staffed Beds:** 226 **Admissions:** 12012 **Census:** 122 **Outpatient Visits:** 144635 **Births:** 3027 **Personnel:** 748

☐ **PARKVIEW COMMUNITY HOSPITAL MEDICAL CENTER (050102)**, 3865 Jackson Street, Zip 92503–3998; tel. 951/688–2211 **A**1 9 10 **F**3 8 12 13 15 29 30 34 35 40 45 46 57 59 60 64 68 70 72 76 77 79 81 84 85 86 87 89 107 108 111 114 115 119 130 132 146 147 148
Primary Contact: Douglas Drumwright, Chief Executive Officer
CFO: Patti Lepe, Chief Financial Officer
CMO: Stephen Carney, M.D., Chief of Staff
CIO: John Ciccarelli, Chief Information Officer
CHR: Stacci Gary, Director Human Resources
CNO: Thomas Santos, R.N., Chief Nursing Officer and Director Quality Services
Web address: www.pchmc.org
**Control:** Other not–for–profit (including NFP Corporation) **Service:** General Medical and Surgical

**Staffed Beds:** 193 **Admissions:** 11040 **Census:** 114 **Outpatient Visits:** 71904 **Births:** 2244 **Total Expense ($000):** 146300 **Payroll Expense ($000):** 55819 **Personnel:** 1034

☐ **RIVERSIDE CENTER FOR BEHAVIORAL MEDICINE (054130)**, 5900 Brockton Avenue, Zip 92506–1862; tel. 951/275–8400 **A**1 9 10 **F**5 98 103 104 105 130 **P**1
Primary Contact: Amrita Rai, Administrator
Web address: www.rcbm.com/
**Control:** Corporation, Investor–owned, for–profit **Service:** Psychiatric

**Staffed Beds:** 50 **Admissions:** 873 **Census:** 15 **Outpatient Visits:** 0 **Births:** 0

⌧ **RIVERSIDE COMMUNITY HOSPITAL (050022)**, 4445 Magnolia Avenue, Zip 92501–4199, Mailing Address: P.O. Box 1669, Zip 92502–1669; tel. 951/788–3000, (Nonreporting) **A**1 2 5 9 10 **S** HCA, Nashville, TN
Primary Contact: Patrick D. Brilliant, President and Chief Executive Officer
COO: Dan Bowers, Chief Operating Officer
CFO: Russell T. Young, Chief Financial Officer
CMO: Joseph Lee, M.D., President Medical Staff
CIO: Cae Swanger, Chief Information Officer
Web address: www.riversidecommunityhospital.com
**Control:** Corporation, Investor–owned, for–profit **Service:** General Medical and Surgical

**Staffed Beds:** 373

*Many Facility Codes have changed. Please refer to the AHA Guide Code Chart.* © 2013 AHA Guide

## ROSEMEAD—Los Angeles County

☐ **BHC ALHAMBRA HOSPITAL (054032)**, 4619 North Rosemead Boulevard, Zip 91770–1478, Mailing Address: P.O. Box 369, Zip 91770–0369; tel. 626/286–1191, (Nonreporting) **A**1 9 10 **S** Universal Health Services, Inc., King of Prussia, PA
Primary Contact: Peggy Minnick, R.N., Chief Executive Officer
CFO: Michelle Jackson, Chief Financial Officer
CMO: Wakelin McNeel, M.D., Medical Director
CIO: Debbie Irvin, Director Health Information Management
CHR: Venus Taylor, Director Human Resources
Web address: www.bhcalhambra.com
**Control:** Corporation, Investor–owned, for–profit **Service:** Psychiatric

**Staffed Beds:** 85

**SILVER LAKE MEDICAL CENTER–INGLESIDE HOSPITAL** See Silver Lake Medical Center, Los Angeles

## ROSEVILLE—Placer County

☒ **KAISER PERMANENTE ROSEVILLE MEDICAL CENTER (050772)**, (Formerly Roseville Medical Center), 1600 Eureka Road, Zip 95661–3027; tel. 916/784–4000, (Nonreporting) **A**1 10 **S** Kaiser Foundation Hospitals, Oakland, CA
Primary Contact: Edward S. Glavis, Senior Vice President and Area Manager
Web address: www.kp.org
**Control:** Other not–for–profit (including NFP Corporation) **Service:** General Medical and Surgical

**Staffed Beds:** 340

☒ **SUTTER ROSEVILLE MEDICAL CENTER (050309)**, One Medical Plaza, Zip 95661–3037; tel. 916/781–1000, (Total facility includes 30 beds in nursing home–type unit) **A**1 2 5 9 10 **F**1 8 12 15 18 19 20 21 22 23 24 25 26 27 28 29 30 31 34 35 40 43 45 46 55 56 57 70 72 74 75 76 78 81 82 84 89 90 91 93 107 108 109 111 114 119 126 130 131 146 147 148 **S** Sutter Health, Sacramento, CA
Primary Contact: Patrick R. Brady, Chief Executive Officer
COO: Dionne Miller, Chief Operating Officer
CFO: Gary Hubschman, Administrative Director Finance
CMO: Stuart Bostrom, M.D., Director Medical Affairs
CIO: Nancy Turner, Director Communications
CHR: Lynda Dasaro, Director Human Resources
CNO: Barbara J. Nelson, Ph.D., Chief Nursing Executive
Web address: www.sutterroseville.org
**Control:** Other not–for–profit (including NFP Corporation) **Service:** General Medical and Surgical

**Staffed Beds:** 358 **Admissions:** 20088 **Census:** 248 **Outpatient Visits:** 144438 **Births:** 2965 **Total Expense ($000):** 398187 **Payroll Expense ($000):** 127764 **Personnel:** 2088

## SACRAMENTO—Sacramento County

☐ **HERITAGE OAKS HOSPITAL (054104)**, 4250 Auburn Boulevard, Zip 95841–4164; tel. 916/489–3336 **A**1 3 5 9 10 **F**2 38 87 98 99 100 101 102 103 104 105 130 **S** Universal Health Services, Inc., King of Prussia, PA
Primary Contact: Shawn Silva, Chief Executive Officer
CFO: Art Wong, Chief Financial Officer
CMO: Joseph Sison, M.D., Medical Director
CHR: Lisa Myers, Director Human Resources
Web address: www.heritageoakshospital.com
**Control:** Corporation, Investor–owned, for–profit **Service:** Psychiatric

**Staffed Beds:** 120 **Admissions:** 4165 **Census:** 98 **Outpatient Visits:** 16419 **Births:** 0 **Total Expense ($000):** 20583 **Payroll Expense ($000):** 11826

☒ **KAISER PERMANENTE SACRAMENTO MEDICAL CENTER (050425)**, (Formerly Sacramento Medical Center), 2025 Morse Avenue, Zip 95825–2115; tel. 916/973–5000 **A**1 3 5 10 **F**3 8 15 17 18 20 29 31 35 40 45 46 48 49 50 56 60 64 68 70 74 75 77 78 79 81 82 84 85 107 108 111 114 115 119 130 146 148 **S** Kaiser Foundation Hospitals, Oakland, CA
Primary Contact: Ronald Groepper, Senior Vice President and Area Manager
CFO: Jim Eldridge, Area Financial Officer
CMO: Chris Palkowski, M.D., Physician in Chief
CIO: Philip Fasano, Chief Information Officer
CHR: Gay Westfall, Senior Vice President Human Resources
Web address: www.kp.org
**Control:** Other not–for–profit (including NFP Corporation) **Service:** General Medical and Surgical

**Staffed Beds:** 287 **Admissions:** 10008 **Census:** 119 **Outpatient Visits:** 83815 **Births:** 0 **Personnel:** 2327

☒ **KAISER PERMANENTE SOUTH SACRAMENTO MEDICAL CENTER (050674)**, (Formerly South Sacramento Medical Center), 6600 Bruceville Road, Zip 95823–4671; tel. 916/688–2430 **A**1 3 5 10 **F**3 8 12 13 15 16 20 22 29 30 31 34 35 40 43 44 49 50 58 59 61 62 63 64 65 68 70 73 74 75 76 77 78 79 81 82 84 85 86 87 88 93 96 97 98 100 104 107 108 109 110 111 114 115 119 126 128 129 130 131 134 135 144 146 147 148 **S** Kaiser Foundation Hospitals, Oakland, CA
Primary Contact: Patricia Rodriguez, Senior Vice President and Area Manager
CIO: Kathleen McKenna, Public Affairs Leader
Web address: www.kp.org
**Control:** Other not–for–profit (including NFP Corporation) **Service:** General Medical and Surgical

**Staffed Beds:** 181 **Admissions:** 11767 **Census:** 112 **Outpatient Visits:** 84199 **Births:** 2362 **Personnel:** 1246

☒ △ **MERCY GENERAL HOSPITAL (050017)**, 4001 J Street, Zip 95819–3600; tel. 916/453–4545, (Total facility includes 38 beds in nursing home–type unit) **A**1 2 3 5 7 9 10 **F**3 8 11 13 15 17 18 20 22 24 26 28 29 31 34 35 37 39 40 42 43 45 46 49 50 51 53 56 57 58 59 63 64 66 68 70 74 75 76 77 78 79 81 82 83 84 85 87 90 93 94 96 99 107 108 111 114 115 118 119 126 128 130 131 132 135 143 145 146 147 148 **P**3 5 **S** Dignity Health, San Francisco, CA
Primary Contact: Edmundo Castaneda, President
COO: Patricia Monczewski, Chief Operating Officer
CFO: Ronald Kroll, Chief Financial Officer
CMO: Robert Wiebe, M.D., Chief Medical Officer
CHR: Cyndi Kirch, Vice President Human Resources
Web address: www.mercygeneral.org
**Control:** Other not–for–profit (including NFP Corporation) **Service:** General Medical and Surgical

**Staffed Beds:** 286 **Admissions:** 17943 **Census:** 237 **Outpatient Visits:** 145567 **Births:** 2662 **Total Expense ($000):** 490560 **Payroll Expense ($000):** 181364 **Personnel:** 1912

☒ **METHODIST HOSPITAL OF SACRAMENTO (050590)**, 7500 Hospital Drive, Zip 95823–5477; tel. 916/423–3000, (Total facility includes 160 beds in nursing home–type unit) **A**1 9 10 **F**3 8 12 13 17 29 30 34 35 37 39 40 41 47 49 50 59 60 61 64 68 70 72 74 75 76 77 79 81 84 85 86 87 89 93 96 97 107 108 111 116 117 118 119 126 128 130 131 132 143 146 147 148 **P**5 **S** Dignity Health, San Francisco, CA
Primary Contact: Eugene Bassett, President and Chief Executive Officer
CHR: Christopher Joyce, Vice President Human Resources
Web address: www.methodistsacramento.org
**Control:** Other not–for–profit (including NFP Corporation) **Service:** General Medical and Surgical

**Staffed Beds:** 325 **Admissions:** 9106 **Census:** 234 **Outpatient Visits:** 63355 **Births:** 1311 **Total Expense ($000):** 227681 **Payroll Expense ($000):** 103357 **Personnel:** 810

☐ **SHRINERS HOSPITALS FOR CHILDREN–NORTHERN CALIFORNIA (053311)**, 2425 Stockton Boulevard, Zip 95817–2215; tel. 916/453–2000, (Nonreporting) **A**1 3 5 9 10 **S** Shriners Hospitals for Children, Tampa, FL
Primary Contact: Margaret Bryan, Administrator
COO: Margaret Bryan, Administrator
CFO: William Dalby, Director Fiscal Services
CIO: John Bevel, Manager Information Systems
CHR: Deborah Rubens, Director Human Resources
Web address: www.shrinershospitalsforchildren.org/Hospitals/Locations/NorthernCalifornia.aspx
**Control:** Other not–for–profit (including NFP Corporation) **Service:** Children's general

**Staffed Beds:** 70

☐ **SIERRA VISTA HOSPITAL (054087)**, 8001 Bruceville Road, Zip 95823–2329; tel. 916/288–0300 **A**1 9 10 **F**98 99 100 101 102 103 104 105 **S** Universal Health Services, Inc., King of Prussia, PA
Primary Contact: Mike Zauner, Chief Executive Officer
COO: Barbara Roush, Chief Operating Officer
CFO: Irene McMillan, Chief Financial Officer
CMO: Okechukwu Nwangburuka, M.D., Medical Director
CIO: Mark Grip, Executive Director Business Development
CHR: David Lish, Director Human Resources
**Control:** Corporation, Investor–owned, for–profit **Service:** Psychiatric

**Staffed Beds:** 120 **Admissions:** 5750 **Census:** 100 **Outpatient Visits:** 5195 **Births:** 0 **Total Expense ($000):** 27410 **Payroll Expense ($000):** 12169 **Personnel:** 283

**CA**

---

**Hospital, Medicare Provider Number, Address, Telephone, Approval, Facility, and Physician Codes, Health Care System**

★ American Hospital Association (AHA) membership
☐ The Joint Commission accreditation
◇ DNV Healthcare Inc. accreditation
○ Healthcare Facilities Accreditation Program
△ Commission on Accreditation of Rehabilitation Facilities (CARF) accreditation

✠ **SUTTER CENTER FOR PSYCHIATRY (054096)**, 7700 Folsom Boulevard, Zip 95826–2608; tel. 916/386–3000 **A**1 9 10 **F**29 30 35 68 98 99 100 101 102 103 104 105 130 132 **S** Sutter Health, Sacramento, CA
Primary Contact: John W. Boyd, PsyD, Chief Administrative Officer
CFO: Pamela Ansley, Director Finance
CMO: Cindy Thygeson, M.D., Director Medical Affairs
CHR: Kristin Daniels, Manager Human Resources
Web address: www.sutterpsychiatry.org
**Control:** Other not–for–profit (including NFP Corporation) **Service:** Psychiatric

> **Staffed Beds:** 69 **Admissions:** 2668 **Census:** 49 **Outpatient Visits:** 4077
> **Births:** 0 **Total Expense ($000):** 21344 **Payroll Expense ($000):** 10919
> **Personnel:** 158

✠ **SUTTER MEDICAL CENTER, SACRAMENTO (050108)**, 5151 F Street, Zip 95819–3295; tel. 916/454–3333, (Includes SUTTER CHILDREN'S CENTER, 5151 F. Street, Zip 95819–3223; tel. 800/478–8837; SUTTER GENERAL HOSPITAL, 2801 L Street, Zip 95816; tel. 916/454–2222), (Total facility includes 100 beds in nursing home–type unit) **A**1 2 3 5 9 10 **F**12 15 17 18 19 20 21 22 23 24 25 26 27 28 29 30 31 35 37 40 46 47 48 49 52 55 56 59 64 68 70 72 74 75 76 77 78 79 81 85 86 87 88 89 93 98 99 100 101 102 103 104 105 107 108 109 110 111 114 115 119 124 126 128 129 130 132 136 137 146 147 148 **S** Sutter Health, Sacramento, CA
Primary Contact: Carrie Owen–Plietz, Chief Executive Officer
CFO: Richard SooHoo, Chief Financial Officer
CMO: Mark Leibenhaut, M.D., Chief of Staff
CIO: Julie Montera, Director Information Technology
CHR: Laurie Rose, Director Human Resources
Web address: www.sutterhealth.org
**Control:** Other not–for–profit (including NFP Corporation) **Service:** General Medical and Surgical

> **Staffed Beds:** 659 **Admissions:** 30785 **Census:** 443 **Outpatient Visits:** 187911 **Births:** 5699 **Total Expense ($000):** 796710 **Payroll Expense ($000):** 248287 **Personnel:** 3025

✠ **UNIVERSITY OF CALIFORNIA, DAVIS MEDICAL CENTER (050599)**, 2315 Stockton Boulevard, Zip 95817–2282; tel. 916/734–2011, (Includes UNIVERSITY OF CALIFORNIA DAVIS CHILDREN'S HOSPITAL, 2315 Stockton Boulevard, Zip 95817–2201; tel. 800/282–3284) **A**1 2 3 5 8 9 10 **F**3 6 8 9 11 12 13 15 16 17 18 19 20 21 22 23 24 25 26 27 28 29 30 31 32 34 35 36 37 38 39 40 41 43 44 45 46 47 48 49 50 51 52 53 54 55 56 57 58 59 60 61 62 63 64 65 66 68 70 71 72 74 75 76 77 78 79 80 81 82 83 84 85 86 87 88 89 90 91 92 93 94 96 97 99 100 101 102 103 104 107 108 110 111 114 115 116 117 118 119 120 121 122 123 124 126 129 130 131 132 134 135 136 138 141 142 143 144 145 146 147 148 **P**6 **S** University of California–Systemwide Administration, Oakland, CA
Primary Contact: Ann Madden Rice, Chief Executive Officer
COO: Vincent Johnson, Chief Operating Officer
CFO: Timothy Maurice, Chief Financial Officer
CMO: Allan Siefkin, M.D., Chief Medical Officer
CIO: Michael N. Minear, Chief Information Officer
CHR: Stephen Chilcott, Associate Director Human Resources
Web address: www.ucdmc.ucdavis.edu
**Control:** Other not–for–profit (including NFP Corporation) **Service:** General Medical and Surgical

> **Staffed Beds:** 581 **Admissions:** 31453 **Census:** 462 **Outpatient Visits:** 1131126 **Births:** 1877 **Total Expense ($000):** 1292420 **Payroll Expense ($000):** 594712 **Personnel:** 6511

### SAINT HELENA—Napa County

✠ **ST. HELENA HOSPITAL NAPA VALLEY (050013)**, (Formerly St. Helena Hospital), 10 Woodland Road, Zip 94574–9554; tel. 707/963–3611, (Nonreporting) **A**1 9 10 **S** Adventist Health, Roseville, CA
Primary Contact: Terry Newmyer, President and Chief Executive Officer
CFO: Edward A. McDonald, Senior Vice President and Chief Financial Officer
CIO: Mons Jensen, Information Systems Team Leader
CHR: Mark Fowler, Executive Director Human Resources
Web address: www.sthelenahospital.org
**Control:** Church–operated, Nongovernment, not–for profit **Service:** General Medical and Surgical

> **Staffed Beds:** 116

### SALINAS—Monterey County

✠ **NATIVIDAD MEDICAL CENTER (050248)**, 1441 Constitution Boulevard, Zip 93906–3100, Mailing Address: P.O. Box 81611, Zip 93912–1611; tel. 831/647–7611, (Nonreporting) **A**1 3 5 9 10
Primary Contact: Harry Weis, Chief Executive Officer
CMO: Gary Gray, D.O., Chief Medical Officer
CIO: Kirk Larson, Chief Information Officer
CHR: Janine Bouyea, Director Human Resources
Web address: www.natividad.com
**Control:** County–Government, nonfederal **Service:** General Medical and Surgical

> **Staffed Beds:** 137

✠ **SALINAS VALLEY MEMORIAL HEALTHCARE SYSTEM (050334)**, 450 East Romie Lane, Zip 93901–4098; tel. 831/757–4333 **A**1 2 9 10 **F**13 15 18 20 22 24 26 29 31 34 35 40 44 45 46 47 48 49 50 55 57 58 59 60 61 63 68 74 75 77 78 79 81 82 83 84 85 86 87 93 94 107 108 110 111 112 114 115 116 117 118 119 124 126 129 130 132 133 134 146 147 148
Primary Contact: Pete Delgado, Chief Executive Officer
COO: James Griffith, Chief Operating Officer
CFO: Augustine Lopez, Chief Financial Officer
CMO: Andrew Wilson, M.D., Interim Chief Medical Officer
CIO: Audrey Parks, Senior Administrative Director Information Technology
CHR: Michelle B. Childs, Executive Administrative Director Human Resources
CNO: Louella Freeman, Chief Nursing Officer
Web address: www.svmh.com
**Control:** Hospital district or authority, Government, nonfederal **Service:** General Medical and Surgical

> **Staffed Beds:** 185 **Admissions:** 10575 **Census:** 123 **Outpatient Visits:** 84000 **Births:** 2000 **Total Expense ($000):** 336076 **Payroll Expense ($000):** 144556

### SAN ANDREAS—Calaveras County

✠ **MARK TWAIN ST. JOSEPH'S HOSPITAL (051332)**, 768 Mountain Ranch Road, Zip 95249–9707; tel. 209/754–3521, (Nonreporting) **A**1 9 10 18 **S** Dignity Health, San Francisco, CA
Primary Contact: Craig J. Marks, FACHE, President
CFO: Jacob Lewis, Chief Financial Officer
CHR: Nancy Vargas, Director Human Resources
Web address: www.marktwainhospital.com
**Control:** Other not–for–profit (including NFP Corporation) **Service:** General Medical and Surgical

> **Staffed Beds:** 25

### SAN BERNARDINO—San Bernardino County

☐ △ **BALLARD REHABILITATION HOSPITAL (053037)**, (Formerly Robert H. Ballard Rehabilitation Hospital), 1760 West 16th Street, Zip 92411–1160; tel. 909/473–1200 **A**1 7 9 10 **F**29 64 90 93 130 132 148 **S** Vibra Healthcare, Mechanicsburg, PA
Primary Contact: Mary Miles Hunt, Chief Executive Officer
Web address: www.ballardrehab.com
**Control:** Corporation, Investor–owned, for–profit **Service:** Rehabilitation

> **Staffed Beds:** 40 **Admissions:** 1025 **Census:** 37 **Outpatient Visits:** 6664 **Births:** 0 **Total Expense ($000):** 18921 **Payroll Expense ($000):** 9414 **Personnel:** 192

✠ **COMMUNITY HOSPITAL OF SAN BERNARDINO (050089)**, 1805 Medical Center Drive, Zip 92411–1214; tel. 909/887–6333, (Nonreporting) **A**1 9 10 **S** Dignity Health, San Francisco, CA
Primary Contact: June Collison, President
CFO: Ed Sorenson, Vice President Finance and Chief Financial Officer
CIO: Robert Redden, Site Director Information Technology
CHR: Denice C. Findlay, Director Human Resources
Web address: www.chsb.org
**Control:** Other not–for–profit (including NFP Corporation) **Service:** General Medical and Surgical

> **Staffed Beds:** 321

✠ **ST. BERNARDINE MEDICAL CENTER (050129)**, 2101 North Waterman Avenue, Zip 92404–4836; tel. 909/883–8711, (Nonreporting) **A**1 2 9 10 **S** Dignity Health, San Francisco, CA
Primary Contact: Steven R. Barron, President and Senior Vice President Operations Dignity Health Southern California East Service Area
CFO: Darryl VandenBosch, Vice President and Chief Financial Officer
CMO: Betty Daniels, M.D., Chief of Staff
CIO: James Croker, Director Information Systems
CHR: Dee Webb, Vice President Human Resources
Web address: www.stbernardinemedicalcenter.com
**Control:** Other not–for–profit (including NFP Corporation) **Service:** General Medical and Surgical

> **Staffed Beds:** 250

### SAN DIEGO—San Diego County

✠ **ALVARADO HOSPITAL (050757)**, 6655 Alvarado Road, Zip 92120–5208; tel. 619/287–3270 **A**1 2 9 10 **F**3 7 12 15 17 18 20 22 24 26 28 29 31 34 35 36 40 46 53 55 56 59 60 61 64 65 68 70 74 75 77 78 79 80 81 82 84 86 87 90 93 96 107 108 111 114 115 118 119 129 130 132 146 148 **S** Prime Healthcare Services, Ontario, CA
Primary Contact: Robin Gomez, Administrator
CFO: Brian Kleven, Chief Financial Officer
CIO: Eric Logie, Director Information Systems
CNO: Peggy Bailey, Chief Nursing Officer
Web address: www.alvaradohospital.com
**Control:** Corporation, Investor–owned, for–profit **Service:** General Medical and Surgical

> **Staffed Beds:** 83 **Admissions:** 7083 **Census:** 83 **Outpatient Visits:** 47854 **Births:** 0 **Total Expense ($000):** 131697 **Payroll Expense ($000):** 7244 **Personnel:** 720

*Many Facility Codes have changed. Please refer to the AHA Guide Code Chart.*

© 2013 AHA Guide

☐ **AURORA BEHAVIORAL HEALTH CARE (054095)**, 11878 Avenue of Industry, Zip 92128–3423; tel. 858/487–3200, (Nonreporting) **A**1 9 10 **S** Aurora Behavioral Health Care, Corona, CA
Primary Contact: James S. Plummer, Chief Executive Officer
COO: Linda Achber, Director Clinical Services
CFO: Tim Sides, Chief Financial Officer
CMO: Thomas Flanagan, M.D., Medical Director
CIO: Alain Azcona, Director Business Development
CHR: Susan Haas, Director Human Resources
Web address: www.sandiego.aurorabehavioral.com/
**Control:** Corporation, Investor–owned, for–profit **Service:** Psychiatric

| **Staffed Beds: 80** |
| --- |

⊞ **KAISER PERMANENTE SAN DIEGO MEDICAL CENTER (050515)**, (Formerly San Diego Medical Center), 4647 Zion Avenue, Zip 92120–2507; tel. 619/528–5000 **A**1 3 5 10 **F**3 8 13 14 15 29 30 31 34 40 41 43 44 45 46 47 48 49 50 51 54 55 56 57 58 59 60 61 62 63 64 65 68 70 71 72 74 75 76 77 78 79 81 82 83 84 85 86 87 89 93 97 100 102 103 104 107 108 111 114 115 117 118 119 130 131 132 143 144 146 148 **S** Kaiser Foundation Hospitals, Oakland, CA
Primary Contact: Mary Ann Barnes, Senior Vice President and Executive Director
COO: Joan Burritt, R.N., Chief Operating Officer
CFO: Lynette Seid, Area Chief Financial Officer
CMO: Paul E. Bernstein, M.D., Area Medical Director
CIO: Matthew T. Ebaugh, Area Information Officer
CHR: Cherie L. Sampson, Director Human Resources
CNO: Joan Burritt, R.N., Interim Chief Nurse Executive
Web address: www.kaiserpermanente.org
**Control:** Other not–for–profit (including NFP Corporation) **Service:** General Medical and Surgical

| **Staffed Beds: 414 Admissions: 27889 Census: 294 Outpatient Visits: 159319 Births: 4577 Personnel: 3384** |
| --- |

⊞ **KINDRED HOSPITAL–SAN DIEGO (052036)**, 1940 El Cajon Boulevard, Zip 92104–1096; tel. 619/543–4500, (Nonreporting) **A**1 9 10 **S** Kindred Healthcare, Louisville, KY
Primary Contact: Cathryn Branch, R.N., Chief Executive Officer
COO: Patricia Cavaness, Chief Clinical Officer
CFO: Gene Fantano, Controller
CMO: Davies Wong, M.D., Medical Director
CHR: Jeffrey Supko, District Director Human Resources
CNO: Maureen Bodme, Chief Clinical Officer
CNO: Catherine Rivera, Nurse Manager
Web address: www.kindredsandiego.com
**Control:** Corporation, Investor–owned, for–profit **Service:** Long–Term Acute Care hospital

| **Staffed Beds: 70** |
| --- |

⊞ **NAVAL MEDICAL CENTER SAN DIEGO**, (Formerly Naval Medical Center), 34800 Bob Wilson Drive, Zip 92134–5000; tel. 619/532–6400, (Nonreporting) **A**1 2 3 5 **S** Bureau of Medicine and Surgery, Department of the Navy, Washington, DC
Primary Contact: Captain Christopher Irwin, Director, Administration
CFO: Captain O. G. Haugen, Director Resources
CIO: Lieutenant D. V. Gonzales, Head Information Technology Management
Web address: www.med.navy.mil/sites/nmcsd/Pages/default.aspx
**Control:** Navy, Government, federal **Service:** General Medical and Surgical

| **Staffed Beds: 285** |
| --- |

☐ **PROMISE HOSPITAL OF SAN DIEGO (052051)**, 5550 University Avenue, Zip 92105–2307; tel. 619/582–3800, (Nonreporting) **A**1 9 10 **S** Promise Healthcare, Boca Raton, FL
Primary Contact: Martha J. Heubach, Chief Executive Officer
COO: Tim Clark, Chief Operating Officer
CFO: Jim McCabe, Chief Financial Officer
CMO: Larry Emdur, M.D., Chief of Staff
CIO: Jim Wilson, Vice President Information Technology
CHR: Stacia Rasina, Director Human Resources
Web address: www.promisesandiego.com
**Control:** Corporation, Investor–owned, for–profit **Service:** Long–Term Acute Care hospital

| **Staffed Beds: 100** |
| --- |

⊞ **RADY CHILDREN'S HOSPITAL – SAN DIEGO (053303)**, 3020 Children's Way, Zip 92123–4282; tel. 858/576–1700, (Total facility includes 43 beds in nursing home–type unit) **A**1 3 5 9 10 **F**1 3 4 7 8 9 10 11 12 16 17 19 21 23 25 26 27 28 29 31 32 34 35 36 38 39 40 41 43 45 46 47 48 50 54 55 57 58 59 60 62 64 65 67 68 70 72 73 74 75 77 78 79 80 81 82 83 84 85 86 87 88 89 90 91 92 93 94 98 99 100 101 102 104 105 107 108 111 114 115 118 119 128 129 130 131 132 133 134 135 136 138 139 141 143 144 145 146 **P**3 5
Primary Contact: Kathleen Ann Sellick, President and Chief Executive Officer
COO: Meg Norton, Senior Vice President and Chief Operating Officer
CFO: Roger Roux, Senior Vice President Financial Affairs and Chief Financial Officer
CMO: Irvin A. Kaufman, M.D., Senior Vice President Health Affairs and Chief Medical Officer
CIO: Albert Oriol, Vice President Information Management and Chief Information Officer
CHR: Mamoon Syed, Vice President Human Resources
Web address: www.rchsd.org
**Control:** Other not–for–profit (including NFP Corporation) **Service:** Children's general

| **Staffed Beds: 377 Admissions: 16087 Census: 206 Outpatient Visits: 159161 Births: 0 Total Expense ($000): 689908 Payroll Expense ($000): 229480 Personnel: 3339** |
| --- |

☐ **SAN DIEGO COUNTY PSYCHIATRIC HOSPITAL (054114)**, 3853 Rosecrans Street, Zip 92110–3115, Mailing Address: P.O. Box 85524, Zip 92186–5524; tel. 619/692–8211, (Nonreporting) **A**1 10
Primary Contact: Izabela Karmach, R.N., Administrator
COO: Izabela Karmach, R.N., Administrator
CFO: Raul J. Loyo–Rodriguez, Administrative Analyst III
CMO: Michael Krelstein, M.D., Medical Director
CIO: Linda Cannon, Chief Medical Records Services
CHR: Francisco Puentes, Human Resource Officer
Web address: www.sdcounty.ca.gov
**Control:** County–Government, nonfederal **Service:** Psychiatric

| **Staffed Beds: 357** |
| --- |

⊞ **SCRIPPS MERCY HOSPITAL (050077)**, 4077 Fifth Avenue, Zip 92103–2105; tel. 619/294–8111, (Includes SCRIPPS MERCY HOSPITAL CHULA VISTA, 435 H Street, Chula Vista, Zip 91912–6617, Mailing Address: P.O. Box 1537, Zip 91910–1537; tel. 619/691–7000) **A**1 2 3 5 9 10 **F**3 8 11 12 13 14 15 17 18 20 22 24 26 28 29 30 31 32 34 35 39 40 43 44 45 46 47 48 50 51 54 56 57 58 59 61 64 65 66 68 70 73 74 75 76 77 78 79 81 82 83 84 85 86 87 92 93 97 98 100 101 102 103 104 105 107 108 110 111 114 115 118 119 126 129 130 132 134 135 141 146 147 148 **P**3 5 7 **S** Scripps Health, San Diego, CA
Primary Contact: Thomas A. Gammiere, Chief Executive, Senior Vice President
CFO: Edward Turk, Vice President Finance
CMO: Davis Cracroft, M.D., Senior Director Medical Affairs
CIO: Drexel DeFord, Chief Information Officer
Web address: www.scrippshealth.org
**Control:** Other not–for–profit (including NFP Corporation) **Service:** General Medical and Surgical

| **Staffed Beds: 433 Admissions: 33209 Census: 416 Outpatient Visits: 170626 Births: 4163 Total Expense ($000): 634561 Payroll Expense ($000): 248239 Personnel: 3307** |
| --- |

⊞ △ **SHARP MEMORIAL HOSPITAL (050100)**, 7901 Frost Street, Zip 92123–2701; tel. 858/939–3400 **A**1 2 7 9 10 **F**3 8 11 12 15 18 20 22 24 26 28 29 30 31 33 34 35 36 40 43 44 45 46 49 55 56 57 58 59 60 62 64 65 68 70 74 75 77 78 79 81 82 84 85 86 87 90 91 93 94 96 97 107 108 110 114 115 119 120 121 123 124 126 129 130 131 132 135 137 138 142 143 145 146 148 **P**3 5 **S** Sharp HealthCare, San Diego, CA
Primary Contact: Tim Smith, Chief Executive Officer
COO: Janie Kramer, Chief Operating Officer
CFO: Kevin Thompson, Chief Financial Officer
CMO: Ronald MacIntyre, M.D., Chief Medical Officer
CMO: Richard Santore, M.D., Chief Medical Officer
CIO: William T. Spooner, Senior Vice President and Chief Information Officer
CHR: Diane Delaney, Vice President Human Resources
CHR: Connie Duquette, Director Human Resources
Web address: www.sharp.com
**Control:** Other not–for–profit (including NFP Corporation) **Service:** General Medical and Surgical

| **Staffed Beds: 368 Admissions: 19513 Census: 264 Outpatient Visits: 372689 Births: 0 Total Expense ($000): 597826 Payroll Expense ($000): 221437 Personnel: 3089** |
| --- |

**CA**

---

**Hospital, Medicare Provider Number, Address, Telephone, Approval, Facility, and Physician Codes, Health Care System**

★ American Hospital Association (AHA) membership
☐ The Joint Commission accreditation
◇ DNV Healthcare Inc. accreditation
○ Healthcare Facilities Accreditation Program
△ Commission on Accreditation of Rehabilitation Facilities (CARF) accreditation

⊞ **SHARP MESA VISTA HOSPITAL (054145)**, 7850 Vista Hill Avenue, Zip 92123–2717; tel. 858/278–4110, (Includes SHARP MCDONALD CENTER, 7989 Linda Vista Road, Zip 92111–5106; tel. 858/637–6920) **A**1 9 10 **F**4 5 29 35 40 43 56 58 64 87 98 99 100 101 102 103 104 105 130 132 143 **S** Sharp HealthCare, San Diego, CA
Primary Contact: Kathi Lencioni, Chief Executive Officer
CFO: Kevin Thompson, Chief Financial Officer
CMO: Michael Plopper, M.D., Chief Medical Officer
CIO: William T. Spooner, Senior Vice President Information Systems
CHR: Carlisle Lewis, III, Senior Vice President Legal and Human Resources
CNO: Cheryl Odell, Chief Nursing Officer
Web address: www.sharp.com
**Control:** Other not–for–profit (including NFP Corporation) **Service:** Psychiatric

**Staffed Beds:** 163 **Admissions:** 6063 **Census:** 121 **Outpatient Visits:** 92039 **Births:** 0 **Total Expense ($000):** 64834 **Payroll Expense ($000):** 37977 **Personnel:** 532

⊞ **UC SAN DIEGO HEALTH SYSTEM (050025)**, 200 West Arbor Drive, Zip 92103–1911; tel. 619/543–6222 **A**1 2 3 5 8 9 10 **F**3 6 9 11 12 13 15 16 17 18 20 22 24 26 29 30 31 34 36 37 40 43 44 45 46 47 48 49 50 51 55 56 57 58 59 60 61 64 65 66 68 70 72 73 74 75 76 77 78 79 80 81 82 84 85 86 87 92 93 97 98 99 100 101 102 103 107 108 109 110 111 113 114 115 117 118 119 120 121 123 124 126 129 130 131 132 136 137 138 139 140 141 142 144 145 146 147 148 **P**1 **S** University of California–Systemwide Administration, Oakland, CA
Primary Contact: Paul S. Viviano, Chief Executive Officer
COO: Margarita Baggett, MSN, Interim Chief Operating Officer
CFO: Lori Donaldson, Chief Financial Officer
CMO: Angela Scioscia, M.D., Chief Medical Officer
CIO: Ed Babakanian, Chief Information Officer
CHR: Paul A. Craig, R.N., Chief Human Resources and Risk Officer
CNO: Margarita Baggett, MSN, Chief Nursing Officer
Web address: www.health.ucsd.edu
**Control:** State–Government, nonfederal **Service:** General Medical and Surgical

**Staffed Beds:** 582 **Admissions:** 26801 **Census:** 420 **Outpatient Visits:** 656918 **Births:** 2545 **Total Expense ($000):** 953763 **Payroll Expense ($000):** 379668 **Personnel:** 5403

⊞ △ **VETERANS AFFAIRS SAN DIEGO HEALTHCARE SYSTEM**, 3350 LaJolla Village Drive, Zip 92161–0002; tel. 858/552–8585, (Total facility includes 39 beds in nursing home–type unit) **A**1 2 3 5 7 8 **F**3 4 5 8 12 15 18 20 22 24 26 29 30 31 34 35 36 38 39 40 44 45 46 47 48 49 54 55 56 58 59 60 61 62 63 64 68 70 71 74 75 77 78 79 81 82 83 84 85 86 87 91 92 93 94 96 97 98 100 101 102 103 104 107 108 110 111 114 115 116 117 118 119 126 127 128 129 130 131 132 133 135 143 145 146 147 148 **S** Department of Veterans Affairs, Washington, DC
Primary Contact: Jeffrey T. Gering, Director
COO: Cynthia Abair, Associate Director
CFO: Ronald Larson, Chief Financial Officer
CMO: Robert M. Smith, M.D., Chief of Staff
CIO: Ruey Keller, Acting Chief Information Officer
CHR: Stephanie Wright, Director Human Resources Management
Web address: www.sandiego.va.gov
**Control:** Veterans Affairs, Government, federal **Service:** General Medical and Surgical

**Staffed Beds:** 232 **Admissions:** 7402 **Census:** 149 **Outpatient Visits:** 779039 **Total Expense ($000):** 562760 **Payroll Expense ($000):** 238039 **Personnel:** 2845

☐ **VIBRA HOSPITAL OF SAN DIEGO (052044)**, 555 Washington Street, Zip 92103–2289; tel. 619/260–8300, (Nonreporting) **A**1 9 10 **S** Vibra Healthcare, Mechanicsburg, PA
Primary Contact: Natalie Germuska, R.N., MSN, Chief Executive Officer
COO: Nancy Wiewiora, Chief Operating Officer
CMO: John Fox, M.D., Chief Medical Officer
CHR: Wes Burns, Director Human Resources
Web address: www.vhsandiego.com/
**Control:** Corporation, Investor–owned, for–profit **Service:** Long–Term Acute Care hospital

**Staffed Beds:** 57

**SAN DIMAS—Los Angeles County**

☐ **SAN DIMAS COMMUNITY HOSPITAL (050588)**, 1350 West Covina Boulevard, Zip 91773–3219; tel. 909/599–6811 **A**1 9 10 **F**3 8 13 15 29 30 40 45 46 49 50 70 76 79 81 85 107 108 110 115 119 130 146 148 **S** Prime Healthcare Services, Ontario, CA
Primary Contact: Gregory Brentano, Chief Executive Officer
CFO: Dan Galles, Chief Financial Officer
CMO: Zuhair Yahya, M.D., Chief Medical Officer
CIO: Jason Beckett, Director Information Services
CHR: Arti Dhuper, Director Human Resources
Web address: www.sandimashospital.com
**Control:** Corporation, Investor–owned, for–profit **Service:** General Medical and Surgical

**Staffed Beds:** 101 **Admissions:** 4263 **Census:** 35 **Outpatient Visits:** 22287 **Births:** 433 **Total Expense ($000):** 55881 **Payroll Expense ($000):** 18184 **Personnel:** 347

**SAN FRANCISCO—San Francisco County**

⊞ △ **CALIFORNIA PACIFIC MEDICAL CENTER (050047)**, 2333 Buchanan Street, Zip 94115–1925, Mailing Address: P.O. Box 7999, Zip 94120–7999; tel. 415/600–6000, (Includes CALIFORNIA PACIFIC MEDICAL CENTER–DAVIES CAMPUS, Castro and Duboce Streets, Zip 94114; tel. 415/565–6000), (Total facility includes 139 beds in nursing home–type unit) **A**1 2 3 5 7 8 9 10 **F**2 6 7 8 12 13 15 17 18 19 20 22 24 26 27 28 29 30 31 32 34 35 36 38 39 40 46 51 52 55 56 57 58 59 60 61 63 65 68 70 72 74 76 77 78 79 81 82 84 85 86 87 88 89 90 93 96 97 98 101 102 104 107 108 110 111 114 115 117 118 119 121 126 128 130 132 133 135 136 137 138 139 141 142 143 144 145 146 147 148 **S** Sutter Health, Sacramento, CA
Primary Contact: Warren S. Browner, M.D., M.P.H., Chief Executive Officer
CFO: John Gates, Vice President Finance and Chief Financial Officer
CMO: Allan Pont, M.D., Vice President Medical Affairs
CIO: Craig Vercruysse, Chief Information Officer
Web address: www.cpmc.org
**Control:** Other not–for–profit (including NFP Corporation) **Service:** General Medical and Surgical

**Staffed Beds:** 785 **Admissions:** 28433 **Census:** 438 **Outpatient Visits:** 453821 **Births:** 5513 **Total Expense ($000):** 953650 **Payroll Expense ($000):** 348433 **Personnel:** 4185

⊞ **CHINESE HOSPITAL (050407)**, 845 Jackson Street, Zip 94133–4899; tel. 415/982–2400 **A**1 9 10 **F**3 11 15 18 29 30 31 34 35 40 45 47 49 50 57 59 60 64 65 70 75 77 78 79 81 86 87 97 107 108 110 115 118 119 130 132 135 145 146 147 **P**5
Primary Contact: Brenda Yee, R.N., MSN, Chief Executive Officer
COO: Linda Schumacher, Chief Operating Officer
CFO: Thomas Bolger, Chief Financial Officer
CMO: James Yan, M.D., Chief of Staff
CIO: Helen Lee, Manager Information Systems
CHR: Karen Chow, Director Human Resources
CNO: Peggy Cmiel, R.N., Chief Nursing Officer
Web address: www.chinesehospital-sf.org
**Control:** Other not–for–profit (including NFP Corporation) **Service:** General Medical and Surgical

**Staffed Beds:** 40 **Admissions:** 1800 **Census:** 28 **Outpatient Visits:** 69008 **Births:** 0 **Total Expense ($000):** 94127 **Payroll Expense ($000):** 27264 **Personnel:** 316

**JEWISH HOME OF SAN FRANCISCO (054089)**, 302 Silver Avenue, Zip 94112–1510; tel. 415/334–2500, (Nonreporting) **A**10
Primary Contact: Daniel R. Ruth, President and Chief Executive Officer
CFO: Kevin Potter, Chief Financial Officer
CNO: Edwin Cabigao, Chief Nursing Officer
Web address: www.jhsf.org
**Control:** Partnership for–profit, Osteopathic **Service:** Psychiatric

**Staffed Beds:** 12

⊞ **KAISER PERMANENTE SAN FRANCISCO MEDICAL CENTER (050076)**, (Formerly San Francisco Medical Center), 2425 Geary Boulevard, Zip 94115–3358; tel. 415/833–2000 **A**1 3 5 10 **F**3 8 13 15 17 18 19 20 21 22 23 24 26 28 29 30 31 32 33 35 40 41 44 45 46 49 50 52 60 61 62 64 65 66 68 70 72 74 75 76 77 78 79 81 82 84 85 86 87 89 100 107 108 111 119 130 141 146 **P**2 **S** Kaiser Foundation Hospitals, Oakland, CA
Primary Contact: Christine Robisch, Senior Vice President and Area Manager
COO: Helen Archer–Duste, Chief Operating Officer
CFO: Alex Khoo, Interim Area Finance Officer
CMO: Robert Mithun, M.D., Physician in Chief
CIO: Peti Arunamata, Interim Area Director Information Technology
CHR: Diane J. Easterwood, Human Resources Business Partner
Web address: www.kaiserpermanente.org
**Control:** Other not–for–profit (including NFP Corporation) **Service:** General Medical and Surgical

**Staffed Beds:** 215 **Admissions:** 12539 **Census:** 163 **Outpatient Visits:** 58650 **Births:** 2894 **Personnel:** 2749

★ **LAGUNA HONDA HOSPITAL AND REHABILITATION CENTER (050668)**, (GACH with Distinct Part SNF Se), 375 Laguna Honda Boulevard, Zip 94116–1499; tel. 415/759–2300, (Total facility includes 769 beds in nursing home–type unit) **A**10 **F**3 29 30 53 56 61 63 64 65 74 75 77 82 83 84 90 92 93 94 100 103 104 128 130 132 135 146 148 **P**1
Primary Contact: Mivic Hirose, Executive Director
COO: Michael R. Llewellyn, Chief Operating Officer
CFO: Tess Navarro, Chief Financial Officer
CMO: Colleen Riley, M.D., Medical Director
CIO: Pat Skala, Chief Information Officer
CHR: Willie Ramirez, Manager Labor Relations
Web address: www.lagunahonda.org/
**Control:** City–County, Government, nonfederal **Service:** Other specialty

**Staffed Beds:** 780 **Admissions:** 1097 **Census:** 757 **Outpatient Visits:** 24065 **Births:** 0 **Total Expense ($000):** 203183 **Payroll Expense ($000):** 108643 **Personnel:** 1379

*Many Facility Codes have changed. Please refer to the AHA Guide Code Chart.* © 2013 AHA Guide

☒ △ **SAINT FRANCIS MEMORIAL HOSPITAL (050152)**, 900 Hyde Street, Zip 94109–4899, Mailing Address: P.O. Box 7726, Zip 94120–7726; tel. 415/353–6000, (Nonreporting) **A**1 2 7 9 10 **S** Dignity Health, San Francisco, CA
Primary Contact: Thomas G. Hennessy, President and Chief Executive Officer
COO: James Jackson, Chief Operating Officer
CFO: Alan Fox, Chief Financial Officer
CHR: Richard Mead, Senior Director Human Resources
Web address: www.saintfrancismemorial.org
**Control:** Other not–for–profit (including NFP Corporation) **Service:** General Medical and Surgical

**Staffed Beds: 239**

☒ **SAN FRANCISCO GENERAL HOSPITAL MEDICAL CENTER (050228)**, 1001 Potrero Avenue, Zip 94110–3594; tel. 415/206–8000, (Nonreporting) **A**1 2 3 5 8 10
Primary Contact: Sue Currin, R.N., MS, Chief Executive Officer
COO: Sharon McCole–Wicher, R.N., Chief Nursing Officer
CFO: Valerie Inouye, Chief Financial Officer
CMO: John Luce, M.D., Chief Medical Officer
CIO: Pat Skala, Chief Information Officer
Web address: www.sfdph.org
**Control:** City–County, Government, nonfederal **Service:** General Medical and Surgical

**Staffed Beds: 460**

☒ **SAN FRANCISCO VETERANS AFFAIRS MEDICAL CENTER**, (Formerly Veterans Affairs Medical Center), 4150 Clement Street, Zip 94121–1598; tel. 415/221–4810, (Total facility includes 120 beds in nursing home–type unit) **A**1 2 3 5 **F**5 8 12 17 18 20 22 24 26 28 29 30 31 34 35 37 38 39 40 45 46 47 48 49 50 54 56 57 58 59 60 61 62 63 64 65 70 74 75 77 78 79 81 82 83 84 86 87 92 93 94 97 98 100 101 102 103 104 105 106 107 108 109 111 112 114 115 116 117 118 119 126 127 128 129 130 132 135 143 144 145 146 147 148 **P**1 **S** Department of Veterans Affairs, Washington, DC
Primary Contact: C. Diana Nicoll, M.D., Ph.D., Director
COO: Ezra R. Safdie, Associate Director
CFO: Brian Kelly, Acting Chief Fiscal Service
CIO: Judith A. Ringler, Chief Information Resources Management
CHR: Terrence Vail, Acting Chief Human Resources Management Services
Web address: www.sanfrancisco.va.gov/
**Control:** Veterans Affairs, Government, federal **Service:** General Medical and Surgical

**Staffed Beds: 244 Admissions: 5420 Census: 189 Outpatient Visits: 595173 Births: 0 Total Expense ($000): 547321 Payroll Expense ($000): 281653 Personnel: 2357**

★ **ST. LUKE'S HOSPITAL (050055)**, 3555 Cesar Chavez Street, Zip 94110–4490; tel. 415/600–6000, (Total facility includes 59 beds in nursing home–type unit) **A**5 10 **F**1 4 13 17 18 20 29 34 35 40 67 68 70 72 73 76 77 78 79 80 84 85 87 88 89 90 93 97 98 107 108 110 111 114 118 119 128 130 143 146 147 **S** Sutter Health, Sacramento, CA
Primary Contact: Warren S. Browner, M.D., M.P.H., Chief Executive Officer
COO: Rick Stevens, Chief Administrative Officer
CFO: John Gates, Chief Financial Officer
CMO: Jerome Franz, M.D., Chief Medical Staff
CIO: Rob Seide, Manager Marketing and Communications
CHR: Linda Isaacs, Vice President Human Resources
CNO: Diana M. Karner, R.N., Chief Nursing Officer
Web address: www.stlukes–sf.org
**Control:** Other not–for–profit (including NFP Corporation) **Service:** General Medical and Surgical

**Staffed Beds: 173 Admissions: 4168 Census: 98 Outpatient Visits: 79626 Births: 934 Total Expense ($000): 119734 Payroll Expense ($000): 52728 Personnel: 623**

☒ **ST. MARY'S MEDICAL CENTER (050457)**, 450 Stanyan Street, Zip 94117–1019; tel. 415/668–1000 **A**1 2 3 5 9 10 **F**3 11 12 15 18 20 22 24 26 28 29 30 31 34 35 40 45 46 47 49 51 56 57 58 59 61 64 66 68 70 74 75 77 78 79 81 82 83 84 85 87 90 91 92 93 98 99 101 102 107 108 110 111 114 115 119 120 128 130 131 132 143 146 148 **S** Dignity Health, San Francisco, CA
Primary Contact: Anna Cheung, President
COO: Deborah Kolhede, Vice President and Chief Operating Officer
CFO: Eric Brettner, Vice President and Chief Financial Officer
CMO: Francis Charlton, Jr., M.D., Chief Medical Staff
CHR: Barbara Morrissett, Vice President Human Resources
CNO: Barbara Eusebio, R.N., Vice President, Chief Nurse Executive
Web address: www.stmarysmedicalcenter.com
**Control:** Other not–for–profit (including NFP Corporation) **Service:** General Medical and Surgical

**Staffed Beds: 232 Admissions: 6642 Census: 103 Outpatient Visits: 130685 Births: 0 Total Expense ($000): 223416 Payroll Expense ($000): 103261**

☒ **UCSF MEDICAL CENTER (050454)**, 500 Parnassus Avenue, Zip 94143–0296, Mailing Address: 500 Parnassus Avenue, Box 0296, Zip 94143–0296; tel. 415/476–1000, (Includes UCSF BENIOFF CHILDREN'S HOSPITAL, 500 Parnassus Avenue, Zip 94143–2203, Mailing Address: 505 Parnassus Avenue, Zip 94143–2203; tel. 888/689–8273) **A**1 2 3 5 8 9 10 **F**3 6 7 8 9 11 12 13 14 15 17 18 19 21 22 23 24 25 26 27 29 30 31 32 33 34 35 36 37 39 40 44 45 46 47 48 49 50 51 52 53 54 55 56 57 58 59 60 61 62 63 64 65 66 68 70 72 74 75 76 77 78 79 81 82 83 84 85 86 87 88 89 92 93 94 95 96 97 99 100 101 102 103 104 105 107 108 109 110 111 112 113 114 115 116 117 118 119 120 121 123 124 126 129 130 131 132 134 135 136 137 138 139 140 141 142 144 145 146 147 148 **P**6 **S** University of California–Systemwide Administration, Oakland, CA
Primary Contact: Mark R. Laret, Chief Executive Officer
COO: Ken M. Jones, Interim Chief Operating Officer
CFO: Susan B. Moore, Interim Chief Financial Officer
CMO: Josh Adler, M.D., Interim Co–Chief Medical Officer
CIO: Larry Lotenero, Chief Information Officer
CHR: David Odato, Chief Administrative and Chief Human Resources Officer
Web address: www.ucsfhealth.org
**Control:** Other not–for–profit (including NFP Corporation) **Service:** General Medical and Surgical

**Staffed Beds: 650 Admissions: 28826 Census: 487 Outpatient Visits: 943079 Births: 1833 Total Expense ($000): 1881549 Payroll Expense ($000): 740809 Personnel: 7049**

**VETERANS AFFAIRS MEDICAL CENTER** See San Francisco Veterans Affairs Medical Center

### SAN GABRIEL—Los Angeles County

☐ **SAN GABRIEL VALLEY MEDICAL CENTER (050132)**, 438 West Las Tunas Drive, Zip 91776–1216, Mailing Address: P.O. Box 1507, Zip 91778–1507; tel. 626/289–5454, (Nonreporting) **A**1 9 10 **S** AHMC & Healthcare, Inc., Alhambra, CA
Primary Contact: Howard Ternes, Chief Executive Officer
COO: Harold Way, Chief Financial Officer and Chief Operating Officer
CFO: Harold Way, Chief Financial Officer and Chief Operating Officer
CIO: Bernie Sauer, Director Information Technology
CHR: Victor Voisard, Director Human Resources
Web address: www.sgvmc.org
**Control:** Partnership, Investor–owned, for–profit **Service:** General Medical and Surgical

**Staffed Beds: 269**

### SAN JOSE—Santa Clara County

☒ **GOOD SAMARITAN HOSPITAL (050380)**, 2425 Samaritan Drive, Zip 95124–3997, Mailing Address: P.O. Box 240002, Zip 95154–2402; tel. 408/559–2011 **A**1 2 9 10 **F**2 3 5 8 11 12 13 15 17 18 19 20 21 22 23 24 25 26 27 28 29 30 31 34 35 37 38 40 44 45 46 47 48 49 50 54 57 58 59 60 63 64 68 70 72 74 75 76 77 78 79 81 82 83 84 85 86 87 88 89 90 93 96 98 101 102 104 105 107 108 110 111 114 115 116 117 118 119 120 123 124 126 130 132 146 147 148 **S** HCA, Nashville, TN
Primary Contact: Paul Beaupre, M.D., Chief Executive Officer
COO: Robert Krieger, Interim Chief Operating Officer
CFO: Lana Aran, Chief Financial Officer
CMO: Arthur Douville, M.D., Chief Medical Officer
CIO: Darrell O'Dell, Director Information Services
CHR: John Omel, Interim Vice President Human Resources
CNO: Dian Adams, R.N., Chief Nursing Officer
Web address: www.goodsamsanjose.com
**Control:** Corporation, Investor–owned, for–profit **Service:** General Medical and Surgical

**Staffed Beds: 373 Admissions: 16068 Census: 220 Outpatient Visits: 132877 Births: 3455 Total Expense ($000): 319138 Payroll Expense ($000): 175135 Personnel: 1284**

☒ **KAISER PERMANENTE SAN JOSE MEDICAL CENTER (050604)**, (Formerly San Jose Medical Center), 250 Hospital Parkway, Zip 95119–1199; tel. 408/972–7000 **A**1 10 **F**3 8 13 17 18 20 22 29 30 31 35 40 46 49 51 56 68 70 72 73 74 76 78 79 81 82 84 85 87 89 104 107 110 111 114 115 119 130 135 141 146 148 **S** Kaiser Foundation Hospitals, Oakland, CA
Primary Contact: Irene Chavez, Senior Vice President and Area Manager
COO: Terry L. Austen, Senior Vice President and Area Manager
CFO: Stephen L. Kalsman, Area Finance Officer
CMO: Raj Bhandari, M.D., Physician–in–Chief
CIO: Ernie Japec, Area Information Officer
CHR: Susan Franzella, Human Resource Business Partner
Web address: www.kaiserpermanente.org
**Control:** Other not–for–profit (including NFP Corporation) **Service:** General Medical and Surgical

**Staffed Beds: 217 Admissions: 10606 Census: 126 Outpatient Visits: 57511 Births: 2064 Personnel: 1379**

---

**Hospital, Medicare Provider Number, Address, Telephone, Approval, Facility, and Physician Codes, Health Care System**

★ American Hospital Association (AHA) membership
☐ The Joint Commission accreditation
◇ DNV Healthcare Inc. accreditation
○ Healthcare Facilities Accreditation Program
△ Commission on Accreditation of Rehabilitation Facilities (CARF) accreditation

✠ **O'CONNOR HOSPITAL (050153)**, 2105 Forest Avenue, Zip 95128–1471; tel. 408/947–2500 **A**1 2 9 10 **F**11 13 15 18 19 20 22 24 26 28 29 30 31 34 35 37 40 44 46 48 49 50 53 54 57 59 60 64 66 68 74 75 77 78 79 81 84 85 86 87 93 97 100 107 108 110 111 114 116 117 118 119 121 123 130 131 132 135 146 147 148 **S** Daughters of Charity Health System, Los Altos Hills, CA
Primary Contact: James F. Dover, FACHE, President and Chief Executive Officer
COO: Ronald J. Galonsky, Chief Operating Officer
CFO: David W. Carroll, Chief Financial Officer
CMO: George Block, M.D., Chief Medical Officer
CIO: Richard Hutsell, Vice President and Chief Information Officer
CHR: Julie Hatcher, Vice President Human Resources
CNO: Judy A. Watland, R.N., Chief Nursing Officer
Web address: www.oconnorhospital.org
**Control:** Other not–for–profit (including NFP Corporation) **Service:** General Medical and Surgical

Staffed Beds: 202 Admissions: 11936 Census: 133 Outpatient Visits: 151312 Births: 3302 Total Expense ($000): 307029 Payroll Expense ($000): 135757

✠ **REGIONAL MEDICAL CENTER OF SAN JOSE (050125)**, 225 North Jackson Avenue, Zip 95116–1603; tel. 408/259–5000, (Nonreporting) **A**1 9 10 **S** HCA, Nashville, TN
Primary Contact: Michael T. Johnson, Chief Executive Officer
COO: Brian J. Knecht, Chief Operating Officer
CFO: Raju Iyer, Chief Financial Officer
CMO: William Scott, M.D., Vice President Medical Affairs
CIO: Shirley Joyal, Director Information Systems
CHR: Nancy Clark, Vice President Human Resources
Web address: www.regionalmedicalsanjose.com
**Control:** Partnership, Investor–owned, for–profit **Service:** General Medical and Surgical

Staffed Beds: 216

☐ △ **SANTA CLARA VALLEY MEDICAL CENTER (050038)**, 751 South Bascom Avenue, Zip 95128–2604; tel. 408/885–5000 **A**1 3 5 7 9 10 **F**3 5 9 12 13 15 16 17 18 19 20 21 22 23 24 25 26 27 28 29 30 31 32 34 35 39 40 43 45 46 47 48 49 50 51 52 55 56 58 59 60 61 64 65 66 68 70 71 72 73 74 75 76 77 78 79 80 81 82 83 84 85 86 87 88 89 90 92 93 97 98 99 100 101 102 103 104 107 108 109 110 111 112 114 115 116 117 118 119 120 121 122 123 124 129 130 131 132 134 135 142 143 144 146 147 148 **P**6
Primary Contact: Linda Smith, FACHE, Chief Executive Officer
CFO: David S. McGrew, Chief Financial Officer
CMO: Alfonso F. Banuelos, Jr., M.D., Chief Medical Officer
CIO: Lee Herrmann, Chief Healthcare Technology Officer
CHR: David Manson, Manager Human Resources
CNO: Trudy Johnson, R.N., Chief Nursing Officer
Web address: www.scvmed.org
**Control:** County–Government, nonfederal **Service:** General Medical and Surgical

Staffed Beds: 321 Admissions: 21790 Census: 312 Outpatient Visits: 850430 Births: 4045 Total Expense ($000): 1115711 Payroll Expense ($000): 419854

### SAN LEANDRO—Alameda County

**ALAMEDA COUNTY MEDICAL CENTER–FAIRMONT CAMPUS** See Alameda County Medical Center, Oakland

✠ **KINDRED HOSPITAL–SAN FRANCISCO BAY AREA (052034)**, 2800 Benedict Drive, Zip 94577–6840; tel. 510/357–8300, (Nonreporting) **A**1 9 10 **S** Kindred Healthcare, Louisville, KY
Primary Contact: Dianne Chartier, R.N., Interim Chief Executive Officer
COO: Mary Schwind, R.N., Chief Clinical Officer
CFO: Ziba Aflak, Chief Financial Officer
CHR: Laurel Scharber, Coordinator Human Resources
Web address: www.kindredhospitalsfba.com
**Control:** Corporation, Investor–owned, for–profit **Service:** Long–Term Acute Care hospital

Staffed Beds: 78

☐ **WILLOW ROCK CENTER (054149)**, 2050 Fairmont Drive, Zip 94578–1001; tel. 510/895–5502 **A**1 10 **F**29 34 57 98 99 101
Primary Contact: Anne L. Bakar, President
Web address: www.tbhcare.com
**Control:** Individual, Investor–owned, for–profit **Service:** Children's hospital psychiatric

Staffed Beds: 16 Admissions: 542 Census: 9 Outpatient Visits: 0 Births: 0 Total Expense ($000): 5281 Payroll Expense ($000): 2321 Personnel: 46

### SAN LUIS OBISPO—San Luis Obispo County

**CALIFORNIA MENS COLONY HOSPITAL**, Highway 1, Zip 93409–8101, Mailing Address: P.O. Box 8101, Zip 93403–8101; tel. 805/547–7913, (Nonreporting)
Primary Contact: Galen Kirn, Administrator
CFO: William Cook, Associate Warden Business Service
CIO: Terry Knight, Public Information Officer and Administrative Assistant
Web address: www.yaca.ca.gov/visitors/fac_prison_cmc.html
**Control:** State–Government, nonfederal **Service:** Hospital unit of an institution (prison hospital, college infirmary, etc.)

Staffed Beds: 39

✠ **FRENCH HOSPITAL MEDICAL CENTER (050232)**, 1911 Johnson Avenue, Zip 93401–4131; tel. 805/543–5353 **A**1 9 10 **F**8 11 15 18 20 22 24 28 29 30 34 35 40 46 50 53 54 57 59 64 68 70 75 76 77 78 79 81 84 85 86 87 89 97 100 107 108 110 111 114 115 119 124 130 132 146 147 148 **S** Dignity Health, San Francisco, CA
Primary Contact: Alan Iftiniuk, Chief Executive Officer
COO: Carla A. Adams, Chief Operating Officer
CFO: Sue Andersen, Chief Financial Officer
CMO: J. Trees Ritter, D.O., Chief of Staff
CIO: Cyndi Lang, Director Information Services
CHR: Kristin Flynn, Manager Human Resources
CNO: Carla A. Adams, Chief Nursing Officer
Web address: www.frenchmedicalcenter.org
**Control:** Other not–for–profit (including NFP Corporation) **Service:** General Medical and Surgical

Staffed Beds: 112 Admissions: 4435 Census: 39 Outpatient Visits: 98322 Births: 640 Total Expense ($000): 99075 Payroll Expense ($000): 35888 Personnel: 359

✠ **SIERRA VISTA REGIONAL MEDICAL CENTER (050506)**, 1010 Murray Avenue, Zip 93405–1806, Mailing Address: P.O. Box 1367, Zip 93406–1367; tel. 805/546–7600 **A**1 2 9 10 19 **F**1 3 4 11 13 15 16 17 18 20 29 31 34 35 38 39 40 45 46 49 50 51 57 64 65 67 70 72 73 74 75 76 77 78 79 80 81 84 85 86 88 89 90 98 107 108 110 115 119 126 128 130 131 132 145 146 147 148 **S** TENET Healthcare Corporation, Dallas, TX
Primary Contact: Candace L. Markwith, Chief Executive Officer
COO: Joseph DeSchryver, Chief Operating Officer
CFO: Rollie Pirkl, Chief Financial Officer
CIO: Robert Leonard, Director Information Services
CHR: Bill Peterson, Chief Human Resources Director
CNO: Christie Gonder, Chief Nursing Officer
Web address: www.sierravistaregional.com
**Control:** Corporation, Investor–owned, for–profit **Service:** General Medical and Surgical

Staffed Beds: 164 Admissions: 5576 Census: 64 Outpatient Visits: 52163 Births: 1281 Total Expense ($000): 108799 Payroll Expense ($000): 50169 Personnel: 691

### SAN MATEO—San Mateo County

**MILLS HOSPITAL** See Mills–Peninsula Health Services, Burlingame

☐ **SAN MATEO MEDICAL CENTER (050113)**, 222 West 39th Avenue, Zip 94403–4398; tel. 650/573–2222, (Nonreporting) **A**1 3 5 9 10
Primary Contact: Susan Ehrlich, M.D., Chief Executive Officer
COO: John Thomas, Chief Operating Officer
CFO: Philip Fortunato, Interim Chief Financial Officer
CMO: Chester Kunnappilly, M.D., Chief Medical Officer and Chief Quality Officer
CIO: Michael Aratow, M.D., Chief Information Officer
CHR: Sonya Siebe, Manager Human Resources
CNO: Liz Evans, Chief Nursing Officer
Web address: www.sanmateomedicalcenter.org
**Control:** County–Government, nonfederal **Service:** General Medical and Surgical

Staffed Beds: 307

### SAN PABLO—Contra Costa County

☐ **DOCTORS MEDICAL CENTER–SAN PABLO CAMPUS (050079)**, 2000 Vale Road, Zip 94806–3808; tel. 510/970–5000, (Nonreporting) **A**1 2 9 10
Primary Contact: Dawn M. Gideon, Interim Chief Executive Officer
COO: Kathy White, R.N., Interim Chief Operating Officer
CFO: James Boatman, Chief Financial Officer
CMO: Laurel Hodgson, M.D., President Medical Staff
CIO: Phyllis Moore, Director Information Systems and Data Center
CHR: John Hardy, Vice President Human Resources
CNO: Kathy White, R.N., Interim Chief Nursing Officer
Web address: www.doctorsmedicalcenter.org
**Control:** Hospital district or authority, Government, nonfederal **Service:** General Medical and Surgical

Staffed Beds: 140

### SAN PEDRO—Los Angeles County, See Los Angeles

*Many Facility Codes have changed. Please refer to the AHA Guide Code Chart.*

© 2013 AHA Guide

**CA**

## SAN RAFAEL—Marin County

☒ **KAISER PERMANENTE SAN RAFAEL MEDICAL CENTER (050510)**, (Formerly San Rafael Medical Center), 99 Montecillo Road, Zip 94903–3308; tel. 415/444–2000 **A**1 10 **F**3 8 15 20 29 30 31 34 35 40 41 43 45 46 47 48 49 50 56 57 59 61 62 64 65 68 70 74 75 76 77 78 79 81 82 84 85 86 87 89 93 107 108 110 111 114 118 119 129 130 131 132 135 144 146 147 148 **P**3 **S** Kaiser Foundation Hospitals, Oakland, CA
Primary Contact: Judy Coffey, Senior Vice President and Area Manager
COO: Tony Fiorello, R.N., Chief Operating and Chief Nursing Officer
CFO: John Groesbeck, Area Finance Officer
CMO: Gary Mizono, M.D., Physician–in–Chief
CIO: Stanley Dobrawa, Area Technology Director
CHR: Rudy Collins, Human Resources Business Partner
CNO: Tony Fiorello, R.N., Chief Operating and Chief Nursing Officer
Web address: www.kaiserpermanente.org
**Control:** Other not–for–profit (including NFP Corporation) **Service:** General Medical and Surgical

**Staffed Beds:** 116 **Admissions:** 4863 **Census:** 52 **Outpatient Visits:** 28976 **Births:** 0 **Personnel:** 1429

## SAN RAMON—Contra Costa County

☒ **SAN RAMON REGIONAL MEDICAL CENTER (050689)**, 6001 Norris Canyon Road, Zip 94583–5400; tel. 925/275–9200 **A**1 9 10 **F**3 8 11 13 15 17 18 20 22 24 26 28 29 30 31 34 35 37 40 45 46 47 48 49 53 57 59 64 70 72 74 75 76 77 78 79 81 84 85 86 89 93 107 108 110 114 118 119 126 130 131 132 146 147 148 **S** TENET Healthcare Corporation, Dallas, TX
Primary Contact: Gary Sloan, Chief Executive Officer
COO: Susan C. Micheletti, Chief Operating Officer
CFO: Beenu Chadha, Chief Financial Officer
CMO: Erik Gracer, M.D., Chief of Staff
CIO: Guy Tennyson, Director Information Systems and Telecommunications
CHR: Dennis Mills, Director Human Resources
CNO: Pam Pshea, R.N., Chief Nursing Officer
Web address: www.sanramonmedctr.com
**Control:** Corporation, Investor–owned, for–profit **Service:** General Medical and Surgical

**Staffed Beds:** 123 **Admissions:** 4421 **Census:** 46 **Outpatient Visits:** 73697 **Births:** 708 **Total Expense ($000):** 122518 **Payroll Expense ($000):** 69827 **Personnel:** 575

## SANTA ANA—Orange County

☐ **COASTAL COMMUNITIES HOSPITAL (050747)**, 2701 South Bristol Street, Zip 92704–6201; tel. 714/754–5454 **A**1 9 10 **F**1 3 4 7 8 13 14 17 29 30 34 35 40 50 56 57 60 64 65 67 68 70 75 76 77 79 81 82 86 87 89 90 93 98 101 103 104 105 107 111 119 128 130 143 146 147 **S** Integrated Healthcare, Santa Ana, CA
Primary Contact: Luke Tharasri, Chief Executive Officer
CFO: Patricia Henry, Chief Financial Officer
CHR: Gretchen Lindeman, Director Human Resources
Web address: www.coastalcommhospital.com
**Control:** Corporation, Investor–owned, for–profit **Service:** General Medical and Surgical

**Staffed Beds:** 178 **Admissions:** 4398 **Census:** 93 **Outpatient Visits:** 30516 **Births:** 1367 **Total Expense ($000):** 62135 **Payroll Expense ($000):** 40637 **Personnel:** 515

☐ **WESTERN MEDICAL CENTER–SANTA ANA (050746)**, 1001 North Tustin Avenue, Zip 92705–3577; tel. 714/835–3555, (Nonreporting) **A**1 3 5 9 10 **S** Integrated Healthcare, Santa Ana, CA
Primary Contact: Daniel Brothman, Chief Executive Officer
COO: Doug Norris, Administrator and Chief Operating Officer
CFO: Kathy Hammack, Chief Financial Officer
CMO: Seifolah Esfandiari, M.D., Chief of Staff
CIO: Nova Stewart, Chief Information Officer
CHR: Milas H. Kennington, Vice President, Human Resources
CNO: Patricia Rives, R.N., Chief Nursing Officer
Web address: www.westernmedicalcenter.com
**Control:** Corporation, Investor–owned, for–profit **Service:** General Medical and Surgical

**Staffed Beds:** 282

## SANTA BARBARA—Santa Barbara County

**COTTAGE REHABILITATION HOSPITAL** See Santa Barbara Cottage Hospital

☒ **GOLETA VALLEY COTTAGE HOSPITAL (050357)**, 351 South Patterson Avenue, Zip 93111–2496, Mailing Address: Box 6306, Zip 93160–6306; tel. 805/967–3411 **A**1 9 10 **F**8 11 12 15 29 40 65 68 70 79 81 107 110 114 119 124 130 148 **S** Cottage Health System, Santa Barbara, CA
Primary Contact: Ronald C. Werft, President and Chief Executive Officer
COO: Steven A. Fellows, Executive Vice President and Chief Operating Officer
CFO: Joan Bricher, Senior Vice President Finance and Chief Financial Officer
CMO: Edmund Wroblewski, M.D., Vice President Medical Affairs and Chief Medical Officer
CIO: Alberto Kywi, Chief Information Officer
CHR: Patrice Ryan, Vice President Human Resources
Web address: www.sbch.org
**Control:** Other not–for–profit (including NFP Corporation) **Service:** General Medical and Surgical

**Staffed Beds:** 72 **Admissions:** 1526 **Census:** 40 **Outpatient Visits:** 38162 **Births:** 0 **Total Expense ($000):** 59561 **Payroll Expense ($000):** 24871 **Personnel:** 291

☒ △ **SANTA BARBARA COTTAGE HOSPITAL (050396)**, 400 West Pueblo Street, Zip 93105–4390, Mailing Address: P.O. Box 689, Zip 93102–0689; tel. 805/682–7111, (Includes COTTAGE CHILDREN'S HOSPITAL, 400 West Pueblo Street, Zip 93105–4353; tel. 877/247–3260; COTTAGE REHABILITATION HOSPITAL, 2415 De la Vina Street, Zip 93105–3819; tel. 805/687–7444; Melinda Staveley, President and Chief Executive Officer) **A**1 2 3 5 7 9 10 **F**3 4 5 8 11 12 13 15 17 18 20 22 24 26 28 29 30 31 34 35 40 43 46 50 53 54 57 58 59 60 64 68 70 72 74 75 76 78 79 81 84 86 88 89 90 91 92 93 96 98 100 102 103 104 106 107 110 111 114 115 119 126 130 132 135 146 148 **S** Cottage Health System, Santa Barbara, CA
Primary Contact: Ronald C. Werft, President and Chief Executive Officer
COO: Steven A. Fellows, Executive Vice President and Chief Operating Officer
CFO: Joan Bricher, Senior Vice President Finance and Chief Financial Officer
CMO: Edmund Wroblewski, M.D., Vice President Medical Affairs and Chief Medical Officer
CIO: Alberto Kywi, Chief Information Officer
CHR: Patrice Ryan, Vice President Human Resources
Web address: www.cottagehealthsystem.org
**Control:** Other not–for–profit (including NFP Corporation) **Service:** General Medical and Surgical

**Staffed Beds:** 351 **Admissions:** 18144 **Census:** 227 **Outpatient Visits:** 126458 **Births:** 2287 **Total Expense ($000):** 510868 **Payroll Expense ($000):** 181535 **Personnel:** 2253

**SANTA BARBARA COUNTY PSYCHIATRIC HEALTH FACILITY (054125)**, 315 Camino Del Remedio, Zip 93110–1332; tel. 805/681–5244 **A**10 **F**75 87 98 130 132 133 143
Primary Contact: Ann Detrick, Director
Web address: www.countyofsb.org
**Control:** County–Government, nonfederal **Service:** Psychiatric

**Staffed Beds:** 16 **Admissions:** 450 **Census:** 14 **Outpatient Visits:** 0 **Births:** 0

## SANTA CLARA—Santa Clara County

☒ **KAISER PERMANENTE SANTA CLARA MEDICAL CENTER (050071)**, (Formerly Santa Clara Medical Center), 700 Lawrence Expressway, Zip 95051–5173; tel. 408/851–1000 **A**1 3 5 10 **F**17 34 40 41 44 45 48 49 50 51 52 53 54 55 56 57 58 59 60 61 62 63 64 65 68 70 71 72 74 75 76 77 78 79 81 82 83 84 85 86 87 88 89 91 92 93 94 96 97 99 100 101 104 107 108 109 110 111 114 115 116 117 118 119 120 121 123 124 126 129 130 131 132 134 135 144 146 147 148 **P**3 **S** Kaiser Foundation Hospitals, Oakland, CA
Primary Contact: Christopher L. Boyd, Senior Vice President and Area Manager
COO: Susan G. Murphy, Chief Operating Officer
CFO: Carol Reeves, Interim Area Finance Officer
CMO: Susan Smarr, M.D., Physician–in–Chief
CIO: Scott May, Area Director Technology
CHR: Robert Hyde, Human Resources Business Partner
CNO: Anne M. Goldfisher, R.N., Chief Nursing Officer
Web address: www.kaiserpermanente.org
**Control:** Other not–for–profit (including NFP Corporation) **Service:** General Medical and Surgical

**Staffed Beds:** 327 **Admissions:** 21207 **Census:** 253 **Outpatient Visits:** 1417167 **Births:** 4503 **Personnel:** 4150

---

**Hospital, Medicare Provider Number, Address, Telephone, Approval, Facility, and Physician Codes, Health Care System**

★ American Hospital Association (AHA) membership
☐ The Joint Commission accreditation
◇ DNV Healthcare Inc. accreditation
○ Healthcare Facilities Accreditation Program
△ Commission on Accreditation of Rehabilitation Facilities (CARF) accreditation

**CA**

## SANTA CRUZ—Santa Cruz County

⊠ **DOMINICAN HOSPITAL (050242)**, 1555 Soquel Drive, Zip 95065–1794; tel. 831/462–7700, (Nonreporting) **A**1 2 9 10 **S** Dignity Health, San Francisco, CA
Primary Contact: Nanette Mickiewicz, M.D., President
COO: Chris Wernke, Chief Operating Officer
CFO: Rick Harron, Chief Financial Officer
CMO: Freddie Weinstein, M.D., Chief Medical Officer
CIO: Lee Vanderpool, Vice President
CHR: Vicki Miranda, Vice President Human Resources
Web address: www.dominicanhospital.org
**Control:** Church–operated, Nongovernment, not–for profit **Service:** General Medical and Surgical

**Staffed Beds:** 276

⊠ **SUTTER MATERNITY AND SURGERY CENTER OF SANTA CRUZ (050714)**, 2900 Chanticleer Avenue, Zip 95065–1816; tel. 831/477–2200 **A**1 9 10 **F**3 13 51 57 76 79 81 132 146 **S** Sutter Health, Sacramento, CA
Primary Contact: Stephen Gray, Chief Executive Officer
CFO: Iftikhar Hussain, Chief Financial Officer
CMO: Matthew Hansman, M.D., Chief of Staff
CIO: Michael Reandeau, Regional Chief Information Officer
CHR: Maynard Jenkins, Regional Vice President for Human Resources
CNO: Jacci Sterling, R.N., Chief Nursing Executive
Web address: www.suttermatsurg.org
**Control:** Other not–for–profit (including NFP Corporation) **Service:** General Medical and Surgical

**Staffed Beds:** 28 **Admissions:** 1645 **Census:** 11 **Outpatient Visits:** 8736 **Births:** 976 **Total Expense ($000):** 50395 **Payroll Expense ($000):** 16786 **Personnel:** 177

## SANTA MARIA—Santa Barbara County

⊠ **MARIAN MEDICAL CENTER (050107)**, 1400 East Church Street, Zip 93454–5906; tel. 805/739–3000, (Total facility includes 95 beds in nursing home–type unit) **A**1 2 9 10 **F**3 8 11 12 13 15 17 18 20 22 24 28 29 30 31 34 35 36 37 39 40 46 49 50 53 54 56 57 58 59 60 62 63 64 65 66 68 69 72 74 75 76 77 78 79 81 82 84 85 86 87 89 93 97 100 107 108 110 111 114 117 118 119 126 127 128 130 132 134 135 143 146 147 148 **S** Dignity Health, San Francisco, CA
Primary Contact: Charles J. Cova, President and Chief Executive Officer and Senior Vice President Operations Dignity Health Central Co
CFO: Sue Andersen, Chief Financial Officer
CMO: Chuck Merrill, M.D., Vice President Medical Affairs
CIO: Patricia Haase, Director Information Technology and Communications
CHR: Susan Winsell, Vice President Human Resources
Web address: www.marianmedicalcenter.org
**Control:** Church–operated, Nongovernment, not–for profit **Service:** General Medical and Surgical

**Staffed Beds:** 286 **Admissions:** 11178 **Census:** 189 **Outpatient Visits:** 191272 **Births:** 2722 **Total Expense ($000):** 239364 **Payroll Expense ($000):** 97295 **Personnel:** 1123

## SANTA MONICA—Los Angeles County

⊠ **SAINT JOHN'S HEALTH CENTER (050290)**, 2121 Santa Monica Boulevard, Zip 90404–2303; tel. 310/829–5511 **A**1 2 9 10 **F**8 11 13 15 18 20 22 24 26 29 30 34 35 40 46 49 58 70 72 74 75 76 78 79 81 82 83 84 93 97 107 108 109 111 112 114 115 119 121 124 126 130 131 **S** SCL Health System, Denver, CO
Primary Contact: Michael L. Wall, FACHE, Interim President and Chief Executive Officer
COO: Kenneth L. Meehan, Interim Chief Operating Officer
CFO: Michelle Mok, Chief Financial Officer
CIO: Martha Ponce, Director Information Technologies and Telecommunications
CHR: Steven Sharrer, Vice President Human Resources
CNO: Dawna Hendel, R.N., Chief Nursing Officer and Vice President Patient Care Services
Web address: www.newstjohns.org/home.aspx
**Control:** Other not–for–profit (including NFP Corporation) **Service:** General Medical and Surgical

**Staffed Beds:** 234 **Admissions:** 12628 **Census:** 134 **Outpatient Visits:** 189935 **Births:** 1979 **Total Expense ($000):** 693305 **Payroll Expense ($000):** 103982 **Personnel:** 1412

⊠ **SANTA MONICA–UCLA MEDICAL CENTER AND ORTHOPAEDIC HOSPITAL (050112)**, 1250 16th Street, Zip 90404–1249; tel. 310/319–4000 **A**1 3 5 9 10 **F**3 8 9 11 12 13 15 18 20 22 24 25 27 29 30 31 34 35 37 40 41 45 46 47 48 49 50 52 54 55 56 57 58 59 64 65 68 70 72 74 75 76 78 79 81 82 84 85 86 87 89 93 96 97 102 107 108 110 111 114 115 116 117 118 119 130 131 143 145 146 147 **P**6 **S** University of California–Systemwide Administration, Oakland, CA
Primary Contact: Paul Watkins, Chief Administrative Officer
COO: Posie Carpenter, R.N., Chief Administrative Officer
CFO: Paul Staton, Chief Financial Officer
CMO: James Atkinson, M.D., Medical Director
CIO: Virginia McFerran, Chief Information Officer
CHR: Mark Speare, Senior Associate Director Patient Relations and Human Resources
Web address: www.healthcare.ucla.edu
**Control:** State–Government, nonfederal **Service:** General Medical and Surgical

**Staffed Beds:** 266 **Admissions:** 14458 **Census:** 204 **Outpatient Visits:** 150452 **Births:** 1261 **Total Expense ($000):** 360280 **Payroll Expense ($000):** 141620 **Personnel:** 1672

## SANTA ROSA—Sonoma County

⊠ **KAISER PERMANENTE SANTA ROSA MEDICAL CENTER (050690)**, (Formerly Santa Rosa Medical Center), 401 Bicentennial Way, Zip 95403–2192; tel. 707/571–4000 **A**1 10 **F**3 13 15 30 31 40 41 44 45 49 51 60 62 64 68 70 72 74 76 77 78 79 81 83 85 89 100 107 108 110 111 114 115 119 130 146 **S** Kaiser Foundation Hospitals, Oakland, CA
Primary Contact: Judy Coffey, Senior Vice President and Area Manager
COO: Susan Janvrin, R.N., Chief Operating and Chief Nursing Officer
CFO: John Groesbeck, Area Finance Officer
CMO: Kirk Pappas, M.D., Physician–in–Chief
CIO: Stanley Dobrawa, Area Technology Director
CHR: Rudy Collins, Human Resources Business Partner
CNO: Susan Janvrin, R.N., Chief Operating and Chief Nursing Officer
Web address: www.kaiserpermanente.org
**Control:** Other not–for–profit (including NFP Corporation) **Service:** General Medical and Surgical

**Staffed Beds:** 117 **Admissions:** 8395 **Census:** 84 **Outpatient Visits:** 52752 **Births:** 1889 **Personnel:** 1751

⊠ **SANTA ROSA MEMORIAL HOSPITAL (050174)**, 1165 Montgomery Drive, Zip 95405–4897, Mailing Address: P.O. Box 522, Zip 95402–0522; tel. 707/546–3210 **A**1 2 9 10 **F**3 8 11 12 13 15 18 20 22 24 26 28 29 30 31 34 35 39 40 43 44 45 46 47 48 49 51 54 56 58 59 60 64 65 66 68 70 71 72 74 75 76 77 78 79 81 82 84 85 86 87 89 90 92 93 102 104 105 107 108 111 115 119 130 143 144 146 148 **S** St. Joseph Health, Irvine, CA
Primary Contact: Todd Salnas, President and Chief Executive Officer
COO: David Ziolkowski, Chief Operating Officer
CFO: Mich Riccioni, Chief Financial Officer
CMO: Gary Greensweig, D.O., Chief Medical Officer
CIO: Anna Shields, Executive Director Information Systems
CHR: Debra Miller, Vice President Human Resources
CNO: Rhonda Foster, Interim Chief Nursing Officer
Web address: www.stjosephhealth.org
**Control:** Other not–for–profit (including NFP Corporation) **Service:** General Medical and Surgical

**Staffed Beds:** 272 **Admissions:** 12602 **Census:** 158 **Outpatient Visits:** 168064 **Births:** 948 **Total Expense ($000):** 349853 **Payroll Expense ($000):** 105215 **Personnel:** 1232

⊠ **SUTTER MEDICAL CENTER OF SANTA ROSA, CHANATE CAMPUS (050291)**, 3325 Chanate Road, Zip 95404–1707; tel. 707/576–4000, (Includes WARRACK CAMPUS, 2449 Summerfield Road, Zip 95405–7815; tel. 707/576–4200) **A**1 3 5 9 10 **F**3 12 13 18 20 22 24 26 31 34 35 39 40 46 49 50 51 56 65 68 70 72 74 75 76 77 78 79 81 82 84 85 87 93 107 108 111 114 119 130 143 146 148 **S** Sutter Health, Sacramento, CA
Primary Contact: Mike Purvis, Chief Administrative Officer
CFO: Avery Schlesenberg, Chief Financial Officer
CMO: Robert Heckey, M.D., Chief of Staff
CHR: Steve Morales, Director Human Resources
Web address: www.sutterhealth.org
**Control:** Other not–for–profit (including NFP Corporation) **Service:** General Medical and Surgical

**Staffed Beds:** 135 **Admissions:** 6122 **Census:** 68 **Outpatient Visits:** 47875 **Births:** 1645 **Total Expense ($000):** 167667 **Payroll Expense ($000):** 60172 **Personnel:** 498

## SEBASTOPOL—Sonoma County

★ ○ **PALM DRIVE HOSPITAL (050385)**, 501 Petaluma Avenue, Zip 95472–4281; tel. 707/823–8511, (Nonreporting) **A**9 10 11
Primary Contact: Thomas M. Harlan, Chief Executive Officer
CFO: David Glassburn, Interim Chief Financial Officer
CMO: Richard Powers, M.D., Chief of Staff
CIO: Bruce Espinosa, Manager Information Systems
CHR: Raoul McDuff, Director Human Resources
Web address: www.palmdrivehospital.org
**Control:** Other not–for–profit (including NFP Corporation) **Service:** General Medical and Surgical

**Staffed Beds:** 47

*Many Facility Codes have changed. Please refer to the AHA Guide Code Chart.*    © 2013 AHA Guide

**SEPULVEDA—Los Angeles County, See Los Angeles**

**SHERMAN OAKS—Los Angeles County, See Los Angeles**

**SIMI VALLEY—Ventura County**

✠ **SIMI VALLEY HOSPITAL AND HEALTH CARE SERVICES (050236)**, 2975 North Sycamore Drive, Zip 93065–1201; tel. 805/955–6000, (Nonreporting) **A**1 2 9 10 **S** Adventist Health, Roseville, CA
Primary Contact: Kim S. Milstien, President and Chief Executive Officer
CFO: John Beaman, Senior Vice President and Chief Financial Officer
CFO: Jon Giese, Vice President and Chief Financial Officer
CMO: John Dingilian, M.D., Chief Medical Staff
CIO: Jeff Brown, Interim Director Information Systems
CHR: Sandy Werner, Director Human Resources
CNO: Caroline Esparza, Sr. VP to Patient Care Executive
Web address: www.simivalleyhospital.com
**Control:** Church–operated, Nongovernment, not–for profit **Service:** General Medical and Surgical

Staffed Beds: 82

**SOLVANG—Santa Barbara County**

✠ **SANTA YNEZ VALLEY COTTAGE HOSPITAL (051331)**, 2050 Viborg Road, Zip 93463–2295; tel. 805/688–6431 **A**1 9 10 18 **F**15 28 40 57 68 81 85 107 111 114 119 143 146 **S** Cottage Health System, Santa Barbara, CA
Primary Contact: Ronald C. Werft, President and Chief Executive Officer
COO: Steven A. Fellows, Executive Vice President and Chief Operating Officer
CFO: Joan Bricher, Senior Vice President Finance and Chief Financial Officer
CMO: Edmund Wroblewski, M.D., Vice President Medical Affairs and Chief Medical Officer
CIO: Alberto Kywi, Chief Information Officer
CHR: Patrice Ryan, Vice President Human Resources
Web address: www.cottagehealthsystem.org
**Control:** Other not–for–profit (including NFP Corporation) **Service:** General Medical and Surgical

Staffed Beds: 10 Admissions: 228 Census: 2 Outpatient Visits: 17256 Births: 0 Total Expense ($000): 12833 Payroll Expense ($000): 6141 Personnel: 66

**SONOMA—Sonoma County**

✠ **SONOMA VALLEY HOSPITAL (050090)**, 347 Andrieux Street, Zip 95476–6811, Mailing Address: P.O. Box 600, Zip 95476–0600; tel. 707/935–5000, (Nonreporting) **A**1 9 10
Primary Contact: Kelly Mather, Chief Executive Officer
CFO: Richard Reid, Chief Financial Officer
CMO: Robert Cohen, M.D., Chief Medical Officer
CIO: Fe Sendaydiego, Director Information Systems
CHR: Paula M. Davis, Chief Human Resources Officer
CNO: Leslie Lovejoy, R.N., Chief Nursing and Quality Officer
Web address: www.svh.com
**Control:** Hospital district or authority, Government, nonfederal **Service:** General Medical and Surgical

Staffed Beds: 65

**SONORA—Tuolumne County**

✠ **SONORA REGIONAL MEDICAL CENTER (050335)**, 1000 Greenley Road, Zip 95370–5200; tel. 209/536–5000, (Total facility includes 68 beds in nursing home–type unit) **A**1 9 10 **F**3 11 13 15 17 18 20 28 29 30 31 34 35 39 40 49 54 56 57 59 62 63 64 70 71 75 76 77 78 79 81 84 85 86 87 93 97 107 108 110 114 115 118 119 120 121 127 128 130 131 132 133 143 144 146 148 **P**6 **S** Adventist Health, Roseville, CA
Primary Contact: Jeff Eller, FACHE, President and Chief Executive Officer
CFO: Andrew Jahn, Vice President Finance
CMO: Ed Clinite, D.O., Chief of Staff
CIO: Bruce Chan, Director Business Planning and Marketing
CHR: Rick A. Dodds, Vice President Human Resources
CNO: Julie Kline, Senior Vice President Patient Services
Web address: www.sonoramedicalcenter.org/
**Control:** Church–operated, Nongovernment, not–for profit **Service:** General Medical and Surgical

Staffed Beds: 152 Admissions: 4783 Census: 116 Outpatient Visits: 288542 Births: 528 Total Expense ($000): 181050 Payroll Expense ($000): 69384 Personnel: 1087

**SOUTH EL MONTE—Los Angeles County**

☐ **GREATER EL MONTE COMMUNITY HOSPITAL (050738)**, 1701 Santa Anita Avenue, Zip 91733–3411; tel. 626/579–7777, (Nonreporting) **A**1 9 10 **S** AHMC & Healthcare, Inc., Alhambra, CA
Primary Contact: Jose Ortega, Chief Executive Officer
COO: Jose Ortega, Chief Executive Officer
CFO: Mary Anne Monje, Chief Financial Officer
CMO: Kamalakar Rambhatla, M.D., Chief of Staff
CIO: Jay Geldhof, Director Information Systems
CHR: Jason Jaquez, Director Human Resources
Web address: www.greaterelmonte.com
**Control:** Hospital district or authority, Government, nonfederal **Service:** General Medical and Surgical

Staffed Beds: 46

**SOUTH LAKE TAHOE—El Dorado County**

✠ **BARTON MEMORIAL HOSPITAL (050352)**, (Formerly Barton Healthcare System), 2170 South Avenue, Zip 96150–7026, Mailing Address: P.O. Box 9578, Zip 96158–9578; tel. 530/541–3420, (Total facility includes 48 beds in nursing home–type unit) **A**1 9 10 20 **F**3 8 11 13 15 18 29 30 32 34 35 38 40 45 46 47 48 50 54 57 59 62 63 64 65 66 68 70 74 75 76 77 79 81 82 83 84 85 86 87 89 90 92 93 94 96 97 99 100 104 107 109 110 111 112 113 114 115 116 117 118 119 121 122 123 124 126 127 128 129 130 131 132 133 143 144 146 147 148
Primary Contact: John G. Williams, President and Chief Executive Officer
COO: Kathy Cocking, R.N., Vice President Operations
CFO: Richard P. Derby, Vice President Finance
CMO: Clint Purvance, M.D., Chief Medical Officer
CHR: LeAnne Kankel, Vice President Human Relations
CNO: Mary J. Bittner, R.N., Vice President Nursing
Web address: www.bartonhealth.org
**Control:** Other not–for–profit (including NFP Corporation) **Service:** General Medical and Surgical

Staffed Beds: 111 Admissions: 2351 Census: 63 Outpatient Visits: 154957 Births: 372 Total Expense ($000): 104546 Payroll Expense ($000): 45250 Personnel: 790

**SOUTH SAN FRANCISCO—San Mateo County**

✠ **KAISER PERMANENTE SOUTH SAN FRANCISCO (050070)**, (Formerly South San Francisco Medical Center), 1200 El Camino Real, Zip 94080–3299; tel. 650/742–2000 **A**1 10 **F**3 5 8 12 15 18 29 30 31 32 34 35 36 40 45 46 47 48 49 50 51 53 54 55 56 57 58 59 64 65 68 70 74 75 77 78 79 81 82 84 85 86 87 91 92 93 94 95 96 97 99 100 101 103 104 107 108 110 111 114 115 118 119 120 121 123 124 129 130 131 132 135 146 147 148 **P**6 **S** Kaiser Foundation Hospitals, Oakland, CA
Primary Contact: Frank T. Beirne, Senior Vice President and Area Manager
CFO: Mark Okashima, Area Finance Officer
CMO: Michelle Caughey, M.D., Physician In Chief
CIO: Angel Shew, Director Area Technology
CHR: Sharon Barncord, Human Resource Business Partner
Web address: www.kaiserpermanente.org
**Control:** Other not–for–profit (including NFP Corporation) **Service:** General Medical and Surgical

Staffed Beds: 120 Admissions: 5677 Census: 58 Outpatient Visits: 469034 Births: 0 Personnel: 1462

**STOCKTON—San Joaquin County**

☐ **DAMERON HOSPITAL (050122)**, 525 West Acacia Street, Zip 95203–2484; tel. 209/944–5550, (Nonreporting) **A**1 9 10
Primary Contact: Lorraine P. Auerbach, President and Chief Executive Officer
COO: Nicholas Arismendi, Chief Operating Officer
CFO: Cyrus E. Dah, Chief Financial Officer
CMO: Bradley Reinke, M.D., Chief of Staff
CIO: Glenn Whipple, Chief Information Officer
CHR: Maria Junez, Director Human Resources
CNO: Janine Hawkins, R.N., Chief Nursing Officer
Web address: www.dameronhospital.org
**Control:** Other not–for–profit (including NFP Corporation) **Service:** General Medical and Surgical

Staffed Beds: 188

⊞ **ST. JOSEPH'S BEHAVIORAL HEALTH CENTER (054123)**, 2510 North California Street, Zip 95204–5502; tel. 209/461–2000 **A1** 9 10 **F5** 29 38 68 98 100 101 103 104 105 130 132 143 146 **S** Dignity Health, San Francisco, CA
Primary Contact: Paul Rains, R.N., MSN, President
CFO: Nikki Ochoa, Interim Chief Financial Officer
CMO: David Robinson, D.O., Medical Director
CHR: Nancy Vargas, Chief Human Resources
CNO: Alan Hall, Chief Nursing Officer
Web address: www.stjosephscanhelp.org
**Control:** Church–operated, Nongovernment, not–for profit **Service:** Psychiatric

| Staffed Beds: 35 Admissions: 1560 Census: 28 Outpatient Visits: 9335 Births: 0 Total Expense ($000): 13270 Payroll Expense ($000): 7431 Personnel: 108 |
| --- |

⊞ **ST. JOSEPH'S MEDICAL CENTER (050084)**, 1800 North California Street, Zip 95204–6019, Mailing Address: P.O. Box 213008, Zip 95213–9008; tel. 209/943–2000, (Nonreporting) **A1** 2 9 10 **S** Dignity Health, San Francisco, CA
Primary Contact: Donald J. Wiley, President and Chief Executive Officer
COO: Michael R. Ricks, Chief Operating Officer
CFO: Nikki Ochoa, Interim Chief Financial Officer
CMO: Susan McDonald, M.D., Vice President
CIO: Randall Gamino, Director Perot Site
CHR: Nancy Vargas, Vice President Human Resources
Web address: www.stjosephsCARES.org
**Control:** Church–operated, Nongovernment, not–for profit **Service:** General Medical and Surgical

| Staffed Beds: 273 |
| --- |

### SUN CITY—Riverside County

☐ **MENIFEE VALLEY MEDICAL CENTER (050684)**, 28400 McCall Boulevard, Zip 92585–9537; tel. 951/679–8888, (Nonreporting) **A1** 9 10 **S** Physicians for Healthy Hospitals, Hemet, CA
Primary Contact: Joel Bergenfeld, Chief Executive Officer
CFO: Michael Garko, Chief Financial Officer
CHR: Michele Bird, Chief Human Resources Officer
Web address: www.valleyhealthsystem.com
**Control:** Hospital district or authority, Government, nonfederal **Service:** General Medical and Surgical

| Staffed Beds: 82 |
| --- |

### SUN VALLEY—Los Angeles County, See Los Angeles

### SUSANVILLE—Lassen County

⊞ **BANNER LASSEN MEDICAL CENTER (051320)**, 1800 Spring Ridge Drive, Zip 96130–6100; tel. 530/252–2000 **A1** 9 10 18 **F3** 11 13 15 29 31 34 35 40 45 50 56 57 59 64 68 75 76 77 78 79 81 85 87 92 107 108 110 111 114 119 129 146 148 **S** Banner Health, Phoenix, AZ
Primary Contact: Bob S. Edwards, Jr., FACHE, Chief Executive Officer
CFO: Shelby Diede, Chief Financial Officer
CMO: Hal Meadows, M.D., Chief Medical Officer
CHR: Melinda Moore, Chief Human Resources Officer
CNO: Catherine S. Harshbarger, R.N., Chief Nursing Officer
Web address: www.bannerhealth.com/Locations/California/Banner+Lassen+Medical+Center
**Control:** Other not–for–profit (including NFP Corporation) **Service:** General Medical and Surgical

| Staffed Beds: 25 Admissions: 1253 Census: 12 Outpatient Visits: 46689 Births: 264 Total Expense ($000): 29975 Payroll Expense ($000): 12645 Personnel: 168 |
| --- |

### SYLMAR—Los Angeles County, See Los Angeles

### TARZANA—Los Angeles County, See Los Angeles

### TEHACHAPI—Kern County

★ ◇ **TEHACHAPI VALLEY HEALTHCARE DISTRICT (051301)**, 115 West E Street, Zip 93561–1607, Mailing Address: P.O. Box 1900, Zip 93581–1900; tel. 661/823–3000 **A**9 10 18 21 **F**29 40 54 57 59 81 82 93 107 127 130 132 133
Primary Contact: Alan J. Burgess, FACHE, Chief Executive Officer
CFO: William J. Van Noy, Chief Financial Officer
CMO: Susan Cribbs, D.O., Chief of Staff
CIO: Dusty Colvard, Manager Information Technology
CHR: Susan Nelson–Jones, Director Human Resources
CNO: Juliana Kay Kirby, R.N., Chief Nursing Officer and Directo of Nursing
Web address: www.tvhd.org
**Control:** Hospital district or authority, Government, nonfederal **Service:** General Medical and Surgical

| Staffed Beds: 20 Admissions: 136 Census: 9 Outpatient Visits: 34085 Births: 0 Total Expense ($000): 18862 Payroll Expense ($000): 7742 Personnel: 185 |
| --- |

### TEMPLETON—San Luis Obispo County

⊞ **TWIN CITIES COMMUNITY HOSPITAL (050633)**, 1100 Las Tablas Road, Zip 93465–9704; tel. 805/434–3500 **A1** 9 10 **F13** 15 29 30 31 34 35 37 38 40 45 46 54 55 57 58 59 64 65 74 75 77 78 79 81 82 84 97 107 111 115 119 130 132 144 147 **P3 S** TENET Healthcare Corporation, Dallas, TX
Primary Contact: Mark P. Lisa, FACHE, Chief Executive Officer
CFO: Paul Posmoga, Chief Financial Officer
CMO: Paula Moore, R.N., Chief Nursing Officer
CIO: Scott Harrison, Director Information Systems
CHR: Eloise Rendon, Director Human Resources
Web address: www.twincitieshospital.com
**Control:** Corporation, Investor–owned, for–profit **Service:** General Medical and Surgical

| Staffed Beds: 122 Admissions: 5089 Census: 52 Outpatient Visits: 43868 Births: 734 Total Expense ($000): 77744 Payroll Expense ($000): 30171 |
| --- |

### THOUSAND OAKS—Ventura County

⊞ **LOS ROBLES HOSPITAL AND MEDICAL CENTER (050549)**, 215 West Janss Road, Zip 91360–1847; tel. 805/497–2727, (Nonreporting) **A1** 2 9 10 **S** HCA, Nashville, TN
Primary Contact: Gregory R. Angle, President and Chief Executive Officer
CFO: Debra J. Herwaldt, Chief Financial Officer
CMO: Barry Thall, M.D., Medical Director
CIO: Dan Isozaki, Director Information Management
CHR: Dayle Dalton, Vice President Human Resources
CNO: Cynthia J. Johnson, R.N., Chief Nursing Officer
Web address: www.losrobleshospital.com
**Control:** Corporation, Investor–owned, for–profit **Service:** General Medical and Surgical

| Staffed Beds: 273 |
| --- |

◇ **THOUSAND OAKS SURGICAL HOSPITAL (050749)**, 401 East Rolling Oaks Drive, Zip 91361–1050; tel. 805/777–7750, (Nonreporting) **A**9 10 21
Primary Contact: Robert C. Shaw, President and Chief Executive Officer
CFO: Craig Corley, Chief Financial Officer
CMO: Steven Bansbach, M.D., Medical Director
CIO: Michael Lashley, Network Administrator
CHR: Jean Callahan, Manager Human Resources
Web address: www.toshospital.com
**Control:** Partnership, Investor–owned, for–profit **Service:** General Medical and Surgical

| Staffed Beds: 21 |
| --- |

### TORRANCE—Los Angeles County

☐ **DEL AMO HOSPITAL (054053)**, 23700 Camino Del Sol, Zip 90505–5000; tel. 310/530–1151, (Nonreporting) **A1** 9 10 **S** Universal Health Services, Inc., King of Prussia, PA
Primary Contact: Lisa K. Montes, Chief Executive Officer
Web address: www.delamohospital.com
**Control:** Corporation, Investor–owned, for–profit **Service:** Psychiatric

| Staffed Beds: 70 |
| --- |

☐ **LAC–HARBOR–UNIVERSITY OF CALIFORNIA AT LOS ANGELES MEDICAL CENTER (050376)**, 1000 West Carson Street, Zip 90502–2004; tel. 310/222–2345, (Nonreporting) **A1** 2 3 5 8 10 **S** Los Angeles County–Department of Health Services, Los Angeles, CA
Primary Contact: Delvecchio Finley, Chief Executive Officer
CFO: Jody Nakasuji, Chief Financial Officer
CMO: Gail Anderson, Jr., M.D., Chief Medical Officer
CIO: Sandy Mungovan, Chief Information Officer
CHR: Karyl Smith, Director Human Resources
Web address: www.humc.edu
**Control:** County–Government, nonfederal **Service:** General Medical and Surgical

| Staffed Beds: 350 |
| --- |

⊞ **PROVIDENCE LITTLE COMPANY OF MARY MEDICAL CENTER (050353)**, 4101 Torrance Boulevard, Zip 90503–4607; tel. 310/540–7676, (Total facility includes 77 beds in nursing home–type unit) **A1** 2 9 10 **F8** 11 13 14 15 18 19 20 22 24 26 28 29 30 34 35 40 46 57 59 60 62 64 68 70 72 74 75 76 77 78 79 81 82 85 86 87 89 93 107 108 110 111 114 118 119 120 121 123 126 128 130 132 133 143 144 145 146 147 148 **S** Providence Health & Services, Renton, WA
Primary Contact: Elizabeth Dunne, Chief Executive Officer
CFO: Elizabeth Zuanich, Chief Financial Officer
CMO: Laurence Eason, M.D., Chief Medical Officer
CIO: Douglas Jones, Regional Chief Information Officer
Web address: www.lcmweb.org
**Control:** Other not–for–profit (including NFP Corporation) **Service:** General Medical and Surgical

| Staffed Beds: 379 Admissions: 20914 Census: 249 Outpatient Visits: 221398 Births: 2722 Total Expense ($000): 320186 Payroll Expense ($000): 122595 Personnel: 1600 |
| --- |

*Many Facility Codes have changed. Please refer to the AHA Guide Code Chart.* © 2013 AHA Guide

✠ **TORRANCE MEMORIAL MEDICAL CENTER (050351)**, 3330 Lomita Boulevard, Zip 90505–5002; tel. 310/325–9110 **A**1 2 9 10 **F**3 5 8 11 12 13 14 15 16 17 18 20 22 24 26 28 29 30 31 34 35 36 37 40 41 46 47 49 50 51 54 57 58 59 60 62 63 64 70 72 74 75 76 77 78 79 81 82 83 84 85 86 87 89 91 93 96 107 108 109 110 111 114 115 116 117 118 119 120 121 123 126 128 129 130 132 134 135 143 144 145 146 147 148
Primary Contact: Craig Leach, President and Chief Executive Officer
CMO: David Rand, M.D., Chief of Staff
CIO: Robert Proto, Director Information Systems
CHR: Lois Michael, Vice President Human Resources
Web address: www.torrancememorial.org
**Control:** Other not–for–profit (including NFP Corporation) **Service:** General Medical and Surgical

> **Staffed Beds:** 377 **Admissions:** 24269 **Census:** 276 **Outpatient Visits:** 258637 **Total Expense ($000):** 448263 **Payroll Expense ($000):** 171010 **Personnel:** 2640

### TRACY—San Joaquin County

✠ **SUTTER TRACY COMMUNITY HOSPITAL (050313)**, 1420 North Tracy Boulevard, Zip 95376–3497; tel. 209/835–1500 **A**1 9 10 **F**3 11 13 15 18 29 30 31 34 35 40 43 45 46 49 50 54 57 59 60 64 68 70 74 75 76 78 79 81 82 85 93 97 107 110 111 115 118 119 124 130 132 135 146 **S** Sutter Health, Sacramento, CA
Primary Contact: David M. Thompson, Chief Executive Officer
COO: Doug Archer, Assistant Administrator
CFO: Eric Dalton, Chief Financial Officer
CIO: Karen Mudd, Director Marketing and Public Affairs
CHR: Melanie Wallace, Manager Human Resources
Web address: www.suttertracy.org
**Control:** Other not–for–profit (including NFP Corporation) **Service:** General Medical and Surgical

> **Staffed Beds:** 82 **Admissions:** 3777 **Census:** 38 **Outpatient Visits:** 97311 **Births:** 630 **Total Expense ($000):** 96042 **Payroll Expense ($000):** 32346 **Personnel:** 456

### TRAVIS AFB—Solano County

✠ **DAVID GRANT MEDICAL CENTER**, 101 Bodin Circle, Zip 94535–1809; tel. 707/423–7300 **A**1 3 5 **F**5 7 8 12 13 14 15 17 18 19 20 22 24 26 29 30 31 32 33 34 35 36 38 39 40 41 43 45 46 47 48 49 50 53 54 57 58 59 60 61 64 65 68 70 74 75 76 77 78 79 81 86 87 92 93 94 96 97 98 99 100 101 104 105 106 107 108 109 110 111 114 115 116 117 118 119 120 121 122 123 124 130 131 132 135 143 144 145 146 147 148 **S** Department of the Air Force, Washington, DC
Primary Contact: Colonel Brian T. Hayes, Commander
CFO: Major Jonathan Richards, Chief Financial Officer
CMO: Colonel Chris Scharenbrock, M.D., Chief Medical Staff
Web address: www.travis.af.mil/units/dgmc/index.asp
**Control:** Other not–for–profit (including NFP Corporation) **Service:** General Medical and Surgical

> **Staffed Beds:** 116 **Admissions:** 6220 **Census:** 60 **Outpatient Visits:** 398221 **Births:** 474 **Personnel:** 2481

### TRUCKEE—Nevada County

**TAHOE FOREST HOSPITAL DISTRICT (051328)**, 10121 Pine Avenue, Zip 96161–4856, Mailing Address: P.O. Box 759, Zip 96160–0759; tel. 530/587–6011, (Nonreporting) **A**2 5 9 10 18 **S** Tahoe Forest Health System, Truckee, CA
Primary Contact: Robert A. Schapper, Chief Executive Officer
CFO: Crystal Betts, Chief Financial Officer
CMO: Richard Ganong, M.D., Chief of Staff
CIO: Mark Griffiths, Chief Systems Innovation Officer
CHR: Marcie Mortensson, Chief Human Resources Officer
Web address: www.tfhd.com
**Control:** Hospital district or authority, Government, nonfederal **Service:** General Medical and Surgical

> **Staffed Beds:** 25

### TULARE—Tulare County

✠ ◇ **TULARE REGIONAL MEDICAL CENTER (050359)**, 869 North Cherry Street, Zip 93274–2207; tel. 559/688–0821 **A**1 9 10 21 **F**3 11 13 15 20 26 29 31 34 35 40 45 46 47 48 49 50 53 56 57 59 60 62 64 65 66 68 70 71 73 74 75 76 77 78 79 81 85 86 89 93 97 107 108 110 111 118 119 126 127 129 130 131 132 135 146 147 148
Primary Contact: Shawn Bolouki, Chief Executive Officer
CFO: Michael Bernstein, Chief Financial Officer
CMO: Pradeep Kamboj, M.D., Chief Medical Staff
CIO: Jim Peelgren, Chief Information Officer
CHR: John Barbadian, Vice President Human Resources
CNO: Patricia Mathewson, Chief Nursing Officer
Web address: www.tulareregional.org
**Control:** Hospital district or authority, Government, nonfederal **Service:** General Medical and Surgical

> **Staffed Beds:** 103 **Admissions:** 4231 **Census:** 45 **Outpatient Visits:** 97933 **Births:** 975 **Total Expense ($000):** 83294 **Payroll Expense ($000):** 28236 **Personnel:** 443

### TURLOCK—Stanislaus County

✠ **EMANUEL MEDICAL CENTER (050179)**, 825 Delbon Avenue, Zip 95382–2016, Mailing Address: P.O. Box 819005, Zip 95381–9005; tel. 209/667–4200, (Total facility includes 145 beds in nursing home–type unit) **A**1 2 9 10 **F**3 8 10 11 12 13 15 18 20 22 24 29 30 31 34 35 39 40 47 48 49 54 59 60 63 64 68 70 73 75 76 77 78 79 81 89 93 97 107 108 110 111 114 115 118 119 120 121 123 128 130 132 146 147
Primary Contact: John R. Sigsbury, President and Chief Executive Officer
COO: Michael T. Iltis, Vice President Professional Services
CFO: David Neapolitan, Chief Financial Officer
CMO: David Canton, D.O., Vice President Medical Affairs
CIO: Ken Hoach, Assistant Vice President and Chief Information Officer
CHR: Terry Gray, Vice President Human Resources
CNO: Constance Fairchilds, R.N., Vice President Patient Care Services
Web address: www.emanuelmed.org
**Control:** Church–operated, Nongovernment, not–for profit **Service:** General Medical and Surgical

> **Staffed Beds:** 354 **Admissions:** 9694 **Census:** 239 **Outpatient Visits:** 84922 **Births:** 1333 **Total Expense ($000):** 196504 **Payroll Expense ($000):** 71924 **Personnel:** 1152

### TUSTIN—Orange County

✠ **HEALTHSOUTH TUSTIN REHABILITATION HOSPITAL (053034)**, 14851 Yorba Street, Zip 92780–2925; tel. 714/832–9200 **A**1 9 10 **F**29 34 57 60 74 75 77 82 90 94 130 132 **S** HEALTHSOUTH Corporation, Birmingham, AL
Primary Contact: Diana C. Hanyak, Chief Executive Officer
CFO: Paula Redmond, Controller
CMO: Rodric Bell, M.D., Medical Director
CHR: JoAnn Roiz, PHR, Director Human Resources
Web address: www.tustinrehab.com
**Control:** Corporation, Investor–owned, for–profit **Service:** Rehabilitation

> **Staffed Beds:** 48 **Admissions:** 1388 **Census:** 41 **Outpatient Visits:** 0 **Births:** 0 **Total Expense ($000):** 19269 **Payroll Expense ($000):** 10199

○ **NEWPORT SPECIALTY HOSPITAL (052053)**, 14662 Newport Avenue, Zip 92780–6064; tel. 714/838–9600, (Nonreporting) **A**9 10 11
Primary Contact: Richard Luna, President and Chief Executive Officer
COO: Kara Bourne, R.N., Chief Nursing Officer and Chief Operating Officer
CIO: Darla Kennedy, Chief Information Officer
CHR: Aprille Major, Director Human Resources
Web address: www.newportspecialtyhospital.com/
**Control:** Corporation, Investor–owned, for–profit **Service:** Long–Term Acute Care hospital

> **Staffed Beds:** 155

### TWENTYNINE PALMS—San Bernardino County

✠ **ROBERT E. BUSH NAVAL HOSPITAL**, (Formerly Naval Hospital), Zip 92278; tel. 760/830–2190, (Nonreporting) **A**1 **S** Bureau of Medicine and Surgery, Department of the Navy, Washington, DC
Primary Contact: Lieutenant Commander Brennan Autry, Director Administration
COO: Captain Cynthia J. Gantt, Executive Officer
CFO: Lieutenant Commander Amy Sulog, Comptroller
CMO: Commander Michael E. Cardenas, M.D., Director Medical Services
CHR: Virginia Ward, Human Resources Officer
CNO: Captain Sandra Mason, Director Nursing Services and Senior Nurse Executive
Web address: www.med.navy.mil/sites/nhtp/Pages/default.aspx
**Control:** Navy, Government, federal **Service:** General Medical and Surgical

> **Staffed Beds:** 39

**CA**

---

**Hospital, Medicare Provider Number, Address, Telephone, Approval, Facility, and Physician Codes, Health Care System**

★ American Hospital Association (AHA) membership
☐ The Joint Commission accreditation
◇ DNV Healthcare Inc. accreditation
○ Healthcare Facilities Accreditation Program
△ Commission on Accreditation of Rehabilitation Facilities (CARF) accreditation

## UKIAH—Mendocino County

☒ **UKIAH VALLEY MEDICAL CENTER (050301)**, 275 Hospital Drive, Zip 95482–4531; tel. 707/462–3111 **A**1 5 9 10 19 **F**3 8 11 12 13 15 18 29 30 31 32 34 35 38 40 43 44 45 46 48 49 50 51 54 57 59 60 64 65 68 70 72 75 76 77 78 79 81 82 84 85 86 87 93 94 97 107 108 110 111 114 115 116 117 118 119 127 130 131 132 135 144 146 147 148 **S** Adventist Health, Roseville, CA
Primary Contact: Gwen Matthews, R.N., MSN, Chief Executive Officer
CIO: David Eastman, Site Director
CHR: Rebecca Ryan, Interim Director Human Resources and Employee Health
Web address: www.adventisthealth.org
**Control:** Church–operated, Nongovernment, not–for profit **Service:** General Medical and Surgical

**Staffed Beds:** 48 **Admissions:** 4105 **Census:** 33 **Outpatient Visits:** 218237 **Births:** 909 **Total Expense ($000):** 108772 **Payroll Expense ($000):** 37161 **Personnel:** 623

## UPLAND—San Bernardino County

☒ **SAN ANTONIO COMMUNITY HOSPITAL (050099)**, 999 San Bernardino Road, Zip 91786–4920, Mailing Address: Box 5001, Zip 91785–5001; tel. 909/985–2811 **A**1 2 9 10 **F**3 8 11 13 15 17 18 20 22 24 26 28 29 31 35 38 40 45 46 49 50 54 57 59 60 61 64 65 69 70 72 74 75 76 77 78 79 80 81 82 83 84 85 86 87 89 91 92 93 94 107 108 110 111 114 115 118 119 121 123 124 130 132 146 147 148
Primary Contact: Harris F. Koenig, President and Chief Executive Officer
CFO: Roger Parsons, Senior Vice President Finance
CMO: Thomas Easter, M.D., President Medical Staff
CIO: Perry Strength, Director Information Services
CHR: Lynn Kelly, Vice President Human Resources
Web address: www.sach.org
**Control:** Other not–for–profit (including NFP Corporation) **Service:** General Medical and Surgical

**Staffed Beds:** 279 **Admissions:** 15073 **Census:** 151 **Outpatient Visits:** 210808 **Births:** 2155 **Total Expense ($000):** 272380 **Payroll Expense ($000):** 114780 **Personnel:** 1562

## VACAVILLE—Solano County

**CALIFORNIA MEDICAL FACILITY**, 1600 California Drive, Zip 95696–2000; tel. 707/448–6841, (Nonreporting)
Primary Contact: Mary Lou Dunlap, Correctional Health Services Administrator
CMO: Raymond Andreasen, M.D., Chief Medical Officer–Inpatient
Web address: www.cya.ca.gov/visitors/fac_prison_cmf.html
**Control:** State–Government, nonfederal **Service:** Hospital unit of an institution (prison hospital, college infimary, etc.)

**Staffed Beds:** 215

☒ **KAISER PERMANENTE VACAVILLE MEDICAL CENTER (050767)**, (Formerly Vacaville Medical Center), 1 Quality Drive, Zip 95688–9494; tel. 707/624–4000, (Nonreporting) **A**1 10 **S** Kaiser Foundation Hospitals, Oakland, CA
Primary Contact: Max Villalobos, Senior Vice President
Web address: www.kp.org
**Control:** Other not–for–profit (including NFP Corporation) **Service:** General Medical and Surgical

**Staffed Beds:** 64

**NORTHBAY VACAVALLEY HOSPITAL** See NorthBay Medical Center, Fairfield

## VALENCIA—Los Angeles County

☒ **HENRY MAYO NEWHALL MEMORIAL HOSPITAL (050624)**, 23845 McBean Parkway, Zip 91355–2083; tel. 661/253–8000 **A**1 2 9 10 **F**3 7 8 11 15 17 18 20 22 24 26 28 29 30 31 34 35 40 43 45 49 54 57 59 60 64 70 72 74 76 77 78 79 81 84 85 86 87 90 93 98 102 104 107 108 109 110 114 115 118 119 130 132 135 146 147 148 **P**5
Primary Contact: Roger E. Seaver, President and Chief Executive Officer
COO: John V. Schleif, Senior Vice President and Chief Operating Officer
CFO: C. R. Hudson, Senior Vice President and Chief Financial Officer
CMO: Richard Frankenstein, M.D., Vice President and Chief Medical Officer
CIO: Cindy Peterson, Vice President and Chief Information Officer
CHR: Mark Puleo, Vice President and Chief Human Resources Officer
CNO: Larry R. Kidd, R.N., Vice President and Chief Nursing Officer
Web address: www.henrymayo.com
**Control:** Other not–for–profit (including NFP Corporation) **Service:** General Medical and Surgical

**Staffed Beds:** 238 **Admissions:** 11727 **Census:** 145 **Outpatient Visits:** 90474 **Births:** 1181 **Total Expense ($000):** 224059 **Payroll Expense ($000):** 69530 **Personnel:** 1243

## VALLEJO—Solano County

☒ △ **KAISER PERMANENTE VALLEJO MEDICAL CENTER (050073)**, (Formerly Vallejo Medical Center), 975 Sereno Drive, Zip 94589–2441; tel. 707/651–1000, (Nonreporting) **A**1 7 10 **S** Kaiser Foundation Hospitals, Oakland, CA
Primary Contact: Max Villalobos, Senior Vice President and Area Manager
COO: Karen Grisnak, R.N., Chief Operating Officer and Assistant Administrator Quality Services
CFO: Joseph D'Angina, Area Finance Officer
CMO: Steven Stricker, M.D., Physician in Chief
CIO: Gale Austin–Moore, Director Area Technology
CHR: Sherri Stegge, Director Human Resources
Web address: www.kaiserpermanente.org
**Control:** Other not–for–profit (including NFP Corporation) **Service:** General Medical and Surgical

**Staffed Beds:** 248

☒ **ST. HELENA HOSPITAL–CENTER FOR BEHAVIORAL HEALTH (054074)**, 525 Oregon Street, Zip 94590–3201; tel. 707/648–2200 **A**1 9 10 **F**29 30 35 50 64 65 68 98 99 104 105 130 146 **S** Adventist Health, Roseville, CA
Primary Contact: Terry Newmyer, President and Chief Executive Officer
CFO: Edward A. McDonald, Chief Financial Officer
Web address: www.sthelenahospital.org/Behavioral/
**Control:** Other not–for–profit (including NFP Corporation) **Service:** Psychiatric

**Staffed Beds:** 61 **Admissions:** 2400 **Census:** 56 **Births:** 0

☒ **SUTTER SOLANO MEDICAL CENTER (050101)**, 300 Hospital Drive, Zip 94589–2574, Mailing Address: P.O. Box 3189, Zip 94590–0669; tel. 707/554–4444 **A**1 2 9 10 **F**3 8 11 13 15 18 26 29 30 31 34 35 40 45 49 50 51 55 57 58 59 64 68 70 74 75 76 77 78 79 81 84 85 86 87 89 90 100 107 108 110 111 114 118 119 120 121 123 124 130 132 146 **S** Sutter Health, Sacramento, CA
Primary Contact: Theresa Glubka, Chief Executive Officer
CFO: Cynthia van Hoff, Chief Financial Officer
CHR: Jean Willhite, Director Human Resources
Web address: www.suttersolano.org
**Control:** Other not–for–profit (including NFP Corporation) **Service:** General Medical and Surgical

**Staffed Beds:** 102 **Admissions:** 4946 **Census:** 50 **Outpatient Visits:** 67869 **Births:** 659 **Total Expense ($000):** 133142 **Payroll Expense ($000):** 43370 **Personnel:** 461

## VAN NUYS—Los Angeles County, See Los Angeles

## VENTURA—Ventura County

☐ **AURORA VISTA DEL MAR HOSPITAL (054077)**, 801 Seneca Street, Zip 93001–1411; tel. 805/653–6434, (Nonreporting) **A**1 9 10 **S** Aurora Behavioral Health Care, Corona, CA
Primary Contact: Mayla Krebsbach, Chief Executive Officer
COO: Sherri Block, Chief Operating Officer
CFO: Cory Delello, Chief Financial Officer
CMO: Robert M. Carvalho, M.D., Medical Director
Web address: www.vistadelmarhospital.com
**Control:** Corporation, Investor–owned, for–profit **Service:** Psychiatric

**Staffed Beds:** 87

☒ ◇ **COMMUNITY MEMORIAL HEALTH SYSTEM (050394)**, 147 North Brent Street, Zip 93003–2854; tel. 805/652–5011, (Includes COMMUNITY MEMORIAL HOSPITAL, 147 North Brent Street, tel. 805/652–5011; OJAI VALLEY COMMUNITY HOSPITAL, 1306 Maricopa Highway, Ojai, Zip 93023–3163; tel. 805/646–1401; Haady Lashkari, Chief Administrative Officer), (Nonreporting) **A**1 2 9 10 21
Primary Contact: Gary Wilde, President and Chief Executive Officer
COO: Adam Thunell, Chief Operating Officer and Vice President Operations
CFO: David Glyer, Vice President Finance
CMO: Stanley Frochtzwajg, M.D., Chief Medical Officer
CIO: Ron Sandifer, Chief Information Officer
CHR: Diany Klein, Vice President Human Resources
Web address: www.cmhshealth.org
**Control:** Other not–for–profit (including NFP Corporation) **Service:** General Medical and Surgical

**Staffed Beds:** 345

☐ **VENTURA COUNTY MEDICAL CENTER (050159)**, 3291 Loma Vista Road, Zip 93003–3099; tel. 805/652–6000, (Nonreporting) **A**1 9 10
Primary Contact: Robert Gonzalez, M.D., Director
COO: Christina B. Thielst, Chief Operating Officer
CFO: Catherine Rodriguez, Chief Financial Officer
CIO: David Herzog, Chief Information Officer
CHR: Maria Teran, Personnel Officer
Web address: www.vchca.org
**Control:** County–Government, nonfederal **Service:** General Medical and Surgical

**Staffed Beds:** 160

*Many Facility Codes have changed. Please refer to the AHA Guide Code Chart.*    © 2013 AHA Guide

**CA**

## VICTORVILLE—San Bernardino County

★ ○ **DESERT VALLEY HOSPITAL (050709)**, 16850 Bear Valley Road, Zip 92395–5794; tel. 760/241–8000, (Nonreporting) **A**9 10 11 **S** Prime Healthcare Services, Ontario, CA
Primary Contact: Margaret R. Peterson, Ph.D., R.N., Chief Executive Officer
COO: Luis Leon, Chief Operating Officer
CFO: Martin Mansukhani, Chief Financial Officer
CIO: Sreekant Gotti, Director Information Systems
CHR: Arti Dhuper, Regional Director Human Resources
CNO: Phyllis Armstrong, R.N., Interim Chief Nursing Officer
Web address: www.dvmc.com
**Control:** Corporation, Investor–owned, for–profit **Service:** General Medical and Surgical

**Staffed Beds:** 75

○ **VICTOR VALLEY COMMUNITY HOSPITAL (050517)**, 15248 Eleventh Street, Zip 92395–3704; tel. 760/245–8691, (Nonreporting) **A**9 10 11 **S** Prime Healthcare Services, Ontario, CA
Primary Contact: Suzanne Richards, R.N., M.P.H., Interim Chief Executive Officer
COO: Doreen Dann, R.N., Chief Operating Officer
CIO: Joe Archer, Chief Information Officer
CHR: Cesar Lugo, Director Human Resources
Web address: www.vvch.org
**Control:** Other not–for–profit (including NFP Corporation) **Service:** General Medical and Surgical

**Staffed Beds:** 115

## VISALIA—Tulare County

⊠ △ **KAWEAH DELTA MEDICAL CENTER (050057)**, 400 West Mineral King Boulevard, Zip 93291–6263; tel. 559/624–2000, (Includes SOUTH CAMPUS, 1633 South Court Street, Zip 93277; tel. 559/624–6090), (Total facility includes 58 beds in nursing home–type unit) **A**1 7 9 10 **F**3 5 13 15 17 18 20 22 24 26 28 29 30 31 34 35 40 41 43 45 49 50 51 53 54 56 57 59 60 62 63 64 65 68 70 73 74 75 76 77 78 79 81 82 84 85 86 87 89 90 93 97 98 99 100 101 102 103 104 107 108 110 111 114 116 117 118 119 123 124 126 127 128 129 130 131 132 134 135 144 146 147 148 **P**7
Primary Contact: Lindsay K. Mann, Chief Executive Officer
CFO: Gary Herbst, Senior Vice President and Chief Financial Officer
CMO: Mark Garfield, M.D., Vice President and Chief Medical Officer
CIO: Dave Gravender, Vice President and Chief Information Officer
CHR: Debbie Wood, Vice President Human Resources
Web address: www.kaweahdelta.org
**Control:** Hospital district or authority, Government, nonfederal **Service:** General Medical and Surgical

**Staffed Beds:** 421 **Admissions:** 23026 **Census:** 360 **Outpatient Visits:** 601078 **Births:** 4217 **Total Expense ($000):** 422535 **Payroll Expense ($000):** 182647 **Personnel:** 2995

## WALNUT CREEK—Contra Costa County

⊠ △ **JOHN MUIR MEDICAL CENTER, WALNUT CREEK (050180)**, 1601 Ygnacio Valley Road, Zip 94598–3194; tel. 925/939–3000 **A**1 2 7 9 10 **F**1 3 4 11 13 15 16 17 18 20 22 24 26 28 29 30 31 34 35 37 39 40 43 44 45 46 47 49 50 54 56 57 58 59 60 62 64 65 67 68 70 72 73 74 75 76 77 78 79 80 81 82 84 85 86 87 88 89 90 93 96 98 100 102 107 108 110 118 119 120 121 123 124 126 128 130 131 132 135 141 145 146 147 148 **P**3 4 5 **S** John Muir Health, Walnut Creek, CA
Primary Contact: Jane Willemsen, Chief Administrative Officer
COO: Raymond Nassief, Senior Vice President Operations and Clinical Transformation
CFO: Michael Moody, Senior Vice President and Chief Financial Officer
CMO: Irving Pike, M.D., Chief Medical Officer
CIO: Jim Wesley, Interim Chief Information Officer
CHR: Alice A. Villanueva, Senior Vice President Human Resources
CNO: Debra Pendergast, Senior Vice President Patient Care Services and Chief Nursing Officer
Web address: www.jmmdhs.com/index.php/jmmdhs_jmmc.html
**Control:** Other not–for–profit (including NFP Corporation) **Service:** General Medical and Surgical

**Staffed Beds:** 367 **Admissions:** 17831 **Census:** 240 **Outpatient Visits:** 309157 **Births:** 2630 **Total Expense ($000):** 709293 **Payroll Expense ($000):** 276198 **Personnel:** 2457

⊠ **KAISER PERMANENTE WALNUT CREEK MEDICAL CENTER (050072)**, (Formerly Walnut Creek Medical Center), 1425 South Main Street, Zip 94596–5300; tel. 925/295–4000, (Includes KAISER FOUNDATION HOSPITAL, 200 Muir Road, Martinez, Zip 94553–4696; tel. 510/372–1000) **A**1 3 5 10 **F**3 5 8 9 13 15 18 29 30 31 32 34 35 36 38 40 45 49 50 54 56 57 59 60 61 62 63 64 65 68 70 73 74 75 76 77 78 79 81 82 83 84 85 86 87 89 91 92 93 94 96 97 99 100 101 102 103 104 107 108 110 111 114 115 116 117 118 119 126 130 132 134 135 144 146 147 148 **S** Kaiser Foundation Hospitals, Oakland, CA
Primary Contact: Colleen McKeown, Senior Vice President and Area Manager
CFO: Yakesun Wing, Business Strategy and Finance Leader
CIO: Kevin Wheeler, Information Technology Leader
Web address: www.kaiserpermanente.org
**Control:** Other not–for–profit (including NFP Corporation) **Service:** General Medical and Surgical

**Staffed Beds:** 233 **Admissions:** 14885 **Census:** 175 **Births:** 3608 **Personnel:** 3281

## WATSONVILLE—Santa Cruz County

⊠ **WATSONVILLE COMMUNITY HOSPITAL (050194)**, 75 Nielson Street, Zip 95076–2468; tel. 831/724–4741, (Nonreporting) **A**1 9 10 **S** Community Health Systems, Inc., Franklin, TN
Primary Contact: Audra Earle, Chief Executive Officer
CFO: Dennis T. Bynum, Interim Chief Financial Officer
CMO: Robert Weber, M.D., Chief Medical Staff
CIO: Sergio Nell, Director Information Systems
CHR: Jeri Gilbert, Director Human Resources
CNO: Sherri Stout–Torres, Chief Nursing Officer
Web address: www.watsonvillehospital.com
**Control:** Other not–for–profit (including NFP Corporation) **Service:** General Medical and Surgical

**Staffed Beds:** 106

## WEAVERVILLE—Trinity County

**TRINITY HOSPITAL (051315)**, 60 Easter Avenue, Zip 96093, Mailing Address: P.O. Box 1229, Zip 96093 1229; tel. 530/623 5541, (Total facility includes 26 beds in nursing home–type unit) **A**9 10 18 **F**3 11 29 30 34 39 40 45 57 62 64 81 107 114 119 128 130 133
Primary Contact: Thomas Pyper, Chief Executive Officer
COO: Thomas Pyper, Chief Executive Officer
CMO: Hank Edelstein, M.D., Chief of Staff
CIO: Jennifer Van Matre, Director Finance and Information Technology
CHR: Nanci Hankerd, Manager Human Resources
CNO: Veena Vangari, R.N., Director of Nursing
Web address: www.mcmedical.org
**Control:** Hospital district or authority, Government, nonfederal **Service:** General Medical and Surgical

**Staffed Beds:** 47 **Admissions:** 420 **Census:** 25 **Outpatient Visits:** 36564 **Births:** 0 **Total Expense ($000):** 14379 **Payroll Expense ($000):** 6479 **Personnel:** 145

## WEST COVINA—Los Angeles County

☐ **DOCTORS HOSPITAL OF WEST COVINA (050096)**, 725 South Orange Avenue, Zip 91790–2614; tel. 626/338–8481, (Total facility includes 24 beds in nursing home–type unit) **A**1 9 10 **F**81 93 104 105 128 130 132
Primary Contact: Gerald H. Wallman, Administrator
CFO: Kami Horvat, Chief Financial Officer
CMO: Nashat Ateia, M.D., Chief of Staff
CHR: Lourdes Meza, Coordinator Human Resources
CNO: Rita Lawrence, Director of Nursing
**Control:** Corporation, Investor–owned, for–profit **Service:** General Medical and Surgical

**Staffed Beds:** 51 **Admissions:** 149 **Census:** 22 **Outpatient Visits:** 4033 **Personnel:** 118

## WEST HILLS—Los Angeles County, See Los Angeles

## WEST LOS ANGELES—Los Angeles County, See Los Angeles

## WESTMINSTER—Orange County

⊠ **KINDRED HOSPITAL–WESTMINSTER (052035)**, 200 Hospital Circle, Zip 92683–3910; tel. 714/893–4541, (Nonreporting) **A**1 9 10 **S** Kindred Healthcare, Louisville, KY
Primary Contact: Brooke Saunders, Administrator
CFO: Dale Wagner, Chief Financial Officer
Web address: www.khwestminster.com/
**Control:** Corporation, Investor–owned, for–profit **Service:** Long–Term Acute Care hospital

**Staffed Beds:** 99

---

**Hospital, Medicare Provider Number, Address, Telephone, Approval, Facility, and Physician Codes, Health Care System**

★ American Hospital Association (AHA) membership
☐ The Joint Commission accreditation
◇ DNV Healthcare Inc. accreditation
○ Healthcare Facilities Accreditation Program
△ Commission on Accreditation of Rehabilitation Facilities (CARF) accreditation

## WHITTIER—Los Angeles County

✠ **PRESBYTERIAN INTERCOMMUNITY HOSPITAL (050169)**, 12401 Washington Boulevard, Zip 90602–1099; tel. 562/698–0811, (Total facility includes 35 beds in nursing home–type unit) **A**1 2 9 10 **F**3 11 13 14 15 17 18 20 22 24 26 28 29 30 31 34 35 36 37 40 44 45 46 49 50 51 54 55 56 57 58 59 60 61 62 63 64 65 66 68 69 70 71 72 74 75 76 77 78 79 81 84 85 86 87 89 90 92 93 96 107 108 110 111 114 115 116 117 118 119 120 121 123 124 128 130 131 132 135 143 145 146 147 148 **P**3 5
Primary Contact: James R. West, President and Chief Executive Officer
CFO: Mitchell T. Thomas, Chief Financial Officer
CMO: Rosalio J. Lopez, M.D., Senior Vice President and Chief Medical Officer
CIO: Peggy Chulack, Chief Administrative Officer and Chief Information Officer
CHR: Lon Orey, Vice President Human Resources
Web address: www.whittierpres.com
**Control:** Other not–for–profit (including NFP Corporation) **Service:** General Medical and Surgical

**Staffed Beds:** 444 **Admissions:** 17585 **Census:** 219 **Outpatient Visits:** 236026 **Births:** 3495 **Total Expense ($000):** 437816 **Payroll Expense ($000):** 158591 **Personnel:** 2665

☐ **WHITTIER HOSPITAL MEDICAL CENTER (050735)**, 9080 Colima Road, Zip 90605–1600; tel. 562/945–3561, (Nonreporting) **A**1 9 10 **S** AHMC & Healthcare, Inc., Alhambra, CA
Primary Contact: Richard Castro, Chief Executive Officer
COO: Mary Anne Monje, Chief Financial Officer and Chief Operating Officer
CFO: Mary Anne Monje, Chief Financial Officer and Chief Operating Officer
CIO: Jay Geldhof, Director Information Systems
CHR: Tamera Jones, Director Human Resources
Web address: www.whittierhospital.com
**Control:** Corporation, Investor–owned, for–profit **Service:** General Medical and Surgical

**Staffed Beds:** 100

## WILLITS—Mendocino County

✠ **FRANK R. HOWARD MEMORIAL HOSPITAL (051310)**, One Madrone Street, Zip 95490–4225; tel. 707/459–6801 **A**1 9 10 18 **F**11 15 29 30 34 35 40 57 59 68 70 75 79 81 93 107 110 111 115 119 131 132 133 135 146 147 148 **S** Adventist Health, Roseville, CA
Primary Contact: Rick Bockmann, Chief Executive Officer
CFO: Carlton Jacobson, Vice President Finance
Web address: www.howardhospital.com
**Control:** Church–operated, Nongovernment, not–for profit **Service:** General Medical and Surgical

**Staffed Beds:** 25 **Admissions:** 1356 **Census:** 16 **Outpatient Visits:** 35804 **Births:** 2 **Total Expense ($000):** 41882 **Payroll Expense ($000):** 16768 **Personnel:** 204

## WILLOWS—Glenn County

**GLENN MEDICAL CENTER (051306)**, 1133 West Sycamore Street, Zip 95988–2601; tel. 530/934–1800, (Nonreporting) **A**9 10 18
Primary Contact: Woody J. Laughnan, Jr., Administrator
CFO: Gary Pea, Chief Financial Officer
CMO: Mark Garrison, Chief of Staff
CHR: Deborah McMillan, Director Human Resources
Web address: www.glennmed.org
**Control:** Other not–for–profit (including NFP Corporation) **Service:** General Medical and Surgical

**Staffed Beds:** 15

## WOODLAND—Yolo County

✠ **WOODLAND HEALTHCARE (050127)**, 1325 Cottonwood Street, Zip 95695–5199; tel. 530/662–3961, (Nonreporting) **A**1 5 9 10 **S** Dignity Health, San Francisco, CA
Primary Contact: H. Kevin Vaziri, President
Web address: www.woodlandhealthcare.org
**Control:** Other not–for–profit (including NFP Corporation) **Service:** General Medical and Surgical

**Staffed Beds:** 111

## WOODLAND HILLS—Los Angeles County, See Los Angeles

## YREKA—Siskiyou County

☐ **FAIRCHILD MEDICAL CENTER (051316)**, 444 Bruce Street, Zip 96097–3450; tel. 530/842–4121, (Nonreporting) **A**1 9 10 18
Primary Contact: Jonathon Andrus, Chief Executive Officer
CFO: Kelly Martin, Chief Financial Officer
CMO: David Della Lana, M.D., Chief of Staff
CIO: Joan Munson, Manager Information Systems
CHR: Joann Sarmento, Manager Human Resources
CNO: Kathy Shelvock, R.N., Assistant Administrator Patient Care Services
Web address: www.fairchildmed.org
**Control:** Other not–for–profit (including NFP Corporation) **Service:** General Medical and Surgical

**Staffed Beds:** 25

## YUBA CITY—Sutter County

**FREMONT MEDICAL CENTER** See Fremont–Rideout Health Group, Marysville

☐ **SUTTER SURGICAL HOSPITAL – NORTH VALLEY (050766)**, 455 Plumas Boulevard, Zip 95991–5074; tel. 530/749–5700 **A**1 9 10 **F**3 29 30 34 47 57 64 68 81 82 85 111 124 146
Primary Contact: Toni Morris, Chief Executive Officer
COO: David Cooke, Chief Nursing Officer
CFO: Renee Schroyer, Chief Financial Officer
CHR: Cynthia Jeter, Director Human Resources
Web address: www.sshnv.org
**Control:** Corporation, Investor–owned, for–profit **Service:** Surgical

**Staffed Beds:** 14 **Admissions:** 528 **Census:** 4 **Outpatient Visits:** 2626 **Births:** 0 **Total Expense ($000):** 19448 **Payroll Expense ($000):** 5264 **Personnel:** 101

*Many Facility Codes have changed. Please refer to the AHA Guide Code Chart.* © 2013 AHA Guide

# COLORADO

## ALAMOSA—Alamosa County

★ **SAN LUIS VALLEY REGIONAL MEDICAL CENTER (060008)**, 106 Blanca Avenue, Zip 81101–2393; tel. 719/589–2511 **A**9 10 20 **F**3 7 11 13 15 29 30 31 33 40 43 53 70 75 76 77 78 79 81 85 93 104 107 111 114 119 129 130 131 146 147 148 **P**6
Primary Contact: Konnie Martin, Chief Executive Officer
CFO: Shane Mortensen, Chief Financial Officer
CMO: Gregory McAuliffe, M.D., Chief Medical Officer
CIO: Patricia Allvin, Account Executive Information Technology
CHR: Mandy Lee Crockett, Director Human Resources
Web address: www.slvrmc.org
**Control:** Other not–for–profit (including NFP Corporation) **Service:** General Medical and Surgical

**Staffed Beds: 44 Admissions: 2224 Census: 18 Outpatient Visits: 100806 Births: 524 Total Expense ($000): 57072 Payroll Expense ($000): 32502 Personnel: 494**

## ASPEN—Pitkin County

✠ **ASPEN VALLEY HOSPITAL DISTRICT (061324)**, 401 Castle Creek Road, Zip 81611–1159; tel. 970/925–1120, (Nonreporting) **A**1 9 10 18
Primary Contact: John Sarpa, Interim Chief Executive Officer
CFO: Terry Collins, Chief Financial Officer
CMO: J. Christopher Beck, D.O., President Medical Staff
CIO: Ginny Dyche, Director Community Relations
CHR: Alicia Miller, Director Human Resources
CNO: Elaine Gerson, Chief Clinical Officer and General Counsel
Web address: www.avhaspen.org
**Control:** Hospital district or authority, Government, nonfederal **Service:** General Medical and Surgical

**Staffed Beds: 25**

## AURORA—Adams County

✠ **CHILDREN'S HOSPITAL COLORADO (063301)**, 13123 East 16th Avenue, Zip 80045–7106; tel. 720/777–1234 **A**1 3 5 9 10 **F**3 11 12 13 14 17 19 21 23 25 27 28 29 30 31 32 34 35 36 38 39 40 41 42 43 44 45 46 48 49 50 53 54 55 58 59 60 61 64 65 66 68 71 72 74 75 77 78 79 81 82 84 85 86 87 88 89 91 92 93 95 96 97 98 99 100 101 102 104 105 107 108 111 113 114 115 116 117 118 126 129 130 131 132 134 136 137 138 139 141 144 145 146 147 148 **P**8
Primary Contact: James E. Shmerling, President and Chief Executive Officer
COO: Jena Hausmann, Executive Vice President and Chief Operating Officer
CFO: Len Dryer, Chief Financial Officer
CMO: Joan Bothner, M.D., Chief Medical Officer
CIO: Mary Ann Leach, Vice President and Chief Information Officer
CHR: Michael Wukitsch, Chief Human Resources Officer
Web address: www.thechildrenshospital.org
**Control:** Other not–for–profit (including NFP Corporation) **Service:** Children's general

**Staffed Beds: 440 Admissions: 14259 Census: 236 Outpatient Visits: 574422 Births: 25 Total Expense ($000): 688555 Payroll Expense ($000): 291082 Personnel: 4500**

✠ **KINDRED HOSPITAL–AURORA (062013)**, 700 Potomac Street 2nd Floor, Zip 80011–6844; tel. 720/857–8333, (Nonreporting) **A**1 9 10 **S** Kindred Healthcare, Louisville, KY
Primary Contact: Nicole Reinhardt, Chief Executive Officer
Web address: www.khaurora.com/
**Control:** Corporation, Investor–owned, for–profit **Service:** Long–Term Acute Care hospital

**Staffed Beds: 37**

✠ **MEDICAL CENTER OF AURORA (060100)**, 1501 South Potomac Street, Zip 80012–5411; tel. 303/695–2600, (Includes MEDICAL CENTER OF AURORA NORTH, 700 Potomac Street, Zip 80011–6792; tel. 303/363–7200; SOUTH CAMPUS, 1501 South Potomac, Zip 80012; tel. 303/695–2600), (Nonreporting) **A**1 2 9 10 **S** HCA, Nashville, TN
Primary Contact: Richard A. Hammett, Chief Executive Officer
COO: Mary Berrigan, Chief Operating Officer
Web address: www.auroramed.com
**Control:** Corporation, Investor–owned, for–profit **Service:** General Medical and Surgical

**Staffed Beds: 303**

✠ △ **SPALDING REHABILITATION HOSPITAL (063027)**, 900 Potomac Steet, Zip 80011–6716; tel. 303/367–1166, (Nonreporting) **A**1 7 10 **S** HCA, Nashville, TN
Primary Contact: Cynthia Kreutz, Chief Executive Officer
COO: Debbie Petersen, R.N., Chief Operating Officer and Chief Nursing Officer
CFO: Joyce Webber, Chief Financial Officer
CHR: Donna Greeley, Director Human Resources
CNO: Debbie Petersen, R.N., Chief Operating Officer and Chief Nursing Officer
Web address: www.spaldingrehab.com
**Control:** Partnership, Investor–owned, for–profit **Service:** Rehabilitation

**Staffed Beds: 40**

✠ **UNIVERSITY OF COLORADO HOSPITAL (060024)**, 12605 East 16th Avenue, Zip 80045–2545; tel. 720/848–0000 **A**1 2 3 5 8 9 10 **F**3 4 5 6 8 9 11 12 13 15 16 17 18 20 22 24 25 28 30 31 33 34 35 36 37 38 39 40 43 44 45 46 47 48 49 50 52 53 54 55 56 57 58 59 60 61 64 65 68 70 72 74 75 76 77 78 79 81 82 84 85 86 87 90 92 93 94 96 97 99 100 101 102 103 104 107 108 110 111 113 114 115 117 118 119 120 121 123 124 126 130 131 132 134 135 136 137 138 139 140 141 142 146 147 148 **S** University of Colorado Health, Fort Collins, CO
Primary Contact: Bruce Schroffel, President and Chief Executive Officer
COO: John Harney, Chief Operating Officer
CFO: Anthony C. DeFurio, Vice President and Chief Financial Officer
CMO: Greg Stiegmann, M.D., Vice President Clinical Affairs
CIO: Steve Hess, Vice President Information Services and Chief Information Officer
CHR: Darryl Varnado, Vice President Human Resources
Web address: www.uch.edu
**Control:** Hospital district or authority, Government, nonfederal **Service:** General Medical and Surgical

**Staffed Beds: 467 Admissions: 24791 Census: 380 Outpatient Visits: 780307 Births: 3054 Total Expense ($000): 820374 Payroll Expense ($000): 288165 Personnel: 5021**

## BOULDER—Boulder County

✠ △ **BOULDER COMMUNITY HOSPITAL (060027)**, 1100 Balsam Avenue, Zip 80304–3496, Mailing Address: P.O. Box 9019, Zip 80301–9019; tel. 303/440–2273, (Includes BOULDER COMMUNITY FOOTHILLS HOSPITAL, 4747 Arapahoe Avenue, Zip 80303–1133, Mailing Address: P.O. Box 9047, Zip 80301–9047; tel. 720/854–7000) **A**1 2 3 5 7 9 10 **F**18 19 20 22 24 25 26 28 29 30 34 37 40 43 50 53 54 57 59 60 62 64 68 70 72 74 75 76 77 78 79 81 82 87 90 97 98 107 111 116 119 124 126 129 130 131 144 146 147 148 **P**4 5
Primary Contact: David P. Gehant, President and Chief Executive Officer
CFO: Bill Munson, Vice President and Chief Financial Officer
Web address: www.bch.org
**Control:** Other not–for–profit (including NFP Corporation) **Service:** General Medical and Surgical

**Staffed Beds: 178 Admissions: 8690 Census: 100 Outpatient Visits: 416372 Births: 1294 Total Expense ($000): 281073 Payroll Expense ($000): 122890 Personnel: 1778**

## BRIGHTON—Adams County

✠ **PLATTE VALLEY MEDICAL CENTER (060004)**, 1600 Prairie Center Parkway, Zip 80601–4006; tel. 303/498–1600 **A**1 5 9 10 **F**3 7 13 15 18 20 22 26 28 29 30 31 35 40 43 45 49 57 68 70 72 74 75 76 77 78 79 81 85 87 89 90 92 93 107 108 110 111 115 119 130 132 135 146 147 148
Primary Contact: John R. Hicks, President and Chief Executive Officer
COO: Kurt Gensert, R.N., Vice President Operations
CFO: Harold Dupper, Chief Financial Officer
CMO: Kirk Quackenbush, M.D., Chief of Staff
CIO: Darrell Messersmith, Director Information Systems
CHR: Jackie J. Dunkin, Director Human Resources
Web address: www.pvmc.org
**Control:** Other not–for–profit (including NFP Corporation) **Service:** General Medical and Surgical

**Staffed Beds: 70 Admissions: 3258 Census: 25 Outpatient Visits: 64851 Births: 948 Total Expense ($000): 89433 Payroll Expense ($000): 30065 Personnel: 550**

CO

---

**Hospital, Medicare Provider Number, Address, Telephone, Approval, Facility, and Physician Codes, Health Care System**

★ American Hospital Association (AHA) membership
☐ The Joint Commission accreditation
◇ DNV Healthcare Inc. accreditation
○ Healthcare Facilities Accreditation Program
△ Commission on Accreditation of Rehabilitation Facilities (CARF) accreditation

## BRUSH—Morgan County

★ **EAST MORGAN COUNTY HOSPITAL (061303)**, 2400 West Edison Street, Zip 80723–1640; tel. 970/842–6200 **A**9 10 18 **F**8 11 15 28 29 30 31 34 35 36 40 45 50 51 53 57 59 64 68 70 75 77 78 79 81 85 87 93 96 97 107 108 110 111 115 119 127 130 131 132 133 146 148 **P**6 **S** Banner Health, Phoenix, AZ
Primary Contact: Linda Thorpe, Chief Executive Officer
CFO: James Cussins, Chief Financial Officer
CMO: Jay Talluri, M.D., Chief Medical Officer
CIO: Michael S. Warden, Senior Vice President and Chief Information Officer
CHR: Jeannie Gallagher, Human Resource Generalist
CNO: Patience M. Samples, R.N., Chief Nursing Officer
Web address: www.emchbrush.com
**Control:** Other not–for–profit (including NFP Corporation) **Service:** General Medical and Surgical

**Staffed Beds:** 19 **Admissions:** 601 **Census:** 6 **Outpatient Visits:** 72607 **Births:** 0 **Total Expense ($000):** 21836 **Payroll Expense ($000):** 10900 **Personnel:** 131

## BURLINGTON—Kit Carson County

★ **KIT CARSON COUNTY MEMORIAL HOSPITAL (061313)**, 286 16th Street, Zip 80807–1697; tel. 719/346–5311, (Nonreporting) **A**9 10 18
Primary Contact: Donald Wade, Interim Chief Executive Officer
CFO: Mona Ebsen, Chief Financial Officer
CMO: James Perez, M.D., Chief Medical Officer
CIO: Arlan Tanner, Chief Information Officer
CHR: Robin Konecne, Manager Human Resources
Web address: www.kccmh.org
**Control:** Hospital district or authority, Government, nonfederal **Service:** General Medical and Surgical

**Staffed Beds:** 19

## CANON CITY—Fremont County

⊠ **ST. THOMAS MORE HOSPITAL (060016)**, 1338 Phay Avenue, Zip 81212–2302; tel. 719/285–2000 **A**1 9 10 20 **F**3 8 11 12 13 14 15 29 30 34 35 40 43 51 53 57 59 64 66 69 70 75 76 77 79 81 82 85 86 87 89 93 97 107 108 110 111 119 127 128 129 131 132 133 135 146 147 148 **S** Catholic Health Initiatives, Englewood, CO
Primary Contact: Sheri Trahern, CPA, MBA, FACHE, Chief Administrative and Chief Financial Officer
COO: Rick Kamerzell, Vice President Operations
CFO: Sheri Trahern, Chief Administrative Officer and Chief Financial Officer
CMO: Victoria King, M.D., Chief Medical Officer
CIO: Jennifer Kemp, Director Marketing and Public Relations
CHR: Stan Miller, Executive Director Human Resources
Web address: www.stmhospital.org
**Control:** Church–operated, Nongovernment, not–for profit **Service:** General Medical and Surgical

**Staffed Beds:** 55 **Admissions:** 2087 **Census:** 20 **Outpatient Visits:** 46210 **Births:** 232 **Total Expense ($000):** 38823 **Payroll Expense ($000):** 15360 **Personnel:** 318

## CHEYENNE WELLS—Cheyenne County

★ **KEEFE MEMORIAL HOSPITAL (060043)**, 602 North 6th Street West, Zip 80810, Mailing Address: P.O. Box 578, Zip 80810–0578; tel. 719/767–5661 **A**9 10 20 **F**3 15 40 43 56 57 59 64 81 89 91 93 107 119 127 133 147 **P**6
Primary Contact: Jim Murphy, Interim Administrator
CFO: Kara Hoover, Controller and Director Human Resources
CMO: Christopher Williams, M.D., Chief of Staff
CHR: Kara Hoover, Controller and Director Human Resources
Web address: www.keefememorialhospital.org
**Control:** County–Government, nonfederal **Service:** General Medical and Surgical

**Staffed Beds:** 11 **Admissions:** 71 **Census:** 1 **Outpatient Visits:** 3436 **Births:** 0 **Total Expense ($000):** 4683 **Payroll Expense ($000):** 1929 **Personnel:** 43

## COLORADO SPRINGS—El Paso County

☐ **CEDAR SPRINGS HOSPITAL (064009)**, (Formerly Cedar Springs Behavioral Health System), 2135 Southgate Road, Zip 80906–2693; tel. 719/633–4114, (Nonreporting) **A**1 9 10 **S** Universal Health Services, Inc., King of Prussia, PA
Primary Contact: A. Elaine Crnkovic, Chief Executive Officer
CFO: Cynthia D. Deboer, Chief Financial Officer
CMO: Larry Shores, M.D., Executive Medical Director
CHR: Jessica McCoy, Director Human Resources
CNO: Jodi Mattson, Director of Nursing
Web address: www.cedarspringsbhs.com
**Control:** Corporation, Investor–owned, for–profit **Service:** Psychiatric

**Staffed Beds:** 110

⊠ **HEALTHSOUTH REHABILITATION HOSPITAL OF COLORADO SPRINGS (063030)**, 325 Parkside Drive, Zip 80910–3134; tel. 719/630–8000, (Nonreporting) **A**1 10 **S** HEALTHSOUTH Corporation, Birmingham, AL
Primary Contact: Stephen Schaefer, Chief Executive Officer
CFO: Pat Penrod, Controller
CHR: Diana Crepeau, Director Human Resources
Web address: www.healthsouthcoloradosprings.com
**Control:** Corporation, Investor–owned, for–profit **Service:** Rehabilitation

**Staffed Beds:** 64

⊠ △ **MEMORIAL HEALTH SYSTEM (060022)**, 1400 East Boulder Street, Zip 80909–5599, Mailing Address: P.O. Box 1326, Zip 80901–1326, (Includes MEMORIAL HOSPITAL FOR CHILDREN, 1400 East Boulder Street, Zip 80909–5533; tel. 719/365–5000), (Nonreporting) **A**1 2 7 9 10 **S** University of Colorado Health, Fort Collins, CO
Primary Contact: Michael A. Scialdone, Interim Chief Executive Officer
CFO: Michael A. Scialdone, Chief Financial Officer
Web address: www.memorialhealthsystem.com
**Control:** City–Government, nonfederal **Service:** General Medical and Surgical

**Staffed Beds:** 548

☐ **PEAK VIEW BEHAVIORAL HEALTH (064026)**, 7353 Sisters Grove, Zip 80923–2615; tel. 719/444–8484 **A**1 9 10 **F**29 38 50 98 99 100 101 102 103 104 105 130 **S** Strategic Behavioral Health, LLC, Memphis, TN
Primary Contact: Gary Miller, Chief Executive Officer
Web address: www.strategicbh.com/peakview.html
**Control:** Corporation, Investor–owned, for–profit **Service:** Psychiatric

**Staffed Beds:** 92 **Admissions:** 1365 **Census:** 32 **Outpatient Visits:** 0 **Births:** 0 **Personnel:** 125

⊠ △ **PENROSE–ST. FRANCIS HEALTH SERVICES (060031)**, 2222 North Nevada Avenue, Zip 80907–6799, Mailing Address: P.O. Box 7021, Zip 80933–7021; tel. 719/776–5000, (Includes PENROSE HOSPITAL, 2215 North Cascade Avenue, Zip 80907, Mailing Address: P.O. Box 7021, Zip 80933–7021; tel. 719/776–5000; ST. FRANCIS MEDICAL CENTER, 6001 East Woodmen Road, Zip 80923–2601; tel. 719/776–5000), (Nonreporting) **A**1 2 7 9 10 **S** Catholic Health Initiatives, Englewood, CO
Primary Contact: Margaret D. Sabin, President and Chief Executive Officer
COO: Andrea C. Coleman, Chief Operating Officer
CIO: Tanya Bell, Public Information Officer
CHR: James Humphrey, Director Human and Educational Resources
Web address: www.penrosestfrancis.org
**Control:** Church–operated, Nongovernment, not–for profit **Service:** General Medical and Surgical

**Staffed Beds:** 405

⊠ **SELECT LONG TERM CARE HOSPITAL – COLORADO SPRINGS (062016)**, 6001 East Woodmen Road, 6th Floor, Zip 80923–2601; tel. 719/571–6000, (Nonreporting) **A**1 9 10 **S** Select Medical Corporation, Mechanicsburg, PA
Primary Contact: James Elton, Chief Executive Officer
CMO: Dave Call, M.D., Medical Director
CHR: Lisa Gayler, Director Human Resources
CNO: Cathrine Viccellio, Chief Nursing Officer
Web address: www.selectmedical.com
**Control:** Corporation, Investor–owned, for–profit **Service:** Long–Term Acute Care hospital

**Staffed Beds:** 30

## CORTEZ—Montezuma County

⊠ ◇ **SOUTHWEST MEMORIAL HOSPITAL (061327)**, 1311 North Mildred Road, Zip 81321–2299; tel. 970/565–6666 **A**1 9 10 21 **F**3 7 11 13 15 28 29 31 34 35 40 47 48 50 54 59 64 65 70 75 76 79 81 82 85 87 93 97 107 108 110 111 115 127 129 130 131 133 147 148 **P**1
Primary Contact: Kent Helwig, Chief Executive Officer
CFO: John Nadone, Chief Financial Officer
CIO: David Cabana, Director Management Information Systems
CHR: Jim Bob Wynes, Director Human Resources
CNO: Liz Sellers, R.N., Chief Nursing Officer
Web address: www.swhealth.org
**Control:** Other not–for–profit (including NFP Corporation) **Service:** General Medical and Surgical

**Staffed Beds:** 25 **Admissions:** 1178 **Census:** 9 **Outpatient Visits:** 47012 **Births:** 183 **Total Expense ($000):** 47220 **Payroll Expense ($000):** 19152 **Personnel:** 343

**CO**

*Many Facility Codes have changed. Please refer to the AHA Guide Code Chart.*
© 2013 AHA Guide

**CRAIG—Moffat County**

☒ **MEMORIAL HOSPITAL AT CRAIG (061314)**, (Formerly Memorial Hospital), 750 Hospital Loop, Zip 81625–8750; tel. 970/824–9411 **A**1 9 10 18 **F**3 7 11 13 15 29 31 32 34 35 40 43 45 49 50 51 57 59 68 70 75 76 77 78 79 81 85 86 87 91 93 97 102 107 108 110 111 112 114 119 129 130 131 132 133 135 146 147 148 **S** QHR, Brentwood, TN
Primary Contact: James Christian Smolik, Chief Executive Officer
COO: Beka Warren, R.N., Interim Chief Clinical Officer
CFO: Bryan Chalmers, Chief Financial Officer
CMO: Larry Kipe, M.D., Chief of Staff
CIO: Samantha Johnston, Chief Organizational Excellence
CHR: Jade Wilhite, Manager Human Resource
Web address: www.thememorialhospital.com
**Control:** County–Government, nonfederal **Service:** General Medical and Surgical

**Staffed Beds:** 25 **Admissions:** 730 **Census:** 7 **Outpatient Visits:** 29225 **Births:** 129 **Total Expense ($000):** 31675 **Payroll Expense ($000):** 12685 **Personnel:** 189

**DEL NORTE—Rio Grande County**

★ **RIO GRANDE HOSPITAL (061301)**, 310 County Road 14, Zip 81132–8758; tel. 719/657–2510 **A**9 10 18 **F**34 40 43 57 65 81 93 107 111 115 127 129 133 **P**6
Primary Contact: Arlene Harms, Chief Executive Officer
CFO: Greg Porter, Chief Financial Officer
CMO: Heidi E. Helgeson, M.D., Chief Medical Officer
CIO: Yael DeFaye, Director, Information Technology
CHR: Paula Warner–Pacheco, Chief Human Resources
CNO: Beverly Martinez, Director of Nursing
Web address: www.rio–grande–hospital.org/
**Control:** Other not–for–profit (including NFP Corporation) **Service:** General Medical and Surgical

**Staffed Beds:** 17 **Admissions:** 354 **Census:** 3 **Outpatient Visits:** 36178 **Births:** 0 **Total Expense ($000):** 12349 **Payroll Expense ($000):** 5439 **Personnel:** 110

**DELTA—Delta County**

☒ **DELTA COUNTY MEMORIAL HOSPITAL (060071)**, 1501 East 3rd Street, Zip 81416–2815, Mailing Address: P.O. Box 10100, Zip 81416–0008; tel. 970/874–7681 **A**1 9 10 **F**3 11 13 15 28 29 30 31 34 40 43 45 50 57 59 62 70 75 76 77 78 79 81 85 87 93 107 108 110 111 114 115 119 124 127 129 146 147 148 **P**5 8
Primary Contact: Jason Cleckler, Chief Executive Officer
CFO: Bev Carlson, Chief Financial Officer
CMO: John P. Knutson, M.D., Chief Medical Staff
CIO: Mitch Van Scoyk, Manager Information Systems
CHR: Larry Vincent, Director Human Resources
Web address: www.deltahospital.org
**Control:** Hospital district or authority, Government, nonfederal **Service:** General Medical and Surgical

**Staffed Beds:** 49 **Admissions:** 2193 **Census:** 19 **Outpatient Visits:** 78252 **Births:** 220 **Total Expense ($000):** 65071 **Payroll Expense ($000):** 25258 **Personnel:** 598

**DENVER—Denver, Adams and Arapaho Coun Counties**

☒ **COLORADO ACUTE LONG TERM HOSPITAL (062012)**, 1690 North Meade Street, Zip 80204–1552; tel. 303/264–6900, (Nonreporting) **A**1 9 10 **S** LifeCare Management Services, Plano, TX
Primary Contact: Craig Bailey, MS, Chief Executive Officer and Administrator
Web address: www.lifecare–hospitals.com/hospital/colorado
**Control:** Corporation, Investor–owned, for–profit **Service:** Long–Term Acute Care hospital

**Staffed Beds:** 63

☐ **COLORADO MENTAL HEALTH INSTITUTE AT FORT LOGAN (064003)**, 3520 West Oxford Avenue, Zip 80236–3197; tel. 303/761–0220, (Nonreporting) **A**1 3 5 10
Primary Contact: Elizabeth M. Stillman, Acting Director
CFO: Bob Fries, Director Fiscal Services
CIO: Billie Busby, Assistant Director
Web address: www.cdhs.state.co.us/cmhifl
**Control:** State–Government, nonfederal **Service:** Psychiatric

**Staffed Beds:** 297

☐ **DENVER HEALTH MEDICAL CENTER (060011)**, 777 Bannock Street, Zip 80204–4507; tel. 303/436–6000 **A**1 3 5 9 10 **F**3 4 5 7 8 11 12 13 15 18 19 20 22 26 28 29 30 31 32 34 35 37 38 39 40 41 42 43 44 45 46 49 50 53 54 55 56 57 58 59 60 61 64 65 66 68 70 71 72 74 75 76 77 78 79 80 81 82 85 86 87 88 89 90 92 93 94 97 98 99 100 102 103 104 107 108 110 111 114 115 118 119 127 129 130 131 132 134 135 143 144 146 147 148 **P**6
Primary Contact: Arthur A. Gonzalez, Dr.PH, FACHE, Chief Executive Officer
COO: Stephanie Thomas, Chief Operating Officer
CFO: Peg Burnette, Chief Financial Officer
CMO: Philip Mehler, M.D., Chief Medical Officer
CIO: Gregory M. Veltri, Chief Information Officer
CHR: Greg Rossman, Chief Human Resource Officer
CNO: Kathy Boyle, R.N., Chief Nursing Officer
Web address: www.denverhealth.org
**Control:** Hospital district or authority, Government, nonfederal **Service:** General Medical and Surgical

**Staffed Beds:** 409 **Admissions:** 22073 **Census:** 285 **Outpatient Visits:** 819912 **Births:** 3177 **Total Expense ($000):** 749824 **Payroll Expense ($000):** 355739 **Personnel:** 5225

☒ **EXEMPLA SAINT JOSEPH HOSPITAL (060028)**, 1835 Franklin Street, Zip 80218–1126; tel. 303/837–7111 **A**1 3 5 9 10 **F**3 8 11 12 13 15 18 20 22 24 26 28 29 30 31 34 35 37 40 43 45 46 49 50 55 58 60 63 64 66 68 70 71 72 74 75 76 77 78 79 81 82 84 85 87 93 107 108 110 111 114 115 116 117 119 120 121 123 124 126 130 145 146 **P**6 7 **S** SCL Health System, Denver, CO
Primary Contact: Bain J. Farris, President and Chief Executive Officer
COO: Barbara A. Jahn, Chief Operating Officer
CFO: Brad Ludford, Vice President Finance
CMO: Shawn Dufford, M.D., Vice President Medical Affairs and Chief Medical Officer
CNO: Mary Shepler, R.N., Vice President and Chief Nursing Officer
Web address: www.exempla.org
**Control:** Other not–for–profit (including NFP Corporation) **Service:** General Medical and Surgical

**Staffed Beds:** 369 **Admissions:** 18514 **Census:** 225 **Outpatient Visits:** 251412 **Births:** 3854 **Total Expense ($000):** 429540 **Payroll Expense ($000):** 141819 **Personnel:** 2108

☒ **KINDRED HOSPITAL–DENVER (062009)**, 1920 High Street, Zip 80218–1213; tel. 303/320–5871, (Nonreporting) **A**1 9 10 **S** Kindred Healthcare, Louisville, KY
Primary Contact: Harvey Ross, Chief Executive Officer
CFO: Tim Stecker, Chief Financial Officer
CMO: Eric Yaeger, M.D., Medical Director
Web address: www.kh–denver.com
**Control:** Corporation, Investor–owned, for–profit **Service:** Long–Term Acute Care hospital

**Staffed Beds:** 68

☒ **NATIONAL JEWISH HEALTH (060107)**, (AllerCardio Resp Rheum ID GI), 1400 Jackson Street, Zip 80206–2762; tel. 303/388–4461 **A**1 3 5 9 10 **F**3 9 11 12 18 20 28 29 30 31 32 34 35 36 44 45 46 47 48 50 53 54 55 57 58 59 61 64 65 66 68 74 75 77 78 84 86 87 89 90 93 96 97 98 99 100 101 104 107 108 111 114 115 116 117 118 119 127 129 130 132 134 135 143 146 **P**6
Primary Contact: Michael Salem, M.D., President and Chief Executive Officer
COO: Ron Berge, Executive Vice President and Chief Operating Officer
CFO: Christine Forkner, Executive Vice President and Chief Financial Officer
CMO: Gary Cott, M.D., Executive Vice President Medical and Clinical Services
CIO: Lots Pook, Chief Information Officer
CHR: Susan Roll, Chief Human Resources
Web address: www.njhealth.org
**Control:** Other not–for–profit (including NFP Corporation) **Service:** Other specialty

**Staffed Beds:** 46 **Admissions:** 72 **Census:** 1 **Outpatient Visits:** 87405 **Births:** 0 **Total Expense ($000):** 204762 **Payroll Expense ($000):** 107658 **Personnel:** 1521

**CO**

---

**Hospital, Medicare Provider Number, Address, Telephone, Approval, Facility, and Physician Codes, Health Care System**

★ American Hospital Association (AHA) membership
☐ The Joint Commission accreditation
◇ DNV Healthcare Inc. accreditation
○ Healthcare Facilities Accreditation Program
△ Commission on Accreditation of Rehabilitation Facilities (CARF) accreditation

✠ **PORTER ADVENTIST HOSPITAL (060064)**, 2525 South Downing Street, Zip 80210–5876; tel. 303/778–1955 **A**1 2 9 10 **F**3 5 8 11 15 18 20 22 24 26 28 29 30 31 34 35 36 37 38 40 45 46 47 48 49 50 54 55 56 57 58 59 60 64 65 68 70 74 75 77 78 79 81 82 84 85 86 87 90 91 92 93 96 97 98 100 101 102 103 104 105 106 107 108 109 110 111 112 114 115 116 117 118 119 120 121 122 123 124 125 126 129 130 131 138 139 141 142 146 147 148 **P**6 **S** Adventist Health System Sunbelt Health Care Corporation, Altamonte Springs, FL
Primary Contact: Randall L. Haffner, Ph.D., Chief Executive Officer
CFO: Andrew Gaasch, Chief Financial Officer
CMO: Diane McCallister, M.D., Chief Medical Officer
CHR: Oz Muller, Director Human Resources
CNO: Sharon H. Pappas, R.N., Chief Nursing Officer
Web address: www.centura.org
**Control:** Church–operated, Nongovernment, not–for profit **Service:** General Medical and Surgical

Staffed Beds: 250 Admissions: 10796 Census: 141 Outpatient Visits: 66538 Births: 0 Total Expense ($000): 233203 Payroll Expense ($000): 77574 Personnel: 1156

✠ △ **PRESBYTERIAN–ST. LUKE'S MEDICAL CENTER (060014)**, 1719 East 19th Avenue, Zip 80218–1281; tel. 303/839–6000, (Includes ROCKY MOUNTAIN HOSPITAL FOR CHILDREN, 1719 East 19th Avenue, Zip 80218–1235; tel. 720/754–1000) **A**1 2 3 5 7 9 10 **F**3 8 9 11 12 13 14 15 18 19 20 21 22 23 24 25 26 28 29 30 31 34 35 37 40 41 43 44 45 46 47 48 49 50 51 54 55 56 57 58 59 60 61 63 64 65 66 68 70 72 73 74 75 76 78 79 80 81 82 83 84 85 86 87 88 89 93 96 97 100 107 108 110 111 112 114 115 116 117 119 120 121 123 124 127 129 130 131 132 134 136 138 145 146 147 148 **P**2 3 4 6 **S** HCA, Nashville, TN
Primary Contact: Madeleine Roberson, Chief Executive Officer
CMO: Reginald Washington, M.D., Chief Medical Officer
CIO: Jay Williams, Director Information Services
CHR: Shane Buer, Director Human Resources
Web address: www.pslmc.com
**Control:** Corporation, Investor–owned, for–profit **Service:** General Medical and Surgical

Staffed Beds: 389 Admissions: 11109 Census: 210 Outpatient Visits: 90561 Births: 1469 Personnel: 1657

✠ **ROSE MEDICAL CENTER (060032)**, 4567 East Ninth Avenue, Zip 80220–3941; tel. 303/320–2121 **A**1 2 3 5 9 10 **F**3 8 11 12 13 15 18 20 22 24 26 28 29 30 31 34 35 40 44 45 49 50 53 54 55 58 59 60 61 64 68 70 72 74 75 76 77 78 79 81 82 84 85 87 89 92 93 94 97 102 107 108 110 111 112 114 115 116 117 118 119 120 121 122 123 126 129 130 131 132 135 143 146 147 148 **P**6 8 **S** HCA, Nashville, TN
Primary Contact: Kenneth H. Feiler, Chief Executive Officer
COO: Elizabeth Hunsicker, Chief Operating Officer
CFO: Jac Connelly, Chief Financial Officer
CIO: Dave Trevathan, Director Information Systems
CHR: Clarence McDavid, Vice President Human Resources
Web address: www.rosebabies.com
**Control:** Individual, Investor–owned, for–profit **Service:** General Medical and Surgical

Staffed Beds: 262 Admissions: 12352 Census: 130 Outpatient Visits: 78119

**SELECT SPECIALTY HOSPITAL DENVER SOUTH** See Select Specialty Hospital–Denver

✠ **SELECT SPECIALTY HOSPITAL–DENVER (062015)**, 1719 East 19th Avenue, 5th Floor, Zip 80218–1235; tel. 303/563–3700, (Includes SELECT SPECIALTY HOSPITAL DENVER SOUTH, 2525 South Downing Street, Zip 80210–5817; tel. 303/715–7373), (Nonreporting) **A**1 9 10 **S** Select Medical Corporation, Mechanicsburg, PA
Primary Contact: Deborah Dale, Chief Executive Officer
Web address: www.selectspecialtyhospitals.com/company/locations/denver.aspx
**Control:** Corporation, Investor–owned, for–profit **Service:** Long–Term Acute Care hospital

Staffed Beds: 65

✠ △ **VETERANS AFFAIRS EASTERN COLORADO HEALTH CARE SYSTEM**, 1055 Clermont Street, Zip 80220–3877; tel. 303/399–8020, (Total facility includes 100 beds in nursing home–type unit) **A**1 3 5 7 **F**3 18 20 22 24 26 29 30 31 35 36 38 39 40 44 46 47 48 49 50 53 54 55 56 57 58 59 60 61 63 64 65 68 70 74 75 77 78 79 80 81 82 83 84 85 87 90 91 92 93 94 95 96 97 98 100 101 102 103 104 106 107 108 111 114 115 119 126 127 128 129 130 132 135 144 146 147 148 **S** Department of Veterans Affairs, Washington, DC
Primary Contact: Lynette A. Roff, Director
CFO: Eliott R. Vanderstek, Chief Fiscal Service
CMO: Ellen Mangione, M.D., Chief of Staff
CIO: Don Huckaby, Chief Information Management Service
CHR: Lorene Connel, Chief Human Resources Management Service
Web address: www.denver.va.gov/
**Control:** Veterans Affairs, Government, federal **Service:** General Medical and Surgical

Staffed Beds: 229 Admissions: 4858 Census: 89 Outpatient Visits: 810202 Births: 0 Total Expense ($000): 530657 Payroll Expense ($000): 253748 Personnel: 2293

**DURANGO—La Plata County**

**ANIMAS SURGICAL HOSPITAL (060117)**, 575 Rivergate Lane, Zip 81301–7487; tel. 970/247–3537, (Nonreporting) **A**9 10
Primary Contact: Brett Gosney, Chief Executive Officer
Web address: www.animassurgical.com/index.htm
**Control:** Corporation, Investor–owned, for–profit **Service:** Surgical

Staffed Beds: 12

✠ **MERCY REGIONAL MEDICAL CENTER (060013)**, 1010 Three Springs Boulevard, Zip 81301–8296; tel. 970/247–4311 **A**1 2 9 10 20 **F**11 13 15 17 18 20 22 24 26 27 28 29 30 31 35 36 40 42 43 50 59 60 61 66 70 72 73 76 79 81 84 85 87 89 94 96 107 111 115 119 127 129 130 131 132 133 135 146 147 148 **P**6 **S** Catholic Health Initiatives, Englewood, CO
Primary Contact: Thomas Gessel, FACHE, President and Chief Executive Officer
CFO: Jane Strobel, Interim Chief Financial Officer
CMO: John A K Boyd, M.D., Vice President Mission and Medical Affairs and Chief Medical Officer
CIO: Neil Stock, Director Technology and Facilities
CHR: Cathy Roberts, Director Human Resources
CNO: Nancy Hoyt, R.N., Vice President Operations/Clinical and Chief Nursing Officer
Web address: www.mercydurango.org
**Control:** Church–operated, Nongovernment, not–for profit **Service:** General Medical and Surgical

Staffed Beds: 82 Admissions: 4575 Census: 41 Outpatient Visits: 89454 Births: 920 Total Expense ($000): 121323 Payroll Expense ($000): 48775 Personnel: 791

**EADS—Kiowa County**

★ **WEISBROD MEMORIAL COUNTY HOSPITAL (061300)**, 1208 Luther Street, Zip 81036, Mailing Address: P.O. Box 817, Zip 81036–0817; tel. 719/438–5401 **A**9 10 18 **F**34 40 57 59 62 65 67 127 129 133
Primary Contact: Thomas Henton, Chief Executive Officer
CFO: Shannon Dixon, Manager Business Office
CMO: Jeff Waggoner, M.D., Chief of Staff
CHR: Shannon Dixon, Manager Business Office
Web address: www.weisbrod.org
**Control:** County–Government, nonfederal **Service:** General Medical and Surgical

Staffed Beds: 42 Admissions: 38 Census: 1 Outpatient Visits: 10574 Births: 0 Total Expense ($000): 17162 Payroll Expense ($000): 3136 Personnel: 60

**ENGLEWOOD—Arapahoe County**

✠ **CRAIG HOSPITAL (062011)**, 3425 South Clarkson Street, Zip 80113–2899; tel. 303/789–8000 **A**1 3 5 9 10 **F**29 30 34 35 36 44 50 53 58 64 68 74 75 77 81 86 87 90 91 93 95 96 97 104 130 132 146 148
Primary Contact: Michael L. Fordyce, President and Chief Executive Officer
COO: Dana Polonsky, Vice President of Clinical Services
CFO: Julie Keegan, Vice President Finance
CMO: Thomas E. Balazy, M.D., Medical Director
CIO: Chris Watkins, Director of Information Technology
CHR: Stacy L. Abel, Director Human Resources
CNO: Diane Reinhard, R.N., Vice President of Patient Care Services
Web address: www.craighospital.org
**Control:** Other not–for–profit (including NFP Corporation) **Service:** Rehabilitation

Staffed Beds: 85 Admissions: 505 Census: 74 Outpatient Visits: 4761 Births: 0 Total Expense ($000): 69614 Payroll Expense ($000): 33702 Personnel: 626

✠ **SWEDISH MEDICAL CENTER (060034)**, 501 East Hampden Avenue, Zip 80113–2702; tel. 303/788–5000 **A**1 2 3 5 9 10 **F**3 7 8 11 12 13 15 18 20 22 24 26 29 30 31 34 35 38 39 40 42 43 44 45 47 48 49 50 53 55 57 58 59 60 64 66 68 70 72 73 74 75 76 77 78 79 81 82 84 85 86 87 88 90 92 97 102 107 108 109 111 114 115 116 117 118 119 120 121 122 123 124 126 129 130 131 132 146 147 148 **P**8 **S** HCA, Nashville, TN
Primary Contact: Mary M. White, Chief Executive Officer
COO: Daniel Miller, Chief Operating Officer
CFO: Kathy Ashenfelter, Chief Financial Officer
CMO: Patricia Howell, M.D., President Medical Staff
CIO: Robert Hollowell, Director Information Systems
CHR: Lisa Morris, Vice President Human Resources
CNO: Karleen Goerke, R.N., Chief Nursing Officer
Web address: www.swedishhospital.com
**Control:** Partnership, Investor–owned, for–profit **Service:** General Medical and Surgical

Staffed Beds: 343 Admissions: 19728 Census: 250 Outpatient Visits: 119975 Births: 2086

**CO**

*Many Facility Codes have changed. Please refer to the AHA Guide Code Chart.*

© 2013 AHA Guide

**ESTES PARK—Larimer County**

★ **ESTES PARK MEDICAL CENTER (061312)**, 555 Prospect Avenue, Zip 80517–6312, Mailing Address: P.O. Box 2740, Zip 80517–2740; tel. 970/586–2317, (Nonreporting) **A**9 10 18
Primary Contact: Roberta Suzanne Swenson, R.N., M.P.H., Interim Chief Executive Officer
CFO: Sam Radke, Vice President of Finance
CMO: Chris Daley, M.D., Chief of Staff
CIO: Gary Hall, Vice President of Information Technology
CHR: Robert Stansel, Vice President of Human Resources
CNO: Roberta Suzanne Swenson, R.N., Vice President of Patient Services
Web address: www.epmedcenter.com
**Control:** Hospital district or authority, Government, nonfederal **Service:** General Medical and Surgical

**Staffed Beds:** 68

**FORT CARSON—El Paso County**

⊠ **EVANS U. S. ARMY COMMUNITY HOSPITAL**, 1650 Cochrane Circle, Building 7500, Zip 80913–4613; tel. 719/526–7200, (Nonreporting) **A**1 9 **S** Department of the Army, Office of the Surgeon General, Falls Church, VA
Primary Contact: Colonel Jimmie O. Keenan, Commander
CFO: Major Bradley Robinson, Chief Financial Officer
CMO: Colonel James Terrio, M.D., Chief Medical Officer
CHR: Lieutenant Colonel Lory Gurr, Chief Human Resources Division
Web address: www.evans.amedd.army.mil
**Control:** Army, Government, federal **Service:** General Medical and Surgical

**Staffed Beds:** 57

**FORT COLLINS—Larimer County**

⊠ **POUDRE VALLEY HOSPITAL (060010)**, 1024 South Lemay Avenue, Zip 80524–3998; tel. 970/495–7000, (Includes MOUNTAIN CREST HOSPITAL, 4601 Corbett Drive, Zip 80525; tel. 970/270–4800), (Data for 182 days) **A**1 2 9 10 **F**3 5 7 11 12 13 14 15 18 20 22 28 29 30 31 32 34 35 37 38 39 40 43 45 46 47 48 49 50 53 54 55 57 58 59 60 61 64 65 66 68 69 70 72 73 74 75 76 77 78 79 80 81 82 84 85 86 87 89 90 93 94 96 98 99 100 101 102 103 104 105 106 107 108 110 111 114 115 118 119 120 124 126 129 130 131 132 134 135 144 146 147 148 **P**5 6 **S** University of Colorado Health, Fort Collins, CO
Primary Contact: Kevin L. Unger, FACHE, President and Chief Executive Officer
COO: Dan Robinson, Vice President Operations
CFO: Stephanie Doughty, Chief Financial Officer
CMO: William Neff, M.D., Chief Medical Officer
CIO: Fernando Pedroza, Chief Information Officer
CHR: Patti Oakes, Interim Vice President Human Resources
Web address: www.pvhs.org
**Control:** Other not–for–profit (including NFP Corporation) **Service:** General Medical and Surgical

**Staffed Beds:** 232 **Admissions:** 7243 **Census:** 152 **Outpatient Visits:** 252136 **Births:** 1250 **Total Expense ($000):** 150866 **Payroll Expense ($000):** 60915 **Personnel:** 1594

**FORT MORGAN—Morgan County**

⊠ **COLORADO PLAINS MEDICAL CENTER (060044)**, 1000 Lincoln Street, Zip 80701–3298; tel. 970/867–3391 **A**1 9 10 20 **F**3 11 13 15 28 29 31 34 35 40 43 44 45 48 50 51 53 56 57 59 62 64 70 75 76 77 79 81 86 87 97 98 99 100 101 102 103 104 105 107 108 110 111 119 129 130 131 133 146 147 148 **P**6 **S** LifePoint Hospitals, Inc., Brentwood, TN
Primary Contact: Michael N. Patterson, Chief Executive Officer
CFO: Christina Patton, Chief Financial Officer
CHR: Janet Brinkman, Director Human Resources
CNO: Sonya Bass, MS, Chief Nursing Officer
Web address: www.coloradoplainsmedicalcenter.com
**Control:** Corporation, Investor–owned, for–profit **Service:** General Medical and Surgical

**Staffed Beds:** 50 **Admissions:** 1634 **Census:** 18 **Outpatient Visits:** 86302 **Births:** 449 **Total Expense ($000):** 41957 **Payroll Expense ($000):** 17481 **Personnel:** 211

**FRISCO—Summit County**

⊠ **ST. ANTHONY SUMMIT MEDICAL CENTER (060118)**, 340 Peak One Drive, Zip 80443, Mailing Address: P.O. Box 738, Zip 80443–0738; tel. 970/668–3300, (Includes ST. ANTHONY GRANBY MEDICAL CENTER, 480 East Agate, Granby, Zip 80446, Mailing Address: P.O. Box 397, Zip 80446; tel. 970/887–7400; Paul J. Chodkowski, Chief Executive Officer) **A**1 9 10 **F**3 34 40 42 43 45 57 59 68 70 75 76 77 79 81 82 84 85 97 107 110 111 119 129 130 132 144 146 147 **S** Catholic Health Initiatives, Englewood, CO
Primary Contact: Paul J. Chodkowski, Chief Executive Officer
CFO: David Thompson, Chief Financial Officer
CHR: Dana Laverdiere, Generalist
Web address: www.summitmedicalcenter.org
**Control:** Church–operated, Nongovernment, not–for profit **Service:** General Medical and Surgical

**Staffed Beds:** 34 **Admissions:** 1306 **Census:** 10 **Outpatient Visits:** 19502 **Births:** 363 **Total Expense ($000):** 46491 **Payroll Expense ($000):** 13821 **Personnel:** 151

**FRUITA—Mesa County**

★ **FAMILY HEALTH WEST (061302)**, 300 West Ottley Avenue, Zip 81521–2118, Mailing Address: P.O. Box 130, Zip 81521–0130; tel. 970/858–9871, (Nonreporting) **A**9 10 18
Primary Contact: Mark J. Francis, President Chief Executive Officer and Hospital Administrator
CFO: Jason McCormick, Vice President Finance and Chief Financial Officer
CMO: Michael Hughes, M.D., Medical Director
CIO: Camille Ficklin, Director Information Services
CHR: Kelly Murphy, Director Human Resources
Web address: www.familyhealthwest.org
**Control:** Other not–for–profit (including NFP Corporation) **Service:** General Medical and Surgical

**Staffed Beds:** 130

**GLENWOOD SPRINGS—Garfield County**

⊠ **VALLEY VIEW HOSPITAL (060075)**, 1906 Blake Avenue, Zip 81601–4259; tel. 970/945–6535 **A**1 9 10 20 **F**3 11 13 14 15 18 20 22 28 29 30 31 34 35 36 38 40 43 45 49 50 51 55 57 58 59 64 65 68 69 70 74 75 76 77 78 80 81 82 85 86 87 93 96 97 100 104 107 108 110 111 114 115 116 117 118 119 120 121 123 124 129 130 131 132 135 145 146 147 148
Primary Contact: Gary L. Brewer, Chief Executive Officer
COO: Deb Wiepking, MSN, Chief Clinical Officer
CFO: Larry L. Dupper, Chief Financial Officer
CMO: Brian Murphy, M.D., Chief of Staff
CIO: Ron Hines, Director Information Technology
CHR: Daniel Biggs, Director Human Resources
Web address: www.vvh.org
**Control:** Other not–for–profit (including NFP Corporation) **Service:** General Medical and Surgical

**Staffed Beds:** 49 **Admissions:** 2716 **Census:** 30 **Outpatient Visits:** 95030 **Births:** 717 **Total Expense ($000):** 134317 **Payroll Expense ($000):** 57369 **Personnel:** 707

**GRANBY—Grand County**

**ST. ANTHONY GRANBY MEDICAL CENTER** See St. Anthony Summit Medical Center, Frisco

**GRAND JUNCTION—Mesa County**

**COLORADO WEST PSYCHIATRIC HOSPITAL (064023)**, 515 28 3/4 Road, Zip 81501–5016; tel. 970/263–4918, (Nonreporting) **A**9 10
Primary Contact: Sharon Raggio, President and Chief Executive Officer
CNO: LaCinda Kelleher, Director of Nursing
Web address: www.cwrmhc.org
**Control:** Other not–for–profit (including NFP Corporation) **Service:** Psychiatric

**Staffed Beds:** 32

⊠ ○ **COMMUNITY HOSPITAL (060054)**, 2021 North 12th Street, Zip 81501–2999; tel. 970/242–0920, (Nonreporting) **A**1 9 10 11 **S** QHR, Brentwood, TN
Primary Contact: Chris Thomas, FACHE, President and Chief Executive Officer
CFO: Wesley D. White, Chief Financial Officer
CMO: Donald Nicolay, M.D., Chief Medical Officer
CIO: Mike Kansgen, Director Information Services
CHR: Laurie K. Sinner, Director Human Resources
Web address: www.yourcommunityhospital.com
**Control:** Other not–for–profit (including NFP Corporation) **Service:** General Medical and Surgical

**Staffed Beds:** 44

CO

---

**Hospital, Medicare Provider Number, Address, Telephone, Approval, Facility, and Physician Codes, Health Care System**

★ American Hospital Association (AHA) membership
☐ The Joint Commission accreditation
◇ DNV Healthcare Inc. accreditation
○ Healthcare Facilities Accreditation Program
△ Commission on Accreditation of Rehabilitation Facilities (CARF) accreditation

⊠ **GRAND JUNCTION VETERANS AFFAIRS MEDICAL CENTER**, (Formerly Veterans Affairs Medical Center), 2121 North Avenue, Zip 81501–6428; tel. 970/242–0731, (Nonreporting) **A**1 **S** Department of Veterans Affairs, Washington, DC
Primary Contact: Terry S. Atienza, Director
COO: Patricia A. Hitt, Associate Director
CFO: Laquita Gruver, Fiscal Officer
CMO: William R. Berryman, M.D., Chief of Staff
CIO: Craig Frerichs, Chief Information Technology Service
CHR: William Chester, Manager Human Resources
Web address: www.grandjunction.va.gov/
**Control:** Veterans Affairs, Government, federal **Service:** General Medical and Surgical

**Staffed Beds:** 23

---

⊠ **ST. MARY'S HOSPITAL AND MEDICAL CENTER (060023)**, 2635 North 7th Street, Zip 81501–8209, Mailing Address: P.O. Box 1628, Zip 81502–1628; tel. 970/298–2273 **A**1 2 3 10 **F**3 7 12 13 14 15 17 18 20 22 24 26 28 29 30 31 34 35 37 40 43 44 45 49 50 51 53 54 55 57 58 59 61 64 67 68 69 70 72 74 75 76 77 78 79 81 82 85 86 87 89 90 91 93 96 97 100 102 107 108 109 110 111 114 115 116 117 119 121 123 124 126 129 130 131 132 135 145 146 147 148 **P**6 **S** SCL Health System, Denver, CO
Primary Contact: Michael J. McBride, FACHE, President and Chief Executive Officer
COO: Reza Kaleel, Executive Vice President and Chief Operating Officer
CFO: Forest Binder, Vice President Finance
CMO: John C. Beeson, M.D., Vice President Medical Affairs
CIO: Jane Wild, Director Information Technology
CHR: Judy White House, Vice President Human Resources
CNO: Shelley Peterson, Vice President Patient Services and Chief Nursing Officer
Web address: www.stmarygj.com
**Control:** Church–operated, Nongovernment, not–for profit **Service:** General Medical and Surgical

**Staffed Beds:** 324 **Admissions:** 12414 **Census:** 147 **Outpatient Visits:** 360775 **Births:** 2175 **Total Expense ($000):** 318136 **Payroll Expense ($000):** 121075 **Personnel:** 1572

**VETERANS AFFAIRS MEDICAL CENTER** See Grand Junction Veterans Affairs Medical Center

### GREELEY—Weld County

⊠ **NORTH COLORADO MEDICAL CENTER (060001)**, 1801 16th Street, Zip 80631–5154; tel. 970/352–4121 **A**1 2 9 10 **F**3 5 11 12 13 14 15 17 18 19 20 22 24 26 28 29 30 31 32 34 35 37 39 40 43 45 46 48 49 50 51 53 54 57 59 61 64 65 66 68 70 71 72 74 75 76 77 78 79 81 84 85 86 87 89 91 92 93 96 97 98 99 100 101 102 103 104 105 107 108 110 111 114 115 116 117 118 119 120 121 123 124 126 129 130 131 132 135 136 141 142 143 145 146 147 148 **P**6 **S** Banner Health, Phoenix, AZ
Primary Contact: Richard O. Sutton, Chief Executive Officer
CFO: Mary McCabe, Chief Financial Officer
CMO: Sheldon Stadnyk, M.D., Chief Medical Officer
CHR: Jimmy Duncan, Chief Human Resource Officer
Web address: www.ncmcgreeley.com
**Control:** Other not–for–profit (including NFP Corporation) **Service:** General Medical and Surgical

**Staffed Beds:** 258 **Admissions:** 14520 **Census:** 148 **Outpatient Visits:** 507675 **Births:** 2007 **Total Expense ($000):** 339365 **Payroll Expense ($000):** 119948 **Personnel:** 1789

### GUNNISON—Gunnison County

⊠ **GUNNISON VALLEY HOSPITAL (061320)**, 711 North Taylor Street, Zip 81230–2296; tel. 970/641–1456, (Nonreporting) **A**1 9 10 18
Primary Contact: Robert J. Santilli, Chief Executive Officer
COO: Betsy Bair, Chief Operating Officer
CFO: David Freshour, Chief Financial Officer
CMO: John S. Tarr, M.D., Chief Medical Officer
CIO: Trevor Smith, Chief Management Information Services
CHR: Elaine Crumpton, Director Human Resources
Web address: www.gvh–colorado.org
**Control:** County–Government, nonfederal **Service:** General Medical and Surgical

**Staffed Beds:** 24

### HAXTUN—Phillips County

★ **HAXTUN HOSPITAL DISTRICT (061304)**, 235 West Fletcher Street, Zip 80731–2737; tel. 970/774–6123, (Nonreporting) **A**9 10 18
Primary Contact: Don Burris, Chief Executive Officer
CFO: Sandra Lambrecht, Chief Financial Officer
CMO: Lila Statz, M.D., Chief of Staff
CHR: Brenda Lechman, Director Human Resources
Web address: www.haxtunhealth.org
**Control:** Hospital district or authority, Government, nonfederal **Service:** General Medical and Surgical

**Staffed Beds:** 25

### HOLYOKE—Phillips County

★ **MELISSA MEMORIAL HOSPITAL (061305)**, 1001 East Johnson Street, Zip 80734–1854; tel. 970/854–2241, (Nonreporting) **A**9 10 18
Primary Contact: John J. Ayoub, FACHE, Chief Executive Officer
CFO: Gregory J. Was, CPA, Chief Financial Officer
CMO: Dennis Jelden, M.D., Chief of Staff
CHR: Sharon Greenman, Director Human Resources
CNO: Claudia Powell, R.N., Director of Nursing
Web address: www.melissamemorial.org
**Control:** Hospital district or authority, Government, nonfederal **Service:** General Medical and Surgical

**Staffed Beds:** 15

### HUGO—Lincoln County

**LINCOLN COMMUNITY HOSPITAL AND NURSING HOME (061306)**, 111 6th Street, Zip 80821–0248, Mailing Address: P.O. Box 248, Zip 80821–0248; tel. 719/743–2421, (Nonreporting) **A**9 10 18
Primary Contact: Herman Schreivogel, Chief Executive Officer
CFO: Herman Schreivogel, Chief Executive Officer
CMO: John E. Fox, M.D., Chief of Staff
Web address: www.lincolncommunityhospitalandnursinghome.com
**Control:** County–Government, nonfederal **Service:** General Medical and Surgical

**Staffed Beds:** 50

### JOHNSTOWN—Larimer County

☐ **NORTHERN COLORADO LONG TERM ACUTE HOSPITAL (062017)**, 4401A Union Street, Zip 80534; tel. 970/619–3663, (Nonreporting) **A**1 9 10 **S** Ernest Health, Inc., Albuquerque, NM
Primary Contact: Dawn Morrissey, Chief Operating Officer
Web address: www.ncltah.ernesthealth.com/
**Control:** Partnership, Investor–owned, for–profit **Service:** Long–Term Acute Care hospital

**Staffed Beds:** 20

⊠ **NORTHERN COLORADO REHABILITATION HOSPITAL (063033)**, 4401 Union Street, Zip 80534–2800; tel. 970/619–3400, (Nonreporting) **A**1 10 **S** Ernest Health, Inc., Albuquerque, NM
Primary Contact: Sharon Scheller, Chief Executive Officer
CFO: Ken R. Derrington, Chief Financial Officer
CMO: Indria S. Lanig, M.D., Medical Director
CHR: Jill Scanlon, Director Human Resources
CNO: Rhonda Carolus, Director of Nursing Operations
Web address: www.ncrh.ernesthealth.com
**Control:** Corporation, Investor–owned, for–profit **Service:** Rehabilitation

**Staffed Beds:** 40

### JULESBURG—Sedgwick County

**SEDGWICK COUNTY HEALTH CENTER (061310)**, 900 Cedar Street, Zip 80737–1199; tel. 970/474–3323, (Nonreporting) **A**9 10 18
Primary Contact: David Garnas, Chief Executive Officer
COO: David Garnas, Chief Executive Officer
CFO: Karla Dunker, Director Finance
CMO: Donald Regier, M.D., Chief Medical Officer
CHR: Sonja Bell, Coordinator Human Resources
**Control:** County–Government, nonfederal **Service:** General Medical and Surgical

**Staffed Beds:** 64

### KREMMLING—Grand County

★ **MIDDLE PARK MEDICAL CENTER (061318)**, (Formerly Kremmling Memorial Hospital), 214 South Fourth Street, Zip 80459, Mailing Address: P.O. Box 399, Zip 80459–0399; tel. 970/724–3442, (Nonreporting) **A**9 10 18
Primary Contact: Cole White, Chief Executive Officer
CMO: Mark Paulsen, M.D., Medical Director
CIO: Eric Murray, Manager Public Relations
CHR: Marianne Hayes, Director Human Resources
Web address: www.mpmc.org
**Control:** Hospital district or authority, Government, nonfederal **Service:** General Medical and Surgical

**Staffed Beds:** 19

### LA JARA—Conejos County

★ **CONEJOS COUNTY HOSPITAL (061308)**, 19021 U.S. Highway 285, Zip 81140–0639, Mailing Address: P.O. Box 639, Zip 81140–0639; tel. 719/274–5121, (Nonreporting) **A**9 10 18
Primary Contact: Henry Garvin, Chief Executive Officer
CFO: Pat Cooper, Comptroller
CMO: Vaughn Jackson, M.D., Chief of Staff
CIO: Kathy Rogers, Vice President Marketing
CHR: Delilah Chavez, Human Resources Assistant
Web address: www.cchco.org
**Control:** Hospital district or authority, Government, nonfederal **Service:** General Medical and Surgical

**Staffed Beds:** 17

**CO**

*Many Facility Codes have changed. Please refer to the AHA Guide Code Chart.*
© 2013 AHA Guide

**LA JUNTA—Otero County**

☒ **ARKANSAS VALLEY REGIONAL MEDICAL CENTER (060036)**, 1100 Carson Avenue, Zip 81050–2799; tel. 719/383–6000, (Total facility includes 99 beds in nursing home–type unit) **A**1 9 10 20 **F**3 8 11 13 15 29 31 34 35 40 43 45 57 59 64 67 68 70 75 76 77 78 79 81 84 85 86 87 89 93 97 107 108 110 111 115 118 119 128 129 130 132 145 147 148 **P**6 **S** QHR, Brentwood, TN
Primary Contact: Lynn Crowell, Chief Executive Officer
CFO: Janette Bender, Chief Financial Officer
CMO: Michael Martino, M.D., Chief of Staff
CIO: Rocky Ackelson, Director Information Services
CHR: Kerri Kimsey, Director Human Resources
Web address: www.avrmc.org
**Control:** Other not–for–profit (including NFP Corporation) **Service:** General Medical and Surgical

**Staffed Beds:** 163 **Admissions:** 1887 **Census:** 102 **Outpatient Visits:** 45862 **Births:** 306 **Total Expense ($000):** 41334 **Payroll Expense ($000):** 18508 **Personnel:** 438

**LAFAYETTE—Boulder County**

☒ **EXEMPLA GOOD SAMARITAN MEDICAL CENTER (060116)**, 200 Exempla Circle, Zip 80026–3370; tel. 303/689–4000 **A**1 9 10 **F**3 11 12 13 15 18 20 22 28 29 30 31 34 35 36 40 43 45 46 49 51 55 57 59 60 63 64 68 70 72 74 75 76 77 78 79 80 81 84 85 86 87 91 92 93 94 100 102 107 108 110 111 114 115 119 126 130 132 143 145 146 147 148 **P**6 **S** SCL Health System, Denver, CO
Primary Contact: David Hamm, President and Chief Executive Officer
COO: Susan Kerschen, MS, Vice President Chief Nursing Officer
CFO: John Higgins, Vice President Finance
CMO: Robert Billerbeck, M.D., Vice President and Chief Medical Officer
CHR: Amy Pacey, Vice President Human Resources
Web address: www.exempla.org
**Control:** Other not–for–profit (including NFP Corporation) **Service:** General Medical and Surgical

**Staffed Beds:** 190 **Admissions:** 13232 **Census:** 139 **Outpatient Visits:** 111225 **Births:** 2473 **Total Expense ($000):** 223973 **Payroll Expense ($000):** 78143 **Personnel:** 1229

**LAKEWOOD—Jefferson County**

☐ **ORTHOCOLORADO HOSPITAL (060124)**, 11650 West 2nd Place, Zip 80228–1527; tel. 720/321–5000, (Nonreporting) **A**1 5 9
Primary Contact: Jude Torchia, Chief Executive Officer
Web address: www.orthocolorado.org
**Control:** Partnership, Investor–owned, for–profit **Service:** Orthopedic

**Staffed Beds:** 48

☒ **ST. ANTHONY HOSPITAL (060015)**, 11600 West Second Place, Zip 80228–1527; tel. 720/321–0000 **A**1 2 3 5 9 10 **F**3 7 11 12 13 17 18 20 22 24 26 28 29 30 31 34 35 36 40 43 45 46 47 48 49 50 53 56 57 59 64 68 70 74 75 76 77 78 79 81 82 84 85 87 90 92 93 96 97 102 107 108 114 115 118 119 120 121 123 124 126 129 130 132 133 134 135 146 147 148 **S** Catholic Health Initiatives, Englewood, CO
Primary Contact: Jeffrey Brickman, FACHE, President and Chief Executive Officer
COO: Patrick Green, Chief Operating Officer
CFO: David Thompson, Chief Financial Officer
CMO: Christopher Ott, M.D., Interim Chief Medical Officer
CIO: Dana Moore, Senior Vice President Information Services
CHR: Sheryl Blythe, Director Human Resources
CHR: Michelle Fornier–Johnson, Group Vice President Human Resources
Web address: www.stanthonyhosp.org
**Control:** Church–operated, Nongovernment, not–for profit **Service:** General Medical and Surgical

**Staffed Beds:** 222 **Admissions:** 10780 **Census:** 157 **Outpatient Visits:** 63367 **Births:** 0 **Total Expense ($000):** 270627 **Payroll Expense ($000):** 77728 **Personnel:** 1107

**LAMAR—Prowers County**

★ **PROWERS MEDICAL CENTER (061323)**, 401 Kendall Drive, Zip 81052–3993; tel. 719/336–4343 **A**9 10 18 **F**3 11 13 15 28 29 31 34 35 40 45 56 57 59 62 64 65 68 70 76 78 81 85 89 90 93 97 107 111 119 124 127 128 130 133 146 147 148 **P**3 6 **S** QHR, Brentwood, TN
Primary Contact: Craig Loveless, Interim Chief Executive Officer
COO: Karen Bryant, Chief Support Services Officer
CFO: Audrey Kane, Interim Chief Financial Officer
CMO: Barry Portner, M.D., Chief of Staff
CIO: Jason Spano, Manager Information Technology
CHR: Karen Bryant, Chief Support Services Officer
Web address: www.prowersmedical.com
**Control:** Hospital district or authority, Government, nonfederal **Service:** General Medical and Surgical

**Staffed Beds:** 25 **Admissions:** 739 **Census:** 10 **Outpatient Visits:** 41142 **Births:** 150 **Total Expense ($000):** 23830 **Payroll Expense ($000):** 10479 **Personnel:** 227

**LEADVILLE—Lake County**

★ **ST. VINCENT GENERAL HOSPITAL DISTRICT (061319)**, 822 West 4th Street, Zip 80461–3897; tel. 719/486–0230, (Nonreporting) **A**9 10 18 **S** QHR, Brentwood, TN
Primary Contact: Joyce Beck, Interim Chief Executive Officer
CFO: Michael Choate, Interim Chief Financial Officer
CMO: William Bradshaw, M.D., Chief of Staff
CHR: Dawn Nelson, Director Human Resources
Web address: www.svghd.org
**Control:** Hospital district or authority, Government, nonfederal **Service:** General Medical and Surgical

**Staffed Beds:** 25

**LITTLETON—Jefferson County**

**FEDERAL CORRECTIONAL INSTITUTE HOSPITAL**, 9595 West Quincy Street, Zip 80123–1159; tel. 303/985–1566, (Nonreporting)
Primary Contact: Mark Ippolito, Administrator
**Control:** Department of Justice, Government, federal **Service:** Hospital unit of an institution (prison hospital, college infimary, etc.)

**Staffed Beds:** 6

☐ **HIGHLANDS BEHAVIORAL HEALTH SYSTEM (064024)**, 8565 South Poplar Way, Zip 80130–3602; tel. 720/348–2800, (Nonreporting) **A**1 9 10 **S** Universal Health Services, Inc., King of Prussia, PA
Primary Contact: Shawn Lemon, Interim Chief Executive Officer
Web address: www.highlandsbhs.com
**Control:** Corporation, Investor–owned, for–profit **Service:** Psychiatric

**Staffed Beds:** 86

☒ **LITTLETON ADVENTIST HOSPITAL (060113)**, 7700 South Broadway Street, Zip 80122–2628; tel. 303/730–8900 **A**1 9 10 **F**3 11 13 15 17 18 20 22 29 30 31 34 35 36 37 40 41 42 43 45 46 47 48 49 53 54 55 57 59 64 68 70 72 74 75 76 77 78 79 81 82 83 84 85 87 89 92 93 97 107 108 110 111 114 115 116 117 118 119 126 129 130 131 132 135 146 147 148 **P**6 **S** Adventist Health System Sunbelt Health Care Corporation, Altamonte Springs, FL
Primary Contact: Brett Spenst, Chief Executive Officer
COO: Geoff Lawton, Vice President Operations
CFO: Jeffrey Eitel, Chief Financial Officer
CMO: Lawrence Wood, M.D., Chief Medical Officer
CIO: Eric Mooss, Director Information Technology
CHR: Rita K. Arthur, Director Human Resources
Web address: www.centura.org
**Control:** Church–operated, Nongovernment, not–for profit **Service:** General Medical and Surgical

**Staffed Beds:** 202 **Admissions:** 9713 **Census:** 111 **Outpatient Visits:** 84600 **Births:** 1684 **Total Expense ($000):** 186477 **Payroll Expense ($000):** 64253 **Personnel:** 910

CO

---

**Hospital, Medicare Provider Number, Address, Telephone, Approval, Facility, and Physician Codes, Health Care System**

★ American Hospital Association (AHA) membership
☐ The Joint Commission accreditation
◇ DNV Healthcare Inc. accreditation
○ Healthcare Facilities Accreditation Program
△ Commission on Accreditation of Rehabilitation Facilities (CARF) accreditation

**CO**

## LONE TREE—Douglas County

⊞ **SKY RIDGE MEDICAL CENTER (060112)**, 10101 Ridge Gate Parkway, Zip 80124–5522; tel. 720/225–1000 **A**1 2 9 10 **F**3 5 8 11 12 13 15 17 18 20 22 24 28 29 30 31 34 35 36 37 39 40 43 45 46 47 48 49 56 57 59 61 64 70 72 74 75 76 77 78 79 81 82 84 85 86 87 89 93 97 107 108 111 114 115 119 120 121 123 126 129 130 131 146 147 148 **P**3 6 8 **S** HCA, Nashville, TN
Primary Contact: Maureen Tarrant, Chief Executive Officer
COO: Susan Hicks, Chief Operating Officer
CFO: Craig Sammons, Chief Financial Officer
CMO: James Lingle, M.D., President Medical Staff
CIO: Ralph Crow, Director Information Technology and Systems
CHR: Linda Pruiett, Vice President Human Resources
Web address: www.skyridgemedcenter.com
**Control:** Corporation, Investor–owned, for-profit **Service:** General Medical and Surgical

**Staffed Beds:** 184 **Admissions:** 14160 **Census:** 137 **Outpatient Visits:** 91830 **Births:** 3773 **Total Expense ($000):** 200305 **Payroll Expense ($000):** 63328 **Personnel:** 967

## LONGMONT—Boulder County

⊞ **LONGMONT UNITED HOSPITAL (060003)**, 1950 West Mountain View Avenue, Zip 80501–3162, Mailing Address: P.O. Box 1659, Zip 80502–1659; tel. 303/651–5111, (Total facility includes 15 beds in nursing home–type unit) **A**1 2 9 10 **F**2 3 11 13 15 18 20 22 28 29 30 31 34 35 36 37 39 40 43 44 45 47 48 49 50 53 54 56 57 59 61 64 68 70 73 74 75 76 77 78 79 81 82 84 85 86 87 89 92 93 107 108 110 111 114 115 118 119 121 123 126 128 129 130 131 132 135 146 148 **P**6
Primary Contact: Mitchell C. Carson, President and Chief Executive Officer
CFO: Neil W. Bertrand, Chief Financial Officer
CMO: John Bradley, M.D., Chief of Staff
CMO: David Burnham, M.D., Chief of Staff
CIO: John Peterson, Vice President Information Systems
CHR: Warren Laughlin, Vice President Human Resources
CNO: Nancy Driscoll, R.N., Chief Nursing Officer
Web address: www.luhcares.org
**Control:** Other not–for–profit (including NFP Corporation) **Service:** General Medical and Surgical

**Staffed Beds:** 146 **Admissions:** 7669 **Census:** 85 **Outpatient Visits:** 127789 **Births:** 1097 **Total Expense ($000):** 167195 **Payroll Expense ($000):** 64712 **Personnel:** 1057

## LOUISVILLE—Boulder County

⊞ **AVISTA ADVENTIST HOSPITAL (060103)**, 100 Health Park Drive, Zip 80027–9583; tel. 303/673–1000 **A**1 9 10 **F**3 8 11 13 15 17 18 20 22 29 30 31 34 40 43 44 45 47 48 49 50 59 60 62 63 64 68 70 72 73 74 75 76 77 78 79 80 81 82 85 86 87 89 93 107 108 111 114 115 119 129 130 131 132 135 146 147 148 **P**4 6 **S** Adventist Health System Sunbelt Health Care Corporation, Altamonte Springs, FL
Primary Contact: Dennis Barts, Chief Executive Officer
COO: David A. Smith, Vice President and Chief Operating Officer
CFO: Cheryl Curry, Vice President Finance
CMO: David Ehrenberger, M.D., Chief Medical Officer
CHR: Derek Morgan, Director Human Resources
Web address: www.avistahospital.org
**Control:** Church–operated, Nongovernment, not–for profit **Service:** General Medical and Surgical

**Staffed Beds:** 114 **Admissions:** 4429 **Census:** 41 **Outpatient Visits:** 45087 **Births:** 2075 **Total Expense ($000):** 77004 **Payroll Expense ($000):** 31551 **Personnel:** 429

☐ **CENTENNIAL PEAKS HOSPITAL (064007)**, 2255 South 88th Street, Zip 80027–9716; tel. 303/673–9990, (Nonreporting) **A**1 9 10 **S** Universal Health Services, Inc., King of Prussia, PA
Primary Contact: Elicia Bunch, Chief Executive Officer
CFO: Tim Ryan, Director Finance
CMO: Michael Zona, M.D., Medical Director
CHR: Tawnya Nordstrom, Director Human Resources
Web address: www.centennialpeaks.com
**Control:** Other not–for–profit (including NFP Corporation) **Service:** Psychiatric

**Staffed Beds:** 72

## LOVELAND—Larimer County

⊞ **MCKEE MEDICAL CENTER (060030)**, 2000 Boise Avenue, Zip 80538–4281; tel. 970/669–4640 **A**1 2 9 10 **F**2 3 8 11 12 13 15 18 20 22 28 30 31 34 35 38 40 43 46 49 50 54 56 57 59 60 61 62 64 68 70 74 75 76 77 78 79 80 81 82 85 86 87 93 97 104 107 108 110 111 114 115 119 121 123 126 129 130 132 133 134 135 144 146 147 148 **P**6 **S** Banner Health, Phoenix, AZ
Primary Contact: Marilyn Schock, Chief Executive Officer
COO: Leslie Martin, Associate Administrator
CFO: Lori Sehrt, Chief Financial Officer
CMO: Bert Honea, M.D., Medical Director
CIO: Steve Rains, Director Information Services
CHR: Darlene Alvis, Chief Human Resources Officer
CNO: Debra Fox, Chief Nursing Officer
Web address: www.mckeeloveland.com
**Control:** Other not–for–profit (including NFP Corporation) **Service:** General Medical and Surgical

**Staffed Beds:** 105 **Admissions:** 5849 **Census:** 50 **Outpatient Visits:** 176533 **Births:** 782 **Total Expense ($000):** 122844 **Payroll Expense ($000):** 43905 **Personnel:** 667

⊞ **MEDICAL CENTER OF THE ROCKIES (060119)**, 2500 Rocky Mountain Avenue, Zip 80538–9004; tel. 970/624–2500, (Data for 182 days) **A**1 9 10 **F**3 11 13 14 15 17 18 20 22 24 26 28 29 30 31 34 35 37 39 40 43 45 47 49 50 55 57 58 59 60 61 64 65 68 70 74 75 76 77 78 79 80 81 82 84 85 86 87 89 93 107 108 110 111 114 118 119 120 126 130 131 132 134 135 146 147 148 **P**5 6 **S** University of Colorado Health, Fort Collins, CO
Primary Contact: George E. Hayes, FACHE, President and Chief Executive Officer
CFO: Stephanie Doughty, Chief Financial Officer
CMO: William Neff, M.D., Chief Medical Officer
CIO: Steve Hess, Vice President & Chief Information Officer
CIO: Fernando Pedroza, Director Information Systems
CHR: Patti Oakes, Director Human Resources
Web address: www.medctrrockies.org
**Control:** Other not–for–profit (including NFP Corporation) **Service:** General Medical and Surgical

**Staffed Beds:** 146 **Admissions:** 3825 **Census:** 81 **Outpatient Visits:** 82326 **Births:** 311 **Total Expense ($000):** 98291 **Payroll Expense ($000):** 30736 **Personnel:** 858

## MEEKER—Rio Blanco County

★ **PIONEERS MEDICAL CENTER (061325)**, 345 Cleveland Street, Zip 81641–3238; tel. 970/878–5047, (Includes WALBRIDGE MEMORIAL CONVALESCENT WING ), (Total facility includes 31 beds in nursing home–type unit) **A**9 10 18 **F**1 15 28 29 34 35 40 45 53 57 59 62 64 65 67 68 69 75 76 77 81 85 89 93 97 107 110 114 119 127 130 133 135 143 **P**6 **S** QHR, Brentwood, TN
Primary Contact: Kenneth Harman, Chief Executive Officer
COO: Drew Varland, Chief Nursing Officer and Chief Operating Officer
CFO: James W. Worrell, Chief Financial Officer
CMO: Albert Krueger, M.D., Chief of Staff
CIO: Curtis Cooper, Manager Information Systems
CHR: Twyla Jensen, Director Human Resources
Web address: www.pioneershospital.com
**Control:** Hospital district or authority, Government, nonfederal **Service:** General Medical and Surgical

**Staffed Beds:** 46 **Admissions:** 169 **Census:** 28 **Outpatient Visits:** 10089 **Births:** 1 **Total Expense ($000):** 12920 **Payroll Expense ($000):** 6232 **Personnel:** 126

## MONTROSE—Montrose County

⊞ **MONTROSE MEMORIAL HOSPITAL (060006)**, 800 South Third Street, Zip 81401–4212; tel. 970/249–2211 **A**1 9 10 20 **F**3 12 13 15 17 18 20 22 28 29 30 31 34 35 40 43 45 46 51 57 66 70 73 74 75 76 78 79 80 81 82 85 88 89 90 93 107 108 110 111 115 119 126 127 129 130 131 146 **P**5 8 **S** QHR, Brentwood, TN
Primary Contact: David L. Hample, Chief Executive Officer
COO: Mary E. Snyder, Chief Operations Officer
CFO: Stephan A. Wilson, Chief Financial Officer
CMO: Richard Shannon, M.D., Chief of Staff
CIO: Carlos Lovera, Director Information Systems
CHR: Kathy McKie, Director Human Resources
Web address: www.montrosehospital.com
**Control:** Other not–for–profit (including NFP Corporation) **Service:** General Medical and Surgical

**Staffed Beds:** 69 **Admissions:** 3141 **Census:** 30 **Outpatient Visits:** 96149 **Births:** 469 **Total Expense ($000):** 80207 **Payroll Expense ($000):** 25937 **Personnel:** 489

## PAGOSA SPRINGS—Archuleta County

**PAGOSA SPRINGS MEDICAL CENTER (061328)**, 95 South Pagosa Boulevard, Zip 81147–8329; tel. 970/731–3700, (Nonreporting) **A**9 10 18
Primary Contact: Bradley Cochennet, Chief Executive Officer
**Control:** Other not–for–profit (including NFP Corporation) **Service:** General Medical and Surgical

**Staffed Beds:** 11

*Many Facility Codes have changed. Please refer to the AHA Guide Code Chart.*

© 2013 AHA Guide

CO

## PARKER—Douglas County

**PARKER ADVENTIST HOSPITAL (060114)**, 9395 Crown Crest Boulevard, Zip 80138–8573; tel. 303/269–4000 **A**1 9 10 **F**3 11 12 13 15 20 22 29 30 31 34 35 36 38 40 43 45 46 49 50 54 55 57 59 64 70 72 73 74 75 76 77 78 79 81 82 83 84 85 87 93 96 97 107 110 111 114 115 116 117 119 126 129 130 131 135 146 147 148 **P**6 **S** Adventist Health System Sunbelt Health Care Corporation, Altamonte Springs, FL
Primary Contact: Morre Dean, Chief Executive Officer
CFO: Andrew Gaasch, Chief Financial Officer
CMO: Todd Mydler, M.D., Chief Medical Officer
Web address: www.parkerhospital.org
**Control:** Church–operated, Nongovernment, not–for profit **Service:** General Medical and Surgical

**Staffed Beds:** 143 **Admissions:** 7459 **Census:** 74 **Outpatient Visits:** 57304 **Births:** 1536 **Total Expense ($000):** 142064 **Payroll Expense ($000):** 46047 **Personnel:** 610

## PUEBLO—Pueblo County

**COLORADO MENTAL HEALTH INSTITUTE AT PUEBLO (060115)**, 1600 West 24th Street, Zip 81003–1499; tel. 719/546–4000, (Nonreporting) **A**1 3 5 10
Primary Contact: John R. DeQuardo, M.D., Superintendent
CFO: Jim Duff, Chief Financial Officer
CMO: Al Singleton, M.D., Chief Psychiatry and Chief Medical Staff
CIO: Eunice Wolther, Public Information Officer
CHR: Mary Young, Director Human Resources
Web address: www.cdhs.state.co.us/cmhip
**Control:** State–Government, nonfederal **Service:** Psychiatric

**Staffed Beds:** 514

**HAVEN BEHAVIORAL WAR HEROES HOSPITAL (064025)**, 1008 Minnequa Avenue, Suite 6100, Zip 81004–3733; tel. 719/546–6000, (Nonreporting) **A**1 10 **S** Haven Behavioral Healthcare, Nashville, TN
Primary Contact: Carrin Harper, M.D., Chief Executive Officer
**Control:** Corporation, Investor–owned, for–profit **Service:** Psychiatric

**Staffed Beds:** 20

△ **PARKVIEW MEDICAL CENTER (060020)**, 400 West 16th Street, Zip 81003–2781; tel. 719/584–4000, (Total facility includes 20 beds in nursing home–type unit) **A**1 7 9 10 **F**2 3 4 5 8 11 13 15 18 20 22 24 28 29 30 31 34 35 37 38 40 42 43 45 46 49 50 51 53 56 57 58 59 62 64 70 73 74 75 76 78 79 81 82 84 85 86 87 89 90 93 94 95 96 97 98 99 100 101 102 103 104 105 107 108 111 114 115 116 118 119 124 128 129 130 132 135 141 146 147 148 **P**6 8
Primary Contact: Michael T. Baxter, Chief Executive Officer
COO: Timothy Allen, Senior Vice President and Chief Operating Officer
CFO: William Patterson, Chief Financial Officer
CMO: Steve Nafziger, M.D., Vice President Medical Affairs
CIO: Steve Shirley, Chief Information Officer
CHR: Darrin Smith, Vice President Human Resources
Web address: www.parkviewmc.org
**Control:** Other not–for–profit (including NFP Corporation) **Service:** General Medical and Surgical

**Staffed Beds:** 370 **Admissions:** 13747 **Census:** 214 **Outpatient Visits:** 183102 **Births:** 1556 **Total Expense ($000):** 267959 **Payroll Expense ($000):** 101829 **Personnel:** 1987

**ST. MARY–CORWIN MEDICAL CENTER (060012)**, 1008 Minnequa Avenue, Zip 81004–3798; tel. 719/557–4000 **A**1 2 9 10 12 13 **F**3 13 15 18 20 22 26 28 29 30 31 34 35 40 43 45 47 48 49 50 51 53 55 57 58 59 64 68 70 72 73 75 76 78 79 81 82 84 85 86 87 89 90 107 108 110 111 114 115 117 119 120 121 123 124 126 129 130 131 132 135 146 147 148 **P**6 **S** Catholic Health Initiatives, Englewood, CO
Primary Contact: Brian Moore, Chief Executive Officer
COO: Michael Cafasso, Vice President Operations
CFO: Sheri Trahern, Chief Financial Officer
CMO: Stephen Brown, M.D., Chief Medical Officer
CHR: Rudy Krasovec, Director Human Resources
Web address: www.centura.org
**Control:** Church–operated, Nongovernment, not–for profit **Service:** General Medical and Surgical

**Staffed Beds:** 202 **Admissions:** 6860 **Census:** 84 **Outpatient Visits:** 87797 **Births:** 577 **Total Expense ($000):** 142733 **Payroll Expense ($000):** 53061 **Personnel:** 875

## RANGELY—Rio Blanco County

★ **RANGELY DISTRICT HOSPITAL (061307)**, 511 South White Avenue, Zip 81648–2104; tel. 970/675–5011, (Nonreporting) **A**9 10 18
Primary Contact: Nick Goshe, Chief Executive Officer
CFO: Jim Dillon, Chief Financial Officer
CMO: Chris Adams, M.D., Physician
CHR: Kristin Beery, Executive Assistant and Director Human Resources
Web address: www.rangelyhospital.com
**Control:** Hospital district or authority, Government, nonfederal **Service:** General Medical and Surgical

**Staffed Beds:** 25

## RIFLE—Garfield County

★ **GRAND RIVER HOSPITAL DISTRICT (061317)**, 501 Airport Road, Zip 81650–8510, Mailing Address: P.O. Box 912, Zip 81650–0912; tel. 970/625–1510, (Total facility includes 57 beds in nursing home–type unit) **A**9 10 18 **F**3 11 12 15 29 34 35 39 40 41 43 45 50 57 59 64 68 69 75 77 79 81 85 87 93 96 97 107 108 110 111 112 114 118 119 127 128 129 130 131 132 133 144 145 146 148 **P**6
Primary Contact: James Coombs, Chief Executive Officer
COO: Mary Desormeau, Chief Nursing Officer
CMO: Gary Meyer, M.D., Chief of Staff
CIO: Diana Murray, Director Information Systems
CHR: Michael Weerts, Director Human Resources
CNO: Mary Desormeau, Chief Nursing Officer
Web address: www.grhd.org
**Control:** Hospital district or authority, Government, nonfederal **Service:** General Medical and Surgical

**Staffed Beds:** 70 **Admissions:** 545 **Census:** 48 **Outpatient Visits:** 54698 **Births:** 0 **Total Expense ($000):** 44769 **Payroll Expense ($000):** 20718 **Personnel:** 258

## SALIDA—Chaffee County

★ **HEART OF THE ROCKIES REGIONAL MEDICAL CENTER (061322)**, 1000 Rush Drive, Zip 81201–9627, Mailing Address: P.O. Box 429, Zip 81201–0429; tel. 719/530–2200 **A**9 10 18 **F**3 11 13 15 28 29 31 34 35 40 43 45 50 54 57 64 68 70 75 76 77 78 79 81 82 85 89 93 97 107 110 111 114 117 119 127 129 130 131 133 135 146 147 148
Primary Contact: Kenneth W. Leisher, Chief Executive Officer
CFO: Lesley Fagerberg, Vice President Fiscal Services
CMO: James Wigington, M.D., Chief of Staff
CIO: Andy Waldbart, Department Manager
CHR: Barbara J. Abel, Vice President Human Resources
CNO: Peg Arnett, Interim Vice President of Nursing
Web address: www.hrrmc.com
**Control:** Hospital district or authority, Government, nonfederal **Service:** General Medical and Surgical

**Staffed Beds:** 25 **Admissions:** 1075 **Census:** 10 **Outpatient Visits:** 38959 **Births:** 126 **Total Expense ($000):** 37177 **Payroll Expense ($000):** 13742 **Personnel:** 262

## SPRINGFIELD—Baca County

★ **SOUTHEAST COLORADO HOSPITAL DISTRICT (061311)**, 373 East Tenth Avenue, Zip 81073–1699; tel. 719/523–4501, (Total facility includes 56 beds in nursing home–type unit) **A**9 10 18 **F**3 6 7 11 29 34 35 40 42 45 50 56 57 62 63 66 68 81 93 97 107 127 133 147 148 **P**6
Primary Contact: Robert W. Omer, FACHE, Chief Executive Officer and Administrator
CFO: James L. Forrest, Jr., Chief Financial Officer
CMO: Frank McDonald, D.O., Chief of Staff
CIO: Bobby L. Schaller, Chief Engineer
CHR: Sherrilyn Turner, Director Human Resources
Web address: www.sechosp.org
**Control:** Hospital district or authority, Government, nonfederal **Service:** General Medical and Surgical

**Staffed Beds:** 79 **Admissions:** 196 **Census:** 48 **Outpatient Visits:** 41745 **Births:** 0 **Total Expense ($000):** 11653 **Payroll Expense ($000):** 5176 **Personnel:** 159

**CO**

## STEAMBOAT SPRINGS—Routt County

☒ **YAMPA VALLEY MEDICAL CENTER (060049)**, 1024 Central Park Drive, Zip 80487–8813; tel. 970/879–1322, (Total facility includes 59 beds in nursing home–type unit) **A**1 9 10 20 **F**3 11 13 15 18 28 29 30 31 34 35 36 40 43 45 46 48 49 50 51 57 64 68 70 73 75 76 77 78 79 81 82 84 85 86 87 93 107 110 111 115 119 128 129 130 131 132 133 135 143 146 147
Primary Contact: Frank May, Chief Executive Officer
CFO: Robert Flake, Chief Financial Officer
CMO: Larry Bookman, D.O., Chief Medical Officer
CIO: Mark Albright, Director of Information Services
CHR: Soniya Fidler, Senior Director Human Resources
CNO: Marie Timlin, R.N., Chief Nursing Officer
Web address: www.yvmc.org
**Control:** Other not–for–profit (including NFP Corporation) **Service:** General Medical and Surgical

**Staffed Beds:** 98 **Admissions:** 1676 **Census:** 69 **Outpatient Visits:** 62090
**Births:** 266 **Total Expense ($000):** 74075 **Payroll Expense ($000):** 26707
**Personnel:** 424

## STERLING—Logan County

☒ **STERLING REGIONAL MEDCENTER (060076)**, 615 Fairhurst Street, Zip 80751–4523; tel. 970/522–0122 **A**1 9 10 20 **F**3 13 15 18 19 28 29 30 31 32 34 40 41 43 44 45 50 51 57 59 60 64 68 69 70 75 76 77 78 79 81 82 85 86 87 93 97 107 108 110 111 114 118 119 127 129 130 131 143 146 148 **P**6 **S** Banner Health, Phoenix, AZ
Primary Contact: Julie Klein, Chief Executive Officer
CFO: Pamela Stieb, Chief Financial Officer
CMO: Thomas Soper, D.O., Medical Director
CHR: Randy Brigham, Chief Human Resource Officer
Web address: www.bannerhealth.com/Locations/Colorado/Sterling+Regional+MedCenter
**Control:** Other not–for–profit (including NFP Corporation) **Service:** General Medical and Surgical

**Staffed Beds:** 25 **Admissions:** 1249 **Census:** 10 **Outpatient Visits:** 114633
**Births:** 189 **Total Expense ($000):** 43026 **Payroll Expense ($000):** 16971
**Personnel:** 233

## THORNTON—Adams County

**HAVEN BEHAVIORAL SENIOR CARE OF NORTH DENVER (064018)**, 8451 Pearl Street, Suite 100, Zip 80229–4804; tel. 303/288–7807, (Nonreporting) **A**10 **S** Haven Behavioral Healthcare, Nashville, TN
Primary Contact: Marc McComas, Executive Director
Web address: www.havenbehavioral.com/seniorcare/denver
**Control:** Corporation, Investor–owned, for–profit **Service:** Psychiatric

**Staffed Beds:** 40

☒ **NORTH SUBURBAN MEDICAL CENTER (060065)**, 9191 Grant Street, Zip 80229–4341; tel. 303/451–7800 **A**1 9 10 **F**3 11 12 13 15 18 20 22 29 30 35 40 43 45 59 60 64 68 70 72 74 75 76 79 80 81 82 84 85 87 89 107 108 111 115 119 129 130 132 135 146 **S** HCA, Nashville, TN
Primary Contact: Jennifer Alderfer, Chief Executive Officer
CFO: Deborah Hart, Chief Financial Officer
CIO: Jeff Schnoor, Director Information Technology and Systems
CHR: Suzanne Kelley, Director Human Resources
CNO: Erica Rossitto, R.N., Chief Nursing Officer
Web address: www.northsuburban.com
**Control:** Corporation, Investor–owned, for–profit **Service:** General Medical and Surgical

**Staffed Beds:** 115 **Admissions:** 7092 **Census:** 74 **Outpatient Visits:** 87464
**Births:** 1364 **Total Expense ($000):** 99456 **Payroll Expense ($000):** 40771
**Personnel:** 553

☐ **VIBRA HOSPITAL OF DENVER (062014)**, 8451 Pearl Street, Zip 80229–4804; tel. 303/288–3000, (Nonreporting) **A**1 9 10 **S** Vibra Healthcare, Mechanicsburg, PA
Primary Contact: Jan Eyer, Chief Executive Officer
CMO: Peter Cahill, M.D., President Medical Staff
CHR: Lorna Fulton, Director Human Resources
Web address: www.vhdenver.com
**Control:** Corporation, Investor–owned, for–profit **Service:** Long–Term Acute Care hospital

**Staffed Beds:** 71

## TRINIDAD—Las Animas County

☒ **MT. SAN RAFAEL HOSPITAL (061321)**, 410 Benedicta Avenue, Zip 81082–2093; tel. 719/846–9213 **A**1 9 10 18 **F**3 11 15 28 40 43 45 50 57 59 68 75 77 81 82 85 87 93 107 108 111 114 119 127 129 133 148 **P**6
Primary Contact: Robert Quist, Chief Executive Officer
CFO: Woody Hathaway, Chief Financial Officer
CMO: Gerald Cichocki, M.D., Chief of Staff
CHR: Lori Silva, Director Human Resources
Web address: www.msrhc.org
**Control:** Other not–for–profit (including NFP Corporation) **Service:** General Medical and Surgical

**Staffed Beds:** 25 **Admissions:** 804 **Census:** 9 **Outpatient Visits:** 39427
**Births:** 0 **Total Expense ($000):** 24538 **Payroll Expense ($000):** 10366
**Personnel:** 194

## VAIL—Eagle County

☒ **VAIL VALLEY MEDICAL CENTER (060096)**, 181 West Meadow Drive, Zip 81657–5242, Mailing Address: P.O. Box 40000, Zip 81658–7520; tel. 970/476–2451, (Nonreporting) **A**1 9 10 20
Primary Contact: Doris Kirchner, Chief Executive Officer
COO: Tom Kyllo, Executive Vice President
CFO: Shaun J. Scanlon, Senior Vice President Finance and Chief Financial Officer
CMO: John Woodland, M.D., Medical Director
CIO: Dave Pluta, Chief Information Officer
CHR: David Blackwell, Vice President Human Resources
Web address: www.vvmc.com
**Control:** Other not–for–profit (including NFP Corporation) **Service:** General Medical and Surgical

**Staffed Beds:** 58

## WALSENBURG—Huerfano County

★ **SPANISH PEAKS REGIONAL HEALTH CENTER (061316)**, 23500 U.S. Highway 160, Zip 81089–9524; tel. 719/738–5100 **A**9 10 18 **F**11 28 34 35 40 45 50 57 59 64 79 81 82 85 93 97 107 111 114 119 127 129 131 133 147 148 **P**6
Primary Contact: Todd Oberheu, Chief Executive Officer
CFO: Richard L. Corradino, Chief Financial Officer
CMO: Thomas Hoffeld, M.D., Chief of Staff
CHR: Tony Marostica, Director Human Resources
CNO: Darlene Colt, R.N., Chief Nursing Officer
Web address: www.sprhc.org
**Control:** Hospital district or authority, Government, nonfederal **Service:** General Medical and Surgical

**Staffed Beds:** 20 **Admissions:** 286 **Census:** 4 **Outpatient Visits:** 35409
**Births:** 0 **Total Expense ($000):** 13985 **Payroll Expense ($000):** 7811
**Personnel:** 135

## WESTMINSTER—Jefferson County

**CLEO WALLACE CENTERS HOSPITAL**, 8405 Church Ranch Boulevard, Zip 80021–3918; tel. 303/466–7391, (Nonreporting) **A**9
Primary Contact: Michael J. Montgomery, President and Chief Executive Officer
CFO: Jonelle A. Roberts, Chief Financial Officer
Web address: www.devereux.org
**Control:** Other not–for–profit (including NFP Corporation) **Service:** Children's hospital psychiatric

**Staffed Beds:** 61

☒ **ST. ANTHONY NORTH HOSPITAL (060104)**, 2551 West 84th Avenue, Zip 80031–3807; tel. 303/426–2151 **A**1 9 10 **F**3 11 13 15 18 20 22 26 28 29 30 31 34 35 36 40 43 45 46 49 54 57 60 63 64 65 68 70 72 74 75 76 77 78 79 81 85 87 92 93 97 102 107 108 110 114 115 119 129 130 146 147 148 **S** Catholic Health Initiatives, Englewood, CO
Primary Contact: Carole Peet, R.N., MSN, President and Chief Executive Officer
CFO: Alison Mizer, Chief Financial Officer
CIO: Dana Moore, Senior Vice President Information Services
CHR: Robert Archibold, Director, Human Resources
CNO: Carol A. Butler, R.N., VP Patient Care Services & Operations
Web address: www.stanthonynorth.org
**Control:** Church–operated, Nongovernment, not–for profit **Service:** General Medical and Surgical

**Staffed Beds:** 138 **Admissions:** 6409 **Census:** 67 **Outpatient Visits:** 62649
**Births:** 911 **Total Expense ($000):** 136961 **Payroll Expense ($000):** 37176
**Personnel:** 743

*Many Facility Codes have changed. Please refer to the AHA Guide Code Chart.* © 2013 AHA Guide

**WHEAT RIDGE—Jefferson County**

☒ **EXEMPLA LUTHERAN MEDICAL CENTER (060009)**, 8300 West 38th Avenue, Zip 80033–6005; tel. 303/425–4500, (Includes EXEMPLA WEST PINES, 3400 Lutheran Parkway, Zip 80033; tel. 303/467–4000), (Total facility includes 114 beds in nursing home–type unit) **A**1 2 9 10 **F**3 4 5 10 11 13 15 18 20 22 24 26 28 29 30 31 33 34 35 36 40 43 45 47 48 49 50 54 55 58 59 60 62 63 64 67 68 70 72 74 75 76 77 78 79 81 84 85 86 87 94 98 100 101 102 103 104 105 107 108 110 111 114 115 119 120 121 123 124 125 126 128 129 130 132 146 147 148 **P**6 **S** SCL Health System, Denver, CO
Primary Contact: Grant Wicklund, President and Chief Executive Officer
COO: Peggy Cain Price, Vice President and Chief Operating Officer
CFO: Karen Scremin, Vice President Finance
CMO: David Munch, M.D., Vice President and Chief Clinical and Quality Officer
CHR: Scott Day, Vice President Human Resources
Web address: www.exempla.org
**Control:** Other not–for–profit (including NFP Corporation) **Service:** General Medical and Surgical

**Staffed Beds:** 494 **Admissions:** 17728 **Census:** 348 **Outpatient Visits:** 170676 **Births:** 2764 **Total Expense ($000):** 289484 **Payroll Expense ($000):** 112213 **Personnel:** 1538

**WOODLAND PARK—Teller County**

◇ **PIKES PEAK REGIONAL HOSPITAL (061326)**, 16420 West Highway 24, Zip 80863; tel. 719/687–9999 **A**9 10 18 21 **F**3 15 29 30 34 40 43 45 50 57 59 64 65 66 68 77 79 81 82 93 97 107 110 111 119 133 146 **S** IASIS Healthcare, Franklin, TN
Primary Contact: Terry Buckner, Chief Executive Officer
CFO: Kimberly Monvesky, Chief Financial Officer
CMO: Kurt Wever, M.D., Chief of Staff
CHR: Arianne Randolph, Director Human Resources
CNO: Rodney Bice, R.N., Chief Nursing Officer
Web address: www.pprmc.org
**Control:** Corporation, Investor–owned, for–profit **Service:** General Medical and Surgical

**Staffed Beds:** 15 **Admissions:** 556 **Census:** 6 **Outpatient Visits:** 22942 **Births:** 0 **Total Expense ($000):** 17281 **Payroll Expense ($000):** 6585

**WRAY—Yuma County**

**WRAY COMMUNITY DISTRICT HOSPITAL (061309)**, 1017 West 7th Street, Zip 80758–1420; tel. 970/332–4811, (Nonreporting) **A**9 10 18
Primary Contact: Edward Finley, Administrator
CFO: Jennie Sullivan, Director Finance
CMO: Monte Uyemura, M.D., Chief of Staff
Web address: www.wcdh.org
**Control:** Hospital district or authority, Government, nonfederal **Service:** General Medical and Surgical

**Staffed Beds:** 16

**YUMA—Yuma County**

★ **YUMA DISTRICT HOSPITAL (061315)**, 1000 West 8th Avenue, Zip 80759–2641; tel. 970/848–5405 **A**9 10 18 **F**3 11 13 15 28 29 30 31 34 35 36 40 43 44 50 53 57 59 62 64 65 68 74 75 76 77 78 79 81 82 87 93 97 99 101 102 103 104 107 111 115 119 127 130 133 148 **P**6
Primary Contact: John Gardner, Chief Executive Officer
COO: Lyndia Loppe, Chief Operating Officer
CFO: Cathy Wolff, Vice President Financial Services and Chief Financial Officer
CMO: John Wolz, M.D., Chief Medical Staff
CIO: Jason Hawley, Manager Information Services
CHR: Gini Adams, Director Employee and Public Relations
CNO: Beth Saxton, R.N., Vice President Patient Care Services
Web address: www.yumahospital.org
**Control:** Hospital district or authority, Government, nonfederal **Service:** General Medical and Surgical

**Staffed Beds:** 12 **Admissions:** 266 **Census:** 3 **Outpatient Visits:** 44976 **Births:** 7 **Total Expense ($000):** 19356 **Payroll Expense ($000):** 8386 **Personnel:** 127

**CO**

**Hospital, Medicare Provider Number, Address, Telephone, Approval, Facility, and Physician Codes, Health Care System**

★ American Hospital Association (AHA) membership
☐ The Joint Commission accreditation
◇ DNV Healthcare Inc. accreditation
○ Healthcare Facilities Accreditation Program
△ Commission on Accreditation of Rehabilitation Facilities (CARF) accreditation

© 2013 AHA Guide    *Many Facility Codes have changed. Please refer to the AHA Guide Code Chart.*    Hospitals **A107**

# CONNECTICUT

## BETHLEHEM—Litchfield County

**WELLSPRING FOUNDATION**, 21 Arch Bridge Road, Zip 06751–1612, Mailing Address: P.O. Box 370, Zip 06751–0370; tel. 203/266–7235, (Nonreporting) **A**9
Primary Contact: Richard E. Beauvais, Ph.D., Chief Executive Officer
CFO: Richard E. Beauvais, Ph.D., Chief Executive Officer
Web address: www.wellspring.org
**Control:** Other not–for–profit (including NFP Corporation) **Service:** Psychiatric

Staffed Beds: 36

## BRANFORD—New Haven County

**THE CONNECTICUT HOSPICE (070038)**, 100 Double Beach Road, Zip 06405–4909; tel. 203/315–7500, (Nonreporting) **A**1 10
Primary Contact: Rosemary Johnson Hurzeler, President and Chief Executive Officer
Web address: www.hospice.com
**Control:** Other not–for–profit (including NFP Corporation) **Service:** Other specialty

Staffed Beds: 52

## BRIDGEPORT—Fairfield County

**BRIDGEPORT HOSPITAL (070010)**, 267 Grant Street, Zip 06610–2805, Mailing Address: P.O. Box 5000, Zip 06610–0120; tel. 203/384–3000 **A**1 2 3 5 6 8 9 10 **F**3 5 6 8 11 12 13 15 16 18 19 20 22 24 26 28 29 30 31 32 34 35 36 38 40 41 43 44 45 46 47 48 49 50 51 55 56 57 58 59 64 65 66 68 70 74 75 76 77 78 79 80 81 82 84 85 86 87 90 93 96 97 98 99 100 101 102 103 104 105 107 108 110 111 114 117 118 119 120 121 123 124 126 129 130 131 132 134 135 144 145 146 147 148 **P**3 **S** Yale New Haven Health System, New Haven, CT
Primary Contact: William M. Jennings, President and Chief Executive Officer
COO: Norman G. Roth, Executive Vice President and Chief Operating Officer
CFO: Patrick McCabe, Senior Vice President Finance and Chief Financial Officer
CMO: Michael Ivy, M.D., Senior Vice President for Medical Affairs and Chief Medical Officer
CIO: Daniel Barchi, Senior Vice President, Technical Services and Chief Information Officer
CHR: Melissa Turner, Senior Vice President Human Resources
CNO: MaryEllen Kosturko, R.N., Senior Vice President Patient Care Operations and Chief Nursing Officer
Web address: www.bridgeporthospital.org
**Control:** Other not–for–profit (including NFP Corporation) **Service:** General Medical and Surgical

Staffed Beds: 337 Admissions: 16959 Census: 262 Outpatient Visits: 288419 Births: 2080 Total Expense ($000): 403987 Payroll Expense ($000): 144214 Personnel: 1895

**SOUTHWEST CONNECTICUT MENTAL HEALTH SYSTEM (074012)**, 97 Middle Street, Zip 06604–4410; tel. 203/551–7400, (Nonreporting) **A**1 9 10 **S** Connecticut Department of Mental Health and Addiction Services, Hartford, CT
Primary Contact: Daniel Wartenberg, PsyD, Acting Chief Executive Officer
CFO: Magnus Ezeji, Chief Financial Officer
CMO: Stephen R. Atkins, M.D., Medical Director
CIO: Paula Zwally, Director Quality Improvement Services and Compliance
CHR: Paula DeBarros, Director Human Resources
Web address: www.ct.gov/dmhas/cwp/view.asp?a=2946&q=378936
**Control:** State–Government, nonfederal **Service:** Psychiatric

Staffed Beds: 62

**ST. VINCENT'S MEDICAL CENTER (070028)**, 2800 Main Street, Zip 06606–4292; tel. 203/576–5454, (Includes ST. VINCENT'S BEHAVIORAL HEALTH, 47 Long Lots Road, Westport, Zip 06880–3800; tel. 203/221–8802; James McCreath, Ph.D., President and Chief Executive Officer) **A**1 2 3 5 9 10 **F**3 4 5 8 12 13 15 17 18 20 22 24 26 28 29 30 31 34 35 36 38 40 43 44 45 46 47 48 49 50 53 54 55 56 57 58 59 60 61 63 64 65 66 68 70 71 74 75 76 77 78 79 80 81 82 83 84 85 86 87 90 91 92 93 96 97 98 99 100 101 102 103 104 105 106 107 108 110 111 114 115 117 118 119 120 121 123 124 126 130 132 134 143 144 145 146 147 148 **P**1 **S** Ascension Health, Saint Louis, MO
Primary Contact: Susan L. Davis, R.N., Ed.D., FACHE, Chief Executive Officer
CFO: John Gleckler, Chief Financial Officer
CMO: Stuart Marcus, M.D., Senior Vice President and Chief Medical Officer
CIO: Betsy Thornquist, Chief Information Officer
CHR: Steven Younes, Vice President, Chief Human Resources Officer and Employment Counsel
Web address: www.stvincents.org
**Control:** Other not–for–profit (including NFP Corporation) **Service:** General Medical and Surgical

Staffed Beds: 414 Admissions: 20912 Census: 327 Outpatient Visits: 448934 Births: 1046 Total Expense ($000): 373660 Payroll Expense ($000): 185441 Personnel: 2318

## BRISTOL—Hartford County

**BRISTOL HOSPITAL (070029)**, Brewster Road, Zip 06011, Mailing Address: P.O. Box 977, Zip 06011–0977; tel. 860/585–3000, (Nonreporting) **A**1 2 5 9 10
Primary Contact: Kurt A. Barwis, FACHE, President and Chief Executive Officer
COO: Marc D. Edelman, Vice President Operations
CFO: Peter Freytag, Senior Vice President Finance and Chief Financial Officer
CMO: Leonard Banco, M.D., Senior Vice President and Chief Medical Officer
CIO: David Rackliffe, Assistant Vice President Information Services
CHR: Jeanine Reckdenwald, Vice President Human Resources and Support Services
Web address: www.bristolhospital.org
**Control:** Other not–for–profit (including NFP Corporation) **Service:** General Medical and Surgical

Staffed Beds: 134

## DANBURY—Fairfield County

**DANBURY HOSPITAL (070033)**, 24 Hospital Avenue, Zip 06810–6099; tel. 203/739–7000 **A**1 2 3 5 8 9 10 **F**3 4 5 8 9 12 13 14 15 17 18 20 22 24 26 28 29 30 31 32 33 34 35 36 37 38 39 40 43 44 45 46 47 48 49 50 51 54 55 56 57 58 59 60 61 64 65 66 68 70 72 73 74 75 76 77 78 79 80 81 82 83 84 85 86 87 89 90 93 94 96 97 98 99 100 101 102 103 104 105 107 108 109 110 111 112 114 115 116 117 118 119 120 121 123 124 126 129 130 131 132 134 135 144 145 146 147 148 **P**6 7 8 **S** Western Connecticut Health Network, Danbury, CT
Primary Contact: John M. Murphy, M.D., President and Chief Executive Officer
COO: Michael Daglio, Chief Operating Officer
CFO: Steven Rosenberg, Chief Financial Officer
CMO: Matthew Miller, M.D., Vice President Medical Affairs
CIO: Kathleen DeMatteo, Chief Information Officer
CHR: Phyllis Zappala, Vice President Human Resources
CHR: Phyllis F. Zappala, Senior Vice President
CNO: Moreen Donahue, R.N., Chief Nursing Executive
Web address: www.danburyhospital.org
**Control:** Other not–for–profit (including NFP Corporation) **Service:** General Medical and Surgical

Staffed Beds: 344 Admissions: 17862 Census: 239 Outpatient Visits: 429070 Births: 2001 Total Expense ($000): 500530 Payroll Expense ($000): 192567 Personnel: 2400

## DERBY—New Haven County

**GRIFFIN HOSPITAL (070031)**, 130 Division Street, Zip 06418–1326; tel. 203/735–7421 **A**1 2 9 10 **F**3 5 8 12 13 15 18 28 29 30 31 34 35 36 38 40 45 49 50 51 53 56 57 58 59 64 65 68 70 71 74 75 76 77 78 79 81 82 85 86 87 93 94 96 97 98 99 100 101 102 103 104 105 107 108 110 111 112 114 116 117 118 119 120 121 129 130 132 134 135 144 146 147 148
Primary Contact: Patrick Charmel, President and Chief Executive Officer
CMO: Kenneth V. Schwartz, M.D., Medical Director
CIO: George Tomas, Director Information Services
CHR: Steve Mordecai, Director Human Resources
CNO: Barbara J. Stumpo, R.N., Vice President Patient Care Services
Web address: www.griffinhealth.org
**Control:** Other not–for–profit (including NFP Corporation) **Service:** General Medical and Surgical

Staffed Beds: 111 Admissions: 6446 Census: 76 Outpatient Visits: 196386 Births: 621 Total Expense ($000): 129116 Payroll Expense ($000): 52662 Personnel: 876

## FARMINGTON—Hartford County

**UNIVERSITY OF CONNECTICUT HEALTH CENTER, JOHN DEMPSEY HOSPITAL (070036)**, 263 Farmington Avenue, Zip 06032–1941; tel. 860/679–2000 **A**1 2 3 5 8 9 10 12 13 19 **F**3 5 6 7 8 9 11 13 15 18 20 22 24 26 29 30 31 34 35 37 38 39 40 44 45 46 47 48 49 50 51 52 54 55 56 57 58 59 60 64 65 66 68 70 74 75 76 77 78 79 81 82 84 85 86 87 91 92 93 94 97 98 99 100 101 102 103 104 105 107 108 110 111 114 115 117 118 119 120 121 123 124 126 129 130 131 132 133 135 143 145 146 147 148 **P**6
Primary Contact: Mike H. Summerer, M.D., Chief Executive Officer
COO: Anne Diamond, JD, Chief Operating Officer
CFO: John Biancamano, Chief Financial Officer
CMO: Richard Simon, M.D., Chief of Staff
CIO: Sandra Armstrong, Chief Information Officer
CHR: Carolle Andrews, Interim Chief Human Resources Officer
CNO: Ellen Leone, R.N., Chief Nursing Officer
Web address: www.uchc.edu
**Control:** State–Government, nonfederal **Service:** General Medical and Surgical

Staffed Beds: 174 Admissions: 8078 Census: 113 Outpatient Visits: 278850 Births: 473 Total Expense ($000): 303434 Payroll Expense ($000): 106047 Personnel: 1403

*Many Facility Codes have changed. Please refer to the AHA Guide Code Chart.*

## GREENWICH—Fairfield County

⊠ **GREENWICH HOSPITAL (070018)**, 5 Perryridge Road, Zip 06830–4697;
tel. 203/863–3000 **A**1 2 3 5 9 10 **F**3 5 8 11 12 13 15 18 20 22 26 28 29 30
31 32 34 35 36 37 39 40 44 45 46 47 48 49 50 51 52 54 55 56 57 58 59
61 63 64 65 66 68 70 72 74 75 76 77 78 79 80 81 82 84 85 86 87 89 93
96 97 99 100 101 102 103 104 107 108 109 110 111 114 115 116 117
118 119 120 121 123 124 126 129 130 131 132 134 135 146 147 148 **P**2
3 5 **S** Yale New Haven Health System, New Haven, CT
Primary Contact: Frank A. Corvino, President and Chief Executive Officer
COO: Quinton J. Friesen, Executive Vice President and Chief Operating Officer
CFO: Eugene Colucci, Vice President Finance
CMO: A. Michael Marino, M.D., Senior Vice President Medical Administration
CIO: James Weeks, Chief Information Officer
Web address: www.greenhosp.org
**Control:** Other not–for–profit (including NFP Corporation) **Service:** General
Medical and Surgical

**Staffed Beds:** 174 **Admissions:** 11039 **Census:** 127 **Outpatient Visits:**
397931 **Births:** 2225 **Total Expense ($000):** 298517 **Payroll Expense
($000):** 114802 **Personnel:** 1488

## HARTFORD—Hartford County

⊠ **CONNECTICUT CHILDREN'S MEDICAL CENTER (073300)**, 282 Washington
Street, Zip 06106–3322; tel. 860/545–9000, (Nonreporting) **A**1 3 5 9 10
Primary Contact: Martin J. Gavin, President and Chief Executive Officer
CFO: Gerald J. Boisvert, Vice President and Chief Financial Officer
CMO: Paul Dworkin, M.D., Physician–in–Chief
CIO: Kelly R. Styles, Vice President and Chief Information Officer
CHR: Elizabeth Rudden, Vice President Human Resources
Web address: www.ccmckids.org
**Control:** Other not–for–profit (including NFP Corporation) **Service:** Children's
general

**Staffed Beds:** 166

⊠ **HARTFORD HOSPITAL (070025)**, 80 Seymour Street, Zip 06102–8000,
Mailing Address: P.O. Box 5037, Zip 06102–5037; tel. 860/545–5000, (Includes
INSTITUTE OF LIVING, 400 Washington Street, Zip 06106–3392;
tel. 860/545–7000), (Total facility includes 104 beds in nursing home–type unit)
**A**1 2 3 5 8 9 10 **F**2 3 5 6 7 8 9 10 11 12 13 15 17 18 20 22 24 26 28 29
30 31 34 35 36 37 38 39 40 43 44 45 46 47 48 49 50 51 52 53 54 55 56
57 58 59 60 61 63 64 65 66 68 70 71 74 75 76 77 78 79 80 81 82 83 84
85 86 87 91 92 93 94 96 97 98 99 100 101 102 103 104 105 106 107 108
110 111 114 115 116 117 118 119 120 121 123 124 125 126 128 129 130
131 132 135 137 138 139 141 145 146 147 148 **P**6 8 **S** Hartford Healthcare,
Hartford, CT
Primary Contact: Jeffrey A. Flaks, President and Chief Executive Officer
CMO: Stuart Markowitz, M.D., Chief Medical Officer
CIO: Stephan O'Neill, Vice President Information Services
CHR: Richard McAloon, Vice President Human Resources
Web address: www.harthosp.org
**Control:** Other not–for–profit (including NFP Corporation) **Service:** General
Medical and Surgical

**Staffed Beds:** 798 **Admissions:** 37997 **Census:** 707 **Outpatient Visits:**
212461 **Births:** 3605 **Total Expense ($000):** 1035271 **Payroll Expense
($000):** 459506 **Personnel:** 5857

⊠ **MOUNT SINAI REHABILITATION HOSPITAL (073025)**, 490 Blue Hills Avenue,
Zip 06112–1513; tel. 860/714–3500 **A**1 10 **F**29 30 34 54 58 59 64 68 74 75
82 90 91 92 93 94 95 96 130 131 132 **P**6 8 **S** Saint Francis Care, Inc.,
Hartford, CT
Primary Contact: Christopher M. Dadlez, President and Chief Executive Officer
Web address: www.stfranciscare.org
**Control:** Other not–for–profit (including NFP Corporation) **Service:** Rehabilitation

**Staffed Beds:** 30 **Admissions:** 650 **Census:** 25 **Outpatient Visits:** 36988
**Births:** 0 **Total Expense ($000):** 24129 **Payroll Expense ($000):** 11634
**Personnel:** 143

⊠ **SAINT FRANCIS HOSPITAL AND MEDICAL CENTER (070002)**, 114
Woodland Street, Zip 06105–1208; tel. 860/714–4000 **A**1 2 3 5 8 9 10 **F**3 8
11 12 13 15 17 18 20 22 24 26 28 29 30 31 34 35 36 38 39 40 43 46 47
48 49 50 53 54 55 56 57 58 59 61 64 65 66 68 70 72 74 75 76 77 78 79
81 82 84 85 87 92 93 94 95 96 97 98 99 100 101 102 103 104 107 111
115 117 118 119 120 121 123 124 126 129 130 131 132 134 135 144 145
146 147 148 **P**8 **S** Saint Francis Care, Inc., Hartford, CT
Primary Contact: Christopher M. Dadlez, President and Chief Executive Officer
COO: Kathleen M. Roche, R.N., Executive Vice President and Chief Operating
Officer
CFO: John N. Giamalis, Senior Vice President and Chief Financial Officer
CMO: Rolf W. Knoll, M.D., Senior Vice President and Chief Medical Officer
CIO: Linda Shanley, Vice President and Chief Information Officer
CHR: Dawn L. Bryant, Senior Vice President and Chief Human Resource Officer
Web address: www.saintfranciscare.com
**Control:** Church–operated, Nongovernment, not–for profit **Service:** General
Medical and Surgical

**Staffed Beds:** 569 **Admissions:** 29379 **Census:** 412 **Outpatient Visits:**
286701 **Births:** 2995 **Total Expense ($000):** 674831 **Payroll Expense
($000):** 243950 **Personnel:** 4342

## MANCHESTER—Hartford County

⊠ **MANCHESTER MEMORIAL HOSPITAL (070027)**, 71 Haynes Street,
Zip 06040–4188; tel. 860/646–1222 **A**1 2 5 9 10 **F**3 4 5 11 13 15 18 24 28
29 30 31 32 34 35 36 38 39 40 45 48 49 50 51 56 57 58 59 61 63 64 65
70 72 74 75 76 77 78 79 80 81 84 85 86 87 89 93 98 99 100 101 102 103
104 105 107 108 110 111 114 116 118 119 126 129 130 131 132 134 135
141 142 146 148 **P**1 5 6 **S** Eastern Connecticut Health Network,
Manchester, CT
Primary Contact: Peter J. Karl, President and Chief Executive Officer
COO: Kathleen Sims, Vice President Operations
CFO: Kevin G. Murphy, Senior Vice President Finance and Chief Financial Officer
CMO: Joel R. Reich, M.D., Senior Vice President Medical Affairs
CIO: Charles Covin, Chief Information Officer
CHR: Deborah Gogliettino, Senior Vice President Human Resources
Web address: www.echn.org
**Control:** Other not–for–profit (including NFP Corporation) **Service:** General
Medical and Surgical

**Staffed Beds:** 156 **Admissions:** 7616 **Census:** 113 **Outpatient Visits:**
363278 **Births:** 1236 **Total Expense ($000):** 184446 **Payroll Expense
($000):** 81550 **Personnel:** 1098

## MANSFIELD CENTER—Tolland County

☐ **NATCHAUG HOSPITAL (074008)**, 189 Storrs Road, Zip 06250–1683;
tel. 860/456–1311 **A**1 9 10 **F**5 98 99 100 104 105 106 **S** Hartford Healthcare,
Hartford, CT
Primary Contact: Stephen W. Larcen, Ph.D., President and Chief Executive Officer
COO: Sharon Hinton, Chief Nursing Officer
CFO: Paul V. Maloney, Chief Financial Officer
CMO: Deborah Weidner, M.D., Chief Medical Officer
CIO: Brian Jaworowski, Director Management Information Systems
CHR: Janet Keown, Director Human Resources
Web address: www.natchaug.org
**Control:** Other not–for–profit (including NFP Corporation) **Service:** Psychiatric

**Staffed Beds:** 57 **Admissions:** 1938 **Census:** 49 **Outpatient Visits:** 51750
**Births:** 0

## MERIDEN—New Haven County

⊠ **MIDSTATE MEDICAL CENTER (070017)**, 435 Lewis Avenue, Zip 06451–2101;
tel. 203/694–8200 **A**1 2 9 10 **F**3 11 12 13 15 18 28 29 30 31 34 35 36 38
39 40 44 45 46 48 49 50 51 53 54 56 57 59 61 62 63 64 68 70 74 75 76
78 79 81 82 84 85 86 87 97 98 102 107 108 110 111 114 115 117 118
119 120 121 123 124 126 129 130 131 132 144 145 146 147 148
**S** Hartford Healthcare, Hartford, CT
Primary Contact: Lucille A. Janatka, President and Chief Executive Officer
CFO: Ralph W. Becker, Chief Financial Officer
CMO: Kenneth R. Kurz, M.D., Chief of Staff
CIO: Jennifer Comerford, Manager Information Services
CHR: Ken Cesca, Vice President Human Resources
Web address: www.midstatemedical.org
**Control:** Other not–for–profit (including NFP Corporation) **Service:** General
Medical and Surgical

**Staffed Beds:** 134 **Admissions:** 9388 **Census:** 110 **Outpatient Visits:**
176615 **Births:** 923 **Total Expense ($000):** 214845 **Payroll Expense
($000):** 75939 **Personnel:** 1056

CT

## MIDDLETOWN—Middlesex County

☐ **ALBERT J. SOLNIT PSYCHIATRIC CENTER – SOUTH CAMPUS**, (Formerly Riverview Hospital for Children and Youth), 915 River Road, Zip 06457–3921, Mailing Address: P.O. Box 2792, Zip 06457–9292; tel. 860/704–4000, (Nonreporting) **A**1 3 5
Primary Contact: Michelle Sarofin, Superintendent
CFO: Connie Tessarzik, Business Manager
CMO: Lesley Siegel, M.D., Medical Director
CIO: Andrew J A Kass, M.D., Assistant Superintendent
Web address: www.ct.gov/
**Control:** State–Government, nonfederal **Service:** Children's hospital psychiatric

**Staffed Beds:** 102

☐ **CONNECTICUT VALLEY HOSPITAL (074003)**, Eastern Drive, Zip 06457–3947, Mailing Address: PO BOX 351, Zip 06457–7023; tel. 860/262–5000, (Includes WHITING FORENSIC DIVISION OF CONNECTICUT VALLEY HOSPITAL, O'Brien Drive, Zip 06457, Mailing Address: Box 70, Zip 06457–3942; tel. 203/344–2541) **A**1 3 5 9 10 **F**3 4 11 30 34 39 50 53 56 57 58 59 60 61 63 65 66 68 75 77 82 84 86 87 91 92 94 96 97 98 101 103 130 132 135 143 146 147 148 **S** Connecticut Department of Mental Health and Addiction Services, Hartford, CT
Primary Contact: Helene M. Vartelas, Chief Executive Officer
CFO: Paul Derdeyn, Director Fiscal Services and Plant Operations
CMO: Stuart Forman, M.D., Chief Professional Services
CHR: Shawn Kuhn, Facility Director Human Resources
Web address: www.ct.gov/dmhas/cwp/view.asp?a=3519&q=416778
**Control:** State–Government, nonfederal **Service:** Psychiatric

**Staffed Beds:** 604 **Admissions:** 3367 **Census:** 564 **Outpatient Visits:** 0 **Births:** 0 **Personnel:** 1623

☒ **MIDDLESEX HOSPITAL (070020)**, 28 Crescent Street, Zip 06457–3650; tel. 860/358–6000 **A**1 2 3 5 9 10 **F**3 5 8 12 13 15 18 20 22 24 28 29 30 31 32 34 35 36 38 40 42 49 50 51 54 55 57 58 59 60 61 62 63 64 65 68 70 73 74 75 76 77 78 79 81 82 83 84 85 86 87 89 92 93 94 97 98 99 100 101 102 103 104 105 106 107 108 110 111 114 115 116 117 118 119 120 121 123 124 125 126 129 130 131 132 134 135 145 146 147 148 **P**6
Primary Contact: Vincent G. Capece, Jr., President and Chief Executive Officer
CFO: Susan Martin, Vice President Finance
CMO: Arthur V. McDowell, III, M.D., Vice President Clinical Affairs
CIO: Ludwig Johnson, Vice President Information Technology
CHR: Gregory B. Nokes, Vice President Human Resources
CNO: Jacquelyn Calamari, MSN, Vice President and Chief Nursing Officer
Web address: www.middlesexhospital.org
**Control:** Other not–for–profit (including NFP Corporation) **Service:** General Medical and Surgical

**Staffed Beds:** 215 **Admissions:** 13039 **Census:** 153 **Outpatient Visits:** 1443691 **Births:** 1140 **Total Expense ($000):** 322338 **Payroll Expense ($000):** 161675 **Personnel:** 1826

**WHITING FORENSIC DIVISION OF CONNECTICUT VALLEY HOSPITAL** See Connecticut Valley Hospital

## MILFORD—New Haven County

☒ **MILFORD HOSPITAL (070019)**, 300 Seaside Avenue, Zip 06460–4603; tel. 203/876–4000, (Nonreporting) **A**1 9 10
Primary Contact: Joseph Pelaccia, President and Chief Executive Officer
COO: Lloyd Friedman, M.D., Vice President Medical Affairs and Chief Operating Officer
CFO: Joseph Pelaccia, President and Chief Executive Officer
CMO: Lloyd Friedman, M.D., Vice President Medical Affairs and Chief Operating Officer
CIO: Marilyn Christensen, Director Information Technology
CHR: Jeffrey Komornik, Director Human Resources
Web address: www.milfordhospital.org
**Control:** Other not–for–profit (including NFP Corporation) **Service:** General Medical and Surgical

**Staffed Beds:** 87

## NEW BRITAIN—Hartford County

☒ △ **HOSPITAL FOR SPECIAL CARE (072004)**, 2150 Corbin Avenue, Zip 06053–2298; tel. 860/223–2761, (Nonreporting) **A**1 3 5 7 10
Primary Contact: John J. Votto, D.O., President and Chief Executive Officer
CFO: Laurie A. Whelan, Senior Vice President Finance and Chief Financial Officer
CMO: Paul Scalise, M.D., Chief Pulmonary Medicine and Internal Medicine
CIO: Stan Jankowski, Vice President and Chief Information Officer
CHR: Judi Trczinski, Vice President and Chief Human Resources Officer
Web address: www.hfsc.org
**Control:** Other not–for–profit (including NFP Corporation) **Service:** Long–Term Acute Care hospital

**Staffed Beds:** 219

☒ **THE HOSPITAL OF CENTRAL CONNECTICUT (070035)**, 100 Grand Street, Zip 06052–2017, Mailing Address: P.O. Box 100, Zip 06050–0100; tel. 860/224–5011, (Includes BRADLEY MEMORIAL, 81 Meriden Avenue, Southington, Zip 06489–3297; tel. 860/276–5000; NEW BRITAIN GENERAL, 100 Grand Street, Mailing Address: P.O. Box 100, Zip 06050–0100; tel. 860/224–5011) **A**1 2 3 5 8 9 10 **F**2 3 4 11 12 13 15 17 18 20 22 27 28 29 30 31 34 35 38 40 44 45 49 50 51 52 53 54 57 58 59 60 61 62 64 65 66 68 70 72 74 75 76 77 78 79 81 84 85 86 87 89 93 97 98 99 100 101 102 103 104 105 107 108 110 111 114 115 116 117 118 119 120 121 123 124 126 129 130 131 132 135 142 143 144 146 147 148 **P**6 **S** Hartford Healthcare, Hartford, CT
Primary Contact: Clarence J. Silvia, President and Chief Executive Officer
CFO: Brian Rogoz, Vice President Finance and Treasurer
CIO: Frank Pinto, Chief Information Officer
CHR: Elizabeth A. Lynch, Vice President Human Resources
Web address: www.thocc.org
**Control:** Other not–for–profit (including NFP Corporation) **Service:** General Medical and Surgical

**Staffed Beds:** 229 **Admissions:** 16602 **Census:** 195 **Outpatient Visits:** 412374 **Births:** 1640 **Total Expense ($000):** 366780 **Payroll Expense ($000):** 165293 **Personnel:** 1943

## NEW CANAAN—Fairfield County

☐ **SILVER HILL HOSPITAL (074014)**, 208 Valley Road, Zip 06840–3899; tel. 203/966–3561, (Nonreporting) **A**1 9 10
Primary Contact: Sigurd H. Ackerman, M.D., President and Chief Executive Officer
COO: Elizabeth Moore, Chief Operating Officer
CFO: Ruurd Leegstra, Chief Financial Officer
CMO: Sigurd H. Ackerman, M.D., President and Chief Executive Officer
CIO: Maria Klinga, Director Management Information Systems
CHR: Juliana Rich, Director Human Resources
Web address: www.silverhillhospital.org
**Control:** Other not–for–profit (including NFP Corporation) **Service:** Psychiatric

**Staffed Beds:** 60

## NEW HAVEN—New Haven County

☐ **CONNECTICUT MENTAL HEALTH CENTER (074011)**, 34 Park Street, Zip 06519–1109, Mailing Address: P.O. Box 1842, Zip 06508–1842; tel. 203/974–7144, (Nonreporting) **A**1 3 5 9 10 **S** Connecticut Department of Mental Health and Addiction Services, Hartford, CT
Primary Contact: Michael Sernyak, M.D., Director
COO: Robert Cole, Chief Operating Officer
CFO: Robert Cole, Chief Operating Officer
CMO: Jeanne Steines, D.O., Medical Director
CIO: Paul Moore, Chief Information Officer
CHR: Carolyn Wallace, Director Human Resources
Web address: www.ct.gov/dmhas/cwp/view.asp?a=2906&q=334596
**Control:** State–Government, nonfederal **Service:** Psychiatric

**Staffed Beds:** 39

**HOSPITAL OF SAINT RAPHAEL** See Yale–New Haven Hospital–Saint Raphael Campus

☒ **YALE–NEW HAVEN HOSPITAL (070022)**, 20 York Street, Zip 06510–3202; tel. 203/688–4242, (Includes YALE–NEW HAVEN CHILDREN'S HOSPITAL, 1 Park Street, Zip 06504–8901; tel. 203/688–4242; YALE–NEW HAVEN HOSPITAL–SAINT RAPHAEL CAMPUS, 1450 Chapel Street, Zip 06511–4405; tel. 203/789–3000; Christopher M. O'Connor, President and Chief Executive Officer; YALE–NEW HAVEN PSYCHIATRIC HOSPITAL, 184 Liberty Street, Zip 06519–1625; tel. 203/688–9704; Paul Haeberle, Executive Director), (Total facility includes 114 beds in nursing home–type unit) **A**1 2 3 5 8 9 10 **F**3 5 6 8 9 11 12 13 14 15 17 18 19 20 21 22 23 24 25 26 27 28 29 30 31 32 34 35 36 37 38 39 40 41 42 43 44 45 46 47 48 49 50 51 52 53 54 55 56 57 58 59 61 64 65 66 68 70 71 72 73 74 75 76 77 78 79 80 81 82 84 85 86 87 88 89 90 91 92 93 94 96 97 98 99 100 101 102 103 104 105 107 108 109 110 111 112 114 115 116 117 118 119 120 121 123 124 126 128 129 130 131 132 133 134 135 136 137 138 139 141 142 143 144 145 146 147 148 **P**2 3 5 6 **S** Yale New Haven Health System, New Haven, CT
Primary Contact: Marna P. Borgstrom, Chief Executive Officer
COO: Richard D'Aquila, President and Chief Operating Officer
CFO: James Staten, Senior Vice President Finance
CMO: Peter N. Herbert, M.D., Senior Vice President Medical Affairs and Chief of Staff
CIO: Mark Andersen, Senior Vice President Information Systems and Chief Information Officer
CHR: Kevin A. Myatt, Senior Vice President Human Resources
Web address: www.ynhh.org
**Control:** Other not–for–profit (including NFP Corporation) **Service:** General Medical and Surgical

**Staffed Beds:** 1571 **Admissions:** 54412 **Census:** 768 **Outpatient Visits:** 774085 **Births:** 5015 **Total Expense ($000):** 1621822 **Payroll Expense ($000):** 585247 **Personnel:** 10838

*Many Facility Codes have changed. Please refer to the AHA Guide Code Chart.*

© 2013 AHA Guide

**NEW LONDON—New London County**

✉ △ **LAWRENCE + MEMORIAL HOSPITAL (070007)**, 365 Montauk Avenue, Zip 06320–4769; tel. 860/442–0711 **A**1 2 7 9 10 **F**2 3 7 8 11 13 15 17 18 20 22 26 28 29 30 31 32 34 35 36 38 39 40 41 42 45 46 47 48 49 50 51 54 56 57 59 60 61 64 65 66 68 70 72 74 75 76 77 78 79 81 82 84 85 86 87 89 90 93 98 99 100 101 102 103 104 105 107 108 110 111 114 115 116 117 118 119 120 121 123 124 126 129 130 132 134 135 144 146 147 148 **P**3 6 **S** Lawrence+Memorial Health System, New London, CT
Primary Contact: Bruce D. Cummings, President and Chief Executive Officer
COO: Daniel Rissi, M.D., Vice President, Chief Medical and Clinical Operations Officer
CFO: Lugene A. Inzana, Vice President and Chief Financial and Support Services Officer
CMO: Daniel Rissi, M.D., Chief Medical and Clinical Operations
CIO: Kimberly Kalajainen, Vice President and Chief Information Officer
CHR: Donna Epps, Vice President and Chief Human Resources Officer
CNO: Lauren Williams, R.N., Vice President of Professional Services and Chief Nursing Officer
Web address: www.lmhospital.org
**Control:** Other not–for–profit (including NFP Corporation) **Service:** General Medical and Surgical

**Staffed Beds:** 256 **Admissions:** 13404 **Census:** 178 **Outpatient Visits:** 275141 **Births:** 1498 **Total Expense ($000):** 305815 **Payroll Expense ($000):** 145714

**NEW MILFORD—Litchfield County**

✉ ○ **NEW MILFORD HOSPITAL (070015)**, 21 Elm Street, Zip 06776–2993; tel. 860/355–2611 **A**1 2 5 9 10 11 19 **F**3 8 13 14 15 17 18 28 29 30 31 32 34 35 36 38 39 40 45 46 47 48 49 50 51 53 55 57 58 59 61 62 63 64 65 68 70 74 75 76 77 78 79 81 82 84 85 86 87 89 99 100 101 102 107 108 109 110 111 115 116 117 119 120 121 122 123 124 129 130 132 133 134 135 145 146 147 148 **P**1 6 7 **S** Western Connecticut Health Network, Danbury, CT
Primary Contact: Deborah K. Weymouth, Executive Director and Senior Vice President
CFO: Steven Rosenberg, Senior Vice President, Chief Financial Officer and Treasurer
CMO: Fred Browne, M.D., Chief Medical Officer and Vice President Medical Affairs
CIO: Peter Courtway, Chief Information Officer
CHR: Phyllis F. Zappala, Senior Vice President Human Resources
Web address: www.newmilfordhospital.org
**Control:** Other not–for–profit (including NFP Corporation) **Service:** General Medical and Surgical

**Staffed Beds:** 59 **Admissions:** 2045 **Census:** 22 **Outpatient Visits:** 73581 **Births:** 243 **Total Expense ($000):** 85185 **Payroll Expense ($000):** 33589 **Personnel:** 336

**NORWALK—Fairfield County**

✉ △ **NORWALK HOSPITAL (070034)**, 34 Maple Street, Zip 06850–3894; tel. 203/852–2000 **A**1 2 3 5 7 9 10 **F**3 5 7 8 11 12 13 15 17 18 20 22 26 28 29 30 31 34 35 36 39 40 43 44 45 46 47 48 49 50 51 53 54 55 57 58 59 64 66 68 70 72 74 75 76 77 78 79 80 81 82 85 87 89 90 91 93 96 98 100 101 102 103 104 107 108 110 111 114 115 117 118 119 120 121 123 124 126 129 130 132 135 145 146 148 **P**6
Primary Contact: Daniel J. DeBarba, Jr., President and Chief Executive Officer
CFO: Michael Kruzick, Acting Chief Financial Officer
CMO: Michael Marks, M.D., Chief of Staff
CHR: Anthony Aceto, Vice President Human Resources
Web address: www.norwalkhospital.org
**Control:** Other not–for–profit (including NFP Corporation) **Service:** General Medical and Surgical

**Staffed Beds:** 300 **Admissions:** 11161 **Census:** 174 **Outpatient Visits:** 223837 **Births:** 1644 **Total Expense ($000):** 338421 **Payroll Expense ($000):** 133582 **Personnel:** 1665

**NORWICH—New London County**

✉ **THE WILLIAM W. BACKUS HOSPITAL (070024)**, 326 Washington Street, Zip 06360–2740; tel. 860/889–8331 **A**1 2 3 5 9 10 **F**3 9 11 12 13 15 18 20 26 28 29 30 31 34 35 36 40 42 43 45 46 49 50 51 54 57 58 59 61 62 63 64 65 70 71 74 75 76 78 79 81 82 84 85 86 87 89 92 93 97 98 100 101 102 103 104 105 107 108 110 111 114 115 116 117 118 119 120 121 126 130 132 133 134 135 144 145 146 147 148
Primary Contact: David Whitehead, President and Chief Executive Officer
CFO: Daniel E. Lohr, Senior Vice President and Chief Financial Officer
CMO: Peter H. Shea, M.D., Senior Vice President and Chief Medical Officer
CIO: Pamela M. Muccilli, Vice President and Chief Information Officer
CHR: Theresa L. Buss, Vice President, Human Resources and Organizational Development
Web address: www.backushospital.org
**Control:** Other not–for–profit (including NFP Corporation) **Service:** General Medical and Surgical

**Staffed Beds:** 184 **Admissions:** 10974 **Census:** 130 **Outpatient Visits:** 440605 **Births:** 916 **Total Expense ($000):** 256654 **Payroll Expense ($000):** 114140 **Personnel:** 1418

**PUTNAM—Windham County**

✉ **DAY KIMBALL HOSPITAL (070003)**, 320 Pomfret Street, Zip 06260–1836, Mailing Address: P.O. Box 6001, Zip 06260–0901; tel. 860/928–6541, (Nonreporting) **A**1 9 10
Primary Contact: Robert E. Smanik, FACHE, President and Chief Executive Officer
COO: Donald St. Onge, Chief Operating Officer
CFO: Christopher Ferraro, Chief Financial Officer
CMO: Douglas Waite, M.D., Vice President Medical Affairs
CIO: Marilyn Rath, Co–Director Management Information Systems and Chief Information Officer
CHR: Nancy Contillo, Director Human Resources
Web address: www.daykimball.org
**Control:** Other not–for–profit (including NFP Corporation) **Service:** General Medical and Surgical

**Staffed Beds:** 63

**ROCKY HILL—Hartford County**

**VETERANS HOME AND HOSPITAL (072006)**, 287 West Street, Zip 06067–3501; tel. 860/616–3703 **A**10 **F**30 39 56 82 84 85 90 91 100 128 130 132 135 143 146 148
Primary Contact: Margaret Concannon, Administrator
CFO: Gregory J. Gioia, Chief Fiscal and Administrative Services
CMO: Michael M. Cebrik, M.D., Director Medical Staff
Web address: www.state.ct.us/ctva/
**Control:** State–Government, nonfederal **Service:** Chronic disease

**Staffed Beds:** 125 **Admissions:** 40 **Census:** 106 **Births:** 0

**SHARON—Litchfield County**

☐ **SHARON HOSPITAL (070004)**, 50 Hospital Hill Road, Zip 06069–2096, Mailing Address: P.O. Box 789, Zip 06069–0789; tel. 860/364–4000, (Nonreporting) **A**1 2 9 10 20 **S** RegionalCare Hospital Partners, Brentwood, TN
Primary Contact: Kim Lumia, President and Chief Executive Officer
CFO: Carolyn Allen, Chief Financial Officer
CMO: Michael Parker, M.D., Chief of Staff
CHR: Kathleen Berlinghoff, Director Human Resources
Web address: www.sharonhospital.com
**Control:** Corporation, Investor–owned, for–profit **Service:** General Medical and Surgical

**Staffed Beds:** 78

**SOMERS—Tolland County**

**CONNECTICUT DEPARTMENT OF CORRECTION'S HOSPITAL**, 100 Bilton Road, Zip 06071–1059, Mailing Address: P.O. Box 100, Zip 06071–0100; tel. 860/749–8391, (Nonreporting)
Primary Contact: Edward A. Blanchette, M.D., Director
**Control:** State–Government, nonfederal **Service:** Hospital unit of an institution (prison hospital, college infirmary, etc.)

**Staffed Beds:** 29

**SOUTHINGTON—Hartford County**

**BRADLEY MEMORIAL** See The Hospital of Central Connecticut, New Britain

CT

---

**Hospital, Medicare Provider Number, Address, Telephone, Approval, Facility, and Physician Codes, Health Care System**

★ American Hospital Association (AHA) membership
☐ The Joint Commission accreditation
◇ DNV Healthcare Inc. accreditation
○ Healthcare Facilities Accreditation Program
△ Commission on Accreditation of Rehabilitation Facilities (CARF) accreditation

## STAFFORD SPRINGS—Tolland County

☒ **JOHNSON MEMORIAL HOSPITAL (070008)**, 201 Chestnut Hill Road,
Zip 06076–4005; tel. 860/684–4251, (Nonreporting) **A**1 2 9 10 **S** Saint Francis
Care, Inc., Hartford, CT
Primary Contact: Stuart E. Rosenberg, Chief Executive Officer
CFO: John Grish, Chief Financial Officer
CHR: Donna M. Megliola, Assistant Vice President
Web address: www.jmmc.com
**Control:** Other not–for–profit (including NFP Corporation) **Service:** General
Medical and Surgical

**Staffed Beds:** 72

## STAMFORD—Fairfield County

☒ **STAMFORD HOSPITAL (070006)**, 30 Shelburne Road, Zip 06902–3628,
Mailing Address: P.O. Box 9317, Zip 06904–9317; tel. 203/276–1000 **A**1 2 3 5
8 9 10 **F**3 8 11 12 13 15 17 18 20 22 24 26 28 29 30 31 32 34 35 36 37
38 40 41 43 44 45 46 47 48 49 50 52 53 54 55 57 58 59 60 61 64 65 66
68 70 71 72 73 74 75 76 77 78 79 81 82 84 85 86 87 89 90 91 92 93 95
96 97 98 100 101 102 103 104 107 108 110 111 114 115 116 117 118
119 120 121 123 124 126 129 130 131 132 135 144 145 146 147 148
**P**6 8
Primary Contact: Brian G. Grissler, President and Chief Executive Officer
COO: Kathleen A. Silard, R.N., Executive Vice President Operations and Chief
Operating Officer
CFO: Kevin Gage, Chief Financial Officer
CMO: Sharon Kiely, M.D., Senior Vice President Medical Affairs and Chief Medical
Officer
CIO: David Taylor, Vice President Information Systems and Chief Information
Officer
CHR: Elaine Guglielmo, Vice President Human Resources and Organizational
Development
CNO: Ellen M. Komar, R.N., Vice President Patient Care Services
Web address: www.stamhealth.org
**Control:** Other not–for–profit (including NFP Corporation) **Service:** General
Medical and Surgical

**Staffed Beds:** 305 **Admissions:** 12334 **Census:** 177 **Outpatient Visits:**
408830 **Births:** 1960 **Total Expense ($000):** 430187 **Payroll Expense**
**($000):** 176514 **Personnel:** 1996

## TORRINGTON—Litchfield County

☒ **THE CHARLOTTE HUNGERFORD HOSPITAL (070011)**, 540 Litchfield Street,
Zip 06790–6679, Mailing Address: P.O. Box 988, Zip 06790–0988;
tel. 860/496–6666 **A**1 2 9 10 **F**13 15 18 28 29 30 31 33 34 35 38 40 42 45
47 48 49 50 51 57 59 60 63 64 68 70 74 75 76 78 79 80 81 82 83 85 87
89 93 94 97 98 99 100 102 104 105 108 110 115 116 118 119 120 121
123 129 130 131 132 144 145 146 148 **P**6
Primary Contact: Daniel J. McIntyre, President and Chief Executive Officer
CFO: Susan Schapp, Vice President Finance and Treasurer
CMO: Mark Prete, M.D., Vice President Medical Affairs
CHR: R. James Elliott, Vice President Human Resources
Web address: www.charlottehungerford.org
**Control:** Other not–for–profit (including NFP Corporation) **Service:** General
Medical and Surgical

**Staffed Beds:** 72 **Admissions:** 5962 **Census:** 67 **Outpatient Visits:** 230370
**Births:** 376 **Total Expense ($000):** 118757 **Payroll Expense ($000):** 54929
**Personnel:** 651

## VERNON ROCKVILLE—Tolland County

☒ **ROCKVILLE GENERAL HOSPITAL (070012)**, 31 Union Street,
Zip 06066–3160; tel. 860/872–0501 **A**1 10 **F**3 11 15 18 24 28 29 30 34 35
36 38 39 40 44 45 49 50 51 54 56 57 59 60 61 63 64 65 66 70 74 75 78
79 81 82 84 85 86 87 89 90 93 97 98 107 108 110 111 114 118 119 124
130 131 132 135 142 146 147 148 **P**1 5 6 **S** Eastern Connecticut Health
Network, Manchester, CT
Primary Contact: Peter J. Karl, President and Chief Executive Officer
COO: Kathleen Sims, Vice President Operations
CFO: Kevin G. Murphy, Senior Vice President Finance and Chief Financial Officer
CMO: Joel R. Reich, M.D., Senior Vice President Medical Affairs
CIO: Charles Covin, Chief Information Officer
CHR: Deborah Gogliettino, Senior Vice President Human Resources
Web address: www.echn.org
**Control:** Other not–for–profit (including NFP Corporation) **Service:** General
Medical and Surgical

**Staffed Beds:** 47 **Admissions:** 2501 **Census:** 36 **Outpatient Visits:** 100863
**Births:** 0 **Total Expense ($000):** 74039 **Payroll Expense ($000):** 30268
**Personnel:** 321

## WALLINGFORD—New Haven County

☐ △ **GAYLORD HOSPITAL (072003)**, Gaylord Farm Road, Zip 06492–7048,
Mailing Address: P.O. Box 400, Zip 06492–7048; tel. 203/284–2800 **A**1 5 7 10
**F**1 29 30 64 68 75 87 91 92 93 95 96 107 114 119 129 130 131 132
146 148
Primary Contact: George M. Kyriacou, President and Chief Executive Officer
CFO: Janine L. Epright, Vice President and Chief Financial Officer
CMO: Luis Teba, M.D., Vice President and Chief Medical Officer
CIO: Brian Richard, Director Information Technology
CHR: Wally G. Harper, Vice President Human Resources
CNO: Charlotte Hyatt, MSN, Vice President Clinical Services
Web address: www.gaylord.org
**Control:** Other not–for–profit (including NFP Corporation) **Service:** Long–Term
Acute Care hospital

**Staffed Beds:** 125 **Admissions:** 1411 **Census:** 110 **Outpatient Visits:** 58095
**Births:** 0 **Total Expense ($000):** 75323 **Payroll Expense ($000):** 39160
**Personnel:** 497

★ **MASONICARE HEALTH CENTER (070039)**, 22 Masonic Avenue,
Zip 06492–3048, Mailing Address: P.O. Box 70, Zip 06492–7001;
tel. 203/679–5900, (Nonreporting) **A**3 5 6 10
Primary Contact: Stephen B. McPherson, President
CFO: James F. Standish, Chief Financial Officer
CMO: Ronald Schwartz, M.D., Medical Director
CHR: Douglas T. Barrett, Senior Vice President Human Resources
Web address: www.masonicare.org
**Control:** Other not–for–profit (including NFP Corporation) **Service:** Other specialty

**Staffed Beds:** 65

## WATERBURY—New Haven County

☒ **SAINT MARY'S HOSPITAL (070016)**, 56 Franklin Street, Zip 06706–1281;
tel. 203/709–6000 **A**1 2 3 5 9 10 **F**3 5 8 11 12 13 15 17 18 20 22 24 28 29
30 31 32 34 35 36 37 39 40 41 43 45 49 50 53 54 57 59 64 70 72 74 75
76 77 78 79 80 81 85 87 93 96 98 100 102 104 105 107 108 110 111 112
114 115 118 119 126 129 130 132 135 144 146 147 **P**6
Primary Contact: Chad W. Wable, President and Chief Executive Officer
COO: Michael Novak, Vice President Operations
CFO: Chris Hayes, Interim Corporate Director of Finance
CMO: Steve Holland, M.D., Chief Medical Officer
CIO: Carolyn Orrell, Chief Information Officer
CHR: M. Clark Kearney, Vice President Human Resources
CNO: Elizabeth Bozzuto, R.N., Interim Chief Nursing Officer and Vice President
Surgical Services
Web address: www.stmh.org
**Control:** Church–operated, Nongovernment, not–for profit **Service:** General
Medical and Surgical

**Staffed Beds:** 168 **Admissions:** 11280 **Census:** 133 **Outpatient Visits:**
238980 **Births:** 933 **Total Expense ($000):** 218385 **Payroll Expense**
**($000):** 84599 **Personnel:** 1119

☒ **WATERBURY HOSPITAL (070005)**, 64 Robbins Street, Zip 06708–2600;
tel. 203/573–6000, (Nonreporting) **A**1 2 3 5 9 10
Primary Contact: Darlene Stromstad, FACHE, President and Chief Executive
Officer
CFO: Colleen M. Scott, Vice President Finance
CMO: David Puzzuto, M.D., Vice President Medical Affairs and Chief Medical
Officer
CIO: Michael J. Cemeno, Chief Information Officer
CHR: Diane Woolley, Vice President Human Resources
CNO: Sandra Ladarola, Chief Nursing Officer
Web address: www.waterburyhospital.org
**Control:** Other not–for–profit (including NFP Corporation) **Service:** General
Medical and Surgical

**Staffed Beds:** 214

## WEST HARTFORD—Hartford County

★ **THE HOSPITAL AT HEBREW HEALTH CARE (070040)**, 1 Abrahms Boulevard,
Zip 06117–1525; tel. 860/523–3800, (Nonreporting) **A**10
Primary Contact: Bonnie B. Gauthier, President and Chief Executive Officer
COO: Kathy Mon, Vice President Operations
CFO: David Houle, Executive Vice President and Chief Financial Officer
CMO: Henry Schneiderman, M.D., Vice President Medical Services and Physician
in Chief
CHR: Carmella Ross, Manager Human Resources
Web address: www.hebrewhealthcare.org
**Control:** Other not–for–profit (including NFP Corporation) **Service:** Other specialty

**Staffed Beds:** 322

*Many Facility Codes have changed. Please refer to the AHA Guide Code Chart.*
© 2013 AHA Guide

CT

## WEST HAVEN—New Haven County

☒ △ **VETERANS AFFAIRS CONNECTICUT HEALTHCARE SYSTEM**, 950 Campbell Avenue, Zip 06516–2770; tel. 203/932–5711, (Includes WEST HAVEN DIVISION, 950 Campbell Avenue, Zip 06516–2700; tel. 203/932–5711), (Total facility includes 32 beds in nursing home–type unit) **A**1 2 3 5 7 8 **F**4 5 8 11 17 18 20 22 24 26 29 30 31 33 34 35 38 39 40 45 46 47 49 50 53 54 56 57 58 59 60 61 62 63 64 65 67 70 74 75 77 78 79 81 82 83 84 85 86 87 93 94 96 97 98 100 101 102 104 105 106 107 108 111 115 117 118 119 126 128 129 130 132 135 143 145 146 147 148 **P**6 **S** Department of Veterans Affairs, Washington, DC
Primary Contact: Janice M. Boss, MS, Director
CFO: Joseph LaMadeleine, Chief Financial Officer
CMO: Michael Ebert, M.D., Chief of Staff
CIO: Joseph Erdos, M.D., Chief Information Officer
CHR: Mark Bain, Chief Human Resources
Web address: www.va.gov/sta/guide/home.asp
**Control:** Veterans Affairs, Government, federal **Service:** General Medical and Surgical

**Staffed Beds:** 197 **Admissions:** 6402 **Census:** 183 **Outpatient Visits:** 709373 **Births:** 0 **Total Expense ($000):** 501693 **Payroll Expense ($000):** 216574 **Personnel:** 2651

## WESTPORT—Fairfield County

**ST. VINCENT'S BEHAVIORAL HEALTH** See St. Vincent's Medical Center, Bridgeport

## WILLIMANTIC—Windham County

**WINDHAM COMMUNITY MEMORIAL HOSPITAL** See Windham Hospital

☒ **WINDHAM HOSPITAL (070021)**, 112 Mansfield Avenue, Zip 06226–2040; tel. 860/456–9116, (Nonreporting) **A**1 5 9 10 **S** Hartford Healthcare, Hartford, CT
Primary Contact: Stephen W. Larcen, Ph.D., President and Chief Executive Officer
COO: Cary Trantalis, R.N., Vice President Operations
CMO: Charles Shooks, M.D., Chief of Staff
CIO: Kevin Tupper, Director Information Technology
CHR: Marty Levine, Vice President Human Resources
CNO: Michael J. Dion, R.N., Vice President Patient Care Services
Web address: www.windhamhospital.org
**Control:** Other not–for–profit (including NFP Corporation) **Service:** General Medical and Surgical

**Staffed Beds:** 79

CT

---

**Hospital, Medicare Provider Number, Address, Telephone, Approval, Facility, and Physician Codes, Health Care System**

★ American Hospital Association (AHA) membership
☐ The Joint Commission accreditation
◇ DNV Healthcare Inc. accreditation
○ Healthcare Facilities Accreditation Program
△ Commission on Accreditation of Rehabilitation Facilities (CARF) accreditation

# DELAWARE

## DOVER—Kent County

☒ △ **BAYHEALTH MEDICAL CENTER (080004)**, 640 South State Street,
Zip 19901–3530; tel. 302/674–4700, (Includes BAYHEALTH MEDICAL CENTER
AT KENT GENERAL, 640 South State Street, Zip 19901–3597; BAYHEALTH
MEDICAL CENTER, MILFORD MEMORIAL HOSPITAL, 21 West Clarke Avenue,
Milford, Zip 19963–1840, Mailing Address: P.O. Box 199, Zip 19963–0199;
tel. 302/430–5738; Michael Ashton, Administrator) **A**1 2 5 7 9 10 **F**3 8 11 12
13 15 17 18 20 22 24 26 28 29 30 31 32 34 35 38 40 41 43 44 45 47 48
49 50 51 53 54 55 57 58 59 60 61 62 64 67 68 70 72 73 74 75 76 77 78
79 81 82 84 85 86 87 88 89 90 93 94 98 99 100 101 102 103 104 107 108
110 111 114 115 117 118 119 120 121 123 124 126 129 130 131 132 134
135 144 146 147 148
Primary Contact: Terry Murphy, President and Chief Executive Officer
COO: Deborah Watson, Senior Vice President and Chief Operating Officer
CFO: Earl P. Tanis, Senior Vice President Financial Operations
CMO: Gary M. Siegelman, M.D., Senior Vice President and Chief Medical Officer
CIO: Terry Feinour, Senior Vice President Corporate Services
Web address: www.bayhealth.org
**Control:** Other not–for–profit (including NFP Corporation) **Service:** General
Medical and Surgical

> **Staffed Beds:** 316 **Admissions:** 17307 **Census:** 247 **Outpatient Visits:**
> 565884 **Births:** 2236 **Total Expense ($000):** 432778 **Payroll Expense**
> **($000):** 175939 **Personnel:** 2791

☐ **DOVER BEHAVIORAL HEALTH SYSTEM (084004)**, 725 Horsepond Road,
Zip 19901–7232; tel. 302/741–0140 **A**1 9 10 **F**5 98 99 102 105 130 **P**6
**S** Universal Health Services, Inc., King of Prussia, PA
Primary Contact: Rod Letterman, Chief Executive Officer
Web address: www.doverbehavioral.com
**Control:** Corporation, Investor–owned, for–profit **Service:** Psychiatric

> **Staffed Beds:** 72 **Admissions:** 3001 **Census:** 61 **Outpatient Visits:** 746
> **Births:** 0

## LEWES—Sussex County

☒ **BEEBE MEDICAL CENTER (080007)**, 424 Savannah Road, Zip 19958–1462;
tel. 302/645–3300 **A**1 2 6 9 10 19 **F**2 3 8 11 12 13 15 17 18 20 22 24 28
29 30 31 32 34 35 36 38 40 43 49 50 51 54 55 56 57 58 59 60 61 62 64
65 68 70 74 75 76 77 78 79 80 81 83 85 87 89 93 97 100 107 108 109
110 111 114 116 117 118 119 121 129 130 132 134 135 143 146 147 148
Primary Contact: Jeffrey M. Fried, FACHE, President and Chief Executive Officer
COO: Thomas Steiner, Chief Operating Officer
CFO: Paul Pernice, Vice President Finance
CMO: Andrejs Strauss, M.D., Interim Vice President Medical Affairs
CIO: Barbara P. Vugrinec, Vice President Information Systems
CHR: Catherine Halen, Vice President Human Resources
CNO: Paul E. Minnick, R.N., Vice President Patient Services
Web address: www.beebemed.org
**Control:** Other not–for–profit (including NFP Corporation) **Service:** General
Medical and Surgical

> **Staffed Beds:** 155 **Admissions:** 8761 **Census:** 99 **Outpatient Visits:** 493697
> **Births:** 889 **Total Expense ($000):** 255131 **Payroll Expense ($000):** 92515
> **Personnel:** 1622

## MILFORD—Sussex County

**BAYHEALTH MEDICAL CENTER, MILFORD MEMORIAL HOSPITAL** See
Bayhealth Medical Center, Dover

## NEW CASTLE—New Castle County

☐ **DELAWARE PSYCHIATRIC CENTER (084001)**, 1901 North Dupont Highway,
Zip 19720–1199; tel. 302/255–2700, (Nonreporting) **A**1 3 5 10
Primary Contact: Kevin Ann Huckshorn, R.N., MSN, Director
CIO: James Nau, Manager Computer and Applications Support
Web address: www.dhss.delaware.gov
**Control:** State–Government, nonfederal **Service:** Psychiatric

> **Staffed Beds:** 189

☐ **MEADOW WOOD BEHAVIORAL HEALTH SYSTEM (084003)**, 575 South
Dupont Highway, Zip 19720–4606; tel. 302/328–3330, (Nonreporting) **A**1 9 10
**S** Acadia Healthcare Company, Inc., Franklin, TN
Primary Contact: Bill A. Mason, Chief Executive Officer
CFO: John Greenly, Chief Financial Officer
Web address: www.meadowwoodhospital.com
**Control:** Corporation, Investor–owned, for–profit **Service:** Psychiatric

> **Staffed Beds:** 53

## NEWARK—New Castle County

☒ △ **CHRISTIANA CARE HEALTH SYSTEM (080001)**, 4755 Ogletown–Stanton
Road, Zip 19718–0002, Mailing Address: P.O. Box 6001, Zip 19714–6001;
tel. 302/733–1000, (Includes CHRISTIANA HOSPITAL, 201 South Broom Street,
Wilmington, Zip 19805, Mailing Address: P.O. Box 2653, Zip 19805;
tel. 302/658–6711; WILMINGTON HOSPITAL, 501 West 14th Street, Wilmington,
Zip 19801, Mailing Address: Box 1668, Zip 19899; tel. 302/733–1000) **A**1 2 3
5 7 8 9 10 12 13 **F**2 3 6 7 8 11 12 13 15 17 18 20 22 24 26 28 29 30 31
32 34 35 36 37 38 39 40 43 44 45 46 47 48 49 50 53 54 55 56 57 58 59
60 61 62 64 65 66 68 70 72 74 75 76 77 78 79 80 81 82 84 85 86 87 88
89 90 92 93 94 96 97 98 99 100 101 102 103 104 105 107 108 110 111
114 115 116 117 118 119 120 121 123 124 126 129 130 131 132 134 135
136 138 143 145 146 147 148 **P**6 **S** Christiana Care Health System,
Wilmington, DE
Primary Contact: Robert J. Laskowski, M.D., President and Chief Executive Officer
COO: Gary W. Ferguson, Executive Vice President and Chief Operating Officer
CFO: Thomas L. Corrigan, Senior Vice President Finance, Managed Care and Chief
Financial Officer
CMO: Janice E. Nevin, M.D., Chief Medical Officer
CIO: Randall Gaboriault, Chief Information Officer
CHR: Audrey C. Van Luven, Senior Vice President and Chief Human Resources
Officer
Web address: www.christianacare.org
**Control:** Other not–for–profit (including NFP Corporation) **Service:** General
Medical and Surgical

> **Staffed Beds:** 985 **Admissions:** 53684 **Census:** 738 **Outpatient Visits:**
> 530560 **Births:** 6594 **Total Expense ($000):** 1292415 **Payroll Expense**
> **($000):** 620369 **Personnel:** 9031

☐ **ROCKFORD CENTER (084002)**, 100 Rockford Drive, Zip 19713–2121;
tel. 302/996–5480 **A**1 9 10 **F**98 99 103 104 105 **P**6 8 **S** Universal Health
Services, Inc., King of Prussia, PA
Primary Contact: John F. McKenna, Chief Executive Officer and Managing Director
COO: Shawn Walsh, Chief Operating Officer
CFO: Kumar Purohit, Chief Financial Officer
CHR: Jessi Jeppi, Director Human Resources
Web address: www.rockfordcenter.com
**Control:** Corporation, Investor–owned, for–profit **Service:** Psychiatric

> **Staffed Beds:** 118 **Admissions:** 4714 **Census:** 117 **Outpatient Visits:** 15348
> **Births:** 0 **Total Expense ($000):** 20764 **Payroll Expense ($000):** 11382
> **Personnel:** 237

## SEAFORD—Sussex County

☒ **NANTICOKE MEMORIAL HOSPITAL (080006)**, 801 Middleford Road,
Zip 19973–3636; tel. 302/629–6611 **A**1 2 9 10 **F**3 11 13 15 17 18 20 22 28
29 30 31 32 34 35 40 43 47 48 49 50 51 57 59 65 68 70 74 75 76 77 79
81 85 86 87 89 90 93 107 108 109 110 111 115 117 119 120 121 123 124
129 130 132 135 146 147 148
Primary Contact: Steven A. Rose, R.N., Chief Executive Officer
COO: Tom Brown, Senior Vice President
CFO: Denise Jester, Interim Chief Financial Officer
CIO: Susan Godesky, Director Information Technology
CHR: Barbara A. Hendricks, Vice President, Human Resources and Support
Services
Web address: www.nanticoke.org
**Control:** Other not–for–profit (including NFP Corporation) **Service:** General
Medical and Surgical

> **Staffed Beds:** 98 **Admissions:** 5298 **Census:** 53 **Outpatient Visits:** 117683
> **Births:** 864 **Total Expense ($000):** 109288 **Payroll Expense ($000):** 39181
> **Personnel:** 735

## WILMINGTON—New Castle County

☒ △ **ALFRED I. DUPONT HOSPITAL FOR CHILDREN (083300)**, 1600
Rockland Road, Zip 19803–3616, Mailing Address: Box 269, Zip 19899–0269;
tel. 302/651–4000 **A**1 3 5 7 10 **F**3 7 8 9 11 12 17 19 21 23 25 27 28 29 30
31 32 34 35 36 38 39 41 43 45 46 47 48 50 54 55 58 59 60 61 63 64 65
67 68 72 74 75 78 79 81 82 83 85 86 87 88 89 90 91 92 93 94 97 99 102
104 107 111 112 114 115 116 117 118 119 126 127 129 130 131 132 134
136 137 138 139 140 143 144 146 148 **S** Nemours, Jacksonville, FL
Primary Contact: Kevin B. Churchwell, M.D., Chief Executive Officer
COO: Paul D. Kempinski, Chief Operating Officer
CFO: William N. Britton, Associate Administrator Finance
CMO: Brent R. King, Chief Medical Officer and Chief Physician
CIO: Ann Altoe, Senior Director Information Systems and Security Officer
Web address: www.nemours.org
**Control:** Other not–for–profit (including NFP Corporation) **Service:** Children's
general

> **Staffed Beds:** 195 **Admissions:** 8798 **Census:** 127 **Outpatient Visits:**
> 178239 **Births:** 0 **Total Expense ($000):** 344354 **Payroll Expense ($000):**
> 117729 **Personnel:** 2610

**CHRISTIANA HOSPITAL** See Christiana Care Health System, Newark

☒ **SELECT SPECIALTY HOSPITAL–WILMINGTON (082000)**, 701 North Clayton Street, 5th Floor, Zip 19805–3948; tel. 302/421–4545, (Nonreporting) **A**1 10 **S** Select Medical Corporation, Mechanicsburg, PA
Primary Contact: Claudia Ann Eisenmann, Chief Executive Officer
COO: Pam Lawson, Director Clinical Services
CFO: Melissa Smith, Vice President and Controller
CMO: John Chabalko, M.D., Medical Director
CHR: Shannon Oberman, Coordinator Human Resources
Web address: www.selectspecialtyhospitals.com/company/locations/wilmington.aspx
**Control:** Corporation, Investor–owned, for–profit **Service:** Long–Term Acute Care hospital

**Staffed Beds:** 35

☒ **ST. FRANCIS HOSPITAL (080003)**, Seventh and Clayton Streets, Zip 19805–0500, Mailing Address: P.O. Box 2500, Zip 19805–0500; tel. 302/421–4100, (Nonreporting) **A**1 2 3 5 9 10 **S** Catholic Health East, Newtown Square, PA
Primary Contact: Brian E. Dietz, FACHE, Interim President and Chief Executive officer
CIO: Paul W. Rowe, Director Information Technology
CHR: Charlene J. Wilson, Vice President Human Resources
Web address: www.stfrancishealthcare.org
**Control:** Other not–for–profit (including NFP Corporation) **Service:** General Medical and Surgical

**Staffed Beds:** 214

☒ **VETERANS AFFAIRS MEDICAL CENTER**, 1601 Kirkwood Highway, Zip 19805–4989; tel. 302/994–2511, (Nonreporting) **A**1 2 3 5 8 **S** Department of Veterans Affairs, Washington, DC
Primary Contact: Daniel Hendee, Director
CFO: Mary Ann Kozel, Chief Fiscal
CMO: Enrique Guttin, M.D., Chief of Staff
CIO: Scott Vlars, Chief Information Technology Services
CHR: Louis McCloskey, Chief Human Resources
Web address: www.va.gov/wilmington
**Control:** Veterans Affairs, Government, federal **Service:** General Medical and Surgical

**Staffed Beds:** 120

**WILMINGTON HOSPITAL** See Christiana Care Health System, Newark

**DE**

# DISTRICT OF COLUMBIA

**WASHINGTON—District Of Columbia County**

⊞ **CHILDREN'S NATIONAL MEDICAL CENTER (093300)**, 111 Michigan Avenue N.W., Zip 20010–2916; tel. 202/476–5000 **A**1 3 5 8 9 10 **F**3 5 7 8 11 12 14 17 18 19 20 21 22 23 25 27 28 29 30 31 32 34 35 38 39 40 41 42 43 44 48 49 50 54 55 57 58 59 60 61 64 65 66 68 71 72 74 75 77 78 79 81 82 83 84 85 86 87 88 89 93 97 98 99 100 101 102 104 107 111 112 115 116 117 118 119 126 129 130 131 132 133 134 135 136 137 142 143 144 146 148 **P**6
Primary Contact: Kurt Newman, M.D., President and Chief Executive Officer
COO: Kathleen Gorman, Chief Operating Officer and Executive Vice President Patient Care Services
CFO: Douglas Myers, Executive Vice President and Chief Financial Officer
CMO: Mark L. Batshaw, M.D., Interim Chief Medical Officer and Chief Academic Officer
CIO: Cherie Pardue, Interim Chief Information Officer
CHR: Jack Gottschalk, Interim Vice President Human Resources
CNO: Nellie C. Robinson, R.N., Executive Vice President, Patient Services & Chief Nursing Officer
Web address: www.childrensnational.org
**Control:** Other not–for–profit (including NFP Corporation) **Service:** Children's general

**Staffed Beds:** 303 **Admissions:** 14595 **Census:** 237 **Outpatient Visits:** 457657 **Births:** 0 **Total Expense ($000):** 672931 **Payroll Expense ($000):** 302140 **Personnel:** 5820

⊞ △ **GEORGE WASHINGTON UNIVERSITY HOSPITAL (090001)**, 900 23rd Street N.W., Zip 20037–2342; tel. 202/715–4000 **A**1 2 3 5 7 8 9 10 **F**3 8 11 12 13 15 17 18 20 22 24 26 29 30 31 34 35 36 37 39 40 43 44 45 46 47 48 49 50 57 58 59 61 64 68 70 72 74 75 77 78 79 81 82 83 84 85 86 87 90 93 94 95 96 98 100 101 102 107 108 110 111 114 115 116 117 118 119 120 121 123 126 129 130 131 136 141 146 147 148 **S** Universal Health Services, Inc., King of Prussia, PA
Primary Contact: Barry A. Wolfman, Chief Executive Officer and Managing Director
COO: Kimberly Russo, Chief Operating Officer
CFO: Richard Davis, Chief Financial Officer
CMO: Gary Little, M.D., Medical Director
CIO: Louis Duhe, Senior Director Information Technology
CHR: Erin Fagan, Manager Human Resources
CNO: Jennifer Kirby, R.N., Chief Nursing Officer
Web address: www.gwhospital.com
**Control:** Partnership, Investor–owned, for–profit **Service:** General Medical and Surgical

**Staffed Beds:** 363 **Admissions:** 17962 **Census:** 233 **Outpatient Visits:** 178677 **Births:** 2209 **Total Expense ($000):** 318894 **Payroll Expense ($000):** 127062 **Personnel:** 1626

⊞ **HOWARD UNIVERSITY HOSPITAL (090003)**, 2041 Georgia Avenue N.W., Zip 20060–0002; tel. 202/865–6100 **A**1 2 3 5 8 9 10 **F**3 8 12 13 15 17 18 24 26 28 29 30 31 32 34 35 36 38 39 40 41 43 44 45 46 50 54 55 56 57 58 59 60 61 64 65 66 68 70 71 72 73 74 75 76 77 78 79 81 82 85 86 87 89 93 97 98 99 100 101 102 103 104 107 108 110 111 114 115 118 119 123 124 129 130 132 146 147 148 **P**4
Primary Contact: Herbert Buchanan, Chief Executive Officer
COO: Paul Mullings, Chief Operating Officer
CMO: Thomas E. Gaiter, M.D., Chief Medical Officer
CIO: Bernie Galla, Interim Director Management Information Systems
CHR: Anthony Jacks, Director Human Resources
Web address: www.huhosp.org
**Control:** Other not–for–profit (including NFP Corporation) **Service:** General Medical and Surgical

**Staffed Beds:** 241 **Admissions:** 11015 **Census:** 142 **Outpatient Visits:** 191568 **Births:** 757 **Total Expense ($000):** 403004 **Payroll Expense ($000):** 120377 **Personnel:** 2104

⊞ **MEDSTAR GEORGETOWN UNIVERSITY HOSPITAL (090004)**, 3800 Reservoir Road N.W., Zip 20007–2197; tel. 202/444–2000 **A**1 2 3 5 8 9 10 **F**3 9 11 13 15 18 26 28 29 30 31 32 34 37 40 44 45 46 47 48 49 50 51 55 57 58 59 60 61 64 65 66 68 70 71 72 73 74 75 76 77 78 79 80 81 82 84 85 86 87 88 89 92 93 97 98 99 100 102 103 104 105 107 108 110 111 114 115 116 117 118 119 120 121 123 124 126 129 130 131 132 134 138 139 142 145 146 147 148 **P**6 **S** MedStar Health, Columbia, MD
Primary Contact: Richard L. Goldberg, M.D., President
COO: Michael Sachtleben, Chief Operating Officer
CFO: Paul Warda, Chief Financial Officer
CMO: Stephen R. T. Evans, M.D., Vice President Medical Affairs and Medical Director
CIO: Catherine Szenczy, Senior Vice President and Chief Information Officer
CHR: Mary Jo Schweickhardt, Vice President Human Resources
Web address: www.georgetownuniversityhospital.org
**Control:** Other not–for–profit (including NFP Corporation) **Service:** General Medical and Surgical

**Staffed Beds:** 396 **Admissions:** 15601 **Census:** 298 **Outpatient Visits:** 690454 **Births:** 952 **Total Expense ($000):** 791345 **Payroll Expense ($000):** 329516 **Personnel:** 4177

⊞ △ **MEDSTAR NATIONAL REHABILITATION HOSPITAL (093025)**, 102 Irving Street N.W., Zip 20010–2949; tel. 202/877–1000 **A**1 3 5 7 9 10 **F**3 9 28 29 30 34 35 43 52 54 58 64 68 74 75 79 82 86 90 91 92 93 94 95 96 119 129 130 131 132 146 **P**6 **S** MedStar Health, Columbia, MD
Primary Contact: John D. Rockwood, President
CFO: Michael Boemmel, Vice President and Chief Financial Officer
CMO: Michael R. Yochelson, M.D., Vice President and Medical Director
CHR: Pamela Ashby, Vice President Human Resources
CNO: Rosemary C. Welch, R.N., Vice President and Chief Nursing Officer
Web address: www.medstarnrh.org
**Control:** Other not–for–profit (including NFP Corporation) **Service:** Rehabilitation

**Staffed Beds:** 137 **Admissions:** 2222 **Census:** 103 **Outpatient Visits:** 218226 **Births:** 0 **Total Expense ($000):** 95668 **Payroll Expense ($000):** 50388 **Personnel:** 1042

⊞ **MEDSTAR WASHINGTON HOSPITAL CENTER (090011)**, 110 Irving Street N.W., Zip 20010–3017; tel. 202/877–7000 **A**1 2 3 5 8 9 10 **F**3 5 9 12 13 14 15 16 17 18 19 20 22 24 26 28 29 30 31 32 34 35 36 37 38 39 40 43 44 45 46 47 48 49 50 54 55 56 57 58 59 60 61 64 65 66 68 70 71 72 73 74 75 76 77 78 79 80 81 82 84 85 86 87 92 97 98 100 101 102 103 104 105 107 108 110 111 114 115 116 117 118 119 120 121 123 124 126 130 131 132 134 135 137 138 142 144 145 146 147 148 **P**1 6 7 **S** MedStar Health, Columbia, MD
Primary Contact: John Sullivan, President
COO: Catherine Monge, Senior Vice President Operations
CFO: Douglas A. Zehner, Senior Vice President and Chief Financia Officer
CMO: Janis M. Orlowski, M.D., Senior Vice President Medical Affairs and Chief Medical Officer
CIO: Joe Brothman, Vice President Information Systems
CHR: James P. Hill, Senior Vice President Human Resources
CNO: Susan Eckert, R.N., Senior Vice President and Chief Nursing Officer
Web address: www.whcenter.org
**Control:** Other not–for–profit (including NFP Corporation) **Service:** General Medical and Surgical

**Staffed Beds:** 777 **Admissions:** 37560 **Census:** 593 **Outpatient Visits:** 409517 **Births:** 3567 **Total Expense ($000):** 1039545 **Payroll Expense ($000):** 486493 **Personnel:** 5583

⊞ **PROVIDENCE HOSPITAL (090006)**, 1150 Varnum Street N.E., Zip 20017–2104; tel. 202/269–7000, (Total facility includes 252 beds in nursing home–type unit) **A**1 2 3 5 9 10 **F**3 4 5 12 13 15 17 20 26 29 30 31 34 35 40 42 43 45 46 49 50 53 54 56 57 58 59 61 63 64 65 66 68 69 70 72 74 75 76 77 78 79 81 82 83 84 85 86 87 91 92 93 94 95 96 97 98 102 103 104 105 106 107 108 111 114 118 119 126 128 129 130 131 132 134 135 143 146 147 148 **P**6 **S** Ascension Health, Saint Louis, MO
Primary Contact: Amy E. Freeman, President and Chief Executive Officer
CFO: Rick Talento, Senior Vice President and Chief Financial Officer
CMO: Raymond L. Cox, M.D., Chief Medical Officer
CIO: Alan Wyman, Chief Information Officer
CHR: Matt Lasecki, Interim Vice President Human Resources
CNO: Thedosia Munford, Senior Vice President and Chief Nursing Officer
Web address: www.provhosp.org
**Control:** Other not–for–profit (including NFP Corporation) **Service:** General Medical and Surgical

**Staffed Beds:** 541 **Admissions:** 13442 **Census:** 401 **Outpatient Visits:** 118175 **Births:** 2195 **Total Expense ($000):** 188238 **Payroll Expense ($000):** 96273 **Personnel:** 1376

DC

*Many Facility Codes have changed. Please refer to the AHA Guide Code Chart.*
© 2013 AHA Guide

☐ **PSYCHIATRIC INSTITUTE OF WASHINGTON (094004)**, 4228 Wisconsin Avenue N.W., Zip 20016–2138; tel. 202/885–5600, (Nonreporting) **A**1 5 9 10
Primary Contact: Kenneth F. Courage, President and Chief Executive Officer
COO: Carol Desjeunes, Chief Operating Officer
CFO: Charles J. Baumgardner, Vice President Corporate Operations
CMO: Howard Hoffman, M.D., Medical Director
CIO: Hector Benedi, Coordinator Information Systems
CHR: Randy Kellar, Director Human Resources
Web address: www.psychinstitute.com
**Control:** Corporation, Investor–owned, for–profit **Service:** Psychiatric

**Staffed Beds:** 114

⊠ **SIBLEY MEMORIAL HOSPITAL (090005)**, 5255 Loughboro Road N.W., Zip 20016–2633; tel. 202/537–4000, (Total facility includes 45 beds in nursing home–type unit) **A**1 2 3 5 9 10 **F**3 6 8 10 12 13 14 15 17 18 20 22 29 30 31 34 35 40 46 47 48 51 53 55 56 57 59 60 62 64 65 68 70 73 74 75 76 77 78 79 81 82 84 85 86 87 92 93 96 98 100 102 103 105 107 108 109 110 111 114 117 119 120 121 123 124 126 128 129 130 131 132 135 141 145 146 147 148 **S** Johns Hopkins Health System, Baltimore, MD
Primary Contact: Richard O. Davis, Ph.D., President and Chief Executive Officer
COO: Stephen C. McDonnell, Senior Vice President, Chief Financial Officer and Chief Operating Officer
CFO: Stephen C. McDonnell, Senior Vice President, Chief Financial Officer and Chief Operating Officer
CMO: Peter E. Petrucci, M.D., Vice President Patient Safety, Quality and Medical Affairs
CIO: Kenda Tavakoli, Vice President Information Technology and Chief Information Officer
CHR: Queenie C. Plater, Vice President and Chief Human Resources Officer
Web address: www.sibley.org
**Control:** Other not–for–profit (including NFP Corporation) **Service:** General Medical and Surgical

**Staffed Beds:** 246 **Admissions:** 11853 **Census:** 159 **Outpatient Visits:** 91264 **Births:** 3545 **Total Expense ($000):** 217590 **Payroll Expense ($000):** 104526 **Personnel:** 1471

☐ **SPECIALTY HOSPITAL OF WASHINGTON (092002)**, 700 Constitution Avenue N.E., Zip 20002–6058; tel. 202/546–5700, (Nonreporting) **A**1 10 **S** Specialty Hospitals of America, LLC, Portsmouth, NH
Primary Contact: Susan P. Bailey, R.N., Chief Executive Officer
CFO: Ed Clark, Vice President Finance
CMO: Manisha Singal, M.D., Medical Director
CHR: Margaret A. Fisher, Executive Director Human Resources
Web address: www.specialtyhospitalofwashington.com
**Control:** Corporation, Investor–owned, for–profit **Service:** Long–Term Acute Care hospital

**Staffed Beds:** 177

☐ **SPECIALTY HOSPITAL OF WASHINGTON–HADLEY (092003)**, 4601 Martin Luther King Jr. Avenue, S.W., Zip 20032–1131; tel. 202/574–5700, (Nonreporting) **A**1 10 **S** Specialty Hospitals of America, LLC, Portsmouth, NH
Primary Contact: Peter Miller, FACHE, Chief Executive Officer
CFO: Ronald Davis, Chief Financial Officer
CMO: Samir Al–Khouri, M.D., Medical Director
CHR: Bing Lechoco, Director Human Resources
**Control:** Corporation, Investor–owned, for–profit **Service:** Long–Term Acute Care hospital

**Staffed Beds:** 82

★ **ST. ELIZABETHS HOSPITAL (094001)**, 1100 Alabama Avenue S.E., Zip 20032–4540; tel. 202/562–4000 **A**3 5 10 **F**30 39 56 59 65 74 75 86 91 98 99 103 130 135 146 148
Primary Contact: Patrick J. Canavan, PsyD, Chief Executive Officer
COO: Anthea Seymour, Chief Operating Officer
CMO: Bernard Arons, M.D., Director Medical Affairs
CIO: Walter Vallierre, Chief Administrative Officer
CHR: James Gallo, Chief Human Resources Officer
Web address: www.dmh.dc.gov
**Control:** City–Government, nonfederal **Service:** Psychiatric

**Staffed Beds:** 292 **Admissions:** 400 **Census:** 269 **Outpatient Visits:** 0 **Births:** 0 **Payroll Expense ($000):** 54730 **Personnel:** 769

⊠ △ **THE HSC PEDIATRIC CENTER**, 1731 Bunker Hill Road N.E., Zip 20017–3096; tel. 202/832–4400 **A**1 7 9 **F**3 29 30 32 34 35 39 64 65 68 74 75 77 80 84 86 87 90 91 93 94 130 132 143 146 148 **P**6
Primary Contact: Bruce Goldman, Chief Operating Officer
COO: Bruce Goldman, Chief Operating Officer
CFO: Nancy J. Southers, Vice President and Chief Financial Officer
CMO: Michael Hauser, M.D., Chief Medical Officer
CIO: Eugene Greer, Chief Information Officer
CHR: Lynne Hostetter, Vice President Human Resources
Web address: www.hscpediatriccenter.org/
**Control:** Other not–for–profit (including NFP Corporation) **Service:** Children's chronic disease

**Staffed Beds:** 118 **Admissions:** 318 **Census:** 53 **Outpatient Visits:** 9536 **Births:** 0 **Total Expense ($000):** 42588 **Payroll Expense ($000):** 18703 **Personnel:** 312

☐ **UNITED MEDICAL CENTER (090008)**, 1310 Southern Avenue S.E., Zip 20032–4623; tel. 202/574–6000, (Total facility includes 120 beds in nursing home–type unit) **A**1 9 10 **F**3 13 15 18 29 30 35 40 45 46 50 60 61 64 65 70 74 75 76 77 79 81 85 87 91 93 96 97 98 100 102 107 108 110 111 114 119 130 146 147 148
Primary Contact: David R. Small, Interim Chief Executive Officer
CFO: Ronald P. Walker, Interim Chief Financial Officer
CMO: Cyril Allen, M.D., Chief Medical Officer
CIO: Janice Akintewe, Director Information Technology
CHR: Jackie Johnson, Vice President Human Resources
CNO: Jean C. Phaire, Executive Vice President Patient Care Services and Chief Nursing Executive
Web address: www.united–medicalcenter.com
**Control:** State–Government, nonfederal **Service:** General Medical and Surgical

**Staffed Beds:** 354 **Admissions:** 5862 **Census:** 199 **Outpatient Visits:** 77165 **Births:** 558 **Total Expense ($000):** 107662 **Payroll Expense ($000):** 52986 **Personnel:** 601

**VETERANS AFFAIRS MEDICAL CENTER** See Washington DC Veterans Affairs Medical Center

⊠ △ **WASHINGTON DC VETERANS AFFAIRS MEDICAL CENTER**, (Formerly Veterans Affairs Medical Center), 50 Irving Street N.W., Zip 20422–0002; tel. 202/745–8000, (Nonreporting) **A**1 2 3 5 7 9 **S** Department of Veterans Affairs, Washington, DC
Primary Contact: Brian A. Hawkins, Director
CFO: Frank Filosa, Fiscal Manager
CIO: Amanda Graves, Chief Information Systems
Web address: www.washingtondc.va.gov/
**Control:** Veterans Affairs, Government, federal **Service:** General Medical and Surgical

**Staffed Beds:** 291

**DC**

---

**Hospital, Medicare Provider Number, Address, Telephone, Approval, Facility, and Physician Codes, Health Care System**

★ American Hospital Association (AHA) membership
☐ The Joint Commission accreditation ◇ DNV Healthcare Inc. accreditation
○ Healthcare Facilities Accreditation Program
△ Commission on Accreditation of Rehabilitation Facilities (CARF) accreditation

© 2013 AHA Guide    *Many Facility Codes have changed. Please refer to the AHA Guide Code Chart.*    Hospitals **A117**

# FLORIDA

### ALTAMONTE SPRINGS—Seminole County

**FLORIDA HOSPITAL–ALTAMONTE** See Florida Hospital, Orlando

### APALACHICOLA—Franklin County

**GEORGE E. WEEMS MEMORIAL HOSPITAL (101305)**, 135 Avenue G.,
Zip 32320–1613, Mailing Address: P.O. Box 580, Zip 32329–0580;
tel. 850/653–8853, (Nonreporting) **A**9 10 18
Primary Contact: Ray Brownsworth, Chief Executive Officer
CFO: James Robinson, Chief Financial Officer
CIO: Dennis Peterson, Chief Information Officer
CHR: Ginny Grimer, Director Human Resources
CNO: Cindy Drapal, Chief Nursing Officer
Web address: www.weemsmemorial.com
**Control:** Partnership, Investor–owned, for–profit **Service:** General Medical and
Surgical

**Staffed Beds:** 25

### APOPKA—Orange County

**FLORIDA HOSPITAL–APOPKA** See Florida Hospital, Orlando

### ARCADIA—Desoto County

☐ **DESOTO MEMORIAL HOSPITAL (100175)**, 900 North Robert Avenue,
Zip 34266–8712, Mailing Address: P.O. Box 2180, Zip 34265–2180;
tel. 863/494–3535, (Nonreporting) **A**1 9 10 20
Primary Contact: Vincent A. Sica, President and Chief Executive Officer
CFO: Joe Amato, Interim Chief Financial Officer
CMO: Kayum Mohammadbhoy, M.D., Chief of Staff
CIO: Annie Curnow, Coordinator Medical Staff and Public Relations
CHR: Lois Hilton, Director Human Resources
Web address: www.dmh.org
**Control:** Other not–for–profit (including NFP Corporation) **Service:** General
Medical and Surgical

**Staffed Beds:** 49

### ATLANTIS—Palm Beach County

⊠ **J. F. K. MEDICAL CENTER (100080)**, 5301 South Congress Avenue,
Zip 33462–1197; tel. 561/965–7300, (Nonreporting) **A**1 2 3 5 9 10 **S** HCA,
Nashville, TN
Primary Contact: Gina Melby, Chief Executive Officer
CFO: Jim Leamon, Chief Financial Officer
CMO: Charles Posternack, M.D., Chief Medical Officer
CIO: Jane Stewart, Director Information Services
CHR: Trudy Bromley, Vice President Human Resources
Web address: www.jfkmc.com
**Control:** Corporation, Investor–owned, for–profit **Service:** General Medical and
Surgical

**Staffed Beds:** 424

### AVENTURA—Miami–Dade County

⊠ **AVENTURA HOSPITAL AND MEDICAL CENTER (100131)**, 20900 Biscayne
Boulevard, Zip 33180–1407; tel. 305/682–7000, (Nonreporting) **A**1 2 9 10
**S** HCA, Nashville, TN
Primary Contact: Dianne Goldenberg, Chief Executive Officer
COO: Lorna Kernizan, Chief Operating Officer
CFO: Alisa Bert, Chief Financial Officer
CMO: Charles Shenker, M.D., Chief of Staff
Web address: www.aventurahospital.com
**Control:** Corporation, Investor–owned, for–profit **Service:** General Medical and
Surgical

**Staffed Beds:** 359

### BARTOW—Polk County

☐ **BARTOW REGIONAL MEDICAL CENTER (100121)**, 2200 Osprey Boulevard,
Zip 33830–3308, Mailing Address: P.O. Box 1050, Zip 33831–1050;
tel. 863/533–8111, (Nonreporting) **A**1 9 10 **S** Health Management Associates,
Naples, FL
Primary Contact: Philip Minden, Chief Executive Officer
CFO: Michael Boscia, Chief Financial Officer
CMO: Stuart Patterson, M.D., Chief of Staff
CIO: Vilakon Champavannarath, Director Information Systems
CHR: Marie Horton, Director Associate Relations
Web address: www.bartowregional.com
**Control:** Corporation, Investor–owned, for–profit **Service:** General Medical and
Surgical

**Staffed Beds:** 72

### BAY PINES—Pinellas County

⊠ △ **BAY PINES VETERANS AFFAIRS MEDICAL CENTER**, (Formerly Veterans
Affairs Medical Center), 10000 Bay Pines Boulevard, Zip 33744–8200, Mailing
Address: P.O. Box 5005, Zip 33744–5005; tel. 727/398–6661, (Total facility
includes 134 beds in nursing home–type unit) **A**1 2 3 5 7 9 **F**3 4 5 8 12 15 18
20 22 26 28 29 30 31 36 38 39 40 45 46 47 49 51 53 54 56 57 58 59 60
61 62 63 64 65 68 70 74 75 77 78 79 81 82 83 84 85 86 87 90 91 92 93
94 97 98 102 103 104 106 107 108 110 111 114 115 116 117 118 119
120 121 123 128 129 130 131 132 135 143 144 146 147 148 **P**6
**S** Department of Veterans Affairs, Washington, DC
Primary Contact: Suzanne M. Klinker, Director
COO: Kris Brown, Associate Director
CFO: Jeanine Ergle, Chief Financial Officer
CMO: George F. Van Buskirk, M.D., Chief of Staff
CIO: John Williams, Chief Information Officer
CHR: Paula Buchele, Chief Human Resources
Web address: www.baypines.va.gov/
**Control:** Veterans Affairs, Government, federal **Service:** General Medical and
Surgical

**Staffed Beds:** 394 **Admissions:** 12591 **Census:** 310 **Outpatient Visits:**
1305940 **Births:** 0 **Personnel:** 3635

### BELLE GLADE—Palm Beach County

**GLADES GENERAL HOSPITAL** See Lakeside Medical Center

⊠ **LAKESIDE MEDICAL CENTER (100130)**, 39200 Hooker Highway,
Zip 33430–5368; tel. 561/996–6571 **A**1 9 10 **F**3 11 13 15 18 29 30 34 35
40 45 46 50 54 59 68 70 76 81 85 87 89 93 97 107 108 110 111 114 119
130 132 135 148
Primary Contact: Thomas J. Leach, Administrator
COO: Nancy L. O'Neal, Director Operations
CFO: Larry Singleton, Chief Financial Officer
CMO: Ron Wiewora, M.D., Chief Medical Officer
CIO: Adam Levenson, Manager Information Systems
CHR: Matthew Morgan, Manager Human Resources
Web address: www.lakesidemedical.org
**Control:** Hospital district or authority, Government, nonfederal **Service:** General
Medical and Surgical

**Staffed Beds:** 70 **Admissions:** 3056 **Census:** 30 **Outpatient Visits:** 32446
**Births:** 539 **Total Expense ($000):** 38624 **Payroll Expense ($000):** 17788
**Personnel:** 300

### BLOUNTSTOWN—Calhoun County

★ **CALHOUN–LIBERTY HOSPITAL (101304)**, 20370 N.E. Burns Avenue,
Zip 32424–1045, Mailing Address: P.O. Box 419, Zip 32424–0419;
tel. 850/674–5411 **A**9 10 18 **F**3 7 34 40 45 50 54 57 59 66 107 110 114
119 127 133 135
Primary Contact: Phillip Hill, Interim Chief Executive Officer
CFO: Nathan Ebersole, Controller
CIO: Michael Flowers, Director Information Management
CHR: Lynn Pitts, Director Human Resources
Web address: www.calhoun–libertyhospital.com
**Control:** Other not–for–profit (including NFP Corporation) **Service:** General
Medical and Surgical

**Staffed Beds:** 25 **Admissions:** 688 **Census:** 17 **Outpatient Visits:** 22399
**Births:** 0 **Total Expense ($000):** 9905 **Payroll Expense ($000):** 4616
**Personnel:** 146

### BOCA RATON—Palm Beach County

**BOCA RATON COMMUNITY HOSPITAL** See Boca Raton Regional Hospital

☐ **BOCA RATON REGIONAL HOSPITAL (100168)**, 800 Meadows Road,
Zip 33486–2368; tel. 561/955–7100 **A**1 2 5 9 10 **F**3 8 11 13 15 17 18 20 22
24 26 28 29 30 31 34 35 37 40 44 45 46 47 48 49 50 51 53 54 55 56 57
58 59 60 62 64 68 70 71 72 74 75 76 77 78 79 81 82 84 85 86 87 91 92
93 94 96 97 100 102 103 107 108 109 110 111 112 114 115 116 117 118
119 120 121 123 124 126 130 131 132 135 144 145 146 147 148 **P**6
Primary Contact: Jerry J. Fedele, President and Chief Executive Officer
COO: Karen Poole, Chief Operating Officer
CFO: Richard Jones, Vice President and Chief Financial Officer
CMO: M. Joseph Grennan, Jr., M.D., Vice President Medical Affairs
CIO: Robin Hildwein, Chief Information Officer
CHR: Mindy Raymond, Vice President Human Resources
Web address: www.brrh.com
**Control:** Other not–for–profit (including NFP Corporation) **Service:** General
Medical and Surgical

**Staffed Beds:** 394 **Admissions:** 15989 **Census:** 194 **Outpatient Visits:**
331842 **Births:** 1821 **Total Expense ($000):** 344022 **Payroll Expense
($000):** 125563 **Personnel:** 1914

FL

⊠ **WEST BOCA MEDICAL CENTER (100268)**, 21644 State Road 7,
Zip 33428–1899; tel. 561/488–8000, (Nonreporting) **A**1 5 9 10 **S** TENET
Healthcare Corporation, Dallas, TX
Primary Contact: Mitchell S. Feldman, Chief Executive Officer
COO: Laura A. Cillo, Chief Operating Officer
CFO: Brook Thomas, Chief Financial Officer
CMO: Jack L. Harari, M.D., Chief Medical Officer
CIO: Linda–Jean Long, Marketing Director
CHR: Stephanie Sherman, Chief Human Resources Officer
CNO: Ruth Schwarzkopf, R.N., Chief Nursing Officer
Web address: www.westbocamedctr.com
**Control:** Corporation, Investor–owned, for–profit **Service:** General Medical and
Surgical

**Staffed Beds:** 195

### BONIFAY—Holmes County

☐ **DOCTORS MEMORIAL HOSPITAL (101307)**, 2600 Hospital Drive,
Zip 32425–4264, Mailing Address: P.O. Box 188, Zip 32425–0188;
tel. 850/547–8000 **A**1 9 10 18 **F**3 11 15 29 30 40 45 57 59 64 70 77 81 90
93 107 110 114 119 131 133 146 148
Primary Contact: Joann Baker, Administrator
CFO: Haley Green, Chief Financial Officer
CMO: Leisa Bailey, M.D., Chief of Staff
CIO: Scott Scurlock, Chief Information Officer
CHR: Christy Booth, Chief Human Resources Officer
Web address: www.doctorsmemorialhospital.com
**Control:** Hospital district or authority, Government, nonfederal **Service:** General
Medical and Surgical

**Staffed Beds:** 20 **Admissions:** 1089 **Census:** 11 **Outpatient Visits:** 16051
**Births:** 0 **Total Expense ($000):** 13040 **Payroll Expense ($000):** 5269
**Personnel:** 134

### BOYNTON BEACH—Palm Beach County

☐ **BETHESDA MEMORIAL HOSPITAL (100002)**, 2815 South Seacrest Boulevard,
Zip 33435–7995; tel. 561/737–7733 **A**1 2 5 9 10 **F**3 8 12 13 15 17 18 20 22
24 26 28 29 30 31 34 35 40 41 45 46 49 50 51 56 58 60 61 64 68 70 72
74 75 76 77 78 79 81 86 87 88 89 90 93 94 96 107 110 111 114 115 119
120 121 123 124 126 129 130 131 132 133 143 146 148
Primary Contact: Roger L. Kirk, President and Chief Executive Officer
CFO: Joanne Aquilina, Vice President Finance and Chief Financial Officer
CMO: Albert Biehl, M.D., Vice President Medical Affairs
CIO: Leslie Durham, Vice President Information Systems
CHR: Regina Crafa, Vice President Human Resources
Web address: www.bethesdaweb.com
**Control:** Other not–for–profit (including NFP Corporation) **Service:** General
Medical and Surgical

**Staffed Beds:** 401 **Admissions:** 20735 **Census:** 291 **Outpatient Visits:**
237431 **Births:** 2931 **Total Expense ($000):** 245373 **Payroll Expense
($000):** 94344 **Personnel:** 1664

### BRADENTON—Manatee County

⊠ △ **BLAKE MEDICAL CENTER (100213)**, 2020 59th Street West,
Zip 34209–4669; tel. 941/792–6611, (Nonreporting) **A**1 2 7 9 10 **S** HCA,
Nashville, TN
Primary Contact: Daniel J. Friedrich, III, Chief Executive Officer
COO: Justin Doss, Chief Operating Officer
CFO: Priscilla Parrish, Chief Financial Officer
CMO: Lawrence Lieberman, M.D., Medical Director
CIO: Shannon Piatkowski, Director Information Technology
CHR: Veronica Lequeux, Vice President Human Resources
Web address: www.blakemedicalcenter.com
**Control:** Corporation, Investor–owned, for–profit **Service:** General Medical and
Surgical

**Staffed Beds:** 294

☐ **LAKEWOOD RANCH MEDICAL CENTER (100299)**, 8330 Lakewood Ranch
Boulevard, Zip 34202–5174; tel. 941/782–2100, (Nonreporting) **A**1 9 10
**S** Universal Health Services, Inc., King of Prussia, PA
Primary Contact: Linda S. Widra, FACHE, Ph.D., R.N., Interim Chief Executive
Officer
COO: Linda S. Widra, FACHE, Chief Operating Officer
CFO: Gerald Christine, Chief Financial Officer
CHR: Trish Morales, Director Human Resources
Web address: www.lakewoodranchmedicalcenter.com
**Control:** Corporation, Investor–owned, for–profit **Service:** General Medical and
Surgical

**Staffed Beds:** 120

**MANATEE GLENS HOSPITAL AND ADDICTION CENTER (104040)**,
(Substance Abuse, Mental Health), 2020 26th Avenue East, Zip 34208–7753,
Mailing Address: P.O. Box 9478, Zip 34206–9478; tel. 941/782–4600 **A**9 10 **F**4
61 98 99 100 102 103 104 132
Primary Contact: Mary Ruiz, Chief Executive Officer
COO: Deborah Kostroun, Chief Operating Officer
CFO: Don Biles, Chief Financial Officer
CMO: Jose Zaglul, M.D., Chief Medical Officer
CIO: Chris Mitchell, Director Information Systems
CHR: Chris McKenna, Director Human Resources
Web address: www.manateeglens.org
**Control:** Other not–for–profit (including NFP Corporation) **Service:** Other specialty

**Staffed Beds:** 75 **Admissions:** 3426 **Census:** 54 **Births:** 0 **Total Expense
($000):** 26247

☐ **MANATEE MEMORIAL HOSPITAL (100035)**, 206 Second Street East,
Zip 34208–1000; tel. 941/746–5111, (Nonreporting) **A**1 2 5 9 10 **S** Universal
Health Services, Inc., King of Prussia, PA
Primary Contact: Kevin DiLallo, Chief Executive Officer
COO: Richard Fletcher, Chief Operating Officer
CFO: Mark A. Tierney, Chief Financial Officer
CMO: Waguih El Masry, M.D., Chief of Staff
CIO: Troy Beaubien, Director Information Services
CHR: Sheree Threewits, Director Human Resources
CNO: Darlette Tice, Chief Nursing Officer
Web address: www.manateememorial.com
**Control:** Partnership, Investor–owned, for–profit **Service:** General Medical and
Surgical

**Staffed Beds:** 319

**MANATEE PALMS YOUTH SERVICES**, 4480 51st Street West,
Zip 34210–2855; tel. 941/792–2222, (Nonreporting) **A**9 **S** Universal Health
Services, Inc., King of Prussia, PA
Primary Contact: Kerry Knott, Chief Executive Officer
CFO: Linda Weymouth, Chief Financial Officer
CMO: Jaime Barker, M.D., Medical Director
Web address: www.mpys.com
**Control:** Corporation, Investor–owned, for–profit **Service:** Children's hospital
psychiatric

**Staffed Beds:** 60

### BRANDON—Hillsborough County

⊠ **BRANDON REGIONAL HOSPITAL (100243)**, 119 Oakfield Drive,
Zip 33511–5779; tel. 813/681–5551, (Nonreporting) **A**1 5 9 10 **S** HCA,
Nashville, TN
Primary Contact: Bland Eng, Chief Executive Officer
COO: Janice Balzano, Chief Operating Officer
COO: Alicia Schulhof, Chief Operating Officer
CFO: Michael T. Terrell, Chief Financial Officer
CMO: Craig Smestad, M.D., Chief Medical Officer
CIO: Shannon Piatkowski, Chief Information Officer
CHR: Patrick Kerrwood, Vice President Human Resources
CNO: Susan Laber, R.N., Chief Nursing Officer
Web address: www.brandonhospital.com
**Control:** Corporation, Investor–owned, for–profit **Service:** General Medical and
Surgical

**Staffed Beds:** 359

### BROOKSVILLE—Hernando County

☐ **BAYFRONT HEALTH BROOKSVILLE (100071)**, (Formerly Brooksville Regional
Hospital), 17240 Cortez Boulevard, Zip 34601–8921, Mailing Address: P.O. Box
37, Zip 34605–0037; tel. 352/796–5111, (Includes SPRING HILL REGIONAL
HOSPITAL, 10461 Quality Drive, Spring Hill, Zip 34609–9634;
tel. 352/688–8200; Patrick Maloney, Market Chief Executive Officer),
(Nonreporting) **A**1 9 10 **S** Health Management Associates, Naples, FL
Primary Contact: Kenneth R. Wicker, Chief Executive Officer
COO: Scott Hartsell, Chief Operating Officer
CFO: Matthew Seagroves, Chief Financial Officer
CMO: Mohammad A. Joud, M.D., Chief of Staff
CIO: Lee Burch, Director Management Information Systems
CHR: Claudia L. Jack, Director Associate Relations
Web address: www.brooksvilleregionalhospital.org
**Control:** Corporation, Investor–owned, for–profit **Service:** General Medical and
Surgical

**Staffed Beds:** 120

---

**Hospital, Medicare Provider Number, Address, Telephone, Approval, Facility, and Physician Codes, Health Care System**

★ American Hospital Association (AHA) membership
☐ The Joint Commission accreditation
◇ DNV Healthcare Inc. accreditation
○ Healthcare Facilities Accreditation Program
△ Commission on Accreditation of Rehabilitation Facilities (CARF) accreditation

FL

⊠ **HEALTHSOUTH REHABILITATION HOSPITAL OF SPRING HILL (103042)**, 12440 Cortez Boulevard, Zip 34613–2628; tel. 352/592–4250 **A**1 9 10 **F**29 34 57 62 64 77 90 93 96 132 **S** HEALTHSOUTH Corporation, Birmingham, AL
Primary Contact: Lori Bedard, Chief Executive Officer
CFO: Debbie Punzirudu, Controller
CMO: Charles Dempsey, M.D., Medical Director
CIO: Myra Merillo, Supervisor Health Information Management
CHR: Ava McLellan, Coordinator Human Resources
Web address: www.healthsouthspringhill.com
**Control:** Corporation, Investor–owned, for–profit **Service:** Rehabilitation

Staffed Beds: 80 Admissions: 1556 Census: 65 Outpatient Visits: 9187 Births: 0 Total Expense ($000): 19897 Payroll Expense ($000): 11141 Personnel: 234

⊠ **OAK HILL HOSPITAL (100264)**, 11375 Cortez Boulevard, Zip 34613–5409; tel. 352/596–6632 **A**1 2 9 10 **F**3 11 15 17 18 20 22 24 26 29 30 31 34 35 40 41 45 46 48 49 50 51 56 57 59 64 70 74 75 77 78 79 81 85 87 93 107 108 110 111 114 118 119 126 130 131 132 146 147 148 **S** HCA, Nashville, TN
Primary Contact: Mickey Smith, Chief Executive Officer
COO: Sonia I. Gonzalez, R.N., Chief Operating Officer
CFO: Chance Phillips, Chief Financial Officer
CMO: Ganesh Chari, M.D., Chief of Staff
CIO: Cindy Peters, Chief Information Officer
CHR: Charles Snider, Vice President Human Resources
CNO: Melissa Bennett, R.N., Chief Nursing Officer
Web address: www.oakhillhospital.com
**Control:** Corporation, Investor–owned, for–profit **Service:** General Medical and Surgical

Staffed Beds: 234 Admissions: 13666 Census: 163 Outpatient Visits: 74293 Births: 0 Total Expense ($000): 134776 Payroll Expense ($000): 51686 Personnel: 871

☐ **SPRINGBROOK HOSPITAL (104057)**, 7007 Grove Road, Zip 34609–8610; tel. 352/596–4306, (Nonreporting) **A**1 9 10
Primary Contact: James E. O'Shea, Administrator
Web address: www.springbrookhospital.org/
**Control:** Other not–for–profit (including NFP Corporation) **Service:** Psychiatric

Staffed Beds: 50

### CAPE CORAL—Lee County

★ ◇ **CAPE CORAL HOSPITAL (100244)**, 636 Del Prado Boulevard, Zip 33990–2695; tel. 239/424–2000 **A**9 10 21 **F**3 11 13 14 15 17 18 20 22 28 29 30 31 34 35 40 45 46 48 50 51 52 53 57 59 60 65 66 68 70 74 75 76 79 81 82 84 85 86 87 89 93 94 97 107 110 111 115 119 129 130 132 135 146 147 148 **S** Lee Memorial Health System, Fort Myers, FL
Primary Contact: James R. Nathan, President and Chief Executive Officer
COO: Lawrence Antonucci, M.D., Chief Operating Officer
CFO: Mike German, Chief Financial Officer
CMO: Mark Greenberg, M.D., Chief Medical Officer
CIO: Mike Smith, Chief Information Officer
CHR: Jon C. Cecil, Chief Human Resource Officer
Web address: www.leememorial.org
**Control:** Hospital district or authority, Government, nonfederal **Service:** General Medical and Surgical

Staffed Beds: 291 Admissions: 14583 Census: 170 Outpatient Visits: 227411 Births: 1252

### CELEBRATION—Osceola County

**FLORIDA HOSPITAL CELEBRATION HEALTH** See Florida Hospital, Orlando

### CHATTAHOOCHEE—Gadsden County

△ **FLORIDA STATE HOSPITAL (104000)**, U.S. Highway 90 East, Zip 32324–1000, Mailing Address: P.O. Box 1000, Zip 32324–1000; tel. 850/663–7536, (Nonreporting) **A**7 10
Primary Contact: Diane R. James, Administrator
CFO: Denise Smith, Director Financial Services
Web address: www.dcf.state.fl.us/institutions/fsh
**Control:** State–Government, nonfederal **Service:** Psychiatric

Staffed Beds: 987

### CHIPLEY—Washington County

☐ **NORTHWEST FLORIDA COMMUNITY HOSPITAL (101308)**, 1360 Brickyard Road, Zip 32428–6303, Mailing Address: P.O. Box 889, Zip 32428–0889; tel. 850/638–1610, (Total facility includes 34 beds in nursing home–type unit) **A**1 9 10 18 **F**3 11 15 18 29 30 34 35 40 45 57 59 62 68 81 82 85 93 104 107 111 114 119 127 128 129 130 131 133 135 146 148 **S** Alliant Management Services, Louisville, KY
Primary Contact: Patrick A. Schlenker, FACHE, President and Chief Executive Officer
COO: Janet Kinney, Chief Operating Officer
CFO: Marcey Black, Chief Financial Officer
CHR: Sue Byrd, Coordinator Human Resources
CNO: Joan Beard, Chief Nursing Officer
Web address: www.nfch.org
**Control:** Corporation, Investor–owned, for–profit **Service:** General Medical and Surgical

Staffed Beds: 59 Admissions: 696 Census: 40 Outpatient Visits: 48129 Births: 0 Total Expense ($000): 22197 Payroll Expense ($000): 8813 Personnel: 209

### CLEARWATER—Pinellas County

⊠ **MORTON PLANT HOSPITAL (100127)**, 300 Pinellas Street, Zip 33756–3804, Mailing Address: P.O. Box 210, Zip 33757–0210; tel. 727/462–7000, (Total facility includes 120 beds in nursing home–type unit) **A**1 2 3 5 9 10 **F**3 5 6 11 13 15 17 18 20 22 24 26 28 29 30 31 34 35 37 38 40 42 45 46 48 49 50 51 53 54 55 56 57 58 59 60 61 62 64 65 66 68 70 72 74 75 76 77 78 79 80 81 82 84 85 86 87 98 99 100 101 102 103 104 107 108 109 110 111 114 115 116 117 118 119 120 121 123 124 126 128 129 130 131 132 143 144 145 146 147 148 **P**6 **S** Morton Plant Mease Health Care, Clearwater, FL
Primary Contact: Glenn D. Waters, FACHE, President
COO: N. Kristopher Hoce, Chief Operating Officer
CFO: Carl Tremonti, Chief Financial Officer
CMO: Donald Pocock, M.D., Chief Medical Officer
CHR: Sharon Collotta, Director Human Resources
CNO: Lisa Johnson, R.N., Chief Nursing Executive
Web address: www.mortonplant.com
**Control:** Other not–for–profit (including NFP Corporation) **Service:** General Medical and Surgical

Staffed Beds: 666 Admissions: 25624 Census: 415 Outpatient Visits: 104567 Births: 2461 Total Expense ($000): 399361 Payroll Expense ($000): 130660 Personnel: 2562

☐ **WINDMOOR HEALTHCARE OF CLEARWATER (104017)**, 11300 U.S. 19 North, Zip 33764; tel. 727/541–2646, (Nonreporting) **A**1 9 10 **S** Universal Health Services, Inc., King of Prussia, PA
Primary Contact: Wendy Merson, Chief Executive Officer
Web address: www.windmoor.com
**Control:** Corporation, Investor–owned, for–profit **Service:** Psychiatric

Staffed Beds: 120

### CLERMONT—Lake County

☐ **SOUTH LAKE HOSPITAL (100051)**, 1900 Don Wickham Drive, Zip 34711–1979; tel. 352/394–4071 **A**1 9 10 **F**3 8 11 13 15 18 20 22 26 29 30 31 32 34 35 37 40 45 46 47 48 49 50 51 53 54 57 59 60 62 64 66 68 70 74 75 76 77 78 79 81 82 85 86 87 89 92 93 107 108 110 111 114 115 117 119 124 126 127 130 131 132 135 145 146 147 148 **P**6 **S** Orlando Health, Orlando, FL
Primary Contact: John Moore, Chief Executive Officer
CFO: Lance Sewell, Chief Financial Officer
CMO: Michael Goler, M.D., Chief Medical Officer
CHR: Sue Brown, Administrator Human Resources
Web address: www.southlakehospital.com
**Control:** Hospital district or authority, Government, nonfederal **Service:** General Medical and Surgical

Staffed Beds: 122 Admissions: 7101 Census: 76 Outpatient Visits: 99141 Births: 693 Total Expense ($000): 128031 Payroll Expense ($000): 51087 Personnel: 943

### CLEWISTON—Hendry County

⊠ **HENDRY REGIONAL MEDICAL CENTER (101309)**, 524 West Sagamore Avenue, Zip 33440–3514; tel. 863/902–3000 **A**1 9 10 18 **F**3 11 15 18 29 34 35 40 45 50 57 59 64 65 68 70 75 77 79 81 82 85 93 97 107 110 111 113 114 119 127 130 133 135 146 148 **P**6 **S** QHR, Brentwood, TN
Primary Contact: R. D. Williams, Chief Executive Officer
CFO: William F. Stoltzfus, Interim Chief Financial Officer
CMO: Karim Kaki, M.D., Chief Medical Director
CIO: Leon Hoover, Director Information Systems
CHR: Lisa Miller, Director Human Resources
Web address: www.hendryregional.org
**Control:** Hospital district or authority, Government, nonfederal **Service:** General Medical and Surgical

Staffed Beds: 25 Admissions: 964 Census: 8 Outpatient Visits: 36372 Births: 0 Total Expense ($000): 28159 Payroll Expense ($000): 11693 Personnel: 211

**FL**

*Many Facility Codes have changed. Please refer to the AHA Guide Code Chart.* © 2013 AHA Guide

## COCOA BEACH—Brevard County

☒ **HEALTH FIRST CAPE CANAVERAL HOSPITAL (100177)**, (Formerly Cape Canaveral Hospital), 701 West Cocoa Beach Causeway, Zip 32931–5595, Mailing Address: P.O. Box 320069, Zip 32932–0069; tel. 321/799–7111 **A**1 9 10 **F**3 11 13 15 18 20 22 26 29 30 31 34 35 40 43 44 45 46 47 48 49 51 54 56 57 59 60 62 64 65 68 70 74 75 76 78 79 81 82 85 86 87 91 92 93 103 107 108 110 111 114 115 116 117 119 124 129 130 132 143 146 147 **P**6 7 **S** Health First, Inc., Rockledge, FL
Primary Contact: Wes Ott, Chief Operating Officer
CFO: Robert Galloway, Senior Vice President Finance and Chief Financial Officer
CMO: Rodney Moore, M.D., Vice President Medical Affairs
CIO: Rich Rogers, Senior Vice President Support Services and Chief Information Officer
CHR: Robert W. Suttles, Vice President Human Resources
Web address: www.health–first.org
**Control:** Other not–for–profit (including NFP Corporation) **Service:** General Medical and Surgical

**Staffed Beds:** 145 **Admissions:** 5692 **Census:** 70 **Outpatient Visits:** 106665 **Births:** 649 **Total Expense ($000):** 91901 **Payroll Expense ($000):** 40200 **Personnel:** 439

## CORAL GABLES—Miami-Dade County

☒ **BAPTIST HEALTH SOUTH FLORIDA, DOCTORS HOSPITAL (100296)**, 5000 University Drive, Zip 33146–2094; tel. 786/308–3000 **A**1 9 10 **F**3 11 18 29 30 31 34 35 37 40 45 47 49 53 57 58 60 63 64 68 70 74 75 77 78 79 81 82 84 85 86 87 93 94 100 102 107 108 111 114 115 119 124 126 130 131 132 135 143 146 148 **S** Baptist Health South Florida, Coral Gables, FL
Primary Contact: Nelson Lazo, Chief Executive Officer
CFO: Maria J. Yanez, Chief Financial Officer
Web address: www.baptisthealth.net
**Control:** Other not–for–profit (including NFP Corporation) **Service:** General Medical and Surgical

**Staffed Beds:** 146 **Admissions:** 6530 **Census:** 100 **Outpatient Visits:** 63782 **Births:** 0 **Total Expense ($000):** 173234 **Payroll Expense ($000):** 56109 **Personnel:** 930

☒ **CORAL GABLES HOSPITAL (100183)**, 3100 Douglas Road, Zip 33134–6914; tel. 305/445–8461, (Nonreporting) **A**1 9 10 **S** TENET Healthcare Corporation, Dallas, TX
Primary Contact: Jeffrey M. Welch, Chief Executive Officer
COO: Caridad Nieves, Chief Nursing Officer and Chief Operating Officer
Web address: www.coralgableshospital.com
**Control:** Corporation, Investor–owned, for–profit **Service:** General Medical and Surgical

**Staffed Beds:** 256

## CORAL SPRINGS—Broward County

☒ **BROWARD HEALTH CORAL SPRINGS (100276)**, 3000 Coral Hills Drive, Zip 33065–4108; tel. 954/344–3000 **A**1 9 10 **F**3 11 12 13 15 17 20 29 31 34 35 40 48 51 55 57 58 59 61 63 64 66 68 70 72 74 75 76 77 78 79 80 81 82 84 85 86 87 88 89 93 96 107 108 111 114 115 118 119 129 130 131 132 143 146 147 148 **S** Broward Health, Fort Lauderdale, FL
Primary Contact: Drew Grossman, Chief Executive Officer
COO: Kimberley Graham, R.N., Chief Nursing Officer and Chief Operating Officer
CFO: Arthur Wallace, Chief Financial Officer
CMO: Carrie Greenspan, M.D., Chief of Staff
CHR: Robert Diano, Director Human Resources
CNO: Kimberley Graham, R.N., Chief Nursing Officer and Chief Operating Officer
Web address: www.browardhealth.org
**Control:** Hospital district or authority, Government, nonfederal **Service:** General Medical and Surgical

**Staffed Beds:** 182 **Admissions:** 13223 **Census:** 138 **Outpatient Visits:** 129915 **Births:** 2399 **Total Expense ($000):** 142161 **Payroll Expense ($000):** 59751 **Personnel:** 939

## CRESTVIEW—Okaloosa County

☒ **NORTH OKALOOSA MEDICAL CENTER (100122)**, 151 Redstone Avenue S.E., Zip 32539–6026; tel. 850/689–8100 **A**1 9 10 **F**3 8 11 13 15 18 20 22 28 29 30 34 35 40 51 53 54 59 67 70 75 76 79 81 85 86 89 93 97 107 110 111 114 115 116 117 119 127 130 131 146 147 148 **S** Community Health Systems, Inc., Franklin, TN
Primary Contact: David W. Fuller, Chief Executive Officer
COO: Heath Evans, Assistant Chief Executive Officer
CFO: Jim Andrews, Chief Financial Officer
CMO: Michael Foley, M.D., Chief Medical Officer
CIO: Jenny Zeitler, Network Administrator
CHR: Melody M. Miller–Collette, Director Human Resources
CNO: Nina Perez, R.N., Chief Nursing Officer
Web address: www.northokaloosa.com
**Control:** Corporation, Investor–owned, for–profit **Service:** General Medical and Surgical

**Staffed Beds:** 110 **Admissions:** 5992 **Census:** 58 **Outpatient Visits:** 79062 **Births:** 449 **Personnel:** 619

## CRYSTAL RIVER—Citrus County

☐ **SEVEN RIVERS REGIONAL MEDICAL CENTER (100249)**, 6201 North Suncoast Boulevard, Zip 34428–6712; tel. 352/795–6560, (Nonreporting) **A**1 9 10 19 **S** Health Management Associates, Naples, FL
Primary Contact: Joyce A. Brancato, Chief Executive Officer
COO: DeAnna Beverly, Chief Operating Officer
CFO: Steven Miller, Chief Financial Officer
CHR: Joann Mramor, Director Human Resources
CNO: Cynthia Heitzman, R.N., Chief Nursing Officer
Web address: www.srrmc.com
**Control:** Corporation, Investor–owned, for–profit **Service:** General Medical and Surgical

**Staffed Beds:** 128

## DADE CITY—Pasco County

☐ **BAYFRONT HEALTH DADE CITY (100211)**, (Formerly Pasco Regional Medical Center), 13100 Fort King Road, Zip 33525–5294; tel. 352/521–1100, (Nonreporting) **A**1 9 10 **S** Health Management Associates, Naples, FL
Primary Contact: Shauna McKinnon, Chief Executive Officer
CFO: Linda Stockton, Chief Financial Officer
CMO: Petros Tsambiras, M.D., Chief of Staff
CIO: Cheryl Kaufman, Director Health Information Management
CHR: Tabatha Wallace, Director Human Resources
Web address: www.pascoregionalmc.com
**Control:** Corporation, Investor–owned, for–profit **Service:** General Medical and Surgical

**Staffed Beds:** 120

## DAVENPORT—Polk County

☐ **HEART OF FLORIDA REGIONAL MEDICAL CENTER (100137)**, 40100 Highway 27, Zip 33837–5906; tel. 863/422–4971, (Nonreporting) **A**1 9 10 **S** Health Management Associates, Naples, FL
Primary Contact: Donnie Breeding, Chief Executive Officer
COO: Brent Burish, Chief Operating Officer
CFO: Tonja Mosley, Chief Financial Officer
CMO: Mohamed Razak, M.D., Chief of Staff
CIO: Louis Jones, Director Management Information Systems
CHR: Joan Allard, Director Human Resources
CNO: Anne E. Carey, R.N., Chief Nursing Officer
Web address: www.heartofflorida.com
**Control:** Corporation, Investor–owned, for–profit **Service:** General Medical and Surgical

**Staffed Beds:** 194

FL

---

**Hospital, Medicare Provider Number, Address, Telephone, Approval, Facility, and Physician Codes, Health Care System**

★ American Hospital Association (AHA) membership
☐ The Joint Commission accreditation
◇ DNV Healthcare Inc. accreditation
○ Healthcare Facilities Accreditation Program
△ Commission on Accreditation of Rehabilitation Facilities (CARF) accreditation

## DAYTONA BEACH—Volusia County

☒ **FLORIDA HOSPITAL MEMORIAL MEDICAL CENTER (100068)**, 301 Memorial Medical Parkway, Zip 32117–5167; tel. 386/676–6000, (Includes FLORIDA HOSPITAL–OCEANSIDE, 264 South Atlantic Avenue, Ormond Beach, Zip 32176–8192; tel. 386/672–4161) **A**1 2 9 10 **F**2 3 11 12 13 15 17 18 20 22 24 26 28 29 30 31 32 34 35 40 42 45 46 47 54 57 58 59 68 70 74 75 76 77 78 79 81 82 86 87 90 91 92 93 97 100 107 108 109 110 111 112 114 116 117 119 120 121 123 124 130 131 132 135 144 146 147 148 **P**6
**S** Adventist Health System Sunbelt Health Care Corporation, Altamonte Springs, FL
Primary Contact: Daryl Tol, Chief Executive Officer
COO: Darlinda Copeland, Chief Operating Officer
CFO: Debora Thomas, Chief Financial Officer
CHR: Connie Schott, Administrative Assistant
Web address: www.floridahospitalmemorial.org
**Control:** Church–operated, Nongovernment, not–for profit **Service:** General Medical and Surgical

**Staffed Beds:** 211 **Admissions:** 13527 **Census:** 183 **Outpatient Visits:** 129684 **Births:** 1408 **Total Expense ($000):** 206135 **Payroll Expense ($000):** 79707 **Personnel:** 2067

☒ **HALIFAX HEALTH MEDICAL CENTER OF DAYTONA BEACH (100017)**, 303 North Clyde Morris Boulevard, Zip 32114–2700; tel. 386/254–4000, (Includes HALIFAX BEHAVIORAL SERVICES, 841 Jimmy Ann Drive, Zip 32117–4599; tel. 904/274–5333; HALIFAX HEALTH MEDICAL CENTER OF PORT ORANGE, 1041 Dunlawton Avenue, Port Orange, Zip 32127; tel. 386/322–4700; Ann Martorano, Administrator) **A**1 2 3 5 9 10 **F**3 11 12 13 17 18 20 22 24 26 28 29 30 31 40 42 43 45 46 47 49 53 55 60 65 70 72 76 77 78 79 81 85 86 87 88 89 98 99 100 101 102 103 107 108 111 114 115 118 119 120 121 123 124 126 130 131 132 135 138 146 147 148
Primary Contact: Jeff Feasel, Chief Executive Officer
CFO: Eric Peburn, Chief Financial Officer
CMO: Donald Stoner, M.D., Chief Medical Officer
CHR: Albert L. Alexander, Chief Human Resources Officer
Web address: www.halifax.org
**Control:** Hospital district or authority, Government, nonfederal **Service:** General Medical and Surgical

**Staffed Beds:** 582 **Admissions:** 22770 **Census:** 321 **Outpatient Visits:** 268055 **Births:** 1879 **Total Expense ($000):** 428718 **Payroll Expense ($000):** 175431 **Personnel:** 3138

## DEERFIELD BEACH—Broward County

☒ △ **BROWARD HEALTH NORTH (100086)**, (Formerly North Broward Medical Center), 201 East Sample Road, Zip 33064–3502; tel. 954/941–8300 **A**1 2 7 10 **F**3 6 11 15 17 18 20 28 29 30 34 35 37 40 43 45 46 49 51 55 57 58 59 60 61 64 66 68 70 74 75 77 78 79 80 81 82 83 84 85 86 87 90 92 93 94 96 100 107 108 110 111 114 115 117 118 119 120 121 123 124 129 130 131 132 143 145 146 148 **S** Broward Health, Fort Lauderdale, FL
Primary Contact: Pauline Grant, FACHE, Chief Executive Officer
COO: Kevin Fusco, Chief Operating Officer
CFO: Robert Bugg, Chief Financial Officer
CMO: Douglas Ford, M.D., Chief of Staff
CIO: Doris Crain, Vice President and Chief Information Officer
CHR: Grace King, Regional Chief Human Resources
CNO: Bettiann S. Ruditz, Chief Nursing Officer
Web address: www.browardhealth.org
**Control:** Hospital district or authority, Government, nonfederal **Service:** General Medical and Surgical

**Staffed Beds:** 342 **Admissions:** 13878 **Census:** 213 **Outpatient Visits:** 116992 **Births:** 0 **Total Expense ($000):** 209604 **Payroll Expense ($000):** 80700 **Personnel:** 1229

## DEFUNIAK SPRINGS—Walton County

**HEALTHMARK REGIONAL MEDICAL CENTER (100081)**, 4413 U.S. Highway 331 South, Zip 32435–6307; tel. 850/951–4500 **A**9 10 **F**3 11 40 45 62 70 75 81 93 107 111 115 119 127 143 **P**6
Primary Contact: James H. Thompson, Ph.D., FACHE, Owner and Chief Executive Officer
COO: Gerald C. Beard, Chief Operating Officer
CFO: Jim Brewer, M.P.H., Chief Financial Officer
CMO: John H. Thomas, M.D., Chief of Staff
CIO: Nikki Galloway, Director Personnel and Administrative Secretary
CHR: Nikki Galloway, Director Personnel and Administrative Secretary
Web address: www.healthmarkregional.com
**Control:** Individual, Investor–owned, for–profit **Service:** General Medical and Surgical

**Staffed Beds:** 50 **Admissions:** 927 **Census:** 11 **Outpatient Visits:** 18578 **Births:** 0 **Total Expense ($000):** 10812 **Payroll Expense ($000):** 5063 **Personnel:** 108

## DELAND—Volusia County

☒ **FLORIDA HOSPITAL DELAND (100045)**, 701 West Plymouth Avenue, Zip 32720–3236; tel. 386/943–4522 **A**1 9 10 **F**3 4 13 15 18 20 22 26 28 29 30 31 34 35 37 38 40 45 46 47 48 49 50 54 55 56 57 58 59 60 64 70 74 75 76 77 78 79 80 81 84 85 86 87 93 97 98 100 102 107 108 109 110 111 112 114 115 116 117 119 120 124 126 129 130 131 132 135 146 147
**S** Adventist Health System Sunbelt Health Care Corporation, Altamonte Springs, FL
Primary Contact: Mark LaRose, President and Chief Executive Officer
COO: Randy Surber, Chief Operating Officer
CFO: Nigel Hinds, Chief Financial Officer
CMO: Mark Hollmann, M.D., Chief of Staff
CIO: Kevin Piper, Director Information Systems
CHR: Opal R. Howard, SPHR, Director Human Resources
CNO: Patricia Ann Stark, R.N., CNO
Web address: www.fhdeland.org
**Control:** Other not–for–profit (including NFP Corporation) **Service:** General Medical and Surgical

**Staffed Beds:** 156 **Admissions:** 9027 **Census:** 95 **Outpatient Visits:** 115209 **Births:** 749 **Total Expense ($000):** 116632 **Payroll Expense ($000):** 44118 **Personnel:** 744

## DELRAY BEACH—Palm Beach County

☒ **DELRAY MEDICAL CENTER (100258)**, 5352 Linton Boulevard, Zip 33484–6580; tel. 561/498–4440, (Includes FAIR OAKS PAVILION, 5440 Linton Boulevard, Zip 33484–6578; tel. 561/495–1000; PINECREST REHABILITATION HOSPITAL, 5360 Linton Boulevard, Zip 33484–6538; tel. 561/495–0400) **A**1 9 10 **F**3 4 11 12 15 17 18 20 22 24 29 31 34 35 37 38 40 41 43 45 46 47 49 50 56 57 58 59 60 64 65 67 70 74 75 77 78 79 80 81 82 84 85 87 90 91 93 94 96 98 100 101 102 103 104 107 108 111 114 115 118 119 126 129 130 131 132 133 135 143 144 146 147 148
**S** TENET Healthcare Corporation, Dallas, TX
Primary Contact: Mark Bryan, Chief Executive Officer
CMO: Anthony Dardano, M.D., Chief Medical Officer
CIO: Robens Rosena, Director Information Systems
CHR: Shannon Wills, Director Human Resources
Web address: www.delraymedicalctr.com
**Control:** Corporation, Investor–owned, for–profit **Service:** General Medical and Surgical

**Staffed Beds:** 493 **Admissions:** 18680 **Census:** 264 **Outpatient Visits:** 76823 **Births:** 0

## DUNEDIN—Pinellas County

☐ **BAYCARE ALLIANT HOSPITAL (102021)**, 601 Main Street, Zip 34698–5848; tel. 727/736–9999 **A**1 9 10 **F**1 3 18 28 29 30 34 84 91 130 148
Primary Contact: Jacqueline Arocho, Administrator
CFO: John Proni, CPA, Manager Finance
CMO: Leonard Dunn, M.D., Chief Medical Officer
CHR: Darlene Shelton, Coordinator Team Resources
CNO: Karen Duffy, R.N., Director Patient Care Services
Web address: www.baycare.org
**Control:** Other not–for–profit (including NFP Corporation) **Service:** Long–Term Acute Care hospital

**Staffed Beds:** 38 **Admissions:** 379 **Census:** 28 **Outpatient Visits:** 0 **Births:** 0 **Total Expense ($000):** 15554 **Payroll Expense ($000):** 5575 **Personnel:** 88

☐ **MEASE DUNEDIN HOSPITAL (100043)**, (Formerly Mease Hospital Dunedin), 601 Main Street, Zip 34698–5891, Mailing Address: P.O. Box 760, Zip 34697–0760; tel. 727/733–1111 **A**1 9 10 **F**3 12 15 17 18 20 22 26 29 30 31 34 37 40 44 45 49 59 60 64 68 70 75 77 78 79 81 84 85 86 87 93 107 108 110 111 114 118 119 130 132 143 145 146 **P**6 **S** Morton Plant Mease Health Care, Clearwater, FL
Primary Contact: Glenn D. Waters, FACHE, President and Chief Executive Officer
COO: Lou Galdieri, R.N., Chief Operating Officer and Administrator
CFO: Carl Tremonti, Chief Financial Officer
CMO: Donald Pocock, M.D., Chief Medical Officer
CHR: Sharon Collotta, Director Human Resources
Web address: www.mpmhealth.com
**Control:** Other not–for–profit (including NFP Corporation) **Service:** General Medical and Surgical

**Staffed Beds:** 124 **Admissions:** 4955 **Census:** 60 **Outpatient Visits:** 33738 **Births:** 0 **Total Expense ($000):** 84279 **Payroll Expense ($000):** 27535 **Personnel:** 388

## EGLIN AFB—Okaloosa County

☒ **U. S. AIR FORCE REGIONAL HOSPITAL**, 307 Boatner Road, Suite 114, Zip 32542–1282; tel. 850/883–8221, (Nonreporting) **A**1 3 5 **S** Department of the Air Force, Washington, DC
Primary Contact: Colonel Gianna Zeh, Commander
Web address: www.eglin.af.mil
**Control:** Air Force, Government, federal **Service:** General Medical and Surgical

**Staffed Beds:** 57

*Many Facility Codes have changed. Please refer to the AHA Guide Code Chart.* © 2013 AHA Guide

## ENGLEWOOD—Sarasota County

⊠ **ENGLEWOOD COMMUNITY HOSPITAL (100267)**, 700 Medical Boulevard, Zip 34223–3978; tel. 941/475–6571, (Nonreporting) **A**1 9 10 **S** HCA, Nashville, TN
Primary Contact: Dale Alward, Chief Executive Officer
COO: Alex Chang, Chief Operating Officer
CMO: Eric Pressman, D.O., Chair Department of Medicine
CHR: Linda V. Smith, Director Human Resources
CHR: Tony Welch, VP Human Resources
CNO: Kathleen Pace, MSN, Chief Nursing Officer
Web address: www.englewoodcommunityhospital.com
**Control:** Corporation, Investor–owned, for–profit **Service:** General Medical and Surgical

**Staffed Beds:** 100

## FERNANDINA BEACH—Nassau County

⊠ **BAPTIST MEDICAL CENTER NASSAU (100140)**, 1250 South 18th Street, Zip 32034–3098; tel. 904/321–3500 **A**1 9 10 **F**3 11 13 15 29 30 34 35 40 45 49 64 70 76 81 82 85 91 92 93 102 107 108 110 111 114 115 119 124 129 132 135 146 148 **S** Baptist Health, Jacksonville, FL
Primary Contact: Stephen Lee, FACHE, President
COO: Patricia K. Hausauer, Director Finance
CFO: Patricia K. Hausauer, Director Finance
CHR: Katherine Howard, Director Human Resources
CNO: Barbara S. Gingher, R.N., Assistant Administrator for Patient Care Services
Web address: www.community.e–baptisthealth.com/bmc/nassau/index.html
**Control:** Other not–for–profit (including NFP Corporation) **Service:** General Medical and Surgical

**Staffed Beds:** 52 **Admissions:** 3158 **Census:** 27 **Outpatient Visits:** 63495
**Births:** 558 **Total Expense ($000):** 58147 **Payroll Expense ($000):** 17047
**Personnel:** 327

## FORT LAUDERDALE—Broward County

☐ **ATLANTIC SHORES HOSPITAL (104065)**, 4545 North Federal Highway, Zip 33308–5274; tel. 954/771–2711, (Nonreporting) **A**1 9 10 **S** Universal Health Services, Inc., King of Prussia, PA
Primary Contact: Manuel R. Llano, Chief Executive Officer
COO: Karin Carol, Chief Operating Officer
Web address: www.atlanticshoreshospital.com
**Control:** Corporation, Investor–owned, for–profit **Service:** Psychiatric

**Staffed Beds:** 72

⊠ **BROWARD HEALTH IMPERIAL POINT (100200)**, (Formerly Imperial Point Medical Center), 6401 North Federal Highway, Zip 33308–1495; tel. 954/776–8500 **A**1 9 10 **F**3 11 12 15 20 29 31 34 35 40 45 51 53 55 57 58 59 61 63 64 66 68 70 74 75 77 78 79 80 81 82 84 85 86 87 93 98 100 102 104 105 107 108 111 114 115 118 119 129 130 131 132 143 146 147 148 **S** Broward Health, Fort Lauderdale, FL
Primary Contact: Alice Taylor, R.N., MSN, Chief Executive Officer
CFO: Susan Newton, Chief Financial Officer
CHR: Melanie Hatcher, Region Director Human Resources
Web address: www.browardhealth.org
**Control:** Hospital district or authority, Government, nonfederal **Service:** General Medical and Surgical

**Staffed Beds:** 180 **Admissions:** 8302 **Census:** 103 **Outpatient Visits:** 89699
**Births:** 0 **Total Expense ($000):** 104502 **Payroll Expense ($000):** 42292
**Personnel:** 1078

⊠ **BROWARD HEALTH MEDICAL CENTER (100039)**, (Formerly Broward General Medical Center), 1600 South Andrews Avenue, Zip 33316–2510; tel. 954/355–4400, (Includes CHRIS EVERT CHILDRENS HOSPITAL, 1600 South Andrews Avenue, tel. 954/355–4400; Calvin E. Glidewell, Jr., Chief Executive Officer) **A**1 2 5 9 10 12 13 **F**3 11 13 15 17 18 20 22 24 26 28 29 30 31 34 35 40 43 45 48 49 51 53 57 59 60 61 62 63 64 65 66 68 70 71 72 73 74 75 76 77 78 79 80 81 82 83 84 85 87 88 89 93 94 98 100 102 105 107 108 110 111 114 115 116 117 119 120 121 129 130 139 146 **S** Broward Health, Fort Lauderdale, FL
Primary Contact: Calvin E. Glidewell, Jr., Chief Executive Officer
CFO: Mark Doyle, Chief Financial Officer
CMO: Rajiv Chokshi, M.D., Chief of Staff
CIO: Doris Crain, Vice President Information Services
CHR: Dionne Wong, Vice President and Chief Human Resources Officer
Web address: www.browardhealth.org
**Control:** Hospital district or authority, Government, nonfederal **Service:** General Medical and Surgical

**Staffed Beds:** 656 **Admissions:** 29012 **Census:** 416 **Outpatient Visits:** 276345 **Births:** 3394 **Total Expense ($000):** 439642 **Payroll Expense ($000):** 176077 **Personnel:** 2929

☐ **FORT LAUDERDALE HOSPITAL (104026)**, 1601 East Las Olas Boulevard, Zip 33301–2393; tel. 954/463–4321, (Nonreporting) **A**1 9 10 **S** Universal Health Services, Inc., King of Prussia, PA
Primary Contact: Manuel R. Llano, Chief Executive Officer
CFO: Gina Lee, Chief Financial Officer
Web address: www.fortlauderdalehospital.org
**Control:** Corporation, Investor–owned, for–profit **Service:** Psychiatric

**Staffed Beds:** 100

⊠ **HEALTHSOUTH SUNRISE REHABILITATION HOSPITAL (103028)**, 4399 Nob Hill Road, Zip 33351–5899; tel. 954/749–0300 **A**1 10 **F**3 29 62 82 90 91 93 95 96 132 **S** HEALTHSOUTH Corporation, Birmingham, AL
Primary Contact: Kevin R. Conn, Chief Executive Officer
COO: Jay de los Reyes, Chief Operating Officer
CFO: Ruth Goodstein, Controller
CMO: Scott Tannenbaum, M.D., Medical Director
CIO: Angela Manning, Director Health Information Services
CHR: Barbara Dunkiel, Director Human Resources
CNO: Omaira D. Riano, Chief Nursing Officer
Web address: www.healthsouthsunrise.com
**Control:** Corporation, Investor–owned, for–profit **Service:** Rehabilitation

**Staffed Beds:** 126 **Admissions:** 2327 **Census:** 91 **Outpatient Visits:** 30894
**Births:** 0 **Total Expense ($000):** 33911 **Payroll Expense ($000):** 17847
**Personnel:** 358

⊠ **HOLY CROSS HOSPITAL (100073)**, 4725 North Federal Highway, Zip 33308–4668, Mailing Address: P.O. Box 23460, Zip 33307–3460; tel. 954/771–8000, (Nonreporting) **A**1 2 9 10 **S** Catholic Health East, Newtown Square, PA
Primary Contact: Patrick Taylor, M.D., President and Chief Executive Officer
COO: Luisa Gutman, Senior Vice President and Chief Operating Officer
CFO: Linda Wilford, CPA, Senior Vice President and Chief Financial Officer
CMO: Kenneth Homer, M.D., Chief Medical Officer
CIO: Jeff Smith, Chief Information Officer
CHR: Luisa Gutman, Vice President Human Resources
CNO: Margaret Scheaffel, R.N., Vice President and Chief Nursing Officer
Web address: www.holy–cross.com
**Control:** Church–operated, Nongovernment, not–for profit **Service:** General Medical and Surgical

**Staffed Beds:** 571

**IMPERIAL POINT MEDICAL CENTER** See Broward Health Imperial Point

⊠ **KINDRED HOSPITAL SOUTH FLORIDA–FORT LAUDERDALE (102010)**, 1516 East Las Olas Boulevard, Zip 33301–2399; tel. 954/764–8900, (Includes KINDRED HOSPITAL SOUTH FLORIDA–CORAL GABLES, 5190 S.W. Eighth Street, Coral Gables, Zip 33134–2495; tel. 305/445–1364; Charles Doten, Chief Executive Officer; KINDRED HOSPITAL SOUTH FLORIDA–HOLLYWOOD, 1859 Van Buren Street, Hollywood, Zip 33020–5127; tel. 954/920–9000; Craig A. Hoover, Administrator) **A**1 9 10 **F**1 3 29 34 45 46 48 56 70 75 77 82 87 91 92 130 132 148 **S** Kindred Healthcare, Louisville, KY
Primary Contact: Theodore L. Welding, Administrator
CFO: Dean Card, Chief Financial Officer
Web address: www.khfortlauderdale.com/
**Control:** Corporation, Investor–owned, for–profit **Service:** Children's Long–Term Acute Care

**Staffed Beds:** 70 **Admissions:** 637 **Census:** 47 **Outpatient Visits:** 0 **Births:** 0

⊠ **NORTH SHORE MEDICAL CENTER, FLORIDA MEDICAL CENTER CAMPUS (100210)**, (Formerly Florida Medical Center), 5000 West Oakland Park Boulevard, Zip 33313–1585; tel. 954/735–6000, (Nonreporting) **A**1 9 10 **S** TENET Healthcare Corporation, Dallas, TX
Primary Contact: Gabrielle Finley–Hazle, Chief Executive Officer
Web address: www.fmc–campus.com
**Control:** Partnership, Investor–owned, for–profit **Service:** General Medical and Surgical

**Staffed Beds:** 459

**NORTH SHORE MEDICAL CENTER, FLORIDA MEDICAL CENTER CAMPUS** See Florida Medical Center

## FORT MYERS—Lee County

**CHILDREN'S HOSPITAL OF SOUTHWEST FLORIDA** See Lee Memorial Hospital

**FL**

---

**Hospital, Medicare Provider Number, Address, Telephone, Approval, Facility, and Physician Codes, Health Care System**

★ American Hospital Association (AHA) membership
☐ The Joint Commission accreditation
◇ DNV Healthcare Inc. accreditation
○ Healthcare Facilities Accreditation Program
△ Commission on Accreditation of Rehabilitation Facilities (CARF) accreditation

☒ ◇ **GULF COAST MEDICAL CENTER (100220)**, 13681 Doctor's Way, Zip 33912–4300; tel. 239/343–1000 **A**1 9 10 21 **F**3 11 13 17 18 20 22 24 26 28 29 30 40 45 49 60 64 70 74 76 77 79 80 81 84 92 93 107 108 111 113 117 119 130 138 146 **S** Lee Memorial Health System, Fort Myers, FL
Primary Contact: James R. Nathan, President and Chief Executive Officer
COO: Lawrence Antonucci, M.D., Chief Operating Officer
CFO: Mike German, Chief Financial Officer
CMO: Mark Greenberg, M.D., Medical Director
CIO: Mike Smith, Chief Information Officer
CHR: Jon C. Cecil, Chief Human Resource Officer
CNO: Donna Giannuzzi, R.N., Chief Patient Care Officer
Web address: www.leememorial.org
**Control:** Hospital district or authority, Government, nonfederal **Service:** General Medical and Surgical

**Staffed Beds:** 349 **Admissions:** 22620 **Census:** 281 **Outpatient Visits:** 54089 **Births:** 1592

★ △ ◇ **LEE MEMORIAL HOSPITAL (100012)**, 2776 Cleveland Avenue, Zip 33901–5855, Mailing Address: P.O. Box 2218, Zip 33902–2218; tel. 239/332–1111, (Includes CHILDREN'S HOSPITAL OF SOUTHWEST FLORIDA, 9981 South HealthPark Drive, Zip 33908; tel. 239/433–7799; HEALTHPARK MEDICAL CENTER, 9981 South HealthPark Drive, Zip 33908; tel. 239/433–7799; THE REHABILITATION HOSPITAL, 2776 Cleveland Avenue, Zip 33901; tel. 239/332–1111), (Total facility includes 112 beds in nursing home–type unit) **A**2 7 9 10 21 **F**3 11 13 14 15 17 18 19 20 21 22 24 26 28 29 30 31 32 34 35 38 40 41 43 45 48 50 51 53 54 56 57 58 59 61 62 64 65 68 70 72 73 74 75 76 77 78 79 80 81 82 84 85 86 87 88 89 90 93 94 97 98 100 102 103 104 105 106 107 108 110 111 113 114 115 116 117 119 126 128 129 130 131 132 134 135 146 147 148 **S** Lee Memorial Health System, Fort Myers, FL
Primary Contact: James R. Nathan, President and Chief Executive Officer
COO: Lawrence Antonucci, M.D., Chief Operating Officer
CMO: Chuck Krivenko, M.D., Chief Medical Officer, Clinical and Quality Services
CIO: Mike Smith, Chief Information Officer
CHR: Jon C. Cecil, Chief Human Resource Officer
Web address: www.leememorial.org
**Control:** Hospital district or authority, Government, nonfederal **Service:** General Medical and Surgical

**Staffed Beds:** 835 **Admissions:** 39388 **Census:** 634 **Outpatient Visits:** 162646 **Births:** 3530

◇ **PARK ROYAL HOSPITAL (104074)**, 9241 Park Royal Drive, Zip 33908–9204; tel. 239/985–2700, (Nonreporting) **A**9 10 21 **S** Acadia Healthcare Company, Inc., Franklin, TN
Primary Contact: Michael K. Evans, Chief Executive Officer
CFO: Amy Ciampa, Chief Financial Officer
CHR: Robert Raynor, Human Resources Director
Web address: www.ParkRoyalHospital.com
**Control:** Corporation, Investor–owned, for–profit **Service:** Psychiatric

**Staffed Beds:** 76

### FORT PIERCE—St. Lucie County

☒ **LAWNWOOD REGIONAL MEDICAL CENTER (100246)**, 1700 South 23rd Street, Zip 34950–4803; tel. 772/461–4000, (Includes LAWNWOOD PAVILION, 1860 North Lawnwood Circle, Zip 34950, Mailing Address: P.O. Box 1540, Zip 34954–1540; tel. 361/466–1500), (Nonreporting) **A**1 9 10 **S** HCA, Nashville, TN
Primary Contact: Rodney R. Smith, Chief Executive Officer
CFO: Robert Dunwoody, Chief Financial Officer
CIO: Eric Castle, Director Information Services
CHR: Pam Burchell, Director Human Resources
Web address: www.lawnwoodmed.com
**Control:** Corporation, Investor–owned, for–profit **Service:** General Medical and Surgical

**Staffed Beds:** 331

### FORT WALTON BEACH—Okaloosa County

☒ △ **FORT WALTON BEACH MEDICAL CENTER (100223)**, 1000 Mar–Walt Drive, Zip 32547–6795; tel. 850/862–1111, (Nonreporting) **A**1 2 7 9 10 **S** HCA, Nashville, TN
Primary Contact: Mitchell P. Mongell, FACHE, Chief Executive Officer
CFO: Vincent N. Wyatt, Chief Financial Officer
CMO: Colonel Tama Van Decar, M.D., Chief Medical Officer
CIO: Lance Penton, Director Information Technology and Systems
CHR: Anna Garland, Director Human Resources
Web address: www.fwbmc.com
**Control:** Corporation, Investor–owned, for–profit **Service:** General Medical and Surgical

**Staffed Beds:** 257

### GAINESVILLE—Alachua County

☒ **MALCOM RANDALL VETERANS AFFAIRS MEDICAL CENTER**, 1601 S.W. Archer Road, Zip 32608–1197; tel. 352/376–1611, (Total facility includes 33 beds in nursing home–type unit) **A**1 3 5 **F**3 8 9 10 11 15 18 20 24 26 28 29 30 31 33 34 35 38 39 40 45 46 47 48 49 50 51 53 54 56 57 58 59 60 61 62 63 64 65 66 68 70 74 75 77 78 79 81 82 83 84 85 86 87 91 92 93 94 97 98 99 100 101 102 103 104 105 106 107 108 109 111 114 115 116 117 119 127 128 129 130 132 133 135 136 143 144 145 146 147 148 **P**1 3 **S** Department of Veterans Affairs, Washington, DC
Primary Contact: Thomas Wisnieski, FACHE, Director
COO: Thomas Sutton, Associate Director
CFO: Jim Taylor, Chief Business Office
CMO: Brad Bender, M.D., Chief of Staff
CIO: Deborah Michel–Ogborn, Chief Information Resource Management
CHR: Michelle Manderino, Chief Human Resources
Web address: www.northflorida.va.gov/
**Control:** Veterans Affairs, Government, federal **Service:** General Medical and Surgical

**Staffed Beds:** 277 **Admissions:** 7259 **Census:** 117 **Outpatient Visits:** 572570 **Births:** 0 **Personnel:** 3252

☒ **NORTH FLORIDA REGIONAL MEDICAL CENTER (100204)**, 6500 Newberry Road, Zip 32605–4392, Mailing Address: P.O. Box 147006, Zip 32614–7006; tel. 352/333–4000, (Nonreporting) **A**1 2 9 10 **S** HCA, Nashville, TN
Primary Contact: Ward Boston, III, Chief Executive Officer
COO: Matt Davis, Chief Operating Officer
CFO: Eric Lawson, Chief Financial Officer
CIO: Deborah Bush, Director Information Services
CHR: William Coorpender, Assistant Vice President Human Resources
Web address: www.nfrmc.com
**Control:** Corporation, Investor–owned, for–profit **Service:** General Medical and Surgical

**Staffed Beds:** 349

☒ **SELECT SPECIALTY HOSPITAL–GAINESVILLE (102022)**, 2708 S.W. Archer Road, Zip 32608–1316; tel. 352/337–3240, (Nonreporting) **A**1 9 10 **S** Select Medical Corporation, Mechanicsburg, PA
Primary Contact: Cheryl Hayes, Chief Executive Officer
Web address: www.selectspecialtyhospitals.com/company/locations/gainesville.aspx
**Control:** Corporation, Investor–owned, for–profit **Service:** Long–Term Acute Care hospital

**Staffed Beds:** 44

☒ △ **SHANDS AT THE UNIVERSITY OF FLORIDA (100113)**, 1600 S.W. Archer Road, Zip 32610–3003, Mailing Address: P.O. Box 100326, Zip 32610–0326; tel. 352/265–0111, (Includes SHANDS CANCER HOSPITAL, 1515 S.W. Archer Road, Zip 32608–1134; tel. 352/265–0111; SHANDS HOSPITAL FOR CHILDREN, 1600 S.W. Archer Road, Mailing Address: P.O. Box 100335, Zip 32610–0335; tel. 352/265–0111; SHANDS REHAB HOSPITAL, 4101 N.W. 89th Boulevard, Zip 32606–3813; tel. 352/265–5499; Marina T. Cecchini, Administrator; SHANDS VISTA, 4101 N.W. 89th Boulevard, Zip 32606, Mailing Address: P.O. Box 24059, Zip 32602; tel. 352/265–5491; Marina T. Cecchini, Administrator) **A**1 2 3 5 7 8 9 10 **F**2 3 4 5 6 7 8 9 11 12 13 15 16 17 18 19 20 21 22 23 24 25 26 27 29 30 31 32 34 35 36 37 38 39 40 41 43 44 45 46 47 48 49 50 51 52 53 54 55 56 57 58 59 60 61 62 64 65 66 68 69 70 72 73 74 75 76 77 78 79 80 81 82 84 85 86 87 88 89 90 91 93 94 96 97 98 99 100 101 102 103 104 105 107 108 109 110 111 114 115 116 117 118 119 120 121 123 124 126 129 130 131 132 134 135 136 137 138 139 140 141 142 143 144 145 146 147 148 **P**6 **S** Shands HealthCare, Gainesville, FL
Primary Contact: Timothy M. Goldfarb, Chief Executive Officer
CFO: William J. Robinson, Senior Vice President and Treasurer
CMO: Timothy C. Flynn, M.D., Chief of Staff
CIO: Kari Cassel, Senior Vice President and Chief Information Officer
CHR: Janet L. Christie, Senior Vice President Human Resources
Web address: www.shands.org
**Control:** Other not–for–profit (including NFP Corporation) **Service:** General Medical and Surgical

**Staffed Beds:** 946 **Admissions:** 41669 **Census:** 737 **Outpatient Visits:** 792099 **Births:** 2899 **Total Expense ($000):** 1084244 **Payroll Expense ($000):** 373562 **Personnel:** 7221

**SHANDS REHAB HOSPITAL** See Shands at the University of Florida

### GRACEVILLE—Jackson County

**CAMPBELLTON GRACEVILLE HOSPITAL (101302)**, 5429 College Drive, Zip 32440–1897; tel. 850/263–4431 **A**9 10 18 **F**3 28 29 30 34 35 40 54 59 63 64 65 67 77 83 84 94 97 107 119 127 128 130 133 135 148
Primary Contact: Jimmy Rigsby, Chief Executive Officer
CFO: Dena Cooper, Chief Financial Officer
CMO: Steve Davis, M.D., Chief Medical Officer
CHR: Judy Austin, Director Human Resources
Web address: www.pahn.org/cgh.cfm
**Control:** Hospital district or authority, Government, nonfederal **Service:** General Medical and Surgical

**Staffed Beds:** 25 **Admissions:** 215 **Census:** 2 **Outpatient Visits:** 5129 **Births:** 0 **Total Expense ($000):** 6224 **Payroll Expense ($000):** 4472 **Personnel:** 93

*Many Facility Codes have changed. Please refer to the AHA Guide Code Chart.*

© 2013 AHA Guide

FL

## GREEN COVE SPRINGS—Clay County

☒ **KINDRED HOSPITAL NORTH FLORIDA (102015)**, 801 Oak Street, Zip 32043–4317; tel. 904/284–9230, (Nonreporting) **A**1 9 10 **S** Kindred Healthcare, Louisville, KY
Primary Contact: Hoyt Ross, Chief Executive Officer
CFO: Dean Cocchi, Chief Financial Officer
CFO: Steve Hart, Controller
CMO: Lionel J. Gatien, D.O., Chief of Staff
CIO: Rick Chapman, Chief Information Officer
CNO: Susan Drago, R.N., Chief Clinical Officer
Web address: www.khnorthflorida.com
**Control:** Corporation, Investor–owned, for–profit **Service:** Long–Term Acute Care hospital

**Staffed Beds:** 80

## GULF BREEZE—Santa Rosa County

☒ **GULF BREEZE HOSPITAL (100266)**, 1110 Gulf Breeze Parkway, Zip 32561–4884; tel. 850/934–2000 **A**1 9 10 **F**3 8 11 15 29 30 31 40 44 45 46 50 54 57 59 64 68 70 74 75 78 79 81 85 86 93 107 108 111 114 119 120 121 123 129 130 131 132 143 146 147 **P**4 6 **S** Baptist Health Care Corporation, Pensacola, FL
Primary Contact: Robert Harriman, M.D., Administrator
CFO: Kerry Vermillion, Senior Vice President Finance and Chief Financial Officer
Web address: www.ebaptisthealthcare.org/GulfBreezeHospital/
**Control:** Other not–for–profit (including NFP Corporation) **Service:** General Medical and Surgical

**Staffed Beds:** 77 **Admissions:** 4417 **Census:** 44 **Outpatient Visits:** 114115 **Births:** 0 **Total Expense ($000):** 85010 **Payroll Expense ($000):** 23447 **Personnel:** 463

## HIALEAH—Miami–Dade County

☒ **HIALEAH HOSPITAL (100053)**, 651 East 25th Street, Zip 33013–3878; tel. 305/693–6100 **A**1 9 10 **F**3 12 13 15 18 24 29 31 34 40 41 49 56 57 59 60 61 68 70 72 74 76 77 79 81 82 85 93 107 111 115 119 126 130 132 147 148 **S** TENET Healthcare Corporation, Dallas, TX
Primary Contact: Ben A. Rodriguez, Chief Executive Officer
COO: Patrick Downes, Chief Operating Officer
CFO: Arthur West, Chief Financial Officer
CHR: Yamila Castro, Director Human Resources
Web address: www.hialeahhosp.com
**Control:** Corporation, Investor–owned, for–profit **Service:** General Medical and Surgical

**Staffed Beds:** 160 **Admissions:** 11292 **Census:** 152 **Births:** 1252 **Personnel:** 577

☐ **PALM SPRINGS GENERAL HOSPITAL (100050)**, 1475 West 49th Street, Zip 33012–3275, Mailing Address: P.O. Box 2804, Zip 33012–2804; tel. 305/558–2500, (Nonreporting) **A**1 10
Primary Contact: George Caballo, Chief Executive Officer
CFO: Tony Milian, Chief Financial Officer
CHR: Lourdes Anton, Director Human Resources
**Control:** Corporation, Investor–owned, for–profit **Service:** General Medical and Surgical

**Staffed Beds:** 190

☒ **PALMETTO GENERAL HOSPITAL (100187)**, 2001 West 68th Street, Zip 33016–1898; tel. 305/823–5000, (Nonreporting) **A**1 9 10 12 13 **S** TENET Healthcare Corporation, Dallas, TX
Primary Contact: Ana J. Mederos, Chief Executive Officer
COO: Georgina Diaz, Chief Operating Officer
CFO: Oscar Vicente, Chief Financial Officer
CMO: Eloy Roman, M.D., Chief of Staff
CHR: Ana Gonzalez–Fajardo, Human Resources Director
Web address: www.palmettogeneral.com
**Control:** Corporation, Investor–owned, for–profit **Service:** General Medical and Surgical

**Staffed Beds:** 360

**SOUTHERN WINDS HOSPITAL** See Westchester General Hospital, Miami

## HOLLYWOOD—Broward County

☐ **HOLLYWOOD PAVILION (104015)**, 1201 North 37th Avenue, Zip 33021–5498; tel. 954/962–1355, (Nonreporting) **A**1 9 10
Primary Contact: Karen Kallen–Zury, Chief Executive Officer
COO: Christopher Gabel, Chief Operating Officer
CFO: Rocky Davidson, Chief Financial Officer
CHR: Len Alpert, Director Human Resources
Web address: www.hollywoodpavilion.com
**Control:** Corporation, Investor–owned, for–profit **Service:** Psychiatric

**Staffed Beds:** 46

☒ △ **MEMORIAL REGIONAL HOSPITAL (100038)**, 3501 Johnson Street, Zip 33021–5421; tel. 954/987–2000 **A**1 2 3 5 7 9 10 **F**3 4 5 7 8 11 12 13 15 16 17 18 19 20 21 22 23 24 25 26 27 28 29 30 31 34 35 36 37 38 39 40 41 42 43 44 45 46 47 49 50 51 53 54 55 56 57 58 59 60 61 62 64 65 66 67 68 70 71 72 73 74 75 76 77 78 79 80 81 82 84 85 87 88 89 90 93 96 97 98 99 100 101 102 103 104 105 107 108 110 111 113 118 119 120 121 123 130 131 132 134 135 137 145 146 147 148 **S** Memorial Healthcare System, Hollywood, FL
Primary Contact: Zeff Ross, FACHE, Senior Vice President and Chief Executive Officer
COO: Angeline M. Marano, Chief Operating Officer
CFO: David Smith, Chief Financial Officer
CMO: Stanley Marks, M.D., Chief Medical Officer
CIO: Forest Blanton, Administrator Process Engineering
CHR: Ray Kendrick, Chief Human Resources Officer
CNO: Maggie Hansen, R.N., Chief Nursing Officer
Web address: www.mhs.net
**Control:** Hospital district or authority, Government, nonfederal **Service:** General Medical and Surgical

**Staffed Beds:** 757 **Admissions:** 30840 **Census:** 463 **Outpatient Visits:** 374431 **Births:** 4272 **Total Expense ($000):** 642702 **Payroll Expense ($000):** 265104 **Personnel:** 4069

★ △ **MEMORIAL REGIONAL HOSPITAL SOUTH**, 3600 Washington Street, Zip 33021–8216; tel. 954/966–4500, (Includes JOE DIMAGGIO CHILDREN'S HOSPITAL, 1000 Joe DiMaggio Drive, Zip 33021–5426; tel. 954/987–2000; Chantal Leconte, Chief Executive Officer), (Nonreporting) **A**7 9 10 **S** Memorial Healthcare System, Hollywood, FL
Primary Contact: Douglas Zaren, FACHE, Administrator
CFO: Veronica Bautista, Chief Financial Officer
CHR: Vivian Sandler, Director Human Resources
Web address: www.memorialregionalsouth.com
**Control:** Hospital district or authority, Government, nonfederal **Service:** General Medical and Surgical

**Staffed Beds:** 280

☐ **SOUTH FLORIDA STATE HOSPITAL (104001)**, 800 East Cypress Drive, Zip 33025–4543; tel. 954/392–3000, (Nonreporting) **A**1 10
Primary Contact: Lee Packett, Administrator
Web address: www.sfsh.org
**Control:** State–Government, nonfederal **Service:** Psychiatric

**Staffed Beds:** 355

## HOMESTEAD—Miami–Dade County

☒ **BAPTIST HEALTH SOUTH FLORIDA, HOMESTEAD HOSPITAL (100125)**, 975 Baptist Way, Zip 33033–7600; tel. 786/243–8000 **A**1 9 10 **F**3 11 13 15 18 29 30 31 34 35 40 41 45 47 49 50 51 53 57 59 60 61 63 64 68 70 74 75 76 78 79 81 82 84 85 86 87 89 93 102 107 108 110 111 114 115 119 129 130 131 132 134 135 145 146 147 148 **S** Baptist Health South Florida, Coral Gables, FL
Primary Contact: Bill Duquette, Chief Executive Officer
COO: Kenneth R. Spell, Vice President Operations
CFO: Erik Long, Controller
CMO: Steven Fletcher, M.D., Chief of Staff
CIO: Mimi Taylor, Corporate Vice President Information Technology
CHR: Corey Heller, Corporate Vice President and Chief Human Resources Officer
CNO: Nancy Gail Gordon, R.N., CNO and VP of Nursing
Web address: www.baptisthealth.net
**Control:** Other not–for–profit (including NFP Corporation) **Service:** General Medical and Surgical

**Staffed Beds:** 142 **Admissions:** 9810 **Census:** 90 **Outpatient Visits:** 114867 **Births:** 1458 **Total Expense ($000):** 185836 **Payroll Expense ($000):** 70688 **Personnel:** 1107

FL

---

**Hospital, Medicare Provider Number, Address, Telephone, Approval, Facility, and Physician Codes, Health Care System**

★ American Hospital Association (AHA) membership
☐ The Joint Commission accreditation
◇ DNV Healthcare Inc. accreditation
○ Healthcare Facilities Accreditation Program
△ Commission on Accreditation of Rehabilitation Facilities (CARF) accreditation

## HUDSON—Pasco County

☒ **REGIONAL MEDICAL CENTER–BAYONET POINT (100256)**, 14000 Fivay Road, Zip 34667–7199; tel. 727/869–5400, (Nonreporting) **A**1 2 9 10 **S** HCA, Nashville, TN
Primary Contact: Shayne George, Chief Executive Officer
COO: Shalin Shah, Chief Operating Officer
CFO: Thomas Lawhorne, Chief Financial Officer
CMO: Joseph Pino, M.D., Chief Medical Officer
CIO: Stephen Goldstein, Director Information Systems
CHR: Douglas B. Goodman, Vice President
CHR: Patrick Kerrwood, Vice President Human Resources
Web address: www.rmchealth.com
**Control:** Corporation, Investor–owned, for–profit **Service:** General Medical and Surgical

Staffed Beds: 290

## INVERNESS—Citrus County

☒ **CITRUS MEMORIAL HEALTH SYSTEM (100023)**, 502 West Highland Boulevard, Zip 34452–4754; tel. 352/726–1551 **A**1 9 10 19 **F**8 11 15 18 20 22 24 28 29 30 31 34 35 40 44 45 46 47 48 49 50 54 57 59 60 61 62 64 68 70 75 76 77 78 79 81 85 86 89 93 97 107 108 110 111 114 115 118 119 129 130 132 135 144 146 147 148 **P**6
Primary Contact: Ryan D. Beaty, President and Chief Executive Officer
COO: Jerrald Deloach, Chief Operating Officer
CFO: Mark Williams, Chief Financial Officer
CMO: Ralph Abadier, M.D., Chief of Staff
CIO: Tyler Whetstine, Director of Information Systems
CHR: Lee Glotzback, Director Human Resources
CNO: Linda M. McCarthy, R.N., VP/ Chief Nursing Officer
Web address: www.citrusmh.com
**Control:** Other not–for–profit (including NFP Corporation) **Service:** General Medical and Surgical

Staffed Beds: 198 Admissions: 10325 Census: 118 Outpatient Visits: 184917 Births: 574 Total Expense ($000): 155760 Payroll Expense ($000): 58739 Personnel: 1144

## JACKSONVILLE—Duval County

☒ **BAPTIST MEDICAL CENTER JACKSONVILLE (100088)**, (Formerly Baptist Medical Center), 800 Prudential Drive, Zip 32207–8202; tel. 904/202–2000, (Includes BAPTIST MEDICAL CENTER SOUTH, 14550 St. Augustine Road, Zip 32258–2160; tel. 904/821–6000; Ronald G. Robinson, Administrator; WOLFSON CHILDREN'S HOSPITAL, 800 Prudential Drive, Zip 32207; tel. 904/202–8000; Michael D. Aubin, President) **A**1 2 3 5 9 10 **F**3 5 8 11 12 13 15 17 18 19 20 21 22 23 24 25 26 27 28 30 31 32 34 35 36 37 38 39 40 41 45 46 47 48 49 50 51 53 55 56 57 58 59 60 61 62 64 68 70 72 73 74 75 76 78 79 80 81 82 83 85 87 88 89 92 93 94 98 99 100 101 102 103 104 105 107 108 109 110 111 112 113 114 115 116 117 118 119 120 121 123 124 126 129 130 132 134 135 136 146 147 148 **P**6 **S** Baptist Health, Jacksonville, FL
Primary Contact: Michael A. Mayo, FACHE, President
COO: John F. Wilbanks, FACHE, Chief Operating Officer
CFO: Mike Lukaszewski, Chief Financial Officer
CMO: Keith L. Stein, M.D., Senior Vice President Medical Affairs and Chief Medical Officer
CIO: Roland Garcia, Senior Vice President and Chief Information Officer
CHR: M. Beth Mehaffey, Vice President Human Resources
Web address: www.e-baptisthealth.com
**Control:** Other not–for–profit (including NFP Corporation) **Service:** General Medical and Surgical

Staffed Beds: 844 Admissions: 39762 Census: 543 Outpatient Visits: 438005 Births: 4096 Total Expense ($000): 789834 Payroll Expense ($000): 246038 Personnel: 5464

☒ △ **BROOKS REHABILITATION HOSPITAL (103039)**, 3599 University Boulevard South, Zip 32216–4252; tel. 904/345–7600 **A**1 7 9 10 **F**29 30 54 62 64 90 91 93 95 96 130 132 146
Primary Contact: Douglas Baer, Chief Executive Officer
COO: Michael Spigel, Executive Vice President & Chief Operating Officer
CFO: Douglas Baer, Chief Executive Officer
CMO: Trevor Paris, M.D., Medical Director
CIO: Karen Green, Chief Information Officer
CHR: Karen Gallagher, Vice President Human Resources and Learning
CNO: Joanne Hoertz, Vice President of Nursing
Web address: www.brookshealth.org
**Control:** Other not–for–profit (including NFP Corporation) **Service:** Rehabilitation

Staffed Beds: 140 Admissions: 3129 Census: 130 Outpatient Visits: 226087 Births: 0 Total Expense ($000): 72286 Payroll Expense ($000): 29128 Personnel: 383

☒ **MAYO CLINIC JACKSONVILLE (100151)**, 4500 San Pablo Road South, Zip 32224–1865; tel. 904/953–2000 **A**1 2 3 5 8 9 10 **F**3 6 9 12 15 17 18 20 22 24 26 28 29 30 31 34 35 37 40 45 46 47 48 49 50 51 54 55 56 57 58 59 60 64 65 68 70 74 75 77 78 79 81 82 84 85 86 87 92 93 96 97 100 107 108 110 111 112 114 115 116 117 118 119 120 121 123 124 126 129 130 131 132 135 136 137 138 139 140 141 142 145 146 147 148 **P**6
**S** Mayo Clinic Health System, Rochester, MN
Primary Contact: Hilary G. Mathews, MS, R.N., Administrator
COO: Hilary G. Mathews, MS, Administrator
CFO: Mary Hoffman, Chief Financial Officer
CMO: Nancy Dawson, M.D., Medical Director
CIO: Cheryl Croft, Chairman Information Services
CHR: Daniel Tomlinson, Chair Human Resources
CNO: Debra Harrison, MS, Chief Nursing Officer
Web address: www.mayoclinic.org
**Control:** Other not–for–profit (including NFP Corporation) **Service:** General Medical and Surgical

Staffed Beds: 214 Admissions: 12547 Census: 176 Outpatient Visits: 48508 Births: 0 Total Expense ($000): 354903 Payroll Expense ($000): 74868 Personnel: 1616

☒ **MEMORIAL HOSPITAL JACKSONVILLE (100179)**, 3625 University Boulevard South, Zip 32216–4207, Mailing Address: P.O. Box 16325, Zip 32245–6325; tel. 904/399–6111, (Nonreporting) **A**1 2 9 10 **S** HCA, Nashville, TN
Primary Contact: James F. O'Loughlin, President and Chief Executive Officer
CFO: Ashley F. Johnson, Chief Financial Officer
CMO: Gary Winfield, M.D., Medical Director
CHR: Laura DeMotte, Vice President Human Resources
Web address: www.memorialhospitaljax.com
**Control:** Corporation, Investor–owned, for–profit **Service:** General Medical and Surgical

Staffed Beds: 425

☒ **NAVAL HOSPITAL JACKSONVILLE**, (Formerly Naval Hospital), 2080 Child Street, Zip 32214–5000; tel. 904/542–7300, (Nonreporting) **A**1 3 5 **S** Bureau of Medicine and Surgery, Department of the Navy, Washington, DC
Primary Contact: Captain Ruby Tennyson, Director Administration
CFO: Lieutenant Commander Michael Gregonis, Comptroller
CMO: Captain Christopher Quarles, M.D., Director Medical Services
CIO: Mike Haytaian, Head Director Information Resources Management
CHR: Captain Ruby Tennyson, Director Administration
Web address: www.med.navy.mil/SITES/NAVALHOSPITALJAX/Pages/default.aspx
**Control:** Navy, Government, federal **Service:** General Medical and Surgical

Staffed Beds: 64

☐ **RIVER POINT BEHAVIORAL HEALTH (104016)**, 6300 Beach Boulevard, Zip 32216–2782; tel. 904/724–9202, (Nonreporting) **A**1 9 10 **S** Universal Health Services, Inc., King of Prussia, PA
Primary Contact: Gayle Eckerd, Chief Executive Officer
CFO: Jenni Stackhouse, Chief Financial Officer
CIO: Bill Willis, Director Information Technology
CHR: Cathy Calhoun, Director Human Resources
Web address: www.riverpointbehavioral.com
**Control:** Corporation, Investor–owned, for–profit **Service:** Psychiatric

Staffed Beds: 92

☒ **SHANDS JACKSONVILLE MEDICAL CENTER (100001)**, 655 West Eighth Street, Zip 32209–6595; tel. 904/244–0411, (Total facility includes 56 beds in nursing home–type unit) **A**1 2 3 5 8 9 10 **F**3 5 8 11 12 13 15 17 18 19 20 22 24 25 26 28 29 30 31 32 33 34 35 36 37 38 39 40 41 43 44 45 46 47 49 50 51 52 53 54 56 57 58 59 60 61 62 64 65 66 68 70 71 72 73 74 75 76 77 78 79 80 81 82 84 85 86 87 88 89 92 93 94 96 97 98 99 100 101 102 103 104 105 107 108 109 110 111 114 115 116 117 118 119 120 121 123 124 126 128 129 130 131 132 134 135 141 145 146 147 148 **S** Shands HealthCare, Gainesville, FL
Primary Contact: Russell Armistead, Chief Executive Officer
COO: Greg Miller, Senior Vice President Operations
CFO: Mike Gleason, Vice President and Chief Financial Officer
CMO: David Vukich, M.D., Senior Vice President, Chief Medical Officer and Chief Quality Officer
CIO: Kari Cassel, Senior Vice President and Chief Information Officer
CHR: Lesli Ward, Vice President Human Resources
Web address: www.shandsjacksonville.org
**Control:** Other not–for–profit (including NFP Corporation) **Service:** General Medical and Surgical

Staffed Beds: 620 Admissions: 26476 Census: 435 Outpatient Visits: 386758 Births: 2999 Total Expense ($000): 539515 Payroll Expense ($000): 194372 Personnel: 3727

**FL**

*Many Facility Codes have changed. Please refer to the AHA Guide Code Chart.*          © 2013 AHA Guide

⊠ **SPECIALTY HOSPITAL JACKSONVILLE (102012)**, 4901 Richard Street, Zip 32207–7328; tel. 904/737–3120, (Nonreporting) **A**1 9 10 **S** HCA, Nashville, TN
Primary Contact: Barbara Walsh, Chief Executive Officer
CFO: Billy Wilcox, Chief Financial Officer
CMO: Wendell H. Williams, Jr., M.D., Medical Director
CIO: Liz Rhodes, Director Information Services
CHR: Lisa Ayala, R.N., Director Human Resources
Web address: www.specialtyhospitaljax.com
**Control:** Corporation, Investor–owned, for–profit **Service:** Long–Term Acute Care hospital

| Staffed Beds: 62 |
| --- |

⊠ **ST. VINCENT'S MEDICAL CENTER RIVERSIDE (100040)**, 1 Shircliff Way, Zip 32204–4748, Mailing Address: P.O. Box 2982, Zip 32203–2982; tel. 904/308–7300 **A**1 2 3 5 9 10 13 **F**3 12 13 15 17 18 20 22 24 26 28 29 30 31 34 35 38 40 45 46 47 48 49 50 51 53 54 56 57 58 59 60 61 64 65 66 68 70 71 72 74 75 76 78 79 81 84 85 86 87 93 94 96 97 107 108 110 111 114 115 116 117 118 119 120 121 123 124 126 129 130 131 132 133 135 143 146 147 148 **S** Ascension Health, Saint Louis, MO
Primary Contact: Moody L. Chisholm, President & Chief Executive Officer
COO: Donnie Romine, Chief Operating Officer
CFO: Mark Doyle, Chief Financial Officer
CMO: Phil Perry, M.D., Chief Medical Officer
CIO: Ann Carey, Vice President and Chief Information Officer
CHR: Janice G. Lipsky, R.N., System Vice President Human Resources and Organizational Development
CNO: Rose Rivers, R.N., Chief Nursing Officer
Web address: www.jaxhealth.com
**Control:** Church–operated, Nongovernment, not–for profit **Service:** General Medical and Surgical

| Staffed Beds: 501 Admissions: 27420 Census: 339 Outpatient Visits: 144446 Births: 1708 Total Expense ($000): 394524 Payroll Expense ($000): 123467 Personnel: 2390 |
| --- |

⊠ **ST. VINCENT'S MEDICAL CENTER SOUTHSIDE (100307)**, 4201 Belfort Road, Zip 32216–1431; tel. 904/296–3700 **A**1 3 5 9 10 **F**3 12 13 15 18 20 22 26 29 30 31 34 35 37 40 44 45 47 49 51 57 59 60 64 65 70 72 74 75 76 78 79 81 82 85 86 87 93 96 107 108 110 111 114 115 119 126 128 129 130 131 132 143 146 147 148 **S** Ascension Health, Saint Louis, MO
Primary Contact: Moody L. Chisholm, President and Chief Executive Officer
COO: Donnie Romine, Chief Operating Officer
CFO: Mark Doyle, Chief Financial Officer
CMO: Phil Perry, M.D., Chief Medical Officer
CIO: Beth Fagin, Manager Information Systems
CHR: Edwina Coulliette, Manager Human Resources
CNO: Lorraine Keith, FACHE, Chief Nursing Officer
Web address: www.jaxhealth.com
**Control:** Church–operated, Nongovernment, not–for profit **Service:** General Medical and Surgical

| Staffed Beds: 269 Admissions: 11796 Census: 152 Outpatient Visits: 37170 Births: 1304 Total Expense ($000): 169079 Payroll Expense ($000): 46692 Personnel: 834 |
| --- |

☐ **WEKIVA SPRINGS CENTER FOR WOMEN (104069)**, 3947 Salisbury Road, Zip 32216–6115; tel. 904/296–3533, (Nonreporting) **A**1 9 10 **S** Universal Health Services, Inc., King of Prussia, PA
Primary Contact: Gayle Eckerd, Chief Executive Officer
Web address: www.wekivacenter.com
**Control:** Other not–for–profit (including NFP Corporation) **Service:** Psychiatric

| Staffed Beds: 60 |
| --- |

### JACKSONVILLE BEACH—Duval County

⊠ **BAPTIST MEDICAL CENTER BEACHES (100117)**, 1350 13th Avenue South, Zip 32250–3205; tel. 904/627–2900 **A**1 9 10 **F**3 8 11 13 15 18 28 29 30 31 36 40 43 45 49 50 53 54 57 59 61 64 74 75 76 77 78 79 80 81 82 85 86 93 107 108 110 111 114 115 118 119 129 130 146 147 148 **S** Baptist Health, Jacksonville, FL
Primary Contact: Joseph M. Mitrick, FACHE, President
COO: John F. Wilbanks, FACHE, Chief Operating Officer
CFO: Mike Lukaszewski, Chief Financial Officer
CMO: Keith L. Stein, M.D., Chief Medical Officer
CIO: Roland Garcia, Senior Vice President and Chief Information Officer
CHR: Dana Voiselle, Director Human Resources
Web address: www.community.e–baptisthealth.com/bmc/beaches/index.html
**Control:** Other not–for–profit (including NFP Corporation) **Service:** General Medical and Surgical

| Staffed Beds: 136 Admissions: 7409 Census: 82 Outpatient Visits: 90767 Births: 1104 Total Expense ($000): 98783 Payroll Expense ($000): 34314 Personnel: 690 |
| --- |

### JAY—Santa Rosa County

★ **JAY HOSPITAL (100048)**, 14114 South Alabama Street, Zip 32565–1219; tel. 850/675–8000 **A**9 10 **F**3 11 15 18 29 30 34 35 40 45 46 48 49 50 57 59 64 75 77 81 82 85 93 107 114 119 130 132 133 135 146 147 **S** Baptist Health Care Corporation, Pensacola, FL
Primary Contact: Michael T. Hutchins, Administrator
CFO: Keith Strickling, Chief Accountant
CMO: Marian Stewart, M.D., Chief of Staff
CHR: Chanda Gay, Manager Human Resources
Web address: www.bhcpns.org/jayhospital/
**Control:** Other not–for–profit (including NFP Corporation) **Service:** General Medical and Surgical

| Staffed Beds: 49 Admissions: 629 Census: 10 Outpatient Visits: 21378 Births: 0 Total Expense ($000): 10900 Payroll Expense ($000): 4758 Personnel: 96 |
| --- |

### JUPITER—Palm Beach County

⊠ **JUPITER MEDICAL CENTER (100253)**, 1210 South Old Dixie Highway, Zip 33458–7299; tel. 561/747–2234, (Total facility includes 120 beds in nursing home–type unit) **A**1 2 9 10 **F**3 11 12 13 15 18 20 28 29 30 31 34 35 37 40 47 48 49 50 53 54 55 57 58 59 68 70 71 74 75 76 77 78 79 80 81 82 84 85 86 87 93 107 108 109 110 111 114 115 116 117 118 119 120 121 123 126 129 130 132 135 143 146 147 148 **P**4
Primary Contact: John D. Couris, President and Chief Executive Officer
CFO: Stephen J. Grigsby, Chief Financial Officer
CIO: Mike Fehr, Vice President Operations and Chief Information Officer
CHR: John Wolf, Chief Human Resources Officer
Web address: www.jupitermed.com
**Control:** Other not–for–profit (including NFP Corporation) **Service:** General Medical and Surgical

| Staffed Beds: 283 Admissions: 10243 Census: 209 Outpatient Visits: 127760 Births: 1084 Total Expense ($000): 186458 Payroll Expense ($000): 73669 Personnel: 1291 |
| --- |

### KEY WEST—Monroe County

☐ **LOWER KEYS MEDICAL CENTER (100150)**, 5900 College Road, Zip 33040–4396, Mailing Address: P.O. Box 9107, Zip 33041 9107; tel. 305/294–5531, (Includes DE POO HOSPITAL, 1200 Kennedy Drive, Zip 33041; tel. 305/294–4692), (Nonreporting) **A**1 9 10 **S** Health Management Associates, Naples, FL
Primary Contact: Nicki L. Will–Mowery, Ph.D., Chief Executive Officer
COO: Meylan Love–Watler, Chief Operating Officer
CFO: Dale Guffey, Chief Financial Officer
CMO: Jerome Covington, M.D., Chief Medical Officer
CIO: Les Jackson, Manager Information Systems
CHR: Donald Canalejo, Director Human Resources
Web address: www.lkmc.com
**Control:** Corporation, Investor–owned, for–profit **Service:** General Medical and Surgical

| Staffed Beds: 90 |
| --- |

### KISSIMMEE—Osceola County

**FLORIDA HOSPITAL KISSIMMEE** See Florida Hospital, Orlando

⊠ **OSCEOLA REGIONAL MEDICAL CENTER (100110)**, 700 West Oak Street, Zip 34741–4996; tel. 407/846–2266, (Nonreporting) **A**1 2 5 9 10 **S** HCA, Nashville, TN
Primary Contact: Robert M. Krieger, Chief Executive Officer
COO: David Cashwell, Chief Operating Officer
CFO: Glenn Romig, Chief Financial Officer
CMO: Aida Sanchez–Jimenez, M.D., Chief Medical Officer
CHR: Sylvia Lollis, Director Human Resources
CNO: Sonya Quintana, R.N., Chief Nursing Officer
Web address: www.osceolaregional.com
**Control:** Corporation, Investor–owned, for–profit **Service:** General Medical and Surgical

| Staffed Beds: 235 |
| --- |

FL

---

**Hospital, Medicare Provider Number, Address, Telephone, Approval, Facility, and Physician Codes, Health Care System**

★ American Hospital Association (AHA) membership
☐ The Joint Commission accreditation
◇ DNV Healthcare Inc. accreditation
○ Healthcare Facilities Accreditation Program
△ Commission on Accreditation of Rehabilitation Facilities (CARF) accreditation

## LAKE BUTLER—Union County

**LAKE BUTLER HOSPITAL HAND SURGERY CENTER (101303)**, 850 East Main Street, Zip 32054–1353, Mailing Address: P.O. Box 748, Zip 32054–0748; tel. 386/496–2323, (Nonreporting) **A**9 10 18
Primary Contact: Pamela B. Howard, R.N., Administrator
CFO: Paula Webb, Chief Financial Officer
CMO: Cynthia Larimer, M.D., Medical Director Emergency Room
CIO: Jennifer Thomas, Director Public Relations
CHR: Diane Cason, Supervisor Personnel and Payroll
CNO: Johnette Davis, Director of Nursing
Web address: www.lakebutlerhospital.com
**Control:** Corporation, Investor–owned, for–profit **Service:** General Medical and Surgical

**Staffed Beds: 25**

**RECEPTION AND MEDICAL CENTER**, State Road 231 South, Zip 32054, Mailing Address: P.O. Box 628, Zip 32054–0628; tel. 386/496–6000 **F**3 29 30 31 38 39 54 59 61 65 78 85 97 100 101 102 103 104 130 143 144 148
Primary Contact: Herbert L. Hall, Administrator
Web address: www.dc.state.fl.us
**Control:** State–Government, nonfederal **Service:** Hospital unit of an institution (prison hospital, college infimary, etc.)

**Staffed Beds: 120 Admissions: 1706 Census: 79 Outpatient Visits: 24799 Births: 0 Personnel: 101**

## LAKE CITY—Columbia County

⊠ **LAKE CITY MEDICAL CENTER (100156)**, 340 N.W. Commerce Drive, Zip 32055–4709; tel. 386/719–9000, (Nonreporting) **A**1 9 10 **S** HCA, Nashville, TN
Primary Contact: Mark Robinson, FACHE, Chief Executive Officer
COO: Jennifer B. Adams, Chief Operating Officer and Chief Financial Officer
CFO: Jennifer B. Adams, Chief Operating Officer and Chief Financial Officer
CMO: Miguel Tepedino, M.D., Chief Medicine
CIO: Taylor Dickerson, Chief Information Officer
CHR: Steve Gordon, Director Human Resources
CNO: Barbara Kinder, R.N., Chief Nursing Officer
Web address: www.lakecitymedical.com
**Control:** Corporation, Investor–owned, for–profit **Service:** General Medical and Surgical

**Staffed Beds: 67**

★ △ **LAKE CITY VETERANS AFFAIRS MEDICAL CENTER**, (Formerly Veterans Affairs Medical Center), 619 South Marion Avenue, Zip 32025–5898; tel. 386/755–3016, (Total facility includes 230 beds in nursing home–type unit) **A**7 **F**1 3 5 6 8 18 28 29 30 31 33 35 38 39 40 45 46 54 56 57 58 59 61 62 63 65 66 68 70 75 77 78 81 82 83 84 85 86 87 91 93 94 97 100 101 102 103 104 106 107 111 114 115 119 127 130 132 135 143 144 146 147 148 **S** Department of Veterans Affairs, Washington, DC
Primary Contact: Thomas Wisnieski, FACHE, Director
CIO: James Hudson, Assistant Chief Information Resource Management
Web address: www.northflorida.va.gov/
**Control:** Veterans Affairs, Government, federal **Service:** General Medical and Surgical

**Staffed Beds: 277 Admissions: 1282 Census: 18 Outpatient Visits: 198211 Births: 0 Personnel: 1015**

☐ **SHANDS LAKE SHORE REGIONAL MEDICAL CENTER (100102)**, (Formerly Shands Lake Shore), 368 N.E. Franklin Street, Zip 32055–3047; tel. 386/292–8000, (Nonreporting) **A**1 9 10 **S** Health Management Associates, Naples, FL
Primary Contact: Rhonda Kay Sherrod, R.N., MSN, Administrator
CMO: Ricardo Rosato, M.D., President Medical Staff
CHR: Janice Jackson, Director Human Resources
Web address: www.shandslakeshore.com
**Control:** Partnership, Investor–owned, for–profit **Service:** General Medical and Surgical

**Staffed Beds: 90**

**VETERANS AFFAIRS MEDICAL CENTER** See Lake City Veterans Affairs Medical Center

## LAKE WALES—Polk County

⊠ **LAKE WALES MEDICAL CENTER (100099)**, 410 South 11th Street, Zip 33853–4256; tel. 863/676–1433 **A**1 9 10 **F**3 11 15 18 20 29 30 34 35 40 45 46 49 50 57 59 64 70 74 75 79 81 82 85 86 87 89 91 92 93 94 96 107 108 110 111 114 115 119 124 129 131 132 146 147 148 **S** Community Health Systems, Inc., Franklin, TN
Primary Contact: Scott M. Smith, Chief Executive Officer
CFO: Danny Warren, Chief Financial Officer
CMO: James Nelson, M.D., Chief Medical Staff
CMO: Sunil Nihalani, M.D., Chief Medical Staff
CIO: Erwin Jaropillo, Director Information Systems
CHR: Renee Latterner, Director Human Resources
CNO: Lee Clack, R.N., Chief Nursing Officer
Web address: www.lakewalesmedicalcenter.com
**Control:** Corporation, Investor–owned, for–profit **Service:** General Medical and Surgical

**Staffed Beds: 131 Admissions: 5264 Census: 60 Outpatient Visits: 46654 Births: 0 Total Expense ($000): 65967 Payroll Expense ($000): 21722 Personnel: 461**

## LAKE WORTH—Palm Beach County

⊠ **SELECT SPECIALTY HOSPITAL–PALM BEACH (102023)**, 3060 Melaleuca Lane, Zip 33461–5174; tel. 561/357–7200, (Nonreporting) **A**1 9 10 **S** Select Medical Corporation, Mechanicsburg, PA
Primary Contact: Larry Melby, Chief Executive Officer
Web address: www.selectspecialtyhospitals.com/company/locations/palmbeach.aspx
**Control:** Corporation, Investor–owned, for–profit **Service:** Long–Term Acute Care hospital

**Staffed Beds: 60**

## LAKELAND—Polk County

⊠ **LAKELAND REGIONAL MEDICAL CENTER (100157)**, 1324 Lakeland Hills Boulevard, Zip 33805–4543, Mailing Address: P.O. Box 95448, Zip 33804–5448; tel. 863/687–1100 **A**1 2 3 5 9 10 **F**3 4 11 13 17 18 20 22 24 26 28 29 30 31 34 37 38 40 41 43 44 45 46 47 49 51 55 56 57 58 59 60 61 64 65 66 70 71 72 74 75 76 77 78 79 80 81 82 83 84 85 86 87 88 89 93 98 99 100 101 102 103 104 107 108 109 110 111 114 115 118 119 120 121 123 124 126 130 132 135 143 144 146 147 148 **P**6
Primary Contact: Mack Reavis, M.D., President and Chief Medical Officer
CFO: Evan Jones, Chief Financial Officer
CMO: Mack Reavis, M.D., President and Chief Medical Officer
CIO: Mary Ford, Vice President and Chief Information Officer
CHR: Jeffery L. Payne, Vice President Human Resources
Web address: www.lrmc.com
**Control:** Other not–for–profit (including NFP Corporation) **Service:** General Medical and Surgical

**Staffed Beds: 828 Admissions: 36789 Census: 488 Outpatient Visits: 222156 Births: 3290 Total Expense ($000): 513600 Payroll Expense ($000): 211517 Personnel: 3836**

## LAND O'LAKES—Pasco County

⊠ **FLORIDA HOSPITAL AT CONNERTON LONG TERM ACUTE CARE (102026)**, 9441 Health Center Drive, Zip 34637–5837; tel. 813/903–3701 **A**1 9 10 **F**29 30 34 70 119 146 148 **S** Adventist Health System Sunbelt Health Care Corporation, Altamonte Springs, FL
Primary Contact: Debi Martoccio, R.N., Chief Operating Officer
COO: Debi Martoccio, R.N., Chief Operating Officer
CMO: Sharad Patel, M.D., Medical Director
CNO: Therese Murphy, Chief Nursing Officer
Web address: www.elevatinghealthcare.org
**Control:** Church–operated, Nongovernment, not–for profit **Service:** Long–Term Acute Care hospital

**Staffed Beds: 50 Admissions: 580 Census: 47 Outpatient Visits: 0 Births: 0 Total Expense ($000): 21325 Payroll Expense ($000): 9151 Personnel: 173**

## LARGO—Pinellas County

⊠ **HEALTHSOUTH REHABILITATION HOSPITAL (103037)**, 901 North Clearwater–Largo Road, Zip 33770–4126; tel. 727/586–2999, (Nonreporting) **A**1 9 10 **S** HEALTHSOUTH Corporation, Birmingham, AL
Primary Contact: Donald D. Evans, Chief Executive Officer
CFO: Judith Johnson, Controller
CMO: Richard A. Liles, M.D., Medical Director
CHR: Jackie Chalk, Director Human Resources
CNO: Pattie Brenner, R.N., Chief Nursing Officer
Web address: www.healthsouthlargo.com
**Control:** Corporation, Investor–owned, for–profit **Service:** Rehabilitation

**Staffed Beds: 70**

**FL**

✠ **LARGO MEDICAL CENTER (100248)**, 201 14th Street S.W., Zip 33770–3133, Mailing Address: P.O. Box 2905, Zip 33779–2905; tel. 727/588–5200, (Nonreporting) **A**1 2 5 9 10 12 13 **S** HCA, Nashville, TN
Primary Contact: Anthony M. Degina, President and Chief Executive Officer
CFO: Robert E. Billings, Chief Financial Officer
CIO: Silvia Padro, Director Information Services
CHR: Eileen M. Corning, Director Human Resources
Web address: www.largomedical.com
**Control:** Corporation, Investor–owned, for–profit **Service:** General Medical and Surgical

**Staffed Beds:** 243

**SUN COAST HOSPITAL (100015)**, 2025 Indian Rocks Road, Zip 33774–1096, Mailing Address: P.O. Box 2025, Zip 33779–2025; tel. 727/581–9474, (Nonreporting) **A**9
Primary Contact: Darrell Lentz, Chief Executive Officer
COO: Nita Kasan, Chief Operating Officer and Chief Nursing Officer
Web address: www.suncoasthealthcare.com
**Control:** Other not–for–profit (including NFP Corporation) **Service:** General Medical and Surgical

**Staffed Beds:** 300

### LAUDERDALE LAKES—Broward County

☐ △ **ST. ANTHONY'S REHABILITATION HOSPITAL (103027)**, 3485 N.W. 30th Street, Zip 33311–1890; tel. 954/739–6233 **A**1 7 9 10 **F**28 29 30 34 35 64 68 74 79 90 91 93 94 95 96 130 131 132 148 **S** Catholic Health Services, Lauderdale Lakes, FL
Primary Contact: Joseph M. Catania, Chief Executive Officer
Web address: www.catholichealthservices.org
**Control:** Church–operated, Nongovernment, not–for profit **Service:** Rehabilitation

**Staffed Beds:** 26 **Admissions:** 539 **Census:** 20 **Outpatient Visits:** 2307 **Births:** 0 **Total Expense ($000):** 8631 **Payroll Expense ($000):** 2711 **Personnel:** 60

### LEESBURG—Lake County

✠ △ **LEESBURG REGIONAL MEDICAL CENTER (100084)**, 600 East Dixie Avenue, Zip 34748–5999; tel. 352/323–5762 **A**1 2 7 9 10 **F**3 8 11 13 15 17 18 20 22 24 26 28 29 30 31 34 35 40 42 45 53 54 57 59 60 64 66 68 70 74 75 76 77 78 79 81 82 85 87 89 90 93 96 107 110 111 114 115 119 130 132 144 146 148 **S** Central Florida Health Alliance, Leesburg, FL
Primary Contact: Donald G. Henderson, FACHE, President and Chief Executive Officer
CFO: Dale E. Hocking, Chief Financial Officer
CMO: Daniel Carlson, M.D., Senior Vice President and Chief Medical Officer
CIO: Nancy Vester, Vice President Information Technology
CNO: Cynde Gamache, R.N., Vice President and Chief Clinical Officer
Web address: www.cfhalliance.org
**Control:** Other not–for–profit (including NFP Corporation) **Service:** General Medical and Surgical

**Staffed Beds:** 331 **Admissions:** 15958 **Census:** 202 **Outpatient Visits:** 78350 **Births:** 1548 **Total Expense ($000):** 225036 **Payroll Expense ($000):** 78825

**LIFESTREAM BEHAVIORAL CENTER (104018)**, 2020 Tally Road, Zip 34748–3426, Mailing Address: P.O. Box 491000, Zip 34749–1000; tel. 352/315–7500, (Nonreporting) **A**9 10
Primary Contact: Jonathan M. Cherry, President and Chief Executive Officer
Web address: www.lsbc.net
**Control:** Other not–for–profit (including NFP Corporation) **Service:** Psychiatric

**Staffed Beds:** 18

### LEHIGH ACRES—Lee County

☐ **LEHIGH REGIONAL MEDICAL CENTER (100107)**, 1500 Lee Boulevard, Zip 33936–4835; tel. 239/369–2101, (Nonreporting) **A**1 10 **S** Health Management Associates, Naples, FL
Primary Contact: Joanie Jeannette, MSN, Chief Executive Officer
COO: Harlo McCall, Chief Operating Officer
CFO: Bob Pulley, Interim Chief Financial Officer
CMO: Madhava Pally, M.D., Chief of Staff
CIO: Jeff Hampton, Director Information Systems
CHR: Carmen Bech de Garcia, Director Human Resources
Web address: www.lehighregional.com
**Control:** Corporation, Investor–owned, for–profit **Service:** General Medical and Surgical

**Staffed Beds:** 88

### LIVE OAK—Suwannee County

☐ **SHANDS LIVE OAK REGIONAL MEDICAL CENTER (101301)**, (Formerly Shands Live Oak), 1100 S.W. 11th Street, Zip 32064–3608; tel. 386/362–0800 **A**1 9 10 18 **F**11 15 18 29 34 35 40 45 50 56 57 59 75 79 81 91 92 93 97 102 107 108 111 119 127 135 146 148 **S** Health Management Associates, Naples, FL
Primary Contact: Richard Huth, Chief Executive Officer
Web address: www.shands.org
**Control:** Corporation, Investor–owned, for–profit **Service:** General Medical and Surgical

**Staffed Beds:** 25 **Admissions:** 1340 **Census:** 15 **Births:** 0

### LOXAHATCHEE—Palm Beach County

✠ **PALMS WEST HOSPITAL (100269)**, 13001 Southern Boulevard, Zip 33470–9203; tel. 561/798–3300 **A**1 9 10 12 13 **F**3 8 13 15 18 19 20 22 29 30 31 34 35 39 40 41 45 46 49 50 51 56 57 58 59 60 64 68 70 74 75 76 77 78 79 81 82 84 85 87 88 89 93 107 108 110 111 114 119 126 130 131 132 146 147 148 **S** HCA, Nashville, TN
Primary Contact: Eric Goldman, Chief Executive Officer
COO: Laura Hilbert, Interim Chief Operating Officer
CFO: Joseph M. Paul, Chief Financial Officer
CIO: Fariba Borjian, Chief Information Officer
CHR: Marcy Mills–Mathews, Director Human Resources
Web address: www.palmswesthospital.com
**Control:** Corporation, Investor–owned, for–profit **Service:** General Medical and Surgical

**Staffed Beds:** 166 **Admissions:** 12378 **Census:** 130 **Outpatient Visits:** 78362 **Births:** 1123 **Total Expense ($000):** 130559 **Payroll Expense ($000):** 44552 **Personnel:** 545

### MACCLENNY—Baker County

**ED FRASER MEMORIAL HOSPITAL AND BAKER COMMUNITY HEALTH CENTER (100134)**, 159 North Third Street, Zip 32063–2103, Mailing Address: P.O. Box 484, Zip 32063–0484; tel. 904/259–3151, (Nonreporting) **A**9 10 20
Primary Contact: Dennis R. Markos, Chief Executive Officer
CFO: Maria Allen, Chief Financial Officer
CMO: Mark Hardin, M.D., Medical Director
CIO: Kelly Lowery, Director Health Information Management
CHR: Linda Fries, Director Personnel
Web address: www.bcmedsvcs.com
**Control:** Other not–for–profit (including NFP Corporation) **Service:** General Medical and Surgical

**Staffed Beds:** 68

### MADISON—Madison County

**MADISON COUNTY MEMORIAL HOSPITAL (101311)**, 309 N.E. Marion Street, Zip 32340–2561; tel. 850/973–2271, (Nonreporting) **A**9 10 18
Primary Contact: David Abercrombie, Chief Executive Officer
COO: Tammy Stevens, Chief Operating Officer
CFO: Patrick Halfhill, Chief Financial Officer
CMO: Brett Perkins, M.D., Chief Medical Staff
CIO: Patrick Stiff, Coordinator Information Technology
CHR: Cindi Burnett, Chief Human Resources Officer
Web address: www.mcmh.us/
**Control:** Other not–for–profit (including NFP Corporation) **Service:** General Medical and Surgical

**Staffed Beds:** 25

### MARATHON—Monroe County

✠ **FISHERMEN'S HOSPITAL (101312)**, 3301 Overseas Highway, Zip 33050–2329; tel. 305/743–5533 **A**1 9 10 18 20 **F**3 8 11 15 17 18 29 30 34 35 40 45 46 50 51 57 59 68 70 75 77 79 81 82 85 91 93 107 108 110 111 114 119 124 141 146 **P**6 8 **S** QHR, Brentwood, TN
Primary Contact: Hal W. Leftwich, FACHE, Chief Executive Officer
CMO: Harlan Pettit, M.D., Chief of Staff
CIO: Joe Brake, Director Information Services
CHR: Michele Teller, Director Human Resources
Web address: www.fishermenshospital.com
**Control:** Other not–for–profit (including NFP Corporation) **Service:** General Medical and Surgical

**Staffed Beds:** 25 **Admissions:** 642 **Census:** 6 **Births:** 0 **Total Expense ($000):** 25430 **Payroll Expense ($000):** 10555 **Personnel:** 211

**FL**

---

**Hospital, Medicare Provider Number, Address, Telephone, Approval, Facility, and Physician Codes, Health Care System**

★ American Hospital Association (AHA) membership
☐ The Joint Commission accreditation
◇ DNV Healthcare Inc. accreditation
○ Healthcare Facilities Accreditation Program
△ Commission on Accreditation of Rehabilitation Facilities (CARF) accreditation

## MARGATE—Broward County

✠ **NORTHWEST MEDICAL CENTER (100189)**, 2801 North State Road 7, Zip 33063–5727; tel. 954/974–0400 **A**1 9 10 **F**3 8 11 12 13 15 17 18 22 24 26 29 31 34 35 40 41 44 45 46 47 49 50 53 56 57 59 60 61 63 64 65 68 70 73 74 75 76 77 78 79 80 81 82 83 85 86 87 89 93 107 108 110 111 114 115 117 118 119 126 129 130 131 132 135 146 147 148 **S** HCA, Nashville, TN
Primary Contact: Mark Rader, FACHE, Chief Executive Officer
COO: Stacy Modlin, Chief Operating Officer
CFO: Gary Mervak, Chief Financial Officer
CMO: Peter Gach, M.D., Chief of Staff
CHR: Scott Mazo, Vice President Human Resources
Web address: www.northwestmed.com
**Control:** Corporation, Investor–owned, for–profit **Service:** General Medical and Surgical

**Staffed Beds:** 223 **Admissions:** 13970 **Census:** 144 **Outpatient Visits:** 66312 **Births:** 1403 **Total Expense ($000):** 141758 **Payroll Expense ($000):** 55275 **Personnel:** 603

## MARIANNA—Jackson County

✠ **JACKSON HOSPITAL (100142)**, 4250 Hospital Drive, Zip 32446–1917, Mailing Address: P.O. Box 1608, Zip 32447–5608; tel. 850/526–2200 **A**1 9 10 20 **F**3 13 15 29 30 31 34 35 40 41 45 46 49 56 57 59 70 71 76 78 79 81 83 85 87 97 107 108 110 111 112 114 119 127 130 133 135 146 147 148 **P**3 **S** QHR, Brentwood, TN
Primary Contact: Larry Meese, Chief Executive Officer
CFO: Kevin Rovito, Chief Financial Officer
CMO: Doyle Bosse, M.D., Chief Medical Officer
CIO: Beth Medlock, Manager Information Technology
CHR: Brooke G. Donaldson, Assistant Administrator Human Resources
CNO: Robbin K. Catt, Chief Nursing Officer
Web address: www.jacksonhosp.com
**Control:** Hospital district or authority, Government, nonfederal **Service:** General Medical and Surgical

**Staffed Beds:** 62 **Admissions:** 3035 **Census:** 35 **Outpatient Visits:** 68472 **Births:** 480 **Total Expense ($000):** 45255 **Payroll Expense ($000):** 21406 **Personnel:** 416

## MELBOURNE—Brevard County

☐ **CIRCLES OF CARE (104024)**, 400 East Sheridan Road, Zip 32901–3184; tel. 321/722–5200, (Nonreporting) **A**1 9 10
Primary Contact: James B. Whitaker, President
CFO: David L. Feldman, Executive Vice President and Treasurer
CMO: Jose Alvarez, M.D., Chief Medical Staff
CHR: Linda Brannon, Vice President Human Resources
Web address: www.circlesofcare.org
**Control:** Other not–for–profit (including NFP Corporation) **Service:** Psychiatric

**Staffed Beds:** 134

**DEVEREUX HOSPITAL AND CHILDREN'S CENTER OF FLORIDA**, 8000 Devereux Drive, Zip 32940–7907; tel. 321/242–9100, (Nonreporting) **S** Devereux, Villanova, PA
Primary Contact: Steven Murphy, Executive Director
COO: Amy Blakely, Assistant Executive Director Operations
CFO: Pamela Griffith, Director Administrative Services
CMO: Emilio Roig, M.D., Network Medical Director
CIO: Rob Fensterer, Director Information Services
Web address: www.devereux.org
**Control:** Other not–for–profit (including NFP Corporation) **Service:** Children's hospital psychiatric

**Staffed Beds:** 100

✠ **HEALTH FIRST HOLMES REGIONAL MEDICAL CENTER (100019)**, (Formerly Holmes Regional Medical Center), 1350 South Hickory Street, Zip 32901–3224; tel. 321/434–7000 **A**1 5 9 10 **F**3 7 11 13 15 17 18 20 22 24 26 29 30 31 34 35 40 43 45 46 47 48 49 56 57 59 60 65 68 70 72 73 74 75 76 77 78 79 81 82 83 84 85 87 89 91 92 93 100 107 108 110 111 114 115 116 117 118 119 124 126 129 130 132 146 147 148 **P**6 7 **S** Health First, Inc., Rockledge, FL
Primary Contact: Sean Gregory, President
CFO: Robert Galloway, Senior Vice President Finance and Chief Financial Officer
CMO: Scott Gettings, M.D., Vice President and Chief Medical Officer
CIO: Rich Rogers, Senior Vice President Support Services and Chief Information Officer
CHR: Robert W. Suttles, Vice President Human Resources
Web address: www.health-first.org
**Control:** Other not–for–profit (including NFP Corporation) **Service:** General Medical and Surgical

**Staffed Beds:** 514 **Admissions:** 25460 **Census:** 374 **Outpatient Visits:** 214580 **Births:** 2420 **Total Expense ($000):** 308123 **Payroll Expense ($000):** 148618 **Personnel:** 1744

**HEALTH FIRST PALM BAY HOSPITAL (100316)**, (Formerly Palm Bay Hospital), 1425 Malabar Road N.E., Zip 32907–2506; tel. 321/434–8000 **A**10 **F**3 11 15 18 20 29 30 34 40 45 49 51 57 59 60 65 68 70 74 75 79 81 84 85 87 91 92 93 107 108 110 111 114 115 118 119 130 132 143 145 146 **P**6 7 **S** Health First, Inc., Rockledge, FL
Primary Contact: Judy Gizinski, Chief Operating Officer
COO: J. Stuart Mitchell, Executive Vice President and Chief Operating Officer
CFO: Joseph G. Felkner, Senior Vice President and Chief Financial Officer
CMO: Scott Gettings, M.D., Vice President Medical Affairs
CIO: Christi C. Rushnell, Vice President Information Technology
CHR: Robert W. Suttles, Vice President Human Resources
CNO: Suzanne Woods, R.N., Vice President Nursing and Chief Nursing Officer
Web address: www.health-first.org
**Control:** Other not–for–profit (including NFP Corporation) **Service:** General Medical and Surgical

**Staffed Beds:** 119 **Admissions:** 5305 **Census:** 72 **Outpatient Visits:** 76390 **Births:** 0 **Total Expense ($000):** 71900 **Payroll Expense ($000):** 30864 **Personnel:** 323

☐ **HEALTH FIRST VIERA HOSPITAL (100315)**, (Formerly Viera Hospital), 8745 North Wickham Road, Zip 32940–5997; tel. 321/434–9164 **A**1 9 10 **F**3 11 12 15 18 20 22 26 29 30 31 34 35 38 40 44 45 46 47 48 49 50 51 55 56 57 59 60 64 68 70 74 75 77 78 79 81 82 85 86 87 93 94 97 107 108 110 111 115 116 117 119 124 126 132 145 146 148 **P**6 **S** Health First, Inc., Rockledge, FL
Primary Contact: Deborah Leiper, Chief Operating Officer
Web address: www.vierahospital.org
**Control:** Other not–for–profit (including NFP Corporation) **Service:** General Medical and Surgical

**Staffed Beds:** 84 **Admissions:** 3059 **Census:** 36 **Outpatient Visits:** 43131 **Total Expense ($000):** 69851 **Payroll Expense ($000):** 24642 **Personnel:** 296

✠ **HEALTHSOUTH SEA PINES REHABILITATION HOSPITAL (103034)**, 101 East Florida Avenue, Zip 32901–8301; tel. 321/984–4600 **A**1 9 10 **F**29 34 59 62 64 68 79 82 86 87 91 93 94 95 96 130 132 148 **S** HEALTHSOUTH Corporation, Birmingham, AL
Primary Contact: Denise B. McGrath, Chief Executive Officer
CFO: Dana Edwards, Chief Financial Officer
CMO: Stuart P. Miller, M.D., Medical Director
CHR: James L. Henry, Director Human Resources
Web address: www.healthsouthseapines.com
**Control:** Corporation, Investor–owned, for–profit **Service:** Rehabilitation

**Staffed Beds:** 90 **Admissions:** 1357 **Census:** 55 **Outpatient Visits:** 5845 **Births:** 0 **Total Expense ($000):** 14721 **Payroll Expense ($000):** 10694 **Personnel:** 166

✠ **KINDRED HOSPITAL MELBOURNE (102027)**, 765 West Nasa Boulevard, Zip 32901–1815; tel. 321/733–5725 **A**1 5 9 **F**1 3 29 107 114 148 **S** Kindred Healthcare, Louisville, KY
Primary Contact: Angelica Cotshott, Chief Executive Officer
Web address: www.khmelbourne.com
**Control:** Corporation, Investor–owned, for–profit **Service:** Long–Term Acute Care hospital

**Staffed Beds:** 42 **Admissions:** 415 **Census:** 32 **Outpatient Visits:** 0 **Births:** 0

☐ **WUESTHOFF MEDICAL CENTER – MELBOURNE (100291)**, 250 North Wickham Road, Zip 32935–8625; tel. 321/752–1200 **A**1 9 10 **F**3 11 12 13 15 18 20 22 29 30 38 40 49 50 51 57 59 60 64 68 70 74 75 76 77 79 80 81 85 87 89 93 102 107 108 111 114 115 116 117 119 126 130 131 132 135 144 146 147 148 **S** Health Management Associates, Naples, FL
Primary Contact: Jeannette Skinner, R.N., FACHE, Chief Executive Officer
CFO: Steve Bender, Chief Financial Officer
Web address: www.wuesthoff.org
**Control:** Corporation, Investor–owned, for–profit **Service:** General Medical and Surgical

**Staffed Beds:** 119 **Admissions:** 5318 **Census:** 69 **Births:** 404

FL

**MIAMI—Miami–Dade County**

⊠ △ **BAPTIST HEALTH SOUTH FLORIDA, BAPTIST HOSPITAL OF MIAMI (100008)**, 8900 North Kendall Drive, Zip 33176–2197; tel. 786/596–1960, (Includes BAPTIST CHILDREN'S HOSPITAL, 8900 North Kendall Drive, Zip 33176–2118; tel. 786/596–1960) **A**1 2 3 5 7 9 10 **F**3 8 11 13 15 17 18 19 20 22 24 26 28 29 30 31 32 33 34 35 36 37 38 39 40 41 45 46 47 49 50 51 53 54 55 56 57 58 59 60 61 62 63 64 66 68 70 72 73 74 75 76 77 78 79 81 82 84 85 86 87 88 89 90 91 92 93 96 100 102 107 108 109 110 111 114 115 116 117 118 119 120 121 123 124 126 129 130 132 135 144 145 146 147 148 **S** Baptist Health South Florida, Coral Gables, FL
Primary Contact: Bo Boulenger, Chief Executive Officer
COO: Randall Lee, Vice President and Chief Operating Officer
CFO: Ralph E. Lawson, Executive Vice President and Chief Financial Officer
CMO: Mark J. Hauser, M.D., Chief Medical Officer
CIO: Mimi Taylor, Corporate Vice President Information Technology
CHR: Corey Heller, Corporate Vice President and Chief Human Resources Officer
Web address: www.baptisthealth.net
**Control:** Other not–for–profit (including NFP Corporation) **Service:** General Medical and Surgical

**Staffed Beds:** 672 **Admissions:** 34926 **Census:** 477 **Outpatient Visits:** 355051 **Births:** 4141 **Total Expense ($000):** 765125 **Payroll Expense ($000):** 265111 **Personnel:** 4180

⊠ **BAPTIST HEALTH SOUTH FLORIDA, SOUTH MIAMI HOSPITAL (100154)**, 6200 S.W. 73rd Street, Zip 33143–4679; tel. 786/662–4000 **A**1 9 10 **F**3 4 5 11 12 13 15 17 18 20 22 24 26 28 29 30 31 34 35 36 40 46 48 49 50 51 52 53 54 57 58 59 60 61 64 68 70 72 73 74 75 76 77 78 79 81 82 84 85 86 87 93 107 108 110 111 114 115 116 117 118 119 120 121 123 124 126 129 130 132 135 144 146 147 148 **S** Baptist Health South Florida, Coral Gables, FL
Primary Contact: Lincoln S. Mendez, Chief Executive Officer
COO: Jeanette Stone, Vice President Operations
CFO: Berta Rufat, Controller
CMO: Yvonne Johnson, M.D., President Medical Staff
CIO: Mimi Taylor, Vice President Information Technology
CHR: Diana Montenegro, Director Human Resources
Web address: www.baptisthealth.net
**Control:** Other not–for–profit (including NFP Corporation) **Service:** General Medical and Surgical

**Staffed Beds:** 374 **Admissions:** 15324 **Census:** 204 **Outpatient Visits:** 244185 **Births:** 4229 **Total Expense ($000):** 463814 **Payroll Expense ($000):** 141117 **Personnel:** 2291

⊠ **BAPTIST HEALTH SOUTH FLORIDA, WEST KENDALL BAPTIST HOSPITAL (100314)**, 9555 S.W. 162nd Avenue, Zip 33196–6408; tel. 786/467–2000 **A**1 10 **F**3 13 18 19 29 30 31 34 35 40 41 45 49 50 51 53 57 58 59 60 63 64 68 70 74 75 76 78 79 81 82 84 85 86 87 93 100 102 107 108 109 111 114 115 119 130 131 132 135 146 147 148 **S** Baptist Health South Florida, Coral Gables, FL
Primary Contact: Javier Hernandez–Lichtl, Chief Executive Officer
CFO: Odalys Remigio, Assistant Vice President, Finance
CMO: Juan–Carlos Verdeja, M.D., President of Medical Staff
CHR: Hilde Zamora de Aguero, Human Resources Site Director
CNO: Denise H. Harris, R.N., Chief Nursing Officer
Web address: www.baptisthealth.net/en/facilities/West–Kendall–Baptist–Hospital/Pages/default.aspx
**Control:** Other not–for–profit (including NFP Corporation) **Service:** General Medical and Surgical

**Staffed Beds:** 133 **Admissions:** 5486 **Census:** 61 **Outpatient Visits:** 58097 **Births:** 570 **Total Expense ($000):** 204220 **Payroll Expense ($000):** 49634 **Personnel:** 865

⊠ **BASCOM PALMER EYE INSTITUTE–ANNE BATES LEACH EYE HOSPITAL (100240)**, 900 N.W. 17th Street, Zip 33136–1199, Mailing Address: Box 016880, Zip 33101–6880; tel. 305/326–6000 **A**1 3 5 9 10 **F**8 34 40 43 44 50 54 55 57 58 59 64 66 68 71 74 75 77 78 79 81 85 86 87 90 93 94 111 119 129 130 131 132 135 141 146 **P**6 **S** University of Miami Health System, Miami, FL
Primary Contact: Michael B. Gittelman, Administrator
COO: Charles Pappas, M.D., Chief Operating Officer
CFO: Harry Rohrer, Chief Financial Officer
CMO: Eduardo Alfonso, M.D., Chairman Ophthalmology
CHR: Paul Hudgins, Associate Vice President Human Resources
Web address: www.bascompalmer.org
**Control:** Other not–for–profit (including NFP Corporation) **Service:** Eye, ear, nose, and throat

**Staffed Beds:** 58 **Admissions:** 115 **Census:** 1 **Outpatient Visits:** 231520 **Births:** 0 **Total Expense ($000):** 99189 **Payroll Expense ($000):** 30666 **Personnel:** 837

**HEALTHSOUTH REHABILITATION HOSPITAL** See HEALTHSOUTH Rehabilitation Hospital of Miami

⊠ **HEALTHSOUTH REHABILITATION HOSPITAL OF MIAMI (103038)**, 20601 Old Cutler Road, Zip 33189–2400; tel. 305/251–3800, (Nonreporting) **A**1 9 10 **S** HEALTHSOUTH Corporation, Birmingham, AL
Primary Contact: Elizabeth L. Izquierdo, CPA, Chief Executive Officer
CFO: Reyna Hernandez, Chief Financial Officer
CHR: Susan Riley, Director Human Resources
Web address: www.healthsouthmiami.com
**Control:** Corporation, Investor–owned, for–profit **Service:** Rehabilitation

**Staffed Beds:** 60

**HIGHLAND PARK HOSPITAL** See Jackson Health System

☐ △ **JACKSON HEALTH SYSTEM (100022)**, 1611 N.W. 12th Avenue, Zip 33136–1005; tel. 305/585–1111, (Includes HIGHLAND PARK HOSPITAL, 1695 N.W. Ninth Avenue, Zip 33136; tel. 305/355–8234; HOLTZ CHILDREN'S HOSPITAL, 1611 N.W. 12th Avenue, tel. 305/585–5437; Daniel Armstrong, Chief Administrative Officer; JACKSON MEMORIAL HOSPITAL, 1611 N.W. 12th Avenue, Zip 33136; tel. 305/585–6661; Alex Contreras–Soto, Senior Vice President and Chief Administrative Officer; JACKSON NORTH MEDICAL CENTER, 160 N.W. 170th Street, North Miami Beach, Zip 33169–5576; tel. 305/651–1100; Sandy Sears, Senior Vice President and Chief Administrative Officer; JACKSON SOUTH COMMUNITY HOSPITAL, 9333 S.W. 152nd Street, Zip 33157–1780; tel. 305/251–2500; Martha Garcia, Senior Vice President and Chief Administrative Officer), (Total facility includes 322 beds in nursing home–type unit) **A**1 3 5 7 8 9 10 **F**1 3 4 5 9 11 12 13 15 16 17 19 20 21 22 23 24 25 26 27 28 29 30 31 34 35 36 38 39 40 41 43 44 45 49 50 51 54 56 57 58 59 60 61 63 64 65 66 68 70 72 73 74 75 76 77 78 79 80 81 82 83 84 85 86 87 88 89 90 91 92 93 94 96 97 98 99 100 101 102 103 104 105 106 107 108 110 111 114 115 117 118 119 120 121 126 128 129 130 131 132 134 135 136 137 138 139 140 141 142 146 147 148 **P**6
Primary Contact: Carlos A. Migoya, President and Chief Executive Officer
COO: Don S. Steigman, Chief Operating Officer
CFO: Mark T. Knight, Executive Vice President and Chief Financial Officer
CMO: Michael K. Butler, M.D., Executive Vice President and Chief Medical Officer
CIO: Fernando Martinez, Vice President and Chief Information Officer
CHR: Trummell Valdera, Senior Vice President and Chief Human Resources Officer
Web address: www.um–jmh.org
**Control:** County–Government, nonfederal **Service:** General Medical and Surgical

**Staffed Beds:** 1892 **Admissions:** 60203 **Census:** 1043 **Outpatient Visits:** 336453 **Births:** 6433 **Total Expense ($000):** 1568699 **Payroll Expense ($000):** 687743 **Personnel:** 8645

**JACKSON SOUTH COMMUNITY HOSPITAL** See Jackson Health System

⊠ **KENDALL REGIONAL MEDICAL CENTER (100209)**, 11750 Bird Road, Zip 33175–3530; tel. 305/223–3000, (Nonreporting) **A**1 9 10 **S** HCA, Nashville, TN
Primary Contact: Scott A. Cihak, Chief Executive Officer
COO: Elizabeth Durrence, Chief Operating Officer
CFO: Ricardo Pavon, Chief Financial Officer
CIO: Ralph Ruiz, Director Information Technology and Services
CHR: Tom Nesbit, Director Human Resources
Web address: www.kendallmed.com
**Control:** Partnership, Investor–owned, for–profit **Service:** General Medical and Surgical

**Staffed Beds:** 300

☐ **METROPOLITAN HOSPITAL OF MIAMI (100076)**, 5959 N.W. Seventh Street, Zip 33126–3198; tel. 305/264–1000, (Nonreporting) **A**1 9 10
Primary Contact: Ismael Roque–Velasco, M.D., Chief Executive Officer
CFO: Vivian Acevedo, Chief Financial Officer
CIO: Frank Canovaca, Director Management Information Systems
CHR: Mirelis Asper, Human Resources Generalist
Web address: www.mhmiami.com
**Control:** Corporation, Investor–owned, for–profit **Service:** General Medical and Surgical

**Staffed Beds:** 146

**FL**

---

**Hospital, Medicare Provider Number, Address, Telephone, Approval, Facility, and Physician Codes, Health Care System**

★ American Hospital Association (AHA) membership
☐ The Joint Commission accreditation
◇ DNV Healthcare Inc. accreditation
○ Healthcare Facilities Accreditation Program
△ Commission on Accreditation of Rehabilitation Facilities (CARF) accreditation

✠ **MIAMI CHILDREN'S HOSPITAL (103301)**, 3100 S.W. 62nd Avenue, Zip 33155–3009; tel. 305/666–6511 **A**1 2 3 5 8 9 10 12 13 **F**1 3 4 7 8 9 16 17 19 20 21 22 23 25 27 29 30 31 32 34 35 36 38 39 40 42 43 44 45 46 50 53 54 55 57 58 59 60 61 64 65 66 67 68 70 71 72 73 74 75 77 78 79 80 81 82 85 86 87 88 89 90 93 97 98 99 100 101 102 104 105 106 107 108 111 114 116 117 118 119 127 128 129 130 131 132 134 136 144 146 **P**6
Primary Contact: M. Narendra Kini, M.D., President and Chief Executive Officer
COO: Kevin R. Hammeran, Executive Vice President and Chief Operating Officer
CFO: Pedro Alfaro, Vice President and Chief Financial Officer
CMO: Deise Granado–Villar, M.D., Chief Medical Officer and Senior Vice President Medical Affairs
CIO: Edward Martinez, Chief Information Officer
Web address: www.mch.com
**Control:** Other not–for–profit (including NFP Corporation) **Service:** Children's general

**Staffed Beds:** 272 **Admissions:** 11550 **Census:** 179 **Outpatient Visits:** 433915 **Births:** 0 **Total Expense ($000):** 503041 **Payroll Expense ($000):** 227263 **Personnel:** 3412

✠ **MIAMI JEWISH HOME AND HOSPITAL FOR AGED (100277)**, 5200 N.E. Second Avenue, Zip 33137–2706; tel. 305/751–8626, (Nonreporting) **A**1 3 5 10
Primary Contact: Jeffrey P. Freimark, Chief Executive Officer
CFO: Lisa Jo Desmarteau, Chief Financial Officer
CMO: Brian Kiedrowski, M.D., Chief Medical Director
CHR: Larry McDonald, Director Human Resources
Web address: www.mjhha.org
**Control:** Other not–for–profit (including NFP Corporation) **Service:** General Medical and Surgical

**Staffed Beds:** 32

✠ △ **MIAMI VETERANS AFFAIRS HEALTHCARE SYSTEM**, (Formerly Veterans Affairs Medical Center), 1201 N.W. 16th Street, Zip 33125–1624; tel. 305/575–7000, (Nonreporting) **A**1 3 5 7 **S** Department of Veterans Affairs, Washington, DC
Primary Contact: Paul M. Russo, FACHE, Director
COO: Paul D. Magalian, Associate Director
CFO: Rick Hunter, Chief Financial Officer
CMO: John Vara, M.D., Chief of Staff
CIO: Bill Tyson, Chief Information Officer
CHR: Larry Brinkman, Chief Human Resources
Web address: www.miami.va.gov/
**Control:** Veterans Affairs, Government, federal **Service:** General Medical and Surgical

**Staffed Beds:** 401

✠ **NORTH SHORE MEDICAL CENTER (100029)**, 1100 N.W. 95th Street, Zip 33150–2098; tel. 305/835–6000 **A**1 2 9 10 **F**1 4 13 15 16 17 20 29 31 34 35 40 45 46 51 57 59 64 67 68 70 72 73 74 76 77 78 79 80 81 82 86 87 88 89 90 91 93 98 100 107 111 119 128 129 130 148 **S** TENET Healthcare Corporation, Dallas, TX
Primary Contact: Manuel Linares, Chief Executive Officer
COO: Patricia Sechi, Chief Operating Officer
CFO: Alex Fernandez, Chief Financial Officer
CMO: Susan Baker, M.D., Chief of Staff
CIO: Luis Estrada, Director Multifacility Information Systems
CHR: Carmen Gomez, Director Human Resources
CNO: Rita Hess, R.N., Chief Nursing Officer
Web address: www.northshoremedical.com
**Control:** Corporation, Investor–owned, for–profit **Service:** General Medical and Surgical

**Staffed Beds:** 357 **Admissions:** 12603 **Census:** 182 **Outpatient Visits:** 75700 **Births:** 1875 **Total Expense ($000):** 132452 **Payroll Expense ($000):** 57072

✠ **SELECT SPECIALTY HOSPITAL–MIAMI (102001)**, 955 N.W. 3rd Street, Zip 33128–1274; tel. 305/416–5700, (Nonreporting) **A**1 9 10 **S** Select Medical Corporation, Mechanicsburg, PA
Primary Contact: Dionisio Bencomo, Chief Executive Officer
Web address: www.selectspecialtyhospitals.com/company/locations/miami.aspx
**Control:** Corporation, Investor–owned, for–profit **Service:** Long–Term Acute Care hospital

**Staffed Beds:** 40

☐ **SISTER EMMANUEL HOSPITAL (102016)**, 3663 South Miami Avenue, Zip 33133–4253; tel. 305/285–2939, (Nonreporting) **A**1 9 10
Primary Contact: Shed Boren, Administrator and Chief Executive Officer
CFO: Miguel Vasquez, Chief Financial Officer
CMO: Hugo Gonzalez, M.D., Chief Medical Officer
CIO: Macarena Restrepo, Manager Business Office
CHR: Kathy Mainieri, Human Resource Specialist
Web address: www.sisteremmanuelhospital.org/
**Control:** Church–operated, Nongovernment, not–for profit **Service:** Long–Term Acute Care hospital

**Staffed Beds:** 29

✠ **UNIVERSITY OF MIAMI HOSPITAL (100009)**, 1400 N.W. 12th Avenue, Zip 33136–1003; tel. 305/325–5511 **A**1 2 3 5 9 10 **F**3 8 11 15 17 18 20 22 24 26 29 30 31 34 35 36 38 39 40 44 45 46 47 48 49 50 51 54 57 58 59 60 63 64 66 68 70 71 74 75 77 78 79 80 81 82 84 85 86 87 92 93 96 97 98 100 102 105 107 108 109 110 111 114 115 117 118 119 120 121 123 124 126 130 131 135 136 141 146 148 **S** University of Miami Health System, Miami, FL
Primary Contact: Daniel J. Snyder, Chief Executive Officer
COO: David Zambrana, R.N., Chief Operating Officer and Chief Nursing Officer
CFO: Darryl Caulton, Chief Financial Officer
CFO: Harry Rohrer, Chief Financial Officer
CMO: Francisco Kerdel, M.D., President Medical Staff
CIO: Craig Scott, Interim Director Management Information Systems
CHR: Errol Douglas, Director Human Resources
Web address: www.umiamihospital.com
**Control:** Other not–for–profit (including NFP Corporation) **Service:** General Medical and Surgical

**Staffed Beds:** 525 **Admissions:** 20546 **Census:** 337 **Outpatient Visits:** 104950 **Births:** 0 **Total Expense ($000):** 359930 **Payroll Expense ($000):** 108633 **Personnel:** 1887

✠ **UNIVERSITY OF MIAMI HOSPITAL AND CLINICS (100079)**, 1475 N.W. 12th Avenue, Zip 33136–1002; tel. 305/243–1000 **A**1 2 3 5 9 10 **F**3 9 11 15 29 30 31 34 35 36 38 44 45 46 47 48 49 50 54 55 57 58 59 60 61 64 65 68 70 74 75 77 78 79 80 81 82 84 85 86 87 97 99 100 101 102 103 104 107 108 110 111 114 115 117 118 119 120 121 123 124 126 130 132 135 136 141 145 146 147 148 **P**6 **S** University of Miami Health System, Miami, FL
Primary Contact: Richard R. Ballard, Administrator
COO: Joseph B. Natoli, Senior Vice President Business and Finance and Chief Financial Officer
CFO: Harry Rohrer, Chief Financial Officer
CMO: W. Jarrad Goodwin, M.D., Director
CHR: Paul Hudgins, Associate Vice President Human Resources
Web address: www.uhealthsystem.com
**Control:** Other not–for–profit (including NFP Corporation) **Service:** General Medical and Surgical

**Staffed Beds:** 40 **Admissions:** 1362 **Census:** 22 **Outpatient Visits:** 305656 **Births:** 0 **Total Expense ($000):** 274149 **Payroll Expense ($000):** 58153 **Personnel:** 1005

**VETERANS AFFAIRS MEDICAL CENTER** See Miami Veterans Affairs Healthcare System

✠ △ **WEST GABLES REHABILITATION HOSPITAL (103036)**, 2525 S.W. 75th Avenue, Zip 33155–2800; tel. 305/262–6800, (Nonreporting) **A**1 7 9 10 **S** Select Medical Corporation, Mechanicsburg, PA
Primary Contact: Walter Concepcion, Chief Executive Officer
CFO: Sara Reohr, Regional Controller
CMO: Jose L. Vargas, M.D., Medical Director
CHR: Barbara Etchason, HR Manager
CNO: Constance Hughes, Director of Nursing
Web address: www.westgablesrehabhospital.com/
**Control:** Corporation, Investor–owned, for–profit **Service:** Rehabilitation

**Staffed Beds:** 60

○ **WESTCHESTER GENERAL HOSPITAL (100284)**, 2500 S.W. 75th Avenue, Zip 33155–2805; tel. 305/264–5252, (Includes SOUTHERN WINDS HOSPITAL, 4225 West 20th Street, Hialeah, Zip 33012–5835; tel. 305/558–9700) **A**9 10 11 12 13 **F**3 15 18 29 31 40 45 49 56 65 70 74 75 77 78 79 81 85 87 98 99 100 102 103 107 108 110 114 115 119 130
Primary Contact: Gilda Baldwin, Chief Executive Officer
CFO: Henry Brown, Chief Financial Officer
CMO: Rogelio Zaldivar, M.D., Medical Director
CHR: Alicia Lund, Director Human Resources
Web address: www.westchesterhospital.com
**Control:** Corporation, Investor–owned, for–profit **Service:** General Medical and Surgical

**Staffed Beds:** 197 **Admissions:** 8487 **Census:** 139 **Outpatient Visits:** 31491 **Births:** 0 **Total Expense ($000):** 65275 **Payroll Expense ($000):** 31956 **Personnel:** 567

**MIAMI BEACH—Dade County**

**MIAMI HEART CAMPUS AT MOUNT SINAI MEDICAL CENTER** See Mount Sinai Medical Center

FL

□ △ **MOUNT SINAI MEDICAL CENTER (100034)**, 4300 Alton Road, Zip 33140–2948; tel. 305/674–2121, (Includes MIAMI HEART CAMPUS AT MOUNT SINAI MEDICAL CENTER, 4701 North Meridian Avenue, Zip 33140–2910; tel. 305/672–1111) **A**1 2 3 5 7 8 9 10 13 **F**1 3 4 6 8 13 14 15 16 17 18 20 22 24 26 28 29 30 31 34 35 37 39 40 42 43 44 45 46 47 48 49 50 51 53 54 55 56 57 58 59 60 61 62 64 65 66 67 70 71 72 73 74 75 76 77 78 79 80 81 82 83 84 85 86 87 88 89 90 91 92 93 96 97 98 100 101 102 103 104 107 108 109 110 111 114 115 116 117 118 119 120 121 122 123 124 126 128 129 130 131 132 135 137 143 145 146 147 148
Primary Contact: Steven D. Sonenreich, President and Chief Executive Officer
CFO: Alex A. Mendez, Executive Vice President of Operations and Chief Financial Officer
CMO: Robert Goldszer, M.D., Senior Vice President and Chief Medical Officer
CIO: Tom Gillette, Vice President and Chief Information Officer
CHR: Georgia McLean, Director Human Resources
Web address: www.msmc.com
**Control:** Other not–for–profit (including NFP Corporation) **Service:** General Medical and Surgical

**Staffed Beds:** 613 **Admissions:** 22126 **Census:** 364 **Outpatient Visits:** 182321 **Births:** 2786 **Total Expense ($000):** 419559 **Payroll Expense ($000):** 158578 **Personnel:** 3373

### MILTON—Santa Rosa County

□ **SANTA ROSA MEDICAL CENTER (100124)**, 1450 Berryhill Road, Zip 32570–5062, Mailing Address: P.O. Box 648, Zip 32572–0648; tel. 850/626–7762, (Nonreporting) **A**1 9 10 **S** Health Management Associates, Naples, FL
Primary Contact: Phillip L. Wright, FACHE, Chief Executive Officer
CFO: Kay Burns, Chief Financial Officer
CIO: Rick Payne, Director Information Systems
Web address: www.santarosamedicalcenter.org
**Control:** Corporation, Investor–owned, for–profit **Service:** General Medical and Surgical

**Staffed Beds:** 105

**WEST FLORIDA COMMUNITY CARE CENTER (104027)**, 5500 Stewart Street, Zip 32570–4304; tel. 850/983–5500, (Nonreporting) **A**10
Primary Contact: Carmen Paroby, Chief Executive Officer
**Control:** Other not–for–profit (including NFP Corporation) **Service:** Psychiatric

**Staffed Beds:** 100

### MIRAMAR—Broward County

☒ **MEMORIAL HOSPITAL MIRAMAR (100285)**, 1901 S.W. 172nd Avenue, Zip 33029–5592; tel. 954/538–5000 **A**1 9 10 **F**3 13 15 29 30 40 41 45 49 50 57 59 61 64 68 70 72 74 75 76 77 78 79 81 82 85 86 87 91 93 96 107 108 109 110 111 114 115 118 119 126 130 131 132 146 **S** Memorial Healthcare System, Hollywood, FL
Primary Contact: Leah A. Carpenter, Administrator and Chief Executive Officer
CFO: Judy Sada, Chief Financial Officer
CMO: Stanley Marks, M.D., Chief Medical Officer
CIO: Forest Blanton, Senior VP and Chief Information Officer
CHR: Ray Kendrick, Chief Human Resources Officer
CNO: Denise Reynolds, Chief Nursing Officer
Web address: www.mhs.net
**Control:** Hospital district or authority, Government, nonfederal **Service:** General Medical and Surgical

**Staffed Beds:** 178 **Admissions:** 9884 **Census:** 97 **Outpatient Visits:** 121480 **Births:** 3249 **Total Expense ($000):** 175765 **Payroll Expense ($000):** 60953 **Personnel:** 774

### MIRAMAR BEACH—Walton County

☒ **SACRED HEART HOSPITAL ON THE EMERALD COAST (100292)**, 7800 Highway 98 West, Zip 32550; tel. 850/278–3000 **A**1 9 10 **F**3 11 13 15 18 20 22 26 28 29 30 31 34 35 36 40 44 50 51 53 57 58 59 60 64 68 70 74 75 76 78 79 81 82 84 85 86 87 93 96 107 108 110 111 114 115 118 119 121 123 124 130 132 135 146 147 148 **P**7 **S** Ascension Health, Saint Louis, MO
Primary Contact: Roger L. Hall, President
Web address: www.sacredheartemerald.org
**Control:** Other not–for–profit (including NFP Corporation) **Service:** General Medical and Surgical

**Staffed Beds:** 58 **Admissions:** 4232 **Census:** 35 **Outpatient Visits:** 83742 **Births:** 893 **Total Expense ($000):** 70406 **Payroll Expense ($000):** 23948 **Personnel:** 386

### NAPLES—Collier County

☒ △ **NCH DOWNTOWN NAPLES HOSPITAL (100018)**, 350 Seventh Street North, Zip 34102–5754, Mailing Address: P.O. Box 413029, Zip 34101–3029; tel. 239/436–5000, (Includes NCH NORTH NAPLES HOSPITAL, 11190 Health Park Boulevard, Zip 34110–5729, Mailing Address: 11190 Health Park Boulevard, Zip 34110–5729; tel. 239/552–7000) **A**1 2 7 9 10 **F**3 11 12 22 24 26 28 29 30 31 34 37 40 41 45 47 49 50 53 56 57 59 64 68 70 72 74 75 76 77 78 79 80 81 84 85 86 87 88 89 90 92 93 95 96 98 100 102 103 107 108 111 114 119 126 130 146 147
Primary Contact: Allen S. Weiss, M.D., President and Chief Executive Officer
COO: Phillip C. Dutcher, Chief Operating Officer
CFO: Vicki Hale, Chief Financial Officer
CMO: Aurora Estevez, M.D., Chief Medical Officer
CIO: Susan Wolff, Chief Information Officer
Web address: www.nchmd.org
**Control:** Other not–for–profit (including NFP Corporation) **Service:** General Medical and Surgical

**Staffed Beds:** 684 **Admissions:** 31536 **Census:** 376 **Outpatient Visits:** 286824 **Births:** 2961 **Total Expense ($000):** 394601 **Payroll Expense ($000):** 154048 **Personnel:** 2846

□ **PHYSICIANS REGIONAL MEDICAL CENTER – PINE RIDGE (100286)**, 6101 Pine Ridge Road, Zip 34119–3900; tel. 239/348–4000, (Includes PHYSICIANS REGIONAL MEDICAL CENTER, 8300 Collier Boulevard, Zip 34114; tel. 239/354–6000; C. Scott Campbell, Market Chief Executive Officer), (Nonreporting) **A**1 9 10 **S** Health Management Associates, Naples, FL
Primary Contact: C. Scott Campbell, Market Chief Executive Officer
CIO: Lisa Gardiner, Director Marketing and Public Relations
CHR: Andrew Nottidge, Director Human Resources
Web address: www.physiciansregional.com
**Control:** Corporation, Investor–owned, for–profit **Service:** General Medical and Surgical

**Staffed Beds:** 70

□ **WILLOUGH HEALTHCARE SYSTEM (104063)**, 9001 Tamiami Trail East, Zip 34113–3304; tel. 239/775–4500, (Nonreporting) **A**1 9 10
Primary Contact: James E. O'Shea, Administrator
CFO: Steve Baldwin, Vice President Finance
Web address: www.thewilloughatnaples.com/
**Control:** Corporation, Investor–owned, for–profit **Service:** Psychiatric

**Staffed Beds:** 80

### NEW PORT RICHEY—Pasco County

**COMMUNITY HOSPITAL** See Medical Center of Trinity, Trinity

☒ △ **MORTON PLANT NORTH BAY HOSPITAL (100063)**, 6600 Madison Street, Zip 34652–1900; tel. 727/842–8468 **A**1 7 9 10 **F**3 11 18 20 22 29 30 31 34 35 40 44 45 47 48 49 50 57 58 59 64 68 70 74 75 77 78 79 81 84 85 86 87 90 93 96 98 99 100 102 107 108 109 111 114 115 118 119 129 130 132 135 143 146 148 **P**6 **S** Morton Plant Mease Health Care, Clearwater, FL
Primary Contact: Glenn D. Waters, FACHE, President
COO: Hal Ziecheck, Chief Operating Officer
CFO: Carl Tremonti, Chief Financial Officer
CMO: Donald Pocock, M.D., Chief Medical Officer
CHR: Sharon Collotta, Director Team Resources
CNO: Lisa Johnson, R.N., Chief Nursing Executive
Web address: www.mpmhealth.com
**Control:** Other not–for–profit (including NFP Corporation) **Service:** General Medical and Surgical

**Staffed Beds:** 226 **Admissions:** 11294 **Census:** 144 **Outpatient Visits:** 34299 **Births:** 0 **Total Expense ($000):** 95474 **Payroll Expense ($000):** 40413 **Personnel:** 611

### NEW SMYRNA BEACH—Volusia County

☒ **BERT FISH MEDICAL CENTER (100014)**, 401 Palmetto Street, Zip 32168–7399; tel. 386/424–5000, (Nonreporting) **A**1 9 10
Primary Contact: Steven W. Harrell, FACHE, Interim Chief Executive Officer
COO: Steven W. Harrell, FACHE, Chief Operating Officer
CFO: Al W. Allred, Chief Financial Officer
CMO: Rajesh Ailani, M.D., Chief Medical Staff
CIO: Debbie Burgess, Director Information Services
CHR: Nancy K. Evolga, Executive Director Human Resources
CNO: Linda Breum, R.N., Chief Nursing Officer
Web address: www.bertfish.com
**Control:** Hospital district or authority, Government, nonfederal **Service:** General Medical and Surgical

**Staffed Beds:** 112

**FL**

---

**Hospital, Medicare Provider Number, Address, Telephone, Approval, Facility, and Physician Codes, Health Care System**

★ American Hospital Association (AHA) membership
□ The Joint Commission accreditation
◇ DNV Healthcare Inc. accreditation
○ Healthcare Facilities Accreditation Program
△ Commission on Accreditation of Rehabilitation Facilities (CARF) accreditation

**NICEVILLE—Okaloosa County**

⊞ **TWIN CITIES HOSPITAL (100054)**, 2190 Highway 85 North, Zip 32578–1045; tel. 850/678–4131, (Nonreporting) **A**1 9 10 **S** HCA, Nashville, TN
Primary Contact: David Whalen, Chief Executive Officer
CFO: Mark Day, Chief Financial Officer
CHR: Cyndi Ronca, Director Human Resources
Web address: www.tchealthcare.com
**Control:** Corporation, Investor–owned, for–profit **Service:** General Medical and Surgical

| Staffed Beds: 57 |
| --- |

**NORTH MIAMI—Miami–Dade County**

⊞ △ **ST. CATHERINE'S REHABILITATION HOSPITAL (103026)**, 1050 N.E. 125th Street, Zip 33161–5881; tel. 305/357–1735, (Nonreporting) **A**1 7 9 10 **S** Catholic Health Services, Lauderdale Lakes, FL
Primary Contact: Jaime Gonzalez, Administrator
COO: Jim Ball, Chief Operating Officer
CFO: Mary Jo Frick, Director Finance
CMO: Miriam Feliz, M.D., Medical Director
Web address: www.catholichealthservices.org
**Control:** Other not–for–profit (including NFP Corporation) **Service:** Rehabilitation

| Staffed Beds: 60 |
| --- |

**NORTH MIAMI BEACH—Dade County**

**JACKSON NORTH MEDICAL CENTER** See Jackson Health System, Miami

**OCALA—Marion County**

⊞ **HEALTHSOUTH REHABILITATION HOSPITAL OF OCALA (103043)**, 2275 S.W. 22nd Lane, Zip 34471–7710; tel. 352/282–4000, (Nonreporting) **A**1 **S** HEALTHSOUTH Corporation, Birmingham, AL
Primary Contact: Ellen Witterstaeter, FACHE, Chief Executive Officer
CFO: Rocco Corsaro, Controller
CMO: Amy Clunn, M.D., Medical Director
CHR: Donna Howard, Human Resources Director
CNO: Wendy Milam, Chief Nursing Officer
Web address: www.healthsouthocala.com
**Control:** Corporation, Investor–owned, for–profit **Service:** Rehabilitation

| Staffed Beds: 40 |
| --- |

⊞ **KINDRED HOSPITAL OCALA (102019)**, 1500 S.W. 1st Avenue, Zip 34471–6504; tel. 352/369–0513, (Nonreporting) **A**1 9 10 **S** Kindred Healthcare, Louisville, KY
Primary Contact: Merlene Bhoorasingh, Administrator
CFO: Dean Cocchi, Chief Financial Officer
Web address: www.kindredocala.com/
**Control:** Corporation, Investor–owned, for–profit **Service:** Long–Term Acute Care hospital

| Staffed Beds: 31 |
| --- |

**MARION–CITRUS MENTAL HEALTH CENTERS (104068)**, 5664 S.W. 60th Avenue, Zip 34474–5677; tel. 352/291–5500, (Nonreporting) **A**9 10
Primary Contact: Charles R. Powell, Director
Web address: www.thecenters.us
**Control:** Corporation, Investor–owned, for–profit **Service:** Psychiatric

| Staffed Beds: 40 |
| --- |

⊞ **MUNROE REGIONAL MEDICAL CENTER (100062)**, 1500 S.W. 1st Avenue, Zip 34471–6504, Mailing Address: P.O. Box 6000, Zip 34478–6000; tel. 352/351–7200 **A**1 3 5 9 10 **F**3 11 12 13 15 17 18 20 22 24 26 28 29 30 34 35 36 37 40 41 42 45 46 47 48 49 51 53 54 56 57 58 59 60 64 65 67 70 71 74 75 76 77 79 81 83 84 85 86 87 89 93 96 107 111 114 115 119 120 124 126 130 131 132 134 135 146 147 148 **P**6 8
Primary Contact: Stephen A. Purves, FACHE, President and Chief Executive Officer
COO: Paul Clark, Senior Vice President and Chief Operating Officer
CFO: Richard Mutarelli, Chief Financial Officer
CMO: Lon McPherson, M.D., Senior Vice President Medical Affairs and Chief Quality Officer
CIO: Carl Candullo, Chief Information Officer
CHR: Pamela W. Michell, R.N., Vice President and Chief Nursing Officer
CHR: Daniel O'Connor, Vice President Human Resources
CNO: Pamela W. Michell, R.N., Chief Nursing Officer
Web address: www.munroeregional.com
**Control:** Hospital district or authority, Government, nonfederal **Service:** General Medical and Surgical

| Staffed Beds: 420 **Admissions:** 21901 **Census:** 284 **Outpatient Visits:** 153092 **Births:** 2550 **Total Expense ($000):** 306998 **Payroll Expense ($000):** 119245 **Personnel:** 2425 |
| --- |

⊞ **OCALA REGIONAL MEDICAL CENTER (100212)**, 1431 S.W. First Avenue, Zip 34471–6500, Mailing Address: P.O. Box 2200, Zip 34478–2200; tel. 352/401–1000, (Includes WEST MARION COMMUNITY HOSPITAL, 4600 S.W. 46th Court, Zip 34471; tel. 352/291–3000), (Nonreporting) **A**1 2 9 10 **S** HCA, Nashville, TN
Primary Contact: Randy McVay, Chief Executive Officer
CMO: Art Osberg, M.D., Vice President and Chief Medical Officer
CIO: Taylor Dickerson, Director Information Services
CHR: Wayne Nielsen, Director Human Resources
Web address: www.ocalaregional.com
**Control:** Corporation, Investor–owned, for–profit **Service:** General Medical and Surgical

| Staffed Beds: 270 |
| --- |

**THE VINES (104071)**, 3130 S.W. 27th Avenue, Zip 34471–4306; tel. 352/671–3130, (Nonreporting) **A**9 10 **S** Universal Health Services, Inc., King of Prussia, PA
Primary Contact: Stephen Quintyne, Chief Executive Officer
Web address: www.thevineshospital.com
**Control:** Corporation, Investor–owned, for–profit **Service:** Psychiatric

| Staffed Beds: 90 |
| --- |

**OCOEE—Orange County**

⊞ **HEALTH CENTRAL (100030)**, 10000 West Colonial Drive, Zip 34761–3499; tel. 407/296–1000, (Total facility includes 228 beds in nursing home–type unit) **A**1 9 10 **F**3 8 11 12 13 15 17 18 20 22 26 28 29 30 34 35 37 40 45 49 50 51 57 59 60 70 73 74 76 79 81 85 86 87 89 93 97 107 108 110 111 115 119 128 129 130 132 144 146 148 **P**6 **S** Orlando Health, Orlando, FL
Primary Contact: Gregory P. Ohe, President and Chief Executive Officer
COO: Jennifer McCarthy, Chief Operating Officer
CFO: Michael E. Mueller, Chief Financial Officer
CMO: James Barton Rodier, M.D., Chief Quality Officer
CIO: John M. Sills, Chief Information Officer
CHR: John Sullivan, Vice President Human Resources
CNO: Susan E. Jackson, R.N., Senior Vice President
Web address: www.healthcentral.org
**Control:** Other not–for–profit (including NFP Corporation) **Service:** General Medical and Surgical

| Staffed Beds: 399 **Admissions:** 11334 **Census:** 328 **Outpatient Visits:** 115875 **Births:** 777 **Total Expense ($000):** 161550 **Payroll Expense ($000):** 71611 **Personnel:** 1077 |
| --- |

**OKEECHOBEE—Okeechobee County**

⊞ **RAULERSON HOSPITAL (100252)**, 1796 Highway 441 North, Zip 34972–1918, Mailing Address: P.O. Box 1307, Zip 34973–1307; tel. 863/763–2151, (Nonreporting) **A**1 9 10 20 **S** HCA, Nashville, TN
Primary Contact: Robert H. Lee, President
CFO: Heather Garvey, Chief Financial Officer
CMO: Mohammad Riaz, M.D., Chief of Staff
CIO: Doug Schneider, Director Information Systems
CHR: Janis Stevens, Director Human Resources
Web address: www.raulersonhospital.com
**Control:** Corporation, Investor–owned, for–profit **Service:** General Medical and Surgical

| Staffed Beds: 100 |
| --- |

**ORANGE CITY—Volusia County**

⊞ **FLORIDA HOSPITAL FISH MEMORIAL (100072)**, 1055 Saxon Boulevard, Zip 32763–8468; tel. 386/917–5000 **A**1 9 10 **F**1 3 4 11 15 16 17 20 28 29 30 31 34 35 37 40 45 48 49 59 64 67 70 72 73 74 75 76 77 78 79 80 81 82 85 87 88 89 90 91 92 93 98 100 104 107 108 110 111 114 115 116 117 118 119 120 121 128 129 130 132 135 144 146 147 148 **P**8 **S** Adventist Health System Sunbelt Health Care Corporation, Altamonte Springs, FL
Primary Contact: Ed Noseworthy, President and Chief Executive Officer
COO: Danielle Johnson, Chief Operating Officer
CFO: Eric Osterly, Chief Financial Officer
CIO: Trish Stebbins, Director Management Information Systems
CHR: Bonne S. Macpherson, Director Human Resources
CNO: Jennifer Shull, R.N., Chief Nursing Officer
Web address: www.fhfishmemorial.org
**Control:** Church–operated, Nongovernment, not–for profit **Service:** General Medical and Surgical

| Staffed Beds: 175 **Admissions:** 7978 **Census:** 96 **Outpatient Visits:** 60415 **Births:** 4 **Total Expense ($000):** 120905 **Payroll Expense ($000):** 44347 **Personnel:** 818 |
| --- |

*Many Facility Codes have changed. Please refer to the AHA Guide Code Chart.*    © 2013 AHA Guide

FL

## ORANGE PARK—Clay County

☒ **ORANGE PARK MEDICAL CENTER (100226)**, 2001 Kingsley Avenue, Zip 32073–5156; tel. 904/276–8500, (Nonreporting) **A**1 2 9 10 **S** HCA, Nashville, TN
Primary Contact: Thomas R. Pentz, President and Chief Executive Officer
COO: Marsha A. Easley, Chief Operating Officer
CFO: Bryce DeHaven, Chief Financial Officer
CMO: Lawrence Coots, M.D., Chief Medical Officer
CIO: Karen Parish, Director Information Systems
CHR: Thomas R. Pentz, Chief Executive Officer
CNO: Kathy Hester, Chief Nursing Officer
Web address: www.opmedical.com
**Control:** Corporation, Investor–owned, for–profit **Service:** General Medical and Surgical

**Staffed Beds:** 230

## ORLANDO—Orange County

**ARNOLD PALMER CHILDREN'S HOSPITAL** See Orlando Regional Medical Center

☐ **CENTRAL FLORIDA BEHAVIORAL HOSPITAL (104072)**, 6601 Central Florida Parkway, Zip 32821–8064; tel. 407/370–0111, (Nonreporting) **A**1 5 9 10 **S** Universal Health Services, Inc., King of Prussia, PA
Primary Contact: Vickie Lewis, Chief Executive Officer
Web address: www.centralfloridabehavioral.com
**Control:** Other not–for–profit (including NFP Corporation) **Service:** Psychiatric

**Staffed Beds:** 120

☒ △ ◇ **FLORIDA HOSPITAL (100007)**, 601 East Rollins Street, Zip 32803–1248; tel. 407/303–6611, (Includes DISNEY CHILDREN'S HOSPITAL, 601 East Rollins Street, tel. 407/303–9732; FLORIDA HOSPITAL CELEBRATION HEALTH, 400 Celebration Place, Celebration, Zip 34747; tel. 407/303–4000; Monica Reed, M.D., Administrator; FLORIDA HOSPITAL EAST ORLANDO, 7727 Lake Underhill Drive, Zip 32822; tel. 407/277–8110; FLORIDA HOSPITAL KISSIMMEE, 2450 North Orange Blossom Trai, Kissimmee, Zip 34741; tel. 407/846–4343; William Haupt, Administrator; FLORIDA HOSPITAL–ALTAMONTE, 601 East Altamonte Drive, Altamonte Springs, Zip 32701; tel. 407/830–4321; Rob Fulbright, Administrator; FLORIDA HOSPITAL–APOPKA, 201 North Park Avenue, Apopka, Zip 32703; tel. 407/889–2566; Verbelee Neilsen Swanson, Administrator; WINTER PARK MEMORIAL HOSPITAL, 200 North Lakemont Avenue, Winter Park, Zip 32792–3273; tel. 407/646–7000; Ken Bradley, Administrator) **A**1 2 3 5 7 8 9 10 21 **F**1 3 6 / 9 11 12 13 15 17 18 19 20 21 22 23 24 25 26 27 28 29 30 31 32 34 35 36 37 38 39 40 41 44 45 46 47 48 49 50 51 53 54 55 56 57 58 59 60 61 62 64 65 66 67 68 70 71 72 73 74 75 76 77 78 79 80 81 82 84 85 86 87 88 89 90 91 92 93 94 96 97 98 100 102 103 104 107 108 110 111 112 114 115 116 117 118 119 120 121 123 124 126 128 129 130 131 132 134 135 136 137 138 139 140 141 142 145 146 147 148 **P**1 6 8 **S** Adventist Health System Sunbelt Health Care Corporation, Altamonte Springs, FL
Primary Contact: Lars D. Houmann, President
COO: Brian Paradis, Chief Operating Officer
CFO: Eddie Soler, Chief Financial Officer
CMO: David Moorhead, M.D., Chief Medical Officer
CIO: Andy Crowder, Chief Information Officer
CHR: Sheryl Dodds, Chief Clinical Officer
Web address: www.flhosp.org
**Control:** Other not–for–profit (including NFP Corporation) **Service:** General Medical and Surgical

**Staffed Beds:** 2338 **Admissions:** 130100 **Census:** 1700 **Outpatient Visits:** 974896 **Births:** 9675 **Total Expense ($000):** 3113048 **Payroll Expense ($000):** 856672 **Personnel:** 16363

**LAKESIDE BEHAVIORAL HEALTHCARE–PRINCETON PLAZA (104067)**, 1800 Mercy Drive, Zip 32808–5646; tel. 407/875–3700, (Nonreporting) **A**5 9 10
Primary Contact: Jerry Kassab, President and Chief Executive Officer
Web address: www.lakesidecares.org
**Control:** Other not–for–profit (including NFP Corporation) **Service:** Psychiatric

**Staffed Beds:** 56

☒ **NEMOURS CHILDREN'S HOSPITAL (103304)**, 13535 Nemours Parkway, Zip 32827–7402; tel. 407/567–4000, (Nonreporting) **A**1 5 9 10 **S** Nemours, Jacksonville, FL
Primary Contact: Roger A. Oxendale, Chief Executive Officer
Web address: www.nemours.org
**Control:** Other not–for–profit (including NFP Corporation) **Service:** Children's general

**Staffed Beds:** 95

☒ **ORLANDO REGIONAL MEDICAL CENTER (100006)**, 1414 Kuhl Avenue, Zip 32806–2093; tel. 407/841–5111, (Includes ARNOLD PALMER CHILDREN'S HOSPITAL, 92 West Miller Street, Zip 32806; tel. 407/649–6960; John Bozard, President; ORLANDO REGIONAL SOUTH SEMINOLE HOSPITAL, 555 West State Road 434, Longwood, Zip 32750–4999; tel. 407/767–1200; Karen Frenier, President; ORLANDO REGIONAL–LUCERNE, 818 Main Lane, Zip 32801–3727; tel. 321/841–4200; WINNIE PALMER HOSPITAL FOR WOMEN AND BABIES, 83 West Miller Street, Zip 32806; tel. 321/843–2201; Kathy Swanson, President) **A**1 2 3 5 8 9 10 **F**3 4 5 8 11 12 13 15 16 17 18 19 20 21 22 23 24 25 26 27 28 29 30 31 34 35 37 40 41 43 44 45 46 49 50 51 53 54 55 57 58 59 60 61 62 64 68 70 71 72 73 74 75 76 77 78 79 80 81 82 84 85 86 87 88 89 90 91 92 93 94 96 97 98 99 100 101 102 103 104 107 108 110 111 114 115 116 117 118 119 120 121 123 124 126 129 130 131 132 134 135 146 147 148 **P**6 **S** Orlando Health, Orlando, FL
Primary Contact: Shannon Elswick, President
CFO: Paul Goldstein, Vice President Finance and Chief Financial Officer
CMO: Timothy Bullard, M.D., Chief of Staff
CIO: Rick Schooler, Vice President and Chief Information Officer
CHR: Nancy Dinon, Vice President Human Resources
Web address: www.orhs.org
**Control:** Other not–for–profit (including NFP Corporation) **Service:** General Medical and Surgical

**Staffed Beds:** 1468 **Admissions:** 80628 **Census:** 1111 **Outpatient Visits:** 732526 **Births:** 13528 **Total Expense ($000):** 1488120 **Payroll Expense ($000):** 622070 **Personnel:** 13946

☒ **SELECT SPECIALTY HOSPITAL–ORLANDO (102003)**, 2250 Bedford Road, Zip 32803–1443; tel. 407/303–7869, (Includes SELECT SPECIALTY HOSPITAL–ORLANDO SOUTH, 5579 South Orange Avenue, Zip 32809–3493; tel. 407/241–4800), (Nonreporting) **A**1 9 10 **S** Select Medical Corporation, Mechanicsburg, PA
Primary Contact: Nellie Castroman, Chief Executive Officer
Web address: www.selectspecialtyhospitals.com/company/locations/orlando.aspx
**Control:** Corporation, Investor–owned, for–profit **Service:** Long–Term Acute Care hospital

**Staffed Beds:** 75

**SELECT SPECIALTY HOSPITAL–ORLANDO SOUTH** See Select Specialty Hospital–Orlando

**WINNIE PALMER HOSPITAL FOR WOMEN AND BABIES** See Orlando Regional Medical Center

## OXFORD—Sumter County

**PROMISE HOSPITAL OF FLORIDA AT THE VILLAGES (102028)**, 5050 County Road, Zip 34484; tel. 352/689–6400 **A**10 **F**3 29 30 34 45 50 57 59 60 70 130 146 148 **S** Promise Healthcare, Boca Raton, FL
Primary Contact: Steven M. Klein, Chief Executive Officer
Web address: www.promise–villages.com
**Control:** Corporation, Investor–owned, for–profit **Service:** General Medical and Surgical

**Staffed Beds:** 40 **Admissions:** 192 **Census:** 13 **Births:** 0

## PALATKA—Putnam County

☒ **PUTNAM COMMUNITY MEDICAL CENTER (100232)**, Highway 20 West, Zip 32177–8118, Mailing Address: P.O. Box 778, Zip 32178–0778; tel. 386/328–5711, (Nonreporting) **A**1 9 10 19 **S** LifePoint Hospitals, Inc., Brentwood, TN
Primary Contact: Jerry Christine, Chief Executive Officer
CFO: Debra Noyes, Chief Financial Officer
CMO: Joseph Stillword, Chief of Staff
CIO: Yvette A. Jones, HIM Director
CHR: John Schneider, Human Resources Director
CNO: Carol Negoshian, MSN, Chief Nursing Officer
Web address: www.pcmcfl.com
**Control:** Corporation, Investor–owned, for–profit **Service:** General Medical and Surgical

**Staffed Beds:** 99

## PALM BEACH GARDENS—Palm Beach County

☒ **PALM BEACH GARDENS MEDICAL CENTER (100176)**, 3360 Burns Road, Zip 33410–4323; tel. 561/622–1411, (Nonreporting) **A**1 9 10 **S** TENET Healthcare Corporation, Dallas, TX
Primary Contact: Larry Coomes, Chief Executive Officer
CFO: Judi Stimson–Rusin, Chief Financial Officer
CIO: James Vega, Director Information Systems
CHR: Kevin Caracciolo, Chief Human Resources Officer
Web address: www.pbgmc.com
**Control:** Corporation, Investor–owned, for–profit **Service:** General Medical and Surgical

**Staffed Beds:** 199

FL

---

**Hospital, Medicare Provider Number, Address, Telephone, Approval, Facility, and Physician Codes, Health Care System**

★ American Hospital Association (AHA) membership
☐ The Joint Commission accreditation
◇ DNV Healthcare Inc. accreditation
◯ Healthcare Facilities Accreditation Program
△ Commission on Accreditation of Rehabilitation Facilities (CARF) accreditation

## PALM COAST—Flagler County

✠ **FLORIDA HOSPITAL–FLAGLER (100118)**, 60 Memorial Medical Parkway, Zip 32164–5980; tel. 386/586–2000 **A**1 2 9 10 **F**11 15 18 20 22 28 29 30 31 34 35 40 45 46 47 49 50 51 54 57 59 60 62 63 64 68 70 74 75 77 78 79 81 85 86 87 93 97 107 108 110 111 114 115 117 119 120 121 123 124 126 130 132 135 144 146 147 **P**6 **S** Adventist Health System Sunbelt Health Care Corporation, Altamonte Springs, FL
Primary Contact: Kenneth R. Mattison, Chief Executive Officer
CFO: Valerie Ziesmer, Chief Financial Officer
CMO: John Walsh, M.D., Chief Medical Officer
CHR: Joshua I. Champion, Director
CNO: Ellen R. Lenkevich, Chief Nursing Officer
Web address: www.floridahospitalflagler.com/
**Control:** Church–operated, Nongovernment, not–for profit **Service:** General Medical and Surgical

**Staffed Beds:** 99 **Admissions:** 6752 **Census:** 73 **Outpatient Visits:** 63149
**Births:** 0 **Total Expense ($000):** 106164 **Payroll Expense ($000):** 38456
**Personnel:** 784

## PANAMA CITY—Bay County

✠ **BAY MEDICAL CENTER SACRED HEART (100026)**, (Formerly Bay Medical Center), 615 North Bonita Avenue, Zip 32401–3600, Mailing Address: P.O. Box 59515, Zip 32412–0515; tel. 850/769–1511 **A**1 2 9 10 **F**3 7 8 11 13 14 15 17 18 20 22 24 26 28 29 30 34 35 40 41 42 45 49 53 54 57 58 59 60 61 64 65 68 70 74 75 77 78 79 80 81 82 87 93 107 108 109 110 111 114 119 121 123 126 129 130 131 132 134 135 143 144 146 147 148 **S** LHP Hospital Group, Plano, TX
Primary Contact: Barry L. Keel, Chief Executive Officer
COO: Daniel R. Morgan, Chief Operating Officer
CFO: Christopher Brooks, Vice President Finance
CMO: Ingrid Rachesky, M.D., President Medical Staff
CIO: Tom Bialorvcki, Chief Information Officer
CHR: Donna Baird, Vice President Corporate Services
Web address: www.baymedical.org
**Control:** Corporation, Investor–owned, for–profit **Service:** General Medical and Surgical

**Staffed Beds:** 273 **Admissions:** 15903 **Census:** 202 **Outpatient Visits:** 181860 **Births:** 271 **Total Expense ($000):** 251879 **Payroll Expense ($000):** 92229 **Personnel:** 1387

☐ **EMERALD COAST BEHAVIORAL HOSPITAL (104073)**, 1940 Harrison Avenue, Zip 32405–4542; tel. 850/763–0017, (Nonreporting) **A**1 9 10 **S** Universal Health Services, Inc., King of Prussia, PA
Primary Contact: Tim Bedford, Chief Executive Officer
Web address: www.emeraldcoastbehavioral.com
**Control:** Corporation, Investor–owned, for–profit **Service:** Psychiatric

**Staffed Beds:** 80

✠ **GULF COAST MEDICAL CENTER (100242)**, 449 West 23rd Street, Zip 32405–4593, Mailing Address: P.O. Box 15309, Zip 32406–5309; tel. 850/769–8341 **A**1 2 9 10 **F**8 12 13 15 20 22 26 29 30 31 34 35 37 39 40 41 46 47 48 49 51 54 56 57 59 60 64 68 74 75 77 78 79 81 85 86 87 93 107 108 109 111 114 116 117 118 119 126 130 131 132 135 144 146 147 148 **S** HCA, Nashville, TN
Primary Contact: Carlton Ulmer, Chief Executive Officer
COO: Nancy Dodson, Chief Operating Officer
CFO: Laurie Haynes, Chief Financial Officer
CHR: Wanda Salley, Administrative Director Human Resources
Web address: www.egulfcoastmedical.com
**Control:** Corporation, Investor–owned, for–profit **Service:** General Medical and Surgical

**Staffed Beds:** 176 **Admissions:** 11664 **Census:** 117 **Outpatient Visits:** 112788 **Births:** 2469 **Total Expense ($000):** 128589 **Payroll Expense ($000):** 40004 **Personnel:** 589

✠ **HEALTHSOUTH EMERALD COAST REHABILITATION HOSPITAL (103040)**, 1847 Florida Avenue, Zip 32405–4640; tel. 850/914–8600 **A**1 9 10 **F**3 28 29 34 57 59 64 68 75 77 85 86 87 90 91 93 95 96 129 130 131 132 146 148 **S** HEALTHSOUTH Corporation, Birmingham, AL
Primary Contact: Tony N. Bennett, Chief Executive Officer
CFO: Angela Eddins, Controller
CMO: Michael Hennigan, M.D., Medical Director
CHR: Traci Powell, Director Human Resources
Web address: www.healthsouthpanamacity.com
**Control:** Corporation, Investor–owned, for–profit **Service:** Rehabilitation

**Staffed Beds:** 75 **Admissions:** 1428 **Census:** 52 **Outpatient Visits:** 5489
**Births:** 0 **Total Expense ($000):** 17928 **Payroll Expense ($000):** 10074
**Personnel:** 207

✠ **SELECT SPECIALTY HOSPITAL–PANAMA CITY (102017)**, 615 North Bonita Avenue, 3rd Floor, Zip 32401–3623; tel. 850/767–3180, (Nonreporting) **A**1 9 10 **S** Select Medical Corporation, Mechanicsburg, PA
Primary Contact: Debra R. Gibson, Chief Executive Officer
CMO: Amir Manzoor, M.D., Medical Director
Web address: www.selectspecialtyhospitals.com/company/locations/panamacity.aspx
**Control:** Corporation, Investor–owned, for–profit **Service:** Long–Term Acute Care hospital

**Staffed Beds:** 30

## PEMBROKE PINES—Broward County

✠ **MEMORIAL HOSPITAL PEMBROKE (100230)**, 7800 Sheridan Street, Zip 33024–2536; tel. 954/883–8482 **A**1 9 10 **F**3 8 12 17 29 30 40 45 46 47 48 49 50 51 59 60 64 70 79 81 82 83 85 86 87 107 111 114 115 119 129 130 132 144 146 148 **S** Memorial Healthcare System, Hollywood, FL
Primary Contact: Keith W. Gallagher, FACHE, Administrator and Chief Executive Officer
CFO: Joseph Stuczynski, Assistant Administrator Finance and Support
CMO: Stanley Marks, M.D., Chief Medical Officer
CIO: Forest Blanton, Chief Information Officer
CHR: Margie Vargas, Director Human Resources
CNO: Judy Frum, R.N., Chief Nursing Officer
Web address: www.memorialpembroke.com/
**Control:** Hospital district or authority, Government, nonfederal **Service:** General Medical and Surgical

**Staffed Beds:** 149 **Admissions:** 6214 **Census:** 70 **Outpatient Visits:** 114274
**Births:** 0 **Total Expense ($000):** 116696 **Payroll Expense ($000):** 49565

✠ **MEMORIAL HOSPITAL WEST (100281)**, 703 North Flamingo Road, Zip 33028–1014; tel. 954/436–5000 **A**1 9 10 **F**3 13 15 17 18 20 22 26 28 29 30 31 34 35 36 40 41 45 46 47 49 51 53 55 56 57 59 60 61 64 68 70 72 74 75 76 79 81 82 85 87 91 92 93 107 108 110 111 114 115 118 119 120 121 123 124 126 130 131 132 136 145 146 147 148 **S** Memorial Healthcare System, Hollywood, FL
Primary Contact: C. Kennon Hetlage, FACHE, Administrator and Chief Executive Officer
COO: Sue E. Bradford, R.N., Chief Nursing Officer
CFO: Walter Bussell, Chief Financial Officer
CMO: Eric Freling, M.D., Director Medical Staff Affairs
CMO: Miguel Venereo, M.D., Director Medical Staff
CIO: Forest Blanton, Chief Information Officer
CHR: Christopher Perry, Director Human Resources
CNO: Grisel Fernandez–Bravo, R.N., Chief Nursing Officer
Web address: www.mhs.net
**Control:** Hospital district or authority, Government, nonfederal **Service:** General Medical and Surgical

**Staffed Beds:** 384 **Admissions:** 21539 **Census:** 252 **Outpatient Visits:** 268134 **Births:** 4357 **Total Expense ($000):** 420769 **Payroll Expense ($000):** 136738 **Personnel:** 1852

## PENSACOLA—Escambia County

✠ **BAPTIST HOSPITAL (100093)**, 1000 West Moreno, Zip 32501–2316, Mailing Address: P.O. Box 17500, Zip 32522–7500; tel. 850/434–4011 **A**1 2 9 10 **F**3 7 8 11 12 13 15 17 18 20 22 24 26 28 29 30 31 34 35 37 40 43 45 46 47 48 49 50 51 52 54 55 56 57 58 59 60 61 62 63 64 67 70 74 75 76 77 78 79 81 82 84 85 86 87 92 93 97 98 99 100 101 102 103 104 107 108 110 111 114 115 116 117 118 119 120 121 123 124 126 129 130 131 132 135 144 146 147 148 **P**4 6 **S** Baptist Health Care Corporation, Pensacola, FL
Primary Contact: David Wildebrandt, Administrator
CFO: Kerry Vermillion, Senior Vice President Finance and Chief Financial Officer
CMO: Coy Irvin, M.D., Vice President and Chief Medical Officer
CIO: Robert Johnson, Vice President and Chief Information Officer
CHR: Glenn Carnathan, Vice President Human Resources
Web address: www.ebaptisthealthcare.org
**Control:** Other not–for–profit (including NFP Corporation) **Service:** General Medical and Surgical

**Staffed Beds:** 339 **Admissions:** 17362 **Census:** 221 **Outpatient Visits:** 250715 **Births:** 998 **Total Expense ($000):** 295777 **Payroll Expense ($000):** 85846 **Personnel:** 1493

✠ **NAVAL HOSPITAL PENSACOLA**, (Formerly Naval Hospital), 6000 West Highway 98, Zip 32512–0003; tel. 850/505–6413 **A**1 3 5 **F**3 5 13 15 18 29 30 32 33 34 35 38 39 40 45 49 50 51 53 54 55 57 58 59 64 65 68 70 74 75 76 77 79 81 85 86 87 92 93 97 100 101 102 104 107 108 110 111 114 115 118 119 124 129 130 131 135 146 147 148 **S** Bureau of Medicine and Surgery, Department of the Navy, Washington, DC
Primary Contact: Commander Devin Morrison, Director Administration
COO: Commander Chris O'Donnell, Director for Administration
CMO: Captain Connie Stamateris, M.D., Director Medical Services
CHR: Commander Ron Martel, Director for Administration
Web address: www.med.navy.mil/sites/pcola/Pages/default.aspx
**Control:** Navy, Government, federal **Service:** General Medical and Surgical

**Staffed Beds:** 28 **Admissions:** 2002 **Census:** 13 **Outpatient Visits:** 628409
**Births:** 490 **Personnel:** 1874

**REHABILITATION INSTITUTE OF WEST FLORIDA** See West Florida Hospital

FL

☒ **SACRED HEART HOSPITAL OF PENSACOLA (100025)**, 5151 North Ninth Avenue, Zip 32504–8795, Mailing Address: P.O. Box 2700, Zip 32513–2700; tel. 850/416–7000 **A**1 2 3 5 9 10 13 **F**3 7 8 11 12 13 15 17 18 20 22 24 26 28 29 30 31 32 34 35 39 40 41 43 44 45 46 49 50 54 56 57 58 59 64 68 70 71 72 73 74 75 76 77 78 79 80 81 82 84 85 86 87 88 89 92 93 97 107 108 110 111 114 115 116 117 118 119 120 121 123 124 126 130 131 132 135 146 147 148 **P**7 **S** Ascension Health, Saint Louis, MO
Primary Contact: Henry Stovall, President
COO: Kerry Eaton, R.N., Chief Operating Officer
CFO: Buddy Elmore, Chief Financial Officer
CMO: Paul T. Baroco, M.D., Chief Medical Officer
CMO: James Ward, M.D., Chief Medical Officer
CIO: Kathy Ross, Chief Information Officer
CHR: Carol Whittington, Chief Human Resources Officer
CNO: Amy Wilson, Interim Chief Nursing Officer
Web address: www.sacred–heart.org
**Control:** Other not–for–profit (including NFP Corporation) **Service:** General Medical and Surgical

**Staffed Beds:** 466 **Admissions:** 25865 **Census:** 325 **Outpatient Visits:** 346353 **Births:** 3641 **Total Expense ($000):** 365007 **Payroll Expense ($000):** 117408 **Personnel:** 2530

☒ **SELECT SPECIALTY HOSPITAL–PENSACOLA (102024)**, 7000 Cobble Creek Drive, Zip 32504–8638; tel. 850/473–4800, (Nonreporting) **A**1 9 10 **S** Select Medical Corporation, Mechanicsburg, PA
Primary Contact: David Goodson, Chief Executive Officer
CMO: John Bray, M.D., Medical Director
Web address: www.selectspecialtyhospitals.com/company/locations/pensacola.aspx
**Control:** Corporation, Investor–owned, for–profit **Service:** Long–Term Acute Care hospital

**Staffed Beds:** 54

☒ **WEST FLORIDA HOSPITAL (100231)**, 8383 North Davis Highway, Zip 32514–6088; tel. 850/494–4000, (Includes REHABILITATION INSTITUTE OF WEST FLORIDA, 8383 North Davis Highway, Zip 32514, Mailing Address: P.O. Box 18900, Zip 32523; tel. 850/494–6000; THE PAVILION, 8383 North Davis Highway, Zip 32523, Mailing Address: P.O. Box 18900, Zip 32523; tel. 904/494–5000), (Nonreporting) **A**1 2 9 10 **S** HCA, Nashville, TN
Primary Contact: Brian Baumgardner, Chief Executive Officer
COO: Robert Peterson, Chief Operating Officer
CFO: Randy Butler, Chief Financial Officer
CIO: Jeff Amerson, Director Information System
CHR: Karen Oliver, Vice President Human Resources
Web address: www.westfloridahospital.com
**Control:** Corporation, Investor–owned, for–profit **Service:** General Medical and Surgical

**Staffed Beds:** 339

**PERRY—Taylor County**

**DOCTOR'S MEMORIAL HOSPITAL (100106)**, 333 North Byron Butler Parkway, Zip 32347–2300; tel. 850/584–0800 **A**9 10 20 **F**3 7 11 15 29 30 34 35 40 45 50 57 59 62 70 81 85 89 93 107 110 111 114 119 127 129 132 133 146 **P**6
Primary Contact: Geri Forbes, Chief Executive Officer
CFO: James L. Leis, Jr., Chief Financial Officer
CMO: Ron Emerick, M.D., Chief of Staff
CIO: Joseph Sprinkle, Chief Information Officer
CHR: Diana McRory, Director Human Resources
CNO: Michael Windham, Chief Nursing Officer
Web address: www.doctorsmemorial.com
**Control:** Other not–for–profit (including NFP Corporation) **Service:** General Medical and Surgical

**Staffed Beds:** 45 **Admissions:** 961 **Census:** 8 **Outpatient Visits:** 25028 **Births:** 0 **Total Expense ($000):** 27847 **Payroll Expense ($000):** 12058 **Personnel:** 263

**PLANT CITY—Hillsborough County**

☒ **SOUTH FLORIDA BAPTIST HOSPITAL (100132)**, 301 North Alexander Street, Zip 33563–4303, Mailing Address: Drawer H, Zip 33564–9058; tel. 813/757–1200 **A**1 9 10 **F**3 11 12 13 15 18 20 22 29 30 31 34 35 40 44 45 47 48 49 51 57 59 64 68 70 71 74 75 76 77 78 79 81 85 86 87 89 93 94 107 108 110 111 114 115 117 118 119 126 130 131 132 135 146 148 **P**7 **S** Catholic Health East, Newtown Square, PA
Primary Contact: Stephen Nierman, Interim Chief Executive Officer
COO: Stephen Nierman, Chief Executive Officer
CFO: Cathy Yoder, Chief Financial Officer
CMO: Mark Vaaler, M.D., Chief Medical Officer
CHR: Juanita Radford, Coordinator Team Resource
Web address: www.sjbhealth.org
**Control:** Other not–for–profit (including NFP Corporation) **Service:** General Medical and Surgical

**Staffed Beds:** 147 **Admissions:** 5934 **Census:** 61 **Outpatient Visits:** 58794 **Births:** 365 **Total Expense ($000):** 81055 **Payroll Expense ($000):** 32876 **Personnel:** 583

**PLANTATION—Broward County**

☒ **PLANTATION GENERAL HOSPITAL (100167)**, 401 N.W. 42nd Avenue, Zip 33317–2882; tel. 954/587–5010, (Includes MERCY HOSPITAL – A CAMPUS OF PLANTATION GENERAL HOSPITAL, 3663 South Miami Avenue, Miami, Zip 33133–4237; tel. 305/854–4400; Barbara Simmons, R.N., Chief Executive Officer), (Nonreporting) **A**1 2 9 10 **S** HCA, Nashville, TN
Primary Contact: Randy Gross, Chief Executive Officer
COO: Bryan Miller, Chief Operating Officer
CFO: Irfan Mirza, Chief Financial Officer
CIO: David Irizarri, Director Management Information Systems
CHR: Linda Bryan, Vice President Human Resources
CNO: Dolores Skaare, R.N., Chief Nursing Officer
Web address: www.plantationgeneral.com
**Control:** Corporation, Investor–owned, for–profit **Service:** General Medical and Surgical

**Staffed Beds:** 264

☒ **WESTSIDE REGIONAL MEDICAL CENTER (100228)**, 8201 West Broward Boulevard, Zip 33324–2701; tel. 954/473–6600 **A**1 2 9 10 **F**3 11 15 17 18 20 22 24 26 29 30 31 34 35 40 44 45 48 49 50 57 59 60 68 70 74 75 77 78 79 80 81 82 85 86 87 93 107 108 110 111 114 115 117 119 126 129 130 131 132 135 145 146 148 **S** HCA, Nashville, TN
Primary Contact: Lee B. Chaykin, Chief Executive Officer
COO: Shana Sappington–Crittenden, Chief Operating Officer
CFO: Kevin Corcoran, Chief Financial Officer
CMO: Brian Weinstein, M.D., Chief of Staff
CIO: Andres Blanco, Director Management Information Systems
CHR: Maria Rivera, Director Human Resources
Web address: www.westsideregional.com
**Control:** Corporation, Investor–owned, for–profit **Service:** General Medical and Surgical

**Staffed Beds:** 215 **Admissions:** 12664 **Census:** 145 **Outpatient Visits:** 58145 **Births:** 0 **Total Expense ($000):** 126908 **Payroll Expense ($000):** 48914 **Personnel:** 624

**PORT CHARLOTTE—Charlotte County**

☐ **BAYFRONT HEALTH PORT CHARLOTTE (100077)**, (Formerly Peace River Regional Medical Center), 2500 Harbor Boulevard, Zip 33952–5000; tel. 941/766–4122, (Nonreporting) **A**1 9 10 **S** Health Management Associates, Naples, FL
Primary Contact: Richard H. Satcher, Market Chief Executive Officer
CFO: Robert Stiekes, Chief Financial Officer
CIO: Ted Bailey, Vice President Information Systems
Web address: www.peaceriverregional.com
**Control:** Corporation, Investor–owned, for–profit **Service:** General Medical and Surgical

**Staffed Beds:** 190

☒ △ **FAWCETT MEMORIAL HOSPITAL (100236)**, 21298 Olean Boulevard, Zip 33952–6765, Mailing Address: P.O. Box 494960, Punta Gorda, Zip 33949–4960; tel. 941/629–1181, (Nonreporting) **A**1 2 7 9 10 **S** HCA, Nashville, TN
Primary Contact: Thomas J. Rice, FACHE, President and Chief Executive Officer
COO: Alex Chang, Vice President and Chief Operating Officer
CFO: James P. Burns, Vice President and Chief Financial Officer
CHR: Tony Welch, Vice President Human Resources
Web address: www.fawcetthospital.com
**Control:** Corporation, Investor–owned, for–profit **Service:** General Medical and Surgical

**Staffed Beds:** 238

**FL**

## PORT ST. JOE—Gulf County

☒ **SACRED HEART HOSPITAL ON THE GULF (100313)**, 3801 East Highway 98, Zip 32456–5318; tel. 850/229–5600 **A**1 9 10 **F**3 11 15 29 30 31 34 35 40 44 45 48 50 54 57 59 64 68 79 81 85 89 90 93 107 110 114 119 130 131 133 146 147 **P**7 **S** Ascension Health, Saint Louis, MO
Primary Contact: Roger L. Hall, President
Web address: www.sacred-heart.org/gulf/
**Control:** Other not–for–profit (including NFP Corporation) **Service:** General Medical and Surgical

**Staffed Beds:** 19 **Admissions:** 493 **Census:** 4 **Outpatient Visits:** 15840 **Births:** 0 **Total Expense ($000):** 17770 **Payroll Expense ($000):** 5420 **Personnel:** 82

## PORT ST. LUCIE—St. Lucie County

☐ **PORT ST. LUCIE HOSPITAL (104070)**, 2550 S.E. Walton Road, Zip 34952–7168; tel. 772/335–0400, (Nonreporting) **A**1 9 10
Primary Contact: John Sannuto, Chief Executive Officer
Web address: www.portstluciehospitalinc.com
**Control:** Other not–for–profit (including NFP Corporation) **Service:** Psychiatric

**Staffed Beds:** 75

☒ **ST. LUCIE MEDICAL CENTER (100260)**, 1800 S.E. Tiffany Avenue, Zip 34952–7521; tel. 772/335–4000, (Nonreporting) **A**1 2 9 10 13 **S** HCA, Nashville, TN
Primary Contact: Gary Cantrell, President and Chief Executive Officer
COO: Calvin Thomas, IV, Chief Operating Officer
CFO: Kevin Keeling, Chief Financial Officer
Web address: www.stluciemed.com
**Control:** Corporation, Investor–owned, for–profit **Service:** General Medical and Surgical

**Staffed Beds:** 194

## PUNTA GORDA—Charlotte County

☐ **BAYFRONT HEALTH PUNTA GORDA (100047)**, (Formerly Charlotte Regional Medical Center), 809 East Marion Avenue, Zip 33950–3819, Mailing Address: P.O. Box 51–1328, Zip 33951–1328; tel. 941/639–3131 **A**1 9 10 **F**3 17 18 28 29 30 31 34 35 36 38 39 40 44 45 50 53 54 56 57 59 60 64 68 70 74 75 77 78 79 81 85 86 87 93 94 98 100 101 102 103 107 108 110 111 115 118 119 126 130 131 132 135 146 148 **S** Health Management Associates, Naples, FL
Primary Contact: Jose F. Morillo, Chief Executive Officer
CFO: Cheryl Tibbett, Chief Financial Officer
Web address: www.charlotteregional.com
**Control:** Corporation, Investor–owned, for–profit **Service:** General Medical and Surgical

**Staffed Beds:** 208 **Admissions:** 6524 **Census:** 104 **Births:** 0 **Personnel:** 512

## RIVIERA BEACH—Palm Beach County

☒ **KINDRED HOSPITAL THE PALM BEACHES (102025)**, 5555 West Blue Heron Boulevard, Zip 33418–7813; tel. 561/840–0754 **A**1 9 10 **F**1 3 18 29 30 45 48 70 74 75 77 79 82 84 85 91 97 100 107 114 145 148 **P**5 **S** Kindred Healthcare, Louisville, KY
Primary Contact: Timothy Page, Chief Executive Officer
Web address: www.khthepalmbeaches.com/
**Control:** Corporation, Investor–owned, for–profit **Service:** Long–Term Acute Care hospital

**Staffed Beds:** 70 **Admissions:** 549 **Census:** 40 **Outpatient Visits:** 0 **Births:** 0 **Total Expense ($000):** 17401 **Payroll Expense ($000):** 8148

## ROCKLEDGE—Brevard County

☐ **WUESTHOFF MEDICAL CENTER – ROCKLEDGE (100092)**, 110 Longwood Avenue, Zip 32955–2887; Box 565002, Mail Stop 1, Zip 32956–5002; tel. 321/636–2211 **A**1 9 10 **F**3 11 13 15 17 18 20 22 24 26 28 29 30 31 34 40 49 50 51 54 56 57 58 59 60 61 62 64 68 70 72 74 75 76 77 78 79 80 81 82 84 85 86 87 89 92 93 98 100 101 102 103 107 108 111 114 115 119 126 129 130 131 132 135 144 146 147 148 **S** Health Management Associates, Naples, FL
Primary Contact: Timothy J. Cerullo, Chief Executive Officer
CFO: Richard Haun, Chief Financial Officer
CMO: Vinay Mehindru, M.D., Medical Director
CIO: David Barnhart, Director Information Systems
CHR: Marchita H. Marino, Vice President Human Resources
Web address: www.wuesthoff.org
**Control:** Corporation, Investor–owned, for–profit **Service:** General Medical and Surgical

**Staffed Beds:** 298 **Admissions:** 12707 **Census:** 168 **Outpatient Visits:** 239862 **Births:** 552 **Total Expense ($000):** 162374 **Payroll Expense ($000):** 68562 **Personnel:** 2188

## SAFETY HARBOR—Pinellas County

☐ **MEASE COUNTRYSIDE HOSPITAL (100265)**, 3231 McMullen–Booth Road, Zip 34695–6607, Mailing Address: P.O. Box 1098, Zip 34695–1098; tel. 727/725–6222 **A**1 2 9 10 **F**3 13 15 17 18 20 22 26 28 29 30 31 34 37 40 41 44 45 46 49 51 59 60 64 68 70 72 73 75 76 77 78 79 81 84 85 86 87 89 93 107 108 109 111 114 115 116 117 118 119 126 129 130 131 132 143 145 146 147 148 **P**6 **S** Morton Plant Mease Health Care, Clearwater, FL
Primary Contact: Glenn D. Waters, FACHE, President
COO: Lou Galdieri, R.N., Chief Operating Officer and Administrator
CFO: Carl Tremonti, Chief Financial Officer
CMO: Donald Pocock, M.D., Chief Medical Officer
CHR: Sharon Collotta, Director Human Resources
Web address: www.mpmhealth.com
**Control:** Other not–for–profit (including NFP Corporation) **Service:** General Medical and Surgical

**Staffed Beds:** 300 **Admissions:** 16433 **Census:** 197 **Outpatient Visits:** 112999 **Births:** 2075 **Total Expense ($000):** 213030 **Payroll Expense ($000):** 79285 **Personnel:** 1208

## SAINT AUGUSTINE—St. Johns County

☐ **FLAGLER HOSPITAL (100090)**, 400 Health Park Boulevard, Zip 32086–5784; tel. 904/819–5155, (Nonreporting) **A**1 2 9 10 20
Primary Contact: Joseph S. Gordy, President
COO: Jason P. Barrett, Chief Operating Officer
CFO: Lynda I. Kirker, Chief Financial Officer
CMO: Douglas Dew, M.D., President Medical Staff
CIO: Bill Rieger, Chief Information Officer
CHR: Jeff Hurley, Vice President Human Resources
Web address: www.flaglerhospital.org
**Control:** Other not–for–profit (including NFP Corporation) **Service:** General Medical and Surgical

**Staffed Beds:** 336

## SAINT CLOUD—Osceola County

☐ **ST. CLOUD REGIONAL MEDICAL CENTER (100302)**, 2906 17th Street, Zip 34769–6099; tel. 407/892–2135 **A**1 9 10 **F**3 15 18 29 30 34 35 40 45 46 49 51 57 59 70 74 75 77 78 79 81 82 85 86 87 91 93 94 96 97 107 108 110 111 115 119 146 **S** Health Management Associates, Naples, FL
Primary Contact: Robert Brooks, Chief Executive Officer
COO: Tom Patrias, Chief Operating Officer
CMO: Paul Thorne, M.D., Chief Medical Director
CIO: James Devlin, Director Information Systems
CHR: Daniel Avila, Director Human Resources
Web address: www.stcloudregional.com
**Control:** Corporation, Investor–owned, for–profit **Service:** General Medical and Surgical

**Staffed Beds:** 84 **Admissions:** 4545 **Census:** 51 **Births:** 0

## SAINT PETERSBURG—Pinellas County

☒ **ALL CHILDREN'S HOSPITAL (103300)**, 501 6th Avenue South, Zip 33701–4634; tel. 727/898–7451 **A**1 3 5 8 9 10 **F**3 11 17 18 19 20 21 22 23 24 25 26 27 29 30 31 32 34 35 36 37 39 40 41 43 44 45 46 47 48 49 50 54 55 57 58 59 60 61 64 65 68 72 73 74 75 77 78 79 81 82 84 85 86 87 88 89 92 93 96 97 99 100 107 111 114 115 116 118 119 129 130 131 132 134 135 136 137 141 142 143 144 146 148 **P**6 **S** Johns Hopkins Health System, Baltimore, MD
Primary Contact: Jonathan M. Ellen, M.D., President
CFO: Nancy Templin, Vice President Finance and Chief Financial Officer
CMO: Michael Epstein, M.D., Senior Vice President Medical Affairs
CIO: Cal Popovich, Vice President Information Technology
CHR: Jay Kuhns, Vice President Human Resources
Web address: www.allkids.org
**Control:** Other not–for–profit (including NFP Corporation) **Service:** Children's general

**Staffed Beds:** 259 **Admissions:** 8830 **Census:** 200 **Outpatient Visits:** 328616 **Births:** 0 **Total Expense ($000):** 350634 **Payroll Expense ($000):** 146061 **Personnel:** 2827

☒ △ **BAYFRONT HEALTH ST. PETERSBURG (100032)**, (Formerly Bayfront Medical Center), 701 Sixth Street South, Zip 33701–4891; tel. 727/823–1234, (Nonreporting) **A**1 3 5 7 9 10 **S** Health Management Associates, Naples, FL
Primary Contact: Kathryn Gillette, President and Chief Executive Officer
COO: Eric Feder, Executive Vice President and Chief Operating Officer
CFO: Bob Thornton, Executive Vice President and Chief Financial Officer
CMO: David Weiland, M.D., Vice President Medical Affairs
CIO: Jennifer Greenman, Chief Information Officer
CHR: Deborah Menendez, Vice President Human Resources
CNO: Karen Long, R.N., Vice President Nursing
Web address: www.bayfront.org
**Control:** Corporation, Investor–owned, for–profit **Service:** General Medical and Surgical

**Staffed Beds:** 395

*Many Facility Codes have changed. Please refer to the AHA Guide Code Chart.* © 2013 AHA Guide

✠ **EDWARD WHITE HOSPITAL (100239)**, 2323 Ninth Avenue North, Zip 33713–6898, Mailing Address: P.O. Box 12018, Zip 33733–2018; tel. 727/323–1111, (Nonreporting) **A**1 9 10 **S** HCA, Nashville, TN
Primary Contact: Sharon Hayes, Chief Executive Officer
COO: Richard S. Frank, Vice President Operations
CFO: Peggy Gatliff, Chief Financial Officer
CMO: Fadi Saba, M.D., Chief of Staff
CIO: Donna Leitenberger, Director Information Services
CHR: Bonnie O'Laskey, Vice President Human Resources
Web address: www.edwardwhitehospital.com
**Control:** Corporation, Investor–owned, for–profit **Service:** General Medical and Surgical

Staffed Beds: 110

✠ **NORTHSIDE HOSPITAL AND HEART INSTITUTE (100238)**, 6000 49th Street North, Zip 33709–2145; tel. 727/521–4411 **A**1 9 10 12 13 **F**3 17 18 20 22 24 26 28 29 30 31 34 35 40 45 49 50 51 53 56 57 58 59 64 65 70 74 75 77 78 79 81 85 92 93 107 108 111 114 115 118 119 135 146 **S** HCA, Nashville, TN
Primary Contact: Dia Nichols, Chief Executive Officer
COO: Mark Miller, Chief Operating Officer
CFO: Shalin Shah, Chief Financial Officer
CIO: Steve McDonald, Director Information Systems
CHR: Maggie Miklos, Director Human Resources
Web address: www.northsidehospital.com
**Control:** Corporation, Investor–owned, for–profit **Service:** General Medical and Surgical

Staffed Beds: 225 Admissions: 8946 Census: 108 Outpatient Visits: 40122 Births: 0 Total Expense ($000): 109922 Payroll Expense ($000): 43180 Personnel: 524

△ ◇ **PALMS OF PASADENA HOSPITAL (100126)**, 1501 Pasadena Avenue South, Zip 33707–3798; tel. 727/381–1000, (Nonreporting) **A**7 9 10 21 **S** IASIS Healthcare, Franklin, TN
Primary Contact: Brian I. Flynn, Chief Executive Officer
CMO: David Long, M.D., Chief of Staff
CIO: Ron Truitt, Director Information Services
CHR: Karen Casteel, Director Human Resources
Web address: www.palmspasadena.com
**Control:** Corporation, Investor–owned, for–profit **Service:** General Medical and Surgical

Staffed Beds: 307

✠ **ST. ANTHONY'S HOSPITAL (100067)**, 1200 Seventh Avenue North, Zip 33705–1388, Mailing Address: P.O. Box 12588, Zip 33733–2588; tel. 727/825–1100, (Total facility includes 28 beds in nursing home–type unit) **A**1 2 5 9 10 **F**3 11 12 15 17 18 20 22 26 28 29 30 31 34 35 40 44 45 46 49 51 57 59 60 64 68 70 74 75 77 78 79 81 84 85 86 87 93 98 100 102 103 107 108 110 111 114 115 117 118 119 121 123 124 126 128 129 130 131 132 135 146 148 **P**6 **S** Catholic Health East, Newtown Square, PA
Primary Contact: William G. Ulbricht, President
COO: Ronald J. Colaguori, Vice President Operations
CFO: Susan Olds, Chief Financial Officer
CMO: Teresa Bradley, M.D., Vice President Medical Affairs
CIO: Lindsey Jarrell, Vice President Information Services
CHR: James S. Bacon, Director Team Resources
Web address: www.stanthonys.com/
**Control:** Church–operated, Nongovernment, not–for profit **Service:** General Medical and Surgical

Staffed Beds: 344 Admissions: 14362 Census: 221 Outpatient Visits: 74641 Births: 0 Total Expense ($000): 184421 Payroll Expense ($000): 79912 Personnel: 1348

✠ **ST. PETERSBURG GENERAL HOSPITAL (100180)**, 6500 38th Avenue North, Zip 33710–1629; tel. 727/384–1414, (Nonreporting) **A**1 2 9 10 12 13 **S** HCA, Nashville, TN
Primary Contact: Robert B. Conroy, Jr., Chief Executive Officer
COO: Stephanie McNulty, Chief Operating Officer
CFO: Andrew Smith, CFO
CHR: Guy Samuel, Director Human Resources
CNO: JoAnne Cattell, Chief Nursing Officer
Web address: www.stpetegeneral.com
**Control:** Corporation, Investor–owned, for–profit **Service:** General Medical and Surgical

Staffed Beds: 219

**SANFORD—Seminole County**

✠ **CENTRAL FLORIDA REGIONAL HOSPITAL (100161)**, 1401 West Seminole Boulevard, Zip 32771–6764; tel. 407/321–4500, (Nonreporting) **A**1 9 10 **S** HCA, Nashville, TN
Primary Contact: Wendy H. Brandon, Chief Executive Officer
COO: Bobby McCullough, Chief Operating Officer
CIO: Nancy Ryerson, Director Information Systems
CHR: Karla Langlotz, Director Human Resources
Web address: www.centralfloridaregional.com
**Control:** Corporation, Investor–owned, for–profit **Service:** General Medical and Surgical

Staffed Beds: 226

**SARASOTA—Sarasota County**

✠ **COMPLEX CARE HOSPITAL AT RIDGELAKE (102018)**, 6150 Edgelake Drive, Zip 34240–8803; tel. 941/342–3000, (Nonreporting) **A**1 10 **S** LifeCare Management Services, Plano, TX
Primary Contact: Danny R. Edwards, Administrator
CFO: Leah Drabant, Director of Finance
CMO: Craig Harcup, M.D., Hospital Medical Director
CHR: Jennifer Sparks, Human Resources Generalist
CNO: Timothy Mitchell, R.N., Chief Nursing Officer
Web address: www.lifecare–hospitals.com/hospital.php?id=23
**Control:** Corporation, Investor–owned, for–profit **Service:** Long–Term Acute Care hospital

Staffed Beds: 40

✠ **DOCTORS HOSPITAL OF SARASOTA (100166)**, 5731 Bee Ridge Road, Zip 34233–5056; tel. 941/342–1100, (Nonreporting) **A**1 2 9 10 **S** HCA, Nashville, TN
Primary Contact: Robert C. Meade, Chief Executive Officer
COO: Valerie L. Powell–Stafford, Chief Operating Officer
CFO: Charles Schwaner, III, Chief Financial Officer
CHR: Theresa Levering, Director Human Resources
Web address: www.doctorsofsarasota.com
**Control:** Corporation, Investor–owned, for–profit **Service:** General Medical and Surgical

Staffed Beds: 168

✠ △ **HEALTHSOUTH REHABILITATION HOSPITAL OF SARASOTA (103031)**, 6400 Edgelake Drive, Zip 34240–8813; tel. 941/921–8600 **A**1 7 9 10 **F**74 75 79 86 90 91 95 96 103 132 135 148 **S** HEALTHSOUTH Corporation, Birmingham, AL
Primary Contact: Marcus Braz, Chief Executive Officer
CFO: Barbara Bierut, Chief Financial Officer
CMO: Alexander De Jesus, M.D., Medical Director
CHR: Brenda Benner, Director Human Resources
CHR: Marivee Jerome, Senior Human Resources Business Partner
CNO: Jacqueline Juenger, R.N., Chief Nursing Officer
Web address: www.healthsouthsarasota.com
**Control:** Corporation, Investor–owned, for–profit **Service:** Rehabilitation

Staffed Beds: 96 Admissions: 2019 Census: 76 Outpatient Visits: 669 Births: 0 Total Expense ($000): 27783 Payroll Expense ($000): 12048 Personnel: 242

**HEALTHSOUTH RIDGELAKE HOSPITAL** See Complex Care Hospital at Ridgelake

☐ △ **SARASOTA MEMORIAL HOSPITAL (100087)**, 1700 South Tamiami Trail, Zip 34239–3555; tel. 941/917–9000 **A**1 2 3 5 7 9 10 **F**3 5 6 7 8 11 12 13 15 17 18 20 22 24 26 28 29 30 31 32 34 35 36 37 38 39 40 42 44 45 46 47 48 49 50 51 53 54 55 56 57 58 59 60 64 66 68 70 72 73 74 75 76 77 78 79 80 81 82 84 85 86 87 89 90 91 93 95 96 98 99 100 101 102 103 104 105 107 108 110 111 114 115 116 117 118 119 124 126 129 130 131 132 135 143 144 145 146 147 148
Primary Contact: Gwen MacKenzie, R.N., Chief Executive Officer
COO: Michael L. Harrington, Chief Operating Officer
CFO: Bill Woeltjen, Chief Financial Officer
CMO: Parlane Reid, M.D., Chief Medical Officer
CIO: Denis Baker, Chief Information Officer
CHR: Laurie Bennett, Director Human Resources
Web address: www.smh.com
**Control:** Hospital district or authority, Government, nonfederal **Service:** General Medical and Surgical

Staffed Beds: 628 Admissions: 24187 Census: 324 Outpatient Visits: 519121 Births: 3068 Total Expense ($000): 442733 Payroll Expense ($000): 169394 Personnel: 3507

FL

---

## SEBASTIAN—Indian River County

☐ **SEBASTIAN RIVER MEDICAL CENTER (100217)**, 13695 North U.S. Highway 1, Zip 32958–3230, Mailing Address: Box 780838, Zip 32978–0838; tel. 772/589-3186 **A**1 9 10 **F**3 11 12 15 18 20 22 28 29 31 34 40 41 45 46 49 50 51 57 59 60 62 63 64 68 70 74 75 77 78 79 81 82 83 84 85 86 87 89 90 91 92 93 107 110 111 114 115 116 119 126 129 130 132 145 146 148 **P**8 **S** Health Management Associates, Naples, FL
Primary Contact: Steven Salyer, Chief Executive Officer
CFO: John McEachern, Controller
CMO: Ralph Geiger, M.D., Chief of Staff
CHR: Kam Storey, Director Human Resources
Web address: www.sebastianrivermedical.com
**Control:** Corporation, Investor–owned, for–profit **Service:** General Medical and Surgical

**Staffed Beds:** 115 **Admissions:** 4669 **Census:** 57 **Births:** 0 **Personnel:** 471

## SEBRING—Highlands County

✠ **FLORIDA HOSPITAL HEARTLAND MEDICAL CENTER (100109)**, 4200 Sun'n Lake Boulevard, Zip 33872–1986, Mailing Address: P.O. Box 9400, Zip 33871–9400; tel. 863/314-4466 **A**1 9 10 19 **F**8 11 13 15 18 20 22 24 28 29 30 34 35 37 40 44 45 49 50 51 53 54 57 59 60 62 64 70 75 76 79 81 82 86 87 89 98 100 101 103 104 107 108 110 111 114 118 119 127 129 130 132 133 134 146 147 148 **P**6 **S** Adventist Health System Sunbelt Health Care Corporation, Altamonte Springs, FL
Primary Contact: Timothy W. Cook, President and Chief Executive Officer
COO: Isaac Palmer, Chief Operating Officer
CFO: Dima Didenko, Vice President and Chief Financial Officer
CMO: Jorge F. Gonzalez, M.D., Chief Medical Officer
CHR: Anthony Stahl, Director Human Resources
Web address: www.fhheartland.org/
**Control:** Church–operated, Nongovernment, not–for profit **Service:** General Medical and Surgical

**Staffed Beds:** 214 **Admissions:** 12011 **Census:** 155 **Outpatient Visits:** 157553 **Births:** 748 **Total Expense ($000):** 167370 **Payroll Expense ($000):** 71229 **Personnel:** 1056

☐ **HIGHLANDS REGIONAL MEDICAL CENTER (100049)**, 3600 South Highlands Avenue, Zip 33870–5495, Mailing Address: Drawer 2066, Zip 33871–2066; tel. 863/471-5800, (Nonreporting) **A**1 9 10 19 **S** Health Management Associates, Naples, FL
Primary Contact: Brian Hess, Chief Executive Officer
COO: Kristen Kopinsky, Chief Operating Officer
CFO: Vicki DeRenzis, Chief Financial Officer
CMO: Robert Nudence, M.D., Chief of Staff
CIO: Felix Garcia, Director Health Information Services
CNO: Kari Bolin, R.N., Chief Nursing Officer
Web address: www.highlandsregional.com
**Control:** Corporation, Investor–owned, for–profit **Service:** General Medical and Surgical

**Staffed Beds:** 126

## SOUTH MIAMI—Miami–Dade County

☐ **LARKIN COMMUNITY HOSPITAL (100181)**, 7031 S.W. 62nd Avenue, Zip 33143–4781; tel. 305/284-7500 **A**1 9 10 13 **F**3 8 11 12 18 29 31 34 35 40 45 46 49 51 56 57 59 62 65 70 74 75 78 79 81 82 85 86 87 98 102 103 105 107 108 111 114 117 118 119 124 130 135 143 148
Primary Contact: Sandra Sosa–Guerrero, Chief Executive Officer
COO: George J. Michel, Chief Operating Officer
CFO: Edgar Castillo, Chief Financial Officer
CMO: Jose David Suarez, M.D., Chief of Staff
CIO: Orlando Suarez, Manager Information Technology
CHR: Carlos R. Garcia, Vice President Clinical Services
CNO: Manuel Fernandez, Vice President Nursing
Web address: www.larkinhospital.com
**Control:** Individual, Investor–owned, for–profit **Service:** General Medical and Surgical

**Staffed Beds:** 146 **Admissions:** 5714 **Census:** 79 **Outpatient Visits:** 9646 **Births:** 0 **Total Expense ($000):** 70481 **Payroll Expense ($000):** 31176 **Personnel:** 848

## STARKE—Bradford County

**SHANDS STARKE** See Shands Starke Regional Medical Center

☐ **SHANDS STARKE REGIONAL MEDICAL CENTER (101310)**, 922 East Call Street, Zip 32091–3699; tel. 904/368-2300 **A**1 9 10 18 **F**3 11 15 29 30 34 35 40 44 45 50 57 59 64 68 75 77 81 85 93 97 107 111 114 119 127 129 131 132 135 **P**6 **S** Health Management Associates, Naples, FL
Primary Contact: Brent Burish, Chief Executive Officer
Web address: www.shands.org
**Control:** Partnership, Investor–owned, for–profit **Service:** General Medical and Surgical

**Staffed Beds:** 25 **Admissions:** 1616 **Census:** 14 **Births:** 0

## STUART—Martin County

✠ **MARTIN HEALTH SYSTEM (100044)**, 200 S.E. Hospital Avenue, Zip 34994–2346, Mailing Address: P.O. Box 9010, Zip 34995–9010; tel. 772/287-5200, (Includes MARTIN MEMORIAL HOSPITAL SOUTH, 2100 S.E. Salerno Road, Zip 34997; tel. 772/223–2300) **A**1 2 9 10 **F**3 8 11 12 13 15 17 18 20 22 24 26 28 29 30 31 35 36 37 40 42 45 46 47 49 50 51 53 55 60 64 68 70 72 74 75 76 77 78 79 81 82 85 86 87 89 91 93 94 95 107 108 110 111 114 115 117 118 119 120 121 123 124 126 129 130 132 143 144 146 **P**6
Primary Contact: Mark E. Robitaille, President and Chief Executive Officer
CFO: Mark Cocorullo, Senior Vice President and Chief Financial Officer
CMO: Howard M. Robbins, M.D., Senior Vice President and Chief Medical Officer
CIO: Edmund Collins, Chief Information Officer
Web address: www.mmhs.com
**Control:** Other not–for–profit (including NFP Corporation) **Service:** General Medical and Surgical

**Staffed Beds:** 321 **Admissions:** 16100 **Census:** 199 **Outpatient Visits:** 94637 **Births:** 1656 **Total Expense ($000):** 292278 **Payroll Expense ($000):** 127202 **Personnel:** 2342

## SUN CITY CENTER—Hillsborough County

✠ **SOUTH BAY HOSPITAL (100259)**, 4016 Sun City Center Boulevard, Zip 33573–5298; tel. 813/634-3301 **A**1 9 10 **F**3 15 18 29 30 31 34 35 37 40 45 49 50 57 59 64 68 70 74 75 77 78 79 81 82 85 86 87 93 107 108 110 111 114 118 119 132 146 148 **S** HCA, Nashville, TN
Primary Contact: Sharon L. Roush, Chief Executive Officer
COO: Gary Malaer, Chief Operating Officer
CFO: Shawn Gregory, Chief Financial Officer
CIO: Danny Waters, Director Information Technology and Systems
CHR: Dana Wheeler, Director Human Resources
CNO: Terrie Jefferson, R.N., Chief Nursing Officer
Web address: www.southbayhospital.com
**Control:** Corporation, Investor–owned, for–profit **Service:** General Medical and Surgical

**Staffed Beds:** 112 **Admissions:** 7078 **Census:** 88 **Outpatient Visits:** 34852 **Births:** 0 **Total Expense ($000):** 69472 **Payroll Expense ($000):** 23922 **Personnel:** 355

## TALLAHASSEE—Leon County

✠ **CAPITAL REGIONAL MEDICAL CENTER (100254)**, 2626 Capital Medical Boulevard, Zip 32308–4499; tel. 850/325-5000, (Nonreporting) **A**1 2 9 10 **S** HCA, Nashville, TN
Primary Contact: Brian Cook, FACHE, Chief Executive Officer
CFO: Michael Gordian, Chief Financial Officer
CMO: Steve West, M.D., Chief Medical Officer
CIO: Robert A. Steed, Director Information Systems
CHR: Louise Truitt, Vice President Human Resources
Web address: www.capitalregionalmedicalcenter.com
**Control:** Individual, Investor–owned, for–profit **Service:** General Medical and Surgical

**Staffed Beds:** 198

**EASTSIDE PSYCHIATRIC HOSPITAL (104059)**, 2634 Capital Circle N.E., Zip 32308–4106; tel. 850/523-3333, (Nonreporting) **A**9 10
Primary Contact: Jay A. Reeve, President and Chief Executive Officer
COO: Sue Conger, Chief Operating Officer
CFO: Virginia Kelly, Chief Financial Officer
CMO: Ludmila de Faria, M.D., Chief Medical Officer
CIO: Thad Moorer, Chief Information Officer
CHR: Candy Landry, Chief Human Resource Officer
CNO: Judy Goreau, R.N., Director of Nursing
Web address: www.apalacheecenter.org
**Control:** Other not–for–profit (including NFP Corporation) **Service:** Psychiatric

**Staffed Beds:** 24

✠ **HEALTHSOUTH REHABILITATION HOSPITAL OF TALLAHASSEE (103033)**, 1675 Riggins Road, Zip 32308–5315; tel. 850/656-4800 **A**1 9 10 **F**29 34 35 56 57 60 64 74 75 77 78 79 82 86 90 93 95 96 130 132 143 146 148 **S** HEALTHSOUTH Corporation, Birmingham, AL
Primary Contact: Dale Neely, Chief Executive Officer
CFO: Jennifer Spooner, Controller
CMO: Robert Rowland, M.D., Medical Director
CIO: Charles O'Keefe, Director Health Information Services
CHR: Shelia Schiefelbein, Director Human Resources
Web address: www.healthsouthtallahassee.com
**Control:** Corporation, Investor–owned, for–profit **Service:** Rehabilitation

**Staffed Beds:** 76 **Admissions:** 1176 **Census:** 45 **Outpatient Visits:** 4663 **Births:** 0 **Total Expense ($000):** 17067 **Payroll Expense ($000):** 7629 **Personnel:** 155

FL

✠ **SELECT SPECIALTY HOSPITAL–TALLAHASSEE (102020)**, 1554 Surgeons Drive, Zip 32308–4631; tel. 850/219–6800, (Nonreporting) **A**1 9 10 **S** Select Medical Corporation, Mechanicsburg, PA
Primary Contact: Lora Davis, Chief Executive Officer
Web address: www.selectspecialtyhospitals.com/company/locations/tallahassee.aspx
**Control:** Corporation, Investor–owned, for–profit **Service:** Long–Term Acute Care hospital

**Staffed Beds:** 29

✠ **TALLAHASSEE MEMORIAL HEALTHCARE (100135)**, 1300 Miccosukee Road, Zip 32308–5054; tel. 850/431–1155, (Total facility includes 42 beds in nursing home–type unit) **A**1 2 3 5 9 10 **F**2 3 5 6 8 11 12 15 17 18 19 20 22 24 26 28 29 30 31 34 35 37 40 43 45 46 47 48 49 50 51 53 54 55 56 57 58 59 60 61 62 64 65 67 70 72 73 74 75 76 77 78 79 80 81 82 84 85 86 87 88 89 91 93 96 97 98 99 100 102 103 104 107 108 110 113 114 115 117 118 119 120 121 123 124 126 127 128 129 130 131 132 135 143 144 146 147 148 **P**6
Primary Contact: G. Mark O'Bryant, President and Chief Executive Officer
COO: Jason H. Moore, Vice President and Chief Operating Officer
CFO: William A. Giudice, Vice President and Chief Financial Officer
CMO: Dean Watson, M.D., Chief Medical Officer
CIO: Don Lindsey, Vice President and Chief Information Officer
CHR: Steven W. Adriaanse, Vice President and Chief Human Resources Officer
Web address: www.tmh.org
**Control:** Other not–for–profit (including NFP Corporation) **Service:** General Medical and Surgical

**Staffed Beds:** 489 **Admissions:** 26051 **Census:** 355 **Outpatient Visits:** 560371 **Births:** 3614 **Total Expense ($000):** 451788 **Payroll Expense ($000):** 188081 **Personnel:** 3528

### TAMARAC—Broward County

✠ **UNIVERSITY HOSPITAL AND MEDICAL CENTER (100224)**, 7201 North University Drive, Zip 33321–2996; tel. 954/721–2200, (Includes UNIVERSITY PAVILION, 7425 North University Drive, Zip 33328; tel. 305/722–9933), (Nonreporting) **A**1 9 10 **S** HCA, Nashville, TN
Primary Contact: Joseph D. Melchiode, Chief Executive Officer
CFO: Aurelio Gonzalez, Chief Financial Officer
CMO: Ran Abrahamy, M.D., Chief of Staff
CIO: Tom Scharff, Director Information Services
Web address: www.uhmchealth.com
**Control:** Corporation, Investor–owned, for–profit **Service:** General Medical and Surgical

**Staffed Beds:** 317

### TAMPA—Hillsborough County

✠ △ **FLORIDA HOSPITAL TAMPA (100173)**, 3100 East Fletcher Avenue, Zip 33613–4688; tel. 813/971–6000 **A**1 2 3 5 7 10 **F**3 8 11 12 13 15 17 18 20 22 24 26 28 29 30 31 34 35 40 41 44 45 46 47 48 49 50 53 54 57 58 59 62 64 70 72 73 74 75 76 78 79 80 81 82 84 85 87 88 89 90 92 93 96 107 108 109 110 111 114 115 116 117 118 119 120 121 123 124 126 129 130 132 135 143 146 147 148 **S** Adventist Health System Sunbelt Health Care Corporation, Altamonte Springs, FL
Primary Contact: John R. Harding, Chief Executive Officer
COO: Jeffrey Oskin, Vice President Ancillary and Support Services
CFO: Marvin A. Kurtz, Senior Vice President Finance and Chief Financial Officer
CMO: Brad Bjornstad, M.D., Vice President and Chief Medical Officer
CIO: Brigitte W. Shaw, Chief Operating Officer, Pepin Heart Hospital
CHR: James Hackman, Corporate Vice President Human Resources
Web address: www.uch.org
**Control:** Other not–for–profit (including NFP Corporation) **Service:** General Medical and Surgical

**Staffed Beds:** 365 **Admissions:** 21553 **Census:** 292 **Outpatient Visits:** 71530 **Births:** 1945 **Total Expense ($000):** 299714 **Payroll Expense ($000):** 114458 **Personnel:** 2268

✠ **FLORIDA HOSPITAL–CARROLLWOOD (100069)**, 7171 North Dale Mabry Highway, Zip 33614–2665; tel. 813/932–2222 **A**1 10 **F**3 8 11 15 29 30 31 34 35 40 44 45 48 49 50 53 54 56 57 58 59 60 61 62 64 65 68 70 74 75 77 78 79 80 81 82 85 86 87 92 93 97 107 111 114 119 130 131 132 143 146 148 **S** Adventist Health System Sunbelt Health Care Corporation, Altamonte Springs, FL
Primary Contact: Joel Johnson, Chief Executive Officer
COO: Mary C. Whillock, R.N., Associate Nursing Officer and Chief Operating Officer
CFO: Marvin A. Kurtz, Chief Financial Officer
Web address: www.uch.org
**Control:** Church–operated, Nongovernment, not–for profit **Service:** General Medical and Surgical

**Staffed Beds:** 90 **Admissions:** 4764 **Census:** 48 **Outpatient Visits:** 54274 **Births:** 0 **Total Expense ($000):** 97466 **Payroll Expense ($000):** 27014 **Personnel:** 520

✠ **H. LEE MOFFITT CANCER CENTER AND RESEARCH INSTITUTE (100271)**, 12902 Magnolia Drive, Zip 33612–9497; tel. 813/972–4673 **A**1 2 3 5 8 9 10 **F**3 8 11 15 26 29 30 31 34 35 36 37 44 45 46 47 48 49 50 54 55 56 57 58 59 63 64 68 70 71 74 75 77 78 79 81 82 83 84 85 86 87 90 91 92 93 96 97 98 100 101 103 104 107 108 109 110 111 113 114 115 116 117 118 119 120 121 123 124 126 130 132 134 135 136 141 144 146 147 148 **P**6
Primary Contact: Alan F. List, M.D., President and Chief Executive Officer
COO: John A. Kolosky, Executive Vice President and Chief Operating Officer
CFO: Janene Culumber, Vice President and Chief Financial Officer
CMO: W. Michael Alberts, M.D., Vice President Medical Affairs
CIO: Mark Hulse, Vice President and Chief Information Officer
CHR: Yvette Tremonti, Vice President Human Resources
Web address: www.moffitt.org
**Control:** Other not–for–profit (including NFP Corporation) **Service:** Cancer

**Staffed Beds:** 206 **Admissions:** 9216 **Census:** 160 **Outpatient Visits:** 324085 **Births:** 0 **Total Expense ($000):** 772012 **Payroll Expense ($000):** 313006 **Personnel:** 4056

✠ △ **JAMES A. HALEY VETERANS' HOSPITAL**, 13000 Bruce B. Downs Boulevard, Zip 33612–4745; tel. 813/972–2000, (Total facility includes 118 beds in nursing home–type unit) **A**1 3 5 7 8 **F**1 3 5 9 12 15 17 18 20 22 24 26 28 29 30 31 33 34 35 36 38 39 40 45 46 47 48 49 50 51 53 54 55 56 57 58 59 60 61 62 63 64 65 70 71 74 75 77 78 79 80 81 82 83 84 85 86 87 90 91 92 93 94 95 96 97 98 100 101 102 103 104 105 106 107 108 109 110 111 113 114 115 116 117 118 119 120 121 123 127 128 129 130 131 132 135 143 144 146 147 148 **P**1 **S** Department of Veterans Affairs, Washington, DC
Primary Contact: Kathleen R. Fogarty, Director
COO: Michael C. Jorge, Ph.D., Associate Director
CFO: Rita Mercier, Manager Finance
CMO: Edward Cutolo, Jr., M.D., Chief of Staff
CIO: Jose Seymour, Chief Information Resource Management
CHR: Neal C. Hamilton, Chief Human Resources
Web address: www.tampa.va.gov/
**Control:** Veterans Affairs, Government, federal **Service:** General Medical and Surgical

**Staffed Beds:** 566 **Admissions:** 12325 **Census:** 361 **Outpatient Visits:** 1172421 **Total Expense ($000):** 789576 **Payroll Expense ($000):** 334030 **Personnel:** 4454

✠ **KINDRED HOSPITAL BAY AREA–TAMPA (102009)**, 4555 South Manhattan Avenue, Zip 33611–2397; tel. 813/839–6341, (Includes KINDRED HOSPITAL–BAY AREA ST. PETERSBURG, 3030 Sixth Street South, Saint Petersburg, Zip 33705–3720; tel. 727/894–8719; Kimberly Probus, Chief Executive Officer), (Nonreporting) **A**1 10 **S** Kindred Healthcare, Louisville, KY
Primary Contact: Julie Feasel, Chief Executive Officer
CFO: Frank Billy, Chief Financial Officer
CHR: Michael Grimes, Manager Human Resources
Web address: www.khtampa.com/
**Control:** Corporation, Investor–owned, for–profit **Service:** Long–Term Acute Care hospital

**Staffed Beds:** 155

✠ **KINDRED HOSPITAL–CENTRAL TAMPA (102013)**, 4801 North Howard Avenue, Zip 33603–1411; tel. 813/874–7575, (Nonreporting) **A**1 9 10 **S** Kindred Healthcare, Louisville, KY
Primary Contact: Debra Plummer, Chief Executive Officer
CFO: John Miner, Chief Financial Officer
Web address: www.kindredcentraltampa.com/
**Control:** Corporation, Investor–owned, for–profit **Service:** Long–Term Acute Care hospital

**Staffed Beds:** 96

◇ **MEMORIAL HOSPITAL OF TAMPA (100206)**, 2901 Swann Avenue, Zip 33609–4057; tel. 813/873–6400, (Nonreporting) **A**5 9 10 21 **S** IASIS Healthcare, Franklin, TN
Primary Contact: John J. Mainieri, Chief Executive Officer
CFO: Shelley V. Kolseth, Chief Financial Officer
CIO: John Riton, Director Information Services
Web address: www.memorialhospitaltampa.com
**Control:** Corporation, Investor–owned, for–profit **Service:** General Medical and Surgical

**Staffed Beds:** 139

FL

---

**Hospital, Medicare Provider Number, Address, Telephone, Approval, Facility, and Physician Codes, Health Care System**

★ American Hospital Association (AHA) membership
☐ The Joint Commission accreditation
◇ DNV Healthcare Inc. accreditation
◯ Healthcare Facilities Accreditation Program
△ Commission on Accreditation of Rehabilitation Facilities (CARF) accreditation

☐ **SHRINERS HOSPITALS FOR CHILDREN–TAMPA (103303)**, 12502 USF Pine Drive, Zip 33612–9499; tel. 813/972–2250 **A**1 3 5 9 10 **F**3 34 35 50 57 64 68 74 77 79 81 85 89 91 93 94 107 131 146 **S** Shriners Hospitals for Children, Tampa, FL
Primary Contact: David A. Ferrell, Regional Administrator
CFO: Ruth Gregos, Director Finance
CMO: Dennis Grogan, M.D., Chief of Staff
Web address: www.shrinershospitalsforchildren.org/Hospitals/Locations/Tampa.aspx
**Control:** Other not–for–profit (including NFP Corporation) **Service:** Children's orthopedic

> **Staffed Beds:** 25 **Admissions:** 357 **Census:** 2 **Outpatient Visits:** 11731
> **Births:** 0 **Personnel:** 168

✠ **ST. JOSEPH'S HOSPITAL (100075)**, 3001 West Martin Luther King Jr. Boulevard, Zip 33607–6387, Mailing Address: P.O. Box 4227, Zip 33677–4227; tel. 813/870–4000, (Includes ST. JOSEPH'S CHILDREN'S HOSPITAL OF TAMPA, 3001 Dr. Martin Luther King Jr. Boulevard, Zip 33607; tel. 813/554–8500; ST. JOSEPH'S WOMEN'S HOSPITAL – TAMPA, 3030 West Dr. Martin L. King Boulevard, Zip 33607–6394; tel. 813/872–2950; Kimberly Guy, Chief Operating Officer) **A**1 2 3 5 9 10 **F**3 7 11 12 13 15 17 18 19 20 21 22 23 24 25 26 27 28 29 30 31 33 34 35 37 39 40 41 43 44 45 46 48 49 51 55 57 58 59 64 65 66 68 70 71 72 73 74 75 76 77 78 79 81 82 84 85 86 87 88 89 93 94 98 99 100 101 102 107 108 110 111 114 115 118 119 120 121 123 124 126 127 129 130 131 132 135 145 146 147 148 **P**7 **S** Catholic Health East, Newtown Square, PA
Primary Contact: Lorraine Lutton, President
CFO: Cathy Yoder, Chief Financial Officer
CMO: Mark Vaaler, M.D., Vice President Medical Staff Affairs
CIO: Lindsey Jarrell, Vice President Information Services
CHR: Pat Teeuwen, Director Team Resources
Web address: www.sjbhealth.org
**Control:** Other not–for–profit (including NFP Corporation) **Service:** General Medical and Surgical

> **Staffed Beds:** 964 **Admissions:** 52598 **Census:** 657 **Outpatient Visits:** 289588 **Births:** 7596 **Total Expense ($000):** 675560 **Payroll Expense ($000):** 254524 **Personnel:** 4395

✠ △ **TAMPA GENERAL HOSPITAL (100128)**, 1 Tampa General Circle, Zip 33606–3571, Mailing Address: P.O. Box 1289, Zip 33601–1289; tel. 813/844–7000, (Includes TAMPA GENERAL HOSPITAL CHILDREN'S MEDICAL CENTER, 1 Tampa General Circle, tel. 813/844–7000) **A**1 3 5 7 8 9 10 **F**3 7 8 9 11 12 13 15 16 17 18 19 20 22 24 26 28 29 30 31 32 34 35 36 37 40 41 43 44 45 46 47 48 49 50 51 52 53 54 55 56 57 58 59 60 61 64 65 66 68 70 72 73 74 75 76 77 78 79 81 82 83 84 85 86 87 88 89 90 91 92 93 94 96 97 98 100 101 102 103 107 108 109 110 111 114 115 119 120 121 123 124 126 129 130 131 132 134 135 137 138 139 140 141 142 143 145 146 147 148 **P**6
Primary Contact: James R. Burkhart, FACHE, President and Chief Executive Officer
COO: Deana Nelson, R.N., Executive Vice President and Chief Operating Officer
CFO: Steve Short, Executive Vice President Finance and Administration
CMO: Sally Houston, M.D., Senior Vice President and Chief Medical Officer
CIO: Elizabeth Lindsay–Wood, Vice President Information Systems
CHR: Chris Roederer, Vice President Human Resources
CNO: Janet Davis, R.N., Senior Vice President and Chief Nursing Officer
Web address: www.tgh.org
**Control:** Other not–for–profit (including NFP Corporation) **Service:** General Medical and Surgical

> **Staffed Beds:** 1018 **Admissions:** 40522 **Census:** 730 **Outpatient Visits:** 263658 **Births:** 5330 **Total Expense ($000):** 976788 **Payroll Expense ($000):** 380396 **Personnel:** 6454

◇ **TOWN AND COUNTRY HOSPITAL (100255)**, 6001 Webb Road, Zip 33615–3291; tel. 813/888–7060, (Nonreporting) **A**5 9 10 21 **S** IASIS Healthcare, Franklin, TN
Primary Contact: Dale Johns, Administrator
CMO: Patrick Horan, M.D., Chief of Staff
CIO: Larry Mohammed, Director Information Systems
CHR: Judy Miller, Director Human Resources
Web address: www.townandcountryhospital.com
**Control:** Partnership, Investor–owned, for–profit **Service:** General Medical and Surgical

> **Staffed Beds:** 200

✠ **FLORIDA HOSPITAL NORTH PINELLAS (100055)**, 1395 South Pinellas Avenue, Zip 34689–3790; tel. 727/942–5000 **A**1 5 9 10 **F**3 11 13 15 17 18 20 22 26 28 29 30 31 34 35 40 45 48 49 50 57 59 64 70 71 75 76 78 79 81 93 94 96 97 107 108 110 111 114 117 119 128 129 130 131 132 146 147 148 **S** Adventist Health System Sunbelt Health Care Corporation, Altamonte Springs, FL
Primary Contact: Bruce Bergherm, Chief Executive Officer
COO: Karen Owensby, R.N., Chief Operating Officer and Chief Nursing Officer
COO: Amy Patterson, Chief Operating Officer and Chief Nursing Officer
CFO: Michael Mewhirter, Chief Financial Officer
CMO: Nicolas Pavouris, M.D., Chief of Medical Staff
CMO: Nicolas Pavouris, M.D., President Medical Staff
CIO: Francisco Manalo, Director of Information Services
CHR: Vernon Elarbee, Director of Human Resources
CNO: Karen Owensby, R.N., Chief Operating Officer and Chief Nursing Officer
Web address: www.fhnorthpinellas.com/
**Control:** Church–operated, Nongovernment, not–for profit **Service:** General Medical and Surgical

> **Staffed Beds:** 168 **Admissions:** 4707 **Census:** 58 **Outpatient Visits:** 20802 **Births:** 196 **Total Expense ($000):** 78591 **Payroll Expense ($000):** 25645 **Personnel:** 497

✠ **FLORIDA HOSPITAL WATERMAN (100057)**, 1000 Waterman Way, Zip 32778–5266; tel. 352/253–3333 **A**1 2 9 10 **F**3 11 13 17 18 20 22 24 26 28 29 30 31 34 35 40 45 49 50 54 57 59 62 64 66 70 74 75 76 77 78 79 81 85 89 93 107 108 110 111 114 115 116 117 118 119 120 121 123 132 135 146 148 **P**8 **S** Adventist Health System Sunbelt Health Care Corporation, Altamonte Springs, FL
Primary Contact: David Ottati, Chief Executive Officer
COO: Carrie L. Fish, Senior Vice President and Chief Operating Officer
CFO: Frances H. Crunk, Vice President and Chief Financial Officer
CMO: Vinay Mehindru, M.D., Vice President/Chief Medical Officer
CHR: Madge Springer, Director Human Resources
CNO: Patricia R. Dolan, R.N., Vice President/ Chief Nursing Officer
Web address: www.fhwat.org
**Control:** Church–operated, Nongovernment, not–for profit **Service:** General Medical and Surgical

> **Staffed Beds:** 269 **Admissions:** 14068 **Census:** 165 **Outpatient Visits:** 113749 **Births:** 702 **Total Expense ($000):** 190672 **Payroll Expense ($000):** 68764 **Personnel:** 1160

✠ **BAPTIST HEALTH SOUTH FLORIDA, MARINERS HOSPITAL (101313)**, 91500 Overseas Highway, Zip 33070–2547; tel. 305/434–3000 **A**1 9 10 18 20 **F**3 11 15 18 28 29 30 31 34 35 40 45 47 50 53 57 59 68 70 74 75 78 79 81 84 85 93 97 102 107 108 110 111 114 115 119 129 130 131 132 133 146 147 148 **P**8 **S** Baptist Health South Florida, Coral Gables, FL
Primary Contact: Rick Freeburg, Chief Executive Officer
CFO: Erik Long, Controller
CIO: Mimi Taylor, Vice President Information Technology
CHR: John Williamson, Human Resources Site Manager
Web address: www.baptisthealth.net/en/facilities/mariners–hospital/Pages/default.aspx
**Control:** Other not–for–profit (including NFP Corporation) **Service:** General Medical and Surgical

> **Staffed Beds:** 25 **Admissions:** 605 **Census:** 6 **Outpatient Visits:** 31533 **Births:** 0 **Total Expense ($000):** 52724 **Payroll Expense ($000):** 14636 **Personnel:** 214

✠ **THE VILLAGES HEALTH SYSTEM (100290)**, 1451 El Camino Real, Zip 32159–0041; tel. 352/751–8000 **A**1 9 10 **F**11 15 17 18 20 22 24 26 29 30 31 34 35 40 45 53 57 64 70 74 78 81 86 93 107 111 114 119 146 **S** Central Florida Health Alliance, Leesburg, FL
Primary Contact: Donald G. Henderson, FACHE, President and Chief Executive Officer
CFO: Dale E. Hocking, Senior Vice President and Chief Financial Officer
CMO: Daniel Carlson, M.D., Senior Vice President Medical Affairs and Chief Medical Officer
CIO: Nancy Vester, Vice President and Chief Information Officer
CNO: Rosemary Reiner, MSN, Vice President and Chief Clinical Officer
Web address: www.cfhalliance.org
**Control:** Other not–for–profit (including NFP Corporation) **Service:** General Medical and Surgical

> **Staffed Beds:** 223 **Admissions:** 12857 **Census:** 143 **Outpatient Visits:** 57207 **Births:** 0 **Total Expense ($000):** 137449 **Payroll Expense ($000):** 48571

**THE VILLAGES REGIONAL HOSPITAL** See The Villages Health System

**FL**

## TITUSVILLE—Brevard County

☐ **PARRISH MEDICAL CENTER (100028)**, 951 North Washington Avenue, Zip 32796–2163; tel. 321/268–6111, (Nonreporting) A1 2 9 10
Primary Contact: George Mikitarian, Jr., Chief Executive Officer
CFO: Timothy K. Skeldon, Senior Vice President and Chief Financial Officer
CMO: Lisa Alexanda, M.D., Vice President Medical Affairs
CIO: William Moore, Chief Information Officer
CHR: Roberta Chaildin, Manager Human Resources
Web address: www.parrishmed.com
**Control:** Hospital district or authority, Government, nonfederal **Service:** General Medical and Surgical

| Staffed Beds: 163 |
|---|

## TRINITY—Pasco County

**COMMUNITY HOSPITAL** See Medical Center of Trinity

☒ **MEDICAL CENTER OF TRINITY (100191)**, 9330 State Road 54, Zip 34655–1808, Mailing Address: P.O. Box 996, New Port Richey, Zip 34656–0996; tel. 727/834–4900 A1 2 5 10 F8 11 13 15 18 20 22 26 29 30 31 34 35 38 40 45 46 47 48 49 57 59 60 67 68 70 74 75 76 77 78 79 80 81 82 84 85 86 87 93 94 98 102 103 107 108 110 111 119 126 130 132 135 146 147 148 S HCA, Nashville, TN
Primary Contact: Leigh Massengill, Chief Executive Officer
COO: Mary Ann Knight, Chief Operating Officer
COO: Thibaut vanMarcke, Chief Operating Officer
CFO: Michael Wyers, Chief Financial Officer
CMO: Linda Badillo, M.D., Chief of Medical Staff
CIO: Kurt Hornung, Director
CHR: Christena Miano, Human Resources Director
CNO: Nancy Maysilles, R.N., Chief Nursing Officer
Web address: www.medicalcentertrinity.com
**Control:** Corporation, Investor–owned, for–profit **Service:** General Medical and Surgical

| Staffed Beds: 282 Admissions: 14534 Census: 179 Outpatient Visits: 66205 Births: 935 Total Expense ($000): 137132 Payroll Expense ($000): 53139 Personnel: 932 |
|---|

## VENICE—Sarasota County

☐ **VENICE REGIONAL MEDICAL CENTER (100070)**, 540 The Rialto, Zip 34285–2900; tel. 941/485–7711, (Nonreporting) A1 9 10 S Health Management Associates, Naples, FL
Primary Contact: Peter Wozniak, MS, R.N., Chief Executive Officer
CFO: Fred Ashworth, Chief Financial Officer
CHR: Dana Wheeler, Director Human Resources
Web address: www.veniceregional.com
**Control:** Corporation, Investor–owned, for–profit **Service:** General Medical and Surgical

| Staffed Beds: 220 |
|---|

## VERO BEACH—Indian River County

☒ **HEALTHSOUTH TREASURE COAST REHABILITATION HOSPITAL (103032)**, 1600 37th Street, Zip 32960–4863; tel. 772/778–2100 A1 9 10 F90 93 S HEALTHSOUTH Corporation, Birmingham, AL
Primary Contact: Carol Sim, Chief Executive Officer
CFO: Kevin Hardy, Chief Financial Officer
CMO: Jimmy Wayne Lockhart, M.D., Medical Director
CHR: Pearl Shisler, Director Human Resources
Web address: www.healthsouthtreasurecoast.com
**Control:** Corporation, Investor–owned, for–profit **Service:** Rehabilitation

| Staffed Beds: 90 Admissions: 1450 Census: 54 Outpatient Visits: 8334 Births: 0 Total Expense ($000): 17773 Payroll Expense ($000): 9742 Personnel: 193 |
|---|

☒ **INDIAN RIVER MEDICAL CENTER (100105)**, 1000 36th Street, Zip 32960–6592; tel. 772/567–4311 A1 2 9 10 F3 11 12 13 17 18 20 22 24 26 28 29 30 31 34 35 37 40 44 49 50 51 57 58 59 60 61 64 70 74 75 76 77 78 79 80 81 82 83 84 85 86 87 89 92 93 96 97 98 99 100 101 102 103 104 107 108 111 114 115 118 119 120 121 123 126 129 130 131 132 135 144 146 147 148 P6
Primary Contact: Jeffrey L. Susi, President and Chief Executive Officer
CFO: Wael Fakhry, Senior Vice President and Chief Financial Officer
CHR: Barbara Horne, R.N., Vice President and Chief Human Resource Development Officer
Web address: www.irmc.cc
**Control:** Other not–for–profit (including NFP Corporation) **Service:** General Medical and Surgical

| Staffed Beds: 245 Admissions: 14696 Census: 172 Outpatient Visits: 160576 Births: 1057 Total Expense ($000): 192138 Payroll Expense ($000): 85820 Personnel: 1419 |
|---|

## WAUCHULA—Hardee County

☒ **FLORIDA HOSPITAL WAUCHULA (101300)**, 533 West Carlton Street, Zip 33873–3407; tel. 863/773–3101, (Nonreporting) A1 9 10 18 S Adventist Health System Sunbelt Health Care Corporation, Altamonte Springs, FL
Primary Contact: Linda Adler, Administrator
COO: Isaac Palmer, Chief Operating Officer
CFO: Dima Didenko, Vice President and Chief Financial Officer
CHR: Michelle F. Myers, Director Human Resources
Web address: www.fh.floridahospital.com/heartland/home.aspx
**Control:** Church–operated, Nongovernment, not–for profit **Service:** General Medical and Surgical

| Staffed Beds: 25 |
|---|

## WESLEY CHAPEL—Pasco County

★ **FLORIDA HOSPITAL WESLEY CHAPEL (100319)**, 2600 Bruce B. Downs Bouelvard, Zip 33544–9207; tel. 813/929–5000, (Nonreporting) A5 9 10 S Adventist Health System Sunbelt Health Care Corporation, Altamonte Springs, FL
Primary Contact: Brian Adams, Chief Executive Officer
**Control:** Other not–for–profit (including NFP Corporation) **Service:** General Medical and Surgical

| Staffed Beds: 83 |
|---|

## WEST PALM BEACH—Palm Beach County

☒ **GOOD SAMARITAN MEDICAL CENTER (100287)**, 1309 North Flagler Drive, Zip 33401–3499; tel. 561/655–5511, (Nonreporting) A1 2 9 10 S TENET Healthcare Corporation, Dallas, TX
Primary Contact: Mark Nosacka, Chief Executive Officer
CFO: Cynthia McCauley, Chief Financial Officer
CIO: Candace Helms, Director Information Services
CHR: Amy Linsin, Chief Human Resources Officer
Web address: www.goodsamaritanmc.com
**Control:** Corporation, Investor–owned, for–profit **Service:** General Medical and Surgical

| Staffed Beds: 174 |
|---|

☐ **JEROME GOLDEN CENTER FOR BEHAVIORAL HEALTH, INC. (104008)**, 1041 45th Street, Zip 33407–2494; tel. 561/383–8000, (Nonreporting) A1 10
Primary Contact: Linda De Piano, Ph.D., Chief Executive Officer
CFO: Pat Priola, Chief Financial Officer
CMO: Suresh Rajpara, M.D., Chief Medical Officer
CIO: Emiliano Fernandez, Director Information Services
CHR: Diane B. White, Director Human Resources
Web address: www.jeromegoldencenter.org
**Control:** Other not–for–profit (including NFP Corporation) **Service:** Psychiatric

| Staffed Beds: 44 |
|---|

**PALM BEACH CHILDREN'S HOSPITAL** See St. Mary's Medical Center

☒ △ **ST. MARY'S MEDICAL CENTER (100288)**, 901 45th Street, Zip 33407–2495; tel. 561/844–6300, (Includes PALM BEACH CHILDREN'S HOSPITAL, 901 45th Street, Zip 33407; tel. 561/844–6300) A1 5 7 9 10 F3 6 8 11 13 15 17 18 19 20 21 23 24 25 29 30 31 34 35 38 39 40 41 43 44 45 47 48 49 50 51 56 57 58 59 60 64 65 68 70 72 73 74 75 76 77 78 79 80 81 85 86 87 88 89 90 92 93 94 96 98 100 101 102 103 107 108 110 111 114 115 119 120 121 123 130 131 132 134 135 146 147 148 S TENET Healthcare Corporation, Dallas, TX
Primary Contact: Davide M. Carbone, FACHE, Chief Executive Officer
CFO: Tom Schlemmer, Chief Financial Officer
CMO: Jeffrey David, D.O., Chief Medical Officer
CIO: Rich Avato, Director
CHR: Sandy Wyant, Director Human Resources
Web address: www.stmarysmc.com
**Control:** Corporation, Investor–owned, for–profit **Service:** General Medical and Surgical

| Staffed Beds: 464 Admissions: 17806 Census: 296 Outpatient Visits: 110888 Births: 3444 Total Expense ($000): 224662 Payroll Expense ($000): 97935 Personnel: 1357 |
|---|

**VETERANS AFFAIRS MEDICAL CENTER** See West Palm Beach Veterans Affairs Medical Center

---

**Hospital, Medicare Provider Number, Address, Telephone, Approval, Facility, and Physician Codes, Health Care System**

★ American Hospital Association (AHA) membership
☐ The Joint Commission accreditation
◇ DNV Healthcare Inc. accreditation
○ Healthcare Facilities Accreditation Program
△ Commission on Accreditation of Rehabilitation Facilities (CARF) accreditation

FL

☐ **WELLINGTON REGIONAL MEDICAL CENTER (100275)**, 10101 Forest Hill Boulevard, Zip 33414–6199; tel. 561/798–8500, (Nonreporting) **A**1 9 10 12 13 **S** Universal Health Services, Inc., King of Prussia, PA
Primary Contact: Robbin Lee, Interim Chief Executive Officer
CFO: Woody White, Chief Financial Officer
CMO: Gordon Johnson, M.D., Chief of Staff
CIO: Pierre Bergeron, Director Information Services
CHR: Mary Jo Garski, Director Human Resources
CNO: Michelle Epps, MSN, Chief Nursing Officer
Web address: www.wellingtonregional.com
**Control:** Corporation, Investor–owned, for–profit **Service:** General Medical and Surgical

> **Staffed Beds:** 158

☒ △ **WEST PALM BEACH VETERANS AFFAIRS MEDICAL CENTER**, (Formerly Veterans Affairs Medical Center), 7305 North Military Trail, Zip 33410–6400; tel. 561/422–8262, (Nonreporting) **A**1 3 5 7 9 **S** Department of Veterans Affairs, Washington, DC
Primary Contact: Charleen R. Szabo, FACHE, Director
CFO: Lori Hancock, Chief Business Officer
CMO: Deepak Mandi, M.D., Chief of Staff
CIO: Karen Gabaldon, Chief Management Information Systems
CHR: David Green, Chief Human Resources
Web address: www.westpalmbeach.va.gov/
**Control:** Veterans Affairs, Government, federal **Service:** General Medical and Surgical

> **Staffed Beds:** 133

☒ ○ **WEST PALM HOSPITAL (100234)**, (Formerly Columbia Hospital), 2201 45th Street, Zip 33407–2047; tel. 561/842–6141 **A**1 9 10 11 12 13 **F**3 20 29 34 35 40 45 57 59 60 70 79 81 82 93 98 99 101 102 103 104 105 107 110 111 119 146 148 **S** HCA, Nashville, TN
Primary Contact: Dana Oaks, Chief Executive Officer
COO: Patrick Connor, Chief Operating Officer
CFO: Oon Soo Ung, Chief Financial Officer
CMO: Paul Seltzer, M.D., Chief of Staff
CIO: Martha Stinson, Director
CHR: Donna Boyle, Director
Web address: www.westpalmhospital.com
**Control:** Corporation, Investor–owned, for–profit **Service:** General Medical and Surgical

> **Staffed Beds:** 245 **Admissions:** 9912 **Census:** 109

### WESTON—Broward County

☒ **CLEVELAND CLINIC FLORIDA (100289)**, 3100 Weston Road, Zip 33331–3602; tel. 954/659–6001 **A**1 2 3 5 9 10 **F**3 8 12 15 18 20 22 24 26 28 29 30 31 34 35 37 40 44 45 46 47 48 49 50 51 54 55 56 57 58 59 60 61 63 64 65 68 70 74 75 77 78 79 80 81 82 85 86 87 91 92 93 97 100 101 107 108 109 110 111 114 115 116 117 119 126 129 130 131 132 135 136 141 145 146 147 148 **P**6 **S** Cleveland Clinic Health System, Cleveland, OH
Primary Contact: Bernardo Fernandez, M.D., Chief Executive Officer
COO: Liz Matuk, Executive Director, Administrative and Clinical Services
COO: Marty Sargeant, Chief Operating Officer
CFO: Keith Nilsson, Chief Financial Officer
CMO: Juan Nogueras, M.D., Chief of Staff
CIO: John Santangelo, Director Information Technology
CHR: Paula Adamson, Manager Human Resources
CHR: Stuart Thompson, Director Human Resources
CNO: Kerry Major, R.N., Chief Nursing Officer
Web address: www.clevelandclinic.org/florida
**Control:** Other not–for–profit (including NFP Corporation) **Service:** General Medical and Surgical

> **Staffed Beds:** 155 **Admissions:** 9811 **Census:** 120 **Outpatient Visits:** 149372 **Births:** 0 **Total Expense ($000):** 171343 **Payroll Expense ($000):** 63387 **Personnel:** 1269

### WILLISTON—Levy County

**TRI–COUNTY HOSPITAL – WILLISTON (100139)**, 125 S.W. Seventh Street, Zip 32696–2403; tel. 352/528–2801, (Nonreporting) **A**9 10
Primary Contact: Jerry E. Gillman, Chief Executive Officer
CFO: Barbara Miller, Manager Business Office
CMO: Jeremie Young, M.D., Chief of Staff
CHR: Karla Dass, Director Human Resources
Web address: www.tricountyhosp.com/
**Control:** Partnership, Investor–owned, for–profit **Service:** General Medical and Surgical

> **Staffed Beds:** 20

### WINTER HAVEN—Polk County

☒ △ **WINTER HAVEN HOSPITAL (100052)**, 200 Avenue F. N.E., Zip 33881–4193; tel. 863/293–1121 **A**1 7 9 10 **F**3 8 11 13 14 15 17 18 20 22 24 26 28 29 30 31 34 36 40 45 49 52 57 58 59 60 64 68 70 72 73 74 75 76 77 78 79 81 82 84 85 86 87 89 90 93 94 98 100 101 102 103 104 107 108 110 111 114 115 118 119 121 123 126 130 132 135 144 146 147 148 **P**6
Primary Contact: Lance W. Anastasio, President
COO: Mary Jo Schreiber, R.N., Vice President Patient Services
CFO: David MacDougall, Vice President Finance
CMO: Donald I. Gale, M.D., Vice President Medical Affairs
CIO: Pat Mongoven, Director Information Systems
Web address: www.winterhavenhospital.org
**Control:** Other not–for–profit (including NFP Corporation) **Service:** General Medical and Surgical

> **Staffed Beds:** 519 **Admissions:** 16833 **Census:** 203 **Outpatient Visits:** 274506 **Births:** 1659 **Total Expense ($000):** 247708 **Payroll Expense ($000):** 117791 **Personnel:** 2587

### WINTER PARK—Orange County

**WINTER PARK MEMORIAL HOSPITAL** See Florida Hospital, Orlando

### ZEPHYRHILLS—Pasco County

☒ **FLORIDA HOSPITAL ZEPHYRHILLS (100046)**, 7050 Gall Boulevard, Zip 33541–1399; tel. 813/788–0411 **A**1 5 9 10 **F**13 15 17 18 20 22 24 26 28 29 30 34 35 40 51 53 59 62 70 74 76 79 81 87 93 107 108 110 111 114 119 126 130 135 144 146 147 148 **S** Adventist Health System Sunbelt Health Care Corporation, Altamonte Springs, FL
COO: Donald E. Welch, Chief Operating Officer
CFO: Paul Ziegele, Chief Financial Officer
CIO: Kelley Sasser, Director Information Systems
CHR: Laura Asaftei, Administrative Director
CNO: Ruth Hemphill, R.N., Chief Nursing Officer
Web address: www.fhzeph.org
**Control:** Church–operated, Nongovernment, not–for profit **Service:** General Medical and Surgical

> **Staffed Beds:** 139 **Admissions:** 10101 **Census:** 102 **Outpatient Visits:** 146588 **Births:** 470 **Total Expense ($000):** 138221 **Payroll Expense ($000):** 56754 **Personnel:** 1014

**FL**

*Many Facility Codes have changed. Please refer to the AHA Guide Code Chart.*
© 2013 AHA Guide

# GEORGIA

## ADEL—Cook County

☒ **COOK MEDICAL CENTER–A CAMPUS OF TIFT REGIONAL MEDICAL CENTER (110101)**, 706 North Parrish Avenue, Zip 31620–1511; tel. 229/896–8000, (Nonreporting) **A**1 9
Primary Contact: Michael L. Purvis, Chief Executive Officer
COO: Kim Wills, Chief Operating Officer
CIO: Barry Medley, Director Information Systems
CHR: Shirley Padgett, Director Human Resources
Web address: www.cookmedicalcenter.com
**Control:** Corporation, Investor–owned, for–profit **Service:** General Medical and Surgical

**Staffed Beds:** 155

## ALBANY—Dougherty County

☒ **PHOEBE NORTH (110163)**, 2000 Palmyra Road, Zip 31701–1528, Mailing Address: P.O. Box 1908, Zip 31702–1908; tel. 229/434–2000, (Nonreporting) **A**1 9 10 **S** Phoebe Putney Health System, Albany, GA
Primary Contact: Thomas Sullivan, Chief Transition Officer
CFO: Karen Hayes, Chief Financial Officer
CHR: Tracy St. Amant, Director Human Resources
Web address: www.palmyramedicalcenters.com
**Control:** Hospital district or authority, Government, nonfederal **Service:** General Medical and Surgical

**Staffed Beds:** 102

☒ ◇ **PHOEBE PUTNEY MEMORIAL HOSPITAL (110007)**, 417 Third Avenue, Zip 31701–1943, Mailing Address: P.O. Box 1828, Zip 31702–1828; tel. 229/883–1800, (Nonreporting) **A**1 2 3 5 9 10 21 **S** Phoebe Putney Health System, Albany, GA
Primary Contact: Joel Wernick, President and Chief Executive Officer
CFO: Kerry Loudermilk, Senior Vice President and Chief Financial Officer
CMO: Douglas Patten, M.D., Chief Medical Officer
CIO: Jesse Diaz, Chief Information Officer
CHR: David J. Baranski, Vice President Human Resources
Web address: www.phoebeputney.com
**Control:** Other not–for–profit (including NFP Corporation) **Service:** General Medical and Surgical

**Staffed Beds:** 440

## ALMA—Bacon County

☒ **BACON COUNTY HOSPITAL AND HEALTH SYSTEM (111327)**, 302 South Wayne Street, Zip 31510–2922, Mailing Address: P.O. Drawer 1987, Zip 31510–0987; tel. 912/632–8961, (Nonreporting) **A**1 9 10 18
Primary Contact: Cindy R. Turner, Chief Executive Officer
COO: Cindy R. Turner, Chief Executive Officer
CFO: Kyle Kimmel, Chief Financial Officer
CMO: Lou Ellen Hutcheson, M.D., Chief of Staff
CHR: Jackie Lewis, Director Human Resources
CNO: Deanna Williams, R.N., Director of Nursing
Web address: www.baconcountyhospital.com
**Control:** Other not–for–profit (including NFP Corporation) **Service:** General Medical and Surgical

**Staffed Beds:** 113

## AMERICUS—Sumter County

☒ ◇ **PHOEBE SUMTER MEDICAL CENTER (110044)**, 126 Highway 280 West, Zip 31719; tel. 229/924–6011, (Nonreporting) **A**1 9 10 21 **S** Phoebe Putney Health System, Albany, GA
Primary Contact: Keith J. Petersen, Chief Executive Officer
CFO: Laurie Hair, Chief Financial Officer
CMO: Andrew Carlson, M.D., Vice President Medical Staff Services
CIO: Becky Lightner, Director Information Systems
CHR: Deatrice Harris, Supervisor Human Resources and Employment
Web address: www.phoebesumter.org
**Control:** Other not–for–profit (including NFP Corporation) **Service:** General Medical and Surgical

**Staffed Beds:** 45

## ATHENS—Clarke County

☒ **ATHENS REGIONAL MEDICAL CENTER (110074)**, 1199 Prince Avenue, Zip 30606–2797; tel. 706/475–7000 **A**1 2 9 10 **F**3 8 11 13 15 17 18 20 22 24 26 28 29 30 31 34 35 36 40 43 45 46 47 48 51 54 56 57 59 60 62 68 70 72 73 74 76 77 78 79 80 81 83 84 85 86 87 89 92 93 94 96 107 108 110 111 116 117 119 120 121 123 124 129 130 131 132 135 145 146 147 148
Primary Contact: James G. Thaw, President and Chief Executive Officer
COO: Linda Della Torre, Senior Vice President and Chief Operating Officer
CFO: W. Larry Webb, Senior Vice President and Chief Financial Officer
CMO: Mark J. Costantino, M.D., Interim Chief Medical Officer
CIO: Steve W. Davis, Interim Chief Information Officer
CHR: Kevin Thigpen, Vice President Human Resources
Web address: www.armc.org
**Control:** Other not–for–profit (including NFP Corporation) **Service:** General Medical and Surgical

**Staffed Beds:** 343 **Admissions:** 18259 **Census:** 209 **Outpatient Visits:** 292689 **Births:** 2634 **Total Expense ($000):** 356761 **Payroll Expense ($000):** 134172 **Personnel:** 2325

☐ **LANDMARK HOSPITAL OF ATHENS (112017)**, 775 Sunset Drive, Zip 30606–2211; tel. 706/425–1500 **A**1 10 **F**1 3 29 30 45 84 119 130 148 **S** Landmark Hospitals, Cape Girardeau, MO
Primary Contact: Tommy Jackson, Chief Executive Officer
Web address: www.landmarkhospitals.com
**Control:** Individual, Investor–owned, for–profit **Service:** Long–Term Acute Care hospital

**Staffed Beds:** 42 **Admissions:** 446 **Census:** 32 **Outpatient Visits:** 0 **Births:** 0 **Personnel:** 121

☒ △ **ST. MARY'S HEALTH CARE SYSTEM (110006)**, 1230 Baxter Street, Zip 30606–3791; tel. 706/389–3000, (Nonreporting) **A**1 7 9 10 **S** Catholic Health East, Newtown Square, PA
Primary Contact: Donald McKenna, President and Chief Executive Officer
CFO: Marty Hutson, Chief Financial Officer
CMO: Bruce Middendorf, M.D., Chief Medical Officer
CIO: Kerry Vaughn, Chief Information Officer
CHR: Jeff English, Vice President Human Resources
CNO: Nina Evans, R.N., Vice President and Chief Nursing Officer
Web address: www.stmarysathens.com
**Control:** Church–operated, Nongovernment, not–for profit **Service:** General Medical and Surgical

**Staffed Beds:** 165

## ATLANTA—Fulton and De Kalb County

**ANCHOR HOSPITAL (114032)**, 5454 Yorktowne Drive, Zip 30349–5317; tel. 770/991–6044, (Nonreporting) **A**9 10 **S** Universal Health Services, Inc., King of Prussia, PA
Primary Contact: Margaret P. Collier, Chief Executive Officer and Managing Director
COO: Jennifer Morgan, Chief Executive Officer and Managing Director
CMO: Joel Kirson, M.D., Medical Director
Web address: www.anchorhospital.com
**Control:** Corporation, Investor–owned, for–profit **Service:** Alcoholism and other chemical dependency

**Staffed Beds:** 111

**GA**

✠ **ATLANTA MEDICAL CENTER (110115)**, 303 Parkway Drive N.E., Zip 30312–1212; tel. 404/265–4000 **A**1 3 5 8 9 10 **F**11 12 13 15 17 18 20 22 24 26 28 29 30 31 34 35 36 37 38 40 43 44 45 46 50 53 54 56 57 59 60 61 64 65 66 68 70 72 73 74 75 76 77 78 79 81 84 85 86 87 89 90 93 96 97 98 100 101 102 103 104 107 108 111 114 118 119 129 130 132 134 144 146 147 148 **P**3 7 8 **S** TENET Healthcare Corporation, Dallas, TX
Primary Contact: William T. Moore, Chief Executive Officer
COO: Robert Russell, Chief Operating Officer
CFO: Lisa Napier, Chief Financial Officer
CMO: Pano Lamis, M.D., Medical Director
CIO: Maryland McCarty, Director Information Systems
CHR: Troy Bond, Chief Human Resources Officer
CNO: Jacqueline Herd, R.N., Chief Nursing Officer
Web address: www.atlantamedcenter.com
**Control:** Corporation, Investor–owned, for–profit **Service:** General Medical and Surgical

> **Staffed Beds:** 403 **Admissions:** 14096 **Census:** 211 **Outpatient Visits:** 88356 **Births:** 3281 **Total Expense ($000):** 232341 **Payroll Expense ($000):** 77899 **Personnel:** 1338

✠ **ATLANTA MEDICAL CENTER – SOUTH CAMPUS (110219)**, (Formerly South Fulton Medical Center), 1170 Cleveland Avenue, Zip 30344–3665; tel. 404/466–1170 **A**1 2 10 **F**3 11 15 17 18 20 22 29 30 31 40 45 48 49 50 53 57 59 60 61 63 64 66 68 74 75 77 79 81 93 94 98 100 101 102 107 108 110 111 114 115 119 129 130 146 148 **S** TENET Healthcare Corporation, Dallas, TX
Primary Contact: Daniel Jackson, Chief Administrative Officer
CFO: Jacob Spruit, Jr., Chief Financial Officer
CMO: Albert Barrocas, M.D., Chief Medical Officer
Web address: www.southfultonmedicalcenter.com
**Control:** Corporation, Investor–owned, for–profit **Service:** General Medical and Surgical

> **Staffed Beds:** 174 **Admissions:** 5725 **Census:** 77 **Outpatient Visits:** 80293 **Births:** 738 **Total Expense ($000):** 93608 **Payroll Expense ($000):** 42436 **Personnel:** 505

☐ △ **CHILDREN'S HEALTHCARE OF ATLANTA (113301)**, 1600 Tullie Circle, N.E., Zip 30329–2303; tel. 404/325–6000, (Includes CHILDREN'S HEALTHCARE OF ATLANTA AT EGLESTON, 1600 Tullie Circle, Zip 30329; tel. 404/325–6000; CHILDREN'S HEALTHCARE OF ATLANTA AT SCOTTISH RITE, 1001 Johnson Ferry Road N.E., Zip 30342–1600; tel. 404/256–5252), (Nonreporting) **A**1 3 5 7 8 9 10
Primary Contact: Donna W. Hyland, President and Chief Executive Officer
COO: Carolyn Kenny, Executive Vice President Clinical Care
CFO: Ruth Fowler, Senior Vice President and Chief Financial Officer
CMO: Daniel Salinas, M.D., Senior Vice President and Chief Medical Officer
CIO: Praveen Chopra, Chief Information and Supply Chain Officer
CHR: Linda Matzigkeit, Senior Vice President Human Resources
Web address: www.choa.org
**Control:** Other not–for–profit (including NFP Corporation) **Service:** Children's general

> **Staffed Beds:** 496

✠ △ **EMORY UNIVERSITY HOSPITAL (110010)**, 1364 Clifton Road N.E., Zip 30322–1102; tel. 404/712–2000, (Includes EMORY UNIVERSITY ORTHOPAEDIC AND SPINE HOSPITAL, 1455 Montreal Road, Tucker, Zip 30084; tel. 404/251–3600; June Conner, R.N., Chief Operating Officer) **A**1 2 3 5 7 8 9 10 **F**3 11 12 14 15 17 18 20 22 24 26 28 29 30 31 34 35 37 38 40 44 45 46 47 49 50 55 57 58 59 60 64 68 70 74 75 77 78 79 80 81 82 83 84 85 86 87 90 92 93 98 100 101 102 103 104 107 108 110 111 112 114 115 116 117 118 119 120 121 123 124 126 130 131 132 135 136 137 138 139 140 141 142 145 146 147 148 **P**1 6 **S** Emory Healthcare, Atlanta, GA
Primary Contact: Robert J. Bachman, Chief Operating Officer
CMO: Ira Horowitz, M.D., Chief Medical Officer
CIO: Dedra Cantrell, Chief Information Officer
CHR: Margaret A. Bloomquist, Assistant Administrator Human Resources
Web address: www.emoryhealthcare.org
**Control:** Other not–for–profit (including NFP Corporation) **Service:** General Medical and Surgical

> **Staffed Beds:** 579 **Admissions:** 25332 **Census:** 460 **Outpatient Visits:** 157794 **Births:** 0 **Total Expense ($000):** 710938 **Payroll Expense ($000):** 231482 **Personnel:** 3379

✠ **EMORY UNIVERSITY HOSPITAL MIDTOWN (110078)**, 550 Peachtree Street N.E., Zip 30308–2247; tel. 404/686–4411 **A**1 2 3 5 8 9 10 **F**3 11 12 13 15 17 18 20 22 24 26 28 29 30 31 35 38 40 44 46 50 51 52 55 57 58 59 60 61 64 68 70 72 73 74 75 76 77 78 79 80 81 83 84 85 86 87 92 93 100 102 104 107 108 110 111 114 115 116 117 118 119 120 121 123 124 126 130 131 132 134 135 146 147 148 **S** Emory Healthcare, Atlanta, GA
Primary Contact: Dane C. Peterson, Chief Operating Officer
COO: Dane C. Peterson, Chief Operating Officer
CFO: Greg E. Anderson, Chief Financial Officer
CMO: James P. Steinberg, M.D., Chief Medical Officer
CIO: Dedra Cantrell, Chief Information Officer
CHR: Dallis Howard–Crow, Chief Human Resources Officer
Web address: www.emoryhealthcare.org
**Control:** Other not–for–profit (including NFP Corporation) **Service:** General Medical and Surgical

> **Staffed Beds:** 435 **Admissions:** 20448 **Census:** 295 **Outpatient Visits:** 172872 **Births:** 3586 **Total Expense ($000):** 501034 **Payroll Expense ($000):** 153583 **Personnel:** 2370

✠ **GRADY MEMORIAL HOSPITAL (110079)**, 80 Jesse Hill Jr. Drive S.E., Zip 30303–3031, Mailing Address: P.O. Box 26189, Zip 30303–0004; tel. 404/616–1000, (Total facility includes 255 beds in nursing home–type unit) **A**1 2 3 5 8 9 10 **F**3 5 7 8 13 15 16 17 18 20 22 24 26 29 30 31 34 35 39 40 43 44 45 50 51 52 53 54 56 57 59 60 61 62 64 65 66 68 70 72 73 74 75 76 77 78 79 80 81 82 84 85 86 87 93 97 98 99 100 101 102 103 104 105 106 107 108 109 110 111 113 114 115 116 117 118 119 120 121 123 130 132 134 135 136 137 138 139 140 141 142 143 144 146 147 148 **P**6
Primary Contact: John M. Haupert, FACHE, Chief Executive Officer
COO: Christopher R. Mosley, FACHE, Chief Operating Officer
CFO: Sue McCarthy, Chief Financial Officer
CMO: Curtis Lewis, M.D., Chief of Staff
CIO: Deborah Cancilla, Chief Information Officer
CHR: Althea Williams, Senior Vice President Human Resources
Web address: www.gradyhealthsystem.org
**Control:** Other not–for–profit (including NFP Corporation) **Service:** General Medical and Surgical

> **Staffed Beds:** 916 **Admissions:** 26840 **Census:** 676 **Outpatient Visits:** 552159 **Births:** 2087 **Total Expense ($000):** 433749 **Payroll Expense ($000):** 264625 **Personnel:** 4711

✠ **KINDRED HOSPITAL–ATLANTA (112004)**, 705 Juniper Street N.E., Zip 30308–1307; tel. 404/873–2871 **A**1 9 10 **F**1 3 29 30 57 60 63 75 82 86 87 92 96 120 130 132 148 **S** Kindred Healthcare, Louisville, KY
Primary Contact: Michael Schmitt, M.D., Chief Executive Officer
CFO: Phillip Johnson, CPA, Chief Financial Officer
CMO: David N. DeRuyter, M.D., President Medical Staff
CHR: Armetria Gibson, Human Resources Generalist
CNO: Annette Harrilson, Chief Clinical Officer
Web address: www.kindredatlanta.com/
**Control:** Partnership, Investor–owned, for–profit **Service:** Long–Term Acute Care hospital

> **Staffed Beds:** 70 **Admissions:** 500 **Census:** 49 **Outpatient Visits:** 0 **Births:** 0 **Total Expense ($000):** 20089 **Payroll Expense ($000):** 9954 **Personnel:** 181

✠ **NORTHSIDE HOSPITAL (110161)**, 1000 Johnson Ferry Road N.E., Zip 30342–1611; tel. 404/851–8000 **A**1 2 9 10 **F**3 5 8 11 12 13 15 17 18 20 22 26 28 29 30 31 34 35 40 44 45 46 47 48 49 50 54 55 57 58 59 60 64 68 70 71 72 73 74 75 76 77 78 79 80 81 82 84 85 86 87 93 100 104 105 107 108 110 111 114 115 117 118 119 120 121 123 124 129 130 132 135 136 145 146 147 148 **S** Northside Healthcare System, Atlanta, GA
Primary Contact: Robert Quattrocchi, President and Chief Executive Officer
CFO: Debbie Mitcham, Chief Financial Officer
CIO: Tina Wakim, Vice President Information
CHR: Dwight Hill, Vice President Human Resources
Web address: www.northside.com
**Control:** Other not–for–profit (including NFP Corporation) **Service:** General Medical and Surgical

> **Staffed Beds:** 551 **Admissions:** 32554 **Census:** 381 **Outpatient Visits:** 385166 **Births:** 14770 **Total Expense ($000):** 759819 **Payroll Expense ($000):** 294329 **Personnel:** 4945

☐ **PEACHFORD BEHAVIORAL HEALTH SYSTEM (114010)**, 2151 Peachford Road, Zip 30338–6599; tel. 770/455–3200 **A**1 9 10 **F**4 5 29 34 35 38 56 57 71 98 99 100 101 102 103 104 105 130 132 134 **P**8 **S** Universal Health Services, Inc., King of Prussia, PA
Primary Contact: Matthew Crouch, Chief Executive Officer and Managing Director
COO: Sharon Stackhouse, Assistant Administrator and Director Risk Management
CFO: April Hughes, Chief Financial Officer
CMO: Asaf Aleem, M.D., Medical Director
CHR: Clay Boyles, Director Human Resources
Web address: www.peachfordhospital.com
**Control:** Corporation, Investor–owned, for–profit **Service:** Psychiatric

> **Staffed Beds:** 246 **Admissions:** 8316 **Census:** 196 **Outpatient Visits:** 0 **Births:** 0 **Total Expense ($000):** 36399 **Payroll Expense ($000):** 17632 **Personnel:** 175

**GA**

**PIEDMONT HOSPITAL (110083)**, 1968 Peachtree Road N.W., Zip 30309–1281; tel. 404/605–5000 **A**1 2 3 5 9 10 **F**3 8 11 12 13 15 17 18 20 22 24 26 28 29 30 31 34 35 40 45 46 47 48 49 50 51 53 54 55 56 57 58 59 60 63 64 65 68 70 72 73 74 75 76 77 78 79 81 82 84 85 86 87 93 107 108 110 111 112 114 115 116 117 118 119 120 121 123 124 126 129 130 131 132 135 137 138 139 142 143 146 147 148 **S** Piedmont Healthcare, Atlanta, GA
Primary Contact: Leslie A. Donahue, President and Chief Executive Officer
CFO: Thomas Arnold, Chief Financial Officer
CMO: Matthew Schreiber, M.D., Chief Medical Officer
CIO: Mark Pasquale, Vice President Information Systems
CHR: Steve Karasick, Interim Vice President Human Resources
Web address: www.piedmonthospital.org
**Control:** Other not–for–profit (including NFP Corporation) **Service:** General Medical and Surgical

**Staffed Beds:** 484 **Admissions:** 24929 **Census:** 381 **Outpatient Visits:** 258381 **Births:** 3571 **Personnel:** 2951

**SAINT JOSEPH'S HOSPITAL OF ATLANTA (110082)**, 5665 Peachtree Dunwoody Road N.E., Zip 30342–1701; tel. 678/843–7001 **A**1 2 9 10 **F**3 11 15 17 18 20 22 24 26 28 29 30 31 34 35 37 40 44 45 46 47 49 50 51 53 54 55 57 58 59 60 64 68 70 71 74 75 78 79 81 82 84 85 87 107 108 110 111 114 115 116 117 118 119 120 121 123 124 126 130 132 135 137 145 146 147 **P**1 6 **S** Emory Healthcare, Atlanta, GA
Primary Contact: Scott Schmidly, Chief Executive Officer
CFO: Kevin Brenan, Chief Financial Officer
CMO: Paul Scheinberg, M.D., Chief of Staff
CIO: Dedra Cantrell, Chief Information Officer
CHR: Audra Farish, Vice President Human Resources
Web address: www.stjosephsatlanta.org
**Control:** Other not–for–profit (including NFP Corporation) **Service:** General Medical and Surgical

**Staffed Beds:** 253 **Admissions:** 13039 **Census:** 183 **Outpatient Visits:** 193440 **Births:** 0 **Total Expense ($000):** 327246 **Payroll Expense ($000):** 102442 **Personnel:** 1513

**SELECT SPECIALTY HOSPITAL–ATLANTA (112009)**, 550 Peachtree Street N.E., Zip 30308–2247; tel. 404/686–2270, (Nonreporting) **A**1 9 10 **S** Select Medical Corporation, Mechanicsburg, PA
Primary Contact: Dwayne Hooks, Jr., R.N., Chief Executive Officer
Web address: www.selectspecialtyhospitals.com/company/locations/atlanta.aspx
**Control:** Corporation, Investor–owned, for–profit **Service:** Long–Term Acute Care hospital

**Staffed Beds:** 30

**SHEPHERD CENTER (112003)**, 2020 Peachtree Road N.W., Zip 30309–1465; tel. 404/352–2020, (Nonreporting) **A**1 3 5 7 9 10
Primary Contact: Gary R. Ulicny, Ph.D., President and Chief Executive Officer
COO: Sarah Morrison, Vice President Clinical Services
CFO: Stephen B. Holleman, Chief Financial Officer
CMO: Donald P. Leslie, M.D., Medical Director
CIO: Michael L. Jones, Ph.D., Chief Information Officer
CHR: Betsy Fox, Director Human Resources
CNO: Tamara King, R.N., Chief Nurse Executive
Web address: www.shepherd.org
**Control:** Other not–for–profit (including NFP Corporation) **Service:** Long–Term Acute Care hospital

**Staffed Beds:** 100

**WESLEY WOODS GERIATRIC HOSPITAL OF EMORY UNIVERSITY (110203)**, (Multi–Discrip Geri Hospital), 1821 Clifton Road N.E., Zip 30329–4021; tel. 404/728–6200, (Total facility includes 250 beds in nursing home–type unit) **A**1 3 5 9 10 **F**3 6 10 11 29 30 34 35 38 39 50 54 56 58 59 60 64 65 67 68 74 75 77 84 86 87 90 93 96 98 100 101 102 103 104 105 107 119 125 128 129 130 132 143 146 148 **S** Emory Healthcare, Atlanta, GA
Primary Contact: William Such, Chief Executive Officer
CFO: Greg E. Anderson, Chief Financial Officer
CMO: Frank Brown, M.D., Chief Medical Officer
CIO: Dedra Cantrell, Chief Information Officer
CHR: Dallis Howard–Crow, Chief Human Resources Officer
Web address: www.emoryhealthcare.org
**Control:** Other not–for–profit (including NFP Corporation) **Service:** Other specialty

**Staffed Beds:** 276 **Admissions:** 2422 **Census:** 273 **Outpatient Visits:** 15550 **Births:** 0 **Total Expense ($000):** 40732 **Payroll Expense ($000):** 23077 **Personnel:** 433

**WESLEY WOODS LONG TERM CARE HOSPITAL (112005)**, 1821 Clifton Road N.E., 2nd Floor, Zip 30329–4021; tel. 404/728–6200 **A**1 10 **F**1 3 11 29 30 34 56 68 74 75 77 82 85 87 94 **P**1 6 **S** Emory Healthcare, Atlanta, GA
Primary Contact: William Such, Chief Executive Officer
CFO: Theodore Saunders, Assistant Controller
CMO: Jeffrey Mikell, M.D., Chief Medical Officer
CIO: Vicky Goziah, Software Administrator
Web address: www.emoryhealthcare.org
**Control:** Other not–for–profit (including NFP Corporation) **Service:** Long–Term Acute Care hospital

**Staffed Beds:** 18 **Admissions:** 198 **Census:** 16 **Outpatient Visits:** 0 **Births:** 0 **Total Expense ($000):** 9347 **Payroll Expense ($000):** 2811 **Personnel:** 48

## AUGUSTA—Richmond County

**CHARLIE NORWOOD VETERANS AFFAIRS MEDICAL CENTER**, (Formerly Veterans Affairs Medical Center), 1 Freedom Way, Zip 30904–6285; tel. 706/733–0188, (Nonreporting) **A**1 2 3 5 7 **S** Department of Veterans Affairs, Washington, DC
Primary Contact: Robert U. Hamilton, Director
CFO: Earline Corder, Chief Fiscal
CMO: Thomas Kiernan, M.D., Chief of Staff
CIO: Susan Lloyd, Chief Health Information Management and Revenue Administration
CHR: Linda Dailey, Acting Chief Human Resources Officer
Web address: www.augusta.va.gov/
**Control:** Veterans Affairs, Government, federal **Service:** General Medical and Surgical

**Staffed Beds:** 338

**DOCTORS HOSPITAL (110177)**, 3651 Wheeler Road, Zip 30909–6426; tel. 706/651–3232 **A**1 2 5 9 10 **F**1 4 8 12 13 15 16 17 18 22 29 30 31 34 39 40 41 43 46 49 50 51 57 59 60 64 67 70 71 72 73 74 75 76 77 78 79 80 81 82 84 85 87 88 89 90 91 92 93 94 96 97 98 107 108 110 111 114 116 117 119 120 121 123 124 126 128 129 130 131 132 135 141 146 147 148 **P**1 **S** HCA, Nashville, TN
Primary Contact: Douglas Welch, Chief Executive Officer
CIO: Dona Hornung, Director Information and Technology Services
Web address: www.doctors–hospital.net
**Control:** Corporation, Investor–owned, for–profit **Service:** General Medical and Surgical

**Staffed Beds:** 307 **Admissions:** 13241 **Census:** 178 **Outpatient Visits:** 95270 **Total Expense ($000):** 238153 **Payroll Expense ($000):** 61246 **Personnel:** 912

**EAST CENTRAL REGIONAL HOSPITAL (114029)**, 3405 Mike Padgett Highway, Zip 30906–3897; tel. 706/792–7000, (Includes EAST CENTRAL REGIONAL HOSPITAL, 100 Myrtle Boulevard, Gracewood, Zip 30812–1299; tel. 706/790–2011), (Total facility includes 391 beds in nursing home–type unit) **A**1 5 10 **F**29 34 38 39 59 65 67 75 77 86 87 96 98 101 128 130 143 **P**6
Primary Contact: Nan M. Lewis, Administrator
CFO: Terry Tribble, Chief Financial Officer
Web address: www.augustareg.dhr.state.ga.us
**Control:** State–Government, nonfederal **Service:** Psychiatric

**Staffed Beds:** 552 **Admissions:** 1205 **Census:** 420 **Outpatient Visits:** 0 **Births:** 0

**GEORGIA REGENTS MEDICAL CENTER (110034)**, (Formerly Georgia Health Sciences Medical Center), 1120 15th Street, Zip 30912–0004; tel. 706/721–0211, (Includes CHILDREN'S HOSPITAL OF GEORGIA, 1446 Harper Street, Zip 30912–0012; tel. 706/721–5437) **A**1 2 3 5 8 9 10 13 **F**3 5 6 11 12 13 14 15 17 18 19 20 21 22 23 24 25 26 27 28 29 30 31 32 34 35 36 38 39 40 41 43 44 45 46 48 49 50 51 54 55 56 58 59 66 68 70 72 73 74 75 76 77 78 79 81 82 84 85 86 87 88 89 91 92 93 97 98 99 100 101 102 103 104 107 108 111 113 115 116 117 118 119 120 121 123 124 126 127 129 130 131 132 134 135 136 138 141 142 143 145 146 147 148 **P**3 7
Primary Contact: David S. Hefner, President and Chief Executive Officer
CMO: William Kanto, M.D., Acting Senior Vice President and Chief Medical Officer
CIO: Richard R. Bias, Acting Vice President Information Systems and Chief Information Officer
CHR: Derek Carissimi, Vice President Human Resources
Web address: www.grhealth.org
**Control:** Other not–for–profit (including NFP Corporation) **Service:** General Medical and Surgical

**Staffed Beds:** 460 **Admissions:** 19447 **Census:** 319 **Outpatient Visits:** 466554 **Births:** 689 **Total Expense ($000):** 542799 **Payroll Expense ($000):** 202391 **Personnel:** 3253

**GA**

---

**Hospital, Medicare Provider Number, Address, Telephone, Approval, Facility, and Physician Codes, Health Care System**

★ American Hospital Association (AHA) membership
□ The Joint Commission accreditation
◇ DNV Healthcare Inc. accreditation
○ Healthcare Facilities Accreditation Program
△ Commission on Accreditation of Rehabilitation Facilities (CARF) accreditation

⊠ △ **HEALTHSOUTH WALTON REHABILITATION HOSPITAL (113026)**, (Formerly Walton Rehabilitation Hospital), 1355 Independence Drive, Zip 30901–1037; tel. 706/724–7746, (Nonreporting) **A**1 5 7 9 10 **S** HEALTHSOUTH Corporation, Birmingham, AL
Primary Contact: Deborah S. Guthrie, Chief Executive Officer
COO: Bob Orsini, Chief Operating Officer
CMO: Pamela Salazar, M.D., Chief of Staff
CIO: Ann Keller, Manager Health Information Management
CHR: Volante Henderson, Manager Human Resources
Web address: www.healthsouthwalton.com/
**Control:** Corporation, Investor–owned, for–profit **Service:** Rehabilitation

Staffed Beds: 58

**MEDICAL COLLEGE OF GEORGIA HEALTH** See Georgia Regents Medical Center

⊠ **SELECT SPECIALTY HOSPITAL–AUGUSTA (112013)**, 1537 Walton Way, Zip 30904–3764; tel. 706/731–1169 **A**1 9 10 **F**1 29 30 107 108 130 148 **S** Select Medical Corporation, Mechanicsburg, PA
Primary Contact: Curtis L. Roberts, Chief Executive Officer
CHR: Terrie Richardson, Coordinator Human Resources
CNO: Kim Pippin, Chief Nursing Officer
Web address: www.selectspecialtyhospitals.com/company/locations/augusta.aspx
**Control:** Corporation, Investor–owned, for–profit **Service:** Long–Term Acute Care hospital

Staffed Beds: 80 Admissions: 881 Census: 64 Outpatient Visits: 0 Births: 0 Total Expense ($000): 29018 Payroll Expense ($000): 12994

⊠ **TRINITY HOSPITAL OF AUGUSTA (110039)**, 2260 Wrightsboro Road, Zip 30904–4726; tel. 706/481–7000, (Nonreporting) **A**1 5 9 10 **S** Community Health Systems, Inc., Franklin, TN
Primary Contact: Jason Studley, Chief Executive Officer
CFO: Marc Nakagawa, Chief Financial Officer
CMO: Lawrence LaHatte, M.D., Chief of Staff
CIO: Charlotte Choate, Director Information Systems
CHR: Connie Martin, Director Human Resources
Web address: www.trinityofaugusta.com
**Control:** Corporation, Investor–owned, for–profit **Service:** General Medical and Surgical

Staffed Beds: 105

⊠ **UNIVERSITY HOSPITAL (110028)**, (Formerly University Health Care System), 1350 Walton Way, Zip 30901–2629; tel. 706/722–9011 **A**1 2 3 5 9 10 **F**3 13 15 17 18 20 22 24 26 28 29 30 31 34 35 37 38 40 41 44 48 49 50 53 54 56 57 59 60 62 63 64 68 70 72 73 74 75 76 77 78 79 80 81 82 83 84 85 86 87 89 93 97 100 107 108 114 115 116 118 119 126 129 130 132 134 135 144 146 147 148 **P**8 **S** University Health Care System, Augusta, GA
Primary Contact: Marilyn A. Bowcutt, R.N., MSN, President
CFO: David Belkoski, Executive Vice President and Chief Financial Officer
CMO: William L. Farr, M.D., Chief Medical Officer
CIO: Leslie Clonch, Vice President and Chief Information Officer
Web address: www.universityhealth.org
**Control:** Other not–for–profit (including NFP Corporation) **Service:** General Medical and Surgical

Staffed Beds: 490 Admissions: 21652 Census: 303 Outpatient Visits: 263139 Births: 3211 Total Expense ($000): 365283 Payroll Expense ($000): 142715 Personnel: 2346

**VETERANS AFFAIRS MEDICAL CENTER** See Charlie Norwood Veterans Affairs Medical Center

**WALTON REHABILITATION HOSPITAL** See HEALTHSOUTH Walton Rehabilitation Hospital

**AUSTELL—Cobb County**

⊠ △ **WELLSTAR COBB HOSPITAL (110143)**, 3950 Austell Road, Zip 30106–1121; tel. 770/732–4000 **A**1 3 5 7 9 10 **F**3 4 11 13 15 16 17 18 20 22 26 28 29 30 31 37 38 40 41 44 45 48 49 50 53 54 58 59 60 61 62 64 66 68 70 72 73 74 75 76 77 78 79 80 81 82 84 85 86 87 90 93 94 96 98 100 101 102 103 104 105 106 107 108 110 111 114 115 118 119 126 130 132 141 146 147 148 **P**1 6 **S** WellStar Health System, Marietta, GA
Primary Contact: Kem Mullins, FACHE, President
COO: Ilona Wozniak, Vice President and Chief Operating Officer
CFO: Darold Etheridge, Vice President and Chief Financial Officer
CMO: Don Campbell, M.D., Senior Vice President and Chief Medical Officer
CMO: Thomas McNamara, D.O., Vice President Medical Management
CHR: Joseph W. Herzberg, Assistant Vice President Human Resources
CHR: Alma Stanfield, Director Human Resources
Web address: www.wellstar.org
**Control:** Other not–for–profit (including NFP Corporation) **Service:** General Medical and Surgical

Staffed Beds: 372 Admissions: 21960 Census: 272 Outpatient Visits: 230595 Births: 4056 Personnel: 2013

**BAINBRIDGE—Decatur County**

☐ **MEMORIAL HOSPITAL AND MANOR (110132)**, 1500 East Shotwell Street, Zip 39819–4256; tel. 229/246–3500, (Nonreporting) **A**1 9 10
Primary Contact: William J. Walker, Jr., Chief Executive Officer
COO: Lee Harris, Assistant Administrator Support Services
CFO: Karen Faircloth, Chief Financial Officer
CMO: Shawn Surratt, M.D., Chief of Staff
CIO: Nelda Moore, Director Data Processing
CHR: Angel Sykes, Director Human Resources
CNO: Cynthia Vickers, R.N., Assistant Administrator for Nursing Services
Web address: www.mh–m.org
**Control:** Hospital district or authority, Government, nonfederal **Service:** General Medical and Surgical

Staffed Beds: 80

**BAXLEY—Appling County**

◇ **APPLING HEALTHCARE SYSTEM (110071)**, 163 East Tollison Street, Zip 31513–0120; tel. 912/367–9841, (Nonreporting) **A**9 10 20 21
Primary Contact: Dale Spell, Chief Executive Officer
COO: Dale Spell, Chief Executive Officer
CFO: Farell Turner, Chief Financial Officer
CIO: Brian Snow, Manager Information Systems
CHR: Carla McLendon, Director Human Resources
Web address: www.appling–hospital.org
**Control:** County–Government, nonfederal **Service:** General Medical and Surgical

Staffed Beds: 150

**BLAIRSVILLE—Union County**

⊠ **UNION GENERAL HOSPITAL (110051)**, 35 Hospital Road, Zip 30512–3139; tel. 706/745–2111, (Nonreporting) **A**1 9 10 20
Primary Contact: Rebecca T. Dyer, Administrator
COO: Mike Gowder, Assistant Administrator
CFO: Tim Henry, Chief Financial Officer
CMO: Andre Schaeffer, M.D., Chief of Staff
CHR: Kathy Hood, Administrative Assistant
Web address: www.uniongeneralhospital.com
**Control:** Hospital district or authority, Government, nonfederal **Service:** General Medical and Surgical

Staffed Beds: 195

**BLAKELY—Early County**

⊠ ◇ **PIONEER COMMUNITY HOSPITAL OF EARLY (111314)**, 11740 Columbia Street, Zip 39823–2574; tel. 229/723–4241, (Nonreporting) **A**1 9 10 18 21 **S** Pioneer Health Services, Magee, MS
Primary Contact: Greg Havard, Administrator
Web address: www.pchearly.com
**Control:** Corporation, Investor–owned, for–profit **Service:** General Medical and Surgical

Staffed Beds: 152

**BLUE RIDGE—Fannin County**

⊠ **FANNIN REGIONAL HOSPITAL (110189)**, 2855 Old Highway 5, Zip 30513–6248; tel. 706/632–3711, (Nonreporting) **A**1 9 10 **S** Community Health Systems, Inc., Franklin, TN
Primary Contact: David S. Sanders, Chief Executive Officer
CFO: Rodney Sisk, Chief Financial Officer
CIO: Timothy Snider, Manager Information Systems
CHR: Terrasina Ensley, Director Human Resources
CNO: Julia Barnett, Chief Nursing Officer
Web address: www.fanninregionalhospital.com
**Control:** Corporation, Investor–owned, for–profit **Service:** General Medical and Surgical

Staffed Beds: 50

**BREMEN—Haralson County**

⊠ **HIGGINS GENERAL HOSPITAL (111320)**, 200 Allen Memorial Drive, Zip 30110–2012; tel. 770/824–2000, (Nonreporting) **A**1 9 10 18 **S** Tanner Health System, Carrollton, GA
Primary Contact: Michael Alexander, Administrator
CIO: Dianne Reed, Director Information Systems
CHR: Vivian C. Barr, Director Human Resources
Web address: www.tanner.org/Main/HigginsGeneralHospitalBremen.aspx
**Control:** Other not–for–profit (including NFP Corporation) **Service:** General Medical and Surgical

Staffed Beds: 25

*Many Facility Codes have changed. Please refer to the AHA Guide Code Chart.*
© 2013 AHA Guide

## BRUNSWICK—Glynn County

☒ **SOUTHEAST GEORGIA HEALTH SYSTEM BRUNSWICK CAMPUS (110025)**, 2415 Parkwood Drive, Zip 31520–4722, Mailing Address: P.O. Box 1518, Zip 31521–1518; tel. 912/466–7000, (Total facility includes 220 beds in nursing home–type unit) **A**1 2 9 10 F3 11 12 13 17 18 20 22 26 28 29 30 31 34 35 37 40 44 45 46 47 48 49 50 51 54 57 59 64 68 70 71 73 74 75 76 77 78 79 81 85 86 87 89 90 91 93 94 96 100 107 108 110 111 114 117 119 120 121 124 126 129 131 132 135 144 146 147 148 **P**5 **S** Southeast Georgia Health System, Brunswick, GA
Primary Contact: Gary R. Colberg, FACHE, President and Chief Executive Officer
CFO: Michael D. Scherneck, Executive Vice President and Chief Financial Officer
CMO: Terry Reynolds, M.D., Chief of Staff
CIO: Chuck Bumgardner, Director Information Systems
CHR: Patrick D. Ebri, Ph.D., Vice President, Human Resources
Web address: www.sghs.org
**Control:** Hospital district or authority, Government, nonfederal **Service:** General Medical and Surgical

**Staffed Beds:** 366 **Admissions:** 11736 **Census:** 364 **Outpatient Visits:** 190528 **Births:** 1301 **Total Expense ($000):** 266582 **Payroll Expense ($000):** 112436 **Personnel:** 1506

## CAIRO—Grady County

☒ **GRADY GENERAL HOSPITAL (110121)**, 1155 Fifth Street S.E., Zip 39828–3142, Mailing Address: P.O. Box 360, Zip 39828–0360; tel. 229/377–1150 **A**1 9 10 F3 11 12 13 15 18 29 34 35 40 45 50 57 59 68 70 75 76 79 81 85 86 87 91 92 93 107 110 111 115 119 130 133 146 **P**6 **S** Archbold Medical Center, Thomasville, GA
Primary Contact: LaDon Toole, Chief Operating Officer and Administrator
COO: LaDon Toole, Chief Operating Officer and Administrator
CFO: Skip Hightower, Chief Financial Officer
CMO: Stephen Ruberdall, M.D., Chief Medical Officer
CIO: William Zimmermann, Chief Information Officer
CHR: Michelle Pledger, Coordinator Human Resources
Web address: www.archbold.org
**Control:** Hospital district or authority, Government, nonfederal **Service:** General Medical and Surgical

**Staffed Beds:** 48 **Admissions:** 1302 **Census:** 16 **Outpatient Visits:** 41007 **Births:** 231 **Total Expense ($000):** 20327 **Payroll Expense ($000):** 8436 **Personnel:** 139

## CALHOUN—Gordon County

☒ ○ **GORDON HOSPITAL (110023)**, 1035 Red Bud Road, Zip 30701–2082, Mailing Address: P.O. Box 12938, Zip 30703–7013; tel. 706/629–2895 **A**1 2 9 10 11 19 F3 7 11 13 15 18 20 29 30 31 34 35 37 40 46 57 59 62 64 70 75 76 77 78 79 81 82 85 86 87 93 107 108 111 115 119 120 121 123 129 130 135 144 146 147 148 **P**1 6 **S** Adventist Health System Sunbelt Health Care Corporation, Altamonte Springs, FL
Primary Contact: Pete M. Weber, President and Chief Executive Officer
COO: Steve Hannah, Chief Operating Officer
CFO: Cory Reeves, Chief Financial Officer
CMO: Will Theus, M.D., Chief of Staff
CHR: Jeni Hasselbrack, Director Human Resources
Web address: www.gordonhospital.com
**Control:** Church–operated, Nongovernment, not–for profit **Service:** General Medical and Surgical

**Staffed Beds:** 85 **Admissions:** 4838 **Census:** 51 **Outpatient Visits:** 172304 **Births:** 586 **Total Expense ($000):** 92181 **Payroll Expense ($000):** 37027 **Personnel:** 747

## CAMILLA—Mitchell County

☒ **MITCHELL COUNTY HOSPITAL (111331)**, 90 East Stephens Street, Zip 31730–1836, Mailing Address: P.O. Box 639, Zip 31730–0639; tel. 229/336–5284, (Total facility includes 156 beds in nursing home–type unit) **A**1 9 10 18 F3 11 15 18 29 34 35 40 50 57 59 68 75 87 93 97 107 111 114 119 127 128 130 133 146 **P**6 **S** Archbold Medical Center, Thomasville, GA
Primary Contact: Mark E. Kimball, Administrator
COO: Kevin C. Taylor, Chief Operating Officer
CFO: Skip Hightower, Senior Vice President and Chief Financial Officer
CIO: William Zimmermann, Chief Information Officer
CHR: Vickie County–Teemer, Coordinator Human Resources
Web address: www.archbold.org
**Control:** Hospital district or authority, Government, nonfederal **Service:** General Medical and Surgical

**Staffed Beds:** 181 **Admissions:** 393 **Census:** 166 **Outpatient Visits:** 26932 **Births:** 0 **Total Expense ($000):** 24966 **Payroll Expense ($000):** 10589 **Personnel:** 274

## CANTON—Cherokee County

☒ **NORTHSIDE HOSPITAL–CHEROKEE (110008)**, 201 Hospital Road, Zip 30114–2408, Mailing Address: P.O. Box 906, Zip 30169–0906; tel. 770/720–5100 **A**1 9 10 F3 8 11 12 13 15 18 20 22 26 29 30 31 34 35 40 44 45 50 54 57 59 60 64 68 70 73 74 75 76 78 79 81 82 85 86 87 93 107 108 110 111 114 119 120 121 123 126 129 130 132 146 147 148 **S** Northside Healthcare System, Atlanta, GA
Primary Contact: William M. Hayes, Chief Executive Officer
COO: Mike Patterson, Director of Operations
CFO: Brian Jennette, Chief Financial Officer
CMO: Alexander Kessler, M.D., Chief of Staff
CIO: Bill Dunford, Manager
CHR: Roslyn Roberts, Manager
CNO: Jan Johnson, R.N., Chief Nursing Officer
Web address: www.northside.com
**Control:** Other not–for–profit (including NFP Corporation) **Service:** General Medical and Surgical

**Staffed Beds:** 88 **Admissions:** 4946 **Census:** 59 **Outpatient Visits:** 90427 **Births:** 973 **Total Expense ($000):** 105775 **Payroll Expense ($000):** 43432 **Personnel:** 738

## CARROLLTON—Carroll County

☒ **TANNER MEDICAL CENTER–CARROLLTON (110011)**, (Formerly Tanner Medical Center), 705 Dixie Street, Zip 30117–3818; tel. 770/836–9666, (Nonreporting) **A**1 9 10 **S** Tanner Health System, Carrollton, GA
Primary Contact: Deborah Matthews, Administrator
CHR: Vivian C. Barr, Director Human Resources
Web address: www.tanner.org
**Control:** Other not–for–profit (including NFP Corporation) **Service:** General Medical and Surgical

**Staffed Beds:** 201

## CARTERSVILLE—Bartow County

☒ **CARTERSVILLE MEDICAL CENTER (110030)**, 960 Joe Frank Harris Parkway, Zip 30120–2129; tel. 770/382–1530, (Nonreporting) **A**1 2 9 10 **S** HCA, Nashville, TN
Primary Contact: Keith Sandlin, Chief Executive Officer
Web address: www.cartersvillemedical.com
**Control:** Corporation, Investor–owned, for–profit **Service:** General Medical and Surgical

**Staffed Beds:** 80

## CEDARTOWN—Polk County

☒ **POLK MEDICAL CENTER (111330)**, 424 North Main Street, Zip 30125–2698; tel. 770/748–2500, (Data for 91 days) **A**1 10 18 F3 7 15 28 29 30 34 35 40 42 50 57 59 64 75 91 93 97 107 108 110 114 119 129 130 132 133 146 147 148
Primary Contact: Kim Scoggins, Administrator
CHR: Jeanna Smith, Administrative Assistant and Human Resources Officer
Web address: www.polkmedicalcenter.com
**Control:** Hospital district or authority, Government, nonfederal **Service:** General Medical and Surgical

**Staffed Beds:** 25 **Admissions:** 32 **Census:** 3 **Outpatient Visits:** 7448 **Births:** 0 **Total Expense ($000):** 9237 **Payroll Expense ($000):** 1647 **Personnel:** 90

## CHATSWORTH—Murray County

☐ **MURRAY MEDICAL CENTER (110050)**, 707 Old Dalton Ellijay Road, Zip 30705–2060, Mailing Address: P.O. Box 1406, Zip 30705–1406; tel. 706/695–4564, (Data for 335 days) **A**1 9 10 F3 7 15 29 34 40 45 46 57 81 107 111 114 119 146
Primary Contact: James C. Hazel, FACHE, Chief Executive Officer
CFO: Jana Briley, Director Financial Services
CMO: Michael A. Witt, M.D., Chief of Staff
CIO: Cynthia Austin, Manager Health Information Management
CHR: Jason Hopkins, Director Human Resources
Web address: www.murraymedical.org/
**Control:** Hospital district or authority, Government, nonfederal **Service:** General Medical and Surgical

**Staffed Beds:** 33 **Admissions:** 1341 **Census:** 7 **Outpatient Visits:** 27874 **Births:** 0 **Total Expense ($000):** 11383 **Payroll Expense ($000):** 5948 **Personnel:** 140

GA

---

**Hospital, Medicare Provider Number, Address, Telephone, Approval, Facility, and Physician Codes, Health Care System**

★ American Hospital Association (AHA) membership
☐ The Joint Commission accreditation
◇ DNV Healthcare Inc. accreditation
○ Healthcare Facilities Accreditation Program
△ Commission on Accreditation of Rehabilitation Facilities (CARF) accreditation

## CLAXTON—Evans County

⊠ **EVANS MEMORIAL HOSPITAL (110142)**, 200 North River Street, Zip 30417–1659, Mailing Address: P.O. Box 518, Zip 30417–0518; tel. 912/739–2611, (Total facility includes 120 beds in nursing home–type unit) **A**1 9 10 **F**3 15 34 40 45 53 57 59 68 81 93 97 107 108 110 111 115 119 127 128 130 135 146
Primary Contact: Martha F. Tatum, Chief Executive Officer
CFO: John Wiggins, Chief Financial Officer
CMO: Yelandra Daniels, M.D., Chief of Staff
CIO: Steve Schmidt, Director Information Systems
CHR: Gina Waters, Director Human Resources
CNO: Nikki NeSmith, Chief Nursing Officer
Web address: www.evansmemorialhospital.org
**Control:** Hospital district or authority, Government, nonfederal **Service:** General Medical and Surgical

**Staffed Beds:** 150 **Admissions:** 979 **Census:** 86 **Outpatient Visits:** 31250 **Births:** 0 **Total Expense ($000):** 19351 **Payroll Expense ($000):** 7115 **Personnel:** 246

## CLAYTON—Rabun County

**MOUNTAIN LAKES MEDICAL CENTER (111336)**, 196 Ridgecrest Circle, Zip 30525–4111; tel. 706/782–4233, (Nonreporting) **A**9 10 18
Primary Contact: Kim Ingram, Chief Executive Officer
CFO: Jimmy Norman, Chief Financial Officer
CHR: Charles Harbaugh, Director Human Resources
Web address: www.mountainlakesmedicalcenter.com
**Control:** Hospital district or authority, Government, nonfederal **Service:** General Medical and Surgical

**Staffed Beds:** 24

## COCHRAN—Bleckley County

☐ ◇ **BLECKLEY MEMORIAL HOSPITAL (111302)**, 145 East Peacock Street, Zip 31014–7846, Mailing Address: P.O. Box 536, Zip 31014–0536; tel. 478/934–6211, (Nonreporting) **A**1 9 10 18 21
Primary Contact: Nikki Paulk, Chief Executive Officer
**Control:** Hospital district or authority, Government, nonfederal **Service:** General Medical and Surgical

**Staffed Beds:** 25

## COLQUITT—Miller County

**MILLER COUNTY HOSPITAL (111305)**, 209 North Cuthbert Street, Zip 39837–3518, Mailing Address: P.O. Box 7, Zip 39837–0007; tel. 229/758–3385, (Total facility includes 97 beds in nursing home–type unit) **A**9 10 18 **F**8 13 15 29 30 34 35 40 44 45 50 56 57 59 64 65 66 68 75 77 79 81 85 87 93 97 103 104 107 108 111 114 119 127 128 129 130 133 135 143 145 146 148
Primary Contact: Robin Rau, Chief Executive Officer
CFO: Jill Brown, Chief Financial Officer
CMO: Lamar Brand, M.D., Chief of Staff
CIO: Keith Lovering, Information Technician
CHR: Sharon Calhoun, R.N., Director Quality Management
CNO: Shawn Whittaker, Chief Nursing Officer
Web address: www.millercountyhospital.com
**Control:** Hospital district or authority, Government, nonfederal **Service:** General Medical and Surgical

**Staffed Beds:** 122 **Admissions:** 701 **Census:** 103 **Outpatient Visits:** 28702 **Births:** 0 **Total Expense ($000):** 18184 **Payroll Expense ($000):** 9649 **Personnel:** 241

## COLUMBUS—Muscogee County

**BRADLEY CENTER OF ST. FRANCIS** See St. Francis Hospital

⊠ **COLUMBUS SPECIALTY HOSPITAL (112012)**, 710 Center Street, 9th Floor, Zip 31901–1527; tel. 706/321–6712 **A**1 9 10 **F**1 3 29 30 130 148
Primary Contact: Robert Saulnier, R.N., MSN, Chief Executive Officer
CFO: William Eckstein, Chief Financial Officer
CHR: Melissa Lassiter, Coordinator Human Resources
CNO: Robert Saulnier, R.N., Chief Executive Officer
Web address: www.columbusspecialtyhospital.net
**Control:** Other not–for–profit (including NFP Corporation) **Service:** Long–Term Acute Care hospital

**Staffed Beds:** 50 **Admissions:** 373 **Census:** 26 **Outpatient Visits:** 0 **Births:** 0 **Total Expense ($000):** 15013 **Payroll Expense ($000):** 5853 **Personnel:** 127

⊠ **DOCTORS HOSPITAL OF COLUMBUS (110186)**, 616 19th Street, Zip 31901–1528, Mailing Address: P.O. Box 2188, Zip 31902–2188; tel. 706/494–4262, (Nonreporting) **A**1 9 10 **S** Columbus Regional Healthcare System, Columbus, GA
Primary Contact: Tamara L. Jackson, R.N., MSN, FACHE, Chief Executive Officer
CMO: Thomas L. Theus, M.D., Chief of Medicine
CIO: Ryan Sanders, Director Information Services
Web address: www.doctorshospital.net
**Control:** Other not–for–profit (including NFP Corporation) **Service:** General Medical and Surgical

**Staffed Beds:** 171

⊠ **HUGHSTON HOSPITAL (110200)**, 100 Frist Court, Zip 31909–3578, Mailing Address: P.O. Box 7188, Zip 31908–7188; tel. 706/494–2100, (Nonreporting) **A**1 9 10 **S** Columbus Regional Healthcare System, Columbus, GA
Primary Contact: Butch Wheeler, FACHE, Chief Executive Officer
COO: Michelle Breitfelder, Chief Operating Officer
CFO: Roland Thacker, Chief Financial Officer
CMO: Lyle Norwood, M.D., Chief of Staff
CIO: Douglas Colburn, Chief Information Officer
CHR: Becky Augustyniak, Director Human Resources
Web address: www.hughstonhospital.com
**Control:** Hospital district or authority, Government, nonfederal **Service:** Orthopedic

**Staffed Beds:** 100

⊠ **ST. FRANCIS HOSPITAL (110129)**, 2122 Manchester Expressway, Zip 31904–6878, Mailing Address: P.O. Box 7000, Zip 31908–7000; tel. 706/596–4000, (Includes BRADLEY CENTER OF ST. FRANCIS, 2000 16th Avenue, Zip 31906–0308; tel. 706/320–3700) **A**1 3 5 9 10 **F**3 4 10 11 15 17 18 20 22 24 26 28 29 30 31 34 35 40 45 46 49 50 51 53 54 56 57 58 59 60 63 64 70 74 75 77 78 79 81 82 85 86 92 93 94 98 99 100 101 102 103 104 105 106 107 108 110 111 119 126 129 130 144 145 146 147 148 **P**6
Primary Contact: Robert P. Granger, President and Chief Executive Officer
COO: Kevin Sass, FACHE, Chief Operating Officer
CFO: Matthew Moore, Senior Vice President and Chief Financial Officer
CMO: Bobbi Farber, M.D., Chief Medical Officer
CHR: E. Rick Lowe, FACHE, Senior Vice President and Chief Administrative Officer
Web address: www.sfhga.com
**Control:** Other not–for–profit (including NFP Corporation) **Service:** General Medical and Surgical

**Staffed Beds:** 321 **Admissions:** 13806 **Census:** 179 **Outpatient Visits:** 147748 **Births:** 0 **Total Expense ($000):** 193967 **Payroll Expense ($000):** 71733 **Personnel:** 1657

⊠ **THE MEDICAL CENTER (110064)**, 710 Center Street, Zip 31901–1527, Mailing Address: P.O. Box 951, Zip 31902–0951; tel. 706/571–1000, (Nonreporting) **A**1 2 3 5 9 10 12 13 **S** Columbus Regional Healthcare System, Columbus, GA
Primary Contact: Ryan Chandler, President and Chief Executive Officer
CMO: Andrew P. Morley, Jr., M.D., Senior Vice President and Chief Medical Officer
CIO: Joseph T. Wood, Vice President and Chief Information Officer
CHR: Wayne Joiner, Vice President Human Resources
Web address: www.columbusregional.com
**Control:** Other not–for–profit (including NFP Corporation) **Service:** General Medical and Surgical

**Staffed Beds:** 497

☐ **WEST CENTRAL GEORGIA REGIONAL HOSPITAL (114013)**, 3000 Schatulga Road, Zip 31907–3117, Mailing Address: P.O. Box 12435, Zip 31917–2435; tel. 706/568–5000, (Nonreporting) **A**1 10
Primary Contact: John L. Robertson, Administrator
COO: Larmar Cunningham, Chief Operating Officer
CMO: Abiodun Famakinwa, M.D., Acting Clinical Director
CIO: Ron Buchanan, Director Information Services
CHR: Coreg Burns, Human Resources Lead
Web address: www.wcgrh.org
**Control:** State–Government, nonfederal **Service:** Psychiatric

**Staffed Beds:** 145

## COMMERCE—Jackson County

⊠ **NORTHRIDGE MEDICAL CENTER (110040)**, 70 Medical Center Drive, Zip 30529–1078; tel. 706/335–1000, (Nonreporting) **A**1 9 10
Primary Contact: Richard L. Clark, Interim Chief Executive Officer
CFO: Larry W. Ebert, Jr., Chief Financial Officer
CMO: Narasimhulu Neelagaru, M.D., Chief of Staff
CIO: Vince Jarnagin, Manager Information Technology
CHR: Robin Daniel, Director of Human Resources
CNO: Maura Cobb, R.N., Chief Nursing Officer
Web address: www.northridgemc.com
**Control:** Partnership, Investor–owned, for–profit **Service:** General Medical and Surgical

**Staffed Beds:** 257

*Many Facility Codes have changed. Please refer to the AHA Guide Code Chart.*
© 2013 AHA Guide

GA

## CONYERS—Rockdale County

⊠ **ROCKDALE MEDICAL CENTER (110091)**, 1412 Milstead Avenue N.E., Zip 30012–3877; tel. 770/918–3000 **A**1 9 10 **F**3 11 13 15 18 20 28 29 30 31 34 35 36 40 45 46 47 49 57 59 62 64 68 70 73 74 75 76 78 79 81 82 85 86 87 92 93 107 108 110 111 114 115 118 119 126 130 131 132 135 145 146 147 148 **S** LifePoint Hospitals, Inc., Brentwood, TN
Primary Contact: Deborah Armstrong, Chief Executive Officer
COO: James Atkins, Chief Operating Officer
CFO: James Hughey, Chief Financial Officer
CMO: Lisa Gillespie, M.D., Chief Medical Officer
CIO: Gail Waldo, Director Information Technology
CHR: Marianne Freeman, Vice President Human Resources
CNO: Deborah Almauhy, R.N., Chief Nursing Officer
Web address: www.rockdalemedicalcenter.org
**Control:** Corporation, Investor–owned, for–profit **Service:** General Medical and Surgical

**Staffed Beds:** 146 **Admissions:** 8464 **Census:** 102 **Outpatient Visits:** 125018 **Births:** 1902 **Total Expense ($000):** 99289 **Payroll Expense ($000):** 44683 **Personnel:** 728

## CORDELE—Crisp County

⊠ **CRISP REGIONAL HOSPITAL (110104)**, 902 North Seventh Street, Zip 31015–3234; tel. 229/276–3100, (Total facility includes 143 beds in nursing home–type unit) **A**1 9 10 20 **F**3 10 11 13 15 28 29 30 31 34 35 40 44 45 48 50 51 54 56 57 58 59 60 61 62 63 64 65 68 70 75 77 78 81 84 85 86 87 90 93 96 97 107 108 110 111 115 125 127 128 129 132 133 135 144 146 147 148 **P**2 8
Primary Contact: Steven Gautney, Chief Executive Officer
COO: Mary Jim Montgomery, R.N., Chief Operating Officer
CFO: Jessica Y. Carter, Chief Financial Officer
CMO: David Kavtaradze, M.D., Chief of Staff
CHR: George M. Laurin, Interim Director Human Resources
CNO: Marsha L. Mulderig, R.N., Chief Nursing Officer
Web address: www.crispregional.org
**Control:** County–Government, nonfederal **Service:** General Medical and Surgical

**Staffed Beds:** 216 **Admissions:** 3254 **Census:** 135 **Outpatient Visits:** 101913 **Births:** 329 **Personnel:** 620

## COVINGTON—Newton County

⊠ **NEWTON MEDICAL CENTER (110018)**, 5126 Hospital Drive, Zip 30014–2567; tel. 770/786–7053 **A**1 9 10 **F**7 11 12 13 15 18 20 28 29 30 31 34 35 40 49 59 62 64 70 72 74 75 76 78 79 81 85 87 89 93 97 107 108 111 119 130 131 132 141 142 146 147 148
Primary Contact: James F. Weadick, Administrator and Chief Executive Officer
CFO: Troy Brooks, Assistant Administrator Fiscal Services
CMO: Mark C. Hanson, M.D., Chief of Staff
CIO: Steve Dickstein, Director
CHR: Greg Richardson, Director Human Resources
CNO: Patricia A. Waller, R.N., Assistant Administrator Patient Care Services
Web address: www.newtonmedical.com
**Control:** Other not–for–profit (including NFP Corporation) **Service:** General Medical and Surgical

**Staffed Beds:** 101 **Admissions:** 5522 **Census:** 51 **Outpatient Visits:** 249966 **Births:** 676 **Total Expense ($000):** 80730 **Payroll Expense ($000):** 36112 **Personnel:** 684

## CUMMING—Forsyth County

⊠ **NORTHSIDE HOSPITAL–FORSYTH (110005)**, 1200 Northside Forsyth Drive, Zip 30041–7659; tel. 770/844–3200 **A**1 9 10 **F**3 8 11 12 13 15 18 20 22 26 28 29 30 31 34 35 40 44 45 49 50 57 59 60 64 68 70 71 73 74 75 76 78 79 81 82 85 86 87 93 107 108 110 111 114 115 117 119 120 121 123 124 126 129 130 132 135 146 147 148 **S** Northside Healthcare System, Atlanta, GA
Primary Contact: Lynn Jackson, Administrator
CFO: Mitch Logan, Director Finance
Web address: www.northside.com
**Control:** Other not–for–profit (including NFP Corporation) **Service:** General Medical and Surgical

**Staffed Beds:** 213 **Admissions:** 11090 **Census:** 149 **Outpatient Visits:** 176900 **Births:** 2371 **Total Expense ($000):** 252154 **Payroll Expense ($000):** 85950 **Personnel:** 1610

## CUTHBERT—Randolph County

⊠ ◇ **SOUTHWEST GEORGIA REGIONAL MEDICAL CENTER (111300)**, 361 Randolph Street, Zip 39840–6127; tel. 229/732–2181, (Nonreporting) **A**1 9 10 18 21
Primary Contact: Derrick A. Frazier, Chief Executive Officer
CFO: Brent Rigsby, Chief Financial Officer
Web address: www.phoebeputney.com/
**Control:** Hospital district or authority, Government, nonfederal **Service:** General Medical and Surgical

**Staffed Beds:** 105

## DAHLONEGA—Lumpkin County

☐ **CHESTATEE REGIONAL HOSPITAL (110187)**, 227 Mountain Drive, Zip 30533–1606; tel. 706/864–6136 **A**1 9 10 **F**3 13 15 29 34 49 50 54 57 59 64 65 76 79 81 85 86 87 105 107 108 110 111 114 119 127 129 130 133 143 146 147 **P**8 **S** Sunlink Health Systems, Atlanta, GA
Primary Contact: Larry R. Jeter, Chief Executive Officer
CFO: Molly Lindquist, Interim Chief Financial Officer
CMO: Richard Wherry, M.D., Chief of Staff
CHR: Barbara Patrick, Director Human Resources
CNO: Barbara Arnau, R.N., Chief Nursing Officer
Web address: www.chestateeregionalhospital.com
**Control:** Corporation, Investor–owned, for–profit **Service:** General Medical and Surgical

**Staffed Beds:** 49 **Admissions:** 1478 **Census:** 12 **Outpatient Visits:** 22515 **Births:** 194 **Total Expense ($000):** 17133 **Payroll Expense ($000):** 7273 **Personnel:** 142

## DALLAS—Paulding County

⊠ **WELLSTAR PAULDING HOSPITAL (110042)**, 600 West Memorial Drive, Zip 30132–4117; tel. 770/445–4411, (Total facility includes 182 beds in nursing home–type unit) **A**1 9 10 **F**3 11 15 28 29 30 37 38 40 44 45 50 54 55 59 61 64 68 70 75 77 78 79 81 82 85 86 87 102 104 107 108 110 111 114 118 119 120 121 123 128 129 130 146 **P**1 6 **S** WellStar Health System, Marietta, GA
Primary Contact: Mark Haney, President
CFO: Marsha Burke, Senior Vice President Financial Services
Web address: www.wellstar.org
**Control:** Other not–for–profit (including NFP Corporation) **Service:** General Medical and Surgical

**Staffed Beds:** 216 **Admissions:** 2128 **Census:** 191 **Outpatient Visits:** 100549 **Births:** 0 **Personnel:** 496

## DALTON—Whitfield County

⊠ **HAMILTON MEDICAL CENTER (110001)**, 1200 Memorial Drive, Zip 30720–2529, Mailing Address: P.O. Box 1168, Zip 30722–1168; tel. 706/272–6000 **A**1 2 9 10 19 **F**3 4 5 8 12 13 15 18 20 22 26 28 29 30 31 34 35 40 43 44 45 46 48 49 50 51 53 54 57 59 60 62 63 64 68 70 72 74 75 76 77 78 79 81 82 83 84 85 86 87 89 93 96 97 98 100 101 102 103 104 105 107 108 110 111 114 115 116 117 118 119 120 121 123 126 129 130 131 132 135 144 146 147 148
Primary Contact: Jeffrey D. Myers, President and Chief Executive Officer
COO: Sandra D. McKenzie, Executive Vice President and Chief Operating Officer
CFO: Gary L. Howard, Senior VP and Chief Financial Officer
CMO: Stephen G. Rohm, M.D., VP and Chief Medical Officer
CIO: John M. Forrester, Director Information Services
CHR: Steven Pound, Vice President Human Resources
CNO: Cathy Ferguson, R.N., VP and Chief Nursing Officer
Web address: www.hamiltonhealth.com
**Control:** Other not–for–profit (including NFP Corporation) **Service:** General Medical and Surgical

**Staffed Beds:** 230 **Admissions:** 10807 **Census:** 113 **Outpatient Visits:** 253004 **Births:** 1780 **Personnel:** 1007

## DECATUR—Dekalb County

⊠ △ **ATLANTA VETERANS AFFAIRS MEDICAL CENTER**, (Formerly Veterans Affairs Medical Center), 1670 Clairmont Road, Zip 30033–4004; tel. 404/321–6111, (Nonreporting) **A**1 2 3 5 7 8 **S** Department of Veterans Affairs, Washington, DC
Primary Contact: Leslie Wiggins, Director
CFO: Pamela Watkins, Chief Financial Officer
CMO: David Bower, M.D., Chief of Staff
CIO: William Brock, Chief Information Officer
CHR: Zeta Ferguson, Chief Human Resources
CNO: Sandy Leake, MSN, Associate Director, Nursing and Patient Care Services
Web address: www.atlanta.va.gov/
**Control:** Veterans Affairs, Government, federal **Service:** General Medical and Surgical

**Staffed Beds:** 239

**GA**

---

**Hospital, Medicare Provider Number, Address, Telephone, Approval, Facility, and Physician Codes, Health Care System**

★ American Hospital Association (AHA) membership
☐ The Joint Commission accreditation
◇ DNV Healthcare Inc. accreditation
○ Healthcare Facilities Accreditation Program
△ Commission on Accreditation of Rehabilitation Facilities (CARF) accreditation

---

☐ **DEKALB MEDICAL AT DOWNTOWN DECATUR (112006)**, 450 North Candler Street, Zip 30030–2671; tel. 404/501–6700 **A**1 5 9 10 **F**1 3 29 30 50 60 74 75 77 79 87 107 119 130 148 **S** DeKalb Regional Health System, Decatur, GA
Primary Contact: John Shelton, President and Chief Executive Officer
COO: John Shelton, Executive Vice President and Chief Operating Officer
CMO: David Snyder, M.D., Chief of Staff
CHR: Tom Crawford, Vice President Human Resources
Web address: www.dekalbmedicalcenter.org
**Control:** Other not–for–profit (including NFP Corporation) **Service:** Long–Term Acute Care hospital

**Staffed Beds:** 44 **Admissions:** 279 **Census:** 24 **Outpatient Visits:** 0 **Births:** 0 **Personnel:** 161

☒ **DEKALB MEDICAL AT NORTH DECATUR (110076)**, 2701 North Decatur Road, Zip 30033–5995; tel. 404/501–1000 **A**1 2 3 9 10 **F**3 11 12 13 15 18 20 22 26 28 29 30 31 34 35 38 40 45 48 49 50 53 55 56 57 58 59 60 64 67 70 71 72 73 74 75 76 77 78 79 81 85 90 93 96 97 98 100 102 105 107 108 110 111 114 115 117 119 120 121 124 126 129 130 131 132 134 135 146 147 148 **P**1 **S** DeKalb Regional Health System, Decatur, GA
Primary Contact: John Shelton, President and Chief Executive Officer
COO: Dane Henry, Executive Vice President and Chief Operating Officer
CFO: Mal Underwood, Interim Sr. VP and Chief Financial Officer
CMO: Duane Barclay, D.O., Vice President Physician Support Services
CIO: Mark Trocino, Chief Information Officer
CHR: Joel Schuessler, Interim Vice President Human Resources
CNO: Cherie Kunik, R.N., Interim Vice President Patient Care Services & CNO
Web address: www.dekalbmedical.org
**Control:** Other not–for–profit (including NFP Corporation) **Service:** General Medical and Surgical

**Staffed Beds:** 418 **Admissions:** 21093 **Census:** 261 **Outpatient Visits:** 171346 **Births:** 5230 **Personnel:** 1416

☐ **GEORGIA REGIONAL HOSPITAL AT ATLANTA (114019)**, 3073 Panthersville Road, Zip 30034–3828; tel. 404/243–2100, (Nonreporting) **A**1 3 5 10
Primary Contact: Susan Trueblood, Chief Executive Officer
COO: Sonny Slate, Chief Operating Officer
CFO: Reginald Jones, Business Manager
CMO: Emile Risby, M.D., Clinical Director
CIO: Elfie Early, Manager Data Services
CHR: Lorraine Farr, Manager Human Resources
Web address: www.atlantareg.dhr.state.ga.us
**Control:** State–Government, nonfederal **Service:** Psychiatric

**Staffed Beds:** 354

**VETERANS AFFAIRS MEDICAL CENTER** See Atlanta Veterans Affairs Medical Center

**DEMOREST—Habersham County**

☒ **HABERSHAM MEDICAL CENTER (110041)**, 541 Historic Highway 441, Zip 30535–3118, Mailing Address: P.O. Box 37, Zip 30535–0037; tel. 706/754–2161, (Total facility includes 84 beds in nursing home–type unit) **A**1 9 10 **F**3 7 11 13 15 28 29 30 35 38 40 45 53 54 57 59 62 64 68 70 77 79 81 82 85 86 87 93 107 108 111 114 116 117 119 124 128 129 130 131 132 133 146 147 **P**7
Primary Contact: Jack Fulbright, Acting Chief Executive Officer
CFO: James Peterson, Senior Vice President Finance
CMO: James Hamilton, M.D., Chief of Staff
CIO: Roger Ivester, Manager Information Systems
CHR: Wanda Hardman, Director Human Resources
Web address: www.hcmcmed.org
**Control:** Hospital district or authority, Government, nonfederal **Service:** General Medical and Surgical

**Staffed Beds:** 137 **Admissions:** 2469 **Census:** 104 **Outpatient Visits:** 95667 **Births:** 401 **Total Expense ($000):** 46283 **Payroll Expense ($000):** 20161 **Personnel:** 531

**DONALSONVILLE—Seminole County**

☐ ◇ **DONALSONVILLE HOSPITAL (110194)**, 102 Hospital Circle, Zip 39845–1199; tel. 229/524–5217, (Total facility includes 75 beds in nursing home–type unit) **A**1 9 10 21 **F**34 40 45 46 57 59 64 68 76 77 81 87 93 107 108 110 114 119 128 133 147 148
Primary Contact: Charles H. Orrick, Administrator
CFO: James Moody, Chief Financial Officer
CMO: C. O. Walker, M.D., Chief of Staff
CHR: Jo Adams, Director Human Resources
**Control:** Other not–for–profit (including NFP Corporation) **Service:** General Medical and Surgical

**Staffed Beds:** 140 **Admissions:** 1901 **Census:** 77 **Outpatient Visits:** 25003 **Births:** 260 **Total Expense ($000):** 30542 **Payroll Expense ($000):** 12437 **Personnel:** 389

**DOUGLAS—Coffee County**

☒ **COFFEE REGIONAL MEDICAL CENTER (110089)**, 1101 Ocilla Road, Zip 31533–2207, Mailing Address: P.O. Box 1287, Zip 31534–1287; tel. 912/384–1900 **A**1 9 10 20 **F**3 7 8 11 13 15 18 20 28 29 30 32 34 35 40 45 47 49 50 51 53 54 56 57 59 61 65 68 70 75 76 77 78 79 81 82 85 86 87 89 97 107 108 110 111 114 115 119 127 129 130 131 132 135 143 144 146 147 148 **P**8
Primary Contact: George L. Heck, III, President and Chief Executive Officer
CFO: Donald C. Lewis, Jr., Vice President and Chief Financial Officer
CIO: George L. Heck, III, President and Chief Executive Officer
CHR: Laura Bloom, Director Human Resources
Web address: www.coffeeregional.org
**Control:** Other not–for–profit (including NFP Corporation) **Service:** General Medical and Surgical

**Staffed Beds:** 88 **Admissions:** 5913 **Census:** 61 **Outpatient Visits:** 120000 **Births:** 583 **Total Expense ($000):** 76226 **Payroll Expense ($000):** 30787 **Personnel:** 708

**DOUGLASVILLE—Douglas County**

☒ **WELLSTAR DOUGLAS HOSPITAL (110184)**, 8954 Hospital Drive, Zip 30134–2282; tel. 770/949–1500 **A**1 2 9 10 **F**3 11 13 15 20 22 28 29 30 31 37 38 40 44 45 48 49 50 51 54 58 59 60 61 64 68 70 74 75 76 77 78 79 81 82 85 86 87 93 94 102 107 108 110 111 114 115 117 118 119 129 130 132 146 147 **P**1 6 **S** WellStar Health System, Marietta, GA
Primary Contact: Craig A. Owens, President
CFO: Bradley Greene, Chief Financial Officer
CMO: Noel Holtz, M.D., Chief Medical Officer
CIO: Ronald Strachan, Chief Information Officer
CHR: Danyale Ziglor, Assistant Director Human Resources
Web address: www.wellstar.org
**Control:** Other not–for–profit (including NFP Corporation) **Service:** General Medical and Surgical

**Staffed Beds:** 102 **Admissions:** 6826 **Census:** 74 **Outpatient Visits:** 130706 **Births:** 486 **Personnel:** 723

**YOUTH VILLAGES INNER HARBOUR CAMPUS**, 4685 Dorsett Shoals Road, Zip 30135–4999; tel. 770/942–2391, (Nonreporting)
Primary Contact: Patrick Lawler, Chief Executive Officer
CFO: J. Steve Lewis, Director Finance
CIO: Laura Sellers, Director Information Systems
CHR: Sherry Kollmeyer, Vice President Human Resources
Web address: www.innerharbour.org
**Control:** Other not–for–profit (including NFP Corporation) **Service:** Children's hospital psychiatric

**Staffed Beds:** 176

**DUBLIN—Laurens County**

☒ **CARL VINSON VETERANS AFFAIRS MEDICAL CENTER**, 1826 Veterans Boulevard, Zip 31021–3620; tel. 478/272–1210, (Nonreporting) **A**1 **S** Department of Veterans Affairs, Washington, DC
Primary Contact: John S. Goldman, Director
CFO: Marcy Chambless, Manager Business Office
CMO: Eva Martin, M.D., Chief of Staff
CIO: Sandra Clem, Manager Information Management
CHR: Teresa L. Lindsey, Supervisor Human Resources
Web address: www.dublin.va.gov/
**Control:** Veterans Affairs, Government, federal **Service:** General Medical and Surgical

**Staffed Beds:** 178

☒ **FAIRVIEW PARK HOSPITAL (110125)**, 200 Industrial Boulevard, Zip 31021–2997, Mailing Address: P.O. Box 1408, Zip 31040–1408; tel. 478/275–2000, (Nonreporting) **A**1 9 10 19 **S** HCA, Nashville, TN
Primary Contact: Donald R. Avery, FACHE, President and Chief Executive Officer
COO: Michael Hoskins, Chief Operating Officer
CFO: Ted Short, Chief Financial Officer
CMO: David G. Shores, D.O., President Medical Staff
CIO: Marsha Morris, Manager Information Services
CHR: Jeff Bruton, Director Human Resources
Web address: www.fairviewparkhospital.com
**Control:** Corporation, Investor–owned, for–profit **Service:** General Medical and Surgical

**Staffed Beds:** 168

**DULUTH—De Kalb County**

**GWINNETT MEDICAL CENTER–DULUTH** See Gwinnett Hospital System, Lawrenceville

GA

*Many Facility Codes have changed. Please refer to the AHA Guide Code Chart.* © 2013 AHA Guide

## EAST POINT—Fulton County

✠ **REGENCY HOSPITAL OF SOUTH ATLANTA (112014)**, 1170 Cleveland Avenue, 4th Floor, Zip 30344–3615; tel. 404/466–6250, (Nonreporting) **A**1 10 **S** Select Medical Corporation, Mechanicsburg, PA
Primary Contact: Alisa Jett, Chief Executive Officer
Web address: www.regencyhospital.com
**Control:** Corporation, Investor–owned, for–profit **Service:** Long–Term Acute Care hospital

**Staffed Beds:** 37

## EASTMAN—Dodge County

◇ **DODGE COUNTY HOSPITAL (110092)**, 901 Griffin Avenue, Zip 31023–6720, Mailing Address: P.O. Box 4309, Zip 31023–4309; tel. 478/374–4000 **A**9 10 21 **F**3 11 13 15 29 30 31 40 45 53 57 59 64 69 70 75 76 79 81 85 86 107 108 111 114 119 146 147
Primary Contact: Kevin Bierschenk, Chief Executive Officer
CFO: Jan Hamrick, Chief Financial Officer
CIO: Victor Woodard, Manager Information Technology
CHR: Wendy Selph, Director Human Resources
CNO: Sandra M. Campbell, R.N., Chief Nursing Officer
Web address: www.dodgecountyhospital.com
**Control:** Hospital district or authority, Government, nonfederal **Service:** General Medical and Surgical

**Staffed Beds:** 25 **Admissions:** 1592 **Census:** 18 **Outpatient Visits:** 38339 **Births:** 147 **Total Expense ($000):** 19369 **Payroll Expense ($000):** 8297 **Personnel:** 224

## EATONTON—Putnam County

☐ **PUTNAM GENERAL HOSPITAL (111313)**, 101 Lake Oconee Parkway, Zip 31024–6054; tel. 706/485–2711, (Nonreporting) **A**1 9 10 18
Primary Contact: Darrell M. Oglesby, Administrator
CFO: Brenda Jarrell, Chief Financial Officer
CMO: Omar Akhras, M.D., Chief of Staff
CIO: Steven Cason, Chief Information Officer
CHR: Ellen Ellard, Director Human Resources
Web address: www.putnamgeneral.com
**Control:** Hospital district or authority, Government, nonfederal **Service:** General Medical and Surgical

**Staffed Beds:** 25

## ELBERTON—Elbert County

✠ **ELBERT MEMORIAL HOSPITAL (110026)**, 4 Medical Drive, Zip 30635–1897; tel. 706/283–3151, (Nonreporting) **A**1 9 10
Primary Contact: James Yarborough, FACHE, Interim Chief Executive Officer
CFO: Doug Faircloth, Interim Chief Financial Officer
CIO: Andy Chapin, Director Information Technology
CHR: Georgian Walton, Director Human Resources
Web address: www.emhcare.net
**Control:** Hospital district or authority, Government, nonfederal **Service:** General Medical and Surgical

**Staffed Beds:** 42

## ELLIJAY—Gilmer County

☐ **NORTH GEORGIA MEDICAL CENTER (110205)**, 1362 South Main Street, Zip 30540–5410, Mailing Address: P.O. Box 2239, Zip 30540–0025; tel. 706/276–4741, (Nonreporting) **A**1 9 10 **S** Sunlink Health Systems, Atlanta, GA
Primary Contact: Jeffrey Dunn, Chief Executive Officer
COO: Jeffrey Dunn, Chief Executive Officer
CFO: Debbie Self, Chief Financial Officer
CMO: Kelvin Haim, M.D., Chief of Staff
CHR: Mary Beth Ralston, Manager Human Resources
Web address: www.northgeorgiamedicalcenter.com
**Control:** Corporation, Investor–owned, for–profit **Service:** General Medical and Surgical

**Staffed Beds:** 150

## FAYETTEVILLE—Fayette County

✠ **PIEDMONT FAYETTE HOSPITAL (110215)**, 1255 Highway 54 West, Zip 30214–4526; tel. 770/719–7000, (Nonreporting) **A**1 2 9 10 **S** Piedmont Healthcare, Atlanta, GA
Primary Contact: J. Michael Burnett, President and Chief Administrative Officer
COO: Michael Burnett, Chief Operating Officer
CMO: Frederick Willms, M.D., Vice President Medical Affairs
CIO: Mark Pasquale, Vice President Information Services and Chief Information Officer
CHR: Catherine Crisler, Executive Director Human Resources
Web address: www.fayettehospital.org
**Control:** Other not–for–profit (including NFP Corporation) **Service:** General Medical and Surgical

**Staffed Beds:** 148

## FITZGERALD—Ben Hill County

☐ ◇ **DORMINY MEDICAL CENTER (110073)**, 200 Perry House Road, Zip 31750–8857, Mailing Address: P.O. Box 1447, Zip 31750–1447; tel. 229/424–7100, (Nonreporting) **A**1 9 10 21
Primary Contact: Warren Manley, Administrator
COO: Debbie Thomas, Chief Operating Officer
CFO: Paige Wynn, Chief Financial Officer
CMO: Thomas Mann, M.D., Chief of Staff
CIO: Mike James, Director Management Information Systems
CHR: Denise Steverson, Director Human Resources
CNO: Staci Mims, Chief Nursing Officer
Web address: www.dorminymedical.org
**Control:** Hospital district or authority, Government, nonfederal **Service:** General Medical and Surgical

**Staffed Beds:** 67

## FOLKSTON—Charlton County

**CHARLTON MEMORIAL HOSPITAL (111315)**, 2449 Third Street, Zip 31537–8919, Mailing Address: P.O. Box 188, Zip 31537–0188; tel. 912/496–2531, (Nonreporting) **A**9 10 18
Primary Contact: H. D. Cannington, Chief Executive Officer
CFO: Kim Savage, Interim Controller
CMO: Albert Thompson, M.D., Chief of Staff
CHR: Darlene Tail, Director Human Resources
Web address: www.southcoast.org/charlton/
**Control:** Hospital district or authority, Government, nonfederal **Service:** General Medical and Surgical

**Staffed Beds:** 22

## FORSYTH—Monroe County

☐ **MONROE COUNTY HOSPITAL (111318)**, 88 Martin Luther King Jr. Drive, Zip 31029–1682, Mailing Address: P.O. Box 1068, Zip 31029–1068; tel. 478/994–2521 **A**1 9 10 18 **F**3 11 15 29 35 40 57 59 68 75 81 107 111 114 119 132 133 146 148 **P**1 2
Primary Contact: Kay A. Floyd, R.N., Chief Executive Officer
CFO: Marlene McLennan, Controller
CMO: Jeremy Goodwin, M.D., President, Medical Staff
CIO: Donna Hogg, Supervisor Medical Records
CHR: Deborah Flowers, Director Human Resources
CNO: Casey Fleckenstein, Medical and Surgical Nurse Manager
Web address: www.monroehospital.org
**Control:** Hospital district or authority, Government, nonfederal **Service:** General Medical and Surgical

**Staffed Beds:** 25 **Admissions:** 488 **Census:** 7 **Outpatient Visits:** 24491 **Births:** 0 **Total Expense ($000):** 10564 **Payroll Expense ($000):** 4336 **Personnel:** 123

## FORT BENNING—Muscogee County

✠ **MARTIN ARMY COMMUNITY HOSPITAL**, 7950 Martin Loop, Zip 31905–5648, Mailing Address: 7950 Martin Loop, B9200, Room 010, Zip 31905–5648; tel. 706/544–2516, (Nonreporting) **A**1 3 5 **S** Department of the Army, Office of the Surgeon General, Falls Church, VA
Primary Contact: Colonel Timothy E. Lamb, Commander
CHR: Major Bernita Hightower, Chief Human Resources
Web address: www.martin.amedd.army.mil
**Control:** Army, Government, federal **Service:** General Medical and Surgical

**Staffed Beds:** 57

**GA**

---

**Hospital, Medicare Provider Number, Address, Telephone, Approval, Facility, and Physician Codes, Health Care System**

★ American Hospital Association (AHA) membership
☐ The Joint Commission accreditation
◇ DNV Healthcare Inc. accreditation
○ Healthcare Facilities Accreditation Program
∧ Commission on Accreditation of Rehabilitation Facilities (CARF) accreditation

## FORT GORDON—Richmond County

✉ **DWIGHT DAVID EISENHOWER ARMY MEDICAL CENTER**, 300 West Hospital Road, Zip 30905–5741; tel. 706/787–5811 **A**1 2 3 5 **F**3 4 5 7 8 9 11 12 14 15 17 18 20 22 24 26 29 30 31 33 34 35 36 37 38 39 43 44 45 46 47 48 49 50 51 53 54 56 57 58 59 60 61 64 65 68 70 74 75 77 78 79 80 81 82 85 86 87 91 93 94 97 98 99 100 101 102 104 105 106 107 108 111 114 116 117 118 119 122 129 130 131 132 135 143 144 145 146 147 148 **P**6 **S** Department of the Army, Office of the Surgeon General, Falls Church, VA
Primary Contact: Commander Christopher M. Castle, Commander
CMO: Colonel James M. Baunchalk, Deputy Chief Clinical Services
CIO: Major Joseph A. Ponce, Chief Information Management
CHR: Elizabeth Shelt, Civilian Personnel Officer
Web address: www.ddeamc.amedd.army.mil
**Control:** Army, Government, federal **Service:** General Medical and Surgical

**Staffed Beds:** 107 **Admissions:** 4359 **Census:** 61 **Outpatient Visits:** 620120 **Births:** 0

## FORT OGLETHORPE—Catoosa County

☐ **ERLANGER AT HUTCHESON (110004)**, 100 Gross Crescent Circle, Zip 30742–3669; tel. 706/858–2000, (Nonreporting) **A**1 9 10 **S** Erlanger Health System, Chattanooga, TN
Primary Contact: Roger Forgey, President and Chief Executive Officer
CFO: Denise Baker, Interim Chief Financial Officer
CMO: Maria Bowers, M.D., Chief of Staff
CIO: Ruth Wright, Director Information Services
CHR: Ella Cowden, Director Human Resources
Web address: www.hutcheson.org
**Control:** Hospital district or authority, Government, nonfederal **Service:** General Medical and Surgical

**Staffed Beds:** 185

## FORT VALLEY—Peach County

☐ **PEACH REGIONAL MEDICAL CENTER (111310)**, 601 Blue Bird Boulevard, Zip 31030–4599, Mailing Address: P.O. Box 1799, Zip 31030–1799; tel. 478/825–8691, (Nonreporting) **A**1 9 10 18
Primary Contact: Nancy Peed, Administrator and Chief Executive Officer
CFO: Lisa Urbistondo, Chief Financial Officer
CMO: Crystal Brown, M.D., Medical Director
CNO: Brenda Goodman, Chief Nursing Officer
Web address: www.peachregional.org
**Control:** Hospital district or authority, Government, nonfederal **Service:** General Medical and Surgical

**Staffed Beds:** 25

## GAINESVILLE—Hall County

✉ △ ◇ **NORTHEAST GEORGIA MEDICAL CENTER (110029)**, 743 Spring Street N.E., Zip 30501–3899; tel. 770/219–3553, (Total facility includes 260 beds in nursing home–type unit) **A**1 2 7 9 10 19 21 **F**3 4 5 7 11 12 13 15 17 18 20 22 24 26 28 29 30 31 34 35 38 39 40 44 45 47 48 49 50 51 54 56 57 58 59 60 61 63 64 65 66 68 70 72 73 74 75 76 77 78 79 81 82 85 86 87 89 90 93 98 99 100 101 102 103 104 105 106 107 108 110 111 114 115 116 117 119 120 121 123 124 126 128 129 130 131 132 143 144 146 147 148 **P**6
Primary Contact: Carol H. Burrell, President and Chief Executive Officer
CFO: Tony Herdener, Vice President Systems and Finance
CMO: Jim Bailey, M.D., Chief Medical Officer
CIO: Mark Jennings, Director Information Systems
Web address: www.nghs.com
**Control:** Other not–for–profit (including NFP Corporation) **Service:** General Medical and Surgical

**Staffed Beds:** 513 **Admissions:** 26974 **Census:** 314 **Outpatient Visits:** 341148 **Births:** 3553 **Total Expense ($000):** 518110 **Payroll Expense ($000):** 192540

## GLENWOOD—Wheeler County

☐ ◇ **LOWER OCONEE COMMUNITY HOSPITAL (111321)**, 111 Third Street, Zip 30428–3764, Mailing Address: P.O. Box 398, Zip 30428–0398; tel. 912/523–5113, (Nonreporting) **A**1 9 10 18 21
Primary Contact: Peyton A. Smith, Chief Executive Officer
CFO: David R. Pike, Chief Financial Officer
CHR: Sheila Heaton, Chief Human Resources Officer
**Control:** Other not–for–profit (including NFP Corporation) **Service:** General Medical and Surgical

**Staffed Beds:** 25

## GRACEWOOD—Richmond County

**EAST CENTRAL REGIONAL HOSPITAL** See East Central Regional Hospital, Augusta

## GREENSBORO—Greene County

✉ **ST. MARY'S GOOD SAMARITAN HOSPITAL (111329)**, (Formerly Good Samaritan Hospital), 1201 Siloam Highway, Zip 30642–2811; tel. 706/453–7331 **A**1 9 10 18 **F**3 11 15 18 29 30 34 35 40 50 56 57 59 64 65 75 79 81 86 87 89 93 107 111 115 119 128 129 130 133 135 148 **S** Catholic Health East, Newtown Square, PA
Primary Contact: D. Montez Carter, President
CMO: Dave Ringer, M.D., Chief of Staff
CHR: Angela C. Adams, Director Human Resources
Web address: www.stmarysgoodsam.org
**Control:** Church–operated, Nongovernment, not–for profit **Service:** General Medical and Surgical

**Staffed Beds:** 25 **Admissions:** 329 **Census:** 4 **Outpatient Visits:** 18736 **Births:** 0 **Total Expense ($000):** 7795 **Payroll Expense ($000):** 5726 **Personnel:** 150

## GRIFFIN—Spalding County

✉ **SPALDING REGIONAL MEDICAL CENTER (110031)**, 601 South Eighth Street, Zip 30224–4294; Mailing Address: P.O. Drawer V, Zip 30224–1168; tel. 770/228–2721 **A**1 2 9 10 **F**3 7 11 13 15 18 20 22 29 30 31 34 35 40 49 50 51 53 54 57 59 64 70 73 74 75 76 77 78 79 81 85 89 93 107 108 110 111 114 115 119 129 130 131 135 143 146 147 148 **P**8 **S** TENET Healthcare Corporation, Dallas, TX
Primary Contact: John A. Quinn, Chief Executive Officer
COO: Christopher Locke, Chief Operating Officer
CFO: Tamara Ison, Chief Financial Officer
CIO: Steve Brown, Director Information Systems
CHR: Amanda Remington, Director Human Resources
CNO: Wadra McCullough, Chief Nursing Officer
Web address: www.spaldingregional.com
**Control:** Corporation, Investor–owned, for–profit **Service:** General Medical and Surgical

**Staffed Beds:** 160 **Admissions:** 8479 **Census:** 91 **Outpatient Visits:** 99183 **Births:** 879 **Total Expense ($000):** 88908 **Payroll Expense ($000):** 37749 **Personnel:** 704

## HAWKINSVILLE—Pulaski County

☐ ◇ **TAYLOR REGIONAL HOSPITAL (110135)**, Macon Highway, Zip 31036, Mailing Address: P.O. Box 1297, Zip 31036–7297; tel. 478/783–0200, (Nonreporting) **A**1 9 10 21
Primary Contact: Dan S. Maddock, President
CFO: Lisa Halliday, Director Accounting Services
CMO: Al Baggett, M.D., Interim Chief of Staff
CIO: Dawn Warnock, Director Medical Records
Web address: www.taylorregional.org
**Control:** Other not–for–profit (including NFP Corporation) **Service:** General Medical and Surgical

**Staffed Beds:** 55

## HAZLEHURST—Jeff Davis County

☐ **JEFF DAVIS HOSPITAL (111333)**, 1215 South Tallahassee Street, Zip 31539–2921, Mailing Address: P.O. Box 1690, Zip 31539–1690; tel. 912/375–7781, (Nonreporting) **A**1 9 10 18
Primary Contact: Gerald A. Schoendienst, Chief Executive Officer
**Control:** Hospital district or authority, Government, nonfederal **Service:** General Medical and Surgical

**Staffed Beds:** 25

## HIAWASSEE—Towns County

**CHATUGE REGIONAL HOSPITAL AND NURSING HOME (111324)**, 110 Main Street, Zip 30546–3408, Mailing Address: P.O. Box 509, Zip 30546–0509; tel. 706/896–2222, (Nonreporting) **A**9 10 18
Primary Contact: R. Lewis Kelley, Administrator
CFO: Tim Henry, Accountant
CMO: Robert F. Stahlkuppe, M.D., Chief of Staff
CIO: Walt Stafford, Director Information Technology
CHR: Rita Bradshaw, Director Human Resources
Web address: www.chatugeregionalhospital.org
**Control:** County–Government, nonfederal **Service:** General Medical and Surgical

**Staffed Beds:** 137

## HINESVILLE—Liberty County

☐ **LIBERTY REGIONAL MEDICAL CENTER (111335)**, 462 Elma G. Miles Parkway, Zip 31313–4000, Mailing Address: P.O. Box 919, Zip 31310–0919; tel. 912/369–9400, (Nonreporting) **A**1 9 10 18
Primary Contact: H. Scott Kroell, Jr., Chief Executive Officer
CFO: Sam Johnson, Chief Financial Officer
Web address: www.libertyregional.org
**Control:** Hospital district or authority, Government, nonfederal **Service:** General Medical and Surgical

**Staffed Beds:** 133

**GA**

*Many Facility Codes have changed. Please refer to the AHA Guide Code Chart.*   © 2013 AHA Guide

☒ **WINN ARMY COMMUNITY HOSPITAL**, 1061 Harmon Avenue,
Zip 31314–5641, Mailing Address: 1061 Harmon Avenue, Suite 2311B,
Zip 31314–5641; tel. 912/435–6965, (Nonreporting) **A**1 3 5 **S** Department of
the Army, Office of the Surgeon General, Falls Church, VA
Primary Contact: Colonel Ronald Place, M.D., Commander
COO: Jose A. Bonilla, Deputy Commander Administration
CMO: Richard Malish, M.D., Deputy Commander Clinical Services
CIO: Arthur N. Kirshner, Chief Information Management
CHR: Major Yvette McCrea, Chief Human Resources
CNO: Colonel Sharon Brown, Deputy Commande Nursing
Web address: www.winn.amedd.army.mil/
**Control:** Army, Government, federal **Service:** General Medical and Surgical

Staffed Beds: 79

### HOMERVILLE—Clinch County

★ **CLINCH MEMORIAL HOSPITAL (111308)**, 1050 Valdosta Highway,
Zip 31634–9701, Mailing Address: P.O. Box 516, Zip 31634–0516;
tel. 912/487–5211 **A**9 10 18 **F**3 7 15 34 40 45 57 59 64 77 91 93 107 110
111 114 119 129 130 133 135 145 146
Primary Contact: Phillip Cook, Administrator
CFO: Sandra Hughes, Chief Financial Officer
CMO: Samuel Cobarrubias, M.D., Chief of Staff
CIO: Shelly Studebaker, Director Management Information Systems
CHR: Shelly Studebaker, Manager Human Resources
Web address: www.sgmc.org/healthsystem/clinchmemorial.htm
**Control:** County–Government, nonfederal **Service:** General Medical and Surgical

Staffed Beds: 25 Admissions: 332 Census: 4 Outpatient Visits: 14169
Births: 0 Total Expense ($000): 10174 Payroll Expense ($000): 3757
Personnel: 105

### JACKSON—Butts County

★ **SYLVAN GROVE HOSPITAL (111319)**, 1050 McDonough Road,
Zip 30233–1599; tel. 770/775–7861 **A**9 10 18 **F**15 29 34 35 40 50 57 59 68
77 93 107 119 130 133 **S** TENET Healthcare Corporation, Dallas, TX
Primary Contact: John A. Quinn, Chief Executive Officer
CFO: Tamara Ison, Chief Financial Officer
CIO: Steve Brown, Chief Information Officer
CHR: Amanda Remington, Director Human Resources
Web address: www.sylvangrovehospital.com
**Control:** Corporation, Investor owned, for-profit **Service:** General Medical and Surgical

Staffed Beds: 23 Admissions: 506 Census: 14 Outpatient Visits: 17613
Births: 0 Total Expense ($000): 6890 Payroll Expense ($000): 4656
Personnel: 77

### JASPER—Pickens County

☒ **PIEDMONT MOUNTAINSIDE HOSPITAL (110225)**, 1266 Highway 515 South,
Zip 30143–4872; tel. 706/692–2441 **A**1 9 10 **F**3 13 15 20 28 29 34 35 40
45 46 47 49 57 64 70 76 77 79 81 85 107 108 110 111 114 115 119 129
130 132 135 148 **S** Piedmont Healthcare, Atlanta, GA
Primary Contact: Denise Ray, President and Chief Administrative Officer
CMO: Folsom Proctor, III, M.D., Vice President and Chief Medical Officer
CHR: Connie McLendon, Director Human Resources
Web address: www.piedmontmountainsidehospital.org
**Control:** Other not–for–profit (including NFP Corporation) **Service:** General
Medical and Surgical

Staffed Beds: 48 Admissions: 2875 Census: 29 Outpatient Visits: 39328
Births: 323 Total Expense ($000): 53052 Payroll Expense ($000): 19882
Personnel: 316

### JESUP—Wayne County

☐ **WAYNE MEMORIAL HOSPITAL (110124)**, 865 South First Street,
Zip 31545–0210, Mailing Address: P.O. Box 410, Zip 31598–0410;
tel. 912/427–6811, (Nonreporting) **A**1 9 10 20
Primary Contact: Joseph P. Ierardi, Chief Executive Officer
CFO: Greg Jones, Chief Financial Officer
CMO: Dan Collipp, M.D., Chief of Staff
CIO: Deborah Six, Coordinator Data Processing
CHR: John McIwain, Director Human Resources
Web address: www.wmhweb.com
**Control:** County–Government, nonfederal **Service:** General Medical and Surgical

Staffed Beds: 84

### JOHNS CREEK—Fulton County

☒ **EMORY JOHNS CREEK HOSPITAL (110230)**, 6325 Hospital Parkway,
Zip 30097–5775; tel. 678/474–7000 **A**1 10 **F**3 11 12 13 15 18 20 22 24 26
29 30 31 34 35 40 46 47 49 51 57 59 64 68 70 72 74 75 76 77 78 79 81
82 93 107 108 110 111 115 116 117 119 126 129 130 132 146 148 **P**1 6
**S** Emory Healthcare, Atlanta, GA
Primary Contact: Craig McCoy, Chief Executive Officer
COO: Laurie Hansen, Associate Administrator
CFO: JoAnn Manning, Chief Financial Officer
CMO: Alan Wang, M.D., Chief Medical Officer
CIO: Jose Diaz, Director Information Systems
CHR: Jennifer Elizabeth Garber, Vice President Human Resources
CNO: Marilyn Margolis, Chief Nursing Officer
Web address: www.emoryjohnscreek.com
**Control:** Other not–for–profit (including NFP Corporation) **Service:** General
Medical and Surgical

Staffed Beds: 84 Admissions: 5286 Census: 60 Outpatient Visits: 50574
Births: 839 Total Expense ($000): 108784 Payroll Expense ($000): 36458
Personnel: 551

### KENNESAW—Cobb County

**DEVEREUX GEORGIA TREATMENT NETWORK**, 1291 Stanley Road N.W.,
Zip 30152–4359; tel. 770/427–0147 **F**98 99 106 **S** Devereux, Villanova, PA
Primary Contact: Gwendolyn Skinner, Executive Director
COO: Mary H. Esposito, Assistant Executive Director
CFO: Kathy Goggin, Director Administrative Services
CMO: Yolanda Graham, M.D., Medical Director
CIO: Sam Maguta, Coordinator Information Systems
CHR: Rudie Delien, Director Human Resources
CNO: Amber Boyd, Nurse Practitioner and Director of Nursing
Web address: www.devereuxga.org
**Control:** Other not–for–profit (including NFP Corporation) **Service:** Children's
hospital psychiatric

Staffed Beds: 100 Admissions: 214 Census: 65 Outpatient Visits: 0 Births:
0 Total Expense ($000): 17122 Payroll Expense ($000): 9584 Personnel:
235

### LA GRANGE—Troup County

☒ **WEST GEORGIA HEALTH (110016)**, 1514 Vernon Road, Zip 30240–4199;
tel. 706/882–1411, (Total facility includes 260 beds in nursing home–type unit)
**A**1 2 9 10 19 **F**2 3 8 11 12 13 15 18 20 22 26 28 29 30 31 34 35 40 47 48
49 50 51 54 56 57 58 59 62 63 64 66 68 70 73 74 75 76 77 78 79 80 81
82 85 86 89 92 93 96 102 107 108 110 111 114 115 116 117 119 120 121
123 128 129 130 132 135 146 147 **P**6
Primary Contact: Gerald N. Fulks, President and Chief Executive Officer
COO: Charis Acree, Senior Vice President
CFO: Paul R. Perrotti, CPA, Chief Financial Officer
CHR: Tommy Britt, Director Human Resources
Web address: www.wghealth.org/
**Control:** Other not–for–profit (including NFP Corporation) **Service:** General
Medical and Surgical

Staffed Beds: 420 Admissions: 7399 Census: 316 Outpatient Visits:
131274 Births: 954 Total Expense ($000): 167625 Payroll Expense
($000): 64578 Personnel: 1317

### LAKELAND—Lanier County

☒ **LOUIS SMITH MEMORIAL HOSPITAL (111326)**, 116 West Thigpen Avenue,
Zip 31635–1011; tel. 229/482–3110, (Nonreporting) **A**1 9 10 18
Primary Contact: Neil W. Ginty, Administrator
CFO: Libby Flemming, Controller and Chief Information Officer
CMO: Bruce Herrington, M.D., Chief Medical Officer
CIO: Libby Flemming, Controller and Chief Information Officer
CHR: Vicki Dinkins, Director Human Resources
Web address: www.sgmc.org
**Control:** Other not–for–profit (including NFP Corporation) **Service:** Other specialty

Staffed Beds: 87

**GA**

---

**Hospital, Medicare Provider Number, Address, Telephone, Approval, Facility, and Physician Codes, Health Care System**

★ American Hospital Association (AHA) membership
☐ The Joint Commission accreditation
◇ DNV Healthcare Inc. accreditation
○ Healthcare Facilities Accreditation Program
△ Commission on Accreditation of Rehabilitation Facilities (CARF) accreditation

© 2013 AHA Guide    *Many Facility Codes have changed. Please refer to the AHA Guide Code Chart.*    Hospitals **A155**

## LAVONIA—Franklin County

☒ **TY COBB REGIONAL MEDICAL CENTER (110027)**, 367 Clear Creek Parkway, Zip 30553–4173; tel. 706/356–7800, (Data for 184 days) **A**1 9 10 **F**3 11 13 15 18 29 30 34 35 40 42 45 46 50 53 57 59 70 75 76 77 81 84 85 87 93 107 108 111 115 119 129 130 146 **S** Ty Cobb Healthcare System, Inc., Royston, GA
Primary Contact: Gregory K. Hearn, Chief Executive Officer
CFO: Kimberly Massey, Chief Financial Officer
CNO: Evelyn Murphy, R.N., Chief Nursing Officer
Web address: www.tycobbhealthcare.org
**Control:** Other not–for–profit (including NFP Corporation) **Service:** General Medical and Surgical

**Staffed Beds: 35 Admissions:** 749 **Census: 14 Outpatient Visits:** 27398 **Births: 138 Total Expense ($000):** 17809

## LAWRENCEVILLE—Gwinnett County

☒ **GWINNETT HOSPITAL SYSTEM (110087)**, 1000 Medical Center Boulevard, Zip 30046–7694, Mailing Address: P.O. Box 348, Zip 30046–0348; tel. 678/312–4321, (Includes GWINNETT MEDICAL CENTER, 1000 Medical Center Boulevard, Zip 30245, Mailing Address: Box 348, Zip 30246; tel. 770/995–4321; GWINNETT MEDICAL CENTER–DULUTH, 3620 Howell Ferry Road, Duluth, Zip 30096; tel. 678/312–6800), (Total facility includes 89 beds in nursing home–type unit) **A**1 2 9 10 **F**3 8 11 12 13 15 17 18 20 22 24 26 28 29 30 31 34 35 36 38 40 43 44 46 47 48 49 50 54 55 56 58 59 64 65 66 67 68 70 71 72 73 74 75 76 77 78 79 81 82 84 85 86 87 90 93 95 96 107 108 110 111 114 117 118 119 126 128 129 130 131 132 134 135 146 147 148 **P**8
Primary Contact: Philip R. Wolfe, President and Chief Executive Officer
COO: Thomas Shepherd, Chief Operating Officer
CFO: Thomas Y. McBride, III, Executive Vice President and Chief Financial Officer
CMO: Alan Bier, M.D., Executive Vice President and Chief Medical Officer
CIO: Ed Brown, Senior Vice President and Chief Information Officer
CHR: Steve Nadeau, Senior Vice President Human Resources
Web address: www.gwinnettmedicalcenter.org
**Control:** Other not–for–profit (including NFP Corporation) **Service:** General Medical and Surgical

**Staffed Beds: 508 Admissions:** 27186 **Census: 424 Outpatient Visits:** 345394 **Births: 4819 Total Expense ($000):** 484945 **Payroll Expense ($000):** 202776 **Personnel:** 3411

☐ **SUMMITRIDGE HOSPITAL (114004)**, 250 Scenic Highway, Zip 30046–5675; tel. 678/442–5800, (Nonreporting) **A**1 10
Primary Contact: Margaret P. Collier, Chief Executive Officer
Web address: www.summitridgehospital.net
**Control:** Other not–for–profit (including NFP Corporation) **Service:** Psychiatric

**Staffed Beds: 25**

## LITHONIA—Dekalb County

☐ **DEKALB MEDICAL AT HILLANDALE (110226)**, 2801 DeKalb Medical Parkway, Zip 30058–4996; tel. 404/501–8700 **A**1 9 10 **F**3 11 12 15 18 29 30 35 40 45 49 50 60 70 74 75 77 79 81 93 107 108 110 111 114 119 130 146 **P**1 **S** DeKalb Regional Health System, Decatur, GA
Primary Contact: John Shelton, President and Chief Executive Officer
COO: John Shelton, Chief Operating Officer
CMO: Duane Barclay, D.O., Chief Medical Officer
CIO: Mark Trocino, Chief Information Officer
CHR: Tom Crawford, Vice President Human Resources
Web address: www.dekalbmedical.org
**Control:** Other not–for–profit (including NFP Corporation) **Service:** General Medical and Surgical

**Staffed Beds: 100 Admissions:** 5423 **Census: 65 Outpatient Visits:** 96545 **Births: 0 Personnel:** 434

## LOUISVILLE—Jefferson County

☐ **JEFFERSON HOSPITAL (110100)**, 1067 Peachtree Street, Zip 30434–1599; tel. 478/625–7000 **A**1 9 10 20 **F**11 15 30 34 40 45 53 54 57 59 63 64 65 66 79 81 85 89 93 97 107 109 114 119 127 129 133 135 **P**6
Primary Contact: Ralph X. Randall, FACHE, Chief Executive Officer
CFO: Michael J. Sombar, Jr., Chief Financial Officer
CIO: Ricky Wasden, Manager Information Technology
CHR: Catherine Hall, Manager Human Resources
Web address: www.jeffersonhosp.com
**Control:** City–County, Government, nonfederal **Service:** General Medical and Surgical

**Staffed Beds: 37 Admissions:** 595 **Census: 7 Outpatient Visits:** 72898 **Births: 2 Total Expense ($000):** 13440 **Payroll Expense ($000):** 6757 **Personnel:** 159

## MACON—Bibb County

☒ **CENTRAL GEORGIA REHABILITATION HOSPITAL (113029)**, 3351 Northside Drive, Zip 31210–2587; tel. 478/201–6500, (Nonreporting) **A**1 9 10
Primary Contact: Elbert T. McQueen, President and Chief Executive Officer
CFO: Beverly Owens, Controller
CMO: Allison Scheetz, M.D., Medical Director
Web address: www.centralgarehab.com
**Control:** Other not–for–profit (including NFP Corporation) **Service:** Rehabilitation

**Staffed Beds: 58**

☒ **COLISEUM CENTER FOR BEHAVIORAL HEALTH (114015)**, (Formerly Coliseum Psychiatric Center), 340 Hospital Drive, Zip 31217–3838; tel. 478/741–1355 **A**1 9 10 **F**3 4 5 29 30 35 38 56 75 98 100 101 102 103 104 105 130 132 **S** HCA, Nashville, TN
Primary Contact: James W. Eyler, FACHE, Chief Executive Officer
Web address: www.coliseumhealthsystem.com
**Control:** Corporation, Investor–owned, for–profit **Service:** Psychiatric

**Staffed Beds: 44 Admissions:** 1373 **Census: 28 Outpatient Visits:** 3506 **Births: 0 Personnel:** 94

☒ **COLISEUM MEDICAL CENTERS (110164)**, 350 Hospital Drive, Zip 31217–3871; tel. 478/765–7000, (Nonreporting) **A**1 2 9 10 **S** HCA, Nashville, TN
Primary Contact: Charles G. Briscoe, FACHE, Chief Executive Officer
COO: David A. Portwood, Chief Operating Officer
CFO: Roger Simmons, Chief Financial Officer
CMO: Larry Grant, M.D., Chief Medical Officer
CIO: Joan Morstad, Director Information Systems
CHR: Pat Lattrell, Director Human Resources
Web address: www.coliseumhealthsystem.com
**Control:** Corporation, Investor–owned, for–profit **Service:** General Medical and Surgical

**Staffed Beds: 227**

☒ **COLISEUM NORTHSIDE HOSPITAL (110201)**, 400 Charter Boulevard, Zip 31210–4853, Mailing Address: P.O. Box 4627, Zip 31208–4627; tel. 478/757–8200, (Nonreporting) **A**1 9 10 **S** HCA, Nashville, TN
Primary Contact: Mike Sherrod, Chief Executive Officer
CFO: Roger Simmons, Chief Financial Officer
CHR: Pat Luttrell, Director Human Resources
Web address: www.coliseumhealthsystem.com
**Control:** Corporation, Investor–owned, for–profit **Service:** General Medical and Surgical

**Staffed Beds: 103**

☒ **MEDICAL CENTER OF CENTRAL GEORGIA (110107)**, 777 Hemlock Street, Zip 31201–2155; tel. 478/633–1000, (Includes CHILDREN'S HOSPITAL, 777 Hemlock Street, tel. 478/633–1000) **A**1 2 3 5 8 9 10 **F**3 5 7 8 11 12 13 14 15 17 18 20 22 24 26 28 29 30 31 32 34 35 36 39 40 43 44 45 46 47 48 49 50 51 53 54 56 57 58 59 60 61 62 63 64 65 66 68 70 72 73 74 75 76 77 78 79 81 82 83 84 85 86 87 88 89 92 93 94 97 98 99 100 101 102 103 104 105 107 108 110 111 114 115 119 126 130 132 135 143 144 145 146 147 148 **P**1
Primary Contact: Ninfa Saunders, Chief Executive Officer
COO: Joseph D. Lavelle, Executive Vice President and Chief Operating Officer
CFO: Rhonda Perry, Chief Financial Officer
CMO: James M. Cunningham, M.D., Vice President Medical Affairs
CIO: William Avenel, Assistant Vice President Information Services
CHR: Lori W. Cassidy, FACHE, Assistant Vice President
Web address: www.mccg.org
**Control:** Hospital district or authority, Government, nonfederal **Service:** General Medical and Surgical

**Staffed Beds: 659 Admissions:** 32993 **Census: 470 Outpatient Visits:** 367885 **Births: 2631 Total Expense ($000):** 612930 **Payroll Expense ($000):** 233021 **Personnel:** 4327

☒ **REGENCY HOSPITAL OF CENTRAL GEORGIA (112016)**, 535 Coliseum Drive, Zip 31217–0104; tel. 478/803–7300, (Nonreporting) **A**1 9 10 **S** Select Medical Corporation, Mechanicsburg, PA
Primary Contact: Michael S. Boggs, Chief Executive Officer
Web address: www.regencyhospital.com
**Control:** Corporation, Investor–owned, for–profit **Service:** Long–Term Acute Care hospital

**Staffed Beds: 34**

*Many Facility Codes have changed. Please refer to the AHA Guide Code Chart.*

© 2013 AHA Guide

## MADISON—Morgan County

☐ **MORGAN MEMORIAL HOSPITAL (111304)**, 1077 South Main Street,
Zip 30650–2073, Mailing Address: P.O. Box 860, Zip 30650–0860;
tel. 706/342–1667, (Nonreporting) **A**1 9 10 18
Primary Contact: Ralph Castillo, Chief Executive Officer
CFO: Courtney Moore, CPA, Chief Financial Officer
CMO: Eduardo M. Cossio, M.D., Chief of Staff
CIO: Patrick Cook, Vice President Support Services
CHR: Sarah Logan, Manager Human Resources
Web address: www.mmh.org
**Control:** Hospital district or authority, Government, nonfederal **Service:** General Medical and Surgical

**Staffed Beds:** 41

## MARIETTA—Cobb County

✠ △ **WELLSTAR KENNESTONE HOSPITAL (110035)**, 677 Church Street,
Zip 30060–1148; tel. 770/793–5000 **A**1 2 3 5 7 9 10 **F**3 8 10 11 12 13 15
17 18 20 22 24 26 28 29 30 31 37 38 40 41 43 44 45 46 47 48 49 50 53
54 58 59 60 61 64 66 68 70 72 73 74 75 76 77 78 79 80 81 82 84 85 86
87 90 93 94 96 100 102 107 108 110 111 114 115 117 118 119 120 121
123 124 125 126 130 132 141 146 147 148 **P**1 6 **S** WellStar Health System,
Marietta, GA
Primary Contact: Dan Woods, President
COO: Michael L. Graue, Executive Vice President and Chief Operating Officer
CFO: A. James Budzinski, Vice President and Chief Financial Officer
CIO: Ronald Strachan, Senior Vice President and Chief Information Officer
CHR: David W. Anderson, Executive Vice President Human Resources and Chief Compliance Officer
Web address: www.wellstar.org
**Control:** Other not–for–profit (including NFP Corporation) **Service:** General Medical and Surgical

**Staffed Beds:** 580 **Admissions:** 36735 **Census:** 468 **Outpatient Visits:**
441335 **Births:** 5366 **Personnel:** 4000

✠ **WELLSTAR WINDY HILL HOSPITAL (112007)**, 2540 Windy Hill Road,
Zip 30067–8632; tel. 770/644–1000 **A**1 2 9 10 **F**1 3 5 11 15 29 30 44 45 50
51 58 60 61 64 68 75 77 79 81 85 86 87 93 100 101 107 108 110 111 114
118 119 129 130 141 146 148 **P**1 6 **S** WellStar Health System, Marietta, GA
Primary Contact: Lou Little, President
CFO: Marsha Burke, Senior Vice President and Chief Financial Officer
CMO: Larry Haldeman, M.D., Executive Vice President and Chief Medical Officer
CIO: Leigh Cox, Chief Information Officer
Web address: www.wellstar.org
**Control:** Other not–for–profit (including NFP Corporation) **Service:** Long–Term Acute Care hospital

**Staffed Beds:** 55 **Admissions:** 377 **Census:** 32 **Outpatient Visits:** 23153
**Births:** 0 **Personnel:** 270

## METTER—Candler County

☐ **CANDLER COUNTY HOSPITAL (111334)**, 400 Cedar Street, Zip 30439–3338,
Mailing Address: P.O. Box 597, Zip 30439–0597; tel. 912/685–5741,
(Nonreporting) **A**1 9 10 18
Primary Contact: Stephen C. Shepherd, Chief Executive Officer
Web address: www.candlercountyhospital.com
**Control:** Hospital district or authority, Government, nonfederal **Service:** General Medical and Surgical

**Staffed Beds:** 25

## MILLEDGEVILLE—Baldwin County

☐ **CENTRAL STATE HOSPITAL**, 620 Broad Street, Zip 31062–0001;
tel. 478/445–4128, (Total facility includes 205 beds in nursing home–type unit)
**A**1 9 10 **F**15 30 39 53 57 59 75 86 87 97 98 100 103 107 108 110 114 119
128 130 **P**6
Primary Contact: Randall Hines, Interim Administrator
COO: Terry McGee, Chief Operations Officer
CMO: Scott VanSant, M.D., Chief Medical Officer
CIO: Betsy Bradley, Coordinator Performance Improvement
CHR: Myra Holloway, Director Human Resources Management
Web address: www.centralstatehospital.org
**Control:** State–Government, nonfederal **Service:** Psychiatric

**Staffed Beds:** 389 **Admissions:** 67 **Census:** 406 **Outpatient Visits:** 0 **Births:**
0 **Total Expense ($000):** 102564 **Payroll Expense ($000):** 46061
**Personnel:** 1377

☐ **OCONEE REGIONAL MEDICAL CENTER (110150)**, 821 North Cobb Street,
Zip 31061–2351, Mailing Address: P.O. Box 690, Zip 31059–0690;
tel. 478/454–3500, (Total facility includes 15 beds in nursing home–type unit) **A**1
9 10 19 **F**3 11 13 15 28 29 30 31 34 35 37 40 45 46 49 50 53 57 59 64 68
70 75 76 78 79 80 81 82 85 86 87 89 107 108 110 111 114 116 117 119
120 121 123 128 132 135 146 147 148 **S** Oconee Regional Health Systems,
Milledgeville, GA
Primary Contact: Jean Aycock, President and Chief Executive Officer
CFO: Brenda Qualls, Chief Financial Officer
Web address: www.oconeeregional.com
**Control:** Other not–for–profit (including NFP Corporation) **Service:** General Medical and Surgical

**Staffed Beds:** 90 **Admissions:** 4017 **Census:** 56 **Outpatient Visits:** 125506
**Births:** 564 **Total Expense ($000):** 70811 **Payroll Expense ($000):** 26567
**Personnel:** 524

## MILLEN—Jenkins County

**JENKINS COUNTY HOSPITAL (111311)**, 931 East Winthrope Avenue,
Zip 30442–1839; tel. 478/982–4221, (Nonreporting) **A**9 10 18
Primary Contact: Brad Trower, Administrator
**Control:** Hospital district or authority, Government, nonfederal **Service:** General Medical and Surgical

**Staffed Beds:** 25

## MONROE—Walton County

☐ **CLEARVIEW REGIONAL MEDICAL CENTER (110046)**, (Formerly Walton
Regional Medical Center), 2151 West Spring Street, Zip 30655–3115;
tel. 770/267–8461, (Nonreporting) **A**1 9 10 **S** Health Management Associates,
Naples, FL
Primary Contact: J. T. Barnhart, Chief Executive Officer
COO: Jon–Paul Croom, Chief Operating Officer
CMO: Terry Chongulia, M.D., Chief of Staff
CIO: Ed Stanley, Director Information Systems
CHR: Michele Monsrud, Director Human Resources
Web address: www.waltonregional.com
**Control:** Corporation, Investor–owned, for–profit **Service:** General Medical and Surgical

**Staffed Beds:** 115

## MONTEZUMA—Macon County

☐ ◇ **FLINT RIVER COMMUNITY HOSPITAL (110190)**, 509 Sumter Street,
Zip 31063–1733, Mailing Address: P.O. Box 770, Zip 31063–2502;
tel. 478/472–3100, (Nonreporting) **A**1 9 10 21
Primary Contact: Frank Schupp, Chief Executive Officer
CFO: Lara Busbee, Chief Financial Officer
CMO: Christopher Inhulsen, M.D., Chief of Staff
CIO: Shawn Reddick, Director Information Management
CHR: Tricia Johnson, Coordinator Human Resources
Web address: www.flintriverhospital.com/
**Control:** Corporation, Investor–owned, for–profit **Service:** General Medical and Surgical

**Staffed Beds:** 49

## MONTICELLO—Jasper County

**JASPER MEMORIAL HOSPITAL (111303)**, 898 College Street,
Zip 31064–1258; tel. 706/468–6411, (Total facility includes 55 beds in nursing
home–type unit) **A**9 10 18 **F**11 18 29 34 40 57 59 65 77 93 97 107 111 119
128 133 146 148 **P**6 **S** Oconee Regional Health Systems, Milledgeville, GA
Primary Contact: Jan Gaston, Administrator
CFO: Stuart Abney, Controller
CHR: Laura Hammonds, Assistant Administrator
CNO: Tammy Honeycutt, R.N., Director of Nursing
Web address: www.jaspermemorialhospital.org
**Control:** Other not–for–profit (including NFP Corporation) **Service:** General Medical and Surgical

**Staffed Beds:** 67 **Admissions:** 175 **Census:** 56 **Outpatient Visits:** 10114
**Births:** 0 **Total Expense ($000):** 8420 **Payroll Expense ($000):** 4345
**Personnel:** 116

**GA**

---

**Hospital, Medicare Provider Number, Address, Telephone, Approval, Facility, and Physician Codes, Health Care System**

★ American Hospital Association (AHA) membership
☐ The Joint Commission accreditation ◇ DNV Healthcare Inc. accreditation
○ Healthcare Facilities Accreditation Program
△ Commission on Accreditation of Rehabilitation Facilities (CARF) accreditation

**MOULTRIE—Colquitt County**

⊠ ○ **COLQUITT REGIONAL MEDICAL CENTER (110105)**, 3131 South Main Street, Zip 31768–6925, Mailing Address: P.O. Box 40, Zip 31776–0040; tel. 229/985–3420 **A**1 9 10 11 **F**3 7 11 12 13 15 17 20 29 30 31 32 34 35 39 40 45 47 48 49 56 57 59 60 61 62 63 65 68 70 74 75 76 77 78 79 81 82 85 86 87 89 91 93 97 107 108 110 111 115 119 126 127 129 130 131 132 135 143 144 146 147 148
Primary Contact: James L. Matney, President and Chief Executive Officer
CFO: W. Larry Sims, Chief Financial Officer and Vice President Financial Services
CMO: D. W. Adcock, M.D., Medical Director
CIO: Mitch Hiers, Director Information Services
CHR: Dawn Johns, Director Human Resources
Web address: www.colquittregional.com
**Control:** Hospital district or authority, Government, nonfederal **Service:** General Medical and Surgical

**Staffed Beds:** 99 **Admissions:** 4017 **Census:** 45 **Outpatient Visits:** 109837 **Births:** 482 **Total Expense ($000):** 73589 **Payroll Expense ($000):** 29642 **Personnel:** 678

**TURNING POINT HOSPITAL (110209)**, 3015 Veterans Parkway South, Zip 31788–6705, Mailing Address: P.O. Box 1177, Zip 31776–1177; tel. 229/985–4815 **A**9 10 **F**4 5 75 87 98 104 105 130 135 143 **P**6 **S** Universal Health Services, Inc., King of Prussia, PA
Primary Contact: Ben Marion, Chief Executive Officer and Managing Director
COO: Judy Payne, R.N., Chief Operating Officer
CFO: Edwin Bennett, Controller
CHR: Michelle Reddick, Director Human Resources
CNO: Faith Connell, Director of Nursing
Web address: www.turningpointcare.com
**Control:** Corporation, Investor–owned, for–profit **Service:** Alcoholism and other chemical dependency

**Staffed Beds:** 59 **Admissions:** 2771 **Census:** 34 **Outpatient Visits:** 17719 **Births:** 0 **Total Expense ($000):** 14182 **Payroll Expense ($000):** 6565 **Personnel:** 157

**NASHVILLE—Berrien County**

☐ **SOUTH GEORGIA MEDICAL CENTER BERRIEN CAMPUS (110112)**, (Formerly Berrien County Hospital), 1221 East McPherson Avenue, Zip 31639–2326, Mailing Address: P.O. Box 665, Zip 31639–0665; tel. 229/543–7100, (Nonreporting) **A**1 9 10
Primary Contact: Neil W. Ginty, Administrator
CFO: Stephanie Fletcher, Chief Financial Officer
Web address: www.berrienhospital.com
**Control:** Corporation, Investor–owned, for–profit **Service:** General Medical and Surgical

**Staffed Beds:** 39

**NEWNAN—Coweta County**

⊠ **PIEDMONT NEWNAN HOSPITAL (110229)**, 745 Poplar Road, Zip 30265–1618; tel. 770/253–1912 **A**1 9 10 **F**8 11 13 15 17 18 20 22 28 29 31 34 35 40 45 49 51 53 54 57 59 64 68 70 72 73 74 75 76 77 78 79 81 82 85 87 89 93 107 108 110 115 116 119 129 130 132 135 146 147 148 **S** Piedmont Healthcare, Atlanta, GA
Primary Contact: G. Michael Bass, President and Chief Executive Officer
COO: Nathan Nipper, Vice President and Chief Operating Officer
CFO: John Miles, Chief Financial Officer
CMO: Jeffrey R. Folk, M.D., Vice President Medical Affairs and Chief Medical Officer
CIO: Sandra Romanow, Director Management Information Systems
CHR: Virginia H. Lyles, Vice President Human Resources
Web address: www.piedmontnewnan.org
**Control:** Other not–for–profit (including NFP Corporation) **Service:** General Medical and Surgical

**Staffed Beds:** 143 **Admissions:** 5636 **Census:** 61 **Outpatient Visits:** 88457 **Births:** 622 **Total Expense ($000):** 96255 **Payroll Expense ($000):** 42572 **Personnel:** 836

☐ **SOUTHEASTERN REGIONAL MEDICAL CENTER**, 600 Parkway N., Zip 30265–8000; tel. 770/400–6000, (Nonreporting) **A**1 **S** Cancer Treatment Centers of America, Schaumburg, IL
Primary Contact: Anne Meisner, MSN, President and Chief Executive Officer
COO: David Kent, Chief Operating Officer
CFO: Scott Walker, Chief Financial Officer
CNO: Gloria V. Barnes, Assistant Vice President Patient Care Services
Web address: www.cancercenter.com/southeastern–hospital.cfm
**Control:** Corporation, Investor–owned, for–profit **Service:** Cancer

**Staffed Beds:** 25

**OCILLA—Irwin County**

⊠ **IRWIN COUNTY HOSPITAL (110130)**, 710 North Irwin Avenue, Zip 31774–5011; tel. 229/468–3800, (Nonreporting) **A**1 9 10
Primary Contact: Sue Spivey, Administrator
CFO: Tami Gray, Chief Financial Officer
CMO: Ashfaq Saiyed, M.D., Medical Director
CHR: Becky Edwards, Manager Human Resources
Web address: www.irwincntyhospital.com
**Control:** County–Government, nonfederal **Service:** General Medical and Surgical

**Staffed Beds:** 64

**PERRY—Houston County**

⊠ **PERRY HOSPITAL (110153)**, 1120 Morningside Drive, Zip 31069–2906; tel. 478/987–3600 **A**1 9 10 **F**3 11 15 29 30 34 35 39 40 45 48 49 50 51 56 57 58 59 61 68 70 75 79 81 82 85 86 87 89 100 107 110 114 115 119 129 130 131 132 133 134 135 146 147 148 **S** Houston Healthcare System, Warner Robins, GA
Primary Contact: David Campbell, Administrator
CFO: Sean Whilden, Chief Financial Officer
CMO: Jefferson Davis, M.D., Medical Director
CIO: Robert Rhodes, Director Information Systems
CHR: Michael O'Hara, Senior Executive Director
CNO: Melinda D. Hartley, R.N., Vice President Patient Care Services
Web address: www.hhc.org
**Control:** Other not–for–profit (including NFP Corporation) **Service:** General Medical and Surgical

**Staffed Beds:** 39 **Admissions:** 1497 **Census:** 18 **Outpatient Visits:** 38813 **Births:** 0 **Total Expense ($000):** 24824 **Payroll Expense ($000):** 9542 **Personnel:** 221

**QUITMAN—Brooks County**

⊠ **BROOKS COUNTY HOSPITAL (111332)**, 903 North Court Street, Zip 31643–1315, Mailing Address: P.O. Box 5000, Zip 31643–5000; tel. 229/263–4171 **A**1 9 10 18 **F**3 11 15 18 29 34 35 40 50 57 59 68 75 86 87 93 97 107 111 119 127 130 133 146 **P**6 **S** Archbold Medical Center, Thomasville, GA
Primary Contact: Kenneth D. Rhudy, Chief Executive Officer
CFO: Skip Hightower, Chief Financial Officer
CMO: Michael Sopt, M.D., Chief of Staff
CHR: Janet Eldridge, Director Human Resources and Personnel
CNO: Nancy M. Williams, R.N., Director of Nursing
Web address: www.archbold.org
**Control:** Hospital district or authority, Government, nonfederal **Service:** General Medical and Surgical

**Staffed Beds:** 25 **Admissions:** 481 **Census:** 16 **Outpatient Visits:** 19588 **Births:** 0 **Total Expense ($000):** 11895 **Payroll Expense ($000):** 5036 **Personnel:** 92

**REIDSVILLE—Tattnall County**

★ **OPTIM MEDICAL CENTER – TATTNALL (111323)**, (Formerly Doctors Hospital of Tattnall), 247 South Main Street, Zip 30453–4605; tel. 912/557–1000, (Nonreporting) **A**9 10 18
Primary Contact: Brad Trower, Administrator
Web address: www.tattnallhospital.com
**Control:** Corporation, Investor–owned, for–profit **Service:** Orthopedic

**Staffed Beds:** 25

**RIVERDALE—Clayton County**

☐ **RIVERWOODS BEHAVIORAL HEALTH SYSTEM (114035)**, 233 Medical Center Drive, Zip 30274–2640; tel. 770/991–8500, (Nonreporting) **A**1 5 10 **S** Acadia Healthcare Company, Inc., Franklin, TN
Primary Contact: Kirk Kureska, Chief Executive Officer
COO: Jenifer Harcourt, Chief Operating Officer
CFO: Tricia Nelson, Chief Financial Officer
CMO: Mahaveer Vakharia, M.D., Medical Director
CIO: Hema Patel, Director Medical Records
CHR: Tareka Beasley, Director Human Resources
Web address: www.riverwoodsbehavioral.com
**Control:** Corporation, Investor–owned, for–profit **Service:** Psychiatric

**Staffed Beds:** 75

⊠ **SOUTHERN CRESCENT HOSPITAL FOR SPECIALTY CARE (112015)**, 11 Upper Riverdale Road S.W., 6th Floor, Zip 30274–2615; tel. 770/897–7603 **A**1 10 **F**1 29 30 35 44 75 77 82 84 87 148 **S** Dubuis Health System, Houston, TX
Primary Contact: Janice Hamilton–Crawford, Administrator
Web address: www.dubuis.org/SouthernCrescentHospitalforSpecialtyCare
**Control:** Church–operated, Nongovernment, not–for profit **Service:** Long–Term Acute Care hospital

**Staffed Beds:** 30 **Admissions:** 289 **Census:** 20 **Outpatient Visits:** 0 **Births:** 0 **Total Expense ($000):** 10289 **Payroll Expense ($000):** 4003 **Personnel:** 59

**GA**

*Many Facility Codes have changed. Please refer to the AHA Guide Code Chart.*

© 2013 AHA Guide

☐ **SOUTHERN REGIONAL MEDICAL CENTER (110165)**, 11 Upper Riverdale Road S.W., Zip 30274–2615; tel. 770/991–8000, (Nonreporting) **A**1 2 3 5 9 10
Primary Contact: Stephen W. Mahan, President and Chief Executive Officer
COO: Therese O. Sucher, Senior Vice President Operations
CFO: Richard G. Stovall, Senior Vice President Fiscal Services and Chief Financial Officer
CMO: Willie Cochran, Jr., M.D., Chief of Staff
CIO: Karen Moore, Vice President Information Technology and Chief Information Officer
CHR: Norma Adams, Director Human Resources
Web address: www.southernregional.org
**Control:** Other not–for–profit (including NFP Corporation) **Service:** General Medical and Surgical

**Staffed Beds:** 274

### ROME—Floyd County

✠ **FLOYD MEDICAL CENTER (110054)**, 304 Turner McCall Boulevard, Zip 30165–5621, Mailing Address: P.O. Box 233, Zip 30162–0233; tel. 706/509–5000 **A**1 2 3 5 9 10 13 19 **F**3 4 5 6 7 8 9 11 12 13 15 17 18 20 22 26 28 29 30 31 32 34 35 36 37 38 39 40 43 44 45 46 48 49 50 51 53 54 56 57 58 59 61 63 64 65 66 68 70 71 72 74 75 76 77 78 79 81 82 84 85 86 87 88 89 90 93 96 97 98 100 101 102 103 104 105 107 108 110 111 114 115 118 119 129 130 131 132 134 135 143 144 146 147 148
Primary Contact: Kurt Stuenkel, FACHE, President and Chief Executive Officer
COO: Warren Alston Rigas, Executive Vice President and Chief Operating Officer
CFO: Rick Sheerin, Vice President Fiscal Services
CMO: Dee B. Russell, M.D., Vice President & Chief of Medical Affairs
CIO: Jeff Budda, Chief Information Officer
CHR: Beth Bradford, Director Human Resources
CNO: Sheila Bennett, R.N., Vice President & Chief Nursing Officer
Web address: www.floyd.org
**Control:** Other not–for–profit (including NFP Corporation) **Service:** General Medical and Surgical

**Staffed Beds:** 299 **Admissions:** 13903 **Census:** 189 **Outpatient Visits:** 252796 **Births:** 2200 **Total Expense ($000):** 309940 **Payroll Expense ($000):** 130248 **Personnel:** 2238

★ **KINDRED HOSPITAL ROME (112010)**, 304 Turner McCall Boulevard, Zip 30165–5621; tel. 706/378–6800 **A**9 10 **F**1 3 29 82 148 **S** Kindred Healthcare, Louisville, KY
Primary Contact: Susan M. Stovall, Chief Executive Officer
Web address: www.kindredrome.com
**Control:** Partnership, Investor–owned, for–profit **Service:** Long–Term Acute Care hospital

**Staffed Beds:** 45 **Admissions:** 454 **Census:** 32 **Outpatient Visits:** 0 **Births:** 0 **Personnel:** 75

✠ **REDMOND REGIONAL MEDICAL CENTER (110168)**, 501 Redmond Road, Zip 30165–1415, Mailing Address: P.O. Box 107001, Zip 30162–7001; tel. 706/291–0291, (Nonreporting) **A**1 2 9 10 19 **S** HCA, Nashville, TN
Primary Contact: John Quinlivan, Chief Executive Officer
COO: Patrick Trammel, Chief Operating Officer
CFO: Ken Metteauer, Chief Financial Officer
CMO: Julie Coffman Barnes, M.D., Chief Medical Officer
CIO: Brad Treglown, Director Information Systems
CHR: Patsy Adams, Director Human Resources
CNO: Kay Rhodes, R.N., Chief Nursing Officer
Web address: www.redmondregional.com
**Control:** Corporation, Investor–owned, for–profit **Service:** General Medical and Surgical

**Staffed Beds:** 230

**SPECIALTY HOSPITAL** See Kindred Hospital Rome

### ROSWELL—Fulton County

✠ **NORTH FULTON REGIONAL HOSPITAL (110198)**, 3000 Hospital Boulevard, Zip 30076–3899; tel. 770/751–2500, (Nonreporting) **A**1 9 10 **S** TENET Healthcare Corporation, Dallas, TX
Primary Contact: Deborah C. Keel, Chief Executive Officer
CFO: Sherry Henderson, Chief Financial Officer
CHR: Susan Brown, Chief Human Resources Officer
Web address: www.northfultonregional.com
**Control:** Corporation, Investor–owned, for–profit **Service:** General Medical and Surgical

**Staffed Beds:** 196

### SAINT MARYS—Camden County

✠ **SOUTHEAST GEORGIA HEALTH SYSTEM CAMDEN CAMPUS (110146)**, 2000 Dan Proctor Drive, Zip 31558–3810; tel. 912/576–6200 **A**1 9 10 20 **F**3 11 13 15 29 30 34 35 40 45 46 47 48 49 50 54 57 59 64 68 70 71 75 76 77 78 79 81 85 86 87 90 93 94 96 107 108 110 111 114 119 129 131 132 146 **P**5 **S** Southeast Georgia Health System, Brunswick, GA
Primary Contact: Howard W. Sepp, Jr., FACHE, Vice President and Administrator
CFO: Michael D. Scherneck, Executive Vice President
CMO: Robert Wilson, M.D., Chief of Staff
CHR: Patrick D. Ebri, Ph.D., Vice President Human Resources
Web address: www.sghs.org
**Control:** City–County, Government, nonfederal **Service:** General Medical and Surgical

**Staffed Beds:** 17 **Admissions:** 1821 **Census:** 17 **Outpatient Visits:** 78291 **Births:** 716 **Total Expense ($000):** 37495 **Payroll Expense ($000):** 14602 **Personnel:** 280

### SAINT SIMONS ISLAND—Glynn County

☐ **SAINT SIMONS BY–THE–SEA HOSPITAL (114016)**, 2927 Demere Road, Zip 31522–1620; tel. 912/638–1999, (Nonreporting) **A**1 9 10 **S** Universal Health Services, Inc., King of Prussia, PA
Primary Contact: Monica Cook, Interim Chief Executive Officer
CMO: Kim Masters, M.D., Medical Director
CIO: Chisty Mosely, Director Information Management
Web address: www.ssbythesea.com
**Control:** Corporation, Investor–owned, for–profit **Service:** Psychiatric

**Staffed Beds:** 101

### SANDERSVILLE—Washington County

☐ **WASHINGTON COUNTY REGIONAL MEDICAL CENTER (110086)**, 610 Sparta Road, Zip 31082–1860, Mailing Address: P.O. Box 636, Zip 31082–0636; tel. 478/240–2000, (Nonreporting) **A**1 9 10 20
Primary Contact: Jimmy Childre, Jr., Interim Chief Executive Officer
CFO: Cythia Parker, Fiscal Director
CMO: Robert Wright, M.D., Chief of Staff
CHR: Gayle Prince, Director Human Resources
Web address: www.wcrmc.com
**Control:** Hospital district or authority, Government, nonfederal **Service:** General Medical and Surgical

**Staffed Beds:** 116

### SAVANNAH—Chatham County

✠ △ **CANDLER HOSPITAL (110024)**, 5353 Reynolds Street, Zip 31405–6015; tel. 912/819–6000, (Total facility includes 11 beds in nursing home–type unit) **A**1 2 7 9 10 **F**2 3 11 13 15 18 20 29 30 31 32 34 35 36 37 38 39 40 44 45 46 47 48 49 50 53 54 57 58 59 60 61 64 65 68 70 71 73 74 75 76 77 78 80 81 82 84 85 86 87 89 90 93 94 96 107 108 110 111 115 117 118 119 120 121 123 124 126 128 129 130 131 132 135 146 147 148
Primary Contact: Paul P. Hinchey, President and Chief Executive Officer
CFO: Gregory J. Schaack, CPA, Vice President and Chief Financial Officer
CMO: James Scott, M.D., Vice President Medical Affairs
CIO: George Evans, Vice President and Chief Information Officer
CHR: Don Stubbs, Vice President Human Resources
Web address: www.sjchs.org
**Control:** Church–operated, Nongovernment, not–for profit **Service:** General Medical and Surgical

**Staffed Beds:** 285 **Admissions:** 12068 **Census:** 188 **Outpatient Visits:** 334032 **Births:** 2970 **Total Expense ($000):** 206422 **Payroll Expense ($000):** 83989 **Personnel:** 1602

☐ **COASTAL HARBOR TREATMENT CENTER (114008)**, 1150 Cornell Avenue, Zip 31406–2702; tel. 912/354–3911 **A**1 9 10 **F**56 59 98 99 101 102 103 104 106 130 **P**5 6 **S** Universal Health Services, Inc., King of Prussia, PA
Primary Contact: Ray Heckerman, Chief Executive Officer and Managing Director
COO: Ray Heckerman, Chief Executive Officer and Managing Director
CFO: Garry Ege, Chief Financial Officer
CMO: Ed Merves, M.D., Medical Director
CHR: Kellie Carlson, Director Human Resources
CNO: Jillisa Thornton, Director of Nursing
Web address: www.coastalharbor.com
**Control:** Corporation, Investor–owned, for–profit **Service:** Psychiatric

**Staffed Beds:** 195 **Admissions:** 2375 **Census:** 134 **Outpatient Visits:** 13737 **Births:** 0 **Total Expense ($000):** 24330 **Payroll Expense ($000):** 11162 **Personnel:** 286

**GEORGE AND MARIE BACKUS CHILDREN'S HOSPITAL** See Memorial Children's Hospital

**GA**

---

**Hospital, Medicare Provider Number, Address, Telephone, Approval, Facility, and Physician Codes, Health Care System**

★ American Hospital Association (AHA) membership
☐ The Joint Commission accreditation
◇ DNV Healthcare Inc. accreditation
◯ Healthcare Facilities Accreditation Program
△ Commission on Accreditation of Rehabilitation Facilities (CARF) accreditation

☐ **GEORGIA REGIONAL HOSPITAL AT SAVANNAH (114028)**, 1915 Eisenhower Drive, Zip 31406–5098; tel. 912/356–2011, (Nonreporting) **A**1 10
Primary Contact: Andy Mannich, Regional Administrator
COO: Thomas F. Kurtz, Jr., Chief Operating Officer
CFO: Janet Edenfield, Director Financial Services
CMO: Donald Manning, M.D., Clinical Director
CHR: Jamekia Powers, Assistant Director Human Resources
Web address: www.garegionalsavannah.com
**Control:** State–Government, nonfederal **Service:** Psychiatric

Staffed Beds: 105

☒ △ **MEMORIAL HEALTH (110036)**, 4700 Waters Avenue, Zip 31404–6283, Mailing Address: P.O. Box 23089, Zip 31403–3089; tel. 912/350–8000, (Includes MEMORIAL CHILDREN'S HOSPITAL, 4700 Waters Avenue, Zip 31404–6220, Mailing Address: PO Box 23089, Zip 31403–3089; tel. 912/350–1543) **A**1 2 3 5 7 8 10 **F**3 8 11 12 13 14 15 17 18 19 20 22 24 26 28 29 30 31 32 34 35 36 37 39 40 41 43 44 45 46 49 50 52 53 54 55 56 57 58 59 60 61 64 65 66 68 70 71 72 73 74 75 76 77 78 79 80 81 82 83 84 85 86 87 88 89 90 92 93 96 97 98 100 101 102 103 104 107 110 111 115 117 118 119 120 121 122 123 124 126 129 130 131 132 135 143 144 146 147 148 **P**6
Primary Contact: Margaret Gill, Chief Executive Officer
CFO: Darcy Davis, Senior Vice President and Chief Financial Officer
CMO: Ramon V. Meguiar, M.D., Senior Vice President and Chief Medical Officer
CIO: Patricia A. Lavely, FACHE, Chief Information Officer
CHR: Richard J. Roche, Vice President Human Resources and Support Services
Web address: www.memorialhealth.com
**Control:** Other not–for–profit (including NFP Corporation) **Service:** General Medical and Surgical

Staffed Beds: 535 Admissions: 27296 Census: 397 Outpatient Visits: 269265 Births: 2878 Total Expense ($000): 451461 Payroll Expense ($000): 186380 Personnel: 3435

☒ **SELECT SPECIALTY HOSPITAL–SAVANNAH (112011)**, 5353 Reynolds Street, 4 South, Zip 31405–6015; tel. 912/819–7972, (Nonreporting) **A**1 9 10 **S** Select Medical Corporation, Mechanicsburg, PA
Primary Contact: James H. Rogers, FACHE, Chief Executive Officer
Web address: www.selectspecialtyhospitals.com/company/locations/savannah.aspx
**Control:** Corporation, Investor–owned, for–profit **Service:** Long–Term Acute Care hospital

Staffed Beds: 36

**ST. JOSEPH'S CANDLER HOSPITAL** See Candler Hospital

☐ △ **ST. JOSEPH'S HOSPITAL (110043)**, 11705 Mercy Boulevard, Zip 31419–1791; tel. 912/819–4100, (Total facility includes 11 beds in nursing home–type unit) **A**1 2 7 9 10 **F**3 11 16 17 18 20 22 24 26 28 29 36 44 45 50 51 55 57 58 59 60 61 65 68 70 74 75 77 79 80 81 82 84 85 86 87 90 93 94 96 107 108 110 114 115 119 126 128 130 131 132 135 146 148
Primary Contact: Paul P. Hinchey, President and Chief Executive Officer
CFO: Gregory J. Schaack, CPA, Vice President and Chief Financial Officer
CMO: James Jackson, M.D., Vice President Medical Affairs
CIO: John Adkins, Vice President and Chief Information Officer
CHR: Don Stubbs, Vice President Human Resources
Web address: www.sjchs.org
**Control:** Church–operated, Nongovernment, not–for profit **Service:** General Medical and Surgical

Staffed Beds: 237 Admissions: 10739 Census: 180 Outpatient Visits: 136584 Births: 0 Total Expense ($000): 178774 Payroll Expense ($000): 65073 Personnel: 1201

**SMYRNA—Cobb County**

☒ **EMORY–ADVENTIST HOSPITAL (110183)**, 3949 South Cobb Drive S.E., Zip 30080–6300; tel. 770/434–0710 **A**1 9 10 **F**11 15 29 30 34 35 40 44 45 48 49 50 56 57 59 64 68 74 75 79 81 82 84 85 87 92 93 97 107 109 110 111 112 114 119 130 146 **S** Adventist Health System Sunbelt Health Care Corporation, Altamonte Springs, FL
Primary Contact: Dennis Kiley, President
COO: Ed Moyer, Chief Operating Officer
CFO: Carol Hazen, Vice President Finance
CHR: Shelli K. Johnson, Director Human Resources
Web address: www.emoryadventist.org
**Control:** Church–operated, Nongovernment, not–for profit **Service:** General Medical and Surgical

Staffed Beds: 52 Admissions: 1547 Census: 16 Outpatient Visits: 45833 Births: 0 Personnel: 327

☒ **RIDGEVIEW INSTITUTE (114012)**, 3995 South Cobb Drive S.E., Zip 30080–6397; tel. 770/434–4567, (Nonreporting) **A**1 5 9 10
Primary Contact: Paul Hackman, Chief Executive Officer
CFO: Jerry Magnison, Chief Financial Officer
CMO: Thomas Bradford Johns, M.D., Medical Director
CIO: Lynn Leger, Director Information Systems
CHR: Betty Sonderman, Manager Human Resources
Web address: www.ridgeviewinstitute.com
**Control:** Other not–for–profit (including NFP Corporation) **Service:** Psychiatric

Staffed Beds: 92

**SNELLVILLE—Gwinnett County**

☒ **EASTSIDE MEDICAL CENTER (110192)**, 1700 Medical Way, Zip 30078–2195; tel. 770/979–0200 **A**1 2 9 10 **F**3 11 13 15 20 22 26 28 29 30 31 34 37 39 40 41 45 49 50 54 56 57 59 64 70 72 73 74 75 76 77 78 79 81 82 85 86 87 90 93 94 96 98 101 103 105 107 108 110 111 112 114 115 118 119 126 129 130 131 132 144 146 147 148 **S** HCA, Nashville, TN
Primary Contact: Kimberly Ryan, Chief Executive Officer
COO: Callie Andrews, Chief Operating Officer
CFO: Tom Jackson, Chief Financial Officer
CMO: Michael O'Neill, M.D., Chief Medical Officer
CIO: Pattie Page, Director Marketing and Public Relations
CHR: Nancy Dwyer, Vice President Human Resources
Web address: www.eastsidemedical.com
**Control:** Corporation, Investor–owned, for–profit **Service:** General Medical and Surgical

Staffed Beds: 247 Admissions: 10897 Census: 152 Outpatient Visits: 137824 Births: 1511 Total Expense ($000): 147922 Payroll Expense ($000): 55417 Personnel: 1029

**SPRINGFIELD—Effingham County**

☒ **EFFINGHAM HOSPITAL (111306)**, 459 Highway 119 South, Zip 31329–3021, Mailing Address: P.O. Box 386, Zip 31329–0386; tel. 912/754–6451, (Total facility includes 105 beds in nursing home–type unit) **A**1 9 10 18 **F**3 11 15 18 19 28 29 34 40 45 46 50 54 56 59 64 65 67 77 79 81 86 87 93 97 107 108 110 111 119 127 128 130 131 133 146 147 **P**6
Primary Contact: Norma J. Morgan, Chief Executive Officer
CFO: Ed Brown, Chief Financial Officer
CMO: George W. Brelsford, M.D., Chief Medical Staff
CIO: Bart Hunter, Manager Information Technology
CHR: Vicky Little, Director Human Resources
Web address: www.effinghamhospital.com
**Control:** Hospital district or authority, Government, nonfederal **Service:** General Medical and Surgical

Staffed Beds: 120 Admissions: 270 Census: 106 Outpatient Visits: 38794 Births: 0 Total Expense ($000): 30313 Payroll Expense ($000): 13564 Personnel: 348

**STATESBORO—Bulloch County**

☐ **EAST GEORGIA REGIONAL MEDICAL CENTER (110075)**, 1499 Fair Road, Zip 30458–1683, Mailing Address: P.O. Box 1048, Zip 30459–1048; tel. 912/486–1000 **A**1 9 10 19 **F**3 11 13 15 18 20 22 26 29 35 37 40 45 46 47 48 49 51 54 57 59 60 64 67 70 74 75 76 77 78 79 81 82 85 87 89 93 107 108 110 111 112 114 115 116 117 118 119 126 129 132 145 146 147 148 **P**5 **S** Health Management Associates, Naples, FL
Primary Contact: Robert F. Bigley, President and Chief Executive Officer
COO: Cindi Butcher, Chief Operating Officer
CFO: Eric Smith, Chief Financial Officer
CMO: Benjamin Oldham, M.D., Chief of Staff
CIO: Marisa Smith, Director Information Services
CHR: Michael Black, Director Human Resources
CNO: Mary Anderson, R.N., Chief Nursing Officer
Web address: www.eastgeorgiaregional.com
**Control:** Corporation, Investor–owned, for–profit **Service:** General Medical and Surgical

Staffed Beds: 150 Admissions: 8912 Census: 90 Outpatient Visits: 136731 Births: 1533 Personnel: 642

**WILLINGWAY HOSPITAL**, 311 Jones Mill Road, Zip 30458–4765; tel. 912/764–6236 **A**9 **F**4 5
Primary Contact: Jimmy Mooney, Chief Executive Officer
CFO: Barbara S. Reid, Chief Financial Officer
CMO: Robert W. Mooney, M.D., Medical Director
Web address: www.willingway.com
**Control:** Corporation, Investor–owned, for–profit **Service:** Alcoholism and other chemical dependency

Staffed Beds: 40 Admissions: 412 Census: 30 Outpatient Visits: 3130 Births: 0 Total Expense ($000): 7264 Payroll Expense ($000): 3675 Personnel: 94

*Many Facility Codes have changed. Please refer to the AHA Guide Code Chart.*

**GA**

## STOCKBRIDGE—Henry County

⊠ **HENRY MEDICAL CENTER (110191)**, 1133 Eagle's Landing Parkway, Zip 30281–5099; tel. 678/604–1000, (Total facility includes 89 beds in nursing home–type unit) **A**1 2 9 10 **F**3 8 11 13 15 18 20 26 28 29 30 31 34 35 37 40 42 45 46 49 53 54 57 59 60 61 64 70 72 73 74 75 76 77 78 79 81 85 86 93 100 102 107 108 110 111 114 115 118 119 124 130 132 135 144 146 147 148 **S** Piedmont Healthcare, Atlanta, GA
Primary Contact: Charles F. Scott, President and Chief Executive Officer
CFO: Danny Harris, Vice President and Chief Financial Officer
CMO: Jorge Spinolo, M.D., Chief of Staff
CIO: Terry Wilk, Chief Information Officer
CHR: Maribeth Ledford, Director Human Resources
Web address: www.henrymedical.com
**Control:** Hospital district or authority, Government, nonfederal **Service:** General Medical and Surgical

Staffed Beds: 289 **Admissions:** 11886 **Census:** 134 **Outpatient Visits:** 143413 **Births:** 2077 **Personnel:** 1242

## SWAINSBORO—Emanuel County

☐ ◇ **EMANUEL MEDICAL CENTER (110109)**, 117 Kite Road, Zip 30401–3231, Mailing Address: P.O. Box 879, Zip 30401–0879; tel. 478/289–1100, (Total facility includes 49 beds in nursing home–type unit) **A**1 9 10 20 21 **F**3 7 11 13 15 29 30 34 40 50 57 59 64 68 70 76 79 81 85 86 87 107 110 111 114 118 119 124 127 128 129 130 132 133 146 147
Primary Contact: Brian L. Riddle, Sr., FACHE, Chief Executive Officer
CFO: Rhonda Durden, Chief Financial Officer
CMO: Cedric Porter, M.D., President Medical Staff
CIO: Dave Flanders, Director Information Technology Systems
CHR: Ellen Boyd, Director Human Resources
Web address: www.emanuelmedical.org
**Control:** Hospital district or authority, Government, nonfederal **Service:** General Medical and Surgical

Staffed Beds: 91 **Admissions:** 1509 **Census:** 63 **Outpatient Visits:** 22528 **Births:** 102 **Total Expense ($000):** 22501 **Payroll Expense ($000):** 11096 **Personnel:** 267

## SYLVANIA—Screven County

★ **SCREVEN COUNTY HOSPITAL (111312)**, 215 Mims Road, Zip 30467–2097; tel. 912/564–7426, (Nonreporting) **A**9 10 18
Primary Contact: Brad Trower, Chief Executive Officer
CFO: Marsha Carroll, Director Financial Services
**Control:** County–Government, nonfederal **Service:** General Medical and Surgical

Staffed Beds: 25

## SYLVESTER—Worth County

⊠ ◇ **PHOEBE WORTH MEDICAL CENTER (111328)**, 807 South Isabella Street, Zip 31791–7554, Mailing Address: P.O. Box 545, Zip 31791–0545; tel. 229/776–6961, (Nonreporting) **A**1 9 10 18 21 **S** Phoebe Putney Health System, Albany, GA
Primary Contact: Kim Gilman, Chief Administrative Officer
CFO: John Graham, Chief Financial Officer
CMO: Natu M. Patel, M.D., Chief of Staff
CHR: Chris Foreman, Director
Web address: www.phoebeputney.com
**Control:** Other not–for–profit (including NFP Corporation) **Service:** General Medical and Surgical

Staffed Beds: 25

## THOMASTON—Upson County

⊠ ◇ **UPSON REGIONAL MEDICAL CENTER (110002)**, 801 West Gordon Street, Zip 30286–3426, Mailing Address: P.O. Box 1059, Zip 30286–0027; tel. 706/647–8111 **A**1 9 10 21 **F**3 11 13 15 28 29 30 31 34 35 36 40 45 46 49 50 53 57 59 61 64 70 75 76 78 79 80 81 82 85 86 87 89 107 108 110 111 114 115 118 119 124 130 132 133 135 148 **P**6 **S** HealthTech Management Services, Franklin, TN
Primary Contact: David L. Castleberry, Chief Executive Officer
CFO: John Williams, Chief Financial Officer
CIO: George Curtis, Director Information Technology Services
CHR: Rich Williams, Director Human Resources
Web address: www.urmc.org
**Control:** Other not–for–profit (including NFP Corporation) **Service:** General Medical and Surgical

Staffed Beds: 75 **Admissions:** 3650 **Census:** 36 **Outpatient Visits:** 77482 **Births:** 466 **Total Expense ($000):** 58602 **Payroll Expense ($000):** 23516 **Personnel:** 518

## THOMASVILLE—Thomas County

⊠ **JOHN D. ARCHBOLD MEMORIAL HOSPITAL (110038)**, 915 Gordon Avenue, Zip 31792–6614, Mailing Address: P.O. Box 1018, Zip 31799–1018; tel. 229/228–2000, (Total facility includes 64 beds in nursing home–type unit) **A**1 2 9 10 19 **F**3 4 5 8 11 12 13 15 17 18 20 22 26 28 29 30 31 34 36 38 40 43 45 46 47 48 49 50 51 57 59 60 64 68 70 74 75 76 77 78 79 81 82 86 87 89 90 93 98 101 102 103 104 105 106 107 108 110 111 114 115 116 117 118 119 121 123 124 126 127 128 129 130 131 132 143 144 146 147 148 **P**6 **S** Archbold Medical Center, Thomasville, GA
Primary Contact: J. Perry Mustian, President and Chief Executive Officer
COO: Kevin C. Taylor, Chief Operating Officer
CFO: Skip Hightower, Senior Vice President and Chief Financial Officer
CIO: William Zimmermann, Senior Vice President Information Services
CHR: Zach Wheeler, Senior Vice President Human Resources
Web address: www.archbold.org
**Control:** Other not–for–profit (including NFP Corporation) **Service:** General Medical and Surgical

Staffed Beds: 293 **Admissions:** 10650 **Census:** 222 **Outpatient Visits:** 196552 **Births:** 853 **Total Expense ($000):** 214576 **Payroll Expense ($000):** 78618 **Personnel:** 1533

☐ **SOUTHWESTERN STATE HOSPITAL (114021)**, Pine Tree Boulevard, Zip 31792, Mailing Address: P.O. Box 1378, Zip 31799–1378; tel. 229/227–2833, (Nonreporting) **A**1 10
Primary Contact: Hilary Hoo–You, Regional Administrator
COO: Susie Oates, Assistant Superintendent for Administration
CFO: Charles Barton, Business Manager
CMO: Joseph B. LeRoy, M.D., Clinical Director
CIO: Loma Owens, Data Manager
CHR: Clifton Mitchell, Manager Human Resources
Web address: www.swsh.org
**Control:** State–Government, nonfederal **Service:** Psychiatric

Staffed Beds: 236

## THOMSON—McDuffie County

★ ◇ **UNIVERSITY HOSPITAL MCDUFFIE (110111)**, 521 Hill Street S.W., Zip 30824–2199; tel. 706/595–1411 **A**9 10 21 **F**3 7 11 15 29 30 40 45 50 57 59 63 64 68 79 81 82 87 93 107 110 114 119 129 130 132 146 148 **S** University Health Care System, Augusta, GA
Primary Contact: Sandra I. McVicker, R.N., MSN, President
CFO: Pat Parris, Chief Financial Officer
CIO: Lisa Tucker, Chief Information Officer
CHR: Belinda H. Campbell, Director Human Resources, Legal Compliance and Risk Management
Web address: www.mrmc.org
**Control:** Other not–for–profit (including NFP Corporation) **Service:** General Medical and Surgical

Staffed Beds: 25 **Admissions:** 209 **Census:** 2 **Outpatient Visits:** 16202 **Births:** 0 **Total Expense ($000):** 7580 **Payroll Expense ($000):** 3045 **Personnel:** 137

## TIFTON—Tift County

⊠ **TIFT REGIONAL MEDICAL CENTER (110095)**, 901 East 18th Street, Zip 31794–3648, Mailing Address: Drawer 747, Zip 31793–0747; tel. 229/382–7120, (Total facility includes 15 beds in nursing–type unit) **A**1 2 9 10 19 **F**3 8 9 11 13 15 18 20 22 26 28 29 31 34 35 40 45 47 49 50 54 57 59 60 63 64 68 70 74 75 76 77 78 79 81 82 84 85 86 87 89 92 93 97 107 108 110 111 114 118 119 120 121 123 126 127 128 129 130 132 135 143 144 146 147 148 **P**6
Primary Contact: William T. Richardson, President and Chief Executive Officer
COO: Sarah Thompson, Vice President Operations
CFO: Dennis L. Crum, Vice President and Chief Financial Officer
CMO: Raymond Moreno, M.D., Vice President Medical Affairs
CIO: Guy McAllister, Assistant Vice President and Chief Information Officer
CHR: Ellen Eaton, Director Human Resources
Web address: www.tiftregional.com
**Control:** Hospital district or authority, Government, nonfederal **Service:** General Medical and Surgical

Staffed Beds: 191 **Admissions:** 10836 **Census:** 128 **Outpatient Visits:** 163179 **Births:** 1045 **Total Expense ($000):** 243607 **Payroll Expense ($000):** 88925 **Personnel:** 1561

**GA**

**Hospital, Medicare Provider Number, Address, Telephone, Approval, Facility, and Physician Codes, Health Care System**

★ American Hospital Association (AHA) membership
☐ The Joint Commission accreditation
◇ DNV Healthcare Inc. accreditation
○ Healthcare Facilities Accreditation Program
△ Commission on Accreditation of Rehabilitation Facilities (CARF) accreditation

## TOCCOA—Stephens County

☒ **STEPHENS COUNTY HOSPITAL (110032)**, 163 Hospital Drive, Zip 30577–6820; tel. 706/282–4200, (Total facility includes 92 beds in nursing home–type unit) **A**1 9 10 **F**3 7 11 13 15 28 30 34 35 40 51 57 59 60 64 68 70 73 75 76 77 79 81 85 86 89 93 107 110 111 114 119 125 129 130 146 148
Primary Contact: Edward C. Gambrell, Jr., Administrator
CFO: Jeff Laird, Controller
CHR: Diane Hardeman, Director Personnel
Web address: www.stephenscountyhospital.com
**Control:** Hospital district or authority, Government, nonfederal **Service:** General Medical and Surgical

**Staffed Beds:** 188 **Admissions:** 2834 **Census:** 135 **Outpatient Visits:** 40712 **Births:** 496 **Total Expense ($000):** 48255 **Payroll Expense ($000):** 22637 **Personnel:** 484

## VALDOSTA—Lowndes County

☒ **SOUTH GEORGIA MEDICAL CENTER (110122)**, 2501 North Patterson Street, Zip 31602–1735; Mailing Address: P.O. Box 1727, Zip 31603–1727; tel. 229/333–1000, (Includes GREENLEAF CENTER, 2209 Pineview Drive, Zip 31602–7316; tel. 229/247–4357; SMITH NORTHVIEW HOSPITAL, 4280 North Valdosta Road, Zip 31602, Mailing Address: P.O. Box 10010, Zip 31604; tel. 229/671–2000; Sammie Dixon, M.D., Interim Chief Executive Officer) **A**1 2 9 10 19 **F**3 4 5 7 8 11 13 15 19 20 22 24 26 28 29 30 31 32 34 35 37 38 39 40 45 46 47 49 50 51 54 56 57 59 60 61 64 68 70 71 74 75 76 77 78 79 81 82 85 86 87 89 90 95 96 97 98 99 100 101 102 103 104 105 107 108 110 111 113 114 115 117 118 119 120 121 123 124 126 129 130 131 132 134 135 143 144 146 147 148 **P**6
Primary Contact: Randy Sauls, Chief Executive Officer and Administrator
CFO: Greg Hembree, Chief Financial Officer
CMO: Kimberly Megow, M.D., Chief Medical Officer
CIO: Bob Foster, Assistant Administrator Information Services
CHR: Charles Eidson, Assistant Administrator Human Resources
Web address: www.sgmc.org
**Control:** Hospital district or authority, Government, nonfederal **Service:** General Medical and Surgical

**Staffed Beds:** 380 **Admissions:** 17275 **Census:** 222 **Outpatient Visits:** 245312 **Births:** 2228 **Total Expense ($000):** 306628 **Payroll Expense ($000):** 106076 **Personnel:** 2365

## VIDALIA—Toombs County

☒ **MEADOWS REGIONAL MEDICAL CENTER (110128)**, One Meadows Parkway, Zip 30474–8759, Mailing Address: P.O. Box 1048, Zip 30475–1048; tel. 912/535–5555 **A**1 9 10 20 **F**11 13 15 18 20 22 29 30 31 34 35 37 40 45 46 49 50 51 53 54 57 59 60 61 62 64 68 70 74 75 76 77 78 79 81 85 86 87 93 97 107 108 110 111 115 118 119 124 127 129 130 131 132 146 147 148 **P**6
Primary Contact: Alan Kent, Chief Executive Officer
COO: Shirley Hoskins, Chief Operating Officer
CFO: John Cornell, Vice President Finance
CIO: Charles Bondurant, Chief Information Officer
Web address: www.meadowsregional.org
**Control:** Other not–for–profit (including NFP Corporation) **Service:** General Medical and Surgical

**Staffed Beds:** 57 **Admissions:** 4370 **Census:** 39 **Outpatient Visits:** 58627 **Births:** 791 **Total Expense ($000):** 76177 **Payroll Expense ($000):** 25874

## VILLA RICA—Carroll County

☒ **TANNER MEDICAL CENTER–VILLA RICA (110015)**, 601 Dallas Road, Zip 30180–1202, Mailing Address: P.O. Box 638, Zip 30180–0638; tel. 770/456–3100, (Nonreporting) **A**1 9 10 **S** Tanner Health System, Carrollton, GA
Primary Contact: Taylor Powers, Administrator
Web address: www.tanner.org
**Control:** Other not–for–profit (including NFP Corporation) **Service:** General Medical and Surgical

**Staffed Beds:** 39

## WARM SPRINGS—Meriwether County

☐ **ROOSEVELT WARM SPRINGS INSTITUTE FOR REHABILITATION (113028)**, 6135 Roosevelt Highway, Zip 31830–2757, Mailing Address: P.O. Box 1000, Zip 31830–1000; tel. 706/655–5000, (Nonreporting) **A**1 9 10
Primary Contact: Greg Schmieg, Executive Director
CFO: David Cawthon, Director Financial Services
CMO: Burton McDaniel, M.D., Medical Director
CIO: Martin Harmon, Director Public Relations
CHR: Bill Bulloch, Director Human Resources
Web address: www.rooseveltrehab.org
**Control:** State–Government, nonfederal **Service:** Rehabilitation

**Staffed Beds:** 52

☐ **ROOSEVELT WARM SPRINGS LTAC HOSPITAL (112000)**, 6135 Roosevelt Highway, Zip 31830–2757; tel. 708/655–5000, (Nonreporting) **A**1 10
Primary Contact: Greg Schmieg, Executive Director
CFO: Ann Poston, Director Financial Services
CMO: W. Burton McDaniel, Jr., M.D., Physician Executive
CIO: Rufus Braddy, Director Management Information Systems
CHR: Kathy Albritton, Director Human Resources
Web address: www.rooseveltrehab.org/medical.php
**Control:** State–Government, nonfederal **Service:** Long–Term Acute Care hospital

**Staffed Beds:** 30

☒ **WARM SPRINGS MEDICAL CENTER (111316)**, 5995 Spring Street, Zip 31830–2149, Mailing Address: P.O. Box 8, Zip 31830–0008; tel. 706/655–3331, (Nonreporting) **A**1 9 10 18
Primary Contact: Richard Buchanan, Interim Chief Executive Officer
CFO: Karen Blanton, Chief Financial Officer
CMO: Alan Thompson, M.D., President Medical Staff
CIO: Milo Varnadoe, Director Information Systems
CHR: Barbara Nolan, Manager Human Resources
Web address: www.warmspringsmc.org
**Control:** Hospital district or authority, Government, nonfederal **Service:** General Medical and Surgical

**Staffed Beds:** 104

## WARNER ROBINS—Houston County

☒ **HOUSTON MEDICAL CENTER (110069)**, 1601 Watson Boulevard, Zip 31093–3431, Mailing Address: P.O. Box 2886, Zip 31099–2886; tel. 478/922–4281 **A**1 9 10 **F**3 11 13 15 18 20 22 28 29 30 31 34 35 38 39 40 45 48 49 50 51 54 56 57 58 59 60 61 64 68 70 73 74 75 76 78 79 81 82 85 86 87 89 96 98 100 101 102 103 104 107 108 110 111 114 115 118 119 129 130 131 132 134 135 144 146 147 148 **P**6 **S** Houston Healthcare System, Warner Robins, GA
Primary Contact: Cary Martin, Chief Executive Officer
CFO: Frank R. Powell, Chief Financial Officer
CFO: Sean Whilden, Chief Financil Officer
CIO: Robert Rhodes, Chief Information Officer
CHR: Michael O'Hara, Senior Executive Director Human Resources
Web address: www.hhc.org
**Control:** Other not–for–profit (including NFP Corporation) **Service:** General Medical and Surgical

**Staffed Beds:** 237 **Admissions:** 14179 **Census:** 175 **Outpatient Visits:** 252948 **Births:** 2146 **Total Expense ($000):** 198430 **Payroll Expense ($000):** 80414 **Personnel:** 1888

## WASHINGTON—Wilkes County

☐ **WILLS MEMORIAL HOSPITAL (111325)**, 120 Gordon Street, Zip 30673–1602, Mailing Address: P.O. Box 370, Zip 30673–0370; tel. 706/678–2151, (Nonreporting) **A**1 9 10 18
Primary Contact: Jane Echols, Chief Executive Officer
CFO: Cliff Cooper, Chief Financial Officer
CHR: Tom Urban, Director Human Resources
Web address: www.willsmemorialhospital.com
**Control:** Hospital district or authority, Government, nonfederal **Service:** General Medical and Surgical

**Staffed Beds:** 25

## WAYCROSS—Ware County

☒ **MAYO CLINIC HEALTH SYSTEM IN WAYCROSS (110003)**, 410 Darling Avenue, Zip 31501–6357, Mailing Address: P.O. Box 139, Zip 31502–0139; tel. 912/283–3030 **A**1 2 3 5 9 10 **F**3 13 15 17 18 20 22 28 29 30 34 35 40 45 49 51 57 59 60 70 73 74 75 76 77 78 79 80 81 85 87 89 90 92 93 98 107 108 111 114 115 116 117 118 119 129 130 132 135 146 **P**6 **S** Mayo Clinic Health System, Rochester, MN
Primary Contact: Robert M. Trimm, Chief Administrative Officer
COO: Windell Smith, Chief Operating Officer
CFO: Katrina Wheeler, Chief Financial Officer
CMO: John Butler, M.D., Director Medical Staff
CIO: Barry Rudd, Chief Information Officer
Web address: www.satilla.org
**Control:** Other not–for–profit (including NFP Corporation) **Service:** General Medical and Surgical

**Staffed Beds:** 199 **Admissions:** 7301 **Census:** 98 **Outpatient Visits:** 132741 **Births:** 570 **Total Expense ($000):** 115300 **Payroll Expense ($000):** 45350 **Personnel:** 999

## WAYNESBORO—Burke County

☐ **BURKE MEDICAL CENTER (110113)**, 351 Liberty Street, Zip 30830–9686; tel. 706/554–4435, (Nonreporting) **A**1 9 10
Primary Contact: Jennifer A. Royal, Administrator
CFO: Dianne Stewart, Controller
CHR: Danette Highsmith, Director Human Resources
Web address: www.burkemedical.net
**Control:** Hospital district or authority, Government, nonfederal **Service:** General Medical and Surgical

**Staffed Beds:** 40

**GA**

*Many Facility Codes have changed. Please refer to the AHA Guide Code Chart.*
© 2013 AHA Guide

☐ **BARROW REGIONAL MEDICAL CENTER (110045)**, 316 North Broad Street,
Zip 30680–2150, Mailing Address: P.O. Box 688, Zip 30680–0688;
tel. 770/867–3400 **A**1 9 10 **F**3 11 12 13 29 34 40 45 50 51 57 59 64 68 70
74 75 76 77 79 81 93 107 108 110 111 114 119 124 129 130 132 135 146
147 148 **S** Health Management Associates, Naples, FL
Primary Contact: Todd Dixon, R.N., Chief Executive Officer
COO: Joshua Self, Chief Operating Officer
CFO: Jared Whipkey, Chief Financial Officer
CMO: William Lytollis, M.D., Chief of Staff
CIO: Ed Stanley, Director Information Systems
CHR: Tina Jackson, Director Human Resources
Web address: www.barrowregional.com
**Control:** Corporation, Investor–owned, for–profit **Service:** General Medical and
Surgical

**Staffed Beds:** 56 **Admissions:** 2415 **Census:** 21 **Outpatient Visits:** 46518
**Births:** 115 **Personnel:** 238

---

**Hospital, Medicare Provider Number, Address, Telephone, Approval, Facility, and Physician Codes, Health Care System**

★ American Hospital Association (AHA) membership  ◯ Healthcare Facilities Accreditation Program
☐ The Joint Commission accreditation  ◇ DNV Healthcare Inc. accreditation  △ Commission on Accreditation of Rehabilitation Facilities (CARF) accreditation

GA

# HAWAII

## AIEA—Honolulu County

**✠ PALI MOMI MEDICAL CENTER (120026)**, 98–1079 Moanalua Road, Zip 96701–4713; tel. 808/486–6000 **A**1 2 5 9 10 **F**3 8 12 15 18 20 22 26 29 30 31 34 35 40 45 46 47 49 50 57 58 59 60 64 65 67 68 69 70 74 75 77 78 79 81 82 83 85 86 87 92 107 108 110 111 114 115 119 130 132 135 142 146 147 148 **P**5 **S** Hawaii Pacific Health, Honolulu, HI
Primary Contact: Jen Chahanovich, Chief Executive Officer
CFO: David Okabe, Executive Vice President, Chief Financial Officer and Treasurer
CMO: Mark Pitts, M.D., Chief of Staff
CIO: Steve Robertson, Senior Vice President
CHR: Gail Lerch, R.N., Vice President Human Resources
Web address: www.kapiolani.org
**Control:** Other not–for–profit (including NFP Corporation) **Service:** General Medical and Surgical

**Staffed Beds:** 126 **Admissions:** 6455 **Census:** 115 **Outpatient Visits:** 139906 **Births:** 0 **Total Expense ($000):** 163471 **Payroll Expense ($000):** 62863 **Personnel:** 1010

## EWA BEACH—Honolulu County

**✠ KAHI MOHALA BEHAVIORAL HEALTH (124001)**, 91–2301 Old Fort Weaver Road, Zip 96706–3602; tel. 808/671–8511 **A**1 9 10 **F**8 11 13 15 18 29 30 34 35 40 45 46 51 54 56 57 59 60 61 64 65 66 68 71 75 77 79 81 85 86 87 91 93 97 98 99 100 101 104 105 106 107 109 110 111 113 115 117 118 127 130 131 133 135 146 147 148 **P**6 **S** Sutter Health, Sacramento, CA
Primary Contact: Leonard Licina, Chief Executive Officer
CFO: Rose Choy, Chief Financial Officer
CMO: Steven Chaplin, M.D., Medical Director
CHR: Christina Enoka, Director Human Resources and Risk Management
Web address: www.kahimohala.org
**Control:** Other not–for–profit (including NFP Corporation) **Service:** Psychiatric

**Staffed Beds:** 66 **Admissions:** 1251 **Census:** 66 **Outpatient Visits:** 4001 **Births:** 0 **Total Expense ($000):** 20437 **Payroll Expense ($000):** 9649 **Personnel:** 176

## HILO—Hawaii County

**✠ HILO MEDICAL CENTER (120005)**, 1190 Waianuenue Avenue, Zip 96720–2089; tel. 808/932–3000, (Total facility includes 112 beds in nursing home–type unit) **A**1 5 9 10 20 **F**3 17 18 20 29 30 31 34 40 43 50 51 57 59 62 67 70 74 75 76 77 78 79 81 85 86 87 93 98 100 101 102 103 107 111 114 119 121 123 128 130 135 146 148 **P**5 6 **S** Hawaii Health Systems Corporation, Honolulu, HI
Primary Contact: Howard N. Ainsley, Regional Chief Executive Officer
COO: Julie–Beth Ako, Director, Systems Services
CFO: Money Atwal, Chief Financial Officer
CMO: Ted Peskin, M.D., Acute Care Medical Director
CIO: Money Atwal, Chief Information Officer
CHR: Holly Ka'Akimaka, Director Human Resources
CNO: Dan Brinkman, Chief Nurse Executive
Web address: www.hmc.hhsc.org
**Control:** State–Government, nonfederal **Service:** General Medical and Surgical

**Staffed Beds:** 276 **Admissions:** 7312 **Census:** 219 **Outpatient Visits:** 65892 **Births:** 1117 **Total Expense ($000):** 167241 **Payroll Expense ($000):** 61041 **Personnel:** 866

## HONOKAA—Hawaii County

**★ HALE HO'OLA HAMAKUA (121307)**, 45–547 Plumeria Street, Zip 96727–6902; tel. 808/775–7211, (Nonreporting) **A**5 9 10 18 **S** Hawaii Health Systems Corporation, Honolulu, HI
Primary Contact: Cathy Meyer–Uyehara, Administrator
CFO: Harlan Seo, Accountant
CMO: Gretchen Salmon, M.D., Medical Director
Web address: www.hhsc.org
**Control:** State–Government, nonfederal **Service:** General Medical and Surgical

**Staffed Beds:** 52

## HONOLULU—Honolulu County

**✠ KAISER PERMANENTE MEDICAL CENTER (120011)**, 3288 Moanalua Road, Zip 96819–1469; tel. 808/432–0000, (Total facility includes 24 beds in nursing home–type unit) **A**1 3 5 10 **F**3 12 13 15 17 18 19 20 21 22 24 26 29 30 31 32 34 35 36 38 40 41 45 46 47 48 49 50 51 54 55 56 57 58 59 60 61 62 64 65 70 71 72 74 75 76 77 78 79 81 82 83 84 85 86 87 89 92 93 94 97 99 100 101 104 107 108 110 111 115 116 117 119 128 129 130 131 133 134 135 144 146 148 **P**1 **S** Kaiser Foundation Hospitals, Oakland, CA
Primary Contact: Peter E. Makowski, Administrator
CFO: Thomas Risse, Chief Financial Officer and Vice President Business Services
CMO: James Griffith, M.D., Associate Medical Director and Professional Chief of Staff
CIO: Brian Yoshii, Vice President Information Technology
CHR: Arlene F. Peasnall, Senior Vice President Human Resources
CNO: Linda Puu, Chief Nursing Officer
Web address: www.kaiserpermanente.org
**Control:** Other not–for–profit (including NFP Corporation) **Service:** General Medical and Surgical

**Staffed Beds:** 235 **Admissions:** 11403 **Census:** 194 **Outpatient Visits:** 61733 **Births:** 1603 **Personnel:** 1788

**☐ KAPIOLANI MEDICAL CENTER FOR WOMEN & CHILDREN (123300)**, 1319 Punahou Street, Zip 96826–1001; tel. 808/983–6000, (Nonreporting) **A**1 2 3 5 9 10 **S** Hawaii Pacific Health, Honolulu, HI
Primary Contact: Martha Smith, Chief Executive Officer
CFO: David Okabe, Senior Vice President, Chief Financial Officer and Treasurer
CIO: Steve Robertson, Vice President
CHR: Gail Lerch, R.N., Vice President
Web address: www.kapiolani.org
**Control:** Other not–for–profit (including NFP Corporation) **Service:** Children's general

**Staffed Beds:** 225

**✠ KUAKINI MEDICAL CENTER (120007)**, 347 North Kuakini Street, Zip 96817–2381; tel. 808/536–2236 **A**1 2 3 5 9 10 **F**3 15 17 18 20 22 24 26 28 29 31 34 35 40 45 46 49 57 58 59 60 68 70 74 75 77 78 79 80 81 82 85 86 87 107 108 110 111 115 117 118 119 121 129 130 131 132 145 146 147 148 **P**1
Primary Contact: Gary K. Kajiwara, President and Chief Executive Officer
COO: Gregg Oishi, Senior Vice President and Chief Operating Officer
CFO: Quin Ogawa, Vice President and Chief Financial Officer
CMO: Nobuyuki Miki, M.D., Vice President Medical Affairs
CIO: Gary K. Kajiwara, President and Chief Executive Officer
CHR: Ann N. Choy, Manager Human Resources and Payroll
Web address: www.kuakini.org
**Control:** Other not–for–profit (including NFP Corporation) **Service:** General Medical and Surgical

**Staffed Beds:** 94 **Admissions:** 5954 **Census:** 108 **Outpatient Visits:** 59801 **Births:** 0 **Total Expense ($000):** 133641 **Payroll Expense ($000):** 62711 **Personnel:** 908

**★ LEAHI HOSPITAL (122001)**, 3675 Kilauea Avenue, Zip 96816–2398; tel. 808/733–8000, (Nonreporting) **A**9 10 **S** Hawaii Health Systems Corporation, Honolulu, HI
Primary Contact: Vincent H. S. Lee, FACHE, Regional Chief Executive Officer
CFO: Edward Chu, Chief Financial Officer
CMO: Albert Yazawa, M.D., Regional Medical Director
CHR: Russel Higa, JD, Regional Director Human Resources
CNO: Amy Vasunaga, Chief Nurse Executive
Web address: www.hhsc.org
**Control:** State–Government, nonfederal **Service:** Long–Term Acute Care hospital

**Staffed Beds:** 188

**HI**

*Many Facility Codes have changed. Please refer to the AHA Guide Code Chart.*
© 2013 AHA Guide

✠ **QUEEN'S MEDICAL CENTER (120001)**, 1301 Punchbowl Street,
Zip 96813–2499; tel. 808/538–9011, (Total facility includes 28 beds in nursing
home–type unit) **A**1 2 3 5 9 10 **F**3 5 11 12 13 15 17 18 20 22 24 26 28 29
31 34 35 37 38 39 40 43 44 45 46 47 48 49 50 51 55 56 57 59 60 61 62
63 64 66 68 70 73 74 75 76 77 78 79 81 82 84 85 86 87 93 96 97 98 99
100 101 102 103 104 105 107 108 110 111 114 115 117 119 120 121 124
126 128 129 130 131 132 135 136 143 146 147 148 **S** Queen's Health
Systems, Honolulu, HI
Primary Contact: Arthur A. Ushijima, President
COO: Mark Yamakawa, Chief Operating Officer
CFO: Richard Keene, Chief Financial Officer
CMO: Gerard Akaka, M.D., Vice President Medical Affairs
CIO: Hunter Praywell, Vice President Information Technology and Chief Information
Officer
CHR: Bert Kido, Vice President Human Resources
CNO: Cynthia Kamikawa, R.N., Vice President Nursing Emergency Department and
Trauma and Chief Nursing Officer
Web address: www.queens.org
**Control:** Other not–for–profit (including NFP Corporation) **Service:** General
Medical and Surgical

**Staffed Beds: 495 Admissions: 25152 Census: 408 Outpatient Visits:**
**334159 Births: 2379**

✠ **REHABILITATION HOSPITAL OF THE PACIFIC (123025)**, 226 North Kuakini
Street, Zip 96817–2488; tel. 808/531–3511 **A**1 9 10 **F**3 11 28 29 34 54 64
74 75 77 79 90 91 93 94 95 96 130 131 132 143 146 147 148
Primary Contact: Timothy J. Roe, President and Chief Executive Officer
CFO: Ty Tomimoto, Acting Vice President Financial Affairs
CHR: Faye Miyamoto, Vice President Human Resources
CNO: AMy Parungao, Director of Nursing
Web address: www.rehabhospital.org
**Control:** Other not–for–profit (including NFP Corporation) **Service:** Rehabilitation

**Staffed Beds: 66 Admissions: 1331 Census: 51 Outpatient Visits: 40132**
**Births: 0 Total Expense ($000): 37252 Payroll Expense ($000): 18242**
**Personnel: 269**

☐ **SHRINERS HOSPITALS FOR CHILDREN–HONOLULU (123301)**, 1310
Punahou Street, Zip 96826–1099; tel. 808/941–4466 **A**1 3 5 9 10 **F**3 29 35 39
58 64 75 77 79 81 85 89 93 94 119 130 132 146 **P**6 **S** Shriners Hospitals for
Children, Tampa, FL
Primary Contact: Gene Raynaud, Administrator
CFO: Patricia Miyasawa, CPA, Director Fiscal Service
CMO: Arabella Leet, M.D., Chief of Staff
CIO: Ross Imada, Director Information Systems
CHR: Derek Ito, Director Human Resources
CNO: Andrea Kubota, R.N., Director Patient Care Services
Web address: www.shrinershospitalsforchildren.org/Hospitals/Locations/Honolulu.
aspx
**Control:** Other not–for–profit (including NFP Corporation) **Service:** Children's
orthopedic

**Staffed Beds: 16 Admissions: 219 Census: 3 Outpatient Visits: 10219**
**Births: 0 Personnel: 138**

☐ **STRAUB CLINIC & HOSPITAL (120022)**, 888 South King Street,
Zip 96813–3097; tel. 808/522–4000 **A**1 2 3 5 9 10 **F**3 9 12 15 16 17 18 20
21 22 23 24 26 27 29 30 31 34 40 45 47 49 54 56 57 59 64 65 68 70 74
75 77 78 79 81 82 84 85 86 87 93 94 97 104 107 108 110 111 114 118
119 129 130 131 132 135 143 144 146 148 **P**6 **S** Hawaii Pacific Health,
Honolulu, HI
Primary Contact: Art Gladstone, R.N., Chief Executive Officer
CFO: David Okabe, Executive Vice President, Chief Financial Officer and Treasurer
CMO: Kenneth Robbins, M.D., Chief Medical Officer
CIO: Steve Robertson, Executive Vice President and Chief Information Officer
CHR: Gail Lerch, R.N., Executive Vice President Human Resources
Web address: www.straubhealth.org
**Control:** Other not–for–profit (including NFP Corporation) **Service:** General
Medical and Surgical

**Staffed Beds: 111 Admissions: 7243 Census: 113 Outpatient Visits:**
**758846 Births: 0 Total Expense ($000): 235186 Payroll Expense ($000):**
**145851 Personnel: 1574**

✠ **TRIPLER ARMY MEDICAL CENTER**, 1 Jarret White Road, Zip 96859–5001;
tel. 808/433–6661, (Nonreporting) **A**1 2 3 5 **S** Department of the Army, Office of
the Surgeon General, Falls Church, VA
Primary Contact: Brigadier General Dennis Doyle, Commanding General
CIO: Major Donna E. Beed, Division Chief Information Management
CHR: Colonel Lisa P. Chisholm, Troop Commander
Web address: www.tamc.amedd.army.mil
**Control:** Army, Government, federal **Service:** General Medical and Surgical

**Staffed Beds: 198**

**KAHUKU—Honolulu County**

**KAHUKU MEDICAL CENTER (121304)**, 56–117 Pualalea Street,
Zip 96731–2052; tel. 808/293–9221, (Total facility includes 10 beds in nursing
home–type unit) **A**9 10 18 **F**3 26 34 40 43 46 50 57 59 67 68 69 77 86 87 90
91 92 93 94 119 128 130 133 134 146
Primary Contact: Stephany Vaioleti, Administrator
CFO: Francis Daquioag, Controller
CMO: P. Douglas Nielson, M.D., Chief of Staff
Web address: www.hhsc.org/oahu/kahuku/index.html
**Control:** State–Government, nonfederal **Service:** Long–Term Acute Care hospital

**Staffed Beds: 21 Admissions: 147 Census: 14 Outpatient Visits: 4755**
**Births: 0 Total Expense ($000): 9343 Payroll Expense ($000): 3929**
**Personnel: 100**

**KAILUA—Honolulu County**

✠ **CASTLE MEDICAL CENTER (120006)**, 640 Ulukahiki Street, Zip 96734–4454;
tel. 808/263–5500 **A**1 3 5 9 10 **F**8 12 13 15 18 20 22 24 29 30 31 34 35 40
45 49 51 57 59 62 64 68 70 71 74 75 76 77 78 79 81 84 93 98 102 107
108 111 115 119 126 130 132 135 146 147 148 **P**6 8 **S** Adventist Health,
Roseville, CA
Primary Contact: Kathryn A. Raethel, R.N., M.P.H., President and Chief Executive
Officer
CFO: Wendi Barber, Vice President Finance
CMO: Alan Cheung, M.D., Vice President Medical Affairs
CIO: Brian Rothe, Site Director Information Systems
CHR: Adele S. Hoe, Director Human Resources
Web address: www.castlemed.org
**Control:** Church–operated, Nongovernment, not–for profit **Service:** General
Medical and Surgical

**Staffed Beds: 160 Admissions: 7497 Census: 95 Outpatient Visits: 110875**
**Births: 1002 Total Expense ($000): 127809 Payroll Expense ($000):**
**57521 Personnel: 1017**

**KAMUELA—Hawaii County**

☐ **NORTH HAWAII COMMUNITY HOSPITAL (120028)**, 67–1125 Mamalahoa
Highway, Zip 96743–8496; tel. 808/885–4444 **A**1 5 9 10 20 **F**3 8 13 15 18 24
26 29 31 34 35 36 40 43 46 50 53 57 58 59 62 68 70 76 77 78 79 81 84
85 93 97 107 108 110 111 115 119 130 142 146 147 148 **P**6
Primary Contact: Lowell W. Johnson, FACHE, Interim Chief Executive Officer
CMO: Dana Lee, M.D., Chief of Staff
CHR: Bill Brown, Vice President Human Resources
Web address: www.northhawaiicommunityhospital.org
**Control:** Other not–for–profit (including NFP Corporation) **Service:** General
Medical and Surgical

**Staffed Beds: 33 Admissions: 2560 Census: 19 Outpatient Visits: 44777**
**Births: 655 Total Expense ($000): 54496 Payroll Expense ($000): 24203**
**Personnel: 302**

**KANEOHE—Honolulu County**

☐ **HAWAII STATE HOSPITAL**, 45–710 Keaahala Road, Zip 96744–3597;
tel. 808/236 8237 **A**1 3 5 **F**34 39 59 75 77 98 101 102 103 105 106 130
132 135 143 146
Primary Contact: Mark Fridovich, Ph.D., Administrator
COO: William T. Elliott, Associate Administrator Administrative and Support
Services
CFO: Anthony Fraiola, Business Manager
CMO: James Westphal, M.D., Medical Director
CIO: John Jansen, Management Information Specialist
CHR: Karen Hara, Personnel Management Specialist
CNO: Leona Guest, Chief Nursing Unit
Web address: www.hshweb.health.state.hi.us
**Control:** State–Government, nonfederal **Service:** Psychiatric

**Staffed Beds: 178 Admissions: 291 Census: 188 Outpatient Visits: 0**
**Births: 0 Total Expense ($000): 50683 Personnel: 605**

**KAPAA—Kauai County**

★ **SAMUEL MAHELONA MEMORIAL HOSPITAL (121306)**, 4800 Kawaihau Road,
Zip 96746–1971; tel. 808/822–4961, (Nonreporting) **A**9 10 18 **S** Hawaii Health
Systems Corporation, Honolulu, HI
Primary Contact: Jerry Walker, Interim Regional Chief Executive Officer
CFO: Michael Perel, Regional Chief Financial Officer
CMO: Gerald Tomory, M.D., Regional Medical Director
CIO: Sandra McMaster, Regional Chief Information Officer
CHR: Lani Aranio, Regional Director Human Resources
Web address: www.smmh.hhsc.org
**Control:** State–Government, nonfederal **Service:** General Medical and Surgical

**Staffed Beds: 80**

**HI**

---

**Hospital, Medicare Provider Number, Address, Telephone, Approval, Facility, and Physician Codes, Health Care System**

★ American Hospital Association (AHA) membership
☐ The Joint Commission accreditation
◇ DNV Healthcare Inc. accreditation
◯ Healthcare Facilities Accreditation Program
△ Commission on Accreditation of Rehabilitation Facilities (CARF) accreditation

### KAUNAKAKAI—Maui County

✠ **MOLOKAI GENERAL HOSPITAL (121303)**, Zip 96748–0408;
tel. 808/553–5331, (Total facility includes 2 beds in nursing home–type unit) **A**1
5 9 10 18 **F**1 3 4 16 17 34 40 41 44 50 57 59 63 64 65 66 67 68 69 70 72
73 75 76 77 78 80 81 82 84 87 88 89 90 91 93 97 98 107 110 115 119
127 130 133 134 135 147 148 **P**6 **S** Queen's Health Systems, Honolulu, HI
Primary Contact: Janice Kalanihuia, President
CFO: Alyne Kikukawa, Accountant
CMO: William Thomas, Jr., M.D., Medical Director Clinical and Internal Affairs
CIO: Randy Lite, Vice President
CHR: Lei Mokiao, Coordinator Human Resources
Web address: www.queens.org
**Control:** Other not–for–profit (including NFP Corporation) **Service:** General
Medical and Surgical

**Staffed Beds:** 15 **Admissions:** 116 **Census:** 4 **Outpatient Visits:** 36574
**Births:** 39 **Total Expense ($000):** 12242 **Payroll Expense ($000):** 4498
**Personnel:** 81

### KEALAKEKUA—Hawaii County

✠ **KONA COMMUNITY HOSPITAL (120019)**, 79–1019 Haukapila Street,
Zip 96750–7920; tel. 808/322–9311 **A**1 5 9 10 20 **F**11 15 29 30 31 34 35
40 43 44 50 67 70 71 76 77 78 79 81 84 98 107 108 109 111 119 120 121
123 127 128 130 133 **S** Hawaii Health Systems Corporation, Honolulu, HI
Primary Contact: Jay E. Kreuzer, FACHE, Chief Executive Officer
CFO: Dean Herzog, Chief Financial Officer
CMO: Kathleen Rokavec, M.D., Medical Director
CHR: Kathryn Salomon, Director Human Resources
CNO: Patricia Kalua, Chief Nurse Executive
Web address: www.kch.hhsc.org
**Control:** Other not–for–profit (including NFP Corporation) **Service:** General
Medical and Surgical

**Staffed Beds:** 94 **Admissions:** 3153 **Census:** 49 **Outpatient Visits:** 21812
**Births:** 443 **Total Expense ($000):** 55025 **Payroll Expense ($000):** 27104
**Personnel:** 474

### KOHALA—Hawaii County

★ **KOHALA HOSPITAL (121302)**, 54–383 Hospital Road, Zip 96755, Mailing
Address: P.O. Box 10, Kapaau, Zip 96755–0010; tel. 808/889–6211, (Total
facility includes 24 beds in nursing home–type unit) **A**9 10 18 **F**40 67 107 128
**S** Hawaii Health Systems Corporation, Honolulu, HI
Primary Contact: Eugene Amar, Jr., Administrator
CMO: Silvia Sonnenschein, M.D., Chief of Staff
Web address: www.koh.hhsc.org
**Control:** State–Government, nonfederal **Service:** General Medical and Surgical

**Staffed Beds:** 28 **Admissions:** 25 **Census:** 21 **Outpatient Visits:** 2389
**Births:** 0 **Total Expense ($000):** 7373 **Payroll Expense ($000):** 3251
**Personnel:** 55

### KULA—Maui County

★ **KULA HOSPITAL (121308)**, 100 Keokea Place, Zip 96790–7450;
tel. 808/878–1221, (Nonreporting) **A**5 9 10 18 **S** Hawaii Health Systems
Corporation, Honolulu, HI
Primary Contact: Nick Hughey, Administrator
CFO: Nerissa Garrity, Chief Financial Officer
CMO: Nicole Apoliona, M.D., Medical Director
Web address: www.hhsc.org
**Control:** State–Government, nonfederal **Service:** General Medical and Surgical

**Staffed Beds:** 6

### LANAI CITY—Maui County

★ **LANAI COMMUNITY HOSPITAL (121305)**, (Critical Access Hospital), 628
Seventh Street, Zip 96763–0650, Mailing Address: P.O. Box 630650,
Zip 96763–0650; tel. 808/565–8450, (Total facility includes 10 beds in nursing
home–type unit) **A**9 10 18 **F**40 67 128 **P**6 **S** Hawaii Health Systems Corporation,
Honolulu, HI
Primary Contact: Nick Hughey, Administrator
Web address: www.lch.hhsc.org
**Control:** State–Government, nonfederal **Service:** General Medical and Surgical

**Staffed Beds:** 24 **Admissions:** 26 **Census:** 9 **Outpatient Visits:** 3449 **Births:**
0 **Personnel:** 35

### LIHUE—Kauai County

☐ **WILCOX MEMORIAL HOSPITAL (120014)**, 3–3420 Kuhio Highway,
Zip 96766–1099; tel. 808/245–1100 **A**1 5 9 10 20 **F**3 13 15 18 28 29 30 31
34 35 40 43 46 47 48 49 50 57 59 60 64 68 70 74 75 76 77 78 79 81 84
85 91 93 97 102 107 108 110 111 114 115 119 130 133 135 146 147 148
**S** Hawaii Pacific Health, Honolulu, HI
Primary Contact: Kathleen Clark, President and Chief Executive Officer
CFO: David Okabe, Executive Vice President, Chief Financial Officer and Treasurer
CMO: Christopher Jordan, M.D., President Medical Staff
CIO: Steve Robertson, Executive Vice President Revenue Cycle Management and
Chief Information Officer
CHR: Monica Reisner, Director Human Resources Operations
CNO: Nancy Wilson, Chief Nurse Executive
Web address: www.wilcoxhealth.org
**Control:** Other not–for–profit (including NFP Corporation) **Service:** General
Medical and Surgical

**Staffed Beds:** 64 **Admissions:** 3530 **Census:** 45 **Outpatient Visits:** 76744
**Births:** 522 **Total Expense ($000):** 80422 **Payroll Expense ($000):** 29452
**Personnel:** 655

### PAHALA—Hawaii County

★ **KAU HOSPITAL (121301)**, (Critical Access Hospital), 1 Kamani Street,
Zip 96777, Mailing Address: P.O. Box 40, Zip 96777–0040; tel. 808/928–2050,
(Total facility includes 16 beds in nursing home–type unit) **A**9 10 18 **F**2 40 127
128 133 146 **S** Hawaii Health Systems Corporation, Honolulu, HI
Primary Contact: Merilyn Harris, Administrator
CFO: Susan Kingsley, Accountant
CMO: Clifford Field, M.D., Medical Director
Web address: www.hhsc.org
**Control:** State–Government, nonfederal **Service:** General Medical and Surgical

**Staffed Beds:** 21 **Admissions:** 4 **Census:** 15 **Outpatient Visits:** 2073 **Births:**
0 **Total Expense ($000):** 6931 **Payroll Expense ($000):** 4761

### WAHIAWA—Honolulu County

✠ **WAHIAWA GENERAL HOSPITAL (120004)**, 128 Lehua Street,
Zip 96786–2036; tel. 808/621–8411, (Total facility includes 93 beds in nursing
home–type unit) **A**1 3 5 9 10 **F**1 3 4 8 11 15 16 17 29 31 40 56 62 67 70 72
73 75 76 77 78 79 80 81 85 86 87 88 89 90 93 98 103 107 108 109
110 115 119 128 130 132 145 146 147 148 **P**8
Primary Contact: R. Don Olden, Chief Executive Officer
COO: R. Don Olden, Chief Executive Officer
CMO: Timothy Whiteside, M.D., Chief of Staff
CIO: Jason Fujinaka, Manager Information System
CHR: Richard Aea, Director Human Resources
Web address: www.wahiawageneral.org
**Control:** Other not–for–profit (including NFP Corporation) **Service:** General
Medical and Surgical

**Staffed Beds:** 160 **Admissions:** 2555 **Census:** 118 **Outpatient Visits:** 29620
**Births:** 0 **Total Expense ($000):** 51334 **Payroll Expense ($000):** 24349
**Personnel:** 381

### WAILUKU—Maui County

✠ **MAUI MEMORIAL MEDICAL CENTER (120002)**, 221 Mahalani Street,
Zip 96793–2581; tel. 808/244–9056, (Nonreporting) **A**1 5 9 10 20 **S** Hawaii
Health Systems Corporation, Honolulu, HI
Primary Contact: Wesley Lo, Regional Chief Executive Officer
CIO: Dana Mendoza, Chief Information Officer
Web address: www.mmmc.hhsc.org
**Control:** State–Government, nonfederal **Service:** General Medical and Surgical

**Staffed Beds:** 213

### WAIMEA—Kauai County

✠ **KAUAI VETERANS MEMORIAL HOSPITAL (121300)**, Waimea Canyon Road,
Zip 96796, Mailing Address: P.O. Box 337, Zip 96796–0337;
tel. 808/338–9431, (Nonreporting) **A**1 9 10 18 **S** Hawaii Health Systems
Corporation, Honolulu, HI
Primary Contact: Jerry Walker, Interim Regional Chief Executive Officer
CFO: Michael Perel, Regional Chief Financial Officer
CMO: Gerald Tomory, M.D., Regional Medical Director
CIO: Sandra McMaster, Regional Chief Information Officer
CHR: Solette Perry, Regional Director Human Resources
Web address: www.kvmh.hhsc.org
**Control:** State–Government, nonfederal **Service:** General Medical and Surgical

**Staffed Beds:** 45

**HI**

*Many Facility Codes have changed. Please refer to the AHA Guide Code Chart.*
© 2013 AHA Guide

# IDAHO

### AMERICAN FALLS—Power County

★ **POWER COUNTY HOSPITAL DISTRICT (131304)**, 510 Roosevelt Road,
Zip 83211–1362, Mailing Address: P.O. Box 420, Zip 83211–0420;
tel. 208/226–3200, (Nonreporting) **A**9 10 18
Primary Contact: Dallas Clinger, Administrator
COO: Rock Roy, Professional Services Director
CFO: Shauna Croft, Chief Financial Officer
CMO: Bret Timmons, D.O., Chief Medical Staff
CIO: Mindy Earl, Health Information Manager
CHR: Norma Hartley, Director Human Resources
CNO: Daniel Kuta, R.N., Director of Nursing
Web address: www.pchd.net
**Control:** Hospital district or authority, Government, nonfederal **Service:** General
Medical and Surgical

| Staffed Beds: 36 |
|---|

### ARCO—Butte County

**LOST RIVERS MEDICAL CENTER (131324)**, (Formerly Lost Rivers District
Hospital), 551 Highland Drive, Zip 83213–9771, Mailing Address: P.O. Box 145,
Zip 83213–0145; tel. 208/527–8206, (Nonreporting) **A**9 10 18
Primary Contact: Kim Dahlman, Administrator
COO: Kim Dahlman, Administrator
CFO: Kim Dahlman, Administrator
CMO: Jeffrey Haskell, M.D., Chief Medical Staff
CIO: Leann Wartchow, Assistant Chief Executive Officer and Certified Risk
Manager
CHR: Leann Wartchow, Assistant Chief Executive Officer and Certified Risk
Manager
Web address: www.lostrivershospital.com
**Control:** Hospital district or authority, Government, nonfederal **Service:** General
Medical and Surgical

| Staffed Beds: 43 |
|---|

### BLACKFOOT—Bingham County

✉ **BINGHAM MEMORIAL HOSPITAL (131325)**, 98 Poplar Street,
Zip 83221–1799; tel. 208/785–4100, (Total facility includes 70 beds in nursing
home–type unit) **A**1 9 10 18 **F**2 3 12 13 15 18 20 26 29 34 35 37 39 40 45
47 50 55 56 57 58 59 64 68 70 74 76 77 79 81 82 85 86 87 93 97 107
108 109 110 111 115 119 127 128 129 130 131 132 133 134 135 144 146
147 148
Primary Contact: Louis D. Kraml, FACHE, Chief Executive Officer
COO: Dan Cochran, Chief Operating Officer
CFO: Jeff Daniels, Chief Financial Officer
CMO: Gary Call, M.D., Chief Medical Officer
CIO: Jack York, Director Information Systems
CHR: Dinah Karren, Director Human Resources
Web address: www.binghammemorial.org
**Control:** Other not–for–profit (including NFP Corporation) **Service:** General
Medical and Surgical

| Staffed Beds: 95 Admissions: 1759 Census: 60 Outpatient Visits: 50099 Births: 377 Total Expense ($000): 76469 Payroll Expense ($000): 33266 Personnel: 516 |
|---|

**MOUNTAIN RIVER BIRTHING AND SURGERY CENTER (130067)**, 350 North
Meridian Street, Zip 83221–1625; tel. 208/782–0300 **A**9 10 **F**3 79 81 85 86
87 107 130 135 148
Primary Contact: Louis D. Kraml, FACHE, Chief Executive Officer
**Control:** Corporation, Investor–owned, for–profit **Service:** Surgical

| Staffed Beds: 8 Admissions: 140 Census: 1 Outpatient Visits: 5121 Births: 0 Total Expense ($000): 5844 Payroll Expense ($000): 792 Personnel: 20 |
|---|

□ **STATE HOSPITAL SOUTH (134010)**, 700 East Alice Street, Zip 83221–4925,
Mailing Address: P.O. Box 400, Zip 83221–0400; tel. 208/785–1200,
(Nonreporting) **A**1 10
Primary Contact: Tracey Sessions, Administrator
COO: Greg Horton, Director Support Services
CFO: Eric Price, Financial Specialist, Senior
CMO: Kelly Palmer, M.D., Medical Director
CIO: Julie Sutton, Director Performance Improvement
CHR: Heidi Anderson, Human Resources Specialist
CNO: Randy Walker, Director Nursing Services
Web address: www.healthandwelfare.idaho.gov
**Control:** State–Government, nonfederal **Service:** Psychiatric

| Staffed Beds: 77 |
|---|

### BOISE—Ada County

**BOISE BEHAVIORAL HEALTH HOSPITAL (134009)**, 8050 Northview Street,
Zip 83704–7126; tel. 208/327–0504 **A**5 9 10 **F**4 29 30 34 35 38 57 65 98
100 101 102 103 104 130 132 **P**1
Primary Contact: Phil Herink, Chief Executive Officer
CFO: Phil Herink, Chief Executive Officer
CMO: David Kent, M.D., Chief Medical Officer
CIO: Debra Alexander, Chief Information Officer
CHR: Kathy Cady, Coordinator Human Resources, Accounts Payable and Payroll
Web address: www.sunh.com
**Control:** Corporation, Investor–owned, for–profit **Service:** Psychiatric

| Staffed Beds: 22 Admissions: 423 Census: 18 Outpatient Visits: 7561 Births: 0 |
|---|

✉ △ **BOISE VETERANS AFFAIRS MEDICAL CENTER**, (Formerly Veterans Affairs
Medical Center), 500 West Fort Street, Zip 83702–4598; tel. 208/422–1000,
(Total facility includes 24 beds in nursing home–type unit) **A**1 3 5 7 9 **F**1 2 3 4 5
8 9 10 12 16 29 30 31 34 35 38 39 40 43 45 46 47 50 53 54 56 57 58 59
60 61 62 63 64 65 66 67 68 71 74 75 77 78 79 80 81 82 83 84 85 86 87
90 91 92 93 94 96 97 98 100 101 102 103 104 105 106 107 108 111 112
119 120 121 122 123 124 127 128 129 130 132 133 135 143 144 145 146
147 148 **S** Department of Veterans Affairs, Washington, DC
Primary Contact: David P. Wood, FACHE, Director
CFO: Ron Blanton, Chief Fiscal Services
CMO: Paul Lambert, M.D., Chief of Staff
CHR: Randy Turner, Chief Human Resource Management Services
Web address: www.boise.va.gov/
**Control:** Veterans Affairs, Government, federal **Service:** General Medical and
Surgical

| Staffed Beds: 85 Admissions: 3258 Census: 59 Outpatient Visits: 334584 Births: 0 Total Expense ($000): 180000 Payroll Expense ($000): 106000 Personnel: 1031 |
|---|

★ △ **ELKS REHAB HOSPITAL (133025)**, 600 North Robbins Road,
Zip 83702–4565, Mailing Address: P.O. Box 1100, Zip 83701–1100;
tel. 208/489–4444, (Nonreporting) **A**5 7 10
Primary Contact: Joseph P. Caroselli, Chief Executive Officer
COO: Melissa Honsinger, Chief Operating Officer
CFO: Doug Lewis, Chief Financial Officer
CMO: Lee Kornfield, M.D., Medical Director
CIO: Scott Pyrah, Director Information Systems
CHR: Jim Atkins, Director Employee Services
Web address: www.idahoelksrehab.org
**Control:** Other not–for–profit (including NFP Corporation) **Service:** Rehabilitation

| Staffed Beds: 31 |
|---|

**IDAHO ELKS REHABILITATION HOSPITAL** See Elks Rehab Hospital

□ **INTERMOUNTAIN HOSPITAL (134002)**, 303 North Allumbaugh Street,
Zip 83704–9208; tel. 208/377–8400, (Nonreporting) **A**1 9 10 **S** Universal Health
Services, Inc., King of Prussia, PA
Primary Contact: Jeffrey F. Morrell, Chief Executive Officer
CMO: Harry Silsby, M.D., Medical Director
CHR: Angela Billingsley, Director Human Resources
Web address: www.intermountainhospital.com
**Control:** Corporation, Investor–owned, for–profit **Service:** Psychiatric

| Staffed Beds: 140 |
|---|

---

**Hospital, Medicare Provider Number, Address, Telephone, Approval, Facility, and Physician Codes, Health Care System**

★ American Hospital Association (AHA) membership
□ The Joint Commission accreditation
◇ DNV Healthcare Inc. accreditation
○ Healthcare Facilities Accreditation Program
△ Commission on Accreditation of Rehabilitation Facilities (CARF) accreditation

**ID**

⌧ △ **SAINT ALPHONSUS REGIONAL MEDICAL CENTER (130007)**, 1055 North Curtis Road, Zip 83706–1309; tel. 208/367–2121 **A**1 2 3 5 7 9 10 **F**3 5 7 8 9 11 12 13 14 15 17 18 20 22 24 26 28 29 30 31 32 33 34 35 36 37 38 39 40 42 43 44 45 48 49 50 52 54 55 56 57 58 59 61 64 65 68 70 71 72 74 75 76 77 78 79 81 82 84 85 86 87 89 90 91 93 94 96 97 98 99 100 101 102 104 107 108 110 111 114 115 116 117 118 119 120 121 123 124 126 127 128 129 130 131 132 135 144 146 147 148 **P**6 8 **S** Trinity Health, Livonia, MI
Primary Contact: Rodney D. Reider, President
CFO: Kenneth Fry, Chief Financial Officer
CMO: Steve Brown, M.D., Chief Quality Officer
CIO: Dwight Pond, TIS Boise
CHR: Susan Bundgard, Vice President Human Resources
CNO: Sherry Parks, R.N., Chief Nursing Officer
Web address: www.saintalphonsus.org
**Control:** Church–operated, Nongovernment, not–for profit **Service:** General Medical and Surgical

> **Staffed Beds:** 399 **Admissions:** 16530 **Census:** 208 **Outpatient Visits:** 797058 **Births:** 1141 **Total Expense ($000):** 339507 **Payroll Expense ($000):** 182515 **Personnel:** 3029

☐ **SOUTHWEST IDAHO ADVANCED CARE HOSPITAL (132003)**, 6651 West Franklin Road, Zip 83709–0914; tel. 208/376–5700, (Nonreporting) **A**1 9 10 **S** Ernest Health, Inc., Albuquerque, NM
Primary Contact: Nolan Hoffer, Chief Executive Officer
Web address: www.siach.ernesthealth.com/
**Control:** Corporation, Investor–owned, for–profit **Service:** Long–Term Acute Care hospital

> **Staffed Beds:** 40

⌧ **ST. LUKE'S REGIONAL MEDICAL CENTER (130006)**, 190 East Bannock Street, Zip 83712–6241; tel. 208/381–2222, (Includes ST. LUKE'S CHILDREN'S HOSPITAL, 190 East Bannock Street, tel. 208/381–1200; ST. LUKE'S MERIDIAN MEDICAL CENTER, 520 South Eagle Road, Meridian, Zip 83642; tel. 208/706–5000) **A**1 2 3 5 9 10 **F**7 8 11 12 13 15 17 18 19 20 21 22 23 24 25 26 27 28 29 30 31 32 34 35 36 37 40 41 46 47 48 49 53 54 56 57 59 61 62 63 64 68 69 70 71 72 74 75 76 77 78 79 81 82 84 86 87 88 89 107 108 110 111 114 115 117 118 119 126 127 129 130 131 132 134 136 144 146 147 **S** St. Luke's Health System, Boise, ID
Primary Contact: Chris Roth, Chief Executive Officer
COO: Kathy D. Moore, Chief Operating Officer
CFO: Jeff Taylor, Vice President Finance
CMO: Bart Hill, M.D., Vice President Medical Affairs
CHR: Maureen O'Keeffe, Vice President Human Resources
Web address: www.stlukesonline.org/boise
**Control:** Other not–for–profit (including NFP Corporation) **Service:** General Medical and Surgical

> **Staffed Beds:** 583 **Admissions:** 28081 **Census:** 293 **Outpatient Visits:** 1137257 **Births:** 5054 **Total Expense ($000):** 967306 **Payroll Expense ($000):** 395657 **Personnel:** 7121

☐ **TREASURE VALLEY HOSPITAL (130063)**, 8800 West Emerald Street, Zip 83704–8205; tel. 208/373–5000, (Nonreporting) **A**1 9 10
Primary Contact: Nick Genna, Administrator
CMO: Jeffrey Hessing, M.D., Medical Director
CHR: Kathleen Phelps, Director Human Resources
Web address: www.treasurevalleyhospital.com
**Control:** Corporation, Investor–owned, for–profit **Service:** General Medical and Surgical

> **Staffed Beds:** 9

**VETERANS AFFAIRS MEDICAL CENTER** See Boise Veterans Affairs Medical Center

### BONNERS FERRY—Boundary County

★ **BOUNDARY COMMUNITY HOSPITAL (131301)**, 6640 Kaniksu Street, Zip 83805–7532; tel. 208/267–3141, (Includes BOUNDARY COUNTY NURSING HOME ), (Total facility includes 28 beds in nursing home–type unit) **A**9 10 18 **F**3 11 15 35 40 45 50 57 59 65 75 77 79 81 85 87 93 107 110 111 114 119 128 130 133 143 146 148
Primary Contact: Craig A. Johnson, Chief Executive Officer and Chief Financial Officer
COO: Jeffery Perkins, Chief Operating Officer
CFO: Craig A. Johnson, Chief Executive Officer and Chief Financial Officer
CHR: Ann Coughlin, Director Human Resources
CNO: Tari Yourzek, Chief Nursing Officer
Web address: www.boundaryhospital.org
**Control:** County–Government, nonfederal **Service:** General Medical and Surgical

> **Staffed Beds:** 48 **Admissions:** 239 **Census:** 31 **Outpatient Visits:** 20786 **Births:** 0 **Total Expense ($000):** 10929 **Payroll Expense ($000):** 5970 **Personnel:** 144

### BURLEY—Cassia County

⌧ **CASSIA REGIONAL MEDICAL CENTER (131326)**, 1501 Hiland Avenue, Zip 83318–2688; tel. 208/678–4444 **A**1 9 10 18 **F**3 7 8 11 13 15 18 28 29 30 34 35 38 40 41 50 57 59 64 68 70 74 75 76 77 79 81 82 83 85 86 93 97 107 108 110 111 114 119 129 130 131 132 146 147 148 **P**6 **S** Intermountain Healthcare, Inc., Salt Lake City, UT
Primary Contact: Rod Barton, Administrator
CFO: Mark Christensen, Assistant Administrator Finance and Chief Financial Officer
CMO: Fred Wood, M.D., Medical Director
CIO: Carie Call, Director Computer Support
CHR: Keri Perrigot, Assistant Administrator Human Resources
CNO: Michele Pond–Bell, R.N., Administrator Nursing
Web address: www.cassiaregional.org
**Control:** Other not–for–profit (including NFP Corporation) **Service:** General Medical and Surgical

> **Staffed Beds:** 25 **Admissions:** 1678 **Census:** 13 **Outpatient Visits:** 103437 **Births:** 668 **Total Expense ($000):** 41355 **Payroll Expense ($000):** 17454 **Personnel:** 314

### CALDWELL—Canyon County

⌧ **WEST VALLEY MEDICAL CENTER (130014)**, 1717 Arlington, Zip 83605–4802; tel. 208/459–4641, (Nonreporting) **A**1 9 10 **S** HCA, Nashville, TN
Primary Contact: Julie Taylor, Chief Executive Officer
COO: Cory Davis, Chief Operating Officer
CFO: Kate Fowler, Chief Financial Officer
CHR: Senta Cornelius, Director Human Resources
CNO: Edith E. Irving, R.N., Chief Nursing Officer
Web address: www.westvalleymedctr.com
**Control:** Corporation, Investor–owned, for–profit **Service:** General Medical and Surgical

> **Staffed Beds:** 118

### CASCADE—Valley County

★ **CASCADE MEDICAL CENTER (131308)**, 402 Old State Highway, Zip 83611, Mailing Address: P.O. Box 1330, Zip 83611–1330; tel. 208/382–4242 **A**9 10 18 **F**11 29 32 34 40 45 53 57 59 64 65 67 87 89 93 97 102 107 114 127 128 130 131 133 135 147 **P**6
Primary Contact: Virgil Boss, Administrator
CMO: Douglas Hill, M.D., Medical Director
Web address: www.cascademedicalcenter.net
**Control:** Hospital district or authority, Government, nonfederal **Service:** General Medical and Surgical

> **Staffed Beds:** 10 **Admissions:** 21 **Census:** 1 **Outpatient Visits:** 7695 **Births:** 0 **Total Expense ($000):** 3380 **Payroll Expense ($000):** 1869 **Personnel:** 29

### COEUR D'ALENE—Kootenai County

⌧ **KOOTENAI MEDICAL CENTER (130049)**, 2003 Kootenai Health Way, Zip 83814–2677; tel. 208/666–2000, (Includes NORTH IDAHO BEHAVIORAL HEALTH, DIVISION OF KOOTENAI MEDICAL CENTER, 2301 North Ironwood Place, Zip 83814–2650; tel. 208/765–4800) **A**1 2 9 10 19 **F**2 3 4 5 8 11 12 13 15 17 18 20 22 24 26 28 29 30 31 34 35 37 39 40 41 44 45 46 47 48 49 50 53 54 55 56 57 58 59 60 63 64 65 68 70 72 73 74 75 76 77 78 79 81 82 83 84 85 86 87 89 90 91 93 96 97 98 99 100 101 102 104 107 108 110 111 114 115 116 117 118 119 120 121 123 124 126 127 129 130 131 132 134 135 143 144 146 148 **P**2 6
Primary Contact: Jon Ness, Chief Executive Officer
CMO: Joseph Bujak, M.D., Vice President Medical Affairs
CHR: Daniel Klocko, Vice President Human Resources
Web address: www.kmc.org
**Control:** Hospital district or authority, Government, nonfederal **Service:** General Medical and Surgical

> **Staffed Beds:** 254 **Admissions:** 11305 **Census:** 165 **Outpatient Visits:** 328662 **Births:** 1635 **Total Expense ($000):** 290285 **Payroll Expense ($000):** 127190 **Personnel:** 1886

### COTTONWOOD—Idaho County

★ **ST. MARY'S HOSPITAL (131321)**, Lewiston and North Streets, Zip 83522–9750, Mailing Address: P.O. Box 137, Zip 83522–0137; tel. 208/962–3251, (Nonreporting) **A**9 10 18 **S** Essentia Health, Duluth, MN
Primary Contact: Lenne Bonner, Interim Chief Executive Officer
COO: Larry Barker, Chief Operating Officer
CFO: Lenne Bonner, Chief Financial Officer
CHR: Debbie Schumacher, Manager Human Resource
Web address: www.smh–cvhc.org/getpage.php?name=index
**Control:** Other not–for–profit (including NFP Corporation) **Service:** General Medical and Surgical

> **Staffed Beds:** 28

**ID**

*Many Facility Codes have changed. Please refer to the AHA Guide Code Chart.*

© 2013 AHA Guide

## DRIGGS—Teton County

★ **TETON VALLEY HEALTH CARE (131313)**, (Formerly Teton Valley Hospital and Surgicenter), 120 East Howard Street, Zip 83422–5112; tel. 208/354–2383, (Nonreporting) **A**9 10 18
Primary Contact: Keith Gnagey, Chief Executive Officer
CFO: Jason Hotchkiss, Controller
CMO: Chad Horrocks, M.D., Chief of Staff
CIO: Chuck Fischer, Director Information Technology Systems
CHR: Dory Harris, Manager Human Resource
CNO: Angela Booker, Director of Nursing Services
Web address: www.tvhcare.org
**Control:** County–Government, nonfederal **Service:** General Medical and Surgical

**Staffed Beds:** 13

## EMMETT—Gem County

★ **WALTER KNOX MEMORIAL HOSPITAL (131318)**, 1202 East Locust Street, Zip 83617–2715; tel. 208/365–3561, (Nonreporting) **A**9 10 18
Primary Contact: John N. Olson, Chief Executive Officer
CFO: Larry Droppers, Chief Financial Officer
CHR: Susan Vahlberg, Director Employee and Community Relations
Web address: www.wkmh.org
**Control:** County–Government, nonfederal **Service:** General Medical and Surgical

**Staffed Beds:** 16

## GOODING—Gooding County

★ **NORTH CANYON MEDICAL CENTER (131302)**, 267 North Canyon Drive, Zip 83330–5500; tel. 208/934–4433 **A**9 10 18 **F**3 11 15 29 34 35 40 44 45 46 47 48 50 53 57 59 64 68 75 77 81 85 86 87 89 90 93 107 110 114 119 129 130 133 135 146 **S** St. Luke's Health System, Boise, ID
Primary Contact: David Butler, Chief Executive Officer
CFO: Rod Larsen, Chief Financial Officer
CMO: Reid Lofgran, D.O., Chief of Staff
CIO: Paul Castronova, Chief Information Officer
CHR: Sara Otto, Director Human Resources
Web address: www.goodinghospital.org
**Control:** Other not–for–profit (including NFP Corporation) **Service:** General Medical and Surgical

**Staffed Beds:** 15 **Admissions:** 639 **Census:** 6 **Outpatient Visits:** 19920 **Births:** 0 **Total Expense ($000):** 17119 **Payroll Expense ($000):** 4941 **Personnel:** 125

## GRANGEVILLE—Idaho County

★ **SYRINGA HOSPITAL AND CLINICS (131315)**, 607 West Main Street, Zip 83530–1396; tel. 208/983–1700 **A**9 10 18 **F**29 30 34 35 40 45 54 57 63 64 65 76 82 85 91 100 135 147 **P**6 8
Primary Contact: Joseph Cladouhos, Chief Executive Officer
CFO: Betty A. Watson, Chief Financial Officer
CMO: Cheryl Mallory, M.D., Chief Medical Officer
CHR: Katy Eimers, Human Resources Officer
Web address: www.syringahospital.org
**Control:** Hospital district or authority, Government, nonfederal **Service:** General Medical and Surgical

**Staffed Beds:** 16 **Admissions:** 377 **Census:** 4 **Births:** 42 **Personnel:** 44

## IDAHO FALLS—Bonneville County

⊠ **EASTERN IDAHO REGIONAL MEDICAL CENTER (130018)**, 3100 Channing Way, Zip 83404–7533, Mailing Address: P.O. Box 2077, Zip 83403–2077; tel. 208/529–6111, (Total facility includes 16 beds in nursing home–type unit) **A**1 2 9 10 **F**3 7 11 12 13 15 18 20 21 22 23 24 28 29 30 31 34 35 36 39 40 43 44 46 49 50 51 53 57 59 64 65 67 68 70 72 74 75 76 77 78 79 81 82 85 86 87 89 90 91 92 93 98 99 100 102 106 107 108 111 114 115 118 119 120 121 123 128 129 130 131 132 135 146 147 148 **S** HCA, Nashville, TN
Primary Contact: Douglas Crabtree, Chief Executive Officer
COO: Sandee Moore, Chief Operating Officer
CFO: Jeffrey D. Baiocco, Chief Financial Officer
CMO: Todd Williams, M.D., President Medical Staff
CHR: Wendy Andersen, Director Human Resources
CNO: Kathleen Nelson, R.N., Chief Nursing Officer
Web address: www.eirmc.com
**Control:** Corporation, Investor–owned, for–profit **Service:** General Medical and Surgical

**Staffed Beds:** 309 **Admissions:** 11923 **Census:** 175 **Outpatient Visits:** 177537 **Births:** 1628 **Total Expense ($000):** 172559 **Payroll Expense ($000):** 65936 **Personnel:** 1196

**MOUNTAIN VIEW HOSPITAL (130065)**, 2325 Coronado Street, Zip 83404–7407; tel. 208/557–2700, (Nonreporting) **A**9 10
Primary Contact: James Adamson, Chief Executive Officer
COO: Peter Fabrick, Vice President Clinical Operations
CHR: Eilene Horne, Manager Human Resources
Web address: www.mountainviewhospital.org
**Control:** Corporation, Investor–owned, for–profit **Service:** General Medical and Surgical

**Staffed Beds:** 42

## JEROME—Jerome County

★ **ST. LUKE'S JEROME (131310)**, (Formerly St. Benedicts Family Medical Center), 709 North Lincoln Street, Zip 83338–1851, Mailing Address: P.O. Box 586, Zip 83338–0586; tel. 208/324–4301 **A**9 10 18 **F**7 13 15 29 30 32 34 39 40 56 57 59 64 65 68 77 79 81 86 87 97 107 111 119 127 133 146 147 **P**6 **S** St. Luke's Health System, Boise, ID
Primary Contact: Curtis Maier, Administrative Director
CMO: H. Peter Doble, M.D., Director Medical Staff Affairs
CHR: Dee Hartzell, Manager Human Resources
Web address: www.stlukesonline.org/jerome/
**Control:** Other not–for–profit (including NFP Corporation) **Service:** General Medical and Surgical

**Staffed Beds:** 25 **Admissions:** 533 **Census:** 7 **Outpatient Visits:** 38830 **Births:** 189 **Total Expense ($000):** 16521 **Payroll Expense ($000):** 8672 **Personnel:** 158

## KELLOGG—Shoshone County

◇ **SHOSHONE MEDICAL CENTER (131314)**, 25 Jacobs Gulch, Zip 83837–2023; tel. 208/784–1221 **A**9 10 18 21 **F**29 34 40 45 53 57 59 64 77 79 81 94 107 108 111 115 119 129 133 145
Primary Contact: Gary Moore, Chief Executive Officer
CFO: Jerry Brantz, Chief Financial Officer
CMO: Berri Swasand, M.D., Chief of Staff
CIO: Russ Allred, Manager Information Systems
CHR: Joanna Radford, Chief Human Resources Officer
Web address: www.shoshonehealth.com
**Control:** Hospital district or authority, Government, nonfederal **Service:** General Medical and Surgical

**Staffed Beds:** 25 **Admissions:** 436 **Census:** 6 **Outpatient Visits:** 13289 **Total Expense ($000):** 9388 **Payroll Expense ($000):** 4368 **Personnel:** 97

## KETCHUM—Blaine County

⊠ **ST. LUKE'S WOOD RIVER MEDICAL CENTER (131323)**, 100 Hospital Drive, Zip 83340, Mailing Address: P.O. Box 100, Zip 83340–0100; tel. 208/727–8800 **A**1 9 10 18 **F**3 7 8 11 13 15 29 30 31 34 35 36 37 43 45 50 54 57 59 64 68 70 74 75 76 79 81 85 86 97 107 108 110 111 114 119 126 130 131 132 133 134 135 141 143 145 146 147 **S** St. Luke's Health System, Boise, ID
Primary Contact: Cody Langbehn, Chief Executive Officer
CFO: Carl Hollingsworth, Chief Financial Officer
Web address: www.slrmc.org
**Control:** Other not–for–profit (including NFP Corporation) **Service:** General Medical and Surgical

**Staffed Beds:** 25 **Admissions:** 1192 **Census:** 8 **Outpatient Visits:** 78548 **Births:** 234 **Total Expense ($000):** 51679 **Payroll Expense ($000):** 23294 **Personnel:** 316

## LEWISTON—Nez Perce County

⊠ **ST. JOSEPH REGIONAL MEDICAL CENTER (130003)**, 415 Sixth Street, Zip 83501–2431; tel. 208/743–2511 **A**1 2 9 10 **F**11 13 15 18 20 22 30 31 34 35 38 40 41 43 45 46 50 53 54 57 58 59 63 64 68 69 70 71 74 75 76 77 79 81 83 84 86 87 89 91 92 93 94 97 98 100 101 102 103 104 106 107 108 110 111 114 115 116 117 118 119 120 121 124 129 130 132 133 135 144 146 **P**6 **S** Ascension Health, Saint Louis, MO
Primary Contact: Timothy Sayler, President and Chief Executive Officer
CFO: Thomas Safley, Chief Financial Officer
CMO: Jay Hunter, M.D., Chief of Staff
CIO: Collin Lamb, Director Management Information Systems
CHR: Brenda J. Forge, Vice President Human Resources
Web address: www.sjrmc.org
**Control:** Church–operated, Nongovernment, not–for profit **Service:** General Medical and Surgical

**Staffed Beds:** 119 **Admissions:** 4950 **Census:** 63 **Outpatient Visits:** 117201 **Births:** 755

ID

---

**Hospital, Medicare Provider Number, Address, Telephone, Approval, Facility, and Physician Codes, Health Care System**

★ American Hospital Association (AHA) membership
☐ The Joint Commission accreditation ◇ DNV Healthcare Inc. accreditation
○ Healthcare Facilities Accreditation Program
△ Commission on Accreditation of Rehabilitation Facilities (CARF) accreditation

**MALAD CITY—Oneida County**

**ONEIDA COUNTY HOSPITAL (131303)**, 150 North 200 West,
Zip 83252–1239, Mailing Address: Box 126, Zip 83252–0126;
tel. 208/766–2231, (Nonreporting) **A**10 18
Primary Contact: Todd V. Winder, Administrator and Chief Executive Officer
CFO: Cindy Howard, Director Financial Services
CHR: Kathy Hubbard, Manager Human Resources
Web address: www.oneidahospital.com
**Control:** County–Government, nonfederal **Service:** General Medical and Surgical

**Staffed Beds:** 11

**MCCALL—Valley County**

★ **ST. LUKE'S MCCALL (131312)**, 1000 State Street, Zip 83638–3704;
tel. 208/634–2221 **A**5 9 10 18 **F**3 8 9 11 15 30 32 34 35 36 38 40 45 46 50
57 59 64 68 70 76 79 81 85 86 87 93 97 107 115 119 130 132 133 134
135 146 **S** St. Luke's Health System, Boise, ID
Primary Contact: Michael A. Fenello, Chief Executive Officer
CFO: Matt Groenig, Vice President Finance
CHR: Cindy E. Paget, Human Resources Manager
Web address: www.mccallhosp.org
**Control:** Other not–for–profit (including NFP Corporation) **Service:** General
Medical and Surgical

**Staffed Beds:** 15 **Admissions:** 432 **Census:** 3 **Outpatient Visits:** 45289
**Births:** 91 **Total Expense ($000):** 21734 **Payroll Expense ($000):** 11883
**Personnel:** 170

**MERIDIAN—Ada County**

✉ **COMPLEX CARE HOSPITAL OF IDAHO (132002)**, 2131 South Bonito Way,
Zip 83642–1659; tel. 877/801–2244, (Nonreporting) **A**1 10 **S** LifeCare
Management Services, Plano, TX
Primary Contact: Colin O'Sullivan, Administrator
Web address: www.lifecare–hospitals.com
**Control:** Corporation, Investor–owned, for–profit **Service:** Long–Term Acute Care
hospital

**Staffed Beds:** 35

**ST. LUKE'S MERIDIAN MEDICAL CENTER** See St. Luke's Regional Medical
Center, Boise

**MONTPELIER—Bear Lake County**

★ **BEAR LAKE MEMORIAL HOSPITAL (131316)**, 164 South Fifth Street,
Zip 83254–1597; tel. 208/847–1630, (Total facility includes 36 beds in nursing
home–type unit) **A**9 10 18 **F**2 5 10 11 12 18 34 40 45 50 53 56 57 59 60 62
70 75 76 79 81 85 87 93 97 99 101 105 107 114 119 120 126 127 128
133 135 146
Primary Contact: Rodney D. Jacobson, Administrator
Web address: www.blmhospital.com
**Control:** County–Government, nonfederal **Service:** General Medical and Surgical

**Staffed Beds:** 57 **Admissions:** 477 **Census:** 41 **Outpatient Visits:** 4443
**Births:** 94 **Total Expense ($000):** 17460 **Payroll Expense ($000):** 7762
**Personnel:** 146

**MOSCOW—Latah County**

✉ **GRITMAN MEDICAL CENTER (131327)**, 700 South Main Street,
Zip 83843–3056; tel. 208/882–4511 **A**1 9 10 18 **F**3 8 11 13 15 19 28 29 34
35 36 37 40 45 46 49 51 53 54 56 57 59 60 64 65 70 75 76 77 79 81 82
84 85 86 87 89 93 96 107 108 110 111 113 114 119 127 129 130 131 132
135 143 146 147 148 **P**5 **S** QHR, Brentwood, TN
Primary Contact: Kara Besst, President and Chief Executive Officer
CFO: Lisa Mae Wood, Chief Financial Officer
CMO: John Visger, M.D., Chief Medical Staff
CIO: Kane Francetich, Chief Information Officer
CHR: Dennis Cockrell, Director Human Resources
CNO: Deena R. Rauch, R.N., Chief Nursing Officer
Web address: www.gritman.org
**Control:** Other not–for–profit (including NFP Corporation) **Service:** General
Medical and Surgical

**Staffed Beds:** 25 **Admissions:** 1523 **Census:** 13 **Outpatient Visits:** 61505
**Births:** 373 **Total Expense ($000):** 43408 **Payroll Expense ($000):** 19944
**Personnel:** 341

**MOUNTAIN HOME—Elmore County**

★ **ST. LUKE'S ELMORE (131311)**, (Formerly Elmore Medical Center), 895 North
Sixth East Street, Zip 83647–2207, Mailing Address: P.O. Box 1270,
Zip 83647–1270; tel. 208/587–8401, (Total facility includes 38 beds in nursing
home–type unit) **A**9 10 18 **F**3 7 11 13 29 30 34 35 40 45 57 64 75 76 77 81
89 107 111 114 119 127 128 129 130 133 146 **S** St. Luke's Health System,
Boise, ID
Primary Contact: Gregory L. Maurer, Administrator
COO: Betty Van Gheluwe, Chief Operating Officer
CFO: Tricia Senger, Chief Financial Officer
CNO: Debbie Plemmons, MSN, Chief Nursing Officer
Web address: www.elmoremedicalcenter.org
**Control:** Hospital district or authority, Government, nonfederal **Service:** General
Medical and Surgical

**Staffed Beds:** 57 **Admissions:** 652 **Census:** 28 **Outpatient Visits:** 38873
**Births:** 115 **Total Expense ($000):** 22155 **Payroll Expense ($000):** 8917
**Personnel:** 230

**MOUNTAIN HOME AFB—Elmore County**

✉ **U. S. AIR FORCE CLINIC**, 90 Hope Drive, Building 600, Zip 83648–1057;
tel. 208/828–7610, (Nonreporting) **A**1 9 **S** Department of the Air Force,
Washington, DC
Primary Contact: Lieutenant Colonel Gregory W. Carson, Administrator
CFO: Robert Magnuson, Business Operations Flight Chief
CIO: Richard Broemeling, Information Systems Flight Commander
**Control:** Air Force, Government, federal **Service:** General Medical and Surgical

**Staffed Beds:** 10

**NAMPA—Canyon County**

**MERCY MEDICAL CENTER** See Saint Alphonsus Medical Center – Nampa

✉ **SAINT ALPHONSUS MEDICAL CENTER – NAMPA (130013)**, 1512 12th
Avenue Road, Zip 83686–6008; tel. 208/463–5000 **A**1 9 10 **F**3 11 12 13 15
18 20 22 28 29 30 34 35 37 40 43 44 45 49 50 54 55 57 59 64 67 68 69
70 75 76 77 78 79 81 82 85 86 87 89 107 108 110 111 114 115 118 119
126 129 130 132 135 141 143 145 146 147 148 **P**8 **S** Trinity Health,
Livonia, MI
Primary Contact: Karl Keeler, Chief Executive Officer
CFO: Richard Caffrey, Interim Assistant Chief Financial Officer
CIO: Daniel Wright, Director Information Technology
Web address: www.mercynampa.org
**Control:** Church–operated, Nongovernment, not–for profit **Service:** General
Medical and Surgical

**Staffed Beds:** 118 **Admissions:** 5195 **Census:** 41 **Outpatient Visits:** 108723
**Births:** 1144 **Total Expense ($000):** 77012 **Payroll Expense ($000):** 28386
**Personnel:** 671

**OROFINO—Clearwater County**

★ **CLEARWATER VALLEY HOSPITAL AND CLINICS (131320)**, 301 Cedar,
Zip 83544–9029; tel. 208/476–4555, (Nonreporting) **A**9 10 18 **S** Essentia
Health, Duluth, MN
Primary Contact: Lenne Bonner, Interim Chief Executive Officer
COO: Larry Barker, Chief Operating Officer
CFO: Lenne Bonner, Chief Financial Officer
Web address: www.smh–cvhc.org
**Control:** Other not–for–profit (including NFP Corporation) **Service:** General
Medical and Surgical

**Staffed Beds:** 23

**STATE HOSPITAL NORTH**, 300 Hospital Drive, Zip 83544–9034;
tel. 208/476–4511, (Nonreporting)
Primary Contact: Debra Manfull, Interim Chief Executive Officer
CMO: Karla Eisele, M.D., Clinical Director
CIO: James Sarbacher, Chief Information Officer
CHR: Heather Vandenbark, Human Resources Specialist
Web address: www.healthandwelfare.idaho.gov
**Control:** State–Government, nonfederal **Service:** Psychiatric

**Staffed Beds:** 60

ID

*Many Facility Codes have changed. Please refer to the AHA Guide Code Chart.*

## POCATELLO—Bannock County

✠ **PORTNEUF MEDICAL CENTER (130028)**, 777 Hospital Way,
Zip 83201–5175; tel. 208/239–1000 **A**1 2 3 5 9 10 20 **F**3 7 8 11 12 13 14
15 17 18 19 20 22 24 28 29 30 31 34 35 37 39 40 44 45 46 49 50 51 54
56 57 58 59 60 61 64 68 70 71 72 74 75 76 77 78 79 80 81 82 85 86 87
88 89 90 93 96 97 98 100 101 102 103 104 105 107 108 109 110 111 114
115 116 117 118 119 121 123 126 129 130 132 135 143 144 146 147 148
**P**6 **S** LHP Hospital Group, Plano, TX
Primary Contact: John Abreu, Interim Chief executive Officer
CFO: John Abreu, Vice President and Chief Financial Officer
CHR: Scott Lowe, Administrative Director Human Resources
CNO: Michael E. Zielaskiewicz, R.N., Vice President Patient Care Services and
Chief Nursing Officer
Web address: www.portmed.org
**Control:** Corporation, Investor–owned, for–profit **Service:** General Medical and
Surgical

**Staffed Beds:** 175 **Admissions:** 8878 **Census:** 91 **Outpatient Visits:** 192879
**Births:** 1556 **Total Expense ($000):** 180028 **Payroll Expense ($000):**
72592 **Personnel:** 1096

**SAFE HAVEN HOSPITAL OF POCATELLO (134011)**, 1200 Hospital Way,
Zip 83201–2708; tel. 208/232–2570, (Total facility includes 75 beds in nursing
home–type unit) **A**10 **F**98 101 102 103 104 130 143 **P**6
Primary Contact: Josiah Dahlstrom, Administrator
Web address: www.safehavenhealthcare.org/safehaven_hospital/index.html
**Control:** Partnership, Investor–owned, for–profit **Service:** Psychiatric

**Staffed Beds:** 87 **Admissions:** 638 **Census:** 77 **Outpatient Visits:** 0 **Births:**
0

## POST FALLS—Kootenai County

☐ **NORTHERN IDAHO ADVANCED CARE HOSPITAL (132001)**, 600 North Cecil
Road, Zip 83854–6200; tel. 208/262–2800, (Nonreporting) **A**1 9 10 **S** Ernest
Health, Inc., Albuquerque, NM
Primary Contact: Maria Godley, R.N., Chief Executive Officer
Web address: www.niach.ernesthealth.com
**Control:** Corporation, Investor–owned, for–profit **Service:** Long–Term Acute Care
hospital

**Staffed Beds:** 40

☐ **NORTHWEST SPECIALTY HOSPITAL (130066)**, 1593 East Polston Avenue,
Zip 83854–5326; tel. 208/262–2300, (Nonreporting) **A**1 9 10 **S** National
Surgical Hospitals, Chicago, IL
Primary Contact: Vaughn Ward, Chief Executive Officer
Web address: www.northwestspecialtyhospital.com
**Control:** Corporation, Investor–owned, for–profit **Service:** Surgical

**Staffed Beds:** 22

## PRESTON—Franklin County

★ **FRANKLIN COUNTY MEDICAL CENTER (131322)**, 44 North First East Street,
Zip 83263–1399; tel. 208/852–0137, (Nonreporting) **A**9 10 18
Primary Contact: Michael G. Andrus, Administrator and Chief Executive Officer
CFO: Paul Smart, CPA, Chief Financial Officer
CHR: Courtney Dursteler, Chief Human Resources Officer
CNO: LuAnn Nielsen, R.N., Chief Nursing Officer
Web address: www.fcmc.org
**Control:** County–Government, nonfederal **Service:** General Medical and Surgical

**Staffed Beds:** 65

## REXBURG—Madison County

★ ◇ **MADISON MEMORIAL HOSPITAL (130025)**, 450 East Main Street,
Zip 83440–2048, Mailing Address: P.O. Box 310, Zip 83440–0310;
tel. 208/359–6900 **A**9 10 21 **F**3 8 11 13 15 29 30 31 34 35 40 41 45 49
59 65 66 68 70 72 74 75 76 77 78 79 81 82 85 86 87 89 91 93 96 107
108 111 115 118 119 130 146 147 148 **P**8
Primary Contact: Rachel Ann Gonzales, MSN, R.N., Chief Executive Officer
CFO: Cecil Ricks, Interim Chief Financial Officer
CMO: Clay C. Prince, Chief Medical Officer
CNO: Terry Conrad, R.N., Interim CNO
Web address: www.madisonhospital.org
**Control:** County–Government, nonfederal **Service:** General Medical and Surgical

**Staffed Beds:** 69 **Admissions:** 4490 **Census:** 23 **Outpatient Visits:** 24069
**Births:** 1486 **Total Expense ($000):** 48634 **Payroll Expense ($000):** 18498
**Personnel:** 401

## RUPERT—Minidoka County

★ **MINIDOKA MEMORIAL HOSPITAL (131319)**, 1224 Eighth Street,
Zip 83350–1599; tel. 208/436–0481, (Total facility includes 46 beds in nursing
home type unit) **A**9 10 18 **F**3 7 11 15 18 29 30 34 35 37 40 45 50 56 57 59
62 63 64 65 68 70 75 77 79 81 83 84 85 86 87 97 107 108 111 114 119
127 128 130 131 132 133 134 143 146 147 148 **P**1 3 5
Primary Contact: Carl Hanson, Administrator
COO: Joel Rogers, Chief Operating Officer
CFO: Jason Gibbons, Chief Financial Officer
CMO: Jeff Swenson, M.D., Chief of Staff
CHR: Tammy Hanks, Director Human Resources
Web address: www.minidokamemorial.com
**Control:** County–Government, nonfederal **Service:** General Medical and Surgical

**Staffed Beds:** 74 **Admissions:** 640 **Census:** 49 **Outpatient Visits:** 14920
**Births:** 0 **Total Expense ($000):** 20833 **Payroll Expense ($000):** 9604
**Personnel:** 201

**MINIDOKA MEMORIAL HOSPITAL AND EXTENDED CARE FACILITY** See
Minidoka Memorial Hospital

## SAINT MARIES—Benewah County

★ **BENEWAH COMMUNITY HOSPITAL (131317)**, 229 South Seventh Street,
Zip 83861–1803; tel. 208/245–5551 **A**9 10 18 **F**8 13 29 30 31 34 35 40 45
57 59 64 75 76 78 79 81 82 84 85 92 93 97 99 100 101 103 104 107 111
114 119 127 129 131 133 135 146 **P**6 **S** QHR, Brentwood, TN
Primary Contact: Christopher Noland, FACHE, Interim Chief Executive Officer
COO: Debbie S. Kerns, Director Human Resources and Chief Operating Officer
CFO: Lori Stoltz, Chief Financial Officer
CMO: Richard Thurston, M.D., Chief of Staff
CHR: Debbie S. Kerns, Director Human Resources and Chief Operating Officer
CNO: Kim Wilson, Director of Nursing
Web address: www.bchmed.org
**Control:** County–Government, nonfederal **Service:** General Medical and Surgical

**Staffed Beds:** 19 **Admissions:** 386 **Census:** 3 **Outpatient Visits:** 18542
**Births:** 50 **Total Expense ($000):** 17974 **Payroll Expense ($000):** 6522

## SALMON—Lemhi County

★ **STEELE MEMORIAL MEDICAL CENTER (131305)**, 203 South Daisy Street,
Zip 83467–4709; tel. 208/756–5600 **A**9 10 18 **F**3 11 13 15 28 29 31 34 35
40 45 55 57 59 64 65 66 68 75 76 77 78 79 81 82 85 86 87 90 93 97 104
107 111 115 119 127 129 131 132 133 135 145 146 148 **P**6 **S** QHR,
Brentwood, TN
Primary Contact: Jeff Hill, Chief Executive Officer
COO: Abner King, Chief Operating Officer
CFO: Gregory Hexum, Chief Financial Officer
CMO: Adam Deutchman, M.D., Chief of Staff
CNO: Stephanie Orr, R.N., Chief Nursing Officer
Web address: www.steelemh.org
**Control:** County–Government, nonfederal **Service:** General Medical and Surgical

**Staffed Beds:** 18 **Admissions:** 370 **Census:** 3 **Outpatient Visits:** 27137
**Births:** 34 **Total Expense ($000):** 11146 **Payroll Expense ($000):** 6049
**Personnel:** 130

## SANDPOINT—Bonner County

✠ **BONNER GENERAL HOSPITAL (131328)**, 520 North Third Avenue,
Zip 83864–1507, Mailing Address: Box 1448, Zip 83864–0877;
tel. 208/263–1441 **A**1 9 10 18 **F**3 11 13 15 17 22 26 28 29 30 34 35 40 45
46 47 48 54 57 59 62 63 64 68 75 76 77 79 81 85 86 87 93 102 107 108
110 111 114 118 119 130 131 132 142 144 146 **P**8
Primary Contact: Sheryl Rickard, Chief Executive Officer
CFO: Norilina Harvel, Chief Financial Officer
CIO: Bob Hess, Chief Information Officer
CHR: Brad Waterbury, Director Human Resources
CNO: Linda Rammler, R.N., Chief Nursing Officer
Web address: www.bonnergeneral.org/index.php
**Control:** Other not–for–profit (including NFP Corporation) **Service:** General
Medical and Surgical

**Staffed Beds:** 25 **Admissions:** 1616 **Census:** 13 **Outpatient Visits:** 57426
**Births:** 335 **Total Expense ($000):** 40787 **Payroll Expense ($000):** 16956
**Personnel:** 288

**ID**

---

**Hospital, Medicare Provider Number, Address, Telephone, Approval, Facility, and Physician Codes, Health Care System**

★ American Hospital Association (AHA) membership
☐ The Joint Commission accreditation
◇ DNV Healthcare Inc. accreditation
○ Healthcare Facilities Accreditation Program
△ Commission on Accreditation of Rehabilitation Facilities (CARF) accreditation

## SODA SPRINGS—Caribou County

★ **CARIBOU MEMORIAL HOSPITAL AND LIVING CENTER (131309)**, 300 South Third West, Zip 83276–1598; tel. 208/547–3341, (Total facility includes 30 beds in nursing home–type unit) **A**9 10 18 **F**11 13 18 29 34 40 57 59 70 76 79 81 82 85 93 100 107 119 127 128 130 133 143 148
Primary Contact: John L. Hoopes, Chief Executive Officer
CFO: Leota Carver, Chief Financial Officer
CMO: John K. Franson, M.D., Chief Medical Staff
CIO: Kathey Peck, Manager Health Information
CHR: Michael D. Peck, Assistant Administrator
Web address: www.cariboumemorial.org
**Control:** County–Government, nonfederal **Service:** General Medical and Surgical

| | |
|---|---|
| **Staffed Beds:** 55 **Admissions:** 365 **Census:** 24 **Outpatient Visits:** 11603 **Births:** 28 **Total Expense ($000):** 11041 **Personnel:** 156 | |

## TWIN FALLS—Twin Falls County

✠ **ST. LUKE'S MAGIC VALLEY MEDICAL CENTER (130002)**, 801 Pole Line Road West, Zip 83301–5810, Mailing Address: P.O. Box 409, Zip 83303–0409; tel. 208/814–0000 **A**1 2 5 9 10 **F**3 4 5 7 8 11 13 15 18 20 22 29 30 31 35 40 57 62 63 68 70 72 76 77 78 79 81 85 87 89 90 93 96 98 107 110 111 114 119 130 146 **S** St. Luke's Health System, Boise, ID
Primary Contact: James L. Angle, FACHE, Chief Executive Officer
Web address: www.stlukesonline.org
**Control:** Other not–for–profit (including NFP Corporation) **Service:** General Medical and Surgical

| | |
|---|---|
| **Staffed Beds:** 197 **Admissions:** 9574 **Census:** 99 **Outpatient Visits:** 527386 **Births:** 1675 **Total Expense ($000):** 242921 **Payroll Expense ($000):** 77991 **Personnel:** 1832 | |

## WEISER—Washington County

★ ◇ **WEISER MEMORIAL HOSPITAL (131307)**, 645 East Fifth Street, Zip 83672–2202; tel. 208/549–0370, (Nonreporting) **A**9 10 18 21 **S** St. Luke's Health System, Boise, ID
Primary Contact: Tom Murphy, Chief Executive Officer
CFO: Nate Coburn, Chief Financial Officer
CMO: Suzanna D. Hubele, M.D., Chief of Staff
CHR: Terri Kautz, Manager Human Resources
CNO: Reuben J. DeKastle, Chief Nursing Officer
Web address: www.weisermemorialhospital.org
**Control:** Hospital district or authority, Government, nonfederal **Service:** General Medical and Surgical

| | |
|---|---|
| **Staffed Beds:** 25 | |

**ID**

*Many Facility Codes have changed. Please refer to the AHA Guide Code Chart.*
© 2013 AHA Guide

# ILLINOIS

## ALEDO—Mercer County

★ **MERCER COUNTY HOSPITAL (141304)**, 409 N.W. Ninth Avenue,
Zip 61231–1296; tel. 309/582–5301 **A**9 10 18 **F**3 11 15 29 30 34 35 40 45
54 56 57 59 64 69 77 79 81 85 87 93 97 107 108 114 119 127 128 130
131 133 146 147 **S** Genesis Health System, Davenport, IA
Primary Contact: Ted Rogalski, Chief Executive Officer
COO: Myron Higgins, Chief Operating Officer
CFO: Sandy Moore, Interim CFO
CMO: Dennis Palmer, D.O., Chief of Staff
CIO: Marcia Kelly, Manager, IT
CHR: Myron Higgins, Chief Operating Officer
CNO: Shelley Wiborg, MS, Chief Nursing Officer
Web address: www.mercerhospital.org
**Control:** County–Government, nonfederal **Service:** General Medical and Surgical

**Staffed Beds:** 22 **Admissions:** 313 **Census:** 4 **Outpatient Visits:** 33800
**Births:** 0 **Total Expense ($000):** 12410 **Payroll Expense ($000):** 5586
**Personnel:** 115

## ALTON—Madison County

⊠ **ALTON MEMORIAL HOSPITAL (140002)**, One Memorial Drive,
Zip 62002–6722; tel. 618/463–7311, (Total facility includes 88 beds in nursing
home–type unit) **A**1 9 10 **F**3 6 7 11 13 15 18 20 22 29 30 31 34 35 38 39 40
45 46 49 50 56 57 59 64 70 74 75 76 77 78 79 81 85 86 87 89 92 93 96
98 103 104 107 108 110 111 114 115 116 117 118 119 120 121 123 128
129 131 132 146 148 **S** BJC HealthCare, Saint Louis, MO
Primary Contact: David A. Braasch, President
COO: Doug Pytlinski, Vice President Administration
CFO: Brad Goacher, Director Finance
CMO: David Burnside, M.D., Chief Medical Officer
CIO: David Weiss, Vice President Information System
CHR: Tina Kristoff, Manager Human Resources
Web address: www.altonmemorialhospital.org
**Control:** Other not–for–profit (including NFP Corporation) **Service:** General
Medical and Surgical

**Staffed Beds:** 253 **Admissions:** 6998 **Census:** 140 **Outpatient Visits:**
136351 **Births:** 637 **Total Expense ($000):** 124848 **Payroll Expense
($000):** 45918 **Personnel:** 715

☐ **ALTON MENTAL HEALTH CENTER (144016)**, 4500 College Avenue,
Zip 62002–5099; tel. 618/474–3800, (Nonreporting) **A**1 10 **S** Division of Mental
Health, Department of Human Services, Springfield, IL
Primary Contact: Brian E. Thomas, Administrator
CFO: Susan Shobe, Director Administration and Support Services
CMO: Claudia Kachigion, M.D., Medical Director
**Control:** State–Government, nonfederal **Service:** Psychiatric

**Staffed Beds:** 165

⊠ **SAINT ANTHONY'S HEALTH CENTER (140052)**, 1 Saint Anthony's Way,
Zip 62002–4579, Mailing Address: P.O. Box 340, Zip 62002–0340;
tel. 618/465–2571, (Includes SAINT CLARE'S HOSPITAL, 915 East Fifth Street,
Zip 62002–6434; tel. 618/463–5151), (Total facility includes 26 beds in nursing
home–type unit) **A**1 2 9 10 **F**2 3 5 10 11 13 15 18 20 22 26 29 30 31 32 34
35 36 37 38 39 40 41 44 45 46 47 48 49 50 51 54 56 57 58 59 61 62 63
64 65 70 74 75 76 78 79 81 82 84 85 86 87 89 90 91 92 93 94 95 96 99
100 101 102 104 107 108 110 111 114 115 117 119 120 121 123 128
129 130 131 132 134 135 146 147 148 **P**6
Primary Contact: Evert J. Kuiper, President & Chief Executive Officer
CFO: Mike Nelson, Chief Financial Officer
CMO: Larry Burch, M.D., Vice President Medical Affairs
CIO: Michael Russo, Chief Administrative Officer
CHR: Sister Mary Mikela, Vice President Mission Stewardship
Web address: www.sahc.org
**Control:** Church–operated, Nongovernment, not–for profit **Service:** General
Medical and Surgical

**Staffed Beds:** 199 **Admissions:** 4520 **Census:** 64 **Outpatient Visits:** 132219
**Births:** 389 **Total Expense ($000):** 75271 **Payroll Expense ($000):** 30203
**Personnel:** 536

## ANNA—Union County

☐ **CHOATE MENTAL HEALTH CENTER (144038)**, 1000 North Main Street,
Zip 62906–1699; tel. 618/833–5161, (Nonreporting) **A**1 10 **S** Division of Mental
Health, Department of Human Services, Springfield, IL
Primary Contact: Elaine Ray, Administrator
COO: Elaine Ray, Administrator
CMO: John Larcas, M.D., Acting Medical Director
CIO: Cindy Flamm, Manager Quality
CHR: Tammy Tellor, Acting Director Human Resources
**Control:** State–Government, nonfederal **Service:** Psychiatric

**Staffed Beds:** 79

⊠ **UNION COUNTY HOSPITAL (141342)**, 517 North Main Street,
Zip 62906–1696; tel. 618/833–4511, (Total facility includes 22 beds in nursing
home–type unit) **A**1 9 10 18 **F**3 11 15 28 29 30 34 35 40 45 49 50 57 59 64
68 75 77 81 85 87 93 97 107 110 114 119 127 130 133 146 148 **P**6
**S** Community Health Systems, Inc., Franklin, TN
Primary Contact: James R. Farris, FACHE, Chief Executive Officer
COO: Jeanette L. Hook, R.N., Chief Nursing Officer
CFO: Terry Paligo, Chief Financial Officer
CMO: Christine Lucas, M.D., Chief of Staff
CIO: John Hegger, Director Information Systems
CHR: Tammy Samuels, Director Human Resources
Web address: www.unioncountyhospital.com
**Control:** Corporation, Investor–owned, for–profit **Service:** General Medical and
Surgical

**Staffed Beds:** 47 **Admissions:** 772 **Census:** 26 **Outpatient Visits:** 31584
**Births:** 3 **Total Expense ($000):** 16600 **Payroll Expense ($000):** 8251
**Personnel:** 157

## ARLINGTON HEIGHTS—Cook County

⊠ **NORTHWEST COMMUNITY HOSPITAL (140252)**, 800 West Central Road,
Zip 60005–2392; tel. 847/618–1000 **A**1 2 9 10 **F**3 4 5 13 15 17 18 20 22 24
25 26 28 29 30 31 32 34 35 37 38 39 40 41 43 44 45 46 47 49 50 54 55
56 57 59 61 62 63 64 65 66 68 70 71 72 73 74 75 76 77 78 79 81 82 84
85 86 87 89 90 92 93 96 98 99 100 101 102 103 104 105 106 107 108
110 111 114 115 116 117 118 119 120 121 123 124 126 129 130 131 132
135 144 145 146 147 148 **P**5 8
Primary Contact: Bruce K. Crowther, President and Chief Executive Officer
COO: Michael B. Zenn, Executive Vice President, Chief Operating Officer and Chief
Financial Officer
CFO: Michael B. Zenn, Executive Vice President, Chief Operating Officer and Chief
Financial Officer
CMO: Leighton B. Smith, M.D., Vice President Medical Affairs
CIO: George Morris, Vice President Information Technology and Chief Information
Officer
CHR: Mark Lusson, Vice President Human Resources
Web address: www.nch.org
**Control:** Other not–for–profit (including NFP Corporation) **Service:** General
Medical and Surgical

**Staffed Beds:** 386 **Admissions:** 21356 **Census:** 238 **Outpatient Visits:**
358339 **Births:** 2908 **Total Expense ($000):** 430363 **Payroll Expense
($000):** 188467 **Personnel:** 2897

## AURORA—Du Page and Kane Counties

⊠ **PRESENCE MERCY MEDICAL CENTER (140174)**, (Formerly Provena Mercy
Medical Center), 1325 North Highland Avenue, Zip 60506–1449;
tel. 630/859–2222 **A**1 2 9 10 **F**3 5 12 13 15 18 20 22 24 26 28 29 30 31 34
35 36 38 40 45 46 49 56 57 59 61 65 68 70 73 75 76 77 78 79 81 82 85
86 87 93 97 98 99 100 101 102 103 104 105 107 111 114 115 119 125
130 132 135 144 146 147 **P**5 **S** Presence Health, Chicago, IL
Primary Contact: Maureen A. Bryant, FACHE, President and Chief Executive Officer
COO: Mary Vonderau, Vice President Strategy and Operations
CHR: Diane Hargreaves, Vice President Human Resources
Web address: www.provena.org/mercy/
**Control:** Other not–for–profit (including NFP Corporation) **Service:** General
Medical and Surgical

**Staffed Beds:** 123 **Admissions:** 9829 **Census:** 123 **Outpatient Visits:**
269976 **Births:** 609 **Total Expense ($000):** 183240 **Payroll Expense
($000):** 57100 **Personnel:** 887

**PROVENA MERCY MEDICAL CENTER** See Presence Mercy Medical Center

✉ △ **RUSH–COPLEY MEDICAL CENTER (140029)**, 2000 Ogden Avenue, Zip 60504–7222; tel. 630/978–6200 **A**1 2 3 5 7 9 10 **F**3 7 9 13 15 17 18 19 20 22 24 25 28 29 30 31 32 34 35 36 37 38 39 40 42 43 44 45 46 47 49 50 51 52 53 54 55 56 57 58 59 60 61 62 64 65 66 68 70 72 73 74 75 76 77 78 79 81 82 84 85 86 87 89 90 92 93 96 97 99 104 107 108 110 111 114 115 117 118 119 120 121 123 130 131 132 134 135 143 144 145 146 147 148 **P**6 **S** Rush University Medical Center, Chicago, IL
Primary Contact: Barry C. Finn, President and Chief Executive Officer
COO: John A. Diederich, Senior Vice President Operations and Chief Operating Officer
CFO: Brenda VanWyhe, Senior Vice President Finance and Chief Financial Officer
CMO: Steve B. Lowenthal, M.D., Senior Vice President Medical Affairs and Chief Medical Officer
CIO: Dennis DeMasie, Vice President Information Systems and Chief Information Officer
CHR: Darla Mullner, Director Human Resources
CNO: Mary Shilkaitis, Vice President Patient Care and Chief Nursing Officer
Web address: www.rushcopley.com
**Control:** Other not–for–profit (including NFP Corporation) **Service:** General Medical and Surgical

**Staffed Beds:** 210 **Admissions:** 12950 **Census:** 151 **Outpatient Visits:** 196230 **Births:** 3172 **Total Expense ($000):** 242125 **Payroll Expense ($000):** 96132 **Personnel:** 1478

### BARRINGTON—Lake County

✉ ◇ **ADVOCATE GOOD SHEPHERD HOSPITAL (140291)**, 450 West Highway 22, Zip 60010–1919; tel. 847/381–0123 **A**1 2 9 10 21 **F**3 11 12 13 15 17 18 19 20 22 24 26 28 29 30 31 34 35 36 37 40 43 45 46 47 48 49 54 57 59 63 64 65 68 70 74 75 76 77 78 79 81 82 84 87 89 91 92 93 94 97 100 101 102 103 104 105 107 110 111 114 115 118 119 120 121 123 126 129 130 132 135 146 **P**8 **S** Advocate Health Care, Downers Grove, IL
Primary Contact: Karen A. Lambert, President
COO: Doug Ryder, Vice President Clinical Operations and Service Lines
CFO: George Teufel, Vice President Finance
CMO: Barry Rosen, M.D., Vice President Medical Management
CIO: Adem Arslani, Director Information Systems
CHR: Robert F. Scott, Vice President Human Resources
Web address: www.advocatehealth.com/gshp/
**Control:** Church–operated, Nongovernment, not–for profit **Service:** General Medical and Surgical

**Staffed Beds:** 169 **Admissions:** 9750 **Census:** 98 **Outpatient Visits:** 223822 **Births:** 1421 **Total Expense ($000):** 219302 **Payroll Expense ($000):** 76093 **Personnel:** 751

### BELLEVILLE—St. Clair County

★ ○ **MEMORIAL HOSPITAL (140185)**, 4500 Memorial Drive, Zip 62226–5399; tel. 618/233–7750, (Total facility includes 70 beds in nursing home–type unit) **A**9 10 11 **F**3 11 13 15 18 20 22 24 26 28 29 30 31 34 39 40 45 46 49 51 53 54 57 59 60 62 64 70 71 74 75 76 77 79 81 82 84 85 86 87 89 92 93 94 96 107 108 110 111 112 114 115 118 119 128 129 130 131 132 135 145 146 147 148 **P**6 8
Primary Contact: Mark J. Turner, President and Chief Executive Officer
COO: Michael T. McManus, Chief Operating Officer
CFO: Amy Thomas, Vice President Finance
CMO: William Casperson, M.D., Vice President Medical Affairs
CIO: Jennifer Meinkoth, Chief Information Officer
CHR: John C. Ziegler, FACHE, Vice Presidnet Human Resources
CNO: Nancy R. Weston, R.N., Vice President Nursing Services
Web address: www.memhosp.com
**Control:** Other not–for–profit (including NFP Corporation) **Service:** General Medical and Surgical

**Staffed Beds:** 345 **Admissions:** 17364 **Census:** 246 **Outpatient Visits:** 338088 **Births:** 1545 **Total Expense ($000):** 241715 **Payroll Expense ($000):** 105097 **Personnel:** 2302

✉ △ **ST. ELIZABETH'S HOSPITAL (140187)**, 211 South Third Street, Zip 62220–1998; tel. 618/234–2120 **A**1 3 5 7 9 10 **F**3 4 5 11 13 15 18 20 22 24 26 28 29 30 35 39 40 45 50 53 54 56 57 59 60 64 65 68 70 74 75 76 77 78 79 81 82 85 86 87 90 93 97 98 100 101 102 103 104 105 107 108 111 115 116 117 118 119 121 124 129 130 131 132 135 144 146 147 148 **P**6 8 **S** Hospital Sisters Health System, Springfield, IL
Primary Contact: Maryann Reese, R.N., FACHE, President and Chief Executive Officer
CFO: Leslie Eckert, Chief Financial Officer
CMO: Shelly Harkins, M.D., Chief Medical Officer
CIO: Dana Stephens, Director Information Technology
CHR: Margaret Dolan, Director People Services
CNO: Shelley Harris, MSN, Chief Nursing Officer
Web address: www.steliz.org
**Control:** Church–operated, Nongovernment, not–for profit **Service:** General Medical and Surgical

**Staffed Beds:** 260 **Admissions:** 11380 **Census:** 126 **Outpatient Visits:** 176824 **Births:** 1058 **Total Expense ($000):** 163387 **Payroll Expense ($000):** 56062 **Personnel:** 1118

### BENTON—Franklin County

★ **FRANKLIN HOSPITAL DISTRICT (141321)**, 201 Bailey Lane, Zip 62812–1969; tel. 618/439–3161 **A**9 10 18 **F**11 15 29 30 34 35 40 45 56 57 59 66 75 77 81 93 97 107 114 119 127 132 133 **P**6 **S** Alliant Management Services, Louisville, KY
Primary Contact: Hervey E. Davis, Chief Executive Officer
COO: Michael J. Budnick, FACHE, Chief Operating Officer and Clinic Manager
CFO: Howard Schou, Chief Financial Officer
CMO: David Hartman, M.D., Chief of Staff
CIO: David Williams, Director Information Technology
CHR: Nancy Seibert, Director Human Resources
CNO: Terri Hermann, R.N., Chief Nursing Officer
Web address: www.franklinhospital.net
**Control:** Hospital district or authority, Government, nonfederal **Service:** General Medical and Surgical

**Staffed Beds:** 25 **Admissions:** 290 **Census:** 3 **Outpatient Visits:** 21808 **Births:** 0 **Total Expense ($000):** 9276 **Payroll Expense ($000):** 6792 **Personnel:** 149

### BERWYN—Cook County

✉ **UNITYHEALTH MACNEAL HOSPITAL (140054)**, (Formerly MacNeal Hospital), 3249 South Oak Park Avenue, Zip 60402–0715; tel. 708/783–9100 **A**1 2 3 5 8 9 10 13 **F**3 5 13 15 18 19 20 22 24 26 28 29 30 31 34 35 37 40 43 45 46 47 49 50 54 56 57 58 59 64 65 68 70 73 74 75 76 78 79 81 82 84 85 86 87 89 92 93 96 97 98 100 101 102 103 104 105 107 108 110 111 114 117 119 120 121 126 130 131 132 146 147 148 **P**5 8 **S** Vanguard Health Systems, Nashville, TN
Primary Contact: J. Scott Steiner, Interim Chief Executive Officer
COO: J. Scott Steiner, Chief Operating Officer
CFO: Michael A. Lawrence, Chief Financial Officer
CMO: Charles Bareis, M.D., Medical Director
CIO: Nora Ellis, Market Chief Information Officer
CHR: Maggie Shontz, VP, Human Resources
Web address: www.macneal.com
**Control:** Corporation, Investor–owned, for–profit **Service:** General Medical and Surgical

**Staffed Beds:** 371 **Admissions:** 16903 **Census:** 219 **Outpatient Visits:** 202717 **Births:** 1884 **Total Expense ($000):** 197961 **Payroll Expense ($000):** 99698 **Personnel:** 2198

### BLOOMINGTON—Mclean County

✉ **OSF ST. JOSEPH MEDICAL CENTER (140162)**, 2200 East Washington Street, Zip 61701–4323; tel. 309/662–3311, (Total facility includes 12 beds in nursing home–type unit) **A**1 2 9 10 **F**3 11 12 13 15 18 20 22 24 28 29 30 31 34 35 37 40 43 45 49 50 51 54 57 59 60 61 64 65 66 68 70 74 75 76 77 78 79 81 82 84 85 86 87 89 92 93 96 97 107 108 110 111 114 115 118 119 127 128 130 131 132 135 144 146 147 148 **P**6 **S** OSF Healthcare System, Peoria, IL
Primary Contact: Kenneth J. Natzke, President and Chief Executive Officer
COO: Lawrence E. Wills, Vice President Operations
CFO: John R. Zell, Chief Financial Officer
CMO: Paul E. Pedersen, M.D., Vice President and Chief Medical Officer
CHR: Sue A. Herriott, Director Human Resources
Web address: www.osfstjoseph.org
**Control:** Church–operated, Nongovernment, not–for profit **Service:** General Medical and Surgical

**Staffed Beds:** 149 **Admissions:** 6839 **Census:** 69 **Outpatient Visits:** 349702 **Births:** 1081 **Total Expense ($000):** 147177 **Payroll Expense ($000):** 66492 **Personnel:** 893

### BLUE ISLAND—Cook County

✉ **METROSOUTH MEDICAL CENTER (140118)**, 12935 South Gregory Street, Zip 60406–2470; tel. 708/597–2000, (Nonreporting) **A**1 9 10 **S** Community Health Systems, Inc., Franklin, TN
Primary Contact: Enrique Beckmann, M.D., Ph.D., President and Chief Executive Officer
COO: Barbara Fideli, Chief Operating Officer, Non–clinical Services
CFO: Pamela Cassara, Chief Financial Officer
CMO: Enrique Beckmann, M.D., President and Chief Executive Officer
CIO: Bashirat Hahn, Chief Information Officer
CHR: Jackie Montgomery, Director Human Resources
CNO: Linda M. St. Julien, R.N., Chief Nursing Officer and Chief Operating Officer of Clinical Services
Web address: www.metrosouthmedicalcenter.com
**Control:** Corporation, Investor–owned, for–profit **Service:** General Medical and Surgical

**Staffed Beds:** 180

*Many Facility Codes have changed. Please refer to the AHA Guide Code Chart.* © 2013 AHA Guide

IL

## BOLINGBROOK—Will County

✠ **ADVENTIST BOLINGBROOK HOSPITAL (140304)**, 500 Remington Boulevard, Zip 60440–4906; tel. 630/312–5000 **A**1 9 10 **F**3 11 12 13 15 18 20 22 28 29 30 31 33 34 35 36 37 39 40 43 45 46 47 49 50 51 52 54 56 57 58 59 60 61 64 65 66 68 70 73 74 75 76 78 79 81 82 85 86 87 92 93 96 107 108 110 111 114 115 119 129 130 131 132 145 146 147 **P**7 8 **S** Adventist Health System Sunbelt Health Care Corporation, Altamonte Springs, FL
Primary Contact: Rick Mace, Chief Executive Officer
CFO: Mike Murrill, Vice President and Chief Financial Officer
CMO: Richard Carroll, M.D., Chief Medical officer
CIO: John McLendon, Senior Vice President and Chief Information Officer
CNO: Jolene Albaugh, R.N., Vice President and Chief Nursing Officer
Web address: www.keepingyouwell.com/abh/
**Control:** Church–operated, Nongovernment, not–for profit **Service:** General Medical and Surgical

**Staffed Beds:** 148 **Admissions:** 5419 **Census:** 50 **Outpatient Visits:** 82098
**Births:** 925 **Total Expense ($000):** 96633 **Payroll Expense ($000):** 32878
**Personnel:** 568

## BREESE—Clinton County

✠ **ST. JOSEPH'S HOSPITAL (140145)**, 9515 Holy Cross Lane, Zip 62230–3618; tel. 618/526–4511 **A**1 9 10 **F**3 11 15 28 29 30 32 34 35 40 43 50 53 56 57 59 68 70 76 79 81 85 89 93 103 107 108 110 111 115 118 119 127 129 130 131 132 134 135 144 146 148 **S** Hospital Sisters Health System, Springfield, IL
Primary Contact: Mark D. Klosterman, FACHE, President and Chief Executive Officer
CFO: John Jeffries, Chief Financial Officer
CHR: Kathryn Mines, Director Human Resources
Web address: www.stjoebreese.com
**Control:** Church–operated, Nongovernment, not–for profit **Service:** General Medical and Surgical

**Staffed Beds:** 47 **Admissions:** 1509 **Census:** 11 **Outpatient Visits:** 94521
**Births:** 530 **Total Expense ($000):** 42225 **Payroll Expense ($000):** 14288
**Personnel:** 309

## CANTON—Fulton County

✠ **GRAHAM HOSPITAL (140001)**, 210 West Walnut Street, Zip 61520–2497; tel. 309/647–5240, (Total facility includes 50 beds in nursing home–type unit) **A**1 6 9 10 20 **F**3 10 11 13 15 26 28 29 30 32 34 35 40 45 50 53 54 56 57 59 62 63 64 65 67 70 75 76 77 79 81 82 85 87 89 91 93 97 107 108 110 111 115 119 124 127 128 129 130 131 132 135 143 144 145 146 **P**3
Primary Contact: Robert G. Senneff, FACHE, President and Chief Executive Officer
CFO: Jim Stratton, Vice President Finance
Web address: www.grahamhospital.org
**Control:** Other not–for–profit (including NFP Corporation) **Service:** General Medical and Surgical

**Staffed Beds:** 93 **Admissions:** 2845 **Census:** 57 **Outpatient Visits:** 194477
**Births:** 248 **Total Expense ($000):** 69745 **Payroll Expense ($000):** 28968
**Personnel:** 531

## CARBONDALE—Jackson County

✠ **MEMORIAL HOSPITAL OF CARBONDALE (140164)**, 405 West Jackson Street, Zip 62901–1467, Mailing Address: P.O. Box 10000, Zip 62902–9000; tel. 618/549–0721 **A**1 2 3 5 9 10 13 19 **F**3 11 13 18 20 22 24 26 28 29 30 31 34 35 40 45 48 49 54 56 57 59 64 68 70 72 74 75 76 77 78 79 81 82 83 84 85 86 87 89 107 108 111 114 115 119 120 121 126 130 131 132 135 145 146 147 **S** Southern Illinois Hospital Services, Carbondale, IL
Primary Contact: Bart Millstead, Administrator
CMO: James D. Miller, M.D., Chief Medical Officer
CIO: Frank Sears, Vice President Information Services
Web address: www.sih.net
**Control:** Other not–for–profit (including NFP Corporation) **Service:** General Medical and Surgical

**Staffed Beds:** 159 **Admissions:** 10204 **Census:** 93 **Outpatient Visits:** 113450 **Births:** 2054 **Total Expense ($000):** 211040 **Payroll Expense ($000):** 52714 **Personnel:** 936

## CARLINVILLE—Macoupin County

★ **CARLINVILLE AREA HOSPITAL (141347)**, 20733 North Broad Street, Zip 62626–1499; tel. 217/854–3141 **A**9 10 18 **F**11 15 28 29 34 35 40 45 64 77 79 81 91 93 107 110 115 129 133 **P**6 **S** HealthTech Management Services, Franklin, TN
Primary Contact: Kenneth G. Reid, President and Chief Executive Officer
CMO: Julie Fleischer, M.D., President Medical Staff
CIO: Jerod Cottingham, Director Information Systems
CHR: Tracy Koster, Director Human Resources
Web address: www.cahcare.com
**Control:** Other not–for–profit (including NFP Corporation) **Service:** General Medical and Surgical

**Staffed Beds:** 25 **Admissions:** 651 **Census:** 10 **Outpatient Visits:** 22090
**Births:** 0 **Total Expense ($000):** 18398 **Payroll Expense ($000):** 6476
**Personnel:** 149

## CARROLLTON—Greene County

**THOMAS H. BOYD MEMORIAL HOSPITAL (141300)**, 800 School Street, Zip 62016–1498; tel. 217/942–6946, (Includes REISCH MEMORIAL NURSING HOME ), (Nonreporting) **A**9 10 18
Primary Contact: Deborah Campbell, Administrator
CHR: Lisa Eldridge, Human Resources Officer
**Control:** Other not–for–profit (including NFP Corporation) **Service:** General Medical and Surgical

**Staffed Beds:** 25

## CARTHAGE—Hancock County

☐ **MEMORIAL HOSPITAL (141305)**, 1454 North County Road 2050, Zip 62321–3551, Mailing Address: P.O. Box 160, Zip 62321–0160; tel. 217/357–8500 **A**1 9 10 18 **F**3 11 13 15 29 30 31 34 35 36 40 45 56 57 59 64 75 76 80 81 82 85 103 107 108 110 115 119 125 127 129 130 132 133 144 146
Primary Contact: Ada Bair, Chief Executive Officer
CFO: Teresa Smith, Chief Financial Officer
CIO: Syndi Horn, Director Information Systems
CHR: Dan Smith, Director Human Resources
CNO: Florine Dixon, Vice President Clinical Services
Web address: www.mhtlc.org
**Control:** Other not–for–profit (including NFP Corporation) **Service:** General Medical and Surgical

**Staffed Beds:** 18 **Admissions:** 500 **Census:** 7 **Outpatient Visits:** 18644
**Births:** 116 **Total Expense ($000):** 19375 **Payroll Expense ($000):** 8260
**Personnel:** 173

## CENTRALIA—Marion County

✠ **ST. MARY'S HOSPITAL (140034)**, 400 North Pleasant Avenue, Zip 62801–3056; tel. 618/436–8000 **A**1 2 9 10 **F**3 5 11 13 15 18 20 26 28 29 30 31 32 34 35 37 38 40 44 45 50 54 57 59 61 64 68 70 73 74 75 76 77 78 79 80 81 82 84 85 86 87 89 90 91 92 93 94 98 99 100 101 102 103 104 105 107 108 110 111 114 118 119 120 121 129 130 131 132 135 146 147 148 **P**6 8 **S** SSM Health Care, Saint Louis, MO
Primary Contact: Bruce Merrell, FACHE, President
COO: Mark A. Clark, Vice President Operations
CFO: Kay Tinsley, Vice President Finance
CMO: Rajendra Shroff, M.D., Administrative Medical Director
CIO: Ralph Caudill, Director Information Systems
CHR: Thomas W. Blythe, Vice President Human Resources
Web address: www.smgsi.com
**Control:** Church–operated, Nongovernment, not–for profit **Service:** General Medical and Surgical

**Staffed Beds:** 113 **Admissions:** 6264 **Census:** 68 **Outpatient Visits:** 207103
**Births:** 334 **Total Expense ($000):** 98821 **Payroll Expense ($000):** 37860
**Personnel:** 848

IL

---

| Hospital, Medicare Provider Number, Address, Telephone, Approval, Facility, and Physician Codes, Health Care System |
| --- |

★ American Hospital Association (AHA) membership
☐ The Joint Commission accreditation
◇ DNV Healthcare Inc. accreditation
○ Healthcare Facilities Accreditation Program
△ Commission on Accreditation of Rehabilitation Facilities (CARF) accreditation

## CENTREVILLE—St. Clair County

□ **TOUCHETTE REGIONAL HOSPITALS (140077)**, 5900 Bond Avenue, Zip 62207–2326; tel. 618/332–3060 **A**1 9 10 **F**3 11 13 15 18 29 30 31 40 45 47 50 54 55 62 64 68 70 73 75 76 78 79 81 85 87 89 92 98 99 101 102 104 105 107 110 114 119 125 130 143 146 148 **P**6
Primary Contact: Larry W. McCulley, President and Chief Executive Officer
COO: Tom Mikkelson, M.D., Interim Chief Operating Officer
CFO: John Majchrzak, Chief Financial Officer
CMO: Tom Mikkelson, M.D., Vice President Medical Affairs
CIO: Michael Nichols, Corporate Vice President Information Technology
CHR: Wardell Sullivan, Director Human Resources
Web address: www.touchette.org
**Control:** Other not–for–profit (including NFP Corporation) **Service:** General Medical and Surgical

**Staffed Beds:** 119 **Admissions:** 2608 **Census:** 28 **Outpatient Visits:** 58017 **Births:** 287 **Total Expense ($000):** 63012 **Payroll Expense ($000):** 27598 **Personnel:** 449

## CHAMPAIGN—Champaign County

□ **THE PAVILION (144029)**, 809 West Church Street, Zip 61820–3399; tel. 217/373–1700, (Nonreporting) **A**1 9 10 **S** Universal Health Services, Inc., King of Prussia, PA
Primary Contact: Joseph Sheehy, Chief Executive Officer and Managing Director
CFO: Edith Frasca, Controller and Chief Financial Officer
Web address: www.pavilionhospital.com
**Control:** Corporation, Investor–owned, for–profit **Service:** Psychiatric

**Staffed Beds:** 46

## CHESTER—Randolph County

□ **CHESTER MENTAL HEALTH CENTER**, Chester Road, Zip 62233–0031, Mailing Address: Box 31, Zip 62233–0031; tel. 618/826–4571 **A**1 **F**29 30 39 86 98 106 130 **P**6 **S** Division of Mental Health, Department of Human Services, Springfield, IL
Primary Contact: Melissa Gross, Interim Administrator
**Control:** State–Government, nonfederal **Service:** Psychiatric

**Staffed Beds:** 245 **Admissions:** 258 **Census:** 239 **Outpatient Visits:** 0 **Births:** 0 **Total Expense ($000):** 33780 **Payroll Expense ($000):** 27764 **Personnel:** 400

□ **MEMORIAL HOSPITAL (141338)**, 1900 State Street, Zip 62233–1116, Mailing Address: P.O. Box 609, Zip 62233–0609; tel. 618/826–4581, (Nonreporting) **A**1 9 10 18
Primary Contact: Steven A. Hayes, Administrator
CFO: Gail Miesner, Chief Financial Officer
CMO: Alan Liefer, M.D., President Medical Staff
CIO: Becky Bunselmeyer, Director Information Services
CHR: May Rose, Director Human Resources
Web address: www.mhchester.com
**Control:** Hospital district or authority, Government, nonfederal **Service:** General Medical and Surgical

**Staffed Beds:** 25

## CHICAGO—Cook County

⊞ **ADVOCATE ILLINOIS MASONIC MEDICAL CENTER (140182)**, 836 West Wellington Avenue, Zip 60657–5147; tel. 773/975–1600 **A**1 2 3 5 8 9 10 12 13 **F**3 5 13 15 17 18 19 20 22 24 26 28 29 30 31 32 33 34 35 36 38 39 40 43 44 45 46 47 48 49 50 53 54 55 56 57 58 59 60 61 64 66 68 70 71 72 73 74 75 76 77 78 79 81 82 84 85 86 87 89 90 92 93 96 97 98 99 100 101 102 103 104 107 108 110 111 115 117 118 119 120 121 123 124 126 130 131 132 134 135 141 143 146 147 148 **P**6 8 **S** Advocate Health Care, Downers Grove, IL
Primary Contact: Susan Nordstrom Lopez, President
CFO: Jack Gilbert, Vice President Finance and Support Services
CMO: Robert Zadylak, M.D., Vice President Medical Management
CIO: John Alban, Interim Director Information Systems
CHR: Marc Senesac, Vice President Human Resources
CNO: Donna J. King, R.N., Vice President Clinical Operations and Chief Nursing Executive
Web address: www.advocatehealth.com/masonic
**Control:** Other not–for–profit (including NFP Corporation) **Service:** General Medical and Surgical

**Staffed Beds:** 330 **Admissions:** 15926 **Census:** 200 **Outpatient Visits:** 186546 **Births:** 2492 **Total Expense ($000):** 315515 **Payroll Expense ($000):** 134713 **Personnel:** 2167

⊞ ◇ **ADVOCATE TRINITY HOSPITAL (140048)**, 2320 East 93rd Street, Zip 60617–3983; tel. 773/967–2000 **A**1 9 10 21 **F**1 3 4 11 13 15 16 17 18 20 22 24 28 29 30 31 34 35 40 45 49 50 56 57 58 59 60 61 65 67 68 70 72 73 74 75 76 77 78 79 80 81 82 87 88 89 90 92 93 98 107 108 110 111 114 115 119 126 128 129 130 132 143 146 148 **P**5 8 **S** Advocate Health Care, Downers Grove, IL
Primary Contact: Jonathan R. Bruss, President
CFO: Maureen Morrison, Vice President Financial Services
CMO: Dianna Grant, M.D., Vice President Medical Management
CIO: Brenda Aranda, Director Communications and Government Relations
Web address: www.advocatehealth.com/trinity
**Control:** Other not–for–profit (including NFP Corporation) **Service:** General Medical and Surgical

**Staffed Beds:** 188 **Admissions:** 12032 **Census:** 122 **Outpatient Visits:** 76781 **Births:** 1207 **Total Expense ($000):** 157241 **Payroll Expense ($000):** 59408 **Personnel:** 938

⊞ **ANN & ROBERT H. LURIE CHILDREN'S HOSPITAL OF CHICAGO (143300)**, 225 East Chicago Avenue, Zip 60611–2991; tel. 312/227–4000 **A**1 3 5 8 9 10 **F**3 8 9 11 12 17 18 19 21 23 25 27 29 30 31 32 34 35 36 37 38 39 40 41 43 44 45 46 48 49 50 51 54 55 57 58 59 60 61 64 65 68 72 74 75 77 78 79 81 82 84 85 86 87 88 89 91 92 93 94 96 97 98 99 100 101 102 104 105 107 108 111 113 114 115 116 117 118 119 124 126 129 130 131 132 134 136 137 138 139 142 144 146 148
Primary Contact: Patrick M. Magoon, President and Chief Executive Officer
COO: Gordon B. Bass, Chief Operating Officer
CFO: Paula Noble, Chief Financial Officer and Treasurer
CMO: Michael Kelleher, Chief Medical Officer
CIO: Stan Krok, Chief Information Officer
CHR: Barbara Bowman, Chief Human Resource Officer
Web address: www.luriechildrens.org
**Control:** Other not–for–profit (including NFP Corporation) **Service:** Children's general

**Staffed Beds:** 288 **Admissions:** 10997 **Census:** 184 **Outpatient Visits:** 512625 **Births:** 0 **Total Expense ($000):** 575169 **Payroll Expense ($000):** 247179 **Personnel:** 3817

□ **AURORA CHICAGO LAKESHORE HOSPITAL (144005)**, 4840 North Marine Drive, Zip 60640–4296; tel. 773/878–9700 **A**1 3 5 9 10 **F**4 5 35 98 99 100 101 104 105 130 132 **S** Aurora Behavioral Health Care, Corona, CA
Primary Contact: C. Alan Eaks, Chief Executive Officer
CFO: Carol Peart, Chief Financial Officer
CMO: Peter Nierman, M.D., Chief Medical Officer
CHR: Johanne Jeanty, Director Human Resources
Web address: www.chicagolakeshorehospital.com
**Control:** Corporation, Investor–owned, for–profit **Service:** Psychiatric

**Staffed Beds:** 115 **Admissions:** 3244 **Census:** 108 **Outpatient Visits:** 9217 **Births:** 0

**BERNARD MITCHELL HOSPITAL** See University of Chicago Medical Center

**CHICAGO LYING–IN HOSPITAL** See University of Chicago Medical Center

□ **CHICAGO–READ MENTAL HEALTH CENTER (144010)**, 4200 North Oak Park Avenue, Zip 60634–1457; tel. 773/794–4000, (Nonreporting) **A**1 10 **S** Division of Mental Health, Department of Human Services, Springfield, IL
Primary Contact: Thomas Simpatico, M.D., Facility Director and Network System Manager
**Control:** State–Government, nonfederal **Service:** Psychiatric

**Staffed Beds:** 200

**CHILDREN'S MEMORIAL HOSPITAL** See Ann & Robert H. Lurie Children's Hospital of Chicago

⊞ **HARTGROVE HOSPITAL (144026)**, 5730 West Roosevelt Road, Zip 60644–1580; tel. 773/413–1700, (Nonreporting) **A**1 10 **S** Universal Health Services, Inc., King of Prussia, PA
Primary Contact: Steven Airhart, Chief Executive Officer
CFO: Srbo Nikolic, Chief Financial Officer
CMO: Johnny Williamson, M.D., Chief Medical Officer
CHR: Anthony Rivera, Director Human Resources
CNO: Jody Bhambra, Chief Nursing Officer
Web address: www.hartgrovehospital.com
**Control:** Corporation, Investor–owned, for–profit **Service:** Psychiatric

**Staffed Beds:** 128

★ ○ **HOLY CROSS HOSPITAL (140133)**, 2701 West 68th Street, Zip 60629–1882; tel. 773/884–9000, (Nonreporting) **A**9 10 11
Primary Contact: Lori Pacura, R.N., MSN, Senior Vice President
COO: Paul M. Teodo, Chief Operating Officer
CFO: Loren Chandler, Interim, Vice President and Chief Financial Officer
CMO: Catherine Kallal, M.D., Chief Medical Officer
CIO: Ken Slawkowski, Interim Director Information Systems
CHR: Doris Gutierrez, Director Human Resources
CNO: Katherine Loeb, R.N., Interim Vice President, Patient Care Services
Web address: www.holycrosshospital.org
**Control:** Corporation, Investor–owned, for–profit **Service:** General Medical and Surgical

**Staffed Beds:** 160

IL

*Many Facility Codes have changed. Please refer to the AHA Guide Code Chart.*   © 2013 AHA Guide

☐ △ **JACKSON PARK HOSPITAL AND MEDICAL CENTER (140177)**, 7531 Stony Island Avenue, Zip 60649–3993; tel. 773/947–7500 **A**1 7 9 10 **F**2 3 13 15 18 26 29 30 31 32 34 35 38 40 44 45 50 56 57 59 60 61 63 64 65 66 68 70 74 75 76 77 78 79 81 82 83 84 85 86 87 92 93 97 98 102 103 104 105 107 108 115 119 130 134 135 144 147 148
Primary Contact: William Dorsey, M.D., Board Chairman and Chief Executive Officer
COO: Randall Smith, Executive Vice President
CFO: Nelson Vasquez, Vice President Finance
CMO: Bangalore Murthy, M.D., Director Medical Staff
CIO: Thomas Pankow, Chief Information Officer
CHR: Tracey Jones, Director Human Resources
Web address: www.jacksonparkhospital.org
**Control:** Other not–for–profit (including NFP Corporation) **Service:** General Medical and Surgical

**Staffed Beds:** 260 **Admissions:** 10000 **Census:** 111 **Outpatient Visits:** 56169 **Births:** 253 **Total Expense ($000):** 94560 **Payroll Expense ($000):** 40273 **Personnel:** 643

☒ △ **JESSE BROWN VETERANS AFFAIRS MEDICAL CENTER**, (Formerly Jesse Brown Veterans Affairs Chicago Health Care System), 820 South Damen, Zip 60612–3776; tel. 312/569–8387, (Nonreporting) **A**1 3 5 7 8 **S** Department of Veterans Affairs, Washington, DC
Primary Contact: Mario V. DeSantis, Acting Medical Center Director
COO: Michelle Blakely, Associate Director
CFO: Kalpana Mehta, Chief Fiscal Services
CMO: Wendy W. Brown, M.D., Chief of Staff
CIO: Howard Loewenstein, Chief Information Resource Management Services
CHR: Wayne Davis, Manager Human Resources
Web address: www.chicago.va.gov/
**Control:** Veterans Affairs, Government, federal **Service:** General Medical and Surgical

**Staffed Beds:** 240

☒ **JOHN H. STROGER JR. HOSPITAL OF COOK COUNTY (140124)**, 1901 West Harrison Street, Zip 60612–3714; tel. 312/864–6000 **A**1 2 3 5 8 9 10 13 **F**3 5 11 13 15 16 17 18 19 20 22 24 28 29 30 31 35 36 38 39 40 41 42 43 44 45 46 47 48 49 52 54 55 56 58 59 60 61 64 65 68 70 72 74 75 76 77 78 79 81 82 84 85 86 87 88 89 91 92 93 94 97 99 100 101 102 103 104 107 108 110 111 114 115 118 119 121 123 129 130 132 134 135 146 147 148 **P**6 **S** Cook County Health and Hospitals System, Chicago, IL
Primary Contact: John Jay Shannon, M.D., Interim Chief Operating Officer
COO: John Jay Shannon, M.D., Interim Chief Operating Officer
CFO: John R. Morales, Chief Financial Officer
CMO: Claudia Fegan, M.D., Chief Medical Officer
CIO: Bala Hota, Interim Chief Information Officer
CHR: Paris I. Partee, Associate Administrator and Director Human Resources
CNO: Antoinette Williams, Chief Nursing Officer
Web address: www.cookcountyhealth.net
**Control:** County–Government, nonfederal **Service:** General Medical and Surgical

**Staffed Beds:** 460 **Admissions:** 23420 **Census:** 301 **Outpatient Visits:** 812242 **Births:** 863 **Total Expense ($000):** 721282 **Payroll Expense ($000):** 371899 **Personnel:** 5513

**JOHNSTON R. BOWMAN HEALTH CENTER** See Rush University Medical Center

**KINDRED CHICAGO LAKESHORE** See Kindred Chicago–Central Hospital

☒ **KINDRED CHICAGO–CENTRAL HOSPITAL (142009)**, 4058 West Melrose Street, Zip 60641–4797; tel. 773/736–7000, (Includes KINDRED CHICAGO LAKESHORE, 6130 North Sheridan Road, Zip 60660; tel. 773/381–1222; Diane Otteman, Chief Executive Officer; KINDRED HOSPITAL CHICAGO NORTH, 2544 West Montrose Avenue, Zip 60618–1589; tel. 773/267–2622; Larry Foster, R.N., MSN, Chief Executive Officer), (Nonreporting) **A**1 9 10 **S** Kindred Healthcare, Louisville, KY
Primary Contact: Bruce Carey, Chief Executive Officer
COO: Joanne Garcia, Chief Operating Officer
CFO: Mary Treacy Shiff, Chief Financial Officer
Web address: www.khchicagocentral.com
**Control:** Corporation, Investor–owned, for–profit **Service:** Long–Term Acute Care hospital

**Staffed Beds:** 54

**KINDRED HOSPITAL CHICAGO NORTH** See Kindred Chicago–Central Hospital

☒ **LA RABIDA CHILDREN'S HOSPITAL (143301)**, 6501 South Promontory Drive, Zip 60649–1003; tel. 773/363–6700 **A**1 3 5 9 10 **F**3 12 28 29 30 32 34 35 38 40 41 50 57 58 59 64 65 74 75 77 79 82 85 86 87 89 91 93 96 97 99 100 102 104 130 132 134 143 144 146 148 **P**6
Primary Contact: Brenda J. Wolf, President and Chief Executive Officer
CFO: Mark Renfree, Chief Financial Officer
CMO: Dilek Bishku, M.D., Vice President Medical Affairs
CIO: Timothy Diamond, Chief Information Officer
CHR: Frances Lefkow, Director Human Resources
Web address: www.larabida.org
**Control:** Other not–for–profit (including NFP Corporation) **Service:** Children's chronic disease

**Staffed Beds:** 49 **Admissions:** 768 **Census:** 23 **Outpatient Visits:** 32431 **Births:** 0 **Total Expense ($000):** 49246 **Payroll Expense ($000):** 22455 **Personnel:** 441

☐ **LORETTO HOSPITAL (140083)**, 645 South Central Avenue, Zip 60644–5059; tel. 773/626–4300 **A**1 10 **F**2 3 4 5 15 18 29 30 31 34 35 38 40 44 45 50 54 57 59 60 61 64 65 68 70 74 75 78 79 81 85 86 87 89 92 93 98 102 103 104 105 106 107 108 115 119 130 132 143 146 147 148
Primary Contact: Sonia Mehta, M.D., Chief Executive Officer and Chief Medical Officer
CFO: John Valles, Senior Vice President and Chief Financial Officer
CMO: Sonia Mehta, M.D., Chief Executive Officer and Chief Medical Officer
CIO: Ron Warren, Director Information Systems
CHR: Ruby Isom, Associate Vice President Human Resources
CNO: Marc Trznadel, Chief Nursing Officer
Web address: www.lorettohospital.org
**Control:** Other not–for–profit (including NFP Corporation) **Service:** General Medical and Surgical

**Staffed Beds:** 176 **Admissions:** 5920 **Census:** 92 **Outpatient Visits:** 34637 **Births:** 0 **Total Expense ($000):** 67392 **Payroll Expense ($000):** 32230 **Personnel:** 497

★ ○ **MERCY HOSPITAL AND MEDICAL CENTER (140158)**, 2525 South Michigan Avenue, Zip 60616–2333; tel. 312/567–2000 **A**2 3 5 9 10 11 **F**3 5 12 13 15 17 18 20 22 24 26 28 29 30 31 32 34 35 36 40 44 45 46 49 50 51 52 53 54 55 56 57 58 59 61 64 65 66 70 73 74 76 77 78 79 81 82 85 86 87 89 90 92 93 96 97 98 99 100 101 102 103 104 105 107 108 110 111 114 115 117 118 119 121 123 124 126 130 131 132 133 134 135 143 144 145 146 147 148 **P**5 6 **S** Trinity Health, Livonia, MI
Primary Contact: Carol L. Schneider, President and Chief Executive Officer
COO: Richard Cerceo, Executive Vice President and Chief Operating Officer
CFO: Thomas J. Garvey, Chief Financial Officer
CMO: Warren Furey, M.D., Vice President Medical Affairs
CIO: Margaret Delaney, Chief Information Officer
CHR: Nancy L. Hill–Davis, Vice President Human Resources and Risk Management
Web address: www.mercy–chicago.org
**Control:** Other not–for–profit (including NFP Corporation) **Service:** General Medical and Surgical

**Staffed Beds:** 421 **Admissions:** 14972 **Census:** 177 **Outpatient Visits:** 377736 **Births:** 2558 **Total Expense ($000):** 241961 **Payroll Expense ($000):** 100154 **Personnel:** 1556

○ **METHODIST HOSPITAL OF CHICAGO (140197)**, 5025 North Paulina Street, Zip 60640–2772; tel. 773/271–9040, (Nonreporting) **A**9 10 11
Primary Contact: Steven H. Friedman, Ph.D., Executive Vice President
CFO: Harold Reisler, Controller
CIO: Bernie Ziegler, Manager Information Systems
Web address: www.bethanymethodist.org
**Control:** Other not–for–profit (including NFP Corporation) **Service:** General Medical and Surgical

**Staffed Beds:** 189

☒ △ **MOUNT SINAI HOSPITAL (140018)**, California Avenue at 15th Street, Zip 60608–1729; tel. 773/542–2000, (Includes SINAI CHILDREN'S HOSPITAL, California Avenue at 15th Street, Zip 60608; tel. 888/287–4624), (Nonreporting) **A**1 2 3 5 7 8 9 10 12 13 **S** Sinai Health System, Chicago, IL
Primary Contact: Alan H. Channing, President and Chief Executive Officer
COO: Karen Teitelbaum, Executive Vice President and Chief Operating Officer
CFO: Charles Weis, Chief Financial Officer
CMO: Jack Garon, M.D., Chief Medical Officer
CIO: Peter Ingram, Vice President and Chief Information Officer
CHR: Andrew Wissel, Director Human Resources
Web address: www.sinai.org
**Control:** Other not–for–profit (including NFP Corporation) **Service:** General Medical and Surgical

**Staffed Beds:** 290

IL

**Hospital, Medicare Provider Number, Address, Telephone, Approval, Facility, and Physician Codes, Health Care System**

★ American Hospital Association (AHA) membership
☐ The Joint Commission accreditation
◇ DNV Healthcare Inc. accreditation
○ Healthcare Facilities Accreditation Program
△ Commission on Accreditation of Rehabilitation Facilities (CARF) accreditation

© 2013 AHA Guide     *Many Facility Codes have changed. Please refer to the AHA Guide Code Chart.*     Hospitals **A177**

⊠ **NORTHWESTERN MEMORIAL HOSPITAL (140281)**, 251 East Huron Street, Zip 60611–2908; tel. 312/926–2000, (Includes PRENTICE WOMEN'S HOSPITAL, 250 East Superior Street, Zip 60611; tel. 312/926–2000; STONE INSTITUTE OF PSYCHIATRY, 320 East Huron Street, Zip 60611; tel. 312/926–2000) **A**1 2 3 5 8 9 10 **F**3 4 5 6 8 9 11 12 13 14 15 17 18 20 22 24 26 28 29 30 31 32 33 34 35 36 37 38 39 40 43 44 45 46 47 48 49 50 51 52 53 54 55 57 58 59 60 61 62 63 64 65 66 68 70 72 73 74 75 76 77 78 79 80 81 82 83 84 85 86 87 92 93 97 98 99 100 101 102 103 104 105 106 107 108 110 111 114 115 116 117 118 119 120 121 123 124 126 129 130 131 132 134 135 136 137 138 139 141 142 143 144 145 146 147 148 **P**5 6 **S** Northwestern Memorial Healthcare, Chicago, IL
Primary Contact: Dean M. Harrison, President and Chief Executive Officer
COO: Dennis M. Murphy, Executive Vice President and Chief Operating Officer
CFO: Peter J. McCanna, Executive Vice President Administration and Chief Financial Officer
CMO: Michael G. Ankin, M.D., Vice President Medical Affairs & Chief Medical Officer
CIO: Timothy R. Zoph, Senior Vice President and Chief Information Officer
CHR: Dean Manheimer, Senior Vice President Human Resources
Web address: www.nmh.org
**Control:** Other not–for–profit (including NFP Corporation) **Service:** General Medical and Surgical

**Staffed Beds:** 885 **Admissions:** 51006 **Census:** 692 **Outpatient Visits:** 656445 **Births:** 12715 **Total Expense ($000):** 1372951 **Payroll Expense ($000):** 436440 **Personnel:** 6945

**NORWEGIAN AMERICAN HOSPITAL (140206)**, 1044 North Francisco Avenue, Zip 60622–2743; tel. 773/292–8200 **A**3 5 6 9 10 **F**5 13 15 18 19 20 22 29 31 32 34 35 36 38 39 40 44 45 46 47 48 49 50 56 57 59 63 64 65 68 70 71 74 75 76 77 78 79 81 82 84 86 87 89 91 92 93 94 96 97 98 100 101 102 103 107 110 111 114 118 119 130 143 146 147 148 **P**8
Primary Contact: Jose R. Sanchez, President and Chief Executive Officer
CFO: Duane Fitch, CPA, Chief Financial Officer
CMO: Mark Loafman, M.D., Vice President Medical Affairs
CIO: James Filkins, Chief Information Officer
CHR: Marcia Powers, Vice President Human Resources
Web address: www.nahospital.org
**Control:** Other not–for–profit (including NFP Corporation) **Service:** General Medical and Surgical

**Staffed Beds:** 170 **Admissions:** 7872 **Census:** 94 **Outpatient Visits:** 82501 **Births:** 1354 **Total Expense ($000):** 96946 **Payroll Expense ($000):** 44854 **Personnel:** 729

**OUR LADY OF THE RESURRECTION MEDICAL CENTER** See Presence Our Lady of the Resurrection Medical Center

**PRENTICE WOMEN'S HOSPITAL** See Northwestern Memorial Hospital

★ ○ **PRESENCE OUR LADY OF THE RESURRECTION MEDICAL CENTER (140251)**, (Formerly Our Lady of the Resurrection Medical Center), 5645 West Addison Street, Zip 60634–4403; tel. 773/282–7000, (Total facility includes 66 beds in nursing home–type unit) **A**9 10 11 **F**3 8 15 18 20 22 28 29 30 31 34 35 36 39 40 43 44 45 49 50 53 56 57 58 59 60 64 68 70 74 75 79 81 82 85 86 92 93 96 107 111 114 115 119 128 130 132 142 144 146 147 148 **P**5 **S** Presence Health, Chicago, IL
Primary Contact: John D. Baird, President and Chief Executive Officer
COO: Dennis FitzMaurice, Vice President, Professional Services
CFO: Donna Diblik, Chief Financial Officer
CMO: David Bordo, M.D., Vice President, Medical Affairs/Chief Medical Officer
CIO: George Chessum, Senior Vice President and Chief Information Officer
CHR: Ivy McKinley, Director Human Resources
CNO: Maryanne Bajgrowicz, Vice President, Patient Care Services/Chief Nursing Officer
Web address: www.presencehealth.org
**Control:** Church–operated, Nongovernment, not–for profit **Service:** General Medical and Surgical

**Staffed Beds:** 279 **Admissions:** 8987 **Census:** 132 **Outpatient Visits:** 119218 **Births:** 2 **Total Expense ($000):** 120906 **Payroll Expense ($000):** 45497 **Personnel:** 764

★ ○ △ **PRESENCE RESURRECTION MEDICAL CENTER (140117)**, (Formerly Resurrection Medical Center), 7435 West Talcott Avenue, Zip 60631–3746; tel. 773/774–8000, (Nonreporting) **A**2 3 5 7 9 10 11 13 **S** Presence Health, Chicago, IL
Primary Contact: John D. Baird, Chief Executive Officer
CMO: Victor McKarry, M.D., President Medical Staff
CIO: George Chessum, Senior Vice President Information Systems and Chief Information Officer
CHR: Paul Skiem, Senior Vice President Human Resources
Web address: www.reshealthcare.org
**Control:** Church–operated, Nongovernment, not–for profit **Service:** General Medical and Surgical

**Staffed Beds:** 402

★ ○ **PRESENCE SAINT JOSEPH HOSPITAL (140224)**, (Formerly Saint Joseph Hospital), 2900 North Lake Shore Drive, Zip 60657–6274; tel. 773/665–3000, (Nonreporting) **A**2 3 5 9 10 11 **S** Presence Health, Chicago, IL
Primary Contact: Roberta Luskin–Hawk, M.D., President and Chief Executive Officer
CFO: Stanley Kazmierczak, Controller
CMO: M. Todd Grendon, M.D., President Medical Staff
CIO: George Chessum, Senior Vice President Information Systems and Chief Information Officer
CHR: Denise Brown, Vice President Human Resources
Web address: www.reshealth.org
**Control:** Church–operated, Nongovernment, not–for profit **Service:** General Medical and Surgical

**Staffed Beds:** 327

★ ○ **PRESENCE SAINTS MARY & ELIZABETH MEDICAL CENTER (140180)**, (Formerly Saints Mary & Elizabeth Medical Center), 2233 West Division Street, Zip 60622–3086; tel. 312/770–2000, (Includes SAINTS MARY & ELIZABETH MEDICAL CENTER, CLAREMONT AVENUE, 1431 North Claremont Avenue, Zip 60622–1791; tel. 773/278–2000; Margaret McDermott, Chief Executive Officer), (Total facility includes 26 beds in nursing home–type unit) **A**2 9 10 11 **F**3 4 5 13 15 17 18 19 20 22 24 26 28 29 30 31 32 34 35 36 40 45 47 49 50 51 57 58 59 60 64 65 66 68 70 72 74 75 76 77 78 79 81 82 85 86 87 89 90 92 93 96 97 98 99 100 101 102 103 104 105 106 107 108 110 111 114 115 117 118 119 121 123 128 129 130 132 135 143 146 147 148 **S** Presence Health, Chicago, IL
Primary Contact: Martin H. Judd, President and Chief Executive Officer
CFO: Kenneth A. Kautzer, Senior Vice President Finance and Treasurer
CIO: Steven Smith, Chief Information Officer
Web address: www.smemc.reshealth.org
**Control:** Church–operated, Nongovernment, not–for profit **Service:** General Medical and Surgical

**Staffed Beds:** 493 **Admissions:** 21266 **Census:** 319 **Outpatient Visits:** 193734 **Births:** 1611

⊠ **PROVIDENT HOSPITAL OF COOK COUNTY (140300)**, 500 East 51st Street, Zip 60615–2494; tel. 312/572–2000, (Nonreporting) **A**1 3 5 9 10 **S** Cook County Health and Hospitals System, Chicago, IL
Primary Contact: Thomas J. Dohm, Interim Chief Operating Officer
COO: Michele T. Thompson, Deputy Chief Operating Officer
CFO: Barbara Patterson, Chief Financial Officer
CMO: Aaron Hamb, M.D., Chief Medical Officer
CIO: Donna Hart, Chief Information Officer
Web address: www.ccbhs.org/pages/ProvidentHospitalofCookCounty.htm
**Control:** County–Government, nonfederal **Service:** General Medical and Surgical

**Staffed Beds:** 25

⊠ **REHABILITATION INSTITUTE OF CHICAGO (143026)**, 345 East Superior Street, Zip 60611–2654; tel. 312/238–1000, (Nonreporting) **A**1 3 5 9 10
Primary Contact: Joanne C. Smith, M.D., President and Chief Executive Officer
COO: Peggy Kirk, Senior Vice President Clinical Operations
CFO: Ed Case, Executive Vice President and Chief Financial Officer
CMO: James Sliwa, M.D., Chief Medical Officer
CIO: Tim McKula, Vice President Information Systems and Chief Information Officer
CHR: Lois Huggins, Chief Human Resources Officer and Senior Vice President Human Resources
Web address: www.ric.org
**Control:** Other not–for–profit (including NFP Corporation) **Service:** Rehabilitation

**Staffed Beds:** 182

**RESURRECTION MEDICAL CENTER** See Presence Resurrection Medical Center

★ **RML SPECIALTY HOSPITAL (142012)**, 3435 West Van Buren Street, Zip 60624–3312; tel. 773/826–6300 **F**1 3 18 29 30 31 40 50 58 74 85 87 107 114 119 130 132 146 148
Primary Contact: James R. Prister, President and Chief Executive Officer
COO: Ken Pawola, Chief Operating Officer
CFO: Tom Pater, Vice President Finance and Chief Financial Officer
CMO: Joseph Rosman, M.D., Chief Medical Director
CIO: Julie Ames, Chief Information Officer
CHR: John Landstrom, Vice President Human Resources and Operations
Web address: www.rmlspecialtyhospital.org
**Control:** Other not–for–profit (including NFP Corporation) **Service:** Long–Term Acute Care hospital

**Staffed Beds:** 68 **Admissions:** 508 **Census:** 44 **Outpatient Visits:** 618 **Births:** 0 **Total Expense ($000):** 28391 **Payroll Expense ($000):** 14496 **Personnel:** 264

○ **ROSELAND COMMUNITY HOSPITAL (140068)**, 45 West 111th Street, Zip 60628–4294; tel. 773/995–3000, (Nonreporting) **A**9 10 11
Primary Contact: Timothy Egan, Chief Restructuring Officer and President
CMO: Rogelio Cave, M.D., Medical Director
CIO: William Spence, Director
CHR: Brenda Mitchell, Director Human Resources
Web address: www.roselandhospital.org
**Control:** Other not–for–profit (including NFP Corporation) **Service:** General Medical and Surgical

**Staffed Beds:** 115

IL

⊠ △ **RUSH UNIVERSITY MEDICAL CENTER (140119)**, 1653 West Congress Parkway, Zip 60612–3833; tel. 312/942–5000, (Includes JOHNSTON R. BOWMAN HEALTH CENTER, 700 South Paulina, Zip 60612; tel. 312/942–7000; RUSH CHILDREN'S HOSPITAL, 1653 Wes Congress Parkway, tel. 888/352–7874) **A**1 2 3 5 7 8 9 10 **F**2 3 6 8 9 11 12 13 14 15 17 18 19 20 21 22 23 24 25 26 27 29 30 31 32 34 35 36 38 39 40 41 43 44 45 46 47 48 49 50 51 52 55 56 57 58 59 60 61 62 63 64 65 66 68 70 72 73 74 75 76 77 78 79 80 81 82 83 84 85 86 87 88 89 90 91 92 93 94 95 96 97 98 99 100 101 102 103 104 105 107 108 111 114 115 117 118 119 120 121 123 124 125 126 129 130 131 132 134 135 136 137 138 139 141 142 145 146 147 148 **P**8 **S** Rush University Medical Center, Chicago, IL
Primary Contact: Peter W. Butler, President and Chief Operating Officer
CMO: David A. Ansell, M.D., Vice President and Chief Medical Officer
CIO: Lac Tran, Senior Vice President Information Services
CHR: Sheri L. Marker, Vice President Human Resources
CNO: Cynthia Barginere, MSN, Vice President Clinical Nursing and Chief Nursing Officer
Web address: www.rush.edu
**Control:** Other not–for–profit (including NFP Corporation) **Service:** General Medical and Surgical

**Staffed Beds:** 669 **Admissions:** 30810 **Census:** 473 **Outpatient Visits:** 424264 **Births:** 2084 **Total Expense ($000):** 876448 **Payroll Expense ($000):** 281986 **Personnel:** 7695

⊠ **SAINT ANTHONY HOSPITAL (140095)**, 2875 West 19th Street, Zip 60623–3596; tel. 773/484–1000 **A**1 3 5 9 10 **F**3 13 15 18 19 29 30 31 32 33 34 35 40 41 44 49 50 51 53 54 56 57 59 64 65 68 70 74 75 76 77 78 79 81 82 85 86 87 89 93 96 97 98 100 101 102 104 105 107 110 111 115 118 119 130 131 132 143 144 146 147 148 **P**8
Primary Contact: Guy A. Medaglia, President and Chief Executive Officer
CFO: Charles R. Brobst, Senior Vice President and Chief Financial Officer
CIO: Mark Jennings, Chief Information Officer
CHR: Michelle C. Morgan, Chief Human Resource Manager
CNO: Jill Stemmerman, R.N., Vice President Nursing
Web address: www.saintanthonyhospital.org
**Control:** Church–operated, Nongovernment, not–for profit **Service:** General Medical and Surgical

**Staffed Beds:** 151 **Admissions:** 7059 **Census:** 82 **Outpatient Visits:** 110944 **Births:** 1849 **Total Expense ($000):** 96133 **Payroll Expense ($000):** 46765 **Personnel:** 634

**SAINT JOSEPH HOSPITAL** See Presence Saint Joseph Hospital

**SAINTS MARY & ELIZABETH MEDICAL CENTER** See Presence Saints Mary & Elizabeth Medical Center

⊠ △ **SCHWAB REHABILITATION HOSPITAL (143025)**, 1401 South California Avenue, Zip 60608–1858; tel. 773/522–2010, (Nonreporting) **A**1 3 5 7 9 10 **S** Sinai Health System, Chicago, IL
Primary Contact: Alan H. Channing, President and Chief Executive Officer
COO: Karen Teitelbaum, Executive Vice President and Chief Operating Officer
CFO: Charles Weis, Chief Financial Officer
CMO: Susan Rayner, M.D., Executive Vice President
CIO: Peter Ingram, Vice President and Chief Information Officer
CHR: Andrew Wissel, Director Human Resources
Web address: www.schwabrehab.org
**Control:** Other not–for–profit (including NFP Corporation) **Service:** Rehabilitation

**Staffed Beds:** 101

☐ **SHRINERS HOSPITALS FOR CHILDREN–CHICAGO (143302)**, 2211 North Oak Park Avenue, Zip 60707–3392; tel. 773/622–5400, (Nonreporting) **A**1 3 5 10 **S** Shriners Hospitals for Children, Tampa, FL
Primary Contact: Mark L. Niederpruem, FACHE, Administrator
CFO: Philip Magid, Director Fiscal Services
CMO: Jeffrey D. Ackman, M.D., Chief of Staff
CIO: Robert Gilb, Director Information Services
CHR: James E. Pawlowicz, Director Human Resources
Web address: www.shrinershospitalsforchildren.org/Hospitals/Locations/Chicago.aspx
**Control:** Other not–for–profit (including NFP Corporation) **Service:** Children's orthopedic

**Staffed Beds:** 36

☐ ○ **SOUTH SHORE HOSPITAL (140181)**, 8012 South Crandon Avenue, Zip 60617–1124; tel. 773/768–0810 **A**1 10 11 **F**3 4 15 18 22 29 35 40 46 59 61 65 70 75 79 81 82 85 86 87 93 98 103 107 110 114 115 119 130 148
Primary Contact: Jesus M. Ong, President
CFO: Timothy Caveney, Chief Financial Officer
CMO: Abraham Jacob, M.D., President Medical Staff
CIO: Jim Ritchie, Director Management Information Systems
CHR: Roger Rak, Director Human Resources
Web address: www.southshorehospital.com
**Control:** Other not–for–profit (including NFP Corporation) **Service:** General Medical and Surgical

**Staffed Beds:** 137 **Admissions:** 3913 **Census:** 67 **Outpatient Visits:** 25339 **Births:** 0 **Total Expense ($000):** 41852 **Payroll Expense ($000):** 20223

☐ △ **ST. BERNARD HOSPITAL AND HEALTH CARE CENTER (140103)**, 326 West 64th Street, Zip 60621–3146; tel. 773/962–3900, (Nonreporting) **A**1 7 9 10
Primary Contact: Sister Elizabeth Van Straten, President and Chief Executive Officer
COO: Janet G. Nohos, Executive Vice President
CFO: Guy Alton, Chief Financial Officer
CIO: Guy Alton, Chief Financial Officer
CHR: Donna Dertz, Director Human Resources
Web address: www.stbernardhospital.com
**Control:** Church–operated, Nongovernment, not–for profit **Service:** General Medical and Surgical

**Staffed Beds:** 100

★ ○ **SWEDISH COVENANT HOSPITAL (140114)**, 5145 North California Avenue, Zip 60625–3661; tel. 773/878–8200 **A**2 9 10 11 12 13 **F**3 12 13 15 18 19 20 22 24 26 28 29 30 31 32 34 35 36 38 39 40 43 45 46 47 49 50 53 56 57 58 59 60 62 64 68 70 74 75 76 78 79 81 82 84 85 86 87 89 90 92 93 96 97 98 100 101 102 103 104 105 107 108 110 111 114 115 117 118 119 121 123 124 126 128 129 130 131 132 134 135 143 146 147 148 **P**1 5 7
Primary Contact: Mark Newton, President and Chief Executive Officer
COO: Anthony Guaccio, Senior Vice President & Chief Operating Officer
CFO: Gary M. Krugel, Senior Vice President Operations and Chief Financial Officer
CIO: Karen Sheehan, Director Information Systems
CNO: Mary Shehan, R.N., Senior Vice President and Chief Nursing Officer
Web address: www.schosp.org
**Control:** Church–operated, Nongovernment, not–for profit **Service:** General Medical and Surgical

**Staffed Beds:** 279 **Admissions:** 14589 **Census:** 196 **Outpatient Visits:** 247737 **Births:** 2087 **Total Expense ($000):** 257149 **Payroll Expense ($000):** 98293 **Personnel:** 1863

○ **THOREK MEMORIAL HOSPITAL (140115)**, 850 West Irving Park Road, Zip 60613–3077; tel. 773/525–6780, (Nonreporting) **A**2 9 10 11
Primary Contact: Edward Budd, President and Chief Executive Officer
COO: Peter N. Kamberos, Chief Operating Officer
CFO: Kevin J. Higdon, Chief Financial Officer
CMO: James Diesfeld, M.D., President Medical Staff
CIO: Eric Dodd, Chief Information Officer
CHR: Brett Wakefield, Director Human Resources
CNO: Mary McCahill, Chief Nursing Officer
Web address: www.thorek.org
**Control:** Other not–for–profit (including NFP Corporation) **Service:** General Medical and Surgical

**Staffed Beds:** 134

⊠ **UNITYHEALTH LOUIS A. WEISS MEMORIAL HOSPITAL (140082)**, (Formerly Louis A. Weiss Memorial Hospital), 4646 North Marine Drive, Zip 60640–5759; tel. 773/878–8700 **A**1 2 3 5 9 10 **F**3 8 9 15 17 18 20 22 24 28 29 30 31 34 35 36 37 40 44 45 49 56 57 58 59 62 64 65 66 68 70 74 75 77 78 79 81 82 84 85 86 87 90 92 93 96 97 98 100 101 102 103 107 108 110 111 114 118 119 121 126 129 130 131 132 135 141 143 144 146 147 148 **P**6 **S** Vanguard Health Systems, Nashville, TN
Primary Contact: Anthony Tedeschi, M.D., M.P.H., Chief Executive Officer and Chief Medical Officer
COO: James M. Renneker, MSN, Chief Operating Officer and Chief Nursing Officer
CFO: Jeffrey L. Meigs, Chief Financial Officer
CMO: Anthony Tedeschi, M.D., Chief Executive Officer and Chief Medical Officer
CIO: Thomas Crawford, Chicago Market Chief Information Officer
CHR: Keoni Nader, Director Human Resources
Web address: www.weisshospital.com
**Control:** Corporation, Investor–owned, for–profit **Service:** General Medical and Surgical

**Staffed Beds:** 184 **Admissions:** 6696 **Census:** 96 **Outpatient Visits:** 79344 **Births:** 0 **Total Expense ($000):** 118004 **Payroll Expense ($000):** 52581 **Personnel:** 663

IL

---

**Hospital, Medicare Provider Number, Address, Telephone, Approval, Facility, and Physician Codes, Health Care System**

★ American Hospital Association (AHA) membership
☐ The Joint Commission accreditation
◇ DNV Healthcare Inc. accreditation
○ Healthcare Facilities Accreditation Program
△ Commission on Accreditation of Rehabilitation Facilities (CARF) accreditation

**UNIVERSITY OF CHICAGO COMER CHILDREN'S HOSPITAL** See University of Chicago Medical Center

☒ **UNIVERSITY OF CHICAGO MEDICAL CENTER (140088)**, 5841 South Maryland Avenue, Zip 60637–1447; tel. 773/702–1000, (Includes BERNARD MITCHELL HOSPITAL, 950 East 59th Street, Zip 60637; CHICAGO LYING–IN HOSPITAL, 950 East 59th Street, Zip 60637; tel. 312/684–6100; UNIVERSITY OF CHICAGO COMER CHILDREN'S HOSPITAL, 5721 South Maryland Avenue, Zip 60637; tel. 312/702–6168) **A**1 2 3 5 8 9 10 **F**3 6 9 11 12 13 14 15 16 17 18 19 20 21 22 23 24 25 26 27 28 29 30 31 32 34 35 36 37 38 40 41 43 44 45 46 47 48 49 50 51 52 54 55 56 57 58 59 60 61 63 64 69 70 71 72 73 74 75 76 77 78 79 80 81 82 83 84 85 86 87 88 89 92 93 97 100 101 102 104 107 108 110 111 114 115 116 117 118 119 120 121 123 124 126 129 130 131 132 134 135 136 137 138 139 140 141 142 143 144 145 146 147 148 **P**1
Primary Contact: Kenneth Polonsky, M.D., Chief Executive Officer
CFO: Richard Miller, Vice President Finance
CMO: Harvey Golomb, M.D., Chief Medical Officer
CIO: Eric Yablonka, Vice President and Chief Information Officer
CHR: Larry Callahan, Interim Vice President and Chief Human Resources Officer
Web address: www.uchospitals.edu
**Control:** Other not–for–profit (including NFP Corporation) **Service:** General Medical and Surgical

**Staffed Beds:** 577 **Admissions:** 24218 **Census:** 399 **Outpatient Visits:** 649194 **Births:** 1464 **Total Expense ($000):** 1170723 **Payroll Expense ($000):** 413601 **Personnel:** 7195

☒ △ **UNIVERSITY OF ILLINOIS HOSPITAL & HEALTH SCIENCES SYSTEM (140150)**, 1740 West Taylor Street, Zip 60612–7232; tel. 312/996–7000 **A**1 2 3 5 7 8 9 10 **F**3 12 13 14 15 17 18 19 20 21 22 23 24 25 26 27 28 29 30 31 32 34 35 37 38 39 40 41 45 46 47 48 49 50 52 54 55 56 57 58 59 60 61 64 65 66 68 70 72 73 74 75 76 77 78 79 81 82 84 85 86 87 88 89 90 91 92 93 96 97 98 99 100 101 102 103 104 107 108 110 111 114 115 116 117 118 119 120 121 123 124 126 129 130 131 132 134 135 136 138 139 141 142 144 145 146 147 148 **P**4
Primary Contact: Bryan Becker, Interim Chief Executive Officer
COO: David Loffing, Chief Operating Officer
CFO: William Devoney, Chief Financial Officer
CMO: William Chamberlin, M.D., Chief Medical Officer
CIO: Rose Ann Laureto, Chief Information Officer
CHR: John R. Loya, Vice Chancellor Human Resources
Web address: www.hospital.uillinois.edu/
**Control:** State–Government, nonfederal **Service:** General Medical and Surgical

**Staffed Beds:** 483 **Admissions:** 18763 **Census:** 321 **Outpatient Visits:** 455175 **Births:** 2489 **Total Expense ($000):** 733562 **Payroll Expense ($000):** 282103 **Personnel:** 6881

### CHICAGO HEIGHTS—Cook County

**ST. JAMES HOSPITAL AND HEALTH CENTERS – CHICAGO HEIGHTS CAMPUS** See Franciscan St. James Hospital and Health Centers, Olympia Fields

### CLINTON—De Witt County

★ **DR. JOHN WARNER HOSPITAL (141303)**, 422 West White Street, Zip 61727–2272; tel. 217/935–9571 **A**9 10 18 **F**3 7 15 28 29 34 40 45 53 57 59 64 68 70 75 81 82 85 87 93 97 107 110 127 129 130 132 133 **P**6
Primary Contact: Earl N. Sheehy, Chief Executive Officer
CFO: Donna Wisner, Chief Financial Officer
CMO: Brit Williams, M.D., President Medical Staff
CIO: Larry Schleicher, Manager Information Services
CHR: Jennie Wernecke, Human Resources Manager
CNO: Heidi Cook, Chief Nursing Officer
Web address: www.djwhospital.org
**Control:** City–Government, nonfederal **Service:** General Medical and Surgical

**Staffed Beds:** 25 **Admissions:** 278 **Census:** 3 **Outpatient Visits:** 17347 **Births:** 0 **Total Expense ($000):** 17386 **Payroll Expense ($000):** 7352 **Personnel:** 157

### DANVILLE—Vermilion County

☒ **PRESENCE UNITED SAMARITANS MEDICAL CENTER (140093)**, (Formerly Provena United Samaritans Medical Center), 812 North Logan, Zip 61832–3788; tel. 217/443–5000 **A**1 2 5 9 10 19 **F**3 8 11 13 15 18 20 28 29 30 31 34 35 40 45 46 47 48 49 50 57 59 64 70 74 75 76 77 78 79 81 82 83 85 86 87 89 93 102 107 108 110 111 114 115 118 119 120 121 124 129 130 132 135 146 147 **S** Presence Health, Chicago, IL
Primary Contact: Michael L. Brown, President and Chief Executive Officer
COO: Jennifer Cord, Vice President of Operations
CFO: Deborah Schimerowski, Chief Financial Officer
CMO: Charles Canver, M.D., Chief Medical Officer
CIO: Paula Keele, Manager Information Systems
CIO: Jason Wheatley, Manager Information Systems
CHR: Janet S. Payne, Vice President Human Resources
CNO: Molly Nicholson, R.N., Vice President of Patient Care/Chief Nurse Executive
Web address: www.provena.org/usmc
**Control:** Church–operated, Nongovernment, not–for profit **Service:** General Medical and Surgical

**Staffed Beds:** 127 **Admissions:** 6383 **Census:** 58 **Outpatient Visits:** 197084 **Births:** 663 **Total Expense ($000):** 97419 **Payroll Expense ($000):** 35837 **Personnel:** 700

☒ △ **VETERANS AFFAIRS ILLIANA HEALTH CARE SYSTEM**, 1900 East Main Street, Zip 61832–5198; tel. 217/554–3000, (Total facility includes 152 beds in nursing home–type unit) **A**1 3 5 7 9 **F**1 3 5 6 8 12 29 30 33 34 35 36 38 39 44 45 46 50 51 53 54 56 57 59 61 62 63 64 65 66 74 75 77 79 81 82 83 84 85 86 87 91 92 93 94 96 97 98 100 101 102 103 104 106 107 108 111 119 127 128 129 130 132 135 144 146 147 148 **P**6 **S** Department of Veterans Affairs, Washington, DC
Primary Contact: Emma Metcalf, MSN, R.N., Director
COO: Diana Carranza, Associate Director
CFO: Becky Tissier, Chief Fiscal Service
CMO: Khiem Tran, M.D., Acting Chief of Staff
CIO: Sherry Boone, Chief Information Resource Management
CHR: Connie Ohl, Acting Chief Human Resources
Web address: www.danville.va.gov/
**Control:** Veterans Affairs, Government, federal **Service:** General Medical and Surgical

**Staffed Beds:** 221 **Admissions:** 2996 **Census:** 181 **Outpatient Visits:** 340266 **Births:** 0 **Total Expense ($000):** 226089 **Payroll Expense ($000):** 121812 **Personnel:** 1547

### DECATUR—Macon County

☒ △ **DECATUR MEMORIAL HOSPITAL (140135)**, 2300 North Edward Street, Zip 62526–4192; tel. 217/876–8121 **A**1 2 3 5 7 9 10 19 **F**3 11 12 13 14 15 17 18 20 22 24 26 28 29 30 31 34 40 45 46 47 48 49 51 53 54 56 57 58 59 60 61 62 63 64 65 69 70 73 74 75 76 77 78 79 81 82 86 87 89 91 92 93 94 96 107 108 110 111 112 114 115 116 117 118 119 120 121 123 126 129 130 131 132 133 143 144 145 146 147 148 **P**8
Primary Contact: Kenneth L. Smithmier, President and Chief Executive Officer
COO: Timothy D. Stone, Executive Vice President and Chief Operating Officer
CFO: Gary G. Peacock, Senior Vice President and Chief Financial Officer
CMO: Michael Zia, M.D., Vice President Quality Systems and Medical Affairs
CIO: James Blackwell, Director Information Systems
CHR: Kevin Horath, Director Human Resources
CNO: Linda L. Fahey, MS, Vice President and Chief Nurse Executive
Web address: www.dmhcares.org
**Control:** Other not–for–profit (including NFP Corporation) **Service:** General Medical and Surgical

**Staffed Beds:** 188 **Admissions:** 11251 **Census:** 111 **Outpatient Visits:** 301194 **Births:** 1009 **Total Expense ($000):** 291645 **Payroll Expense ($000):** 115536 **Personnel:** 2089

☒ △ **ST. MARY'S HOSPITAL (140166)**, 1800 East Lake Shore Drive, Zip 62521–3883; tel. 217/464–2966, (Total facility includes 14 beds in nursing home–type unit) **A**1 3 5 7 9 10 **F**2 3 5 11 13 15 18 20 22 28 29 30 31 34 35 40 44 45 50 54 56 57 59 64 66 70 74 75 76 77 78 79 81 82 85 86 87 89 90 92 93 96 98 99 100 101 102 103 104 105 107 108 110 111 114 115 117 119 120 121 123 124 128 129 130 131 132 141 142 146 148 **P**7 **S** Hospital Sisters Health System, Springfield, IL
Primary Contact: Kevin F. Kast, President and Chief Executive Officer
COO: Theresa Rutherford, R.N., Chief Operating Officer
CFO: Rebecca Colker, Chief Financial Officer
CHR: Terri Kuhle, Director Human Resources
Web address: www.stmarysdecatur.com
**Control:** Church–operated, Nongovernment, not–for profit **Service:** General Medical and Surgical

**Staffed Beds:** 232 **Admissions:** 8305 **Census:** 119 **Outpatient Visits:** 166148 **Births:** 588 **Total Expense ($000):** 141989 **Payroll Expense ($000):** 43796 **Personnel:** 888

### DEKALB—DeKalb County

☒ **KISHWAUKEE HOSPITAL (140286)**, (Formerly Kishwaukee Community Hospital), 1 Kish Hospital Drive, Zip 60115–9602, Mailing Address: P.O. Box 707, Zip 60115–0707; tel. 815/756–1521 **A**1 2 9 10 **F**3 8 11 13 15 18 20 22 26 28 29 30 31 32 34 35 36 37 40 43 45 46 48 49 57 58 59 60 64 68 70 71 73 74 75 76 77 78 79 81 82 85 86 87 89 93 96 102 104 107 108 110 111 114 115 117 118 119 129 130 131 132 133 135 143 145 146 147 148 **P**8 **S** Kish Health System, DeKalb, IL
Primary Contact: Brad Copple, President
COO: Brad Copple, President
CFO: Loren Foelske, Vice President Finance
CMO: Michael Kulisz, D.O., Chief Medical Officer
CIO: Heath Bell, Chief Information Officer
CHR: Mark Thate, Vice President Human Resources
CNO: Pamela Duffy, Vice President Patient Care Services and Chief Nursing Officer
Web address: www.kishhospital.org
**Control:** Other not–for–profit (including NFP Corporation) **Service:** General Medical and Surgical

**Staffed Beds:** 98 **Admissions:** 5803 **Census:** 56 **Outpatient Visits:** 142280 **Births:** 874 **Total Expense ($000):** 145203 **Payroll Expense ($000):** 41749 **Personnel:** 742

### DES PLAINES—Cook County

**HOLY FAMILY MEDICAL CENTER** See Presence Holy Family Medical Center

**IL**

☐ **MARYVILLE BEHAVIORAL HEALTH HOSPITAL**, (Formerly Maryville Scott Nolan Center), 555 Wilson Lane, Zip 60016–4729; tel. 847/768–5430, (Nonreporting) **A**1 9
Primary Contact: Joseph Novak, PsyD, Chief Executive Officer
CFO: Timothy J. Morgan, Chief Financial Officer
CMO: Shiraz Butt, M.D., Medical Director
CHR: Betty Barnes, Director Human Resources
CNO: Barbara Preib, Director of Nursing
Web address: www.maryvilleacademy.org
**Control:** Church–operated, Nongovernment, not–for profit **Service:** Children's hospital psychiatric

**Staffed Beds: 113**

★ ○ **PRESENCE HOLY FAMILY MEDICAL CENTER (142011)**, (Formerly Holy Family Medical Center), 100 North River Road, Zip 60016–1255; tel. 847/297–1800, (Nonreporting) **A**9 10 11 **S** Presence Health, Chicago, IL
Primary Contact: Pamela Bell, R.N., President and Chief Executive Officer
CMO: Manish Tanna, M.D., President Medical Staff
CIO: George Chessum, Senior Vice President Information Systems and Chief Information Officer
CHR: Paul Skiem, Senior Vice President Human Resources
CNO: Marti Edwards, MSN, Vice President Patient Care Services
Web address: www.presencehealth.org
**Control:** Church–operated, Nongovernment, not–for profit **Service:** Long–Term Acute Care hospital

**Staffed Beds: 118**

### DIXON—Lee County

★ **KATHERINE SHAW BETHEA HOSPITAL (140012)**, 403 East First Street, Zip 61021–3187; tel. 815/288–5531 **A**3 5 9 10 **F**3 11 13 15 18 20 22 28 29 30 31 32 34 35 36 38 39 40 43 44 45 46 47 49 50 54 56 57 59 62 64 65 66 69 70 74 75 76 77 78 79 81 82 85 86 87 89 91 92 93 94 96 97 98 100 101 102 103 104 107 108 110 111 115 118 119 127 129 130 131 132 135 145 146 147 **P**6
Primary Contact: David L. Schreiner, FACHE, President and Chief Executive Officer
CFO: Debra Didier, Vice President and Chief Financial Officer
CMO: Tim Appenheimer, M.D., Vice President and Chief Medical Officer
CIO: Timothy W. Broos, Vice President and Chief Information Officer
CHR: Suzanne M. Ravlin, Director Human Resources
CNO: Linda Clemen, R.N., Vice President and Chief Nursing Officer
Web address: www.ksbhospital.com
**Control:** Other not–for–profit (including NFP Corporation) **Service:** General Medical and Surgical

**Staffed Beds: 80 Admissions: 4457 Census: 40 Outpatient Visits: 172391 Births: 352 Total Expense ($000): 124979 Payroll Expense ($000): 61816 Personnel: 821**

### DOWNERS GROVE—Dupage County

⊠ ◇ **ADVOCATE GOOD SAMARITAN HOSPITAL (140288)**, 3815 Highland Avenue, Zip 60515–1590; tel. 630/275–5900, (Nonreporting) **A**1 2 3 5 9 10 21 **S** Advocate Health Care, Downers Grove, IL
Primary Contact: David Fox, President
COO: Marjorie A. Maurer, MSN, Vice President Operations and Chief Nursing Executive
CFO: Mary Treacy–Shiff, Vice President Finance
CMO: Charles Derus, M.D., Vice President Medical Management
CHR: Elizabeth Calby, Vice President Human Resources
Web address: www.advocatehealth.com/gsam
**Control:** Church–operated, Nongovernment, not–for profit **Service:** General Medical and Surgical

**Staffed Beds: 326**

### DU QUOIN—Perry County

⊠ **MARSHALL BROWNING HOSPITAL (141331)**, 900 North Washington Street, Zip 62832–1233, Mailing Address: P.O. Box 192, Zip 62832–0192; tel. 618/542–2146 **A**1 9 10 18 **F**3 11 15 28 29 35 40 50 59 81 85 93 107 108 110 114 119 125 127 129 131 133
Primary Contact: Edwin A. Gast, Chief Executive Officer
CFO: Brice Harsy, Chief Financial Officer
CHR: Sarah J. Dickey, Director Human Resources
Web address: www.mbhdq.com
**Control:** Other not–for–profit (including NFP Corporation) **Service:** General Medical and Surgical

**Staffed Beds: 25 Admissions: 614 Census: 8 Outpatient Visits: 29601 Births: 0 Total Expense ($000): 16352 Payroll Expense ($000): 6844 Personnel: 139**

### EFFINGHAM—Effingham County

⊠ **ST. ANTHONY'S MEMORIAL HOSPITAL (140032)**, 503 North Maple Street, Zip 62401–2099; tel. 217/342–2121, (Total facility includes 13 beds in nursing home–type unit) **A**1 2 9 10 19 **F**3 8 11 13 15 18 19 29 20 31 34 37 40 45 57 59 60 62 64 68 70 76 79 81 82 85 89 93 107 110 111 114 115 119 128 129 130 132 146 147 **S** Hospital Sisters Health System, Springfield, IL
Primary Contact: Theresa Rutherford, R.N., MSN, FACHE, President and Chief Executive Officer
CFO: Dave Storm, Director Business Support
CHR: Kal Keitel, Manager Personnel Services
Web address: www.stanthonyshospital.org
**Control:** Church–operated, Nongovernment, not–for profit **Service:** General Medical and Surgical

**Staffed Beds: 146 Admissions: 6868 Census: 69 Outpatient Visits: 254103 Births: 809 Total Expense ($000): 98801 Payroll Expense ($000): 32079 Personnel: 661**

### ELDORADO—Saline County

**FERRELL HOSPITAL (141324)**, 1201 Pine Street, Zip 62930–1634; tel. 618/273–3361, (Nonreporting) **A**9 10 18
Primary Contact: Keith Broach, Chief Executive Officer and President
CFO: James Fraser, Chief Financial Officer
CIO: Doug Rash, Director Information Technology
CHR: Beth Anderton, Vice President Human Resources
Web address: www.ferrellhosp.org
**Control:** Other not–for–profit (including NFP Corporation) **Service:** General Medical and Surgical

**Staffed Beds: 25**

### ELGIN—Kane County

⊠ **ADVOCATE SHERMAN HOSPITAL (140030)**, (Formerly Sherman Hospital), 1425 North Randall Road, Zip 60123–2300; tel. 847/742–9800 **A**1 2 9 10 **F**3 11 13 15 18 19 20 22 24 26 27 28 29 30 31 34 35 38 40 43 45 46 47 48 49 50 55 57 59 64 65 68 70 74 75 76 77 78 79 81 82 85 87 89 93 100 107 108 110 111 114 115 118 119 120 121 126 129 130 132 135 144 146 147 148 **P**8 **S** Advocate Health Care, Downers Grove, IL
Primary Contact: Richard B. Floyd, President and Chief Executive Officer
COO: Linda Deering, R.N., Executive Vice President and Chief Operating Officer
CFO: Eric Krueger, Vice President, Finance and Chief Financial Officer
CMO: Ian V. Jones, M.D., Vice President Clinical Performance
CHR: Katie Bata, Vice President Human Resources
CNO: Judith Balcitis, MS, Vice President, Nursing and Chief Nursing Officer
Web address: www.shermanhealthsystems.com
**Control:** Other not–for–profit (including NFP Corporation) **Service:** General Medical and Surgical

**Staffed Beds: 255 Admissions: 14519 Census: 147 Outpatient Visits: 294602 Births: 2803 Total Expense ($000): 264234 Payroll Expense ($000): 93986 Personnel: 1571**

☐ **ELGIN MENTAL HEALTH CENTER (144037)**, 750 South State Street, Zip 60123–7692; tel. 847/742–1040, (Nonreporting) **A**1 5 10 **S** Division of Mental Health, Department of Human Services, Springfield, IL
Primary Contact: Amparo Lopez, Region Executive Director
CFO: Tajudeen Ibrahim, Interim Business Administrator
CMO: Malini Patel, M.D., Medical Director
CIO: Kelly Callahan, Public Information Officer
CHR: Darek Williams, Director Human Resources
Web address: www.dhs.state.il.us
**Control:** State–Government, nonfederal **Service:** Psychiatric

**Staffed Beds: 500**

⊠ △ **PRESENCE SAINT JOSEPH HOSPITAL (140217)**, (Formerly Provena Saint Joseph Hospital), 77 North Airlite Street, Zip 60123–4912; tel. 847/695–3200 **A**1 2 5 7 9 10 **F**5 11 12 15 17 18 20 22 24 26 28 29 30 31 34 35 36 37 38 40 43 44 49 50 53 54 56 57 58 59 60 61 62 63 64 65 68 69 70 74 75 77 78 79 81 82 84 85 86 87 90 93 94 96 97 98 99 100 101 102 103 104 105 107 108 111 114 115 116 117 119 120 121 123 124 130 132 134 135 143 145 146 147 148 **P**5 **S** Presence Health, Chicago, IL
Primary Contact: Eugene J. McMahon, M.D., President and Chief Executive Officer
COO: Laurence Dry, Vice President, Support and Ambulatory Services
CIO: Trevor O'Malley, Site Manager
CHR: Diane Hargreaves, Vice President Human Resources
Web address: www.provena.org
**Control:** Other not–for–profit (including NFP Corporation) **Service:** General Medical and Surgical

**Staffed Beds: 125 Admissions: 7380 Census: 118 Outpatient Visits: 173588 Births: 0 Total Expense ($000): 140493 Payroll Expense ($000): 52275 Personnel: 709**

**PROVENA SAINT JOSEPH HOSPITAL** See Presence Saint Joseph Hospital
**SHERMAN HOSPITAL** See Advocate Sherman Hospital

---

**Hospital, Medicare Provider Number, Address, Telephone, Approval, Facility, and Physician Codes, Health Care System**

★ American Hospital Association (AHA) membership
☐ The Joint Commission accreditation
◇ DNV Healthcare Inc. accreditation
○ Healthcare Facilities Accreditation Program
△ Commission on Accreditation of Rehabilitation Facilities (CARF) accreditation

IL

## ELK GROVE VILLAGE—Cook County

⊠ △ **ALEXIAN BROTHERS MEDICAL CENTER (140258)**, 800 Biesterfield Road, Zip 60007–3397; tel. 847/437–5500, (Includes ALEXIAN BROTHERS WOMEN & CHILDREN'S HOSPITAL, 1555 Barrington Road, Hoffman Estates, Zip 60169–1019; tel. 847/843–2000; ALEXIAN REHABILITATION HOSPITAL, 935 Beisner Road, Zip 60007; tel. 847/640–5600) **A**1 2 3 5 7 9 10 **F**3 12 13 15 17 18 20 22 24 26 28 29 30 31 34 35 36 37 39 40 41 43 45 46 47 48 49 50 54 55 56 57 58 59 62 63 64 66 70 74 75 76 78 79 81 82 84 85 86 87 89 90 91 92 93 95 96 107 108 110 111 113 114 115 116 117 119 120 121 123 124 126 129 130 132 135 143 144 145 146 147 148 **P**6 **S** Ascension Health, Saint Louis, MO
Primary Contact: John P. Werrbach, Chief Executive Officer
Web address: www.alexian.org
**Control:** Church–operated, Nongovernment, not–for profit **Service:** General Medical and Surgical

**Staffed Beds:** 370 **Admissions:** 19976 **Census:** 277 **Outpatient Visits:** 407024 **Births:** 2301 **Total Expense ($000):** 414361 **Payroll Expense ($000):** 143252 **Personnel:** 2019

## ELMHURST—Dupage County

⊠ **ELMHURST MEMORIAL HOSPITAL (140200)**, 155 East Brush Hill Road, Zip 60126–5658; tel. 331/221–1000, (Total facility includes 38 beds in nursing home–type unit) **A**1 2 9 10 **F**3 5 11 13 15 18 20 22 24 26 28 29 30 31 34 35 38 40 41 42 43 45 46 47 48 49 50 54 57 58 59 62 63 64 65 70 74 75 76 77 78 79 81 82 83 84 85 86 89 92 96 97 98 99 100 101 102 103 104 105 107 108 109 110 111 114 115 119 120 121 126 128 129 130 131 132 144 146 147 148 **P**1 3
Primary Contact: Mary Lou Mastro, President
CFO: James F. Doyle, Senior Vice President Finance and Chief Financial Officer
CMO: Michael Martirano, M.D., President Medical Staff
CIO: Charles Colander, Vice President Information Systems and Chief Information Officer
CHR: Lois Grubb, Vice President Human Resources
Web address: www.emhc.org
**Control:** Other not–for–profit (including NFP Corporation) **Service:** General Medical and Surgical

**Staffed Beds:** 315 **Admissions:** 14105 **Census:** 195 **Outpatient Visits:** 421517 **Births:** 1400 **Total Expense ($000):** 354534 **Payroll Expense ($000):** 142280 **Personnel:** 2359

## EUREKA—Woodford County

★ ◇ **ADVOCATE EUREKA HOSPITAL (141309)**, 101 South Major Street, Zip 61530–1246; tel. 309/467–2371 **A**9 10 18 21 **F**3 15 28 29 30 31 34 35 39 40 44 45 57 59 64 65 67 68 74 75 77 78 79 81 82 85 86 87 89 90 93 107 108 110 111 114 119 128 129 130 132 133 146 **P**8 **S** Advocate Health Care, Downers Grove, IL
Primary Contact: Colleen Kannaday, FACHE, President
COO: Anna Laible, Administrator
CMO: Steven K. Jones, M.D., Medical Director
CIO: David Harper, Director, Site Information Systems
CHR: Tony Coletta, Vice President of Human Resources
CHR: Aron Klein, Vice President of Finance
CNO: Nancy Allen, R.N., Director, Patient Services/CNE
Web address: www.advocatehealth.com/eureka/
**Control:** Church–operated, Nongovernment, not–for profit **Service:** General Medical and Surgical

**Staffed Beds:** 18 **Admissions:** 387 **Census:** 5 **Outpatient Visits:** 32755 **Births:** 0 **Total Expense ($000):** 14397 **Payroll Expense ($000):** 5340 **Personnel:** 103

**EUREKA COMMUNITY HOSPITAL** See Advocate Eureka Hospital

## EVANSTON—Cook County

⊠ **NORTHSHORE UNIVERSITY HEALTH SYSTEM EVANSTON HOSPITAL (140010)**, 1301 Central Street, Zip 60201–1613; tel. 847/570–2000, (Includes NORTHSHORE GLENBROOK HOSPITAL, 2100 Pfingsten Road, Glenview, Zip 60025; tel. 847/657–5800; NORTHSHORE HIGHLAND PARK HOSPITAL, 718 Glenview Avenue, Highland Park, Zip 60035–2497; tel. 847/432–8000) **A**1 2 3 5 8 9 10 **F**2 3 5 8 9 11 12 13 14 15 18 19 20 22 24 26 28 29 30 31 32 34 35 36 37 38 39 40 43 44 45 46 47 48 49 50 54 55 56 57 58 59 60 61 62 63 64 66 68 70 72 74 75 76 77 78 79 81 82 83 84 85 86 87 88 89 90 92 93 96 97 98 99 100 101 102 103 104 105 107 108 109 110 111 114 115 116 117 118 119 120 121 123 124 126 129 132 134 135 136 145 146 147 148 **S** NorthShore University HealthSystem, Evanston, IL
Primary Contact: Douglas M. Silverstein, President
COO: Jeffrey H. Hillebrand, Chief Operating Officer
CFO: Gary Weiss, Chief Financial Officer
CIO: Thomas Smith, Chief Information Officer
CHR: Bill Luehrs, Chief Human Resources Officer
Web address: www.northshore.org
**Control:** Other not–for–profit (including NFP Corporation) **Service:** General Medical and Surgical

**Staffed Beds:** 690 **Admissions:** 39647 **Census:** 509 **Outpatient Visits:** 1946909 **Births:** 4479 **Total Expense ($000):** 1424084 **Payroll Expense ($000):** 446858 **Personnel:** 5948

★ ○ **PRESENCE SAINT FRANCIS HOSPITAL (140080)**, (Formerly Saint Francis Hospital), 355 Ridge Avenue, Zip 60202–3399; tel. 847/316–4000, (Nonreporting) **A**2 3 5 9 10 11 **S** Presence Health, Chicago, IL
Primary Contact: Jeffrey J. Murphy, President and Chief Executive Officer
CMO: David DiLoreto, M.D., Executive Vice President and Chief Medical Officer
CIO: George Chessum, Vice President Information Systems
CHR: Paul Skiem, Senior Vice President Human Resources
Web address: www.reshealth.org
**Control:** Church–operated, Nongovernment, not–for profit **Service:** General Medical and Surgical

**Staffed Beds:** 244

**SAINT FRANCIS HOSPITAL** See Presence Saint Francis Hospital

## EVERGREEN PARK—Cook County

☐ **LITTLE COMPANY OF MARY HOSPITAL AND HEALTH CARE CENTERS (140179)**, 2800 West 95th Street, Zip 60805–2795; tel. 708/422–6200 **A**1 2 9 10 **F**3 5 11 12 13 15 17 18 20 22 23 26 29 30 31 34 35 36 40 41 45 46 47 50 54 56 57 59 60 62 63 64 71 73 74 75 76 77 78 79 81 82 83 84 85 86 87 89 92 93 94 98 100 101 102 103 104 105 107 108 110 111 114 115 119 120 121 124 126 129 130 132 135 144 146 147 148 **P**6 7 8 **S** American Province of Little Company of Mary Sisters, Evergreen Park, IL
Primary Contact: Dennis A. Reilly, President and Chief Executive Officer
COO: Mary Freyer, Chief Operating Officer
CFO: Randy Ruther, Vice President Finance and Chief Financial Officer
CMO: Dan Rowan, M.D., President Medical Staff
CIO: Darryl Mazzuca, Director Management Information Systems
CHR: Colleen Rohan, Director Human Resources
Web address: www.lcmh.org
**Control:** Other not–for–profit (including NFP Corporation) **Service:** General Medical and Surgical

**Staffed Beds:** 288 **Admissions:** 12942 **Census:** 157 **Outpatient Visits:** 175466 **Births:** 1020 **Total Expense ($000):** 180760 **Payroll Expense ($000):** 80027 **Personnel:** 1467

## FAIRFIELD—Wayne County

⊠ **FAIRFIELD MEMORIAL HOSPITAL (141311)**, 303 N.W. 11th Street, Zip 62837–1203; tel. 618/842–2611 **A**1 9 10 **F**3 11 15 18 28 30 31 34 38 40 41 56 57 59 62 64 69 70 75 78 81 87 93 103 104 107 108 111 116 119 127 128 129 130 132 135 145 146 **S** Alliant Management Services, Louisville, KY
Primary Contact: Katherine Bunting, Chief Executive Officer
COO: Dana Shantel Taylor, Director of Organizational Development
CFO: Kathy Clayton, Chief Financial Officer
CMO: Michelle O'Neill, M.D., President Medical Staff
CIO: Bryan Mitchell, Director Information Systems
CHR: Kari Book, Director Human Resources
CNO: Ann Ignas, R.N., Chief Nurse Executive
Web address: www.fairfieldmemorial.org
**Control:** Other not–for–profit (including NFP Corporation) **Service:** General Medical and Surgical

**Staffed Beds:** 55 **Admissions:** 889 **Census:** 26 **Outpatient Visits:** 39406 **Births:** 0 **Total Expense ($000):** 24978 **Payroll Expense ($000):** 10440 **Personnel:** 237

## FLORA—Clay County

⊠ **CLAY COUNTY HOSPITAL (141351)**, 911 Stacy Burk Drive, Zip 62839–3241, Mailing Address: P.O. Box 280, Zip 62839–0280; tel. 618/662–2131, (Nonreporting) **A**1 9 10 18 **S** BJC HealthCare, Saint Louis, MO
Primary Contact: Robert R. Sellers, President
CFO: Melissa Lucas, Chief Financial Officer
CMO: Michael Klingler, M.D., Chief of Staff
CHR: Darla Colwell, Director Human Resources and Marketing
Web address: www.claycountyhospital.org
**Control:** County–Government, nonfederal **Service:** General Medical and Surgical

**Staffed Beds:** 18

## FOREST PARK—Cook County

☐ **RIVEREDGE HOSPITAL (144009)**, 8311 West Roosevelt Road, Zip 60130–2500; tel. 708/771–7000, (Nonreporting) **A**1 5 9 10 **S** Universal Health Services, Inc., King of Prussia, PA
Primary Contact: Carey Carlock, Chief Executive Officer
CFO: Michael E. Nelson, Chief Financial Officer
CMO: Lucyna M. Puszkarska, M.D., Medical Director
CIO: Kyle Heinze, Coordinator Information Technology
CHR: Joseph Baw, Director Human Resources
Web address: www.riveredgehospital.com
**Control:** Corporation, Investor–owned, for–profit **Service:** Psychiatric

**Staffed Beds:** 224

## FREEPORT—Stephenson County

★ **FHN MEMORIAL HOSPITAL (140160)**, 1045 West Stephenson Street, Zip 61032–4899; tel. 815/599–6000 **A**9 10 **F**3 11 13 14 15 18 20 22 28 29 30 31 32 34 38 40 46 47 48 49 50 51 53 57 59 61 63 64 65 68 69 74 75 76 77 78 79 81 82 84 85 86 87 89 93 97 99 100 101 102 103 104 107 108 109 110 111 114 119 129 130 131 132 135 141 146 **P**6 8
Primary Contact: Michael R. Perry, M.D., President and Chief Executive Officer
COO: Sharon K. Summers, R.N., Executive Vice President and Chief Operating Officer
CFO: Michael Clark, Vice President Finance
CMO: Robert D. Geller, M.D., Vice President Medical Affairs
CIO: Mike Willams, Chief Information Officer
CHR: Leonard M. Carter, Vice President Human Resources
CNO: Nancy Cutler, R.N., Vice President Patient Services/CNO
Web address: www.fhn.org
**Control:** Other not–for–profit (including NFP Corporation) **Service:** General Medical and Surgical

| Staffed Beds: 100 Admissions: 4668 Census: 44 Outpatient Visits: 104293 Births: 433 Total Expense ($000): 95901 Payroll Expense ($000): 28586 Personnel: 465 |
| --- |

## GALENA—Jo Daviess County

★ **MIDWEST MEDICAL CENTER (141302)**, One Medical Center Drive, Zip 61036–1697; tel. 815/777–1340, (Nonreporting) **A**9 10 18
Primary Contact: Tracy Bauer, Chief Executive Officer
COO: Steve Busch, Chief Operating Officer
CMO: Grant Westenfelder, M.D., Chief Medical Officer
CHR: Melissa Conley, Director Human Resources
Web address: www.midwestmedicalcenter.org
**Control:** Corporation, Investor–owned, for–profit **Service:** General Medical and Surgical

| Staffed Beds: 25 |
| --- |

## GALESBURG—Knox County

⊠ **GALESBURG COTTAGE HOSPITAL (140040)**, 695 North Kellogg Street, Zip 61401–2885; tel. 309/343–8131, (Nonreporting) **A**1 10 **S** Community Health Systems, Inc., Franklin, TN
Primary Contact: Earl J. Iamar, Chief Executive Officer
COO: Lance Porter, Assistant Chief Executive Officer
CFO: Rob Gasaway, Chief Financial Officer
CMO: Daniel Piper, M.D., President Medical Staff
CIO: Teresa Mach, Director Information Technology
CHR: Nancy Baird, Director Human Resources
CNO: Debra Rickard, R.N., Chief Nursing Officer
Web address: www.cottagehospital.com
**Control:** Other not–for–profit (including NFP Corporation) **Service:** General Medical and Surgical

| Staffed Beds: 119 |
| --- |

⊠ **OSF ST. MARY MEDICAL CENTER (140064)**, 3333 North Seminary Street, Zip 61401–1299; tel. 309/344–3161 **A**1 9 10 **F**3 11 13 14 15 18 20 26 28 29 30 31 34 40 41 43 45 49 51 53 56 57 58 59 61 62 63 68 70 74 75 76 77 78 79 81 82 84 85 86 87 89 93 96 97 107 110 111 114 115 117 119 129 130 132 135 145 146 147 **P**6 **S** OSF Healthcare System, Peoria, IL
Primary Contact: Richard S. Kowalski, FACHE, President and Chief Executive Officer
CFO: Curt Lipe, Vice President, Chief Financial Officer
CMO: Mark Meeker, D.O., Medical Staff President
CIO: Becky Lynch, Manager Business Entity Management and Information Systems
CHR: Roxanna Crosser, Vice President, Operations
CNO: Alice Snyder, Vice President, Chief Nursing Officer
Web address: www.osfstmary.org
**Control:** Church–operated, Nongovernment, not–for profit **Service:** General Medical and Surgical

| Staffed Beds: 90 Admissions: 3503 Census: 37 Outpatient Visits: 146601 Births: 246 Total Expense ($000): 79730 Payroll Expense ($000): 38255 Personnel: 541 |
| --- |

## GENESEO—Henry County

⊠ **HAMMOND–HENRY HOSPITAL (141319)**, 600 North College Avenue, Zip 61254–1099; tel. 309/944–4625, (Total facility includes 38 beds in nursing home–type unit) **A**1 9 10 18 **F**3 8 11 13 15 17 18 28 29 34 35 40 43 44 45 57 59 62 70 75 76 79 81 82 87 88 89 93 107 111 114 119 128 129 130 131 132 133 135 144 146 **S** HealthTech Management Services, Franklin, TN
Primary Contact: Bradley Solberg, FACHE, Chief Executive Officer
CFO: Jodie Criswell, Vice President Fiscal Services
CIO: Heather Henry, Manager Information Systems
CHR: Margaret Chavez, Manager Human Resources
Web address: www.hammondhenry.com
**Control:** Hospital district or authority, Government, nonfederal **Service:** General Medical and Surgical

| Staffed Beds: 61 Admissions: 1281 Census: 46 Outpatient Visits: 89468 Births: 205 Total Expense ($000): 31884 Payroll Expense ($000): 12490 Personnel: 285 |
| --- |

## GENEVA—Kane County

⊠ **DELNOR HOSPITAL (140211)**, 300 Randall Road, Zip 60134–4200; tel. 630/208–3000 **A**1 2 9 10 **F**3 11 12 13 15 18 20 22 26 28 29 30 31 32 34 35 36 39 40 43 44 49 50 53 55 57 59 64 65 68 70 74 75 76 77 78 79 81 82 85 86 87 89 93 94 96 99 100 101 102 104 107 108 110 111 114 115 118 119 120 121 126 129 130 131 132 135 146 147 148 **S** Cadence Health, Winfield, IL
Primary Contact: Robert Friedberg, President
CMO: Mark Daniels, M.D., Vice President Physician Enterprise
CIO: James Kearns, Chief Information Officer
Web address: www.delnor.com
**Control:** Other not–for–profit (including NFP Corporation) **Service:** General Medical and Surgical

| Staffed Beds: 159 Admissions: 8059 Census: 78 Outpatient Visits: 209849 Births: 1492 Total Expense ($000): 172303 Payroll Expense ($000): 64621 Personnel: 976 |
| --- |

## GIBSON CITY—Ford County

⊠ **GIBSON AREA HOSPITAL AND HEALTH SERVICES (141317)**, 1120 North Melvin Street, Zip 60936–1477, Mailing Address: P.O. Box 429, Zip 60936–0429; tel. 217/784–4251, (Includes GIBSON COMMUNITY HOSPITAL NURSING HOME ), (Total facility includes 42 beds in nursing home–type unit) **A**1 5 9 10 18 **F**3 7 11 13 15 28 29 31 34 35 40 43 44 45 49 50 51 53 56 57 59 63 64 65 67 68 69 70 75 76 77 79 81 82 85 87 93 103 107 108 110 111 115 119 127 128 129 131 132 133 143 146 147 148 **P**6 7 8
Primary Contact: Robert C. Schmitt, II, Chief Executive Officer
COO: Robin Rose, R.N., Chief Nursing Officer
CFO: John Jacobson, Chief Financial Officer
CMO: David J. Hagan, M.D., Chief Medical Officer
CIO: Jim Edwards, Executive Director of Information Technology
CHR: Ty Royal, Executive Director of Support Services and Human Resources
CNO: Robin Rose, R.N., Chief Nursing Officer/Chief Operating Officer
Web address: www.gibsonhospital.org
**Control:** Other not–for–profit (including NFP Corporation) **Service:** General Medical and Surgical

| Staffed Beds: 67 Admissions: 1005 Census: 46 Outpatient Visits: 106303 Births: 143 Total Expense ($000): 60987 Payroll Expense ($000): 26574 Personnel: 521 |
| --- |

## GLENDALE HEIGHTS—Dupage County

⊠ **ADVENTIST GLENOAKS HOSPITAL (140292)**, 701 Winthrop Avenue, Zip 60139–1403; tel. 630/545–8000 **A**1 9 10 **F**3 11 13 15 17 18 20 22 26 29 30 31 34 35 38 40 43 45 49 57 58 59 61 64 68 70 72 74 75 76 78 79 81 82 85 86 87 92 93 96 97 98 99 100 101 102 103 104 105 107 108 110 111 114 118 119 130 131 132 146 147 148 **P**7 8 **S** Adventist Health System Sunbelt Health Care Corporation, Altamonte Springs, FL
Primary Contact: Bruce C. Christian, Chief Executive Officer
CFO: Eric Moots, Vice President and Chief Financial Officer
CMO: Richard Carroll, M.D., Chief Medical Officer
CIO: Joe Granneman, Regional Chief Information Officer
CHR: Donald Russell, Vice President
Web address: www.keepingyouwell.com
**Control:** Church–operated, Nongovernment, not–for profit **Service:** General Medical and Surgical

| Staffed Beds: 141 Admissions: 4975 Census: 81 Outpatient Visits: 38161 Births: 396 Total Expense ($000): 76153 Payroll Expense ($000): 33377 Personnel: 573 |
| --- |

## GLENVIEW—Cook County

**NORTHSHORE GLENBROOK HOSPITAL** See NorthShore University Health System Evanston Hospital, Evanston

---

**Hospital, Medicare Provider Number, Address, Telephone, Approval, Facility, and Physician Codes, Health Care System**

★ American Hospital Association (AHA) membership
☐ The Joint Commission accreditation
◇ DNV Healthcare Inc. accreditation
◯ Healthcare Facilities Accreditation Program
△ Commission on Accreditation of Rehabilitation Facilities (CARF) accreditation

IL

## GRANITE CITY—Madison County

⊞ **GATEWAY REGIONAL MEDICAL CENTER (140125)**, 2100 Madison Avenue, Zip 62040–4799; tel. 618/798–3000, (Nonreporting) **A**1 9 10 **S** Community Health Systems, Inc., Franklin, TN
Primary Contact: M. Edward Cunningham, Chief Executive Officer
CFO: Ronald Leazer, Chief Financial Officer
CMO: Mike Adams, M.D., Chief Medical Officer
CIO: Dennis Kampwerth, Director Management Information Systems
CHR: J. Ronald Payton, Director Human Resources
Web address: www.gatewayregional.net
**Control:** Corporation, Investor–owned, for–profit **Service:** General Medical and Surgical

**Staffed Beds:** 337

## GREENVILLE—Bond County

★ ○ **GREENVILLE REGIONAL HOSPITAL (140137)**, 200 Healthcare Drive, Zip 62246–1154; tel. 618/664–1230, (Includes FAIR OAKS ), (Total facility includes 108 beds in nursing home–type unit) **A**9 10 11 **F**2 7 11 13 15 28 29 31 34 40 41 45 49 50 56 57 59 64 68 75 76 77 78 79 81 85 87 89 93 94 95 97 98 100 103 104 107 111 115 119 125 127 128 129 130 131 132 133 135 146 148 **P**6
Primary Contact: Brian Nall, President and Chief Executive Officer
CFO: Sherry Koehler, Chief Financial Officer
CHR: Todd A. Ray, Director Human Resources
CNO: Tammy Lett, R.N., Chief Nursing Officer
Web address: www.greenvilleregionalhospital.com
**Control:** Other not–for–profit (including NFP Corporation) **Service:** General Medical and Surgical

**Staffed Beds:** 150 **Admissions:** 1291 **Census:** 80 **Outpatient Visits:** 41022 **Births:** 205 **Total Expense ($000):** 38303 **Payroll Expense ($000):** 17964 **Personnel:** 320

## HARRISBURG—Saline County

⊞ **HARRISBURG MEDICAL CENTER (140210)**, 100 Drive Warren Tuttle Drive, Zip 62946–2718, Mailing Address: P.O. Box 428, Zip 62946–0428; tel. 618/253–7671 **A**1 9 10 20 **F**3 8 11 15 28 29 30 31 34 40 45 50 56 57 59 61 62 64 75 77 78 81 85 87 89 91 93 97 98 99 100 101 102 103 104 105 107 108 110 114 118 119 127 129 130 131 133 146 148
Primary Contact: Rodney Smith, Chief Executive Officer
CFO: John Riley, Chief Financial Officer
CIO: Rick Pyle, Director Information Systems
CNO: Cindy Ford, R.N., Chief Nursing Officer
Web address: www.harrisburgmc.com
**Control:** Other not–for–profit (including NFP Corporation) **Service:** General Medical and Surgical

**Staffed Beds:** 73 **Admissions:** 2489 **Census:** 32 **Outpatient Visits:** 53594 **Births:** 0 **Total Expense ($000):** 41350 **Payroll Expense ($000):** 20385 **Personnel:** 428

## HARVARD—Mchenry County

⊞ **MERCY HARVARD HOSPITAL (141335)**, 901 Grant Street, Zip 60033–1898, Mailing Address: P.O. Box 850, Zip 60033–0850; tel. 815/943–5431, (Total facility includes 22 beds in nursing home–type unit) **A**1 9 10 18 **F**3 11 12 15 28 29 30 35 40 45 46 53 57 59 64 69 70 75 77 79 81 82 85 87 93 94 96 97 107 108 109 114 119 128 129 130 132 143 146 **P**6 **S** Mercy Health System, Janesville, WI
Primary Contact: Jennifer Hallatt, Chief Operating Officer
CFO: John Cook, Chief Financial Officer
CHR: Heather Niles, Director Human Resources Operations
Web address: www.mercyhealthsystem.org
**Control:** Other not–for–profit (including NFP Corporation) **Service:** General Medical and Surgical

**Staffed Beds:** 35 **Admissions:** 637 **Census:** 22 **Outpatient Visits:** 55458 **Births:** 0 **Total Expense ($000):** 21623 **Payroll Expense ($000):** 9437 **Personnel:** 90

## HARVEY—Cook County

★ △ ◇ **INGALLS MEMORIAL HOSPITAL (140191)**, One Ingalls Drive, Zip 60426–3591; tel. 708/333–2300 **A**2 7 9 10 21 **F**3 5 8 11 13 15 18 20 22 24 26 28 29 30 31 34 35 36 37 40 41 42 43 45 46 47 49 50 51 54 56 57 58 59 60 62 63 64 68 70 74 75 76 77 78 79 81 82 84 85 86 87 89 90 92 93 94 97 98 99 101 102 103 104 105 107 108 110 111 113 114 115 116 117 118 119 120 121 123 124 129 130 131 132 135 143 144 146 147 148 **P**8
Primary Contact: Kurt E. Johnson, President and Chief Executive Officer
CFO: Andrew Stefo, Senior Vice President Finance and Chief Financial Officer
CHR: Aletha Ross, Vice President Human Resources
Web address: www.ingallshealthsystem.org
**Control:** Other not–for–profit (including NFP Corporation) **Service:** General Medical and Surgical

**Staffed Beds:** 344 **Admissions:** 17011 **Census:** 223 **Outpatient Visits:** 373567 **Births:** 1036 **Total Expense ($000):** 270495 **Payroll Expense ($000):** 104004 **Personnel:** 1654

## HAVANA—Mason County

⊞ **MASON DISTRICT HOSPITAL (141313)**, 615 North Promenade Street, Zip 62644–1243, Mailing Address: P.O. Box 530, Zip 62644–0530; tel. 309/543–4431 **A**1 9 10 18 **F**7 8 11 15 18 28 29 30 34 35 40 42 45 49 50 53 54 56 57 59 62 64 65 68 69 75 79 81 93 97 103 107 108 110 114 118 119 127 129 130 132 133 143 146 **P**6
Primary Contact: Harry Wolin, Administrator and Chief Executive Officer
CFO: Robert J. Stolba, Chief Financial Officer
CMO: James T. Brown, M.D., President of Medical Staff
CIO: Aaron Coats, Information Technology Director
CHR: Anne Davis, Director Human Resources
CNO: Carman Wuebbels, R.N., Chief Nursing Officer and Assistant Administrator
Web address: www.masondistricthospital.org
**Control:** Hospital district or authority, Government, nonfederal **Service:** General Medical and Surgical

**Staffed Beds:** 20 **Admissions:** 307 **Census:** 2 **Outpatient Visits:** 24432 **Births:** 0 **Total Expense ($000):** 21307 **Payroll Expense ($000):** 10564 **Personnel:** 223

## HAZEL CREST—Cook County

⊞ ◇ **ADVOCATE SOUTH SUBURBAN HOSPITAL (140250)**, 17800 South Kedzie Avenue, Zip 60429–0989; tel. 708/799–8000, (Total facility includes 37 beds in nursing home–type unit) **A**1 2 9 10 21 **F**3 11 13 15 18 20 22 24 26 28 29 30 31 34 35 36 40 45 46 47 49 50 51 53 57 59 60 63 64 68 70 75 76 78 79 81 82 85 87 89 107 108 110 111 114 115 118 119 126 128 129 130 132 145 146 147 148 **P**8 **S** Advocate Health Care, Downers Grove, IL
Primary Contact: Richard Heim, President
COO: Karen Clark, MS, Vice President Operations
CFO: Brian Kelly, Vice President Finance
CIO: Beth Turek, Site Manager Information Systems
Web address: www.advocatehealth.com/ssub/
**Control:** Church–operated, Nongovernment, not–for profit **Service:** General Medical and Surgical

**Staffed Beds:** 240 **Admissions:** 12306 **Census:** 144 **Outpatient Visits:** 115934 **Births:** 924 **Total Expense ($000):** 187889 **Payroll Expense ($000):** 68291 **Personnel:** 935

## HERRIN—Williamson County

☐ **HERRIN HOSPITAL (140011)**, 201 South 14th Street, Zip 62948–3631; tel. 618/942–2171 **A**1 5 9 10 **F**3 11 12 18 28 29 30 34 35 40 45 47 49 50 54 56 57 59 60 61 64 68 70 74 75 78 79 81 82 84 85 86 87 90 92 93 100 107 108 111 114 115 119 130 131 132 135 143 146 148 **S** Southern Illinois Hospital Services, Carbondale, IL
Primary Contact: Terence Farrell, Administrator
CFO: Michael Kasser, Chief Financial Officer
CMO: Michelle Jenkins, M.D., President Medical Staff
CIO: David Holland, Chief Information Officer
CHR: Teresa A. Lovellette, Manager Human Resources
Web address: www.sih.net
**Control:** Other not–for–profit (including NFP Corporation) **Service:** General Medical and Surgical

**Staffed Beds:** 114 **Admissions:** 5506 **Census:** 75 **Outpatient Visits:** 98562 **Births:** 0 **Total Expense ($000):** 110755 **Payroll Expense ($000):** 32688 **Personnel:** 646

## HIGHLAND—Madison County

⊞ **ST. JOSEPH'S HOSPITAL (141336)**, 1515 Main Street, Zip 62249–1656; tel. 618/654–7421 **A**1 9 10 18 **F**8 11 15 18 26 28 29 30 34 35 40 41 44 45 47 49 51 57 59 64 65 68 69 70 74 75 77 78 81 82 84 85 86 87 90 92 93 97 107 108 110 111 114 119 128 129 130 131 132 133 135 146 147 **S** Hospital Sisters Health System, Springfield, IL
Primary Contact: Peggy A. Sebastian, MSN, R.N., President and Chief Executive Officer
CFO: James Johnson, Chief Financial Officer
CMO: A. Greg Miranda, D.O., President Medical Staff
Web address: www.stjosephshighland.com
**Control:** Church–operated, Nongovernment, not–for profit **Service:** General Medical and Surgical

**Staffed Beds:** 25 **Admissions:** 1120 **Census:** 13 **Outpatient Visits:** 47187 **Births:** 0 **Total Expense ($000):** 29404 **Payroll Expense ($000):** 8668 **Personnel:** 194

## HIGHLAND PARK—Lake County

**NORTHSHORE HIGHLAND PARK HOSPITAL** See NorthShore University Health System Evanston Hospital, Evanston

*Many Facility Codes have changed. Please refer to the AHA Guide Code Chart.*

IL

**HILLSBORO—Montgomery County**

☒ **HILLSBORO AREA HOSPITAL (141332)**, 1200 East Tremont Street, Zip 62049–1900; tel. 217/532–6111 **A**1 9 10 18 **F**10 15 28 29 30 34 35 40 56 57 59 64 65 75 77 79 81 85 86 87 89 92 93 94 97 107 110 115 125 129 130 131 133 135 146 148 **S** HealthTech Management Services, Franklin, TN
Primary Contact: Rex H. Brown, Chief Executive Officer
CFO: Terri L. Carroll, Vice President Financial Services
CHR: Sharon Clark, Director Human Resources
Web address: www.hillsborohealth.org
**Control:** Other not–for–profit (including NFP Corporation) **Service:** General Medical and Surgical

Staffed Beds: 25 Admissions: 519 Census: 7 Outpatient Visits: 22175 Births: 0 Total Expense ($000): 16783 Payroll Expense ($000): 6138 Personnel: 165

**HINES—Cook County**

☒ △ **EDWARD HINES, JR. VETERANS AFFAIRS HOSPITAL**, (Formerly Veterans Affairs Edward Hines, Jr. Hospital), 5000 South Fifth Avenue, Zip 60141–3030, Mailing Address: P.O. Box 5000, Zip 60141–5000; tel. 708/202–8387 **A**1 2 3 5 7 8 **F**1 3 4 5 6 7 9 12 14 15 16 17 18 20 22 24 26 28 29 30 31 34 35 36 38 39 40 44 45 46 47 48 49 50 53 56 57 58 59 60 61 63 64 65 66 68 70 71 74 75 77 78 79 81 82 83 84 86 87 90 91 92 93 94 96 97 98 100 101 102 103 104 105 106 107 108 109 110 111 112 113 115 116 117 119 120 121 122 123 124 126 127 128 129 130 131 132 135 143 144 146 147 148 **S** Department of Veterans Affairs, Washington, DC
Primary Contact: Joan M. Ricard, R.N., FACHE, Director
COO: Nathan L. Geraths, Director
CFO: Raleigh Beard, Chief Fiscal Services
CMO: Barbara Temeck, M.D., Chief of Staff
CIO: Gordon Brown, Chief Information Resources Management
CHR: Clare Hadjuk, Director Human Resources
Web address: www.hines.va.gov/
**Control:** Veterans Affairs, Government, federal **Service:** General Medical and Surgical

Staffed Beds: 450 Admissions: 9800 Census: 437 Outpatient Visits: 770000 Births: 0 Personnel: 3064

☐ **JOHN J. MADDEN MENTAL HEALTH CENTER (144028)**, 1200 South First Avenue, Zip 60141–0800; tel. 708/338–7202, (Nonreporting) **A**1 3 5 10 **S** Division of Mental Health, Department of Human Services, Springfield, IL
Primary Contact: Edith Newman, Interim Administrator
CFO: Janice Evans, Chief Financial Officer
**Control:** State–Government, nonfederal **Service:** Psychiatric

Staffed Beds: 150

**VETERANS AFFAIRS EDWARD HINES, JR. HOSPITAL** See Edward Hines, Jr. Veterans Affairs Hospital

**HINSDALE—DuPage County**

☒ △ **ADVENTIST HINSDALE HOSPITAL (140122)**, 120 North Oak Street, Zip 60521–3890; tel. 630/856–9000 **A**1 2 3 5 7 9 10 13 **F**3 5 8 11 12 13 14 15 18 20 22 24 26 27 28 29 30 31 34 35 37 38 39 40 43 44 45 47 48 49 52 54 55 56 57 58 59 61 62 63 64 68 70 72 73 74 75 76 78 79 81 82 84 85 86 87 88 89 90 92 96 97 98 99 100 101 102 103 104 105 107 108 110 111 114 115 118 119 120 121 123 124 126 129 130 131 132 136 141 146 147 148 **P**7 8 **S** Adventist Health System Sunbelt Health Care Corporation, Altamonte Springs, FL
Primary Contact: Michael Goebel, Chief Executive Officer
CFO: Rebecca Mathis, Vice President and Chief Financial Officer
CMO: Gary Lipinski, M.D., Regional Vice President and Chief Medical Officer
CIO: Joe Granneman, Chief Information Officer
CHR: Donald Russell, Regional Vice President Human Resources
CNO: Shawn O. Tyrrell, R.N., VP/Chief Nursing Officer
Web address: www.keepingyouwell.com
**Control:** Church–operated, Nongovernment, not–for profit **Service:** General Medical and Surgical

Staffed Beds: 277 Admissions: 12839 Census: 156 Outpatient Visits: 270940 Births: 2000 Total Expense ($000): 283804 Payroll Expense ($000): 100118 Personnel: 1891

☒ **RML SPECIALTY HOSPITAL (142010)**, 5601 South County Line Road, Zip 60521–4875; tel. 630/286–4000 **A**1 5 9 10 **F**1 3 18 29 31 50 58 74 85 87 107 114 119 130 132 146 148
Primary Contact: James R. Prister, President and Chief Executive Officer
COO: Ken Pawola, Chief Operating Officer
CFO: Tom Pater, Chief Financial Officer
CMO: John Brofman, M.D., Medical Director
CIO: Julie Ames, Chief Information Officer
CHR: John Landstrom, Director Human Resources
CNO: Maura Hopkins, R.N., Chief Nursing Officer
Web address: www.rmlspecialtyhospital.org
**Control:** Other not–for–profit (including NFP Corporation) **Service:** Long–Term Acute Care hospital

Staffed Beds: 87 Admissions: 849 Census: 71 Outpatient Visits: 0 Births: 0 Total Expense ($000): 47244 Payroll Expense ($000): 23518 Personnel: 372

**HOFFMAN ESTATES—Cook County**

☒ **ALEXIAN BROTHERS BEHAVIORAL HEALTH HOSPITAL (144031)**, 1650 Moon Lake Boulevard, Zip 60169–1010; tel. 847/882–1600 **A**1 5 9 10 **F**4 5 29 30 34 35 44 50 56 58 59 65 68 75 77 87 98 99 100 101 102 103 104 105 130 132 **P**4 **S** Ascension Health, Saint Louis, MO
Primary Contact: Clayton Ciha, President and Chief Executive Officer
COO: Christopher Novak, Chief Operating Officer
CFO: David Jones, Chief Financial Officer
CMO: Gregory Teas, M.D., Chief Medical Officer
CIO: Sherrie Russell, Vice President and Chief Information Officer
CHR: James Lewandowski, Vice President Corporate Human Resources
CNO: Christine Quinlan, MS, Chief Nursing Officer
Web address: www.abbhh.org
**Control:** Church–operated, Nongovernment, not–for profit **Service:** Psychiatric

Staffed Beds: 141 Admissions: 6355 Census: 130 Outpatient Visits: 145084 Births: 0 Total Expense ($000): 61655 Payroll Expense ($000): 33970 Personnel: 557

☒ **ST. ALEXIUS MEDICAL CENTER (140290)**, 1555 Barrington Road, Zip 60169–1019; tel. 847/843–2000 **A**1 2 3 5 9 10 **F**3 12 13 15 17 18 20 22 26 29 30 31 34 35 37 39 40 41 43 45 46 47 48 49 50 54 55 56 57 59 63 70 72 73 74 75 76 77 78 79 81 82 84 85 86 87 88 89 93 107 108 110 111 114 115 119 120 121 126 130 132 145 146 147 148 **P**6 **S** Ascension Health, Saint Louis, MO
Primary Contact: Leonard Wilk, President and Chief Executive Officer
CFO: Sherril Vincent, Vice President Finance/CFO, Alexian Brothers Acute Care Ministries
CMO: Scott Neeley, M.D., Chief Medical Officer
CIO: Sherrie Russell, Chief Information Officer
CHR: Linda Baker, Director Human Resources
CNO: Chris Budzinsky, R.N., Vice President Nursing/CNO Alexian Brothers Acute Care Ministries
Web address: www.stalexius.org
**Control:** Church–operated, Nongovernment, not–for profit **Service:** General Medical and Surgical

Staffed Beds: 305 Admissions: 16334 Census: 189 Outpatient Visits: 241328 Births: 2984 Total Expense ($000): 291973 Payroll Expense ($000): 102615 Personnel: 1450

**HOOPESTON—Vermilion County**

☒ ◇ **HOOPESTON REGIONAL HEALTH CENTER (141316)**, 701 East Orange Street, Zip 60942–1801; tel. 217/283–5531, (Nonreporting) **A**1 9 10 18 21
Primary Contact: Harry Brockus, Chief Executive Officer
COO: Jacqueline Johnson, Chief Clinical Officer
CIO: Bernie McCarty, Director Facilities
CHR: Betsy Morgenroth, Director Human Resources
Web address: www.carle.org
**Control:** Other not–for–profit (including NFP Corporation) **Service:** General Medical and Surgical

Staffed Beds: 99

**HOPEDALE—Tazewell County**

**HOPEDALE MEDICAL COMPLEX (141330)**, 107 Tremont Street, Zip 61747–7525; tel. 309/449–3321, (Nonreporting) **A**9 10 18
Primary Contact: Alfred N. Rossi, M.D., Chief Executive Officer
COO: Mark F. Rossi, Chief Operating Officer and General Counsel
CFO: Larry Kloc, Chief Financial Officer
CHR: Ann Wilson, Acting Director Human Resources
Web address: www.hopedalemc.com
**Control:** Other not–for–profit (including NFP Corporation) **Service:** General Medical and Surgical

Staffed Beds: 25

IL

Hospital, Medicare Provider Number, Address, Telephone, Approval, Facility, and Physician Codes, Health Care System

★ American Hospital Association (AHA) membership
☐ The Joint Commission accreditation
◇ DNV Healthcare Inc. accreditation
○ Healthcare Facilities Accreditation Program
△ Commission on Accreditation of Rehabilitation Facilities (CARF) accreditation

## JACKSONVILLE—Morgan County

✠ **PASSAVANT AREA HOSPITAL (140058)**, 1600 West Walnut Street, Zip 62650–1136; tel. 217/245–9541, (Total facility includes 15 beds in nursing home–type unit) **A**1 9 10 **F**3 8 11 12 13 15 28 29 30 34 35 38 40 45 47 48 50 51 56 57 59 64 68 69 70 71 75 76 77 79 81 82 85 86 87 89 90 93 96 100 102 104 107 108 111 115 119 128 129 130 131 132 146 148 **P**4 6
Primary Contact: Chester A. Wynn, President and Chief Executive Officer
CFO: David Bolen, Vice President and Chief Financial Officer
CMO: Tara Ramsey, M.D., President Medical Staff
CIO: Marc E. Steinberg, Vice President Community Relations and Physician Recruitment
CHR: Rick A. Mogler, Director Human Resources
Web address: www.passavanthospital.com
**Control:** Other not–for–profit (including NFP Corporation) **Service:** General Medical and Surgical

**Staffed Beds:** 108 **Admissions:** 3645 **Census:** 47 **Outpatient Visits:** 82402 **Births:** 351 **Total Expense ($000):** 76570 **Payroll Expense ($000):** 32037 **Personnel:** 732

## JERSEYVILLE—Jersey County

✠ **JERSEY COMMUNITY HOSPITAL (140059)**, 400 Maple Summit Road, Zip 62052–2028, Mailing Address: P.O. Box 426, Zip 62052–0426; tel. 618/498–6402 **A**1 9 10 **F**3 7 8 11 12 13 15 28 29 31 34 35 36 40 45 53 57 59 65 68 69 70 74 75 76 77 79 81 85 86 89 93 107 108 110 111 115 119 129 130 131 132 133 134 135 146 147 148
Primary Contact: Lawrence P. Bear, Administrator and Chief Executive Officer
COO: Lawrence P. Bear, Administrator and Chief Executive Officer
CFO: David Kennett, Chief Financial Officer
CMO: Julie Smith, R.N., Director of Nursing
CIO: Bob Bray, Chief Information Officer
CHR: Sharon K. Sanford, Director Human Resources
Web address: www.jch.org
**Control:** Hospital district or authority, Government, nonfederal **Service:** General Medical and Surgical

**Staffed Beds:** 49 **Admissions:** 1263 **Census:** 10 **Outpatient Visits:** 45105 **Births:** 164 **Total Expense ($000):** 20078 **Payroll Expense ($000):** 11305 **Personnel:** 260

## JOLIET—Will County

✠ △ **PRESENCE SAINT JOSEPH MEDICAL CENTER (140007)**, (Formerly Provena Saint Joseph Medical Center), 333 North Madison Street, Zip 60435–8200; tel. 815/725–7133 **A**1 2 5 7 9 10 **F**3 5 8 11 12 13 15 17 18 20 22 24 26 28 29 30 31 32 34 35 36 37 38 39 40 41 43 44 45 46 49 50 53 54 56 57 58 59 60 65 68 70 72 74 75 76 77 78 79 80 81 82 84 85 86 87 88 89 90 92 93 96 97 98 99 100 101 102 103 105 107 108 110 111 114 115 118 119 120 121 123 124 126 129 130 131 132 134 135 143 144 145 146 147 **P**8 **S** Presence Health, Chicago, IL
Primary Contact: Beth Hughes, President and Chief Executive Officer
COO: Amy Dirks Stevens, Chief Operating Officer
CFO: Gary Gasbarra, Regional Chief Financial Officer
CMO: David R. Franzblau, M.D., Chief Medical Officer
CIO: Russell Soliman, System Manager Client Services and Management Information Services
CHR: Terry S. Solem, System Vice President Human Resources
Web address: www.provena.org/stjoes
**Control:** Church–operated, Nongovernment, not–for profit **Service:** General Medical and Surgical

**Staffed Beds:** 457 **Admissions:** 25025 **Census:** 302 **Outpatient Visits:** 534546 **Births:** 1459 **Total Expense ($000):** 364779 **Payroll Expense ($000):** 135600 **Personnel:** 2085

**PROVENA SAINT JOSEPH MEDICAL CENTER** See Presence Saint Joseph Medical Center

**SILVER CROSS HOSPITAL** See Silver Cross Hospital, New Lenox

## KANKAKEE—Kankakee County

✠ **PRESENCE ST. MARY'S HOSPITAL (140155)**, (Formerly Provena St. Mary's Hospital), 500 West Court Street, Zip 60901–3661; tel. 815/937–2400 **A**1 2 9 10 **F**3 5 11 12 13 15 18 20 22 26 28 29 30 31 32 34 35 36 38 39 40 43 45 48 49 50 53 54 56 57 58 59 60 61 64 65 68 70 74 75 76 77 78 79 81 82 83 84 85 86 87 89 92 93 97 98 99 100 101 102 103 104 105 106 107 108 110 111 114 115 116 119 129 130 131 132 135 143 146 147 148 **S** Presence Health, Chicago, IL
Primary Contact: Amy LaFine, R.N., MSN, President and Chief Executive Officer
CFO: Frank McHugh, Chief Financial Officer
CIO: Russell Soliman, Director Information Services
CNO: Barbara Decker, R.N., Chief Nursing Officer
Web address: www.provena.org/stmarys/
**Control:** Church–operated, Nongovernment, not–for profit **Service:** General Medical and Surgical

**Staffed Beds:** 143 **Admissions:** 6801 **Census:** 78 **Outpatient Visits:** 211272 **Births:** 495 **Total Expense ($000):** 125775 **Payroll Expense ($000):** 41251 **Personnel:** 743

**PROVENA ST. MARY'S HOSPITAL** See Presence St. Mary's Hospital

## RIVERSIDE MEDICAL CENTER

✠ ◇ **RIVERSIDE MEDICAL CENTER (140186)**, 350 North Wall Street, Zip 60901–2901; tel. 815/933–1671 **A**1 2 5 9 10 13 21 **F**3 4 5 6 7 8 9 11 12 13 15 17 18 19 20 22 24 26 28 29 30 31 32 34 35 36 38 39 40 41 43 44 45 46 47 48 49 50 51 54 55 56 57 58 59 61 62 64 65 66 68 70 71 74 75 76 77 78 79 81 82 84 85 86 87 89 90 92 93 96 97 98 99 100 101 102 103 104 105 106 107 108 110 111 114 115 118 119 120 121 123 126 127 129 130 131 132 134 135 141 143 145 146 147 148
Primary Contact: Phillip M. Kambic, Chief Executive Officer
COO: David Duda, Senior Vice President and Chief Operating Officer
CFO: Bill Douglas, Senior Vice President and Chief Financial Officer
CMO: John Jurica, M.D., Vice President Medical Affairs
CIO: Kyle Hansen, Corporate Director Information Systems
CHR: Becky Hinrichs, Vice President Human Resources
CNO: Allen Kelly, R.N., Vice President Procedural Services & CNO
Web address: www.riversidehealthcare.org
**Control:** Other not–for–profit (including NFP Corporation) **Service:** General Medical and Surgical

**Staffed Beds:** 325 **Admissions:** 11043 **Census:** 142 **Outpatient Visits:** 348952 **Births:** 925 **Total Expense ($000):** 225492 **Payroll Expense ($000):** 89946 **Personnel:** 1672

## KEWANEE—Henry County

★ **KEWANEE HOSPITAL (141325)**, 1051 West South Street, Zip 61443–8354, Mailing Address: P.O. Box 747, Zip 61443–0747; tel. 309/852–7500 **A**9 10 18 **F**3 11 15 18 29 31 32 34 35 36 38 40 45 50 57 59 64 65 66 68 70 75 77 78 79 81 82 85 86 87 92 93 96 97 107 108 110 115 119 127 129 131 132 133 135 146 148 **P**6
Primary Contact: Lynn Fulton, Chief Executive Officer
CFO: Preston Becker, Chief Financial Officer
CIO: Jeremy Johnson, Director of Information Technology
CHR: Renee A. Salisbury, Director Human Resources
CNO: Jennifer Junis, MSN, Chief Nursing Officer
Web address: www.kewaneehospital.com
**Control:** Other not–for–profit (including NFP Corporation) **Service:** General Medical and Surgical

**Staffed Beds:** 25 **Admissions:** 661 **Census:** 6 **Outpatient Visits:** 33477 **Births:** 0 **Total Expense ($000):** 25240 **Payroll Expense ($000):** 9594 **Personnel:** 189

## LA GRANGE—Cook County

✠ **ADVENTIST LA GRANGE MEMORIAL HOSPITAL (140065)**, 5101 South Willow Spring Road, Zip 60525–2600; tel. 708/245–9000 **A**1 2 3 5 9 10 13 **F**3 12 13 15 17 18 20 22 24 26 28 29 30 31 34 35 37 39 40 43 44 45 49 50 56 57 58 59 60 61 64 68 70 73 74 75 76 78 79 81 82 85 86 87 93 96 97 100 107 108 110 111 114 115 116 117 119 120 121 123 126 129 130 131 132 135 146 147 148 **P**7 8 **S** Adventist Health System Sunbelt Health Care Corporation, Altamonte Springs, FL
Primary Contact: Lary Davis, President and Chief Executive Officer
COO: Edward Gervain, Chief Operating Officer
CFO: Keith Richardson, Chief Financial Officer
CMO: Gary Lipinski, M.D., Regional Vice President and Chief Medical Officer
CIO: Russ Solimon, Chief Information Officer
CHR: Patty Sanchez, Site Manager Human Resources
Web address: www.keepingyouwell.com
**Control:** Church–operated, Nongovernment, not–for profit **Service:** General Medical and Surgical

**Staffed Beds:** 187 **Admissions:** 8453 **Census:** 103 **Outpatient Visits:** 116700 **Births:** 504 **Total Expense ($000):** 153884 **Payroll Expense ($000):** 55507 **Personnel:** 976

## LAKE FOREST—Lake County

**LAKE FOREST HOSPITAL** See Northwestern Lake Forest Hospital

✠ **NORTHWESTERN LAKE FOREST HOSPITAL (140130)**, 660 North Westmoreland Road, Zip 60045–1696; tel. 847/234–5600, (Total facility includes 72 beds in nursing home–type unit) **A**1 2 3 5 9 10 **F**2 3 8 9 11 13 15 18 20 22 26 28 29 30 31 32 34 35 36 38 40 42 43 44 45 46 48 49 50 51 53 54 56 57 58 59 62 64 65 70 73 74 75 76 77 78 79 81 82 85 86 87 89 92 93 96 97 107 108 110 111 114 115 116 117 119 120 121 123 128 129 130 131 132 135 146 147 148 **P**6 8 **S** Northwestern Memorial Healthcare, Chicago, IL
Primary Contact: Thomas J. McAfee, President
CFO: Matthew J. Flynn, Senior Vice President and Chief Financial Officer
CMO: Michael G. Ankin, M.D., Vice President Medical Affairs & Chief Medical Officer
CIO: Timothy R. Zoph, Senior Vice President and Chief Information Officer
CHR: Marsha Oberrieder, Vice President Operations
CNO: Kimberly Nagy, R.N., Vice President Operations and Chief Nurse Executive
Web address: www.lfh.org
**Control:** Other not–for–profit (including NFP Corporation) **Service:** General Medical and Surgical

**Staffed Beds:** 188 **Admissions:** 9306 **Census:** 134 **Outpatient Visits:** 210078 **Births:** 1662 **Total Expense ($000):** 245067 **Payroll Expense ($000):** 86456 **Personnel:** 1259

IL

*Many Facility Codes have changed. Please refer to the AHA Guide Code Chart.* © 2013 AHA Guide

**LAWRENCEVILLE—Lawrence County**

★ **LAWRENCE COUNTY MEMORIAL HOSPITAL (141344)**, 2200 West State Street, Zip 62439–1852; tel. 618/943–1000 **A**9 10 18 **F**3 11 15 28 30 40 75 81 93 107 114 127 130 133 **S** QHR, Brentwood, TN
Primary Contact: Doug Florkowski, Chief Executive Officer
CFO: Jerry Klein, Chief Financial Officer
CHR: Kim Kendall, Director Human Resources
Web address: www.lcmhosp.org
**Control:** Other not–for–profit (including NFP Corporation) **Service:** General Medical and Surgical

Staffed Beds: 25 Admissions: 790 Census: 8 Outpatient Visits: 30570
Births: 0 Total Expense ($000): 12310 Payroll Expense ($000): 4556
Personnel: 123

**LIBERTYVILLE—Lake County**

⊞ **ADVOCATE CONDELL MEDICAL CENTER (140202)**, 801 South Milwaukee Avenue, Zip 60048–3199; tel. 847/362–2900 **A**1 2 9 10 **F**2 3 11 12 13 15 18 19 20 22 24 26 28 29 30 31 32 34 35 36 37 40 41 43 44 45 46 47 48 49 50 51 53 54 56 57 59 60 64 65 68 70 73 74 75 76 77 78 79 81 82 85 86 87 89 92 93 95 96 107 108 110 111 114 115 117 118 119 120 121 123 126 129 130 131 132 135 144 145 146 147 148 **P**8 **S** Advocate Health Care, Downers Grove, IL
Primary Contact: Dominica Tallarico, President
CFO: David A. Cartwright, Vice President Finance
CMO: Joan Boomsma, M.D., Vice President Medical Management
CIO: Eileen Matzek, Director Information Technology
CHR: Gwenn Leschke, Vice President Human Resources
Web address: www.advocatehealth.com/condell/
**Control:** Other not–for–profit (including NFP Corporation) **Service:** General Medical and Surgical

Staffed Beds: 279 Admissions: 18253 Census: 189 Outpatient Visits: 209180 Births: 2540 Total Expense ($000): 250047 Payroll Expense ($000): 95366 Personnel: 1704

**LINCOLN—Logan County**

⊞ **ABRAHAM LINCOLN MEMORIAL HOSPITAL (141322)**, 200 Stahlhut Drive, Zip 62656–5066; tel. 217/732–2161 **A**1 9 10 18 **F**13 15 28 29 30 34 35 40 57 59 64 71 75 76 77 79 81 82 87 93 107 108 110 111 119 129 130 131 132 133 144 146 **P**5 **S** Memorial Health System, Springfield, IL
Primary Contact: Dolan Dalpoas, President and Chief Executive Officer
COO: Kathleen Vipond, Assistant Administrator and Director
CFO: Andrew Costic, Regional Chief Financial Officer
CMO: Tracy Mizeur, M.D., President Medical Staff
CIO: Darrell Oller, Director Information Systems
CHR: Kaylee Tanner, Human Resources Business Partner
Web address: www.almh.org
**Control:** Other not–for–profit (including NFP Corporation) **Service:** General Medical and Surgical

Staffed Beds: 25 Admissions: 1082 Census: 10 Outpatient Visits: 49719
Births: 208 Total Expense ($000): 35985 Payroll Expense ($000): 13193
Personnel: 267

**LITCHFIELD—Montgomery County**

⊞ **ST. FRANCIS HOSPITAL (141350)**, 1215 Franciscan Drive, Zip 62056–1799, Mailing Address: P.O. Box 1215, Zip 62056–0999; tel. 217/324–2191 **A**1 9 10 18 **F**11 13 15 18 28 29 30 34 35 40 44 45 46 50 56 57 59 64 68 70 74 75 76 77 78 79 81 82 85 86 87 92 93 107 111 114 118 119 129 131 132 133 134 135 146 147 **S** Hospital Sisters Health System, Springfield, IL
Primary Contact: Daniel L. Perryman, President and Chief Executive Officer
COO: Carol Jaco, R.N., Chief Operating Officer and Chief Nursing Officer
CFO: Diane Lindsay, Chief Financial Officer
Web address: www.stfrancis-litchfield.org
**Control:** Church–operated, Nongovernment, not–for profit **Service:** General Medical and Surgical

Staffed Beds: 25 Admissions: 1418 Census: 14 Outpatient Visits: 50244
Births: 416 Total Expense ($000): 29242 Payroll Expense ($000): 10748
Personnel: 198

**MACOMB—Mcdonough County**

⊞ **MCDONOUGH DISTRICT HOSPITAL (140089)**, 525 East Grant Street, Zip 61455–3318; tel. 309/833–4101, (Total facility includes 16 beds in nursing home–type unit) **A**1 9 10 20 **F**2 3 5 7 11 13 15 28 29 31 34 35 40 45 48 51 56 57 59 62 63 64 68 70 75 76 77 78 79 81 82 84 85 86 89 91 93 94 96 97 99 100 101 102 103 104 107 108 110 111 115 116 119 128 129 130 131 132 135 146 148 **P**8
Primary Contact: Kenneth Boyd, Jr., President and Chief Executive Officer
COO: Lori Moon, R.N., Vice President Clinical Operations/Business Development
CFO: Linda Dace, Vice President Finance
CMO: Christopher Stortzum, M.D., President Medical Staff
CIO: Harlan T. Baker, Department Leader Information Systems
CHR: Sue Dexter, Administrative Department Leader Human Resources
CNO: Wanda Foster, R.N., Vice President Nursing
Web address: www.mdh.org
**Control:** Hospital district or authority, Government, nonfederal **Service:** General Medical and Surgical

Staffed Beds: 95 Admissions: 2313 Census: 26 Outpatient Visits: 145043
Births: 331 Total Expense ($000): 60297 Payroll Expense ($000): 29155
Personnel: 540

**MARION—Williamson County**

⊞ **HEARTLAND REGIONAL MEDICAL CENTER (140184)**, 3333 West DeYoung, Zip 62959–5884; tel. 618/998–7000, (Nonreporting) **A**1 9 10 **S** Community Health Systems, Inc., Franklin, TN
Primary Contact: Stephen Lunn, Chief Executive Officer
CFO: Loren Rials, Chief Financial Officer
CHR: Ed Daech, Director Human Resources
Web address: www.heartlandregional.com
**Control:** Corporation, Investor–owned, for–profit **Service:** General Medical and Surgical

Staffed Beds: 92

⊞ **MARION VETERANS AFFAIRS MEDICAL CENTER**, (Formerly Veterans Affairs Medical Center), 2401 West Main Street, Zip 62959–1188; tel. 618/997–5311, (Nonreporting) **A**1 3 5 **S** Department of Veterans Affairs, Washington, DC
Primary Contact: Brent A. Thelen, Ph.D., Interim Director
COO: Frank Kehus, Associate Director for Operations
CFO: Wayne Morris, Chief Financial Officer
CMO: Farhana Hasan, M.D., Chief of Staff
CIO: Clint Bishop, Program Manager
CHR: Tonya L. Searby, Chief Human Resources
CNO: Barbara Southworth, R.N., Associate Director for Patient Care Services
Web address: www.marion.va.gov
**Control:** Veterans Affairs, Government, federal **Service:** General Medical and Surgical

Staffed Beds: 225

**MARYVILLE—Madison County**

⊞ △ **ANDERSON HOSPITAL (140289)**, 6800 State Route 162, Zip 62062–8500; tel. 618/288–5711 **A**1 7 9 10 **F**3 11 13 15 18 20 22 28 29 30 34 35 40 49 51 57 59 62 63 70 74 75 76 78 79 81 82 85 90 93 107 108 110 111 115 118 119 120 124 126 129 130 132 144 146 147 148
Primary Contact: Keith Allen Page, President and Chief Executive Officer
CFO: Michael Marshall, Vice President Finance and Chief Financial Officer
CMO: Michael Mulligan, M.D., President Medical Staff
CIO: Michael Ward, Director Information Services
CHR: Robin Steinmann, Administrative Director Human Resources
CNO: Lisa Klaustermeier, R.N., Chief Nursing Officer
Web address: www.andersonhospital.org
**Control:** Other not–for–profit (including NFP Corporation) **Service:** General Medical and Surgical

Staffed Beds: 154 Admissions: 6963 Census: 75 Outpatient Visits: 178679
Births: 1732 Total Expense ($000): 133121 Payroll Expense ($000): 45788 Personnel: 886

IL

---

| Hospital, Medicare Provider Number, Address, Telephone, Approval, Facility, and Physician Codes, Health Care System | |
|---|---|
| ★ American Hospital Association (AHA) membership | ○ Healthcare Facilities Accreditation Program |
| ☐ The Joint Commission accreditation ◇ DNV Healthcare Inc. accreditation | △ Commission on Accreditation of Rehabilitation Facilities (CARF) accreditation |

## MATTOON—Coles County

✠ **SARAH BUSH LINCOLN HEALTH CENTER (140189)**, 1000 Health Center Drive, Zip 61938–9253, Mailing Address: P.O. Box 372, Zip 61938–0372; tel. 217/258–2525 **A**1 9 10 20 **F**3 11 12 13 15 18 20 22 28 29 30 31 32 34 35 36 38 39 40 44 47 48 49 50 54 56 57 59 61 62 63 64 65 66 68 69 70 71 74 75 76 77 78 79 81 82 84 85 86 87 89 93 97 98 99 100 101 102 103 104 105 107 110 111 115 119 120 121 123 127 129 130 131 132 134 135 144 145 146 147 148 **P**6
Primary Contact: Timothy A. Ols, FACHE, President and Chief Executive Officer
COO: Dennis Pluard, Vice President Operations
CFO: Craig Sheagren, Vice President Finance
CMO: James Hildebrandt, D.O., President Medical Staff
CIO: Mike DeLuca, Vice President Information Systems
CHR: Eric Benson, Vice President Human Resources
CNO: Mary Lou Wild, Vice President Patient Care Services
Web address: www.sarahbush.org
**Control:** Other not–for–profit (including NFP Corporation) **Service:** General Medical and Surgical

**Staffed Beds:** 118 **Admissions:** 6968 **Census:** 67 **Outpatient Visits:** 458201 **Births:** 760 **Total Expense ($000):** 182540 **Payroll Expense ($000):** 92151 **Personnel:** 1457

## MAYWOOD—Cook County

✠ △ **LOYOLA UNIVERSITY MEDICAL CENTER (140276)**, 2160 South First Avenue, Zip 60153–3328; tel. 708/216–9000, (Includes RONALD MCDONALD CHILDREN'S HOSPITAL, 2160 South 1St. Avenue, tel. 888/584–7888) **A**1 2 3 5 7 8 9 10 **F**3 6 7 8 9 11 12 13 14 15 16 17 18 19 20 21 22 23 24 25 26 27 28 29 30 31 32 33 34 35 36 37 38 39 40 41 43 44 45 46 47 48 49 50 51 54 55 56 57 58 59 60 61 62 63 64 65 66 68 70 71 72 73 74 75 76 77 78 79 80 81 82 84 85 86 87 88 89 90 91 92 93 94 96 97 98 99 100 101 102 103 104 107 108 110 114 115 116 117 118 119 120 121 123 124 126 129 130 131 132 134 135 136 137 138 139 140 141 142 143 144 145 146 147 148 **P**6 **S** Trinity Health, Livonia, MI
Primary Contact: Larry M. Goldberg, President and Chief Executive Officer
CFO: Thomas Honan, Interim Chief Financial Officer
CMO: Robert Cherry, M.D., Chief Medical Officer
CIO: Arthur J. Krumrey, Chief Information Officer
CHR: Vicky Piper, Vice President Human Resources
Web address: www.loyolamedicine.org/Medical_Services/index.cfm
**Control:** Other not–for–profit (including NFP Corporation) **Service:** General Medical and Surgical

**Staffed Beds:** 485 **Admissions:** 23871 **Census:** 341 **Outpatient Visits:** 1382350 **Births:** 912 **Total Expense ($000):** 930485 **Payroll Expense ($000):** 456205 **Personnel:** 5893

## MCHENRY—Mchenry County

✠ **CENTEGRA HOSPITAL – MCHENRY (140116)**, 4201 Medical Center Drive, Zip 60050–8409; tel. 815/344–5000 **A**1 2 5 9 10 **F**3 4 11 13 15 18 20 22 24 26 28 29 30 31 34 35 37 38 39 40 43 44 47 49 50 54 55 57 58 59 62 64 68 69 70 74 75 76 78 79 81 85 86 87 90 92 93 96 100 101 102 107 108 110 111 114 115 116 117 118 119 120 121 123 126 129 130 131 132 143 146 147 148 **P**5 **S** Centegra Health System, Crystal Lake, IL
Primary Contact: Michael S. Eesley, Chief Executive Officer
COO: Jason Sciarro, President and Chief Operating Officer
CFO: Robert Rosenberger, Executive Vice President and Chief Financial Officer
CMO: Ted Lorenc, M.D., Vice President Medical Affairs
CIO: David Tomlinson, Senior Vice President, Chief Information Officer
CHR: Bernadette S. Szczepanski, Vice President, Human Resources Development
CNO: Neil W. Murphy, R.N., Senior Vice President and Chief Nursing Officer
Web address: www.centegra.com
**Control:** Other not–for–profit (including NFP Corporation) **Service:** General Medical and Surgical

**Staffed Beds:** 173 **Admissions:** 10413 **Census:** 118 **Outpatient Visits:** 155694 **Births:** 839 **Total Expense ($000):** 226982 **Payroll Expense ($000):** 88207 **Personnel:** 1046

## MCLEANSBORO—Hamilton County

**HAMILTON MEMORIAL HOSPITAL DISTRICT (141326)**, 611 South Marshall Avenue, Zip 62859–1213, Mailing Address: P.O. Box 429, Mc Leansboro, Zip 62859–0429; tel. 618/643–2361 **A**9 10 18 **F**3 11 15 28 29 40 43 57 81 93 107 108 114 119 127 129 130 133
Primary Contact: Randall W. Dauby, Chief Executive Officer
COO: Bradley Futrell, Chief Operating Officer
CFO: Kent Mitchell, Chief Financial Officer
CIO: Don Darnell, Chief Information Officer
CNO: Patty Blazier, Chief Nursing Officer
Web address: www.hmhospital.org
**Control:** Hospital district or authority, Government, nonfederal **Service:** General Medical and Surgical

**Staffed Beds:** 25 **Admissions:** 845 **Census:** 8 **Outpatient Visits:** 37191 **Births:** 0 **Total Expense ($000):** 13352 **Payroll Expense ($000):** 5497 **Personnel:** 124

## MELROSE PARK—Cook County

✠ **GOTTLIEB MEMORIAL HOSPITAL (140008)**, 701 West North Avenue, Zip 60160–1612; tel. 708/681–3200 **A**1 3 5 9 10 **F**2 3 11 12 13 15 18 20 22 24 26 28 29 30 34 35 36 39 40 43 44 45 47 49 53 54 56 57 59 60 62 63 64 65 68 70 74 75 76 77 78 79 81 85 86 87 89 92 93 96 97 98 103 107 108 110 111 114 118 119 128 129 130 132 143 144 146 147 148 **P**8 **S** Trinity Health, Livonia, MI
Primary Contact: Lori Price, President
COO: Ken Fishbain, Chief Operating Officer
CFO: Ellyn Chin, Vice President Finance
CMO: Gerald Luger, M.D., President Medical Staff
CIO: Maurita Adler, Director Information Services
CHR: Brett Wakefield, Vice President Human Resources
Web address: www.gottliebhospital.org
**Control:** Other not–for–profit (including NFP Corporation) **Service:** General Medical and Surgical

**Staffed Beds:** 255 **Admissions:** 8047 **Census:** 130 **Outpatient Visits:** 90817 **Births:** 732 **Total Expense ($000):** 124192 **Payroll Expense ($000):** 52796 **Personnel:** 901

★ ○ **WESTLAKE HOSPITAL (140240)**, (Formerly Westlake Hospital), 1225 Lake Street, Zip 60160–4000; tel. 708/681–3000, (Nonreporting) **A**3 5 9 10 11 **S** Vanguard Health Systems, Nashville, TN
Primary Contact: Joan Ormsby, Interim Chief Executive Officer
COO: Joan Ormsby, Chief Operating Officer
CFO: Gene Smith, M.D., Interim Chief Financial Officer
CMO: Robert Chase, Chief Medical Officer
CHR: Nancy Gunnell, Vice President Human Resources
CNO: Sharon Freyer, Chief Nursing Unit
Web address: www.wlhospital.com/Home.aspx
**Control:** Corporation, Investor–owned, for–profit **Service:** General Medical and Surgical

**Staffed Beds:** 181

## MENDOTA—Lasalle County

★ **MENDOTA COMMUNITY HOSPITAL (141310)**, 1401 East 12th Street, Zip 61342–9216; tel. 815/539–7461 **A**9 10 18 **F**3 11 15 28 29 31 34 40 49 59 62 65 69 70 77 78 79 81 85 93 107 110 111 115 129 130 133 146 148 **P**6
Primary Contact: Lynn E. Klein, Administrator
CFO: Larry Peach, Assistant Administrator and Chief Financial Officer
CMO: William Schuler, M.D., President Medical Staff
CIO: Gilbert Hermosillo, Manager Information Services
CHR: Kimberly Kennedy, Manager Human Resources
Web address: www.mendotahospital.org
**Control:** Other not–for–profit (including NFP Corporation) **Service:** General Medical and Surgical

**Staffed Beds:** 25 **Admissions:** 921 **Census:** 10 **Outpatient Visits:** 57894 **Births:** 0 **Total Expense ($000):** 31838 **Payroll Expense ($000):** 14404 **Personnel:** 242

## METROPOLIS—Massac County

★ **MASSAC MEMORIAL HOSPITAL (141323)**, 28 Chick Street, Zip 62960–2467, Mailing Address: P.O. Box 850, Zip 62960–0850; tel. 618/524–2176, (Nonreporting) **A**9 10 18
Primary Contact: David G. Fuqua, Chief Executive Officer
CFO: Chelle Keplinger, Chief Financial Officer
CHR: Joel Foster, Director Human Resources
CNO: Janet Barrett, R.N., Chief Nurse Executive
Web address: www.massachealth.org
**Control:** Hospital district or authority, Government, nonfederal **Service:** General Medical and Surgical

**Staffed Beds:** 25

## MOLINE—Rock Island County

**TRINITY MOLINE** See Trinity Rock Island, Rock Island

## MONMOUTH—Warren County

★ **OSF HOLY FAMILY MEDICAL CENTER (141318)**, 1000 West Harlem Avenue, Zip 61462–1007; tel. 309/734–3141 **A**9 10 18 **F**11 15 28 29 30 34 40 45 46 50 57 59 64 65 68 75 77 81 85 87 93 97 107 110 115 118 119 127 129 130 132 133 135 145 146 148 **P**6 **S** OSF Healthcare System, Peoria, IL
Primary Contact: H. William Harker, Chief Executive Officer
CFO: Theresa Springer, Chief Financial Officer
CMO: Ruben Medrano, M.D., President Medical Staff
CIO: Lew McCann, Director Management Information Systems
CHR: Irene Kress, Director Human Resources
Web address: www.osfholyfamily.org
**Control:** Church–operated, Nongovernment, not–for profit **Service:** General Medical and Surgical

**Staffed Beds:** 23 **Admissions:** 456 **Census:** 5 **Outpatient Visits:** 76309 **Births:** 0 **Total Expense ($000):** 23531 **Payroll Expense ($000):** 11595 **Personnel:** 194

*Many Facility Codes have changed. Please refer to the AHA Guide Code Chart.*  © 2013 AHA Guide

**IL**

## MONTICELLO—Piatt County

⊠ **KIRBY MEDICAL CENTER (141301)**, 1000 Medical Center Drive,
Zip 61856–2116; tel. 217/762–2115, (Nonreporting) **A**1 5 9 10 18
Primary Contact: Steven Tenhouse, FACHE, Chief Executive Officer
CFO: C. David Harms, Chief Financial Officer
CMO: Narain Mandhan, M.D., President Medical Staff
CIO: Kyle Willams, Chief Information Officer
Web address: www.kirbyhealth.org
**Control:** Other not–for–profit (including NFP Corporation) **Service:** General
Medical and Surgical

**Staffed Beds:** 16

## MORRIS—Grundy County

★ ○ **MORRIS HOSPITAL & HEALTHCARE CENTERS (140101)**, 150 West
High Street, Zip 60450–1497; tel. 815/942–2932 **A**2 9 10 11 **F**3 11 13 15 18
19 20 22 26 28 29 34 35 40 43 47 49 50 54 57 59 64 66 69 70 74 75 76
77 78 79 81 82 85 86 87 89 93 97 99 102 107 108 110 111 114 115 118
119 120 121 123 130 132 135 143 144 146 **P**6
Primary Contact: Mark B. Steadham, President and Chief Executive Officer
COO: Patrick O'Connor, Chief Operating Officer
CFO: Thomas Meyer, Vice President Finance
CIO: Dean M. Marketti, Chief Information Officer
CHR: Erin Murphy–Frobish, Vice President Human Resources
CNO: Carol Havel, R.N., Vice President Patient Care Services
Web address: www.morrishospital.org
**Control:** Other not–for–profit (including NFP Corporation) **Service:** General
Medical and Surgical

**Staffed Beds:** 89 **Admissions:** 4340 **Census:** 43 **Outpatient Visits:** 232165
**Births:** 587 **Total Expense ($000):** 117107 **Payroll Expense ($000):** 48150
**Personnel:** 655

## MORRISON—Whiteside County

★ **MORRISON COMMUNITY HOSPITAL (141329)**, 303 North Jackson Street,
Zip 61270–3042; tel. 815/772–4003, (Total facility includes 29 beds in nursing
home–type unit) **A**9 10 18 **F**7 11 15 29 33 40 41 44 45 50 57 59 64 65 67 68
77 79 81 82 91 93 96 97 99 100 101 102 104 105 107 110 127 128 130
133 143 148 **S** Trinity Health, Livonia, MI
Primary Contact: Pam Pfister, Interim Chief Executive Officer
COO: Pam Pfister, Associate Administrator
CFO: Cami Megli, Controller
CMO: Duncan Dinkha, M.D., Chief of Staff
CIO: Pam Pfister, Associate Administrator
CHR: Kathy Pennock, Director Human Resources
Web address: www.morrisonhospital.com
**Control:** Hospital district or authority, Government, nonfederal **Service:** General
Medical and Surgical

**Staffed Beds:** 36 **Admissions:** 313 **Census:** 36 **Outpatient Visits:** 23163
**Births:** 0 **Total Expense ($000):** 10804 **Payroll Expense ($000):** 4794
**Personnel:** 130

## MOUNT CARMEL—Wabash County

⊠ **WABASH GENERAL HOSPITAL (141327)**, 1418 College Drive,
Zip 62863–2638; tel. 618/262–8621 **A**1 9 10 18 **F**3 7 11 28 29 31 34 40 45
46 50 59 64 75 77 78 79 81 91 92 94 107 110 111 114 119 127 129 130
131 133 135 143 144 **S** Alliant Management Services, Louisville, KY
Primary Contact: Jay Purvis, Administrator
CFO: Steve McGill, Chief Financial Officer
Web address: www.wabashgeneral.com
**Control:** County–Government, nonfederal **Service:** General Medical and Surgical

**Staffed Beds:** 25 **Admissions:** 682 **Census:** 8 **Outpatient Visits:** 39699
**Births:** 0 **Total Expense ($000):** 30303 **Payroll Expense ($000):** 12729
**Personnel:** 261

## MOUNT VERNON—Jefferson County

⊠ **CROSSROADS COMMUNITY HOSPITAL (140294)**, 8 Doctors Park Road,
Zip 62864–6224; tel. 618/244–5500, (Nonreporting) **A**1 9 10 **S** Community
Health Systems, Inc., Franklin, TN
CMO: Norman Cohen, M.D., Chief Medical Officer
CIO: Regina Garrett, Director Health Information Management
CHR: Reva Weems, Director Human Resources
Web address: www.crossroadscommunityhospital.com
**Control:** Corporation, Investor–owned, for–profit **Service:** General Medical and
Surgical

**Staffed Beds:** 41

## GOOD SAMARITAN REGIONAL HEALTH CENTER (140046), 605 North 12th

⊠ **GOOD SAMARITAN REGIONAL HEALTH CENTER (140046)**, 605 North 12th
Street, Zip 62864–2899; tel. 618/242–4600 **A**1 2 9 10 19 **F**3 11 13 15 18 20
22 24 26 28 29 30 31 34 35 38 40 44 45 46 50 51 54 56 57 59 61 64 68
70 74 75 76 77 78 79 80 81 82 84 85 86 87 89 90 93 94 107 108 110 111
114 115 119 126 130 131 132 135 145 146 147 148 **P**6 8 **S** SSM Health
Care, Saint Louis, MO
Primary Contact: Michael D. Warren, President
COO: Chris Adams, Vice President Operations
CFO: Kay Tinsley, Vice President Fiscal Services
CMO: Daniel Hoffman, M.D., Administrative Medical Director
CIO: Steve Murphy, Director Networks
CHR: Thomas W. Blythe, Regional Vice President Human Resources
Web address: www.smgsi.com
**Control:** Church–operated, Nongovernment, not–for profit **Service:** General
Medical and Surgical

**Staffed Beds:** 146 **Admissions:** 6821 **Census:** 70 **Outpatient Visits:** 207028
**Births:** 865 **Total Expense ($000):** 126068 **Payroll Expense ($000):** 45173
**Personnel:** 1046

## MURPHYSBORO—Jackson County

★ **ST. JOSEPH MEMORIAL HOSPITAL (141334)**, 2 South Hospital Drive,
Zip 62966–3333; tel. 618/684–3156 **A**9 10 18 **F**3 11 18 28 29 30 31 34 35
40 45 56 57 59 64 74 75 77 78 79 81 85 86 93 107 114 119 129 130 132
135 146 148 **S** Southern Illinois Hospital Services, Carbondale, IL
Primary Contact: John T. Brothers, R.N., MS, Administrator
CMO: Gerald McClallen, President Medical Staff
CIO: David Holland, Vice President Information Services
CHR: Kelly Stevens, Manager Human Resources
Web address: www.sih.net
**Control:** Other not–for–profit (including NFP Corporation) **Service:** General
Medical and Surgical

**Staffed Beds:** 25 **Admissions:** 928 **Census:** 8 **Outpatient Visits:** 64883
**Births:** 0 **Total Expense ($000):** 42515 **Payroll Expense ($000):** 12140
**Personnel:** 230

## NAPERVILLE—Dupage County

⊠ **EDWARD HOSPITAL (140231)**, 801 South Washington Street,
Zip 60540–7499; tel. 630/527–3000 **A**1 2 9 10 **F**3 13 15 17 18 20 22 24 26
28 29 30 31 32 34 35 37 38 40 41 42 43 45 46 47 49 50 54 55 57 58 59
61 64 68 70 72 73 74 75 76 77 78 79 80 81 82 84 85 86 87 88 89 93 96
97 102 107 108 109 110 111 114 115 117 118 119 120 121 123 124 126
129 130 131 132 135 144 146 147 148 **P**1 6
Primary Contact: Pamela M. Davis, President and Chief Executive Officer
COO: Marianne Spencer, R.N., Vice President Operations and Chief Operating
Officer
CFO: Vincent Pryor, Senior Vice President Finance and Chief Financial Officer
CMO: Brent Smith, M.D., Chief Medical Officer and Vice President Clinical
Integration
CIO: Bobbie Byrne, M.D., Vice President Chief Information Officer
CHR: Dennise Vaughn, Vice President Corporate Resources
CNO: Patti Ludwig–Beymer, Ph.D., Chief Nursing Officer
Web address: www.edward.org
**Control:** Other not–for–profit (including NFP Corporation) **Service:** General
Medical and Surgical

**Staffed Beds:** 349 **Admissions:** 21066 **Census:** 225 **Outpatient Visits:**
485655 **Births:** 3229 **Total Expense ($000):** 462824 **Payroll Expense**
**($000):** 157364 **Personnel:** 2374

⊠ **LINDEN OAKS HOSPITAL AT EDWARD (144035)**, 852 West Street,
Zip 60540–6400; tel. 630/305–5500 **A**1 5 9 10 **F**4 5 29 30 34 35 38 56 57
59 64 68 75 87 98 99 100 101 103 104 105 106 130 132 134 **P**1 6
Primary Contact: Gina Sharp, FACHE, President
COO: Gina Sharp, FACHE, President
CFO: Gina Sharp, FACHE, President
CMO: Barry Rabin, M.D., Medical Director
CIO: Hugh Siddiqui, Senior Applications Analyst
CHR: Dennise Vaughn, Vice President Corporate Resources
CNO: Beth Jelesky, Director Clinical Excellence
Web address: www.edward.org
**Control:** Other not–for–profit (including NFP Corporation) **Service:** Psychiatric

**Staffed Beds:** 101 **Admissions:** 4165 **Census:** 81 **Outpatient Visits:** 45257
**Births:** 0 **Total Expense ($000):** 34714 **Payroll Expense ($000):** 19020
**Personnel:** 353

IL

## NASHVILLE—Washington County

✠ **WASHINGTON COUNTY HOSPITAL (141308)**, 705 South Grand Avenue, Zip 62263–1534; tel. 618/327–8236, (Total facility includes 28 beds in nursing home–type unit) **A**1 9 10 18 **F**28 29 31 34 40 49 57 59 64 65 78 81 85 93 104 107 114 119 127 129 133 145 146 148
Primary Contact: Nancy M. Newby, R.N., Ph.D., FACHE, President and Chief Executive Officer
CFO: Elaine Matzenbacher, Chief Financial Officer
CMO: Alfonso Urdaneta, M.D., President Medical Staff
CIO: Kim Larkin, Chief Information Officer
CHR: Alanna Barker, Director Human Resources
CNO: Tammy Amizich, Chief Nursing Executive
Web address: www.washingtoncountyhospital.org
**Control:** Hospital district or authority, Government, nonfederal **Service:** General Medical and Surgical

**Staffed Beds:** 50 **Admissions:** 275 **Census:** 33 **Outpatient Visits:** 33496 **Births:** 0 **Total Expense ($000):** 13624 **Payroll Expense ($000):** 6190 **Personnel:** 143

## NEW LENOX—Will County

✠ △ **SILVER CROSS HOSPITAL (140213)**, 1900 Silver Cross Boulevard, Zip 60451–9509; tel. 815/300–1100 **A**1 2 7 9 10 **F**3 5 7 11 12 13 15 18 19 20 22 26 27 28 29 30 31 32 34 35 37 38 40 42 43 44 46 47 48 49 50 53 54 57 59 60 62 64 68 70 74 75 76 77 78 79 81 82 84 85 89 90 92 93 96 98 100 101 102 103 104 105 107 108 110 111 114 115 118 119 126 130 131 132 134 135 146 147 148 **P**1 5 8
Primary Contact: Paul Pawlak, President and Chief Executive Officer
COO: Mary Bakken, Executive Vice President and Chief Operating Officer
CFO: William R. Brownlow, Senior Vice President Finance
CMO: Alexander Sosenko, M.D., Chief of Staff
CIO: Kevin Lane, Vice President Information Systems
CHR: Mark Jepson, Vice President
CNO: Peggy Gricus, R.N., Vice President, Patient Care Services and Chief Nursing Officer
Web address: www.silvercross.org
**Control:** Other not–for–profit (including NFP Corporation) **Service:** General Medical and Surgical

**Staffed Beds:** 289 **Admissions:** 16744 **Census:** 180 **Outpatient Visits:** 190250 **Births:** 2111 **Total Expense ($000):** 274302 **Payroll Expense ($000):** 88677 **Personnel:** 1577

## NORMAL—McLean County

✠ **ADVOCATE BROMENN MEDICAL CENTER (140127)**, 1304 Franklin Avenue, Zip 61761–3558, Mailing Address: P.O. Box 2850, Bloomington, Zip 61702–2850; tel. 309/454–1400, (Includes BROMENN REGIONAL MEDICAL CENTER, Virginia and Franklin Streets, Zip 61761, Mailing Address: P.O. Box 2850, Bloomington, Zip 61702–2850; tel. 309/454–1400) **A**1 2 5 10 12 13 **F**2 3 4 12 13 15 17 18 20 22 24 26 28 29 30 31 32 34 35 38 39 40 43 44 45 49 51 54 57 59 64 65 66 70 74 75 76 77 78 79 81 82 83 84 85 86 87 89 90 93 96 97 98 100 101 102 103 107 108 110 111 114 115 118 119 126 130 131 132 135 141 146 147 148 **P**8 **S** Advocate Health Care, Downers Grove, IL
Primary Contact: Colleen Kannaday, FACHE, President
COO: Gary Hagens, Chief Operating Officer and Vice President Medical Affairs
CMO: Gary Hagens, Chief Operating Officer and Vice President Medical Affairs
CIO: Vincent Vitali, Vice President and Chief Information Officer
CHR: Alex Horvath, Vice President Human Resources
Web address: www.bromenn.org
**Control:** Church–operated, Nongovernment, not–for profit **Service:** General Medical and Surgical

**Staffed Beds:** 204 **Admissions:** 9072 **Census:** 96 **Outpatient Visits:** 140967 **Births:** 1435 **Total Expense ($000):** 163431 **Payroll Expense ($000):** 54886 **Personnel:** 946

**ADVOCATE BROMENN REGIONAL MEDICAL CENTER** See Advocate BroMenn Medical Center

## NORTH CHICAGO—Lake County

✠ **CAPTAIN JAMES A. LOVELL FEDERAL HEALTH CARE CENTER**, 3001 Green Bay Road, Zip 60064–3049; tel. 847/688–1900, (Nonreporting) **A**1 3 5 **S** Department of Veterans Affairs, Washington, DC
Primary Contact: Patrick L. Sullivan, FACHE, Director
COO: Marianne Semrad, Associate Director Administrative Services
CFO: Barbara Meadows, Chief Financial Manager
CMO: Tariq Hassan, M.D., Associate Director of Patient Care
CIO: Jonathan Friedman, Public Affairs Officer
CHR: Amy Sanders, Chief Human Resources
CNO: Sarah Fouse, Associate Director of Patient Services
Web address: www.lovell.fhcc.va.gov
**Control:** Veterans Affairs, Government, federal **Service:** Other specialty

**Staffed Beds:** 103

## NORTHLAKE—Cook County

✠ **KINDRED HOSPITAL CHICAGO–NORTHLAKE (142008)**, 365 East North Avenue, Zip 60164–2628; tel. 708/345–8100 **A**1 9 10 **F**1 3 29 45 77 80 85 91 107 119 130 148 **S** Kindred Healthcare, Louisville, KY
Primary Contact: Beverly Foster, Chief Executive Officer
COO: Sandra Buckhoy, Chief Clinical Officer
CFO: Jay Schweikart, Chief Financial Officer
CMO: Maher Najjar, M.D., Medical Director
Web address: www.kindrednorthlake.com/
**Control:** Corporation, Investor–owned, for–profit **Service:** Long–Term Acute Care hospital

**Staffed Beds:** 94 **Admissions:** 622 **Census:** 53 **Outpatient Visits:** 0 **Total Expense ($000):** 25028 **Payroll Expense ($000):** 9848 **Personnel:** 161

## OAK LAWN—Cook County

✠ △ **ADVOCATE CHRIST MEDICAL CENTER (140208)**, 4440 West 95th Street, Zip 60453–2699; tel. 708/684–8000, (Includes ADVOCATE HOPE CHILDREN'S HOSPITAL, 4440 West 95th Street, Zip 60453–2600; tel. 708/684–8000) **A**1 2 3 5 7 8 9 10 13 **F**3 5 6 11 13 15 17 18 19 20 21 22 23 24 25 26 27 28 29 30 31 32 34 35 37 38 39 40 41 43 44 45 46 47 48 49 50 51 52 54 55 56 57 58 59 60 61 62 63 64 65 66 68 69 70 71 72 74 75 76 77 78 79 81 82 84 85 86 87 88 89 90 92 93 96 97 98 99 100 101 102 103 104 105 107 108 109 110 111 114 115 118 119 120 121 123 124 126 129 130 131 132 134 135 137 138 143 145 146 147 148 **P**8 **S** Advocate Health Care, Downers Grove, IL
Primary Contact: Kenneth W. Lukhard, President
COO: Michael Wilkins, Chief Operating Officer
CFO: Robert Pekofske, Vice President Finance
CMO: Robert Stein, M.D., Vice President Medical Management
CIO: Brian Banbury, Director Site Information Systems
Web address: www.advocatehealth.com/christ
**Control:** Other not–for–profit (including NFP Corporation) **Service:** General Medical and Surgical

**Staffed Beds:** 684 **Admissions:** 41511 **Census:** 549 **Outpatient Visits:** 327032 **Births:** 3811 **Total Expense ($000):** 844270 **Payroll Expense ($000):** 321355 **Personnel:** 4265

## OAK PARK—Cook County

✠ △ **RUSH OAK PARK HOSPITAL (140063)**, 520 South Maple Avenue, Zip 60304–1097; tel. 708/383–9300, (Total facility includes 20 beds in nursing home–type unit) **A**1 3 5 7 9 10 **F**3 11 15 18 20 22 29 30 34 35 40 45 47 49 50 56 57 59 64 68 70 74 75 77 79 81 82 85 87 90 92 93 94 96 107 108 111 114 115 119 128 130 145 146 148 **P**8 **S** Wheaton Franciscan Healthcare, Wheaton, IL
Primary Contact: Bruce M. Elegant, President and Chief Executive Officer
COO: James Kaese, Vice President Administration
CFO: Deborah Wilberding, Controller
CMO: Michael R. Silver, M.D., Vice President Medical Affairs
CIO: Dewey Gosnell, Manager
CHR: Cristina Diaz, Director
CNO: Karen Mayer, R.N., VP Patient Care Services
Web address: www.roph.org
**Control:** Church–operated, Nongovernment, not–for profit **Service:** General Medical and Surgical

**Staffed Beds:** 114 **Admissions:** 4373 **Census:** 70 **Outpatient Visits:** 95468 **Births:** 0 **Total Expense ($000):** 98364 **Payroll Expense ($000):** 46299 **Personnel:** 787

★ ○ **WEST SUBURBAN MEDICAL CENTER (140049)**, (Formerly West Suburban Medical Center), 3 Erie Court, Zip 60302–2599; tel. 708/383–6200, (Nonreporting) **A**2 3 5 9 10 11 13 **S** Vanguard Health Systems, Nashville, TN
Primary Contact: Joan Ormsby, Interim Chief Executive Officer
COO: Joan Ormsby, Chief Operating Officer
CFO: Gene Smith, Interim Chief Financial Officer
CMO: Robert Chase, M.D., Chief Medical Officer
CHR: Nancy Gunnell, Vice President Human Resources
CNO: Rosyln Lennon, Chief Nursing Officer
Web address: www.westsuburbanmc.com/Home.aspx
**Control:** Corporation, Investor–owned, for–profit **Service:** General Medical and Surgical

**Staffed Beds:** 172

IL

*Many Facility Codes have changed. Please refer to the AHA Guide Code Chart.*   © 2013 AHA Guide

## OLNEY—Richland County

★ ○ **RICHLAND MEMORIAL HOSPITAL (140147)**, 800 East Locust Street, Zip 62450–2553; tel. 618/395–2131, (Total facility includes 34 beds in nursing home–type unit) **A**9 10 11 **F**3 7 11 13 15 28 29 31 34 35 40 51 57 59 61 62 63 64 68 69 70 75 76 78 79 81 85 87 89 93 97 98 100 102 103 104 107 108 110 111 115 119 128 129 131 132 133 135 143 146 147 **P**6
Primary Contact: David B. Allen, Chief Executive Officer
CFO: Mike Stoverink, Chief Financial Officer
CMO: Robert Nash, M.D., Chief of Staff
CIO: Tim Gillespie, Manager Information Systems
CHR: Jill Van Hyning, Director Human Resources
CNO: Cindy Bailey, R.N., Chief Nursing Officer
Web address: www.richlandmemorial.com
**Control:** Other not–for–profit (including NFP Corporation) **Service:** General Medical and Surgical

**Staffed Beds:** 90 **Admissions:** 2462 **Census:** 28 **Outpatient Visits:** 50578 **Births:** 328 **Total Expense ($000):** 40103 **Payroll Expense ($000):** 17797 **Personnel:** 427

## OLYMPIA FIELDS—Cook County

○ △ **FRANCISCAN ST. JAMES HOSPITAL AND HEALTH CENTERS (140172)**, 20201 South Crawford Avenue, Zip 60461–1010; tel. 708/747–4000, (Includes ST. JAMES HOSPITAL AND HEALTH CENTERS – CHICAGO HEIGHTS CAMPUS, 1423 Chicago Road, Chicago Heights, Zip 60411–3483; tel. 708/756–1000; ST. JAMES HOSPITALS AND HEALTH CENTERS – OLYMPIA FIELDS CAMPUS, 20201 Crawford Avenue, tel. 708/747–4000), (Nonreporting) **A**2 7 9 10 11 12 13 **S** Franciscan Alliance, Mishawaka, IN
Primary Contact: Seth C. R. Warren, President
CIO: Stephen Maes, Director Information Systems
Web address: www.stjameshhc.org
**Control:** Church–operated, Nongovernment, not–for profit **Service:** General Medical and Surgical

**Staffed Beds:** 398

**ST. JAMES HOSPITAL AND HEALTH CENTERS** See Franciscan St. James Hospital and Health Centers

## OTTAWA—Lasalle County

⊠ **OSF SAINT ELIZABETH MEDICAL CENTER (140110)**, (Formerly Ottawa Regional Hospital and Healthcare Center), 1100 East Norris Drive, Zip 61350–1687; tel. 815/433–3100 **A**1 9 10 **F**3 11 13 15 18 28 30 31 34 35 40 43 45 48 49 53 56 57 59 62 63 68 70 75 76 77 79 81 82 84 85 86 87 93 94 98 99 100 101 102 103 104 105 107 108 110 111 115 118 119 130 131 132 135 143 144 146 148 **S** OSF Healthcare System, Peoria, IL
Primary Contact: Robert A. Chaffin, President and Chief Executive Officer
COO: Judy A. Christiansen, R.N., Chief Operating Officer
CFO: Dawn Trompeter, Vice President Finance
CMO: David O. Manigold, M.D., President Medical Staff
CIO: John Maynard, Director Information Systems
CHR: Robert Gibson, Senior Director Operating Services
Web address: www.ottawaregional.org
**Control:** Other not–for–profit (including NFP Corporation) **Service:** General Medical and Surgical

**Staffed Beds:** 90 **Admissions:** 3839 **Census:** 37 **Outpatient Visits:** 193234 **Births:** 389 **Total Expense ($000):** 75474 **Payroll Expense ($000):** 30310 **Personnel:** 531

## PALOS HEIGHTS—Cook County

⊠ **PALOS COMMUNITY HOSPITAL (140062)**, 12251 South 80th Avenue, Zip 60463–0930; tel. 708/923–4000 **A**1 2 9 10 **F**3 4 5 13 15 17 18 20 22 24 26 28 29 30 31 32 34 35 36 38 40 49 50 54 56 57 59 61 62 63 64 69 70 74 75 76 78 79 81 84 85 87 89 93 99 100 102 103 104 105 107 108 110 111 114 115 117 118 119 130 132 135 144 146 147 148 **P**6
Primary Contact: David Manchester, Interim President and Chief Executive Officer
CFO: Hugh Rose, Vice President Fiscal Management
CIO: Peggy Carroll, Chief Information Officer
CHR: Mary Denisienko, Vice President Human Resources
Web address: www.paloscommunityhospital.org
**Control:** Other not–for–profit (including NFP Corporation) **Service:** General Medical and Surgical

**Staffed Beds:** 377 **Admissions:** 17960 **Census:** 213 **Outpatient Visits:** 385069 **Births:** 952 **Total Expense ($000):** 315156 **Payroll Expense ($000):** 16095 **Personnel:** 2328

## PANA—Christian County

★ **PANA COMMUNITY HOSPITAL (141341)**, 101 East Ninth Street, Zip 62557–1785; tel. 217/562–2131 **A**9 10 18 **F**1 3 4 11 15 16 17 28 30 31 34 35 40 53 57 59 62 63 64 67 69 70 72 73 75 78 79 80 81 87 88 89 90 93 94 98 100 104 110 114 127 128 130 131 133 **P**6
Primary Contact: Trina Casner, President and Chief Executive Officer
CMO: Alan Frigy, M.D., President Medical Staff
CIO: Dianne Bailey, Coordinator Information Systems
CHR: Luann Funk, Administrative Assistant and Manager Human Resources
Web address: www.panahospital.com
**Control:** Other not–for–profit (including NFP Corporation) **Service:** General Medical and Surgical

**Staffed Beds:** 22 **Admissions:** 362 **Census:** 3 **Outpatient Visits:** 49887 **Births:** 0 **Total Expense ($000):** 15908 **Payroll Expense ($000):** 7276 **Personnel:** 135

## PARIS—Edgar County

⊠ **PARIS COMMUNITY HOSPITAL (141320)**, 721 East Court Street, Zip 61944–2460; tel. 217/465–4141 **A**1 9 10 18 **F**3 15 28 29 30 31 34 35 40 45 57 59 64 65 67 69 74 75 77 78 79 81 82 85 86 87 89 90 93 107 108 110 111 114 119 127 128 130 131 132 133 144 146 148 **P**6 **S** Alliant Management Services, Louisville, KY
Primary Contact: Randy Simmons, President and Chief Executive Officer
CFO: Terry Brinkley, Vice President Finance
CIO: Gary Taylor, Manager Information Services
CHR: Ollie Smith, Vice President Human Resources
Web address: www.pariscommunityhospital.com
**Control:** Other not–for–profit (including NFP Corporation) **Service:** General Medical and Surgical

**Staffed Beds:** 25 **Admissions:** 485 **Census:** 6 **Outpatient Visits:** 93363 **Births:** 0 **Total Expense ($000):** 34984 **Payroll Expense ($000):** 15724 **Personnel:** 222

## PARK RIDGE—Cook County

⊠ △ ◇ **ADVOCATE LUTHERAN GENERAL HOSPITAL (140223)**, 1775 Dempster Street, Zip 60068–1174; tel. 847/723–2210 **A**1 2 3 5 7 8 9 10 13 21 **F**2 3 5 6 8 9 11 12 13 15 17 18 19 20 21 22 23 24 25 26 27 28 29 30 31 32 34 35 37 38 39 40 41 43 44 45 46 47 48 49 50 53 55 56 57 58 59 60 61 63 64 65 66 68 69 70 72 74 75 76 78 79 80 81 82 84 85 86 87 88 89 90 92 93 94 97 98 99 100 101 102 103 104 105 106 107 108 110 111 112 114 115 116 117 118 119 120 121 123 124 126 129 130 131 132 134 135 136 141 143 146 147 148 **P**6 8 **S** Advocate Health Care, Downers Grove, IL
Primary Contact: Anthony A. Armada, President
COO: Barbara Weber, Chief Operating Officer
CFO: Jim Kelley, Vice President Finance and Support Services
CMO: Michael McKenna, M.D., Vice President Medical Management
CIO: Mark Beitzel, Director Information Systems
CHR: Penny Pilarczyk, Vice President Human Resources
Web address: www.advocatehealth.com/luth/
**Control:** Other not–for–profit (including NFP Corporation) **Service:** General Medical and Surgical

**Staffed Beds:** 624 **Admissions:** 29025 **Census:** 400 **Outpatient Visits:** 302657 **Births:** 4122 **Total Expense ($000):** 605864 **Payroll Expense ($000):** 226466 **Personnel:** 3388

## PEKIN—Tazewell County

⊠ **PEKIN HOSPITAL (140120)**, 600 South 13th Street, Zip 61554–4936; tel. 309/347–1151 **A**1 5 9 10 **F**3 8 11 13 15 18 20 22 28 29 30 31 34 35 40 45 46 47 48 49 50 51 53 57 59 60 62 64 68 69 70 74 75 76 78 79 81 82 85 86 87 89 97 107 108 110 111 115 119 128 129 130 132 135 144 145 146 147 148 **P**1 **S** QHR, Brentwood, TN
Primary Contact: Gary L. Jepson, Chief Executive Officer
CFO: Steve Hall, Chief Financial Officer
CMO: Kathryn Kramer, M.D., President Medical Staff
CHR: Anne Dierker, Vice President Hospital Services
Web address: www.pekinhospital.org
**Control:** Other not–for–profit (including NFP Corporation) **Service:** General Medical and Surgical

**Staffed Beds:** 125 **Admissions:** 3883 **Census:** 47 **Outpatient Visits:** 104661 **Births:** 426 **Total Expense ($000):** 60343 **Payroll Expense ($000):** 28034 **Personnel:** 679

## PEORIA—Peoria County

**GREATER PEORIA SPECIALTY HOSPITAL** See Kindred Hospital Peoria

IL

---

**Hospital, Medicare Provider Number, Address, Telephone, Approval, Facility, and Physician Codes, Health Care System**

★ American Hospital Association (AHA) membership
□ The Joint Commission accreditation
◇ DNV Healthcare Inc. accreditation
○ Healthcare Facilities Accreditation Program
△ Commission on Accreditation of Rehabilitation Facilities (CARF) accreditation

☒ **KINDRED HOSPITAL PEORIA (142013)**, 500 West Romeo B. Garrett Avenue, Zip 61605–2301; tel. 309/680–1500, (Nonreporting) **A**1 9 10 **S** Kindred Healthcare, Louisville, KY
Primary Contact: Robert N. Wright, Chief Executive Officer
Web address: www.khpeoria.com/
**Control:** Corporation, Investor–owned, for–profit **Service:** Long–Term Acute Care hospital

Staffed Beds: 50

**METHODIST MEDICAL CENTER OF ILLINOIS** See UnityPoint Health – Methodist

☒ △ **OSF SAINT FRANCIS MEDICAL CENTER (140067)**, 530 N.E. Glen Oak Avenue, Zip 61637–0001; tel. 309/655–2000, (Includes CHILDREN'S HOSPITAL OF ILLINOIS, 530 N.E. Glen Oak Avenue, tel. 309/655–7171) **A**1 2 3 5 7 8 9 10 **F**3 8 9 11 12 13 15 17 18 19 20 21 22 23 24 25 26 27 28 29 30 31 32 34 35 37 38 39 40 41 42 43 44 45 46 47 48 49 50 51 52 54 56 57 58 59 60 64 65 66 67 68 69 70 72 73 74 75 76 77 78 79 81 82 83 84 85 86 87 88 89 90 91 92 93 94 96 97 99 100 102 104 105 107 108 110 111 114 115 116 117 118 119 120 121 123 124 126 127 129 130 132 134 138 142 143 144 145 146 147 148 **P**6 **S** OSF Healthcare System, Peoria, IL
Primary Contact: Keith E. Steffen, President and Chief Executive Officer
COO: Susan C. Wozniak, R.N., Senior Vice President and Chief Operating Officer
CFO: Ken Harbaugh, Vice President and Chief Financial Officer
CMO: Tim C. Miller, M.D., Vice President, Chief Medical Officer and Director Academy Affairs
CHR: Lynn J. Gillespie, Vice President Human Resources and Organizational Development
Web address: www.osfsaintfrancis.org
**Control:** Church–operated, Nongovernment, not–for profit **Service:** General Medical and Surgical

Staffed Beds: 631 Admissions: 33747 Census: 476 Outpatient Visits: 921342 Births: 2447 Total Expense ($000): 878698 Payroll Expense ($000): 369197 Personnel: 5305

☐ **PROCTOR HOSPITAL (140013)**, 5409 North Knoxville Avenue, Zip 61614–5069; tel. 309/691–1000, (Total facility includes 20 beds in nursing home–type unit) **A**1 3 5 9 10 **F**3 4 5 11 13 15 18 20 22 24 28 29 30 34 40 45 49 51 53 57 59 62 64 65 70 74 75 76 79 81 85 86 87 89 93 98 103 104 105 107 108 110 111 115 118 119 128 129 130 132 135 145 146 148
Primary Contact: Paul E. Macek, President and Chief Executive Officer
CFO: Roger Armstrong, Vice President Finance and Chief Financial Officer
CHR: Linda K. Buck, Vice President Human Resources
Web address: www.proctor.org
**Control:** Other not–for–profit (including NFP Corporation) **Service:** General Medical and Surgical

Staffed Beds: 172 Admissions: 6661 Census: 81 Outpatient Visits: 177392 Births: 623 Total Expense ($000): 108364 Payroll Expense ($000): 38851 Personnel: 822

☒ △ **UNITYPOINT HEALTH – METHODIST (140209)**, (Formerly Methodist Medical Center of Illinois), 221 N.E. Glen Oak Avenue, Zip 61636–4310; tel. 309/672–5522 **A**1 2 3 5 7 10 **F**3 8 9 11 12 13 15 17 18 20 22 24 26 28 29 30 31 32 34 35 36 38 40 43 44 45 46 47 48 49 50 53 54 56 57 58 59 60 62 63 64 68 70 74 75 76 77 78 79 81 82 84 85 86 87 89 90 92 93 96 98 99 100 101 102 103 104 105 107 108 110 111 114 115 116 117 118 119 120 121 126 127 129 130 131 132 134 135 136 143 144 145 146 147 148 **P**8 **S** UnityPoint Health, West Des Moines, IA
Primary Contact: Deborah R. Simon, R.N., President and Chief Executive Officer
CFO: Calvin R. MacKay, Chief Financial Officer
CMO: Rick Anderson, M.D., Senior Vice President Medical Affairs and Chief Medical Officer
CIO: Steven Riney, Vice President Information Technology and Chief Information Officer
CHR: Joy Ledbetter, Director Human Resources
Web address: www.mymethodist.net
**Control:** Other not–for–profit (including NFP Corporation) **Service:** General Medical and Surgical

Staffed Beds: 269 Admissions: 15548 Census: 208 Outpatient Visits: 552335 Births: 1737 Total Expense ($000): 337924 Payroll Expense ($000): 140742 Personnel: 2128

★ **ILLINOIS VALLEY COMMUNITY HOSPITAL (140234)**, 925 West Street, Zip 61354–2757; tel. 815/223–3300 **A**9 10 **F**2 3 11 13 15 28 29 30 35 38 40 45 46 47 49 50 51 54 59 63 64 65 66 68 69 70 74 75 76 77 79 81 82 84 85 87 89 93 96 97 104 107 110 111 115 118 119 127 129 130 132 133 135 143 144 146 147 **P**8
Primary Contact: Tommy Hobbs, Chief Executive Officer
COO: Bobby Smith, Vice President Physician Services and Quality
CFO: Stephen Davis, Chief Financial Officer
CMO: Mario Cote, M.D., Chief of Staff and President Medical Staff
CIO: Nancy McDonnell, Manager Information Systems
CHR: Mary Beth Herron, Director of Human Resources
CNO: Wilma Hart–Flynn, Vice President Patient Care Services/CNO
Web address: www.ivch.org
**Control:** Other not–for–profit (including NFP Corporation) **Service:** General Medical and Surgical

Staffed Beds: 56 Admissions: 2824 Census: 24 Outpatient Visits: 143795 Births: 437 Total Expense ($000): 69615 Payroll Expense ($000): 26815 Personnel: 510

★ **PINCKNEYVILLE COMMUNITY HOSPITAL (141307)**, 101 North Walnut Street, Zip 62274–1099; tel. 618/357–5901 **A**9 10 18 **F**3 15 29 31 34 40 43 45 50 53 57 78 81 85 93 107 108 110 119 127 130 133 148 **P**6
Primary Contact: Thomas J. Hudgins, FACHE, Administrator and Chief Executive Officer
CFO: Kara Jo Carson, Chief Financial Officer
CIO: Tina Grafton, Director Information Technology
CHR: Christie Gajewski, Director Human Resources
CNO: Eva Hopp, Chief Nurse Executive
Web address: www.pvillehosp.org/
**Control:** Hospital district or authority, Government, nonfederal **Service:** General Medical and Surgical

Staffed Beds: 25 Admissions: 483 Census: 6 Outpatient Visits: 46937 Births: 0 Total Expense ($000): 18417 Payroll Expense ($000): 8325 Personnel: 171

☒ **ILLINI COMMUNITY HOSPITAL (141315)**, 640 West Washington Street, Zip 62363–1350; tel. 217/285–2113 **A**1 9 10 18 **F**3 15 18 19 28 30 31 34 40 46 50 53 59 64 65 68 70 75 78 81 82 85 87 89 93 97 107 110 115 119 127 129 130 131 133 146
Primary Contact: Kathy Hull, President and Chief Executive Officer
CFO: Sandra Purcell, Administrative Director Business and Financial Services
CMO: Paul Hibbert, D.O., President Medical Staff
CHR: Becky Myers, Human Resources Specialist
Web address: www.illinihospital.org
**Control:** Other not–for–profit (including NFP Corporation) **Service:** General Medical and Surgical

Staffed Beds: 21 Admissions: 479 Census: 4 Outpatient Visits: 7641 Births: 0 Total Expense ($000): 20683 Payroll Expense ($000): 7628 Personnel: 158

☒ **OSF SAINT JAMES – JOHN W. ALBRECHT MEDICAL CENTER (140161)**, 2500 West Reynolds, Zip 61764–9774; tel. 815/842–2828 **A**1 9 10 20 **F**3 8 11 13 15 18 28 29 30 32 34 35 40 45 50 56 57 59 64 68 70 75 76 77 79 81 82 84 85 86 87 89 90 91 93 96 97 107 110 111 115 117 118 119 127 128 129 130 131 132 133 135 144 146 147 **P**7 **S** OSF Healthcare System, Peoria, IL
Primary Contact: David T. Ochs, President and Chief Executive Officer
CFO: Paula Corrigan, Vice President and Chief Financial Officer
CHR: Kenneth Beutke, Vice President Organization Development and Planning
Web address: www.osfsaintjames.org
**Control:** Church–operated, Nongovernment, not–for profit **Service:** General Medical and Surgical

Staffed Beds: 42 Admissions: 1508 Census: 12 Outpatient Visits: 161047 Births: 230 Total Expense ($000): 63212 Payroll Expense ($000): 24147 Personnel: 330

**PERRY MEMORIAL HOSPITAL (141337)**, 530 Park Avenue East, Zip 61356–2598; tel. 815/875–2811, (Nonreporting) **A**9 10 18
Primary Contact: Rex D. Conger, FACHE, President and Chief Executive Officer
CFO: Patricia Ellison, Chief Financial Officer
CMO: Robert E. Mestan, M.D., Chief of Staff
CIO: Karen Behrens, Director Technology Services
CHR: Karen Russell, Director Human Resources
Web address: www.perry–memorial.org
**Control:** City–Government, nonfederal **Service:** General Medical and Surgical

Staffed Beds: 25

IL

*Many Facility Codes have changed. Please refer to the AHA Guide Code Chart.*

© 2013 AHA Guide

## QUINCY—Adams County

⊞ △ **BLESSING HOSPITAL (140015)**, Broadway at 11th Street,
Zip 62305–7005, Mailing Address: P.O. Box 7005, Zip 62305–7005;
tel. 217/223–1200, (Includes BLESSING HOSPITAL, Broadway & 14th Street,
Zip 62301, Mailing Address: P.O. Box 7005, Zip 62305–7005;
tel. 217/223–1200), (Total facility includes 20 beds in nursing home–type unit)
**A**1 2 3 5 7 9 10 13 **F**3 5 8 11 12 13 15 17 18 20 22 24 28 29 30 31 32 34
35 40 43 44 48 49 50 53 56 57 58 59 60 61 62 63 64 66 68 70 73 74 75
76 77 78 79 81 82 84 85 86 87 89 90 94 96 98 99 100 101 102 103 104
107 108 110 111 114 115 118 119 120 121 123 124 126 127 128 129 130
131 132 135 144 146 147 148 **P**8
Primary Contact: Maureen A. Kahn, R.N., President and Chief Executive Officer
COO: Tim Moore, Chief Accounting Officer and Vice President Ancillary Services
CFO: Patrick M. Gerveler, Vice President Finance and Chief Financial Officer
Web address: www.blessinghospital.org
**Control:** Other not–for–profit (including NFP Corporation) **Service:** General
Medical and Surgical

**Staffed Beds:** 335 **Admissions:** 13160 **Census:** 167 **Outpatient Visits:**
375555 **Births:** 1082 **Total Expense ($000):** 257749 **Payroll Expense**
**($000):** 102715 **Personnel:** 2034

## RED BUD—Randolph County

⊞ **RED BUD REGIONAL HOSPITAL (141348)**, 325 Spring Street,
Zip 62278–1105; tel. 618/282–3831, (Nonreporting) **A**1 9 10 18 **S** Community
Health Systems, Inc., Franklin, TN
Primary Contact: Shane Watson, Chief Executive Officer
CFO: Donald Lovelace, Chief Financial Officer
CMO: Nancy Birner, M.D., President Medical Staff
CIO: Nick Behnken, Supervisor Information Technology
CHR: Lori Brooks, Director Human Resources
CNO: Linda Harbison, Chief Nursing Officer
Web address: www.redbudhospital.com
**Control:** Corporation, Investor–owned, for–profit **Service:** General Medical and
Surgical

**Staffed Beds:** 140

## ROBINSON—Crawford County

⊞ **CRAWFORD MEMORIAL HOSPITAL (141343)**, 1000 North Allen Street,
Zip 62454–1167; tel. 618/544–3131, (Total facility includes 35 beds in nursing
home–type unit) **A**1 9 10 18 **F**3 8 11 12 13 15 28 30 31 40 45 53 56 59 62
64 76 77 78 79 80 81 85 93 107 108 111 119 127 128 129 130 132 133
146 147 **P**6 **S** QHR, Brentwood, TN
Primary Contact: Donald E. Annis, Chief Executive Officer
CFO: Richard Carlson, Chief Financial Officer
CMO: Gary Tennison, D.O., Chief of Staff
CIO: Tim Richard, IT Coordinator
CHR: Kristi Zane, Chief Human Resources Officer
CNO: Sandra Burtron, MS, Chief Nursing Officer
Web address: www.crawfordmh.org
**Control:** Hospital district or authority, Government, nonfederal **Service:** General
Medical and Surgical

**Staffed Beds:** 63 **Admissions:** 1193 **Census:** 28 **Outpatient Visits:** 51096
**Births:** 172 **Total Expense ($000):** 37119 **Payroll Expense ($000):** 16689
**Personnel:** 308

## ROCHELLE—Ogle County

⊞ **ROCHELLE COMMUNITY HOSPITAL (141312)**, 900 North Second Street,
Zip 61068–1764; tel. 815/562–2181 **A**1 9 10 18 **F**3 8 15 29 30 31 34 35 40
41 50 53 57 59 64 68 70 74 75 77 78 81 82 85 86 87 93 97 107 110 115
130 132 133 135 144 146 **P**6
Primary Contact: Mark Batty, Chief Executive Officer
CFO: Lori Gutierrez, Chief Financial Officer
CFO: John M. Ross, Vice President Finance and Chief Financial Officer
CMO: Jason Popp, Chief of Medical Staff
CIO: Scott Stewart, Manager Information Services
CHR: Robert Johns, Senior Vice President Administration
CNO: Jennifer Montgomery, Chief Nursing Officer
Web address: www.rcha.net
**Control:** Other not–for–profit (including NFP Corporation) **Service:** General
Medical and Surgical

**Staffed Beds:** 16 **Admissions:** 611 **Census:** 5 **Outpatient Visits:** 35522
**Births:** 1 **Total Expense ($000):** 24834 **Payroll Expense ($000):** 9224
**Personnel:** 191

## ROCK ISLAND—Rock Island County

⊞ △ **TRINITY ROCK ISLAND (140280)**, 2701 17th Street, Zip 61201–5393;
tel. 309/779–5000, (Includes TRINITY MOLINE, 500 John Deere Road, Moline,
Zip 61265; tel. 309/779–5000), (Total facility includes 29 beds in nursing home–
type unit) **A**1 2 7 9 10 **F**3 5 7 11 12 13 15 18 20 22 24 26 28 29 30 31 34
35 37 38 40 43 44 45 49 50 52 55 59 63 64 70 74 75 76 78 79 81 82 84
85 86 87 89 90 93 96 97 98 99 100 101 102 103 104 105 106 107 108
110 114 115 119 120 121 123 126 128 129 130 132 134 135 143 144 146
147 148 **P**6 8 **S** UnityPoint Health, West Des Moines, IA
Primary Contact: Richard A. Seidler, FACHE, President and Chief Executive Officer
COO: Michael J. Patterson, Vice President Operations
CFO: Greg Pagliuzza, Chief Financial Officer
CMO: Paul McLoone, M.D., Chief Medical Officer
CHR: Jeffery Stolze, Vice President Human Resources
Web address: www.trinityqc.com
**Control:** Other not–for–profit (including NFP Corporation) **Service:** General
Medical and Surgical

**Staffed Beds:** 343 **Admissions:** 15646 **Census:** 197 **Outpatient Visits:**
288366 **Births:** 1583 **Total Expense ($000):** 265755 **Payroll Expense**
**($000):** 91442 **Personnel:** 1877

## ROCKFORD—Winnebago County

☐ **H. DOUGLAS SINGER MENTAL HEALTH AND DEVELOPMENTAL CENTER
(144023)**, 4402 North Main Street, Zip 61103–1278; tel. 815/987–7096,
(Nonreporting) **A**1 **S** Division of Mental Health, Department of Human Services,
Springfield, IL
Primary Contact: Gail Tennant, Director
**Control:** State–Government, nonfederal **Service:** Psychiatric

**Staffed Beds:** 162

⊞ **OSF SAINT ANTHONY MEDICAL CENTER (140233)**, 5666 East State Street,
Zip 61108–2425; tel. 815/226–2000 **A**1 2 5 9 10 **F**3 11 12 13 15 16 17 18
20 22 24 26 28 29 30 31 32 34 35 36 37 38 39 40 41 43 44 45 46 49 50
51 53 55 56 57 58 59 64 66 70 73 74 75 76 77 78 79 81 82 84 85 86 87
89 92 93 107 108 110 111 114 115 116 117 118 119 120 121 123 124
129 130 131 132 135 145 146 147 148 **P**6 **S** OSF Healthcare System,
Peoria, IL
Primary Contact: David A. Schertz, President and Chief Executive Officer
CFO: David Stenerson, Vice President Fiscal Services and Chief Financial Officer
CMO: Eric Benink, M.D., Vice President and Chief Medical Officer
CIO: Kathy Peterson, Director Information Services
CHR: Karen C. Brown, Vice President Strategic Human Resources
Web address: www.osfhealth.com
**Control:** Church–operated, Nongovernment, not–for profit **Service:** General
Medical and Surgical

**Staffed Beds:** 235 **Admissions:** 10536 **Census:** 127 **Outpatient Visits:**
384709 **Births:** 432 **Total Expense ($000):** 328530 **Payroll Expense**
**($000):** 132606 **Personnel:** 1784

⊞ **ROCKFORD MEMORIAL HOSPITAL (140239)**, 2400 North Rockton Avenue,
Zip 61103–3655; tel. 815/971–5000 **A**1 2 5 10 **F**3 11 13 18 19 20 22 24 25
26 27 28 29 30 31 32 34 35 39 40 41 43 44 45 48 49 50 54 55 57 59 63
64 65 68 70 71 72 74 75 76 77 78 79 80 81 82 83 84 85 86 87 88 89 93
97 98 99 100 101 102 103 107 108 111 114 115 118 119 121 123 126
129 130 131 132 135 145 146 147 148 **P**6
Primary Contact: Gary E. Kaatz, President and Chief Executive Officer
COO: Daniel A. Parod, Senior Vice President Hospital and Administrative Affairs
CFO: Henry Seybold, Senior Vice President and Chief Financial Officer
CMO: Milton G. Schmitt, Jr., M.D., Chief Medical Officer
CIO: Dennis P. L'Heureux, Chief Information Officer
CHR: Daniel A. Parod, Senior Vice President Hospital and Administrative Affairs
CNO: Susan Schreier, R.N., Chief Nursing Executive
Web address: www.rhsnet.org
**Control:** Other not–for–profit (including NFP Corporation) **Service:** General
Medical and Surgical

**Staffed Beds:** 297 **Admissions:** 12409 **Census:** 184 **Outpatient Visits:**
451837 **Births:** 1468 **Total Expense ($000):** 268940 **Payroll Expense**
**($000):** 104053 **Personnel:** 2073

IL

**Hospital, Medicare Provider Number, Address, Telephone, Approval, Facility, and Physician Codes, Health Care System**

★ American Hospital Association (AHA) membership
☐ The Joint Commission accreditation ◇ DNV Healthcare Inc. accreditation

○ Healthcare Facilities Accreditation Program
△ Commission on Accreditation of Rehabilitation Facilities (CARF) accreditation

☒ **SWEDISHAMERICAN HOSPITAL (140228)**, 1401 East State Street,
Zip 61104–2315; tel. 815/968–4400 **A**1 2 3 5 9 10 **F**3 13 15 17 18 20 22 24
26 28 29 30 31 34 35 36 37 38 39 40 43 44 45 46 49 50 56 57 58 59 61
64 65 68 70 72 74 75 76 77 78 79 81 82 84 85 86 87 89 92 93 98 99 100
101 102 103 104 105 107 108 110 111 114 115 117 118 119 121 123 129
130 132 146 147 148 **P**6
Primary Contact: William R. Gorski, M.D., President and Chief Executive Officer
COO: Richard Walsh, Executive Vice President and Chief Operating Officer
CFO: Don Haring, Vice President Finance and Treasurer
CMO: Kathleen Kelly, M.D., Chief Medical Officer and Chief Quality Officer
CIO: Phil Wasson, Chief Information Officer
CHR: Jerry Guinane, Vice President Human Resources
Web address: www.swedishamerican.org
**Control:** Other not–for–profit (including NFP Corporation) **Service:** General
Medical and Surgical

| | |
|---|---|
| **Staffed Beds:** 325 **Admissions:** 16482 **Census:** 195 **Outpatient Visits:** 268470 **Births:** 2549 **Total Expense ($000):** 299625 **Payroll Expense ($000):** 114874 **Personnel:** 2033 | |

☒ △ **VAN MATRE HEALTHSOUTH REHABILITATION HOSPITAL (143028)**,
950 South Mulford Road, Zip 61108–4274; tel. 815/381–8500 **A**1 7 9 10 **F**28
29 34 57 64 68 74 75 82 86 90 91 93 95 96 130 131 132 148 **P**5
**S** HEALTHSOUTH Corporation, Birmingham, AL
Primary Contact: Ken Bowman, Chief Executive Officer
CFO: Mark Lundvall, Controller
CMO: Scott Craig, M.D., Medical Director
CIO: Dianne Miller, Director Health Information Management
CHR: Lisa Vitale, Director Human Resources
CNO: Nancy Miller, R.N., Chief Nursing Officer
Web address: www.healthsouth.com
**Control:** Partnership, Investor–owned, for–profit **Service:** Rehabilitation

| | |
|---|---|
| **Staffed Beds:** 50 **Admissions:** 1202 **Census:** 44 **Outpatient Visits:** 7350 **Births:** 0 **Total Expense ($000):** 17042 **Payroll Expense ($000):** 10056 **Personnel:** 128 | |

### ROSICLARE—Hardin County

★ **HARDIN COUNTY GENERAL HOSPITAL (141328)**, 6 Ferrell Road, Zip 62982,
Mailing Address: PO BOX 2467, Zip 62982–2467; tel. 618/285–6634,
(Nonreporting) **A**9 10 18
Primary Contact: Roby D. Williams, Administrator
CFO: Janie Parker, Chief Financial Officer
CMO: Marcos N. Sunga, M.D., Chief of Staff
CHR: Joyce Shelby, Manager Human Resources
Web address: www.ilhcgh.org
**Control:** Other not–for–profit (including NFP Corporation) **Service:** General
Medical and Surgical

| | |
|---|---|
| **Staffed Beds:** 25 | |

### RUSHVILLE—Schuyler County

★ **SARAH D. CULBERTSON MEMORIAL HOSPITAL (141333)**, 238 South
Congress Street, Zip 62681–1472; tel. 217/322–4321, (Total facility includes 24
beds in nursing home–type unit) **A**9 10 18 **F**11 15 18 28 31 34 40 45 57 59 69
77 78 79 81 82 103 107 110 114 119 125 127 129 132 133 146 148
Primary Contact: Lynn E. Stambaugh, R.N., Chief Executive Officer
CFO: Alan Palo, Chief Financial Officer
CMO: S. K. Kanthilal, M.D., President Medical Staff
Web address: www.cmhospital.com
**Control:** Hospital district or authority, Government, nonfederal **Service:** General
Medical and Surgical

| | |
|---|---|
| **Staffed Beds:** 46 **Admissions:** 247 **Census:** 13 **Outpatient Visits:** 47448 **Births:** 0 **Total Expense ($000):** 20022 **Payroll Expense ($000):** 7772 **Personnel:** 154 | |

**IL**

### SALEM—Marion County

★ **SALEM TOWNSHIP HOSPITAL (141345)**, 1201 Ricker Drive, Zip 62881–4263;
tel. 618/548–3194 **A**9 10 18 **F**3 11 15 28 29 34 40 45 50 57 59 63 64 65
70 75 81 85 86 89 93 96 97 107 110 111 114 119 127 129 130 132 133
145 146 148
Primary Contact: Stephanie Hilton–Siebert, President and Chief Executive Officer
CFO: Teresa Stroud, Chief Financial Officer
CMO: Gautam Jha, M.D., Chief of Staff
CIO: Steve Turner, Director Information Technology
CHR: Diane Boswell, Director Human Resources and Marketing
CNO: Kendra Taylor, Director Inpatient Nursing
Web address: www.sthcares.org
**Control:** City–County, Government, nonfederal **Service:** General Medical and
Surgical

| | |
|---|---|
| **Staffed Beds:** 22 **Admissions:** 853 **Census:** 8 **Outpatient Visits:** 40028 **Births:** 0 **Total Expense ($000):** 22448 **Payroll Expense ($000):** 7737 **Personnel:** 205 | |

### SANDWICH—Dekalb County

☒ **VALLEY WEST HOSPITAL (141340)**, (Formerly Valley West Community
Hospital), 11 East Pleasant Avenue, Zip 60548–0901; tel. 815/786–8484 **A**1 9
10 18 **F**11 13 15 18 28 29 30 31 32 34 35 40 45 46 49 51 57 58 59 64 68
70 71 75 76 77 78 79 81 82 85 87 92 107 110 115 119 129 130
131 132 135 146 147 **S** Kish Health System, DeKalb, IL
Primary Contact: Brad Copple, President
COO: David R. Proulx, Assistant Vice President Operations
CFO: Loren Foelske, Vice President Finance
CMO: Michael Kulisz, D.O., Chief Medical Officer
CIO: Heath Bell, Chief Information Officer
CHR: Mark Thate, Vice President Human Resources
CNO: Pamela Duffy, Vice President Patient Services and CNO
Web address: www.vwch.org
**Control:** Other not–for–profit (including NFP Corporation) **Service:** General
Medical and Surgical

| | |
|---|---|
| **Staffed Beds:** 24 **Admissions:** 1197 **Census:** 9 **Outpatient Visits:** 40817 **Births:** 193 **Total Expense ($000):** 40572 **Payroll Expense ($000):** 10983 **Personnel:** 190 | |

### SHELBYVILLE—Shelby County

★ **SHELBY MEMORIAL HOSPITAL (140019)**, 200 South Cedar Street,
Zip 62565–1838; tel. 217/774–3961 **A**9 10 20 **F**3 15 28 29 40 62 64 81 93
107 108 118 119 127 129 132 133 146 **P**5
Primary Contact: Marilyn Sears, President and Chief Executive Officer
CFO: Phil Miller, Chief Financial Officer
CMO: Arnold Agapito, M.D., President Medical Staff
CHR: Amy Koehler, Director Human Resources
Web address: www.mysmh.org
**Control:** Other not–for–profit (including NFP Corporation) **Service:** General
Medical and Surgical

| | |
|---|---|
| **Staffed Beds:** 30 **Admissions:** 679 **Census:** 6 **Outpatient Visits:** 27890 **Births:** 0 **Total Expense ($000):** 15203 **Payroll Expense ($000):** 6770 **Personnel:** 157 | |

### SILVIS—Rock Island County

☒ **GENESIS MEDICAL CENTER, ILLINI CAMPUS (140275)**, 801 Illini Drive,
Zip 61282–1893; tel. 309/281–4000 **A**1 9 10 **F**3 7 11 13 15 18 20 26 28 29
30 31 34 35 38 40 43 44 46 50 53 54 57 59 63 64 68 70 74 75 76 77 78
79 81 82 84 85 86 87 89 97 107 108 110 111 114 119 129 130 131 132
135 146 147 **P**6 **S** Genesis Health System, Davenport, IA
Primary Contact: Florence Spyrow, President
CFO: Mark G. Rogers, Interim Vice President Finance and Chief Financial Officer
CMO: Peter Metcalf, M.D., President Medical Staff
CIO: Robert Frieden, Vice President Information Systems
CHR: Heidi Kahly–McMahon, Vice President Human Resources
Web address: www.genesishealth.com
**Control:** Other not–for–profit (including NFP Corporation) **Service:** General
Medical and Surgical

| | |
|---|---|
| **Staffed Beds:** 101 **Admissions:** 4461 **Census:** 39 **Outpatient Visits:** 108227 **Births:** 600 **Total Expense ($000):** 76799 **Payroll Expense ($000):** 25405 **Personnel:** 488 | |

### SKOKIE—Cook County

☒ **NORTHSHORE UNIVERSITY HEALTH SYSTEM SKOKIE HOSPITAL (140051)**,
9600 Gross Point Road, Zip 60076–1257; tel. 847/677–9600, (Nonreporting)
**A**1 3 5 9 10 **S** NorthShore University HealthSystem, Evanston, IL
Primary Contact: Kristen Murtos, FACHE, President
COO: Anthony Di Lorenzo, Vice President Operations
CMO: Michael Raymond, M.D., Chief Medical Officer
CIO: Kerry Kerlin, Vice President Information Technology
CHR: Richard J. Casey, Assistant Vice President Operations
Web address: www.northshore.org
**Control:** Other not–for–profit (including NFP Corporation) **Service:** General
Medical and Surgical

| | |
|---|---|
| **Staffed Beds:** 234 | |

### SPARTA—Randolph County

**SPARTA COMMUNITY HOSPITAL (141349)**, 818 East Broadway Street,
Zip 62286–1820, Mailing Address: P.O. Box 297, Zip 62286–0297;
tel. 618/443–2177 **A**9 10 18 **F**3 11 15 28 34 35 40 41 53 54 57 59 62 64
75 77 81 89 93 97 107 114 119 127 129 130 132 133 143 146 147 **P**5
Primary Contact: Joann Emge, Chief Executive Officer
COO: Joann Emge, Chief Executive Officer
CFO: Steven A. Bricker, Chief Financial Officer
CMO: Franklin James, Jr., M.D., Chief Medical Staff
CIO: Susan Gutjahr, Reimbursement Specialist
CHR: Darla Shawgo, Director Human Resources
CNO: Lori Clinton, Chief Nursing Officer
Web address: www.spartahospital.com
**Control:** Hospital district or authority, Government, nonfederal **Service:** General
Medical and Surgical

| | |
|---|---|
| **Staffed Beds:** 25 **Admissions:** 833 **Census:** 7 **Outpatient Visits:** 38957 **Births:** 0 **Total Expense ($000):** 26595 **Payroll Expense ($000):** 11534 **Personnel:** 219 | |

*Many Facility Codes have changed. Please refer to the AHA Guide Code Chart.*

**SPRING VALLEY—Bureau County**

**ST. MARGARET'S HOSPITAL (140143)**, 600 East First Street,
Zip 61362–1512; tel. 815/664–5311 **A**9 10 **F**3 11 13 15 28 29 30 31 32 34
35 38 40 44 45 46 47 49 53 57 58 59 63 70 75 76 77 79 81 82 85 87 90
93 96 107 108 110 111 114 118 119 129 130 131 132 133 135 143 144
146 147 148 **P**6 8 **S** Sisters of Mary of the Presentation Health System,
Fargo, ND
Primary Contact: Tim Muntz, President and Chief Executive Officer
CFO: Kim D. Santman, Vice President Finance
CIO: John Sabotta, Director Information Systems
CHR: Cheri D. Adrian, Director Human Resources
Web address: www.aboutsmh.org
**Control:** Church–operated, Nongovernment, not–for profit **Service:** General
Medical and Surgical

**Staffed Beds:** 69 **Admissions:** 2370 **Census:** 21 **Outpatient Visits:** 240934
**Births:** 292 **Total Expense ($000):** 64463 **Payroll Expense ($000):** 28324
**Personnel:** 493

**SPRINGFIELD—Sangamon County**

☐ **ANDREW MCFARLAND MENTAL HEALTH CENTER (144021)**, 901 East
Southwind Road, Zip 62703–5125; tel. 217/786–6994, (Nonreporting) **A**1 3
5 10
Primary Contact: Karen Schweighart, R.N., MS, Administrator
CFO: Jeff Frey, Business Administrator
CIO: Josh Kates, Information Technology Analyst
CHR: Robert Braasch, Administrator Human Resources
**Control:** State–Government, nonfederal **Service:** Psychiatric

**Staffed Beds:** 118

⊞ **KINDRED HOSPITAL SPRINGFIELD (142014)**, 701 North Walnut Street,
Zip 62702–4931; tel. 217/528–1217, (Nonreporting) **A**1 9 10 **S** Kindred
Healthcare, Louisville, KY
Primary Contact: Sally Hoffmann, Interim Chief Executive Officer
Web address: www.kindredspringfield.com/
**Control:** Corporation, Investor–owned, for–profit **Service:** Long–Term Acute Care
hospital

**Staffed Beds:** 50

☐ **LINCOLN PRAIRIE BEHAVIORAL HEALTH CENTER**, 5230 South Sixth Street,
Zip 62703–5128; tel. 217/585–1180 **A**1 3 5 9 **F**35 38 98 99 100 101 104 **P**3
6 **S** Universal Health Services, Inc., King of Prussia, PA
Primary Contact: Mark Littrell, Chief Executive Officer
Web address: www.lincolnprairiebhc.com/
**Control:** Corporation, Investor–owned, for–profit **Service:** Children's hospital
psychiatric

**Staffed Beds:** 88 **Admissions:** 1455 **Census:** 57 **Outpatient Visits:** 5998
**Births:** 0 **Total Expense ($000):** 12247 **Payroll Expense ($000):** 6498
**Personnel:** 214

⊞ △ **MEMORIAL MEDICAL CENTER (140148)**, 701 North First Street,
Zip 62781–0001; tel. 217/788–3000 **A**1 2 3 5 7 8 9 10 **F**3 8 11 12 13 14 15
16 17 18 20 22 24 26 28 29 30 31 32 34 35 36 37 40 43 44 45 46 47 48
49 50 51 54 57 58 59 60 61 63 64 68 69 70 74 75 76 77 78 79 81 82 84
85 86 87 89 90 92 93 96 97 98 100 101 102 103 104 105 107 108 110
111 114 115 116 117 118 119 120 121 124 126 129 130 131 132 134 135
138 141 142 144 145 146 147 148 **P**3 5 **S** Memorial Health System,
Springfield, IL
Primary Contact: Edgar J. Curtis, President and Chief Executive Officer
COO: Douglas L. Rahn, Senior Vice President and Chief Operating Officer
CFO: Robert W. Kay, Senior Vice President and Chief Financial Officer
CMO: Rajesh G. Govindaiah, M.D., Chief Medical Officer
CIO: David B. Graham, M.D., Senior Vice President and Chief Information Officer
CHR: Bradley J. Warren, Senior Vice President and Chief People Officer
CNO: Marsha A. Prater, Ph.D., Senior Vice President and Chief Nursing Officer
Web address: www.memorialmedical.com
**Control:** Other not–for–profit (including NFP Corporation) **Service:** General
Medical and Surgical

**Staffed Beds:** 473 **Admissions:** 25436 **Census:** 336 **Outpatient Visits:**
484595 **Births:** 1770 **Total Expense ($000):** 538201 **Payroll Expense
($000):** 173492 **Personnel:** 3526

⊞ **ST. JOHN'S HOSPITAL (140053)**, 800 East Carpenter Street,
Zip 62769–0002; tel. 217/544–6464, (Includes ST. JOHN'S CHILDREN'S
HOSPITAL, 800 East Carpenter Street, Zip 62769; tel. 217/544–6464), (Total
facility includes 37 beds in nursing home–type unit) **A**1 2 3 5 8 9 10 **F**3 11 12
13 15 17 18 19 20 22 24 26 28 29 30 31 32 34 35 36 37 39 40 41 43 44
45 46 47 48 49 50 51 53 54 56 57 58 59 60 61 62 63 64 66 68 70 72 74
75 76 77 78 79 81 82 84 85 86 87 88 89 92 93 94 98 100 101 102 103
104 107 108 110 111 114 115 117 118 119 120 121 122 123 124 126 128
129 130 131 132 135 145 146 147 148 **S** Hospital Sisters Health System,
Springfield, IL
Primary Contact: Robert P. Ritz, President and Chief Executive Officer
CFO: Larry Ragel, Chief Financial Officer
CMO: Craig Backs, M.D., Medical Director
CIO: Kirk Mahlen, Chief Information Officer
CHR: Joseph W. Bretz, Director Human Resources
Web address: www.st-johns.org
**Control:** Other not–for–profit (including NFP Corporation) **Service:** General
Medical and Surgical

**Staffed Beds:** 430 **Admissions:** 19487 **Census:** 280 **Outpatient Visits:**
244419 **Births:** 1812 **Total Expense ($000):** 425742 **Payroll Expense
($000):** 134598 **Personnel:** 2498

**STAUNTON—Macoupin County**

**COMMUNITY MEMORIAL HOSPITAL (141306)**, 400 Caldwell Street,
Zip 62088–1499; tel. 618/635–2200 **A**9 10 18 **F**3 11 15 28 29 31 34 40 56
57 70 81 85 87 93 103 107 110 115 119 130 132 133 146 **P**6
Primary Contact: Susie Campbell, Chief Executive Officer
CFO: Donald Brunnworth, Chief Financial Officer
CMO: Bryan Siegfried, M.D., President Medical Staff
CIO: Cheryl Horner, Supervisor Data Processing
CHR: Marilyn Herbeck, Coordinator Human Resources
Web address: www.stauntonhospital.org
**Control:** Other not–for–profit (including NFP Corporation) **Service:** General
Medical and Surgical

**Staffed Beds:** 25 **Admissions:** 224 **Census:** 2 **Outpatient Visits:** 27177
**Births:** 0 **Total Expense ($000):** 13383 **Payroll Expense ($000):** 5518
**Personnel:** 133

**STERLING—Whiteside County**

⊞ **CGH MEDICAL CENTER (140043)**, 100 East LeFevre Road, Zip 61081–1279;
tel. 815/625–0400 **A**1 9 10 **F**3 7 8 11 13 15 18 20 22 28 29 30 31 34 35 40
45 47 49 50 51 57 59 62 64 68 70 74 76 78 79 81 85 86 87 89 93 97 107
108 110 111 114 115 118 119 124 129 130 132 133 135 145 146 148 **P**6
Primary Contact: Paul Steinke, D.O., President and Chief Executive Officer
COO: Norm Deets, Vice President and Chief Operating Officer
CFO: Ben Schaab, VP Fiscal Services/ Chief Financial Officer
CMO: Mark Schmelzel, M.D., Vice President and Medical Director
CIO: Kevin Anderson, Director Information Technology
CHR: Thomas J. McCawley, Director Human Resources
CNO: Kristie A. Geil, VP, Chief Nursing Officer
Web address: www.cghmc.com
**Control:** City–Government, nonfederal **Service:** General Medical and Surgical

**Staffed Beds:** 99 **Admissions:** 5589 **Census:** 49 **Outpatient Visits:** 274800
**Births:** 557 **Total Expense ($000):** 147586 **Payroll Expense ($000):** 59951
**Personnel:** 1252

**STREAMWOOD—Cook County**

☐ **STREAMWOOD BEHAVIORAL HEALTH CENTER (144034)**, 1400 East Irving
Park Road, Zip 60107–3203; tel. 630/837–9000, (Nonreporting) **A**1 9 10
**S** Universal Health Services, Inc., King of Prussia, PA
Primary Contact: Ron Weglarz, Chief Executive Officer and Managing Director
COO: Ron Weglarz, Chief Executive Officer and Managing Director
CFO: Karen Williams, Chief Financial Officer
CMO: Joseph McNally, M.D., Medical Director
CHR: Michael Isaacs, Director Human Resources
CNO: Olieth Lightbourne, Chief Nursing Officer
Web address: www.streamwoodhospital.com
**Control:** Corporation, Investor–owned, for–profit **Service:** Children's hospital
psychiatric

**Staffed Beds:** 177

IL

---

**Hospital, Medicare Provider Number, Address, Telephone, Approval, Facility, and Physician Codes, Health Care System**

★ American Hospital Association (AHA) membership
☐ The Joint Commission accreditation
◇ DNV Healthcare Inc. accreditation
○ Healthcare Facilities Accreditation Program
△ Commission on Accreditation of Rehabilitation Facilities (CARF) accreditation

## STREATOR—Lasalle County

☒ **ST. MARY'S HOSPITAL (140026)**, 111 Spring Street, Zip 61364–3399; tel. 815/673–2311, (Total facility includes 30 beds in nursing home–type unit) **A**1 9 10 **F**3 11 13 15 18 28 29 30 31 34 35 40 41 45 47 50 54 56 57 59 62 70 75 76 77 78 79 81 82 84 85 87 89 93 107 108 110 111 115 119 128 130 132 143 146 147 148 **P**8 **S** Hospital Sisters Health System, Springfield, IL
Primary Contact: John T. Flanders, MS, R.N., President and Chief Executive Officer
CFO: Karen S. Clark, Chief Financial Officer
CMO: Larry Jones, M.D., Chief Medical Officer
CIO: Georgene Lansford, Director Information Systems
Web address: www.stmaryshospital.org
**Control:** Church–operated, Nongovernment, not–for profit **Service:** General Medical and Surgical

**Staffed Beds:** 98 **Admissions:** 2162 **Census:** 22 **Outpatient Visits:** 88012 **Births:** 182 **Total Expense ($000):** 53773 **Payroll Expense ($000):** 17050 **Personnel:** 346

## SYCAMORE—Dekalb County

☒ **KINDRED HOSPITAL–SYCAMORE (142006)**, 225 Edward Street, Zip 60178–2137; tel. 815/895–2144 **A**1 10 **F**1 3 29 30 45 46 60 63 68 74 78 80 82 84 85 107 114 130 148 **S** Kindred Healthcare, Louisville, KY
Primary Contact: Cindy Smith, Chief Executive Officer
CFO: Jay Schweikart, Chief Financial Officer
CMO: Thomas Liske, M.D., Chief Medical Officer
CHR: Eileen Strachan, Coordinator Human Resources
Web address: www.kindredhospitalsyc.com/
**Control:** Corporation, Investor–owned, for–profit **Service:** Long–Term Acute Care hospital

**Staffed Beds:** 69 **Admissions:** 497 **Census:** 38 **Outpatient Visits:** 0 **Births:** 0 **Total Expense ($000):** 17300 **Payroll Expense ($000):** 6627 **Personnel:** 138

## TAYLORVILLE—Christian County

☒ **TAYLORVILLE MEMORIAL HOSPITAL (141339)**, 201 East Pleasant Street, Zip 62568–1597; tel. 217/824–3331, (Total facility includes 20 beds in nursing home–type unit) **A**1 5 9 10 18 **F**15 28 29 30 31 34 35 40 45 46 50 57 59 64 75 77 79 81 87 89 93 107 108 110 111 119 128 129 130 131 132 133 144 146 **P**5 **S** Memorial Health System, Springfield, IL
Primary Contact: Daniel J. Raab, President and Chief Executive Officer
CFO: Sue Hill, Director Finance
CHR: Jackie Broaddus, Business Partner
Web address: www.taylorvillememorial.org
**Control:** Other not–for–profit (including NFP Corporation) **Service:** General Medical and Surgical

**Staffed Beds:** 45 **Admissions:** 1396 **Census:** 14 **Outpatient Visits:** 37643 **Total Expense ($000):** 33005 **Payroll Expense ($000):** 12847 **Personnel:** 235

## URBANA—Champaign County

☒ △ ◇ **CARLE FOUNDATION HOSPITAL (140091)**, 611 West Park Street, Zip 61801–2595; tel. 217/383–3311 **A**1 2 3 5 7 9 10 13 21 **F**3 7 8 11 12 13 15 17 20 22 24 26 29 30 34 35 40 43 44 45 46 47 48 49 50 51 53 56 57 58 59 60 61 62 63 64 65 68 70 72 74 75 76 78 79 80 81 84 85 86 87 89 90 91 93 94 96 107 108 110 111 114 115 116 117 119 126 129 130 131 132 135 145 146 148
Primary Contact: James C. Leonard, M.D., President and Chief Executive Officer
COO: John Snyder, Executive Vice President and Chief Operating Officer
CFO: Dennis Hesch, Executive Vice President Finance and Chief Financial Officer
CMO: Kirk Moberg, M.D., Executive Vice President and Chief Medical Officer
CIO: Rick Rinehart, Chief Information Officer
Web address: www.carle.com/hospital
**Control:** Other not–for–profit (including NFP Corporation) **Service:** General Medical and Surgical

**Staffed Beds:** 322 **Admissions:** 19827 **Census:** 267 **Outpatient Visits:** 269648 **Births:** 2575 **Total Expense ($000):** 326570 **Payroll Expense ($000):** 96247 **Personnel:** 1849

☒ △ **PRESENCE COVENANT MEDICAL CENTER (140113)**, (Formerly Provena Covenant Medical Center), 1400 West Park Street, Zip 61801–2396; tel. 217/337–2000 **A**1 3 5 7 9 10 **F**3 7 13 15 18 20 22 24 26 28 29 30 31 34 35 38 40 49 50 56 57 59 61 63 64 65 68 70 74 75 76 78 79 81 82 83 84 85 89 90 93 98 100 101 102 103 107 108 110 111 114 115 119 126 130 132 135 146 147 148 **S** Presence Health, Chicago, IL
Primary Contact: Michael L. Brown, President and Chief Executive Officer
COO: Eric Rhodes, Assistant Vice President of Operations
CFO: Deborah Schimerowski, Vice President Finance and Chief Financial Officer
CMO: Jared Rogers, M.D., Chief Medical Officer
CIO: Jason Wheatley, Manager Information Systems
CHR: Janet S. Payne, Vice President Human Resources
Web address: www.provena.org/covenant
**Control:** Church–operated, Nongovernment, not–for profit **Service:** General Medical and Surgical

**Staffed Beds:** 181 **Admissions:** 8171 **Census:** 87 **Outpatient Visits:** 193289 **Births:** 830 **Total Expense ($000):** 134044 **Payroll Expense ($000):** 42721 **Personnel:** 849

## VANDALIA—Fayette County

☒ **FAYETTE COUNTY HOSPITAL (141346)**, 650 West Taylor Street, Zip 62471–1296; tel. 618/283–1231, (Total facility includes 85 beds in nursing home–type unit) **A**1 9 10 18 **F**3 7 11 15 28 29 30 34 35 40 45 49 57 59 77 80 81 86 93 107 110 111 112 114 116 117 119 127 128 129 130 132 133 145 146 148 **P**5 **S** Alliant Management Services, Louisville, KY
Primary Contact: Gregory D. Starnes, Chief Executive Officer
CFO: Shelley Bay, Chief Financial Officer
CMO: Raymond Ryan, M.D., Chief of Staff
CIO: Susan Crawford, Manager Human Resources
Web address: www.fayettecountyhospital.org
**Control:** Corporation, Investor–owned, for–profit **Service:** General Medical and Surgical

**Staffed Beds:** 110 **Admissions:** 1282 **Census:** 65 **Outpatient Visits:** 31304 **Births:** 0 **Total Expense ($000):** 21439 **Payroll Expense ($000):** 7735 **Personnel:** 252

## WATSEKA—Iroquois County

☒ **IROQUOIS MEMORIAL HOSPITAL AND RESIDENT HOME (140167)**, 200 Fairman Avenue, Zip 60970–1644; tel. 815/432–5841, (Nonreporting) **A**1 9 10 20
Primary Contact: Michael J. Stenger, Interim President and Chief Executive Officer
CFO: Joseph A. Swab, Chief Financial Officer
CMO: Mohammed Razvi, M.D., Chief of Staff
CIO: Tim Smith, Director Information Systems
CHR: Jamie Neumann, Director Human Resources
Web address: www.iroquoismemorial.com
**Control:** Other not–for–profit (including NFP Corporation) **Service:** General Medical and Surgical

**Staffed Beds:** 84

## WAUKEGAN—Lake County

☒ **VISTA MEDICAL CENTER EAST (140084)**, 1324 North Sheridan Road, Zip 60085–2161; tel. 847/360–3000 **A**1 2 9 10 **F**3 12 13 15 18 20 22 24 26 28 29 30 31 34 35 38 39 40 42 43 44 45 46 47 48 49 50 57 59 68 70 73 74 76 78 79 81 82 85 87 89 90 93 100 102 107 108 110 111 114 115 119 126 129 130 132 146 147 148 **P**5 6 **S** Community Health Systems, Inc., Franklin, TN
Primary Contact: Barbara J. Martin, R.N., President and Chief Executive Officer
COO: Kim Needham, Assistant Chief Executive Officer
CFO: Pamela German Hill, Chief Financial Officer
CMO: Michael Scheer, M.D., President Medical Staff
CIO: Cathy Adler–Marks, Director Information Technology
CHR: Nancy Alonso, Vice President Human Resources
Web address: www.vistahealth.com
**Control:** Corporation, Investor–owned, for–profit **Service:** General Medical and Surgical

**Staffed Beds:** 192 **Admissions:** 11193 **Census:** 117 **Outpatient Visits:** 121772 **Births:** 1091 **Total Expense ($000):** 133724 **Payroll Expense ($000):** 52126 **Personnel:** 836

☒ △ **VISTA MEDICAL CENTER WEST (140033)**, 2615 Washington Street, Zip 60085–4988; tel. 847/249–3900 **A**1 7 9 10 **F**29 30 34 35 38 40 42 43 50 56 59 64 68 77 87 90 98 99 101 102 103 104 105 107 119 130 132 135 **P**5 6 **S** Community Health Systems, Inc., Franklin, TN
Primary Contact: Barbara J. Martin, R.N., President and Chief Executive Officer
COO: Kim Needham, Assistant Chief Executive Officer
CFO: Pamela German Hill, Chief Financial Officer
CMO: Wendy Lotts, M.D., President Medical Staff
CIO: Cathy Adler–Marks, Director Information Technology
CHR: Robyn Matsil, Human Resources Director
CNO: Rosetta Speights, R.N., Chief Nursing Officer
Web address: www.vistahealth.com
**Control:** Corporation, Investor–owned, for–profit **Service:** Psychiatric

**Staffed Beds:** 67 **Admissions:** 1833 **Census:** 38 **Outpatient Visits:** 22444 **Births:** 0 **Total Expense ($000):** 15950 **Payroll Expense ($000):** 7537 **Personnel:** 125

## WHEATON—Du Page County

☒ △ **MARIANJOY REHABILITATION HOSPITAL (143027)**, 26 West 171 Roosevelt Road, Zip 60187–0795, Mailing Address: P.O. Box 795, Zip 60187–0795; tel. 630/909–8000, (Total facility includes 20 beds in nursing home–type unit) **A**1 3 5 7 9 10 **F**11 29 30 34 35 36 56 64 68 75 86 87 90 91 93 94 128 132 143 146 148 **P**6 **S** Wheaton Franciscan Healthcare, Wheaton, IL
Primary Contact: Kathleen C. Yosko, President and Chief Executive Officer
COO: John Brady, Vice President Physician Services and Organizational Planning
CFO: Michael Hedderman, Senior Vice President Finance and Chief Financial Officer
CMO: Noel Rao, M.D., Medical Director
CIO: Pat Orrison, Director Information Services
CHR: Teresa Chapman, Vice President Human Resources
Web address: www.marianjoy.org
**Control:** Church–operated, Nongovernment, not–for profit **Service:** Rehabilitation

**Staffed Beds:** 128 **Admissions:** 2939 **Census:** 110 **Outpatient Visits:** 47430 **Births:** 0 **Total Expense ($000):** 68800 **Payroll Expense ($000):** 36394 **Personnel:** 734

IL

*Many Facility Codes have changed. Please refer to the AHA Guide Code Chart.*
© 2013 AHA Guide

**WINFIELD—DuPage County**

✠ **CENTRAL DUPAGE HOSPITAL (140242)**, 25 North Winfield Road, Zip 60190;
tel. 630/933–1600, (Includes BEHAVIORAL HEALTH CENTER, 27 West 350 High
Lake Road, tel. 630/653–4000) **A**1 2 5 9 10 **F**3 4 5 8 11 12 13 15 17 18 19
20 22 24 26 28 29 30 31 34 35 36 37 39 40 41 42 43 44 45 46 47 48 49
50 54 55 57 58 59 64 68 70 72 73 74 75 76 78 79 81 82 84 85 86 87 88
89 91 92 93 94 96 98 99 100 101 102 103 104 105 106 107 108 110 111
112 114 115 116 117 118 119 120 121 122 123 124 126 129 130 132 135
141 142 144 145 146 147 148 **S** Cadence Health, Winfield, IL
Primary Contact: Brian J. Lemon, President
CFO: James Spear, Executive Vice President and Chief Financial Officer
CMO: Kevin Most, D.O., Vice President Medical Affairs
CIO: David Printz, Vice President and Chief Information Officer
Web address: www.cdh.org
**Control:** Other not–for–profit (including NFP Corporation) **Service:** General
Medical and Surgical

**Staffed Beds:** 344 **Admissions:** 23280 **Census:** 251 **Outpatient Visits:**
904822 **Births:** 3081 **Total Expense ($000):** 539359 **Payroll Expense
($000):** 190487 **Personnel:** 2879

**WOODSTOCK—Mchenry County**

✠ **CENTEGRA HOSPITAL – WOODSTOCK (140176)**, 3701 Doty Road,
Zip 60098–7509, Mailing Address: P.O. Box 1990, Zip 60098–1990;
tel. 815/338–2500, (Total facility includes 25 beds in nursing home–type unit) **A**1
2 9 10 **F**3 4 5 11 12 13 15 18 28 29 30 31 34 35 37 38 39 40 43 44 47 49
50 54 57 58 59 64 68 69 70 74 75 76 78 79 81 85 86 87 92 93 98 100
101 102 103 105 107 108 110 111 114 115 118 119 128 129 130 131 132
143 146 147 148 **P**5 **S** Centegra Health System, Crystal Lake, IL
Primary Contact: Michael S. Eesley, Chief Executive Officer
COO: Jason Sciarro, Chief Operating Officer
CFO: Robert Rosenberger, Executive Vice President, Chief Financial Officer
CMO: Ted Lorenc, M.D., Chief Medical Officer
CIO: Paul Solverson, Interim Chief Information Officer
CIO: David Tomlinson, Senior Vice President, Chief Information Officer
CHR: Barbara Jo Johnson, R.N., Senior Vice President Human Resources
Development
CHR: Bernadette S. Szczepanski, Vice President Human Resources Development
CNO: Neil W. Murphy, R.N., Senior Vice President, Chief Nursing Officer
Web address: www.centegra.org
**Control:** Other not–for–profit (including NFP Corporation) **Service:** General
Medical and Surgical

**Staffed Beds:** 135 **Admissions:** 8108 **Census:** 98 **Outpatient Visits:** 126301
**Births:** 942 **Total Expense ($000):** 149506 **Payroll Expense ($000):** 60309
**Personnel:** 757

**ZION—Lake County**

☐ **MIDWESTERN REGIONAL MEDICAL CENTER (140100)**, 2520 Elisha Avenue,
Zip 60099–2587; tel. 847/872–4561, (Nonreporting) **A**1 2 3 5 10 **S** Cancer
Treatment Centers of America, Schaumburg, IL
Primary Contact: Scott Jones, Chief Executive Officer
CFO: Cecilia Taylor, Chief Financial Officer
CMO: Edgar Staren, M.D., Senior Vice President Medical Affairs
CIO: Chad Eckes, Chief Information Officer
CHR: Scott Gallo, Assistant Vice President Talent
Web address: www.cancercenter.com
**Control:** Corporation, Investor–owned, for–profit **Service:** General Medical and
Surgical

**Staffed Beds:** 73

---

**Hospital, Medicare Provider Number, Address, Telephone, Approval, Facility, and Physician Codes, Health Care System**

★ American Hospital Association (AHA) membership
☐ The Joint Commission accreditation
◇ DNV Healthcare Inc. accreditation
○ Healthcare Facilities Accreditation Program
△ Commission on Accreditation of Rehabilitation Facilities (CARF) accreditation

IL

# INDIANA

## ANDERSON—Madison County

☐ **COMMUNITY HOSPITAL OF ANDERSON AND MADISON COUNTY (150113)**, 1515 North Madison Avenue, Zip 46011–3453; tel. 765/298–4242, (Total facility includes 191 beds in nursing home–type unit) **A**1 2 9 10 **F**3 6 10 11 13 15 18 20 22 28 29 30 31 32 34 35 40 44 46 49 50 51 54 56 57 58 59 60 61 64 67 68 70 73 74 75 76 77 78 79 81 85 86 87 89 93 107 108 109 111 114 119 120 121 122 123 126 128 129 130 132 135 143 146 147 148 **P**6 **S** Community Health Network, Indianapolis, IN
Primary Contact: Beth S. Tharp, R.N., President and Chief Executive Officer
Web address: www.communityanderson.com
**Control:** Other not–for–profit (including NFP Corporation) **Service:** General Medical and Surgical

**Staffed Beds:** 318 **Admissions:** 6416 **Census:** 255 **Outpatient Visits:** 177899 **Births:** 810 **Total Expense ($000):** 133998 **Payroll Expense ($000):** 61792 **Personnel:** 1405

⌧ **ST. VINCENT ANDERSON REGIONAL HOSPITAL (150088)**, (Formerly Saint John's Health System), 2015 Jackson Street, Zip 46016–4339; tel. 765/649–2511 **A**1 2 9 10 **F**3 4 5 8 11 14 15 16 18 20 22 28 29 30 31 32 34 35 38 40 44 45 49 50 51 54 56 57 58 59 60 61 62 63 64 65 66 68 70 74 75 76 77 78 79 81 82 84 85 86 87 89 90 92 93 94 96 98 99 100 101 102 103 104 105 106 107 108 110 111 114 116 117 118 119 120 121 123 129 130 132 134 135 144 145 146 147 148 **P**6 **S** Ascension Health, Saint Louis, MO
Primary Contact: Thomas J. VanOsdol, President
COO: David Maxwell, Vice President Operations
CFO: Donald L. Apple, Chief Financial Officer
CMO: Gary Brazel, M.D., Chief Medical Officer
CIO: Robert Pope, Information Technology Director and Ministry Liaison
CHR: Glenn C. Fields, Human Resources
CNO: Nancy Pitcock, Vice President of Nursing and Chief Nursing Officer
Web address: www.stvincent.org/Saint-Johns/Default.aspx
**Control:** Church–operated, Nongovernment, not–for profit **Service:** General Medical and Surgical

**Staffed Beds:** 185 **Admissions:** 7908 **Census:** 103 **Outpatient Visits:** 278709 **Births:** 464 **Total Expense ($000):** 188812 **Payroll Expense ($000):** 72799 **Personnel:** 1024

## ANGOLA—Steuben County

★ △ **CAMERON MEMORIAL COMMUNITY HOSPITAL (151315)**, 416 East Maumee Street, Zip 46703–2015; tel. 260/665–2141 **A**7 9 10 18 **F**3 5 10 11 13 15 28 29 30 34 45 54 57 59 62 63 68 76 77 79 81 82 84 85 87 93 107 108 111 114 116 117 118 119 132 133 144 146
Primary Contact: Gregory T. Burns, President and Chief Executive Officer
CFO: Darryl Faye, Chief Financial Officer
CMO: Berry Miller, M.D., Chief Medical Officer
CHR: Nancy Covell, Director Human Resources
Web address: www.cameronmch.com
**Control:** Other not–for–profit (including NFP Corporation) **Service:** General Medical and Surgical

**Staffed Beds:** 25 **Admissions:** 955 **Census:** 9 **Outpatient Visits:** 102850 **Births:** 158 **Total Expense ($000):** 42670 **Payroll Expense ($000):** 14806 **Personnel:** 341

## AUBURN—Dekalb County

★ **DEKALB HEALTH (150045)**, 1316 East Seventh Street, Zip 46706–2515, Mailing Address: P.O. Box 542, Zip 46706–0542; tel. 260/925–4600 **A**9 10 **F**3 7 11 13 15 28 29 32 34 35 36 40 45 53 56 57 59 62 63 64 70 73 75 76 77 79 81 82 84 85 86 87 89 93 97 104 107 108 110 111 114 115 118 119 129 130 132 135 146 147 148 **P**4 6 8
Primary Contact: Fred Price, R.N., President and Chief Executive Officer
CFO: Amy Crouch, Chief Financial Officer
CMO: Emilio Vazquez, M.D., Chief Medical Officer
CIO: Ed Hobbs, Director Information Services
CHR: Deb Arend Sinclair, Vice President Human Resources
CNO: Donna S. Freund, MSN, Chief Nursing Officer
Web address: www.dekalbhealth.com
**Control:** Other not–for–profit (including NFP Corporation) **Service:** General Medical and Surgical

**Staffed Beds:** 51 **Admissions:** 1878 **Census:** 15 **Outpatient Visits:** 83195 **Births:** 420 **Total Expense ($000):** 55192 **Payroll Expense ($000):** 22256 **Personnel:** 426

**NORTHEASTERN CENTER (154050)**, 1850 Wesley Road, Zip 46706–3653; tel. 260/927–0726, (Nonreporting) **A**10
Primary Contact: Jerry Hollister, Chief Executive Officer
Web address: www.necmh.org
**Control:** Other not–for–profit (including NFP Corporation) **Service:** Psychiatric

**Staffed Beds:** 16

## AVON—Hendricks County

**CLARIAN WEST MEDICAL CENTER** See Indiana University Health West Hospital

⌧ **INDIANA UNIVERSITY HEALTH WEST HOSPITAL (150158)**, 1111 North Ronald Reagan Parkway, Zip 46123–7085; tel. 317/217–3000 **A**1 2 5 9 10 **F**3 13 15 18 20 22 26 28 29 30 34 35 40 45 47 48 49 50 51 57 59 64 70 73 74 75 76 77 78 79 81 82 85 86 87 89 93 100 107 110 111 113 114 115 119 120 121 129 130 132 135 146 147 148 **S** Indiana University Health, Indianapolis, IN
Primary Contact: Matthew D. Bailey, FACHE, President and Chief Executive Officer
COO: Judy Coleman, Chief Operating Officer and Chief Financial Officer
CFO: Judy Coleman, Chief Operating Officer and Chief Financial Officer
CMO: Gregory Spurgin, M.D., Chief of Staff
CHR: Lana Funkhouser, Vice President Human Resources
CNO: Mary Myers, R.N., Chief Nursing Officer
Web address: www.iuhealth.org
**Control:** Other not–for–profit (including NFP Corporation) **Service:** General Medical and Surgical

**Staffed Beds:** 127 **Admissions:** 7232 **Census:** 83 **Outpatient Visits:** 135473 **Births:** 1167 **Total Expense ($000):** 139399 **Payroll Expense ($000):** 47528 **Personnel:** 764

## BATESVILLE—Franklin County

⌧ **MARGARET MARY HEALTH (151329)**, (Formerly Margaret Mary Community Hospital), 321 Mitchell Avenue, Zip 47006–8909, Mailing Address: P.O. Box 226, Zip 47006–0226; tel. 812/934–6624 **A**1 2 9 10 18 **F**3 13 15 28 30 31 34 35 36 39 40 45 46 50 54 56 59 62 63 64 65 70 75 76 77 78 79 81 85 86 87 93 107 108 111 114 118 119 121 123 129 130 131 132 135 144 146 148
Primary Contact: Timothy L. Putnam, FACHE, President and Chief Executive Officer
CFO: Brian Daeger, Vice President Financial Services
CMO: Andrew Poltrack, M.D., Chief of Staff
CIO: Donna Nobbe, Director Information Systems
CHR: Kimberly Inscho, Vice President Community Relations and Human Resources
Web address: www.mmch.org
**Control:** Other not–for–profit (including NFP Corporation) **Service:** General Medical and Surgical

**Staffed Beds:** 25 **Admissions:** 1806 **Census:** 15 **Outpatient Visits:** 152090 **Births:** 369 **Total Expense ($000):** 67534 **Payroll Expense ($000):** 27955 **Personnel:** 438

## BEDFORD—Lawrence County

**BEDFORD REGIONAL MEDICAL CENTER** See Indiana University Health Bedford Hospital

**DUNN MEMORIAL HOSPITAL** See St. Vincent Dunn Hospital

⌧ **INDIANA UNIVERSITY HEALTH BEDFORD HOSPITAL (151328)**, 2900 West 16th Street, Zip 47421–3583; tel. 812/275–1200 **A**1 2 9 10 18 **F**3 7 11 15 18 28 29 30 31 34 35 36 37 38 39 40 41 44 45 46 49 53 57 59 64 65 68 70 71 74 75 77 78 79 81 82 85 86 87 91 92 93 94 97 102 107 108 110 111 115 118 119 129 130 131 132 133 134 135 144 146 **P**6 **S** Indiana University Health, Indianapolis, IN
Primary Contact: Bradford W. Dykes, President and Chief Executive Officer
CFO: Charles L. Shetler, CPA, Chief Financial Officer
CHR: Cindy Smale, Director Human Resources
CNO: Brenda Davis, R.N., Vice President of Patient Services
Web address: www.iuhealth.com
**Control:** Other not–for–profit (including NFP Corporation) **Service:** General Medical and Surgical

**Staffed Beds:** 25 **Admissions:** 1348 **Census:** 15 **Outpatient Visits:** 87382 **Births:** 0 **Total Expense ($000):** 52668 **Payroll Expense ($000):** 25751 **Personnel:** 448

⌧ **ST. VINCENT DUNN HOSPITAL (151335)**, 1600 23rd Street, Zip 47421–4704; tel. 812/275–3331, (Nonreporting) **A**1 9 10 18 **S** Ascension Health, Saint Louis, MO
Primary Contact: Joseph E. Roche, Chief Executive Officer
CFO: Crystal Plano, Controller
CMO: Deborah W. Craton, M.D., Chief Medical Officer
CIO: Chad Damon, Chief Information Officer
CHR: Darci Medlock, Manager Human Resources
Web address: www.stvincent.org/St-Vincent–Dunn/Default.aspx
**Control:** Other not–for–profit (including NFP Corporation) **Service:** General Medical and Surgical

**Staffed Beds:** 25

## BEECH GROVE—Marion County

**ST. FRANCIS HOSPITAL AND HEALTH CENTERS – NORTH CAMPUS** See Franciscan St. Francis Health – Beech Grove

*Many Facility Codes have changed. Please refer to the AHA Guide Code Chart.*
© 2013 AHA Guide

## BLOOMINGTON—Monroe County

**BLOOMINGTON HOSPITAL** See Indiana University Health Bloomington Hospital

☐ **BLOOMINGTON MEADOWS HOSPITAL (154041)**, 3600 North Prow Road, Zip 47404–1616; tel. 812/331–8000 **A**1 9 10 **F**4 98 99 101 102 104 105 106 **S** Universal Health Services, Inc., King of Prussia, PA
Primary Contact: Jean Scallon, Chief Executive Officer
CFO: Becky T. Nyberg, Chief Financial Officer
CMO: Jonathan Bevers, M.D., Medical Director
CHR: Amanda Shettlesworth, Director Human Resources
CNO: Susan Calabrese, Director of Nursing
Web address: www.bloomingtonmeadows.com
**Control:** Corporation, Investor–owned, for–profit **Service:** Psychiatric

**Staffed Beds:** 67 **Admissions:** 1331 **Census:** 49 **Outpatient Visits:** 5428 **Births:** 0 **Total Expense ($000):** 8052 **Payroll Expense ($000):** 5324 **Personnel:** 129

☒ △ **INDIANA UNIVERSITY HEALTH BLOOMINGTON HOSPITAL (150051)**, 601 West Second Street, Zip 47403–2317, Mailing Address: P.O. Box 1149, Zip 47402–1149; tel. 812/336–6821 **A**1 2 5 7 9 10 19 **F**3 7 8 11 12 13 15 17 18 20 22 24 26 28 29 30 31 32 34 35 38 40 45 46 47 48 49 50 53 54 55 57 58 59 60 61 62 63 64 65 68 70 71 74 75 76 77 78 79 81 82 84 85 86 87 89 90 91 92 93 96 97 98 100 101 102 103 104 105 107 108 111 114 115 118 119 120 121 123 126 129 130 131 132 135 143 144 146 147 148 **P**6 **S** Indiana University Health, Indianapolis, IN
Primary Contact: Mark E. Moore, President and Chief Executive Officer
CFO: Jim Myers, Chief Financial Officer
CMO: Ken Marshall, M.D., Chief Medical Officer
CIO: Mark W. McMath, Chief Information Officer
CHR: Steven Deckard, Vice President Human Resources
Web address: www.iuhealth.org
**Control:** Other not–for–profit (including NFP Corporation) **Service:** General Medical and Surgical

**Staffed Beds:** 293 **Admissions:** 12827 **Census:** 151 **Outpatient Visits:** 264793 **Births:** 1977 **Total Expense ($000):** 319050 **Payroll Expense ($000):** 126028 **Personnel:** 2314

☒ **MONROE HOSPITAL (150164)**, 4011 South Monroe Medical Park Boulevard, Zip 47403–8000; tel. 812/825–1111 **A**1 9 10 **F**3 15 18 26 31 34 40 45 46 48 49 51 59 63 65 70 79 81 82 83 84 85 86 107 108 109 110 111 112 115 119 127 129 131 148 **P**6 8
Primary Contact: Joseph E. Roche, Chief Executive Officer
CFO: Dan Urban, Vice President of Finance
CMO: Brian Murphy, M.D., Chief of Staff
CHR: Pamela S. Hoffman, Director of Human Resources
CNO: Mary Jane Fleener, Director of Clinical Services
Web address: www.monroehospital.com
**Control:** Corporation, Investor–owned, for–profit **Service:** General Medical and Surgical

**Staffed Beds:** 32 **Admissions:** 1330 **Census:** 14 **Outpatient Visits:** 50233 **Births:** 0 **Total Expense ($000):** 62574 **Payroll Expense ($000):** 3912 **Personnel:** 215

## BLUFFTON—Wells County

☒ **BLUFFTON REGIONAL MEDICAL CENTER (150075)**, 303 South Main Street, Zip 46714–2503; tel. 260/824–3210, (Total facility includes 13 beds in nursing home–type unit) **A**1 9 10 **F**3 13 15 18 28 29 30 31 34 35 40 46 48 57 59 65 68 70 71 75 76 77 79 81 82 85 89 93 107 110 111 114 119 128 129 130 135 146 147 148 **S** Community Health Systems, Inc., Franklin, TN
Primary Contact: Aaron Garofola, Chief Executive Officer
CFO: Larry DeBolt, Chief Financial Officer
CMO: Kay Johnson, M.D., Chief of Staff
Web address: www.blufftonregional.com
**Control:** Corporation, Investor–owned, for–profit **Service:** General Medical and Surgical

**Staffed Beds:** 79 **Admissions:** 2257 **Census:** 28 **Outpatient Visits:** 60842 **Births:** 249 **Total Expense ($000):** 34901 **Payroll Expense ($000):** 13618 **Personnel:** 264

## BOONVILLE—Warrick County

☒ **ST. MARY'S WARRICK HOSPITAL (151325)**, 1116 Millis Avenue, Zip 47601–2204; tel. 812/897–4800 **A**1 9 10 18 **F**3 11 15 28 29 30 40 45 50 53 56 57 59 64 68 77 79 81 85 89 103 107 111 114 118 119 128 130 132 133 135 146 **S** Ascension Health, Saint Louis, MO
Primary Contact: Carol Godsey, Administrator
COO: Jared Richey, Chief Operating Officer
CFO: Cheryl Richey, Director of Finance
CMO: Peter Rosario, M.D., Chief Medical Officer
CHR: Dorothy Gehlhausen, Manager Human Resources
CNO: Karen Waters, Chief Nursing Officer
Web address: www.stmarys.org/warrick
**Control:** Other not–for–profit (including NFP Corporation) **Service:** General Medical and Surgical

**Staffed Beds:** 35 **Admissions:** 969 **Census:** 18 **Outpatient Visits:** 13296 **Births:** 0 **Total Expense ($000):** 15322 **Payroll Expense ($000):** 6952 **Personnel:** 130

## BRAZIL—Clay County

☒ **ST. VINCENT CLAY HOSPITAL (151309)**, 1206 East National Avenue, Zip 47834–2797, Mailing Address: P.O. Box 489, Zip 47834–0489; tel. 812/442–2500 **A**1 9 10 18 **F**3 11 15 18 29 30 34 35 40 45 50 57 59 65 67 68 75 77 79 81 82 85 86 87 107 108 111 114 119 130 131 133 135 146 148 **S** Ascension Health, Saint Louis, MO
Primary Contact: Jerry Laue, Administrator
CFO: Wayne Knight, Director Finance
CMO: Craig Johnson, D.O., Medical Director
CHR: Jennifer French, Director Organizational Quality
Web address: www.stvincent.org
**Control:** Church–operated, Nongovernment, not–for profit **Service:** General Medical and Surgical

**Staffed Beds:** 25 **Admissions:** 716 **Census:** 8 **Outpatient Visits:** 32665 **Births:** 0 **Total Expense ($000):** 19926 **Payroll Expense ($000):** 7161 **Personnel:** 93

## BREMEN—Marshall County

☒ **COMMUNITY HOSPITAL OF BREMEN (151300)**, 1020 High Road, Zip 46506–1093, Mailing Address: P.O. Box 8, Zip 46506–0008; tel. 574/546–2211 **A**1 9 10 18 **F**3 11 13 15 29 34 35 40 45 50 57 59 64 69 75 76 77 79 81 82 85 89 93 107 110 111 114 119 129 130 132 133 135 146
Primary Contact: David Bailey, FACHE, Chief Executive Officer
CFO: Debra Kipfer, Chief Financial Officer
CMO: Michael McClaid, M.D., President Medical Staff
CIO: Linda Barrett, Vice President of Information Services
CHR: Patricia Board, Vice President Human Resources
CNO: Andrea Koontz, R.N., Vice President of Nursing Services
Web address: www.bremenhospital.com
**Control:** Other not–for–profit (including NFP Corporation) **Service:** General Medical and Surgical

**Staffed Beds:** 24 **Admissions:** 446 **Census:** 4 **Outpatient Visits:** 27146 **Births:** 85 **Total Expense ($000):** 14738 **Payroll Expense ($000):** 5994 **Personnel:** 118

☐ **DOCTOR'S HOSPITAL AND NEUROMUSCULAR CENTER (153040)**, 411 South Whitlock Street, Zip 46506–1626, Mailing Address: P.O. Box 36, Zip 46506–0036; tel. 574/546–3830, (Nonreporting) **A**1 9 10 **S** Physicians Hospital System, Mishawaka, IN
Primary Contact: DeWayne Long, Chief Executive Officer
COO: John M. Day, Chief Operating Officer
CFO: Bernie Hebert, Jr., Chief Financial Officer
CMO: Steven Posar, M.D., Chief of Medicine
CHR: Emyle Kruyer–Collins, Director Human Resources
Web address: www.physicianshospitalsystem.net
**Control:** Partnership, Investor–owned, for–profit **Service:** Rehabilitation

**Staffed Beds:** 20

## CARMEL—Hamilton County

**CLARIAN NORTH MEDICAL CENTER** See Indiana University Health North Hospital

**FRANCISCAN ST. FRANCIS HEALTH–CARMEL**, 12188B North Meridian Street, Zip 46032–4840; tel. 317/705–4500, (Data for 248 days) **A**9 **F**3 15 29 30 31 35 45 57 59 64 78 79 81 85 94 107 111 115 119 146 **P**7 8 **S** Franciscan Alliance, Mishawaka, IN
Primary Contact: Robert J. Brody, Chief Executive Officer
Web address: www.franciscanalliance.org/hospitals/carmel/Pages/default.aspx
**Control:** Church–operated, Nongovernment, not–for profit **Service:** General Medical and Surgical

**Staffed Beds:** 6 **Admissions:** 7 **Census:** 1 **Outpatient Visits:** 1413 **Births:** 0 **Total Expense ($000):** 5644 **Payroll Expense ($000):** 2168 **Personnel:** 32

IN

**Hospital, Medicare Provider Number, Address, Telephone, Approval, Facility, and Physician Codes, Health Care System**

★ American Hospital Association (AHA) membership
☐ The Joint Commission accreditation
◇ DNV Healthcare Inc. accreditation
○ Healthcare Facilities Accreditation Program
△ Commission on Accreditation of Rehabilitation Facilities (CARF) accreditation

✠ **INDIANA UNIVERSITY HEALTH NORTH HOSPITAL (150161)**, 11700 North Meridian Avenue, Zip 46032–4656; tel. 317/688–2000 **A**1 5 9 10 **F**3 13 15 18 19 20 22 25 29 30 31 34 35 36 37 45 47 49 52 53 55 57 59 60 64 68 70 72 74 75 76 78 79 81 85 87 88 89 93 107 108 110 111 115 119 124 126 129 130 132 135 146 147 148 **S** Indiana University Health, Indianapolis, IN
Primary Contact: Jonathan R. Goble, FACHE, President and Chief Executive Officer
COO: Randall C. Yust, Chief Operating Officer and Chief Financial Officer
CFO: Randall C. Yust, Chief Operating Officer and Chief Financial Officer
CIO: Terrence Baker, Manager Information Services
CHR: Angela S. Thompson, Vice President Human Resources and Support Services
CNO: Suzanne Del Boccio, MS, Chief Nursing Officer and Vice President Patient Care Services
Web address: www.iuhealth.org
**Control:** Other not–for–profit (including NFP Corporation) **Service:** General Medical and Surgical

**Staffed Beds:** 161 **Admissions:** 7827 **Census:** 80 **Outpatient Visits:** 123922 **Births:** 2390 **Total Expense ($000):** 206840 **Payroll Expense ($000):** 66916 **Personnel:** 1075

✠ **ST. VINCENT CARMEL HOSPITAL (150157)**, 13500 North Meridian Street, Zip 46032–1456; tel. 317/582–7000, (Nonreporting) **A**1 9 10 **S** Ascension Health, Saint Louis, MO
Primary Contact: Michael D. Chittenden, President
COO: Daniel LaReau, Executive Director Operations and Information
CFO: Robert A. Bates, Executive Director Finance and Chief Financial Officer
CMO: Steven L. Priddy, M.D., Vice President Physician Affairs and Chief Medical Officer
CIO: Daniel LaReau, Executive Director Operations and Information
CHR: Charles Jeffras, Executive Director Human Resources
CNO: Gwynn Perlich, Vice President of Patient Services and Chief Nursing Officer
Web address: www.stvincent.org
**Control:** Church–operated, Nongovernment, not–for profit **Service:** General Medical and Surgical

**Staffed Beds:** 107

## CHARLESTOWN—Clark County

☐ **SAINT CATHERINE REGIONAL HOSPITAL (150163)**, 2200 Market Street, Zip 47111–9553, Mailing Address: P.O. Box 9, Zip 47111–0009; tel. 812/256–3301, (Nonreporting) **A**1 9 10
Primary Contact: Merlyn E. Knapp, President and Chief Executive Officer
CMO: William Garner, M.D., Chief Medical Officer
CIO: Kevin McLaughlin, Director Information Systems
Web address: www.saintcatherinehospital.com
**Control:** Corporation, Investor–owned, for–profit **Service:** General Medical and Surgical

**Staffed Beds:** 64

## CLARKSVILLE—Clark County

○ **KENTUCKIANA MEDICAL CENTER (150176)**, 4601 Medical Plaza Way, Zip 47129–9204; tel. 812/284–6100, (Nonreporting) **A**9 10 11
Primary Contact: Paul Newsom, Chief Operating Officer
Web address: www.kentuckianamedcen.com/
**Control:** Corporation, Investor–owned, for–profit **Service:** General Medical and Surgical

**Staffed Beds:** 40

## CLINTON—Vermillion County

**UNION HOSPITAL CLINTON (151326)**, 801 South Main Street, Zip 47842–2261; tel. 765/832–2451 **A**9 10 18 **F**3 11 15 18 29 30 34 35 40 45 50 57 59 64 65 68 70 75 77 81 85 86 87 93 97 107 108 110 114 119 130 132 133 146 **P**6
Primary Contact: Terri L. Hill, Vice President and Administrator
COO: Scott L. Teffeteller, President and Chief Executive Officer
CFO: Wayne Hutson, Chief Financial Officer
CIO: Kym Pfrank, Vice President Information Systems
CHR: Sally Zuel, Vice President Human Resources
CNO: Rhonda E. Smith, R.N., Chief Nursing Officer
Web address: www.uhhg.org/wcch/index.html
**Control:** Other not–for–profit (including NFP Corporation) **Service:** General Medical and Surgical

**Staffed Beds:** 25 **Admissions:** 1131 **Census:** 8 **Outpatient Visits:** 47509 **Births:** 0 **Total Expense ($000):** 20926 **Payroll Expense ($000):** 9206 **Personnel:** 154

## COLUMBIA CITY—Whitley County

✠ **PARKVIEW WHITLEY HOSPITAL (150101)**, 1260 East State Road 205, Zip 46725–9492; tel. 260/248–9000, (Total facility includes 67 beds in nursing home–type unit) **A**1 9 10 **F**3 7 8 13 15 28 29 34 35 38 40 45 50 54 57 59 64 69 70 75 76 79 81 82 85 89 91 93 96 102 107 108 110 111 114 119 125 128 129 132 135 143 144 146 148 **S** Parkview Health, Fort Wayne, IN
Primary Contact: Scott F. Gabriel, Chief Operating Officer
COO: Scott F. Gabriel, Chief Operating Officer
CFO: Lisa Peppler, Financial Operations Analyst
CMO: Jeffrey Brookes, M.D., Medical Director
CHR: Stephen P. Gagle, Manager Human Resources
CNO: Bridget Dolohanty–Johnson, R.N., Vice President Patient Care Services
Web address: www.parkview.com
**Control:** Other not–for–profit (including NFP Corporation) **Service:** General Medical and Surgical

**Staffed Beds:** 97 **Admissions:** 1805 **Census:** 66 **Outpatient Visits:** 40565 **Births:** 244 **Total Expense ($000):** 43391 **Payroll Expense ($000):** 13279 **Personnel:** 256

## COLUMBUS—Bartholomew County

★ ○ **COLUMBUS REGIONAL HOSPITAL (150112)**, 2400 East 17th Street, Zip 47201–5360; tel. 812/379–4441 **A**2 9 10 11 19 **F**3 7 8 11 12 13 15 18 20 22 24 26 28 29 30 31 34 35 36 38 39 40 45 49 50 51 53 57 58 59 64 66 68 70 73 74 75 76 77 78 79 81 84 85 86 87 89 90 93 98 100 101 102 103 107 108 110 111 113 114 117 118 119 120 121 123 126 129 130 131 132 135 143 144 146 147 148 **P**3 7 8
Primary Contact: James Bickel, Chief Executive Officer
CFO: Marlene Weatherwax, Vice President and Chief Financial Officer
CMO: Thomas Sonderman, M.D., Vice President and Chief Medical Officer
CIO: Diana Boyer, Chief Information Officer
CHR: Joseph Turco, Director Human Resources
CNO: Pamela Missi, R.N., Vice President and Chief Nursing Officer
Web address: www.crh.org
**Control:** County–Government, nonfederal **Service:** General Medical and Surgical

**Staffed Beds:** 198 **Admissions:** 9359 **Census:** 100 **Outpatient Visits:** 236771 **Births:** 1226 **Total Expense ($000):** 215677 **Payroll Expense ($000):** 74569 **Personnel:** 1258

## CONNERSVILLE—Fayette County

○ **FAYETTE REGIONAL HEALTH SYSTEM (150064)**, 1941 Virginia Avenue, Zip 47331–2833; tel. 765/825–5131, (Nonreporting) **A**9 10 11
Primary Contact: Randall White, Chief Executive Officer
CMO: Steven Johnson, D.O., Chief of Staff
CIO: Roy Cupp, Director Management Information Systems
CHR: Rhonda McPherson, Vice President Human Resources
Web address: www.fayetteregional.org
**Control:** Other not–for–profit (including NFP Corporation) **Service:** General Medical and Surgical

**Staffed Beds:** 73

## CORYDON—Harrison County

★ **HARRISON COUNTY HOSPITAL (151331)**, 1141 Hospital Drive North W., Zip 47112–1774; tel. 812/738–4251, (Nonreporting) **A**9 10 18
Primary Contact: Steven L. Taylor, Chief Executive Officer
CFO: Jeff Davis, Chief Financial Officer
CIO: Chuck Wiley, Manager Information Systems
CHR: Angie Phelps Sells, Manager Human Resources
Web address: www.hchin.org
**Control:** County–Government, nonfederal **Service:** General Medical and Surgical

**Staffed Beds:** 25

## CRAWFORDSVILLE—Montgomery County

○ **FRANCISCAN ST. ELIZABETH HEALTH – CRAWFORDSVILLE (150022)**, 1710 Lafayette Road, Zip 47933–1099; tel. 765/362–2800, (Nonreporting) **A**9 10 11 **S** Franciscan Alliance, Mishawaka, IN
Primary Contact: Thomas R. Peck, Chief Executive Officer
COO: Nancy Sennett, R.N., Vice President Nursing Services
CFO: Keith Lauter, Vice President Finance
Web address: www.stclaremedical.org
**Control:** Other not–for–profit (including NFP Corporation) **Service:** General Medical and Surgical

**Staffed Beds:** 76

**ST. CLARE MEDICAL CENTER** See Franciscan St. Elizabeth Health – Crawfordsville

*Many Facility Codes have changed. Please refer to the AHA Guide Code Chart.*
© 2013 AHA Guide

## CROWN POINT—Lake County

○ **FRANCISCAN ST. ANTHONY HEALTH – CROWN POINT (150126)**, 1201 South Main Street, Zip 46307–8483; tel. 219/738–2100, (Nonreporting) **A**2 5 9 10 11 **S** Franciscan Alliance, Mishawaka, IN
Primary Contact: David Ruskowski, President
CFO: Larry Stazinski, Vice President Finance
CMO: John T. King, M.D., Vice President Medical Staff Affairs
CIO: Nader Eskander, Director
CHR: Donna Wimmer, Director Human Resources
Web address: www.stanthonymedicalcenter.com
**Control:** Church–operated, Nongovernment, not–for profit **Service:** General Medical and Surgical

**Staffed Beds:** 254

**PINNACLE HOSPITAL (150166)**, 9301 Connecticut Drive, Zip 46307–7486; tel. 219/756–2100, (Nonreporting) **A**9 10
Primary Contact: Haroon Naz, Chief Executive Officer
Web address: www.pinnaclehealthcare.net
**Control:** Partnership, Investor–owned, for–profit **Service:** General Medical and Surgical

**Staffed Beds:** 18

**ST. ANTHONY MEDICAL CENTER** See Franciscan St. Anthony Health – Crown Point

☐ **VIBRA HOSPITAL OF NORTHWESTERN INDIANA (152028)**, 9509 Georgia Street, Zip 46307–6518; tel. 219/472–2200 **A**1 10 **F**1 29 75 77 85 86 87 130 148 **S** Vibra Healthcare, Mechanicsburg, PA
Primary Contact: Charles Nordyke, Chief Executive Officer
Web address: www.vhnwindiana.com/
**Control:** Corporation, Investor–owned, for–profit **Service:** Long–Term Acute Care hospital

**Staffed Beds:** 40 **Admissions:** 356 **Census:** 35 **Outpatient Visits:** 0 **Births:** 0 **Total Expense ($000):** 15813 **Payroll Expense ($000):** 6686 **Personnel:** 165

## DANVILLE—Hendricks County

★ ○ **HENDRICKS REGIONAL HEALTH (150005)**, 1000 East Main Street, Zip 46122–1948, Mailing Address: P.O. Box 409, Zip 46122–0409; tel. 317/745–4451 **A**2 5 9 10 11 **F**3 8 11 13 15 20 28 29 30 31 32 34 35 40 54 55 56 57 59 60 61 64 66 69 70 73 74 75 76 77 78 79 81 85 86 87 89 93 96 97 107 108 109 110 111 115 117 118 119 120 121 123 129 130 131 132 135 144 146 147 148 **P**6
Primary Contact: Kevin Speer, Chief Executive Officer
CFO: John Komenda, Chief Financial Officer
CMO: John Sparzo, M.D., Vice President Medical Affairs
CIO: Lowell Nicodemus, Director Information Systems
CHR: Gary Lenard, Director Human Resources
Web address: www.hendrickshealth.org
**Control:** County–Government, nonfederal **Service:** General Medical and Surgical

**Staffed Beds:** 127 **Admissions:** 5778 **Census:** 56 **Outpatient Visits:** 321267 **Births:** 1069 **Total Expense ($000):** 189897 **Payroll Expense ($000):** 81146 **Personnel:** 1304

## DECATUR—Adams County

★ **ADAMS MEMORIAL HOSPITAL (151330)**, 1100 Mercer Avenue, Zip 46733–2303, Mailing Address: P.O. Box 151, Zip 46733–0151; tel. 260/724–2145, (Total facility includes 195 beds in nursing home–type unit) **A**9 10 18 **F**3 5 7 10 13 15 29 31 34 35 38 40 45 47 50 53 57 59 64 65 66 67 68 70 74 75 76 77 79 81 82 84 85 86 87 92 93 94 96 97 98 99 100 101 102 103 104 105 106 107 108 110 111 114 119 125 128 129 130 131 132 133 134 135 143 144 145 146 147 148 **P**6
Primary Contact: JoEllen Eidam, Interim Chief Executive Officer
COO: JoEllen Eidam, Chief Operating Officer
CFO: Dane Wheeler, Chief Financial Officer
CMO: Scott Smith, M.D., Chief of Staff
CIO: Nick Nelson, Director Support Services
CHR: Alison Kukelhan, Manager Human Resources
CNO: Jo McIntire, Chief Nursing Officer
Web address: www.adamshospital.com
**Control:** County–Government, nonfederal **Service:** General Medical and Surgical

**Staffed Beds:** 233 **Admissions:** 2378 **Census:** 206 **Outpatient Visits:** 98460 **Births:** 214 **Total Expense ($000):** 70275 **Payroll Expense ($000):** 21009 **Personnel:** 369

## DYER—Lake County

**FRANCISCAN ST. MARGARET HEALTH – DYER** See Franciscan St. Margaret Health – Hammond, Hammond

**SAINT MARGARET MERCY HEALTHCARE CENTERS–SOUTH CAMPUS** See Franciscan St. Margaret Health – Dyer

## EAST CHICAGO—Lake County

⊠ **REGENCY HOSPITAL OF NORTHWEST INDIANA (152024)**, 4321 Fir Street, 4th Floor, Zip 46312–3049; tel. 219/392–7790, (Includes REGENCY HOSPITAL OF PORTER COUNTY, 3630 Willow Creek Road, Portage, Zip 46368; tel. 219/364–3800), (Nonreporting) **A**1 10 **S** Select Medical Corporation, Mechanicsburg, PA
Primary Contact: Victor J. Galfano, FACHE, Chief Executive Officer
Web address: www.regencyhospital.com/company/locations/indiana–northwest–indiana.aspx
**Control:** Corporation, Investor–owned, for–profit **Service:** Long–Term Acute Care hospital

**Staffed Beds:** 25

☐ △ **ST. CATHERINE HOSPITAL (150008)**, 4321 Fir Street, Zip 46312–3097; tel. 219/392–1700 **A**1 5 7 9 10 **F**1 3 5 11 13 15 17 18 20 22 24 26 28 29 30 31 34 35 40 49 50 54 57 58 59 60 61 62 64 68 74 75 76 77 78 79 80 81 82 85 86 87 89 92 93 98 99 100 101 102 103 104 107 108 110 111 114 119 120 129 130 132 135 146 147 148 **P**1 **S** Community Healthcare System, Hammond, IN
Primary Contact: JoAnn Birdzell, Chief Executive Officer and Administrator
COO: Craig Bolda, Chief Operating Officer
CFO: Luis Molina, Chief Financial Officer
CMO: John Griep, M.D., Chief Medical Director
CIO: Gary Weiner, Chief Information Officer
CNO: Paula C. Swenson, R.N., Vice President and Chief Nursing Officer
Web address: www.stcatherinehospital.org
**Control:** Other not–for–profit (including NFP Corporation) **Service:** General Medical and Surgical

**Staffed Beds:** 189 **Admissions:** 8844 **Census:** 116 **Outpatient Visits:** 140926 **Births:** 579 **Total Expense ($000):** 168523 **Payroll Expense ($000):** 58426 **Personnel:** 818

## ELKHART—Elkhart County

★ ○ △ **ELKHART GENERAL HEALTHCARE SYSTEM (150018)**, 600 East Boulevard, Zip 46514–2499, Mailing Address: P.O. Box 1329, Zip 46515–1329; tel. 574/294–2621 **A**2 5 7 9 10 11 **F**3 5 12 14 15 17 18 20 22 24 26 28 29 30 31 34 35 40 45 46 49 50 57 59 60 64 68 69 70 72 74 75 76 77 78 79 81 82 85 86 87 89 90 92 93 98 99 100 102 104 105 107 108 110 111 114 115 118 119 120 121 123 129 130 132 134 135 146 147 148 **P**6
Primary Contact: Greg Losasso, President
CMO: Karl W. Schultz, M.D., Chief of Staff
CIO: David Vick, Chief Information Officer
CHR: Kurt A. Meyer, Vice President Human Resources
CNO: Karra Heggen, R.N., Vice President Nursing
Web address: www.egh.org
**Control:** Other not–for–profit (including NFP Corporation) **Service:** General Medical and Surgical

**Staffed Beds:** 270 **Admissions:** 12462 **Census:** 137 **Outpatient Visits:** 434003 **Births:** 1566 **Total Expense ($000):** 264746 **Payroll Expense ($000):** 90834 **Personnel:** 1624

## ELWOOD—Madison County

⊠ **ST. VINCENT MERCY HOSPITAL (151308)**, 1331 South A Street, Zip 46036–1942; tel. 765/552–4600 **A**1 2 9 10 18 **F**3 8 11 15 18 28 29 30 31 34 35 40 43 44 45 46 47 50 53 57 59 64 67 74 75 78 79 81 82 85 86 87 93 107 108 110 111 114 119 128 129 130 132 133 135 141 146 148 **P**6 **S** Ascension Health, Saint Louis, MO
Primary Contact: Deborah Y. Rasper, FACHE, Administrator
CFO: Joseph Kubala, Chief Financial Officer
CMO: Stephen Berghofer, M.D., Chief Medical Officer
CHR: Barbara Whitenack, Manager Human Resources
CNO: Ann C. Yates, R.N., Director Patient Care and Clinical Services
Web address: www.stvincent.org
**Control:** Church–operated, Nongovernment, not–for profit **Service:** General Medical and Surgical

**Staffed Beds:** 25 **Admissions:** 625 **Census:** 7 **Outpatient Visits:** 35767 **Births:** 0 **Total Expense ($000):** 23389 **Payroll Expense ($000):** 10135 **Personnel:** 132

IN

---

**Hospital, Medicare Provider Number, Address, Telephone, Approval, Facility, and Physician Codes, Health Care System**

★ American Hospital Association (AHA) membership
☐ The Joint Commission accreditation
◇ DNV Healthcare Inc. accreditation
○ Healthcare Facilities Accreditation Program
△ Commission on Accreditation of Rehabilitation Facilities (CARF) accreditation

## EVANSVILLE—Vanderburgh County

★ ○ **DEACONESS HOSPITAL (150082)**, 600 Mary Street, Zip 47710–1658; tel. 812/450–5000, (Includes DEACONESS CROSS POINTE CENTER, 7200 East Indiana Street, Zip 47715; tel. 812/476–7200; Cheryl Rietman, Chief Administrative Officer) **A**2 3 5 9 10 11 **F**3 5 9 11 12 15 17 18 19 20 22 24 26 29 30 31 32 34 35 36 38 39 40 43 44 45 46 49 50 51 53 54 56 57 58 59 60 61 62 63 64 65 66 68 70 71 74 75 77 78 79 81 82 84 85 86 87 88 89 93 94 96 97 98 99 100 101 102 104 105 107 108 110 111 114 115 116 117 118 119 120 121 123 126 129 130 132 134 135 145 146 148 **P**6 **S** Deaconess Health System, Evansville, IN
Primary Contact: Shawn W. McCoy, Chief Administrative Officer
CFO: Cheryl A. Wathen, Interim Chief Financial Officer
CMO: James Porter, M.D., Vice President Medical Affairs
CHR: Larry Pile, Director Human Resources
Web address: www.deaconess.com
**Control:** Other not–for–profit (including NFP Corporation) **Service:** General Medical and Surgical

Staffed Beds: 523 Admissions: 25606 Census: 335 Outpatient Visits: 573867 Births: 0 Total Expense ($000): 520292 Payroll Expense ($000): 198891 Personnel: 3272

**EVANSVILLE PSYCHIATRIC CHILDREN CENTER**, 3300 East Morgan Avenue, Zip 47715–2232; tel. 812/477–6436, (Nonreporting)
Primary Contact: Lottie Cook, Superintendent
Web address: www.khrh.org
**Control:** State–Government, nonfederal **Service:** Children's hospital psychiatric

Staffed Beds: 28

☐ **EVANSVILLE STATE HOSPITAL (154056)**, 3400 Lincoln Avenue, Zip 47714–0146; tel. 812/469–6800 **A**1 10 **F**98 130 132 135 146
Primary Contact: Cathe Fulcher, Superintendent
CFO: Janet Kelsey, Director Business
CMO: Melba Briones, M.D., Medical Director
CHR: Cheryl Lutey, Director Human Resources
**Control:** State–Government, nonfederal **Service:** Psychiatric

Staffed Beds: 168 Admissions: 57 Census: 152 Outpatient Visits: 0 Births: 0 Total Expense ($000): 31759 Payroll Expense ($000): 13404 Personnel: 332

☒ **HEALTHSOUTH DEACONESS REHABILITATION HOSPITAL (153025)**, 4100 Covert Avenue, Zip 47714–5567, Mailing Address: P.O. Box 5349, Zip 47716–5349; tel. 812/476–9983 **A**1 9 10 **F**28 29 64 68 75 87 90 91 93 94 95 96 130 132 143 148 **S** HEALTHSOUTH Corporation, Birmingham, AL
Primary Contact: Barbara Butler, Chief Executive Officer
CFO: Diane Riley, Controller
CMO: Ashok Dhingra, M.D., Executive Medical Director
CHR: Blake Bunner, Director Human Resources
Web address: www.healthsouthdeaconess.com
**Control:** Corporation, Investor–owned, for–profit **Service:** Rehabilitation

Staffed Beds: 80 Admissions: 1561 Census: 63 Outpatient Visits: 7161 Births: 0 Total Expense ($000): 19096 Payroll Expense ($000): 10302 Personnel: 230

☒ **SELECT SPECIALTY HOSPITAL–EVANSVILLE (152014)**, 400 S.E. 4th Street, Zip 47713–1206; tel. 812/421–2500, (Nonreporting) **A**1 10 **S** Select Medical Corporation, Mechanicsburg, PA
Primary Contact: Mike Carney, Chief Executive Officer
Web address: www.selectspecialtyhospitals.com/company/locations/evansville.aspx
**Control:** Corporation, Investor–owned, for–profit **Service:** Long–Term Acute Care hospital

Staffed Beds: 60

☒ △ **ST. MARY'S MEDICAL CENTER OF EVANSVILLE (150100)**, 3700 Washington Avenue, Zip 47714–0541; tel. 812/485–4000 **A**1 2 5 7 9 10 **F**3 8 11 12 13 15 17 18 19 20 22 24 26 28 29 30 31 32 34 35 36 37 39 40 43 45 46 47 48 49 50 51 53 54 55 56 57 58 59 60 61 64 65 66 68 70 71 72 73 74 75 76 77 78 79 80 81 84 85 86 87 88 89 90 92 93 96 97 98 100 101 102 103 107 108 110 111 114 115 116 117 118 119 124 130 131 132 135 143 144 146 147 148 **P**4 6 **S** Ascension Health, Saint Louis, MO
Primary Contact: Timothy A. Flesch, President and Chief Executive Officer
CFO: Kimberly Hodgkinson, Senior Vice President and Chief Financial Officer
CMO: John Gallagher, M.D., Chief Medical Officer
CIO: Cynthia Hyde, Interim Chief Information Officer
CNO: Darcy Ellison, R.N., Senior Vice President, Chief Nursing Officer and Inpatient Flow
Web address: www.stmarys.org
**Control:** Church–operated, Nongovernment, not–for profit **Service:** General Medical and Surgical

Staffed Beds: 433 Admissions: 17126 Census: 230 Outpatient Visits: 346697 Births: 1704 Total Expense ($000): 356875 Payroll Expense ($000): 121572 Personnel: 2336

## FORT WAYNE—Allen County

☒ **DUPONT HOSPITAL (150150)**, 2520 East Dupont Road, Zip 46825–1675; tel. 260/416–3000 **A**1 9 10 **F**3 13 15 20 22 26 29 30 34 35 40 45 49 51 56 57 59 64 65 68 70 72 73 74 75 79 81 82 85 86 87 107 108 111 112 113 114 115 119 124 126 129 131 132 135 141 145 146 147 148 **P**1 5 **S** Community Health Systems, Inc., Franklin, TN
Primary Contact: Chad Towner, Chief Executive Officer
COO: Bonnie Hanson, Chief Operating Officer
CFO: Brian Schneider, Chief Financial Officer
CMO: Theresa Herman, M.D., Chief Medical Officer and Chief Quality Officer
CIO: Keith A. Neuman, Chief Information Officer
Web address: www.thedupontdifference.com
**Control:** Partnership, Investor–owned, for–profit **Service:** General Medical and Surgical

Staffed Beds: 131 Admissions: 4880 Census: 49 Outpatient Visits: 104242 Births: 2157 Total Expense ($000): 79491 Payroll Expense ($000): 28361 Personnel: 471

☒ **LUTHERAN HOSPITAL OF INDIANA (150017)**, 7950 West Jefferson Boulevard, Zip 46804–4140; tel. 260/435–7001 **A**1 2 3 5 9 10 **F**3 7 12 13 15 17 18 19 20 22 24 26 28 29 30 31 32 34 35 39 40 41 43 45 46 48 49 51 57 58 59 60 61 64 68 70 72 74 75 76 77 78 79 80 81 82 84 85 86 87 88 89 92 93 97 107 108 110 111 112 114 115 116 117 118 119 124 126 129 130 132 135 137 138 141 143 145 146 147 **S** Community Health Systems, Inc., Franklin, TN
Primary Contact: Brian Bauer, Chief Executive Officer
COO: Erica Wehrmeister, Chief Operating Officer
CFO: Michael McCullough, Chief Financial Officer
CMO: Geoffrey Randolph, M.D., Chief Medical Officer
CIO: Randy Cox, Chief Information Officer
CHR: Bruce Hamilton, Vice President Human Resources
Web address: www.lutheranhospital.com
**Control:** Corporation, Investor–owned, for–profit **Service:** General Medical and Surgical

Staffed Beds: 396 Admissions: 19029 Census: 262 Outpatient Visits: 435253 Births: 1236 Total Expense ($000): 330143 Payroll Expense ($000): 105830 Personnel: 2443

☒ **ORTHOPAEDIC HOSPITAL OF LUTHERAN HEALTH NETWORK (150168)**, (Formerly Orthopaedic Hospital of Lutheran Health), 7952 West Jefferson Boulevard, Zip 46804–4140; tel. 260/435–2999 **A**1 9 10 **F**29 34 35 37 64 77 79 80 81 82 93 94 96 111 131 **P**8 **S** Community Health Systems, Inc., Franklin, TN
Primary Contact: Kenneth Jones, Chief Executive Officer
CFO: Michael McCullough, Chief Financial Officer
CMO: Steven Fisher, M.D., President Medical Staff
CHR: Bruce Hamilton, Director Human Resources
Web address: www.theorthohospital.com
**Control:** Corporation, Investor–owned, for–profit **Service:** Orthopedic

Staffed Beds: 44 Admissions: 2208 Census: 15 Outpatient Visits: 39712 Births: 0 Total Expense ($000): 45724 Payroll Expense ($000): 10334 Personnel: 204

☐ **PARKVIEW ORTHO HOSPITAL (150167)**, 11130 Parkview Circle Drive, Zip 46845–1735; tel. 260/672–5000 **A**1 9 10 **F**3 29 30 34 42 45 50 58 65 68 79 81 82 84 85 86 87 90 93 94 96 107 119 141
Primary Contact: Julie Fleck, Chief Operating Officer
Web address: www.parkview.com
**Control:** Corporation, Investor–owned, for–profit **Service:** Orthopedic

Staffed Beds: 37 Admissions: 1845 Census: 13 Outpatient Visits: 2193 Births: 0 Total Expense ($000): 43031 Payroll Expense ($000): 5858 Personnel: 132

★ **PARKVIEW REGIONAL MEDICAL CENTER (150021)**, 11109 Parkview Plaza Drive, Zip 46845–1701; tel. 260/373–4000, (Total facility includes 31 beds in nursing home–type unit) **A**9 10 **F**3 5 7 11 13 14 15 17 18 20 22 24 26 28 29 30 31 32 34 35 40 43 44 45 46 49 50 51 53 54 55 57 58 59 60 61 62 63 64 65 68 69 70 72 74 75 76 78 79 81 82 84 85 86 87 88 89 90 92 93 96 98 99 100 101 102 103 104 105 107 108 109 111 114 115 118 119 120 121 123 124 126 128 129 130 131 132 135 141 146 147 148 **S** Parkview Health, Fort Wayne, IN
Primary Contact: Sue Ehinger, Ph.D., President
Web address: www.parkview.com
**Control:** Other not–for–profit (including NFP Corporation) **Service:** General Medical and Surgical

Staffed Beds: 636 Admissions: 28450 Census: 424 Outpatient Visits: 246036 Births: 2790 Total Expense ($000): 596744 Payroll Expense ($000): 174331 Personnel: 3226

*Many Facility Codes have changed. Please refer to the AHA Guide Code Chart.*

© 2013 AHA Guide

⊠ △ **REHABILITATION HOSPITAL OF FORT WAYNE (153030)**, 7970 West Jefferson Boulevard, Zip 46804–4140; tel. 260/435–6100 **A**1 7 9 10 **F**29 30 43 90 93 96 130 132 146 **P**5 **S** Community Health Systems, Inc., Franklin, TN
Primary Contact: Ted Scholten, Chief Operating Officer
COO: Ted Scholten, Chief Operating Officer
CFO: Michael McCullough, Chief Financial Officer
CMO: Thomas Banas, Chief Medical Officer
CIO: Keith A. Neuman, Chief Information Officer
CHR: Deborah Giardina, Director Human Resources and Medical Staff Services
CNO: Shelley Boxell, R.N., Chief Nursing Officer and Quality Coordinator
Web address: www.rehabhospital.com
**Control:** Corporation, Investor–owned, for–profit **Service:** Rehabilitation

**Staffed Beds:** 36 **Admissions:** 470 **Census:** 16 **Outpatient Visits:** 44 **Births:** 0 **Total Expense ($000):** 8402 **Payroll Expense ($000):** 4580 **Personnel:** 92

⊠ **SELECT SPECIALTY HOSPITAL–FORT WAYNE (152016)**, 700 Broadway, 7th Floor, Zip 46802–1402; tel. 260/425–3810, (Nonreporting) **A**1 10 **S** Select Medical Corporation, Mechanicsburg, PA
Primary Contact: Lea Ann Klarner, Chief Executive Officer
CMO: Yogesh Amin, M.D., Medical Director
CNO: Marielle Lael, R.N., Chief Nursing Officer
Web address: www.selectspecialtyhospitals.com/company/locations/fortwayne.aspx
**Control:** Corporation, Investor–owned, for–profit **Service:** Long–Term Acute Care hospital

**Staffed Beds:** 32

⊠ **ST. JOSEPH HOSPITAL (150047)**, 700 Broadway, Zip 46802–1493; tel. 260/425–3000, (Total facility includes 20 beds in nursing home–type unit) **A**1 3 5 9 10 **F**3 4 5 13 15 16 17 18 20 22 24 28 29 30 34 35 38 40 45 46 47 49 50 51 53 54 55 56 57 58 59 64 65 68 69 70 72 74 76 77 79 81 85 87 92 93 96 98 100 101 102 103 104 105 107 108 110 111 114 115 118 119 128 130 132 142 146 147 148 **P**6 **S** Community Health Systems, Inc., Franklin, TN
Primary Contact: Eric N. Looper, Chief Executive Officer
CFO: Pamela Hess, Chief Financial Officer
CIO: Randy Cox, Chief Information Officer
CHR: Steve Heggen, Administrative Director Human Resources
Web address: www.stjoehospital.com
**Control:** Corporation, Investor–owned, for–profit **Service:** General Medical and Surgical

**Staffed Beds:** 182 **Admissions:** 5995 **Census:** 96 **Outpatient Visits:** 118207 **Births:** 434 **Total Expense ($000):** 96783 **Payroll Expense ($000):** 34542 **Personnel:** 708

⊠ **VETERANS AFFAIRS NORTHERN INDIANA HEALTH CARE SYSTEM**, 2121 Lake Avenue, Zip 46805–5100; tel. 260/426–5431, (Includes VETERANS AFFAIRS NORTHERN INDIANA HEALTH CARE SYSTEM–MARION CAMPUS, 1700 East 38th Street, Marion, Zip 46953–4589; tel. 765/674–3321), (Nonreporting) **A**1 **S** Department of Veterans Affairs, Washington, DC
Primary Contact: Denise M. Deitzen, Director
COO: Helen Rhodes, R.N., Associate Director Operations
CFO: Jay H. Vandermark, Chief Financial Officer
CMO: Mark D. Wooten, M.D., Chief of Staff
CIO: David Troyer, Chief Information Officer
CHR: Brian Flynn, Chief Human Resources Officer
Web address: www.northernindiana.va.gov/
**Control:** Veterans Affairs, Government, federal **Service:** General Medical and Surgical

**Staffed Beds:** 26

☐ **VIBRA HOSPITAL OF FORT WAYNE (152027)**, 2200 Randallia Drive, Zip 48605–4638; tel. 260/399–2900 **A**1 10 **F**1 3 18 29 56 60 61 68 78 85 87 148 **S** Vibra Healthcare, Mechanicsburg, PA
Primary Contact: John Pierson, Chief Executive Officer
Web address: www.vhfortwayne.com
**Control:** Corporation, Investor–owned, for–profit **Service:** Long–Term Acute Care hospital

**Staffed Beds:** 24 **Admissions:** 163 **Census:** 10 **Outpatient Visits:** 0 **Births:** 0 **Total Expense ($000):** 6744 **Payroll Expense ($000):** 2793 **Personnel:** 63

**FRANKFORT—Clinton County**

⊠ **ST. VINCENT FRANKFORT HOSPITAL (151316)**, 1300 South Jackson Street, Zip 46041–3394, Mailing Address: P.O. Box 669, Zip 46041–0669; tel. 765/656–3000 **A**1 9 10 18 **F**3 11 13 15 28 29 30 31 34 35 40 45 50 57 59 64 65 68 75 76 77 78 79 81 82 85 86 89 90 93 97 107 111 114 119 130 132 133 135 146 148 **S** Ascension Health, Saint Louis, MO
Primary Contact: Thomas Crawford, Administrator
CFO: Jerry Marks, Chief Financial Officer
CMO: Stephen Tharp, M.D., Medical Director
CHR: Krista Wright, Director Human Resources
Web address: www.stvincent.org
**Control:** Church–operated, Nongovernment, not–for profit **Service:** General Medical and Surgical

**Staffed Beds:** 25 **Admissions:** 911 **Census:** 9 **Outpatient Visits:** 36014 **Births:** 220 **Total Expense ($000):** 23282 **Payroll Expense ($000):** 9047 **Personnel:** 94

**FRANKLIN—Johnson County**

★ ○ **JOHNSON MEMORIAL HOSPITAL (150001)**, 1125 West Jefferson Street, Zip 46131–2140, Mailing Address: P.O. Box 549, Zip 46131–0549; tel. 317/736–3300 **A**2 5 9 10 11 **F**12 13 15 18 20 24 28 29 30 31 34 35 36 40 44 45 49 50 54 57 59 62 64 68 70 74 75 76 77 78 79 81 82 85 87 90 93 97 107 111 113 114 118 119 121 129 130 131 132 134 135 144 146 147 148 **P**8
Primary Contact: Larry Heydon, President and Chief Executive Officer
COO: Steve Wohlford, Chief Operating Officer–Hospital Services
CFO: Andrew Walker, Chief Financial Officer
CMO: John Norris, M.D., Chief Medical Officer
CIO: Scott Krodel, Director Information Systems
CHR: Judy Ware, Director Human Resources
CNO: Anita M. Trackwell, R.N., Chief Nursing Officer
Web address: www.johnsonmemorial.org
**Control:** County–Government, nonfederal **Service:** General Medical and Surgical

**Staffed Beds:** 101 **Admissions:** 2262 **Census:** 28 **Outpatient Visits:** 156266 **Births:** 399 **Total Expense ($000):** 75731 **Payroll Expense ($000):** 36336 **Personnel:** 677

**GARY—Lake County**

☐ ○ △ **METHODIST HOSPITALS (150002)**, 600 Grant Street, Zip 46402–6099; tel. 219/886–4000, (Includes SOUTHLAKE CAMPUS, 8701 Broadway, Merrillville, Zip 46410; tel. 219/738–5500) **A**1 2 3 5 7 9 10 11 **F**3 8 10 11 12 13 15 20 22 24 26 28 29 30 31 32 34 35 37 40 45 47 48 49 50 51 54 55 57 59 62 64 68 70 72 73 74 75 76 77 78 79 81 82 85 86 87 89 90 93 97 98 99 100 101 102 103 104 105 107 108 110 111 114 115 117 119 120 121 123 124 126 130 132 133 146 147 148 **P**6
Primary Contact: Ian McFadden, President and Chief Executive Officer
CMO: Charles O. Davidson, M.D., Vice President Medical Affairs
CIO: Shaw Collins, Director Information Technology
CHR: Joyce McGlory, Vice President Human Resources
Web address: www.methodisthospitals.org
**Control:** Other not–for–profit (including NFP Corporation) **Service:** General Medical and Surgical

**Staffed Beds:** 503 **Admissions:** 17638 **Census:** 287 **Outpatient Visits:** 230763 **Births:** 1494 **Total Expense ($000):** 263480 **Payroll Expense ($000):** 117377 **Personnel:** 1834

**GOSHEN—Elkhart County**

**GOSHEN GENERAL HOSPITAL** See Indiana University Health Goshen Hospital

⊠ **INDIANA UNIVERSITY HEALTH GOSHEN HOSPITAL (150026)**, 200 High Park Avenue, Zip 46526–4899, Mailing Address: P.O. Box 139, Zip 46527–0139; tel. 574/533–2141 **A**1 2 9 10 **F**3 11 12 13 15 18 20 22 26 28 29 30 31 32 34 35 36 37 40 44 45 46 47 48 49 50 51 54 56 57 58 59 62 63 64 65 67 68 70 71 74 75 76 77 78 79 80 81 82 84 85 86 87 89 92 93 96 97 102 107 108 110 111 114 115 116 117 118 119 120 121 123 124 126 129 130 132 135 145 146 147 148 **S** Indiana University Health, Indianapolis, IN
Primary Contact: Randal Christophel, President and Chief Executive Officer
COO: Paulette Brown, Chief Operating Officer
CMO: Randall Cammenga, M.D., Vice President Medical Affairs
CIO: Dolph Voelker, Director Information Services
CHR: Alan Weldy, Vice President Human Resources, Compliance and Legal Services
Web address: www.iuhealth.org
**Control:** Other not–for–profit (including NFP Corporation) **Service:** General Medical and Surgical

**Staffed Beds:** 122 **Admissions:** 6239 **Census:** 55 **Outpatient Visits:** 139083 **Births:** 1238 **Total Expense ($000):** 187012 **Payroll Expense ($000):** 60733 **Personnel:** 1190

IN

---

**Hospital, Medicare Provider Number, Address, Telephone, Approval, Facility, and Physician Codes, Health Care System**

★ American Hospital Association (AHA) membership
☐ The Joint Commission accreditation
◇ DNV Healthcare Inc. accreditation
○ Healthcare Facilities Accreditation Program
△ Commission on Accreditation of Rehabilitation Facilities (CARF) accreditation

**OAKLAWN PSYCHIATRIC CENTER (154031)**, 330 Lakeview Drive, Zip 46528–9365, Mailing Address: P.O. Box 809, Zip 46527–0809; tel. 574/533–1234 **A**9 10 **F**4 5 29 30 35 38 54 56 98 99 100 101 103 104 106 130 146 **P**6
Primary Contact: Laurie N. Nafziger, President and Chief Executive Officer
CFO: Lynn J. Miller, Vice President Financial Services
CMO: Daniel Kinsey, M.D., Medical Director
CIO: Gloria Holub, Manager Communications
CHR: Jill Seifer, Vice President Human Resources
CNO: Elaine G. Miller, Director of Nursing
Web address: www.oaklawn.org
**Control:** Other not–for–profit (including NFP Corporation) **Service:** Psychiatric

**Staffed Beds:** 16 **Admissions:** 822 **Census:** 14 **Outpatient Visits:** 294461 **Births:** 0 **Total Expense ($000):** 35970 **Payroll Expense ($000):** 20755 **Personnel:** 568

### GREENCASTLE—Putnam County

**PUTNAM COUNTY HOSPITAL (151333)**, 1542 Bloomington Street, Zip 46135–2297; tel. 765/653–5121, (Nonreporting) **A**2 9 10 18
Primary Contact: Dennis Weatherford, Chief Executive Officer
CFO: Kevin Fowler, Director Finance
Web address: www.pchosp.org/
**Control:** County–Government, nonfederal **Service:** General Medical and Surgical

**Staffed Beds:** 25

### GREENFIELD—Hancock County

★ ○ **HANCOCK REGIONAL HOSPITAL (150037)**, 801 North State Street, Zip 46140–1270, Mailing Address: P.O. Box 827, Zip 46140–0827; tel. 317/462–5544 **A**5 9 10 11 **F**3 11 12 13 15 17 18 20 22 28 29 30 31 32 34 35 38 40 44 45 47 48 49 50 53 54 56 57 59 62 63 64 66 68 69 70 74 75 76 78 79 81 82 83 84 85 86 87 89 90 93 96 98 103 107 110 111 114 115 119 127 129 130 131 132 134 135 144 146 147 148 **P**2 8
Primary Contact: Robert C. Keen, Ph.D., FACHE, President and Chief Executive Officer
CFO: Rick Edwards, Vice President Finance Services
CMO: Michael Fletcher, M.D., President Medical Staff
CIO: Jon Miller, Team Leader Accounting and Information Services
CHR: Laura L. Nichols, Team Leader Human Resources
CNO: Sherry Gehring, R.N., Vice President Nursing, Inpatient Care and Chief Nursing Officer
Web address: www.hancockregional.org
**Control:** County–Government, nonfederal **Service:** General Medical and Surgical

**Staffed Beds:** 92 **Admissions:** 3142 **Census:** 37 **Outpatient Visits:** 164183 **Births:** 383 **Total Expense ($000):** 97040 **Payroll Expense ($000):** 37853 **Personnel:** 677

### GREENSBURG—Decatur County

⊞ ◇ **DECATUR COUNTY MEMORIAL HOSPITAL (151332)**, 720 North Lincoln Street, Zip 47240–1398; tel. 812/663–4331 **A**1 2 9 10 18 21 **F**3 11 13 15 18 28 29 31 32 34 35 40 45 50 54 56 57 59 62 64 65 68 69 75 76 77 78 79 80 81 82 85 86 87 89 92 93 94 96 97 107 108 110 111 114 115 117 118 119 128 129 130 131 132 133 135 145 146 147 148 **P**6
Primary Contact: Linda V. Simmons, President and Chief Executive Officer
CFO: Michael R. Ruckel, Vice President Finance
CIO: Michael R. Ruckel, Vice President Finance
CHR: Robin Meyer, Vice President Support Services
CNO: Diane McKinney, R.N., Vice President Patient Care Service
Web address: www.dcmh.net
**Control:** County–Government, nonfederal **Service:** General Medical and Surgical

**Staffed Beds:** 25 **Admissions:** 1202 **Census:** 10 **Outpatient Visits:** 114533 **Births:** 271 **Total Expense ($000):** 47180 **Payroll Expense ($000):** 22119 **Personnel:** 402

### GREENWOOD—Johnson County

⊞ **KINDRED HOSPITAL INDIANAPOLIS SOUTH (152008)**, 607 Greenwood Springs Drive, Zip 46143–6377; tel. 317/888–8155 **A**1 10 **F**1 3 29 119 148 **S** Kindred Healthcare, Louisville, KY
Primary Contact: Marc Hurst, Chief Executive Officer
COO: Michelle Estes, Chief Clinical Officer
CFO: William Brenner, Chief Financial Officer
CMO: Steven Samuels, M.D., Medical Director
Web address: www.khindysouth.com/
**Control:** Individual, Investor–owned, for–profit **Service:** Children's Long–Term Acute Care

**Staffed Beds:** 52 **Admissions:** 632 **Census:** 42 **Outpatient Visits:** 0 **Births:** 0 **Total Expense ($000):** 19256 **Payroll Expense ($000):** 8396

□ **VALLE VISTA HOSPITAL (154024)**, 898 East Main Street, Zip 46143–1400; tel. 317/887–1348, (Nonreporting) **A**1 9 10 **S** Universal Health Services, Inc., King of Prussia, PA
Primary Contact: Sherri R. Jewett, Chief Executive Officer
CFO: Anne Knapp, Chief Financial Officer
CMO: Jennifer Comer, M.D., Medical Director
CIO: Karen Hayden, Director Health Information Services, Performance Improvement and Risk Management
CHR: Ismael Santos, Director Human Resources
Web address: www.vallevistahospital.com
**Control:** Corporation, Investor–owned, for–profit **Service:** Psychiatric

**Staffed Beds:** 102

### HAMMOND—Lake County

○ △ **FRANCISCAN ST. MARGARET HEALTH – HAMMOND (150004)**, 5454 Hohman Avenue, Zip 46320–1999; tel. 219/933–2074, (Includes FRANCISCAN ST. MARGARET HEALTH – DYER, 24 Joliet Street, Dyer, Zip 46311–1799; tel. 219/865–2141; SAINT MARGARET MERCY HEALTHCARE CENTERS–NORTH CAMPUS, 5454 Hohman Avenue, Zip 46320; tel. 219/932–2300), (Nonreporting) **A**2 5 7 9 10 11 **S** Franciscan Alliance, Mishawaka, IN
Primary Contact: Thomas J. Gryzbek, President
CFO: Jim Lipinski, Chief Financial Officer
Web address: www.smmhc.com
**Control:** Church–operated, Nongovernment, not–for profit **Service:** General Medical and Surgical

**Staffed Beds:** 500

⊞ **KINDRED HOSPITAL NORTHWEST INDIANA (152012)**, 5454 Hohman Avenue, 5th Floor, Zip 46320–1931; tel. 219/937–9900, (Nonreporting) **A**1 10 **S** Kindred Healthcare, Louisville, KY
Primary Contact: Frank A. Solare, Chief Executive Officer
Web address: www.khnwindiana.com
**Control:** Corporation, Investor–owned, for–profit **Service:** Long–Term Acute Care hospital

**Staffed Beds:** 70

**SAINT MARGARET MERCY HEALTHCARE CENTERS** See Franciscan St. Margaret Health – Hammond

**TRIUMPH HOSPITAL NORTHWEST INDIANA** See Kindred Hospital Northwest Indiana

### HARTFORD CITY—Blackford County

**BLACKFORD COMMUNITY HOSPITAL** See Indiana University Health Blackford Hospital

⊞ **INDIANA UNIVERSITY HEALTH BLACKFORD HOSPITAL (151302)**, 410 Pilgrim Boulevard, Zip 47348–1897; tel. 765/348–0300 **A**1 9 10 18 **F**3 7 11 15 28 29 34 35 40 44 45 50 57 59 64 75 81 85 86 93 107 110 114 119 132 133 135 143 **S** Indiana University Health, Indianapolis, IN
Primary Contact: Steven J. West, Chief Executive Officer
CIO: Robert McKelvey, Chief Information Officer
CHR: John Crosbie, Director Support Services
Web address: www.iuhealth.org
**Control:** Other not–for–profit (including NFP Corporation) **Service:** General Medical and Surgical

**Staffed Beds:** 15 **Admissions:** 588 **Census:** 8 **Outpatient Visits:** 36190 **Births:** 0 **Total Expense ($000):** 11360 **Payroll Expense ($000):** 7360 **Personnel:** 123

### HOBART—Lake County

**HIND GENERAL HOSPITAL**, 101 West 61st Avenue, Zip 46342–6449; tel. 219/947–3030, (Nonreporting)
Primary Contact: Raghu Nayak, Chief Executive Officer
**Control:** Partnership, Investor–owned, for–profit **Service:** General Medical and Surgical

**Staffed Beds:** 8

□ △ **ST. MARY MEDICAL CENTER (150034)**, 1500 South Lake Park Avenue, Zip 46342–6699; tel. 219/942–0551 **A**1 2 7 9 10 12 13 15 18 20 22 24 26 28 29 30 31 34 35 36 38 39 40 45 47 49 50 51 54 57 58 59 60 62 64 65 68 70 74 75 76 77 78 79 80 81 82 85 86 87 89 90 92 93 96 107 108 110 111 114 115 117 119 120 121 123 124 126 129 130 132 134 135 146 147 148 **P**6 8 **S** Community Healthcare System, Hammond, IN
Primary Contact: Janice L. Ryba, JD, Chief Executive Officer
CFO: Mary Sudicky, Chief Financial Officer
CIO: Gary Weiner, Vice President Information Technology and Chief Information Officer
CHR: Tony Ferracane, Vice President Human Resources
Web address: www.comhs.org
**Control:** Other not–for–profit (including NFP Corporation) **Service:** General Medical and Surgical

**Staffed Beds:** 195 **Admissions:** 11469 **Census:** 158 **Outpatient Visits:** 205753 **Births:** 568 **Total Expense ($000):** 199607 **Payroll Expense ($000):** 66470 **Personnel:** 1113

*Many Facility Codes have changed. Please refer to the AHA Guide Code Chart.*

© 2013 AHA Guide

## HUNTINGTON—Huntington County

✉ **PARKVIEW HUNTINGTON HOSPITAL (150091)**, 2001 Stults Road, Zip 46750–1291; tel. 260/355–3000 **A**1 9 10 **F**3 7 8 13 15 28 29 30 31 32 34 35 36 38 39 40 44 45 46 50 53 56 57 59 64 68 69 70 75 76 77 78 79 81 85 86 87 93 96 97 107 108 111 119 130 131 132 134 135 146 148 **S** Parkview Health, Fort Wayne, IN
Primary Contact: Darlene Garrett, Chief Operating Officer
COO: Darlene Garrett, Chief Operating Officer
Web address: www.parkview.com
**Control:** Other not–for–profit (including NFP Corporation) **Service:** General Medical and Surgical

**Staffed Beds:** 36 **Admissions:** 1875 **Census:** 16 **Outpatient Visits:** 40187 **Births:** 369 **Total Expense ($000):** 37257 **Payroll Expense ($000):** 11683 **Personnel:** 239

## INDIANAPOLIS—Marion County

**CLARIAN HEALTH PARTNERS** See Indiana University Health University Hospital

☐ **COMMUNITY HEART AND VASCULAR HOSPITAL (150154)**, (Formerly Indiana Heart Hospital), 8075 North Shadeland Avenue, Zip 46250–2693; tel. 317/621–8000 **A**1 10 **F**11 17 18 20 22 24 26 28 29 30 34 35 40 55 58 59 60 68 69 70 71 74 75 77 80 81 85 87 107 114 115 118 119 130 132 133 135 141 146 148 **S** Community Health Network, Indianapolis, IN
Primary Contact: Thomas A. Malasto, Chief Executive Officer
COO: Susan Holbrook–Preston, Chief Operating Officer and Chief Nursing Officer
CFO: W. Kevin Fowler, Chief Financial Officer
CMO: Robert Shoemaker, M.D., Chief of Staff Community Heart and Vascular
CIO: Ed Koschka, Network Vice President Information Technology and Chief Information Officer
CHR: Sharon McCullough, Director Human Resources
Web address: www.hearthospital.com
**Control:** Other not–for–profit (including NFP Corporation) **Service:** Heart

**Staffed Beds:** 56 **Admissions:** 2863 **Census:** 31 **Births:** 0

☐ △ **COMMUNITY HOSPITAL EAST (150074)**, 1500 North Ritter Avenue, Zip 46219–3095; tel. 317/355–1411, (Nonreporting) **A**1 2 3 5 7 9 10 **S** Community Health Network, Indianapolis, IN
Primary Contact: Robin Ledyard, M.D., M.P.H., President
Web address: www.ecommunity.com/east/
**Control:** Other not–for–profit (including NFP Corporation) **Service:** General Medical and Surgical

**Staffed Beds:** 233

☐ **COMMUNITY HOSPITAL NORTH (150169)**, 7150 Clearvista Drive, Zip 46256–1695; tel. 317/621–6262 **A**1 9 10 **F**3 8 12 15 18 29 30 31 35 38 40 41 42 45 46 47 49 50 52 53 60 61 62 63 65 69 70 72 74 75 76 77 78 79 80 81 83 84 85 87 89 91 92 93 95 97 98 99 100 101 102 103 104 105 106 107 108 110 111 112 114 115 116 117 118 119 120 126 129 130 131 132 133 134 135 146 147 148 **S** Community Health Network, Indianapolis, IN
Primary Contact: Robert Lindeman, M.D., President
COO: Mike Blanchet, President, CHI
CFO: Jeff Kirkham, Chief Financial Officer
CMO: Clif Knight, M.D., Vice President Medical and Academic Affairs
CIO: Edward Koschka, Network Vice President Information Technology and Chief Information Officer
CHR: Jill Parris, Network Vice President Human Resources
Web address: www.ecommunity.com
**Control:** Other not–for–profit (including NFP Corporation) **Service:** General Medical and Surgical

**Staffed Beds:** 389 **Admissions:** 19533 **Census:** 268 **Births:** 750

☐ **COMMUNITY HOSPITAL SOUTH (150128)**, 1402 East County Line Road South, Zip 46227–0963; tel. 317/887–7000, (Nonreporting) **A**1 9 10 **S** Community Health Network, Indianapolis, IN
Primary Contact: Anthony B. Lennen, President
Web address: www.ecommunity.com
**Control:** Other not–for–profit (including NFP Corporation) **Service:** General Medical and Surgical

**Staffed Beds:** 108

○ **COMMUNITY WESTVIEW HOSPITAL (150129)**, 3630 Guion Road, Zip 46222–1699; tel. 317/924–6661, (Nonreporting) **A**3 5 9 10 11 12 13 **S** Community Health Network, Indianapolis, IN
Primary Contact: David C. Williams, D.O., Interim President and Chief Executive Officer
CMO: James M. Williams, D.O., Vice President Medical Affairs
CHR: Emily Rogers, Manager Human Resources
CNO: Deborah Lee, Chief Nursing Officer
Web address: www.westviewhospital.org
**Control:** Other not–for–profit (including NFP Corporation) **Service:** General Medical and Surgical

**Staffed Beds:** 68

☐ **FAIRBANKS (150179)**, 8102 Clearvista Parkway, Zip 46256–4698; tel. 317/849–8222 **A**1 9 10 **F**4 5 29 30 35 36 75 87 100 105 130 132 135 146 **P**8
Primary Contact: Helene M. Cross, President and Chief Executive Officer
COO: Cindy Leigh, Chief Operating Officer
CFO: Barb Elliott, Chief Financial Officer
CMO: Timothy J. Kelly, M.D., Medical Director
CIO: Randy Walls, Manager Information Services
CHR: Sharon Baker, Director Support Services
Web address: www.fairbankscd.org
**Control:** Other not–for–profit (including NFP Corporation) **Service:** Alcoholism and other chemical dependency

**Staffed Beds:** 86 **Admissions:** 3311 **Census:** 56 **Outpatient Visits:** 26235 **Births:** 0 **Total Expense ($000):** 19017 **Payroll Expense ($000):** 9878 **Personnel:** 228

○ △ **FRANCISCAN ST. FRANCIS HEALTH – INDIANAPOLIS (150162)**, 8111 South Emerson Avenue, Zip 46237–8601; tel. 317/528–5000 **A**2 7 9 10 11 **F**8 11 12 13 15 18 22 24 28 29 30 31 32 34 35 36 40 46 47 49 50 55 56 57 60 61 62 63 64 65 66 68 70 72 74 75 76 77 78 79 80 81 82 84 85 86 87 89 90 93 97 107 108 109 110 111 113 115 116 117 118 119 120 121 123 124 126 129 130 131 132 135 144 146 147 148 **P**7 8 **S** Franciscan Alliance, Mishawaka, IN
Primary Contact: Robert J. Brody, President and Chief Executive Officer
COO: D. Keith Jewell, Senior Vice President and Chief Operating Officer
CFO: Jay R. Brehm, Executive Vice President and Chief Financial Officer
CMO: Christopher Doehring, M.D., Vice President Medical Affairs
CIO: Barbara Coulter, Director Information Systems
CHR: Karen S. Sagar, Vice President Human Resources
CNO: Susan McRoberts, R.N., Vice President and Chief Nursing Officer
Web address: www.stfrancishospitals.org
**Control:** Church–operated, Nongovernment, not–for profit **Service:** General Medical and Surgical

**Staffed Beds:** 486 **Admissions:** 19123 **Census:** 246 **Outpatient Visits:** 530771 **Births:** 2213 **Total Expense ($000):** 502246 **Payroll Expense ($000):** 171545 **Personnel:** 2944

○ **INDIANA ORTHOPAEDIC HOSPITAL (150160)**, 8400 Northwest Boulevard, Zip 46278–1381; tel. 317/956–1000, (Nonreporting) **A**9 10 11
Primary Contact: Jane Keller, R.N., Chief Executive Officer
COO: Stacie Vance, Vice President Clinical Services
CFO: Anthony Gioia, Chief Financial Officer
CMO: Jeffrey J. Soldatis, M.D., Chairman Medical Executive Committee
CIO: Paul Frey, Director Information Technology Applications
CHR: Amanda Gleason, Director Human Resources
Web address: www.orthoindy.com
**Control:** Corporation, Investor–owned, for–profit **Service:** Orthopedic

**Staffed Beds:** 37

**INDIANA UNIVERSITY HEALTH METHODIST HOSPITAL** See Indiana University Health University Hospital

✉ **INDIANA UNIVERSITY HEALTH UNIVERSITY HOSPITAL (150056)**, 550 University Boulevard, Zip 46202–5149, Mailing Address: P.O. Box 1367, Zip 46206–1367; tel. 317/944–5000, (Includes INDIANA UNIVERSITY HEALTH METHODIST HOSPITAL, 1701 North Senate Boulevard, Zip 46202, Mailing Address: 1701 North Senate Boulevard, Zip 46202; tel. 317/962–2000; INDIANA UNIVERSITY HOSPITAL, 550 North University Boulevard, Zip 46202–5262; tel. 317/274–5000; IU HEALTH SAXONY HOSPITAL, 13000 East 136th Street, Fishers, Zip 46037–9478; tel. 317/678–2000; Jonathan R. Goble, FACHE, Chief Executive Officer; RILEY HOSPITAL FOR CHILDREN AT INDIANA UNIVERSITY HEALTH, 702 Barnhill Drive, Zip 46202–5225; tel. 317/274–5000; Jeff Sperring, M.D., President and Chief Executive Officer) **A**1 2 3 5 8 9 10 **F**3 4 5 6 7 8 9 11 12 13 15 16 17 18 19 20 21 22 23 24 25 26 27 28 29 30 31 32 33 34 35 36 37 38 39 40 41 43 44 45 46 47 48 49 50 51 52 53 54 55 56 57 58 59 60 61 62 63 64 65 68 69 70 71 72 73 74 75 76 77 78 79 81 82 83 84 85 86 87 88 89 91 92 93 94 96 97 98 99 100 101 102 103 104 105 106 107 108 109 110 111 112 113 114 115 116 117 118 119 120 121 122 123 124 126 129 130 131 132 134 135 136 137 138 139 140 141 144 145 146 147 148 **S** Indiana University Health, Indianapolis, IN
Primary Contact: James G. Terwilliger, President
COO: Dennis F. Murphy, Chief Operating Officer
CIO: Richard F. Johnson, Senior Vice President and Chief Information Officer
Web address: www.iuhealth.org
**Control:** Other not–for–profit (including NFP Corporation) **Service:** General Medical and Surgical

**Staffed Beds:** 1371 **Admissions:** 55379 **Census:** 979 **Outpatient Visits:** 1081735 **Births:** 3903 **Total Expense ($000):** 2406581 **Payroll Expense ($000):** 824517 **Personnel:** 12543

**INDIANA UNIVERSITY HOSPITAL** See Indiana University Health University Hospital

---

**Hospital, Medicare Provider Number, Address, Telephone, Approval, Facility, and Physician Codes, Health Care System**

★ American Hospital Association (AHA) membership
☐ The Joint Commission accreditation
◇ DNV Healthcare Inc. accreditation
○ Healthcare Facilities Accreditation Program
△ Commission on Accreditation of Rehabilitation Facilities (CARF) accreditation

**IN**

⊠ **KINDRED HOSPITAL–INDIANAPOLIS (152007)**, 1700 West 10th Street, Zip 46222–3802; tel. 317/636–4400, (Nonreporting) **A**1 10 **S** Kindred Healthcare, Louisville, KY
Primary Contact: Kristy Walden, R.N., Interim Administrator
CFO: William Brenner, Chief Financial Officer
CHR: Linda Russell, Director Human Resources
Web address: www.kindredhospitalindy.com/
**Control:** Corporation, Investor–owned, for–profit **Service:** Long–Term Acute Care hospital

**Staffed Beds: 59**

☐ **LARUE D. CARTER MEMORIAL HOSPITAL (154008)**, 2601 Cold Spring Road, Zip 46222–2273; tel. 317/941–4000 **A**1 3 5 10 **F**30 31 38 58 68 75 77 86 87 98 99 101 130 135 143
Primary Contact: Lawrence D. Lisak, Superintendent
CFO: Michael Logar, Assistant Superintendent
CMO: Beth Pfau, M.D., Chief Medical Officer
CIO: Denton Gross, Director Information Services
CHR: Rebecca Dutton, Director Human Resources
CNO: Todd Rittman, Director of Nursing
**Control:** State–Government, nonfederal **Service:** Psychiatric

**Staffed Beds: 148 Admissions: 104 Census: 134 Outpatient Visits: 0 Births: 0 Total Expense ($000): 29233 Payroll Expense ($000): 11563 Personnel: 282**

**METHODIST HOSPITAL** See Indiana University Health Methodist Hospital

**OPTIONS BEHAVIORAL HEALTH SYSTEM (154057)**, 5602 Caito Drive, Zip 46226–1346; tel. 317/544–4340, (Nonreporting) **S** Acadia Healthcare Company, Inc., Franklin, TN
Primary Contact: Roxane Harcourt, Chief Executive Officer
**Control:** Corporation, Investor–owned, for–profit **Service:** Psychiatric

**Staffed Beds: 42**

☐ △ **REHABILITATION HOSPITAL OF INDIANA (153028)**, 4141 Shore Drive, Zip 46254–2607; tel. 317/329–2000 **A**1 3 5 7 9 10 **F**28 29 30 33 54 58 64 75 79 86 87 90 91 92 93 96 119 130 131 132 146 148 **P**5
Primary Contact: Daniel B. Woloszyn, Chief Executive Officer
COO: Monte Spence, Chief Operating Officer
CFO: Marjorie Basey, Chief Financial Officer
CMO: Flora Hammond, M.D., Chief Medical Affairs
CHR: Joni Brown, Director Human Resources
Web address: www.rhin.com
**Control:** Other not–for–profit (including NFP Corporation) **Service:** Rehabilitation

**Staffed Beds: 91 Admissions: 1474 Census: 61 Outpatient Visits: 21651 Births: 0 Total Expense ($000): 28401 Payroll Expense ($000): 17818 Personnel: 369**

⊠ △ **RICHARD L. ROUDEBUSH VETERANS AFFAIRS MEDICAL CENTER**, 1481 West Tenth Street, Zip 46202–2884; tel. 317/554–0000 **A**1 2 3 5 7 8 **F**2 3 5 8 18 20 22 24 26 28 29 30 31 33 34 36 38 39 40 45 46 49 50 53 54 56 57 58 59 60 61 62 63 64 65 67 70 74 75 77 78 79 80 81 82 83 84 85 86 87 90 91 92 93 94 97 98 100 101 102 103 104 105 107 111 115 117 119 120 121 126 127 129 130 131 132 135 143 144 146 147 148 **S** Department of Veterans Affairs, Washington, DC
Primary Contact: Thomas Mattice, Director
COO: Major Jeff Nechanicky, Assistant Director
CFO: Paul Pessagno, Chief Financial Officer
CMO: Ken Klotz, M.D., Chief of Staff
CIO: Steve Stoner, Chief Information Officer
Web address: www.indianapolis.va.gov
**Control:** Veterans Affairs, Government, federal **Service:** General Medical and Surgical

**Staffed Beds: 209 Admissions: 7924 Census: 151 Outpatient Visits: 613126 Births: 0 Total Expense ($000): 414920 Payroll Expense ($000): 186350 Personnel: 2633**

**RILEY HOSPITAL FOR CHILDREN** See Riley Hospital for Children at Indiana University Health

**RILEY HOSPITAL FOR CHILDREN AT INDIANA UNIVERSITY HEALTH** See Indiana University Health University Hospital

⊠ **SELECT SPECIALTY HOSPITAL–BEECH GROVE (152013)**, 8060 Knue Road, Zip 46250–1976; tel. 317/783–8985, (Nonreporting) **A**1 10 **S** Select Medical Corporation, Mechanicsburg, PA
Primary Contact: Cheryl G. Gentry, Chief Executive Officer
CHR: Kelly Becker, Administrative Coordinator Human Resources
Web address: www.selectspecialtyhospitals.com/company/locations/indianapolis.aspx
**Control:** Corporation, Investor–owned, for–profit **Service:** Long–Term Acute Care hospital

**Staffed Beds: 45**

**ST. FRANCIS HOSPITAL AND HEALTH CENTERS – SOUTH CAMPUS** See Franciscan St. Francis Health – Indianapolis

★ ○ **ST. VINCENT HEART CENTER OF INDIANA (150153)**, 10580 North Meridian Street, Zip 46290–1028; tel. 317/583–5000 **A**9 10 11 **F**3 18 20 22 24 26 28 29 30 34 35 40 45 46 57 58 59 75 81 85 86 87 107 111 115 119 129 130 135 148 **P**2 **S** Ascension Health, Saint Louis, MO
Primary Contact: Blake A. Dye, President
COO: Mike Schroyer, Chief Operating Officer
CFO: Becky Jacobson, Vice President Finance
CMO: William Storer, M.D., Medical Director
CIO: Roger Strange, Chief Information Officer
CHR: Jane Richardson, Vice President Human Resources
Web address: www.bestheartcare.com
**Control:** Partnership, Investor–owned, for–profit **Service:** Heart

**Staffed Beds: 107 Admissions: 5345 Census: 55 Outpatient Visits: 11047 Births: 0 Total Expense ($000): 108918 Payroll Expense ($000): 31392 Personnel: 347**

⊠ **ST. VINCENT INDIANAPOLIS HOSPITAL (150084)**, 2001 West 86th Street, Zip 46260–1991, Mailing Address: P.O. Box 40970, Zip 46240–0970; tel. 317/338–2345, (Includes PEYTON MANNING CHILDREN'S HOSPITAL, 1707 West 86th Street, Zip 46240, Mailing Address: P.O. Box 40407, Zip 46240; tel. 317/415–5500; Anne Coleman, Administrator; PEYTON MANNING CHILDREN'S HOSPITAL AT ST. VINCENT, 2001 West 86th Street, Zip 46260, Mailing Address: P.O. Box 40970, Zip 46240–0970; tel. 317/415–8111; Anne Coleman, Administrator; ST. VINCENT STRESS CENTER, 8401 Harcourt Road, Zip 46260, Mailing Address: P.O. Box 80160, Zip 46280; tel. 317/338–4600; Sheila Mishler, Chief Executive Officer; ST. VINCENT WOMEN'S HOSPITAL, 8111 Township Line Road, Zip 46260–8043; tel. 317/415–8111; Anne Coleman, Administrator) **A**1 2 3 5 8 9 10 **F**2 3 4 5 7 9 11 13 15 17 18 19 20 21 22 23 24 25 26 27 28 29 30 31 32 34 35 37 38 39 40 41 42 43 44 45 46 47 48 49 50 51 53 54 55 56 57 58 59 61 62 63 64 65 66 68 70 71 72 73 74 75 76 78 79 80 81 82 83 84 85 86 87 88 89 91 92 93 94 96 97 98 99 100 101 102 103 104 105 106 107 108 110 111 114 115 116 117 118 119 120 121 123 124 126 129 130 131 132 134 135 136 137 138 142 143 144 146 147 148 **P**6 **S** Ascension Health, Saint Louis, MO
Primary Contact: Kyle De Fur, FACHE, President
COO: Darcy Burthay, MSN, Chief Nursing Officer and Chief Operating Officer
CFO: Thomas M. Cook, CPA, Chief Financial Officer
CMO: Daniel LeGrand, M.D., Chief Medical Officer
CIO: Brian Peters, Chief Information Officer
CHR: Marty Du Rall, Executive Director Human Resources
Web address: www.stvincent.org
**Control:** Church–operated, Nongovernment, not–for profit **Service:** General Medical and Surgical

**Staffed Beds: 903 Admissions: 35300 Census: 541 Outpatient Visits: 935048 Births: 3801 Total Expense ($000): 1046786 Payroll Expense ($000): 378970 Personnel: 4794**

⊠ **ST. VINCENT SETON SPECIALTY HOSPITAL (152020)**, 8050 Township Line Road, Zip 46260–2478; tel. 317/415–8353 **A**1 9 10 **F**1 29 30 31 35 45 60 78 107 114 119 130 143 148 **S** Ascension Health, Saint Louis, MO
Primary Contact: Peter H. Alexander, Administrator
COO: Troy T. Reiff, Corporate Director Operations
CFO: David M. Girten, Corporate Director Financial Services
CMO: Ronald Reisman, M.D., Chief Medical Director
CHR: Terry A. Wignall, Director Human Resources
Web address: www.stvincent.org/
**Control:** Other not–for–profit (including NFP Corporation) **Service:** Long–Term Acute Care hospital

**Staffed Beds: 74 Admissions: 724 Census: 61 Outpatient Visits: 0 Births: 0 Total Expense ($000): 37426 Payroll Expense ($000): 19505 Personnel: 209**

**WESTVIEW HOSPITAL** See Community Westview Hospital

☐ **WISHARD HEALTH SERVICES (150024)**, 1001 West 10th Street, Zip 46202–2879; tel. 317/630–7033 **A**1 3 5 8 9 10 **F**3 5 7 10 12 13 14 15 16 18 19 20 21 22 28 29 30 31 32 34 35 36 38 39 40 43 44 47 48 50 54 55 56 57 59 61 62 64 65 66 68 70 71 72 74 75 76 77 78 79 81 82 84 85 86 87 93 96 97 98 99 100 101 102 103 104 105 106 107 110 111 116 117 118 119 130 132 134 135 143 144 145 146 147 148
Primary Contact: Lisa E. Harris, M.D., Chief Executive Officer and Medical Director
CFO: Lee Livin, Chief Financial Officer
CMO: Lisa E. Harris, M.D., Chief Executive Officer and Medical Director
CIO: David Shaw, Vice President Information Systems
CHR: Nancy Foster, Vice President Human Resources
Web address: www.wishard.edu
**Control:** County–Government, nonfederal **Service:** General Medical and Surgical

**Staffed Beds: 293 Admissions: 15483 Census: 211 Outpatient Visits: 950592 Births: 2032 Total Expense ($000): 494080 Payroll Expense ($000): 183908 Personnel: 3028**

**IN**

*Many Facility Codes have changed. Please refer to the AHA Guide Code Chart.*  © 2013 AHA Guide

## JASPER—Dubois County

☒ **MEMORIAL HOSPITAL AND HEALTH CARE CENTER (150115)**, 800 West Ninth Street, Zip 47546–2516; tel. 812/996–2345, (Total facility includes 20 beds in nursing home–type unit) **A**1 2 9 10 19 **F**3 7 11 12 13 15 20 22 26 28 29 30 31 34 35 36 38 40 48 51 54 56 57 59 62 64 66 68 70 74 75 76 77 78 79 81 82 84 85 86 87 89 90 93 97 98 100 101 102 103 104 107 108 111 114 115 118 119 121 127 128 129 130 131 132 143 144 146 147 148 **P**6 **S** American Province of Little Company of Mary Sisters, Evergreen Park, IL
Primary Contact: Raymond W. Snowden, President and Chief Executive Officer
CFO: E. Kyle Bennett, Executive Vice President
CMO: Stan Tretter, M.D., President Medical Staff
CIO: Todd Mehringer, Director Information Systems
CHR: Richard Pea, Director Human Resources
CNO: Tonya Heim, R.N., Vice President Patient Services and Chief Nursing Officer
Web address: www.mhhcc.org
**Control:** Church–operated, Nongovernment, not–for profit **Service:** General Medical and Surgical

**Staffed Beds:** 133 **Admissions:** 6305 **Census:** 71 **Outpatient Visits:** 231610 **Births:** 918 **Total Expense ($000):** 150717 **Payroll Expense ($000):** 65173 **Personnel:** 1155

## JEFFERSONVILLE—Clark County

☒ **CLARK MEMORIAL HOSPITAL (150009)**, 1220 Missouri Avenue, Zip 47130–3743, Mailing Address: P.O. Box 69, Zip 47131–0600; tel. 812/282–6631 **A**1 2 3 5 9 10 **F**3 5 8 11 12 13 15 17 18 20 22 26 28 29 30 31 34 35 38 40 45 46 49 50 53 54 56 57 59 64 65 70 74 75 76 77 78 79 81 82 85 86 87 91 92 97 98 100 101 102 103 104 105 107 108 110 111 114 115 119 124 130 132 135 144 145 146 147 148 **P**6
Primary Contact: Martin Padgett, President and Chief Executive Officer
CFO: Kirk Strack, Vice President and Chief Financial Officer
CMO: William Templeton, III, M.D., Medical Director
CIO: Larry Reverman, Director Information Systems
CHR: Fred J. Horlander, Vice President
Web address: www.clarkmemorial.org
**Control:** County–Government, nonfederal **Service:** General Medical and Surgical

**Staffed Beds:** 158 **Admissions:** 13869 **Census:** 152 **Outpatient Visits:** 155866 **Births:** 1535 **Total Expense ($000):** 182824 **Payroll Expense ($000):** 72583 **Personnel:** 1380

☐ **WELLSTONE REGIONAL HOSPITAL (154051)**, 2700 Vissing Park Road, Zip 47130–5989; tel. 812/284–8000 **A**1 9 10 **F**4 5 29 33 34 56 59 71 75 87 98 99 101 103 104 105 130 132 **P**5 **S** Universal Health Services, Inc., King of Prussia, PA
Primary Contact: Greg Stewart, Chief Executive Officer
CFO: Gracia Winsett, Chief Financial Officer
CMO: Asad Ismail, M.D., Medical Director
CHR: Tiffany Smith, Director Human Resources
Web address: www.wellstonehospital.com
**Control:** Corporation, Investor–owned, for–profit **Service:** Psychiatric

**Staffed Beds:** 100 **Admissions:** 3004 **Census:** 76 **Outpatient Visits:** 7266 **Births:** 0 **Total Expense ($000):** 13286 **Payroll Expense ($000):** 8451 **Personnel:** 227

## KENDALLVILLE—Noble County

☒ **PARKVIEW NOBLE HOSPITAL (150146)**, 401 Sawyer Road, Zip 46755–2568; tel. 260/347–8700 **A**1 9 10 **F**3 7 11 13 15 28 29 34 35 40 45 46 47 50 54 57 59 64 70 74 75 76 79 81 82 85 87 93 94 97 107 108 110 111 114 118 119 129 130 132 135 143 145 146 **S** Parkview Health, Fort Wayne, IN
Primary Contact: David C. Hunter, Chief Operating Officer
COO: David C. Hunter, Chief Operating Officer
CFO: Michael P. Browning, Chief Financial Officer
CMO: Phil Corbin, M.D., Chief Medical Officer
CIO: Ron Double, Chief Information Officer
CHR: Rebecca Gonzalez, Manager Human Resources
CNO: Catherine Byrd, Vice President Patient Services
Web address: www.parkview.com
**Control:** Other not–for–profit (including NFP Corporation) **Service:** General Medical and Surgical

**Staffed Beds:** 31 **Admissions:** 1808 **Census:** 15 **Outpatient Visits:** 52636 **Births:** 324 **Total Expense ($000):** 38450 **Payroll Expense ($000):** 11943 **Personnel:** 185

## KNOX—Starke County

☒ **INDIANA UNIVERSITY HEALTH STARKE HOSPITAL (150102)**, 102 East Culver Road, Zip 46534–2216, Mailing Address: P.O. Box 339, Zip 46534–0339; tel. 574/772–6231 **A**1 9 10 **F**3 15 18 28 29 30 34 35 36 40 45 47 50 53 57 59 68 74 75 77 79 81 85 87 93 94 107 108 110 111 114 117 119 130 146 **S** Indiana University Health, Indianapolis, IN
Primary Contact: Jared Beasley, Interim President
CFO: Rosemarie Heise, Vice President Finance
CMO: A. N. Damodaran, M.D., President Medical Staff
CIO: Ashley Norem, Chief Information Systems
CHR: Doug Jesch, Director Human Resources
Web address: www.iuhealth.org/starke/
**Control:** Other not–for–profit (including NFP Corporation) **Service:** General Medical and Surgical

**Staffed Beds:** 20 **Admissions:** 775 **Census:** 6 **Outpatient Visits:** 28142 **Births:** 0 **Total Expense ($000):** 20390 **Payroll Expense ($000):** 7492 **Personnel:** 138

**STARKE MEMORIAL HOSPITAL** See Indiana University Health Starke Hospital

## KOKOMO—Howard County

☒ **COMMUNITY HOWARD REGIONAL HOSPITAL (150007)**, 3500 South Lafountain Street, Zip 46902–3803, Mailing Address: P.O. Box 9011, Zip 46904–9011; tel. 765/453–0702 **A**1 2 9 10 **F**3 7 8 13 15 17 18 20 22 24 26 28 29 30 31 32 34 35 38 40 45 46 50 53 57 58 59 60 62 63 65 66 68 70 71 72 74 75 76 77 78 79 81 82 85 87 89 90 93 96 97 98 99 100 101 102 103 104 105 106 107 108 109 111 115 116 117 119 120 121 123 129 130 131 132 134 135 143 145 146 147 148 **S** Community Health Network, Indianapolis, IN
Primary Contact: James P. Alender, President and Chief Executive Officer
COO: Theodore Brown, Chief Operating Officer
CFO: Alan W. Biggs, Vice President Financial Services
CIO: Sharon Miller, Chief Information Officer
CHR: Michael L. Williams, FACHE, Vice President Human Resources
Web address: www.howardregional.org
**Control:** Other not–for–profit (including NFP Corporation) **Service:** General Medical and Surgical

**Staffed Beds:** 168 **Admissions:** 4608 **Census:** 54 **Outpatient Visits:** 100201 **Births:** 359 **Total Expense ($000):** 132594 **Payroll Expense ($000):** 51959 **Personnel:** 737

☒ **COMMUNITY HOWARD SPECIALTY HOSPITAL (153039)**, 829 North Dixon Road, Zip 46901–7709; tel. 765/452–6700, (Nonreporting) **A**1 9 10 **S** Community Health Network, Indianapolis, IN
Primary Contact: Michelle L. Russell, Administrator
CFO: Julie Pena, Director Finance
CMO: Brad Vossberg, M.D., Chief Rehabilitation
CHR: Kathy Leonard, Manager Human Resources
Web address: www.howardregional.org
**Control:** Corporation, Investor–owned, for–profit **Service:** Rehabilitation

**Staffed Beds:** 30

**HOWARD REGIONAL HEALTH SYSTEM** See Community Howard Regional Hospital

**HOWARD REGIONAL HEALTH SYSTEM WEST CAMPUS SPECIALTY HOSPITAL** See Community Howard Specialty Hospital

☒ **ST. JOSEPH HOSPITAL AND HEALTH CENTER (150010)**, 1907 West Sycamore Street, Zip 46901–4197, Mailing Address: P.O. Box 9010, Zip 46904–9010; tel. 765/452–5611 **A**1 9 10 **F**3 4 5 7 8 13 15 18 19 20 28 29 30 34 35 36 40 44 45 49 50 51 55 57 59 64 66 68 69 70 73 74 75 76 77 78 79 81 82 84 85 86 87 89 90 93 96 97 98 99 100 102 103 104 105 107 108 110 111 114 119 120 121 123 129 130 131 132 135 143 144 145 146 147 **P**6 **S** Ascension Health, Saint Louis, MO
Primary Contact: Kathlene A. Young, MS, FACHE, President and Chief Executive Officer
CFO: Dennis Ressler, Chief Financial Officer
CMO: David L. Williams, M.D., Chief Medical Officer
CIO: Jeffrey Scott, Chief Information Officer
CHR: Cindy Babb, Executive Director Human Resources and Organizational Effectiveness
CNO: Kathleen K. Peoples, R.N., Vice President and Nursing
Web address: www.stjoseph.stvincent.org
**Control:** Church–operated, Nongovernment, not–for profit **Service:** General Medical and Surgical

**Staffed Beds:** 137 **Admissions:** 5392 **Census:** 70 **Outpatient Visits:** 153699 **Births:** 628 **Total Expense ($000):** 105360 **Payroll Expense ($000):** 42820 **Personnel:** 694

**IN**

---

**Hospital, Medicare Provider Number, Address, Telephone, Approval, Facility, and Physician Codes, Health Care System**

★ American Hospital Association (AHA) membership
☐ The Joint Commission accreditation
◇ DNV Healthcare Inc. accreditation
○ Healthcare Facilities Accreditation Program
△ Commission on Accreditation of Rehabilitation Facilities (CARF) accreditation

## LA PORTE—Laporte County

☒ **INDIANA UNIVERSITY HEALTH LA PORTE HOSPITAL (150006)**, 1007 Lincolnway, Zip 46350–3201, Mailing Address: P.O. Box 250, Zip 46352–0250; tel. 219/326–1234, (Total facility includes 55 beds in nursing home–type unit) **A**1 2 5 9 10 19 **F**3 8 11 13 15 17 18 20 22 24 26 28 29 30 31 32 34 35 36 38 39 40 45 46 49 50 51 53 54 56 57 58 59 62 63 64 65 66 67 68 70 71 74 75 76 77 79 81 82 84 85 86 87 89 90 93 96 98 100 101 102 103 107 108 110 111 114 115 118 119 126 128 129 130 131 132 135 144 145 146 147 148 **S** Indiana University Health, Indianapolis, IN
Primary Contact: G. Thor Thordarson, President and Chief Executive Officer
COO: Linda L. Satkoski, R.N., Chief Operating Officer
CFO: Mark Rafalski, CPA, Chief Financial Officer
CMO: William J. Houston, M.D., Medical Director
CIO: Earl Adams, Chief Information Officer
CHR: Connie Ford, Vice President Human Resources
CNO: Pauline Arnold, MSN, Chief Nursing and Quality Officer
Web address: www.iuhealth.org
**Control:** Other not–for–profit (including NFP Corporation) **Service:** General Medical and Surgical

**Staffed Beds:** 204 **Admissions:** 6379 **Census:** 109 **Outpatient Visits:** 114506 **Births:** 660 **Total Expense ($000):** 162858 **Payroll Expense ($000):** 58529 **Personnel:** 1377

**LA PORTE REGIONAL HEALTH SYSTEM** See Indiana University Health La Porte Hospital

## LAFAYETTE—Tippecanoe County

**CLARIAN ARNETT HOSPITAL** See Indiana University Health Arnett Hospital

○ **FRANCISCAN ST. ELIZABETH HEALTH – LAFAYETTE CENTRAL (150003)**, 1501 Hartford Street, Zip 47904–2134; tel. 765/423–6011, (Includes LAFAYETTE HOME HOSPITAL, 2400 South Street, Zip 47904–3052; tel. 765/447–6811; ST. ELIZABETH MEDICAL CENTER, 1501 Hartford Street, Zip 47904–2126; tel. 765/423–6011), (Nonreporting) **A**2 5 6 9 10 11 **S** Franciscan Alliance, Mishawaka, IN
Primary Contact: Terrance E. Wilson, President and Chief Executive Officer
CFO: Keith Lauter, Chief Financial Officer
CMO: Donald B. Edelen, M.D., Vice President Medical Services and Quality Initiatives
CIO: Lisa K. Decker, Director Public Relations and Marketing
CHR: Jan Garvin, Vice President Human Resources
Web address: www.ste.org
**Control:** Other not–for–profit (including NFP Corporation) **Service:** General Medical and Surgical

**Staffed Beds:** 302

○ **FRANCISCAN ST. ELIZABETH HEALTH – LAFAYETTE EAST (150109)**, (Formerly Elizabeth East), 1701 South Creasy Lane, Zip 47905–4972; tel. 765/502–4000, (Nonreporting) **A**10 11 **S** Franciscan Alliance, Mishawaka, IN
Primary Contact: Terrance E. Wilson, President and Chief Executive Officer
Web address: www.ste.org
**Control:** Other not–for–profit (including NFP Corporation) **Service:** General Medical and Surgical

**Staffed Beds:** 140

★ ○ **INDIANA UNIVERSITY HEALTH ARNETT HOSPITAL (150173)**, 5165 McCarty Lane, Zip 47905–8764, Mailing Address: P.O. Box 5545, Zip 47903–5545; tel. 765/448–8000 **A**3 5 9 10 11 **F**3 11 13 15 18 20 22 24 26 28 29 30 31 34 35 40 42 45 46 49 50 51 54 57 59 60 64 65 68 69 70 72 74 75 76 77 78 79 81 82 85 87 89 93 97 99 107 108 110 111 114 115 116 117 118 119 121 129 130 131 144 146 147 148 **P**6 **S** Indiana University Health, Indianapolis, IN
Primary Contact: Alfonso W. Gatmaitan, Chief Executive Officer
COO: Brian T. Shockney, FACHE, Chief Operating Officer
CMO: Jim Bien, M.D., Vice President Quality and Patient Safety
CIO: John Rich, System Director Information Technology
CHR: Koreen H. Kyhnell, Vice President Human Resources
Web address: www.iuhealth.org
**Control:** Other not–for–profit (including NFP Corporation) **Service:** General Medical and Surgical

**Staffed Beds:** 180 **Admissions:** 8792 **Census:** 107 **Outpatient Visits:** 72849 **Births:** 1269 **Total Expense ($000):** 352464 **Payroll Expense ($000):** 148576 **Personnel:** 1817

**ST. ELIZABETH CENTRAL** See Franciscan St. Elizabeth Health – Lafayette Central

☒ **ST. VINCENT SETON SPECIALTY HOSPITAL (152021)**, 1501 Hartford Street, Zip 47904–2134; tel. 765/236–8900 **A**1 10 **F**1 29 30 31 35 60 78 130 148 **S** Ascension Health, Saint Louis, MO
Primary Contact: Peter H. Alexander, Administrator
COO: Troy T. Reiff, Corporate Director Operations
CFO: David M. Girten, Corporate Director Financial Services
CMO: Ronald Reisman, M.D., rireisma@stvincent.org
CHR: Terry A. Wignall, Director Human Resources
Web address: www.stvincent.org
**Control:** Other not–for–profit (including NFP Corporation) **Service:** Long–Term Acute Care hospital

**Staffed Beds:** 30 **Admissions:** 243 **Census:** 16 **Outpatient Visits:** 0 **Births:** 0 **Total Expense ($000):** 10729 **Payroll Expense ($000):** 5412 **Personnel:** 56

☐ **SYCAMORE SPRINGS HOSPITAL (154059)**, 833 Park East Boulevard, Zip 47905–0785; tel. 765/743–4400 **A**1 9 10 **F**4 5 98 102 103 104 105
Primary Contact: David Fletcher–Janzen, Chief Executive Officer
Web address: www.sycamorespringshealth.com
**Control:** Corporation, Investor–owned, for–profit **Service:** Psychiatric

**Staffed Beds:** 48 **Admissions:** 611 **Census:** 11 **Outpatient Visits:** 8401 **Births:** 0 **Total Expense ($000):** 4950 **Payroll Expense ($000):** 2833 **Personnel:** 62

## LAGRANGE—Lagrange County

☒ **PARKVIEW LAGRANGE HOSPITAL (151323)**, 207 North Townline Road, Zip 46761–1325; tel. 260/463–2143 **A**1 9 10 18 **F**3 7 13 15 17 26 29 30 34 35 40 45 50 51 57 59 63 64 70 75 76 79 81 82 83 84 85 86 87 89 90 93 96 107 108 109 110 111 114 118 119 128 129 130 132 133 143 146 148 **S** Parkview Health, Fort Wayne, IN
Primary Contact: Robert T. Myers, Chief Operating Officer
COO: Robert T. Myers, Chief Operating Officer
CFO: Vickie Stanski, Financial Analyst
CMO: Jeffrey Brookes, M.D., Chief Medical Officer
CHR: Rebecca Gonzalez, Director Human Resources
Web address: www.parkview.com
**Control:** Other not–for–profit (including NFP Corporation) **Service:** General Medical and Surgical

**Staffed Beds:** 25 **Admissions:** 1181 **Census:** 11 **Outpatient Visits:** 21885 **Births:** 351 **Total Expense ($000):** 26673 **Payroll Expense ($000):** 8203 **Personnel:** 152

## LAWRENCEBURG—Dearborn County

**COMMUNITY MENTAL HEALTH CENTER (154011)**, 285 Bielby Road, Zip 47025–1055; tel. 812/537–1302 **A**9 10 **F**4 98 99 100 101 102 103 104 105 106 130 135 **P**6
Primary Contact: Tom Talbot, Chief Executive Officer
Web address: www.cmhcinc.org
**Control:** Other not–for–profit (including NFP Corporation) **Service:** Psychiatric

**Staffed Beds:** 14 **Admissions:** 580 **Census:** 8 **Outpatient Visits:** 55327 **Births:** 0 **Total Expense ($000):** 1936 **Payroll Expense ($000):** 907 **Personnel:** 19

★ ○ **DEARBORN COUNTY HOSPITAL (150086)**, 600 Wilson Creek Road, Zip 47025–2751; tel. 812/537–1010 **A**9 10 11 **F**3 11 13 15 20 28 30 31 34 35 37 40 43 44 45 46 47 49 50 57 59 62 63 64 70 75 76 77 78 79 81 84 85 86 87 92 93 107 108 110 111 114 116 117 118 119 130 131 132 146 148 **P**6
Primary Contact: Roger Howard, President and Chief Executive Officer
CFO: Philip A. Meyer, Director Finance
CHR: Pat Sutton, Director Human Resources
Web address: www.dch.org
**Control:** County–Government, nonfederal **Service:** General Medical and Surgical

**Staffed Beds:** 78 **Admissions:** 4141 **Census:** 41 **Outpatient Visits:** 142764 **Births:** 497 **Total Expense ($000):** 77835 **Payroll Expense ($000):** 31465 **Personnel:** 640

*Many Facility Codes have changed. Please refer to the AHA Guide Code Chart.*

© 2013 AHA Guide

## LEBANON—Boone County

✠ **WITHAM MEMORIAL HOSPITAL (150104)**, 2605 North Lebanon Street, Zip 46052–1476, Mailing Address: P.O. Box 1200, Zip 46052–3005; tel. 765/485–8000 **A**1 9 10 **F**3 7 8 13 15 18 20 22 28 29 30 31 34 40 42 45 50 54 56 57 59 60 64 65 68 69 70 75 76 77 79 81 82 83 85 86 87 93 94 97 98 103 107 108 110 111 115 117 118 119 129 130 132 135 141 148 147 148 **P**1
Primary Contact: Raymond V. Ingham, M.D., Ph.D., President and Chief Executive Officer
COO: Diane Feder, MSN, Senior Vice President and Chief Operating Officer
CFO: George Pogas, CPA, Senior Vice President and Chief Financial Officer
CMO: Thomas Cartwright, M.D., Chief of Staff
CMO: C. Layton Elliott, M.D., Chief of Staff
CIO: George Pogas, CPA, Senior Vice President and Chief Financial Officer
CHR: Gary A. Deater, Vice President Administration, Human Resources and Risk Management
CNO: Diane Feder, MSN, Senior Vice President and Chief Operating Officer
Web address: www.witham.org
**Control:** County–Government, nonfederal **Service:** General Medical and Surgical

**Staffed Beds:** 52 **Admissions:** 2532 **Census:** 25 **Outpatient Visits:** 130027 **Births:** 451 **Total Expense ($000):** 88711 **Payroll Expense ($000):** 33768 **Personnel:** 560

## LINTON—Greene County

✠ **GREENE COUNTY GENERAL HOSPITAL (151317)**, 1185 North 1000 W., Zip 47441–5282; tel. 812/847–2281 **A**1 9 10 18 **F**3 11 13 15 18 30 31 34 35 45 57 59 64 65 70 74 76 77 78 79 81 85 89 90 93 107 108 110 114 119 130 133 135 148
Primary Contact: Brenda Reetz, R.N., Chief Executive Officer
CFO: April Settles, Chief Financial Officer
CMO: Owen A. Batterton, M.D., Chief of Staff
CIO: Steve Phillips, Information Officer
CHR: Timothy Norris, Chief Financial Officer
CNO: Lea Ann Camp, MSN, Chief Nursing Officer
Web address: www.greenecountyhospital.com
**Control:** County–Government, nonfederal **Service:** General Medical and Surgical

**Staffed Beds:** 25 **Admissions:** 875 **Census:** 8 **Outpatient Visits:** 16471 **Births:** 62 **Total Expense ($000):** 23437 **Payroll Expense ($000):** 10465 **Personnel:** 209

## LOGANSPORT—Cass County

**FOUR COUNTY COUNSELING CENTER (154035)**, 1015 Michigan Avenue, Zip 46947–1526; tel. 574/722–5151, (Nonreporting) **A**9 10
Primary Contact: C.J. Davis, Chief Executive Officer/ Executive Director
COO: Kim Hazlett, Chief Operating Officer/ Associate Director
CFO: Nancy Street Merriweather, Chief Financial Officer
CNO: Donna Henry, Director of Nursing
Web address: www.fourcounty.org
**Control:** Other not–for–profit (including NFP Corporation) **Service:** Psychiatric

**Staffed Beds:** 15

★ ◯ **LOGANSPORT MEMORIAL HOSPITAL (150072)**, 1101 Michigan Avenue, Zip 46947–1528, Mailing Address: P.O. Box 7013, Zip 46947–7013; tel. 574/753–7541 **A**9 10 11 20 **F**3 11 13 15 28 29 30 32 34 35 36 40 44 45 48 49 50 51 57 59 64 65 68 69 70 75 76 77 78 79 81 85 86 87 93 97 107 108 110 111 114 119 124 129 130 132 133 135 146 147 **P**6
Primary Contact: David J. Ameen, President and Chief Executive Officer
CFO: Julia L. Berndt, Chief Financial Officer
CMO: Charles Montgomery, M.D., Medical Director
CIO: Beth Jump, Chief Information Officer
CHR: Lynda J. Murphy, Vice President Human Resources
Web address: www.logansportmemorial.org
**Control:** County–Government, nonfederal **Service:** General Medical and Surgical

**Staffed Beds:** 83 **Admissions:** 1966 **Census:** 17 **Outpatient Visits:** 95976 **Births:** 521 **Total Expense ($000):** 56855 **Payroll Expense ($000):** 26550 **Personnel:** 519

☐ **LOGANSPORT STATE HOSPITAL**, 1098 South State Road 25, Zip 46947–6723; tel. 574/737–3633 **A**1 **F**30 39 98 106 **P**6
Primary Contact: Robert Clover, Superintendent and Chief Executive Officer
COO: Robert Clover, Assistant Superintendent
CFO: Misty Moss, Director Business Administration
CMO: Danny Meadows, M.D., Medical Director
CIO: Joe McIntosh, Director Management Information Systems
CHR: Dianne Renner, Director Human Resources
Web address: www.lshonline.org
**Control:** State–Government, nonfederal **Service:** Psychiatric

**Staffed Beds:** 170 **Admissions:** 144 **Census:** 1 **Births:** 0

## MADISON—Jefferson County

★ ◯ **KING'S DAUGHTERS' HEALTH (150069)**, (Formerly King's Daughters' Hospital and Health Services), One Bethany Drive, Zip 47250, Mailing Address: P.O. Box 447, Zip 47250–0447; tel. 812/801–0800 **A**2 9 10 11 **F**3 7 8 13 15 20 28 29 30 31 34 40 42 45 48 49 50 57 59 62 63 64 65 68 70 74 75 76 77 78 79 81 82 84 85 86 91 93 94 97 107 108 110 111 115 119 120 121 123 129 130 131 132 134 135 144 145 146 147 148 **P**6
Primary Contact: Carol Dozier, President and Chief Executive Officer
CFO: Steve Meacham, Vice President Finance
CMO: Judy Kuehler, M.D., President Medical Staff
CIO: Linda Darnell, Director Management Information Systems
CHR: Susan Poling, Director Human Resources
Web address: www.kdhmadison.org
**Control:** Other not–for–profit (including NFP Corporation) **Service:** General Medical and Surgical

**Staffed Beds:** 77 **Admissions:** 3684 **Census:** 39 **Outpatient Visits:** 177681 **Births:** 415 **Total Expense ($000):** 98906 **Payroll Expense ($000):** 49146 **Personnel:** 875

☐ **MADISON STATE HOSPITAL (154019)**, 711 Green Road, Zip 47250–2199; tel. 812/265–2611, (Nonreporting) **A**1 10
Primary Contact: Peggy Stephens, M.D., Superintendent and Medical Director
COO: Peggy Stephens, M.D., Superintendent and Medical Director
CFO: Carolyn Copeland, Business Administrator
CMO: Peggy Stephens, M.D., Superintendent and Medical Director
CIO: Ric Martin, Information Specialist
Web address: www.in.gov/fssa/msh
**Control:** State–Government, nonfederal **Service:** Psychiatric

**Staffed Beds:** 150

## MARION—Grant County

☐ **GRANT–BLACKFORD MENTAL HEALTH CENTER (154021)**, 505 North Wabash Avenue, Zip 46952–2608; tel. 765/662–3971, (Nonreporting) **A**1 9 10
Primary Contact: Paul Kuczora, Chief Executive Officer
Web address: www.cornerstone.org/
**Control:** Other not–for–profit (including NFP Corporation) **Service:** Psychiatric

**Staffed Beds:** 16

★ ◯ **MARION GENERAL HOSPITAL (150011)**, 441 North Wabash Avenue, Zip 46952–2690; tel. 765/660–6000 **A**2 9 10 11 **F**3 7 8 11 13 15 18 20 22 26 28 29 30 31 34 35 40 41 45 50 57 58 59 64 65 66 68 70 74 75 76 77 78 79 81 82 85 86 87 89 90 91 92 93 96 97 107 108 110 111 114 115 118 119 129 130 132 135 143 145 146 147 148 **P**6
Primary Contact: Paul L. Usher, President and Chief Executive Officer
COO: Bernadine L. Wallace, MSN, Chief Nursing Officer and Chief Operating Officer
CFO: Robyn L. Powell, Chief Financial Officer
CMO: Edward L. Keppler, M.D., Chief Medical Officer
CIO: Emmanuel Ndow, Chief Information Officer
CHR: Karen Jones, Administrative Director Human Resources
Web address: www.mgh.net
**Control:** Other not–for–profit (including NFP Corporation) **Service:** General Medical and Surgical

**Staffed Beds:** 115 **Admissions:** 5080 **Census:** 55 **Outpatient Visits:** 211669 **Births:** 688 **Total Expense ($000):** 131101 **Payroll Expense ($000):** 43855 **Personnel:** 943

**VETERANS AFFAIRS NORTHERN INDIANA HEALTH CARE SYSTEM–MARION CAMPUS** See Veterans Affairs Northern Indiana Health Care System, Fort Wayne

## MARTINSVILLE—Morgan County

✠ **INDIANA UNIVERSITY HEALTH MORGAN HOSPITAL (150038)**, 2209 John R. Wooden Drive, Zip 46151–1840, Mailing Address: P.O. Box 1717, Zip 46151–0717; tel. 765/342–8441 **A**1 2 9 10 **F**3 8 11 13 15 18 28 29 30 31 32 34 35 40 45 50 55 56 57 59 64 69 70 73 75 76 77 78 79 80 81 82 84 85 86 89 90 93 97 98 103 107 108 110 111 114 119 120 121 123 129 130 132 144 146 147 148 **P**1 6 **S** Indiana University Health, Indianapolis, IN
Primary Contact: Doug Puckett, President and Chief Executive Officer
CFO: Scott Andritsch, Vice President and Chief Financial Officer
CMO: Warren L. Gray, M.D., Chief of Staff
CHR: Charlene Hall, Vice President Human Resources and Guest Support Services
Web address: www.iuhealth.org/morgan/
**Control:** Other not–for–profit (including NFP Corporation) **Service:** General Medical and Surgical

**Staffed Beds:** 92 **Admissions:** 1493 **Census:** 18 **Outpatient Visits:** 65343 **Births:** 218 **Total Expense ($000):** 41190 **Payroll Expense ($000):** 16007 **Personnel:** 322

IN

---

**Hospital, Medicare Provider Number, Address, Telephone, Approval, Facility, and Physician Codes, Health Care System**

★ American Hospital Association (AHA) membership
☐ The Joint Commission accreditation
◇ DNV Healthcare Inc. accreditation
◯ Healthcare Facilities Accreditation Program
△ Commission on Accreditation of Rehabilitation Facilities (CARF) accreditation

## MERRILLVILLE—Lake County

**REGIONAL MENTAL HEALTH CENTER (154020)**, 8555 Taft Street, Zip 46410–6123; tel. 219/769–4005, (Nonreporting) **A**9 10
Primary Contact: Robert D. Krumwied, President and Chief Executive Officer
Web address: www.regionalmentalhealth.org/
**Control:** Corporation, Investor–owned, for–profit **Service:** Psychiatric

**Staffed Beds:** 16

**SOUTHLAKE CAMPUS** See Methodist Hospitals, Gary

## MICHIGAN CITY—Laporte County

○ **FRANCISCAN ST. ANTHONY HEALTH – MICHIGAN CITY (150015)**, 301 West Homer Street, Zip 46360–4358; tel. 219/879–8511, (Nonreporting) **A**2 9 10 11 19 **S** Franciscan Alliance, Mishawaka, IN
Primary Contact: James Callaghan, III, M.D., President
CFO: Jim Lipinski, Regional Chief Financial Officer
CIO: Terry Veith, Director Management Information Systems
CHR: Susan King–Schreiber, Vice President Human Resources
Web address: www.saintanthonymemorial.org
**Control:** Church–operated, Nongovernment, not–for profit **Service:** General Medical and Surgical

**Staffed Beds:** 171

**SAINT ANTHONY MEMORIAL** See Franciscan St. Anthony Health – Michigan City

## MISHAWAKA—St. Joseph County

⊠ **KINDRED HOSPITAL OF NORTHERN INDIANA (152018)**, 215 West Fourth Street, Suite 200, Zip 46544–1917; tel. 574/252–2000, (Nonreporting) **A**1 10 **S** Kindred Healthcare, Louisville, KY
Primary Contact: Christine T. Voorde, Chief Executive Officer
CFO: Christy Henrich, Controller
CMO: Shaya Mokfi, M.D., Medical Director and President Medical Staff
CHR: Brenda Schweizer, Coordinator Human Resources
CNO: Jane G. Mason, R.N., Chief Clinical Officer
Web address: www.khnorthernindiana.com/
**Control:** Corporation, Investor–owned, for–profit **Service:** Long–Term Acute Care hospital

**Staffed Beds:** 32

○ **RIVERCREST SPECIALTY HOSPITAL (152026)**, 1625 East Jefferson Boulevard, Zip 46545–7103; tel. 574/255–1400, (Nonreporting) **A**10 11 **S** Physicians Hospital System, Mishawaka, IN
Primary Contact: Ronni Banks, Administrator
Web address: www.physicianshospitalsystem.net/
**Control:** Partnership, Investor–owned, for–profit **Service:** Long–Term Acute Care hospital

**Staffed Beds:** 30

⊠ **SAINT JOSEPH REGIONAL MEDICAL CENTER (150012)**, 5215 Holy Cross Parkway, Zip 46545–1469; tel. 574/335–5000 **A**1 2 9 10 13 **F**13 15 17 20 21 22 23 24 25 26 28 29 30 31 34 35 39 40 45 46 47 48 49 50 54 57 60 66 68 70 71 72 74 75 76 77 78 79 80 81 87 89 90 93 96 107 108 111 115 117 118 119 120 121 123 124 126 127 129 130 131 132 135 144 145 146 147 148 **S** Trinity Health, Livonia, MI
Primary Contact: Albert Gutierrez, FACHE, President and Chief Executive Officer
CFO: Terry Heck, Vice President Finance and Chief Financial Officer
CIO: Gary L. Miller, Regional Director Information Systems
Web address: www.sjmed.com
**Control:** Other not–for–profit (including NFP Corporation) **Service:** General Medical and Surgical

**Staffed Beds:** 267 **Admissions:** 13900 **Census:** 161 **Outpatient Visits:** 156838 **Births:** 1015 **Total Expense ($000):** 264176 **Payroll Expense ($000):** 75503 **Personnel:** 1506

**TRIUMPH OUR LADY OF PEACE HOSPITAL** See Kindred Hospital of Northern Indiana

○ **UNITY MEDICAL & SURGICAL HOSPITAL (150177)**, 4455 Edison Lakes Parkway, Zip 46545–1442; tel. 574/968–0867, (Nonreporting) **A**9 10 11 **S** Physicians Hospital System, Mishawaka, IN
Primary Contact: John M. Day, Chief Executive Officer
CFO: Bernie Hebert, Jr., Chief Financial Officer
CMO: Viraj Patel, M.D., Chief Medical Officer
CIO: Tim Morningstar, Blue Star
CHR: Emyle Kruyer–Collins, Vice President Human Resources
Web address: www.physicianshospitalsystem.net
**Control:** Corporation, Investor–owned, for–profit **Service:** General Medical and Surgical

**Staffed Beds:** 15

## MONTICELLO—White County

★ **INDIANA UNIVERSITY HEALTH WHITE MEMORIAL HOSPITAL (151312)**, 720 South Sixth Street, Zip 47960–8182; tel. 574/583–7111 **A**9 10 18 **F**3 8 11 13 15 29 30 31 34 35 40 45 50 57 59 62 64 75 76 77 78 80 81 85 91 93 107 108 110 111 114 119 129 133 135 146 147 **S** Indiana University Health, Indianapolis, IN
Primary Contact: Stephanie Long, Chief Executive Officer
COO: Mary Minier, Vice President Operations
CMO: Adel Khdour, M.D., Chief Medical Officer
CIO: Michelle Baker, Director Information Systems
CHR: JoEllyn Brockmeyer, Director Human Resources
CNO: Robin S. Smith, Chief Nursing Officer
Web address: www.iuhealth.org/white–memorial
**Control:** Other not–for–profit (including NFP Corporation) **Service:** General Medical and Surgical

**Staffed Beds:** 25 **Admissions:** 1157 **Census:** 12 **Outpatient Visits:** 62804 **Births:** 151 **Total Expense ($000):** 25728 **Payroll Expense ($000):** 9320 **Personnel:** 217

## MOORESVILLE—Morgan County

○ **FRANCISCAN ST. FRANCIS HEALTH – MOORESVILLE (150057)**, 1201 Hadley Road, Zip 46158–1789; tel. 317/831–1160 **A**9 10 11 **F**8 12 13 15 29 30 31 35 37 46 47 49 50 57 58 59 64 70 75 76 77 78 79 80 81 87 91 107 108 109 110 111 116 117 119 120 121 123 124 129 130 144 145 146 147 **P**7 8 **S** Franciscan Alliance, Mishawaka, IN
Primary Contact: D. Keith Jewell, Interim Chief Executive Officer
COO: D. Keith Jewell, Senior Vice President and Chief Operating Officer
CMO: Donald Kerner, M.D., Vice President Medical Affairs
CIO: Barbara Coulter, Director Information Systems
CHR: John Ross, Vice President
Web address: www.franciscanalliance.org/hospitals/mooresville/Pages/default.aspx
**Control:** Church–operated, Nongovernment, not–for profit **Service:** General Medical and Surgical

**Staffed Beds:** 116 **Admissions:** 3365 **Census:** 29 **Outpatient Visits:** 130818 **Births:** 191 **Total Expense ($000):** 77158 **Payroll Expense ($000):** 21140 **Personnel:** 377

**ST. FRANCIS HOSPITAL–MOORESVILLE** See Franciscan St. Francis Health – Mooresville

## MUNCIE—Delaware County

○ **AMG SPECIALTY HOSPITAL – MUNCIE (152025)**, (Formerly Integra Specialty Hospital), 2401 West University Avenue, 8th Floor, Zip 47303–3428; tel. 765/751–5253, (Data for 214 days) **A**10 11 **F**1 29
Primary Contact: Rodney Midkiff, Chief Executive Officer
CNO: Tina Riegle, R.N., Chief Clinical Officer
Web address: www.amgmuncie.com/
**Control:** Corporation, Investor–owned, for–profit **Service:** Long–Term Acute Care hospital

**Staffed Beds:** 32 **Admissions:** 135 **Census:** 16 **Outpatient Visits:** 0 **Births:** 0 **Total Expense ($000):** 5014 **Payroll Expense ($000):** 2273 **Personnel:** 76

**BALL MEMORIAL HOSPITAL** See Indiana University Health Ball Memorial Hospital

⊠ △ **INDIANA UNIVERSITY HEALTH BALL MEMORIAL HOSPITAL (150089)**, 2401 University Avenue, Zip 47303–3499; tel. 765/747–3111, (Total facility includes 30 beds in nursing home–type unit) **A**1 2 3 5 7 8 9 10 19 **F**3 11 12 13 15 17 18 20 22 24 26 27 28 29 30 31 32 34 35 39 40 41 45 46 49 50 51 53 54 56 57 58 59 60 64 65 66 69 70 72 73 74 75 76 77 78 79 80 81 82 83 84 85 86 87 89 90 91 92 93 94 97 98 99 100 102 107 110 111 114 115 117 118 119 120 121 123 124 126 128 129 130 132 146 147 148 **S** Indiana University Health, Indianapolis, IN
Primary Contact: Michael E. Haley, President and Chief Executive Officer
COO: Lori Luther, Chief Operating Officer
CFO: Carol Seals, Chief Financial Officer
CMO: Jeffrey C. Bird, M.D., Chief Medical Officer
CIO: Robert McKelvey, Director Information System, Mergers and Integrations
CHR: Ann M. McGuire, Vice President Human Resources
Web address: www.iuhealth.org
**Control:** Other not–for–profit (including NFP Corporation) **Service:** General Medical and Surgical

**Staffed Beds:** 346 **Admissions:** 17454 **Census:** 233 **Outpatient Visits:** 328683 **Births:** 1666 **Total Expense ($000):** 338289 **Payroll Expense ($000):** 102253 **Personnel:** 1984

☐ **MERIDIAN HEALTH SERVICES (154053)**, 2401 West University Avenue, Zip 47303–3428; tel. 765/747–3281, (Nonreporting) **A**1 10
Primary Contact: Hank A. Milius, Chief Executive Officer
CMO: Sarfraz Khan, Medical Director
Web address: www.meridianhs.org
**Control:** Other not–for–profit (including NFP Corporation) **Service:** Psychiatric

**Staffed Beds:** 20

**RENAISSANCE SPECIALTY HOSPITAL OF CENTRAL INDIANA** See AMG Specialty Hospital – Muncie

*Many Facility Codes have changed. Please refer to the AHA Guide Code Chart.* © 2013 AHA Guide

## MUNSTER—Lake County

□ △ **COMMUNITY HOSPITAL (150125)**, 901 MacArthur Boulevard, Zip 46321–2959; tel. 219/836–1600 **A1** 2 5 7 9 10 **F3** 8 11 13 15 17 18 20 22 24 26 28 29 31 34 35 40 45 49 50 51 53 54 57 58 59 60 62 64 68 70 72 73 74 75 76 78 79 80 81 82 85 86 87 89 90 92 93 94 96 107 108 110 111 114 115 117 119 120 121 123 124 126 129 130 132 135 144 146 147 148 **P6 S** Community Healthcare System, Hammond, IN
Primary Contact: Donald P. Fesko, Chief Executive Officer and Administrator
CFO: Luis Molina, Vice President Finance and Chief Financial Officer
CMO: Don Henry, M.D., President Medical and Dental Staff
CIO: Gary Weiner, Vice President Information Technology, Chief Information Officer
CHR: Michael Graham, Director Human Resources
CNO: Ronda McKay, MSN, Vice President Patient Care Services, Chief Nursing Officer
Web address: www.comhs.org
**Control:** Other not–for–profit (including NFP Corporation) **Service:** General Medical and Surgical

**Staffed Beds:** 447 **Admissions:** 22147 **Census:** 319 **Outpatient Visits:** 358438 **Births:** 2230 **Total Expense ($000):** 431825 **Payroll Expense ($000):** 167495 **Personnel:** 2473

○ **FRANCISCAN PHYSICIANS HOSPITAL (150165)**, 701 Superior Avenue, Zip 46321–4037; tel. 219/924–1300, (Nonreporting) **A9** 10 11 **S** Franciscan Alliance, Mishawaka, IN
Primary Contact: Barbara M. Greene, President
CFO: Harold E. Collins, JD, Chief Financial Officer
CMO: Vijay D. Gupta, M.D., President and Chief Executive Officer
CIO: Steven Krause, Manager Information Technology
Web address: www.franciscanphysicianshospital.org
**Control:** Partnership, Investor–owned, for–profit **Service:** General Medical and Surgical

**Staffed Beds:** 32

## NEW ALBANY—Floyd County

★ ○ **FLOYD MEMORIAL HOSPITAL AND HEALTH SERVICES (150044)**, 1850 State Street, Zip 47150–4997; tel. 812/949–5500, (Total facility includes 118 beds in nursing home–type unit) **A2** 3 5 9 10 11 **F8** 11 12 13 15 17 18 20 22 24 28 29 30 31 34 35 40 43 49 50 56 57 59 62 64 70 71 74 75 76 77 78 79 80 81 82 85 86 87 89 93 100 107 108 110 111 114 115 116 117 118 119 120 121 123 128 129 130 131 132 135 144 146 147 148
Primary Contact: Mark D. Shugarman, President and Chief Executive Officer
COO: Mark Truman, Vice President of Operations
CFO: Ted Miller, Chief Financial Officer
CMO: Daniel J. Eichenberger, M.D., Medical Director
CIO: Brian Cox, Director Information Systems
CHR: Mike Ford, Vice President Human Resources
Web address: www.floydmemorial.com
**Control:** County–Government, nonfederal **Service:** General Medical and Surgical

**Staffed Beds:** 329 **Admissions:** 14431 **Census:** 210 **Outpatient Visits:** 358308 **Births:** 954 **Total Expense ($000):** 229517 **Payroll Expense ($000):** 100945 **Personnel:** 1995

□ **PHYSICIANS' MEDICAL CENTER (150172)**, 4023 Reas Lane, Zip 47150–2228; tel. 812/206–7660 **A1** 9 10 **F3** 12 45 51 68 79 81 82 85 87 145 **P5**
Primary Contact: Dennis Medley, Administrator
CMO: John Rademaker, M.D., Medical Director
CNO: Rob Jones, Chief Nursing Officer
Web address: www.pmcindiana.com
**Control:** State–Government, nonfederal **Service:** Surgical

**Staffed Beds:** 12 **Admissions:** 285 **Census:** 1 **Outpatient Visits:** 2549 **Births:** 0 **Total Expense ($000):** 6277 **Payroll Expense ($000):** 2656 **Personnel:** 103

⊠ △ **SOUTHERN INDIANA REHABILITATION HOSPITAL (153037)**, 3104 Blackiston Boulevard, Zip 47150–9579; tel. 812/941–8300, (Total facility includes 26 beds in nursing home–type unit) **A1** 7 9 10 **F29** 34 35 57 59 74 75 77 79 86 87 90 91 93 96 128 130 132 135 143 146 **S** Catholic Health Initiatives, Englewood, CO
Primary Contact: Randy L. Napier, President
CFO: Robert Steltenpohl, Controller
CMO: John C. Shaw, M.D., Medical Director
CHR: Lisa Burris, Director Human Resources
CNO: Suzann Byers, Director of Nursing
Web address: www.sirh.org
**Control:** Other not–for–profit (including NFP Corporation) **Service:** Rehabilitation

**Staffed Beds:** 60 **Admissions:** 1387 **Census:** 44 **Outpatient Visits:** 28660 **Births:** 0 **Total Expense ($000):** 17589 **Payroll Expense ($000):** 9305 **Personnel:** 200

## NEW CASTLE—Henry County

★ ○ **HENRY COUNTY HOSPITAL (150030)**, 1000 North 16th Street, Zip 47362–4319; Mailing Address: P.O. Box 490, Zip 47362–0490; tel. 765/521–0890 **A9** 10 11 **F3** 8 11 13 15 18 28 29 30 34 35 40 45 46 50 51 53 57 59 62 63 64 68 70 74 75 76 77 79 81 82 85 87 89 91 92 93 94 97 107 110 111 114 118 119 127 129 130 131 132 135 144 146 147 148 **P1**
Primary Contact: Paul Janssen, President and Chief Executive Officer
COO: Brian K. Ring, Chief Operating Officer
CMO: Wylie McGlothlin, M.D., Chief Medical Officer
CIO: Mike Spencer, Chief Information Officer
CHR: Deanna Malott, Director Human Resources
CNO: Carrie Williams, R.N., Chief Nursing Officer
Web address: www.hcmhcares.org
**Control:** County–Government, nonfederal **Service:** General Medical and Surgical

**Staffed Beds:** 90 **Admissions:** 2617 **Census:** 27 **Outpatient Visits:** 137175 **Births:** 335 **Total Expense ($000):** 62921 **Payroll Expense ($000):** 24016 **Personnel:** 587

## NEWBURGH—Warrick County

□ **BRENTWOOD MEADOWS (154055)**, 4455 Roslin Road, Zip 47630; tel. 812/858–7200 **A1** 9 10 **F4** 5 34 59 67 98 101 104 105 132
Primary Contact: Rosemary Notarantonio, R.N., MSN, Chief Executive Officer
Web address: www.brentwoodmeadows.com
**Control:** Corporation, Investor–owned, for–profit **Service:** Alcoholism and other chemical dependency

**Staffed Beds:** 48 **Admissions:** 1077 **Census:** 21 **Outpatient Visits:** 0 **Births:** 0 **Personnel:** 41

○ **THE HEART HOSPITAL AT DEACONESS GATEWAY (150175)**, 4007 Gateway Boulevard, Zip 47630–8947; tel. 812/842–4784 **A9** 10 11 **F3** 17 18 20 22 24 26 28 29 30 34 35 57 58 59 60 62 63 64 68 81 83 84 85 86 87 107 108 109 111 114 115 116 117 118 119 130 132 **S** Deaconess Health System, Evansville, IN
Primary Contact: Rebecca Malotte, Executive Director and Chief Nursing Officer
Web address: www.deaconess.com/
**Control:** Partnership, Investor–owned, for–profit **Service:** Heart

**Staffed Beds:** 24 **Admissions:** 1697 **Census:** 17 **Outpatient Visits:** 6139 **Births:** 0 **Total Expense ($000):** 39803 **Payroll Expense ($000):** 6365 **Personnel:** 120

★ ○ **THE WOMEN'S HOSPITAL (150149)**, 4199 Gateway Boulevard, Zip 47630–8940; tel. 812/842–4200 **A9** 10 11 **F3** 7 13 29 30 34 35 40 44 50 52 53 55 57 59 63 65 72 75 76 77 81 84 85 86 87 93 119 126 130 132 134 135 146 147 **P6 S** Deaconess Health System, Evansville, IN
Primary Contact: Christina M. Ryan, R.N., Chief Executive Officer
CFO: Tina Cady, Controller
CIO: Liz Adams, Manager Informatics
CHR: Jerri Sue Traylor, Manager Human Resources
CNO: Christina M. Ryan, R.N., Chief Executive Officer and Chief Nursing Officer
Web address: www.deaconess.com
**Control:** Partnership, Investor–owned, for–profit **Service:** Obstetrics and gynecology

**Staffed Beds:** 74 **Admissions:** 3321 **Census:** 44 **Outpatient Visits:** 17181 **Births:** 3016 **Total Expense ($000):** 54905 **Payroll Expense ($000):** 21147 **Personnel:** 419

## NOBLESVILLE—Hamilton County

○ △ **RIVERVIEW HOSPITAL (150059)**, 395 Westfield Road, Zip 46060–1425, Mailing Address: P.O. Box 220, Zip 46061–0220; tel. 317/773–0760, (Nonreporting) **A2** 5 7 9 10 11
Primary Contact: Patricia K. Fox, President and Chief Executive Officer
COO: Lawrence Christman, Chief Financial Officer and Chief Operating Officer
CFO: Lawrence Christman, Chief Financial Officer and Chief Operating Officer
CMO: John Paris, M.D., Chief Medical Officer
CIO: Michael Mover, Chief Information Officer
Web address: www.riverview.org
**Control:** County–Government, nonfederal **Service:** General Medical and Surgical

**Staffed Beds:** 162

---

**Hospital, Medicare Provider Number, Address, Telephone, Approval, Facility, and Physician Codes, Health Care System**

★ American Hospital Association (AHA) membership
□ The Joint Commission accreditation
◇ DNV Healthcare Inc. accreditation
○ Healthcare Facilities Accreditation Program
△ Commission on Accreditation of Rehabilitation Facilities (CARF) accreditation

IN

## NORTH VERNON—Jennings County

⊠ **ST. VINCENT JENNINGS HOSPITAL (151303)**, 301 Henry Street,
Zip 47265–1097; tel. 812/352–4200 **A**1 9 10 18 **F**3 15 29 30 32 34 35 40
44 45 46 47 50 56 57 59 64 65 66 74 77 79 81 85 93 97 107 111 114 119
124 132 133 135 144 146 148 **P**5 **S** Ascension Health, Saint Louis, MO
Primary Contact: Carl W. Risk, II, Administrator
CFO: John Lines, Chief Financial Officer
CMO: Jennifer Stanley, M.D., President Medical Staff
CHR: Kathryn Johnson, Manager Human Resources, Marketing and Public
Relations
CNO: Karen Shaw, Chief Nursing Officer and Director of Clinical Services
Web address: www.stvincent.org
**Control:** Other not–for–profit (including NFP Corporation) **Service:** General
Medical and Surgical

**Staffed Beds:** 25 **Admissions:** 445 **Census:** 4 **Outpatient Visits:** 33927
**Births:** 0 **Total Expense ($000):** 16685 **Payroll Expense ($000):** 6245
**Personnel:** 100

## PAOLI—Orange County

**BLOOMINGTON HOSPITAL OF ORANGE COUNTY** See Indiana University
Health Paoli Hospital

⊠ **INDIANA UNIVERSITY HEALTH PAOLI HOSPITAL (151306)**, 642 West
Hospital Road, Zip 47454–9672, Mailing Address: P.O. Box 499,
Zip 47454–0499; tel. 812/723–2811 **A**1 9 10 18 **F**3 7 13 15 29 30 35 40 45
50 57 59 64 76 77 81 84 85 89 93 107 110 111 114 119 129 132 133 135
146 148 **S** Indiana University Health, Indianapolis, IN
Primary Contact: Larry Bailey, Chief Executive Officer
COO: Candace Isom, Chief Operating Officer
CFO: Sue Brock, Chief Financial Officer
CMO: Dan O'Brien, D.O., Medical Director
CHR: Jessica Fortner, Director Human Resources
Web address: www.iuhealth.org/paoli
**Control:** Other not–for–profit (including NFP Corporation) **Service:** General
Medical and Surgical

**Staffed Beds:** 24 **Admissions:** 508 **Census:** 4 **Outpatient Visits:** 28889
**Births:** 123 **Total Expense ($000):** 23508 **Payroll Expense ($000):** 10498
**Personnel:** 211

## PERU—Miami County

⊠ **DUKES MEMORIAL HOSPITAL (151318)**, 275 West 12th Street,
Zip 46970–1638; tel. 765/472–8000 **A**1 9 10 18 **F**3 7 13 15 17 18 28 29 30
31 34 35 40 41 50 51 57 59 64 68 69 70 75 76 77 79 81 82 85 87 89 90
93 107 108 110 111 115 118 119 129 130 132 133 135 144 146 147 **P**6
**S** Community Health Systems, Inc., Franklin, TN
Primary Contact: Debra Close, Chief Executive Officer
CMO: Neil Stalker, M.D., Chief of Staff
CHR: Kim Black, Manager Human Resources
Web address: www.dukesmemorialhosp.com
**Control:** Corporation, Investor–owned, for–profit **Service:** General Medical and
Surgical

**Staffed Beds:** 25 **Admissions:** 1254 **Census:** 12 **Outpatient Visits:** 41112
**Births:** 216 **Total Expense ($000):** 31766 **Payroll Expense ($000):** 14736
**Personnel:** 264

## PLYMOUTH—Marshall County

☐ **MICHIANA BEHAVIORAL HEALTH CENTER (154047)**, 1800 North Oak Drive,
Zip 46563–3492; tel. 574/936–3784 **A**1 9 10 **F**98 99 105 106 **S** Universal
Health Services, Inc., King of Prussia, PA
Primary Contact: Bryan W. Lett, Chief Executive Officer
CFO: Jeff Calvin, Chief Financial Officer
CMO: Robert Raster, M.D., Medical Director
CIO: Bob Kedalis, Director Business Development
CHR: Becky Nowicki, Director Human Resources
Web address: www.michianabhc.com
**Control:** Corporation, Investor–owned, for–profit **Service:** Psychiatric

**Staffed Beds:** 75 **Admissions:** 1485 **Census:** 55 **Outpatient Visits:** 0 **Births:**
0 **Total Expense ($000):** 10686 **Payroll Expense ($000):** 5076 **Personnel:**
131

⊠ **SAINT JOSEPH REGIONAL MEDICAL CENTER–PLYMOUTH CAMPUS
(150076)**, 1915 Lake Avenue, Zip 46563–9366, Mailing Address: P.O. Box 670,
Zip 46563–0670; tel. 574/936–3181 **A**1 9 10 **F**13 15 24 29 30 31 34 35 40
45 50 54 57 59 66 68 70 74 75 76 78 79 81 87 93 107 108 114 117 119
120 121 122 123 124 129 130 132 145 146 **S** Trinity Health, Livonia, MI
Primary Contact: Albert Gutierrez, FACHE, President and Chief Executive Officer
CFO: Terry Heck, Vice President Finance and Chief Financial Officer
CIO: Gary L. Miller, Regional Director Information Systems
Web address: www.sjmed.com
**Control:** Other not–for–profit (including NFP Corporation) **Service:** General
Medical and Surgical

**Staffed Beds:** 45 **Admissions:** 2257 **Census:** 20 **Outpatient Visits:** 86060
**Births:** 365 **Total Expense ($000):** 40423 **Payroll Expense ($000):** 13563
**Personnel:** 259

## PORTLAND—Jay County

⊠ **JAY COUNTY HOSPITAL (151320)**, 500 West Votaw Street, Zip 47371–1322;
tel. 260/726–7131 **A**1 9 10 18 **F**3 8 11 13 15 28 29 30 32 34 35 40 45 50
57 59 68 70 75 76 77 81 85 86 87 103 107 108 110 111 114 119 129 130
132 133 135 144 146 **P**6 **S** Indiana University Health, Indianapolis, IN
Primary Contact: David W. Hyatt, Chief Executive Officer
CFO: Don Michael, Chief Financial Officer
CIO: Jeff Horn, Coordinator Information Systems
CHR: Jerry Bozell, Administrative Director Human Resources
CNO: Lisa Craiger, Chief Nursing Officer
Web address: www.jaycountyhospital.com
**Control:** County–Government, nonfederal **Service:** General Medical and Surgical

**Staffed Beds:** 35 **Admissions:** 1049 **Census:** 15 **Outpatient Visits:** 47017
**Births:** 74 **Total Expense ($000):** 34690 **Payroll Expense ($000):** 14025
**Personnel:** 327

## PRINCETON—Gibson County

⊠ **GIBSON GENERAL HOSPITAL (151319)**, 1808 Sherman Drive,
Zip 47670–1043; tel. 812/385–3401, (Total facility includes 45 beds in nursing
home–type unit) **A**1 9 10 18 **F**3 5 11 15 28 29 30 31 34 35 38 40 45 54 56
57 59 62 64 68 70 75 77 79 81 89 93 97 99 100 101 102 103 104 107 110
111 115 119 128 129 130 131 132 133 146 148 **P**6 **S** Alliant Management
Services, Louisville, KY
Primary Contact: Emmett C. Schuster, President and Chief Executive Officer
CFO: Ron Harrington, Vice President and Chief Financial Officer
CMO: Thomas Joseph, M.D., Chief of Staff
CIO: Patricia Ping, Director Information Services
CHR: D. Deann Hunt, Director Human Resources
CNO: Lori Phillips, Vice President and Chief Nursing Officer
Web address: www.gibsongeneral.com
**Control:** Other not–for–profit (including NFP Corporation) **Service:** General
Medical and Surgical

**Staffed Beds:** 70 **Admissions:** 861 **Census:** 42 **Outpatient Visits:** 33681
**Births:** 0 **Total Expense ($000):** 24483 **Payroll Expense ($000):** 10561
**Personnel:** 301

## RENSSELAER—Jasper County

★ **JASPER COUNTY HOSPITAL (151324)**, 1104 East Grace Street,
Zip 47978–3296; tel. 219/866–5141 **A**9 10 18 **F**3 11 13 15 28 29 30 31 34
35 39 40 45 49 50 51 53 54 56 57 59 62 63 64 65 68 69 70 74 75 76 77
78 79 81 82 85 86 87 93 96 107 108 110 111 115 118 119 127 129 130
131 132 133 135 148
Primary Contact: Timothy M. Schreeg, President and Chief Executive Officer
CFO: Jeffrey D. Webb, CPA, Chief Financial Officer
CIO: Kirby Reed, Director Information Systems
CHR: Deana Brown, Director Administrative Services
Web address: www.jchh.com
**Control:** County–Government, nonfederal **Service:** General Medical and Surgical

**Staffed Beds:** 27 **Admissions:** 1167 **Census:** 27 **Outpatient Visits:** 10701
**Births:** 73 **Payroll Expense ($000):** 15471 **Personnel:** 346

## RICHMOND—Wayne County

★ ○ **REID HOSPITAL AND HEALTH CARE SERVICES (150048)**, 1100 Reid
Parkway, Zip 47374–1157; tel. 765/983–3000 **A**2 5 9 10 11 **F**3 11 13 15 18
20 22 24 26 27 28 29 30 31 32 34 35 36 39 40 43 44 45 47 49 50 51 54
56 57 59 61 63 64 70 74 75 76 77 78 79 81 82 83 84 85 86 87 89 90 93
96 97 98 100 101 102 103 104 107 108 110 111 114 115 116 117 118
119 120 121 123 126 129 130 131 132 135 144 146 147 148 **P**6 7 8
Primary Contact: Craig C. Kinyon, President
CFO: James Puffenberger, Vice President and Chief Financial Officer
CMO: Thomas Huth, M.D., Vice President Medical Affairs
CIO: Tim Love, Director Information Services
CHR: Scott C. Rauch, Vice President Human Resources
CNO: Kay B. Cartwright, R.N., Vice President and Chief Nursing Officer
Web address: www.reidhosp.com
**Control:** Other not–for–profit (including NFP Corporation) **Service:** General
Medical and Surgical

**Staffed Beds:** 207 **Admissions:** 11500 **Census:** 147 **Outpatient Visits:**
222331 **Births:** 671 **Total Expense ($000):** 339641 **Payroll Expense
($000):** 128078 **Personnel:** 1803

☐ **RICHMOND STATE HOSPITAL (154018)**, 498 N.W. 18th Street,
Zip 47374–2851; tel. 765/966–0511 **A**1 10 **F**29 30 39 68 75 77 87 98 100
101 103 130 132 135 146 **P**6
Primary Contact: Jeffrey Butler, Superintendent
CFO: Dave Shelford, Assistant Superintendent
CMO: Donald Graber, M.D., Medical Director
CIO: Robert Boatman, Director Information Technology
CHR: Sarah Witt, Director Human Resources
Web address: www.richmondstatehospital.org
**Control:** State–Government, nonfederal **Service:** Psychiatric

**Staffed Beds:** 220 **Admissions:** 144 **Census:** 209 **Outpatient Visits:** 0
**Births:** 0 **Total Expense ($000):** 36207 **Payroll Expense ($000):** 18594
**Personnel:** 466

*Many Facility Codes have changed. Please refer to the AHA Guide Code Chart.*  © 2013 AHA Guide

## ROCHESTER—Fulton County

★ **WOODLAWN HOSPITAL (151313)**, 1400 East Ninth Street, Zip 46975–8937; tel. 574/223–3141 **A**9 10 18 **F**3 11 13 15 29 30 31 40 46 56 57 59 63 65 68 69 75 76 77 78 79 81 82 87 93 97 107 108 111 115 116 119 129 130 132 133 135 143 146 148 **P**6
Primary Contact: John L. Alley, Chief Executive Officer
CFO: Dave Cholger, Chief Financial Officer
CHR: Debra J. Lemasters, Director Human Resources
Web address: www.woodlawnhospital.com
**Control:** County–Government, nonfederal **Service:** General Medical and Surgical

**Staffed Beds:** 25 **Admissions:** 1092 **Census:** 11 **Outpatient Visits:** 83562 **Births:** 197 **Total Expense ($000):** 41334 **Payroll Expense ($000):** 18887 **Personnel:** 304

## RUSHVILLE—Rush County

★ **RUSH MEMORIAL HOSPITAL (151304)**, 1300 North Main Street, Zip 46173–1198, Mailing Address: P.O. Box 608, Zip 46173–0608; tel. 765/932–4111 **A**9 10 18 **F**3 7 11 15 18 24 28 29 31 35 36 40 46 51 52 57 59 64 65 74 75 77 78 79 81 85 93 97 107 111 114 117 120 121 122 129 130 131 132 133 135 146 147 148 **P**6
Primary Contact: Bradley Smith, President and Chief Executive Officer
COO: Debbie Jones–Browning, Vice President Operations and Physician Services and Chief Operating Officer
CFO: Karen Meyer, Vice President Finance and Chief Financial Officer
CMO: Daniel Stahl, D.O., Chief of Staff
CIO: Jim Boyer, Vice President Information Technology and Chief Information Officer
CNO: Gretchen Smith, Vice President Nursing and Compliance and Risk
Web address: www.rushmemorial.com
**Control:** County–Government, nonfederal **Service:** General Medical and Surgical

**Staffed Beds:** 25 **Admissions:** 551 **Census:** 5 **Outpatient Visits:** 34879 **Births:** 0 **Total Expense ($000):** 22988 **Payroll Expense ($000):** 10685 **Personnel:** 226

## SALEM—Washington County

☒ **ST. VINCENT SALEM HOSPITAL (151314)**, 911 North Shelby Street, Zip 47167–1694; tel. 812/883–5881 **A**1 9 10 18 **F**3 11 15 28 29 30 32 34 40 45 47 49 57 59 75 77 79 81 82 85 89 93 104 107 111 114 119 129 130 132 133 148 **P**6 **S** Ascension Health, Saint Louis, MO
Primary Contact: Lee Jaeger, FACHE, Chief Executive Officer
CFO: John Lines, Director Financial and Support Services
CMO: S. E. Kemker, M.D., President Medical Staff
CIO: Scott Cox, Manager Information Systems
CHR: Val Potter, Director Human Resources
Web address: www.stvincent.org/St–Vincent–Salem/Default.aspx
**Control:** Other not–for–profit (including NFP Corporation) **Service:** General Medical and Surgical

**Staffed Beds:** 25 **Admissions:** 465 **Census:** 4 **Outpatient Visits:** 38050 **Births:** 0 **Total Expense ($000):** 21848 **Payroll Expense ($000):** 7036 **Personnel:** 109

## SCOTTSBURG—Scott County

☒ **SCOTT MEMORIAL HOSPITAL (151334)**, 1415 North Gardner Street, Zip 47170, Mailing Address: Box 430, Zip 47170–0430; tel. 812/752–3456, (Nonreporting) **A**1 9 10 18 **S** LifePoint Hospitals, Inc., Brentwood, TN
Primary Contact: Jerry Dooley, Interim Chief Executive Officer
CFO: Angela Doan, Chief Financial Officer
Web address: www.scottmemorial.com
**Control:** County–Government, nonfederal **Service:** General Medical and Surgical

**Staffed Beds:** 25

## SEYMOUR—Jackson County

☒ **SCHNECK MEDICAL CENTER (150065)**, 411 West Tipton Street, Zip 47274–2363, Mailing Address: P.O. Box 2349, Zip 47274–5000; tel. 812/522–2349 **A**1 2 9 10 **F**3 8 12 13 15 18 28 29 30 31 34 35 36 40 45 50 51 56 57 58 59 60 61 62 63 64 68 69 70 74 75 76 77 78 79 81 82 83 84 85 86 87 89 93 104 107 110 111 115 116 118 119 120 121 123 124 126 129 130 131 132 133 135 144 146 147 148 **P**8
Primary Contact: Gary A. Meyer, President and Chief Executive Officer
CFO: Warren Forgey, Executive Vice President Fiscal Services and Business Development
CIO: Craig Rice, Director Information
CHR: William Lewis, Vice President Human Resources
Web address: www.schneckmed.org
**Control:** County–Government, nonfederal **Service:** General Medical and Surgical

**Staffed Beds:** 93 **Admissions:** 3830 **Census:** 41 **Outpatient Visits:** 166160 **Births:** 752 **Total Expense ($000):** 108229 **Payroll Expense ($000):** 44794 **Personnel:** 754

## SHELBYVILLE—Shelby County

★ ○ **MAJOR HOSPITAL (150097)**, 150 West Washington Street, Zip 46176–1236; tel. 317/392–3211 **A**9 10 11 **F**3 12 13 15 28 29 30 31 34 35 40 50 57 59 62 63 68 70 73 75 76 77 78 80 81 82 85 89 93 97 107 108 110 111 114 118 119 120 121 123 129 130 132 135 146 147 148 **P**6
Primary Contact: John M. Horner, President and Chief Executive Officer
CFO: Ralph Mercuri, Vice President and Chief Financial Officer
CHR: Nicki Sparling, Manager Human Resources
Web address: www.majorhospital.org
**Control:** City–County, Government, nonfederal **Service:** General Medical and Surgical

**Staffed Beds:** 72 **Admissions:** 2916 **Census:** 27 **Outpatient Visits:** 148407 **Births:** 331 **Total Expense ($000):** 78672 **Payroll Expense ($000):** 32562

## SOUTH BEND—St. Joseph County

☒ △ **MEMORIAL HOSPITAL OF SOUTH BEND (150058)**, 615 North Michigan Street, Zip 46601–1033; tel. 574/647–1000, (Includes MEMORIAL CHILDREN'S HOSPITAL, 615 North Michigan Street, Zip 46601, Mailing Address: 516 North Michigan Street, Zip 46601; tel. 574/647–1000) **A**1 2 3 5 7 9 10 **F**3 7 8 9 13 15 17 18 19 20 22 24 26 29 30 31 35 38 40 43 46 49 50 53 56 59 60 61 64 67 68 70 72 74 75 76 77 78 79 81 82 84 85 86 87 88 89 90 92 93 98 99 102 103 107 108 114 115 116 117 119 121 124 126 129 130 131 132 134 135 146 147 148 **P**8
Primary Contact: Kreg Gruber, President
CFO: Jeff Costello, Chief Financial Officer
CMO: Cheryl Wibbens, M.D., Vice President Medical Staff Affairs
CIO: Steve Huffman, Chief Information Officer
Web address: www.qualityoflife.org
**Control:** Other not–for–profit (including NFP Corporation) **Service:** General Medical and Surgical

**Staffed Beds:** 445 **Admissions:** 20999 **Census:** 250 **Outpatient Visits:** 178010 **Births:** 2815 **Total Expense ($000):** 373686 **Payroll Expense ($000):** 124829 **Personnel:** 2298

## SULLIVAN—Sullivan County

★ **SULLIVAN COUNTY COMMUNITY HOSPITAL (151327)**, 2200 North Section Street, Zip 47882–7523, Mailing Address: P.O. Box 10, Zip 47882–0010; tel. 812/268–4311 **A**9 10 18 **F**3 8 13 15 28 29 32 34 35 40 44 45 47 48 53 56 57 59 61 62 69 70 75 76 77 78 79 81 86 87 93 97 107 110 111 114 127 129 130 131 133 146 147 148 **P**8 **S** QHR, Brentwood, TN
Primary Contact: Michelle Sly–Smith, Chief Executive Officer
CFO: Alan J. Montella, Assistant Administrator Finance
CMO: Gene Bourgasser, M.D., Chief of Staff
CIO: Hap Beckes, Director Information Systems
CHR: Denise Hart, Director Human Resources
Web address: www.schosp.com
**Control:** County–Government, nonfederal **Service:** General Medical and Surgical

**Staffed Beds:** 25 **Admissions:** 1011 **Census:** 8 **Outpatient Visits:** 69022 **Births:** 154 **Total Expense ($000):** 23594 **Payroll Expense ($000):** 9806 **Personnel:** 204

## TELL CITY—Perry County

★ **PERRY COUNTY MEMORIAL HOSPITAL (151322)**, 1 Hospital Road, Zip 47586–2750; tel. 812/547–7011 **A**9 10 18 **F**3 7 11 13 15 28 29 30 31 34 35 38 40 50 56 57 59 62 64 65 68 70 74 75 76 77 78 79 81 86 87 93 102 107 108 110 111 114 118 119 129 130 132 133 135 146 147 **S** Alliant Management Services, Louisville, KY
Primary Contact: Joseph A. Stuber, President and Chief Executive Officer
COO: Becky Elder, Vice President Clinical Services
CMO: Anastacia Lagunzad, M.D., Chief of Staff
CIO: Debbie Kleeman, Manager Information Systems
CHR: Sheila Gaynor, Director Human Resources
Web address: www.pchospital.org
**Control:** County–Government, nonfederal **Service:** General Medical and Surgical

**Staffed Beds:** 25 **Admissions:** 1302 **Census:** 13 **Outpatient Visits:** 75720 **Births:** 76 **Total Expense ($000):** 33745 **Payroll Expense ($000):** 12169 **Personnel:** 271

## TERRE HAUTE—Vigo County

**HAMILTON CENTER (154009)**, 620 Eighth Avenue, Zip 47804–2744; tel. 812/231–8323, (Nonreporting) **A**9 10
Primary Contact: Mel Burks, Chief Executive Officer
COO: Robb Johnson, Director Operations
CFO: Susie Thompson, Executive Director Fiscal Services
CMO: David Hilton, M.D., Medical Director
Web address: www.hamiltoncenter.org
**Control:** State–Government, nonfederal **Service:** Psychiatric

**Staffed Beds:** 16

**IN**

---

**Hospital, Medicare Provider Number, Address, Telephone, Approval, Facility, and Physician Codes, Health Care System**

★ American Hospital Association (AHA) membership
☐ The Joint Commission accreditation
◇ DNV Healthcare Inc. accreditation
○ Healthcare Facilities Accreditation Program
△ Commission on Accreditation of Rehabilitation Facilities (CARF) accreditation

☐ **HARSHA BEHAVIORAL CENTER (154054)**, 1420 East Crossing Boulevard, Zip 47802–5316; tel. 866/644–8880, (Nonreporting) **A**1 9 10
Primary Contact: Roopam Harshawat, Chief Executive Officer
Web address: www.harshacenter.com
**Control:** Corporation, Investor–owned, for–profit **Service:** Psychiatric

Staffed Beds: 36

✠ **TERRE HAUTE REGIONAL HOSPITAL (150046)**, 3901 South Seventh Street, Zip 47802–5709; tel. 812/232–0021 **A**1 2 5 9 10 **F**3 11 13 15 18 20 22 24 26 29 31 34 35 37 40 41 45 46 47 49 57 59 64 65 70 74 76 77 78 79 80 81 82 85 86 89 90 91 92 93 98 102 103 107 108 109 110 111 113 115 119 132 135 144 145 146 147 148 **S** HCA, Nashville, TN
Primary Contact: Mary Ann Conroy, Chief Executive Officer
CMO: Francis Tapia, M.D., President Medical Staff
CIO: Mike Kuckewich, Director Information Systems
Web address: www.regionalhospital.com
**Control:** Corporation, Investor–owned, for–profit **Service:** General Medical and Surgical

Staffed Beds: 208 Admissions: 5857 Census: 73 Outpatient Visits: 50696 Births: 629 Personnel: 645

★ ○ △ **UNION HOSPITAL (150023)**, 1606 North Seventh Street, Zip 47804–2780; tel. 812/238–7000 **A**2 3 5 7 9 10 11 19 **F**3 8 13 15 18 20 22 24 26 28 29 30 31 34 35 36 39 40 45 46 48 49 50 51 53 54 57 59 60 64 68 70 72 73 74 75 76 77 78 79 81 82 85 86 87 89 90 92 93 94 95 96 97 100 107 108 110 111 112 114 115 116 117 118 119 120 121 123 126 127 130 131 132 135 146 147 148 **P**6
Primary Contact: Scott L. Teffeteller, President and Chief Executive Officer
CFO: Wayne Hutson, Chief Financial Officer
CMO: John Bolinger, M.D., Vice President Medical Affairs
CIO: Kym Pfrank, Senior Vice President and Chief Information Officer
CHR: Sally Zuel, Vice President Human Resources and Education
CNO: Rhonda E. Smith, R.N., Vice President Patient Care Services and Chief Nursing Officer
Web address: www.uhhg.org
**Control:** Other not–for–profit (including NFP Corporation) **Service:** General Medical and Surgical

Staffed Beds: 310 Admissions: 16373 Census: 212 Outpatient Visits: 398449 Births: 1721 Total Expense ($000): 382557 Payroll Expense ($000): 116695 Personnel: 1977

### TIPTON—Tipton County

✠ **INDIANA UNIVERSITY HEALTH TIPTON HOSPITAL (151311)**, 1000 South Main Street, Zip 46072–9799; tel. 765/675–8500 **A**1 2 9 10 18 **F**3 11 15 18 28 29 31 34 35 40 45 46 47 48 53 57 58 59 68 70 74 75 77 78 79 81 82 85 86 87 93 94 107 108 110 111 115 119 125 129 130 131 132 133 134 135 146 147 148 **P**8 **S** Indiana University Health, Indianapolis, IN
Primary Contact: Michael Harlowe, President and Chief Executive Officer
CFO: Vern J. Schmaltz, Vice President Finance
Web address: www.iuhealth.org
**Control:** Other not–for–profit (including NFP Corporation) **Service:** General Medical and Surgical

Staffed Beds: 25 Admissions: 1271 Census: 15 Outpatient Visits: 46797 Births: 1 Total Expense ($000): 40628 Payroll Expense ($000): 18721 Personnel: 316

**TIPTON HOSPITAL** See Indiana University Health Tipton Hospital

### VALPARAISO—Porter County

✠ **PORTER REGIONAL HOSPITAL (150035)**, (Formerly Porter–Valparaiso Hospital Campus), 814 La Porte Avenue, Zip 46383–5898; tel. 219/263–4600, (Nonreporting) **A**1 9 10 **S** Community Health Systems, Inc., Franklin, TN
Primary Contact: Jonathan Nalli, Chief Executive Officer
COO: Brian Sinotte, Chief Operating Officer
CFO: Cheryl A. Harmon, Chief Financial Officer
CMO: Ramireddy K. Tummuru, M.D., Chief Medical Officer
CHR: Angie Hampton, Director Human Resources
Web address: www.porterhealth.org
**Control:** Corporation, Investor–owned, for–profit **Service:** General Medical and Surgical

Staffed Beds: 276

**PORTER–STARKE SERVICES (154052)**, 601 Wall Street, Zip 46383–2512; tel. 219/531–3500 **A**10 **F**5 29 66 68 98 99 101 102 103 104 **P**6
Primary Contact: Rocco Schiralli, President/Chief Executive Officer
CFO: Mary Idstein, Chief Financial Officer
CMO: Anand Popli, Medical Director
Web address: www.porterstarke.org
**Control:** Other not–for–profit (including NFP Corporation) **Service:** Psychiatric

Staffed Beds: 16 Admissions: 699 Census: 8 Outpatient Visits: 81958 Births: 0 Total Expense ($000): 14027 Payroll Expense ($000): 8211 Personnel: 194

### VINCENNES—Knox County

✠ △ **GOOD SAMARITAN HOSPITAL (150042)**, 520 South Seventh Street, Zip 47591–1038; tel. 812/882–5220 **A**1 2 7 9 10 19 **F**3 5 8 11 13 15 17 18 20 22 28 29 30 31 32 34 35 38 40 45 46 47 48 49 50 53 54 56 57 59 60 63 64 65 66 67 68 70 74 75 76 77 78 79 81 82 85 87 89 90 92 93 96 97 98 99 100 101 102 103 104 106 107 108 110 111 115 118 119 121 123 129 130 131 132 134 135 143 144 145 146 147 **P**6
Primary Contact: Robert D. McLin, President and Chief Executive Officer
COO: Gerald E. Waldroup, Senior Vice President
CFO: Jerry Stump, Chief Financial Officer
CMO: Charles C. Hedde, M.D., Vice President Medical Affairs
CIO: Charles Christian, Chief Information Officer and Director Information Systems
CHR: Dean Wagoner, Director Human Resources
Web address: www.gshvin.org/goodsamaritan
**Control:** County–Government, nonfederal **Service:** General Medical and Surgical

Staffed Beds: 191 Admissions: 7520 Census: 91 Outpatient Visits: 458056 Births: 526 Total Expense ($000): 178172 Payroll Expense ($000): 83023 Personnel: 1655

### WABASH—Wabash County

✠ **WABASH COUNTY HOSPITAL (151310)**, 710 North East Street, Zip 46992–1924, Mailing Address: P.O. Box 548, Zip 46992–0548; tel. 260/563–3131, (Total facility includes 25 beds in nursing home–type unit) **A**1 9 10 18 **F**3 11 15 32 34 35 53 57 58 59 62 63 64 65 68 69 75 77 80 81 85 86 87 93 97 107 108 111 114 119 128 130 131 132 133 146 147 **S** Alliant Management Services, Louisville, KY
Primary Contact: Marilyn J. Custer–Mitchell, President and Chief Executive Officer
CFO: Jane Bissel, Chief Financial Officer
CMO: Dean Gifford, M.D., Chief of Staff
CIO: David Brinson, Director Information Technology
CHR: Kimberly R. Shininger, Director Human Resources
CNO: Sonia R. Strevy, Chief Nursing Officer
Web address: www.wchospital.com
**Control:** County–Government, nonfederal **Service:** General Medical and Surgical

Staffed Beds: 50 Admissions: 795 Census: 18 Outpatient Visits: 48076 Births: 0 Total Expense ($000): 39394 Payroll Expense ($000): 15372 Personnel: 292

### WARSAW—Kosciusko County

✠ **KOSCIUSKO COMMUNITY HOSPITAL (150133)**, 2101 East Dubois Drive, Zip 46580–3288; tel. 574/267–3200 **A**1 2 9 10 19 **F**3 12 13 15 28 29 30 31 32 34 35 40 42 44 50 51 53 57 58 59 64 65 68 70 74 75 76 77 78 79 81 82 85 86 89 90 92 93 107 108 110 111 115 116 117 118 119 120 121 129 130 131 132 144 146 147 148 **P**6 **S** Community Health Systems, Inc., Franklin, TN
Primary Contact: Stephen R. Miller, Chief Executive Officer
CFO: Douglas J. BeMent, Chief Financial Officer
CFO: Finny Mathew, Chief Operating Officer
CMO: Patrick Silveus, M.D., Medical Director
CIO: Tammy Lukens, Director Information
CHR: Joe Jarboe, Director Human Resources
CNO: Kim Finch, Chief Nursing Officer
Web address: www.kch.com
**Control:** Corporation, Investor–owned, for–profit **Service:** General Medical and Surgical

Staffed Beds: 72 Admissions: 3775 Census: 32 Outpatient Visits: 106331 Births: 709 Total Expense ($000): 80317 Payroll Expense ($000): 23962 Personnel: 473

★ **OTIS R BOWEN CENTER FOR HUMAN SERVICES (154014)**, 850 North Harrison Street, Zip 46580–3163; tel. 574/267–7169 **A**9 10 **F**4 5 29 34 35 38 50 86 87 98 99 100 101 102 103 104 106 127 130 132 134 135 143 **P**1
Primary Contact: Kurt Carlson, Chief Executive Officer
Web address: www.bowencenter.org
**Control:** Other not–for–profit (including NFP Corporation) **Service:** Psychiatric

Staffed Beds: 16 Admissions: 876 Census: 9 Outpatient Visits: 411340 Births: 0 Total Expense ($000): 31873 Payroll Expense ($000): 19329 Personnel: 666

### WASHINGTON—Daviess County

✠ △ **DAVIESS COMMUNITY HOSPITAL (150061)**, 1314 East Walnut Street, Zip 47501–2860, Mailing Address: P.O. Box 760, Zip 47501–0760; tel. 812/254–2760, (Nonreporting) **A**1 7 9 10 **S** QHR, Brentwood, TN
Primary Contact: David Bixler, Chief Executive Officer
CMO: Michael Baker, D.O., Chief of Staff
CIO: Richard Meinhart, Manager Information Systems
CHR: Marilyn Richard, Director Human Resources
Web address: www.dchosp.org
**Control:** County–Government, nonfederal **Service:** General Medical and Surgical

Staffed Beds: 80

*Many Facility Codes have changed. Please refer to the AHA Guide Code Chart.* © 2013 AHA Guide

## WEST LAFAYETTE—Tippecanoe County

★ **RIVER BEND HOSPITAL (154005)**, 2900 North River Road, Zip 47906–3744;
tel. 765/463–2555 **A**9 10 **F**98 102 103
Primary Contact: John R. Walling, President
COO: Tom Gillian, Chief Operating Officer
CFO: Jeff Nagy, Chief Financial Officer
CMO: Richard Rahdert, M.D., Medical Director
CIO: Craig Anderson, Director Management Information Systems
CHR: Jan Shaw, Director Personnel
CNO: Megan Gibson, Nurse Manager
Web address: www.nchsi.com/riverbendhospital.cfm
**Control:** Other not–for–profit (including NFP Corporation) **Service:** Psychiatric

**Staffed Beds:** 16 **Admissions:** 820 **Census:** 12 **Births:** 0

**WABASH VALLEY HOSPITAL** See River Bend Hospital

## WILLIAMSPORT—Warren County

⊠ **ST. VINCENT WILLIAMSPORT HOSPITAL (151307)**, 412 North Monroe
Street, Zip 47993–1049; tel. 765/762–4000, (Nonreporting) **A**1 9 10 18
**S** Ascension Health, Saint Louis, MO
Primary Contact: Jane Craigin, Chief Executive Officer
CFO: Janet Merritt, Chief Financial Officer
Web address: www.stvincent.org
**Control:** Other not–for–profit (including NFP Corporation) **Service:** General
Medical and Surgical

**Staffed Beds:** 16

## WINAMAC—Pulaski County

★ **PULASKI MEMORIAL HOSPITAL (151305)**, 616 East 13th Street,
Zip 46996–1117, Mailing Address: P.O. Box 279, Zip 46996–0279;
tel. 574/946–2100 **A**9 10 18 **F**1 4 11 13 15 18 28 29 30 31 34 35 40 43 45
50 53 57 59 62 63 64 65 67 68 73 75 76 77 78 79 80 81 82 85 86 87 89
90 91 93 96 97 98 107 110 114 119 128 130 131 132 133 135 146 **P**6
Primary Contact: Thomas Barry, Chief Executive Officer
CFO: Gregg Malott, Chief Financial Officer
CMO: Rex Allman, M.D., President Medical Staff
CIO: Jeff Boer, Director Information Technology
CHR: Mark Fenn, Director Human Resources
CNO: Linda Webb, R.N., Chief Nursing Executive
Web address: www.pmhnet.com
**Control:** County–Government, nonfederal **Service:** General Medical and Surgical

**Staffed Beds:** 25 **Admissions:** 625 **Census:** 6 **Outpatient Visits:** 25169
**Births:** 114 **Total Expense ($000):** 20280 **Payroll Expense ($000):** 8643
**Personnel:** 185

## WINCHESTER—Randolph County

⊠ **ST. VINCENT RANDOLPH HOSPITAL (151301)**, 473 Greenville Avenue,
Zip 47394–9436, Mailing Address: P.O. Box 407, Zip 47394–0407;
tel. 765/584–0004 **A**1 9 10 18 **F**3 11 13 15 28 29 30 34 35 40 45 48 50 57
59 64 65 68 75 76 77 79 81 85 86 87 89 93 107 110 111 114 119 124 129
130 131 132 133 135 146 147 148 **S** Ascension Health, Saint Louis, MO
Primary Contact: Francis G. Albarano, Administrator
CFO: John Arthur, Chief Financial Officer
CMO: Daniel Wegg, M.D., Medical Director
CHR: Richard Ross Brodhead, Director Human Resources
CNO: Carla Fouse, Chief Nursing Officer
Web address: www.stvincent.org
**Control:** Other not–for–profit (including NFP Corporation) **Service:** General
Medical and Surgical

**Staffed Beds:** 16 **Admissions:** 1142 **Census:** 10 **Outpatient Visits:** 49906
**Births:** 237 **Total Expense ($000):** 25215 **Payroll Expense ($000):** 10894
**Personnel:** 198

---

**Hospital, Medicare Provider Number, Address, Telephone, Approval, Facility, and Physician Codes, Health Care System**

★ American Hospital Association (AHA) membership
□ The Joint Commission accreditation
◇ DNV Healthcare Inc. accreditation
○ Healthcare Facilities Accreditation Program
△ Commission on Accreditation of Rehabilitation Facilities (CARF) accreditation

IN

# IOWA

## ALBIA—Monroe County

★ **MONROE COUNTY HOSPITAL (161342)**, 6580 165th Street,
Zip 52531–8793; tel. 641/932–2134 **A**9 10 18 **F**1 4 7 8 11 15 16 17 28 29
31 35 40 45 57 59 63 64 67 70 72 73 80 81 85 88 89 90 93 98 107 115
119 127 128 133 135 **P**5 6
Primary Contact: Sara Drobnich, Interim Chief Executive Officer
Web address: www.mchalbia.com
**Control:** County–Government, nonfederal **Service:** General Medical and Surgical

> **Staffed Beds:** 25 **Admissions:** 454 **Census:** 8 **Outpatient Visits:** 50410
> **Births:** 0 **Total Expense ($000):** 15873 **Payroll Expense ($000):** 7033
> **Personnel:** 132

## ALGONA—Kossuth County

★ **KOSSUTH REGIONAL HEALTH CENTER (161353)**, 1515 South Phillips Street,
Zip 50511–3649; tel. 515/295–2451 **A**9 10 18 **F**11 13 15 17 28 29 30 31 32
34 35 36 40 41 43 50 56 57 59 62 63 64 65 67 68 70 75 76 77 78 81 82
84 86 87 89 90 92 93 97 107 114 119 127 128 129 130 131 132 133 135
146 147 **P**8 **S** Trinity Health, Livonia, MI
Primary Contact: Scott A. Curtis, Administrator and Chief Executive Officer
CFO: Dan Myers, Controller
CMO: Michael Lampe, M.D., Chief of Staff
CIO: Nancy Erickson, Administrator Information Systems
CHR: Paula Seely, Manager Human Resources
CNO: Darlene M. Elbert, R.N., Assistant Administrator and Chief Nursing Officer
Web address: www.krhc.com
**Control:** County–Government, nonfederal **Service:** General Medical and Surgical

> **Staffed Beds:** 23 **Admissions:** 808 **Census:** 10 **Outpatient Visits:** 28031
> **Births:** 87 **Total Expense ($000):** 29456 **Payroll Expense ($000):** 9430
> **Personnel:** 177

## AMES—Story County

☒ **MARY GREELEY MEDICAL CENTER (160030)**, 1111 Duff Avenue,
Zip 50010–5745; tel. 515/239–2011, (Total facility includes 11 beds in nursing
home–type unit) **A**1 2 9 10 19 **F**3 7 8 11 12 13 15 17 18 20 22 26 28 29 30
31 34 35 36 37 38 40 43 45 46 49 50 53 55 56 57 58 59 61 62 63 64 65
68 69 70 72 74 75 76 77 78 79 81 82 85 86 89 90 92 93 96 98 99 100
101 102 103 104 107 108 110 111 114 115 118 119 121 123 124 126 128
129 130 131 132 135 145 146 148
Primary Contact: Brian Dieter, President and Chief Executive Officer
CFO: Mike Tretina, Vice President and Chief Financial Officer
CIO: JaNelle Anderson, Director
CHR: Betsy V. Schoeller, Director Human Resources and Education
Web address: www.mgmc.org
**Control:** City–Government, nonfederal **Service:** General Medical and Surgical

> **Staffed Beds:** 192 **Admissions:** 9617 **Census:** 113 **Outpatient Visits:**
> 163479 **Births:** 1030 **Total Expense ($000):** 155375 **Payroll Expense**
> **($000):** 58919 **Personnel:** 1076

## ANAMOSA—Jones County

★ **JONES REGIONAL MEDICAL CENTER (161306)**, 1795 Highway 64 East,
Zip 52205–2112; tel. 319/462–6131 **A**9 10 18 **F**3 7 11 12 15 28 29 31 34
35 38 40 43 45 50 56 57 59 64 68 71 75 81 82 84 85 87 91 93 96 97 99
100 101 102 103 104 107 110 111 114 118 119 130 132 133 135 145 146
148 **P**4 **S** UnityPoint Health, West Des Moines, IA
Primary Contact: Eric Briesemeister, Chief Executive Officer
CFO: Rachel Von Behren, Director Financial Services
CMO: Victor Salas, M.D., President Medical Staff
CHR: Donna Condry, Director Human Resources
Web address: www.jonesregional.org
**Control:** Other not–for–profit (including NFP Corporation) **Service:** General
Medical and Surgical

> **Staffed Beds:** 22 **Admissions:** 584 **Census:** 8 **Outpatient Visits:** 57426
> **Births:** 0 **Total Expense ($000):** 17023 **Payroll Expense ($000):** 5928
> **Personnel:** 129

## ATLANTIC—Cass County

★ **CASS COUNTY MEMORIAL HOSPITAL (161376)**, 1501 East Tenth Street,
Zip 50022–1997; tel. 712/243–3250 **A**9 10 18 **F**11 13 15 28 29 40 57 59 64
69 70 75 76 77 78 81 82 93 98 99 101 102 103 104 105 107 108 111 119
124 127 129 130 132 133 135 147 148 **P**8
Primary Contact: Patricia A. Markham, Administrator and Chief Executive Officer
CFO: Stephen Lewis, Assistant Administrator and Chief Financial Officer
CMO: Chad McCance, M.D., Chief of Staff
CIO: Steve Stark, Chief Information Officer
CHR: Donald D. Johnson, Assistant Administrator Human Resources
CNO: Linda Hemminger, MSN, Assistant Administrator Clinical Services
Web address: www.casshealth.org
**Control:** County–Government, nonfederal **Service:** General Medical and Surgical

> **Staffed Beds:** 33 **Admissions:** 1069 **Census:** 13 **Outpatient Visits:** 95387
> **Births:** 127 **Total Expense ($000):** 33727 **Payroll Expense ($000):** 13976
> **Personnel:** 316

## AUDUBON—Audubon County

**AUDUBON COUNTY MEMORIAL HOSPITAL (161330)**, 515 Pacific Street,
Zip 50025–1056; tel. 712/563–2611 **A**9 10 18 **F**3 11 15 28 31 40 43 45 53
59 64 67 78 79 81 85 90 93 98 104 110 119 127 128 133 135
Primary Contact: Thomas G. Smith, Administrator and Chief Executive Officer
CFO: Karen McGuire, Chief Financial Officer
CMO: James Brokke, M.D., Chief of Staff
CIO: Kelli Burgin, Director Information Technology
Web address: www.acmhhosp.org
**Control:** County–Government, nonfederal **Service:** General Medical and Surgical

> **Staffed Beds:** 25 **Admissions:** 145 **Census:** 2 **Outpatient Visits:** 15390
> **Births:** 0 **Total Expense ($000):** 10063 **Payroll Expense ($000):** 4158
> **Personnel:** 87

## BELMOND—Wright County

★ **IOWA SPECIALTY HOSPITAL–BELMOND (161301)**, 403 First Street S.E.,
Zip 50421–1201; tel. 641/444–3223 **A**9 10 18 **F**3 7 11 15 28 29 32 34 35
40 43 45 46 50 53 56 57 59 62 63 64 65 67 68 75 77 79 81 82 85 87 89
92 93 96 97 107 110 111 119 128 129 131 133 135 146 148 **P**6 **S** Iowa
Specialty Hospitals, Clarion, IA
Primary Contact: Nancy Gabrielson, Administrator and Chief Executive Officer
CFO: Greg Polzin, Chief Financial Officer
CMO: Charles B. Brindle, M.D., Chief Medical Staff
CHR: Reagan Swisher, Director Human Resources
Web address: www.belmondmedicalcenter.com
**Control:** City–Government, nonfederal **Service:** General Medical and Surgical

> **Staffed Beds:** 22 **Admissions:** 466 **Census:** 6 **Outpatient Visits:** 25938
> **Births:** 0 **Total Expense ($000):** 13623 **Payroll Expense ($000):** 3859
> **Personnel:** 97

## BETTENDORF—Scott County

☒ **TRINITY BETTENDORF (160104)**, 4500 Utica Ridge Road, Zip 52722–1626;
tel. 563/742–5000 **A**1 9 10 13 **F**3 7 11 13 15 18 20 22 26 29 30 34 35 37
40 44 45 46 50 57 58 59 63 64 70 74 75 76 79 81 82 84 85 86 87 93 96
97 107 108 110 114 119 129 130 132 135 146 147 148 **P**6 8 **S** UnityPoint
Health, West Des Moines, IA
Primary Contact: Richard A. Seidler, FACHE, President and Chief Executive Officer
COO: Mykl Garrett, Executive Vice President and Chief Operating Officer
CFO: Greg Pagliuzza, Chief Financial Officer
CMO: Paul McLoone, M.D., Chief Medical Officer
CHR: Jeffery Stolze, Vice President Human Resources
Web address: www.trinityqc.com
**Control:** Other not–for–profit (including NFP Corporation) **Service:** General
Medical and Surgical

> **Staffed Beds:** 76 **Admissions:** 3494 **Census:** 28 **Outpatient Visits:** 42625
> **Births:** 593 **Total Expense ($000):** 61887 **Payroll Expense ($000):** 18755
> **Personnel:** 228

## BLOOMFIELD—Davis County

★ **DAVIS COUNTY HOSPITAL (161327)**, 509 North Madison Street, Zip 52537–1271; tel. 641/664–2145, (Total facility includes 32 beds in nursing home–type unit) **A**9 10 18 **F**3 7 11 13 15 29 34 35 40 43 44 45 50 57 59 61 62 63 64 65 67 68 69 75 76 78 79 81 85 86 87 89 97 107 111 119 130 132 133 146 **P**6
Primary Contact: Deborah L. Herzberg, R.N., MS, FACHE, Chief Executive Officer
COO: Debbie Scott, Chief Operating Officer
CMO: Sean Brodale, D.O., Chief Medical Staff
CHR: Pam Young, Human Resources Leader
CNO: Ronda Reimer, R.N., Chief Nursing Officer
Web address: www.daviscountyhospital.org
**Control:** County–Government, nonfederal **Service:** General Medical and Surgical

**Staffed Beds:** 57 **Admissions:** 493 **Census:** 35 **Outpatient Visits:** 22219 **Births:** 58 **Total Expense ($000):** 20998 **Payroll Expense ($000):** 7447 **Personnel:** 162

## BOONE—Boone County

★ **BOONE COUNTY HOSPITAL (161372)**, 1015 Union Street, Zip 50036–4821; tel. 515/432–3140 **A**9 10 18 **F**2 7 11 13 15 28 30 31 34 35 40 43 50 57 59 62 64 65 69 70 75 76 77 78 79 81 85 91 93 97 107 111 114 119 128 132 133 145 146 147 148 **P**6 **S** QHR, Brentwood, TN
Primary Contact: Joseph S. Smith, Chief Executive Officer
CFO: David Mellett, Chief Financial Officer
CMO: Scott Thiel, M.D., Chief of Staff
CIO: Matthew Sabus, Director Information Systems
CHR: Kim K. Schwartz, Assistant Administrator of Human Resources and Physician Services
Web address: www.boonehospital.com
**Control:** County–Government, nonfederal **Service:** General Medical and Surgical

**Staffed Beds:** 25 **Admissions:** 1457 **Census:** 15 **Outpatient Visits:** 69500 **Births:** 139 **Total Expense ($000):** 43309 **Payroll Expense ($000):** 16504 **Personnel:** 321

## BRITT—Hancock County

★ **HANCOCK COUNTY HEALTH SYSTEM (161307)**, (Formerly Hancock County Memorial Hospital), 532 First Street N.W., Zip 50423–1227; tel. 641/843–5000 **A**9 10 18 **F**15 28 29 31 34 35 36 40 43 45 46 53 56 57 59 64 65 75 77 81 82 85 93 97 107 114 119 129 130 131 132 133 146 148 **P**1 **S** Trinity Health, Livonia, MI
Primary Contact: Vance Jackson, FACHE, Administrator and Chief Executive Officer
CFO: Julie Damm, Chief Financial Officer
CMO: Catherine Butler, M.D., Chief Medical Staff
CIO: Julie Damm, Chief Financial Officer
CHR: Denise Jakoubeck, Director Human Resources
Web address: www.trusthchs.com/hancock–county–health–system
**Control:** County–Government, nonfederal **Service:** General Medical and Surgical

**Staffed Beds:** 25 **Admissions:** 547 **Census:** 9 **Outpatient Visits:** 18092 **Births:** 0 **Total Expense ($000):** 14322 **Payroll Expense ($000):** 5182 **Personnel:** 147

## CARROLL—Carroll County

★ **ST. ANTHONY REGIONAL HOSPITAL (160005)**, 311 South Clark Street, Zip 51401–3038, Mailing Address: P.O. Box 628, Zip 51401–0628; tel. 712/792–3581, (Total facility includes 79 beds in nursing home–type unit) **A**9 10 19 20 **F**6 11 13 15 28 29 30 31 34 35 37 38 39 40 43 44 45 46 50 51 56 57 59 60 61 62 63 64 65 67 68 69 70 74 75 76 77 78 79 81 82 84 85 86 87 89 93 97 98 99 100 101 102 103 104 107 108 110 111 115 118 119 125 127 129 130 131 132 133 134 135 145 146 147 148 **P**6
Primary Contact: Edward H. Smith, Jr., President and Chief Executive Officer
CFO: John Munson, Vice President and Chief Financial Officer
CMO: Tracey Wellendorf, M.D., Chief of Staff
CIO: Randy Eischeid, Director Information Systems
CHR: Gina Ramaekers, Director Human Resources
Web address: www.stanthonyhospital.org
**Control:** Church–operated, Nongovernment, not–for profit **Service:** General Medical and Surgical

**Staffed Beds:** 155 **Admissions:** 2346 **Census:** 107 **Outpatient Visits:** 98537 **Births:** 398 **Total Expense ($000):** 59996 **Payroll Expense ($000):** 25018 **Personnel:** 535

## CEDAR FALLS—Black Hawk County

☒ **SARTORI MEMORIAL HOSPITAL (160040)**, 515 College Street, Zip 50613–2500; tel. 319/268–3000 **A**1 9 10 **F**3 7 8 11 12 15 29 30 35 40 43 44 46 53 57 59 64 68 70 75 77 79 81 91 93 97 98 103 107 110 111 119 130 131 132 146 **P**1 6 **S** Wheaton Franciscan Healthcare, Wheaton, IL
Primary Contact: Rose Fowler, MS, Administrator
CFO: Michele Panicucci, Chief Financial Officer
CMO: Paul Franke, M.D., Vice President Medical Affairs
CHR: Vicki L. Parsons, Regional Vice President Human Resources
Web address: www.wheatoniowa.org
**Control:** Church–operated, Nongovernment, not–for profit **Service:** General Medical and Surgical

**Staffed Beds:** 50 **Admissions:** 1399 **Census:** 21 **Outpatient Visits:** 42400 **Births:** 0 **Total Expense ($000):** 29209 **Payroll Expense ($000):** 10593 **Personnel:** 179

## CEDAR RAPIDS—Linn County

☐ **CONTINUING CARE HOSPITAL AT ST. LUKE'S (162002)**, 1026 A Avenue N.E., 6th Floor, Zip 52402–5036; tel. 319/369–8142 **A**1 10 **F**1 3 29 30 75 84 85 148 **S** Dubuis Health System, Houston, TX
Primary Contact: Elly Steffen, Chief Executive Officer and Administrator
CNO: Mary Beth Keuter, Director Patient Care
Web address: www.dubuis.org/ContinuingCareHospitalatStLukes
**Control:** Church–operated, Nongovernment, not–for profit **Service:** Long–Term Acute Care hospital

**Staffed Beds:** 16 **Admissions:** 158 **Census:** 12 **Outpatient Visits:** 0 **Births:** 0 **Total Expense ($000):** 7262 **Payroll Expense ($000):** 2282 **Personnel:** 50

☒ **MERCY MEDICAL CENTER–CEDAR RAPIDS (160079)**, (Formerly Mercy Medical Center), 701 Tenth Street S.E., Zip 52403–1292; tel. 319/398–6011, (Total facility includes 76 beds in nursing home–type unit) **A**1 2 3 5 9 10 **F**3 5 11 13 15 17 18 20 22 26 28 29 30 31 32 34 35 38 40 43 44 49 50 53 54 55 56 57 58 59 60 61 62 63 64 65 67 68 70 71 72 74 75 76 77 78 79 81 82 84 85 86 87 88 89 90 91 92 93 94 98 99 100 101 102 103 104 107 108 109 110 114 115 116 117 118 119 120 121 123 124 126 128 130 131 132 135 143 145 146 147 148 **P**7 8
Primary Contact: Timothy L. Charles, President and Chief Executive Officer
COO: Michael D. Trachta, FACHE, Executive Vice President and Chief Operating Officer
CFO: Philip Peterson, Executive Vice President and Chief Financial Officer
CMO: Mark Valliere, M.D., Senior Vice President Medical Affairs and Chief Medical Officer
CIO: Jeff Cash, Senior Vice President and Chief Information Officer
Web address: www.mercycare.org
**Control:** Church–operated, Nongovernment, not–for profit **Service:** General Medical and Surgical

**Staffed Beds:** 314 **Admissions:** 11907 **Census:** 190 **Outpatient Visits:** 237737 **Births:** 710 **Total Expense ($000):** 251124 **Payroll Expense ($000):** 93937 **Personnel:** 2090

**ST. LUKE'S HOSPITAL** See UnityPoint Health St. Luke's

☒ △ **UNITYPOINT HEALTH ST. LUKE'S (160045)**, (Formerly St. Luke's Hospital), 1026 A Avenue N.E., Zip 52402–3026, Mailing Address: P.O. Box 3026, Zip 52406–3026; tel. 319/369–7211 **A**1 2 3 5 7 9 10 **F**3 5 8 11 12 13 14 15 17 18 19 20 22 24 26 28 29 30 31 32 34 35 36 37 39 40 43 45 46 49 50 54 55 56 57 59 60 61 63 64 65 66 70 72 74 75 76 77 78 79 81 82 84 85 86 87 88 89 90 92 93 95 96 98 99 100 101 103 104 105 107 108 110 111 114 115 118 119 121 126 130 131 132 134 135 145 146 147 148 **P**4 6 **S** UnityPoint Health, West Des Moines, IA
Primary Contact: Theodore E. Townsend, FACHE, President and Chief Executive Officer
CFO: Milton E. Aunan, II, CPA, Vice President and Chief Financial Officer
CMO: Charles W. Schauberger, M.D., Vice President and Chief Medical Officer
CHR: Sue Slattery, Director Human Resources
Web address: www.crstlukes.org
**Control:** Other not–for–profit (including NFP Corporation) **Service:** General Medical and Surgical

**Staffed Beds:** 340 **Admissions:** 16506 **Census:** 214 **Outpatient Visits:** 599160 **Births:** 2577 **Total Expense ($000):** 314406 **Payroll Expense ($000):** 122908 **Personnel:** 2423

**IA**

| Hospital, Medicare Provider Number, Address, Telephone, Approval, Facility, and Physician Codes, Health Care System |
|---|
| ★ American Hospital Association (AHA) membership ○ Healthcare Facilities Accreditation Program ☐ The Joint Commission accreditation ◇ DNV Healthcare Inc. accreditation △ Commission on Accreditation of Rehabilitation Facilities (CARF) accreditation |

## CENTERVILLE—Appanoose County

★ **MERCY MEDICAL CENTER–CENTERVILLE (161377)**, 1 St. Joseph's Drive, Zip 52544–8055; tel. 641/437–4111, (Total facility includes 20 beds in nursing home–type unit) **A**9 10 18 **F**1 3 4 8 11 13 15 16 17 28 29 30 31 34 40 45 46 50 51 54 57 59 60 64 67 70 72 73 75 76 77 78 79 80 81 85 86 87 88 89 90 93 97 98 107 110 111 113 115 117 119 127 128 129 130 132 133 135 **P**6 **S** Catholic Health Initiatives, Englewood, CO
Primary Contact: Clinton J. Christianson, FACHE, President
COO: Lori Rathbun, Vice President Operations
CFO: Lori Rathbun, Vice President Operations
CIO: Ann Young, Vice President Community and Staff Relations
CHR: Tonya Clawson, Manager Human Resources
CNO: Sherri L. Doggett, Vice President Patient Services
Web address: www.mercycenterville.org
**Control:** Church–operated, Nongovernment, not–for profit **Service:** General Medical and Surgical

**Staffed Beds:** 45 **Admissions:** 927 **Census:** 29 **Outpatient Visits:** 89111 **Births:** 81 **Total Expense ($000):** 22698 **Payroll Expense ($000):** 9890 **Personnel:** 184

## CHARITON—Lucas County

★ **LUCAS COUNTY HEALTH CENTER (161341)**, 1200 North Seventh Street, Zip 50049–1258; tel. 641/774–3000 **A**9 10 18 **F**3 5 7 13 15 28 29 31 34 38 40 41 43 44 45 47 50 59 64 68 70 75 76 77 81 86 87 89 93 107 115 119 127 128 130 131 132 133 143 145 146 148
Primary Contact: Veronica Fuhs, Chief Executive Officer
CFO: Larry Brown, Chief Financial Officer
CMO: Philip Sundquist, M.D., Chief Medical Staff
CIO: Brett Grinde, Network Manager
CHR: Lana Kuball, Director Administrative Services
CNO: JoBeth Lawless, Director of Nursing, Nursing Services and Director Emergency Management Services
Web address: www.lchcia.com
**Control:** County–Government, nonfederal **Service:** General Medical and Surgical

**Staffed Beds:** 25 **Admissions:** 423 **Census:** 4 **Outpatient Visits:** 17486 **Births:** 55 **Total Expense ($000):** 17701 **Payroll Expense ($000):** 8348 **Personnel:** 200

## CHARLES CITY—Floyd County

**FLOYD COUNTY MEDICAL CENTER (161347)**, 800 Eleventh Street, Zip 50616–3499; tel. 641/228–6830 **A**9 10 18 **F**3 11 13 15 28 29 31 34 35 40 45 48 57 59 64 69 75 76 79 81 85 89 91 93 97 107 115 119 127 130 132 133 146 148 **S** Mayo Clinic Health System, Rochester, MN
Primary Contact: Bill D. Faust, Administrator
CFO: Ron James, Chief Financial Officer
CHR: Don Nosbisch, Director Human Resources
Web address: www.fcmc.us.com/
**Control:** County–Government, nonfederal **Service:** General Medical and Surgical

**Staffed Beds:** 25 **Admissions:** 1025 **Census:** 12 **Outpatient Visits:** 54087 **Births:** 99 **Total Expense ($000):** 22208 **Payroll Expense ($000):** 8275 **Personnel:** 167

## CHEROKEE—Cherokee County

★ **CHEROKEE REGIONAL MEDICAL CENTER (161362)**, 300 Sioux Valley Drive, Zip 51012–1205; tel. 712/225–5101 **A**9 10 18 **F**7 11 13 15 17 28 29 34 35 40 43 45 53 56 57 59 62 63 64 65 67 68 69 75 76 77 78 81 84 86 87 89 93 96 97 107 111 114 117 119 125 127 128 129 130 131 132 133 135 146 147 148 **P**6
Primary Contact: John M. Comstock, Chief Executive Officer
CFO: Joan Bierman, Vice President Finance
Web address: www.cherokeermc.org
**Control:** Other not–for–profit (including NFP Corporation) **Service:** General Medical and Surgical

**Staffed Beds:** 25 **Admissions:** 1136 **Census:** 12 **Outpatient Visits:** 43963 **Births:** 145 **Total Expense ($000):** 19381 **Payroll Expense ($000):** 8836 **Personnel:** 182

☐ **MENTAL HEALTH INSTITUTE (164002)**, 1251 West Cedar Loop, Zip 51012–1599; tel. 712/225–2594 **A**1 9 10 **F**3 98 99 100 101 102 104 130 **P**6
Primary Contact: Daniel Gillette, M.D., Clinical Director
CFO: Tony Morris, Business Manager
CMO: Daniel Gillette, M.D., Clinical Director
CHR: Mary Ann Hanson, Director Personnel
Web address: www.dhs.state.ia.us
**Control:** State–Government, nonfederal **Service:** Psychiatric

**Staffed Beds:** 37 **Admissions:** 446 **Census:** 29 **Outpatient Visits:** 37 **Births:** 0 **Total Expense ($000):** 13030 **Payroll Expense ($000):** 8832 **Personnel:** 173

## CLARINDA—Page County

★ **CLARINDA REGIONAL HEALTH CENTER (161352)**, 220 Essie Davison Drive, Zip 51632–2915, Mailing Address: P.O. Box 217, Zip 51632–0217; tel. 712/542–2176 **A**9 10 18 **F**3 7 11 15 28 29 31 34 36 40 43 50 57 59 64 65 66 69 74 75 77 78 79 81 85 86 87 93 97 107 110 111 114 118 119 124 127 128 129 130 132 133 135 143 146 148 **P**6
Primary Contact: Christopher R. Stipe, FACHE, Chief Executive Officer
COO: Elaine Otte, Chief Operating Officer
CFO: Melissa Walter, Chief Financial Officer
CHR: Tammie Driftmier, PHR, Director Human Resources
Web address: www.clarindahealth.com
**Control:** City–Government, nonfederal **Service:** General Medical and Surgical

**Staffed Beds:** 25 **Admissions:** 516 **Census:** 4 **Outpatient Visits:** 55969 **Births:** 0 **Total Expense ($000):** 23472 **Payroll Expense ($000):** 9866 **Personnel:** 228

**MENTAL HEALTH INSTITUTE (164005)**, 1800 North 16Th Street, Zip 51632–1101; tel. 712/542–2161, (Total facility includes 20 beds in nursing home–type unit) **A**9 10 **F**67 98 101 103 130 146 **P**6
Primary Contact: Mark Lund, Superintendent
COO: Mark Lund, Superintendent
CFO: Roger Stirle, Business Manager
CMO: Teresa Rosales, M.D., Clinical Director
CIO: Jeri Nielsen, Compliance Officer
CHR: Anna Fengel, Personnel Assistant
Web address: www.dhs.state.ia.us/
**Control:** State–Government, nonfederal **Service:** Psychiatric

**Staffed Beds:** 35 **Admissions:** 207 **Census:** 32 **Outpatient Visits:** 0 **Births:** 0 **Personnel:** 89

## CLARION—Wright County

★ **IOWA SPECIALTY HOSPITAL–CLARION (161302)**, 1316 South Main Street, Zip 50525–2019; tel. 515/532–2811 **A**9 10 18 **F**11 13 15 28 29 31 32 34 35 40 43 45 46 50 56 57 59 63 64 65 68 69 75 76 77 79 81 82 85 87 92 93 97 107 110 111 114 119 125 127 129 131 132 133 134 135 146 148 **P**6 **S** Iowa Specialty Hospitals, Clarion, IA
Primary Contact: Steven J. Simonin, Chief Executive Officer
CFO: Amy McDaniel, Chief Financial Officer
CMO: Jon Ahrendsen, M.D., Chief of Staff
CHR: Holly Martin, Human Resources Leader
Web address: www.wrightmed.com
**Control:** City–Government, nonfederal **Service:** General Medical and Surgical

**Staffed Beds:** 25 **Admissions:** 1439 **Census:** 11 **Outpatient Visits:** 108881 **Births:** 241 **Total Expense ($000):** 45924 **Payroll Expense ($000):** 17721 **Personnel:** 330

## CLINTON—Clinton County

✉ **MERCY MEDICAL CENTER–CLINTON (160080)**, 1410 North Fourth Street, Zip 52732–2940; tel. 563/244–5555, (Includes MERCY SERVICES FOR AGING, 600 14th Avenue North, Zip 52732; tel. 563/244–3888), (Total facility includes 183 beds in nursing home–type unit) **A**1 9 10 **F**3 11 13 15 18 20 22 28 29 30 31 34 35 36 38 40 44 45 47 49 50 53 56 57 59 60 61 62 63 64 68 70 74 75 76 77 78 79 80 81 82 84 85 87 89 90 93 98 99 100 101 102 103 107 108 110 115 118 119 121 123 128 129 130 132 146 148 **S** Trinity Health, Livonia, MI
Primary Contact: Sean J. Williams, President and Chief Executive Officer
CFO: Paul Mangin, Vice President Finance
Web address: www.mercyclinton.com
**Control:** Church–operated, Nongovernment, not–for profit **Service:** General Medical and Surgical

**Staffed Beds:** 319 **Admissions:** 5640 **Census:** 175 **Outpatient Visits:** 51176 **Births:** 471 **Total Expense ($000):** 85064 **Payroll Expense ($000):** 35239 **Personnel:** 785

## CORNING—Adams County

★ **ALEGENT CREIGHTON HEALTH MERCY HOSPITAL (161304)**, (Formerly Alegent Health Mercy Hospital), 603 Rosary Drive, Zip 50841–1683; tel. 641/322–3121 **A**9 10 18 **F**3 11 15 28 30 31 34 40 43 50 53 56 57 59 62 64 67 69 74 75 81 85 107 119 127 128 129 130 133 135 146 147 148 **P**6 **S** Catholic Health Initiatives, Englewood, CO
Primary Contact: Debra Goldsmith, Regional Administrator
CMO: Maen Haddadin, M.D., President Medical Staff
CIO: Kenneth Lawonn, Senior Vice President and Chief Information Officer
CHR: Sandra Lammers, Coordinator Human Resources and Finance
CNO: Jane Carmody DNP, MBA, RN, CENP, R.N., Vice President and System Chief Nursing Officer
Web address: www.alegent.com
**Control:** Church–operated, Nongovernment, not–for profit **Service:** General Medical and Surgical

**Staffed Beds:** 22 **Admissions:** 304 **Census:** 3 **Outpatient Visits:** 56362 **Births:** 0 **Total Expense ($000):** 15471 **Payroll Expense ($000):** 4544 **Personnel:** 122

**IA**

*Many Facility Codes have changed. Please refer to the AHA Guide Code Chart.* © 2013 AHA Guide

**CORYDON—Wayne County**

★ **WAYNE COUNTY HOSPITAL (161358)**, 417 South East Street,
Zip 50060–1860, Mailing Address: P.O. Box 305, Zip 50060–0305;
tel. 641/872–2260 **A**9 10 18 **F**7 10 11 13 15 28 29 34 35 36 39 40 43 51
56 57 59 60 69 70 75 76 77 79 81 85 87 89 91 92 93 97 107 110 114 119
125 127 130 131 132 133 148 **P**6
Primary Contact: Daren Relph, Chief Executive Officer
COO: Michael Thomas, Associate Administrator
CFO: Diane Hook, Chief Financial Officer
CMO: Joel Baker, D.O., Chief Medical Officer
CIO: Laurie Ehrich, Chief Communications Officer
CHR: Dave Carlyle, Director Human Resources
CNO: Sheila Mattly, Chief Nursing Officer
Web address: www.waynecountyhospital.org
**Control:** County–Government, nonfederal **Service:** General Medical and Surgical

**Staffed Beds:** 25 **Admissions:** 645 **Census:** 7 **Outpatient Visits:** 15680
**Births:** 126 **Total Expense ($000):** 21388 **Payroll Expense ($000):** 10202
**Personnel:** 204

**COUNCIL BLUFFS—Pottawattamie County**

⊠ **ALEGENT CREIGHTON HEALTH MERCY HOSPITAL (160028)**, (Formerly
Alegent Health–Mercy Hospital), 800 Mercy Drive, Zip 51503–3128, Mailing
Address: P.O. Box 1C, Zip 51502–3001; tel. 712/328–5000 **A**1 9 10 **F**3 5 11
12 13 15 18 20 22 28 29 30 31 34 35 38 39 40 43 44 47 48 49 50 56 57
59 60 62 64 65 68 70 74 75 76 77 78 79 81 82 84 85 87 89 93 97 98 99
100 101 102 103 104 105 106 107 108 110 111 114 115 119 129 130 132
134 135 143 146 147 148 **P**6 8 **S** Catholic Health Initiatives, Englewood, CO
Primary Contact: Marie E. Knedler, R.N., President
CFO: Amy Knott, Chief Financial Officer
CMO: Joseph Hoagbin, M.D., Chief Quality Officer
CIO: Kenneth Lawonn, Senior Vice President and Chief Information Officer
CHR: Nancy Wallace, Senior Vice President Human Resources
CNO: Jane Carmody DNP, MBA, RN, CENP, R.N., Vice President and System Chief
Nursing Officer
Web address: www.alegent.com/mercy
**Control:** Church–operated, Nongovernment, not–for profit **Service:** General
Medical and Surgical

**Staffed Beds:** 163 **Admissions:** 7828 **Census:** 85 **Outpatient Visits:** 74806
**Births:** 629 **Total Expense ($000):** 115060 **Payroll Expense ($000):** 32426
**Personnel:** 656

**JENNIE EDMUNDSON HOSPITAL** See Methodist Jennie Edmundson Hospital

⊠ **METHODIST JENNIE EDMUNDSON HOSPITAL (160047)**, (Formerly Jennie
Edmundson Hospital), 933 East Pierce Street, Zip 51503–4652, Mailing Address:
P.O. Box 2C, Zip 51502–3002; tel. 712/396–6000 **A**1 2 5 9 10 **F**3 11 13 15
18 20 22 26 28 29 30 31 34 35 39 40 43 44 45 47 49 50 57 58 59 61 64
68 70 74 75 76 78 79 81 82 85 86 87 89 92 93 98 100 101 102 103 107
108 110 111 114 116 118 119 121 123 129 130 131 132 135 143 145 146
147 148 **S** Nebraska Methodist Health System, Inc., Omaha, NE
Primary Contact: Steven P. Baumert, President and Chief Executive Officer
CFO: Linda K. Burt, Corporate Vice President Finance
CMO: Michael A. Romano, M.D., Vice President Medical Affairs
CIO: Roger Hertz, Vice President
CHR: Holly Huerter, Vice President Human Resources
CNO: Peggy Helget, R.N., Vice President Patient SErvices and Chief Nursing
Officer
Web address: www.bestcare.org
**Control:** Other not–for–profit (including NFP Corporation) **Service:** General
Medical and Surgical

**Staffed Beds:** 114 **Admissions:** 5101 **Census:** 60 **Outpatient Visits:** 108276
**Births:** 358 **Total Expense ($000):** 86109 **Payroll Expense ($000):** 34265
**Personnel:** 512

**CRESCO—Howard County**

★ **REGIONAL HEALTH SERVICES OF HOWARD COUNTY (161328)**, 235 Eighth
Avenue West, Zip 52136–1098; tel. 563/547–2101 **A**9 10 18 **F**7 11 13 15 18
28 29 34 40 43 44 57 59 62 63 64 65 68 75 76 77 79 80 81 85 86 87 93
107 110 114 128 130 132 133 146 148 **P**8 **S** Trinity Health, Livonia, MI
Primary Contact: Robin M. Schluter, Chief Executive Officer
CFO: Brenda Moser, Vice President Finance
CMO: Paul Jensen, M.D., Chief of Staff
CIO: Brenda Moser, Chief Information Officer
CHR: Connie Kuennen, Director Human Resources and Community Relations
CNO: Staci Urzak, Director Patient Care Services
Web address: www.rhshc.com
**Control:** County–Government, nonfederal **Service:** General Medical and Surgical

**Staffed Beds:** 20 **Admissions:** 316 **Census:** 4 **Outpatient Visits:** 20661
**Births:** 46 **Total Expense ($000):** 14490 **Payroll Expense ($000):** 5547
**Personnel:** 133

**CRESTON—Union County**

★ **GREATER REGIONAL MEDICAL CENTER (161365)**, 1700 West Townline
Street Suite 3, Zip 50801–1099; tel. 641/782–7091 **A**9 10 18 **F**3 7 11 13 15
28 29 31 34 35 40 43 45 56 57 59 63 64 65 70 75 76 77 78 79 81 82 84
86 93 96 97 107 108 110 111 114 119 120 121 124 125 127 129 130 131
132 133 135 146 148 **P**6 **S** UnityPoint Health, West Des Moines, IA
Primary Contact: Monte Neitzel, Chief Executive Officer
CFO: Matt McCutchan, Chief Financial Officer
CMO: Karen Krogstad, M.D., Chief Medical Officer
CIO: Karla Alford, Chief Information Officer
CHR: Lisa Ross, Human Resources Officer
CNO: Gwen Buck, R.N., Chief Nursing Officer
Web address: www.greaterregional.org
**Control:** County–Government, nonfederal **Service:** General Medical and Surgical

**Staffed Beds:** 25 **Admissions:** 723 **Census:** 7 **Outpatient Visits:** 66823
**Births:** 169 **Total Expense ($000):** 38608 **Payroll Expense ($000):** 16419
**Personnel:** 304

**DAVENPORT—Scott County**

⊠ △ **GENESIS MEDICAL CENTER–DAVENPORT (160033)**, 1227 East
Rusholme Street, Zip 52803–2498; tel. 563/421–1000, (Includes GENESIS
MEDICAL CENTER–EAST CAMPUS, 1227 East Rusholme Street, Zip 52803;
tel. 563/421–1000; GENESIS MEDICAL CENTER–WEST CAMPUS, 1401 West
Central Park, Zip 52804–1769; tel. 563/421–1000) **A**1 2 3 5 7 9 10 **F**3 7 11
12 13 15 18 20 22 24 26 28 29 30 31 34 35 37 38 40 43 44 46 49 50 53
54 57 58 59 60 63 64 68 70 72 74 75 76 77 78 79 80 81 82 84 85 86 87
89 90 91 92 93 94 96 97 98 100 102 107 110 111 114 116 118 119 120
121 123 124 126 129 130 131 132 135 146 147 148 **P**6 **S** Genesis Health
System, Davenport, IA
Primary Contact: Wayne A. Diewald, President
CFO: Mark G. Rogers, Interim Vice President Finance and Chief Financial Officer
CMO: Frank Claudy, M.D., Vice President Medical Staff Affairs
CIO: Robert Frieden, Vice President Information Systems
CHR: Heidi Kahly–McMahon, Interim Vice President Human Resources
Web address: www.genesishealth.com
**Control:** Other not–for–profit (including NFP Corporation) **Service:** General
Medical and Surgical

**Staffed Beds:** 34/ **Admissions:** 1682/ **Census:** 192 **Outpatient Visits:**
179098 **Births:** 2115 **Total Expense ($000):** 314242 **Payroll Expense
($000):** 87634 **Personnel:** 1640

⊠ **SELECT SPECIALTY HOSPITAL–QUAD CITIES (162001)**, 1111 West Kimberly
Road, Zip 52806–5711; tel. 563/468–2000 **A**1 10 **F**1 3 29 75 77 85 100 119
130 148 **S** Select Medical Corporation, Mechanicsburg, PA
Primary Contact: Austin B. Cleveland, Chief Executive Officer
Web address: www.selectspecialtyhospitals.com/company/locations/quadcities.
aspx
**Control:** Corporation, Investor–owned, for–profit **Service:** Long–Term Acute Care
hospital

**Staffed Beds:** 50 **Admissions:** 346 **Census:** 25 **Outpatient Visits:** 0 **Births:**
0 **Total Expense ($000):** 14289 **Payroll Expense ($000):** 5398 **Personnel:**
121

**DE WITT—Clinton County**

⊠ **GENESIS MEDICAL CENTER, DEWITT (161313)**, 1118 11th Street,
Zip 52742–1296; tel. 563/659–4200, (Total facility includes 75 beds in nursing
home–type unit) **A**1 9 10 18 **F**7 11 15 29 30 31 34 35 38 40 43 44 50 53 57
59 64 74 75 77 78 79 81 85 86 87 97 102 107 110 111 114 119 129 130
131 132 133 135 **P**6 **S** Genesis Health System, Davenport, IA
Primary Contact: Curt Coleman, FACHE, Administrator
CMO: Steven Fowler, M.D., President Medical Staff
CHR: Kristin Nicholson, Coordinator Human Resources
CNO: Wanda Haack, MSN, Chief Nursing Officer
Web address: www.genesishealth.com
**Control:** Other not–for–profit (including NFP Corporation) **Service:** General
Medical and Surgical

**Staffed Beds:** 86 **Admissions:** 300 **Census:** 69 **Outpatient Visits:** 18270
**Births:** 0 **Total Expense ($000):** 16030 **Payroll Expense ($000):** 6777
**Personnel:** 113

**IA**

**Hospital, Medicare Provider Number, Address, Telephone, Approval, Facility, and Physician Codes, Health Care System**

★ American Hospital Association (AHA) membership
☐ The Joint Commission accreditation ◇ DNV Healthcare Inc. accreditation
○ Healthcare Facilities Accreditation Program
△ Commission on Accreditation of Rehabilitation Facilities (CARF) accreditation

© 2013 AHA Guide *Many Facility Codes have changed. Please refer to the AHA Guide Code Chart.* Hospitals **A219**

**DECORAH—Winneshiek County**

✠ **WINNESHIEK MEDICAL CENTER (161371)**, 901 Montgomery Street,
Zip 52101–2325; tel. 563/382–2911 **A**1 9 10 18 **F**3 7 8 11 13 15 28 29 31
34 35 38 40 43 45 50 56 57 59 61 62 63 64 68 69 70 75 76 77 78 79 80
81 82 86 87 93 97 102 104 107 110 111 114 119 128 129 130 131 132
133 135 144 146 147 **S** Mayo Clinic Health System, Rochester, MN
Primary Contact: Gretchen M. Dahlen, FACHE, Chief Administrative Officer
COO: David B. Jordahl, FACHE, Chief Operating Officer
CFO: Lynn Luloff, Chief Financial Officer
CMO: Susan Halter, M.D., Chief Medical Officer
CHR: Laurie Bulman, Director Human Resources
Web address: www.winmedical.org
**Control:** County–Government, nonfederal **Service:** General Medical and Surgical

**Staffed Beds:** 25 **Admissions:** 1046 **Census:** 10 **Outpatient Visits:** 58041
**Births:** 221 **Total Expense ($000):** 43616 **Payroll Expense ($000):** 15404
**Personnel:** 346

**DENISON—Crawford County**

★ **CRAWFORD COUNTY MEMORIAL HOSPITAL (161369)**, 100 Medical
Parkway, Zip 51442–2607; tel. 712/265–2500 **A**9 10 18 **F**3 7 8 11 13 15 17
28 29 31 34 35 40 45 56 57 59 64 67 68 70 75 76 77 78 79 81 82 85 87
89 93 97 107 110 111 114 119 127 128 133 135 148 **P**6
Primary Contact: Bill Bruce, FACHE, Chief Executive Officer
CFO: Nancy Carlson, Chief Financial Officer
CIO: Angie Anderson, Director Information Technology
CNO: Diane Arkfeld, R.N., Director of Nursing
Web address: www.ccmhia.com
**Control:** County–Government, nonfederal **Service:** General Medical and Surgical

**Staffed Beds:** 25 **Admissions:** 677 **Census:** 6 **Outpatient Visits:** 38963
**Births:** 127 **Total Expense ($000):** 25138 **Payroll Expense ($000):** 11521
**Personnel:** 192

**DES MOINES—Polk County**

✠ **BROADLAWNS MEDICAL CENTER (160101)**, 1801 Hickman Road,
Zip 50314–1597; tel. 515/282–2200 **A**1 3 5 9 10 **F**2 3 5 11 13 15 18 29 30
31 32 34 35 38 39 40 42 43 44 45 48 50 52 53 56 57 58 59 64 65 66 68
70 74 75 76 77 78 79 81 82 85 86 87 92 93 94 97 98 99 100 101 102 103
104 105 106 107 111 114 119 130 131 132 135 144 146 147 148 **P**6
Primary Contact: Jody J. Jenner, President and Chief Executive Officer
CFO: Al White, CPA, Senior Vice President Business Services
CMO: Vincent Mandracchia, DPM, Chief Medical Officer
CNO: Susan N. Kirstein, R.N., Chief Nursing Officer
Web address: www.broadlawns.org
**Control:** County–Government, nonfederal **Service:** General Medical and Surgical

**Staffed Beds:** 91 **Admissions:** 3568 **Census:** 46 **Outpatient Visits:** 202155
**Births:** 299 **Total Expense ($000):** 119605 **Payroll Expense ($000):** 49726
**Personnel:** 836

**DES MOINES DIVISION** See Veterans Affairs Central Iowa Health Care System

**IOWA LUTHERAN HOSPITAL** See UnityPoint Health – Des Moines

★ △ ◇ **IOWA METHODIST MEDICAL CENTER (160082)**, 1200 Pleasant
Street, Zip 50309–1406; tel. 515/241–6212, (Includes BLANK CHILDREN'S
HOSPITAL, 1200 Pleasant Street, tel. 515/241–5437; JOHN STODDARD CANCER
CENTER, 1221 Pleasant Street, Zip 50309–1423; tel. 515/241–6212;
METHODIST WEST HOSPITAL, 1660 60th Street, West Des Moines,
Zip 50266–7700; tel. 515/343–1000; POWELL CONVALESCENT CENTER, 1200
Pleasant, Zip 50309; RAYMOND BLANK MEMORIAL HOSPITAL FOR CHILDREN,
Zip 50308; YOUNKER MEMORIAL REHABILITATION CENTER, 1200 Pleasant Road,
Zip 50308) **A**2 7 8 9 10 21 **F**3 7 8 11 12 13 17 18 20 22 24 26 29 30 31 32
34 35 39 40 41 43 44 45 46 49 50 53 54 55 56 57 58 59 64 65 66 68
70 71 72 74 75 76 77 78 79 81 82 84 85 86 87 88 89 90 91 92 93 94 96
97 100 107 108 111 115 116 117 118 119 120 121 123 124 126 129 130
131 132 134 135 138 142 146 147 148 **P**6 **S** UnityPoint Health, West Des
Moines, IA
Primary Contact: Eric T. Crowell, President and Chief Executive Officer
COO: Steve R. Stephenson, M.D., Executive Vice President and Chief Operating
Officer
CFO: Joe Corfits, Senior Vice President Finance
CMO: Mark Purtle, M.D., Vice President Medical Affairs
CHR: Joyce McDanel, Vice President Human Resources
Web address: www.iowahealth.org
**Control:** Other not–for–profit (including NFP Corporation) **Service:** General
Medical and Surgical

**Staffed Beds:** 478 **Admissions:** 24515 **Census:** 339 **Outpatient Visits:**
269827 **Births:** 3903 **Total Expense ($000):** 504757 **Payroll Expense**
**($000):** 208557 **Personnel:** 3531

✠ △ **MERCY MEDICAL CENTER–DES MOINES (160083)**, 1111 6th Avenue,
Zip 50314–2611; tel. 515/247–3121, (Includes MERCY FRANKLIN CENTER,
1818 48th Street, Zip 50310; tel. 515/271–6000) **A**1 2 7 9 10 13 **F**3 4 5 6 7
8 9 10 11 13 15 16 17 18 19 20 21 22 23 24 25 26 27 28 29 30 31 32 34
35 36 38 39 40 41 43 44 46 48 49 50 53 54 56 57 58 59 60 61 62 63 64
65 66 68 70 71 72 73 74 75 76 77 78 79 81 82 84 85 86 87 88 89 90 91
92 93 94 96 97 98 99 100 101 102 103 104 105 106 107 108 109 110 111
114 115 116 117 118 119 120 121 123 124 125 126 129 130 131 132 134
135 138 141 142 143 144 145 146 147 148 **P**6 **S** Catholic Health Initiatives,
Englewood, CO
Primary Contact: Robert P. Ritz, President
COO: Jackie Frost–Kunnen, Senior Vice President Operations
CFO: Steven F. Kukla, Senior Vice President and Chief Financial Officer
CMO: Dale Andres, D.O., Senior Vice President Medical Affairs
CIO: Cristina Thomas, Vice President and Chief Information Officer
CHR: Robyn Wilkinson, Senior Vice President Human Resources
Web address: www.mercydesmoines.org
**Control:** Church–operated, Nongovernment, not–for profit **Service:** General
Medical and Surgical

**Staffed Beds:** 567 **Admissions:** 29270 **Census:** 399 **Outpatient Visits:**
249284 **Births:** 4823 **Total Expense ($000):** 561540 **Payroll Expense**
**($000):** 234207 **Personnel:** 3782

★ ◇ **UNITYPOINT HEALTH – DES MOINES (160024)**, (Formerly Iowa Lutheran
Hospital), 700 East University Avenue, Zip 50316–2392; tel. 515/263–5612,
(Total facility includes 16 beds in nursing home–type unit) **A**3 5 9 10 21 **F**3 4 5 8
11 13 15 17 18 20 22 24 26 28 29 30 34 35 38 39 40 43 44 45 49 50 51
53 56 57 58 59 60 61 64 65 68 70 71 74 75 76 79 81 82 84 85 86 87 93
97 98 99 100 101 102 103 104 105 107 108 110 111 114 115 118 119
128 130 132 134 135 142 146 147 148 **P**6 **S** UnityPoint Health, West Des
Moines, IA
Primary Contact: Eric T. Crowell, President and Chief Executive Officer
COO: Eric L. Lothe, Vice President and Administrator
CFO: Joe Corfits, Chief Financial Officer
CMO: Mark Purtle, M.D., Vice President Medical Affairs
CHR: Joyce McDanel, Vice President Human Resources and Education
Web address: www.iowahealth.org
**Control:** Other not–for–profit (including NFP Corporation) **Service:** General
Medical and Surgical

**Staffed Beds:** 187 **Admissions:** 8048 **Census:** 119 **Outpatient Visits:** 55062
**Births:** 399 **Total Expense ($000):** 111068 **Payroll Expense ($000):** 48793
**Personnel:** 842

✠ △ **VETERANS AFFAIRS CENTRAL IOWA HEALTH CARE SYSTEM**, 3600
30th Street, Zip 50310–5753; tel. 515/699–5999, (Includes DES MOINES
DIVISION, 3600 30th Street, Zip 50310–5774; tel. 515/699–5999; KNOXVILLE
DIVISION, 1515 West Pleasant, Knoxville, Zip 50138–3399; tel. 515/842–3101),
(Total facility includes 140 beds in nursing home–type unit) **A**1 3 5 7 9 **F**2 3 5 11
15 18 20 22 28 29 30 31 33 34 35 36 38 39 40 44 46 50 56 57 59 61 62
63 64 65 66 70 71 74 75 77 78 79 80 81 82 83 84 85 86 87 93 94 97 98
100 101 102 103 104 105 106 107 108 111 114 115 118 119 128 129 130
132 135 146 147 148 **S** Department of Veterans Affairs, Washington, DC
Primary Contact: Donald C. Cooper, Director
CMO: Fredrick Bahls, M.D., Chief of Staff
CIO: James Danuser, Chief Information Officer
CHR: Sabrina Owen, Human Resources Officer
Web address: www.centraliowa.va.gov/
**Control:** Veterans Affairs, Government, federal **Service:** General Medical and
Surgical

**Staffed Beds:** 255 **Admissions:** 2895 **Census:** 194 **Outpatient Visits:**
333921 **Births:** 0 **Total Expense ($000):** 224951 **Payroll Expense ($000):**
123767 **Personnel:** 1408

**DUBUQUE—Dubuque County**

**FINLEY HOSPITAL** See UnityPoint Health Finley

✠ △ **MERCY MEDICAL CENTER–DUBUQUE (160069)**, 250 Mercy Drive,
Zip 52001–7360; tel. 563/589–8000, (Total facility includes 40 beds in nursing
home–type unit) **A**1 7 9 10 **F**3 4 5 8 11 13 15 18 20 22 24 26 28 29 30 31
32 34 35 36 38 39 40 43 44 49 50 51 53 56 57 58 59 61 62 64 65 67 70
72 74 75 76 77 78 79 80 81 85 86 87 89 90 91 93 97 98 99 100 101 102
103 104 107 108 111 114 116 119 126 128 129 130 131 132 134 135 143
144 146 147 148 **P**8 **S** Trinity Health, Livonia, MI
Primary Contact: Russell M. Knight, President and Chief Executive Officer
CFO: Robert Shafer, Vice President Finance
CIO: Matt Trimmer, Director Information Services
CNO: Kay Takes, R.N., Vice President Patient Care Services and Chief Nursing
Officer
Web address: www.mercydubuque.com
**Control:** Church–operated, Nongovernment, not–for profit **Service:** General
Medical and Surgical

**Staffed Beds:** 272 **Admissions:** 8714 **Census:** 139 **Outpatient Visits:** 41357
**Births:** 853 **Total Expense ($000):** 137927 **Payroll Expense ($000):** 43418
**Personnel:** 983

**IA**

*Many Facility Codes have changed. Please refer to the AHA Guide Code Chart.* © 2013 AHA Guide

⊞ △ **UNITYPOINT HEALTH FINLEY (160117)**, (Formerly Finley Hospital), 350 North Grandview Avenue, Zip 52001–6392; tel. 563/582–1881 **A**1 7 9 10 **F**3 11 12 13 15 18 20 22 26 28 29 30 31 34 35 39 40 43 44 45 46 48 49 50 53 56 57 59 60 61 62 64 65 69 70 72 74 75 76 77 78 79 81 82 84 85 86 87 90 93 96 97 98 103 107 108 110 111 115 117 118 119 120 121 123 124 126 129 130 131 132 135 144 146 147 148 **P**1 5 **S** UnityPoint Health, West Des Moines, IA
Primary Contact: David R. Brandon, President and Chief Executive Officer
COO: Chad Wolbers, Chief Operating Officer
CFO: Dan Carpenter, Chief Financial Officer
CMO: Bryan Pechous, M.D., Vice President Medical Affairs
CIO: Tim Loeffelholz, Account Executive Information Technology
CHR: Karla Waldbillig, Director Human Resources
CNO: Diana Batchelor, Chief Nursing Officer
Web address: www.finleyhospital.org
**Control:** Other not–for–profit (including NFP Corporation) **Service:** General Medical and Surgical

**Staffed Beds:** 109 **Admissions:** 4699 **Census:** 55 **Outpatient Visits:** 92436 **Births:** 732 **Total Expense ($000):** 92260 **Payroll Expense ($000):** 38394 **Personnel:** 669

**DYERSVILLE—Dubuque County**

★ **MERCY MEDICAL CENTER–DYERSVILLE (161378)**, 1111 Third Street S.W., Zip 52040–1725; tel. 563/875–7101 **A**9 10 18 **F**11 15 34 35 36 39 40 44 50 56 57 59 64 65 75 79 81 85 86 93 119 130 131 132 133 134 135 146 147 **P**8 **S** Trinity Health, Livonia, MI
Primary Contact: Russell M. Knight, President and Chief Executive Officer
CFO: Robert Shafer, Vice President Finance
Web address: www.mercydubuque.com/mercy–dyersville
**Control:** Church–operated, Nongovernment, not–for profit **Service:** General Medical and Surgical

**Staffed Beds:** 25 **Admissions:** 101 **Census:** 3 **Outpatient Visits:** 3981 **Births:** 0 **Total Expense ($000):** 4901 **Payroll Expense ($000):** 2261 **Personnel:** 51

**ELKADER—Clayton County**

★ **CENTRAL COMMUNITY HOSPITAL (161319)**, 901 Davidson Street N.W., Zip 52043–9015; tel. 563/245–7000 **A**9 10 18 **F**7 11 15 18 28 34 35 40 43 50 56 57 59 64 65 67 68 70 75 81 85 86 87 89 102 107 114 128 130 132 133 134 135 143 148 **S** Trinity Health, Livonia, MI
Primary Contact: Frances J. Zichal, Chief Executive Officer
CFO: Patricia Borel, Chief Financial Officer
CIO: Nathan Baker, Manager Information Technology
CHR: Angie Gerndt, Human Resources Manager
CNO: Mary Walters, Chief Nursing Officer
Web address: www.centralcommunityhospital.com
**Control:** Other not–for–profit (including NFP Corporation) **Service:** General Medical and Surgical

**Staffed Beds:** 16 **Admissions:** 217 **Census:** 2 **Outpatient Visits:** 8350 **Births:** 0 **Total Expense ($000):** 5936 **Payroll Expense ($000):** 2013 **Personnel:** 56

**EMMETSBURG—Palo Alto County**

★ **PALO ALTO COUNTY HEALTH SYSTEM (161357)**, 3201 First Street, Zip 50536–2516; tel. 712/852–5500, (Total facility includes 22 beds in nursing home–type unit) **A**9 10 18 **F**3 7 11 15 28 34 35 40 43 45 50 57 59 62 63 64 65 67 68 69 70 75 76 77 79 81 85 87 93 107 110 115 119 125 127 130 132 133 135 143 146 **P**6 **S** Trinity Health, Livonia, MI
Primary Contact: Desiree Einsweiler, Chief Executive Officer
CFO: Renay Hauswirth, Chief Financial Officer
CMO: Frank Veltri, M.D., President Medical Staff
CIO: Randy Beaver, Chief Information Officer
CHR: Kelly Bond, Director Human Resources
Web address: www.pachs.com
**Control:** County–Government, nonfederal **Service:** General Medical and Surgical

**Staffed Beds:** 47 **Admissions:** 426 **Census:** 25 **Outpatient Visits:** 22088 **Births:** 113 **Total Expense ($000):** 21964 **Payroll Expense ($000):** 8171 **Personnel:** 179

**ESTHERVILLE—Emmet County**

★ **AVERA HOLY FAMILY HOSPITAL (161351)**, 826 North Eighth Street, Zip 51334–1598; tel. 712/362–2631 **A**9 10 18 **F**3 11 13 15 28 29 30 31 34 35 40 45 59 62 63 64 68 69 70 75 76 77 78 79 81 85 87 93 107 114 119 130 132 133 146 **P**4 **S** Avera Health, Sioux Falls, SD
Primary Contact: Michael L. Hall, Chief Executive Officer
CMO: James Creech, M.D., Chief of Staff
CHR: Janette Jensen, Manager Human Resources
Web address: www.avera–holyfamily.org
**Control:** Church–operated, Nongovernment, not–for profit **Service:** General Medical and Surgical

**Staffed Beds:** 25 **Admissions:** 772 **Census:** 7 **Outpatient Visits:** 65509 **Births:** 28 **Total Expense ($000):** 22335 **Payroll Expense ($000):** 7951 **Personnel:** 178

**FAIRFIELD—Jefferson County**

★ **JEFFERSON COUNTY HEALTH CENTER (161364)**, 2000 South Main, Zip 52556–9572, Mailing Address: P.O. Box 588, Zip 52556–0010; tel. 641/472–4111 **A**9 10 18 **F**11 15 28 30 31 34 35 36 40 43 45 57 59 67 68 70 75 77 78 79 81 85 89 93 96 102 107 110 114 119 128 129 133 135 143 146 148 **P**5
Primary Contact: Deborah Cardin, R.N., FACHE, MS, Chief Executive Officer
CFO: Gene Irwin, Chief Financial Officer
CHR: Nanette Everly, Manager Human Resources and Administrative Assistant
Web address: www.jeffersoncountyhealthcenter.org
**Control:** County–Government, nonfederal **Service:** General Medical and Surgical

**Staffed Beds:** 25 **Admissions:** 835 **Census:** 13 **Outpatient Visits:** 45975 **Births:** 0 **Total Expense ($000):** 24442 **Payroll Expense ($000):** 8068 **Personnel:** 175

**FORT DODGE—Webster County**

★ ◇ **TRINITY REGIONAL MEDICAL CENTER (160016)**, 802 Kenyon Road, Zip 50501–5795; tel. 515/573–3101 **A**2 9 10 21 **F**3 7 8 11 13 15 18 20 22 24 28 29 30 31 32 34 35 36 40 43 45 48 49 50 53 57 59 60 64 68 70 73 75 76 77 78 79 81 82 84 86 87 89 93 107 108 111 115 118 119 129 130 131 132 135 146 148 **P**6 **S** UnityPoint Health, West Des Moines, IA
Primary Contact: Susan K. Thompson, President and Chief Executive Officer
COO: Troy Martens, Chief Operating Officer
CFO: Mike Dewerff, Chief Financial Officer
CHR: Ted W. Vaughn, Director Human Resources
CNO: Debra Shriver, R.N., Chief Nurse Executive
Web address: www.trmc.org
**Control:** Other not–for–profit (including NFP Corporation) **Service:** General Medical and Surgical

**Staffed Beds:** 113 **Admissions:** 4689 **Census:** 41 **Outpatient Visits:** 105742 **Births:** 532 **Total Expense ($000):** 94836 **Payroll Expense ($000):** 41867 **Personnel:** 685

**FORT MADISON—Lee County**

⊞ **FORT MADISON COMMUNITY HOSPITAL (160122)**, 5445 Avenue O, Zip 52627–9611, Mailing Address: P.O. Box 174, Zip 52627–0174; tel. 319/372–6530 **A**1 9 10 **F**3 11 13 15 28 29 31 34 40 43 45 50 51 53 57 59 62 64 67 68 70 74 75 76 77 78 79 81 85 86 87 90 91 93 94 96 97 99 100 101 102 103 104 107 108 110 111 114 117 118 119 128 129 130 131 132 133 143 144 146 147 148 **P**6 **S** QHR, Brentwood, TN
Primary Contact: C. James Platt, Chief Executive Officer
CFO: Bradley J. Kokjohn, Chief Financial Officer
CMO: David Wenger–Keller, M.D., Chief of Staff
CIO: Shane Tapper, Director Management Information Systems
CHR: Vicki Kokjohn, Director Employee Relations
Web address: www.fmchosp.com
**Control:** Other not–for–profit (including NFP Corporation) **Service:** General Medical and Surgical

**Staffed Beds:** 50 **Admissions:** 1972 **Census:** 19 **Outpatient Visits:** 82608 **Births:** 313 **Total Expense ($000):** 49417 **Payroll Expense ($000):** 24621 **Personnel:** 427

IA

---

**Hospital, Medicare Provider Number, Address, Telephone, Approval, Facility, and Physician Codes, Health Care System**

★ American Hospital Association (AHA) membership
□ The Joint Commission accreditation
◇ DNV Healthcare Inc. accreditation
○ Healthcare Facilities Accreditation Program
△ Commission on Accreditation of Rehabilitation Facilities (CARF) accreditation

### GREENFIELD—Adair County

**ADAIR COUNTY MEMORIAL HOSPITAL (161310)**, 609 S.E. Kent Street, Zip 50849–9454; tel. 641/743–2123 **A**9 10 18 **F**3 7 11 15 18 28 29 31 34 35 36 40 43 45 48 57 59 62 64 65 69 70 75 77 79 81 89 91 93 97 107 108 110 111 114 116 118 119 127 128 129 130 133 146 148 **P**6
Primary Contact: Angela Mortoza, Administrator
CFO: Lisa Blazek, Chief Financial Officer
CMO: Melissa Thompson, M.D., Chief Medical Officer
CIO: Andy Christie, Chief Information Technology
CHR: Angie Shatava, Director Human Resources
Web address: www.adaircountyhealthsystem.org
**Control:** County–Government, nonfederal **Service:** General Medical and Surgical

> **Staffed Beds:** 18 **Admissions:** 170 **Census:** 2 **Outpatient Visits:** 11793
> **Births:** 0 **Total Expense ($000):** 10358 **Payroll Expense ($000):** 3850
> **Personnel:** 96

### GRINNELL—Poweshiek County

★ **GRINNELL REGIONAL MEDICAL CENTER (160147)**, 210 Fourth Avenue, Zip 50112–1898; tel. 641/236–7511 **A**9 10 **F**3 11 12 13 15 28 29 30 31 32 34 35 36 37 38 40 43 44 45 46 47 50 53 54 56 57 59 61 62 63 64 65 66 70 75 76 77 78 79 81 84 85 86 87 89 93 97 107 108 110 111 114 118 119 127 129 130 131 132 133 134 135 146 147 148 **P**6 7
Primary Contact: Todd C. Linden, President and Chief Executive Officer
COO: Suzanne Cooner, R.N., Vice President Operations
CFO: Jack Fritts, Vice President Finance and Chief Financial Officer
CMO: David C. Cranston, M.D., Vice President Medical Staff Affairs
CIO: David L. Ness, Vice President Operations
CHR: Debra S. Nowachek, Director Human Resources
Web address: www.grmc.us
**Control:** Other not–for–profit (including NFP Corporation) **Service:** General Medical and Surgical

> **Staffed Beds:** 49 **Admissions:** 1442 **Census:** 14 **Outpatient Visits:** 48399
> **Births:** 166 **Total Expense ($000):** 42227 **Payroll Expense ($000):** 20715
> **Personnel:** 401

### GRUNDY CENTER—Grundy County

★ **GRUNDY COUNTY MEMORIAL HOSPITAL (161303)**, 201 East J Avenue, Zip 50638–2096; tel. 319/824–5421, (Total facility includes 55 beds in nursing home–type unit) **A**9 10 18 **F**15 28 29 34 35 40 43 57 59 63 67 75 78 79 81 82 86 87 93 107 110 111 114 119 128 129 130 131 132 133 135 146 148 **S** UnityPoint Health, West Des Moines, IA
Primary Contact: Brian Kellar, Chief Executive Officer
COO: Ryan Bingman, Director Operations
CFO: Lisa Zinkula, Chief Financial Officer
CMO: Douglas Cooper, M.D., Chief Medical Officer
CIO: Nicholas Betts, Director Information Technology
CHR: Nicole Larson, Manager Human Resources
Web address: www.grundycountyhospital.com
**Control:** County–Government, nonfederal **Service:** General Medical and Surgical

> **Staffed Beds:** 80 **Admissions:** 391 **Census:** 56 **Outpatient Visits:** 32184
> **Births:** 0 **Total Expense ($000):** 18178 **Payroll Expense ($000):** 7622
> **Personnel:** 151

### GUTHRIE CENTER—Guthrie County

★ **GUTHRIE COUNTY HOSPITAL (161314)**, 710 North 12th Street, Zip 50115–1544; tel. 641/332–2201 **A**9 10 18 **F**11 15 18 28 29 31 34 35 40 43 45 53 56 57 59 64 69 75 77 79 81 85 93 107 110 119 128 130 132 133 143 **S** UnityPoint Health, West Des Moines, IA
Primary Contact: Patrick Peters, Chief Executive Officer
CFO: Melinda Alt, Chief Financial Officer
CMO: Steven Bascom, M.D., Chief Medical Officer
CIO: Jeff Cobb, Information Technologist
CHR: Kimberly Myers, Director Human Resources
CNO: Danielle Navarro, R.N., Chief Nursing Officer
Web address: www.guthriecountyhospital.org
**Control:** County–Government, nonfederal **Service:** General Medical and Surgical

> **Staffed Beds:** 25 **Admissions:** 307 **Census:** 3 **Outpatient Visits:** 35075
> **Births:** 1 **Total Expense ($000):** 13959 **Payroll Expense ($000):** 5942
> **Personnel:** 118

### GUTTENBERG—Clayton County

⊠ **GUTTENBERG MUNICIPAL HOSPITAL (161312)**, 200 Main Street, Zip 52052–9108, Mailing Address: P.O. Box 550, Zip 52052–0550; tel. 563/252–1121 **A**1 9 10 18 **F**3 7 8 11 13 15 28 34 35 40 43 45 50 53 57 59 64 68 76 81 82 85 89 93 102 107 110 111 114 119 128 130 132 133 **P**5 6 **S** UnityPoint Health, West Des Moines, IA
Primary Contact: Kimberley A. Gau, FACHE, Chief Executive Officer
CMO: Andrew Smith, M.D., Chief Medical Staff
CIO: Ken Kaiser, Director Information Technology
CHR: Leigh Ann Judge, Manager Human Resources
CNO: Laura Beyer, Director Patient Care
Web address: www.guttenberghospital.org
**Control:** City–Government, nonfederal **Service:** General Medical and Surgical

> **Staffed Beds:** 20 **Admissions:** 492 **Census:** 5 **Outpatient Visits:** 21966
> **Births:** 40 **Total Expense ($000):** 9980 **Payroll Expense ($000):** 3767
> **Personnel:** 83

### HAMBURG—Fremont County

**GEORGE C GRAPE COMMUNITY HOSPITAL (161324)**, 2959 U.S. Highway 275, Zip 51640–5067; tel. 712/382–1515, (Total facility includes 6 beds in nursing home–type unit) **A**9 10 18 **F**11 15 18 28 31 34 40 43 45 50 53 57 59 62 64 65 68 69 74 75 77 78 79 81 82 85 91 93 107 114 119 128 129 130 131 133 135 148
Primary Contact: Michael O'Neal, Administrator and Chief Executive Officer
CFO: Hilary Christiansen, Chief Financial Officer
CMO: Kelli Woltemath, D.O., Chief Medical Staff
CIO: Nancy Tiemeyer, Director Health Information Management
CHR: Jackie Wertz, Director Human Resources
Web address: www.grapehospital.com
**Control:** Other not–for–profit (including NFP Corporation) **Service:** General Medical and Surgical

> **Staffed Beds:** 25 **Admissions:** 340 **Census:** 9 **Outpatient Visits:** 18309
> **Births:** 0 **Total Expense ($000):** 9905 **Payroll Expense ($000):** 4200
> **Personnel:** 96

### HAMPTON—Franklin County

★ **FRANKLIN GENERAL HOSPITAL (161308)**, 1720 Central Avenue East, Suite A., Zip 50441–1867; tel. 641/456–5000, (Total facility includes 52 beds in nursing home–type unit) **A**9 10 18 **F**7 10 11 15 28 30 31 34 40 43 57 59 63 64 65 67 68 75 77 81 82 85 86 89 90 93 107 111 114 119 127 128 129 130 132 133 135 146 **P**8 **S** Trinity Health, Livonia, MI
Primary Contact: Kim Price, Chief Executive Officer
CFO: Michelle Craighton, Manager Finance
CHR: Victoria Kruse, Manager Human Resources
Web address: www.franklingeneral.com
**Control:** County–Government, nonfederal **Service:** General Medical and Surgical

> **Staffed Beds:** 77 **Admissions:** 305 **Census:** 53 **Outpatient Visits:** 16986
> **Births:** 0 **Total Expense ($000):** 16155 **Payroll Expense ($000):** 5917
> **Personnel:** 142

### HARLAN—Shelby County

★ **MYRTUE MEDICAL CENTER (161374)**, 1213 Garfield Avenue, Zip 51537–2057; tel. 712/755–5161 **A**9 10 18 **F**3 5 11 13 15 28 29 31 32 34 35 38 40 43 45 46 50 53 56 57 59 62 63 64 65 68 75 76 77 78 81 85 87 92 93 97 99 101 102 103 104 107 110 114 127 129 130 131 132 133 135 146 148 **P**6 8
Primary Contact: Barry Jacobsen, Chief Executive Officer
CFO: Sue Blake, Chief Financial Officer
CMO: Sarah Devine, M.D., Chief of Staff
CIO: David Sirek, Chief Information Officer
CHR: Donna Christensen–Mores, Director Human Resources
CNO: Karen Buman, Chief Nurse Executive
Web address: www.myrtuemedical.org
**Control:** County–Government, nonfederal **Service:** General Medical and Surgical

> **Staffed Beds:** 25 **Admissions:** 961 **Census:** 12 **Outpatient Visits:** 84702
> **Births:** 91 **Total Expense ($000):** 31214 **Payroll Expense ($000):** 12899
> **Personnel:** 317

### HAWARDEN—Sioux County

★ **HAWARDEN REGIONAL HEALTHCARE (161311)**, (Formerly Hawarden Community Hospital), 1111 11th Street, Zip 51023–1999; tel. 712/551–3100 **A**9 10 18 **F**11 15 28 29 31 34 35 40 43 53 59 64 67 69 75 77 80 81 89 90 92 93 107 108 119 128 132 133 135 148 **P**3 7 **S** Trinity Health, Livonia, MI
Primary Contact: Jayson Pullman, Chief Executive Officer
CHR: Amy A. Miller, Human Resources Assistant
Web address: www.hawardenregionalhealthcare.com/
**Control:** City–Government, nonfederal **Service:** General Medical and Surgical

> **Staffed Beds:** 18 **Admissions:** 184 **Census:** 3 **Outpatient Visits:** 17835
> **Births:** 0 **Total Expense ($000):** 6649 **Payroll Expense ($000):** 2264
> **Personnel:** 49

### HUMBOLDT—Humboldt County

★ **HUMBOLDT COUNTY MEMORIAL HOSPITAL (161334)**, 1000 North 15th Street, Zip 50548–1008; tel. 515/332–4200, (Total facility includes 28 beds in nursing home–type unit) **A**9 10 18 **F**7 8 10 11 12 14 15 28 29 31 32 34 35 40 41 43 45 47 50 51 59 65 69 75 77 78 79 81 82 85 87 93 102 107 110 111 114 119 125 130 133 134 **S** UnityPoint Health, West Des Moines, IA
Primary Contact: James Atty, Chief Executive Officer
CFO: Betty Etherington, Chief Financial Officer
CHR: Mary Moritz, Administrator Human Resources
Web address: www.humboldthospital.org
**Control:** County–Government, nonfederal **Service:** General Medical and Surgical

> **Staffed Beds:** 49 **Admissions:** 294 **Census:** 34 **Outpatient Visits:** 42469
> **Births:** 0 **Total Expense ($000):** 13002 **Payroll Expense ($000):** 4917
> **Personnel:** 117

**IA**

*Many Facility Codes have changed. Please refer to the AHA Guide Code Chart.*
© 2013 AHA Guide

## IDA GROVE—Ida County

★ **HORN MEMORIAL HOSPITAL (161354)**, 701 East Second Street, Zip 51445–1699; tel. 712/364–3311 **A**9 10 18 **F**11 15 28 29 31 34 40 45 57 59 62 63 64 65 66 68 71 75 77 78 79 81 85 93 97 107 108 110 111 114 119 127 129 130 132 133 135 146 147 148 **P**6
Primary Contact: Marcia Fehring, Interim Chief Executive Officer
CFO: Marcia Fehring, Chief Financial Officer
CIO: Robbie Todd, Director Information Technology
CHR: Lorraine Davis, Vice President Human Resources
CNO: Sharon A. Wellendorf, Chief Nursing Officer
Web address: www.hornmemorialhospital.org
**Control:** Other not–for–profit (including NFP Corporation) **Service:** General Medical and Surgical

**Staffed Beds:** 25 **Admissions:** 521 **Census:** 8 **Outpatient Visits:** 22915 **Births:** 20 **Total Expense ($000):** 16549 **Payroll Expense ($000):** 7063 **Personnel:** 150

## INDEPENDENCE—Buchanan County

★ **BUCHANAN COUNTY HEALTH CENTER (161335)**, 1600 First Street East, Zip 50644–3155; tel. 319/332–0999, (Total facility includes 39 beds in nursing home–type unit) **A**9 10 18 **F**3 11 15 28 29 32 34 35 40 43 45 53 56 57 59 64 65 67 70 75 77 79 81 82 86 87 91 93 107 110 111 114 119 125 129 130 131 132 133 135 146 148
Primary Contact: Danielle Gearhart, Chief Executive Officer
CFO: Ronald Timpe, Associate Administrator
CHR: Shelbie Medina, Chief People Officer
Web address: www.bchealth.info
**Control:** County–Government, nonfederal **Service:** General Medical and Surgical

**Staffed Beds:** 64 **Admissions:** 401 **Census:** 36 **Outpatient Visits:** 45143 **Births:** 0 **Total Expense ($000):** 17484 **Payroll Expense ($000):** 7005 **Personnel:** 169

☐ **MENTAL HEALTH INSTITUTE (164003)**, 2277 Iowa Avenue, Zip 50644–9106; tel. 319/334–2583 **A**1 9 10 **F**65 98 99 101 102 106 130 143 146 **P**6
Primary Contact: Bhasker J. Dave, M.D., Superintendent
CFO: Kevin Jimmerson, Business Manager
CMO: Bhasker J. Dave, M.D., Superintendent
Web address: www.dhs.state.ia.us
**Control:** State–Government, nonfederal **Service:** Psychiatric

**Staffed Beds:** 75 **Admissions:** 277 **Census:** 60 **Outpatient Visits:** 29 **Births:** 0 **Total Expense ($000):** 20693 **Payroll Expense ($000):** 11782 **Personnel:** 235

## IOWA CITY—Johnson County

☒ **IOWA CITY VETERANS AFFAIRS HEALTH CARE SYSTEM**, (Formerly Veterans Affairs Medical Center), 601 Highway 6 West, Zip 52246–2208; tel. 319/338–0581 **A**1 3 5 8 9 **F**3 5 12 18 20 22 24 29 30 31 34 35 38 39 40 43 44 45 46 47 50 51 54 56 57 58 59 60 61 64 70 74 75 78 79 81 82 83 84 85 86 87 91 92 93 94 97 98 100 101 102 103 104 **S** Department of Veterans Affairs, Washington, DC
Primary Contact: Barry D. Sharp, Director
COO: Timothy McMurry, Associate Director Operations
CFO: Kevin Kosek, Chief Financial Officer
CMO: Mark H. Smith, M.D., Chief of Staff
CIO: Dwight Schuessler, Chief Information Officer
CHR: Dan Helle, Human Resources Officer
CNO: Dawn Oxley, R.N., Associate Director Patient Care Services and Nurse Executive
Web address: www.iowacity.va.gov/
**Control:** Veterans Affairs, Government, federal **Service:** General Medical and Surgical

**Staffed Beds:** 65 **Admissions:** 3352 **Census:** 47 **Outpatient Visits:** 432046 **Births:** 0 **Total Expense ($000):** 269054 **Payroll Expense ($000):** 101342 **Personnel:** 1515

☒ **MERCY IOWA CITY (160029)**, 500 East Market Street, Zip 52245–2689; tel. 319/339–0300, (Total facility includes 16 beds in nursing home–type unit) **A**1 2 9 10 **F**3 11 13 15 18 20 22 24 26 28 29 30 31 34 35 36 37 38 40 41 42 43 44 45 48 49 50 51 56 57 58 59 62 63 64 65 70 72 73 74 75 76 77 78 79 81 82 85 86 87 89 97 98 100 101 102 103 107 108 110 111 114 115 118 119 126 128 130 132 135 144 145 146 148 **P**8
Primary Contact: Ronald R. Reed, President and Chief Executive Officer
CFO: Michael G. Heinrich, Executive Vice President and Chief Financial Officer
CMO: Martin Izakovic, M.D., Vice President Medical Staff Affairs and Chief Medical Officer
CIO: Paul Foelsch, Vice President Information Services and Chief Information Officer
CHR: Marie Peeters, Director Human Resources
CNO: Cindy L. Penney, R.N., Vice President Nursing
Web address: www.mercyiowacity.org
**Control:** Church–operated, Nongovernment, not–for profit **Service:** General Medical and Surgical

**Staffed Beds:** 234 **Admissions:** 8273 **Census:** 92 **Outpatient Visits:** 319886 **Births:** 1153 **Total Expense ($000):** 142368 **Payroll Expense ($000):** 58465 **Personnel:** 978

☒ **UNIVERSITY OF IOWA HOSPITALS AND CLINICS (160058)**, 200 Hawkins Drive, Zip 52242–1009; tel. 319/356–1616, (Includes CENTER FOR DISABILITIES AND DEVELOPMENT, 200 Hawkins Drive, Zip 52242; tel. 319/353–6456; CHEMICAL DEPENDENCY CENTER, 200 Hawkins Drive, Oakdale, Zip 52242–1007; tel. 319/384–8765; STATE PSYCHIATRIC HOSPITAL, 200 Hawkins Drive, Zip 52242; tel. 319/356–4658; UNIVERSITY OF IOWA CHILDREN'S HOSPITAL, 200 Hawkins Drive, tel. 319/384–8442) **A**1 2 3 5 8 9 10 **F**3 5 6 7 8 9 11 12 13 14 15 16 17 18 19 20 21 22 23 24 25 26 27 28 29 30 31 32 33 34 35 36 37 38 39 40 43 44 45 46 47 48 49 50 51 52 53 54 55 56 57 58 59 60 61 62 63 64 65 66 68 70 72 73 74 75 76 77 78 79 80 81 82 83 84 85 86 87 88 89 90 91 92 93 94 97 98 99 100 101 102 103 104 105 107 108 109 110 111 114 115 116 117 118 119 120 121 123 124 126 127 129 130 131 132 135 136 137 138 139 140 141 142 143 144 145 146 147 148 **P**1 7
Primary Contact: Kenneth P. Kates, Chief Executive Officer
COO: John H. Staley, Ph.D., Senior Associate Director and Interim Chief Operating Officer
CFO: Kenneth Fisher, Associate Vice President Finance and Chief Financial Officer
CMO: Theresa Brennan, M.D., Chief Medical Officer
CIO: Lee Carmen, Associate Vice President Health Care Information Systems
CHR: Jana Wessels, Associate Vice President Human Resources
Web address: www.uihealthcare.com
**Control:** State Government, nonfederal **Service:** General Medical and Surgical

**Staffed Beds:** 685 **Admissions:** 30537 **Census:** 534 **Outpatient Visits:** 1118444 **Births:** 1950 **Total Expense ($000):** 1055648 **Payroll Expense ($000):** 390921 **Personnel:** 6734

## IOWA FALLS—Hardin County

★ **ELLSWORTH MUNICIPAL HOSPITAL (161380)**, 110 Rocksylvania Avenue, Zip 50126–2400; tel. 641/648–4631 **A**9 10 18 **F**11 13 15 28 34 40 43 45 50 53 57 59 64 65 75 76 77 81 85 86 87 93 97 100 104 107 110 114 119 133 135 **P**6 **S** Trinity Health, Livonia, MI
Primary Contact: Cherelle Montanye–Ireland, Chief Executive Officer
CFO: Betty Riley, Chief Financial Officer
CMO: Kathleen Haverkamp, M.D., Chief Medical Officer
CHR: Cheri Geitz, Director Human Resources
Web address: www.emhia.com
**Control:** City–Government, nonfederal **Service:** General Medical and Surgical

**Staffed Beds:** 23 **Admissions:** 895 **Census:** 10 **Outpatient Visits:** 32496 **Births:** 77 **Total Expense ($000):** 19589 **Payroll Expense ($000):** 9101 **Personnel:** 201

## JEFFERSON—Greene County

★ **GREENE COUNTY MEDICAL CENTER (161325)**, 1000 West Lincolnway, Zip 50129–1645; tel. 515/386–2114, (Total facility includes 65 beds in nursing home–type unit) **A**9 10 18 **F**11 13 15 28 29 34 35 36 40 46 56 57 59 62 63 64 65 67 68 75 76 78 79 81 82 85 93 107 114 119 125 128 130 131 132 133 147 **P**5 6 **S** UnityPoint Health, West Des Moines, IA
Primary Contact: Carl P. Behne, Administrator and Chief Executive Officer
CFO: William Steussy, Chief Financial Officer
CMO: Steven Karber, M.D., Medical Director
CIO: Roger Overby, Executive Director Information Systems
CHR: Tammy Ford, Executive Director Human Resources
CNO: Cynthia Kail, Chief Nursing Officer and Executive Director Public Health
Web address: www.gcmchealth.com
**Control:** County–Government, nonfederal **Service:** General Medical and Surgical

**Staffed Beds:** 90 **Admissions:** 457 **Census:** 60 **Outpatient Visits:** 26829 **Births:** 45 **Total Expense ($000):** 22614 **Payroll Expense ($000):** 10245 **Personnel:** 224

**IA**

---

**Hospital, Medicare Provider Number, Address, Telephone, Approval, Facility, and Physician Codes, Health Care System**

★ American Hospital Association (AHA) membership
☐ The Joint Commission accreditation
◇ DNV Healthcare Inc. accreditation
○ Healthcare Facilities Accreditation Program
△ Commission on Accreditation of Rehabilitation Facilities (CARF) accreditation

## KEOKUK—Lee County

⊠ **KEOKUK AREA HOSPITAL (160008)**, 1600 Morgan Street, Zip 52632–3456; tel. 319/524–7150 **A**1 9 10 **F**1 3 4 11 13 15 16 17 28 29 31 34 35 40 43 45 46 57 59 62 64 67 68 70 72 73 76 79 80 81 85 86 87 88 89 90 93 96 98 100 101 102 107 108 111 114 115 118 119 128 129 130 131 132 133 146 148 **P**6
Primary Contact: Katherine Devine, R.N., Interim Chief Executive Officer
CMO: Kiran Khanolkar, M.D., Chief of Staff
CIO: Linda Schaffner, Chief Information Officer
CHR: Rhonda Schreck, Director Human Resources
CNO: Susan Pankey, Vice President Clinical Services
Web address: www.keokukhealthsystems.org
**Control:** Other not–for–profit (including NFP Corporation) **Service:** General Medical and Surgical

**Staffed Beds:** 61 **Admissions:** 1759 **Census:** 16 **Outpatient Visits:** 36675 **Births:** 147 **Total Expense ($000):** 25745 **Payroll Expense ($000):** 11938 **Personnel:** 296

## KEOSAUQUA—Van Buren County

★ **VAN BUREN COUNTY HOSPITAL (161337)**, 304 Franklin Street, Zip 52565–1164; tel. 319/293–3171 **A**9 10 18 **F**3 7 10 11 13 15 28 29 32 34 35 40 43 45 46 50 57 59 64 65 70 75 76 77 81 85 86 87 89 93 97 102 107 110 111 114 119 125 127 128 130 132 133 135 146 147 148 **P**6
Primary Contact: Jill Kordick, Interim Chief Executive Officer
CFO: Kara McEntee, Chief Financial Officer
CIO: Chris McEntee, Network Specialist
Web address: www.vbch.org
**Control:** County–Government, nonfederal **Service:** General Medical and Surgical

**Staffed Beds:** 25 **Admissions:** 480 **Census:** 5 **Outpatient Visits:** 16238 **Births:** 40 **Total Expense ($000):** 12526 **Payroll Expense ($000):** 6257 **Personnel:** 147

## KNOXVILLE—Marion County

**KNOXVILLE DIVISION** See Veterans Affairs Central Iowa Health Care System, Des Moines

★ ◇ **KNOXVILLE HOSPITAL & CLINICS (161355)**, 1002 South Lincoln Street, Zip 50138–3155; tel. 641/842–2151 **A**9 10 18 21 **F**3 8 11 13 15 28 29 31 34 40 43 45 47 48 49 50 54 57 59 64 65 68 75 76 77 79 81 85 86 93 97 102 107 108 110 111 114 119 129 130 132 133 135 146 147 148 **P**6
Primary Contact: Kevin Kincaid, Chief Executive Officer
COO: Christine Buttell, Chief Operating Officer
CFO: Maggie Hamilton–Beyer, Chief Financial Officer
CMO: Bryon Schaeffer, M.D., Chief of Medical Staff
CIO: Thom Richards, Director Information Technology
CHR: Brian Sims, Director Administrative Services
CNO: Mary Jane Applegate, Chief Nursing Officer
Web address: www.knoxvillehospital.org
**Control:** Other not–for–profit (including NFP Corporation) **Service:** General Medical and Surgical

**Staffed Beds:** 25 **Admissions:** 1093 **Census:** 10 **Outpatient Visits:** 63562 **Births:** 58 **Total Expense ($000):** 24644 **Payroll Expense ($000):** 10841 **Personnel:** 213

## LAKE CITY—Calhoun County

★ **STEWART MEMORIAL COMMUNITY HOSPITAL (161350)**, 1301 West Main, Zip 51449–1585; tel. 712/464–3171 **A**9 10 18 **F**7 11 12 15 28 29 30 31 34 40 43 45 59 62 63 64 65 69 70 75 76 77 78 79 81 82 86 93 94 107 110 119 127 130 133 135 147 **P**5 6
Primary Contact: Leah Glasgo, Administrator and Chief Executive Officer
CFO: Jim Henkenius, Chief Financial Officer
CHR: Bill Albright, Director Human Resources
Web address: www.stewartmemorial.org
**Control:** Other not–for–profit (including NFP Corporation) **Service:** General Medical and Surgical

**Staffed Beds:** 25 **Admissions:** 631 **Census:** 6 **Outpatient Visits:** 49968 **Births:** 80 **Total Expense ($000):** 29984 **Payroll Expense ($000):** 13023 **Personnel:** 231

## LE MARS—Plymouth County

★ **FLOYD VALLEY HOSPITAL (161368)**, 714 Lincoln Street N.E., Zip 51031–3314; tel. 712/546–7871 **A**9 10 18 **F**3 10 11 13 15 28 29 31 32 34 35 40 43 45 53 57 59 62 64 65 67 76 78 79 80 81 85 86 87 89 107 114 119 128 130 132 133 135 146 148 **S** Avera Health, Sioux Falls, SD
Primary Contact: Michael T. Donlin, FACHE, Administrator
CFO: Daryl Friedenbach, Director Fiscal Services
CMO: Shahid Naqvi, M.D., President Medical Staff
CHR: Mary Helen Gibson, Director Human Resources
Web address: www.floydvalleyhospital.org
**Control:** City–Government, nonfederal **Service:** General Medical and Surgical

**Staffed Beds:** 25 **Admissions:** 1090 **Census:** 9 **Outpatient Visits:** 49078 **Births:** 105 **Total Expense ($000):** 31420 **Payroll Expense ($000):** 10747 **Personnel:** 253

## LEON—Decatur County

★ **DECATUR COUNTY HOSPITAL (161340)**, 1405 N.W. Church Street, Zip 50144–1299; tel. 641/446–4871 **A**9 10 18 **F**7 11 15 28 29 31 40 57 59 64 67 68 75 78 79 81 85 93 107 111 114 119 128 130 133
Primary Contact: Lynn Milnes, Chief Executive Officer
CFO: Tara Spidle, Controller
CMO: Larry Richard, M.D., Chief Medical Staff
CHR: Jo Beth Smith, Director Support Services and Human Resources
Web address: www.decaturcountyhospital.org
**Control:** County–Government, nonfederal **Service:** General Medical and Surgical

**Staffed Beds:** 25 **Admissions:** 352 **Census:** 4 **Outpatient Visits:** 12803 **Births:** 0 **Total Expense ($000):** 9297 **Payroll Expense ($000):** 3437 **Personnel:** 91

## MANCHESTER—Delaware County

★ **REGIONAL MEDICAL CENTER (161343)**, 709 West Main Street, #359, Zip 52057–1526, Mailing Address: P.O. Box 359, Zip 52057–0359; tel. 563/927–3232 **A**9 10 18 **F**3 7 11 12 13 15 17 28 29 34 35 36 40 43 44 50 53 57 59 61 62 63 64 65 66 68 70 75 76 77 79 81 82 85 86 89 93 94 97 107 108 110 111 114 119 127 128 129 130 131 132 133 146 148 **P**6
Primary Contact: Lon D. Butikofer, R.N., Ph.D., Chief Executive Officer
CFO: Danette Kramer, Chief Financial Officer
CIO: Amy Mensen, Chief Administrative Officer
CHR: Amy Mensen, Chief Administrative Officer
CNO: Patricia S. Doyle, R.N., Chief Nursing Officer
Web address: www.regmedctr.org
**Control:** County–Government, nonfederal **Service:** General Medical and Surgical

**Staffed Beds:** 25 **Admissions:** 890 **Census:** 9 **Outpatient Visits:** 164091 **Births:** 119 **Total Expense ($000):** 35887 **Payroll Expense ($000):** 17111 **Personnel:** 330

## MANNING—Carroll County

★ **MANNING REGIONAL HEALTHCARE CENTER (161332)**, 410 Main Street, Zip 51455–1093; tel. 712/655–2072, (Total facility includes 56 beds in nursing home–type unit) **A**9 10 18 **F**3 4 5 11 13 15 31 34 35 38 40 43 45 46 50 56 57 59 61 64 68 71 74 75 76 81 85 87 89 92 93 107 108 110 114 119 128 130 132 133 146 148 **P**6
Primary Contact: John O'Brien, Chief Executive Officer
CFO: Abbey Stangl, Chief Financial Officer
CMO: Tracy Kahl, M.D., Chief Medical Officer
CIO: Kim C. Jahn, Director Support Services
CHR: Shelli Lorenzen, Director Human Resources
CNO: Amy S. Dawson, Chief Clinical Officer
Web address: www.mrhcia.com
**Control:** Other not–for–profit (including NFP Corporation) **Service:** General Medical and Surgical

**Staffed Beds:** 73 **Admissions:** 322 **Census:** 56 **Outpatient Visits:** 7803 **Births:** 40 **Total Expense ($000):** 12244 **Payroll Expense ($000):** 5960 **Personnel:** 174

## MAQUOKETA—Jackson County

⊠ **JACKSON COUNTY REGIONAL HEALTH CENTER (161329)**, 700 West Grove Street, Zip 52060–2163; tel. 563/652–2474 **A**1 9 10 18 **F**3 7 11 15 28 34 40 43 45 53 59 62 64 65 75 77 81 87 93 107 110 114 119 129 130 132 133 146 **S** Genesis Health System, Davenport, IA
Primary Contact: Curt Coleman, FACHE, Chief Executive Officer
CFO: Donna Roeder, Chief Financial Officer
CHR: Shannon Langenberg, Director Human Resources
Web address: www.jcrhc.org
**Control:** County–Government, nonfederal **Service:** General Medical and Surgical

**Staffed Beds:** 25 **Admissions:** 210 **Census:** 3 **Outpatient Visits:** 20036 **Births:** 0 **Total Expense ($000):** 12917 **Payroll Expense ($000):** 5230 **Personnel:** 114

## MARENGO—Iowa County

★ **UNITYPOINT HEALTH – MARENGO MEMORIAL HOSPITAL (161317)**, 300 West May Street, Zip 52301–1261, Mailing Address: P.O. Box 228, Zip 52301–0228; tel. 319/642–5543 **A**9 10 18 **F**3 7 28 29 31 34 35 38 40 43 45 50 57 59 60 64 68 69 75 78 81 82 85 87 96 97 107 114 130 133 143 146 **P**5 6 **S** UnityPoint Health, West Des Moines, IA
Primary Contact: Barry Goettsch, Chief Executive Officer
COO: Mikaela Kienitz, Assistant Administrator
CFO: Nancy Kohrt, Chief Financial Officer
CHR: Lesa Waddell, Director Human Resources
Web address: www.marengohospital.org
**Control:** City–Government, nonfederal **Service:** General Medical and Surgical

**Staffed Beds:** 25 **Admissions:** 343 **Census:** 12 **Outpatient Visits:** 22911 **Births:** 0 **Total Expense ($000):** 15961 **Payroll Expense ($000):** 6661 **Personnel:** 137

**IA**

*Many Facility Codes have changed. Please refer to the AHA Guide Code Chart.* © 2013 AHA Guide

## MARSHALLTOWN—Marshall County

★ **MARSHALLTOWN MEDICAL & SURGICAL CENTER (160001)**, 3 South Fourth Avenue, Zip 50158–2998; tel. 641/754–5151, (Total facility includes 26 beds in nursing home–type unit) **A**9 10 **F**3 7 11 13 15 18 20 22 26 27 28 29 30 35 40 41 42 43 44 45 46 48 50 53 54 56 57 59 61 62 64 67 68 70 75 76 77 79 81 82 85 86 87 89 93 94 97 107 111 114 115 119 127 128 129 130 146 147 148
Primary Contact: John Hughes, FACHE, President and Chief Executive Officer
CFO: Robert Downey, Chief Financial Officer
CMO: Milt Van Gundy, M.D., President Medical Staff
CIO: Robert Downey, Chief Financial Officer
CHR: Jill Petermeier, Senior Executive Human Resources
Web address: www.everydaychampions.org
**Control:** Other not–for–profit (including NFP Corporation) **Service:** General Medical and Surgical

**Staffed Beds:** 105 **Admissions:** 3002 **Census:** 27 **Outpatient Visits:** 196904 **Births:** 588 **Total Expense ($000):** 60689 **Payroll Expense ($000):** 28885 **Personnel:** 527

## MASON CITY—Cerro Gordo County

⊠ **MERCY MEDICAL CENTER–NORTH IOWA (160064)**, 1000 Fourth Street S.W., Zip 50401–2800; tel. 641/428–7000 **A**1 2 3 5 9 10 13 **F**3 11 12 13 15 17 18 20 22 24 26 28 29 30 31 32 34 35 36 37 38 39 40 43 44 45 46 47 48 49 50 54 56 57 59 60 61 62 63 64 65 66 68 70 71 72 74 75 76 77 78 79 81 82 84 85 86 87 89 90 92 93 96 97 98 99 100 101 102 103 104 105 107 108 110 111 114 115 117 118 119 120 121 123 125 126 128 129 130 131 132 134 135 144 146 147 148 **P**1 6 **S** Trinity Health, Livonia, MI
Primary Contact: Daniel Varnum, President and Chief Executive Officer
COO: Diane Fischels, Senior Vice President and Chief Operating Officer
CFO: Moni Haxtom, Interim Chief Financial Officer
CMO: Paul Manternach, M.D., Senior Vice President Physician Integration
CIO: Randy Haskins, Director Information Systems
CHR: Jackie Luecht, Chief Human Resources Officer
CNO: Kim Chamberlin, Vice President Patient Services and Chief Nursing Officer
Web address: www.mercynorthiowa.com
**Control:** Church–operated, Nongovernment, not–for profit **Service:** General Medical and Surgical

**Staffed Beds:** 240 **Admissions:** 12916 **Census:** 138 **Outpatient Visits:** 441007 **Births:** 911 **Total Expense ($000):** 316534 **Payroll Expense ($000):** 129528 **Personnel:** 2081

## MISSOURI VALLEY—Harrison County

★ **ALEGENT CREIGHTON HEALTH COMMUNITY MEMORIAL HOSPITAL (161309)**, (Formerly Alegent Health–Community Memorial Hospital), 631 North Eighth Street, Zip 51555–1102; tel. 712/642–2784 **A**9 10 18 **F**3 11 15 18 28 29 30 31 35 39 40 43 45 50 54 59 64 75 77 78 79 81 82 85 93 99 100 102 103 104 107 110 114 119 127 129 133 135 144 146 **P**8 **S** Catholic Health Initiatives, Englewood, CO
Primary Contact: Robert A. Valentine, Regional Administrator
CFO: Matthew Smith, Operations Director Finance and Support Services
CMO: Daniel Richter, M.D., Chief of Staff
CIO: Kenneth Lawonn, Senior Vice President Strategy and Technology
CHR: Julie Brown, Human Resources Specialist
CNO: Jane Carmody DNP, MBA, RN, CENP, R.N., Vice President and System Chief Nursing Officer
Web address: www.alegentcreighton.com/community–memorial
**Control:** Other not–for–profit (including NFP Corporation) **Service:** General Medical and Surgical

**Staffed Beds:** 16 **Admissions:** 531 **Census:** 5 **Outpatient Visits:** 62361 **Births:** 0 **Total Expense ($000):** 21891 **Payroll Expense ($000):** 7059 **Personnel:** 171

## MOUNT AYR—Ringgold County

**RINGGOLD COUNTY HOSPITAL (161373)**, 504 North Cleveland Street, Zip 50854–2201; tel. 641/464–3226 **A**9 10 18 **F**3 7 11 15 28 29 31 35 38 40 56 57 59 60 64 65 81 89 93 107 111 114 119 133 148 **P**6
Primary Contact: Gordon W. Winkler, Administrator and Chief Executive Officer
CFO: Teresa Roberts, Chief Financial Officer
CIO: Jan Lyons, Regional Director Health Improvement Management
CHR: Mitzi Hymbaugh, Chief Personnel
Web address: www.rchmtayr.org
**Control:** County–Government, nonfederal **Service:** General Medical and Surgical

**Staffed Beds:** 16 **Admissions:** 301 **Census:** 2 **Outpatient Visits:** 21607 **Births:** 0 **Total Expense ($000):** 16410 **Payroll Expense ($000):** 5759 **Personnel:** 116

## MOUNT PLEASANT—Henry County

★ **HENRY COUNTY HEALTH CENTER (161356)**, 407 South White Street, Zip 52641–2263; tel. 319/385–3141, (Total facility includes 49 beds in nursing home–type unit) **A**9 10 18 **F**3 7 11 13 15 28 29 31 32 34 35 40 41 43 45 50 57 59 64 65 67 68 70 75 76 77 78 79 81 82 85 86 87 89 93 102 107 108 110 115 118 119 128 129 130 131 132 133 135 143 145 146 148 **P**6
Primary Contact: Robb Gardner, Chief Executive Officer
CFO: David Muhs, Chief Financial Officer
CMO: Steve Davis, M.D., Chief of Staff
CIO: Steve Stewart, Director Information Technology
CHR: Jim Carson, Director Human Resources
CNO: Jodi Geerts, Chief Nursing Officer
Web address: www.hchc.org
**Control:** County–Government, nonfederal **Service:** General Medical and Surgical

**Staffed Beds:** 74 **Admissions:** 720 **Census:** 47 **Outpatient Visits:** 160584 **Births:** 146 **Total Expense ($000):** 30263 **Payroll Expense ($000):** 12690 **Personnel:** 222

**MENTAL HEALTH INSTITUTE (164004)**, 1200 East Washington Street, Zip 52641–1898; tel. 319/385–7231 **A**9 10 **F**4 5 29 75 86 98 100 101 103 130 132 135
Primary Contact: Ron Mullen, Superintendent
CFO: Barb Wheeler, Business Manager
CHR: Janice Creighton, Human Resources Associate
Web address: www.dhs.state.ia.us
**Control:** State–Government, nonfederal **Service:** Alcoholism and other chemical dependency

**Staffed Beds:** 78 **Admissions:** 794 **Census:** 65 **Outpatient Visits:** 75 **Births:** 0 **Total Expense ($000):** 8445 **Payroll Expense ($000):** 4886 **Personnel:** 79

## MUSCATINE—Muscatine County

⊠ **TRINITY MUSCATINE (160013)**, 1518 Mulberry Avenue, Zip 52761–3499; tel. 563/264–9100 **A**1 9 10 20 **F**3 11 13 15 28 31 40 43 46 50 56 57 59 61 64 68 69 70 75 76 79 81 83 85 87 89 102 107 108 110 114 119 129 130 133 148 **S** UnityPoint Health, West Des Moines, IA
Primary Contact: James M. Hayes, Chief Executive Officer
CFO: Greg Pagliuzza, Chief Financial Officer
CMO: Manasi Nadkarni, M.D., Vice President Medical Affairs
CIO: Richard E. Maere, Account Executive Information Technology
CHR: Karla Blaser, Director Human Resources
CNO: Pam Askew, R.N., Vice President Patient Care Services
Web address: www.trinitymuscatine.org
**Control:** Other not–for–profit (including NFP Corporation) **Service:** General Medical and Surgical

**Staffed Beds:** 56 **Admissions:** 1670 **Census:** 14 **Outpatient Visits:** 86296 **Births:** 331 **Total Expense ($000):** 36242 **Payroll Expense ($000):** 14968 **Personnel:** 309

## NEVADA—Story County

★ **STORY COUNTY MEDICAL CENTER (161333)**, 640 South 19th Street, Zip 50201–2902; tel. 515/382–2111, (Total facility includes 60 beds in nursing home–type unit) **A**9 10 18 **F**3 7 11 28 29 31 32 35 36 40 43 50 53 57 59 64 68 75 77 79 81 85 93 97 107 114 127 130 131 132 133 135 143 146 148 **P**6
Primary Contact: Tom Mulrooney, Chief Executive Officer
COO: Julie Schreitmueller, Chief Operating Officer
CFO: Jane Ramthun, Chief Financial Officer
CHR: Kaylee Siebrecht, Director Human Resources
Web address: www.storymedical.org
**Control:** County–Government, nonfederal **Service:** General Medical and Surgical

**Staffed Beds:** 77 **Admissions:** 439 **Census:** 63 **Outpatient Visits:** 28206 **Births:** 0 **Total Expense ($000):** 19253 **Payroll Expense ($000):** 8645 **Personnel:** 175

IA

---

**Hospital, Medicare Provider Number, Address, Telephone, Approval, Facility, and Physician Codes, Health Care System**

★ American Hospital Association (AHA) membership
☐ The Joint Commission accreditation
◇ DNV Healthcare Inc. accreditation
○ Healthcare Facilities Accreditation Program
△ Commission on Accreditation of Rehabilitation Facilities (CARF) accreditation

## NEW HAMPTON—Chickasaw County

★ **MERCY MEDICAL CENTER–NEW HAMPTON (161331)**, 308 North Maple Avenue, Zip 50659–1142; tel. 641/394–4121 **A**9 10 18 **F**3 11 13 15 28 29 34 35 40 43 45 48 56 57 59 64 65 68 74 76 77 79 81 85 93 97 107 108 110 113 114 119 131 133 146 148 **P**1 **S** Trinity Health, Livonia, MI
Primary Contact: Kim Price, Chief Executive Officer
CFO: Jennifer Rapenske, Manager Financial Services
CMO: D. Paul McQuillen, D.O., Chief of Staff
CIO: Randy Haskins, Director Information Systems
CHR: Lisa Heller, Manager Human Resources
CNO: Sherrie L. Laubenthal, R.N., Chief Nursing Officer
Web address: www.mercynewhampton.com
**Control:** Church–operated, Nongovernment, not–for profit **Service:** General Medical and Surgical

**Staffed Beds:** 18 **Admissions:** 426 **Census:** 4 **Outpatient Visits:** 18512 **Births:** 43 **Total Expense ($000):** 14609 **Payroll Expense ($000):** 5368 **Personnel:** 97

## NEWTON—Jasper County

★ ○ **SKIFF MEDICAL CENTER (160032)**, 204 Fourth Avenue East, Zip 50208–3100, Mailing Address: P.O. Box 1006, Zip 50208–1006; tel. 641/792–1273 **A**9 10 11 **F**3 11 13 15 28 29 30 31 34 35 36 40 43 44 45 57 59 62 63 64 65 70 75 76 77 78 79 81 84 85 93 96 102 107 108 110 111 115 118 119 124 130 131 132 133 135 146 148 **P**6
Primary Contact: Steve Long, FACHE, President and Chief Executive Officer
COO: Brett Altman, Clinical Operations Officer
CFO: Mike Anderson, Chief Financial Officer
CIO: Janice Bilmer, Director, Information Services
CHR: Ellen Graber, Director, Human Resources
CNO: Mary Swoboda, R.N., Chief Nursing Officer
Web address: www.skiffmed.com
**Control:** City–Government, nonfederal **Service:** General Medical and Surgical

**Staffed Beds:** 48 **Admissions:** 1776 **Census:** 23 **Outpatient Visits:** 75253 **Births:** 175 **Total Expense ($000):** 37423 **Payroll Expense ($000):** 17624 **Personnel:** 286

## OAKDALE—Johnson County

**IOWA MEDICAL AND CLASSIFICATION CENTER**, Highway 965, Zip 52319, Mailing Address: IMCC, Box A, Zip 52319; tel. 319/626–2391 **F**29 38 39 59 75 98 101 102 103 105 130 132 143
Primary Contact: Daniel Craig, Warden
Web address: www.oakdaleprison.com/
**Control:** State–Government, nonfederal **Service:** Psychiatric

**Staffed Beds:** 28 **Admissions:** 47 **Census:** 22 **Outpatient Visits:** 5 **Births:** 0 **Total Expense ($000):** 2490 **Personnel:** 26

## OELWEIN—Fayette County

★ **MERCY HOSPITAL OF FRANCISCAN SISTERS (161338)**, 201 Eighth Avenue S.E., Zip 50662–2447; tel. 319/283–6000, (Total facility includes 39 beds in nursing home–type unit) **A**9 10 18 **F**7 11 15 29 30 34 35 40 57 59 69 75 79 81 97 107 110 111 119 127 128 130 132 133 146 **P**1 **S** Wheaton Franciscan Healthcare, Wheaton, IL
Primary Contact: Terri Derflinger, Administrator
CFO: Timothy Huber, Manager Financial Support
CHR: Vicki L. Parsons, Regional Vice President Human Resources
Web address: www.covhealth.com
**Control:** Church–operated, Nongovernment, not–for profit **Service:** General Medical and Surgical

**Staffed Beds:** 64 **Admissions:** 329 **Census:** 34 **Outpatient Visits:** 24923 **Births:** 0 **Total Expense ($000):** 12573 **Payroll Expense ($000):** 5510 **Personnel:** 92

## ONAWA—Monona County

★ **BURGESS HEALTH CENTER (161359)**, 1600 Diamond Street, Zip 51040–1548; tel. 712/423–2311 **A**9 10 18 **F**3 7 11 13 15 28 29 31 32 34 35 40 56 57 59 62 63 64 65 70 75 76 77 78 79 81 82 85 89 93 97 99 100 101 103 104 107 114 119 127 130 132 133 135 146 148 **P**6
Primary Contact: Francis G. Tramp, President
CFO: Shawn Gosch, Chief Financial Officer
CMO: John Garred, Sr., M.D., Chief Medical Officer
CIO: Kim Norby, Chief Information Officer
CHR: Denise Trukenmiller, Director Human Resources
Web address: www.burgesshc.org
**Control:** Other not–for–profit (including NFP Corporation) **Service:** General Medical and Surgical

**Staffed Beds:** 25 **Admissions:** 792 **Census:** 9 **Outpatient Visits:** 71804 **Births:** 52 **Total Expense ($000):** 23446 **Payroll Expense ($000):** 9820 **Personnel:** 218

## ORANGE CITY—Sioux County

★ **ORANGE CITY AREA HEALTH SYSTEM (161360)**, 1000 Lincoln Circle S.E., Zip 51041–1862; tel. 712/737–4984, (Total facility includes 79 beds in nursing home–type unit) **A**9 10 18 **F**7 10 11 13 15 18 28 29 31 34 35 40 45 50 53 56 57 59 60 62 63 64 67 68 69 70 75 76 77 78 79 81 82 85 86 87 89 93 97 107 110 111 114 117 119 120 125 127 130 131 132 133 146 147 148 **P**6 **S** Sanford Health, Sioux Falls, SD
Primary Contact: Martin W. Guthmiller, Chief Executive Officer
COO: Daniel P. McCarty, Chief Operating Officer
CFO: Dina Baas, Director Financial Services
CHR: Shari Baker, Director Human Resources
Web address: www.ochealthsystem.org
**Control:** City–Government, nonfederal **Service:** General Medical and Surgical

**Staffed Beds:** 104 **Admissions:** 1002 **Census:** 87 **Outpatient Visits:** 71159 **Births:** 213 **Total Expense ($000):** 37864 **Payroll Expense ($000):** 16443 **Personnel:** 382

## OSAGE—Mitchell County

★ **MITCHELL COUNTY REGIONAL HEALTH CENTER (161323)**, 616 North Eighth Street, Zip 50461–1498; tel. 641/732–6000 **A**9 10 18 **F**7 8 11 15 18 28 29 34 35 40 50 57 59 63 64 65 75 81 85 87 91 93 107 110 114 119 127 130 132 133 144 146 **P**8 **S** Trinity Health, Livonia, MI
Primary Contact: Kevin Runolfson, Chief Executive Officer
CMO: Kelly Ross, M.D., Chief of Staff
CHR: Tom Nelson, Director Human Resources
Web address: www.mitchellcohospital–clinics.com
**Control:** County–Government, nonfederal **Service:** General Medical and Surgical

**Staffed Beds:** 25 **Admissions:** 448 **Census:** 6 **Outpatient Visits:** 57734 **Births:** 0 **Total Expense ($000):** 17512 **Payroll Expense ($000):** 5677 **Personnel:** 133

## OSCEOLA—Clarke County

★ **CLARKE COUNTY HOSPITAL (161348)**, 800 South Fillmore Street, Zip 50213–1619; tel. 641/342–2184 **A**9 10 18 **F**7 11 15 18 28 29 31 34 35 40 45 53 57 59 64 67 68 75 81 89 90 93 94 96 107 111 115 116 117 118 119 128 129 130 133 135 148 **S** UnityPoint Health, West Des Moines, IA
Primary Contact: Brian G. Evans, FACHE, Chief Executive Officer
CFO: Michael Thilges, Chief Financial Officer
CMO: George Fotiadis, M.D., Chief of Staff
CIO: Dennis Blazek, Chief Information Officer
CHR: Kate Emanuel, Director Human Resources
Web address: www.clarkehosp.org
**Control:** County–Government, nonfederal **Service:** General Medical and Surgical

**Staffed Beds:** 25 **Admissions:** 335 **Census:** 13 **Outpatient Visits:** 20401 **Births:** 0 **Total Expense ($000):** 17625 **Payroll Expense ($000):** 5949 **Personnel:** 142

## OSKALOOSA—Mahaska County

⊠ **MAHASKA HEALTH PARTNERSHIP (161379)**, 1229 C Avenue East, Zip 52577–4298; tel. 641/672–3100 **A**1 9 10 18 **F**5 7 11 13 15 28 29 30 31 34 35 40 43 45 47 50 54 56 57 59 62 63 64 68 69 70 75 76 77 78 79 81 87 93 97 98 99 100 101 102 103 104 107 110 111 114 119 129 130 133 135 146 148 **P**6
Primary Contact: Jay Christensen, FACHE, Administrator
CFO: Susan Horras, Chief Financial Officer
CMO: Sreedhar Somisetty, M.D., Chief Medical Officer
CHR: Jacky Bresnahan, Director Human Resources
Web address: www.mahaskahealth.com
**Control:** County–Government, nonfederal **Service:** General Medical and Surgical

**Staffed Beds:** 33 **Admissions:** 1643 **Census:** 18 **Outpatient Visits:** 96210 **Births:** 160 **Total Expense ($000):** 37661 **Payroll Expense ($000):** 23409 **Personnel:** 336

## OTTUMWA—Wapello County

☐ △ **OTTUMWA REGIONAL HEALTH CENTER (160089)**, 1001 Pennsylvania Avenue, Zip 52501–2186; tel. 641/684–2300 **A**1 2 7 9 10 **F**3 6 7 8 10 11 13 15 18 20 22 28 29 30 31 34 35 40 43 45 51 53 56 57 59 60 62 72 76 77 78 79 81 82 85 87 89 90 107 108 110 114 115 118 119 120 121 123 125 126 129 130 131 135 141 142 144 146 147 148 **P**6 **S** RegionalCare Hospital Partners, Brentwood, TN
Primary Contact: Philip G. Dionne, Chief Executive Officer
CFO: Dan Porter, Vice President and Chief Financial Officer
CMO: Kenneth Wayne, M.D., Chief Medical Officer
CHR: JoEllen Randall, Administrative Director Human Resources
Web address: www.ottumwaregionalhealth.com
**Control:** Corporation, Investor–owned, for–profit **Service:** General Medical and Surgical

**Staffed Beds:** 105 **Admissions:** 3370 **Census:** 38 **Outpatient Visits:** 115660 **Births:** 570 **Total Expense ($000):** 80352 **Payroll Expense ($000):** 24879 **Personnel:** 613

IA

*Many Facility Codes have changed. Please refer to the AHA Guide Code Chart.* © 2013 AHA Guide

## PELLA—Marion County

✉ **PELLA REGIONAL HEALTH CENTER (161367)**, 404 Jefferson Street, Zip 50219–1257; tel. 641/628–3150, (Total facility includes 63 beds in nursing home–type unit) **A**1 9 10 18 **F**3 11 13 15 28 29 30 31 34 35 40 43 48 50 57 59 60 62 63 64 65 67 70 75 76 77 78 79 81 85 86 87 93 97 107 108 110 111 115 119 126 127 128 129 130 131 132 133 141 144 146 147 148 **P**6
Primary Contact: Robert D. Kroese, FACHE, Chief Executive Officer
COO: Robert D. Kroese, FACHE, Chief Executive Officer
CFO: Ron Wauters, Chief Financial Officer
CIO: Tait Smock, Manager Information Systems
CHR: Teri Lickteig, HR Director
CNO: Yvonne M. O'Brien, MS, Chief of Nursing
Web address: www.pellahealth.org
**Control:** Other not–for–profit (including NFP Corporation) **Service:** General Medical and Surgical

**Staffed Beds:** 88 **Admissions:** 1659 **Census:** 64 **Outpatient Visits:** 139226
**Births:** 410 **Total Expense ($000):** 49663 **Payroll Expense ($000):** 20530
**Personnel:** 607

## PERRY—Dallas County

★ **DALLAS COUNTY HOSPITAL (161322)**, 610 10th Street, Zip 50220–2221; tel. 515/465–3547 **A**9 10 18 **F**10 11 15 18 28 29 31 34 35 39 40 41 43 57 59 68 75 77 78 79 81 82 85 89 90 93 107 110 111 114 116 119 128 129 132 133 146 147 148
Primary Contact: Matt Wille, Chief Executive Officer
CFO: Sandra Christensen, Chief Financial Officer
CMO: Steven Sohn, M.D., President Medical Staff
CHR: Sherry Smith, Manager Human Resources
Web address: www.dallascohospital.org
**Control:** County–Government, nonfederal **Service:** General Medical and Surgical

**Staffed Beds:** 18 **Admissions:** 287 **Census:** 4 **Outpatient Visits:** 26554
**Births:** 0 **Total Expense ($000):** 13819 **Payroll Expense ($000):** 4233
**Personnel:** 89

## POCAHONTAS—Pocahontas County

★ **POCAHONTAS COMMUNITY HOSPITAL (161305)**, 606 N.W. Seventh Street, Zip 50574–1099; tel. 712/335–3501 **A**9 10 18 **F**7 11 15 28 29 31 35 40 43 45 59 62 63 64 75 77 78 79 81 84 89 93 107 110 119 128 130 132 133 135 146 148 **P**6 **S** UnityPoint Health, West Des Moines, IA
Primary Contact: James D. Roetman, President and Chief Executive Officer
CFO: Lynn Raveling, Chief Financial Officer
Web address: www.pocahontashospital.org
**Control:** City–Government, nonfederal **Service:** General Medical and Surgical

**Staffed Beds:** 20 **Admissions:** 294 **Census:** 4 **Outpatient Visits:** 32904
**Births:** 0 **Total Expense ($000):** 9809 **Payroll Expense ($000):** 3170
**Personnel:** 84

## PRIMGHAR—O'brien County

★ **BAUM HARMON MERCY HOSPITAL (161300)**, 255 North Welch Avenue, Zip 51245–7765, Mailing Address: P.O. Box 528, Zip 51245–0528; tel. 712/957–2300 **A**9 10 18 **F**11 15 28 29 30 31 34 35 40 45 53 57 59 64 67 70 75 77 78 81 89 119 127 128 133 135 **P**6 **S** Trinity Health, Livonia, MI
Primary Contact: David Liebsack, Chief Executive Officer
CFO: Sue E. McCauley, Director Finance
CMO: Shailesh Desai, M.D., Chief of Staff
Web address: www.baumharmon.org
**Control:** Church–operated, Nongovernment, not–for profit **Service:** General Medical and Surgical

**Staffed Beds:** 13 **Admissions:** 152 **Census:** 1 **Outpatient Visits:** 23805
**Births:** 0 **Total Expense ($000):** 7163 **Payroll Expense ($000):** 3432
**Personnel:** 66

## RED OAK—Montgomery County

★ **MONTGOMERY COUNTY MEMORIAL HOSPITAL (161363)**, 2301 Eastern Avenue, Zip 51566–1300, Mailing Address: P.O. Box 498, Zip 51566–0498; tel. 712/623–7000 **A**9 10 18 **F**1 4 11 13 15 16 29 31 34 35 40 44 45 50 53 57 59 62 63 64 67 68 69 70 72 73 75 76 77 78 79 80 81 82 85 86 87 88 89 90 93 98 107 110 111 114 118 119 128 129 130 133 135 146 147 148
Primary Contact: Allen E. Pohren, Administrator
CFO: Rick Leinen, Chief Financial Officer
CMO: William Artherholt, M.D., Chief of Staff
CIO: Ron Kloewer, Chief Information Officer
Web address: www.mcmh.org
**Control:** County–Government, nonfederal **Service:** General Medical and Surgical

**Staffed Beds:** 25 **Admissions:** 1106 **Census:** 16 **Outpatient Visits:** 44104
**Births:** 88 **Total Expense ($000):** 27918 **Payroll Expense ($000):** 12687
**Personnel:** 244

## ROCK RAPIDS—Lyon County

**SANFORD MERRILL MEDICAL CENTER** See Sanford Rock Rapids Medical Center

★ **SANFORD ROCK RAPIDS MEDICAL CENTER (161321)**, (Formerly Sanford Medical Center Rock Rapids), 801 South Greene Street, Zip 51246–1998; tel. 712/472–2591 **A**9 10 18 **F**11 28 31 34 40 41 45 53 57 59 68 77 81 87 89 97 107 119 127 130 131 133 135 146 **P**6 **S** Sanford Health, Sioux Falls, SD
Primary Contact: Tammy Loosbrock, Chief Executive Officer
CFO: Stanley Knobloch, Chief Financial Officer
CMO: David Springer, M.D., President Medical Staff
CHR: Rachel K. Ask, Supervisor Human Resources
Web address: www.sanfordmerrill.org
**Control:** Other not–for–profit (including NFP Corporation) **Service:** General Medical and Surgical

**Staffed Beds:** 16 **Admissions:** 303 **Census:** 3 **Outpatient Visits:** 15929
**Births:** 0 **Total Expense ($000):** 7814 **Payroll Expense ($000):** 3568
**Personnel:** 66

## ROCK VALLEY—Sioux County

★ **HEGG MEMORIAL HEALTH CENTER AVERA (161336)**, 1202 21st Avenue, Zip 51247–1497; tel. 712/476–8000, (Total facility includes 60 beds in nursing home–type unit) **A**9 10 18 **F**3 11 13 15 28 29 31 34 35 36 40 41 43 45 53 57 59 62 64 67 68 70 75 76 77 78 79 81 84 85 89 93 97 107 110 111 114 119 128 130 131 132 133 135 144 147 148 **S** Avera Health, Sioux Falls, SD
Primary Contact: Glenn Zevenbergen, Chief Executive Officer
CFO: Kari Timmer, Chief Financial Officer
CMO: Kevin Post, D.O., Chief Medical Officer
CHR: Tammy Faber, Director Human Resources
CNO: Sherri Kerr, Director of Nursing
Web address: www.hegghc.org
**Control:** Other not–for–profit (including NFP Corporation) **Service:** General Medical and Surgical

**Staffed Beds:** 85 **Admissions:** 343 **Census:** 62 **Outpatient Visits:** 34444
**Births:** 78 **Total Expense ($000):** 15460 **Payroll Expense ($000):** 8008
**Personnel:** 199

## SAC CITY—Sac County

★ **LORING HOSPITAL (161370)**, 211 Highland Avenue, Zip 50583–2424; tel. 712/662–7105 **A**9 10 18 **F**3 11 15 28 29 30 31 34 35 40 45 57 59 62 63 64 68 75 78 79 81 86 87 93 107 110 115 119 125 129 130 132 133 146 **S** UnityPoint Health, West Des Moines, IA
Primary Contact: Michael S. Ketcham, President and Chief Executive Officer
CFO: Angie Fischer, Chief Financial Officer
CMO: Les Marczewski, M.D., Chief Medical Officer
CIO: Kathy Veit, Director Health Information Services
CHR: Becky Pontious, Human Resources/Accounting
CNO: Lori Forneris, R.N., Chief Clinical Officer
Web address: www.loringhospital.org
**Control:** Other not–tor–profit (including NFP Corporation) **Service:** General Medical and Surgical

**Staffed Beds:** 25 **Admissions:** 892 **Census:** 8 **Outpatient Visits:** 23223
**Births:** 0 **Total Expense ($000):** 12143 **Payroll Expense ($000):** 4506
**Personnel:** 115

## SHELDON—O'brien County

★ **SANFORD SHELDON MEDICAL CENTER (161381)**, 118 North Seventh Avenue, Zip 51201–1235, Mailing Address: P.O. Box 250, Zip 51201–0250; tel. 712/324–5041, (Total facility includes 70 beds in nursing home–type unit) **A**9 10 18 **F**11 13 15 28 29 31 34 35 38 40 45 50 53 56 57 59 62 63 64 65 67 68 74 75 76 77 78 79 81 82 84 86 87 91 93 96 97 107 108 109 110 111 114 119 127 129 130 131 132 133 135 146 148 **P**6 **S** Sanford Health, Sioux Falls, SD
Primary Contact: Richard E. Nordahl, Chief Executive Officer
CFO: Deb Rosburg, Chief Financial Officer
CMO: Shane Smith, M.D., Physician
CIO: Scott Moffitt, Director Information Systems
CHR: Dianne Wolthuizen, Director Human Resources
CNO: Joni DeKok, Chief Nursing Officer
Web address: www.sanfordsheldon.org
**Control:** Other not–for–profit (including NFP Corporation) **Service:** General Medical and Surgical

**Staffed Beds:** 95 **Admissions:** 758 **Census:** 67 **Outpatient Visits:** 98637
**Births:** 114 **Total Expense ($000):** 25601 **Payroll Expense ($000):** 11565
**Personnel:** 259

**IA**

---

**Hospital, Medicare Provider Number, Address, Telephone, Approval, Facility, and Physician Codes, Health Care System**

★ American Hospital Association (AHA) membership
☐ The Joint Commission accreditation
◇ DNV Healthcare Inc. accreditation
◯ Healthcare Facilities Accreditation Program
△ Commission on Accreditation of Rehabilitation Facilities (CARF) accreditation

## SHENANDOAH—Page County

★ **SHENANDOAH MEDICAL CENTER (161366)**, 300 Pershing Avenue,
Zip 51601–2355; tel. 712/246–1230, (Total facility includes 53 beds in nursing
home–type unit) **A**9 10 18 **F**3 10 11 13 15 18 28 31 34 36 40 43 45 50 53 56
57 59 62 63 64 67 68 69 70 75 76 77 78 79 81 85 87 93 99 104 107 108
110 111 114 117 118 119 127 129 130 132 133 135 146 147 148 **P**6
Primary Contact: Karen S. Cole, MS, FACHE, Chief Executive Officer
CFO: Sandra Chesshire, Chief Financial Officer
CMO: Jerry Schaaf, M.D., Chief Medical Officer
CIO: John Eckmann, Director Information Systems
CHR: Keli Royal, Director Human Resources
CNO: Victor Bycroft, R.N., Chief Nursing Officer
Web address: www.shenandoahmedcenter.com
**Control:** Other not–for–profit (including NFP Corporation) **Service:** General
Medical and Surgical

**Staffed Beds:** 78 **Admissions:** 707 **Census:** 52 **Outpatient Visits:** 183414
**Births:** 125 **Total Expense ($000):** 25942 **Payroll Expense ($000):** 12071
**Personnel:** 238

## SIBLEY— County

★ **OSCEOLA COMMUNITY HOSPITAL (161345)**, 600 Ninth Avenue North,
Zip 51249–1012, Mailing Address: P.O. Box 258, Zip 51249–0258;
tel. 712/754–2574 **A**9 10 18 **F**3 8 9 10 11 13 15 17 18 26 28 29 31 32 34
35 36 40 43 45 46 49 53 56 57 59 61 62 64 65 67 68 70 75 76 77 78 79
81 82 83 84 85 86 87 89 93 107 108 110 114 119 125 128 129 130 131
132 133 135 143 144 145 146 147 148 **P**5 **S** Avera Health, Sioux Falls, SD
Primary Contact: Janet H. Dykstra, Chief Executive Officer
CFO: Jerri Palsrok, Manager Business Office
CMO: Gregory J. Kosters, D.O., Chief Medical Officer
CIO: Sherry McElroy, Director Health Information Management
Web address: www.osceolacommunityhospital.org
**Control:** Other not–for–profit (including NFP Corporation) **Service:** General
Medical and Surgical

**Staffed Beds:** 25 **Admissions:** 250 **Census:** 2 **Outpatient Visits:** 19254
**Births:** 25 **Total Expense ($000):** 10340 **Payroll Expense ($000):** 3330
**Personnel:** 82

## SIGOURNEY—Keokuk County

**KEOKUK COUNTY HEALTH CENTER (161315)**, 23019 Highway 149,
Zip 52591–8341; tel. 641/622–2720 **A**9 10 18 **F**1 2 3 7 11 12 28 29 30 34
35 38 40 43 45 46 50 56 57 59 63 64 65 67 75 77 82 84 86 87 90 91 93
97 107 128 130 131 132 133 134 135 144 146 148 **P**5 6
Primary Contact: Matthew Ives, Interim Chief Executive Officer and Chief Financial
Officer
CFO: Matthew Ives, Interim Chief Executive Officer and Chief Financial Officer
Web address: www.kchc.net
**Control:** County–Government, nonfederal **Service:** General Medical and Surgical

**Staffed Beds:** 14 **Admissions:** 92 **Census:** 7 **Outpatient Visits:** 7740 **Births:**
0 **Total Expense ($000):** 8786 **Payroll Expense ($000):** 3997 **Personnel:**
88

## SIOUX CENTER—Sioux County

★ **SIOUX CENTER COMMUNITY HOSPITAL AND HEALTH CENTER AVERA
(161346)**, 605 South Main Avenue, Zip 51250–1398; tel. 712/722–1271, (Total
facility includes 69 beds in nursing home–type unit) **A**9 10 18 **F**3 8 10 13 15 17
18 26 28 29 30 31 34 35 40 43 45 56 57 59 62 63 64 67 68 74 75 76
77 78 79 81 82 83 84 85 86 89 93 97 107 110 111 114 119 125 128 130
131 132 133 135 144 146 147 148 **P**6 **S** Avera Health, Sioux Falls, SD
Primary Contact: Kayleen R. Lee, Chief Executive Officer
COO: Marla Toering, Chief Operating Officer
CFO: Jackson Schuiteman, Chief Financial Officer
CHR: Gail Vonk, Director Human Resources and Marketing
Web address: www.schospital.org
**Control:** Other not–for–profit (including NFP Corporation) **Service:** General
Medical and Surgical

**Staffed Beds:** 90 **Admissions:** 655 **Census:** 73 **Outpatient Visits:** 48192
**Births:** 212 **Total Expense ($000):** 27863 **Payroll Expense ($000):** 13150
**Personnel:** 317

## SIOUX CITY—Woodbury County

✉ **MERCY MEDICAL CENTER–SIOUX CITY (160153)**, 801 Fifth Street,
Zip 51101–1326, Mailing Address: P.O. Box 3168, Zip 51102–3168;
tel. 712/279–2010 **A**1 2 3 5 9 10 **F**3 5 11 13 15 17 18 20 22 24 26 28 29
30 31 32 34 35 36 37 38 40 43 44 45 48 49 50 51 55 56 57 59 61 64 65
68 70 71 74 75 76 77 78 79 81 82 84 85 86 87 89 90 92 93 96 97 98 99
100 101 102 103 104 105 107 108 110 111 114 115 118 119 124 126 129
130 132 135 144 146 147 148 **P**6 8 **S** Trinity Health, Livonia, MI
Primary Contact: Robert J. Peebles, President and Chief Executive Officer
COO: Mari Kaptain–Dahlen, Chief Operating Officer
CFO: J. Steven Eavenson, Interim Vice President and Chief Financial Officer
CMO: Larry W. Sellers, M.D., Chief Medical Officer
CIO: Steve Larson, M.D., Director Information Systems
CHR: Julie Anfinson, Director Human Resources
Web address: www.mercysiouxcity.com
**Control:** Church–operated, Nongovernment, not–for profit **Service:** General
Medical and Surgical

**Staffed Beds:** 238 **Admissions:** 10585 **Census:** 138 **Outpatient Visits:**
267928 **Births:** 308 **Total Expense ($000):** 194055 **Payroll Expense
($000):** 79652 **Personnel:** 1262

★ ◇ **UNITYPOINT HEALTH ST. LUKE'S (160146)**, (Formerly St. Luke's
Regional Medical Center), 2720 Stone Park Boulevard, Zip 51104–3734;
tel. 712/279–3500 **A**3 5 9 10 21 **F**3 11 13 15 17 18 20 22 26 28 29 30 32
34 35 39 40 45 49 50 51 54 57 59 60 63 64 68 70 72 73 74 75 76 77 78
79 81 82 84 86 88 89 90 92 93 96 97 98 102 105 107 108 111 114 118
119 126 129 130 131 132 135 142 145 146 147 **P**6 **S** UnityPoint Health, West
Des Moines, IA
Primary Contact: Peter W. Thoreen, FACHE, President and Chief Executive Officer
COO: Lynn Wold, Chief Operation Officer
CFO: James Gobell, Chief Financial Officer
CMO: Richard D. Hildebrand, M.D., Vice President Medical Affairs and Chief
Medical Officer
CIO: James Gobell, Chief Financial Officer
CHR: Gary Johnson, Director Human Resources
CNO: Priscilla Stokes, MS, Vice President Patient Care and Chief Nursing Officer
Web address: www.stlukes.org
**Control:** Other not–for–profit (including NFP Corporation) **Service:** General
Medical and Surgical

**Staffed Beds:** 157 **Admissions:** 9425 **Census:** 106 **Outpatient Visits:** 66086
**Births:** 2018 **Total Expense ($000):** 123891 **Payroll Expense ($000):**
50660 **Personnel:** 1026

## SPENCER—Clay County

★ **SPENCER HOSPITAL (160112)**, 1200 First Avenue East, Suite 1,
Zip 51301–4342; tel. 712/264–6111 **A**9 10 **F**3 7 8 11 13 15 28 29 30 31 34
35 39 40 43 50 53 56 57 59 60 62 63 64 65 69 70 75 76 77 78 79 81 82
84 85 86 87 93 97 98 99 100 101 102 103 104 107 108 109 111 115 118
119 120 121 123 127 129 130 131 132 133 135 146 147 148 **P**5
Primary Contact: William J. Bumgarner, President
COO: Susan Zulk, Vice President Marketing and Fund Development
CFO: Mark Gaworski, Vice President Finance, Chief Financial Officer
CMO: Brian Wilson, D.O., Medical Staff President
CIO: Brenda Marie Tiefenthaler, R.N., Vice President Patient Care and Informatics
CHR: Stephen Duetsch, Vice President Operations and Support
CNO: Brenda Marie Tiefenthaler, R.N., Vice President Patient Care and Informatics
Web address: www.spencerhospital.org
**Control:** City–Government, nonfederal **Service:** General Medical and Surgical

**Staffed Beds:** 80 **Admissions:** 2850 **Census:** 33 **Outpatient Visits:** 120793
**Births:** 265 **Total Expense ($000):** 61422 **Payroll Expense ($000):** 21613
**Personnel:** 470

## SPIRIT LAKE—Dickinson County

★ **LAKES REGIONAL HEALTHCARE (160124)**, Highway 71 South,
Zip 51360–6810, Mailing Address: P.O. Box AB, Zip 51360–0159;
tel. 712/336–1230 **A**9 10 **F**3 7 11 13 15 28 29 30 31 34 35 40 41 43 45 50
57 59 62 63 64 65 69 70 75 76 77 78 79 81 85 93 97 107 111 114 119
128 129 130 132 133 143 146 148
Primary Contact: Jason Harrington, President and Chief Executive Officer
CFO: Steve Alger, Senior Vice President and Chief Financial Officer
Web address: www.lakeshealth.org
**Control:** County–Government, nonfederal **Service:** General Medical and Surgical

**Staffed Beds:** 30 **Admissions:** 897 **Census:** 9 **Outpatient Visits:** 37218
**Births:** 141 **Total Expense ($000):** 28724 **Payroll Expense ($000):** 10527
**Personnel:** 219

**IA**

*Many Facility Codes have changed. Please refer to the AHA Guide Code Chart.* © 2013 AHA Guide

## STORM LAKE—Buena Vista County

✠ **BUENA VISTA REGIONAL MEDICAL CENTER (161375)**, 1525 West Fifth Street, Zip 50588–3027, Mailing Address: P.O. Box 309, Zip 50588–0309; tel. 712/732–4030 **A**1 9 10 18 **F**3 7 8 11 13 15 18 28 29 30 31 34 40 45 53 57 59 62 63 64 68 70 74 75 76 77 78 79 81 82 84 85 86 87 93 96 98 103 107 108 110 111 115 117 118 119 129 130 131 132 133 135 146 147 148 **S** UnityPoint Health, West Des Moines, IA
Primary Contact: Steven Colerick, Chief Executive Officer
CFO: Krista Ketcham, Chief Financial Officer
CMO: Jason Huisenga, D.O., Chief Medical Staff
CIO: Brian Granville, Director Information Technology
CHR: Carrie Turnquist, Director Human Resources
CNO: Dawn M. Bach, MS, Chief Clinical Officer
Web address: www.bvrmc.org
**Control:** County–Government, nonfederal **Service:** General Medical and Surgical

**Staffed Beds:** 35 **Admissions:** 1387 **Census:** 19 **Outpatient Visits:** 74759 **Births:** 332 **Total Expense ($000):** 39966 **Payroll Expense ($000):** 16829 **Personnel:** 351

## SUMNER—Bremer County

★ **COMMUNITY MEMORIAL HOSPITAL (161320)**, 909 West First Street, Zip 50674–1203, Mailing Address: P.O. Box 148, Zip 50674–0148; tel. 563/578–3275 **A**9 10 18 **F**3 11 15 28 29 34 40 45 57 59 64 81 85 86 97 107 114 127 128 129 131 133 135 148 **P**5 6 **S** UnityPoint Health, West Des Moines, IA
Primary Contact: Mary S. Wells, R.N., Chief Executive Officer
CFO: Sara Trainor, Chief Financial Officer
CMO: Troy Buchholz, M.D., Chief Medical Staff
CHR: Robin Elliott, Personnel Officer
CNO: Lynne Niemann, Director Nurses and Patient Care
Web address: www.cmhsumner.org
**Control:** Other not–for–profit (including NFP Corporation) **Service:** General Medical and Surgical

**Staffed Beds:** 16 **Admissions:** 185 **Census:** 2 **Outpatient Visits:** 9862 **Births:** 0 **Total Expense ($000):** 9777 **Payroll Expense ($000):** 3992 **Personnel:** 79

## VINTON—Benton County

★ **VIRGINIA GAY HOSPITAL (161349)**, 502 North Ninth Avenue, Zip 52349–2299; tel. 319/472–6200, (Total facility includes 40 beds in nursing home–type unit) **A**9 10 18 **F**3 15 28 29 34 40 43 45 53 59 62 64 75 77 81 85 86 87 96 97 107 111 114 119 125 127 129 130 131 132 133 143 **P**6
Primary Contact: Michael J. Riege, Chief Executive Officer
COO: Tedd Kipper, Chief Operating Officer
CFO: Julia Meadows, Chief Financial Officer
CMO: Brian Meeker, D.O., President Medical Staff
CHR: Kim Frank, Chief Human Resources Officer
Web address: www.vghinc.com
**Control:** Other not–for–profit (including NFP Corporation) **Service:** General Medical and Surgical

**Staffed Beds:** 65 **Admissions:** 441 **Census:** 43 **Outpatient Visits:** 89867 **Births:** 0 **Total Expense ($000):** 21059 **Payroll Expense ($000):** 10178 **Personnel:** 191

## WASHINGTON—Washington County

★ **WASHINGTON COUNTY HOSPITAL AND CLINICS (161344)**, 400 East Polk Street, Zip 52353–1237, Mailing Address: P.O. Box 909, Zip 52353–0909; tel. 319/653–5481, (Total facility includes 43 beds in nursing home–type unit) **A**9 10 18 **F**3 13 15 28 29 34 40 43 45 53 55 57 59 64 67 68 69 75 76 81 82 84 85 86 93 97 107 110 114 119 130 132 133 135 146 147 148 **P**6
Primary Contact: Dennis Hunger, Chief Executive Officer
CFO: Steve Sanders, Chief Financial Officer
CMO: Donald Miller, M.D., Chief of Staff
CIO: Jennifer Durst, Director Information Services
CHR: Tracy Ousey, Director Human Resources
CNO: Barbara Griswold, Chief Nursing Officer
Web address: www.wchc.org
**Control:** County–Government, nonfederal **Service:** General Medical and Surgical

**Staffed Beds:** 68 **Admissions:** 1412 **Census:** 53 **Outpatient Visits:** 44508 **Births:** 144 **Total Expense ($000):** 23184 **Payroll Expense ($000):** 10828 **Personnel:** 231

## WATERLOO—Black Hawk County

**ALLEN MEMORIAL HOSPITAL** See UnityPoint Health Allen

✠ △ **COVENANT MEDICAL CENTER (160067)**, 3421 West Ninth Street, Zip 50702–5401; tel. 319/272–8000, (Includes KIMBALL–RIDGE CENTER, 2101 Kimball Avenue, Zip 50702; tel. 319/291–3131) **A**1 2 3 5 7 9 10 **F**3 4 5 7 11 13 15 18 19 20 22 26 28 29 30 31 33 34 35 40 43 44 46 49 51 53 57 58 59 60 61 62 64 68 70 71 72 74 75 76 77 78 79 81 82 89 90 93 97 98 99 100 104 105 107 108 110 111 114 115 116 118 119 120 127 129 130 131 132 143 144 146 147 148 **P**1 6 **S** Wheaton Franciscan Healthcare, Wheaton, IL
Primary Contact: Jack Dusenbery, President and Chief Executive Officer
CFO: Michele Panicucci, Senior Vice President and Chief Financial Officer
CMO: Paul Franke, M.D., Vice President Medical Affairs
CIO: Gregory Smith, Chief Information Officer
CHR: Vicki L. Parsons, Regional Vice President Human Resources
Web address: www.wheatoniowa.org
**Control:** Church–operated, Nongovernment, not–for profit **Service:** General Medical and Surgical

**Staffed Beds:** 243 **Admissions:** 9056 **Census:** 101 **Outpatient Visits:** 614956 **Births:** 1456 **Total Expense ($000):** 244111 **Payroll Expense ($000):** 112957 **Personnel:** 1742

✠ **UNITYPOINT HEALTH ALLEN (160110)**, (Formerly Allen Memorial Hospital), 1825 Logan Avenue, Zip 50703–1916; tel. 319/235–3941 **A**1 3 5 9 10 **F**3 8 11 13 15 17 18 20 22 24 26 28 29 30 31 34 35 37 40 43 45 46 48 49 50 51 52 54 56 57 59 63 64 66 68 70 72 74 75 76 77 78 79 81 82 84 85 86 87 88 89 90 91 92 93 96 97 98 99 100 101 102 103 104 107 108 110 111 114 115 118 119 126 127 129 130 132 135 146 147 148 **S** UnityPoint Health, West Des Moines, IA
Primary Contact: Pamela K. Delagardelle, Chief Executive Officer
CFO: Renee Rasmussen, Senior Vice President and Chief Financial Officer
CMO: Jeff Crandall, M.D., Chief Medical Officer
Web address: www.allenhospital.org
**Control:** Other not–for–profit (including NFP Corporation) **Service:** General Medical and Surgical

**Staffed Beds:** 201 **Admissions:** 10545 **Census:** 111 **Outpatient Visits:** 269721 **Births:** 971 **Total Expense ($000):** 200125 **Payroll Expense ($000):** 67062 **Personnel:** 1275

## WAUKON—Allamakee County

★ **VETERANS MEMORIAL HOSPITAL (161318)**, 40 First Street S.E., Zip 52172–2099; tel. 563/568–3411 **A**9 10 18 **F**7 11 13 15 28 31 34 35 40 45 57 59 62 64 65 75 76 78 79 81 107 119 131 132 133 134 144 146
Primary Contact: Michael D. Myers, Chief Executive Officer
CFO: Scott Knode, Chief Financial Officer
CHR: Erin Berns, Director Human Resources
Web address: www.vmhospital.com
**Control:** City–Government, nonfederal **Service:** General Medical and Surgical

**Staffed Beds:** 25 **Admissions:** 721 **Census:** 8 **Outpatient Visits:** 45503 **Births:** 130 **Total Expense ($000):** 14463 **Payroll Expense ($000):** 6030 **Personnel:** 144

## WAVERLY—Bremer County

✠ **WAVERLY HEALTH CENTER (161339)**, 312 Ninth Street S.W., Zip 50677–2999; tel. 319/352–4120 **A**1 9 10 18 **F**3 7 8 11 13 15 28 29 34 35 36 40 43 45 50 57 59 63 64 75 76 77 79 81 85 86 97 107 110 111 114 119 127 130 132 133 134 135 144 146 147 **P**6
Primary Contact: Kyle Richards, Chief Executive Officer
CFO: Lisa Bennett, Chief Financial Officer
CMO: Clay Dahlquist, M.D., Chief Medical Officer
CIO: Jerry Tiedt, Director Information Systems
CHR: Angie Tye, Director Human Resources
CNO: Rhonda DeBuhr, R.N., Chief Clinical and Nursing Officer
Web address: www.waverlyhealthcenter.org
**Control:** City–Government, nonfederal **Service:** General Medical and Surgical

**Staffed Beds:** 25 **Admissions:** 935 **Census:** 9 **Outpatient Visits:** 100940 **Births:** 246 **Total Expense ($000):** 48762 **Payroll Expense ($000):** 22475 **Personnel:** 322

## WEBSTER CITY—Hamilton County

**HAMILTON HOSPITAL** See Van Diest Medical Center

IA

**Hospital, Medicare Provider Number, Address, Telephone, Approval, Facility, and Physician Codes, Health Care System**

★ American Hospital Association (AHA) membership
□ The Joint Commission accreditation
◇ DNV Healthcare Inc. accreditation
○ Healthcare Facilities Accreditation Program
△ Commission on Accreditation of Rehabilitation Facilities (CARF) accreditation

★ **VAN DIEST MEDICAL CENTER (161361)**, 2350 Hospital Drive, Zip 50595–6600; tel. 515/832–9400 **A**9 10 18 **F**3 7 11 13 15 28 29 35 38 40 43 44 45 59 64 75 76 77 79 81 82 85 86 87 89 93 107 111 119 129 130 132 133 135 146 **P**6
Primary Contact: Robert L. Mason, Chief Executive Officer
COO: Janet Naset–Payne, R.N., Chief Operating Officer
CFO: Alice Heinrichs, CPA, Chief Financial Officer
CMO: Mark Andrew, M.D., Chief of Staff
CIO: Dave Dawson, Director Information Services
Web address: www.hamiltonhospital.com
**Control:** County–Government, nonfederal **Service:** General Medical and Surgical

| | |
|---|---|
| **Staffed Beds:** 25 **Admissions:** 1345 **Census:** 14 **Outpatient Visits:** 20032 **Births:** 116 **Total Expense ($000):** 23833 **Payroll Expense ($000):** 8290 **Personnel:** 183 | |

**WEST BURLINGTON—Des Moines County**

✉ △ **GREAT RIVER MEDICAL CENTER (160057)**, 1221 South Gear Avenue, Zip 52655–1681; tel. 319/768–1000, (Total facility includes 165 beds in nursing home–type unit) **A**1 7 9 10 19 **F**3 4 5 7 11 13 15 18 20 22 28 29 30 31 32 34 35 36 38 40 43 48 50 53 57 59 60 62 63 64 67 68 69 70 73 75 76 77 78 79 81 82 84 85 86 87 89 90 91 92 93 96 98 99 100 101 102 103 104 107 108 110 111 114 115 116 117 118 119 121 123 128 129 130 131 132 143 146 147 148 **P**6
Primary Contact: Mark D. Richardson, FACHE, President and Chief Executive Officer
CFO: Todd J. Sladky, Chief Financial Officer
CMO: William Daws, M.D., Chief of Staff
CIO: Gary Davis, Director Information Systems
CHR: Ron Halligan, Vice President Support Services
CHR: James M. Kammerer, Vice President Support Services
CNO: Teresa Colgan, VP of Nursing
Web address: www.greatrivermedical.org
**Control:** Other not–for–profit (including NFP Corporation) **Service:** General Medical and Surgical

| | |
|---|---|
| **Staffed Beds:** 378 **Admissions:** 7469 **Census:** 186 **Outpatient Visits:** 251100 **Births:** 513 **Total Expense ($000):** 146346 **Payroll Expense ($000):** 61217 **Personnel:** 1205 | |

**WEST DES MOINES—Polk County**

★ **MERCY MEDICAL CENTER – WEST LAKES**, 1755 59th Place, Zip 50266–7737; tel. 515/358–8000 **A**9 **F**3 7 11 12 13 15 18 20 22 26 29 30 39 40 41 43 44 50 56 61 62 64 65 68 70 75 76 77 78 79 81 85 86 87 93 96 107 108 111 114 118 119 130 132 135 143 146 **S** Catholic Health Initiatives, Englewood, CO
Primary Contact: Robert P. Ritz, President
COO: Sheryl L. Barnes, MSN, Senior Director Clinical Services
Web address: www.mercywestlakes.org/
**Control:** Church–operated, Nongovernment, not–for profit **Service:** General Medical and Surgical

| | |
|---|---|
| **Staffed Beds:** 82 **Admissions:** 3901 **Census:** 34 **Outpatient Visits:** 21588 **Births:** 262 **Total Expense ($000):** 48928 **Payroll Expense ($000):** 14613 **Personnel:** 266 | |

**UNITYPOINT HEALTH – METHODIST WEST HOSPITAL** See UnityPoint Health – Iowa Methodist Medical Center

**WEST UNION—Fayette County**

★ **PALMER LUTHERAN HEALTH CENTER (161316)**, 112 Jefferson Street, Zip 52175–1022; tel. 563/422–3811 **A**9 10 18 **F**3 8 11 13 15 28 29 30 31 34 40 43 56 57 59 62 63 64 65 68 70 76 77 78 79 81 82 85 86 93 96 107 111 114 119 128 129 130 131 132 133 135 144 146 148
Primary Contact: Debrah Chensvold, FACHE, President and Chief Executive Officer
CFO: Joni Gisleson, Director Finance
CMO: Chaudri Rasool, D.O., Chief of Staff
CIO: Kurt Chicken, Director Support Services
CHR: Cheryl Meyer, Director Human Resources
CNO: Kathy Begalske, Chief Nursing Officer
Web address: www.palmerlutheran.org
**Control:** Other not–for–profit (including NFP Corporation) **Service:** General Medical and Surgical

| | |
|---|---|
| **Staffed Beds:** 25 **Admissions:** 528 **Census:** 6 **Outpatient Visits:** 69013 **Births:** 94 **Total Expense ($000):** 21851 **Payroll Expense ($000):** 8720 **Personnel:** 180 | |

**WINTERSET—Madison County**

★ **MADISON COUNTY HEALTH CARE SYSTEM (161326)**, 300 West Hutchings Street, Zip 50273–2109; tel. 515/462–2373 **A**9 10 18 **F**3 15 18 28 31 35 37 40 43 45 57 59 63 78 79 81 89 93 97 107 110 114 119 127 128 129 130 131 132 133 135 146 **P**6
Primary Contact: Marcia Hendricks, R.N., Chief Executive Officer
COO: Terry E. Simmons, Chief Nursing Officer
CFO: Rebekah Mitchell, Chief Financial Officer
CMO: Jonathan Suddarth, D.O., Chief of Staff
CIO: Gary Mullen, Chief Information Officer
CHR: Jennifer Hannon, Director Human Resources
Web address: www.madisonhealth.com
**Control:** County–Government, nonfederal **Service:** General Medical and Surgical

| | |
|---|---|
| **Staffed Beds:** 25 **Admissions:** 407 **Census:** 5 **Outpatient Visits:** 58790 **Births:** 1 **Total Expense ($000):** 17686 **Payroll Expense ($000):** 7333 **Personnel:** 132 | |

**IA**

*Many Facility Codes have changed. Please refer to the AHA Guide Code Chart.* © 2013 AHA Guide

# KANSAS

## ABILENE—Dickinson County

★ **MEMORIAL HEALTH SYSTEM (171381)**, 511 N.E. Tenth Street, Zip 67410–2153; tel. 785/263–2100, (Total facility includes 77 beds in nursing home–type unit) **A**9 10 18 **F**3 13 15 18 28 29 31 34 36 40 45 53 57 59 62 63 64 68 69 71 75 77 78 79 81 82 85 87 93 98 103 107 108 110 111 114 119 127 128 130 131 132 133 134 135 143 146 148 **P**6
Primary Contact: Mark A. Miller, FACHE, Chief Executive Officer
COO: Bob Brazil, Chief Operating Officer
CFO: Elgin Glanzer, Chief Financial Officer
CMO: W. L. Short, M.D., Chief Medical Officer
CIO: Blaine Cappel, Director Information Systems
CHR: Bob Brazil, Chief Operating Officer
Web address: www.mhsks.org
**Control:** Hospital district or authority, Government, nonfederal **Service:** General Medical and Surgical

**Staffed Beds:** 112 **Admissions:** 887 **Census:** 87 **Outpatient Visits:** 44549 **Births:** 44 **Total Expense ($000):** 20517 **Payroll Expense ($000):** 10680 **Personnel:** 327

## ANDOVER—Butler County

**KANSAS MEDICAL CENTER (170197)**, 1124 West 21st Street, Zip 67002–5500; tel. 316/300–4000 **A**9 10 **F**3 17 18 20 22 24 29 30 40 43 49 51 60 64 68 70 75 77 79 81 82 85 87 102 107 108 115 119 130 131 146 148
Primary Contact: Badr Idbeis, M.D., Chief Executive Officer
COO: Daryl W. Thornton, Chief Operating Officer
CFO: Steven N. Hadley, Chief Financial Officer
Web address: www.ksmedcenter.com/
**Control:** Corporation, Investor–owned, for–profit **Service:** General Medical and Surgical

**Staffed Beds:** 58 **Admissions:** 2782 **Census:** 28 **Outpatient Visits:** 8115 **Births:** 0 **Personnel:** 267

## ANTHONY—Harper County

★ **ANTHONY MEDICAL CENTER (171346)**, 1101 East Spring Street, Zip 67003–2122; tel. 620/842–5111 **A**9 10 18 **F**40 48 53 57 64 67 81 93 97 107 119 127 128 133 **P**6
Primary Contact: J. Bryant Anderson, Administrator and Chief Executive Officer
CFO: Lori Allen, Chief Financial Officer
CHR: Kim Barwick, Vice President Human Resources
**Control:** Hospital district or authority, Government, nonfederal **Service:** General Medical and Surgical

**Staffed Beds:** 25 **Admissions:** 292 **Census:** 9 **Outpatient Visits:** 20958 **Births:** 0 **Total Expense ($000):** 6783 **Payroll Expense ($000):** 3637 **Personnel:** 78

## ARKANSAS CITY—Cowley County

★ **SOUTH CENTRAL KANSAS MEDICAL CENTER (170150)**, 6401 Patterson Parkway, Zip 67005–5701, Mailing Address: P.O. Box 1107, Zip 67005–1107; tel. 620/442–2500 **A**9 10 **F**3 11 12 13 15 29 30 34 35 39 40 45 50 52 59 64 68 70 75 76 77 79 81 82 85 87 93 107 108 110 111 115 119 129 132 133 148
Primary Contact: Steven J. Perkins, Chief Executive Officer
CFO: Holly Beaty, Chief Financial Officer
CMO: David Schmeidler, M.D., Chief Medical Staff
CMO: Kamran Shahzada, M.D., Chief Medical Staff
CHR: Clayton Pappan, Director Human Resources and Marketing
CNO: Patricia Davis, Chief Nursing Officer
Web address: www.sckrmc.org
**Control:** City–Government, nonfederal **Service:** General Medical and Surgical

**Staffed Beds:** 37 **Admissions:** 1104 **Census:** 11 **Outpatient Visits:** 22870 **Births:** 182 **Total Expense ($000):** 15017 **Payroll Expense ($000):** 7528 **Personnel:** 183

## ASHLAND—Clark County

★ **ASHLAND HEALTH CENTER (171304)**, 709 Oak Street, Zip 67831–0188, Mailing Address: P.O. Box 188, Zip 67831–0188; tel. 620/635–2241, (Total facility includes 21 beds in nursing home–type unit) **A**9 10 18 **F**2 30 34 40 53 59 62 64 67 68 85 87 93 107 127 128 133 143 **P**6 **S** Great Plains Health Alliance, Inc., Wichita, KS
Primary Contact: Roger Barnhart, Chief Executive Officer
CFO: Debbie Filson, Chief Financial Officer
CMO: Daniel Shuman, D.O., Chief Medical Officer
CIO: Alan Romans, Director Information Technology
CHR: Debbie Filson, Chief Financial Officer
CNO: Patty Young, R.N., Hospital Director of Nursing
Web address: www.ashlandhc.org
**Control:** Hospital district or authority, Government, nonfederal **Service:** General Medical and Surgical

**Staffed Beds:** 45 **Admissions:** 129 **Census:** 27 **Outpatient Visits:** 12035 **Births:** 0 **Total Expense ($000):** 5995 **Payroll Expense ($000):** 2918 **Personnel:** 70

## ATCHISON—Atchison County

★ **ATCHISON HOSPITAL (171382)**, 800 Raven Hill Drive, Zip 66002–9204; tel. 913/367–2131 **A**9 10 18 **F**3 7 11 12 13 15 28 29 30 31 34 35 40 45 49 50 57 59 62 63 64 68 70 75 76 77 79 81 82 85 87 89 92 93 97 107 108 110 111 114 118 119 127 129 130 131 132 133 135 146 147 **P**6
Primary Contact: John L. Jacobson, Chief Executive Officer
CFO: Gary R. Foll, Chief Financial Officer
CMO: Michael Jones, M.D., Chief of Staff
CIO: Michael Gaul, Manager Information Systems
CHR: Pamela K. Sweger, Director Human Resources
Web address: www.atchisonhospital.org
**Control:** Other not–for–profit (including NFP Corporation) **Service:** General Medical and Surgical

**Staffed Beds:** 25 **Admissions:** 970 **Census:** 9 **Outpatient Visits:** 45981 **Births:** 181 **Total Expense ($000):** 31230 **Payroll Expense ($000):** 14066 **Personnel:** 256

## ATWOOD—Rawlins County

★ **RAWLINS COUNTY HEALTH CENTER (171307)**, 707 Grant Street, Zip 67730–1526, Mailing Address: P.O. Box 47, Zip 67730–0047; tel. 785/626–3211 **A**9 10 18 **F**3 28 29 30 34 40 45 57 59 64 66 68 75 81 83 85 87 93 97 107 114 125 127 128 130 131 132 133 135 146 148 **P**6 **S** Great Plains Health Alliance, Inc., Wichita, KS
Primary Contact: Deanna Freeman, Administrator and Chief Executive Officer
CFO: Heather Prideaux, Director Finance
Web address: www.rchc.us
**Control:** County–Government, nonfederal **Service:** General Medical and Surgical

**Staffed Beds:** 24 **Admissions:** 365 **Census:** 4 **Outpatient Visits:** 20048 **Births:** 0 **Total Expense ($000):** 6855 **Payroll Expense ($000):** 3233 **Personnel:** 67

## BELLEVILLE—Republic County

⊞ **REPUBLIC COUNTY HOSPITAL (171361)**, 2420 G Street, Zip 66935–2400; tel. 785/527–2254, (Total facility includes 38 beds in nursing home–type unit) **A**1 5 9 10 18 **F**3 13 15 28 29 30 31 35 39 40 45 56 57 64 67 68 75 76 77 78 79 81 85 86 87 89 93 107 108 114 119 128 130 131 133 **S** Great Plains Health Alliance, Inc., Wichita, KS
Primary Contact: Blaine K. Miller, Administrator
CFO: Barry Bottger, Chief Financial Officer
Web address: www.rphospital.org
**Control:** Other not–for–profit (including NFP Corporation) **Service:** General Medical and Surgical

**Staffed Beds:** 63 **Admissions:** 1021 **Census:** 41 **Outpatient Visits:** 14351 **Births:** 59 **Total Expense ($000):** 13117 **Payroll Expense ($000):** 6263 **Personnel:** 158

---

**Hospital, Medicare Provider Number, Address, Telephone, Approval, Facility, and Physician Codes, Health Care System**

★ American Hospital Association (AHA) membership
☐ The Joint Commission accreditation
◇ DNV Healthcare Inc. accreditation
○ Healthcare Facilities Accreditation Program
△ Commission on Accreditation of Rehabilitation Facilities (CARF) accreditation

**KS**

## BELOIT—Mitchell County

★ **MITCHELL COUNTY HOSPITAL HEALTH SYSTEMS (171375)**, 400 West Eighth, Zip 67420–1605, Mailing Address: P.O. Box 399, Zip 67420–0399; tel. 785/738–2266, (Total facility includes 40 beds in nursing home–type unit) **A**9 10 18 **F**3 11 13 15 28 29 31 34 40 43 45 48 50 56 59 62 63 64 68 69 74 76 77 81 82 84 86 87 93 98 103 106 107 111 114 119 128 129 130 132 133 148
Primary Contact: David Dick, Chief Executive Officer
CFO: Eldon Koepke, Chief Financial Officer
CIO: Nate Richards, Director Information Technology
CHR: Phyllis Oetting, Director Human Resources
CNO: Jan Kemmerer, Director of Nursing
Web address: www.mchks.com
**Control:** County–Government, nonfederal **Service:** General Medical and Surgical

**Staffed Beds:** 75 **Admissions:** 1306 **Census:** 53 **Outpatient Visits:** 14171 **Births:** 96 **Total Expense ($000):** 24150 **Payroll Expense ($000):** 11095 **Personnel:** 268

## BURLINGTON—Coffey County

★ **COFFEY COUNTY HOSPITAL (170094)**, 801 North Fourth Street, Zip 66839–2602, Mailing Address: P.O. Box 189, Zip 66839–0189; tel. 620/364–2121, (Total facility includes 42 beds in nursing home–type unit) **A**5 9 10 20 **F**3 7 10 11 13 15 17 29 30 31 34 40 45 50 57 59 62 64 65 67 68 70 75 76 77 78 79 81 82 85 87 93 107 110 111 114 119 125 127 128 130 133 146 **P**6
Primary Contact: Karen Smith, Interim Chief Executive Officer
CFO: James H. Garner, Chief Financial Officer
Web address: www.coffeyhealth.org
**Control:** County–Government, nonfederal **Service:** General Medical and Surgical

**Staffed Beds:** 78 **Admissions:** 975 **Census:** 37 **Outpatient Visits:** 14508 **Births:** 90 **Total Expense ($000):** 22360 **Payroll Expense ($000):** 13054 **Personnel:** 167

## CALDWELL—Sumner County

★ **SUMNER COUNTY HOSPITAL DISTRICT ONE (171329)**, 601 South Osage Street, Zip 67022–1654; tel. 620/845–6492 **A**9 10 18 **F**7 11 40 57 62 75 81 93 107 119 133 **P**5
Primary Contact: Virgil Watson, Administrator
CFO: Jennifer Marcrum, Chief Financial Officer
CMO: Jim Blunk, D.O., Chief Medical Officer
CIO: Trey Watson, Network Administrator
Web address: www.schd1.com
**Control:** Hospital district or authority, Government, nonfederal **Service:** General Medical and Surgical

**Staffed Beds:** 15 **Admissions:** 208 **Census:** 3 **Outpatient Visits:** 4178 **Births:** 0 **Total Expense ($000):** 4523 **Payroll Expense ($000):** 1794 **Personnel:** 46

## CHANUTE—Neosho County

★ **NEOSHO MEMORIAL REGIONAL MEDICAL CENTER (171380)**, 629 South Plummer, Zip 66720–1928, Mailing Address: P.O. Box 426, Zip 66720–0426; tel. 620/431–4000 **A**5 9 10 18 **F**3 7 11 13 15 28 29 30 34 40 43 52 53 57 62 63 64 76 77 79 81 82 85 89 93 107 108 110 111 114 119 128 129 130 133 135 143 146 147 **P**8 **S** QHR, Brentwood, TN
Primary Contact: Dennis Franks, FACHE, Chief Executive Officer
CFO: Nancy Woodyard, Chief Financial Officer
CMO: Brian Kueser, M.D., Chief Medical Officer
CIO: Wanda W. Thomas, Director Health Information
CHR: R. C. Rowan, Director Human Resources
Web address: www.nmrmc.com
**Control:** County–Government, nonfederal **Service:** General Medical and Surgical

**Staffed Beds:** 25 **Admissions:** 1843 **Census:** 18 **Outpatient Visits:** 33022 **Births:** 307 **Total Expense ($000):** 40059 **Payroll Expense ($000):** 16968 **Personnel:** 314

## CLAY CENTER—Clay County

★ **CLAY COUNTY MEDICAL CENTER (171371)**, 617 Liberty Street, Zip 67432–1564, Mailing Address: P.O. Box 512, Zip 67432–0512; tel. 785/632–2144 **A**9 10 18 **F**13 15 18 19 28 30 31 40 50 51 53 55 59 63 64 67 68 70 74 75 76 77 78 79 81 82 84 85 86 87 88 89 93 96 108 110 111 114 117 119 128 130 132 133 148
Primary Contact: Ron Bender, Chief Executive Officer
COO: Tyce Young, Patient Services Officer
CFO: Jim Brinkman, Chief Financial Officer
CIO: Jim Seley, Chief Information Officer
CHR: Cindy Rush, Director Human Resources
Web address: www.ccmcks.org
**Control:** County–Government, nonfederal **Service:** General Medical and Surgical

**Staffed Beds:** 25 **Admissions:** 829 **Census:** 10 **Outpatient Visits:** 45143 **Births:** 68 **Total Expense ($000):** 15940 **Payroll Expense ($000):** 7478 **Personnel:** 179

## COFFEYVILLE—Montgomery County

⊠ **COFFEYVILLE REGIONAL MEDICAL CENTER (170145)**, 1400 West Fourth, Zip 67337–3306; tel. 620/251–1200, (Total facility includes 20 beds in nursing home–type unit) **A**1 2 9 10 **F**3 7 11 13 15 28 29 30 31 34 40 45 46 47 50 57 59 62 64 68 70 74 75 76 77 78 79 81 82 85 90 93 97 107 108 110 114 115 119 121 128 130 132 135 145 147 **P**8
Primary Contact: John Smith, Chief Executive Officer
CIO: Chris Crist, Director Information Systems
CHR: Becky McCune, Director Human Resources, Community Relations and Education
CNO: Lori Rexwinkle, Chief Nursing Officer
Web address: www.crmcinc.com
**Control:** Other not–for–profit (including NFP Corporation) **Service:** General Medical and Surgical

**Staffed Beds:** 88 **Admissions:** 2482 **Census:** 32 **Outpatient Visits:** 51105 **Births:** 208 **Total Expense ($000):** 40032 **Payroll Expense ($000):** 15751 **Personnel:** 333

## COLBY—Thomas County

**CITIZENS MEDICAL CENTER (171362)**, 100 East College Drive, Zip 67701–3799; tel. 785/462–7511, (Total facility includes 63 beds in nursing home–type unit) **A**9 10 18 **F**3 11 13 15 28 30 31 34 40 64 67 74 76 78 79 81 85 86 87 93 97 107 108 110 111 114 119 127 130 133 146 **P**6
Primary Contact: Kevan Trenkle, Chief Executive Officer
CFO: Patsy Evans, Chief Financial Officer
CMO: Brewster Kellogg, D.O., Chief Medical Staff
CIO: Rod Williams, Manager Information Systems
CHR: Margaret Kummer, Vice President Human Resources
CNO: Victoria Duffey, Director of Nursing
Web address: www.nwkshealthcare.com
**Control:** Other not–for–profit (including NFP Corporation) **Service:** General Medical and Surgical

**Staffed Beds:** 88 **Admissions:** 496 **Census:** 56 **Outpatient Visits:** 11628 **Births:** 140 **Total Expense ($000):** 22505 **Payroll Expense ($000):** 10931 **Personnel:** 242

## COLDWATER—Comanche County

★ **COMANCHE COUNTY HOSPITAL (171312)**, 202 South Frisco Street, Zip 67029–9101, Mailing Address: HC 65, Box 8A, Zip 67029–9500; tel. 620/582–2144 **A**9 10 18 **F**3 11 30 31 40 43 53 59 61 68 75 78 93 102 128 133 **P**6 **S** Great Plains Health Alliance, Inc., Wichita, KS
Primary Contact: Nancy Zimmerman, R.N., Administrator
CFO: Lisa Brooks, Chief Financial Officer
CMO: Daniel Schowengerdt, M.D., Chief of Staff
CIO: LaNell Wagnon, Director Medical Records
CHR: Lisa Brooks, Chief Financial Officer
CNO: Sandra Dobrinski, Director of Nursing
Web address: www.gpha.com
**Control:** County–Government, nonfederal **Service:** General Medical and Surgical

**Staffed Beds:** 12 **Admissions:** 75 **Census:** 2 **Outpatient Visits:** 12074 **Births:** 0 **Total Expense ($000):** 4377 **Payroll Expense ($000):** 2004 **Personnel:** 45

## COLUMBUS—Cherokee County

★ **MERCY HOSPITAL COLUMBUS (171308)**, 220 North Pennsylvania Avenue, Zip 66725–1110; tel. 620/429–2545 **A**9 10 18 **F**11 15 39 40 45 57 59 77 81 93 119 133 **S** Mercy Health, Chesterfield, MO
Primary Contact: Cindy Neely, Administrator
CMO: Darcy Selenke, M.D., Chief of Staff
Web address: www.mercy.net/northwestarar/practice/mercy–maude–norton–hospital–columbus
**Control:** Church–operated, Nongovernment, not–for profit **Service:** General Medical and Surgical

**Staffed Beds:** 18 **Admissions:** 137 **Census:** 2 **Outpatient Visits:** 11297 **Births:** 0 **Total Expense ($000):** 3573 **Payroll Expense ($000):** 2098 **Personnel:** 51

## CONCORDIA—Cloud County

★ **CLOUD COUNTY HEALTH CENTER (171349)**, 1100 Highland Drive, Zip 66901–3923; tel. 785/243–1234 **A**9 10 18 **F**3 11 13 15 20 28 31 34 35 40 41 45 56 57 59 64 65 70 74 75 76 77 79 81 82 85 86 87 89 93 96 97 102 107 108 114 118 119 127 130 132 133 135 146 148 **P**6
Primary Contact: Rita K. Buurman, Interim Chief Executive Officer
CMO: Justin Poore, D.O., Chief Medical Staff
CIO: Mitch Wing, Network Administrator
CHR: Nicole Nelson, Director Human Resources
Web address: www.cchc.org
**Control:** Other not–for–profit (including NFP Corporation) **Service:** General Medical and Surgical

**Staffed Beds:** 25 **Admissions:** 649 **Census:** 9 **Outpatient Visits:** 23866 **Births:** 34 **Total Expense ($000):** 13722 **Payroll Expense ($000):** 7296 **Personnel:** 151

*Many Facility Codes have changed. Please refer to the AHA Guide Code Chart.* © 2013 AHA Guide

## COUNCIL GROVE—Morris County

★ **MORRIS COUNTY HOSPITAL (171379)**, 600 North Washington Street, Zip 66846–1422; tel. 620/767–6811 **A**9 10 18 **F**7 11 13 15 18 28 31 35 40 45 59 64 65 70 76 77 81 87 93 94 96 107 110 130 132 133 146 148 **P**5
Primary Contact: James H. Reagan, Jr., Ph.D., Chief Executive Officer
CFO: Ron Christenson, Chief Financial Officer
CMO: Joel Hornuug, M.D., Chief Medical Officer
CIO: Bill Lauer, Chief Information Officer
CHR: Don Zimmerman, Director Human Resources
CNO: Stephanne Wolf, Chief Nursing Officer
Web address: www.mrcohosp.com
**Control:** County–Government, nonfederal **Service:** General Medical and Surgical

**Staffed Beds:** 25 **Admissions:** 544 **Census:** 6 **Outpatient Visits:** 14911 **Births:** 49 **Total Expense ($000):** 8920 **Payroll Expense ($000):** 3125 **Personnel:** 92

## DIGHTON—Lane County

★ **LANE COUNTY HOSPITAL (171303)**, 235 West Vine, Zip 67839–0969, Mailing Address: P.O. Box 969, Zip 67839–0969; tel. 620/397–5321, (Total facility includes 14 beds in nursing home–type unit) **A**9 10 18 **F**30 40 56 67 77 85 93 97 127 128 131 133 **P**6 **S** Great Plains Health Alliance, Inc., Wichita, KS
Primary Contact: Donna McGowan, Administrator
CFO: Marcia Gabel, Chief Financial Officer
CMO: Paul Chinburg, M.D., Medical Director
CHR: Dina Casey, Human Resources Officer
Web address: www.lchospital.com
**Control:** County–Government, nonfederal **Service:** General Medical and Surgical

**Staffed Beds:** 31 **Admissions:** 99 **Census:** 20 **Outpatient Visits:** 13867 **Births:** 0 **Total Expense ($000):** 4599 **Payroll Expense ($000):** 2172 **Personnel:** 47

## DODGE CITY—Ford County

☒ **WESTERN PLAINS MEDICAL COMPLEX (170175)**, 3001 Avenue A, Zip 67801–6508, Mailing Address: P.O. Box 1478, Zip 67801–1478; tel. 620/225–8400 **A**1 3 5 9 10 20 **F**3 8 11 13 15 17 18 20 22 28 29 30 34 35 40 50 51 60 64 70 72 73 74 75 76 77 79 81 85 86 87 88 89 90 93 107 108 111 115 119 129 130 133 146 **S** LifePoint Hospitals, Inc., Brentwood, TN
Primary Contact: Michael R. Burroughs, FACHE, Chief Executive Officer
CFO: Scott Hankinson, Chief Financial Officer
CMO: Aye Mya Win, M.D., Chief Medical Staff
CIO: Shawna Culver, Director Information Systems
Web address: www.westernplainsmc.com
**Control:** Corporation, Investor–owned, for–profit **Service:** General Medical and Surgical

**Staffed Beds:** 89 **Admissions:** 1832 **Census:** 20 **Outpatient Visits:** 34141 **Births:** 725 **Personnel:** 250

## EL DORADO—Butler County

☒ **SUSAN B. ALLEN MEMORIAL HOSPITAL (170017)**, 720 West Central Avenue, Zip 67042–2112; tel. 316/321–3300 **A**1 5 9 10 **F**3 11 13 15 28 30 40 45 59 60 62 68 69 70 76 79 81 85 92 93 96 97 98 103 107 108 110 111 115 119 121 123 130 133 146 148
Primary Contact: Gayle Arnett, President and Chief Executive Officer
COO: David Shaw, Vice President and Chief Operating Officer
CFO: Robin Crawford, Vice President and Chief Financial Officer
CIO: Mark Rooker, Director Information Systems
CHR: Gay Kimble, Director Human Resources
Web address: www.sbamh.com
**Control:** Other not–for–profit (including NFP Corporation) **Service:** General Medical and Surgical

**Staffed Beds:** 52 **Admissions:** 1923 **Census:** 20 **Outpatient Visits:** 79635 **Births:** 346 **Total Expense ($000):** 46051 **Payroll Expense ($000):** 18986 **Personnel:** 366

## ELKHART—Morton County

★ **MORTON COUNTY HEALTH SYSTEM (170166)**, 445 Hilltop Street, Zip 67950–0937, Mailing Address: P.O. Box 937, Zip 67950–0937; tel. 620/697–2141, (Total facility includes 80 beds in nursing home–type unit) **A**9 10 20 **F**10 11 15 18 28 29 31 34 40 45 54 56 57 59 64 67 68 70 75 77 79 81 86 87 93 94 96 97 98 99 100 101 102 103 104 107 111 114 119 130 131 132 133 135 143 146 147 148 **P**5 6
Primary Contact: William Wild, Chief Executive Officer
CFO: Jeff Weaver, Chief Financial Officer
CHR: Sonja May, Director Human Resources
Web address: www.mchswecare.com
**Control:** County–Government, nonfederal **Service:** General Medical and Surgical

**Staffed Beds:** 120 **Admissions:** 838 **Census:** 80 **Outpatient Visits:** 23851 **Births:** 0 **Total Expense ($000):** 17922 **Payroll Expense ($000):** 8602 **Personnel:** 225

## ELLINWOOD—Barton County

★ **ELLINWOOD DISTRICT HOSPITAL (171301)**, 605 North Main Street, Zip 67526–1440; tel. 620/564–2548 **A**9 10 18 **F**11 40 64 65 93 107 127 128 133 **P**6 **S** Great Plains Health Alliance, Inc., Wichita, KS
Primary Contact: John Hughes, Administrator
CFO: Penny Stephenson, Chief Financial Officer
CMO: Charles Joslin, M.D., Chief of Staff
CIO: Becky L. Burns, Manager Health Information Management
CHR: Penny Stephenson, Chief Financial Officer
CNO: Aletha Budig, R.N., Director of Nursing
Web address: www.ellinwood.org
**Control:** Other not–for–profit (including NFP Corporation) **Service:** General Medical and Surgical

**Staffed Beds:** 25 **Admissions:** 231 **Census:** 9 **Outpatient Visits:** 14167 **Births:** 0 **Total Expense ($000):** 5545 **Payroll Expense ($000):** 2660 **Personnel:** 61

## ELLSWORTH—Ellsworth County

★ **ELLSWORTH COUNTY MEDICAL CENTER (171327)**, 1604 Aylward Street, Zip 67439–2541, Mailing Address: P.O. Box 87, Zip 67439–0087; tel. 785/472–3111 **A**5 9 10 18 **F**3 11 28 29 34 35 40 45 47 53 57 59 62 64 67 77 85 86 87 93 97 107 114 119 127 128 130 133 135 146 **P**6
Primary Contact: Roger A. Masse, FACHE, Chief Executive Officer
CFO: Preston Sauers, Chief Financial Officer
CIO: Lynette Dick, Director of Support Services
CHR: Sandy Wedel, Director Human Resources
CNO: Laura Stofferson, Director of Nursing
Web address: www.ewmed.com
**Control:** County–Government, nonfederal **Service:** General Medical and Surgical

**Staffed Beds:** 20 **Admissions:** 678 **Census:** 5 **Outpatient Visits:** 19362 **Births:** 0 **Total Expense ($000):** 13223 **Payroll Expense ($000):** 6904 **Personnel:** 141

## EMPORIA—Lyon County

★ ○ **NEWMAN REGIONAL HEALTH (170001)**, 1201 West 12th Avenue, Zip 66801–2597; tel. 620/343–6800 **A**5 9 10 11 20 **F**3 11 13 15 28 29 31 39 40 41 45 51 53 59 61 63 64 65 68 70 76 77 78 79 81 82 84 85 86 87 89 90 93 96 100 102 107 108 111 114 118 119 129 130 131 132 133 135 144 146 147 148 **P**6 **S** QHR, Brentwood, TN
Primary Contact: John Rossfeld, Interim Chief Executive Officer
CFO: Holly French, Chief Financial Officer
CMO: Cy Anderson, M.D., Chief of Staff
CIO: Donald Cope, Director Information Systems
CHR: Kathy Orear, Director Human Resources
CNO: Julia Pyle, R.N., Chief Nursing Officer
Web address: www.newmanrh.org
**Control:** County–Government, nonfederal **Service:** General Medical and Surgical

**Staffed Beds:** 59 **Admissions:** 2430 **Census:** 27 **Outpatient Visits:** 95306 **Births:** 411 **Total Expense ($000):** 51942 **Payroll Expense ($000):** 25006 **Personnel:** 430

## EUREKA—Greenwood County

**GREENWOOD COUNTY HOSPITAL (171339)**, 100 West 16th Street, Zip 67045–1064; tel. 620/583–7451 **A**5 9 10 18 **F**3 40 43 53 62 64 81 93 107 119 127 133 **P**6
Primary Contact: Edward E. Riley, Chief Executive Officer
CFO: Lisa Ramsey, Chief Financial Officer
CIO: Filiberto J. Ojeda, Director Quality Improvement, Risk Management and Information System
CHR: Janel M. Palmer, Director Human Resources
Web address: www.gwch.org
**Control:** County–Government, nonfederal **Service:** General Medical and Surgical

**Staffed Beds:** 25 **Admissions:** 442 **Census:** 4 **Outpatient Visits:** 15522 **Births:** 0 **Total Expense ($000):** 13225 **Payroll Expense ($000):** 6261 **Personnel:** 115

---

**Hospital, Medicare Provider Number, Address, Telephone, Approval, Facility, and Physician Codes, Health Care System**

★ American Hospital Association (AHA) membership
☐ The Joint Commission accreditation
◇ DNV Healthcare Inc. accreditation
○ Healthcare Facilities Accreditation Program
△ Commission on Accreditation of Rehabilitation Facilities (CARF) accreditation

KS

## FORT SCOTT—Bourbon County

⊞ **MERCY HOSPITAL FORT SCOTT (170058)**, 401 Woodland Hills Boulevard, Zip 66701–8797; tel. 620/223–2200 **A**1 5 9 10 **F**3 7 11 13 15 28 29 30 34 35 40 53 57 59 62 65 70 72 75 76 77 79 81 82 84 85 90 93 97 107 108 110 111 114 118 119 127 129 130 131 132 133 143 144 145 146 148 **P**6 **S** Mercy Health, Chesterfield, MO
Primary Contact: Reta K. Baker, President
CFO: Terri Del Chiaro, Chief Financial Officer
CMO: Robert R. Nichols, M.D., Vice President Medical Affairs
CIO: Rose Ludeke, Site Administrator Management Information Systems
CHR: Linda Noll, Executive Director Human Resources
Web address: www.mercykansas.com
**Control:** Church–operated, Nongovernment, not–for profit **Service:** General Medical and Surgical

**Staffed Beds:** 61 **Admissions:** 1795 **Census:** 19 **Outpatient Visits:** 74173 **Births:** 229 **Total Expense ($000):** 33599 **Payroll Expense ($000):** 14520 **Personnel:** 286

## FREDONIA—Wilson County

★ **FREDONIA REGIONAL HOSPITAL (171374)**, 1527 Madison Street, Zip 66736–1751, Mailing Address: P.O. Box 579, Zip 66736–0579; tel. 620/378–2121 **A**9 10 18 **F**3 7 11 15 30 40 81 82 85 93 98 103 107 110 114 119 128 133 **S** Great Plains Health Alliance, Inc., Wichita, KS
Primary Contact: Alan Fisher, Chief Executive Officer
CFO: Wendy Barton, Manager Business Office
CHR: Debbie Marr, Administrative Assistant and Director Human Resources
Web address: www.fredoniaregionalhospital.org
**Control:** City–Government, nonfederal **Service:** General Medical and Surgical

**Staffed Beds:** 34 **Admissions:** 714 **Census:** 13 **Outpatient Visits:** 21885 **Births:** 0 **Total Expense ($000):** 12824 **Payroll Expense ($000):** 4235 **Personnel:** 113

## GARDEN CITY—Finney County

⊞ **ST. CATHERINE HOSPITAL (170023)**, 401 East Spuce Street, Zip 67846–5679; tel. 620/272–2561 **A**1 5 9 10 20 **F**3 8 15 18 20 22 24 29 30 31 34 35 40 45 51 57 59 60 63 64 65 69 70 73 75 76 77 78 79 81 85 87 89 93 97 98 100 102 107 108 109 111 115 116 118 119 120 121 122 123 124 129 130 132 135 146 147 148 **P**5 6 **S** Catholic Health Initiatives, Englewood, CO
Primary Contact: Scott J. Taylor, President and Chief Executive Officer
COO: John Yox, Senior Vice President and Chief Operating Officer
CFO: Amanda Vaughan, Chief Financial Officer
CIO: Lance Kellenbarger, Site Director Information Systems
CHR: Kathy E. Morrison, Executive Director Human Resources
Web address: www.stcath–hosp.org
**Control:** Church–operated, Nongovernment, not–for profit **Service:** General Medical and Surgical

**Staffed Beds:** 110 **Admissions:** 3528 **Census:** 42 **Outpatient Visits:** 130831 **Births:** 770 **Total Expense ($000):** 81567 **Payroll Expense ($000):** 32128 **Personnel:** 536

## GARDNER—Johnson County

★ △ **MEADOWBROOK REHABILITATION HOSPITAL (170180)**, 427 West Main Street, Zip 66030–1183; tel. 913/856–8747, (Total facility includes 42 beds in nursing home–type unit) **A**7 9 10 **F**34 59 80 86 87 91 92 93 130 143 148
Primary Contact: Chris Mattingly, Chief Executive Officer
CFO: Renee Morrow, Business Manager
CMO: Magdy Tadros, M.D., Medical Director
CHR: Carrie Moore, Director Human Resources
Web address: www.meadowbrookrehab.com
**Control:** Corporation, Investor–owned, for–profit **Service:** Rehabilitation

**Staffed Beds:** 54 **Admissions:** 156 **Census:** 50 **Outpatient Visits:** 0 **Births:** 0 **Total Expense ($000):** 9882 **Payroll Expense ($000):** 3842 **Personnel:** 136

## GARNETT—Anderson County

★ **ANDERSON COUNTY HOSPITAL (171316)**, 421 South Maple, Zip 66032–1334, Mailing Address: P.O. Box 309, Zip 66032–0309; tel. 785/448–3131, (Total facility includes 30 beds in nursing home–type unit) **A**9 10 18 **F**3 7 11 15 29 30 34 35 40 41 45 57 59 64 67 75 81 87 93 97 107 108 110 114 127 130 133 135 148 **P**6 **S** Saint Luke's Health System, Kansas City, MO
Primary Contact: Dennis A. Hachenberg, FACHE, Chief Executive Officer
CFO: Vicki L. Mills, Chief Financial Officer
CMO: George A. Pagels, M.D., Senior Vice President and Chief Medical Officer
CHR: Karen Gillespie, Director Human Resources
CNO: Margo L. Williams, R.N., Chief Nursing Officer
Web address: www.saint–lukes.org
**Control:** Other not–for–profit (including NFP Corporation) **Service:** General Medical and Surgical

**Staffed Beds:** 41 **Admissions:** 174 **Census:** 30 **Outpatient Visits:** 40146 **Births:** 0 **Total Expense ($000):** 16901 **Payroll Expense ($000):** 7076 **Personnel:** 137

## GIRARD—Crawford County

★ **GIRARD MEDICAL CENTER (171376)**, 302 North Hospital Drive, Zip 66743–2000; tel. 620/724–8291 **A**9 10 18 **F**3 6 11 12 15 29 34 35 40 43 45 47 50 51 53 56 57 59 62 64 65 75 77 79 81 87 93 97 98 100 101 102 103 104 105 107 114 119 127 128 130 131 132 133 146 148 **P**6
Primary Contact: Michael E. Payne, Administrator
CFO: Holly Koch, Chief Financial Officer
CIO: Jeff Barnes, Director of Information Technology
CHR: Mary Ann Holloway, Manager Human Resources
CNO: Patty Ridings, Director of Nursing
Web address: www.girardmedicalcenter.com
**Control:** Hospital district or authority, Government, nonfederal **Service:** General Medical and Surgical

**Staffed Beds:** 35 **Admissions:** 846 **Census:** 14 **Outpatient Visits:** 26543 **Births:** 0 **Total Expense ($000):** 18736 **Payroll Expense ($000):** 8845 **Personnel:** 199

## GOODLAND—Sherman County

**GOODLAND REGIONAL MEDICAL CENTER (171370)**, 220 West Second Street, Zip 67735–1602; tel. 785/890–3625 **A**9 10 18 **F**3 11 13 15 28 31 34 40 44 45 57 59 64 65 67 69 75 76 79 81 82 85 87 89 93 97 107 114 119 127 128 130 132 133 **P**6
Primary Contact: Jay P. Jolly, Chief Executive Officer
CFO: James Precht, Chief Financial Officer
CIO: Kevin Sanderson, Director Information Systems
CHR: Dale Shields, Director Human Resources
Web address: www.goodlandregional.com
**Control:** County–Government, nonfederal **Service:** General Medical and Surgical

**Staffed Beds:** 25 **Admissions:** 374 **Census:** 4 **Outpatient Visits:** 39968 **Births:** 65 **Total Expense ($000):** 15500 **Payroll Expense ($000):** 6100 **Personnel:** 120

## GREAT BEND—Barton County

**GREAT BEND REGIONAL HOSPITAL (170191)**, 514 Cleveland Street, Zip 67530–3562; tel. 620/792–8833 **A**5 9 10 **F**3 13 29 30 34 40 57 59 64 70 75 76 79 81 82 89 107 111 114 119 127 130 135 147
Primary Contact: Pamela Chambers, Chief Executive Officer
CFO: Larry T. Fore, Controller
CMO: Adina Gregory, Chief Nursing Officer
CIO: Susan Read, Director Information Technology Support
CHR: Ruth Bealer, Director Human Resources
Web address: www.greatbendsurgical.com
**Control:** Partnership, Investor–owned, for–profit **Service:** General Medical and Surgical

**Staffed Beds:** 33 **Admissions:** 1822 **Census:** 16 **Outpatient Visits:** 29214 **Births:** 426 **Total Expense ($000):** 20967 **Payroll Expense ($000):** 10103 **Personnel:** 235

## GREENSBURG—Kiowa County

★ **KIOWA COUNTY MEMORIAL HOSPITAL (171332)**, 721 West Kansas Avenue, Zip 67054–1633; tel. 620/723–3341 **A**9 10 18 **F**3 7 11 40 50 53 59 64 68 107 115 127 128 133 **P**6 **S** Great Plains Health Alliance, Inc., Wichita, KS
Primary Contact: Mary Sweet, Administrator
CFO: Ron Tucker, Business Office Manager
CMO: Nizar Kibar, M.D., Chief Medical Staff
CIO: Jeremy Hoover, Chief Information Officer
CHR: Cathy McFall, Human Resources Manager
CNO: Vanessa Kirk, Director of Nursing
Web address: www.kcmh.net
**Control:** Other not–for–profit (including NFP Corporation) **Service:** General Medical and Surgical

**Staffed Beds:** 15 **Admissions:** 163 **Census:** 4 **Outpatient Visits:** 11286 **Births:** 0 **Total Expense ($000):** 7865 **Payroll Expense ($000):** 2936 **Personnel:** 66

## HANOVER—Washington County

★ **HANOVER HOSPITAL (171365)**, 205 South Hanover, Zip 66945–8924, Mailing Address: P.O. Box 38, Zip 66945–0038; tel. 785/337–2214 **A**5 9 10 18 **F**2 7 40 53 64 69 81 133 143 148 **P**5
Primary Contact: Roger D. Warren, M.D., Administrator
CFO: Sheryl Adam, Chief Financial Officer
CMO: Roger D. Warren, M.D., Administrator
**Control:** Hospital district or authority, Government, nonfederal **Service:** General Medical and Surgical

**Staffed Beds:** 25 **Admissions:** 153 **Census:** 20 **Outpatient Visits:** 1531 **Births:** 1 **Total Expense ($000):** 3380 **Payroll Expense ($000):** 1801 **Personnel:** 47

*Many Facility Codes have changed. Please refer to the AHA Guide Code Chart.* © 2013 AHA Guide

## HARPER—Harper County

★ **HARPER HOSPITAL DISTRICT FIVE (171366)**, 700 West 13th Street, Zip 67058–1401; tel. 620/896–7324 **A**9 10 18 **F**3 10 12 29 32 34 35 40 43 45 46 50 53 57 59 62 64 65 67 68 69 75 77 79 81 84 87 93 97 107 111 114 119 125 127 128 129 130 133 135 146 147 148
Primary Contact: William Widener, Administrator and Chief Executive Officer
CFO: Sandra Owen, Director Fiscal and Accounting
CMO: Ralph Imlay, M.D., Chief of Staff
CIO: Cindi Beadman, Director Medical Records
CHR: Vicki Longbine, Director Human Resources
CNO: Karen Aldis, Director of Nursing
Web address: www.hhd5.com
**Control:** Hospital district or authority, Government, nonfederal **Service:** General Medical and Surgical

**Staffed Beds:** 25 **Admissions:** 322 **Census:** 11 **Outpatient Visits:** 87230 **Births:** 0 **Total Expense ($000):** 7599 **Payroll Expense ($000):** 3782 **Personnel:** 92

## HAYS—Ellis County

★ ◇ **HAYS MEDICAL CENTER (170013)**, 2220 Canterbury Drive, Zip 67601–2370, Mailing Address: P.O. Box 8100, Zip 67601–8100; tel. 785/623–5000 **A**3 5 9 10 21 **F**3 11 12 13 15 17 18 20 22 24 26 28 29 30 31 32 34 35 36 37 38 39 40 43 45 46 49 53 55 56 57 59 60 63 64 65 66 68 69 70 71 72 73 74 75 76 77 78 79 80 81 82 84 85 86 87 89 90 92 93 97 98 100 101 102 103 104 107 108 110 111 115 118 119 120 121 127 129 130 131 132 135 146 147 148 **P**6
Primary Contact: John H. Jeter, M.D., President and Chief Executive Officer
COO: Bryce A. Young, Chief Operating Officer
CFO: Bill Overbey, Chief Financial Officer and Chief Information Officer
CMO: Larry Watts, Chief Medical Officer
CIO: Bill Overbey, Chief Financial Officer and Chief Information Officer
CHR: Bruce Whittington, Vice President Human Resources
CNO: Terry Siek, MSN, Chief Nursing Officer
Web address: www.haysmed.com
**Control:** Other not–for–profit (including NFP Corporation) **Service:** General Medical and Surgical

**Staffed Beds:** 172 **Admissions:** 5963 **Census:** 81 **Outpatient Visits:** 318647 **Births:** 721 **Total Expense ($000):** 188289 **Payroll Expense ($000):** 79579 **Personnel:** 1222

## HERINGTON—Dickinson County

**HERINGTON MUNICIPAL HOSPITAL (171340)**, 100 East Helen Street, Zip 67449–1606; tel. 785/258–2207 **A**9 10 18 **F**15 28 29 40 45 57 64 77 81 93 97 107 114 119 127 133 148
Primary Contact: Michael J. Ryan, Chief Executive Officer
CFO: Patricia M. Moyer, Chief Financial Officer
CMO: John Mosier, D.O., Chief of Staff
CHR: Debbie Stewart, Human Resources Officer
CNO: Kathy Kershner, Director of Nursing
Web address: www.heringtonhospital.org
**Control:** City–Government, nonfederal **Service:** General Medical and Surgical

**Staffed Beds:** 25 **Admissions:** 324 **Census:** 6 **Outpatient Visits:** 14463 **Births:** 0 **Total Expense ($000):** 6354 **Payroll Expense ($000):** 3034 **Personnel:** 71

## HIAWATHA—Brown County

★ **HIAWATHA COMMUNITY HOSPITAL (171341)**, 300 Utah Street, Zip 66434–2314; tel. 785/742–2131 **A**5 9 10 18 **F**8 13 15 40 42 45 62 67 69 70 76 81 85 107 114 119 128 130 133 146 **P**6
Primary Contact: John Moore, Administrator
CFO: Jenny Knudson, Controller
CMO: Bryon Bigham, M.D., Chief of Staff
CIO: Cheryl Wenger, Manager Health Information and Quality Assurance
CHR: Katie Sisk, Director Human Resources
CNO: Lisa Thompson, MSN, Director of Nursing
Web address: www.hch–ks.org
**Control:** Other not–for–profit (including NFP Corporation) **Service:** General Medical and Surgical

**Staffed Beds:** 25 **Admissions:** 992 **Census:** 11 **Outpatient Visits:** 27691 **Births:** 104 **Total Expense ($000):** 22851 **Payroll Expense ($000):** 10234 **Personnel:** 213

## HILL CITY—Graham County

★ **GRAHAM COUNTY HOSPITAL (171325)**, 304 West Prout Street, Zip 67642–1435; tel. 785/421–2121 **A**5 9 10 18 **F**3 11 29 34 40 45 50 53 57 59 64 69 75 81 82 84 93 97 107 127 128 133 148
Primary Contact: Melissa Atkins, CPA, Chief Executive Officer
CHR: Donella Belleau, Director Human Resources
Web address: www.grahamcountyhospital.org
**Control:** County–Government, nonfederal **Service:** General Medical and Surgical

**Staffed Beds:** 25 **Admissions:** 585 **Census:** 6 **Outpatient Visits:** 1018 **Births:** 1 **Total Expense ($000):** 8125 **Payroll Expense ($000):** 3976 **Personnel:** 95

## HILLSBORO—Marion County

★ **HILLSBORO COMMUNITY HOSPITAL (171357)**, 701 South Main Street, Zip 67063–1553; tel. 620/947–3114 **A**9 10 18 **F**3 11 29 30 34 35 40 45 47 50 57 59 64 65 75 77 81 85 86 87 93 107 114 127 130 132 133 146 148 **P**5 6 **S** Rural Community Hospitals of America, Kansas City, MO
Primary Contact: Marion Regier, Chief Executive Officer
COO: Johna Magnuson, Director Nursing
CIO: Marsha Setzkorn–Meyer, Director Public Relations and Marketing
CHR: Wendy McCarty, Director Human Resources
Web address: www.hchks.com
**Control:** Corporation, Investor–owned, for–profit **Service:** General Medical and Surgical

**Staffed Beds:** 10 **Admissions:** 194 **Census:** 3 **Outpatient Visits:** 9910 **Births:** 0 **Total Expense ($000):** 4288 **Payroll Expense ($000):** 2020 **Personnel:** 38

## HOISINGTON—Barton County

★ **CLARA BARTON HOSPITAL (171333)**, 250 West Ninth Street, Zip 67544–1706; tel. 620/653–2114 **A**9 10 18 **F**11 15 28 40 51 56 57 59 64 77 81 85 92 93 97 107 114 119 127 128 133 148 **P**6
Primary Contact: Curt Colson, President and Chief Executive Officer
CFO: James Blackwell, Vice President and Chief Financial Officer
CMO: Josh Durham, D.O., Chief of Staff
CHR: John Moshier, Director Human Resources
CNO: Jane Schepmann, Vice President and Chief Nursing Officer
Web address: www.clarabartonhospital.org
**Control:** Other not–for–profit (including NFP Corporation) **Service:** General Medical and Surgical

**Staffed Beds:** 23 **Admissions:** 507 **Census:** 8 **Outpatient Visits:** 50101 **Births:** 0 **Total Expense ($000):** 16603 **Payroll Expense ($000):** 7998 **Personnel:** 160

## HOLTON—Jackson County

★ **HOLTON COMMUNITY HOSPITAL (171319)**, 1110 Columbine Drive, Zip 66436–8824; tel. 785/364–2116 **A**5 9 10 18 **F**3 11 13 15 18 28 34 40 45 62 63 64 65 75 76 77 81 82 89 90 93 97 107 114 119 127 128 130 131 132 133 135 146 147 148
Primary Contact: Carrie L. Saia, R.N., Chief Executive Officer
CFO: Marlene Kranz, Controller
CMO: Lee Schnee, M.D., Chief Medical Staff
CIO: Sarah A. Larison, Director Health Information Management
CHR: Gretchen Snavely, Director Human Resources
Web address: www.holtonhospital.com
**Control:** Other not–for–profit (including NFP Corporation) **Service:** General Medical and Surgical

**Staffed Beds:** 12 **Admissions:** 355 **Census:** 4 **Outpatient Visits:** 57673 **Births:** 42 **Total Expense ($000):** 10502 **Payroll Expense ($000):** 5224 **Personnel:** 128

## HORTON—Brown County

**HORTON COMMUNITY HOSPITAL (171320)**, 240 West 18th Street, Zip 66439–1245; tel. 785/486–2642 **A**9 10 18 **F**7 15 18 28 29 31 40 45 46 64 81 93 107 114 119 127 128 133 **P**6 **S** Rural Community Hospitals of America, Kansas City, MO
Primary Contact: Christopher Barlow, Chief Executive Officer
CFO: Sue Kidd, Chief Financial Officer
CMO: Galen Seymour, M.D., Chief of Staff
CHR: Ty Compton, Chief Nursing Executive
Web address: www.horton–hospital.com
**Control:** Corporation, Investor–owned, for–profit **Service:** General Medical and Surgical

**Staffed Beds:** 25 **Admissions:** 429 **Census:** 5 **Outpatient Visits:** 1848 **Births:** 0 **Total Expense ($000):** 6560 **Payroll Expense ($000):** 3403 **Personnel:** 67

---

**Hospital, Medicare Provider Number, Address, Telephone, Approval, Facility, and Physician Codes, Health Care System**

★ American Hospital Association (AHA) membership
☐ The Joint Commission accreditation
◇ DNV Healthcare Inc. accreditation
○ Healthcare Facilities Accreditation Program
△ Commission on Accreditation of Rehabilitation Facilities (CARF) accreditation

## HOXIE—Sheridan County

**SHERIDAN COUNTY HEALTH COMPLEX (171347)**, 826 18th Street,
Zip 67740–0167, Mailing Address: P.O. Box 167, Zip 67740–0167;
tel. 785/675–3281, (Total facility includes 35 beds in nursing home–type unit) **A**9
10 18 **F**3 10 11 29 30 31 34 40 45 49 50 53 56 57 59 68 69 81 85 86 93
97 107 119 127 128 130 131 132 133 134 135 146 147 148
Primary Contact: Steven L. Granzow, Chief Executive Officer
CFO: Christine Niblock, Chief Financial Officer
CMO: Thomas R. Plumeri, Chief of Staff
CNO: Maria Zimmerman, R.N., Chief Nursing Officer
Web address: www.sheridancountyhospital.com
**Control:** County–Government, nonfederal **Service:** General Medical and Surgical

**Staffed Beds:** 53 **Admissions:** 212 **Census:** 31 **Outpatient Visits:** 6696
**Births:** 0 **Total Expense ($000):** 6930 **Payroll Expense ($000):** 3730
**Personnel:** 110

## HUGOTON—Stevens County

**STEVENS COUNTY HOSPITAL (171335)**, 1006 South Jackson Street,
Zip 67951–2858, Mailing Address: P.O. Box 10, Zip 67951–0010;
tel. 620/544–8511, (Total facility includes 83 beds in nursing home–type unit) **A**9
10 18 **F**3 11 15 28 29 34 40 45 57 59 62 67 68 81 93 107 119 127 128
130 133 135 146
Primary Contact: Linda Stalcup, Chief Executive Officer
CMO: Samer Al–hashmi, M.D., Chief Medical Staff
Web address: www.healthcarefor the heartland.org
**Control:** County–Government, nonfederal **Service:** General Medical and Surgical

**Staffed Beds:** 100 **Admissions:** 246 **Census:** 62 **Outpatient Visits:** 56211
**Births:** 0 **Total Expense ($000):** 15873 **Payroll Expense ($000):** 7783
**Personnel:** 92

## HUTCHINSON—Reno County

⊠ **HUTCHINSON REGIONAL MEDICAL CENTER (170020)**, 1701 East 23rd
Avenue, Zip 67502–1191; tel. 620/665–2000, (Total facility includes 70 beds in
nursing home–type unit) **A**1 3 5 9 10 **F**3 7 10 11 13 18 20 22 24 28 29 30 31
40 43 47 48 49 50 51 60 62 63 64 67 68 70 74 75 76 77 78 79 81 82 83
84 85 89 90 93 98 102 103 106 107 108 111 114 115 119 120 121 123
125 126 128 129 130 146 148 **P**6
Primary Contact: Kevin J. Miller, FACHE, President and Chief Executive Officer
COO: James McComas, Vice President Operations
CFO: David A. Busatti, Vice President Finance
CMO: Verlin Janzen, M.D., Chief of Staff
CIO: David Mendenhall, Chief Information Officer
CHR: Janet Hamons, Vice President Human Resources
Web address: www.promiseregional.com
**Control:** Other not–for–profit (including NFP Corporation) **Service:** General
Medical and Surgical

**Staffed Beds:** 213 **Admissions:** 7636 **Census:** 180 **Outpatient Visits:**
137129 **Births:** 705 **Total Expense ($000):** 130414 **Payroll Expense
($000):** 49743 **Personnel:** 899

**SUMMIT SURGICAL, LLC (170198)**, 1818 East 23rd Avenue,
Zip 67502–1106; tel. 620/663–4800 **A**9 10 **F**3 29 45 50 64 79 81 82 85 **P**2
Primary Contact: Gordon Funk, Chief Executive Officer
CFO: Kevin Crunkleton, Chief Financial Officer
CMO: Ann Hentzen Page, M.D., Medical Director
CIO: Monty Moore, Director Information Services
CHR: Jonathan D. Funk, Director Human Resources and Marketing
Web address: www.summitks.com/
**Control:** Corporation, Investor–owned, for–profit **Service:** Surgical

**Staffed Beds:** 10 **Admissions:** 232 **Census:** 1 **Outpatient Visits:** 1166
**Births:** 0 **Total Expense ($000):** 4697 **Payroll Expense ($000):** 983
**Personnel:** 23

## INDEPENDENCE—Montgomery County

⊠ **MERCY HOSPITAL INDEPENDENCE (170010)**, 800 West Myrtle Street,
Zip 67301–3240, Mailing Address: P.O. Box 388, Zip 67301–0388;
tel. 620/331–2200 **A**1 9 10 **F**1 3 4 11 13 15 16 17 18 28 30 34 40 45 53 57
59 62 65 67 70 72 73 76 77 79 80 81 84 88 89 90 91 93 97 98 107 108
110 111 114 118 119 127 128 129 130 131 133 135 143 144 146 **P**3 6
**S** Mercy Health, Chesterfield, MO
Primary Contact: Robert Y. Copeland, Jr., FACHE, Interim President
CFO: Terri Del Chiaro, Vice President and Chief Financial Officer
CMO: Chris Lewis, M.D., Vice President Medical Affairs
CHR: Linda Noll, Executive Director Human Resources
Web address: www.mercykansas.com
**Control:** Church–operated, Nongovernment, not–for profit **Service:** General
Medical and Surgical

**Staffed Beds:** 40 **Admissions:** 995 **Census:** 10 **Outpatient Visits:** 50909
**Births:** 257 **Total Expense ($000):** 22616 **Payroll Expense ($000):** 9073
**Personnel:** 180

## IOLA—Allen County

⊠ **ALLEN COUNTY HOSPITAL (171373)**, 101 South First Street,
Zip 66749–3505, Mailing Address: P.O. Box 540, Zip 66749–0540;
tel. 620/365–1000 **A**1 9 10 18 **F**3 11 13 15 29 30 31 34 35 40 49 56 57 59
62 63 64 65 68 70 75 76 77 78 81 82 84 85 86 87 89 93 107 110 114 119
129 130 132 133 146 147 148 **S** HCA, Nashville, TN
Primary Contact: Ron Baker, Chief Executive Officer
CFO: Larry Peterson, Chief Financial Officer
CMO: Tim Spears, D.O., Chief of Staff
CHR: Paula Sell, Director Human Resources
CNO: Patty McGuffin, R.N., Chief Nursing Officer
Web address: www.allencountyhospital.com
**Control:** Corporation, Investor–owned, for–profit **Service:** General Medical and
Surgical

**Staffed Beds:** 25 **Admissions:** 826 **Census:** 10 **Outpatient Visits:** 19932
**Births:** 90 **Total Expense ($000):** 15000 **Payroll Expense ($000):** 6544
**Personnel:** 118

## JETMORE—Hodgeman County

★ **HODGEMAN COUNTY HEALTH CENTER (171369)**, 809 Bramley Street,
Zip 67854–9320, Mailing Address: P.O. Box 310, Zip 67854–0310;
tel. 620/357–8361, (Total facility includes 25 beds in nursing home–type unit)
**A**10 18 **F**3 40 53 67 81 107 114 125 127 130 133 143 **P**4
Primary Contact: Teresa L. Deuel, Chief Executive Officer
Web address: www.hchconline.org
**Control:** County–Government, nonfederal **Service:** General Medical and Surgical

**Staffed Beds:** 38 **Admissions:** 234 **Census:** 25 **Outpatient Visits:** 5752
**Births:** 0 **Total Expense ($000):** 6557 **Payroll Expense ($000):** 2806
**Personnel:** 80

## JOHNSON—Stanton County

**STANTON COUNTY HOSPITAL (171343)**, 404 North Chestnut Street,
Zip 67855–5001, Mailing Address: P.O. Box 779, Zip 67855–0779;
tel. 620/492–6250, (Total facility includes 25 beds in nursing home–type unit) **A**9
10 18 **F**3 13 34 40 41 45 50 56 57 59 64 68 75 76 81 86 87 89 93 97 107
114 127 128 130 132 133 143 146 **P**6
Primary Contact: Jay Tusten, Chief Executive Officer
CFO: Barbara Anderson, Chief Financial Officer
CMO: Charles Weintz, D.O., Chief of Staff
CIO: Marco Medina, Chief Information Officer
CHR: Camille Davidson, Director Human Resources
CNO: Marianne Mills, R.N., Chairperson
Web address: www.stantoncountyhospital.com
**Control:** County–Government, nonfederal **Service:** General Medical and Surgical

**Staffed Beds:** 34 **Admissions:** 126 **Census:** 19 **Outpatient Visits:** 14405
**Births:** 27 **Total Expense ($000):** 6618 **Payroll Expense ($000):** 2882
**Personnel:** 76

## JUNCTION CITY—Geary County

⊠ **GEARY COMMUNITY HOSPITAL (170074)**, 1102 St. Mary's Road,
Zip 66441–4196, Mailing Address: P.O. Box 490, Zip 66441–0490;
tel. 785/238–4131 **A**1 9 10 **F**3 8 11 12 13 15 16 17 18 19 28 29 30 34 35 40 50
56 57 59 61 62 63 64 65 66 70 75 76 77 79 81 85 86 87 90 97 98 103
107 108 109 110 111 113 114 115 118 119 127 129 130 131 132 133 135
143 144 145 146 147 148
Primary Contact: Joseph Stratton, FACHE, Chief Executive Officer
COO: Alice J. Jensen, Chief Operating Officer
CFO: Darren K. Rumford, Chief Financial Officer
CHR: Teto E. Henderson, Director Human Resources
Web address: www.gchks.org
**Control:** County–Government, nonfederal **Service:** General Medical and Surgical

**Staffed Beds:** 65 **Admissions:** 1654 **Census:** 17 **Outpatient Visits:** 56046
**Births:** 310 **Total Expense ($000):** 43956 **Payroll Expense ($000):** 19640
**Personnel:** 394

⊠ **IRWIN ARMY COMMUNITY HOSPITAL**, 600 Caisson Hill Road,
Zip 66442–7037; tel. 785/239–7000, (Nonreporting) **A**1 2 3 5 **S** Department of
the Army, Office of the Surgeon General, Falls Church, VA
Primary Contact: Colonel Barry R. Pockrandt, Commander
COO: Lieutenant Colonel Daniel G. Bonnichsen, Deputy Commander for
Administration
CFO: Lieutenant Colonel Daniel G. Bonnichsen, Deputy Commander for
Administration
CMO: Colonel Craig R. Webb, M.D., Deputy Commander for Clinical Services
CIO: David Dougherty, Chief Information Management Officer
CHR: Dianna Kallenberger, Chief Manpower Branch
CNO: Colonel Robert E. Dettmer, Deputy Commander for Health Services
Web address: www.iach.amedd.army.mil
**Control:** Army, Government, federal **Service:** General Medical and Surgical

**Staffed Beds:** 44

*Many Facility Codes have changed. Please refer to the AHA Guide Code Chart.*  © 2013 AHA Guide

## KANSAS CITY—Wyandotte County

☐ **KVC PSYCHIATRIC HOSPITAL**, 4300 Brenner Drive, Zip 66104–1163; tel. 913/334–0294 **A**1 3 5 **F**98 99 **P**5
Primary Contact: B. Wayne Sims, President and Chief Executive Officer
Web address: www.kvc.org
**Control:** Other not–for–profit (including NFP Corporation) **Service:** Children's hospital psychiatric

> **Staffed Beds:** 67 **Admissions:** 1561 **Census:** 38 **Outpatient Visits:** 0 **Births:** 0 **Total Expense ($000):** 8262 **Payroll Expense ($000):** 3599 **Personnel:** 90

✠ **PROVIDENCE MEDICAL CENTER (170146)**, 8929 Parallel Parkway, Zip 66112–1689; tel. 913/596–4000 **A**1 2 9 10 **F**3 13 15 17 18 20 22 24 28 29 30 31 34 35 40 44 46 49 56 57 59 61 64 68 70 73 74 75 76 77 78 79 80 81 82 84 85 86 93 97 107 108 111 114 115 118 119 120 121 123 124 129 130 131 132 135 146 147 148 **P**6 **S** SCL Health System, Denver, CO
Primary Contact: Randall G. Nyp, FACHE, President and Chief Executive Officer
CFO: Joe Jeans, Vice President Finance
CIO: Kevin Mapes, Regional Information Technology Director
CHR: Winifred Williams, Vice President Human Resources
CNO: Barbara Wertz, Vice President Patient Care Services
Web address: www.providence–health.org
**Control:** Church–operated, Nongovernment, not–for profit **Service:** General Medical and Surgical

> **Staffed Beds:** 168 **Admissions:** 7357 **Census:** 90 **Outpatient Visits:** 135789 **Births:** 779 **Total Expense ($000):** 159894 **Payroll Expense ($000):** 60730 **Personnel:** 850

☐ **RAINBOW MENTAL HEALTH FACILITY (174010)**, 2205 West 36th Avenue, Zip 66103–2107; tel. 913/755–7000 **A**1 10 **F**11 30 50 86 87 98 101 103 130 135 146 **P**6
Primary Contact: Steven F. Ashcraft, Superintendent
CFO: Donna Dean, Chief Financial Officer
CMO: Maria Gustilo, M.D., Medical Director
CHR: Marilyn Williamson, Chief Human Resources Officer
Web address: www.srskansas.org/osh/osh–rmhf_main.html
**Control:** State–Government, nonfederal **Service:** Psychiatric

> **Staffed Beds:** 36 **Admissions:** 635 **Census:** 31 **Outpatient Visits:** 0 **Births:** 0 **Total Expense ($000):** 7453 **Payroll Expense ($000):** 4307 **Personnel:** 128

✠ **SELECT SPECIALTY HOSPITAL–KANSAS CITY (172005)**, 1731 North 90th Street, Zip 66112–1515; tel. 913/732–5900 **A**1 9 10 **F**1 3 18 29 82 85 91 130 148 **P**5 **S** Select Medical Corporation, Mechanicsburg, PA
Primary Contact: Matthew H. Blevins, Chief Executive Officer
Web address: www.selectspecialtyhospitals.com
**Control:** Corporation, Investor–owned, for–profit **Service:** Long–Term Acute Care hospital

> **Staffed Beds:** 40 **Admissions:** 396 **Census:** 28 **Outpatient Visits:** 0 **Births:** 0 **Total Expense ($000):** 15923 **Payroll Expense ($000):** 6350 **Personnel:** 134

✠ △ **THE UNIVERSITY OF KANSAS HOSPITAL (170040)**, 3901 Rainbow Boulevard, Zip 66160–7200; tel. 913/588–5000 **A**1 2 3 5 7 8 9 10 **F**3 8 11 12 13 14 15 16 17 18 20 21 22 23 24 25 26 27 28 29 30 31 32 33 34 35 36 37 38 39 40 41 43 44 45 46 47 48 49 50 51 54 55 56 57 58 59 60 61 63 64 65 66 70 72 74 75 76 77 78 79 80 81 82 83 84 85 86 87 88 89 90 92 93 96 97 98 99 100 101 102 103 104 107 108 110 111 114 115 116 117 118 119 120 121 123 124 126 129 130 131 132 135 136 138 139 141 142 144 145 146 147 148 **P**6
Primary Contact: Bob Page, Chief Executive Officer
COO: Tammy Peterman, R.N., Executive Vice President, Chief Operating Officer and Chief Nursing Officer
CFO: Bill Marting, Senior Vice President and Chief Financial Officer
CMO: H. William Barkman, M.D., Chief of Staff
CIO: Chris Hansen, Senior Vice President Ambulatory Services and Chief Information Officer
CHR: Dwight Kasperbauer, Vice President Human Resources
CNO: Tammy Peterman, R.N., Executive Vice President, Chief Operating Officer and Chief Nursing Officer
Web address: www.kumed.com
**Control:** Hospital district or authority, Government, nonfederal **Service:** General Medical and Surgical

> **Staffed Beds:** 623 **Admissions:** 27380 **Census:** 442 **Outpatient Visits:** 530918 **Births:** 1644 **Total Expense ($000):** 1014599 **Payroll Expense ($000):** 333863 **Personnel:** 5636

## KINGMAN—Kingman County

★ **KINGMAN COMMUNITY HOSPITAL (171378)**, (Formerly Ninnescah Valley Health System), 750 Avenue D. West, Zip 67068–0376; tel. 620/532–3147 **A**9 10 18 **F**3 11 15 17 28 29 31 34 35 40 56 57 59 62 64 67 69 70 75 77 78 81 86 87 89 90 93 97 107 114 119 128 130 132 133 145 146 148
Primary Contact: Gary L. Tiller, Chief Executive Officer
CFO: Kent Hudson, Chief Financial Officer
CIO: Jay Gehring, Director Information Systems
CHR: Nancy Stucky, Director Human Resources and Public Relations
CNO: Nita McFarland, Director of Nursing
Web address: www.kchks.com
**Control:** Other not–for–profit (including NFP Corporation) **Service:** General Medical and Surgical

> **Staffed Beds:** 25 **Admissions:** 631 **Census:** 11 **Outpatient Visits:** 29043 **Births:** 0 **Total Expense ($000):** 10130 **Payroll Expense ($000):** 4933 **Personnel:** 122

## KINSLEY—Edwards County

★ **EDWARDS COUNTY HOSPITAL AND HEALTHCARE CENTER (171317)**, 620 West Eighth Street, Zip 67547–2329, Mailing Address: P.O. Box 99, Zip 67547–0099; tel. 620/659–3621 **A**9 10 18 **F**3 7 11 15 18 19 28 29 30 34 35 39 40 53 56 57 59 64 65 67 68 77 79 81 93 97 98 103 107 110 111 127 128 130 133 146 148
Primary Contact: Robert Krickbaum, Chief Executive Officer
CFO: Jennifer L. Jones, Chief Financial Officer
CMO: Robert Wray, D.O., Chief Medical Staff
CHR: Cheryl Gross, Director Human Resources
Web address: www.edwardscohospital.com
**Control:** County–Government, nonfederal **Service:** General Medical and Surgical

> **Staffed Beds:** 22 **Admissions:** 342 **Census:** 13 **Outpatient Visits:** 9693 **Births:** 0 **Total Expense ($000):** 8769 **Payroll Expense ($000):** 3553 **Personnel:** 65

## KIOWA—Barber County

▲ **KIOWA DISTRICT HOSPITAL AND MANOR (171331)**, 810 Drumm Street, Zip 67070–1626; tel. 620/825–4131, (Total facility includes 34 beds in nursing home–type unit) **A**9 10 18 **F**2 29 40 45 64 81 85 92 93 97 107 111 119 127 130 133 **P**6
Primary Contact: Alden M. Vandeveer, Jr., FACHE, Chief Executive Officer
CFO: Robin Lewis, Chief Financial Officer
CMO: Paul Wilhelm, M.D., Chief of Staff
CHR: Tara Girty, Director Human Resources
**Control:** Hospital district or authority, Government, nonfederal **Service:** General Medical and Surgical

> **Staffed Beds:** 58 **Admissions:** 159 **Census:** 28 **Outpatient Visits:** 6215 **Births:** 0 **Total Expense ($000):** 3643 **Payroll Expense ($000):** 1910 **Personnel:** 57

## LA CROSSE—Rush County

★ **RUSH COUNTY MEMORIAL HOSPITAL (171342)**, 801 Locust Street, Zip 67548–9673, Mailing Address: P.O. Box 520, Zip 67548–0520; tel. 785/222–2545, (Total facility includes 20 beds in nursing home–type unit) **A**9 10 18 **F**40 45 53 63 64 68 77 81 93 97 107 111 114 119 127 133 **P**6
Primary Contact: Duane Fields, Interim Chief Executive Officer
CFO: Duane Fields, Chief Financial Officer
CMO: J. Scott Appling, M.D., Chief of Staff
CHR: Pam Seltman, Director Human Resources
Web address: www.rushcounty.org/
**Control:** County–Government, nonfederal **Service:** General Medical and Surgical

> **Staffed Beds:** 36 **Admissions:** 122 **Census:** 20 **Outpatient Visits:** 5234 **Births:** 0 **Total Expense ($000):** 5543 **Payroll Expense ($000):** 2284 **Personnel:** 69

## LAKIN—Kearny County

**KEARNY COUNTY HOSPITAL (171313)**, 500 Thorpe Street, Zip 67860–9625; tel. 620/355–7111, (Total facility includes 75 beds in nursing home–type unit) **A**5 9 10 18 **F**2 3 6 10 13 28 34 35 40 45 50 56 59 62 64 67 68 69 75 76 81 85 86 89 93 97 107 119 125 128 131 132 133 143 **P**6
Primary Contact: John Loebl, Chief Executive Officer
CFO: ReChelle Kennedy, Chief Financial Officer
CMO: Arlo Reimer, M.D., Chief of Staff
CIO: Scott Good, Manager Information Services
CHR: Donna Winright, Director Human Resources and Senior Services
Web address: www.kearnycountyhospital.com
**Control:** County–Government, nonfederal **Service:** General Medical and Surgical

> **Staffed Beds:** 100 **Admissions:** 450 **Census:** 67 **Outpatient Visits:** 39922 **Births:** 178 **Total Expense ($000):** 16890 **Payroll Expense ($000):** 8902 **Personnel:** 204

---

**Hospital, Medicare Provider Number, Address, Telephone, Approval, Facility, and Physician Codes, Health Care System**

★ American Hospital Association (AHA) membership
☐ The Joint Commission accreditation
◇ DNV Healthcare Inc. accreditation
○ Healthcare Facilities Accreditation Program
△ Commission on Accreditation of Rehabilitation Facilities (CARF) accreditation

**KS**

## LARNED—Pawnee County

☐ **LARNED STATE HOSPITAL (174006)**, 1301 Kansas Highway 264, Zip 67550; tel. 620/285-2131 **A**1 10 **F**30 50 53 57 61 68 75 77 86 87 98 99 101 103 106 130 132 135 143 146
Primary Contact: Robert Connell, PsyD, Superintendent
CFO: Mary Odom, Accountant
CMO: Geoffrey Hammond, M.D., Medical Director
CIO: Sid Smith, Director Information Resources
CHR: Adele Dunn, Director Human Resources
Web address: www.larnedstatehospital.org
**Control:** State-Government, nonfederal **Service:** Psychiatric

**Staffed Beds:** 520 **Admissions:** 1354 **Census:** 498 **Outpatient Visits:** 0 **Births:** 0 **Total Expense ($000):** 53929 **Payroll Expense ($000):** 26436 **Personnel:** 726

★ **PAWNEE VALLEY COMMUNITY HOSPITAL (171345)**, 923 Carroll Avenue, Zip 67550-2429; tel. 620/285-3161 **A**9 10 18 **F**3 11 28 29 30 34 40 45 46 57 68 77 81 84 87 93 102 107 114 119 129 130 131 133 135 148
Primary Contact: Matt Heyn, Administrator
COO: Bryce A. Young, Chief Operating Officer
CFO: Bill Overbey, Chief Financial Officer
CMO: David Sanger, M.D., Chief Medical Officer
CHR: Bruce Whittington, Vice President Human Resources
Web address: www.pawneevalleyhospital.com
**Control:** County-Government, nonfederal **Service:** General Medical and Surgical

**Staffed Beds:** 25 **Admissions:** 284 **Census:** 6 **Outpatient Visits:** 12898 **Births:** 0 **Total Expense ($000):** 9177 **Payroll Expense ($000):** 4164 **Personnel:** 78

## LAWRENCE—Douglas County

⊠ △ **LAWRENCE MEMORIAL HOSPITAL (170137)**, 325 Maine Street, Zip 66044-1360; tel. 785/505-5000, (Total facility includes 12 beds in nursing home–type unit) **A**1 3 5 7 9 10 20 **F**3 11 13 15 18 20 22 26 28 29 30 31 34 36 38 40 44 45 49 50 51 54 55 57 59 61 64 68 70 72 74 75 76 77 78 79 81 82 84 85 86 87 89 90 91 93 94 96 100 102 107 108 110 111 114 115 116 117 118 119 122 126 128 129 130 132 135 145 146 147 148 **P**6 8
Primary Contact: Eugene W. Meyer, President and Chief Executive Officer
COO: Karen J. Shumate, R.N., Chief Operating Officer
CFO: Joe Pedley, CPA, Vice President and Chief Financial Officer
CIO: Jane Maskus, Vice President and Chief Information Officer
CNO: Dana R. Hale, R.N., Vice President Nursing
Web address: www.lmh.org
**Control:** City-Government, nonfederal **Service:** General Medical and Surgical

**Staffed Beds:** 152 **Admissions:** 6655 **Census:** 63 **Outpatient Visits:** 170433 **Births:** 1103 **Total Expense ($000):** 167336 **Payroll Expense ($000):** 69793 **Personnel:** 1156

## LEAVENWORTH—Leavenworth County

**CUSHING MEMORIAL HOSPITAL** See Saint Luke's Cushing Medical Center

**DWIGHT D. EISENHOWER VETERANS AFFAIRS MEDICAL CENTER** See Veterans Affairs Eastern Kansas Health Care System, Topeka

⊠ **SAINT JOHN HOSPITAL (170009)**, 3500 South Fourth Street, Zip 66048-5043; tel. 913/680-6000 **A**1 9 10 **F**3 8 13 15 18 29 30 34 35 40 44 46 54 56 57 59 61 64 65 70 74 75 76 77 78 79 81 82 84 85 93 98 103 107 111 114 118 119 130 132 133 135 146 147 148 **P**6 **S** SCL Health System, Denver, CO
Primary Contact: Randall G. Nyp, FACHE, President and Chief Executive Officer
CFO: Joe Jeans, Chief Financial Officer
CIO: Kevin Mapes, Regional Information Technology Director
CHR: Winifred Williams, Vice President Human Resources
CNO: Barbara Wertz, Vice President Patient Care Services
Web address: www.providence-health.org/sjh
**Control:** Church-operated, Nongovernment, not-for profit **Service:** General Medical and Surgical

**Staffed Beds:** 56 **Admissions:** 1787 **Census:** 26 **Outpatient Visits:** 68088 **Births:** 137 **Total Expense ($000):** 39291 **Payroll Expense ($000):** 16767 **Personnel:** 213

⊠ **SAINT LUKE¥S CUSHING MEDICAL CENTER (170133)**, (Formerly Cushing Memorial Hospital), 711 Marshall Street, Zip 66048-3235; tel. 913/684-1100 **A**1 5 9 10 **F**3 11 13 15 18 28 29 31 34 40 45 50 51 57 59 64 68 70 74 75 76 77 79 81 82 85 87 93 94 98 100 101 102 103 108 110 111 114 119 129 130 131 132 146 148 **S** Saint Luke's Health System, Kansas City, MO
Primary Contact: Adele Ducharme, R.N., MSN, Chief Executive Officer
CFO: Sally Border, Chief Financial Officer
CMO: Kathleen McBratney, M.D., President
CHR: Bertt Matthews, Director Human Resources
CNO: Karin Sundblom, Chief Nursing Officer
Web address: www.https://www.saintlukeshealthsystem.org/location/cushing-memorial-hospital
**Control:** Other not-for-profit (including NFP Corporation) **Service:** General Medical and Surgical

**Staffed Beds:** 52 **Admissions:** 1834 **Census:** 18 **Outpatient Visits:** 32609 **Births:** 161 **Total Expense ($000):** 35868 **Payroll Expense ($000):** 13771 **Personnel:** 255

## LEAWOOD—Johnson County

☐ **DOCTOR'S HOSPITAL (170194)**, 4901 College Boulevard, Zip 66211-1602; tel. 913/529-1801 **A**1 10 **F**39 79 81 82 111 **P**5
Primary Contact: Phil Harness, Chief Executive Officer
Web address: www.dshospital.net
**Control:** Partnership, Investor-owned, for-profit **Service:** General Medical and Surgical

**Staffed Beds:** 6 **Admissions:** 131 **Census:** 1 **Outpatient Visits:** 9159 **Births:** 0 **Total Expense ($000):** 15492 **Payroll Expense ($000):** 1695 **Personnel:** 29

**KANSAS CITY ORTHOPAEDIC INSTITUTE (170188)**, 3651 College Boulevard, Zip 66211-1910; tel. 913/338-4100 **A**3 5 9 10 **F**29 77 79 81 82 93 111
Primary Contact: Charles E. Rhoades, M.D., Chief Executive Officer
CIO: Jim Leveling, Director Information Technology
CHR: Laura Sinclair, Director Human Resources
Web address: www.kcoi.com
**Control:** Partnership, Investor-owned, for-profit **Service:** Orthopedic

**Staffed Beds:** 9 **Admissions:** 699 **Census:** 6 **Outpatient Visits:** 33196 **Births:** 0 **Personnel:** 97

## LENEXA—Johnson County

☐ **MINIMALLY INVASIVE SURGERY CENTER (170199)**, 11217 Lakeview Avenue, Zip 66219-1399; tel. 913/322-7401 **A**1 10 **F**12 81 107 119
Primary Contact: Parajeet Sabharrwal, Administrator
Web address: www.laplose.com/
**Control:** State-Government, nonfederal **Service:** Surgical

**Staffed Beds:** 9 **Admissions:** 100 **Census:** 1 **Outpatient Visits:** 762 **Births:** 0 **Total Expense ($000):** 1097 **Payroll Expense ($000):** 72 **Personnel:** 14

## LEOTI—Wichita County

★ **WICHITA COUNTY HEALTH CENTER (171306)**, 211 East Earl Street, Zip 67861-9620; tel. 620/375-2233, (Total facility includes 12 beds in nursing home–type unit) **A**9 10 18 **F**2 3 11 29 34 35 40 41 45 50 56 57 59 64 67 69 75 77 86 87 89 93 97 107 127 128 130 133 135 146 **P**6
Primary Contact: Victoria J. Hahn, Administrator and Chief Executive Officer
CFO: Janice Campas, Chief Financial Officer
CMO: Jeffrey Alpert, M.D., Medical Director
CHR: Patti Whalen, Manager Human Resources
CNO: Teresa Clark, Director of Nursing
Web address: www.wichitacountyhealthcenter.com
**Control:** County-Government, nonfederal **Service:** General Medical and Surgical

**Staffed Beds:** 37 **Admissions:** 196 **Census:** 18 **Outpatient Visits:** 7691 **Births:** 0 **Total Expense ($000):** 6535 **Payroll Expense ($000):** 3249 **Personnel:** 75

## LIBERAL—Seward County

☐ **SOUTHWEST MEDICAL CENTER (170068)**, 315 West 15th Street, Zip 67901-2455, Mailing Address: Box 1340, Zip 67905-1340; tel. 620/624-1651, (Total facility includes 18 beds in nursing home–type unit) **A**1 9 10 **F**1 3 4 11 13 15 16 17 29 31 34 40 45 48 49 57 59 67 68 70 72 73 75 76 77 79 80 81 85 87 88 89 90 93 96 98 103 104 107 108 110 111 114 118 119 128 129 130 131 145
Primary Contact: Bill Ermann, President and Chief Executive Officer
COO: Michele Gillespie, Vice President of Operations
CFO: Bill Ermann, Vice President and Chief Financial Officer
CIO: Shelley Mayes, Director of Medical Information Services
CHR: Lisa L. Mathes, Director of Human Resources
CNO: Jo L. Harrison, Vice President of Patient Care Services
Web address: www.swmedcenter.com
**Control:** County-Government, nonfederal **Service:** General Medical and Surgical

**Staffed Beds:** 101 **Admissions:** 2011 **Census:** 17 **Outpatient Visits:** 58600 **Births:** 727 **Total Expense ($000):** 41260 **Payroll Expense ($000):** 16818 **Personnel:** 359

## LINCOLN—Lincoln County

**LINCOLN COUNTY HOSPITAL (171360)**, 624 North Second Street, Zip 67455-1738, Mailing Address: P.O. Box 406, Zip 67455-0406; tel. 785/524-4403 **A**9 10 18 **F**11 40 69 107 119 127 133 **P**6
Primary Contact: Greg R. McNeil, Chief Executive Officer
**Control:** County-Government, nonfederal **Service:** General Medical and Surgical

**Staffed Beds:** 14 **Admissions:** 210 **Census:** 2 **Outpatient Visits:** 4694 **Births:** 0 **Total Expense ($000):** 6580 **Payroll Expense ($000):** 2926 **Personnel:** 72

**LINDSBORG—Mcpherson County**

★ **LINDSBORG COMMUNITY HOSPITAL (171358)**, 605 West Lincoln Street,
Zip 67456–2328; tel. 785/227–3308 **A**9 10 18 **F**3 28 29 40 53 59 62 64 67
77 81 93 97 107 115 119 128 130 133 144 **P**6
Primary Contact: Larry VanDerWege, Administrator and Chief Executive Officer
CFO: Laraine Gengler, Chief Financial Officer
CMO: Craig Nickel, M.D., Chief of Staff
CIO: Betty Nelson, Director of Marketing and Development
CHR: Brad Malm, Director Human Resources and Education
CNO: Beth Hedberg, R.N., Director of Nursing
Web address: www.lindsborghospital.org
**Control:** Other not–for–profit (including NFP Corporation) **Service:** General
Medical and Surgical

**Staffed Beds: 25 Admissions:** 306 **Census:** 4 **Outpatient Visits:** 20804
**Births:** 0 **Total Expense ($000):** 6638 **Payroll Expense ($000):** 3246
**Personnel:** 93

**LYONS—Rice County**

★ **RICE COUNTY DISTRICT HOSPITAL (171330)**, 619 South Clark Street,
Zip 67554–3003, Mailing Address: P.O. Box 828, Zip 67554–0828;
tel. 620/257–5173 **A**9 10 18 **F**1 3 10 13 29 30 34 35 40 45 57 67 70 75 76
77 81 89 93 107 125 127 128 130 132 133 143
Primary Contact: George M. Stover, Chief Executive Officer
CFO: Terry Pound, Chief Financial Officer
Web address: www.ricecountyhospital.com
**Control:** Hospital district or authority, Government, nonfederal **Service:** General
Medical and Surgical

**Staffed Beds: 25 Admissions:** 412 **Census:** 17 **Outpatient Visits:** 18017
**Births:** 72 **Total Expense ($000):** 13722 **Payroll Expense ($000):** 6818
**Personnel:** 142

**MANHATTAN—Riley County**

**MANHATTAN SURGICAL CENTER (170190)**, 1829 College Avenue,
Zip 66502–3381; tel. 785/776–5100 **A**9 10 **F**29 45 48 51 77 79 81 82 85
130 131
Primary Contact: Scott Chapman, Administrator
Web address: www.manhattansurgical.com
**Control:** Partnership, Investor–owned, for–profit **Service:** General Medical and
Surgical

**Staffed Beds: 13 Admissions:** 407 **Census:** 2 **Outpatient Visits:** 9992
**Births:** 0 **Personnel:** 77

★ ○ **MERCY REGIONAL HEALTH CENTER (170142)**, 1823 College Avenue,
Zip 66502–3346; tel. 785/776–3322 **A**5 9 10 11 19 **F**3 11 12 13 15 18 20
22 28 29 30 31 34 35 37 40 44 45 46 49 60 64 70 73 74 75 76 77 78 79
81 82 84 85 86 87 89 90 93 96 102 103 104 107 108 110 111 115 119
129 130 132 133 146 147 148 **S** Ascension Health, Saint Louis, MO
Primary Contact: John R. Broberg, FACHE, President and Chief Executive Officer
COO: Carla J. Yost, R.N., Chief Operating Officer
CIO: Andy Gagnon, Director Information Systems
CHR: Marcie Holsteen, Director Human Resources
Web address: www.mercyregional.org
**Control:** Other not–for–profit (including NFP Corporation) **Service:** General
Medical and Surgical

**Staffed Beds: 96 Admissions:** 4879 **Census:** 44 **Outpatient Visits:** 123253
**Births:** 1061 **Total Expense ($000):** 83042 **Payroll Expense ($000):** 33981
**Personnel:** 631

**MANKATO—Jewell County**

**JEWELL COUNTY HOSPITAL (171309)**, 100 Crestvue Avenue,
Zip 66956–2407, Mailing Address: P.O. Box 327, Zip 66956–0327;
tel. 785/378–3137, (Total facility includes 19 beds in nursing home–type unit) **A**9
10 18
Primary Contact: Doyle L. McKimmy, FACHE, Chief Executive Officer
COO: Eric Borden, Chief Operating Officer and Chief Financial Officer
CFO: Eric Borden, Chief Operating Officer and Chief Financial Officer
Web address: www.jewellcountyhospital.com
**Control:** County–Government, nonfederal **Service:** General Medical and Surgical

**Staffed Beds: 41 Admissions:** 82 **Census:** 22 **Outpatient Visits:** 5475
**Births:** 0

**MARION—Marion County**

★ **ST. LUKE HOSPITAL AND LIVING CENTER (171356)**, 535 South Freeborn,
Zip 66861–1256; tel. 620/382–2177, (Total facility includes 32 beds in nursing
home–type unit) **A**9 10 18 **F**3 11 15 28 29 34 40 45 62 64 81 97 107 108
114 127 128 133 **P**6 **S** QHR, Brentwood, TN
Primary Contact: Jeremy Armstrong, FACHE, Chief Executive Officer
CFO: Bev Reid, Chief Financial Officer
CMO: Don Hodson, M.D., Chief Medical Officer
CIO: Jeff Methvin, Manager Information Technology
CHR: Sharon Zogelman, Director Human Resources
CNO: Jeremy Ensey, Chief Nursing Officer
Web address: www.slhmarion.org
**Control:** Hospital district or authority, Government, nonfederal **Service:** General
Medical and Surgical

**Staffed Beds: 37 Admissions:** 159 **Census:** 32 **Outpatient Visits:** 22396
**Births:** 0 **Total Expense ($000):** 8678 **Payroll Expense ($000):** 3438
**Personnel:** 97

**MARYSVILLE—Marshall County**

★ **COMMUNITY MEMORIAL HEALTHCARE (171363)**, 708 North 18th Street,
Zip 66508–1338; tel. 785/562–2311 **A**9 10 18 **F**3 13 15 28 29 30 31 34 35
40 45 50 57 59 62 64 68 69 75 76 77 78 79 81 87 93 94 97 107 108 114
127 128 129 130 131 132 133 135 146 147 148 **P**6
Primary Contact: Curtis R. Hawkinson, Chief Executive Officer
CFO: William H. Storck, Chief Financial Officer
CMO: Michelle Stone, D.O., Chief Medical Staff
CHR: Jessie Schneider, Director Human Resources
Web address: www.cmhcare.org
**Control:** Other not–for–profit (including NFP Corporation) **Service:** General
Medical and Surgical

**Staffed Beds: 25 Admissions:** 605 **Census:** 5 **Outpatient Visits:** 26062
**Births:** 62 **Total Expense ($000):** 20571 **Payroll Expense ($000):** 8866
**Personnel:** 184

**MCPHERSON—Mcpherson County**

★ **MCPHERSON HOSPITAL (170105)**, 1000 Hospital Drive, Zip 67460–2326;
tel. 620/241–2250 **A**5 9 10 **F**3 7 11 13 15 28 34 35 40 45 53 57 59 64 65
70 75 76 77 79 81 82 85 97 107 108 114 119 133 146 **P**6
Primary Contact: Robert Monical, President and Chief Executive Officer
COO: Terri Gehring, Vice President Operations
CHR: Jill Wenger, Vice President Human Resources
Web address: www.mcphersonmemorial.org
**Control:** Other not–for–profit (including NFP Corporation) **Service:** General
Medical and Surgical

**Staffed Beds: 41 Admissions:** 1092 **Census:** 11 **Outpatient Visits:** 34942
**Births:** 170 **Total Expense ($000):** 23219 **Payroll Expense ($000):** 10944
**Personnel:** 275

**MEMORIAL HOSPITAL** See McPherson Hospital

**MEADE—Meade County**

★ **MEADE DISTRICT HOSPITAL (171321)**, 510 East Carthage Street,
Zip 67864–6401, Mailing Address: P.O. Box 820, Zip 67864–0820;
tel. 620/873–2141, (Total facility includes 60 beds in nursing home–type unit) **A**9
10 18 **F**3 15 28 29 34 35 40 45 53 56 57 59 62 64 79 81 82 85 87 93 107
108 114 119 127 128 130 131 133 143 148 **P**6
Primary Contact: Michael P. Thomas, Administrator
CFO: Lori Smith, Chief Financial Officer
CIO: Leighton Miller, Chief Information Officer
Web address: www.meadehospital.com
**Control:** Hospital district or authority, Government, nonfederal **Service:** General
Medical and Surgical

**Staffed Beds: 80 Admissions:** 346 **Census:** 45 **Outpatient Visits:** 9706
**Births:** 0 **Total Expense ($000):** 14378 **Payroll Expense ($000):** 7421
**Personnel:** 189

---

**Hospital, Medicare Provider Number, Address, Telephone, Approval, Facility, and Physician Codes, Health Care System**

★ American Hospital Association (AHA) membership
□ The Joint Commission accreditation
◇ DNV Healthcare Inc. accreditation
○ Healthcare Facilities Accreditation Program
△ Commission on Accreditation of Rehabilitation Facilities (CARF) accreditation

**KS**

## MEDICINE LODGE—Barber County

★ **MEDICINE LODGE MEMORIAL HOSPITAL (171334)**, 710 North Walnut Street, Zip 67104–1019; tel. 620/886–3771 **A**9 10 18 **F**7 11 40 44 45 53 56 64 81 93 107 119 127 128 133 148 **P**6 **S** Great Plains Health Alliance, Inc., Wichita, KS
Primary Contact: Kevin A. White, Administrator
CFO: Thomas G. Lee, Chief Financial Officer
CHR: Johnnie Davis, Director Human Resources
CNO: Kathryn I. Burns, R.N., Director of Nursing
Web address: www.mlmh.net/
**Control:** Hospital district or authority, Government, nonfederal **Service:** General Medical and Surgical

**Staffed Beds:** 25 **Admissions:** 244 **Census:** 14 **Outpatient Visits:** 22944 **Births:** 0 **Total Expense ($000):** 7692 **Payroll Expense ($000):** 4152 **Personnel:** 83

## MINNEAPOLIS—Ottawa County

★ **OTTAWA COUNTY HEALTH CENTER (171328)**, 215 East Eighth, Zip 67467–1902, Mailing Address: P.O. Box 290, Zip 67467–0290; tel. 785/392–2122, (Total facility includes 17 beds in nursing home–type unit) **A**5 9 10 18 **F**10 28 35 40 53 56 62 64 67 69 85 86 93 128 130 133 143 **S** Great Plains Health Alliance, Inc., Wichita, KS
Primary Contact: Jody Parks, Administrator
CFO: Cheryl Lanoue, Chief Financial Officer
CIO: Linda Wright, Director Information
CHR: Jenny Johnson, Chief Human Resource Officer
Web address: www.ottawacountyhealthcenter.com
**Control:** Other not–for–profit (including NFP Corporation) **Service:** General Medical and Surgical

**Staffed Beds:** 42 **Admissions:** 298 **Census:** 31 **Outpatient Visits:** 10724 **Births:** 0 **Total Expense ($000):** 5911 **Payroll Expense ($000):** 3002 **Personnel:** 96

## MINNEOLA—Ford County

★ **MINNEOLA DISTRICT HOSPITAL (171368)**, 212 Main Street, Zip 67865–8511, Mailing Address: P.O. Box 127, Zip 67865–0127; tel. 620/885–4264, (Total facility includes 36 beds in nursing home–type unit) **A**9 10 18 **F**13 29 40 45 46 56 57 64 65 67 81 83 93 102 107 127 128 130 133 148 **P**6 **S** Great Plains Health Alliance, Inc., Wichita, KS
Primary Contact: Deborah Bruner, Chief Executive Officer and Administrator
CFO: Marion Blanton, Chief Financial Officer
CMO: Tony Luna, M.D., Chief of Staff
CHR: Vena Harris, Director Human Resources
Web address: www.minneolahealthcare.com
**Control:** Hospital district or authority, Government, nonfederal **Service:** General Medical and Surgical

**Staffed Beds:** 54 **Admissions:** 501 **Census:** 36 **Outpatient Visits:** 25921 **Births:** 42 **Total Expense ($000):** 10145 **Payroll Expense ($000):** 4937 **Personnel:** 116

## MOUNDRIDGE—Mcpherson County

★ **MERCY HOSPITAL (170075)**, 218 East Pack Street, Zip 67107–8815, Mailing Address: P.O. Box 180, Zip 67107–0180; tel. 620/345–6391 **A**5 9 10 **F**40 56 76 81 89 130 133
Primary Contact: Doyle K. Johnson, Administrator
CFO: Royce Holdeman, Chief Financial Officer
Web address: www.mercyh.org/
**Control:** Church–operated, Nongovernment, not–for profit **Service:** General Medical and Surgical

**Staffed Beds:** 21 **Admissions:** 357 **Census:** 5 **Outpatient Visits:** 8336 **Births:** 40 **Total Expense ($000):** 2924 **Payroll Expense ($000):** 1240 **Personnel:** 46

## NEODESHA—Wilson County

★ **WILSON MEDICAL CENTER (171344)**, 2600 Ottawa Road, Zip 66757–1897, Mailing Address: P.O. Box 360, Zip 66757–0360; tel. 620/325–2611 **A**9 10 18 **F**3 11 29 34 40 45 53 57 59 64 81 82 85 89 93 107 108 115 119 128 133 148 **S** QHR, Brentwood, TN
Primary Contact: Dennis R. Shelby, Chief Executive Officer
CFO: John Gutschenritter, Chief Financial Officer
CIO: Julie Quanstrom, Director Information Systems and Reimbursement Specialist
CHR: Laura Dean, Director Human Resources
CNO: Michelle Bohannon, Director of Nursing Operations and Risk, Compliance, Quality and Safety
Web address: www.wilsonmedical.org
**Control:** County–Government, nonfederal **Service:** General Medical and Surgical

**Staffed Beds:** 15 **Admissions:** 300 **Census:** 5 **Outpatient Visits:** 12146 **Births:** 0 **Total Expense ($000):** 11798 **Payroll Expense ($000):** 4751 **Personnel:** 127

## NESS CITY—Ness County

★ **NESS COUNTY HOSPITAL (171336)**, 312 Custer Street, Zip 67560–1654; tel. 785/798–2291, (Total facility includes 43 beds in nursing home–type unit) **A**9 10 18 **F**3 7 15 28 32 40 45 59 62 65 67 93 107 111 119 125 127 128 133
Primary Contact: Curt Thomas, Administrator
CFO: Debra Frank, Chief Financial Officer
CMO: Mikhail Imseis, M.D., Chief of Staff
CIO: Vicki Howe, Chief Information Officer
CHR: Lori Hensley, Chief Human Resources Officer
CNO: Brenda Dinges, Director of Nursing
Web address: www.nesscountyhospital.com/
**Control:** Hospital district or authority, Government, nonfederal **Service:** General Medical and Surgical

**Staffed Beds:** 63 **Admissions:** 166 **Census:** 42 **Outpatient Visits:** 9609 **Births:** 0 **Total Expense ($000):** 8287 **Payroll Expense ($000):** 3740 **Personnel:** 108

## NEWTON—Harvey County

★ ○ **NEWTON MEDICAL CENTER (170103)**, 600 Medical Center Drive, Zip 67114–8780, Mailing Address: P.O. Box 308, Zip 67114–0308; tel. 316/283–2700 **A**5 9 10 11 **F**3 8 13 15 20 22 28 29 30 40 45 49 51 59 64 68 70 73 75 76 81 85 86 90 103 107 108 110 111 114 118 119 126 130 133 146 147 148 **P**6
Primary Contact: Steven G. Kelly, President and Chief Executive Officer
COO: J. Michael Keller, Vice President Operations
CFO: Todd Kasitz, Chief Financial Officer
CIO: Prableen Singh, Chief Information Officer
CHR: Todd Tangeman, Director Human Resources
Web address: www.newtonmedicalcenter.com
**Control:** Other not–for–profit (including NFP Corporation) **Service:** General Medical and Surgical

**Staffed Beds:** 103 **Admissions:** 2763 **Census:** 37 **Outpatient Visits:** 67101 **Births:** 482 **Total Expense ($000):** 57147 **Payroll Expense ($000):** 25532 **Personnel:** 534

□ **PRAIRIE VIEW (174016)**, 1901 East First Street, Zip 67114–5010, Mailing Address: P.O. Box 467, Zip 67114–0467; tel. 316/284–6400, (Nonreporting) **A**1 9 10
Primary Contact: Jessie Kaye, Chief Executive Officer
CFO: Dan Evans, Vice President Business and Finance
CIO: Merle Enns, Director Information Services
CHR: Joy Robb, Vice President Human Resources
Web address: www.prairieview.org
**Control:** Other not–for–profit (including NFP Corporation) **Service:** Psychiatric

**Staffed Beds:** 38

## NORTON—Norton County

★ **NORTON COUNTY HOSPITAL (171348)**, 102 East Holme, Zip 67654–1406, Mailing Address: P.O. Box 250, Zip 67654–0250; tel. 785/877–3351 **A**5 9 10 18 **F**3 13 15 28 31 34 40 41 45 50 59 64 69 76 78 81 89 93 97 107 110 114 119 127 130 133 135 148 **P**6
Primary Contact: Richard Miller, Administrator and Chief Executive Officer
CFO: Ryan Stover, Chief Financial Officer
CHR: Shannan Hempler, Director Human Resources
Web address: www.ntcohosp.com
**Control:** County–Government, nonfederal **Service:** General Medical and Surgical

**Staffed Beds:** 25 **Admissions:** 645 **Census:** 6 **Outpatient Visits:** 55102 **Births:** 56 **Total Expense ($000):** 10730 **Payroll Expense ($000):** 5379 **Personnel:** 108

## OAKLEY—Logan County

★ **LOGAN COUNTY HOSPITAL (171326)**, 211 Cherry Street, Zip 67748–1201; tel. 785/672–3211, (Total facility includes 46 beds in nursing home–type unit) **A**9 10 18 **F**26 27 28 40 45 50 64 67 69 81 93 107 127 130 133 143 148 **P**5 6
Primary Contact: Darcy Howard, Chief Executive Officer and Chief Financial Officer
CFO: Darcy Howard, Chief Executive Officer and Chief Financial Officer
CMO: Celeste Rains, D.O., Chief of Staff
CIO: Mike Jacobs, Director Information Technology
CHR: Steve Allison, Director Human Resources
Web address: www.logancountyhospital.org
**Control:** County–Government, nonfederal **Service:** General Medical and Surgical

**Staffed Beds:** 71 **Admissions:** 413 **Census:** 45 **Outpatient Visits:** 16546 **Births:** 0 **Total Expense ($000):** 11469 **Payroll Expense ($000):** 5872 **Personnel:** 143

**KS**

*Many Facility Codes have changed. Please refer to the AHA Guide Code Chart.*
© 2013 AHA Guide

## OBERLIN—Decatur County

★ **DECATUR COUNTY HOSPITAL AND CEDAR LIVING CENTER (171352)**, 810 West Columbia Street, Zip 67749–2450, Mailing Address: P.O. Box 268, Zip 67749–0268; tel. 785/475–2208, (Total facility includes 37 beds in nursing home–type unit) **A**9 10 18 **F**3 13 15 28 29 31 34 35 40 45 53 56 57 62 64 69 75 76 78 80 81 84 85 86 93 107 114 127 130 133 135 **P**6
Primary Contact: Johnathan Owens, Chief Executive Officer
CFO: Amanda Fortin, Manager Finance
CMO: Elizabeth Sliter, M.D., Chairman Medical Staff
CIO: Natasha Weishapl, Manager Business Office and Human Resources
CHR: Natasha Weishapl, Manager Business Office and Human Resources
Web address: www.decaturhealthsystems.org
**Control:** County–Government, nonfederal **Service:** General Medical and Surgical

**Staffed Beds: 61 Admissions: 226 Census: 26 Outpatient Visits:** 7775 **Births: 0 Total Expense ($000):** 7010 **Payroll Expense ($000):** 3818 **Personnel:** 86

## OLATHE—Johnson County

☐ **OLATHE MEDICAL CENTER (170049)**, 20333 West 151st Street, Zip 66061–5350; tel. 913/791–4200 **A**1 2 5 9 10 **F**3 8 11 12 13 15 18 20 22 24 26 28 29 30 31 34 35 39 40 41 46 49 56 57 58 59 61 62 63 64 65 68 70 74 75 76 77 78 79 81 82 84 85 86 87 89 93 107 108 110 111 114 115 116 117 118 119 129 130 131 132 135 144 145 146 147 148
Primary Contact: Frank H. Devocelle, President and Chief Executive Officer
CFO: Tierney Grasser, Senior Vice President Finance
CIO: Georeg Dix, Chief Information Officer
CHR: David Klimek, Chief Human Resources Officer
CNO: Elaine Patton, Vice President Nursing
Web address: www.ohsi.com
**Control:** Other not–for–profit (including NFP Corporation) **Service:** General Medical and Surgical

**Staffed Beds: 229 Admissions: 10843 Census: 112 Outpatient Visits:** 302969 **Births:** 1190 **Personnel:** 1371

## ONAGA—Pottawatomie County

★ **COMMUNITY HEALTHCARE SYSTEM (171354)**, 120 West Eighth Street, Zip 66521–9574; tel. 785/889–4272, (Total facility includes 78 beds in nursing home–type unit) **A**9 10 18 **F**2 3 5 6 10 11 12 13 15 29 31 32 34 35 36 40 43 45 50 53 56 57 59 62 64 65 67 70 74 75 76 77 78 79 81 82 84 85 86 87 89 93 97 99 100 101 102 103 104 105 106 107 114 119 125 127 128 130 131 132 133 134 135 143 144 145 146 147 148 **P**6
Primary Contact: Greg Unruh, Chief Executive Officer
COO: Marcia S. Walsh, M.P.H., Chief Operating Officer
CFO: Monica Holthaus, Chief Financial Officer
CMO: Nancy Zidek, M.D., Chief of Staff
CIO: Paul Zidek, Chief Information Officer
CHR: Terry D. Bernatis, Director Human Resources
CNO: Rosalind Lewis, R.N., Chief Nursing Officer
Web address: www.chcsks.org
**Control:** Other not–for–profit (including NFP Corporation) **Service:** General Medical and Surgical

**Staffed Beds: 159 Admissions: 1158 Census: 77 Outpatient Visits:** 99724 **Births:** 107 **Total Expense ($000):** 25268 **Payroll Expense ($000):** 15241 **Personnel:** 358

## OSAWATOMIE—Miami County

☐ **OSAWATOMIE STATE HOSPITAL (174004)**, 500 State Hospital Drive, Zip 66064–1813, Mailing Address: P.O. Box 500, Zip 66064–0500; tel. 913/755–7000 **A**1 10 **F**11 30 50 75 86 87 98 101 103 130 132 135 146 **P**6
Primary Contact: Steven F. Ashcraft, Superintendent
CFO: Donna Dean, Chief Financial Officer
CMO: Maria Gustilo, M.D., Medical Director
CIO: Lester Vohs, Chief Information Management
CHR: Marilyn Williamson, Director Human Resources
Web address: www.srskansas.org/osh/osh-rmhf_info.html
**Control:** State–Government, nonfederal **Service:** Psychiatric

**Staffed Beds: 176 Admissions: 2912 Census: 176 Outpatient Visits:** 0 **Births: 0 Total Expense ($000):** 28967 **Payroll Expense ($000):** 16261 **Personnel:** 328

## OSBORNE—Osborne County

★ **OSBORNE COUNTY MEMORIAL HOSPITAL (171364)**, 424 West New Hampshire Street, Zip 67473–2314, Mailing Address: P.O. Box 70, Zip 67473–0070; tel. 785/346–2121 **A**9 10 18 **F**3 11 13 40 45 64 69 76 81 107 128 133 **P**6 **S** Great Plains Health Alliance, Inc., Wichita, KS
Primary Contact: Kiley Floyd, Administrator
CFO: Linda Murphy, Chief Financial Officer
CMO: Barbara Brown, D.O., Chief of Staff
CIO: Kiley Floyd, Administrator
Web address: www.ocmh.org
**Control:** County–Government, nonfederal **Service:** General Medical and Surgical

**Staffed Beds: 25 Admissions: 301 Census: 7 Outpatient Visits:** 11663 **Births:** 10 **Total Expense ($000):** 5842 **Payroll Expense ($000):** 2722 **Personnel:** 66

## OSWEGO—Labette County

★ **OSWEGO COMMUNITY HOSPITAL (171302)**, 800 Barker Drive, Zip 67356–9014; tel. 620/795–2921 **A**9 10 18 **F**3 9 12 30 32 35 40 57 59 64 65 75 77 93 97 107 127 130 132 133 135 146 147 148 **P**5 **S** Rural Community Hospitals of America, Kansas City, MO
Primary Contact: Daniel Hiben, Chief Executive Officer
CFO: Christina Schlatter, Chief Financial Officer
CMO: Gordon Kern, M.D., Medical Director
CHR: Christina Schlatter, Chief Financial Officer
Web address: www.oswegocommunityhospital.com
**Control:** Corporation, Investor–owned, for–profit **Service:** General Medical and Surgical

**Staffed Beds: 12 Admissions: 127 Census: 5 Outpatient Visits:** 9338 **Births: 0 Total Expense ($000):** 3276 **Payroll Expense ($000):** 2133 **Personnel:** 44

## OTTAWA—Franklin County

⌘ **RANSOM MEMORIAL HOSPITAL (170014)**, 1301 South Main Street, Zip 66067–3598; tel. 785/229–8200 **A**1 5 9 10 **F**3 11 13 15 28 30 34 35 36 40 45 46 49 53 56 57 59 64 70 75 76 77 79 81 82 85 86 92 93 96 97 107 108 110 111 115 118 119 129 130 131 132 133 134 135 144 146 147 148 **P**8
Primary Contact: Larry A. Felix, FACHE, Chief Executive Officer
CFO: Dean Ohmart, Assistant Administrator and Chief Financial Officer
Web address: www.ransom.org
**Control:** County–Government, nonfederal **Service:** General Medical and Surgical

**Staffed Beds: 44 Admissions: 1444 Census: 12 Outpatient Visits:** 101748 **Births:** 173 **Total Expense ($000):** 31271 **Payroll Expense ($000):** 15972 **Personnel:** 293

## OVERLAND PARK—Johnson County

☐ **CHILDREN'S MERCY SOUTH (173300)**, 5808 West 110th Street, Zip 66211–2504; tel. 913/696–8000 **A**1 9 10 **F**3 9 29 30 32 35 36 40 41 44 48 50 59 62 64 68 75 77 79 81 82 85 87 89 93 94 100 101 104 107 111 114 119 129 130 131 132 134 144 146 148 **P**6 8
Primary Contact: Randall L. O'Donnell, Ph.D., President and Chief Executive Officer
CFO: Sandra A J Lawrence, Executive Vice President and Chief Financial Officer
CMO: Charles Roberts, M.D., Medical Director
CIO: Jean Ann Breedlove, Chief Information Officer
CHR: Dan Wright, Vice President Human Resources
Web address: www.childrens-mercy.org
**Control:** Other not–for–profit (including NFP Corporation) **Service:** Children's general

**Staffed Beds: 45 Admissions: 2070 Census: 13 Outpatient Visits:** 83404 **Births: 0 Total Expense ($000):** 85611 **Payroll Expense ($000):** 47730 **Personnel:** 609

**HEARTLAND SPINE & SPECIALTY HOSPITAL** See Heartland Surgical Specialty Hospital

☐ **HEARTLAND SURGICAL SPECIALTY HOSPITAL (170195)**, 10720 Nall Avenue, Zip 66211–1206; tel. 913/754–5000, (Nonreporting) **A**1 9 10
Primary Contact: Don Burman, Chief Executive Officer
CFO: Jesse Saucedo, Chief Financial Officer
CMO: David Anderson, M.D., Medical Director
CIO: Matt Czugala, Manager Information Systems
CHR: Jan Mathieu, Director Human Resources
Web address: www.hssh.org
**Control:** Partnership, Investor–owned, for–profit **Service:** Orthopedic

**Staffed Beds: 48**

---

**Hospital, Medicare Provider Number, Address, Telephone, Approval, Facility, and Physician Codes, Health Care System**

★ American Hospital Association (AHA) membership
☐ The Joint Commission accreditation
◇ DNV Healthcare Inc. accreditation
○ Healthcare Facilities Accreditation Program
△ Commission on Accreditation of Rehabilitation Facilities (CARF) accreditation

KS

✠ **MENORAH MEDICAL CENTER (170182)**, 5721 West 119th Street, Zip 66209–3722; tel. 913/498–6000 **A**1 2 9 10 **F**3 12 13 15 18 20 22 24 26 28 29 30 31 34 35 38 40 45 46 47 49 55 57 58 59 60 64 65 68 70 72 74 75 76 77 78 79 81 82 85 86 87 90 93 97 102 107 108 110 111 114 115 117 119 121 124 126 129 130 131 132 135 144 145 146 147 148 **P**5 **S** HCA, Nashville, TN
Primary Contact: Steven D. Wilkinson, President and Chief Executive Officer
CFO: Deborah Gafford, Chief Financial Officer
Web address: www.menorahmedicalcenter.com
**Control:** Corporation, Investor–owned, for–profit **Service:** General Medical and Surgical

**Staffed Beds:** 158 **Admissions:** 6774 **Census:** 78 **Outpatient Visits:** 72459 **Births:** 1003 **Total Expense ($000):** 153339 **Payroll Expense ($000):** 46517 **Personnel:** 705

✠ **OVERLAND PARK REGIONAL MEDICAL CENTER (170176)**, 10500 Quivira Road, Zip 66215–2306, Mailing Address: P.O. Box 15959, Zip 66215–5959; tel. 913/541–5000 **A**1 9 10 **F**3 13 15 18 20 22 24 26 28 29 30 31 34 35 37 40 43 45 49 50 56 57 59 60 61 64 65 67 70 72 73 74 75 76 77 78 79 81 82 83 84 85 86 87 91 92 93 107 108 110 111 114 119 126 129 130 131 135 145 146 147 148 **S** HCA, Nashville, TN
Primary Contact: Damond Boatwright, Chief Executive Officer
COO: Dean Carucci, Chief Operating Officer
CFO: Shari Collier, Chief Financial Officer
CMO: John A. Romito, M.D., Chief Medical Officer
CHR: Connie Miller, Vice President Human Resources
Web address: www.oprmc.com
**Control:** Corporation, Investor–owned, for–profit **Service:** General Medical and Surgical

**Staffed Beds:** 276 **Admissions:** 10516 **Census:** 142 **Outpatient Visits:** 64302 **Births:** 3270 **Total Expense ($000):** 133963 **Payroll Expense ($000):** 53459 **Personnel:** 770

✠ **SAINT LUKE'S SOUTH HOSPITAL (170185)**, 12300 Metcalf Avenue, Zip 66213–1324; tel. 913/317–7000 **A**1 9 10 **F**3 8 12 13 15 18 20 22 26 28 29 30 31 34 38 40 45 47 49 55 58 59 64 65 70 72 74 75 76 77 78 79 80 81 82 84 85 87 90 93 94 107 108 110 111 114 117 118 119 129 130 131 132 146 148 **S** Saint Luke's Health System, Kansas City, MO
Primary Contact: Jani L. Johnson, President and Chief Executive Officer
CFO: Shelby Frigon, Chief Financial Officer
CMO: Wendell Clarkston, M.D., President Medical Staff
CIO: Deborah Gash, Chief Information Officer
CHR: Donna Kunz, Manager Human Resources
CNO: Julia Woods, R.N., Vice President and Chief Nursing Officer
Web address: www.saint–lukes.org
**Control:** Church–operated, Nongovernment, not–for profit **Service:** General Medical and Surgical

**Staffed Beds:** 110 **Admissions:** 5316 **Census:** 56 **Outpatient Visits:** 80849 **Births:** 1066 **Total Expense ($000):** 103763 **Payroll Expense ($000):** 34896 **Personnel:** 491

☐ **SPECIALTY HOSPITAL OF MID–AMERICA (172004)**, 6509 West 103rd Street, Zip 66212–1728; tel. 913/649–3701, (Total facility includes 52 beds in nursing home–type unit) **A**1 9 10 **F**1 29 60 128 143 **S** Fundamental Long Term Care Holdings, LLC, Sparks Glencoe, MD
Primary Contact: Karen Leverich, Chief Executive Officer
CFO: William Scott, Chief Financial Officer
CHR: Darren Enochs, Director Human Resources
Web address: www.thicare.com/SpecHospOfMidAmerica/
**Control:** Corporation, Investor–owned, for–profit **Service:** Long–Term Acute Care hospital

**Staffed Beds:** 104 **Admissions:** 460 **Census:** 61 **Outpatient Visits:** 0 **Births:** 0 **Total Expense ($000):** 4479 **Payroll Expense ($000):** 3322 **Personnel:** 119

## PAOLA—Miami County

☐ **MIAMI COUNTY MEDICAL CENTER (170109)**, 2100 Baptiste Drive, Zip 66071–1314, Mailing Address: P.O. Box 365, Zip 66071–0365; tel. 913/294–2327 **A**1 5 9 10 **F**3 11 15 30 40 59 61 64 68 75 77 78 79 81 82 85 87 89 90 93 102 107 108 110 111 114 119 127 129 130 131 146 148
Primary Contact: Gerald Wiesner, Administrator
Web address: www.olathehealth.com
**Control:** Other not–for–profit (including NFP Corporation) **Service:** General Medical and Surgical

**Staffed Beds:** 18 **Admissions:** 474 **Census:** 3 **Outpatient Visits:** 31146 **Births:** 0 **Personnel:** 121

## PARSONS—Labette County

★ ○ **LABETTE HEALTH (170120)**, 1902 South U.S. Highway 59, Zip 67357–7404; tel. 620/421–4880 **A**9 10 11 **F**3 7 11 13 15 29 30 34 40 43 53 57 59 62 70 75 76 77 79 81 82 86 90 93 107 111 118 119 127 129 130 131 132 143 146 147 148 **P**6
Primary Contact: Jodi A. Schmidt, President and Chief Executive Officer
CFO: Thomas Macaronas, Chief Financial Officer
CHR: Christina Sykes, Director Human Resources
Web address: www.labettehealth.com
**Control:** County–Government, nonfederal **Service:** General Medical and Surgical

**Staffed Beds:** 55 **Admissions:** 2418 **Census:** 23 **Outpatient Visits:** 71538 **Births:** 267 **Total Expense ($000):** 58143 **Payroll Expense ($000):** 22873 **Personnel:** 522

**PARSONS STATE HOSPITAL AND TRAINING CENTER**, 2601 Gabriel Avenue, Zip 67357–2341, Mailing Address: P.O. Box 738, Zip 67357–0738; tel. 620/421–6550 **F**35 39 67 130 146
Primary Contact: Jerry A. Rea, Ph.D., Superintendent
CFO: John Spare, Accountant
CMO: Rema Menon, M.D., Clinical Director
CIO: Ron Malmstrom, Information Research Specialist
CHR: Tim B. Posch, Business Manager and Director Personnel
Web address: www.pshtc.org
**Control:** State–Government, nonfederal **Service:** Institution for mental retardation

**Staffed Beds:** 188 **Admissions:** 14 **Census:** 180 **Outpatient Visits:** 0 **Births:** 0 **Total Expense ($000):** 26360 **Payroll Expense ($000):** 15080 **Personnel:** 418

## PHILLIPSBURG—Phillips County

★ **PHILLIPS COUNTY HOSPITAL (171353)**, 1150 State Street, Zip 67661–1743, Mailing Address: P.O. Box 607, Zip 67661–0607; tel. 785/543–5226 **A**9 10 18 **F**3 11 15 28 30 31 40 45 50 59 64 68 75 77 78 81 86 87 93 107 114 119 127 128 130 132 133 145 146 148 **P**6 **S** Great Plains Health Alliance, Inc., Wichita, KS
Primary Contact: David Engel, Chief Executive Officer
CFO: Dennis Fredrickson, Chief Financial Officer
CMO: Ben Stephenson, M.D., Chief of Staff
CIO: Steven Seems, Director of Information Technology
CNO: Diane Jarvis, R.N., Director of Nursing
Web address: www.phillipshospital.org
**Control:** Other not–for–profit (including NFP Corporation) **Service:** General Medical and Surgical

**Staffed Beds:** 25 **Admissions:** 292 **Census:** 5 **Outpatient Visits:** 22464 **Births:** 0 **Total Expense ($000):** 8964 **Payroll Expense ($000):** 3766 **Personnel:** 96

## PITTSBURG—Crawford County

✠ **VIA CHRISTI HOSPITAL IN PITTSBURG (170006)**, (Formerly Via Christi Hospital), 1 Mt. Carmel Way, Zip 66762–7587; tel. 620/232–0109 **A**1 2 5 9 10 **F**3 5 8 11 12 13 15 18 20 22 26 28 29 30 31 34 35 40 42 43 45 47 48 50 51 53 54 55 56 57 58 59 62 64 68 69 70 71 73 75 76 77 78 79 80 81 82 84 85 86 89 90 93 99 100 101 103 104 107 108 109 110 111 112 114 115 116 117 118 119 120 121 122 123 129 130 131 132 133 135 143 144 145 146 147 148 **P**8 **S** Ascension Health, Saint Louis, MO
Primary Contact: Randall R. Cason, FACHE, President and Chief Executive Officer
COO: Drew Talbott, Vice President Operations
CFO: Mike Joy, Chief Financial Officer
CIO: Troy Mascher, Director Information Systems
CHR: Connie McCune, Vice President Human Resources
Web address: www.viachristi.org
**Control:** Church–operated, Nongovernment, not–for profit **Service:** General Medical and Surgical

**Staffed Beds:** 111 **Admissions:** 4225 **Census:** 54 **Outpatient Visits:** 119744 **Births:** 562 **Total Expense ($000):** 85759 **Payroll Expense ($000):** 37752 **Personnel:** 671

## PLAINVILLE—Rooks County

★ **ROOKS COUNTY HEALTH CENTER (171311)**, 1210 North Washington Street, Zip 67663–1632, Mailing Address: P.O. Box 389, Zip 67663–0389; tel. 785/434–4553 **A**5 9 10 18 **F**3 11 13 15 28 31 34 40 45 50 57 59 64 77 81 87 93 96 102 107 110 114 119 125 130 133 135 143 144 146 148
Primary Contact: Michael Sinclair, Chief Executive Officer
COO: William D. Stahl, Chief Operating Officer
CFO: Julie Price, Chief Financial Officer
CMO: Lynn Fisher, M.D., Chief of Staff
CIO: Kathy Ramsay, R.N., Director Communications and Development
CHR: Cindi Knipp, Director Human Resources
Web address: www.rookscountyhealthcenter.com
**Control:** Hospital district or authority, Government, nonfederal **Service:** General Medical and Surgical

**Staffed Beds:** 20 **Admissions:** 388 **Census:** 6 **Outpatient Visits:** 16796 **Births:** 33 **Total Expense ($000):** 12604 **Payroll Expense ($000):** 4583 **Personnel:** 132

**KS**

*Many Facility Codes have changed. Please refer to the AHA Guide Code Chart.*
© 2013 AHA Guide

## PRATT—Pratt County

★ **PRATT REGIONAL MEDICAL CENTER (170027)**, 200 Commodore Street, Zip 67124–2903; tel. 620/672–7451, (Total facility includes 47 beds in nursing home–type unit) **A**5 9 10 20 **F**3 11 13 15 30 31 34 40 45 49 56 57 59 61 62 64 68 69 70 75 76 77 79 81 82 85 86 87 89 90 93 107 108 114 118 119 124 127 128 130 131 133 145 146 147 148 **P**6
Primary Contact: Susan M. Page, President and Chief Executive Officer
CFO: Hilary Dolbee, Vice President and Chief Financial Officer
CIO: Stacy Glennie, Director Health Information Services
CHR: Ken Brown, Vice President and Chief Human Resource Officer
CNO: Sherry L. Besser, R.N., Vice President Quality, Risk Management and Chief Nursing Officer
Web address: www.prmc.org
**Control:** Other not–for–profit (including NFP Corporation) **Service:** General Medical and Surgical

**Staffed Beds:** 85 **Admissions:** 1459 **Census:** 55 **Outpatient Visits:** 87355 **Births:** 295 **Total Expense ($000):** 39286 **Payroll Expense ($000):** 19503 **Personnel:** 334

## QUINTER—Gove County

**GOVE COUNTY MEDICAL CENTER (171367)**, 520 West Fifth Street, Zip 67752–9705, Mailing Address: P.O. Box 129, Zip 67752–0129; tel. 785/754–3341, (Total facility includes 49 beds in nursing home–type unit) **A**5 9 10 18 **F**3 11 13 28 29 31 34 40 45 57 62 67 75 81 93 107 119 125 133 135 143 148
Primary Contact: Richard Q. Bergling, Chief Executive Officer
CFO: Joy Bretz, Chief Financial Officer
CHR: Valerie Schneider, Director Human Resources
CNO: Tammy Hutchison, R.N., Director of Nursing
Web address: www.gcmc.ws
**Control:** County–Government, nonfederal **Service:** General Medical and Surgical

**Staffed Beds:** 70 **Admissions:** 695 **Census:** 54 **Outpatient Visits:** 10091 **Births:** 67 **Total Expense ($000):** 13006 **Payroll Expense ($000):** 5913 **Personnel:** 167

## RANSOM—Ness County

★ **GRISELL MEMORIAL HOSPITAL DISTRICT ONE (171300)**, 210 South Vermont Avenue, Zip 67572–9525; tel. 785/731–2231, (Total facility includes 34 beds in nursing home–type unit) **A**9 10 18 **F**3 40 56 67 69 85 93 97 127 128 133 **P**6 **S** Great Plains Health Alliance, Inc., Wichita, KS
Primary Contact: Kristine Ochs, R.N., Administrator
CFO: Tammy Schweitzer, Chief Financial Officer
CMO: Allen McLain, M.D., Chief of Staff
CNO: Joni Pfaff, Chief Nursing Officer
Web address: www.grisellmemorialhospital.org
**Control:** Hospital district or authority, Government, nonfederal **Service:** General Medical and Surgical

**Staffed Beds:** 46 **Admissions:** 55 **Census:** 29 **Outpatient Visits:** 6949 **Births:** 0 **Total Expense ($000):** 4405 **Payroll Expense ($000):** 2335 **Personnel:** 70

## RUSSELL—Russell County

★ **RUSSELL REGIONAL HOSPITAL (171350)**, 200 South Main Street, Zip 67665–2920; tel. 785/483–3131, (Total facility includes 21 beds in nursing home–type unit) **A**9 10 18 **F**7 11 15 29 30 32 34 35 40 50 53 57 59 64 65 66 67 69 75 83 85 87 93 107 110 114 119 127 128 130 131 133 135 145 146 147 148 **P**6
Primary Contact: Harold Courtois, Chief Executive Officer
CFO: Janel Burch, Chief Financial Officer
CMO: Earl Merkel, M.D., Chief of Staff
CIO: David Schraeder, Director Information Systems
CHR: Sharon Collins, Director Human Resources and Executive Administrative Assistant
Web address: www.russellhospital.org
**Control:** Other not–for–profit (including NFP Corporation) **Service:** General Medical and Surgical

**Staffed Beds:** 46 **Admissions:** 382 **Census:** 26 **Outpatient Visits:** 23721 **Births:** 0 **Total Expense ($000):** 13528 **Payroll Expense ($000):** 7343 **Personnel:** 142

## SABETHA—Nemaha County

★ **SABETHA COMMUNITY HOSPITAL (171338)**, 14th and Oregon Streets, Zip 66534–0229, Mailing Address: P.O. Box 229, Zip 66534–0229; tel. 785/284–2121 **A**9 10 18 **F**3 11 13 15 28 34 35 40 45 50 56 57 59 62 63 64 68 75 76 77 78 79 81 82 84 86 93 107 110 114 119 128 130 133 146 148 **P**6 **S** Great Plains Health Alliance, Inc., Wichita, KS
Primary Contact: Lora Key, Chief Executive Officer
CFO: Lori Lackey, Chief Financial Officer
CMO: Kevin Kennally, M.D., Chief of Medical Staff
CIO: Holli Dieckmann, Director Health Information
CHR: Julie K. Holthaus, Director Human Resources
CNO: Stacy Scott, Director of Nursing
Web address: www.sabethahospital.com
**Control:** Other not–for–profit (including NFP Corporation) **Service:** General Medical and Surgical

**Staffed Beds:** 25 **Admissions:** 405 **Census:** 6 **Outpatient Visits:** 42859 **Births:** 48 **Total Expense ($000):** 10777 **Payroll Expense ($000):** 5036 **Personnel:** 102

## SAINT FRANCIS—Cheyenne County

★ **CHEYENNE COUNTY HOSPITAL (171310)**, 210 West First Street, Zip 67756–3540, Mailing Address: P.O. Box 547, Zip 67756–0547; tel. 785/332–2104 **A**5 9 10 18 **F**3 8 11 13 28 29 31 40 57 59 64 65 66 76 77 78 81 85 89 93 97 107 119 127 128 133 148 **P**6 **S** Great Plains Health Alliance, Inc., Wichita, KS
Primary Contact: Judith Ann Rockwood, Administrator
CFO: Heidi Tice, Chief Financial Officer
CMO: Rebecca Allard, M.D., Chief of Staff
CHR: Tabetha Ketzner, Director Human Resources
Web address: www.cheyennecountyhospital.com
**Control:** Other not–for–profit (including NFP Corporation) **Service:** General Medical and Surgical

**Staffed Beds:** 16 **Admissions:** 374 **Census:** 4 **Outpatient Visits:** 19976 **Births:** 20 **Total Expense ($000):** 8410 **Payroll Expense ($000):** 3953 **Personnel:** 80

## SALINA—Saline County

★ ○ **SALINA REGIONAL HEALTH CENTER (170012)**, 400 South Santa Fe Avenue, Zip 67401–4198, Mailing Address: P.O. Box 5080, Zip 67402–5080; tel. 785/452–7000, (Includes SALINA REGIONAL HEALTH CENTER– PENN CAMPUS, 139 North Penn Street, Zip 67401, Mailing Address: P.O. Box 5080, Zip 67402–5080; tel. 913/452–7000; SALINA REGIONAL HEALTH CENTER–SANTA FE CAMPUS, 400 South Santa Fe Avenue, Zip 67401, Mailing Address: Box 5080, Zip 67402–5080; tel. 913/452–7000) **A**2 3 5 9 10 11 **F**3 13 15 20 22 24 26 28 29 30 31 35 40 46 47 48 49 51 53 64 70 71 72 73 74 76 77 78 79 81 85 86 87 89 90 91 92 93 94 98 100 102 103 104 105 107 108 110 111 114 116 117 118 119 120 121 122 123 129 130 143 144 145 146 147 148
Primary Contact: Micheal Terry, President and Chief Executive Officer
COO: Joel Phelps, Chief Operating Officer
CFO: Joe Tallon, Vice President Finance
CIO: Larry Barnes, Vice President Information Technology
CHR: David Moody, Vice President Human Resources
Web address: www.srhc.com
**Control:** Other not–for–profit (including NFP Corporation) **Service:** General Medical and Surgical

**Staffed Beds:** 198 **Admissions:** 8378 **Census:** 104 **Outpatient Visits:** 173732 **Births:** 1203 **Total Expense ($000):** 145481 **Payroll Expense ($000):** 60948 **Personnel:** 1171

**SALINA SURGICAL HOSPITAL (170187)**, 401 South Sante Fe, Zip 67401–4143; tel. 785/827–0610 **A**9 10 **F**29 45 48 49 51 74 79 81 85 131
Primary Contact: LuAnn Puvogel, R.N., Administrator
CFO: Geri Leibham, Manager Business Office
CMO: Michael Johnson, M.D., Medical Director
CIO: Rex Harrell, Information Technologist
CHR: Geri Leibham, Manager Business Office
Web address: www.salinasurgical.com/
**Control:** Partnership, Investor–owned, for–profit **Service:** Surgical

**Staffed Beds:** 16 **Admissions:** 553 **Census:** 4 **Outpatient Visits:** 7240 **Births:** 0 **Total Expense ($000):** 13588 **Payroll Expense ($000):** 4626 **Personnel:** 81

---

**Hospital, Medicare Provider Number, Address, Telephone, Approval, Facility, and Physician Codes, Health Care System**

★ American Hospital Association (AHA) membership
□ The Joint Commission accreditation
◇ DNV Healthcare Inc. accreditation
○ Healthcare Facilities Accreditation Program
△ Commission on Accreditation of Rehabilitation Facilities (CARF) accreditation

**KS**

## SATANTA—Haskell County

★ **SATANTA DISTRICT HOSPITAL (171324)**, 401 South Cheyenne Street, Zip 67870-0159, Mailing Address: P.O. Box 159, Zip 67870-0159; tel. 620/649-2761, (Total facility includes 44 beds in nursing home–type unit) **A**9 10 18 **F**3 11 40 45 57 64 67 68 75 81 93 104 107 119 127 128 130 133 **P**4 **S** Great Plains Health Alliance, Inc., Wichita, KS
Primary Contact: Jeremy Clingenpeel, Administrator
CFO: Libby Anderson, Chief Financial Officer
CMO: Virgilio Taduran, M.D., Chief Medical Officer
CIO: Ben Leppke, Chief Information Officer
CHR: Sam Hett, Manager Human Resources
CNO: Tina Pendergraft, Chief Nursing Officer
Web address: www.satantahospital.org
**Control:** Hospital district or authority, Government, nonfederal **Service:** General Medical and Surgical

**Staffed Beds:** 57 **Admissions:** 229 **Census:** 37 **Outpatient Visits:** 26112 **Births:** 0 **Total Expense ($000):** 12397 **Payroll Expense ($000):** 5247 **Personnel:** 128

## SCOTT CITY—Scott County

★ **SCOTT COUNTY HOSPITAL (171372)**, 310 East Third Street, Zip 67871-1203; tel. 620/872-5811 **A**9 10 18 **F**3 7 13 15 28 29 30 31 35 40 45 57 59 62 64 68 69 75 76 77 81 85 93 107 110 119 127 128 130 133 135 148 **P**6
Primary Contact: Mark Burnett, President and Chief Executive Officer
COO: Karma Huck, Chief Operating Officer
CFO: Joe S. Meyer, Chief Financial Officer
CMO: Elizabeth Hineman, M.D., Chief Medical Staff
CHR: Pamela R. Wheeler, Manager Human Resources
Web address: www.scotthospital.net
**Control:** Other not–for–profit (including NFP Corporation) **Service:** General Medical and Surgical

**Staffed Beds:** 22 **Admissions:** 542 **Census:** 9 **Outpatient Visits:** 16887 **Births:** 64 **Total Expense ($000):** 13615 **Payroll Expense ($000):** 7105 **Personnel:** 187

## SEDAN—Chautauqua County

**SEDAN CITY HOSPITAL (171318)**, 300 North Street, Zip 67361-1051, Mailing Address: P.O. Box C, Zip 67361-0427; tel. 620/725-3115 **A**9 10 18 **F**29 34 40 57 64 107 128 130 133 148 **S** Ascension Health, Saint Louis, MO
Primary Contact: Michelle Williams, Administrator
CFO: Jennifer Seever, Regional Chief Financial Officer
CMO: James McDermott, M.D., Chief of Staff
**Control:** City–Government, nonfederal **Service:** General Medical and Surgical

**Staffed Beds:** 25 **Admissions:** 214 **Census:** 2 **Outpatient Visits:** 7521 **Births:** 0 **Total Expense ($000):** 2651 **Payroll Expense ($000):** 1713 **Personnel:** 37

## SENECA—Nemaha County

★ **NEMAHA VALLEY COMMUNITY HOSPITAL (171315)**, 1600 Community Drive, Zip 66538-9739; tel. 785/336-6181 **A**9 10 18 **F**11 12 13 15 28 31 40 56 57 59 64 75 76 77 78 79 81 84 85 89 93 107 111 114 117 119 127 129 130 131 132 133 **P**6
Primary Contact: Stan Regehr, President and Chief Executive Officer
CFO: Connie Ingwerson, Chief Financial Officer
CHR: Jan Lueb, Coordinator Human Resources
Web address: www.nemvch.org
**Control:** Other not–for–profit (including NFP Corporation) **Service:** General Medical and Surgical

**Staffed Beds:** 24 **Admissions:** 299 **Census:** 4 **Outpatient Visits:** 19914 **Births:** 44 **Total Expense ($000):** 10624 **Payroll Expense ($000):** 5051 **Personnel:** 111

## SHAWNEE MISSION—Johnson County

☒ **MID–AMERICA REHABILITATION HOSPITAL (173026)**, 5701 West 110th Street, Zip 66211-2503; tel. 913/491-2400 **A**1 10 **F**29 35 56 64 86 90 93 132 143 148 **S** HEALTHSOUTH Corporation, Birmingham, AL
Primary Contact: Troy DeDecker, Chief Executive Officer
CFO: Richard Lane, Chief Financial Officer
CMO: Cielo Dehning, M.D., Medical Director
CHR: Holly Ray, Director Human Resources
Web address: www.midamericarehabhospital.com
**Control:** Corporation, Investor–owned, for–profit **Service:** Rehabilitation

**Staffed Beds:** 98 **Admissions:** 2088 **Census:** 76 **Outpatient Visits:** 9188 **Births:** 0 **Total Expense ($000):** 25595 **Payroll Expense ($000):** 12933 **Personnel:** 220

☒ **SHAWNEE MISSION MEDICAL CENTER (170104)**, 9100 West 74th Street, Zip 66204-4004, Mailing Address: Box 2923, Zip 66201-1323; tel. 913/676-2000 **A**1 2 3 5 9 10 **F**3 4 5 8 11 12 13 15 17 18 20 22 24 28 29 30 31 32 34 35 36 40 42 45 47 48 49 52 54 55 56 57 59 60 61 62 64 70 72 74 75 76 77 78 79 81 82 84 85 86 87 89 93 96 98 100 101 102 103 104 105 107 108 110 111 113 114 115 116 118 119 126 129 130 131 132 135 144 146 147 148 **P**6 **S** Adventist Health System Sunbelt Health Care Corporation, Altamonte Springs, FL
Primary Contact: Ken J. Bacon, President and Chief Executive Officer
CFO: Jack W. Wagner, Executive Vice President and Chief Financial Officer
CMO: Leah Ridgway, M.D., President Medical Staff
CIO: Mike Allen, Director Information Services
CHR: Brad Hoffman, Administrative Director Human Resources
Web address: www.shawneemission.org
**Control:** Church–operated, Nongovernment, not–for profit **Service:** General Medical and Surgical

**Staffed Beds:** 376 **Admissions:** 19716 **Census:** 208 **Outpatient Visits:** 524596 **Births:** 3786 **Total Expense ($000):** 328950 **Payroll Expense ($000):** 131633 **Personnel:** 2129

## SMITH CENTER—Smith County

★ **SMITH COUNTY MEMORIAL HOSPITAL (171377)**, 614 South Main Street, Zip 66967-3001; tel. 785/282-6845, (Total facility includes 28 beds in nursing home–type unit) **A**5 9 10 18 **F**2 13 15 28 30 31 40 45 53 64 67 68 69 75 76 81 85 93 107 114 119 127 128 133 **P**6 **S** Great Plains Health Alliance, Inc., Wichita, KS
Primary Contact: Allen Van Driel, FACHE, Administrator
CFO: Julie Williams, Chief Financial Officer
CIO: Tammy Gaston, Chief Information Officer
CHR: Jody Maxwell, Manager Business Office
CNO: Sarah Ragsdale, R.N., Chief Nursing Officer
Web address: www.gpha.com
**Control:** Other not–for–profit (including NFP Corporation) **Service:** General Medical and Surgical

**Staffed Beds:** 53 **Admissions:** 377 **Census:** 27 **Outpatient Visits:** 24727 **Births:** 23 **Total Expense ($000):** 9985 **Payroll Expense ($000):** 4655 **Personnel:** 117

## STAFFORD—Stafford County

★ **STAFFORD COUNTY HOSPITAL (171323)**, 502 South Buckeye Street, Zip 67578-2035, Mailing Address: P.O. Box 190, Zip 67578-0190; tel. 620/234-5221 **A**9 10 18 **F**3 15 29 35 40 57 59 62 64 67 77 93 107 128 130 133 **P**5
Primary Contact: Todd Taylor, Chief Executive Officer
CFO: Janell Goodno, Chief Financial Officer
Web address: www.staffordcountyhospital.org
**Control:** Hospital district or authority, Government, nonfederal **Service:** General Medical and Surgical

**Staffed Beds:** 25 **Admissions:** 95 **Census:** 8 **Outpatient Visits:** 36414 **Births:** 0 **Total Expense ($000):** 3745 **Payroll Expense ($000):** 1619 **Personnel:** 45

## SYRACUSE—Hamilton County

**HAMILTON COUNTY HOSPITAL (171322)**, East Avenue G & Huser Street, Zip 67878-0948, Mailing Address: P.O. Box 948, Zip 67878-0948; tel. 620/384-7461, (Total facility includes 44 beds in nursing home–type unit) **A**9 10 18 **F**3 40 50 64 81 93 107 127 128 133
Primary Contact: Phyllis Horning, Interim Administrator
CFO: Phyllis Horning, Chief Financial Officer
CHR: Angela Talbot, Manager Human Resources
Web address: www.hamiltoncountyhospital.net
**Control:** County–Government, nonfederal **Service:** General Medical and Surgical

**Staffed Beds:** 69 **Admissions:** 228 **Census:** 38 **Outpatient Visits:** 5592 **Births:** 0 **Total Expense ($000):** 6824 **Payroll Expense ($000):** 3499 **Personnel:** 77

## TOPEKA—Shawnee County

**COLMERY–O'NEIL VETERANS AFFAIRS MEDICAL CENTER** See Veterans Affairs Eastern Kansas Health Care System

**KANSAS NEUROLOGICAL INSTITUTE**, 3107 West 21st Street, Zip 66604-3298; tel. 785/296-5301 **F**1 4 16 17 29 30 35 39 67 70 72 73 76 80 88 89 90 91 97 98 128 130 143 146
Primary Contact: Barney Hubert, Superintendent
COO: Barney Hubert, Superintendent
CFO: Sara Mock, Director Administrative Services
CMO: Kimberley Scott, Director Health Care Services
CIO: Cheryl Fuller, Director Information Resources
CHR: Shawna Mercer, Director Human Resources
Web address: www.srsnet.srs.ks.gov/hospitals/kni/
**Control:** State–Government, nonfederal **Service:** Institution for mental retardation

**Staffed Beds:** 152 **Admissions:** 3 **Census:** 152 **Outpatient Visits:** 0 **Births:** 0 **Total Expense ($000):** 26329 **Payroll Expense ($000):** 16318 **Personnel:** 462

*Many Facility Codes have changed. Please refer to the AHA Guide Code Chart.*

**KANSAS REHABILITATION HOSPITAL (173025)**, 1504 S.W. Eighth Avenue, Zip 66606–1632; tel. 785/235–6600 **A**1 9 10 **F**3 29 53 59 62 64 68 75 86 90 91 93 95 96 130 132 148 **S** HEALTHSOUTH Corporation, Birmingham, AL
Primary Contact: Marty Dernier, Chief Executive Officer
CMO: Joseph Sankoorikal, M.D., Chief Medical Staff
CHR: Dina Cox, Director Human Resources
CNO: Carol Swanger, Chief Nursing Officer
Web address: www.kansasrehabhospital.com
**Control:** Corporation, Investor–owned, for–profit **Service:** Rehabilitation

**Staffed Beds:** 59 **Admissions:** 1297 **Census:** 42 **Outpatient Visits:** 18769 **Births:** 0 **Total Expense ($000):** 16172 **Payroll Expense ($000):** 8536 **Personnel:** 167

**SELECT SPECIALTY HOSPITAL–TOPEKA (172006)**, 1700 S.W. Seventh Street, Suite 840, Zip 66606–1660; tel. 785/295–5551 **A**1 10 **F**1 3 29 75 77 85 87 130 148 **S** Select Medical Corporation, Mechanicsburg, PA
Primary Contact: Jon W. Scott, Chief Executive Officer
CMO: Jed McKee, M.D., Medical Director
CNO: Sarah Herrmann, R.N., Chief Nursing Officer
Web address: www.selectspecialtyhospitals.com/company/locations/topeka.aspx
**Control:** Corporation, Investor–owned, for–profit **Service:** Long–Term Acute Care hospital

**Staffed Beds:** 34 **Admissions:** 307 **Census:** 23 **Outpatient Visits:** 0 **Births:** 0 **Total Expense ($000):** 11127 **Payroll Expense ($000):** 4954 **Personnel:** 91

△ **ST. FRANCIS HEALTH CENTER (170016)**, 1700 S.W. 7th Street, Zip 66606–1690; tel. 785/295–8000 **A**1 2 7 9 10 **F**3 12 13 15 18 19 20 22 24 26 28 29 30 31 34 35 40 47 49 50 53 57 59 62 64 70 73 74 75 76 77 78 79 80 81 82 85 86 87 89 90 92 93 95 96 107 108 110 111 114 115 116 117 118 119 120 121 123 126 127 130 131 146 147 **P**6 8 **S** SCL Health System, Denver, CO
Primary Contact: Robert J. Erickson, Chief Executive Officer
COO: Dan Fieker, D.O., Chief Medical Officer and Chief Operating Officer
CFO: Gary Zmrhal, Interim Vice President Finance
CMO: Dan Fieker, D.O., Chief Medical Officer and Chief Operating Officer
CIO: Kevin Mapes, Director Kansas Division System and Technology Service Center
CHR: Byron Waldy, Director Human Resources
CNO: Scott E. Wells, MSN, Chief Nursing Officer
Web address: www.stfrancistopeka.org
**Control:** Church–operated, Nongovernment, not–for profit **Service:** General Medical and Surgical

**Staffed Beds:** 291 **Admissions:** 8969 **Census:** 111 **Outpatient Visits:** 543734 **Births:** 1073 **Total Expense ($000):** 240992 **Payroll Expense ($000):** 99749 **Personnel:** 1440

**STORMONT–VAIL HEALTHCARE (170086)**, 1500 S.W. Tenth Avenue, Zip 66604–1353; tel. 785/354–6000 **A**1 2 5 9 10 **F**3 11 12 13 15 17 18 19 20 22 24 26 28 29 30 31 34 35 37 40 43 45 47 49 51 53 55 56 57 58 59 60 61 64 65 68 69 70 71 72 74 75 76 77 78 79 81 82 83 84 85 86 87 88 89 91 93 94 97 98 99 101 102 103 104 105 107 108 110 111 112 114 115 117 119 120 121 123 129 130 131 132 135 143 144 145 146 147 148 **P**6
Primary Contact: Randall Peterson, President and Chief Executive Officer
COO: Janet Stanek, Executive Vice President
CFO: Kevin Han, Vice President and Chief Financial Officer
CMO: Kent Palmberg, M.D., Senior Vice President and Chief Medical Officer
CIO: Judy Corzine, Administrative Director and Chief Information Officer
CHR: Bernard H. Becker, Vice President and Chief Human Resources Officer
CNO: Carol Perry, R.N., Vice President and Chief Nursing Officer
Web address: www.stormontvail.org
**Control:** Other not–for–profit (including NFP Corporation) **Service:** General Medical and Surgical

**Staffed Beds:** 394 **Admissions:** 20759 **Census:** 244 **Outpatient Visits:** 121233 **Births:** 1947 **Total Expense ($000):** 492151 **Payroll Expense ($000):** 256278 **Personnel:** 3631

△ **VETERANS AFFAIRS EASTERN KANSAS HEALTH CARE SYSTEM**, 2200 Gage Boulevard, Zip 66622–0002; tel. 785/350–3111, (Includes COLMERY–O'NEIL VETERANS AFFAIRS MEDICAL CENTER, 2200 Gage Boulevard, tel. 785/350–3111; DWIGHT D. EISENHOWER VETERANS AFFAIRS MEDICAL CENTER, 4101 S. 4th Street Trafficway, Leavenworth, Zip 66048–5055; tel. 913/682–2000), (Nonreporting) **A**1 3 5 7 **S** Department of Veterans Affairs, Washington, DC
Primary Contact: Anthony Rudy Klopher, FACHE, Director
COO: Karen Glotzbach, Acting Associate Director
CMO: Rajeev Trehan, M.D., Chief of Staff
CIO: Joni Davin, Director Information and Business Management Service Line
Web address: www.topeka.va.gov/
**Control:** Veterans Affairs, Government, federal **Service:** General Medical and Surgical

**Staffed Beds:** 213

**TRIBUNE—Greeley County**

★ **GREELEY COUNTY HEALTH SERVICES (171359)**, 506 Third Street, Zip 67879–9684, Mailing Address: P.O. Box 338, Zip 67879–0338; tel. 620/376–4221, (Total facility includes 32 beds in nursing home–type unit) **A**5 9 10 18 **F**2 3 28 40 45 59 64 65 66 69 81 82 85 93 97 107 114 127 128 133 147 **S** QHR, Brentwood, TN
Primary Contact: Deborah Lehner, Administrator
CFO: James L. Smith, Chief Financial Officer
CMO: Wendel Ellis, D.O., Chief Medical Staff
CIO: Shanon Schneider, Chief Information Officer
CHR: Tiffany Kleymann, Manager Human Resources
CNO: Stephanie Wineinger, Director of Nursing
Web address: www.mygchs.com
**Control:** Other not–for–profit (including NFP Corporation) **Service:** General Medical and Surgical

**Staffed Beds:** 50 **Admissions:** 377 **Census:** 32 **Outpatient Visits:** 11392 **Births:** 0 **Total Expense ($000):** 9584 **Payroll Expense ($000):** 4814 **Personnel:** 112

**ULYSSES—Grant County**

★ **BOB WILSON MEMORIAL GRANT COUNTY HOSPITAL (170110)**, 415 North Main Street, Zip 67880–2133; tel. 620/356–1266 **A**9 10 20 **F**3 11 13 15 29 30 34 35 40 45 50 57 59 62 64 68 75 76 79 81 82 85 86 87 91 93 96 97 107 119 127 130 133 146 148 **P**6
Primary Contact: Arthur H. Frable, Chief Executive Officer
CFO: Robert Jacobi, Chief Financial Officer
CIO: Chris Moffet, Director Information Services
CHR: Tammy Oxford, Director Human Resources
Web address: www.bwmgch.com
**Control:** County–Government, nonfederal **Service:** General Medical and Surgical

**Staffed Beds:** 26 **Admissions:** 342 **Census:** 4 **Outpatient Visits:** 10253 **Births:** 70 **Total Expense ($000):** 11404 **Payroll Expense ($000):** 5476 **Personnel:** 158

**WAKEENEY—Trego County**

★ **TREGO COUNTY–LEMKE MEMORIAL HOSPITAL (171355)**, 320 North 13th Street, Zip 67672–2099; tel. 785/743–2182, (Total facility includes 37 beds in nursing home–type unit) **A**9 10 18 **F**3 8 10 11 15 28 29 34 40 45 53 57 59 62 64 67 69 71 81 86 89 93 107 110 114 127 128 130 133 143 146 148 **P**6 **S** Great Plains Health Alliance, Inc., Wichita, KS
Primary Contact: Don Bates, Interim Chief Executive Officer
CFO: Gail Jensen, Chief Financial Officer
CMO: Gordon Lang, M.D., Chief of Staff
CIO: Jolene Schuster, Director Information Technology
CHR: Cindy Meier, Human Resources and Payroll Coordinator
CNO: Sandy Purinton, Chief Nursing Officer
Web address: www.tclmh.org
**Control:** County–Government, nonfederal **Service:** General Medical and Surgical

**Staffed Beds:** 62 **Admissions:** 960 **Census:** 49 **Outpatient Visits:** 35334 **Births:** 0 **Total Expense ($000):** 15706 **Payroll Expense ($000):** 7221 **Personnel:** 168

**WAMEGO—Pottawatomie County**

★ **WAMEGO CITY HOSPITAL (171337)**, 711 Genn Drive, Zip 66547–1179; tel. 785/456–2295 **A**9 10 18 **F**3 11 15 29 32 34 35 40 45 56 59 64 65 75 77 81 93 97 107 114 119 127 130 132 133 142 143 146 147 148 **P**6
Primary Contact: Shannan Flach, Chief Executive Officer
COO: Brian Smith, Director Risk Management, Quality and Safety
CFO: Keith Zachariasen, Chief Financial Officer
CMO: Roland Darey, M.D., Medical Director
CIO: Wes Janzen, Chief Information Officer
CHR: Marcie Holsteen, Human Resources Officer
CNO: Tresha Flanary, R.N., Chief Clinical Services Officer
Web address: www.wamegocityhospital.com
**Control:** Other not–for–profit (including NFP Corporation) **Service:** General Medical and Surgical

**Staffed Beds:** 18 **Admissions:** 245 **Census:** 3 **Outpatient Visits:** 10696 **Births:** 0 **Total Expense ($000):** 9104 **Payroll Expense ($000):** 4467 **Personnel:** 74

### WASHINGTON—Washington County

**WASHINGTON COUNTY HOSPITAL (171351)**, 304 East Third Street,
Zip 66968–2033; tel. 785/325–2211 **A**5 9 10 18 **F**2 3 11 13 15 28 29 30 31
35 40 45 53 57 64 67 70 76 81 85 89 93 107 114 128 130 133 148 **P**5
Primary Contact: Doyle L. McKimmy, FACHE, Chief Executive Officer
CFO: Linda Rettig, Director Financial Services
Web address: www.washingtoncountyhospital.com
**Control:** County–Government, nonfederal **Service:** General Medical and Surgical

**Staffed Beds:** 25 **Admissions:** 123 **Census:** 6 **Outpatient Visits:** 4720
**Births:** 12 **Total Expense ($000):** 4333 **Payroll Expense ($000):** 1791
**Personnel:** 44

### WELLINGTON—Sumner County

★ **SUMNER REGIONAL MEDICAL CENTER (170039)**, 1323 North A Street,
Zip 67152–4350; tel. 620/326–7451, (Total facility includes 9 beds in nursing
home–type unit) **A**5 9 10 **F**10 11 13 15 31 35 40 45 56 59 76 77 78 79 81 82
85 98 103 107 108 110 111 119 128 129 130
Primary Contact: Leonard Hernandez, President and Chief Executive Officer
CFO: Kim Weaver, CPA, Chief Financial Officer
CIO: Lori Young, Manager Health Information Management
CHR: Allen Keller, Director Human Resources
CNO: Darlene Cooney, Director Nursing
Web address: www.srmcks.org
**Control:** City–Government, nonfederal **Service:** General Medical and Surgical

**Staffed Beds:** 61 **Admissions:** 766 **Census:** 15 **Outpatient Visits:** 19092
**Births:** 128 **Total Expense ($000):** 15245 **Payroll Expense ($000):** 6117
**Personnel:** 131

### WICHITA—Sedgwick County

☐ **AMG SPECIALTY HOSPITAL–WICHITA (172003)**, (Formerly LTAC of Wichita),
8080 East Pawnee Street, Zip 67207–5475; tel. 316/682–0004 **A**1 10 **F**1 29
30 77 143 148 **S** AMG Integrated Healthcare Management, Lafayette, LA
Primary Contact: Robert A. Loepp, Jr., FACHE, Chief Executive Officer
CFO: Myra Dick, Manager Business Office
CIO: Michelle Bradley, Director Health Information Management
CHR: Adrienne Burkholder, Director Human Resources
Web address: www.amgwichita.com/
**Control:** Corporation, Investor–owned, for–profit **Service:** Long–Term Acute Care hospital

**Staffed Beds:** 26 **Admissions:** 255 **Census:** 17 **Outpatient Visits:** 0 **Births:**
0 **Total Expense ($000):** 7621 **Payroll Expense ($000):** 3196 **Personnel:**
92

**KANSAS HEART HOSPITAL (170186)**, 3601 North Webb Road,
Zip 67226–8129; tel. 316/630–5000 **A**9 10 **F**3 17 18 20 22 24 29 30 64 81
86 107 108 115 119 130
Primary Contact: Thomas L. Ashcom, M.D., Ph.D., Chief Executive Officer
COO: I. Lynn Jeane, Chief Operating Officer
CFO: Steve Smith, Chief Financial Officer
CHR: Teresa E. Wolfe, Manager Human Resources
Web address: www.kansasheart.com
**Control:** Corporation, Investor–owned, for–profit **Service:** Heart

**Staffed Beds:** 54 **Admissions:** 1834 **Census:** 21 **Outpatient Visits:** 9313
**Births:** 0 **Personnel:** 177

**KANSAS SPINE HOSPITAL (170196)**, 3333 North Webb Road,
Zip 67226–8123; tel. 316/462–5000 **A**9 10 **F**3 29 79 81 82 85 87 107
111 114
Primary Contact: Thomas M. Schmitt, Chief Executive Officer
CFO: Kevin P. Vaughn, Chief Financial Officer
CIO: Michael Knocke, Chief Information Officer
CHR: Jean–Marie Jimeson, Coordinator Human Resources
Web address: www.ksspine.com
**Control:** Corporation, Investor–owned, for–profit **Service:** General Medical and Surgical

**Staffed Beds:** 38 **Admissions:** 2027 **Census:** 12 **Outpatient Visits:** 4688
**Births:** 0 **Personnel:** 95

**KANSAS SURGERY AND RECOVERY CENTER (170183)**, 2770 North Webb
Road, Zip 67226–8112; tel. 316/634–0090 **A**9 10 **F**51 64 68 81 85 87 107
111 114 119
Primary Contact: Ely Bartal, M.D., Chief Executive Officer
CFO: Ashley Simon, Chief Financial Officer
CMO: Ely Bartal, M.D., Chief Executive Officer and Medical Director
CIO: Jonathan Wells, Supervisor Information Technology
CNO: Becky Bailey, R.N., Director of Nursing
Web address: www.ksrc.org
**Control:** Partnership, Investor–owned, for–profit **Service:** General Medical and Surgical

**Staffed Beds:** 32 **Admissions:** 1477 **Census:** 11 **Outpatient Visits:** 8052
**Births:** 0 **Total Expense ($000):** 23815 **Payroll Expense ($000):** 6346
**Personnel:** 139

⊠ **ROBERT J. DOLE VETERANS AFFAIRS MEDICAL CENTER**, 5500 East
Kellogg, Zip 67218–1607; tel. 316/685–2221, (Nonreporting) **A**1 3 5
**S** Department of Veterans Affairs, Washington, DC
Primary Contact: Kevin Inkley, Interim Director
CFO: Ronald Dreher, Finance Officer
CMO: Kent Murray, M.D., Chief of Staff
CIO: Sharon Williamson, Chief Information Technology
CHR: Nancy Gerstner, Manager Human Resources
Web address: www.wichita.va.gov
**Control:** Veterans Affairs, Government, federal **Service:** General Medical and Surgical

**Staffed Beds:** 41

⊠ **SELECT SPECIALTY HOSPITAL–WICHITA (172007)**, 929 North St. Francis
Street, Zip 67214–3821; tel. 316/261–8303 **A**1 10 **F**1 3 12 18 29 50 56 60
61 75 82 84 85 86 87 130 148 **S** Select Medical Corporation,
Mechanicsburg, PA
Primary Contact: Peggy Cliffe, Chief Executive Officer
Web address: www.selectspecialtyhospitals.com/company/locations/wichita.aspx
**Control:** Corporation, Investor–owned, for–profit **Service:** Long–Term Acute Care hospital

**Staffed Beds:** 58 **Admissions:** 478 **Census:** 36 **Outpatient Visits:** 0 **Births:**
0 **Total Expense ($000):** 17321 **Payroll Expense ($000):** 6332 **Personnel:**
130

⊠ **VIA CHRISTI HOSPITAL ON ST. FRANCIS (170122)**, (Formerly Via Christi
Hospital Wichita), 929 North St. Francis Street, Zip 67214–3882;
tel. 316/268–5000, (Includes GOOD SHEPHERD CAMPUS, 8901 East Orme,
Zip 67207; tel. 316/858–0333; ST. FRANCIS CAMPUS, 929 North St. Francis
Street, tel. 316/268–5000; Sherry Hausmann, President; ST. JOSEPH CAMPUS,
3600 East Harry Street, Zip 67218–3713; tel. 316/685–1111; Claudio J.
Ferraro, President) **A**1 2 3 5 9 10 13 **F**3 5 7 11 12 13 15 16 17 18 19 20 21
22 23 24 26 27 28 29 30 31 32 34 35 38 40 43 44 45 46 48 49 50 51 54
56 57 58 59 60 61 62 64 68 70 72 74 75 76 77 78 79 80 81 82 84 85 86
87 88 89 92 93 97 98 99 100 101 102 103 104 105 107 108 110 111 114
115 116 117 118 119 120 121 123 124 126 130 131 132 135 136 138 141
142 143 146 147 148 **P**6 **S** Ascension Health, Saint Louis, MO
Primary Contact: Sherry Hausmann, President
COO: Laurie Labarca, Executive Vice President and Chief Operating Officer
CFO: Mike Wegner, Chief Financial Officer
CMO: Steven Nesbit, D.O., Chief Medical Officer
CIO: Diana Hilburn, Vice President Information Technology and Chief Information
Officer
CHR: Sherrie String, Vice President Human Resources
Web address: www.via–christi.org
**Control:** Church–operated, Nongovernment, not–for profit **Service:** General
Medical and Surgical

**Staffed Beds:** 751 **Admissions:** 33266 **Census:** 437 **Outpatient Visits:**
329147 **Births:** 2320 **Total Expense ($000):** 519479 **Payroll Expense
($000):** 213310 **Personnel:** 3800

⊠ **VIA CHRISTI HOSPITAL ON ST. TERESA (170200)**, (Formerly Via Christi
Hospital), 14800 West St. Teresa, Zip 67235–9602; tel. 316/796–7000 **A**1 9
10 **F**3 8 13 18 20 22 29 30 34 35 40 45 50 64 68 70 75 76 78 79 81 85 87
90 107 108 111 114 118 119 130 146 147 148 **S** Ascension Health, Saint
Louis, MO
Primary Contact: Kevin Strecker, President
Web address: www.via–christi.org/st-teresa
**Control:** Church–operated, Nongovernment, not–for profit **Service:** General
Medical and Surgical

**Staffed Beds:** 70 **Admissions:** 2041 **Census:** 17 **Outpatient Visits:** 18831
**Births:** 414 **Total Expense ($000):** 42804 **Payroll Expense ($000):** 13887
**Personnel:** 208

**VIA CHRISTI REGIONAL MEDICAL CENTER** See Via Christi Hospital on St.
Francis

⊠ △ **VIA CHRISTI REHABILITATION CENTER (173028)**, 1151 North Rock
Road, Zip 67206–1262; tel. 316/634–3400 **A**1 7 9 10 **F**11 29 30 34 35 44 50
54 57 59 64 77 86 87 90 92 93 94 96 119 129 130 131 132 143 146 148
**S** Ascension Health, Saint Louis, MO
Primary Contact: Cindy LaFleur, President
CMO: Kevin Rieg, M.D., President Medical Staff
Web address: www.via–christi.org
**Control:** Church–operated, Nongovernment, not–for profit **Service:** Rehabilitation

**Staffed Beds:** 58 **Admissions:** 803 **Census:** 26 **Outpatient Visits:** 102960
**Births:** 0 **Total Expense ($000):** 24172 **Payroll Expense ($000):** 12090
**Personnel:** 247

**KS**

*Many Facility Codes have changed. Please refer to the AHA Guide Code Chart.*
© 2013 AHA Guide

⊠ **WESLEY MEDICAL CENTER (170123)**, 550 North Hillside, Zip 67214–4976;
tel. 316/962–2000, (Includes GALICHIA HEART HOSPITAL, 2610 North
Woodlawn, Zip 67220; tel. 316/858–2610; Stephen J. Harris, Chief Executive
Officer; THE CHILDREN'S CENTER AT WESLEY, 550 North Hillside Street,
Zip 67214–4910) **A**1 3 5 9 10 **F**3 7 11 12 13 15 17 18 19 20 22 24 26 28
29 30 31 34 35 39 40 41 42 43 44 45 46 48 49 50 51 54 55 56 57 58 59
60 64 65 68 70 72 73 74 76 78 79 81 85 86 87 88 89 92 93 94 97 100
102 107 108 111 114 115 119 121 123 124 126 129 130 131 132 134 135
146 147 148 **P**6 **S** HCA, Nashville, TN
Primary Contact: Hugh C. Tappan, President and Chief Executive Officer
COO: Bill Voloch, Chief Operating Officer
CFO: Matt Leary, Chief Financial Officer
CMO: Francie H. Ekengren, M.D., Chief Medical Officer
CIO: Larry Forsyth, Director Information System
CHR: Don Morris, Vice President Human Resources
Web address: www.wesleymc.com
**Control:** Corporation, Investor–owned, for–profit **Service:** General Medical and
Surgical

| | |
|---|---|
| **Staffed Beds:** 595 **Admissions:** 23933 **Census:** 303 **Outpatient Visits:** 317415 **Births:** 6271 **Total Expense ($000):** 407756 **Payroll Expense ($000):** 146420 **Personnel:** 2477 | |

⊠ **WESLEY REHABILITATION HOSPITAL (173027)**, 8338 West 13th Street
North, Zip 67212–2984; tel. 316/729–9999 **A**1 9 10 **F**29 34 35 62 64 68 90
91 93 95 96 132 147 148 **S** HEALTHSOUTH Corporation, Birmingham, AL
Primary Contact: James F. Grocholski, FACHE, Chief Executive Officer
CFO: Bob Peck, Chief Financial Officer
CMO: Kevin F. Brown, D.O., Medical Director
CIO: Debbie Patterson, Director Health Information Management
CHR: Betty Shuman, Director Human Resources
Web address: www.wesleyrehabhospital.com
**Control:** Corporation, Investor–owned, for–profit **Service:** Rehabilitation

| | |
|---|---|
| **Staffed Beds:** 65 **Admissions:** 893 **Census:** 33 **Outpatient Visits:** 22112 **Births:** 0 **Total Expense ($000):** 15363 **Payroll Expense ($000):** 7427 **Personnel:** 159 | |

**WICHITA SPECIALTY HOSPITAL** See AMG Specialty Hospital–Wichita

**WINCHESTER—Jefferson County**

★ **F. W. HUSTON MEDICAL CENTER (171314)**, 408 Delaware Street,
Zip 66097–4003; tel. 913/774–4340, (Nonreporting) **A**9 10 18
Primary Contact: LaMont Cook, Administrator
CFO: Shelly Ludwig, Controller
CHR: Lois Wheeler, Manager Human Resources
Web address: www.jcmhospital.org
**Control:** Other not–for–profit (including NFP Corporation) **Service:** General
Medical and Surgical

| | |
|---|---|
| **Staffed Beds:** 74 | |

**JEFFERSON COUNTY MEMORIAL HOSPITAL** See F. W. Huston Medical Center

**WINFIELD—Cowley County**

★ **WILLIAM NEWTON HOSPITAL (171383)**, 1300 East Fifth Street,
Zip 67156–2407; tel. 620/221–2300 **A**5 9 10 18 **F**3 11 13 15 18 28 29 32
34 35 38 39 40 44 45 47 51 57 59 62 64 65 68 70 74 75 76 77 78 79 81
82 85 86 87 93 102 107 108 111 114 118 119 121 123 127 129 130 131
132 133 135 146 147 148
Primary Contact: J. Ben Quinton, Administrator
COO: Tom Embers, Assistant Administrator and Chief Operating Officer
CFO: Debbie Hockenbury, Assistant Administrator and Chief Financial Officer
CMO: Wade Turner, M.D., Chief of Staff
CIO: Randy Mayo, Director Information Technology
CHR: Cathy McClurg, Director Human Resources
CNO: Kristie Ball, Director of Nursing
Web address: www.wnmh.org
**Control:** City–Government, nonfederal **Service:** General Medical and Surgical

| | |
|---|---|
| **Staffed Beds:** 25 **Admissions:** 907 **Census:** 8 **Outpatient Visits:** 60312 **Births:** 182 **Total Expense ($000):** 25525 **Payroll Expense ($000):** 11582 **Personnel:** 260 | |

# KENTUCKY

### ALBANY—Clinton County

**CLINTON COUNTY HOSPITAL (180106)**, 723 Burkesville Road, Zip 42602–1654; tel. 606/387–6421, (Nonreporting) **A**9 10
Primary Contact: John David Mullins, Jr., Administrator
CHR: Pat Beard, Director Human Resources
Web address: www.clintoncountyhospital.com
**Control:** Other not–for–profit (including NFP Corporation) **Service:** General Medical and Surgical

**Staffed Beds:** 42

### ASHLAND—Boyd County

☐ △ **KING'S DAUGHTERS MEDICAL CENTER (180009)**, 2201 Lexington Avenue, Zip 41101–2874, Mailing Address: P.O. Box 151, Zip 41105–0151; tel. 606/408–4000, (Nonreporting) **A**1 2 7 9 10
Primary Contact: Fred L. Jackson, FACHE, Chief Executive Officer
COO: Bob Lucas, Vice President Operations
CFO: Paul L. McDowell, Vice President Finance and Chief Financial Officer
CMO: Phil Fioret, M.D., Vice President Medical Affairs
CIO: David Oliver, Director Information Systems
CHR: Larry Higgins, Vice President Human Resources
Web address: www.kdmc.com
**Control:** Other not–for–profit (including NFP Corporation) **Service:** General Medical and Surgical

**Staffed Beds:** 612

✠ **OUR LADY OF BELLEFONTE HOSPITAL (180036)**, St. Christopher Drive, Zip 41101, Mailing Address: P.O. Box 789, Zip 41105–0789; tel. 606/833–3333 **A**1 2 9 10 12 13 **F**3 4 5 8 11 12 15 18 19 20 28 29 30 31 34 35 37 39 40 44 45 49 50 53 54 55 57 58 59 62 64 65 66 69 70 71 74 75 77 78 79 81 82 84 85 86 87 89 93 96 97 98 100 101 102 103 106 107 108 110 111 114 115 118 119 129 130 131 132 135 143 144 145 146 147 148 **P**7 8 **S** Bon Secours Health System, Inc., Marriottsville, MD
Primary Contact: Kevin Halter, Chief Executive Officer
CFO: Joe Buchheit, Chief Financial Officer
CIO: Mike Gomez, Site Manager Medical Information Systems
CHR: Judy Daniels, Vice President Human Resources
Web address: www.olbh.com
**Control:** Church–operated, Nongovernment, not–for profit **Service:** General Medical and Surgical

**Staffed Beds:** 151 **Admissions:** 6938 **Census:** 73 **Outpatient Visits:** 240557 **Births:** 0 **Total Expense ($000):** 132617 **Payroll Expense ($000):** 43375 **Personnel:** 966

### BARBOURVILLE—Knox County

☐ **KNOX COUNTY HOSPITAL (181328)**, 80 Hospital Drive, Zip 40906–7363, Mailing Address: P.O. Box 10, Zip 40906–0010; tel. 606/546–4175, (Nonreporting) **A**1 9 10 18 **S** Pacer Health Corporation, Miami Lakes, FL
Primary Contact: Gary G. Kendrick, Interim Chief Executive Officer
CFO: Amanda Ellis, Chief Financial Officer
CMO: Kamran Hasni, M.D., Chief of Medical Staff
CIO: Evan Davis, Director Technology and Environmental Services
CHR: Janet Wilder, Director Human Resources
CNO: Brenda Graham, Chief Nursing Officer
Web address: www.knoxcohospital.com
**Control:** Corporation, Investor–owned, for–profit **Service:** General Medical and Surgical

**Staffed Beds:** 25

### BARDSTOWN—Nelson County

✠ **FLAGET MEMORIAL HOSPITAL (180025)**, 4305 New Shepherdsville Road, Zip 40004–9019; tel. 502/350–5000, (Total facility includes 12 beds in nursing home–type unit) **A**1 9 10 **F**11 12 13 15 18 28 29 30 31 34 35 37 40 45 49 59 62 63 64 70 76 78 79 81 82 84 85 87 96 107 111 116 117 119 127 128 129 130 132 144 146 147 148 **P**3 **S** Catholic Health Initiatives, Englewood, CO
Primary Contact: Sue Downs, R.N., MSN, President
COO: Norma Goss, R.N., COO/CNO
CFO: John Bradford, Vice President Finance
CMO: Mark Abramovich, M.D., Chief of Staff
CHR: Deborah Cowles, Vice President Human Resources
CNO: Norma Goss, R.N., COO/CNO
Web address: www.flaget.com
**Control:** Other not–for–profit (including NFP Corporation) **Service:** General Medical and Surgical

**Staffed Beds:** 40 **Admissions:** 2519 **Census:** 23 **Outpatient Visits:** 68694 **Births:** 247 **Total Expense ($000):** 62025 **Payroll Expense ($000):** 20337 **Personnel:** 352

### BENTON—Marshall County

☐ **MARSHALL COUNTY HOSPITAL (181327)**, 615 Old Symsonia Road, Zip 42025–5042, Mailing Address: P.O. Box 630, Zip 42025–0630; tel. 270/527–4800 **A**1 9 10 18 **F**3 7 11 15 18 28 29 30 34 35 40 51 53 57 59 62 77 79 81 85 89 90 93 107 108 119 128 132 133 135 **P**6
Primary Contact: Kathy Long, Chief Executive Officer
CFO: Janice Kelley, Chief Financial Officer
CMO: Glen Van Loon, M.D., Chief of Staff
CIO: Patrick Waters, Director Information Technology
CHR: Jeannie Lee, Director Human Resources
Web address: www.marshallcountyhospital.org
**Control:** Hospital district or authority, Government, nonfederal **Service:** General Medical and Surgical

**Staffed Beds:** 25 **Admissions:** 986 **Census:** 13 **Outpatient Visits:** 18640 **Total Expense ($000):** 18695 **Payroll Expense ($000):** 7634 **Personnel:** 188

### BEREA—Madison County

✠ **SAINT JOSEPH BEREA (181329)**, 305 Estill Street, Zip 40403–1909; tel. 859/986–3151 **A**1 5 9 10 18 **F**3 29 40 45 70 77 79 81 82 91 97 107 111 114 119 133 **P**4 **S** Catholic Health Initiatives, Englewood, CO
Primary Contact: Chris Schweighardt, R.N., MSN, Interim President
COO: Chris Schweighardt, R.N., Chief Nursing Officer and Chief Operating Officer
CMO: Patrick Kelleher, M.D., Chief Medical Staff
CIO: Katie Heckman, Director Community Relations
CHR: Renee Bullock, Vice President Human Resources
Web address: www.saintjosephberea.org
**Control:** Church–operated, Nongovernment, not–for profit **Service:** General Medical and Surgical

**Staffed Beds:** 25 **Admissions:** 1218 **Census:** 14 **Outpatient Visits:** 56921 **Births:** 0 **Total Expense ($000):** 27982 **Payroll Expense ($000):** 10838 **Personnel:** 202

### BOWLING GREEN—Warren County

**COMMONWEALTH REGIONAL SPECIALTY HOSPITAL (182005)**, 250 Park Drive, 6th Floor, Zip 42101–1760, Mailing Address: P.O. Box 90010, Zip 42102–9010; tel. 270/796–6200 **A**10 **F**1 3 29 30 34 35 50 57 68 70 84 85 87 130 135 143 146 148 **S** Commonwealth Health Corporation, Bowling Green, KY
Primary Contact: Emily Howard Martin, Administrator
CFO: Ronald G. Sowell, Executive Vice President
CMO: Doug Thomson, M.D., Chief Medical Officer
CIO: Jean Cherry, Executive Vice President
CHR: Lynn Williams, Vice President
Web address: www.commonwealthregionalspecialtyhospital.org
**Control:** Other not–for–profit (including NFP Corporation) **Service:** Long–Term Acute Care hospital

**Staffed Beds:** 24 **Admissions:** 230 **Census:** 18 **Outpatient Visits:** 0 **Births:** 0 **Personnel:** 57

☐ **MEDICAL CENTER AT BOWLING GREEN (180013)**, 250 Park Street, Zip 42101–1795, Mailing Address: P.O. Box 90010, Zip 42102–9010; tel. 270/745–1000 **A**1 2 9 10 19 **F**1 3 7 13 15 17 18 20 22 24 26 28 29 30 31 32 34 35 37 39 40 46 50 51 56 57 59 60 62 64 68 70 72 74 75 76 78 79 80 81 82 84 85 86 87 89 91 93 98 100 102 103 104 105 107 108 110 111 114 116 117 119 121 123 129 130 132 135 145 146 147 148 **S** Commonwealth Health Corporation, Bowling Green, KY
Primary Contact: Connie Smith, Chief Executive Officer
CFO: Ronald G. Sowell, Executive Vice President
CIO: Jean Cherry, Executive Vice President and Chief Information Officer
CHR: Lynn Williams, Vice President Human Resources
Web address: www.themedicalcenter.org
**Control:** Other not–for–profit (including NFP Corporation) **Service:** General Medical and Surgical

**Staffed Beds:** 337 **Admissions:** 17385 **Census:** 234 **Outpatient Visits:** 114012 **Births:** 2343 **Personnel:** 1627

☐ **RIVENDELL BEHAVIORAL HEALTH (184017)**, 1035 Porter Pike, Zip 42103–9581; tel. 270/843–1199, (Nonreporting) **A**1 9 10 **S** Universal Health Services, Inc., King of Prussia, PA
Primary Contact: Janice Richardson, Chief Executive Officer and Managing Director
CFO: Tim Gore, Chief Financial Officer
Web address: www.rivendellbehavioral.com
**Control:** Corporation, Investor–owned, for–profit **Service:** Psychiatric

**Staffed Beds:** 125

*Many Facility Codes have changed. Please refer to the AHA Guide Code Chart.*    © 2013 AHA Guide

☐ △ **SOUTHERN KENTUCKY REHABILITATION HOSPITAL (183029)**, 1300 Campbell Lane, Zip 42104–4162; tel. 270/782–6900 **A**1 7 9 10 **F**28 29 64 87 90 91 93 95 96 130 132 143 148 **P**5 **S** Vibra Healthcare, Mechanicsburg, PA
Primary Contact: Stuart Locke, Interim Chief Executive Officer
COO: Dana Lewis, Director Clinical Services
CFO: Stuart Locke, Chief Financial Officer
CMO: Jim Farrage, M.D., Medical Director
CHR: Suzanne Cornett, Director Human Resources
Web address: www.skyrehab.com
**Control:** Corporation, Investor–owned, for–profit **Service:** Rehabilitation

Staffed Beds: 60 Admissions: 1541 Census: 44 Outpatient Visits: 3889
Births: 0 Total Expense ($000): 16906 Payroll Expense ($000): 8255
Personnel: 171

☒ **TRISTAR GREENVIEW REGIONAL HOSPITAL (180124)**, (Formerly Greenview Regional Hospital), 1801 Ashley Circle, Zip 42104–3362; tel. 270/793–1000 **A**1 2 9 10 19 **F**3 8 11 15 18 20 22 29 30 31 34 35 37 40 45 46 48 49 50 51 57 59 64 65 68 70 74 75 77 78 79 81 82 85 86 87 107 108 110 111 114 118 119 124 128 130 131 132 133 135 145 146 **S** HCA, Nashville, TN
Primary Contact: Anne Leonard, R.N., Interim Chief Executive Officer
CFO: Richard Patterson, Chief Financial Officer
CMO: Tim Long, M.D., Chief of Staff
CIO: Cyndi Talley, Director Information Systems
CHR: Judy Fulkerson, Director Human Resources
CNO: Anne Leonard, R.N., Chief Nursing Officer
Web address: www.greenviewhospital.com
**Control:** Corporation, Investor–owned, for–profit **Service:** General Medical and Surgical

Staffed Beds: 167 Admissions: 4355 Census: 60 Outpatient Visits: 49042
Births: 0 Total Expense ($000): 61693 Payroll Expense ($000): 21149
Personnel: 462

### BURKESVILLE—Cumberland County

**CUMBERLAND COUNTY HOSPITAL (181317)**, 299 Glasgow Road, Zip 42717–9696, Mailing Address: P.O. Box 280, Zip 42717–0280; tel. 270/864–2511, (Nonreporting) **A**9 10 18
Primary Contact: Richard Neikirk, Chief Executive Officer
CFO: Rick Capps, Chief Financial Officer
CMO: Christian Konsavage, M.D., Chief of Staff
CHR: Martha Young, Director Human Resources
Web address: www.cchospital.org
**Control:** Other not–for–profit (including NFP Corporation) **Service:** General Medical and Surgical

Staffed Beds: 25

### CADIZ—Trigg County

★ **TRIGG COUNTY HOSPITAL (181304)**, 254 Main Street, Zip 42211–9153, Mailing Address: P.O. Box 312, Zip 42211–0312; tel. 270/522–3215, (Nonreporting) **A**9 10 18
Primary Contact: Alisa Coleman, Chief Executive Officer
CFO: Liz Snodgrass, Chief Financial Officer
CMO: Stuart Harris, M.D., Chief of Staff
CHR: Janet James, Director Human Resources
Web address: www.trigghospital.org
**Control:** County–Government, nonfederal **Service:** General Medical and Surgical

Staffed Beds: 25

### CAMPBELLSVILLE—Taylor County

☒ **TAYLOR REGIONAL HOSPITAL (180087)**, 1700 Old Lebanon Road, Zip 42718–9600; tel. 270/465–3561 **A**1 2 9 10 **F**3 8 11 13 15 18 20 28 29 30 31 34 35 39 40 43 45 46 48 49 50 51 54 56 57 59 64 65 68 70 75 76 77 78 79 81 85 86 93 97 107 108 110 111 114 117 118 119 120 127 129 130 134 135 141 143 144 146 147 148 **S** Catholic Health Initiatives, Englewood, CO
Primary Contact: Jane Wheatley, Chief Executive Officer
CFO: David Massengale, Chief Financial Officer
CIO: Gary Neat, Director Information Management Systems
CHR: Andrea Settle, Director Human Resources
Web address: www.trhosp.org
**Control:** Hospital district or authority, Government, nonfederal **Service:** General Medical and Surgical

Staffed Beds: 90 Admissions: 2873 Census: 30 Outpatient Visits: 88046
Births: 280 Total Expense ($000): 63293 Payroll Expense ($000): 29017
Personnel: 551

### CARLISLE—Nicholas County

☐ **NICHOLAS COUNTY HOSPITAL (181303)**, 2323 Concrete Road, Zip 40311–9721, Mailing Address: P.O. Box 232, Zip 40311–0232; tel. 859/289–7181, (Includes JOHNSON–MATHERS NURSING HOME ), (Nonreporting) **A**1 9 10 18
Primary Contact: Benny Nolen, Interim Administrator
CFO: Wesley Berry, Chief Financial Officer
CMO: Osias Villaflor, M.D., Chief Medical Staff
CHR: Wendy Price, Manager Human Resources
Web address: www.johnsonmathers.org
**Control:** Other not–for–profit (including NFP Corporation) **Service:** General Medical and Surgical

Staffed Beds: 16

### CARROLLTON—Carroll County

★ **CARROLL COUNTY MEMORIAL HOSPITAL (181310)**, 309 11th Street, Zip 41008–1400; tel. 502/732–4321 **A**9 10 18 **F**3 11 15 18 28 29 34 40 45 50 56 57 59 68 74 75 77 79 81 82 85 86 93 94 97 107 108 111 114 119 127 128 129 130 133 148 **P**6 **S** Alliant Management Services, Louisville, KY
Primary Contact: Michael A. Kozar, Chief Executive Officer
CFO: Steve Eiqel, Chief Financial Officer
CMO: Kathy Short, D.O., Family Practice
CHR: Kimberly Puckett, Manager Human Resources
CNO: Lisa Penick, R.N., Chief Nursing Officer
Web address: www.ccmhosp.com
**Control:** Hospital district or authority, Government, nonfederal **Service:** General Medical and Surgical

Staffed Beds: 25 Admissions: 768 Census: 2 Outpatient Visits: 11417
Births: 0 Total Expense ($000): 12021 Payroll Expense ($000): 4833
Personnel: 153

### COLUMBIA—Adair County

☐ **WESTLAKE REGIONAL HOSPITAL (180149)**, 901 Westlake Drive, Zip 42728–1123, Mailing Address: P.O. Box 1269, Zip 42728–6269; tel. 270/384–4753 **A**1 9 10 **F**3 11 15 18 28 29 35 45 57 59 79 81 87 93 98 107 114 119 127 130 **P**6
Primary Contact: David D. Rasmussen, Chief Executive Officer
CFO: Ken Doran, Interim Chief Financial Officer
CMO: Gary Partin, M.D., President Medical Staff
CHR: Nanette Kenyon, Director Human Resources
Web address: www.westlakeregionalhospital.com
**Control:** Hospital district or authority, Government, nonfederal **Service:** General Medical and Surgical

Staffed Beds: 32 Admissions: 1065 Census: 12 Outpatient Visits: 17823
Births: 0 Total Expense ($000): 16535 Payroll Expense ($000): 7267
Personnel: 201

### CORBIN—Whitley County

★ ◇ **BAPTIST HEALTH CORBIN (180080)**, (Formerly Baptist Regional Medical Center), 1 Trillium Way, Zip 40701–8420; tel. 606/528–1212 **A**9 10 19 21 **F**1 3 4 5 11 12 13 15 18 20 22 29 30 31 32 34 35 38 40 45 47 48 49 53 54 57 59 64 68 70 73 76 78 79 81 85 86 89 90 93 98 99 100 101 102 103 104 105 107 108 110 111 114 115 118 119 126 130 132 133 135 145 146 147 148 **S** Baptist Health, Louisville, KY
Primary Contact: Larry Gray, President
CIO: Jeff Thurmond, Vice President Information Systems
CNO: Anthony Powers, Vice President Patient Care Services
Web address: www.baptistregional.com
**Control:** Other not–for–profit (including NFP Corporation) **Service:** General Medical and Surgical

Staffed Beds: 273 Admissions: 9735 Census: 124 Outpatient Visits: 101127 Births: 868 Total Expense ($000): 129633 Payroll Expense ($000): 48159 Personnel: 1025

◇ **OAK TREE HOSPITAL (182006)**, 1 Trillium Way, Lower Level, Zip 40701–8727; tel. 606/523–5150 **A**10 21 **F**1 3 4 16 17 29 30 39 50 60 67 70 72 73 76 80 88 89 90 98 128 130 148 **S** Baptist Health, Louisville, KY
Primary Contact: R. Alan Coppock, FACHE, President
CFO: Jeff Hamlin, Director Finance
CMO: Bill Durham, M.D., Chief Medical Officer
CIO: Jackie Lucas, Vice President
CHR: Janice Caldwell, Director Human Resources
Web address: www.oaktreecorbin.com
**Control:** Other not–for–profit (including NFP Corporation) **Service:** Long–Term Acute Care hospital

Staffed Beds: 32 Admissions: 295 Census: 22 Outpatient Visits: 0 Births: 0 Total Expense ($000): 12164 Payroll Expense ($000): 4296 Personnel: 87

---

**Hospital, Medicare Provider Number, Address, Telephone, Approval, Facility, and Physician Codes, Health Care System**

★ American Hospital Association (AHA) membership
☐ The Joint Commission accreditation
◇ DNV Healthcare Inc. accreditation
○ Healthcare Facilities Accreditation Program
△ Commission on Accreditation of Rehabilitation Facilities (CARF) accreditation

## COVINGTON—Kenton County

**NORTHKEY COMMUNITY CARE (184006)**, 502 Farrell Drive,
Zip 41011-3799, Mailing Address: P.O. Box 2680, Zip 41012-2680;
tel. 859/578-3200, (Nonreporting) **A**9 10
Primary Contact: Owen Nichols, PsyD, President and Chief Executive Officer
CFO: John Metzger, Controller
Web address: www.northkey.org
**Control:** Other not-for-profit (including NFP Corporation) **Service:** Children's
hospital psychiatric

Staffed Beds: 25

**ST. ELIZABETH MEDICAL CENTER–NORTH** See St. Elizabeth Covington

## CYNTHIANA—Harrison County

✠ **HARRISON MEMORIAL HOSPITAL (180079)**, 1210 KY Highway 36E,
Zip 41031-7498; tel. 859/234-2300 **A**1 9 10 **F**3 11 13 15 18 20 28 29 30
31 34 35 36 39 40 44 45 47 49 50 53 57 59 61 64 68 69 70 74 75 76 77
78 79 81 82 85 86 87 89 93 97 107 108 111 115 118 119 129 130 131
132 133 135 146 147 148 **P**6 8
Primary Contact: Sheila Currans, Chief Executive Officer
CFO: James Spears, Chief Financial Officer
CIO: Martha Sullivan, Chief Information Officer
CHR: Rebecca Jenkins, Director Human Resources Management
CNO: Wendy Reeder, R.N., Chief Nursing Officer
Web address: www.harrisonmemhosp.com
**Control:** Other not-for-profit (including NFP Corporation) **Service:** General
Medical and Surgical

Staffed Beds: 49 Admissions: 1681 Census: 16 Outpatient Visits: 51090
Births: 222 Total Expense ($000): 32746 Payroll Expense ($000): 14339
Personnel: 267

## DANVILLE—Boyle County

✠ **EPHRAIM MCDOWELL REGIONAL MEDICAL CENTER (180048)**, 217 South
Third Street, Zip 40422-1823; tel. 859/239-1000, (Total facility includes 24
beds in nursing home–type unit) **A**1 5 9 10 19 **F**3 11 13 15 17 18 20 22
29 30 31 32 34 35 40 43 45 46 49 51 53 56 57 59 60 64 65 66 70 73 75
76 77 78 79 81 82 85 87 89 93 96 97 98 100 101 102 103 107 108 110
111 114 117 118 119 125 127 128 129 130 132 144 146 147 148 **P**5
Primary Contact: Vicki A. Darnell, R.N., MSN, President and Chief Executive
Officer
CFO: William R. Snapp, III, Vice President Finance and Chief Financial Officer
CMO: Gary Ahnquist, M.D., President Medical Staff
CIO: Allen Levi, Director Information Services
CHR: Carl Metz, Vice President Human Resources
CNO: Sally Davenport, Vice President of Patient Care Services & CNO
Web address: www.emrmc.org
**Control:** Other not-for-profit (including NFP Corporation) **Service:** General
Medical and Surgical

Staffed Beds: 159 Admissions: 7512 Census: 96 Outpatient Visits: 125183
Births: 626 Total Expense ($000): 116743 Payroll Expense ($000): 46301
Personnel: 978

## EDGEWOOD—Kenton County

✠ **HEALTHSOUTH NORTHERN KENTUCKY REHABILITATION HOSPITAL
(183027)**, 201 Medical Village Drive, Zip 41017-3407; tel. 859/341-2044 **A**1
9 10 **F**64 79 82 90 93 94 **P**6 **S** HEALTHSOUTH Corporation, Birmingham, AL
Primary Contact: Richard R. Evens, Chief Executive Officer
CFO: Lisa McGue, Controller
CMO: Neal Moser, M.D., Medical Director
CHR: Bridgette Keith, Director Human Resources
CNO: Scott Toney, R.N., Chief Nursing Officer
Web address: www.healthsouthkentucky.com
**Control:** Partnership, Investor-owned, for-profit **Service:** Rehabilitation

Staffed Beds: 40 Admissions: 978 Census: 33 Outpatient Visits: 3788
Births: 0

☐ **ST. ELIZABETH EDGEWOOD (180035)**, 1 Medical Village Drive,
Zip 41017-3403; tel. 859/301-2000, (Includes ST. ELIZABETH COVINGTON,
1500 James Simpson Jr. Way, Covington, Zip 41014-1585; tel. 859/655-8800)
**A**1 2 3 5 9 10 **F**3 5 8 13 14 15 17 18 20 22 24 26 28 29 30 31 34 35 36 38
40 44 45 46 47 48 49 50 51 56 63 64 68 70 71 73 74 75 76 77
78 79 80 81 82 83 84 85 86 87 89 92 93 97 98 100 103 104 105 107 108
109 110 111 114 115 116 117 118 119 120 121 123 126 129 130 131 132
135 145 146 147 148 **P**6 **S** St. Elizabeth Healthcare, Edgewood, KY
Primary Contact: John S. Dubis, FACHE, President and Chief Executive Officer
COO: John S. Dubis, FACHE, President and Chief Executive Officer
CFO: Garren Colvin, Senior Vice President and Chief Financial Officer
CMO: Karl Schmitt, M.D., Chief of Staff
CIO: Alex Rodriguez, Vice President and Chief Information Officer
CHR: Martin Oscadal, Vice President Human Resources
Web address: www.stelizabeth.com
**Control:** Church-operated, Nongovernment, not-for profit **Service:** General
Medical and Surgical

Staffed Beds: 502 Admissions: 32282 Census: 347 Outpatient Visits:
770475 Births: 4511 Total Expense ($000): 619914 Payroll Expense
($000): 227575 Personnel: 2987

**ST. ELIZABETH HEALTHCARE–EDGEWOOD** See St. Elizabeth Edgewood

## ELIZABETHTOWN—Hardin County

✠ **HARDIN MEMORIAL HOSPITAL (180012)**, 913 North Dixie Avenue,
Zip 42701-2503; tel. 270/737-1212, (Total facility includes 15 beds in nursing
home–type unit) **A**1 2 5 9 10 19 **F**3 8 11 12 13 15 17 18 20 22 24 28 29 30
31 32 34 35 37 39 40 44 45 48 49 50 51 52 54 57 58 59 64 68 70 71 73
74 75 76 77 78 79 80 81 82 84 85 86 87 89 93 94 96 98 102 107 108 110
111 114 115 117 118 119 120 121 124 126 128 129 130 131 132 134 135
144 146 147 148 **S** Baptist Health, Louisville, KY
Primary Contact: Dennis B. Johnson, President
COO: Diane Logsdon, Vice President Planning and Development
CFO: Elmer Cummings, Vice President and Chief Financial Officer
CMO: Stephen Toadvine, M.D., Chief Medical Officer
CIO: Mark Brookman, Director Information Technology
CHR: Ann Kelley, Director Human Resources
Web address: www.hmh.net
**Control:** County-Government, nonfederal **Service:** General Medical and Surgical

Staffed Beds: 268 Admissions: 12758 Census: 155 Outpatient Visits:
326644 Births: 1603 Total Expense ($000): 205700 Payroll Expense
($000): 87828 Personnel: 1762

✠ **HEALTHSOUTH LAKEVIEW REHABILITATION HOSPITAL (183028)**, 134
Heartland Drive, Zip 42701-2778; tel. 270/769-3100, (Nonreporting) **A**1 10
**S** HEALTHSOUTH Corporation, Birmingham, AL
Primary Contact: Lori Jarboe, Chief Executive Officer
CFO: Scott Hart, Controller
CMO: Vickie Lowe, M.D., Medical Director
CHR: Janet Morris, Director Human Resources
Web address: www.healthsouthlakeview.com
**Control:** Corporation, Investor-owned, for-profit **Service:** Rehabilitation

Staffed Beds: 40

## FLEMINGSBURG—Fleming County

✠ **FLEMING COUNTY HOSPITAL (180053)**, 55 Foundation Drive,
Zip 41041-9815, Mailing Address: P.O. Box 388, Zip 41041-0388;
tel. 606/849-5000 **A**1 9 10 **F**15 28 29 31 34 35 40 45 50 57 59 78 79 81
87 93 107 108 110 111 114 118 119 129 130 133 135 146 **P**6 **S** QHR,
Brentwood, TN
Primary Contact: David M. Faulkner, Chief Executive Officer
CMO: William Bacon, M.D., Chief of Staff
CIO: Don Daugherty, Director Information Systems
CHR: Marsha Mitchell, Director Human Resources
CNO: Lynda Skaggs, Chief Nursing Officer
Web address: www.flemingcountyhospital.org
**Control:** Other not-for-profit (including NFP Corporation) **Service:** General
Medical and Surgical

Staffed Beds: 52 Admissions: 1265 Census: 13 Outpatient Visits: 34094
Births: 0 Total Expense ($000): 22308 Payroll Expense ($000): 9380
Personnel: 190

## FLORENCE—Boone County

☐ **GATEWAY REHABILITATION HOSPITAL (183030)**, 5940 Merchant Street,
Zip 41042-1158; tel. 859/426-2400, (Nonreporting) **A**1 9 10
Primary Contact: Jim Burcham, Chief Executive Officer
Web address: www.gatewayflorence.com/
**Control:** Corporation, Investor-owned, for-profit **Service:** Rehabilitation

Staffed Beds: 40

☐ **ST. ELIZABETH FLORENCE (180045)**, 4900 Houston Road, Zip 41042-4824;
tel. 859/212-5200, (Total facility includes 16 beds in nursing home–type unit) **A**1
9 10 **F**3 11 12 15 18 20 28 29 30 31 34 35 40 44 45 47 48 49 50 55 56 57
59 60 64 71 74 75 77 78 79 80 81 82 85 86 87 92 93 97 98 100 107 108
110 111 115 118 119 128 129 130 132 135 144 146 147 **P**6 **S** St. Elizabeth
Healthcare, Edgewood, KY
Primary Contact: Chris Carle, Senior Vice President and Chief Operating Officer
COO: Chris Carle, Senior Vice President and Chief Operating Officer
CFO: Garren Colvin, Senior Vice President and Chief Financial Officer
CMO: George Hall, M.D., Vice President Medical Affairs
CIO: Alex Rodriguez, Vice President and Chief Information Officer
CHR: Martin Oscadal, Senior Vice President Human Resources
Web address: www.stelizabeth.com
**Control:** Church-operated, Nongovernment, not-for profit **Service:** General
Medical and Surgical

Staffed Beds: 169 Admissions: 10190 Census: 107 Outpatient Visits:
139340 Births: 0 Total Expense ($000): 106030 Payroll Expense ($000):
41832 Personnel: 659

**ST. ELIZABETH HEALTHCARE FLORENCE** See St. Elizabeth Florence

*Many Facility Codes have changed. Please refer to the AHA Guide Code Chart.*

© 2013 AHA Guide

## FORT CAMPBELL—Montgomery County

☒ **COLONEL FLORENCE A. BLANCHFIELD ARMY COMMUNITY HOSPITAL**, 650 Joel Drive, Zip 42223–5318; tel. 270/798–8040, (Nonreporting) **A**1 3 5 **S** Department of the Army, Office of the Surgeon General, Falls Church, VA
Primary Contact: Colonel Paul Cordts, Commander
CMO: Lieutenant Colonel Michael Place, M.D., Deputy Commander Clinical Services
CIO: Gloria K. Davis, Chief Information Management
CHR: Major Travis Burchett, Troop Commander Human Resources
Web address: www.campbell.amedd.army.mil/
**Control:** Army, Government, federal **Service:** General Medical and Surgical

**Staffed Beds:** 66

## FORT KNOX—Hardin County

☒ **IRELAND ARMY COMMUNITY HOSPITAL**, 289 Ireland Avenue, Zip 40121–5111; tel. 502/624–9333, (Nonreporting) **A**1 5 **S** Department of the Army, Office of the Surgeon General, Falls Church, VA
Primary Contact: Colonel Cornelius C. Maher, Commander
Web address: www.iach.knox.amedd.army.mil/
**Control:** Army, Government, federal **Service:** General Medical and Surgical

**Staffed Beds:** 33

## FORT THOMAS—Campbell County

**CARDINAL HILL SPECIALTY HOSPITAL** See Select Specialty Hospital–Northern Kentucky

☒ **SELECT SPECIALTY HOSPITAL–NORTHERN KENTUCKY (182004)**, (Formerly Cardinal Hill Specialty Hospital), 85 North Grand Avenue, Zip 41075–1793; tel. 859/572–3880, (Nonreporting) **A**1 10 **S** Select Medical Corporation, Mechanicsburg, PA
Primary Contact: Matthew Keppler, Chief Executive Officer
Web address: www.selectspecialtyhospitals.com/company/locations/northern–kentucky.aspx
**Control:** Corporation, Investor–owned, for–profit **Service:** Long–Term Acute Care hospital

**Staffed Beds:** 33

☐ **ST. ELIZABETH FORT THOMAS (180001)**, 85 North Grand Avenue, Zip 41075–1796; tel. 859/572–3100, (Total facility includes 26 beds in nursing home–type unit) **A**1 2 9 10 **F**3 4 11 15 17 18 20 28 29 30 31 34 35 40 44 45 47 48 49 50 55 56 57 59 60 61 63 64 70 71 74 75 77 78 79 80 81 82 85 86 87 92 93 97 100 107 108 110 111 114 115 118 119 120 121 123 126 128 129 130 132 135 146 147 **P**6 **S** St. Elizabeth Healthcare, Edgewood, KY
Primary Contact: Thomas Saalfeld, Senior Vice President and Chief Operating Officer
COO: Thomas Saalfeld, Senior Vice President and Chief Operating Officer
CFO: Garren Colvin, Senior Vice President and Chief Financial Officer
CMO: George Hall, M.D., Vice President Medical Affairs
CIO: Alex Rodriguez, Vice President and Chief Information Officer
CHR: Martin Oscadal, Senior Vice President Human Resources
Web address: www.stelizabeth.com
**Control:** Church–operated, Nongovernment, not–for profit **Service:** General Medical and Surgical

**Staffed Beds:** 181 **Admissions:** 7610 **Census:** 102 **Outpatient Visits:** 145850 **Births:** 0 **Total Expense ($000):** 93970 **Payroll Expense ($000):** 39120 **Personnel:** 601

**ST. ELIZABETH HEALTHCARE FORT THOMAS** See St. Elizabeth Fort Thomas

## FRANKFORT—Franklin County

☒ **FRANKFORT REGIONAL MEDICAL CENTER (180127)**, 299 King's Daughters Drive, Zip 40601–4186; tel. 502/875–5240 **A**1 9 10 19 **F**3 13 15 17 18 20 22 28 29 30 31 34 40 45 49 50 51 57 60 64 66 68 70 72 73 75 76 77 78 79 81 82 83 84 85 87 89 93 107 111 119 124 129 130 133 145 146 147 148 **S** HCA, Nashville, TN
Primary Contact: Chip Peal, Chief Executive Officer
CFO: Osman Gruhonjic, Chief Financial Officer
CMO: Willis P. McKee, Jr., M.D., Chief Medical Officer
CIO: Craig Willard, Director Information Technology and Systems
CHR: Bev Young, Director Human Resources
Web address: www.frankfortregional.com
**Control:** Corporation, Investor–owned, for–profit **Service:** Long–Term Acute Care hospital

**Staffed Beds:** 134 **Admissions:** 4400 **Census:** 48 **Outpatient Visits:** 81229 **Births:** 767 **Total Expense ($000):** 68542 **Payroll Expense ($000):** 25968 **Personnel:** 423

## FRANKLIN—Simpson County

☐ **MEDICAL CENTER AT FRANKLIN (181318)**, 1100 Brookhaven Road, Zip 42134–2746; tel. 270/598–4800 **A**1 9 10 18 **F**1 3 4 15 16 17 28 29 30 32 34 35 40 46 57 59 64 67 68 70 72 73 75 76 77 80 81 86 87 88 89 90 93 98 107 111 114 119 127 128 130 133 135 146 148 **S** Commonwealth Health Corporation, Bowling Green, KY
Primary Contact: Eric Hagan, R.N., Vice President/Administrator
CFO: Ronald G. Sowell, Executive Vice President
CIO: Jean Cherry, Executive Vice President
Web address: www.themedicalcenterfranklin.org
**Control:** Other not–for–profit (including NFP Corporation) **Service:** General Medical and Surgical

**Staffed Beds:** 25 **Admissions:** 1341 **Census:** 20 **Outpatient Visits:** 20820 **Births:** 0 **Personnel:** 120

## FULTON—Fulton County

☒ **PARKWAY REGIONAL HOSPITAL (180117)**, 2000 Holiday Lane, Zip 42041–8468; tel. 270/472–2522, (Nonreporting) **A**1 9 10 **S** Community Health Systems, Inc., Franklin, TN
Primary Contact: Rob Calhoun, Chief Executive Officer
CFO: Dana Lawrence, Chief Financial Officer
CMO: F. Gregory Cox, M.D., Chief of Staff
CHR: Janice Bone, Director Human Resources
Web address: www.parkwayregionalhospital.com
**Control:** Corporation, Investor–owned, for–profit **Service:** General Medical and Surgical

**Staffed Beds:** 70

## GEORGETOWN—Scott County

☒ **GEORGETOWN COMMUNITY HOSPITAL (180101)**, 1140 Lexington Road, Zip 40324–9362; tel. 502/868–1100 **A**1 5 9 10 **F**3 11 12 13 15 18 19 28 29 30 31 34 35 40 45 49 50 51 57 59 70 74 75 76 77 78 79 81 82 85 86 87 92 93 107 108 109 110 111 114 115 119 129 130 132 133 146 147 **S** LifePoint Hospitals, Inc., Brentwood, TN
Primary Contact: William Haugh, Administrator
CFO: Patrick C. Bolander, Chief Financial Officer
CMO: Brian Allen, M.D., President Medical Staff
CHR: Marrianne Slonina, Director Human Resources
Web address: www.georgetowncommunityhospital.com
**Control:** Corporation, Investor–owned, for–profit **Service:** General Medical and Surgical

**Staffed Beds:** 58 **Admissions:** 1870 **Census:** 15 **Outpatient Visits:** 52233 **Births:** 153 **Total Expense ($000):** 38443 **Payroll Expense ($000):** 13554 **Personnel:** 264

## GLASGOW—Barren County

☒ **T. J. SAMSON COMMUNITY HOSPITAL (180017)**, 1301 North Race Street, Zip 42141–3483; tel. 270/651–4444, (Total facility includes 16 beds in nursing home–type unit) **A**1 3 5 9 10 19 **F**2 3 11 13 15 18 20 22 24 28 29 30 31 34 40 45 57 59 60 62 63 64 70 71 72 74 75 76 77 78 79 81 82 85 86 87 89 93 97 107 110 111 112 114 119 124 128 129 130 132 135 146 148 **P**5
Primary Contact: Bill Kindred, Chief Executive Officer
COO: Larry Morgan, Controller
CFO: Anthony G. Sudduth, CPA, Chief Financial Officer
CMO: Michael Shadowen, M.D., Chief of Staff
CIO: Debbie Caudel–Logsdon, Director Information System
CHR: LaDonna Rogers, Director Human Resources
Web address: www.tjsamson.org
**Control:** Other not–for–profit (including NFP Corporation) **Service:** General Medical and Surgical

**Staffed Beds:** 196 **Admissions:** 6277 **Census:** 61 **Outpatient Visits:** 101970 **Births:** 1146 **Total Expense ($000):** 123920 **Payroll Expense ($000):** 45535 **Personnel:** 1015

## GREENSBURG—Green County

**JANE TODD CRAWFORD HOSPITAL (181325)**, 202–206 Milby Street, Zip 42743–1100, Mailing Address: P.O. Box 220, Zip 42743–0220; tel. 270/932–4211, (Nonreporting) **A**9 10 18
Primary Contact: Rex A. Tungate, Administrator
CMO: James G. Bland, M.D., Chief of Staff
**Control:** County–Government, nonfederal **Service:** General Medical and Surgical

**Staffed Beds:** 45

---

| Hospital, Medicare Provider Number, Address, Telephone, Approval, Facility, and Physician Codes, Health Care System |
| --- |

★ American Hospital Association (AHA) membership
☐ The Joint Commission accreditation
◇ DNV Healthcare Inc. accreditation
○ Healthcare Facilities Accreditation Program
△ Commission on Accreditation of Rehabilitation Facilities (CARF) accreditation

### GREENVILLE—Muhlenberg County

**☒ MUHLENBERG COMMUNITY HOSPITAL (180004)**, 440 Hopkinsville Street, Zip 42345–1172, Mailing Address: P.O. Box 387, Zip 42345–0387; tel. 270/338–8000, (Total facility includes 45 beds in nursing home–type unit) **A**1 9 10 **F**3 7 8 11 15 28 29 30 34 35 40 50 56 57 59 62 64 65 68 70 75 76 77 79 81 82 85 86 87 89 90 93 94 107 110 111 114 119 127 128 129 130 131 135 146 148 **P**6 **S** Alliant Management Services, Louisville, KY
Primary Contact: John T. Countzler, Chief Executive Officer
CFO: Joseph Swab, Chief Financial Officer
CMO: Vincent P. Genovese, M.D., President Medical Staff
CIO: Alan Trail, Director Information Systems
CHR: Lisa R. Hope, Director Human Resources
CNO: Kathy Mitchell, Chief Nursing Officer
Web address: www.mchky.org
**Control:** Other not–for–profit (including NFP Corporation) **Service:** General Medical and Surgical

**Staffed Beds:** 105 **Admissions:** 2076 **Census:** 57 **Outpatient Visits:** 55587 **Births:** 150 **Total Expense ($000):** 33073 **Payroll Expense ($000):** 14960

### HARDINSBURG—Breckinridge County

**☒ BRECKINRIDGE MEMORIAL HOSPITAL (181319)**, 1011 Old Highway 60, Zip 40143–2597; tel. 270/756–7000, (Total facility includes 18 beds in nursing home–type unit) **A**1 9 10 18 **F**3 15 18 28 29 30 34 35 40 48 49 50 53 56 57 59 62 63 64 65 68 75 77 79 81 82 85 86 87 93 100 107 110 111 119 127 129 130 132 133 135 143 146 148 **P**6 **S** Alliant Management Services, Louisville, KY
Primary Contact: Michael W. Cooper, Chief Executive Officer
CMO: Brian O'Donoghue, M.D., Chief Medical Officer
CIO: Virginia D. Bradley, Chief Information Officer
CHR: Clara Cordelia Hall, Chief Human Resources Officer
Web address: www.breckhealth.org
**Control:** Other not–for–profit (including NFP Corporation) **Service:** General Medical and Surgical

**Staffed Beds:** 43 **Admissions:** 1116 **Census:** 31 **Outpatient Visits:** 35664 **Total Expense ($000):** 18536 **Payroll Expense ($000):** 7912 **Personnel:** 207

### HARLAN—Harlan County

**☐ HARLAN ARH HOSPITAL (180050)**, 81 Ball Park Road, Zip 40831–1792; tel. 606/573–8100 **A**1 9 10 19 **F**3 11 13 15 29 30 32 34 35 40 50 54 57 59 62 64 70 75 76 77 78 79 81 82 85 86 87 89 90 93 97 98 102 103 107 108 111 115 118 119 127 129 130 132 146 147 148 **P**6 **S** Appalachian Regional Healthcare, Inc., Lexington, KY
Primary Contact: Dan Stone, Community Chief Executive Officer
CFO: Brad Burkhart, Assistant Administrator
CHR: Sabra Howard, Manager Human Resources
Web address: www.arh.org
**Control:** Other not–for–profit (including NFP Corporation) **Service:** General Medical and Surgical

**Staffed Beds:** 137 **Admissions:** 4943 **Census:** 59 **Outpatient Visits:** 67261 **Births:** 278 **Total Expense ($000):** 59996 **Payroll Expense ($000):** 17545 **Personnel:** 418

### HARRODSBURG—Mercer County

**☒ JAMES B. HAGGIN MEMORIAL HOSPITAL (181302)**, 464 Linden Avenue, Zip 40330–1862; tel. 859/734–5441, (Nonreporting) **A**1 5 9 10 18 **S** Alliant Management Services, Louisville, KY
Primary Contact: Victoria L. Reed, R.N., FACHE, Chief Executive Officer
CFO: Tony Patterson, Chief Financial Officer
Web address: www.hagginhosp.org
**Control:** Other not–for–profit (including NFP Corporation) **Service:** General Medical and Surgical

**Staffed Beds:** 25

### HARTFORD—Ohio County

**☒ OHIO COUNTY HOSPITAL (181323)**, 1211 Main Street, Zip 42347–1619; tel. 270/298–7411 **A**1 9 10 18 **F**3 11 15 17 18 28 29 30 31 34 35 40 41 45 47 49 54 57 58 59 63 64 65 70 74 75 77 78 79 81 85 88 89 92 93 97 107 108 111 115 119 127 128 129 130 131 132 133 134 135 144 145 146 147 148 **P**6 **S** QHR, Brentwood, TN
Primary Contact: Blaine Pieper, Chief Executive Officer
CFO: John Tichenor, Chief Financial Officer
CMO: Janna Pathi, M.D., Chief Medical Officer
CHR: Sue Wydick, Director Human Resources
Web address: www.ohiocountyhospital.com
**Control:** Other not–for–profit (including NFP Corporation) **Service:** General Medical and Surgical

**Staffed Beds:** 25 **Admissions:** 1101 **Census:** 9 **Outpatient Visits:** 51966 **Births:** 0 **Total Expense ($000):** 28909 **Payroll Expense ($000):** 13958 **Personnel:** 368

### HAZARD—Perry County

**☐ HAZARD ARH REGIONAL MEDICAL CENTER (180029)**, 100 Medical Center Drive, Zip 41701–9421; tel. 606/439–6600 **A**1 2 3 5 9 10 19 **F**3 11 12 13 15 17 18 20 22 24 28 29 30 31 32 34 35 40 43 46 48 50 54 57 59 62 64 70 71 73 74 75 76 77 78 79 81 82 85 86 87 89 90 93 97 98 101 102 103 107 108 110 111 115 116 119 121 124 127 129 130 132 146 147 148 **P**6 **S** Appalachian Regional Healthcare, Inc., Lexington, KY
Primary Contact: Donald R. Fields, Senior Community Chief Executive Officer
COO: Donald R. Fields, Senior Community Chief Executive Officer
CMO: J. D. Miller, M.D., Chief Medical Officer
CIO: Jeff Brady, Director Information Systems
CHR: Sheila Cornett, Manager Human Resources
Web address: www.arh.org
**Control:** Other not–for–profit (including NFP Corporation) **Service:** General Medical and Surgical

**Staffed Beds:** 308 **Admissions:** 13470 **Census:** 206 **Outpatient Visits:** 92109 **Births:** 379 **Total Expense ($000):** 149629 **Payroll Expense ($000):** 36287 **Personnel:** 954

### HENDERSON—Henderson County

**☐ METHODIST HOSPITAL (180056)**, 1305 North Elm Street, Zip 42420–2775, Mailing Address: P.O. Box 48, Zip 42419–0048; tel. 270/827–7700 **A**1 9 10 13 **F**3 11 13 15 18 20 29 30 31 34 35 40 45 46 47 49 50 51 53 57 58 59 64 66 68 70 71 72 74 75 76 77 78 79 81 82 85 86 87 89 92 93 102 107 108 110 111 114 116 119 126 127 129 130 131 132 135 146 147 148 **P**8
Primary Contact: Bruce D. Begley, Executive Director
CFO: Gregory P. Hebbeler, Chief Financial Officer
CMO: Gerald Rightmyer, M.D., Chief of Staff
CIO: Gregory P. Hebbeler, Chief Financial Officer
CHR: Marty Mattingly, Vice President Human Resources
Web address: www.methodisthospital.net
**Control:** Church–operated, Nongovernment, not–for profit **Service:** General Medical and Surgical

**Staffed Beds:** 167 **Admissions:** 5183 **Census:** 67 **Outpatient Visits:** 273797 **Births:** 594 **Total Expense ($000):** 120063 **Payroll Expense ($000):** 37540 **Personnel:** 1036

### HOPKINSVILLE—Christian County

**☐ CUMBERLAND HALL HOSPITAL (184014)**, 270 Walton Way, Zip 42240–6808; tel. 270/886–1919 **A**1 9 10 **F**98 **S** Universal Health Services, Inc., King of Prussia, PA
Primary Contact: James Spruyt, Chief Executive Officer
CFO: Chris Jagoditz, Chief Financial Officer
CMO: Deepak Patel, M.D., Medical Director
CIO: Patricia Gray, Director Health Information Management
CHR: Tracy Thomas, Director Human Resources
CNO: Jackie Wurth, Director of Nursing
Web address: www.cumberlandhallhospital.com
**Control:** Corporation, Investor–owned, for–profit **Service:** Psychiatric

**Staffed Beds:** 97 **Admissions:** 1541 **Census:** 65 **Outpatient Visits:** 0 **Births:** 0 **Total Expense ($000):** 8562 **Payroll Expense ($000):** 4792 **Personnel:** 130

**☒ JENNIE STUART MEDICAL CENTER (180051)**, 320 West 18th Street, Zip 42240–1965, Mailing Address: P.O. Box 2400, Zip 42241–2400; tel. 270/887–0100, (Nonreporting) **A**1 9 10 **S** QHR, Brentwood, TN
Primary Contact: Eric A. Lee, President and Chief Executive Officer
CFO: Samuel L. Brown, CPA, Vice President Financial Services
CMO: Casey Covington, M.D., President Elect, Medical Staff
CIO: Jerry Houston, Director Information Systems
CHR: Austin Moss, Vice President Human Resources
Web address: www.jsmc.org
**Control:** Other not–for–profit (including NFP Corporation) **Service:** General Medical and Surgical

**Staffed Beds:** 139

**☐ WESTERN STATE HOSPITAL (184002)**, Russellville Road, Zip 42240–3017, Mailing Address: P.O. Box 2200, Zip 42241–2200; tel. 270/889–6025 **A**1 10 **F**98 102 103 130 **P**5
Primary Contact: Stephen P. Wiggins, Director
CFO: Jessica Cates, Fiscal Manager
CMO: Nayyar Iqbal, M.D., Director Medical Staff
CIO: Valerie Majors, Director Information Services
CHR: James L. Hayes, Director Human Resources
**Control:** State–Government, nonfederal **Service:** Psychiatric

**Staffed Beds:** 207 **Admissions:** 1930 **Census:** 100 **Outpatient Visits:** 0 **Births:** 0 **Total Expense ($000):** 16240 **Payroll Expense ($000):** 10333 **Personnel:** 633

*Many Facility Codes have changed. Please refer to the AHA Guide Code Chart.* © 2013 AHA Guide

## HORSE CAVE—Hart County

★ **CAVERNA MEMORIAL HOSPITAL (181314)**, 1501 South Dixie Street,
Zip 42749–1477; tel. 270/786–2191 **A**9 10 18 **F**3 15 34 40 57 59 64 70 81
85 89 107 111 114 119 127 128 133 135 **P**6 **S** Alliant Management Services,
Louisville, KY
Primary Contact: Alan B. Alexander, Chief Executive Officer
CFO: Debra Riggs, Chief Financial Officer
CMO: Swaranjik K. Chani, M.D., Chief of Staff
CIO: Brad Lowe, Director Information Systems
CHR: Cathy Szabo, Director Human Resources
CNO: Vanessa Burd, R.N., Chief Nursing Officer
Web address: www.cavernahospital.com
**Control:** Other not–for–profit (including NFP Corporation) **Service:** General
Medical and Surgical

**Staffed Beds:** 25 **Admissions:** 450 **Census:** 4 **Outpatient Visits:** 19961
**Births:** 0 **Total Expense ($000):** 10416 **Payroll Expense ($000):** 4815
**Personnel:** 102

## HYDEN—Leslie County

**MARY BRECKINRIDGE ARH HOSPITAL (181316)**, 130 Kate Ireland Drive,
Zip 41749–9071, Mailing Address: P.O. Box 447–A, Zip 41749–0717;
tel. 606/672–2901, (Nonreporting) **A**9 10 18 **S** Appalachian Regional Healthcare,
Inc., Lexington, KY
Primary Contact: Mallie S. Noble, Administrator
COO: Nathan W. Lee, Chief Executive Officer
CFO: Robert Besten, Chief Financial Officer
CMO: Roy Varghese, M.D., Chief of Staff
CIO: Frank Baker, Chief Information Officer
CHR: Beulah Couch, Director Human Resources
Web address: www.frontiernursing.org
**Control:** Other not–for–profit (including NFP Corporation) **Service:** General
Medical and Surgical

**Staffed Beds:** 25

## IRVINE—Estill County

★ **MARCUM AND WALLACE MEMORIAL HOSPITAL (181301)**, 60 Mercy Court,
Zip 40336–1331; tel. 606/723–2115, (Nonreporting) **A**9 10 18 **S** Catholic Health
Partners, Cincinnati, OH
Primary Contact: Susan Starling, President and Chief Executive Officer
CFO: Della Deerfield, Vice President Finance
CMO: Mark Rukavina, M.D., Chief Medical Staff
CIO: Tracy Bryant, Coordinator Information Technology
CHR: Dana Stepp, Human Resources Officer
Web address: www.marcumandwallace.org
**Control:** Church–operated, Nongovernment, not–for profit **Service:** General
Medical and Surgical

**Staffed Beds:** 25

## JACKSON—Breathitt County

⊠ **KENTUCKY RIVER MEDICAL CENTER (180139)**, 540 Jett Drive,
Zip 41339–9622; tel. 606/666–6000, (Nonreporting) **A**1 9 10 20 **S** Community
Health Systems, Inc., Franklin, TN
Primary Contact: William Chad French, Chief Executive Officer
CFO: Michael Ackley, Chief Financial Officer
CMO: Eunice Johnson, M.D., Chief Medical Staff
CIO: Diana Tyra, Director Health Information
CHR: Naomi Mitchell, Director Human Resources
Web address: www.kentuckyrivermc.com
**Control:** Corporation, Investor–owned, for–profit **Service:** General Medical and
Surgical

**Staffed Beds:** 54

## LA GRANGE—Oldham County

★ ○ **BAPTIST HEALTH LA GRANGE (180138)**, (Formerly Baptist Hospital
Northeast), 1025 New Moody Lane, Zip 40031–9154; tel. 502/222–5388, (Total
facility includes 30 beds in nursing home–type unit) **A**3 5 9 10 11 **F**3 7 11 13 15
18 28 29 30 34 35 36 40 43 45 46 49 50 54 56 57 59 64 68 70 74 75 76
77 78 79 81 82 85 86 87 93 97 107 108 110 111 114 119 128 129 130
131 132 133 135 146 147 148 **P**6 **S** Baptist Health, Louisville, KY
Primary Contact: Chris Roty, President
CFO: Susanne Haynes, Executive Director Finance
CMO: Matt McDanald, M.D., Chief Medical Officer
CIO: Jackie Lucas, Vice President Information Systems
CHR: Jean Harden, Vice President Human Resources
Web address: www.baptistnortheast.com
**Control:** Other not–for–profit (including NFP Corporation) **Service:** General
Medical and Surgical

**Staffed Beds:** 108 **Admissions:** 3158 **Census:** 48 **Outpatient Visits:** 45188
**Births:** 509 **Total Expense ($000):** 48158 **Payroll Expense ($000):** 21264
**Personnel:** 298

## LEBANON—Marion County

⊠ **SPRING VIEW HOSPITAL (180024)**, 320 Loretto Road, Zip 40033–1300;
tel. 270/692–3161 **A**1 9 10 **F**3 11 13 15 28 29 30 34 35 40 45 48 49 50 51
57 59 64 70 75 76 77 79 81 85 86 87 90 92 93 107 108 110 111 114 118
119 130 131 133 135 146 147 148 **P**6 **S** LifePoint Hospitals, Inc.,
Brentwood, TN
Primary Contact: Ruth A. McDaniel, Chief Executive Officer
CFO: Denise Thomas, Chief Financial Officer
CIO: Douglas Bland, Manager Information Services
CHR: Ann Dabney, Manager Human Resources
CNO: Kathleen Ferriell, Chief Nursing Officer
Web address: www.springviewhospital.com
**Control:** Corporation, Investor–owned, for–profit **Service:** General Medical and
Surgical

**Staffed Beds:** 60 **Admissions:** 1704 **Census:** 16 **Outpatient Visits:** 44322
**Births:** 354 **Payroll Expense ($000):** 9734 **Personnel:** 234

## LEITCHFIELD—Grayson County

☐ **TWIN LAKES REGIONAL MEDICAL CENTER (180070)**, 910 Wallace Avenue,
Zip 42754–2414; tel. 270/259–9400, (Data for 364 days) **A**1 9 10 **F**3 11 13
15 28 29 30 31 34 40 53 57 59 68 70 72 76 78 79 81 82 85 86 87 89 93
107 108 110 111 115 118 119 129 130 131 132 133 135 144 146 148 **P**6
**S** Alliant Management Services, Louisville, KY
Primary Contact: Wayne Meriwether, Chief Executive Officer
COO: Deneace Clemons, Chief Operating Officer
CFO: Scott Arndell, Chief Financial Officer
CMO: John Evans, M.D., Chief Medical Officer
CIO: Mandy Bryant, Chief Information Officer
CHR: Mandi Filburn, Director Human Resources
Web address: www.tlrmc.com
**Control:** Other not–for–profit (including NFP Corporation) **Service:** General
Medical and Surgical

**Staffed Beds:** 75 **Admissions:** 2672 **Census:** 29 **Outpatient Visits:** 79369
**Births:** 372 **Total Expense ($000):** 34920 **Payroll Expense ($000):** 12955
**Personnel:** 321

## LEXINGTON—Fayette County

⊠ **BAPTIST HEALTH LEXINGTON (180103)**, (Formerly Central Baptist Hospital),
1740 Nicholasville Road, Zip 40503–1499; tel. 859/260–6100 **A**1 2 9 10 **F**3 11
12 13 15 17 18 20 22 24 26 28 29 30 31 34 35 36 40 44 48 49 53 54 55
56 57 58 59 60 62 64 68 70 72 74 75 76 77 78 79 81 84 85 86 87 89 92
93 97 107 108 110 111 114 115 117 118 119 120 121 124 126 129 130
131 132 135 144 146 147 148 **S** Baptist Health, Louisville, KY
Primary Contact: William G. Sisson, President
COO: Karen S. Hill, R.N., Chief Operating Officer and Chief Nursing Officer
CFO: Bobbie L. Prather, Chief Financial Officer
CMO: Preston Nunelley, M.D., Chief Medical Officer
CIO: Lisa Fluty, Director Information Services
CHR: Lynette Walker, R.N., Vice President Human Resources
Web address: www.centralbap.com
**Control:** Other not–for–profit (including NFP Corporation) **Service:** General
Medical and Surgical

**Staffed Beds:** 344 **Admissions:** 18326 **Census:** 231 **Outpatient Visits:**
237519 **Births:** 3732 **Total Expense ($000):** 373991 **Payroll Expense
($000):** 135642 **Personnel:** 2333

---

**Hospital, Medicare Provider Number, Address, Telephone, Approval, Facility, and Physician Codes, Health Care System**

★ American Hospital Association (AHA) membership
☐ The Joint Commission accreditation
◇ DNV Healthcare Inc. accreditation
○ Healthcare Facilities Accreditation Program
△ Commission on Accreditation of Rehabilitation Facilities (CARF) accreditation

★ △ **CARDINAL HILL REHABILITATION HOSPITAL (183026)**, 2050 Versailles Road, Zip 40504–1405; tel. 859/254–5701, (Total facility includes 74 beds in nursing home–type unit) **A**3 5 7 9 10 **F**2 3 9 11 29 30 32 34 35 38 50 53 56 57 58 59 62 64 65 68 74 75 79 82 86 87 90 91 92 93 94 95 96 128 130 131 132 134 135 143 146 147 148
Primary Contact: Gary Payne, Chief Executive Officer
COO: Beth Monarch, Executive Vice President and Chief Operating Officer
CFO: Marty Lautner, Vice President Finance and Chief Financial Officer
CFO: Timothy Wilson, Vice President Finance and Chief Financial Officer
CMO: William Lester, M.D., Vice President Medical Affairs
CIO: LouAnn Hydor, Director Information Integrity Management
CHR: Tracy Murford, Director Human Resources
Web address: www.cardinalhill.org
**Control:** Other not–for–profit (including NFP Corporation) **Service:** Rehabilitation

**Staffed Beds:** 232 **Admissions:** 2881 **Census:** 102 **Outpatient Visits:** 51118 **Births:** 0 **Total Expense ($000):** 63756 **Payroll Expense ($000):** 35033 **Personnel:** 570

★ **CONTINUING CARE HOSPITAL (182002)**, 150 North Eagle Creek Drive, 5th Floor, Zip 40509–1805; tel. 859/967–5744, (Nonreporting) **A**10 **S** Catholic Health Initiatives, Englewood, CO
Primary Contact: Tonja Williams, MSN, R.N., President
CMO: Michael Miedler, M.D., Chief Medical Officer
CNO: Regina Masters, R.N., Director of Nursing
**Control:** Church–operated, Nongovernment, not–for profit **Service:** Long–Term Acute Care hospital

**Staffed Beds:** 45

☐ **EASTERN STATE HOSPITAL (184004)**, 627 West Fourth Street, Zip 40508–1294; tel. 859/246–7000, (Nonreporting) **A**1 3 5 9 10
Primary Contact: Shannon Ware, President and Chief Executive Officer
COO: Susan M. Griffith, Chief Operations Officer
CFO: Tambara Nalle, Chief Financial Officer
CMO: Scott A. Haas, M.D., Chief Medical Officer
CIO: Bud Stone, Director Information Systems
CHR: Jerry Kersey, Director Employee Relations
CNO: Kristan Mowder, Director Administration and Patient Care Services
Web address: www.bluegrass.org
**Control:** State–Government, nonfederal **Service:** Psychiatric

**Staffed Beds:** 197

**FEDERAL MEDICAL CENTER**, 3301 Leestown Road, Zip 40511–8799; tel. 859/255–6812, (Nonreporting)
Primary Contact: Stephen DeWalt, Warden
CFO: Mike Kinsel, Controller
CMO: Michael Growse, M.D., Clinical Director
**Control:** Department of Justice, Government, federal **Service:** Hospital unit of an institution (prison hospital, college infimary, etc.)

**Staffed Beds:** 22

☐ **RIDGE BEHAVIORAL HEALTH SYSTEM (184009)**, 3050 Rio Dosa Drive, Zip 40509–1540; tel. 859/269–2325, (Nonreporting) **A**1 3 5 9 10 **S** Universal Health Services, Inc., King of Prussia, PA
Primary Contact: Nina W. Eisner, Chief Executive Officer and Managing Director
CFO: Richard McDowell, Chief Financial Officer
CMO: Michael Rieser, M.D., Medical Director
CHR: Samantha Castle, Director Human Resources and Performance Improvement
CNO: Georgia Swank, Chief Nursing Officer
Web address: www.ridgebhs.com
**Control:** Corporation, Investor–owned, for–profit **Service:** Psychiatric

**Staffed Beds:** 110

⊠ **SAINT JOSEPH EAST (180143)**, 150 North Eagle Creek Drive, Zip 40509–1805; tel. 859/967–5000 **A**1 5 9 10 **F**3 8 12 13 15 17 18 20 22 24 26 28 29 30 31 40 47 49 50 60 68 70 72 73 74 75 76 77 78 79 81 82 85 86 89 90 93 107 108 111 115 118 119 120 121 122 123 126 128 129 142 146 147 148 **S** Catholic Health Initiatives, Englewood, CO
Primary Contact: Eric Gilliam, President
COO: Christine Mays, R.N., Chief Operating Officer and Chief Nurse Executive
CFO: Melinda S. Evans, Vice President Finance
CIO: Janie Fergus, Director and Chief Information Officer
CHR: Edward Carthew, Chief Human Resources Officer
Web address: www.sjhlex.org
**Control:** Church–operated, Nongovernment, not–for profit **Service:** General Medical and Surgical

**Staffed Beds:** 183 **Admissions:** 8006 **Census:** 83 **Outpatient Visits:** 107133 **Births:** 2403 **Total Expense ($000):** 132617 **Payroll Expense ($000):** 43038 **Personnel:** 725

⊠ **SAINT JOSEPH HOSPITAL (180010)**, One St. Joseph Drive, Zip 40504–3754; tel. 859/278–3436 **A**1 2 3 5 9 10 **F**1 3 8 11 12 15 17 18 19 20 22 24 25 26 27 28 29 30 31 34 35 37 40 41 42 45 47 49 50 51 54 55 56 57 58 59 62 64 65 66 67 68 70 74 77 78 79 81 82 83 84 85 86 87 89 90 92 93 94 96 97 107 110 111 114 115 116 117 118 119 120 121 123 126 127 129 130 132 135 141 144 146 147 148 **S** Catholic Health Initiatives, Englewood, CO
Primary Contact: John E. Smithhisler, President
COO: Christine Mays, R.N., Chief Operating Officer and Chief Nurse Executive
CFO: Melinda S. Evans, Vice President Finance
CIO: Janie Fergus, Director and Chief Information Officer
CHR: Edward Carthew, Chief Human Resources Officer
Web address: www.sjhlex.org
**Control:** Church–operated, Nongovernment, not–for profit **Service:** General Medical and Surgical

**Staffed Beds:** 298 **Admissions:** 16047 **Census:** 228 **Outpatient Visits:** 109659 **Births:** 0 **Total Expense ($000):** 293488 **Payroll Expense ($000):** 89519 **Personnel:** 1462

⊠ **SELECT SPECIALTY HOSPITAL–LEXINGTON (182003)**, 310 South Limestone Street, 3rd Floor, Zip 40508–3008; tel. 859/226–7096, (Nonreporting) **A**1 10 **S** Select Medical Corporation, Mechanicsburg, PA
Primary Contact: Mary Lou Guinle, FACHE, Chief Executive Officer
Web address: www.selectspecialtyhospitals.com/company/locations/lexington.aspx
**Control:** Corporation, Investor–owned, for–profit **Service:** Long–Term Acute Care hospital

**Staffed Beds:** 41

☐ **SHRINERS HOSPITALS FOR CHILDREN–LEXINGTON (183300)**, 1900 Richmond Road, Zip 40502–1298; tel. 859/266–2101, (Nonreporting) **A**1 3 5 9 10 **S** Shriners Hospitals for Children, Tampa, FL
Primary Contact: Tony Lewgood, Administrator
CFO: Robert Montgomery, Chief Financial Officer
CMO: Chester Tylkowski, M.D., Chief of Staff
CIO: David Brian, Director Information Services
Web address: www.shrinershospitalsforchildren.org/Hospitals/Locations/Lexington.aspx
**Control:** Other not–for–profit (including NFP Corporation) **Service:** Children's orthopedic

**Staffed Beds:** 50

★ **UK HEALTHCARE GOOD SAMARITAN HOSPITAL (180007)**, 310 South Limestone Street, Zip 40508–3008; tel. 859/226–7000 **A**3 5 9 **F**3 28 29 30 40 45 46 49 51 57 59 64 68 70 79 81 82 85 87 97 98 99 100 101 102 103 107 111 113 114 119 129 130 146 147 148 **P**6 **S** UK HealthCare, Lexington, KY
Primary Contact: Anna M. Smith, Chief Administrative Officer
COO: Mark Armstrong, Chief Operating Officer
CFO: Sergio L. Melgar, Vice President Health Affairs and Chief Financial Officer
CMO: Bernie Boulanger, M.D., Chief Medical Officer
CIO: Zed Day, Associate Vice President Information Technology
CHR: Kimberly P. Wilson, Associate Vice President
Web address: www.ukhealthcare.uky.edu/samaritan
**Control:** State–Government, nonfederal **Service:** General Medical and Surgical

**Staffed Beds:** 158 **Admissions:** 8281 **Census:** 113 **Outpatient Visits:** 61548 **Births:** 0 **Total Expense ($000):** 105519 **Payroll Expense ($000):** 34199 **Personnel:** 755

⊠ **UNIVERSITY OF KENTUCKY ALBERT B. CHANDLER HOSPITAL (180067)**, 800 Rose Street, Zip 40536–0293; tel. 859/323–5000, (Includes KENTUCKY CHILDREN'S HOSPITAL, N–100 – 800 Rose Street, tel. 859/257–1000) **A**1 2 3 5 8 9 10 **F**3 5 6 7 9 11 12 13 15 16 17 18 19 20 21 22 23 24 25 26 27 28 29 30 31 32 34 35 36 37 38 39 40 41 43 44 45 46 47 48 49 50 52 54 55 56 57 58 59 60 61 64 65 66 68 70 72 73 74 75 76 77 78 79 81 82 84 85 86 87 88 89 92 93 94 95 96 97 100 102 104 107 108 110 111 113 114 115 118 119 120 121 123 124 126 130 131 132 134 135 136 137 138 139 140 141 142 145 146 147 148 **P**6 **S** UK HealthCare, Lexington, KY
Primary Contact: Anna M. Smith, Chief Administrative Officer
CFO: Jay Sial, Chief Financial Officer
CIO: Tim Tarnowski, Chief Information Officer
CHR: Kimberly P. Wilson, Director Human Resources
Web address: www.ukhealthcare.uky.edu
**Control:** State–Government, nonfederal **Service:** General Medical and Surgical

**Staffed Beds:** 589 **Admissions:** 26189 **Census:** 448 **Outpatient Visits:** 889525 **Births:** 1762 **Total Expense ($000):** 803247 **Payroll Expense ($000):** 240702 **Personnel:** 5328

**UNIVERSITY OF KENTUCKY HOSPITAL** See University of Kentucky Albert B. Chandler Hospital

*Many Facility Codes have changed. Please refer to the AHA Guide Code Chart.*
© 2013 AHA Guide

⊠ **VETERANS AFFAIRS MEDICAL CENTER–LEXINGTON**, 1101 Veterans Drive, Zip 40502–2235; tel. 859/233–4511, (Nonreporting) **A**1 2 3 5 **S** Department of Veterans Affairs, Washington, DC
Primary Contact: DeWayne Hamlin, Director
CFO: Patricia Swisshelm, Acting Chief Fiscal Service
CMO: Joseph Pellecchia, M.D., Chief of Staff
CIO: Michael Gross, Chief Information Officer
CHR: Laura Faulkner, Chief Human Resource Management Service
Web address: www.lexington.va.gov/
**Control:** Veterans Affairs, Government, federal **Service:** General Medical and Surgical

**Staffed Beds:** 199

### LIBERTY—Casey County

☐ **CASEY COUNTY HOSPITAL (181309)**, 187 Wolford Avenue, Zip 42539–3278; tel. 606/787–6275, (Nonreporting) **A**1 9 10 18
Primary Contact: Rex A. Tungate, Administrator
**Control:** County–Government, nonfederal **Service:** General Medical and Surgical

**Staffed Beds:** 24

### LONDON—Laurel County

⊠ **SAINT JOSEPH – LONDON (180011)**, 310 East Ninth Street, Zip 40741–1299; tel. 606/330–6000 **A**1 9 10 19 **F**3 13 15 17 18 20 22 24 26 28 29 30 31 34 35 40 42 49 50 51 57 59 60 61 64 68 70 74 76 78 79 81 82 85 87 89 92 93 107 110 111 114 115 119 129 130 131 146 147 **S** Catholic Health Initiatives, Englewood, CO
Primary Contact: Greg D. Gerard, President
COO: Peggy Green, Chief Operating Officer and Chief Nursing Officer
CFO: Robert Brock, Vice President Finance and Business Development
CMO: John Abe, M.D., Chief of Staff
CIO: Debbie Mullins, Director
CHR: Kevin P. Richie, Senior Human Resources Business Partner
Web address: www.saintjosephhealthsystem.org
**Control:** Church–operated, Nongovernment, not–for profit **Service:** General Medical and Surgical

**Staffed Beds:** 110 **Admissions:** 7931 **Census:** 86 **Outpatient Visits:** 109186 **Births:** 1092 **Total Expense ($000):** 147656 **Payroll Expense ($000):** 47532 **Personnel:** 796

### LOUISA—Lawrence County

⊠ **THREE RIVERS MEDICAL CENTER (180128)**, Highway 644, Zip 41230–9632, Mailing Address: P.O. Box 769, Zip 41230–0769; tel. 606/638–9451 **A**1 9 10 20 **F**3 12 13 15 18 29 34 40 45 49 50 51 57 59 70 76 77 79 81 85 86 87 93 97 98 102 103 104 107 111 115 119 130 132 133 146 **S** Community Health Systems, Inc., Franklin, TN
Primary Contact: Greg Kiser, Chief Executive Officer
CFO: Adam Cruse, Chief Financial Officer
CHR: Pat Hart, Director Human Resources
Web address: www.threeriversmedicalcenter.com
**Control:** Corporation, Investor–owned, for–profit **Service:** General Medical and Surgical

**Staffed Beds:** 80 **Admissions:** 3704 **Census:** 34 **Outpatient Visits:** 41739 **Births:** 173 **Total Expense ($000):** 27572 **Personnel:** 305

### LOUISVILLE—Jefferson County

⊠ △ **BAPTIST HEALTH LOUISVILLE (180130)**, (Formerly Baptist Hospital East), 4000 Kresge Way, Zip 40207–4676; tel. 502/897–8100 **A**1 2 3 5 7 9 10 **F**3 5 8 11 12 13 15 17 18 20 22 24 26 28 29 30 31 33 34 36 37 38 40 41 44 45 46 47 48 49 50 51 53 54 56 57 58 59 60 61 62 64 68 70 72 74 75 76 78 79 81 82 83 84 85 86 87 89 90 93 97 98 100 101 102 103 104 105 107 108 110 111 114 115 116 117 118 119 120 121 123 124 126 129 130 131 132 134 135 145 146 147 148 **S** Baptist Health, Louisville, KY
Primary Contact: David L. Gray, FACHE, President
CFO: Jim Morris, Vice President Finance
CMO: Kenneth Anderson, M.D., Vice President and Chief Medical Officer
CIO: Shari Price, Director Information Services
CHR: Steven Rudolf, Vice President Human Resources
CNO: Karen Newman, Ed.D., Vice President and Chief Nursing Officer
Web address: www.baptisteast.com
**Control:** Other not–for–profit (including NFP Corporation) **Service:** General Medical and Surgical

**Staffed Beds:** 519 **Admissions:** 27071 **Census:** 367 **Outpatient Visits:** 235576 **Births:** 3061 **Total Expense ($000):** 449188 **Payroll Expense ($000):** 169407 **Personnel:** 2901

☐ **CENTRAL STATE HOSPITAL (184015)**, 10510 LaGrange Road, Zip 40223–1228; tel. 502/253–7000, (Nonreporting) **A**1 3 5 10
Primary Contact: Vital Shah, M.D., Director
CFO: Mark Reynolds, Controller
CMO: Vital Shah, M.D., Director
**Control:** State–Government, nonfederal **Service:** Psychiatric

**Staffed Beds:** 116

★ △ **FRAZIER REHAB INSTITUTE**, 220 Abraham Flexner Way, Zip 40202–1887; tel. 502/582–7400, (Data for 182 days) **A**3 5 7 9 **F**28 29 30 34 35 42 44 50 54 56 57 58 59 60 64 68 74 75 77 78 79 82 84 85 86 87 90 91 93 95 96 100 130 131 132 146 148 **P**6 **S** Catholic Health Initiatives, Englewood, CO
Primary Contact: Charles A. Peck, M.D., Interim President
COO: Randy L. Napier, Administrator
CFO: Ronald Farr, Senior Vice President and Chief Financial Officer
CMO: William P. Williamson, M.D., Medical Director
CHR: Lisa Burris, Manager Human Resources
Web address: www.frazierrehab.org
**Control:** Other not–for–profit (including NFP Corporation) **Service:** Rehabilitation

**Staffed Beds:** 79 **Admissions:** 867 **Census:** 67 **Outpatient Visits:** 52269 **Births:** 0 **Total Expense ($000):** 24770 **Payroll Expense ($000):** 9968 **Personnel:** 401

⊠ **JEWISH HOSPITAL (180040)**, 200 Abraham Flexner Way, Zip 40202–1886; tel. 502/587–4011, (Data for 182 days) **A**1 2 3 5 9 10 **F**1 3 8 11 14 15 17 18 20 22 24 26 28 29 30 31 34 35 36 37 40 42 43 44 45 46 47 48 49 50 53 54 56 57 58 59 60 61 64 67 68 70 74 75 76 78 79 80 81 82 84 85 87 89 92 97 98 100 107 108 110 111 112 114 115 116 117 118 119 121 123 124 126 130 131 132 135 136 137 138 139 140 141 142 145 146 **P**6 **S** Catholic Health Initiatives, Englewood, CO
Primary Contact: Charles A. Peck, M.D., Interim President
CFO: Ronald Farr, Chief Financial Officer
CMO: James P. Ketterhagen, M.D., Senior Vice President and Chief Medical Officer
CIO: Thomas Wittman, Chief Information Officer
CHR: Julie McGregor, Vice President and Chief People Officer
CNO: Cheryl Fugatte, Vice President and Chief Nursing Officer
Web address: www.jewishhospital.org
**Control:** Corporation, Investor–owned, for–profit **Service:** General Medical and Surgical

**Staffed Beds:** 387 **Admissions:** 9039 **Census:** 273 **Outpatient Visits:** 132056 **Births:** 0 **Total Expense ($000):** 218793 **Payroll Expense ($000):** 59559 **Personnel:** 1709

**KINDRED HOSPITAL LOUISVILLE AT JEWISH HOSPITAL** See Kindred Hospital–Louisville

⊠ **KINDRED HOSPITAL–LOUISVILLE (182001)**, 1313 Saint Anthony Place, Zip 40204–1740; tel. 502/587–7001, (Includes KINDRED HOSPITAL LOUISVILLE AT JEWISH HOSPITAL, 200 Abraham Flexner Way, 2nd Floor, Zip 40202; tel. 502/587–3999; David Johnson, Chief Executive Officer), (Total facility includes 47 beds in nursing home–type unit) **A**1 3 5 10 **F**1 3 29 45 64 70 81 107 119 128 130 148 **S** Kindred Healthcare, Louisville, KY
Primary Contact: Michael L. Moody, Market Chief Executive Officer
CFO: Debra Michalek, Chief Financial Officer
Web address: www.kindredlouisville.com/
**Control:** Corporation, Investor–owned, for–profit **Service:** Long–Term Acute Care hospital

**Staffed Beds:** 164 **Admissions:** 1007 **Census:** 139 **Outpatient Visits:** 3726 **Births:** 0 **Total Expense ($000):** 57200 **Payroll Expense ($000):** 20894 **Personnel:** 474

★ **KOSAIR CHILDREN'S HOSPITAL**, 231 East Chestnut Street, Zip 40202–1821; tel. 502/629–6000 **A**2 3 5 9 **F**3 8 11 19 21 23 25 27 29 30 31 32 34 35 38 39 40 41 42 43 44 45 50 54 57 58 59 64 65 68 72 74 75 78 79 81 82 84 85 86 87 88 89 92 93 96 98 99 100 101 102 107 108 111 114 119 129 130 132 134 136 137 138 143 146 **S** Norton Healthcare, Louisville, KY
Primary Contact: Thomas D. Kmetz, President
Web address: www.kosairchildrens.com/
**Control:** Other not–for–profit (including NFP Corporation) **Service:** Children's general

**Staffed Beds:** 271 **Admissions:** 10492 **Census:** 208 **Outpatient Visits:** 145510 **Births:** 0 **Total Expense ($000):** 295103 **Payroll Expense ($000):** 96511 **Personnel:** 1591

---

**Hospital, Medicare Provider Number, Address, Telephone, Approval, Facility, and Physician Codes, Health Care System**

★ American Hospital Association (AHA) membership
☐ The Joint Commission accreditation ◇ DNV Healthcare Inc. accreditation

◯ Healthcare Facilities Accreditation Program
△ Commission on Accreditation of Rehabilitation Facilities (CARF) accreditation

★ **NORTON AUDUBON HOSPITAL**, One Audubon Plaza Drive, Zip 40217–1300, Mailing Address: P.O. Box 17550, Zip 40217–0550; tel. 502/636–7111 **A**2 3 5 9 10 **F**3 5 11 15 17 18 20 22 24 26 29 30 31 34 35 37 40 45 46 47 48 49 50 56 57 59 64 68 70 74 75 78 79 81 82 85 86 87 107 108 110 111 112 114 115 118 119 129 130 132 146 147 148 **S** Norton Healthcare, Louisville, KY
Primary Contact: Steven MacLauchlan, President
CFO: Jonathan Presser, Vice President Finance and Operations
Web address: www.nortonhealthcare.com/NortonAudubonHospital
**Control:** Other not–for–profit (including NFP Corporation) **Service:** General Medical and Surgical

| Staffed Beds: 278 Admissions: 14409 Census: 198 Outpatient Visits: 133469 Births: 0 Total Expense ($000): 227671 Payroll Expense ($000): 77970 Personnel: 1299 |

★ **NORTON BROWNSBORO HOSPITAL**, 4960 Norton Healthcare Boulevard, Zip 40241–2831; tel. 502/446–8000 **A**9 10 **F**3 11 12 15 18 20 29 30 31 34 35 37 40 44 45 46 47 48 49 56 57 59 64 68 70 74 75 78 79 81 82 85 86 87 92 107 108 110 111 112 114 115 119 129 130 131 132 143 144 146 148 **S** Norton Healthcare, Louisville, KY
Primary Contact: John D. Harryman, President
CFO: Andy Strausbaugh, Vice President Finance and Operations
Web address: www.nortonhealthcare.com/nortonbrownsborohospital
**Control:** Other not–for–profit (including NFP Corporation) **Service:** General Medical and Surgical

| Staffed Beds: 103 Admissions: 5899 Census: 60 Outpatient Visits: 56840 Births: 0 Total Expense ($000): 116286 Payroll Expense ($000): 34481 Personnel: 641 |

**NORTON HEALTHCARE PAVILION** See Norton Hospital

⊠ **NORTON HOSPITAL (180088)**, 200 East Chestnut Street, Zip 40202–1800, Mailing Address: P.O. Box 35070, Zip 40232–5070; tel. 502/629–8000, (Includes NORTON HEALTHCARE PAVILION, 315 East Broadway, Zip 40202–1703; tel. 502/629–2000) **A**1 2 3 5 9 10 **F**1 3 4 11 12 13 15 16 17 18 20 22 24 26 28 29 30 31 34 35 36 38 39 40 43 44 45 46 49 50 51 53 55 56 57 59 64 67 68 70 72 73 74 75 76 78 79 80 81 82 84 85 86 87 88 90 92 93 96 98 100 101 102 107 108 110 111 114 116 117 118 119 126 128 130 132 146 147 148 **S** Norton Healthcare, Louisville, KY
Primary Contact: Kevin S. Wardell, President
CFO: Carl Amorose, Vice President Finance
Web address: www.nortonhealthcare.com/nortonhospital
**Control:** Other not–for–profit (including NFP Corporation) **Service:** General Medical and Surgical

| Staffed Beds: 370 Admissions: 16768 Census: 253 Outpatient Visits: 98394 Births: 2888 Total Expense ($000): 324242 Payroll Expense ($000): 102537 Personnel: 1638 |

★ **NORTON SUBURBAN HOSPITAL**, 4001 Dutchmans Lane, Zip 40207–4799; tel. 502/893–1000 **A**2 3 5 9 10 **F**3 11 12 13 15 18 20 29 30 31 34 35 40 44 45 47 49 50 56 57 59 64 68 70 72 73 74 75 76 78 79 81 82 85 86 87 107 108 110 111 114 115 118 119 120 121 123 124 126 130 132 146 147 **S** Norton Healthcare, Louisville, KY
Primary Contact: Charlotte Ipsan, President
CFO: Mark Kircher, Associate Vice President Finance
CMO: Steven Hester, M.D., Vice President Medical Affairs
CIO: Joseph DeVenuto, Vice President and Chief Information Officer
Web address: www.nortonhealthcare.com/nortonsuburbanhospital
**Control:** Other not–for–profit (including NFP Corporation) **Service:** General Medical and Surgical

| Staffed Beds: 359 Admissions: 14918 Census: 190 Outpatient Visits: 100503 Births: 5248 Total Expense ($000): 203791 Payroll Expense ($000): 72240 Personnel: 1253 |

★ **OUR LADY OF PEACE**, 2020 Newburg Road, Zip 40205–1879; tel. 502/479–4500, (Data for 182 days) **A**3 5 9 **F**5 29 30 34 35 53 59 68 98 99 100 101 104 105 106 130 132 143 146 **S** Catholic Health Initiatives, Englewood, CO
Primary Contact: Jennifer Nolan, President
COO: Martha S. Mather, Chief Operating Officer and Vice President
CFO: Beckie Kistler, Controller
CHR: Jan Ostbloom, Human Resources Consultant
CNO: Brad Lincks, R.N., Chief Nursing Officer/ Vice President
Web address: www.hopehasaplace.org
**Control:** Other not–for–profit (including NFP Corporation) **Service:** Psychiatric

| Staffed Beds: 261 Admissions: 2725 Census: 206 Outpatient Visits: 11105 Births: 0 Total Expense ($000): 27249 Payroll Expense ($000): 13187 Personnel: 561 |

⊠ **ROBLEY REX VETERANS AFFAIRS MEDICAL CENTER**, (Formerly Veterans Affairs Medical Center–Louisville), 800 Zorn Avenue, Zip 40206–1499; tel. 502/287–4000, (Nonreporting) **A**1 2 3 5 **S** Department of Veterans Affairs, Washington, DC
Primary Contact: Wayne L. Pfeffer, FACHE, Director
CFO: Barbara Roberts, Chief Financial Officer
CMO: Marylee Rothschild, M.D., Chief of Staff
CIO: Augustine Bittner, Chief Information Officer
CHR: Angela Dutton, Chief Human Resources Management Service
Web address: www.louisville.va.gov
**Control:** Veterans Affairs, Government, federal **Service:** General Medical and Surgical

| Staffed Beds: 116 |

★ **STS. MARY & ELIZABETH HOSPITAL**, 1850 Bluegrass Avenue, Zip 40215–1199; tel. 502/361–6000, (Data for 182 days) **A**3 5 9 **F**3 8 11 12 15 18 20 22 29 30 31 34 35 39 40 42 43 44 45 47 49 50 53 54 59 60 64 68 69 70 74 75 78 79 81 82 84 85 86 87 107 108 110 111 114 115 118 119 129 130 132 135 146 147 148 **P**6 **S** Catholic Health Initiatives, Englewood, CO
Primary Contact: Jennifer Nolan, President
COO: Kenneth Johnson, Vice President
CFO: Elaine Hayes, Controller
CMO: Val Slayton, M.D., Vice President Medical Affairs
CHR: Julie McGregor, Director Human Resources
Web address: www.jhsmh.org
**Control:** Other not–for–profit (including NFP Corporation) **Service:** General Medical and Surgical

| Staffed Beds: 163 Admissions: 4842 Census: 118 Outpatient Visits: 75549 Births: 0 Total Expense ($000): 57687 Payroll Expense ($000): 23342 Personnel: 752 |

**TEN BROECK DUPONT** See The Brook at Dupont

☐ **THE BROOK AT DUPONT (184007)**, 1405 Browns Lane, Zip 40207–4608; tel. 502/896–0495, (Nonreporting) **A**1 9 10 **S** Universal Health Services, Inc., King of Prussia, PA
Primary Contact: Paul Andrews, Chief Executive Officer
Web address: www.thebrookhospitals.com/
**Control:** Corporation, Investor–owned, for–profit **Service:** Psychiatric

| Staffed Beds: 66 |

☐ **THE BROOK HOSPITAL – KMI (184008)**, 8521 Old LaGrange Road, Zip 40242–3800; tel. 502/426–6380, (Nonreporting) **A**1 5 9 10 **S** Universal Health Services, Inc., King of Prussia, PA
Primary Contact: Paul Andrews, Chief Executive Officer
COO: Kim Peabody, Chief Operating Officer
CFO: Dennis Collins, Chief Financial Officer
CMO: Timothy Burke, M.D., Medical Director
CIO: Joel Roy, Manager Information Systems
CHR: Christina Taylor, Director Human Resources
Web address: www.thebrookhospitals.com
**Control:** Corporation, Investor–owned, for–profit **Service:** Psychiatric

| Staffed Beds: 110 |

⊠ **UNIVERSITY OF LOUISVILLE HOSPITAL (180141)**, 530 South Jackson Street, Zip 40202–3611; tel. 502/562–3000 **A**1 2 3 5 8 9 10 **F**3 13 15 16 17 18 20 22 24 26 29 30 31 34 35 39 40 43 45 46 47 49 50 51 54 56 57 58 59 60 61 64 65 68 70 71 72 73 74 75 76 78 79 80 81 82 84 85 86 87 92 93 94 98 100 102 104 107 108 110 111 114 115 117 118 119 120 121 123 124 126 130 132 135 136 144 146 148
Primary Contact: Kenneth P. Marshall, Interim President
COO: Kenneth P. Marshall, Senior Vice President and Chief Operating Officer
CMO: Mark P. Pfeifer, M.D., Senior Vice President and Chief Medical Officer
CIO: Troy May, Chief Information Officer
CHR: Gary Bensing, Vice President Human Resources
CNO: Mary Jane Adams, R.N., Senior Vice President and Chief Nursing Officer
Web address: www.ulh.org
**Control:** Other not–for–profit (including NFP Corporation) **Service:** General Medical and Surgical

| Staffed Beds: 329 Admissions: 17148 Census: 259 Outpatient Visits: 197218 Births: 1730 Total Expense ($000): 445156 Payroll Expense ($000): 144674 Personnel: 3015 |

**VETERANS AFFAIRS MEDICAL CENTER–LOUISVILLE** See Robley Rex Veterans Affairs Medical Center

*Many Facility Codes have changed. Please refer to the AHA Guide Code Chart.*

© 2013 AHA Guide

## MADISONVILLE—Hopkins County

☒ **BAPTIST HEALTH MADISONVILLE (180093)**, (Formerly Regional Medical Center of Hopkins County), 900 Hospital Drive, Zip 42431–1694; tel. 270/825–5100, (Total facility includes 20 beds in nursing home–type unit) **A**1 2 3 5 9 10 **F**3 8 11 13 14 18 20 22 24 26 28 29 30 31 34 35 40 44 49 51 53 57 58 59.60 62 63 64 68 70 73 76 78 79 81 85 87 88 89 90 93 96 107 108 111 114 117 118 119 120 121 123 128 129 130 131 132 146 148 **S** Baptist Health, Louisville, KY
Primary Contact: E. Berton Whitaker, FACHE, President
CFO: C. Thomas Moore, Chief Financial Officer
CIO: Sheila Bruce, Director Information System
CHR: David Lang, Vice President Human Resources
Web address: www.troverfoundation.org
**Control:** Other not–for–profit (including NFP Corporation) **Service:** General Medical and Surgical

**Staffed Beds:** 198 **Admissions:** 6270 **Census:** 76 **Outpatient Visits:** 130251 **Births:** 512 **Total Expense ($000):** 99943 **Payroll Expense ($000):** 39735 **Personnel:** 1261

## MANCHESTER—Clay County

☒ ○ **MANCHESTER MEMORIAL HOSPITAL (180043)**, 210 Marie Langdon Drive, Zip 40962–6388; tel. 606/598–5104 **A**1 9 10 11 **F**3 13 15 29 30 34 35 40 45 50 57 59 62 65 68 70 71 75 76 77 81 85 86 87 89 93 97 107 108 110 111 119 127 130 131 135 146 147 **S** Adventist Health System Sunbelt Health Care Corporation, Altamonte Springs, FL
Primary Contact: Erika Skula, President and Chief Executive Officer
CFO: Daniel T. Walker, Vice President Finance and Chief Financial Officer
CMO: Neeraj Mahboob, M.D., Chief Medical Officer
CHR: Joe Skula, Director Human Resources
Web address: www.manchestermemorial.org
**Control:** Church–operated, Nongovernment, not–for profit **Service:** General Medical and Surgical

**Staffed Beds:** 63 **Admissions:** 2775 **Census:** 23 **Outpatient Visits:** 34511 **Births:** 94 **Total Expense ($000):** 51506 **Payroll Expense ($000):** 23070 **Personnel:** 305

## MARION—Crittenden County

☒ **CRITTENDEN COUNTY HOSPITAL (180095)**, 520 West Gum Street, Zip 42064–1516, Mailing Address: P.O. Box 386, Zip 42064–0386; tel. 270/965–5281 **A**1 9 10 20 **F**3 7 11 15 28 29 30 34 35 40 45 50 57 59 62 64 68 70 75 77 81 85 86 87 93 97 107 108 111 119 127 128 129 130 133 146 **P**6
Primary Contact: Jim Christensen, Chief Executive Officer
COO: Robin Curnel, Chief Operating Officer and Chief Nursing Officer
CFO: Tom Hales, CPA, Chief Financial Officer
CMO: Steven Burkhart, M.D., Chief Medical Officer
CIO: Reese Baker, Director Information Systems
CHR: Jan Gregory, Chief of Human Resources
CNO: Robin Curnel, Chief Operating Officer and Chief Nursing Officer
Web address: www.crittenden–health.org
**Control:** Other not–for–profit (including NFP Corporation) **Service:** General Medical and Surgical

**Staffed Beds:** 48 **Admissions:** 1432 **Census:** 17 **Outpatient Visits:** 14853 **Births:** 0 **Total Expense ($000):** 16678 **Payroll Expense ($000):** 8171 **Personnel:** 174

## MARTIN—Floyd County

☒ **SAINT JOSEPH – MARTIN (181305)**, 11203 Main Street, Zip 41649; tel. 606/285–6400 **A**1 9 10 18 **F**3 15 18 28 35 40 56 81 104 111 114 119 127 130 **S** Catholic Health Initiatives, Englewood, CO
Primary Contact: Kathy Stumbo, President
CFO: Robert Brock, Vice President Finance
CMO: John Triplett, D.O., President Medical Staff
CIO: Chris Dye, Director Information Systems
Web address: www.saintjosephmartin.org
**Control:** Church–operated, Nongovernment, not–for profit **Service:** General Medical and Surgical

**Staffed Beds:** 25 **Admissions:** 843 **Census:** 11 **Outpatient Visits:** 29112 **Births:** 0 **Total Expense ($000):** 19813 **Payroll Expense ($000):** 7241 **Personnel:** 136

## MAYFIELD—Graves County

☒ **JACKSON PURCHASE MEDICAL CENTER (180116)**, 1099 Medical Center Circle, Zip 42066–1159; tel. 270/251–4100 **A**1 9 10 19 **F**3 11 12 13 15 18 22 28 29 30 31 34 35 37 40 43 46 47 48 49 51 57 59 64 68 74 75 76 77 79 80 81 85 87 93 97 107 110 111 115 117 119 129 131 132 133 135 143 146 147 148 **P**7 **S** LifePoint Hospitals, Inc., Brentwood, TN
Primary Contact: David Anderson, Chief Executive Officer
COO: Matt Tavenner, Assistant Administrator
CFO: Greg Cook, Chief Financial Officer
CMO: David Zetter, M.D., Chief of Staff
CIO: Tracy Watt, Director Information Systems
CHR: Tressa B. Hargrove, Director Human Resources
Web address: www.jacksonpurchase.com
**Control:** Corporation, Investor–owned, for–profit **Service:** General Medical and Surgical

**Staffed Beds:** 106 **Admissions:** 3343 **Census:** 42 **Outpatient Visits:** 66831 **Births:** 117 **Total Expense ($000):** 52032 **Payroll Expense ($000):** 23447 **Personnel:** 534

## MAYSVILLE—Mason County

☒ **MEADOWVIEW REGIONAL MEDICAL CENTER (180019)**, 989 Medical Park Drive, Zip 41056–8750; tel. 606/759–5311, (Nonreporting) **A**1 9 10 **S** LifePoint Hospitals, Inc., Brentwood, TN
Primary Contact: Robert Parker, Chief Executive Officer
CFO: Clayton Kolodziejczyk, Chief Financial Officer
CMO: Eric Lohman, M.D., Chief of Staff
CHR: Diana Kennedy, Director Human Resources
Web address: www.meadowviewregional.com
**Control:** Corporation, Investor–owned, for–profit **Service:** General Medical and Surgical

**Staffed Beds:** 101

## MCDOWELL—Floyd County

☐ **MCDOWELL ARH HOSPITAL (181331)**, Route 122, Zip 41647, Mailing Address: P.O. Box 247, Zip 41647–0247; tel. 606/377–3400 **A**1 9 10 18 **F**3 11 15 29 30 34 35 40 43 50 57 59 62 64 65 70 73 75 77 81 82 86 87 89 90 93 97 98 107 111 114 119 127 130 133 146 **P**6 **S** Appalachian Regional Healthcare, Inc., Lexington, KY
Primary Contact: Russell Barker, Community Chief Executive Officer
COO: Russell Barker, Community Chief Executive Officer
CFO: Joseph Grossman, Chief Financial Officer
CMO: Mary A. Hall, Chief Medical Staff
CIO: Jeff Brady, Director Information Systems
CHR: Stephanie Owens, Manager Human Resources
Web address: www.arh.org
**Control:** Other not–for–profit (including NFP Corporation) **Service:** General Medical and Surgical

**Staffed Beds:** 25 **Admissions:** 838 **Census:** 8 **Outpatient Visits:** 37210 **Births:** 0 **Total Expense ($000):** 15129 **Payroll Expense ($000):** 5513 **Personnel:** 109

## MIDDLESBORO—Bell County

☐ **MIDDLESBORO ARH HOSPITAL (180020)**, 3600 West Cumberland Avenue, Zip 40965–2614, Mailing Address: P.O. Box 340, Zip 40965–0340; tel. 606/242–1100 **A**1 9 10 **F**3 11 13 15 17 29 30 34 35 39 40 50 57 59 62 64 70 75 76 77 79 81 85 86 87 89 90 93 97 107 108 111 114 118 119 127 130 133 146 147 148 **P**6 **S** Appalachian Regional Healthcare, Inc., Lexington, KY
Primary Contact: Michael Slusher, Community Chief Executive Officer
CFO: Jeremy Hall, Assistant Administrator and Chief Financial Officer
CMO: Rogelio Uy, M.D., Chief of Staff
CIO: Lisa Dooley, Health Information Officer
CHR: Ashley Kelly, Manager Human Resources
Web address: www.arh.org/middlesboro
**Control:** Other not–for–profit (including NFP Corporation) **Service:** General Medical and Surgical

**Staffed Beds:** 96 **Admissions:** 2922 **Census:** 30 **Outpatient Visits:** 57728 **Births:** 336 **Total Expense ($000):** 37429 **Payroll Expense ($000):** 10579 **Personnel:** 235

---

**Hospital, Medicare Provider Number, Address, Telephone, Approval, Facility, and Physician Codes, Health Care System**

★ American Hospital Association (AHA) membership
☐ The Joint Commission accreditation
◇ DNV Healthcare Inc. accreditation
○ Healthcare Facilities Accreditation Program
△ Commission on Accreditation of Rehabilitation Facilities (CARF) accreditation

## MONTICELLO—Wayne County

**WAYNE COUNTY HOSPITAL (181321)**, 166 Hospital Street, Zip 42633–2416; tel. 606/348–9343 **A**9 10 18 **F**3 11 15 29 30 40 47 63 64 81 107 108 110 115 119 127 133 135 146 148
Primary Contact: Joseph Murrell, Chief Executive Officer
CFO: Anne Sawyer, Chief Financial Officer
CMO: Cory Ryan, M.D., Chief of Staff
CIO: Angela Griffin, Privacy Officer
CHR: Mollie Dick, Coordinator Human Resources
Web address: www.waynehospital.org
**Control:** State–Government, nonfederal **Service:** General Medical and Surgical

**Staffed Beds:** 25 **Admissions:** 906 **Census:** 11 **Outpatient Visits:** 25461 **Births:** 1 **Total Expense ($000):** 12997 **Payroll Expense ($000):** 5281 **Personnel:** 156

## MOREHEAD—Rowan County

✠ **ST. CLAIRE REGIONAL MEDICAL CENTER (180018)**, 222 Medical Circle, Zip 40351–1179; tel. 606/783–6500, (Total facility includes 10 beds in nursing home–type unit) **A**1 2 3 5 9 10 **F**3 5 11 13 15 18 20 22 28 29 30 31 34 35 38 39 40 45 48 49 50 51 54 56 57 58 59 60 61 62 63 64 65 68 70 74 75 76 77 78 79 81 82 84 85 86 87 89 90 93 97 98 99 100 101 102 103 104 107 108 111 115 118 119 128 129 130 132 135 146 147 148 **P**6
Primary Contact: Mark J. Neff, FACHE, President and Chief Executive Officer
CFO: G.R. Sonny Jones, Vice President Finance and Chief Financial Officer
CMO: Will L. Melahn, M.D., Vice President Medical Affairs and Chief Medical Officer
CIO: Randy McCleese, Vice President Information Services and Chief Information Officer
CHR: Travis A. Bailey, Vice President Administration
CNO: Lerae Wilson, R.N., Vice President Patient Services and Chief Nursing Officer
Web address: www.st-claire.org
**Control:** Church–operated, Nongovernment, not–for profit **Service:** General Medical and Surgical

**Staffed Beds:** 133 **Admissions:** 5343 **Census:** 57 **Outpatient Visits:** 209417 **Births:** 398 **Total Expense ($000):** 127358 **Payroll Expense ($000):** 64379 **Personnel:** 1070

## MORGANFIELD—Union County

✠ **METHODIST HOSPITAL UNION COUNTY (181306)**, 4604 Highway 60 West, Zip 42437–9570; tel. 270/389–5000 **A**1 9 10 18 **F**3 7 11 15 29 30 34 40 45 53 57 64 75 77 81 85 93 107 114 119 130 133 135 146
Primary Contact: Patrick Donahue, Administrator
CFO: Gregory P. Hebbeler, Chief Financial Officer
CMO: John Holeman, M.D., Chief of Staff
CNO: Peggy F. Creighton, R.N., Director of Nursing Services
Web address: www.methodisthospitaluc.net
**Control:** Church–operated, Nongovernment, not–for profit **Service:** General Medical and Surgical

**Staffed Beds:** 25 **Admissions:** 835 **Census:** 13 **Outpatient Visits:** 23393 **Births:** 0 **Total Expense ($000):** 16989 **Payroll Expense ($000):** 5597 **Personnel:** 136

## MOUNT STERLING—Montgomery County

✠ **SAINT JOSEPH MOUNT STERLING (180064)**, 50 Sterling Avenue, Zip 40353–1158, Mailing Address: P.O. Box 7, Zip 40353–0007; tel. 859/497–5000 **A**1 5 9 10 **F**3 13 15 17 28 29 34 35 40 45 46 57 59 64 70 74 75 76 77 78 79 81 86 87 93 107 108 114 119 129 130 132 133 135 146 147 148 **S** Catholic Health Initiatives, Englewood, CO
Primary Contact: Benny Nolen, President
CFO: Janelle Pugh, Vice President Finance and Operations
CMO: James Rollins, M.D., President Medical Staff
CIO: Jeff Ryder, Director Information Systems
CHR: Cindy Clark, Human Resource Consultant
Web address: www.sjhlex.org
**Control:** Church–operated, Nongovernment, not–for profit **Service:** General Medical and Surgical

**Staffed Beds:** 42 **Admissions:** 2018 **Census:** 23 **Outpatient Visits:** 64524 **Births:** 273 **Total Expense ($000):** 40935 **Payroll Expense ($000):** 12229 **Personnel:** 263

## MOUNT VERNON—Rockcastle County

✠ **ROCKCASTLE REGIONAL HOSPITAL AND RESPIRATORY CARE CENTER (180115)**, 145 Newcomb Avenue, Zip 40456–2728, Mailing Address: P.O. Box 1310, Zip 40456–1310; tel. 606/256–2195, (Nonreporting) **A**1 9 10
Primary Contact: Stephen A. Estes, Chief Executive Officer
CFO: Charles Black, Jr., Chief Financial Officer
CMO: Jon A. Arvin, M.D., Chief Medical Officer
CIO: Maleigha Amyx, Chief Information Officer
CHR: Carmen Poynter, Director Human Resources
CNO: Cynthia Burton, R.N., Chief Nursing Officer
Web address: www.rockcastleregional.org
**Control:** Other not–for–profit (including NFP Corporation) **Service:** General Medical and Surgical

**Staffed Beds:** 119

## MURRAY—Calloway County

✠ **MURRAY–CALLOWAY COUNTY HOSPITAL (180027)**, 803 Poplar Street, Zip 42071–2432; tel. 270/762–1100, (Total facility includes 180 beds in nursing home–type unit) **A**1 2 9 10 19 **F**2 3 7 11 12 13 14 15 18 20 26 28 29 30 31 34 35 40 45 47 48 49 50 51 53 59 62 63 66 68 70 74 75 76 77 78 79 81 82 85 87 90 92 93 97 98 104 107 108 111 114 115 119 121 128 129 130 132 144 146 147 **P**5
Primary Contact: Colonel Jerome Penner, Chief Executive Officer
CFO: Vicki Parks, Vice President
CMO: Robert Tucker, M.D., Chief Medical Officer
CIO: Regina Davison, Director Information Systems
CHR: John R. Wilson, Vice President, Human Resources
CNO: Lisa Ray, R.N., Vice President, Patient Care Services
Web address: www.murrayhospital.org
**Control:** City–County, Government, nonfederal **Service:** General Medical and Surgical

**Staffed Beds:** 285 **Admissions:** 4884 **Census:** 232 **Outpatient Visits:** 112168 **Births:** 611 **Total Expense ($000):** 118998 **Payroll Expense ($000):** 47053 **Personnel:** 1103

## OWENSBORO—Daviess County

✠ △ **OWENSBORO HEALTH REGIONAL HOSPITAL (180038)**, (Formerly Owensboro Medical Health System), 1201 Pleasant Valley Road, Zip 42303–3258; tel. 270/412–2000, (Includes HEALTHPARK, 1006 Ford Avenue, Zip 42301, Mailing Address: P.O. Box 2839, Zip 42302; tel. 270/688–5433), (Total facility includes 30 beds in nursing home–type unit) **A**1 2 5 7 9 10 **F**3 5 11 12 13 15 17 18 20 22 24 26 28 29 30 31 32 34 35 40 45 46 49 53 54 56 57 58 59 61 62 63 64 65 66 70 72 74 75 76 77 78 79 81 82 84 85 86 87 89 90 91 92 93 97 98 100 101 102 103 104 105 107 108 110 111 114 115 116 117 118 119 120 121 123 124 126 128 129 130 131 132 135 144 145 146 147 148 **P**6 8
Primary Contact: Jeffrey B. Barber, Dr.PH, FACHE, President and Chief Executive Officer
COO: Greg Strahan, Chief Operating Officer
CFO: John Hackbarth, CPA, Senior Vice President Finance and Chief Financial Officer
CMO: Wathen Medley, M.D., Chief Medical Officer
CHR: Mia Suter, Chief Administration Officer
Web address: www.omhs.org
**Control:** Other not–for–profit (including NFP Corporation) **Service:** General Medical and Surgical

**Staffed Beds:** 372 **Admissions:** 18055 **Census:** 230 **Outpatient Visits:** 538380 **Births:** 1843 **Total Expense ($000):** 360342 **Payroll Expense ($000):** 120064 **Personnel:** 2577

**RIVERVALLEY BEHAVIORAL HEALTH HOSPITAL (184013)**, 1000 Industrial Drive, Zip 42301–8715; tel. 270/689–6500 **A**9 10 **F**29 59 98 99 100 101 102 104 105 130 **P**6
Primary Contact: Gayle DiCesare, President and Chief Executive Officer
COO: Michelle Parks, Administrator
CFO: J. Michael Mountain, Chief Financial Officer
CMO: David Harmon, D.O., Vice President Medical Services
CIO: Travis Taggart, Director Information Technology
CHR: Cathryn Gaddis, Director Human Resources
Web address: www.rvbh.com
**Control:** Other not–for–profit (including NFP Corporation) **Service:** Children's hospital psychiatric

**Staffed Beds:** 80 **Admissions:** 614 **Census:** 28 **Outpatient Visits:** 0 **Births:** 0 **Total Expense ($000):** 6021 **Payroll Expense ($000):** 3176 **Personnel:** 56

## OWENTON—Owen County

★ **NEW HORIZONS HEALTH SYSTEMS (181312)**, 330 Roland Avenue, Zip 40359–1502; tel. 502/484–3663, (Nonreporting) **A**9 10 18
Primary Contact: Bernard T. Poe, Administrator
COO: Bernard T. Poe, Administrator
CFO: Roger Williams, Chief Financial Officer
CMO: Larry C. Johnson, M.D., Medical Director Rural Health Clinic
CIO: Edward Seale, Chief Information Officer
CHR: Kelly Perkins, Director Human Resources
Web address: www.newhorizonsmedicalcenter.com
**Control:** Other not–for–profit (including NFP Corporation) **Service:** General Medical and Surgical

**Staffed Beds:** 25

*Many Facility Codes have changed. Please refer to the AHA Guide Code Chart.*
© 2013 AHA Guide

## PADUCAH—Mccracken County

⊠ **BAPTIST HEALTH PADUCAH (180104)**, (Formerly Western Baptist Hospital), 2501 Kentucky Avenue, Zip 42003–3200; tel. 270/575–2100, (Total facility includes 24 beds in nursing home–type unit) **A**1 2 9 10 19 **F**13 15 17 18 20 22 24 28 29 30 31 34 35 40 45 46 57 58 59 64 70 72 73 74 75 76 77 78 79 81 84 85 86 87 89 93 97 107 108 110 111 114 115 117 119 121 126 128 129 130 131 132 135 145 146 147 **P**6 8 **S** Baptist Health, Louisville, KY
Primary Contact: Larry O. Barton, FACHE, President
COO: Scott T. Ware, Chief Operating Officer
CFO: Jim Carmain, Vice President Financial and Information Services
CMO: Bradley W. Housman, M.D., Chief Medical Officer
CIO: Mike Cromika, Director Information Services
CHR: Donald L. Brown, Director Human Resources
Web address: www.westernbaptist.com
**Control:** Other not–for–profit (including NFP Corporation) **Service:** General Medical and Surgical

**Staffed Beds:** 320 **Admissions:** 14748 **Census:** 186 **Outpatient Visits:** 143141 **Births:** 1368 **Total Expense ($000):** 238830 **Payroll Expense ($000):** 77371 **Personnel:** 1615

⊠ △ **LOURDES HOSPITAL (180102)**, 1530 Lone Oak Road, Zip 42003–7900, Mailing Address: P.O. Box 7100, Zip 42002–7100; tel. 270/444–2444, (Total facility includes 20 beds in nursing home–type unit) **A**1 7 9 10 19 **F**7 8 11 12 13 15 17 18 20 22 24 26 28 29 30 31 32 34 35 40 42 45 46 54 57 59 60 62 63 64 66 68 70 74 75 76 77 78 79 81 82 83 84 85 87 90 93 96 97 98 100 101 102 103 105 107 110 111 114 115 117 119 127 128 129 130 131 132 135 136 141 143 146 147 148 **P**3 6 **S** Catholic Health Partners, Cincinnati, OH
Primary Contact: Steven Grinnell, President and Chief Executive Officer
CFO: Mark Thompson, Vice President Finance and Chief Financial Officer
CHR: Kim Lindsey, Chief Human Resources Officer
Web address: www.lourdes–pad.org
**Control:** Church–operated, Nongovernment, not–for profit **Service:** General Medical and Surgical

**Staffed Beds:** 280 **Admissions:** 11614 **Census:** 154 **Outpatient Visits:** 235033 **Births:** 289 **Total Expense ($000):** 195036 **Payroll Expense ($000):** 78395

## PAINTSVILLE—Johnson County

☐ **PAUL B. HALL REGIONAL MEDICAL CENTER (180078)**, 625 James S. Trimble Boulevard, Zip 41240–0000; tel. 606/789–3511, (Nonreporting) **A**1 9 10 **S** Health Management Associates, Naples, FL
Primary Contact: Deborah Trimble, R.N., Chief Executive Officer
CFO: Pattie Major, Chief Financial Officer
CMO: F. K. Belhasen, M.D., Medical Director
CHR: Carla J. Stapleton, Director Human Resources
Web address: www.pbhrmc.com
**Control:** Corporation, Investor–owned, for–profit **Service:** General Medical and Surgical

**Staffed Beds:** 72

## PARIS—Bourbon County

⊠ **BOURBON COMMUNITY HOSPITAL (180046)**, 9 Linville Drive, Zip 40361–2196; tel. 859/987–3600 **A**1 9 10 **F**1 3 15 28 29 34 35 38 39 40 44 49 50 51 56 57 59 64 67 68 70 74 75 79 80 81 86 87 93 98 99 100 101 102 103 107 108 110 111 114 119 129 130 133 146 148 **P**7 **S** LifePoint Hospitals, Inc., Brentwood, TN
Primary Contact: Joseph G. Koch, Chief Executive Officer
COO: Donna Davis, Chief Nursing Officer
CFO: Michael Snedegar, Chief Financial Officer
CMO: Hunter Housman, M.D., Chief Medical Officer
CIO: Phil Osborne, Director Information Technology
CHR: Roger K. Davis, Director Human Resources
CNO: Brian Springate, Chief Nursing Officer
Web address: www.bourbonhospital.com
**Control:** Corporation, Investor–owned, for–profit **Service:** General Medical and Surgical

**Staffed Beds:** 58 **Admissions:** 1861 **Census:** 25 **Outpatient Visits:** 26936 **Births:** 0 **Total Expense ($000):** 18925 **Payroll Expense ($000):** 10138 **Personnel:** 175

## PIKEVILLE—Pike County

☐ **PIKEVILLE MEDICAL CENTER (180044)**, 911 Bypass Road, Zip 41501–1689; tel. 606/218–3500 **A**1 2 9 10 13 **F**3 11 12 13 15 18 20 22 24 26 28 29 30 31 34 35 39 40 45 49 50 51 57 59 60 61 62 64 66 68 69 70 72 74 75 76 77 78 79 81 82 84 85 86 87 89 90 93 95 96 97 107 108 110 111 115 116 117 118 119 121 123 124 127 129 130 131 132 135 146 147 148 **P**6
Primary Contact: Walter E. May, President and Chief Executive Officer
COO: Juanita Deskins, Chief Operating Officer
CFO: Michael Hagy, Chief Financial Officer
CMO: William Johnson, M.D., Chief Medical Director
CIO: Bernie Galla, Director Information Services
CNO: Estella Clark, Chief Nursing Officer
Web address: www.pikevillehospital.org
**Control:** Other not–for–profit (including NFP Corporation) **Service:** General Medical and Surgical

**Staffed Beds:** 243 **Admissions:** 11129 **Census:** 161 **Outpatient Visits:** 403107 **Births:** 1043 **Total Expense ($000):** 324690 **Payroll Expense ($000):** 133553 **Personnel:** 2151

## PINEVILLE—Bell County

○ **PINEVILLE COMMUNITY HOSPITAL ASSOCIATION (180021)**, 850 Riverview Avenue, Zip 40977–1452; tel. 606/337–3051, (Nonreporting) **A**9 10 11
Primary Contact: J. Milton Brooks, III, Administrator
CFO: Colan Kelly, Chief Financial Officer
CIO: David Hall, Chief Information Officer
CHR: Greg Nunnelley, Director Human Resources
Web address: www.pinevillehospital.com
**Control:** Other not–for–profit (including NFP Corporation) **Service:** General Medical and Surgical

**Staffed Beds:** 150

## PRESTONSBURG—Floyd County

⊠ ◇ **HIGHLANDS REGIONAL MEDICAL CENTER (180005)**, 5000 Kentucky Route 321, Zip 41653–1273, Mailing Address: P.O. Box 668, Zip 41653–0668; tel. 606/886–8511, (Nonreporting) **A**1 2 5 9 10 19 21
Primary Contact: Harold C. Warman, Jr., FACHE, President and Chief Executive Officer
COO: Chris Hoffman, Chief Operating Officer
CFO: Jack Blackwell, Chief Financial Officer
CIO: J. D. Jackson, Chief Information Officer
CHR: Susan Renee' Ellis, R.N., Vice President of Human Resources
CNO: Terresa O. Booher, Vice President of Patient Care Services
Web address: www.hrmc.org
**Control:** Other not–for–profit (including NFP Corporation) **Service:** General Medical and Surgical

**Staffed Beds:** 145

## PRINCETON—Caldwell County

⊠ **CALDWELL MEDICAL CENTER (181322)**, 100 Medical Center Drive, Zip 42445–2430, Mailing Address: P.O. Box 410, Zip 42445–0410; tel. 270/365–0300 **A**1 9 10 18 **F**11 15 28 29 34 35 40 57 59 62 68 77 81 85 107 108 111 118 119 129 133 135 146 **S** QHR, Brentwood, TN
Primary Contact: Charles D. Lovell, Jr., FACHE, President and Chief Executive Officer
CFO: Shane Whittington, Chief Financial Officer
CHR: Chad A. Walker, Director Human Resources
CNO: Douglas James, Chief Nursing Officer
Web address: www.caldwellhosp.org
**Control:** Other not–for–profit (including NFP Corporation) **Service:** General Medical and Surgical

**Staffed Beds:** 25 **Admissions:** 625 **Census:** 6 **Outpatient Visits:** 30191 **Births:** 0 **Total Expense ($000):** 19634 **Payroll Expense ($000):** 5802 **Personnel:** 140

## RADCLIFF—Hardin County

☐ **LINCOLN TRAIL BEHAVIORAL HEALTH SYSTEM (184012)**, 3909 South Wilson Road, Zip 40160–8944, Mailing Address: P.O. Box 369, Zip 40159–0369; tel. 270/351–9444, (Nonreporting) **A**1 9 10 **S** Universal Health Services, Inc., King of Prussia, PA
Primary Contact: Charles L. Webb, Jr., Chief Executive Officer
CFO: Debbie Ditto, CPA, Controller
CMO: Muhammad W. Sajid, M.D., Medical Director
CHR: Charlotte C. Davis, Director Human Resources
Web address: www.lincolnbehavioral.com
**Control:** Corporation, Investor–owned, for–profit **Service:** Psychiatric

**Staffed Beds:** 67

---

**Hospital, Medicare Provider Number, Address, Telephone, Approval, Facility, and Physician Codes, Health Care System**

★ American Hospital Association (AHA) membership
☐ The Joint Commission accreditation
◇ DNV Healthcare Inc. accreditation
○ Healthcare Facilities Accreditation Program
△ Commission on Accreditation of Rehabilitation Facilities (CARF) accreditation

## RICHMOND—Madison County

★ ○ **BAPTIST HEALTH RICHMOND (180049)**, (Formerly Pattie A. Clay Regional Medical Center), 801 Eastern Bypass, Zip 40475–2405, Mailing Address: P.O. Box 1600, Zip 40476–2603; tel. 859/623–3131 **A**9 10 11 19 **F**3 11 13 18 20 28 29 30 34 35 40 46 48 49 50 51 57 59 64 68 70 75 76 77 79 81 84 85 87 89 91 92 93 107 108 110 111 114 118 119 124 129 130 132 133 144 146 147 148 **S** Baptist Health, Louisville, KY
Primary Contact: Todd Jones, President
CFO: Chris McClurg, Chief Financial Officer
CMO: Tom Cervoni, M.D., Chief of Staff
CHR: Joy M. Benedict, Director Human Resources
Web address: www.baptisthealthrichmond.com
**Control:** Other not–for–profit (including NFP Corporation) **Service:** General Medical and Surgical

**Staffed Beds:** 66 **Admissions:** 2197 **Census:** 22 **Outpatient Visits:** 59799 **Births:** 522 **Total Expense ($000):** 46280 **Payroll Expense ($000):** 18236 **Personnel:** 544

## RUSSELL SPRINGS—Russell County

★ **RUSSELL COUNTY HOSPITAL (181330)**, 153 Dowell Road, Zip 42642–4579, Mailing Address: P.O. Box 1610, Zip 42642–1610; tel. 270/866–4141, (Nonreporting) **A**9 10 18 **S** Baptist Health, Louisville, KY
Primary Contact: Robert L. Ramey, President
CFO: Ken Kimsal, Chief Financial Officer
CMO: Miles Gibson, M.D., Chief of Staff
CIO: Monte Monsanto, Chief Information Systems
CHR: Jennifer Dykes, Director Human Resources
Web address: www.russellcohospital.org
**Control:** County–Government, nonfederal **Service:** General Medical and Surgical

**Staffed Beds:** 25

## RUSSELLVILLE—Logan County

⊠ **LOGAN MEMORIAL HOSPITAL (180066)**, 1625 South Nashville Road, Zip 42276–8834, Mailing Address: P.O. Box 10, Zip 42276–0010; tel. 270/726–4011 **A**1 9 10 **F**15 28 29 30 34 40 45 50 51 57 59 64 75 79 81 85 93 107 110 111 114 119 129 130 132 133 142 146 **S** LifePoint Hospitals, Inc., Brentwood, TN
Primary Contact: Jim Bills, Chief Executive Officer
COO: Julia Murphy, Chief Nursing Officer
CFO: Jason Schmiedt, Chief Financial Officer
CMO: Patrick Hayden, M.D., Chief of Staff
CIO: Mike Katz, Director Information Systems
CHR: Courtney Jackson, Director Human Resources
CNO: Julia Murphy, Chief Nursing Officer
Web address: www.loganmemorial.com
**Control:** Corporation, Investor–owned, for–profit **Service:** General Medical and Surgical

**Staffed Beds:** 53 **Admissions:** 996 **Census:** 14 **Outpatient Visits:** 44737 **Births:** 0

## SALEM—Livingston County

★ **LIVINGSTON HOSPITAL AND HEALTHCARE SERVICES (181320)**, 131 Hospital Drive, Zip 42078–8043; tel. 270/988–2299, (Nonreporting) **A**9 10 18 **S** Alliant Management Services, Louisville, KY
Primary Contact: Mark A. Edwards, Chief Executive Officer
CFO: John Hubbell, Chief Financial Officer
CMO: William Guyette, M.D., President Medical Staff
CIO: Shannan Landreth, Information Systems
CHR: Carla Wiggins, Director Human Resources
CNO: Joanna Stone, Chief Nursing Officer
Web address: www.lhhs.org
**Control:** Other not–for–profit (including NFP Corporation) **Service:** General Medical and Surgical

**Staffed Beds:** 25

## SCOTTSVILLE—Allen County

**MEDICAL CENTER AT SCOTTSVILLE (181324)**, 456 Burnley Road, Zip 42164–6355; tel. 270/622–2800, (Total facility includes 110 beds in nursing home–type unit) **A**9 10 18 **F**1 3 4 15 16 17 28 29 30 34 35 40 56 57 59 64 67 68 70 71 72 73 74 75 76 79 80 81 85 86 87 88 89 90 93 97 98 102 103 104 107 111 113 114 119 127 128 130 132 133 143 146 148 **S** Commonwealth Health Corporation, Bowling Green, KY
Primary Contact: Eric Hagan, R.N., Vice President/Administrator
COO: Connie Smith, Chief Executive Officer and Chief Operating Officer
CFO: Ronald G. Sowell, Chief Financial Officer
CIO: Jean Cherry, Chief Information Officer
CHR: Lynn Williams, Vice President Human Resources
Web address: www.themedicalcenterscottsville.org/
**Control:** Other not–for–profit (including NFP Corporation) **Service:** General Medical and Surgical

**Staffed Beds:** 135 **Admissions:** 660 **Census:** 123 **Outpatient Visits:** 21693 **Births:** 0 **Personnel:** 197

## SHELBYVILLE—Shelby County

⊠ **JEWISH HOSPITAL–SHELBYVILLE (180016)**, 727 Hospital Drive, Zip 40065–1699; tel. 502/647–4000, (Data for 182 days) **A**1 9 10 **F**3 11 15 18 28 29 30 34 35 39 40 44 45 46 50 57 59 64 68 70 75 79 81 82 84 85 87 91 93 107 108 110 111 114 119 129 132 135 146 147 148 **P**6 **S** Catholic Health Initiatives, Englewood, CO
Primary Contact: Michael L. Collins, President
CFO: Erika McGimsey, Controller
CMO: Tony Perez, M.D., President Medical Staff
CHR: Cindy Stewart Rattray, Director Human Resources
Web address: www.jhsmh.org
**Control:** Other not–for–profit (including NFP Corporation) **Service:** General Medical and Surgical

**Staffed Beds:** 41 **Admissions:** 906 **Census:** 19 **Outpatient Visits:** 22024 **Births:** 0 **Total Expense ($000):** 17114 **Payroll Expense ($000):** 5730 **Personnel:** 184

## SOMERSET—Pulaski County

⊠ **LAKE CUMBERLAND REGIONAL HOSPITAL (180132)**, 305 Langdon Street, Zip 42503–2750, Mailing Address: P.O. Box 620, Zip 42502–0620; tel. 606/679–7441, (Total facility includes 12 beds in nursing home–type unit) **A**1 2 9 10 **F**3 8 11 12 13 15 17 18 20 22 24 28 29 30 31 34 35 40 45 47 49 50 54 56 57 59 61 64 65 68 70 73 74 75 76 77 78 79 81 82 85 86 87 89 90 93 97 98 102 103 107 108 109 110 111 114 115 119 120 121 124 125 126 127 128 129 130 132 135 144 146 147 148 **P**5 **S** LifePoint Hospitals, Inc., Brentwood, TN
Primary Contact: Mark T. Brenzel, Chief Executive Officer
CFO: Steve Sloan, Chief Financial Officer
CMO: Michael Citak, M.D., Chief Medical Officer
CIO: Thomas Gilbert, Director Information Technology Services
CHR: James Hughes, Director Human Resources
Web address: www.lakecumberlandhospital.com
**Control:** Corporation, Investor–owned, for–profit **Service:** General Medical and Surgical

**Staffed Beds:** 295 **Admissions:** 12430 **Census:** 156 **Outpatient Visits:** 118221 **Births:** 1400 **Total Expense ($000):** 125415 **Payroll Expense ($000):** 50531 **Personnel:** 1166

## SOUTH WILLIAMSON—Pike County

☐ **WILLIAMSON ARH HOSPITAL (180069)**, 260 Hospital Drive, Zip 41503–4072; tel. 606/237–1710, (Total facility includes 35 beds in nursing home–type unit) **A**1 9 10 **F**3 11 13 15 29 30 34 35 40 43 50 54 57 59 62 64 67 70 74 75 76 77 79 81 82 85 86 87 89 90 93 97 107 108 111 114 115 118 119 127 128 129 130 132 146 147 **P**6 **S** Appalachian Regional Healthcare, Inc., Lexington, KY
Primary Contact: Timothy A. Hatfield, Community Chief Executive Officer
CMO: J. D. Miller, M.D., Vice President Medical Affairs
CIO: Jeff Brady, Chief Information Officer
Web address: www.arh.org
**Control:** Other not–for–profit (including NFP Corporation) **Service:** General Medical and Surgical

**Staffed Beds:** 126 **Admissions:** 2872 **Census:** 57 **Outpatient Visits:** 46565 **Births:** 150 **Total Expense ($000):** 41837 **Payroll Expense ($000):** 11905 **Personnel:** 265

## STANFORD—Lincoln County

⊠ **EPHRAIM MCDOWELL FORT LOGAN HOSPITAL (181315)**, 110 Metker Trail, Zip 40484–1020; tel. 606/365–4600 **A**1 9 10 18 **F**3 11 13 15 29 30 34 35 40 43 57 59 64 76 81 87 89 107 110 111 119 130 133 135 146 **P**5
Primary Contact: Mike Jackson, President and Chief Executive Officer
CFO: William R. Snapp, III, Vice President and Chief Financial Officer
CMO: Naren James, M.D., Chief of Staff
CIO: Sharon McWhorter, Director Information Systems
Web address: www.fortloganhospital.org
**Control:** Other not–for–profit (including NFP Corporation) **Service:** General Medical and Surgical

**Staffed Beds:** 22 **Admissions:** 757 **Census:** 6 **Outpatient Visits:** 41468 **Births:** 320 **Total Expense ($000):** 12738 **Payroll Expense ($000):** 7003 **Personnel:** 147

## TOMPKINSVILLE—Monroe County

⊠ **MONROE COUNTY MEDICAL CENTER (180105)**, 529 Capp Harlan Road, Zip 42167–1840; tel. 270/487–9231 **A**1 9 10 **F**1 2 3 4 7 15 16 17 29 30 34 40 45 57 62 64 67 70 72 73 76 77 80 85 88 89 90 93 94 98 110 111 114 119 128 132 148 **P**6 8 **S** QHR, Brentwood, TN
Primary Contact: Vicky McFall, Chief Executive Officer
CFO: Rickie F. Brown, Chief Financial Officer
CIO: Paul McKiddy, Director Information Technology
CHR: Sue Page, Director Human Resources
Web address: www.mcmccares.com
**Control:** Other not–for–profit (including NFP Corporation) **Service:** General Medical and Surgical

**Staffed Beds:** 49 **Admissions:** 2052 **Census:** 25 **Outpatient Visits:** 45696 **Births:** 0 **Total Expense ($000):** 18719 **Payroll Expense ($000):** 8825

*Many Facility Codes have changed. Please refer to the AHA Guide Code Chart.*

© 2013 AHA Guide

## VERSAILLES—Woodford County

★ **BLUEGRASS COMMUNITY HOSPITAL (181308)**, 360 Amsden Avenue,
Zip 40383–1286; tel. 859/873–3111, (Nonreporting) **A**9 10 18 **S** LifePoint
Hospitals, Inc., Brentwood, TN
Primary Contact: Tommy Haggard, Chief Executive Officer
CFO: Shellie Shouse, Chief Financial Officer
CMO: Jon Sanchez, M.D., Chief of Staff
CHR: Marcia Carter, Director Human Resources
CNO: Kathy Russell, R.N., Chief Nursing Officer
Web address: www.bluegrasscommunityhospital.com
**Control:** Other not–for–profit (including NFP Corporation) **Service:** General
Medical and Surgical

**Staffed Beds:** 25

## WEST LIBERTY—Morgan County

☐ **MORGAN COUNTY ARH HOSPITAL (181307)**, 476 Liberty Road,
Zip 41472–2049, Mailing Address: P.O. Box 579, Zip 41472–0579;
tel. 606/743–3186 **A**1 9 10 18 **F**11 15 29 30 34 35 40 43 54 57 59 62 64
75 82 86 87 93 97 107 114 119 127 129 130 132 133 146 **P**6 **S** Appalachian
Regional Healthcare, Inc., Lexington, KY
Primary Contact: Stephen M. Gavalchik, FACHE, Community Chief Executive
Officer
COO: Paul V. Miles, Chief Operating Officer
CMO: J. D. Miller, M.D., Vice President Medical Affairs
CIO: Jeff Brady, Director Information Systems
CHR: Lisa Redding, Manager Human Resources
Web address: www.arh.org
**Control:** Other not–for–profit (including NFP Corporation) **Service:** General
Medical and Surgical

**Staffed Beds:** 25 **Admissions:** 581 **Census:** 6 **Outpatient Visits:** 25664
**Births:** 0 **Total Expense ($000):** 12976 **Payroll Expense ($000):** 4379
**Personnel:** 100

## WHITESBURG—Letcher County

☐ **WHITESBURG ARH HOSPITAL (180002)**, 240 Hospital Road,
Zip 41858–7627; tel. 606/633–3600 **A**1 9 10 **F**3 11 13 15 29 30 34 35 40
43 50 54 57 59 62 64 70 75 76 77 81 82 85 86 87 89 90 93 97 107 108
111 114 118 119 127 129 130 133 146 147 **P**6 **S** Appalachian Regional
Healthcare, Inc., Lexington, KY
Primary Contact: Dena C. Sparkman, FACHE, Community Chief Executive Officer
COO: Paul V. Miles, Vice President Administration
CFO: Joseph Grossman, Vice President Fiscal Affairs
CMO: Ricky M. Collins, M.D., Chief of Staff
CIO: Brent Styer, Director Information Technology
CHR: Daniel Fitzpatrick, Director Human Resources
Web address: www.arh.org/whitesburg
**Control:** Other not–for–profit (including NFP Corporation) **Service:** General
Medical and Surgical

**Staffed Beds:** 85 **Admissions:** 3508 **Census:** 34 **Outpatient Visits:** 55276
**Births:** 367 **Total Expense ($000):** 38590 **Payroll Expense ($000):** 11380
**Personnel:** 245

## WILLIAMSTOWN—Grant County

**ST. ELIZABETH GRANT (181311)**, 238 Barnes Road, Zip 41097–9482;
tel. 859/824–8240 **A**9 10 18 **F**3 11 15 29 30 31 34 35 38 40 42 44 46 50
57 59 63 64 68 74 75 78 79 82 84 93 97 107 108 110 111 114 119 129
130 131 132 135 146 148 **P**6 **S** St. Elizabeth Healthcare, Edgewood, KY
Primary Contact: John Mitchell, Assistant Vice President Operations
Web address: www.stelizabeth.com
**Control:** Church–operated, Nongovernment, not–for profit **Service:** General
Medical and Surgical

**Staffed Beds:** 16 **Admissions:** 375 **Census:** 3 **Outpatient Visits:** 57650
**Births:** 0 **Total Expense ($000):** 17612 **Payroll Expense ($000):** 6158
**Personnel:** 101

**ST. ELIZABETH MEDICAL CENTER–GRANT COUNTY** See St. Elizabeth Grant

## WINCHESTER—Clark County

★ **CLARK REGIONAL MEDICAL CENTER (180092)**, 175 Hospital Drive,
Zip 40391–9591; tel. 859/745–3500, (Nonreporting) **A**5 9 10 **S** LifePoint
Hospitals, Inc., Brentwood, TN
Primary Contact: Cherie Sibley, R.N., Chief Executive Officer
CMO: Freddie Terrell, M.D., Chief of Staff
Web address: www.clarkregional.org
**Control:** Corporation, Investor–owned, for–profit **Service:** General Medical and
Surgical

**Staffed Beds:** 100

---

Hospital, Medicare Provider Number, Address, Telephone, Approval, Facility, and Physician Codes, Health Care System

★ American Hospital Association (AHA) membership
☐ The Joint Commission accreditation
◇ DNV Healthcare Inc. accreditation
○ Healthcare Facilities Accreditation Program
△ Commission on Accreditation of Rehabilitation Facilities (CARF) accreditation

**LA**

# LOUISIANA

## ABBEVILLE—Vermilion Parish

✠ **ABBEVILLE GENERAL HOSPITAL (190034)**, 118 North Hospital Drive, Zip 70510–4077, Mailing Address: P.O. Box 580, Zip 70511–0580; tel. 337/893–5466 **A**1 9 10 **F**11 13 15 29 30 31 34 40 45 50 54 59 60 64 66 70 75 76 79 81 82 85 86 87 89 97 98 103 105 108 114 119 127 128 130 133 146 **P**6
Primary Contact: Ray A. Landry, Chief Executive Officer
CFO: Troy Hair, Chief Financial Officer
CIO: Kelly Cousins, Director Information Technology
Web address: www.abbgen.net
**Control:** Hospital district or authority, Government, nonfederal **Service:** General Medical and Surgical

Staffed Beds: 60 Admissions: 1917 Census: 30 Outpatient Visits: 65131
Births: 162 Personnel: 363

## ALEXANDRIA—Rapides Parish

◇ **CENTRAL LOUISIANA SURGICAL HOSPITAL (190298)**, 651 North Bolton Avenue, Zip 71301–7449, Mailing Address: P.O. Box 8646, Zip 71306–1646; tel. 318/443–3511 **A**9 10 21 **F**3 12 45 51 64 68 79 81 82 85 86 107 115 118 119 **P**2
Primary Contact: Louise Barker, R.N., Chief Executive Officer
CFO: Michael Fuselier, FACHE, Chief Financial Officer
CMO: Renick Webb, M.D., Chief Medical Director
CHR: Debbie Norman, Director Human Resources
CNO: Carol Wells, R.N., Chief Nursing Officer
Web address: www.clshospital.com
**Control:** Partnership, Investor–owned, for–profit **Service:** Surgical

Staffed Beds: 24 Admissions: 1056 Census: 7 Births: 0

✠ **CHRISTUS ST. FRANCES CABRINI HOSPITAL (190019)**, 3330 Masonic Drive, Zip 71301–3899; tel. 318/487–1122 **A**1 2 9 10 **F**11 12 13 15 18 20 22 24 26 28 29 30 31 34 35 40 41 45 46 49 54 57 58 59 63 64 70 72 74 76 77 78 79 81 82 84 85 87 89 90 93 96 97 108 109 110 111 114 115 116 117 118 119 120 121 126 129 130 131 132 145 146 147 148 **P**6 **S** CHRISTUS Health, Irving, TX
Primary Contact: Stephen F. Wright, President and Chief Executive Officer
COO: Lisa R. Lauve, R.N., Regional Chief Nursing Executive and Chief Operating Officer
CFO: Debbie White, Chief Financial Officer
CIO: Ron Dekeyzer, Regional Management Information Officer
CHR: Wendy White, Regional Vice President Human Resources
Web address: www.cabrini.org/
**Control:** Church–operated, Nongovernment, not–for profit **Service:** General Medical and Surgical

Staffed Beds: 281 Admissions: 12933 Census: 172 Outpatient Visits: 183907 Births: 1110 Total Expense ($000): 194922 Payroll Expense ($000): 64722 Personnel: 1396

☐ **CROSSROADS REGIONAL HOSPITAL (194022)**, 110 John Eskew Drive, Zip 71303; tel. 318/445–5111, (Nonreporting) **A**1 9 10
Primary Contact: Brian Brunson, Chief Executive Officer
Web address: www.crossroadshospital.com
**Control:** Corporation, Investor–owned, for–profit **Service:** Psychiatric

Staffed Beds: 70

✠ **DUBUIS HOSPITAL OF ALEXANDRIA (192012)**, 3330 Masonic Drive, 4th Floor, Zip 71301–3841; tel. 318/448–4938 **A**1 10 **F**1 3 29 77 84 85 148 **S** Dubuis Health System, Houston, TX
Primary Contact: Beth Parsons, R.N., Administrator
CNO: Kimberly Bennett, Director Patient Care
Web address: www.christusdubuis.org/CHRISTUSDubuisHospitalofAlexandriaLA
**Control:** Church–operated, Nongovernment, not–for profit **Service:** Long–Term Acute Care hospital

Staffed Beds: 25 Admissions: 240 Census: 18 Outpatient Visits: 0 Births: 0

✠ **HEALTHSOUTH REHABILITATION HOSPITAL OF ALEXANDRIA (193031)**, 104 North Third Street, Zip 71301–8581; tel. 318/449–1370, (Nonreporting) **A**1 10 **S** HEALTHSOUTH Corporation, Birmingham, AL
Primary Contact: James W. McClung, Chief Executive Officer
CFO: Linda Wright, Chief Finanical Officer
CMO: Vasudeva Dhulipala, M.D., Medical Director
CHR: Suzie Wagner, Director Human Resources
Web address: www.healthsouthalexandria.com
**Control:** Partnership, Investor–owned, for–profit **Service:** Rehabilitation

Staffed Beds: 47

☐ **OCEANS BEHAVIORAL HOSPITAL OF ALEXANDRIA (194096)**, 2621 North Bolton Avenue, Zip 71303–4506; tel. 318/448–8473, (Nonreporting) **A**1 9 10 **S** Oceans Healthcare, Lake Charles, LA
Primary Contact: Gene Amons, Administrator
Web address: www.obha.info/
**Control:** Corporation, Investor–owned, for–profit **Service:** Psychiatric

Staffed Beds: 24

✠ **RAPIDES REGIONAL MEDICAL CENTER (190026)**, 211 Fourth Street, Zip 71301–8421; tel. 318/473–3000 **A**1 2 3 5 9 10 **F**3 11 13 15 17 18 19 20 22 24 26 28 29 30 31 32 34 35 36 38 40 41 43 44 45 46 47 48 49 50 51 52 54 55 57 59 60 61 64 65 68 70 72 74 75 76 77 78 79 81 82 84 85 86 87 88 89 97 107 108 110 111 114 115 118 119 120 121 123 124 129 130 131 132 135 146 147 148 **P**1 **S** HCA, Nashville, TN
Primary Contact: Jason E. Cobb, FACHE, Chief Executive Officer
COO: James R. Beatty, Chief Operating Officer
COO: Cheryl A. Wilson, Chief Operating Officer
CMO: Francis Brian, M.D., Senior Vice President Medical Affairs
CHR: Allen Crain, Director Human Resources
Web address: www.rapidesregional.com
**Control:** Partnership, Investor–owned, for–profit **Service:** General Medical and Surgical

Staffed Beds: 349 Admissions: 16568 Census: 245 Outpatient Visits: 136533 Births: 1911 Total Expense ($000): 199205 Payroll Expense ($000): 75428 Personnel: 1317

☐ **RIVERSIDE HOSPITAL OF LOUISIANA (192043)**, 211 Fourth Street, 5th Floor, Zip 71301–8421; tel. 318/767–2900, (Nonreporting) **A**1 10
Primary Contact: William Bush, Chief Executive Officer
Web address: www.riversidehospital.net
**Control:** Corporation, Investor–owned, for–profit **Service:** Long–Term Acute Care hospital

Staffed Beds: 27

## AMITE—Tangipahoa Parish

★ **HOOD MEMORIAL HOSPITAL (191309)**, 301 West Walnut Street, Zip 70422–2098; tel. 985/748–9485 **A**9 10 18 **F**29 35 40 57 59 64 65 86 97 107 108 119 127 133
Primary Contact: John C. Neal, Chief Executive Officer
CHR: Cynthia Rutherford, Manager Business Office
**Control:** Hospital district or authority, Government, nonfederal **Service:** General Medical and Surgical

Staffed Beds: 25 Admissions: 406 Census: 4 Outpatient Visits: 10126 Births: 0 Total Expense ($000): 7728 Payroll Expense ($000): 3852 Personnel: 93

## ARCADIA—Bienville Parish

**BIENVILLE MEDICAL CENTER (191320)**, 1175 Pine Street, Suite 200, Zip 71001–3122; tel. 318/263–4700, (Nonreporting) **A**9 10 18
Primary Contact: Richard T. Merk, Chief Executive Officer
**Control:** Other not–for–profit (including NFP Corporation) **Service:** General Medical and Surgical

Staffed Beds: 21

## BASTROP—Morehouse Parish

**BASTROP REHABILITATION HOSPITAL (193058)**, 323 West Walnut Street, Zip 71220–4521, Mailing Address: P.O. Box 1531, Zip 71221–1531; tel. 318/556–1191, (Nonreporting) **A**10
Primary Contact: William H. Means, Jr., Administrator
COO: Tena Hughes, R.N., Program Director and Director Nursing
CFO: William H. Means, Jr., Administrator
CMO: James M. Smith, M.D., Medical Director
CIO: Debbie Chunn, Director Medical Records
CHR: Renee Walker, Director Human Resources
**Control:** Corporation, Investor–owned, for–profit **Service:** Rehabilitation

Staffed Beds: 15

☐ **LIBERTY HEALTHCARE SYSTEMS (194083)**, 4673 Eugene Ware Boulevard, Zip 71220–1425; tel. 318/281–2448 **A**1 9 10 **F**98 99 130
Primary Contact: William W. Bing, Chief Executive Officer
Web address: www.libertybh.com/
**Control:** Partnership, Investor–owned, for–profit **Service:** Children's hospital psychiatric

Staffed Beds: 60 Admissions: 949 Census: 24 Outpatient Visits: 0 Births: 0

*Many Facility Codes have changed. Please refer to the AHA Guide Code Chart.*  © 2013 AHA Guide

★ **MOREHOUSE GENERAL HOSPITAL (190116)**, 323 West Walnut Avenue, Zip 71220–4521, Mailing Address: P.O. Box 1060, Zip 71221–1060; tel. 318/283–3600 **A**9 10 **F**3 8 11 13 15 29 34 39 40 45 47 49 50 64 70 75 76 79 81 85 86 87 89 107 111 114 119 127 130 133 143 146 147 148
Primary Contact: Stephen R. Pitts, Chief Executive Officer
CFO: James Allbritton, Chief Financial Officer
CMO: John Coats, M.D., Chief Medical Staff
CIO: B. J. Vail, Director Information Systems
CHR: Debbie Spann, Director Human Resources
CNO: Melinda Jones, R.N., Chief Nursing Officer
Web address: www.mghospital.com
**Control:** Hospital district or authority, Government, nonfederal **Service:** General Medical and Surgical

**Staffed Beds:** 22 **Admissions:** 2012 **Census:** 19 **Outpatient Visits:** 46658 **Births:** 380 **Total Expense ($000):** 29475 **Payroll Expense ($000):** 9943 **Personnel:** 241

## BATON ROUGE—East Baton Rouge Parish

☐ **BATON ROUGE GENERAL MEDICAL CENTER (190065)**, 3600 Florida Street, Zip 70806–3889, Mailing Address: P.O. Box 2511, Zip 70821–2511; tel. 225/387–7000, (Includes BATON ROUGE GENERAL MEDICAL CENTER–BLUEBONNET, 8585 Picardy Avenue, Zip 70809–3679, Mailing Address: P.O. Box 84330, Zip 70884–4330; tel. 225/763–4000) **A**1 2 3 5 6 8 9 10 **F**3 8 11 12 13 15 16 17 18 19 22 24 26 28 29 30 31 34 35 38 40 44 45 46 47 49 50 53 56 57 58 59 60 61 64 65 68 70 72 74 75 76 77 78 79 81 82 84 86 87 88 89 90 93 96 97 98 101 102 103 104 107 108 110 111 114 115 117 118 119 120 121 123 124 126 127 128 129 130 131 132 135 143 144 146 147 148 **P**4 6
Primary Contact: Evelyn Hayes, M.D., Interim President and Chief Executive Officer
COO: Edgardo Tenreiro, Chief Operating Officer
CFO: Kendall Johnson, Chief Financial Officer
CMO: Floyd Roberts, M.D., Chief Medical Officer
CIO: David Hastings, Director Information Technology
CHR: Paul Douglas, Vice President Human Resources
Web address: www.brgeneral.org
**Control:** Other not-for-profit (including NFP Corporation) **Service:** General Medical and Surgical

**Staffed Beds:** 466 **Admissions:** 19218 **Census:** 285 **Outpatient Visits:** 221461 **Births:** 816 **Total Expense ($000):** 305316 **Payroll Expense ($000):** 112941 **Personnel:** 2606

✠ **BATON ROUGE REHABILITATION HOSPITAL (193028)**, 8595 United Plaza Boulevard, Zip 70809–2251; tel. 225/927–0567, (Nonreporting) **A**1 10
Primary Contact: Jacque Shadle, Chief Executive Officer
CFO: Nicholas Hluchy, Business Analyst, Support Services Manager
CMO: Sundararama R. Vatsavai, M.D., Medical Director
CIO: Roxane Bingham, Director Marketing
CHR: Michelle Smith, Coordinator Human Resources
CNO: Derrick Landreneau, Director of Nursing
Web address: www.brrehab.com
**Control:** Corporation, Investor-owned, for-profit **Service:** Rehabilitation

**Staffed Beds:** 80

**BETHESDA REHABILITATION HOSPITAL (193092)**, 7414 Sumrall Drive, Zip 70812–1240, Mailing Address: 8225 Summa Avenue, Suite B., Zip 70809–3422; tel. 225/767–2034, (Nonreporting) **A**10
Primary Contact: Lionel Murphy, Chief Executive Officer and Administrator
**Control:** Corporation, Investor-owned, for-profit **Service:** Rehabilitation

**Staffed Beds:** 18

**HEALTHSOUTH REHABILITATION HOSPITAL OF BATON ROUGE** See Baton Rouge Rehabilitation Hospital

**NEUROMEDICAL CENTER REHABILITATION HOSPITAL (193090)**, 10101 Park Rowe Avenue, Suite 500, Zip 70810–1685; tel. 225/906–2999, (Nonreporting) **A**10 **S** AMG Integrated Healthcare Management, Lafayette, LA
Primary Contact: Jay Ivy, R.N., Chief Executive Officer
Web address: www.theneuromedicalcenter.com
**Control:** Corporation, Investor-owned, for-profit **Service:** Rehabilitation

**Staffed Beds:** 23

**OCEANS BEHAVIORAL HOSPITAL OF BATON ROUGE (194086)**, 11135 Florida Boulevard, Zip 70815–2013; tel. 225/356–7030, (Nonreporting) **A**9 10 **S** Oceans Healthcare, Lake Charles, LA
Primary Contact: Valerie Dalton, R.N., Administrator
Web address: www.obhbr.info/
**Control:** Corporation, Investor-owned, for-profit **Service:** Psychiatric

**Staffed Beds:** 20

⊠ **OCHSNER MEDICAL CENTER–BATON ROUGE (190202)**, 17000 Medical Center Drive, Zip 70816–3224; tel. 225/752–2470, (Nonreporting) **A**1 9 10 **S** Ochsner Health System, New Orleans, LA
Primary Contact: Eric McMillen, Chief Executive Officer
CFO: Barry M. Chambers, CPA, Chief Financial Officer
CMO: F. Ralph Dauterive, M.D., Vice President Medical Affairs
CHR: Chris Atkinson, Director of Human Resources
Web address: www.ochsner.org/page.cfm?id=103
**Control:** Corporation, Investor-owned, for-profit **Service:** General Medical and Surgical

**Staffed Beds:** 115

⊠ **OUR LADY OF THE LAKE REGIONAL MEDICAL CENTER (190064)**, 5000 Hennessy Boulevard, Zip 70808–4375; tel. 225/765–6565, (Includes OUR LADY OF THE LAKE CHILDREN'S HOSPITAL, 5000 Hennessy Boulevard, tel. 225/765–8886), (Total facility includes 390 beds in nursing home–type unit) **A**1 2 3 5 8 9 10 **F**3 4 5 8 10 11 12 14 15 17 18 19 20 21 22 23 24 25 26 28 29 30 31 34 35 37 38 39 40 41 45 46 50 53 54 55 56 57 58 59 61 64 68 70 71 74 75 77 78 79 81 82 84 85 86 87 88 89 90 93 96 97 98 99 100 101 102 103 104 105 107 108 110 111 114 115 116 117 118 119 125 126 127 129 130 131 132 135 141 142 143 146 148 **P**6 **S** Franciscan Missionaries of Our Lady Health System, Inc., Baton Rouge, LA
Primary Contact: K. Scott Wester, FACHE, President and Chief Executive Officer
COO: Terrie Sterling, R.N., Chief Operating Officer
CFO: Jeff Limbocker, Chief Financial Officer
CMO: Richard Vath, M.D., Vice President Medical Affairs
CIO: Stephanie Mills, Vice President Information and Materials Systems
CHR: Cora Ford, Vice President Human Resources
Web address: www.ololrmc.com
**Control:** Church-operated, Nongovernment, not-for profit **Service:** General Medical and Surgical

**Staffed Beds:** 1042 **Admissions:** 33096 **Census:** 729 **Outpatient Visits:** 388638 **Births:** 0 **Total Expense ($000):** 687644 **Payroll Expense ($000):** 270457 **Personnel:** 4433

☐ **PROMISE HOSPITAL BATON ROUGE – MAIN CAMPUS (192045)**, (Formerly Promise Hospital Baton Rouge), 5130 Mancuso Lane, Zip 70809–3583; tel. 225/490–9600, (Nonreporting) **A**1 **S** Promise Healthcare, Boca Raton, FL
Primary Contact: Richard Knowland
COO: Christopher A. Stegall, Regional Chief Financial Officer and Chief Operating Officer
CFO: Christopher A. Stegall, Regional Chief Financial Officer and Chief Operating Officer
CMO: Peter J. Monteyne, M.D., Chief Medical Staff
CHR: Wendy Cobbs, Director Human Resources
Web address: www.promise-batonrouge.com
**Control:** Corporation, Investor-owned, for-profit **Service:** Long-Term Acute Care hospital

**Staffed Beds:** 50

**PROMISE HOSPITAL OF BATON ROUGE – MID–CITY CAMPUS (192004)**, (Formerly Promise Hospital of Baton Rouge), 3600 Florida Boulevard, 4th Floor, Zip 70806–3842; tel. 225/387–7770, (Nonreporting) **A**10 **S** Promise Healthcare, Boca Raton, FL
Primary Contact: Bryan Day, Interim Chief Executive Officer
COO: Michael J. Nolan, Area Chief Operating Officer and Safety
CMO: Subhaker Gummadi, M.D., President Medical Staff
Web address: www.promise-batonrougemidcity.com
**Control:** Corporation, Investor-owned, for-profit **Service:** Long-Term Acute Care hospital

**Staffed Beds:** 28

☐ **PROMISE HOSPITAL OF BATON ROUGE – OCHSNER CAMPUS (192049)**, (Formerly Promise Hospital of Baton Rouge), 17000 Medical Center Drive, 3rd Floor, Zip 70816–3246; tel. 225/236–5440, (Nonreporting) **A**1 10 **S** Promise Healthcare, Boca Raton, FL
Primary Contact: Bryan Day, Interim Chief Executive Officer
COO: Michael J. Nolan, Area Safety Director
CMO: Venkat Banda, M.D., President Medical Staff
CHR: Wendy Cobbs, Director of Human Resources
Web address: www.promise-batonrougeochsner.com
**Control:** Corporation, Investor-owned, for-profit **Service:** Long-Term Acute Care hospital

**Staffed Beds:** 22

---

**Hospital, Medicare Provider Number, Address, Telephone, Approval, Facility, and Physician Codes, Health Care System**

★ American Hospital Association (AHA) membership
☐ The Joint Commission accreditation
◇ DNV Healthcare Inc. accreditation
○ Healthcare Facilities Accreditation Program
△ Commission on Accreditation of Rehabilitation Facilities (CARF) accreditation

**SAGE REHABILITATION HOSPITAL (193078)**, 8000 Summa Avenue, Zip 70809–3423, Mailing Address: P.O. Box 82681, Zip 70884–2681; tel. 225/819–0703, (Total facility includes 15 beds in nursing home–type unit) (Data for 358 days) **A**10 **F**29 54 74 75 77 90 91 93 128 130 **P**2
Primary Contact: Gayla Bryant, Administrator
CMO: Christopher Belleau, M.D., Medical Director
CIO: Garon Leblanc, Chief Plant Operations
CHR: Kathy Ringe, Director Human Resources
Web address: www.sage-rehab.org
**Control:** Individual, Investor–owned, for–profit **Service:** Rehabilitation

**Staffed Beds:** 42 **Admissions:** 324 **Census:** 14 **Outpatient Visits:** 0 **Births:** 0 **Personnel:** 152

☐ **SURGICAL SPECIALTY CENTER OF BATON ROUGE (190251)**, 8080 Bluebonnet Boulevard, Zip 70810–7827; tel. 225/408–8080, (Nonreporting) **A**1 9 10
Primary Contact: Craig P. Hume, Chief Executive Officer
Web address: www.sscbr.com
**Control:** Corporation, Investor–owned, for–profit **Service:** Surgical

**Staffed Beds:** 14

**THE NEUROMEDICAL CENTER SURGICAL HOSPITAL (190266)**, 10105 Park Rowe Avenue, Suite 250, Zip 70810–1684; tel. 225/763–9900, (Nonreporting) **A**9 10
Primary Contact: Robert D. Blair, Chief Executive Officer
CFO: Allison Doherty, Chief Financial Officer
CMO: Shawn Dunn, M.D., Medical Director
CHR: Shannon Juge, Human Resources Representative
Web address: www.theneuromedicalcenter.com
**Control:** Corporation, Investor–owned, for–profit **Service:** Surgical

**Staffed Beds:** 23

✉ **WOMAN'S HOSPITAL (190128)**, 100 Woman's Way, Zip 70817–5100, Mailing Address: P.O. Box 95009, Zip 70895–9009; tel. 225/927–1300 **A**1 2 9 10 **F**3 11 12 13 15 31 32 34 35 36 38 45 50 53 54 57 58 59 61 62 64 65 68 70 71 72 73 74 75 76 77 78 79 81 84 85 86 87 89 93 107 110 111 114 119 126 129 130 132 134 135 146 147 **P**6
Primary Contact: Teri G. Fontenot, FACHE, President and Chief Executive Officer
COO: Jamie Haeuser, Senior Vice President Operations
CFO: Stephanie Anderson, Senior Vice President, Finance and Administration
CMO: Kenneth Brown, M.D., Medical Director
CIO: Paul Kirk, Vice President
CHR: Donna L. Bodin, Vice President
CNO: Patricia R. Johnson, R.N., Senior Vice President
Web address: www.womans.org
**Control:** Other not–for–profit (including NFP Corporation) **Service:** Obstetrics and gynecology

**Staffed Beds:** 226 **Admissions:** 12644 **Census:** 140 **Outpatient Visits:** 113177 **Births:** 8486 **Total Expense ($000):** 210810 **Payroll Expense ($000):** 106856 **Personnel:** 1552

**BERNICE—Union Parish**

**REEVES MEMORIAL MEDICAL CENTER (191326)**, 409 First Street, Zip 71222–4001, Mailing Address: P.O. Box 697, Zip 71222–0697; tel. 318/285–9066, (Nonreporting) **A**9 10 18
Primary Contact: Landon Tooke, Chief Executive Officer
COO: Beth Jones, Chief Operating Officer
CFO: Charolette Thompson, Chief Financial Officer
CMO: R. Brian Harris, M.D., Chief of Staff
CHR: Robin Adams, Director Human Resources
Web address: www.reevesmemorial.com/
**Control:** Hospital district or authority, Government, nonfederal **Service:** General Medical and Surgical

**Staffed Beds:** 11

**TRI–WARD GENERAL HOSPITAL** See Reeves Memorial Medical Center

**BOGALUSA—Washington Parish**

☐ **LSU BOGALUSA MEDICAL CENTER (190095)**, 433 Plaza Street, Zip 70427–3793; tel. 985/730–6700, (Includes AMG SPECIALTY HOSPITAL – BOGALUSA, 621 Columbia Street, Zip 70427–0040; tel. 985/735–1322; BOGALUSA COMMUNITY MEDICAL CENTER, 433 Plaza Street, tel. 985/730–6700) **A**1 3 9 **F**3 11 13 15 18 28 29 34 35 38 40 41 45 49 50 51 56 57 58 59 60 61 64 66 68 70 74 75 76 81 85 86 87 89 93 97 98 104 107 108 111 114 119 130 132 135 141 146 147 148 **P**6 **S** LSU Health Care Services Division, Baton Rouge, LA
Primary Contact: Kurt M. Scott, FACHE, Administrator
CFO: Brooke Cummings, Chief Financial Officer
CMO: Lee Roy Joyner, M.D., Medical Director
CIO: Betina Owens, Chief Information Officer
CHR: Christi Brown, Director Human Resources
Web address: www.lsuhospitals.org
**Control:** State–Government, nonfederal **Service:** General Medical and Surgical

**Staffed Beds:** 74 **Admissions:** 3290 **Census:** 42 **Outpatient Visits:** 121289 **Births:** 171

**BOSSIER CITY—Bossier Parish**

☐ **CORNERSTONE HOSPITAL OF BOSSIER CITY (192006)**, 4900 Medical Drive, Zip 71112–4521; tel. 318/747–9500, (Nonreporting) **A**1 10 **S** Cornerstone Healthcare Group, Dallas, TX
Primary Contact: Sheri Burnette, R.N., Chief Executive Officer and Administrator
CFO: Chad Deardorff, Chief Financial Officer
CMO: James Jackson, M.D., Chief of Staff
Web address: www.chghospitals.com/
**Control:** Corporation, Investor–owned, for–profit **Service:** Long–Term Acute Care hospital

**Staffed Beds:** 54

◇ **PATHWAY REHABILITATION HOSPITAL (193094)**, 4900 Medical Drive, Zip 71112–4521; tel. 318/841–5555, (Nonreporting) **A**10 21
Primary Contact: James Manning, Administrator
Web address: www.pathrehab.com
**Control:** Corporation, Investor–owned, for–profit **Service:** Rehabilitation

**Staffed Beds:** 24

**RED RIVER BEHAVIORAL CENTER (194079)**, 2800 Melrose Avenue, Zip 71111–5870; tel. 318/549–2033 **A**9 10 **F**98 101 103 104 **P**5
Primary Contact: Susan Kottenbrook, Chief Executive Officer
Web address: www.redriverbehavioral.com/
**Control:** Partnership, Investor–owned, for–profit **Service:** Psychiatric

**Staffed Beds:** 20 **Admissions:** 314 **Census:** 13 **Outpatient Visits:** 0 **Births:** 0

**WILLIS–KNIGHTON BOSSIER HEALTH CENTER** See WK Bossier Health Center

✉ △ **WK BOSSIER HEALTH CENTER (190236)**, 2400 Hospital Drive, Zip 71111–2385; tel. 318/212–7000 **A**1 7 9 10 **F**3 8 11 12 13 15 18 20 22 24 28 29 30 34 35 38 40 44 45 46 47 48 49 50 53 54 56 57 59 60 61 64 65 68 70 74 75 76 77 78 79 80 81 82 84 85 86 87 89 93 96 97 100 101 102 103 107 108 109 110 111 114 118 119 126 127 129 130 131 132 135 144 146 147 148 **P**6 7 **S** Willis–Knighton Health System, Shreveport, LA
Primary Contact: Clifford M. Broussard, FACHE, Administrator
COO: Charles D. Daigle, Chief Operating Officer
CFO: Robert D. Huie, Chief Financial Officer
CMO: Charles Powers, M.D., Administrative Medical Director
CIO: Charles Laster, Director Information Management
CHR: Debbie Fortson, Director Human Resources
CNO: Sharon Hudnell, R.N., Chief Nursing Officer
Web address: www.wkhs.com/wkb/
**Control:** Other not–for–profit (including NFP Corporation) **Service:** General Medical and Surgical

**Staffed Beds:** 134 **Admissions:** 10536 **Census:** 91 **Outpatient Visits:** 123337 **Births:** 966 **Personnel:** 881

**BREAUX BRIDGE—St. Martin Parish**

**GENESIS BEHAVIORAL HOSPITAL (194089)**, 606 Latiolais Drive, Zip 70517–4231; tel. 337/442–6084, (Data for 364 days) **A**9 10 **F**64 98 103 104 105 130 **P**1
Primary Contact: Will Alredge, Administrator
**Control:** Corporation, Investor–owned, for–profit **Service:** Psychiatric

**Staffed Beds:** 18 **Admissions:** 410 **Census:** 15 **Outpatient Visits:** 22000 **Births:** 0 **Total Expense ($000):** 5300 **Payroll Expense ($000):** 1995 **Personnel:** 66

★ **ST. MARTIN HOSPITAL (191302)**, 210 Champagne Boulevard, Zip 70517–3700, Mailing Address: P.O. Box 357, Zip 70517–0357; tel. 337/332–2178 **A**9 10 18 **F**1 3 4 16 17 29 34 40 57 64 67 70 72 73 76 77 80 88 89 90 93 98 107 110 119 128 133 **P**8
Primary Contact: Katherine D. Hebert, Chief Executive Officer
CFO: Shadelle Huval, Director Finance
CHR: Rena B. Mouisset, Director Human Resources and Contract Compliance
Web address: www.stmartinhospital.org
**Control:** Other not–for–profit (including NFP Corporation) **Service:** General Medical and Surgical

**Staffed Beds:** 25 **Admissions:** 325 **Census:** 8 **Outpatient Visits:** 17444 **Births:** 0 **Total Expense ($000):** 16406 **Payroll Expense ($000):** 4854 **Personnel:** 136

**BROUSSARD—Lafayette Parish**

☐ **OCEANS BEHAVIORAL HOSPITAL OF BROUSSARD (194073)**, 418 Albertson Parkway, Zip 70518–4971; tel. 337/237–6444, (Nonreporting) **A**1 9 10 **S** Oceans Healthcare, Lake Charles, LA
Primary Contact: Amy Dysart, Administrator
Web address: www.obhb.info/
**Control:** Corporation, Investor–owned, for–profit **Service:** Psychiatric

**Staffed Beds:** 38

*Many Facility Codes have changed. Please refer to the AHA Guide Code Chart.*
© 2013 AHA Guide

## BUNKIE—Avoyelles Parish

**BUNKIE GENERAL HOSPITAL (191311)**, 427 Evergreen Highway, Zip 71322, Mailing Address: P.O. Box 380, Zip 71322–0380; tel. 318/346–6681, (Nonreporting) **A**9 10 18
Primary Contact: Linda F. Deville, Chief Executive Officer
COO: Lonnie L. Dufour, Chief Operating Officer, Chief Information Officer and Director Human Resources
CFO: Terry Willett, Chief Financial Officer
CMO: Mohit Srivastava, M.D., Chief of Staff
CIO: Lonnie L. Dufour, Chief Operating Officer, Chief Information Officer and Director Human Resources
CHR: Lonnie L. Dufour, Chief Operating Officer, Chief Information Officer and Director Human Resource
Web address: www.bunkiegeneral.com
**Control:** Hospital district or authority, Government, nonfederal **Service:** General Medical and Surgical

**Staffed Beds:** 18

## CAMERON—Cameron Parish

◇ **SOUTH CAMERON MEMORIAL HOSPITAL (190307)**, 5360 West Creole Highway, Zip 70631–5127; tel. 337/542–4111, (Nonreporting) **A**10 20 21
Primary Contact: David Byrns, Chief Executive Officer
**Control:** Hospital district or authority, Government, nonfederal **Service:** General Medical and Surgical

**Staffed Beds:** 49

## CHALMETTE—Saint Bernard Parish

☐ **ST. BERNARD PARISH HOSPITAL (190308)**, 8000 West Judge Perez Drive, Zip 70043–1668; tel. 504/826–9500 **A**1 10 **F**8 15 18 20 22 24 29 34 40 45 46 53 57 59 7077 79 81 91 107 108 110 111 114 119 129 148
Primary Contact: Wayne J. Landry, Chief Executive Officer
Web address: www.sbph.net
**Control:** Hospital district or authority, Government, nonfederal **Service:** General Medical and Surgical

**Staffed Beds:** 40 **Admissions:** 331 **Census:** 4

## CHURCH POINT—Acadia Parish

**ACADIA–ST. LANDRY HOSPITAL (191319)**, 810 South Broadway Street, Zip 70525–4497; tel. 337/684–5435, (Nonreporting) **A**9 10 18
Primary Contact: F. Peter Savoy, III, Chief Executive Officer
CFO: Judy Young, Chief Financial Officer
CMO: Ty Hargroder, M.D., Chief of Staff
CHR: Judy Young, Chief Financial Officer
Web address: www.aslh.org
**Control:** Other not–for–profit (including NFP Corporation) **Service:** General Medical and Surgical

**Staffed Beds:** 25

## CLINTON—East Feliciana Parish

**AMG SPECIALTY HOSPITAL–FELICIANA (192041)**, 9725 Grace Lane, Zip 70722–4925; tel. 225/683–1600 **A**10 **F**1 3 29 90 148 **S** AMG Integrated Healthcare Management, Lafayette, LA
Primary Contact: Keith Carruth, Chief Executive Officer
Web address: www.amgfeliciana.com/
**Control:** Corporation, Investor–owned, for–profit **Service:** General Medical and Surgical

**Staffed Beds:** 16 **Admissions:** 140 **Census:** 10 **Outpatient Visits:** 0 **Births:** 0

## COLUMBIA—Caldwell Parish

**CALDWELL MEMORIAL HOSPITAL (190190)**, 411 Main Street, Zip 71418–6704, Mailing Address: P.O. Box 899, Zip 71418–0899; tel. 318/649–6111, (Nonreporting) **A**9 10
Primary Contact: Heather Clark, Chief Executive Officer
COO: Lisa Patrick, Chief Operating Officer
**Control:** Other not–for–profit (including NFP Corporation) **Service:** General Medical and Surgical

**Staffed Beds:** 25

**CITIZENS MEDICAL CENTER (190184)**, 7939 U.S. Highway 165, Zip 71418–1079, Mailing Address: P.O. Box 1079, Zip 71418–1079; tel. 318/649–6106, (Nonreporting) **A**9 10
Primary Contact: Steve Barbo, R.N., Administrator
**Control:** Hospital district or authority, Government, nonfederal **Service:** General Medical and Surgical

**Staffed Beds:** 40

## COUSHATTA—Red River Parish

☒ **CHRISTUS COUSHATTA HEALTH CARE CENTER (191312)**, 1635 Marvel Street, Zip 71019–9022, Mailing Address: P.O. Box 589, Zip 71019–0589; tel. 318/932–2000 **A**1 9 10 18 **F**2 3 15 29 30 34 35 39 40 41 50 54 56 57 59 64 65 66 67 68 75 77 93 97 103 107 110 115 116 117 119 120 127 128 130 133 135 147 148 **S** CHRISTUS Health, Irving, TX
Primary Contact: Gary L. Kempf, Administrator
CFO: Scott Merryman, Chief Financial Officer
CMO: Jonathan Weisul, M.D., Vice President Medical Affairs and Chief Medical Officer
CIO: Bruce Honea, Director Information Services
CHR: Donnette Craig, Director Human Resources
Web address: www.christuscoushatta.org
**Control:** Church–operated, Nongovernment, not–for profit **Service:** Hospital unit of an institution (prison hospital, college infimary, etc.)

**Staffed Beds:** 25 **Admissions:** 1094 **Census:** 11 **Outpatient Visits:** 37569 **Births:** 0 **Total Expense ($000):** 13290 **Payroll Expense ($000):** 5638 **Personnel:** 81

**SPECIALTY REHABILITATION HOSPITAL (193080)**, 1110 Ringgold Avenue Suite B., Zip 71019–9073; tel. 318/932–1770, (Nonreporting) **A**10 **S** Specialty Healthcare, LLC, Leesville, LA
Primary Contact: Craig Ball, Chief Executive Officer
COO: Charlie Ball, Chief Operating Officer
CFO: Connie Ball, Chief Financial Officer
CMO: Jalal Joudeh, M.D., Chief Medical Officer
CHR: Denise Logan, Director Human Resources
Web address: www.specialtyhealthcare.com
**Control:** Individual, Investor–owned, for–profit **Service:** Rehabilitation

**Staffed Beds:** 12

## COVINGTON—St. Tammany Parish

◇ **FAIRWAY MEDICAL CENTER (190267)**, 67252 Industry Lane, Zip 70433–8704; tel. 985/809–9888, (Nonreporting) **A**9 10 21
Primary Contact: Benjamin Patterson, Chief Executive Officer
CFO: Sandy Badinger, Chief Financial Officer
CMO: William Preau, M.D., Medical Director
CIO: Skip Federico, Director Information Systems
CHR: Pam Collins, Director Human Resources
Web address: www.fairwaymedical.com
**Control:** Corporation, Investor–owned, for–profit **Service:** General Medical and Surgical

**Staffed Beds:** 21

**GREENBRIER HOSPITAL (194069)**, 201 Greenbrier Boulevard, Zip 70433–7236; tel. 985/893–2970 **A**9 10 **F**29 35 54 56 64 75 98 100 101 102 103 104 105 130
Primary Contact: William Fuqua, Administrator
CMO: Jason Coe, M.D., Medical Director
Web address: www.mmoinc.com
**Control:** Individual, Investor–owned, for–profit **Service:** Psychiatric

**Staffed Beds:** 60 **Admissions:** 2210 **Census:** 46 **Births:** 0

**GULF STATES LONG TERM ACUTE CARE OF COVINGTON** See Northshore Specialty Hospital

☒ **LAKEVIEW REGIONAL MEDICAL CENTER (190177)**, 95 Judge Tanner Boulevard, Zip 70433–7507; tel. 985/867–3800 **A**1 9 10 **F**11 12 13 15 18 20 22 24 26 27 28 29 34 35 40 49 57 59 64 68 70 75 76 77 78 81 85 89 91 92 93 98 102 103 106 107 108 110 111 114 115 119 130 132 143 144 146 147 **S** HCA, Nashville, TN
Primary Contact: Bret Kolman, Chief Executive Officer
COO: Stephen Robinson, Chief Operating Officer
CFO: Tim Breslin, Chief Financial Officer
CMO: George Barnes, M.D., Medical Director
CIO: Debra Hasling, Director Medical Records
CHR: Lyle Theriot, Director Human Resources
CNO: Bonnie Pratt, R.N., Chief Nursing Officer
Web address: www.lakeviewregional.com
**Control:** Corporation, Investor–owned, for–profit **Service:** General Medical and Surgical

**Staffed Beds:** 172 **Admissions:** 7000 **Census:** 96 **Outpatient Visits:** 39272 **Births:** 863 **Total Expense ($000):** 101804 **Payroll Expense ($000):** 35862 **Personnel:** 612

---

**Hospital, Medicare Provider Number, Address, Telephone, Approval, Facility, and Physician Codes, Health Care System**

★ American Hospital Association (AHA) membership
☐ The Joint Commission accreditation
◇ DNV Healthcare Inc. accreditation
○ Healthcare Facilities Accreditation Program
△ Commission on Accreditation of Rehabilitation Facilities (CARF) accreditation

**LA**

☐ **NORTHSHORE SPECIALTY HOSPITAL (192048)**, 20050 Crestwood Boulevard, Zip 70433–5207; tel. 985/875–7525 **A**1 10 **F**1 29 35 54 60 130 143 148 **S** Post Acute Medical, LLC, Camp Hill, PA
Primary Contact: Stephanie Morvant, Chief Executive Officer
Web address: www.northshoreltach.com
**Control:** Partnership, Investor–owned, for–profit **Service:** Long–Term Acute Care hospital

Staffed Beds: 58 Admissions: 442 Census: 31 Outpatient Visits: 1980
Births: 0 Total Expense ($000): 15747 Payroll Expense ($000): 5799
Personnel: 111

⊠ **REGENCY HOSPITAL OF COVINGTON (192051)**, 195 Highland Park Entrance, Zip 70433–7164; tel. 985/867–3977, (Nonreporting) **A**1 10 **S** Select Medical Corporation, Mechanicsburg, PA
Primary Contact: Kiley P. Cedotal, Chief Executive Officer
CMO: Merrill Laurent, M.D., Medical Director
CHR: Beth Sayler, Director Human Resources
Web address: www.regencyhospital.com
**Control:** Corporation, Investor–owned, for–profit **Service:** Long–Term Acute Care hospital

Staffed Beds: 38

⊠ **ST. TAMMANY PARISH HOSPITAL (190045)**, 1202 South Tyler Street, Zip 70433–2330; tel. 985/898–4000 **A**1 2 9 10 **F**3 8 11 12 13 15 17 18 20 22 24 26 28 29 30 31 34 35 37 40 43 45 48 49 50 54 57 59 62 63 64 65 69 70 72 74 75 76 77 78 79 81 82 84 85 86 87 89 90 92 93 96 97 107 108 109 110 111 114 115 119 124 129 130 132 135 146 147 148 **P**6 7
Primary Contact: Patti M. Ellish, FACHE, President and Chief Executive Officer
COO: Sharon A. Toups, Senior Vice President and Chief Operating Officer
CMO: Robert Capitelli, M.D., Senior Vice President and Chief Medical Officer
CHR: Judy Gracia, Vice President Human Resources
Web address: www.stph.org
**Control:** Hospital district or authority, Government, nonfederal **Service:** General Medical and Surgical

Staffed Beds: 218 Admissions: 11237 Census: 135 Outpatient Visits:
230808 Births: 1484 Total Expense ($000): 211195 Payroll Expense
($000): 85199 Personnel: 1328

### CROWLEY—Acadia Parish

★ **AMERICAN LEGION HOSPITAL (190044)**, 1305 Crowley Rayne Highway, Zip 70526–8202; tel. 337/783–3222, (Nonreporting) **A**9 10
Primary Contact: Terry W. Osborne, CPA, Chief Executive Officer
CFO: Charmaine Vidrine, CPA, Chief Financial Officer
CMO: Neal J. Duhon, M.D., Chief of Staff
**Control:** Other not–for–profit (including NFP Corporation) **Service:** General Medical and Surgical

Staffed Beds: 178

★ **COMPASS BEHAVIORAL CENTER OF CROWLEY (194085)**, 1526 North Avenue I., Zip 70526–2434; tel. 337/788–3380 **A**9 10 **F**64 98 100 101 103 104 105 **P**8 **S** Compass Health, Crowley, LA
Primary Contact: Aimee Monaghan, Administrator
Web address: www.compasshealthcare.com
**Control:** Corporation, Investor–owned, for–profit **Service:** Psychiatric

Staffed Beds: 34 Admissions: 431 Census: 13 Outpatient Visits: 20553
Births: 0 Total Expense ($000): 6783 Payroll Expense ($000): 3664
Personnel: 29

**CROWLEY REHABILITATION HOSPITAL (192050)**, 713 North Avenue L., Zip 70526–3832; tel. 337/783–2859, (Nonreporting) **A**10
Primary Contact: Gil Pinac, Chief Executive Officer
**Control:** Corporation, Investor–owned, for–profit **Service:** Long–Term Acute Care hospital

Staffed Beds: 15

### CUT OFF—Lafourche Parish

★ ◇ **LADY OF THE SEA GENERAL HOSPITAL (191325)**, 200 West 134th Place, Zip 70345–4143; tel. 985/632–6401, (Nonreporting) **A**9 10 18 21
Primary Contact: Don Werner, Chief Executive Officer
CFO: Randy Tabor, Chief Financial Officer
CHR: Bennie Smith, Director Human Resources and Risk Management
Web address: www.losgh.org
**Control:** Hospital district or authority, Government, nonfederal **Service:** General Medical and Surgical

Staffed Beds: 25

### DE RIDDER—Beauregard Parish

⊠ **BEAUREGARD MEMORIAL HOSPITAL (190050)**, 600 South Pine Street, Zip 70634–4942, Mailing Address: P.O. Box 730, Zip 70634–0730; tel. 337/462–7100 **A**1 9 10 **F**3 11 13 15 18 20 26 28 29 30 31 34 35 39 40 45 46 50 53 57 64 70 75 76 78 79 81 85 89 91 93 96 107 108 110 111 114 119 129 130 133 146 148 **P**6
Primary Contact: Nathan Tudor, Chief Executive Officer and Administrator
CFO: Darrell L. Kingham, CPA, Vice President Finance
CMO: Chris Granger, M.D., President Medical Staff
CIO: Meg Jackson, Director Biomedical and Management Information Systems
CHR: Hope Leedom, Director Human Resources
CNO: Jackie Reviel, R.N., Vice President Patient Care Services
Web address: www.beauregard.org
**Control:** Hospital district or authority, Government, nonfederal **Service:** General Medical and Surgical

Staffed Beds: 60 Admissions: 2305 Census: 22 Outpatient Visits: 43701
Births: 363 Total Expense ($000): 34108 Payroll Expense ($000): 15826
Personnel: 314

### DELHI—Richland Parish

**RICHLAND PARISH HOSPITAL (191323)**, 407 Cincinnati Street, Zip 71232–3007; tel. 318/878–5171, (Nonreporting) **A**9 10 18
Primary Contact: Michael W. Carroll, Administrator
CIO: Barbra Hutchison, Director Medical Records
CHR: Patsy Stout, Director Personnel
Web address: www.delhihospital.com
**Control:** Hospital district or authority, Government, nonfederal **Service:** General Medical and Surgical

Staffed Beds: 25

### DENHAM SPRINGS—Livingston Parish

**AMG SPECIALTY HOSPITAL–DENHAM SPRINGS (192008)**, 8375 Florida Boulevard, Zip 70726–7806; tel. 225/665–2664, (Nonreporting) **A**10 **S** AMG Integrated Healthcare Management, Lafayette, LA
Primary Contact: Karen Crayton, Administrator
Web address: www.amgdenham.com/
**Control:** Corporation, Investor–owned, for–profit **Service:** Long–Term Acute Care hospital

Staffed Beds: 117

### DEQUINCY—Calcasieu Parish

☐ **DEQUINCY MEMORIAL HOSPITAL (191307)**, 110 West Fourth Street, Zip 70633–3508, Mailing Address: P.O. Box 1166, Zip 70633–1166; tel. 337/786–1200, (Nonreporting) **A**1 9 10 18
Primary Contact: Michael Ashford, Administrator
CFO: Brandy Maddox, Chief Financial Officer
CMO: Jalal Joudeh, M.D., Chief of Staff
Web address: www.dequincyhospital.com
**Control:** City–Government, nonfederal **Service:** General Medical and Surgical

Staffed Beds: 19

### DERIDDER—Beauregard Parish

☐ **OCEANS BEHAVIORAL HOSPITAL OF DE RIDDER (194081)**, 1420 Blankenship Drive, Zip 70634–4604; tel. 337/460–9472, (Nonreporting) **A**1 9 10 **S** Oceans Healthcare, Lake Charles, LA
Primary Contact: Ronald E. Hand, Administrator
Web address: www.obhd.info/
**Control:** Corporation, Investor–owned, for–profit **Service:** Psychiatric

Staffed Beds: 20

### DONALDSONVILLE—Ascension Parish

⊠ **PREVOST MEMORIAL HOSPITAL (191308)**, 301 Memorial Drive, Zip 70346–4376; tel. 225/473–7931 **A**1 9 10 18 **F**3 11 15 29 40 57 59 107 110 119 133 146
Primary Contact: Vincent A. Cataldo, Administrator
CFO: Jane Arboneaux, Chief Financial Officer
CMO: Michel Y. Hirsch, M.D., Chief Medical Staff
CHR: Linda Cataldo, Human Resources Secretary
Web address: www.prevosthospital.net
**Control:** Hospital district or authority, Government, nonfederal **Service:** General Medical and Surgical

Staffed Beds: 25 Admissions: 90 Census: 1 Outpatient Visits: 22563
Births: 0 Total Expense ($000): 6662

### FARMERVILLE—Union Parish

**LIBERTY HEALTHCARE SYSTEMS** See Serenity Springs Specialty Hospital

**SERENITY SPRINGS SPECIALTY HOSPITAL (194074)**, 309 North Main Street, Zip 71241–2825; tel. 318/368–0110, (Nonreporting) **A**9 10
Primary Contact: Adrian Williams, Chief Executive Officer and Administrator
Web address: www.serenityhospital.com
**Control:** Corporation, Investor–owned, for–profit **Service:** Psychiatric

Staffed Beds: 18

*Many Facility Codes have changed. Please refer to the AHA Guide Code Chart.* © 2013 AHA Guide

**UNION GENERAL HOSPITAL (191301)**, 901 James Avenue, Zip 71241–2234, Mailing Address: P.O. Box 398, Zip 71241–0398; tel. 318/368–9751 **A**9 10 18 **F**15 32 35 40 45 56 81 93 104 107 114 119 127 128 133 143
Primary Contact: Evalyn Ormond, Chief Executive Officer
CFO: William Adcock, Chief Financial Officer
CHR: Sheri Cooper, Director Human Resources
Web address: www.uniongen.com
**Control:** Other not–for–profit (including NFP Corporation) **Service:** General Medical and Surgical

**Staffed Beds:** 25 **Admissions:** 419 **Census:** 6 **Outpatient Visits:** 26641 **Births:** 0 **Total Expense ($000):** 10808 **Payroll Expense ($000):** 4356 **Personnel:** 105

### FERRIDAY—Concordia Parish

**RIVERLAND MEDICAL CENTER (191318)**, 1700 N.E. Wallace Boulevard, Zip 71334–0111, Mailing Address: P.O. Box 111, Zip 71334–0111; tel. 318/757–6551 **A**9 10 18 **F**3 15 29 34 35 38 40 45 57 70 81 85 89 107 108 110 115 119 133 146 148
Primary Contact: Billy Rucker, Administrator
CFO: Lynda Jones, Financial Officer
CMO: J. Kevin Ingram, M.D., Chief of Staff
CIO: Nekisha Smith, Director Medical Records
CHR: Norma Jean Price, Manager Personnel
Web address: www.riverlandmedcenter.com/
**Control:** Hospital district or authority, Government, nonfederal **Service:** General Medical and Surgical

**Staffed Beds:** 25 **Admissions:** 811 **Census:** 8 **Outpatient Visits:** 93400 **Births:** 0 **Total Expense ($000):** 14938 **Personnel:** 137

### FORT POLK—Vernon Parish

☒ **BAYNE–JONES ARMY COMMUNITY HOSPITAL**, 1585 3rd Street, Zip 71459–5102; tel. 337/531–3928 **A**1 **F**8 11 13 15 29 30 32 33 34 35 38 39 40 44 45 46 50 54 57 59 64 65 68 75 77 79 81 82 85 87 97 99 100 101 104 107 110 111 115 119 130 131 132 135 143 144 146 147 148 **S** Department of the Army, Office of the Surgeon General, Falls Church, VA
Primary Contact: Colonel Mark C. Wilhite, Commander
CMO: Colonel Glynda Lucas, M.D., Deputy Commander Clinical Services
CIO: Thomas Baker, Chief Information Management Division
CHR: Captain Lucinda Duncan, Chief Human Resources
Web address: www.polk.amedd.army.mil
**Control:** Army, Government, federal **Service:** General Medical and Surgical

**Staffed Beds:** 22 **Admissions:** 1226 **Census:** 7 **Outpatient Visits:** 260277 **Births:** 543 **Total Expense ($000):** 56000 **Payroll Expense ($000):** 34021

### FRANKLIN—St. Mary Parish

☒ **FRANKLIN FOUNDATION HOSPITAL (191310)**, 1097 Northwest Boulevard, Zip 70538–3407, Mailing Address: P.O. Box 577, Zip 70538–0577; tel. 337/828–0760 **A**1 9 10 18 **F**3 11 13 15 18 26 28 29 34 40 45 50 57 59 68 70 74 75 76 77 79 81 85 93 107 110 111 114 119 130 133 135 146 147 148 **P**6 **S** QHR, Brentwood, TN
Primary Contact: Parker Templeton, FACHE, Chief Executive Officer
CFO: Ron Bailey, Chief Financial Officer
CMO: Jesus Chua, M.D., Chief of Staff
CMO: Sharad Gunda, M.D., Chief of Staff
CIO: Hal Goree, Chief Information Officer
CIO: John Spradlin, Information Systems Director
CHR: Elmo Vinas, Director Human Resources
CNO: Jennifer Wise, Chief Nursing Officer
Web address: www.franklinfoundation.org
**Control:** Hospital district or authority, Government, nonfederal **Service:** General Medical and Surgical

**Staffed Beds:** 22 **Admissions:** 1019 **Census:** 13 **Outpatient Visits:** 25000 **Births:** 109 **Total Expense ($000):** 22789 **Payroll Expense ($000):** 10448 **Personnel:** 174

### FRANKLINTON—Washington Parish

☐ **RIVERSIDE MEDICAL CENTER (191313)**, 1900 Main Street, Zip 70438–3688; tel. 985/839–4431 **A**1 9 10 18 **F**11 15 29 31 34 40 41 53 56 57 59 64 70 75 77 81 86 89 93 97 107 119 127 128 130 132 133 146
Primary Contact: Patricia A. Mizell, Interim Chief Executive Officer
CFO: Patricia A. Mizell, Chief Financial Officer
CMO: Mark James, M.D., Chief of Staff
CIO: Herman Ingram, Director
CHR: John Seal, Director Human Resources
Web address: www.rmchospital.com
**Control:** Hospital district or authority, Government, nonfederal **Service:** General Medical and Surgical

**Staffed Beds:** 25 **Admissions:** 729 **Census:** 8 **Outpatient Visits:** 19629 **Births:** 0

### GONZALES—Ascension Parish

☐ **ASCENSION GONZALES REHABILITATION HOSPITAL (193089)**, 333 East Worthy Road, Zip 70737–4234; tel. 225/450–2231 **A**1 10 **F**3 30 34 35 38 56 57 59 65 68 77 86 87 90 92 96 130 147 **P**5
Primary Contact: Bruce Walker, MSN, R.N., Chief Executive Officer
COO: Shawanza L. Alston, Administrator
CMO: Rosiland Cropper, M.D., Medical Director
Web address: www.agrehab.com
**Control:** Corporation, Investor–owned, for–profit **Service:** Rehabilitation

**Staffed Beds:** 20 **Admissions:** 158 **Census:** 1 **Outpatient Visits:** 0 **Births:** 0 **Personnel:** 27

☐ **SEASIDE HEALTH SYSTEM (194103)**, 615 East Worthy Road, Zip 70737–4240; Mailing Address: TX, tel. 225/238–3043 **A**1 9 10 **F**5 29 38 64 98 100 101 102 103 104 105 106 130 132 **P**5
Primary Contact: Larry Godfrey, Administrator
Web address: www.seasidehc.com
**Control:** Corporation, Investor–owned, for–profit **Service:** Psychiatric

**Staffed Beds:** 24 **Admissions:** 586 **Census:** 19 **Outpatient Visits:** 0 **Births:** 0

**SOUTH BATON ROUGE REHABILITATION HOSPITAL** See Ascension Gonzales Rehabilitation Hospital

☒ **ST. ELIZABETH HOSPITAL (190242)**, 1125 West Highway 30, Zip 70737–5004; tel. 225/647–5000 **A**1 9 10 **F**3 8 11 12 15 29 30 34 35 40 43 45 46 47 48 49 51 57 59 66 70 74 75 79 80 81 82 85 107 108 110 111 114 115 119 130 133 146 **P**6 **S** Franciscan Missionaries of Our Lady Health System, Inc., Baton Rouge, LA
Primary Contact: Robert Burgess, President and Chief Executive Officer
COO: Sue Knight, CPA, Chief Operating Officer
CFO: Scott Richard, Vice President Finance and Chief Financial Officer
CMO: Craig Vitrano, M.D., Medical Director
CIO: Joe Bumpus, Director Information Technology
CHR: Victor Vidaurre, Assistant Vice President Human Resources
Web address: www.steh.com
**Control:** Church–operated, Nongovernment, not–for profit **Service:** General Medical and Surgical

**Staffed Beds:** 48 **Admissions:** 2633 **Census:** 29 **Outpatient Visits:** 278290 **Births:** 0 **Total Expense ($000):** 103317 **Payroll Expense ($000):** 40341 **Personnel:** 756

**ST. JAMES BEHAVIORAL HEALTH HOSPITAL (194088)**, 3136 South Saint Landry Road, Zip 70737–5801; tel. 225/647–7524, (Nonreporting) **A**10
Primary Contact: Rick Bennett, Administrator
COO: Wendell Smith, Chief Operating Officer
CFO: Gopinath Gopalam, Chief Financial Officer
CMO: Lance Bullock, M.D., Medical Director
CHR: Charla Burchfield, Manager Human Resources
Web address: www.sjbhh.com/
**Control:** Corporation, Investor–owned, for–profit **Service:** Psychiatric

**Staffed Beds:** 10

### GREENSBURG—St. Helena Parish

**ST. HELENA PARISH HOSPITAL (191300)**, 16874 Highway 43, Zip 70441–4834; tel. 225/222–6111, (Total facility includes 72 beds in nursing home–type unit) **A**9 10 18 **F**3 7 9 11 14 15 18 26 28 29 30 31 32 33 34 35 36 38 40 41 42 44 53 56 57 58 59 60 63 64 65 66 67 68 71 75 82 83 84 85 86 87 89 90 91 92 93 97 101 102 103 104 105 107 110 119 127 128 133 135 143 148 **P**4 5 7
Primary Contact: Naveed Awan, FACHE, Chief Executive Officer
CFO: Theresa Brinkhaus, Chief Financial Officer
CMO: Anjanette Varnado, M.D., Chief Medical Officer
CHR: Lorraine L. Ballard, Director Human Resources
Web address: www.sthelenaparishhospital.com
**Control:** Hospital district or authority, Government, nonfederal **Service:** General Medical and Surgical

**Staffed Beds:** 97 **Admissions:** 323 **Census:** 13 **Outpatient Visits:** 15791 **Births:** 0

### GRETNA—Jefferson Parish

**UNITED MEDICAL HEALTHWEST–NEW ORLEANS (193074)**, 3201 Wall Boulevard, Suite B., Zip 70056–7755; tel. 504/433–5551, (Nonreporting) **A**9 10
Primary Contact: John Mills, President and Chief Executive Officer
Web address: www.umrhospital.com/
**Control:** Individual, Investor–owned, for–profit **Service:** Rehabilitation

**Staffed Beds:** 15

---

**Hospital, Medicare Provider Number, Address, Telephone, Approval, Facility, and Physician Codes, Health Care System**

★ American Hospital Association (AHA) membership
☐ The Joint Commission accreditation
◇ DNV Healthcare Inc. accreditation
◯ Healthcare Facilities Accreditation Program
△ Commission on Accreditation of Rehabilitation Facilities (CARF) accreditation

**LA**

## HAMMOND—Tangipahoa Parish

◇ **CYPRESS POINTE SURGICAL HOSPITAL (190303)**, 42570 South Airport Road, Zip 70403–0946; tel. 985/510–6200, (Nonreporting) **A**9 10 21
Primary Contact: Don Trexler, Chief Executive Officer
Web address: www.cypresspointsurgical.com
**Control:** Corporation, Investor–owned, for–profit **Service:** Surgical

Staffed Beds: 24

✳ △ **NORTH OAKS MEDICAL CENTER (190015)**, 15790 Paul Vega, M. D. Drive, Zip 70403–1436, Mailing Address: PO Box 2668, Zip 70404–2668; tel. 985/345–2700 **A**1 7 9 10 19 **F**3 13 15 18 20 22 24 26 28 29 30 31 32 34 40 45 49 50 54 56 57 58 59 63 64 68 70 72 73 74 75 76 77 78 79 81 82 84 85 86 87 89 93 94 96 102 103 107 108 110 111 114 115 118 119 126 129 130 131 132 135 143 144 146 147 148 **P**6 **S** North Oaks Health System, Hammond, LA
Primary Contact: Michele K. Sutton, FACHE, Administrator
COO: Michele K. Sutton, FACHE, Administrator
CFO: Shirley Hsing, Senior Vice President and Chief Financial Officer
CMO: Robert Peltier, M.D., Senior Vice President and Chief Medical Officer
CIO: Chris Smith, Vice President Information Technology
CHR: Carolyn Adema, Senior Vice President Human Resources
CNO: Shelly Welch, R.N., Senior Vice President and Chief Nursing Officer
Web address: www.northoaks.org
**Control:** Hospital district or authority, Government, nonfederal **Service:** General Medical and Surgical

Staffed Beds: 251 Admissions: 12608 Census: 176 Outpatient Visits: 382644 Births: 1446 Total Expense ($000): 242857 Payroll Expense ($000): 131953 Personnel: 2363

☐ **NORTH OAKS REHABILITATION HOSPITAL (193044)**, 1900 South Morrison Boulevard, Zip 70403–5742; tel. 504/230–5700 **A**1 10 **F**29 56 75 86 87 90 130 132 143 **P**6 **S** North Oaks Health System, Hammond, LA
Primary Contact: Sybil K. Paulson, R.N., Administrator
Web address: www.northoaks.org
**Control:** Hospital district or authority, Government, nonfederal **Service:** Rehabilitation

Staffed Beds: 27 Admissions: 527 Census: 17 Outpatient Visits: 0 Births: 0 Total Expense ($000): 13122 Payroll Expense ($000): 2702 Personnel: 40

☐ **POST ACUTE SPECIALTY HOSPITAL OF HAMMOND (192036)**, (Formerly Specialty Long Term Acute Care Hospital of Hammond), 42074 Veterans Avenue, Zip 70403–1408; tel. 985/902–8148 **A**1 10 **F**1 75 77 **S** Specialty Healthcare, LLC, Leesville, LA
Primary Contact: Jerry Elenbaas, Administrator
Web address: www.specialtyltch.com/
**Control:** Corporation, Investor–owned, for–profit **Service:** Long–Term Acute Care hospital

Staffed Beds: 40 Admissions: 326 Census: 22 Outpatient Visits: 0 Births: 0 Total Expense ($000): 10942 Payroll Expense ($000): 4786

**UNITED MEDICAL REHABILITATION HOSPITAL (193079)**, 15717 Belle Drive, Zip 70403–1439; tel. 985/340–5998, (Nonreporting) **A**10
Primary Contact: Cyrillia Bonds, Administrator
CFO: Warren Swenson, Chief Financial Officer
CMO: Luis Franco, M.D., Medical Director
CHR: Mark Gros, Director Human Resources
Web address: www.umrhospital.com
**Control:** Corporation, Investor–owned, for–profit **Service:** Rehabilitation

Staffed Beds: 20

## HOMER—Claiborne Parish

**HOMER MEMORIAL HOSPITAL (190114)**, 620 East College Street, Zip 71040–3202; tel. 318/927–2024 **A**9 10 **F**3 15 29 31 35 38 40 45 56 57 62 64 65 70 75 78 81 85 86 87 89 98 101 103 107 108 114 119 128 130 132 133 135 143 148
Primary Contact: Scott M. Landrum, Interim Chief Executive Officer
CFO: Michael Randle, Chief Financial Officer
CMO: Mark Haynes, M.D., Chief of Staff
CIO: Vance Robinson, Chief Information Officer
CHR: William Colvin, Human Resources Officer
CNO: Wendy Burnham, Interim Chief Nursing Officer
CNO: Ginger S. Smith, Chief Nursing Officer
Web address: www.homerhospital.com
**Control:** City–Government, nonfederal **Service:** General Medical and Surgical

Staffed Beds: 60 Admissions: 1985 Census: 31 Outpatient Visits: 22841 Births: 0 Total Expense ($000): 18136 Payroll Expense ($000): 7762 Personnel: 219

## HOUMA—Terrebonne Parish

**AMG SPECIALTY HOSPITAL–HOUMA (192037)**, 629 Dunn Street, Zip 70360–4707; tel. 985/274–0001, (Data for 245 days) **A**10 **F**1 29 130 **S** AMG Integrated Healthcare Management, Lafayette, LA
Primary Contact: Ricky Robeson, Chief Executive Officer
**Control:** Corporation, Investor–owned, for–profit **Service:** Long–Term Acute Care hospital

Staffed Beds: 40 Admissions: 275 Census: 28 Outpatient Visits: 0 Births: 0 Total Expense ($000): 7240 Payroll Expense ($000): 3684 Personnel: 103

**COMPASS BEHAVIORAL CENTER OF HOUMA, INC.**, 4701 West Park Avenue, Zip 70364–4426; tel. 985/876–1715, (Nonreporting) **S** Compass Health, Crowley, LA
Web address: www.compasshealthcare.com/site83.php
**Control: Service:** Psychiatric

Staffed Beds: 20

☐ **LEONARD J. CHABERT MEDICAL CENTER (190183)**, 1978 Industrial Boulevard, Zip 70363–7094; tel. 985/873–2200 **A**1 3 5 9 10 **F**3 15 18 20 29 30 31 34 35 38 39 40 45 46 47 48 49 50 51 55 58 59 60 61 64 65 66 68 70 74 75 77 78 79 81 82 83 84 85 86 87 89 91 92 93 94 97 98 99 100 101 102 103 107 108 109 110 111 114 115 119 120 130 132 143 146 147 148 **P**1 **S** LSU Health Care Services Division, Baton Rouge, LA
Primary Contact: Rhonda G. Green, Administrator
CFO: Elizabeth Callais, Chief Fiscal Officer
CMO: Michael Garcia, M.D., Medical Director
CIO: Susan Arceneaux, R.N., Coordinator Information Technology
CHR: Bain Manning, Director Human Resources
Web address: www.lsuhospitals.org/hospitals/ljc/default.htm
**Control:** State–Government, nonfederal **Service:** General Medical and Surgical

Staffed Beds: 74 Admissions: 4576 Census: 66 Outpatient Visits: 198788 Births: 228 Total Expense ($000): 98355 Payroll Expense ($000): 38973 Personnel: 805

**PHYSICIANS ALLIANCE HOSPITAL OF HOUMA** See AMG Specialty Hospital–Houma

**PHYSICIANS MEDICAL CENTER (190241)**, 218 Corporate Drive, Zip 70360–2768; tel. 985/853–1390, (Nonreporting) **A**9 10
Primary Contact: Connie Martin, Administrator
Web address: www.physicianshouma.com/
**Control:** Partnership, Investor–owned, for–profit **Service:** Surgical

Staffed Beds: 10

✳ △ **TERREBONNE GENERAL MEDICAL CENTER (190008)**, 8166 Main Street, Zip 70360–3498, Mailing Address: P.O. Box 6037, Zip 70361–6037; tel. 985/873–4141, (Total facility includes 8 beds in nursing home–type unit) **A**1 2 7 9 10 **F**8 11 13 14 15 17 18 20 22 24 26 29 30 31 34 35 40 44 49 50 57 58 59 64 65 68 70 72 74 75 76 77 78 79 81 82 84 85 86 87 89 90 92 93 107 108 109 110 111 114 117 118 119 121 123 124 128 130 132 134 135 146 147 148 **P**3 6
Primary Contact: Phyllis Peoples, MSN, R.N., President and Chief Executive Officer
COO: Diane Yeates, Chief Operating Officer
CFO: Dean Verret, Vice President Financial Services
CMO: Richard Abben, M.D., Chief of Staff
CHR: Mickie Rousseau, Director Human Resources
CNO: Teresita McNabb, R.N., Vice President Nursing Services
Web address: www.tgmc.com
**Control:** Hospital district or authority, Government, nonfederal **Service:** General Medical and Surgical

Staffed Beds: 230 Admissions: 9898 Census: 136 Outpatient Visits: 116832 Births: 1900 Total Expense ($000): 184555 Payroll Expense ($000): 65414 Personnel: 1272

## INDEPENDENCE—Tangipahoa Parish

☐ **LALLIE KEMP MEDICAL CENTER (191321)**, 52579 Highway 51 South, Zip 70443–2231; tel. 985/878–9421, (Nonreporting) **A**1 5 9 10 18 **S** LSU Health Care Services Division, Baton Rouge, LA
Primary Contact: Sherre Pack–Hookfin, Administrator
COO: Lisa G. Bruhl, Chief Operating Officer
CFO: Chad Thompson, Chief Financial Officer
CMO: Kathy Willis, M.D., Medical Director
CIO: Charles Tate, Director Information Technology
CHR: Diane Farnham, Acting Director Human Resources
Web address: www.lsuhospitals.org
**Control:** State–Government, nonfederal **Service:** General Medical and Surgical

Staffed Beds: 25

*Many Facility Codes have changed. Please refer to the AHA Guide Code Chart.*

## JACKSON—East Feliciana Parish

☐ **EASTERN LOUISIANA MENTAL HEALTH SYSTEM (194008)**, 4502 Highway 951, Zip 70748–5842, Mailing Address: P.O. Box 498, Zip 70748–0498; tel. 225/634–0100 **A**1 10 **F**29 30 35 39 50 59 75 87 98 100 103 104 106 130 146 **P**6 **S** Louisiana State Hospitals, Baton Rouge, LA
Primary Contact: Patricia Gonzales, Chief Executive Officer
COO: Hampton P S Lea, Chief Operating Officer
CFO: Janet O'Dell, Administrative Director
CMO: John W. Thompson, M.D., Chief of Staff
CIO: Deborah Brandon, Director Total Quality Management
CHR: Evelyn Perkins, Director Human Resources
Web address: www.wwprd.doa.louisiana.gov/laservices/publicpages/ServiceDetail.cfm?service_id=2445
**Control:** State–Government, nonfederal **Service:** Psychiatric

**Staffed Beds:** 473 **Admissions:** 1076 **Census:** 513 **Outpatient Visits:** 18720 **Births:** 0 **Total Expense ($000):** 93232 **Personnel:** 984

**VILLA FELICIANA MEDICAL COMPLEX (190199)**, 5002 Highway 10, Zip 70748–3627, Mailing Address: P.O. Box 438, Zip 70748–0438; tel. 225/634–4017, (Nonreporting) **A**10
Primary Contact: Michael C. Crump, Administrator
CFO: Kim Jelks, Fiscal Officer
CMO: John F. Piker, M.D., Medical Director
CIO: Michael James, Information Technology Technical Support Specialist 1
CHR: Sandra Delatte, Director Human Resources
CNO: Linda Williams, Director of Nursing
Web address: www.dhh.state.la.us/
**Control:** State–Government, nonfederal **Service:** Other specialty

**Staffed Beds:** 10

## JENA—La Salle Parish

★ **LASALLE GENERAL HOSPITAL (190145)**, 187 Ninth Street, Zip 71342 3901, Mailing Address: P.O. Box 2780, Zip 71342–2780; tel. 318/992–9200 **A**9 10 **F**7 11 15 20 29 40 45 53 57 59 62 64 71 81 89 93 107 108 110 114 118 119 127 130 133 **P**6
Primary Contact: Douglas A. Newman, Chief Executive Officer
CHR: Allyson Fannin, Director Human Resources
Web address: www.lasallegeneralhospital.com
**Control:** Hospital district or authority, Government, nonfederal **Service:** General Medical and Surgical

**Staffed Beds:** 49 **Admissions:** 955 **Census:** 10 **Outpatient Visits:** 27186 **Births:** 0 **Total Expense ($000):** 20360 **Payroll Expense ($000):** 9554 **Personnel:** 239

## JENNINGS—Jefferson Davis Parish

☐ **JENNINGS AMERICAN LEGION HOSPITAL (190053)**, 1634 Elton Road, Zip 70546–3614; tel. 337/616–7000 **A**1 9 10 **F**3 11 13 15 18 19 20 21 22 23 28 29 34 35 40 45 46 47 48 50 70 75 79 81 87 108 119 130 133 146 **P**6
Primary Contact: Dana D. Williams, Chief Executive Officer
COO: Keith J. Simpson, Chief Operating Officer
CFO: Pam Primeaux, Chief Financial Officer
CIO: Gary Courrege, Chief Information Officer
CHR: Ruth Carnes, Manager Human Resources
Web address: www.jalh.com
**Control:** Other not–for–profit (including NFP Corporation) **Service:** General Medical and Surgical

**Staffed Beds:** 60 **Admissions:** 3471 **Census:** 35 **Outpatient Visits:** 29779 **Births:** 373 **Total Expense ($000):** 33748 **Payroll Expense ($000):** 14847 **Personnel:** 376

**JENNINGS SENIOR CARE HOSPITAL (194082)**, 1 Hospital Drive, Suite 201, Zip 70546–3641; tel. 337/785–8003, (Nonreporting) **A**9 10
Primary Contact: April Bearb, Administrator
**Control:** Corporation, Investor–owned, for–profit **Service:** Psychiatric

**Staffed Beds:** 18

**MMO WESTEND HOSPITAL (194075)**, (Formerly WestEnd Hospital), 1530 Highway 90 West, Zip 70546–4022; tel. 337/616–8122, (Nonreporting) **A**9 10
Primary Contact: Jessica Adkinson, Administrator
CFO: Ronnie Callais, Chief Financial Officer
CMO: Charles Bramliet, M.D., Medical Director
CHR: Gloria Conner, Director Human Resources
Web address: www.mmoinc.com
**Control:** Corporation, Investor–owned, for–profit **Service:** Psychiatric

**Staffed Beds:** 20

**REHABILITATION HOSPITAL OF JENNINGS (193067)**, 1 Hospital Drive, Suite 101, Zip 70546–3641; tel. 337/821–5353 **A**10 **F**29 34 56 57 75 77 90 130 148
Primary Contact: Michael Holland, M.D., Chief Executive Officer
Web address: www.jenningsrehab.com
**Control:** State–Government, nonfederal **Service:** Rehabilitation

**Staffed Beds:** 16 **Admissions:** 231 **Census:** 9 **Outpatient Visits:** 0 **Births:** 0 **Total Expense ($000):** 1502 **Payroll Expense ($000):** 1292 **Personnel:** 35

## JONESBORO—Jackson Parish

**JACKSON PARISH HOSPITAL (191317)**, 165 Beech Springs Road, Zip 71251–2059; tel. 318/259–4435, (Nonreporting) **A**9 10 18
Primary Contact: Lloyd Monger, Administrator
CFO: David Sanders, Chief Financial Officer
CHR: Elizabeth Cheatwood, Human Resource Director and Administrative Assistant
Web address: www.jacksonparishhospital.com
**Control:** Hospital district or authority, Government, nonfederal **Service:** General Medical and Surgical

**Staffed Beds:** 25

## KAPLAN—Vermilion Parish

**ABROM KAPLAN MEMORIAL HOSPITAL (191322)**, 1310 West Seventh Street, Zip 70548–2910; tel. 337/643–8300, (Nonreporting) **A**9 10 18
Primary Contact: Lyman Trahan, Chief Executive Officer
CFO: Mary Melancon, Chief Financial Officer
CMO: Scott Bergeaux, M.D., Chief Medical Staff
Web address: www.lafayettegeneral.com
**Control:** Hospital district or authority, Government, nonfederal **Service:** General Medical and Surgical

**Staffed Beds:** 35

## KENNER—Jefferson Parish

**LOUISIANA EXTENDED CARE HOSPITAL OF KENNER** See Ochsner Extended Care Hospital of Kenner

☐ **OCEANS BEHAVIORAL HOSPITAL OF GREATER NEW ORLEANS (194098)**, 716 Village Road, Zip 70065–2751; tel. 504/464–8895 **A**1 9 10 **F**56 98 103 104 130 **P**6 **S** Oceans Healthcare, Lake Charles, LA
Primary Contact: Deborah Spier, Administrator
Web address: www.obhgno.info/
**Control:** Other, Government, federal **Service:** Psychiatric

**Staffed Beds:** 30 **Admissions:** 31 **Census:** 1 **Outpatient Visits:** 0 **Births:** 0

☐ **OCHSNER EXTENDED CARE HOSPITAL OF KENNER (192015)**, 180 West Esplanade Avenue, 5th Floor, Zip 70065–2467; tel. 504/464–8590, (Nonreporting) **A**1 10 **S** LHC Group, Lafayette, LA
Primary Contact: Fritz Nelson, Administrator
Web address: www.lhcgroup.com/
**Control:** Corporation, Investor–owned, for–profit **Service:** Long–Term Acute Care hospital

**Staffed Beds:** 34

⊠ **OCHSNER MEDICAL CENTER – KENNER (190274)**, 180 West Esplanade Avenue, Zip 70065–6001; tel. 504/468–8600 **A**1 3 5 8 9 10 **F**1 3 13 15 17 18 20 22 24 26 28 29 30 34 35 37 40 43 45 46 47 49 54 56 57 58 59 60 63 64 65 68 70 72 74 75 76 77 78 79 81 84 85 87 88 89 90 93 97 98 102 107 108 110 111 115 119 120 124 128 129 130 131 132 135 146 147 148 **S** Ochsner Health System, New Orleans, LA
Primary Contact: Paolo Zambito, Chief Executive Officer
COO: Eddy Ramirez, Assistant Vice President Business Development
CFO: Mark Eckert, Vice President Finance
CMO: James Tebbe, M.D., Vice President Medical Affairs
CIO: Dere Krummel, Director Information Systems
CHR: Wendy L. Willis, Assistant Vice President Human Resources
Web address: www.ochsner.org/locations/ochsner_health_center_kenner_w_esplanade_ave/
**Control:** Other not–for–profit (including NFP Corporation) **Service:** General Medical and Surgical

**Staffed Beds:** 119 **Admissions:** 5782 **Census:** 60 **Outpatient Visits:** 104286 **Births:** 1266 **Total Expense ($000):** 92800 **Payroll Expense ($000):** 38397 **Personnel:** 592

**LA**

## KENTWOOD—Tangipahoa Parish

**OCEANS BEHAVIORAL HOSPITAL OF KENTWOOD (194091)**, 921 Avenue G., Zip 70444–2636; tel. 985/229–0717, (Nonreporting) **A**9 10 **S** Oceans Healthcare, Lake Charles, LA
Primary Contact: Gina Isbell, Administrator
Web address: www.obhk.info/
**Control:** Corporation, Investor–owned, for–profit **Service:** Psychiatric

| Staffed Beds: 18 |
| --- |

**SOUTHEAST REGIONAL MEDICAL CENTER (192040)**, 719 Avenue G., Zip 70444–2601; tel. 985/229–9193, (Nonreporting) **A**10
Primary Contact: Lionel Murphy, Chief Executive Officer
**Control:** Corporation, Investor–owned, for–profit **Service:** Long–Term Acute Care hospital

| Staffed Beds: 14 |
| --- |

## KINDER—Allen Parish

★ **ALLEN PARISH HOSPITAL (190133)**, 108 Sixth Avenue, Zip 70648–3187, Mailing Address: P.O. Box 1670, Zip 70648–1670; tel. 337/738–2527, (Nonreporting) **A**9 10
Primary Contact: Becky Rhodes, Interim Chief Executive Officer
COO: Terry Willet, Controller
CFO: Suzette Fatula, Chief Financial Officer
CMO: Ejiro Ughouwa, M.D., Chief of Staff
CIO: Bill Marcantel, Chief Information Systems
CHR: Amand Lambert, Director Human Resources
Web address: www.allenparishhospital.com
**Control:** Hospital district or authority, Government, nonfederal **Service:** General Medical and Surgical

| Staffed Beds: 49 |
| --- |

## LA PLACE—St. John The Baptist Parish

⊠ **RIVER PARISHES HOSPITAL (190175)**, 500 Rue De Sante, Zip 70068–5418; tel. 985/652–7000, (Nonreporting) **A**1 9 10 **S** LifePoint Hospitals, Inc., Brentwood, TN
Primary Contact: Robert Marshall, Chief Executive Officer
CFO: Thomas Ramsey, Chief Financial Officer
CMO: Andrew St. Martin, M.D., Chief of Staff
CHR: Katherine Trepagnier, Director Human Resources
CNO: Joyce Neville, Chief Nursing Officer
Web address: www.riverparisheshospital.com
**Control:** Corporation, Investor–owned, for–profit **Service:** General Medical and Surgical

| Staffed Beds: 106 |
| --- |

## LACOMBE—St. Tammany Parish

☐ **LOUISIANA HEART HOSPITAL (190250)**, (Formerly Louisiana Medical Center and Heart Hospital), 64030 Highway 434, Zip 70445–3456; tel. 985/690–7500, (Nonreporting) **A**1 9 10
Primary Contact: Stephen Blades, Chief Executive Officer and President
CFO: Christopher W. Daniel, Chief Financial Officer
CMO: Vasanth Bethala, M.D., Medical Director
CIO: Alan Chapman, Director Information Systems
CHR: Alana Roche, Director Human Resources
CNO: Glenda Dobson, Vice President Clinical Services
Web address: www.louisianaheart.com
**Control:** Corporation, Investor–owned, for–profit **Service:** Heart

| Staffed Beds: 58 |
| --- |

**MAGNOLIA BEHAVIORAL HEALTHCARE (194080)**, 64026 Highway 434, Suite 300, Zip 70445–5417; tel. 985/882–0226 **A**9 10 **F**56 98 101 103 104 130
Primary Contact: Gerry Morris, Administrator
Web address: www.magnoliabehavioralhealth.com
**Control:** Corporation, Investor–owned, for–profit **Service:** Psychiatric

| Staffed Beds: 16 **Admissions:** 384 **Census:** 14 **Outpatient Visits:** 9822 **Births:** 0 **Total Expense ($000):** 5216 **Payroll Expense ($000):** 2918 |
| --- |

## LAFAYETTE—Lafayette Parish

**ACADIA OPTIMA HOSPITAL (194078)**, (Formerly Optima Specialty Hospital), 1131 Rue De Belier, Zip 70506–6532; tel. 337/991–0571, (Nonreporting) **A**10 **S** Acadia Healthcare Company, Inc., Franklin, TN
Primary Contact: Michael E. Geissler, Chief Executive Officer
Web address: www.optimaspecialtyhospital.com/
**Control:** Corporation, Investor–owned, for–profit **Service:** General Medical and Surgical

| Staffed Beds: 24 |
| --- |

**ACADIA VERMILION HOSPITAL (194044)**, 2520 North University Avenue, Zip 70507–5306; tel. 337/234–5614 **A**9 10 **F**4 5 29 56 64 98 99 100 101 103 104 105 130 132 **P**8 **S** Acadia Healthcare Company, Inc., Franklin, TN
Primary Contact: Joseph Rodriguez, Chief Executive Officer
CFO: Doug Lahasky, Chief Financial Officer
CMO: Bob Winston, M.D., Medical Director
CHR: Claire Rowland, Director Human Resources
Web address: www.acadiavermilion.com
**Control:** Corporation, Investor–owned, for–profit **Service:** Psychiatric

| Staffed Beds: 54 **Admissions:** 2253 **Census:** 47 **Outpatient Visits:** 3885 **Births:** 0 **Total Expense ($000):** 11291 **Payroll Expense ($000):** 5681 **Personnel:** 89 |
| --- |

**AMG SPECIALTY HOSPITAL–LAFAYETTE (192029)**, (Formerly AMG Specialty Hospital – Lafayette), 310 Youngsville Highway, Zip 70508–4524; tel. 337/839–9880 **A**10 **F**1 3 29 30 34 35 50 56 60 75 77 79 91 119 130 135 143 148 **P**5 **S** AMG Integrated Healthcare Management, Lafayette, LA
Primary Contact: Jason Branson, Chief Executive Officer
CFO: Jessica McGee, Chief Financial Officer
CMO: Bradley Blappert, M.D., Chief Medical Officer
CHR: Heather Lamarche, Manager Human Resources
CNO: Mary Bollich, Director of Nurses
Web address: www.amglafayette.com
**Control:** Corporation, Investor–owned, for–profit **Service:** Long–Term Acute Care hospital

| Staffed Beds: 58 **Admissions:** 430 **Census:** 27 **Outpatient Visits:** 0 **Births:** 0 **Personnel:** 85 |
| --- |

**COMMUNITY SPECIALTY HOSPITAL (192020)**, 408 S.E. Evangeline Thruway, Zip 70501–7129; tel. 337/234–4031, (Nonreporting) **A**10
Primary Contact: Mark Goff, Owner and Administrator
COO: John E. Jumonville, III, Chief Operating Officer
CFO: Carolyn Guidry, Business Manager
CMO: John Charles Dugal, M.D., Medical Director
**Control:** Corporation, Investor–owned, for–profit **Service:** Long–Term Acute Care hospital

| Staffed Beds: 22 |
| --- |

⊠ **HEART HOSPITAL OF LAFAYETTE (190263)**, 1105 Kaliste Saloom Road, Zip 70508–5705; tel. 337/521–1000 **A**1 9 10 **F**3 17 18 20 22 24 26 28 29 30 34 35 40 46 50 57 59 64 74 75 81 85 87 107 108 115
Primary Contact: Christina Hockaday, FACHE, Administrator and Chief Operating Officer
CFO: James P. Barbuat, Chief Financial Officer
CHR: Thomas Duhon, Director Human Resources
Web address: www.hearthospitallaf.net
**Control:** Partnership, Investor–owned, for–profit **Service:** Heart

| Staffed Beds: 32 **Admissions:** 1744 **Census:** 16 **Outpatient Visits:** 20233 **Births:** 0 **Total Expense ($000):** 34600 **Payroll Expense ($000):** 10313 **Personnel:** 196 |
| --- |

⊠ **KINDRED HOSPITAL LAFAYETTE (192033)**, 204 Energy Parkway, Zip 70508–3816; tel. 337/232–1905 **A**1 10 **F**1 29 30 34 35 56 57 59 74 75 100 107 135 143 148 **S** Kindred Healthcare, Louisville, KY
Primary Contact: Sharon Black, Chief Executive Officer
CFO: Eva De La Paz, Regional Controller
CMO: Vitalis C. Okechukwu, M.D., President Medical Staff
CHR: Donna Stelly, Human Resources Coordinator
CNO: Major Stephanie Rossyion, Chief Clinical Officer
Web address: www.khlafayette.com
**Control:** Corporation, Investor–owned, for–profit **Service:** Long–Term Acute Care hospital

| Staffed Beds: 50 **Admissions:** 309 **Census:** 22 **Outpatient Visits:** 0 **Births:** 0 **Total Expense ($000):** 10999 **Payroll Expense ($000):** 5109 **Personnel:** 110 |
| --- |

**LAFAYETTE BEHAVIORAL HEALTH**, (Formerly University Medical Center–Psychiatric Unit), 302 Dulles Drive, Zip 70506–3008; tel. 337/262–4190, (Nonreporting)
Primary Contact: Kandy Collins, MSN, Director
Web address: www.lafayettegeneral.com
**Control:** State–Government, nonfederal **Service:** Psychiatric

| Staffed Beds: 20 |
| --- |

*Many Facility Codes have changed. Please refer to the AHA Guide Code Chart.*
© 2013 AHA Guide

**LAFAYETTE GENERAL MEDICAL CENTER (190002)**, 1214 Coolidge Avenue, Zip 70503–2696, Mailing Address: P.O. Box 52009 OCS, Zip 70505–2009; tel. 337/289–7991 **A**1 2 9 10 **F**3 8 11 12 13 15 17 18 19 20 21 22 23 24 26 28 29 30 31 35 40 45 47 48 49 50 51 53 54 56 57 59 64 65 70 72 74 75 76 77 78 79 81 84 85 87 88 89 90 98 100 102 103 107 108 110 111 114 115 117 118 119 120 121 123 124 126 130 132 135 144 146 147 148 **P**8
Primary Contact: David L. Callecod, FACHE, President and Chief Executive Officer
COO: Patrick W. Gandy, Chief Operating Officer
CFO: Roger Mattke, Chief Financial Officer
CMO: Ziad Ashkar, M.D., Chief Medical Officer
CIO: Edwina Mallery, Vice President Information Systems
CHR: Sheena Mitchell, Director Human Resources
CNO: Rebecca Benoit, R.N., Chief Nursing Officer
Web address: www.lafayettegeneral.org
**Control:** Other not–for–profit (including NFP Corporation) **Service:** General Medical and Surgical

**Staffed Beds:** 377 **Admissions:** 15689 **Census:** 212 **Outpatient Visits:** 169836 **Births:** 1843 **Total Expense ($000):** 241040 **Payroll Expense ($000):** 80259 **Personnel:** 1831

**LAFAYETTE GENERAL SURGICAL HOSPITAL (190268)**, 1000 West Pinhook Road, Zip 70503–2460; tel. 337/289–8088 **A**9 10 **F**3 29 51 68 79 81 141 **P**2
Primary Contact: Carrie E. Templeton, FACHE, Chief Executive Officer
CFO: Sandi Hernandez, Controller
CNO: Susan Woollen, R.N., Director of Nursing
Web address: www.lgsh.us
**Control:** Partnership, Investor–owned, for–profit **Service:** General Medical and Surgical

**Staffed Beds:** 10 **Admissions:** 48 **Census:** 1 **Outpatient Visits:** 7947 **Births:** 0 **Total Expense ($000):** 9738 **Payroll Expense ($000):** 2796 **Personnel:** 51

**LAFAYETTE PHYSICAL REHABILITATION HOSPITAL (193093)**, 307 Polly Lane, Zip 70508–4960; tel. 337/314–1111, (Nonreporting) **A**10 **S** AMG Integrated Healthcare Management, Lafayette, LA
Primary Contact: Jonathan Landreth, Chief Executive Officer
**Control:** Corporation, Investor–owned, for–profit **Service:** Rehabilitation

**Staffed Beds:** 32

**LAFAYETTE SURGICAL SPECIALTY HOSPITAL (190259)**, 1101 Kaliste Saloom Road, Zip 70508–5705; tel. 337/769–4100, (Nonreporting) **A**1 9 10 **S** National Surgical Hospitals, Chicago, IL
Primary Contact: Buffy Domingue, Chief Executive Officer
Web address: www.lafayettesurgical.com
**Control:** Corporation, Investor–owned, for–profit **Service:** Surgical

**Staffed Beds:** 20

**LONG TERM ACUTE CARE OF ACADIANA** See AMG Specialty Hospital–Lafayette

**LOUISIANA EXTENDED CARE HOSPITAL OF LAFAYETTE (192032)**, 1214 Coolidge Boulevard, 8th Floor, Zip 70503–2621; tel. 337/289–8180, (Includes EUNICE EXTENDED CARE HOSPITAL, 1879 Highway 190, Eunice, Zip 70535; tel. 337/546–0024; Cayle P. Guillory, Administrator; IBERIA EXTENDED CARE HOSPITAL, 2315 East Main Street, 3rd Floor, New Iberia, Zip 70560–4031; tel. 337/369–1100; Kevin Frank, Administrator), (Nonreporting) **A**10 **S** LHC Group, Lafayette, LA
Primary Contact: Kevin Frank, Administrator
Web address: www.lhcgroup.com
**Control:** Other not–for–profit (including NFP Corporation) **Service:** Long–Term Acute Care hospital

**Staffed Beds:** 42

**OPTIMA SPECIALTY HOSPITAL** See Acadia Optima Hospital

**OUR LADY OF LOURDES REGIONAL MEDICAL CENTER (190102)**, 4801 Ambassador Caffery Parkway, Zip 70508–6917; tel. 337/470–2000 **A**1 2 9 10 **F**3 5 11 16 18 20 22 24 26 28 29 30 31 32 34 35 40 44 45 47 48 49 50 51 53 54 56 57 58 59 60 64 65 66 68 70 71 74 75 77 78 79 81 82 84 85 86 87 90 93 96 107 108 110 111 114 115 117 118 119 126 127 129 130 132 134 135 143 144 145 146 147 148 **P**6 **S** Franciscan Missionaries of Our Lady Health System, Inc., Baton Rouge, LA
Primary Contact: William F. Barrow, II, President and Chief Executive Officer
COO: Robert Davis, III, M.D., Chief Operating Officer
CFO: Kim Hebert, Chief Financial Officer
CMO: Andy Blalock, M.D., Physician Executive
CIO: Nona Mire, Director Information Systems
CHR: Kevin Domingue, Director Human Resources and Medical Affairs
Web address: www.lourdesrmc.com
**Control:** Church–operated, Nongovernment, not–for profit **Service:** General Medical and Surgical

**Staffed Beds:** 186 **Admissions:** 10917 **Census:** 145 **Outpatient Visits:** 161114 **Births:** 0 **Total Expense ($000):** 225039 **Payroll Expense ($000):** 70254 **Personnel:** 1305

**PARK PLACE SURGICAL HOSPITAL (190255)**, 901 Wilson Street, Zip 70503–2439; tel. 337/237–8119, (Nonreporting) **A**9 10
Primary Contact: Brandon Moore, Administrator and Chief Executive Officer
Web address: www.parkplacesurgery.com/
**Control:** Partnership, Investor–owned, for–profit **Service:** Surgical

**Staffed Beds:** 10

**REGIONAL MEDICAL CENTER OF ACADIANA (190205)**, 2810 Ambassador Caffery Parkway, Zip 70506–5906; tel. 337/981–2949, (Includes WOMEN'S AND CHILDREN'S HOSPITAL, 4600 Ambassador Caffery Parkway, Zip 70508–6923, Mailing Address: P.O. Box 88030, Zip 70598–8030; tel. 337/521–9100), (Nonreporting) **A**1 9 10 **S** HCA, Nashville, TN
Primary Contact: Kathy J. Bobbs, FACHE, President Chief Executive Officer
COO: Mario J. Garner, FACHE, Chief Operating Officer
CFO: James Miller, CPA, Chief Financial Officer
CMO: Charles Wyatt, M.D., Medical Director
CHR: Jane Fuller, Director Human Resources
Web address: www.medicalcenterofacadiana.com
**Control:** Corporation, Investor–owned, for–profit **Service:** General Medical and Surgical

**Staffed Beds:** 142

**UNIVERSITY MEDICAL CENTER (190006)**, 2390 West Congress Street, Zip 70506–4298, Mailing Address: P.O. Box 69300, Zip 70596–9300; tel. 337/261–6001, (Nonreporting) **A**1 2 3 5 9 10 **S** LSU Health Care Services Division, Baton Rouge, LA
Primary Contact: Jared Stark, Chief Executive Officer
COO: Glenn L. Craig, Chief Operating Officer
CFO: Karen Gardiner, Director Fiscal Services
CMO: James B. Falterman, Jr., M.D., Medical Director
CIO: J. Barry Daigle, Manager Information Systems
CHR: Jennifer Simms, Director Human Resources
Web address: www.lsuhospitals.org
**Control:** State–Government, nonfederal **Service:** General Medical and Surgical

**Staffed Beds:** 100

**LAKE CHARLES—Calcasieu Parish**

**CALCASIEU OAKS GERIATRIC PSYCHIATRIC HOSPITAL**, 2837 Ernest Street, Zip 70601–8785; tel. 337/439–8111, (Nonreporting) **A**9 **S** Pacer Health Corporation, Miami Lakes, FL
Primary Contact: Charles Getwood, Assistant Chief Executive Officer
**Control:** Corporation, Investor–owned, for–profit **Service:** Psychiatric

**Staffed Beds:** 24

△ **CHRISTUS ST. PATRICK HOSPITAL OF LAKE CHARLES (190027)**, 524 Dr. Michael Debakey Drive, Zip 70601–5799, Mailing Address: P.O. Box 3401, Zip 70602–3401; tel. 337/436–2511 **A**1 2 7 9 10 **F**3 11 12 15 17 18 20 22 24 26 28 29 30 31 32 34 35 38 40 44 45 46 47 48 49 50 56 57 59 61 64 65 68 70 74 75 78 79 81 84 85 86 87 89 90 93 96 98 100 101 102 103 104 105 107 108 110 118 119 120 121 122 123 124 126 130 131 132 134 135 146 147 148 **P**8 **S** CHRISTUS Health, Irving, TX
Primary Contact: Stephen F. Wright, President and Chief Executive Officer
COO: Dianne P. Teal, MSN, Vice President Clinical Operations
CFO: Debbie White, Chief Financial Officer
CMO: David Engleking, M.D., Vice President Medical Affairs
CIO: Allen Abshire, Director Information Services
CHR: Wendy White, Assistant Administrator Human Resources
Web address: www.stpatrickhospital.org
**Control:** Church–operated, Nongovernment, not–for profit **Service:** General Medical and Surgical

**Staffed Beds:** 160 **Admissions:** 7582 **Census:** 115 **Outpatient Visits:** 69683 **Births:** 0 **Total Expense ($000):** 128558 **Payroll Expense ($000):** 39167 **Personnel:** 748

**DUBUIS HOSPITAL OF LAKE CHARLES (192024)**, 524 Dr. Michael DeBakey Drive, 5th Floor, Zip 70601–5725; tel. 337/491–7752 **A**1 10 **F**1 3 29 30 35 75 148 **S** Dubuis Health System, Houston, TX
Primary Contact: William L. Willis, Administrator
CMO: Ron Lewis, M.D., Medical Director
Web address: www.dubuis.org/DubuisHospitalofLakeCharles
**Control:** Church–operated, Nongovernment, not–for profit **Service:** Long–Term Acute Care hospital

**Staffed Beds:** 24 **Admissions:** 214 **Census:** 14 **Outpatient Visits:** 0 **Births:** 0 **Total Expense ($000):** 7127 **Payroll Expense ($000):** 2655 **Personnel:** 57

| Hospital, Medicare Provider Number, Address, Telephone, Approval, Facility, and Physician Codes, Health Care System |
|---|
| ★ American Hospital Association (AHA) membership     ○ Healthcare Facilities Accreditation Program |
| □ The Joint Commission accreditation     ◇ DNV Healthcare Inc. accreditation     △ Commission on Accreditation of Rehabilitation Facilities (CARF) accreditation |

LA

**EXTENDED CARE OF SOUTHWEST LOUISIANA (192019)**, 2837 Ernest Street, Building B., Zip 70601–8785; tel. 337/480–8990 **A**10 **F**1 3 85 130 148
Primary Contact: Ronald Hunt, Chief Executive Officer
Web address: www.lcmh.com/extcare.htm
**Control:** Other not–for–profit (including NFP Corporation) **Service:** Long–Term Acute Care hospital

Staffed Beds: 29 Admissions: 221 Census: 15 Outpatient Visits: 0 Births: 0 Total Expense ($000): 5624

✠ **LAKE CHARLES MEMORIAL HOSPITAL (190060)**, 1701 Oak Park Boulevard, Zip 70601–8911; tel. 337/494–3000, (Includes LAKE CHARLES MEMORIAL HOSPITAL FOR WOMEN, 1900 West Gauthier Road, Zip 70605–7170, tel. 337/480–7000) **A**1 2 3 5 9 10 **F**3 8 11 13 14 15 17 18 20 22 24 25 26 28 29 30 31 34 37 40 43 45 49 50 51 53 56 57 58 60 62 64 66 68 70 71 72 73 74 75 76 77 78 79 81 85 86 87 88 89 90 93 98 99 102 103 107 108 110 111 114 115 119 120 121 123 124 127 129 130 131 132 135 143 144 146 147 148 **P**1 6 7
Primary Contact: Larry M. Graham, FACHE, President and Chief Executive Officer
COO: Timothy O. Coffey, Senior Vice President Operations
CFO: Charles P. Whitson, CPA, Senior Vice President Finance
CMO: Kevin Mocklin, M.D., Director Medical Staff
CIO: Belinda Sommers, Chief Information Officer
CHR: Ginger Consigney, Vice President Human Resources
Web address: www.lcmh.com
**Control:** Other not–for–profit (including NFP Corporation) **Service:** General Medical and Surgical

Staffed Beds: 306 Admissions: 11122 Census: 157 Outpatient Visits: 150403 Births: 1714 Total Expense ($000): 177296 Payroll Expense ($000): 58685 Personnel: 1589

**LAKE CHARLES MEMORIAL HOSPITAL FOR WOMEN** See Lake Charles Memorial Hospital

**OCEANS BEHAVIORAL HOSPITAL OF LAKE CHARLES (194090)**, 302 West Mcneese Street, Zip 70605–5604; tel. 337/474–7581, (Nonreporting) **A**9 10 **S** Oceans Healthcare, Lake Charles, LA
Primary Contact: Christin Bennett, Administrator
Web address: www.obhlc.info/
**Control:** Corporation, Investor–owned, for–profit **Service:** Psychiatric

Staffed Beds: 20

✠ **WOMEN AND CHILDREN'S HOSPITAL (190201)**, 4200 Nelson Road, Zip 70605–4118; tel. 337/474–6370 **A**1 9 10 **F**12 13 15 20 22 29 40 45 46 47 48 49 50 57 70 72 75 76 77 79 81 85 89 91 93 107 110 114 119 130 132 146 147 **S** Community Health Systems, Inc., Franklin, TN
Primary Contact: Bryan S. Bateman, Chief Executive Officer
CFO: Dawn Johnson–Hatcher, Chief Financial Officer
CMO: Floyd Guidry, M.D., Medical Director
CIO: Aaron Cook, Director Information Services
CHR: Charles Buchert, Director Human Resources
CNO: Robbin Odom, R.N., Chief Nursing Officer
Web address: www.women–childrens.com
**Control:** Corporation, Investor–owned, for–profit **Service:** General Medical and Surgical

Staffed Beds: 88 Admissions: 3152 Census: 31 Outpatient Visits: 48436 Births: 1329 Total Expense ($000): 41883 Payroll Expense ($000): 19587 Personnel: 358

**LAKE PROVIDENCE—East Carroll Parish**

**EAST CARROLL PARISH HOSPITAL (190208)**, 336 North Hood Street, Zip 71254–2140; tel. 318/559–4023, (Nonreporting) **A**9 10
Primary Contact: LaDonna Englerth, Administrator
**Control:** Hospital district or authority, Government, nonfederal **Service:** General Medical and Surgical

Staffed Beds: 11

**LEESVILLE—Vernon Parish**

✠ **BYRD REGIONAL HOSPITAL (190164)**, 1020 West Fertitta Boulevard, Zip 71446–4645; tel. 337/239–9041 **A**1 9 10 **F**3 8 13 15 18 20 29 34 37 40 45 48 50 54 57 65 70 76 79 81 87 107 110 111 115 119 133 **P**7
**S** Community Health Systems, Inc., Franklin, TN
Primary Contact: Roger C. LeDoux, Chief Executive Officer
CFO: Wendell Wilkes, Chief Financial Officer
CMO: Hanna Lubbos, M.D., Chief of Staff
CHR: Karolyne Christian, Director Human Resources
Web address: www.byrdregional.com
**Control:** Corporation, Investor–owned, for–profit **Service:** General Medical and Surgical

Staffed Beds: 60 Admissions: 3979 Census: 36 Outpatient Visits: 32846 Births: 399 Total Expense ($000): 32446 Payroll Expense ($000): 14330 Personnel: 387

**DOCTOR'S HOSPITAL OF DEER CREEK (190297)**, 815 South 10th Street, Zip 71446–4611, Mailing Address: P.O. Box 1391, Zip 71496–1391; tel. 337/392–5088 **A**9 10 **F**8 81 89 107
Primary Contact: Jeff Morrow, Chief Executive Officer
CHR: Annette Hillman, Director Human Resources
CNO: Elizabeth Bennett, Director of Nursing
Web address: www.dhdc.md
**Control:** Corporation, Investor–owned, for–profit **Service:** General Medical and Surgical

Staffed Beds: 10 Admissions: 671 Census: 5 Outpatient Visits: 2540 Births: 0 Total Expense ($000): 6524 Payroll Expense ($000): 2044 Personnel: 62

☐ **LEESVILLE REHABILITATION HOSPITAL (193086)**, 900 South 6th Street, Zip 71446–4723; tel. 337/392–8118 **A**1 10 **F**9 29 57 77 90 91 96 130 148
Primary Contact: Jack M. Causey, Administrator and Chief Executive Officer
CMO: Gregory D. Lord, M.D., Chief Medical Officer
CHR: Jackie Rubar, Administrative Assistant and Director Human Resources
Web address: www.leesvillerehab.com
**Control:** Corporation, Investor–owned, for–profit **Service:** Rehabilitation

Staffed Beds: 16 Admissions: 332 Census: 11 Outpatient Visits: 0 Births: 0 Payroll Expense ($000): 1467

☐ **TRI PARISH REHABILITATION HOSPITAL (193050)**, 8088 Hawks Road, Zip 71446–6649; tel. 337/462–8880 **A**1 10 **F**29 64 90 93 148
Primary Contact: Heath Hairgrove, Administrator
Web address: www.triparishrehab.com
**Control:** Corporation, Investor–owned, for–profit **Service:** Rehabilitation

Staffed Beds: 20 Admissions: 266 Census: 13 Births: 0

**LULING—St. Charles Parish**

☐ **SPECIALTY REHABILITATION HOSPITAL OF LULING (193064)**, 1125 Paul Maillard Road, Zip 70070–4351; tel. 985/785–5233, (Nonreporting) **A**1 10 **S** Specialty Healthcare, LLC, Leesville, LA
Primary Contact: Chenell Barnes, Administrator
Web address: www.specialtyhealthcare.com
**Control:** Corporation, Investor–owned, for–profit **Service:** Rehabilitation

Staffed Beds: 21

☐ **ST. CHARLES PARISH HOSPITAL (190079)**, 1057 Paul Maillard Road, Zip 70070–4349, Mailing Address: P.O. Box 87, Zip 70070–0087; tel. 985/785–6242, (Nonreporting) **A**1 9 10
Primary Contact: Fred Martinez, Jr., Chief Executive Officer
COO: Karen Guillot, R.N., Chief Operating Officer
CMO: Chemmele Jayakrishnan, M.D., Chief Medical Staff
CIO: Angela Duet, Director Information Technology
CHR: Carolyn Faucheaux, Director Human Resources
Web address: www.stch.net
**Control:** Hospital district or authority, Government, nonfederal **Service:** General Medical and Surgical

Staffed Beds: 59

**ST. CHARLES SPECIALTY REHABILITATION HOSPITAL (193060)**, 1125 Paul Maillard Road, Zip 70070–4349, Mailing Address: P.O. Box 243, Zip 70070–0243; tel. 985/785–5233, (Nonreporting) **A**10
Primary Contact: Juanita Ann Bates, Administrator
Web address: www.lulingrehab.com
**Control:** County–Government, nonfederal **Service:** Rehabilitation

Staffed Beds: 16

**LUTCHER—St. James Parish**

✠ **ST. JAMES PARISH HOSPITAL (191305)**, 1645 Lutcher Avenue, Zip 70071–5150; tel. 225/869–5512 **A**1 9 10 18 **F**3 15 29 30 34 35 40 45 57 59 64 75 77 81 107 110 111 114 119 128 132 133
Primary Contact: Mary Ellen Pratt, FACHE, Chief Executive Officer
CFO: Tracy L. George, Chief Financial Officer
CIO: Susan Duhon, Director Medical Records
CHR: Lisa Faucheux, Director Human Resources
Web address: www.sjph.org
**Control:** Hospital district or authority, Government, nonfederal **Service:** General Medical and Surgical

Staffed Beds: 20 Admissions: 576 Census: 12 Outpatient Visits: 25036 Births: 0 Total Expense ($000): 19109 Payroll Expense ($000): 7367 Personnel: 157

*Many Facility Codes have changed. Please refer to the AHA Guide Code Chart.*

## MAMOU—Evangeline Parish

☐ **SAVOY MEDICAL CENTER (190025)**, 801 Poinciana Avenue, Zip 70554–2298; tel. 337/468–5261, (Nonreporting) **A**1 9 10
Primary Contact: George Patrick Derouen, Chief Executive Officer
COO: Gerald Fuselier, Chief Operating Officer
CMO: Greg Savoy, M.D., Chief Medical Officer
CIO: Daniel Lahaye, Manager
CHR: Annette Thibodeaux, Director Human Resources
Web address: www.savoymedicalcenter.com
**Control:** Corporation, Investor–owned, for–profit **Service:** General Medical and Surgical

**Staffed Beds:** 180

## MANDEVILLE—St. Tammany Parish

☐ **NORTHLAKE BEHAVIORAL HOSPITAL (194007)**, (Formerly Southeast Louisiana Hospital), 23515 Highway 190, Zip 70448–7334, Mailing Address: P.O. Box 3850, Zip 70470–3850; tel. 985/626–6300, (Nonreporting) **A**1 3 5 10
Primary Contact: Richard Kramer, Interim Chief Executive Officer
COO: Richard Kramer, Chief Operating Officer
CFO: Denise Businelle, Account Administrator
CMO: Girishkumar Shah, M.D., Clinical Director
CIO: Mike Ziemba, Information Technology Project Lead
CHR: Daphne Stewart, Director Human Resources
Web address: www.selh.org
**Control:** State–Government, nonfederal **Service:** Psychiatric

**Staffed Beds:** 153

## MANSFIELD—De Soto Parish

**DE SOTO REGIONAL HEALTH SYSTEM (190118)**, 207 Jefferson Street, Zip 71052–2603, Mailing Address: P.O. Box 1636, Zip 71052–1636; tel. 318/871–3100 **A**9 10 20 **F**3 15 29 31 107 108 110 111 114 115 119 127 130 133 **P**3
Primary Contact: Todd Eppler, Chief Executive Officer
CMO: Leigh Dillard, M.D., Chief of Staff
CHR: Rhonda Potter, Director Human Resources
CNO: Vernadine Mitchell, Chief Nursing Officer
Web address: www.desotoregional.com
**Control:** State–Government, nonfederal **Service:** General Medical and Surgical

**Staffed Beds:** 12 **Admissions:** 800 **Census:** 9 **Outpatient Visits:** 22434 **Births:** 0 **Total Expense ($000):** 18116 **Payroll Expense ($000):** 8071 **Personnel:** 200

## MANY—Sabine Parish

**SABINE MEDICAL CENTER (190218)**, 240 Highland Drive, Zip 71449–3718; tel. 318/256–5691 **A**9 10 20 **F**3 15 27 29 34 40 41 45 50 57 59 64 81 89 107 111 115 119 127 128 130 133 **S** Allegiance Health Management, Shreveport, LA
Primary Contact: Chris Beddoe, Chief Executive Officer
CFO: Frances F. Hopkins, Chief Financial Officer
Web address: www.sabinemedicalcenter.net
**Control:** Individual, Investor–owned, for–profit **Service:** General Medical and Surgical

**Staffed Beds:** 44 **Admissions:** 939 **Census:** 8 **Outpatient Visits:** 56227 **Births:** 0 **Total Expense ($000):** 13615 **Payroll Expense ($000):** 7119 **Personnel:** 139

## MARKSVILLE—Avoyelles Parish

☐ **AVOYELLES HOSPITAL (190099)**, 4231 Highway 1192, Zip 71351–4711, Mailing Address: P.O. Box 249, Zip 71351–0249; tel. 318/253–8611 **A**1 9 10 **F**3 15 29 34 40 56 57 64 65 70 75 81 85 86 107 110 119 133 135 146
Primary Contact: David M. Mitchel, Chief Executive Officer
CMO: Fernando Garcia, M.D., Chief of Staff
CIO: Billy Tingle, Director Information Systems and Respiratory Therapy
CHR: Allison Ferguson, Director Human Resources
Web address: www.avoyelleshospital.com
**Control:** Corporation, Investor–owned, for–profit **Service:** General Medical and Surgical

**Staffed Beds:** 35 **Admissions:** 1515 **Census:** 17 **Outpatient Visits:** 44657 **Births:** 0 **Total Expense ($000):** 10119 **Payroll Expense ($000):** 6646 **Personnel:** 173

## MARRERO—Jefferson Parish

★ **LOUISIANA SPECIALTY HOSPITAL (192007)**, (Formerly Kindred Hospital West–Jefferson), 1111 Medical Center Boulevard, Suite S–550, Zip 70072–3151; tel. 504/349–2470, (Nonreporting) **A**10
Primary Contact: James H. Morgan, Chief Executive Officer
**Control:** Corporation, Investor–owned, for–profit **Service:** Long–Term Acute Care hospital

**Staffed Beds:** 56

✚ △ **WEST JEFFERSON MEDICAL CENTER (190039)**, 1101 Medical Center Boulevard, Zip 70072–3191; tel. 504/347–5511 **A**1 2 3 5 7 9 10 **F**3 6 7 11 12 13 15 17 18 20 22 24 26 28 29 30 31 34 35 37 38 39 40 41 43 45 46 47 49 50 51 53 56 57 59 60 61 64 65 68 70 72 74 75 76 78 79 81 82 84 85 86 87 89 90 91 93 96 97 98 100 101 102 104 105 107 108 110 111 114 115 117 118 119 120 121 124 126 127 129 130 132 135 146 147 148 **P**6
Primary Contact: Nancy R. Cassagne, FACHE, Chief Executive Officer
COO: Angela Greener, Chief Administrative Officer
CMO: Mark Workman, M.D., Chief Medical Officer
CIO: Nicholas Thimis, Chief Information Officer
CHR: Frank Martinez, Vice President Human Resources
CNO: Adonna F. Lowe, R.N., Chief Nursing Officer
Web address: www.wjmc.org
**Control:** Hospital district or authority, Government, nonfederal **Service:** General Medical and Surgical

**Staffed Beds:** 319 **Admissions:** 13192 **Census:** 194 **Outpatient Visits:** 233976 **Births:** 1223 **Total Expense ($000):** 256382 **Payroll Expense ($000):** 91986 **Personnel:** 1722

## METAIRIE—Jefferson Parish

✚ △ **EAST JEFFERSON GENERAL HOSPITAL (190146)**, 4200 Houma Boulevard, Zip 70006–2996; tel. 504/454–4000, (Includes DOCTORS HOSPITAL OF JEFFERSON, 4320 Houma Boulevard, Zip 70006–2973, tel. 504/849–4000) **A**1 2 3 5 7 9 10 **F**3 7 8 11 13 14 15 17 18 20 22 24 26 28 29 30 31 34 35 37 40 45 46 47 48 49 50 51 53 56 57 59 60 64 68 70 72 73 74 75 76 77 78 79 81 82 84 85 86 87 90 91 92 93 94 96 97 98 102 103 107 109 110 111 112 115 116 117 118 119 120 121 122 123 126 128 129 130 131 132 135 145 146 148
Primary Contact: Mark J. Peters, M.D., President and Chief Executive Officer
COO: Janice Kishner, R.N., Chief Operating Officer and Nurse Executive
CFO: Ted Shaw, Interim Chief Financial Officer
CMO: Raymond P. DeCorte, M.D., Chief Medical Officer
CIO: Bernie Clement, Chief Information Officer
CHR: Donna Ammons, Director Human Resources
Web address: www.ejgh.org
**Control:** Hospital district or authority, Government, nonfederal **Service:** General Medical and Surgical

**Staffed Beds:** 437 **Admissions:** 18405 **Census:** 282 **Outpatient Visits:** 202025 **Births:** 1570 **Total Expense ($000):** 332585 **Payroll Expense ($000):** 120951 **Personnel:** 2346

◇ **OMEGA HOSPITAL (190302)**, 2525 Severn Avenue, Zip 70002–5932; tel. 504/832–4200, (Nonreporting) **A**10 21
Primary Contact: Debbie Schenck, Administrator
Web address: www.omega–institute.com
**Control:** Individual, Investor–owned, for–profit **Service:** Surgical

**Staffed Beds:** 10

☐ **ST. THERESA SPECIALTY HOSPITAL (192030)**, 4200 Houma Boulevard, Zip 70006–2970; tel. 504/780–3041 **A**1 10 **F**1 29 30 34 35 87 90 91 100 148
Primary Contact: Glynda Troyo, Chief Executive Officer
Web address: www.stmck.com
**Control:** Corporation, Investor–owned, for–profit **Service:** Children's Long–Term Acute Care

**Staffed Beds:** 73 **Admissions:** 193 **Census:** 18 **Outpatient Visits:** 0 **Births:** 0

---

**Hospital, Medicare Provider Number, Address, Telephone, Approval, Facility, and Physician Codes, Health Care System**

★ American Hospital Association (AHA) membership
☐ The Joint Commission accreditation
◇ DNV Healthcare Inc. accreditation
○ Healthcare Facilities Accreditation Program
△ Commission on Accreditation of Rehabilitation Facilities (CARF) accreditation

**LA**

## MINDEN—Webster Parish

☒ **MINDEN MEDICAL CENTER (190144)**, 1 Medical Plaza, Zip 71055–3330,
Mailing Address: P.O. Box 5003, Zip 71058–5003; tel. 318/377–2321 **A**1 9 10
19 **F**11 13 15 18 20 22 29 30 34 40 45 46 56 57 59 62 64 70 75 76 77 79
81 82 87 89 90 93 98 103 107 111 115 119 129 130 132 146 147 148
**S** LifePoint Hospitals, Inc., Brentwood, TN
Primary Contact: George E. French, III, FACHE, Chief Executive Officer
CFO: Jim Williams, Chief Financial Officer
CMO: G. Max Stell, M.D., Medical Director
CIO: Mace Morgan, Director Information Systems
CHR: Mary Winget, Director Human Resources
CNO: Donna Carter, MSN, Chief Nursing Officer
Web address: www.mindenmedicalcenter.com
**Control:** Corporation, Investor–owned, for–profit **Service:** General Medical and
Surgical

**Staffed Beds:** 161 **Admissions:** 4590 **Census:** 51 **Outpatient Visits:** 44427
**Births:** 702 **Total Expense ($000):** 57753 **Payroll Expense ($000):** 23459
**Personnel:** 484

## MONROE—Ouachita Parish

☐ **E. A. CONWAY MEDICAL CENTER (190011)**, 4864 Jackson Street,
Zip 71202–6497, Mailing Address: P.O. Box 1881, Zip 71210–8005;
tel. 318/330–7000 **A**1 3 5 9 10 **F**11 13 15 30 31 40 43 49 50 54 58 59 61
64 65 66 70 72 74 75 76 77 78 79 81 87 89 92 93 97 98 100 102 107 108
110 111 114 119 130 135 146 **P**1
Primary Contact: H. Aryon McGuire, Administrator
CFO: Linda Lochbrunner, Chief Financial Officer
CMO: LaDonna Ford, M.D., Medical Director
CHR: Kaye Clark, Assistant Director Human Resources Management
Web address: www.conway.lsuhsc.edu
**Control:** State–Government, nonfederal **Service:** General Medical and Surgical

**Staffed Beds:** 158 **Admissions:** 5728 **Census:** 86 **Outpatient Visits:** 145475
**Births:** 836 **Total Expense ($000):** 76908 **Payroll Expense ($000):** 34320
**Personnel:** 781

☐ **MONROE SURGICAL HOSPITAL (190245)**, 2408 Broadmoor Boulevard,
Zip 71201–2963; tel. 318/410–0002, (Nonreporting) **A**1 9 10
Primary Contact: Robyn Hemphill, Interim Chief Executive Officer and Chief
Nursing Officer
Web address: www.monroesurgical.com
**Control:** Corporation, Investor–owned, for–profit **Service:** Surgical

**Staffed Beds:** 10

★ ◇ **P & S SURGICAL HOSPITAL (190246)**, 312 Grammont Street Suite 101,
Zip 71201–7403; tel. 318/388–4040 **A**9 10 21 **F**3 8 12 18 20 22 26 29 34
35 37 49 50 51 64 65 68 75 79 81 82 85 107 111 114 119 130 131 132
135 141 **P**2 7
Primary Contact: Linda S. Holyfield, R.N., MSN, President and Chief Executive
Officer
COO: Terri Hicks, Chief Operating Officer and Chief Financial Officer
CFO: Terri Hicks, Chief Operating Officer and Chief Financial Officer
CMO: Mark Napoli, M.D., Chief of Staff
CHR: Joseph Vicknair, Director Human Resources
CNO: Debbie W. Austin, R.N., Vice President Patient Care Services
Web address: www.pssurgery.com
**Control:** Partnership, Investor–owned, for–profit **Service:** Surgical

**Staffed Beds:** 22 **Admissions:** 650 **Census:** 5 **Outpatient Visits:** 8345
**Births:** 0 **Personnel:** 179

**SPECIALTY EXTENDED CARE HOSPITAL OF MONROE (192016)**, (Formerly
Specialty Extended Care of Monroe), 309 Jackson Street, 7th Floor,
Zip 71201–7407, Mailing Address: P.O. Box 1532, Zip 71210–1532;
tel. 318/966–4126, (Nonreporting) **A**10
Primary Contact: Cleta Munholland, Administrator
Web address: www.ihcgroup.com
**Control:** Church–operated, Nongovernment, not–for profit **Service:** Long–Term
Acute Care hospital

**Staffed Beds:** 32

☒ **ST. FRANCIS MEDICAL CENTER (190125)**, 309 Jackson Street,
Zip 71201–7407, Mailing Address: P.O. Box 1901, Zip 71210–1901;
tel. 318/966–4000, (Includes ST. FRANCIS NORTH HOSPITAL, 3421 Medical Park
Drive, Zip 71203–2399; tel. 318/388–1946; Cindy J. Rogers, FACHE,
Administrator) **A**1 2 9 10 **F**2 3 12 13 15 17 18 19 20 21 22 23 24 26 27 28
29 30 31 32 34 35 37 39 40 44 45 49 50 54 55 56 57 59 64 65 68 69
70 72 74 75 76 77 78 79 81 85 87 88 89 90 92 93 96 97 98 102 103 104
105 107 108 110 111 114 115 116 117 118 119 124 128 129 130 131 132
134 135 144 146 147 148 **P**8 **S** Franciscan Missionaries of Our Lady Health
System, Inc., Baton Rouge, LA
Primary Contact: Louis H. Bremer, Jr., President and Chief Executive Officer
CFO: Ronald E. Hogan, Senior Vice President and Chief Financial Officer
CMO: R. Louis Gavioli, M.D., Vice President Medical Affairs
CIO: Thomas H. Hammond, Chief Information Officer
CHR: James Novak, Vice President, Human Resources
CNO: Darline Smith, R.N., Vice President Patient Care Services and Chief Nursing
Officer
Web address: www.stfran.com
**Control:** Church–operated, Nongovernment, not–for profit **Service:** General
Medical and Surgical

**Staffed Beds:** 343 **Admissions:** 15979 **Census:** 249 **Outpatient Visits:**
239192 **Births:** 2128 **Total Expense ($000):** 247349 **Payroll Expense
($000):** 98016

**ST. FRANCIS SPECIALTY HOSPITAL** See Specialty Extended Care Hospital of
Monroe

## MORGAN CITY—St. Mary Parish

☒ **TECHE REGIONAL MEDICAL CENTER (190014)**, 1125 Marguerite Street,
Zip 70380–1855, Mailing Address: P.O. Box 2308, Zip 70381–2308;
tel. 985/384–2200 **A**1 9 10 20 **F**3 13 15 18 20 22 29 30 31 34 40 45 50 57
60 70 76 79 81 85 89 90 93 98 102 104 105 107 108 110 111 115 119
130 141 146 147 **S** LifePoint Hospitals, Inc., Brentwood, TN
Primary Contact: James P. Frazier, III, Chief Executive Officer
CFO: Michael Mayeux, Chief Financial Officer
CMO: Kimberly Thorguson, M.D., Chief of Staff
CIO: Cheryl Lipari, Manager Information Systems
CHR: Timothy Hebert, Director Human Resources
Web address: www.techeregional.com
**Control:** Corporation, Investor–owned, for–profit **Service:** General Medical and
Surgical

**Staffed Beds:** 165 **Admissions:** 3348 **Census:** 45 **Outpatient Visits:** 51000
**Births:** 414 **Total Expense ($000):** 41417 **Payroll Expense ($000):** 14876
**Personnel:** 269

## NAPOLEONVILLE—Assumption Parish

★ **ASSUMPTION COMMUNITY HOSPITAL (191303)**, 135 Highway 402,
Zip 70390–2217; tel. 985/369–3600 **A**9 10 18 **F**32 34 35 40 57 58 59 64 65
127 135 **S** Franciscan Missionaries of Our Lady Health System, Inc., Baton
Rouge, LA
Primary Contact: Wayne M. Arboneaux, Chief Executive Officer
CHR: Letonia Pierre, Coordinator Human Resources
CNO: Donna Mullings, Director of Nursing
Web address: www.ololrmc.com
**Control:** Other not–for–profit (including NFP Corporation) **Service:** General
Medical and Surgical

**Staffed Beds:** 6 **Admissions:** 76 **Census:** 1 **Outpatient Visits:** 25142 **Births:**
0 **Total Expense ($000):** 5946 **Payroll Expense ($000):** 2275 **Personnel:**
45

## NATCHITOCHES—Natchitoches Parish

**LOUISIANA EXTENDED CARE HOSPITAL OF NATCHITOCHES (192035)**, 501
Keyser Avenue, Zip 71457–6018; tel. 318/354–2044, (Nonreporting) **A**10 **S** LHC
Group, Lafayette, LA
Primary Contact: Kermit Simmons, Administrator
Web address: www.lhcgroup.com
**Control:** Corporation, Investor–owned, for–profit **Service:** Long–Term Acute Care
hospital

**Staffed Beds:** 21

☒ **NATCHITOCHES REGIONAL MEDICAL CENTER (190007)**, 501 Keyser
Avenue, Zip 71457–6036, Mailing Address: P.O. Box 2009, Zip 71457–2009;
tel. 318/214–4200, (Total facility includes 112 beds in nursing home–type unit)
**A**1 9 10 20 **F**2 3 7 8 11 13 15 18 29 34 35 40 45 46 50 56 57 59 68 70 75
76 79 81 87 89 98 103 107 111 115 119 127 128 130 133 135 146 147
148 **P**5 **S** CHRISTUS Health, Irving, TX
Primary Contact: D. Kirk Soileau, Chief Executive Officer
CFO: Billy Page, Chief Financial Officer
CIO: Steve Crowder, Manager Information Technology
CHR: Ernie Scott, Director Human Resources
CNO: Dawna DeBlieux, Chief Nurse Executive
Web address: www.natchitocheshospital.org
**Control:** County–Government, nonfederal **Service:** General Medical and Surgical

**Staffed Beds:** 208 **Admissions:** 2640 **Census:** 26 **Outpatient Visits:** 48443
**Births:** 532 **Total Expense ($000):** 30178 **Payroll Expense ($000):** 17160
**Personnel:** 427

*Many Facility Codes have changed. Please refer to the AHA Guide Code Chart.*

© 2013 AHA Guide

## NEW IBERIA—Iberia Parish

⊠ ○ **DAUTERIVE HOSPITAL (190003)**, 600 North Lewis Street,
Zip 70563–2043; tel. 337/365–7311 **A**1 9 10 11 19 **F**13 15 17 18 28 29 40
56 57 70 76 81 86 87 89 90 93 98 103 107 111 119 130 132 146 **S** HCA,
Nashville, TN
Primary Contact: Gerald A. Fornoff, Interim Chief Executive Officer
CFO: Laura Allen, Chief Financial Officer
CMO: Mike Alvarez, M.D., Chief Medical Officer
CIO: Terry Stewart, Director Information Systems
CHR: Candice Ardoin, Director Human Resources
Web address: www.dauterivehospital.com
**Control:** Corporation, Investor–owned, for–profit **Service:** General Medical and
Surgical

**Staffed Beds:** 103 **Admissions:** 2863 **Census:** 36 **Births:** 443 **Total
Expense ($000):** 51811 **Payroll Expense ($000):** 17520 **Personnel:** 305

☐ **IBERIA MEDICAL CENTER (190054)**, 2315 East Main Street,
Zip 70560–4031, Mailing Address: P.O. Box 13338, Zip 70562–3338;
tel. 337/364–0441 **A**1 9 10 **F**3 11 13 15 18 20 22 28 29 30 31 34 39 40 45
46 47 48 49 50 57 68 70 72 74 75 76 77 78 79 81 85 87 88 89 93 97 107
108 110 115 119 127 130 146 148 **P**6 **S** HealthTech Management Services,
Franklin, TN
Primary Contact: John A. Tucker, Chief Executive Officer
COO: Shane P. Myers, Chief Operating Officer
CFO: Wally Piekarczyk, Chief Financial Officer
CMO: Ellen Mullen, M.D., Chief of Staff
CIO: Ross Leleux, Chief Information Officer
CHR: Lori Spann, Director Human Resources
Web address: www.iberiamedicalcenter.com
**Control:** Hospital district or authority, Government, nonfederal **Service:** General
Medical and Surgical

**Staffed Beds:** 84 **Admissions:** 3649 **Census:** 33 **Outpatient Visits:** 86135
**Births:** 387 **Total Expense ($000):** 55205 **Payroll Expense ($000):** 22526
**Personnel:** 477

☐ **IBERIA REHABILITATION HOSPITAL (190304)**, 532 Jefferson Terrace,
Zip 70560–4948; tel. 337/364–6923, (Nonreporting) **A**1 9 10
Primary Contact: Athan Oliver, Administrator and Chief Executive Officer
Web address: www.iberiarehab.net/
**Control:** Partnership, Investor–owned, for–profit **Service:** Rehabilitation

**Staffed Beds:** 24

## NEW ORLEANS—Orleans Parish

**BEACON BEHAVIORAL HOSPITAL – NEW ORLEANS (194084)**, 14500 Hayne
Boulevard, Suite 200, Zip 70128–1751; tel. 504/210–0460, (Nonreporting)
**A**9 10
Primary Contact: Jessica Scallion, Administrator
**Control:** Corporation, Investor–owned, for–profit **Service:** Psychiatric

**Staffed Beds:** 24

☐ △ **CHILDREN'S HOSPITAL (193300)**, 200 Henry Clay Avenue,
Zip 70118–5720; tel. 504/899–9511 **A**1 2 3 5 7 9 10 **F**3 8 9 11 16 17 19 21
23 25 27 29 30 31 32 34 35 36 39 40 41 43 50 54 55 57 58 59 60 61 64
65 66 71 72 74 75 78 79 80 81 82 84 85 86 87 88 89 90 93 97 98 99 100
102 104 107 108 111 113 115 119 129 130 131 132 136 138 141 144 146
148 **P**4 8
Primary Contact: Steve Worley, President and Chief Executive Officer
CFO: Greg Feirn, Senior Vice President and Chief Financial Officer
CMO: Alan M. Robson, M.D., Senior Vice President and Medical Director
CIO: Tammy Reites, Vice President Patient Financial Services
CHR: Doug Mittelstaedt, Vice President Human Resources
CNO: Diane Michel, Vice President Nursing
Web address: www.chnola.org
**Control:** Other not–for–profit (including NFP Corporation) **Service:** Children's
general

**Staffed Beds:** 200 **Admissions:** 7482 **Census:** 130 **Outpatient Visits:**
440017 **Births:** 0 **Personnel:** 1664

☐ **COMMUNITY CARE HOSPITAL (194056)**, 1421 General Taylor Street,
Zip 70115–3717; tel. 504/899–2500, (Nonreporting) **A**1 10
Primary Contact: Paul B. Kavanaugh, President and Chief Executive Officer
Web address: www.communitycarehospital.com
**Control:** State–Government, nonfederal **Service:** Psychiatric

**Staffed Beds:** 36

☐ **INTERIM LSU PUBLIC HOSPITAL (190005)**, 2021 Perdido Street,
Zip 70112–1396; tel. 504/903–3000, (Nonreporting) **A**1 2 5 8 9 10
Primary Contact: Cindy Nuesslein, Chief Executive Officer
COO: Adler Voltaire, Chief Administrative Officer
CFO: Ed Burke, Chief Financial Officer
CMO: Cathi E. Fontenot, M.D., Medical Director
CIO: Mitch Perlin, Chief Information Officer
CHR: Ronald Broadus, Assistant Administrator Human Resources
Web address: www.umcno.bizzuka.com/Default.asp
**Control:** Other not–for–profit (including NFP Corporation) **Service:** General
Medical and Surgical

**Staffed Beds:** 255

⊠ **KINDRED HOSPITAL–NEW ORLEANS (192009)**, 3601 Coliseum Street,
Zip 70115–3606; tel. 504/899–1555 **A**1 9 10 **F**1 28 29 30 46 75 77 86 87
91 96 98 103 130 143 148 **S** Kindred Healthcare, Louisville, KY
Primary Contact: Thomas Alexander, Chief Executive Officer
CFO: Mary Kay Nations, Chief Financial Officer
Web address: www.kindredhospitalnola.com
**Control:** Corporation, Investor–owned, for–profit **Service:** Long–Term Acute Care
hospital

**Staffed Beds:** 75 **Admissions:** 572 **Census:** 42 **Outpatient Visits:** 0 **Births:**
0 **Total Expense ($000):** 21368 **Payroll Expense ($000):** 9256

⊠ **OCHSNER BAPTIST MEDICAL CENTER (190135)**, 2700 Napoleon Avenue,
Zip 70115–6914; tel. 504/899–9311 **A**1 9 10 **F**3 15 20 22 29 30 34 37 40
41 45 46 47 48 49 50 53 54 57 59 60 64 70 74 75 77 79 81 82 83 107
109 110 111 114 115 119 126 129 130 135 **P**8 **S** Ochsner Health System,
New Orleans, LA
Primary Contact: Dawn Anuszkiewicz, Chief Executive Officer
COO: Ava Jo Collins, Vice President Operations
CFO: Christy Migaud, Controller
CMO: Allen Brown, M.D., Vice President Medical Affairs
CHR: Bill Ramsey, Director Human Resources
CNO: Donna Martin, R.N., Chief Nursing Officer
Web address: www.ochsner.org
**Control:** Other not–for–profit (including NFP Corporation) **Service:** General
Medical and Surgical

**Staffed Beds:** 55 **Admissions:** 3306 **Census:** 35 **Outpatient Visits:** 45560
**Births:** 0 **Total Expense ($000):** 70723 **Payroll Expense ($000):** 21350
**Personnel:** 392

⊠ △ **OCHSNER MEDICAL CENTER (190036)**, 1514 Jefferson Highway,
Zip 70121–2429; tel. 504/842–3000, (Includes OCHSNER MEDICAL CENTER –
WEST BANK, 2500 Belle Chasse Highway, Gretna, Zip 70056–7127;
tel. 504/392–3131; Travis Capers, Chief Executive Officer; OCHSNER MEDICAL
CENTER FOR CHILDREN, 1514 Jefferson Highway, tel. 504/842–3000), (Total
facility includes 32 beds in nursing home–type unit) **A**1 2 3 5 7 8 9 10 **F**2 3 5 8
9 11 12 13 14 15 17 18 19 20 21 22 23 24 25 26 27 28 29 30 31 32 34 37
38 40 41 43 44 45 46 47 48 49 50 51 54 55 56 57 58 59 60 61 64 65 68
70 72 74 75 76 77 78 79 81 84 85 86 87 88 89 90 93 94 96 97 98 99 100
101 102 103 104 105 107 108 110 111 113 114 115 117 118 119 120 121
123 124 126 128 129 130 131 132 134 135 136 137 138 139 140 141 142
145 146 147 148 **P**6 **S** Ochsner Health System, New Orleans, LA
Primary Contact: Robert Wolterman, Chief Executive Officer
CFO: Scott J. Posecai, Executive Vice President and Chief Financial Officer
CMO: Patrick J. Quinlan, M.D., Chief Executive Officer
CIO: Lynn Witherspoon, Vice President and Chief Information Officer
CHR: Joan Mollohan, Vice President Human Resources
Web address: www.ochsner.org
**Control:** Other not–for–profit (including NFP Corporation) **Service:** General
Medical and Surgical

**Staffed Beds:** 771 **Admissions:** 34367 **Census:** 507 **Outpatient Visits:**
382000 **Births:** 3475 **Total Expense ($000):** 837216 **Payroll Expense
($000):** 299872 **Personnel:** 5827

**PSYCHIATRIC PAVILION NEW ORLEANS** See Beacon Behavioral Hospital –
New Orleans

☐ **RIVER OAKS HOSPITAL (194031)**, 1525 River Oaks Road West,
Zip 70123–2162; tel. 504/734–1740, (Includes RIVER OAKS CHILD AND
ADOLESCENT HOSPITAL, 1525 River Oaks Road West, tel. 504/734–1740) **A**1 9
10 **F**4 5 29 40 98 99 102 105 130 **S** Universal Health Services, Inc., King of
Prussia, PA
Primary Contact: Evelyn Nolting, Chief Executive Officer and Managing Director
CFO: James Todd, Chief Financial Officer
CMO: Lincoln Paine, M.D., Medical Director
CIO: Vincent Chastelain, Director Business Development
CHR: Wanda Hoffmann, Director Human Resources
Web address: www.riveroakshospital.com
**Control:** Corporation, Investor–owned, for–profit **Service:** Psychiatric

**Staffed Beds:** 126 **Admissions:** 3267 **Census:** 79 **Outpatient Visits:** 0
**Births:** 0 **Total Expense ($000):** 15899 **Payroll Expense ($000):** 7546

---

**Hospital, Medicare Provider Number, Address, Telephone, Approval, Facility, and Physician Codes, Health Care System**

★ American Hospital Association (AHA) membership
☐ The Joint Commission accreditation
◇ DNV Healthcare Inc. accreditation
○ Healthcare Facilities Accreditation Program
△ Commission on Accreditation of Rehabilitation Facilities (CARF) accreditation

**SEASIDE BEHAVIORAL CENTER (194100)**, 4201 Woodland Drive, Zip 70131–7339; tel. 504/393–4223, (Nonreporting) **A**9 10
Primary Contact: Mary L. Matamoros, R.N., Chief Executive Officer
**Control:** Partnership, Investor–owned, for–profit **Service:** Psychiatric

Staffed Beds: 24

☐ **ST. CATHERINE MEMORIAL HOSPITAL (192023)**, 14500 Hayne Boulevard, Zip 70128–1751; tel. 504/210–3000, (Nonreporting) **A**1 10
Primary Contact: John Gray, Administrator
Web address: www.stcatherine–hospital.com
**Control:** Corporation, Investor–owned, for–profit **Service:** Long–Term Acute Care hospital

Staffed Beds: 21

★ ◇ **ST. CHARLES SURGICAL HOSPITAL (190300)**, 1717 Saint Charles Avenue, Zip 70130–5223; tel. 504/529–6600, (Nonreporting) **A**10 21
Primary Contact: Cheri Saltaformaggio, Chief Executive Officer
Web address: www.scsh.com
**Control:** Corporation, Investor–owned, for–profit **Service:** Surgical

Staffed Beds: 17

✠ △ **TOURO INFIRMARY (190046)**, 1401 Foucher Street, Zip 70115–3593; tel. 504/897–7011, (Includes TOURO REHABILITATION CENTER, 1401 Foucher Street, Zip 70115–3515; tel. 504/897–8560) **A**1 2 3 5 7 9 10 **F**3 8 10 11 13 15 18 20 22 24 28 29 30 31 34 35 36 37 39 40 43 44 45 50 53 54 55 57 59 60 61 62 63 64 68 70 72 74 75 76 77 78 79 81 83 84 85 86 87 90 93 96 97 107 108 109 110 111 114 115 116 117 118 119 120 121 123 124 125 126 128 130 131 132 135 143 146 147 148 **P**8
Primary Contact: James T. Montgomery, FACHE, President
COO: Susan Pitoscia, MSN, Chief Operating Officer
CIO: Jeff Lott, Director Information Services
CHR: Chad Courrege, Vice President Human Resources
Web address: www.touro.com
**Control:** Other not–for–profit (including NFP Corporation) **Service:** General Medical and Surgical

Staffed Beds: 411 Admissions: 14153 Census: 202 Outpatient Visits: 266864 Births: 3069 Total Expense ($000): 247519 Payroll Expense ($000): 83899 Personnel: 1271

✠ **TULANE MEDICAL CENTER (190176)**, 1415 Tulane Avenue, Zip 70112–2600; tel. 504/988–5263, (Includes TULANE–LAKESIDE HOSPITAL, 4700 South I. 10 Service Road West, Metairie, Zip 70001–1269; tel. 504/780–4200), (Nonreporting) **A**1 2 3 5 8 9 10 **S** HCA, Nashville, TN
Primary Contact: Robert Lynch, M.D., Chief Executive Officer
COO: Jennifer Eslinger, Chief Operating Officer
CFO: Robert Hatcher, Chief Financial Officer
CMO: John Pigott, M.D., Chief Medical Officer
CIO: Sue Rachuig, Director Information Services
CHR: Beth Babin, Vice President Human Resources
CNO: Danita S. Sullivan, R.N., Chief Nursing Officer
Web address: www.tuhc.com
**Control:** Corporation, Investor–owned, for–profit **Service:** General Medical and Surgical

Staffed Beds: 327

### NEW ROADS—Pointe Coupee Parish

★ **POINTE COUPEE GENERAL HOSPITAL (191316)**, 2202 False River Drive, Zip 70760–2614; tel. 225/638–6331 **A**9 10 18 **F**29 40 45 77 81 87 93 107 111 125 133
Primary Contact: Chad E. Olinde, Administrator and Chief Executive Officer
CFO: John Cazayoux, Chief Financial Officer
CMO: Carol Smothers, M.D., Chief of Staff
CHR: Lisa Patterson, Director Human Resources
Web address: www.pcgh.org
**Control:** Hospital district or authority, Government, nonfederal **Service:** General Medical and Surgical

Staffed Beds: 25 Admissions: 727 Census: 10 Outpatient Visits: 24425 Births: 0 Total Expense ($000): 16429 Payroll Expense ($000): 6842 Personnel: 160

### OAK GROVE—West Carroll Parish

**WEST CARROLL MEMORIAL HOSPITAL (190081)**, 706 Ross Street, Zip 71263–9798; tel. 318/428–3237, (Nonreporting) **A**9 10
Primary Contact: R. Randall Morris, Administrator
**Control:** Other not–for–profit (including NFP Corporation) **Service:** General Medical and Surgical

Staffed Beds: 21

### OAKDALE—Allen Parish

☐ **OAKDALE COMMUNITY HOSPITAL (190106)**, 130 North Hospital Drive, Zip 71463–3035, Mailing Address: P.O. Box 629, Zip 71463–0629; tel. 318/335–3700, (Nonreporting) **A**1 9 10
Primary Contact: Calvin Green, Chief Executive Officer
CFO: Michael Fontenot, Interim Chief Financial Officer
CMO: Tommy Davis, M.D., Chief of Staff
CIO: Melissa Welch, Director Health Information Management
CHR: Dana Blood, Director Human Resources
Web address: www.oakdalecommunityhospital.com/
**Control:** Partnership, Investor–owned, for–profit **Service:** General Medical and Surgical

Staffed Beds: 27

### OLLA—Caldwell Parish

**HARDTNER MEDICAL CENTER (191315)**, 1102 North Pine Road, Zip 71465–4804; tel. 318/495–3131, (Nonreporting) **A**9 10 18
Primary Contact: Paul G. Mathews, CPA, Administrator
CIO: Destini Bubrig, Director Health Information Management
Web address: www.hardtnermedical.com
**Control:** Hospital district or authority, Government, nonfederal **Service:** General Medical and Surgical

Staffed Beds: 35

### OPELOUSAS—St. Landry Parish

☐ **OCEANS BEHAVIORAL HOSPITAL OF OPELOUSAS (194095)**, 1310 Heather Drive, Zip 70570–7714; tel. 337/948–8820, (Nonreporting) **A**1 9 10 **S** Oceans Healthcare, Lake Charles, LA
Primary Contact: Remi Savoy, Administrator
Web address: www.obho.info/
**Control:** Corporation, Investor–owned, for–profit **Service:** Psychiatric

Staffed Beds: 20

✠ **OPELOUSAS GENERAL HEALTH SYSTEM (190017)**, 539 East Prudhomme Street, Zip 70570–6499, Mailing Address: P.O. Box 1389, Zip 70571–1389; tel. 337/948–3011, (Includes OPELOUSAS GENERAL HEALTH SYSTEM–SOUTH CAMPUS, 3983 I–49 South Service Road, Zip 70570–8975; tel. 337/948–2100) **A**1 2 9 10 19 **F**3 13 15 18 20 22 28 29 30 31 34 35 38 40 49 51 57 59 61 70 73 74 75 76 77 78 79 80 81 86 87 89 90 93 98 103 104 107 108 110 111 114 117 118 119 121 129 130 132 135 146 147 **S** QHR, Brentwood, TN
Primary Contact: Mark E. Marley, FACHE, President and Chief Executive Officer
COO: Bob Hardy, Chief Operating Officer
CFO: James B. Juneau, Chief Financial Officer
CMO: Derek Metoyer, M.D., Chief of Staff
CIO: Jared Lormand, Vice President Information Technology
CHR: Suzanne F. Kidder, Director Human Resources
CNO: Karen Gremillion, R.N., Chief Nursing Officer
Web address: www.opelousasgeneral.com
**Control:** Hospital district or authority, Government, nonfederal **Service:** General Medical and Surgical

Staffed Beds: 231 Admissions: 8766 Census: 114 Outpatient Visits: 122355 Births: 1044 Total Expense ($000): 122635 Payroll Expense ($000): 45503 Personnel: 967

**ST. LANDRY EXTENDED CARE HOSPITAL (192034)**, 3983 I–49 South Service Road, 2nd Floor, Zip 70570; tel. 337/948–5184, (Includes EVANGELINE EXTENDED CARE HOSPITAL–MAMOU, 801 Poinciana Avenue, Mamou, Zip 70554–2243; tel. 337/468–4203), (Nonreporting) **A**10
Primary Contact: Biff David, Administrator
Web address: www.lhcgroup.com
**Control:** Corporation, Investor–owned, for–profit **Service:** Long–Term Acute Care hospital

Staffed Beds: 23

### PINEVILLE—Rapides Parish

✠ **ALEXANDRIA VETERANS AFFAIRS HEALTH CARE SYSTEM**, (Formerly Veterans Affairs Medical Center – Alexandria), 2495 Shreveport Highway, 71 N., Zip 71360–4044, Mailing Address: P.O. Box 69004, Alexandria, Zip 71306–9004; tel. 318/473–0010, (Nonreporting) **A**1 3 5 **S** Department of Veterans Affairs, Washington, DC
Primary Contact: Martin J. Traxler, Director
CFO: Denise Morton, Chief Financial Officer
CMO: Hollis Reed, M.D., Chief of Staff
CIO: David Thurmond, Chief Information Resource Management Service
CHR: Cindy Twilligear, Manager Human Resources
Web address: www.alexandria.va.gov/
**Control:** Veterans Affairs, Government, federal **Service:** General Medical and Surgical

Staffed Beds: 143

*Many Facility Codes have changed. Please refer to the AHA Guide Code Chart.*
© 2013 AHA Guide

**CENTRAL LOUISIANA STATE HOSPITAL (194025)**, 242 West Shamrock Avenue, Zip 71360–6439, Mailing Address: P.O. Box 5031, Zip 71361–5031; tel. 318/484–6200, (Nonreporting) **A**1 10 **S** Louisiana State Hospitals, Baton Rouge, LA
COO: Paul Benoit, Associate Administrator
CFO: Tina Darbonne, Chief Financial Officer
CMO: L. Lee Tynes, Jr., M.D., Medical Director
CIO: William Haynes, Director Information Technology
CHR: Tom Crout, MS, Director Human Resources
Web address: www.dhh.la.gov/omh/inpatient–serv/clsh.htm
**Control:** State–Government, nonfederal **Service:** Psychiatric

**Staffed Beds:** 128

**HUEY P. LONG MEDICAL CENTER (190009)**, 352 Hospital Boulevard, Zip 71360–6903, Mailing Address: P.O. Box 5352, Zip 71361–5352; tel. 318/448–0811 **A**1 3 5 9 10 **F**3 8 11 15 18 19 29 30 31 32 35 38 39 40 43 46 50 54 57 59 61 64 65 66 70 75 77 78 79 81 85 86 87 89 93 97 98 102 107 114 119 130 132 135 146 147 148 **P**6
Primary Contact: Gary L. Crockett, Administrator
CFO: Beldia Bebee, Acting Chief Financial Officer
CMO: David Barnard, M.D., Medical Director
CIO: Mickey Roberts, Director Information Systems
CHR: Marsha Crittle, Director Human Resources
Web address: www.lsuhscshreveport.edu/index.php?src=gendocs&ref=HP–Long&submenu=HP–Long
**Control:** State–Government, nonfederal **Service:** General Medical and Surgical

**Staffed Beds:** 60 **Admissions:** 2076 **Census:** 38 **Outpatient Visits:** 72503 **Births:** 0 **Total Expense ($000):** 48386 **Payroll Expense ($000):** 21070 **Personnel:** 478

**VETERANS AFFAIRS MEDICAL CENTER – ALEXANDRIA** See Alexandria Veterans Affairs Health Care System

**PLAQUEMINE—Iberville Parish**

**MMO REHABILITATION AND WELLNESS CENTER (193070)**, 59213 Riverwest Drive, Zip 70764–6552; tel. 225/687–8100, (Nonreporting) **A**10
Primary Contact: Bridget Suire, Acting Administrator
Web address: www.mmoinc.com
**Control:** Other not–for–profit (including NFP Corporation) **Service:** Rehabilitation

**Staffed Beds:** 8

**RACELAND—Lafourche Parish**

⊠ **OCHSNER ST. ANNE GENERAL HOSPITAL (191324)**, 4608 Highway 1, Zip 70394–2623; tel. 985/537–6841, (Nonreporting) **A**1 9 10 18 **S** Ochsner Health System, New Orleans, LA
Primary Contact: Milton D. Bourgeois, Jr., Chief Executive Officer
CHR: Ann Ritchie, Director Human Resources
Web address: www.ochsnerstanne.org
**Control:** Other not–for–profit (including NFP Corporation) **Service:** General Medical and Surgical

**Staffed Beds:** 38

**RAYNE—Acadia Parish**

**PHOENIX BEHAVIORAL HOSPITAL (194097)**, 2021 Crowley Rayne Highway, Zip 70578–4027; tel. 337/788–0091, (Nonreporting) **A**1 9 10
Primary Contact: Joseph Tidwell, Administrator
**Control:** Corporation, Investor–owned, for–profit **Service:** Psychiatric

**Staffed Beds:** 18

**RAYVILLE—Richland Parish**

★ **RICHARDSON MEDICAL CENTER (190151)**, 254 Highway 3048 Christian Drive, Zip 71269–0388, Mailing Address: P.O. Box 388, Zip 71269–0388; tel. 318/728–4181, (Nonreporting) **A**9 10
Primary Contact: James W. Barrett, Jr., Chief Executive Officer
CFO: Shawnia Taylor, Chief Financial Officer
CMO: David Thompson, M.D., Chief of Staff
CHR: Rita Brown, Director Human Resources
Web address: www.richardsonmed.org
**Control:** Hospital district or authority, Government, nonfederal **Service:** General Medical and Surgical

**Staffed Beds:** 38

**RUSTON—Lincoln Parish**

**ALLEGIANCE HEALTH CENTER OF RUSTON (194087)**, 1401 Ezelle Street, Zip 71270–7218; tel. 318/255–8085, (Nonreporting) **A**9 10 **S** Allegiance Health Management, Shreveport, LA
Primary Contact: Donna K. Thompson, Chief Executive Officer
Web address: www.ahmgt.com
**Control:** Corporation, Investor–owned, for–profit **Service:** Psychiatric

**Staffed Beds:** 14

**GREEN CLINIC SURGICAL HOSPITAL (190257)**, 1118 Farmerville Street, Zip 71270–5914; tel. 318/232–7700, (Nonreporting) **A**9 10
Primary Contact: Chad Conner, Interim Administrator
Web address: www.gcsurgical.com
**Control:** Corporation, Investor–owned, for–profit **Service:** Other specialty

**Staffed Beds:** 13

⊠ **LIFECARE SPECIALTY HOSPITAL OF NORTH LOUISIANA (192022)**, 1401 Ezell Street, Zip 71270–7218; tel. 318/251–3126 **A**1 10 **F**1 **S** LifeCare Management Services, Plano, TX
Primary Contact: Brent Martin, Chief Executive Officer
Web address: www.lifecare–hospitals.com/hospital.php?id=19
**Control:** Corporation, Investor–owned, for–profit **Service:** Children's Long–Term Acute Care

**Staffed Beds:** 70 **Admissions:** 369 **Census:** 39 **Births:** 0 **Outpatient Visits:** 0

⊠ **NORTHERN LOUISIANA MEDICAL CENTER (190086)**, 401 East Vaughn Avenue, Zip 71270–5950; tel. 318/254–2100, (Nonreporting) **A**1 9 10 19 **S** Community Health Systems, Inc., Franklin, TN
Primary Contact: Brady Dubois, Interim Chief Executive Officer
CFO: Frank Malek, Chief Financial Officer
CMO: Derek McClusky, M.D., Chief of Staff
CIO: Heather Nolan, Director Information Services
CHR: Tonya Duggan, Director Human Resources
Web address: www.northernlouisianamedicalcenter.com
**Control:** Other not–for–profit (including NFP Corporation) **Service:** General Medical and Surgical

**Staffed Beds:** 91

**SAINT FRANCISVILLE—West Feliciana Parish**

⊠ **WEST FELICIANA PARISH HOSPITAL (191306)**, 5266 Commerce Street, Zip 70775, Mailing Address: P.O. Box 368, Zip 70775–0368; tel. 225/635–3811 **A**1 9 10 18 **F**34 35 40 57 58 81 107 119 128 130 133 135 143
Primary Contact: Lee Chastant, M.D., Chief Executive Officer
CFO: Linda Harvey, Chief Financial Officer
CHR: Neta F. Leake, Administrative Assistant Human Resources
Web address: www.wfph.org
**Control:** Hospital district or authority, Government, nonfederal **Service:** General Medical and Surgical

**Staffed Beds:** 22 **Admissions:** 82 **Census:** 1 **Outpatient Visits:** 23130 **Births:** 0 **Total Expense ($000):** 15016 **Payroll Expense ($000):** 5453 **Personnel:** 105

**SHREVEPORT—Caddo Parish**

**BRENTWOOD HOSPITAL (194020)**, 1006 Highland Avenue, Zip 71101–4103; tel. 318/678–7500 **A**1 9 10 **F**4 5 98 99 105 **P**6 **S** Universal Health Services, Inc., King of Prussia, PA
Primary Contact: William Weaver, Chief Executive Officer
CFO: Kisha Scruggs, Chief Financial Officer
Web address: www.brentwoodbehavioral.com
**Control:** Corporation, Investor–owned, for–profit **Service:** Psychiatric

**Staffed Beds:** 172 **Admissions:** 5032 **Census:** 130 **Outpatient Visits:** 2739 **Births:** 0 **Total Expense ($000):** 19345 **Payroll Expense ($000):** 10818 **Personnel:** 266

---

**Hospital, Medicare Provider Number, Address, Telephone, Approval, Facility, and Physician Codes, Health Care System**

★ American Hospital Association (AHA) membership
☐ The Joint Commission accreditation
◇ DNV Healthcare Inc. accreditation
○ Healthcare Facilities Accreditation Program
△ Commission on Accreditation of Rehabilitation Facilities (CARF) accreditation

✠ **CHRISTUS SCHUMPERT MEDICAL CENTER (190041)**, (Formerly CHRISTUS Health Shreveport–Bossier), One St. Mary Place, Zip 71101–4399; tel. 318/681–4500, (Includes CHRISTUS HIGHLAND MEDICAL CENTER, 1453 East Bert Kouns Industrial Loop, Zip 71105–6050; tel. 318/681–5000; CHRISTUS SCHUMPERT MEDICAL CENTER, One St. Mary Place, tel. 318/681–4500; CHRISTUS SCHUMPERT SUTTON CHILDREN'S MEDICAL CENTER, One Saint Mary Place, Zip 71101; tel. 318/424–5437) **A**1 2 3 5 9 10 **F**3 7 11 12 13 15 17 18 20 22 24 26 29 30 31 32 34 35 40 41 43 45 46 47 48 49 53 54 56 57 58 59 60 61 64 70 72 74 75 76 77 78 79 81 82 85 86 87 88 89 90 93 96 97 102 107 108 110 111 114 115 119 120 121 123 124 126 130 131 132 134 135 143 146 147 148 **S** CHRISTUS Health, Irving, TX
Primary Contact: Stephen F. Wright, President and Chief Executive Officer
COO: William Lunn, M.D., Chief Operating Officer
CFO: Frank Canova, Jr., Chief Financial Officer
CMO: Deirdre Barfield, M.D., Vice President Medical Affairs and Chief Medical Officer
CIO: Jeff Davis, Market Information Officer
CHR: Wendy White, Vice President Human Resources
Web address: www.christusschumpert.org
**Control:** Church–operated, Nongovernment, not–for profit **Service:** General Medical and Surgical

**Staffed Beds:** 302 **Admissions:** 12621 **Census:** 167 **Outpatient Visits:** 188266 **Births:** 1219 **Total Expense ($000):** 229480 **Payroll Expense ($000):** 74811 **Personnel:** 1235

✠ **DUBUIS HOSPITAL OF SHREVEPORT (192025)**, One St. Mary Place, 6th Floor, Zip 71101; tel. 318/221–3802, (Nonreporting) **A**1 10 **S** Dubuis Health System, Houston, TX
Primary Contact: Holly Powell, Interim Administrator
Web address: www.dubuis.org/shreveport
**Control:** Church–operated, Nongovernment, not–for profit **Service:** Long–Term Acute Care hospital

**Staffed Beds:** 36

✠ **LIFECARE HOSPITALS OF SHREVEPORT (192011)**, 9320 Linwood Avenue, Zip 71106–7003; tel. 318/688–8504, (Includes LIFECARE HOSPITALS OF SHREVEPORT–WILLIS KNIGHTON, 8001 Youree Drive, Zip 71115–2302; Keith Cox, Chief Executive Officer and Administrator; LIFECARE HOSPITALS OF SOUTH SHREVEPORT–WILLIS KNIGHTON NORTH, 2550 Kings Highway, Zip 71103–3922; Keith Cox, Chief Executive Officer and Administrator), (Nonreporting) **A**1 9 10 **S** LifeCare Management Services, Plano, TX
Primary Contact: Keith Cox, Administrator
Web address: www.lifecare–hospitals.com
**Control:** Corporation, Investor–owned, for–profit **Service:** Long–Term Acute Care hospital

**Staffed Beds:** 119

☐ **LSU HEALTH SCIENCES CENTER (190098)**, (Formerly LSU Medical Center–University Hospital), 1501 Kings Highway, Zip 71103–4228, Mailing Address: P.O. Box 33932, Zip 71130–3932; tel. 318/675–5000, (Includes CHILDREN'S HOSPITAL OF SHREVEPORT, 1501 Kings Highway, Mailing Address: PO Box 33932, Zip 71130–3932; tel. 318/675–5000) **A**1 2 3 5 9 10 **F**3 8 11 13 14 15 16 18 19 20 21 22 23 24 26 27 29 30 31 32 35 36 39 40 43 47 49 50 51 54 55 59 60 61 64 66 68 70 72 74 75 76 77 78 79 80 81 82 85 88 93 97 98 99 100 101 102 103 104 107 108 110 111 114 115 118 119 120 121 123 124 129 130 135 136 146 147 148
Primary Contact: Joseph M. Miciotto, Administrator
COO: Betty Johnson, Associate Administrator
CFO: Harold White, Vice Chancellor
CMO: Kevin Sittig, M.D., Senior Associate Dean and Chief Medical Officer
CIO: Marcus Hobgood, Director Information Services
CHR: David Fuqua, Director Human Resources Management
Web address: www.lsuhscshreveport.edu
**Control:** State–Government, nonfederal **Service:** General Medical and Surgical

**Staffed Beds:** 459 **Admissions:** 20424 **Census:** 319 **Outpatient Visits:** 409127 **Births:** 1541 **Payroll Expense ($000):** 174329

✠ **OVERTON BROOKS VETERANS AFFAIRS MEDICAL CENTER**, 510 East Stoner Avenue, Zip 71101–4295; tel. 318/221–8411, (Nonreporting) **A**1 2 3 5 **S** Department of Veterans Affairs, Washington, DC
Primary Contact: Shirley Bealer, Medical Center Director
CFO: Kim Lane, Chief Fiscal Service
CIO: Janey Taylor, Chief Information and Technology
CHR: Michael L. Palmer, Chief Human Resources Management
Web address: www.shreveport.va.gov/
**Control:** Veterans Affairs, Government, federal **Service:** General Medical and Surgical

**Staffed Beds:** 100

**PHYSICIANS BEHAVIORAL HOSPITAL (194094)**, 2025 Desoto Street, Zip 71103–4717; tel. 318/550–0520, (Nonreporting) **A**9 10
Primary Contact: Tom McCardell, Administrator
**Control:** Corporation, Investor–owned, for–profit **Service:** Psychiatric

**Staffed Beds:** 12

☐ **PROMISE HOSPITAL OF LOUISIANA – SHREVEPORT CAMPUS (192010)**, 1800 Irving Place, Zip 71101–4608; tel. 318/425–4096, (Includes PROMISE HOSPITAL OF LOUISIANA – BOSSIER CITY CAMPUS, 2525 Viking Drive, Bossier City, Zip 71111–2103; tel. 318/841–2525), (Nonreporting) **A**1 9 10 **S** Promise Healthcare, Boca Raton, FL
Primary Contact: Rick Stockton, Chief Executive Officer
Web address: www.promise–shreveport.com
**Control:** Corporation, Investor–owned, for–profit **Service:** Long–Term Acute Care hospital

**Staffed Beds:** 146

**PROMISE SPECIALTY HOSPITAL OF SHREVEPORT** See Promise Hospital of Louisiana – Shreveport Campus

☐ **SHRINERS HOSPITALS FOR CHILDREN–SHREVEPORT (193301)**, (Formerly Shriners Hospitals for Children, Shreveport), 3100 Samford Avenue, Zip 71103–4289; tel. 318/222–5704 **A**1 3 5 9 10 **F**34 50 59 64 68 79 81 85 89 93 94 119 130 131 146 **S** Shriners Hospitals for Children, Tampa, FL
Primary Contact: Garry Kim Green, FACHE, Administrator
CFO: Lori Lucas, Director Fiscal Services
CMO: Philip E. Gates, M.D., Chief of Staff
CIO: Kim Crockett, Director Management Information Systems
CHR: Rena Arbuthnot, Director Human Resources
CNO: Gail Rains, R.N., Director Patient Care Services
Web address: www.shrinershospitalsforchildren.org/Hospitals/Locations/Shreveport.aspx
**Control:** Other not–for–profit (including NFP Corporation) **Service:** Children's orthopedic

**Staffed Beds:** 45 **Admissions:** 268 **Census:** 2 **Outpatient Visits:** 10804 **Births:** 0 **Personnel:** 162

**SPECIALISTS HOSPITAL – SHREVEPORT (190278)**, 1500 Line Avenue, Zip 71101–4639; tel. 318/213–3800, (Nonreporting) **A**9 10
Primary Contact: Kandi Moore, Administrator
Web address: www.specialistshospitalshreveport.com/
**Control:** Corporation, Investor–owned, for–profit **Service:** General Medical and Surgical

**Staffed Beds:** 15

✠ △ **WILLIS–KNIGHTON MEDICAL CENTER (190111)**, 2600 Greenwood Road, Zip 71103–3908, Mailing Address: P.O. Box 32600, Zip 71130–2600; tel. 318/212–4600, (Includes WILLIS–KNIGHTON PIERREMONT HEALTH CENTER, 8001 Youree Drive, Zip 71115; tel. 318/212–3000; WILLIS–KNIGHTON SOUTH – THE CENTER FOR WOMEN'S HEALTH, 2510 Bert Kouns Industrial Loop, Zip 71118; tel. 318/212–5000; Keri Elrod, Administrator) **A**1 2 3 5 7 9 10 **F**3 17 70 72 81 88 90 98 128 **P**6 7 **S** Willis–Knighton Health System, Shreveport, LA
Primary Contact: Jaf Fielder, Vice President and Administrator
COO: Charles D. Daigle, Senior Vice President and Chief Operating Officer
CFO: Robert D. Huie, Executive Vice President and Chief Financial Officer
CMO: Frederick Kinder, M.D., Chief of Staff
CIO: Charles Laster, Director Information Management
CHR: Jaf Fielder, Vice President and Administrator
Web address: www.wkhs.com
**Control:** Other not–for–profit (including NFP Corporation) **Service:** General Medical and Surgical

**Staffed Beds:** 896 **Admissions:** 37303 **Census:** 445 **Outpatient Visits:** 382393 **Births:** 2931 **Personnel:** 4349

**SLIDELL—St. Tammany Parish**

**AMG SPECIALTY HOSPITAL–SLIDELL (192046)**, 1400 Lindberg Drive, Zip 70458–8056; tel. 985/326–0440, (Nonreporting) **A**10 **S** AMG Integrated Healthcare Management, Lafayette, LA
Primary Contact: Richard Daughdrill, R.N., Chief Executive Officer
COO: Gene Smith, Senior Vice President Operations
CFO: Jessica McGee, Chief Financial Officer
CMO: Marie Mahoney, M.D., Chief Medical Officer
CHR: Kim Hernandez, Director Human Resources
Web address: www.amgslidell.com/
**Control:** Partnership, Investor–owned, for–profit **Service:** Long–Term Acute Care hospital

**Staffed Beds:** 40

**CYPRESS POINTE HOSPITAL EAST (190256)**, 989 Robert Boulevard, Zip 70458–2009; tel. 985/690–8200, (Nonreporting) **A**9 10
Primary Contact: Sarah C. Garvin, Chief Executive Officer
**Control:** Corporation, Investor–owned, for–profit **Service:** Other specialty

**Staffed Beds:** 10

**NORTHSHORE REGIONAL MEDICAL CENTER** See Ochsner Medical Center – North Shore

*Many Facility Codes have changed. Please refer to the AHA Guide Code Chart.*     © 2013 AHA Guide

⊠ **OCHSNER MEDICAL CENTER – NORTH SHORE (190204)**, 100 Medical Center Drive, Zip 70461–5520; tel. 985/646–5000 **A**1 9 10 **F**3 13 15 18 20 22 24 26 29 30 31 34 35 40 41 44 45 46 49 50 51 57 59 61 62 64 68 70 72 74 75 76 77 78 79 81 84 85 86 87 88 89 90 91 93 95 96 97 102 107 108 109 110 111 113 114 116 117 118 119 129 130 132 135 146 147 148 **S** Ochsner Health System, New Orleans, LA
Primary Contact: Polly J. Davenport, R.N., Chief Executive Officer
COO: Alan Hodges, Chief Operating Officer
CFO: Forrest Whichard, Chief Financial Officer
CMO: James Newcomb, M.D., Vice President Medical
CHR: Terri Joseph-Taylor, Chief Human Resource Manager
CNO: Cheryl Woods, Chief Nursing Officer
Web address: www.ochsner.org/locations/northshore
**Control:** Other not–for–profit (including NFP Corporation) **Service:** General Medical and Surgical

**Staffed Beds:** 110 **Admissions:** 4829 **Census:** 59 **Outpatient Visits:** 58409 **Births:** 437 **Total Expense ($000):** 80601 **Payroll Expense ($000):** 33159 **Personnel:** 465

⊠ **SLIDELL MEMORIAL HOSPITAL (190040)**, 1001 Gause Boulevard, Zip 70458–2987; tel. 985/643–2200, (Nonreporting) **A**1 2 3 5 9 10
Primary Contact: John William Davis, Chief Executive Officer and Chief Financial Officer
CFO: John William Davis, Chief Executive Officer and Chief Financial Officer
Web address: www.slidellmemorial.org
**Control:** Hospital district or authority, Government, nonfederal **Service:** General Medical and Surgical

**Staffed Beds:** 170

☐ **SOUTHERN SURGICAL HOSPITAL (190270)**, 1700 Lindberg Drive, Zip 70458–8062; tel. 985/641–0600 **A**1 9 10 **F**8 12 29 57 70 79 81 82 107 111 130 132
Primary Contact: Michael J. Pisciotta, Chief Executive Officer
CFO: Michael J. Maurin, Chief Financial Officer
CMO: J. Gosey, M.D., Medical Director
CIO: Buddy Graves, Chief Information Officer
CHR: Lorrie Alfred, Director Human Resources
Web address: www.sshla.com/
**Control:** Partnership, Investor–owned, for–profit **Service:** Surgical

**Staffed Beds:** 37 **Admissions:** 1400 **Census:** 8 **Outpatient Visits:** 0 **Births:** 0

### SPRINGHILL—Webster Parish

☐ **SPRINGHILL MEDICAL CENTER (190088)**, 2001 Doctors Drive, Zip 71075–4526, Mailing Address: P.O. Box 920, Zip 71075–0920; tel. 318/539–1000 **A**1 9 10 **F**3 15 18 26 29 30 34 35 40 45 46 47 48 49 50 51 57 59 64 65 68 70 75 79 81 82 85 86 87 93 98 103 104 107 108 110 111 114 119 127 129 130 131 133 148 **P**6
Primary Contact: Vince Sedminik, Chief Executive Officer
CFO: Layla Chase, Chief Financial Officer
CMO: Michelle Pardue, M.D., Chief Medical Staff
CIO: Brian Griffin, Director Information Services
CHR: Derek Melancon, Director Human Resources and Marketing
CNO: Dana Jones, R.N., Chief Nursing Officer
Web address: www.smccare.com
**Control:** Other not–for–profit (including NFP Corporation) **Service:** General Medical and Surgical

**Staffed Beds:** 58 **Admissions:** 1099 **Census:** 13 **Outpatient Visits:** 37096 **Births:** 0 **Total Expense ($000):** 13957 **Payroll Expense ($000):** 6476 **Personnel:** 225

### STERLINGTON—Ouachita Parish

**STERLINGTON REHABILITATION HOSPITAL (193069)**, 111 Highway 2, Zip 71280–3009, Mailing Address: P.O. Box 627, Zip 71280–0627; tel. 318/665–9950, (Nonreporting) **A**10
Primary Contact: Cathy Martin, Administrator
Web address: www.www.sterlingtonrehab.com
**Control:** Corporation, Investor–owned, for–profit **Service:** Rehabilitation

**Staffed Beds:** 19

### SULPHUR—Calcasieu Parish

☐ **CORNERSTONE HOSPITAL OF SOUTHWEST LOUISIANA (192013)**, 703 Cypress Street, Zip 70663–5053; tel. 337/527–1102, (Nonreporting) **A**1 10 **S** Cornerstone Healthcare Group, Dallas, TX
Primary Contact: Robert R. Lafleur, Chief Executive Officer
CFO: Amy Bryant, Chief Financial Officer
Web address: www.chghospitals.com/chswl.html
**Control:** Partnership, Investor–owned, for–profit **Service:** Long–Term Acute Care hospital

**Staffed Beds:** 30

☐ **WEST CALCASIEU CAMERON HOSPITAL (190013)**, 701 Cypress Street, Zip 70663–5000, Mailing Address: P.O. Box 2509, Zip 70664–2509; tel. 337/527–4240 **A**1 9 10 **F**3 7 11 13 15 18 20 22 26 28 29 30 31 32 34 35 37 38 40 44 45 46 50 53 54 57 59 62 64 65 68 70 75 76 77 78 79 81 85 86 89 93 94 107 108 109 110 111 115 118 119 127 130 132 134 145 146 148 **P**6
Primary Contact: Jane Doucet Fruge, R.N., Chief Executive Officer
COO: Janie Fruge, Chief Operating Officer and Chief Nursing Officer
CFO: Tammy Broussard, Chief Financial Officer
CIO: Trey Rion, Chief Information Officer
CHR: Christi Kingsley, Director Human Resources
Web address: www.wcch.com
**Control:** Hospital district or authority, Government, nonfederal **Service:** General Medical and Surgical

**Staffed Beds:** 79 **Admissions:** 3260 **Census:** 35 **Outpatient Visits:** 83710 **Births:** 218 **Total Expense ($000):** 59684 **Payroll Expense ($000):** 24753 **Personnel:** 570

### TALLULAH—Madison Parish

**MADISON PARISH HOSPITAL (191314)**, 900 Johnson Street, Zip 71282–4537, Mailing Address: P.O. Box 1559, Zip 71284–1559; tel. 318/574–2374, (Nonreporting) **A**9 10 18
Primary Contact: Scott G. Barrilleaux, FACHE, Chief Executive Officer
CIO: Charles Whitaker, Director Information Technology
CHR: Chasity Whitaker, Administrative Assistant
Web address: www.madisonparishhospital.com
**Control:** Other not–for–profit (including NFP Corporation) **Service:** General Medical and Surgical

**Staffed Beds:** 25

### THIBODAUX—Lafourche Parish

⊠ △ **THIBODAUX REGIONAL MEDICAL CENTER (190004)**, 602 North Acadia Road, Zip 70301–4847, Mailing Address: P.O. Box 1118, Zip 70302–1118; tel. 985/447–5500 **A**1 2 7 9 10 **F**3 8 11 12 13 15 18 19 20 22 24 28 29 30 31 32 34 40 46 49 57 59 62 64 70 73 74 75 76 77 78 79 81 85 86 87 90 92 93 96 97 98 103 104 105 107 108 110 111 115 116 117 119 120 121 123 124 126 127 129 130 131 132 146 147 148
Primary Contact: Greg K. Stock, Chief Executive Officer
COO: Kim Keene, Vice President Professional Services
CFO: Steve C. Gaubert, Chief Financial Officer
CMO: Greg Chaisson, M.D., Chief Medical Staff
CIO: Terry Evans, Chief Information Officer
CHR: Eric Degravelle, Director Human Resources
Web address: www.thibodaux.com
**Control:** Hospital district or authority, Government, nonfederal **Service:** General Medical and Surgical

**Staffed Beds:** 140 **Admissions:** 7929 **Census:** 91 **Outpatient Visits:** 139808 **Births:** 834 **Total Expense ($000):** 128504 **Payroll Expense ($000):** 50532 **Personnel:** 902

### VIDALIA—Concordia Parish

☐ **PROMISE HOSPITAL OF MISS LOU (192028)**, 209 Front Street, Zip 71373–2837; tel. 318/336–6500, (Nonreporting) **A**1 10 **S** Promise Healthcare, Boca Raton, FL
Primary Contact: Benny Costello, Chief Executive Officer
COO: Howard B. Koslow, President and Chief Executive Officer
CFO: Larry Leder, Chief Financial Officer
CMO: Barry Tillman, M.D., Chief Medical Staff
CIO: Elizabeth Carpenter, Director Quality Assurance and Quality Improvement and Assistant Administrator
CHR: Roxan Houghton, Director Human Resources
Web address: www.promise–misslou.com
**Control:** Corporation, Investor–owned, for–profit **Service:** Long–Term Acute Care hospital

**Staffed Beds:** 40

---

**Hospital, Medicare Provider Number, Address, Telephone, Approval, Facility, and Physician Codes, Health Care System**

★ American Hospital Association (AHA) membership
☐ The Joint Commission accreditation
◇ DNV Healthcare Inc. accreditation
○ Healthcare Facilities Accreditation Program
△ Commission on Accreditation of Rehabilitation Facilities (CARF) accreditation

**LA**

### VILLE PLATTE—Evangeline Parish

⌧ **MERCY REGIONAL MEDICAL CENTER (190167)**, 800 East Main Street, Zip 70586–4618, Mailing Address: P.O. Box 349, Zip 70586–0349; tel. 337/363–5684, (Includes ACADIAN MEDICAL CENTER, 3501 Highway 190, Eunice, Zip 70535–5129; tel. 337/580–7500) **A**1 9 10 **F**3 8 11 13 15 29 30 31 34 35 38 40 45 51 53 55 57 59 64 65 70 75 76 77 78 79 81 82 83 84 85 86 87 89 90 91 92 93 94 96 97 107 108 110 111 114 119 130 131 132 133 135 146 147 148 **S** LifePoint Hospitals, Inc., Brentwood, TN
Primary Contact: Robert Alan Daugherty, Chief Executive Officer
COO: Sandy Morein, Chief Operating Officer
CFO: Lori Petrie, Chief Financial Officer
CMO: Brandon Fontenot, M.D., Chief of Staff
CIO: Courtney Bieber, Director Information Systems
CHR: Sue Thomas, Director Human Resources
Web address: www.mercyregionalmedicalcenter.com
**Control:** Corporation, Investor–owned, for–profit **Service:** General Medical and Surgical

**Staffed Beds:** 70 **Admissions:** 3992 **Census:** 52 **Outpatient Visits:** 39510 **Births:** 515 **Total Expense ($000):** 65012 **Payroll Expense ($000):** 22153 **Personnel:** 464

### VIVIAN—Caddo Parish

**NORTH CADDO MEDICAL CENTER (191304)**, 1000 South Spruce Street, Zip 71082–3232, Mailing Address: P.O. Box 792, Zip 71082–0792; tel. 318/375–3235, (Nonreporting) **A**5 6 9 10 18
Primary Contact: David C. Jones, Administrator
CFO: Carol Reisz, Chief Financial Officer
CMO: John H. Haynes, Jr., M.D., Chief of Medical Staff
CIO: Allyson Allums, Director Medical Records
CHR: Lanell Audirsch, Administrative Assistant
Web address: www.northcaddomedicalcenter.com
**Control:** Hospital district or authority, Government, nonfederal **Service:** General Medical and Surgical

**Staffed Beds:** 25

### WEST MONROE—Ouachita Parish

☐ **CORNERSTONE HOSPITAL–WEST MONROE (192031)**, 6198 Cypress Street, Zip 71291–9010; tel. 318/396–5600, (Nonreporting) **A**1 10 **S** Cornerstone Healthcare Group, Dallas, TX
Primary Contact: Chris Simpson, Chief Executive Officer
COO: Jay Quintana, Vice President Operations
CFO: Laura Nowell, Chief Financial Officer
CMO: Khaled Shafici, M.D., President Medical Staff
CIO: Adam Davis, Chief Information Officer
CHR: Dan Perkins, Corporate Director Human Resources
Web address: www.chghospitals.com/chwm.html
**Control:** Corporation, Investor–owned, for–profit **Service:** Long–Term Acute Care hospital

**Staffed Beds:** 40

◇ **GLENWOOD REGIONAL MEDICAL CENTER (190160)**, 503 McMillan Road, Zip 71291–5327; tel. 318/329–4200 **A**2 9 10 21 **F**3 5 8 11 13 15 17 18 20 22 24 26 28 29 30 31 32 34 35 37 40 42 43 45 46 49 50 54 56 57 59 60 64 65 68 70 71 72 74 75 76 77 78 79 81 85 86 87 89 90 92 93 94 96 98 103 104 106 107 108 109 110 111 114 115 116 117 118 119 126 128 129 130 132 133 135 144 146 147 148 **P**8 **S** IASIS Healthcare, Franklin, TN
Primary Contact: Ronald J. Elder, Chief Executive Officer
COO: Larry D. Walker, Chief Operating Officer
CFO: John DeSantis, Chief Financial Officer
CMO: John Maxwell, M.D., Chief of Staff
CIO: Ronnie Maxwell, Director Information Systems
CHR: Jan Walker, Director Human Resources
CNO: Sharon Lewis, Chief Nursing Officer
Web address: www.grmc.com
**Control:** Corporation, Investor–owned, for–profit **Service:** General Medical and Surgical

**Staffed Beds:** 247 **Admissions:** 12045 **Census:** 165 **Outpatient Visits:** 72156 **Births:** 976 **Total Expense ($000):** 118226 **Payroll Expense ($000):** 43344 **Personnel:** 889

**LOUISIANA EXTENDED CARE HOSPITAL WEST MONROE (192055)**, 503 McMillan Road, 3rd Floor, Zip 71291–5327; tel. 318/329–4300, (Nonreporting) **A**10 **S** LHC Group, Lafayette, LA
Primary Contact: Cleta Munholland, Administrator
**Control:** Corporation, Investor–owned, for–profit **Service:** Long–Term Acute Care hospital

**Staffed Beds:** 18

◇ **OUACHITA COMMUNITY HOSPITAL (190261)**, 1275 Glenwood Drive, Zip 71291–5539; tel. 318/322–1339 **A**9 10 21 **F**3 12 34 35 37 45 56 57 65 75 79 81 82 85 132 135
Primary Contact: Robert L. Colvin, Administrator
CFO: John DeSantis, Chief Financial Officer
CMO: H. Jerrel Fontenot, M.D., Medical Director
CMO: Brenda Wallace, R.N., Chief Nursing Officer
Web address: www.ouachitacommunityhospital.com
**Control:** Partnership, Investor–owned, for–profit **Service:** Surgical

**Staffed Beds:** 10 **Admissions:** 105 **Census:** 1 **Outpatient Visits:** 2400 **Births:** 0 **Total Expense ($000):** 5239 **Payroll Expense ($000):** 1758 **Personnel:** 31

### WINNFIELD—Winn Parish

☐ **SPECIALTY HOSPITAL OF WINNFIELD (192052)**, 915 First Street, Zip 71483–2945; tel. 318/648–0212 **A**1 10 **F**1 29 34 35 148
Primary Contact: William Bush, Chief Executive Officer
CFO: Charlie Jurek, Business Office Manager
CIO: Shamada Venzant, Manager Health Information
**Control:** Partnership, Investor–owned, for–profit **Service:** Long–Term Acute Care hospital

**Staffed Beds:** 20 **Admissions:** 20 **Census:** 11 **Outpatient Visits:** 0 **Births:** 0 **Total Expense ($000):** 3872 **Payroll Expense ($000):** 1793 **Personnel:** 63

**WINN PARISH MEDICAL CENTER (190090)**, 301 West Boundary Street, Zip 71483–3427, Mailing Address: P.O. Box 152, Zip 71483–0152; tel. 318/648–3000, (Nonreporting) **A**9 10
Primary Contact: Bryan Bogle, Interim Chief Executive Officer
CFO: Leah Lashley, Chief Financial Officer
CMO: Julio Iglesias, M.D., Chief of Staff
CHR: Kimberly Ingles, Director Human Resources
Web address: www.winnparishmedical.com
**Control:** Partnership, Investor–owned, for–profit **Service:** General Medical and Surgical

**Staffed Beds:** 60

**WOODLANDS BEHAVIORAL CENTER (194076)**, 1400 West Court Street, Zip 71483–2650, Mailing Address: P.O. Box 138, Zip 71483–0138; tel. 318/628–5445, (Nonreporting) **A**9 10
Primary Contact: Bobby G. Jordan, Administrator
Web address: www.woodlandsbehavioral.com/
**Control:** Corporation, Investor–owned, for–profit **Service:** Psychiatric

**Staffed Beds:** 19

### WINNSBORO—Franklin Parish

★ **FRANKLIN MEDICAL CENTER (190140)**, 2106 Loop Road, Zip 71295–3344, Mailing Address: P.O. Box 1300, Zip 71295–1300; tel. 318/435–9411, (Nonreporting) **A**9 10
Primary Contact: Blake Kramer, Chief Executive Officer
CMO: Jay Busby, M.D., President Medical Staff
CIO: Judy Ogden, Director Information Technology
Web address: www.fmc–cares.com
**Control:** Hospital district or authority, Government, nonfederal **Service:** General Medical and Surgical

**Staffed Beds:** 43

### ZACHARY—East Baton Rouge Parish

⌧ **LANE REGIONAL MEDICAL CENTER (190020)**, 6300 Main Street, Zip 70791–4037; tel. 225/658–4000, (Total facility includes 38 beds in nursing home–type unit) **A**1 9 10 **F**3 11 13 15 18 20 22 26 29 31 34 35 36 39 40 45 46 48 50 54 56 57 59 62 64 67 70 73 75 76 77 79 80 81 85 87 90 93 107 108 110 111 114 115 119 130 144 146 148 **P**6
Primary Contact: Randall M. Olson, Chief Executive Officer
CFO: Mark Anderson, Chief Financial Officer
CMO: David Rabalais, M.D., Chief Medical Staff
CIO: Scarlet Collier, Chief Information Officer
CHR: David Beck, Chief Operating Officer and Director Human Resources
CNO: Jennifer S. Johnson, R.N., Chief Nursing Officer
Web address: www.lanermc.org
**Control:** Hospital district or authority, Government, nonfederal **Service:** General Medical and Surgical

**Staffed Beds:** 180 **Admissions:** 4655 **Census:** 97 **Births:** 531

*Many Facility Codes have changed. Please refer to the AHA Guide Code Chart.*

© 2013 AHA Guide

# MAINE

## AUGUSTA—Kennebec County

**★ MAINE VETERANS AFFAIRS MEDICAL CENTER**, (Formerly Veterans Affairs Medical Center), 1 VA Center, Zip 04330–6719; tel. 207/623–8411, (Total facility includes 100 beds in nursing home–type unit) **A**1 **F**3 5 8 18 20 28 29 30 31 33 34 35 38 39 40 42 44 45 50 53 54 56 57 58 59 60 61 62 63 64 65 66 68 70 71 74 75 77 78 79 81 82 83 84 85 87 91 93 94 97 98 100 102 103 104 105 107 111 112 115 119 127 129 130 132 135 143 146 147 148 **P**6 **S** Department of Veterans Affairs, Washington, DC
Primary Contact: Ryan S. Lilly, Acting Director
CFO: Daniel Howard, Chief Financial Officer
CMO: Timothy J. Richardson, M.D., Chief of Staff
CIO: Richard McNaughton, Chief Information Management Service
CHR: Christine Miller, Chief Human Resources Management Services
Web address: www.maine.va.gov/
**Control:** Veterans Affairs, Government, federal **Service:** General Medical and Surgical

Staffed Beds: 181 Admissions: 2506 Census: 112 Outpatient Visits: 411047 Births: 0 Total Expense ($000): 276164 Payroll Expense ($000): 120385 Personnel: 710

**MAINEGENERAL MEDICAL CENTER–AUGUSTA CAMPUS** See MaineGeneral Medical Center–Waterville Campus, Waterville

**☐ RIVERVIEW PSYCHIATRIC CENTER (204007)**, 250 Arsenal Street, 11 State House Station, Zip 04330; tel. 207/624–3900 **A**1 10 **F**29 30 39 64 75 86 87 97 98 100 101 103 104 130 132 135 **P**6
Primary Contact: Mary Louise McEwen, Superintendent
CFO: Jenny Boyden, Chief Financial Officer
CMO: William Nelson, M.D., Medical Director
CHR: Kristine Albert, Personnel Officer
CNO: Tami Cooper, Acting Director of Nursing
Web address: www.state.me.us/dhhs/riverview
**Control:** State–Government, nonfederal **Service:** Psychiatric

Staffed Beds: 92 Admissions: 288 Census: 92 Outpatient Visits: 9433 Births: 0 Total Expense ($000): 30784 Payroll Expense ($000): 13191 Personnel: 294

**VETERANS AFFAIRS MEDICAL CENTER** See Maine Veterans Affairs Medical Center

## BANGOR—Penobscot County

**☐ DOROTHEA DIX PSYCHIATRIC CENTER (204004)**, 656 State Street, Zip 04401–5609, Mailing Address: P.O. Box 926, Zip 04402–0926; tel. 207/941–4000, (Nonreporting) **A**1 10
Primary Contact: Linda O. Abernethy, MSN, R.N., Superintendent
COO: Sharon Sprague, Director Therapeutic Services
CFO: Steven Thebarge, Chief Operating Officer and Chief Financial Officer
CMO: Marjorie Snyder, M.D., Clinical Director
CIO: Larry Larson, Management Analyst
CHR: Ruth Mullaney, Personnel Officer
Web address: www.maine.gov/dhhs/ddpc/index.shtml
**Control:** State–Government, nonfederal **Service:** Psychiatric

Staffed Beds: 51

**★ EASTERN MAINE MEDICAL CENTER (200033)**, 489 State Street, Zip 04401–6674, Mailing Address: P.O. Box 404, Zip 04402–0404; tel. 207/973–7000, (Includes ROSS SKILLED NURSING FACILITY ) **A**1 2 3 5 9 10 13 **F**3 11 12 13 15 17 18 19 20 22 24 26 28 29 30 31 34 36 37 39 40 43 44 45 46 47 48 49 50 51 53 54 55 57 58 59 60 61 64 70 72 74 75 76 77 78 79 81 82 84 85 86 87 88 89 90 92 93 94 96 97 102 107 108 110 111 114 115 118 119 120 121 123 124 126 129 130 131 132 144 145 146 147 148 **P**6 **S** Eastern Maine Healthcare Systems, Brewer, ME
Primary Contact: Deborah Carey Johnson, R.N., President and Chief Executive Officer
CFO: Elmer Doucette, Vice President and Chief Financial Officer
CMO: James Raczek, M.D., Sr. Vice President of Operations and Chief Medical Officer
CIO: Catherine Bruno, FACHE, Chief Information Officer
CHR: Greg Howat, Vice President Human Resources
CNO: Jodi Galli, Chief Nursing Officer
Web address: www.emh.org
**Control:** Other not–for–profit (including NFP Corporation) **Service:** General Medical and Surgical

Staffed Beds: 357 Admissions: 20101 Census: 282 Outpatient Visits: 414750 Births: 1644 Total Expense ($000): 594903 Payroll Expense ($000): 241882 Personnel: 3478

**★ ST. JOSEPH HOSPITAL (200001)**, 360 Broadway, Zip 04401–3979, Mailing Address: P.O. Box 403, Zip 04402–0403; tel. 207/262–1000 **A**1 9 10 **F**8 15 18 28 29 30 31 35 40 45 48 49 51 55 56 57 62 63 64 70 74 75 78 79 81 82 84 86 87 107 108 110 115 118 119 129 130 132 135 146 147 148 **S** Covenant Health Systems, Inc., Tewksbury, MA
Primary Contact: Mary Prybylo, President and Chief Executive Officer
CFO: Wayne Woodford, Executive Vice President and Chief Financial Officer
CMO: David Renedo, M.D., Chief of Staff
CIO: Karen Bowling, Chief Information Officer
CHR: Patricia Brezovsky, Director Human Resources
Web address: www.sjhhealth.com
**Control:** Church–operated, Nongovernment, not–for profit **Service:** General Medical and Surgical

Staffed Beds: 84 Admissions: 6196 Census: 50 Outpatient Visits: 107978 Births: 0 Total Expense ($000): 90329 Payroll Expense ($000): 36656 Personnel: 702

**★ THE ACADIA HOSPITAL (204006)**, 268 Stillwater Avenue, Zip 04401–3945, Mailing Address: P.O. Box 422, Zip 04402–0422; tel. 207/973–6100 **A**1 10 **F**5 29 30 50 57 66 68 75 77 87 98 99 100 101 103 104 105 130 132 **P**6 **S** Eastern Maine Healthcare Systems, Brewer, ME
Primary Contact: Daniel B. Coffey, President and Chief Executive Officer
CFO: Marie Suitter, Chief Financial Officer
CMO: Anthony Ng, M.D., Vice President and Chief Medical Officer
CIO: Jeanne Paradis, Director Information Services
CHR: Ted Helberg, Vice President, Human Resources
CNO: Karen Clements, R.N., Vice President, Chief Nursing Officer
Web address: www.acadiahospital.org
**Control:** Other not–for–profit (including NFP Corporation) **Service:** Psychiatric

Staffed Beds: 68 Admissions: 1440 Census: 55 Outpatient Visits: 95623 Births: 0 Total Expense ($000): 45732 Payroll Expense ($000): 25247 Personnel: 439

## BAR HARBOR—Hancock County

**★ MOUNT DESERT ISLAND HOSPITAL (201304)**, 10 Wayman Lane, Zip 04609–1625, Mailing Address: P.O. Box 8, Zip 04609–0008; tel. 207/288–5081 **A**9 10 18 **F**3 5 6 10 11 13 15 28 29 31 34 35 36 40 54 56 57 59 64 65 70 74 75 76 77 78 79 81 82 84 85 87 91 92 93 97 99 100 101 104 107 108 114 119 125 127 130 131 132 133 135 145 146 147 **P**6 7
Primary Contact: Arthur J. Blank, President and Chief Executive Officer
CFO: Christina Harding, Vice President Finance
CMO: Julian Kuffler, M.D., President Medical Staff
CIO: Mark White, Director Information Services
CHR: Joanne Harris, Director Human Resources
CNO: Barbara A. Hannon, R.N., VP Nursing
Web address: www.mdihospital.org
**Control:** Other not–for–profit (including NFP Corporation) **Service:** General Medical and Surgical

Staffed Beds: 25 Admissions: 1029 Census: 9 Outpatient Visits: 173970 Births: 112 Total Expense ($000): 54751 Payroll Expense ($000): 23524 Personnel: 403

## BELFAST—Waldo County

**WALDO COUNTY GENERAL HOSPITAL (201312)**, 118 Northport Avenue, Zip 04915–6072, Mailing Address: P.O. Box 287, Zip 04915–0287; tel. 207/338–2500 **A**9 10 18 **F**3 11 13 15 18 19 28 29 30 31 35 40 45 46 51 57 59 62 63 64 65 70 74 75 76 78 79 81 83 85 93 97 107 108 110 111 114 117 118 119 127 129 130 132 133 135 145 146 147 148 **P**8 **S** MaineHealth, Portland, ME
Primary Contact: Mark A. Biscone, Executive Director
COO: Dan Bennett, Director Operations
CFO: Linda Drinkwater, Chief Financial Officer
CMO: Kent Clark, M.D., Chief Medical Affairs and Quality
CIO: David Felton, Manager Information Systems
CHR: Karen Littlefield, Manager Human Resources
CNO: Teri R. Young–Hise, Director of Nursing
Web address: www.wchi.com
**Control:** Other not–for–profit (including NFP Corporation) **Service:** General Medical and Surgical

Staffed Beds: 25 Admissions: 1518 Census: 15 Outpatient Visits: 128680 Births: 147 Total Expense ($000): 66139 Payroll Expense ($000): 34058 Personnel: 483

---

**Hospital, Medicare Provider Number, Address, Telephone, Approval, Facility, and Physician Codes, Health Care System**

★ American Hospital Association (AHA) membership
☐ The Joint Commission accreditation
◇ DNV Healthcare Inc. accreditation
○ Healthcare Facilities Accreditation Program
△ Commission on Accreditation of Rehabilitation Facilities (CARF) accreditation

**ME**

### BIDDEFORD—York County

⊞ **SOUTHERN MAINE MEDICAL CENTER (200019)**, One Medical Center Drive, Zip 04005–9496, Mailing Address: P.O. Box 626, Zip 04005–0626; tel. 207/283–7000 **A**1 2 10 **F**3 5 8 11 12 13 15 18 20 22 24 28 29 30 34 35 36 38 40 42 44 45 46 47 48 49 50 51 54 57 58 59 65 66 68 70 74 75 76 77 78 79 81 85 86 87 89 93 98 99 100 101 102 103 104 105 107 108 110 111 114 115 118 119 129 130 132 135 146 147 148 **P**6 **S** MaineHealth, Portland, ME
Primary Contact: Edward J. McGeachey, President and Chief Executive Officer
COO: Frank Lavoie, M.D., Executive Vice President and Chief Operating Officer
CFO: Norman Belair, Chief Financial Officer and Vice President Finance
CMO: Robert Fernandez, M.D., Chief Medical Staff
CIO: Mary Jane Kamps, Chief Information Officer
CHR: Lorraine Bouchard, Vice President Human Resources
CNO: Patricia M. Camire, MS, Chief Nursing Officer
Web address: www.smmc.org
**Control:** Other not–for–profit (including NFP Corporation) **Service:** General Medical and Surgical

**Staffed Beds:** 110 **Admissions:** 5576 **Census:** 60 **Outpatient Visits:** 287851
**Births:** 545 **Total Expense ($000):** 157291 **Payroll Expense ($000):** 79359
**Personnel:** 1132

### BLUE HILL—Hancock County

★ **BLUE HILL MEMORIAL HOSPITAL (201300)**, 57 Water Street, Zip 04614–5231, Mailing Address: P.O. Box 1029, Zip 04614–1029; tel. 207/374–3400, (Nonreporting) **A**9 10 18 **S** Eastern Maine Healthcare Systems, Brewer, ME
Primary Contact: Gregory E. Roraff, President and Chief Executive Officer
CFO: Scott Oxley, Interim Chief Financial Officer
CMO: Kathleen Ober, M.D., Chief Medical Officer
CHR: David Wheaton, Director Human Resources
Web address: www.bhmh.org
**Control:** Other not–for–profit (including NFP Corporation) **Service:** General Medical and Surgical

**Staffed Beds:** 25

### BOOTHBAY HARBOR—Lincoln County

★ **ST. ANDREWS HOSPITAL AND HEALTHCARE CENTER (201302)**, 6 St. Andrews Lane, Zip 04538–1732, Mailing Address: P.O. Box 417, Zip 04538–0417; tel. 207/633–2121, (Total facility includes 54 beds in nursing home–type unit) **A**9 10 18 **F**3 6 10 11 15 29 30 34 35 40 43 44 45 50 56 57 59 64 65 67 75 79 81 85 87 93 96 97 107 110 114 119 125 127 128 130 132 133 135 143 146 148 **P**6 **S** MaineHealth, Portland, ME
Primary Contact: James W. Donovan, President and Chief Executive Officer
COO: Cynthia Leavitt, R.N., Senior Vice President, Hospital Operations
CFO: Wayne Printy, Chief Financial Officer and Senior Vice President Finance
CMO: Russell Mack, M.D., Chief Medical Officer
CIO: Brooks Betts, Vice President and Chief Information Officer
CHR: Thomas R. Girard, Vice President Human Resources
Web address: www.lincolncountyhealthcare.org
**Control:** Other not–for–profit (including NFP Corporation) **Service:** General Medical and Surgical

**Staffed Beds:** 73 **Admissions:** 288 **Census:** 60 **Outpatient Visits:** 23944
**Births:** 0 **Total Expense ($000):** 18599 **Payroll Expense ($000):** 6426
**Personnel:** 155

### BRIDGTON—Cumberland County

★ **BRIDGTON HOSPITAL (201310)**, 10 Hospital Drive, Zip 04009–1148; tel. 207/647–6000 **A**9 10 18 **F**3 11 13 15 29 30 31 34 35 40 45 50 53 54 57 59 65 70 75 76 78 79 81 85 86 93 97 107 108 110 111 114 119 128 130 131 132 133 135 143 144 146 147 148 **P**8
Primary Contact: R. David Frum, President
COO: John A. Ludwig, R.N., Vice President Administration
CFO: Philip Morissette, Chief Financial Officer
CMO: Suzanne Dater, M.D., President Medical Staff
CHR: Joyce McPhetres, Vice President Human Resources
Web address: www.bridgtonhospital.org
**Control:** Other not–for–profit (including NFP Corporation) **Service:** General Medical and Surgical

**Staffed Beds:** 22 **Admissions:** 1205 **Census:** 11 **Outpatient Visits:** 104731
**Births:** 120 **Total Expense ($000):** 40439 **Payroll Expense ($000):** 15939
**Personnel:** 259

### BRUNSWICK—Cumberland County

⊞ **MID COAST HOSPITAL (200021)**, 123 Medical Center Drive, Zip 04011–2652; tel. 207/729–0181 **A**1 2 10 **F**3 5 11 12 13 15 18 20 28 29 30 31 32 34 35 36 40 41 44 45 46 47 48 49 51 53 54 57 58 59 61 64 66 68 70 74 75 76 77 78 79 81 82 84 85 86 87 89 92 93 97 98 103 105 107 108 110 111 115 118 119 129 130 131 132 134 135 144 146 147 148 **P**6
Primary Contact: Lois N. Skillings, R.N., MSN, President and Chief Executive Officer
COO: Philip A. Ortolani, Vice President Operations
CFO: Robert N. McCue, Vice President Finance
CMO: Scott Mills, M.D., Vice President Medical Staff Administration and Chief Medical Officer
CIO: Gale Stoy, Manager Information Systems
Web address: www.midcoasthealth.com
**Control:** Other not–for–profit (including NFP Corporation) **Service:** General Medical and Surgical

**Staffed Beds:** 92 **Admissions:** 4630 **Census:** 54 **Outpatient Visits:** 180678
**Births:** 586 **Total Expense ($000):** 117861 **Payroll Expense ($000):** 55180
**Personnel:** 832

★ **PARKVIEW ADVENTIST MEDICAL CENTER (200025)**, 329 Maine Street, Zip 04011–3398; tel. 207/373–2000 **A**9 10 **F**11 15 29 30 31 34 35 36 37 38 40 45 50 56 59 61 64 65 66 68 70 75 77 78 79 81 82 85 86 87 89 90 93 107 108 110 111 114 116 117 119 129 130 132 135 145 146 147 **P**8
Primary Contact: Randee Reynolds, President
CFO: Scott Heatley, Controller
CMO: Ramesh Gaindh, M.D., President Medical Staff
CIO: Bill McQuaid, Assistant Vice President and Chief Information Officer
CHR: Robin White, Assistant Vice President Human Resources
Web address: www.parkviewamc.org
**Control:** Church–operated, Nongovernment, not–for profit **Service:** General Medical and Surgical

**Staffed Beds:** 55 **Admissions:** 971 **Census:** 10 **Outpatient Visits:** 64391
**Births:** 0 **Total Expense ($000):** 32943 **Payroll Expense ($000):** 11159
**Personnel:** 181

### CALAIS—Washington County

★ **CALAIS REGIONAL HOSPITAL (201305)**, 24 Hospital Lane, Zip 04619–1398; tel. 207/454–7521 **A**9 10 18 **F**3 11 13 15 18 28 29 31 32 34 35 36 40 42 45 46 50 57 59 62 64 65 68 70 75 76 77 79 81 84 85 89 90 93 97 107 108 110 111 114 119 127 129 130 132 133 146 147 148 **P**6 **S** QHR, Brentwood, TN
Primary Contact: Michael K. Lally, Chief Executive Officer
CFO: Nancy Glidden, Chief Financial Officer
CMO: Robert Chagrasulis, M.D., Chief of Staff
CIO: Dee Dee Travis, Director Community Relations
CHR: Kristi K. Saunders, Director and Compliance Officer
CNO: Cheryl Zwingman–Bagley, R.N., Chief Nursing Officer
Web address: www.calaishospital.com
**Control:** Other not–for–profit (including NFP Corporation) **Service:** General Medical and Surgical

**Staffed Beds:** 25 **Admissions:** 889 **Census:** 7 **Outpatient Visits:** 31700
**Births:** 71 **Total Expense ($000):** 33953 **Payroll Expense ($000):** 11203
**Personnel:** 240

### CARIBOU—Aroostook County

⊞ **CARY MEDICAL CENTER (200031)**, 163 Van Buren Road, Suite 1, Zip 04736–3567; tel. 207/498–3111, (Total facility includes 9 beds in nursing home–type unit) **A**1 9 10 **F**3 8 11 13 15 28 29 31 32 34 35 36 38 40 43 44 51 53 54 56 57 59 61 64 67 68 70 75 76 77 78 79 81 82 84 85 86 87 89 90 93 97 107 108 111 115 118 119 121 130 131 132 135 144 146 147 148 **S** QHR, Brentwood, TN
Primary Contact: Kris A. Doody, R.N., Chief Executive Officer
COO: Shawn Anderson, Chief Operating Officer
CFO: Galen Dickinson, Chief Financial Officer
CMO: Beth Collamore, M.D., Chief of Staff
CIO: Dave Silsbee, Chief Information Officer
CHR: Paula A. Parent, R.N., Director Human Resources and Nursing Administration
Web address: www.carymedicalcenter.org
**Control:** City–Government, nonfederal **Service:** General Medical and Surgical

**Staffed Beds:** 49 **Admissions:** 1904 **Census:** 30 **Outpatient Visits:** 77224
**Births:** 229 **Total Expense ($000):** 50041 **Payroll Expense ($000):** 20109
**Personnel:** 418

*Many Facility Codes have changed. Please refer to the AHA Guide Code Chart.*
© 2013 AHA Guide

## DAMARISCOTTA—Lincoln County

★ **MILES MEMORIAL HOSPITAL (200002)**, 35 Miles Street, Zip 04543–4047;
tel. 207/563–1234 **A**9 10 20 **F**3 11 13 15 29 30 32 34 35 40 43 44 45 50
57 59 64 65 70 75 76 79 81 85 86 87 93 96 97 107 108 110 111 114 118
119 127 130 132 133 135 146 147 148 **P**6 **S** MaineHealth, Portland, ME
Primary Contact: James W. Donovan, President and Chief Executive Officer
COO: Cynthia Leavitt, R.N., Senior Vice President, Hospital Operations
CFO: Wayne Printy, Chief Financial Officer and Senior Vice President Finance
CMO: Russell Mack, M.D., Chief Medical Officer
CIO: Brooks Betts, Vice President and Chief Information Officer
CHR: Thomas R. Girard, Vice President Human Resources
Web address: www.lchcare.org
**Control:** Other not–for–profit (including NFP Corporation) **Service:** General
Medical and Surgical

**Staffed Beds:** 38 **Admissions:** 1625 **Census:** 19 **Outpatient Visits:** 88809
**Births:** 124 **Total Expense ($000):** 54860 **Payroll Expense ($000):** 14448
**Personnel:** 358

## DOVER–FOXCROFT—Piscataquis County

★ **MAYO REGIONAL HOSPITAL (201309)**, 897 West Main Street,
Zip 04426–1099; tel. 207/564–8401 **A**9 10 18 **F**3 5 7 8 11 13 15 29 30 31
34 35 38 40 45 50 57 59 64 65 70 75 76 77 78 79 81 85 86 87 93 94 97
99 100 104 107 110 114 118 119 127 128 129 130 133 146 147 148
Primary Contact: Edward J. Hannon, Chief Executive Officer
CFO: Jim Fowle, Interim Chief Financial Officer
CMO: Richard Evans, M.D., President Medical Staff
CHR: Kenneth S. Proctor, MS, Director Human Resources
Web address: www.mayohospital.com
**Control:** Hospital district or authority, Government, nonfederal **Service:** General
Medical and Surgical

**Staffed Beds:** 25 **Admissions:** 1112 **Census:** 11 **Outpatient Visits:** 107477
**Births:** 137 **Total Expense ($000):** 45096 **Payroll Expense ($000):** 24444
**Personnel:** 432

## ELLSWORTH—Hancock County

⊞ **MAINE COAST MEMORIAL HOSPITAL (200050)**, 50 Union Street,
Zip 04605–1599; tel. 207/664–5311 **A**1 9 10 **F**13 15 18 28 29 31 34 35 40
45 51 55 57 59 61 64 65 68 70 74 75 76 77 78 79 81 84 85 93 97 107
108 111 115 119 129 130 132 133 144 146 147 148 **P**6
Primary Contact: Charles D. Therrien, Chief Executive Officer
COO: Barbara Hocking, R.N., Chief Operating Officer
CFO: Chris Frauenhofer, Chief Financial Officer
CMO: Sheena Whittaker, M.D., President Medical Staff
CIO: Mary Jo MacLaughlin, Director Information Systems
CHR: Karen Dickson, Director, Human Resources
CNO: Barbara Hocking, R.N., Chief Nursing Officer
Web address: www.mainehospital.org
**Control:** Other not–for–profit (including NFP Corporation) **Service:** General
Medical and Surgical

**Staffed Beds:** 48 **Admissions:** 2706 **Census:** 24 **Outpatient Visits:** 118676
**Births:** 286 **Total Expense ($000):** 81036 **Payroll Expense ($000):** 41877
**Personnel:** 544

## FARMINGTON—Franklin County

⊞ **FRANKLIN MEMORIAL HOSPITAL (200037)**, 111 Franklin Health Commons,
Zip 04938–6144; tel. 207/778–6031 **A**1 9 10 20 **F**3 5 7 8 11 13 15 28 29 30
31 32 34 35 36 40 41 45 46 50 51 54 56 59 61 64 65 70 75 76 77 78 79
81 82 83 84 85 86 87 89 93 97 99 104 107 108 110 111 115 118 119 129
130 131 132 135 146 147 148 **P**6 8
Primary Contact: Rebecca L. Ryder, R.N., President and Chief Executive Officer
COO: Gerald Cayer, Executive Vice President and Chief Operating Officer
CFO: Wayne Bennett, Chief Financial Officer
CMO: Michael Rowland, M.D., Vice President Medical Affairs
CIO: Ralph Johnson, Chief Information Officer
CHR: Joline Hart, Vice President Human Resources
CNO: Pam Ernest, R.N., CNO/ VP Patient Care Services
Web address: www.fchn.org
**Control:** Other not–for–profit (including NFP Corporation) **Service:** General
Medical and Surgical

**Staffed Beds:** 48 **Admissions:** 2640 **Census:** 24 **Outpatient Visits:** 154852
**Births:** 327 **Total Expense ($000):** 83687 **Payroll Expense ($000):** 40963
**Personnel:** 702

## FORT FAIRFIELD—Aroostook County

**COMMUNITY GENERAL HEALTH CENTER** See The Aroostook Medical Center,
Presque Isle

## FORT KENT—Aroostook County

⊞ **NORTHERN MAINE MEDICAL CENTER (200052)**, 194 East Main Street,
Zip 04743–1497; tel. 207/834–3155, (Total facility includes 45 beds in nursing
home–type unit) **A**1 10 20 **F**13 15 28 29 31 34 40 45 53 54 57 59 62 64 67
68 70 75 76 77 78 79 81 82 86 87 98 99 100 101 102 103 104 107 108
111 115 119 127 128 130 131 132 135 146 147 **P**6
Primary Contact: Peter Sirois, Interim Chief Executive Officer
COO: Joanne Fortin, R.N., Director of Clinical Services
COO: Peter Sirois, Associate Administrator
CFO: Roger Lagasse, Chief Financial Officer
CMO: Michael Sullivan, M.D., Chief Medical Officer
CIO: Adam Landry, Coordinator Computer Systems
CHR: Robin Damboise, Director Human Resources
CNO: Cheryl Daigle, R.N., Director of Nursing
Web address: www.nmmc.org
**Control:** Other not–for–profit (including NFP Corporation) **Service:** General
Medical and Surgical

**Staffed Beds:** 81 **Admissions:** 1370 **Census:** 59 **Outpatient Visits:** 52714
**Births:** 62 **Total Expense ($000):** 43829 **Payroll Expense ($000):** 24103
**Personnel:** 421

## GREENVILLE—Piscataquis County

★ **CHARLES A. DEAN MEMORIAL HOSPITAL (201301)**, 364 Pritham Avenue,
Zip 04441–1395, Mailing Address: P.O. Box 1129, Zip 04441–1129;
tel. 207/695–5200, (Nonreporting) **A**10 18 **S** Eastern Maine Healthcare Systems,
Brewer, ME
Primary Contact: Geno Murray, President and Chief Executive Officer
CFO: Edward Olivier, Chief Financial Officer
CMO: Darin Peck, M.D., Chief of Staff
Web address: www.cadean.org
**Control:** Other not–for–profit (including NFP Corporation) **Service:** General
Medical and Surgical

**Staffed Beds:** 36

## HOULTON—Aroostook County

★ **HOULTON REGIONAL HOSPITAL (201308)**, 20 Hartford Street,
Zip 04730–1891; tel. 207/532–9471, (Total facility includes 18 beds in nursing
home type unit) **A**9 10 18 **F**1 3 4 11 13 15 16 17 28 29 30 34 40 43 51 59
65 67 70 72 73 75 76 79 80 81 85 86 87 88 89 90 93 97 98 107 108 110
111 114 119 127 128 130 132 135 146 148 **P**5
Primary Contact: Thomas J. Moakler, Chief Executive Officer
CFO: Cindy Daigle, Chief Financial Officer
CHR: Vicky Moody, Director Human Resources
Web address: www.houlton.net/hrh
**Control:** Other not–for–profit (including NFP Corporation) **Service:** General
Medical and Surgical

**Staffed Beds:** 43 **Admissions:** 1412 **Census:** 29 **Outpatient Visits:** 95940
**Births:** 156 **Total Expense ($000):** 44013 **Payroll Expense ($000):** 21390
**Personnel:** 355

## LEWISTON—Androscoggin County

⊞ △ **CENTRAL MAINE MEDICAL CENTER (200024)**, 300 Main Street,
Zip 04240–7027; tel. 207/795–0111 **A**1 2 3 5 7 9 10 13 **F**3 11 12 13 15 18
19 20 22 24 26 28 29 30 31 32 34 35 36 40 41 43 44 45 46 47 48 49 50
51 52 53 55 57 58 59 61 64 65 66 67 68 70 71 73 74 75 76 77 78 79 81
82 84 85 86 87 89 90 91 92 93 97 102 107 108 110 114 115 118 119 120
121 123 124 129 130 131 132 135 143 144 146 147 148 **P**8
Primary Contact: Tina Legere, President
CFO: Matthew Cox, Chief Financial Officer
CMO: Edmund Claxton, M.D., President, Medical Staff
CIO: Denis Tanguay, Chief Information Officer
CHR: Kirk Miklavic, Director, Human Resources
CNO: Sharron Sieleman, R.N., VP, Nursing
Web address: www.cmmc.org
**Control:** Other not–for–profit (including NFP Corporation) **Service:** General
Medical and Surgical

**Staffed Beds:** 190 **Admissions:** 9444 **Census:** 111 **Outpatient Visits:**
785996 **Births:** 732 **Total Expense ($000):** 306660 **Payroll Expense
($000):** 136703 **Personnel:** 1642

---

**Hospital, Medicare Provider Number, Address, Telephone, Approval, Facility, and Physician Codes, Health Care System**

★ American Hospital Association (AHA) membership
☐ The Joint Commission accreditation
◇ DNV Healthcare Inc. accreditation
○ Healthcare Facilities Accreditation Program
△ Commission on Accreditation of Rehabilitation Facilities (CARF) accreditation

⊠ **ST. MARY'S REGIONAL MEDICAL CENTER (200034)**, 330 Sabattus Street, Zip 04240–5553, Mailing Address: P.O. Box 291, Zip 04243–0291; tel. 207/777–8100 **A**1 2 10 **F**1 3 4 5 7 11 13 15 16 17 18 20 28 29 30 31 34 35 40 44 45 46 49 50 51 53 54 57 58 59 60 61 64 65 67 68 70 72 73 74 75 76 77 78 79 80 81 82 84 85 86 87 88 89 90 91 93 96 97 98 99 100 101 102 103 104 105 107 108 110 111 114 116 117 118 119 128 129 130 132 134 135 144 146 147 148 **P**1 6 **S** Covenant Health Systems, Inc., Tewksbury, MA
Primary Contact: Lee T. Myles, President and Chief Executive Officer
COO: Susan Keiler, Chief Operating Officer
CFO: Carolyn Kasabian, Chief Financial Officer
CMO: Ira Shapiro, M.D., Chief Medical Officer
CIO: Rene Dumont, CIO/ Vice President Strategic Growth
CHR: Kevin Healey, Vice President Human Resources
Web address: www.stmarysmaine.com
**Control:** Other not–for–profit (including NFP Corporation) **Service:** General Medical and Surgical

**Staffed Beds:** 171 **Admissions:** 6285 **Census:** 85 **Outpatient Visits:** 315341 **Births:** 599 **Total Expense ($000):** 148697 **Payroll Expense ($000):** 71133 **Personnel:** 960

**LINCOLN—Penobscot County**

★ **PENOBSCOT VALLEY HOSPITAL (201303)**, 7 Transalpine Road, Zip 04457–4222, Mailing Address: P.O. Box 368, Zip 04457–0368; tel. 207/794–3321 **A**10 18 **F**3 7 8 11 13 15 26 28 29 30 34 40 41 45 50 53 57 59 64 65 68 70 76 77 79 81 84 85 89 90 93 107 108 114 119 127 128 130 132 133 135 146 147 148 **P**6 **S** QHR, Brentwood, TN
Primary Contact: David A. Shannon, Chief Executive Officer
CFO: Ann Marie Rush, Chief Financial Officer
CHR: Sarah Loman, Director Human Resources
Web address: www.pvhme.org
**Control:** Other not–for–profit (including NFP Corporation) **Service:** General Medical and Surgical

**Staffed Beds:** 25 **Admissions:** 853 **Census:** 7 **Outpatient Visits:** 38778 **Births:** 81 **Total Expense ($000):** 26594 **Payroll Expense ($000):** 10775 **Personnel:** 177

**MACHIAS—Washington County**

★ **DOWN EAST COMMUNITY HOSPITAL (201311)**, 11 Hospital Drive, Zip 04654–3325; tel. 207/255–3356, (Total facility includes 28 beds in nursing home–type unit) **A**9 10 18 **F**3 8 13 15 28 29 34 35 40 43 56 57 59 63 64 65 75 76 77 79 81 82 83 84 85 89 90 93 97 107 108 110 111 119 127 128 129 130 146 147 148 **P**6
Primary Contact: Douglas T. Jones, President and Chief Executive Officer
CFO: Lynnette Parr, Chief Financial Officer
CMO: Kara Dwight, Chief of Staff
CIO: Lynnette Parr, Chief Financial Officer
CHR: Ernestine O. Reisman, Vice President Human Resources
CNO: Rob Janssen, Vice President, Nursing Services
Web address: www.dech.org
**Control:** Other not–for–profit (including NFP Corporation) **Service:** General Medical and Surgical

**Staffed Beds:** 53 **Admissions:** 953 **Census:** 34 **Outpatient Visits:** 31053 **Births:** 132 **Total Expense ($000):** 38734 **Payroll Expense ($000):** 17935 **Personnel:** 241

**MARS HILL—Aroostook County**

**AROOSTOOK HEALTH CENTER** See The Aroostook Medical Center, Presque Isle

**MILLINOCKET—Penobscot County**

★ **MILLINOCKET REGIONAL HOSPITAL (201307)**, 200 Somerset Street, Zip 04462–1298; tel. 207/723–5161 **A**9 10 18 **F**3 8 11 15 28 29 30 31 34 35 37 40 43 47 48 50 53 55 59 64 65 75 79 81 84 85 86 87 89 93 97 107 108 115 128 130 133 135 147 **P**6
Primary Contact: Marie E. Vienneau, R.N., Chief Executive Officer
CFO: Christine McLaughlin, Chief Financial Officer
CMO: Daniel Herbert, M.D., Medical Administrative Officer
CIO: Tom Folsom, Manager Information Systems
CHR: Lisa Arsenault, Director Human Resources
Web address: www.mrhme.org
**Control:** Other not–for–profit (including NFP Corporation) **Service:** General Medical and Surgical

**Staffed Beds:** 25 **Admissions:** 1023 **Census:** 11 **Outpatient Visits:** 33594 **Births:** 1 **Total Expense ($000):** 27739 **Payroll Expense ($000):** 13692 **Personnel:** 194

**NORWAY—Oxford County**

★ **STEPHENS MEMORIAL HOSPITAL (201315)**, 181 Main Street, Zip 04268–5664; tel. 207/743–5933 **A**9 10 18 **F**3 7 13 15 28 29 30 31 34 35 40 43 45 57 59 61 64 65 68 70 75 76 78 79 81 84 85 86 89 93 96 97 102 107 108 110 111 115 117 130 132 146 **S** MaineHealth, Portland, ME
Primary Contact: Timothy A. Churchill, President
CMO: Gregory Hardy, M.D., President Medical Staff
CHR: Roberta Metivier, Vice President Human Resources and Administrator, Western Main Nursing Home
Web address: www.wmhcc.com
**Control:** Other not–for–profit (including NFP Corporation) **Service:** General Medical and Surgical

**Staffed Beds:** 25 **Admissions:** 1430 **Census:** 13 **Outpatient Visits:** 104959 **Births:** 168 **Total Expense ($000):** 53769 **Payroll Expense ($000):** 23374 **Personnel:** 402

**PITTSFIELD—Somerset County**

⊠ **SEBASTICOOK VALLEY HEALTH (201313)**, 447 North Main Street, Zip 04967–3707; tel. 207/487–4000 **A**1 9 10 18 **F**7 11 15 28 29 35 40 45 50 51 57 59 64 65 70 75 78 79 81 85 87 93 96 97 107 108 111 115 118 119 127 129 130 132 133 135 143 146 147 148 **P**6 **S** Eastern Maine Healthcare Systems, Brewer, ME
Primary Contact: Terri Vieira, Interim Chief Executive Officer
COO: Terri Vieira, Vice President Operations
CFO: Randal Clark, Vice President Finance
CMO: Howard Margolskee, M.D., Chief of Staff
CIO: Michael Peterson, Vice President Ancillary and Support Services and Chief Information Officer
CHR: Liisa H. Janelle, Vice President Human Resources
Web address: www.sebasticookvalleyhealth.org
**Control:** Other not–for–profit (including NFP Corporation) **Service:** General Medical and Surgical

**Staffed Beds:** 25 **Admissions:** 845 **Census:** 11 **Outpatient Visits:** 96018 **Births:** 0 **Total Expense ($000):** 33773 **Payroll Expense ($000):** 15974 **Personnel:** 292

**PORTLAND—Cumberland County**

⊠ △ **MAINE MEDICAL CENTER (200009)**, 22 Bramhall Street, Zip 04102–3175; tel. 207/662–0111, (Includes BARBARA BUSH CHILDREN'S HOSPITAL, 22 Bramhall Street, Zip 04102–3134; tel. 207/662–0111; MAINE MEDICAL CENTER, BRIGHTON CAMPUS, 335 Brighton Avenue, Zip 04102–9735, Mailing Address: P.O. Box 9735, Zip 04102–9735; tel. 207/879–8000) **A**1 2 3 5 7 8 10 **F**3 5 8 11 12 13 15 16 17 18 19 20 21 22 23 24 25 26 27 29 30 31 32 34 35 36 38 40 41 42 43 44 45 46 47 48 49 50 51 52 54 55 56 57 58 59 60 61 64 65 66 68 70 72 73 74 75 76 78 79 81 82 83 84 85 86 87 88 89 92 97 98 99 100 101 102 103 104 105 107 108 110 111 115 117 118 119 120 121 123 124 126 129 130 131 132 134 135 138 141 142 144 145 146 147 148 **P**4 6 8 **S** MaineHealth, Portland, ME
Primary Contact: Richard W. Petersen, President and Chief Executive Officer
COO: Jeff Sanders, Chief Operating Officer
CFO: John E. Heye, Chief Financial Officer
CMO: Peter Bates, M.D., Vice President Medical Affairs and Chief Medical Officer
CIO: Barry Blumenfeld, M.D., Chief Information Officer
CHR: Lisa McIlwain, Senior Director Talent Management
CHR: Judy West, Vice President Human Resources
Web address: www.mmc.org
**Control:** Other not–for–profit (including NFP Corporation) **Service:** General Medical and Surgical

**Staffed Beds:** 637 **Admissions:** 28354 **Census:** 405 **Outpatient Visits:** 490703 **Births:** 1641 **Total Expense ($000):** 862212 **Payroll Expense ($000):** 348614 **Personnel:** 5622

⊠ **MERCY HOSPITAL OF PORTLAND (200008)**, 144 State Street, Zip 04101–3795; tel. 207/879–3000 **A**1 2 10 **F**4 5 11 13 15 18 20 26 29 30 31 34 35 36 40 44 45 48 49 50 51 54 56 57 58 59 61 64 68 70 74 75 76 77 78 79 81 82 84 86 87 93 97 100 102 104 105 107 108 110 111 115 119 130 132 135 143 144 146 147 148 **P**6 **S** Catholic Health East, Newtown Square, PA
Primary Contact: Eileen F. Skinner, FACHE, President and Chief Executive Officer
COO: Robert Nutter, COO, Vice President of Human Resources and Support Services
CFO: Anthony Marple, Vice President of Strategy
CMO: Scott Rusk, M.D., Vice President Medical Administration
CIO: Don Huff, Interim Chief Information Officer
CHR: Elizabeth B. Christensen, Director, Human Resources
CNO: Bette Neville, R.N., Interim CNO and Director of Nursing
Web address: www.mercyhospitalstories.org/cms/
**Control:** Church–operated, Nongovernment, not–for profit **Service:** General Medical and Surgical

**Staffed Beds:** 148 **Admissions:** 7517 **Census:** 72 **Outpatient Visits:** 353632 **Births:** 866 **Total Expense ($000):** 216735 **Payroll Expense ($000):** 95874 **Personnel:** 1019

*Many Facility Codes have changed. Please refer to the AHA Guide Code Chart.*  © 2013 AHA Guide

ME

**ME**

⊠ **NEW ENGLAND REHABILITATION HOSPITAL OF PORTLAND (203025)**, 335 Brighton Avenue, Zip 04102–2363; tel. 207/775–4000 **A**1 10 **F**29 34 35 60 68 75 79 82 90 93 95 96 130 131 132 135 143 146 **S** HEALTHSOUTH Corporation, Birmingham, AL
Primary Contact: Jeanine Chesley, Chief Executive Officer
CMO: Elissa Charbonneau, D.O., Medical Director
CHR: Leigh Baade, Director Human Resources
Web address: www.nerhp.org
**Control:** Partnership, Investor–owned, for–profit **Service:** Rehabilitation

**Staffed Beds:** 90 **Admissions:** 1930 **Census:** 72 **Outpatient Visits:** 14650 **Births:** 0 **Total Expense ($000):** 21856 **Payroll Expense ($000):** 13677 **Personnel:** 227

### PRESQUE ISLE—Aroostook County

⊠ **THE AROOSTOOK MEDICAL CENTER (200018)**, 140 Academy Street, Zip 04769–3171, Mailing Address: P.O. Box 151, Zip 04769–0151; tel. 207/768–4000, (Includes AROOSTOOK HEALTH CENTER, 15 Highland Avenue, Mars Hill, Zip 04758; tel. 207/768–4900; ARTHUR R. GOULD MEMORIAL HOSPITAL, 140 Academy Street, Zip 04769, Mailing Address: P.O. Box 151, Zip 04769; tel. 207/768–4000; COMMUNITY GENERAL HEALTH CENTER, 3 Green Street, Fort Fairfield, Zip 04742; tel. 207/768–4700), (Total facility includes 64 beds in nursing home–type unit) **A**1 10 **F**3 7 8 12 13 15 18 20 28 29 30 31 32 34 35 36 38 40 43 45 46 50 51 52 53 54 56 57 59 60 61 63 64 65 67 68 69 70 74 75 76 77 78 79 80 81 82 84 85 86 87 89 90 91 92 93 96 97 99 104 107 108 110 114 115 118 119 121 123 128 129 130 131 132 134 135 143 146 147 148 **P**6 **S** Eastern Maine Healthcare Systems, Brewer, ME
Primary Contact: Sylvia Getman, President and Chief Executive Officer
COO: Jay Reynolds, M.D., Chief Operating Officer and Chief Medical Officer
CFO: C. Bruce Sandstrom, Vice President and Chief Financial Officer
CMO: Jay Reynolds, M.D., Vice President Medical Affairs and Chief Operating Officer
CIO: Catherine Bruno, FACHE, Chief Information Officer
CHR: Thomas Umphrey, Senior Vice President Human Resources
Web address: www.tamc.org
**Control:** Other not–for–profit (including NFP Corporation) **Service:** General Medical and Surgical

**Staffed Beds:** 122 **Admissions:** 2136 **Census:** 84 **Outpatient Visits:** 187244 **Births:** 216 **Total Expense ($000):** 104235 **Payroll Expense ($000):** 54194 **Personnel:** 839

### ROCKPORT—Knox County

⊠ **PEN BAY MEDICAL CENTER (200063)**, 6 Glen Cove Drive, Zip 04856–4240; tel. 207/596–8000, (Total facility includes 84 beds in nursing home–type unit) **A**1 2 10 20 **F**3 4 5 6 13 15 17 18 28 29 30 31 32 34 35 40 43 45 51 58 59 61 64 65 67 70 74 75 76 77 78 79 81 82 83 85 86 87 89 93 97 98 100 107 114 118 119 128 129 130 131 132 134 135 144 146 147 148 **P**1 **S** MaineHealth, Portland, ME
Primary Contact: Wade C. Johnson, MS, FACHE, Chief Executive Officer
COO: Eric Waters, Vice President Operations
CFO: Maura Kelly, Vice President Fiscal Services
CMO: Dana L. Goldsmith, M.D., Vice President Medical Affairs
CIO: Brooks Betts, Director Information Systems and Chief Information Officer
CHR: Thomas R. Girard, Vice President Human Resources
Web address: www.penbayhealthcare.org
**Control:** Other not–for–profit (including NFP Corporation) **Service:** General Medical and Surgical

**Staffed Beds:** 165 **Admissions:** 3863 **Census:** 112 **Outpatient Visits:** 160782 **Births:** 285 **Total Expense ($000):** 120008 **Payroll Expense ($000):** 57596 **Personnel:** 824

**PENOBSCOT BAY MEDICAL CENTER** See Pen Bay Medical Center

### RUMFORD—Oxford County

★ **RUMFORD HOSPITAL (201306)**, 420 Franklin Street, Zip 04276–2145; tel. 207/369–1000 **A**9 10 18 **F**3 8 11 13 15 18 28 29 31 34 35 38 40 45 50 53 57 59 64 65 70 75 76 77 78 79 81 82 84 85 87 89 93 94 97 107 111 114 119 127 128 130 132 133 146 148 **P**6 8
Primary Contact: R. David Frum, President
Web address: www.rumfordhospital.org
**Control:** Other not–for–profit (including NFP Corporation) **Service:** General Medical and Surgical

**Staffed Beds:** 21 **Admissions:** 1131 **Census:** 14 **Outpatient Visits:** 82822 **Births:** 63 **Total Expense ($000):** 34612 **Payroll Expense ($000):** 13852 **Personnel:** 245

### SANFORD—York County

⊠ **HENRIETTA D. GOODALL HOSPITAL (200040)**, 25 June Street, Zip 04073–2645; tel. 207/324–4310, (Total facility includes 112 beds in nursing home–type unit) **A**1 2 9 10 **F**2 3 6 10 13 15 18 26 27 28 29 30 31 32 34 35 40 45 47 50 59 64 65 67 70 73 75 76 77 79 81 82 85 87 89 90 93 97 107 108 111 114 118 119 125 128 129 131 134 144 145 146 147 **P**6
Primary Contact: Patricia Aprile, Chief Executive Officer
CFO: Dan Forgues, Chief Financial Officer
CMO: Mukesh Bhargava, M.D., Vice President Medical Affairs
CIO: Charles Caruso, Chief Information Officer
CHR: Carolyn Burgess, Director Human Resources
Web address: www.goodallhospital.org
**Control:** Other not–for–profit (including NFP Corporation) **Service:** General Medical and Surgical

**Staffed Beds:** 157 **Admissions:** 2361 **Census:** 126 **Outpatient Visits:** 192961 **Births:** 187 **Total Expense ($000):** 89509 **Payroll Expense ($000):** 40405 **Personnel:** 696

### SKOWHEGAN—Somerset County

★ **REDINGTON–FAIRVIEW GENERAL HOSPITAL (201314)**, Fairview Avenue, Zip 04976, Mailing Address: P.O. Box 468, Zip 04976–0468; tel. 207/474–5121 **A**9 10 18 **F**3 7 11 13 15 18 28 29 30 31 35 40 50 53 56 57 59 65 68 70 74 75 76 77 78 79 81 82 85 92 93 97 107 108 110 114 115 118 119 131 132 134 135 146 147 **P**6
Primary Contact: Richard Willett, Chief Executive Officer
CFO: Dana Kempton, Associate Director and Chief Financial Officer
CMO: Michael Lambke, M.D., Medical Director
CHR: Deborah Buckingham, R.N., Director Human Resources
CNO: Sherry L. Rogers, MS, Chief Nursing Officer
Web address: www.rfgh.net
**Control:** Other not–for–profit (including NFP Corporation) **Service:** General Medical and Surgical

**Staffed Beds:** 25 **Admissions:** 1543 **Census:** 13 **Outpatient Visits:** 80046 **Births:** 153 **Total Expense ($000):** 68114 **Payroll Expense ($000):** 27358 **Personnel:** 498

### WATERVILLE—Kennebec County

★ ○ **INLAND HOSPITAL (200041)**, 200 Kennedy Memorial Drive, Zip 04901–4595; tel. 207/861–3000 **A**9 10 11 **F**3 13 15 18 28 29 30 34 35 36 40 45 48 50 51 54 57 59 64 65 68 70 74 75 76 79 81 82 85 86 89 93 97 107 108 110 111 115 118 119 127 129 132 135 144 146 147 148 **S** Eastern Maine Healthcare Systems, Brewer, ME
Primary Contact: John Dalton, President and Chief Executive Officer
COO: Daniel Booth, Vice President Operations and Chief Human Resources Officer
CFO: Dean Bither, Chief Financial Officer
CIO: Kevin Dieterich, Director Information Services
CHR: Daniel Booth, Vice President Operations and Chief Human Resources Officer
Web address: www.inlandhospital.org
**Control:** Other not–for–profit (including NFP Corporation) **Service:** General Medical and Surgical

**Staffed Beds:** 46 **Admissions:** 1350 **Census:** 12 **Outpatient Visits:** 91655 **Births:** 369 **Total Expense ($000):** 72664 **Payroll Expense ($000):** 31970 **Personnel:** 447

⊠ **MAINEGENERAL MEDICAL CENTER–WATERVILLE CAMPUS (200039)**, 149 North Street, Zip 04901–4974; tel. 207/872–1000, (Includes MAINEGENERAL MEDICAL CENTER–AUGUSTA CAMPUS, 6 East Chestnut Street, Augusta, Zip 04330–9988; tel. 207/626–1000; Chuck Hays, President) **A**1 2 10 **F**3 4 5 11 12 13 15 20 22 26 28 29 30 31 34 35 40 44 45 46 51 54 55 57 58 59 60 63 64 65 66 70 74 75 76 77 78 79 81 82 84 85 86 87 89 90 93 94 96 97 98 99 100 101 102 103 104 107 108 110 115 116 117 119 120 121 123 124 126 129 130 131 132 135 143 144 145 146 147 148
Primary Contact: Chuck Hays, President
CMO: Steve Diaz, M.D., Chief Medical Officer
CIO: Daniel Burgess, Chief Information Officer
CHR: Rebecca Lamey, Vice President Human Resources
Web address: www.mainegeneral.org
**Control:** Other not–for–profit (including NFP Corporation) **Service:** General Medical and Surgical

**Staffed Beds:** 258 **Admissions:** 11026 **Census:** 146

---

**Hospital, Medicare Provider Number, Address, Telephone, Approval, Facility, and Physician Codes, Health Care System**

★ American Hospital Association (AHA) membership
□ The Joint Commission accreditation
◇ DNV Healthcare Inc. accreditation
○ Healthcare Facilities Accreditation Program
△ Commission on Accreditation of Rehabilitation Facilities (CARF) accreditation

## WESTBROOK—Cumberland County

☒ **SPRING HARBOR HOSPITAL (204005)**, 123 Andover Road, Zip 04092–3850;
tel. 207/761–2200 **A**1 10 **F**4 5 29 50 59 68 75 87 98 99 101 130 132 135
138 146 **P**6 **S** MaineHealth, Portland, ME
Primary Contact: Dennis P. King, Chief Executive Officer
COO: Richard Hanley, Chief Operating Officer
CFO: Gregory Bowers, Chief Financial Officer
CMO: Girard Robinson, M.D., Chief Medical Officer
CIO: Chris Simons, Director Health Information Management and Utilization Review
Web address: www.springharbor.org
**Control:** Other not–for–profit (including NFP Corporation) **Service:** Psychiatric

**Staffed Beds:** 88 **Admissions:** 2315 **Census:** 78 **Outpatient Visits:** 0 **Births:**
0 **Total Expense ($000):** 31341 **Payroll Expense ($000):** 16944
**Personnel:** 317

## YORK—York County

★ **YORK HOSPITAL (200020)**, 15 Hospital Drive, Zip 03909–1099;
tel. 207/363–4321 **A**2 9 10 **F**3 5 8 11 13 15 17 18 20 22 26 28 29 30 31 32
34 36 40 42 43 45 48 49 50 53 54 56 57 59 62 64 65 69 70 71 74 75 76
77 78 79 81 85 87 89 90 92 93 96 97 100 103 104 107 108 110 111 112
114 119 129 130 131 132 135 143 144 146 148 **P**6
Primary Contact: Jud Knox, President
COO: Stephen Pelletier, Leader Guest Services
CFO: Robin LaBonte, Leader Financial Care
CMO: Lawrence Petrovich, M.D., Chief Medical Officer
CIO: Robin LaBonte, Leader Financial Care
CHR: Olivia Chayer, Lead Human Resources
CNO: Kathy Lane, Leader–ICU, Home Care, MedSurg
Web address: www.yorkhospital.com
**Control:** Other not–for–profit (including NFP Corporation) **Service:** General
Medical and Surgical

**Staffed Beds:** 79 **Admissions:** 3622 **Census:** 40 **Outpatient Visits:** 319242
**Births:** 323 **Total Expense ($000):** 152406 **Payroll Expense ($000):** 64498
**Personnel:** 970

*Many Facility Codes have changed. Please refer to the AHA Guide Code Chart.*

# MARYLAND

MD

## ANNAPOLIS—Anne Arundel County

✠ **ANNE ARUNDEL MEDICAL CENTER (210023)**, 2001 Medical Parkway, Zip 21401–3019; tel. 443/481–1000, (Total facility includes 40 beds in nursing home–type unit) **A**1 2 5 9 10 **F**3 4 5 9 11 12 13 14 15 18 20 22 26 28 29 30 31 32 34 35 36 37 38 39 40 41 44 45 46 49 50 51 53 54 55 56 57 58 59 60 61 63 64 65 66 68 70 71 72 74 75 76 77 78 79 81 82 84 85 86 87 89 91 92 93 94 96 97 100 102 107 108 110 111 114 115 116 117 118 119 120 121 123 124 126 129 130 131 132 134 135 145 146 147 148
Primary Contact: Victoria Bayless, President and Chief Executive Officer
COO: Sherry Perkins, Ph.D., Chief Operating Officer and Chief Nursing Officer
CFO: Robert Reilly, Vice President and Chief Financial Officer
CMO: Joseph Moser, M.D., Vice President Medical Staff Affairs
CIO: Douglas A. Abel, Chief Information Officer
CHR: Nancy Luttrell, Vice President Human Resources
Web address: www.aahs.org
**Control:** Other not–for–profit (including NFP Corporation) **Service:** General Medical and Surgical

**Staffed Beds:** 406 **Admissions:** 28540 **Census:** 301 **Outpatient Visits:** 533870 **Births:** 5308 **Total Expense ($000):** 480287 **Payroll Expense ($000):** 177121 **Personnel:** 3366

## BALTIMORE—Baltimore City County

✠ **BON SECOURS BALTIMORE HEALTH SYSTEM (210013)**, 2000 West Baltimore Street, Zip 21223–1558; tel. 410/362–3000 **A**1 9 10 **F**3 11 15 18 20 26 29 30 31 40 44 45 59 60 64 66 70 78 79 81 84 85 87 98 99 100 101 102 103 104 105 107 108 110 111 115 119 130 143 146 148 **P**6 **S** Bon Secours Health System, Inc., Marriottsville, MD
Primary Contact: Samuel Lee Ross, M.D., MS, Chief Executive Officer
CFO: Richard Jones, Chief Financial Officer
CMO: Sidney Mir, M.D., Vice President Medical Affairs and Chief Medical Officer
CIO: Sanjay Purushotham, Executive Director Information Systems
CNO: Lesia Douglas, R.N., Vice President Patient Care Services and Chief Nurse Executive
Web address: www.bonsecoursbaltimore.com
**Control:** Church–operated, Nongovernment, not–for profit **Service:** General Medical and Surgical

**Staffed Beds:** 93 **Admissions:** 6521 **Census:** 80 **Outpatient Visits:** 394852 **Births:** 0 **Total Expense ($000):** 123758 **Payroll Expense ($000):** 48887 **Personnel:** 819

**FRANKLIN SQUARE HOSPITAL CENTER** See MedStar Franklin Square Medical Center

**GOOD SAMARITAN HOSPITAL OF MARYLAND** See MedStar Good Samaritan Hospital

✠ **GREATER BALTIMORE MEDICAL CENTER (210044)**, 6701 North Charles Street, Zip 21204–6892; tel. 443/849–2000, (Nonreporting) **A**1 2 3 5 9 10
Primary Contact: John B. Chessare, M.D., M.P.H., FACHE, President and Chief Executive Officer
COO: Keith R. Poisson, Executive Vice President and Chief Operating Officer
CFO: Eric L. Melchior, Executive Vice President and Chief Financial Officer
CMO: John R. Saunders, M.D., Senior Vice President Medical Affairs and Chief Medical Officer
CIO: Tressa Springmann, Chief Information Officer
CHR: Delois Simpson–Tuggle, Vice President Human Resources and Organizational Development and Chief Human Resources Officer
CNO: Jody Porter, R.N., Senior Vice President Patient Care Services and Chief Nursing Officer
Web address: www.gbmc.org
**Control:** Other not–for–profit (including NFP Corporation) **Service:** General Medical and Surgical

**Staffed Beds:** 249

**HARBOR HOSPITAL** See MedStar Harbor Hospital

✠ **JOHNS HOPKINS BAYVIEW MEDICAL CENTER (210029)**, 4940 Eastern Avenue, Zip 21224–2780; tel. 410/550–0100, (Total facility includes 138 beds in nursing home–type unit) **A**1 2 3 5 8 9 10 **F**1 2 3 4 5 6 8 9 10 11 12 13 15 16 17 18 20 22 26 28 29 30 31 32 34 35 36 38 39 40 43 44 45 47 48 49 50 51 54 55 56 57 58 59 60 61 64 65 66 67 68 70 71 72 73 74 75 76 77 78 79 80 81 82 84 85 86 87 88 89 90 92 93 94 97 98 99 100 101 102 103 104 105 107 111 114 115 116 118 119 120 126 128 129 130 131 132 134 135 141 143 145 146 147 148 **S** Johns Hopkins Health System, Baltimore, MD
Primary Contact: Richard G. Bennett, M.D., President
COO: Charlie Reuland, Sc.D., Executive Vice President and Chief Operating Officer
CFO: Carl H. Francioli, Vice President Finance
CIO: Sandy Reckert, Director Communications and Public Affairs
CHR: Craig R. Brodian, Vice President Human Resources
Web address: www.hopkinsbayview.org
**Control:** Other not–for–profit (including NFP Corporation) **Service:** General Medical and Surgical

**Staffed Beds:** 477 **Admissions:** 22227 **Census:** 383 **Outpatient Visits:** 459166 **Births:** 1530 **Total Expense ($000):** 403629 **Payroll Expense ($000):** 145744 **Personnel:** 3226

✠ △ **JOHNS HOPKINS HOSPITAL (210009)**, 600 North Wolfe Street, Zip 21287–2182; tel. 410/955–5000, (Includes JOHNS HOPKINS CHILDREN'S CENTER, 600 North Wolfe Street, Zip 21287–0005; tel. 410/955–5000) **A**1 2 3 5 7 8 9 10 **F**3 5 6 7 8 9 11 13 14 15 16 17 18 19 20 21 22 23 24 25 26 27 28 29 30 31 32 34 35 36 38 39 40 41 43 44 45 46 47 48 49 50 52 54 55 56 57 58 59 60 61 63 64 65 66 68 70 72 74 75 76 77 78 79 80 81 82 84 85 86 87 88 89 90 92 93 94 96 97 98 99 100 101 102 103 104 105 107 108 110 111 112 114 115 116 117 118 119 120 121 123 124 126 129 130 131 132 134 135 136 137 138 139 140 141 142 143 145 146 147 148 **S** Johns Hopkins Health System, Baltimore, MD
Primary Contact: Ronald R. Peterson, President
COO: Judy A. Reitz, Sc.D., Executive Vice President and Chief Operating Officer
CFO: Ronald J. Werthman, Senior Vice President Finance, Chief Financial Officer and Treasurer
CMO: Redonda G. Miller, M.D., Vice President Medical Affairs
CIO: Stephanie L. Reel, Senior Vice President Information Services
CHR: Pamela Paulk, Senior Vice President Human Resources
Web address: www.hopkinsmedicine.org
**Control:** Other not–for–profit (including NFP Corporation) **Service:** General Medical and Surgical

**Staffed Beds:** 951 **Admissions:** 46673 **Census:** 770 **Outpatient Visits:** 538609 **Births:** 1990 **Total Expense ($000):** 1690857 **Payroll Expense ($000):** 526287 **Personnel:** 9338

☐ △ **KENNEDY KRIEGER INSTITUTE (213301)**, 707 North Broadway, Zip 21205–1890; tel. 443/923–9200, (Nonreporting) **A**1 3 5 7 9 10
Primary Contact: Gary W. Goldstein, M.D., President and Chief Executive Officer
COO: James M. Anders, Jr., Administrator and Chief Operating Officer
CFO: Michael J. Neuman, Vice President Finance
CMO: Michael V. Johnston, M.D., Chief Medical Officer and Senior Vice President Medical Programs
CIO: Kenneth Davis, Assistant Vice President Information Systems
CHR: Michael Loughran, Vice President Human Resources
Web address: www.kennedykrieger.org
**Control:** Other not–for–profit (including NFP Corporation) **Service:** Children's other specialty

**Staffed Beds:** 70

✠ △ **KERNAN ORTHOPAEDICS AND REHABILITATION (210058)**, 2200 Kernan Drive, Zip 21207–6697; tel. 410/448–2500, (Nonreporting) **A**1 3 5 7 9 10 **S** University of Maryland Medical System, Baltimore, MD
Primary Contact: Michael Jablonover, M.D., President and Chief Executive Officer
COO: Juanita D. Robbins, Chief Operating and Development Officer
CFO: W. Walter Augustin, III, CPA, Vice President Financial Services and Chief Financial Officer
CMO: John P. Straumanis, M.D., Vice President Medical Affairs and Chief Medical Officer
CIO: Linda Hines, Vice President Information Technology and Information Systems
CHR: David Swift, Vice President Human Resources, Volunteer and Community Services
Web address: www.kernan.org
**Control:** Other not–for–profit (including NFP Corporation) **Service:** Rehabilitation

**Staffed Beds:** 104

---

**Hospital, Medicare Provider Number, Address, Telephone, Approval, Facility, and Physician Codes, Health Care System**

★ American Hospital Association (AHA) membership
☐ The Joint Commission accreditation
◇ DNV Healthcare Inc. accreditation
○ Healthcare Facilities Accreditation Program
△ Commission on Accreditation of Rehabilitation Facilities (CARF) accreditation

☒ △ **LEVINDALE HEBREW GERIATRIC CENTER AND HOSPITAL (212005)**, 2434 West Belvedere Avenue, Zip 21215–5267; tel. 410/466–8700, (Total facility includes 361 beds in nursing home–type unit) **A**1 7 9 10 **F**2 11 29 30 50 56 60 63 68 69 82 84 87 93 103 104 105 128 130 132 146 148 **P**6 **S** LifeBridge Health, Baltimore, MD
Primary Contact: Aric Spitulnik, President and Chief Operating Officer
CMO: Susan M. Levy, M.D., Vice President Medical Affairs
CIO: Karen Barker, Vice President and Chief Information Officer
CHR: Cheryl T. Boyer, Vice President Human Resources
CNO: Cathy M. Gallo, Vice President and Chief Nursing Officer
Web address: www.sinai–balt.com
**Control:** Other not–for–profit (including NFP Corporation) **Service:** Long–Term Acute Care hospital

**Staffed Beds:** 481 **Admissions:** 1915 **Census:** 401 **Outpatient Visits:** 25023 **Births:** 0 **Total Expense ($000):** 87145 **Payroll Expense ($000):** 38495 **Personnel:** 840

☒ △ **MARYLAND GENERAL HOSPITAL (210038)**, 827 Linden Avenue, Zip 21201–4606; tel. 410/225–8000 **A**1 3 5 7 9 10 **F**5 11 13 15 18 20 29 30 31 34 35 40 44 45 49 50 51 56 57 59 60 61 64 65 66 68 70 74 75 76 77 78 79 81 82 85 87 90 93 94 96 97 98 100 101 102 103 104 106 107 108 111 114 115 118 119 129 130 143 147 148 **S** University of Maryland Medical System, Baltimore, MD
Primary Contact: Sylvia Smith Johnson, President and Chief Executive Officer
COO: Donald Ray, Vice President of Operations
CFO: Brian Bailey, Chief Administrative and Financial Officer
CMO: W. Eugene Egerton, M.D., Chief Medical Officer
CIO: Jon P. Burns, Senior Vice President and Chief Information Officer
CHR: David Swift, Vice President Human Resources
CNO: Edward Streyle, MS, Senior Vice President and Chief Nursing Officer
Web address: www.marylandgeneral.org
**Control:** Other not–for–profit (including NFP Corporation) **Service:** General Medical and Surgical

**Staffed Beds:** 212 **Admissions:** 8870 **Census:** 107 **Outpatient Visits:** 111965 **Births:** 615 **Total Expense ($000):** 168208 **Payroll Expense ($000):** 66696 **Personnel:** 1123

☒ **MEDSTAR FRANKLIN SQUARE MEDICAL CENTER (210015)**, 9000 Franklin Square Drive, Zip 21237–3901; tel. 443/777–7000 **A**1 2 3 5 8 9 10 **F**3 5 11 12 13 14 15 18 20 22 26 28 29 30 31 32 34 35 36 37 38 39 40 41 44 45 46 47 48 49 50 51 55 56 57 58 59 60 61 64 65 66 70 71 72 74 75 76 77 78 79 81 82 85 86 87 89 92 93 94 97 98 99 100 101 102 103 104 107 108 109 110 111 115 118 119 126 129 130 131 132 134 135 145 146 147 148 **P**6 **S** MedStar Health, Columbia, MD
Primary Contact: Samuel E. Moskowitz, President
CFO: Robert P. Lally, Jr., Vice President Finance
CMO: Tony Sclama, M.D., Vice President Medical Affairs
CIO: Stephen Mannion, Assistant Vice President Information Systems Customer Service
CHR: Karen Robertson–Keck, Vice President Human Resources
CNO: Lawrence F. Strassner III, R.N., Vice President, Patient Care Services and Chief Nursing Officer
Web address: www.medstarfranklin.org
**Control:** Other not–for–profit (including NFP Corporation) **Service:** General Medical and Surgical

**Staffed Beds:** 377 **Admissions:** 22186 **Census:** 263 **Outpatient Visits:** 469216 **Births:** 2477 **Total Expense ($000):** 443333 **Payroll Expense ($000):** 188880 **Personnel:** 3182

☒ △ **MEDSTAR GOOD SAMARITAN HOSPITAL (210056)**, 5601 Loch Raven Boulevard, Zip 21239–2995; tel. 443/444–8000, (Total facility includes 30 beds in nursing home–type unit) **A**1 2 3 5 7 9 10 **F**3 9 11 14 15 17 18 20 26 28 29 30 31 34 35 36 37 38 40 44 45 50 51 53 55 56 57 58 59 60 61 65 66 68 70 74 75 77 78 79 80 81 82 84 85 86 87 90 91 93 96 97 99 100 101 102 103 104 107 108 110 111 114 118 119 121 124 128 129 130 131 132 135 146 148 **S** MedStar Health, Columbia, MD
Primary Contact: Jeffrey A. Matton, President
CFO: Deana Stout, Vice President Financial Services
Web address: www.goodsam–md.org
**Control:** Other not–for–profit (including NFP Corporation) **Service:** General Medical and Surgical

**Staffed Beds:** 308 **Admissions:** 15725 **Census:** 221 **Outpatient Visits:** 164783 **Births:** 0 **Total Expense ($000):** 305894 **Payroll Expense ($000):** 126569 **Personnel:** 1906

☒ **MEDSTAR HARBOR HOSPITAL (210034)**, 3001 South Hanover Street, Zip 21225–1290; tel. 410/350–3200 **A**1 2 3 5 9 10 **F**3 9 11 13 14 15 18 20 26 29 30 31 34 35 36 40 44 45 46 48 49 50 51 53 55 56 57 58 59 60 61 64 65 66 68 70 72 74 75 76 77 78 79 81 82 84 85 86 87 89 92 93 94 97 102 103 107 108 110 111 114 119 120 121 129 130 131 132 135 146 147 **P**6 **S** MedStar Health, Columbia, MD
Primary Contact: Dennis W. Pullin, Chief Executive Officer
CFO: David R. Pitman, Vice President Finance
CMO: Allan Birenberg, Vice President Medical Affairs
CIO: David B. Smith, Assistant Vice President Information Services
CHR: Pamela S. Williams, Vice President Human Resources
Web address: www.harborhospital.org
**Control:** Other not–for–profit (including NFP Corporation) **Service:** General Medical and Surgical

**Staffed Beds:** 192 **Admissions:** 10096 **Census:** 117 **Outpatient Visits:** 184535 **Births:** 1439 **Total Expense ($000):** 201549 **Payroll Expense ($000):** 81644 **Personnel:** 1248

☒ △ **MEDSTAR UNION MEMORIAL HOSPITAL (210024)**, 201 East University Parkway, Zip 21218–2895; tel. 410/554–2000 **A**1 2 3 5 7 9 10 **F**3 5 8 9 11 14 15 17 18 20 22 24 26 28 29 30 31 34 35 37 38 39 40 41 43 44 45 46 47 48 49 50 51 52 53 54 55 56 57 58 59 60 61 63 64 65 66 70 74 75 77 78 79 80 81 82 84 85 86 87 89 90 91 92 93 94 96 97 98 100 101 102 103 104 105 107 108 110 111 114 115 118 119 120 121 123 129 130 131 132 135 142 146 148 **P**6 **S** MedStar Health, Columbia, MD
Primary Contact: Bradley Chambers, President
COO: Neil MacDonald, Vice President Operations
CFO: Joseph B. Smith, Vice President Finance
CMO: Stuart Bell, M.D., Vice President Medical Affairs
CIO: Catherine Szenczy, Senior Vice President and Chief Information Officer
CHR: Holly Phipps–Adams, Vice President Human Resources
CNO: Sharon A. Bottcher, R.N., Vice President Patient Care Services
Web address: www.unionmemorial.org
**Control:** Other not–for–profit (including NFP Corporation) **Service:** General Medical and Surgical

**Staffed Beds:** 238 **Admissions:** 14914 **Census:** 170 **Outpatient Visits:** 164838 **Births:** 0 **Total Expense ($000):** 424514 **Payroll Expense ($000):** 163165 **Personnel:** 2202

☒ **MERCY MEDICAL CENTER (210008)**, 301 St. Paul Place, Zip 21202–2165; tel. 410/332–9000 **A**1 2 3 5 8 9 10 **F**3 4 8 11 13 14 15 17 18 20 29 30 31 34 35 36 37 39 40 41 44 45 46 47 48 49 50 51 55 57 58 59 64 65 66 68 70 72 74 75 76 77 78 79 81 82 85 86 87 89 92 93 94 100 102 107 108 110 111 114 115 116 117 118 119 120 121 123 124 126 128 129 130 132 135 141 142 143 144 145 146 147 148 **P**6
Primary Contact: Thomas R. Mullen, President and Chief Executive Officer
COO: Susan D. Finlayson, R.N., Senior Vice President of Operations
CFO: John E. Topper, Senior Vice President and Chief Financial Officer
CMO: Scott A. Spier, M.D., Senior Vice President Medical Affairs
CIO: Kathleen Perry, Vice President and Chief Information Officer
CHR: Tammy Janus, Vice President Human Resources
Web address: www.mdmercy.com
**Control:** Church–operated, Nongovernment, not–for profit **Service:** General Medical and Surgical

**Staffed Beds:** 281 **Admissions:** 17371 **Census:** 204 **Outpatient Visits:** 330090 **Births:** 2705 **Total Expense ($000):** 444570 **Payroll Expense ($000):** 151528 **Personnel:** 3412

☒ △ **MT. WASHINGTON PEDIATRIC HOSPITAL (213300)**, (PEDIATRIC SPECIALTY), 1708 West Rogers Avenue, Zip 21209–4545; tel. 410/578–8600 **A**1 3 5 7 9 10 **F**12 29 32 34 46 48 50 54 57 64 68 74 75 77 79 80 87 90 91 93 94 96 99 100 101 104 119 129 130 131 132 133 146 148 **P**6 **S** University of Maryland Medical System, Baltimore, MD
Primary Contact: Sheldon J. Stein, President and Chief Executive Officer
CFO: Mary Miller, Vice President Finance and Business Development
CMO: Richard Katz, M.D., Vice President Medical Affairs
CIO: Tim Brady, Director Information Systems
CHR: Thomas J. Ellis, Vice President Human Resources
Web address: www.mwph.org
**Control:** Other not–for–profit (including NFP Corporation) **Service:** Children's other specialty

**Staffed Beds:** 61 **Admissions:** 692 **Census:** 55 **Outpatient Visits:** 38695 **Births:** 0 **Total Expense ($000):** 46690 **Payroll Expense ($000):** 25849 **Personnel:** 472

*Many Facility Codes have changed. Please refer to the AHA Guide Code Chart.*

✠ **SAINT AGNES HOSPITAL (210011)**, 900 Caton Avenue, Zip 21229–5201; tel. 410/368–6000 **A**1 2 3 5 9 10 **F**3 8 11 12 13 14 15 17 18 20 22 26 28 29 30 31 32 34 35 40 41 44 46 49 50 53 54 55 56 57 58 59 60 61 64 65 68 70 72 74 75 76 77 78 79 81 82 84 85 86 87 88 89 92 93 96 97 102 103 107 108 110 111 114 115 117 118 119 120 121 123 124 126 129 130 131 132 134 135 144 146 147 148 **P**6 **S** Ascension Health, Saint Louis, MO
Primary Contact: Bonnie Phipps, President and Chief Executive Officer
CFO: Scott Furniss, Senior Vice President and Chief Financial Officer
CMO: Adrian Long, M.D., Executive Vice President and Chief Medical Officer
CIO: William Greskovich, Chief Information Officer
CHR: James Bobbitt, Vice President Human Resources
Web address: www.stagnes.org
**Control:** Church–operated, Nongovernment, not–for profit **Service:** General Medical and Surgical

**Staffed Beds:** 344 **Admissions:** 19122 **Census:** 214 **Outpatient Visits:** 514590 **Births:** 1889 **Total Expense ($000):** 379702 **Payroll Expense ($000):** 200322 **Personnel:** 2701

☐ **SHEPPARD PRATT HEALTH SYSTEM (214000)**, (Formerly Sheppard and Enoch Pratt Hospital), 6501 North Charles Street, Zip 21204–6819, Mailing Address: P.O. Box 6815, Zip 21285–6815; tel. 410/938–3000 **A**1 3 5 9 10 **F**10 30 35 38 56 58 64 75 87 98 99 101 103 104 105 106 130 132 143 144 146
Primary Contact: Steven S. Sharfstein, M.D., President and Chief Executive Officer
CFO: Patricia Pinkerton, Vice President and Chief Financial Officer
CMO: Robert Roca, M.D., Vice President Medical Affairs
CIO: Greg Merkle, Director Information Systems
CHR: Cathy Doughty, Vice President Human Resources
CNO: Ernestine Y. Cosby, Vice President Clinical Services and Chief Nursing Officer
Web address: www.sheppardpratt.org
**Control:** Other not–for–profit (including NFP Corporation) **Service:** Psychiatric

**Staffed Beds:** 336 **Admissions:** 9453 **Census:** 287 **Outpatient Visits:** 41703 **Births:** 0 **Total Expense ($000):** 185978 **Payroll Expense ($000):** 89301 **Personnel:** 2002

✠ △ **SINAI HOSPITAL OF BALTIMORE (210012)**, 2401 West Belvedere Avenue, Zip 21215–5271; tel. 410/601–9000 **A**1 2 3 5 7 9 10 **F**3 5 6 8 9 11 12 13 15 17 18 20 22 24 26 28 29 30 31 32 34 35 36 37 38 39 40 41 43 44 45 46 47 48 49 50 55 57 58 59 60 61 64 65 66 68 70 72 73 74 75 76 77 78 79 81 82 85 86 87 88 89 90 92 93 94 95 96 97 98 100 101 102 103 104 105 107 108 110 111 114 115 117 118 119 120 121 123 124 126 129 130 132 134 135 143 146 147 **P**6 **S** LifeBridge Health, Baltimore, MD
Primary Contact: Amy Perry, President
CFO: David Krajewski, Senior Vice President and Chief Financial Officer
CMO: Daniel C. Silverman, M.D., Vice President and Chief Medical Officer
CIO: Karen Barker, Vice President and Chief Information Officer
CHR: Cheryl T. Boyer, Vice President Human Resources
CNO: Diane Johnson, R.N., Vice President Patient Care Services and Chief Nursing Officer
Web address: www.lifebridgehealth.org
**Control:** Other not–for–profit (including NFP Corporation) **Service:** General Medical and Surgical

**Staffed Beds:** 460 **Admissions:** 27229 **Census:** 350 **Outpatient Visits:** 180943 **Births:** 2245 **Total Expense ($000):** 691053 **Payroll Expense ($000):** 297916 **Personnel:** 4202

☐ **SPRING GROVE HOSPITAL CENTER (214018)**, 55 Wade Avenue, Zip 21228–4663; tel. 410/402–6000, (Nonreporting) **A**1 3 5 9 10
Primary Contact: David S. Helsel, M.D., Chief Executive Officer
CFO: Edward Swartz, Chief Financial Officer
CMO: Devika Krishnan, M.D., Clinical Director and Chief of Staff
Web address: www.springgrove.com
**Control:** State–Government, nonfederal **Service:** Psychiatric

**Staffed Beds:** 365

**UNION MEMORIAL HOSPITAL** See MedStar Union Memorial Hospital

✠ **UNIVERSITY OF MARYLAND MEDICAL CENTER (210002)**, 22 South Greene Street, Zip 21201–1595; tel. 410/328–8667, (Includes UNIVERSITY OF MARYLAND HOSPITAL FOR CHILDREN, 22 South Greene Street, Zip 21201–1544; tel. 800/492–5538) **A**1 2 3 5 8 9 10 **F**3 4 5 6 7 9 11 12 13 14 15 16 17 18 19 20 21 22 23 24 25 26 27 28 29 30 31 32 34 35 36 38 39 40 41 43 44 45 46 47 48 49 50 51 52 54 55 56 57 58 59 60 61 64 65 66 67 68 70 71 72 73 74 75 76 77 78 79 80 81 82 84 85 86 87 88 89 90 92 93 94 97 98 99 100 101 102 103 104 105 106 107 108 109 110 111 114 115 116 117 118 119 120 121 123 124 126 128 129 130 131 132 134 135 136 137 139 140 141 142 143 144 145 146 147 148 **P**6 **S** University of Maryland Medical System, Baltimore, MD
Primary Contact: Jeffrey A. Rivest, FACHE, President and Chief Executive Officer
CFO: Keith D. Persinger, Senior Vice President Finance and Chief Financial Officer
CMO: Jonathan Gottlieb, M.D., Senior Vice President and Chief Medical Officer
CIO: Jon P. Burns, Chief Information Officer
CHR: R. Keith Allen, Senior Vice President Human Resources
Web address: www.umm.edu
**Control:** Other not–for–profit (including NFP Corporation) **Service:** General Medical and Surgical

**Staffed Beds:** 698 **Admissions:** 36968 **Census:** 605 **Outpatient Visits:** 261955 **Births:** 1531 **Total Expense ($000):** 1417044 **Payroll Expense ($000):** 423424 **Personnel:** 9106

✠ △ **VETERANS AFFAIRS MARYLAND HEALTH CARE SYSTEM–BALTIMORE DIVISION**, 10 North Greene Street, Zip 21201–1524; tel. 410/605–7001, (Includes VETERANS AFFAIRS MARYLAND HEALTH CARE SYSTEM–PERRY POINT DIVISION, Circle Drive, Perry Point, Zip 21902; tel. 410/642–2411; Dennis H. Smith, Director), (Nonreporting) **A**1 2 3 5 7 8 9 **S** Department of Veterans Affairs, Washington, DC
Primary Contact: Dennis H. Smith, Director
CFO: Major Tom Scheffler, Chief Fiscal Officer
CMO: Dorothy Snow, M.D., Chief of Staff
CIO: Sharon Zielinski, Chief Information Resource Officer
CHR: Jeff Craig, Chief Human Resource Management
Web address: www.maryland.va.gov/
**Control:** Veterans Affairs, Government, federal **Service:** General Medical and Surgical

**Staffed Beds:** 727

**BEL AIR—Harford County**

☐ **UPPER CHESAPEAKE MEDICAL CENTER (210049)**, 500 Upper Chesapeake Drive, Zip 21014–4324; tel. 443/643–1000 **A**1 2 9 10 **F**3 11 13 15 18 20 22 26 28 29 30 31 34 35 36 38 40 41 42 45 46 49 50 51 54 57 59 64 64 65 68 70 71 74 75 76 77 78 79 81 82 84 85 86 87 89 92 93 96 107 108 110 111 114 115 118 119 130 131 132 143 146 147 **S** Upper Chesapeake Health System, Bel Air, MD
Primary Contact: Lyle Ernest Sheldon, FACHE, President and Chief Executive Officer
CFO: Joseph E. Hoffman, III, Executive Vice President and Chief Financial Officer
CMO: Peggy Vaughan, M.D., Senior Vice President Medical Affairs
CIO: Rick Casteel, Vice President Management Information Systems and Chief Information Officer
CHR: Toni M. Shivery, Vice President Human Resources
Web address: www.uchs.org
**Control:** Other not–for–profit (including NFP Corporation) **Service:** General Medical and Surgical

**Staffed Beds:** 182 **Admissions:** 12968 **Census:** 130 **Outpatient Visits:** 175496 **Births:** 1340 **Total Expense ($000):** 225852 **Payroll Expense ($000):** 84042 **Personnel:** 1443

**BERLIN—Worcester County**

✠ **ATLANTIC GENERAL HOSPITAL (210061)**, 9733 Healthway Drive, Zip 21811–1155; tel. 410/641–1100 **A**1 9 10 **F**3 8 11 12 15 17 18 29 30 31 34 35 38 40 45 50 54 57 58 59 64 65 66 70 74 75 77 78 79 81 84 85 87 92 97 99 104 107 108 110 111 114 119 129 132 135 144 146 147 148 **P**7
Primary Contact: Michael A. Franklin, FACHE, President and Chief Executive Officer
COO: Kim Justice, Vice President Planning and Operations
CFO: Cheryl Nottingham, Chief Financial Officer
CMO: Stephen F. Waters, M.D., Medical Director
CIO: Barbara Riddell, Vice President Information Services
CHR: Jim Brannon, Vice President Human Resources
CNO: Colleen Wareing, Vice President Patient Care Services
Web address: www.atlanticgeneral.org
**Control:** Other not–for–profit (including NFP Corporation) **Service:** General Medical and Surgical

**Staffed Beds:** 58 **Admissions:** 3054 **Census:** 34 **Outpatient Visits:** 102606 **Births:** 0 **Total Expense ($000):** 87084 **Payroll Expense ($000):** 38794 **Personnel:** 611

---

**Hospital, Medicare Provider Number, Address, Telephone, Approval, Facility, and Physician Codes, Health Care System**

★ American Hospital Association (AHA) membership
☐ The Joint Commission accreditation
◇ DNV Healthcare Inc. accreditation
○ Healthcare Facilities Accreditation Program
△ Commission on Accreditation of Rehabilitation Facilities (CARF) accreditation

**BETHESDA—Montgomery County**

☒ **NATIONAL INSTITUTES OF HEALTH CLINICAL CENTER**, (Biomedical Research), 9000 Rockville Pike, Building 10, Room 6–2551, Zip 20892–1504; tel. 301/496–4000, (Includes CHILDREN'S INN AT NIH, 7 West Drive, Zip 20814–1509; tel. 301/496–5672) **A**1 3 5 8 **F**3 4 5 8 14 15 20 22 26 30 31 36 39 45 52 53 55 58 59 60 61 64 65 68 70 74 75 77 78 79 81 82 84 85 86 87 89 91 92 93 94 95 96 98 99 100 101 104 105 107 108 110 111 112 114 115 116 117 118 119 120 121 124 126 129 130 132 135 136 141 142 145 146 148 **S** U. S. Indian Health Service, Rockville, MD
Primary Contact: John I. Gallin, M.D., Director
COO: Maureen E. Gormley, R.N., Chief Operating Officer
CFO: Maria Joyce, Chief Financial Officer
CMO: David K. Henderson, M.D., Deputy Director Clinical Care
CIO: Jon W. McKeeby, Chief Information Officer
CHR: Bonnie Tuma, Human Resources Team Lead
Web address: www.clinicalcenter.nih.gov
**Control:** Public Health Service, Government, federal **Service:** Other specialty

Staffed Beds: 161 Admissions: 5916 Census: 150 Outpatient Visits: 102169 Births: 0 Total Expense ($000): 400483 Payroll Expense ($000): 171008 Personnel: 1875

**NATIONAL NAVAL MEDICAL CENTER** See Walter Reed National Military Medical Center

☒ **SUBURBAN HOSPITAL (210022)**, 8600 Old Georgetown Road, Zip 20814–1497; tel. 301/896–3100 **A**1 2 3 5 9 10 **F**3 5 8 11 15 17 18 20 22 24 26 28 29 30 31 34 35 36 37 38 39 40 43 44 45 46 49 50 51 53 54 56 57 58 59 60 64 70 71 74 75 77 78 79 81 82 84 85 86 87 89 92 93 98 99 100 101 102 103 104 105 107 108 110 111 114 115 117 118 119 120 121 123 126 129 130 132 134 135 146 147 148 **P**6 **S** Johns Hopkins Health System, Baltimore, MD
Primary Contact: Gene E. Green, M.D., President
COO: Jacky Schultz, R.N., Executive Vice President and Chief Operating Officer
CFO: Marty Basso, Senior Vice President Finance
CMO: Robert Rothstein, M.D., Vice President Medical Affairs
CIO: Christopher T. Timbers, Vice President and Chief Information Officer
CHR: Dennis Parnell, Senior Vice President Human Resources
CNO: Barbara Stewart Jacobs, MSN, Chief Nurse Officer
Web address: www.suburbanhospital.org
**Control:** Other not–for–profit (including NFP Corporation) **Service:** General Medical and Surgical

Staffed Beds: 233 Admissions: 14171 Census: 166 Outpatient Visits: 126248 Births: 0 Total Expense ($000): 248726 Payroll Expense ($000): 99822 Personnel: 1336

☒ **WALTER REED NATIONAL MILITARY MEDICAL CENTER**, 8901 Wisconsin Avenue, Zip 20889–5600; tel. 301/295–4611, (Nonreporting) **A**1 2 3 5 **S** Bureau of Medicine and Surgery, Department of the Navy, Washington, DC
Primary Contact: Colonel John M. Gaal, Deputy Commander Administration
CFO: Commander Joseph Pickel, Director Resource Management
CMO: Paul Florentino, M.D., Director Medical Services
CIO: Commander Cayetano Thornton, Chief Information Officer
CHR: Captain Jaime Carroll, Department Head
Web address: www.wrnmmc.capmed.mil/SitePages/home.aspx
**Control:** Navy, Government, federal **Service:** General Medical and Surgical

Staffed Beds: 240

**CAMBRIDGE—Dorchester County**

☒ **DORCHESTER GENERAL HOSPITAL**, 300 Byrn Street, Zip 21613–1908; tel. 410/228–5511 **A**1 9 **F**3 11 15 18 19 20 22 28 29 30 31 39 40 45 57 59 64 68 70 74 75 77 78 79 81 82 85 87 91 93 98 99 100 102 103 104 107 108 111 113 118 119 130 132 **S** University of Maryland Medical System, Baltimore, MD
Primary Contact: Kenneth D. Kozel, FACHE, President and Chief Executive Officer
COO: Gerard M. Walsh, Senior Vice President and Chief Operating Officer
CFO: Walter Zajac, Senior Vice President and Chief Financial Officer
CMO: Michael Tooke, M.D., Vice President Medical Affairs
CIO: Elizabeth Fish, Chief Information Officer
CHR: Michael Zimmerman, Vice President Human Resources
Web address: www.shorehealth.org
**Control:** Other not–for–profit (including NFP Corporation) **Service:** General Medical and Surgical

Staffed Beds: 43 Admissions: 2844 Census: 31 Outpatient Visits: 117065 Births: 0 Total Expense ($000): 43435 Payroll Expense ($000): 20086 Personnel: 264

☐ **EASTERN SHORE HOSPITAL CENTER (214002)**, 5262 Woods Road, Zip 21613–3796, Mailing Address: P.O. Box 800, Zip 21613–0800; tel. 410/221–2525, (Nonreporting) **A**1 9 10
Primary Contact: Mary Kay Noren, Chief Executive Officer
COO: Randy L. Bradford, Assistant Superintendent
CFO: Ida Bundick, Chief Financial Officer
CMO: David Pytlewski, M.D., Clinical Director
CHR: Cassandra Stanley, Director Personnel
Web address: www.dhmh.state.md.us/eshc
**Control:** State–Government, nonfederal **Service:** Psychiatric

Staffed Beds: 76

**CHESTERTOWN—Kent County**

☒ **CHESTER RIVER HEALTH SYSTEM (210030)**, 100 Brown Street, Zip 21620–1499; tel. 410/778–3300 **A**1 9 10 **F**3 11 15 18 19 20 28 29 30 31 34 35 39 40 41 42 45 46 47 50 53 55 56 57 59 60 62 63 64 65 68 70 75 78 79 80 81 82 85 87 97 102 107 110 111 115 119 128 129 130 132 143 146 147 **S** University of Maryland Medical System, Baltimore, MD
Primary Contact: James E. Ross, FACHE, President and Chief Executive Officer
COO: Scott D. Burleson, Executive Vice President
CFO: Samuel Marinelli, Vice President Finance and Chief Financial Officer
CMO: Stanley Minken, M.D., Chief Medical Officer
CIO: Elizabeth Fish, Senior Director Site Executive and Information Technology
CHR: Patricia Kuhl, Vice President Human Resources
CNO: Mary Jo Keefe, R.N., Vice President Patient Care Services and Chief Nursing Officer
Web address: www.chesterriverhealth.org
**Control:** Other not–for–profit (including NFP Corporation) **Service:** General Medical and Surgical

Staffed Beds: 46 Admissions: 2666 Census: 30 Outpatient Visits: 52070 Births: 157 Total Expense ($000): 54293 Payroll Expense ($000): 23195 Personnel: 298

**CHESTER RIVER HOSPITAL CENTER** See Chester River Health System

**CHEVERLY—Prince George's County**

**GLADYS SPELLMAN SPECIALTY HOSPITAL AND NURSING CENTER**, 2900 Mercy Lane, Zip 20785–1157; tel. 301/618–2010, (Nonreporting)
Primary Contact: Stewart R. Seitz, Chief Executive Officer
CFO: Ketty Taboado, Chief Financial Officer
CMO: Paul A. Devore, M.D., Medical Director
CIO: Dennis Lilik, Chief Information Officer
CHR: Michael Jacobs, Vice President Human Resources
Web address: www.dimensionshealth.org
**Control:** Corporation, Investor–owned, for–profit **Service:** Chronic disease

Staffed Beds: 30

☐ **PRINCE GEORGE'S HOSPITAL CENTER (210003)**, 3001 Hospital Drive, Zip 20785–1189; tel. 301/618–2000 **A**1 3 5 9 10 **F**3 11 13 15 18 19 20 22 24 26 28 29 31 34 35 38 40 42 43 45 46 47 48 49 50 54 55 56 57 59 60 61 63 64 65 66 68 69 70 72 74 75 76 77 78 79 81 82 84 85 86 87 89 92 93 97 98 100 101 102 103 104 105 107 108 110 111 114 115 118 119 130 131 132 134 135 142 144 146 148 **P**6 **S** Dimensions Healthcare System, Cheverly, MD
Primary Contact: John A. O'Brien, FACHE, President
CMO: David Goldman, M.D., Vice President Medical Affairs and Education
CIO: Dennis Lilik, Chief Information Officer
CHR: Michael Jacobs, Vice President Human Resources
Web address: www.princegeorgeshospital.org
**Control:** Other not–for–profit (including NFP Corporation) **Service:** General Medical and Surgical

Staffed Beds: 302 Admissions: 11365 Census: 160 Outpatient Visits: 94836 Births: 2150 Total Expense ($000): 238032 Payroll Expense ($000): 106414 Personnel: 1599

**CLINTON—Prince George's County**

☒ **MEDSTAR SOUTHERN MARYLAND HOSPITAL CENTER (210062)**, (Formerly Southern Maryland Hospital Center), 7503 Surratts Road, Zip 20735–3358; tel. 301/868–8000, (Total facility includes 24 beds in nursing home–type unit) (Data for 344 days) **A**1 2 9 10 **F**3 12 13 17 18 20 22 26 28 29 30 31 32 34 35 36 37 39 40 44 45 46 47 48 49 50 57 59 64 65 70 71 73 74 75 76 77 78 79 81 82 85 86 87 89 91 92 93 96 98 100 101 102 103 105 107 108 114 115 118 119 128 129 130 132 135 143 145 146 147 148 **P**6 **S** MedStar Health, Columbia, MD
Primary Contact: Michael J. Chiaramonte, Chief Executive Officer
CFO: Charles R. Stewart, Vice President Business, Finance and Corporate Compliance
CMO: J. Andrew Sumner, M.D., Vice President Medical Affairs
CIO: Lou Mavromatis, Vice President Data Processing
CHR: Paul Zeller, Vice President Human Resources
Web address: www.smhchealth.org
**Control:** Corporation, Investor–owned, for–profit **Service:** General Medical and Surgical

Staffed Beds: 262 Admissions: 16091 Census: 174 Outpatient Visits: 108258 Births: 1877 Total Expense ($000): 230872 Payroll Expense ($000): 86013 Personnel: 1506

**SOUTHERN MARYLAND HOSPITAL CENTER** See MedStar Southern Maryland Hospital Center

*Many Facility Codes have changed. Please refer to the AHA Guide Code Chart.*   © 2013 AHA Guide

## COLUMBIA—Howard County

☒ **HOWARD COUNTY GENERAL HOSPITAL (210048)**, 5755 Cedar Lane, Zip 21044–2999; tel. 410/740–7890 **A**1 2 5 9 10 **F**3 8 11 13 15 18 20 22 26 28 29 30 31 32 34 35 36 39 40 41 44 45 46 47 49 50 51 55 56 57 58 59 61 64 68 70 72 74 75 76 77 78 79 81 82 84 85 86 87 89 91 92 93 94 96 98 100 101 102 103 107 108 110 111 114 115 119 130 131 132 134 135 146 147 148 **S** Johns Hopkins Health System, Baltimore, MD
Primary Contact: Victor A. Broccolino, President and Chief Executive Officer
COO: Jay H. Blackman, Senior Vice President and Chief Operating Officer
CFO: James Young, Senior Vice President Finance and Chief Financial Officer
CIO: Rick Edwards, Director Information Systems
CHR: Dorothy Brillantes, Senior Vice President Human Resources
Web address: www.hcgh.org
**Control:** Other not–for–profit (including NFP Corporation) **Service:** General Medical and Surgical

**Staffed Beds:** 256 **Admissions:** 15667 **Census:** 178 **Outpatient Visits:** 155504 **Births:** 3333 **Total Expense ($000):** 167717 **Payroll Expense ($000):** 85834 **Personnel:** 1380

## CRISFIELD—Somerset County

☐ **MCCREADY FOUNDATION (210045)**, (Formerly McCready Health Services Foundation), 201 Hall Highway, Zip 21817–1299; tel. 410/968–1200, (Nonreporting) **A**1 9 10
Primary Contact: Robert Jones, Chief Executive Officer
CFO: Gary W. Broadwater, Chief Financial Officer
Web address: www.mccreadyfoundation.org
**Control:** Other not–for–profit (including NFP Corporation) **Service:** General Medical and Surgical

**Staffed Beds:** 89

## CUMBERLAND—Allegany County

☐ **THOMAS B. FINAN CENTER (214012)**, 10102 Country Club Road S.E., Zip 21502–8339, Mailing Address: P.O. Box 1722, Zip 21501–1722; tel. 301/777–2240, (Nonreporting) **A**1 9 10
Primary Contact: Judith Hott, Chief Executive Officer
COO: John Cullen, Assistant Superintendent
CFO: Craig Alexander, Fiscal Specialist
CMO: Linda de Hoyos, M.D., Clinical Director
CHR: Chris Loney, Director Personnel
CNO: Gayle Walter, Director of Nursing
Web address: www.dhmh.state.md.us
**Control:** State–Government, nonfederal **Service:** Psychiatric

**Staffed Beds:** 80

☒ △ **WESTERN MARYLAND REGIONAL MEDICAL CENTER (210027)**, 12500 Willowbrook Road, Zip 21502–6393, Mailing Address: P.O. Box 539, Zip 21501–0539; tel. 240/964–7000, (Total facility includes 88 beds in nursing home–type unit) **A**1 2 7 9 10 **F**3 5 11 13 14 15 17 18 20 22 24 26 28 29 30 31 32 34 35 38 40 43 44 45 50 51 54 56 57 59 60 62 63 64 68 69 70 73 74 75 76 77 78 79 80 81 82 84 85 86 87 89 90 93 94 96 97 98 100 102 103 104 107 108 110 111 114 115 116 117 118 119 120 121 123 128 129 130 132 135 144 146 148 **P**6
Primary Contact: Barry P. Ronan, President and Chief Executive Officer
COO: Thomas C. Dowdell, FACHE, Senior Vice President and Chief Operating Officer
CFO: Kimberly S. Repac, Senior Vice President and Chief Financial Officer
CMO: George Garrow, M.D., Senior Vice President and Chief Medical Officer
CIO: William Byers, Vice President and Chief Information Officer
CHR: Mark J. Sullivan, Vice President Human Resources
CNO: Nancy D. Adams, R.N., Senior Vice President and Chief Nurse Executive
Web address: www.wmhs.com
**Control:** Other not–for–profit (including NFP Corporation) **Service:** General Medical and Surgical

**Staffed Beds:** 371 **Admissions:** 13932 **Census:** 249 **Outpatient Visits:** 527275 **Births:** 993 **Total Expense ($000):** 305799 **Payroll Expense ($000):** 109711 **Personnel:** 1903

## EAST NEW MARKET—Dorchester County

**WARWICK MANOR BEHAVIORAL HEALTH**, 3680 Warwick Road, Zip 21631–1420; tel. 410/943–8108, (Nonreporting)
Primary Contact: Marie McBee, Chief Executive Officer
Web address: www.warwickmanor.org/
**Control:** Corporation, Investor–owned, for–profit **Service:** Alcoholism and other chemical dependency

**Staffed Beds:** 42

## EASTON—Talbot County

☒ △ **MEMORIAL HOSPITAL AT EASTON MARYLAND (210037)**, 219 South Washington Street, Zip 21601–2996; tel. 410/822–1000 **A**1 2 7 9 10 **F**3 8 11 13 15 18 20 22 28 29 30 31 34 37 39 40 42 45 49 51 54 57 58 59 60 62 63 64 65 70 74 76 78 79 81 82 83 84 85 86 90 91 93 100 102 107 108 111 114 116 117 118 119 120 121 123 124 126 129 130 132 144 147 148 **P**3 **S** University of Maryland Medical System, Baltimore, MD
Primary Contact: Kenneth D. Kozel, FACHE, President and Chief Executive Officer
COO: Gerard M. Walsh, Senior Vice President and Chief Operating Officer
CFO: Walter Zajac, Senior Vice President and Chief Financial Officer
CMO: Michael Tooke, M.D., Chief Medical Officer
CIO: Elizabeth Fish, Chief Information Officer
CHR: Michael Zimmerman, Vice President Human Resources
CNO: Christopher J. Parker, R.N., Chief Nursing Officer
Web address: www.shorehealth.org
**Control:** Other not–for–profit (including NFP Corporation) **Service:** General Medical and Surgical

**Staffed Beds:** 114 **Admissions:** 8314 **Census:** 89 **Outpatient Visits:** 373382 **Births:** 1004 **Total Expense ($000):** 167428 **Payroll Expense ($000):** 61645 **Personnel:** 1046

## ELKTON—Cecil County

☒ △ **UNION HOSPITAL (210032)**, 106 Bow Street, Zip 21921–5596; tel. 410/398–4000 **A**1 2 3 5 7 9 10 **F**2 3 11 13 15 18 26 29 30 31 34 35 40 44 45 46 49 50 51 54 57 59 61 63 64 69 70 74 75 76 77 78 79 81 82 84 85 86 87 89 92 97 98 100 102 104 105 107 108 110 111 114 118 119 129 130 131 132 135 146 147 148 **P**6
Primary Contact: Kenneth S. Lewis, M.D., JD, President and Chief Executive Officer
COO: David N. Gipson, Senior Vice President and Chief Clinical Operations Officer
CFO: Laurie Beyer, Senior Vice President and Chief Financial Officer
CMO: Jose Ma, M.D., Vice President Medical Affairs
CIO: Mary Jane Kamps, Chief Information Officer
CHR: Peter Gloggner, Vice President Human Resources
Web address: www.uhcc.com
**Control:** Other not–for–profit (including NFP Corporation) **Service:** General Medical and Surgical

**Staffed Beds:** 119 **Admissions:** 6346 **Census:** 65 **Outpatient Visits:** 166210 **Births:** 683 **Total Expense ($000):** 134531 **Payroll Expense ($000):** 59119 **Personnel:** 907

## FORT WASHINGTON—Prince George's County

☒ **FORT WASHINGTON MEDICAL CENTER (210060)**, 11711 Livingston Road, Zip 20744–5164; tel. 301/292–7000 **A**1 9 10 **F**3 29 34 35 40 45 46 47 49 50 57 59 64 66 70 71 74 75 79 81 85 87 92 107 108 110 119 130
Primary Contact: Verna Stroman Meacham, President and Chief Executive Officer
CFO: Joseph B. Tucker, Senior Vice President and Chief Financial Officer
CMO: Elias Debbas, M.D., President Medical Staff
CIO: Fred Ashby, Director Information Technology
CHR: Alexander Morris, Corporate Director Human Resources
CNO: Marjorie Quint–Bouzid, Chief Nursing Officer and Vice President Patient Care Services
Web address: www.fortwashingtonmc.org
**Control:** Other not–for–profit (including NFP Corporation) **Service:** General Medical and Surgical

**Staffed Beds:** 37 **Admissions:** 2185 **Census:** 22 **Outpatient Visits:** 55726 **Births:** 0 **Total Expense ($000):** 38280 **Payroll Expense ($000):** 18879 **Personnel:** 298

## FREDERICK—Frederick County

☒ **FREDERICK MEMORIAL HOSPITAL (210005)**, 400 West Seventh Street, Zip 21701–4593; tel. 240/566–3300, (Nonreporting) **A**1 2 5 9 10
Primary Contact: Thomas A. Kleinhanzl, President and Chief Executive Officer
COO: John R. Verbus, Senior Vice President and Chief Operating Officer
CFO: Michelle K. Mahan, Senior Vice President and Chief Financial Officer
CMO: Manuel Casiano, M.D., Vice President Medical Affairs
CIO: David Quirke, Vice President Information Services
CHR: Terry O'Malley, Vice President Human Resources
Web address: www.fmh.org
**Control:** Other not–for–profit (including NFP Corporation) **Service:** General Medical and Surgical

**Staffed Beds:** 308

**MD**

## GLEN BURNIE—Anne Arundel County

✠ **BALTIMORE WASHINGTON MEDICAL CENTER (210043)**, 301 Hospital Drive, Zip 21061–5899; tel. 410/787–4000 **A**1 2 9 10 **F**8 10 11 13 14 18 20 22 26 28 29 30 31 34 35 40 42 44 45 46 48 49 50 54 55 56 57 58 59 60 64 65 68 70 73 74 75 76 77 78 79 81 82 84 85 87 89 93 94 98 100 102 105 107 108 111 114 115 118 119 120 121 123 126 129 130 131 132 135 146 147 148 **P**6 **S** University of Maryland Medical System, Baltimore, MD
Primary Contact: Karen E. Olscamp, President and Chief Executive Officer
COO: Ronald J. Andro, Senior Vice President and Chief Operating Officer
CFO: Al Pietsch, CPA, Senior Vice President and Chief Financial Officer
CMO: Lawrence Linder, M.D., Senior Vice President and Chief Medical Officer
CIO: Linda Hines, Vice President and Site Executive
CHR: Frank Venuto, Vice President Human Resources
Web address: www.bwmc.umms.org
**Control:** Other not–for–profit (including NFP Corporation) **Service:** General Medical and Surgical

| | |
|---|---|
| **Staffed Beds:** 323 **Admissions:** 19375 **Census:** 227 **Outpatient Visits:** 138357 **Births:** 832 **Total Expense ($000):** 325035 **Payroll Expense ($000):** 129025 **Personnel:** 2280 | |

## HAGERSTOWN—Washington County

☐ **BROOK LANE HEALTH SERVICES (214003)**, 13218 Brook Lane Drive, Zip 21742–1435, Mailing Address: P.O. Box 1945, Zip 21742–1945; tel. 301/733–0330 **A**1 9 10 **F**5 26 27 30 56 68 98 99 100 101 103 104 105 130 143 146 **P**4 6
Primary Contact: R. Lynn Rushing, Chief Executive Officer
CFO: Floyd Klauka, Chief Financial Officer
CIO: Sharon Gladfelter, Health Information Officer
CHR: Patricia Bourdeau, Director Human Resources
Web address: www.brooklane.org
**Control:** Other not–for–profit (including NFP Corporation) **Service:** Psychiatric

| | |
|---|---|
| **Staffed Beds:** 43 **Admissions:** 1973 **Census:** 34 **Outpatient Visits:** 53907 **Births:** 0 **Total Expense ($000):** 20537 **Payroll Expense ($000):** 12486 **Personnel:** 301 | |

✠ △ **MERITUS MEDICAL CENTER (210001)**, 11116 Medical Campus Road, Zip 21742–6710; tel. 301/790–8000 **A**1 2 7 9 10 **F**3 5 11 12 13 15 17 18 20 22 26 28 29 30 31 34 35 38 40 43 44 49 51 52 54 56 57 58 59 60 61 62 64 65 70 74 75 76 77 78 79 81 82 83 84 85 86 87 89 90 93 94 96 97 98 99 100 101 102 103 104 105 107 108 111 114 115 118 119 120 121 123 130 131 132 135 143 144 145 146 147 148 **P**6 8
Primary Contact: Joseph P. Ross, President and Chief Executive Officer
COO: Deborah Addo–Samuels, Senior Vice President and Chief Operating Officer
CFO: Raymond A. Grahe, Senior Vice President Strategic Ventures and Chief Financial Officer
CMO: Robert L. Brooks, M.D., Vice President Medical Affairs
CMO: Heather Lorenzo, M.D., Vice President and Chief Medical Officer
CIO: Jake Dorst, Vice President and Chief Information Officer
CIO: Carey O. Leverett, Vice President Information Services
CHR: Kelly Corbi, Chief Administrative Officer and Vice President Human Resources and Development
CNO: Jesus Cepero, Ph.D., Vice President Nursing and Chief Nursing Officer
Web address: www.meritushealth.com
**Control:** Other not–for–profit (including NFP Corporation) **Service:** General Medical and Surgical

| | |
|---|---|
| **Staffed Beds:** 272 **Admissions:** 15533 **Census:** 183 **Outpatient Visits:** 204459 **Births:** 1976 **Total Expense ($000):** 282643 **Payroll Expense ($000):** 115284 **Personnel:** 1924 | |

**WASHINGTON COUNTY HEALTH SYSTEM** See Meritus Medical Center

☐ △ **WESTERN MARYLAND HOSPITAL CENTER (212002)**, 1500 Pennsylvania Avenue, Zip 21742–3194; tel. 301/791–4400, (Nonreporting) **A**1 7 9 10
Primary Contact: Cynthia Miller Pellegrino, Chief Executive Officer
COO: David Davis, Chief Operating Officer
CFO: Kelly Edmonds, Chief Financial Officer
CMO: Monica Stallworth, M.D., Chief of Staff
CIO: Ron Keplinger, Chief Information Officer
CHR: David Davis, Chief Operating Officer
Web address: www.wmhc.us
**Control:** State–Government, nonfederal **Service:** Long–Term Acute Care hospital

| | |
|---|---|
| **Staffed Beds:** 120 | |

## HAVRE DE GRACE—Harford County

☐ **HARFORD MEMORIAL HOSPITAL (210006)**, 501 South Union Avenue, Zip 21078–3493; tel. 443/843–5000 **A**1 2 9 10 **F**3 11 12 15 28 29 30 31 34 35 36 38 40 42 46 49 50 51 57 59 60 64 65 66 68 70 71 74 75 77 78 79 81 82 84 85 86 87 92 93 96 98 102 103 104 107 108 110 111 114 115 118 119 129 130 131 132 135 146 148 **S** Upper Chesapeake Health System, Bel Air, MD
Primary Contact: Lyle Ernest Sheldon, FACHE, President and Chief Executive Officer
CFO: Joseph E. Hoffman, III, Executive Vice President and Chief Financial Officer
CMO: Peggy Vaughan, M.D., Senior Vice President Medical Affairs
CIO: Rick Casteel, Vice President Management Information Systems and Chief Information Officer
CHR: Toni M. Shivery, Vice President Human Resources
Web address: www.uchs.org
**Control:** Other not–for–profit (including NFP Corporation) **Service:** General Medical and Surgical

| | |
|---|---|
| **Staffed Beds:** 104 **Admissions:** 5132 **Census:** 63 **Outpatient Visits:** 93162 **Births:** 0 **Total Expense ($000):** 83529 **Payroll Expense ($000):** 37743 **Personnel:** 690 | |

## JESSUP—Howard County

☐ **CLIFTON T. PERKINS HOSPITAL CENTER**, 8450 Dorsey Run Road, Zip 20794–9486; tel. 410/724–3000, (Nonreporting) **A**1 3 5
Primary Contact: Sheilah Davenport, JD, MS, R.N., Chief Executive Officer and Superintendent
COO: Steve Mason, Assistant Superintendent and Chief Operating Officer
CFO: George Parnel, Chief Financial Officer
CMO: Muhammed Ajanah, M.D., Clinical Director
CIO: Chanda Hamilton, Chief Information Officer
CHR: Beverly Stacie, Director Human Resources
Web address: www.dhmh.state.md.us/perkins/
**Control:** State–Government, nonfederal **Service:** Psychiatric

| | |
|---|---|
| **Staffed Beds:** 218 | |

## LA PLATA—Charles County

✠ **UNIVERSITY OF MARYLAND CHARLES REGIONAL MEDICAL CENTER (210035)**, (Formerly Civista Health), 5 Garrett Avenue, Zip 20646–5960, Mailing Address: P.O. Box 1070, Zip 20646–1070; tel. 301/609–4000 **A**1 2 9 10 **F**3 11 13 15 18 20 28 29 30 31 34 35 36 40 45 50 51 57 59 60 61 64 70 74 76 77 78 79 81 82 85 86 87 89 93 107 108 111 114 115 118 119 129 130 132 145 146 148 **S** University of Maryland Medical System, Baltimore, MD
Primary Contact: Noel A. Cervino, President and Chief Executive Officer
CFO: Erik Boas, Vice President Finance
CMO: Sanjeeb Mishra, M.D., Chief of Staff
CIO: Kevin Burbules, Chief Information Officer
CHR: Stacey Cook, Director Human Resources
Web address: www.civista.org
**Control:** Other not–for–profit (including NFP Corporation) **Service:** General Medical and Surgical

| | |
|---|---|
| **Staffed Beds:** 124 **Admissions:** 7105 **Census:** 80 **Outpatient Visits:** 58754 **Births:** 701 **Total Expense ($000):** 96010 **Payroll Expense ($000):** 43980 **Personnel:** 708 | |

## LANHAM—Prince George's County

✠ **DOCTORS COMMUNITY HOSPITAL (210051)**, 8118 Good Luck Road, Zip 20706–3574; tel. 301/552–8118 **A**1 9 10 **F**12 15 18 28 29 30 34 35 40 57 59 60 64 70 75 77 78 79 81 82 93 107 110 111 114 115 119 126 130 146
Primary Contact: Philip B. Down, Chief Executive Officer
COO: Paul Grenaldo, Executive Vice President and Chief Operating Officer
CFO: Dennis P. Scanlon, Vice President Finance
CMO: Gabriel Jaffe, M.D., Vice President Medical Affairs
CIO: Alan Johnson, Chief Information Officer
CHR: Charlene B. Lundgren, Vice President
Web address: www.dchweb.org
**Control:** Other not–for–profit (including NFP Corporation) **Service:** General Medical and Surgical

| | |
|---|---|
| **Staffed Beds:** 219 **Admissions:** 12052 **Census:** 148 **Outpatient Visits:** 119236 **Births:** 0 **Total Expense ($000):** 176880 **Payroll Expense ($000):** 76856 **Personnel:** 1250 | |

*Many Facility Codes have changed. Please refer to the AHA Guide Code Chart.*

**LAUREL—Prince George's County**

☐ △ **LAUREL REGIONAL HOSPITAL (210055)**, 7300 Van Dusen Road, Zip 20707–9463; tel. 301/725–4300 **A**1 7 9 10 **F**1 3 11 13 15 18 20 29 30 31 34 35 40 46 49 50 51 57 59 60 61 63 64 65 66 68 69 70 74 75 76 77 78 79 80 81 82 84 85 87 90 92 93 98 100 102 103 104 105 107 108 110 111 114 115 118 119 129 130 132 146 148 **P**6 **S** Dimensions Healthcare System, Cheverly, MD
Primary Contact: John Spearman, President and Chief Operating Officer
COO: John A. O'Brien, FACHE, Chief Operating Officer
CMO: Gita Shah, M.D., Vice President Medical Affairs
CIO: Dennis Lilik, Chief Information Officer
CHR: Michael Jacobs, Vice President Human Resources
Web address: www.laurelregionalhospital.org
**Control:** Other not–for–profit (including NFP Corporation) **Service:** General Medical and Surgical

**Staffed Beds:** 166 **Admissions:** 5630 **Census:** 81 **Outpatient Visits:** 42141 **Births:** 1006 **Total Expense ($000):** 111741 **Payroll Expense ($000):** 48480 **Personnel:** 679

**LEONARDTOWN—St. Mary's County**

☒ **MEDSTAR ST. MARY'S HOSPITAL (210028)**, 25500 Point Lookout Road, Zip 20650–2015, Mailing Address: P.O. Box 527, Zip 20650–0527; tel. 301/475–6001 **A**1 2 9 10 **F**3 11 13 15 18 28 29 30 31 32 34 35 36 39 40 44 45 48 50 51 53 54 56 57 59 60 63 64 65 66 68 70 71 74 75 76 77 78 79 81 82 84 85 86 87 89 93 98 100 101 102 103 104 105 107 108 110 111 114 115 118 119 129 130 132 134 135 144 146 147 148 **P**6 **S** MedStar Health, Columbia, MD
Primary Contact: Christine R. Wray, President
CFO: Richard Braam, Vice President Finance
CMO: Avani D. Shah, M.D., Chief of Medical Staff
CIO: Donald Sirk, Director Information Systems
CHR: Evelyn Campos–Diaz, Director Human Resources
CNO: Mary Lou Watson, MS, Vice President Nursing
Web address: www.medstarstmarys.org
**Control:** Other not–for–profit (including NFP Corporation) **Service:** General Medical and Surgical

**Staffed Beds:** 90 **Admissions:** 7581 **Census:** 63 **Outpatient Visits:** 261448 **Births:** 1091 **Total Expense ($000):** 120811 **Payroll Expense ($000):** 53061 **Personnel:** 904

**OAKLAND—Garrett County**

☒ **GARRETT COUNTY MEMORIAL HOSPITAL (210017)**, 251 North Fourth Street, Zip 21550–1375; tel. 301/533–4000, (Total facility includes 10 beds in nursing home–type unit) **A**1 9 10 **F**3 11 13 28 29 30 31 32 34 35 38 40 45 53 56 57 59 64 65 70 75 76 78 79 81 82 85 87 89 102 107 108 109 114 118 119 128 130 135 146 148 **P**6 7
Primary Contact: Donald P. Battista, President and Chief Executive Officer
COO: Denise R. Liston, R.N., Vice President Clinical and Support Services
CFO: Tracy Lipscomb, Vice President Financial Services and Chief Financial Officer
CIO: Stephen Peterson, Director Information Systems
CHR: Annette Livengood, Vice President Human Resources
Web address: www.gcmh.com
**Control:** Other not–for–profit (including NFP Corporation) **Service:** General Medical and Surgical

**Staffed Beds:** 56 **Admissions:** 2179 **Census:** 27 **Outpatient Visits:** 73661 **Births:** 279 **Total Expense ($000):** 40662 **Payroll Expense ($000):** 16015 **Personnel:** 313

**OLNEY—Montgomery County**

☒ **MEDSTAR MONTGOMERY MEDICAL CENTER (210018)**, 18101 Prince Philip Drive, Zip 20832–1512; tel. 301/774–8882 **A**1 2 9 10 **F**3 5 11 12 13 18 20 26 28 29 30 31 34 35 37 38 40 41 45 46 48 49 50 51 53 55 56 57 59 62 65 70 74 75 76 77 78 79 80 81 84 85 86 89 92 93 98 99 100 102 103 104 105 107 108 114 115 118 119 126 129 130 132 134 135 146 **S** MedStar Health, Columbia, MD
Primary Contact: Peter W. Monge, President
CFO: David A. Havrilla, Chief Financial Officer
CMO: Roger Leonard, M.D., Vice President Medical Affairs
CHR: Kevin Mell, Vice President Operations
Web address: www.montgomerygeneral.com
**Control:** Other not–for–profit (including NFP Corporation) **Service:** General Medical and Surgical

**Staffed Beds:** 158 **Admissions:** 9205 **Census:** 98 **Outpatient Visits:** 68835 **Births:** 727 **Total Expense ($000):** 137669 **Payroll Expense ($000):** 56939 **Personnel:** 834

**PERRY POINT—Cecil County**

**VETERANS AFFAIRS MARYLAND HEALTH CARE SYSTEM–PERRY POINT DIVISION** See Veterans Affairs Maryland Health Care System–Baltimore Division, Baltimore

**PRINCE FREDERICK—Calvert County**

☒ **CALVERT MEMORIAL HOSPITAL (210039)**, 100 Hospital Road, Zip 20678–4017; tel. 410/535–4000, (Total facility includes 18 beds in nursing home–type unit) **A**1 2 9 10 **F**3 8 11 13 15 18 28 29 30 31 32 33 34 35 36 38 40 49 50 54 57 59 62 68 70 75 76 77 78 79 81 82 84 85 86 87 89 98 99 101 102 105 107 108 111 114 118 119 129 130 131 132 134 135 144 146 147 148 **P**4
Primary Contact: James J. Xinis, President and Chief Executive Officer
COO: Dean Teague, Chief Operating Officer
CFO: Robert Kertis, Vice President Finance
CMO: Barbara Estes, M.D., Chief of Staff
CIO: Ed Grogan, Vice President Information Services and Chief Information Officer
CHR: Anthony M. Bladen, Vice President Human Resources
CNO: Robert McWhirt, Vice President Patient Care Services and Chief Nursing Executive
Web address: www.calverthospital.com
**Control:** Other not–for–profit (including NFP Corporation) **Service:** General Medical and Surgical

**Staffed Beds:** 116 **Admissions:** 7764 **Census:** 80 **Outpatient Visits:** 135950 **Births:** 859 **Total Expense ($000):** 130770 **Payroll Expense ($000):** 57440 **Personnel:** 924

**RANDALLSTOWN—Baltimore County**

☒ **NORTHWEST HOSPITAL (210040)**, 5401 Old Court Road, Zip 21133–5185; tel. 410/521–2200, (Total facility includes 29 beds in nursing home–type unit) **A**1 2 9 10 **F**3 8 11 12 15 18 20 26 28 29 30 31 34 35 36 37 38 40 45 50 56 57 59 60 63 64 68 70 74 75 77 78 79 80 81 82 83 84 85 86 87 92 93 97 98 100 102 107 110 111 114 115 119 126 128 129 130 131 132 135 146 147 148 **S** LifeBridge Health, Baltimore, MD
Primary Contact: Brian M. White, President
CMO: Ronald L. Ginsberg, M.D., Vice President Medical Affairs
CIO: Karen Barker, Vice President and Chief Information Officer
CHR: Valerie Brandenburg, Director Human Resources
Web address: www.lifebridgehealth.org
**Control:** Other not–for–profit (including NFP Corporation) **Service:** General Medical and Surgical

**Staffed Beds:** 244 **Admissions:** 14462 **Census:** 188 **Outpatient Visits:** 120341 **Births:** 0 **Total Expense ($000):** 201990 **Payroll Expense ($000):** 82711 **Personnel:** 1314

**ROCKVILLE—Montgomery County**

☒ **ADVENTIST BEHAVIORAL HEALTH ROCKVILLE (214013)**, 14901 Broschart Road, Zip 20850–3318; tel. 301/251–4500, (Nonreporting) **A**1 9 10 **S** Adventist HealthCare, Gaithersburg, MD
Primary Contact: Kevin Young, FACHE, President
CFO: Randy Reimer, Chief Financial Officer
CMO: Peter H. Levine, M.D., Executive Medical Director Behavioral Health Services
CIO: Kathleen Dyer, Vice President and Chief Information Officer
CHR: Mary Cloutier, Director Human Resources
Web address: www.adventistbehavioralhealth.com
**Control:** Other not–for–profit (including NFP Corporation) **Service:** Psychiatric

**Staffed Beds:** 283

☒ △ **ADVENTIST REHABILITATION HOSPITAL OF MARYLAND (213029)**, 9909 Medical Center Drive, Zip 20850–6361; tel. 240/864–6000, (Nonreporting) **A**1 7 9 10 **S** Adventist HealthCare, Gaithersburg, MD
Primary Contact: Brent Reitz, Vice President and Administrator
CFO: Val C. Daniels, Chief Financial Officer
CMO: Terrence P. Sheehan, M.D., Medical Director
CHR: Ana S. Doll, Manager Human Resources
Web address: www.adventistrehab.com
**Control:** Other not–for–profit (including NFP Corporation) **Service:** Rehabilitation

**Staffed Beds:** 77

**POTOMAC RIDGE BEHAVIORAL HEALTH** See Adventist Behavioral Health Rockville

---

**Hospital, Medicare Provider Number, Address, Telephone, Approval, Facility, and Physician Codes, Health Care System**

★ American Hospital Association (AHA) membership
☐ The Joint Commission accreditation
◇ DNV Healthcare Inc. accreditation
○ Healthcare Facilities Accreditation Program
△ Commission on Accreditation of Rehabilitation Facilities (CARF) accreditation

MD

✠ **SHADY GROVE ADVENTIST HOSPITAL (210057)**, 9901 Medical Center Drive, Zip 20850–3395; tel. 240/826–6000, (Nonreporting) **A**1 2 9 10 **S** Adventist HealthCare, Gaithersburg, MD
Primary Contact: John Sackett, Chief Executive Officer
CFO: Daniel Cochran, Vice President and Chief Financial Officer
CMO: Stephen Lakner, M.D., President Medical and Affiliate Staff
CIO: Kathleen Dyer, Vice President and Chief Information Officer
CHR: Eric Brown, Senior Business Partner
CNO: Skip Margot, Vice President Patient Care Services and Chief Nurse Executive
Web address: www.adventisthealthcare.com
**Control:** Church–operated, Nongovernment, not–for profit **Service:** General Medical and Surgical

**Staffed Beds: 327**

**MD**

### SALISBURY—Wicomico County

☐ **DEER'S HEAD HOSPITAL CENTER (212003)**, 351 Deer's Head Hospital Road, Zip 21801–3201, Mailing Address: P.O. Box 2018, Zip 21802–2018; tel. 410/543–4000, (Total facility includes 57 beds in nursing home–type unit) **A**1 9 10 **F**1 3 11 28 29 30 44 50 56 57 59 60 61 65 68 75 77 82 84 85 86 87 90 91 93 94 96 128 130 132 135 146 148 **P**6
Primary Contact: Sandra K. Smith, Chief Executive Officer
CFO: Kenneth Waller, Fiscal Administrator
CMO: Thomas F. Kelly, M.D., Medical Director
CIO: Mac Beattie, Computer Network Specialist
CHR: Michael Dollinger, Personnel Administrator
Web address: www.deershead.org
**Control:** State–Government, nonfederal **Service:** Chronic disease

**Staffed Beds: 81 Admissions: 151 Census: 68 Outpatient Visits: 13631 Births: 0 Total Expense ($000): 21764 Payroll Expense ($000): 9763 Personnel: 217**

✠ △ **HEALTHSOUTH CHESAPEAKE REHABILITATION HOSPITAL (213028)**, 220 Tilghman Road, Zip 21804–1921; tel. 410/546–4600, (Nonreporting) **A**1 7 9 10 **S** HEALTHSOUTH Corporation, Birmingham, AL
Primary Contact: Steven Walas, Chief Executive Officer
CFO: Karen Rounsley, Controller
CHR: Belinda Thompson, Coordinator Human Resources
Web address: www.healthsouthchesapeake.com
**Control:** Corporation, Investor–owned, for–profit **Service:** Rehabilitation

**Staffed Beds: 54**

✠ **PENINSULA REGIONAL MEDICAL CENTER (210019)**, (Formerly Peninsula Regional Health System), 100 East Carroll Street, Zip 21801–5422; tel. 410/546–6400, (Total facility includes 30 beds in nursing home–type unit) **A**1 2 9 10 **F**3 12 13 15 17 18 20 22 24 26 28 29 30 31 34 35 40 43 45 46 47 48 49 50 51 53 54 57 58 59 60 61 62 64 68 70 71 72 74 75 76 77 78 79 81 82 84 85 87 89 93 96 97 98 100 102 107 108 110 111 114 115 116 117 118 119 120 121 123 124 126 128 130 143 144 145 146 147 148 **P**5 8
Primary Contact: Margaret Naleppa, President and Chief Executive Officer
COO: Cindy Lunsford, Executive Vice President and Chief Operating Officer
CFO: Bruce Ritchie, Vice President of Finance and Chief Financial Officer
CMO: Charles B. Silvia, M.D., Chief Medical Officer and Vice President Medical Affairs
CIO: Raymond Adkins, Chief Information Officer
CHR: Scott Peterson, Vice President of People and Organizational Development
CNO: Karen C. Poisker, MSN, Vice President Patient Care Services and Chief Nursing Officer
Web address: www.peninsula.org
**Control:** Other not–for–profit (including NFP Corporation) **Service:** General Medical and Surgical

**Staffed Beds: 403 Admissions: 19917 Census: 248 Outpatient Visits: 506217 Births: 2037 Total Expense ($000): 363167 Payroll Expense ($000): 146085 Personnel: 2482**

### SILVER SPRING—Montgomery County

✠ **HOLY CROSS HOSPITAL (210004)**, 1500 Forest Glen Road, Zip 20910–1487; tel. 301/754–7000 **A**1 2 3 5 8 9 10 **F**2 3 11 12 13 15 17 18 19 20 22 26 29 30 31 32 34 35 36 37 39 40 41 45 46 49 50 54 55 56 57 58 59 60 64 66 68 70 72 74 75 76 77 78 79 81 82 84 85 86 87 89 93 97 100 107 108 110 111 114 115 119 120 121 123 124 126 129 130 131 132 134 135 144 146 147 **S** Trinity Health, Livonia, MI
Primary Contact: Judith Rogers, R.N., Ph.D., President and Chief Executive Officer
COO: Judith Rogers, R.N., President and Chief Executive Officer
CFO: Anne Gillis, Chief Financial Officer
CMO: Blair Eig, M.D., Senior Vice President Medical Affairs
CIO: Heather Smith, Director Information Services
CHR: J. Manuel Ocasio, Vice President Human Resources
CNO: Celia Guarino, R.N., Vice President and Chief Nursing Officer
Web address: www.holycrosshealth.org
**Control:** Church–operated, Nongovernment, not–for profit **Service:** General Medical and Surgical

**Staffed Beds: 425 Admissions: 32287 Census: 348 Outpatient Visits: 178712 Births: 8661 Total Expense ($000): 286778 Payroll Expense ($000): 165419 Personnel: 2245**

**SAINT LUKE INSTITUTE**, 8901 New Hampshire Avenue, Zip 20903–3611; tel. 301/445–7970, (Nonreporting)
Primary Contact: Father Stephen J. Rossetti, Ph.D., President and Chief Executive Officer
COO: Sister Danile Lynch, Chief Operating Officer
Web address: www.sli.org
**Control:** Other not–for–profit (including NFP Corporation) **Service:** Psychiatric

**Staffed Beds: 24**

### SYKESVILLE—Carroll County

☐ **SPRINGFIELD HOSPITAL CENTER (214004)**, 6655 Sykesville Road, Zip 21784–7966; tel. 410/970–7000 **A**1 9 10 **F**11 35 39 44 53 56 57 68 75 77 86 87 98 101 103 130 132 135 146 **P**6
Primary Contact: Paula A. Langmead, Chief Executive Officer
COO: Barry Stabile, Chief Operating Officer
CFO: Dallas Snyder, Chief Financial Officer
CMO: Jonathan D. Book, M.D., Clinical Director
CMO: Gloria Merek, Director of Nursing
CIO: Denise Maskell, Chief Information Officer
CHR: Sherry L. Miller, Director Human Resources
Web address: www.dhmh.state.md.us/springfield
**Control:** State–Government, nonfederal **Service:** Psychiatric

**Staffed Beds: 220 Admissions: 380 Census: 262 Outpatient Visits: 0 Births: 0 Total Expense ($000): 71254 Payroll Expense ($000): 39783 Personnel: 809**

### TAKOMA PARK—Montgomery County

✠ △ **WASHINGTON ADVENTIST HOSPITAL (210016)**, 7600 Carroll Avenue, Zip 20912–6392; tel. 301/891–7600, (Nonreporting) **A**1 2 3 5 7 9 10 **S** Adventist HealthCare, Gaithersburg, MD
Primary Contact: Joyce Newmyer, President
Web address: www.adventisthealthcare.com
**Control:** Other not–for–profit (including NFP Corporation) **Service:** General Medical and Surgical

**Staffed Beds: 204**

### TOWSON—Baltimore County

✠ **UNIVERSITY OF MARYLAND ST. JOSEPH MEDICAL CENTER (210007)**, (Formerly St. Joseph Medical Center), 7601 Osler Drive, Zip 21204–7582; tel. 410/337–1000 **A**1 2 9 **F**3 11 13 15 17 18 20 22 24 26 28 29 30 31 34 35 36 37 40 41 44 45 46 47 48 49 50 55 56 57 58 59 60 61 64 65 66 68 70 71 72 74 75 76 77 78 79 81 82 85 86 87 89 91 92 93 97 98 99 100 101 102 103 104 105 107 108 110 114 115 118 119 120 121 122 123 124 126 129 130 131 132 134 135 144 146 147 148 **P**6 **S** University of Maryland Medical System, Baltimore, MD
Primary Contact: Mohan Suntha, M.D., President and Chief Executive Officer
COO: Craig Carmichael, Vice President, Operations
CFO: Richard Imbimbo, Chief Financial Officer
CMO: Gail Cunningham, Interim Chief Medical Officer
CIO: Sean Shuffield, Regional Chief Information Officer
CHR: Dianne Wassall, Director Human Resources
CNO: Pamela Jamieson, Vice President Patient Care Services and Chief Nursing Officer
Web address: www.sjmcmd.org
**Control:** Church–operated, Nongovernment, not–for profit **Service:** General Medical and Surgical

**Staffed Beds: 320 Admissions: 16127 Census: 173 Outpatient Visits: 154956 Births: 2036 Total Expense ($000): 351152 Payroll Expense ($000): 126483 Personnel: 1830**

### WESTMINSTER—Carroll County

✠ **CARROLL HOSPITAL CENTER (210033)**, 200 Memorial Avenue, Zip 21157–5799; tel. 410/848–3000 **A**1 2 9 10 **F**3 5 11 13 15 18 19 20 22 26 28 29 30 31 32 34 35 36 37 38 39 40 44 45 49 50 51 55 56 57 58 59 62 63 64 65 68 70 75 76 77 78 79 81 82 83 84 85 86 87 89 93 94 98 99 100 101 102 103 104 105 107 108 109 111 114 115 118 119 120 121 126 129 130 131 132 135 145 146 147 148 **P**6 8
Primary Contact: John M. Sernulka, Chief Executive Officer
CFO: Kevin Kelbly, Senior Vice President Finance and Corporate Fiscal Affairs
CMO: Kevin Smothers, M.D., Senior Vice President Medical Affairs and Chief Medical and Quality Officer
CIO: Kim Moreau, Assistant Vice President Information Systems
CHR: Tracey Ellison, Vice President Human Resources
CNO: Stephanie Reid, R.N., Vice President of Quality and Chief Nursing Officer
Web address: www.carrollhospitalcenter.org
**Control:** Other not–for–profit (including NFP Corporation) **Service:** General Medical and Surgical

**Staffed Beds: 189 Admissions: 12276 Census: 110 Outpatient Visits: 173143 Births: 1128 Total Expense ($000): 273864 Payroll Expense ($000): 111427 Personnel: 1455**

*Many Facility Codes have changed. Please refer to the AHA Guide Code Chart.*    © 2013 AHA Guide

# MASSACHUSETTS

**MA**

## ANDOVER—Essex County

**ISHAM HEALTH CENTER**, 180 Main Street, Zip 01810–4161;
tel. 978/749–4455, (Nonreporting)
Primary Contact: Catherine Golas, Administrator
Web address: www.andover.edu
**Control:** Other not-for-profit (including NFP Corporation) **Service:** Children's
other specialty

**Staffed Beds:** 20

## ATHOL—Worcester County

☐ **ATHOL MEMORIAL HOSPITAL (221303)**, 2033 Main Street, Zip 01331–3598;
tel. 978/249–3511, (Nonreporting) **A**1 9 10 18
Primary Contact: James Meehan, Interim Chief Executive Officer
COO: Lucille Songer, Acting Chief Operating Officer
CFO: Dean Fleming, Chief Financial Officer
CMO: Donald Mruk, M.D., President Medical Staff
CIO: Lorrie Bernard, Manager Patient Accounts and Information Systems
CHR: John G. Kelleher, Manager Human Resources
CNO: Lucille Songer, Chief Nursing Officer
Web address: www.atholhospital.org
**Control:** Other not-for-profit (including NFP Corporation) **Service:** General
Medical and Surgical

**Staffed Beds:** 12

## ATTLEBORO—Bristol County

☐ **ARBOUR–FULLER HOSPITAL (224021)**, 200 May Street, Zip 02703–5520;
tel. 508/761–8500, (Nonreporting) **A**1 9 10 **S** Universal Health Services, Inc.,
King of Prussia, PA
Primary Contact: Kevin Burchill, Chief Executive Officer
CFO: James Rollins, Chief Financial Officer
CMO: Aminadav Zakai, M.D., Medical Director
CHR: Brian Jenkins, Director Human Resources
Web address: www.arbourhealth.com
**Control:** Corporation, Investor–owned, for–profit **Service:** Psychiatric

**Staffed Beds:** 46

☒ **STURDY MEMORIAL HOSPITAL (220008)**, 211 Park Street, Zip 02703–3137,
Mailing Address: PO Box 2963, Zip 02703–0963; tel. 508/222–5200 **A**1 2 9 10
**F**3 8 13 15 18 20 28 29 30 31 32 34 35 36 39 40 44 45 46 49 50 54 56 57
58 59 61 64 70 74 75 76 77 78 79 81 82 85 86 87 89 93 97 100 107 108
109 110 111 115 118 119 129 130 131 132 134 144 146 147 148 **P**6
Primary Contact: Linda Shyavitz, President and Chief Executive Officer
CFO: Joseph Casey, Chief Financial Officer
CMO: Daniel Pietro, M.D., Medical Director
CHR: Cheryl Barrows, Vice President Human Resources
Web address: www.sturdymemorial.org
**Control:** Other not-for-profit (including NFP Corporation) **Service:** General
Medical and Surgical

**Staffed Beds:** 128 **Admissions:** 5951 **Census:** 68 **Outpatient Visits:** 225000
**Births:** 814 **Total Expense ($000):** 145584 **Payroll Expense ($000):** 76362
**Personnel:** 999

## AYER—Middlesex County

☐ **NASHOBA VALLEY MEDICAL CENTER (220098)**, 200 Groton Road,
Zip 01432–3300; tel. 978/784–9000, (Nonreporting) **A**1 9 10 **S** Steward Health
Care System, LLC, Boston, MA
Primary Contact: Steven P. Roach, Chief Executive Officer
CFO: Ben Moll, Assistant Chief Financial Officer
CMO: Michael Older, M.D., President Medical Staff
CIO: Armen Arakelian, Chief Information Officer
Web address: www.nashobamed.com
**Control:** Corporation, Investor–owned, for–profit **Service:** General Medical and
Surgical

**Staffed Beds:** 42

## BEDFORD—Middlesex County

☒ △ **EDITH NOURSE ROGERS MEMORIAL VETERANS HOSPITAL**, 200
Springs Road, Zip 01730–1198; tel. 781/687–2000, (Nonreporting) **A**1 3 5 7
**S** Department of Veterans Affairs, Washington, DC
Primary Contact: Christine Croteau, Acting Director
COO: Mark Fontaine–Westhart, Associate Director
CMO: Dan Berlowitz, Acting Chief of Staff
CIO: Stephen Roberts, Chief Information Officer
CHR: Robert Colpitts, Chief Human Resources Officer
CNO: Mary Ann Petrillo, Acting Associate Director, Nursing
Web address: www.befrod.va.gov
**Control:** Veterans Affairs, Government, federal **Service:** Psychiatric

**Staffed Beds:** 461

## BELMONT—Middlesex County

☒ **MCLEAN HOSPITAL (224007)**, 115 Mill Street, Zip 02478–1064;
tel. 617/855–2000 **A**1 3 5 9 10 **F**4 5 11 29 50 53 56 58 64 68 74 77 86 98
99 100 101 103 104 105 106 111 119 130 132 134 146 **P**6 **S** Partners
HealthCare System, Inc., Boston, MA
Primary Contact: Scott L. Rauch, M.D., President
COO: Michele L. Gougeon, Executive Vice President and Chief Operating Officer
CFO: David A. Lagasse, Senior Vice President Fiscal Affairs
CMO: Joseph Gold, M.D., Chief Medical Officer
CIO: Andrew Laband, Chief Information Officer
CHR: Jean Mansfield, Director Human Resources
CNO: Linda Flaherly, R.N., Senior Vice President, Patient Care Services
Web address: www.mclean.harvard.edu
**Control:** Other not-for-profit (including NFP Corporation) **Service:** Psychiatric

**Staffed Beds:** 177 **Admissions:** 6074 **Census:** 158 **Outpatient Visits:**
110808 **Births:** 0 **Total Expense ($000):** 171234 **Payroll Expense ($000):**
73160 **Personnel:** 1509

## BEVERLY—Essex County

☒ **BEVERLY HOSPITAL (220033)**, 85 Herrick Street, Zip 01915–1777;
tel. 978/922–3000, (Includes ADDISON GILBERT HOSPITAL, 298 Washington
Street, Gloucester, Zip 01930–4887; tel. 978/283–4000) **A**1 2 5 9 10 **F**3 5 8
11 12 13 15 18 20 22 26 28 29 30 31 32 34 35 40 43 44 45 46 47 48 49
50 51 53 54 55 56 57 59 60 61 63 64 65 68 70 73 74 75 76 77 78 79 81
82 83 84 85 86 87 89 91 92 93 96 97 98 100 102 103 104 105 107 108
110 111 114 115 119 129 130 131 132 134 135 141 142 145 146 147 148
**P**1 6 **S** Lahey Health, Burlington, MA
Primary Contact: Denis S. Conroy, President
COO: Pauline Pike, Chief Operating Officer
CFO: Gary P. Marlow, Chief Financial Officer
CMO: Peter H. Short, M.D., Senior Vice President Medical Affairs
CIO: Robert Laramie, Chief Information Officer
CHR: Althea C Lyons, Vice President Human Resources and Development
Web address: www.beverlyhospital.org
**Control:** Other not-for-profit (including NFP Corporation) **Service:** General
Medical and Surgical

**Staffed Beds:** 320 **Admissions:** 15945 **Census:** 176 **Outpatient Visits:**
462160 **Births:** 2199 **Total Expense ($000):** 326338 **Payroll Expense**
**($000):** 154598 **Personnel:** 2035

## BOSTON—Suffolk County

☐ **ARBOUR HOSPITAL (224013)**, 49 Robinwood Avenue, Zip 02130–2156;
tel. 617/522–4400, (Nonreporting) **A**1 9 10 **S** Universal Health Services, Inc.,
King of Prussia, PA
Primary Contact: Jean–Charles Constant, Interim Chief Executive Officer
Web address: www.arbourhealth.com
**Control:** Other not-for-profit (including NFP Corporation) **Service:** Psychiatric

**Staffed Beds:** 118

---

**Hospital, Medicare Provider Number, Address, Telephone, Approval, Facility, and Physician Codes, Health Care System**

★ American Hospital Association (AHA) membership
☐ The Joint Commission accreditation
◇ DNV Healthcare Inc. accreditation
○ Healthcare Facilities Accreditation Program
△ Commission on Accreditation of Rehabilitation Facilities (CARF) accreditation

**BETH ISRAEL DEACONESS MEDICAL CENTER (220086)**, 330 Brookline Avenue, Zip 02215–5491; tel. 617/667–7000, (Includes BETH ISRAEL DEACONESS HOSPITAL–NEEDHAM CAMPUS, 148 Chestnut Street, Needham, Zip 02492; tel. 781/453–3000; John M. Fogarty, President and Chief Executive Officer) **A**1 2 3 5 8 9 10 **F**3 6 9 10 11 12 13 14 15 16 17 18 20 22 24 26 28 29 30 31 34 35 36 38 40 43 44 45 46 47 48 49 50 51 53 54 55 56 57 58 59 60 61 63 64 65 66 68 70 72 73 74 75 76 77 78 79 81 82 84 85 86 87 91 92 93 94 97 98 100 101 102 103 104 107 108 109 110 111 112 113 114 115 116 117 118 119 120 121 123 124 126 130 131 132 135 136 138 139 142 143 145 146 147 148 **P**5 7
Primary Contact: Kevin Tabb, M.D., President and Chief Executive Officer
COO: Nancy A. Formella, R.N., Chief Operating Officer
CFO: Steven P. Fischer, Chief Financial Officer
CIO: John Halamka, M.D., Chief Information Officer
CHR: Lisa Zankman, Senior Vice President Human Resources
Web address: www.bidmc.harvard.edu
**Control:** Other not–for–profit (including NFP Corporation) **Service:** General Medical and Surgical

**Staffed Beds:** 649 **Admissions:** 33194 **Census:** 467 **Outpatient Visits:** 619336 **Births:** 4760 **Total Expense ($000):** 1336725 **Payroll Expense ($000):** 528299 **Personnel:** 7173

**BOSTON CHILDREN'S HOSPITAL (223302)**, (Formerly Children's Hospital Boston), 300 Longwood Avenue, Zip 02115–5737; tel. 617/355–6000 **A**1 3 5 8 9 10 **F**3 5 8 11 12 14 18 19 20 21 22 23 24 25 26 27 28 29 30 31 32 34 35 36 37 38 39 40 41 43 44 45 46 48 49 50 51 54 55 57 58 59 60 61 62 63 64 65 67 68 72 74 75 77 78 79 80 81 82 83 84 85 86 87 88 89 92 93 94 97 98 99 100 101 102 104 107 108 109 111 112 113 114 115 116 117 118 119 120 121 123 124 126 129 130 131 132 134 135 136 137 138 139 140 141 142 143 144 146 147 148 **P**3 5
Primary Contact: James Mandell, M.D., Chief Executive Officer
COO: Sandra Fenwick, President and Chief Operating Officer
CFO: David Kirshner, Senior Vice President and Chief Financial Officer
CIO: Daniel Nigrin, M.D., Vice President Information Services and Chief Information Officer
CHR: Inez Stewart, Vice President
Web address: www.childrenshospital.org/
**Control:** Other not–for–profit (including NFP Corporation) **Service:** Children's general

**Staffed Beds:** 395 **Admissions:** 15748 **Census:** 281 **Outpatient Visits:** 659005 **Births:** 0 **Total Expense ($000):** 1238428 **Payroll Expense ($000):** 448486 **Personnel:** 8322

△ **BOSTON MEDICAL CENTER (220031)**, 1 Boston Medical Center Place, Zip 02118–2908; tel. 617/638–8000 **A**1 2 3 5 7 8 9 10 **F**3 5 8 9 12 13 15 17 18 20 22 24 26 28 29 30 31 32 34 35 36 38 40 41 43 44 45 46 47 48 49 50 51 54 55 56 57 58 59 61 64 65 66 68 70 72 73 74 75 76 77 78 79 81 82 84 85 86 87 88 89 90 93 97 99 100 101 102 103 104 107 108 110 111 114 116 117 118 119 120 121 123 124 126 129 130 131 132 134 135 136 138 142 143 144 145 146 147 148 **P**7
Primary Contact: Kate Walsh, President and Chief Executive Officer
CFO: Ronald E. Bartlett, Chief Financial Officer
CMO: Ravin Davidoff, M.D., Chief Medical Officer
CHR: Stephanie Lovell, Vice President and General Counsel
Web address: www.bmc.org
**Control:** Other not–for–profit (including NFP Corporation) **Service:** General Medical and Surgical

**Staffed Beds:** 454 **Admissions:** 24067 **Census:** 314 **Outpatient Visits:** 1006661 **Births:** 2422 **Total Expense ($000):** 972914 **Payroll Expense ($000):** 364304 **Personnel:** 5004

**BRIGHAM AND WOMEN'S FAULKNER HOSPITAL (220119)**, (Formerly Faulkner Hospital), 1153 Centre Street, Zip 02130–3446; tel. 617/983–7000 **A**1 3 5 8 9 10 **F**3 4 5 11 12 15 18 28 29 30 34 35 40 45 46 54 55 56 57 59 60 64 65 68 70 74 75 77 79 81 82 85 86 87 91 93 94 98 100 101 102 103 104 105 107 108 110 111 114 115 119 124 126 129 130 131 132 135 145 146 147 **S** Partners HealthCare System, Inc., Boston, MA
Primary Contact: Michael Gustafson, M.D., Chief Operating Officer
COO: Michael Gustafson, M.D., Chief Operating Officer
CFO: Vincent McDermott, Executive Director Finance
CMO: Stephen C. Wright, M.D., Chief Medical Officer
CIO: Jim Anzeveno, Chief Information Officer
CHR: Rebecca Blair, Vice President Human Resources and Service Excellence
Web address: www.brighamandwomensfaulkner.org/index.asp
**Control:** Other not–for–profit (including NFP Corporation) **Service:** General Medical and Surgical

**Staffed Beds:** 86 **Admissions:** 7572 **Census:** 92 **Outpatient Visits:** 188250 **Births:** 0 **Total Expense ($000):** 186300 **Payroll Expense ($000):** 83972 **Personnel:** 1160

**BRIGHAM AND WOMEN'S HOSPITAL (220110)**, 75 Francis Street, Zip 02115–6110; tel. 617/732–5500 **A**1 3 5 8 9 10 **F**3 5 6 8 9 11 12 13 14 15 16 17 18 20 22 24 26 28 29 30 31 32 33 34 35 36 37 38 39 40 43 44 45 46 47 48 49 50 51 52 54 55 56 57 58 59 60 61 64 65 66 68 70 71 72 74 75 76 77 78 79 81 82 83 84 85 86 87 92 93 97 99 100 101 102 103 104 105 107 108 110 111 112 114 115 116 117 118 119 120 121 123 124 126 129 130 131 132 133 134 135 136 137 138 140 141 142 143 144 145 146 147 148 **P**6 **S** Partners HealthCare System, Inc., Boston, MA
Primary Contact: Elizabeth Nabel, M.D., President
COO: Mairead Hickey, Ph.D., Executive Vice President and Chief Operating Officer
CFO: Michael Reney, Chief Financial Officer
CMO: Stanley Ashley, M.D., Chief Medical Officer
CIO: William C. Johnston, Interim Vice President, Information System
CHR: Julie Celano, Vice President Human Resources
CNO: Jacqueline G. Somerville, R.N., Senior Vice President for Patient Care Services and Chief Nursing Officer
Web address: www.brighamandwomens.org
**Control:** Other not–for–profit (including NFP Corporation) **Service:** General Medical and Surgical

**Staffed Beds:** 779 **Admissions:** 45352 **Census:** 698 **Outpatient Visits:** 809935 **Births:** 7736 **Total Expense ($000):** 2285611 **Payroll Expense ($000):** 668137 **Personnel:** 12651

☐ **CARNEY HOSPITAL (220017)**, 2100 Dorchester Avenue, Zip 02124–5615; tel. 617/296–4000, (Nonreporting) **A**1 2 3 5 9 10 **S** Steward Health Care System, LLC, Boston, MA
Primary Contact: Andrew Davis, President
COO: Christian Stroucken, Chief Operating Officer
CFO: David McGrail, Vice President Finance
CMO: Alexander White, Vice President Medical Affairs
CHR: Mary Orlandi, Manager Human Resources
Web address: www.carneyhospital.org
**Control:** Corporation, Investor–owned, for–profit **Service:** General Medical and Surgical

**Staffed Beds:** 120

**DANA–FARBER CANCER INSTITUTE (220162)**, 44 Binney Street, Zip 02115–6084; tel. 617/632–3000 **A**1 3 5 9 10 **F**3 11 14 15 29 30 31 34 35 36 44 50 54 55 57 58 59 64 65 66 68 71 75 77 78 82 83 84 85 86 87 99 100 101 104 107 108 110 111 114 115 117 119 120 121 123 124 130 132 134 135 136 146 147 148 **P**6
Primary Contact: Edward J. Benz, Jr., M.D., President and Chief Executive Officer
COO: Dorothy E. Puhy, Executive Vice President and Chief Operating Officer
CMO: Lawrence N. Shulman, M.D., Senior Vice President Medical Affairs and Chief Medical Officer
CIO: Jeffrey R. Kessler, Vice President Information Services
CHR: Emily Barclay, Vice President Human Resources
Web address: www.dana–farber.org
**Control:** Other not–for–profit (including NFP Corporation) **Service:** General Medical and Surgical

**Staffed Beds:** 30 **Admissions:** 1146 **Census:** 27 **Outpatient Visits:** 341918 **Births:** 0 **Total Expense ($000):** 971447 **Payroll Expense ($000):** 295832 **Personnel:** 3912

**DR. SOLOMON CARTER FULLER MENTAL HEALTH CENTER (224040)**, 85 East Newton Street, Zip 02118–2340; tel. 617/626–8700, (Nonreporting) **A**3 5 6 10
Primary Contact: Mary–Louise White, M.D., Chief Executive Officer
**Control:** Other not–for–profit (including NFP Corporation) **Service:** Psychiatric

**Staffed Beds:** 32

**FRANCISCAN HOSPITAL FOR CHILDREN (223300)**, 30 Warren Street, Zip 02135–3680; tel. 617/254–3800 **A**1 3 5 9 10 **F**5 28 30 32 39 75 77 79 81 90 91 93 95 96 98 99 104 106 107 130 132 134 143 **P**5
Primary Contact: John D. Nash, FACHE, President and Chief Executive Officer
COO: Donna Polselli, Chief Operating Officer
CFO: Alex Denucci, Chief Financial Officer
CMO: Jane E. O'Brien, M.D., Medical Director
CHR: Steven Snyder, Vice President Human Resources
Web address: www.franciscanhospital.org
**Control:** Other not–for–profit (including NFP Corporation) **Service:** Children's rehabilitation

**Staffed Beds:** 112 **Admissions:** 759 **Census:** 57 **Outpatient Visits:** 31596 **Births:** 0 **Total Expense ($000):** 52307 **Payroll Expense ($000):** 25193 **Personnel:** 490

△ **HEBREW REHABILITATION CENTER (222007)**, 1200 Centre Street, Zip 02131–1097; tel. 617/323–8000, (Total facility includes 50 beds in nursing home–type unit) **A**7 10 **F**1 2 18 29 30 34 39 50 53 56 58 59 60 64 65 68 69 75 77 82 93 100 103 104 119 128 130 143 146 148 **P**6
Primary Contact: Louis J. Woolf, President
COO: Mary K. Moscato, Chief Operating Officer–Hebrew Rehabilitation Center and Hebrew Senior Life Health Care Services
CFO: James Hart, Chief Financial Officer
CMO: Rob Schreiber, M.D., Chief Medical Officer
CIO: Fran Hinckley, Chief Information Officer
CHR: Alessandra de Vaca, Chief Administrative Officer
CNO: Tammy B. Retalic, R.N., Vice President Nursing and Patient and Family Centered Care
Web address: www.hebrewseniorlife.org
**Control:** Other not–for–profit (including NFP Corporation) **Service:** Long–Term Acute Care hospital

**Staffed Beds:** 725 **Admissions:** 1443 **Census:** 679 **Outpatient Visits:** 12383 **Births:** 0 **Total Expense ($000):** 119718 **Payroll Expense ($000):** 74481 **Personnel:** 1279

☐ **MASSACHUSETTS EYE AND EAR INFIRMARY (220075)**, 243 Charles Street, Zip 02114–3002; tel. 617/523–7900 **A**1 3 5 9 10 **F**3 7 8 11 29 30 31 34 35 36 40 41 44 50 54 55 56 57 58 59 64 65 66 68 74 75 77 78 81 82 85 86 87 89 107 111 114 119 130 132 141 143 144 146 148 **P**6
Primary Contact: John R. Fernandez, President and Chief Executive Officer
CFO: Peter J. Chinetti, Chief Financial Officer
CIO: Alec Cheloff, Chief Information Officer
CHR: Christine Regan, Vice President Human Resources
Web address: www.masseyeandear.org
**Control:** Other not–for–profit (including NFP Corporation) **Service:** Eye, ear, nose, and throat

**Staffed Beds:** 41 **Admissions:** 1475 **Census:** 15 **Outpatient Visits:** 323418 **Births:** 0 **Total Expense ($000):** 198449 **Payroll Expense ($000):** 63873 **Personnel:** 1724

⊞ **MASSACHUSETTS GENERAL HOSPITAL (220071)**, 55 Fruit Street, Zip 02114–2696; tel. 617/726–2000, (Includes MASSGENERAL HOSPITAL FOR CHILDREN, 55 Fruit Street, Zip 02114–2621; tel. 888/644–3248) **A**1 3 5 8 9 10 **F**2 3 5 6 8 9 11 12 13 14 15 16 17 18 19 20 21 22 23 24 25 26 27 28 29 30 31 33 34 35 36 37 38 39 40 43 44 45 46 47 48 49 50 51 52 53 54 55 56 57 58 59 60 61 62 63 64 65 66 68 70 71 72 74 75 76 77 78 79 80 81 82 84 85 86 87 88 89 91 92 93 94 95 96 97 98 99 100 101 102 103 104 107 108 110 111 112 113 114 115 116 117 118 119 120 121 122 123 124 126 129 130 131 132 134 135 136 137 138 139 140 141 142 143 144 145 146 147 148 **P**6 7 **S** Partners HealthCare System, Inc., Boston, MA
Primary Contact: Peter L. Slavin, M.D., President
CFO: Sally Mason Boemer, Senior Vice President Finance
CMO: Britain Nicholson, M.D., Chief Medical Officer
CIO: James W. Noga, Chief Information Officer
CHR: Jeff Davis, Senior Vice President Human Resources
Web address: www.massgeneral.org
**Control:** Other not–for–profit (including NFP Corporation) **Service:** General Medical and Surgical

**Staffed Beds:** 947 **Admissions:** 48587 **Census:** 773 **Outpatient Visits:** 957452 **Births:** 3699 **Total Expense ($000):** 2934610 **Payroll Expense ($000):** 942187 **Personnel:** 16296

⊞ **NEW ENGLAND BAPTIST HOSPITAL (220088)**, 125 Parker Hill Avenue, Zip 02120–2847; tel. 617/754–5800 **A**1 3 5 9 10 **F**3 8 9 11 14 18 20 29 30 34 35 36 37 44 45 50 51 54 57 58 59 60 64 65 68 70 74 75 77 79 81 82 85 86 87 91 92 93 96 97 100 107 108 111 119 130 131 132 141 143 144 146 148 **P**8
Primary Contact: Trish Hannon, FACHE, President and Chief Executive Officer
CFO: Thomas Gheringhelli, Chief Financial Officer
CHR: Linda Thompson, Vice President Human Resources
Web address: www.nebh.org
**Control:** Other not–for–profit (including NFP Corporation) **Service:** Orthopedic

**Staffed Beds:** 118 **Admissions:** 7619 **Census:** 70 **Outpatient Visits:** 144831 **Births:** 0 **Total Expense ($000):** 206984 **Payroll Expense ($000):** 74590 **Personnel:** 1049

⊞ **RADIUS SPECIALTY HOSPITAL BOSTON (222010)**, 59 Townsend Street, Zip 02119–1318; tel. 617/989–8400, (Nonreporting) **A**1 10
Primary Contact: Daniel Mitchell, Chief Operating Officer
COO: Daniel Mitchell, Chief Operating Officer
CMO: Raul Octaviani, M.D., Chief Medical Officer
CHR: Christine Bresnahan, Manager Human Resources
Web address: www.radiushospital.com
**Control:** Corporation, Investor–owned, for–profit **Service:** Long–Term Acute Care hospital

**Staffed Beds:** 98

☐ **SHRINERS HOSPITALS FOR CHILDREN–BOSTON BURNS HOSPITAL (223304)**, (Formerly Shriners Hospitals for Children–Boston), (Pediatric Burns, Orthopaedics), 51 Blossom Street, Zip 02114–2601; tel. 617/722–3000 **A**1 3 5 10 **F**3 16 29 30 34 35 57 64 68 75 77 79 81 85 86 87 93 99 104 130 132 141 143 146 148 **S** Shriners Hospitals for Children, Tampa, FL
Primary Contact: C. Thomas D'Esmond, FACHE, Administrator
CFO: Maria Chung, CPA, Director Fiscal Services
CMO: Ronald G. Tompkins, M.D., Chief of Staff and Director Research
CIO: Kenneth Ward, Regional Director Information Services
CHR: Sharyn D. Gazit, Director Human Resources
Web address: www.shrinershospitalsforchildren.org/Hospitals/Locations/Boston.aspx
**Control:** Other not–for–profit (including NFP Corporation) **Service:** Children's other specialty

**Staffed Beds:** 30 **Admissions:** 515 **Census:** 9 **Outpatient Visits:** 5639 **Births:** 0 **Personnel:** 184

⊞ △ **SPAULDING REHABILITATION HOSPITAL (223034)**, 125 Nashua Street, Zip 02114–1198; tel. 617/573–7000 **A**1 3 5 7 10 **F**3 7 29 30 34 35 36 39 50 57 58 59 60 64 74 75 77 82 85 86 87 90 91 92 93 94 95 96 100 104 119 129 130 131 132 143 146 148 **P**8 **S** Partners HealthCare System, Inc., Boston, MA
Primary Contact: David E. Storto, President
COO: Maureen Banks, R.N., Chief Operating Officer
CFO: Mary Shaughnessy, Vice President Finance
CMO: Ross Zafonte, D.O., Chief, Physical Medicine and Rehabilitation and Vice President Medical Affairs, Research and Education
CIO: John Campbell, Director Management Information Systems
CHR: Russell Averna, Director Human Resources
Web address: www.spauldingrehab.org
**Control:** Other not–for–profit (including NFP Corporation) **Service:** Rehabilitation

**Staffed Beds:** 196 **Admissions:** 2371 **Census:** 143 **Outpatient Visits:** 156437 **Births:** 0 **Total Expense ($000):** 111217 **Payroll Expense ($000):** 56346 **Personnel:** 886

⊞ **TUFTS MEDICAL CENTER (220116)**, 800 Washington Street, Zip 02111–1552; tel. 617/636–5000 **A**1 2 3 5 8 9 10 **F**3 12 13 14 15 17 18 19 20 21 22 23 24 25 26 27 28 29 31 32 34 35 39 40 41 43 44 45 47 49 50 51 52 55 56 57 58 59 61 64 65 68 70 71 72 74 75 76 77 78 79 81 82 84 85 86 87 88 89 93 97 98 99 100 102 104 107 108 111 114 115 116 117 118 119 120 121 123 124 126 129 130 131 132 134 135 136 137 138 143 146 147 148 **P**3
Primary Contact: Eric J. Beyer, President and Chief Executive Officer
CFO: C. Okey Agba, Senior Vice President, Chief Financial Officer and Treasurer
CMO: David Fairchild, M.D., Chief Medical Officer
CIO: William Shickolovich, Chief Information Officer
Web address: www.tuftsmedicalcenter.org
**Control:** Other not–for–profit (including NFP Corporation) **Service:** General Medical and Surgical

**Staffed Beds:** 284 **Admissions:** 20001 **Census:** 273 **Outpatient Visits:** 404101 **Births:** 1178 **Total Expense ($000):** 605616 **Payroll Expense ($000):** 249935 **Personnel:** 4134

★ △ **VETERANS AFFAIRS BOSTON HEALTHCARE SYSTEM**, 1400 VFW Parkway, Zip 02132–4927; tel. 857/203–6000, (Nonreporting) **A**3 5 7 8 **S** Department of Veterans Affairs, Washington, DC
Primary Contact: Michael E. Lawson, Director
CFO: Joe Costa, Chief Financial Officer
CMO: Brian Hoffman, M.D., Chief Medical Services
CIO: David M. Goodman, Ph.D., Chief Information Officer
CHR: William Warfield, Chief Human Resources Management
Web address: www.boston.va.gov/
**Control:** Veterans Affairs, Government, federal **Service:** General Medical and Surgical

**Staffed Beds:** 361

**VETERANS AFFAIRS MEDICAL CENTER** See Brockton Veterans Affairs Medical Center, Brockton

## BRADFORD—Essex County

⊞ △ **WHITTIER REHABILITATION HOSPITAL (222047)**, 145 Ward Hill Avenue, Zip 01835–6928; tel. 978/372–8000, (Nonreporting) **A**1 7 10 **S** Whittier Health Network, Haverhill, MA
Primary Contact: Alfred J. Arcidi, M.D., Senior Vice President
Web address: www.whittierhealth.com
**Control:** Partnership, Investor–owned, for–profit **Service:** Long–Term Acute Care hospital

**Staffed Beds:** 60

---

**Hospital, Medicare Provider Number, Address, Telephone, Approval, Facility, and Physician Codes, Health Care System**

★ American Hospital Association (AHA) membership
☐ The Joint Commission accreditation   ◇ DNV Healthcare Inc. accreditation
◯ Healthcare Facilities Accreditation Program
△ Commission on Accreditation of Rehabilitation Facilities (CARF) accreditation

**MA**

### BRAINTREE—Norfolk County

☐ **BRAINTREE REHABILITATION HOSPITAL (223027)**, 250 Pond Street, Zip 02184–5351; tel. 781/348–2500 **A**1 5 10 **F**29 34 35 54 57 59 64 74 75 77 78 79 86 87 90 91 92 93 94 95 101 108 119 130 131 132 146 148 **P**5 **S** Five Star Quality Care, Newton, MA
Primary Contact: Randy Doherty, CPA, Chief Executive Officer
CFO: Thomas Whalen, Chief Financial Officer
CMO: Arthur Williams, M.D., Medical Director
CHR: Tara Spellacy, Director Human Resources
Web address: www.braintreerehabhospital.com
**Control:** Corporation, Investor–owned, for–profit **Service:** Rehabilitation

**Staffed Beds:** 187 **Admissions:** 2279 **Census:** 96 **Outpatient Visits:** 112040
**Births:** 0 **Total Expense ($000):** 51960 **Payroll Expense ($000):** 32832
**Personnel:** 582

### BRIDGEWATER—Plymouth County

**BRIDGEWATER STATE HOSPITAL**, 20 Administration Road, Zip 02324–3201; tel. 508/279–4521, (Nonreporting) **A**3 5
Primary Contact: Kenneth W. Nelson, Superintendent
CFO: Diane Wholley, Director Fiscal Services
**Control:** State–Government, nonfederal **Service:** Psychiatric

**Staffed Beds:** 350

### BRIGHTON—Suffolk County

**CARITAS ST. ELIZABETH'S MEDICAL CENTER** See St. Elizabeth's Medical Center

☒ **KINDRED HOSPITAL–BOSTON (222045)**, 1515 Commonwealth Avenue, Zip 02135–3617; tel. 617/254–1100, (Nonreporting) **A**1 10 **S** Kindred Healthcare, Louisville, KY
Primary Contact: Susan Downey, R.N., MS, Chief Executive Officer
CFO: Lawrence J. Toye, Chief Financial Officer
CMO: Mark Rohrer, M.D., Chief Medical Officer
Web address: www.kindredbos.com/
**Control:** Corporation, Investor–owned, for–profit **Service:** Long–Term Acute Care hospital

**Staffed Beds:** 59

☐ **ST. ELIZABETH'S MEDICAL CENTER (220036)**, 736 Cambridge Street, Zip 02135–2997; tel. 617/789–3000, (Nonreporting) **A**1 2 3 5 8 9 10 **S** Steward Health Care System, LLC, Boston, MA
Primary Contact: Kevin R. Hannifan, President
COO: Nathan Howell, Chief Operating Officer
CFO: Jeffrey P. Dion, Vice President Finance
CIO: Joseph Schmitt, Chief Information Officer
CHR: Claudia Henderson, Chief Human Resources
CNO: Suzanne G. McLaughlin, R.N., Chief Nursing Officer and Vice President Patient Care
Web address: www.stewardhealth.org/St_Elizabeths
**Control:** Corporation, Investor–owned, for–profit **Service:** General Medical and Surgical

**Staffed Beds:** 338

### BROCKTON—Plymouth County

☒ △ **BROCKTON VETERANS AFFAIRS MEDICAL CENTER**, 940 Belmont Street, Zip 02301–5596; tel. 508/583–4500, (Includes VETERANS AFFAIRS MEDICAL CENTER, 1400 VFW Parkway, West Roxbury, Boston, Zip 02132, Mailing Address: 1400 VVF Parkway, West Roxbury, Zip 02132; tel. 617/323–7700; William H. Kelleher, Director), (Nonreporting) **A**1 3 5 7 8 **S** Department of Veterans Affairs, Washington, DC
Primary Contact: Michael E. Lawson, Director
CFO: Joe Costa, Acting Chief Fiscal Officer
Web address: www.boston.va.gov/
**Control:** Veterans Affairs, Government, federal **Service:** General Medical and Surgical

**Staffed Beds:** 375

**CARITAS GOOD SAMARITAN MEDICAL CENTER** See Good Samaritan Medical Center

☐ **GOOD SAMARITAN MEDICAL CENTER (220111)**, 235 North Pearl Street, Zip 02301–1794; tel. 508/427–3000, (Includes GOOD SAMARITAN MEDICAL CENTER – CUSHING CAMPUS, 235 North Pearl Street, Zip 02401–1794; tel. 508/427–3000), (Nonreporting) **A**1 2 3 5 9 10 **S** Steward Health Care System, LLC, Boston, MA
Primary Contact: Jeffrey H. Liebman, President
COO: Donna Rubinate, R.N., Chief Operating Officer
CFO: Thomas Whalen, Vice President Finance
CMO: Scott Stewart, M.D., Vice President Medical Management
CIO: Lori Caswell, Director Information Technology
CHR: David J. Cronin, Regional Vice President Human Resources
Web address: www.stewardhealth.org/Good–Samaritan
**Control:** Corporation, Investor–owned, for–profit **Service:** General Medical and Surgical

**Staffed Beds:** 189

☒ **SIGNATURE HEALTHCARE BROCKTON HOSPITAL (220052)**, 680 Centre Street, Zip 02302–3395; tel. 508/941–7000, (Total facility includes 29 beds in nursing home–type unit) **A**1 2 6 9 10 **F**11 12 13 15 17 18 20 22 24 28 29 30 31 32 34 35 38 40 45 46 47 48 49 50 51 52 54 55 56 57 58 59 60 61 64 65 66 68 70 73 74 75 76 77 78 79 81 82 84 85 87 89 93 97 98 100 101 102 103 104 105 107 108 110 111 114 117 118 119 120 121 123 128 130 131 132 135 143 144 146 147 148 **P**6 8
Primary Contact: Kim Norton Hollon, FACHE, Chief Executive Officer
CFO: James Papadakos, Chief Financial Officer
CIO: Paul J. Pettinato, M.D., Chief Information Officer
CHR: David Fisher, Vice President Human Resources
CNO: Kim Walsh, Chief Nursing Officer
Web address: www.signature–healthcare.org
**Control:** Other not–for–profit (including NFP Corporation) **Service:** General Medical and Surgical

**Staffed Beds:** 245 **Admissions:** 12746 **Census:** 146 **Outpatient Visits:** 363168 **Births:** 991 **Total Expense ($000):** 198520 **Payroll Expense ($000):** 88165 **Personnel:** 1319

### BROOKLINE—Norfolk County

☐ **ARBOUR H. R. I. HOSPITAL (224018)**, 227 Babcock Street, Zip 02446–6799; tel. 617/731–3200, (Nonreporting) **A**1 9 10 **S** Universal Health Services, Inc., King of Prussia, PA
Primary Contact: Patrick Moallemian, Chief Executive Officer and Managing Director
CFO: James Rollins, Chief Financial Officer
CMO: Anthony Raynes, M.D., Psychiatrist in Chief
CHR: Kris Munson, Director Human Resources
Web address: www.arbourhealth.com
**Control:** Corporation, Investor–owned, for–profit **Service:** Psychiatric

**Staffed Beds:** 68

☐ **BOURNEWOOD HEALTH SYSTEMS (224022)**, 300 South Street, Zip 02467–3658; tel. 617/469–0300 **A**1 3 5 9 10 **F**4 5 98 99 104 105 130 132 **P**1
Primary Contact: Nasir A. Khan, M.D., Chief Executive Officer
CFO: Michael Gale, Chief Financial Officer
CMO: Carmel Heinsohn, M.D., Medical Director
CHR: Paula Berardi, Manager Human Resources
Web address: www.bournewood.com
**Control:** Corporation, Investor–owned, for–profit **Service:** Psychiatric

**Staffed Beds:** 81 **Admissions:** 3661 **Census:** 76 **Outpatient Visits:** 11313
**Births:** 0 **Total Expense ($000):** 20058 **Payroll Expense ($000):** 12080
**Personnel:** 181

### BURLINGTON—Middlesex County

☒ **LAHEY HOSPITAL & MEDICAL CENTER, BURLINGTON (220171)**, (Formerly Lahey Clinic Hospital), 41 Mall Road, Zip 01805–0001; tel. 781/744–5100, (Includes LAHEY MEDICAL CENTER, PEABODY, 1 Essex Center Drive, Peabody, Zip 01960–2901; tel. 978/538–4000) **A**1 2 3 5 8 9 10 **F**3 5 8 9 11 12 14 15 17 18 20 22 24 26 28 29 30 31 34 35 36 37 38 40 42 43 44 45 46 47 48 49 50 51 53 54 55 56 57 58 59 61 64 65 66 68 70 74 75 77 78 79 81 82 84 85 86 87 91 92 93 96 97 99 100 101 102 103 104 107 108 110 111 114 115 116 117 118 119 120 121 123 124 126 129 130 131 132 135 136 138 139 141 142 143 144 145 146 147 148 **P**6 **S** Lahey Health, Burlington, MA
Primary Contact: Howard R. Grant, JD, M.D., President and Chief Executive Officer
COO: Donald F. Snell, Executive Vice President and Chief Operating Officer
CFO: Timothy P. O'Connor, Executive Vice President and Chief Financial Officer
CMO: Richard W. Nesto, M.D., Executive Vice President and Chief Medical Officer
CIO: Bruce Metz, Ph.D., Chief Information Officer
CHR: Joan M. Robbio, Senior Vice President and Chief Human Resources Officer
Web address: www.lahey.org
**Control:** Other not–for–profit (including NFP Corporation) **Service:** General Medical and Surgical

**Staffed Beds:** 327 **Admissions:** 21849 **Census:** 278 **Outpatient Visits:** 938633 **Births:** 0 **Total Expense ($000):** 733318 **Payroll Expense ($000):** 256028 **Personnel:** 5025

*Many Facility Codes have changed. Please refer to the AHA Guide Code Chart.*
© 2013 AHA Guide

## CAMBRIDGE—Middlesex County

✠ **CAMBRIDGE HEALTH ALLIANCE (220011)**, 1493 Cambridge Street, Zip 02139–1099; tel. 617/665–1000, (Includes CAMBRIDGE HOSPITAL, 1493 Cambridge Street, tel. 617/498–1000; SOMERVILLE HOSPITAL, 230 Highland Avenue, Somerville, Zip 02143; tel. 617/666–4400; WHIDDEN MEMORIAL HOSPITAL, 103 Garland Street, Everett, Zip 02149–5095; tel. 617/389–6270) **A**1 2 3 5 8 9 10 **F**5 11 13 15 29 30 31 32 34 35 36 38 39 40 44 45 46 47 48 49 50 51 56 57 58 59 61 64 65 66 68 70 75 76 77 78 79 81 82 86 87 93 97 98 99 100 101 102 103 104 107 108 110 111 114 115 119 129 130 131 132 134 135 143 146 147 148 **P**6
Primary Contact: Patrick R. Wardell, Chief Executive Officer
COO: Allison Bayer, Executive Vice President and Chief Operating Officer
CFO: Robert DeVey, Chief Financial Officer
CMO: David Bor, M.D., Chief of Medicine
CIO: Judith S. Klickstein, Chief Information Officer
CHR: Joan Bennett, Senior Vice President Human Resources
Web address: www.challiance.org
**Control:** Hospital district or authority, Government, nonfederal **Service:** General Medical and Surgical

**Staffed Beds:** 219 **Admissions:** 12121 **Census:** 162 **Outpatient Visits:** 669464 **Births:** 1345 **Total Expense ($000):** 536203 **Payroll Expense ($000):** 296498 **Personnel:** 2594

✠ **MOUNT AUBURN HOSPITAL (220002)**, 330 Mount Auburn Street, Zip 02138–5597; tel. 617/492–3500 **A**1 2 3 5 8 9 10 **F**3 5 11 12 13 14 15 17 18 20 22 24 26 28 29 30 31 34 35 37 40 45 49 50 51 52 55 56 57 58 59 60 61 62 64 65 68 70 73 74 75 76 77 78 79 81 82 86 87 93 97 98 100 101 102 103 104 107 108 110 111 114 115 117 118 119 120 121 123 124 126 129 130 131 132 135 144 145 146 147 **P**5 6 7
Primary Contact: Jeanette G. Clough, President and Chief Executive Officer
COO: Nicholas T. Dileso, R.N., Chief Operating Officer
CFO: William Sullivan, Chief Financial Officer
CMO: A. Kim Saal, M.D., President Medical Staff
CIO: Bob Todd, Director Information Systems
CHR: Tom Fabiano, Director Human Resources
Web address: www.mountauburnhospital.org
**Control:** Other not-for-profit (including NFP Corporation) **Service:** General Medical and Surgical

**Staffed Beds:** 203 **Admissions:** 11800 **Census:** 134 **Outpatient Visits:** 176364 **Births:** 2390 **Total Expense ($000):** 292066 **Payroll Expense ($000):** 135853 **Personnel:** 2361

**SPAULDING HOSPITAL CAMBRIDGE** See Spaulding Hospital for Continuing Medical Care Cambridge

✠ **SPAULDING HOSPITAL FOR CONTINUING MEDICAL CARE CAMBRIDGE (222000)**, 1575 Cambridge Street, Zip 02138–4308; tel. 617/876–4344, (Nonreporting) **A**1 10 **S** Partners HealthCare System, Inc., Boston, MA
Primary Contact: Maureen Banks, R.N., MS, President
COO: Timothy Lynch, Vice President Operations
CFO: Michael J. Keller, Vice President Financial Affairs and Chief Financial Officer
CMO: Jonathon Schwartz, M.D., Medical Director and Chief Medical Officer
CIO: John Wilder, Director Information Systems
CHR: Jack Carroll, Senior Director Human Resources
Web address: www.spauldingnetwork.org
**Control:** Other not-for-profit (including NFP Corporation) **Service:** Long-Term Acute Care hospital

**Staffed Beds:** 180

## CANTON—Norfolk County

✠ **MASSACHUSETTS HOSPITAL SCHOOL (222025)**, 3 Randolph Street, Zip 02021–2351; tel. 781/828–2440, (Nonreporting) **A**1 10 **S** Massachusetts Department of Public Health, Boston, MA
Primary Contact: Brian V. Devin, Chief Executive Officer
CFO: Sharon Porter, Chief Financial Officer
CMO: Aruna Sachdev, M.D., Medical Director
CIO: Robert Lima, Director Information Systems
CHR: Trish Scully, Manager Employment Services
Web address: www.mhsf.us/
**Control:** State-Government, nonfederal **Service:** Children's Long-Term Acute Care

**Staffed Beds:** 93

## CLINTON—Worcester County

★ ◇ **CLINTON HOSPITAL (220058)**, 201 Highland Street, Zip 01510–1096; tel. 978/368–3000, (Nonreporting) **A**3 5 9 10 21 **S** UMass Memorial Health Care, Inc., Worcester, MA
Primary Contact: Sheila Daly, President and Chief Executive Officer
CFO: Steven McCue, Chief Financial Officer
CHR: Martha Chiarchiaro, Vice President Human Resources
CNO: Charlene Elie, Vice President Patient Care Services
Web address: www.clintonhospital.org
**Control:** Other not for profit (including NFP Corporation) **Service:** General Medical and Surgical

**Staffed Beds:** 41

## CONCORD—Middlesex County

✠ **EMERSON HOSPITAL (220084)**, 133 Old Road to Nine Acre Corner, Zip 01742–9120; tel. 978/369–1400 **A**1 5 9 10 **F**3 7 8 11 12 13 14 15 17 18 28 29 30 31 32 34 35 36 37 38 40 45 48 49 50 51 54 57 59 60 62 64 65 68 74 75 76 77 78 79 81 85 86 87 93 98 100 101 102 103 104 105 107 110 111 114 115 119 121 128 129 130 131 132 141 145 146 148 **P**5 8
Primary Contact: Christine C. Schuster, R.N., President and Chief Executive Officer
CFO: John O. Wilhelm, Jr., Senior Vice President and Chief Financial Officer
CMO: C. Gregory Martin, M.D., Chief Medical Officer
CIO: John O. Wilhelm, Jr., Senior Vice President and Chief Financial Officer
CHR: Eric Stastny, Vice President Human Resources
Web address: www.emersonhospital.org
**Control:** Other not-for-profit (including NFP Corporation) **Service:** General Medical and Surgical

**Staffed Beds:** 170 **Admissions:** 8183 **Census:** 108 **Outpatient Visits:** 245823 **Births:** 1131 **Total Expense ($000):** 179878 **Payroll Expense ($000):** 83461 **Personnel:** 963

## EAST SANDWICH—Barnstable County

✠ **SPAULDING REHABILITATION HOSPITAL CAPE COD (223032)**, 311 Service Road, Zip 02537–1370; tel. 508/833–4000 **A**1 10 **F**3 30 36 54 56 64 74 75 79 82 90 91 92 93 94 96 100 130 131 132 146 147 148 **S** Partners HealthCare System, Inc., Boston, MA
Primary Contact: Maureen Banks, R.N., MS, President and Chief Executive Officer
COO: Stephanie Nadolny, Vice President Clinical Services
CFO: Mary Shaughnessy, Vice President Finance
CMO: David Lowell, M.D., Medical Director
CIO: John Campbell, Chief Information Officer
CHR: Del Pontremoli, Director Human Resources
Web address: www.rhci.org
**Control:** Other not-for-profit (including NFP Corporation) **Service:** Rehabilitation

**Staffed Beds:** 60 **Admissions:** 1135 **Census:** 39 **Outpatient Visits:** 90971 **Births:** 0 **Total Expense ($000):** 32902 **Payroll Expense ($000):** 17480 **Personnel:** 397

## EVERETT—Middlesex County

**WHIDDEN MEMORIAL HOSPITAL** See Cambridge Health Alliance, Cambridge

## FALL RIVER—Bristol County

**CHARLTON MEMORIAL HOSPITAL** See Southcoast Hospitals Group

☐ **DR. J. CORRIGAN MENTAL HEALTH CENTER (224028)**, 49 Hillside Street, Zip 02720–5266; tel. 508/235–7200, (Nonreporting) **A**1 10 **S** Massachusetts Department of Mental Health, Boston, MA
Primary Contact: Steve Figueiredo, Director
**Control:** State-Government, nonfederal **Service:** Psychiatric

**Staffed Beds:** 16

☐ **SAINT ANNE'S HOSPITAL (220020)**, 795 Middle Street, Zip 02721–1798; tel. 508/674–5741 **A**1 2 9 10 **F**2 8 15 18 29 30 31 32 34 35 37 40 41 45 47 49 50 51 57 59 61 64 68 70 75 77 78 79 81 82 84 85 86 87 89 91 93 98 99 101 102 103 104 105 107 108 109 110 114 115 116 117 118 119 120 121 123 124 129 130 132 135 143 146 147 148 **P**5 6 **S** Steward Health Care System, LLC, Boston, MA
Primary Contact: Craig A. Jesiolowski, FACHE, President
CFO: Michael Bushell, Vice President Finance, Business Development and Support Services
CMO: Harvey Kowaloff, M.D., Vice President Medical Affairs
CHR: Lisa Berry, Director
CNO: Carole Billington, R.N., Vice President Patient Care Services
Web address: www.saintanneshospital.org
**Control:** Corporation, Investor-owned, for-profit **Service:** General Medical and Surgical

**Staffed Beds:** 160 **Admissions:** 7160 **Census:** 92 **Outpatient Visits:** 288716 **Births:** 0 **Personnel:** 875

---

**Hospital, Medicare Provider Number, Address, Telephone, Approval, Facility, and Physician Codes, Health Care System**

★ American Hospital Association (AHA) membership
☐ The Joint Commission accreditation ◇ DNV Healthcare Inc. accreditation
○ Healthcare Facilities Accreditation Program
△ Commission on Accreditation of Rehabilitation Facilities (CARF) accreditation

MA

**MA**

✠ **SOUTHCOAST HOSPITALS GROUP (220074)**, 363 Highland Avenue, Zip 02720–3703; tel. 508/679–3131, (Includes CHARLTON MEMORIAL HOSPITAL, 363 Highland Avenue, tel. 508/679–3131; ST. LUKE'S HOSPITAL, 101 Page Street, New Bedford, Zip 02740; tel. 508/997–1515; TOBEY HOSPITAL, 43 High Street, Wareham, Zip 02571; tel. 508/295–0880) **A**1 2 9 10 **F**3 8 11 12 13 14 15 17 18 20 22 24 26 28 29 30 31 32 34 35 36 37 40 41 44 45 47 48 49 50 51 54 55 56 57 58 59 60 61 64 68 70 71 73 74 75 76 77 78 79 81 82 83 84 85 86 87 89 90 91 92 93 98 101 102 103 107 108 110 111 114 115 117 118 119 120 121 123 124 126 130 131 132 134 144 146 147 148 **P**5 6
Primary Contact: Keith A. Hovan, R.N., President and Chief Executive Officer
COO: Linda Bodenmann, Chief Operating Officer
CIO: Christopher Baldwin, Vice President Information Systems
CHR: David DeJesus, Vice President Human Resources
Web address: www.southcoast.org
**Control:** Other not–for–profit (including NFP Corporation) **Service:** General Medical and Surgical

**Staffed Beds:** 743 **Admissions:** 38303 **Census:** 510 **Outpatient Visits:** 941487 **Births:** 3417 **Total Expense ($000):** 653042 **Payroll Expense ($000):** 312477 **Personnel:** 4254

### FALMOUTH—Barnstable County

✠ **FALMOUTH HOSPITAL (220135)**, 100 Ter Heun Drive, Zip 02540–2599; tel. 508/548–5300 **A**1 2 9 10 **F**3 8 11 13 15 18 20 28 29 30 34 35 36 38 40 45 50 51 53 54 57 59 60 61 64 65 68 70 74 75 76 77 78 79 81 82 85 86 87 89 92 93 96 102 107 108 110 111 114 118 119 129 130 131 132 135 143 146 147 148 **P**5 6 8 **S** Cape Cod Healthcare, Inc., Hyannis, MA
Primary Contact: Hugh J. Kelleher, Chief Operating Officer
COO: Hugh J. Kelleher, Chief Operating Officer
CFO: Michael Connors, Senior Vice President and Chief Financial Officer
CMO: Herb Gray, M.D., Chief Medical Officer
CIO: Sheryl Crowley, Chief Information Officer
CHR: David Ryan, Vice President Human Resources
Web address: www.capecodhealth.org
**Control:** Other not–for–profit (including NFP Corporation) **Service:** General Medical and Surgical

**Staffed Beds:** 95 **Admissions:** 5905 **Census:** 64 **Outpatient Visits:** 168138 **Births:** 499 **Total Expense ($000):** 136513 **Payroll Expense ($000):** 59782 **Personnel:** 521

### FRAMINGHAM—Middlesex County

✠ **METROWEST MEDICAL CENTER (220175)**, 115 Lincoln Street, Zip 01702–6342; tel. 508/383–1000, (Includes FRAMINGHAM UNION HOSPITAL, 115 Lincoln Street, Zip 01702; tel. 508/383–1000; LEONARD MORSE HOSPITAL, 67 Union Street, Natick, Zip 01760; tel. 508/650–7000) **A**1 2 3 5 9 10 **F**3 5 12 13 14 15 18 20 22 26 28 29 30 31 32 34 35 36 40 44 45 49 50 54 56 57 59 61 62 63 64 65 68 70 72 74 75 76 77 78 79 81 82 85 86 87 89 93 97 98 99 100 102 103 105 107 108 110 114 115 118 119 120 121 129 130 131 132 134 135 143 144 146 147 148 **S** Vanguard Health Systems, Nashville, TN
Primary Contact: Charles Orlando, Interim Chief Executive Officer
CFO: Roger D. Wiseman, Chief Financial Officer
CMO: Michael Gottlieb, M.D., Chief Medical Officer
CIO: Michael Hebert, Director Technology
CHR: Rebecca Heffernan, Director Human Resources
Web address: www.mwmc.com
**Control:** Corporation, Investor–owned, for–profit **Service:** General Medical and Surgical

**Staffed Beds:** 155 **Admissions:** 13689 **Census:** 149 **Outpatient Visits:** 384984 **Births:** 887 **Total Expense ($000):** 251173 **Payroll Expense ($000):** 122870 **Personnel:** 1855

### GARDNER—Worcester County

✠ **HEYWOOD HOSPITAL (220095)**, 242 Green Street, Zip 01440–1373; tel. 978/632–3420, (Nonreporting) **A**1 5 9 10
Primary Contact: Winfield S. Brown, President and Chief Executive Officer
CFO: Robert Crosby, Senior Vice President and Chief Financial Officer
CHR: Thomas Cady, Vice President Human Resources
Web address: www.heywood.org
**Control:** Other not–for–profit (including NFP Corporation) **Service:** General Medical and Surgical

**Staffed Beds:** 128

### GLOUCESTER—Essex County

**ADDISON GILBERT HOSPITAL** See Beverly Hospital, Beverly

### GREAT BARRINGTON—Berkshire County

✠ **FAIRVIEW HOSPITAL (221302)**, 29 Lewis Avenue, Zip 01230–1713; tel. 413/528–0790 **A**1 9 10 18 **F**3 11 13 15 18 26 29 30 34 35 40 45 46 49 50 54 57 59 64 65 68 70 75 76 79 81 85 86 87 89 93 94 97 107 108 110 114 119 130 131 132 133 135 146 147 148 **P**6 **S** Berkshire Health Systems, Inc., Pittsfield, MA
Primary Contact: Eugene A. Dellea, President
COO: Doreen M. Sylvia–Hutchinson, Vice President Operations and Chief Nurse Executive
CFO: Anthony Rinaldi, Executive Vice President
CMO: Brian Burke, M.D., President Medical Staff
CHR: Laura Farkas, Director Human Resources
Web address: www.bhs1.org/body_fh.cfm?id=39
**Control:** Other not–for–profit (including NFP Corporation) **Service:** General Medical and Surgical

**Staffed Beds:** 24 **Admissions:** 961 **Census:** 8 **Outpatient Visits:** 70241 **Births:** 144 **Total Expense ($000):** 41737 **Payroll Expense ($000):** 20227 **Personnel:** 214

### GREENFIELD—Franklin County

✠ **BAYSTATE FRANKLIN MEDICAL CENTER (220016)**, 164 High Street, Zip 01301–2613; tel. 413/773–0211 **A**1 2 9 10 **F**3 7 11 12 13 14 15 18 24 28 29 30 31 34 36 40 45 46 47 48 49 50 51 55 57 59 60 64 68 70 74 75 76 77 78 79 81 82 85 86 87 89 93 98 105 107 108 110 111 115 118 119 129 130 131 132 146 147 **S** Baystate Health, Inc., Springfield, MA
Primary Contact: Charles Gijanto, President, Baystate Northern Region
COO: Gina Campbell, Chief Operating Officer
CFO: Andrea Nathanson, Director Finance
CMO: Jacques Blanchet, M.D., Director Medical Affairs
CHR: Jill Wyman, Interim Director Human Resources
Web address: www.baystatehealth.com/fmc
**Control:** Other not–for–profit (including NFP Corporation) **Service:** General Medical and Surgical

**Staffed Beds:** 90 **Admissions:** 3882 **Census:** 50 **Outpatient Visits:** 113623 **Births:** 462 **Total Expense ($000):** 78737 **Payroll Expense ($000):** 33302 **Personnel:** 422

### HAVERHILL—Essex County

**BALDPATE HOSPITAL (224033)**, 83 Baldpate Road, Zip 01833–2303; tel. 978/352–2131, (Nonreporting) **A**9 10
Primary Contact: Lucille M. Batal, Administrator
Web address: www.baldpateh.com
**Control:** Corporation, Investor–owned, for–profit **Service:** Psychiatric

**Staffed Beds:** 59

☐ **MERRIMACK VALLEY HOSPITAL (220174)**, 140 Lincoln Avenue, Zip 01830–6798; tel. 978/374–2000, (Nonreporting) **A**1 9 10 **S** Steward Health Care System, LLC, Boston, MA
Primary Contact: Michael F. Collins, Chief Executive Officer
COO: Diane Lovallo, R.N., Chief Nursing Officer
CMO: George Kwass, M.D., Chief of Staff
CIO: Mark Nightingale, Senior Administrator
CHR: Gina Lagana, Director Human Resources
Web address: www.steward.org/merrimack-valley
**Control:** Corporation, Investor–owned, for–profit **Service:** General Medical and Surgical

**Staffed Beds:** 90

**WHITTIER PAVILION (224039)**, (Formerly Whittier Pavillion), 76 Summer Street, Zip 01830–5814; tel. 978/373–8222, (Nonreporting) **A**9 10 **S** Whittier Health Network, Haverhill, MA
Primary Contact: Alfred L. Arcidi, M.D., Chief Executive Officer
Web address: www.whittierhealth.com
**Control:** Partnership, Investor–owned, for–profit **Service:** Psychiatric

**Staffed Beds:** 65

### HOLYOKE—Hampden County

✠ **HOLYOKE MEDICAL CENTER (220024)**, 575 Beech Street, Zip 01040–2223; tel. 413/534–2500 **A**1 2 5 9 10 **F**3 5 10 14 15 17 18 28 29 31 34 35 38 40 44 45 46 49 50 57 59 64 65 68 70 74 75 76 77 78 79 81 82 85 86 87 89 91 92 93 96 98 100 101 102 104 105 107 108 110 111 114 118 119 124 129 130 132 135 143 145 146 147 148 **P**8
Primary Contact: Hank J. Porten, FACHE, President and Chief Executive Officer
CFO: Antonio Correia, Chief Financial Officer
CMO: Karen Ferroni, M.D., Medical Director
CIO: Carl Cameron, Director Information Systems
CHR: Mary Kelleher, Vice President Human Resources
Web address: www.holyokehealth.com
**Control:** Other not–for–profit (including NFP Corporation) **Service:** General Medical and Surgical

**Staffed Beds:** 198 **Admissions:** 5720 **Census:** 74 **Outpatient Visits:** 276760 **Births:** 436 **Total Expense ($000):** 121288 **Payroll Expense ($000):** 64198 **Personnel:** 913

**SOLDIERS' HOME IN HOLYOKE (220153)**, (Non–acute LTC), 110 Cherry Street, Zip 01040–7002; tel. 413/532–9475 **F**6 12 30 35 54 56 57 63 75 77 82 84 146 148
Primary Contact: Paul Barabani, Superintendent
COO: Lee Anne St Martin, Director Operations
CFO: Anthony Di Stefano, Director Finance
CMO: David Clinton, M.D., Medical Director
CIO: Anthony Di Stefano, Coordinator Management Information Systems
CHR: James M. Black, Director Administration
CNO: Pamela Quirk, Director of Nursing
Web address: www.mass.gov/hly
**Control:** State–Government, nonfederal **Service:** Other specialty

**Staffed Beds:** 264 **Admissions:** 196 **Census:** 264 **Outpatient Visits:** 8335 **Births:** 0 **Total Expense ($000):** 20425 **Personnel:** 287

**HYANNIS—Barnstable County**

⊠ **CAPE COD HOSPITAL (220012)**, 27 Park Street, Zip 02601–5230; tel. 508/771–1800 **A**1 2 5 9 10 20 **F**3 11 13 14 15 17 18 20 22 24 26 29 30 31 34 35 37 38 40 44 45 49 50 51 54 57 58 59 60 61 64 65 66 68 70 74 75 76 77 78 79 81 82 85 86 87 89 93 96 97 98 99 100 101 102 103 104 105 106 107 108 110 111 114 118 119 120 121 123 124 126 130 131 132 143 146 147 **P**5 6 8 **S** Cape Cod Healthcare, Inc., Hyannis, MA
Primary Contact: Michael K. Lauf, President and Chief Executive Officer
CFO: Michael Connors, Senior Vice President and Chief Financial Officer
CMO: James D. Butterick, M.D., Chief Medical Officer
CIO: John E. Kilroy, Vice President and Chief Information Officer
Web address: www.capecodhealth.org
**Control:** Other not–for–profit (including NFP Corporation) **Service:** General Medical and Surgical

**Staffed Beds:** 259 **Admissions:** 15429 **Census:** 179 **Outpatient Visits:** 684761 **Births:** 821 **Total Expense ($000):** 391120 **Payroll Expense ($000):** 150204 **Personnel:** 1419

**JAMAICA PLAIN—Suffolk County**

⊠ **LEMUEL SHATTUCK HOSPITAL (222006)**, 170 Morton Street, Zip 02130–3735; tel. 617/522–8110 **A**1 3 10 **F**5 8 15 18 29 30 31 39 45 50 54 58 59 60 61 64 65 68 70 74 75 77 78 79 81 87 93 94 97 98 103 106 107 108 110 114 115 118 119 130 135 146 148 **P**6 **S** Massachusetts Department of Public Health, Boston, MA
Primary Contact: Paul Romary, Chief Executive Officer
CFO: Mike Donovan, Chief Financial Officer
CMO: Kenneth Freedman, M.D., Chief Medical Officer
CIO: Kathryn Noonan, Director Information Management
CHR: Jill Sampson, Director Human Resources
Web address: www.mass.gov/shattuckhospital
**Control:** State–Government, nonfederal **Service:** General Medical and Surgical

**Staffed Beds:** 260 **Admissions:** 1607 **Census:** 232 **Outpatient Visits:** 23617 **Births:** 0 **Total Expense ($000):** 171857 **Payroll Expense ($000):** 53535 **Personnel:** 749

**LAWRENCE—Essex County**

⊠ **LAWRENCE GENERAL HOSPITAL (220010)**, 1 General Street, Zip 01841–2961, Mailing Address: P.O. Box 189, Zip 01842–0389; tel. 978/683–4000 **A**1 2 9 10 **F**7 11 12 13 15 16 17 20 22 28 29 30 34 35 40 43 45 46 49 50 51 57 59 60 65 68 70 73 74 75 76 77 78 79 81 85 87 88 89 100 107 108 110 114 115 119 130 132 135 144 146 147 148 **P**5 6 8
Primary Contact: Dianne J. Anderson, MS, R.N., President and Chief Executive Officer
COO: Denise S. Palumbo, MSN, Executive Vice President and Chief Operating Officer
CFO: Deborah J. Wilson, Senior Vice President and Chief Financial Officer
CMO: Neil S. Meehan, D.O., Chief Medical Officer and Chief Medical Information Officer
CIO: Jeffrey L. Brown, Director Information Systems
CHR: Cynthia Phelan, Vice President Human Resources
CNO: Elizabeth Hale, R.N., Vice President Patient Services and Chief Nursing Officer
Web address: www.lawrencegeneral.org
**Control:** Other not–for–profit (including NFP Corporation) **Service:** General Medical and Surgical

**Staffed Beds:** 189 **Admissions:** 10861 **Census:** 108 **Outpatient Visits:** 222623 **Births:** 1513 **Total Expense ($000):** 191446 **Payroll Expense ($000):** 97148 **Personnel:** 1063

**LEEDS—Hampshire County**

⊠ △ **VA CENTRAL WESTERN MASSACHUSETTS HEALTHCARE SYSTEM**, (Formerly Veterans Affairs Medical Center), 421 North Main Street, Zip 01053–9764; tel. 413/582–3000, (Nonreporting) **A**1 7 **S** Department of Veterans Affairs, Washington, DC
Primary Contact: Roger L. Johnson, Director
COO: Richard Tremaine, Associate Director
CFO: David Cichocki, Chief Fiscal Officer
CMO: Neil Nusbaum, M.D., Chief of Staff
CIO: Michael Marley, Chief Information Officer
CHR: Michelle Krause, Manager Human Resources
Web address: www.centralwesternmass.va.gov/
**Control:** Veterans Affairs, Government, federal **Service:** Psychiatric

**Staffed Beds:** 167

**LEOMINSTER—Worcester County**

⊠ △ **HEALTH ALLIANCE HOSPITALS (220001)**, 60 Hospital Road, Zip 01453–2205; tel. 978/466–2000 **A**1 2 5 7 9 10 13 **F**3 13 15 28 29 30 31 34 35 36 40 46 47 49 50 51 59 62 63 64 68 70 74 75 76 77 78 79 81 82 84 85 86 87 89 92 93 97 100 107 108 110 114 115 118 119 130 131 132 135 144 146 147 **P**6 **S** UMass Memorial Health Care, Inc., Worcester, MA
Primary Contact: Patrick L. Muldoon, FACHE, President and Chief Executive Officer
CFO: Michael Cofone, Chief Financial Officer
CMO: Daniel H. O'Leary, M.D., Chief Medical Officer
CIO: Margaret Campbell, Vice President, Associate Chief Information Officer
CHR: Cynthia Ring, Vice President Human Resources
Web address: www.healthalliance.com
**Control:** Other not–for–profit (including NFP Corporation) **Service:** General Medical and Surgical

**Staffed Beds:** 83 **Admissions:** 6648 **Census:** 73 **Outpatient Visits:** 255375 **Births:** 969 **Total Expense ($000):** 150669 **Payroll Expense ($000):** 65224 **Personnel:** 878

**LOWELL—Middlesex County**

⊠ **LOWELL GENERAL HOSPITAL (220063)**, 295 Varnum Avenue, Zip 01854–2134; tel. 978/937–6000, (Includes LOWELL GENERAL HOSPITAL, SAINTS CAMPUS, 1 Hospital Drive, Zip 01852–1311, tel. 978/458–1411), (Nonreporting) **A**1 2 3 5 9 10
Primary Contact: Normand E. Deschene, FACHE, President and Chief Executive Officer
COO: Joseph White, Executive Vice President and Chief Operating Officer
CFO: Susan Green, Chief Financial Officer
CMO: Wayne Pasanen, M.D., Vice President Medical Affairs
CIO: Maureen Belley, Director Information Services
CHR: Peter Zarrilla, Vice President and Chief Human Resources Officer
Web address: www.lowellgeneral.org
**Control:** Other not–for–profit (including NFP Corporation) **Service:** General Medical and Surgical

**Staffed Beds:** 300

**LUDLOW—Hampden County**

**SAINTS MEDICAL CENTER** See Lowell General Hospital

⊠ **HEALTHSOUTH REHABILITATION HOSPITAL OF WESTERN MASSACHUSETTS (223030)**, 14 Chestnut Place, Zip 01056–3476; tel. 413/589–7581, (Nonreporting) **A**1 10 **S** HEALTHSOUTH Corporation, Birmingham, AL
Primary Contact: Victoria Healy, Chief Executive Officer
CMO: Adnan Dahdul, M.D., Medical Director
CHR: Mary Mazza, Director Human Resources
CNO: Deborah Cabanas, R.N., Chief Nursing Officer
Web address: www.healthsouthrehab.org
**Control:** Corporation, Investor–owned, for–profit **Service:** Rehabilitation

**Staffed Beds:** 53

**LYNN—Essex County**

**UNION CAMPUS** See North Shore Medical Center, Salem

**UNION HOSPITAL** See Union Campus

MA

---

**Hospital, Medicare Provider Number, Address, Telephone, Approval, Facility, and Physician Codes, Health Care System**

★ American Hospital Association (AHA) membership
☐ The Joint Commission accreditation    ◇ DNV Healthcare Inc. accreditation

◯ Healthcare Facilities Accreditation Program
△ Commission on Accreditation of Rehabilitation Facilities (CARF) accreditation

**MA**

### MARLBOROUGH—Bristol County

☒ **UMASS MEMORIAL–MARLBOROUGH HOSPITAL (220049)**, 157 Union Street, Zip 01752–1297; tel. 508/481–5000 **A**1 5 9 10 **F**3 11 15 18 28 29 30 31 34 35 40 49 50 57 68 70 75 77 78 79 81 85 93 98 100 101 105 107 114 119 132 141 146 147 **S** UMass Memorial Health Care, Inc., Worcester, MA
Primary Contact: Candra Szymanski, MS, R.N., Interim President and Chief Executive Officer
COO: Candra Szymanski, MS, Chief Operating Officer
CFO: Jeff Dion, Chief Financial Officer
CFO: Steven McCue, Chief Financial Officer
CMO: Lalita Matta, M.D., Chief Medical Officer and Vice President Medical Affairs
CHR: Suzanne Parsons, Vice President Human Resources
CNO: Mary Brown, Chief Nursing Officer
Web address: www.marlboroughhospital.org
**Control:** Other not–for–profit (including NFP Corporation) **Service:** General Medical and Surgical

**Staffed Beds: 67 Admissions:** 4076 **Census:** 50 **Births:** 0

### MEDFORD—Middlesex County

**LAWRENCE MEMORIAL HOSPITAL OF MEDFORD** See Hallmark Health System, Melrose

### MELROSE—Middlesex County

☒ **HALLMARK HEALTH SYSTEM (220070)**, 585 Lebanon Street, Zip 02176–3225; tel. 781/979–3000, (Includes LAWRENCE MEMORIAL HOSPITAL OF MEDFORD, 170 Governors Avenue, Medford, Zip 02155–1643; tel. 781/306–6000; MELROSE–WAKEFIELD HOSPITAL, 585 Lebanon Street, Zip 02176; tel. 781/979–3000; Michael V. Sack, FACHE, Chief Executive Officer) **A**1 2 5 10 **F**2 3 11 12 13 15 18 20 22 26 28 29 30 31 34 35 38 40 45 46 47 49 50 51 54 55 56 57 58 59 60 61 62 63 64 65 68 70 72 74 75 76 77 78 79 81 82 84 85 86 87 93 97 98 100 101 102 103 104 107 108 110 111 114 115 119 120 121 123 130 131 132 135 141 143 144 146 147 **P**5 6
Primary Contact: Michael V. Sack, FACHE, President and Chief Executive Officer
CFO: James A. Nania, System Vice President and Chief Financial Officer
CIO: Richard A. Pozniak, Director Marketing and Communications
CHR: Richard Kenny, Vice President Human Resources
Web address: www.hallmarkhealth.org
**Control:** Other not–for–profit (including NFP Corporation) **Service:** General Medical and Surgical

**Staffed Beds: 297 Admissions:** 13242 **Census:** 180 **Outpatient Visits:** 548821 **Births:** 1000 **Total Expense ($000):** 263557 **Payroll Expense ($000):** 133001 **Personnel:** 1564

### METHUEN—Essex County

☐ **HOLY FAMILY HOSPITAL AND MEDICAL CENTER (220080)**, 70 East Street, Zip 01844–4597; tel. 978/687–0151, (Nonreporting) **A**1 2 5 9 10 **S** Steward Health Care System, LLC, Boston, MA
Primary Contact: Lester P. Schindel, President and Chief Executive Officer
COO: Martha M. McDrury, R.N., Chief Operating Officer and Chief Nursing Officer
CFO: Kevin Kilday, Vice President Finance
CMO: Paul Allen, M.D., Vice President Medical Affairs
CHR: Deborah Bradshaw, Director Human Resources
CNO: Martha M. McDrury, R.N., Chief Operating Officer and Chief Nursing Officer
Web address: www.stewardhealth.org/Holy–Family–Hospital
**Control:** Corporation, Investor–owned, for–profit **Service:** General Medical and Surgical

**Staffed Beds: 239**

### MILFORD—Worcester County

☒ **MILFORD REGIONAL MEDICAL CENTER (220090)**, 14 Prospect Street, Zip 01757–3003; tel. 508/473–1190, (Includes WHITINSVILLE MEDICAL CENTER, 18 Granite Street, Whitinsville, Zip 01588; tel. 508/234–6311) **A**1 2 5 9 10 **F**3 11 13 15 18 20 28 29 30 31 32 34 35 40 41 49 50 51 52 57 59 62 63 64 65 68 70 74 75 76 77 78 79 80 81 82 83 84 85 86 87 89 93 107 108 110 114 115 118 119 124 130 131 132 134 135 146 147 148 **P**6
Primary Contact: Francis M. Saba, Chief Executive Officer
CFO: Edward Kelly, President
CMO: William Muller, M.D., Vice President Medical Affairs
CIO: Larry Fraize, Director Management Information Systems
CHR: Linda Greasom, Vice President Human Resources
Web address: www.milfordregional.org
**Control:** Other not–for–profit (including NFP Corporation) **Service:** General Medical and Surgical

**Staffed Beds: 121 Admissions:** 7972 **Census:** 79 **Outpatient Visits:** 413386 **Births:** 954 **Total Expense ($000):** 180578 **Payroll Expense ($000):** 85861 **Personnel:** 1439

### MILTON—Norfolk County

☐ **BETH ISRAEL DEACONESS HOSPITAL–MILTON (220108)**, (Formerly Milton Hospital), 199 Reedsdale Road, Zip 02186–3926; tel. 617/696–4600, (Nonreporting) **A**1 9 10
Primary Contact: Doris Sinkevich, R.N., MS, Interim Chief Executive Officer
CFO: Jason Radzevich, Vice President Finance
CIO: Jean Fernandez, Chief Information Officer
CHR: Kathleen Harrington, Vice President Human Resources
Web address: www.miltonhospital.org
**Control:** Other not–for–profit (including NFP Corporation) **Service:** General Medical and Surgical

**Staffed Beds: 82**

### NANTUCKET—Nantucket County

☒ **NANTUCKET COTTAGE HOSPITAL (220177)**, 57 Prospect Street, Zip 02554–2799; tel. 508/825–8100 **A**1 9 10 **F**13 15 28 29 31 35 40 45 50 57 59 60 64 68 70 75 76 77 78 79 81 82 84 85 86 87 89 93 100 102 107 110 111 115 119 130 132 133 147 148 **P**5 **S** Partners HealthCare System, Inc., Boston, MA
Primary Contact: Margot Hartmann, M.D., Ph.D., President and Chief Executive Officer
CFO: David J. Burke, Director Finance and Chief Financial Officer
CMO: Timothy J. Lepore, FACS, Medical Director
CIO: Terry Hughes, Manager Management Information Systems
CHR: Grace Hull, Director Human Resources
Web address: www.nantuckethospital.org
**Control:** Other not–for–profit (including NFP Corporation) **Service:** General Medical and Surgical

**Staffed Beds: 19 Admissions:** 639 **Census:** 5 **Outpatient Visits:** 24188 **Births:** 123 **Total Expense ($000):** 27168 **Payroll Expense ($000):** 15064 **Personnel:** 193

### NATICK—Middlesex County

**LEONARD MORSE HOSPITAL** See MetroWest Medical Center, Framingham

### NEEDHAM—Norfolk County

**BETH ISRAEL DEACONESS HOSPITAL–NEEDHAM CAMPUS** See Beth Israel Deaconess Medical Center, Boston

### NEW BEDFORD—Bristol County

☐ **NEW BEDFORD REHABILITATION HOSPITAL (222043)**, 4499 Acushnet Avenue, Zip 02745–4707; tel. 508/995–6900 **A**1 10 **F**1 12 18 28 29 50 56 57 64 74 75 77 79 87 93 94 96 101 103 104 130 135 146 148 **P**6 **S** Vibra Healthcare, Mechanicsburg, PA
Primary Contact: Edward B. Leary, Chief Executive Officer
CFO: Cheryl Perry, Chief Financial Officer
CMO: Albert Loerinc, M.D., Medical Director
CHR: Ilene Mirabella, Director Human Resources
Web address: www.newbedfordrehab.com
**Control:** Corporation, Investor–owned, for–profit **Service:** Children's Long–Term Acute Care

**Staffed Beds: 90 Admissions:** 559 **Census:** 76 **Outpatient Visits:** 4592 **Births:** 0 **Total Expense ($000):** 24554 **Payroll Expense ($000):** 13029 **Personnel:** 145

**ST. LUKE'S HOSPITAL** See Southcoast Hospitals Group, Fall River

### NEWBURYPORT—Essex County

☒ **ANNA JAQUES HOSPITAL (220029)**, 25 Highland Avenue, Zip 01950–3894; tel. 978/463–1000 **A**1 9 10 **F**3 13 14 15 18 20 26 28 29 31 34 40 43 45 50 51 64 70 75 76 77 78 79 81 82 85 89 93 98 102 105 107 108 110 111 115 116 117 118 119 129 130 135 146 148 **P**8
Primary Contact: Delia O'Connor, FACHE, President and Chief Executive Officer
CFO: Mark L. Goldstein, Chief Financial Officer
CMO: Gail Fayre, M.D., Medical Director
CIO: Robert Buchanan, Chief Information Officer
CHR: Stephen Salvo, Vice President Human Resources
CNO: Richard Maki, R.N., Vice President Nursing and Chief Nursing Officer
Web address: www.ajh.org
**Control:** Other not–for–profit (including NFP Corporation) **Service:** General Medical and Surgical

**Staffed Beds: 123 Admissions:** 7106 **Census:** 83 **Outpatient Visits:** 235713 **Births:** 618 **Total Expense ($000):** 111626 **Payroll Expense ($000):** 51299 **Personnel:** 688

*Many Facility Codes have changed. Please refer to the AHA Guide Code Chart.*

© 2013 AHA Guide

## NEWTON LOWER FALLS—Middlesex County

☒ **NEWTON–WELLESLEY HOSPITAL (220101)**, 2014 Washington Street, Zip 02462–1699; tel. 617/243–6000, (Includes MASSGENERAL FOR CHILDREN AT NEWTON-WELLESLEY HOSPITAL, 2000 Washington Street, Newton, Zip 02462–1650; tel. 617/243–6585) **A**1 2 3 5 9 10 **F**3 8 11 12 13 15 18 28 29 30 31 32 34 35 38 40 41 44 45 46 49 50 51 52 53 54 55 56 57 58 59 60 61 63 64 65 68 70 72 74 75 76 77 78 79 81 82 84 85 86 87 89 93 94 97 98 100 101 102 107 108 110 111 113 114 115 116 117 118 119 129 130 131 132 135 143 144 146 147 148 **P**1 6 **S** Partners HealthCare System, Inc., Boston, MA
Primary Contact: Patrick Jordan, III, Interim President
COO: Elaine Bridge, R.N., Interim Chief Operating Officer
CFO: Daniel Gross, Senior Vice President Finance and Chief Financial Officer
CMO: Leslie Selbovitz, M.D., Senior Vice President Medical Affairs
CIO: Scott T. MacLean, Chief Information Officer
CHR: Beth Taylor, Director Human Resources
CNO: Elaine Bridge, R.N., Chief Nursing Officer
Web address: www.nwh.org
**Control:** Other not–for–profit (including NFP Corporation) **Service:** General Medical and Surgical

**Staffed Beds:** 216 **Admissions:** 16405 **Census:** 180 **Outpatient Visits:** 559722 **Births:** 4124 **Total Expense ($000):** 384989 **Payroll Expense ($000):** 177891 **Personnel:** 2319

## NORTH ADAMS—Berkshire County

☐ **NORTH ADAMS REGIONAL HOSPITAL (220051)**, 71 Hospital Avenue, Zip 01247–2584; tel. 413/664–5000, (Nonreporting) **A**1 9 10
Primary Contact: Timothy P. Jones, President and Chief Executive Officer
COO: Arthur B. Scott, Vice President Operations
CFO: Christopher Hickey, Chief Financial Officer
CMO: Jeffrey Bath, M.D., President Medical Staff
CIO: Charles Groh, Interim Chief Information Officer
CHR: Paul Kulp, Director Human Resources
Web address: www.nbhealth.org
**Control:** Other not–for–profit (including NFP Corporation) **Service:** General Medical and Surgical

**Staffed Beds:** 36

## NORTHAMPTON—Hampshire County

☒ **COOLEY DICKINSON HOSPITAL (220015)**, 30 Locust Street, Zip 01060–2093, Mailing Address: P.O. Box 5001, Zip 01061–5001; tel. 413/582–2000 **A**1 2 9 10 **F**3 11 13 14 15 18 20 26 28 29 30 31 34 35 36 38 39 40 49 50 51 54 56 57 59 60 61 64 68 70 74 75 76 78 79 81 82 85 86 87 89 93 96 98 100 102 107 108 110 111 114 115 119 120 121 123 126 130 131 132 134 135 144 146 147 148 **P**8
Primary Contact: Craig N. Melin, President and Chief Executive Officer
CFO: Edith S. Peter, Chief Financial Officer and Vice President Finance
CIO: Wayne Freeberg, Chief Information Officer
CHR: Wilmont Davis, Vice President Human Resources
Web address: www.cooley–dickinson.org
**Control:** Other not–for–profit (including NFP Corporation) **Service:** General Medical and Surgical

**Staffed Beds:** 86 **Admissions:** 7908 **Census:** 80 **Outpatient Visits:** 232425 **Births:** 855 **Total Expense ($000):** 145977 **Payroll Expense ($000):** 64549 **Personnel:** 876

## NORWOOD—Norfolk County

☐ **NORWOOD HOSPITAL (220126)**, 800 Washington Street, Zip 02062–3487; tel. 781/769–4000 **A**1 2 5 9 10 **F**7 12 13 15 17 18 20 22 24 26 28 29 30 31 32 34 35 37 40 41 44 45 48 49 50 56 57 59 60 65 68 70 74 75 76 77 78 79 81 82 87 89 91 93 98 100 102 103 107 108 110 111 114 115 116 118 119 121 122 123 124 126 129 130 132 146 148 **S** Steward Health Care System, LLC, Boston, MA
Primary Contact: Emily L. Holliman, President
COO: William P. Fleming, Chief Operating Officer
CFO: Mark Johnson, Chief Financial Officer
CHR: Kimberly Brosnan, Director Human Resources
CNO: Kathleen Davidson, Vice President, Patient Care Services and Chief Nursing Officer
CNO: Matthew Lowry, M.D., Vice President of Medical Affairs
Web address: www.stewardhealth.org/Norwood–Hospital
**Control:** Corporation, Investor–owned, for–profit **Service:** General Medical and Surgical

**Staffed Beds:** 188 **Admissions:** 12833 **Census:** 165 **Outpatient Visits:** 132616 **Births:** 481

## OAK BLUFFS—Dukes County

☒ **MARTHA'S VINEYARD HOSPITAL (221300)**, One Hospital Road, Zip 02557, Mailing Address: P.O. Box 1477, Zip 02557–1477; tel. 508/693–0410 **A**1 9 10 18 **F**3 8 13 15 18 28 29 30 31 39 40 45 50 57 68 70 75 76 78 79 81 85 86 89 93 97 107 110 111 115 119 130 133 146 147 **P**6 **S** Partners HealthCare System, Inc., Boston, MA
Primary Contact: Timothy J. Walsh, Chief Executive Officer
CFO: Thomas Lenkowski, Chief Financial Officer
CMO: Pieter Pil, M.D., Chief Medical Staff
CHR: Ken Chisholm, Director Human Resources
CNO: Carol A. Bardwell, R.N., Chief Nurse Executive
Web address: www.marthasvineyardhospital.org
**Control:** Other not–for–profit (including NFP Corporation) **Service:** General Medical and Surgical

**Staffed Beds:** 25 **Admissions:** 1372 **Census:** 14 **Outpatient Visits:** 86219 **Births:** 141 **Total Expense ($000):** 58157 **Payroll Expense ($000):** 29322 **Personnel:** 270

## PALMER—Hampden County

☒ **WING MEMORIAL HOSPITAL AND MEDICAL CENTERS (220030)**, 40 Wright Street, Zip 01069–1138; tel. 413/283–7651 **A**1 5 9 10 **F**3 5 11 12 15 18 29 30 31 33 34 36 37 40 49 50 51 56 57 59 61 62 63 64 65 68 70 74 75 77 78 79 81 82 85 89 92 93 97 98 99 100 101 102 103 104 107 108 110 115 118 119 129 130 131 132 146 147 148 **P**6 **S** UMass Memorial Health Care, Inc., Worcester, MA
Primary Contact: Janice A. Kucewicz, R.N., Interim President and Chief Executive Officer
CFO: Keary T. Allicon, Vice President Finance and Chief Financial Officer
CMO: David L. Maguire, M.D., Vice President Medical Affairs
CIO: Kenneth Riley, Director Information Systems
CHR: Thomas Guilfoil, Director Human Resources
Web address: www.winghealth.org
**Control:** Other not–for–profit (including NFP Corporation) **Service:** General Medical and Surgical

**Staffed Beds:** 74 **Admissions:** 3227 **Census:** 48 **Outpatient Visits:** 247692 **Births:** 0 **Total Expense ($000):** 89028 **Payroll Expense ($000):** 40967 **Personnel:** 678

## PEABODY—Essex County

☒ **KINDRED HOSPITAL BOSTON–NORTH SHORE (222044)**, 15 King Street, Zip 01960–4379; tel. 978/531–2900, (Nonreporting) **A**1 10 **S** Kindred Healthcare, Louisville, KY
Primary Contact: Yolande Wilson, Chief Executive Officer
CFO: John Couillard, Chief Financial Officer
CMO: M. Akbarian, M.D., Medical Director
CHR: Jan Pray, Coordinator Payroll and Benefits
Web address: www.kindredbns.com
**Control:** Corporation, Investor–owned, for–profit **Service:** Long–Term Acute Care hospital

**Staffed Beds:** 50

## PEMBROKE—Plymouth County

**PEMBROKE HOSPITAL**, 199 Oak Street, Zip 02359–1953; tel. 781/829–7000, (Nonreporting) **A**9 **S** Universal Health Services, Inc., King of Prussia, PA
Primary Contact: Thomas P. Hickey, Chief Executive Officer and Managing Director
CFO: Diane Airosus, Chief Financial Officer
CMO: Gary Jacobson, M.D., Chief Medical Officer
Web address: www.arbourhealth.com/organizations/pembroke–hospital/
**Control:** Partnership, Investor–owned, for–profit **Service:** Psychiatric

**Staffed Beds:** 80

MA

---

**Hospital, Medicare Provider Number, Address, Telephone, Approval, Facility, and Physician Codes, Health Care System**

★ American Hospital Association (AHA) membership
☐ The Joint Commission accreditation      ◇ DNV Healthcare Inc. accreditation

○ Healthcare Facilities Accreditation Program
△ Commission on Accreditation of Rehabilitation Facilities (CARF) accreditation

**PITTSFIELD—Berkshire County**

✠ **BERKSHIRE MEDICAL CENTER (220046)**, 725 North Street,
Zip 01201–4124; tel. 413/447–2000, (Includes HILLCREST HOSPITAL, 165 Tor
Court, Zip 01201–3099, Mailing Address: Box 1155, Zip 01202–1155;
tel. 413/443–4761) **A**1 2 3 5 8 9 10 12 13 **F**3 4 5 8 12 13 14 15 17 18 20
26 28 29 30 31 32 34 35 38 39 40 43 44 49 50 51 53 54 55 56 57 58 59
60 61 62 64 65 68 70 71 74 75 76 77 78 79 81 82 84 85 86 87 89 90 93
96 98 99 100 101 102 103 104 105 107 108 110 111 112 114 115 118
119 120 121 123 124 126 129 130 131 132 134 135 144 145 146 147 148
**P**6 **S** Berkshire Health Systems, Inc., Pittsfield, MA
Primary Contact: David E. Phelps, President and Chief Executive Officer
CFO: Darlene Rodowicz, Chief Financial Officer
CMO: Robert Cella, M.D., Vice President Medical Affairs
CHR: Arthur D. Milano, Vice President Human Resources
Web address: www.bhs1.org/body_bmc.cfm?id=43
**Control:** Other not–for–profit (including NFP Corporation) **Service:** General
Medical and Surgical

> **Staffed Beds:** 253 **Admissions:** 13111 **Census:** 168 **Outpatient Visits:**
> 456923 **Births:** 719 **Total Expense ($000):** 313732 **Payroll Expense**
> **($000):** 154242 **Personnel:** 2011

**PLYMOUTH—Plymouth County**

✠ **JORDAN HOSPITAL (220060)**, 275 Sandwich Street, Zip 02360–2196;
tel. 508/746–2000 **A**1 2 9 10 **F**3 13 15 17 18 20 28 29 30 31 34 35 36 37
40 44 45 51 57 58 59 61 62 64 68 70 73 74 75 76 77 78 79 81 82 85 86
87 89 93 96 98 100 102 103 104 107 108 109 110 111 115 117 118 119
120 121 123 126 129 130 131 132 134 135 143 144 146 147 148 **P**6
Primary Contact: Peter J. Holden, President and Chief Executive Officer
COO: James E. Fanale, M.D., Senior Vice President System Development
CFO: Joseph Iannoni, Vice President Finance
CIO: James Albert, Chief Information Officer
CNO: Donna Doherty, R.N., Vice President of Nursing and Chief Nursing Officer
Web address: www.jordanhospital.org
**Control:** Other not–for–profit (including NFP Corporation) **Service:** General
Medical and Surgical

> **Staffed Beds:** 155 **Admissions:** 9498 **Census:** 113 **Outpatient Visits:**
> 258430 **Births:** 690 **Total Expense ($000):** 193023 **Payroll Expense**
> **($000):** 81049 **Personnel:** 932

**POCASSET—Barnstable County**

☐ **CAPE COD & ISLAND COMMUNITY MENTAL HEALTH CENTER (224031)**,
830 County Road, Zip 02559–2110; tel. 508/564–9600, (Nonreporting) **A**1 10
Primary Contact: Steven Jochim, Administrator
**Control:** Other not–for–profit (including NFP Corporation) **Service:** Psychiatric

> **Staffed Beds:** 24

**QUINCY—Norfolk County**

☐ **QUINCY MEDICAL CENTER (220067)**, 114 Whitwell Street, Zip 02169–1899;
tel. 617/773–6100, (Nonreporting) **A**1 3 5 9 10 **S** Steward Health Care System,
LLC, Boston, MA
Primary Contact: Daniel J. Knell, MSN, President
COO: Susan Takacs, Chief Operating Officer
CMO: Apurv Gupta, M.D., Chief Medical Officer
CHR: Victor Munger, Vice President Human Resources
Web address: www.quincymc.org
**Control:** Other not–for–profit (including NFP Corporation) **Service:** General
Medical and Surgical

> **Staffed Beds:** 116

**ROCHDALE—Worcester County**

**KINDRED HOSPITAL PARK VIEW–CENTRAL MASSACHUSETTS** See Kindred
Hospital Park View, Springfield

**SALEM—Essex County**

**NORTH SHORE CHILDREN'S HOSPITAL** See MassGeneral for Children at North
Shore Medical Center

**NORTH SHORE MEDICAL CENTER (220035)**, 81 Highland Avenue,
Zip 01970–2714; tel. 978/741–1200, (Includes MASSGENERAL FOR CHILDREN
AT NORTH SHORE MEDICAL CENTER, 57 Highland Avenue, Zip 01970–6508;
tel. 978/745–2100; SALEM CAMPUS, 81 Highland Avenue, Zip 01970;
tel. 978/741–1200; UNION CAMPUS, 500 Lynnfield Street, Lynn,
Zip 01904–1487; tel. 781/581–9200) **A**1 3 5 9 10 **F**5 12 13 15 17 18 20 22
24 26 28 29 30 31 32 34 35 36 38 40 43 45 46 49 50 51 55 57 59 61 63
64 68 70 73 74 75 76 77 78 79 81 82 84 85 86 87 89 93 98 99 100 101
102 103 104 105 107 108 111 114 116 118 119 121 123 129 130 131 132
135 143 146 147 148 **P**6 8 **S** Partners HealthCare System, Inc., Boston, MA
Primary Contact: Robert G. Norton, President and Chief Executive Officer
CFO: Sally Mason Boemer, Chief Financial Officer
CMO: Mitchell S. Rein, M.D., Chief Medical Officer
CIO: Patricia George, Chief Information Officer
CHR: Arthur Bowes, Senior Vice President Human Resources
Web address: www.nsmc.partners.org
**Control:** Other not–for–profit (including NFP Corporation) **Service:** General
Medical and Surgical

> **Staffed Beds:** 411 **Admissions:** 18695 **Census:** 243 **Outpatient Visits:**
> 658802 **Births:** 1382 **Total Expense ($000):** 439187 **Payroll Expense**
> **($000):** 198155 **Personnel:** 2385

**SALEM HOSPITAL** See Salem Campus

✠ △ **SPAULDING HOSPITAL FOR CONTINUING MEDICAL CARE NORTH
SHORE (222026)**, 1 Dove Avenue, Zip 01970–2999; tel. 978/825–8900,
(Nonreporting) **A**1 7 10 **S** Partners HealthCare System, Inc., Boston, MA
Primary Contact: Maureen Banks, R.N., MS, President
COO: Joanne Fucile, R.N., Vice President Patient Care Services
CFO: Virginia Mirisola, Fiscal Director
CIO: Robert Sawyer, Senior Project Specialist
CHR: Colleen M. Moran, Director Human Resources
Web address: www.shaughnessy–kaplan.org
**Control:** Other not–for–profit (including NFP Corporation) **Service:** Long–Term
Acute Care hospital

> **Staffed Beds:** 160

**SOMERVILLE—Middlesex County**

**SOMERVILLE HOSPITAL** See Cambridge Health Alliance, Cambridge

**SOUTH WEYMOUTH—Norfolk County**

✠ **SOUTH SHORE HOSPITAL (220100)**, 55 Fogg Road, Zip 02190–2432;
tel. 781/624–8000 **A**1 2 3 5 9 10 **F**3 7 11 13 15 17 18 20 22 24 26 28 29
30 31 32 34 35 36 37 40 41 43 44 45 46 49 50 51 53 54 55 57 58 59 60
62 63 64 65 68 70 72 73 74 75 76 78 79 81 82 84 85 86 87 89 91 92 93
107 108 110 111 114 115 118 119 124 126 129 130 132 134 135 143 146
147 148 **P**1
Primary Contact: Richard H. Aubut, R.N., President and Chief Executive Officer
COO: Joseph Cahill, Executive Vice President and Chief Operating Officer
CFO: Michael Cullen, Senior Vice President and Chief Financial Officer
CMO: John Stevenson, M.D., Senior Vice President and Chief Medical Officer
CIO: Del Dixon, Chief Information Officer
CHR: Robert Wheeler, Vice President Human Resources
Web address: www.southshorehospital.org
**Control:** Other not–for–profit (including NFP Corporation) **Service:** General
Medical and Surgical

> **Staffed Beds:** 329 **Admissions:** 22269 **Census:** 245 **Outpatient Visits:**
> 517060 **Births:** 3435 **Total Expense ($000):** 440819 **Payroll Expense**
> **($000):** 210641 **Personnel:** 2986

**SOUTHBRIDGE—Worcester County**

✠ **HARRINGTON MEMORIAL HOSPITAL (220019)**, 100 South Street,
Zip 01550–4051; tel. 508/765–9771 **A**1 5 10 **F**3 5 8 11 13 15 17 18 19 28
29 30 31 32 34 35 38 39 40 42 45 48 49 50 51 54 57 59 61 64 65 68 70
71 74 75 76 77 78 79 81 82 85 86 87 89 92 93 94 96 98 99 100 101 102
103 104 107 108 110 111 114 115 117 118 119 120 123 129 130 131 132
134 135 146 147 148 **P**8
Primary Contact: Edward H. Moore, President and Chief Executive Officer
COO: Douglas Crapser, Executive Vice President
CFO: Thomas Sullivan, Vice President Fiscal Services
CMO: Arthur Russo, M.D., Director Medical Affairs
CIO: Hadley Zabinsky, Chief Information Officer
CHR: Charlene Richard, Director Human Resources
Web address: www.harringtonhospital.org
**Control:** Other not–for–profit (including NFP Corporation) **Service:** General
Medical and Surgical

> **Staffed Beds:** 114 **Admissions:** 4160 **Census:** 51 **Outpatient Visits:** 319211
> **Births:** 306 **Total Expense ($000):** 118206 **Payroll Expense ($000):** 52137
> **Personnel:** 644

*Many Facility Codes have changed. Please refer to the AHA Guide Code Chart.*
© 2013 AHA Guide

MA

## SPRINGFIELD—Hampden County

⊞ **BAYSTATE MEDICAL CENTER (220077)**, 759 Chestnut Street,
Zip 01199–0001; tel. 413/794–0000, (Includes BAYSTATE CHILDREN'S
HOSPITAL, 759 Chestnut Street, Zip 01199–1001; tel. 413/794–0000) **A**1 2 3 5
8 9 10 **F**1 3 4 5 8 12 13 14 15 16 17 18 19 20 22 24 26 28 29 30 31 32 34
35 38 40 41 43 44 45 46 47 48 49 50 51 52 53 54 55 56 57 58 59 60 61
64 65 66 67 68 70 72 73 74 75 76 77 78 79 80 81 82 85 86 87 88 89 90
91 92 93 97 98 99 100 101 102 103 104 105 107 108 110 111 113 114
115 118 119 120 121 123 124 126 128 129 130 131 132 135 138 141 143
145 146 147 148 **P**8 **S** Baystate Health, Inc., Springfield, MA
Primary Contact: Mark R. Tolosky, JD, FACHE, President and Chief Executive
Officer
COO: Gregory A. Harb, FACHE, Executive Vice President and Chief Operating
Officer
CFO: Keith C McLean Shinaman, Senior Vice President Finance
CMO: Loring S. Flint, Jr., M.D., Senior Vice President Medical Affairs
CIO: Mark Gorrell, Vice President Information Services
CHR: Paula C. Squires, Senior Vice President Human Resources
Web address: www.baystatehealth.org/bmc
**Control:** Other not–for–profit (including NFP Corporation) **Service:** General
Medical and Surgical

**Staffed Beds:** 716 **Admissions:** 33944 **Census:** 469 **Outpatient Visits:**
820103 **Births:** 4114 **Total Expense ($000):** 869276 **Payroll Expense**
**($000):** 338634 **Personnel:** 6583

⊞ **KINDRED HOSPITAL PARK VIEW (222046)**, 1400 State Street,
Zip 01109–2550; tel. 413/726–6700, (Includes KINDRED HOSPITAL PARK
VIEW–CENTRAL MASSACHUSETTS, 111 Huntoon Memorial Highway, Rochdale,
Zip 01542; tel. 508/892–6000; Scott MacLean, Administrator), (Nonreporting) **A**1
10 **S** Kindred Healthcare, Louisville, KY
Primary Contact: Jake Socha, Chief Executive Officer
CFO: Anna Dyrkacz, Chief Financial Officer
CHR: Donna Ciarefella, Director Human Resources
Web address: www.khparkview.com/
**Control:** Corporation, Investor–owned, for–profit **Service:** Long–Term Acute Care
hospital

**Staffed Beds:** 202

⊞ △ **MERCY MEDICAL CENTER (220066)**, 271 Carew Street,
Zip 01104–2398, Mailing Address: P.O. Box 9012, Zip 01102–9012;
tel. 413/748–9000 **A**1 2 7 9 10 **F**3 4 5 8 11 12 13 15 18 28 29 30 31 35 40
45 46 49 50 51 56 57 59 64 68 70 74 76 77 78 79 81 82 85 89 90 93 96
98 99 102 103 104 105 107 108 110 111 114 115 118 119 120 121 123
124 126 129 130 132 135 143 144 146 147 148 **S** Catholic Health East,
Newtown Square, PA
Primary Contact: Daniel P. Moen, President and Chief Executive Officer
CIO: Joan Methe, Chief Information Officer
CHR: Leonard F. Pansa, Senior Vice President Human Resources
Web address: www.mercycares.com
**Control:** Other not–for–profit (including NFP Corporation) **Service:** General
Medical and Surgical

**Staffed Beds:** 301 **Admissions:** 14524 **Census:** 231 **Outpatient Visits:**
425066 **Births:** 1264 **Total Expense ($000):** 211328 **Payroll Expense**
**($000):** 90430

☐ **SHRINERS HOSPITALS FOR CHILDREN–SPRINGFIELD (223303)**, (Formerly
Shriners Hospitals for Children, Springfield), 516 Carew Street, Zip 01104–2396;
tel. 413/787–2000 **A**1 3 5 10 **F**11 29 34 35 37 39 44 50 58 59 62 64 68 74
75 77 79 81 85 86 87 89 91 92 93 94 96 108 119 130 146 148 **P**6
**S** Shriners Hospitals for Children, Tampa, FL
Primary Contact: Charles Walczak, FACHE, Regional Administrator
COO: Charles Walczak, FACHE, Regional Administrator
CFO: Richard Fulkerson, Director Fiscal Services
CMO: David M. Drvaric, M.D., Chief of Staff
CIO: Kenneth Ward, Director Information Services
CHR: Kathleen Bachetti, Director Human Resources
Web address: www.shrinershospitalsforchildren.org/Hospitals/Locations/
Springfield.aspx
**Control:** Other not–for–profit (including NFP Corporation) **Service:** Children's
orthopedic

**Staffed Beds:** 20 **Admissions:** 160 **Census:** 3 **Outpatient Visits:** 12881
**Births:** 0 **Total Expense ($000):** 21112 **Payroll Expense ($000):** 9752
**Personnel:** 147

## STOCKBRIDGE—Berkshire County

⊞ **AUSTEN RIGGS CENTER**, 25 Main Street, Zip 01262, Mailing Address: P.O. Box
962, Zip 01262–0962; tel. 413/298–5511 **A**1 3 5 **F**98 105 106
Primary Contact: James Sacksteder, M.D., Director Operations
CFO: Chauncey Collins, M.D., Director Operations
CMO: James Sacksteder, M.D., Medical Director and Chief Executive Officer
CIO: Ave Schwartz, Chief Information Officer
CHR: Bertha Mary Connelley, Director Human Resources
Web address: www.austenriggs.org
**Control:** Other not–for–profit (including NFP Corporation) **Service:** Psychiatric

**Staffed Beds:** 74 **Admissions:** 85 **Census:** 60 **Outpatient Visits:** 0 **Births:** 0
**Total Expense ($000):** 16387 **Payroll Expense ($000):** 8554 **Personnel:**
141

## STOUGHTON—Norfolk County

⊞ **KINDRED HOSPITAL NORTHEAST–STOUGHTON (222002)**, 909 Sumner
Street, 1st Floor, Zip 02072–3396; tel. 781/297–8200, (Nonreporting) **A**1 10
**S** Kindred Healthcare, Louisville, KY
Primary Contact: Robert A. Gundersen, Market Chief Executive Officer
Web address: www.khstoughton.com
**Control:** Corporation, Investor–owned, for–profit **Service:** Long–Term Acute Care
hospital

**Staffed Beds:** 170

⊞ △ **NEW ENGLAND SINAI HOSPITAL AND REHABILITATION CENTER**
**(222027)**, 150 York Street, Zip 02072–1881; tel. 781/344–0600,
(Nonreporting) **A**1 3 5 7 10 **S** Steward Health Care System, LLC, Boston, MA
Primary Contact: Judith C. Waterston, R.N., MS, President and Chief Executive
Officer
CFO: Victoria Lobban, Vice President Finance
CMO: Lawrence S. Hotes, M.D., Chief Medical Officer
CIO: Francine Sousa, Director Management Information Service
CNO: Janet M. Madigan, MS, Vice President for Patient Care Services
Web address: www.newenglandsinai.org
**Control:** Other not–for–profit (including NFP Corporation) **Service:** Long–Term
Acute Care hospital

**Staffed Beds:** 212

## TAUNTON—Bristol County

☐ **MORTON HOSPITAL AND MEDICAL CENTER (220073)**, 88 Washington
Street, Zip 02780–2465; tel. 508/828–7000, (Nonreporting) **A**1 2 9 10
**S** Steward Health Care System, LLC, Boston, MA
Primary Contact: Kimberly S. Bassett, R.N., President
CFO: Carmen Acker, Chief Financial Officer
CIO: Harry Lemieux, Chief Information and Innovation Officer
CHR: Cara Hart, Director Human Resources
Web address: www.mortonhospital.org
**Control:** Other not–for–profit (including NFP Corporation) **Service:** General
Medical and Surgical

**Staffed Beds:** 154

☐ **TAUNTON STATE HOSPITAL (224001)**, 60 Hodges Avenue Extension,
Zip 02780–3034, Mailing Address: PO Box 4007, Zip 02780–0997;
tel. 508/977–3000, (Nonreporting) **A**1 10 **S** Massachusetts Department of Mental
Health, Boston, MA
Primary Contact: Roberta H. Guez, Chief Operating Officer
COO: Roberta H. Guez, Chief Operating Officer
CHR: Trish Scully, Director Human Resources
**Control:** State–Government, nonfederal **Service:** Psychiatric

**Staffed Beds:** 185

## TEWKSBURY—Middlesex County

☐ **TEWKSBURY HOSPITAL (222003)**, 365 East Street, Zip 01876–1998;
tel. 978/851–7321 **A**1 10 **F**1 3 30 39 60 65 68 74 75 77 82 83 84 85 86 87
91 96 98 100 103 130 132 135 148 **P**2 6 **S** Massachusetts Department of
Public Health, Boston, MA
Primary Contact: Debra Tosti, Chief Executive Officer
CFO: Maureen DiPalma, Director Finance
Web address: www.mass.gov
**Control:** State–Government, nonfederal **Service:** Long–Term Acute Care hospital

**Staffed Beds:** 381 **Admissions:** 578 **Census:** 321 **Outpatient Visits:** 0
**Births:** 0 **Total Expense ($000):** 51130 **Payroll Expense ($000):** 35888
**Personnel:** 628

---

**Hospital, Medicare Provider Number, Address, Telephone, Approval, Facility, and Physician Codes, Health Care System**

★ American Hospital Association (AHA) membership
☐ The Joint Commission accreditation      ◇ DNV Healthcare Inc. accreditation
○ Healthcare Facilities Accreditation Program
△ Commission on Accreditation of Rehabilitation Facilities (CARF) accreditation

## WALTHAM—Middlesex County

☐ **WALDEN PSYCHIATRIC CARE (224038)**, 9 Hope Avenue, Zip 02453–2741; tel. 781/647–6700, (Nonreporting) A1 9 10
Primary Contact: Stuart Koman, Ph.D., President and Chief Executive Officer
Web address: www.waldenbehavioralcare.com/
**Control:** Other not-for-profit (including NFP Corporation) **Service:** Psychiatric

**Staffed Beds:** 45

## WARE—Hampshire County

✠ **BAYSTATE MARY LANE HOSPITAL (220050)**, 85 South Street, Zip 01082–1697; tel. 413/967–6211, (Nonreporting) A1 9 10 **S** Baystate Health, Inc., Springfield, MA
Primary Contact: Charles Gijanto, President
COO: Mohammed Shafeeq Ahmed, M.D., Chief Operating Officer and Chief Medical Officer
COO: Gregory A. Harb, FACHE, Executive Vice President and Chief Operating Officer
CFO: Curtis Davis, Director Finance
CMO: Mohammed Shafeeq Ahmed, M.D., Chief Operating Officer and Chief Medical Officer
CIO: Joel L. Vengco, MS, Vice President and Chief Information Officer, Baystate Health
CHR: Donna Arsenault, Director Human Resources
CNO: Lisa Beaudry, M.P.H., Director, Patient Care
Web address: www.baystatehealth.com
**Control:** Other not-for-profit (including NFP Corporation) **Service:** General Medical and Surgical

**Staffed Beds:** 25

## WAREHAM—Plymouth County

**TOBEY HOSPITAL** See Southcoast Hospitals Group, Fall River

## WESTBOROUGH—Worcester County

☐ **WHITTIER REHABILITATION HOSPITAL (222048)**, 150 Flanders Road, Zip 01581–1017; tel. 508/871–2000, (Nonreporting) A1 10 **S** Whittier Health Network, Haverhill, MA
Primary Contact: Alfred J. Arcidi, M.D., Senior Vice President
Web address: www.whittierhealth.com
**Control:** Partnership, Investor-owned, for-profit **Service:** Long–Term Acute Care hospital

**Staffed Beds:** 74

## WESTFIELD—Hampden County

✠ **NOBLE HOSPITAL (220065)**, 115 West Silver Street, Zip 01085–3628; tel. 413/568–2811 A1 2 5 9 10 **F**8 14 15 18 29 30 31 34 35 40 57 59 68 70 75 77 78 79 80 81 86 87 89 90 93 98 100 101 102 103 104 105 107 108 110 111 115 116 117 119 130 132 146 147 148 **P**8
Primary Contact: Ron Bryant, President and Chief Executive Officer
CFO: John Shaver, Chief Financial Officer
CMO: Stanley Strzempko, M.D., Vice President Medical Affairs and Chief Medical Officer
CIO: Steven Cummings, Chief Operating Officer and Chief Information Officer
CHR: Joanne Ollson, Vice President Human Resources
CNO: Diane Brunelle, MSN, Vice President of Patient Care Services and Chief Nursing Officer
Web address: www.noblehealth.org
**Control:** Other not-for-profit (including NFP Corporation) **Service:** General Medical and Surgical

**Staffed Beds:** 97 **Admissions:** 3525 **Census:** 52 **Outpatient Visits:** 106782 **Births:** 0 **Total Expense ($000):** 52956 **Payroll Expense ($000):** 23819 **Personnel:** 303

☐ **WESTERN MASSACHUSETTS HOSPITAL (222023)**, 91 East Mountain Road, Zip 01085–1801; tel. 413/562–4131, (Nonreporting) A1 10 **S** Massachusetts Department of Public Health, Boston, MA
Primary Contact: Derrick Tallman, Chief Executive Officer
CMO: Chabilal Neergheen, M.D., Medical Director
CHR: James E. Duggan, Director Human Resources
Web address: www.mass.gov/eohhs/gov/departments/dph/programs/western–massachusetts–hospital.html
**Control:** State–Government, nonfederal **Service:** Long–Term Acute Care hospital

**Staffed Beds:** 70

## WESTWOOD—Norfolk County

☐ **WESTWOOD LODGE HOSPITAL (224023)**, 45 Clapboardtree Street, Zip 02090–2903; tel. 781/762–7764 A1 9 10 **F**29 98 99 105 **S** Universal Health Services, Inc., King of Prussia, PA
Primary Contact: Gregory Brownstein, Chief Executive Officer
CFO: Charles Denno, Chief Financial Officer
Web address: www.arbourhealth.com
**Control:** Corporation, Investor-owned, for-profit **Service:** Psychiatric

**Staffed Beds:** 130 **Admissions:** 3681 **Census:** 104 **Outpatient Visits:** 0 **Births:** 0

## WHITINSVILLE—Worcester County

**WHITINSVILLE MEDICAL CENTER** See Milford Regional Medical Center, Milford

## WINCHESTER—Middlesex County

✠ **WINCHESTER HOSPITAL (220105)**, 41 Highland Avenue, Zip 01890–1496; tel. 781/729–9000 A1 2 3 5 9 10 **F**3 8 12 13 15 18 26 28 29 30 31 32 34 35 36 38 40 41 44 45 46 49 50 51 54 55 56 57 59 62 64 68 70 73 74 75 76 77 78 79 81 82 85 86 87 89 92 93 107 108 110 111 114 115 118 119 120 121 126 129 130 131 132 135 144 145 146 147 148
Primary Contact: Kevin F. Smith, President and Chief Executive Officer
CFO: Matthew Woods, Executive Vice President Finance and Chief Financial Officer
CMO: Richard Iseke, M.D., Vice President Medical Affairs
CHR: Anne Lang, Vice President Human Resources and Compliance and Privacy Officer
CNO: Kathy Schuler, R.N., Vice President of Patient Care Services
Web address: www.winchesterhospital.org
**Control:** Other not-for-profit (including NFP Corporation) **Service:** General Medical and Surgical

**Staffed Beds:** 200 **Admissions:** 12621 **Census:** 131 **Outpatient Visits:** 588259 **Births:** 1861 **Total Expense ($000):** 264762 **Payroll Expense ($000):** 124040 **Personnel:** 1892

## WOBURN—Middlesex County

☐ **NEW ENGLAND REHABILITATION HOSPITAL (223026)**, Two Rehabilitation Way, Zip 01801–6098; tel. 781/935–5050, (Nonreporting) A1 10 **S** Five Star Quality Care, Newton, MA
Primary Contact: Joel Rudin, Chief Executive Officer
CFO: Lester Felege, Controller
CMO: A. Deniz Ozel, M.D., Medical Director
CHR: Annamarie Cronin, Director Human Resources
Web address: www.newenglandrehab.com
**Control:** Corporation, Investor-owned, for-profit **Service:** Rehabilitation

**Staffed Beds:** 210

## WORCESTER—Worcester County

**ADCARE HOSPITAL OF WORCESTER (220062)**, 107 Lincoln Street, Zip 01605–2499; tel. 508/799–9000, (Nonreporting) A5 9 10
Primary Contact: David W. Hillis, President and Chief Executive Officer
COO: Jeffrey W. Hillis, Chief Operating Officer
CFO: Christine Judycki–Crepeault, Chief Financial Officer
CMO: Ronald F. Pike, M.D., Medical Director
CHR: Joan L. Bertrand, Vice President Human Resources
Web address: www.adcare.com
**Control:** Other not-for-profit (including NFP Corporation) **Service:** Alcoholism and other chemical dependency

**Staffed Beds:** 114

✠ **FAIRLAWN REHABILITATION HOSPITAL (223029)**, 189 May Street, Zip 01602–4339; tel. 508/791–6351 A1 3 5 10 **F**3 28 29 34 35 56 57 59 64 74 75 77 79 82 86 87 90 91 93 95 96 130 132 135 146 148 **P**8 **S** HEALTHSOUTH Corporation, Birmingham, AL
Primary Contact: R. David Richer, Chief Executive Officer
CFO: John Flaherty, Controller
CMO: Peter Bagley, M.D., Medical Director
CIO: Elizabeth Hemingway, Director Health Information
CHR: Rosalie Lawless, Director Human Resources
Web address: www.fairlawnrehab.org
**Control:** Corporation, Investor-owned, for-profit **Service:** Rehabilitation

**Staffed Beds:** 110 **Admissions:** 2356 **Census:** 88 **Outpatient Visits:** 9460 **Births:** 0 **Total Expense ($000):** 28863 **Payroll Expense ($000):** 16498 **Personnel:** 280

✠ **SAINT VINCENT HOSPITAL (220176)**, 123 Summer Street, Zip 01608–1216; tel. 508/363–5000 A1 2 3 5 9 10 **F**12 13 15 17 18 20 22 24 26 28 29 30 31 35 38 40 45 46 47 48 49 50 57 59 60 64 68 70 74 75 76 77 78 79 81 82 84 85 86 87 89 92 93 97 98 100 101 102 107 108 110 111 114 115 116 117 118 119 120 121 123 124 126 129 130 131 132 135 146 147 **S** Vanguard Health Systems, Nashville, TN
Primary Contact: Erik G. Wexler, President and Chief Executive Officer
COO: Deborah Bitsoli, Chief Operating Officer
CFO: Stephen Gilmore, Chief Financial Officer
CMO: Octavio Diaz, M.D., Chief Medical Officer
CIO: Tara Jones, Director Information Services
CHR: Jan Peters, Vice President Human Resources
Web address: www.stvincenthospital.com
**Control:** Corporation, Investor-owned, for-profit **Service:** General Medical and Surgical

**Staffed Beds:** 321 **Admissions:** 17757 **Census:** 175 **Outpatient Visits:** 239931 **Births:** 1914 **Total Expense ($000):** 295339 **Payroll Expense ($000):** 133723 **Personnel:** 1363

*Many Facility Codes have changed. Please refer to the AHA Guide Code Chart.* © 2013 AHA Guide

⊠ **UMASS MEMORIAL MEDICAL CENTER (220163)**, 119 Belmont Street,
Zip 01605–2982; tel. 508/334–1000, (Includes HAHNEMANN CAMPUS, 281
Lincoln Street, Zip 01605; tel. 508/334–1000; MEMORIAL CAMPUS, 119
Belmont Street, Zip 01605; tel. 508/334–1000; UMASS MEMORIAL CHILDREN'S
MEDICAL CENTER, 55 Lake Avenue North, Zip 01655–0002; tel. 508/334–1000;
UNIVERSITY CAMPUS, 55 Lake Avenue North, Zip 01655–0002;
tel. 508/334–1000) **A**1 2 3 5 8 9 10 **F**3 5 7 8 9 12 13 14 15 16 17 18 19 20
22 24 25 26 28 29 30 31 32 34 38 40 41 43 45 46 47 48 49 50 51 52 55
56 58 59 60 61 64 65 68 70 71 72 73 74 75 76 77 78 79 81 82 83 84 85
87 88 89 91 92 93 97 98 99 100 101 102 103 104 105 107 108 110 114
115 118 119 120 121 123 124 126 127 129 130 131 132 133 134 135 136
138 139 142 144 145 146 147 148 **P**1 6 8 **S** UMass Memorial Health Care,
Inc., Worcester, MA
Primary Contact: Eric Dickson, M.D., President and Chief Executive Officer
COO: Andrew Sussman, M.D., Chief Operating Officer
CFO: Therese Day, Chief Financial Officer
CMO: Stephen Tosi, M.D., Chief Medical Officer
CIO: George Brenkle, Chief Information Officer
Web address: www.umassmemorial.org
**Control:** Other not–for–profit (including NFP Corporation) **Service:** General
Medical and Surgical

**Staffed Beds:** 687 **Admissions:** 41454 **Census:** 562 **Outpatient Visits:**
1054217 **Births:** 3978 **Total Expense ($000):** 1331575 **Payroll Expense
($000):** 467889 **Personnel:** 8490

☐ **WORCESTER RECOVERY CENTER AND HOSPITAL (224032)**, (Formerly
Worcester State Hospital), 305 Belmont Street, Zip 01604–1695;
tel. 508/368–3300, (Nonreporting) **A**1 3 5 10 **S** Massachusetts Department of
Mental Health, Boston, MA
Primary Contact: Anthony Riccitelli, Chief Operating Officer
COO: Anthony Riccitelli, Chief Operating Officer
CMO: Kathleen Whitley, R.N., Director Clinical and Professional Service
CIO: Ron Medciros, Director Applied Information Technology
**Control:** State–Government, nonfederal **Service:** Psychiatric

**Staffed Beds:** 126

**MA**

---

**Hospital, Medicare Provider Number, Address, Telephone, Approval, Facility, and Physician Codes, Health Care System**

★  American Hospital Association (AHA) membership
☐  The Joint Commission accreditation       ◇  DNV Healthcare Inc. accreditation

○  Healthcare Facilities Accreditation Program
△  Commission on Accreditation of Rehabilitation Facilities (CARF) accreditation

# MICHIGAN

**MI**

## ADRIAN—Lenawee County

★ ○ **PROMEDICA BIXBY HOSPITAL (230005)**, 818 Riverside Avenue, Zip 49221–1446; tel. 517/265–0900 **A**2 9 10 11 **F**3 11 13 15 18 20 28 30 31 34 40 45 46 50 51 57 59 60 64 65 68 70 74 75 76 77 78 79 81 82 85 92 93 100 102 103 104 107 108 110 111 114 117 118 119 120 121 126 130 131 132 135 141 145 146 148 **P**6 7 8 **S** ProMedica Health System, Toledo, OH
Primary Contact: Timothy Jakacki, President
CFO: Bernie Nawrocki, Administrative Director Finance
CMO: Julie Yaroch, D.O., Vice President Medical Affairs
CIO: Carol Boyce, Administrative Director Support Services
CHR: Cathy J. Davis, Director Human Resources
CNO: Kathryn M. Greenlee, R.N., Vice President, Clinical Services/CNO
Web address: www.promedica.org
**Control:** Other not–for–profit (including NFP Corporation) **Service:** General Medical and Surgical

**Staffed Beds:** 66 **Admissions:** 4152 **Census:** 41 **Outpatient Visits:** 145764
**Births:** 737 **Total Expense ($000):** 70516 **Payroll Expense ($000):** 26245
**Personnel:** 556

## ALLEGAN—Allegan County

★ △ ◇ **ALLEGAN GENERAL HOSPITAL (231328)**, 555 Linn Street, Zip 49010–1524; tel. 269/673–8424 **A**7 9 10 18 21 **F**3 12 15 28 29 31 32 34 35 40 45 47 48 50 57 59 62 64 65 68 70 75 77 78 79 81 85 86 87 93 96 99 100 101 104 107 108 110 114 119 127 129 130 131 132 135 145 146 **S** QHR, Brentwood, TN
Primary Contact: Gerald J. Barbini, President and Chief Executive Officer
CFO: Richard Harning, Vice President Finance and Chief Financial Officer
CMO: Nabil Nouna, M.D., Chief of Staff
CIO: David Federinko, Chief Information Officer
CHR: Denise A. Eberth, Director Human Resources
Web address: www.aghosp.org
**Control:** Other not–for–profit (including NFP Corporation) **Service:** General Medical and Surgical

**Staffed Beds:** 25 **Admissions:** 831 **Census:** 8 **Outpatient Visits:** 82729
**Births:** 0 **Total Expense ($000):** 43089 **Payroll Expense ($000):** 18048
**Personnel:** 290

## ALMA—Gratiot County

**GRATIOT MEDICAL CENTER** See MidMichigan Medical Center–Gratiot

⊠ △ **MIDMICHIGAN MEDICAL CENTER–GRATIOT (230030)**, 300 East Warwick Drive, Zip 48801–1014; tel. 989/463–1101 **A**1 7 9 10 19 **F**3 11 12 13 15 18 20 28 29 31 32 34 35 40 50 51 55 56 57 59 60 61 64 65 68 70 74 75 76 77 78 79 81 82 85 89 90 92 93 96 98 100 101 102 103 105 107 108 110 111 114 115 116 117 118 119 124 127 129 130 132 135 144 145 146 148 **S** MidMichigan Health, Midland, MI
Primary Contact: Mark A. Santamaria, President
CFO: Victor Morgan, Chief Financial Officer
CIO: Michael Larson, Chief Information Officer
Web address: www.midmichigan.org/gratiot
**Control:** Other not–for–profit (including NFP Corporation) **Service:** General Medical and Surgical

**Staffed Beds:** 100 **Admissions:** 5242 **Census:** 65 **Outpatient Visits:** 140823
**Births:** 562 **Total Expense ($000):** 109828 **Payroll Expense ($000):** 38737
**Personnel:** 623

## ALPENA—Alpena County

⊠ **ALPENA REGIONAL MEDICAL CENTER (230036)**, 1501 West Chisholm Street, Zip 49707–1401; tel. 989/356–7390 **A**1 2 9 10 **F**3 5 11 13 14 15 20 22 28 29 31 34 35 40 43 44 45 46 47 48 49 50 59 62 64 65 70 71 73 74 75 76 77 78 79 81 82 85 86 87 90 93 96 97 98 99 100 101 102 103 104 106 107 108 110 111 114 115 118 119 129 130 131 132 135 146 147 148 **P**6
Primary Contact: Karmon T. Bjella, Chief Executive Officer
COO: Aldean J. Moe, Chief Operating Officer
CFO: George J. Smart, VP Finance & IT
CHR: Diane Shields, Chief Human Resources Officer
CNO: Gayle Bruski, R.N., Chief Nursing Officer
Web address: www.alpenaregionalmedicalcenter.org
**Control:** County–Government, nonfederal **Service:** General Medical and Surgical

**Staffed Beds:** 125 **Admissions:** 4611 **Census:** 60 **Outpatient Visits:** 205679
**Births:** 360 **Total Expense ($000):** 124665 **Payroll Expense ($000):** 47551
**Personnel:** 864

## ANN ARBOR—Washtenaw County

⊠ **UNIVERSITY OF MICHIGAN HOSPITALS AND HEALTH CENTERS (230046)**, 1500 East Medical Center Drive, Zip 48109–5000; tel. 734/936–4000, (Includes C.S. MOTT CHILDREN'S HOSPITAL, 1500 East Medical Center Drive, Zip 48109–5475; tel. 734/936–4000) **A**1 2 3 5 8 9 10 **F**3 5 6 8 9 11 12 13 15 16 17 18 19 20 21 22 23 24 25 26 27 28 29 30 31 32 34 35 36 37 38 39 40 41 43 44 45 46 47 48 49 50 51 52 53 54 55 56 57 58 59 60 61 62 64 65 66 68 69 70 72 74 75 76 77 78 79 80 81 82 84 85 86 87 88 89 90 91 92 93 94 95 97 98 99 100 101 102 103 104 107 108 110 111 114 115 116 117 118 119 120 121 123 124 126 127 129 130 131 132 134 135 136 137 138 139 140 141 142 145 146 147 148 **P**6
Primary Contact: Douglas Strong, Chief Executive Officer
COO: Tony Denton, JD, Chief Operating Officer
CFO: Paul Castillo, Chief Financial Officer
CMO: Darrell Campbell, M.D., Chief Clinical Affairs
CIO: Sue Schade, Chief Information Officer
CHR: Deborah Childs, Chief Human Resources Officer
Web address: www.med.umich.edu
**Control:** Other not–for–profit (including NFP Corporation) **Service:** General Medical and Surgical

**Staffed Beds:** 899 **Admissions:** 45412 **Census:** 758 **Outpatient Visits:** 1969216 **Births:** 3787 **Total Expense ($000):** 2245866 **Payroll Expense ($000):** 859092 **Personnel:** 13969

⊠ △ **VETERANS AFFAIRS ANN ARBOR HEALTHCARE SYSTEM**, 2215 Fuller Road, Zip 48105–2399; tel. 734/769–7100, (Total facility includes 40 beds in nursing home–type unit) **A**1 2 3 5 7 8 9 **F**3 5 12 18 20 22 24 26 28 29 30 31 34 35 36 38 39 40 45 46 48 49 50 54 56 57 58 59 60 61 62 63 64 65 68 70 71 74 75 77 78 79 80 81 82 83 84 85 86 87 91 92 93 94 96 97 98 100 101 102 103 104 105 107 108 111 114 116 117 119 121 123 126 128 129 130 132 135 143 144 146 147 148 **P**6 **S** Department of Veterans Affairs, Washington, DC
Primary Contact: Robert P. McDivitt, FACHE, Director
COO: Randall Ritter, Associate Director
CFO: Walter Zawisza, Chief Financial Officer
CMO: Eric Young, M.D., Chief of Staff
CIO: Rob Whitehurst, Chief, Office of Information and Technology
CHR: James S. Lodge, Chief Human Resources
CNO: Stacey Breedveld, R.N., Associate Director for Patient Care
Web address: www.annarbor.va.gov
**Control:** Veterans Affairs, Government, federal **Service:** General Medical and Surgical

**Staffed Beds:** 145 **Admissions:** 5604 **Census:** 87 **Outpatient Visits:** 504542
**Births:** 0 **Total Expense ($000):** 384839 **Payroll Expense ($000):** 162691
**Personnel:** 2981

## AUBURN HILLS—Oakland County

☐ **HAVENWYCK HOSPITAL (234023)**, 1525 University Drive, Zip 48326–2673; tel. 248/373–9200 **A**1 9 10 **F**98 99 102 105 130 **P**8 **S** Universal Health Services, Inc., King of Prussia, PA
Primary Contact: David C. Bell, Chief Executive Officer
CFO: Mirhee Chun, Chief Financial Officer
Web address: www.havenwyckhospital.com
**Control:** Corporation, Investor–owned, for–profit **Service:** Psychiatric

**Staffed Beds:** 251 **Admissions:** 5950 **Census:** 199 **Outpatient Visits:** 4243
**Births:** 0 **Total Expense ($000):** 40214 **Payroll Expense ($000):** 14713
**Personnel:** 303

## BAD AXE—Huron County

**HURON MEDICAL CENTER (230118)**, 1100 South Van Dyke Road, Zip 48413–9615; tel. 989/269–9521 **A**9 10 20 **F**3 11 13 14 15 18 20 28 29 31 32 34 35 40 45 53 56 57 59 64 70 74 75 76 77 78 79 81 82 85 90 93 97 107 108 114 119 126 127 130 132 134 135 144 146 **P**6
Primary Contact: Janet Sternberg, President and Chief Executive Officer
CFO: Jeffery Longbrake, Chief Financial Officer
CMO: Jerome Yaklic, M.D., Chief of Staff
CHR: Nancy Bouck, Director Human Resources
Web address: www.huronmedicalcenter.org
**Control:** Other not–for–profit (including NFP Corporation) **Service:** General Medical and Surgical

**Staffed Beds:** 36 **Admissions:** 1638 **Census:** 14 **Outpatient Visits:** 55926
**Births:** 365 **Total Expense ($000):** 41772 **Payroll Expense ($000):** 16572
**Personnel:** 344

*Many Facility Codes have changed. Please refer to the AHA Guide Code Chart.*
© 2013 AHA Guide

## BATTLE CREEK—Calhoun County

☒ △ **BATTLE CREEK VETERANS AFFAIRS MEDICAL CENTER**, (Formerly Veterans Affairs Medical Center), 5500 Armstrong Road, Zip 49037–7314; tel. 269/966–5600, (Total facility includes 104 beds in nursing home–type unit) **A**1 7 9 **F**3 4 5 12 29 30 34 36 38 39 50 53 54 56 57 58 59 61 62 63 64 65 68 74 75 77 82 83 84 86 87 91 92 93 94 96 97 98 100 101 102 103 104 106 107 108 119 127 128 130 132 135 141 143 144 146 147 148 **S** Department of Veterans Affairs, Washington, DC
Primary Contact: Mary Beth Skupien, Director
COO: Edward G. Dornoff, Associate Director
CFO: James M. Rupert, Chief Fiscal Services
CMO: Wilfredo Rodriguez, M.D., Chief of Staff
CIO: Scott Hershberger, Acting Chief Information Management Services
CHR: Palma Simkins, Chief Human Resources Management Services
CNO: Kay Bower, Associate Director for Patient Care Services
Web address: www.battlecreek.va.gov/
**Control:** Veterans Affairs, Government, federal **Service:** Psychiatric

**Staffed Beds:** 204 **Admissions:** 2769 **Census:** 237 **Outpatient Visits:** 399933 **Births:** 0 **Personnel:** 1481

☒ **BRONSON BATTLE CREEK (230075)**, 300 North Avenue, Zip 49017–3307; tel. 269/966–8000, (Includes FIELDSTONE CENTER, 165 North Washington Avenue, Zip 49037; tel. 616/964–7121; MAIN CAMPUS, 300 North Avenue, Zip 49017; tel. 616/966–8000) **A**1 2 9 10 **F**3 5 6 9 11 13 15 18 20 26 28 29 30 31 34 35 38 40 43 44 45 46 49 50 51 54 55 56 57 58 59 60 64 65 66 68 70 71 74 75 76 77 78 79 81 82 84 85 87 92 93 98 100 101 102 103 104 107 108 110 111 114 115 117 118 119 120 121 123 126 129 130 131 132 135 143 144 146 147 148 **P**6 8 **S** Bronson Healthcare Group, Inc., Kalamazoo, MI
Primary Contact: Anne Regling, Interim Chief Executive Officer
CFO: Anne Regling, Interim Chief Financial Officer
CMO: Thomas Ignaczak, M.D., Interim Vice President Medical Affairs
CIO: Jim Keller, Director Information Services
CHR: Cathy Edwards, Director Organization and Talent Effectiveness
Web address: www.bchealth.com
**Control:** Other not–for–profit (including NFP Corporation) **Service:** General Medical and Surgical

**Staffed Beds:** 218 **Admissions:** 9490 **Census:** 110 **Outpatient Visits:** 217308 **Births:** 884 **Total Expense ($000):** 196802 **Payroll Expense ($000):** 82394 **Personnel:** 1221

☒ **SELECT SPECIALTY HOSPITAL–BATTLE CREEK (232035)**, 300 North Avenue, Zip 49017–3307; tel. 269/964–9075, (Nonreporting) **A**1 9 10 **S** Select Medical Corporation, Mechanicsburg, PA
Primary Contact: Robert Padalino, Interim Chief Executive Officer
Web address: www.selectspecialtyhospitals.com/company/locations/battlecreek.aspx
**Control:** Corporation, Investor–owned, for–profit **Service:** Long–Term Acute Care hospital

**Staffed Beds:** 25

☐ **SOUTHWEST REGIONAL REHABILITATION CENTER (233025)**, 393 East Roosevelt Avenue, Zip 49017–3333; tel. 269/965–3206 **A**1 9 10 **F**3 29 64 90 93 96 130 132 146 148 **P**6
Primary Contact: Kevin Arnold, President and Chief Executive Officer
COO: Amy Davis, Chief Operating Officer
CFO: Bruce Hart, Chief Financial Officer
CMO: Mehmet Yilmaz, M.D., Medical Director
CIO: Rick Albaugh, Manager Information Services
CHR: Karol A. Jenney, Director Business Operations
Web address: www.sw–rehab.org
**Control:** Other not–for–profit (including NFP Corporation) **Service:** Rehabilitation

**Staffed Beds:** 26 **Admissions:** 624 **Census:** 17 **Outpatient Visits:** 13338 **Births:** 0 **Total Expense ($000):** 12569 **Payroll Expense ($000):** 6715 **Personnel:** 125

**VETERANS AFFAIRS MEDICAL CENTER** See Battle Creek Veterans Affairs Medical Center

## BAY CITY—Bay County

☒ △ **MCLAREN BAY REGION (230041)**, 1900 Columbus Avenue, Zip 48708–6831; tel. 989/894–3000, (Includes BAY REGIONAL MEDICAL CENTER–WEST CAMPUS, 3250 East Midland Road, Zip 48706; tel. 989/667–6750) **A**1 2 7 9 10 12 13 **F**3 7 11 13 15 17 18 20 22 24 26 28 29 30 31 32 34 35 36 38 40 44 49 50 57 58 59 64 65 68 70 73 74 75 76 78 79 81 82 85 86 87 89 90 92 93 96 97 98 100 102 103 107 108 110 111 114 115 119 120 121 123 124 129 130 131 132 135 141 143 146 147 148 **P**6 **S** McLaren Health Care Corporation, Flint, MI
Primary Contact: Alice M. Gerard, President and Chief Executive Officer
CFO: Brian Kay, Chief Financial Officer
CMO: Ashok Vashishta, M.D., Vice President Medical Affairs
CIO: Curt Valley, Customer Site Manager
CHR: Joseph A. Lyons, Vice President Human Resources
Web address: www.bayregional.org
**Control:** Other not–for–profit (including NFP Corporation) **Service:** General Medical and Surgical

**Staffed Beds:** 338 **Admissions:** 15669 **Census:** 207 **Outpatient Visits:** 363396 **Births:** 897 **Total Expense ($000):** 266771 **Payroll Expense ($000):** 114104 **Personnel:** 1824

☒ ○ **MCLAREN BAY SPECIAL CARE (232020)**, 3250 East Midland Road, Suite 1, Zip 48706–2835; tel. 989/667–6802 **A**1 9 10 11 **F**1 3 29 31 79 87 96 148 **S** McLaren Health Care Corporation, Flint, MI
Primary Contact: Cheryl A. Burzynski, President
CFO: Brian Kay, Chief Financial Officer
CMO: Janet Sutton, M.D., Medical Director
CIO: Darren Frye, Manager
CHR: Greg Purtell, Vice President Human Resources
Web address: www.bayspecialcare.org
**Control:** Other not–for–profit (including NFP Corporation) **Service:** Long–Term Acute Care hospital

**Staffed Beds:** 26 **Admissions:** 330 **Census:** 24 **Outpatient Visits:** 0 **Births:** 0 **Total Expense ($000):** 7617 **Payroll Expense ($000):** 3919 **Personnel:** 71

## BERRIEN CENTER—Berrien County

☐ **LAKELAND SPECIALTY HOSPITAL–BERRIEN CENTER (232025)**, 6418 Deans Hill Road, Zip 49102–9750; tel. 269/473–3003, (Total facility includes 166 beds in nursing home–type unit) **A**1 9 10 **F**1 3 84 90 128 **P**4 **S** Lakeland Healthcare, Saint Joseph, MI
Primary Contact: Loren Hamel, M.D., President and Chief Executive Officer
Web address: www.lakelandhealth.org
**Control:** Other not–for–profit (including NFP Corporation) **Service:** Long–Term Acute Care hospital

**Staffed Beds:** 183 **Admissions:** 486 **Census:** 138 **Outpatient Visits:** 0 **Births:** 0

## BIG RAPIDS—Mecosta County

☒ **MECOSTA COUNTY MEDICAL CENTER (230093)**, 605 Oak Street, Zip 49307–2099; tel. 231/796–8691 **A**1 9 10 20 **F**3 11 13 15 17 28 29 34 40 43 45 59 62 64 65 75 76 77 79 81 85 86 87 89 90 93 107 108 110 111 115 119 124 127 129 130 132 135 146 148 **P**1
Primary Contact: Thomas E. Daugherty, Administrator
CFO: Joseph W. Hohenberger, Chief Financial Officer
Web address: www.mcmcbr.com
**Control:** County–Government, nonfederal **Service:** General Medical and Surgical

**Staffed Beds:** 35 **Admissions:** 2449 **Census:** 19 **Outpatient Visits:** 128645 **Births:** 636 **Total Expense ($000):** 53568 **Payroll Expense ($000):** 24078 **Personnel:** 459

## BRIGHTON—Livingston County

★ **BRIGHTON CENTER FOR RECOVERY (230279)**, 12851 Grand River Road, Zip 48116–8506; tel. 810/227–1211 **A**10 **F**4 5 35 68 75 104 132 **P**3 5 6 7 8 **S** Ascension Health, Saint Louis, MO
Primary Contact: Raymond Waller, Director
CFO: Jackie Hill, Chief Financial Officer
CMO: Jeffrey Berger, M.D., Chief Medical Officer
CIO: Melissa Whelan, Director Health Information
CHR: Carol Tucker, Worklife Services Consultant
Web address: www.brightonhospital.org
**Control:** Other not–for–profit (including NFP Corporation) **Service:** Alcoholism and other chemical dependency

**Staffed Beds:** 99 **Admissions:** 4172 **Census:** 94 **Outpatient Visits:** 26777 **Births:** 0 **Total Expense ($000):** 16803 **Payroll Expense ($000):** 8648 **Personnel:** 98

MI

---

**Hospital, Medicare Provider Number, Address, Telephone, Approval, Facility, and Physician Codes, Health Care System**

★ American Hospital Association (AHA) membership
☐ The Joint Commission accreditation          ◇ DNV Healthcare Inc. accreditation

○ Healthcare Facilities Accreditation Program
△ Commission on Accreditation of Rehabilitation Facilities (CARF) accreditation

## CADILLAC—Wexford County

☒ **MERCY HOSPITAL CADILLAC (230081)**, 400 Hobart Street, Zip 49601–2389;
tel. 231/876–7200 **A**1 9 10 20 **F**3 11 13 15 18 28 29 30 34 35 40 44 45 50
51 59 64 68 70 75 76 77 78 79 81 82 85 87 89 93 97 107 108 111 114
116 119 129 130 132 146 147 148 **P**6 8 **S** Trinity Health, Livonia, MI
Primary Contact: John L. MacLeod, President and Chief Executive Officer
COO: Mary L. Neff, R.N., Chief Operating Officer and Chief Nursing Officer
CFO: Lori Swarts, Controller and Interim Vice President
CMO: Gerald Dudek, M.D., Chief of Staff
CIO: Randi Oehlers, Site Director Management Information Systems
CHR: Michael Stebbins, Director Organization and Talent Effectiveness
CNO: Mary L. Neff, R.N., Chief Nursing Officer
Web address: www.munsonhealthcare.org
**Control:** Church–operated, Nongovernment, not–for profit **Service:** General
Medical and Surgical

**Staffed Beds:** 65 **Admissions:** 3830 **Census:** 33 **Outpatient Visits:** 80058
**Births:** 288 **Total Expense ($000):** 64113 **Payroll Expense ($000):** 23120
**Personnel:** 530

## CARO—Tuscola County

☐ **CARO CENTER (234025)**, 2000 Chambers Road, Zip 48723–9296;
tel. 989/673–3191, (Nonreporting) **A**1 9 10
Primary Contact: Rose Laskowski, R.N., Director
COO: Rose Laskowski, R.N., Director
CFO: Mary Jo Drzewiecki–Burger, Administrative Manager
CMO: William Clark, M.D., Chief Clinical Affairs
CIO: Michele Wills, Registered Health Information Administrator
CHR: Barbara Frank, Human Resource Specialist
**Control:** State–Government, nonfederal **Service:** Psychiatric

**Staffed Beds:** 193

★ **CARO COMMUNITY HOSPITAL (231329)**, 401 North Hooper Street,
Zip 48723–1476, Mailing Address: P.O. Box 435, Zip 48723–0435;
tel. 989/673–3141 **A**9 10 18 **F**3 11 15 18 29 40 45 50 57 59 65 75 81 82
85 87 92 93 97 107 108 110 114 118 119 129 130 135 **P**6
Primary Contact: Marc Augsburger, President and Chief Executive Officer
CFO: Ron Srebinski, Chief Financial Officer
Web address: www.cch–mi.org
**Control:** Other not–for–profit (including NFP Corporation) **Service:** General
Medical and Surgical

**Staffed Beds:** 25 **Admissions:** 162 **Census:** 1 **Outpatient Visits:** 30966
**Births:** 0 **Total Expense ($000):** 12376 **Payroll Expense ($000):** 4737
**Personnel:** 100

## CARSON CITY—Montcalm County

★ ○ **CARSON CITY HOSPITAL (230208)**, 406 East Elm Street,
Zip 48811–9693, Mailing Address: P.O. Box 879, Zip 48811–0879;
tel. 989/584–3131 **A**9 10 11 19 **F**11 13 15 29 30 31 34 35 37 40 45 46 57
59 62 65 68 70 74 75 76 77 78 79 81 82 93 97 98 100 101 102 104 107
108 110 111 115 119 126 127 130 132 135 146 147 148 **P**8
Primary Contact: Matthew J. Thompson, Chief Executive Officer
CFO: Duane Miller, Senior Vice President Finance
CMO: Robert Seals, D.O., Medical Director
CIO: Richard Terry, Vice President & Chief Information Officer
CHR: Georgette Russell, Vice President of Talent & Organizational Effectiveness
CNO: Nancy Weaver, Vice President of Nursing, Chief Nursing Officer
Web address: www.carsoncityhospital.com
**Control:** Other not–for–profit (including NFP Corporation) **Service:** General
Medical and Surgical

**Staffed Beds:** 62 **Admissions:** 1915 **Census:** 17 **Outpatient Visits:** 68729
**Births:** 349 **Total Expense ($000):** 58823 **Payroll Expense ($000):** 29248
**Personnel:** 495

## CASS CITY—Tuscola County

★ **HILLS & DALES GENERAL HOSPITAL (231316)**, 4675 Hill Street,
Zip 48726–1099; tel. 989/872–2121 **A**9 10 18 **F**3 11 15 29 30 31 32 34 35
40 46 53 56 57 59 61 64 70 75 77 79 81 85 86 87 93 97 100 108 109 110
115 118 119 127 129 130 131 132 135 144 146 147 148 **P**5 6
Primary Contact: Michael J. Falatko, FACHE, President and Chief Executive Officer
COO: Jean Anthony, Chief Operating Officer and Vice President Patient Services
CFO: Kenneth Baranski, Chief Financial Officer
CMO: Nancy Wade, M.D., Chief of Staff
CHR: Tom Bardwell, Vice President Human Resources
CNO: Jennifer TerBush, Director of Nursing
Web address: www.hdghmi.org
**Control:** Other not–for–profit (including NFP Corporation) **Service:** General
Medical and Surgical

**Staffed Beds:** 25 **Admissions:** 545 **Census:** 5 **Outpatient Visits:** 58534
**Births:** 0 **Total Expense ($000):** 22668 **Payroll Expense ($000):** 10164
**Personnel:** 184

## CHARLEVOIX—Charlevoix County

☒ **CHARLEVOIX AREA HOSPITAL (231322)**, 14700 Lake Shore Drive,
Zip 49720–1999; tel. 231/547–4024 **A**1 9 10 18 **F**11 13 15 28 32 34 35 40
57 59 70 75 76 77 78 79 81 82 89 93 107 108 111 115 119 129 130 131
132 133 135 144 146
Primary Contact: Lyn Jenks, Chief Executive Officer
COO: Christine Wilhelm, Vice President Operations
CFO: Joseph Schodde, Vice President Financial Services
CIO: David Priest, Director Information Systems
CHR: Patty Fitzgerald, Staff Services
Web address: www.cah.org
**Control:** Other not–for–profit (including NFP Corporation) **Service:** General
Medical and Surgical

**Staffed Beds:** 25 **Admissions:** 855 **Census:** 7 **Outpatient Visits:** 28306
**Births:** 216 **Total Expense ($000):** 34064 **Payroll Expense ($000):** 16491
**Personnel:** 326

## CHARLOTTE—Eaton County

☒ △ **HAYES GREEN BEACH MEMORIAL HOSPITAL (231327)**, 321 East Harris
Street, Zip 48813–1629; tel. 517/543–1050 **A**1 7 9 10 18 **F**3 7 11 15 18 26
28 29 34 35 36 40 45 46 50 53 57 59 62 64 65 68 69 75 77 79 81 82 85
87 89 92 93 97 107 108 110 111 114 118 119 129 130 131 132 135 143
144 146 148 **P**6 **S** QHR, Brentwood, TN
Primary Contact: Matthew Rush, President and Chief Executive Officer
CFO: Kim Capps, Chief Financial Officer
CMO: Robert Leeser, M.D., Chief Medical Officer
CIO: Kim Capps, Chief Financial Officer
CHR: Jennifer Bucienski, Director Human Resources
Web address: www.hgbhealth.com
**Control:** Other not–for–profit (including NFP Corporation) **Service:** General
Medical and Surgical

**Staffed Beds:** 25 **Admissions:** 712 **Census:** 6 **Outpatient Visits:** 147658
**Births:** 0 **Total Expense ($000):** 49133 **Payroll Expense ($000):** 19940
**Personnel:** 378

## CHELSEA—Washtenaw County

☒ **CHELSEA COMMUNITY HOSPITAL (230259)**, 775 South Main Street,
Zip 48118–1383; tel. 734/475–1311 **A**1 3 5 9 10 **F**1 3 5 8 9 11 15 28 29 30
31 34 35 36 40 45 51 53 59 62 64 65 68 70 75 77 78 79 81 82 85 86 87
90 91 93 97 98 99 100 101 104 107 110 111 114 115 119 128 129 130
131 132 134 135 146 147 148 **S** Trinity Health, Livonia, MI
Primary Contact: Nancy Kay Graebner, President and Chief Executive Officer
CFO: James Birchler, Vice President Finance
CMO: Larry Handelsman, M.D., Vice President Medical Affairs
CIO: Sherry Brown, Director Information Services
CHR: Cindy Harrison, Vice President Human Resources
Web address: www.cch.org
**Control:** Other not–for–profit (including NFP Corporation) **Service:** General
Medical and Surgical

**Staffed Beds:** 102 **Admissions:** 4164 **Census:** 53 **Outpatient Visits:** 160358
**Births:** 0 **Total Expense ($000):** 105137 **Payroll Expense ($000):** 46647
**Personnel:** 617

## CLARE—Clare County

☒ **MIDMICHIGAN MEDICAL CENTER–CLARE (230180)**, 703 North McEwan
Street, Zip 48617–1440; tel. 989/802–5000 **A**1 5 9 10 **F**3 11 15 18 20 28 29
30 31 34 35 40 45 50 53 57 59 61 64 70 75 77 79 81 85 87 89 93 97 107
108 110 114 118 119 127 129 130 132 135 144 146 **S** MidMichigan Health,
Midland, MI
Primary Contact: Raymond Stover, President and Chief Executive Officer
CFO: Josh Wiggins, Vice President Controller
CMO: David Bremer, D.O., Chief of Staff
CIO: Michael Larson, Vice President Chief Inofmation Officer
CNO: Glenn King, R.N., Vice President, Chief Nursing Officer
Web address: www.midmichigan.org
**Control:** Other not–for–profit (including NFP Corporation) **Service:** General
Medical and Surgical

**Staffed Beds:** 49 **Admissions:** 1646 **Census:** 13 **Outpatient Visits:** 106442
**Births:** 0 **Total Expense ($000):** 50113 **Payroll Expense ($000):** 15217
**Personnel:** 259

MI

*Many Facility Codes have changed. Please refer to the AHA Guide Code Chart.*
© 2013 AHA Guide

## CLINTON TOWNSHIP—Macomb County

⊞ △ **HENRY FORD MACOMB HOSPITALS (230047)**, 15855 19 Mile Road, Zip 48038–6324; tel. 586/263–2300, (Includes HENRY FORD MACOMB HOSPITAL – MOUNT CLEMENS CAMPUS, 215 North Avenue, Mount Clemens, Zip 48043; tel. 586/466–9300; ST. JOSEPH'S MERCY HOSPITAL–WEST, 15855 19 Mile Road, Zip 48038; tel. 586/263–2707; ST. JOSEPH'S MERCY–NORTH, 80650 North Van Dyke, Romeo, Zip 48065; tel. 810/798–3551) **A**1 2 7 9 10 12 13 **F**3 7 11 12 13 15 18 19 20 22 24 26 28 29 30 31 32 34 35 36 38 40 43 44 45 46 47 49 50 51 54 56 57 58 59 60 61 64 65 66 68 69 70 74 75 76 77 78 79 81 82 84 85 86 87 89 90 92 93 96 97 98 99 100 101 102 103 104 105 107 108 110 111 114 115 117 118 119 120 121 124 126 129 131 132 134 144 146 147 148 **P**6 8 **S** Henry Ford Health System, Detroit, MI
Primary Contact: Barbara Rossmann, R.N., President and Chief Executive Officer
COO: Gary Beaulac, Chief Operating Officer
CFO: Terry Goodbalian, Vice President Finance and Chief Financial Officer
CMO: Charles Kelly, D.O., Vice President Medical Affairs and Chief Medical Officer
CIO: Cathy Geiger, Director Information Systems
CHR: Joel Gibson, Vice President Human Resources
Web address: www.henryfordmacomb.com
**Control:** Other not–for–profit (including NFP Corporation) **Service:** General Medical and Surgical

**Staffed Beds:** 433 **Admissions:** 24059 **Census:** 357 **Outpatient Visits:** 439100 **Births:** 1667 **Total Expense ($000):** 433440 **Payroll Expense ($000):** 176968 **Personnel:** 2730

## COLDWATER—Branch County

⊞ **COMMUNITY HEALTH CENTER OF BRANCH COUNTY (230022)**, 274 East Chicago Street, Zip 49036–2041; tel. 517/279–5400 **A**1 9 10 13 19 **F**3 5 8 11 12 13 15 28 29 30 31 34 37 40 43 45 57 59 61 62 63 64 65 70 74 75 76 78 79 81 84 85 87 89 91 92 93 96 97 98 100 101 102 103 104 107 108 110 111 115 116 117 118 119 127 129 130 132 135 146 148 **P**6 8
Primary Contact: Randy DeGroot, President and Chief Executive Officer
COO: Mary R. Rose, R.N., Chief Clinical Officer
CFO: Steve Anderson, Chief Financial Officer
CMO: Joudat Daoud, M.D., Chief of Staff
CIO: Joel Lederman, Director Information Systems
CHR: Amy Jensen, Director Human Resources
Web address: www.chcbc.com
**Control:** County–Government, nonfederal **Service:** General Medical and Surgical

**Staffed Beds:** 96 **Admissions:** 3602 **Census:** 38 **Outpatient Visits:** 156681 **Births:** 283 **Total Expense ($000):** 67813 **Payroll Expense ($000):** 30061 **Personnel:** 500

## COMMERCE TOWNSHIP—Oakland County

⊞ **DMC HURON VALLEY–SINAI HOSPITAL (230277)**, (Formerly Huron Valley–Sinai Hospital), 1 William Carls Drive, Zip 48382–2201; tel. 248/937–3300 **A**1 9 10 12 **F**3 11 12 13 15 18 20 22 26 28 29 30 31 34 35 37 39 40 44 45 46 48 49 50 51 57 58 59 60 61 64 65 68 70 74 75 76 77 78 79 80 81 82 84 85 86 87 89 92 107 108 110 111 114 115 117 119 120 121 123 124 126 129 130 131 132 135 141 146 147 148 **P**6 8
**S** Vanguard Health Systems, Nashville, TN
Primary Contact: Lynn M. Torossian, President
COO: Karen Fordham, Vice President Chief Operating Officer
CFO: William Lantzy, Vice President Finance
CMO: Marc Bocknek, D.O., Vice President Medical Affairs
CHR: Ayanna Weber, Director Human Resources
CNO: Cathy Grant, R.N., Associate Vice President, Patient Services
Web address: www.hvsh.org
**Control:** Corporation, Investor–owned, for–profit **Service:** General Medical and Surgical

**Staffed Beds:** 153 **Admissions:** 9295 **Census:** 104 **Outpatient Visits:** 91071 **Births:** 1326 **Total Expense ($000):** 168785 **Payroll Expense ($000):** 56408 **Personnel:** 913

## DEARBORN—Wayne County

⊞ **OAKWOOD HOSPITAL & MEDICAL CENTER–DEARBORN (230020)**, 18101 Oakwood Boulevard, Zip 48124–4089, Mailing Address: P.O. Box 2500, Zip 48123–2500; tel. 313/593–7000 **A**1 2 3 5 8 9 10 **F**3 11 12 13 15 17 18 20 22 24 26 28 29 30 31 32 34 35 37 38 39 40 43 44 46 47 49 50 52 55 56 57 58 59 60 61 64 65 68 70 72 74 75 76 77 78 79 80 81 82 84 85 86 87 89 92 93 96 97 100 102 107 108 110 111 114 115 118 119 120 121 123 124 126 130 131 132 135 146 147 148 **P**8 **S** Oakwood Healthcare, Inc., Dearborn, MI
Primary Contact: Douglas D. Welday, Division President
CFO: Douglas D. Welday, Division President
CMO: Malcolm S. Henoch, M.D., Chief Medical Officer
CIO: Paula Smith, Leader Information Services and Chief Information Officer
CHR: John Paul Conway, Executive Vice President Human Resources
Web address: www.oakwood.org
**Control:** Other not–for–profit (including NFP Corporation) **Service:** General Medical and Surgical

**Staffed Beds:** 555 **Admissions:** 30806 **Census:** 432 **Outpatient Visits:** 181111 **Births:** 4071 **Total Expense ($000):** 592398 **Payroll Expense ($000):** 213896 **Personnel:** 3130

## DECKERVILLE—Sanilac County

**DECKERVILLE COMMUNITY HOSPITAL (231311)**, 3559 Pine Street, Zip 48427–7703, Mailing Address: P.O. Box 126, Zip 48427–0126; tel. 810/376–2835, (Nonreporting) **A**9 10 18
Primary Contact: Ethan Lipkind, President and Chief Executive Officer
COO: David West, Chief Operating Officer
CFO: Michael Beeman, Chief Financial Officer
CMO: Levi Guerrero, M.D., Chief of Staff
Web address: www.deckervillehosp.org
**Control:** Other not–for–profit (including NFP Corporation) **Service:** General Medical and Surgical

**Staffed Beds:** 15

## DETROIT—Wayne County

**BCA STONECREST HOSPITAL** See Stonecrest Center

⊞ △ **CHILDREN'S HOSPITAL OF MICHIGAN (233300)**, 3901 Beaubien Street, Zip 48201–2119; tel. 313/745–5437 **A**1 3 5 7 9 10 **F**3 7 11 16 17 18 19 20 21 22 23 24 25 26 27 29 30 31 32 34 35 38 39 40 41 43 44 45 48 49 50 51 54 55 57 58 59 60 61 63 64 65 68 72 74 75 77 78 79 80 81 82 84 85 86 87 88 89 90 91 92 93 94 95 96 97 99 100 101 102 107 108 111 114 115 116 117 118 119 120 121 123 124 129 130 131 132 134 136 137 138 139 141 144 146 148 **P**6 8 **S** Vanguard Health Systems, Nashville, TN
Primary Contact: Herman B. Gray, M.D., President
CFO: Joseph Scallen, Jr., Chief Financial Officer
CMO: Charles Barone, M.D., Vice President Medical Affairs
CIO: Srinivasan Suresh, M.D., Chief Medical Information Officer
CHR: Tarry Paylor, Director Human Resources
Web address: www.chmkids.org
**Control:** Corporation, Investor–owned, for–profit **Service:** Children's general

**Staffed Beds:** 222 **Admissions:** 10640 **Census:** 139 **Outpatient Visits:** 259009 **Births:** 0 **Total Expense ($000):** 338493 **Payroll Expense ($000):** 125491 **Personnel:** 1826

⊞ △ **DETROIT RECEIVING HOSPITAL/UNIVERSITY HEALTH CENTER (230273)**, 4201 Saint Antoine Street, Zip 48201–2153; tel. 313/745–3000 **A**1 3 5 7 9 10 **F**3 16 17 18 29 30 34 35 38 40 42 43 44 49 50 56 57 58 59 61 64 65 66 68 70 74 75 77 79 81 82 84 85 87 97 98 99 100 102 103 104 107 114 115 119 129 130 131 132 135 141 143 144 146 148 **P**1 6
**S** Vanguard Health Systems, Nashville, TN
Primary Contact: Iris Taylor, Ph.D., R.N., President
COO: Jeff Dawkins, Chief Operating Officer
CFO: Gloria Larkins, Vice President Finance
CMO: Safwan Badr, M.D., Executive Vice President and Chief Medical Officer
CIO: Michael LeRoy, Senior Vice President and Chief Information Officer
CHR: Paulette Griffin, Vice President Human Resources
Web address: www.dmc.org
**Control:** Corporation, Investor–owned, for–profit **Service:** General Medical and Surgical

**Staffed Beds:** 268 **Admissions:** 14275 **Census:** 189 **Outpatient Visits:** 178687 **Births:** 0 **Total Expense ($000):** 375303 **Payroll Expense ($000):** 99898 **Personnel:** 1585

**HARPER UNIVERSITY HOSPITAL** See Harper University Hospital/Hutzel Women's Hospital

---

**Hospital, Medicare Provider Number, Address, Telephone, Approval, Facility, and Physician Codes, Health Care System**

★ American Hospital Association (AHA) membership
□ The Joint Commission accreditation
◇ DNV Healthcare Inc. accreditation
○ Healthcare Facilities Accreditation Program
△ Commission on Accreditation of Rehabilitation Facilities (CARF) accreditation

✠ **HARPER UNIVERSITY HOSPITAL/HUTZEL WOMEN'S HOSPITAL (230104)**, 3990 John R Street, Zip 48201–2018; tel. 313/745–8040, (Includes DMC SURGERY HOSPITAL, 30671 Stephenson Highway, Madison Heights, Zip 48071–1678; tel. 248/733–2200; Frank P. Iacobell, President; HUTZEL HOSPITAL, 4707 St. Antoine Boulevard, Zip 48201–0154; tel. 313/745–6211) **A**1 3 5 9 10 **F**3 8 9 11 12 13 15 16 17 18 20 22 24 26 28 29 30 34 35 36 39 40 42 44 45 46 47 48 49 50 51 52 54 55 56 57 58 59 60 61 63 64 65 66 68 70 72 73 74 75 76 77 78 79 80 81 82 83 84 85 86 87 92 94 97 98 100 107 108 109 111 112 114 115 119 124 126 130 131 132 133 134 135 136 138 141 143 146 147 148 **P**6 8 **S** Vanguard Health Systems, Nashville, TN
Primary Contact: Patricia Wilkerson–Uddyback, M.D., Interim President
COO: Valerie Gibson, Chief Operating Officer
CFO: Tina Wood, Vice President Finance
CMO: Reginald J. Eadie, M.D., Vice President Medical Affairs
CIO: Michael LeRoy, Senior Vice President and Chief Information Officer
CHR: Deloris Hunt, Corporate Vice President Human Resources
Web address: www.harperhospital.org
**Control:** Corporation, Investor–owned, for–profit **Service:** General Medical and Surgical

**Staffed Beds:** 535 **Admissions:** 19936 **Census:** 281 **Outpatient Visits:** 208820 **Births:** 4826 **Total Expense ($000):** 544487 **Payroll Expense ($000):** 171784 **Personnel:** 2825

✠ **HENRY FORD HOSPITAL (230053)**, 2799 West Grand Boulevard, Zip 48202–2608; tel. 313/916–2600 **A**1 2 3 5 8 9 10 **F**3 5 6 8 9 11 12 15 17 18 19 20 22 24 26 27 28 29 30 31 32 33 34 35 36 38 39 40 42 43 44 45 46 47 48 49 50 51 52 53 54 55 56 57 58 59 60 61 63 64 65 66 68 70 71 72 73 74 75 76 77 78 79 80 81 82 83 84 85 86 87 89 91 92 93 94 96 97 99 100 101 102 103 104 105 107 108 110 111 112 113 114 115 116 117 118 119 120 121 123 124 126 129 130 131 132 134 135 136 137 138 139 140 141 142 144 145 146 147 148 **P**6 **S** Henry Ford Health System, Detroit, MI
Primary Contact: John Popovich, M.D., President and Chief Executive Officer
COO: Veronica Hall, R.N., Chief Operating Officer
CFO: Joseph Schmitt, III, Senior Vice President Finance and Chief Financial Officer
CIO: Mary Alice Annecharico, Chief Information Officer
CHR: Kathy Oswald, Senior Vice President and Chief Human Resources Officer
CNO: Gwen Gnam, R.N., Chief Nursing Officer
Web address: www.henryfordhealth.org
**Control:** Other not–for–profit (including NFP Corporation) **Service:** General Medical and Surgical

**Staffed Beds:** 751 **Admissions:** 43774 **Census:** 610 **Outpatient Visits:** 2078907 **Births:** 1677 **Total Expense ($000):** 1649097 **Payroll Expense ($000):** 812782 **Personnel:** 9869

✠ △ **JOHN D. DINGELL VETERANS AFFAIRS MEDICAL CENTER**, 4646 John R Street, Zip 48201–1932; tel. 313/576–1000, (Total facility includes 109 beds in nursing home–type unit) **A**1 2 3 5 7 8 9 **F**3 4 5 8 9 11 12 17 18 20 26 28 29 30 31 34 35 36 38 39 40 44 45 49 50 54 56 57 58 59 60 61 62 63 64 65 66 67 68 70 74 75 77 78 79 80 81 82 83 84 85 86 87 90 93 94 97 98 100 101 102 103 104 105 107 108 111 114 115 118 119 121 123 127 128 129 130 132 135 143 144 145 146 147 148 **P**6 **S** Department of Veterans Affairs, Washington, DC
Primary Contact: Pamela J. Reeves, M.D., Director
COO: Brent A. Thelen, Ph.D., Associate Director
CFO: Sherry Kilgore, Chief Financial Management Service
CMO: Scott Gruber, M.D., Chief of Staff
CIO: Jonathan Small, Chief Operations Information and Technology
CHR: Kathleen Osinski, Chief Human Resources Service
CNO: Ann Herm, Associate Director Patient Care Services
Web address: www.detroit.va.gov/
**Control:** Veterans Affairs, Government, federal **Service:** General Medical and Surgical

**Staffed Beds:** 188 **Admissions:** 4948 **Census:** 63 **Outpatient Visits:** 469185 **Births:** 0 **Total Expense ($000):** 316535 **Payroll Expense ($000):** 198821 **Personnel:** 2012

✠ **KARMANOS CANCER CENTER (230297)**, 4100 John R Street, Zip 48201–2013; tel. 313/576–8670 **A**1 2 3 5 9 10 **F**3 14 15 29 31 34 35 36 38 39 44 50 54 55 56 57 58 59 63 64 65 68 70 74 75 78 79 81 82 83 84 85 86 87 100 107 108 110 111 114 115 116 117 118 119 120 121 123 124 126 130 132 135 136 146 147 148 **P**6
Primary Contact: Gerold Bepler, M.D., Ph.D., President and Chief Executive Officer
COO: Gary Morrison, Chief Operating Officer
CFO: Michael Grisdela, Chief Financial Officer
CMO: George Yoo, M.D., Chief Medical Officer
CIO: Scott McCarter, Chief Information Officer
CHR: David Jansen, Vice President Human Resources
Web address: www.karmanos.org
**Control:** Other not–for–profit (including NFP Corporation) **Service:** Cancer

**Staffed Beds:** 90 **Admissions:** 3881 **Census:** 72 **Outpatient Visits:** 170301 **Births:** 0 **Total Expense ($000):** 232184 **Payroll Expense ($000):** 55056 **Personnel:** 1120

✠ **KINDRED HOSPITAL DETROIT (232027)**, 4777 East Outer Drive, Zip 48234–3241; tel. 313/369–5800, (Nonreporting) **A**1 9 10 **S** Kindred Healthcare, Louisville, KY
Primary Contact: Jan Turk, Chief Executive Officer
CFO: Steven Smith, Chief Financial Officer
CMO: Christopher Hughes, M.D., Medical Director
CHR: John Lucido, Director Human Resources
Web address: www.kindreddetroit.com/
**Control:** Corporation, Investor–owned, for–profit **Service:** Long–Term Acute Care hospital

**Staffed Beds:** 77

✠ △ **REHABILITATION INSTITUTE OF MICHIGAN (233027)**, 261 Mack Boulevard, Zip 48201–2495; tel. 313/745–1203 **A**1 3 5 7 9 10 **F**3 28 29 30 34 35 36 40 42 43 44 50 53 58 64 68 86 87 90 91 92 93 94 95 96 119 130 131 132 134 146 148 **P**6 8 **S** Vanguard Health Systems, Nashville, TN
Primary Contact: William H. Restum, Ph.D., President
COO: Patty Jobbitt, Vice President Operations
CFO: Kevin Smith, Vice President Finance and Support Services
CMO: Ali Bitar, M.D., Vice President Medical Affairs
CHR: Paul Sturgis, Vice President Human Resources
CNO: Julia Libcke, R.N., VP Patient Care Services
Web address: www.rimrehab.org
**Control:** Corporation, Investor–owned, for–profit **Service:** Rehabilitation

**Staffed Beds:** 74 **Admissions:** 1201 **Census:** 60 **Outpatient Visits:** 247241 **Births:** 0 **Total Expense ($000):** 79758 **Payroll Expense ($000):** 38601 **Personnel:** 688

✠ **SELECT SPECIALTY HOSPITAL–NORTHWEST DETROIT (232032)**, 6071 West Outer Drrive, Zip 48235–2624; tel. 313/966–4747, (Nonreporting) **A**1 9 10 **S** Select Medical Corporation, Mechanicsburg, PA
Primary Contact: Marilouise Riska, Chief Executive Officer
Web address: www.selectspecialtyhospitals.com/company/locations/northwestdetroit.aspx
**Control:** Corporation, Investor–owned, for–profit **Service:** Long–Term Acute Care hospital

**Staffed Beds:** 36

✠ **SINAI–GRACE HOSPITAL (230024)**, 6071 West Outer Drive, Zip 48235–2679; tel. 313/966–3300 **A**1 3 5 8 9 10 13 **F**3 5 7 8 11 13 15 17 18 20 22 24 26 28 29 30 31 32 34 35 37 38 39 40 43 44 45 47 49 50 51 52 54 55 56 57 58 59 60 61 63 64 65 66 68 70 72 74 75 76 77 78 79 80 81 82 83 84 85 86 87 90 93 94 96 97 98 100 101 102 103 104 107 108 110 111 114 115 117 118 119 120 121 123 126 129 130 131 132 134 135 143 144 146 147 148 **P**6 8 **S** Vanguard Health Systems, Nashville, TN
Primary Contact: Reginald J. Eadie, M.D., President
CFO: Michael Prusatis, Vice President Finance
CMO: Matthew Griffin, M.D., Vice President Medical Affairs
CHR: Paulette Griffin, Director Human Resources
Web address: www.sinaigrace.org
**Control:** Corporation, Investor–owned, for–profit **Service:** General Medical and Surgical

**Staffed Beds:** 310 **Admissions:** 18952 **Census:** 270 **Outpatient Visits:** 216225 **Births:** 1476 **Total Expense ($000):** 391001 **Payroll Expense ($000):** 132307 **Personnel:** 2281

✠ **ST. JOHN HOSPITAL AND MEDICAL CENTER (230165)**, 22101 Moross Road, Zip 48236–2148; tel. 313/343–4000 **A**1 2 3 5 8 9 10 **F**3 8 9 11 12 13 14 15 17 18 20 22 24 26 28 29 32 34 35 36 37 38 39 40 41 42 43 44 45 46 47 48 49 50 54 55 56 57 58 59 60 61 63 64 65 66 68 70 72 73 74 75 76 77 78 79 80 81 82 84 85 86 87 88 89 90 91 92 93 95 96 97 98 100 101 102 103 107 108 110 111 114 115 116 117 118 119 120 121 123 124 126 130 131 132 135 138 141 142 143 144 146 147 148 **P**3 6 7 8 **S** Ascension Health, Saint Louis, MO
Primary Contact: David Brooks, Chief Executive Officer
CFO: Tomasine Marx, Chief Financial Officer
CMO: Michael Haynes, M.D., Chief Medical Officer
CIO: Claudia Allen, Chief Information Officer
CHR: Mary Naber, Senior Vice President Worklife Services
CNO: Maryann Barnes, MS, Vice President and Chief Nursing Officer East Region
Web address: www.stjohn.org
**Control:** Church–operated, Nongovernment, not–for profit **Service:** General Medical and Surgical

**Staffed Beds:** 673 **Admissions:** 34148 **Census:** 454 **Outpatient Visits:** 893875 **Births:** 3384 **Total Expense ($000):** 711521 **Payroll Expense ($000):** 265807 **Personnel:** 4188

☐ **STONECREST CENTER (234038)**, (Formerly BCA Stonecrest Hospital), 15000 Gratiot Avenue, Zip 48205–1973; tel. 313/245–0600 **A**1 9 10 **F**3 29 50 68 87 98 99 102 103 130 132 135 **P**6 **S** Acadia Healthcare Company, Inc., Franklin, TN
Primary Contact: Steve Savage, Chief Executive Officer and Chief Operating Officer
Web address: www.bcastonecrestcenter.com
**Control:** Corporation, Investor–owned, for–profit **Service:** Psychiatric

**Staffed Beds:** 81 **Admissions:** 2213 **Census:** 70 **Outpatient Visits:** 0 **Births:** 0 **Total Expense ($000):** 16451 **Payroll Expense ($000):** 6620 **Personnel:** 138

*Many Facility Codes have changed. Please refer to the AHA Guide Code Chart.*      © 2013 AHA Guide

**TRIUMPH HOSPITAL DETROIT** See Kindred Hospital Detroit

## DOWAGIAC—Cass County

☒ **BORGESS–LEE MEMORIAL HOSPITAL (231315)**, 420 West High Street, Zip 49047–1943; tel. 269/782–8681 **A**1 9 10 18 **F**3 11 15 18 29 30 31 34 35 40 41 50 54 57 59 64 65 68 70 75 77 78 79 81 85 86 87 93 97 100 104 107 108 114 119 127 128 130 132 133 135 146 148 **P**6 **S** Ascension Health, Saint Louis, MO
Primary Contact: John Ryder, Interim Administrator and Chief Operating Officer
COO: John Ryder, Chief Operating Officer
CFO: Ken Holst, Chief Financial Officer
CMO: Don Bouchard, D.O., Chief of Staff
CHR: Pete Krueger, Director Human Resources
Web address: www.borgess.com
**Control:** Church–operated, Nongovernment, not–for profit **Service:** General Medical and Surgical

**Staffed Beds:** 25 **Admissions:** 836 **Census:** 8 **Outpatient Visits:** 107264 **Births:** 0 **Total Expense ($000):** 27812 **Payroll Expense ($000):** 13017 **Personnel:** 223

## EAST CHINA—St. Clair County

☒ **ST. JOHN RIVER DISTRICT HOSPITAL (230241)**, 4100 River Road, Zip 48054–2909; tel. 810/329–7111 **A**1 9 10 **F**3 7 11 13 15 18 20 29 31 34 35 36 40 44 49 50 55 56 59 60 63 64 65 68 70 74 75 76 77 78 79 81 82 84 85 87 89 92 93 97 102 107 108 110 111 115 116 117 119 129 130 132 146 147 148 **P**3 6 7 8 **S** Ascension Health, Saint Louis, MO
Primary Contact: Frank W. Poma, President
CFO: Tomasine Marx, Chief Financial Officer
CMO: H. Lee Bacheldor, D.O., Medical Director
CHR: Dawn Beindit, Director Work Life Services
Web address: www.stjohn.org
**Control:** Church–operated, Nongovernment, not–for profit **Service:** General Medical and Surgical

**Staffed Beds:** 68 **Admissions:** 1810 **Census:** 17 **Outpatient Visits:** 60204 **Births:** 298 **Total Expense ($000):** 42543 **Payroll Expense ($000):** 17715 **Personnel:** 312

## EATON RAPIDS—Eaton County

☒ **EATON RAPIDS MEDICAL CENTER (231324)**, 1500 South Main Street, Zip 48827–1952, Mailing Address: P.O. Box 130, Zip 48827–0130; tel. 517/663–2671, (Nonreporting) **A**1 9 10 18
Primary Contact: Timothy Johnson, President and Chief Executive Officer
CFO: Shari Glynn, Vice President Finance and Chief Financial Officer
CMO: Ashok K. Gupta, M.D., Chief of Staff
CIO: Mark Rodge, Director Information Systems
CHR: Laurie Field, Director Human Resources
Web address: www.eatonrapidsmedicalcenter.org
**Control:** Other not–for–profit (including NFP Corporation) **Service:** General Medical and Surgical

**Staffed Beds:** 20

## ESCANABA—Delta County

☒ **OSF ST. FRANCIS HOSPITAL (231337)**, 3401 Ludington Street, Zip 49829–1377; tel. 906/786–3311, (Nonreporting) **A**1 9 10 20 **S** OSF Healthcare System, Peoria, IL
Primary Contact: David Lord, President and Chief Executive Officer
CFO: Jim Wayne, Chief Financial Officer
CMO: Mark Povich, D.O., Medical Director
CIO: Mark Irving, Manager Management Information Systems
CHR: Elizabeth Zorza, Assistant Administrator
Web address: www.osfstfrancis.org
**Control:** Church–operated, Nongovernment, not–for profit **Service:** General Medical and Surgical

**Staffed Beds:** 48

## FARMINGTON HILLS—Oakland County

★ ○ **BOTSFORD HOSPITAL (230151)**, 28050 Grand River Avenue, Zip 48336–5933; tel. 248/471–8000 **A**9 10 11 12 13 **F**3 8 9 11 12 13 15 17 18 20 22 26 28 29 30 31 32 34 35 36 38 39 40 41 43 44 45 46 47 48 49 50 51 53 54 56 57 58 59 60 61 63 64 65 68 70 74 75 76 77 78 79 80 81 82 83 84 85 86 87 89 90 92 93 94 96 97 98 100 101 102 103 107 108 110 111 114 115 118 119 120 121 123 124 126 129 130 131 132 134 135 144 146 147 148 **P**1 5 6
Primary Contact: Paul E. LaCasse, D.O., President and Chief Executive Officer
CFO: David Marcellino, Executive Vice President and Chief Operating Officer
CMO: David Walters, D.O., Vice President and Chief Medical Officer
CIO: John Czahor, Chief Information Officer
CHR: Barbara Palmer, Corporate Vice President Human Resources
Web address: www.botsford.org
**Control:** Other not–for–profit (including NFP Corporation) **Service:** General Medical and Surgical

**Staffed Beds:** 306 **Admissions:** 15765 **Census:** 211 **Outpatient Visits:** 479734 **Births:** 816 **Total Expense ($000):** 278616 **Payroll Expense ($000):** 134960 **Personnel:** 2129

## FERNDALE—Oakland County

☒ **HENRY FORD KINGSWOOD HOSPITAL (234011)**, 10300 West Eight Mile Road, Zip 48220–2100; tel. 248/398–3200 **A**1 9 10 **F**4 29 30 32 34 35 44 50 56 57 59 68 75 77 82 86 87 98 99 101 103 130 134 135 **P**6 **S** Henry Ford Health System, Detroit, MI
Primary Contact: C. Edward Coffey, M.D., Chief Executive Officer and Director Behavioral Health Services
CFO: Tony Gaglio, Chief Financial Officer
CMO: Taft Parson, M.D., Medical Director
CNO: Cheryl Taylor, R.N., Director of Nursing
Web address: www.henryford.com
**Control:** Other not–for–profit (including NFP Corporation) **Service:** Psychiatric

**Staffed Beds:** 100 **Admissions:** 3791 **Census:** 63 **Outpatient Visits:** 0 **Births:** 0 **Total Expense ($000):** 17264 **Payroll Expense ($000):** 10584 **Personnel:** 180

## FLINT—Genesee County

☒ **HURLEY MEDICAL CENTER (230132)**, One Hurley Plaza, Zip 48503–5993; tel. 810/262–6887, (Includes HURLEY CHILDREN'S HOSPITAL, 1 Hurley Plaza, Zip 48503–5902) **A**1 2 3 5 8 9 10 **F**3 5 11 12 13 15 16 17 18 19 20 22 26 28 29 30 31 32 35 39 40 41 43 45 46 47 50 52 53 54 55 56 57 58 59 61 64 66 70 72 74 75 76 77 78 79 80 81 82 84 85 86 87 88 89 90 93 96 97 98 100 101 102 103 104 107 108 110 111 114 115 118 119 120 121 123 124 129 130 131 132 135 141 143 146 147 148
Primary Contact: Melany Gavulic, President & Chief Executive Officer
COO: Melany Gavulic, Senior Vice President Operations & COO
CFO: Cass Wisniewski, Interim Chief Financial Officer
CMO: Michael Jaggi, D.O., Vice President and Chief Medical Officer
CIO: Gary Townsend, Chief Information Officer
CHR: Beth Brophy, Interim VP for Human Resources
CNO: Teresa Bourque, Sr. Administrator for Nursing/Chief Nurse
Web address: www.hurleymc.com
**Control:** City–Government, nonfederal **Service:** General Medical and Surgical

**Staffed Beds:** 418 **Admissions:** 18995 **Census:** 267 **Outpatient Visits:** 411504 **Births:** 2544 **Total Expense ($000):** 362940 **Payroll Expense ($000):** 155886 **Personnel:** 2270

☒ **MCLAREN FLINT (230141)**, 401 South Ballenger Highway, Zip 48532–3685; tel. 810/342–2000 **A**1 2 3 5 8 9 10 **F**3 5 11 12 13 15 17 18 20 22 24 26 28 29 30 31 32 34 35 36 38 39 40 43 44 45 46 49 50 52 53 54 55 56 57 58 59 60 61 64 68 70 74 75 76 77 78 79 81 82 85 86 87 89 90 93 96 97 98 99 100 101 102 103 104 105 107 108 114 115 118 119 120 121 123 124 126 129 130 131 132 135 141 144 146 147 148 **P**6 7 **S** McLaren Health Care Corporation, Flint, MI
Primary Contact: Donald C. Kooy, President and Chief Executive Officer
COO: Brent Wheeler, Vice President Ancillary and Support Services
CFO: Rick Wyles, Chief Financial Officer
CIO: Gayle Consiglio, Chief Information Officer
CHR: Timothy G. Srock, Vice President Human Resources
Web address: www.mclarenregional.org
**Control:** Other not–for–profit (including NFP Corporation) **Service:** General Medical and Surgical

**Staffed Beds:** 350 **Admissions:** 21341 **Census:** 266 **Outpatient Visits:** 401670 **Births:** 579 **Total Expense ($000):** 387039 **Payroll Expense ($000):** 166367 **Personnel:** 2549

MI

MI

✠ **SELECT SPECIALTY HOSPITAL–FLINT (232012)**, 401 South Ballenger Highway, 5th Floor Central, Zip 48532–3638; tel. 810/342–4500, (Nonreporting) **A**1 9 10 **S** Select Medical Corporation, Mechanicsburg, PA
Primary Contact: Don Shook, Chief Executive Officer
CMO: Jitendra P. Katneni, M.D., Medical Director
CHR: Gayle Barthel, Coordinator Human Resources
CNO: Nicole McLean, Chief Nursing Officer
Web address: www.selectspecialtyhospitals.com/company/locations/flint.aspx
**Control:** Corporation, Investor–owned, for–profit **Service:** Long–Term Acute Care hospital

Staffed Beds: 26

---

**FRANKFORT—Benzie County**

★ **PAUL OLIVER MEMORIAL HOSPITAL (231300)**, 224 Park Avenue, Zip 49635–9658; tel. 231/352–2200, (Total facility includes 39 beds in nursing home–type unit) **A**9 10 18 **F**11 15 28 30 34 35 40 45 46 50 53 57 59 64 75 77 81 86 93 107 110 111 115 119 129 130 132 133 143 146 148 **S** Munson Healthcare, Traverse City, MI
Primary Contact: James D. Austin, FACHE, Administrator
COO: Peter Marinoff, Director Operations
CMO: Gerard Mahoney, M.D., Chief of Staff
CHR: Julie Banktson, Manager Human Resources
Web address: www.munsonhealthcare.org
**Control:** Other not–for–profit (including NFP Corporation) **Service:** General Medical and Surgical

Staffed Beds: 47 Admissions: 101 Census: 35 Outpatient Visits: 43741
Births: 0 Total Expense ($000): 16172 Payroll Expense ($000): 4889
Personnel: 120

---

**FREMONT—Newaygo County**

✠ **SPECTRUM HEALTH GERBER MEMORIAL (230106)**, 212 South Sullivan Avenue, Zip 49412–1548; tel. 231/924–3300 **A**1 9 10 **F**3 11 13 15 28 29 31 32 34 35 36 40 43 45 48 50 53 59 62 64 68 70 75 76 77 78 79 81 86 87 93 96 107 108 110 111 115 118 119 127 129 130 131 132 135 146 147 **S** Spectrum Health, Grand Rapids, MI
Primary Contact: Randall Stasik, President and Chief Executive Officer
COO: Janice Stone, Vice President Clinical Integration
CFO: Kevin J. Cawley, Interim Vice President Finance
CMO: Kevin Gerth, M.D., Chief of Staff
CIO: Patrick Whiteside, Manager Technology Information Systems
CHR: Christine Schurkamp, Senior Human Resources Business Partner
CNO: Patti Wethington, R.N., Chief Nursing Officer
Web address: www.spectrumhealth.org
**Control:** Other not–for–profit (including NFP Corporation) **Service:** General Medical and Surgical

Staffed Beds: 40 Admissions: 2225 Census: 18 Outpatient Visits: 109353
Births: 451 Total Expense ($000): 65217 Payroll Expense ($000): 28164
Personnel: 538

---

**GARDEN CITY—Wayne County**

★ ○ **GARDEN CITY HOSPITAL (230244)**, 6245 North Inkster Road, Zip 48135–4001; tel. 734/421–3300 **A**9 10 11 12 13 **F**3 4 11 13 15 17 18 20 22 26 28 29 31 34 35 36 40 43 44 45 46 47 49 50 51 57 59 62 64 65 68 70 71 74 75 76 77 78 79 80 81 82 85 87 89 90 91 92 93 96 97 107 110 111 112 114 115 119 129 130 131 132 135 143 146 148 **P**5 6
Primary Contact: Gary R. Ley, President and Chief Executive Officer
CFO: Timothy Jodway, Chief Financial Officer
CMO: Kirsten Waarala, D.O., Vice President Medical Services
CIO: Albert Fadool, Director Information Systems
CHR: Steven Solomon, Vice President Human Resources
CNO: Bette Fitz, Chief Nursing Officer
Web address: www.gchosp.org
**Control:** Other not–for–profit (including NFP Corporation) **Service:** General Medical and Surgical

Staffed Beds: 167 Admissions: 9298 Census: 113 Outpatient Visits: 137655 Births: 612 Total Expense ($000): 131510 Payroll Expense ($000): 57594 Personnel: 1041

---

**GAYLORD—Otsego County**

✠ **OTSEGO MEMORIAL HOSPITAL (230133)**, 825 North Center Avenue, Zip 49735–1592; tel. 989/731–2100, (Includes MCREYNOLDS HALL ), (Total facility includes 34 beds in nursing home–type unit) **A**1 9 10 20 **F**3 13 15 28 29 31 32 34 35 36 37 40 43 44 45 46 49 50 51 54 56 57 59 60 64 65 70 74 75 76 77 78 79 81 82 85 86 87 93 96 97 107 108 110 111 115 118 119 124 127 128 129 130 131 132 134 135 144 146 147 148 **P**6 7
Primary Contact: Thomas R. Lemon, Chief Executive Officer
COO: James D. Flickema, VP, Professional & Ancillary Services
CFO: Robert Courtois, Vice President Finance
CMO: Peter Handley, M.D., Chief of Staff
CIO: Timothy Hella, Chief Information Officer
CHR: Terra Deming, Director Human Resources
CNO: Diane Fisher, R.N., VP, Patient Care Services
Web address: www.myomh.org
**Control:** Other not–for–profit (including NFP Corporation) **Service:** General Medical and Surgical

Staffed Beds: 80 Admissions: 1670 Census: 46 Outpatient Visits: 181322
Births: 256 Total Expense ($000): 72602 Payroll Expense ($000): 33351
Personnel: 590

---

**GLADWIN—Gladwin County**

✠ **MIDMICHIGAN MEDICAL CENTER–GLADWIN (231325)**, 515 Quarter Street, Zip 48624–1959; tel. 989/426–9286 **A**1 5 9 10 18 **F**3 11 15 18 28 29 30 31 34 35 40 45 53 57 59 64 75 77 81 85 86 89 93 97 107 108 110 114 118 119 127 129 130 132 135 143 146 **S** MidMichigan Health, Midland, MI
Primary Contact: Raymond Stover, President and Chief Executive Officer
CFO: Josh Wiggins, Vice President and Controller
CMO: Marcelino Barreto, M.D., Chief Medical Staff
CIO: Michael Larson, Vice President and Chief Information Officer
CNO: Glenn King, R.N., Vice President and Chief Nursing Officer
Web address: www.midmichigan.org
**Control:** Other not–for–profit (including NFP Corporation) **Service:** General Medical and Surgical

Staffed Beds: 25 Admissions: 624 Census: 5 Outpatient Visits: 59870
Births: 0 Total Expense ($000): 26980 Payroll Expense ($000): 7783
Personnel: 126

---

**GRAND BLANC—Genesee County**

✠ △ **GENESYS REGIONAL MEDICAL CENTER (230197)**, One Genesys Parkway, Zip 48439–8066; tel. 810/606–5000 **A**1 2 3 5 7 9 10 12 13 **F**3 11 13 15 17 18 20 22 24 26 28 29 30 31 34 35 37 40 43 44 45 46 47 48 49 50 51 54 56 58 59 60 61 64 68 70 74 75 76 77 78 79 81 82 84 85 86 87 89 90 92 93 96 97 102 107 108 110 111 114 115 117 118 119 129 130 132 135 145 146 147 148 **P**6 **S** Ascension Health, Saint Louis, MO
Primary Contact: Elizabeth Aderholdt, President
COO: Christopher Palazzolo, Senior Vice President and Chief Operating Officer
CFO: Nancy Haywood, Chief Financial Officer
CMO: James C. Bonnette, M.D., Chief Clinical Officer
CIO: Daniel Stross, Chief Information Officer
CNO: Julie A. Gorczyca, R.N., Chief Nursing Officer
Web address: www.genesys.org
**Control:** Church–operated, Nongovernment, not–for profit **Service:** General Medical and Surgical

Staffed Beds: 410 Admissions: 20720 Census: 276 Outpatient Visits: 627134 Births: 2158 Total Expense ($000): 413604 Payroll Expense ($000): 182235 Personnel: 2610

---

**GRAND HAVEN—Ottawa County**

✠ ◇ **NORTH OTTAWA COMMUNITY HOSPITAL (230174)**, 1309 Sheldon Road, Zip 49417–2488; tel. 616/842–3600, (Nonreporting) **A**1 9 10 21
Primary Contact: Shelleye Yaklin, President and Chief Executive Officer
CFO: Donald J. Longpre, Vice President Finance and Chief Financial Officer
CMO: Haney Assaad, Chief of Staff
CHR: Carla Wallis, Director Human Resources
CNO: Cindy Van Kampen, Chief Nursing Officer
Web address: www.noch.org
**Control:** Other not–for–profit (including NFP Corporation) **Service:** General Medical and Surgical

Staffed Beds: 39

---

**GRAND RAPIDS—Kent County**

☐ **FOREST VIEW PSYCHIATRIC HOSPITAL (234030)**, 1055 Medical Park Drive S.E., Zip 49546–3607; tel. 616/942–9610 **A**1 9 10 **F**75 87 98 99 100 101 102 104 105 130 132 **S** Universal Health Services, Inc., King of Prussia, PA
Primary Contact: Andrew Hotaling, Chief Executive Officer
CFO: Gabrielle Gale, Chief Financial Officer
CMO: James VanHaren, M.D., Medical Director
CHR: Mike Henderson, Director Human Resources
Web address: www.forestviewhospital.com
**Control:** Corporation, Investor–owned, for–profit **Service:** Psychiatric

Staffed Beds: 82 Admissions: 2385 Census: 70 Outpatient Visits: 9195
Births: 0 Total Expense ($000): 17438 Payroll Expense ($000): 7137
Personnel: 122

*Many Facility Codes have changed. Please refer to the AHA Guide Code Chart.*    © 2013 AHA Guide

**GREAT LAKES SPECIALTY HOSPITAL–GRAND RAPIDS CAMPUS (232026)**, (Formerly Great Lakes Specialty Hospital–Oak Campus), 200 Jefferson Avenue S.E., 5th Floor, Zip 49503–4502; tel. 616/965–8701, (Nonreporting) **A**1 9 10 **S** Select Medical Corporation, Mechanicsburg, PA
Primary Contact: Brian Pangle, Chief Executive Officer
CMO: Mark J. Ivey, M.D., Medical Director
CNO: Tracie Peterson, R.N., Chief Nursing Officer
Web address: www.selectmedicalcorp.com
**Control:** Corporation, Investor–owned, for–profit **Service:** Long–Term Acute Care hospital

**Staffed Beds:** 20

**LIFECARE HOSPITALS OF WESTERN MICHIGAN** See Great Lakes Specialty Hospital–Grand Rapids Campus

△ **MARY FREE BED REHABILITATION HOSPITAL (233026)**, 235 Wealthy Street S.E., Zip 49503–5247; tel. 616/242–0300 **A**1 7 9 10 **F**30 34 54 56 58 64 68 75 77 78 79 82 86 90 91 92 93 94 95 96 100 104 119 130 131 132 143 146 **P**6
Primary Contact: Kent Riddle, Chief Executive Officer
COO: Bruce A. Brasser, R.N., VP of Inpatient and Network Operations
CFO: Randall DeNeff, Vice President Finance
CMO: John Butzer, M.D., Medical Director
CIO: Jeff Burns, Manager of Information Technology
CHR: Kelli Miller, Vice President Human Resources
CNO: Connie A. Brown–Olds, R.N., Chief Nursing Officer
Web address: www.maryfreebed.com
**Control:** Other not–for–profit (including NFP Corporation) **Service:** Rehabilitation

**Staffed Beds:** 80 **Admissions:** 1075 **Census:** 53 **Outpatient Visits:** 62822 **Births:** 0 **Total Expense ($000):** 52593 **Payroll Expense ($000):** 29600 **Personnel:** 735

**PINE REST CHRISTIAN MENTAL HEALTH SERVICES (234006)**, 300 68th Street S.E., Zip 49548–6927, Mailing Address: P.O. Box 165, Zip 49501–0165; tel. 616/455–5000 **A**1 5 9 10 **F**2 4 5 6 29 30 32 34 35 38 43 55 56 58 59 66 68 75 77 82 86 87 91 93 98 99 100 101 102 103 104 105 106 130 132 134 135 146 **P**6
Primary Contact: Mark C. Eastburg, Ph.D., President and Chief Executive Officer
COO: Robert Nykamp, Vice President and Chief Operating Officer
CFO: Paul H. Karsten, Vice President Finance and Chief Financial Officer
CMO: Alan Armstrong, M.D., Chief Medical Officer
Web address: www.pinerest.org
**Control:** Other not–for–profit (including NFP Corporation) **Service:** Psychiatric

**Staffed Beds:** 442 **Admissions:** 5631 **Census:** 146 **Outpatient Visits:** 276601 **Births:** 0 **Total Expense ($000):** 102900 **Payroll Expense ($000):** 56600 **Personnel:** 1196

**SAINT MARY'S HEALTH CARE (230059)**, 200 Jefferson Avenue S.E., Zip 49503–4598; tel. 616/685–5000 **A**1 2 3 5 9 10 **F**3 8 13 15 18 20 22 26 28 29 30 31 34 35 36 37 40 43 44 45 46 48 49 50 53 54 56 57 58 59 60 61 64 66 68 70 72 74 75 76 77 78 79 80 81 82 83 84 85 86 87 97 98 99 100 102 105 107 108 110 111 114 115 116 117 118 119 120 121 123 124 126 129 130 131 132 135 138 144 146 147 148 **P**1 6 **S** Trinity Health, Livonia, MI
Primary Contact: Philip H. McCorkle, Jr., President and Chief Executive Officer
COO: Randall J. Wagner, Chief Operating Officer
CFO: Steve Pirog, Vice President Finance
CMO: David Baumgartner, M.D., Vice President Medical Affairs
CMO: Rolland Mambourg, M.D., Vice President Medical Affairs
CIO: Jim Keller, Site Director Information Services
CHR: Thomas Karel, Vice President Organization and Talent Effectiveness
CNO: Elizabeth A. Murphy, R.N., Vice President for Patient Care Services
Web address: www.mercyhealthsaintmarys.org
**Control:** Church–operated, Nongovernment, not–for profit **Service:** General Medical and Surgical

**Staffed Beds:** 356 **Admissions:** 20584 **Census:** 270 **Outpatient Visits:** 900572 **Births:** 2134 **Total Expense ($000):** 452176 **Payroll Expense ($000):** 120798 **Personnel:** 2252

**SPECTRUM HEALTH – GRAND RAPIDS (230038)**, (Formerly Spectrum Health Butterworth Hospital), 100 Michigan Street N.E., Zip 49503–2560; tel. 616/774–7444, (Includes HELEN DEVOS CHILDREN'S HOSPITAL, 100 Michigan Street N.E., tel. 616/391–9000; SPECTRUM HEALTH, 100 Michigan Street N.E., Zip 49503–2551; tel. 616/391–1774; SPECTRUM HEALTH – BLODGETT CAMPUS, 1840 Wealthy Street S.E., Zip 49506–2921; tel. 616/774–7444) **A**1 2 3 5 9 10 **F**3 7 8 9 11 12 13 15 16 17 18 19 20 21 22 23 24 25 26 27 28 29 30 31 32 34 35 36 37 38 40 41 43 44 49 50 51 52 54 55 56 57 58 59 60 61 64 65 66 68 70 71 72 73 74 75 76 77 78 79 80 81 82 84 85 86 87 88 89 93 99 100 107 108 110 111 114 115 116 117 118 119 120 121 123 124 126 129 130 131 132 134 135 136 137 138 143 144 145 146 147 148 **P**5 6 **S** Spectrum Health, Grand Rapids, MI
Primary Contact: Kevin Splaine, President
COO: Lisa Shannon, Chief Operating Officer
CFO: Ronald Knaus, Vice President Finance
CMO: Ralph Rogers, M.D., Vice President Medical Affairs and Chief Medical Officer
CIO: Michael Rosencrance, Vice President Information Services
CHR: David Beach, Vice President Human Resources
CNO: Shawn Ulreich, R.N., Vice President Clinical Operations and Chief Nursing Executive
Web address: www.spectrum–health.org
**Control:** Other not–for–profit (including NFP Corporation) **Service:** General Medical and Surgical

**Staffed Beds:** 1048 **Admissions:** 59852 **Census:** 640 **Outpatient Visits:** 1293375 **Births:** 7393 **Total Expense ($000):** 1414340 **Payroll Expense ($000):** 442582 **Personnel:** 7726

△ **SPECTRUM HEALTH SPECIAL CARE HOSPITAL (232029)**, 750 Fuller Avenue N.E., Zip 49503–1995; tel. 616/486–3000, (Nonreporting) **A**1 7 9 10 **S** Spectrum Health, Grand Rapids, MI
Primary Contact: Chuck Tozer, Administrator
COO: Linda Joel, Vice President Operations
CFO: Larry Oberst, Vice President Finance
CMO: Peter Sholler, M.D., Medical Director
CIO: Mary Nader, Director Information Technology
CHR: Mark Pakkala, Director Human Resources
CNO: Jennifer Groeneweg, R.N., Director of Nursing
Web address: www.spectrum–health.org
**Control:** Other not–for–profit (including NFP Corporation) **Service:** Long–Term Acute Care hospital

**Staffed Beds:** 36

### GRAYLING—Crawford County

**MERCY HOSPITAL GRAYLING (230058)**, 1100 East Michigan Avenue, Zip 49738–1312; tel. 989/348–5461, (Total facility includes 39 beds in nursing home–type unit) **A**1 9 10 20 **F**3 11 13 15 28 29 30 32 34 35 36 38 40 44 45 50 51 54 56 57 58 59 64 65 66 70 75 76 77 79 81 85 86 87 93 97 107 108 111 115 119 127 129 130 131 135 146 147 148 **P**6 8 **S** Trinity Health, Livonia, MI
Primary Contact: Stephanie J. Riemer–Matuzak, Chief Executive Officer
COO: Kirsten Korth–White, Vice President Operations
CFO: William Lubaway, Chief Financial Officer
CHR: Kirsten Korth–White, Vice President Operations
Web address: www.mercygrayling.munsonhealthcare.org/
**Control:** Church–operated, Nongovernment, not–for profit **Service:** General Medical and Surgical

**Staffed Beds:** 94 **Admissions:** 3321 **Census:** 61 **Outpatient Visits:** 140404 **Births:** 302 **Total Expense ($000):** 73350 **Payroll Expense ($000):** 27468 **Personnel:** 442

### GREENVILLE—Montcalm County

**SPECTRUM HEALTH UNITED HOSPITAL (230035)**, 615 South Bower Street, Zip 48838–2614; tel. 616/754–4691, (Includes SPECTRUM HEALTH KELSEY HOSPITAL, 418 Washington Avenue, Lakeview, Zip 48850; tel. 989/352–7211), (Total facility includes 70 beds in nursing home–type unit) **A**1 9 10 **F**3 8 11 13 15 18 29 31 32 34 35 40 41 43 44 45 50 57 62 64 65 70 75 76 77 78 79 81 85 86 87 89 93 97 107 108 110 111 114 115 119 124 127 128 129 130 131 132 133 135 146 147 148 **P**8 **S** Spectrum Health, Grand Rapids, MI
Primary Contact: Christina Freese–Decker, President
COO: Priscillia Mahar, Chief Clinical Officer
CFO: Ryan K. Johnson, Vice President Finance
CMO: Kevin O'Connor, D.O., President Medical Staff
CIO: David Dutmers, Manager Technology Information System
CHR: Vicki Jensen, Senior Human Resource Business Partner
CNO: Brian Brasser, Chief Nursing Officer
Web address: www.spectrum–health.org/
**Control:** Other not–for–profit (including NFP Corporation) **Service:** General Medical and Surgical

**Staffed Beds:** 116 **Admissions:** 3013 **Census:** 88 **Outpatient Visits:** 157404 **Births:** 421 **Total Expense ($000):** 73931 **Payroll Expense ($000):** 29938 **Personnel:** 607

MI

**Hospital, Medicare Provider Number, Address, Telephone, Approval, Facility, and Physician Codes, Health Care System**

★ American Hospital Association (AHA) membership
☐ The Joint Commission accreditation    ◇ DNV Healthcare Inc. accreditation
○ Healthcare Facilities Accreditation Program
△ Commission on Accreditation of Rehabilitation Facilities (CARF) accreditation

© 2013 AHA Guide    *Many Facility Codes have changed. Please refer to the AHA Guide Code Chart.*    Hospitals **A315**

## GROSSE POINTE—Wayne County

✠ **BEAUMONT HOSPITAL GROSSE POINTE (230089)**, 468 Cadieux Road, Zip 48230–1507; tel. 313/473–1000 **A**1 3 5 9 10 **F**3 11 12 13 15 18 20 22 26 28 29 30 31 34 35 36 39 40 44 45 46 49 50 51 53 54 57 58 59 60 61 63 64 65 66 68 69 70 71 74 75 76 77 78 79 81 82 83 85 86 87 89 92 93 94 96 97 100 107 108 110 111 114 115 117 118 119 124 126 129 130 131 132 135 146 147 148 **P**6 **S** Beaumont Health System, Royal Oak, MI
Primary Contact: Richard P. Swaine, President
COO: Chris Stesney–Ridenour, Vice President Operations
CFO: Nickolas A. Vitale, Senior Vice President and Chief Financial Officer
CMO: Donna Hoban, M.D., Senior Vice President and Physician–in–Chief
CIO: Subra Sripada, Senior Vice President and Chief Information Officer
CHR: Jay T. Holden, Vice President, Human Resources
CNO: Phyllis Reynolds, R.N., VP, Nursing
Web address: www.beaumont.edu/grosse–pointe–hospital–campus
**Control:** Other not–for–profit (including NFP Corporation) **Service:** General Medical and Surgical

**Staffed Beds:** 250 **Admissions:** 10974 **Census:** 122 **Outpatient Visits:** 271740 **Births:** 568 **Total Expense ($000):** 164559 **Payroll Expense ($000):** 51099 **Personnel:** 1116

✠ **SELECT SPECIALTY HOSPITAL–GROSSE POINTE (232038)**, 468 Cadieux Road, 3 North West, Zip 48230–1507; tel. 313/473–6131, (Nonreporting) **A**1 9 10 **S** Select Medical Corporation, Mechanicsburg, PA
Primary Contact: Miriam Deemer, Chief Executive Officer
Web address: www.selectspecialtyhospitals.com/company/locations/grossepointe.aspx
**Control:** Corporation, Investor–owned, for–profit **Service:** Long–Term Acute Care hospital

**Staffed Beds:** 30

## HANCOCK—Houghton County

✠ **PORTAGE HEALTH (230108)**, 500 Campus Drive, Zip 49930–1569; tel. 906/483–1000, (Total facility includes 60 beds in nursing home–type unit) **A**1 9 10 20 **F**3 7 8 11 13 15 28 29 30 31 32 34 35 40 43 50 53 54 56 57 59 60 62 63 64 65 67 68 69 70 75 76 77 78 79 81 84 85 86 87 89 90 93 94 97 107 108 110 111 115 119 127 129 130 131 132 133 144 145 146 147 148 **P**6
Primary Contact: James Bogan, FACHE, President and Chief Executive Officer
CFO: Brian Donahue, Chief Financial Officer
CMO: Kirk Lufkin, M.D., Chief Medical Officer
CIO: John Steenport, Director Information Technology
CHR: Robbyn Lucier, Director Human Resources
Web address: www.portagehealth.org
**Control:** Other not–for–profit (including NFP Corporation) **Service:** General Medical and Surgical

**Staffed Beds:** 96 **Admissions:** 1530 **Census:** 73 **Outpatient Visits:** 110058 **Births:** 339 **Total Expense ($000):** 77028 **Payroll Expense ($000):** 35537 **Personnel:** 588

## HARBOR BEACH—Huron County

**HARBOR BEACH COMMUNITY HOSPITAL (231313)**, 210 South First Street, Zip 48441–1236; tel. 989/479–3201, (Total facility includes 39 beds in nursing home–type unit) **A**9 10 18 **F**2 3 15 29 35 40 56 57 59 64 75 81 86 93 107 108 110 114 118 119 127 128 130 132 133 146 147 148 **P**6
Primary Contact: Edward L. Gamache, President and Chief Executive Officer
CFO: Jill Wehner, Vice President Financial Services
CMO: Richard Lloyd, D.O., Chief of Staff
CIO: Tami Nickrand, Director Information Technology
CHR: Tina Osantoski, Director Human Resources
Web address: www.hbch.org
**Control:** Other not–for–profit (including NFP Corporation) **Service:** General Medical and Surgical

**Staffed Beds:** 54 **Admissions:** 144 **Census:** 33 **Outpatient Visits:** 10595 **Births:** 0 **Total Expense ($000):** 11344 **Payroll Expense ($000):** 4850 **Personnel:** 127

## HASTINGS—Barry County

✠ **PENNOCK HOSPITAL (230040)**, 1009 West Green Street, Zip 49058–1710; tel. 269/945–3451 **A**1 9 10 **F**3 11 13 15 29 30 32 34 35 36 39 40 44 45 50 53 54 56 57 59 62 63 64 65 69 70 74 75 76 77 79 81 82 84 85 86 87 89 91 93 96 97 107 108 110 111 115 119 125 129 130 131 132 135 144 146 147 148 **P**6 8
Primary Contact: Sheryl Lewis Blake, FACHE, Chief Executive Officer
COO: Carla Wilson–Neil, Chief Operating Officer
CFO: Connie Downs, Chief Financial Officer
CHR: Anita Henderson, Director Human Resources
Web address: www.pennockhealth.com
**Control:** Other not–for–profit (including NFP Corporation) **Service:** General Medical and Surgical

**Staffed Beds:** 58 **Admissions:** 2668 **Census:** 27 **Outpatient Visits:** 425369 **Births:** 371 **Total Expense ($000):** 56515 **Payroll Expense ($000):** 24473 **Personnel:** 444

## HILLSDALE—Hillsdale County

★ ○ **HILLSDALE COMMUNITY HEALTH CENTER (230037)**, 168 South Howell Street, Zip 49242–2081; tel. 517/437–4451, (Total facility includes 21 beds in nursing home–type unit) **A**9 10 11 12 13 19 **F**3 11 12 13 15 28 29 31 34 35 37 38 40 45 48 50 59 62 70 74 75 76 78 79 81 82 87 89 93 97 98 102 104 107 110 111 115 119 127 128 130 131 132 135 146 147 148 **P**6 8
Primary Contact: Duke Anderson, President and Chief Executive Officer
CFO: Valerie Fetters, Chief Financial Officer
CMO: Barry Collins, D.O., Chief of Staff
CIO: Steve Rausch, Manager Information Technology
CHR: Mike Pacheco, Human Resources Manager
CNO: Julie Walters, Chief Nursing Officer
Web address: www.hchc.com
**Control:** Other not–for–profit (including NFP Corporation) **Service:** General Medical and Surgical

**Staffed Beds:** 84 **Admissions:** 3506 **Census:** 53 **Outpatient Visits:** 123268 **Births:** 305 **Total Expense ($000):** 55904 **Payroll Expense ($000):** 21200 **Personnel:** 389

## HOLLAND—Ottawa County

★ ◇ **HOLLAND HOSPITAL (230072)**, 602 Michigan Avenue, Zip 49423–4999; tel. 616/392–5141, (Nonreporting) **A**9 10 21
Primary Contact: Dale Sowders, President and Chief Executive Officer
CFO: Terry L. Steele, Vice President Finance and Chief Financial Officer
CMO: William Vandervliet, M.D., Vice President Medical Affairs
CIO: Randy J. Paruch, Director, Information Systems
CHR: Chuck Kohlruss, Vice President Human Resources and Operations Support
CNO: Patti J. VanDort, MSN, President Nursing/Chief Nursing Officer
Web address: www.hollandhospital.org
**Control:** Other not–for–profit (including NFP Corporation) **Service:** General Medical and Surgical

**Staffed Beds:** 130

## HOWELL—Livingston County

✠ **ST. JOSEPH MERCY LIVINGSTON HOSPITAL (230069)**, 620 Byron Road, Zip 48843–1093; tel. 517/545–6000 **A**1 3 5 9 10 13 **F**3 5 8 11 15 18 28 29 30 31 34 35 40 41 42 45 51 54 56 57 59 62 63 64 65 68 70 74 75 77 78 79 81 82 83 84 85 86 87 93 97 100 104 107 108 110 111 114 115 119 120 129 130 131 132 135 141 145 146 147 148 **P**5 **S** Trinity Health, Livonia, MI
Primary Contact: Robert F. Casalou, President and Chief Executive Officer
COO: Michael J. Markel, MSN, Executive Director of Operations
CFO: Charles Hoffman, Vice President Financial Services and Chief Financial Officer
CMO: Mark Baumeier, M.D., Chief of Staff
CIO: Frank Rademacher, Director, Information Systems
CHR: Kenneth Antczak, Vice President Human Resources
CNO: Joyce Young, R.N., VP, Patient Services & Chief Nursing Officer
Web address: www.stjoeslivingston.org/livingston
**Control:** Church–operated, Nongovernment, not–for profit **Service:** General Medical and Surgical

**Staffed Beds:** 36 **Admissions:** 3212 **Census:** 29 **Outpatient Visits:** 307225 **Births:** 0 **Total Expense ($000):** 109899 **Payroll Expense ($000):** 38220 **Personnel:** 650

## IONIA—Ionia County

✠ **SPARROW IONIA HOSPITAL (231331)**, 479 Lafayette Street, Zip 48846–1834, Mailing Address: Box 1001, Zip 48846–6001; tel. 616/523–1400 **A**1 9 10 18 **F**3 12 15 29 31 34 35 40 45 50 54 57 59 64 65 69 70 74 75 77 78 79 81 85 89 93 107 108 110 115 119 127 129 130 131 146 148 **S** Sparrow Health System, Lansing, MI
Primary Contact: William Roeser, President and Chief Executive Officer
COO: George W. Rutherford, Vice President and Chief Operating Officer
CFO: Mark Brisboe, Vice President and Chief Financial Officer
CMO: Amy Jentz, M.D., Chief of Staff
CIO: Bob Neal, Director Information Technology
CHR: Jolene Jacobs, Director Human Resources
Web address: www.sparrow.org/sparrowionia
**Control:** Other not–for–profit (including NFP Corporation) **Service:** General Medical and Surgical

**Staffed Beds:** 25 **Admissions:** 516 **Census:** 4 **Outpatient Visits:** 55126 **Births:** 0 **Total Expense ($000):** 28215 **Payroll Expense ($000):** 12776 **Personnel:** 225

**MI**

*Many Facility Codes have changed. Please refer to the AHA Guide Code Chart.*
© 2013 AHA Guide

## IRON MOUNTAIN—Dickinson County

✠ **DICKINSON COUNTY HEALTHCARE SYSTEM (230055)**, 1721 South Stephenson Avenue, Zip 49801–3637; tel. 906/774–1313 **A**1 9 10 20 **F**3 11 13 15 17 18 28 29 31 34 35 40 45 46 51 53 56 57 59 61 62 64 67 68 70 74 75 76 77 79 81 85 86 87 89 91 92 93 96 97 107 108 110 111 114 115 119 121 123 127 129 130 131 132 133 135 145 146 148 **P**6
Primary Contact: John Schon, Administrator and Chief Executive Officer
COO: Jeff Gussert, Director Operations
CFO: Eileen Sparpana, Director Finance
CMO: Don Kube, M.D., Chief of Staff
CIO: Dean Decremer, Chief Information Officer
CHR: Paula Swartout, HR Manager
CNO: Susan Hadley, R.N., Director of Nursing
Web address: www.dchs.org
**Control:** County–Government, nonfederal **Service:** General Medical and Surgical

**Staffed Beds:** 96 **Admissions:** 3289 **Census:** 33 **Outpatient Visits:** 237979 **Births:** 438 **Total Expense ($000):** 85142 **Payroll Expense ($000):** 37860 **Personnel:** 613

✠ **OSCAR G. JOHNSON VETERANS AFFAIRS MEDICAL CENTER**, (Formerly Veterans Affairs Medical Center), 325 East H Street, Zip 49801–4792; tel. 906/774–3300, (Nonreporting) **A**1 9 **S** Department of Veterans Affairs, Washington, DC
Primary Contact: James W. Rice, Director
Web address: www.ironmountain.va.gov/
**Control:** Veterans Affairs, Government, federal **Service:** General Medical and Surgical

**Staffed Beds:** 17

**VETERANS AFFAIRS MEDICAL CENTER** See Oscar G. Johnson Veterans Affairs Medical Center

## IRON RIVER—Iron County

✠ **NORTHSTAR HEALTH SYSTEM (231318)**, 1400 West Ice Lake Road, Zip 49935–9526; tel. 906/265–6121 **A**1 9 10 18 **F**7 11 15 28 29 31 32 33 34 35 40 43 50 53 54 56 57 59 60 62 63 64 70 75 77 78 79 81 86 87 89 93 97 104 107 111 115 119 128 130 131 132 133 135 144 145 146 147 148
Primary Contact: Connie L. Koutouzos, R.N., MSN, Chief Executive Officer and President
COO: Robert Lindberg, R.N., Chief Operating Officer and Chief Nursing Officer
CFO: Glenn E. Dobson, Chief Financial Officer
CMO: Ronald Dalton, M.D., Chief Medical Officer
CMO: Kim Mahler, M.D., Chief Medical Officer
CHR: Carol Bastianello, Director Employee Services
Web address: www.northstarhs.org
**Control:** Other not–for–profit (including NFP Corporation) **Service:** General Medical and Surgical

**Staffed Beds:** 25 **Admissions:** 850 **Census:** 9 **Outpatient Visits:** 61486 **Births:** 0 **Total Expense ($000):** 38618 **Payroll Expense ($000):** 15267 **Personnel:** 281

## IRONWOOD—Gogebic County

✠ **ASPIRUS GRAND VIEW HOSPITAL (231333)**, N10561 Grand View Lane, Zip 49938–9622; tel. 906/932–2525 **A**1 9 10 18 **F**3 11 13 15 28 29 31 34 35 40 44 45 50 56 57 59 62 63 64 65 66 70 75 76 77 78 81 85 86 87 89 97 100 101 102 103 104 105 107 108 110 114 119 120 121 129 130 132 133 144 146 147 148 **P**6 **S** Aspirus, Inc., Wausau, WI
Primary Contact: Charles Nelson, Chief Executive Officer
COO: Paula L. Chermside, Chief Operating Officer
CFO: Charmaine Chiantello, Chief Financial Officer
CMO: Jeffrey Edwards, M.D., Chief Medical Staff
CIO: Ron Eyer, Manager Information Services
CHR: Keri Kartheiser, Manager Human Resources
Web address: www.gvh.org
**Control:** Other not–for–profit (including NFP Corporation) **Service:** General Medical and Surgical

**Staffed Beds:** 25 **Admissions:** 1031 **Census:** 10 **Outpatient Visits:** 63696 **Births:** 150 **Total Expense ($000):** 28612 **Payroll Expense ($000):** 10791 **Personnel:** 251

## ISHPEMING—Marquette County

★ **BELL HOSPITAL (231321)**, 901 Lakeshore Drive, Zip 49849–1367; tel. 906/486–4431 **A**9 10 18 **F**3 7 11 13 15 29 30 32 34 35 40 50 53 57 59 65 68 70 75 76 77 79 81 82 85 87 89 92 93 96 97 107 108 110 119 129 131 133 135 144 146 147 **P**6
Primary Contact: Floyd D. Bounds, Chief Executive Officer
COO: Barbara Larson, R.N., Chief Operating Officer
CFO: Darin Sizemore, Controller
CMO: Shahar Madjar, M.D., Chief of Staff
CHR: Ruth Solinski, Vice President Organizational Development
Web address: www.bellmemorial.org
**Control:** Other not–for–profit (including NFP Corporation) **Service:** General Medical and Surgical

**Staffed Beds:** 25 **Admissions:** 1335 **Census:** 8 **Outpatient Visits:** 83805 **Births:** 262 **Total Expense ($000):** 40812 **Payroll Expense ($000):** 16563 **Personnel:** 259

## JACKSON—Jackson County

✠ **ALLEGIANCE HEALTH (230092)**, 205 North East Avenue, Zip 49201–1753; tel. 517/788–4800, (Total facility includes 20 beds in nursing home–type unit) **A**1 2 3 5 9 10 **F**3 4 5 6 7 8 9 11 13 15 17 18 20 22 24 26 28 29 30 31 34 35 38 40 44 45 46 47 48 49 50 51 53 54 56 57 58 59 61 62 63 64 65 68 69 70 73 74 75 76 77 78 79 81 82 84 85 87 89 92 93 96 98 99 100 101 102 103 104 105 106 107 108 110 111 112 114 115 118 119 121 126 128 129 130 131 132 134 135 146 147 148 **P**6
Primary Contact: Georgia R. Fojtasek, President and Chief Executive Officer
COO: Karen Chaprnka, Senior Vice President and Chief Operating Officer
CFO: Jeanne Wickens, Chief Financial Officer
CMO: Ray King, M.D., Senior Vice President and Chief Medical Officer
CIO: Richard Warren, Vice President Health Information Systems
CHR: Cheryl Lamborn, Vice President Human Resources
CNO: Jacalyn A. Liebowitz, Vice President Patient Care Continuum & CNO
Web address: www.allegiancehealth.org
**Control:** Other not–for–profit (including NFP Corporation) **Service:** General Medical and Surgical

**Staffed Beds:** 303 **Admissions:** 18609 **Census:** 221 **Outpatient Visits:** 579257 **Births:** 1669 **Total Expense ($000):** 409952 **Payroll Expense ($000):** 180452 **Personnel:** 3238

✠ **CARELINK OF JACKSON (232036)**, 110 North Elm Avenue, Zip 49202–3595; tel. 517/787–1440, (Nonreporting) **A**1 9 10
Primary Contact: J. Mark Fall, Chief Executive Officer
CFO: Dale L. Friesen, Chief Financial Officer
CMO: Gregg Patten, M.D., Chief Medical Officer
Web address: www.carelinkofjackson.org
**Control:** Other not–for–profit (including NFP Corporation) **Service:** Long–Term Acute Care hospital

**Staffed Beds:** 44

**DUANE L. WATERS HOSPITAL**, 3857 Cooper Street, Zip 49201–7521; tel. 517/780–5600, (Nonreporting)
Primary Contact: Gerald De Voss, Acting Administrator
**Control:** State–Government, nonfederal **Service:** Hospital unit of an institution (prison hospital, college infimary, etc.)

**Staffed Beds:** 150

## KALAMAZOO—Kalamazoo County

✠ △ **BORGESS MEDICAL CENTER (230117)**, 1521 Gull Road, Zip 49048–1640; tel. 269/226–7000 **A**1 3 5 7 9 10 **F**1 3 7 8 9 11 12 13 15 17 18 20 22 24 26 28 29 30 31 33 34 35 37 38 39 40 43 44 45 46 49 50 53 54 56 57 58 59 60 61 64 68 70 74 75 76 77 78 79 81 82 84 85 86 87 90 91 92 93 94 96 97 98 99 100 101 102 103 104 105 107 108 110 114 115 118 119 126 129 130 131 132 135 144 146 147 148 **P**1 3 6 **S** Ascension Health, Saint Louis, MO
Primary Contact: Paul A. Spaude, FACHE, President and Chief Executive Officer
COO: Mark Anthony, Executive Vice President and Chief Operating Officer
CFO: Richard Felbinger, Senior Vice President and Chief Financial Officer
CMO: Anthony F. Oliva, D.O., Sr. Vice President & Chief Medical Officer
CIO: Donna Roach, Chief Information Officer
CHR: Laura Lentenbrink, Vice President, Human Resources
CNO: Lois J. Van Donselaar, R.N., Vice President & Chief Nursing Officer
Web address: www.borgess.com
**Control:** Church–operated, Nongovernment, not–for profit **Service:** General Medical and Surgical

**Staffed Beds:** 387 **Admissions:** 19429 **Census:** 246 **Outpatient Visits:** 497358 **Births:** 1369 **Total Expense ($000):** 452563 **Payroll Expense ($000):** 171266 **Personnel:** 2154

MI

---

**Hospital, Medicare Provider Number, Address, Telephone, Approval, Facility, and Physician Codes, Health Care System**

★ American Hospital Association (AHA) membership
☐ The Joint Commission accreditation   ◇ DNV Healthcare Inc. accreditation
○ Healthcare Facilities Accreditation Program
△ Commission on Accreditation of Rehabilitation Facilities (CARF) accreditation

✠ **BRONSON METHODIST HOSPITAL (230017)**, 601 John Street, Zip 49007–5346; tel. 269/341–6000, (Includes BRONSON VICKSBURG HOSPITAL, 13326 North Boulevard, Vicksburg, Zip 49097–1099; tel. 269/649–2321; Frank J. Sardone, President and Chief Executive Officer; CHILDREN'S HOSPITAL AT BRONSON, 601 John Street, Zip 49007–5341; tel. 269/341–7654) **A**1 3 5 9 10 **F**3 9 11 12 13 15 16 17 18 19 20 22 24 26 28 29 30 31 32 34 35 37 39 40 41 42 43 44 45 46 47 49 50 51 55 56 57 58 59 60 61 62 64 65 66 68 70 71 72 74 75 76 77 78 79 80 81 82 83 84 85 86 87 88 89 92 93 97 102 107 108 110 111 114 115 117 118 119 126 130 131 132 134 135 141 145 146 147 148 **P**6 **S** Bronson Healthcare Group, Inc., Kalamazoo, MI
Primary Contact: Frank J. Sardone, President and Chief Executive Officer
COO: Kenneth L. Taft, Executive Vice President and Chief Operating Officer
CFO: Mary Meitz, Vice President Finance
CMO: Scott Larson, M.D., Vice President Medical Affairs and Chief Medical Officer
CHR: John Hayden, Vice President and Chief Human Resources Officer
Web address: www.bronsonhealth.com
**Control:** Other not–for–profit (including NFP Corporation) **Service:** General Medical and Surgical

> **Staffed Beds:** 415 **Admissions:** 21519 **Census:** 277 **Outpatient Visits:** 586394 **Births:** 3465 **Total Expense ($000):** 578263 **Payroll Expense ($000):** 235177 **Personnel:** 3168

☐ **KALAMAZOO PSYCHIATRIC HOSPITAL (234026)**, 1312 Oakland Drive, Zip 49008–1205; tel. 269/337–3000 **A**1 9 10 12 13 **F**3 39 50 53 56 65 75 77 86 87 97 98 101 103 130 132 135 143 146 **P**6
Primary Contact: James J. Coleman, Ed.D., Director
COO: James J. Coleman, Ed.D., Director
CFO: Sue Glenn, Director Administrative Services
CMO: N. Gajare, M.D., Chief Clinical Affairs
CIO: Gerry Wood, Information Technologist
CHR: Kerry Bloom, Director Human Resources
**Control:** State–Government, nonfederal **Service:** Psychiatric

> **Staffed Beds:** 203 **Admissions:** 480 **Census:** 187 **Outpatient Visits:** 0 **Births:** 0 **Payroll Expense ($000):** 26074 **Personnel:** 506

### KALKASKA—Kalkaska County

★ **KALKASKA MEMORIAL HEALTH CENTER (231301)**, 419 South Coral Street, Zip 49646–2503; tel. 231/258–7500, (Total facility includes 88 beds in nursing home–type unit) **A**9 10 18 **F**2 7 10 15 28 34 35 40 44 45 50 56 57 59 60 64 65 66 78 81 84 87 93 97 107 110 119 127 128 129 130 132 134 143 144 146 147 148 **S** Munson Healthcare, Traverse City, MI
Primary Contact: James D. Austin, FACHE, Administrator
COO: Sheila Atwood, R.N., Chief Operating Officer
CMO: Jeremy Holmes, D.O., Chief of Staff
CHR: Kimberly Babcock, Administrator Human Resources
CNO: Christine Bissonette, R.N., Chief Nursing Officer
Web address: www.munsonhealthcare.org
**Control:** Hospital district or authority, Government, nonfederal **Service:** General Medical and Surgical

> **Staffed Beds:** 96 **Admissions:** 170 **Census:** 84 **Outpatient Visits:** 63471 **Births:** 0 **Total Expense ($000):** 30475 **Payroll Expense ($000):** 11027 **Personnel:** 239

### L'ANSE—L'Anse County

☐ **BARAGA COUNTY MEMORIAL HOSPITAL (231307)**, 18341 U.S. Highway 41, Zip 49946–8024; tel. 906/524–3300 **A**1 9 10 18 **F**3 5 11 15 28 31 34 40 45 53 57 59 62 63 64 74 77 78 79 81 82 84 85 89 93 107 108 110 114 118 119 127 130 132 133 146 **P**6
Primary Contact: Tim E. Zwickey, Chief Executive Officer
CFO: Gail Jestila–Peltola, Chief Financial Officer
CMO: Todd Ingram, M.D., Chief of Staff
CIO: Taylor Makela, Director Information Technology
CHR: Carol Seppanen, Director Human Resources
CNO: Becky D'Agostino, R.N., Director of Nursing
Web address: www.bcmh.org
**Control:** County–Government, nonfederal **Service:** General Medical and Surgical

> **Staffed Beds:** 15 **Admissions:** 523 **Census:** 5 **Outpatient Visits:** 25023 **Births:** 0 **Total Expense ($000):** 18725 **Payroll Expense ($000):** 6949 **Personnel:** 102

### LAKEVIEW—Montcalm County

**SPECTRUM HEALTH KELSEY HOSPITAL** See Spectrum Health United Hospital, Greenville

### LANSING—Ingham County

★ ○ **McLAREN GREATER LANSING (230167)**, 401 West Greenlawn Avenue, Zip 48910–2819; tel. 517/975–6000, (Includes INGHAM REGIONAL MEDICAL CENTER, GREENLAWN CAMPUS, 401 West Greenlawn Avenue, tel. 517/334–2121; McLAREN ORTHOPEDIC HOSPITAL, 2727 South Pennsylvania Avenue, Zip 48910–3490; tel. 517/975–6000; Rick Wright, President and Chief Executive Officer) **A**2 3 5 9 10 11 12 13 **F**3 5 8 11 13 15 17 18 20 24 25 26 28 29 30 31 34 35 37 40 44 45 49 50 51 55 56 57 58 59 60 61 63 64 65 66 70 74 75 76 77 78 79 80 81 82 83 84 85 86 87 89 90 93 97 98 100 101 102 103 104 105 107 108 110 111 114 115 116 117 118 119 120 121 124 126 129 130 131 132 135 146 147 148 **P**8 **S** McLaren Health Care Corporation, Flint, MI
Primary Contact: Rick Wright, President and Chief Executive Officer
CFO: Kevin Lanciotti, Chief Financial Officer
CMO: Thomas Petroff, D.O., Vice President Medical Affairs
CHR: Laurie Brewis, Vice President Human Resources
Web address: www.irmc.org
**Control:** Other not–for–profit (including NFP Corporation) **Service:** General Medical and Surgical

> **Staffed Beds:** 322 **Admissions:** 15352 **Census:** 180 **Outpatient Visits:** 348851 **Births:** 1268 **Total Expense ($000):** 286512 **Payroll Expense ($000):** 112266 **Personnel:** 1757

✠ ○ △ **SPARROW HOSPITAL (230230)**, 1215 East Michigan Avenue, Zip 48912–1811; tel. 517/364–1000, (Includes SPARROW REGIONAL CHILDREN'S CENTER, 1215 East Michigan Avenue, tel. 517/364–1000) **A**1 2 3 5 7 9 10 11 12 13 **F**2 3 4 5 11 12 13 15 17 18 20 22 24 26 28 29 30 31 32 34 35 36 38 40 41 43 44 45 46 49 50 51 54 55 56 57 58 59 60 63 64 65 66 68 70 72 74 75 76 77 78 79 81 82 84 85 86 87 88 89 90 92 93 96 97 98 99 100 101 102 103 104 105 107 108 110 114 115 117 118 119 120 121 123 124 126 128 129 130 131 132 135 143 144 146 147 148 **P**1 6 **S** Sparrow Health System, Lansing, MI
Primary Contact: Dennis A. Swan, JD, FACHE, President and Chief Executive Officer
COO: Joseph Ruth, Executive Vice President and Chief Operating Officer
CFO: Paula Reichle, Executive Vice President and Chief Operating Officer
CMO: Brian D. Schroeder, M.D., Senior Vice President Medical Affairs
CIO: Thomas Bres, Vice President and Chief Information Officer
CHR: Donald Davis, Vice President Human Resources
Web address: www.sparrow.org
**Control:** Other not–for–profit (including NFP Corporation) **Service:** General Medical and Surgical

> **Staffed Beds:** 638 **Admissions:** 32734 **Census:** 450 **Outpatient Visits:** 641566 **Births:** 4209 **Total Expense ($000):** 762320 **Payroll Expense ($000):** 351219 **Personnel:** 5136

★ ○ **SPARROW SPECIALTY HOSPITAL (232037)**, 1210 West Saginaw Street, Zip 48915–1927; Mailing Address: P.O. Box 85201, Zip 48915–1927; tel. 517/364–6800 **A**9 10 11 **F**1 3 29 30 36 60 68 85 100 101 119 130 148 **S** Sparrow Health System, Lansing, MI
Primary Contact: Kira Carter–Robertson, President and Chief Executive Officer
CFO: David Przybylski, Interim Controller
CMO: Paul Entler, D.O., Medical Director
CHR: LaChelle Flowers, Administrative Assistant Human Resources
CHR: Lucy M. Vail, Director HR Partner Relationships
CNO: Tina Gross, Director of Clinical Services
Web address: www.sparrowspecialty.org
**Control:** Other not–for–profit (including NFP Corporation) **Service:** Long–Term Acute Care hospital

> **Staffed Beds:** 36 **Admissions:** 304 **Census:** 25 **Outpatient Visits:** 0 **Births:** 0 **Total Expense ($000):** 12114 **Payroll Expense ($000):** 5893 **Personnel:** 132

### LAPEER—Lapeer County

★ ○ **McLAREN LAPEER REGION (230193)**, 1375 North Main Street, Zip 48446–1350; tel. 810/667–5500, (Total facility includes 19 beds in nursing home–type unit) **A**2 9 10 11 **F**3 11 13 15 18 20 28 29 30 31 34 40 45 46 49 50 51 54 56 57 59 64 68 70 74 75 76 77 78 79 81 82 83 85 86 87 92 93 97 98 102 107 108 111 114 115 119 123 124 128 129 130 131 132 135 144 146 148 **S** McLaren Health Care Corporation, Flint, MI
Primary Contact: Barton Buxton, Ed.D., President and Chief Executive Officer
COO: Thomas Mee, R.N., Vice President Operations
CFO: Mary Beth Callahan, Chief Financial Officer
CMO: Gary Salem, M.D., Vice President Medical Affairs
CIO: Gayle Consiglio, Chief Information Officer
CHR: Amy Dorr, Vice President Human Resources
Web address: www.lapeerregional.org
**Control:** Other not–for–profit (including NFP Corporation) **Service:** General Medical and Surgical

> **Staffed Beds:** 157 **Admissions:** 7598 **Census:** 89 **Outpatient Visits:** 129476 **Births:** 553 **Total Expense ($000):** 109177 **Payroll Expense ($000):** 41236 **Personnel:** 644

*Many Facility Codes have changed. Please refer to the AHA Guide Code Chart.* © 2013 AHA Guide

MI

MI

## LAURIUM—Houghton County

☒ **ASPIRUS KEWEENAW HOSPITAL (231319)**, 205 Osceola Street,
Zip 49913–2134; tel. 906/337–6500 **A**1 9 10 18 **F**3 7 11 13 15 17 18 28 29
30 31 35 40 45 52 53 56 57 59 61 62 63 70 76 78 79 81 87 89 93 107
108 110 115 119 127 129 130 131 132 133 135 145 146 147 **P**6 **S** Aspirus,
Inc., Wausau, WI
Primary Contact: Charles Nelson, Chief Executive Officer
COO: Michael Hauswirth, Chief Operating Officer
CFO: Craig Aittama, Chief Financial Officer
CMO: Glenn Kauppila, D.O., Chief of Staff
CIO: Dave Olsson, Director of Marketing
CHR: Chad D. Rowe, Director Human Resources
CNO: Grace Tousignant, R.N., Chief Nursing Officer
Web address: www.aspiruskeweenaw.org
**Control:** Other not–for–profit (including NFP Corporation) **Service:** General
Medical and Surgical

**Staffed Beds:** 25 **Admissions:** 1074 **Census:** 10 **Outpatient Visits:** 37031
**Births:** 86 **Total Expense ($000):** 34720 **Payroll Expense ($000):** 17419
**Personnel:** 357

## LINCOLN PARK—Wayne County

☐ **VIBRA HOSPITAL OF SOUTHEASTERN MICHIGAN (232019)**, 26400 West
Outer Drive, Zip 48146–2088; tel. 313/386–2000, (Nonreporting) **A**1 9 10
**S** Vibra Healthcare, Mechanicsburg, PA
Primary Contact: Scott Deig, FACHE, Chief Executive Officer
COO: Cindy Brassinger, Chief Operating Officer
CFO: Douglas Morris, Chief Financial Officer
CHR: Karen D. Gray, Director Human Resources
Web address: www.vhsemichigan.com/
**Control:** Corporation, Investor–owned, for–profit **Service:** Long–Term Acute Care
hospital

**Staffed Beds:** 140

## LIVONIA—Wayne County

☒ **ST. MARY MERCY HOSPITAL (230002)**, 36475 Five Mile Road,
Zip 48154–1988; tel. 734/655–4800 **A**1 2 9 10 **F**3 4 5 12 13 15 18 20 22 26
29 30 31 34 35 38 40 45 46 47 49 50 51 56 57 58 59 64 68 70 74 75 76
78 79 81 83 84 85 87 90 93 98 100 101 102 103 104 107 108 110 111
114 115 116 117 118 119 120 121 126 129 130 132 135 143 145 146 147
148 **P**6 **S** Trinity Health, Livonia, MI
Primary Contact: David A. Spivey, President and Chief Executive Officer
COO: C. W. Lauderbach, Jr., Vice President Clinical Services
CFO: Mike Samyn, Vice President, Finance and Chief Financial Officer
CIO: Janet Yim, Director Information Services
CHR: Kenneth Antczak, Vice President Human Resources
Web address: www.stmarymercy.org
**Control:** Church–operated, Nongovernment, not–for profit **Service:** General
Medical and Surgical

**Staffed Beds:** 289 **Admissions:** 17098 **Census:** 217 **Outpatient Visits:**
180120 **Births:** 694 **Total Expense ($000):** 220384 **Payroll Expense**
**($000):** 89690 **Personnel:** 1431

## LUDINGTON—Mason County

◇ **MEMORIAL MEDICAL CENTER OF WEST MICHIGAN (230110)**, One Atkinson
Drive, Zip 49431–1906; tel. 231/843–2591 **A**9 10 20 21 **F**8 11 13 15 17 28
29 34 35 40 45 49 51 57 59 62 68 70 75 76 77 78 79 81 82 85 92 93 98
100 102 103 107 108 110 111 114 118 119 129 130 131 132 135 146 147
Primary Contact: Mark Vipperman, President and Chief Executive Officer
COO: Timothy Heinrich, Senior Vice President and Chief Operating Officer
CFO: Kerri Nelson, Chief Financial Officer
CMO: Stanley Seuferer, D.O., Chief of Staff
CIO: Daryl Crowley, Director Information Services
CHR: James Wood, Director Human Resources
Web address: www.mmcwm.org
**Control:** Other not–for–profit (including NFP Corporation) **Service:** General
Medical and Surgical

**Staffed Beds:** 80 **Admissions:** 2204 **Census:** 26 **Outpatient Visits:** 94802
**Births:** 358 **Total Expense ($000):** 57388 **Payroll Expense ($000):** 22824
**Personnel:** 477

## MADISON HEIGHTS—Oakland County

**DMC SURGERY HOSPITAL** See Harper University Hospital/Hutzel Women's
Hospital, Detroit

## MANISTEE—Manistee County

**WEST SHORE MEDICAL CENTER (231335)**, 1465 East Parkdale Avenue,
Zip 49660–9709; tel. 231/398–1000 **A**9 10 18 **F**3 7 11 13 15 17 28 29 32
34 39 40 46 53 54 57 59 74 75 76 77 79 81 85 86 93 97 107 108 110 111
115 118 119 129 132 135 146 147 148 **P**6
Primary Contact: James Barker, President
COO: Donn J. Lemmer, Vice President Finance
CFO: Donn J. Lemmer, Vice President Finance
Web address: www.westshoremedcenter.org
**Control:** County–Government, nonfederal **Service:** General Medical and Surgical

**Staffed Beds:** 25 **Admissions:** 1553 **Census:** 14 **Outpatient Visits:** 91390
**Births:** 175 **Total Expense ($000):** 51494 **Payroll Expense ($000):** 23442
**Personnel:** 311

## MANISTIQUE—Schoolcraft County

★ **SCHOOLCRAFT MEMORIAL HOSPITAL (231303)**, 500 Main Street,
Zip 49854–1599; tel. 906/341–3200 **A**9 10 18 **F**3 10 11 15 28 29 30 31 32
34 35 40 41 44 45 50 53 56 57 59 62 63 64 65 70 75 77 78 79 81 84 85
86 87 89 93 97 107 108 110 114 118 119 127 128 129 130 132 133 144
146 147 148 **P**6
Primary Contact: George H. Montgomery, Chief Executive Officer
CMO: Randy Olli, M.D., Chief Medical Officer
CIO: Kent La Croix, IT Supervisor
CHR: Gina Lindquist, Director Human Resources
CNO: Cindy Olli, R.N., Chief Nursing Officer
Web address: www.scmh.org
**Control:** County–Government, nonfederal **Service:** General Medical and Surgical

**Staffed Beds:** 18 **Admissions:** 474 **Census:** 5 **Outpatient Visits:** 39695
**Births:** 0 **Total Expense ($000):** 22834 **Payroll Expense ($000):** 11402
**Personnel:** 189

## MARLETTE—Sanilac County

☐ **MARLETTE REGIONAL HOSPITAL (231330)**, 2770 Main Street,
Zip 48453–1141, Mailing Address: P.O. Box 307, Zip 48453–0307;
tel. 989/635–4000, (Nonreporting) **A**1 9 10 18
Primary Contact: Daniel Babcock, Chief Executive Officer
CFO: James L. Singles, Chief Financial Officer
CMO: William Starbird, M.D., Chief of Staff
CIO: Kyle Estep, Manager Information Technology
CHR: Connie Kennedy, Director Human Resources
Web address: www.marletteregionalhospital.org
**Control:** Other not–for–profit (including NFP Corporation) **Service:** General
Medical and Surgical

**Staffed Beds:** 74

## MARQUETTE—Marquette County

☒ **MARQUETTE GENERAL HEALTH SYSTEM (230054)**, 580 West College
Avenue, Zip 49855–2736; tel. 906/228–9440 **A**1 2 3 5 9 10 13 **F**3 4 5 7 8 11
12 13 14 15 17 18 20 22 24 26 28 29 30 31 32 34 35 37 38 40 43 45 46
48 49 50 51 55 56 57 58 59 60 62 63 64 65 68 70 72 74 75 76 77 78 79
81 82 85 86 87 90 93 94 98 99 100 101 102 103 104 107 108 110 111
114 115 116 117 118 119 120 121 122 123 124 127 129 130 131 132 135
143 145 146 147 148 **P**6
Primary Contact: A. Gary Muller, FACHE, President and Chief Executive Officer
COO: Edward D. Banos, Chief Operating Officer
CFO: Jerry L. Worden, Chief Financial Officer
CMO: Tom Noren, M.D., Chief Medical Officer
CIO: David Graser, Chief Information Officer
CHR: David Smith, Senior Director Human Resources
CNO: Dagmar Ann Raica, R.N., Chief Nursing Officer
Web address: www.mgh.org
**Control:** Other not–for–profit (including NFP Corporation) **Service:** General
Medical and Surgical

**Staffed Beds:** 268 **Admissions:** 9865 **Census:** 142 **Outpatient Visits:**
239851 **Births:** 724 **Total Expense ($000):** 316393 **Payroll Expense**
**($000):** 126564 **Personnel:** 2045

---

## MARSHALL—Calhoun County

★ ◇ **OAKLAWN HOSPITAL (230217)**, 200 North Madison Street, Zip 49068–1199; tel. 269/781–4271 **A**9 10 21 **F**3 11 13 15 18 19 26 28 29 30 31 32 34 35 36 37 38 40 44 45 46 48 50 53 54 57 58 59 60 62 63 64 65 68 69 70 74 75 76 77 78 79 81 82 85 86 87 89 93 94 97 98 99 100 101 102 103 104 105 106 107 108 110 111 114 115 117 118 119 126 129 130 131 132 135 146 147 148 **P**1 6
Primary Contact: Ginger Williams, M.D., President and Chief Executive Officer
CFO: Colleen Koppenhaver, Chief Financial Officer
CIO: Natalie Spivak, Director Information Services
CHR: Jan Sinclair, Director Personnel
Web address: www.oaklawnhospital.org
**Control:** Other not–for–profit (including NFP Corporation) **Service:** General Medical and Surgical

**Staffed Beds:** 78 **Admissions:** 3805 **Census:** 40 **Outpatient Visits:** 162707 **Births:** 686 **Total Expense ($000):** 107737 **Payroll Expense ($000):** 48081 **Personnel:** 825

## MIDLAND—Midland County

✠ **MIDMICHIGAN MEDICAL CENTER–MIDLAND (230222)**, 4000 Wellness Drive, Zip 48670–2000; tel. 989/839–3000 **A**1 2 3 5 9 10 20 **F**3 7 11 12 13 15 17 18 20 22 24 26 28 29 30 31 34 40 44 45 46 48 49 50 53 54 55 57 58 59 64 65 68 70 74 75 76 77 78 79 81 85 86 87 89 92 93 96 97 98 100 101 102 104 107 108 110 111 115 118 123 124 126 129 130 131 132 135 146 147 148 **S** MidMichigan Health, Midland, MI
Primary Contact: Gregory H. Rogers, President
CFO: Scott D. Currie, Vice President and Chief Financial Officer
CMO: James Bicknell, M.D., Medical Director
CIO: C. Harlan Goodrich, Vice President and Chief Information Officer
Web address: www.midmichigan.org
**Control:** Other not–for–profit (including NFP Corporation) **Service:** General Medical and Surgical

**Staffed Beds:** 265 **Admissions:** 12710 **Census:** 123 **Outpatient Visits:** 286884 **Births:** 1169 **Total Expense ($000):** 331304 **Payroll Expense ($000):** 97067 **Personnel:** 1814

## MONROE—Monroe County

✠ **MERCY MEMORIAL HOSPITAL SYSTEM (230099)**, 718 North Macomb Street, Zip 48162–7815; tel. 734/240–8400, (Total facility includes 70 beds in nursing home–type unit) **A**1 2 9 10 **F**3 5 8 11 13 15 18 20 28 29 30 34 35 38 40 43 44 45 46 49 50 51 54 56 57 59 62 63 64 65 69 70 71 74 75 76 77 79 81 84 85 86 87 89 92 93 97 98 99 100 101 102 103 104 107 108 109 110 111 113 114 115 116 117 118 119 126 129 130 131 132 135 144 145 146 147 148 **P**6
Primary Contact: Annette S. Phillips, President and Chief Executive Officer
CFO: Thomas Schilling, Chief Financial Officer and Senior Vice President Finance
CMO: Mark Sherrard, D.O., Chief Medical Officer and Senior Vice President Medical Affairs
CIO: Bruce Kelly, Chief Information Officer
CNO: Pamela A. Urbanski, R.N., Chief Nursing Officer, Senior Vice President, Patient Care Services
Web address: www.mercymemorial.org
**Control:** Other not–for–profit (including NFP Corporation) **Service:** General Medical and Surgical

**Staffed Beds:** 179 **Admissions:** 9856 **Census:** 112 **Outpatient Visits:** 177453 **Births:** 856 **Total Expense ($000):** 161141 **Payroll Expense ($000):** 70180 **Personnel:** 1299

## MOUNT CLEMENS—Macomb County

**HENRY FORD MACOMB HOSPITAL – MOUNT CLEMENS CAMPUS** See Henry Ford Macomb Hospitals, Clinton Township

★ ○ **MCLAREN MACOMB (230227)**, 1000 Harrington Boulevard, Zip 48043–2992; tel. 586/493–8000 **A**2 9 10 11 12 13 **F**3 7 8 12 13 15 18 20 22 24 26 28 29 30 31 34 35 36 37 39 40 42 43 45 47 48 49 50 51 52 54 57 58 59 60 61 62 63 64 65 66 68 70 71 74 75 76 77 78 79 81 82 85 86 87 89 92 93 97 100 102 107 108 109 110 111 112 114 115 116 117 118 119 120 121 124 126 129 130 131 132 135 145 146 147 148 **P**8 **S** McLaren Health Care Corporation, Flint, MI
Primary Contact: Mark S. O'Halla, President and Chief Executive Officer
COO: Sue Durst, R.N., Vice President Plant Operations
CMO: Michael K. Smith, D.O., Vice President Medical Affairs
CNO: Patricia Rosenberg, R.N., Vice President Patient Care Services and Chief Nursing Officer
Web address: www.mcrmc.org
**Control:** Other not–for–profit (including NFP Corporation) **Service:** General Medical and Surgical

**Staffed Beds:** 288 **Admissions:** 14341 **Census:** 156 **Outpatient Visits:** 154669 **Births:** 944 **Total Expense ($000):** 270120 **Payroll Expense ($000):** 106712 **Personnel:** 1661

✠ **SELECT SPECIALTY HOSPITAL–MACOMB COUNTY (232023)**, 215 North Avenue, Zip 48043–1700; tel. 586/307–9000, (Nonreporting) **A**1 9 10 **S** Select Medical Corporation, Mechanicsburg, PA
Primary Contact: Jon P. O'Malley, Chief Executive Officer
Web address: www.selectspecialtyhospitals.com/company/locations/macomb.aspx
**Control:** Corporation, Investor–owned, for–profit **Service:** Long–Term Acute Care hospital

**Staffed Beds:** 30

## MOUNT PLEASANT—Isabella County

★ ○ **MCLAREN CENTRAL MICHIGAN (230080)**, 1221 South Drive, Zip 48858–3257; tel. 989/772–6700 **A**9 10 11 **F**3 12 13 15 18 20 22 26 28 29 30 31 34 35 40 44 45 48 49 50 54 57 59 62 64 65 68 70 74 75 76 77 78 79 81 82 85 86 87 89 96 97 107 108 110 111 114 117 118 119 120 121 123 124 129 130 131 132 144 145 146 147 **P**1 **S** McLaren Health Care Corporation, Flint, MI
Primary Contact: William P. Lawrence, President and Chief Executive Officer
CFO: Gregg Beeg, Chief Financial Officer
CMO: Ashok Vashishta, M.D., Vice President Medical Affairs
CIO: Nicolette Zalud, Customer Site Manager
CHR: Carolyn Potter, Vice President Human Resources
CNO: Sheri Myers, Vice President Patient Care Services
Web address: www.cmch.org
**Control:** Other not–for–profit (including NFP Corporation) **Service:** General Medical and Surgical

**Staffed Beds:** 78 **Admissions:** 3802 **Census:** 30 **Outpatient Visits:** 217697 **Births:** 552 **Total Expense ($000):** 85389 **Payroll Expense ($000):** 38187 **Personnel:** 596

## MUNISING—Alger County

**MUNISING MEMORIAL HOSPITAL (231308)**, 1500 Sand Point Road, Zip 49862–1406; tel. 906/387–4110, (Nonreporting) **A**9 10 18
Primary Contact: Kevin P. Calhoun, Chief Executive Officer
CFO: Barb Trombley, Director Financial Services
CMO: Christine Krueger, M.D., Chief of Staff
CHR: Melissa Hall, Human Resources
Web address: www.munisingmemorial.org
**Control:** Other not–for–profit (including NFP Corporation) **Service:** General Medical and Surgical

**Staffed Beds:** 25

## MUSKEGON—Muskegon County

✠ **GREAT LAKES SPECIALTY HOSPITAL–MUSKEGON (232021)**, (Formerly Great Lakes Specialty Hospital–Hackley Campus), 1700 Clinton Street, South 2, Zip 49442–5502; tel. 231/728–5811, (Nonreporting) **A**1 9 10 **S** Select Medical Corporation, Mechanicsburg, PA
Primary Contact: Mark Holcomb, Administrator
Web address: www.selectmedical.com
**Control:** Corporation, Investor–owned, for–profit **Service:** Long–Term Acute Care hospital

**Staffed Beds:** 31

**GREAT LAKES SPECIALTY HOSPITAL–MUSKEGON** See Great Lakes Specialty Hospital–Hackley Campus

✠ **MERCY HEALTH PARTNERS, HACKLEY CAMPUS (230066)**, 1700 Clinton Street, Zip 49442–5502, Mailing Address: P.O. Box 3302, Zip 49443–3302; tel. 231/726–3511 **A**1 2 9 10 **F**3 11 12 13 15 26 29 30 35 39 40 45 49 50 51 53 54 57 59 61 64 68 70 74 76 77 79 81 82 84 85 87 89 90 91 93 96 97 98 99 100 101 102 103 104 105 106 107 108 109 111 114 115 116 117 118 119 127 144 146 147 148 **S** Trinity Health, Livonia, MI
Primary Contact: Roger Spoelman, President and Chief Executive Officer
COO: Greg Loomis, Chief Operating Officer
CFO: Gary Allore, Chief Financial Officer
CMO: F. Remington Sprague, M.D., Chief Medical Officer
CIO: William Stefl, Director Information Systems
Web address: www.mercyhealthmuskegon.com
**Control:** Other not–for–profit (including NFP Corporation) **Service:** General Medical and Surgical

**Staffed Beds:** 213 **Admissions:** 8953 **Census:** 97 **Outpatient Visits:** 272622 **Births:** 2135 **Total Expense ($000):** 163105 **Payroll Expense ($000):** 59451 **Personnel:** 1093

*Many Facility Codes have changed. Please refer to the AHA Guide Code Chart.*
© 2013 AHA Guide

MI

☒ ○ **MERCY HEALTH PARTNERS, MERCY CAMPUS (230004)**, 1500 East Sherman Boulevard, Zip 49444–1849; tel. 231/672–2000, (Includes MERCY HEALTH PARTNERS–MUSKEGON GENERAL CAMPUS, 1700 Oak Avenue, Zip 49442; tel. 231/672–3311) **A**1 2 9 10 11 12 13 **F**3 11 12 15 18 20 22 24 26 28 29 30 31 34 35 40 44 50 51 53 54 56 57 58 59 64 68 70 74 75 77 78 79 81 82 84 85 86 87 91 93 94 97 107 108 111 114 115 116 117 118 119 120 121 122 123 124 129 130 131 132 135 144 146 147 148 **P**6 8 **S** Trinity Health, Livonia, MI
Primary Contact: Roger Spoelman, President and Chief Executive Officer
COO: Greg Loomis, Chief Operation Officer
CFO: Gary Allore, Chief Financial Officer
CMO: F. Remington Sprague, M.D., Chief Medical Officer
Web address: www.mghp.com
**Control:** Other not–for–profit (including NFP Corporation) **Service:** General Medical and Surgical

**Staffed Beds:** 188 **Admissions:** 9329 **Census:** 104 **Outpatient Visits:** 635401 **Births:** 0 **Total Expense ($000):** 284422 **Payroll Expense ($000):** 121615 **Personnel:** 1855

### NEW BALTIMORE—Macomb County

**HARBOR OAKS HOSPITAL (234021)**, 35031 23 Mile Road, Zip 48047–3649; tel. 586/725–5777, (Nonreporting) **A**9 10 **S** Acadia Healthcare Company, Inc., Franklin, TN
Primary Contact: Sari Abromovich, Chief Executive Officer
CFO: Michael Ferguson, Chief Financial Officer
CMO: James D. Adamo, M.D., Medical Director
CHR: DeShawna Boden, Director Human Resources
Web address: www.harboroaks.com
**Control:** Corporation, Investor–owned, for–profit **Service:** Psychiatric

**Staffed Beds:** 45

### NEWBERRY—Luce County

☒ ◇ **HELEN NEWBERRY JOY HOSPITAL (231304)**, 502 West Harrie Street, Zip 49868–1209; tel. 906/293–9200, (Includes HELEN NEWBERRY JOY HOSPITAL ANNEX ), (Total facility includes 48 beds in nursing home–type unit) **A**1 9 10 18 21 **F**15 28 29 30 31 32 34 35 36 38 40 44 45 53 57 59 63 64 65 75 78 81 85 86 87 93 97 107 108 114 118 119 127 128 129 130 131 132 133 134 135 143 144 146 148 **P**6
Primary Contact: Scott Pillion, Chief Executive Officer
CMO: Raghu Rao, M.D., Chief of Staff
CIO: Michelle Sears, Director Information Systems
CHR: Roger Bergh, Director Human Resources
Web address: www.hnjh.org
**Control:** County–Government, nonfederal **Service:** General Medical and Surgical

**Staffed Beds:** 73 **Admissions:** 622 **Census:** 51 **Outpatient Visits:** 65749 **Births:** 0 **Total Expense ($000):** 30274 **Payroll Expense ($000):** 14153 **Personnel:** 307

### NORTHVILLE—Wayne County

☐ **HAWTHORN CENTER**, 18471 Haggerty Road, Zip 48168–9575; tel. 248/735–6771, (Nonreporting) **A**1 9
Primary Contact: Roy Kelly, Facility Director
CIO: Robert W. Bailey, Chief Information Officer
**Control:** State–Government, nonfederal **Service:** Children's hospital psychiatric

**Staffed Beds:** 69

### NOVI—Oakland County

**PROVIDENCE PARK HOSPITAL** See Providence Hospital, Southfield

### ONTONAGON—Ontonagon County

☒ **ASPIRUS ONTONAGON HOSPITAL (231309)**, 601 South Seventh Street, Zip 49953–1459; tel. 906/884–8000, (Nonreporting) **A**1 9 10 18 **S** Aspirus, Inc., Wausau, WI
Primary Contact: Charles Nelson, Chief Executive Officer
COO: Michael Hauswirth, Chief Operating Officer
CFO: Craig Aittama, Chief Financial Officer
CMO: John Austin, M.D., Director Medical Staff
CHR: Gina Linna, Manager Human Resources
CNO: Deanna Wilson, VP Patient Care Services/Site Manager
Web address: www.aspirus–ontonagon.org
**Control:** City–Government, nonfederal **Service:** General Medical and Surgical

**Staffed Beds:** 18

### OWOSSO—Shiawassee County

☒ **MEMORIAL HEALTHCARE (230121)**, 826 West King Street, Zip 48867–2120; tel. 989/723–5211, (Total facility includes 17 beds in nursing home–type unit) **A**1 2 5 9 10 **F**11 12 13 15 28 29 30 31 32 34 35 36 40 45 46 47 49 50 51 56 57 58 59 62 63 64 65 69 70 74 75 76 78 79 81 82 85 87 89 93 98 100 101 102 103 107 108 111 115 119 127 128 129 130 131 132 143 144 146 148 **P**6 7
Primary Contact: Brian Long, Interim President and Chief Executive Officer
CFO: Brian Long, Vice President Finance
CMO: Wael Salman, M.D., Vice President Medical Affairs
CIO: Frank Fear, Chief Information Officer
CHR: Ruthann Liagre, Vice President Human Resources
CNO: Dawn Blackwell, R.N., VP of Patient Care Services
Web address: www.memorialhealthcare.org
**Control:** Other not–for–profit (including NFP Corporation) **Service:** General Medical and Surgical

**Staffed Beds:** 134 **Admissions:** 3747 **Census:** 62 **Outpatient Visits:** 361703 **Births:** 451 **Total Expense ($000):** 102425 **Payroll Expense ($000):** 45234 **Personnel:** 905

### PAW PAW—Van Buren County

☒ **BRONSON LAKEVIEW HOSPITAL (231332)**, 408 Hazen Street, Zip 49079–1019, Mailing Address: P.O. Box 209, Zip 49079–0209; tel. 269/657–3141 **A**1 10 18 **F**3 6 11 15 29 30 34 35 40 44 56 57 59 64 65 66 68 74 75 77 79 81 82 85 86 87 93 98 100 101 102 103 107 110 114 119 127 129 130 146 147 148 **P**6 **S** Bronson Healthcare Group, Inc., Kalamazoo, MI
Primary Contact: Sally L. Berglin, Chief Executive Officer
COO: Sally L. Berglin, Vice President
CMO: Ravinder P. Mediratta, M.D., Chief of Staff
CHR: John Hayden, Senior Vice President and Chief Human Resources Officer
Web address: www.bronsonhealth.com/lakeview
**Control:** Other not–for–profit (including NFP Corporation) **Service:** General Medical and Surgical

**Staffed Beds:** 35 **Admissions:** 893 **Census:** 13 **Outpatient Visits:** 195687 **Births:** 0 **Total Expense ($000):** 38090 **Payroll Expense ($000):** 13231 **Personnel:** 341

### PETOSKEY—Emmet County

☒ △ **MCLAREN NORTHERN MICHIGAN (230105)**, 416 Connable Avenue, Zip 49770–2297; tel. 231/487–4000, (Data for 274 days) **A**1 2 7 9 10 **F**3 12 13 15 17 18 20 22 24 26 28 29 30 31 32 34 35 36 38 40 42 43 44 45 49 50 51 53 57 58 59 60 64 68 70 74 75 76 77 78 79 81 82 85 86 87 89 90 91 93 94 96 107 108 110 111 114 115 119 120 121 123 124 129 130 132 135 146 148 **S** McLaren Health Care Corporation, Flint, MI
Primary Contact: Reezie DeVet, R.N., Ph.D., President and Chief Executive Officer
COO: Mary–Anne D. Ponti, R.N., Chief Operating Officer and Chief Nurse Executive
CFO: Stephen J. Scannell, Chief Financial Officer
CMO: Kirk Lufkin, M.D., VPMA
CIO: Mark Gray, Chief Information Officer
CHR: Gene Kaminski, Vice President Human Resources
CNO: Jennifer Woods, R.N., Chief Nursing Officer
Web address: www.northernhealth.org
**Control:** Other not–for–profit (including NFP Corporation) **Service:** General Medical and Surgical

**Staffed Beds:** 178 **Admissions:** 6734 **Census:** 94 **Outpatient Visits:** 139886 **Births:** 511 **Total Expense ($000):** 136797 **Payroll Expense ($000):** 48145 **Personnel:** 1170

### PIGEON—Huron County

☒ **SCHEURER HOSPITAL (231310)**, 170 North Caseville Road, Zip 48755–9781; tel. 989/453–3223, (Total facility includes 19 beds in nursing home–type unit) **A**1 9 10 18 **F**3 7 10 11 15 28 29 30 31 34 36 40 44 45 50 53 54 56 57 59 64 68 69 75 77 78 79 81 85 86 87 91 93 97 107 108 110 114 119 125 127 130 131 132 133 143 146 **P**6
Primary Contact: Dwight Gascho, President and Chief Executive Officer
CFO: Terry Lutz, Chief Financial Officer
CMO: Scott Reiter, D.O., Chief of Staff
CIO: Suzanne LeMaire, Manager Health Information Management Services and Corporate Compliance Officer
CHR: Gregory S. Foy, Human Resources System Leader
CNO: Sue Lathrom, Director of Nursing/Patient Care System Leader
Web address: www.scheurer.org
**Control:** Other not–for–profit (including NFP Corporation) **Service:** General Medical and Surgical

**Staffed Beds:** 44 **Admissions:** 571 **Census:** 23 **Outpatient Visits:** 45649 **Births:** 0 **Total Expense ($000):** 31425 **Payroll Expense ($000):** 15465 **Personnel:** 320

**MI**

---

**Hospital, Medicare Provider Number, Address, Telephone, Approval, Facility, and Physician Codes, Health Care System**

★ American Hospital Association (AHA) membership
☐ The Joint Commission accreditation
◇ DNV Healthcare Inc. accreditation
○ Healthcare Facilities Accreditation Program
△ Commission on Accreditation of Rehabilitation Facilities (CARF) accreditation

## PLAINWELL—Allegan County

✠ **BORGESS–PIPP HOSPITAL (232034)**, 411 Naomi Street, Zip 49080–1222; tel. 269/685–6811, (Nonreporting) **A**1 9 10 **S** Ascension Health, Saint Louis, MO
Primary Contact: John Ryder, Administrator and Chief Executive Officer
Web address: www.borgess.com
**Control:** Other not–for–profit (including NFP Corporation) **Service:** Long–Term Acute Care hospital

**Staffed Beds:** 43

## PONTIAC—Oakland County

☐ **DOCTORS' HOSPITAL OF MICHIGAN (230013)**, 461 West Huron Street, Zip 48341–1601; tel. 248/857–7200, (Nonreporting) **A**1 9 10
Primary Contact: Robert Barrow, Chief Executive Officer
COO: Dennis Franks, Vice President Operations
CFO: Dennis Franks, Interim Chief Financial Officer
CMO: Ray Breitenbach, M.D., Chief of Staff
CIO: Albert Sinisi, Director Information Systems
Web address: www.dhofm.com
**Control:** Other not–for–profit (including NFP Corporation) **Service:** General Medical and Surgical

**Staffed Beds:** 106

★ ○ **MCLAREN OAKLAND (230207)**, 50 North Perry Street, Zip 48342–2253; tel. 248/338–5000, (Total facility includes 120 beds in nursing home–type unit) **A**9 10 11 12 13 **F**3 4 7 8 11 12 14 15 18 20 24 26 28 29 30 31 32 33 34 35 36 40 42 43 44 45 50 53 54 57 59 62 63 64 65 66 68 70 74 75 77 78 79 81 82 90 92 93 94 98 103 107 108 111 114 118 119 124 128 131 132 135 136 137 138 139 140 141 142 143 144 146 148 **P**4 8 **S** McLaren Health Care Corporation, Flint, MI
Primary Contact: Clarence Sevillian, President and Chief Executive Officer
CFO: Fred Korte, Chief Financial Officer
CMO: Steven Calkin, D.O., Vice President Medical Affairs
CIO: Darin Boka, Chief Information Officer
CIO: Teresa Rodges, Executive Director Marketing and Public Relations
CHR: Laura Gibbard, Vice President Human Resources
Web address: www.pohmedical.org
**Control:** Other not–for–profit (including NFP Corporation) **Service:** General Medical and Surgical

**Staffed Beds:** 285 **Admissions:** 6223 **Census:** 199 **Outpatient Visits:** 167322 **Births:** 0 **Total Expense ($000):** 144983 **Payroll Expense ($000):** 56730 **Personnel:** 1067

✠ **SELECT SPECIALTY HOSPITAL–PONTIAC (232030)**, 44405 Woodward Avenue, 8th Floor, Zip 48341–5023; tel. 248/452–5252, (Nonreporting) **A**1 9 10 **S** Select Medical Corporation, Mechanicsburg, PA
Primary Contact: Peggy Kingston, Chief Executive Officer
CMO: Fadi Salloum, M.D., Medical Director
CNO: Catherine Folson, MSN, Chief Nursing Officer
Web address: www.selectspecialtyhospitals.com/company/locations/pontiac.aspx
**Control:** Corporation, Investor–owned, for–profit **Service:** Long–Term Acute Care hospital

**Staffed Beds:** 30

✠ **ST. JOSEPH MERCY OAKLAND (230029)**, 44405 Woodward Avenue, Zip 48341–5023; tel. 248/858–3000 **A**1 2 3 5 9 10 12 13 **F**3 8 12 13 15 17 18 20 22 24 26 28 29 30 31 34 35 36 37 38 39 40 43 44 45 46 47 48 49 50 51 53 54 55 56 57 58 59 61 64 65 66 68 70 72 74 75 76 77 78 79 81 82 84 85 86 87 89 90 92 93 94 97 98 100 101 102 103 105 107 108 110 111 114 115 118 119 126 129 130 131 132 135 144 146 147 148 **P**6 **S** Trinity Health, Livonia, MI
Primary Contact: Jack Weiner, President and Chief Executive Officer
COO: Barbara Hertzler, Chief Operating Officer
CFO: Michael Gusho, Chief Financial Officer
CMO: Donald Bignotti, M.D., Vice President Medical Affairs
CIO: Robert Jones, Director Management Information Systems
CHR: Martha Murphy, Vice President Human Resources
CNO: Ann McDonald–Upton, Chief Nursing Officer
Web address: www.stjoesoakland.com
**Control:** Church–operated, Nongovernment, not–for profit **Service:** General Medical and Surgical

**Staffed Beds:** 409 **Admissions:** 19726 **Census:** 276 **Outpatient Visits:** 343441 **Births:** 1903 **Total Expense ($000):** 385589 **Payroll Expense ($000):** 150258 **Personnel:** 2906

## PORT HURON—St. Clair County

✠ **PORT HURON HOSPITAL (230216)**, 1221 Pine Grove Avenue, Zip 48060–3511; tel. 810/987–5000 **A**1 2 9 10 **F**3 5 11 12 13 15 17 18 20 22 24 26 29 30 31 32 34 35 36 39 40 44 45 46 48 49 50 51 54 56 57 58 59 61 64 65 66 68 70 72 74 75 76 78 79 81 82 84 85 86 87 89 92 93 96 97 98 99 100 101 102 103 104 107 108 110 111 114 115 116 117 118 119 124 130 131 132 134 135 144 145 146 147 148 **P**6 **S** Blue Water Health Services Corporation, Port Huron, MI
Primary Contact: Thomas D. DeFauw, FACHE, President and Chief Executive Officer
COO: David S. McEwen, Vice President Operations
CFO: John Liston, Chief Financial Officer
CMO: Michael W. Tawney, D.O., Vice President Medical Affairs
CIO: Mark Richard, Chief Information Officer
CHR: Doris A. Seidl, Vice President Human Resources
CNO: Jennifer Montgomery, R.N., Vice President, Nursing
Web address: www.porthuronhospital.org
**Control:** Other not–for–profit (including NFP Corporation) **Service:** General Medical and Surgical

**Staffed Beds:** 186 **Admissions:** 11108 **Census:** 133 **Outpatient Visits:** 165204 **Births:** 1248 **Total Expense ($000):** 156187 **Payroll Expense ($000):** 64913 **Personnel:** 1230

✠ **ST. JOSEPH MERCY PORT HURON (230031)**, 2601 Electric Avenue, Zip 48060–6518; tel. 810/985–1500 **A**1 2 9 10 **F**3 11 12 15 18 20 29 30 31 34 35 37 40 43 45 49 50 54 56 57 58 59 61 62 63 64 66 70 74 75 77 78 79 81 82 83 85 86 87 89 90 93 96 97 107 108 110 114 116 118 119 120 121 123 126 130 131 132 135 146 147 148 **P**6 8 **S** Trinity Health, Livonia, MI
Primary Contact: Rebekah Smith, R.N., President and Chief Executive Officer
CFO: Deborah Armstrong, Chief Financial Officer
CMO: Philip Matich, M.D., Vice President Medical Affairs
CIO: Peggy Assessor, Director Information Services
CHR: Robert Gunn, Vice President Human Resources
Web address: www.mercyporthuron.com
**Control:** Church–operated, Nongovernment, not–for profit **Service:** General Medical and Surgical

**Staffed Beds:** 119 **Admissions:** 4068 **Census:** 50 **Outpatient Visits:** 124614 **Births:** 0 **Total Expense ($000):** 80545 **Payroll Expense ($000):** 29900 **Personnel:** 634

## REED CITY—Osceola County

✠ **SPECTRUM HEALTH REED CITY HOSPITAL (231323)**, 300 North Patterson Road, Zip 49677–8041, Mailing Address: P.O. Box 75, Zip 49677–0075; tel. 231/832–3271, (Total facility includes 50 beds in nursing home–type unit) **A**1 9 10 18 **F**3 15 29 30 31 34 35 40 45 50 53 54 57 59 64 65 70 75 77 78 79 81 84 85 86 87 93 97 107 108 110 111 114 118 119 120 121 123 124 127 128 129 130 131 133 146 147 **P**6 **S** Spectrum Health, Grand Rapids, MI
Primary Contact: Sam Daugherty, Ed.D., President
COO: Cathy Rybicki, Chief Operating Officer
CFO: Thomas Knoerl, Vice President Finance
CMO: Thomas Campana, M.D., Chief of Staff
CIO: Brandi Johnson, Technolgy Information Systems Site Manager
CHR: Kris Miller, Senior Human Resources Business Partner
CNO: Scott Lombard, Acting Chief Nursing Officer
Web address: www.reedcity.spectrum–health.org
**Control:** Other not–for–profit (including NFP Corporation) **Service:** General Medical and Surgical

**Staffed Beds:** 75 **Admissions:** 811 **Census:** 56 **Outpatient Visits:** 375716 **Births:** 0 **Total Expense ($000):** 47238 **Payroll Expense ($000):** 17841 **Personnel:** 414

## ROCHESTER—Oakland County

☐ △ **CRITTENTON HOSPITAL MEDICAL CENTER (230254)**, 1101 West University Drive, Zip 48307–1831; tel. 248/652–5000 **A**1 2 3 5 7 9 10 **F**3 11 12 13 15 17 18 20 22 24 26 28 29 30 31 32 34 35 36 37 39 40 44 45 46 47 48 49 50 51 53 54 55 57 58 59 60 62 63 64 65 68 70 73 74 75 76 77 78 79 81 82 84 85 86 87 89 90 92 93 94 96 97 98 100 101 102 107 108 110 114 115 118 119 126 129 130 131 132 134 135 143 144 146 147 148
Primary Contact: Frank Sottile, M.D., Interim Chief Executive Officer
COO: Gregory A. Partamian, Chief Operating Officer
CFO: Donna Kopinski, Chief Financial Officer
CMO: Frank Sottile, M.D., Chief Medical Officer
CIO: Tom Ventameglia, Director Information Systems
Web address: www.crittenton.com
**Control:** Other not–for–profit (including NFP Corporation) **Service:** General Medical and Surgical

**Staffed Beds:** 254 **Admissions:** 12859 **Census:** 167 **Outpatient Visits:** 206846 **Births:** 1279 **Total Expense ($000):** 164211 **Payroll Expense ($000):** 86480 **Personnel:** 1231

*Many Facility Codes have changed. Please refer to the AHA Guide Code Chart.*
© 2013 AHA Guide

## ROGERS CITY—Presque Isle County

☐ **ROGERS CITY REHABILITATION HOSPITAL (233029)**, 555 North Bradley Highway, Suite C., Zip 49779–1539; tel. 989/734–7545 **A**1 9 10 **F**90 93 **P**5
Primary Contact: Joyal Pavey, Executive Director
CFO: Dylan Moore, Controller
CMO: Diana Hernandez Drozdowicz, M.D., Medical Director
Web address: www.rogerscityrehab.com
**Control:** Corporation, Investor–owned, for–profit **Service:** Rehabilitation

**Staffed Beds:** 28 **Admissions:** 184 **Census:** 6 **Outpatient Visits:** 1774
**Births:** 0 **Total Expense ($000):** 3846 **Payroll Expense ($000):** 1270
**Personnel:** 42

## ROMEO—Macomb County

**ST. JOSEPH'S MERCY–NORTH** See Henry Ford Macomb Hospitals, Clinton Township

## ROYAL OAK—Oakland County

☒ **BEAUMONT HOSPITAL – ROYAL OAK (230130)**, 3601 West Thirteen Mile Road, Zip 48073–6712; tel. 248/898–5000, (Includes BEAUMONT CHILDREN'S HOSPITAL, 3601 West 13 Mile Road, tel. 248/898–5000) **A**1 2 3 5 8 9 10 13 **F**3 5 6 11 12 13 14 15 17 18 19 20 22 24 26 28 29 30 31 32 36 37 38 39 40 41 43 44 45 46 47 48 49 50 51 54 55 56 57 58 59 60 61 62 63 64 65 66 68 70 71 72 74 75 76 77 78 79 80 81 82 83 84 85 86 87 88 89 90 91 92 93 94 95 96 97 98 99 100 101 102 103 104 105 107 108 109 110 111 114 115 116 117 118 119 120 121 123 124 126 129 130 131 132 134 135 138 139 141 142 143 144 145 146 147 148 **P**6 **S** Beaumont Health System, Royal Oak, MI
Primary Contact: Shane Cerone, President
COO: Gene Michalski, Executive Vice President and Chief Operating Officer
CFO: Nickolas A. Vitale, Executive Vice President and Chief Financial Officer
CMO: Ananias C. Diokno, M.D., Executive Vice President and Chief Medical Officer
CIO: Subra Sripada, Senior Vice President and Chief Information Officer
Web address: www.beaumont.edu/royal-oak-hospital-campus
**Control:** Other not–for–profit (including NFP Corporation) **Service:** General Medical and Surgical

**Staffed Beds:** 1070 **Admissions:** 57024 **Census:** 828 **Outpatient Visits:** 1382655 **Births:** 4946 **Total Expense ($000):** 1175433 **Payroll Expense ($000):** 369191 **Personnel:** 8126

## SAGINAW—Saginaw County

☒ **ALEDA E. LUTZ VETERANS AFFAIRS MEDICAL CENTER**, 1500 Weiss Street, Zip 48602–5298; tel. 989/497–2500, (Total facility includes 35 beds in nursing home–type unit) **A**1 9 **F**3 5 8 11 15 18 29 30 31 34 35 36 38 39 44 45 50 53 54 56 57 58 59 61 63 64 68 74 75 77 78 81 82 83 84 85 86 87 93 94 97 100 101 102 103 104 107 108 119 127 128 130 131 132 133 135 136 137 138 139 140 141 142 143 144 146 147 148 **P**6 **S** Department of Veterans Affairs, Washington, DC
Primary Contact: Major Jeff Nechanicky, Acting Medical Center Director
CFO: Jeff Drew, Fiscal Officer
CIO: Stephanie Young, Chief Information Technology
CHR: Kathy Seymour, Acting Chief Human Resources Management Service
Web address: www.saginaw.va.gov/
**Control:** Veterans Affairs, Government, federal **Service:** General Medical and Surgical

**Staffed Beds:** 100 **Admissions:** 1362 **Census:** 45 **Outpatient Visits:** 331172 **Births:** 0 **Total Expense ($000):** 163841 **Payroll Expense ($000):** 66203 **Personnel:** 1001

★ ○ △ **COVENANT MEDICAL CENTER (230070)**, 1447 North Harrison Street, Zip 48602–4727; tel. 989/583–0000, (Includes COVENANT MEDICAL CENTER–COOPER, 700 Cooper Avenue, Zip 48602–5399; tel. 517/583–0000; COVENANT MEDICAL CENTER–HARRISON, 1447 North Harrison Street, Zip 48602–4785; tel. 517/583–0000), (Total facility includes 20 beds in nursing home–type unit) **A**2 3 5 7 9 10 11 12 13 15 17 18 19 20 22 24 25 26 27 28 29 30 31 35 36 40 41 42 43 45 46 47 48 49 50 54 57 58 59 60 61 62 63 64 65 70 72 74 75 76 77 78 79 81 82 83 84 86 87 88 89 90 91 92 93 94 97 107 108 110 111 113 114 115 118 119 120 121 123 124 126 128 129 130 131 132 135 143 144 146 147 148 **P**7 8
Primary Contact: Spencer Maidlow, President and Chief Executive Officer
COO: Edward Bruff, Executive Vice President and Chief Operating Officer
CFO: Mark E. Gronda, Vice President and Chief Financial Officer
CMO: John Kosanovich, M.D., Vice President Covenant Healthcare and Chief Executive Officer Covenant Medical Group
CIO: Keith Grantham, Director Information Technology
CHR: Al Van Arsdal, Director Human Resources
Web address: www.covenanthealthcare.com
**Control:** Other not–for–profit (including NFP Corporation) **Service:** General Medical and Surgical

**Staffed Beds:** 532 **Admissions:** 27942 **Census:** 365 **Outpatient Visits:** 482358 **Births:** 3064 **Total Expense ($000):** 489240 **Payroll Expense ($000):** 212446

☐ **HEALTHSOURCE SAGINAW (230275)**, (LTC Rehab Psych Chem Dependenc), 3340 Hospital Road, Zip 48603–9622, Mailing Address: P.O. Box 6280, Zip 48608–6280; tel. 989/790–7700, (Total facility includes 213 beds in nursing home–type unit) **A**1 9 10 **F**4 5 11 56 57 66 74 75 77 82 86 87 90 91 93 94 95 98 99 100 101 103 104 128 130 132 135 143 146 148 **P**6
Primary Contact: Lester Heyboer, Jr., President and Chief Executive Officer
CFO: Lisa Lapham, Chief Financial Officer
CMO: Daniel Duffy, D.O., Chief Medical Director
CIO: Randall Sanborn, Director Information Technology
CHR: Rebecca Oster, Director Human Resources
Web address: www.healthsourcesaginaw.org
**Control:** Hospital district or authority, Government, nonfederal **Service:** Other specialty

**Staffed Beds:** 319 **Admissions:** 3291 **Census:** 261 **Outpatient Visits:** 3123 **Births:** 0 **Total Expense ($000):** 41010 **Payroll Expense ($000):** 19618 **Personnel:** 478

☒ **SELECT SPECIALTY HOSPITAL–SAGINAW (232033)**, 1447 North Harrison Street, 8th Floor, Zip 48602–4785; tel. 989/583–4235, (Nonreporting) **A**1 9 10 **S** Select Medical Corporation, Mechanicsburg, PA
Primary Contact: Dawn Frisbie, Chief Executive Officer
Web address: www.selectspecialtyhospitals.com/company/locations/saginaw.aspx
**Control:** Corporation, Investor–owned, for–profit **Service:** Long–Term Acute Care hospital

**Staffed Beds:** 32

☒ **ST. MARY'S OF MICHIGAN (230077)**, 800 South Washington Avenue, Zip 48601–2594; tel. 989/907–8000 **A**1 2 3 5 9 10 **F**2 3 11 15 17 18 20 22 24 26 28 29 30 31 34 35 36 40 42 43 44 45 49 50 51 54 57 58 59 64 66 68 70 74 75 77 78 79 80 81 82 85 86 87 92 93 96 97 100 102 107 108 110 111 114 115 118 119 120 121 123 124 126 129 130 132 146 148 **P**6 8 **S** Ascension Health, Saint Louis, MO
Primary Contact: John R. Graham, President and Chief Executive Officer
COO: Rick L. Ohle, Chief Operating Officer
CFO: Gina Butcher, Chief Financial Officer
CIO: David Wanner, Chief Information Officer
CHR: Ron Haase, Vice President Human Resources
Web address: www.stmarysofmichigan.org
**Control:** Church–operated, Nongovernment, not–for profit **Service:** General Medical and Surgical

**Staffed Beds:** 236 **Admissions:** 11293 **Census:** 168 **Outpatient Visits:** 166778 **Births:** 0 **Total Expense ($000):** 253365 **Payroll Expense ($000):** 98801 **Personnel:** 1795

## SAINT IGNACE—Mackinac County

★ **MACKINAC STRAITS HEALTH SYSTEM (231306)**, 1140 North State Street, Zip 49781–1048; tel. 906/643–8585, (Total facility includes 48 beds in nursing home–type unit) **A**9 10 18 **F**15 28 31 32 40 42 53 54 56 59 60 64 65 77 78 91 93 97 104 107 111 114 119 127 128 130 132 133 144 146 147 **P**6
Primary Contact: Rodney M. Nelson, Chief Executive Officer
CFO: Jason Anderson, Chief Financial Officer
CMO: John Stephenson, M.D., Chief of Staff
CHR: Karen Cheeseman, Director Human Resources
Web address: www.mshosp.org
**Control:** Other not–for–profit (including NFP Corporation) **Service:** General Medical and Surgical

**Staffed Beds:** 63 **Admissions:** 370 **Census:** 48 **Outpatient Visits:** 29519 **Births:** 0 **Total Expense ($000):** 30267 **Payroll Expense ($000):** 10217 **Personnel:** 197

## SAINT JOHNS—Clinton County

☒ **SPARROW CLINTON HOSPITAL (231326)**, 805 South Oakland Street, Zip 48879–2253; tel. 989/227–3400 **A**1 9 10 18 **F**8 11 15 18 19 31 32 34 35 40 45 53 57 59 64 70 75 77 78 79 81 85 93 107 110 111 114 119 129 130 131 133 145 146 148 **P**6 **S** Sparrow Health System, Lansing, MI
Primary Contact: Edward Bruun, President and Chief Executive Officer
COO: Kevin A. Price, Vice President and Chief Operating Officer
CFO: Mark Brisboe, Vice President & CFO
CMO: Gregory Holzhei, D.O., Chief of Staff
CHR: Lucy M. Vail, Director Human Resources & Partner Relations
Web address: www.clintonmemorial.org
**Control:** Other not–for–profit (including NFP Corporation) **Service:** General Medical and Surgical

**Staffed Beds:** 25 **Admissions:** 747 **Census:** 6 **Outpatient Visits:** 56305 **Births:** 0 **Total Expense ($000):** 38077 **Payroll Expense ($000):** 14878 **Personnel:** 206

**MI**

---

**Hospital, Medicare Provider Number, Address, Telephone, Approval, Facility, and Physician Codes, Health Care System**

★ American Hospital Association (AHA) membership
☐ The Joint Commission accreditation
◇ DNV Healthcare Inc. accreditation
○ Healthcare Facilities Accreditation Program
△ Commission on Accreditation of Rehabilitation Facilities (CARF) accreditation

## SAINT JOSEPH—Berrien County

☐ **LAKELAND REGIONAL MEDICAL CENTER–ST. JOSEPH (230021)**, 1234 Napier Avenue, Zip 49085–2158; tel. 269/983–8300, (Nonreporting) **A**1 2 9 10 13 **S** Lakeland Healthcare, Saint Joseph, MI
Primary Contact: Loren Hamel, M.D., President and Chief Executive Officer
CFO: Timothy Calhoun, Vice President Finance and Chief Financial Officer
CMO: Stephen Hempel, M.D., President Medical Staff
CIO: Emily Gallay, Vice President and Chief Information Officer
CHR: Gerard Guinane, Vice President Human Resources and Diversity Management
Web address: www.lakelandhealth.org
**Control:** Other not–for–profit (including NFP Corporation) **Service:** General Medical and Surgical

**Staffed Beds: 250**

## SALINE—Washtenaw County

☐ **CENTER FOR FORENSIC PSYCHIATRY (234041)**, 8303 Platt Road, Zip 48176–9773, Mailing Address: P.O. Box 2060, Ann Arbor, Zip 48106–2060; tel. 734/429–2531 **A**1 10 **F**30 39 98 130
Primary Contact: Carol E. Holden, Director
Web address: www.michigan.gov
**Control:** State–Government, nonfederal **Service:** Psychiatric

**Staffed Beds: 210 Admissions: 235 Census: 210 Outpatient Visits: 0 Births: 0 Total Expense ($000): 64899 Payroll Expense ($000): 33863 Personnel: 505**

## SANDUSKY—Sanilac County

**MCKENZIE HEALTH SYSTEM (231314)**, 120 North Delaware Street, Zip 48471–1087; tel. 810/648–3770, (Nonreporting) **A**9 10 18
Primary Contact: Steve Barnett, MS, President and Chief Executive Officer
COO: Janet Herbert, R.N., Chief Operating Officer
CFO: Amy Ruedisueli, Chief Financial Officer
CMO: Mark E. English, M.D., Chief of Staff
CHR: Carrie Krampits, Director Human Resources
CNO: Tammy Cliff, R.N., Director Nursing Services
Web address: www.mckenziehealth.org
**Control:** Other not–for–profit (including NFP Corporation) **Service:** General Medical and Surgical

**Staffed Beds: 25**

## SAULT SAINTE MARIE—Chippewa County

⊞ ◇ **WAR MEMORIAL HOSPITAL (230239)**, 500 Osborn Boulevard, Zip 49783–1884; tel. 906/635–4460, (Total facility includes 51 beds in nursing home–type unit) **A**1 9 10 20 21 **F**3 11 12 13 15 18 28 29 30 31 34 35 36 38 40 43 44 45 50 53 54 56 57 58 59 60 61 62 64 65 66 68 70 74 75 76 77 78 79 81 82 84 85 87 92 93 97 98 100 101 104 107 108 110 111 115 117 119 127 128 129 130 131 132 133 135 143 144 146 147 148
Primary Contact: David B. Jahn, President and Chief Executive Officer
COO: Marla Bunker, Vice President Nursing and Chief Operating Officer
CFO: Kevin Kalchik, Chief Financial Officer
CMO: Ted Ludwig, Chief Medical Officer
CIO: Steve Pietrangelo, Director Information Services
CHR: Susan Sliger, Director Human Resources
CNO: Sue Tetzlaff, Vice President of Nursing
Web address: www.warmemorialhospital.org
**Control:** Other not–for–profit (including NFP Corporation) **Service:** General Medical and Surgical

**Staffed Beds: 135 Admissions: 3502 Census: 91 Outpatient Visits: 150793 Births: 331 Total Expense ($000): 96159 Payroll Expense ($000): 35499 Personnel: 778**

## SHELBY—Oceana County

⊞ **MERCY HEALTH PARTNERS, LAKESHORE CAMPUS (231320)**, 72 South State Street, Zip 49455–1299; tel. 231/861–2156 **A**1 9 10 18 **F**3 11 15 29 30 34 35 40 57 59 68 81 85 87 89 97 107 111 115 119 127 129 132 146 **S** Trinity Health, Livonia, MI
Primary Contact: Jay Bryan, President and Chief Executive Officer
CFO: Mark Gross, Senior Business Director Finance
Web address: www.mercyhealthmuskegon.com
**Control:** Other not–for–profit (including NFP Corporation) **Service:** General Medical and Surgical

**Staffed Beds: 24 Admissions: 357 Census: 3 Outpatient Visits: 20369 Births: 0 Total Expense ($000): 22826 Payroll Expense ($000): 10003 Personnel: 148**

## SHERIDAN—Montcalm County

★ **SHERIDAN COMMUNITY HOSPITAL (231312)**, 301 North Main Street, Zip 48884–9235, Mailing Address: P.O. Box 279, Zip 48884–0279; tel. 989/291–3261, (Nonreporting) **A**9 10 18
Primary Contact: Randolph K. Flechsig, Administrator
COO: Steve Scott, Chief Operating Officer
CFO: Randolph K. Flechsig, Administrator
CMO: Maria Charlotte Alvarez, M.D., Chief of Staff
CIO: David Bussler, Chief Information Officer
CHR: Sharon Bowers, R.N., Manager of Community, Public and Employee Relations
CNO: Elizabeth Edwards, R.N., Director, Nursing Services
Web address: www.sheridanhospital.com
**Control:** Other not–for–profit (including NFP Corporation) **Service:** General Medical and Surgical

**Staffed Beds: 22**

## SOUTH HAVEN—Van Buren County

**SOUTH HAVEN COMMUNITY HOSPITAL** See South Haven Health System

⊞ **SOUTH HAVEN HEALTH SYSTEM (230085)**, 955 South Bailey Avenue, Zip 49090–6743; tel. 269/637–5271 **A**1 9 10 **F**3 11 13 15 28 29 30 31 34 35 36 40 41 53 57 59 62 64 65 68 75 76 77 78 79 81 85 87 89 93 95 96 97 107 108 110 112 115 118 119 127 129 130 132 135 146 147 148 **P**4
Primary Contact: Joanne Urbanski, President and Chief Executive Officer
CFO: Jim Wheeler, Executive Vice President and Chief Financial Officer
CMO: Maura Buckingham, D.O., Chief of Staff
CIO: Dennis Sorenson, Supervisor Information Technology
CHR: Bill Wood, Director Human Resources
Web address: www.shch.org
**Control:** Hospital district or authority, Government, nonfederal **Service:** General Medical and Surgical

**Staffed Beds: 33 Admissions: 1100 Census: 8 Outpatient Visits: 122394 Births: 420 Total Expense ($000): 38322 Payroll Expense ($000): 17437 Personnel: 334**

## SOUTHFIELD—Oakland County

★ ○ **OAKLAND REGIONAL HOSPITAL (230301)**, 22401 Foster Winter Drive, Zip 48075–3724; tel. 248/423–5100, (Total facility includes 26 beds in nursing home–type unit) **A**9 10 11 **F**45 79 81 82 85 90 93 111 128
Primary Contact: Daniel R. Babb, Chief Executive Officer
COO: Amelia Jones, Chief Operating Officer
CMO: Robert Barbosa, D.O., Chief Medical Officer
CIO: Bill Moncrief, ORH IT Client Executive
CHR: Gordon Meyer, Director Human Resources
Web address: www.oaklandregionalhospital.com
**Control:** Corporation, Investor–owned, for–profit **Service:** General Medical and Surgical

**Staffed Beds: 71 Admissions: 778 Census: 26 Outpatient Visits: 10565 Births: 0 Total Expense ($000): 26289 Payroll Expense ($000): 7250 Personnel: 102**

⊞ **PROVIDENCE HOSPITAL (230019)**, 16001 West Nine Mile Road, Zip 48075–4818, Mailing Address: P.O. Box 2043, Zip 48037–2043; tel. 248/424–3000, (Includes PROVIDENCE PARK HOSPITAL, 47601 Grand River Avebue, Novi, Zip 48374–1233; tel. 248/465–4100; Peter Karadjoff, President) **A**1 2 3 5 9 10 **F**3 5 8 9 11 12 13 15 17 18 20 22 24 26 28 29 30 31 34 35 36 38 39 40 44 45 46 47 48 49 50 51 54 55 56 57 58 59 60 61 63 64 65 66 68 70 72 74 75 76 77 78 79 80 81 82 84 85 86 87 89 90 92 93 97 98 99 100 101 102 103 104 105 107 108 110 111 114 115 116 117 118 119 120 121 123 126 129 130 131 132 135 141 143 146 147 148 **P**3 6 7 8 **S** Ascension Health, Saint Louis, MO
Primary Contact: Michael Wiemann, M.D., President
CFO: Douglas Winner, Chief Financial Officer
CHR: Sue Gronbach, Director Human Resources
Web address: www.providence-stjohnhealth.org
**Control:** Church–operated, Nongovernment, not–for profit **Service:** General Medical and Surgical

**Staffed Beds: 565 Admissions: 33224 Census: 410 Outpatient Visits: 316592 Births: 3940 Total Expense ($000): 601844 Payroll Expense ($000): 239142 Personnel: 3977**

⊞ **STRAITH HOSPITAL FOR SPECIAL SURGERY (230071)**, 23901 Lahser Road, Zip 48033–6035; tel. 248/357–3360 **A**1 9 10 **F**29 81 91 130 141 148 **P**5
Primary Contact: Gregory R. Hoose, Chief Executive Officer
CFO: H. Roger Jones, Chief Financial Officer
Web address: www.straith.org/
**Control:** Other not–for–profit (including NFP Corporation) **Service:** General Medical and Surgical

**Staffed Beds: 24 Admissions: 647 Census: 13 Outpatient Visits: 1284 Births: 0 Total Expense ($000): 9889 Payroll Expense ($000): 4150 Personnel: 93**

*Many Facility Codes have changed. Please refer to the AHA Guide Code Chart.*    © 2013 AHA Guide

**STANDISH—Arenac County**

✠ **ST. MARY'S OF MICHIGAN STANDISH HOSPITAL (231305)**, 805 West Cedar Street, Zip 48658–9526; tel. 989/846–4521, (Total facility includes 39 beds in nursing home–type unit) **A**1 9 10 18 **F**3 8 11 15 17 28 29 30 34 35 38 40 45 50 54 56 57 59 64 65 66 77 81 82 84 85 87 93 107 108 110 114 115 118 119 127 128 130 132 133 135 143 146 147 **P**6 **S** Ascension Health, Saint Louis, MO
Primary Contact: Rose Goick, MSN, Administrative Director of Operations
CFO: Tony Doud, Controller
CMO: Jaya Sankaran, M.D., Chief of Staff
CIO: Tammy Copes, Director Information Systems
CHR: Renee Reetz, Director Human Resources
Web address: www.stmarysofmichigan.org/standish
**Control:** Other not–for–profit (including NFP Corporation) **Service:** General Medical and Surgical

| | |
|---|---|
| **Staffed Beds:** 64 **Admissions:** 1027 **Census:** 39 **Outpatient Visits:** 43337 **Births:** 0 **Total Expense ($000):** 21629 **Payroll Expense ($000):** 9734 **Personnel:** 203 | |

**STURGIS—St. Joseph County**

★ ◇ **STURGIS HOSPITAL (230096)**, 916 Myrtle Street, Zip 49091–2326; tel. 269/651–7824 **A**9 10 21 **F**3 11 13 15 28 29 30 31 34 35 40 42 45 46 49 50 57 59 62 63 64 65 68 70 75 76 77 78 79 81 82 85 87 89 93 97 102 107 108 115 118 119 127 129 130 132 144 146 147 148 **P**6 **S** QHR, Brentwood, TN
Primary Contact: Robert J. LaBarge, Chief Executive Officer
CFO: David Miller, Chief Financial Officer
CMO: Keyar Patel, M.D., President Medical Staff
CIO: Rita Denison, Manager Information Systems
CHR: Mary Kay Schultz, Director Human Resources
CNO: Charlotte J. Pavilanis, R.N., Director of Patient Care Services
Web address: www.sturgishospital.com
**Control:** Other not–for–profit (including NFP Corporation) **Service:** General Medical and Surgical

| | |
|---|---|
| **Staffed Beds:** 49 **Admissions:** 1445 **Census:** 11 **Outpatient Visits:** 92064 **Births:** 381 **Total Expense ($000):** 40996 **Payroll Expense ($000):** 18082 **Personnel:** 255 | |

**TAWAS CITY—Iosco County**

✠ **ST. JOSEPH HEALTH SYSTEM (230100)**, 200 Hemlock Street, Zip 48763–9237, Mailing Address: P.O. Box 659, Zip 48764–0659; tel. 989/362–3411, (Nonreporting) **A**1 9 10 20 **S** Ascension Health, Saint Louis, MO
Primary Contact: Ann M. Balfour, R.N., President
CFO: Linda Stancill, Vice President and Chief Financial Officer
CHR: Nancy Bodenner, Director Human Resources
Web address: www.sjhsys.org
**Control:** Other not–for–profit (including NFP Corporation) **Service:** General Medical and Surgical

| | |
|---|---|
| **Staffed Beds:** 20 | |

**TAYLOR—Wayne County**

✠ **OAKWOOD HERITAGE HOSPITAL (230270)**, 10000 Telegraph Road, Zip 48180–3330; tel. 313/295–5000 **A**1 3 5 9 10 **F**3 11 15 29 30 34 37 38 39 40 44 49 50 56 57 59 60 61 64 65 68 70 74 75 78 79 81 82 84 85 86 87 90 92 93 96 98 100 101 102 103 105 107 108 111 114 115 118 119 128 130 131 132 135 146 148 **P**8 **S** Oakwood Healthcare, Inc., Dearborn, MI
Primary Contact: Kelly C. Smith, Division President
CFO: Mark Deming, Controller
CMO: Vijay Khanna, M.D., Chief of Staff
CIO: Paula Smith, Chief Information Officer
CHR: Sherry Huffman, Administrator Human Resources
Web address: www.oakwood.org
**Control:** Other not–for–profit (including NFP Corporation) **Service:** General Medical and Surgical

| | |
|---|---|
| **Staffed Beds:** 145 **Admissions:** 7962 **Census:** 133 **Outpatient Visits:** 67116 **Births:** 0 **Total Expense ($000):** 128982 **Payroll Expense ($000):** 51301 **Personnel:** 758 | |

✠ **SELECT SPECIALTY HOSPITAL–DOWNRIVER (232031)**, 10000 Telegraph Road, 2nd Floor, Zip 48180–3330; tel. 313/375–7075, (Nonreporting) **A**1 9 10 **S** Select Medical Corporation, Mechanicsburg, PA
Primary Contact: Martin T. Carmody, Chief Executive Officer
CMO: Roderick Boyer, M.D., Medical Director
CHR: Barb Wierzbicki, Manager Human Resources
Web address: www.selectspecialtyhospitals.com/company/locations/downriver.aspx
**Control:** Corporation, Investor–owned, for–profit **Service:** Long–Term Acute Care hospital

| | |
|---|---|
| **Staffed Beds:** 40 | |

**TECUMSEH—Lenawee County**

★ **PROMEDICA HERRICK HOSPITAL (231334)**, 500 East Pottawatamie Street, Zip 49286–2018; tel. 517/424–3000, (Total facility includes 25 beds in nursing home–type unit) **A**9 10 18 **F**3 11 15 18 30 34 35 38 40 45 46 47 50 53 57 59 60 65 68 70 74 75 77 79 81 85 93 94 98 99 100 101 102 104 107 108 110 114 119 128 129 130 131 132 135 141 142 145 146 147 **P**6 7 8 **S** ProMedica Health System, Toledo, OH
Primary Contact: Timothy Jakacki, President
CFO: Bernie Nawrocki, Administrative Director Finance
CMO: Julie Yaroch, D.O., Vice President Medical Affairs
CIO: Carol Boyce, Administrative Director Support Services
CHR: Cathy J. Davis, Director Human Resources
CNO: Kathryn M. Greenlee, R.N., Vice President, Clinical Services/CNO
Web address: www.promedica.org
**Control:** Other not–for–profit (including NFP Corporation) **Service:** General Medical and Surgical

| | |
|---|---|
| **Staffed Beds:** 60 **Admissions:** 1581 **Census:** 37 **Outpatient Visits:** 47062 **Births:** 0 **Total Expense ($000):** 35604 **Payroll Expense ($000):** 11904 **Personnel:** 162 | |

**THREE RIVERS—St. Joseph County**

✠ **THREE RIVERS HEALTH (230015)**, 701 South Health Parkway, Zip 49093–8352; tel. 269/278–1145, (Nonreporting) **A**1 9 10 **S** QHR, Brentwood, TN
Primary Contact: William B. Russell, Chief Executive Officer
COO: Laurie Herbert, Vice President Operations
CFO: Steve Andrews, Chief Financial Officer
CIO: Dave Parks, Chief Information Officer
Web address: www.threerivershealth.org
**Control:** Hospital district or authority, Government, nonfederal **Service:** General Medical and Surgical

| | |
|---|---|
| **Staffed Beds:** 35 | |

**TRAVERSE CITY—Grand Traverse County**

✠ △ **MUNSON MEDICAL CENTER (230097)**, 1105 Sixth Street, Zip 49684–2386; tel. 231/935–5000 **A**1 2 3 5 7 9 10 12 13 **F**3 4 5 6 11 12 13 15 17 18 20 22 24 26 28 29 30 31 34 35 36 38 39 40 43 44 45 46 48 49 50 53 54 55 56 57 58 59 60 61 62 63 64 65 68 70 71 72 74 75 76 77 78 79 81 82 84 85 86 87 89 90 92 93 94 96 97 98 100 101 102 103 104 105 107 108 110 111 114 115 116 117 118 119 120 121 123 124 126 129 130 131 132 134 135 141 142 143 144 145 146 147 148 **P**6 **S** Munson Healthcare, Traverse City, MI
Primary Contact: Alfred E. Pilong, President
COO: Kathleen A. McManus, Executive Vice President/Chief Operating Officer
CFO: Mark A. Helper, Vice President, Chief Financial Officer
CMO: David S. McGreaham, M.D., Vice President Medical Affairs
CIO: Christopher J. Podges, Vice President and Chief Information Officer
CHR: Sue Peters, Vice President Human Resources
CNO: James Fischer, R.N., Vice President Patient Care Services/Chief Nursing Officer
Web address: www.munsonhealthcare.org
**Control:** Other not–for–profit (including NFP Corporation) **Service:** General Medical and Surgical

| | |
|---|---|
| **Staffed Beds:** 391 **Admissions:** 22549 **Census:** 284 **Outpatient Visits:** 489661 **Births:** 1909 **Total Expense ($000):** 467142 **Payroll Expense ($000):** 183675 **Personnel:** 2957 | |

**TRENTON—Wayne County**

✠ ○ **OAKWOOD SOUTHSHORE MEDICAL CENTER (230176)**, 5450 Fort Street, Zip 48183–4625; tel. 734/671–3800 **A**1 9 10 11 12 13 **F**3 8 11 13 15 17 18 20 22 26 28 29 30 31 34 35 38 39 40 43 44 46 47 49 50 56 57 59 60 61 64 65 68 70 74 75 76 78 79 80 81 82 85 86 87 92 93 96 100 102 107 108 110 111 115 118 119 130 131 132 135 146 147 148 **P**8 **S** Oakwood Healthcare, Inc., Dearborn, MI
Primary Contact: Edith M. Hughes, R.N., President
COO: J. Joseph Diederich, Executive Vice President and Chief Operating Officer
CFO: Patricia Vannoy, Controller
CMO: Iqbal Nasir, M.D., Chief of Staff
CIO: Paula Smith, Vice President Information Services and Chief Information Officer
CHR: Juliet Hafford, Director Human Resources
Web address: www.oakwood.org
**Control:** Other not–for–profit (including NFP Corporation) **Service:** General Medical and Surgical

| | |
|---|---|
| **Staffed Beds:** 144 **Admissions:** 8714 **Census:** 96 **Outpatient Visits:** 67578 **Births:** 691 **Total Expense ($000):** 136530 **Payroll Expense ($000):** 47489 **Personnel:** 679 | |

**MI**

---

**Hospital, Medicare Provider Number, Address, Telephone, Approval, Facility, and Physician Codes, Health Care System**

★ American Hospital Association (AHA) membership
☐ The Joint Commission accreditation
◇ DNV Healthcare Inc. accreditation
○ Healthcare Facilities Accreditation Program
△ Commission on Accreditation of Rehabilitation Facilities (CARF) accreditation

**TROY—Oakland County**

✠ **BEAUMONT HOSPITAL – TROY (230269)**, 44201 Dequindre Road, Zip 48085–1117; tel. 248/964–5000 **A**1 3 5 9 10 **F**3 11 12 13 14 15 17 18 20 22 24 26 28 29 30 31 32 34 35 36 39 40 44 45 46 47 48 49 50 51 54 55 56 57 58 59 60 61 62 63 64 65 66 68 70 71 72 74 75 76 77 78 79 80 81 82 84 85 86 87 89 90 91 92 93 94 96 97 100 102 103 107 108 109 110 111 114 115 117 118 119 120 121 123 126 129 130 131 132 135 141 142 143 145 146 147 148 **P**6 **S** Beaumont Health System, Royal Oak, MI
Primary Contact: Nancy Susick, MSN, President
CFO: Mark Leonard, Vice President Finance
CMO: Roger Howard, M.D., Senior Vice President and Medical Director
CIO: Subra Sripada, Senior Vice President and Chief Information Officer
CHR: Lisa Ouelette, Director Human Resources
Web address: www.beaumont.edu/troy–hospital–campus
**Control:** Other not–for–profit (including NFP Corporation) **Service:** General Medical and Surgical

**Staffed Beds:** 418 **Admissions:** 29996 **Census:** 318 **Outpatient Visits:** 865447 **Births:** 3343 **Total Expense ($000):** 488818 **Payroll Expense ($000):** 196246 **Personnel:** 2928

**VICKSBURG—Kalamazoo County**

**BRONSON VICKSBURG HOSPITAL** See Bronson Methodist Hospital, Kalamazoo

**WARREN—Macomb County**

☐ **BEHAVIORAL CENTER OF MICHIGAN (234041)**, 4050 East 12 Mile Road, Zip 48092–2534; tel. 586/261–2266, (Nonreporting) **A**1 9 10
Primary Contact: Ryan Gunabalan, Chief Executive Officer
COO: Efren Lusterio, Director of Nursing
CFO: Mark Corey, Chief Financial Officer
CMO: Eleanor Medina, M.D., Chief Medical Officer
CIO: Kashmira Khade, Coordinator Non–Clinical Services
CHR: Erin R. Youngblood, Chief Human Resources Officer
Web address: www.behavioralcenter.com
**Control:** Corporation, Investor–owned, for–profit **Service:** Psychiatric

**Staffed Beds:** 42

☐ **SOUTHEAST MICHIGAN SURGICAL HOSPITAL (230264)**, 21230 Dequindre, Zip 48091–2287; tel. 586/427–1000, (Nonreporting) **A**1 9 10 **S** National Surgical Hospitals, Chicago, IL
Primary Contact: Yvonne Kughn, Chief Executive Officer
CMO: Benjamin Paolucci, D.O., Chief of Staff
CHR: Dawn Meiers, Coordinator Medical Staff and Personnel Services
Web address: www.nshinc.com
**Control:** Corporation, Investor–owned, for–profit **Service:** Surgical

**Staffed Beds:** 13

✠ ◯ **ST. JOHN MACOMB–OAKLAND HOSPITAL (230195)**, 11800 East 12 Mile Road, Zip 48093–3472; tel. 586/573–5000, (Includes ST. JOHN MACOMB–OAKLAND HOSPITAL, MACOMB CENTER, 11800 East Twelve Mile Road, tel. 586/573–5000; ST. JOHN MACOMB–OAKLAND HOSPITAL, OAKLAND CENTER, 27351 Dequindre, Madison Heights, Zip 48071–3487; tel. 248/967–7000) **A**1 9 10 11 12 13 **F**3 11 12 13 15 17 18 20 22 24 26 28 29 30 31 34 35 36 38 39 40 43 44 45 46 47 48 49 50 51 56 57 58 59 60 61 63 64 65 68 70 74 75 76 77 78 79 80 81 82 84 85 86 87 90 91 92 93 96 97 98 100 101 102 103 105 107 108 110 114 115 116 117 119 121 123 126 129 130 131 132 135 141 143 146 147 148 **P**3 6 7 8 **S** Ascension Health, Saint Louis, MO
Primary Contact: Terry Hamilton, President
CFO: Tomasine Marx, Chief Financial Officer
CMO: Gary L. Berg, D.O., Chief Medical Officer
CIO: Mary Kay LaChance, Director Information Systems
CHR: Joanne E. Tuscany, Director Worklife Services
CNO: Constance O'Malley, Chief Nursing Officer
Web address: www.stjohnprovidence.org/macomb
**Control:** Church–operated, Nongovernment, not–for profit **Service:** General Medical and Surgical

**Staffed Beds:** 495 **Admissions:** 27766 **Census:** 370 **Outpatient Visits:** 442153 **Births:** 1198 **Total Expense ($000):** 377692 **Payroll Expense ($000):** 160424 **Personnel:** 2730

**WATERVLIET—Berrien County**

**COMMUNITY HOSPITAL** See Lakeland Community Hospital Watervliet

☐ △ **LAKELAND COMMUNITY HOSPITAL WATERVLIET (230078)**, 400 Medical Park Drive, Zip 49098–9225; tel. 269/463–3111 **A**1 7 9 10 **F**3 11 15 29 30 34 35 38 40 45 50 54 57 59 68 70 75 77 79 81 85 86 87 90 93 97 107 119 127 130 131 132 135 144 146 **S** Lakeland Healthcare, Saint Joseph, MI
Primary Contact: Ray Cruse, Chief Executive Officer
CFO: Chris Kuhlmann, Chief Financial Officer
CHR: Heather West, Director Human Resources
**Control:** Other not–for–profit (including NFP Corporation) **Service:** General Medical and Surgical

**Staffed Beds:** 38 **Admissions:** 854 **Census:** 10 **Outpatient Visits:** 44702 **Births:** 0 **Total Expense ($000):** 25728 **Payroll Expense ($000):** 12142 **Personnel:** 211

**WAYNE—Wayne County**

✠ **OAKWOOD ANNAPOLIS HOSPITAL (230142)**, 33155 Annapolis Street, Zip 48184–2405; tel. 734/467–4000 **A**1 9 10 13 **F**3 11 13 15 18 20 22 26 28 29 30 31 34 35 38 40 43 44 47 49 50 57 59 60 61 64 65 68 70 74 75 76 78 79 80 81 82 84 85 86 87 92 93 96 100 102 107 108 111 114 115 118 119 130 131 132 135 146 147 148 **P**8 **S** Oakwood Healthcare, Inc., Dearborn, MI
Primary Contact: Eric W. Widner, Division President
COO: J. Joseph Diederich, Executive Vice President and Chief Operating Officer
CFO: Roy Birmingham, Controller
CMO: Ashok Jain, M.D., Chief of Staff
CIO: Paula Smith, Senior Vice President Chief Information Officer
CHR: Robert L. James, Director Human Resources
CNO: Diane L. Hartley, R.N., Director of Patient Care Services
Web address: www.oakwood.org
**Control:** Other not–for–profit (including NFP Corporation) **Service:** General Medical and Surgical

**Staffed Beds:** 204 **Admissions:** 8514 **Census:** 93 **Outpatient Visits:** 100904 **Births:** 849 **Total Expense ($000):** 136262 **Payroll Expense ($000):** 55604 **Personnel:** 800

**WEST BLOOMFIELD—Oakland County**

★ ◇ **HENRY FORD WEST BLOOMFIELD HOSPITAL (230302)**, 6777 West Maple Road, Zip 48322–3013; tel. 248/661–4100 **A**9 10 21 **F**3 11 12 13 15 18 20 22 26 28 29 30 31 32 33 34 35 36 38 40 44 45 46 47 49 50 51 53 55 56 57 58 59 60 61 64 65 68 70 74 75 76 77 78 79 81 82 84 85 86 87 89 93 97 100 102 103 107 108 110 111 114 115 116 117 118 119 120 121 123 124 126 129 130 131 132 135 143 146 147 148 **P**6 **S** Henry Ford Health System, Detroit, MI
Primary Contact: MaryClaire Dangel–Palmer, Chief Operating Officer
COO: Christine Zambrini, Chief Operating Officer and Chief Nursing Officer
Web address: www.henryford.com
**Control:** Other not–for–profit (including NFP Corporation) **Service:** General Medical and Surgical

**Staffed Beds:** 191 **Admissions:** 13132 **Census:** 139 **Outpatient Visits:** 359541 **Births:** 1647 **Total Expense ($000):** 247938 **Payroll Expense ($000):** 95937 **Personnel:** 1566

**WEST BRANCH—Ogemaw County**

★ ◯ **WEST BRANCH REGIONAL MEDICAL CENTER (230095)**, 2463 South M–30, Zip 48661–1199; tel. 989/345–3660 **A**9 10 11 20 **F**3 11 15 17 20 28 29 30 34 35 40 50 57 59 63 64 75 77 79 81 84 93 107 111 114 115 117 119 130 146 148 **P**6
Primary Contact: Edward A. Napierala, FACHE, Chief Executive Officer
CFO: Robert McGrail, Chief Financial Officer
CMO: Patrick Morse, M.D., President Medical Staff
CIO: Doug Danitz, Director Information Technology
CHR: Dane J. Turner, Director Human Resources
CNO: Noreen B. Connolly, MS, Chief Nurse Executive
Web address: www.wbrmc.com
**Control:** City–Government, nonfederal **Service:** General Medical and Surgical

**Staffed Beds:** 88 **Admissions:** 2218 **Census:** 25 **Outpatient Visits:** 70297 **Births:** 0 **Total Expense ($000):** 38598 **Payroll Expense ($000):** 13085 **Personnel:** 305

**WESTLAND—Wayne County**

☐ **WALTER P. REUTHER PSYCHIATRIC HOSPITAL (234035)**, 30901 Palmer Road, Zip 48186–5389; tel. 734/367–8400, (Nonreporting) **A**1 9 10
Primary Contact: Ron Denstedt, Acting Director
CMO: Venkata Lingam, M.D., Chief Clinical Affairs
CHR: Gerald Gibson, Director Human Resources
Web address: www.mhweb.org/wayne/reuther.htm
**Control:** State–Government, nonfederal **Service:** Psychiatric

**Staffed Beds:** 239

*Many Facility Codes have changed. Please refer to the AHA Guide Code Chart.*    © 2013 AHA Guide

## WYANDOTTE—Wayne County

★ △ ◇ **HENRY FORD WYANDOTTE HOSPITAL (230146)**, 2333 Biddle Avenue, Zip 48192–4668; tel. 734/246–6000 **A**7 9 10 12 13 21 **F**3 8 11 12 13 15 17 18 20 22 26 28 29 30 31 32 34 35 36 38 40 42 44 45 46 47 49 50 51 54 56 57 58 59 60 64 65 66 68 69 70 74 75 76 77 78 79 80 81 82 84 85 86 87 90 92 93 94 96 98 100 101 102 103 107 108 110 111 114 115 116 117 118 119 126 129 130 131 132 135 146 147 148 **P**6 **S** Henry Ford Health System, Detroit, MI
Primary Contact: Denise Brooks–Williams, President and Chief Executive Officer
COO: Rand O'Leary, Senior Vice President and Chief Operating Officer
CFO: James J. Miller, Vice President and Chief Financial Officer
CMO: Dennis R. Lemanski, D.O., Senior Vice President Medical Affairs and Medical Education/CMO
CMO: Mohinder S. Singh–Sandhu, M.D., President Medical Staff
CIO: Mary Alice Annecharico, Senior VP and CIO, Henry Ford Health System
CIO: Arthur K. Gross, FACHE, Executive Vice President and Chief Information Officer
CHR: Aline S. Lafferty, Vice President Human Resources
CNO: Josephine Sclafani Wahl, R.N., VP, Patient Care Services & CNO
Web address: www.henryfordhealth.org
**Control:** Other not–for–profit (including NFP Corporation) **Service:** General Medical and Surgical

**Staffed Beds:** 348 **Admissions:** 18446 **Census:** 239 **Outpatient Visits:** 336772 **Births:** 1363 **Total Expense ($000):** 264677 **Payroll Expense ($000):** 111717 **Personnel:** 1956

## WYOMING—Kent County

★ ○ **METRO HEALTH HOSPITAL (230236)**, 5900 Byron Center Avenue S.W., Zip 49519–9606, Mailing Address: P.O. Box 916, Zip 49509–0916; tel. 616/252–7200 **A**9 10 11 12 13 **F**3 12 13 15 18 20 22 24 26 29 30 31 34 35 40 44 45 49 50 51 54 57 58 59 64 65 70 71 74 75 76 77 78 79 80 81 82 85 86 87 91 92 93 94 96 97 107 108 110 111 114 115 117 119 126 129 130 131 132 135 146 147 148 **P**8
Primary Contact: Michael D. Faas, President and Chief Executive Officer
COO: Jamal Ghani, Chief Operating Officer
CFO: Tim Susterich, Chief Financial Officer
CMO: William Cunningham, D.O., Chief Medical Officer
CIO: William Lewkowski, Executive Vice President Information Services and Chief Information Officer
CHR: Floyd Wilson, Jr., Executive Vice President Human Resources
Web address: www.metrohealth.net
**Control:** Other not–for–profit (including NFP Corporation) **Service:** General Medical and Surgical

**Staffed Beds:** 208 **Admissions:** 9483 **Census:** 139 **Outpatient Visits:** 407179 **Births:** 1799 **Total Expense ($000):** 258335 **Payroll Expense ($000):** 92165 **Personnel:** 1729

## YPSILANTI—Washtenaw County

☐ **FOREST HEALTH MEDICAL CENTER (230144)**, 135 South Prospect Street, Zip 48198–7914; tel. 734/547–4700 **A**1 9 10 **F**12 30 46 64 75 79 81 82 85 119 130 132
Primary Contact: Trevor J. Dyksterhouse, President
COO: Trevor J. Dyksterhouse, President
CFO: Dan Miller, Vice President Finance
CMO: Steven Poplawski, M.D., Medical Director
CIO: Steve Jerant, Vice President Information Technology
CHR: Karen Pinto, Coordinator Human Resources
Web address: www.barixclinics.com
**Control:** Corporation, Investor–owned, for–profit **Service:** General Medical and Surgical

**Staffed Beds:** 24 **Admissions:** 1555 **Census:** 5 **Outpatient Visits:** 6241 **Births:** 0 **Personnel:** 45

⊠ **SELECT SPECIALTY HOSPITAL–ANN ARBOR (232024)**, 5301 East Huron River Drive, 7th Floor, Zip 48197–1051; tel. 734/712–0111, (Nonreporting) **A**1 9 10 **S** Select Medical Corporation, Mechanicsburg, PA
Primary Contact: John F. O'Malley, FACHE, Chief Executive Officer
CMO: Jim Hayner, M.D., Medical Director
CHR: Cambrea Baker, Coordinator Human Resources
Web address: www.selectspecialtyhospitals.com/company/locations/annarbor.aspx
**Control:** Corporation, Investor–owned, for–profit **Service:** Long–Term Acute Care hospital

**Staffed Beds:** 36

⊠ **ST. JOSEPH MERCY HOSPITAL (230156)**, 5301 Mcauley Drive, Zip 48197–1051, Mailing Address: P.O. Box 995, Ann Arbor, Zip 48106–0995; tel. 734/712–3456 **A**1 3 5 8 10 **F**3 4 5 6 8 9 11 12 13 15 17 18 19 20 22 24 26 28 29 30 31 32 33 34 35 36 37 38 40 41 42 43 44 45 46 50 51 53 54 56 57 58 59 60 61 62 63 64 65 66 67 68 70 71 72 73 74 75 76 77 78 79 80 81 82 83 84 85 86 87 89 90 91 92 93 94 97 98 99 100 101 102 103 104 105 107 108 109 110 111 114 115 117 118 119 120 121 123 124 125 126 128 129 130 131 132 134 135 141 143 144 145 146 147 **P**5 **S** Trinity Health, Livonia, MI
Primary Contact: Robert F. Casalou, President and Chief Executive Officer
CFO: Kathy O'Connor, Vice President, Finance and Chief Financial Officer
CMO: Rolland Mambourg, M.D., Vice President Physician Services
CIO: Joan Hurray, Regional Director Information Services
CHR: Kathleen Rhine, Vice President Administrative Services and Chief Operating Officer
Web address: www.sjmercyhealth.org
**Control:** Church–operated, Nongovernment, not–for profit **Service:** General Medical and Surgical

**Staffed Beds:** 537 **Admissions:** 32363 **Census:** 386 **Outpatient Visits:** 1202602 **Births:** 3690 **Total Expense ($000):** 720893 **Payroll Expense ($000):** 268771 **Personnel:** 5604

## ZEELAND—Ottawa County

⊠ **SPECTRUM HEALTH ZEELAND COMMUNITY HOSPITAL (230003)**, 8333 Felch Street, Zip 49464–2608; tel. 616/772–4644 **A**1 9 10 **F**3 12 13 15 17 18 29 34 35 40 45 54 57 59 63 64 65 68 69 70 75 76 79 81 85 89 90 93 97 107 110 111 115 119 129 130 132 135 144 146 **S** Spectrum Health, Grand Rapids, MI
Primary Contact: Henry A. Veenstra, President
CFO: Ryan J. Powers, Vice President Finance
CMO: Dale Terpstra, D.O., Vice President Physician Services
CIO: Imran Syed, Manager Technology Information Services
CHR: Jennifer F. Becksvoort, Senior Human Resource Business Partner
CNO: Jane Czerew, Vice President Clinical Services and Quality
Web address: www.spectrumhealth.org/zeeland
**Control:** Other not–for–profit (including NFP Corporation) **Service:** General Medical and Surgical

**Staffed Beds:** 57 **Admissions:** 2213 **Census:** 19 **Outpatient Visits:** 81381 **Births:** 520 **Total Expense ($000):** 50045 **Payroll Expense ($000):** 19527 **Personnel:** 298

**ZEELAND COMMUNITY HOSPITAL** See Spectrum Health Zeeland Community Hospital

MI

---

**Hospital, Medicare Provider Number, Address, Telephone, Approval, Facility, and Physician Codes, Health Care System**

★ American Hospital Association (AHA) membership
☐ The Joint Commission accreditation
◇ DNV Healthcare Inc. accreditation
○ Healthcare Facilities Accreditation Program
△ Commission on Accreditation of Rehabilitation Facilities (CARF) accreditation

# MINNESOTA

**MN**

### ADA—Norman County

**BRIDGES MEDICAL CENTER** See Essentia Health Ada

★ **ESSENTIA HEALTH ADA (241313)**, 201 9th Street West, Zip 56510–1279; tel. 218/784–5000, (Nonreporting) **A**9 10 18 **S** Essentia Health, Duluth, MN
Primary Contact: Ryan Hill, Interim Chief Executive Officer
CFO: Ryan Hill, Chief Financial Officer
CMO: Jeff Peterson, M.D., Chief of Staff
CHR: Shayla Hennenberg, Director Human Resources
Web address: www.essentiahealth.org
**Control:** Other not–for–profit (including NFP Corporation) **Service:** General Medical and Surgical

**Staffed Beds:** 14

### AITKIN—Crow Wing County

⊠ **RIVERWOOD HEALTHCARE CENTER (241305)**, 200 Bunker Hill Drive, Zip 56431–1865; tel. 218/927–2121 **A**1 9 10 18 **F**3 8 11 13 15 28 29 31 32 34 35 40 43 45 54 56 57 59 64 65 70 75 76 77 78 79 81 82 86 87 93 97 104 107 110 111 114 119 127 129 130 131 132 133 135 144 145 146 147 148 **P**6
Primary Contact: Chad D. Cooper, Chief Executive Officer
CFO: Kent Dumonseau, Chief Financial Officer
CMO: Mark Heggem, M.D., Chief Medical Officer
CIO: Daryl Kallevig, Chief Information Officer
CHR: Cindi Hills, Director Human Resources
CNO: Kristine Layne, R.N., Chief Nursing Officer
Web address: www.riverwoodhealthcare.com
**Control:** Other not–for–profit (including NFP Corporation) **Service:** General Medical and Surgical

**Staffed Beds:** 25 **Admissions:** 1122 **Census:** 10 **Outpatient Visits:** 67848
**Births:** 63 **Total Expense ($000):** 47648 **Payroll Expense ($000):** 19134
**Personnel:** 314

### ALBANY—Stearns County

★ **ALBANY AREA HOSPITAL AND MEDICAL CENTER (241331)**, 300 Third Avenue, Zip 56307–9363; tel. 320/845–2121, (Data for 364 days) **A**9 10 18 **F**1 4 13 15 16 17 30 34 35 40 45 50 59 64 65 67 70 72 73 76 77 79 80 81 88 89 90 93 98 107 114 119 127 128 129 130 132 133 135 146 **P**6 **S** Catholic Health Initiatives, Englewood, CO
Primary Contact: Sandra Day, Administrator, Chief Nursing Officer
CFO: Steve Smith, Chief Financial Officer
CMO: Aaron Gersch, M.D., Chief of Staff
CHR: Bernie Cekalla, Manager Human Resources
CNO: Sandra Day, Administrator, Chief Nursing Officer
Web address: www.albanyareahospital.com
**Control:** Church–operated, Nongovernment, not–for profit **Service:** General Medical and Surgical

**Staffed Beds:** 17 **Admissions:** 247 **Census:** 3 **Outpatient Visits:** 28134
**Births:** 45 **Total Expense ($000):** 11279 **Payroll Expense ($000):** 4795
**Personnel:** 69

### ALBERT LEA—Freeborn County

☐ **MAYO CLINIC HEALTH SYSTEM IN ALBERT LEA (240043)**, 404 West Fountain Street, Zip 56007–2473; tel. 507/373–2384, (Nonreporting) **A**1 5 9 10 **S** Mayo Clinic Health System, Rochester, MN
Primary Contact: Mark Ciota, M.D., Chief Executive Officer
CFO: Sheri Dankert, Chief Financial Officer
CMO: John Grzybowski, M.D., Medical Director
CHR: Monica Fleegel, Director Human Resources
CNO: Lori Routh, R.N., Nurse Administrator
Web address: www.almedcenter.org
**Control:** Other not–for–profit (including NFP Corporation) **Service:** General Medical and Surgical

**Staffed Beds:** 129

### ALEXANDRIA—Sherburne County

☐ **COMMUNITY BEHAVIORAL HEALTH HOSPITAL – ALEXANDRIA (244012)**, 1610 8th Avenue East, Zip 56308–2472; tel. 320/335–6201, (Nonreporting) **A**1 10 **S** Minnesota Department of Human Services, Saint Paul, MN
Primary Contact: Pamela R. Bajari, R.N., Interim Administrator
CFO: Shirley Jacobson, Chief Financial Officer
Web address: www.health.state.mn.us
**Control:** State–Government, nonfederal **Service:** Psychiatric

**Staffed Beds:** 16

★ ○ **DOUGLAS COUNTY HOSPITAL (240030)**, 111 17th Avenue East, Zip 56308–3798; tel. 320/762–1511 **A**2 9 10 11 **F**3 8 11 13 15 28 30 31 34 36 40 43 45 57 61 64 68 69 70 76 77 78 79 81 85 86 89 93 107 108 111 115 117 119 129 130 131 132 135 146 **P**6
Primary Contact: Carl P. Vaagenes, Chief Executive Officer
CFO: Nate Meyer, Director Finance
CHR: Sister Patrice Kiefer, Director Human Resources
Web address: www.dchospital.com
**Control:** County–Government, nonfederal **Service:** General Medical and Surgical

**Staffed Beds:** 99 **Admissions:** 3758 **Census:** 39 **Outpatient Visits:** 56555
**Births:** 587

### ANNANDALE—Wright County

☐ **COMMUNITY BEHAVIORAL HEALTH HOSPITAL – ANNANDALE (244011)**, 400 Annandale Boulevard, Zip 55302–3141; tel. 651/259–3850, (Nonreporting) **A**1 10 **S** Minnesota Department of Human Services, Saint Paul, MN
Primary Contact: Pamela Barger, R.N., Interim Administrator
Web address: www.health.state.mn.us
**Control:** State–Government, nonfederal **Service:** Psychiatric

**Staffed Beds:** 16

### ANOKA—Anoka County

☐ **ANOKA–METROPOLITAN REGIONAL TREATMENT CENTER (244002)**, 3301 Seventh Avenue, Zip 55303–4516; tel. 763/712–4000, (Nonreporting) **A**1 10 **S** Minnesota Department of Human Services, Saint Paul, MN
Primary Contact: Nancy Webster–Smith, Administrator
Web address: www.health.state.mn.us
**Control:** State–Government, nonfederal **Service:** Psychiatric

**Staffed Beds:** 112

### APPLETON—Swift County

★ **APPLETON AREA HEALTH SERVICES (241341)**, 30 South Behl Street, Zip 56208–1699; tel. 320/289–2422, (Nonreporting) **A**9 10 18
Primary Contact: Jeffrey A. Cook, Chief Executive Officer
CFO: Anne Kells, Interim Chief Financial Officer
Web address: www.appletonareahealth.com
**Control:** City–Government, nonfederal **Service:** General Medical and Surgical

**Staffed Beds:** 68

### ARLINGTON—Sibley County

★ **SIBLEY MEDICAL CENTER (241311)**, 601 West Chandler Street, Zip 55307–2127; tel. 507/964–2271 **A**9 10 18 **F**8 15 28 29 31 34 35 38 40 41 42 43 45 50 56 57 59 62 64 65 66 67 68 75 77 78 79 81 85 89 92 93 97 100 102 107 114 119 127 128 129 133 143 144 145 148 **P**6
Primary Contact: Todd Sandberg, Chief Executive Officer and Administrator
CFO: Darla Anderson, Chief Financial Officer
CMO: Ehtaisham Mohammed, M.D., Chief Medical Officer
CIO: Chris Bulau, Manager Information Technology
CHR: Sara Christiansen, Interim Director Human Resources
CNO: Sandy Domeier, Director Patient Care Services
Web address: www.sibleymedical.org
**Control:** City–Government, nonfederal **Service:** General Medical and Surgical

**Staffed Beds:** 17 **Admissions:** 141 **Census:** 2 **Outpatient Visits:** 9571
**Births:** 0 **Total Expense ($000):** 11451 **Personnel:** 81

### AURORA—St. Louis County

★ **ESSENTIA HEALTH NORTHERN PINES (241340)**, 5211 Highway 110, Zip 55705–1599; tel. 218/229–2211, (Total facility includes 50 beds in nursing home–type unit) **A**9 10 18 **F**28 29 34 38 40 43 50 56 59 65 75 77 79 81 87 91 93 97 107 128 130 133 **S** Essentia Health, Duluth, MN
Primary Contact: Laura Ackman, Chief Operating Officer and Administrator
CFO: Barbara Johnson, Chief Financial Officer
CMO: Michelle Oman, D.O., Chief Medical Officer
CHR: Kim Carlson, Director Human Resources
CNO: Cindy Loe, Director of Nursing
Web address: www.essentiahealth.org/NorthernPines/FindaClinic/Essentia–HealthNorthern–Pines–36.aspx
**Control:** Other not–for–profit (including NFP Corporation) **Service:** General Medical and Surgical

**Staffed Beds:** 58 **Admissions:** 293 **Census:** 50 **Outpatient Visits:** 4856
**Births:** 0 **Total Expense ($000):** 13273 **Payroll Expense ($000):** 6182
**Personnel:** 119

**WHITE COMMUNITY HOSPITAL** See Essentia Health Northern Pines

*Many Facility Codes have changed. Please refer to the AHA Guide Code Chart.*

## AUSTIN—Mower County

☐ **MAYO CLINIC HEALTH SYSTEM IN AUSTIN (240117)**, 1000 First Drive N.W., Zip 55912–2904; tel. 507/433–7351, (Nonreporting) **A**1 5 9 10 **S** Mayo Clinic Health System, Rochester, MN
Primary Contact: Mark Ciota, M.D., Chief Executive Officer
CFO: Sheri Dankert, Vice President Finance
CMO: Cynthia Dube, M.D., Medical Director
CIO: Tammy Kritzer, Vice President Clinic Operations
CHR: Rodney Nording, Vice President Organizational Support
CNO: Lori Routh, R.N., Nurse Administrator
Web address: www.austinmedicalcenter.org
**Control:** Other not–for–profit (including NFP Corporation) **Service:** General Medical and Surgical

Staffed Beds: 82

## BAGLEY—Clearwater County

★ **SANFORD BAGLEY MEDICAL CENTER (241328)**, 203 Fourth Street N.W., Zip 56621–8307; tel. 218/694–6501, (Nonreporting) **A**9 10 18 **S** Sanford Health, Sioux Falls, SD
Primary Contact: Kirby Johnson, Administrator
CFO: Rachel Rosenbush, Account Manager
CMO: Esther Potti, M.D., Chief Medical Staff
Web address: www.clearwaterhealthservices.com
**Control:** County–Government, nonfederal **Service:** General Medical and Surgical

Staffed Beds: 95

## BAUDETTE—Lake Of The Woods County

★ **LAKEWOOD HEALTH CENTER (241301)**, 600 Main Avenue South, Zip 56623–2855; tel. 218/634–2120, (Total facility includes 40 beds in nursing home–type unit) **A**9 10 18 **F**3 7 10 15 28 30 31 34 35 40 45 50 53 57 64 66 68 79 81 85 89 107 119 128 130 133 **P**6 **S** Catholic Health Initiatives, Englewood, CO
Primary Contact: Jason Breuer, President
CFO: Lynn Ellis, Chief Financial Officer
CIO: Darlene Bushaw, Information Technology Systems Site Lead
CHR: Lois Slick, Director Human Resources
Web address: www.lakewoodhealthcenter.org
**Control:** Church–operated, Nongovernment, not–for profit **Service:** General Medical and Surgical

Staffed Beds: 55 Admissions: 263 Census: 42 Outpatient Visits: 23420 Births: 0 Total Expense ($000): 13561 Payroll Expense ($000): 6016 Personnel: 131

## BAXTER—Crow Wing County

☐ **COMMUNITY BEHAVIORAL HEALTH HOSPITAL – BAXTER (244015)**, 14241 Grand Oaks Drive, Zip 56425–8749; tel. 218/316–3101, (Nonreporting) **A**1 10 **S** Minnesota Department of Human Services, Saint Paul, MN
Primary Contact: Richard G. Slieter, Jr., Administrator
**Control:** State–Government, nonfederal **Service:** Psychiatric

Staffed Beds: 16

## BEMIDJI—Beltrami County

☐ **COMMUNITY BEHAVIORAL HEALTH HOSPITAL – BEMIDJI (244014)**, 800 Bemidji Avenue North, Zip 56601–3054; tel. 218/308–2400, (Nonreporting) **A**1 10 **S** Minnesota Department of Human Services, Saint Paul, MN
Primary Contact: Richard G. Slieter, Jr., Administrator
**Control:** State–Government, nonfederal **Service:** Psychiatric

Staffed Beds: 16

**NORTH COUNTRY REGIONAL HOSPITAL** See Sanford Bemidji Medical Center

★ **SANFORD BEMIDJI MEDICAL CENTER (240100)**, 1300 Anne Street N.W., Zip 56601–5103; tel. 218/751–5430, (Total facility includes 78 beds in nursing home–type unit) **A**9 10 **F**3 7 8 10 11 13 14 15 20 22 28 29 30 31 34 35 40 44 45 46 50 51 53 54 56 57 59 62 63 64 65 70 74 75 76 77 78 79 81 85 86 87 90 93 103 107 108 110 111 114 115 117 119 120 121 123 124 125 127 128 129 130 131 132 133 135 141 142 144 145 146 148 **P**6 **S** Sanford Health, Sioux Falls, SD
Primary Contact: Joy E. Johnson, Interim President
CFO: Craig Boyer, Vice President Finance
CMO: Daniel DeKrey, M.D., Chief of Staff
CIO: Dan Moffatt, Chief Information Officer
Web address: www.nchs.com
**Control:** Other not–for–profit (including NFP Corporation) **Service:** General Medical and Surgical

Staffed Beds: 196 Admissions: 6125 Census: 144 Outpatient Visits: 262210 Births: 987 Total Expense ($000): 104957 Payroll Expense ($000): 47275 Personnel: 961

## BENSON—Swift County

★ **SWIFT COUNTY–BENSON HOSPITAL (241365)**, 1815 Wisconsin Avenue, Zip 56215–1653; tel. 320/843–1311, (Nonreporting) **A**9 10 18
Primary Contact: Frank Lawatsch, Chief Executive Officer
CFO: Jayne Thielke, Chief Financial Officer
CMO: Roger Bauer, M.D., Chief Medical Officer
CIO: Jayne Thielke, Chief Financial Officer
CHR: Stella Kalthoff, Administrative Assistant, Manager Human Resources and Coordinator Quality Improvement
Web address: www.scbh.org
**Control:** Hospital district or authority, Government, nonfederal **Service:** General Medical and Surgical

Staffed Beds: 18

## BIGFORK—Itasca County

★ **BIGFORK VALLEY HOSPITAL (241316)**, 258 Pine Tree Drive, Zip 56628, Mailing Address: P.O. Box 258, Zip 56628–0258; tel. 218/743–3177, (Nonreporting) **A**9 10 18
Primary Contact: Daniel Odegaard, Chief Executive Officer
CFO: Karen M. Campbell, Director Finance
CMO: George Rounds, M.D., Chief of Staff
CIO: Sally Sedgwick, Manager Public Relations and Marketing
CHR: Jennifer Drotts, Manager Human Resources
Web address: www.bigforkvalley.org
**Control:** Hospital district or authority, Government, nonfederal **Service:** General Medical and Surgical

Staffed Beds: 60

## BLUE EARTH—Faribault County

⊞ **UNITED HOSPITAL DISTRICT (241369)**, 515 South Moore Street, Zip 56013–2158, Mailing Address: P.O. Box 160, Zip 56013–0160; tel. 507/526–3273, (Nonreporting) **A**1 9 10 18
Primary Contact: Jeffrey M. Lang, Chief Executive Officer
CFO: Larry Lee, Chief Financial Officer
Web address: www.uhd.org
**Control:** Hospital district or authority, Government, nonfederal **Service:** General Medical and Surgical

Staffed Beds: 41

## BRAINERD—Crow Wing County

☐ **ESSENTIA HEALTH ST. JOSEPH'S MEDICAL CENTER (240075)**, 523 North Third Street, Zip 56401–3098; tel. 218/829–2861, (Nonreporting) **A**1 2 9 10 **S** Essentia Health, Duluth, MN
Primary Contact: Adam Rees, President
CFO: James Winch, Vice President Finance
CMO: David Boran, M.D., Chief Medical Officer
CHR: Dale Benson, Vice President Human Resources
Web address: www.sjmcmn.org
**Control:** Church–operated, Nongovernment, not–for profit **Service:** General Medical and Surgical

Staffed Beds: 162

☐ **MINNESOTA NEUROREHABILITATION HOSPITAL (243025)**, 11615 State Avenue, Zip 56401–7306; tel. 218/828–6123, (Nonreporting) **A**1
Primary Contact: Dawn Barnard, Administrator
**Control:** State–Government, nonfederal **Service:** Rehabilitation

Staffed Beds: 15

**ST. JOSEPH'S MEDICAL CENTER** See Essentia Health St. Joseph's Medical Center

## BRECKENRIDGE—Wilkin County

★ **ST. FRANCIS HEALTHCARE CAMPUS (241377)**, 2400 St. Francis Drive, Zip 56520–1025; tel. 218/643–3000, (Total facility includes 120 beds in nursing home–type unit) **A**5 9 10 18 **F**3 5 8 11 13 15 17 28 29 30 32 34 35 38 39 40 43 45 46 50 53 56 57 59 64 70 75 76 77 79 81 87 89 93 96 97 99 100 101 102 103 104 107 110 111 115 119 125 127 128 129 130 131 132 133 143 146 **P**6 **S** Catholic Health Initiatives, Englewood, CO
Primary Contact: David A. Nelson, President
CFO: Nancy Whitney, Chief Financial Officer
Web address: www.sfcare.org
**Control:** Church–operated, Nongovernment, not–for profit **Service:** General Medical and Surgical

Staffed Beds: 145 Admissions: 1020 Census: 120 Outpatient Visits: 22220 Births: 168 Total Expense ($000): 30962 Payroll Expense ($000): 12592 Personnel: 301

MN

---

**Hospital, Medicare Provider Number, Address, Telephone, Approval, Facility, and Physician Codes, Health Care System**

★ American Hospital Association (AHA) membership
☐ The Joint Commission accreditation     ◇ DNV Healthcare Inc. accreditation

○ Healthcare Facilities Accreditation Program
△ Commission on Accreditation of Rehabilitation Facilities (CARF) accreditation

## BUFFALO—Wright County

⊞ **BUFFALO HOSPITAL (240076)**, 303 Catlin Street, Zip 55313–1947;
tel. 763/682–1212 **A**1 9 10 **F**3 11 13 15 18 28 29 31 32 34 35 36 40 43 44
45 57 59 64 75 76 78 79 80 81 85 86 87 89 93 107 110 111 114 118 119
129 130 131 132 135 146 148 **S** Allina Health, Minneapolis, MN
Primary Contact: Jennifer Myster, President
COO: Laura Jenkins, Director Operations Finance and Business Development
CFO: Sandra Matrella, Manager Finance
CMO: Corey Martin, M.D., Director Medical Affairs
CIO: Lois Nevinski, Manager Information Services
CHR: Nikki Mills, Director Human Resources and Operations
CNO: Gretchen A. Frederick, R.N., Director Patient Care Services
Web address: www.buffalohospital.org
**Control:** Other not–for–profit (including NFP Corporation) **Service:** General
Medical and Surgical

**Staffed Beds:** 44 **Admissions:** 2648 **Census:** 17 **Outpatient Visits:** 70727
**Births:** 884 **Total Expense ($000):** 60036 **Payroll Expense ($000):** 23907
**Personnel:** 327

## BURNSVILLE—Dakota County

⊞ **FAIRVIEW RIDGES HOSPITAL (240207)**, 201 East Nicollet Boulevard,
Zip 55337–5799; tel. 952/892–2000 **A**1 2 3 9 10 **F**3 11 13 15 18 20 22 28
29 30 31 34 35 36 40 41 43 44 45 49 50 51 55 57 64 68 70 72 74 75 76
77 78 79 81 82 84 85 87 89 93 100 107 108 110 111 114 118 119 126
130 132 146 148 **P**6 **S** Fairview Health Services, Minneapolis, MN
Primary Contact: Beth Krehbiel, President and Chief Executive Officer
COO: Brian A. Knapp, Vice President Operations
CFO: Alan Lem, Vice President Finance
CMO: Lizbeth Thomas, M.D., Vice President Medical Affairs
CHR: Mary Kaphings, Director Human Resources
CNO: Carol Koeppel–Olsen, R.N., Vice President Patient Care Services
Web address: www.fairview.org
**Control:** Other not–for–profit (including NFP Corporation) **Service:** General
Medical and Surgical

**Staffed Beds:** 165 **Admissions:** 11725 **Census:** 107 **Outpatient Visits:**
101903 **Births:** 2636 **Total Expense ($000):** 154523 **Payroll Expense
($000):** 78463 **Personnel:** 966

## CAMBRIDGE—Isanti County

⊞ **CAMBRIDGE MEDICAL CENTER (240020)**, 701 South Dellwood Street,
Zip 55008–1920; tel. 763/689–7700 **A**1 9 10 **F**3 4 5 11 13 14 15 18 28 29
30 31 32 34 35 38 40 43 45 50 56 57 59 61 64 65 69 70 74 75 76 77 78
79 81 82 85 86 87 89 93 97 98 99 100 101 102 103 104 107 108 111 114
119 125 129 130 131 132 134 135 144 145 146 147 148 **P**5 6 **S** Allina
Health, Minneapolis, MN
Primary Contact: Gary Shaw, President
CFO: Nancy Treacy, Director Finance
CHR: Diane Rasmussen, Director Human Resources
CNO: Mari J. Holt, R.N., Directo Patient Care Services
Web address: www.allina.com/ahs/cambridge.nsf
**Control:** Other not–for–profit (including NFP Corporation) **Service:** General
Medical and Surgical

**Staffed Beds:** 78 **Admissions:** 3672 **Census:** 41 **Outpatient Visits:** 90954
**Births:** 457 **Total Expense ($000):** 75228 **Payroll Expense ($000):** 29966
**Personnel:** 655

## CANBY—Yellow Medicine County

★ **SANFORD CANBY MEDICAL CENTER (241347)**, (Formerly Sanford Medical
Center Canby), 112 St. Olaf Avenue South, Zip 56220–1433;
tel. 507/223–7277, (Includes SENIOR HAVEN CONVALESCENT NURSING CENTER
), (Total facility includes 68 beds in nursing home–type unit) **A**9 10 **F**2 3 7 10
11 13 15 28 29 31 35 39 40 45 46 49 53 56 59 60 62 64 65 70 71 75 76
81 89 93 107 110 119 128 130 132 133 143 144 **P**6 **S** Sanford Health, Sioux
Falls, SD
Primary Contact: Lori Sisk, R.N., Chief Executive Officer
CFO: Allison Nelson, Chief Financial Officer
CMO: Maritza Lopez, M.D., Chief of Staff
CIO: Cheryl L. Ferguson, Associate Administrator
Web address: www.sanfordcanby.org
**Control:** Other not–for–profit (including NFP Corporation) **Service:** General
Medical and Surgical

**Staffed Beds:** 93 **Admissions:** 451 **Census:** 73 **Outpatient Visits:** 28076
**Births:** 37 **Total Expense ($000):** 21056 **Payroll Expense ($000):** 10229
**Personnel:** 209

## CANNON FALLS—Goodhue County

⊞ **MAYO CLINIC HEALTH SYSTEM IN CANNON FALLS (241346)**, 1116 West
Mill Street, Zip 55009–1898; tel. 507/263–4221, (Nonreporting) **A**1 9 10 18
**S** Mayo Clinic Health System, Rochester, MN
Primary Contact: Thomas J. Witt, M.D., President and Chief Executive Officer
COO: Glenn Christian, Administrator
CFO: Edward A. Tusa, Chief Financial Officer
CMO: Tarlochan Turna, M.D., Medical Director
CHR: Mary Garlets, Director Human Resources
Web address: www.mayoclinichealthsystem.org/locations/cannon–falls
**Control:** Hospital district or authority, Government, nonfederal **Service:** General
Medical and Surgical

**Staffed Beds:** 21

## CASS LAKE—Cass County

★ **U. S. PUBLIC HEALTH SERVICE INDIAN HOSPITAL (241358)**, 7th Street &
Grant Utley Avenue N.W., Zip 56633, Mailing Address: Rural Route 3, Box 211,
Zip 56633; tel. 218/335–3200, (Nonreporting) **A**5 9 10 18 **S** U. S. Indian Health
Service, Rockville, MD
Primary Contact: Norine Smith, Chief Executive Officer
CFO: Randall Jordan, Budget Analyst
Web address: www.ihs.gov
**Control:** PHS, Indian Service, Government, federal **Service:** General Medical and
Surgical

**Staffed Beds:** 11

## CLOQUET—Carlton County

★ **COMMUNITY MEMORIAL HOSPITAL (241364)**, 512 Skyline Boulevard,
Zip 55720–1199; tel. 218/879–4641, (Nonreporting) **A**9 10 18
Primary Contact: Rick Breuer, Chief Executive Officer and Administrator
CFO: Brad Anderson, Chief Financial Officer
CIO: Jason Stoeke, Director Management Information Systems
CHR: Cory Glad, Director Human Resources
Web address: www.cloquethospital.com
**Control:** Other not–for–profit (including NFP Corporation) **Service:** General
Medical and Surgical

**Staffed Beds:** 113

## COOK—St. Louis County

★ **COOK HOSPITAL AND CONVALESCENT NURSING CARE UNIT (241312)**, 10
Fifth Street S.E., Zip 55723–9745; tel. 218/666–5945, (Total facility includes 28
beds in nursing home–type unit) **A**9 10 18 **F**2 3 11 15 28 29 35 40 53 56 57
64 77 81 93 96 107 110 111 119 128 130 133 148
Primary Contact: Allen J. Vogt, Chief Executive Officer
CFO: Kaylee S. Hoard, Chief Financial Officer
Web address: www.cookhospital.org
**Control:** Hospital district or authority, Government, nonfederal **Service:** General
Medical and Surgical

**Staffed Beds:** 42 **Admissions:** 361 **Census:** 29 **Outpatient Visits:** 15597
**Births:** 0 **Total Expense ($000):** 11210 **Payroll Expense ($000):** 4946
**Personnel:** 109

## COON RAPIDS—Anoka County

⊞ **MERCY HOSPITAL (240115)**, 4050 Coon Rapids Boulevard, Zip 55433–2586;
tel. 763/236–6000 **A**1 2 3 5 9 10 **F**3 8 11 13 17 18 20 22 24 26 28 29 30
31 34 35 36 37 38 40 43 45 49 53 55 59 63 64 65 68 69 70 74 75 76 77
78 79 81 82 85 87 89 93 97 98 99 100 101 102 103 104 105 107 108 111
115 119 126 130 132 135 146 147 148 **P**4 5 6 **S** Allina Health,
Minneapolis, MN
Primary Contact: Sara J. Criger, President
COO: Brandi Lunneborg, Vice President Operations
CFO: Earl Beitzel, Vice President Finance
CMO: Ryan Else, M.D., Interim Vice President Medical Affairs
CIO: Susan Heichert, Chief Information Officer
CHR: Nancy Watson, Director Human Resources
CNO: MariBeth Olson, R.N., Vice President Patient Care Services
Web address: www.allinamercy.org
**Control:** Other not–for–profit (including NFP Corporation) **Service:** General
Medical and Surgical

**Staffed Beds:** 254 **Admissions:** 20659 **Census:** 201 **Outpatient Visits:**
136411 **Births:** 2006 **Total Expense ($000):** 359564 **Payroll Expense
($000):** 133070 **Personnel:** 1488

*Many Facility Codes have changed. Please refer to the AHA Guide Code Chart.* © 2013 AHA Guide

## CROOKSTON—Polk County

★ **RIVERVIEW HEALTH (241320)**, 323 South Minnesota Street, Zip 56716–1601; tel. 218/281–9200, (Nonreporting) **A**5 9 10 18
Primary Contact: Carrie Michalski, President and Chief Executive Officer
CFO: William Bennett, Chief Financial Officer
CMO: Mirza Baig, M.D., Chief of Staff
CIO: Chris Bruggeman, Chief Information Officer
CHR: Jean Tate, Manager Human Resources
Web address: www.riverviewhealth.org
**Control:** Other not–for–profit (including NFP Corporation) **Service:** General Medical and Surgical

**Staffed Beds: 52**

## CROSBY—Crow Wing County

⊠ **CUYUNA REGIONAL MEDICAL CENTER (241353)**, 320 East Main Street, Zip 56441–1690; tel. 218/546–7000, (Total facility includes 120 beds in nursing home–type unit) **A**1 9 10 18 **F**3 7 12 13 15 18 28 29 31 34 35 40 43 45 46 47 48 49 50 51 56 57 59 62 63 64 65 68 70 75 76 77 78 79 81 82 84 85 86 87 91 92 93 94 97 99 100 101 103 104 107 110 111 115 116 117 118 119 124 127 128 130 131 132 133 143 144 146 147 148 **P**6
Primary Contact: John H. Solheim, Chief Executive Officer
COO: Theresa Sullivan, Chief Operating Officer
CFO: Kyle Bauer, Chief Financial Officer
CMO: George Kuhlmann, M.D., Chief of Staff
CHR: Rebecca A. Thiesfeld, Executive Director Human Resources
Web address: www.cuyunamed.org
**Control:** Hospital district or authority, Government, nonfederal **Service:** General Medical and Surgical

**Staffed Beds: 145 Admissions: 2469 Census: 127 Outpatient Visits:** 67921 **Births: 278 Total Expense ($000):** 73151 **Payroll Expense ($000):** 28659 **Personnel: 577**

## DAWSON—Lac Qui Parle County

**JOHNSON MEMORIAL HEALTH SERVICES (241314)**, 1282 Walnut Street, Zip 56232–2333; tel. 320/769–4323, (Total facility includes 56 beds in nursing home–type unit) **A**9 10 18 **F**3 7 8 11 13 15 28 34 40 43 56 57 62 64 65 68 71 76 77 81 85 93 107 110 111 119 127 128 130 133 135 145 146 **P**6
Primary Contact: Kathy Johnson, Administrator
CFO: Crystal Bothun, Chief Financial Officer
CMO: Ralph Gerbig, M.D., Chief of Staff
CIO: Derrick Ochsendorf, Manager Information Technology and Systems
CHR: Ellen Alberg, Director Human Resources
CNO: Lori Andreas, Director Patient Care Services
Web address: www.jmhsdawson.com
**Control:** Hospital district or authority, Government, nonfederal **Service:** General Medical and Surgical

**Staffed Beds: 79 Admissions: 310 Census: 57 Outpatient Visits:** 2101 **Births: 10 Total Expense ($000):** 13370 **Payroll Expense ($000):** 6981 **Personnel: 77**

## DEER RIVER—Itasca County

★ **ESSENTIA HEALTH–DEER RIVER (241360)**, (Formerly Deer River HealthCare Center), 115 10th Avenue N.E., Zip 56636–8795; tel. 218/246–2900, (Nonreporting) **A**9 10 18
Primary Contact: Jeffry Stampohar, Chief Executive Officer
CMO: David Goodall, M.D., Chief Medical Staff
CHR: Brittany Mohler, Director Human Resources
Web address: www.drhc.org
**Control:** Other not–for–profit (including NFP Corporation) **Service:** General Medical and Surgical

**Staffed Beds: 52**

## DETROIT LAKES—Becker County

⊠ **ESSENTIA HEALTH ST. MARY'S HOSPITAL – DETROIT LAKES (240101)**, 1027 Washington Avenue, Zip 56501–3409; tel. 218/847–5611, (Total facility includes 96 beds in nursing home–type unit) **A**1 5 9 10 **F**7 10 11 13 15 18 28 29 30 31 33 40 41 43 56 57 59 62 64 65 70 75 76 77 81 89 93 97 104 107 110 111 119 125 128 130 131 132 135 144 146 147 148 **S** Essentia Health, Duluth, MN
Primary Contact: Peter Jacobson, President
CFO: Ryan Hill, Chief Financial Officer
CMO: Rich Vetter, M.D., Associate Chief
CIO: Ken Gilles, Associate Chief Information Officer
CHR: Diane Sundrud, Human Resource Service Partner
CNO: Diana Johnson, R.N., Chief Nursing Officer
Web address: www.trustedcareforlife.org
**Control:** Other not–for–profit (including NFP Corporation) **Service:** General Medical and Surgical

**Staffed Beds: 131 Admissions: 2884 Census: 32 Outpatient Visits:** 15545 **Births: 523 Total Expense ($000):** 74517 **Payroll Expense ($000):** 33511 **Personnel: 585**

**ST. MARY'S INNOVIS HEALTH** See Essentia Health St. Mary's Hospital – Detroit Lakes

## DULUTH—St. Louis County

⊠ △ **ESSENTIA HEALTH DULUTH (240019)**, 502 East Second Street, Zip 55805–1982; tel. 218/727–8762 **A**1 3 5 7 9 10 **F**3 5 11 12 15 16 29 30 31 32 34 35 49 50 51 52 54 55 56 57 59 61 64 65 70 74 75 77 78 79 81 82 84 85 86 87 90 92 93 94 96 97 98 99 100 101 103 104 105 107 108 110 111 114 115 116 117 118 119 120 121 123 124 129 130 131 132 134 135 141 144 146 147 148 **P**6 **S** Essentia Health, Duluth, MN
Primary Contact: Barb Wessberg, Administrator
CFO: Barbara Johnson, Chief Financial Officer
CMO: Hugh Renier, M.D., Vice President Medical Affairs
CIO: Dennis Dassenko, Chief Information Officer
CHR: Diane Davidson, Senior Vice President Human Resources
Web address: www.smdcmedicalcenter.org
**Control:** Other not–for–profit (including NFP Corporation) **Service:** General Medical and Surgical

**Staffed Beds: 154 Admissions: 4157 Census: 74 Outpatient Visits:** 37558 **Births: 13 Total Expense ($000):** 352051 **Payroll Expense ($000):** 195237 **Personnel: 2852**

⊠ **ESSENTIA HEALTH ST. MARY'S MEDICAL CENTER (240002)**, 407 East Third Street, Zip 55805–1984; tel. 218/786–4000, (Includes ST. MARY'S CHILDREN'S HOSPITAL, 407 East Third Street, Zip 55805–1950; tel. 218/786–5437) **A**1 2 3 5 9 10 **F**3 11 12 13 17 18 20 22 24 26 28 29 30 34 35 37 38 40 43 45 46 47 48 49 50 57 59 63 65 67 70 72 74 76 78 79 81 83 84 85 86 87 88 89 102 107 108 111 115 119 126 129 130 132 135 141 146 **P**6 **S** Essentia Health, Duluth, MN
Primary Contact: Daniel B. McGinty, Administrator
CMO: Hugh Renier, M.D., Vice President Medical Affairs
CIO: Tess Jettergren, Director Clinical Informatics
CHR: Glen Porter, Vice President Human Resources
Web address: www.essentiahealth.org/StMarysMedicalCenter/FindaClinic/ Essentia–HealthSt–Marys–Medical–Center–46.aspx
**Control:** Other not–for–profit (including NFP Corporation) **Service:** General Medical and Surgical

**Staffed Beds: 341 Admissions: 16962 Census: 210 Outpatient Visits:** 94379 **Births: 1295 Total Expense ($000):** 304545 **Payroll Expense ($000):** 122208 **Personnel: 2023**

**SMDC MEDICAL CENTER** See Essentia Health Duluth

⊠ △ **ST. LUKE'S HOSPITAL (240047)**, 915 East First Street, Zip 55805–2193; tel. 218/249–5555 **A**1 2 3 5 7 9 10 **F**3 8 9 11 12 13 15 17 18 20 22 24 26 28 29 30 31 34 35 39 40 43 46 47 48 49 51 53 54 57 58 59 60 61 62 63 64 65 70 74 75 76 77 78 79 81 82 83 84 85 86 87 89 90 92 93 97 98 100 101 102 103 104 107 108 110 111 114 115 116 118 119 120 121 123 124 126 129 130 131 132 144 146 148 **P**6
Primary Contact: John Strange, President and Chief Executive Officer
CMO: Gary Peterson, M.D., Vice President Medical Affairs and Medical Director
CIO: Clark Averill, Director Information Technology
CHR: Marla Halvorson, Director Human Resources
CNO: Susan Hamel, Chief Nursing Officer
Web address: www.slhduluth.com
**Control:** Other not–for–profit (including NFP Corporation) **Service:** General Medical and Surgical

**Staffed Beds: 267 Admissions: 10595 Census: 127 Outpatient Visits:** 153283 **Births: 880 Total Expense ($000):** 334175 **Payroll Expense ($000):** 163374 **Personnel: 1798**

**ST. MARY'S MEDICAL CENTER** See Essentia Health St. Mary's Medical Center

MN

---

**Hospital, Medicare Provider Number, Address, Telephone, Approval, Facility, and Physician Codes, Health Care System**

★ American Hospital Association (AHA) membership
☐ The Joint Commission accreditation   ◇ DNV Healthcare Inc. accreditation
○ Healthcare Facilities Accreditation Program
△ Commission on Accreditation of Rehabilitation Facilities (CARF) accreditation

**MN**

## EDINA—Hennepin County

⊠ **FAIRVIEW SOUTHDALE HOSPITAL (240078)**, 6401 France Avenue South, Zip 55435-2199; tel. 952/924-5000 **A**1 2 3 5 9 10 **F**3 5 8 11 12 13 15 17 18 20 22 24 26 28 29 30 31 34 35 38 40 43 49 50 51 55 57 59 60 64 65 69 70 73 74 75 76 78 79 81 82 84 87 92 93 94 98 100 102 107 108 109 110 111 114 115 116 119 121 124 126 129 130 131 132 134 135 146 147 148 **P**6 **S** Fairview Health Services, Minneapolis, MN
Primary Contact: Bradley Beard, President
CFO: Alan Lem, Vice President Finance
CHR: Rich Lutz, Director Human Resources
CNO: Judith Pechacek, R.N., Vice President Patient Care
Web address: www.fairview.org
**Control:** Other not-for-profit (including NFP Corporation) **Service:** General Medical and Surgical

**Staffed Beds:** 326 **Admissions:** 18255 **Census:** 199 **Outpatient Visits:** 126912 **Births:** 3138 **Total Expense ($000):** 364524 **Payroll Expense ($000):** 144068 **Personnel:** 1756

## ELBOW LAKE—Grant County

**ELEAH MEDICAL CENTER** See Prairie Ridge Hospital and Health Services

★ **PRAIRIE RIDGE HOSPITAL AND HEALTH SERVICES (241379)**, 930 First Street N.E., Zip 56531-4611; tel. 218/685-4461 **A**9 10 18 **F**7 15 28 31 40 43 45 46 47 48 53 59 64 65 67 81 90 93 97 107 128 133 135 147 148 **P**5
Primary Contact: Thomas Kooiman, Chief Executive Officer
CFO: Claude Priest, Chief Financial Officer
CMO: Larry Rapp, M.D., Chief Medical Officer
Web address: www.eleahmed.org
**Control:** Other not-for-profit (including NFP Corporation) **Service:** General Medical and Surgical

**Staffed Beds:** 20 **Admissions:** 194 **Census:** 2 **Outpatient Visits:** 25519 **Births:** 0 **Total Expense ($000):** 13916 **Payroll Expense ($000):** 3827 **Personnel:** 109

## ELY—St. Louis County

★ **ELY–BLOOMENSON COMMUNITY HOSPITAL (241318)**, 328 West Conan Street, Zip 55731-1198; tel. 218/365-3271 **A**9 10 18 **F**13 15 28 31 40 45 53 62 64 76 81 107 110 119 130 133 148 **P**6
Primary Contact: John Fossum, Chief Executive Officer and Administrator
CFO: Scott Kellerman, Chief Financial Officer
CHR: Richard Rand, Director Human Resources
Web address: www.ebch.org
**Control:** Other not-for-profit (including NFP Corporation) **Service:** General Medical and Surgical

**Staffed Beds:** 25 **Admissions:** 349 **Census:** 3 **Outpatient Visits:** 8598 **Births:** 30 **Total Expense ($000):** 15529 **Payroll Expense ($000):** 4907

## FAIRMONT—Martin County

⊠ **MAYO CLINIC HEALTH SYSTEM IN FAIRMONT (240166)**, 800 Medical Center Drive, Zip 56031-4575; tel. 507/238-8100, (Includes LUTZ WING CONVALESCENT AND NURSING CARE UNIT ), (Total facility includes 40 beds in nursing home–type unit) **A**1 9 10 20 **F**3 8 11 13 15 17 18 28 29 30 31 34 40 43 59 64 65 68 75 76 77 78 79 81 82 84 85 86 87 92 93 97 99 100 101 103 104 107 108 110 111 115 118 119 128 129 130 132 133 144 146 **P**6 **S** Mayo Clinic Health System, Rochester, MN
Primary Contact: Robert Bartingale, Administrator
COO: Gayle B. Hansen, R.N., Chief Operating Officer
CFO: Brian Suter, Chief Financial Officer
CMO: Rufus Rodriguez, M.D., Medical Director
Web address: www.fairmontmedicalcenter.org
**Control:** Other not-for-profit (including NFP Corporation) **Service:** General Medical and Surgical

**Staffed Beds:** 96 **Admissions:** 2105 **Census:** 57 **Outpatient Visits:** 160654 **Births:** 236 **Total Expense ($000):** 80374 **Payroll Expense ($000):** 37657 **Personnel:** 643

## FARIBAULT—Rice County

★ **DISTRICT ONE HOSPITAL (240071)**, 200 State Avenue, Zip 55021-6345; tel. 507/334-6451, (Nonreporting) **A**9 10
Primary Contact: Stephen J. Pribyl, FACHE, Chief Executive Officer
COO: Joan Boysen, Chief Operating Officer
CFO: Rick Miller, Chief Financial Officer
CMO: Brant Barr, M.D., Chief Medical Officer
CIO: Glenn Gregersen, Director Information Technology
CHR: Lucy G. Dupree, Director Human Resources
CNO: Lynette Dickson, Director Clinical Operations and Director of Nursing
Web address: www.districtonehospital.com
**Control:** Hospital district or authority, Government, nonfederal **Service:** General Medical and Surgical

**Staffed Beds:** 42

## FERGUS FALLS—Otter Tail County

☐ **COMMUNITY BEHAVIORAL HEALTH HOSPITAL – FERGUS FALLS (244013)**, 1801 West Alcott Avenue, Zip 56537-2661, Mailing Address: P.O. Box 478, Zip 56538-0478; tel. 218/332-5001, (Nonreporting) **A**1 9 10 **S** Minnesota Department of Human Services, Saint Paul, MN
Primary Contact: Derrick A. Jones, Administrator
**Control:** State–Government, nonfederal **Service:** Psychiatric

**Staffed Beds:** 16

⊠ △ **LAKE REGION HEALTHCARE (240052)**, (Formerly Lake Region Healthcare Corporation), 712 South Cascade Street, Zip 56537-2900, Mailing Address: P.O. Box 728, Zip 56538-0728; tel. 218/736-8000 **A**1 7 9 10 20 **F**3 10 11 13 15 17 28 29 30 31 32 33 34 35 36 40 41 43 44 45 50 51 53 54 56 57 58 59 61 64 65 68 70 74 75 76 77 78 79 81 84 85 86 87 89 90 92 93 94 96 98 100 101 102 103 104 107 108 110 111 115 117 118 119 120 121 123 130 131 132 135 144 146 147 148
Primary Contact: Larry A. Schulz, Chief Executive Officer
CFO: Brett Longtin, Chief Financial Officer
CMO: Wade Swenson, M.D., Chief of Staff
CIO: Wade A. Jurkas, Director Computer Information Systems
CHR: Cheryl Buck, Vice President Human Resources
CNO: Lucia E. Anderson, Senior Vice President Nursing and Chief Nurse Executive
Web address: www.lrhc.org
**Control:** Other not-for-profit (including NFP Corporation) **Service:** General Medical and Surgical

**Staffed Beds:** 108 **Admissions:** 3050 **Census:** 33 **Outpatient Visits:** 54033 **Births:** 319 **Total Expense ($000):** 102774 **Payroll Expense ($000):** 37058 **Personnel:** 750

## FOSSTON—Polk County

★ **ESSENTIA HEALTH FOSSTON (241357)**, 900 Hilligoss Boulevard S.E., Zip 56542-1599; tel. 218/435-1133, (Nonreporting) **A**9 10 18 **S** Essentia Health, Duluth, MN
Primary Contact: Kevin Gish, Administrator and Vice President
CFO: Kim Bodensteiner, Chief Financial Officer
CIO: Abe Deusterman, Manager Information Technology
CHR: Diane Sundrud, Director Human Resources
Web address: www.firstcare.org
**Control:** Other not-for-profit (including NFP Corporation) **Service:** General Medical and Surgical

**Staffed Beds:** 75

**FIRST CARE MEDICAL SERVICES** See Essentia Health Fosston

## FRIDLEY—Anoka County

⊠ **UNITY HOSPITAL (240132)**, 550 Osborne Road N.E., Zip 55432-2799; tel. 763/236-5000 **A**1 2 5 9 10 **F**3 4 5 11 12 13 15 18 20 22 24 26 28 29 30 31 34 35 36 40 43 45 49 50 53 55 56 57 59 64 65 69 70 73 75 76 77 78 79 81 82 85 86 87 89 93 97 98 99 100 101 102 103 104 107 108 111 114 115 119 130 132 135 145 146 147 148 **S** Allina Health, Minneapolis, MN
Primary Contact: Lori Wightman, R.N., MSN, FACHE, President
COO: Patrick Belland, Vice President Operations
CFO: Lisa K. Anderson, Vice President Finance
CMO: Paul Kettler, M.D., Vice President Medical Affairs
CIO: Susan Heichert, Chief Information Officer
CHR: Kenneth E. Auer, Director Human Resources
CNO: Julianne Lapensky, MS, Vice President Patient Care Services
Web address: www.allina.com
**Control:** Other not-for-profit (including NFP Corporation) **Service:** General Medical and Surgical

**Staffed Beds:** 220 **Admissions:** 12479 **Census:** 131 **Outpatient Visits:** 94858 **Births:** 1192 **Total Expense ($000):** 174421 **Payroll Expense ($000):** 74726 **Personnel:** 904

## GLENCOE—Mcleod County

★ **GLENCOE REGIONAL HEALTH SERVICES (241355)**, 1805 Hennepin Avenue North, Zip 55336-1416; tel. 320/864-3121, (Total facility includes 110 beds in nursing home–type unit) **A**9 10 18 **F**2 7 8 15 17 28 29 31 34 40 43 48 56 64 68 70 75 76 77 81 86 87 89 93 97 107 110 114 119 125 128 130 132 133 135 145 146 **P**6 **S** HealthPartners, Bloomington, MN
Primary Contact: Jon D. Braband, FACHE, President and Chief Executive Officer
CFO: John C. Doidge, Vice President Finance
CMO: John H. Bergseng, D.O., Vice President Medical Affairs
CIO: Tony Alsleben, Director Information Technology
CHR: Jill Hatlestad, Vice President Human Resources and Organizational Support
CNO: Gayle Sturgis, Vice President Nursing
Web address: www.grhsonline.org
**Control:** Other not-for-profit (including NFP Corporation) **Service:** General Medical and Surgical

**Staffed Beds:** 135 **Admissions:** 1118 **Census:** 106 **Outpatient Visits:** 25458 **Births:** 201 **Total Expense ($000):** 47094 **Payroll Expense ($000):** 22942 **Personnel:** 391

*Many Facility Codes have changed. Please refer to the AHA Guide Code Chart.*

## GLENWOOD—Pope County

★ **GLACIAL RIDGE HEALTH SYSTEM (241376)**, 10 Fourth Avenue S.E.,
Zip 56334–1898; tel. 320/634–4521 **A**9 10 18 **F**7 11 12 13 15 17 28 31 34
35 40 41 43 53 59 62 63 64 75 76 81 107 110 114 119 127 130 133 146
148 **P**6
Primary Contact: Kirk A. Stensrud, Chief Executive Officer
CFO: Kyle Chase, Chief Financial Officer
CMO: Robert Montenegro, M.D., Chief of Staff
CIO: Heidi Engle, Manager Information Technology
CHR: Gordon Paulson, Manager Personnel
Web address: www.glacialridge.org
**Control:** Hospital district or authority, Government, nonfederal **Service:** General
Medical and Surgical

**Staffed Beds:** 19 **Admissions:** 712 **Census:** 6 **Outpatient Visits:** 13282
**Births:** 65 **Total Expense ($000):** 21493 **Payroll Expense ($000):** 10081
**Personnel:** 176

## GOLDEN VALLEY—Hennepin County

⊞ **REGENCY HOSPITAL OF MINNEAPOLIS (242005)**, 1300 Hidden Lakes
Parkway, Zip 55422–4286; tel. 763/588–2750, (Nonreporting) **A**1 10 **S** Select
Medical Corporation, Mechanicsburg, PA
Primary Contact: John P. Allen, Chief Executive Officer
COO: Jan Cwynar, Vice President Operations
CMO: Norm Yunis, M.D., Medical Director
Web address: www.regencyhospital.com
**Control:** Corporation, Investor–owned, for–profit **Service:** Long–Term Acute Care
hospital

**Staffed Beds:** 54

## GRACEVILLE—Big Stone County

**ESSENTIA HEALTH–HOLY TRINITY HOSPITAL (241321)**, 115 West Second
Street, Zip 56240–4845, Mailing Address: P.O. Box 157, Zip 56240–0157;
tel. 320/748–7223, (Nonreporting) **A**9 10 18 **S** Essentia Health, Duluth, MN
Primary Contact: John Campion, Administrator
CMO: Arthur Van Vranken, M.D., Chief Medical Officer
CIO: Brad Tostenson, Chief Information Officer
CHR: Jenny Lee, Human Resources Generalist
CNO: Jill Johnsrud, Director of Nursing
Web address: www.essentiahealth.org/HolyTrinityHospital/FindaClinic/Essentia–
HealthHoly–Trinity–Hospital–96.aspx
**Control:** Other not–for–profit (including NFP Corporation) **Service:** General
Medical and Surgical

**Staffed Beds:** 65

**GRACEVILLE HEALTH CENTER** See Essentia Health–Holy Trinity Hospital

## GRAND MARAIS—Cook County

**COOK COUNTY NORTH SHORE HOSPITAL (241317)**, 515 5th Avenue West,
Zip 55604–3017; tel. 218/387–3040, (Total facility includes 37 beds in nursing
home–type unit) **A**9 10 18 **F**7 11 13 15 28 31 34 40 43 45 56 59 62 64 76 77
84 85 89 93 107 110 111 114 119 128 130 133
Primary Contact: Kimber L. Wraalstad, FACHE, Administrator
CFO: Yvonne Gennrich, Controller
CHR: Shelly Starkey, Personnel Coordinator
CNO: Bridget Sobieck, Director of Nursing
Web address: www.nshorehospital.com
**Control:** Hospital district or authority, Government, nonfederal **Service:** General
Medical and Surgical

**Staffed Beds:** 53 **Admissions:** 179 **Census:** 41 **Outpatient Visits:** 9391
**Births:** 9 **Total Expense ($000):** 13079 **Payroll Expense ($000):** 5914
**Personnel:** 118

## GRAND RAPIDS—Itasca County

⊞ **GRAND ITASCA CLINIC AND HOSPITAL (240064)**, 1601 Golf Course Road,
Zip 55744–8648; tel. 218/326–5000 **A**1 9 10 20 **F**3 11 12 13 15 17 18 28
29 30 31 33 35 36 38 40 43 44 45 50 53 56 61 62 64 65 70 71 75 76 77
78 81 82 85 86 87 90 93 96 97 107 108 110 111 115 118 119 129 130
131 132 135 141 146 147 148 **P**6
Primary Contact: Michael Youso, Chief Executive Officer
CHR: Robert Cocker, Vice President Organizational Effectiveness
Web address: www.granditasca.org
**Control:** Other not–for–profit (including NFP Corporation) **Service:** General
Medical and Surgical

**Staffed Beds:** 45 **Admissions:** 2207 **Census:** 19 **Outpatient Visits:** 171513
**Births:** 329 **Total Expense ($000):** 71718 **Payroll Expense ($000):** 37735
**Personnel:** 464

## GRANITE FALLS—Yellow Medicine County

★ **GRANITE FALLS MUNICIPAL HOSPITAL AND MANOR (241343)**, 345 Tenth
Avenue, Zip 56241–1499; tel. 320/564–3111, (Total facility includes 57 beds in
nursing home–type unit) **A**9 10 18 **F**3 7 13 15 28 34 40 43 45 56 57 59 62 64
69 71 76 79 81 84 85 93 107 128 129 130 133 143
Primary Contact: George Gerlach, Chief Executive Officer
CFO: Val Hoffman, Chief Financial Officer
CIO: Kris Wilke, Manager Health Information
CHR: Sue Tollefson, Coordinator Payroll Personnel
CNO: Patty Massman, Director of Nursing
Web address: www.granitefallshealthcare.com
**Control:** City–Government, nonfederal **Service:** General Medical and Surgical

**Staffed Beds:** 82 **Admissions:** 583 **Census:** 51 **Outpatient Visits:** 26698
**Births:** 38 **Total Expense ($000):** 16848 **Payroll Expense ($000):** 8104
**Personnel:** 145

## HALLOCK—Kittson County

★ **KITTSON MEMORIAL HEALTHCARE CENTER (241336)**, 1010 South Birch
Street, Zip 56728–4215, Mailing Address: P.O. Box 700, Zip 56728–0700;
tel. 218/843–3612, (Total facility includes 70 beds in nursing home–type unit) **A**9
10 18 **F**7 10 11 15 34 40 45 53 59 62 63 81 127 128 133
Primary Contact: Richard J. Failing, Chief Executive Officer
CFO: Jeni Schwenzfeier, Chief Financial Officer
CMO: Thomas Lohstreter, M.D., Chief of Staff
CIO: Holly Knutson, Manager Information Technology
CHR: Carlene Cole, Manager Human Resources
Web address: www.kmhc.net
**Control:** Other not–for–profit (including NFP Corporation) **Service:** General
Medical and Surgical

**Staffed Beds:** 85 **Admissions:** 157 **Census:** 69 **Outpatient Visits:** 9800
**Births:** 0 **Total Expense ($000):** 12280 **Payroll Expense ($000):** 5719
**Personnel:** 189

## HASTINGS—Dakota County

☐ **REGINA MEDICAL CENTER (240059)**, 1175 Nininger Road, Zip 55033–1098;
tel. 651/480–4100, (Nonreporting) **A**1 9 10
Primary Contact: Ty W. Erickson, Chief Executive Officer
CFO: Greg Kopp, Chief Financial Officer
CMO: James Noreen, M.D., Chief Medical Officer
CHR: Kirstin D. Swenson, Director Human Resources
Web address: www.reginamedical.org
**Control:** Other not–for–profit (including NFP Corporation) **Service:** General
Medical and Surgical

**Staffed Beds:** 115

## HENDRICKS—Lincoln County

★ **HENDRICKS COMMUNITY HOSPITAL (241339)**, 503 East Lincoln Street,
Zip 56136–9598, Mailing Address: P.O. Box 106, Zip 56136–0106;
tel. 507/275–3134, (Total facility includes 55 beds in nursing home–type unit) **A**9
10 18 **F**2 3 7 10 11 15 17 28 29 31 34 35 40 59 62 63 70 81 89 93 125
127 128 130 132 133 146
Primary Contact: Jeffrey Gollaher, Chief Executive Officer
CMO: Tabb McCluskey, M.D., Chief Medical Officer
CHR: Lynn R. Olson, Director Human Resources
Web address: www.hendrickshosp.org
**Control:** Other not–for–profit (including NFP Corporation) **Service:** General
Medical and Surgical

**Staffed Beds:** 67 **Admissions:** 199 **Census:** 58 **Outpatient Visits:** 11658
**Births:** 0 **Total Expense ($000):** 12200 **Payroll Expense ($000):** 6280
**Personnel:** 112

**MN**

---

**Hospital, Medicare Provider Number, Address, Telephone, Approval, Facility, and Physician Codes, Health Care System**

★ American Hospital Association (AHA) membership
☐ The Joint Commission accreditation
◇ DNV Healthcare Inc. accreditation
○ Healthcare Facilities Accreditation Program
△ Commission on Accreditation of Rehabilitation Facilities (CARF) accreditation

**HIBBING—St. Louis County**

⊠ **RANGE REGIONAL HEALTH SERVICES (240040)**, 750 East 34th Street,
Zip 55746–4600; tel. 218/262–4881 **A**1 2 9 10 **F**3 11 13 15 28 29 30 34 35
40 43 45 48 49 59 64 70 75 76 77 81 85 86 89 93 98 102 107 108 110
111 115 116 119 120 121 129 130 143 144 146 147 148 **P**6 **S** Fairview
Health Services, Minneapolis, MN
Primary Contact: Debra K. Boardman, FACHE, President and Chief Executive
Officer
COO: Vicky Korynta, Senior Vice President and Chief Operating Officer
CFO: John D. Kritz, Senior Vice President and Chief Financial Officer
CMO: Jim Hartert, M.D., Senior Vice President and Medical Director
CIO: Jessica Valento, Director Information Systems
CHR: Mitch Vincent, Vice President Organizational Support
CNO: Connie Harle, Chief Nursing Officer
Web address: www.range.fairview.org
**Control:** Other not–for–profit (including NFP Corporation) **Service:** General
Medical and Surgical

> **Staffed Beds:** 85 **Admissions:** 3044 **Census:** 36 **Outpatient Visits:** 143885
> **Births:** 336 **Total Expense ($000):** 98217 **Payroll Expense ($000):** 48599
> **Personnel:** 686

**HUTCHINSON—Mcleod County**

⊠ **HUTCHINSON HEALTH (240187)**, (Formerly Hutchinson Area Health Care),
1095 Highway 15 South, Zip 55350–3182; tel. 320/234–5000 **A**1 9 10 20 **F**2 3
5 11 13 15 28 29 31 34 35 36 38 40 43 45 56 57 59 64 69 70 75 76 77 78
79 81 82 85 87 93 98 99 100 101 102 103 104 107 110 111 115 119 127
129 130 131 132 146 147 148 **S** Allina Health, Minneapolis, MN
Primary Contact: Steven Mulder, M.D., President and Chief Executive Officer
CFO: Pamela Larson, Division Director Financial Services
CIO: Pamela Larson, Division Director Financial Services
CHR: Rebecca Streich, Manager Human Resources and Education Manager
Web address: www.hutchhealth.com
**Control:** Other not–for–profit (including NFP Corporation) **Service:** General
Medical and Surgical

> **Staffed Beds:** 57 **Admissions:** 2261 **Census:** 22 **Outpatient Visits:** 86387
> **Births:** 259 **Total Expense ($000):** 59237 **Payroll Expense ($000):** 22853
> **Personnel:** 364

**INTERNATIONAL FALLS—Koochiching County**

⊠ **RAINY LAKE MEDICAL CENTER (241322)**, 1400 Highway 71,
Zip 56649–2189; tel. 218/283–4481 **A**1 9 10 18 **F**11 13 15 28 29 31 34 40
42 43 45 50 64 76 77 81 85 89 90 93 102 119 128 133 144 148 **S** QHR,
Brentwood, TN
Primary Contact: Bob Haley, Interim Chief Executive Officer
CMO: Douglas A. Johnson, M.D., Chief of Staff
CIO: Michael Blesi, Director Information Technology
Web address: www.rainylakemedical.com
**Control:** Other not–for–profit (including NFP Corporation) **Service:** General
Medical and Surgical

> **Staffed Beds:** 25 **Admissions:** 530 **Census:** 5 **Outpatient Visits:** 75129
> **Births:** 57 **Total Expense ($000):** 24001 **Payroll Expense ($000):** 7750
> **Personnel:** 141

**JACKSON—Jackson County**

★ **SANFORD JACKSON MEDICAL CENTER (241315)**, 1430 North Highway,
Zip 56143–1093; tel. 507/847–2420 **A**9 10 18 **F**1 3 15 18 28 29 31 34 35
40 43 45 46 50 56 57 59 64 65 67 68 75 77 78 79 81 82 85 86 87 89 90
93 97 107 108 110 111 114 118 119 127 128 129 131 132 133 148 **P**6
**S** Sanford Health, Sioux Falls, SD
Primary Contact: Mary J. Ruyter, Chief Executive Officer
CFO: Gail Eike, Chief Financial Officer
CMO: Sister Marie Paul Lockerd, M.D., Chief Medical Officer
CNO: Dawn Schnell, Chief Nursing Officer
Web address: www.sanfordjackson.org
**Control:** Other not–for–profit (including NFP Corporation) **Service:** General
Medical and Surgical

> **Staffed Beds:** 16 **Admissions:** 112 **Census:** 1 **Outpatient Visits:** 23297
> **Births:** 0 **Total Expense ($000):** 6493 **Payroll Expense ($000):** 2553
> **Personnel:** 60

**LAKE CITY—Goodhue County**

⊠ **MAYO CLINIC HEALTH SYSTEM IN LAKE CITY (241338)**, 500 West Grant
Street, Zip 55041–1143; tel. 651/345–3321, (Nonreporting) **A**1 9 10 18 **S** Mayo
Clinic Health System, Rochester, MN
Primary Contact: Susan M. Stiene, R.N., MS, Interim Chief Administrative Officer
CFO: David Biren, Chief Financial Officer
CMO: Dennis Spano, M.D., Medical Director
CHR: Jacqueline Ryan, Director Human Resources
Web address: www.lakecitymedicalcenter.org
**Control:** Other not–for–profit (including NFP Corporation) **Service:** General
Medical and Surgical

> **Staffed Beds:** 108

**LE SUEUR—Le Sueur County**

**MINNESOTA VALLEY HEALTH CENTER (241375)**, 621 South Fourth Street,
Zip 56058–2298; tel. 507/665–3375, (Includes GARDENVIEW NURSING HOME ),
(Nonreporting) **A**9 10 18 **S** Essentia Health, Duluth, MN
Primary Contact: Pam Williams, Chief Executive Officer
CFO: Patricia Schlegel, Executive Director Finance
CMO: Carolyn Stelter, M.D., Chief of Staff
CHR: Bonnie Barnhardt, Executive Director Human Resources
Web address: www.mvhc.org
**Control:** Other not–for–profit (including NFP Corporation) **Service:** General
Medical and Surgical

> **Staffed Beds:** 110

**LITCHFIELD—Meeker County**

★ **MEEKER MEMORIAL HOSPITAL (241366)**, 612 South Sibley Avenue,
Zip 55355–3398; tel. 320/693–3242 **A**9 10 18 **F**11 13 15 28 29 31 34 40 43
45 57 59 70 75 76 77 78 81 89 90 93 103 107 110 111 114 119 130 132
133 146 148
Primary Contact: Kyle R. Rasmussen, Chief Executive Officer
CFO: Stephen Plaisance, Chief Financial Officer
CMO: Tim Peterson, M.D., Chief of Staff
CIO: Connie Liimatta, Director Medical Records and Business Office
CHR: Cindi Twardy, Manager Human Resources
CNO: Ann Lien, R.N., Chief Nursing Officer
Web address: www.meekermemorial.org
**Control:** County–Government, nonfederal **Service:** General Medical and Surgical

> **Staffed Beds:** 39 **Admissions:** 1074 **Census:** 15 **Outpatient Visits:** 23868
> **Births:** 131 **Total Expense ($000):** 26000 **Payroll Expense ($000):** 9244
> **Personnel:** 154

**LITTLE FALLS—Morrison County**

⊠ **ST. GABRIEL'S HOSPITAL (241370)**, 815 Second Street S.E.,
Zip 56345–3596; tel. 320/632–5441 **A**1 9 10 18 **F**3 11 13 15 26 28 29 30
31 34 40 43 45 59 62 63 64 65 68 70 75 76 77 79 81 84 85 86 87 93 107
108 110 111 115 119 127 128 130 131 132 133 146 **P**6 **S** Catholic Health
Initiatives, Englewood, CO
Primary Contact: Joseph Messmer, Interim President
CMO: Thomas Stoy, M.D., Chief of Staff
CHR: Barb Miller, Director Human Resources
Web address: www.stgabriels.com
**Control:** Church–operated, Nongovernment, not–for profit **Service:** General
Medical and Surgical

> **Staffed Beds:** 25 **Admissions:** 1402 **Census:** 13 **Outpatient Visits:** 45028
> **Births:** 170 **Total Expense ($000):** 45240 **Payroll Expense ($000):** 15573
> **Personnel:** 241

**LONG PRAIRIE—Todd County**

★ **CENTRACARE HEALTH–LONG PRAIRIE (241326)**, (Formerly CentraCare
Health System – Long Prairie), 20 Ninth Street S.E., Zip 56347–1404;
tel. 320/732–2141, (Nonreporting) **A**9 10 18 **S** CentraCare Health, Saint
Cloud, MN
Primary Contact: Daniel J. Swenson, FACHE, Administrator and Chief Executive
Officer
CFO: Larry Knutson, Director Finance
CMO: Rene Eldidy, M.D., Chief of Staff
Web address: www.centracare.com
**Control:** Other not–for–profit (including NFP Corporation) **Service:** General
Medical and Surgical

> **Staffed Beds:** 20

**LONG PRAIRIE MEMORIAL HOSPITAL AND HOME** See CentraCare
Health–Long Prairie

**LUVERNE—Rock County**

★ **SANFORD LUVERNE MEDICAL CENTER (241371)**, 1600 North Kniss Avenue,
Zip 56156–1067; tel. 507/283–2321 **A**9 10 18 **F**3 4 5 7 8 11 13 15 18 19 28
29 31 32 34 35 40 43 45 56 57 59 63 64 65 67 68 74 75 76 77 78 79 81
82 83 84 85 86 87 90 93 96 97 107 111 114 118 119 128 129 131 132
133 135 146 147 148 **P**6 **S** Sanford Health, Sioux Falls, SD
Primary Contact: Tammy Loosbrock, Chief Executive Officer
CFO: Stanley Knobloch, Chief Financial Officer
CMO: Richard P. Morgan, M.D., Chief of Staff
Web address: www.sanfordluverne.com
**Control:** Other not–for–profit (including NFP Corporation) **Service:** General
Medical and Surgical

> **Staffed Beds:** 25 **Admissions:** 605 **Census:** 6 **Outpatient Visits:** 28697
> **Births:** 113 **Total Expense ($000):** 21149 **Payroll Expense ($000):** 8840
> **Personnel:** 201

**MN**

*Many Facility Codes have changed. Please refer to the AHA Guide Code Chart.*   © 2013 AHA Guide

**MADELIA—Watonwan County**

☒ **MADELIA COMMUNITY HOSPITAL (241323)**, 121 Drew Avenue S.E., Zip 56062–1899; tel. 507/642-3255 **A**1 3 5 9 10 18 **F**11 13 15 34 35 40 57 59 62 64 68 69 75 76 77 81 84 85 86 93 102 107 110 114 128 130 132 133 144 145
Primary Contact: Candace Fenske, Chief Executive Officer
CFO: Donna M. Klinkner, Chief Financial Officer
CMO: Timothy Bachenberg, M.D., Chief Medical Officer
CIO: Marie Schneeberger, Director of Health
CHR: Donna M. Klinkner, Chief Financial Officer
CNO: Deidre Hruby, Director of Patient Care
Web address: www.mchospital.org
**Control:** Other not–for–profit (including NFP Corporation) **Service:** General Medical and Surgical

**Staffed Beds:** 21 **Admissions:** 172 **Census:** 3 **Outpatient Visits:** 4529 **Births:** 1 **Total Expense ($000):** 10353 **Payroll Expense ($000):** 3634 **Personnel:** 58

**MADISON—Lac Qui Parle County**

★ **MADISON HOSPITAL (241372)**, 900 Second Avenue, Zip 56256–1006; tel. 320/598-7556 **A**9 10 18 **F**10 11 15 28 29 30 34 40 43 57 59 62 64 65 76 77 79 81 84 89 93 97 107 110 111 119 127 130 132 133 145 147 **P**5
Primary Contact: Steven T. Moburg, Chief Executive Officer
CFO: Carol Borgerson, Business Office Manager and Chief Financial Officer
CIO: Jerry Harberts, Information Technologist
CHR: Bridget Sabin, Director Human Resources
Web address: www.madisonlutheranhome.com
**Control:** Other not–for–profit (including NFP Corporation) **Service:** General Medical and Surgical

**Staffed Beds:** 12 **Admissions:** 227 **Census:** 2 **Outpatient Visits:** 13912 **Births:** 5 **Total Expense ($000):** 6155 **Payroll Expense ($000):** 2101 **Personnel:** 55

**MAHNOMEN—Mahnomen County**

★ **MAHNOMEN HEALTH CENTER (241300)**, 414 West Jefferson Avenue, Zip 56557–4912, Mailing Address: P.O. Box 396, Zip 56557–0396; tel. 218/935-2511, (Total facility includes 48 beds in nursing home–type unit) **A**9 10 18 **F**3 7 11 15 28 29 34 35 40 41 43 56 57 59 62 63 64 65 68 77 85 86 87 91 93 100 107 108 110 111 119 127 128 130 131 132 133 135 148 **S** Sanford Health, Sioux Falls, SD
Primary Contact: Susan K. Klassen, Chief Executive Officer and Administrator
CFO: Mary Pazdernik, Chief Financial Officer
CMO: Anju Gurung, M.D., Chief Medical Officer
CHR: Kristi Stall, Chief Human Resources Officer
Web address: www.mahnomenhealthcenter.com
**Control:** City–County, Government, nonfederal **Service:** General Medical and Surgical

**Staffed Beds:** 68 **Admissions:** 195 **Census:** 37 **Outpatient Visits:** 8120 **Births:** 0 **Total Expense ($000):** 8120 **Payroll Expense ($000):** 2949 **Personnel:** 90

**MANKATO—Blue Earth County**

☒ **MAYO CLINIC HEALTH SYSTEM IN MANKATO (240093)**, 1025 Marsh Street, Zip 56001–4752, Mailing Address: P.O. Box 8673, Zip 56002–8673; tel. 507/625-4031 **A**1 3 5 9 10 **F**3 5 11 12 13 15 18 20 22 26 27 28 29 30 31 33 34 35 36 38 39 40 41 43 45 49 53 54 57 58 59 60 61 62 63 64 65 66 68 70 74 75 76 77 78 79 81 82 83 84 85 86 87 89 91 92 93 97 98 99 100 102 103 104 107 108 110 111 114 115 116 118 119 120 121 123 126 127 129 130 132 135 144 146 147 148 **P**6 **S** Mayo Clinic Health System, Rochester, MN
Primary Contact: Gregory Kutcher, M.D., President and Chief Executive Officer
CFO: Stanley Marczak, Chief Financial Officer
CMO: Brian Whited, M.D., Medical Director
CIO: Thomas Borowski, Chief Information Officer
CHR: Julie Oliver, Chief Human Resources Officer
Web address: www.isj–mhs.org
**Control:** Other not–for–profit (including NFP Corporation) **Service:** General Medical and Surgical

**Staffed Beds:** 166 **Admissions:** 10670 **Census:** 108 **Outpatient Visits:** 366383 **Births:** 1486 **Total Expense ($000):** 274484 **Payroll Expense ($000):** 144408 **Personnel:** 1757

**MAPLE GROVE—Hennepin County**

☒ ◇ **MAPLE GROVE HOSPITAL (240214)**, 9875 Hospital Drive, Zip 55369–4648; tel. 763/581-1000 **A**1 9 10 21 **F**3 13 15 18 29 30 40 45 60 68 70 73 76 77 79 81 84 85 89 100 102 107 108 111 115 118 119 130 146 148 **P**8 **S** North Memorial Health Care, Robbinsdale, MN
Primary Contact: Andrew S. Cochrane, Chief Executive Officer
CFO: Jason Weaver, Finance Manager
CHR: Kate J. Law, Director Human Resources
Web address: www.maplegrovehospital.org
**Control:** Other not–for–profit (including NFP Corporation) **Service:** General Medical and Surgical

**Staffed Beds:** 90 **Admissions:** 7132 **Census:** 49 **Outpatient Visits:** 33367 **Births:** 3662

**MARSHALL—Lyon County**

☒ **AVERA MARSHALL REGIONAL MEDICAL CENTER (241359)**, 300 South Bruce Street, Zip 56258–3900; tel. 507/532-9661, (Total facility includes 76 beds in nursing home–type unit) **A**1 9 10 18 **F**2 8 11 12 13 15 28 29 30 31 34 35 40 43 54 56 57 59 64 68 70 76 78 79 81 82 84 93 97 98 99 100 101 102 103 104 105 107 110 111 115 118 119 128 129 130 131 133 134 146 147 148 **P**6 **S** Avera Health, Sioux Falls, SD
Primary Contact: Mary B. Maertens, FACHE, President and Chief Executive Officer
CFO: Sharon Williams, Vice President Finance and Information Technology
CMO: Steven Meister, M.D., Chief of Staff
CIO: Sharon Williams, Vice President Finance and Information Technology
CHR: Amber Crowley, Vice President Human Resources
Web address: www.averamarshall.org
**Control:** Other not–for–profit (including NFP Corporation) **Service:** General Medical and Surgical

**Staffed Beds:** 111 **Admissions:** 1980 **Census:** 94 **Outpatient Visits:** 37893 **Births:** 453 **Total Expense ($000):** 57101 **Payroll Expense ($000):** 25603 **Personnel:** 336

**MELROSE—Stearns County**

★ **CENTRACARE HEALTH–MELROSE (241330)**, 525 Main Street West, Zip 56352–1043; tel. 320/256-4231, (Nonreporting) **A**9 10 18 **S** CentraCare Health, Saint Cloud, MN
Primary Contact: Gerry Gilbertson, FACHE, Administrator
COO: Gerry Gilbertson, FACHE, Administrator
CFO: Adam Paulson, Director Finance
CMO: Dante Beretta, M.D., Chief of Staff
CIO: Janet Kruzel, Health Information Manager
CHR: Joyce Chan, Chief Human Resources Officer
CNO: Keri Wimmer, R.N., Patient Care Director
Web address: www.centracare.com
**Control:** Other not–for–profit (including NFP Corporation) **Service:** General Medical and Surgical

**Staffed Beds:** 93

**MINNEAPOLIS—Hennepin County**

☒ **ABBOTT NORTHWESTERN HOSPITAL (240057)**, 800 East 28th Street, Zip 55407–3799; tel. 612/863-4000, (Includes SISTER KENNY REHABILITATION INSTITUTE, 810 East 27th Street, Zip 55407; tel. 612/874-4000) **A**1 2 3 5 8 9 10 **F**3 8 9 12 13 15 17 18 19 20 22 24 26 28 29 30 31 34 35 36 37 38 39 40 41 42 43 44 45 46 47 48 49 50 51 52 53 54 55 56 57 58 59 60 61 63 64 65 66 68 70 71 74 75 76 77 78 79 81 82 83 84 85 86 87 90 91 92 93 94 95 96 97 98 99 100 101 102 103 104 105 107 108 109 110 111 112 113 114 115 116 117 118 119 120 121 123 124 126 129 130 131 132 135 136 137 138 141 143 144 145 146 147 148 **P**6 **S** Allina Health, Minneapolis, MN
Primary Contact: Ben Bache–Wiig, M.D., President
CFO: Brian Weinreis, Vice President Operations and Finance
CHR: Margaret Butler, Vice President Human Resources
Web address: www.abbottnorthwestern.com
**Control:** Other not–for–profit (including NFP Corporation) **Service:** General Medical and Surgical

**Staffed Beds:** 631 **Admissions:** 37570 **Census:** 455 **Outpatient Visits:** 403196 **Births:** 4189 **Total Expense ($000):** 939903 **Payroll Expense ($000):** 371876 **Personnel:** 3735

**MN**

---

**Hospital, Medicare Provider Number, Address, Telephone, Approval, Facility, and Physician Codes, Health Care System**

★ American Hospital Association (AHA) membership
☐ The Joint Commission accreditation
◇ DNV Healthcare Inc. accreditation
○ Healthcare Facilities Accreditation Program
△ Commission on Accreditation of Rehabilitation Facilities (CARF) accreditation

□ **CHILDREN'S HOSPITALS AND CLINICS OF MINNESOTA (243302)**, 2525 Chicago Avenue South, Zip 55404–4518; tel. 612/813–6100 **A**1 3 5 10 **F**3 8 9 11 12 17 18 19 20 21 22 23 24 25 26 27 28 29 30 31 32 34 35 36 38 39 40 41 43 44 48 50 51 54 55 57 58 59 60 61 62 63 64 65 66 68 72 73 74 75 77 78 79 80 81 82 84 85 86 87 88 89 92 93 97 99 100 101 102 104 107 108 109 111 112 114 115 117 118 119 129 130 131 132 134 135 136 143 145 146 148 **P**6 8 **S** Children's Hospitals and Clinics of Minnesota, Minneapolis, MN
Primary Contact: Alan L. Goldbloom, M.D., Chief Executive Officer
COO: David S. Overman, Chief Operating Officer
CFO: Jerry Massmann, Chief Financial Officer
CMO: Phillip M. Kibort, M.D., Vice President Medical Affairs and Chief Medical Officer
CIO: Jeffrey D. Young, Chief Information Officer
CHR: David Brumbaugh, Vice President Human Resources
Web address: www.childrensmn.org
**Control:** Other not–for–profit (including NFP Corporation) **Service:** Children's general

**Staffed Beds:** 381 **Admissions:** 12586 **Census:** 238 **Outpatient Visits:** 437518 **Births:** 0 **Total Expense ($000):** 605592 **Payroll Expense ($000):** 283523 **Personnel:** 3260

**FAIRVIEW RIVERSIDE HOSPITAL** See University of Minnesota Medical Center, Fairview

□ △ **HENNEPIN COUNTY MEDICAL CENTER (240004)**, 701 Park Avenue South, Zip 55415–1829; tel. 612/873–3000, (Includes HCMC DEPARTMENT OF PEDIATRICS, 701 Park Avenue, Zip 55415–1623; tel. 612/873–2064) **A**1 2 3 5 7 8 9 10 **F**3 5 7 11 12 13 15 16 18 20 22 24 26 28 29 30 31 32 33 34 35 36 38 39 40 41 43 44 45 46 48 49 50 51 53 54 55 56 57 58 59 60 61 64 65 66 68 70 72 74 75 76 77 78 79 81 82 84 85 86 87 88 89 90 92 93 94 96 97 98 99 100 101 102 103 104 105 107 108 110 111 112 114 115 117 118 119 120 121 129 130 131 132 134 135 138 141 144 146 147 148 **P**5 6 8
Primary Contact: Jon Pryor, Chief Executive Officer
CFO: Larry Kryzaniak, Chief Financial Officer
CMO: Michael Belzer, M.D., Medical Director
CHR: Hilary Marden–Resnik, Vice President Human Resources
Web address: www.hcmc.org
**Control:** County–Government, nonfederal **Service:** General Medical and Surgical

**Staffed Beds:** 443 **Admissions:** 21554 **Census:** 339 **Outpatient Visits:** 632292 **Births:** 2357 **Total Expense ($000):** 720243 **Payroll Expense ($000):** 394057 **Personnel:** 4859

✠ △ **MINNEAPOLIS VETERANS AFFAIRS HEALTH CARE SYSTEM**, One Veterans Drive, Zip 55417–2399; tel. 612/725–2000, (Nonreporting) **A**1 2 3 5 7 8 **S** Department of Veterans Affairs, Washington, DC
Primary Contact: Patrick J. Kelly, FACHE, Director
COO: Kurt Thielen, Manager Business Office
CFO: LeAnn Stomberg, Chief Financial Officer
CMO: Kent Crossley, M.D., Acting Chief of Staff
CIO: Karl Reid, Chief Information Officer
CHR: Kevin Upham, Chief Human Resources Officer
CNO: Helen Pearlman, Nurse Executive
Web address: www.minneapolis.va.gov
**Control:** Veterans Affairs, Government, federal **Service:** General Medical and Surgical

**Staffed Beds:** 305

✠ **PHILLIPS EYE INSTITUTE (240196)**, 2215 Park Avenue, Zip 55404–3756; tel. 612/775–8800 **A**1 9 10 **F**81 **S** Allina Health, Minneapolis, MN
Primary Contact: Joan M. Arbach, Interim President
CFO: Chris Verdon, Director Finance
CMO: Emmett Carpel, M.D., Medical Director and Chief of Staff
CNO: Margaret Watry, Director of Patient Care Services and Nurse Executive
Web address: www.allinahealth.org/ahs/pei.nsf/
**Control:** Other not–for–profit (including NFP Corporation) **Service:** Eye, ear, nose, and throat

**Staffed Beds:** 8 **Admissions:** 141 **Census:** 1 **Outpatient Visits:** 14517 **Births:** 0 **Total Expense ($000):** 29454 **Payroll Expense ($000):** 9193 **Personnel:** 116

□ **SHRINERS HOSPITALS FOR CHILDREN–TWIN CITIES (243303)**, (Formerly Shriners Hospitals for Children, Twin Cities), 2025 East River Parkway, Zip 55414–3696; tel. 612/596–6100, (Nonreporting) **A**1 3 5 10 **S** Shriners Hospitals for Children, Tampa, FL
Primary Contact: Charles C. Lobeck, Administrator
CMO: Kenneth Guidera, M.D., Chief of Staff
CHR: Karen Frigen, Director Human Resources
Web address: www.shrinershospitalsforchildren.org/Hospitals/Locations/twincities.aspx
**Control:** Other not–for–profit (including NFP Corporation) **Service:** Children's orthopedic

**Staffed Beds:** 40

**SISTER KENNY REHABILITATION INSTITUTE** See Abbott Northwestern Hospital

**ST. MARY'S HOSPITAL AND REHABILITATION CENTER** See University of Minnesota Medical Center, Fairview

**UNIVERSITY OF MINNESOTA HOSPITAL AND CLINIC** See University of Minnesota Medical Center, Fairview

✠ **UNIVERSITY OF MINNESOTA MEDICAL CENTER, FAIRVIEW (240080)**, 2450 Riverside Avenue, Zip 55454–1400; tel. 612/672–6000, (Includes FAIRVIEW RIVERSIDE HOSPITAL, 2312 South Sixth Street, Zip 55454; tel. 612/371–6300; ST. MARY'S HOSPITAL AND REHABILITATION CENTER, 2414 South Seventh Street, Zip 55454; tel. 612/338–2229; UNIVERSITY OF MINNESOTA CHILDREN'S HOSPITAL, FAIRVIEW, 420 Delaware Street, S.E., Zip 55455–0341; tel. 888/543–7866; UNIVERSITY OF MINNESOTA HOSPITAL AND CLINIC, 420 S.E. Delaware Street, Zip 55455–0392; tel. 612/626–3000), (Total facility includes 36 beds in nursing home–type unit) **A**1 3 5 8 9 10 **F**2 3 4 5 6 8 9 11 12 13 14 15 17 18 19 20 21 22 23 24 25 26 27 28 29 30 31 32 33 34 35 36 37 38 39 40 41 43 44 45 46 47 48 49 50 51 52 54 55 56 57 58 59 60 61 64 65 66 67 68 70 71 72 73 74 75 76 77 78 79 80 81 82 83 84 85 86 87 88 89 90 91 92 93 96 97 98 99 100 101 102 103 104 105 106 107 108 110 111 112 114 115 116 117 118 119 120 121 123 124 126 128 129 130 131 132 134 135 136 137 138 139 140 141 142 143 145 146 147 148 **P**5 **S** Fairview Health Services, Minneapolis, MN
Primary Contact: Carolyn Wilson, President
CFO: Steven Hill, Vice President Finance
CHR: Charles McIntosh, Senior Director Human Resources
Web address: www.fairview.org
**Control:** Other not–for–profit (including NFP Corporation) **Service:** General Medical and Surgical

**Staffed Beds:** 825 **Admissions:** 34256 **Census:** 581 **Outpatient Visits:** 729391 **Births:** 2512 **Total Expense ($000):** 1211050 **Payroll Expense ($000):** 434155 **Personnel:** 6296

**VETERANS AFFAIRS MEDICAL CENTER** See Minneapolis Veterans Affairs Health Care System

**MONTEVIDEO—Chippewa County**

★ **CHIPPEWA COUNTY–MONTEVIDEO HOSPITAL (241325)**, 824 North 11th Street, Zip 56265–1683; tel. 320/269–8877 **A**9 10 18 **F**7 13 15 28 29 30 31 34 40 43 57 59 62 77 78 79 81 93 107 110 114 119 133 146 148 **P**7
Primary Contact: Mark E. Paulson, Chief Executive Officer
CFO: Darlene Boike, Chief Financial Officer
CIO: Jane Myhre, MS, Director Health Information
CNO: Linda M. Nelson, R.N., Director of Nursing Services
Web address: www.montevideomedical.com
**Control:** City–County, Government, nonfederal **Service:** General Medical and Surgical

**Staffed Beds:** 25 **Admissions:** 792 **Census:** 7 **Outpatient Visits:** 33688 **Births:** 115 **Total Expense ($000):** 37445 **Payroll Expense ($000):** 14409 **Personnel:** 238

**MONTICELLO—Wright County**

✠ **CENTRACARE HEALTH–MONTICELLO (241362)**, (Formerly New River Medical Center), 1013 Hart Boulevard, Zip 55362–8230; tel. 763/295–2945, (Nonreporting) **A**1 3 5 9 10 18 **S** CentraCare Health, Saint Cloud, MN
Primary Contact: Mary Ellen Wells, Administrator
CFO: Nancy Friesen, Chief Financial Officer
CMO: Mark Dietz, Chief Medical Officer
CIO: Ruth Kremer, Director Information Services
CHR: Kathy Voss, Director Human Resources
CNO: Euretta Sorenson, R.N., Chief Nursing Officer
Web address: www.newrivermedical.com
**Control:** Hospital district or authority, Government, nonfederal **Service:** General Medical and Surgical

**Staffed Beds:** 25

**MOOSE LAKE—Carlton County**

★ **MERCY HOSPITAL (241350)**, 710 South Kenwood Avenue, Zip 55767–9405; tel. 218/485–4481 **A**9 10 18 **F**3 7 8 11 13 15 28 29 31 34 35 40 43 45 46 53 57 59 62 64 68 70 75 76 77 79 81 85 86 87 89 93 107 111 114 119 130 131 132 133 135 143 144 146 148
Primary Contact: Jason T. Douglas, Chief Executive Officer
CFO: Gregg Chartrand, Chief Financial Officer
CHR: Sonya Towle, Director Human Resources
CNO: Donita Korpela, R.N., Director of Patient Care Services
Web address: www.mercymooselake.org
**Control:** Hospital district or authority, Government, nonfederal **Service:** General Medical and Surgical

**Staffed Beds:** 25 **Admissions:** 881 **Census:** 7 **Outpatient Visits:** 25333 **Births:** 122 **Total Expense ($000):** 29169 **Payroll Expense ($000):** 13057 **Personnel:** 209

*Many Facility Codes have changed. Please refer to the AHA Guide Code Chart.*
© 2013 AHA Guide

MN

## MORA—Kanabec County

✠ **FIRSTLIGHT HEALTH SYSTEM (241367)**, 301 South Highway 65,
Zip 55051–1899; tel. 320/679–1212 **A**1 9 10 18 **F**3 7 11 13 15 28 30 31 34
35 40 43 51 53 57 63 70 75 76 77 78 79 81 84 85 87 93 94 107 108 110
111 115 118 119 130 132 133 135 146 148
Primary Contact: Randy Ulseth, Chief Executive Officer
COO: Christine M. Kimbler, R.N., Chief Operating Officer
CFO: David H. Amundson, Chief Financial Officer
CMO: Scott Lagaard, M.D., Chief of Staff
CHR: Kim Carlson, Director Human Resources
Web address: www.firstlighthealthsystem.org
**Control:** County–Government, nonfederal **Service:** General Medical and Surgical

| | |
|---|---|
| **Staffed Beds:** 25 **Admissions:** 1130 **Census:** 7 **Outpatient Visits:** 32000 **Births:** 112 **Total Expense ($000):** 47245 **Payroll Expense ($000):** 16982 **Personnel:** 301 | |

## MORRIS—Stevens County

★ **STEVENS COMMUNITY MEDICAL CENTER (241363)**, 400 East First Street,
Zip 56267–1408, Mailing Address: P.O. Box 660, Zip 56267–0660;
tel. 320/589–1313 **A**9 10 18 **F**3 11 12 13 15 28 29 31 34 35 40 44 45 50
57 59 64 70 76 79 81 85 86 87 89 97 107 111 114 119 130 131 132 133
135 145 146 148 **P**6
Primary Contact: John Rau, President and Chief Executive Officer
CFO: Kerrie McEvilly, Director Finance and Information Systems
CIO: Kerrie McEvilly, Director Finance and Information Systems
CHR: Karla Larson, Director Human Resources
Web address: www.scmcinc.org
**Control:** Other not–for–profit (including NFP Corporation) **Service:** General
Medical and Surgical

| | |
|---|---|
| **Staffed Beds:** 25 **Admissions:** 1074 **Census:** 9 **Outpatient Visits:** 71917 **Births:** 91 **Total Expense ($000):** 36497 **Payroll Expense ($000):** 17677 **Personnel:** 257 | |

## NEW PRAGUE—Scott County

✠ **MAYO CLINIC HEALTH SYSTEM IN NEW PRAGUE (241361)**, 301 Second
Street N.E., Zip 56071–1799; tel. 952/758–4431 **A**1 9 10 18 **F**8 11 13 15 17
28 29 30 31 34 35 36 39 40 43 46 53 57 59 63 64 68 70 74 75 76 77 78
79 81 82 85 87 89 90 93 97 107 108 111 114 117 119 125 129 130 131
132 133 135 146 147 **P**6 **S** Mayo Clinic Health System, Rochester, MN
Primary Contact: Mary J. Klimp, FACHE, Chief Administrative Officer
COO: Anna L. Herrmann, JD, Assistant Administrator
CMO: Marty Herrmann, M.D., Medical Director
CNO: Laura Hopkins, Director of Nursing
Web address: www.mayoclinichealthsystem.org/locations/new-prague
**Control:** Other not–for–profit (including NFP Corporation) **Service:** General
Medical and Surgical

| | |
|---|---|
| **Staffed Beds:** 25 **Admissions:** 872 **Census:** 9 **Outpatient Visits:** 30339 **Births:** 157 **Total Expense ($000):** 35522 **Payroll Expense ($000):** 15302 **Personnel:** 222 | |

## NEW ULM—Brown County

✠ **NEW ULM MEDICAL CENTER (241378)**, 1324 Fifth Street North,
Zip 56073–1553; tel. 507/217–5000 **A**1 9 10 18 **F**3 4 5 11 13 15 28 29 31
32 34 35 36 40 43 45 55 56 57 59 62 63 64 65 68 70 75 76 77 78 79 81
82 85 87 93 94 97 98 99 100 101 102 103 104 107 108 111 114 119 129
130 131 132 135 144 146 148 **S** Allina Health, Minneapolis, MN
Primary Contact: Toby Freier, President
CFO: Toby Freier, President
CMO: Joan Krikava, M.D., Director Medical Affairs
CIO: Toby Freier, President
CHR: Anne Makepeace, Director Human Resources
Web address: www.newulmmedicalcenter.com
**Control:** Other not–for–profit (including NFP Corporation) **Service:** General
Medical and Surgical

| | |
|---|---|
| **Staffed Beds:** 45 **Admissions:** 2493 **Census:** 20 **Outpatient Visits:** 109040 **Births:** 319 **Total Expense ($000):** 68904 **Payroll Expense ($000):** 22976 **Personnel:** 343 | |

## NORTHFIELD—Dakota County

★ **NORTHFIELD HOSPITAL (240014)**, 2000 North Avenue, Zip 55057–1498;
tel. 507/646–1000, (Includes LONG TERM CARE CENTER ), (Total facility includes
40 beds in nursing home–type unit) **A**9 10 **F**3 7 11 15 29 30 31 34 35 40 43
45 46 47 48 49 57 59 62 63 64 68 69 70 75 76 77 78 79 81 85 86 87 93
94 97 107 110 111 113 115 117 119 120 128 129 130 131 132 133 146
147 **P**6
Primary Contact: Steve Underdahl, Chief Executive Officer
CFO: Timothy L. Gronseth, Vice President and Chief Financial Officer
CMO: Jeff Meland, M.D., Vice President, Chief Medical Officer
CHR: Kirsten Budin, Director Human Resources
Web address: www.northfieldhospital.org
**Control:** City–Government, nonfederal **Service:** General Medical and Surgical

| | |
|---|---|
| **Staffed Beds:** 77 **Admissions:** 1812 **Census:** 51 **Outpatient Visits:** 119341 **Births:** 511 **Total Expense ($000):** 72802 **Payroll Expense ($000):** 29563 **Personnel:** 462 | |

## OLIVIA—Renville County

**RC HOSPITAL AND CLINICS (241306)**, 611 East Fairview Avenue,
Zip 56277–4213; tel. 320/523–1261, (Nonreporting) **A**9 10 18
Primary Contact: Nathan Blad, Chief Executive Officer
CFO: Nathan Blad, Chief Financial Officer
CIO: Cherry Weigel, Director Health Information Management
Web address: www.rchospital.com
**Control:** County–Government, nonfederal **Service:** General Medical and Surgical

| | |
|---|---|
| **Staffed Beds:** 25 | |

## ONAMIA—Mille Lacs County

★ **MILLE LACS HEALTH SYSTEM (241356)**, 200 North Elm Street,
Zip 56359–7901; tel. 320/532–3154, (Total facility includes 57 beds in nursing
home–type unit) **A**9 10 18 **F**7 11 13 15 28 29 30 31 33 34 40 43 45 59 62 63
64 75 76 77 81 85 93 98 103 107 110 114 127 129 130 132 133 135
144 **P**6
Primary Contact: Bill Nelson, Chief Executive Officer
COO: Kim Kucera, Chief Operating Officer
CFO: John Unzen, Chief Financial Officer
CMO: Thomas H. Bracken, M.D., Vice President Medical Affairs
CHR: Fern Gershone, Vice President Human Resources
Web address: www.mlhealth.org
**Control:** Other not–for–profit (including NFP Corporation) **Service:** General
Medical and Surgical

| | |
|---|---|
| **Staffed Beds:** 85 **Admissions:** 940 **Census:** 70 **Outpatient Visits:** 22205 **Births:** 52 **Total Expense ($000):** 37406 **Payroll Expense ($000):** 17433 **Personnel:** 384 | |

## ORTONVILLE—Big Stone County

★ **ORTONVILLE AREA HEALTH SERVICES (241342)**, 450 Eastvold Avenue,
Zip 56278–1133; tel. 320/839–2502, (Total facility includes 64 beds in nursing
home–type unit) **A**5 9 10 18 **F**2 3 11 13 15 18 19 28 30 31 34 35 40 44 45
49 50 55 57 59 62 63 64 65 68 69 74 75 76 77 78 79 81 82 84 85 86 87
89 92 93 107 111 114 117 119 128 130 131 133 135 146 **P**4 **S** Sanford
Health, Sioux Falls, SD
Primary Contact: Richard M. Ash, Chief Executive Officer
CFO: James Foster, Chief Financial Officer and Assistant Administrator
CMO: Robert Ross, M.D., Chief of Staff
CIO: Barbara Voecks, Chief Information Officer
CHR: Kim McCrea, Chief Human Resources Officer
CNO: Jennifer Wiik, Chief Nursing Officer
Web address: www.oahs.us
**Control:** City–Government, nonfederal **Service:** General Medical and Surgical

| | |
|---|---|
| **Staffed Beds:** 89 **Admissions:** 545 **Census:** 61 **Outpatient Visits:** 43793 **Births:** 73 **Total Expense ($000):** 22226 **Payroll Expense ($000):** 7196 **Personnel:** 176 | |

## OWATONNA—Steele County

✠ **OWATONNA HOSPITAL (240069)**, 2250 N.W. 26th Street, Zip 55060–5503;
tel. 507/451–3850 **A**1 9 10 **F**11 13 28 29 34 35 40 57 76 77 79 80 81 89
93 98 100 101 102 103 107 108 119 129 130 131 145 **S** Allina Health,
Minneapolis, MN
Primary Contact: David L. Albrecht, President
CFO: Mark T. Gillen, Director Finance and Operations
CHR: Mark Sevenich, Director Human Resources
Web address: www.owatonnahospital.com
**Control:** Other not–for–profit (including NFP Corporation) **Service:** General
Medical and Surgical

| | |
|---|---|
| **Staffed Beds:** 43 **Admissions:** 2703 **Census:** 24 **Outpatient Visits:** 32269 **Births:** 516 **Total Expense ($000):** 45374 **Payroll Expense ($000):** 15880 **Personnel:** 204 | |

**MN**

## PARK RAPIDS—Hubbard County

☒ **ST. JOSEPH'S AREA HEALTH SERVICES (241380)**, 600 Pleasant Avenue, Zip 56470–1431; tel. 218/732–3311 **A**1 5 9 10 18 **F**3 11 12 13 15 28 29 30 32 34 35 39 40 43 45 47 57 59 62 63 64 65 70 75 76 77 79 81 82 84 85 93 107 108 110 111 114 118 119 129 130 131 132 133 134 146 **S** Catholic Health Initiatives, Englewood, CO
Primary Contact: Benjamin Koppelman, President
CFO: Jay Ross, Chief Financial Officer
CFO: Brent Schmidt, Chief Financial Officer
CMO: Darryl Beehler, D.O., Chief of Staff
CHR: John Tormanen, Director Mission and Human Resources
CNO: Deb Haagenson, R.N., Vice President of Patient Care
Web address: www.sjahs.org
**Control:** Church–operated, Nongovernment, not–for profit **Service:** General Medical and Surgical

**Staffed Beds:** 25 **Admissions:** 1603 **Census:** 15 **Outpatient Visits:** 34189 **Births:** 129 **Total Expense ($000):** 42718 **Payroll Expense ($000):** 17357 **Personnel:** 269

## PAYNESVILLE—Stearns County

★ **PAYNESVILLE AREA HEALTH CARE SYSTEM (241349)**, 200 West 1st Street, Zip 56362–1496; tel. 320/243–3767, (Total facility includes 52 beds in nursing home–type unit) **A**9 10 18 **F**7 10 11 13 15 17 28 31 40 43 56 64 75 81 85 107 115 119 125 127 128 130 133 143 145 146 148 **P**8
Primary Contact: Dennis C. Miley, Chief Executive Officer
COO: Greg Wilson, Chief Operating Officer and Chief Financial Officer
CFO: Greg Wilson, Chief Operating Officer and Chief Financial Officer
CIO: Gary Smith, Manager Information Technology
CHR: Paulette Hagen, Director Human Resources
Web address: www.pahcs.org
**Control:** Hospital district or authority, Government, nonfederal **Service:** General Medical and Surgical

**Staffed Beds:** 77 **Admissions:** 529 **Census:** 56 **Outpatient Visits:** 19369 **Births:** 78 **Total Expense ($000):** 35511 **Payroll Expense ($000):** 14083 **Personnel:** 232

## PERHAM—Otter Tail County

☒ **PERHAM HEALTH (241373)**, 1000 Coney Street West, Zip 56573–1199; tel. 218/347–4500, (Total facility includes 96 beds in nursing home–type unit) **A**1 9 10 18 **F**3 10 13 15 28 33 40 43 45 57 69 76 77 81 85 89 90 93 107 110 111 115 128 130 133 144 146 **S** Sanford Health, Sioux Falls, SD
Primary Contact: Chuck Hofius, Chief Executive Officer
CFO: Brad D. Wurgler, Chief Financial Officer
CMO: Corey Nyhus, M.D., President Medical Staff
CIO: Jim Rieber, Director Information Systems
CHR: Kathy Johnson, Director Human Resources
CNO: Bonnie Johnson, R.N., Vice President of Patient Services
Web address: www.perhamhealth.org
**Control:** Hospital district or authority, Government, nonfederal **Service:** General Medical and Surgical

**Staffed Beds:** 121 **Admissions:** 1038 **Census:** 99 **Outpatient Visits:** 22570 **Births:** 125 **Total Expense ($000):** 38407 **Payroll Expense ($000):** 16690

## PINE CITY—Pine County

**LAKESIDE MEDICAL CENTER (240211)**, 129 East Sixth Avenue, Zip 55063; tel. 320/629–2542, (Nonreporting) **A**9
Primary Contact: Max Blaufuss, Administrator and Chief Executive Officer
Web address: www.lmc–pcac.com
**Control:** Corporation, Investor–owned, for–profit **Service:** Other specialty

**Staffed Beds:** 10

## PIPESTONE—Pipestone County

★ **PIPESTONE COUNTY MEDICAL CENTER AVERA (241374)**, 916 4th Avenue S.W., Zip 56164–1890; tel. 507/825–5811, (Data for 182 days) **A**9 10 18 **F**8 13 15 28 29 31 34 40 45 53 57 59 62 63 64 65 68 75 76 77 81 82 85 93 107 110 111 114 119 130 131 132 133 135 146 148 **P**6 **S** Avera Health, Sioux Falls, SD
Primary Contact: Bradley D. Burris, Chief Executive Officer
CFO: Dave Keeler, Chief Financial Officer
CHR: Judy Raschke, Director Human Resources
Web address: www.pcmchealth.org
**Control:** County–Government, nonfederal **Service:** General Medical and Surgical

**Staffed Beds:** 25 **Admissions:** 186 **Census:** 3 **Outpatient Visits:** 16314 **Births:** 33 **Total Expense ($000):** 11206 **Payroll Expense ($000):** 4993 **Personnel:** 173

## PRINCETON—Sherburne County

☒ **FAIRVIEW NORTHLAND MEDICAL CENTER (240141)**, 911 Northland Drive, Zip 55371–2173; tel. 763/389–1313 **A**1 5 9 10 **F**3 11 13 15 18 19 20 28 29 30 31 32 34 35 40 45 46 50 57 59 64 70 75 76 77 81 85 87 89 91 93 107 110 111 114 115 119 130 132 146 **P**6 **S** Fairview Health Services, Minneapolis, MN
Primary Contact: John W. Herman, Chief Executive Officer
CFO: Kim Ericson, Vice President Finance
CMO: Greg Schoen, M.D., Regional Medical Director
Web address: www.northland.fairview.org
**Control:** Other not–for–profit (including NFP Corporation) **Service:** General Medical and Surgical

**Staffed Beds:** 31 **Admissions:** 1855 **Census:** 13 **Outpatient Visits:** 49907 **Births:** 524 **Total Expense ($000):** 53861 **Payroll Expense ($000):** 23013 **Personnel:** 250

## RED WING—Goodhue County

☒ **MAYO CLINIC HEALTH SYSTEM IN RED WING (240018)**, 701 Hewitt Boulevard, Zip 55066–2848, Mailing Address: P.O. Box 95, Zip 55066–0095; tel. 651/267–5000, (Nonreporting) **A**1 9 10 **S** Mayo Clinic Health System, Rochester, MN
Primary Contact: Thomas J. Witt, M.D., President and Chief Executive Officer
CFO: Mike Larson, Chief Financial Officer
CMO: Jack Alexander, M.D., Chief Medical Officer
CIO: Kendra Shaw, Manager Information Services
CHR: Kim Trittin, Manager Human Resources
Web address: www.mayoclinichealthsystem.org/locations/red–wing
**Control:** Other not–for–profit (including NFP Corporation) **Service:** General Medical and Surgical

**Staffed Beds:** 134

## REDLAKE—Beltrami County

☐ **U.S. PUBLIC HEALTH SERVICE INDIAN HOSPITAL (240206)**, Highway 1, Zip 56671, Mailing Address: P.O. Box 497, Zip 56671–0497; tel. 218/679–3912, (Nonreporting) **A**1 9 10 **S** U. S. Indian Health Service, Rockville, MD
Primary Contact: Mark Karzon, Chief Executive Officer
CMO: John Robinson, M.D., Clinical Director
Web address: www.ihs.gov
**Control:** PHS, Indian Service, Government, federal **Service:** General Medical and Surgical

**Staffed Beds:** 19

## REDWOOD FALLS—Redwood County

★ **REDWOOD AREA HOSPITAL (241351)**, 100 Fallwood Road, Zip 56283–1828; tel. 507/637–4500, (Nonreporting) **A**9 10 18
Primary Contact: Bryan Lydick, Chief Executive Officer
CFO: Connie Bloedow, Interim Chief Financial Officer
CIO: Tom Balko, Manager Information Systems
CHR: Jody Rindfleisch, Manager Human Resources
CNO: Dawn Allen, R.N., Chief Clinical Officer
Web address: www.redwoodareahospital.org
**Control:** City–Government, nonfederal **Service:** General Medical and Surgical

**Staffed Beds:** 25

## ROBBINSDALE—Hennepin County

☒ △ ◇ **NORTH MEMORIAL MEDICAL CENTER (240001)**, (Formerly North Memorial Health Care), 3300 Oakdale Avenue North, Zip 55422–2926; tel. 763/520–5200 **A**1 2 3 5 7 9 10 21 **F**3 7 11 13 15 17 18 20 22 24 26 28 29 30 31 32 34 35 38 40 43 44 45 46 49 50 53 54 55 56 57 58 59 60 62 63 64 68 70 72 73 74 75 76 77 78 81 82 83 84 85 86 87 89 90 91 92 93 96 97 98 100 102 103 104 105 107 108 110 111 114 115 117 118 119 124 126 129 130 132 133 135 143 144 146 147 148 **P**6 8 **S** North Memorial Health Care, Robbinsdale, MN
Primary Contact: Loren L. Taylor, Chief Executive Officer
COO: Andrew S. Cochrane, President Hospital Operations
CMO: J. Kevin Croston, M.D., Chief Medical Officer
CIO: Patrick Taffe, Vice President Information Services
CHR: David Abrams, Vice President Human Resources
CNO: Ginger L. Malone, MSN, Chief Nursing Officer
Web address: www.northmemorial.com
**Control:** Other not–for–profit (including NFP Corporation) **Service:** General Medical and Surgical

**Staffed Beds:** 355 **Admissions:** 21734 **Census:** 242 **Outpatient Visits:** 562152 **Births:** 1173 **Total Expense ($000):** 650925 **Payroll Expense ($000):** 308607 **Personnel:** 3995

*Many Facility Codes have changed. Please refer to the AHA Guide Code Chart.*
© 2013 AHA Guide

## ROCHESTER—Olmsted County

☐ **COMMUNITY BEHAVIORAL HEALTH HOSPITAL – ROCHESTER**, 251 Wood
Lake Drive S.E., Zip 55904–5530; tel. 507/206–2561, (Nonreporting) **A**1 9
**S** Minnesota Department of Human Services, Saint Paul, MN
Primary Contact: Lisa Costello, R.N., Interim Administrator
Web address: www.health.state.mn.us
**Control:** State–Government, nonfederal **Service:** Psychiatric

**Staffed Beds:** 16

⊠ △ **MAYO CLINIC – SAINT MARYS HOSPITAL (240010)**, 1216 Second
Street S.W., Zip 55902–1970; tel. 507/255–5123, (Includes MAYO EUGENIO
LITTA CHILDREN'S HOSPITAL, 200 First Street, S.W., Zip 55905–0001;
tel. 507/255–5123), (Nonreporting) **A**1 3 5 7 8 9 10 **S** Mayo Clinic Health
System, Rochester, MN
Primary Contact: Lynn Frederick, Administrator
COO: Shirley Weis, Chief Administrative Officer
CFO: Brad Schmidt, Chief Financial Officer
CMO: Michael Rock, M.D., Chief Medical Officer
CIO: Jessica Grosset, Director Information Technology
CHR: Ken Schneider, Chair Human Resources
Web address: www.mayoclinic.org
**Control:** Other not–for–profit (including NFP Corporation) **Service:** General
Medical and Surgical

**Staffed Beds:** 797

★ **OLMSTED MEDICAL CENTER (240006)**, 1650 Fourth Street S.E.,
Zip 55904–4717, Mailing Address: 210 Ninth Street S.E., Zip 55904–6756;
tel. 507/288–3443 **A**9 10 **F**3 11 12 13 15 28 30 34 40 45 50 54 57 58 59
64 65 68 74 75 76 77 79 80 81 82 85 86 87 92 93 97 99 100 104 107 108
110 111 115 119 129 130 131 135 144 147 148 **P**6
Primary Contact: Roy A. Yawn, M.D., President
CFO: Kevin A. Higgins, Chief Financial Officer
CMO: David E. Westgard, M.D., Chief Medical Officer
CIO: Susan M. Schuett, Chief Information Officer
CHR: David P. Johnson, Director Human Resources
Web address: www.olmmed.org
**Control:** Other not–for–profit (including NFP Corporation) **Service:** General
Medical and Surgical

**Staffed Beds:** 38 **Admissions:** 1950 **Census:** 13 **Outpatient Visits:** 331593
**Births:** 822 **Total Expense ($000):** 151080 **Payroll Expense ($000):** 78185
**Personnel:** 871

⊠ **ROCHESTER METHODIST HOSPITAL (240061)**, (Formerly Mayo Clinic –
Methodist Hospital), 201 West Center Street, Zip 55902–3084;
tel. 507/266–7890, (Nonreporting) **A**1 3 5 9 10 **S** Mayo Clinic Health System,
Rochester, MN
Primary Contact: Lynn Frederick, Administrator
COO: Shirley Weis, Chief Administrative Officer
CFO: Brad Schmidt, Chief Financial Officer
CMO: Michael Rock, M.D., Chief Medical Officer
CIO: Jessica Grosset, Director Information Technology
CHR: Ken Schneider, Chair Human Resources
CNO: Pamela O. Johnson, MS, Chief Nursing Officer
Web address: www.mayoclinic.org
**Control:** Other not–for–profit (including NFP Corporation) **Service:** General
Medical and Surgical

**Staffed Beds:** 335

## ROSEAU—Roseau County

⊠ **LIFECARE MEDICAL CENTER (241344)**, 715 Delmore Avenue,
Zip 56751–1599; tel. 218/463–2500, (Total facility includes 100 beds in nursing
home–type unit) **A**1 5 9 10 18 **F**3 7 10 11 13 15 28 29 30 31 32 34 35 36 40
43 45 53 56 57 59 62 63 64 65 68 75 76 77 81 82 84 85 86 93 104 107
110 111 115 118 119 128 129 130 132 133 135 144 146 147 148 **P**6
Primary Contact: Keith Okeson, President and Chief Executive Officer
COO: Susan C. Lisell, Vice President of Clinical Services
CFO: Cathy Huss, Chief Financial Officer
CIO: Kevin Schumacher, Director of Information Services
CHR: Carol Klotz, Director Human Resources
CNO: Roxanne Fabian, Director of Nursing–Acute Care
Web address: www.lifecaremedicalcenter.org
**Control:** Other not–for–profit (including NFP Corporation) **Service:** General
Medical and Surgical

**Staffed Beds:** 125 **Admissions:** 818 **Census:** 104 **Outpatient Visits:** 35878
**Births:** 170 **Total Expense ($000):** 34112 **Payroll Expense ($000):** 15699
**Personnel:** 301

## SAINT CLOUD—Stearns County

⊠ △ **ST. CLOUD HOSPITAL (240036)**, 1406 Sixth Avenue North,
Zip 56303–1901; tel. 320/251–2700 **A**1 2 3 5 7 9 10 13 20 **F**3 5 11 12 13
14 15 17 18 19 20 22 24 26 27 28 29 30 31 32 34 35 36 39 40 43
44 45 46 47 48 49 50 51 54 56 57 58 59 60 61 62 63 64 66 68 69 70 72
74 75 76 77 78 79 80 81 82 84 85 86 87 88 89 90 92 93 94 96 97 98 99
100 101 102 103 104 105 106 107 108 110 111 114 115 117 118 119 120
121 123 124 126 129 130 131 132 134 135 141 145 146 147 148 **P**6
**S** CentraCare Health, Saint Cloud, MN
Primary Contact: Craig J. Broman, FACHE, President
COO: Linda Chmielewski, R.N., Vice President Operations
CFO: Greg Klugherz, Vice President Corporate Services and Chief Financial Officer
CMO: Mark Matthias, M.D., Vice President of Medical Affairs
CIO: Amy Porwoll, Vice President of Information Systems
CHR: Duane Rasmusson, Vice President Human Resources
CNO: Linda Chmielewski, R.N., Vice President Operations
Web address: www.centracare.com
**Control:** Other not–for–profit (including NFP Corporation) **Service:** General
Medical and Surgical

**Staffed Beds:** 485 **Admissions:** 26687 **Census:** 295 **Outpatient Visits:**
435148 **Births:** 2409 **Total Expense ($000):** 565682 **Payroll Expense**
**($000):** 238516 **Personnel:** 4235

⊠ △ **ST. CLOUD VETERANS AFFAIRS HEALTH CARE SYSTEM**, 4801 Veterans
Drive, Zip 56303–2099; tel. 320/252–1670, (Total facility includes 225 beds in
nursing home–type unit) **A**1 7 **F**2 3 4 5 11 12 15 18 28 29 30 31 35 36 39 46
47 50 53 54 56 58 59 61 63 64 65 68 75 77 78 79 81 82 83 84 87 93 94
97 98 100 102 103 104 105 106 107 115 119 128 130 132 135 143 144
146 147 148 **P**6 **S** Department of Veterans Affairs, Washington, DC
Primary Contact: Barry I. Bahl, Director
COO: Barry I. Bahl, Director
CFO: Joseph Schmitz, Chief Financial Officer
CMO: Susan Markstrom, M.D., Chief of Staff
CIO: Denise Hanson, Information Technology Specialist
CHR: Lisa Rosendahl, Director Human Resources
CNO: Meri Hauge, R.N., Associate Director of Patient Care Services and Nurse
Executive
Web address: www.stcloud.va.gov
**Control:** Veterans Affairs, Government, federal **Service:** General Medical and
Surgical

**Staffed Beds:** 388 **Admissions:** 2523 **Census:** 350 **Outpatient Visits:**
368960 **Births:** 0 **Total Expense ($000):** 215194 **Payroll Expense ($000):**
98642 **Personnel:** 1454

**VETERANS AFFAIRS MEDICAL CENTER** See St. Cloud Veterans Affairs Health
Care System

## SAINT JAMES—Watonwan County

⊠ **MAYO CLINIC HEALTH SYSTEM IN SAINT JAMES (241333)**, 1101 Moulton
and Parsons Drive, Zip 56081–5550; tel. 507/375–3261 **A**1 9 10 18 **F**3 15 18
28 34 35 40 43 53 57 59 75 77 79 81 86 87 97 107 110 114 119 127 128
130 132 133 135 144 146 148 **P**6 **S** Mayo Clinic Health System,
Rochester, MN
Primary Contact: Ryan J. Smith, Administrator
COO: Mark Fratzke, R.N., Chief Nursing Officer and Chief Operating Officer
CFO: James Tarasovich, Chief Financial Officer
CMO: Jennifer Langbehn, Medical Director
CIO: Thomas Borowski, Chief Information Officer
CHR: Gayle B. Hansen, R.N., Chief Integration Officer
CNO: Mark Fratzke, R.N., Chief Nursing Officer and Chief Operating Officer
Web address: www.mayoclinichealthsystem.org/locations/st-james
**Control:** Other not–for–profit (including NFP Corporation) **Service:** General
Medical and Surgical

**Staffed Beds:** 13 **Admissions:** 215 **Census:** 4 **Outpatient Visits:** 39527
**Births:** 0 **Total Expense ($000):** 16217 **Payroll Expense ($000):** 5448
**Personnel:** 59

## SAINT LOUIS PARK—Hennepin County

⊠ △ **PARK NICOLLET METHODIST HOSPITAL (240053)**, 6500 Excelsior
Boulevard, Zip 55426–4702; Mailing Address: Minneapolis, tel. 952/993–5000,
(Nonreporting) **A**1 2 3 5 7 9 10 **S** HealthPartners, Bloomington, MN
Primary Contact: David Abelson, M.D., President and Chief Executive Officer
COO: Michael Kaupa, Executive Vice President and Chief Operating Officer
CFO: Sheila McMillan, Chief Financial Officer
CMO: Steven Connelly, M.D., Chief Medical Officer
CIO: Julie Flaschenriem, Chief Information Officer
CHR: Paul Dominski, Vice President Human Resources
CNO: Roxanna L. Gapstur, Ph.D., Chief Nursing Officer
Web address: www.parknicollet.com
**Control:** Other not–for–profit (including NFP Corporation) **Service:** General
Medical and Surgical

**Staffed Beds:** 426

**MN**

---

**Hospital, Medicare Provider Number, Address, Telephone, Approval, Facility, and Physician Codes, Health Care System**

★ American Hospital Association (AHA) membership
☐ The Joint Commission accreditation    ◇ DNV Healthcare Inc. accreditation
○ Healthcare Facilities Accreditation Program
△ Commission on Accreditation of Rehabilitation Facilities (CARF) accreditation

## SAINT PAUL—Ramsey County

☒ △ **BETHESDA HOSPITAL (242004)**, (Formerly HealthEast Bethesda Hospital), 559 Capitol Boulevard, Zip 55103–2101; tel. 651/232–2000 **A**1 3 5 7 9 10 **F**1 3 6 11 29 30 38 44 45 50 53 56 60 61 64 68 74 75 77 79 85 86 87 91 93 100 101 103 104 105 107 111 114 119 130 132 146 **P**8 **S** HealthEast Care System, Saint Paul, MN
Primary Contact: Catherine Barr, Senior Vice President and President, Bethesda Hospital
CFO: Lea Jilek, Director Finance
CMO: Stephen J. Kolar, M.D., Vice President Medical Affairs
CIO: Mac McClurkan, Chief Information Officer
Web address: www.healtheast.org
**Control:** Other not–for–profit (including NFP Corporation) **Service:** Long–Term Acute Care hospital

**Staffed Beds:** 126 **Admissions:** 1218 **Census:** 103 **Outpatient Visits:** 9589 **Births:** 0 **Total Expense ($000):** 77181 **Payroll Expense ($000):** 35204 **Personnel:** 500

☒ **CHILDREN'S HOSPITALS AND CLINICS OF MINNESOTA (243301)**, 345 North Smith Avenue, Zip 55102–2346; tel. 651/220–6000, (Nonreporting) **A**1 3 5 9 **S** Children's Hospitals and Clinics of Minnesota, Minneapolis, MN
Primary Contact: Alan L. Goldbloom, M.D., Chief Executive Officer
COO: David S. Overman, Chief Operating Officer
CFO: Jerry Massmann, Chief Financial Officer
CMO: Phillip M. Kibort, M.D., Vice President Medical Affairs and Chief Medical Officer
CIO: Jeffrey D. Young, Chief Information Officer
CHR: David Brumbaugh, Vice President Human Resources
Web address: www.childrensmn.org
**Control:** Other not–for–profit (including NFP Corporation) **Service:** Children's general

**Staffed Beds:** 133

☐ △ **GILLETTE CHILDREN'S SPECIALTY HEALTHCARE (243300)**, (Pediatric Specialty Hospital), 200 East University Avenue, Zip 55101–2598; tel. 651/291–2848 **A**1 3 5 7 9 10 **F**3 29 30 35 36 39 50 54 64 68 71 74 79 81 82 84 85 88 89 90 91 92 93 94 107 111 115 119 129 130 146 **P**6
Primary Contact: Margaret E. Perryman, President and Chief Executive Officer
CFO: James Haddican, Vice President Finance
CMO: Steven Koop, M.D., Medical Director
CIO: Jennifer Fall, Chief Information Officer
CHR: Betty Rivard, Vice President Human Resources
Web address: www.gillettechildrens.org
**Control:** Other not–for–profit (including NFP Corporation) **Service:** Children's other specialty

**Staffed Beds:** 60 **Admissions:** 2545 **Census:** 33 **Outpatient Visits:** 147984 **Births:** 0 **Total Expense ($000):** 183816 **Payroll Expense ($000):** 89451 **Personnel:** 1070

☐ △ **REGIONS HOSPITAL (240106)**, 640 Jackson Street, Zip 55101–2595; tel. 651/254–3456 **A**1 2 3 5 7 8 9 10 **F**3 4 5 8 13 15 16 17 18 20 22 24 26 28 29 30 31 34 35 36 38 40 42 43 45 46 47 49 50 51 53 54 55 56 57 58 59 60 64 65 68 70 71 74 75 76 77 78 79 81 82 84 85 86 87 89 90 92 93 96 98 100 101 102 103 104 105 106 107 108 109 110 111 112 114 115 116 117 119 120 121 122 124 126 128 129 130 131 132 135 143 146 147 148 **S** HealthPartners, Bloomington, MN
Primary Contact: Brock D. Nelson, President and Chief Executive Officer
CFO: Heidi Conrad, Vice President and Chief Financial Officer
CMO: George J. Isham, M.D., Chief Health Officer and Medical Director Health Plan
CIO: Kim LaReau, Vice President and Chief Information Officer
Web address: www.regionshospital.com
**Control:** Other not–for–profit (including NFP Corporation) **Service:** General Medical and Surgical

**Staffed Beds:** 454 **Admissions:** 25048 **Census:** 334 **Outpatient Visits:** 129657 **Births:** 2544 **Total Expense ($000):** 594708 **Payroll Expense ($000):** 284942 **Personnel:** 2863

☒ **ST. JOHN'S HOSPITAL (240210)**, 1575 Beam Avenue, Zip 55109–1126; tel. 651/232–7000 **A**1 2 10 **F**3 13 15 28 29 30 31 34 35 36 37 38 40 43 44 50 54 55 57 59 60 61 63 64 68 70 72 74 75 76 77 78 79 81 85 86 87 89 93 96 97 100 102 104 107 108 110 111 114 115 117 118 119 121 123 126 130 131 132 146 147 148 **P**8 **S** HealthEast Care System, Saint Paul, MN
Primary Contact: Scott L. North, FACHE, Senior Vice President and President of Acute Care Hospitals
CMO: John Kvasnicka, M.D., Medical Director
CIO: Mac McClurkan, Chief Information Officer
CHR: Mary Arnold, Interim Vice President Human Resources
Web address: www.stjohnshospital–mn.org
**Control:** Other not–for–profit (including NFP Corporation) **Service:** General Medical and Surgical

**Staffed Beds:** 192 **Admissions:** 14476 **Census:** 120 **Outpatient Visits:** 214864 **Births:** 2701 **Total Expense ($000):** 234234 **Payroll Expense ($000):** 83422 **Personnel:** 1143

☒ **ST. JOSEPH'S HOSPITAL (240063)**, 45 West 10th Street, Zip 55102–1053; tel. 651/232–3000 **A**1 2 3 5 9 10 **F**3 4 5 11 12 13 15 17 18 20 22 24 26 28 29 30 31 34 35 36 37 38 40 43 44 46 49 50 56 57 58 59 60 61 63 64 68 70 74 75 76 77 78 79 81 83 84 85 87 92 93 96 98 100 101 102 103 104 105 107 108 111 114 119 120 121 124 130 132 146 147 148 **P**8 **S** HealthEast Care System, Saint Paul, MN
Primary Contact: Scott L. North, FACHE, Senior Vice President and President of Acute Care Hospitals
CMO: Stephen J. Kolar, M.D., Vice President Medical Affairs
Web address: www.healtheast.org
**Control:** Other not–for–profit (including NFP Corporation) **Service:** General Medical and Surgical

**Staffed Beds:** 232 **Admissions:** 12738 **Census:** 177 **Outpatient Visits:** 121274 **Births:** 1209 **Total Expense ($000):** 258255 **Payroll Expense ($000):** 96048 **Personnel:** 1397

☒ △ **UNITED HOSPITAL (240038)**, 333 North Smith Avenue, Zip 55102–2389; tel. 651/241–8000, (Nonreporting) **A**1 2 3 5 7 9 10 **S** Allina Health, Minneapolis, MN
Primary Contact: Thomas O'Connor, President
CFO: John Bien, Vice President Finance
CMO: Daniel Foley, M.D., Vice President Medical Affairs
CHR: James McGlade, Director Human Resources
Web address: www.allina.com
**Control:** Other not–for–profit (including NFP Corporation) **Service:** General Medical and Surgical

**Staffed Beds:** 398

## SAINT PETER—Nicollet County

☐ **COMMUNITY BEHAVIORAL HEALTH HOSPITAL – ST. PETER (244010)**, 2000 Klein Street, Zip 56082–5800; tel. 507/933–5001, (Nonreporting) **A**1 5 10 **S** Minnesota Department of Human Services, Saint Paul, MN
Primary Contact: Marlene Schnichels, R.N., Interim Administrator
CFO: Shirley Jacobson, Chief Financial Officer
Web address: www.health.state.mn.us
**Control:** State–Government, nonfederal **Service:** Psychiatric

**Staffed Beds:** 16

★ ◇ **RIVER'S EDGE HOSPITAL AND CLINIC (241334)**, 1900 North Sunrise Drive, Zip 56082–5376; tel. 507/931–2200, (Nonreporting) **A**5 9 10 18 21
Primary Contact: Colleen A. Spike, Chief Executive Officer
CFO: Curt Savstrom, Chief Financial Officer and Chief Information Officer
CMO: Michael Sparacino, M.D., Chief Medical Staff
CIO: Curt Savstrom, Chief Financial Officer and Chief Information Officer
CHR: Tammie Hudspith, Director Human Resources
Web address: www.riversedgehealth.org
**Control:** City–Government, nonfederal **Service:** General Medical and Surgical

**Staffed Beds:** 17

## SANDSTONE—Pine County

★ **ESSENTIA HEALTH SANDSTONE (241309)**, 109 Court Avenue South, Zip 55072–5120; tel. 320/245–2212, (Nonreporting) **A**9 10 18 **S** Essentia Health, Duluth, MN
Primary Contact: Michael D. Hedrix, Interim Chief Executive Officer
CFO: Chris Johnson, Assistant Administrator and Chief Financial Officer
CMO: Sarah Aldredge, M.D., Chief Medical Officer
Web address: www.pinemedicalcenter.org
**Control:** Hospital district or authority, Government, nonfederal **Service:** General Medical and Surgical

**Staffed Beds:** 85

## SAUK CENTRE—Stearns County

★ **CENTRACARE HEALTH–SAUK CENTRE (241368)**, (Formerly St. Michael's Hospital and Nursing Home), 425 North Elm Street, Zip 56378–1010; tel. 320/352–2221, (Nonreporting) **A**9 10 18 **S** CentraCare Health, Saint Cloud, MN
Primary Contact: Delano Christianson, Administrator
CFO: Delano Christianson, Administrator
Web address: www.centracare.com/hospitals/sauk_centre/index.html
**Control:** City–Government, nonfederal **Service:** General Medical and Surgical

**Staffed Beds:** 85

*Many Facility Codes have changed. Please refer to the AHA Guide Code Chart.*
© 2013 AHA Guide

## SHAKOPEE—Scott County

☒ **ST. FRANCIS REGIONAL MEDICAL CENTER (240104)**, 1455 St. Francis Avenue, Zip 55379–3380; tel. 952/428–3000 **A**1 2 5 9 10 **F**3 11 12 13 14 15 28 29 30 31 34 35 36 38 40 43 45 46 50 51 53 57 58 59 68 70 73 75 76 77 78 79 81 82 84 86 87 89 93 107 108 110 111 115 117 119 120 124 129 130 131 132 135 144 146 147 148 **P**3 **S** Allina Health, Minneapolis, MN
Primary Contact: Michael A. Baumgartner, President
CFO: Cynthia Vincent, Vice President Finance
CMO: Brian Prokosch, M.D., Vice President Medical Affairs
CIO: Joe Delveaux, Manager Information Services
CHR: Ann Glaves, Vice President Human Resources
CNO: Debora Ryan, R.N., Vice President Patient Care
Web address: www.stfrancis–shakopee.com
**Control:** Other not–for–profit (including NFP Corporation) **Service:** General Medical and Surgical

**Staffed Beds: 86 Admissions: 5675 Census: 42 Outpatient Visits:** 110974 **Births:** 1311 **Total Expense ($000):** 72707 **Payroll Expense ($000):** 40041 **Personnel:** 489

## SLAYTON—Murray County

★ **MURRAY COUNTY MEDICAL CENTER (241319)**, 2042 Juniper Avenue, Zip 56172–1017; tel. 507/836–6111 **A**9 10 18 **F**3 7 8 11 28 29 31 32 34 35 40 43 45 53 56 57 59 64 65 70 75 79 81 85 86 87 93 97 107 119 127 129 130 131 132 133 135 146 148 **P**5 **S** Sanford Health, Sioux Falls, SD
Primary Contact: Meldon L. Snow, Chief Executive Officer
CFO: Renee Logan, Chief Financial Officer
CMO: Joyce Tarbet, M.D., Chief Medical Officer
CIO: Justin Keller, Director Information Technology
CHR: Nancy Andert, Director Human Resources
CNO: Shari Achterhoff, R.N., Chief Nursing Officer
Web address: www.murraycountymed.org
**Control:** County–Government, nonfederal **Service:** General Medical and Surgical

**Staffed Beds: 18 Admissions: 394 Census: 4 Births:** 0

## SLEEPY EYE—Brown County

**SLEEPY EYE MEDICAL CENTER (241327)**, 400 Fourth Avenue N.W., Zip 56085–1109, Mailing Address: P.O. Box 323, Zip 56085 0323; tel. 507/794–3571 **A**9 10 18 **F**13 15 28 34 40 43 45 59 68 76 77 81 91 93 107 114 119 127 129 130 133 **P**6
Primary Contact: Kevin Sellheim, Chief Executive Officer
CHR: Connie Dahlberg, Director Business and Employee
CNO: Sue Schweiss, Director of Nursing
Web address: www.semedicalcenter.org
**Control:** City–Government, nonfederal **Service:** General Medical and Surgical

**Staffed Beds: 17 Admissions: 333 Census: 3 Outpatient Visits:** 11076 **Births:** 21 **Total Expense ($000):** 9788 **Payroll Expense ($000):** 4680 **Personnel:** 92

## SPRINGFIELD—Brown County

☐ **MAYO CLINIC HEALTH SYSTEM IN SPRINGFIELD (241352)**, 625 North Jackson Avenue, Zip 56087–1714, Mailing Address: P.O. Box 146, Zip 56087–0146; tel. 507/723–6201 **A**1 9 10 18 **F**3 15 28 32 34 39 40 45 57 59 65 75 81 85 89 93 97 107 110 114 128 133 135 146 148 **P**6 **S** Mayo Clinic Health System, Rochester, MN
Primary Contact: Scott D. Thoreson, FACHE, Administrator
COO: Scott D. Thoreson, FACHE, Administrator
CFO: James Tarasovich, Chief Financial Officer
CMO: Annette Schmit–Cline, M.D., Medical Director
CIO: Margo Woodford, Assistant Administrator
CHR: Marian Schoper, Manager Human Resources
Web address: www.smc–mhs.org
**Control:** Other not–for–profit (including NFP Corporation) **Service:** General Medical and Surgical

**Staffed Beds: 24 Admissions: 206 Census: 3 Outpatient Visits:** 24698 **Births:** 0 **Total Expense ($000):** 14899 **Payroll Expense ($000):** 5555 **Personnel:** 66

## STAPLES—Wadena County

**LAKEWOOD HEALTH SYSTEM (241329)**, 49725 County 83, Zip 56479–5280; tel. 218/894–1515, (Total facility includes 100 beds in nursing home–type unit) **A**9 10 18 **F**3 6 7 8 10 11 12 13 15 28 29 30 31 34 35 36 39 40 43 50 52 53 56 57 59 62 63 64 65 68 75 77 78 79 81 82 84 85 86 87 93 98 99 100 101 102 103 104 105 107 110 114 119 125 127 128 129 130 131 132 133 135 143 146 147 148 **P**7
Primary Contact: Tim Rice, President and Chief Executive Officer
CFO: Jim Dregney, Chief Financial Officer
CMO: John Halfen, M.D., Medical Director
CIO: Jeff Osegard, Chief Information Officer
CHR: Janet Jacobson, Director Human Resources
Web address: www.lakewoodhealthsystem.com
**Control:** Other not–for–profit (including NFP Corporation) **Service:** General Medical and Surgical

**Staffed Beds: 135 Admissions: 1651 Census: 113 Outpatient Visits:** 226789 **Births:** 443 **Total Expense ($000):** 86757 **Payroll Expense ($000):** 35895 **Personnel:** 771

## STILLWATER—Washington County

☒ **LAKEVIEW HOSPITAL (240066)**, 927 Churchill Street West, Zip 55082–6605; tel. 651/439–5330, (Nonreporting) **A**1 5 9 10 **S** HealthPartners, Bloomington, MN
Primary Contact: Curt Geissler, President
CFO: Doug Johnson, Chief Financial Officer
CMO: Charles Bransford, M.D., Medical Director
CIO: Carol Lundstrom, Interim Director Information Systems
CHR: Angy Duchesneau, Senior Director Human Resources
CNO: Jo Sittlow, Senior Director of Patient Care and Chief Nursing Officer
Web address: www.lakeview.org
**Control:** Other not–for–profit (including NFP Corporation) **Service:** General Medical and Surgical

**Staffed Beds: 66**

## THIEF RIVER FALLS—Pennington County

**MERITCARE THIEF RIVER FALLS NORTHWEST MEDICAL CENTER** See Sanford Thief River Falls Medical Center

★ **SANFORD THIEF RIVER FALLS MEDICAL CENTER (241381)**, (Formerly Sanford Medical Center Thief River Falls), 120 LaBree Avenue South, Zip 56701–2840; tel. 218/681–4240 **A**9 10 18 **F**3 8 11 13 15 28 29 31 33 34 39 40 43 45 50 53 54 57 64 68 70 76 77 78 79 81 85 86 87 93 94 96 98 99 100 101 102 104 106 107 110 111 114 119 129 131 132 133 135 144 146 147 **P**6 **S** Sanford Health, Sioux Falls, SD
Primary Contact: Brian J. Carlson, FACHE, Chief Executive Officer
COO: Rob Lovejoy, Chief Operating Officer
CFO: Casey R. Johnson, Chief Financial Officer
CMO: Janell Hudson, M.D., Chief Clinical Officer
CHR: Rob Lovejoy, Chief Operating Officer
Web address: www.sanfordhealth.org
**Control:** Other not–for–profit (including NFP Corporation) **Service:** General Medical and Surgical

**Staffed Beds: 35 Admissions: 1888 Census: 19 Outpatient Visits:** 43961 **Births:** 293 **Total Expense ($000):** 58855 **Payroll Expense ($000):** 21970 **Personnel:** 521

## TRACY—Lyon County

★ **SANFORD TRACY MEDICAL CENTER (241303)**, 251 Fifth Street East, Zip 56175–1536; tel. 507/629–3200 **A**9 10 18 **F**3 11 28 31 32 34 40 41 56 57 59 62 64 68 71 77 81 85 87 89 93 97 107 108 111 125 129 130 131 132 133 135 143 **S** Sanford Health, Sioux Falls, SD
Primary Contact: Stacy Barstad, Chief Executive Officer
CFO: Jerry Thompson, Chief Financial Officer
CMO: Louisa Paul, M.D., Chief Medical Officer
CIO: Janet Theisen, Chief Information Officer
CHR: Becky Foster, Manager Human Resources
Web address: www.sanfordtracy.org
**Control:** Other not–for–profit (including NFP Corporation) **Service:** General Medical and Surgical

**Staffed Beds: 25 Admissions: 205 Census: 2 Outpatient Visits:** 18938 **Births:** 0 **Total Expense ($000):** 10120 **Payroll Expense ($000):** 4835 **Personnel:** 100

**MN**

---

**Hospital, Medicare Provider Number, Address, Telephone, Approval, Facility, and Physician Codes, Health Care System**

★ American Hospital Association (AHA) membership
☐ The Joint Commission accreditation
◇ DNV Healthcare Inc. accreditation
○ Healthcare Facilities Accreditation Program
△ Commission on Accreditation of Rehabilitation Facilities (CARF) accreditation

MN

## TWO HARBORS—Lake County

**LAKE VIEW MEMORIAL HOSPITAL (241308)**, 325 11th Avenue, Zip 55616–1360; tel. 218/834–7300 **A**9 10 18 **F**5 10 15 17 28 35 40 43 53 59 63 64 75 77 81 82 84 93 111 114 119 130 133 144 148
Primary Contact: Jo Ann R. Hoag, R.N., Chief Executive Officer
CFO: Susan Benjamin, Chief Financial Officer
Web address: www.lvmhospital.com
**Control:** Other not–for–profit (including NFP Corporation) **Service:** General Medical and Surgical

**Staffed Beds:** 17 **Admissions:** 215 **Census:** 5 **Outpatient Visits:** 31663
**Births:** 0 **Total Expense ($000):** 12945 **Payroll Expense ($000):** 5271
**Personnel:** 85

## TYLER—Lincoln County

**TYLER HEALTHCARE CENTER AVERA (241348)**, 240 Willow Street, Zip 56178–1166; tel. 507/247–5521, (Nonreporting) **A**9 10 18 **S** Avera Health, Sioux Falls, SD
Primary Contact: Dale K. Kruger, Chief Executive Officer and Chief Financial Officer
CFO: Dale K. Kruger, Chief Executive Officer and Chief Financial Officer
Web address: www.www1.avera.org/amck/regionalfacilities/tyler/index.aspx
**Control:** Other not–for–profit (including NFP Corporation) **Service:** General Medical and Surgical

**Staffed Beds:** 56

## VIRGINIA—St. Louis County

⊠ △ **ESSENTIA HEALTH–VIRGINIA (240084)**, (Formerly Virginia Regional Medical Center), 901 Ninth Street North, Zip 55792–2398; tel. 218/741–3340, (Nonreporting) **A**1 7 9 10
Primary Contact: Daniel Milbridge, Administrator and Chief Operating Officer
CFO: Steven Feltman, CPA, Interim Chief Financial Officer
CIO: Brenda Skorich, Manager Business and Medical Records
CNO: Michelle Fleming, Chief Nursing Officer
Web address: www.vrmc.org
**Control:** City–Government, nonfederal **Service:** General Medical and Surgical

**Staffed Beds:** 173

## WABASHA—Wabasha County

★ **SAINT ELIZABETH'S MEDICAL CENTER (241335)**, 1200 Grant Boulevard West, Zip 55981–1042; tel. 651/565–4531, (Total facility includes 146 beds in nursing home–type unit) **A**9 10 18 **F**1 2 4 6 10 11 12 13 15 16 17 28 29 30 34 35 40 43 45 46 49 50 53 56 59 62 65 67 70 72 73 75 76 77 80 81 85 88 89 90 93 94 98 107 110 114 119 125 128 130 133 143 145 146 148 **S** Ascension Health, Saint Louis, MO
Primary Contact: Thomas Crowley, President and Chief Executive Officer
CFO: John Wolfe, Chief Financial Officer
CMO: Brian E. Kelly, M.D., President Medical Staff
CHR: Jim Root, Vice President Human Resources
CNO: Kathy Lueders, R.N., Director of Nursing–Acute Care
Web address: www.stelizabethswabasha.org
**Control:** Church–operated, Nongovernment, not–for profit **Service:** General Medical and Surgical

**Staffed Beds:** 166 **Admissions:** 524 **Census:** 150 **Outpatient Visits:** 23508
**Births:** 70 **Total Expense ($000):** 23367 **Payroll Expense ($000):** 11270
**Personnel:** 280

## WACONIA—Carver County

★ ◇ **RIDGEVIEW MEDICAL CENTER (240056)**, 500 South Maple Street, Zip 55387–1791; tel. 952/442–2191 **A**2 9 10 21 **F**3 7 8 12 13 15 18 20 22 28 29 30 31 32 34 35 36 38 40 43 45 48 49 54 57 58 59 62 63 64 65 66 68 70 73 74 75 76 77 78 79 81 84 85 86 87 89 93 96 98 107 108 110 111 114 115 118 119 126 129 130 131 132 135 144 146 147 148 **P**6
Primary Contact: Robert Stevens, President and Chief Executive Officer
CFO: Gordon Gablenz, Vice President Finance
CIO: Tamara Korbel, Director Management Information Systems
CHR: Sarah M. Hastings, Vice President Human Resources
Web address: www.ridgeviewmedical.org
**Control:** Other not–for–profit (including NFP Corporation) **Service:** General Medical and Surgical

**Staffed Beds:** 102 **Admissions:** 4748 **Census:** 46 **Outpatient Visits:** 153883
**Births:** 1366 **Total Expense ($000):** 171577 **Payroll Expense ($000):** 81299 **Personnel:** 1237

## WADENA—Wadena County

☐ **TRI–COUNTY HOSPITAL (241354)**, 415 Jefferson Street North, Zip 56482–1297; tel. 218/631–3510 **A**1 9 10 18 **F**3 7 11 13 15 17 28 31 34 35 40 50 54 57 59 64 65 70 75 76 77 81 85 86 89 93 99 104 107 110 111 114 119 127 129 130 131 132 133 135 146 147 148 **P**6
Primary Contact: Joel Beiswenger, Chief Executive Officer
CFO: Kim Aagard, Chief Financial Officer
CMO: John Pate, M.D., Chief Medical Officer
CIO: Bill Blaha, Manager Information Technology
CHR: Lisa Reddick, Director Organizational Resources
CNO: Kathy Kleen, Chief Nursing Officer
Web address: www.tricountyhospital.org
**Control:** Other not–for–profit (including NFP Corporation) **Service:** General Medical and Surgical

**Staffed Beds:** 25 **Admissions:** 1446 **Census:** 11 **Outpatient Visits:** 155673
**Births:** 161 **Total Expense ($000):** 44876 **Payroll Expense ($000):** 17158
**Personnel:** 352

## WARREN—Marshall County

★ **NORTH VALLEY HEALTH CENTER (241337)**, 109 South Minnesota Street, Zip 56762–1499; tel. 218/745–4211, (Nonreporting) **A**9 10 18
Primary Contact: Ashley King, Chief Executive Officer
CFO: Mitchell Kotrba, Chief Financial Officer
Web address: www.nvhc.net
**Control:** Other not–for–profit (including NFP Corporation) **Service:** General Medical and Surgical

**Staffed Beds:** 20

## WASECA—Waseca County

⊠ **MAYO CLINIC HEALTH SYSTEM IN WASECA (241345)**, 501 North State Street, Zip 56093–2811; tel. 507/835–1210 **A**1 5 9 10 18 **F**3 8 11 15 18 28 29 30 31 32 34 35 40 45 50 53 56 57 59 63 64 65 68 74 75 77 79 81 87 90 93 97 103 104 107 110 111 114 119 128 130 131 132 133 143 144 146 147 148 **P**6 **S** Mayo Clinic Health System, Rochester, MN
Primary Contact: Jeffrey Carlson, Administrator
CMO: Daniel Stahl, M.D., Medical Director
Web address: www.mayoclinichealthsystem.org
**Control:** Other not–for–profit (including NFP Corporation) **Service:** General Medical and Surgical

**Staffed Beds:** 25 **Admissions:** 336 **Census:** 6 **Outpatient Visits:** 53123
**Births:** 0 **Total Expense ($000):** 18568 **Payroll Expense ($000):** 7943
**Personnel:** 96

## WESTBROOK—Cottonwood County

★ **SANFORD WESTBROOK MEDICAL CENTER (241302)**, 920 Bell Avenue, Zip 56183–9669, Mailing Address: P.O. Box 188, Zip 56183–0188; tel. 507/274–6121 **A**9 10 18 **F**3 31 34 40 56 57 59 62 64 68 71 75 77 81 85 89 91 93 97 99 100 101 102 103 104 107 108 111 125 130 131 132 133 135 143 **P**6 **S** Sanford Health, Sioux Falls, SD
Primary Contact: Stacy Barstad, Chief Executive Officer
COO: Gordon Kopperud, Director Operations
CFO: Jerry Thompson, Chief Financial Officer
CIO: Janet Theisen, Chief Information Officer
CHR: Becky Foster, Manager Human Resources
Web address: www.sanfordwestbrook.org
**Control:** Other not–for–profit (including NFP Corporation) **Service:** General Medical and Surgical

**Staffed Beds:** 6 **Admissions:** 90 **Census:** 1 **Outpatient Visits:** 10454 **Births:** 0 **Total Expense ($000):** 5773 **Payroll Expense ($000):** 2556 **Personnel:** 40

## WHEATON—Traverse County

★ **SANFORD WHEATON MEDICAL CENTER (241304)**, 401 12th Street North, Zip 56296–1099; tel. 320/563–8226 **A**9 10 18 **F**3 7 11 15 17 18 28 29 30 34 40 43 45 57 59 64 65 81 86 89 90 97 107 110 114 115 119 127 128 132 133 **S** Sanford Health, Sioux Falls, SD
Primary Contact: JoAnn M. Foltz, R.N., Chief Executive Officer
CFO: Shane Ayres, Chief Financial Officer
CHR: Brenda Petersen, Director Human Resources
Web address: www.sanfordhealth.org
**Control:** Other not–for–profit (including NFP Corporation) **Service:** General Medical and Surgical

**Staffed Beds:** 15 **Admissions:** 111 **Census:** 1 **Outpatient Visits:** 7343
**Births:** 0 **Total Expense ($000):** 6536 **Payroll Expense ($000):** 2591
**Personnel:** 55

## WILLMAR—Kandiyohi County

☐ **CHILD AND ADOLESCENT BEHAVIORAL HEALTH SERVICES (244005)**, 1701 Technology Drive Northeast, Zip 56201–2275; tel. 320/231–5421, (Nonreporting) **A**1 10
Primary Contact: Mark Kragenbring, Administrator
Web address: www.dhs.state.mn.us
**Control:** County–Government, nonfederal **Service:** Psychiatric

**Staffed Beds:** 16

*Many Facility Codes have changed. Please refer to the AHA Guide Code Chart.*

© 2013 AHA Guide

☒ **RICE MEMORIAL HOSPITAL (240088)**, 301 Becker Avenue S.W., Zip 56201–3395; tel. 320/235–4543, (Total facility includes 78 beds in nursing home–type unit) **A**1 2 9 10 **F**7 11 12 13 15 18 28 29 30 31 34 35 36 39 40 43 45 47 48 49 57 59 60 63 64 68 70 73 75 76 77 78 79 81 82 84 86 87 89 90 93 98 100 101 102 103 104 105 107 108 111 114 118 119 121 128 129 130 131 132 135 146 147 148
Primary Contact: Michael Schramm, Chief Executive Officer
CIO: Teri Beyer, Chief Information Officer
CHR: Dale Hustedt, Associate Administrator Administrative Services
Web address: www.ricehospital.com
**Control:** City–Government, nonfederal **Service:** General Medical and Surgical

| | |
|---|---|
| **Staffed Beds:** 188 **Admissions:** 3741 **Census:** 110 **Outpatient Visits:** 67773 **Births:** 764 **Total Expense ($000):** 102466 **Payroll Expense ($000):** 42206 **Personnel:** 573 | |

### WINDOM—Cottonwood County

★ **WINDOM AREA HOSPITAL (241332)**, 2150 Hospital Drive, Zip 56101–1287, Mailing Address: P.O. Box 339, Zip 56101–0339; tel. 507/831–2400 **A**9 10 18 **F**11 13 15 28 31 34 35 40 45 53 57 59 76 77 81 93 107 115 119 130 133 148 **S** Sanford Health, Sioux Falls, SD
Primary Contact: Geraldine F. Burmeister, FACHE, Chief Executive Officer
CFO: Kim Armstrong, Chief Financial Officer
CIO: Lori Ling, Information Technician
CHR: Katie Slette, Director Human Resources and Marketing
CNO: Kari Witte, Director of Patient Care
Web address: www.windomareahospital.com
**Control:** City–Government, nonfederal **Service:** General Medical and Surgical

| | |
|---|---|
| **Staffed Beds:** 25 **Admissions:** 452 **Census:** 4 **Outpatient Visits:** 21486 **Births:** 128 **Total Expense ($000):** 13678 **Payroll Expense ($000):** 5492 **Personnel:** 111 | |

### WINONA—Winona County

★ **WINONA HEALTH (240044)**, 855 Mankato Avenue, Zip 55987–4868, Mailing Address: P.O. Box 5600, Zip 55987–0600; tel. 507/454–3650 **A**9 10 20 **F**11 13 15 28 29 30 31 32 34 35 38 40 43 50 53 56 57 59 60 61 70 74 75 76 77 78 79 81 82 84 85 86 87 89 93 96 97 98 99 100 101 102 103 104 107 108 110 111 115 118 119 127 129 130 131 132 135 144 146 147 148 **P**6
Primary Contact: Rachelle H. Schultz, President and Chief Executive Officer
CFO: Michael Allen, Chief Financial Officer
CMO: Charles Shepard, M.D., Medical Director
CHR: Bill Gould, Chief People Resource Officer
Web address: www.winonahealth.org
**Control:** Other not–for–profit (including NFP Corporation) **Service:** General Medical and Surgical

| | |
|---|---|
| **Staffed Beds:** 53 **Admissions:** 2783 **Census:** 26 **Outpatient Visits:** 147027 **Births:** 347 **Total Expense ($000):** 109289 **Payroll Expense ($000):** 45118 **Personnel:** 890 | |

### WOODBURY—Washington County

☒ **WOODWINDS HEALTH CAMPUS (240213)**, 1925 Woodwinds Drive, Zip 55125–4445; tel. 651/232–0228 **A**1 5 9 10 **F**3 13 15 28 29 30 31 34 35 36 37 38 40 43 44 49 50 57 58 59 61 63 64 68 70 74 75 76 77 78 79 81 85 86 87 93 107 108 111 114 119 129 130 132 135 146 **P**8 **S** HealthEast Care System, Saint Paul, MN
Primary Contact: Scott L. North, FACHE, Senior Vice President and President of Acute Care Hospitals
CFO: Robert D. Gill, Chief Financial Officer
CMO: Lynne Lillie, M.D., Medical Director
CIO: Mac McClurkan, Chief Information Officer
CHR: Tammy Arrigoni, Human Resources Lead
Web address: www.woodwinds.org
**Control:** Other not–for–profit (including NFP Corporation) **Service:** General Medical and Surgical

| | |
|---|---|
| **Staffed Beds:** 86 **Admissions:** 7481 **Census:** 56 **Outpatient Visits:** 89100 **Births:** 1762 **Total Expense ($000):** 82731 **Payroll Expense ($000):** 43493 **Personnel:** 584 | |

### WORTHINGTON—Nobles County

**SANFORD REGIONAL HOSPITAL WORTHINGTON** See Sanford Worthington Medical Center

★ **SANFORD WORTHINGTON MEDICAL CENTER (240022)**, 1018 Sixth Avenue, Zip 56187–2202, Mailing Address: P.O. Box 997, Zip 56187–0997; tel. 507/372–2941 **A**9 10 **F**3 11 13 15 17 18 19 26 27 28 31 34 35 40 43 45 50 57 59 60 62 64 68 69 70 75 76 78 79 81 85 86 89 90 93 97 107 110 111 114 116 119 120 121 126 128 129 130 131 132 133 135 144 146 147 148 **S** Sanford Health, Sioux Falls, SD
Primary Contact: Michael Hammer, Chief Executive Officer
COO: Jeffrey J. Rotert, Chief Operating Officer
CFO: Linda Wagner, Chief Financial Officer
CMO: James D. Harris, M.D., Chief of Staff
CHR: Jeffrey J. Rotert, Chief Operating Officer
CNO: Jennifer Weg, R.N., Chief Nursing Officer
Web address: www.sanfordregionalworthington.org
**Control:** Other not–for–profit (including NFP Corporation) **Service:** General Medical and Surgical

| | |
|---|---|
| **Staffed Beds:** 48 **Admissions:** 1350 **Census:** 10 **Outpatient Visits:** 57814 **Births:** 388 **Total Expense ($000):** 28461 **Payroll Expense ($000):** 12318 **Personnel:** 215 | |

### WYOMING—Chisago County

☒ **FAIRVIEW LAKES HEALTH SERVICES (240050)**, 5200 Fairview Boulevard, Zip 55092–8013; tel. 651/982–7000 **A**1 9 10 **F**3 11 13 15 28 29 30 31 32 34 35 37 40 43 45 51 52 53 54 56 57 59 62 63 64 65 68 70 75 76 77 78 79 81 82 83 84 85 86 87 93 97 107 110 111 114 115 119 129 130 131 132 134 143 144 146 147 148 **P**6 **S** Fairview Health Services, Minneapolis, MN
Primary Contact: Steven C. Housh, President
CFO: Kim Ericson, Vice President Finance
CMO: David Milbrandt, M.D., Vice President Medical Affairs
CHR: Don Moschkau, Director Human Resources
CNO: Mary Jo Brueggeman, R.N., Vice President Patient Care
Web address: www.fairview.org/
**Control:** Other not–for–profit (including NFP Corporation) **Service:** General Medical and Surgical

| | |
|---|---|
| **Staffed Beds:** 47 **Admissions:** 3535 **Census:** 26 **Outpatient Visits:** 92524 **Births:** 693 **Personnel:** 485 | |

**MN**

---

**Hospital, Medicare Provider Number, Address, Telephone, Approval, Facility, and Physician Codes, Health Care System**

★ American Hospital Association (AHA) membership
☐ The Joint Commission accreditation
◇ DNV Healthcare Inc. accreditation
○ Healthcare Facilities Accreditation Program
△ Commission on Accreditation of Rehabilitation Facilities (CARF) accreditation

# MISSISSIPPI

### ABERDEEN—Monroe County

★ ◇ **PIONEER COMMUNITY HOSPITAL OF ABERDEEN (251302)**, 400 South Chestnut Street, Zip 39730–3335, Mailing Address: P.O. Box 548, Zip 39730–0548; tel. 662/369–2455 **A**9 10 18 21 **F**29 35 40 43 53 70 75 81 86 87 89 90 93 97 98 103 107 119 128 130 131 133 **S** Pioneer Health Services, Magee, MS
Primary Contact: Sean Johnson, Administrator
CFO: Julie Gieger, Chief Financial Officer
CMO: Kevin Hayes, M.D., Chief of Staff
CHR: Lee Rob, Director Human Resources
Web address: www.pchaberdeen.com
**Control:** Corporation, Investor–owned, for–profit **Service:** General Medical and Surgical

**Staffed Beds:** 35 **Admissions:** 432 **Census:** 7 **Outpatient Visits:** 3737 **Births:** 0 **Personnel:** 191

### ACKERMAN—Choctaw County

★ ◇ **PIONEER COMMUNITY HOSPITAL OF CHOCTAW (251310)**, 311 West Cherry Street, Zip 39735–8708; tel. 662/285–6235, (Total facility includes 60 beds in nursing home–type unit) **A**9 10 18 21 **F**29 40 43 70 77 87 89 93 107 119 128 130 133 143 **S** Pioneer Health Services, Magee, MS
Primary Contact: Sean Johnson, Chief Executive Officer
Web address: www.pchchoctaw.com
**Control:** Corporation, Investor–owned, for–profit **Service:** General Medical and Surgical

**Staffed Beds:** 72 **Admissions:** 225 **Census:** 47 **Outpatient Visits:** 12998 **Births:** 0 **Personnel:** 160

### AMORY—Monroe County

☐ **GILMORE MEMORIAL REGIONAL MEDICAL CENTER (250025)**, 1105 Earl Frye Boulevard, Zip 38821–5500, Mailing Address: P.O. Box 459, Zip 38821–0459; tel. 662/256–7111 **A**1 9 10 **F**13 15 17 29 35 40 43 53 70 72 73 75 76 77 81 86 87 88 89 90 93 107 108 111 119 130 147 **P**6 **S** Health Management Associates, Naples, FL
Primary Contact: J. Allen Tyra, Chief Executive Officer
CFO: Jimmy Young, Chief Financial Officer
CMO: William Rogers, Chief Medical Officer
CIO: Jeff Wideman, Director Information Systems
CHR: Angie L. Weaver, Director Human Resources
Web address: www.gilmorehealth.com
**Control:** Corporation, Investor–owned, for–profit **Service:** General Medical and Surgical

**Staffed Beds:** 95 **Admissions:** 3391 **Census:** 35 **Outpatient Visits:** 49008 **Births:** 562 **Personnel:** 272

### BATESVILLE—Panola County

**BATESVILLE SPECIALTY HOSPITAL (252011)**, 303 Medical Center Drive, Zip 38606–8608; tel. 662/712–2484, (Nonreporting) **A**10
Primary Contact: Candace Eldib, Administrator
**Control:** Other not–for–profit (including NFP Corporation) **Service:** Long–Term Acute Care hospital

**Staffed Beds:** 12

**TRI–LAKES MEDICAL CENTER (250128)**, 303 Medical Center Drive, Zip 38606–8608; tel. 662/563–5611 **A**9 10 **F**3 4 5 11 12 13 15 29 30 31 32 34 35 38 40 43 45 56 57 59 64 65 68 70 74 76 77 81 85 87 89 97 98 100 101 102 103 104 107 108 114 119 127 129 130 132 135 143 147 **S** Health Management Associates, Naples, FL
Primary Contact: Wes Sigler, Chief Executive Officer
COO: Vince Brummett, Director Administrative Services
CMO: Michael R. Hovens, M.D., Chief Medical Officer
CIO: Will Morris, Director Information Technology
Web address: www.trilakesmc.com
**Control:** Corporation, Investor–owned, for–profit **Service:** General Medical and Surgical

**Staffed Beds:** 112 **Admissions:** 3491 **Census:** 48 **Outpatient Visits:** 19575 **Births:** 195 **Personnel:** 304

### BAY SAINT LOUIS—Hancock County

☒ **HANCOCK MEDICAL CENTER (250162)**, 149 Drinkwater Boulevard, Zip 39520–1658, Mailing Address: P.O. Box 2790, Zip 39521–2790; tel. 228/467–8600 **A**1 10 **F**3 11 13 15 17 18 28 29 31 32 34 35 39 40 43 45 51 57 59 64 68 70 75 76 77 79 81 85 86 87 89 90 93 97 107 108 110 111 115 118 119 129 130 131 135 144 145 147 148 **S** QHR, Brentwood, TN
Primary Contact: Craig R. Cudworth, Interim Chief Executive Officer
CNO: Angela Gambino, R.N., Chief Nursing Officer
Web address: www.hmc.org
**Control:** County–Government, nonfederal **Service:** General Medical and Surgical

**Staffed Beds:** 47 **Admissions:** 2011 **Census:** 18 **Outpatient Visits:** 75422 **Births:** 187 **Total Expense ($000):** 38295 **Payroll Expense ($000):** 18350 **Personnel:** 343

### BAY SPRINGS—Jasper County

★ **JASPER GENERAL HOSPITAL (250018)**, 15 A South Sixth Street, Zip 39422–9738, Mailing Address: P.O. Box 527, Zip 39422–0527; tel. 601/764–2101, (Includes JASPER COUNTY NURSING HOME ), (Total facility includes 110 beds in nursing home–type unit) **A**9 10 **F**62 70 128 130 133
Primary Contact: M. Kenneth Posey, FACHE, Administrator
CFO: Steve Green, Comptroller
CMO: A. K. Lay, Sr., M.D., Chief Medical Officer
CHR: JoAnn Boyd, Administrative Assistant
**Control:** County–Government, nonfederal **Service:** General Medical and Surgical

**Staffed Beds:** 126 **Admissions:** 45 **Census:** 108 **Outpatient Visits:** 0 **Births:** 0 **Personnel:** 47

### BELZONI—Humphreys County

**PATIENT'S CHOICE MEDICAL CENTER OF HUMPHREYS COUNTY (251311)**, (Formerly Patient's Choice Medical Center), 500 CCC Road, Zip 39038–3806, Mailing Address: P.O. Box 510, Zip 39038–0510; tel. 662/247–3831 **A**9 10 18 **F**13 29 40 43 70 76 89 90 93 97 98 103 130 133
Primary Contact: Paula Lang, Chief Executive Officer
CHR: Ruth Hayes, Director Human Resources
**Control:** Corporation, Investor–owned, for–profit **Service:** General Medical and Surgical

**Staffed Beds:** 34 **Admissions:** 571 **Census:** 9 **Outpatient Visits:** 7360 **Births:** 0 **Personnel:** 87

### BILOXI—Harrison County

☐ **BILOXI REGIONAL MEDICAL CENTER (250007)**, 150 Reynoir Street, Zip 39530–4199, Mailing Address: P.O. Box 128, Zip 39533–0128; tel. 228/432–1571 **A**1 9 10 **F**3 11 12 13 15 17 18 20 29 31 34 35 37 40 43 45 46 47 48 49 50 54 59 61 64 65 68 70 73 74 75 76 77 78 79 81 85 86 87 89 90 93 97 98 100 102 103 104 105 107 108 110 111 114 115 117 118 119 126 130 135 143 147 148 **S** Health Management Associates, Naples, FL
Primary Contact: Monte J. Bostwick, Chief Executive Officer
CFO: Mark Wack, Chief Financial Officer
CMO: David Harris, M.D., President Medical Affairs
CHR: Brian Stanford, Director Human Resources
Web address: www.biloxiregional.net
**Control:** Corporation, Investor–owned, for–profit **Service:** General Medical and Surgical

**Staffed Beds:** 198 **Admissions:** 7267 **Census:** 102 **Outpatient Visits:** 94658 **Births:** 753 **Total Expense ($000):** 92186 **Payroll Expense ($000):** 31271 **Personnel:** 812

☒ △ **VETERANS AFFAIRS GULF COAST VETERANS HEALTH CARE SYSTEM**, 400 Veterans Avenue, Zip 39531–2410; tel. 228/523–5000, (Nonreporting) **A**1 3 5 7 **S** Department of Veterans Affairs, Washington, DC
Primary Contact: Anthony L. Dawson, FACHE, Director
COO: Deborah M. Johnson, Associate Director
CFO: Teresa Pisarich, Acting Chief Financial Officer
CMO: Barry–Lewis Harris, II, M.D., Chief of Staff
CIO: David D. Wagner, Chief Information Management Service
CHR: Johnnie M. Jones, Acting Chief Human Resource Management and Workforce Development Service
Web address: www.biloxi.va.gov/
**Control:** Veterans Affairs, Government, federal **Service:** General Medical and Surgical

**Staffed Beds:** 392

*Many Facility Codes have changed. Please refer to the AHA Guide Code Chart.*   © 2013 AHA Guide

## BOONEVILLE—Prentiss County

**⊞ BAPTIST MEMORIAL HOSPITAL–BOONEVILLE (250044)**, 100 Hospital Street, Zip 38829–3359; tel. 662/720–5000 **A**1 9 10 **F**3 11 15 17 28 29 30 40 43 70 75 81 87 89 90 93 98 103 107 108 111 118 119 130 132 133 **S** Baptist Memorial Health Care Corporation, Memphis, TN
Primary Contact: James Grantham, Administrator and Chief Executive Officer
CFO: Donavan Leonard, Chief Financial Officer
CMO: Nathan Baldwin, M.D., President Medical Staff
CIO: Linda Chaffin, Director Medical Review
CHR: Shannon Bolen, Director Human Resources
Web address: www.bmhcc.org/booneville
**Control:** Other not–for–profit (including NFP Corporation) **Service:** General Medical and Surgical

**Staffed Beds:** 66 **Admissions:** 1190 **Census:** 18 **Outpatient Visits:** 32206 **Births:** 0 **Total Expense ($000):** 22714 **Payroll Expense ($000):** 8862 **Personnel:** 224

## BRANDON—Rankin County

**☐ CROSSGATES RIVER OAKS HOSPITAL (250096)**, 350 Crossgates Boulevard, Zip 39042–2698; tel. 601/825–2811 **A**1 9 10 **F**3 11 16 17 18 29 30 40 41 43 45 64 70 74 77 78 79 81 85 87 89 90 93 97 98 103 107 108 110 111 114 119 129 130 135 **P**8 **S** Health Management Associates, Naples, FL
Primary Contact: Glen M. Silverman, Chief Executive Officer
CFO: Brad Sinclair, Chief Financial Officer
CMO: Edward Rigdon, M.D., Chief Medical Officer
CIO: Christy Murphy, Director Health Information Systems
CHR: Mark Cook, Director Human Resources
Web address: www.crossgatesriveroaks.com
**Control:** Corporation, Investor–owned, for–profit **Service:** General Medical and Surgical

**Staffed Beds:** 149 **Admissions:** 5062 **Census:** 68 **Outpatient Visits:** 72648 **Births:** 0 **Total Expense ($000):** 52105 **Payroll Expense ($000):** 19739 **Personnel:** 346

## BROOKHAVEN—Lincoln County

**⊞ ◇ KING'S DAUGHTERS MEDICAL CENTER (250057)**, 427 Highway 51 North, Zip 39601–2350, Mailing Address: P.O. Box 948, Zip 39602–0948; tel. 601/833–6011 **A**1 9 10 20 21 **F**3 7 11 13 15 17 28 29 34 35 39 40 41 43 45 51 53 54 57 59 60 61 64 65 68 70 73 75 76 77 79 80 81 85 88 89 93 94 96 97 107 108 111 114 115 118 119 126 129 130 131 132 135 143 147 148 **S** QHR, Brentwood, TN
Primary Contact: Alvin Hoover, FACHE, Chief Executive Officer
COO: Phil Campbell, Chief Operating Officer
CFO: Randy B. Pirtle, Chief Financial Officer
CMO: Leigh Cher Gray, M.D., Chief of Staff
CIO: Carl Smith, Director Information Systems
CHR: Celine Craig, Director Human Resources
CNO: Cheri Walker, R.N., Chief Nursing Officer
Web address: www.kdmc.org
**Control:** Other not–for–profit (including NFP Corporation) **Service:** General Medical and Surgical

**Staffed Beds:** 103 **Admissions:** 3522 **Census:** 30 **Outpatient Visits:** 36578 **Births:** 635 **Total Expense ($000):** 63000 **Payroll Expense ($000):** 27784 **Personnel:** 561

## CALHOUN CITY—Calhoun County

**★ CALHOUN HEALTH SERVICES (251331)**, 140 Burke–Calhoun City Road, Zip 38916–9690; tel. 662/628–6611, (Total facility includes 120 beds in nursing home–type unit) **A**9 10 **F**40 43 70 87 89 93 98 103 107 119 128 130 133 **S** North Mississippi Health Services, Inc., Tupelo, MS
Primary Contact: James P. Franklin, Administrator
CFO: Mandy Suber, Controller
CMO: Guy Farmer, M.D., President Medical Staff
Web address: www.nmhs.net/calhoun_city
**Control:** City–County, Government, nonfederal **Service:** General Medical and Surgical

**Staffed Beds:** 150 **Admissions:** 427 **Census:** 108 **Outpatient Visits:** 5410 **Births:** 0 **Personnel:** 278

## CANTON—Madison County

**MADISON RIVER OAKS MEDICAL CENTER (250038)**, Highway 16 East, Zip 39046–8823, Mailing Address: P.O. Box 1607, Zip 39046–1607; tel. 601/859–1331 **A**9 10 **F**13 15 29 35 40 43 70 76 81 87 89 107 108 130 **S** Health Management Associates, Naples, FL
Primary Contact: L. Dwayne Blalock, Chief Executive Officer
CFO: Ken Warriner, Chief Financial Officer
CMO: Robert Tatum, M.D., Chief of Staff
CIO: Michelle Hughes, Director Health Information Management
CHR: Jackie Williams, Director Human Resources
Web address: www.madisonriveroaks.com
**Control:** Partnership, Investor–owned, for–profit **Service:** General Medical and Surgical

**Staffed Beds:** 67 **Admissions:** 2251 **Census:** 19 **Outpatient Visits:** 21871 **Births:** 414 **Personnel:** 238

## CARTHAGE—Leake County

**★ BAPTIST MEDICAL CENTER LEAKE (251315)**, 310 Ellis Street, Zip 39051–3809, Mailing Address: P.O. Box 909, Zip 39051–0909; tel. 601/267–1100, (Total facility includes 44 beds in nursing home–type unit) **A**9 10 18 **F**3 29 32 34 40 41 43 46 57 59 65 66 70 87 107 110 114 119 127 130 133 135 **P**6 **S** Mississippi Baptist Health System, Jackson, MS
Primary Contact: C. Gerald Cotton, Interim Chief Executive Officer
COO: C. Gerald Cotton, Interim Chief Operating Officer
CFO: David Jackson, Chief Financial Officer
CMO: Doug Perry, M.D., Chief of Staff
Web address: www.mbhs.com/locations/baptist–medical–center–leake/
**Control:** Other not–for–profit (including NFP Corporation) **Service:** General Medical and Surgical

**Staffed Beds:** 69 **Admissions:** 811 **Census:** 50 **Outpatient Visits:** 21292 **Births:** 2 **Total Expense ($000):** 7230 **Payroll Expense ($000):** 3679 **Personnel:** 181

## CENTREVILLE—Wilkinson County

**⊞ FIELD MEMORIAL COMMUNITY HOSPITAL (251309)**, 270 West Main Street, Zip 39631, Mailing Address: P.O. Box 639, Zip 39631–0639; tel. 601/645–5221 **A**1 9 10 18 **F**15 18 29 30 34 39 40 43 45 57 59 61 64 70 75 77 79 81 89 90 93 107 108 114 130 133 135
Primary Contact: Chad Netterville, Administrator
CFO: Jacquelyn Richoux, Chief Financial Officer
CHR: Debbie Willingham, Administrative Assistant
Web address: www.fmch.org
**Control:** County–Government, nonfederal **Service:** General Medical and Surgical

**Staffed Beds:** 25 **Admissions:** 534 **Census:** 6 **Outpatient Visits:** 14693 **Births:** 0 **Total Expense ($000):** 15632 **Payroll Expense ($000):** 7635 **Personnel:** 153

## CHARLESTON—Tallahatchie County

**TALLAHATCHIE GENERAL HOSPITAL (251304)**, 201 South Market, Zip 38921–2236, Mailing Address: P.O. Box 230, Zip 38921–0240; tel. 662/647–5535, (Total facility includes 98 beds in nursing home–type unit) **A**9 10 18 **F**29 39 40 70 87 107 128 130 133 **P**6
Primary Contact: Jim Blackwood, Chief Executive Officer
CFO: Sammie Bell, Jr., Chief Financial Officer
**Control:** County–Government, nonfederal **Service:** General Medical and Surgical

**Staffed Beds:** 116 **Admissions:** 331 **Census:** 96 **Outpatient Visits:** 0 **Births:** 0 **Personnel:** 271

## CLARKSDALE—Coahoma County

**☐ △ NORTHWEST MISSISSIPPI REGIONAL MEDICAL CENTER (250042)**, 1970 Hospital Drive, Zip 38614–7202, Mailing Address: P.O. Box 1218, Zip 38614–1218; tel. 662/627–3211 **A**1 7 9 10 19 **F**3 13 15 17 18 20 22 28 29 30 31 34 35 40 43 46 49 50 57 59 64 65 70 74 76 79 81 85 86 87 89 90 92 93 107 108 110 111 114 115 118 119 126 129 130 132 **S** Health Management Associates, Naples, FL
Primary Contact: William G. Buck, Chief Executive Officer
COO: Joseph Webb, Chief Operating Officer
CFO: Steve Marinelli, Chief Financial Officer
CMO: Rodney Baine, M.D., Chief of Staff
CIO: Kayla Carpenter, Health Information Management Systems Officer
CHR: Sarah Dale Shaffer, Director Human Resources
Web address: www.northwestregional.org
**Control:** Corporation, Investor–owned, for–profit **Service:** General Medical and Surgical

**Staffed Beds:** 195 **Admissions:** 5680 **Census:** 60 **Outpatient Visits:** 50398 **Births:** 836 **Total Expense ($000):** 58545 **Payroll Expense ($000):** 21424 **Personnel:** 444

## CLEVELAND—Bolivar County

✉ **BOLIVAR MEDICAL CENTER (250093)**, 901 East Sunflower Road, Zip 38732–2833, Mailing Address: P.O. Box 1380, Zip 38732–1380; tel. 662/846–0061, (Total facility includes 35 beds in nursing home–type unit) **A**1 9 10 20 **F**13 15 17 29 35 39 40 43 56 60 70 73 76 81 87 88 89 93 103 107 108 111 116 118 119 128 130 132 133 **S** LifePoint Hospitals, Inc., Brentwood, TN
Primary Contact: Scott M. Smith, Chief Executive Officer
CFO: Chad Miller, Chief Financial Officer
CMO: Michael Portner, M.D., Chief Medical Staff
CIO: Dusty Griffith, Director Information Systems
CHR: David Kent, Director Human Resources
Web address: www.bolivarmedical.com
**Control:** Corporation, Investor–owned, for–profit **Service:** General Medical and Surgical

**Staffed Beds:** 127 **Admissions:** 3700 **Census:** 74 **Outpatient Visits:** 53207 **Births:** 437 **Personnel:** 382

## COLLINS—Covington County

✉ ◇ **COVINGTON COUNTY HOSPITAL (251325)**, Gerald McRaney Street, Zip 39428–3899, Mailing Address: P.O. Box 1149, Zip 39428–1149; tel. 601/765–6711, (Total facility includes 60 beds in nursing home–type unit) **A**1 9 10 18 21 **F**40 43 70 81 89 93 103 107 119 128 130 133 144
Primary Contact: Paul V. Peiffer, Chief Executive Officer
CFO: Kirstie Evans, Chief Financial Officer
CHR: Lee Robb, Director Human Resources
Web address: www.covingtoncountyhospital.com
**Control:** County–Government, nonfederal **Service:** General Medical and Surgical

**Staffed Beds:** 94 **Admissions:** 615 **Census:** 53 **Outpatient Visits:** 33145 **Births:** 0 **Personnel:** 243

## COLUMBIA—Marion County

**MARION GENERAL HOSPITAL (250085)**, 1560 Sumrall Road, Zip 39429–2654, Mailing Address: P.O. Box 630, Zip 39429–0630; tel. 601/736–6303 **A**9 10 **F**29 35 39 40 43 61 62 70 75 81 87 89 90 93 97 107 108 111 119 131 133 144
Primary Contact: Bryan K. Maxie, Administrator
CFO: Randall Pigott, Chief Financial Officer
CMO: Jeff Johnson, M.D., Chief Medical Staff
CIO: Donny Bracey, Director Information Services
**Control:** County–Government, nonfederal **Service:** General Medical and Surgical

**Staffed Beds:** 49 **Admissions:** 854 **Census:** 10 **Outpatient Visits:** 29467 **Births:** 0 **Personnel:** 132

## COLUMBUS—Lowndes County

✉ **BAPTIST MEMORIAL HOSPITAL–GOLDEN TRIANGLE (250100)**, 2520 Fifth Street North, Zip 39705–2095, Mailing Address: P.O. Box 1307, Zip 39703–1307; tel. 662/244–1000 **A**1 9 10 19 **F**3 4 5 7 11 13 15 17 18 20 22 24 26 28 29 30 31 34 39 40 41 43 45 47 49 50 51 57 59 61 64 65 70 73 75 76 77 78 79 80 81 83 84 85 87 88 89 93 96 98 100 102 104 105 106 107 108 109 110 111 114 115 116 117 118 119 120 121 123 124 126 129 130 132 134 135 147 148 **P**6 **S** Baptist Memorial Health Care Corporation, Memphis, TN
Primary Contact: Paul Cade, Administrator and Chief Executive Officer
CFO: Jimmy Robertson, Chief Financial Officer
CMO: John E. Reed, M.D., Medical Director
CIO: Sheila Bardwell, Director Information Systems
CHR: Bob McCallister, Director Human Resources
CNO: Mary Ellen Sumrall, Chief Nursing Officer
Web address: www.baptistonline.org/golden–triangle/
**Control:** Other not–for–profit (including NFP Corporation) **Service:** General Medical and Surgical

**Staffed Beds:** 249 **Admissions:** 7655 **Census:** 102 **Outpatient Visits:** 103774 **Births:** 900 **Total Expense ($000):** 126293 **Payroll Expense ($000):** 42340 **Personnel:** 948

## CORINTH—Alcorn County

☐ **MAGNOLIA REGIONAL HEALTH CENTER (250009)**, 611 Alcorn Drive, Zip 38834–9321; tel. 662/293–1000 **A**1 9 10 13 19 **F**13 15 17 29 35 39 40 43 51 53 62 63 70 75 76 77 78 81 86 87 89 93 98 100 101 102 103 107 108 111 116 118 119 130 131 132 143 147 **P**7 8
Primary Contact: Ronny Humes, President and Chief Executive Officer
COO: Angela Nowlin, Senior Vice President, Operations
CFO: Jeff Taylor, Senior Vice President Finance
CMO: Felton Combest, M.D., Vice President Medical Affairs
CIO: David Parker, Vice President Information Technology
CHR: Regenia Brown, Vice President Human Resources
CNO: Pam Wallis, Vice President, Nursing Services
Web address: www.mrhc.org
**Control:** City–County, Government, nonfederal **Service:** General Medical and Surgical

**Staffed Beds:** 164 **Admissions:** 7530 **Census:** 95 **Outpatient Visits:** 155688 **Births:** 532 **Personnel:** 1074

## DE KALB—Kemper County

★ ◇ **JOHN C. STENNIS MEMORIAL HOSPITAL (251335)**, 14365 Highway 16 West, Zip 39328–7974; tel. 769/486–1000 **A**9 10 21 **F**29 40 43 70 75 107 119 133 **P**6 **S** Rush Health Systems, Meridian, MS
Primary Contact: Michael Nester, Administrator
Web address: www.johncstennismemorialhospital.com/jcsmh/
**Control:** Other not–for–profit (including NFP Corporation) **Service:** General Medical and Surgical

**Staffed Beds:** 25 **Admissions:** 113 **Census:** 1 **Outpatient Visits:** 4171 **Births:** 0 **Personnel:** 79

## EUPORA—Webster County

✉ **NORTH MISSISSIPPI MEDICAL CENTER–EUPORA (250020)**, 70 Medical Plaza, Zip 39744–4018; tel. 662/258–6221, (Total facility includes 35 beds in nursing home–type unit) **A**1 9 10 **F**3 7 28 32 34 35 40 43 50 53 54 57 59 64 65 70 71 75 86 87 89 98 107 115 119 128 129 130 132 133 135 **S** North Mississippi Health Services, Inc., Tupelo, MS
Primary Contact: John R. Jones, Administrator
CFO: Adonna Mitchell, Director Fiscal Services
CMO: Charles Ozborn, M.D., Chief of Staff
CIO: Shirley Griffin, Director Health Information
CHR: Dorothy Castle, Director Human Resources
Web address: www.nmhs.net/eupora
**Control:** Other not–for–profit (including NFP Corporation) **Service:** General Medical and Surgical

**Staffed Beds:** 73 **Admissions:** 1109 **Census:** 51 **Outpatient Visits:** 17277 **Births:** 0 **Total Expense ($000):** 19684 **Payroll Expense ($000):** 8315 **Personnel:** 210

## FAYETTE—Jefferson County

**JEFFERSON COUNTY HOSPITAL (250060)**, 870 South Main Street, Zip 39069–5695, Mailing Address: P.O. Box 577, Zip 39069–0577; tel. 601/786–3401 **A**9 10 **F**40 70 98 103
Primary Contact: Jerry Kennedy, Administrator
CFO: Jerry Kennedy, Administrator
CMO: Khar Omolara, M.D., Chief Medical Staff
CHR: Patricia Selmon, Director Public Relations and Chief Human Resources
**Control:** County–Government, nonfederal **Service:** General Medical and Surgical

**Staffed Beds:** 30 **Admissions:** 785 **Census:** 19 **Outpatient Visits:** 0 **Births:** 0 **Personnel:** 87

## FLOWOOD—Rankin County

✉ **RIVER OAKS HOSPITAL (250138)**, 1030 River Oaks Drive, Zip 39232–9553, Mailing Address: P.O. Box 5100, Jackson, Zip 39296–5100; tel. 601/932–1030 **A**1 10 **F**3 11 12 13 15 17 18 20 29 33 35 39 40 43 45 49 51 60 61 63 70 72 73 74 75 76 77 78 79 81 85 87 89 90 93 110 111 115 126 130 147 **S** Health Management Associates, Naples, FL
Primary Contact: Timothy W. Mitchell, Chief Executive Officer
COO: Joan Strayham, R.N., Chief Operating Officer
CFO: Brad Sinclair, Chief Financial Officer
CMO: C. Ron Cannon, M.D., Medical Director
CIO: Pat Jones, Director Information Systems
CHR: Warren Weed, Director Human Resources
CNO: Sherry P. Cook, R.N., Chief Nursing Executive
Web address: www.riveroakshosp.com
**Control:** Corporation, Investor–owned, for–profit **Service:** General Medical and Surgical

**Staffed Beds:** 158 **Admissions:** 6096 **Census:** 60 **Outpatient Visits:** 63152 **Births:** 1853 **Personnel:** 701

☐ **WOMAN'S HOSPITAL (250136)**, 1026 North Flowood Drive, Zip 39232–9532, Mailing Address: P.O. Box 4546, Jackson, Zip 39296–4546; tel. 601/932–1000 **A**1 10 **F**8 13 15 30 34 35 39 59 64 70 72 73 76 81 85 105 108 119 130 147 **S** Health Management Associates, Naples, FL
Primary Contact: Sherry J. Pitts, Chief Executive Officer
CFO: Jeff Bedford, Executive Vice President and Chief Financial Officer
CMO: Edra Kimmel, M.D., Chief of Staff
CHR: Warren Weed, Director Associate Relations
Web address: www.womanshospitalms.com
**Control:** Corporation, Investor–owned, for–profit **Service:** Obstetrics and gynecology

**Staffed Beds:** 60 **Admissions:** 2100 **Census:** 18 **Outpatient Visits:** 17107 **Births:** 1496 **Personnel:** 211

*Many Facility Codes have changed. Please refer to the AHA Guide Code Chart.*

**FOREST—Scott County**

★ ◇ **S. E. LACKEY MEMORIAL HOSPITAL (251300)**, 330 Broad Street, Zip 39074–3508, Mailing Address: P.O. Box 428, Zip 39074–0428; tel. 601/469–4151, (Total facility includes 20 beds in nursing home–type unit) **A**9 10 18 21 **F**15 29 35 39 40 43 56 70 81 86 89 98 107 108 111 119 128 130 133 **P**5 6 **S** Pioneer Health Services, Magee, MS
Primary Contact: Donna Riser, Administrator
CFO: Julie Gieger, Chief Financial Officer
CMO: John Paul Lee, M.D., Chief of Staff
CIO: Eddie Pope, Chief Information Officer
CHR: Donn Paul, Chief Human Resources
Web address: www.lackeymemorialhospital.com
**Control:** Other not–for–profit (including NFP Corporation) **Service:** General Medical and Surgical

**Staffed Beds:** 55 **Admissions:** 1010 **Census:** 35 **Outpatient Visits:** 39224 **Births:** 0 **Personnel:** 223

**GREENVILLE—Washington County**

◇ **ALLEGIANCE SPECIALTY HOSPITAL OF GREENVILLE (250166)**, 300 South Washington Avenue, 3rd Floor, Zip 38701–4719; tel. 662/332–7344 **A**10 21 **F**29 70 87 130 **S** Allegiance Health Management, Shreveport, LA
Primary Contact: Vernail Herzog, Chief Executive Officer
Web address: www.ahmgt.com
**Control:** Corporation, Investor–owned, for–profit **Service:** Long–Term Acute Care hospital

**Staffed Beds:** 39 **Admissions:** 151 **Census:** 10 **Outpatient Visits:** 0 **Births:** 0 **Personnel:** 63

⊠ **DELTA REGIONAL MEDICAL CENTER (250082)**, 1400 East Union Street, Zip 38703–3246; tel. 662/378–3783, (Includes THE KING'S DAUGHTERS HOSPITAL, 300 Washington Avenue, Zip 38701–3614, Mailing Address: P.O. Box 1857, Zip 38702–1857; tel. 662/378–2020) **A**1 9 10 19 **F**3 4 7 8 13 15 17 18 20 22 24 28 29 30 35 40 43 49 51 56 59 62 63 65 70 72 73 74 75 76 77 78 79 81 84 85 89 90 93 97 98 103 104 107 108 111 116 118 119 127 129 130 131 132 135 144 147 **P**6 8
Primary Contact: Stansel Harvey, FACHE, Chief Executive Officer
CFO: Courtney Phillips, Chief Financial Officer
CIO: Shane Coleman, Director Information Services
CHR: Alphe Wells, Vice President Human Resources and Support Services
Web address: www.deltaregional.com
**Control:** County–Government, nonfederal **Service:** General Medical and Surgical

**Staffed Beds:** 217 **Admissions:** 8000 **Census:** 122 **Outpatient Visits:** 90706 **Births:** 880 **Total Expense ($000):** 117394 **Payroll Expense ($000):** 52106 **Personnel:** 908

**GREENWOOD—Leflore County**

**AMG SPECIALTY HOSPITAL–GREENWOOD (252010)**, (Formerly LTAC Hospital of Greenwood), 1401 River Road Floor 2, Zip 38930–4030; tel. 662/459–2681 **A**9 10 **F**130 **S** AMG Integrated Healthcare Management, Lafayette, LA
Primary Contact: Jennifer Wallace, Chief Executive Officer
CMO: Gutti Rao, M.D., Medical Director
CIO: Larry Bramlett, Chief Information Officer
CHR: Shelia Brown, Director Human Resources
Web address: www.amggreenwood.com/
**Control:** Partnership, Investor–owned, for–profit **Service:** Long–Term Acute Care hospital

**Staffed Beds:** 40 **Admissions:** 393 **Census:** 27 **Outpatient Visits:** 0 **Births:** 0 **Total Expense ($000):** 11052 **Payroll Expense ($000):** 4974 **Personnel:** 75

☐ △ **GREENWOOD LEFLORE HOSPITAL (250099)**, 1401 River Road, Zip 38930–4030, Mailing Address: Drawer 1410, Zip 38935–1410; tel. 662/459–7000 **A**1 7 9 10 19 **F**3 8 13 15 17 18 20 28 29 31 32 35 39 40 43 45 50 53 56 57 59 61 68 70 74 75 76 79 81 85 86 87 89 90 93 94 96 98 103 108 110 111 114 118 119 127 129 130 132 145 146 147 148 **P**6 8
Primary Contact: James H. Jackson, Jr., Executive Director
COO: Jeff Curtis, Chief Operating Officer
CMO: A. Randle White, M.D., Chief Medical Staff
CIO: Mark S. Hutson, Chief Information Officer
CHR: Key Britt, Associate Director
Web address: www.glh.org
**Control:** City–County, Government, nonfederal **Service:** General Medical and Surgical

**Staffed Beds:** 196 **Admissions:** 7103 **Census:** 96 **Outpatient Visits:** 170141 **Births:** 619 **Personnel:** 966

**GRENADA—Grenada County**

★ ◇ **GRENADA LAKE MEDICAL CENTER (250015)**, 960 Avent Drive, Zip 38901–5230; tel. 662/227–7000 **A**9 10 20 21 **F**3 8 11 13 14 15 17 29 30 35 39 40 43 49 53 57 60 62 64 70 73 76 77 79 80 81 87 89 90 93 94 96 97 107 108 111 114 118 127 128 130 143 146 147
Primary Contact: Charles L. Denton, Chief Executive Officer
CFO: Keith Heartsill, Chief Financial Officer
CMO: David Simmons, M.D., Chief of Staff
CIO: Sarah Longest, Chief Information Officer
CHR: Ken Baker, Administrative Director Human Resources
Web address: www.glmc.net
**Control:** County–Government, nonfederal **Service:** General Medical and Surgical

**Staffed Beds:** 140 **Admissions:** 2842 **Census:** 36 **Outpatient Visits:** 52333 **Births:** 409 **Total Expense ($000):** 48829 **Payroll Expense ($000):** 19135 **Personnel:** 426

**GULFPORT—Harrison County**

⊠ **GARDEN PARK MEDICAL CENTER (250123)**, 15200 Community Road, Zip 39503–3085, Mailing Address: P.O. Box 1240, Zip 39502–1240; tel. 228/575–7000 **A**1 9 10 **F**13 15 29 35 40 70 76 78 81 86 87 89 90 93 97 98 103 107 108 111 118 119 130 147 **S** HCA, Nashville, TN
Primary Contact: Brenda M. Waltz, FACHE, Chief Executive Officer
COO: Daphne David, Chief Operating Officer
CFO: Regina Ramazani, Chief Financial Officer
CIO: Jackson Balch, IT Director
CHR: Krystyna Varnado, Director Human Resources
CNO: Cheryl Thompson, Chief Nursing Officer
Web address: www.gpmedical.com
**Control:** Corporation, Investor–owned, for–profit **Service:** General Medical and Surgical

**Staffed Beds:** 130 **Admissions:** 3699 **Census:** 44 **Outpatient Visits:** 71075 **Births:** 464 **Personnel:** 417

⊠ △ **MEMORIAL HOSPITAL AT GULFPORT (250019)**, 4500 13th Street, Zip 39501–2569, Mailing Address: P.O. Box 1810, Zip 39502–1810; tel. 228/867–4000, (Includes MEMORIAL BEHAVIORAL HEALTH, 11150 Highway 49 North, Zip 39503 4110; tel. 228/831 1700; Michael A. Zieman, Administrator) **A**1 2 7 9 10 **F**2 3 4 5 8 11 13 15 17 18 20 22 24 26 28 29 30 31 34 35 38 40 43 45 48 49 50 51 53 57 59 64 65 70 71 72 73 74 76 77 78 79 80 81 85 87 89 90 92 93 95 96 98 99 100 101 102 104 105 107 108 110 111 115 116 117 118 119 120 121 124 126 130 132 135 148 **P**3 8
Primary Contact: Gary G. Marchand, President and Chief Executive Officer
CFO: Jeffrey T. Steiner, Vice President Finance
CMO: Nancy Downs, M.D., Vice President Medical Affairs
CIO: Richard Ferrans, M.D., Vice President and Medical Information Officer
Web address: www.gulfportmemorial.com
**Control:** City–County, Government, nonfederal **Service:** General Medical and Surgical

**Staffed Beds:** 445 **Admissions:** 16354 **Census:** 241 **Outpatient Visits:** 436491 **Births:** 1434 **Total Expense ($000):** 366985 **Payroll Expense ($000):** 166485 **Personnel:** 2560

⊠ **SELECT SPECIALTY HOSPITAL–GULF COAST (252005)**, 1520 Broad Avenue, Suite 300, Zip 39501–3601; tel. 228/575–7500 **A**1 10 **F**70 87 90 130 **S** Select Medical Corporation, Mechanicsburg, PA
Primary Contact: John O'Keefe, Chief Executive Officer
Web address: www.selectspecialtyhospitals.com/company/locations/gulfcoast.aspx
**Control:** Corporation, Investor–owned, for–profit **Service:** Long–Term Acute Care hospital

**Staffed Beds:** 61 **Admissions:** 233 **Census:** 19 **Outpatient Visits:** 0 **Births:** 0 **Personnel:** 106

**HATTIESBURG—Forrest County**

★ △ ◇ **FORREST GENERAL HOSPITAL (250078)**, 6051 U.S. Highway 49, Zip 39401–7200, Mailing Address: P.O. Box 16389, Zip 39404–6389; tel. 601/288–7000 **A**2 3 5 7 9 10 19 21 **F**3 4 5 8 15 17 18 20 22 24 26 28 29 30 31 32 34 35 37 45 46 48 49 50 53 54 57 58 59 60 62 63 64 68 70 72 73 74 75 76 77 78 79 80 81 84 85 86 87 88 89 90 92 93 94 95 96 98 99 100 102 103 104 107 108 111 114 115 118 119 120 121 123 128 130 131 132 135 147 148 **P**8
Primary Contact: Evan S. Dillard, M.P.H., FACHE, President and Chief Executive Officer
CFO: Andy Woodward, Chief Financial Officer
CMO: Steven E. Farrell, M.D., Chief Medical Officer
CIO: G. Edward Tucker, Jr., Vice President Corporate Services
Web address: www.forrestgeneral.com
**Control:** County–Government, nonfederal **Service:** General Medical and Surgical

**Staffed Beds:** 512 **Admissions:** 26246 **Census:** 331 **Outpatient Visits:** 136746 **Births:** 2249 **Total Expense ($000):** 339502 **Payroll Expense ($000):** 134619 **Personnel:** 2651

**MS**

---

**Hospital, Medicare Provider Number, Address, Telephone, Approval, Facility, and Physician Codes, Health Care System**

★ American Hospital Association (AHA) membership
☐ The Joint Commission accreditation
◇ DNV Healthcare Inc. accreditation
◯ Healthcare Facilities Accreditation Program
△ Commission on Accreditation of Rehabilitation Facilities (CARF) accreditation

⊠ **REGENCY HOSPITAL OF HATTIESBURG (252009)**, 6051 U.S. Highway 495, 5th Floor, Zip 39401–6031; tel. 601/288–8510 **A**1 10 **F**40 70 **S** Select Medical Corporation, Mechanicsburg, PA
Primary Contact: Kathy A. Viator, R.N., Chief Executive Officer
CMO: Ralph Kahler, M.D., Medical Director
CHR: Jared Burns, Coordinator Human Resources
Web address: www.regencyhospital.com/hattiesburg
**Control:** Corporation, Investor–owned, for–profit **Service:** Long–Term Acute Care hospital

**Staffed Beds:** 33 **Admissions:** 420 **Census:** 29 **Outpatient Visits:** 0 **Births:** 0 **Personnel:** 114

⊠ **WESLEY MEDICAL CENTER (250094)**, 5001 Hardy Street, Zip 39402–1308, Mailing Address: P.O. Box 16509, Zip 39404–6509; tel. 601/268–8000 **A**1 9 10 19 **F**13 15 17 29 35 39 40 53 60 61 70 72 73 75 76 77 78 81 87 89 90 93 97 107 108 111 118 119 130 132 **P**6 7 **S** Community Health Systems, Inc., Franklin, TN
Primary Contact: Michael Neuendorf, Chief Executive Officer
COO: Travis Sisson, Chief Operating Officer
CFO: Randy Humphrey, Chief Financial Officer
CMO: William Reno, III, M.D., President Medical Staff
CIO: William Toon, Director Information Technology
CHR: Terry Trigg, Director Human Resources
Web address: www.wesley.com
**Control:** Corporation, Investor–owned, for–profit **Service:** General Medical and Surgical

**Staffed Beds:** 211 **Admissions:** 8801 **Census:** 112 **Outpatient Visits:** 92591 **Births:** 1488 **Personnel:** 992

### HAZLEHURST—Copiah County

★ **HARDY WILSON MEMORIAL HOSPITAL (251327)**, 233 Magnolia Street, Zip 39083–2228, Mailing Address: P.O. Box 889, Zip 39083–0889; tel. 601/894–4541 **A**9 10 18 **F**15 34 35 39 40 42 45 56 57 59 65 68 70 71 75 81 90 93 98 103 107 111 119 130 133 148
Primary Contact: Larry Joe Walker, Administrator and Chief Executive Officer
Web address: www.hardywilsonhospital.com
**Control:** County–Government, nonfederal **Service:** General Medical and Surgical

**Staffed Beds:** 25 **Admissions:** 746 **Census:** 15 **Outpatient Visits:** 13383 **Births:** 0 **Total Expense ($000):** 10015 **Payroll Expense ($000):** 5970 **Personnel:** 194

### HOLLY SPRINGS—Marshall County

**ALLIANCE HEALTHCARE SYSTEM (250012)**, 1430 Highway 4 East, Zip 38635–2140, Mailing Address: P.O. Box 6000, Zip 38634–6000; tel. 662/252–1212 **A**9 10 20 **F**15 29 35 43 70 75 81 87 89 98 103 107 119 130 132 133 143
Primary Contact: Perry E. Williams, Sr., Administrator and Chief Executive Officer
COO: Cecelia Bost, Chief Operating Officer
CFO: William F. Magee, Chief Financial Officer
CMO: Subbu Rayudu, M.D., Chief of Staff
CIO: Saul Mbenga, Manager Information Technology
CHR: Judy Eggers, Manager Human Resources
Web address: www.alliancehealth.us
**Control:** Corporation, Investor–owned, for–profit **Service:** General Medical and Surgical

**Staffed Beds:** 40 **Admissions:** 567 **Census:** 8 **Outpatient Visits:** 8173 **Births:** 0 **Personnel:** 91

### HOUSTON—Chickasaw County

☐ **TRACE REGIONAL HOSPITAL (250017)**, Highway 8 East, Zip 38851–9396, Mailing Address: P.O. Box 626, Zip 38851–0626; tel. 662/456–3700 **A**1 9 10 **F**15 35 40 61 70 75 89 90 93 98 103 107 111 119 128 130 133 **P**6 **S** Sunlink Health Systems, Atlanta, GA
Primary Contact: Gary L. Staten, Chief Executive Officer
CFO: Pamela W. Cook, Chief Financial Officer
CMO: J. Ronald Staten, M.D., Chief of Staff
CHR: Carol Colbert, Director Human Resources
Web address: www.traceregional.com
**Control:** Corporation, Investor–owned, for–profit **Service:** General Medical and Surgical

**Staffed Beds:** 84 **Admissions:** 795 **Census:** 12 **Outpatient Visits:** 20801 **Births:** 0 **Personnel:** 231

### INDIANOLA—Sunflower County

★ **SOUTH SUNFLOWER COUNTY HOSPITAL (250095)**, 121 East Baker Street, Zip 38751–2498; tel. 662/887–5235 **A**9 10 20 **F**13 15 17 40 43 45 70 76 81 107 110 111 114 119 130 **P**8
Primary Contact: Harold J. Blessitt, Administrator
COO: Barbara Prichard, Assistant Administrator
CFO: Meredith Taylor, Comptroller
CMO: Wade Dowell, M.D., Chief of Staff
CIO: Julie Sterling, Manager Information System
**Control:** County–Government, nonfederal **Service:** General Medical and Surgical

**Staffed Beds:** 49 **Admissions:** 1186 **Census:** 10 **Outpatient Visits:** 12292 **Births:** 194 **Total Expense ($000):** 21100 **Payroll Expense ($000):** 7527 **Personnel:** 134

### IUKA—Tishomingo County

⊠ **NORTH MISSISSIPPI MEDICAL CENTER–IUKA (250002)**, 1777 Curtis Drive, Zip 38852–1001, Mailing Address: P.O. Box 860, Zip 38852–0860; tel. 662/423–6051 **A**1 9 10 **F**17 29 35 40 43 53 70 75 86 87 89 90 93 107 108 111 119 130 132 133 134 **S** North Mississippi Health Services, Inc., Tupelo, MS
Primary Contact: Fred A. Truesdale, Jr., Administrator
CFO: Betty Moore, Business Manager
CMO: Margaret Glynn, M.D., Chief Medical Officer
CIO: Fred A. Truesdale, Jr., Administrator
CHR: Jane Chamblee, Manager Human Resources
Web address: www.nmhs.net
**Control:** Other not–for–profit (including NFP Corporation) **Service:** General Medical and Surgical

**Staffed Beds:** 48 **Admissions:** 701 **Census:** 6 **Outpatient Visits:** 10571 **Births:** 0 **Personnel:** 153

### JACKSON—Hinds County

☐ **BRENTWOOD BEHAVIORAL HEALTHCARE OF MISSISSIPPI (254007)**, 3531 East Lakeland Drive, Zip 39232–8839; tel. 601/936–2024 **A**1 10 **F**35 98 99 100 101 102 104 130 134 **S** Universal Health Services, Inc., King of Prussia, PA
Primary Contact: Michael J. Carney, Chief Executive Officer
Web address: www.brentwoodjackson.com
**Control:** Corporation, Investor–owned, for–profit **Service:** Psychiatric

**Staffed Beds:** 105 **Admissions:** 2535 **Census:** 65 **Outpatient Visits:** 0 **Births:** 0 **Personnel:** 172

☐ **CENTRAL MISSISSIPPI MEDICAL CENTER (250072)**, 1850 Chadwick Drive, Zip 39204–3479, Mailing Address: P.O. Box 59001, Zip 39284–9001; tel. 601/376–1000 **A**1 2 9 10 **F**13 15 17 29 35 40 43 51 61 70 72 73 75 76 77 78 80 81 86 87 89 90 93 97 98 100 102 103 104 107 108 111 116 118 119 130 132 147 **P**4 **S** Health Management Associates, Naples, FL
Primary Contact: Charlotte W. Dupre', Chief Executive Officer
CHR: Kevin Korner, Director Human Resources
Web address: www.centralmississippimedicalcenter.com
**Control:** Corporation, Investor–owned, for–profit **Service:** General Medical and Surgical

**Staffed Beds:** 367 **Admissions:** 7906 **Census:** 106 **Outpatient Visits:** 50034 **Births:** 776 **Personnel:** 596

⊠ △ **G.V. (SONNY) MONTGOMERY VETERANS AFFAIRS MEDICAL CENTER**, 1500 East Woodrow Wilson Drive, Zip 39216–5199; tel. 601/362–4471, (Nonreporting) **A**1 2 3 5 7 **S** Department of Veterans Affairs, Washington, DC
Primary Contact: Joe Battle, Interim Director
COO: Jed Fillingim, Acting Chief Operating Officer and Associate Director
CFO: Joy Willis, Acting Chief Fiscal Service
CMO: Kent Kirchner, M.D., Chief of Staff
CIO: Robert Wolak, Chief Information Resource Management Service
CHR: Sam Evans, Chief Human Resources Management
Web address: www.jackson.va.gov/
**Control:** Veterans Affairs, Government, federal **Service:** General Medical and Surgical

**Staffed Beds:** 323

⊠ △ **METHODIST REHABILITATION CENTER (250152)**, 1350 Woodrow Wilson Drive, Zip 39216–5198; tel. 601/981–2611, (Total facility includes 60 beds in nursing home–type unit) **A**1 3 5 7 9 10 **F**29 35 70 77 81 86 87 90 93 119 130 132 143
Primary Contact: Mark A. Adams, President and Chief Executive Officer
COO: Joseph M. Morette, Executive Vice President
CFO: Gary Armstrong, Executive Vice President
CIO: Gary Armstrong, Executive Vice President
CHR: Steve Hope, Vice President Corporate Services
Web address: www.methodistrehab.org
**Control:** Other not–for–profit (including NFP Corporation) **Service:** Rehabilitation

**Staffed Beds:** 184 **Admissions:** 1105 **Census:** 107 **Outpatient Visits:** 37118 **Births:** 0 **Personnel:** 514

⊠ **MISSISSIPPI BAPTIST MEDICAL CENTER (250102)**, 1225 North State Street, Zip 39202–2064; tel. 601/968–1000 **A**1 2 3 5 9 10 **F**3 4 5 8 11 12 13 15 17 18 19 20 22 24 26 27 28 29 30 31 34 35 36 39 40 41 44 45 46 47 48 49 50 51 52 54 55 57 59 61 64 65 68 70 71 72 73 74 75 76 78 79 80 81 85 86 89 90 91 92 93 94 98 100 103 104 105 107 108 109 110 111 114 115 116 117 118 119 120 121 122 123 124 126 127 129 130 132 144 145 146 147 148 **S** Mississippi Baptist Health System, Jackson, MS
Primary Contact: Kerry R. Tirman, JD, FACHE, President
CFO: Russell W. York, Chief Financial Officer
CMO: Eric A. McVey, M.D., Vice President and Chief Medical Officer
CIO: Steve M. Stanic, Vice President and Chief Information Officer
CHR: Lee Ann Foreman, Vice President Human Resources
CNO: Bobbie K. Ware, R.N., Vice President/Patient Care/Chief Nursing Officer
Web address: www.mbhs.org
**Control:** Other not–for–profit (including NFP Corporation) **Service:** General Medical and Surgical

**Staffed Beds:** 638 **Admissions:** 19208 **Census:** 290 **Outpatient Visits:** 160138 **Births:** 1248 **Total Expense ($000):** 331876 **Payroll Expense ($000):** 114047 **Personnel:** 2769

*Many Facility Codes have changed. Please refer to the AHA Guide Code Chart.*

© 2013 AHA Guide

⊠ **MISSISSIPPI HOSPITAL FOR RESTORATIVE CARE (252003)**, 1225 North State Street, Zip 39202–2097, Mailing Address: P.O. Box 23695, Zip 39225–3695; tel. 601/968–1000 **A**1 10 **F**29 39 56 61 70 80 89 130 **P**7 **S** Mississippi Baptist Health System, Jackson, MS
Primary Contact: Bobbie K. Ware, R.N., FACHE, Chief Executive Officer and Chief Nursing Officer
CFO: Russell W. York, Vice President and Chief Financial Officer
CMO: Holland M. Addison, M.D., Medical Director
CIO: Steve M. Stanic, Vice President and Chief Information Officer
CHR: Lee Ann Foreman, Vice President Human Resources
Web address: www.mbhs.org
**Control:** Other not–for–profit (including NFP Corporation) **Service:** Long–Term Acute Care hospital

| | |
|---|---|
| **Staffed Beds:** 25 **Admissions:** 260 **Census:** 20 **Outpatient Visits:** 0 **Births:** 0 **Personnel:** 60 | |

⊠ **REGENCY HOSPITAL OF JACKSON (252012)**, 969 Lakeland Drive, 6th Floor, Zip 39216–4643; tel. 601/364–6200 **A**1 10 **F**29 70 130 **S** Select Medical Corporation, Mechanicsburg, PA
Primary Contact: Lorie Powell, Interim Chief Executive Officer
Web address: www.regencyhospital.com
**Control:** Corporation, Investor–owned, for–profit **Service:** Long–Term Acute Care hospital

| | |
|---|---|
| **Staffed Beds:** 36 **Admissions:** 325 **Census:** 22 **Outpatient Visits:** 0 **Births:** 0 **Personnel:** 93 | |

⊠ **SELECT SPECIALTY HOSPITAL–JACKSON (252007)**, 5903 Ridgewood Road, Suite 100, Zip 39211–3700; tel. 601/899–3800 **A**1 10 **F**93 130 **S** Select Medical Corporation, Mechanicsburg, PA
Primary Contact: Chandler Ewing, Chief Executive Officer
CFO: Melissa Smith, Controller
CIO: Jacqueline Barnes, Manager Health Information
CHR: Vicki Watson, Manager Human Resources
Web address: www.selectspecialtyhospitals.com/company/locations/jackson.aspx
**Control:** Corporation, Investor–owned, for–profit **Service:** Long–Term Acute Care hospital

| | |
|---|---|
| **Staffed Beds:** 53 **Admissions:** 656 **Census:** 45 **Outpatient Visits:** 0 **Births:** 0 **Personnel:** 208 | |

⊠ **ST. DOMINIC–JACKSON MEMORIAL HOSPITAL (250048)**, 969 Lakeland Drive, Zip 39216–4606; tel. 601/200–2000 **A**1 2 3 5 9 10 **F**3 4 5 11 12 13 15 17 18 20 22 24 26 28 29 30 31 34 35 36 37 38 39 40 43 47 49 51 53 58 60 61 64 65 68 70 72 73 74 75 76 77 78 79 80 81 84 85 86 89 90 92 93 97 98 100 101 102 103 106 107 108 109 110 111 114 115 116 117 118 119 120 121 123 124 126 130 131 147 148 **P**8
Primary Contact: Lester K. Diamond, President
CFO: Jennifer Sinclair, Vice President Finance
CMO: Robert L. Mobley, M.D., Executive Vice President Medical Affairs and Quality
CIO: Keith Van Camp, Vice President Information Services
CHR: Lorraine Washington, Vice President Human Resources
Web address: www.stdom.com
**Control:** Other not–for–profit (including NFP Corporation) **Service:** General Medical and Surgical

| | |
|---|---|
| **Staffed Beds:** 477 **Admissions:** 31624 **Census:** 350 **Outpatient Visits:** 183440 **Births:** 1351 **Total Expense ($000):** 369750 **Payroll Expense ($000):** 147198 **Personnel:** 2643 | |

⊠ △ **UNIVERSITY HOSPITALS AND HEALTH SYSTEM, UNIVERSITY OF MISSISSIPPI MEDICAL CENTER (250001)**, 2500 North State Street, Zip 39216–4505; tel. 601/984–1000, (Includes BLAIR E. BATSON HOSPITAL FOR CHILDREN, 2500 North State State Room W019, Zip 39216–4500; tel. 601/984–1000; CHILDREN'S HEALTHCARE OF MISSISSIPPI, 2500 North State Street, Zip 39216–4500) **A**1 2 3 5 7 8 9 10 **F**3 7 8 12 13 15 17 18 19 20 21 22 23 24 25 26 27 28 29 30 31 32 34 35 37 38 39 40 43 44 45 46 47 48 49 50 52 53 54 56 57 58 59 60 61 64 65 66 68 70 72 73 74 75 76 77 78 79 80 81 84 85 86 87 88 89 90 92 93 94 96 97 98 99 100 101 102 103 104 107 108 110 111 112 114 115 116 117 118 119 120 121 124 126 127 129 130 131 132 134 135 136 137 138 141 143 144 147 148 **P**6
Primary Contact: Janet Y. Harris, R.N., MSN, Chief Executive Officer and Chief Nursing Officer
CFO: Dan Janicak, Chief Financial Officer
CMO: William H. Cleland, M.D., Chief Medical Officer
CIO: Charles Enicks, Chief Information Officer
CHR: Michael Estes, Director Human Resources
Web address: www.umc.edu
**Control:** State–Government, nonfederal **Service:** General Medical and Surgical

| | |
|---|---|
| **Staffed Beds:** 675 **Admissions:** 28489 **Census:** 491 **Outpatient Visits:** 226224 **Births:** 2389 **Total Expense ($000):** 736424 **Payroll Expense ($000):** 317298 **Personnel:** 5015 | |

**KEESLER AFB—Harrison County**

⊠ **U. S. AIR FORCE MEDICAL CENTER KEESLER**, 301 Fisher Street, Room 1A132, Zip 39534–2519; tel. 228/376–2550, (Nonreporting) **A**1 2 3 5 **S** Department of the Air Force, Washington, DC
Primary Contact: Colonel Robert Cothron, USAF, MSC, Administrator
COO: Brigadier General James Dougherty, Commander
CFO: Major Brenda Yi, Director Medical Resource Management and Chief Financial Officer
CMO: Colonel James Gasque, M.D., Chief Hospital Services
CIO: Major Samuel Silverthorne, Chief Information Officer
CHR: Major Brenda Yi, Director Medical Resource Management and Chief Financial Officer
Web address: www.keesler.af.mil
**Control:** Air Force, Government, federal **Service:** General Medical and Surgical

| | |
|---|---|
| **Staffed Beds:** 56 | |

**KILMICHAEL—Montgomery County**

★ **KILMICHAEL HOSPITAL (250051)**, 301 Lamar Avenue, Zip 39747–9002, Mailing Address: P.O. Box 188, Zip 39747–0188; tel. 662/262–4311 **A**9 10 **F**70 89 133 **P**1
Primary Contact: Calvin D. Johnson, Administrator
**Control:** County–Government, nonfederal **Service:** General Medical and Surgical

| | |
|---|---|
| **Staffed Beds:** 19 **Admissions:** 183 **Census:** 2 **Outpatient Visits:** 0 **Births:** 0 **Personnel:** 35 | |

**KOSCIUSKO—Attala County**

★ **MONTFORT JONES MEMORIAL HOSPITAL (250059)**, 220 Highway 12 West, Zip 39090–3208, Mailing Address: P.O. Box 887, Zip 39090–0887; tel. 662/289–4311 **A**9 10 **F**3 15 17 30 34 35 39 40 42 43 57 59 70 74 81 89 90 93 96 103 107 108 110 114 117 118 119 130 133 145 148
Primary Contact: John Dawson, Chief Executive Officer
CFO: James Thomas, Chief Financial Officer
CIO: Jimmy Chesteen, Director Information Technology
CHR: Linnie Pearson, Coordinator Human Resources and Benefits
CNO: Allison Schuler, R.N., Chief Nursing Officer
Web address: www.montfortjones.com
**Control:** County–Government, nonfederal **Service:** General Medical and Surgical

| | |
|---|---|
| **Staffed Beds:** 71 **Admissions:** 1394 **Census:** 18 **Outpatient Visits:** 23015 **Births:** 0 **Total Expense ($000):** 14606 **Payroll Expense ($000):** 5973 **Personnel:** 102 | |

**LAUREL—Jones County**

★ ◇ **SOUTH CENTRAL REGIONAL MEDICAL CENTER (250058)**, 1220 Jefferson Street, Zip 39440–4374, Mailing Address: P.O. Box 607, Zip 39441–0607; tel. 601/426–4000, (Total facility includes 239 beds in nursing home–type unit) **A**9 10 21 **F**3 4 7 10 12 13 15 17 18 20 28 29 30 31 34 35 37 40 43 48 49 51 53 56 57 59 62 63 64 68 70 73 74 75 76 77 78 79 81 84 85 86 87 89 90 92 93 100 102 103 104 105 108 110 111 114 115 117 118 119 127 128 130 131 132 134 143 144 146 147 148 **P**6
Primary Contact: G. Douglas Higginbotham, President and Chief Executive Officer
CFO: Tom Canizaro, Vice President and Chief Financial Officer
CMO: James Holston, M.D., Vice President and Chief Quality Officer
CIO: Linda Gavin, Associate Executive Director Marketing and Physician Recruitment
CHR: Janet Staples, Vice President Human Resources
CNO: Beth W. Endom, R.N., Vice President and Chief Nursing Officer
Web address: www.scrmc.com
**Control:** County–Government, nonfederal **Service:** General Medical and Surgical

| | |
|---|---|
| **Staffed Beds:** 433 **Admissions:** 8031 **Census:** 323 **Outpatient Visits:** 77428 **Births:** 813 **Total Expense ($000):** 133824 **Payroll Expense ($000):** 67586 **Personnel:** 1531 | |

**LEAKESVILLE—Greene County**

**GREENE COUNTY HOSPITAL (251329)**, 1017 Jackson Avenue, Zip 39451–9105; tel. 601/394–4139 **A**9 10 18 **F**40 43 70 107 133
Primary Contact: Deborah Berry, Director of Operations
CFO: Debbie Brannan, Chief Financial Officer
CMO: Larry Henderson, M.D., Medical Director
CHR: Carla Shows, Payroll Clerk
Web address: www.georgeregional.com
**Control:** County–Government, nonfederal **Service:** General Medical and Surgical

| | |
|---|---|
| **Staffed Beds:** 3 **Admissions:** 23 **Census:** 1 **Outpatient Visits:** 2963 **Births:** 0 **Personnel:** 52 | |

**MS**

**Hospital, Medicare Provider Number, Address, Telephone, Approval, Facility, and Physician Codes, Health Care System**

★ American Hospital Association (AHA) membership
□ The Joint Commission accreditation
◇ DNV Healthcare Inc. accreditation
○ Healthcare Facilities Accreditation Program
△ Commission on Accreditation of Rehabilitation Facilities (CARF) accreditation

## LEXINGTON—Holmes County

✉ **HOLMES COUNTY HOSPITAL AND CLINICS (251319)**, 239 Bowling Green Road, Zip 39095–5167; tel. 662/834–1321 **A**1 9 10 18 **F**3 11 15 29 34 35 40 43 45 49 56 57 59 64 65 70 86 87 89 93 107 108 111 114 119 127 130 133 135 **P**6
Primary Contact: Phillip L. Grady, Administrator
COO: Dewery Montgomery, Chief Operating Officer
CFO: Dan Janicak, Chief Financial Officer
CMO: Mark Smothers, M.D., Chief Medical Staff
CIO: Paula Pepper, Lan Administrator
CHR: Gloria Bordelon, Human Resources Generalist
**Control:** State–Government, nonfederal **Service:** General Medical and Surgical

**Staffed Beds:** 25 **Admissions:** 344 **Census:** 3 **Outpatient Visits:** 11796 **Births:** 0 **Total Expense ($000):** 12371 **Payroll Expense ($000):** 6292 **Personnel:** 111

## LOUISVILLE—Winston County

**WINSTON MEDICAL CENTER (250027)**, 562 East Main Street, Zip 39339–2742, Mailing Address: P.O. Box 967, Zip 39339–0967; tel. 662/773–6211, (Total facility includes 120 beds in nursing home–type unit) **A**9 10 20 **F**3 15 29 32 34 35 40 43 45 57 59 66 70 81 89 93 103 107 108 110 114 119 128 130 133
Primary Contact: Lee McCall, Administrator
Web address: www.winstonmedical.org
**Control:** Other not–for–profit (including NFP Corporation) **Service:** General Medical and Surgical

**Staffed Beds:** 161 **Admissions:** 665 **Census:** 123 **Outpatient Visits:** 21880 **Births:** 0 **Total Expense ($000):** 18814 **Payroll Expense ($000):** 6368 **Personnel:** 198

## LUCEDALE—Jackson County

**GEORGE REGIONAL HOSPITAL (250036)**, (Formerly George County Hospital), 859 Winter Street, Zip 39452–6603, Mailing Address: P.O. Box 607, Zip 39452–0607; tel. 601/947–3161 **A**9 10 20 **F**3 11 13 15 17 18 30 34 35 40 43 45 47 48 49 53 54 57 59 65 68 70 76 81 86 87 93 107 108 111 119 130 133 135 146 148 **P**8
Primary Contact: Paul A. Gardner, CPA, Administrator
CFO: Debbie Brannan, Chief Financial Officer
CMO: Seth Scott, M.D., Chief of Staff
CHR: Carla Shows, Payroll Clerk
Web address: www.georgeregional.com
**Control:** County–Government, nonfederal **Service:** General Medical and Surgical

**Staffed Beds:** 48 **Admissions:** 1415 **Census:** 14 **Outpatient Visits:** 39922 **Births:** 176 **Personnel:** 360

## MACON—Noxubee County

**NOXUBEE GENERAL HOSPITAL (251307)**, 606 North Jefferson Street, Zip 39341–2242, Mailing Address: P.O. Box 480, Zip 39341–0480; tel. 662/726–4231, (Total facility includes 60 beds in nursing home–type unit) **A**9 10 18 **F**40 43 70 89 107 128 130 133
Primary Contact: Danny H. McKay, Administrator
Web address: www.noxubeemedical.com
**Control:** County–Government, nonfederal **Service:** General Medical and Surgical

**Staffed Beds:** 85 **Admissions:** 788 **Census:** 63 **Outpatient Visits:** 4011 **Births:** 0 **Personnel:** 168

## MAGEE—Simpson County

★ **MAGEE GENERAL HOSPITAL (250124)**, 300 Third Avenue S.E., Zip 39111–3698; tel. 601/849–5070 **A**9 10 **F**13 15 29 35 40 43 70 76 81 89 107 111 119 130 133
Primary Contact: Althea H. Crumpton, Administrator
CFO: Melissa Bruntlett, Chief Financial Officer
CMO: Kelli Smith, M.D., Chief of Staff
CIO: Kirby Craft, Chief Information Officer
CHR: Steve Beckham, Director Human Resources
CNO: Cindy McIntyre, R.N., Administrative Director Clinical Services
Web address: www.mghosp.org
**Control:** Other not–for–profit (including NFP Corporation) **Service:** General Medical and Surgical

**Staffed Beds:** 61 **Admissions:** 1461 **Census:** 16 **Outpatient Visits:** 52268 **Births:** 307 **Personnel:** 255

## MAGNOLIA—Pike County

**BEACHAM MEMORIAL HOSPITAL (250049)**, 205 North Cherry Street, Zip 39652–2819, Mailing Address: P.O. Box 351, Zip 39652–0351; tel. 601/783–2351 **A**9 10 **F**35 70 107 133
Primary Contact: Guy Geller, Administrator and Chief Executive Officer
CMO: Lucius Lampton, M.D., Medical Director
CHR: Jackie McKenzie, Director Administrative Services
Web address: www.beachammemhos.com
**Control:** Other not–for–profit (including NFP Corporation) **Service:** General Medical and Surgical

**Staffed Beds:** 37 **Admissions:** 792 **Census:** 13 **Outpatient Visits:** 0 **Births:** 0 **Personnel:** 91

## MARKS—Quitman County

**QUITMAN COUNTY HOSPITAL (251314)**, 340 Getwell Drive, Zip 38646–9785; tel. 662/326–8031 **A**9 10 18 **F**3 40 43 56 70 89 90 103 107 114 119 133
Primary Contact: Stephen Nichols, Chief Executive Officer
CFO: Jane Moore, Director, Fiscal Services
CMO: James E. Warrington, Sr., M.D., Chief of Staff
CHR: Sandra Biffle, Personnel Clerk
CNO: Dana Hall, Director of Nursing
**Control:** Corporation, Investor–owned, for–profit **Service:** General Medical and Surgical

**Staffed Beds:** 33 **Admissions:** 627 **Census:** 9 **Outpatient Visits:** 10355 **Births:** 0 **Personnel:** 116

## MCCOMB—Pike County

★ ◇ **SOUTHWEST MISSISSIPPI REGIONAL MEDICAL CENTER (250097)**, 215 Marion Avenue, Zip 39648–2705, Mailing Address: P.O. Box 1307, Zip 39649–1307; tel. 601/249–5500 **A**9 10 19 21 **F**13 15 17 29 39 40 43 53 70 72 73 75 76 77 78 81 86 87 89 93 107 108 111 118 119 130 131 132 **P**6 **S** Southwest Health Systems, Mccomb, MS
Primary Contact: Norman M. Price, FACHE, Chief Executive Officer
COO: Richard Williams, Chief Operating Officer
CFO: Reece Nunnery, Chief Financial Officer
CMO: Kevin Richardson, M.D., Chief of Staff
CIO: Mike Moak, Chief Information Officer
CHR: Don Haskins, Administrative Director Human Resources
CNO: Katie McKinley, Assistant Administrator/Nursing
Web address: www.smrmc.com
**Control:** Hospital district or authority, Government, nonfederal **Service:** General Medical and Surgical

**Staffed Beds:** 143 **Admissions:** 6899 **Census:** 65 **Outpatient Visits:** 88309 **Births:** 875 **Personnel:** 968

## MEADVILLE—Franklin County

**FRANKLIN COUNTY MEMORIAL HOSPITAL (251330)**, 40 Union Church Road, Zip 39653–8336, Mailing Address: P.O. Box 636, Zip 39653–0636; tel. 601/384–5801 **A**9 10 **F**29 35 40 43 56 70 81 86 89 93 98 103 107 119 130 133 143 **P**6
Primary Contact: Mike Boleware, Administrator
Web address: www.fcmh.net
**Control:** County–Government, nonfederal **Service:** General Medical and Surgical

**Staffed Beds:** 35 **Admissions:** 380 **Census:** 8 **Outpatient Visits:** 25019 **Births:** 0 **Personnel:** 184

## MENDENHALL—Simpson County

**SIMPSON GENERAL HOSPITAL (251317)**, 1842 Simpson Highway 149, Zip 39114–3438; tel. 601/847–2221 **A**9 10 18 **F**35 40 53 56 61 70 81 86 87 90 98 103 107 119 130 132 133 134 **P**5 7
Primary Contact: Randall Neely, Chief Executive Officer
COO: Al Gary, COO
CFO: Al Gary, COO
CMO: Chip Holbrook, M.D., Chief of Staff
CIO: David Welch, Director Information Technology
CHR: Randall Neely, CEO
CNO: Sharon Burnham, Director of Nursing
Web address: www.simpsongeneralhospital.com
**Control:** Other not–for–profit (including NFP Corporation) **Service:** General Medical and Surgical

**Staffed Beds:** 35 **Admissions:** 743 **Census:** 11 **Outpatient Visits:** 9947 **Births:** 0 **Personnel:** 97

## MERIDIAN—Lauderdale County

☐ **ALLIANCE HEALTH CENTER (250151)**, 5000 Highway 39 North, Zip 39301–1021; tel. 601/483–6211 **A**1 9 10 **F**4 35 70 86 87 98 99 101 102 103 **P**6 **S** Universal Health Services, Inc., King of Prussia, PA
Primary Contact: James Miller, Interim Chief Executive Officer
CFO: Robert Jackson, Chief Financial Officer
CMO: Terry Jordan, M.D., Chief of Staff
CIO: Brenda Smith, Director Financial Services
CHR: Shrea Johnson, Director Human Resources
Web address: www.alliancehealthcenter.com
**Control:** Corporation, Investor–owned, for–profit **Service:** Psychiatric

**Staffed Beds:** 134 **Admissions:** 2445 **Census:** 73 **Outpatient Visits:** 0 **Births:** 0 **Personnel:** 220

*Many Facility Codes have changed. Please refer to the AHA Guide Code Chart.*   © 2013 AHA Guide

MS

⊞ **ANDERSON REGIONAL MEDICAL CENTER (250104)**, 2124 14th Street, Zip 39301–4040; tel. 601/553–6000 **A**1 2 9 10 19 **F**3 13 15 17 18 20 22 24 28 30 31 34 35 39 40 43 45 46 47 48 49 50 53 54 57 59 64 68 70 72 73 74 75 76 77 78 79 80 81 84 85 86 87 88 89 90 93 94 98 107 108 109 110 115 116 117 118 119 126 129 130 131 132 135 145 148 **P**7 8
Primary Contact: L. Ray Humphreys, Chief Executive Officer
CFO: Anthony C. Rispoli, Vice President Finance
CHR: Irby Lang, Vice President Human Resources
Web address: www.jarmc.org
**Control:** Other not–for–profit (including NFP Corporation) **Service:** General Medical and Surgical

**Staffed Beds:** 260 **Admissions:** 10226 **Census:** 144 **Outpatient Visits:** 109832 **Births:** 1225 **Total Expense ($000):** 159209 **Payroll Expense ($000):** 63280 **Personnel:** 1065

☐ △ **ANDERSON REGIONAL MEDICAL CENTER–SOUTH CAMPUS (250081)**, 1102 Constitution Avenue, Zip 39301–4001; tel. 601/693–2511 **A**1 7 9 10 **F**3 4 11 15 29 30 34 35 53 57 59 60 61 64 65 68 70 75 81 85 86 87 90 96 97 98 106 107 114 119 127 130 132 133 135 144 148 **P**7 8
Primary Contact: Ray Humphreys, Chief Executive Officer
CFO: Anthony C. Rispoli, Vice President Finance
CMO: Bradley Boone, M.D., Chief Medical Staff
CHR: Jamie Shuster, Director Associate Relations
Web address: www.jarmc.org
**Control:** Other not–for–profit (including NFP Corporation) **Service:** General Medical and Surgical

**Staffed Beds:** 69 **Admissions:** 550 **Census:** 16 **Outpatient Visits:** 34313 **Births:** 0 **Total Expense ($000):** 30312 **Payroll Expense ($000):** 8608 **Personnel:** 167

**EAST MISSISSIPPI STATE HOSPITAL**, 4555 Highland Park Drive, Zip 39307–5498, Mailing Address: Box 4128, West Station, Zip 39304–4128; tel. 601/482–6186 **F**4 29 56 87 98 99 101 103 128 130 **S** Mississippi State Department of Mental Health, Jackson, MS
Primary Contact: Charles Carlisle, Director
CFO: Geri Rutledge, Director Business
CMO: Gloria Gomez, M.D., Medical Director
CIO: Susie Broadhead, Director Public Information
CHR: Shearmaine Calaway, Director Human Resources
Web address: www.emsh.state.ms.us
**Control:** State–Government, nonfederal **Service:** Psychiatric

**Staffed Beds:** 251 **Admissions:** 1052 **Census:** 247 **Outpatient Visits:** 0 **Births:** 0 **Personnel:** 784

⊞ **REGENCY HOSPITAL OF MERIDIAN (252006)**, 1102 Constitution Avenue, 2nd Floor, Zip 39301–4001; tel. 601/484–7900 **A**1 10 **F**40 70 **S** Select Medical Corporation, Mechanicsburg, PA
Primary Contact: Clifton Quinn, Chief Executive Officer
Web address: www.regencyhospital.com
**Control:** Corporation, Investor–owned, for–profit **Service:** Long–Term Acute Care hospital

**Staffed Beds:** 40 **Admissions:** 402 **Census:** 29 **Outpatient Visits:** 0 **Births:** 0 **Personnel:** 111

**RILEY HOSPITAL** See Anderson Regional Medical Center–South Campus

★ ◇ **RUSH FOUNDATION HOSPITAL (250069)**, 1314 19th Avenue, Zip 39301–4195; tel. 601/483–0011 **A**9 10 19 21 **F**13 15 17 29 35 39 40 43 70 72 73 76 77 81 86 89 90 93 97 107 108 118 119 130 131 147 **P**3 8 **S** Rush Health Systems, Meridian, MS
Primary Contact: Christopher Rush, Vice President and Administrator
COO: Morris A. Reece, Executive Vice President and Chief Operating Officer
CMO: W. Scot Bell, M.D., Chief Medical Officer
CIO: Angela Sherrill, Corporate Director Information System
CHR: Donnie Smith, Director Human Resources
Web address: www.rushhealthsystems.org/rfh/
**Control:** Other not–for–profit (including NFP Corporation) **Service:** General Medical and Surgical

**Staffed Beds:** 182 **Admissions:** 5826 **Census:** 78 **Outpatient Visits:** 28752 **Births:** 853 **Personnel:** 904

★ **SPECIALTY HOSPITAL OF MERIDIAN (252004)**, 1314 19th Avenue, Zip 39301–4116; tel. 601/703–4211 **A**9 10 **F**70 78 87 133 144 **P**6 **S** Rush Health Systems, Meridian, MS
Primary Contact: Elizabeth C. Mitchell, Vice President and Administrator
CFO: Lexie Fuller, Controller
CMO: Richmond Alexander, M.D., President Medical Staff
CIO: Angela Sherrill, Corporate Director Information System
Web address: www.specialtyhospitalofmeridian.com/shm/
**Control:** Other not–for–profit (including NFP Corporation) **Service:** Long–Term Acute Care hospital

**Staffed Beds:** 49 **Admissions:** 565 **Census:** 47 **Outpatient Visits:** 0 **Births:** 0 **Personnel:** 148

**MONTICELLO—Lawrence County**

**LAWRENCE COUNTY HOSPITAL (251305)**, Highway 84 East, Zip 39654–0788, Mailing Address: P.O. Box 788, Zip 39654–0788; tel. 601/587–4051 **A**9 10 18 **F**39 40 43 70 86 87 107 119 130 133 **S** Southwest Health Systems, Mccomb, MS
Primary Contact: Semmes Ross, Jr., Administrator
CFO: Jennifer Moak, Business Office Manager
Web address: www.smrmc.com
**Control:** County–Government, nonfederal **Service:** General Medical and Surgical

**Staffed Beds:** 25 **Admissions:** 443 **Census:** 4 **Outpatient Visits:** 0 **Births:** 0 **Personnel:** 123

**MORTON—Scott County**

★ **SCOTT REGIONAL HOSPITAL (251323)**, 317 Highway 13 South, Zip 39117–3353, Mailing Address: P.O. Box 259, Zip 39117–0259; tel. 601/732–6301 **A**9 10 18 **F**35 40 43 70 77 81 89 93 107 111 119 130 133 **S** Rush Health Systems, Meridian, MS
Primary Contact: Michael R. Edwards, Administrator
CFO: Paul S. Black, Chief Financial Officer
CHR: Amy Sugg, Director Human Resources
Web address: www.scottregional.org/srh/
**Control:** Other not–for–profit (including NFP Corporation) **Service:** General Medical and Surgical

**Staffed Beds:** 25 **Admissions:** 700 **Census:** 7 **Outpatient Visits:** 12851 **Births:** 0 **Personnel:** 119

**NATCHEZ—Adams County**

☐ **NATCHEZ COMMUNITY HOSPITAL (250122)**, 129 Jefferson Davis Boulevard, Zip 39120–5100, Mailing Address: P.O. Box 1203, Zip 39121–1203; tel. 601/445–6200 **A**1 9 10 **F**13 17 29 35 40 43 51 60 61 70 73 76 78 81 87 89 93 103 107 108 119 130 **P**6 **S** Health Management Associates, Naples, FL
Primary Contact: Eric Robinson, Chief Executive Officer
CFO: Warren Ladner, Chief Financial Officer
CHR: Hal Harrington, Director Human Resources
Web address: www.natchezcommunityhospital.com/default.aspx
**Control:** Partnership, Investor–owned, for–profit **Service:** General Medical and Surgical

**Staffed Beds:** 101 **Admissions:** 3698 **Census:** 43 **Outpatient Visits:** 40076 **Births:** 516 **Personnel:** 269

☐ △ **NATCHEZ REGIONAL MEDICAL CENTER (250084)**, 54 Seargent S Prentiss Drive, Zip 39120–4726; tel. 601/443–2100 **A**1 7 9 10 **F**13 15 17 29 35 40 43 60 70 73 75 76 77 78 81 86 87 88 89 90 93 107 108 111 116 119 130 131 132 134 147 **P**3
Primary Contact: William R. Heburn, Chief Executive Officer
CFO: Charles Mack, Vice President Finance and Chief Financial Officer
CMO: John O'Brien, M.D., Chief of Staff
CIO: Walt Roddy, Director Information Management Systems
CHR: Sherri L. Clifton–LeMay, Director Human Resources
Web address: www.natchezregional.com
**Control:** County–Government, nonfederal **Service:** General Medical and Surgical

**Staffed Beds:** 155 **Admissions:** 3161 **Census:** 39 **Outpatient Visits:** 36244 **Births:** 447 **Personnel:** 283

MS

---

**Hospital, Medicare Provider Number, Address, Telephone, Approval, Facility, and Physician Codes, Health Care System**

★ American Hospital Association (AHA) membership
☐ The Joint Commission accreditation
◇ DNV Healthcare Inc. accreditation
◯ Healthcare Facilities Accreditation Program
△ Commission on Accreditation of Rehabilitation Facilities (CARF) accreditation

## NEW ALBANY—Union County

☒ **BAPTIST MEMORIAL HOSPITAL–UNION COUNTY (250006)**, 200 Highway 30 West, Zip 38652–3112; tel. 662/538–7631 **A**1 9 10 **F**3 7 11 13 15 17 29 30 34 35 39 40 41 51 53 57 59 70 75 76 77 79 81 84 85 86 87 89 90 93 107 108 110 111 114 118 119 132 133 135 147 148 **S** Baptist Memorial Health Care Corporation, Memphis, TN
Primary Contact: Walter Grace, Chief Executive Officer and Administrator
CFO: Kim High, Chief Financial Officer
CMO: Justin Lohmeier, M.D., Chief of Staff
CIO: Missy Coltharp, Director
CHR: Lori Goode, Director Human Resources
CNO: Randy White, Chief Nursing Officer
Web address: www.baptistonline.org/union-county/
**Control:** Other not–for–profit (including NFP Corporation) **Service:** General Medical and Surgical

**Staffed Beds:** 153 **Admissions:** 3849 **Census:** 34 **Outpatient Visits:** 47563 **Births:** 1099 **Total Expense ($000):** 48355 **Payroll Expense ($000):** 18018 **Personnel:** 533

## NEWTON—Newton County

**NEWTON REGIONAL HOSPITAL** See Pioneer Community Hospital of Newton

★ ◇ **PIONEER COMMUNITY HOSPITAL OF NEWTON (251332)**, 9421 Eastside Drive, Zip 39345–8063; tel. 601/683–2031 **A**9 10 18 21 **F**3 11 29 34 35 39 40 43 45 46 53 57 64 65 68 70 77 79 81 89 90 93 98 103 107 111 114 119 127 130 133 148 **P**6 **S** Pioneer Health Services, Magee, MS
Primary Contact: Mark Norman, Administrator
CFO: Julie Gieger, Chief Financial Officer
CMO: Sohaib Arair, M.D., Chairman of Medical Staff
CIO: Eric Two Bears, Chief Information Officer
CHR: Tracy Rushing, Executive Assistant Human Resources and Payroll
CNO: Christie Malbrough, Director of Nursing
Web address: www.pchnewton.com
**Control:** Corporation, Investor–owned, for–profit **Service:** General Medical and Surgical

**Staffed Beds:** 30 **Admissions:** 821 **Census:** 11 **Outpatient Visits:** 10778 **Births:** 0 **Personnel:** 135

## OCEAN SPRINGS—Jackson County

**OCEAN SPRINGS HOSPITAL** See Singing River Health System, Pascagoula

## OLIVE BRANCH—Desoto County

☐ **PARKWOOD BEHAVIORAL HEALTH SYSTEM (254005)**, 8135 Goodman Road, Zip 38654–2103; tel. 662/895–4900, (Total facility includes 40 beds in nursing home–type unit) **A**1 9 10 **F**4 5 29 34 35 54 64 75 86 87 98 99 100 101 102 104 105 106 130 **S** Universal Health Services, Inc., King of Prussia, PA
Primary Contact: Ethan Permenter, Chief Executive Officer
CFO: Sandra Wallace, Chief Financial Officer
CMO: Paul King, M.D., Medical Director
CHR: Audrey Johnson, Director Human Resources
CNO: Alicia Plunkett, Director of Nursing
Web address: www.parkwoodbhs.com
**Control:** Corporation, Investor–owned, for–profit **Service:** Psychiatric

**Staffed Beds:** 128 **Admissions:** 2432 **Census:** 106 **Outpatient Visits:** 0 **Births:** 0 **Personnel:** 220

## OXFORD—Lafayette County

☒ △ **BAPTIST MEMORIAL HOSPITAL–NORTH MISSISSIPPI (250034)**, 2301 South Lamar Boulevard, Zip 38655–5373, Mailing Address: P.O. Box 946, Zip 38655–6002; tel. 662/232–8100 **A**1 2 7 9 10 19 **F**3 7 11 12 13 15 17 18 20 22 24 26 28 29 30 31 34 35 39 40 43 45 47 48 49 50 53 57 59 64 68 70 73 74 76 78 79 81 84 85 86 87 89 90 96 105 107 108 110 111 114 115 116 117 118 119 120 121 123 126 129 130 131 132 141 145 147 148 **S** Baptist Memorial Health Care Corporation, Memphis, TN
Primary Contact: William C. Henning, Administrator and Chief Executive Officer
CFO: Dana Williams, Assistant Administrator and Chief Financial Officer
CMO: Brett Lampton, M.D., Chief of Staff
CIO: Linda Britt, Director Information Systems
CHR: Dennis Fisher, Director Human Resources
Web address: www.baptistonline.org/north–mississippi/
**Control:** Other not–for–profit (including NFP Corporation) **Service:** General Medical and Surgical

**Staffed Beds:** 217 **Admissions:** 7664 **Census:** 100 **Outpatient Visits:** 70481 **Births:** 890 **Total Expense ($000):** 148134 **Payroll Expense ($000):** 45713 **Personnel:** 981

## PASCAGOULA—Jackson County

☒ △ **SINGING RIVER HEALTH SYSTEM (250040)**, 2809 Denny Avenue, Zip 39581–5301; tel. 228/809–5000, (Includes OCEAN SPRINGS HOSPITAL, 3109 Bienville Boulevard, Ocean Springs, Zip 39564–4361; tel. 228/818–1111; Heath Thompson, R.N., Administrator; SINGING RIVER HOSPITAL, 2809 Denny Avenue, tel. 228/809–5000; Davis Walton, Administrator) **A**1 2 7 9 10 **F**3 13 15 17 18 20 22 24 26 28 29 31 34 38 39 40 43 44 47 48 49 50 53 54 57 58 59 61 64 68 70 73 74 76 78 79 80 81 85 86 87 88 89 90 92 98 100 101 102 103 104 107 108 111 114 115 118 119 120 121 123 126 127 129 130 135 144 145 148
Primary Contact: Chris Anderson, Chief Executive Officer
COO: Kevin Holland, Chief Operating Officer
CFO: Michael E. Crews, Chief Financial Officer
CMO: Larry D. Shoemaker, M.D., Chief Medical Officer
CIO: Chris Oubre, Director Information Systems
CHR: Nebo Carter, Chief Human Resources Officer
Web address: www.mysrhs.com
**Control:** County–Government, nonfederal **Service:** General Medical and Surgical

**Staffed Beds:** 381 **Admissions:** 17995 **Census:** 218 **Outpatient Visits:** 432593 **Births:** 1440 **Total Expense ($000):** 376531 **Payroll Expense ($000):** 151400 **Personnel:** 1740

## PHILADELPHIA—Neshoba County

☐ **CHOCTAW HEALTH CENTER (250127)**, 210 Hospital Circle, Zip 39350–6781; tel. 601/656–2211, (Nonreporting) **A**1 9 10
Primary Contact: Gary Ben, Administrator
CFO: Donita Stephens, Director Financial Services
CMO: Chandrashekhar V. Joshi, M.D., Chief of Staff
CIO: Charlene Sam, Manager Health Information
CHR: Linda McMillan, Human Resources Specialist
Web address: www.choctaw.org
**Control:** PHS, Indian Service, Government, federal **Service:** General Medical and Surgical

**Staffed Beds:** 25

**NESHOBA COUNTY GENERAL HOSPITAL (250043)**, 1001 Holland Avenue, Zip 39350–2161, Mailing Address: P.O. Box 648, Zip 39350–0648; tel. 601/663–1200, (Total facility includes 160 beds in nursing home–type unit) **A**9 10 20 **F**15 29 35 81 87 90 103 107 108 111 118 119 128 130 132 133 143 144
Primary Contact: Lawrence Graeber, Chief Executive Officer
CFO: Calvin J. Brummund, Interim Chief Financial Officer
CMO: Walt Willis, M.D., Medical Director
CHR: Hedda Stewart, Director Human Resources
Web address: www.neshobageneral.com
**Control:** County–Government, nonfederal **Service:** General Medical and Surgical

**Staffed Beds:** 208 **Admissions:** 1412 **Census:** 167 **Outpatient Visits:** 66801 **Births:** 0 **Personnel:** 425

## PICAYUNE—Pearl River County

**HIGHLAND COMMUNITY HOSPITAL (250117)**, 801 Goodyear Boulevard, Zip 39466–3221, Mailing Address: P.O. Box 909, Zip 39466–0909; tel. 601/798–4711 **A**9 10 **F**13 15 29 40 43 70 75 76 81 86 87 89 93 107 108 111 119 130 131 147
Primary Contact: Mark Stockstill, R.N., Administrator
CFO: Bryan N. Stevens, Chief Financial Officer
CHR: Josh Lowery, Director Human Resources
CNO: MaryBeth Cooper, R.N., Chief Nursing Officer
Web address: www.highlandch.com
**Control:** County–Government, nonfederal **Service:** General Medical and Surgical

**Staffed Beds:** 56 **Admissions:** 1968 **Census:** 16 **Outpatient Visits:** 40975 **Births:** 292 **Personnel:** 294

## PONTOTOC—Pontotoc County

☒ **NORTH MISSISSIPPI MEDICAL CENTER–PONTOTOC HOSPITAL AND NURSING HOME (251308)**, 176 South Main Street, Zip 38863–3311, Mailing Address: P.O. Box 790, Zip 38863–0790; tel. 662/488–7640, (Total facility includes 44 beds in nursing home–type unit) **A**1 9 10 18 **F**35 40 43 70 86 87 90 107 119 128 130 133 **S** North Mississippi Health Services, Inc., Tupelo, MS
Primary Contact: Fred B. Hood, FACHE, Administrator
CFO: M. Denise Heard, Director Business Services
CHR: P. Marie Barnes, Director, Human Resources
CNO: Cathy Waldrop, Director, Hospital Nursing Services
Web address: www.nmhs.net
**Control:** Other not–for–profit (including NFP Corporation) **Service:** General Medical and Surgical

**Staffed Beds:** 69 **Admissions:** 375 **Census:** 47 **Outpatient Visits:** 16690 **Births:** 0 **Personnel:** 166

MS

*Many Facility Codes have changed. Please refer to the AHA Guide Code Chart.* © 2013 AHA Guide

**POPLARVILLE—Pearl River County**

**PEARL RIVER COUNTY HOSPITAL (251333)**, 305 West Moody Street,
Zip 39470–7338, Mailing Address: P.O. Box 392, Zip 39470–0392;
tel. 601/795–4543, (Total facility includes 126 beds in nursing home–type unit)
**A**9 10 **F**35 40 43 70 93 107 119 130 133 143
Primary Contact: Steve Vaughan, Chief Executive Officer
CNO: Lisa Brown, Director of Nursing
**Control:** County–Government, nonfederal **Service:** General Medical and Surgical

**Staffed Beds:** 150 **Admissions:** 195 **Census:** 103 **Outpatient Visits:** 7216
**Births:** 0 **Personnel:** 280

**PORT GIBSON—Claiborne County**

☐ **PATIENT'S CHOICE MEDICAL CENTER OF CLAIBORNE COUNTY (251320)**,
123 McComb Avenue, Zip 39150–2915, Mailing Address: P.O. Box 1004,
Zip 39150–1004; tel. 601/437–5141 **A**1 9 10 18 **F**40 43 70 89 90 98 103
119 130 133
Primary Contact: William Cockrell, Administrator and Chief Executive Officer
CFO: Linda Caho–Mooney, Chief Financial Officer
CIO: Ada Ratliff, Chief Information Officer
Web address: www.claibornehospital.net/
**Control:** County–Government, nonfederal **Service:** General Medical and Surgical

**Staffed Beds:** 32 **Admissions:** 632 **Census:** 9 **Outpatient Visits:** 5288
**Births:** 0 **Personnel:** 83

**PRENTISS—Jefferson Davis County**

**JEFFERSON DAVIS COMMUNITY HOSPITAL (251326)**, 1102 Rose Street,
Zip 39474–5200, Mailing Address: P.O. Box 1288, Zip 39474–1288;
tel. 601/792–4276, (Total facility includes 60 beds in nursing home–type unit) **A**9
10 18 **F**35 40 43 53 56 70 86 87 89 90 93 98 103 107 111 119 128 130
132 133
Primary Contact: Bryan K. Maxie, Chief Executive Officer
CFO: Paul S. Black, Chief Financial Officer
CHR: Diane Daughdrill, Director Human Resources
Web address: www.jdchospital.com
**Control:** County–Government, nonfederal **Service:** General Medical and Surgical

**Staffed Beds:** 95 **Admissions:** 389 **Census:** 58 **Outpatient Visits:** 11927
**Births:** 1 **Personnel:** 112

**PURVIS—Lamar County**

☐ **SOUTH MISSISSIPPI STATE HOSPITAL (254008)**, 823 Highway 589,
Zip 39475–4194; tel. 601/794–0100 **A**1 10 **F**3 50 98 130 **S** Mississippi State
Department of Mental Health, Jackson, MS
Primary Contact: Clint Ashley, Director
Web address: www.smsh.state.ms.us
**Control:** State–Government, nonfederal **Service:** Psychiatric

**Staffed Beds:** 50 **Admissions:** 697 **Census:** 46 **Outpatient Visits:** 0 **Births:**
0 **Personnel:** 104

**QUITMAN—Clarke County**

★ **H. C. WATKINS MEMORIAL HOSPITAL (251316)**, 605 South Archusa Avenue,
Zip 39355–2331; tel. 601/776–6925 **A**9 10 18 **F**29 40 43 70 81 89 103 107
130 133 **S** Rush Health Systems, Meridian, MS
Primary Contact: Clinton Eaves, Administrator
CFO: Paul S. Black, Controller
CMO: O. Wayne Byrd, M.D., Chief of Staff
CIO: Melinda Smith, Chief Information Systems
CHR: Leigh Moore, Administrative Assistant Human Resources
Web address: www.watkinsmemorialhospital.com/hcwmh/
**Control:** Other not–for–profit (including NFP Corporation) **Service:** General
Medical and Surgical

**Staffed Beds:** 25 **Admissions:** 444 **Census:** 5 **Outpatient Visits:** 6053
**Births:** 0 **Personnel:** 135

**RALEIGH—Smith County**

**PATIENTS CHOICE MEDICAL CENTER OF SMITH COUNTY (250163)**, 347
Magnolia Drive, Zip 39153–6011; tel. 601/782–9997 **A**10 **F**70 98 103 130 **P**6
Primary Contact: Tim Cockrell, Chief Executive Officer
**Control:** Corporation, Investor–owned, for–profit **Service:** General Medical and
Surgical

**Staffed Beds:** 10 **Admissions:** 160 **Census:** 7 **Outpatient Visits:** 863 **Births:**
0 **Personnel:** 6

**RICHTON—Perry County**

**PERRY COUNTY GENERAL HOSPITAL (251306)**, 206 Bay Avenue,
Zip 39476–2941; tel. 601/788–6316 **A**9 10 18 **F**40 43 70 107 119 133
Primary Contact: David Paris, Chief Executive Officer
Web address: www.pcghospital.com/
**Control:** Partnership, Investor–owned, for–profit **Service:** General Medical and
Surgical

**Staffed Beds:** 22 **Admissions:** 170 **Census:** 2 **Outpatient Visits:** 0 **Births:** 0
**Personnel:** 66

**RIPLEY—Tippah County**

⊠ **TIPPAH COUNTY HOSPITAL (250010)**, 1005 City Avenue North,
Zip 38663–1414, Mailing Address: P.O. Box 499, Zip 38663–0499;
tel. 662/837–9221, (Total facility includes 40 beds in nursing home–type unit) **A**1
9 10 20 **F**15 29 40 43 53 70 81 89 107 119 128 130 133
Primary Contact: Tom Hood, Administrator
CFO: Charles Knight, Chief Financial Officer
CMO: Charles M. Elliott, M.D., Chief of Staff
CHR: Margaret Weeks, Manager Personnel
Web address: www.tippahcounty.ripley.ms/hospital.html
**Control:** County–Government, nonfederal **Service:** General Medical and Surgical

**Staffed Beds:** 69 **Admissions:** 737 **Census:** 46 **Outpatient Visits:** 14626
**Births:** 0 **Personnel:** 196

**ROLLING FORK—Sharkey County**

**SHARKEY–ISSAQUENA COMMUNITY HOSPITAL (250079)**, 108 South Fourth
Street, Zip 39159–5146, Mailing Address: P.O. Box 339, Zip 39159–0339;
tel. 662/873–4396 **A**9 10 **F**40 53 56 70 89 103 107 111 119
Primary Contact: Jerry Keever, Administrator
**Control:** County–Government, nonfederal **Service:** General Medical and Surgical

**Staffed Beds:** 29 **Admissions:** 475 **Census:** 7 **Outpatient Visits:** 2752
**Births:** 0 **Personnel:** 70

**RULEVILLE—Sunflower County**

★ **NORTH SUNFLOWER MEDICAL CENTER (251318)**, 840 North Oak Avenue,
Zip 38771–3227, Mailing Address: P.O. Box 369, Zip 38771–0369;
tel. 662/756–2711, (Total facility includes 60 beds in nursing home–type unit) **A**9
10 18 **F**15 29 35 40 43 53 56 70 75 77 81 87 90 93 97 103 107 108 119
128 130 132 133 134 143 **P**6
Primary Contact: Wayne Walters, Administrator
COO: Sam Miller, Chief Operating Officer
CFO: Charlotte Sherwood, Chief Financial Officer
CMO: Vicente Luciano, M.D., Chief of Staff
CIO: Roger Goss, Director, Information Services
CHR: Robbie Taylor, Director Human Resources
CNO: Lisa Miller, R.N., Director of Nursing
Web address: www.northsunflower.com
**Control:** County–Government, nonfederal **Service:** General Medical and Surgical

**Staffed Beds:** 95 **Admissions:** 923 **Census:** 73 **Outpatient Visits:** 24364
**Births:** 0 **Personnel:** 403

**SENATOBIA—Tate County**

☐ **NORTH OAK REGIONAL MEDICAL CENTER (250126)**, 401 Getwell Drive,
Zip 38668–2213, Mailing Address: P.O. Box 648, Zip 38668–0648;
tel. 662/562–3100 **A**1 9 10 **F**35 40 43 56 70 86 89 98 103 107 119 130
Primary Contact: Sonja Graham, Chief Executive Officer
CMO: Pravinchandra Patel, M.D., Chief Medical Officer
CHR: Vickie Barksdale, Manager Human Resources
Web address: www.normc.org
**Control:** Corporation, Investor–owned, for–profit **Service:** General Medical and
Surgical

**Staffed Beds:** 53 **Admissions:** 1157 **Census:** 15 **Outpatient Visits:** 12659
**Births:** 0 **Personnel:** 109

MS

---

**Hospital, Medicare Provider Number, Address, Telephone, Approval, Facility, and Physician Codes, Health Care System**

★ American Hospital Association (AHA) membership
☐ The Joint Commission accreditation    ◇ DNV Healthcare Inc. accreditation
○ Healthcare Facilities Accreditation Program
△ Commission on Accreditation of Rehabilitation Facilities (CARF) accreditation

## SOUTHAVEN—Desoto County

✉ △ **BAPTIST MEMORIAL HOSPITAL–DESOTO (250141)**, 7601 Southcrest Parkway, Zip 38671–4742; tel. 662/772–4000 **A**1 7 9 10 **F**3 8 11 13 15 17 18 20 22 24 26 28 29 30 31 34 35 40 43 46 47 48 49 50 51 57 60 61 64 68 70 73 74 75 76 77 78 79 80 81 84 85 86 87 90 93 96 107 108 111 114 115 116 118 119 120 121 123 126 129 130 131 132 135 143 144 147 148 **S** Baptist Memorial Health Care Corporation, Memphis, TN
Primary Contact: James Huffman, Chief Executive Officer and Administrator
CFO: Kimberly Young, Chief Financial Officer
CHR: Walter Banks, Director Human Resources
Web address: www.baptistonline.org/desoto/
**Control:** Other not–for–profit (including NFP Corporation) **Service:** General Medical and Surgical

**Staffed Beds:** 263 **Admissions:** 15848 **Census:** 213 **Outpatient Visits:** 104511 **Births:** 1937 **Total Expense ($000):** 253303 **Payroll Expense ($000):** 86417 **Personnel:** 1710

## STARKVILLE—Oktibbeha County

★ ◇ **OCH REGIONAL MEDICAL CENTER (250050)**, 400 Hospital Road, Zip 39759–2163, Mailing Address: P.O. Box 1506, Zip 39760–1506; tel. 662/323–4320 **A**9 10 21 **F**3 7 11 13 15 17 28 29 32 34 35 39 40 41 43 45 47 48 51 53 57 59 61 64 65 66 70 73 74 75 76 77 79 81 85 87 88 89 90 93 97 98 107 108 110 111 114 115 118 119 126 127 129 130 131 132 133 135 147 **P**6
Primary Contact: Richard G. Hilton, Administrator and Chief Executive Officer
COO: Mike Andrews, Assistant Administrator and Chief Operating Officer
CIO: Chamath Wijewardane, Director Information Technology
CHR: Mike Andrews, Assistant Administrator and Chief Operating Officer
Web address: www.och.org
**Control:** County–Government, nonfederal **Service:** General Medical and Surgical

**Staffed Beds:** 96 **Admissions:** 2868 **Census:** 32 **Outpatient Visits:** 215530 **Births:** 982 **Total Expense ($000):** 62289 **Payroll Expense ($000):** 31801 **Personnel:** 590

## TUPELO—Lee County

✉ △ **NORTH MISSISSIPPI MEDICAL CENTER – TUPELO (250004)**, 830 South Gloster Street, Zip 38801–4934; tel. 662/377–3000, (Total facility includes 107 beds in nursing home–type unit) **A**1 2 3 5 7 9 10 19 **F**3 4 5 7 11 12 13 15 17 18 20 22 24 26 28 29 30 31 34 35 37 38 40 41 43 44 50 51 53 54 56 57 58 59 61 62 63 64 65 68 70 71 72 73 74 75 76 77 78 79 80 81 83 84 85 86 87 88 89 90 91 92 93 96 97 98 100 101 103 104 106 107 108 109 110 111 112 113 114 115 116 117 118 119 120 130 131 132 134 135 146 147 148 **S** North Mississippi Health Services, Inc., Tupelo, MS
Primary Contact: Timothy H. Moore, Chief Executive Officer
CIO: Tom Bozeman, Chief Information Officer
CHR: Rodger Brown, Vice President Human Resources
Web address: www.nmhs.net
**Control:** Other not–for–profit (including NFP Corporation) **Service:** General Medical and Surgical

**Staffed Beds:** 757 **Admissions:** 24844 **Census:** 474 **Outpatient Visits:** 246332 **Births:** 2138 **Total Expense ($000):** 544823 **Payroll Expense ($000):** 192582 **Personnel:** 3791

☐ **NORTH MISSISSIPPI STATE HOSPITAL (254009)**, 1937 Briar Ridge Road, Zip 38804–5963; tel. 662/690–4200 **A**1 10 **F**3 29 30 34 87 98 101 106 130 132 143 146 **S** Mississippi State Department of Mental Health, Jackson, MS
Primary Contact: Paul A. Callens, Ph.D., Director
CFO: Joe Rials, Director Fiscal Services
CMO: Ken Lippincott, M.D., Chief of Staff
CIO: James Wilhite, Director Systems Information
Web address: www.nmsh.state.ms.us
**Control:** State–Government, nonfederal **Service:** Psychiatric

**Staffed Beds:** 50 **Admissions:** 558 **Census:** 46 **Outpatient Visits:** 0 **Births:** 0 **Total Expense ($000):** 8283 **Payroll Expense ($000):** 4041 **Personnel:** 107

## TYLERTOWN—Walthall County

★ **WALTHALL COUNTY GENERAL HOSPITAL (251324)**, 100 Hospital Drive, Zip 39667–2099; tel. 601/876–2122 **A**9 10 18 **F**40 43 70 81 89 93 107 119 130 133
Primary Contact: Bryan K. Maxie, Administrator
Web address: www.walthallhospitalms.org
**Control:** County–Government, nonfederal **Service:** General Medical and Surgical

**Staffed Beds:** 25 **Admissions:** 364 **Census:** 3 **Outpatient Visits:** 15476 **Births:** 0 **Personnel:** 100

## UNION—Newton County

★ **LAIRD HOSPITAL (251322)**, 25117 Highway 15, Zip 39365–9099; tel. 601/774–8214 **A**9 10 18 **F**15 29 35 40 43 70 87 89 93 107 119 130 132 133 **S** Rush Health Systems, Meridian, MS
Primary Contact: Thomas G. Bartlett, III, Administrator
COO: Morris A. Reece, EVP/COO
CFO: Jennifer Flint, Chief Financial Officer
CMO: John Mutziger, M.D., Chief Medical Officer
CIO: Angela Sherrill, Chief Information Officer
CHR: Donnie Smith, Chief Human Resources Officer
CNO: Pam Rigdon, Director Nursing
Web address: www.lairdhospital.com/lh/
**Control:** Other not–for–profit (including NFP Corporation) **Service:** General Medical and Surgical

**Staffed Beds:** 25 **Admissions:** 440 **Census:** 4 **Outpatient Visits:** 15791 **Births:** 0 **Personnel:** 164

## VICKSBURG—Warren County

**PROMISE HOSPITAL OF VICKSBURG (252008)**, 1111 North Frontage Road, 2nd Floor, Zip 39180–5102; tel. 601/619–3526 **A**10 **F**70 90 **S** Promise Healthcare, Boca Raton, FL
Primary Contact: Mike Harrell, Chief Executive Officer
COO: Dawn Posey, Chief Operating Officer
CFO: Christopher A. Stegall, Regional Chief Financial Officer and Chief Operating Officer
CMO: Daniel Edney, M.D., Chief of Staff
CIO: Barbara Whiting, Director Health Information Management
CHR: Debbie Carson, Director Human Resources
Web address: www.promise–vicksburg.com
**Control:** Corporation, Investor–owned, for–profit **Service:** Long–Term Acute Care hospital

**Staffed Beds:** 33 **Admissions:** 358 **Census:** 25 **Outpatient Visits:** 0 **Births:** 0 **Personnel:** 69

✉ **RIVER REGION MEDICAL CENTER (250031)**, 2100 Highway 61 North, Zip 39183–8211, Mailing Address: P.O. Box 590, Zip 39181–0590; tel. 601/883–5000, (Includes RIVER REGION WEST CAMPUS, 1111 North Frontage Road, Zip 39180–5102; tel. 601/883–5000) **A**1 9 10 **F**4 13 15 17 29 35 39 40 43 51 56 60 70 73 75 76 77 78 81 87 89 90 93 97 98 100 101 102 103 107 108 111 118 119 130 131 132 147 **S** Community Health Systems, Inc., Franklin, TN
Primary Contact: Doug Sills, Chief Executive Officer
CFO: John Milazzo, Chief Financial Officer
CMO: W. Briggs Hopson, M.D., Clinical Medical Director
CIO: J. B. White, Director Information Systems
CHR: Rebecca Columbus, Vice President Human Resources
Web address: www.riverregion.com
**Control:** Corporation, Investor–owned, for–profit **Service:** General Medical and Surgical

**Staffed Beds:** 297 **Admissions:** 9935 **Census:** 151 **Outpatient Visits:** 140299 **Births:** 685 **Personnel:** 1020

## WATER VALLEY—Yalobusha County

**YALOBUSHA GENERAL HOSPITAL (250061)**, 630 South Main, Zip 38965–3468, Mailing Address: P.O. Box 728, Zip 38965–0728; tel. 662/473–1411, (Total facility includes 122 beds in nursing home–type unit) **A**9 10 **F**3 7 29 33 59 70 107 119 127 128 130 133 143 **P**6
Primary Contact: Terry Varner, Administrator
COO: Ashlee Langdon, Controller
CHR: Katie Rotenberry–Baggett, Administrative Assistant and Human Resources
Web address: www.yalobushageneral.com/
**Control:** County–Government, nonfederal **Service:** General Medical and Surgical

**Staffed Beds:** 148 **Admissions:** 480 **Census:** 121 **Outpatient Visits:** 4537 **Births:** 0 **Total Expense ($000):** 18340 **Payroll Expense ($000):** 11582 **Personnel:** 212

## WAYNESBORO—Wayne County

☐ **WAYNE GENERAL HOSPITAL (250077)**, 950 Matthew Drive, Zip 39367–2590, Mailing Address: P.O. Box 1249, Zip 39367–1249; tel. 601/735–5151 **A**1 9 10 20 **F**13 15 35 39 40 43 53 61 62 63 70 75 76 81 86 88 89 90 93 107 108 111 119 130 132 133
Primary Contact: Donald Hemeter, Administrator
Web address: www.waynegeneralhospital.org
**Control:** County–Government, nonfederal **Service:** General Medical and Surgical

**Staffed Beds:** 80 **Admissions:** 2031 **Census:** 25 **Outpatient Visits:** 33251 **Births:** 225 **Personnel:** 341

*Many Facility Codes have changed. Please refer to the AHA Guide Code Chart.* © 2013 AHA Guide

**MS**

**WEST POINT—Clay County**

☒ **NORTH MISSISSIPPI MEDICAL CENTER–WEST POINT (250067)**, 835 Medical Center Drive, Zip 39773–9320; tel. 662/495–2300 **A**1 9 10 **F**3 7 8 11 13 15 17 28 29 30 31 32 34 35 40 42 43 45 48 53 57 59 64 65 70 73 75 76 78 79 80 81 85 86 87 89 90 97 107 108 109 110 111 114 119 120 129 130 132 133 135 143 145 147 148 **S** North Mississippi Health Services, Inc., Tupelo, MS
Primary Contact: James W. Hahn, Administrator
CFO: Kay Lawler, Business Office Manager
CMO: Timothy E. Whittle, M.D., Chief Medical Staff
CHR: Brenda Johnson, Director Human Resources
CNO: Jane Windle, R.N., Director of Nurses
Web address: www.nmhs.net/westpoint
**Control:** Other not–for–profit (including NFP Corporation) **Service:** General Medical and Surgical

**Staffed Beds:** 60 **Admissions:** 1818 **Census:** 18 **Outpatient Visits:** 46480 **Births:** 357 **Total Expense ($000):** 28650 **Payroll Expense ($000):** 13528 **Personnel:** 267

**WHITFIELD—Rankin County**

☒ **MISSISSIPPI STATE HOSPITAL (254010)**, 3550 Highway 468 West, Zip 39193–5529, Mailing Address: P.O. Box 157–A, Zip 39193–0157; tel. 601/351–8000, (Includes WHITFIELD MEDICAL SURGICAL HOSPITAL, Oak Circle, Zip 39193; tel. 601/351–8023), (Total facility includes 423 beds in nursing home–type unit) **A**1 9 10 **F**4 29 39 70 75 87 89 98 99 100 101 102 103 104 105 107 119 128 130 143 **P**1 **S** Mississippi State Department of Mental Health, Jackson, MS
Primary Contact: James G. Chastain, FACHE, Director
COO: Kelly R. Breland, CPA, Director Support Services
CFO: Warren Williams, CPA, Director Fiscal Services
CMO: Duncan Stone, D.D.S., Chief Medical Staff
CIO: James Dunaway, Director Information Management
CHR: Katie Storr, Director Personnel
Web address: www.msh.state.ms.us
**Control:** State–Government, nonfederal **Service:** Psychiatric

**Staffed Beds:** 875 **Admissions:** 2777 **Census:** 813 **Outpatient Visits:** 4102 **Births:** 0 **Personnel:** 1382

**WIGGINS—Stone County**

**STONE COUNTY HOSPITAL (251303)**, 1434 East Central Avenue, Zip 39577–9602; tel. 601/928–6600 **A**9 10 18 **F**29 40 43 70 77 81 86 87 89 90 97 107 111 119 130 133 **P**6
Primary Contact: Julie Cain, Administrator
Web address: www.schospital.net/
**Control:** Corporation, Investor–owned, for–profit **Service:** General Medical and Surgical

**Staffed Beds:** 25 **Admissions:** 491 **Census:** 4 **Outpatient Visits:** 7317 **Births:** 0 **Personnel:** 171

**WINONA—Montgomery County**

**TYLER HOLMES MEMORIAL HOSPITAL (251312)**, 409 Tyler Holmes Drive, Zip 38967–1599; tel. 662/283–4114 **A**9 10 18 **F**11 34 35 40 43 57 59 66 70 87 107 108 114 119 130 133 135 148 **P**8
Primary Contact: Rosamond M. Tyler, Administrator
CFO: Cori Bailey, Accountant
CHR: Becky Corley, Director Human Resources
**Control:** County–Government, nonfederal **Service:** General Medical and Surgical

**Staffed Beds:** 25 **Admissions:** 639 **Census:** 6 **Outpatient Visits:** 13543 **Births:** 0 **Total Expense ($000):** 11026 **Payroll Expense ($000):** 4822 **Personnel:** 141

**YAZOO CITY—Yazoo County**

★ **KING'S DAUGHTERS HOSPITAL (251313)**, 823 Grand Avenue, Zip 39194–3233; tel. 662/746–2261 **A**9 10 18 **F**11 15 29 40 41 45 53 56 64 70 81 89 93 97 103 107 108 110 111 112 115 119 133 148
Primary Contact: Daryl W. Weaver, Chief Executive Officer
COO: Marsha Jones, R.N., Director Nursing
CFO: Robert E. Harper, Chief Financial Officer
CMO: Heath Scott, M.D., Chief of Staff
CHR: Stephanie Washington, Director Community Relations and Human Resources
Web address: www.kdhyazoo.com
**Control:** Other not–for–profit (including NFP Corporation) **Service:** General Medical and Surgical

**Staffed Beds:** 35 **Admissions:** 1016 **Census:** 13 **Outpatient Visits:** 19324 **Births:** 4 **Total Expense ($000):** 19111 **Payroll Expense ($000):** 8043 **Personnel:** 171

MS

# MISSOURI

## ALBANY—Gentry County

★ **NORTHWEST MEDICAL CENTER (261328)**, 705 North College Street, Zip 64402–1433; tel. 660/726–3941 **A**9 10 18 **F**3 11 15 28 29 34 35 40 44 45 50 56 57 59 62 64 68 75 77 81 85 86 87 90 93 97 104 107 108 110 111 114 118 119 127 128 130 131 133 135 148 **P**6
Primary Contact: Jon D. Doolittle, President and Chief Executive Officer
COO: Jon D. Doolittle, President and Chief Executive Officer
CMO: Jackie Miller, D.O., Chief of Staff
CIO: James Crouch, Vice President Technical Services
CHR: Vickie Cline, Director Human Resources
Web address: www.northwestmedicalcenter.org
**Control:** Other not–for–profit (including NFP Corporation) **Service:** General Medical and Surgical

**Staffed Beds:** 25 **Admissions:** 746 **Census:** 9 **Outpatient Visits:** 41880
**Births:** 0 **Total Expense ($000):** 13535 **Payroll Expense ($000):** 6786
**Personnel:** 166

## APPLETON CITY—St. Clair County

★ **ELLETT MEMORIAL HOSPITAL (261301)**, 610 North Ohio Avenue, Zip 64724–1609, Mailing Address: P.O. Box 6, Zip 64724–0006; tel. 660/476–2111 **A**9 10 18 **F**3 7 11 18 34 40 45 59 64 65 68 77 79 81 90 93 107 111 114 119 127 128 129 130 133 143 **P**6
Primary Contact: Raymond M. Magers, Chief Executive Officer
CFO: Tom Hollis, Chief Financial Officer
CMO: James Wirkkula, M.D., Chief Medical Officer
Web address: www.ellettmemorial.com
**Control:** Hospital district or authority, Government, nonfederal **Service:** General Medical and Surgical

**Staffed Beds:** 12 **Admissions:** 204 **Census:** 4 **Outpatient Visits:** 11518
**Births:** 0 **Total Expense ($000):** 7427 **Payroll Expense ($000):** 3346
**Personnel:** 75

## AURORA—Lawrence County

⊞ **MERCY HOSPITAL AURORA (261316)**, 500 Porter Street, Zip 65605–2365; tel. 417/678–2122 **A**1 9 10 18 **F**3 11 13 15 28 29 30 34 35 40 41 45 50 57 59 64 65 75 76 77 81 85 86 87 89 92 93 94 96 107 108 110 111 114 119 129 130 132 133 135 148 **P**6 **S** Mercy Health, Chesterfield, MO
Primary Contact: Douglas M. Stroemel, President
COO: David Steinmann, VP/COO
CFO: Sherry Clouse Day, CPA, VP Finance/ Regional Chief Financial Officer
CMO: Christie Hurt, M.D., Chief of Staff and Medical Director
CHR: George Roden, Vice President Human Resources
CNO: Nicki Gamet, R.N., VP/Chief Nursing Officer
Web address: www.stjohns.com/aboutus/aurora.aspx
**Control:** Church–operated, Nongovernment, not–for profit **Service:** General Medical and Surgical

**Staffed Beds:** 25 **Admissions:** 673 **Census:** 5 **Outpatient Visits:** 27883
**Births:** 231 **Total Expense ($000):** 13356 **Payroll Expense ($000):** 8280
**Personnel:** 159

## BELTON—Cass County

⊞ **BELTON REGIONAL MEDICAL CENTER (260214)**, 17065 South 71 Highway, Zip 64012–4631; tel. 816/348–1200 **A**1 2 9 10 **F**3 15 18 29 30 31 34 35 37 40 43 45 57 59 65 68 70 74 75 77 78 79 81 82 85 87 90 93 107 108 110 111 118 119 129 130 131 132 146 **P**5 **S** HCA, Nashville, TN
Primary Contact: Todd Krass, R.N., Chief Executive Officer
COO: Nicole Smith Hendricks, Vice President Operations
CFO: Susan Shreeve, Chief Financial Officer
CMO: Douglas Bradley, M.D., Vice President Medical Affairs
CIO: Sarah Bloom, Director Information Systems
CHR: Yvonne Brewington, Director Human Resources
CNO: Karen Lee, MSN, Chief Nursing Officer
Web address: www.beltonregionalmedicalcenter.com
**Control:** Corporation, Investor–owned, for–profit **Service:** General Medical and Surgical

**Staffed Beds:** 38 **Admissions:** 1869 **Census:** 17 **Outpatient Visits:** 95249
**Births:** 0 **Total Expense ($000):** 32146 **Payroll Expense ($000):** 13071
**Personnel:** 172

**RESEARCH BELTON HOSPITAL** See Belton Regional Medical Center

## BETHANY—Harrison County

★ **HARRISON COUNTY COMMUNITY HOSPITAL (261312)**, 2600 Miller Street, Zip 64424–2701, Mailing Address: P.O. Box 428, Zip 64424–0428; tel. 660/425–2211 **A**9 10 18 **F**3 11 15 28 29 34 40 44 45 50 53 54 57 59 62 64 65 66 67 68 75 77 79 81 82 87 89 90 93 96 107 108 110 111 114 119 127 128 129 130 133 143 145 146 147 148 **P**5
Primary Contact: James W. Fairchild, FACHE, Chief Executive Officer
CFO: Christina Gillespie, Chief Financial Officer
CIO: Brenda Siemer, Director of Information Technology
CHR: Brenda Gabriel, Director Human Resources
CNO: Crystal Hicks, R.N., Chief Nursing Officer
Web address: www.hcchospital.org
**Control:** Hospital district or authority, Government, nonfederal **Service:** General Medical and Surgical

**Staffed Beds:** 20 **Admissions:** 352 **Census:** 4 **Outpatient Visits:** 27052
**Births:** 0 **Total Expense ($000):** 13996 **Payroll Expense ($000):** 6384
**Personnel:** 169

## BLUE SPRINGS—Jackson County

⊞ **ST. MARY'S MEDICAL CENTER (260193)**, 201 West R. D. Mize Road, Zip 64014–2518; tel. 816/228–5900 **A**1 9 10 13 **F**3 8 11 13 15 18 20 22 28 29 30 31 34 35 40 49 50 53 56 57 59 60 64 68 70 72 74 75 76 77 78 79 81 82 84 85 86 87 90 93 96 107 108 110 111 115 118 119 121 123 129 130 132 135 143 146 147 148 **S** Ascension Health, Saint Louis, MO
Primary Contact: Annette Small, R.N., Chief Executive Officer
CFO: Steven R. Cleary, Vice President Finance
CMO: Stephens Stoops, M.D., Chief Medical Officer
Web address: www.carondelethealth.org
**Control:** Church–operated, Nongovernment, not–for profit **Service:** General Medical and Surgical

**Staffed Beds:** 131 **Admissions:** 4743 **Census:** 52 **Outpatient Visits:** 89561
**Births:** 615 **Total Expense ($000):** 64898 **Payroll Expense ($000):** 26150
**Personnel:** 466

## BOLIVAR—Polk County

⊞ **CITIZENS MEMORIAL HOSPITAL (260195)**, 1500 North Oakland Avenue, Zip 65613–3011; tel. 417/326–6000 **A**1 9 10 20 **F**3 7 11 13 15 18 20 22 26 28 29 31 34 35 36 39 40 43 50 51 56 57 59 62 63 64 66 68 70 74 75 76 77 78 79 80 81 82 83 84 85 86 87 89 90 93 94 96 98 100 102 103 104 107 108 110 111 115 117 119 127 128 129 130 131 132 133 135 143 146 147 148 **P**6
Primary Contact: Donald J. Babb, Chief Executive Officer
COO: Jeff Miller, Chief Operating Officer
CFO: Gary D. Fullbright, Comptroller
CMO: Steven Butcher, D.O., Director Medical Affairs
CIO: Denni McColm, Chief Information Officer
CHR: Jeremy MacLaughlin, Director Human Resources
CNO: Pamela A. Reese, FACHE, Chief Clinical Officer
Web address: www.citizensmemorial.com
**Control:** Hospital district or authority, Government, nonfederal **Service:** General Medical and Surgical

**Staffed Beds:** 62 **Admissions:** 3125 **Census:** 31 **Outpatient Visits:** 288195
**Births:** 527 **Total Expense ($000):** 90202 **Payroll Expense ($000):** 45993
**Personnel:** 889

## BONNE TERRE—St. Francois County

⊞ **PARKLAND HEALTH CENTER–BONNE TERRE (261315)**, 7245 Raider Road, Zip 63628–3767; tel. 573/358–1400 **A**1 9 10 18 **F**3 11 29 30 31 34 35 40 50 53 57 59 64 65 75 77 78 86 90 93 107 129 130 135 146 **S** BJC HealthCare, Saint Louis, MO
Primary Contact: Steven R. Marler, Administrator
CFO: Cheri L. Goldsmith, Director Financial Services
CMO: Brett M. Dickinson, M.D., Chief of Staff
CHR: Sheri Graham, Director Human Resources and Administrative Services
Web address: www.parklandhealthcenter.org
**Control:** Other not–for–profit (including NFP Corporation) **Service:** General Medical and Surgical

**Staffed Beds:** 3 **Admissions:** 5 **Census:** 1 **Outpatient Visits:** 21944 **Births:** 0 **Personnel:** 63

*Many Facility Codes have changed. Please refer to the AHA Guide Code Chart.*

MO

## BOONVILLE—Cooper County

★ **COOPER COUNTY MEMORIAL HOSPITAL (260004)**, 17651 B Highway, Zip 65233–2839, Mailing Address: P.O. Box 88, Zip 65233–0088; tel. 660/882–7461, (Total facility includes 14 beds in nursing home–type unit) **A**9 10 20 **F**3 7 11 28 29 34 35 40 45 53 57 59 62 64 67 68 75 79 81 85 89 93 94 107 111 114 119 127 128 130 131 132 133 135 146 148 **S** University of Missouri Health Care, Columbia, MO
Primary Contact: Allen J. Waldo, FACHE, CPA, Chief Executive Officer
CFO: Patricia Nowlin, Director of Accounting
CMO: Robert Koch, M.D., Chief Medical Staff
CIO: Steve Weekley, Director Information Technology
CHR: Kim Ashcraft, Director Human Resources
CNO: Nancy Fredrich, R.N., Chief Clinical Officer
Web address: www.coopercmh.com
**Control:** County–Government, nonfederal **Service:** General Medical and Surgical

**Staffed Beds:** 32 **Admissions:** 292 **Census:** 10 **Outpatient Visits:** 36631 **Births:** 0 **Total Expense ($000):** 11177 **Payroll Expense ($000):** 5593 **Personnel:** 149

## BRANSON—Taney County

✉ △ **COX MEDICAL CENTER BRANSON (260094)**, (Formerly Skaggs Regional Medical Center), 251 Skaggs Road, Zip 65616–2031, Mailing Address: P.O. Box 650, Zip 65615–0650; tel. 417/335–7000 **A**1 5 7 9 10 **F**3 8 11 13 15 17 18 20 22 26 28 29 31 32 34 35 40 41 44 45 46 47 50 51 53 56 57 59 60 61 62 63 64 65 66 68 70 74 75 76 77 78 79 80 81 82 84 85 86 87 89 90 93 97 98 100 103 106 107 108 110 111 114 119 121 123 124 127 129 130 131 132 135 143 144 146 147 148 **P**3 6 8 **S** CoxHealth, Springfield, MO
Primary Contact: William K. Mahoney, President and Chief Executive Officer
CFO: David Strong, Chief Financial Officer/Vice President Finance
CIO: Michael Elley, Chief Information Officer
CHR: Carol Murrow, Vice President Business Development
CNO: Sheryl Tilus, R.N., Vice President Clinical Services/Chief Nursing Officer
Web address: www.skaggs.net
**Control:** Other not–for–profit (including NFP Corporation) **Service:** General Medical and Surgical

**Staffed Beds:** 126 **Admissions:** 6366 **Census:** 72 **Outpatient Visits:** 236504 **Births:** 556 **Total Expense ($000):** 116724 **Payroll Expense ($000):** 56372 **Personnel:** 1063

## BRIDGETON—St. Louis County

✉ **SSM DEPAUL HEALTH CENTER (260104)**, 12303 De Paul Drive, Zip 63044–2512; tel. 314/344–6000, (Total facility includes 54 beds in nursing home–type unit) **A**1 2 9 10 **F**3 5 11 12 13 15 17 18 20 22 24 28 29 31 33 34 35 36 38 40 43 44 49 50 51 53 55 56 57 59 60 61 64 68 69 70 73 74 75 76 78 79 81 82 84 85 86 87 89 98 99 100 101 102 103 104 105 107 108 111 114 115 117 119 120 121 124 126 128 130 132 135 143 146 147 148 **P**6 8 **S** SSM Health Care, Saint Louis, MO
Primary Contact: Sean Hogan, President
COO: Lee Bernstein, Regional Executive Vice President and Chief Operating Officer
CFO: Hal Holder, Director Finance
CMO: John Moore, M.D., Vice President, Medical Affairs
CIO: Matt Woodall, Director Information Management
CHR: Patricia Campbell, Vice President Human Resources
CNO: Kathleen Bonser, R.N., Vice President, Nursing/CNO
Web address: www.ssmdepaul.com
**Control:** Church–operated, Nongovernment, not–for profit **Service:** General Medical and Surgical

**Staffed Beds:** 476 **Admissions:** 21203 **Census:** 327 **Outpatient Visits:** 217822 **Births:** 1098 **Total Expense ($000):** 288087 **Payroll Expense ($000):** 105019 **Personnel:** 1798

**SSM REHABILITATION HOSPITAL**, 12380 De Paul Drive, Zip 63044–2511; tel. 314/447–9700 **A**9 **F**3 29 35 44 64 74 75 77 79 85 87 90 91 93 94 96 130 131 132 148 **P**6
Primary Contact: Timothy Wadman, Chief Executive Officer
Web address: www.ssm–select.com/locations/inpatientrehab.aspx
**Control:** Partnership, Investor–owned, for–profit **Service:** Rehabilitation

**Staffed Beds:** 95 **Admissions:** 1698 **Census:** 67 **Outpatient Visits:** 255330 **Births:** 0 **Total Expense ($000):** 65911 **Payroll Expense ($000):** 36983 **Personnel:** 573

## BROOKFIELD—Linn County

**GENERAL JOHN J. PERSHING MEMORIAL HOSPITAL (261307)**, 130 East Lockling Avenue, Zip 64628–2337, Mailing Address: P.O. Box 408, Zip 64628–0408; tel. 660/258–2222 **A**9 10 18 **F**11 15 28 29 36 40 44 54 57 59 63 64 75 81 87 93 97 107 111 114 119 127 130 133 146 **P**6
Primary Contact: Phil Hamilton, R.N., Chief Executive Officer
CFO: Gary R. Tandy, Chief Financial Officer
CMO: B. K. Knowles, D.O., Chief of Staff
CIO: Elaine Sutton, Chief Information Officer
CHR: Amy Sayre, Director Human Resources
Web address: www.pershinghealthsystem.com
**Control:** Other not–for–profit (including NFP Corporation) **Service:** General Medical and Surgical

**Staffed Beds:** 25 **Admissions:** 851 **Census:** 9 **Outpatient Visits:** 63860 **Births:** 0 **Total Expense ($000):** 15530 **Payroll Expense ($000):** 6520 **Personnel:** 146

## BUTLER—Bates County

**BATES COUNTY MEMORIAL HOSPITAL (260034)**, 615 West Nursery Street, Zip 64730–1840, Mailing Address: P.O. Box 370, Zip 64730–0370; tel. 660/200–7000 **A**9 10 20 **F**3 7 11 15 28 29 30 31 34 40 50 57 59 64 68 70 77 79 81 87 90 93 107 108 109 110 111 115 118 119 127 129 130 132 133 143 **P**6
Primary Contact: Wendell R. Harris, CPA, Ph.D., Chief Executive Officer
CFO: Wendell R. Harris, CPA, Chief Executive Officer
CMO: Joseph Brewster, M.D., Chief of Staff
CIO: Marcia Cook, Director Information Technology
CHR: Melinda Jackson, Director Human Resources
Web address: www.bcmhospital.com
**Control:** County–Government, nonfederal **Service:** General Medical and Surgical

**Staffed Beds:** 49 **Admissions:** 925 **Census:** 11 **Outpatient Visits:** 66929 **Births:** 0 **Total Expense ($000):** 29365 **Payroll Expense ($000):** 13459 **Personnel:** 265

## CAMERON—Clinton County

**CAMERON REGIONAL MEDICAL CENTER (260057)**, 1600 East Evergreen, Zip 64429–2400, Mailing Address: P.O. Box 557, Zip 64429–0557; tel. 816/632–2101 **A**9 10 **F**3 11 13 15 18 28 29 30 31 34 35 39 40 46 47 49 56 57 59 61 62 63 64 67 70 74 75 76 77 78 79 81 82 84 85 86 87 89 90 98 100 104 107 110 111 115 119 128 129 130 131 133 143 146 147 148 **P**6
Primary Contact: Joseph F. Abrutz, Jr., Administrator
CFO: Rosa Patti, Chief Financial Officer
CIO: Bill Walser, Coordinator Technology
CHR: Pat Bestgen, Manager Human Resources
Web address: www.cameronregional.org
**Control:** Other not–for–profit (including NFP Corporation) **Service:** General Medical and Surgical

**Staffed Beds:** 58 **Admissions:** 2139 **Census:** 32 **Outpatient Visits:** 412617 **Births:** 132 **Total Expense ($000):** 33386 **Payroll Expense ($000):** 19934 **Personnel:** 341

## CAPE GIRARDEAU—Cape Girardeau County

☐ **LANDMARK HOSPITAL (262015)**, 3255 Independence Street, Zip 63701–4914; tel. 573/335–1091 **A**1 9 10 **F**1 29 75 119 130 148 **S** Landmark Hospitals, Cape Girardeau, MO
Primary Contact: Rodney Brown, Chief Executive Officer
COO: Michael L. Norman, Executive Vice President and Chief Operating Officer
CFO: Richard H. Hogan, CPA, Chief Financial Officer
CMO: William Fritsch, M.D., Medical Director
CIO: Renee Hesselrode, Director Health Information Management
CHR: Angela Kisner, Director Human Resources and Coordinator Medical Staff
Web address: www.landmarkhospitals.com
**Control:** Partnership, Investor–owned, for–profit **Service:** Long–Term Acute Care hospital

**Staffed Beds:** 30 **Admissions:** 347 **Census:** 25 **Outpatient Visits:** 0 **Births:** 0 **Total Expense ($000):** 13817 **Payroll Expense ($000):** 4930 **Personnel:** 128

MO

---

**Hospital, Medicare Provider Number, Address, Telephone, Approval, Facility, and Physician Codes, Health Care System**

★ American Hospital Association (AHA) membership
☐ The Joint Commission accreditation
◇ DNV Healthcare Inc. accreditation
○ Healthcare Facilities Accreditation Program
△ Commission on Accreditation of Rehabilitation Facilities (CARF) accreditation

⊞ **SAINT FRANCIS MEDICAL CENTER (260183)**, 211 St. Francis Drive, Zip 63703–5049; tel. 573/331–3000 **A**1 2 9 10 19 **F**3 9 11 12 13 15 17 18 20 22 24 26 28 29 30 31 32 34 35 39 40 43 44 45 46 47 48 49 50 53 54 55 56 57 58 59 60 61 62 64 65 70 72 73 74 75 76 77 78 79 80 81 82 83 84 85 86 87 89 90 91 92 93 97 107 108 109 110 111 114 115 117 118 119 120 121 123 124 126 129 130 131 132 135 141 142 143 144 145 146 147 148 **P**6
Primary Contact: Steven C. Bjelich, President and Chief Executive Officer
COO: Marilyn K. Curtis, Vice President, Professional Services
CFO: Tony Balsano, Vice President Finance
CMO: James Schell, M.D., Vice President Medical Affairs
CIO: Diane Gammon, Director Information Systems
CHR: Teri Kreitzer, Director Human Resources
CNO: Jeannie Fadler, R.N., Vice President, Patient Care Services
Web address: www.sfmc.net
**Control:** Church–operated, Nongovernment, not–for profit **Service:** General Medical and Surgical

**Staffed Beds: 282 Admissions: 11415 Census: 162 Outpatient Visits:** 336915 **Births: 1089 Total Expense ($000): 329570 Payroll Expense ($000): 141034 Personnel: 2091**

⊞ **SOUTHEAST HOSPITAL (260110)**, 1701 Lacey Street, Zip 63701–5230; tel. 573/334–4822 **A**1 2 9 10 19 **F**3 11 12 13 15 17 18 20 22 24 26 28 29 30 31 32 34 35 40 45 49 50 51 53 54 57 58 59 60 61 62 63 64 65 68 70 72 73 74 75 76 77 78 79 80 81 82 85 86 87 88 89 90 92 93 96 97 98 100 102 103 107 108 110 111 114 115 119 120 121 123 124 126 127 129 130 131 132 144 146 147 148 **P**6 **S** SoutheastHEALTH, Cape Girardeau, MO
Primary Contact: Wayne Smith, President and Chief Executive Officer
CFO: David Strong, Vice President and Chief Financial Officer
CMO: Lee Taylor, M.D., Vice President and Chief Medical Officer
CIO: Jay McGuire, Director Information Systems
Web address: www.sehealth.org/
**Control:** Other not–for–profit (including NFP Corporation) **Service:** General Medical and Surgical

**Staffed Beds: 221 Admissions: 10331 Census: 124 Outpatient Visits:** 322379 **Births: 856 Total Expense ($000): 263310 Payroll Expense ($000): 114067 Personnel: 2059**

### CARROLLTON—Carroll County

★ **CARROLL COUNTY MEMORIAL HOSPITAL (261332)**, 1502 North Jefferson Street, Zip 64633–1948; tel. 660/542–1695 **A**9 10 18 **F**3 11 15 28 29 30 34 35 38 40 45 53 56 57 59 62 64 65 75 77 79 86 87 90 91 93 103 104 107 108 110 111 114 117 119 129 130 131 132 133 143 146 **P**6
Primary Contact: Jeff A. Tindle, Chief Executive Officer
CMO: Timothy Reid, M.D., Chief Medical Staff
CHR: Karen Pfaff, Director Human Resources
Web address: www.carrollcountyhospital.org
**Control:** Other not–for–profit (including NFP Corporation) **Service:** General Medical and Surgical

**Staffed Beds: 25 Admissions: 317 Census: 4 Outpatient Visits: 38904 Births: 1 Total Expense ($000): 11620 Payroll Expense ($000): 5166 Personnel: 126**

### CARTHAGE—Jasper County

★ **MERCY MCCUNE–BROOKS HOSPITAL (260228)**, 3125 Drive Russell Smith Way, Zip 64836–7402; tel. 417/358–8121, (Data for 182 days) **A**9 10 **F**3 7 11 13 15 28 29 30 34 35 40 45 50 53 57 59 62 64 68 69 70 75 76 79 81 89 90 98 104 107 111 114 119 129 130 131 132 133 135 146 147 **P**6 **S** Mercy Health, Chesterfield, MO
Primary Contact: Robert Y. Copeland, Jr., FACHE, Chief Executive Officer
CFO: Tony Wright, Chief Financial Officer
CIO: Ken Masters, Director Information Systems
CHR: Tracy G. Lemmons, Director Human Resources
Web address: www.mccune–brooks.org
**Control:** Church–operated, Nongovernment, not–for profit **Service:** General Medical and Surgical

**Staffed Beds: 25 Admissions: 1309 Census: 25 Outpatient Visits: 49044 Births: 133 Total Expense ($000): 27767 Payroll Expense ($000): 9775 Personnel: 381**

### CASSVILLE—Barry County

⊞ **MERCY HOSPITAL CASSVILLE (261317)**, 94 Main Street, Zip 65625–1610; tel. 417/847–6000 **A**1 9 10 18 **F**3 11 15 28 29 30 34 40 41 45 50 53 57 59 64 65 75 77 81 85 86 87 89 92 93 94 96 107 110 111 114 119 132 133 135 148 **P**6 **S** Mercy Health, Chesterfield, MO
Primary Contact: Douglas M. Stroemel, President
COO: David Steinmann, Chief Operating Officer
CFO: Sherry Clouse Day, CPA, Chief Financial Officer
CMO: Jamie Zengotita, M.D., Chief Medical Staff
CHR: George Roden, Vice President Human Resources
CNO: Nicki Garnet, R.N., Chief Nursing Officer
Web address: www.mercy.net/northwestar/practice/mercy–hospital–cassville
**Control:** Church–operated, Nongovernment, not–for profit **Service:** General Medical and Surgical

**Staffed Beds: 18 Admissions: 258 Census: 2 Outpatient Visits: 24535 Births: 0 Total Expense ($000): 10856 Payroll Expense ($000): 6344 Personnel: 114**

### CHESTERFIELD—St. Louis County

**DUBUIS HOSPITAL OF ST. LOUIS** See Mercy Continuing Care Hospital

⊞ **MERCY CONTINUING CARE HOSPITAL (262012)**, 13190 South Outer Forty Road, Zip 63017–5917; tel. 314/392–6380 **A**1 9 10 **F**1 3 29 30 130 148 **S** Dubuis Health System, Houston, TX
Primary Contact: Matthew B. Schweigert, Administrator
CFO: Paul Veillon, CPA, Chief Financial Officer
CMO: Rekha Lakshmanan, M.D., Medical Director
CNO: Jennifer Ryder, Director of Nursing
Web address: www.dubuis.org/mercycontinuingcarehospital
**Control:** Other not–for–profit (including NFP Corporation) **Service:** Long–Term Acute Care hospital

**Staffed Beds: 54 Admissions: 313 Census: 24 Outpatient Visits: 0 Births: 0 Total Expense ($000): 14588 Payroll Expense ($000): 7343 Personnel: 89**

⊞ △ **MERCY REHABILITATION HOSPITAL (263029)**, 14561 North Outer Forty Road, Zip 63017; tel. 314/881–4000 **A**1 7 9 10 **F**16 29 30 75 90 91 130 132 143 148 **S** Mercy Health, Chesterfield, MO
Primary Contact: Donna M. Flannery, Chief Executive Officer
CFO: Jerry Wise, Controller
CMO: Siresha Samudrala, M.D., Medical Director
Web address: www.stjohnsmercyrehab.com
**Control:** Partnership, Investor–owned, for–profit **Service:** Rehabilitation

**Staffed Beds: 90 Admissions: 1316 Census: 53 Outpatient Visits: 0 Births: 0 Total Expense ($000): 22769 Payroll Expense ($000): 9932 Personnel: 197**

⊞ **ST. LUKE'S HOSPITAL (260179)**, 232 South Woods Mill Road, Zip 63017–3417; tel. 314/434–1500, (Total facility includes 140 beds in nursing home–type unit) **A**1 2 3 5 9 10 **F**3 10 11 12 13 15 17 18 20 22 24 26 28 29 30 31 32 34 35 36 39 40 41 42 44 45 46 48 49 50 52 53 54 55 56 57 58 59 60 61 62 63 64 65 66 68 69 70 71 73 74 75 76 77 78 79 81 82 83 84 85 86 87 89 90 93 97 107 108 110 111 114 115 117 118 119 120 121 123 124 126 128 129 130 131 132 133 146 145 146 147 148 **P**6 8
Primary Contact: Gary R. Olson, President and Chief Executive Officer
CFO: Scott Johnson, Vice President Finance
CIO: William Meyers, Chief Information Officer
CHR: Janette Taaffe, Administrator Human Resources
Web address: www.stlukes–stl.com
**Control:** Church–operated, Nongovernment, not–for profit **Service:** General Medical and Surgical

**Staffed Beds: 585 Admissions: 16815 Census: 308 Outpatient Visits:** 750827 **Births: 1967 Total Expense ($000): 423382 Payroll Expense ($000): 188657 Personnel: 3120**

⊞ **ST. LUKE'S REHABILITATION HOSPITAL (263030)**, 14709 Olive Boulevard, Zip 63017–2221; tel. 314/317–5700 **A**1 9 10 **F**3 12 28 29 34 54 75 79 90 93 94 96 100 119 130 132 148 **P**8 **S** Kindred Healthcare, Louisville, KY
Primary Contact: Elizabeth A. Cooley, R.N., Chief Executive Officer
Web address: www.khrehabstluke.com
**Control:** Partnership, Investor–owned, for–profit **Service:** Rehabilitation

**Staffed Beds: 35 Admissions: 555 Census: 21 Outpatient Visits: 9157 Births: 0 Total Expense ($000): 9209 Payroll Expense ($000): 3664 Personnel: 68**

### CHILLICOTHE—Livingston County

⊞ **HEDRICK MEDICAL CENTER (261321)**, 100 Central Avenue, Zip 64601–1554; tel. 660/646–1480 **A**1 9 10 18 **F**3 11 13 15 18 28 29 30 31 34 35 40 41 44 50 57 59 64 65 68 69 70 74 75 76 77 78 79 81 82 85 86 87 89 90 92 93 96 97 100 102 104 107 108 111 115 118 119 127 128 129 130 131 133 146 147 148 **P**6 **S** Saint Luke's Health System, Kansas City, MO
Primary Contact: Matthew J. Wenzel, Chief Executive Officer
CFO: Dana Hoover, Chief Financial Officer
CMO: George A. Pagels, M.D., President and Chief Executive Officer
CHR: Lisa Hecker, Director Human Resources
Web address: www.saintlukeshealthsystem.org
**Control:** Other not–for–profit (including NFP Corporation) **Service:** General Medical and Surgical

**Staffed Beds: 25 Admissions: 948 Census: 12 Outpatient Visits: 81609 Births: 180 Total Expense ($000): 31144 Payroll Expense ($000): 13395 Personnel: 258**

**MO**

*Many Facility Codes have changed. Please refer to the AHA Guide Code Chart.*   © 2013 AHA Guide

## CLINTON—Henry County

☒ **GOLDEN VALLEY MEMORIAL HEALTHCARE (260175)**, 1600 North Second Street, Zip 64735–1192; tel. 660/885–5511 **A**1 9 10 **F**3 7 11 13 15 18 28 29 30 31 34 35 40 45 47 48 49 53 57 59 61 62 64 68 70 74 75 76 77 78 79 81 85 86 87 90 93 96 107 108 111 115 118 119 127 128 129 130 131 132 133 143 146 147 148
Primary Contact: Randy S. Wertz, Chief Executive Officer
CFO: Gordon Glass, Chief Financial Officer
CIO: James Begin, Director Information Technology
CHR: Roger Cook, Director Human Resources
CNO: Mark D. Mattes, R.N., Assistant Administrator/Patient Care Services
Web address: www.gvmh.org
**Control:** Hospital district or authority, Government, nonfederal **Service:** General Medical and Surgical

**Staffed Beds:** 56 **Admissions:** 2825 **Census:** 29 **Outpatient Visits:** 227871
**Births:** 339 **Total Expense ($000):** 54987 **Payroll Expense ($000):** 31584
**Personnel:** 598

## COLUMBIA—Boone County

☒ **BOONE HOSPITAL CENTER (260068)**, 1600 East Broadway,
Zip 65201–5844; tel. 573/815–8000 **A**1 2 3 5 9 10 **F**3 7 11 12 13 15 17 18 20 22 24 26 28 29 30 31 34 35 46 47 48 49 50 51 53 56 57 59 60 61 64 65 68 70 71 72 73 74 75 76 77 78 79 80 81 82 84 85 86 87 89 90 93 96 97 107 108 110 111 114 115 117 118 119 126 129 130 131 132 135 145 146 147 148 **S** BJC HealthCare, Saint Louis, MO
Primary Contact: Randy Morrow, Interim Chief Executive Officer
CFO: Randy Morrow, Vice President and Chief Operating Officer
CMO: Jerry Kennett, M.D., Chief Medical Officer
CHR: Michelle Zvanut, Vice President Human Resources
Web address: www.boone.org
**Control:** Other not–for–profit (including NFP Corporation) **Service:** General Medical and Surgical

**Staffed Beds:** 360 **Admissions:** 17003 **Census:** 199 **Outpatient Visits:** 162454 **Births:** 2196 **Total Expense ($000):** 286994 **Payroll Expense ($000):** 78997 **Personnel:** 1751

**ELLIS FISCHEL CANCER CENTER** See University of Missouri Hospitals and Clinics

☒ △ **HARRY S. TRUMAN MEMORIAL VETERANS HOSPITAL**, 800 Hospital Drive, Zip 65201–5275; tel. 573/814–6000, (Total facility includes 41 beds in nursing home–type unit) **A**1 3 5 7 **F**3 4 5 17 18 20 22 24 28 29 30 31 34 35 39 40 44 49 54 56 58 59 61 62 63 64 67 70 74 75 78 79 81 82 84 85 86 87 90 92 93 94 97 98 100 101 102 103 104 105 106 107 108 111 115 116 118 119 127 128 129 130 132 135 146 147 **P**6 **S** Department of Veterans Affairs, Washington, DC
Primary Contact: Sallie Houser–Hanfelder, FACHE, Director
COO: Robert G. Ritter, Associate Director
CFO: Paul Hopkins, Chief Financial Officer
CMO: Lana Zerrer, M.D., Chief of Staff
CIO: Donna Krause, Chief Information Officer
CHR: Jimmy Powell, Manager Human Resources
Web address: www.columbiamo.va.gov
**Control:** Veterans Affairs, Government, federal **Service:** General Medical and Surgical

**Staffed Beds:** 126 **Admissions:** 3847 **Census:** 83 **Outpatient Visits:** 643921
**Births:** 0 **Total Expense ($000):** 273796 **Payroll Expense ($000):** 93744
**Personnel:** 1439

☒ **HOWARD A. RUSK REHABILITATION CENTER (263027)**, 315 Business Loop 70 West, Zip 65203–3248; tel. 573/817–2703 **A**1 3 5 9 10 **F**29 34 59 64 75 90 93 95 96 132 143 148 **S** HEALTHSOUTH Corporation, Birmingham, AL
Primary Contact: Bruce Eady, Chief Executive Officer
CFO: Ted Weatherford, Chief Financial Officer
CMO: Gregory Worsowicz, M.D., Medical Director
CHR: Robin Prater, Director Human Resources
CNO: Mary Schnell, R.N., Chief Nursing Officer
Web address: www.ruskrehab.com
**Control:** Partnership, Investor–owned, for–profit **Service:** Rehabilitation

**Staffed Beds:** 60 **Admissions:** 1050 **Census:** 46 **Outpatient Visits:** 8648
**Births:** 0 **Total Expense ($000):** 18349 **Payroll Expense ($000):** 8488
**Personnel:** 178

☐ **LANDMARK HOSPITAL OF COLUMBIA (262020)**, 604 Old 63 North, Zip 65201–6308; tel. 573/499–6600 **A**1 3 5 9 10 **F**1 29 75 148 **S** Landmark Hospitals, Cape Girardeau, MO
Primary Contact: Shannon Canard, Chief Executive Officer
Web address: www.landmarkhospitals.com
**Control:** Partnership, Investor–owned, for–profit **Service:** Long–Term Acute Care hospital

**Staffed Beds:** 42 **Admissions:** 442 **Census:** 31 **Outpatient Visits:** 0 **Births:** 0 **Total Expense ($000):** 16520 **Payroll Expense ($000):** 5205 **Personnel:** 104

☒ **UNIVERSITY OF MISSOURI HOSPITALS AND CLINICS (260141)**, One Hospital Drive, Zip 65212–0001; tel. 573/882–4141, (Includes ELLIS FISCHEL CANCER CENTER, 115 Business Loop 70 West, Zip 65203; tel. 573/882–5460) **A**1 2 3 5 8 9 10 **F**3 4 7 9 11 12 13 15 16 17 18 19 20 22 24 26 28 29 30 31 32 34 35 37 38 39 40 41 43 44 45 46 47 48 49 50 51 52 53 54 55 56 57 58 59 60 61 64 65 68 70 71 72 73 74 75 76 77 78 79 81 82 84 85 86 87 88 89 92 93 97 98 99 100 101 102 104 107 108 110 111 114 115 117 118 119 120 121 123 124 126 129 130 131 132 134 135 138 141 142 144 146 147 148 **P**1 6 **S** University of Missouri Health Care, Columbia, MO
Primary Contact: Mitchell L. Wasden, Ed.D., Chief Executive Officer and Chief Operating Officer
COO: Anita Larsen, R.N., Interim Chief Operating Officer
CFO: Kevin Necas, Chief Financial Officer
CMO: Les Hall, M.D., Chief Medical Officer
CHR: Sue Kopfle, Chief Human Resources Officer
Web address: www.muhealth.org
**Control:** State–Government, nonfederal **Service:** General Medical and Surgical

**Staffed Beds:** 463 **Admissions:** 21770 **Census:** 295 **Outpatient Visits:** 762967 **Births:** 1761 **Total Expense ($000):** 556245 **Payroll Expense ($000):** 216028 **Personnel:** 4503

★ **WOMEN'S AND CHILDREN'S HOSPITAL (260178)**, 404 Keene Street, Zip 65201–6626; tel. 573/875–9000, (Nonreporting) **A**9 **S** University of Missouri Health Care, Columbia, MO
Primary Contact: Keri Simon, Executive Director
CFO: Kevin Necas, Chief Financial Officer
CMO: Les Hall, M.D., Chief of Staff
CIO: Joanne Burns, Chief Information Officer
CHR: Sue Kopfle, Chief Human Resources Officer
CNO: Anita Larsen, R.N., Chief Nursing Officer
Web address: www.muchildrenshospital.org
**Control:** State–Government, nonfederal **Service:** Children's general

**Staffed Beds:** 108

## CRYSTAL CITY—Jefferson County

○ △ **MERCY HOSPITAL JEFFERSON (260023)**, (Formerly Jefferson Regional Medical Center), Highway 61 South, Zip 63019, Mailing Address: P.O. Box 350, Zip 63019–0350; tel. 636/933–1000 **A**7 9 10 11 **F**3 4 5 7 8 11 12 13 15 18 20 22 24 26 28 29 30 34 35 37 40 44 45 49 50 51 53 54 57 59 62 63 64 70 74 75 76 77 79 81 82 84 85 86 87 89 90 92 93 94 96 97 98 100 101 102 103 104 107 110 111 114 115 116 117 118 119 129 130 131 132 135 143 144 146 147 148 **P**6 **S** Mercy Health, Chesterfield, MO
Primary Contact: Eric Ammons, President
CMO: Mark Briete, M.D., Vice President Medical Affairs
CIO: Jan Poneta, Director Information Services
CHR: Saundra G. Turner, Director Human Resources
Web address: www.jhsmo.com
**Control:** Other not–for–profit (including NFP Corporation) **Service:** General Medical and Surgical

**Staffed Beds:** 215 **Admissions:** 11412 **Census:** 122 **Outpatient Visits:** 108377 **Births:** 508 **Total Expense ($000):** 98851 **Payroll Expense ($000):** 48099 **Personnel:** 1137

## DEXTER—Stoddard County

**SOUTHEAST HEALTH CENTER OF STODDARD COUNTY (260160)**, (Formerly Missouri Southern Healthcare), 1200 North One Mile Road, Zip 63841–1000; tel. 573/624–5566 **A**9 10 **F**3 11 15 29 34 39 40 45 57 59 62 65 70 75 77 80 81 85 89 90 93 97 107 108 114 119 127 128 130 133 135 **P**6 **S** SoutheastHEALTH, Cape Girardeau, MO
Primary Contact: Adam Bracks, Chief Executive Officer
CHR: Judy Bowling, Director Human Resources
Web address: www.sehealth.org
**Control:** Corporation, Investor–owned, for–profit **Service:** General Medical and Surgical

**Staffed Beds:** 45 **Admissions:** 1108 **Census:** 9 **Outpatient Visits:** 102333
**Births:** 0 **Total Expense ($000):** 9024 **Payroll Expense ($000):** 5790
**Personnel:** 159

**MO**

---

**Hospital, Medicare Provider Number, Address, Telephone, Approval, Facility, and Physician Codes, Health Care System**

★ American Hospital Association (AHA) membership
☐ The Joint Commission accreditation
◇ DNV Healthcare Inc. accreditation
○ Healthcare Facilities Accreditation Program
△ Commission on Accreditation of Rehabilitation Facilities (CARF) accreditation

### DONIPHAN—Ripley County

★ **SOUTHEAST HEALTH CENTER OF RIPLEY COUNTY (260080)**, 109 Plum Street, Zip 63935–1299; tel. 573/996–2141 **A**9 10 **F**11 29 40 59 62 65 87 93 107 115 119 127 130 135 **S** SoutheastHEALTH, Cape Girardeau, MO
Primary Contact: Christy Hardin, Interim Administrator
CFO: Rickie Maples, Interim Chief Financial Officer
CMO: Ureej Mansoor, M.D., Chief of Staff
CIO: Riley March, Manager Information Technology
CHR: Peggy Teasdale, Director Human Resources
Web address: www.sehealth.org/southeast–health–center–of–ripley–county/SoutheastHEALTH.aspx?nd=41
**Control:** County–Government, nonfederal **Service:** General Medical and Surgical

**Staffed Beds:** 21 **Admissions:** 308 **Census:** 3 **Outpatient Visits:** 26576 **Births:** 0 **Total Expense ($000):** 8022 **Payroll Expense ($000):** 4941 **Personnel:** 113

### EL DORADO SPRINGS—Cedar County

**CEDAR COUNTY MEMORIAL HOSPITAL (261323)**, 1401 South Park Street, Zip 64744–2037; tel. 417/876–2511 **A**9 10 18 **F**11 13 15 18 28 29 30 34 35 40 45 53 56 57 59 62 64 65 68 74 75 76 77 81 85 86 87 89 93 102 107 110 111 114 119 127 129 130 133 146 147 148 **P**6
Primary Contact: Jana Witt, Chief Executive Officer
CFO: Carla Gilbert, Controller
CMO: George Methven, M.D., Chief Medical Staff
CIO: Lois Willmore, Supervisor Health Information Management
CHR: Diana Pyle, Director Human Resources
Web address: www.cedarcountyhospital.org
**Control:** County–Government, nonfederal **Service:** General Medical and Surgical

**Staffed Beds:** 25 **Admissions:** 577 **Census:** 11 **Outpatient Visits:** 36101 **Births:** 60 **Total Expense ($000):** 11254 **Payroll Expense ($000):** 5101 **Personnel:** 127

**SOUTHWEST MISSOURI PSYCHIATRIC REHABILITATION CENTER (264027)**, 1301 Industrial Parkway East, Zip 64744–6263; tel. 417/876–1000 **A**10 **F**98 101 102
Primary Contact: Denise Norbury, Regional Executive Officer
CFO: Ronald Chandler, Accountant II
CMO: Ronald Lacey, M.D., Medical Director
CHR: James Stacy, Director Human Resources
**Control:** State–Government, nonfederal **Service:** Psychiatric

**Staffed Beds:** 16 **Admissions:** 122 **Census:** 15 **Outpatient Visits:** 0 **Births:** 0 **Total Expense ($000):** 3567 **Payroll Expense ($000):** 2611 **Personnel:** 6

### ELLINGTON— County

**SOUTHEAST HEALTH CENTER OF REYNOLDS COUNTY (261304)**, (Formerly Advanced Healthcare Medical Center), 100 Highway 21 South, Zip 63638, Mailing Address: Rural Route 4, Box 4269, Zip 63638–9409; tel. 573/663–2511 **A**9 10 18 **F**3 40 62 64 87 107 111 114 119 127 130 133 **P**6 **S** SoutheastHEALTH, Cape Girardeau, MO
Primary Contact: Bernadean Anseln, Chief Executive Officer
COO: Steve Myers, Assistant Administrator
CFO: Katie Caudel, Controller
CIO: Thomas Barker, Director Information
**Control:** Partnership, Investor–owned, for–profit **Service:** General Medical and Surgical

**Staffed Beds:** 12 **Admissions:** 288 **Census:** 3 **Outpatient Visits:** 55049 **Births:** 0 **Personnel:** 14

### EXCELSIOR SPRINGS—Clay County

⊞ **EXCELSIOR SPRINGS HOSPITAL (261322)**, 1700 Rainbow Boulevard, Zip 64024–1190; tel. 816/630–6081, (Total facility includes 80 beds in nursing home–type unit) **A**1 9 10 18 **F**3 10 11 15 18 29 30 31 32 34 35 39 40 45 49 56 57 59 62 63 64 67 68 70 75 77 78 79 81 82 84 85 86 89 90 93 102 107 108 110 111 114 116 117 118 119 125 128 129 130 132 133 135 143 146 147
Primary Contact: Sally S. Nance, Chief Executive Officer
CFO: Dennis Hartman, Chief Financial Officer
CMO: Manoch Kuangparichat, M.D., President Medical Staff
CIO: Alicia Harrison, Data Management Officer
CHR: Joni Schwan, Director Human Resources
Web address: www.esmc.org
**Control:** City–Government, nonfederal **Service:** General Medical and Surgical

**Staffed Beds:** 105 **Admissions:** 461 **Census:** 76 **Outpatient Visits:** 21644 **Births:** 0 **Total Expense ($000):** 21111 **Payroll Expense ($000):** 9797 **Personnel:** 237

### FAIRFAX—Atchison County

**COMMUNITY HOSPITAL ASSOCIATION** See Community Hospital–Fairfax

★ **COMMUNITY HOSPITAL–FAIRFAX (261303)**, 26136 U.S. Highway 59, Zip 64446–9105, Mailing Address: P.O. Box 107, Zip 64446–0107; tel. 660/686–2211 **A**9 10 18 **F**3 11 13 15 28 30 34 40 45 57 59 62 64 67 76 79 81 85 87 89 93 107 110 114 119 128 130 133
Primary Contact: Myra L. Evans, Chief Executive Officer
COO: Rhonda Evans, R.N., Chief Operating Officer
CFO: Suzanne Southard, Director Finance
CMO: Aron Burke, M.D., Chief Medical Officer
CIO: Michelle Oswald, Director of Information Systems
CHR: Deanna Lamb, Director of Human Resources
Web address: www.fairfaxmed.com
**Control:** Other not–for–profit (including NFP Corporation) **Service:** General Medical and Surgical

**Staffed Beds:** 18 **Admissions:** 571 **Census:** 6 **Outpatient Visits:** 15568 **Births:** 35 **Total Expense ($000):** 10861 **Payroll Expense ($000):** 3911 **Personnel:** 95

### FARMINGTON—St. Francois County

○ **MINERAL AREA REGIONAL MEDICAL CENTER (260116)**, 1212 Weber Road, Zip 63640–3325; tel. 573/756–4581 **A**9 10 11 19 **F**3 12 13 15 28 29 30 34 40 45 50 57 59 60 62 64 68 70 76 77 79 81 85 89 90 93 98 100 102 103 107 111 114 119 129 130 132 133 146 147 **S** Capella Healthcare, Franklin, TN
Primary Contact: Lynn M. Mergen, Chief Executive Officer
CFO: Paul Rogers, Chief Financial Officer
CMO: Richard Secor, Jr., M.D., Chief of Staff
CIO: Jim Smith, Director Information Systems
CHR: Regina K. Sons, Administrative Director Human Ressources and Volunteer Services Associate Ethics and Compliance Officer
Web address: www.marmc.net
**Control:** Corporation, Investor–owned, for–profit **Service:** General Medical and Surgical

**Staffed Beds:** 98 **Admissions:** 3276 **Census:** 39 **Outpatient Visits:** 81927 **Births:** 389 **Total Expense ($000):** 39999 **Payroll Expense ($000):** 15858 **Personnel:** 406

⊞ **PARKLAND HEALTH CENTER (260163)**, 1101 West Liberty Street, Zip 63640–1921; tel. 573/756–6451 **A**1 9 10 **F**3 11 13 15 28 29 30 34 35 39 40 44 45 46 49 50 51 53 57 59 60 61 64 65 68 69 70 74 75 76 77 79 81 85 86 87 89 93 98 103 107 108 111 115 118 119 130 132 135 143 146 147 148 **S** BJC HealthCare, Saint Louis, MO
Primary Contact: Thomas P. Karl, President
CFO: Cheri L. Goldsmith, Director Financial Services
CMO: Brett M. Dickinson, M.D., Chief of Staff
CHR: Sheri Graham, Director Human Resources and Administrative Services
Web address: www.parklandhealthcenter.org
**Control:** Other not–for–profit (including NFP Corporation) **Service:** General Medical and Surgical

**Staffed Beds:** 98 **Admissions:** 3831 **Census:** 35 **Outpatient Visits:** 87631 **Births:** 469 **Total Expense ($000):** 68600 **Payroll Expense ($000):** 23578 **Personnel:** 496

□ **SOUTHEAST MISSOURI MENTAL HEALTH CENTER (264005)**, 1010 West Columbia Street, Zip 63640–2997; tel. 573/218–6792 **A**1 10 **F**4 30 39 53 65 75 77 86 87 93 97 98 101 103 106 130 132 135 143 146
Primary Contact: Julie Inman, Regional Executive Officer
COO: Melissa Ring, Ph.D., Chief Operating Officer
CMO: Jay Englehart, M.D., Medical Director
CHR: Mark Remspecher, Director Human Resources
Web address: www.dmh.missouri.gov/southeast/
**Control:** State–Government, nonfederal **Service:** Psychiatric

**Staffed Beds:** 298 **Admissions:** 298 **Census:** 287 **Outpatient Visits:** 0 **Births:** 0 **Total Expense ($000):** 49770 **Payroll Expense ($000):** 28210 **Personnel:** 813

### FENTON—St. Louis County

⊞ **SSM ST. CLARE HEALTH CENTER (260081)**, 1015 Bowles Avenue, Zip 63026–2394; tel. 636/496–2000 **A**1 9 10 **F**3 11 13 15 17 18 20 22 24 28 29 30 31 34 35 40 44 45 50 51 53 54 56 57 59 61 64 65 70 73 74 75 76 78 79 81 82 84 85 86 87 100 102 103 107 108 110 111 114 115 117 118 119 130 132 135 143 146 147 148 **P**6 8 **S** SSM Health Care, Saint Louis, MO
Primary Contact: Lee Bernstein, Interim President
COO: Kelly Pearce, Vice President of Operations
CFO: Karen Rewerts, Vice President Finance and Chief Financial Officer
CMO: Timothy J. Pratt, M.D., Vice President of Medical Affairs/Chief Medical Officer
CIO: Leighton Wassilak, Manager, Information Systems/ Telecommunications
CHR: Patricia Campbell, Vice President Human Resources
CNO: Mary Brobst, R.N., Vice President of Nursing
Web address: www.ssmstclare.com
**Control:** Church–operated, Nongovernment, not–for profit **Service:** General Medical and Surgical

**Staffed Beds:** 184 **Admissions:** 11768 **Census:** 119 **Outpatient Visits:** 117098 **Births:** 1404 **Total Expense ($000):** 160866 **Payroll Expense ($000):** 56120 **Personnel:** 922

*Many Facility Codes have changed. Please refer to the AHA Guide Code Chart.* © 2013 AHA Guide

MO

## FORT LEONARD WOOD—Pulaski County

✠ **GENERAL LEONARD WOOD ARMY COMMUNITY HOSPITAL**, 126 Missouri Avenue, Zip 65473–8952; tel. 573/596–0414, (Nonreporting) **A**1 **S** Department of the Army, Office of the Surgeon General, Falls Church, VA
Primary Contact: Colonel Marie Dominguez, Commander
CFO: Major Michael Hogan, Chief Resource Management
CMO: Lieutenant Colonel John Lowery, M.D., Deputy Commander Clinical Services
CHR: Major Sandra Roper, Chief Human Resources
Web address: www.glwach.amedd.army.mil/
**Control:** Army, Government, federal **Service:** General Medical and Surgical

**Staffed Beds:** 54

## FREDERICKTOWN—Madison County

**MADISON MEDICAL CENTER (261302)**, 611 West Main Street, Zip 63645–1111; tel. 573/783–3341, (Total facility includes 80 beds in nursing home–type unit) **A**9 10 18 **F**6 11 15 18 28 31 35 40 45 59 62 64 67 70 74 77 78 79 81 85 87 92 93 97 103 107 111 119 127 128 129 130 133 146
Primary Contact: Lisa Twidwell, Administrator
CMO: P. A. George, M.D., Chief of Staff
CHR: Jennifer Penuel, Director Human Resources
Web address: www.madisonmedicalcenter.net
**Control:** County–Government, nonfederal **Service:** General Medical and Surgical

**Staffed Beds:** 97 **Admissions:** 652 **Census:** 81 **Outpatient Visits:** 60179 **Births:** 0 **Total Expense ($000):** 14499 **Payroll Expense ($000):** 8674 **Personnel:** 253

## FULTON—Callaway County

☐ **CALLAWAY COMMUNITY HOSPITAL (260209)**, 10 South Hospital Drive, Zip 65251–2510; tel. 573/642–3376 **A**1 3 5 9 10 **F**3 11 15 29 30 34 35 40 45 50 57 59 67 68 81 85 89 90 93 97 98 103 107 108 111 114 119 127 128 130 131 133 135 **S** Sunlink Health Systems, Atlanta, GA
Primary Contact: Allen D. AufderHeide, Chief Executive Officer
COO: Chuck Baker, R.N., Chief Operating Officer and Chief Nursing Officer
CHR: Martie Jeney, Director Human Resources
Web address: www.mycallaway.org
**Control:** Corporation, Investor–owned, for–profit **Service:** General Medical and Surgical

**Staffed Beds:** 37 **Admissions:** 406 **Census:** 3 **Outpatient Visits:** 40950 **Births:** 0 **Total Expense ($000):** 11771 **Payroll Expense ($000):** 6078

☐ **FULTON STATE HOSPITAL (264004)**, 600 East Fifth Street, Zip 65251–1753; tel. 573/592–4100 **A**1 3 5 10 **F**3 4 11 29 30 39 44 50 53 56 57 58 59 65 75 77 82 86 87 98 100 101 102 103 130 132 135 143 146 **P**6
Primary Contact: Robert Reitz, Ph.D., Regional Executive Officer
COO: Marty Ann Martin–Forman, Chief Operating Officer
CFO: J. Kenneth Lyle, Jr., Chief Financial Officer
CMO: Bruce Harry, M.D., Clinical Director
CIO: Robert Smith, Chief Information Officer
CHR: Lori Hollinger, Manager Human Resources
Web address: www.dmh.missouri.gov/fulton
**Control:** State–Government, nonfederal **Service:** Psychiatric

**Staffed Beds:** 366 **Admissions:** 186 **Census:** 310 **Outpatient Visits:** 0 **Births:** 0 **Total Expense ($000):** 82299 **Payroll Expense ($000):** 40210 **Personnel:** 1115

## HANNIBAL—Marion County

✠ **HANNIBAL REGIONAL HOSPITAL (260025)**, 6000 Hospital Drive, Zip 63401–6887, Mailing Address: P.O. Box 551, Zip 63401–0551; tel. 573/248–1300 **A**1 2 9 10 **F**3 11 13 15 18 20 22 26 28 30 31 35 39 40 45 47 49 51 57 59 60 62 64 68 70 74 75 76 77 78 79 81 82 85 86 87 89 90 92 93 96 97 100 102 104 107 108 110 111 115 117 118 119 120 121 123 124 127 129 130 131 132 144 145 146 148 **P**1
Primary Contact: C. Todd Ahrens, President and Chief Executive Officer
CFO: Roger J. Dix, Senior Vice President and Chief Financial Officer
CMO: Roderick Bartlett, M.D., President Medical Staff
CIO: Jeff W. Evans, Vice President Information and Technology
CHR: Penny Nunley, Vice President Human Resources
Web address: www.hrhonline.org
**Control:** Other not–for–profit (including NFP Corporation) **Service:** General Medical and Surgical

**Staffed Beds:** 91 **Admissions:** 4701 **Census:** 46 **Outpatient Visits:** 128303 **Births:** 580 **Total Expense ($000):** 99843 **Payroll Expense ($000):** 50874 **Personnel:** 806

## HARRISONVILLE—Cass County

✠ **CASS REGIONAL MEDICAL CENTER (261324)**, 2800 East Rock Haven Road, Zip 64701–4411; tel. 816/380–3474 **A**1 9 10 18 **F**11 15 18 28 29 30 31 32 34 35 37 39 40 45 48 50 54 56 57 59 64 65 66 68 70 74 75 77 78 79 81 84 85 86 87 89 92 93 96 97 98 110 111 114 115 119 127 129 130 131 132 133 135 146 147 148 **P**6
Primary Contact: John Christopher Lang, Chief Executive Officer
CFO: Brent Probasco, Chief Financial Officer
CIO: Cynthia Miltenberger, Director Organizational Effectiveness
CHR: Carla Wallen, Manager Human Resources
Web address: www.cassregional.org
**Control:** County–Government, nonfederal **Service:** General Medical and Surgical

**Staffed Beds:** 35 **Admissions:** 1740 **Census:** 21 **Outpatient Visits:** 104604 **Births:** 0 **Total Expense ($000):** 47185 **Payroll Expense ($000):** 20943 **Personnel:** 379

## HAYTI—Pemiscot County

**PEMISCOT MEMORIAL HEALTH SYSTEM (260070)**, 946 East Road, Zip 63851–1245, Mailing Address: P.O. Box 489, Zip 63851–0489; tel. 573/359–1372, (Total facility includes 66 beds in nursing home–type unit) **A**9 10 **F**3 7 11 13 15 17 28 29 30 34 39 40 50 57 59 64 67 68 70 75 76 77 79 81 82 85 87 89 90 93 97 98 99 103 104 107 111 119 127 128 130 133 143 144 146 147 148 **P**6
Primary Contact: Jack Pennington, Chief Executive Officer
CFO: Kerry L. Noble, Chief Financial Officer
CHR: Jackie Powell, Director Human Resources
Web address: www.pemiscot.org/
**Control:** County–Government, nonfederal **Service:** General Medical and Surgical

**Staffed Beds:** 167 **Admissions:** 2110 **Census:** 74 **Outpatient Visits:** 34585 **Births:** 96 **Total Expense ($000):** 41124 **Payroll Expense ($000):** 18366 **Personnel:** 492

## HERMANN—Gasconade County

★ **HERMANN AREA DISTRICT HOSPITAL (261314)**, 509 West 18th Street, Zip 65041–1547, Mailing Address: P.O. Box 470, Zip 65041–0470; tel. 573/486–2191 **A**9 10 18 **F**3 11 15 18 28 29 30 34 35 40 41 44 45 53 56 57 59 62 63 64 67 68 69 71 75 77 78 81 85 86 87 89 90 93 96 97 104 107 111 114 119 127 128 129 130 132 133 135 143 146 **P**6
Primary Contact: Dan McKinney, Administrator
COO: Matt Siebert, Assistant Administrator of Ancillary Services
CFO: Denise Witthaus, Assistant Administrator Finance
CMO: Jeremy Tallery, D.O., Chief of Staff
CIO: Chris Gooch, Information Technology Director
CHR: Carol Schaefer, Human Resources
CNO: Sue Daller, R.N., Assistant Administrator of Nursing
Web address: www.hadh.org
**Control:** Hospital district or authority, Government, nonfederal **Service:** General Medical and Surgical

**Staffed Beds:** 24 **Admissions:** 452 **Census:** 9 **Outpatient Visits:** 58667 **Births:** 0 **Total Expense ($000):** 15514 **Payroll Expense ($000):** 7748 **Personnel:** 178

## HOUSTON—Texas County

**TEXAS COUNTY MEMORIAL HOSPITAL (260024)**, 1333 South Sam Houston Boulevard, Zip 65483–2046; tel. 417/967–3311 **A**9 10 20 **F**3 7 13 15 28 29 34 40 45 53 57 59 62 63 64 70 76 81 85 86 87 89 93 97 107 111 114 119 127 129 130 133 143 148 **P**6
Primary Contact: Wesley E. Murray, Chief Executive Officer
CFO: Linda Pamperien, Chief Financial Officer
CMO: Charles Mueller, M.D., Chief of Staff
CHR: Anita Kuhn, Controller
Web address: www.tcmh.org
**Control:** County–Government, nonfederal **Service:** General Medical and Surgical

**Staffed Beds:** 47 **Admissions:** 1847 **Census:** 20 **Outpatient Visits:** 111557 **Births:** 281 **Total Expense ($000):** 22630 **Payroll Expense ($000):** 15990 **Personnel:** 365

MO

---

**Hospital, Medicare Provider Number, Address, Telephone, Approval, Facility, and Physician Codes, Health Care System**

★ American Hospital Association (AHA) membership
☐ The Joint Commission accreditation
◇ DNV Healthcare Inc. accreditation
○ Healthcare Facilities Accreditation Program
△ Commission on Accreditation of Rehabilitation Facilities (CARF) accreditation

### INDEPENDENCE—Jackson County

✠ **CENTERPOINT MEDICAL CENTER (260095)**, 19600 East 39th Street, Zip 64057–2301; tel. 816/698–7000 **A**1 2 9 10 **F**3 8 13 15 17 18 20 22 24 26 28 29 30 31 34 35 38 40 43 49 50 54 55 56 57 59 60 64 70 71 72 73 74 75 76 77 78 79 80 81 82 83 84 85 86 87 92 93 107 108 110 111 114 115 119 126 129 130 131 132 135 144 145 146 147 148 **S** HCA, Nashville, TN
Primary Contact: David R. Williams, Chief Executive Officer
COO: Phil Buttell, Chief Operating Officer
CFO: James H. Brown, Chief Financial Officer
CMO: Christopher Sullivan, M.D., Chief Medical Officer
CIO: Carl Sifers, Director Information Technology and System Services
CHR: Kyla Stoltz, Vice President Human Resources
Web address: www.centerpointmedical.com
**Control:** Corporation, Investor–owned, for–profit **Service:** General Medical and Surgical

**Staffed Beds:** 221 **Admissions:** 13993 **Census:** 159 **Outpatient Visits:** 138187 **Births:** 1473 **Total Expense ($000):** 171780 **Payroll Expense ($000):** 64312 **Personnel:** 892

### JEFFERSON CITY—Cole County

✠ **CAPITAL REGION MEDICAL CENTER (260047)**, 1125 Madison Street, Zip 65101–5200, Mailing Address: P.O. Box 1128, Zip 65102–1128; tel. 573/632–5000 **A**1 3 5 9 10 12 13 **F**3 5 11 13 15 17 18 20 22 24 26 28 29 30 31 32 34 35 36 38 40 45 46 47 48 49 51 53 54 56 57 58 59 61 62 64 65 66 70 73 74 75 76 77 78 79 80 81 85 87 89 90 92 93 94 97 99 100 102 104 107 108 110 111 114 118 119 120 121 129 130 131 132 135 144 146 147 **P**2 6 **S** University of Missouri Health Care, Columbia, MO
Primary Contact: Edward F. Farnsworth, FACHE, President
COO: Janet Weckenborg, FACHE, VP Operations
CFO: James McMillan, Vice President Finance
CMO: Lorenzo McKnelly, D.O., Chief of Staff
CIO: Jason Cecil, Chief Information Officer
CHR: Robert Mazur, Vice President Human Resources
CNO: Tawny Sandifer, R.N., Vice President Patient Care
Web address: www.crmc.org
**Control:** Other not–for–profit (including NFP Corporation) **Service:** General Medical and Surgical

**Staffed Beds:** 114 **Admissions:** 6687 **Census:** 70 **Outpatient Visits:** 455828 **Births:** 768 **Total Expense ($000):** 152159 **Payroll Expense ($000):** 70227 **Personnel:** 1216

✠ **ST. MARYS HEALTH CENTER (260011)**, 100 St. Marys Medical Plaza, Zip 65101–1602; tel. 573/761–7000 **A**1 9 10 19 **F**3 11 13 15 17 18 20 22 24 28 29 30 31 32 34 35 40 44 45 49 50 57 59 64 70 73 74 75 76 77 78 79 80 81 82 84 85 86 87 89 93 96 98 100 101 102 103 104 107 108 110 111 114 115 118 119 129 130 131 132 135 141 142 144 146 147 148 **P**6 **S** SSM Health Care, Saint Louis, MO
Primary Contact: R. Brent VanConia, President
COO: Anthony Houston, Executive Vice President
CMO: John Lucio, D.O., Vice President Medical Affairs
CHR: Susan Mankoski, Vice President Human Resources
CNO: Grace McBride, Vice President Acute Care Services
Web address: www.lethealingbegin.com
**Control:** Church–operated, Nongovernment, not–for profit **Service:** General Medical and Surgical

**Staffed Beds:** 139 **Admissions:** 8067 **Census:** 90 **Outpatient Visits:** 225534 **Births:** 615 **Total Expense ($000):** 130597 **Payroll Expense ($000):** 48753 **Personnel:** 878

### JOPLIN—Newton County

★ ○ **FREEMAN HOSPITAL WEST (260137)**, 1102 West 32nd Street, Zip 64804–3503; tel. 417/347–1111, (Includes FREEMAN HOSPITAL EAST, 932 East 34th Street, Zip 64804–3999; tel. 417/623–4640), (Total facility includes 32 beds in nursing home–type unit) **A**9 10 11 13 **F**3 8 11 13 15 17 18 20 22 24 26 28 29 30 31 34 35 36 37 38 39 40 42 43 44 45 46 47 48 49 50 54 56 57 58 59 60 61 62 64 65 68 70 71 72 73 74 75 76 77 78 79 81 82 84 85 86 87 89 90 93 96 97 98 100 102 103 107 108 110 111 114 115 117 119 124 128 129 130 131 132 135 144 145 146 147 148 **P**1 6 **S** Freeman Health System, Joplin, MO
Primary Contact: Paula F. Baker, President and Chief Executive Officer
COO: Joe L. Kirk, Executive Vice President
CFO: Steve W. Graddy, Chief Financial Officer
CMO: Richard D. Schooler, M.D., Chief Medical Officer
CIO: Sue Annesser, Director Information Technology
CHR: Deborah Chiodo, Director Human Resources
Web address: www.freemanhealth.com
**Control:** Other not–for–profit (including NFP Corporation) **Service:** General Medical and Surgical

**Staffed Beds:** 413 **Admissions:** 19602 **Census:** 287 **Outpatient Visits:** 712445 **Births:** 2770 **Total Expense ($000):** 374850 **Payroll Expense ($000):** 196209 **Personnel:** 3076

☐ **LANDMARK HOSPITAL OF JOPLIN (262016)**, 2040 West 32nd Street, Zip 64804–3512; tel. 417/627–1300 **A**1 9 10 **F**1 29 75 119 130 148 **S** Landmark Hospitals, Cape Girardeau, MO
Primary Contact: Kenneth D'Amico, Chief Executive Officer
COO: Trish Shuler, Chief Clinical Officer
CFO: Richard H. Hogan, CPA, Chief Financial Officer
CMO: Ronald Williams, M.D., Medical Director
CHR: Teresa Woodward, Director Human Resources
Web address: www.landmarkhospitals.com
**Control:** Partnership, Investor–owned, for–profit **Service:** Long–Term Acute Care hospital

**Staffed Beds:** 30 **Admissions:** 360 **Census:** 24 **Outpatient Visits:** 0 **Births:** 0 **Total Expense ($000):** 14504 **Payroll Expense ($000):** 5434 **Personnel:** 119

✠ △ **MERCY HOSPITAL JOPLIN (260001)**, 2817 South St. John's Boulevard, Zip 64804–1626; tel. 417/781–2727, (Includes ST. JOHN'S REHABILITATION CENTER, 2727 McClelland Boulevard, Zip 64804; tel. 417/659–6716) **A**1 2 7 10 **F**4 5 7 11 12 13 15 17 18 20 22 24 26 28 29 30 31 34 35 37 38 39 40 43 44 45 49 50 54 57 58 59 60 61 62 63 64 65 66 68 70 73 74 75 76 77 78 79 81 82 83 84 85 86 87 90 93 94 97 98 99 100 101 102 103 104 105 106 107 108 110 111 114 115 117 118 119 126 127 129 130 131 132 134 135 144 146 147 148 **P**6 **S** Mercy Health, Chesterfield, MO
Primary Contact: Gary W. Pulsipher, President and Chief Executive Officer
COO: Dottie Bringle, R.N., Chief Operating Officer and Chief Nursing Officer
CFO: Shelly Hunter, Chief Financial Officer
CIO: Robert Honeywell, Site Administrator
CHR: Scott Watson, JD, Vice President Human Resources and Support Services
Web address: www.stj.com
**Control:** Church–operated, Nongovernment, not–for profit **Service:** General Medical and Surgical

**Staffed Beds:** 180 **Admissions:** 4374 **Census:** 52 **Outpatient Visits:** 118339 **Births:** 95 **Total Expense ($000):** 208739 **Payroll Expense ($000):** 55459 **Personnel:** 1106

### KANSAS CITY—Jackson County

☐ **CENTER FOR BEHAVIORAL MEDICINE (264008)**, 1000 East 24th Street, Zip 64108–2776; tel. 816/512–7000 **A**1 3 5 10 **F**4 35 36 38 50 53 98
Primary Contact: Denise Norbury, Chief Executive Officer
COO: Scott Carter, Chief Operating Officer
CFO: Randy Riley, Chief Financial Officer
CMO: Stuart J. Munro, M.D., Clinical Director
CIO: Rob Curren, Director Information Technology
CHR: Silva Ward, Director Human Resources
Web address: www.dmhonline.dmh.state.mo.us
**Control:** State–Government, nonfederal **Service:** Psychiatric

**Staffed Beds:** 65 **Admissions:** 60 **Census:** 63 **Outpatient Visits:** 0 **Births:** 0 **Total Expense ($000):** 23293 **Payroll Expense ($000):** 13156 **Personnel:** 352

✠ **CHILDREN'S MERCY HOSPITALS AND CLINICS (263302)**, 2401 Gillham Road, Zip 64108–4619; tel. 816/234–3000 **A**1 2 3 5 8 9 10 **F**3 7 8 9 11 12 16 19 20 21 22 23 24 25 26 27 29 30 31 32 34 35 36 39 40 41 43 44 48 49 50 54 55 57 58 59 60 61 62 64 65 68 72 73 74 75 77 78 79 81 82 84 85 86 87 88 89 90 91 92 93 94 96 97 100 101 104 107 108 111 114 117 118 119 130 131 132 134 136 138 139 141 142 144 146 148 **P**6 8
Primary Contact: Randall L. O'Donnell, Ph.D., President and Chief Executive Officer
COO: Jo W. Stueve, Co–Chief Operating Officer
CFO: Sandra A J Lawrence, Executive Vice President and Chief Financial Officer
CMO: V. Fred Burry, M.D., Executive Medical Director
CIO: Jean Ann Breedlove, Chief Information Officer
CHR: Dan Wright, Vice President Human Resources
Web address: www.childrensmercy.org
**Control:** Other not–for–profit (including NFP Corporation) **Service:** Children's general

**Staffed Beds:** 265 **Admissions:** 11327 **Census:** 197 **Outpatient Visits:** 357881 **Births:** 92 **Total Expense ($000):** 710589 **Payroll Expense ($000):** 358358 **Personnel:** 5172

✠ **CRITTENTON CHILDREN'S CENTER (264018)**, 10918 Elm Avenue, Zip 64134–4108; tel. 816/765–6600 **A**1 10 **F**5 29 30 32 34 35 68 75 77 86 87 98 99 100 101 102 104 106 130 132 146 **P**6 **S** Saint Luke's Health System, Kansas City, MO
Primary Contact: Janine Hron, Chief Executive Officer
COO: JoAnn McDonough, Director Operations and Chief Nursing Officer
CFO: Willard Staron, Chief Financial Officer
CMO: Eileen Duggan, M.D., Medical Director
CIO: Deborah Gash, Vice President and Chief Information Officer
CHR: Shawna Roath, Director Human Resources
Web address: www.crittentonkc.org
**Control:** Other not–for–profit (including NFP Corporation) **Service:** Children's hospital psychiatric

**Staffed Beds:** 46 **Admissions:** 2298 **Census:** 38 **Outpatient Visits:** 13567 **Births:** 0 **Total Expense ($000):** 24067 **Payroll Expense ($000):** 14062 **Personnel:** 182

*Many Facility Codes have changed. Please refer to the AHA Guide Code Chart.*

⊠ △ **KANSAS CITY VETERANS AFFAIRS MEDICAL CENTER**, (Formerly Veterans Affairs Medical Center), 4801 East Linwood Boulevard, Zip 64128–2226; tel. 816/861–4700, (Nonreporting) **A**1 2 3 5 7 **S** Department of Veterans Affairs, Washington, DC
Primary Contact: Kent D. Hill, Director
CFO: Charles Henning, Program Director Business
Web address: www.kansascity.va.gov/
**Control:** Veterans Affairs, Government, federal **Service:** General Medical and Surgical

**Staffed Beds:** 157

⊠ **KINDRED HOSPITAL KANSAS CITY (262011)**, 8701 Troost Avenue, Zip 64131–2767; tel. 816/995–2000 **A**1 9 10 **F**1 3 18 29 30 60 70 75 80 85 100 107 130 148 **S** Kindred Healthcare, Louisville, KY
Primary Contact: Aaron Anothayanontha, Chief Executive Officer
COO: Stephenie Hashmi, Chief Clinical Officer
CFO: Maureen Roach, Chief Financial Officer
Web address: www.kindredhospitalkc.com
**Control:** Corporation, Investor–owned, for–profit **Service:** Long–Term Acute Care hospital

**Staffed Beds:** 130 **Admissions:** 632 **Census:** 52 **Outpatient Visits:** 0 **Births:** 0 **Total Expense ($000):** 30779 **Payroll Expense ($000):** 9170 **Personnel:** 176

⊠ **KINDRED HOSPITAL NORTHLAND (262018)**, 500 Northwest 68th Street, Zip 64118–2455; tel. 816/420–6300 **A**1 9 10 **F**1 18 28 29 30 60 77 82 84 85 100 130 148 **S** Kindred Healthcare, Louisville, KY
Primary Contact: H. Frank Schneider, Chief Executive Officer
CFO: Austin Walker, Accounting Manager
CMO: Sean R. Muldoon, M.D., Senior Vice President & Chief Medical Officer–Kindred Healthcare, Hospital Divison
CHR: Jeffrey Sopko, West Region Director of HR
CNO: Julie Duben, Chief Clinical Officer
Web address: www.khnorthland.com
**Control:** Corporation, Investor–owned, for–profit **Service:** Long–Term Acute Care hospital

**Staffed Beds:** 35 **Admissions:** 389 **Census:** 28 **Outpatient Visits:** 0 **Births:** 0 **Total Expense ($000):** 15142 **Payroll Expense ($000):** 5062 **Personnel:** 118

**NORTHLAND LTAC HOSPITAL** See Kindred Hospital Northland

⊠ **RESEARCH MEDICAL CENTER (260027)**, 2316 East Meyer Boulevard, Zip 64132–1136; tel. 816/276–4000 **A**1 2 3 5 9 10 **F**3 4 8 11 13 15 17 18 20 22 24 26 28 29 30 31 34 35 38 39 40 42 43 45 46 47 49 50 51 52 53 55 57 58 59 60 61 64 68 70 72 73 74 75 76 77 78 79 80 81 82 84 85 86 87 90 93 94 96 97 98 107 108 110 111 114 115 116 118 119 120 121 122 124 129 130 131 132 134 135 138 143 146 147 148 **S** HCA, Nashville, TN
Primary Contact: Kevin J. Hicks, President and Chief Executive Officer
COO: Jacqueline DeSouza, Chief Operating Officer
CFO: Susan Shreeve, Chief Financial Officer
CMO: George Liesmann, M.D., Chief Medical Officer
CIO: Tressy McKinney, Director Information Services
CHR: Dennis K. Johnson, Vice President Human Resources
Web address: www.researchmedicalcenter.com
**Control:** Corporation, Investor–owned, for–profit **Service:** General Medical and Surgical

**Staffed Beds:** 366 **Admissions:** 15130 **Census:** 210 **Outpatient Visits:** 157609 **Births:** 1498 **Total Expense ($000):** 274386 **Payroll Expense ($000):** 95677 **Personnel:** 1527

⊠ **RESEARCH PSYCHIATRIC CENTER (264016)**, 2323 East 63rd Street, Zip 64130–3462; tel. 816/444–8161 **A**1 10 **F**4 5 29 35 87 98 99 100 101 102 103 104 105 130 **S** HCA, Nashville, TN
Primary Contact: Richard Failla, Chief Executive Officer
COO: Kevin Walker, Vice President Operations
CFO: Susan Shreeve, Chief Financial Officer
CMO: Steven Segraves, M.D., Medical Director
CIO: Matt Untch, Controller
CHR: Peggy Tyson, Director Human Resources
CNO: Carmen Kynard, R.N., Chief Nursing Officer
Web address: www.researchpsychiatriccenter.com
**Control:** Corporation, Investor–owned, for–profit **Service:** Psychiatric

**Staffed Beds:** 100 **Admissions:** 3902 **Census:** 71 **Outpatient Visits:** 7256 **Births:** 0 **Total Expense ($000):** 21255 **Payroll Expense ($000):** 10085 **Personnel:** 199

⊠ **SAINT LUKE'S HOSPITAL OF KANSAS CITY (260138)**, 4401 Wornall Road, Zip 64111–3220; tel. 816/932–9886, (Includes SAINT LUKE'S CANCER INSTITUTE, 4321 Washington, Medical Plaza III, Suite 5100, Zip 64111–3214; tel. 816/932–2823) **A**1 2 3 5 8 9 10 **F**3 9 11 12 13 15 17 18 20 22 24 25 26 28 29 30 31 32 34 35 36 37 38 39 40 43 44 45 46 47 48 49 50 53 55 56 57 58 59 60 61 62 64 65 66 68 70 71 72 73 74 75 76 77 78 79 81 82 84 85 86 87 89 90 91 92 93 94 95 96 97 100 101 102 104 107 108 110 111 114 115 116 117 118 119 120 121 123 124 126 129 130 131 132 135 137 138 139 141 146 147 148 **P**6 **S** Saint Luke's Health System, Kansas City, MO
Primary Contact: Julie L. Quirin, FACHE, Chief Executive Officer
COO: Brad Simmons, Chief Operating Officer
CFO: Amy Nachtigal, Chief Financial Officer
CMO: John Yeast, M.D., Director Medical Affairs
CIO: Deborah Gash, Chief Information Officer
CHR: Doris Rogers, Vice President Human Resources
CNO: Debra White, Chief Nursing Officer
Web address: www.saint–lukes.org
**Control:** Church–operated, Nongovernment, not–for profit **Service:** General Medical and Surgical

**Staffed Beds:** 410 **Admissions:** 19771 **Census:** 290 **Outpatient Visits:** 227215 **Births:** 2235 **Total Expense ($000):** 511674 **Payroll Expense ($000):** 165781 **Personnel:** 3112

⊠ **SAINT LUKE'S NORTH HOSPITAL – BARRY ROAD (260062)**, 5830 N.W. Barry Road, Zip 64154–2778; tel. 816/891–6000, (Includes SAINT LUKE'S NORTH HOSPITAL–SMITHVILLE CAMPUS, 601 South 169 Highway, Smithville, Zip 64089–9317; tel. 816/532–3700) **A**1 9 10 **F**3 11 13 15 17 18 20 22 26 28 29 30 31 32 34 35 36 38 40 44 45 49 50 53 56 57 59 60 64 68 69 70 71 73 74 75 76 77 79 81 82 84 85 86 87 90 92 93 96 97 98 99 100 101 102 103 104 105 107 108 110 111 114 115 117 118 119 129 130 131 132 134 135 141 143 146 147 148 **S** Saint Luke's Health System, Kansas City, MO
Primary Contact: Kevin T. Trimble, FACHE, President and Chief Executive Officer
CFO: Julie Murphy, Chief Financial Officer
CIO: Carolyn Masoner, Director Information Services
CHR: Alan L. Abramovitz, Director Human Resources
Web address: www.saint–lukes.org
**Control:** Church–operated, Nongovernment, not–for profit **Service:** General Medical and Surgical

**Staffed Beds:** 137 **Admissions:** 6884 **Census:** 80 **Outpatient Visits:** 90436 **Births:** 871 **Total Expense ($000):** 97288 **Payroll Expense ($000):** 39710 **Personnel:** 696

⊠ **SELECT SPECIALTY HOSPITAL–WESTERN MISSOURI (262014)**, 2316 East Meyer Boulevard, 3 West, Zip 64132–1136; tel. 816/276–3300 **A**1 9 10 **F**1 3 29 77 84 85 86 148 **S** Select Medical Corporation, Mechanicsburg, PA
Primary Contact: Matthew Paul Pearson, Chief Executive Officer
Web address: www.selectspecialtyhospitals.com/company/locations/westernmissouri.aspx
**Control:** Corporation, Investor–owned, for–profit **Service:** Long–Term Acute Care hospital

**Staffed Beds:** 34 **Admissions:** 371 **Census:** 27 **Outpatient Visits:** 0 **Births:** 0 **Total Expense ($000):** 13561 **Payroll Expense ($000):** 5854 **Personnel:** 90

⊠ **ST. JOSEPH MEDICAL CENTER (260085)**, 1000 Carondelet Drive, Zip 64114–4673; tel. 816/942–4400 **A**1 2 9 10 **F**3 11 13 15 17 18 20 22 24 26 28 29 30 31 34 35 36 40 45 46 47 49 50 51 56 57 59 60 64 68 70 71 72 74 75 76 77 78 79 80 81 82 84 85 86 87 90 96 107 108 110 111 114 115 116 118 119 129 130 132 135 146 147 148 **S** Ascension Health, Saint Louis, MO
Primary Contact: Michael A. Dorsey, FACHE, Chief Executive Officer
CFO: Steven R. Cleary, Vice President Finance
CMO: Stephens Stoops, M.D., Chief Medical Officer
CIO: Maggie Ratliff, Chief Information Officer
CHR: Dawn L. Bryant, Vice President Organizational Development
CNO: Debra Ohnoutka, Chief Nursing Officer
Web address: www.carondelethealth.org
**Control:** Other not–for–profit (including NFP Corporation) **Service:** General Medical and Surgical

**Staffed Beds:** 191 **Admissions:** 9993 **Census:** 132 **Outpatient Visits:** 120652 **Births:** 1067 **Total Expense ($000):** 154431 **Payroll Expense ($000):** 52847 **Personnel:** 930

MO

⊠ **TRUMAN MEDICAL CENTER–HOSPITAL HILL (260048)**, 2301 Holmes Street, Zip 64108–2640; tel. 816/404–1000 **A**1 2 3 5 8 9 10 **F**3 4 5 11 12 13 15 17 18 20 22 26 28 29 30 31 34 35 36 38 39 40 41 43 44 45 46 48 49 50 52 53 55 57 58 59 61 64 65 66 68 70 71 72 74 75 76 77 78 79 81 82 84 85 86 87 90 93 94 97 98 99 100 101 102 103 104 107 108 110 111 114 115 119 129 130 131 132 134 135 143 146 147 148 **P**5 **S** Truman Medical Centers, Kansas City, MO
Primary Contact: John W. Bluford, President and Chief Executive Officer
COO: Catherine D. Disch, Executive Vice President and Chief Operating Officer
CFO: Allen Johnson, Chief Financial Officer
CMO: Mark Steele, M.D., Chief Medical Officer
CIO: Mitzi Cardenas, Chief Information Officer
CHR: CiCi Rojas, Vice President Community Engagement
Web address: www.trumed.org
**Control:** Other not–for–profit (including NFP Corporation) **Service:** General Medical and Surgical

**Staffed Beds:** 272 **Admissions:** 13882 **Census:** 180 **Outpatient Visits:** 616723 **Births:** 2119 **Total Expense ($000):** 339202 **Payroll Expense ($000):** 144813 **Personnel:** 2738

⊠ **TRUMAN MEDICAL CENTER–LAKEWOOD (260102)**, 7900 Lee's Summit Road, Zip 64139–1236; tel. 816/404–7000, (Total facility includes 188 beds in nursing home–type unit) **A**1 3 5 9 10 **F**3 4 5 6 11 13 15 29 30 32 34 35 36 38 39 40 41 44 45 50 53 54 56 57 58 59 64 65 66 67 68 70 71 74 75 76 77 78 79 81 85 86 87 89 90 92 93 94 96 97 98 99 100 101 102 103 104 107 111 112 114 119 129 130 131 132 134 135 143 146 147 **P**5 6 **S** Truman Medical Centers, Kansas City, MO
Primary Contact: John W. Bluford, President and Chief Executive Officer
COO: Charlie Shields, Chief Operating Officer
CFO: Allen Johnson, Chief Financial Officer
CFO: Daniel J. Williams, Senior Director Finance
CMO: Mark Steele, M.D., Chief Medical Officer
CIO: Mitzi Cardenas, Chief Information Officer
CHR: CiCi Rojas, Vice President Community Engagement
CNO: Lynette Wheeler, MSN, Chief Nursing Officer
Web address: www.trumed.org
**Control:** Other not–for–profit (including NFP Corporation) **Service:** General Medical and Surgical

**Staffed Beds:** 333 **Admissions:** 5402 **Census:** 227 **Outpatient Visits:** 396525 **Births:** 1110 **Total Expense ($000):** 125537 **Payroll Expense ($000):** 57938 **Personnel:** 913

⊠ **TWO RIVERS BEHAVIORAL HEALTH SYSTEM (264017)**, 5121 Raytown Road, Zip 64133–2141; tel. 816/382–6300 **A**1 10 **F**4 5 29 30 34 35 38 75 86 87 98 99 101 102 103 104 105 130 132 134 143 **P**6 **S** Universal Health Services, Inc., King of Prussia, PA
Primary Contact: Scott Hullinger, Chief Executive Officer
CFO: Michael Delaney, Chief Financial Officer
CMO: Shahbaz Khan, M.D., Medical Director
CIO: Michael Witt, Director of Information Technology
CHR: Troy Angell, Director Human Resources
CNO: Rebecca Clark, Chief Nursing Officer
Web address: www.tworivershospital.com
**Control:** Corporation, Investor–owned, for–profit **Service:** Psychiatric

**Staffed Beds:** 105 **Admissions:** 3156 **Census:** 51 **Outpatient Visits:** 5644 **Births:** 0 **Total Expense ($000):** 14940 **Payroll Expense ($000):** 7481 **Personnel:** 106

**VETERANS AFFAIRS MEDICAL CENTER** See Kansas City Veterans Affairs Medical Center

☐ **TWIN RIVERS REGIONAL MEDICAL CENTER (260015)**, 1301 First Street, Zip 63857–2508, Mailing Address: P.O. Box 728, Zip 63857–0728; tel. 573/888–4522 **A**1 9 10 **F**3 11 13 15 18 29 30 31 35 40 50 56 57 59 60 64 68 70 75 76 78 79 81 85 89 90 98 99 100 101 102 103 104 107 108 110 111 114 115 117 119 127 129 130 135 146 147 148 **S** Health Management Associates, Naples, FL
Primary Contact: Kenneth James, Chief Executive Officer
CFO: Tiffany Berry, Chief Financial Officer
CHR: Sherry Malone, Director Human Resources
Web address: www.twinriversmedctr.com
**Control:** Corporation, Investor–owned, for–profit **Service:** General Medical and Surgical

**Staffed Beds:** 116 **Admissions:** 3954 **Census:** 35 **Outpatient Visits:** 75044 **Births:** 412 **Total Expense ($000):** 32657 **Payroll Expense ($000):** 15177 **Personnel:** 344

★ ○ **NORTHEAST REGIONAL MEDICAL CENTER (260022)**, 315 South Osteopathy, Zip 63501–6401, Mailing Address: P.O. Box C8502, Zip 63501–8599; tel. 660/785–1000 **A**9 10 11 12 13 **F**3 12 13 15 18 20 28 29 30 34 35 39 40 43 45 46 49 50 51 53 57 59 60 62 64 68 70 74 75 76 77 79 81 82 85 86 87 89 90 93 107 108 110 111 114 115 119 127 129 130 131 132 133 135 146 147 148 **P**5 **S** Community Health Systems, Inc., Franklin, TN
Primary Contact: Eric A. Barber, Chief Executive Officer
COO: Ranee C. Brayton, R.N., Associate Chief Executive Officer
CFO: Tom Luebbering, Chief Financial Officer
CMO: John Bailey, D.O., Chief of Staff
CIO: Chad Tatro, Supervisor Information Systems
CHR: Jim Bergman, Director Human Resources
CNO: Cindy Carter, Chief Nursing Officer
Web address: www.nermc.com
**Control:** Corporation, Investor–owned, for–profit **Service:** General Medical and Surgical

**Staffed Beds:** 115 **Admissions:** 3212 **Census:** 35 **Outpatient Visits:** 78871 **Births:** 473 **Total Expense ($000):** 50784 **Payroll Expense ($000):** 18781 **Personnel:** 467

⊠ **SSM ST. JOSEPH HOSPITAL WEST (260200)**, 100 Medical Plaza, Zip 63367–1366; tel. 636/625–5200 **A**1 9 10 **F**3 11 13 15 17 20 22 28 29 30 31 34 35 36 38 40 41 43 44 49 50 51 53 55 56 57 59 60 61 64 68 70 73 74 75 76 78 79 81 82 84 85 86 87 89 102 107 108 110 111 114 118 119 120 121 129 130 132 135 146 147 148 **P**6 8 **S** SSM Health Care, Saint Louis, MO
Primary Contact: Lisle Wescott, President
CFO: Hal Holder, Director Finance
CMO: Michael Handler, M.D., Vice President Medical Administration
CIO: Sharon Gardner, Manager Information Systems
CHR: Annie Kessler, Human Resources Consultant
Web address: www.ssmstjoseph.com
**Control:** Church–operated, Nongovernment, not–for profit **Service:** General Medical and Surgical

**Staffed Beds:** 126 **Admissions:** 8485 **Census:** 79 **Outpatient Visits:** 134404 **Births:** 1108 **Total Expense ($000):** 113631 **Payroll Expense ($000):** 47185 **Personnel:** 722

**BARTON COUNTY MEMORIAL HOSPITAL (261325)**, 29 N.W. First Lane, Zip 64759–8105; tel. 417/681–5100 **A**9 10 18 **F**3 11 15 18 28 30 34 35 36 39 40 44 45 50 57 59 64 68 75 77 79 81 85 86 87 89 90 93 97 107 108 110 111 114 119 127 128 129 130 131 132 133 135 143 146 148
Primary Contact: Wendy Duvall, Chief Executive Officer
COO: Virginia Rutledge, Assistant Administrator
CIO: Brad Butler, Network Administrator
CHR: Sheila Boice, Director Human Resources
Web address: www.bcmh.net
**Control:** County–Government, nonfederal **Service:** General Medical and Surgical

**Staffed Beds:** 25 **Admissions:** 1478 **Census:** 16 **Outpatient Visits:** 61449 **Births:** 0 **Total Expense ($000):** 20170 **Payroll Expense ($000):** 7722 **Personnel:** 208

⊠ **MERCY HOSPITAL LEBANON (260059)**, 100 Hospital Drive, Zip 65536–9210; tel. 417/533–6100 **A**1 9 10 **F**3 11 13 15 28 29 30 31 32 35 36 37 40 50 53 57 59 64 65 68 70 71 75 76 77 78 79 81 82 83 85 86 87 89 90 93 107 108 110 111 114 119 129 130 131 132 133 135 144 146 147 148 **P**6 **S** Mercy Health, Chesterfield, MO
Primary Contact: Michael J. Gillen, FACHE, President
CFO: Douglas M. Hoban, Vice President and Chief Financial Officer
Web address: www.stjohnslebanon.com
**Control:** Church–operated, Nongovernment, not–for profit **Service:** General Medical and Surgical

**Staffed Beds:** 62 **Admissions:** 2527 **Census:** 19 **Outpatient Visits:** 145078 **Births:** 383 **Total Expense ($000):** 60868 **Payroll Expense ($000):** 26423 **Personnel:** 541

*Many Facility Codes have changed. Please refer to the AHA Guide Code Chart.*          © 2013 AHA Guide

**LEE'S SUMMIT—Jackson County**

☒ **LEE'S SUMMIT MEDICAL CENTER (260190)**, 2100 S.E. Blue Parkway, Zip 64063–1007; tel. 816/282–5000 **A**1 9 10 **F**3 15 18 20 22 28 29 30 31 34 40 43 49 57 59 60 64 65 68 69 70 74 75 77 78 79 81 82 84 85 87 93 107 108 110 111 114 119 129 130 131 132 145 146 148 **S** HCA, Nashville, TN
Primary Contact: Jacqueline DeSouza, Chief Executive Officer
CFO: Heath King, Chief Financial Officer
CIO: Evan Kenney, Manager Information Technology Systems
CHR: DeeDee Hawman, Director Human Resources
Web address: www.leessummitmedicalcenter.com
**Control:** Corporation, Investor–owned, for–profit **Service:** General Medical and Surgical

| | |
|---|---|
| **Staffed Beds:** 64 **Admissions:** 3519 **Census:** 33 **Outpatient Visits:** 93128 **Births:** 0 **Total Expense ($000):** 59234 **Payroll Expense ($000):** 27233 **Personnel:** 305 | |

☒ **SAINT LUKE'S EAST HOSPITAL (260216)**, 100 N.E. Saint Luke's Boulevard, Zip 64086–6000; tel. 816/347–5000 **A**1 9 10 **F**3 13 15 17 18 20 22 26 28 29 30 31 34 35 38 40 43 45 49 50 56 57 59 60 64 68 70 73 74 75 76 78 79 80 81 82 84 85 86 87 92 93 94 96 107 108 110 111 114 115 117 118 119 126 129 130 132 145 146 147 148 **S** Saint Luke's Health System, Kansas City, MO
Primary Contact: Ronald L. Baker, Chief Executive Officer
COO: Gloria Solis, R.N., Chief Operating Officer and Chief Nursing Officer
Web address: www.saint–lukes.org
**Control:** Church–operated, Nongovernment, not–for profit **Service:** General Medical and Surgical

| | |
|---|---|
| **Staffed Beds:** 125 **Admissions:** 8151 **Census:** 79 **Outpatient Visits:** 110290 **Births:** 1529 **Total Expense ($000):** 126957 **Payroll Expense ($000):** 45853 **Personnel:** 742 | |

**LEXINGTON—Lafayette County**

☒ **LAFAYETTE REGIONAL HEALTH CENTER (261320)**, 1500 State Street, Zip 64067–1107; tel. 660/259–2203 **A**1 9 10 18 **F**11 15 29 31 40 49 64 68 70 75 78 79 81 85 93 107 110 111 114 116 119 127 129 130 133 147 **P**6 **S** HCA, Nashville, TN
Primary Contact: Darrel Box, Chief Executive Officer
CFO: Teri James, Chief Financial Officer
CHR: Lee Tagai, Director Human Resources
CNO: Kim Leakey, R.N., Chief Nursing Officer
Web address: www.lafayetteregionalhealthcenter.com
**Control:** Corporation, Investor–owned, for–profit **Service:** General Medical and Surgical

| | |
|---|---|
| **Staffed Beds:** 25 **Admissions:** 1124 **Census:** 11 **Outpatient Visits:** 80958 **Births:** 0 **Total Expense ($000):** 22641 **Payroll Expense ($000):** 10110 **Personnel:** 204 | |

**LIBERTY—Clay County**

☒ **LIBERTY HOSPITAL (260177)**, 2525 Glenn Hendren Drive, Zip 64068–9600, Mailing Address: P.O. Box 1002, Zip 64069–1002; tel. 816/781–7200 **A**1 2 9 10 **F**3 9 11 13 15 18 20 22 24 28 29 30 31 34 35 40 43 44 47 49 56 59 62 63 64 66 68 69 70 73 74 75 76 77 78 79 80 81 82 84 85 86 87 89 92 93 96 97 102 107 108 110 111 114 115 118 119 126 129 130 132 143 146 148
Primary Contact: David Feess, President and Chief Executive Officer
CFO: Gregg Mages, Interim Chief Financial Officer
CHR: Patti L. Downey, Vice President, Human Resources
Web address: www.Libertyhospital.org
**Control:** Hospital district or authority, Government, nonfederal **Service:** General Medical and Surgical

| | |
|---|---|
| **Staffed Beds:** 250 **Admissions:** 12386 **Census:** 135 **Outpatient Visits:** 244564 **Births:** 1111 **Total Expense ($000):** 177733 **Payroll Expense ($000):** 87097 **Personnel:** 1336 | |

**LOUISIANA—Pike County**

☒ **PIKE COUNTY MEMORIAL HOSPITAL (261333)**, 2305 Georgia Street, Zip 63353–2559; tel. 573/754–5531 **A**1 9 10 18 **F**3 7 11 15 18 28 29 30 34 35 40 50 53 54 56 57 59 64 65 68 74 75 77 79 81 85 86 87 89 90 93 97 107 114 127 130 131 132 133 147 148
Primary Contact: Lorraine L. Harness, Administrator
CFO: Ann Perry, Chief Financial Officer
CIO: Jeremy Gruen, Director Information Systems
CHR: Dan Jones, Director Human Resources
Web address: www.pcmh–mo.org
**Control:** County–Government, nonfederal **Service:** General Medical and Surgical

| | |
|---|---|
| **Staffed Beds:** 25 **Admissions:** 642 **Census:** 6 **Outpatient Visits:** 37448 **Births:** 0 **Total Expense ($000):** 12022 **Payroll Expense ($000):** 6904 **Personnel:** 163 | |

**MACON—Macon County**

★ **SAMARITAN MEMORIAL HOSPITAL (261313)**, 1205 North Missouri Street, Zip 63552–2095; tel. 660/385–8700 **A**9 10 18 **F**3 7 8 15 28 29 30 31 34 35 40 45 53 56 57 58 59 60 61 63 64 65 66 68 71 75 77 78 79 81 82 83 84 85 86 93 94 107 111 115 119 127 128 129 130 131 132 133 135 143 146 148 **P**5
Primary Contact: Bernard A. Orman, Jr., Administrator
CFO: Susan Spencer, Chief Financial Officer
CHR: Suzanne Britt, Director Human Resources
Web address: www.samaritanhospital.net
**Control:** County–Government, nonfederal **Service:** General Medical and Surgical

| | |
|---|---|
| **Staffed Beds:** 25 **Admissions:** 704 **Census:** 12 **Outpatient Visits:** 60604 **Births:** 0 **Total Expense ($000):** 20397 **Payroll Expense ($000):** 8067 **Personnel:** 168 | |

**MARSHALL—Saline County**

★ **FITZGIBBON HOSPITAL (260142)**, 2305 South 65 Highway, Zip 65340–0250, Mailing Address: P.O. Box 250, Zip 65340–0250; tel. 660/886–7431 **A**5 9 10 **F**3 11 13 15 30 31 35 40 45 53 57 59 62 63 64 68 70 74 75 76 77 78 79 81 82 84 85 87 90 93 98 103 104 107 110 111 115 118 120 121 122 127 128 129 130 131 132 133 143 146 147 148
Primary Contact: Ronald A. Ott, Chief Executive Officer
COO: Dennis Sousley, Vice President of Clinical Services
CFO: Roberta Nienhueser, Chief Financial Officer
CMO: Darin Haug, D.O., Chief Medical Officer
CIO: Tom Jones, Manager Information Technology
CHR: Myron Lite, Director Human Resources
CNO: Kathryn Lynne Ott, MSN, Vice President Patient Care Services/Chief Nursing Officer
Web address: www.fitzgibbon.org
**Control:** Other not–for–profit (including NFP Corporation) **Service:** General Medical and Surgical

| | |
|---|---|
| **Staffed Beds:** 52 **Admissions:** 2439 **Census:** 22 **Outpatient Visits:** 104897 **Births:** 292 **Total Expense ($000):** 35298 **Payroll Expense ($000):** 19858 **Personnel:** 520 | |

**MARYLAND HEIGHTS—St. Louis County**

★ **RANKEN JORDAN – A PEDIATRIC SPECIALTY HOSPITAL (263303)**, 11365 Dorsett Road, Zip 63043–3411; tel. 314/872–6400 **A**9 10 **F**1 3 12 16 29 30 32 35 44 50 64 80 82 86 87 89 90 91 92 93 94 96 99 104 130 132 143 146 148 **P**6
Primary Contact: Laureen K. Tanner, R.N., MSN, FACHE, President and Chief Executive Officer
COO: Brett Moorehouse, FACHE, Vice President and Chief Operating Officer
CFO: Jean Bardwell, Vice President and Chief Financial Officer
CMO: Nicholas Holekamp, M.D., Medical Director
CIO: Jean Bardwell, Vice President and Chief Financial Officer
CHR: Thomas M. Irvin, Administrator Human Resources
Web address: www.rankenjordan.org
**Control:** Other not–for–profit (including NFP Corporation) **Service:** Children's rehabilitation

| | |
|---|---|
| **Staffed Beds:** 34 **Admissions:** 244 **Census:** 29 **Outpatient Visits:** 6986 **Births:** 0 **Total Expense ($000):** 25261 **Payroll Expense ($000):** 13108 **Personnel:** 252 | |

**MARYVILLE—Nodaway County**

☒ **ST. FRANCIS HOSPITAL AND HEALTH SERVICES (260050)**, 2016 South Main Street, Zip 64468–2655; tel. 660/562–2600 **A**1 9 10 20 **F**3 8 11 13 15 18 28 29 30 34 35 38 40 45 57 59 64 65 70 75 76 77 79 81 82 84 85 89 93 96 97 98 99 100 101 102 103 104 105 107 111 114 119 127 128 130 131 133 135 141 142 146 **P**6 **S** SSM Health Care, Saint Louis, MO
Primary Contact: Gray Cox, President
COO: Cathy New, Vice President Clinical Services
CFO: Jocelyn Skidmore, Director Finance
CMO: Shellie Faris, M.D., President Medical Staff
CIO: Dave Lewis, Director Information Services
CHR: Martha Archer, Director Human Resources
Web address: www.stfrancismaryville.com
**Control:** Church–operated, Nongovernment, not–for profit **Service:** General Medical and Surgical

| | |
|---|---|
| **Staffed Beds:** 57 **Admissions:** 1433 **Census:** 17 **Outpatient Visits:** 84388 **Births:** 319 **Total Expense ($000):** 58687 **Payroll Expense ($000):** 26862 **Personnel:** 402 | |

**MO**

---

| Hospital, Medicare Provider Number, Address, Telephone, Approval, Facility, and Physician Codes, Health Care System | |
|---|---|
| ★ American Hospital Association (AHA) membership | ○ Healthcare Facilities Accreditation Program |
| ☐ The Joint Commission accreditation    ◇ DNV Healthcare Inc. accreditation | △ Commission on Accreditation of Rehabilitation Facilities (CARF) accreditation |

## MEMPHIS—Scotland County

★ **SCOTLAND COUNTY HOSPITAL (261310)**, 450 Sigler Avenue,
Zip 63555–1726; tel. 660/465–8511, (Nonreporting) **A**9 10 18
Primary Contact: Marcia R. Dial, Administrator and Chief Executive Officer
CFO: Sheryl Templeton, Chief Financial Officer
CMO: Randy Tobler, M.D., Chief Medical Officer
CIO: Angela Schmitter, Director Health Information Management
CHR: Tammy Newland, Coordinator Human Resources
Web address: www.scotlandcountyhospital.com
**Control:** Hospital district or authority, Government, nonfederal **Service:** General Medical and Surgical

**Staffed Beds:** 25

**SCOTLAND COUNTY MEMORIAL HOSPITAL** See Scotland County Hospital

## MEXICO—Audrain County

☐ △ **AUDRAIN MEDICAL CENTER (260064)**, 620 East Monroe Street,
Zip 65265–2919; tel. 573/582–5000 **A**1 2 7 9 10 **F**3 11 13 15 18 20 22 26
28 29 30 31 34 40 45 53 54 57 59 64 65 70 73 74 75 76 77 78 79 81 85
86 87 89 90 93 107 108 110 111 114 118 119 121 127 129 130 131 132
146 147 **P**6 **S** SSM Health Care, Saint Louis, MO
Primary Contact: David A. Neuendorf, FACHE, President and Chief Executive Officer
COO: David A. Neuendorf, FACHE, President and Chief Executive Officer
CFO: Greg Shaw, Vice President and Chief Financial Officer
CMO: Michael Quinlan, M.D., Chief of Staff
CIO: Dawn Evans, Manager Information Technology
CHR: Christy Smiley, Director Human Resources
Web address: www.audrainmedicalcenter.com
**Control:** Other not–for–profit (including NFP Corporation) **Service:** General Medical and Surgical

**Staffed Beds:** 49 **Admissions:** 2117 **Census:** 19 **Outpatient Visits:** 151277
**Births:** 146 **Total Expense ($000):** 54711 **Payroll Expense ($000):** 22466
**Personnel:** 443

## MILAN—Sullivan County

★ **SULLIVAN COUNTY MEMORIAL HOSPITAL (261306)**, 630 West Third Street,
Zip 63556–1076; tel. 660/265–4212, (Total facility includes 14 beds in nursing home–type unit) **A**9 10 18 **F**28 29 32 34 35 40 53 57 59 67 68 75 77 79 87
97 107 111 114 119 127 128 130 133 146 147 148 **P**5 6
Primary Contact: Jerry Dover, Chief Executive Officer
COO: Amy J. Michael, Chief Operating Officer
CFO: Amy J. Michael, Chief Operating Officer
CMO: Thomas Williams, D.O., Chief of Staff
CIO: Jody Biston, Director Risk Management and Physician Clinic
CHR: Valerie Johnson, Director Human Resources
CHR: Billie Ryals, Human Resources Director
CNO: Carol Fordyce, Director of Patient Care Services
Web address: www.scmhospital.org
**Control:** County–Government, nonfederal **Service:** General Medical and Surgical

**Staffed Beds:** 39 **Admissions:** 331 **Census:** 24 **Outpatient Visits:** 18858
**Births:** 0 **Total Expense ($000):** 6367 **Payroll Expense ($000):** 3146
**Personnel:** 91

## MOBERLY—Randolph County

☒ **MOBERLY REGIONAL MEDICAL CENTER (260074)**, 1515 Union Avenue,
Zip 65270–9449; tel. 660/263–8400 **A**1 9 10 20 **F**3 13 15 18 20 22 26 28
29 34 35 38 39 40 44 45 46 49 50 51 53 56 57 59 64 65 70 74 75 76 77
79 80 81 85 86 87 89 93 97 98 100 103 107 108 110 111 114 117 118
119 127 129 130 131 132 133 135 146 147 148 **S** Community Health Systems, Inc., Franklin, TN
Primary Contact: Christian Jones, Chief Executive Officer
CFO: Tracey Matheis, Chief Financial Officer
CMO: Philip Stitzer, D.O., Chief Medical Officer
CIO: Doris Whelan, Chief Information Officer
CHR: Tim Clark, Director Human Resources
Web address: www.moberlyhospital.com
**Control:** Corporation, Investor–owned, for–profit **Service:** General Medical and Surgical

**Staffed Beds:** 94 **Admissions:** 2867 **Census:** 43 **Outpatient Visits:** 51902
**Births:** 212 **Total Expense ($000):** 46117 **Payroll Expense ($000):** 17243
**Personnel:** 340

## MONETT—Barry County

☐ **COX MONETT (261329)**, 801 North Lincoln Avenue, Zip 65708–1641;
tel. 417/235–3144 **A**1 9 10 18 **F**3 11 13 15 28 29 31 32 34 35 40 45 50 53
56 57 59 64 68 76 77 81 85 89 90 93 107 111 114 119 127 128 129 130
131 133 135 146 147 **P**6 **S** CoxHealth, Springfield, MO
Primary Contact: Genice Maroc, FACHE, Administrator and Chief Executive Officer
CFO: R. Martin Williams, Director Financial Services
CHR: Pamela Foland, Director Human Resources
Web address: www.coxhealth.com
**Control:** Other not–for–profit (including NFP Corporation) **Service:** General Medical and Surgical

**Staffed Beds:** 25 **Admissions:** 828 **Census:** 6 **Outpatient Visits:** 60044
**Births:** 328 **Total Expense ($000):** 24507 **Payroll Expense ($000):** 13340
**Personnel:** 224

## MOUNT VERNON—Lawrence County

☒ △ **MISSOURI REHABILITATION CENTER (262001)**, 600 North Main Street,
Zip 65712–1004; tel. 417/466–3711 **A**1 7 10 **F**1 3 11 28 29 30 44 50 53 57
59 64 68 70 75 77 87 90 91 93 96 119 129 130 135 143 146 148 **P**6
**S** University of Missouri Health Care, Columbia, MO
Primary Contact: Mike Powell, Executive Director
CFO: Amy Baker, Associate Director Finance Services
CMO: Jennie Gorham, D.O., Co–Medical Director
CIO: Tom Collier, Manager Information Systems
CHR: David Thiessen, Associate Director Support Services
CNO: Gail Getzendaner, Interim Director of Nursing
Web address: www.muhealth.org/mrcrehab
**Control:** State–Government, nonfederal **Service:** Long–Term Acute Care hospital

**Staffed Beds:** 63 **Admissions:** 338 **Census:** 35 **Outpatient Visits:** 52138
**Births:** 0 **Total Expense ($000):** 32208 **Payroll Expense ($000):** 17153
**Personnel:** 335

## MOUNTAIN VIEW—Howell County

☒ **MERCY ST. FRANCIS HOSPITAL (261335)**, 100 West Highway 60,
Zip 65548–7125; tel. 417/934–7000 **A**1 9 10 18 **F**11 15 28 29 30 34 40 45
50 57 59 64 75 81 85 89 93 107 110 111 114 119 129 132 133 **P**6 **S** Mercy Health, Chesterfield, MO
Primary Contact: Jonathan O. Wade, President and Chief Executive Officer
CFO: Sherry Clouse Day, CPA, Chief Financial Officer
CMO: Barry Spoon, M.D., Chief of Staff
CIO: Jana Murray, Manager Medical Records
CHR: Tracy Smith, Director Human Resources
Web address: www.stjohns.com/aboutus/stfrancis.aspx
**Control:** Church–operated, Nongovernment, not–for profit **Service:** General Medical and Surgical

**Staffed Beds:** 20 **Admissions:** 469 **Census:** 5 **Outpatient Visits:** 11450
**Births:** 0 **Total Expense ($000):** 13125 **Payroll Expense ($000):** 6631
**Personnel:** 138

## NEOSHO—Newton County

★ **FREEMAN NEOSHO HOSPITAL (261331)**, 113 West Hickory Street,
Zip 64850–1705; tel. 417/455–4352 **A**9 10 18 **F**3 7 11 15 28 29 30 34 35
40 43 44 45 47 56 57 59 64 68 70 75 77 79 81 85 86 87 89 90 93 97 107
111 114 119 128 130 131 132 133 146 148 **S** Freeman Health System, Joplin, MO
Primary Contact: Paula F. Baker, President and Chief Executive Officer
CFO: Steve W. Graddy, Chief Financial Officer
CMO: Rodney McFarland, M.D., Medical Director
CIO: Sue Annesser, Director Information Systems
CHR: Deborah Chiodo, Director Human Resources
Web address: www.freemanhealth.com
**Control:** Other not–for–profit (including NFP Corporation) **Service:** General Medical and Surgical

**Staffed Beds:** 25 **Admissions:** 1706 **Census:** 20 **Outpatient Visits:** 48588
**Births:** 0 **Total Expense ($000):** 15399 **Payroll Expense ($000):** 9557
**Personnel:** 167

## NEVADA—Vernon County

☐ **HEARTLAND BEHAVIORAL HEALTH SERVICES**, 1500 West Ashland Street,
Zip 64772–1710; tel. 417/667–2666 **A**1 **F**98 99 101 102 **S** Universal Health Services, Inc., King of Prussia, PA
Primary Contact: Alyson Wysong–Harder, Chief Executive Officer
CFO: Terri Graves, Chief Financial Officer
CMO: Ahmad Tarar, M.D., Medical Director
CHR: Carri Compton–Ogle, Administrative Officer
Web address: www.heartlandbehavioral.com
**Control:** Corporation, Investor–owned, for–profit **Service:** Psychiatric

**Staffed Beds:** 37 **Admissions:** 1198 **Census:** 32 **Outpatient Visits:** 0 **Births:** 0 **Total Expense ($000):** 14181 **Payroll Expense ($000):** 6887 **Personnel:** 88

**MO**

*Many Facility Codes have changed. Please refer to the AHA Guide Code Chart.*
© 2013 AHA Guide

**NEVADA REGIONAL MEDICAL CENTER (260061)**, 800 South Ash Street, Zip 64772–3223; tel. 417/667-3355 **A**1 9 10 **F**3 11 13 15 18 26 27 28 29 30 31 32 34 35 39 40 41 45 50 54 57 59 62 63 64 65 70 74 75 76 77 78 79 81 82 84 85 86 87 89 90 91 93 94 96 98 101 102 103 104 107 110 111 114 119 127 129 130 131 132 133 135 143 144 146 148 **S** QHR, Brentwood, TN
Primary Contact: Judith K. Feuquay, Chief Executive Officer
CMO: Scott Beard, M.D., Chief of Staff
CIO: Jeffrey Price, Director Information Technology
CHR: Patty Gaughan, Human Resource Administrative Officer
Web address: www.nrmchealth.com
**Control:** City–Government, nonfederal **Service:** General Medical and Surgical

**Staffed Beds:** 71 **Admissions:** 2429 **Census:** 30 **Outpatient Visits:** 72851 **Births:** 304 **Total Expense ($000):** 31020 **Payroll Expense ($000):** 14101 **Personnel:** 350

### NORTH KANSAS CITY—Clay County

**NORTH KANSAS CITY HOSPITAL (260096)**, 2800 Clay Edwards Drive, Zip 64116–3220; tel. 816/691-2000 **A**1 2 5 9 10 **F**3 11 12 13 15–17 18 20 22 24 26 28 29 30 31 34 35 37 38 39 40 43 44 45 46 47 48 49 50 53 57 58 59 62 63 64 70 72 74 75 76 77 78 79 80 81 82 83 84 85 86 87 89 90 93 96 107 108 110 111 114 115 118 119 120 121 123 126 129 130 132 135 146 147
Primary Contact: Peggy Schmitt, President and Chief Executive Officer
COO: Jody Abbott, Senior Vice President and Chief Operating Officer
CFO: Jim McNey, Vice President Finance and Chief Financial Officer
CMO: Gary L. Carter, M.D., Medical Director of Quality
CIO: Art Fisk, Chief Information Officer
CHR: Beverly Johnson, Vice President Human Resources
CNO: Sarah G. Fields, R.N., Vice President Nursing
Web address: www.nkch.org
**Control:** City–Government, nonfederal **Service:** General Medical and Surgical

**Staffed Beds:** 415 **Admissions:** 20060 **Census:** 238 **Outpatient Visits:** 225686 **Births:** 1288 **Total Expense ($000):** 360815 **Payroll Expense ($000):** 143969 **Personnel:** 2405

### OSAGE BEACH—Camden County

**LAKE REGIONAL HEALTH SYSTEM (260186)**, 54 Hospital Drive, Zip 65065–3050; tel. 573/348-8000, (Total facility includes 16 beds in nursing home–type unit) **A**1 2 9 10 **F**3 11 12 13 15 17 18 20 22 24 28 29 30 31 32 34 35 38 40 43 44 45 48 49 50 51 53 57 59 60 62 64 65 68 70 74 75 76 77 78 79 81 82 84 85 86 87 89 93 96 107 108 110 111 114 115 118 119 121 127 128 129 130 131 132 135 144 145 146 148 **P**6
Primary Contact: Michael E. Henze, Chief Executive Officer
COO: Vicki L. Franklin, Senior Vice President and Chief Operating Officer
CFO: David Halsell, Senior Vice President and Chief Financial Officer
CMO: Robert Hyatt, M.D., Senior Vice President Medical Affairs
CIO: Scott Poest, Chief Information Officer
CHR: Tom Williams, Director Human Resources
CNO: Janice L. Dungan, Senior Vice President Clinical Services
Web address: www.lakeregional.com
**Control:** Other not–for–profit (including NFP Corporation) **Service:** General Medical and Surgical

**Staffed Beds:** 116 **Admissions:** 6472 **Census:** 77 **Outpatient Visits:** 286211 **Births:** 700 **Total Expense ($000):** 152138 **Payroll Expense ($000):** 70042 **Personnel:** 1166

### OSCEOLA—St. Clair County

★ **SAC–OSAGE HOSPITAL (260147)**, Junction Highways 13 & Business 13, Zip 64776–0426, Mailing Address: P.O. Box 426, Zip 64776–0426; tel. 417/646-8181 **A**9 10 20 **F**3 7 8 11 15 29 30 34 35 40 49 57 69 75 77 79 81 83 89 90 93 107 111 119 127 128 133 146 **P**6
Primary Contact: Bryan D. Coffey, Chief Executive Officer
CMO: Niko van Zanten, M.D., Chief of Staff
CNO: Patricia Turner, R.N., Director of Nursing
Web address: www.sac-osagehospital.com
**Control:** Hospital district or authority, Government, nonfederal **Service:** General Medical and Surgical

**Staffed Beds:** 47 **Admissions:** 385 **Census:** 5 **Outpatient Visits:** 14183 **Births:** 0 **Total Expense ($000):** 7040 **Payroll Expense ($000):** 3450 **Personnel:** 78

### PERRYVILLE—Perry County

**PERRY COUNTY MEMORIAL HOSPITAL (261311)**, 434 North West Street, Zip 63775–1398; tel. 573/547-2536 **A**1 9 10 18 **F**3 7 8 11 13 15 29 30 31 34 35 40 44 48 51 53 54 56 57 59 62 64 66 68 75 76 77 78 79 81 85 87 89 90 92 93 97 99 100 101 102 103 104 107 111 114 117 119 129 130 131 132 133 135 143 144 145 147 148
Primary Contact: Patrick E. Carron, FACHE, President and Chief Executive Officer
COO: Lee Clinton, FACHE, Vice President Operations
CFO: Randall Wolf, Vice President Finance
CMO: Michael Steele, M.D., Chief of Staff
CIO: Ron Heuring, Director Information Systems
CHR: Christopher Wibbenmeyer, Director Human Resources
Web address: www.pchmo.org
**Control:** Other not–for–profit (including NFP Corporation) **Service:** General Medical and Surgical

**Staffed Beds:** 25 **Admissions:** 959 **Census:** 13 **Outpatient Visits:** 48236 **Births:** 146 **Total Expense ($000):** 26575 **Payroll Expense ($000):** 10992 **Personnel:** 306

### PILOT KNOB—Iron County

**IRON COUNTY HOSPITAL (261336)**, 301 North Highway 21, Zip 63663–0548, Mailing Address: P.O. Box 548, Zip 63663–0548; tel. 573/546-1260 **A**9 10 18 **F**11 15 35 40 57 90 93 107 111 114 119 127 128 129 130 133
Primary Contact: Terry Nichols, Chief Executive Officer
Web address: www.ironhospital.com
**Control:** Hospital district or authority, Government, nonfederal **Service:** General Medical and Surgical

**Staffed Beds:** 15 **Admissions:** 319 **Census:** 4 **Outpatient Visits:** 18211 **Births:** 0 **Total Expense ($000):** 7553 **Payroll Expense ($000):** 2539 **Personnel:** 47

### POPLAR BLUFF—Butler County

**BLACK RIVER MEDICAL CENTER (560227)**, (Acute Care no Surgery), 217 Physicians Park Drive, Zip 63901–3956, Mailing Address: 219 Physicians Park Drive, Zip 63901–3956; tel. 573/727-9080, (Data for 197 days) **A**1 9 **F**3 29 40 41 80 107 108 110 111 119
Primary Contact: Christy Montgomery Shawan, Chief Operating Officer
Web address: www.poplarbluffmedical.com
**Control:** Other not–for–profit (including NFP Corporation) **Service:** Other specialty

**Staffed Beds:** 3 **Admissions:** 134 **Census:** 1 **Outpatient Visits:** 0 **Births:** 0 **Total Expense ($000):** 6630 **Payroll Expense ($000):** 2542 **Personnel:** 120

**JOHN J. PERSHING VETERANS AFFAIRS MEDICAL CENTER**, 1500 North Westwood Boulevard, Zip 63901–3318; tel. 573/686-4151, (Total facility includes 40 beds in nursing home–type unit) **A**1 **F**3 5 11 15 29 30 33 34 36 38 39 40 45 53 54 56 59 62 63 64 65 75 77 79 81 83 84 86 87 90 93 94 97 100 104 107 111 114 119 127 128 129 130 135 143 144 146 147 **S** Department of Veterans Affairs, Washington, DC
Primary Contact: Marjorie Hedstrom, Director
COO: Stan Skorniak, MS, Associate Medical Center Director
CFO: Kristy Siebert, Manager Finance
CMO: Vijayachandran Nair, M.D., Chief of Staff
CIO: Janice Vernon, Supervisory Information Technology Specialist
CHR: Genise Denton, Manager Human Resources
Web address: www.poplarbluff.va.gov
**Control:** Veterans Affairs, Government, federal **Service:** General Medical and Surgical

**Staffed Beds:** 58 **Admissions:** 1521 **Census:** 41 **Outpatient Visits:** 119836 **Births:** 0 **Total Expense ($000):** 114829 **Payroll Expense ($000):** 35001 **Personnel:** 558

MO

---

**Hospital, Medicare Provider Number, Address, Telephone, Approval, Facility, and Physician Codes, Health Care System**

★ American Hospital Association (AHA) membership
☐ The Joint Commission accreditation
◇ DNV Healthcare Inc. accreditation
○ Healthcare Facilities Accreditation Program
△ Commission on Accreditation of Rehabilitation Facilities (CARF) accreditation

✠ △ **POPLAR BLUFF REGIONAL MEDICAL CENTER (260119)**, 3100 Oak Grove Road, Zip 63901, Mailing Address: P.O. Box 88, Zip 63902–0088; tel. 573/776–2000, (Includes POPLAR BLUFF REGIONAL MEDICAL CENTER–SOUTH CAMPUS, 621 Pine Boulevard, tel. 573/785–7721) **A**1 2 7 9 10 19 **F**3 4 11 13 15 17 18 20 22 24 28 29 31 35 40 45 46 49 50 51 53 54 57 59 60 64 65 68 70 74 75 76 77 78 79 81 82 85 87 89 90 93 98 102 107 108 111 114 117 118 119 121 126 127 130 131 132 146 148 **P**6 **S** Health Management Associates, Naples, FL
Primary Contact: Charles L. Stewart, Chief Executive Officer
COO: Lavah Lowe, Chief Operating Officer
CFO: Kevin Fowler, Chief Financial Officer
CMO: Austin Tinsley, M.D., Chief Medical Officer
CIO: Gary Dollins, Director Management Information Systems
CHR: Denise Rushin, Director Human Resources
CNO: Melissa A. Samuelson, R.N., Chief Nurse Executive
Web address: www.poplarbluffregional.com
**Control:** Individual, Investor–owned, for–profit **Service:** General Medical and Surgical

> **Staffed Beds:** 287 **Admissions:** 11395 **Census:** 122 **Outpatient Visits:** 161149 **Births:** 1222 **Total Expense ($000):** 125145 **Payroll Expense ($000):** 41315 **Personnel:** 1001

### POTOSI—Washington County

★ **WASHINGTON COUNTY MEMORIAL HOSPITAL (261308)**, 300 Health Way, Zip 63664–1420; tel. 573/438–5451 **A**9 10 18 **F**3 11 15 28 29 33 34 35 40 45 57 59 64 65 74 75 77 79 81 87 90 93 97 98 104 106 107 108 111 114 119 127 129 130 133 144 145 146 147 148 **P**6
Primary Contact: Leah Osbahr, Administrator
COO: Leah Osbahr, CEO
CFO: Debbie Pratt, Chief Financial Officer
CMO: James Hawk, M.D., Chief of Staff
CMO: James Weber, D.O., Chief of Staff
CIO: Andrew Schrum, Director Information Systems
CHR: Hopie Jenkins, Director Personnel
CNO: Beverly Williams, R.N., Chief Nursing Officer
Web address: www.wcmhosp.org
**Control:** County–Government, nonfederal **Service:** General Medical and Surgical

> **Staffed Beds:** 25 **Admissions:** 821 **Census:** 15 **Outpatient Visits:** 74280 **Births:** 0 **Total Expense ($000):** 22612 **Payroll Expense ($000):** 11525 **Personnel:** 276

### RICHMOND—Ray County

**RAY COUNTY MEMORIAL HOSPITAL (261327)**, 904 Wollard Boulevard, Zip 64085–2229; tel. 816/470–5432 **A**9 10 18 **F**3 11 15 29 40 62 64 68 74 75 78 79 81 82 85 87 93 107 108 110 111 115 116 119 130 133 146
Primary Contact: Robert Littleton, Administrator
CFO: Donald Harr, Controller
CHR: Donna Strain, Director Human Resources
Web address: www.raycountyhospital.com
**Control:** County–Government, nonfederal **Service:** General Medical and Surgical

> **Staffed Beds:** 25 **Admissions:** 916 **Census:** 10 **Outpatient Visits:** 19224 **Births:** 0 **Total Expense ($000):** 16879 **Payroll Expense ($000):** 8516 **Personnel:** 199

### ROLLA—Phelps County

✠ △ **PHELPS COUNTY REGIONAL MEDICAL CENTER (260017)**, 1000 West Tenth Street, Zip 65401–2905; tel. 573/458–8899, (Total facility includes 20 beds in nursing home–type unit) **A**1 2 7 9 10 **F**3 7 8 11 13 15 17 18 20 26 27 28 29 30 31 34 35 39 40 45 47 48 49 51 57 59 60 63 68 70 73 74 75 76 77 78 79 81 85 86 89 90 93 96 98 100 101 102 103 104 107 110 111 114 115 116 117 118 119 121 127 128 129 131 132 135 143 144 146 148
Primary Contact: John Denbo, Chief Executive Officer
COO: Ellis Hawkins, Senior Vice President and Chief Operating Officer
CFO: Edward Clayton, Chief Financial Officer
CMO: Donald James, D.O., Chief Medical Officer
CIO: David Dawdy, Director Information Technology
CHR: Frank A. Lazzaro, III, Chief Human Resources Officer
CNO: Regenia Stull, R.N., Chief Nurse Executive
Web address: www.pcrmc.com
**Control:** County–Government, nonfederal **Service:** General Medical and Surgical

> **Staffed Beds:** 204 **Admissions:** 6775 **Census:** 92 **Outpatient Visits:** 240735 **Births:** 835 **Total Expense ($000):** 123596 **Payroll Expense ($000):** 54952 **Personnel:** 1314

### SAINT CHARLES—St. Charles County

✠ **CENTERPOINTE HOSPITAL (264012)**, 4801 Weldon Spring Parkway, Zip 63304–9101; tel. 636/441–7300 **A**1 9 10 **F**4 5 34 35 38 54 87 98 99 100 101 102 103 104 105 106 130 132 143
Primary Contact: Azfar Malik, M.D., Chief Executive Officer and Chief Medical Officer
COO: Susan Mathis, Chief Operating Officer
CFO: Tariq F. Malik, CPA, Acting Chief Financial Officer
CMO: Azfar Malik, M.D., Chief Executive Officer and Chief Medical Officer
CIO: Jennifer Bourn, Coordinator Health Information Systems
CHR: Kelli White, Manager Human Resources
Web address: www.centerpointehospital.com
**Control:** Corporation, Investor–owned, for–profit **Service:** Psychiatric

> **Staffed Beds:** 150 **Admissions:** 4151 **Census:** 90 **Outpatient Visits:** 57073 **Births:** 0 **Total Expense ($000):** 31231 **Payroll Expense ($000):** 16066 **Personnel:** 348

✠ **PROGRESS WEST HEALTHCARE CENTER (260219)**, Two Progress Point, Zip 63368–2208; tel. 636/344–2273 **A**1 9 10 **F**3 13 15 18 20 22 29 30 40 41 45 49 51 57 59 60 70 76 79 81 85 87 89 107 110 111 115 118 119 130 135 146 **S** BJC HealthCare, Saint Louis, MO
Primary Contact: Larry Tracy, FACHE, President
CFO: Glen Schweagel, Chief Financial Officer
CMO: Kenneth Hacker, M.D., Chief of Staff
CIO: Michael Kelly, Information Systems Account Executive
Web address: www.progresswesthealthcare.org
**Control:** Other not–for–profit (including NFP Corporation) **Service:** General Medical and Surgical

> **Staffed Beds:** 42 **Admissions:** 2854 **Census:** 25 **Outpatient Visits:** 45854 **Births:** 500 **Total Expense ($000):** 60866 **Payroll Expense ($000):** 18608 **Personnel:** 294

✠ **SELECT SPECIALTY HOSPITAL–ST. LOUIS (262013)**, 300 First Capitol Drive, Unit 1, Zip 63301–2844; tel. 636/947–5010 **A**1 9 10 **F**1 29 74 75 77 87 107 148 **S** Select Medical Corporation, Mechanicsburg, PA
Primary Contact: Patrice L. Komoroski, Ph.D., R.N., Chief Executive Officer
Web address: www.selectspecialtyhospitals.com/company/locations/stlouis.aspx
**Control:** Corporation, Investor–owned, for–profit **Service:** Long–Term Acute Care hospital

> **Staffed Beds:** 33 **Admissions:** 364 **Census:** 30 **Outpatient Visits:** 0 **Births:** 0 **Total Expense ($000):** 16821 **Payroll Expense ($000):** 6939 **Personnel:** 113

✠ **SSM ST. JOSEPH HEALTH CENTER (260005)**, 300 First Capitol Drive, Zip 63301–2844; tel. 636/947–5000, (Includes SSM ST. JOSEPH HEALTH CENTER – WENTZVILLE, 500 Medical Drive, Wentzville, Zip 63385–3421; tel. 636/327–1000) **A**1 2 9 10 **F**3 5 11 13 15 17 18 20 22 24 26 28 29 30 31 34 35 36 38 39 40 41 43 44 45 46 49 50 51 53 54 55 56 57 58 59 60 61 64 68 70 73 74 75 76 78 79 81 82 85 86 87 90 96 97 98 99 100 101 102 103 104 105 107 108 110 111 114 118 119 120 121 129 130 132 134 135 143 146 147 148 **P**6 8 **S** SSM Health Care, Saint Louis, MO
Primary Contact: Gaspare Calvaruso, President
COO: Lee Bernstein, Regional Executive Vice President and Chief Operating Officer
CFO: Hal Holder, Vice President Finance
CIO: Margaret Feilner, Director Information Services
CHR: Michael R. Garcia, Vice President Human Resources
Web address: www.ssmstjoseph.com
**Control:** Church–operated, Nongovernment, not–for profit **Service:** General Medical and Surgical

> **Staffed Beds:** 331 **Admissions:** 14182 **Census:** 194 **Outpatient Visits:** 158740 **Births:** 811 **Total Expense ($000):** 181684 **Payroll Expense ($000):** 72614 **Personnel:** 1204

### SAINT JOSEPH—Buchanan County

★ **HEARTLAND LONG TERM ACUTE CARE HOSPITAL (262019)**, 5325 Faraon Street, Zip 64506–3488; tel. 816/271–6000 **A**9 10 **F**1 3 29 86 130
Primary Contact: James Mikes, Administrator
Web address: www.heartland–health.com
**Control:** Other not–for–profit (including NFP Corporation) **Service:** Long–Term Acute Care hospital

> **Staffed Beds:** 41 **Admissions:** 260 **Census:** 26 **Outpatient Visits:** 0 **Births:** 0 **Total Expense ($000):** 12800 **Payroll Expense ($000):** 3680 **Personnel:** 68

*Many Facility Codes have changed. Please refer to the AHA Guide Code Chart.* © 2013 AHA Guide

✠ **HEARTLAND REGIONAL MEDICAL CENTER (260006)**, 5325 Faraon Street, Zip 64506–3488; tel. 816/271–6000 **A**1 2 9 10 20 **F**3 8 9 11 12 13 15 17 18 20 22 24 26 28 29 30 31 33 34 35 36 37 39 40 43 45 47 49 50 53 54 57 58 59 62 63 64 65 66 70 71 74 75 76 77 78 79 80 81 82 84 85 86 87 89 92 93 94 96 97 98 100 102 103 104 107 108 110 111 114 115 118 119 120 121 123 124 129 130 131 135 144 146 147 148 **P**6
Primary Contact: Samuel Mark Laney, M.D., President and Chief Executive Officer
COO: Curt Kretzinger, Chief Operating Officer
CFO: John P. Wilson, Chief Financial Officer
CIO: Joe Boyce, M.D., Chief Information Officer
CHR: Michael Pulido, Process Leader Human Resources
Web address: www.heartland–health.com
**Control:** Other not–for–profit (including NFP Corporation) **Service:** General Medical and Surgical

> **Staffed Beds:** 352 **Admissions:** 17718 **Census:** 208 **Outpatient Visits:** 1064952 **Births:** 1713 **Total Expense ($000):** 443399 **Payroll Expense ($000):** 219737 **Personnel:** 3215

☐ **NORTHWEST MISSOURI PSYCHIATRIC REHABILITATION CENTER (264007)**, 3505 Frederick Avenue, Zip 64506–2914; tel. 816/387–2300 **A**1 10 **F**4 29 34 50 58 59 65 75 77 86 87 98 101 102 103 130 135 146 **P**6
Primary Contact: Denise Norbury, Chief Executive Officer
COO: Mary Attebury, Chief Operating Officer
CFO: Randy Riley, Fiscal and Administrative Manager
CMO: James B. Reynolds, M.D., Medical Director
CIO: Eduardo Abaricia, Director Information Technology
CHR: Mary Blakey Gorman, Director Human Resources
Web address: www.dmh.missouri.gov/hr/faclist.htm
**Control:** State–Government, nonfederal **Service:** Psychiatric

> **Staffed Beds:** 108 **Admissions:** 50 **Census:** 108 **Outpatient Visits:** 0 **Births:** 0 **Total Expense ($000):** 21296 **Payroll Expense ($000):** 10435 **Personnel:** 290

### SAINT LOUIS—St. Louis City County

✠ **BARNES–JEWISH HOSPITAL (260032)**, 1 Barnes–Jewish Hospital Plaza, Zip 63110–1003; tel. 314/747–3000, (Total facility includes 120 beds in nursing home–type unit) **A**1 2 3 5 8 9 10 **F**3 4 8 9 11 12 13 14 15 16 17 18 19 20 21 22 23 24 25 26 28 29 30 31 34 35 36 37 38 39 40 43 44 45 46 47 48 49 50 51 52 53 54 55 56 57 58 59 60 61 64 65 66 68 70 71 73 74 75 76 77 78 79 80 81 82 84 85 86 87 89 90 91 92 93 94 95 96 97 98 100 101 102 103 104 105 107 108 109 110 111 112 114 115 116 117 118 119 120 121 123 124 126 128 129 130 131 132 134 135 136 137 138 139 140 141 142 143 144 145 146 147 148 **P**6 **S** BJC HealthCare, Saint Louis, MO
Primary Contact: Richard J. Liekweg, President
CFO: Mark Krieger, Vice President and Chief Financial Officer
CMO: John Lynch, M.D., Vice President and Chief Medical Officer
CIO: Jerry Vuchak, Vice President Information Systems
CHR: John Beatty, Vice President Human Resources
CNO: Coreen Vlodarchyk, R.N., Vice President, Patient Care Services and Chief Nursing Officer
Web address: www.barnesjewish.org
**Control:** Other not–for–profit (including NFP Corporation) **Service:** General Medical and Surgical

> **Staffed Beds:** 1310 **Admissions:** 57461 **Census:** 941 **Outpatient Visits:** 696744 **Births:** 3283 **Total Expense ($000):** 2325054 **Payroll Expense ($000):** 529312 **Personnel:** 9759

✠ **BARNES–JEWISH WEST COUNTY HOSPITAL (260162)**, 12634 Olive Boulevard, Zip 63141–6337; tel. 314/996–8000 **A**1 3 5 9 10 **F**3 12 15 18 29 30 34 35 40 46 47 49 50 51 53 57 59 64 65 68 70 74 75 77 78 79 81 82 85 90 93 100 107 108 111 114 115 117 119 120 121 126 129 130 131 146 **S** BJC HealthCare, Saint Louis, MO
Primary Contact: Doug Black, President
CFO: Diane M. Glen, Assistant Administrator
CMO: Sam B. Bhayani, Chief Medical Officer
CIO: Jerry Vuchak, Vice President Information Systems
CNO: Marianne Fournie, R.N., Chief Nursing Officer
Web address: www.barnesjewishwestcounty.org
**Control:** Other not–for–profit (including NFP Corporation) **Service:** General Medical and Surgical

> **Staffed Beds:** 77 **Admissions:** 2906 **Census:** 27 **Outpatient Visits:** 106689 **Births:** 0 **Total Expense ($000):** 141955 **Payroll Expense ($000):** 28402 **Personnel:** 435

✠ **CHRISTIAN HOSPITAL (260180)**, 11133 Dunn Road, Zip 63136–6119; tel. 314/653–5000 **A**1 2 9 10 **F**3 5 7 8 11 15 17 18 20 22 24 26 28 29 30 31 34 35 40 42 45 46 47 49 50 51 53 54 56 57 58 59 60 63 65 68 69 70 71 74 75 77 78 79 80 81 82 84 85 86 87 90 92 93 94 96 98 100 101 102 103 104 105 107 110 111 114 115 116 117 118 119 120 121 123 126 129 130 132 135 146 147 148 **P**6 **S** BJC HealthCare, Saint Louis, MO
Primary Contact: Ronald B. McMullen, President
CMO: Sebastian Rueckert, M.D., Chief Medical Officer
CIO: Michael Kelly, Vice President
CHR: Bryan Hartwick, Vice President Human Resources
CNO: Jennifer Cordia, Vice President and Chief Nursing Executive
Web address: www.christianhospital.org
**Control:** Other not–for–profit (including NFP Corporation) **Service:** General Medical and Surgical

> **Staffed Beds:** 258 **Admissions:** 15672 **Census:** 223 **Outpatient Visits:** 284215 **Births:** 0 **Total Expense ($000):** 288688 **Payroll Expense ($000):** 106559 **Personnel:** 1708

★ ○ **DES PERES HOSPITAL (260176)**, 2345 Dougherty Ferry Road, Zip 63122–3313; tel. 314/966–9100 **A**3 5 9 10 11 12 13 **F**3 12 15 17 18 20 22 24 26 29 30 31 34 35 36 40 44 49 50 54 56 57 58 59 60 64 68 69 70 74 75 77 79 81 85 86 87 93 103 107 111 114 119 130 131 132 135 143 146 148 **S** TENET Healthcare Corporation, Dallas, TX
Primary Contact: John A. Grah, JD, FACHE, Chief Executive Officer
COO: Benson Chacko, Chief Operating Officer
CFO: Rhonda Rogers, Chief Financial Officer
CMO: Karen Webb, M.D., Chief Medical Officer
CIO: Kay Hannon, Director Information Systems
CHR: Ron Birlew, Director Human Resources
Web address: www.despereshospital.com
**Control:** Corporation, Investor–owned, for–profit **Service:** General Medical and Surgical

> **Staffed Beds:** 143 **Admissions:** 5588 **Census:** 62 **Outpatient Visits:** 31212 **Births:** 0 **Total Expense ($000):** 115282 **Payroll Expense ($000):** 35412 **Personnel:** 616

☐ **HAWTHORN CHILDREN PSYCHIATRIC HOSPITAL**, 1901 Pennsylvania, Zip 63133–1325; tel. 314/512–7800 **A**1 **F**98 99 106 **P**6
Primary Contact: Laurent D. Javois, Regional Executive Officer
COO: Marcia F. Perry, Chief Operating Officer
CFO: James D. Martin, Chief Financial Officer
CMO: Joshua Calhoun, M.D., Medical Director
CIO: Richard Moore, Director Information Technology
CHR: Donna Harris, Director Human Resources
Web address: www.dmh.missouri.gov/hcph/
**Control:** State–Government, nonfederal **Service:** Children's hospital psychiatric

> **Staffed Beds:** 52 **Admissions:** 139 **Census:** 39 **Outpatient Visits:** 0 **Births:** 0 **Total Expense ($000):** 12483 **Payroll Expense ($000):** 7416 **Personnel:** 222

✠ **KINDRED HOSPITAL–ST. LOUIS (262010)**, 4930 Lindell Boulevard, Zip 63108–1510; tel. 314/361–8700, (Includes KINDRED HOSPITAL ST. LOUIS–ST. ANTHONY'S, 10018 Kennerly Road, 3rd Floor, Zip 63128; tel. 314/525–8100; Robert S. Adcock, Chief Executive Officer) **A**1 9 10 **F**1 3 29 77 80 85 130 148 **S** Kindred Healthcare, Louisville, KY
Primary Contact: Stacy M. Howard, R.N., Chief Executive Officer
COO: Dakota Redd, R.N., Chief Clinical Officer
CFO: Maureen Roach, Senior Chief Financial Officer
CMO: Michael Holtzman, M.D., Medical Director
CIO: Thomas C. Christman, Director Plant Operations
CHR: Cindy Sander, Coordinator Human Resources
Web address: www.kindredstlouis.com/
**Control:** Corporation, Investor–owned, for–profit **Service:** Long–Term Acute Care hospital

> **Staffed Beds:** 98 **Admissions:** 689 **Census:** 51 **Outpatient Visits:** 0 **Births:** 0 **Total Expense ($000):** 30779 **Payroll Expense ($000):** 11519 **Personnel:** 198

MO

---

**Hospital, Medicare Provider Number, Address, Telephone, Approval, Facility, and Physician Codes, Health Care System**

★ American Hospital Association (AHA) membership
☐ The Joint Commission accreditation  ◇ DNV Healthcare Inc. accreditation
○ Healthcare Facilities Accreditation Program
△ Commission on Accreditation of Rehabilitation Facilities (CARF) accreditation

⊠ **MERCY HOSPITAL ST. LOUIS (260020)**, 615 South New Ballas Road, Zip 63141–8277; tel. 314/569–6000, (Includes MERCY CHILDREN'S HOSPITAL ST. LOUIS, 615 South New Ballas Road, Zip 63141–8221; tel. 314/251–6000), (Total facility includes 120 beds in nursing home–type unit) **A**1 2 3 5 8 9 10 **F**1 3 4 5 8 11 12 13 14 15 16 17 18 19 20 22 24 25 26 28 29 30 31 32 33 34 35 36 38 39 40 41 43 45 46 47 48 49 50 51 52 53 54 55 56 57 58 59 60 61 64 66 67 68 69 70 71 72 73 74 75 76 77 78 79 80 81 82 84 85 86 87 88 89 90 92 93 94 96 97 98 99 100 101 102 103 104 105 106 107 108 110 111 114 115 116 117 118 119 120 121 123 124 126 128 129 130 131 132 134 135 143 144 146 147 148 **P**6 8 **S** Mercy Health, Chesterfield, MO
Primary Contact: Jeffrey A. Johnston, President
COO: Eric J. Eoloff, Chief Operating Officer
CFO: Cheryl Matejka, Chief Financial Officer
CMO: Paul Hintze, M.D., Vice President Medical Affairs
CIO: Eugene Roth, Vice President Information Services
CHR: Rocky Ruello, Vice President Human Resources
Web address: www.mercy.net/stlouismo
**Control:** Other not–for–profit (including NFP Corporation) **Service:** General Medical and Surgical

| | | |
|---|---|---|
| **Staffed Beds:** 979 **Admissions:** 39926 **Census:** 599 **Outpatient Visits:** 861442 **Births:** 7889 **Total Expense ($000):** 721215 **Payroll Expense ($000):** 276346 **Personnel:** 4556 | | |

☐ **METROPOLITAN ST. LOUIS PSYCHIATRIC CENTER (264025)**, 5351 Delmar, Zip 63112–3198; tel. 314/877–0500, (Nonreporting) **A**1 3 5 10 **S**11 30 98 130 146
Primary Contact: Laurent D. Javois, Regional Executive Officer
COO: Anthony J. Cuneo, Chief Operating Officer
CFO: James D. Martin, Chief Financial Officer
CIO: Richard Moore, Director Information Technology
CHR: Donna Harris, Director Human Resources
Web address: www.dmh.missouri.gov/mpc
**Control:** State–Government, nonfederal **Service:** Psychiatric

| | | |
|---|---|---|
| **Staffed Beds:** 50 **Admissions:** 68 **Census:** 42 **Outpatient Visits:** 0 **Births:** 0 **Total Expense ($000):** 13265 **Payroll Expense ($000):** 6504 **Personnel:** 183 | | |

⊠ **MISSOURI BAPTIST MEDICAL CENTER (260108)**, 3015 North Ballas Road, Zip 63131–2329; tel. 314/996–5000 **A**1 2 3 5 9 10 **F**3 11 13 14 17 18 19 20 22 24 26 29 30 31 34 35 40 41 45 46 48 49 50 51 52 54 55 57 58 59 60 61 64 65 68 70 71 72 74 75 76 77 78 79 81 83 84 85 86 87 89 90 93 94 96 107 108 109 110 111 114 115 116 119 120 121 123 124 126 130 131 132 145 146 147 148 **P**6 **S** BJC HealthCare, Saint Louis, MO
Primary Contact: John Antes, President
CFO: Augusto A. Noronha, Vice President Finance and Chief Financial Officer
CMO: Timothy Ranney, M.D., Vice President Medical Affairs and Chief Medical Officer
CIO: Derrick Marcum, Director Information Systems
CHR: Sandra G. Young, Vice President Human Resources
CNO: Tim Mislan, MS, Vice President Patient Care Services
Web address: www.missouribaptistmedicalcenter.org
**Control:** Other not–for–profit (including NFP Corporation) **Service:** General Medical and Surgical

| | | |
|---|---|---|
| **Staffed Beds:** 445 **Admissions:** 24048 **Census:** 255 **Outpatient Visits:** 312871 **Births:** 4096 **Total Expense ($000):** 685136 **Payroll Expense ($000):** 157156 **Personnel:** 2447 | | |

⊠ **SAINT LOUIS UNIVERSITY HOSPITAL (260105)**, 3635 Vista at Grand Boulevard, Zip 63110–0250, Mailing Address: P.O. Box 15250, Zip 63110–0250; tel. 314/577–8000 **A**1 2 3 5 8 9 10 **F**3 6 7 8 9 11 14 15 17 18 20 22 24 26 28 29 30 31 34 35 36 38 39 40 43 44 45 46 47 48 49 50 51 55 56 57 58 59 60 61 63 64 65 69 70 74 75 77 78 79 81 82 84 85 86 87 90 91 92 93 94 96 97 98 100 101 102 103 104 107 108 110 111 112 114 115 116 117 118 119 120 121 123 124 126 129 130 131 132 135 136 138 139 141 142 146 148 **P**1 **S** TENET Healthcare Corporation, Dallas, TX
Primary Contact: Phillip E. Sowa, Chief Executive Officer
CFO: Raymond Alvey, Chief Financial Officer
CMO: Karen Webb, M.D., Chief Medical Officer
CIO: Patrick Brennan, Director Information System Technology
CHR: Vera W. Daniel, Chief Human Resources Officer
Web address: www.sluhospital.com
**Control:** Corporation, Investor–owned, for–profit **Service:** General Medical and Surgical

| | | |
|---|---|---|
| **Staffed Beds:** 332 **Admissions:** 15074 **Census:** 239 **Outpatient Visits:** 121545 **Births:** 0 **Total Expense ($000):** 364318 **Payroll Expense ($000):** 85707 **Personnel:** 1371 | | |

☐ **SHRINERS HOSPITALS FOR CHILDREN–ST. LOUIS (263304)**, (Formerly Shriners Hospitals for Children, St. Louis), 2001 South Lindbergh Boulevard, Zip 63131–3597; tel. 314/432–3600 **A**1 3 5 9 10 **F**3 29 34 57 59 64 65 74 75 79 81 85 86 87 89 93 94 97 130 131 132 146 148 **S** Shriners Hospitals for Children, Tampa, FL
Primary Contact: John Gloss, FACHE, Administrator
CFO: Sandra K. Lawson, Interim Director Fiscal Services
CMO: Perry L. Schoenecker, M.D., Chief of Staff
CIO: Jeanne Hall, Director Information Systems
CHR: Mark Venable, Interim Director Human Resources
Web address: www.shrinershospitalsforchildren.org/Hospitals/Locations/Stlouis.aspx
**Control:** Other not–for–profit (including NFP Corporation) **Service:** Children's orthopedic

| | | |
|---|---|---|
| **Staffed Beds:** 42 **Admissions:** 455 **Census:** 9 **Outpatient Visits:** 10653 **Births:** 0 **Total Expense ($000):** 27916 **Payroll Expense ($000):** 10788 **Personnel:** 199 | | |

★ **SSM CARDINAL GLENNON CHILDREN'S MEDICAL CENTER (269807)**, 1465 South Grand Boulevard, Zip 63104–1095; tel. 314/577–5600 **A**3 5 8 9 10 **F**3 8 11 19 21 23 25 27 29 30 31 32 34 35 38 39 40 41 43 44 46 47 48 49 50 51 54 55 57 59 60 61 64 65 66 68 72 73 74 75 77 78 79 80 81 82 84 85 86 87 88 89 90 93 94 97 99 100 101 102 104 107 111 114 115 119 127 129 130 131 132 133 136 137 138 139 141 142 146 148 **P**6 8 **S** SSM Health Care, Saint Louis, MO
Primary Contact: Sherlyn Hailstone, MSN, R.N., FACHE, President
CFO: Karen Rewerts, Vice President Finance
CMO: Susan Heaney, M.D., Vice President Medical Affairs
CIO: Michael Paasch, Regional Vice President and Chief Information Officer
CHR: Mary Jane Brecklin, Network Vice President, South Operating Group
Web address: www.cardinalglennon.com
**Control:** Church–operated, Nongovernment, not–for profit **Service:** Children's general

| | | |
|---|---|---|
| **Staffed Beds:** 176 **Admissions:** 7517 **Census:** 136 **Outpatient Visits:** 199657 **Births:** 0 **Total Expense ($000):** 276955 **Payroll Expense ($000):** 94654 **Personnel:** 1564 | | |

⊠ **SSM ST. MARY'S HEALTH CENTER (260091)**, 6420 Clayton Road, Zip 63117–1811; tel. 314/768–8000 **A**1 2 5 8 9 10 **F**3 4 13 15 17 18 20 22 24 26 28 29 30 31 34 35 37 38 40 44 45 46 47 48 50 55 58 59 60 61 64 66 70 72 73 74 75 76 78 79 81 82 84 85 86 87 97 98 100 101 102 103 104 105 107 108 110 111 114 115 119 120 121 129 130 132 135 143 146 147 148 **P**6 8 **S** SSM Health Care, Saint Louis, MO
Primary Contact: Kathleen R. Becker, M.P.H., JD, President
CFO: Jo Bertram, Vice President Finance
CMO: Darren E. Wethers, M.D., President Medical Staff
CIO: Robert Curran, Director Health Information Management
Web address: www.stmarys-stlouis.com
**Control:** Church–operated, Nongovernment, not–for profit **Service:** General Medical and Surgical

| | | |
|---|---|---|
| **Staffed Beds:** 381 **Admissions:** 19283 **Census:** 257 **Outpatient Visits:** 196408 **Births:** 3190 **Total Expense ($000):** 271375 **Payroll Expense ($000):** 104599 **Personnel:** 1716 | | |

☐ **ST. ALEXIUS HOSPITAL – BROADWAY CAMPUS (260210)**, 3933 South Broadway, Zip 63118–4601; tel. 314/865–3333, (Includes SOUTHPOINTE HOSPITAL, 2639 Miami Street, Zip 63118–3929; tel. 314/772–1456; ST. ALEXIUS HOSPITAL – FOREST PARK CAMPUS, 6150 Oakland Avenue, Zip 63139–3215; tel. 314/768–3000; Michael J. Motte, Chief Executive Officer) **A**1 6 9 10 **F**3 12 15 20 29 30 35 38 39 40 56 57 59 60 68 70 74 77 78 79 81 86 87 98 101 102 103 104 107 108 110 111 118 119 130 143 146 148 **P**6 **S** Success Healthcare, Boca Raton, FL
Primary Contact: Michael J. Motte, Chief Executive Officer
CFO: Matthew Brandt, Chief Financial Officer
CIO: Jennifer Schempp, Manager Information Systems
Web address: www.stalexiushospital.com
**Control:** Corporation, Investor–owned, for–profit **Service:** General Medical and Surgical

| | | |
|---|---|---|
| **Staffed Beds:** 189 **Admissions:** 5427 **Census:** 116 **Outpatient Visits:** 33383 **Births:** 0 **Total Expense ($000):** 57672 **Payroll Expense ($000):** 33827 **Personnel:** 676 | | |

⊠ △ **ST. ANTHONY'S MEDICAL CENTER (260077)**, 10010 Kennerly Road, Zip 63128–2106; tel. 314/525–1000 **A**1 2 7 9 10 **F**3 4 5 8 11 12 13 15 17 18 20 22 24 26 28 29 30 31 32 34 35 37 38 40 41 42 43 47 49 50 51 53 54 56 57 59 60 61 62 63 64 65 68 69 70 73 74 75 76 77 78 79 80 81 82 84 85 86 87 89 90 91 92 93 94 95 96 97 98 99 100 101 102 103 104 105 107 108 110 111 114 118 119 120 121 122 123 124 129 130 131 132 135 143 144 146 147 148 **P**6
Primary Contact: Michael Rindler, Chief Executive Officer
CFO: John Skeans, Chief Financial Officer
CMO: David Morton, M.D., Chief Medical Officer
CIO: Jim Weldon, Chief Information Officer
CNO: Cathi Blise, Interim Chief Nursing Officer
Web address: www.stanthonysmedcenter.com
**Control:** Other not–for–profit (including NFP Corporation) **Service:** General Medical and Surgical

| | | |
|---|---|---|
| **Staffed Beds:** 585 **Admissions:** 28329 **Census:** 353 **Outpatient Visits:** 651693 **Births:** 1392 **Total Expense ($000):** 438814 **Payroll Expense ($000):** 206487 **Personnel:** 4114 | | |

*Many Facility Codes have changed. Please refer to the AHA Guide Code Chart.*    © 2013 AHA Guide

MO

**ST. JOHN'S MERCY CHILDREN'S HOSPITAL** See Mercy Children's Hospital St. Louis

**ST. JOHN'S MERCY MEDICAL CENTER** See Mercy Hospital St. Louis

☒ △ **ST. LOUIS CHILDREN'S HOSPITAL (263301)**, One Children's Place, Zip 63110–1002; tel. 314/454–6000 **A**1 3 5 7 8 9 10 **F**3 5 7 11 16 17 19 20 21 22 23 25 26 27 29 30 31 32 34 35 38 39 40 41 42 43 44 45 46 47 48 49 50 54 57 58 59 60 61 62 63 64 65 68 71 72 74 75 77 78 79 81 82 83 84 85 86 87 88 89 90 92 93 96 99 100 101 102 104 107 108 109 111 112 114 115 119 129 130 131 132 134 135 136 137 138 139 140 141 142 143 144 145 146 148 **S** BJC HealthCare, Saint Louis, MO
Primary Contact: Joan Magruder, President
CFO: Doug Vanderslice, Vice President and Chief Financial Officer
CMO: F. Sessions Cole, M.D., Chief Medical Officer
CHR: David Cook, Vice President Human Resources
Web address: www.stlouischildrens.org
**Control:** Other not–for–profit (including NFP Corporation) **Service:** Children's general

**Staffed Beds:** 258 **Admissions:** 11275 **Census:** 197 **Outpatient Visits:** 152965 **Births:** 0 **Total Expense ($000):** 842217 **Payroll Expense ($000):** 146039 **Personnel:** 2638

☐ **ST. LOUIS PSYCHIATRIC REHABILITATION CENTER (264010)**, 5300 Arsenal Street, Zip 63139–1463; tel. 314/877–6500 **A**1 10 **F**11 30 39 65 68 75 86 87 98 100 101 106 130 143 146
Primary Contact: Laurent D. Javois, Regional Executive Officer
COO: H. Andrew Mannich, Chief Operating Officer
CFO: James D. Martin, Chief Financial Officer
CMO: Roy Wilson, M.D., Medical Director
CIO: Richard Moore, Director Information Technology
CHR: Donna Harris, Director Human Resources
Web address: www.dmh.missouri.gov
**Control:** State–Government, nonfederal **Service:** Psychiatric

**Staffed Beds:** 180 **Admissions:** 8 **Census:** 180 **Outpatient Visits:** 0 **Births:** 0 **Total Expense ($000):** 37226 **Payroll Expense ($000):** 17418 **Personnel:** 513

☐ **ST. LOUIS REGIONAL PSYCHIATRIC STABILIZATION CENTER**, 5355 Delmar Boulevard, Zip 63112–3146; tel. 314/932–7110, (Data for 344 days) **A**1 **F**29 30 98 119 130 **P**5
Primary Contact: John M. Eiler, President
Web address: www.stlpsc.org
**Control:** Other not–for–profit (including NFP Corporation) **Service:** Psychiatric

**Staffed Beds:** 25 **Admissions:** 549 **Census:** 8 **Outpatient Visits:** 0 **Births:** 0 **Total Expense ($000):** 5609 **Payroll Expense ($000):** 3460 **Personnel:** 62

☒ △ **THE REHABILITATION INSTITUTE OF ST. LOUIS (263028)**, 4455 Duncan Avenue, Zip 63110–1111; tel. 314/658–3800 **A**1 7 9 10 **F**29 44 56 58 64 68 74 75 79 82 87 90 91 93 94 100 130 132 143 146 148 **S** HEALTHSOUTH Corporation, Birmingham, AL
Primary Contact: Jon McDowell, FACHE, Chief Executive Officer
CFO: Tara Diebling, Chief Financial Officer
CMO: David Carr, M.D., Physician Medical Director
CIO: Sherrie Marshall, Health Information Management Services Director
CHR: Christina Devine, Director Human Resources
CNO: Dakota Redd, R.N., Chief Nursing Officer
Web address: www.rehabinstitutestl.com
**Control:** Partnership, Investor–owned, for–profit **Service:** Rehabilitation

**Staffed Beds:** 96 **Admissions:** 1887 **Census:** 80 **Outpatient Visits:** 39597 **Births:** 0 **Total Expense ($000):** 33715 **Payroll Expense ($000):** 17487 **Personnel:** 296

☒ △ **VETERANS AFFAIRS ST. LOUIS HEALTH CARE SYSTEM**, (Formerly Veterans Affairs Medical Center), 915 North Grand, Zip 63106–1621; tel. 314/652–4100, (Total facility includes 71 beds in nursing home–type unit) **A**1 3 5 7 **F**1 3 4 5 8 12 15 17 18 20 22 26 28 29 30 31 33 34 35 38 39 40 45 49 50 54 56 57 58 59 60 61 62 63 64 65 66 70 74 75 77 78 79 81 82 83 84 85 86 87 90 91 92 93 94 97 98 100 101 102 103 104 105 106 107 108 109 110 111 114 115 116 117 118 119 120 121 122 123 126 127 128 129 130 131 132 135 143 144 145 146 147 148 **S** Department of Veterans Affairs, Washington, DC
Primary Contact: Marc Magill, Acting Director
CFO: Karen Westerheide, Chief Financial Officer
CMO: Nathan Ravi, M.D., Chief of Staff
CIO: Steve Warmbold, Director Information Management Service Line
CHR: Marie Lewis, Human Resources Liaison
Web address: www.stlouis.va.gov/
**Control:** Veterans Affairs, Government, federal **Service:** General Medical and Surgical

**Staffed Beds:** 356 **Admissions:** 10582 **Census:** 241 **Outpatient Visits:** 702799 **Births:** 0 **Total Expense ($000):** 413308 **Payroll Expense ($000):** 235293 **Personnel:** 2522

## SAINT PETERS—St. Charles County

☒ **BARNES–JEWISH ST. PETERS HOSPITAL (260191)**, 10 Hospital Drive, Zip 63376–1659; tel. 636/916–9000 **A**1 5 9 10 **F**3 8 11 13 15 18 20 22 28 29 30 31 34 35 40 41 49 57 59 64 70 75 76 77 78 79 81 85 86 87 90 93 107 108 110 111 114 115 118 119 120 121 123 124 129 130 132 135 146 147 148 **S** BJC HealthCare, Saint Louis, MO
Primary Contact: Larry Tracy, FACHE, President
COO: Ann Abad, Vice President Operations
CFO: Glen Schweagel, Vice President Finance
CMO: Dan Bergmann, M.D., Chief Medical Officer
CNO: Jill Skyles, R.N., Vice President Patient Care Services
Web address: www.bjsph.org/
**Control:** Other not–for–profit (including NFP Corporation) **Service:** General Medical and Surgical

**Staffed Beds:** 113 **Admissions:** 6071 **Census:** 66 **Outpatient Visits:** 119896 **Births:** 436 **Total Expense ($000):** 115445 **Payroll Expense ($000):** 39365 **Personnel:** 618

## SALEM—Dent County

★ **SALEM MEMORIAL DISTRICT HOSPITAL (261318)**, Highway 72 North, Zip 65560–0774; Mailing Address: P.O. Box 774, Zip 65560–0774; tel. 573/729–6626, (Total facility includes 18 beds in nursing home–type unit) **A**9 10 18 **F**3 7 11 29 30 34 40 59 60 62 67 75 81 85 87 89 107 115 119 127 128 130 133 135 146
Primary Contact: Dennis P. Pryor, Administrator
CFO: Stephanie Wofford, Controller
CMO: Ryan Pharr, M.D., Chief Medical Staff
CHR: Gina Bobbitt, Director Human Resources
Web address: www.smdh.net
**Control:** Hospital district or authority, Government, nonfederal **Service:** General Medical and Surgical

**Staffed Beds:** 43 **Admissions:** 708 **Census:** 29 **Outpatient Visits:** 36438 **Births:** 0 **Total Expense ($000):** 15394 **Payroll Expense ($000):** 7586 **Personnel:** 173

## SEDALIA—Pettis County

☒ **BOTHWELL REGIONAL HEALTH CENTER (260009)**, 601 East 14th Street, Zip 65301–5972, Mailing Address: P.O. Box 1706, Zip 65302–1706; tel. 660/826–8833, (Total facility includes 10 beds in nursing home–type unit) **A**1 9 10 **F**3 11 13 14 15 18 20 22 28 29 30 31 34 35 39 40 51 54 56 57 59 60 62 63 64 65 68 70 73 74 75 76 77 78 79 80 81 82 84 85 86 87 89 92 93 107 108 110 111 114 115 116 117 118 119 120 121 123 124 127 128 129 130 131 132 135 146 147 148
Primary Contact: John M. Dawes, FACHE, Chief Executive Officer
COO: Mark I. Hirshberg, Chief Operating Officer
CFO: Jimmy Robertson, Jr., Chief Financial Officer
CIO: Tom Fairfax, Director Information Systems
CHR: Deb Clemmer, Vice President Human Resources
Web address: www.brhc.org
**Control:** City–Government, nonfederal **Service:** General Medical and Surgical

**Staffed Beds:** 132 **Admissions:** 5489 **Census:** 60 **Outpatient Visits:** 184821 **Births:** 558 **Total Expense ($000):** 85080 **Payroll Expense ($000):** 36735 **Personnel:** 762

## SIKESTON—Scott County

☐ △ **MISSOURI DELTA MEDICAL CENTER (260113)**, 1008 North Main Street, Zip 63801–5044; tel. 573/471–1600 **A**1 7 9 10 **F**3 11 13 15 18 28 29 30 31 32 34 35 39 40 44 50 51 53 54 56 57 59 62 64 68 70 74 75 76 77 78 79 81 82 84 85 86 87 89 90 93 97 98 103 107 108 109 110 111 115 116 117 118 119 127 129 130 131 132 144 146 147 148 **P**6
Primary Contact: Jason Schrumpf, President
CFO: Jon Branstetter, Vice President Finance
Web address: www.missouridelta.com
**Control:** Other not–for–profit (including NFP Corporation) **Service:** General Medical and Surgical

**Staffed Beds:** 160 **Admissions:** 4634 **Census:** 61 **Outpatient Visits:** 216420 **Births:** 468 **Total Expense ($000):** 75815 **Payroll Expense ($000):** 41553 **Personnel:** 728

**MO**

| Hospital, Medicare Provider Number, Address, Telephone, Approval, Facility, and Physician Codes, Health Care System | |
|---|---|
| ★ American Hospital Association (AHA) membership | ○ Healthcare Facilities Accreditation Program |
| ☐ The Joint Commission accreditation ◇ DNV Healthcare Inc. accreditation | △ Commission on Accreditation of Rehabilitation Facilities (CARF) accreditation |

## SPRINGFIELD—Greene County

☐ **LAKELAND BEHAVIORAL HEALTH SYSTEM (264024)**, 440 South Market Street, Zip 65806–2026; tel. 417/865–5581 **A**1 10 **F**98 99 130 **S** Acadia Healthcare Company, Inc., Franklin, TN
Primary Contact: Keith A. Furman, Chief Executive Officer
CFO: Rick Crump, Chief Financial Officer
CMO: Richard Aiken, M.D., Vice President and Medical Director
CHR: Dave England, Director Human Resources
Web address: www.lakeland–hospital.com
**Control:** Corporation, Investor–owned, for–profit **Service:** Children's hospital psychiatric

**Staffed Beds:** 86 **Admissions:** 1605 **Census:** 67 **Outpatient Visits:** 0 **Births:** 0 **Total Expense ($000):** 17191 **Payroll Expense ($000):** 9687 **Personnel:** 248

⊠ △ **LESTER E. COX MEDICAL CENTERS (260040)**, 1423 North Jefferson Street, Zip 65802–1988; tel. 417/269–3000, (Includes LESTER E. COX MEDICAL CENTER NORTH, 1423 North Jefferson Avenue, Zip 65802; tel. 417/269–3000; LESTER E. COX MEDICAL CENTER SOUTH, 3801 South National Avenue, Zip 65807; tel. 417/269–6000) **A**1 2 3 5 7 9 10 **F**3 4 5 7 11 12 13 15 17 18 19 20 22 24 26 28 29 30 31 32 34 35 38 39 40 42 43 44 45 46 47 49 50 51 52 53 54 55 56 57 58 59 60 61 62 64 65 68 69 70 71 72 74 75 76 77 78 79 80 81 82 84 85 86 87 88 89 90 92 93 95 96 97 98 99 100 101 102 103 104 107 108 110 111 114 115 117 118 119 120 121 126 127 128 129 130 131 132 135 143 144 146 147 148 **P**3 6 **S** CoxHealth, Springfield, MO
Primary Contact: Steven D. Edwards, President and Chief Executive Officer
CFO: Jacob McWay, Senior Vice President and Chief Financial Officer
CMO: Dan Sontheimer, M.D., Vice President Medical Affairs
CIO: Bruce Robison, Vice President and Chief Information Officer
CHR: John Hursh, Vice President Human Resources
Web address: www.coxhealth.com
**Control:** Other not–for–profit (including NFP Corporation) **Service:** General Medical and Surgical

**Staffed Beds:** 647 **Admissions:** 31136 **Census:** 427 **Outpatient Visits:** 1330215 **Births:** 3146 **Total Expense ($000):** 781310 **Payroll Expense ($000):** 325305 **Personnel:** 6602

⊠ △ **MERCY HOSPITAL SPRINGFIELD (260065)**, 1235 East Cherokee Street, Zip 65804–2263; tel. 417/820–2000, (Includes ST. JOHN'S CHILDREN'S HOSPITAL, 1235 East Cherokee Street, Zip 65804–2203; tel. 417/820–2000), (Total facility includes 25 beds in nursing home–type unit) **A**1 2 3 5 7 9 10 **F**3 5 6 7 8 9 11 12 13 15 16 17 18 20 22 24 26 28 30 31 34 36 38 39 40 43 44 48 49 50 51 53 54 55 56 57 59 60 61 62 63 64 65 68 70 71 72 73 74 75 76 77 78 79 81 82 84 85 86 87 88 89 90 91 93 94 97 98 100 101 102 103 104 107 108 111 114 116 117 118 119 120 121 123 124 126 128 129 130 131 132 134 135 143 144 146 147 148 **P**6 8 **S** Mercy Health, Chesterfield, MO
Primary Contact: Robert Steele, M.D., President
COO: Jay Guffey, Senior Vice President and Chief Operating Officer
CMO: Allan Allphin, M.D., Chief of Staff
CHR: Trisha Holbert, Vice President Human Resources
Web address: www.stjohns.com
**Control:** Church–operated, Nongovernment, not–for profit **Service:** General Medical and Surgical

**Staffed Beds:** 678 **Admissions:** 34190 **Census:** 467 **Outpatient Visits:** 597044 **Births:** 2989 **Total Expense ($000):** 1024962 **Payroll Expense ($000):** 246131 **Personnel:** 5380

○ **OZARKS COMMUNITY HOSPITAL (260207)**, 2828 North National, Zip 65803–4306; tel. 417/837–4000 **A**9 10 11 **F**3 29 39 40 42 45 54 56 59 65 68 74 75 77 78 79 81 82 85 86 87 89 90 93 97 98 100 103 104 107 108 111 114 119 127 129 130 143 144 147 148 **P**6
Primary Contact: Alexis Brown, Administrator
CFO: Janet Taylor, CPA, Chief Financial Officer
Web address: www.ochonline.com
**Control:** Corporation, Investor–owned, for–profit **Service:** General Medical and Surgical

**Staffed Beds:** 28 **Admissions:** 988 **Census:** 16 **Outpatient Visits:** 241463 **Births:** 0 **Total Expense ($000):** 44236 **Payroll Expense ($000):** 15529 **Personnel:** 566

⊠ **SELECT SPECIALTY HOSPITAL–SPRINGFIELD (262017)**, 1630 East Primrose Street, Zip 65804–7929; tel. 417/885–4700 **A**1 10 **F**1 3 29 45 70 85 90 107 112 114 148 **S** Select Medical Corporation, Mechanicsburg, PA
Primary Contact: Julie De Jean, Chief Executive Officer
CHR: Tonya Eddington, Coordinator Human Resources
Web address: www.selectspecialtyhospitals.com/company/locations/springfield.aspx
**Control:** Corporation, Investor–owned, for–profit **Service:** Long–Term Acute Care hospital

**Staffed Beds:** 44 **Admissions:** 584 **Census:** 40 **Outpatient Visits:** 0 **Births:** 0 **Total Expense ($000):** 21390 **Payroll Expense ($000):** 7374 **Personnel:** 161

## STE. GENEVIEVE—Ste. Genevieve County

★ **STE. GENEVIEVE COUNTY MEMORIAL HOSPITAL (261330)**, 800 Suite Genevieve Drive, Zip 63670–1434; tel. 573/883–2751 **A**10 18 **F**3 11 13 15 18 28 29 31 34 35 39 40 50 53 56 57 59 62 64 65 68 75 76 77 78 79 81 82 85 86 87 89 92 93 107 111 115 119 124 127 129 130 131 132 133 135 146 147 148 **P**6
Primary Contact: Thomas Keim, Chief Executive Officer
CFO: Susan Eckenfels, Chief Financial Officer
CMO: Bhargav Kanani, M.D., Chief of Staff
CIO: Marsha Norris, Director Information Systems
CHR: Sarah Jo Kelley, Director Human Resources
Web address: www.stegenevievehospital.org
**Control:** County–Government, nonfederal **Service:** General Medical and Surgical

**Staffed Beds:** 25 **Admissions:** 1115 **Census:** 12 **Outpatient Visits:** 98159 **Births:** 113 **Total Expense ($000):** 30777 **Payroll Expense ($000):** 13890 **Personnel:** 274

## SULLIVAN—Crawford County

★ **MISSOURI BAPTIST SULLIVAN HOSPITAL (260115)**, 751 Sappington Bridge Road, Zip 63080–2354; tel. 573/468–4186 **A**9 **F**3 4 7 11 13 15 28 29 30 31 35 40 53 56 57 59 63 64 65 68 70 75 76 77 78 79 81 82 83 84 85 86 87 89 90 93 97 98 102 103 104 107 111 115 119 127 129 130 131 133 146 **S** BJC HealthCare, Saint Louis, MO
Primary Contact: Tony Schwarz, President
CFO: Christinia Lashmett, Director Financial Services
CMO: Roger Rembecki, M.D., Chief of Staff
CHR: Kathleen Reed, Manager Human Resources
Web address: www.missouribaptistsullivan.org
**Control:** Other not–for–profit (including NFP Corporation) **Service:** General Medical and Surgical

**Staffed Beds:** 35 **Admissions:** 1912 **Census:** 22 **Outpatient Visits:** 89533 **Births:** 272 **Total Expense ($000):** 41503 **Payroll Expense ($000):** 17067 **Personnel:** 355

## SWEET SPRINGS—Saline County

**I–70 COMMUNITY HOSPITAL (261334)**, 105 Hospital Drive, Zip 65351–2229; tel. 660/335–4700 **A**9 10 18 **F**3 11 29 34 35 40 45 59 64 65 68 75 83 85 87 89 90 93 107 111 114 119 127 128 129 133 143 148 **S** Rural Community Hospitals of America, Kansas City, MO
Primary Contact: Julie Davenport, Chief Executive Officer
CFO: Gary Clifton, Chief Financial Officer
CMO: Deborah Herrmann, M.D., Chief of Staff
CIO: Debra Harris, Director Medical Records
CHR: Diane Steinkuhler, Administrative Assistant Human Resources
Web address: www.i70medcenter.com
**Control:** Corporation, Investor–owned, for–profit **Service:** General Medical and Surgical

**Staffed Beds:** 15 **Admissions:** 280 **Census:** 3 **Outpatient Visits:** 23028 **Births:** 0 **Total Expense ($000):** 6941 **Payroll Expense ($000):** 3223 **Personnel:** 56

## TRENTON—Grundy County

★ **WRIGHT MEMORIAL HOSPITAL (261309)**, 191 Iowa Boulevard, Zip 64683–8343, Mailing Address: P.O. Box 628, Zip 64683–0628; tel. 660/358–5700 **A**9 10 18 **F**3 11 13 15 28 29 30 31 34 35 40 45 50 57 59 62 63 64 68 75 76 77 78 79 81 82 84 85 87 89 90 93 102 104 107 108 111 115 119 127 129 130 133 146 148 **P**1 **S** Saint Luke's Health System, Kansas City, MO
Primary Contact: Gary W. Jordan, FACHE, Chief Executive Officer
CFO: Leslie Reed, Chief Financial Officer
CMO: Gerald C. Zabielski, M.D., Chief Medical Staff
CHR: Jenny Donovan, Director Human Resources
Web address: www.saintlukeshealthsystem.org
**Control:** Other not–for–profit (including NFP Corporation) **Service:** General Medical and Surgical

**Staffed Beds:** 25 **Admissions:** 778 **Census:** 8 **Outpatient Visits:** 64851 **Births:** 194 **Total Expense ($000):** 25062 **Payroll Expense ($000):** 9667 **Personnel:** 178

## TROY—Lincoln County

☐ **LINCOLN COUNTY MEDICAL CENTER (261319)**, 1000 East Cherry Street, Zip 63379–1513; tel. 636/528–8551 **A**1 9 10 18 **F**3 11 15 17 18 28 29 30 34 35 40 44 45 50 51 57 59 62 64 65 68 70 75 77 79 81 85 86 87 89 90 93 107 110 111 114 119 127 129 130 131 132 133 135 146 148 **P**6
Primary Contact: Patrick G. Bira, JD, FACHE, Chief Executive Officer
CIO: Travis Boyd, Manager Information Technology
CHR: Toni Price, Director Human Resources
Web address: www.lcmctroy.com
**Control:** County–Government, nonfederal **Service:** General Medical and Surgical

**Staffed Beds:** 25 **Admissions:** 997 **Census:** 12 **Outpatient Visits:** 76109 **Births:** 0 **Total Expense ($000):** 32050 **Payroll Expense ($000):** 16472 **Personnel:** 298

**MO**

*Many Facility Codes have changed. Please refer to the AHA Guide Code Chart.*
© 2013 AHA Guide

**UNIONVILLE—Putnam County**

**PUTNAM COUNTY MEMORIAL HOSPITAL (261305)**, 1926 Oak Street,
Zip 63565–1180, Mailing Address: P.O. Box 389, Zip 63565–0389;
tel. 660/947–2411 **A**9 10 18 **F**3 15 28 29 34 35 40 45 50 57 59 64 65 75
77 81 85 87 89 90 93 97 107 111 114 119 127 128 129 130 133 **P**5
Primary Contact: Cindy Cummings, Chief Executive Officer
CMO: W. Stephen Casady, M.D., Chief of Staff
CHR: Judy Green, Director Human Resources
Web address: www.pcmhosp.com
**Control:** County–Government, nonfederal **Service:** General Medical and Surgical

**Staffed Beds:** 15 **Admissions:** 197 **Census:** 2 **Outpatient Visits:** 10323
**Births:** 0 **Total Expense ($000):** 6683 **Payroll Expense ($000):** 2680
**Personnel:** 72

**WARRENSBURG—Johnson County**

**WESTERN MISSOURI MEDICAL CENTER (260097)**, 403 Burkarth Road,
Zip 64093–3101; tel. 660/747–2500 **A**1 9 10 20 **F**3 8 11 12 13 15 17 18 28
29 30 31 32 34 35 40 45 47 57 59 61 64 65 68 70 75 76 77 78 79 81 82
85 89 90 93 102 107 108 110 111 115 118 119 127 129 130 131 132 133
135 146 147 148 **P**6
Primary Contact: Susan M. Stiles, President and Chief Executive Officer
COO: Michael L. Gasparini, Vice President Clinical Services and Chief Operating
Officer
CFO: Terri Bradley, CPA, Vice President Financial Services and Chief Financial
Officer
CMO: Michael Misko, M.D., Vice President Medical Staff Services and Chief
Medical Officer
CIO: Carol McKinney, Director Information Services
CHR: Dennis Long, Director Human Resources
Web address: www.wmmc.com
**Control:** County–Government, nonfederal **Service:** General Medical and Surgical

**Staffed Beds:** 72 **Admissions:** 3275 **Census:** 31 **Outpatient Visits:** 127906
**Births:** 759 **Total Expense ($000):** 66231 **Payroll Expense ($000):** 28075
**Personnel:** 517

**WASHINGTON—Franklin County**

**MERCY HOSPITAL WASHINGTON (260052)**, 901 East Fifth Street,
Zip 63090–3127; tel. 636/239–8000 **A**1 9 10 **F**3 4 8 11 12 13 14 15 17 18
20 22 28 29 30 31 32 34 35 40 43 46 48 49 50 52 53 57 59 61 64 66 68
69 70 73 75 76 77 78 79 80 81 82 84 85 87 89 90 93 94 96 97 99 100
101 104 107 108 110 111 114 116 117 118 119 120 121 127 129 130 131
132 134 135 144 146 147 148 **P**6 8 **S** Mercy Health, Chesterfield, MO
Primary Contact: Terri L. McLain, FACHE, President
COO: Joan Frost, R.N., Chief Operating Officer/Chief Nursing Officer
CFO: Cheryl Matejka, Chief Financial Officer
CMO: Thomas Riechers, M.D., Chief Medical Staff
CIO: Michael McCreary, Chief of Services
CHR: Frank Lenoir, Executive Director Human Resources
CNO: Joan Frost, R.N., Chief Operating Officer/Chief Nursing Officer
Web address: www.mercy.net
**Control:** Other not–for–profit (including NFP Corporation) **Service:** General
Medical and Surgical

**Staffed Beds:** 187 **Admissions:** 5658 **Census:** 49 **Outpatient Visits:** 173009
**Births:** 867 **Total Expense ($000):** 92511 **Payroll Expense ($000):** 40598
**Personnel:** 590

**WENTZVILLE—St. Charles County**

**SSM ST. JOSEPH HEALTH CENTER – WENTZVILLE** See SSM St. Joseph
Health Center, Saint Charles

**WEST PLAINS—Howell County**

**OZARKS MEDICAL CENTER (260078)**, 1100 Kentucky Avenue,
Zip 65775–2029, Mailing Address: P.O. Box 1100, Zip 65775–1100;
tel. 417/256–9111 **A**1 9 10 **F**2 3 5 11 13 15 17 18 20 22 24 28 29 30 31 34
38 40 44 45 49 57 59 61 62 63 64 68 70 74 75 76 77 78 79 81 82 84 85
86 87 89 90 93 94 98 99 100 101 102 103 104 107 108 110 111 115 118
119 120 121 127 129 130 131 132 135 144 145 146 147 148 **P**8
Primary Contact: David M. Zechman, FACHE, President and Chief Executive Officer
COO: Jeanne M. Looper, Chief Operating Officer
CFO: Michael Gross, Senior Vice President, Finance/Business Development
CMO: Edward R. Henegar, D.O., Vice President, Medical Affairs
CIO: Edward Boys, Chief Information Officer
CHR: Greg Shannon, Director Human Resources
CNO: Marcia Robson, R.N., Chief Nursing Officer
Web address: www.ozarksmedicalcenter.com
**Control:** Other not–for–profit (including NFP Corporation) **Service:** General
Medical and Surgical

**Staffed Beds:** 114 **Admissions:** 6190 **Census:** 61 **Outpatient Visits:** 543296
**Births:** 682 **Total Expense ($000):** 108168 **Payroll Expense ($000):** 63067
**Personnel:** 1117

**WINDSOR—Henry County**

☐ **ROYAL OAKS HOSPITAL (264020)**, 307 North Main, Zip 65360–1449;
tel. 660/647–2182 **A**1 3 5 10 **F**30 98 99 100 101 102 103 104 105
Primary Contact: Alan W. Greiman, Administrator
Web address: www.royal–oaks–hospital.org
**Control:** Other not–for–profit (including NFP Corporation) **Service:** Psychiatric

**Staffed Beds:** 41 **Admissions:** 1337 **Census:** 30 **Outpatient Visits:** 0 **Births:**
0 **Total Expense ($000):** 11064 **Payroll Expense ($000):** 6092 **Personnel:**
154

MO

# MONTANA

## ANACONDA—Deer Lodge County

★ **COMMUNITY HOSPITAL OF ANACONDA (271335)**, 401 West Pennsylvania Street, Zip 59711; tel. 406/563–8500, (Total facility includes 62 beds in nursing home–type unit) **A**9 10 18 **F**1 3 6 8 11 13 15 29 30 31 34 40 43 45 50 57 59 62 63 64 75 77 79 81 82 87 93 107 110 111 114 119 128 130 133 135 143 144 146 **P**6 **S** Providence Health & Services, Renton, WA
Primary Contact: Steve McNeece, Chief Executive Officer
COO: Laura Austin, Chief Financial Officer and Chief Operating Officer
CFO: Laura Austin, Chief Financial Officer and Chief Operating Officer
CMO: Shawna Baker, M.D., Chief of Staff
CIO: Laura Austin, Chief Financial Officer and Chief Operating Officer
CHR: Meg Hickey–Boynton, Director Human Resources and Marketing
CNO: Jamie Johnson, R.N., VP of Nursing
Web address: www.communityhospitalofanaconda.org
**Control:** Other not–for–profit (including NFP Corporation) **Service:** General Medical and Surgical

**Staffed Beds:** 87 **Admissions:** 975 **Census:** 66 **Outpatient Visits:** 47063 **Births:** 50 **Total Expense ($000):** 34411 **Payroll Expense ($000):** 14613 **Personnel:** 246

## BAKER—Fallon County

**FALLON MEDICAL COMPLEX (271301)**, 202 South 4th Street West, Zip 59313–9156, Mailing Address: P.O. Box 820, Zip 59313–0820; tel. 406/778–3331, (Total facility includes 15 beds in nursing home–type unit) **A**9 10 18 **F**11 15 28 32 34 36 40 56 57 59 62 64 65 68 69 75 81 93 97 107 110 114 119 127 128 130 133 146 148 **P**6
Primary Contact: David Espeland, Chief Executive Officer
CFO: Selena Nelson, Chief Financial Officer
CMO: Darryl Espeland, D.O., Chief Medical Staff
Web address: www.fallonmedical.org
**Control:** Other not–for–profit (including NFP Corporation) **Service:** General Medical and Surgical

**Staffed Beds:** 40 **Admissions:** 219 **Census:** 34 **Outpatient Visits:** 20910 **Births:** 0 **Total Expense ($000):** 8057 **Payroll Expense ($000):** 3848 **Personnel:** 99

## BIG SANDY—Chouteau County

★ **BIG SANDY MEDICAL CENTER (271311)**, 166 Montana Avenue East, Zip 59520–8474, Mailing Address: P.O. Box 530, Zip 59520–0530; tel. 406/378–2188, (Total facility includes 22 beds in nursing home–type unit) **A**9 10 18 **F**40 64 93 127 128 133
Primary Contact: Harry Bold, Administrator
CFO: Nora Grubb, Chief Financial Officer
Web address: www.bsmc.org
**Control:** Other not–for–profit (including NFP Corporation) **Service:** General Medical and Surgical

**Staffed Beds:** 30 **Admissions:** 109 **Census:** 20 **Outpatient Visits:** 4123 **Births:** 0 **Total Expense ($000):** 3110 **Payroll Expense ($000):** 1791 **Personnel:** 38

## BIG TIMBER—Sweet Grass County

★ **PIONEER MEDICAL CENTER (271313)**, 301 West Seventh Avenue, Zip 59011–7893, Mailing Address: P.O. Box 1228, Zip 59011–1228; tel. 406/932–4603, (Total facility includes 25 beds in nursing home–type unit) **A**9 10 18 **F**2 7 10 29 34 35 40 41 45 57 59 63 64 65 69 75 77 93 97 107 114 127 128 130 131 132 133 **P**3 6
Primary Contact: Erik Wood, Chief Executive Officer
CFO: Kyle Gee, Chief Financial Officer
CMO: Benjamin P. Bullington, M.D., Chief of Staff
CHR: Miki Gregorich, Director Human Resources
CNO: Randi Pike, Director of Nursing
Web address: www.pmcmt.org/
**Control:** County–Government, nonfederal **Service:** General Medical and Surgical

**Staffed Beds:** 50 **Admissions:** 124 **Census:** 36 **Outpatient Visits:** 7077 **Births:** 0 **Total Expense ($000):** 5736 **Payroll Expense ($000):** 2571 **Personnel:** 93

## BILLINGS—Yellowstone County

☐ **ADVANCED CARE HOSPITAL OF MONTANA (272001)**, 3528 Gabel Road, Zip 59102–7307; tel. 406/373–8000, (Nonreporting) **A**1 9 10 **S** Ernest Health, Inc., Albuquerque, NM
Primary Contact: Kerry Ashment, Chief Executive Officer
Web address: www.achm.ernesthealth.com
**Control:** Corporation, Investor–owned, for–profit **Service:** Long–Term Acute Care hospital

**Staffed Beds:** 40

⊠ **BILLINGS CLINIC (270004)**, 2800 10th Avenue North, Zip 59101–0703, Mailing Address: P.O. Box 37000, Zip 59107–7000; tel. 406/657–4000, (Total facility includes 125 beds in nursing home–type unit) **A**1 2 9 10 **F**3 7 8 9 10 11 12 13 15 17 18 20 22 24 26 28 29 30 31 32 34 35 36 38 40 43 44 45 46 48 49 50 51 52 54 55 56 57 58 59 60 61 63 64 65 66 68 70 71 72 74 75 76 77 78 79 81 82 84 85 86 87 91 92 93 97 98 99 100 101 102 103 104 105 107 108 110 111 114 115 116 117 118 119 120 121 124 126 128 129 130 131 132 134 135 143 144 146 147 148 **P**6
Primary Contact: Nicholas Wolter, M.D., President and Chief Executive Officer
CFO: Connie F. Prewitt, Chief Financial Officer
CMO: Mark C. Rumans, M.D., Physician in Chief
CIO: Chris E. Stevens, Chief Information Officer
CHR: Kellee J. Fisk, Vice President People Resources
Web address: www.billingsclinic.com
**Control:** Other not–for–profit (including NFP Corporation) **Service:** General Medical and Surgical

**Staffed Beds:** 388 **Admissions:** 14525 **Census:** 277 **Outpatient Visits:** 971259 **Births:** 1368 **Total Expense ($000):** 474094 **Payroll Expense ($000):** 234736 **Personnel:** 3157

⊠ △ **ST. VINCENT HEALTHCARE (270049)**, 1233 North 30th Street, Zip 59101–0165, Mailing Address: P.O. Box 35200, Zip 59107–5200; tel. 406/237–7000 **A**1 2 7 9 10 **F**3 8 11 12 13 15 17 18 19 20 22 24 28 29 30 31 32 34 35 36 37 38 39 40 43 44 45 47 49 50 51 56 57 59 60 61 64 68 70 71 72 74 75 76 77 78 79 81 82 84 85 86 87 88 89 90 92 93 97 99 100 101 103 104 107 108 111 114 115 116 117 118 119 120 121 123 124 125 126 129 130 131 132 134 135 143 144 145 146 147 148 **P**6 **S** SCL Health System, Denver, CO
Primary Contact: Jason Barker, Chief Executive Officer
CMO: Michael Schweitzer, M.D., Chief Medical Officer
CIO: Al Rooney, Director Information Systems
Web address: www.svh–mt.org
**Control:** Church–operated, Nongovernment, not–for profit **Service:** General Medical and Surgical

**Staffed Beds:** 249 **Admissions:** 11878 **Census:** 144 **Outpatient Visits:** 443775 **Births:** 1391 **Total Expense ($000):** 320533 **Payroll Expense ($000):** 126202 **Personnel:** 1711

## BOZEMAN—Gallatin County

⊠ **BOZEMAN DEACONESS HOSPITAL (270057)**, 915 Highland Boulevard, Zip 59715–6902; tel. 406/585–5000, (Nonreporting) **A**1 2 9 10 20
Primary Contact: Kevin M. Pitzer, President and Chief Executive Officer
Web address: www.bozemandeaconess.org
**Control:** Other not–for–profit (including NFP Corporation) **Service:** General Medical and Surgical

**Staffed Beds:** 70

## BUTTE—Silver Bow County

⊠ **ST. JAMES HEALTHCARE (270017)**, 400 South Clark Street, Zip 59701–2328; tel. 406/723–2500 **A**1 9 10 **F**3 11 13 15 18 20 22 26 28 29 30 31 34 35 40 43 45 46 47 48 49 50 51 54 56 57 59 64 65 68 70 72 75 76 77 78 79 81 82 83 85 87 89 93 97 102 107 108 111 114 115 116 117 118 119 120 121 122 123 126 127 130 131 132 135 146 147 148 **P**6 **S** SCL Health System, Denver, CO
Primary Contact: Charles T. Wright, President and Chief Executive Officer
CFO: Jay Doyle, Chief Financial Officer
CMO: Dennis Salisbury, M.D., Vice President for Medical Affairs
CHR: Trisha Palmer, Director
CNO: Shannon S. Holland, R.N., Vice Presient of Patient Care Service
Web address: www.stjameshealthcare.org
**Control:** Other not–for–profit (including NFP Corporation) **Service:** General Medical and Surgical

**Staffed Beds:** 58 **Admissions:** 3647 **Census:** 36 **Outpatient Visits:** 62075 **Births:** 457 **Total Expense ($000):** 71019 **Payroll Expense ($000):** 27629 **Personnel:** 525

## CHESTER—Liberty County

**LIBERTY MEDICAL CENTER (271334)**, 315 West Madison Avenue, Zip 59522, Mailing Address: P.O. Box 705, Zip 59522–0705; tel. 406/759–5181, (Nonreporting) **A**9 10 18
Primary Contact: Dustin Ahrens, Chief Executive Officer
CFO: Shari Meissner, Chief Financial Officer
CMO: Anna Earl, M.D., Chief of Staff
CIO: Marilyn Snyder, Chief Information Officer
CHR: Jane Allen, Director Human Resources and Payroll
Web address: www.lchnh.org
**Control:** Other not–for–profit (including NFP Corporation) **Service:** General Medical and Surgical

**Staffed Beds:** 25

MT

*Many Facility Codes have changed. Please refer to the AHA Guide Code Chart.*

© 2013 AHA Guide

## CHOTEAU—Teton County

★ **TETON MEDICAL CENTER (271307)**, 915 4th Street North West, Zip 59422–9123; tel. 406/466–5763, (Total facility includes 30 beds in nursing home–type unit) **A**9 10 18 **F**2 3 15 34 35 40 41 53 54 56 57 59 63 64 68 77 87 93 107 127 128 130 131 133 143 146 **P**6
Primary Contact: Louie King, Administrator
Web address: www.tetonmedicalcenter.net
**Control:** Hospital district or authority, Government, nonfederal **Service:** General Medical and Surgical

**Staffed Beds:** 40 **Admissions:** 224 **Census:** 29 **Outpatient Visits:** 8246 **Births:** 0 **Total Expense ($000):** 6630 **Payroll Expense ($000):** 3844 **Personnel:** 95

## CIRCLE—McCone County

★ **MCCONE COUNTY HEALTH CENTER (271305)**, 605 Sullivan Avenue, Zip 59215, Mailing Address: P.O. Box 48, Zip 59215–0048; tel. 406/485–3381 **A**9 10 18 **F**2 3 11 40 41 65 133 135 143 146
Primary Contact: Nancy Rosaaen, Chief Executive Officer
CFO: Nancy Rosaaen, Chief Executive Officer
CHR: Jacque Gardner, Administrative Assistant, Clinic Manager, Co–Chief Financial Officer and Chief Human Resources
Web address: www.mcconehealth.org/
**Control:** County–Government, nonfederal **Service:** General Medical and Surgical

**Staffed Beds:** 25 **Admissions:** 65 **Census:** 24 **Outpatient Visits:** 3799 **Births:** 0 **Total Expense ($000):** 3131 **Payroll Expense ($000):** 1550 **Personnel:** 41

## COLUMBUS—Stillwater County

★ **STILLWATER COMMUNITY HOSPITAL (271330)**, 44 West Fourth Avenue North, Zip 59019–0959, Mailing Address: P.O. Box 959, Zip 59019–0959; tel. 406/322–5316 **A**9 10 18 **F**10 15 28 29 32 35 40 45 46 56 57 59 62 65 69 75 93 107 128 130 133 145 **P**1 3
Primary Contact: Tim Russell, Administrator
Web address: www.billingsclinic.com
**Control:** Other not–for–profit (including NFP Corporation) **Service:** General Medical and Surgical

**Staffed Beds:** 23 **Admissions:** 177 **Census:** 2 **Outpatient Visits:** 9164 **Births:** 0 **Total Expense ($000):** 5606 **Payroll Expense ($000):** 1797 **Personnel:** 36

## CONRAD—Pondera County

**PONDERA MEDICAL CENTER (271324)**, 805 Sunset Boulevard, Zip 59425–1717, Mailing Address: P.O. Box 758, Zip 59425–0758; tel. 406/271–3211, (Total facility includes 59 beds in nursing home–type unit) **A**9 10 18 **F**1 2 3 6 7 11 13 15 28 29 35 40 43 53 57 59 62 65 66 76 77 81 87 91 97 102 107 108 114 119 128 130 133 144 146 **P**6
Primary Contact: Wayne Ogburn, Chief Executive Officer
CFO: Dave Doran, Chief Financial Officer
CMO: Peter Barran, M.D., Chief of Staff
CIO: Sean Kavawaha, Supervisor Information Technology and Information Systems
CHR: J. D. Duncan, Director Human Resources
Web address: www.ponderamedical.com
**Control:** Other not–for–profit (including NFP Corporation) **Service:** General Medical and Surgical

**Staffed Beds:** 79 **Admissions:** 209 **Census:** 55 **Outpatient Visits:** 7826 **Births:** 44 **Personnel:** 167

## CROW AGENCY—Big Horn County

**CROW/NORTHERN CHEYENNE HOSPITAL (271339)**, 10110 South 7650 East, Zip 59022–0009, Mailing Address: P.O. Box 9, Zip 59022–0009; tel. 406/638–2626, (Nonreporting) **A**10 18 **S** U. S. Indian Health Service, Rockville, MD
Primary Contact: Clayton Old Elk, Service Unit Director
CMO: Jim Upchurch, M.D., Chief Medical Officer
CIO: Melanie Falls Down, Site Manager
Web address: www.ihs.gov/facilitiesservices/areaoffices/billings/crow/index.asp
**Control:** Public Health Service, Government, federal **Service:** General Medical and Surgical

**Staffed Beds:** 24

## CULBERTSON—Roosevelt County

★ **ROOSEVELT MEDICAL CENTER (271308)**, 818 Second Avenue East, Zip 59218, Mailing Address: P.O. Box 419, Zip 59218–0419; tel. 406/787–6401 **A**9 10 18 **F**1 2 3 7 11 15 34 35 40 43 50 56 57 59 65 69 93 97 119 127 128 130 133 143 146 **P**6
Primary Contact: Audrey Stromberg, Administrator
CFO: Carolyn Casterline, Financial Director
Web address: www.roosmem.org
**Control:** Other not–for–profit (including NFP Corporation) **Service:** General Medical and Surgical

**Staffed Beds:** 25 **Admissions:** 56 **Census:** 21 **Outpatient Visits:** 7751 **Births:** 0 **Total Expense ($000):** 4322 **Payroll Expense ($000):** 2465 **Personnel:** 63

## CUT BANK—Glacier County

**NORTHERN ROCKIES MEDICAL CENTER (271337)**, 802 Second Street S.E., Zip 59427–3329; tel. 406/873–2251 **A**9 10 18 **F**8 11 29 34 40 50 57 59 64 65 66 81 89 91 93 97 107 108 119 127 129 130 133 **P**4 6
Primary Contact: Cherie Taylor, Chief Executive Officer
CFO: Treasure Berkram, Chief Financial Officer
CMO: Adron Medley, M.D., Chief Medical Staff
CHR: Kandie Lemieux, Administrative Assistant and Director Human Resources
Web address: www.nmrcinc.org
**Control:** Other not–for–profit (including NFP Corporation) **Service:** General Medical and Surgical

**Staffed Beds:** 13 **Admissions:** 156 **Census:** 1 **Outpatient Visits:** 12832 **Births:** 0 **Total Expense ($000):** 6807 **Payroll Expense ($000):** 3727 **Personnel:** 79

## DEER LODGE—Powell County

**DEER LODGE MEDICAL CENTER (271314)**, (Formerly Powell County Medical Center), 1101 Texas Avenue, Zip 59722–1828; tel. 406/846–2212, (Nonreporting) **A**9 10 18
Primary Contact: Tony Pfaff, Interim Chief Executive Officer
CFO: Jaena Richards, Chief Financial Officer
CMO: Michelle Corbin, M.D., Chief of Staff
CIO: Chris Foster, Director Health Information Management
Web address: www.pcmh.org
**Control:** Other not–for–profit (including NFP Corporation) **Service:** General Medical and Surgical

**Staffed Beds:** 16

## DILLON—Beaverhead County

★ **BARRETT HOSPITAL & HEALTHCARE (271318)**, 600 Highway 91 South, Zip 59725–7379; tel. 406/683–3000 **A**9 10 18 **F**3 13 15 28 29 32 34 35 37 38 40 43 44 45 50 57 59 62 63 64 65 68 70 75 76 77 79 81 82 83 84 85 86 87 93 94 97 107 108 110 111 115 118 119 120 130 131 132 133 146 148 **P**5 6 **S** HealthTech Management Services, Franklin, TN
Primary Contact: Ken Westman, Chief Executive Officer
CFO: Dick Achter, Chief Financial Officer
CMO: Cindy Christenson, Chief Clinical Officer
CIO: Dick Achter, Chief Financial Officer
Web address: www.barretthospital.org
**Control:** Hospital district or authority, Government, nonfederal **Service:** General Medical and Surgical

**Staffed Beds:** 25 **Admissions:** 766 **Census:** 7 **Outpatient Visits:** 31195 **Births:** 89 **Total Expense ($000):** 26931 **Payroll Expense ($000):** 12604 **Personnel:** 222

## EKALAKA—Carter County

**DAHL MEMORIAL HEALTHCARE ASSOCIATION (271302)**, 215 Sandy Street, Zip 59324, Mailing Address: P.O. Box 46, Zip 59324–0046; tel. 406/775–8730, (Total facility includes 23 beds in nursing home–type unit) **A**9 10 18 **F**2 7 40 41 57 59 65 69 127 128 130 131 133 135 143 146 148 **P**6
Primary Contact: Nadine Elmore, Chief Executive Officer
CFO: Nadine Elmore, Chief Executive Officer
CMO: Dale Diede, M.D., Medical Provider
CIO: Rhonda Knapp, Director Human Resources
CHR: Rhonda Knapp, Director Human Resources
Web address: www.dahlmemorial.com
**Control:** Other not–for–profit (including NFP Corporation) **Service:** General Medical and Surgical

**Staffed Beds:** 31 **Admissions:** 37 **Census:** 16 **Outpatient Visits:** 2868 **Births:** 0 **Total Expense ($000):** 2492 **Payroll Expense ($000):** 1162 **Personnel:** 34

**MT**

---

**Hospital, Medicare Provider Number, Address, Telephone, Approval, Facility, and Physician Codes, Health Care System**

★ American Hospital Association (AHA) membership
☐ The Joint Commission accreditation
◇ DNV Healthcare Inc. accreditation
◯ Healthcare Facilities Accreditation Program
△ Commission on Accreditation of Rehabilitation Facilities (CARF) accreditation

### ENNIS—Madison County

**MADISON VALLEY MEDICAL CENTER (271329)**, 305 North Main Street, Zip 59729–8001, Mailing Address: P.O. Box 397, Zip 59729–0397; tel. 406/682–4222 **A**9 10 18 **F**3 11 40 57 67 81 104 107 119 128 133 135 **P**6
Primary Contact: John Bishop, Chief Financial Officer
CFO: John Bishop, Chief Financial Officer
CMO: Cindy Sharp, M.D., Chief Medical Officer
CIO: Bo Nix, Chief Information Officer
Web address: www.mvhospital–clinic.com
**Control:** Hospital district or authority, Government, nonfederal **Service:** General Medical and Surgical

**Staffed Beds:** 10 **Admissions:** 70 **Census:** 1 **Outpatient Visits:** 18303 **Births:** 0 **Total Expense ($000):** 5625 **Payroll Expense ($000):** 1613 **Personnel:** 41

### FORSYTH—Rosebud County

★ **ROSEBUD HEALTH CARE CENTER (271327)**, 383 North 17th Avenue, Zip 59327–0268, Mailing Address: P.O. Box 268, Zip 59327–0268; tel. 406/346–2161, (Nonreporting) **A**9 10 18
Primary Contact: Ryan Tooke, Interim Chief Executive Officer
CFO: Ryan Tooke, Chief Financial Officer
CMO: William Anderson, M.D., Medical Director
CHR: Karla Allies, Director Human Resources
Web address: www.rosebudhealthcare.com/
**Control:** Other not–for–profit (including NFP Corporation) **Service:** General Medical and Surgical

**Staffed Beds:** 55

### FORT BENTON—Chouteau County

★ **MISSOURI RIVER MEDICAL CENTER (271304)**, 1501 St. Charles Street, Zip 59442–0249, Mailing Address: P.O. Box 249, Zip 59442–0249; tel. 406/622–3331, (Total facility includes 41 beds in nursing home–type unit) **A**9 10 18 **F**2 3 10 40 57 59 63 64 67 84 89 90 93 107 114 119 127 128 130 131 133 135 143 146 **P**5 **S** Benefis Health System, Great Falls, MT
Primary Contact: Jay Pottenger, Administrator
CFO: Lynn Asbeck, Manager Business Office
CHR: Carolyn Johnsrud, Manager Human Resources
Web address: www.mrmcfb.org
**Control:** Hospital district or authority, Government, nonfederal **Service:** Long–Term Acute Care hospital

**Staffed Beds:** 52 **Admissions:** 139 **Census:** 30 **Outpatient Visits:** 5921 **Total Expense ($000):** 5171 **Payroll Expense ($000):** 2712 **Personnel:** 90

### FORT HARRISON—Lewis And Clark County

✉ **VETERANS AFFAIRS MONTANA HEALTH CARE SYSTEM**, 3687 Veterans Drive, Zip 59636–9703, Mailing Address: P.O. Box 1500, Zip 59636–1500; tel. 406/442–6410, (Nonreporting) **A**1 **S** Department of Veterans Affairs, Washington, DC
Primary Contact: Steven W. Young, Acting Director
CFO: Brian Gustafson, Chief Financial Officer
CMO: Kurt Werner, M.D., Chief of Staff
CIO: Paul Gauthier, Chief Information Resources Management
CHR: Aggie Hamilton, Chief Human Resources
Web address: www.montana.va.gov/
**Control:** Veterans Affairs, Government, federal **Service:** General Medical and Surgical

**Staffed Beds:** 65

### GLASGOW—Valley County

✉ **FRANCES MAHON DEACONESS HOSPITAL (271316)**, 621 Third Street South, Zip 59230–2699; tel. 406/228–3500 **A**1 9 10 18 **F**3 7 11 13 15 28 29 30 31 34 35 40 43 53 56 57 59 61 64 70 75 76 78 79 81 82 86 87 89 93 100 102 105 107 108 110 111 114 118 119 127 128 130 131 133 135 145 146 **P**6 7
Primary Contact: Randall G. Holom, Chief Executive Officer
COO: Ellen Guttenberg, Chief Operating Officer
CFO: Del Gienger, Director Financial Services
CMO: Gordon Bell, M.D., Chief of Staff
CIO: David L. Nixdorf, Director Support Services
CHR: Shelly Van Buren, Director Human Resources
CNO: Brenda Koessl, R.N., Director of Nursing Services
Web address: www.fmdh.org
**Control:** Other not–for–profit (including NFP Corporation) **Service:** General Medical and Surgical

**Staffed Beds:** 25 **Admissions:** 579 **Census:** 6 **Outpatient Visits:** 34198 **Births:** 116 **Total Expense ($000):** 18609 **Payroll Expense ($000):** 9089 **Personnel:** 165

### GLENDIVE—Dawson County

★ **GLENDIVE MEDICAL CENTER (271332)**, 202 Prospect Drive, Zip 59330–1999; tel. 406/345–3306, (Total facility includes 71 beds in nursing home–type unit) **A**9 10 18 **F**3 10 11 13 15 28 29 30 31 35 38 40 41 43 50 56 57 59 61 62 63 64 67 69 70 75 76 77 78 79 81 82 87 89 93 94 98 102 103 104 107 108 111 115 119 127 128 130 131 132 133 143 144 146 147 148 **P**6 7 8
Primary Contact: Parker Powell, Interim Chief Executive Officer
CFO: Barbara Markham, Chief Financial Officer
CMO: Kevin Maxwell, M.D., Chief of Staff
CIO: Matthew Shahan, Director Information Systems
CHR: Joetta J. Pearcy, Director, Human Resources
Web address: www.gmc.org
**Control:** Other not–for–profit (including NFP Corporation) **Service:** General Medical and Surgical

**Staffed Beds:** 96 **Admissions:** 920 **Census:** 52 **Outpatient Visits:** 28605 **Births:** 102 **Total Expense ($000):** 27927 **Payroll Expense ($000):** 12501 **Personnel:** 249

### GREAT FALLS—Cascade County

✉ △ **BENEFIS HOSPITALS (270012)**, 1101 26th Street South, Zip 59405–5104; tel. 406/455–5000, (Includes BENEFIS HEALTH CARE–EAST CAMPUS, 1101 26th Street, Zip 59405; tel. 406/761–1200; BENEFIS HEALTH CARE–WEST CAMPUS, 500 15th Avenue South, Zip 59405, Mailing Address: P.O. Box 5013, Zip 59403–5013; tel. 406/727–3333), (Total facility includes 146 beds in nursing home–type unit) **A**1 2 7 9 10 20 **F**3 4 5 6 8 11 12 13 15 17 18 20 22 24 28 29 30 31 34 35 37 38 40 43 45 48 49 50 54 55 56 57 58 59 60 61 62 63 64 65 70 71 72 73 74 75 76 77 78 79 80 81 82 83 84 85 86 87 88 89 90 92 93 96 97 98 100 101 102 103 104 105 107 108 110 111 113 114 115 119 120 121 123 124 126 127 128 129 130 131 132 133 134 135 136 141 143 144 145 146 147 **P**4 5 7 8 **S** Benefis Health System, Great Falls, MT
Primary Contact: John H. Goodnow, Chief Executive Officer
COO: Julie Hickethier, R.N., Senior Vice President
CFO: Douglas Davenport, System Chief Financial Officer
CMO: Paul Dolan, M.D., Chief Medical Affairs Officer
CIO: Lee Roath, System Chief Information Officer
CHR: Terry Olinger, System Chief Human Resources Officer
Web address: www.benefis.org
**Control:** Other not–for–profit (including NFP Corporation) **Service:** General Medical and Surgical

**Staffed Beds:** 463 **Admissions:** 12698 **Census:** 290 **Outpatient Visits:** 351241 **Births:** 1438 **Total Expense ($000):** 327075 **Payroll Expense ($000):** 136281 **Personnel:** 2152

**GREAT FALLS CLINIC MEDICAL CENTER (270086)**, 1411 9th Street South, Zip 59405–4507; tel. 406/216–8000, (Nonreporting) **A**9 10
Primary Contact: Patrick M. Hermanson, Administrator
COO: Vicki Newmiller, Chief Operating Officer
CFO: Cheryl Cornwell, Chief Financial Officer
CMO: Nicholas Bonfilio, M.D., Chief of Staff
Web address: www.greatfallsclinicmedicalcenter.com
**Control:** Corporation, Investor–owned, for–profit **Service:** Surgical

**Staffed Beds:** 20

### HAMILTON—Ravalli County

★ **MARCUS DALY MEMORIAL HOSPITAL (271340)**, 1200 Westwood Drive, Zip 59840–2345; tel. 406/363–2211 **A**9 10 18 **F**1 3 7 8 11 13 15 17 28 30 34 35 40 45 50 57 59 62 63 64 65 70 74 75 76 77 79 81 83 84 89 93 97 102 105 107 110 111 115 119 127 128 129 130 131 132 133 144 145 146 148
Primary Contact: John M. Bartos, Chief Executive Officer
CFO: Donja Erdman, Chief Financial Officer
CMO: John Moreland, M.D., Chief Medical Officer
CHR: Debbie M. Morris, Director Human Resources
Web address: www.mdmh.org
**Control:** Other not–for–profit (including NFP Corporation) **Service:** General Medical and Surgical

**Staffed Beds:** 37 **Admissions:** 1257 **Census:** 11 **Outpatient Visits:** 45453 **Births:** 154 **Total Expense ($000):** 45939 **Payroll Expense ($000):** 22497 **Personnel:** 417

### HARDIN—Big Horn County

★ **BIG HORN COUNTY MEMORIAL HOSPITAL (271338)**, 17 North Miles Avenue, Zip 59034–2323; tel. 406/665–2310, (Total facility includes 36 beds in nursing home–type unit) **A**9 10 18 **F**10 11 13 15 28 29 40 43 50 57 59 64 65 68 75 77 81 85 86 87 93 107 110 111 114 119 125 128 130 132 133 143 146
Primary Contact: George Minder, Chief Executive Officer
CFO: Roxie Cain, Chief Financial Officer
Web address: www.bighornhospital.org
**Control:** Other not–for–profit (including NFP Corporation) **Service:** General Medical and Surgical

**Staffed Beds:** 61 **Admissions:** 359 **Census:** 49 **Outpatient Visits:** 8040 **Births:** 51 **Total Expense ($000):** 12221 **Payroll Expense ($000):** 6902 **Personnel:** 159

**MT**

*Many Facility Codes have changed. Please refer to the AHA Guide Code Chart.*
© 2013 AHA Guide

## HARLEM—Blaine County

**FORT BELKNAP U. S. PUBLIC HEALTH SERVICE INDIAN HOSPITAL (271315)**, 669 Agency Main Street, Zip 59526–9455; tel. 406/353–3100, (Nonreporting) **A**10 18 **S** U. S. Indian Health Service, Rockville, MD
Primary Contact: Steve Fox, Chief Executive Officer
CIO: Mikki Grant, Chief Information Officer
CHR: Mary H. Mount, Administrative Officer
Web address: www.ihs.gov
**Control:** PHS, Indian Service, Government, federal **Service:** General Medical and Surgical

**Staffed Beds:** 6

## HARLOWTON—Wheatland County

★ **WHEATLAND MEMORIAL HEALTHCARE (271321)**, 530 Third Street North West, Zip 59036, Mailing Address: P.O. Box 287, Zip 59036–0287; tel. 406/632–4351, (Nonreporting) **A**9 10 18
Primary Contact: Lauri Ann Cooney, Interim Chief Executive Officer
CFO: Kathie R. Newland, Controller
CMO: Kris Cunningham, M.D., Chief of Staff
CIO: Russ Young, Network Administrator
CHR: Peggy Hiner, Executive Secretary and Manager Human Resources
CNO: Lauri Ann Cooney, Director Nursing
Web address: www.wheatlandmemorial.org
**Control:** Other not–for–profit (including NFP Corporation) **Service:** General Medical and Surgical

**Staffed Beds:** 25

## HAVRE—Hill County

★ **NORTHERN MONTANA HOSPITAL (270032)**, 30 13th Street, Zip 59501–5222, Mailing Address: P.O. Box 1231, Zip 59501–1231; tel. 406/265–2211, (Total facility includes 102 beds in nursing home–type unit) **A**9 10 20 **F**10 11 13 15 28 29 34 35 36 38 40 50 53 56 57 59 60 63 64 68 70 75 76 77 79 81 82 84 85 89 93 97 99 101 102 103 104 105 107 108 110 111 115 118 119 127 128 129 130 132 133 135 146 148 **P**6
Primary Contact: David Henry, President and Chief Executive Officer
CFO: Kim Lucke, Vice President Finance
CHR: Bonnie O'Neill, Vice President Employee Services
CNO: Brenda L. Sturm, MSN, Vice President, Patient Care Services
Web address: www.nmhcare.org
**Control:** Other not–for–profit (including NFP Corporation) **Service:** General Medical and Surgical

**Staffed Beds:** 129 **Admissions:** 1647 **Census:** 112 **Outpatient Visits:** 88358 **Births:** 397 **Total Expense ($000):** 47209 **Payroll Expense ($000):** 26598 **Personnel:** 488

## HELENA—Lewis And Clark County

⊞ **SHODAIR CHILDREN'S HOSPITAL (274004)**, 2755 Colonial Drive, Zip 59601–4926, Mailing Address: P.O. Box 5539, Zip 59604–5539; tel. 406/444–7500 **A**1 9 10 **F**55 98 99 101 104 106 130 **P**6
Primary Contact: John P. Casey, Administrator
COO: John P. Casey, Administrator
CFO: Ron Wiens, Chief Financial Officer
CMO: Heather Zaluski, M.D., President Medical Staff
CIO: Judy Jackson, Director Health Information Management and Privacy Officer
Web address: www.shodairhospital.org
**Control:** Other not–for–profit (including NFP Corporation) **Service:** Children's hospital psychiatric

**Staffed Beds:** 88 **Admissions:** 800 **Census:** 65 **Outpatient Visits:** 3501 **Births:** 0 **Total Expense ($000):** 20430 **Payroll Expense ($000):** 11813 **Personnel:** 204

⊞ **ST. PETER'S HOSPITAL (270003)**, 2475 Broadway, Zip 59601–4928; tel. 406/442–2480 **A**1 2 9 10 20 **F**3 7 11 13 15 18 20 22 28 29 30 31 34 35 40 45 46 50 51 54 56 57 59 60 62 63 64 65 70 74 75 76 78 79 81 82 84 92 93 98 102 103 107 108 110 111 114 115 116 117 119 120 121 122 129 130 132 133 135 143 144 146 147 148 **P**6
Primary Contact: Nate Olson, Chief Executive Officer
CFO: John Green, Vice President Finance
CIO: Tammy K. Buyok, Vice President Support Services
CHR: Thomas Gregg, Vice President Human Resources
Web address: www.stpetes.org
**Control:** Other not–for–profit (including NFP Corporation) **Service:** General Medical and Surgical

**Staffed Beds:** 123 **Admissions:** 5606 **Census:** 64 **Outpatient Visits:** 158158 **Births:** 755 **Total Expense ($000):** 160208 **Payroll Expense ($000):** 61983 **Personnel:** 961

## JORDAN—Garfield County

**GARFIELD COUNTY HEALTH CENTER (271310)**, 332 Leavitt Avenue, Zip 59337, Mailing Address: P.O. Box 389, Zip 59337–0389; tel. 406/557–2500, (Nonreporting) **A**9 10 18
Primary Contact: Hanz Arnston, R.N., Chief Executive Officer
CFO: Sandi Williams, Manager Business Officer
CMO: Daniel Muniak, M.D., Chief Medical Officer
CIO: Sandi Williams, Manager Business Officer
**Control:** County–Government, nonfederal **Service:** General Medical and Surgical

**Staffed Beds:** 4

## KALISPELL—Flathead County

**HEALTHCENTER NORTHWEST** See The HealthCenter

★ △ **KALISPELL REGIONAL MEDICAL CENTER (270051)**, 310 Sunnyview Lane, Zip 59901–3129; tel. 406/752–5111, (Includes PATHWAYS TREATMENT CENTER, 200 Heritage Way, Zip 59901; tel. 406/756–3950) **A**7 9 10 **F**3 4 5 8 13 15 18 20 22 24 26 28 29 30 31 35 36 40 43 45 46 49 50 56 57 58 59 62 63 64 68 70 72 74 75 76 77 78 79 81 84 85 86 87 90 98 99 100 101 102 104 105 107 108 114 115 118 119 120 121 123 126 129 130 131 132 143 144 145 146 147 148 **P**6
Primary Contact: Velinda Stevens, President
COO: Ted W. Hirsch, Senior Executive Director
CFO: Charles T. Pearce, Chief Financial and Information Officer
CHR: Deb Wilson, Director Human Resources
Web address: www.krmc.org
**Control:** Other not–for–profit (including NFP Corporation) **Service:** General Medical and Surgical

**Staffed Beds:** 163 **Admissions:** 7763 **Census:** 87 **Outpatient Visits:** 181022 **Births:** 659 **Total Expense ($000):** 203925 **Payroll Expense ($000):** 92431 **Personnel:** 2130

★ **THE HEALTHCENTER (270087)**, 320 Sunnyview Lane, Zip 59901–3129; tel. 406/751–7550 **A**9 10 **F**3 8 15 31 36 39 64 68 74 78 79 81 82 85 87 100 107 110 111 114 115 117 119 126 147 **P**2
Primary Contact: Tate J. Kreitinger, Chief Executive Officer
CMO: Craig Eddy, M.D., Chief Medical Officer
CIO: Charles T. Pearce, CFIO
CHR: Susan Stevens, Director Human Resources
CNO: Victoria Johnson, R.N., Nursing Director of Surgical and Medical Services
Web address: www.krmc.org
**Control:** Corporation, Investor–owned, for–profit **Service:** General Medical and Surgical

**Staffed Beds:** 30 **Admissions:** 699 **Census:** 4 **Outpatient Visits:** 38462 **Births:** 0 **Total Expense ($000):** 32098 **Payroll Expense ($000):** 6582 **Personnel:** 134

## LEWISTOWN—Fergus County

★ **CENTRAL MONTANA MEDICAL CENTER (271345)**, 408 Wendell Avenue, Zip 59457–2261; tel. 406/535–7711, (Total facility includes 65 beds in nursing home–type unit) **A**9 10 18 **F**3 7 11 13 15 28 29 30 31 34 35 40 43 45 46 50 53 56 57 59 62 63 64 65 75 76 77 78 79 81 82 85 86 87 89 93 97 100 102 105 107 108 110 111 115 119 128 129 130 131 132 133 135 143 146 148 **P**6 **S** QHR, Brentwood, TN
Primary Contact: Lee Rhodes, Chief Executive Officer
COO: Dianne Scotten, Chief Clinical Officer
CFO: Alan Aldrich, Chief Financial Officer
CHR: Torie A. Lynch, Manager Human Resources
Web address: www.cmmccares.com
**Control:** Other not–for–profit (including NFP Corporation) **Service:** General Medical and Surgical

**Staffed Beds:** 90 **Admissions:** 924 **Census:** 57 **Outpatient Visits:** 48020 **Births:** 92 **Total Expense ($000):** 26014 **Payroll Expense ($000):** 13491 **Personnel:** 309

MT

---

**Hospital, Medicare Provider Number, Address, Telephone, Approval, Facility, and Physician Codes, Health Care System**

★ American Hospital Association (AHA) membership
☐ The Joint Commission accreditation
◇ DNV Healthcare Inc. accreditation
○ Healthcare Facilities Accreditation Program
△ Commission on Accreditation of Rehabilitation Facilities (CARF) accreditation

## LIBBY—Lincoln County

★ **ST. JOHN'S LUTHERAN HOSPITAL (271320)**, 350 Louisiana Avenue, Zip 59923–2130; tel. 406/293–0100 **A**5 9 10 18 **F**3 11 13 15 17 28 29 30 31 34 35 40 45 56 57 59 64 68 70 75 76 77 79 81 82 84 85 86 87 89 91 93 97 102 107 110 111 114 119 129 130 131 132 133 135 144 146 147 148 **P**6
Primary Contact: Bruce Whitfield, CPA, Chief Executive Officer and Chief Financial Officer
CFO: Bruce Whitfield, CPA, Chief Executive Officer and Chief Financial Officer
CMO: Jay Maloney, M.D., Chief of Staff
Web address: www.sjlh.com
**Control:** Other not–for–profit (including NFP Corporation) **Service:** General Medical and Surgical

**Staffed Beds:** 25 **Admissions:** 932 **Census:** 10 **Outpatient Visits:** 34421 **Births:** 117 **Total Expense ($000):** 28174 **Payroll Expense ($000):** 12972 **Personnel:** 202

## LIVINGSTON—Park County

★ **LIVINGSTON MEMORIAL HOSPITAL (271317)**, 504 South 13th Street, Zip 59047–3727; tel. 406/222–3541 **A**9 10 18 **F**13 15 17 28 29 34 35 36 40 43 45 50 57 59 62 63 64 65 66 67 68 70 75 76 77 78 79 81 82 85 86 87 89 93 102 107 108 110 111 114 119 124 128 129 130 131 133 135 **P**3
Primary Contact: Bren Lowe, Chief Executive Officer
CFO: Melanie Emter, Director Finance
CMO: Michelle Donaldson, M.D., President Medical Staff
CHR: Connie Dunn, Director Human Resources
Web address: www.livingstonhealthcare.org
**Control:** Other not–for–profit (including NFP Corporation) **Service:** General Medical and Surgical

**Staffed Beds:** 25 **Admissions:** 884 **Census:** 9 **Outpatient Visits:** 22971 **Births:** 96 **Total Expense ($000):** 29125 **Payroll Expense ($000):** 14609 **Personnel:** 274

## MALTA—Phillips County

★ **PHILLIPS COUNTY HOSPITAL (271312)**, 417 South Fourth East, Zip 59538–8825, Mailing Address: P.O. Box 640, Zip 59538–0640; tel. 406/654–1100 **A**9 10 18 **F**3 28 29 30 31 32 34 35 40 41 43 45 56 58 59 62 64 65 67 78 90 93 97 107 114 127 128 130 133 148 **P**4
Primary Contact: Ward C. VanWichen, Chief Executive Officer
CFO: Stephanie Denham, Chief Financial Officer and Human Resources Officer
CMO: Ed Medina, M.D., Medical Director
CHR: Stephanie Denham, Chief Financial Officer and Human Resources Officer
CNO: Lonna Crowder, Director of Nursing
Web address: www.phillipscountyhospital.com
**Control:** Other not–for–profit (including NFP Corporation) **Service:** General Medical and Surgical

**Staffed Beds:** 6 **Admissions:** 199 **Census:** 2 **Outpatient Visits:** 7015 **Births:** 0 **Total Expense ($000):** 4903 **Payroll Expense ($000):** 2466 **Personnel:** 56

## MILES CITY—Custer County

⊠ **HOLY ROSARY HEALTHCARE (271347)**, 2600 Wilson Street, Zip 59301–5094; tel. 406/233–2600, (Total facility includes 65 beds in nursing home–type unit) **A**1 9 10 **F**3 13 15 26 28 29 30 31 32 34 35 40 41 45 48 56 57 59 63 64 65 68 70 75 76 77 78 79 81 84 85 89 93 97 102 107 108 110 111 115 119 124 127 129 130 131 133 135 143 144 146 147 148 **P**6
**S** SCL Health System, Denver, CO
Primary Contact: Paul Lewis, Chief Executive Officer
CFO: Calvin Carey, VP Finance and Support Services
CHR: Cathy Rodenbaugh, Director Human Resources
CNO: Lisa Sanford, VP Patient Care/CNO
Web address: www.holyrosaryhealthcare.org
**Control:** Church–operated, Nongovernment, not–for profit **Service:** General Medical and Surgical

**Staffed Beds:** 90 **Admissions:** 1645 **Census:** 71 **Outpatient Visits:** 56866 **Births:** 248 **Total Expense ($000):** 37849 **Payroll Expense ($000):** 16839 **Personnel:** 278

## MISSOULA—Missoula County

⊠ △ **COMMUNITY MEDICAL CENTER (270023)**, 2827 Fort Missoula Road, Zip 59804–7408; tel. 406/728–4100 **A**1 7 9 10 19 **F**2 3 11 13 17 18 20 22 26 28 29 30 31 34 35 37 40 43 45 46 47 48 49 51 54 57 59 64 65 68 70 72 73 74 75 76 78 79 81 82 83 84 85 87 88 89 90 91 92 93 94 96 97 107 108 110 115 116 117 118 119 126 130 132 134 135 143 144 145 146 147 148 **P**6 7
Primary Contact: Stephen G. Carlson, President and Chief Executive Officer
COO: Devin Huntley, Vice President Operations
CFO: David Richhart, Vice President Fiscal Services
CMO: Jonathan Weisul, M.D., Chief Medical Officer and Vice President Innovation
CIO: Leigh Thurston, Vice President Information Systems
CHR: Joe Schmier, Director Human Resources, Payroll & Employee Health
CNO: Jan Perry, R.N., Vice President Patient Care Services
Web address: www.communitymed.org
**Control:** Other not–for–profit (including NFP Corporation) **Service:** General Medical and Surgical

**Staffed Beds:** 133 **Admissions:** 5061 **Census:** 58 **Outpatient Visits:** 127695 **Births:** 1450 **Total Expense ($000):** 144824 **Payroll Expense ($000):** 58498 **Personnel:** 928

⊠ △ **ST. PATRICK HOSPITAL (270014)**, 500 West Broadway, Zip 59802–4096, Mailing Address: P.O. Box 4587, Zip 59806–4587; tel. 406/543–7271 **A**1 2 5 7 9 10 19 **F**3 5 8 11 12 15 18 19 20 21 22 23 24 25 26 27 28 29 30 31 34 35 36 38 40 43 45 49 50 53 57 58 59 61 64 65 68 70 74 75 77 78 79 81 82 84 85 86 88 89 90 92 93 96 97 98 99 100 101 102 103 104 105 107 108 110 111 113 114 115 116 117 118 119 121 123 124 126 127 129 130 131 132 135 141 146 147 148 **S** Providence Health & Services, Renton, WA
Primary Contact: Jeff Fee, Chief Executive Officer
COO: Craig E. Aasved, Chief Operating Officer
CHR: Karyn Trainor, Director Human Resources
Web address: www.saintpatrick.org
**Control:** Church–operated, Nongovernment, not–for profit **Service:** General Medical and Surgical

**Staffed Beds:** 193 **Admissions:** 8586 **Census:** 114 **Outpatient Visits:** 179939 **Births:** 0 **Total Expense ($000):** 207755 **Payroll Expense ($000):** 61099 **Personnel:** 1391

## PHILIPSBURG—Granite County

**GRANITE COUNTY MEDICAL CENTER (271303)**, 310 Sansome Street, Zip 59858–0729, Mailing Address: P.O. Box 729, Zip 59858–0729; tel. 406/859–3271, (Nonreporting) **A**9 10 18
Primary Contact: Daniel W. Boatman, Chief Executive Officer
CFO: Susan Ossello, Chief Financial Officer
CMO: John Moore, M.D., Medical Director
Web address: www.gcmedcenter.org/
**Control:** County–Government, nonfederal **Service:** General Medical and Surgical

**Staffed Beds:** 9

## PLAINS—Sanders County

★ **CLARK FORK VALLEY HOSPITAL (271323)**, 10 Kruger Road, Zip 59859, Mailing Address: P.O. Box 768, Zip 59859–0768; tel. 406/826–4800, (Total facility includes 28 beds in nursing home–type unit) **A**9 10 18 **F**3 11 13 15 18 29 30 32 34 35 36 40 43 44 45 50 57 58 59 62 63 64 65 68 70 74 75 76 77 81 82 83 84 85 89 93 97 107 110 114 118 119 127 128 130 133 143 146 147 148 **P**6
Primary Contact: Gregory S. Hanson, M.D., Chief Executive Officer
CFO: Carla Neiman, Chief Financial Officer
CMO: Sharon Nichols, D.O., Chief of Staff
CIO: Carla Neiman, Chief Financial Officer
CHR: Barry Fowler, Director Human and System Resources
CNO: Dawn Lynch, R.N., Director of Patient Care Services
Web address: www.cfvh.org
**Control:** Other not–for–profit (including NFP Corporation) **Service:** General Medical and Surgical

**Staffed Beds:** 44 **Admissions:** 430 **Census:** 28 **Outpatient Visits:** 37845 **Births:** 36 **Total Expense ($000):** 15351 **Payroll Expense ($000):** 7292 **Personnel:** 118

## PLENTYWOOD—Sheridan County

**SHERIDAN MEMORIAL HOSPITAL (271322)**, 440 West Laurel Avenue, Zip 59254–1596; tel. 406/765–1420, (Total facility includes 78 beds in nursing home–type unit) **A**9 10 18 **F**3 7 11 13 15 17 35 40 57 59 62 63 75 77 81 93 107 110 114 119 127 128 130 132 133 145 146 147
Primary Contact: Sandra Christensen, Chief Executive Officer
Web address: www.sheridanhospital.org
**Control:** Other not–for–profit (including NFP Corporation) **Service:** General Medical and Surgical

**Staffed Beds:** 97 **Admissions:** 299 **Census:** 52 **Outpatient Visits:** 12350 **Births:** 0 **Total Expense ($000):** 10506 **Payroll Expense ($000):** 5423 **Personnel:** 164

MT

*Many Facility Codes have changed. Please refer to the AHA Guide Code Chart.*
© 2013 AHA Guide

## POLSON—Lake County

**✶ ST. JOSEPH HOSPITAL (271343)**, 6 Thirteenth Avenue East, Zip 59860–5315, Mailing Address: P.O. Box 1010, Zip 59860–1010; tel. 406/883–5377 **A**1 9 10 18 **F**3 10 13 15 28 29 30 34 35 40 43 46 50 57 59 64 68 75 76 77 79 81 82 84 85 87 89 93 97 100 102 107 111 114 119 125 127 129 130 131 133 146 147 148 **P**6 **S** Providence Health & Services, Renton, WA
Primary Contact: James R. Kiser, II, Chief Executive Officer
COO: Colleen Nielsen, Director Operations
CFO: Kirk Bodlovic, Vice President and Chief Financial Officer
CMO: Kelly Bagnell, M.D., Chief of Staff
Web address: www.saintjoes.org
**Control:** Church–operated, Nongovernment, not–for profit **Service:** General Medical and Surgical

**Staffed Beds:** 22 **Admissions:** 615 **Census:** 6 **Outpatient Visits:** 62144 **Births:** 136 **Total Expense ($000):** 25578 **Payroll Expense ($000):** 11617 **Personnel:** 194

## POPLAR—Roosevelt County

**✶ POPLAR COMMUNITY HOSPITAL (271300)**, H and Court Avenue, Zip 59255, Mailing Address: P.O. Box 38, Zip 59255–0038; tel. 406/768–3452 **A**9 10 18 **F**3 7 40 43 50 57 59 69 75 114 130 133 143 **P**3 6
Primary Contact: Margaret B. Norgaard, Chief Executive Officer
CHR: Annie Block, Director Human Resources
Web address: www.nemhs.net
**Control:** Other not–for–profit (including NFP Corporation) **Service:** General Medical and Surgical

**Staffed Beds:** 20 **Admissions:** 111 **Census:** 6 **Outpatient Visits:** 8705 **Births:** 0 **Total Expense ($000):** 6701 **Payroll Expense ($000):** 2833

## RED LODGE—Carbon County

**✶ BEARTOOTH BILLINGS CLINIC (271326)**, 2525 North Broadway, Zip 59068–9222, Mailing Address: P.O. Box 590, Zip 59068–0590; tel. 406/446–2345 **A**9 10 18 **F**3 11 15 18 28 29 34 35 40 43 44 45 50 56 57 59 62 63 64 65 68 75 77 81 85 86 87 93 94 96 97 107 110 114 119 130 131 133 135 146 148 **P**6
Primary Contact: Kelley Evans, Chief Executive Officer
CFO: Kyle Gee, Chief Financial Officer
CMO: William George, M.D., Chief of Staff
CIO: Susan Scott, Director Medical Records
CHR: Katie Nordstrom, Director Human Resources
Web address: www.beartoothbillingsclinic.org
**Control:** Other not–for–profit (including NFP Corporation) **Service:** General Medical and Surgical

**Staffed Beds:** 10 **Admissions:** 223 **Census:** 3 **Outpatient Visits:** 54166 **Births:** 0 **Total Expense ($000):** 11161 **Payroll Expense ($000):** 3262 **Personnel:** 78

## RONAN—Lake County

**✶ ST. LUKE COMMUNITY HEALTHCARE (271325)**, (Formerly St. Luke Community Hospital), 107 Sixth Avenue S.W., Zip 59864–2634; tel. 406/676–4441, (Total facility includes 75 beds in nursing home–type unit) **A**9 10 18 **F**2 13 15 28 29 34 40 43 45 53 54 57 59 61 64 65 75 76 77 79 81 85 93 97 107 108 110 111 115 119 127 128 129 131 133 135 144 145 **P**6
Primary Contact: Shane H. Roberts, Chief Executive Officer
COO: Steve J. Todd, Chief Operating Officer
CFO: Paul Soukup, Chief Financial Officer
CMO: Paul D. Gochis, M.D., Chief of Staff
CHR: Theresa Jones, Manager Human Resources
Web address: www.stlukehealthnet.org
**Control:** Other not–for–profit (including NFP Corporation) **Service:** General Medical and Surgical

**Staffed Beds:** 105 **Admissions:** 1063 **Census:** 64 **Outpatient Visits:** 72122 **Births:** 157 **Total Expense ($000):** 33083 **Payroll Expense ($000):** 16601 **Personnel:** 303

## ROUNDUP—Musselshell County

**✶ ROUNDUP MEMORIAL HEALTHCARE (271346)**, 1202 Third Street West, Zip 59072–1816, Mailing Address: P.O. Box 40, Zip 59072–0040; tel. 406/323–2301 **A**9 10 18 **F**11 29 30 34 35 40 45 50 57 59 65 66 67 85 87 97 102 107 119 127 128 130 132 133 146 **P**6
Primary Contact: Bradley Howell, Chief Executive Officer
CMO: Terry D. Jones, M.D., Interim Chief of Staff
CHR: Michelle Clement, Executive Assistant/Human Resources Director
CNO: Alena Keller, Chief Nursing Officer
Web address: www.rmhmt.org/
**Control:** Other not–for–profit (including NFP Corporation) **Service:** General Medical and Surgical

**Staffed Beds:** 25 **Admissions:** 132 **Census:** 20 **Outpatient Visits:** 12063 **Births:** 0 **Total Expense ($000):** 4881 **Payroll Expense ($000):** 2331 **Personnel:** 66

## SAINT MARY—Glacier County

**U. S. PUBLIC HEALTH SERVICE BLACKFEET COMMUNITY HOSPITAL (270074)**, Zip 59417–0760; Mailing Address: Browning, tel. 406/338–6100, (Nonreporting) **A**5 10 **S** U. S. Indian Health Service, Rockville, MD
Primary Contact: Merlin Gilham, Chief Executive Officer
Web address: www.ihs.gov
**Control:** PHS, Indian Service, Government, federal **Service:** General Medical and Surgical

**Staffed Beds:** 25

## SCOBEY—Daniels County

**DANIELS MEMORIAL HEALTHCARE CENTER (271342)**, 105 Fifth Avenue East, Zip 59263, Mailing Address: P.O. Box 400, Zip 59263–0400; tel. 406/487–2296, (Total facility includes 30 beds in nursing home–type unit) **A**9 10 18 **F**2 11 29 31 34 35 40 43 50 56 57 59 64 65 67 69 75 77 85 86 87 91 93 97 102 103 107 114 127 130 131 132 133 143 146 148 **P**6
Primary Contact: David Hubbard, Chief Executive Officer
CMO: Don Sawdey, M.D., Medical Director
CHR: Edith Huda, Director Human Resources
Web address: www.danielsmemorialhealthcare.org
**Control:** Hospital district or authority, Government, nonfederal **Service:** General Medical and Surgical

**Staffed Beds:** 54 **Admissions:** 202 **Census:** 30 **Outpatient Visits:** 5491 **Births:** 0 **Total Expense ($000):** 6264 **Payroll Expense ($000):** 3146 **Personnel:** 95

## SHELBY—Toole County

**✶ MARIAS MEDICAL CENTER (271328)**, 640 Park Drive, Zip 59474–1663, Mailing Address: P.O. Box 915, Zip 59474–0915; tel. 406/434–3200, (Total facility includes 63 beds in nursing home–type unit) **A**9 10 18 **F**7 10 11 13 15 17 40 43 45 56 57 59 64 70 75 76 77 78 79 81 82 89 93 107 110 111 115 119 125 128 129 130 133
Primary Contact: Mark A. Cross, Chief Executive Officer
CFO: Melissa Ostberg, Chief Financial Officer
CMO: Charles G. Marlge, M.D., Chief of Staff
CIO: Jayce Yarn, Director Information Technology
CHR: Cindy Lamb, Director Human Resources
Web address: www.mmcmt.org
**Control:** County–Government, nonfederal **Service:** General Medical and Surgical

**Staffed Beds:** 88 **Admissions:** 420 **Census:** 46 **Outpatient Visits:** 13019 **Births:** 19 **Total Expense ($000):** 15693 **Payroll Expense ($000):** 6423 **Personnel:** 115

## SHERIDAN—Madison County

**✶ RUBY VALLEY HOSPITAL (271319)**, 220 East Crofoot Street, Zip 59749–7714, Mailing Address: P.O. Box 336, Zip 59749–0336; tel. 406/842–5453 **A**9 10 18 **F**2 11 28 29 34 35 38 40 50 56 57 59 64 65 66 71 75 77 82 86 90 91 93 97 119 127 128 130 133 135 147 148 **P**6
Primary Contact: John H. Semingson, Chief Executive Officer
CFO: Dennis Holschbach, Chief Financial Officer and Director Human Resources
CMO: Roman Hendrickson, M.D., Medical Director
CHR: Dennis Holschbach, Chief Financial Officer and Director Human Resources
CNO: Ted Woirhaye, R.N., Director of Nursing
Web address: www.rubyvalleyhospital.com/
**Control:** Hospital district or authority, Government, nonfederal **Service:** General Medical and Surgical

**Staffed Beds:** 8 **Admissions:** 187 **Census:** 2 **Outpatient Visits:** 5043 **Births:** 0 **Total Expense ($000):** 4398 **Payroll Expense ($000):** 2710 **Personnel:** 49

MT

---

**Hospital, Medicare Provider Number, Address, Telephone, Approval, Facility, and Physician Codes, Health Care System**

✶ American Hospital Association (AHA) membership
☐ The Joint Commission accreditation
◇ DNV Healthcare Inc. accreditation
○ Healthcare Facilities Accreditation Program
△ Commission on Accreditation of Rehabilitation Facilities (CARF) accreditation

### SIDNEY—Richland County

★ **SIDNEY HEALTH CENTER (271344)**, 216 14th Avenue S.W.,
Zip 59270–3586; tel. 406/488–2100, (Total facility includes 93 beds in nursing
home–type unit) **A**9 10 18 **F**2 3 13 15 17 28 30 31 34 35 40 45 50 56 57 59
62 63 64 70 75 76 78 79 81 82 84 85 86 87 89 93 96 107 108 110 115
119 120 121 122 123 125 128 129 130 133 144 145 146 147 148 **P**6 7
Primary Contact: Richard Haraldson, Chief Executive Officer
CFO: Tina Montgomery, Chief Financial Officer
CMO: Rajohn Karanjai, M.D., Chief Medical Officer
CIO: Brian Fay, Director Information Systems
CHR: Lisa Aisenbrey, Administrator Human Resources and Support Services
Web address: www.sidneyhealth.org
**Control:** Other not–for–profit (including NFP Corporation) **Service:** General
Medical and Surgical

| **Staffed Beds:** 118 **Admissions:** 957 **Census:** 85 **Outpatient Visits:** 38558 **Births:** 150 **Total Expense ($000):** 45071 **Payroll Expense ($000):** 17770 **Personnel:** 438 |
| --- |

### SUPERIOR—Mineral County

★ **MINERAL COMMUNITY HOSPITAL (271331)**, 1208 6th Avenue East,
Zip 59872–9618, Mailing Address: P.O. Box 66, Zip 59872–0066;
tel. 406/822–4841, (Nonreporting) **A**9 10 18
Primary Contact: Steven D. Carty, Chief Executive Officer
CFO: Cliff Case, Chief Financial Officer
CMO: Patrick Tufts, M.D., Medical Director
CHR: Stacy Conrow–Ververis, Director Human Resources
Web address: www.mineralcommunityhospital.com/
**Control:** Other not–for–profit (including NFP Corporation) **Service:** General
Medical and Surgical

| **Staffed Beds:** 25 |
| --- |

### TERRY—Prairie County

**PRAIRIE COMMUNITY HEALTH CENTER** See Prairie Community Hospital

★ **PRAIRIE COMMUNITY HOSPITAL (271309)**, 312 South Adams Avenue,
Zip 59349–0156, Mailing Address: P.O. Box 156, Zip 59349–0156;
tel. 406/635–5511 **A**9 10 18 **F**1 3 32 34 40 43 57 59 64 65 67 69 75 87 90
127 128 133 135 146 147 148 **P**6
Primary Contact: Parker Powell, Administrator
CFO: Laurie Chandler, Financial Officer
CMO: Joseph M. Leal, Jr., M.D., Medical Director
CIO: Laurie Chandler, Chairman
CNO: Kay Schaaf, Chief Nursing Officer
Web address: www.prairiecommunityhospital.org/
**Control:** Hospital district or authority, Government, nonfederal **Service:** General
Medical and Surgical

| **Staffed Beds:** 22 **Admissions:** 32 **Census:** 21 **Outpatient Visits:** 3119 **Births:** 0 **Total Expense ($000):** 2120 **Payroll Expense ($000):** 892 **Personnel:** 32 |
| --- |

### TOWNSEND—Broadwater County

**BROADWATER HEALTH CENTER (271333)**, 110 North Oak Street,
Zip 59644–2306; tel. 406/266–3186, (Nonreporting) **A**9 10 18
Primary Contact: Jan Kalgaard, Administrator
CFO: Lorrie Vennes, Chief Financial Officer
Web address: www.broadwaterhealthcenter.com
**Control:** County–Government, nonfederal **Service:** General Medical and Surgical

| **Staffed Beds:** 44 |
| --- |

### WARM SPRINGS—Deer Lodge County

**MONTANA STATE HOSPITAL (274086)**, 300 Garnet Way, Zip 59756–0300,
Mailing Address: P.O. Box 300, Zip 59756–0300; tel. 406/693–7000 **A**10 **F**29
38 39 50 59 66 68 74 75 77 86 97 98 100 103 106 119 130 132 135 **P**6
Primary Contact: John W. Glueckert, Administrator
CFO: Tracey Sweeney, Director Business and Support Services
CMO: Thomas Gray, M.D., Medical Director
CIO: Billie Holmlund, Director Information Services
CHR: Todd Thun, Director Human Resources
Web address: www.msh.mt.gov
**Control:** State–Government, nonfederal **Service:** Psychiatric

| **Staffed Beds:** 201 **Admissions:** 640 **Census:** 163 **Outpatient Visits:** 0 **Births:** 0 **Total Expense ($000):** 30284 **Payroll Expense ($000):** 16630 **Personnel:** 402 |
| --- |

### WHITE SULPHUR SPRINGS—Meagher County

**MOUNTAINVIEW MEDICAL CENTER (271306)**, 16 West Main Street,
Zip 59645–9036, Mailing Address: P.O. Box Q, Zip 59645–0817;
tel. 406/547–3321, (Nonreporting) **A**9 10 18
Primary Contact: Aaron Rogers, Chief Executive Officer
Web address: www.mvmc.org
**Control:** Other not–for–profit (including NFP Corporation) **Service:** General
Medical and Surgical

| **Staffed Beds:** 25 |
| --- |

### WHITEFISH—Flathead County

★ **NORTH VALLEY HOSPITAL (271336)**, 1600 Hospital Way, Zip 59937–7849;
tel. 406/863–3500 **A**9 10 18 **F**3 11 13 15 28 29 30 31 34 35 37 40 43 45
50 51 54 56 57 59 64 68 70 75 76 79 81 82 85 86 87 97 100 102 103 104
107 110 111 115 119 126 127 129 130 131 132 133 135 144 146 148
**S** QHR, Brentwood, TN
Primary Contact: Jason A. Spring, FACHE, Chief Executive Officer
COO: Maura G. Fields, R.N., Chief Clinical Officer
CFO: Marilyn Hays, Chief Financial Officer
CIO: Michael Barnes, Chief Information Officer
CHR: Susan G. Catt, Director Human Resources
Web address: www.nvhosp.org
**Control:** Other not–for–profit (including NFP Corporation) **Service:** General
Medical and Surgical

| **Staffed Beds:** 25 **Admissions:** 1550 **Census:** 13 **Outpatient Visits:** 47043 **Births:** 483 **Total Expense ($000):** 40868 **Payroll Expense ($000):** 13525 **Personnel:** 282 |
| --- |

### WOLF POINT—Roosevelt County

★ **TRINITY HOSPITAL (271341)**, 315 Knapp Street, Zip 59201–1826;
tel. 406/653–6500, (Total facility includes 60 beds in nursing home–type unit) **A**9
10 18 **F**2 3 6 7 8 13 15 29 31 32 34 40 41 43 45 50 56 57 59 64 67 69 70
75 76 78 81 89 92 110 119 120 125 127 128 130 133 143 145
Primary Contact: Margaret B. Norgaard, Chief Executive Officer
Web address: www.nemhs.net
**Control:** Other not–for–profit (including NFP Corporation) **Service:** General
Medical and Surgical

| **Staffed Beds:** 82 **Admissions:** 444 **Census:** 69 **Outpatient Visits:** 15363 **Births:** 126 **Total Expense ($000):** 14239 **Payroll Expense ($000):** 6019 **Personnel:** 175 |
| --- |

MT

*Many Facility Codes have changed. Please refer to the AHA Guide Code Chart.*
© 2013 AHA Guide

# NEBRASKA

## AINSWORTH—Brown County

**BROWN COUNTY HOSPITAL (281325)**, 945 East Zero Street,
Zip 69210–1547; tel. 402/387–2800 **A**9 10 18 **F**15 28 31 40 45 57 59 62 64
75 77 78 79 81 93 94 107 110 111 114 119 130 133 148 **P**6
Primary Contact: Shannon Sorensen, Chief Executive Officer
CFO: Matt Sells, CPA, Chief Financial Officer
CMO: Annette Miller, M.D., Medical Staff Chairman
CIO: Mike Depko, Director Information Technology
CHR: Lisa Fischer, Director Human Resources
Web address: www.browncountyhospital.org
**Control:** County–Government, nonfederal **Service:** General Medical and Surgical

**Staffed Beds:** 18 **Admissions:** 191 **Census:** 1 **Outpatient Visits:** 10194
**Births:** 0 **Total Expense ($000):** 6753 **Payroll Expense ($000):** 2818
**Personnel:** 74

## ALBION—Boone County

★ **BOONE COUNTY HEALTH CENTER (281334)**, 723 West Fairview Street,
Zip 68620–1725, Mailing Address: P.O. Box 151, Zip 68620–0151;
tel. 402/395–2191, (Nonreporting) **A**9 10 18
Primary Contact: Victor N. Lee, FACHE, President and Chief Executive Officer
CFO: Mandy Kumm, Vice President Fiscal Services
CIO: Larry Zoucha, Chief Information Officer
CHR: Jennifer Beierman, Director Human Resources
Web address: www.boonecohealth.org
**Control:** County–Government, nonfederal **Service:** General Medical and Surgical

**Staffed Beds:** 25

## ALLIANCE—Box Butte County

⊠ **BOX BUTTE GENERAL HOSPITAL (281360)**, 2101 Box Butte Avenue,
Zip 69301–4445, Mailing Address: P.O. Box 810, Zip 69301–0810;
tcl. 308/762–6660 **A**1 9 10 18 **F**3 5 11 13 15 28 29 31 32 34 35 36 38 40
43 50 53 57 59 60 64 68 69 75 77 78 79 81 82 85 86 87 92 93 97 100
101 104 107 108 111 114 116 118 119 127 129 130 131 132 133 134 135
146 148
Primary Contact: Dan Griess, Chief Executive Officer
COO: Jim Parks, Chief Operating Officer
CFO: Tracy E. Jatczak, CPA, Chief Financial Officer
CMO: John J. Ruffing, Jr., M.D., Chief of Staff
CIO: Jim Parks, Chief Operating Officer
CHR: Rebecca Sisler, Director Human Resources
Web address: www.bbgh.org
**Control:** County–Government, nonfederal **Service:** General Medical and Surgical

**Staffed Beds:** 25 **Admissions:** 1001 **Census:** 11 **Outpatient Visits:** 34251
**Births:** 76 **Total Expense ($000):** 29743 **Payroll Expense ($000):** 12925
**Personnel:** 255

## ALMA—Harlan County

★ **HARLAN COUNTY HEALTH SYSTEM (281300)**, 717 North Brown Street,
Zip 68920–2132, Mailing Address: P.O. Box 836, Zip 68920–0836;
tel. 308/928–2151 **A**9 10 18 **F**3 11 15 29 30 31 40 46 50 64 75 81 85 86
93 107 110 114 119 127 128 130 132 133 135 **P**6 **S** Great Plains Health
Alliance, Inc., Wichita, KS
Primary Contact: Manuela Wolf, Interim Chief Executive Officer
CFO: Sue Lans, Comptroller
CMO: Anton Smolik, M.D., Chief of Medical Staff
CIO: Bob Kentner, Coordinator Information Systems
CHR: Peg Howart, Coordinator Human Resources and Benefits
Web address: www.harlancountyhealth.com
**Control:** County–Government, nonfederal **Service:** General Medical and Surgical

**Staffed Beds:** 19 **Admissions:** 175 **Census:** 3 **Outpatient Visits:** 18469
**Births:** 0 **Total Expense ($000):** 7615 **Payroll Expense ($000):** 3147
**Personnel:** 57

## ATKINSON—Holt County

**WEST HOLT MEMORIAL HOSPITAL (281343)**, 406 West Neely Street,
Zip 68713–4801; tel. 402/925–2811, (Nonreporting) **A**9 10 18 **S** Faith Regional
Health Services, Norfolk, NE
Primary Contact: Michael F. Coyle, Chief Executive Officer
CFO: Karen Nollette, Chief Financial Officer
CMO: John Tubbs, M.D., Chief of Staff
CIO: Mark Johnson, Chief Information Officer
CHR: Margaret Linse, Administrative Secretary and Director Human Resources
Web address: www.westholtmed.org
**Control:** Other not–for–profit (including NFP Corporation) **Service:** General
Medical and Surgical

**Staffed Beds:** 18

## AUBURN—Nemaha County

★ ◇ **NEMAHA COUNTY HOSPITAL (281324)**, 2022 13th Street,
Zip 68305–1799; tel. 402/274–4366 **A**9 10 18 21 **F**1 3 4 7 11 12 13 15 16
17 28 29 30 31 35 40 43 62 64 67 68 70 72 73 74 75 76 77 78 79 80 81
82 85 87 88 89 90 93 94 98 107 110 111 114 117 119 128 129 133 135
141 147 148
Primary Contact: Marty Fattig, Chief Executive Officer
COO: Kermit Moore, R.N., Chief Operating Officer and Chief Nursing Officer
CFO: Stacy Taylor, Chief Financial Officer
CHR: Susie Shupp, Director Human Resources
Web address: www.nchnet.org
**Control:** County–Government, nonfederal **Service:** General Medical and Surgical

**Staffed Beds:** 20 **Admissions:** 272 **Census:** 4 **Outpatient Visits:** 19269
**Births:** 0 **Total Expense ($000):** 10891 **Payroll Expense ($000):** 4243
**Personnel:** 75

## AURORA—Hamilton County

★ **MEMORIAL COMMUNITY HEALTH (281320)**, 1423 Seventh Street,
Zip 68818–1197; tel. 402/694–3171, (Nonreporting) **A**9 10 18
Primary Contact: Diane R. Keller, Chief Executive Officer
CFO: Phil Fendt, Chief Financial Officer
CMO: Timothy Widhelm, M.D., Chief of Staff
CHR: Laurie Andrews, Chief Human Resources Officer
Web address: www.memorialcommunityhealth.org
**Control:** Other not–for–profit (including NFP Corporation) **Service:** General
Medical and Surgical

**Staffed Beds:** 64

**MEMORIAL HOSPITAL** See Memorial Community Health

## BASSETT—Rock County

**ROCK COUNTY HOSPITAL (281333)**, 102 East South Street,
Zip 68714–5508; tel. 402/684–3366, (Total facility includes 30 beds in nursing
home–type unit) **A**9 10 18 **F**7 11 28 40 53 57 81 84 107 127 128 133
Primary Contact: Stacey A. Knox, Administrator
CMO: John I. Cherry, M.D., Chief of Staff
CHR: Jackie Carpenter, Office Manager
Web address: www.rockcountyhospital.com
**Control:** County–Government, nonfederal **Service:** General Medical and Surgical

**Staffed Beds:** 54 **Admissions:** 284 **Census:** 32 **Outpatient Visits:** 5479
**Births:** 0 **Total Expense ($000):** 5125 **Payroll Expense ($000):** 2724
**Personnel:** 73

NE

---

**Hospital, Medicare Provider Number, Address, Telephone, Approval, Facility, and Physician Codes, Health Care System**

★ American Hospital Association (AHA) membership
☐ The Joint Commission accreditation
◇ DNV Healthcare Inc. accreditation

○ Healthcare Facilities Accreditation Program
△ Commission on Accreditation of Rehabilitation Facilities (CARF) accreditation

## BEATRICE—Gage County

☒ **BEATRICE COMMUNITY HOSPITAL AND HEALTH CENTER (281364)**, 4800 Hospital Parkway, Zip 68310–6906, Mailing Address: P.O. Box 278, Zip 68310–0278; tel. 402/228–3344 **A**1 9 10 18 **F**3 13 15 28 31 34 35 40 45 57 62 63 64 65 68 69 70 75 76 78 79 81 85 87 93 107 108 110 111 114 118 119 127 129 130 132 133 135 146 147
Primary Contact: Thomas W. Sommers, FACHE, President and Chief Executive Officer
CFO: Alan W. Streeter, Chief Financial Officer
CMO: Brett Studley, M.D., Chief of Staff
CHR: Charlotte Campbell, Chief Human Resources Officer
CNO: Julie L. Jones, R.N., Chief Nursing Officer
Web address: www.beatricecommunityhospital.com
**Control:** Other not–for–profit (including NFP Corporation) **Service:** General Medical and Surgical

**Staffed Beds:** 25 **Admissions:** 941 **Census:** 7 **Outpatient Visits:** 145495 **Births:** 191 **Total Expense ($000):** 47453 **Payroll Expense ($000):** 20121 **Personnel:** 333

## BELLEVUE—Sarpy County

☐ **BELLEVUE MEDICAL CENTER (280132)**, 2500 Bellevue Medical Center Drive, Zip 68123–1591; tel. 402/763–3000, (Nonreporting) **A**1 3 5 9 10
Primary Contact: Paulette Davidson, Chief Executive Officer
CMO: Marlin G. Stahl, M.D., Chief Medical Officer
Web address: www.bellevuemed.com
**Control:** Partnership, Investor–owned, for–profit **Service:** General Medical and Surgical

**Staffed Beds:** 55

## BENKELMAN—Dundy County

★ **DUNDY COUNTY HOSPITAL (281340)**, 1313 North Cheyenne Street, Zip 69021–3074, Mailing Address: P.O. Box 626, Zip 69021–0626; tel. 308/423–2204, (Nonreporting) **A**9 10 18
Primary Contact: Rita A. Jones, Chief Executive Officer
COO: Wendy Elkins, Director Operations
CFO: Dwana Roschewski, Director Fiscal Services
CMO: Lori Stonehocker, D.O., Chief Medical Staff
CIO: Anna Elliot, Head Information Technology
CHR: Sandy Noffsinger, Executive Assistant, Risk Manager and Director Marketing
Web address: www.bwtelcom.net/dch
**Control:** County–Government, nonfederal **Service:** General Medical and Surgical

**Staffed Beds:** 14

## BLAIR—Washington County

**MEMORIAL COMMUNITY HOSPITAL AND HEALTH SYSTEM (281359)**, 810 North 22nd Street, Zip 68008–1199, Mailing Address: P.O. Box 250, Zip 68008–0250; tel. 402/426–2182, (Nonreporting) **A**9 10 18
Primary Contact: Robert C. Copple, FACHE, Interim Administrator
CMO: John F. Simonson, M.D., President Medical Staff
CNO: Jane Carmody DNP, MBA, RN, CENP, R.N., Vice President and System Chief Nursing Officer
Web address: www.mchhs.org
**Control:** Other not–for–profit (including NFP Corporation) **Service:** General Medical and Surgical

**Staffed Beds:** 25

## BRIDGEPORT—Morrill County

**MORRILL COUNTY COMMUNITY HOSPITAL (281318)**, 1313 S Street, Zip 69336–0579, Mailing Address: P.O. Box 579, Zip 69336–0579; tel. 308/262–1616, (Nonreporting) **A**9 10 18
Primary Contact: Vail Oleson, Chief Executive Officer
COO: Robin Stuart, Chief Operating Officer
Web address: www.morrillcountyhospital.org
**Control:** County–Government, nonfederal **Service:** General Medical and Surgical

**Staffed Beds:** 20

## BROKEN BOW—Custer County

**JENNIE M. MELHAM MEMORIAL MEDICAL CENTER (281365)**, 145 Memorial Drive, Zip 68822–1378, Mailing Address: P.O. Box 250, Zip 68822–0250; tel. 308/872–4100, (Nonreporting) **A**9 10 18
Primary Contact: Michael J. Steckler, President and Chief Executive Officer
CFO: Tim Schuckman, Chief Financial Officer
CIO: Tim Schuckman, Chief Financial Officer
Web address: www.brokenbow-ne.com/community/healthcare/melham.htm
**Control:** Other not–for–profit (including NFP Corporation) **Service:** General Medical and Surgical

**Staffed Beds:** 25

## CALLAWAY—Custer County

★ **CALLAWAY DISTRICT HOSPITAL (281335)**, 211 East Kimball, Zip 68825–2589, Mailing Address: P.O. Box 100, Zip 68825–0100; tel. 308/836–2228, (Nonreporting) **A**9 10 18
Primary Contact: Marvin Neth, Administrator
CHR: Carol Koch, Manager Human Resources
Web address: www.callaway-ne.com/hospital/
**Control:** Hospital district or authority, Government, nonfederal **Service:** General Medical and Surgical

**Staffed Beds:** 12

## CAMBRIDGE—Furnas County

★ **TRI VALLEY HEALTH SYSTEM (281348)**, 1305 West Highway 6 and 34, Zip 69022–0488, Mailing Address: P.O. Box 488, Zip 69022–0488; tel. 308/697–3329, (Nonreporting) **A**9 10 18 **S** HealthTech Management Services, Franklin, TN
Primary Contact: Roger W. Steinkruger, Chief Executive Officer
CFO: Diana Rippe, Chief Financial Officer
CMO: Shelly Kasper–Cope, M.D., Chief of Staff
CIO: Doug Hall, Director Information Systems
CHR: Tammy Claussen, Human Resources Executive
Web address: www.trivalleyhealth.com
**Control:** Other not–for–profit (including NFP Corporation) **Service:** General Medical and Surgical

**Staffed Beds:** 51

## CENTRAL CITY—Merrick County

★ **LITZENBERG MEMORIAL COUNTY HOSPITAL (281328)**, 1715 26th Street, Zip 68826–9620; tel. 308/946–3015, (Total facility includes 45 beds in nursing home–type unit) **A**9 10 18 **F**40 45 57 59 64 67 75 77 79 81 91 92 93 107 110 114 119 128 130 132 133 145 **P**4
Primary Contact: Tad M. Hunt, MS, Chief Executive Officer
Web address: www.lmchealth.com
**Control:** County–Government, nonfederal **Service:** General Medical and Surgical

**Staffed Beds:** 65 **Admissions:** 458 **Census:** 41 **Outpatient Visits:** 10378 **Births:** 0 **Total Expense ($000):** 11957 **Payroll Expense ($000):** 4569 **Personnel:** 102

## CHADRON—Dawes County

★ **CHADRON COMMUNITY HOSPITAL AND HEALTH SERVICES (281341)**, 825 Centennial Drive, Zip 69337–9400; tel. 308/432–5586, (Nonreporting) **A**5 9 10 18
Primary Contact: Harold L. Krueger, Jr., Chief Executive Officer
CFO: Russ Bohnenkamp, Director Finance
CMO: Jerry McLain, M.D., Chief of Staff
CIO: Anna Turman, Chief Information Officer
CHR: Ellen Krueger, Director Human Resources
CNO: Cheryl Cassiday, R.N., Director of Nursing
Web address: www.chadronhospital.com
**Control:** Other not–for–profit (including NFP Corporation) **Service:** General Medical and Surgical

**Staffed Beds:** 25

## COLUMBUS—Platte County

☒ **COLUMBUS COMMUNITY HOSPITAL (280111)**, 4600 38th Street, Zip 68601–1664, Mailing Address: P.O. Box 1800, Zip 68602–1800; tel. 402/564–7118, (Total facility includes 4 beds in nursing home–type unit) **A**1 9 10 20 **F**3 8 11 13 15 17 28 29 34 35 37 38 39 40 43 45 57 59 62 63 64 65 68 69 70 75 76 77 79 81 82 84 85 86 87 93 107 108 110 111 115 116 117 118 119 127 128 129 130 131 132 133 135 146 148 **P**8
Primary Contact: Michael T. Hansen, FACHE, President and Chief Executive Officer
COO: James P. Goulet, Vice President Operations
CFO: J. Joseph Barbaglia, Vice President Financial Services
CMO: Mark Howerter, M.D., President Medical Staff
CIO: Cheryl Tira, Director Information Systems
CHR: Scott E. Messersmith, Director Human Resources
Web address: www.columbushosp.org
**Control:** Other not–for–profit (including NFP Corporation) **Service:** General Medical and Surgical

**Staffed Beds:** 51 **Admissions:** 2416 **Census:** 19 **Outpatient Visits:** 55598 **Births:** 606 **Total Expense ($000):** 57891 **Payroll Expense ($000):** 25295 **Personnel:** 423

## COZAD—Dawson County

★ **COZAD COMMUNITY HOSPITAL (281327)**, 300 East 12th Street, Zip 69130–1505, Mailing Address: P.O. Box 108, Zip 69130–0108; tel. 308/784–2261, (Nonreporting) **A**9 10 18
Primary Contact: Lyle E. Davis, Administrator
Web address: www.cozadhealthcare.com
**Control:** Hospital district or authority, Government, nonfederal **Service:** General Medical and Surgical

**Staffed Beds:** 21

NE

## CREIGHTON—Knox County

★ **AVERA CREIGHTON HOSPITAL (281331)**, 1503 Main Street,
Zip 68729–3007, Mailing Address: P.O. Box 186, Zip 68729–0186;
tel. 402/358–5700, (Total facility includes 47 beds in nursing home–type unit) **A**9
10 18 **F**8 11 15 28 29 31 34 35 40 45 46 50 53 56 57 59 62 64 65 75 77
78 81 84 90 93 107 110 127 128 130 131 133 146 147 148 **P**6 **S** Avera
Health, Sioux Falls, SD
Primary Contact: Mark Schulte, Chief Executive Officer
CFO: Gregory Beckmann, Finance Controller
CHR: Candace Timmerman, Director Human Resources
CNO: Jean M. Henes, R.N., Director of Nursing
Web address: www.avera.org/creighton/
**Control:** Other not–for–profit (including NFP Corporation) **Service:** General
Medical and Surgical

> **Staffed Beds:** 54 **Admissions:** 377 **Census:** 43 **Outpatient Visits:** 5817
> **Births:** 0 **Total Expense ($000):** 9044 **Payroll Expense ($000):** 4153
> **Personnel:** 95

## CRETE—Saline County

★ **CRETE AREA MEDICAL CENTER (281354)**, 2910 Betten Drive,
Zip 68333–3084, Mailing Address: P.O. Box 220, Zip 68333–0220;
tel. 402/826–2102 **A**9 10 18 **F**13 15 28 29 31 34 40 43 57 59 64 65 68 78
79 81 93 97 107 111 114 117 119 127 129 130 131 133 143 146 147 **P**6
**S** Bryan Health, Lincoln, NE
Primary Contact: Carol Friesen, President and Chief Executive Officer
CFO: Bryce Betke, Chief Financial Officer
CIO: Sheri Thompson, Director Information Technology
CHR: Bobbie Wilson, Director Human Resources
Web address: www.creteareamedicalcenter.com
**Control:** Other not–for–profit (including NFP Corporation) **Service:** General
Medical and Surgical

> **Staffed Beds:** 24 **Admissions:** 428 **Census:** 4 **Outpatient Visits:** 54124
> **Births:** 95 **Total Expense ($000):** 18734 **Payroll Expense ($000):** 7304
> **Personnel:** 132

## DAVID CITY—Butler County

★ **BUTLER COUNTY HEALTH CARE CENTER (281332)**, 372 South Ninth Street,
Zip 68632–2116; tel. 402/367–1200 **A**9 10 18 **F**7 13 15 28 29 30 31 34 37
40 45 46 53 56 57 59 63 64 71 75 76 77 78 79 81 82 93 107 110 114 119
126 130 131 133 135 143 145 146
Primary Contact: Donald T. Naiberk, Administrator
CFO: Ron Jones, Chief Financial Officer
CMO: Victor Thoendel, M.D., Chief Medical Officer
CIO: Cindy Neesen, Director of Information Technology
CHR: Andra Vandenberg, Director Human Resources
CNO: Sue M. Birkel, R.N., Director of Nursing
Web address: www.bchccnet.org
**Control:** County–Government, nonfederal **Service:** General Medical and Surgical

> **Staffed Beds:** 20 **Admissions:** 814 **Census:** 5 **Outpatient Visits:** 17805
> **Births:** 85 **Total Expense ($000):** 11724 **Payroll Expense ($000):** 5247

## ELKHORN—Douglas County

**METHODIST WOMEN'S HOSPITAL** See Nebraska Methodist Hospital, Omaha

## FAIRBURY—Jefferson County

★ **JEFFERSON COMMUNITY HEALTH CENTER (281319)**, 2200 H Street,
Zip 68352–1119, Mailing Address: P.O. Box 277, Zip 68352–0277;
tel. 402/729–3351, (Total facility includes 39 beds in nursing home–type unit) **A**9
10 18 **F**2 3 13 15 28 29 30 31 34 35 40 42 45 50 53 57 59 62 75 76 77 78
79 81 85 86 87 93 107 110 114 119 128 130 131 132 133 135 146 **P**5
Primary Contact: William L. Welch, FACHE, Chief Executive Officer
CFO: Chad Jurgens, Chief Financial Officer
CIO: Dennis Ahl, Director Information Technology
CHR: Sandra A. Bauer, Director Human Resources
Web address: www.jchc.us
**Control:** Other not–for–profit (including NFP Corporation) **Service:** General
Medical and Surgical

> **Staffed Beds:** 64 **Admissions:** 359 **Census:** 42 **Outpatient Visits:** 17562
> **Births:** 38 **Total Expense ($000):** 14948 **Payroll Expense ($000):** 6351
> **Personnel:** 159

## FALLS CITY—Richardson County

★ **COMMUNITY MEDICAL CENTER (281352)**, 3307 Barada Street,
Zip 68355–2470, Mailing Address: P.O. Box 399, Zip 68355–0399;
tel. 402/245–2428 **A**9 10 18 **F**3 13 15 28 31 34 35 40 43 45 57 59 75 76
78 81 85 93 97 107 111 119 127 130 133 135 **P**6
Primary Contact: Ryan C. Larsen, FACHE, Chief Executive Officer
CFO: Scott Sawyer, Chief Financial Officer
CIO: Karen Brown, Director Health Information
CHR: Shannon Weinmann, Director Human Resources
Web address: www.cmcfc.org
**Control:** Other not–for–profit (including NFP Corporation) **Service:** General
Medical and Surgical

> **Staffed Beds:** 24 **Admissions:** 892 **Census:** 11 **Outpatient Visits:** 45462
> **Births:** 61 **Total Expense ($000):** 18783 **Payroll Expense ($000):** 6787
> **Personnel:** 162

## FRANKLIN—Franklin County

★ **FRANKLIN COUNTY MEMORIAL HOSPITAL (281311)**, 1406 Q Street,
Zip 68939–0315, Mailing Address: P.O. Box 315, Zip 68939–0315;
tel. 308/425–6221, (Nonreporting) **A**9 10 18
Primary Contact: Linda Bush, Chief Executive Officer
CFO: Amy Richards, Accounting
CMO: Linda Mazour, M.D., President
CIO: Cathy Webber, Chief Information Officer
Web address: www.fcmh.com
**Control:** County–Government, nonfederal **Service:** General Medical and Surgical

> **Staffed Beds:** 14

## FREMONT—Dodge County

☐ **FREMONT AREA MEDICAL CENTER (280077)**, 450 East 23rd Street,
Zip 68025–2387; tel. 402/721–1610, (Nonreporting) **A**1 2 9 10
Primary Contact: Patrick M. Booth, Chief Executive Officer
CFO: David G. Hanen, Vice President and Chief Financial Officer
Web address: www.famc.org
**Control:** County–Government, nonfederal **Service:** General Medical and Surgical

> **Staffed Beds:** 202

## FRIEND—Saline County

**WARREN MEMORIAL HOSPITAL (281330)**, 905 Second Street,
Zip 68359–1133; tel. 402/947–2541, (Nonreporting) **A**9 10 18
Primary Contact: John W. Wilson, Chief Executive Officer
CFO: Daniel R. Bartz, CPA, Chief Financial Officer
CMO: Roger Meyer, M.D., Chief of Staff
CIO: Mary Kay Carrithers, Manager Health Information
CHR: Jamie Tuttle, Coordinator Human Resources
Web address: www.warrenmemorialhospital.org
**Control:** City–Government, nonfederal **Service:** General Medical and Surgical

> **Staffed Beds:** 60

## GENEVA—Fillmore County

**FILLMORE COUNTY HOSPITAL (281301)**, 1900 F Street, Zip 68361–1325,
Mailing Address: P.O. Box 193, Zip 68361–0193; tel. 402/759–3167,
(Nonreporting) **A**9 10 18
Primary Contact: Paul Utemark, Chief Executive Officer
CFO: Jeanne Ackland, Director of Finance
CMO: John Jacobsen, M.D., Chief of Staff
CIO: Tyler Gewecke, Information Technology Technician
CHR: Abby Tuberville, Human Resource Generalist
Web address: www.fhsofgeneva.org
**Control:** County–Government, nonfederal **Service:** General Medical and Surgical

> **Staffed Beds:** 25

## GENOA—Nance County

**GENOA COMMUNITY HOSPITAL (281312)**, 706 Ewing Avenue,
Zip 68640–3035, Mailing Address: P.O. Box 310, Zip 68640–0310;
tel. 402/993–2283, (Total facility includes 39 beds in nursing home–type unit) **A**9
10 18 **F**10 34 40 43 45 46 57 59 64 65 67 75 77 81 93 107 111 119 127
128 130 131 132 133 **P**5
Primary Contact: Larry E. Schrage, Administrator
CFO: Jennifer Wieck, Business Manager
CMO: Brian Buhlke, M.D., Medical Director
CHR: Kari Reeg, Manager Human Resources
Web address: www.genoamedical.org/
**Control:** City–Government, nonfederal **Service:** General Medical and Surgical

> **Staffed Beds:** 58 **Admissions:** 169 **Census:** 34 **Outpatient Visits:** 7397
> **Births:** 0

**NE**

**Hospital, Medicare Provider Number, Address, Telephone, Approval, Facility, and Physician Codes, Health Care System**

★ American Hospital Association (AHA) membership
☐ The Joint Commission accreditation
◇ DNV Healthcare Inc. accreditation
○ Healthcare Facilities Accreditation Program
△ Commission on Accreditation of Rehabilitation Facilities (CARF) accreditation

© 2013 AHA Guide    *Many Facility Codes have changed. Please refer to the AHA Guide Code Chart.*    Hospitals **A383**

**GORDON—Sheridan County**

★ **GORDON MEMORIAL HOSPITAL (281358)**, 300 East Eighth Street,
Zip 69343–1123; tel. 308/282–0401, (Nonreporting) **A**9 10 18
Primary Contact: James B. McHugh, Interim Chief Executive Officer
CFO: Heidi Cushing, Director Finance
CMO: Christopher P. Costa, M.D., Chief of Staff
CIO: Ray Waldron, Director Information Technology
CHR: Shelley Beguin, Director Human Resources
Web address: www.gordonmemorial.org
**Control:** Hospital district or authority, Government, nonfederal **Service:** General Medical and Surgical

**Staffed Beds:** 25

**GOTHENBURG—Dawson County**

★ **GOTHENBURG MEMORIAL HOSPITAL (281313)**, 910 20th Street,
Zip 69138–1237, Mailing Address: P.O. Box 469, Zip 69138–0469;
tel. 308/537–3661 **A**9 10 18 **F**3 8 13 15 18 19 28 29 34 35 38 40 41 43 44
45 46 50 53 56 57 59 63 64 65 68 75 76 77 79 81 84 85 86 87 91 93 94
96 102 107 110 111 114 119 129 130 132 133 135 143 148
Primary Contact: Mick Brant, Chief Executive Officer
CFO: Taci Bartlett, Chief Financial Officer
CMO: Craig Bartruff, M.D., Medical Director
CHR: Lisa Gieken, Director Human Resources
Web address: www.ghospital.org
**Control:** Hospital district or authority, Government, nonfederal **Service:** General Medical and Surgical

**Staffed Beds:** 12 **Admissions:** 196 **Census:** 1 **Outpatient Visits:** 16345
**Births:** 28 **Total Expense ($000):** 8080 **Payroll Expense ($000):** 2611
**Personnel:** 69

**GRAND ISLAND—Hall County**

⊞ **SAINT FRANCIS MEDICAL CENTER (280023)**, 2620 West Faidley Avenue,
Zip 68803–4297, Mailing Address: P.O. Box 9804, Zip 68802–9804;
tel. 308/384–4600, (Includes SAINT FRANCIS MEMORIAL HEALTH CENTER, 2116
West Faidley Avenue, Zip 68803, Mailing Address: P.O. Box 9804, Zip 68802;
tel. 308/384–4600), (Total facility includes 34 beds in nursing home–type unit)
**A**1 2 3 5 9 10 19 **F**3 5 11 12 13 15 17 18 20 22 28 30 31 34 35 40 43 45
47 51 53 59 60 63 64 65 68 70 72 74 75 76 77 78 79 81 82 84 85 89 90
91 97 104 105 110 120 121 123 128 129 130 132 135 145 146 148
**S** Catholic Health Initiatives, Englewood, CO
Primary Contact: Daniel P. McElligott, FACHE, President and Chief Executive Officer
CFO: Lisa Webb, Vice President Finance and Chief Financial Officer
CMO: Mike Horn, M.D., Vice President Medical Affairs
CIO: Michael Foley, Director Information Systems
CHR: Lee Elliott, Vice President Human Resources and Fund Development
Web address: www.saintfrancisgi.org
**Control:** Church–operated, Nongovernment, not–for profit **Service:** General Medical and Surgical

**Staffed Beds:** 190 **Admissions:** 6493 **Census:** 87 **Outpatient Visits:** 192983
**Births:** 903 **Total Expense ($000):** 139524 **Payroll Expense ($000):** 49093
**Personnel:** 942

**GRANT—Perkins County**

★ **PERKINS COUNTY HEALTH SERVICES (281356)**, 900 Lincoln Avenue,
Zip 69140–3095; tel. 308/352–7200, (Includes GOLDEN OURS CONVALESCENT
HOME ), (Nonreporting) **A**9 10 18
Primary Contact: James LeBrun, Chief Executive Officer
COO: Tim Rowley, Chief Operating Officer
CFO: Tiffany Weber, Chief Financial Officer
CMO: Kristi Kohl, M.D., Chief Medical Officer
CIO: Jennifer Baumgartner, Chief Information Officer
CHR: Alicia Fraley, Chief Human Resources
CNO: Dana McArtor, R.N., Director of Nursing
Web address: www.pchsgrant.com
**Control:** Hospital district or authority, Government, nonfederal **Service:** General Medical and Surgical

**Staffed Beds:** 70

**HASTINGS—Adams County**

**HASTINGS REGIONAL CENTER**, 4200 West Second Street, Zip 68901–9700,
Mailing Address: P.O. Box 579, Zip 68902–0579; tel. 402/462–1971,
(Nonreporting) **A**9
Primary Contact: William R. Gibson, Chief Executive Officer
COO: Marj A. Colburn, Facility Operating Officer, Risk Manager and Performance Improvement Coordinator
CMO: Gene Wyse, D.O., Medical Director
CIO: Nancy Kinyoun, Director Health Information Management
CHR: LaDene Madson, Director Human Resources
Web address: www.dhhs.ne.gov
**Control:** State–Government, nonfederal **Service:** Other specialty

**Staffed Beds:** 156

⊞ **MARY LANNING HEALTHCARE (280032)**, 715 North St. Joseph Avenue,
Zip 68901–4497; tel. 402/463–4521 **A**1 2 9 10 **F**11 13 15 17 28 30 31 34
35 37 40 43 46 53 54 59 62 63 64 66 68 70 72 74 75 76 77 78 79 81 84
85 86 87 89 90 93 96 97 98 100 101 102 103 104 105 107 108 110 111
114 115 118 119 120 121 128 135 146 147 148
Primary Contact: Mark Callahan, Interim President and Chief Executive Officer
CMO: Joe Davis, M.D., Vice President Medical Affairs
CIO: George Sullivan, Director Management Information Systems
Web address: www.marylanning.org
**Control:** Other not–for–profit (including NFP Corporation) **Service:** General Medical and Surgical

**Staffed Beds:** 148 **Admissions:** 4821 **Census:** 59 **Outpatient Visits:** 143474
**Births:** 729 **Total Expense ($000):** 107538 **Payroll Expense ($000):** 45584
**Personnel:** 874

**HEBRON—Thayer County**

★ **THAYER COUNTY HEALTH SERVICES (281304)**, 120 Park Avenue,
Zip 68370–2019, Mailing Address: P.O. Box 49, Zip 68370–0049;
tel. 402/768–6041, (Nonreporting) **A**9 10 18
Primary Contact: Joyce Beck, Administrator
COO: Susan L. Moore, R.N., Director Nursing
CFO: Michael Pracheil, Chief Financial Officer
CMO: Michelle Kuhlmann, M.D., Director Medical Staff
CIO: Dan Engle, Chief Information Officer
Web address: www.thayercountyhealth.com
**Control:** County–Government, nonfederal **Service:** General Medical and Surgical

**Staffed Beds:** 19

**HENDERSON—York County**

**HENDERSON HEALTH CARE SERVICES (281308)**, 1621 Front Street,
Zip 68371–9802; tel. 402/723–4512, (Nonreporting) **A**9 10 18
Primary Contact: Cheryl Brown, Administrator
CMO: James M. Ohrt, M.D., Director Medical Staff
CHR: Lynette Friesen, Manager Human Resources
Web address: www.hendersonhealthcare.org/getpage.php?name=message
**Control:** Other not–for–profit (including NFP Corporation) **Service:** General Medical and Surgical

**Staffed Beds:** 56

**HOLDREGE—Phelps County**

⊞ **PHELPS MEMORIAL HEALTH CENTER (281362)**, 1215 Tibbals Street,
Zip 68949–1255; tel. 308/995–2211, (Nonreporting) **A**1 9 10 18 **S** QHR,
Brentwood, TN
Primary Contact: Mark Harrel, Chief Executive Officer
CFO: Loren D. Schroder, Chief Financial Officer
CMO: Stuart Embury, M.D., Chief Medical Officer
CIO: Leora Smith, Information System and Health Information Management Team Leader
CHR: Cindy Jackson, Director Human Resources
Web address: www.phelpsmemorial.com
**Control:** Other not–for–profit (including NFP Corporation) **Service:** General Medical and Surgical

**Staffed Beds:** 25

**IMPERIAL—Chase County**

**CHASE COUNTY COMMUNITY HOSPITAL (281351)**, 600 West 12th Street,
Zip 69033–3130, Mailing Address: P.O. Box 819, Zip 69033–0819;
tel. 308/882–7111 **A**9 10 18 **F**11 15 28 29 30 31 34 35 40 41 42 43 45 57
59 64 75 76 78 79 81 90 91 93 107 110 114 127 128 133 **P**6
Primary Contact: Gary Bieganski, LFACHE, Interim Chief Executive Officer
CFO: Renee Fink, CPA, Chief Financial Officer
CMO: Jonathan Richman, M.D., Chief of Staff
CIO: Jen Harris, Director Health Information Management
CHR: Julie Sharp, Supervisor Human Resources
Web address: www.chasecountyhospital.com
**Control:** County–Government, nonfederal **Service:** General Medical and Surgical

**Staffed Beds:** 22 **Admissions:** 25 **Census:** 1 **Outpatient Visits:** 16787 **Total
Expense ($000):** 10574 **Payroll Expense ($000):** 4661 **Personnel:** 89

**KEARNEY—Buffalo County**

**GOOD SAMARITAN HEALTH SYSTEMS** See Good Samaritan Hospital

**NE**

**GOOD SAMARITAN HOSPITAL (280009)**, 10 East 31st Street, Zip 68847–2926, Mailing Address: P.O. Box 1990, Zip 68848–1990; tel. 308/865–7100, (Includes RICHARD H. YOUNG HOSPITAL, 1755 Prairie View Place, Zip 68848, Mailing Address: P.O. Box 1750, Zip 68848–1705; tel. 308/865–2000), (Total facility includes 21 beds in nursing home–type unit) **A**1 2 3 5 9 10 **F**3 7 9 12 13 15 18 20 22 24 28 29 30 31 34 35 37 40 43 44 45 46 48 49 50 51 53 57 58 59 60 64 68 69 70 71 72 74 75 76 77 78 79 80 81 82 83 84 85 86 87 89 90 92 93 98 99 101 102 103 104 107 108 110 111 114 115 116 117 118 119 120 121 123 124 126 128 129 130 132 134 135 146 148 **P**6 8 **S** Catholic Health Initiatives, Englewood, CO
Primary Contact: Michael H. Schnieders, FACHE, President and Chief Executive Officer
CFO: George Harms, Chief Financial Officer
CIO: Tanya Arthur, Chief Information Officer
CHR: Robert Cunningham, Vice President Human Resources
Web address: www.gshs.org
**Control:** Church–operated, Nongovernment, not–for profit **Service:** General Medical and Surgical

**Staffed Beds:** 229 **Admissions:** 10210 **Census:** 142 **Outpatient Visits:** 58403 **Births:** 992 **Total Expense ($000):** 179297 **Payroll Expense ($000):** 59665 **Personnel:** 1132

## KIMBALL—Kimball County

★ **KIMBALL HEALTH SERVICES (281305)**, 505 South Burg Street, Zip 69145–1398; tel. 308/235–1952, (Nonreporting) **A**9 10 18
Primary Contact: Ken Hunter, R.N., Chief Executive Officer
CFO: David Usher, Chief Financial Officer
CMO: Richard Jay, M.D., Chief of Staff
CIO: Nicole Nielan, Director Information Technology
CHR: James R. Imler, Director Human Resources
CNO: Chad Jay, Chief Nursing Officer
Web address: www.kimballhealth.org
**Control:** County–Government, nonfederal **Service:** General Medical and Surgical

**Staffed Beds:** 12

## LEXINGTON—Dawson County

★ **LEXINGTON REGIONAL HEALTH CENTER (281361)**, 1201 North Erie Street, Zip 68850–1560, Mailing Address: P.O. Box 980, Zip 68850–0980; tel. 308/324–5651, (Nonreporting) **A**9 10 18
Primary Contact: Leslie Marsh, Chief Executive Officer
CFO: Wade Eschenbrenner, Chief Financial Officer
CMO: Francisca Acosta–Carlson, M.D., Chief of Staff
CIO: Robb Hanna, Executive Director Information Technology
CHR: Jill Denker, Executive Director Human Resources
CNO: Dana Steiner, R.N., Executive Director of Nursing Services
Web address: www.lexingtonregional.org
**Control:** Hospital district or authority, Government, nonfederal **Service:** General Medical and Surgical

**Staffed Beds:** 25

## LINCOLN—Lancaster County

△ **BRYAN MEDICAL CENTER (280003)**, (Formerly BryanLGH Medical Center), 1600 South 48th Street, Zip 68506–1299; tel. 402/489–0200, (Includes BRYAN MEDICAL CENTER–EAST, 1600 South 48th Street, tel. 402/489–0200; BRYAN MEDICAL CENTER–WEST, 2300 South 16th Street, Zip 68502–3781; tel. 402/475–1011) **A**1 2 7 9 10 **F**3 4 5 8 12 13 15 17 18 19 20 22 24 26 28 29 30 31 34 35 37 38 39 40 43 45 46 47 48 49 50 54 56 57 58 59 61 64 68 70 71 72 74 75 76 78 79 81 82 84 85 86 87 89 90 92 93 96 98 99 101 102 103 104 105 107 108 110 111 112 114 115 117 118 119 120 123 124 126 129 130 131 132 145 146 147 148 **S** Bryan Health, Lincoln, NE
Primary Contact: John T. Woodrich, President and Chief Operating Officer
CFO: Russell Gronewold, Chief Financial Officer
CMO: Carolyn Cody, M.D., Vice President Medical Affairs
CIO: George Carr, Chief Information Officer
CHR: Jan Garvin, Vice President Human Resources
CNO: Lisa M. Vail, R.N., Chief Nursing Officer and Vice President of Patient Care Services
Web address: www.bryanhealth.com
**Control:** Other not–for–profit (including NFP Corporation) **Service:** General Medical and Surgical

**Staffed Beds:** 351 **Admissions:** 21857 **Census:** 260 **Outpatient Visits:** 222453 **Births:** 2591 **Total Expense ($000):** 416973 **Payroll Expense ($000):** 148411 **Personnel:** 2629

**LINCOLN DIVISION** See Veterans Affairs Nebraska–Western Iowa Health Care System

□ **LINCOLN REGIONAL CENTER (284003)**, West Prospector Place and South Folsom, Zip 68522–2299, Mailing Address: P.O. Box 94949, Zip 68509–4949; tel. 402/479–5207 **A**1 9 10 **F**39 75 77 86 87 97 98 99 100 101 105 106 107 130 135 143 **P**6
Primary Contact: William R. Gibson, Chief Executive Officer
COO: Stacey Werth–Sweeney, Facility Operating Officer
CFO: Randy Willey, Business Manager
CMO: Vijay Dewan, M.D., Clinical Director
CHR: Scott Rasmussen, Director Human Resources
Web address: www.hhs.state.ne.us/beh/rc
**Control:** State–Government, nonfederal **Service:** Psychiatric

**Staffed Beds:** 224 **Admissions:** 181 **Census:** 181 **Outpatient Visits:** 71 **Births:** 0 **Total Expense ($000):** 34705 **Payroll Expense ($000):** 20757 **Personnel:** 556

**LINCOLN SURGICAL HOSPITAL (280127)**, 1710 South 70th Street, Suite 200, Zip 68506–1677; tel. 402/484–9090, (Nonreporting) **A**9 10
Primary Contact: Robb Linafelter, Chief Executive Officer
Web address: www.lincolnsurgery.com
**Control:** Corporation, Investor–owned, for–profit **Service:** Other specialty

**Staffed Beds:** 7

★ △ **MADONNA REHABILITATION HOSPITAL (282000)**, 5401 South Street, Zip 68506–2134; tel. 402/489–7102, (Total facility includes 125 beds in nursing home–type unit) **A**7 9 10 **F**1 10 28 29 30 32 34 35 36 50 53 54 56 57 58 59 64 65 67 74 75 77 79 82 84 86 87 90 91 92 93 94 95 96 128 130 131 132 135 143 146 148 **P**4 6
Primary Contact: Marsha Lommel, FACHE, President and Chief Executive Officer
COO: Paul Dongilli, Jr., Ph.D., Executive Vice President and Chief Operating Officer
CFO: Victor J. Witkowicz, Senior Vice President and Chief Financial Officer
CMO: Thomas Stadler, M.D., Vice President Medical Affairs and Chief Medical Officer
CIO: David Rolfe, Chief Information Officer
CHR: Lou Ann Manske, Director Human Resources
Web address: www.madonna.org
**Control:** Other not–for–profit (including NFP Corporation) **Service:** Rehabilitation

**Staffed Beds:** 300 **Admissions:** 1775 **Census:** 218 **Outpatient Visits:** 60327 **Births:** 0 **Total Expense ($000):** 90348 **Payroll Expense ($000):** 56580 **Personnel:** 1156

★ **NEBRASKA HEART HOSPITAL (280128)**, (Formerly Nebraska Heart Institute and Heart Hospital), 7500 South 91st Street, Zip 68526–9437; tel. 402/327–2700, (Nonreporting) **A**9 10 **S** Catholic Health Initiatives, Englewood, CO
Primary Contact: Kent Reckewey, M.D., Chief Executive Officer
CFO: Dan Schonlau, Chief Financial Officer
CHR: Jamie N. Carlson, Chief Human Resources Officer
Web address: www.neheart.com
**Control:** Other not–for–profit (including NFP Corporation) **Service:** Heart

**Staffed Beds:** 52

**NEBRASKA PENAL AND CORRECTIONAL HOSPITAL**, 14th And Pioneer Streets, Zip 68501; tel. 402/471–3161, (Nonreporting)
Primary Contact: George E. Lewis, M.D., Medical Officer
Web address: www.corrections.nebraska.gov
**Control:** State–Government, nonfederal **Service:** Hospital unit of an institution (prison hospital, college infimary, etc.)

**Staffed Beds:** 12

△ **SAINT ELIZABETH REGIONAL MEDICAL CENTER (280020)**, 555 South 70th Street, Zip 68510–2494; tel. 402/219–8000 **A**1 2 3 5 9 10 **F**3 8 11 12 13 15 16 28 29 30 31 34 35 37 39 40 44 45 46 47 48 49 50 51 55 58 59 60 61 64 65 68 70 72 74 75 76 78 79 80 81 84 85 86 87 89 92 107 108 110 111 114 115 116 117 118 119 120 121 123 124 126 129 130 131 132 135 144 145 146 147 148 **S** Catholic Health Initiatives, Englewood, CO
Primary Contact: Kim S. Moore, President and Chief Executive Officer
CFO: Jeanette Wojtalewicz, Vice President Finance
CMO: Cary Ward, M.D., Chief Medical Officer
CIO: Richard Bohaty, Director Information Technology
CHR: Cody Koch, Director Human Resources
Web address: www.saintelizabethonline.com
**Control:** Other not–for–profit (including NFP Corporation) **Service:** General Medical and Surgical

**Staffed Beds:** 260 **Admissions:** 12755 **Census:** 144 **Outpatient Visits:** 106365 **Births:** 2151 **Total Expense ($000):** 221574 **Payroll Expense ($000):** 68805 **Personnel:** 1143

**NE**

---

**Hospital, Medicare Provider Number, Address, Telephone, Approval, Facility, and Physician Codes, Health Care System**

★ American Hospital Association (AHA) membership
□ The Joint Commission accreditation ◇ DNV Healthcare Inc. accreditation
○ Healthcare Facilities Accreditation Program
△ Commission on Accreditation of Rehabilitation Facilities (CARF) accreditation

★ **VETERANS AFFAIRS NEBRASKA–WESTERN IOWA HEALTH CARE SYSTEM**,
600 South 70th Street, Zip 68510–2493; tel. 402/489–3802, (Includes LINCOLN
DIVISION, 600 South 70th Street, tel. 402/489–3802), (Nonreporting) **A**9
**S** Department of Veterans Affairs, Washington, DC
Primary Contact: Marci Mylan, Director
CIO: David Daiker, Chief Information Resource Management
CHR: Dave Peters, Chief Human Resources Officer
Web address: www.nebraska.va.gov/
**Control:** Veterans Affairs, Government, federal **Service:** General Medical and
Surgical

Staffed Beds: 186

### LYNCH—Boyd County

**NIOBRARA VALLEY HOSPITAL (281303)**, 401 South Fifth Street,
Zip 68746–0118, Mailing Address: P.O. Box 118, Zip 68746–0118;
tel. 402/569–2451 **A**9 10 18 **F**11 40 57 59 64 81 93 107 128 133 **S** Faith
Regional Health Services, Norfolk, NE
Primary Contact: Kelly Kalkowski, Chief Executive Officer
CFO: Martha Nelson, Chief Financial Officer
Web address: www.ci.lynch.ne.us/health.htm
**Control:** Other not–for–profit (including NFP Corporation) **Service:** General
Medical and Surgical

Staffed Beds: 20 Admissions: 38 Census: 1 Outpatient Visits: 1975 Births:
0 Total Expense ($000): 1982 Payroll Expense ($000): 813 Personnel: 23

### MCCOOK—Red Willow County

⊠ **COMMUNITY HOSPITAL (281363)**, 1301 East H Street, Zip 69001–1328,
Mailing Address: P.O. Box 1328, Zip 69001–1328; tel. 308/344–2650 **A**1 9 10
18 **F**3 11 13 15 28 31 34 35 40 43 57 59 62 63 64 68 74 75 77 78 79 81
82 85 86 87 90 94 107 110 111 114 118 119 124 127 129 130 132 133
135 146 147 148 **P**3 6
Primary Contact: James P. Ulrich, Jr., President and Chief Executive Officer
CFO: Troy Bruntz, Vice President Finance and Chief Financial Officer
CMO: Walter Eskildsen, M.D., Chief of Staff
CIO: Lori Beeby, Director Information Systems
CHR: Leanne R. Miller, Director Human Resources
Web address: www.chmccook.org
**Control:** Other not–for–profit (including NFP Corporation) **Service:** General
Medical and Surgical

Staffed Beds: 25 Admissions: 846 Census: 8 Outpatient Visits: 29434
Births: 121 Total Expense ($000): 33748 Payroll Expense ($000): 12188
Personnel: 206

### MINDEN—Kearney County

★ **KEARNEY COUNTY HEALTH SERVICES (281306)**, 727 East First Street,
Zip 68959–1705; tel. 308/832–3400, (Total facility includes 34 beds in nursing
home–type unit) **A**9 10 18 **F**10 15 18 28 34 40 43 45 56 59 64 65 81 86 97
107 110 114 119 127 128 130 133 143 146 148
Primary Contact: Fred J. Meis, Chief Executive Officer
CFO: Rebekah Mussman, Chief Financial Officer
CMO: Eddie Pierce, M.D., Chief Medical Staff
CHR: Donna Dyke, Human Resources Officer
Web address: www.kchs.org
**Control:** County–Government, nonfederal **Service:** General Medical and Surgical

Staffed Beds: 44 Admissions: 182 Census: 26 Outpatient Visits: 7960
Births: 0 Total Expense ($000): 8347 Payroll Expense ($000): 4403

### NEBRASKA CITY—Otoe County

★ **ST. MARY'S COMMUNITY HOSPITAL (281342)**, 1314 Third Avenue,
Zip 68410–1930; tel. 402/873–3321 **A**9 10 18 **F**3 13 15 17 28 31 35 40 45
64 67 68 69 70 75 76 78 79 81 82 85 87 89 107 110 111 114 118 119 128
129 132 133 135 148 **S** Catholic Health Initiatives, Englewood, CO
Primary Contact: Daniel J. Kelly, President and Chief Executive Officer
CFO: Shawn Closner, Vice President Finance
CMO: Jonathan Stelling, M.D., Chief Medical Officer
CNO: Brenda Jean Sebek, R.N., Chief Nursing Officer
Web address: www.stmaryshospitalnecity.org
**Control:** Church–operated, Nongovernment, not–for profit **Service:** General
Medical and Surgical

Staffed Beds: 18 Admissions: 478 Census: 5 Outpatient Visits: 30151
Births: 119 Total Expense ($000): 15868 Payroll Expense ($000): 6226
Personnel: 122

### NELIGH—Antelope County

★ **ANTELOPE MEMORIAL HOSPITAL (281326)**, 102 West Ninth Street,
Zip 68756–1114, Mailing Address: P.O. Box 229, Zip 68756–0229;
tel. 402/887–4151, (Nonreporting) **A**9 10 18
Primary Contact: Jack W. Green, Administrator
CFO: Martha Nelson, Chief Financial Officer
CMO: Troy Dawson, M.D., President Medical Staff
CIO: Kevin Trease, Chief Information Officer
CHR: Mary A. Schwager, Director Human Resources
CNO: Merry Sprout, R.N., Chief Nursing Officer
Web address: www.amhne.org/
**Control:** Other not–for–profit (including NFP Corporation) **Service:** General
Medical and Surgical

Staffed Beds: 25

### NORFOLK—Madison County

⊞ **FAITH REGIONAL HEALTH SERVICES (280125)**, 2700 West Norfolk Avenue,
Zip 68701–4438, Mailing Address: P.O. Box 869, Zip 68702–0869;
tel. 402/644–7201, (Includes EAST CAMPUS, 1500 Koenigstein Avenue,
Zip 68701; tel. 402/371–3402; WEST CAMPUS, 2700 Norfolk Avenue,
Zip 68701, Mailing Address: P.O. Box 869, Zip 68702–0869;
tel. 402/371–4880), (Nonreporting) **A**1 2 3 5 9 10 20 **S** Faith Regional Health
Services, Norfolk, NE
Primary Contact: Tim Auwarter, Interim President and Chief Executive Officer
CFO: Johnathan Wilker, Vice President Finance and Chief Financial Officer
CMO: Dean O. French, M.D., Chief of Staff
CHR: Janet Pinkelman, Director Human Resources
Web address: www.frhs.org
**Control:** Other not–for–profit (including NFP Corporation) **Service:** General
Medical and Surgical

Staffed Beds: 146

**NORFOLK REGIONAL CENTER (284004)**, 1700 North Victory Road,
Zip 68701–6859, Mailing Address: P.O. Box 1209, Zip 68702–1209;
tel. 402/370–3400, (Nonreporting) **A**9
Primary Contact: William R. Gibson, Chief Executive Officer
COO: Stephen O'Neill, Clinical Director
CFO: Randy Willey, Business Manager
CMO: Daniel Sturgis, Ph.D., Director Psychology
CIO: Marilyn Blunck, Director Health Information Management
CHR: Jim McElfresh, Manager Human Resources
Web address: www.hhss.ne.gov/beh/rc/nrcserv.htm
**Control:** State–Government, nonfederal **Service:** Psychiatric

Staffed Beds: 179

### NORTH PLATTE—Lincoln County

⊠ **GREAT PLAINS REGIONAL MEDICAL CENTER (280065)**, 601 West Leota
Street, Zip 69101–6598, Mailing Address: P.O. Box 1167, Zip 69103–1167;
tel. 308/696–8000 **A**1 2 3 5 9 10 **F**3 8 12 13 15 18 20 22 28 29 30 31 34
35 40 43 45 48 50 51 57 59 60 62 63 68 70 72 74 75 76 78 79 81 82 84
89 93 98 99 102 103 104 105 107 108 110 111 115 116 117 119 120 121
122 124 129 130 131 132 146 147 148 **P**8
Primary Contact: Gregory A. Nielsen, President
COO: Melvin McNea, Chief Operating Officer
CFO: Krystal Claymore, Chief Financial Officer
CIO: Brandon Kelliher, IT Operations Officer
CHR: Kelly Hurt, VP Human Resources
CNO: Todd Greenfield, Chief Nursing Officer
Web address: www.gprmc.com
**Control:** Other not–for–profit (including NFP Corporation) **Service:** General
Medical and Surgical

Staffed Beds: 101 Admissions: 5013 Census: 47 Outpatient Visits: 250751
Births: 534 Total Expense ($000): 120272 Payroll Expense ($000): 48223
Personnel: 771

### O'NEILL—Holt County

★ **AVERA ST. ANTHONY'S HOSPITAL (281329)**, 302 North Second Street,
Zip 68763–1514, Mailing Address: P.O. Box 270, Oneill, Zip 68763–0270;
tel. 402/336–2611 **A**9 10 18 **F**3 8 13 15 28 29 30 31 32 34 35 38 40 45 46
48 52 56 57 59 60 61 62 64 65 68 74 75 76 77 78 79 81 82 86 87 90 91
93 94 96 107 108 111 112 114 119 120 124 127 129 130 131 133 135
143 146 148 **P**1 6 **S** Avera Health, Sioux Falls, SD
Primary Contact: Ronald J. Cork, President and Chief Executive Officer
CFO: Michael Garman, Chief Financial Officer
CMO: Preston Renshaw, M.D., Chief Medical Officer
CIO: Michael Garman, Chief Financial Officer
CHR: Crystal Kahle, Director Human Resources and Marketing
Web address: www.avera.org/st-anthonys
**Control:** Church–operated, Nongovernment, not–for profit **Service:** General
Medical and Surgical

Staffed Beds: 25 Admissions: 811 Census: 9 Outpatient Visits: 40610
Births: 163 Total Expense ($000): 33366 Payroll Expense ($000): 12792
Personnel: 227

*Many Facility Codes have changed. Please refer to the AHA Guide Code Chart.*

© 2013 AHA Guide

**NE**

## OAKLAND—Burt County

★ **OAKLAND MERCY HOSPITAL (281321)**, 601 East Second Street, Zip 68045–1499; tel. 402/685–5601 **A**9 10 18 **F**11 15 28 29 30 31 34 35 40 44 50 57 59 75 81 93 97 107 119 127 128 132 133 148 **P**6 **S** Trinity Health, Livonia, MI
Primary Contact: John W. Werner, Chief Executive Officer
CFO: David M A Jensen, Chief Financial Officer
CHR: Karolyn McEnroy, Business Office Manager
Web address: www.oaklandhospital.org
**Control:** Church–operated, Nongovernment, not–for profit **Service:** General Medical and Surgical

**Staffed Beds:** 18 **Admissions:** 153 **Census:** 2 **Outpatient Visits:** 6833 **Births:** 0 **Total Expense ($000):** 6363 **Payroll Expense ($000):** 3054 **Personnel:** 58

## OGALLALA—Keith County

★ **OGALLALA COMMUNITY HOSPITAL (281355)**, 2601 North Spruce Street, Zip 69153–2465; tel. 308/284–4011 **A**9 10 18 **F**3 13 15 18 19 29 30 31 35 40 43 46 57 59 76 77 78 79 81 85 87 89 93 97 107 110 114 119 129 133 148 **P**6 **S** Banner Health, Phoenix, AZ
Primary Contact: Sharon Lind, MSN, Chief Executive Officer
CFO: Dena Klockman, Chief Financial Officer
CMO: Kurt Johnson, M.D., Chief of Staff
CHR: Bethany Childers, Manager People Resources
Web address: www.bannerhealth.com/Locations/Nebraska/Ogallala+Community+Hospital
**Control:** Other not–for–profit (including NFP Corporation) **Service:** General Medical and Surgical

**Staffed Beds:** 18 **Admissions:** 582 **Census:** 6 **Outpatient Visits:** 43347 **Births:** 81 **Total Expense ($000):** 14621 **Payroll Expense ($000):** 5803 **Personnel:** 93

## OMAHA—Douglas County

⊠ **ALEGENT CREIGHTON HEALTH BERGAN MERCY MEDICAL CENTER (280060)**, (Formerly Alegent Health–Bergan Mercy Medical Center), 7500 Mercy Road, Zip 68124–2319; tel. 402/398–6060, (Includes LASTING HOPE RECOVERY CENTER, 415 South 25th Avenue, Zip 68131; tel. 402/717–5300; Robin Conyers, Administrator) **A**1 2 3 5 9 10 **F**3 8 11 13 15 17 18 20 22 24 26 28 29 30 31 32 34 35 37 38 39 40 42 43 44 45 46 47 48 49 50 51 53 54 55 56 57 59 60 61 62 63 64 65 68 70 72 74 75 76 77 78 79 80 81 82 83 84 85 86 87 89 92 93 97 98 100 102 105 107 108 109 110 111 114 115 116 117 118 119 120 121 123 124 126 127 130 131 132 134 143 144 145 146 147 148 **P**6 8 **S** Catholic Health Initiatives, Englewood, CO
Primary Contact: Marie E. Knedler, R.N., President
CFO: Amy Knott, Chief Financial Officer
CIO: Kenneth Lawonn, Senior Vice President Strategy & Technology
CHR: Nancy Wallace, Vice President Human Resources
CNO: Jane Carmody DNP, MBA, RN, CENP, R.N., Vice President and System Chief Nursing Officer
Web address: www.alegent.com/bergan
**Control:** Church–operated, Nongovernment, not for profit **Service:** General Medical and Surgical

**Staffed Beds:** 341 **Admissions:** 15946 **Census:** 221 **Outpatient Visits:** 353908 **Births:** 3316 **Total Expense ($000):** 230544 **Payroll Expense ($000):** 90730 **Personnel:** 1638

⊠ △ **ALEGENT CREIGHTON HEALTH IMMANUEL MEDICAL CENTER (280081)**, (Formerly Alegent Health–Immanuel Medical Center), 6901 North 72nd Street, Zip 68122–1799; tel. 402/572–2121, (Total facility includes 165 beds in nursing home–type unit) **A**1 2 3 5 7 9 10 **F**3 4 5 6 11 12 13 15 17 18 20 22 26 28 29 30 31 32 34 35 36 37 38 39 40 42 43 44 45 46 49 50 53 55 56 57 58 59 62 63 64 68 70 72 73 74 75 76 77 78 79 80 81 82 83 84 85 86 87 88 89 90 91 92 93 96 97 98 99 100 101 102 103 104 105 106 107 108 109 110 111 114 115 117 118 119 120 121 123 124 126 128 129 130 131 132 134 136 142 145 146 147 148 **P**6 8 **S** Catholic Health Initiatives, Englewood, CO
Primary Contact: Ann Schumacher, R.N., MSN, President
CFO: Tim H. Schnack, Chief Financial Officer
CIO: Kenneth Lawonn, Senior Vice President Strategy and Technology
CHR: Nancy Wallace, Vice President Human Resources
CNO: Jane Carmody DNP, MBA, RN, CENP, R.N., Chief Nursing Officer
Web address: www.alegent.com/immanuel
**Control:** Church–operated, Nongovernment, not–for–profit **Service:** General Medical and Surgical

**Staffed Beds:** 285 **Admissions:** 9523 **Census:** 162 **Outpatient Visits:** 232360 **Births:** 573 **Total Expense ($000):** 180692 **Payroll Expense ($000):** 59627 **Personnel:** 1234

⊠ **ALEGENT CREIGHTON HEALTH LAKESIDE HOSPITAL (280130)**, (Formerly Alegent Health–Lakeside Hospital), 16901 Lakeside Hills Court, Zip 68130–2318; tel. 402/717–8000 **A**1 2 9 10 **F**3 8 12 13 15 17 18 20 22 26 28 29 30 31 32 34 35 36 38 39 40 44 45 46 49 53 54 55 56 59 60 63 64 68 70 72 73 74 75 76 77 78 79 80 81 82 83 84 85 86 93 94 97 99 100 102 103 104 107 108 110 111 114 115 118 119 120 121 123 124 126 129 130 131 132 134 143 146 147 148 **P**6 8 **S** Catholic Health Initiatives, Englewood, CO
Primary Contact: Cindy Alloway, President
CFO: Ryan Reinke, Chief Financial Officer
CMO: Patricia Murdock–Langan, Medical Director
CIO: Kenneth Lawonn, Senior Vice President and Chief Information Officer
CHR: Nancy Wallace, Vice President Human Resources
CNO: Jane Carmody DNP, MBA, RN, CENP, R.N., Vice President and System Chief Nursing Officer
Web address: www.alegent.org
**Control:** Church–operated, Nongovernment, not–for profit **Service:** General Medical and Surgical

**Staffed Beds:** 137 **Admissions:** 7188 **Census:** 64 **Outpatient Visits:** 170884 **Births:** 1156 **Total Expense ($000):** 110454 **Payroll Expense ($000):** 33030 **Personnel:** 757

⊠ **ALEGENT CREIGHTON HEALTH–CREIGHTON UNIVERSITY MEDICAL CENTER (280030)**, (Formerly Creighton University Medical Center), 601 North 30th Street, Zip 68131–2197; tel. 402/449–4000 **A**1 3 5 8 9 10 **F**3 11 12 13 15 17 18 20 22 24 26 28 29 30 31 32 34 35 38 40 41 43 45 46 47 48 49 50 51 52 53 54 56 57 58 59 60 61 64 65 68 70 72 73 74 75 76 77 78 79 81 82 85 88 89 93 96 97 107 108 109 110 111 114 115 119 120 121 124 126 129 130 131 132 141 143 146 147 148 **P**6 8 **S** Catholic Health Initiatives, Englewood, CO
Primary Contact: Kevin J. Nokels, FACHE, President
COO: Parveen Chand, Chief Operating Officer
CFO: Tim H. Schnack, Chief Financial Officer
CMO: Robert Dunlay, M.D., Chief Medical Officer
CIO: Rick Sweeney, Director Information Services
CHR: Kristine Nielsen, Interim Chief Human Resources Officer
Web address: www.alegentcreighton.com
**Control:** Church–operated, Nongovernment, not–for profit **Service:** General Medical and Surgical

**Staffed Beds:** 223 **Admissions:** 8125 **Census:** 107 **Outpatient Visits:** 85619 **Births:** 1251 **Total Expense ($000):** 176788 **Payroll Expense ($000):** 43590 **Personnel:** 1182

☐ **BOYS TOWN NATIONAL RESEARCH HOSPITAL (283300)**, 555 North 30th Street, Zip 68131–2198; tel. 402/498–6511 **A**1 3 5 9 10 **F**3 34 35 58 65 68 79 81 86 87 97 99 104 106 107 108 111 119 129 130 131 **P**6
Primary Contact: John K. Arch, FACHE, Administrator
CFO: Leigh Jean Koinzan, Director Finance
CMO: Patrick E. Brookhouser, M.D., Director and Chief Medical Officer
CIO: Ann Ducey, Chief Information Officer
CHR: Michael Gell, Director Human Resources
Web address: www.boystownhospital.org
**Control:** Other not–for–profit (including NFP Corporation) **Service:** Children's general

**Staffed Beds:** 129 **Admissions:** 317 **Census:** 2 **Outpatient Visits:** 208396 **Births:** 0 **Total Expense ($000):** 84571 **Payroll Expense ($000):** 37697 **Personnel:** 797

⊠ **CHILDREN'S HOSPITAL AND MEDICAL CENTER (283301)**, 8200 Dodge Street, Zip 68114–4113; tel. 402/955–5400 **A**1 3 5 9 10 **F**3 7 11 12 19 21 23 25 27 29 30 31 32 34 35 41 43 45 46 48 49 50 54 55 59 62 64 68 72 74 75 77 78 79 81 82 84 85 88 89 92 93 99 104 107 108 111 114 115 119 126 129 130 132 143 144 145 146 148 **P**6
Primary Contact: Gary A. Perkins, FACHE, President and Chief Executive Officer
COO: Kathy L. English, R.N., Executive Vice President and Chief Operating Officer
CFO: Michael Brown, Senior Vice President Finance and Chief Financial Officer
CMO: Carl H. Gumbiner, M.D., Senior Vice President Medical Affairs and Chief Medical Officer
CIO: George Reynolds, M.D., Vice President, Chief Information Officer and Chief Medical Information Officer
CHR: Corliss Lovstad, Vice President Human Resources
CNO: Debbie Arnow, R.N., VP Patient Care & Chief Nursing Officer
Web address: www.childrensomaha.org
**Control:** Other not–for–profit (including NFP Corporation) **Service:** Children's general

**Staffed Beds:** 124 **Admissions:** 4742 **Census:** 86 **Outpatient Visits:** 289638 **Births:** 0 **Total Expense ($000):** 259878 **Payroll Expense ($000):** 109014 **Personnel:** 1519

NE

---

**Hospital, Medicare Provider Number, Address, Telephone, Approval, Facility, and Physician Codes, Health Care System**

★ American Hospital Association (AHA) membership
☐ The Joint Commission accreditation
◇ DNV Healthcare Inc. accreditation
○ Healthcare Facilities Accreditation Program
△ Commission on Accreditation of Rehabilitation Facilities (CARF) accreditation

---

★ ○ **DOUGLAS COUNTY COMMUNITY MENTAL HEALTH CENTER (284009)**, 4102 Woolworth Avenue, Zip 68105–1899; tel. 402/444–7000 **A**3 5 9 10 11 **F**29 35 64 66 68 98 104 105 130 132 **P**6
Primary Contact: John Sheehan, Chief Executive Officer
CFO: DeDe Will, Director Finance
CMO: Sidney A. Kauzlarich, M.D., Medical Director
CIO: Dianne Wallace, County Information Manager
CHR: Lee A. Lazure, Director Civil Service Commission
CNO: Marti Christensen, Director of Psychiatric Nursing
Web address: www.co.douglas.ne.us
**Control:** County–Government, nonfederal **Service:** Psychiatric

| | |
|---|---|
| **Staffed Beds:** 18 **Admissions:** 911 **Census:** 14 **Outpatient Visits:** 21864 **Births:** 0 | |

**MIDWEST SURGICAL HOSPITAL (280131)**, 7915 Farnam Drive, Zip 68114–4504; tel. 402/399–1900, (Nonreporting) **A**9 10
Primary Contact: Charles Livingston, Chief Executive Officer
Web address: www.mwsurgicalhospital.com
**Control:** Corporation, Investor–owned, for–profit **Service:** Surgical

| |
|---|
| **Staffed Beds:** 19 |

⊠ **NEBRASKA MEDICAL CENTER (280013)**, 987400 Nebraska Medical Center, Zip 68198–7400; tel. 402/552–2000 **A**1 2 3 5 8 9 10 **F**3 11 12 13 15 16 17 18 20 22 24 26 28 29 30 31 34 37 38 40 41 43 44 45 46 47 48 49 50 53 54 57 58 59 61 64 65 68 70 72 74 76 77 78 79 80 81 82 84 85 86 87 88 89 92 93 94 96 97 98 101 107 108 110 111 113 114 115 116 117 118 119 120 121 123 124 126 129 130 131 132 135 136 137 138 139 141 142 145 146 147 148 **P**5 8
Primary Contact: Glenn A. Fosdick, FACHE, President and Chief Executive Officer
COO: Joe B. Graham, Chief Operating Officer
CFO: William S. Dinsmoor, Chief Financial Officer
CMO: Stephen B. Smith, M.D., Chief Medical Officer
CIO: Lianne Stevens, Vice President Information Technology
CHR: Tadd M. Pullin, Interim Vice President, Human Resources
CNO: Rosanna D. Morris, R.N., CNO & Senior VP Patient Care Services
Web address: www.nebraskamed.com
**Control:** Other not–for–profit (including NFP Corporation) **Service:** General Medical and Surgical

| | |
|---|---|
| **Staffed Beds:** 495 **Admissions:** 23848 **Census:** 357 **Outpatient Visits:** 427312 **Births:** 1802 **Total Expense ($000):** 695089 **Payroll Expense ($000):** 252111 **Personnel:** 5100 | |

⊠ △ **NEBRASKA METHODIST HOSPITAL (280040)**, 8303 Dodge Street, Zip 68114–4199; tel. 402/354–4000, (Includes METHODIST WOMEN'S HOSPITAL, 707 North 190th Plaza, Elkhorn, Zip 68022–3974; tel. 402/815–4000; Susan Korth, M.P.H., Ph.D., Vice President and Chief Operating Officer) **A**1 2 3 5 7 9 10 **F**3 8 11 12 13 15 17 18 20 22 24 26 28 29 30 31 34 35 40 45 46 47 48 49 50 51 52 53 54 55 56 57 58 59 62 63 64 65 66 68 70 72 74 75 76 77 78 79 81 82 83 84 85 86 87 90 91 92 93 96 100 101 104 107 108 110 111 114 115 116 117 118 119 120 121 123 124 126 129 130 132 135 143 146 147 148 **P**6 8 **S** Nebraska Methodist Health System, Inc., Omaha, NE
Primary Contact: Stephen L. Goeser, FACHE, President and Chief Executive Officer
CFO: Linda K. Burt, Corporate Vice President Finance
CMO: William Shiffermiller, M.D., Vice President Medical Affairs
CIO: Roger Hertz, Vice President Information Technology
CHR: Holly Huerter, Vice President Human Resources
Web address: www.bestcare.org
**Control:** Other not–for–profit (including NFP Corporation) **Service:** General Medical and Surgical

| | |
|---|---|
| **Staffed Beds:** 460 **Admissions:** 17124 **Census:** 239 **Outpatient Visits:** 125264 **Births:** 3696 **Total Expense ($000):** 397166 **Payroll Expense ($000):** 144136 **Personnel:** 2104 | |

□ **NEBRASKA ORTHOPAEDIC HOSPITAL (280129)**, 2808 South 143rd Plaza, Zip 68144–5611; tel. 402/637–0600 **A**1 3 5 9 10 **F**3 9 29 34 35 37 39 40 44 50 57 58 59 64 77 79 81 82 85 86 87 93 94 96 111 131 141 142 **P**6
Primary Contact: Tom Macy, FACHE, Chief Executive Officer
COO: Mark E. Longacre, FACHE, Chief Operating Officer
CFO: Anna McCaslin, Chief Financial Officer
CMO: Ian Crabb, M.D., Medical Director
CIO: Tim Pugsley, Manager Information Technology
CHR: Kathleen Kelley–Robinson, Manager Human Resources
Web address: www.nohmail.com
**Control:** Partnership, Investor–owned, for–profit **Service:** Orthopedic

| | |
|---|---|
| **Staffed Beds:** 24 **Admissions:** 1510 **Census:** 11 **Outpatient Visits:** 58175 **Births:** 0 **Total Expense ($000):** 58023 **Payroll Expense ($000):** 17206 **Personnel:** 293 | |

⊠ **NEBRASKA SPINE HOSPITAL (280133)**, 6901 North 72nd Street, Suite 20300, Zip 68122–1755, Mailing Address: 6901 North 72nd Street, Zip 68122–1709; tel. 402/572–3000, (Nonreporting) **A**1 9 10 **S** Catholic Health Initiatives, Englewood, CO
Primary Contact: Troy P. Stockman, Chief Executive Officer
Web address: www.nebraskaspinehospital.com
**Control:** Partnership, Investor–owned, for–profit **Service:** Orthopedic

| |
|---|
| **Staffed Beds:** 34 |

⊠ **SELECT SPECIALTY HOSPITAL–OMAHA (282001)**, 1870 South 75th Street, Zip 68124–1700; tel. 402/361–5700, (Nonreporting) **A**1 9 10 **S** Select Medical Corporation, Mechanicsburg, PA
Primary Contact: Thomas N. Theroult, Chief Executive Officer
CMO: Guillermo Huerta, M.D., Chief Medical Officer
CMO: Antonio Saquaton, M.D., Chief Medical Officer
CIO: Cynde McCall, R.N., Chief Nursing Officer
CHR: Nicole Nelson, Human Resources Coordinator
CNO: Cynde McCall, R.N., Chief Nursing Officer
Web address: www.selectspecialtyhospitals.com/company/locations/omahacentral.aspx
**Control:** Corporation, Investor–owned, for–profit **Service:** Long–Term Acute Care hospital

| |
|---|
| **Staffed Beds:** 52 |

⊠ **VETERANS AFFAIRS MEDICAL CENTER**, 4101 Woolworth Avenue, Zip 68105–1873; tel. 402/346–8800, (Nonreporting) **A**1 2 3 5 8 9 **S** Department of Veterans Affairs, Washington, DC
Primary Contact: Nancy A. Gregory, Acting Director
COO: Katie Landwehr, Acting Associate Director
CFO: Kirk Kay, Chief Financial Officer
CMO: Thomas Lynch, M.D., Chief of Staff
CIO: John Horner, Manager Business Office
CHR: Cheryl M. DeWispelare, Chief Human Resources Officer
Web address: www.nebraska.va.gov/
**Control:** Veterans Affairs, Government, federal **Service:** General Medical and Surgical

| |
|---|
| **Staffed Beds:** 100 |

### ORD—Valley County

★ **VALLEY COUNTY HEALTH SYSTEM (281353)**, 2707 L. Street, Zip 68862–1275; tel. 308/728–4200, (Nonreporting) **A**9 10 18
Primary Contact: William T. Sugg, President and Chief Executive Officer
CFO: Ashley Woodward, Director Financial Services
CMO: Jennifer Bengston, M.D., Chief Medical Officer
CIO: Shane Molacek, Chief Information Officer
CHR: Tricia Richards, Director Human Resources
Web address: www.valleycountyhospital.org
**Control:** County–Government, nonfederal **Service:** General Medical and Surgical

| |
|---|
| **Staffed Beds:** 85 |

### OSCEOLA—Polk County

**ANNIE JEFFREY MEMORIAL COUNTY HEALTH CENTER (281314)**, 531 Beebe Street, Zip 68651–5537, Mailing Address: P.O. Box 428, Zip 68651–0428; tel. 402/747–2031, (Nonreporting) **A**9 10 18
Primary Contact: Joseph W. Lohrman, Chief Executive Officer
CFO: Joseph W. Lohrman, Chief Executive Officer
CMO: David Jameson, M.D., Chief of Staff
CIO: Frank Vrba, Chief Information Officer
CHR: Sue Leif, R.N., Director Human Resources
Web address: www.ajhc.org
**Control:** County–Government, nonfederal **Service:** General Medical and Surgical

| |
|---|
| **Staffed Beds:** 21 |

### OSHKOSH—Garden County

**GARDEN COUNTY HEALTH SERVICES (281310)**, 1100 West Second Street, Zip 69154–6152; tel. 308/772–3283, (Nonreporting) **A**9 10 18
Primary Contact: Jimmie W. Hansel, Ph.D., Chief Executive Officer
CFO: Jennifer Moffat, Staff Accountant
CMO: Harold Keenan, M.D., Chief Medical Officer
CIO: DeeDee Waltman, Information Officer
CHR: Dodi Moffat, Supervisor Human Resources
Web address: www.gchealth.org
**Control:** County–Government, nonfederal **Service:** General Medical and Surgical

| |
|---|
| **Staffed Beds:** 50 |

### OSMOND—Pierce County

★ **OSMOND GENERAL HOSPITAL (281347)**, 402 North Maple Street, Zip 68765–5726, Mailing Address: P.O. Box 429, Zip 68765–0429; tel. 402/748–3393, (Nonreporting) **A**9 10 18
Primary Contact: Celine M. Mlady, Chief Executive Officer
CFO: Jodi Aschoff, Chief Financial Officer
CMO: David Mwebe, M.D., Chief of Staff
Web address: www.osmondhospital.com
**Control:** Other not–for–profit (including NFP Corporation) **Service:** General Medical and Surgical

| |
|---|
| **Staffed Beds:** 25 |

*Many Facility Codes have changed. Please refer to the AHA Guide Code Chart.* © 2013 AHA Guide

## PAPILLION—Sarpy County

☒ **ALEGENT CREIGHTON HEALTH MIDLANDS HOSPITAL (280105)**, (Formerly Alegent Health–Midlands Hospital), 11111 South 84th Street, Zip 68046–4122; tel. 402/593–3000 **A**1 2 9 10 **F**3 11 13 15 17 18 20 22 26 28 29 30 34 35 36 38 40 44 45 46 49 50 51 53 56 57 59 60 61 62 63 64 65 68 70 76 77 79 81 84 85 86 87 93 97 107 110 111 114 115 117 118 119 129 130 131 132 135 143 146 147 **P**6 8 **S** Catholic Health Initiatives, Englewood, CO
Primary Contact: Cindy Alloway, President
CFO: Ryan Reinke, Chief Financial Officer
CMO: Jeffrey Strohmyer, M.D., Chief Medical Officer
CIO: Kenneth Lawonn, Senior Vice President and Chief Information Officer
CHR: Nancy Wallace, Interim Senior Vice President Human Resources
Web address: www.alegent.org/midlands
**Control:** Church–operated, Nongovernment, not–for profit **Service:** General Medical and Surgical

**Staffed Beds:** 61 **Admissions:** 1890 **Census:** 17 **Outpatient Visits:** 72899 **Births:** 298 **Total Expense ($000):** 51102 **Payroll Expense ($000):** 15659 **Personnel:** 347

## PAWNEE CITY—Pawnee County

★ **PAWNEE COUNTY MEMORIAL HOSPITAL AND RURAL HEALTH CLINIC (281302)**, (Formerly Pawnee County Memorial Hospital), 600 I Street, Zip 68420–3001, Mailing Address: P.O. Box 433, Zip 68420–0433; tel. 402/852–2231 **A**9 10 18 **F**7 15 18 28 30 31 34 40 43 45 57 59 65 75 77 79 81 82 93 97 102 107 110 114 119 127 129 130 132 133 135 147 **P**5
Primary Contact: James A. Kubik, Administrator
CHR: Jennifer Bartels, Director Human Resources
CNO: Kris Meyer, R.N., Director of Nursing
Web address: www.pawneehospital.com
**Control:** County–Government, nonfederal **Service:** General Medical and Surgical

**Staffed Beds:** 11 **Admissions:** 67 **Census:** 1 **Outpatient Visits:** 5381 **Births:** 0 **Total Expense ($000):** 3898 **Payroll Expense ($000):** 2554

## PENDER—Thurston County

★ **PENDER COMMUNITY HOSPITAL (281349)**, 100 Hospital Drive, Zip 68047–0100, Mailing Address: P.O. Box 100, Zip 68047–0100; tel. 402/385–3083, (Nonreporting) **A**9 10 18 **S** Trinity Health, Livonia, MI
Primary Contact: Roger W. Lenz, Interim Chief Executive Officer
COO: Melissa Kelly, Chief Operating Officer
CFO: Melissa Kelly, Chief Financial Officer
CMO: Matt Timm, M.D., Medical Director
CIO: Teresa Heise, Coordinator Management Information Systems
CHR: Nancy Suhr, Manager Human Resources
CNO: Katie Peterson, R.N., Director of Nursing
Web address: www.pendercommunityhospital.com
**Control:** Hospital district or authority, Government, nonfederal **Service:** General Medical and Surgical

**Staffed Beds:** 67

## PLAINVIEW—Pierce County

★ **ALEGENT CREIGHTON HEALTH PLAINVIEW HOSPITAL (281346)**, 704 North Third Street, Zip 68769–2047, Mailing Address: P.O. Box 489, Zip 68769–0489; tel. 402/582–4245, (Nonreporting) **A**9 10 18 **S** Catholic Health Initiatives, Englewood, CO
Primary Contact: Richard B. Gamel, Administrator
CFO: Rebecca Lambrecht, Manager Finance
CMO: W. Brad Lockee, M.D., Chief of Staff
CHR: Diane Blair, Human Resources and Admissions
Web address: www.alegentcreighton.com/plainview–hospital
**Control:** Church–operated, Nongovernment, not–for profit **Service:** General Medical and Surgical

**Staffed Beds:** 16

## RED CLOUD—Webster County

**WEBSTER COUNTY COMMUNITY HOSPITAL (281316)**, Sixth Avenue and Franklin Street, Zip 68970–0465, Mailing Address: P.O. Box 465, Zip 68970–0465; tel. 402/746–5600, (Nonreporting) **A**9 10 18
Primary Contact: Marianna Harris, Administrator
CFO: Marcia Olson, Business Office Manager
CMO: Michele Durr, M.D., Medical Director
CIO: Eilleen Berry, Manager Information Technology
CHR: Marcia Olson, Business Office Manager
Web address: www.websterhospital.org
**Control:** County–Government, nonfederal **Service:** General Medical and Surgical

**Staffed Beds:** 16

## SAINT PAUL—Howard County

**HOWARD COUNTY COMMUNITY HOSPITAL** See Howard County Medical Center

★ **HOWARD COUNTY MEDICAL CENTER (281338)**, 1113 Sherman Street, Zip 68873–1546, Mailing Address: P.O. Box 406, Zip 68873–0406; tel. 308/754–4421 **A**9 10 18 **F**3 11 13 28 29 34 40 43 45 57 59 68 81 85 93 107 114 119 127 128 130 133 135 146
Primary Contact: Arlan D. Johnson, Chief Executive Officer
CFO: Thomas Parish, Chief Financial Officer
CMO: Jared Kramer, M.D., Chief of Staff
CIO: Kari Pierson, Manager
CHR: Shauna Graham, Director Human Resources
Web address: www.hcchmc.org
**Control:** County–Government, nonfederal **Service:** General Medical and Surgical

**Staffed Beds:** 25 **Admissions:** 319 **Census:** 8 **Outpatient Visits:** 22494 **Births:** 48 **Total Expense ($000):** 13425 **Payroll Expense ($000):** 6666 **Personnel:** 149

## SCHUYLER—Colfax County

★ **ALEGENT CREIGHTON HEALTH–MEMORIAL HOSPITAL, SCHUYLER (281323)**, (Formerly Alegent Health–Memorial Hospital), 104 West 17th Street, Zip 68661–1304; tel. 402/352–2441, (Nonreporting) **A**9 10 18 **S** Catholic Health Initiatives, Englewood, CO
Primary Contact: Connie Peters, R.N., Regional Administrator
CFO: Tim H. Schnack, Chief Financial Officer
CIO: Kenneth Lawonn, Senior Vice President and Chief Information Officer
CHR: Nancy Wallace, Vice President Human Resources
CNO: Jane Carmody DNP, MBA, RN, CENP, R.N., Vice President and System Chief Nursing Officer
Web address: www.alegent.org
**Control:** Church–operated, Nongovernment, not–for profit **Service:** General Medical and Surgical

**Staffed Beds:** 25

## SCOTTSBLUFF—Scotts Bluff County

☒ △ **REGIONAL WEST MEDICAL CENTER (280061)**, 4021 Avenue B, Zip 69361–4695; tel. 308/635–3711, (Total facility includes 18 beds in nursing home–type unit) **A**1 2 3 5 7 9 10 **F**8 11 12 14 15 17 28 29 30 40 43 45 47 59 62 64 65 68 69 70 72 74 76 77 78 81 85 89 90 92 93 98 107 108 110 111 114 115 119 120 121 128 129 130 146 147 148
Primary Contact: Todd Sorensen, M.D., Chief Executive Officer
CFO: David Griffiths, Vice President and Chief Financial Officer
CIO: Lisa Bewley, Vice President and Chief Information Officer
CHR: Steve Hodges, Vice President Human Resources
Web address: www.rwhs.org
**Control:** Other not–for–profit (including NFP Corporation) **Service:** General Medical and Surgical

**Staffed Beds:** 145 **Admissions:** 7648 **Census:** 84 **Outpatient Visits:** 343119 **Births:** 835 **Total Expense ($000):** 189622 **Payroll Expense ($000):** 63091 **Personnel:** 1134

## SEWARD—Seward County

★ **MEMORIAL HEALTH CARE SYSTEMS (281339)**, 300 North Columbia Avenue, Zip 68434–2228; tel. 402/643–2971, (Nonreporting) **A**9 10 18
Primary Contact: Roger J. Reamer, Chief Executive Officer
CFO: Greg Jerger, Chief Financial Officer
CMO: Tricia Sams, M.D., Medical Director
CIO: Carol Carlson, Director Community Relations
Web address: www.mhcs.us
**Control:** Other not–for–profit (including NFP Corporation) **Service:** General Medical and Surgical

**Staffed Beds:** 36

## SIDNEY—Cheyenne County

★ **SIDNEY REGIONAL MEDICAL CENTER (281357)**, 645 Osage Street, Zip 69162–1799; tel. 308/254–5825, (Total facility includes 63 beds in nursing home–type unit) **A**5 9 10 18 **F**34 40 44 45 50 53 56 57 59 62 63 64 65 70 75 77 81 85 87 90 92 93 107 110 127 128 130 131 132 133 135 143 146 **P**6
Primary Contact: Jason Petik, Chief Executive Officer
CFO: Kelly Utley, Chief Financial Officer
CMO: Mandy Shaw, M.D., Chief of Staff
Web address: www.sidneyrmc.com
**Control:** Other not–for–profit (including NFP Corporation) **Service:** Long–Term Acute Care hospital

**Staffed Beds:** 88 **Admissions:** 790 **Census:** 59 **Outpatient Visits:** 74863 **Births:** 60 **Total Expense ($000):** 31929 **Payroll Expense ($000):** 15266 **Personnel:** 297

**NE**

---

**Hospital, Medicare Provider Number, Address, Telephone, Approval, Facility, and Physician Codes, Health Care System**

★ American Hospital Association (AHA) membership
☐ The Joint Commission accreditation ◇ DNV Healthcare Inc. accreditation
○ Healthcare Facilities Accreditation Program
△ Commission on Accreditation of Rehabilitation Facilities (CARF) accreditation

## SUPERIOR—Nuckolls County

★ **BRODSTONE MEMORIAL HOSPITAL (281315)**, 520 East Tenth Street, Zip 68978-1225, Mailing Address: P.O. Box 187, Zip 68978-0187; tel. 402/879-3281 **A**9 10 18 **F**3 7 11 13 15 18 28 29 30 31 34 39 40 41 45 48 50 56 57 59 62 64 65 67 68 70 74 75 76 77 79 81 85 86 87 89 93 97 107 110 111 114 119 127 128 129 130 131 132 133 135 146 148
Primary Contact: John E. Keelan, Administrator and Chief Executive Officer
COO: Dena C. Alvarez, R.N., COO & Chief Compliance Officer
CFO: Sandy Borden, Chief Financial Officer
CMO: Timothy Blecha, M.D., Medical Director
CIO: Tim Hiatt, Chief Information Officer
CHR: Jeremy Littrell, Director Human Resources
CNO: Kori Field, Director of Nursing
Web address: www.brodstonehospital.org
**Control:** Other not-for-profit (including NFP Corporation) **Service:** General Medical and Surgical

**Staffed Beds:** 25 **Admissions:** 515 **Census:** 6 **Outpatient Visits:** 17515 **Births:** 34 **Total Expense ($000):** 18143 **Payroll Expense ($000):** 8230 **Personnel:** 171

## SYRACUSE—Otoe County

★ **COMMUNITY MEMORIAL HOSPITAL (281309)**, 1579 Midland Street, Zip 68446-9732, Mailing Address: P.O. Box N., Zip 68446-0518; tel. 402/269-2011 **A**9 10 18 **F**3 11 15 28 29 40 43 45 53 59 62 64 79 81 82 89 93 107 110 127 128 133
Primary Contact: Michael Harvey, Chief Executive Officer
COO: Julie Werner, Chief Operating Officer
CFO: Michael Harvey, Chief Executive Officer
CFO: Jenn Seckinger, Chief Financial Officer
CMO: Zak Tempelmeyer, M.D., Chief Medical Staff
CIO: Matthew Steinblock, Systems Administrator
CHR: Karrie Beach, Director Human Resources
CNO: Pat Howell, Chief Nursing Officer
Web address: www.syracusecmh.org
**Control:** Hospital district or authority, Government, nonfederal **Service:** General Medical and Surgical

**Staffed Beds:** 12 **Admissions:** 126 **Census:** 1 **Outpatient Visits:** 16799 **Births:** 0 **Total Expense ($000):** 10393 **Payroll Expense ($000):** 5324 **Personnel:** 102

## TECUMSEH—Johnson County

★ **JOHNSON COUNTY HOSPITAL (281350)**, 202 High Street, Zip 68450-2443, Mailing Address: P.O. Box 599, Zip 68450-0599; tel. 402/335-3361, (Nonreporting) **A**9 10 18
Primary Contact: Diane Newman, Administrator
COO: Diane Newman, Administrator
CFO: Janice Oehm, Manager Business Office
CMO: Keith Shuey, M.D., Chief Medical Staff
CIO: Fred Pooch, Supervisor Information Technology
CHR: Susan Hessheimer, Director Human Resources
Web address: www.jchosp.com
**Control:** County-Government, nonfederal **Service:** General Medical and Surgical

**Staffed Beds:** 25

## TILDEN—Madison County

**TILDEN COMMUNITY HOSPITAL (281317)**, 308 West Second Street, Zip 68781-4760, Mailing Address: P.O. Box 340, Zip 68781-0340; tel. 402/368-5343 **A**9 10 18 **F**3 17 34 35 40 57 59 64 87 93 97 107 114 127 128 133 **S** Faith Regional Health Services, Norfolk, NE
Primary Contact: Lon Knievel, Chief Executive Officer
CFO: Sarah Mitchell, Chief Financial Officer
CMO: Kelly Ellis, D.O., Chief Medical Officer
CIO: Sarah Mitchell, Chief Financial Officer
CHR: Lon Knievel, Chief Executive Officer
Web address: www.tildenhospital.org
**Control:** City-Government, nonfederal **Service:** General Medical and Surgical

**Staffed Beds:** 12 **Admissions:** 79 **Census:** 1 **Outpatient Visits:** 292 **Births:** 0 **Total Expense ($000):** 3891

## VALENTINE—Cherry County

★ **CHERRY COUNTY HOSPITAL (281344)**, 510 North Green Street, Zip 69201-1932, Mailing Address: P.O. Box 410, Zip 69201-0410; tel. 402/376-2525, (Nonreporting) **A**5 9 10 18
Primary Contact: Brent A. Peterson, Administrator
CFO: Peggy Snell, Chief Finance Officer
**Control:** County-Government, nonfederal **Service:** General Medical and Surgical

**Staffed Beds:** 25

## WAHOO—Saunders County

★ **SAUNDERS MEDICAL CENTER (281307)**, 1760 County Road J., Zip 68066-4152; tel. 402/443-4191, (Nonreporting) **A**9 10 18
Primary Contact: Kenneth W. Archer, Chief Executive Officer
CMO: Leo L. Meduna, M.D., Chief Medical Officer
CIO: Carrie Stephens, Coordinator Information Systems
CHR: Karen Leise, Coordinator Human Resources
Web address: www.saundersmedicalcenter.com
**Control:** County-Government, nonfederal **Service:** General Medical and Surgical

**Staffed Beds:** 87

## WAYNE—Wayne County

★ **PROVIDENCE MEDICAL CENTER (281345)**, 1200 Providence Road, Zip 68787-1299; tel. 402/375-3800, (Nonreporting) **A**9 10 18
Primary Contact: Thomas J. Lee, Administrator/CEO
CFO: Kim Hixson, Chief Financial Officer
CHR: Sonja Hunke, Director Human Resources
Web address: www.providencemedical.com
**Control:** Other not-for-profit (including NFP Corporation) **Service:** General Medical and Surgical

**Staffed Beds:** 25

## WEST POINT—Cuming County

★ **ST. FRANCIS MEMORIAL HOSPITAL (281322)**, 430 North Monitor Street, Zip 68788-1555; tel. 402/372-2404, (Total facility includes 63 beds in nursing home-type unit) **A**9 10 18 **F**3 6 11 13 15 28 29 30 31 34 35 40 43 45 53 57 59 62 63 64 68 75 76 77 78 79 81 82 85 86 90 92 93 94 98 99 100 103 107 111 114 119 127 128 129 130 131 132 133 135 146 147 148 **P**6 **S** Franciscan Sisters of Christian Charity Sponsored Ministries, Inc., Manitowoc, WI
Primary Contact: Ronald O. Briggs, FACHE, President and Chief Executive Officer
CFO: Dennis Dinslage, Vice President Finance and Chief Financial Officer
CMO: Scott Green, M.D., Chief of Staff
CIO: Jean Meiergerd, Chief Information Officer
CHR: Terri Ridder, Director Human Resources
Web address: www.fcswp.org
**Control:** Church-operated, Nongovernment, not-for profit **Service:** General Medical and Surgical

**Staffed Beds:** 92 **Admissions:** 587 **Census:** 69 **Outpatient Visits:** 69280 **Births:** 62 **Total Expense ($000):** 26546 **Payroll Expense ($000):** 12698 **Personnel:** 217

## WINNEBAGO—Thurston County

☐ **U. S. PUBLIC HEALTH SERVICE INDIAN HOSPITAL (280119)**, Highway 7577, Zip 68071; tel. 402/878-2231, (Nonreporting) **A**1 9 10 **S** U. S. Indian Health Service, Rockville, MD
Primary Contact: Sheriann Moore, Service Unit Director
CFO: Audrey Parker, Budget Analyst
Web address: www.ihs.gov
**Control:** PHS, Indian Service, Government, federal **Service:** General Medical and Surgical

**Staffed Beds:** 30

## YORK—York County

★ **YORK GENERAL HOSPITAL (281336)**, 2222 North Lincoln Avenue, Zip 68467-1095; tel. 402/362-6671, (Total facility includes 129 beds in nursing home-type unit) **A**9 10 18 **F**3 10 11 12 13 15 28 29 31 34 35 40 45 53 56 57 59 60 62 64 68 70 75 76 77 78 79 81 82 85 86 87 89 93 96 107 108 110 111 115 117 118 119 125 128 129 130 131 132 133 145 146 148
Primary Contact: Charles K. Schulz, Chief Executive Officer
COO: Jane Thompson, Administrator and Chief Operating Officer
CFO: Bob McQuistan, Vice President Finance
CMO: Daniel Growney, M.D., Chief of Staff
CIO: John Temple, Director Information Systems
CHR: Cathy Norquest, Director Human Resources
CNO: Jenny Obermier, VP, Director of Nursing
Web address: www.yorkgeneral.org
**Control:** Other not-for-profit (including NFP Corporation) **Service:** General Medical and Surgical

**Staffed Beds:** 154 **Admissions:** 1012 **Census:** 120 **Outpatient Visits:** 44554 **Births:** 109 **Total Expense ($000):** 36907 **Payroll Expense ($000):** 17044 **Personnel:** 401

*Many Facility Codes have changed. Please refer to the AHA Guide Code Chart.*
© 2013 AHA Guide

NE

# NEVADA

## BATTLE MOUNTAIN—Lander County

**BATTLE MOUNTAIN GENERAL HOSPITAL (291303)**, 535 South Humboldt Street, Zip 89820–1988; tel. 775/635–2550, (Nonreporting) **A**9 10 18
Primary Contact: Philip S. Hanna, Administrator
CFO: Cindy Fagg, Fiscal Officer
CMO: George Mardini, M.D., Chief of Staff
CIO: Terry Dunn, Director Information Technology
CHR: Lori Sherbondy, Director Human Resources
Web address: www.bmgh.org
**Control:** Hospital district or authority, Government, nonfederal **Service:** General Medical and Surgical

**Staffed Beds: 7**

## BOULDER CITY—Clark County

**BOULDER CITY HOSPITAL (291309)**, 901 Adams Boulevard, Zip 89005–2213; tel. 702/293–4111, (Nonreporting) **A**9 10 18
Primary Contact: Thomas Maher, Chief Executive Officer and Administrator
CFO: Frey Belete, Controller
CMO: Jim Chiang, M.D., Chief of Staff
CIO: Scott Brooks, Manager Information Technology
CHR: Dianna Todd, Director Human Resources
Web address: www.bouldercityhospital.org
**Control:** Other not-for-profit (including NFP Corporation) **Service:** General Medical and Surgical

**Staffed Beds: 63**

## CALIENTE—Lincoln County

**GROVER C. DILS MEDICAL CENTER (291312)**, 700 North Spring Street, Zip 89008, Mailing Address: P.O. Box 1010, Zip 89008–1010; tel. 775/726–3171, (Nonreporting) **A**9 10 18
Primary Contact: Jason Bleak, Administrator and Chief Executive Officer
COO: Jason Bleak, Administrator and Chief Executive Officer
CFO: Sherlyn Fackrell, Finance Controller
CMO: R. William Katschke, Jr., M.D., Medical Director
CHR: Rozanne Mangum, Administrative Assistant and Director Human Resources
Web address: www.dilsmedicalcenter.org
**Control:** Other not-for-profit (including NFP Corporation) **Service:** Other specialty

**Staffed Beds: 20**

## CARSON CITY—Carson City County

**CARSON TAHOE CONTINUING CARE HOSPITAL (292008)**, 775 Fleischmann Way, 2nd Floor, Zip 89703–2995; tel. 775/445–7795, (Nonreporting) **A**9 10
Primary Contact: Neal Duncan, Chief Executive Officer
Web address: www.carsontahoe.com
**Control:** Other not-for-profit (including NFP Corporation) **Service:** Long–Term Acute Care hospital

**Staffed Beds: 29**

**CARSON TAHOE REGIONAL HEALTHCARE (290019)**, 1600 Medical Parkway, Zip 89703–4625, Mailing Address: P.O. Box 2168, Zip 89702–2168; tel. 775/445–8672 **A**1 2 9 10 **F**3 4 5 8 11 12 13 15 17 18 20 22 24 28 29 30 31 34 35 38 40 42 48 49 57 59 64 65 68 70 74 75 76 77 78 79 81 85 86 87 89 90 91 93 98 99 100 101 102 103 104 105 107 108 111 114 119 120 121 123 124 130 132 135 144 146 147 148
Primary Contact: Edward L. Epperson, Chief Executive Officer
COO: Douglas Self, Chief Operating Officer
CFO: Ann Beck, Vice President Finance
CMO: Jeffrey Sanders, M.D., Chief of Staff
CIO: Cheri Glockner, Director Development
CHR: Carie Wilkens, Director of Human Resources
CNO: Cathy Dinauer, MSN, Vice President Patient Care
Web address: www.carsontahoe.com
**Control:** Other not-for-profit (including NFP Corporation) **Service:** General Medical and Surgical

**Staffed Beds: 190 Admissions: 10161 Census: 119 Outpatient Visits: 221434 Births: 893 Total Expense ($000): 187242 Payroll Expense ($000): 72129 Personnel: 1076**

**SIERRA SURGERY HOSPITAL (290051)**, 1400 Medical Parkway, Zip 89703–4624; tel. 775/883–1700, (Nonreporting) **A**1 9 10
Primary Contact: Alan C. Olive, Chief Executive Officer
CFO: Sheryl Hayden, Chief Financial Officer
Web address: www.sierrasurgery.com
**Control:** Partnership, Investor–owned, for–profit **Service:** Surgical

**Staffed Beds: 15**

## ELKO—Elko County

**NORTHEASTERN NEVADA REGIONAL HOSPITAL (290008)**, 2001 Errecart Boulevard, Zip 89801–8333; tel. 775/738–5151, (Nonreporting) **A**1 9 10 20 **S** LifePoint Hospitals, Inc., Brentwood, TN
Primary Contact: Gene Miller, Chief Executive Officer
COO: Ann Cariker, Chief Operating Officer
CFO: Grant Trollope, Chief Financial Officer
CIO: Jeff Morgan, Director Information Systems
CNO: Dona E. Townsend, Chief Nursing Officer
Web address: www.nnrhospital.com
**Control:** Corporation, Investor–owned, for–profit **Service:** General Medical and Surgical

**Staffed Beds: 50**

## ELY—White Pine County

**WILLIAM BEE RIRIE HOSPITAL (291302)**, 1500 Avenue H, Zip 89301–2699; tel. 775/289–3001 **A**1 9 10 18 **F**8 13 15 29 31 32 35 40 44 45 50 57 59 64 65 66 68 75 76 77 79 81 82 85 86 87 89 93 107 108 111 114 119 127 129 130 135 **P**6
Primary Contact: Jan Jensen, R.N., Chief Executive Officer and Administrator
CMO: G. N. Christensen, M.D., Chief Medical Officer
CIO: Destin Brandis, Chief Information Officer
CHR: Vicki Pereace, Manager Human Resources
Web address: www.elynevadahospital.org
**Control:** Hospital district or authority, Government, nonfederal **Service:** General Medical and Surgical

**Staffed Beds: 12 Admissions: 585 Census: 4 Outpatient Visits: 32579 Births: 94 Total Expense ($000): 26220 Payroll Expense ($000): 13094 Personnel: 93**

## FALLON—Churchill County

**BANNER CHURCHILL COMMUNITY HOSPITAL (290006)**, 801 East Williams Avenue, Zip 89406–3052; tel. 775/867–7000 **A**1 9 10 20 **F**3 7 11 13 15 26 27 29 30 31 34 35 40 45 47 50 57 59 65 68 70 75 76 77 78 79 81 85 86 87 93 97 107 108 110 111 114 118 119 130 146 148 **P**6 **S** Banner Health, Phoenix, AZ
Primary Contact: John D'Angelo, Chief Executive Officer
CFO: Steven Fraker, Chief Financial Officer
CMO: Sukhbir Pannce, M.D., Chief Medical Officer
Web address: www.bannerhealth.com/Locations/Nevada/Banner+Churchill+Community+Hospital
**Control:** Other not-for-profit (including NFP Corporation) **Service:** General Medical and Surgical

**Staffed Beds: 40 Admissions: 2215 Census: 20 Outpatient Visits: 98899 Births: 381 Total Expense ($000): 37435 Payroll Expense ($000): 16026 Personnel: 243**

## GARDNERVILLE—Douglas County

★ **CARSON VALLEY MEDICAL CENTER (291306)**, 1107 Highway 395, Zip 89410; tel. 775/782–1500 **A**9 10 18 **F**11 15 29 31 34 35 40 45 47 48 50 53 54 56 57 59 60 64 68 70 75 77 79 81 93 103 107 108 110 111 115 118 119 127 129 130 132 133 135 144 146 148
Primary Contact: Susan Davila, Chief Executive Officer and Administrator
CFO: Marcus Armstrong, Chief Financial Officer
CNO: Linda Rowe, R.N., Chief Nursing Officer
Web address: www.carsonvalleymedicalcenter.com
**Control:** Other not–for–profit (including NFP Corporation) **Service:** General Medical and Surgical

**Staffed Beds: 23 Admissions: 741 Census: 6 Outpatient Visits: 115284 Births: 0 Total Expense ($000): 38057 Payroll Expense ($000): 14634 Personnel: 211**

NV

---

**Hospital, Medicare Provider Number, Address, Telephone, Approval, Facility, and Physician Codes, Health Care System**

★ American Hospital Association (AHA) membership
□ The Joint Commission accreditation      ◇ DNV Healthcare Inc. accreditation

○ Healthcare Facilities Accreditation Program
△ Commission on Accreditation of Rehabilitation Facilities (CARF) accreditation

## HAWTHORNE—Mineral County

**MOUNT GRANT GENERAL HOSPITAL (291300)**, First and A Street, Zip 89415, Mailing Address: P.O. Box 1510, Zip 89415–1510; tel. 775/945–2461, (Nonreporting) **A**9 10 18
Primary Contact: Richard Munger, Administrator
Web address: www.mtgrantgenhospital.org/
**Control:** Other not–for–profit (including NFP Corporation) **Service:** General Medical and Surgical

| Staffed Beds: 11 |
|---|

## HENDERSON—Clark County

☒ **HEALTHSOUTH REHABILITATION HOSPITAL – HENDERSON (293032)**, 10301 Jeffreys Street, Zip 89052–3922; tel. 702/939–9400 **A**1 10 **F**29 34 35 56 57 59 62 64 74 75 79 86 90 93 94 95 130 132 143 148 **S** HEALTHSOUTH Corporation, Birmingham, AL
Primary Contact: Earl Greenia, FACHE, Chief Executive Officer
CFO: Robert Bollard, Chief Financial Officer
Web address: www.hendersonrehabhospital.com
**Control:** Corporation, Investor–owned, for–profit **Service:** Rehabilitation

| Staffed Beds: 90 Admissions: 1640 Census: 63 Outpatient Visits: 12888 Births: 0 Total Expense ($000): 18398 Payroll Expense ($000): 11367 Personnel: 190 |
|---|

**SEVEN HILLS BEHAVIORAL INSTITUTE (294012)**, 3021 West Horizon Ridge Parkway, Zip 89052–3990; tel. 702/646–5000 **A**9 10 **F**4 98 99 102 104 105 **S** Acadia Healthcare Company, Inc., Franklin, TN
Primary Contact: John Hull, Chief Executive Officer
CMO: Keith Breiland, M.D., Medical Director
Web address: www.sevenhillsbi.com
**Control:** Corporation, Investor–owned, for–profit **Service:** Psychiatric

| Staffed Beds: 58 Admissions: 2776 Census: 50 Outpatient Visits: 1704 Births: 0 Total Expense ($000): 11657 Payroll Expense ($000): 5212 Personnel: 93 |
|---|

☒ **ST. ROSE DOMINICAN HOSPITALS – ROSE DE LIMA CAMPUS (290012)**, 102 East Lake Mead Parkway, Zip 89015–5524; tel. 702/616–5000 **A**1 9 10 **F**3 8 12 15 18 20 28 29 30 31 32 34 35 38 40 44 45 49 50 57 59 62 63 64 65 68 70 74 75 77 78 79 81 82 84 85 86 87 90 93 96 102 107 108 111 114 119 130 131 132 135 143 146 147 148 **S** Dignity Health, San Francisco, CA
Primary Contact: Teressa Conley, Interim President and Chief Executive Officer
COO: Teressa Conley, Vice President and Chief Operating Officer
CFO: Kevin Walters, Chief Financial Officer
CMO: Stephen K. Jones, M.D., Vice President Medical Staff Affairs
CIO: Sharon Hester, Site Manager Information Technology
Web address: www.strosehospitals.org
**Control:** Church–operated, Nongovernment, not–for profit **Service:** General Medical and Surgical

| Staffed Beds: 119 Admissions: 6529 Census: 90 Outpatient Visits: 42943 Births: 0 Total Expense ($000): 131659 Payroll Expense ($000): 60164 Personnel: 677 |
|---|

☒ **ST. ROSE DOMINICAN HOSPITALS – SIENA CAMPUS (290045)**, 3001 St. Rose Parkway, Zip 89052; tel. 702/616–5000 **A**1 3 5 9 10 **F**3 7 13 15 18 20 21 22 23 24 26 28 29 30 31 32 34 35 38 40 41 43 44 45 46 50 57 59 64 68 70 72 74 75 76 77 78 79 81 82 83 84 85 86 87 88 89 93 102 107 108 110 111 114 115 119 126 130 131 132 135 146 147 148 **P**6 **S** Dignity Health, San Francisco, CA
Primary Contact: Rod A. Davis, FACHE, President and Chief Executive Officer and Senior Vice President Operations Dignity Health Nevada
COO: Teressa Conley, Chief Operating Officer
CFO: Kevin Walters, Chief Financial Officer
CMO: Stephen K. Jones, M.D., Vice President Medical Staff Affairs
CIO: Sharon Hester, Site Manager Information Technology
CHR: LeRoy Walker, Vice President Human Resources
Web address: www.strosehospitals.com
**Control:** Church–operated, Nongovernment, not–for profit **Service:** General Medical and Surgical

| Staffed Beds: 219 Admissions: 16785 Census: 191 Outpatient Visits: 73111 Births: 3428 Total Expense ($000): 292185 Payroll Expense ($000): 127126 Personnel: 1633 |
|---|

## INCLINE VILLAGE—Washoe County

○ **INCLINE VILLAGE COMMUNITY HOSPITAL (291301)**, 880 Alder Avenue, Zip 89451–8335; tel. 775/833–4100, (Nonreporting) **A**3 5 9 10 11 18 **S** Tahoe Forest Health System, Truckee, CA
Primary Contact: Judy Newland, R.N., Chief Nursing Officer
COO: Virginia Razo, Chief Operating Officer
CFO: Crystal Betts, Chief Financial Officer
CIO: Mark Griffiths, Director Management Information Systems
CHR: Jayne O'Flanagan, Director Human Resources
Web address: www.tfhd.com
**Control:** Hospital district or authority, Government, nonfederal **Service:** General Medical and Surgical

| Staffed Beds: 6 |
|---|

## LAS VEGAS—Clark County

☐ **CENTENNIAL HILLS HOSPITAL MEDICAL CENTER (290054)**, 6900 North Durango Drive, Zip 89149–4409; tel. 702/835–9700, (Nonreporting) **A**1 9 10 **S** Universal Health Services, Inc., King of Prussia, PA
Primary Contact: Sajit Pullarkat, Chief Executive Officer and Managing Director
Web address: www.centennialhillshospital.com
**Control:** Corporation, Investor–owned, for–profit **Service:** General Medical and Surgical

| Staffed Beds: 171 |
|---|

☒ **COMPLEX CARE HOSPITAL AT TENAYA (292006)**, 2500 North Tenaya, Zip 89128–0482; tel. 702/562–2021, (Nonreporting) **A**1 9 10 **S** LifeCare Management Services, Plano, TX
Primary Contact: Timothy C. Deaton, Administrator
CFO: Deborah Gerke, Chief Financial Officer
CMO: C. Dean Milne, D.O., Medical Director
CIO: Lynn Tunson, Manager Medical Records
CHR: Debra Tafoya, Director Human Resources
Web address: www.lifecare–hospitals.com
**Control:** Corporation, Investor–owned, for–profit **Service:** Long–Term Acute Care hospital

| Staffed Beds: 70 |
|---|

☐ **DESERT SPRINGS HOSPITAL MEDICAL CENTER (290022)**, 2075 East Flamingo Road, Zip 89119–5121; tel. 702/733–8800, (Nonreporting) **A**1 9 10 **S** Universal Health Services, Inc., King of Prussia, PA
Primary Contact: Samuel Kaufman, Chief Executive Officer and Managing Director
CFO: Lynn Kennington, Chief Financial Officer
CMO: Adel R. Shehata, M.D., Medical Director
CIO: Tom Schoenig, System Director Information Services
CHR: Shirley A. Shadwick, Administrator Human Resources
Web address: www.desertspringshospital.com
**Control:** Corporation, Investor–owned, for–profit **Service:** General Medical and Surgical

| Staffed Beds: 346 |
|---|

**DESERT WILLOW TREATMENT CENTER**, 6171 West Charleston Boulevard, Zip 89146–1126; tel. 702/486–8900, (Nonreporting) **A**3 5
Primary Contact: Linda Santangelo, Ph.D., Director
**Control:** State–Government, nonfederal **Service:** Psychiatric

| Staffed Beds: 58 |
|---|

**HARMON MEDICAL AND REHABILITATION HOSPITAL (290042)**, 2170 East Harmon Avenue, Zip 89119–7840; tel. 702/794–0100, (Nonreporting) **A**10 **S** Fundamental Long Term Care Holdings, LLC, Sparks Glencoe, MD
Primary Contact: Bonnie Essex Hillegass, Chief Executive Officer
**Control:** Corporation, Investor–owned, for–profit **Service:** Rehabilitation

| Staffed Beds: 118 |
|---|

☒ **HEALTHSOUTH DESERT CANYON REHABILITATION HOSPITAL (293033)**, 9175 West Oquendo Road, Zip 89148–1234; tel. 702/252–7342 **A**1 10 **F**3 29 77 79 90 91 93 **S** HEALTHSOUTH Corporation, Birmingham, AL
Primary Contact: Deanna Martin, MSN, Chief Executive Officer
Web address: www.healthsouthdesertcanyon.com
**Control:** Corporation, Investor–owned, for–profit **Service:** Rehabilitation

| Staffed Beds: 50 Admissions: 1154 Census: 41 Outpatient Visits: 3463 Births: 0 Total Expense ($000): 19008 Payroll Expense ($000): 8017 Personnel: 136 |
|---|

☒ **HEALTHSOUTH REHABILITATION HOSPITAL–LAS VEGAS (293026)**, 1250 South Valley View Boulevard, Zip 89102–1861; tel. 702/877–8898 **A**1 10 **F**3 28 29 57 60 65 68 74 75 77 79 90 95 96 130 132 143 148 **S** HEALTHSOUTH Corporation, Birmingham, AL
Primary Contact: Michael Ward, Chief Executive Officer
CFO: Sherilene DeLeon, Controller
CMO: Farzin Farhang, M.D., Medical Director
CHR: Gina Lewis, Director Human Resources
CNO: Elizabeth Solomon, R.N., Regional Quality/Risk Director and Interim Chief Nursing Officer
Web address: www.healthsouthlasvegas.com
**Control:** Corporation, Investor–owned, for–profit **Service:** Rehabilitation

| Staffed Beds: 79 Admissions: 1615 Census: 54 Outpatient Visits: 0 Births: 0 Total Expense ($000): 17986 Payroll Expense ($000): 10189 Personnel: 227 |
|---|

NV

*Many Facility Codes have changed. Please refer to the AHA Guide Code Chart.* © 2013 AHA Guide

☐ **HORIZON SPECIALTY HOSPITAL (292003)**, 640 Desert Lane,
Zip 89106–4207; tel. 702/382-3155 **A**1 9 10 **F**1 12 28 29 60 119 130 148
**S** Fundamental Long Term Care Holdings, LLC, Sparks Glencoe, MD
Primary Contact: William Fox, Chief Executive Officer
CFO: Darnell Bennett, Director Finance
CMO: Syed Rahman, M.D., Chief of Staff
CIO: Azena Ansi, Manager Health Information Management
CHR: Melvin Layugan, Director Human Resources
**Control:** Corporation, Investor–owned, for–profit **Service:** Long–Term Acute Care
hospital

> **Staffed Beds:** 49 **Admissions:** 842 **Census:** 38 **Outpatient Visits:** 0 **Births:**
> 0 **Total Expense ($000):** 16115 **Payroll Expense ($000):** 6555 **Personnel:**
> 115

**KINDRED HOSPITAL LAS VEGAS, DESERT SPRINGS CAMPUS** See Kindred
Hospital Las Vegas–Sahara

☒ **KINDRED HOSPITAL LAS VEGAS–SAHARA (292002)**, 5110 West Sahara
Avenue, Zip 89146–3406; tel. 702/871-1418, (Includes KINDRED HOSPITAL LAS
VEGAS, DESERT SPRINGS CAMPUS, 2075 East Flamingo Road, Suite 114,
Zip 89119; tel. 702/894–5728; KINDRED HOSPITAL–FLAMINGO, 2250 East
Flamingo Road, Zip 89119; tel. 702/871–1418), (Nonreporting) **A**1 9 10
**S** Kindred Healthcare, Louisville, KY
Primary Contact: Carol Lee O'Connor, Interim Chief Executive Officer
CFO: William Lysaght, Chief Financial Officer
CMO: Paul Stewart, M.D., Medical Director
CHR: Jim Sturgeon, Area Director Human Resources
Web address: www.kindredhospitallvs.com/
**Control:** Corporation, Investor–owned, for–profit **Service:** Long–Term Acute Care
hospital

> **Staffed Beds:** 238

☐ **MONTEVISTA HOSPITAL (294009)**, 5900 West Rochelle Avenue,
Zip 89103–3327; tel. 702/364–1111 **A**1 9 10 **F**5 98 99 102 103 104 105 130
133 **S** Strategic Behavioral Health, LLC, Memphis, TN
Primary Contact: Kreg Gillman, Chief Executive Officer
CFO: Ben Winbery, Chief Financial Officer
CMO: William Bauer, M.D., Medical Director
CHR: Carol Nelson, Director Human Resources
Web address: www.montevistahospital.com
**Control:** Corporation, Investor–owned, for–profit **Service:** Psychiatric

> **Staffed Beds:** 90 **Admissions:** 3067 **Census:** 73 **Outpatient Visits:** 13383
> **Births:** 0 **Total Expense ($000):** 17477 **Payroll Expense ($000):** 9841
> **Personnel:** 216

☒ **MOUNTAINVIEW HOSPITAL (290039)**, 3100 North Tenaya Way,
Zip 89128–0436; tel. 702/255–5000, (Nonreporting) **A**1 3 5 9 10 **S** HCA,
Nashville, TN
Primary Contact: William Wagnon, Chief Executive Officer
CFO: Lana Arad, Chief Financial Officer
CMO: Jack Collier, M.D., Chief of Staff
CHR: Robert Nettles, Director Human Resources
Web address: www.mountainview–hospital.com
**Control:** Corporation, Investor owned, for profit **Service:** General Medical and
Surgical

> **Staffed Beds:** 235

**PROGRESSIVE HOSPITAL (292007)**, 4015 South McLeod Drive,
Zip 89121–4305; tel. 702/433–2200 **A**9 10 **F**1 29 30 85 130 148 **P**5
Primary Contact: Rosemary Thiele, Chief Executive Officer
Web address: www.progressivehospital.com/
**Control:** Partnership, Investor–owned, for–profit **Service:** Long–Term Acute Care
hospital

> **Staffed Beds:** 24 **Admissions:** 173 **Census:** 14 **Outpatient Visits:** 0 **Births:**
> 0 **Total Expense ($000):** 7001 **Payroll Expense ($000):** 3181 **Personnel:**
> 66

☐ **RED ROCK BEHAVIORAL HOSPITAL (294008)**, 5975 West Twain Avenue,
Zip 89103–1237; tel. 702/214–8099 **A**1 9 10 **F**98 101 103 **S** Strategic
Behavioral Health, LLC, Memphis, TN
Primary Contact: Toby Davis, Chief Executive Officer
Web address: www.redrockhospital.com
**Control:** Other not–for–profit (including NFP Corporation) **Service:** Psychiatric

> **Staffed Beds:** 21 **Admissions:** 522 **Census:** 19 **Outpatient Visits:** 0 **Total**
> **Expense ($000):** 3858 **Payroll Expense ($000):** 2088 **Personnel:** 27

☒ **SOUTHERN HILLS HOSPITAL AND MEDICAL CENTER (290047)**, 9300 West
Sunset Road, Zip 89148–4844; tel. 702/880–2100 **A**1 9 10 **F**3 13 15 17 18
20 22 26 29 40 43 45 57 59 68 70 72 74 75 76 77 78 79 81 85 87 98 107
108 109 110 111 113 114 119 130 135 146 147 **P**5 **S** HCA, Nashville, TN
Primary Contact: Kimball Anderson, FACHE, Chief Executive Officer
COO: Andrea Davis, Assistant Administrator
CFO: Michael Herron, Chief Financial Officer
CIO: Joe Grandiosi, Director Information Technology
CHR: Tim Black, Director Human Resources
CNO: Natalie Ransom, Chief Nursing Officer
Web address: www.southernhillshospital.com
**Control:** Corporation, Investor–owned, for–profit **Service:** General Medical and
Surgical

> **Staffed Beds:** 134 **Admissions:** 7071 **Census:** 81 **Outpatient Visits:** 29597
> **Births:** 1264 **Total Expense ($000):** 105501 **Payroll Expense ($000):**
> 38421

☐ **SOUTHERN NEVADA ADULT MENTAL HEALTH SERVICES (294002)**, 6161
West Charleston Boulevard, Zip 89146–1126; tel. 702/486–6000, (Nonreporting)
**A**1 3 5 10
Primary Contact: James Northrop, Director
Web address: www.mhds.state.nv.us
**Control:** State–Government, nonfederal **Service:** Psychiatric

> **Staffed Beds:** 190

☐ **SPRING MOUNTAIN SAHARA (294010)**, 5460 West Sahara, Zip 89146–3307;
tel. 702/216–8900 **A**1 9 10 **F**29 56 64 98 103 104 130 **S** Universal Health
Services, Inc., King of Prussia, PA
Primary Contact: Darryl S. Dubroca, Chief Executive Officer and Managing
Director
Web address: www.springmountainsahara.com
**Control:** Corporation, Investor–owned, for–profit **Service:** Psychiatric

> **Staffed Beds:** 30 **Admissions:** 784 **Census:** 23 **Outpatient Visits:** 2387
> **Births:** 0 **Total Expense ($000):** 4386 **Payroll Expense ($000):** 2715
> **Personnel:** 47

☐ **SPRING MOUNTAIN TREATMENT CENTER (294011)**, 7000 West Spring
Mountain Road, Zip 89117–3816; tel. 702/873–2400 **A**1 5 9 10 **F**29 98 99 105
130 **S** Universal Health Services, Inc., King of Prussia, PA
Primary Contact: Darryl S. Dubroca, Chief Executive Officer and Managing
Director
Web address: www.healthsouth.com
**Control:** Corporation, Investor–owned, for–profit **Service:** Psychiatric

> **Staffed Beds:** 82 **Admissions:** 2778 **Census:** 59 **Outpatient Visits:** 2039
> **Births:** 0 **Total Expense ($000):** 12118 **Payroll Expense ($000):** 6473
> **Personnel:** 162

☐ **SPRING VALLEY HOSPITAL MEDICAL CENTER (290046)**, 5400 South
Rainbow Boulevard, Zip 89118–1859; tel. 702/853–3000, (Nonreporting) **A**1 9
10 **S** Universal Health Services, Inc., King of Prussia, PA
Primary Contact: Leonard Freehof, Chief Executive Officer and Managing Director
COO: Mason VanHouweling, Chief Operating Officer
CFO: Leanne Shields, Chief Financial Officer
CMO: Dan McBride, M.D., Chief of Staff
CHR: Angelique Davison, Administrator Human Resources
Web address: www.springvalleyhospital.com
**Control:** Corporation, Investor–owned, for–profit **Service:** General Medical and
Surgical

> **Staffed Beds:** 169

☒ **ST. ROSE DOMINICAN HOSPITALS – SAN MARTIN CAMPUS (290053)**,
8280 West Warm Springs Road, Zip 89113–3612; tel. 702/492–8000 **A**1 9 10
**F**3 8 13 15 18 20 22 24 26 28 29 30 31 32 34 35 38 40 44 45 47 49 50 57
59 64 68 70 73 74 75 76 77 78 79 80 81 82 84 85 86 87 93 102 107 108
110 111 115 119 126 130 131 132 135 146 147 148 **S** Dignity Health, San
Francisco, CA
Primary Contact: Victoria J. VanMeetren, President
COO: Teressa Conley, Chief Operating Officer
CFO: Kevin Walters, Chief Financial Officer
CMO: Stephen K. Jones, M.D., Chief Medical Officer
CIO: Sharon Hester, Site Manager Information Technology
CHR: LeRoy Walker, Vice President Human Resources
Web address: www.strosehospitals.org
**Control:** Church–operated, Nongovernment, not–for profit **Service:** General
Medical and Surgical

> **Staffed Beds:** 147 **Admissions:** 8183 **Census:** 96 **Outpatient Visits:** 32725
> **Births:** 904 **Total Expense ($000):** 165600 **Payroll Expense ($000):** 63578
> **Personnel:** 677

NV

---

☐ **SUMMERLIN HOSPITAL MEDICAL CENTER (290041)**, 657 Town Center Drive, Zip 89144–6367; tel. 702/233–7000, (Nonreporting) **A**1 9 10 **S** Universal Health Services, Inc., King of Prussia, PA
Primary Contact: Robert S. Freymuller, Chief Executive Officer
CFO: Vanessa Kochevar, Chief Financial Officer
Web address: www.summerlinhospital.com
**Control:** Corporation, Investor–owned, for–profit **Service:** General Medical and Surgical

**Staffed Beds:** 148

⊠ △ **SUNRISE HOSPITAL AND MEDICAL CENTER (290003)**, 3186 Maryland Parkway, Zip 89109–2306, Mailing Address: P.O. Box 98530, Zip 89193; tel. 702/731–8000, (Includes SUNRISE CHILDREN'S HOSPITAL ) **A**1 2 3 5 7 9 10 **F**3 11 12 13 15 17 18 19 20 21 22 23 24 25 26 27 29 30 31 34 35 39 40 41 43 45 46 49 50 57 58 59 60 61 64 65 68 70 72 74 75 76 77 78 79 81 82 84 85 86 88 89 90 92 96 107 108 110 111 114 115 116 117 118 119 124 126 129 130 132 135 146 147 148 **S** HCA, Nashville, TN
Primary Contact: Todd Sklamberg, President
CFO: Daniel Perritt, Chief Financial Officer
CMO: Katherine Keeley, M.D., Chief of Staff
CIO: Alan Burt, Director Information Services
Web address: www.sunrisehospital.com
**Control:** Corporation, Investor–owned, for–profit **Service:** General Medical and Surgical

**Staffed Beds:** 641 **Admissions:** 28586 **Census:** 418 **Outpatient Visits:** 161155 **Births:** 4231 **Total Expense ($000):** 445492 **Payroll Expense ($000):** 182519 **Personnel:** 2356

⊠ **UNIVERSITY MEDICAL CENTER (290007)**, 1800 West Charleston Boulevard, Zip 89102–2386; tel. 702/383–2000, (Includes CHILDREN'S HOSPITAL OF NEVADA AT UMC, 1800 West Charleston Boulevard, Zip 89102–2329; tel. 702/383–2000) **A**1 2 3 5 8 9 10 **F**3 12 13 15 16 17 18 19 20 21 22 23 24 26 27 28 29 30 31 34 35 40 41 43 44 45 46 47 48 49 50 54 55 57 58 59 60 61 64 65 66 67 68 70 72 73 74 75 76 77 78 79 81 82 83 85 87 88 89 92 93 107 111 112 114 115 118 119 130 132 138 141 144 146 147 148 **P**1 8
Primary Contact: Brian G. Brannman, Chief Executive Officer
CFO: George Stevens, Chief Financial Officer
CMO: Dale Carrison, M.D., Chief of Staff
CIO: Ernie McKinley, Chief Information Officer
CHR: John Espinoza, Chief Human Resources Officer
Web address: www.umcsn.com
**Control:** County–Government, nonfederal **Service:** General Medical and Surgical

**Staffed Beds:** 541 **Admissions:** 30746 **Census:** 361 **Outpatient Visits:** 788865 **Births:** 3468 **Total Expense ($000):** 578119 **Payroll Expense ($000):** 222248 **Personnel:** 3522

☐ **VALLEY HOSPITAL MEDICAL CENTER (290021)**, 620 Shadow Lane, Zip 89106–4119; tel. 702/388–4000, (Nonreporting) **A**1 9 10 12 13 **S** Universal Health Services, Inc., King of Prussia, PA
Primary Contact: Jay Finnegan, Chief Executive Officer
CFO: Betsy A. Sponsler, Chief Financial Officer
CMO: Dost Wattoo, M.D., Chief of Staff
CIO: Tom Schoenig, Regional Director Information Services
CHR: Dana Thorne, Administrator Human Resources
Web address: www.valleyhospital.net
**Control:** Corporation, Investor–owned, for–profit **Service:** General Medical and Surgical

**Staffed Beds:** 365

### LOVELOCK—Pershing County

**PERSHING GENERAL HOSPITAL (291304)**, 855 Sixth Street, Zip 89419, Mailing Address: P.O. Box 661, Zip 89419–0661; tel. 775/273–2621, (Total facility includes 25 beds in nursing home–type unit) **A**9 10 18 **F**40 57 93 97 103 107 114 127 128 130 133
Primary Contact: Patty Goldsworthy, Interim Chief Executive Officer and Administrator
CFO: Marjorie Skinner, Director Finance
CMO: Yousri Gadallah, M.D., Chief Medical Officer
CIO: Jim Weeldreyer, Manager Information Technology
CHR: Cynthia Hixenbaugh, Director Human Resources
Web address: www.pershinghospital.org
**Control:** Hospital district or authority, Government, nonfederal **Service:** Long–Term Acute Care hospital

**Staffed Beds:** 38 **Admissions:** 69 **Census:** 20 **Outpatient Visits:** 16591 **Total Expense ($000):** 8175 **Payroll Expense ($000):** 3197 **Personnel:** 77

### MESQUITE—Clark County

⊠ **MESA VIEW REGIONAL HOSPITAL (291307)**, 1299 Bertha Howe Avenue, Zip 89027–7500; tel. 702/346–8040, (Nonreporting) **A**1 9 10 18 **S** Community Health Systems, Inc., Franklin, TN
Primary Contact: Patricia Holden, Chief Executive Officer
CFO: Eric S. Hardy, Chief Financial Officer
CHR: Matthew Anderson, Director Human Resources
Web address: www.mesaviewhospital.com
**Control:** Corporation, Investor–owned, for–profit **Service:** General Medical and Surgical

**Staffed Beds:** 25

### NELLIS AFB—Clark County

⊠ **MIKE O'CALLAGHAN FEDERAL HOSPITAL**, 4700 Las Vegas Boulevard North, Suite 2419, Zip 89191–6600; tel. 702/653–2000, (Nonreporting) **A**1 3 5 **S** Department of the Air Force, Washington, DC
Primary Contact: Colonel Christian Benjamin, USAF, MC, Commander
COO: Colonel Linnes L. Chester, USAF, Administrator
CFO: Major Kari Turkal–Barrett, Flight Commander Resource Management Officer
CMO: Lieutenant Colonel Markham Brown, M.D., Chief Medical Staff
CIO: Major Kevin Seeley, Chief Information Officer
Web address: www.lasvegas.va.gov/
**Control:** Air Force, Government, federal **Service:** General Medical and Surgical

**Staffed Beds:** 46

### NORTH LAS VEGAS—Clark County

◇ **NORTH VISTA HOSPITAL (290005)**, 1409 East Lake Mead Boulevard, Zip 89030–7197; tel. 702/649–7711, (Nonreporting) **A**9 10 21 **S** IASIS Healthcare, Franklin, TN
Primary Contact: Cathy N. Story, Interim Chief Executive Officer
COO: Michael Heindel, Chief Operating Officer
CFO: Kim Forbes–Daniels, Chief Financial Officer
Web address: www.northvistahospital.com
**Control:** Corporation, Investor–owned, for–profit **Service:** General Medical and Surgical

**Staffed Beds:** 198

★ **VETERANS AFFAIRS SOUTHERN NEVADA HEALTHCARE SYSTEM**, 6900 North Pecos Road, Mailing Address: P.O. Box 360001, Zip 89036–8108; tel. 702/791–9000 **A**5 **F**15 18 20 22 30 31 33 34 35 38 39 50 54 55 56 57 59 62 64 65 66 71 74 75 77 78 79 81 82 83 84 86 87 90 93 94 97 98 100 101 102 103 104 105 107 108 109 110 111 112 113 114 115 116 117 118 119 120 121 122 123 124 126 130 132 135 143 146 147 148 **P**6 **S** Department of Veterans Affairs, Washington, DC
Primary Contact: Isabel Duff, MS, Acting Director
CFO: Richard O. Hays, Chief Fiscal Service
CMO: Ramanujam Komanduri, M.D., Chief of Staff
Web address: www.lasvegas.va.gov/
**Control:** Veterans Affairs, Government, federal **Service:** General Medical and Surgical

**Staffed Beds:** 58 **Admissions:** 4435 **Census:** 48 **Outpatient Visits:** 552800 **Births:** 0 **Total Expense ($000):** 213126 **Payroll Expense ($000):** 163889 **Personnel:** 3225

### PAHRUMP—Nye County

★ **DESERT VIEW HOSPITAL (291311)**, 360 South Lola Lane, Zip 89048–0884; tel. 775/751–7500 **A**9 10 18 **F**3 15 18 29 34 40 57 81 86 87 107 111 119 133 148 **P**6 **S** Rural Health Group, Nephi, UT
Primary Contact: Kelly H. Adams, Chief Executive Officer
CMO: Fredric Siegel, M.D., Chief of Staff
CHR: Alecia Riddle, Manager Human Resources
CNO: Ellen Maborang, Chief Nursing Officer
Web address: www.desertviewhospital.com
**Control:** Corporation, Investor–owned, for–profit **Service:** General Medical and Surgical

**Staffed Beds:** 25 **Admissions:** 1734 **Census:** 14 **Births:** 0 **Total Expense ($000):** 20264 **Payroll Expense ($000):** 8170 **Personnel:** 162

**DESERT VIEW REGIONAL MEDICAL CENTER** See Desert View Hospital

**NV**

*Many Facility Codes have changed. Please refer to the AHA Guide Code Chart.* © 2013 AHA Guide

## RENO—Washoe County

⊠ **RENOWN REGIONAL MEDICAL CENTER (290001)**, 1155 Mill Street, Zip 89502–1576; tel. 775/982–4100, (Includes RENOWN CHILDREN'S HOSPITAL, 1155 Mill Street, tel. 775/982–5437) **A**1 2 3 5 9 10 **F**3 5 11 13 15 17 18 19 20 21 22 23 24 25 26 27 28 29 30 31 32 34 35 37 40 41 43 45 49 54 56 57 58 59 60 61 62 64 65 66 68 70 72 73 74 75 76 77 78 79 81 82 84 85 86 87 88 89 93 99 100 101 102 103 104 105 107 108 109 110 111 114 115 118 119 120 121 123 124 126 130 131 132 135 144 145 146 147 148 **S** Renown Health, Reno, NV
Primary Contact: Gregory E. Boyer, Chief Executive Officer
COO: Kris Gaw, Chief Operating Officer
CFO: Sam King, Chief Financial Officer
CMO: Charles Johnson, M.D., Chief of Staff
CIO: Charles Scully, Chief Information Officer
CHR: Michelle Sanchez–Bickley, Vice President Human Resources
Web address: www.renown.org
**Control:** Other not–for–profit (including NFP Corporation) **Service:** General Medical and Surgical

**Staffed Beds:** 608 **Admissions:** 27864 **Census:** 397 **Outpatient Visits:** 335138 **Births:** 3220 **Total Expense ($000):** 471535 **Payroll Expense ($000):** 147768 **Personnel:** 2786

★ △ **RENOWN REHABILITATION HOSPITAL**, 1495 Mill Street, Zip 89502–1479; tel. 775/982–3500 **A**3 5 7 **F**29 54 77 82 90 93 96 143 148 **P**5 6 **S** Renown Health, Reno, NV
Primary Contact: Allan E. Hanssen, Interim Administrator
COO: Kris Gaw, Chief Operating Officer
CFO: Dawn Ahner, Chief Financial Officer
CIO: Charles Scully, Chief Information Officer
CHR: Michelle Sanchez–Bickley, Vice President Human Resources
CNO: Gail P. Green, R.N., Chief Nursing Officer
Web address: www.renown.org
**Control:** Other not–for–profit (including NFP Corporation) **Service:** Rehabilitation

**Staffed Beds:** 62 **Admissions:** 983 **Census:** 41 **Outpatient Visits:** 20910 **Births:** 0 **Total Expense ($000):** 21028 **Payroll Expense ($000):** 10706 **Personnel:** 181

⊠ **RENOWN SOUTH MEADOWS MEDICAL CENTER (290049)**, 10101 Double R Boulevard, Zip 89521–5931; tel. 775/982–7000 **A**1 3 5 9 10 **F**8 10 12 29 30 35 39 40 46 49 68 70 74 75 79 81 84 85 87 93 97 107 108 111 119 125 130 131 146 **S** Renown Health, Reno, NV
Primary Contact: Allan E. Hanssen, Interim Administrator
COO: Kris Gaw, Chief Operating Officer
CFO: Cora Case, Chief Financial Officer
CMO: Max Jackson, M.D., Chief Medical Officer
CIO: Charles Scully, Chief Information Officer
CHR: Michelle Sanchez–Bickley, Vice President Human Resources
CNO: Gail P. Green, R.N., Chief Nursing Officer
Web address: www.renown.org
**Control:** Other not–for–profit (including NFP Corporation) **Service:** General Medical and Surgical

**Staffed Beds:** 76 **Admissions:** 2923 **Census:** 25 **Outpatient Visits:** 57822 **Births:** 0 **Total Expense ($000):** 60471 **Payroll Expense ($000):** 20390 **Personnel:** 348

⊠ **SAINT MARY'S REGIONAL MEDICAL CENTER (290009)**, 235 West Sixth Street, Zip 89503–4548; tel. 775/770–3000, (Data for 184 days) **A**1 2 3 5 9 10 **F**3 12 13 15 17 18 20 22 24 28 29 30 31 35 39 40 45 46 47 48 49 53 54 56 58 62 63 64 70 72 74 75 76 77 78 79 81 82 84 85 87 89 93 95 102 107 108 110 111 114 115 118 119 120 121 124 126 130 132 146 147 148 **S** Prime Healthcare Services, Ontario, CA
Primary Contact: Helen Lidholm, Chief Executive Officer
CFO: John R. Deakyne, Chief Financial Officer
CIO: Cindy Mullins, Director Information Technology
CHR: David Milovich, Vice President Human Resources
Web address: www.saintmarysreno.org
**Control:** Corporation, Investor–owned, for–profit **Service:** General Medical and Surgical

**Staffed Beds:** 272 **Admissions:** 7827 **Census:** 147 **Outpatient Visits:** 68062 **Births:** 869 **Total Expense ($000):** 110584 **Payroll Expense ($000):** 38191 **Personnel:** 1132

⊠ **TAHOE PACIFIC HOSPITALS (292004)**, 201 West Liberty Street, Suite 310, Zip 89501–2017; tel. 775/355–5970, (Includes TAHOE PACIFIC HOSPITALS – WEST, 235 West Sixth Street, 5th Floor, Zip 89503–4548), (Nonreporting) **A**1 9 10 **S** LifeCare Management Services, Plano, TX
Primary Contact: Colin O'Sullivan, Administrator
COO: Theresa Fegan, Chief Clinical Officer
CFO: Nena Swenson, Financial Manager
CMO: T. Brian Callister, M.D., Chief Medical Officer
CIO: Kaylene Reeves, Director
CHR: Nelson Coy, Director Human Resources
Web address: www.lifecare–hospitals.com
**Control:** Corporation, Investor–owned, for–profit **Service:** Long–Term Acute Care hospital

**Staffed Beds:** 60

⊠ **VETERANS AFFAIRS SIERRA NEVADA HEALTH CARE SYSTEM**, 975 Kirman Avenue, Zip 89502–0993; tel. 775/786–7200, (Total facility includes 60 beds in nursing home–type unit) **A**1 3 5 **F**1 3 5 18 20 22 26 28 29 30 31 34 35 36 38 39 40 44 45 46 50 54 56 57 58 59 60 61 62 63 64 68 70 74 75 77 78 79 81 82 83 84 85 86 87 91 92 93 94 96 97 98 100 103 104 106 107 108 111 114 115 119 129 130 132 135 143 144 146 147 148 **S** Department of Veterans Affairs, Washington, DC
Primary Contact: Kurt W. Schlegelmilch, M.D., FACHE, Director
COO: Michael C. Tadych, Associate Director
CFO: Kathy Munday, Chief Financial Officer
CMO: Steven Brilliant, M.D., Chief of Staff
CIO: Jack Smith, Acting Chief Information Resources Management Service
CHR: Debbie Jenkins, Chief Human Resources Management Service
Web address: www.reno.va.gov/
**Control:** Veterans Affairs, Government, federal **Service:** General Medical and Surgical

**Staffed Beds:** 124 **Admissions:** 4076 **Census:** 105 **Outpatient Visits:** 379039 **Births:** 0 **Personnel:** 1261

☐ **WEST HILLS HOSPITAL (294003)**, 1240 East Ninth Street, Zip 89512–2964; tel. 775/323–0478 **A**1 9 10 **F**4 5 98 99 101 103 104 **S** Universal Health Services, Inc., King of Prussia, PA
Primary Contact: Darryl S. Dubroca, Interim Chief Executive Officer
CFO: Erich Koch, Chief Financial Officer
CMO: Philip Rich, M.D., Chief Medical Officer
CHR: Don Gay, Director Human Resources
Web address: www.westhillshospital.net
**Control:** Corporation, Investor–owned, for–profit **Service:** Psychiatric

**Staffed Beds:** 190 **Admissions:** 2193 **Census:** 41 **Outpatient Visits:** 0 **Births:** 0 **Total Expense ($000):** 10924 **Payroll Expense ($000):** 6025

**WILLOW SPRINGS CENTER**, 690 Edison Way, Zip 89502–4135; tel. 775/858–3303 **A**3 5 **F**98 99 104 106
Primary Contact: Jim Serratt, Chief Executive Officer
CFO: Diahann Barrera, Chief Financial Officer
CMO: Jason Walenta, M.D., Medical Director
Web address: www.willowspringscenter.com
**Control:** Corporation, Investor–owned, for–profit **Service:** Children's hospital psychiatric

**Staffed Beds:** 116 **Admissions:** 370 **Census:** 93 **Outpatient Visits:** 8036 **Births:** 0 **Total Expense ($000):** 14663 **Payroll Expense ($000):** 8005 **Personnel:** 148

## SPARKS—Washoe County

☐ **NORTHERN NEVADA ADULT MENTAL HEALTH SERVICES (294000)**, 480 Galletti Way, Zip 89431–5564; tel. 775/688–2001 **A**1 3 5 9 10 **F**98 99 102 104 106 130 132
Primary Contact: Cody Phinney, Administrator
CFO: Elizabeth O'Brien, Chief Financial Officer
CIO: Lois Repass, Quality Assurance Specialist and Coordinator Performance Improvement
Web address: www.mhds.state.nv.us/
**Control:** State–Government, nonfederal **Service:** Psychiatric

**Staffed Beds:** 30 **Admissions:** 563 **Census:** 15 **Outpatient Visits:** 83960 **Births:** 0 **Total Expense ($000):** 15620 **Payroll Expense ($000):** 12420 **Personnel:** 244

NV

---

**Hospital, Medicare Provider Number, Address, Telephone, Approval, Facility, and Physician Codes, Health Care System**

★ American Hospital Association (AHA) membership
☐ The Joint Commission accreditation   ◇ DNV Healthcare Inc. accreditation
○ Healthcare Facilities Accreditation Program
△ Commission on Accreditation of Rehabilitation Facilities (CARF) accreditation

☐ **NORTHERN NEVADA MEDICAL CENTER (290032)**, 2375 East Prater Way,
Zip 89434–9641; tel. 775/331–7000 **A**1 9 10 **F**2 6 7 11 14 15 18 19 20 22
24 26 29 33 34 37 40 44 45 46 57 59 60 61 64 70 74 75 79 81 82 86 87
90 93 97 98 100 101 102 103 104 105 107 111 119 126 130 131 135 146
147 148 **S** Universal Health Services, Inc., King of Prussia, PA
Primary Contact: Alan C. Olive, Chief Executive Officer
COO: Tiffany Meert, Chief Operating Officer
CFO: Ryan Heit, Chief Financial Officer
CHR: Patricia Downs, Director Human Resources
Web address: www.nnmc.com
**Control:** Corporation, Investor–owned, for–profit **Service:** General Medical and
Surgical

**Staffed Beds:** 108 **Admissions:** 3767 **Census:** 50 **Outpatient Visits:** 43985
**Total Expense ($000):** 54493 **Payroll Expense ($000):** 21497 **Personnel:**
306

### TONOPAH—Nye County

**NYE REGIONAL MEDICAL CENTER (290020)**, 825 South Main Street,
Zip 89049, Mailing Address: P.O. Box 391, Zip 89049–0391;
tel. 775/482–6233, (Nonreporting) **A**9 10 20
Primary Contact: Mercy Peterson, Interim Chief Executive Officer
CMO: Vincent Scoccia, D.O., Chief Medical Staff
CIO: Mercy Peterson, Assistant Administrator
CHR: Leilani Gordon, Director Human Resources and Payroll
Web address: www.nyeregional.org
**Control:** Corporation, Investor–owned, for–profit **Service:** General Medical and
Surgical

**Staffed Beds:** 44

### WINNEMUCCA—Humboldt County

★ **HUMBOLDT GENERAL HOSPITAL (291308)**, 118 East Haskell Street,
Zip 89445–3299; tel. 775/623–5222, (Nonreporting) **A**9 10 18
Primary Contact: James G. Parrish, FACHE, Chief Executive Officer
COO: Craig Prest, Director Operation Services
CFO: Larry Hutcheson, Chief Financial Officer and Director Administrative Services
CMO: Richard M. Ingle, M.D., Chief of Staff
CIO: Larry Hutcheson, Chief Financial Officer and Director Administrative Services
CHR: Rose Marie Green, Director Human Resources
Web address: www.hghospital.ws
**Control:** Hospital district or authority, Government, nonfederal **Service:** General
Medical and Surgical

**Staffed Beds:** 52

### YERINGTON—Lyon County

**SOUTH LYON MEDICAL CENTER (290002)**, 213 South Whitacre,
Zip 89447–2561, Mailing Address: P.O. Box 940, Zip 89447–0940;
tel. 775/463–2301, (Nonreporting) **A**9 10 20
Primary Contact: Kim O. Crandell, Administrator
Web address: www.southlyonmedicalcenter.org
**Control:** Other not–for–profit (including NFP Corporation) **Service:** General
Medical and Surgical

**Staffed Beds:** 63

**NV**

# NEW HAMPSHIRE

## BERLIN—Coos County

**ANDROSCOGGIN VALLEY HOSPITAL (301310)**, 59 Page Hill Road,
Zip 03570–3531; tel. 603/752–2200 **A**10 18 **F**3 8 11 12 13 15 17 28 29 30
34 40 41 43 45 47 57 59 61 62 63 64 67 70 74 75 76 77 79 81 82 85 89
92 93 102 107 108 114 119 128 129 130 131 132 133 146 147 **P**6
Primary Contact: Russell G. Keene, Chief Executive Officer
CFO: Jeremy Roberge, Director Reimbursement
CMO: Keith M. Shute, M.D., Senior Vice President Medical Affairs and Clinical
Services
CIO: Linda M. Laperle, Vice President Administrative Services
CHR: James A. Wheeler, Vice President Human Relations and Community
Development
Web address: www.avhnh.org
**Control:** Other not–for–profit (including NFP Corporation) **Service:** General
Medical and Surgical

> **Staffed Beds:** 25 **Admissions:** 1182 **Census:** 14 **Outpatient Visits:** 65754
> **Births:** 109 **Total Expense ($000):** 53214 **Payroll Expense ($000):** 24432
> **Personnel:** 322

## CLAREMONT—Sullivan County

**VALLEY REGIONAL HOSPITAL (301308)**, 243 Elm Street, Zip 03743–4921;
tel. 603/542–7771 **A**1 9 10 18 **F**2 3 11 13 14 15 28 29 34 35 38 40 43 45
49 50 51 54 57 59 62 63 64 68 70 74 75 77 79 81 84 85 87 93 97 104
107 108 110 114 118 119 130 132 133 135 146 147 **P**6
Primary Contact: Peter J. Wright, Chief Executive Officer
CFO: Steven Monette, Chief Financial Officer
CMO: Carol F. Boerner, M.D., President Medical Staff
CIO: Patricia Witthaus, Director Information Services
CHR: Gregg Burdett, Vice President Administration and Physician Services
Web address: www.vrh.org
**Control:** Other not–for–profit (including NFP Corporation) **Service:** General
Medical and Surgical

> **Staffed Beds:** 25 **Admissions:** 1025 **Census:** 12 **Outpatient Visits:** 72417
> **Births:** 57 **Total Expense ($000):** 41546 **Payroll Expense ($000):** 17531
> **Personnel:** 356

## COLEBROOK—Coos County

★ **UPPER CONNECTICUT VALLEY HOSPITAL (301300)**, 181 Corliss Lane,
Zip 03576–3207; tel. 603/237–4971 **A**9 10 18 **F**3 15 29 30 31 34 35 40 43
45 50 56 57 59 64 67 68 75 78 79 81 85 93 102 107 110 114 119 128 130
133 134 135 146 147 148 **P**6
Primary Contact: Charles White, Chief Administrative Officer
CMO: Gerald Westover, M.D., Medical Director
Web address: www.ucvh.org
**Control:** Other not–for–profit (including NFP Corporation) **Service:** General
Medical and Surgical

> **Staffed Beds:** 16 **Admissions:** 334 **Census:** 5 **Outpatient Visits:** 16625
> **Births:** 0 **Total Expense ($000):** 14148 **Payroll Expense ($000):** 5825
> **Personnel:** 90

## CONCORD—Merrimack County

⊠ ◇ **CONCORD HOSPITAL (300001)**, 250 Pleasant Street, Zip 03301–2598;
tel. 603/225–2711 **A**1 2 3 5 9 10 21 **F**3 8 12 13 14 15 17 18 20 22 24 26
28 29 30 31 33 34 35 36 37 38 39 40 42 43 44 46 49 50 51 53 54 55 56
57 58 59 61 64 65 66 68 69 70 71 74 75 76 77 78 79 80 81 82 83 84 85
86 87 89 93 97 98 99 100 101 102 103 104 105 107 108 110 111 114 115
118 119 120 121 126 129 130 131 132 134 135 144 145 146 147 148 **P**6
Primary Contact: Michael B. Green, President and Chief Executive Officer
COO: Joseph M. Conley, Chief Operating Officer
CFO: Bruce R. Burns, Chief Financial Officer
CMO: David F. Green, M.D., Chief Medical Officer
CIO: Deane Morrison, Chief Information Officer
CHR: Robin A. Moore, Vice President Human Resources
Web address: www.concordhospital.org
**Control:** Other not–for–profit (including NFP Corporation) **Service:** General
Medical and Surgical

> **Staffed Beds:** 237 **Admissions:** 12445 **Census:** 140 **Outpatient Visits:**
> 698895 **Births:** 1287 **Total Expense ($000):** 370603 **Payroll Expense**
> **($000):** 171888 **Personnel:** 2726

⊠ **HEALTHSOUTH REHABILITATION HOSPITAL (303027)**, 254 Pleasant Street,
Zip 03301–2508; tel. 603/226–9800 **A**1 10 **F**29 34 35 64 74 75 79 90 93 95
96 130 132 **S** HEALTHSOUTH Corporation, Birmingham, AL
Primary Contact: Catherine Devaney, Chief Executive Officer
CFO: Jeanine Chesley, Controller
CMO: Safwan Kazmouz, M.D., Chief Medical Director
CHR: Myra Nixon, Director Human Resources
CNO: Joseph Adamski, Chief Nursing Officer
Web address: www.healthsouthrehabconcordnh.com
**Control:** Corporation, Investor–owned, for–profit **Service:** Rehabilitation

> **Staffed Beds:** 50 **Admissions:** 887 **Census:** 32 **Outpatient Visits:** 4762
> **Births:** 0 **Total Expense ($000):** 16519 **Payroll Expense ($000):** 6665
> **Personnel:** 128

☐ **NEW HAMPSHIRE HOSPITAL (304000)**, 36 Clinton Street, Zip 03301–2359;
tel. 603/271–5300 **A**1 10 **F**3 29 30 39 56 57 61 68 74 75 77 86 87 98 99
101 103 130 135 146 **P**4 6
Primary Contact: Robert J. MacLeod, Chief Executive Officer
CFO: Jamie Dall, Director Finance and Support Operations
CMO: David G. Folks, M.D., Chief Medical Officer
CHR: Mark Bussiere, Administrator Human Resources
Web address: www.dhhs.state.nh.us./dhhs/default.htm
**Control:** State–Government, nonfederal **Service:** Psychiatric

> **Staffed Beds:** 152 **Admissions:** 2369 **Census:** 148 **Outpatient Visits:** 0
> **Births:** 0 **Total Expense ($000):** 56236 **Payroll Expense ($000):** 31579
> **Personnel:** 631

## DERRY—Rockingham County

⊠ **PARKLAND MEDICAL CENTER (300017)**, One Parkland Drive,
Zip 03038–2750; tel. 603/432–1500, (Nonreporting) **A**1 2 9 10 **S** HCA,
Nashville, TN
Primary Contact: Chris Accashian, Chief Executive Officer
COO: Jeff Scionti, Chief Operating Officer
CIO: Brad George, Director Information Systems
CHR: Molly Lahti, Director Human Resources
Web address: www.parklandmedicalcenter.com
**Control:** Corporation, Investor–owned, for–profit **Service:** General Medical and
Surgical

> **Staffed Beds:** 82

## DOVER—Strafford County

⊠ **WENTWORTH–DOUGLASS HOSPITAL (300018)**, 789 Central Avenue,
Zip 03820–2589; tel. 603/742–5252 **A**1 2 9 10 **F**3 11 13 15 17 18 19 20 22
26 28 29 30 31 32 34 35 36 39 40 41 42 43 44 45 46 47 49 50 51 54 55
57 58 59 61 62 63 64 65 68 70 73 74 75 76 77 78 79 81 82 84 85 86 87
89 92 93 94 97 100 101 107 108 110 111 114 115 116 117 118 119 120
121 123 124 126 129 130 131 132 134 135 143 144 145 146 147 148
**P**6 8
Primary Contact: Gregory J. Walker, Chief Executive Officer
COO: Daniel N. Dunn, Vice President Operations
CFO: Peter Walcek, Vice President Finance
CMO: Paul Cass, D.O., Chief Medical & Clinical Integration Officer
CIO: Jeffrey Pollock, Chief Information Officer
CHR: Erin Flanigan, Vice President Human Resources
CNO: Sheila Woolley, R.N., Vice President, Patient Care Services
Web address: www.wdhospital.com
**Control:** Other not–for–profit (including NFP Corporation) **Service:** General
Medical and Surgical

> **Staffed Beds:** 124 **Admissions:** 6679 **Census:** 75 **Outpatient Visits:** 231636
> **Births:** 987 **Total Expense ($000):** 211617 **Payroll Expense ($000):** 87452
> **Personnel:** 1441

**NH**

---

**Hospital, Medicare Provider Number, Address, Telephone, Approval, Facility, and Physician Codes, Health Care System**

★ American Hospital Association (AHA) membership
☐ The Joint Commission accreditation ◇ DNV Healthcare Inc. accreditation

○ Healthcare Facilities Accreditation Program
△ Commission on Accreditation of Rehabilitation Facilities (CARF) accreditation

## EXETER—Rockingham County

⊠ ◇ **EXETER HOSPITAL (300023)**, 5 Alumni Drive, Zip 03833–2128;
tel. 603/778–7311 **A**1 2 9 10 19 21 **F**3 8 13 14 15 18 20 22 26 28 29 30 31
32 34 35 36 37 38 40 44 45 46 47 48 49 50 51 52 54 65 70
74 75 76 77 78 79 80 81 84 85 86 87 89 93 107 108 110 111 114 118 119
120 121 123 124 129 130 131 132 135 143 144 146 147 148
Primary Contact: Kevin J. Callahan, President and Chief Executive Officer
COO: Susan Burns–Tisdale, Senior Vice President Clinical Operations
CFO: Kevin J. O'Leary, Senior Vice President and Chief Financial Officer
CMO: Nancy Braese, D.O., President Medical Staff
CIO: David Briden, Chief Information Officer
CHR: Christopher Callahan, Vice President Human Resources
CNO: Susan Burns–Tisdale, Senior Vice President Clinical Operations, Interim CNO
Web address: www.ehr.org
**Control:** Other not–for–profit (including NFP Corporation) **Service:** General
Medical and Surgical

**Staffed Beds:** 99 **Admissions:** 5740 **Census:** 60 **Outpatient Visits:** 172637
**Births:** 712 **Total Expense ($000):** 186168 **Payroll Expense ($000):** 65705
**Personnel:** 1138

## FRANKLIN—Merrimack County

★ **FRANKLIN REGIONAL HOSPITAL (301306)**, 15 Aiken Avenue,
Zip 03235–1299; tel. 603/934–2060 **A**10 18 **F**11 15 18 29 30 31 34 35 36
40 44 45 46 47 48 49 50 57 58 59 61 64 65 66 68 70 74 75 77 78 79 81
82 83 84 85 86 87 93 97 99 100 101 102 103 116 119 127 128 130 131
132 133 135 146 147 148 **P**4 6 **S** LRGHealthcare, Laconia, NH
Primary Contact: Thomas Clairmont, President
CFO: Henry D. Lipman, Executive Vice President and Chief Financial Officer
CMO: Peter Walkley, M.D., Chief of Staff
CIO: Red Hutchinson, Chief Information Officer
Web address: www.lrgh.org
**Control:** Other not–for–profit (including NFP Corporation) **Service:** General
Medical and Surgical

**Staffed Beds:** 25 **Admissions:** 1592 **Census:** 18 **Outpatient Visits:** 70025
**Births:** 0 **Total Expense ($000):** 37573 **Payroll Expense ($000):** 13960
**Personnel:** 221

## GREENFIELD—Hillsborough County

**CROTCHED MOUNTAIN REHABILITATION CENTER**, 1 Verney Drive,
Zip 03047–5000; tel. 603/547–3311, (Nonreporting)
Primary Contact: Donald L. Shumway, Chief Executive Officer
COO: Michael Redmond, Senior Vice President and Chief Operating Officer
CFO: Joseph Fermano, Vice President Finance and Chief Financial Officer
CMO: W. Carl Cooley, M.D., Chief Medical Officer
CHR: Lorrie Rudis, Director Human Resources
Web address: www.cmf.org
**Control:** Other not–for–profit (including NFP Corporation) **Service:** Rehabilitation

**Staffed Beds:** 181

## HAMPSTEAD—Rockingham County

☐ **HAMPSTEAD HOSPITAL (304001)**, 218 East Road, Zip 03841–2305;
tel. 603/329–5311, (Nonreporting) **A**1 10
Primary Contact: Phillip J. Kubiak, President
COO: Cynthia A. Gove, Chief Operating Officer
CFO: John J. Whittier, Vice President Finance
CMO: Bienvenido Manzanero, M.D., Medical Director
CIO: Sandra J. Lucia, Director Health Information and Corporate Compliance
Officer
CHR: Lisa M. Ryan, Coordinator Human Resources
Web address: www.hampsteadhospital.com
**Control:** Corporation, Investor–owned, for–profit **Service:** Psychiatric

**Staffed Beds:** 60

## KEENE—Cheshire County

⊠ **CHESHIRE MEDICAL CENTER (300019)**, 580 Court Street, Zip 03431–1718;
tel. 603/354–5400, (Data for 274 days) **A**1 2 9 10 **F**3 12 13 15 17 18 28 29
30 31 34 35 38 40 43 44 45 46 49 51 53 56 59 61 64 65 68 70 74 75 76
77 78 79 81 82 84 85 86 87 89 90 91 92 93 94 96 97 98 99 100 101 102
103 104 105 107 108 110 111 114 115 118 119 121 129 130 131 132 133
135 146 147 148
Primary Contact: Arthur W. Nichols, President and Chief Executive Officer
CFO: Jill I. Batty, Chief Financial Officer
CMO: Don Caruso, M.D., Chief Medical Officer
CIO: Peter Malloy, Chief Information Officer
CHR: Julie Green, Vice President Human Resources
CNO: Cynthia Coughlin, MS, Chief Nursing Officer
Web address: www.cheshire–med.com
**Control:** Other not–for–profit (including NFP Corporation) **Service:** General
Medical and Surgical

**Staffed Beds:** 140 **Admissions:** 3072 **Census:** 55 **Outpatient Visits:** 119413
**Births:** 358 **Total Expense ($000):** 109962 **Payroll Expense ($000):** 39863
**Personnel:** 1066

## LACONIA—Belknap County

★ **LAKES REGION GENERAL HOSPITAL (300005)**, 80 Highland Street,
Zip 03246–3298; tel. 603/524–3211 **A**10 **F**3 5 7 8 11 13 15 18 28 29 30 31
32 34 35 36 39 40 43 44 45 46 47 48 49 50 53 56 57 58 59 60 61 64 65
66 68 70 74 75 76 77 78 79 81 82 83 84 85 86 87 89 93 97 98 99 100
101 102 103 107 114 118 119 129 130 131 132 133 135 144 146 147 148
**P**4 6 **S** LRGHealthcare, Laconia, NH
Primary Contact: Thomas Clairmont, President
CFO: Henry D. Lipman, Senior Vice President, Financial Strategy and External
Relations
CMO: Peter Walkley, M.D., Chief Medical Officer
CIO: Kevin Irish, Chief Information Officer
CHR: Suzanne Stiles, Chief Human Resources Officer & Sr. Vice
President/Administrative and Support Services
CNO: Ellen Wolff, R.N., Chief Nursing Officer/Senior VP/Patient Care Services
Web address: www.lrgh.org
**Control:** Other not–for–profit (including NFP Corporation) **Service:** General
Medical and Surgical

**Staffed Beds:** 88 **Admissions:** 4211 **Census:** 61 **Outpatient Visits:** 196771
**Births:** 361 **Total Expense ($000):** 169525 **Payroll Expense ($000):** 80893
**Personnel:** 1041

## LANCASTER—Coos County

★ **WEEKS MEDICAL CENTER (301303)**, 173 Middle Street, Zip 03584–3508;
tel. 603/788–4911 **A**9 10 18 **F**3 11 15 18 28 29 30 31 32 34 35 36 40 45
50 51 56 57 59 61 62 63 64 65 66 68 70 71 75 77 78 79 81 85 87 89 91
92 93 94 97 100 104 107 108 110 111 114 116 117 118 119 127 130 131
132 133 134 135 146 147 148 **P**6
Primary Contact: Scott W. Howe, Chief Executive Officer
CFO: Celeste Pitts, Chief Financial Officer
CMO: Lars Nielson, M.D., Chief Medical Officer
CIO: Darrell Bodnar, Director Information
CHR: Linda Rexford, Director Human Resources
CNO: Donna Walker, Chief Nurse Executive
Web address: www.weeksmedical.org
**Control:** Other not–for–profit (including NFP Corporation) **Service:** General
Medical and Surgical

**Staffed Beds:** 25 **Admissions:** 767 **Census:** 10 **Outpatient Visits:** 78081
**Births:** 0 **Total Expense ($000):** 41710 **Payroll Expense ($000):** 20783
**Personnel:** 335

## LEBANON—Grafton County

★ **ALICE PECK DAY MEMORIAL HOSPITAL (301305)**, 10 Alice Peck Day Drive,
Zip 03766–2650; tel. 603/448–3121 **A**9 10 18 **F**3 11 13 15 29 34 35 36 37
39 40 41 42 45 47 50 51 54 56 57 59 63 64 65 66 67 75 76 77 79 81 82
83 84 85 93 97 100 107 110 113 114 115 119 128 129 130 131 133 135
145 146 147 148 **P**5 6
Primary Contact: Susan E. Mooney, M.D., President and Chief Executive Officer
COO: J. Todd Miller, Vice President and Chief Operating Officer
CFO: Evalie M. Crosby, CPA, Vice President Finance and Chief Financial Officer
CMO: Randy Lea, M.D., Vice President and Chief Medical Officer
CIO: Lorraine Nichols, Director Information Services
CHR: Brenda Blair, Association Vice President Human Resources and
Organizational Learning
CNO: Beverley A. Rankin, R.N., Vice President & Chief Nursing Officer
Web address: www.alicepeckday.org
**Control:** Other not–for–profit (including NFP Corporation) **Service:** General
Medical and Surgical

**Staffed Beds:** 25 **Admissions:** 936 **Census:** 14 **Outpatient Visits:** 98984
**Births:** 319 **Total Expense ($000):** 50011 **Payroll Expense ($000):** 27963
**Personnel:** 371

⊠ **DARTMOUTH–HITCHCOCK MEDICAL CENTER (300003)**, One Medical Center
Drive, Zip 03756–0001; tel. 603/650–5000, (Includes CHILDREN'S HOSPITAL AT
DARTMOUTH, One Medical Center Drive, Zip 03756; tel. 603/650–5000) **A**1 3 5
8 9 10 **F**3 5 6 7 8 9 11 12 13 14 15 17 18 19 20 21 22 23 24 25 26 27 28
29 30 31 32 34 35 36 37 38 39 40 41 43 44 45 46 47 48 49 50 51 52 53
54 55 56 57 58 59 60 61 63 64 65 66 68 70 71 72 74 75 76 77 78 79 80
81 82 84 85 86 87 88 89 91 92 93 94 96 97 98 99 100 101 102 103 104
105 107 108 110 111 114 115 116 117 118 119 120 121 123 124 126 129
130 131 132 134 135 136 138 141 142 143 145 146 147 148 **P**6
Primary Contact: James Weinstein, M.D., President and Chief Executive Officer
COO: Stephen J. LeBlanc, Chief Operating Officer
CFO: Daniel Jantzen, Chief Financial Officer
CMO: John R. Butterly, M.D., Medical Director
CIO: Peter A. Johnson, Vice President Information Services
CHR: Richard B. Davis, Chief Human Resources Officer
Web address: www.hitchcock.org
**Control:** Other not–for–profit (including NFP Corporation) **Service:** General
Medical and Surgical

**Staffed Beds:** 388 **Admissions:** 19732 **Census:** 308 **Outpatient Visits:**
840204 **Births:** 1023 **Total Expense ($000):** 1010923 **Payroll Expense**
**($000):** 465268 **Personnel:** 5637

**NH**

*Many Facility Codes have changed. Please refer to the AHA Guide Code Chart.*
© 2013 AHA Guide

## LITTLETON—Grafton County

★ **LITTLETON REGIONAL HOSPITAL (301302)**, 600 Saint Johnsbury Road,
Zip 03561–3442; tel. 603/444–9000 **A**9 10 18 **F**1 3 11 13 15 16 18 26 28
29 31 32 34 35 36 38 40 43 44 45 49 50 51 56 57 59 64 65 67 70 73 74
75 76 77 78 79 80 81 84 85 86 87 89 90 92 93 96 97 107 108 110 111
115 118 119 128 129 130 131 132 133 143 146 147 148 **P**6
Primary Contact: Warren K. West, FACHE, Chief Executive Officer
CFO: Robert L. Fotter, Chief Financial Officer
CIO: Scott Vachon, Director Information Technology
CHR: Georgene Novak, Director Human Resources
CNO: Linda Gilmore, Chief Nursing Officer/Chief Administrative Officer
Web address: www.littletonhospital.org
**Control:** Other not–for–profit (including NFP Corporation) **Service:** General
Medical and Surgical

**Staffed Beds:** 25 **Admissions:** 1259 **Census:** 11 **Outpatient Visits:** 52249
**Births:** 257 **Total Expense ($000):** 70473 **Payroll Expense ($000):** 28476
**Personnel:** 371

## MANCHESTER—Hillsborough County

✠ **CATHOLIC MEDICAL CENTER (300034)**, 100 McGregor Street,
Zip 03102–3770; tel. 603/668–3545 **A**1 2 10 **F**3 9 11 12 13 15 18 20 22 24
26 28 29 30 31 32 34 35 36 37 38 39 40 41 43 44 46 47 48 49 50 53 57
58 59 60 61 63 64 65 66 70 71 73 74 75 76 77 78 79 80 81 82 84 85 86
87 90 93 96 100 102 104 105 107 108 110 111 114 115 118 119 124 126
129 130 131 132 134 135 143 144 146 147 148 **P**6
Primary Contact: Joseph Pepe, M.D., President and Chief Executive Officer
CFO: Edward L. Dudley, III, Senior Vice President and Chief Financial Officer
CMO: Matthew Greenston, M.D., Interim Chief Medical Officer
CIO: Brian Tew, Vice President and Chief Information Officer
CHR: Scott Watkins, Director Human Resources
CNO: Robert A. Duhaime, R.N., Senior Vice President Clinical Operations and Chief
Nursing Officer
Web address: www.catholicmedicalcenter.org
**Control:** Other not–for–profit (including NFP Corporation) **Service:** General
Medical and Surgical

**Staffed Beds:** 233 **Admissions:** 9701 **Census:** 128 **Outpatient Visits:**
175784 **Births:** 1034 **Total Expense ($000):** 274796 **Payroll Expense**
**($000):** 114895 **Personnel:** 1375

✠ △ **ELLIOT HOSPITAL (300012)**, One Elliot Way, Zip 03103–3502;
tel. 603/669–5300 **A**1 2 7 9 10 **F**3 8 9 11 12 13 15 18 20 22 26 28 29 30
31 32 34 35 36 37 38 39 40 41 42 43 44 45 46 47 48 49 50 51 53 54 55
56 57 59 64 65 68 70 72 74 75 76 77 78 79 81 82 83 84 85 86 87 88 89
93 97 98 99 100 101 102 103 107 108 110 111 114 115 118 119 120 121
123 124 126 129 130 131 132 134 135 144 146 147 148 **P**6
Primary Contact: Douglas F. Dean, Jr., President and Chief Executive Officer
CFO: Richard Elwell, Senior Vice President and Chief Financial Officer
CMO: Greg Baxter, M.D., Vice President Medical Affairs
CIO: Denise Purington, Vice President and Chief Information Officer
CHR: Sabrina M. Granville, Vice President Human Resources
Web address: www.elliothospital.org
**Control:** Other not–for–profit (including NFP Corporation) **Service:** General
Medical and Surgical

**Staffed Beds:** 279 **Admissions:** 12791 **Census:** 169 **Outpatient Visits:**
516395 **Births:** 1778 **Total Expense ($000):** 295895 **Payroll Expense**
**($000):** 119253 **Personnel:** 2754

★ **MANCHESTER VETERANS AFFAIRS MEDICAL CENTER**, (Formerly Veterans
Affairs Medical Center), 718 Smyth Road, Zip 03104–4098; tel. 603/624–4366,
(Nonreporting) **A**5 **S** Department of Veterans Affairs, Washington, DC
Primary Contact: Marc Levenson, M.D., Director
COO: Richard T. Rose, Associate Director
CFO: Frank Ryan, Chief Financial Officer
CMO: Andrew Breuder, M.D., Chief of Staff
CIO: John Foote, Chief Information Officer
CHR: Mary Ellen Kenney, Chief Human Services
Web address: www.manchester.va.gov/
**Control:** Veterans Affairs, Government, federal **Service:** Rehabilitation

**Staffed Beds:** 90

**VETERANS AFFAIRS MEDICAL CENTER** See Manchester Veterans Affairs
Medical Center

## NASHUA—Hillsborough County

✠ **SOUTHERN NEW HAMPSHIRE MEDICAL CENTER (300020)**, 8 Prospect
Street, Zip 03060–3925, Mailing Address: P.O. Box 2014, Zip 03061–2014;
tel. 603/577–2000, (Nonreporting) **A**1 2 3 5 9 10
Primary Contact: Thomas E. Wilhelmsen, Jr., President and Chief Executive Officer
CFO: Michael S. Rose, Senior Vice President Finance and Chief Financial Officer
CMO: Stephanie Wolf–Rosenblum, M.D., Chief Medical Officer
CIO: Andrew Watt, M.D., Vice President, Chief Information Officer and Chief
Medical Information Officer
CHR: Merryll Rosenfeld, Vice President Human Resources
Web address: www.snhmc.org
**Control:** Other not–for–profit (including NFP Corporation) **Service:** General
Medical and Surgical

**Staffed Beds:** 166

✠ △ **ST. JOSEPH HOSPITAL (300011)**, 172 Kinsley Street, Zip 03060–3648;
tel. 603/882–3000 **A**1 2 7 10 **F**3 11 13 15 18 20 28 29 30 31 32 34 35 36
40 42 43 44 49 50 51 54 56 57 59 61 62 63 64 65 68 70 74 75 76 77 78
79 81 82 83 84 85 86 87 89 90 93 97 98 103 104 107 108 110 111 115
116 117 119 126 129 130 132 135 146 147 148 **P**6 8 **S** Covenant Health
Systems, Inc., Tewksbury, MA
Primary Contact: Richard Boehler, M.D., President and Chief Executive Officer
COO: Pam Duchene, R.N., Vice President Patient Care Services
CFO: Richard Plamondon, Vice President Finance and Chief Financial Officer
CIO: Keith A. Choinka, Vice President Information Systems and Chief Information
Officer
CHR: Jacqueline Woolley, Vice President Human Resources
Web address: www.stjosephhospital.com
**Control:** Church–operated, Nongovernment, not–for profit **Service:** General
Medical and Surgical

**Staffed Beds:** 144 **Admissions:** 6156 **Census:** 90 **Outpatient Visits:** 194691
**Births:** 485 **Total Expense ($000):** 160342 **Payroll Expense ($000):** 68828
**Personnel:** 1053

## NEW LONDON—Merrimack County

★ **NEW LONDON HOSPITAL (301304)**, 273 County Road, Zip 03257–5736;
tel. 603/526–2911, (Total facility includes 58 beds in nursing home–type unit) **A**9
10 18 **F**3 7 11 15 18 29 30 31 32 34 40 41 45 50 51 54 56 57 59 64 67 70
74 75 77 78 79 81 82 84 85 87 89 93 94 97 100 102 107 110 111 114 119
127 128 129 130 131 133 134 146 147 148 **P**6
Primary Contact: Bruce King, President and Chief Executive Officer
CFO: Donald Griffin, CPA, Chief Financial Officer
CMO: Steven Powell, M.D., Chief Medical Officer
CIO: David Foss, Senior Director Information Systems
CHR: Catherine Bardier, Senior Director Human Resources
Web address: www.newlondonhospital.org
**Control:** Other not–for–profit (including NFP Corporation) **Service:** General
Medical and Surgical

**Staffed Beds:** 83 **Admissions:** 1145 **Census:** 66 **Outpatient Visits:** 163491
**Births:** 0 **Total Expense ($000):** 54767 **Payroll Expense ($000):** 27153
**Personnel:** 415

## NORTH CONWAY—Carroll County

**MEMORIAL HOSPITAL (301307)**, 3073 White Mountain Highway,
Zip 03860–7101, Mailing Address: P.O. Box 5001, Zip 03860–5001;
tel. 603/356–5461, (Total facility includes 45 beds in nursing home–type unit) **A**9
10 18 **F**3 11 13 15 28 29 30 31 34 35 36 40 43 45 50 51 57 59 64 67 68
70 75 76 77 78 79 81 82 85 86 87 90 94 96 97 105 107 110 115 119 128
129 130 131 132 133 144 146 147 **P**6
Primary Contact: Scott McKinnon, President and Chief Executive Officer
COO: Steven J. Wyrsch, R.N., Senior Vice President, Operations and Chief
Operating Officer
CFO: John Newton, Vice President Financial and Support Services and Chief
Financial Officer
CMO: Ray Rabideau, M.D., Medical Director
CIO: Curtis Kerbs, Vice President Information Services
CHR: Margaret Phillips, Director Human Resources
CNO: Ethnee Garner, Vice President Nursing Services
Web address: www.memorialhospitalnh.org
**Control:** Other not–for–profit (including NFP Corporation) **Service:** General
Medical and Surgical

**Staffed Beds:** 70 **Admissions:** 1662 **Census:** 55 **Outpatient Visits:** 59495
**Births:** 257 **Total Expense ($000):** 61908 **Payroll Expense ($000):** 17775
**Personnel:** 387

**NH**

## PETERBOROUGH—Hillsborough County

★ **MONADNOCK COMMUNITY HOSPITAL (301309)**, 452 Old Street Road,
Zip 03458–1295; tel. 603/924–7191 **A**5 9 10 18 **F**3 13 15 28 29 30 31 34
35 36 38 39 40 41 44 45 50 53 56 57 59 64 65 70 74 75 76 77 78 79 81
82 85 86 87 89 93 97 99 100 101 102 103 104 107 108 110 115 118 119
130 131 132 133 134 135 141 142 146 147 148 **P**6
Primary Contact: Peter L. Gosline, Chief Executive Officer
CFO: Richard Scheinblum, Chief Financial Officer
CMO: Philip Vuocolo, M.D., Chief Medical Officer
CIO: Carol Roosa, Chief Information Officer
CNO: Vicki Loughery, R.N., Chief Nursing Officer
Web address: www.monadnockhospital.org
**Control:** Other not–for–profit (including NFP Corporation) **Service:** General
Medical and Surgical

**Staffed Beds:** 25 **Admissions:** 1377 **Census:** 13 **Outpatient Visits:** 75854
**Births:** 312 **Total Expense ($000):** 74579 **Payroll Expense ($000):** 31380
**Personnel:** 537

## PLYMOUTH—Grafton County

★ **SPEARE MEMORIAL HOSPITAL (301311)**, 16 Hospital Road,
Zip 03264–1199; tel. 603/536–1120 **A**9 10 18 **F**3 13 15 28 29 30 31 32 34
35 39 40 45 53 54 57 59 64 70 75 76 77 78 79 81 84 85 93 94 97 107
110 111 113 114 119 127 129 130 131 132 133 144 146 147 **P**8
Primary Contact: Michelle McEwen, President and Chief Executive Officer
CFO: Richard F. Werkowski, Chief Financial Officer
CMO: Joseph Ebner, M.D., Chief Medical Officer
CIO: Alexis Jeannotte, Director Information Technology
CHR: Laurie Bolognani, Human Resources Officer
CNO: Kristine Hering, R.N., Chief Nursing Officer
Web address: www.spearehospital.com
**Control:** Other not–for–profit (including NFP Corporation) **Service:** General
Medical and Surgical

**Staffed Beds:** 25 **Admissions:** 1247 **Census:** 11 **Outpatient Visits:** 80124
**Births:** 175 **Total Expense ($000):** 47740 **Payroll Expense ($000):** 22718
**Personnel:** 301

## PORTSMOUTH—Rockingham County

⊠ **PORTSMOUTH REGIONAL HOSPITAL (300029)**, 333 Borthwick Avenue,
Zip 03801–7128; tel. 603/436–5110, (Nonreporting) **A**1 2 9 10 **S** HCA,
Nashville, TN
Primary Contact: Anne Jamieson, FACHE, Chief Executive Officer
COO: Stuart Hemming, Chief Operating Officer
CFO: Richard Senger, Chief Financial Officer
CMO: Tim Pike, M.D., Chief Medical Officer
CIO: Ed Sovetskhy, Director Information Services
CHR: Jackie Brayton, Vice President Human Resources
Web address: www.portsmouthhospital.com
**Control:** Corporation, Investor–owned, for–profit **Service:** General Medical and
Surgical

**Staffed Beds:** 165

## ROCHESTER—Strafford County

★ **FRISBIE MEMORIAL HOSPITAL (300014)**, 11 Whitehall Road,
Zip 03867–3297; tel. 603/332–5211 **A**9 10 **F**3 7 11 13 17 18 20 21 28 29
31 32 34 35 40 42 45 46 49 50 56 57 59 64 68 70 75 76 77 78 79 81 82
83 86 87 89 93 97 98 103 104 105 107 111 115 117 118 119 129 130 132
135 146 147 **P**5 8
Primary Contact: Alvin D. Felgar, President and Chief Executive Officer
CFO: John A. Marzinzik, Vice President Finance
CMO: Susan Gaire, M.D., President Medical Staff
CHR: Carol Themelis, Vice President Human Resources
Web address: www.frisbiehospital.com
**Control:** Other not–for–profit (including NFP Corporation) **Service:** General
Medical and Surgical

**Staffed Beds:** 82 **Admissions:** 3422 **Census:** 40 **Outpatient Visits:** 136194
**Births:** 385 **Total Expense ($000):** 125786 **Payroll Expense ($000):** 53525
**Personnel:** 790

## SALEM—Rockingham County

☐ △ **NORTHEAST REHABILITATION HOSPITAL (303026)**, 70 Butler Street,
Zip 03079–3925; tel. 603/893–2900 **A**1 7 10 **F**29 30 34 35 54 57 62 64 68
74 75 77 79 82 85 86 87 90 93 95 96 130 131 132 135 146
Primary Contact: John F. Prochilo, Chief Executive Officer and Administrator
COO: Robert Kotsonis, Chief Operating Officer
CFO: Charles Champagne, Chief Financial Officer
CMO: James A. Whitlock, Jr., M.D., Medical Director
CIO: Larry Frank, Director Information Systems
CHR: Thomas A. Prince, Vice President Operations and Human Resources
CNO: Marie Sullivan, R.N., Chief Nursing Officer and Administrator
Web address: www.northeastrehab.com
**Control:** Corporation, Investor–owned, for–profit **Service:** Rehabilitation

**Staffed Beds:** 135 **Admissions:** 2671 **Census:** 95 **Outpatient Visits:** 177355
**Births:** 0 **Total Expense ($000):** 60685 **Payroll Expense ($000):** 33547
**Personnel:** 755

## WOLFEBORO—Carroll County

★ **HUGGINS HOSPITAL (301312)**, 240 South Main Street, Zip 03894–4455,
Mailing Address: P.O. Box 912, Zip 03894–0912; tel. 603/569–7500 **A**9 10 18
**F**2 3 10 11 15 28 30 44 45 50 56 57 59 64 65 70 74 75 79 81 85 86 87 93
97 107 110 111 114 119 125 130 131 132 133 135 146 147 **P**6
Primary Contact: Michael Connelly, President
CFO: Jeremy Roberge, Chief Financial Officer
CMO: John Boornazian, M.D., Chief Medical Officer
CIO: Pam McGovern, Director Technology
CHR: Laura Stauss, Director of Human Resources
Web address: www.hugginshospital.org
**Control:** Other not–for–profit (including NFP Corporation) **Service:** General
Medical and Surgical

**Staffed Beds:** 25 **Admissions:** 999 **Census:** 16 **Outpatient Visits:** 143190
**Births:** 0 **Total Expense ($000):** 54101 **Payroll Expense ($000):** 24447
**Personnel:** 363

## WOODSVILLE—Grafton County

★ **COTTAGE HOSPITAL (301301)**, 90 Swiftwater Road, Zip 03785–1421, Mailing
Address: P.O. Box 2001, Zip 03785–2001; tel. 603/747–9000 **A**9 10 18 **F**3 11
13 15 18 28 29 30 31 34 35 40 43 46 49 50 59 64 65 67 68 70 74 75 76
77 78 79 81 82 84 85 87 89 93 97 107 111 114 119 127 128 130 132 133
135 146 147 148
Primary Contact: Maria Ryan, Ph.D., Chief Executive Officer
COO: Lori Hughes, R.N., Chief Nursing Officer, Vice President Operations and
Patient Care Services
CFO: Steven L. Plant, Chief Financial Officer
CIO: Rick Fredrick, Director Information Technology
CHR: Gerry J. Graham, Director Human Resources
CNO: Lori Hughes, R.N., Chief Nursing Officer, Vice President Operations &
Patient Care Services
Web address: www.cottagehospital.org
**Control:** Other not–for–profit (including NFP Corporation) **Service:** General
Medical and Surgical

**Staffed Beds:** 25 **Admissions:** 729 **Census:** 7 **Outpatient Visits:** 47257
**Births:** 91 **Total Expense ($000):** 28892 **Payroll Expense ($000):** 12422
**Personnel:** 215

**NH**

*Many Facility Codes have changed. Please refer to the AHA Guide Code Chart.*
© 2013 AHA Guide

# NEW JERSEY

## ATLANTIC CITY—Atlantic County

★ ◇ **ACUITY SPECIALTY HOSPITAL OF NEW JERSEY (312023)**, 1925 Pacific Avenue, 7th Floor, Zip 08401–6713; tel. 609/441–2122, (Nonreporting) **A**10 21 **S** AcuityHealthcare, LP, Charlotte, NC
Primary Contact: Kerry McLane, Interim Chief Executive Officer
Web address: www.acuityhealthcare.net
**Control:** Corporation, Investor–owned, for–profit **Service:** Long–Term Acute Care hospital

**Staffed Beds:** 30

✠ **ATLANTICARE REGIONAL MEDICAL CENTER (310064)**, 1925 Pacific Avenue, Zip 08401–6713; tel. 609/441–8994, (Includes ATLANTICARE REGIONAL MEDICAL CENTER–MAINLAND DIVISION, Jimmie Leeds Road, Pomona, Zip 08240; tel. 609/652–1000) **A**1 2 9 10 **F**3 7 11 12 13 15 16 17 18 20 22 24 26 29 30 31 34 35 36 37 38 40 41 42 43 45 46 47 48 49 50 54 57 58 59 60 61 64 66 67 68 70 71 72 73 74 75 76 78 79 80 81 82 84 85 86 87 88 89 90 93 97 98 99 100 102 103 104 105 106 107 108 110 111 114 115 116 117 118 119 120 121 123 124 126 130 132 135 143 146 147 148 **P**6 **S** AtlantiCare, Egg Harbor Township, NJ
Primary Contact: Lori Herndon, R.N., President and Chief Executive Officer
COO: Lori Herndon, R.N., President and Chief Executive Officer
CFO: Walter Greiner, Chief Financial Officer
CMO: Marilouise Vendetti, M.D., Chief Medical Officer
CHR: Richard Lovering, Corporate Vice President Human Resources and Organizational Development
Web address: www.atlanticare.org
**Control:** Other not–for–profit (including NFP Corporation) **Service:** General Medical and Surgical

**Staffed Beds:** 534 **Admissions:** 30327 **Census:** 391 **Outpatient Visits:** 313895 **Births:** 2511 **Total Expense ($000):** 605289 **Payroll Expense ($000):** 253780 **Personnel:** 3357

## BAYONNE—Hudson County

☐ **BAYONNE MEDICAL CENTER (310025)**, 29th Street & Avenue E., Zip 07002–4699; tel. 201/858–5000 **A**1 2 6 9 10 **F**3 7 8 15 18 20 22 28 29 31 34 40 46 49 57 59 60 66 70 74 77 78 79 81 82 85 87 98 100 102 103 107 108 110 111 114 116 118 119 120 121 123 128 130 132 143 147 148
Primary Contact: Mark Spektor, M.D., President and Chief Executive Officer
CFO: David Paulosky, Chief Financial Officer
CIO: Don Lutz, Chief Information Officer
CHR: Jennifer Dobin, Vice President Human Resources
Web address: www.bayonnemedicalcenter.org
**Control:** Corporation, Investor–owned, for–profit **Service:** General Medical and Surgical

**Staffed Beds:** 173 **Admissions:** 6496 **Census:** 99 **Outpatient Visits:** 57007 **Total Expense ($000):** 164364 **Payroll Expense ($000):** 49960

## BELLE MEAD—Somerset County

✠ **CARRIER CLINIC (314012)**, 252 County Route 601, Zip 08502–0147, Mailing Address: P.O. Box 147, Zip 08502–0147; tel. 908/281–1000, (Nonreporting) **A**1 3 5 9 10
Primary Contact: Donald J. Parker, President and Chief Executive Officer
COO: Mary Pawlikowski, Vice President and Chief Operating Officer
CFO: Randolph Jacobson, Chief Financial Officer
CMO: Marie Hasson, M.D., Medical Director
CIO: Peter Schwartz, Manager Information Services
CHR: Trish Toole, Vice President Administrative Services
CNO: Carol Kosztyo, R.N., Vice President, Patient Care Services
Web address: www.carrierclinic.org
**Control:** Other not–for–profit (including NFP Corporation) **Service:** Psychiatric

**Staffed Beds:** 270

**EAST MOUNTAIN HOSPITAL (314026)**, 252 County Route 601, Zip 08502; tel. 908/281–1500, (Nonreporting) **A**10
Primary Contact: Michael Voorhees, MS, Executive Director
CFO: Randolph Jacobson, Chief Financial Officer
CMO: Bohdan Cehelyk, M.D., Chief Medical Officer
CIO: Peter Schwartz, Director Information Systems
CHR: Patricia Toole, Vice President Human Resources
CNO: Deborah Charette, Director of Nursing
Web address: www.eastmountainhospital.com
**Control:** Corporation, Investor–owned, for–profit **Service:** Psychiatric

**Staffed Beds:** 16

## BELLEVILLE—Essex County

✠ **CLARA MAASS MEDICAL CENTER (310009)**, One Clara Maass Drive, Zip 07109–3557; tel. 973/450–2000 **A**1 2 3 5 9 10 **F**1 3 4 8 11 12 13 15 16 17 18 19 20 22 28 29 30 31 34 35 38 40 44 45 47 49 50 51 55 56 57 58 59 60 61 62 63 64 66 67 68 70 72 73 74 75 76 78 79 80 81 82 83 84 85 86 87 88 89 90 91 92 93 94 98 101 102 103 107 108 110 111 114 115 116 117 118 119 120 121 123 126 128 129 130 132 143 146 147 148 **S** Barnabas Health, West Orange, NJ
Primary Contact: Mary Ellen Clyne, Ph.D., President and Chief Executive Officer
CIO: Michael McTigue, Chief Information Officer
Web address: www.barnabashealth.org/hospitals/clara_maass/index.html
**Control:** Other not–for–profit (including NFP Corporation) **Service:** General Medical and Surgical

**Staffed Beds:** 429 **Admissions:** 18162 **Census:** 236 **Outpatient Visits:** 126093 **Births:** 1557 **Total Expense ($000):** 239872 **Payroll Expense ($000):** 102094 **Personnel:** 1505

## BERKELEY HEIGHTS—Union County

★ **RUNNELLS SPECIALIZED HOSPITAL OF UNION COUNTY (314027)**, 40 Watchung Way, Zip 07922–2618; tel. 908/771–5700, (Nonreporting) **A**9 10
Primary Contact: Susan Palma, MS, R.N., Administrator
CFO: Michael Drummond, Chief Financial Officer
CMO: Raymond Lanza, D.O., Medical Director
CIO: Margaret A. Salisbury, Director Marketing
CHR: Greg Hardoby, Director Personnel
Web address: www.ucnj.org/runnells
**Control:** County–Government, nonfederal **Service:** Other specialty

**Staffed Beds:** 344

## BERLIN—Camden County

★ **VIRTUA BERLIN (310022)**, 100 Townsend Avenue, Zip 08009–9035; tel. 856/322–3000 **A**9 10 **F**3 11 29 30 34 35 38 40 45 46 47 48 49 50 55 56 57 63 64 65 68 70 74 75 81 82 84 85 87 90 92 93 100 107 108 111 115 119 130 146 148 **S** Virtua Health, Marlton, NJ
Primary Contact: Christopher A. Chekouras, Vice President and Chief Operating Officer
CFO: Robert Segin, Chief Financial Officer
CMO: John Matsinger, M.D., Medical Director
CIO: Alfred Campanella, Vice President and Chief Information Officer
CHR: Michael Pepe, Ph.D., Chief Human Resources Officer
Web address: www.virtua.org
**Control:** Other not–for–profit (including NFP Corporation) **Service:** General Medical and Surgical

**Staffed Beds:** 83 **Admissions:** 3740 **Census:** 50 **Outpatient Visits:** 32994 **Births:** 0 **Total Expense ($000):** 76634 **Payroll Expense ($000):** 26705 **Personnel:** 308

## BLACKWOOD—Camden County

✠ **CAMDEN COUNTY HEALTH SERVICES CENTER (314018)**, 425 Woodbury Turnersville Road, Zip 08012–2960; tel. 856/374–6600, (Total facility includes 300 beds in nursing home–type unit) **A**1 9 10 **F**4 56 65 84 87 98 100 103 128 130 135 146 148 **P**6
Primary Contact: Gene Lynam, Interim Chief Executive Officer
COO: Gene Lynam, Chief Operating Officer and Treasurer
CFO: Gene Lynam, Chief Operating Officer and Treasurer
CMO: Michael S. DeShields, M.D., Director Medical Affairs
CIO: Richard Behm, Director Information Technology
CHR: Brian Eisen, Director Human Resources
Web address: www.cchsc.com
**Control:** County–Government, nonfederal **Service:** Psychiatric

**Staffed Beds:** 450 **Admissions:** 1133 **Census:** 426 **Outpatient Visits:** 57 **Births:** 0 **Total Expense ($000):** 77048 **Payroll Expense ($000):** 33043 **Personnel:** 484

## BOONTON TOWNSHIP—Morris County

**SAINT CLARE'S HOSPITAL/BOONTON TOWNSHIP** See Saint Clare's Health System, Denville

**NJ**

## BRICK—Ocean County

☐ **SHORE REHABILITATION INSTITUTE (313033)**, (Formerly Shore Rehabilitation Hospital), 425 Jack Martin Boulevard, Zip 08724–7732; tel. 732/836–4500, (Nonreporting) **A**1 10
Primary Contact: Amit Mohan, Executive Director
Web address: www.oceanmedicalcenter.com
**Control:** Other not–for–profit (including NFP Corporation) **Service:** Rehabilitation

**Staffed Beds:** 40

## BRICK TOWNSHIP—Ocean County

⊠ **OCEAN MEDICAL CENTER (310052)**, 425 Jack Martin Boulevard, Zip 08724–7732; tel. 732/840–2200 **A**1 2 9 10 **F**3 5 6 11 13 15 17 18 20 22 28 29 30 31 32 40 41 42 44 45 46 47 49 53 55 56 59 60 64 65 66 68 70 73 74 75 76 78 79 80 81 82 84 85 86 87 89 92 93 97 100 101 103 107 108 110 111 114 115 117 119 120 121 123 129 130 132 135 144 146 147 148 **P**7 **S** Meridian Health, Wall Township, NJ
Primary Contact: Dean Q. Lin, FACHE, President
COO: Regina Foley, R.N., Vice President Nursing and Operations
CFO: John Gantner, Executive Vice President Finance
CMO: James Clarke, M.D., Vice President Medical Affairs and Clinical Effectiveness
CIO: Rebecca Weber, Senior Vice President and Chief Information Officer
Web address: www.meridianhealth.com
**Control:** Other not–for–profit (including NFP Corporation) **Service:** General Medical and Surgical

**Staffed Beds:** 265 **Admissions:** 13772 **Census:** 188 **Outpatient Visits:** 153969 **Births:** 958 **Total Expense ($000):** 233697 **Payroll Expense ($000):** 92174 **Personnel:** 1061

## BRIDGETON—Cumberland County

**BRIDGETON HEALTH CENTER** See Inspira Medical Center–Vineland, Vineland

## BROWNS MILLS—Burlington County

☐ **DEBORAH HEART AND LUNG CENTER (310031)**, 200 Trenton Road, Zip 08015–1705; tel. 609/893–6611, (Nonreporting) **A**1 3 5 9 10 13
Primary Contact: Joseph P. Chirichella, President and Chief Executive Officer
CFO: R. Grant Leidy, Vice President Finance
CMO: Lynn McGrath, M.D., Vice President Medical Affairs
CHR: James Carlino, Vice President Human Resources
Web address: www.deborah.org
**Control:** Other not–for–profit (including NFP Corporation) **Service:** Other specialty

**Staffed Beds:** 89

## CAMDEN—Camden County

⊠ **COOPER HEALTH SYSTEM (310014)**, One Cooper Plaza, Zip 08103–1489; tel. 856/342–2000, (Includes CHILDEN'S REGIONAL HOSPITAL AT COOPER, One Cooper Plaza, Zip 08103; tel. 800/826–6737), (Nonreporting) **A**1 2 3 5 8 9 10 13
Primary Contact: John P. Sheridan, Jr., President and Chief Executive Officer
COO: Adrienne Kirby, Ph.D., Chief Operating Officer
CFO: Douglas E. Shirley, Senior Executive Vice President and Chief Financial Officer
CMO: Carolyn Bekes, M.D., Chief Medical Officer
CHR: Douglas Allen, Vice President Human Resources
Web address: www.cooperhealth.org
**Control:** Other not–for–profit (including NFP Corporation) **Service:** General Medical and Surgical

**Staffed Beds:** 493

⊠ △ **OUR LADY OF LOURDES MEDICAL CENTER (310029)**, 1600 Haddon Avenue, Zip 08103–3117; tel. 856/757–3500 **A**1 2 6 7 9 10 **F**3 11 12 13 15 17 18 20 22 24 26 28 29 30 31 32 34 35 36 37 38 40 44 46 47 49 50 55 56 57 58 59 60 61 64 65 66 68 70 71 72 73 74 75 76 78 79 81 82 84 85 86 87 89 90 95 96 100 107 108 110 111 114 115 118 119 126 130 132 134 135 138 139 142 146 147 148 **S** Catholic Health East, Newtown Square, PA
Primary Contact: Alexander J. Hatala, FACHE, President and Chief Executive Officer
COO: Mark Nessel, Chief Operating Officer
CFO: Michael Hammond, Chief Financial Officer
CMO: Alan R. Pope, M.D., Vice President Medical Affairs
CIO: Maureen Hetu, Chief Information Officer
CHR: Richard P. Kropp, Vice President Human Resources
CNO: Audrey Jadczak, R.N., Chief Nursing Officer
Web address: www.lourdesnet.org
**Control:** Other not–for–profit (including NFP Corporation) **Service:** General Medical and Surgical

**Staffed Beds:** 350 **Admissions:** 13682 **Census:** 197 **Outpatient Visits:** 124362 **Births:** 1127 **Total Expense ($000):** 261627 **Payroll Expense ($000):** 100620 **Personnel:** 1537

## CAPE MAY COURT HOUSE—Cape May County

⊠ **CAPE REGIONAL MEDICAL CENTER (310011)**, Two Stone Harbor Boulevard, Zip 08210–9990; tel. 609/463–2000 **A**1 2 9 10 **F**3 8 11 13 15 18 20 28 29 30 31 34 35 40 44 45 46 49 50 53 57 59 64 70 74 75 76 77 78 79 81 82 84 85 86 87 89 91 93 97 107 111 114 118 119 120 121 123 130 132 135 143 146 148
Primary Contact: Joanne Carrocino, FACHE, President and Chief Executive Officer
CFO: Mark Gill, Vice President Finance and Chief Financial Officer
CMO: Richard Falivena, D.O., Vice President Medical Affairs
CIO: Richard Wheatley, Chief Information Officer
CHR: Byron Hunter, Vice President Human Resources
Web address: www.caperegional.com
**Control:** Other not–for–profit (including NFP Corporation) **Service:** General Medical and Surgical

**Staffed Beds:** 180 **Admissions:** 9271 **Census:** 94 **Outpatient Visits:** 167428 **Births:** 533 **Total Expense ($000):** 112831 **Payroll Expense ($000):** 49320 **Personnel:** 890

## CEDAR GROVE—Essex County

☐ **ESSEX COUNTY HOSPITAL CENTER (314020)**, 204 Grove Avenue, Zip 07009–1436; tel. 973/571–2800, (Nonreporting) **A**1 10
Primary Contact: Lucia A. Guarini, Administrator
CFO: Lonnie Hughes, Comptroller
CMO: N. Elangovan, M.D., Medical Director
CIO: John Rosas, Compliance Officer
CHR: BettyAnn Jannuzzi, Supervisor Personnel
Web address: www.essexcountynj.org
**Control:** County–Government, nonfederal **Service:** Psychiatric

**Staffed Beds:** 180

## CHERRY HILL—Camden County

⊠ ○ **KENNEDY HEALTH SYSTEM (310086)**, (Formerly Kennedy Memorial Hospitals–University Medical Center), 2201 Chapel Avenue West, Zip 08002–2048, Mailing Address: P.O. Box 1916, Voorhees, Zip 08043–9016; tel. 856/488–6500, (Includes KENNEDY UNIVERSITY HOSPITAL – STRATFORD, 18 East Laurel Road, Stratford, Zip 08084; tel. 609/346–6000; KENNEDY UNIVERSITY HOSPITAL – WASHINGTON TOWNSHIP, 435 Hurffville–Cross Keys Road, Turnersville, Zip 08012; tel. 609/582–2500) **A**1 10 11 12 **F**3 4 5 7 8 11 12 13 15 18 20 22 29 30 31 32 34 35 38 39 40 44 46 49 50 54 55 56 57 59 60 61 62 64 65 66 68 70 72 73 74 75 76 78 79 81 82 84 85 86 87 89 93 97 98 99 100 101 102 103 104 105 107 108 110 111 114 115 117 118 119 121 123 126 129 130 131 132 134 143 146 147 148
Primary Contact: Martin A. Bieber, President and Chief Executive Officer
CFO: Gary G. Terrinoni, Chief Financial Officer and Senior Vice President
CIO: Thomas Balcavage, Vice President Information Systems and Chief Information Officer
CHR: Anneliese McMenamin, Vice President Human Resources
Web address: www.kennedyhealth.org
**Control:** Other not–for–profit (including NFP Corporation) **Service:** General Medical and Surgical

**Staffed Beds:** 483 **Admissions:** 29169 **Census:** 346 **Outpatient Visits:** 382333 **Births:** 1036 **Total Expense ($000):** 447959 **Payroll Expense ($000):** 182026 **Personnel:** 3047

**KENNEDY MEMORIAL HOSPITALS–UNIVERSITY MEDICAL CENTER** See Kennedy Health System

## CHESTER—Morris County

**KESSLER INSTITUTE FOR REHABILITATION** See Kessler Institute for Rehabilitation, West Orange

*Many Facility Codes have changed. Please refer to the AHA Guide Code Chart.*

© 2013 AHA Guide

**NJ**

## DENVILLE—Morris County

☒ **SAINT CLARE'S HEALTH SYSTEM (310050)**, 25 Pocono Road,
Zip 07834–2954; tel. 973/625–6000, (Includes SAINT CLARE'S
HOSPITAL/BOONTON TOWNSHIP, 130 Powerville Road, Boonton Township,
Zip 07005; tel. 973/316–1800; SAINT CLARE'S HOSPITAL/DENVILLE, 25 Pocono
Road, Zip 07834; tel. 973/625–6000; SAINT CLARE'S HOSPITAL/SUSSEX, 20
Walnut Street, Sussex, Zip 07461; tel. 973/702–2200; ST. CLARE'S
HOSPITAL/DOVER, 400 West Blackwell Street, Dover, Zip 07801–3311;
tel. 973/989–3000), (Total facility includes 118 beds in nursing home–type unit)
**A**1 2 9 10 **F**1 3 4 5 7 10 11 12 13 14 15 18 20 22 26 28 29 30 31 32 34 35
36 38 40 41 44 45 46 47 48 49 50 51 54 56 57 58 59 61 62 64 65 66 67
68 70 71 73 74 75 76 77 78 79 81 82 83 84 85 86 87 89 90 92 93 97 98
99 100 101 102 103 104 105 106 107 108 109 110 111 112 114 116 117
118 119 120 121 123 125 126 127 128 129 130 131 132 134 135 143 145
146 147 **P**5 **S** Catholic Health Initiatives, Englewood, CO
Primary Contact: Leslie D. Hirsch, FACHE, President and Chief Executive Officer
CFO: Gordon A. King, Interim Chief Financial Officer
CMO: Alma Ratcliffe, M.D., Executive Vice President Medical Staff and Business
Development
CIO: Tero Caamano, Director Information Technology
CHR: Gail C. Cohen, Vice President Human Resources
Web address: www.saintclares.org
**Control:** Church–operated, Nongovernment, not–for profit **Service:** General
Medical and Surgical

**Staffed Beds:** 433 **Admissions:** 17494 **Census:** 213 **Outpatient Visits:**
236437 **Births:** 1311 **Total Expense ($000):** 344397 **Payroll Expense
($000):** 143723 **Personnel:** 2004

**SAINT CLARE'S HOSPITAL/DENVILLE** See Saint Clare's Health System

## DOVER—Morris County

☒ **KINDRED HOSPITAL–NEW JERSEY MORRIS COUNTY (312020)**, 400 West
Blackwell Street, Zip 07801–2525; tel. 973/537–3818, (Includes KINDRED
HOSPITAL NEW JERSEY – RAHWAY, 865 Stone Street, Rahway, Zip 07065;
tel. 732/453–2950; Sharon Rosetti, R.N., Chief Executive Officer; KINDRED
HOSPITAL NEW JERSEY – WAYNE, 224 Hamburg Turnpike, Wayne, Zip 07470;
tel. 973/636–7200; Alice M. O'Connor, R.N., Administrator), (Nonreporting) **A**1
10 **S** Kindred Healthcare, Louisville, KY
Primary Contact: Wayne D. Blanchard, Chief Executive Officer
CFO: Rishab Punjabi, Chief Financial Officer
CHR: Neil Rosner, Area Director Human Resources
Web address: www.khmorriscounty.com/
**Control:** Corporation, Investor–owned, for–profit **Service:** Long–Term Acute Care
hospital

**Staffed Beds:** 117

## EAST ORANGE—Essex County

☒ **EAST ORANGE GENERAL HOSPITAL (310083)**, 300 Central Avenue,
Zip 07018–2897; tel. 973/672–8400 **A**1 9 10 **F**11 15 18 29 30 34 35 38 40
45 46 53 57 59 60 61 68 70 71 74 77 79 81 84 93 97 98 99 102 104 105
106 107 108 110 111 114 119 130 148 **P**6
Primary Contact: Kevin J. Slavin, FACHE, President and Chief Executive Officer
CFO: Al Aboud, Chief Financial Officer
CMO: Valentine Burroughs, M.D., Chief Medical Officer
CIO: Thomas Ciccarelli, Chief Information Officer
CHR: Chester Banks, Director Human Resources
CNO: Mary Anne Marra, R.N., Vice President/Chief Nursing Officer
Web address: www.evh.org
**Control:** Other not–for–profit (including NFP Corporation) **Service:** General
Medical and Surgical

**Staffed Beds:** 190 **Admissions:** 7550 **Census:** 135 **Outpatient Visits:**
101589 **Births:** 0 **Total Expense ($000):** 109501 **Payroll Expense ($000):**
53851 **Personnel:** 977

☒ △ **VETERANS AFFAIRS NEW JERSEY HEALTH CARE SYSTEM**, 385
Tremont Avenue, Zip 07018–1095; tel. 973/676–1000, (Includes EAST ORANGE
DIVISION, 385 Tremont Avenue, tel. 973/676–1000; LYONS DIVISION, 151
Knollcroft Road, Lyons, Zip 07939–9998; tel. 908/647–0180) **A**1 2 3 5 7 **F**3 4
5 11 15 18 20 24 29 30 31 33 35 38 39 40 45 46 50 53 54 56 57 58 59 60
61 62 64 68 70 71 74 75 77 78 79 81 82 83 84 85 86 87 91 92 93 94 96
97 98 100 101 102 103 104 105 106 107 111 114 119 121 122 128 129
130 132 133 135 143 146 147 148 **P**6 **S** Department of Veterans Affairs,
Washington, DC
Primary Contact: Kenneth H. Mizrach, Director
COO: Kenneth H. Mizrach, Director
CFO: Tyrone Taylor, Chief Financial Officer
CMO: Steven L. Lieberman, M.D., Chief of Staff
CIO: Marsha Evens, Acting Chief Information Resource Management
CHR: Joseph Capodiferro, Chief Human and Learning Resources
Web address: www.newjersey.va.gov/
**Control:** Veterans Affairs, Government, federal **Service:** General Medical and
Surgical

**Staffed Beds:** 439 **Admissions:** 4958 **Census:** 107 **Outpatient Visits:** 20005
**Births:** 0 **Personnel:** 1262

## EDISON—Middlesex County

★ △ **JFK JOHNSON REHABILITATION INSTITUTE**, 65 James Street,
Zip 08820–3947; tel. 732/321–7050, (Nonreporting) **A**7 **S** JFK Health System,
Edison, NJ
Primary Contact: Anthony Cuzzola, Vice President Rehabilitation Services
CIO: Louis H. Hermans, Vice President Information Systems
Web address: www.njrehab.org
**Control:** Other not–for–profit (including NFP Corporation) **Service:** Rehabilitation

**Staffed Beds:** 92

☒ **JFK MEDICAL CENTER (310108)**, 65 James Street, Zip 08820–3947;
tel. 732/321–7000, (Nonreporting) **A**1 2 3 5 9 10 **S** JFK Health System,
Edison, NJ
Primary Contact: Raymond F. Fredericks, President and CEO
COO: Scott Gebhard, Executive VP and Chief Operating Officer
CFO: Richard C. Smith, Senior Vice President and Chief Financial Officer
CMO: William F. Oser, M.D., Senior Vice President and Chief Medical Officer
CIO: Louis H. Hermans, Vice President Information Systems
CHR: Shirley Higgins–Bowers, Vice President Human Resources
CNO: Patricia G. Rackovan, Senior Vice President & Chief Nurse Executive
Web address: www.jfkmc.org
**Control:** Other not–for–profit (including NFP Corporation) **Service:** General
Medical and Surgical

**Staffed Beds:** 441

## ELIZABETH—Union County

☒ **TRINITAS REGIONAL MEDICAL CENTER (310027)**, 225 Williamson Street,
Zip 07202–3625; tel. 908/994–5000, (Includes TRINITAS HOSPITAL, 925 East
Jersey Street, Zip 07201; tel. 908/994–5000; TRINITAS HOSPITAL – NEW POINT
CAMPUS, 655 East Jersey Street, Zip 07206; tel. 201/351–9000), (Total facility
includes 120 beds in nursing home–type unit) **A**1 2 6 9 10 13 **F**3 5 7 11 12 13
15 17 18 20 22 28 29 30 31 32 34 35 36 38 40 44 45 46 48 49 53 54 56
57 58 59 60 61 64 65 66 68 70 73 74 75 76 77 78 79 81 82 83 84 85 86
87 93 97 98 99 100 101 102 103 104 105 106 107 108 110 111 114 118
119 120 121 123 124 126 128 129 130 132 134 135 143 146 147 **P**6
Primary Contact: Gary S. Horan, FACHE, President and Chief Executive Officer
CFO: Karen Lumpp, Senior Vice President and Chief Financial Officer
CMO: William McHugh, M.D., Chief Medical Officer
CIO: Judy Comitto, Vice President Information Services and Chief Information
Officer
CHR: Glenn Nacion, Vice President Human Resources
Web address: www.trinitashospital.com
**Control:** Other not–for–profit (including NFP Corporation) **Service:** General
Medical and Surgical

**Staffed Beds:** 454 **Admissions:** 15740 **Census:** 381 **Outpatient Visits:**
447247 **Births:** 2179 **Total Expense ($000):** 284869 **Payroll Expense
($000):** 129551 **Personnel:** 2290

**NJ**

---

**Hospital, Medicare Provider Number, Address, Telephone, Approval, Facility, and Physician Codes, Health Care System**

★ American Hospital Association (AHA) membership
☐ The Joint Commission accreditation ◇ DNV Healthcare Inc. accreditation

○ Healthcare Facilities Accreditation Program
△ Commission on Accreditation of Rehabilitation Facilities (CARF) accreditation

## ELMER—Salem County

★ ◇ **INSPIRA MEDICAL CENTER–ELMER (310069)**, (Formerly South Jersey Healthcare – Elmer Hospital), 501 West Front Street, Zip 08318–2101; tel. 856/363–1000 **A**9 10 21 **F**3 11 12 13 15 28 29 30 34 38 40 44 50 57 59 64 68 70 74 75 76 77 78 79 81 82 85 86 87 89 93 107 108 110 111 119 130 131 132 134 146 147 148 **S** Inspira Health Network, Vineland, NJ
Primary Contact: Chester B. Kaletkowski, President and Chief Executive Officer
COO: David Yhlen, Chief Operating Officer
CFO: John A. DiAngelo, Senior Vice President Finance and Chief Financial Officer
CMO: Steven C. Linn, M.D., Chief Medical Officer
CIO: Thomas Pacek, Vice President Information Systems and Chief Information Officer
CHR: Erich Florentine, Chief People Officer
Web address: www.sjhealthcare.net
**Control:** Other not–for–profit (including NFP Corporation) **Service:** General Medical and Surgical

**Staffed Beds:** 88 **Admissions:** 2799 **Census:** 41 **Outpatient Visits:** 62796 **Births:** 336 **Total Expense ($000):** 58908 **Payroll Expense ($000):** 26399 **Personnel:** 302

## ENGLEWOOD—Bergen County

⊠ **ENGLEWOOD HOSPITAL AND MEDICAL CENTER (310045)**, 350 Engle Street, Zip 07631–1898; tel. 201/894–3000 **A**1 2 3 5 9 10 **F**7 8 12 13 15 17 18 19 20 22 24 26 28 29 30 31 34 35 36 38 40 45 46 49 50 51 54 55 56 57 58 59 60 64 70 72 74 75 76 77 78 79 81 82 83 84 85 86 87 89 91 92 93 94 98 99 100 101 102 103 104 105 106 107 108 109 110 111 112 114 115 116 117 118 119 120 121 124 126 129 130 143 145 146 148 **P**6 7
Primary Contact: Warren Geller, President and Chief Executive Officer
CFO: Anthony T. Orlando, Senior Vice President Finance
CMO: Stephen Brunnquell, M.D., President Medical Staff
CIO: Ronald Fuschillo, Chief Information Officer
CHR: Patricia Wilson, Vice President Human Resources
CNO: Madelyn Pearson, R.N., Sr. Vice President Patient Care Services
Web address: www.englewoodhospital.com
**Control:** Other not–for–profit (including NFP Corporation) **Service:** General Medical and Surgical

**Staffed Beds:** 297 **Admissions:** 15739 **Census:** 195 **Outpatient Visits:** 604829 **Births:** 1962 **Total Expense ($000):** 374142 **Payroll Expense ($000):** 132588 **Personnel:** 2086

## FLEMINGTON—Hunterdon County

⊠ **HUNTERDON MEDICAL CENTER (310005)**, 2100 Wescott Drive, Zip 08822–4604; tel. 908/788–6100 **A**1 2 3 5 9 10 **F**3 4 5 11 12 13 14 15 18 20 22 27 28 29 30 31 32 34 35 38 40 45 46 47 48 49 53 54 55 56 57 58 59 60 61 62 64 65 68 70 71 74 75 76 77 78 79 81 82 83 84 85 86 87 89 91 92 93 94 97 98 99 100 101 102 103 104 105 106 107 108 110 114 118 119 121 123 127 129 130 131 132 134 135 146 147 148 **P**1 5
Primary Contact: Robert P. Wise, FACHE, President and Chief Executive Officer
COO: Lawrence N. Grand, Executive Vice President and Chief Operating Officer
CFO: Daniel J. Deets, Chief Financial Officer
CIO: Glenn Mamary, Chief Information Officer
CHR: Violet Kocsis, Vice President Human Resources and Development
CNO: Patricia Steingall, R.N., Vice President, Patient Care Services
Web address: www.hunterdonhealthcare.org
**Control:** Other not–for–profit (including NFP Corporation) **Service:** General Medical and Surgical

**Staffed Beds:** 178 **Admissions:** 8476 **Census:** 105 **Outpatient Visits:** 623348 **Births:** 953 **Total Expense ($000):** 208349 **Payroll Expense ($000):** 122613 **Personnel:** 1877

## FREEHOLD—Monmouth County

⊠ **CENTRASTATE HEALTHCARE SYSTEM (310111)**, 901 West Main Street, Zip 07728–2549; tel. 732/431–2000 **A**1 2 3 5 9 10 **F**3 11 12 13 15 18 19 20 28 29 30 31 32 34 35 36 38 40 41 45 46 49 50 57 58 59 61 64 65 66 70 73 74 75 76 77 78 79 81 82 84 86 87 89 92 93 97 98 100 101 102 107 108 110 114 118 119 120 121 123 124 126 129 130 131 132 134 135 144 146 147 148
Primary Contact: John Gribbin, FACHE, President and Chief Executive Officer
COO: Daniel J. Messina, Ph.D., Senior Vice President and Chief Operating Officer
CFO: John Dellocono, Senior Vice President and Chief Financial Officer
CMO: Jack H. Dworkin, M.D., Vice President Medical Affairs and Chief Medical Officer
CIO: Indranil Ganguly, Vice President and Chief Information Officer
CHR: Fran Keane, Vice President Human Resources
Web address: www.centrastate.com
**Control:** Other not–for–profit (including NFP Corporation) **Service:** General Medical and Surgical

**Staffed Beds:** 273 **Admissions:** 14444 **Census:** 163 **Outpatient Visits:** 254422 **Births:** 1524 **Total Expense ($000):** 226184 **Payroll Expense ($000):** 94749 **Personnel:** 1451

## HACKENSACK—Bergen County

⊠ **HACKENSACK UNIVERSITY MEDICAL CENTER (310001)**, 30 Prospect Avenue, Zip 07601–1914; tel. 201/996–2000, (Includes THE JOSEPH M. SANZARI CHILDREN'S HOSPITAL, 30 Prospect Avenue, tel. 201/996–2000) **A**1 2 3 5 8 9 10 **F**2 3 4 5 6 7 8 9 10 11 12 13 14 15 16 17 18 19 20 22 24 26 27 28 29 30 31 32 34 35 36 37 38 39 40 41 42 43 44 45 46 47 48 49 50 51 52 53 54 55 56 57 58 59 60 61 64 65 66 68 69 70 71 72 73 74 75 76 77 78 79 81 82 84 85 86 87 88 89 90 91 92 93 94 96 97 98 99 100 101 102 103 104 107 108 109 110 111 113 114 115 116 117 118 119 120 121 123 124 126 129 130 131 132 134 135 136 138 141 142 143 144 145 146 147 148 **P**1 5 6
Primary Contact: Robert C. Garrett, FACHE, President and Chief Executive Officer
COO: Ketul J. Patel, Executive Vice President and Chief Operations and Strategy Officer
CFO: Robert Glenning, Executive Vice President Finance and Chief Financial Officer
CMO: Peter A. Gross, M.D., Senior Vice President and Chief Medical Officer
CHR: Nancy R. Corcoran, Senior Vice President Human Resources and Quality Service
Web address: www.hackensackumc.org/
**Control:** Other not–for–profit (including NFP Corporation) **Service:** General Medical and Surgical

**Staffed Beds:** 685 **Admissions:** 70638 **Census:** 605 **Outpatient Visits:** 2927191 **Births:** 6144 **Total Expense ($000):** 1360597 **Payroll Expense ($000):** 575507 **Personnel:** 7243

## HACKETTSTOWN—Warren County

★ **HACKETTSTOWN REGIONAL MEDICAL CENTER (310115)**, 651 Willow Grove Street, Zip 07840–1799; tel. 908/852–5100, (Nonreporting) **A**9 10 **S** Adventist HealthCare, Gaithersburg, MD
Primary Contact: Jason C. Coe, President and Chief Executive Officer
COO: Stella Visaggio, Chief Operating Officer
CFO: Robert Peterson, Chief Financial Officer
CMO: Kenneth Janowski, M.D., Chief Medical Officer
CIO: Dorothy Cox, Manager Information Systems
CHR: Jeanne Jepson, Director Human Resources
CNO: Linda Ambacher, Interim Chief Nursing Officer
Web address: www.hrmcnj.org
**Control:** Church–operated, Nongovernment, not–for profit **Service:** General Medical and Surgical

**Staffed Beds:** 111

## HAMILTON—Mercer County

⊠ **ROBERT WOOD JOHNSON UNIVERSITY HOSPITAL AT HAMILTON (310110)**, One Hamilton Health Place, Zip 08690–3599; tel. 609/586–7900 **A**1 2 5 9 10 **F**3 8 9 11 12 13 15 17 18 22 26 28 29 30 31 32 34 35 36 39 40 41 44 46 47 48 49 50 51 53 54 55 56 57 58 59 60 61 63 64 65 66 68 69 70 71 73 74 75 76 77 78 79 81 82 84 85 86 87 92 93 96 97 100 102 103 107 108 110 111 114 115 116 117 118 119 120 121 123 124 129 130 131 132 134 135 143 144 145 146 147 148 **P**6 **S** Robert Wood Johnson Health System & Network, New Brunswick, NJ
Primary Contact: Anthony J. Cimino, President and Chief Executive Officer
COO: Barbara H. Smith, Senior Vice President & Chief Operating Officer
CFO: James M. Maher, Senior Vice President and Chief Financial Officer
CMO: Ronald Ryder, D.O., President of the Medical Staff
CNO: Lisa Breza, R.N., Vice President and Chief Nursing Officer
Web address: www.rwjhamilton.org
**Control:** Other not–for–profit (including NFP Corporation) **Service:** General Medical and Surgical

**Staffed Beds:** 242 **Admissions:** 11774 **Census:** 140 **Outpatient Visits:** 223035 **Births:** 1141 **Total Expense ($000):** 186016 **Payroll Expense ($000):** 78950 **Personnel:** 1136

## HAMMONTON—Camden County

☐ **ANCORA PSYCHIATRIC HOSPITAL (314005)**, 301 Spring Garden Road, Zip 08037–9699; tel. 609/561–1700 **A**1 10 **F**30 39 56 68 75 87 97 98 130 135 143 146 **P**6 **S** Division of Mental Health and Addiction Services, Department of Human Services, State of New Jersey, Trenton, NJ
Primary Contact: Allan Boyer, Chief Executive Officer
COO: John Lubitsky, Deputy Chief Executive Officer Support Services
CFO: John Holmes, Business Manager
CMO: David Roat, D.O., Acting Medical Director
CIO: Charlene Ruberti, Director Information Technology Development
CHR: Alfred Filipini, Manager Human Resources
CNO: Catherine Jones, Chief Nursing Officer
Web address: www.state.nj.us/humanservices/dmhs/oshm/aph/
**Control:** State–Government, nonfederal **Service:** Psychiatric

**Staffed Beds:** 500 **Admissions:** 762 **Census:** 489 **Outpatient Visits:** 0 **Births:** 0 **Total Expense ($000):** 141205 **Payroll Expense ($000):** 85341 **Personnel:** 1658

**NJ**

*Many Facility Codes have changed. Please refer to the AHA Guide Code Chart.*  © 2013 AHA Guide

**HOBOKEN—Hudson County**

☐ **HOBOKEN UNIVERSITY MEDICAL CENTER (310040)**, 308 Willow Avenue, Zip 07030–3889; tel. 201/418–1000, (Nonreporting) **A**1 3 5 9 10
Primary Contact: Paul A. Walker, FACHE, President and Chief Executive Officer
CFO: Vincent Riccitelli, Vice President and Chief Financial Officer
CMO: Joseph Kozel, M.D., President Medical Staff
CIO: Lior Blik, Chief Information Officer
CHR: Yleana Contrera, Executive Director Human Resources
Web address: www.hobokenumc.com
**Control:** Corporation, Investor–owned, for–profit **Service:** General Medical and Surgical

Staffed Beds: 204

**HOLMDEL—Monmouth County**

⊠ **BAYSHORE COMMUNITY HOSPITAL (310112)**, 727 North Beers Street, Zip 07733–1598; tel. 732/739–5900 **A**1 2 9 10 **F**3 8 11 12 15 18 20 28 29 30 31 40 41 45 49 50 51 56 60 64 65 66 68 70 74 75 78 79 81 82 84 85 87 92 93 97 107 108 110 111 114 116 117 118 119 129 130 132 135 145 146 147 148 **P**7 **S** Meridian Health, Wall Township, NJ
Primary Contact: Timothy J. Hogan, FACHE, Regional President
COO: Anthony V. Cava, Chief Operating Officer
CFO: John Gantner, Executive Vice President Finance and Partner Company Operations
CMO: L. Scott Larsen, M.D., Vice President Medical Affairs
CIO: Rebecca Weber, Senior Vice President and Chief Information Officer
Web address: www.bchs.com
**Control:** Other not–for–profit (including NFP Corporation) **Service:** General Medical and Surgical

Staffed Beds: 147 Admissions: 7255 Census: 101 Outpatient Visits: 78895 Births: 0 Total Expense ($000): 107214 Payroll Expense ($000): 48612 Personnel: 632

**JERSEY CITY—Hudson County**

☐ **CHRIST HOSPITAL (310016)**, 176 Palisade Avenue, Zip 07306–1196, Mailing Address: 176 Palisades Avenue, Zip 07306–1196; tel. 201/795–8200, (Nonreporting) **A**1 6 9 10 12 13
Primary Contact: Peter A. Kelly, President and Chief Executive Officer
CFO: George A. Popko, Senior Vice President and Chief Financial Officer
CMO: Bhavani P. Mekala, M.D., President Medical Staff
CIO: Marty Grossman, Director Information Technology
CHR: Eileen Clyne, Director Human Resources
Web address: www.christhospital.org
**Control:** Other not–for–profit (including NFP Corporation) **Service:** General Medical and Surgical

Staffed Beds: 381

☐ ◇ **LIBERTYHEALTH–JERSEY CITY MEDICAL CENTER (310074)**, 355 Grand Street, Zip 07302–4321; tel. 201/915–2000 **A**1 3 5 9 10 21 **F**5 7 8 11 12 13 15 17 18 20 22 24 26 28 29 30 31 34 35 38 39 40 41 43 44 45 46 47 48 49 50 51 52 55 56 57 58 59 60 61 63 64 65 68 70 71 72 73 74 75 76 77 78 79 81 82 84 85 87 89 91 93 94 96 97 98 99 100 101 102 104 105 106 107 108 110 111 112 114 115 119 130 132 134 135 144 146 147 148
Primary Contact: Joseph F. Scott, FACHE, President and Chief Executive Officer
CFO: Paul R. Goldberg, Chief Financial Officer
CMO: Kenneth Garay, M.D., Chief Medical Officer
CIO: Stephen Li, Vice President Management Information Systems
CHR: Mary Cataudella, Corporate Director Human Resources
Web address: www.libertyhcs.org
**Control:** Other not–for–profit (including NFP Corporation) **Service:** General Medical and Surgical

Staffed Beds: 316 Admissions: 15608 Census: 198 Outpatient Visits: 262968 Births: 1808 Total Expense ($000): 314710 Payroll Expense ($000): 130951 Personnel: 1959

**LAKEWOOD—Ocean County**

⊠ **KIMBALL MEDICAL CENTER (310084)**, 600 River Avenue, Zip 08701–5237; tel. 732/363–1900 **A**1 2 9 10 **F**3 11 13 15 18 20 28 29 30 31 32 34 35 36 38 40 41 43 44 50 54 56 57 58 59 60 61 64 68 70 73 74 75 76 77 78 79 81 82 84 86 87 89 93 96 97 98 100 101 102 103 104 105 107 108 111 114 117 119 130 131 132 133 134 135 146 147 148 **S** Barnabas Health, West Orange, NJ
Primary Contact: Michael Mimoso, FACHE, President and Chief Executive Officer
CFO: Thomas Percello, Chief Financial Officer
CMO: Todd Phillips, M.D., Interim Vice President, Medical Affairs
CIO: Chris Butler, Deputy CIO/System Vice President
CHR: Michele Schweers, Vice President Human Resources
CNO: Judy Colorado, R.N., Vice President, Patient Care Services
Web address: www.barnabashealth.org/hospitals/kimbal_medical/index.html
**Control:** Other not–for–profit (including NFP Corporation) **Service:** General Medical and Surgical

Staffed Beds: 240 Admissions: 9874 Census: 149 Outpatient Visits: 103369 Births: 893 Total Expense ($000): 140221 Payroll Expense ($000): 58934 Personnel: 850

**SPECIALTY HOSPITAL AT KIMBALL (312013)**, 600 River Avenue, 4 West, Zip 08701–5237; tel. 732/942–3588, (Nonreporting) **A**10
Primary Contact: Violeta Peters, R.N., Chief Executive Officer
CFO: Richard L. Cassady, Chief Financial Officer
CMO: Howard Lebowitz, M.D., Chief Medical Officer
CHR: Mary Pat Napolitano, Director Human Resources
Web address: www.acutecarehs.com
**Control:** Corporation, Investor–owned, for–profit **Service:** Long–Term Acute Care hospital

Staffed Beds: 50

**LAWRENCEVILLE—Mercer County**

⊠ **ST. LAWRENCE REHABILITATION CENTER (313027)**, 2381 Lawrenceville Road, Zip 08648–2025; tel. 609/896–9500, (Total facility includes 57 beds in nursing home–type unit) **A**1 10 **F**29 30 34 35 57 64 68 90 93 96 108 119 128 130 132 143 146 148
Primary Contact: Darlene S. Hanley, R.N., President and Chief Executive Officer
COO: Shirley Pukala, R.N., Assistant Administrator of Operations
CFO: Thomas W. Boyle, Chief Financial Officer
CMO: Kevin McGuigan, M.D., Medical Director
CIO: Jane Millner, Director Community Relations and Development
CHR: John Levi, Director of Human Resources
CNO: Magdalena Sokolowski, R.N., Director of Nursing
Web address: www.slrc.org
**Control:** Church–operated, Nongovernment, not–for profit **Service:** Rehabilitation

Staffed Beds: 109 Admissions: 2398 Census: 100 Outpatient Visits: 21857 Births: 0 Total Expense ($000): 30539 Payroll Expense ($000): 18338 Personnel: 351

**LIVINGSTON—Essex County**

⊠ **SAINT BARNABAS MEDICAL CENTER (310076)**, 94 Old Short Hills Road, Zip 07039–5672; tel. 973/322–5000 **A**1 2 3 5 8 9 10 12 13 **F**2 3 11 12 13 16 17 18 19 20 22 24 26 28 29 30 31 32 34 35 40 41 46 49 55 57 58 59 64 65 66 68 69 70 72 73 74 75 77 78 79 80 81 82 85 86 87 88 92 93 97 107 108 111 114 115 118 119 120 121 123 124 126 129 130 132 134 135 138 142 146 147 148 **P**5 **S** Barnabas Health, West Orange, NJ
Primary Contact: John F. Bonamo, M.D., MS, President and Chief Executive Officer
CFO: Patrick Ahearn, Senior Vice President Finance and Administrative Services
CMO: Gregory Rokosz, D.O., Senior Vice President Medical and Academic Affairs
CIO: Michael McTigue, Chief Information Officer
CHR: Arnold D. Manzo, Vice President Human Resources
Web address: www.barnabashealth.org/hospitals/saint_barnabas/index.html
**Control:** Other not–for–profit (including NFP Corporation) **Service:** General Medical and Surgical

Staffed Beds: 577 Admissions: 32809 Census: 403 Outpatient Visits: 189987 Births: 5645 Total Expense ($000): 519438 Payroll Expense ($000): 215562 Personnel: 3006

NJ

---

**Hospital, Medicare Provider Number, Address, Telephone, Approval, Facility, and Physician Codes, Health Care System**

★ American Hospital Association (AHA) membership
☐ The Joint Commission accreditation
◇ DNV Healthcare Inc. accreditation
○ Healthcare Facilities Accreditation Program
△ Commission on Accreditation of Rehabilitation Facilities (CARF) accreditation

## LONG BRANCH—Monmouth County

☒ **MONMOUTH MEDICAL CENTER (310075)**, 300 Second Avenue, Zip 07740–6303; tel. 732/222–5200, (Includes CHILDREN'S HOSPITAL AT MONMOUTH MEDICAL CENTER, 300 Second Avenue, tel. 732/222–5200) **A**1 2 3 5 8 9 10 **F**1 3 5 8 9 11 12 13 14 15 17 18 19 20 22 28 29 30 31 32 34 35 36 38 40 41 45 46 47 48 49 50 51 52 53 54 55 56 57 58 59 60 61 63 64 65 66 68 70 72 73 74 75 76 77 78 79 81 82 83 84 85 86 87 88 89 97 98 99 100 101 102 103 104 105 106 107 108 109 110 111 112 114 115 119 120 121 123 124 126 129 130 131 132 133 134 135 143 144 145 146 147 148 **P**5 6 **S** Barnabas Health, West Orange, NJ
Primary Contact: Frank J. Vozos, M.D., FACS, President and Chief Executive Officer
COO: Bill Arnold, Chief Operating Officer
CFO: Gerald Tofani, Chief Financial Officer
CMO: Eric Burkett, M.D., Vice President Medical Affairs
CIO: Paul Garrin, Chief Information Officer
CHR: Glenn Oppito, Vice President Human Resources
Web address: www.barnabashealth.org/hospitals/monmouth_medical/index.html
**Control:** Other not–for–profit (including NFP Corporation) **Service:** General Medical and Surgical

**Staffed Beds: 329 Admissions: 18088 Census: 228 Outpatient Visits:** 190686 **Births: 4491 Total Expense ($000): 316630 Payroll Expense ($000):** 123923 **Personnel:** 1813

## LYONS—Somerset County

**LYONS DIVISION** See Veterans Affairs New Jersey Health Care System, East Orange

## MANAHAWKIN—Ocean County

☒ **SOUTHERN OCEAN MEDICAL CENTER (310113)**, 1140 Route 72 West, Zip 08050–2499; tel. 609/978–8900, (Total facility includes 20 beds in nursing home–type unit) **A**1 2 9 10 **F**3 11 12 13 15 18 20 28 29 30 31 32 40 44 45 46 51 54 56 59 64 65 66 68 70 74 76 77 78 79 81 82 84 85 86 87 92 93 97 107 108 110 111 114 118 119 128 129 130 132 135 144 146 147 148 **P**7 **S** Meridian Health, Wall Township, NJ
Primary Contact: Joseph P. Coyle, President
COO: E. Joseph Hummel, Chief Strategy Officer
CFO: John Gantner, Executive Vice President Finance and Partner Company Operations
CIO: Rebecca Weber, Senior Vice President and Chief Information Officer
Web address: www.soch.com
**Control:** Other not–for–profit (including NFP Corporation) **Service:** General Medical and Surgical

**Staffed Beds: 132 Admissions: 6412 Census: 87 Outpatient Visits: 102041 Births: 330 Total Expense ($000): 122322 Payroll Expense ($000): 50137 Personnel: 592**

## MARLTON—Burlington County

☐ △ **MARLTON REHABILITATION HOSPITAL (313032)**, 92 Brick Road, Zip 08053–2177; tel. 856/988–8778 **A**1 7 10 **F**34 50 57 59 60 64 68 75 77 85 86 87 90 91 92 93 94 95 96 107 111 114 116 119 130 132 148 **P**8 **S** Vibra Healthcare, Mechanicsburg, PA
Primary Contact: Michael Long, MS, Chief Executive Officer
CFO: Stuart Moss, Chief Financial Officer
CMO: Kenneth Wu, M.D., Medical Director
CHR: Joanne Cornava, Director Human Resources
Web address: www.marltonrehab.com
**Control:** Corporation, Investor–owned, for–profit **Service:** Rehabilitation

**Staffed Beds: 51 Admissions: 1551 Census: 48 Outpatient Visits: 17374 Births: 0 Total Expense ($000): 20925 Payroll Expense ($000): 10164 Personnel: 112**

☒ **VIRTUA MARLTON**, 90 Brick Road, Zip 08053–2177; tel. 856/355–6000 **A**1 2 9 **F**20 22 26 29 31 40 45 49 56 60 64 68 70 75 78 79 81 82 84 85 87 93 107 111 119 129 130 146 148 **S** Virtua Health, Marlton, NJ
Primary Contact: Gary L. Long, Chief Operating Officer
COO: Gary L. Long, Chief Operating Officer
CFO: Robert Segin, Executive Vice President & Chief Financial Officer
CMO: James P. Dwyer, D.O., Chief Medical Officer
CIO: Alfred Campanella, Chief Information Officer
CHR: Michael Pepe, Ph.D., Chief Human Resources
CNO: Ann Campbell, Chief Nursing Officer
Web address: www.virtua.org
**Control:** Other not–for–profit (including NFP Corporation) **Service:** General Medical and Surgical

**Staffed Beds: 192 Admissions: 10264 Census: 132 Outpatient Visits:** 49037 **Births: 0 Total Expense ($000): 206527 Payroll Expense ($000):** 57923 **Personnel:** 738

☐ **WEISMAN CHILDREN'S REHABILITATION HOSPITAL (313302)**, 92 Brick Road 3rd Floor, Zip 08053–2177; tel. 856/489–4520, (Nonreporting) **A**1 10
Primary Contact: Thomas J. Lonergan, Chief Executive Officer
CMO: Connie Domingo, M.D., Medical Director
CIO: Darren Pedersen, Coordinator Information Technology
CHR: Eileen Dumsha, Manager Employee Relations
Web address: www.weismanchildrens.com
**Control:** Corporation, Investor–owned, for–profit **Service:** Children's rehabilitation

**Staffed Beds: 24**

## MONTCLAIR—Essex County

☒ **HACKENSACK UNIVERSITY MEDICAL CENTER MOUNTAINSIDE (310054)**, 1 Bay Avenue, Zip 07042–4898; tel. 973/429–6000, (Data for 184 days) **A**1 2 3 5 6 9 10 **F**3 8 12 13 14 15 18 20 22 26 28 29 30 31 34 35 38 39 40 44 45 46 48 49 50 51 52 53 54 55 56 57 59 60 66 67 68 70 73 74 75 76 77 78 79 81 82 84 85 86 87 89 91 93 94 97 98 102 103 104 105 107 108 109 110 111 114 115 116 117 118 119 120 121 123 124 126 128 129 130 131 132 134 135 144 145 146 147 148 **P**5 **S** LHP Hospital Group, Plano, TX
Primary Contact: John A. Fromhold, Chief Executive Officer
COO: Ed Devaney, Vice President and Chief Operating Officer
CHR: Fran Corridon, Vice President Human Resources and Shared Services
Web address: www.mountainsidenow.com
**Control:** Corporation, Investor–owned, for–profit **Service:** General Medical and Surgical

**Staffed Beds: 228 Admissions: 8005 Census: 315 Births: 1285 Total Expense ($000): 96067 Payroll Expense ($000): 43813 Personnel: 1377**

## MORRIS PLAINS—Morris County

☐ **GREYSTONE PARK PSYCHIATRIC HOSPITAL (314016)**, 59 Koch Avenue, Zip 07950–4400; tel. 973/538–1800 **A**1 **F**39 68 77 87 98 99 101 103 130 135 143 146 **S** Division of Mental Health and Addiction Services, Department of Human Services, State of New Jersey, Trenton, NJ
Primary Contact: Janet J. Monroe, R.N., Chief Executive Officer
COO: John Whitenack, Chief Operating Officer
CFO: Jack Frey, Business Manager
CMO: Milton Luria, M.D., Chief of Medicine
CHR: Jerri Casazza, Manager Human Resources
Web address: www.state.nj.us/humanservices/dmhs/oshm/gpph/
**Control:** State–Government, nonfederal **Service:** Psychiatric

**Staffed Beds: 506 Admissions: 524 Census: 476 Outpatient Visits: 0 Births: 0 Personnel: 622**

## MORRISTOWN—Morris County

☒ **MORRISTOWN MEDICAL CENTER (310015)**, 100 Madison Avenue, Zip 07960–6136; tel. 973/971–5000, (Includes REHABILITATION INSTITUTE AT THE MOUNT KEMBLE DIVISION ; GORYEB CHILDREN'S HOSPITAL, 100 Madison Avenue, tel. 800/247–9580), (Total facility includes 40 beds in nursing home–type unit) **A**1 2 3 5 8 9 10 **F**3 5 6 7 8 9 11 12 13 14 15 17 18 19 20 22 24 26 28 29 30 31 32 33 34 35 36 37 38 39 40 41 43 44 45 46 47 48 49 50 51 52 53 54 55 56 57 58 59 60 61 62 63 64 65 66 68 69 70 71 72 73 74 75 76 77 78 79 81 82 83 84 85 86 87 88 89 90 91 92 93 94 95 96 97 98 99 100 101 102 103 104 105 107 108 109 110 111 114 115 116 117 118 119 120 121 123 126 128 129 130 131 132 134 135 141 143 144 145 146 147 148 **P**2 3 5 6 **S** Atlantic Health, Morristown, NJ
Primary Contact: David J. Shulkin, M.D., President and Chief Executive Officer
COO: Joanne M. Conroy, M.D., Executive Vice President and Chief Operating Officer
CFO: Kevin Shanley, Vice President Finance and Chief Financial Officer
CMO: Joanne M. Conroy, M.D., Executive Vice President and Chief Operating Officer
CIO: Linda Reed, Vice President and Chief Information Officer
CHR: Andrew L. Kovach, Vice President Human Resources and Chief Administrative Officer
Web address: www.atlantichealth.org/Morristown/
**Control:** Other not–for–profit (including NFP Corporation) **Service:** General Medical and Surgical

**Staffed Beds: 656 Admissions: 34871 Census: 519 Outpatient Visits:** 323066 **Births: 4033 Total Expense ($000): 820013 Payroll Expense ($000): 359439 Personnel: 5363**

## MOUNT HOLLY—Burlington County

☒ **VIRTUA MEMORIAL (310057)**, 175 Madison Avenue, Zip 08060–2099; tel. 609/267–0700 **A**1 3 5 9 10 **F**3 11 12 13 15 18 20 22 28 29 30 31 40 41 45 48 49 56 59 60 70 73 74 75 76 77 78 79 81 85 86 87 89 92 93 98 102 105 107 108 110 111 114 115 118 119 120 126 129 130 143 146 147 148 **S** Virtua Health, Marlton, NJ
Primary Contact: Matthew Zuino, Vice President
CFO: Robert Segin, Chief Financial Officer
CMO: James P. Dwyer, D.O., Executive Vice President and Chief Medical Officer
CHR: E. D. Dunn, Vice President Human Resources
Web address: www.virtua.org
**Control:** Other not–for–profit (including NFP Corporation) **Service:** General Medical and Surgical

**Staffed Beds: 325 Admissions: 18201 Census: 236 Outpatient Visits:** 177066 **Births: 2534 Total Expense ($000): 282098 Payroll Expense ($000):** 89479 **Personnel:** 1310

*Many Facility Codes have changed. Please refer to the AHA Guide Code Chart.*
© 2013 AHA Guide

**NJ**

**VIRTUA MEMORIAL HOSPITAL BURLINGTON COUNTY** See Virtua Memorial

## NEPTUNE—Monmouth County

☒ **JERSEY SHORE UNIVERSITY MEDICAL CENTER (310073)**, 1945 Route 33, Zip 07754–0397; tel. 732/775–5500, (Includes K. HOVNANIAN CHILDREN'S HOSPITAL, 1945 State Route 33, Zip 07753–4859; tel. 800/560–9990) **A**1 2 3 5 8 9 10 13 **F**3 5 8 11 12 13 17 18 19 20 22 24 26 28 29 30 31 32 38 39 40 41 43 45 46 47 49 50 54 55 59 60 61 63 64 66 68 70 72 73 74 75 76 78 79 80 81 82 84 85 86 87 88 89 92 93 94 96 97 98 99 100 101 102 103 104 105 107 108 111 114 115 117 118 119 120 121 123 126 129 130 131 132 135 144 146 147 148 **P**7 **S** Meridian Health, Wall Township, NJ
Primary Contact: Steven G. Littleson, FACHE, President
COO: Robert H. Adams, Vice President Operations
CFO: John Gantner, Executive Vice President Finance and Partner Company Operations
CMO: David Kountz, M.D., Senior Vice President Medical Affairs
CIO: Rebecca Weber, Senior Vice President and Chief Information Officer
Web address: www.meridianhealth.com
**Control:** Other not–for–profit (including NFP Corporation) **Service:** General Medical and Surgical

**Staffed Beds:** 546 **Admissions:** 26398 **Census:** 390 **Outpatient Visits:** 210690 **Births:** 2083 **Total Expense ($000):** 549510 **Payroll Expense ($000):** 215045 **Personnel:** 2654

## NEW BRUNSWICK—Middlesex County

☐ △ **CHILDREN'S SPECIALIZED HOSPITAL–PSE&G (313300)**, (Formerly Children's Specialized Hospital), 200 Somerset Street, Zip 08901–1942; tel. 732/258–7000, (Includes CHILDREN'S SPECIALIZED HOSPITAL, 150 New Providence Road, Mountainside, Zip 07092–2590; tel. 908/233–3720), (Nonreporting) **A**1 3 5 7 10 **S** Robert Wood Johnson Health System & Network, New Brunswick, NJ
Primary Contact: Amy B. Mansue, President and Chief Executive Officer
COO: Warren E. Moore, Executive Vice President and Chief Operating Officer
CFO: Joseph J. Dobosh, Jr., Vice President and Chief Financial Officer
CMO: Frank V. Castello, M.D., Medical Director
CIO: Pat DeMartino, Chief Information Officer
CHR: William Dwyer, Vice President Human Resources
Web address: www.childrens-specialized.org
**Control:** Other not–for–profit (including NFP Corporation) **Service:** Children's rehabilitation

**Staffed Beds:** 126

☒ **ROBERT WOOD JOHNSON UNIVERSITY HOSPITAL (310038)**, 1 Robert Wood Johnson Place, Zip 08901–1928; tel. 732/828–3000, (Includes BRISTOL–MYERS SQUIBB CHILDREN'S HOSPITAL, One Robert Wood Johnson Place, Zip 08901, Mailing Address: P.O. Box 2601, Zip 08903–2601; tel. 732/828–3000) **A**1 2 3 5 8 9 10 **F**3 6 7 8 9 11 12 13 14 15 17 18 19 20 22 24 26 28 29 30 31 32 34 35 37 38 39 40 41 43 44 45 46 47 48 49 50 51 52 53 54 55 56 57 58 59 60 61 62 63 64 65 66 68 70 71 72 73 74 75 76 77 78 79 81 82 83 84 85 86 87 88 89 91 92 93 94 96 97 99 100 102 104 107 108 109 110 111 112 113 114 115 116 117 118 119 120 121 123 124 126 129 130 131 132 134 135 136 137 138 141 142 143 146 147 148 **P**6 **S** Robert Wood Johnson Health System & Network, New Brunswick, NJ
Primary Contact: Stephen K. Jones, President and Chief Executive Officer
COO: Vincent D. Joseph, Executive Vice President and Chief Operating Officer
CFO: Brian M. Reilly, Chief Financial Officer
CMO: Joshua M. Bershad, M.D., Senior Vice President Medical Affairs and Chief Medical Officer
CIO: Robert G. Irwin, Vice President Information Systems
CHR: Martin S. Everhart, Senior Vice President Human Resources
Web address: www.rwjuh.edu
**Control:** Other not–for–profit (including NFP Corporation) **Service:** General Medical and Surgical

**Staffed Beds:** 610 **Admissions:** 32267 **Census:** 493 **Outpatient Visits:** 260916 **Births:** 2335 **Total Expense ($000):** 753269 **Payroll Expense ($000):** 290398 **Personnel:** 3977

☒ **SAINT PETER'S UNIVERSITY HOSPITAL (310070)**, 254 Easton Avenue, Zip 08901–1780; tel. 732/745–8600, (Includes THE CHILDREN'S HOSPITAL AT SAINT PETER'S UNIVERSITY, 254 Easton Avenue, Zip 08901–1766; tel. 732/565–5437) **A**1 2 3 5 8 9 10 **F**2 3 11 12 13 15 17 18 19 20 21 22 26 27 28 29 30 31 32 34 35 37 38 39 40 41 44 45 46 49 50 51 54 55 56 57 58 59 60 61 64 65 66 68 70 71 72 73 74 75 76 77 78 79 81 82 83 84 85 86 87 88 89 91 92 93 94 95 96 97 100 102 105 107 108 110 111 113 114 115 118 119 120 121 123 126 129 130 131 132 135 143 144 145 146 147 148 **P**3 6
Primary Contact: Ronald C. Rak, JD, Chief Executive Officer
COO: Patricia Carroll, Senior Vice President and Chief Operating Officer
CFO: Garrick J. Stoldt, Vice President and Chief Financial Officer
CMO: Anthony Passannante, Jr., M.D., Vice President, Chief Medical Officer and Co–Chief Quality Officer
CIO: Frank DiSanzo, Vice President and Chief Information Officer
CHR: Susan Ballestero, Vice President Human Resources
Web address: www.saintpetersuh.com
**Control:** Church–operated, Nongovernment, not–for profit **Service:** General Medical and Surgical

**Staffed Beds:** 374 **Admissions:** 20210 **Census:** 246 **Outpatient Visits:** 342970 **Births:** 5809 **Total Expense ($000):** 394156 **Payroll Expense ($000):** 196218 **Personnel:** 2702

## NEWARK—Essex County

☒ **NEWARK BETH ISRAEL MEDICAL CENTER (310002)**, 201 Lyons Avenue, Zip 07112–2027; tel. 973/926–7000, (Includes CHILDREN'S HOSPITAL OF NEW JERSEY, 201 Lyons Avenue, tel. 973/926–7000) **A**1 2 3 5 8 9 10 12 13 **F**2 3 12 15 17 18 19 20 21 22 23 24 25 26 27 28 29 30 31 32 34 35 38 39 40 41 44 46 47 48 49 50 55 56 57 58 59 60 61 64 68 70 71 72 73 74 75 76 77 78 79 81 82 84 85 86 87 88 89 92 93 97 99 100 101 102 104 105 107 108 110 111 114 115 117 119 120 121 126 129 130 131 132 135 137 138 140 141 142 143 146 147 148 **P**8 **S** Barnabas Health, West Orange, NJ
Primary Contact: John A. Brennan, M.D., M.P.H., President and Chief Executive Officer
COO: Darrell K. Terry, Sr., Senior Vice President Operations
CFO: Veronica Zeichner, Chief Financial Officer
CHR: Zach Lipner, Vice President Human Resources
Web address: www.barnabashealth.org/hospitals/newark_beth_israel/index.html
**Control:** Other not–for–profit (including NFP Corporation) **Service:** General Medical and Surgical

**Staffed Beds:** 408 **Admissions:** 22613 **Census:** 399 **Outpatient Visits:** 295397 **Births:** 3543 **Total Expense ($000):** 522105 **Payroll Expense ($000):** 253099 **Personnel:** 3158

☒ **SAINT MICHAEL'S MEDICAL CENTER (310096)**, 111 Central Avenue, Zip 07102–1909; tel. 973/877–5549 **A**1 2 3 5 9 10 **F**3 5 12 15 17 18 20 22 24 26 29 30 31 34 35 37 38 40 45 47 48 49 50 51 57 58 59 60 61 64 66 68 70 74 75 77 78 79 81 82 85 87 91 92 93 97 98 100 102 107 108 110 111 114 119 121 126 130 132 143 146 148 **S** Catholic Health East, Newtown Square, PA
Primary Contact: David A. Ricci, President and Chief Executive Officer
CFO: John S. Grywalski, Jr., CPA, Chief Financial Officer
CMO: Sebastian Dovi, M.D., Interim Chief Medical Officer
CIO: Angelo Schittone, Chief Information Officer
CHR: Mary Beth Rose, Vice President Human Resources
Web address: www.smmcnj.org
**Control:** Church–operated, Nongovernment, not–for profit **Service:** General Medical and Surgical

**Staffed Beds:** 170 **Admissions:** 9194 **Census:** 136 **Outpatient Visits:** 89978 **Births:** 0 **Total Expense ($000):** 238990 **Payroll Expense ($000):** 80929 **Personnel:** 1046

☒ **UNIVERSITY OF MEDICINE AND DENTISTRY OF NEW JERSEY–UNIVERSITY HOSPITAL (310119)**, 150 Bergen Street, Zip 07103–2496; tel. 973/972–4300 **A**1 2 3 5 8 9 10 **F**1 3 4 7 11 15 16 17 18 19 20 22 24 26 28 29 30 31 32 34 35 37 38 39 40 41 43 44 45 46 47 49 50 52 55 56 57 58 59 60 61 64 65 66 67 68 70 71 72 73 74 75 76 77 78 79 80 81 82 84 85 86 87 88 89 90 92 93 94 97 98 100 102 103 107 108 110 111 112 113 114 116 117 119 121 123 124 126 128 130 131 132 133 134 135 139 144 145 146 147 148
Primary Contact: James R. Gonzalez, Acting President and Chief Executive Officer
CFO: Thomas M. Daly, Chief Financial Officer
CMO: Suzanne Atkin, M.D., Chief of Staff and Associate Dean Clinical Affairs
CIO: Richard Tunnell, Director Information Systems Technology and Health Management Information Systems
CHR: Gerard Garcia, Acting Vice President Human Resources
Web address: www.umdnj.edu
**Control:** State–Government, nonfederal **Service:** General Medical and Surgical

**Staffed Beds:** 281 **Admissions:** 17016 **Census:** 245 **Outpatient Visits:** 262802 **Births:** 1228 **Total Expense ($000):** 563588 **Payroll Expense ($000):** 262807 **Personnel:** 3084

**NJ**

## NEWTON—Sussex County

☒ **NEWTON MEDICAL CENTER (310028)**, 175 High Street, Zip 07860–1004; tel. 973/383–2121 **A**1 2 9 10 **F**3 4 5 6 8 9 11 12 13 14 15 17 18 19 20 26 28 29 30 31 32 33 34 35 37 38 39 40 41 44 45 46 47 48 49 50 53 54 55 56 57 58 59 60 61 62 64 65 66 68 69 70 71 73 74 75 76 77 78 79 81 82 83 84 85 86 87 89 91 92 93 94 95 96 97 98 99 100 101 102 103 104 105 106 107 108 110 111 114 118 119 126 129 130 131 132 134 135 143 145 146 147 148 **P**6 **S** Atlantic Health, Morristown, NJ
Primary Contact: Thomas J. Senker, FACHE, President and Chief Executive Officer
COO: Thomas J. Senker, FACHE, President and Chief Executive Officer
CFO: Kevin Lenahan, Director Corporate Accounting, Budgets, Grants and Reimbursements
CMO: David Lazarus, M.D., Medical Director Clinical Affairs
CIO: Linda Reed, Vice President Information Systems and Chief Information Officer
CHR: Andrew L. Kovach, Vice President Human Resources and Chief Administrative Officer
Web address: www.atlantichealth.org/newton/
**Control:** Other not–for–profit (including NFP Corporation) **Service:** General Medical and Surgical

**Staffed Beds:** 148 **Admissions:** 7599 **Census:** 93 **Outpatient Visits:** 92360 **Births:** 544 **Total Expense ($000):** 133664 **Payroll Expense ($000):** 64171 **Personnel:** 886

## NORTH BERGEN—Hudson County

☒ **PALISADES MEDICAL CENTER (310003)**, 7600 River Road, Zip 07047–6217; tel. 201/854–5000 **A**1 3 5 10 **F**11 12 13 15 18 20 28 29 30 34 35 38 40 45 49 56 57 59 68 74 75 77 78 79 81 84 85 86 87 91 92 93 102 104 107 111 115 119 129 130 132 143 146 147 148
Primary Contact: Bruce J. Markowitz, President and Chief Executive Officer
COO: David J. Berkowitz, Vice President and Chief Operating Officer
CFO: John Calandriello, Vice President and Chief Financial Officer
CMO: Suresh Raina, M.D., Vice President Medical Staff and Chief Medical Officer
CIO: Glenn Hunsberger, Director Management Information Systems
CHR: Donna Cahill, Vice President Human Resources
Web address: www.palisadesmedical.org
**Control:** Other not–for–profit (including NFP Corporation) **Service:** General Medical and Surgical

**Staffed Beds:** 180 **Admissions:** 9949 **Census:** 122 **Outpatient Visits:** 83434 **Births:** 1522 **Total Expense ($000):** 135175 **Payroll Expense ($000):** 62273 **Personnel:** 771

## OLD BRIDGE—Middlesex County

**OLD BRIDGE DIVISION** See Raritan Bay Medical Center, Perth Amboy

## PARAMUS—Bergen County

☐ **BERGEN REGIONAL MEDICAL CENTER (310058)**, 230 East Ridgewood Avenue, Zip 07652–4142; tel. 201/967–4000, (Nonreporting) **A**1 10
Primary Contact: Joseph S. Orlando, President
COO: Susan Mendelowitz, Executive Vice President and Chief Operating Officer
CFO: Connie Magdangal, Executive Vice President and Chief Financial Officer
CMO: Robert M. Harris, M.D., President Medical and Dental Staff
CIO: Ronald Li, Vice President Management Information Systems
CHR: Guy Mennonna, Senior Vice President Human Resources
Web address: www.bergenregional.com
**Control:** County–Government, nonfederal **Service:** Psychiatric

**Staffed Beds:** 432

## PASSAIC—Passaic County

☒ **ST. MARY'S HOSPITAL (310006)**, 350 Boulevard, Zip 07055–2840; tel. 973/365–4300, (Nonreporting) **A**1 9 10
Primary Contact: Edward Condit, President and Chief Executive Officer
CFO: Nicholas Lanza, Controller
CMO: Ronald Poblete, M.D., President Medical and Dental Staff
CHR: Cathy Lynch–Kilic, Vice President Human Resources
Web address: www.smh–passaic.org
**Control:** Other not–for–profit (including NFP Corporation) **Service:** General Medical and Surgical

**Staffed Beds:** 269

## PATERSON—Passaic County

★ ◇ **ST. JOSEPH'S REGIONAL MEDICAL CENTER (310019)**, 703 Main Street, Zip 07503–2691; tel. 973/754–2000, (Includes ST. JOSEPH'S CHILDREN'S HOSPITAL, 703 Main Street, Zip 07503–2621; tel. 973/754–2500; ST. JOSEPH'S WAYNE HOSPITAL, 224 Hamburg Turnpike, Wayne, Zip 07470–2100; tel. 973/942–6900; Daniel B. Kline, Administrator), (Total facility includes 151 beds in nursing home–type unit) **A**2 3 5 9 10 12 13 21 **F**3 5 7 8 11 12 13 14 15 17 18 19 20 21 22 23 24 25 26 27 28 29 30 31 32 34 35 37 38 39 40 41 43 44 45 46 47 48 49 50 54 55 56 57 58 59 60 61 62 63 64 65 66 68 70 71 72 73 74 75 76 77 78 79 81 82 83 84 85 86 87 88 89 90 92 93 96 97 98 99 100 101 102 103 104 105 107 108 109 110 111 112 114 115 116 117 118 119 120 121 123 126 129 130 131 132 133 134 135 143 144 145 146 147 148 **P**3 5 6
Primary Contact: William A. McDonald, President and Chief Executive Officer
COO: Gloria A. Kunze, R.N., Vice President Operations
CFO: Jack Robinson, Chief Financial Officer
CMO: James Labagnara, M.D., Vice President Medical Affairs
CIO: James Cavanagh, Chief Information Officer
CHR: John Bruno, Vice President Human Resources
Web address: www.stjosephshealth.org
**Control:** Church–operated, Nongovernment, not–for profit **Service:** General Medical and Surgical

**Staffed Beds:** 700 **Admissions:** 34298 **Census:** 511 **Outpatient Visits:** 350099 **Births:** 3367 **Total Expense ($000):** 688363 **Payroll Expense ($000):** 321087 **Personnel:** 4384

## PEAPACK—Somerset County

☐ **MATHENY MEDICAL AND EDUCATIONAL CENTER (312014)**, (special hospital/med. complex/), 65 Highland Avenue, Zip 07977, Mailing Address: P.O. Box 339, Zip 07977–0339; tel. 908/234–0011 **A**1 5 10 **F**2 29 35 39 64 82 86 87 93 100 130 146 147 148 **P**6
Primary Contact: Steven M. Proctor, President
COO: Christopher King, Director Operations and Administrative Services
CFO: Wayne Guberman, Director Finance
CMO: Gary E. Eddey, M.D., Medical Director
CIO: Ron Daniel, Manager Information Systems
CHR: Nancy Petrillo, Director Human Resources
Web address: www.matheny.org
**Control:** Other not–for–profit (including NFP Corporation) **Service:** Other specialty

**Staffed Beds:** 102 **Admissions:** 7 **Census:** 99 **Outpatient Visits:** 1849 **Births:** 0 **Total Expense ($000):** 45400 **Payroll Expense ($000):** 28421 **Personnel:** 498

## PENNINGTON—Mercer County

☒ **CAPITAL HEALTH MEDICAL CENTER–HOPEWELL (310044)**, 1 Capital Way, Zip 08534–2520; tel. 609/303–4000 **A**1 2 5 6 9 10 **F**3 7 8 11 13 15 18 19 20 22 26 27 29 30 31 32 34 35 39 40 41 44 45 46 47 48 49 50 51 54 55 57 58 59 60 64 65 66 68 69 70 73 74 75 76 77 78 79 81 82 84 85 86 87 89 90 93 94 96 97 102 107 108 109 110 111 114 115 117 118 119 120 121 123 124 126 129 130 132 135 143 144 145 146 147 148 **S** Capital Health, Trenton, NJ
Primary Contact: Al Maghazehe, Ph.D., FACHE, Chief Executive Officer
COO: Larry DiSanto, Executive Vice President and Chief Operating Officer
CFO: Shane Fleming, Chief Financial Officer
CMO: Robert Remstein, D.O., Vice President Medical Affairs
CIO: Eugene Grochala, Vice President Information Systems
CHR: J. Scott Clemmensen, Vice President Human Resources and Leadership Enhancement
Web address: www.capitalhealth.org
**Control:** Other not–for–profit (including NFP Corporation) **Service:** General Medical and Surgical

**Staffed Beds:** 223 **Admissions:** 12797 **Census:** 139 **Outpatient Visits:** 112535 **Births:** 1953 **Personnel:** 1273

## PERTH AMBOY—Middlesex County

☐ **CARE ONE AT RARITAN BAY MEDICAL CENTER (312018)**, 530 New Brunswick Avenue, Zip 08861–3654; tel. 732/324–6090, (Nonreporting) **A**1 10
Primary Contact: Sharon Bready, R.N., Chief Executive Officer
CFO: Richard Burguillos, Chief Financial Officer
Web address: www.care–one.com
**Control:** Corporation, Investor–owned, for–profit **Service:** Long–Term Acute Care hospital

**Staffed Beds:** 30

✠ **RARITAN BAY MEDICAL CENTER (310039)**, 530 New Brunswick Avenue, Zip 08861–3654; tel. 732/442–3700, (Includes OLD BRIDGE DIVISION, One Hospital Plaza, Old Bridge, Zip 08857; tel. 732/360–1000; PERTH AMBOY DIVISION, 530 New Brunswick Avenue, Zip 08861–3685; tel. 732/442–3700) **A**1 3 5 9 10 **F**5 7 9 11 12 13 15 18 20 22 26 29 30 31 34 35 36 38 39 40 45 46 49 50 51 54 56 57 59 60 61 64 65 66 68 70 74 75 76 77 78 79 81 82 87 89 92 93 94 97 98 100 101 102 103 104 107 108 110 111 114 115 117 119 129 130 132 143 146 147 148 **P**6
Primary Contact: Michael R. D'Agnes, FACHE, President and Chief Executive Officer
COO: Vincent Costantino, Vice President Operations and Human Resources
CFO: Thomas Shanahan, Chief Financial Officer and Senior Vice President
CMO: Michael Ciencewicki, M.D., Vice President Medical Affairs
CHR: Vincent Costantino, Vice President Operations and Human Resources
Web address: www.rbmc.org
**Control:** Other not–for–profit (including NFP Corporation) **Service:** General Medical and Surgical

**Staffed Beds:** 277 **Admissions:** 13439 **Census:** 182 **Outpatient Visits:** 150440 **Births:** 1264 **Total Expense ($000):** 228080 **Payroll Expense ($000):** 103522 **Personnel:** 1729

## PHILLIPSBURG—Warren County

✠ **ST. LUKE'S HOSPITAL – WARREN CAMPUS (310060)**, 185 Roseberry Street, Zip 08865–1690; tel. 908/859–6700 **A**1 2 3 5 9 10 13 **F**2 3 8 11 15 18 20 28 29 30 31 34 35 39 40 45 48 49 53 56 59 61 64 65 66 68 70 74 75 77 78 79 81 82 85 86 87 91 92 93 97 98 100 102 103 104 106 107 108 110 111 114 118 119 124 129 130 131 132 134 146 147 148 **S** St. Luke's University Health Network, Bethlehem, PA
Primary Contact: Scott R. Wolfe, CPA, President
COO: Alice Wilson, FACHE, Vice President Administration
CFO: Carl M. Alberto, Vice President Finance and Chief Financial Officer
CMO: Edward Gilkey, M.D., Vice President Medical Affairs
CIO: Debbie Bowlby, Director Information Systems
CHR: Morgan G. Mahl, Director Human Resources
CNO: Gail Newton, R.N., Vice President Patient Care Services
Web address: www.warrenhospital.org
**Control:** Other not–for–profit (including NFP Corporation) **Service:** General Medical and Surgical

**Staffed Beds:** 140 **Admissions:** 5847 **Census:** 74 **Outpatient Visits:** 109864 **Births:** 0 **Total Expense ($000):** 111660 **Payroll Expense ($000):** 46673 **Personnel:** 975

## PISCATAWAY—Middlesex County

**UNIVERSITY OF MEDICINE AND DENTISTRY OF NEW JERSEY, UNIVERSITY BEHAVIORAL HEALTHCARE (314011)**, 671 Hoes Lane, Zip 08854–8021, Mailing Address: P.O. Box 1392, Zip 08855–1392; tel. 732/235–5900 **A**3 5 9 10 **F**87 98 99 101 102 103 104 105 106 **P**6
Primary Contact: Christopher O. Kosseff, President and Chief Executive Officer
COO: Susan Furrer, PsyD, Acting Chief Operating Officer and Executive Director Behavioral Research and Training Institute
CFO: Alan Weinkrantz, Chief Financial Officer
CMO: Theresa Miskimen, M.D., Vice President Medical Services
CIO: Leon Garfinkel, Director Information Services
Web address: www.umdnj.edu
**Control:** State–Government, nonfederal **Service:** Psychiatric

**Staffed Beds:** 48 **Admissions:** 1080 **Census:** 38 **Outpatient Visits:** 76682 **Births:** 0 **Personnel:** 72

## PLAINSBORO—Middlesex County

**UNIVERSITY MEDICAL CENTER AT PRINCETON** See University Medical Center of Princeton at Plainsboro

✠ **UNIVERSITY MEDICAL CENTER OF PRINCETON AT PLAINSBORO (310010)**, One Plainsboro Road, Zip 08536–1913; tel. 609/853–7100, (Includes ACUTE GENERAL HOSPITAL, MERWICK UNIT–EXTENDED CARE AND REHABILITATION, PRINCETON HOUSE UNIT–COMMUNITY MENTAL HEALTH AND SUBSTANCE ABUSE ) **A**1 2 3 5 9 10 **F**3 4 5 8 11 12 13 14 15 17 18 19 20 22 26 28 29 30 31 32 34 35 36 38 39 40 41 45 46 49 50 51 53 54 55 56 57 58 59 60 62 63 64 65 66 68 70 73 74 75 76 77 78 79 81 82 85 86 87 89 90 91 92 93 96 97 98 99 100 101 102 103 104 105 107 108 110 111 114 115 118 119 120 121 124 126 129 130 132 134 135 143 146 147 148 **P**6
Primary Contact: Mark T. Jones, President
CFO: Bruce Traub, Chief Financial Officer
CMO: Linda Sieglen, M.D., Vice President Medical Affairs
CIO: Anne Searle, Chief Information Officer
CHR: Marcia M. Telthorster, Vice President Human Resources
CNO: Susan G. Lorenz, R.N., Vice President, Patient Care Services & Chief Nursing Officer
Web address: www.princetonhcs.org
**Control:** Other not–for–profit (including NFP Corporation) **Service:** General Medical and Surgical

**Staffed Beds:** 338 **Admissions:** 16679 **Census:** 248 **Outpatient Visits:** 795528 **Total Expense ($000):** 354194 **Payroll Expense ($000):** 136218 **Personnel:** 2761

## POMONA—Atlantic County

**ATLANTICARE REGIONAL MEDICAL CENTER–MAINLAND DIVISION** See AtlantiCare Regional Medical Center, Atlantic City

✠ △ **BACHARACH INSTITUTE FOR REHABILITATION (313030)**, 61 West Jimmie Leeds Road, Zip 08240–9102, Mailing Address: P.O. Box 723, Zip 08240–0723; tel. 609/652–7000, (Nonreporting) **A**1 7 10
Primary Contact: Richard J. Kathrins, Ph.D, President and Chief Executive Officer
CFO: Jeanne Vuksta, Chief Financial Officer
CMO: Craig Anmuth, M.D., Medical Director
CIO: Jeff Rees, Director Information Systems
CHR: Diane Croshaw, Vice President Human Resources
Web address: www.bacharach.org
**Control:** Other not–for–profit (including NFP Corporation) **Service:** Rehabilitation

**Staffed Beds:** 80

## POMPTON PLAINS—Morris County

✠ **CHILTON HOSPITAL (310017)**, 97 West Parkway, Zip 07444–1696; tel. 973/831–5000 **A**1 2 9 10 **F**3 7 11 12 13 15 17 18 19 20 22 28 29 30 31 32 34 35 38 40 41 44 45 47 49 50 54 57 59 64 65 66 70 73 74 75 76 77 78 79 81 82 84 85 86 87 89 93 97 102 107 108 109 110 111 114 115 118 119 121 123 126 129 130 131 132 135 146 147 148 **P**6
Primary Contact: Deborah Zastocki, R.N., FACHE, FACHE, President and Chief Executive Officer
COO: Thomas Scott, Chief Operating Officer
CFO: Michael Richetti, Chief Financial Officer
CMO: Charles Ross, M.D., Vice President Medical Affairs
CIO: Karen S. Smith, Director Information Services
CHR: Julia McGovern, Vice President Human Resources
Web address: www.chiltonmemorial.org
**Control:** Other not for profit (including NFP Corporation) **Service:** General Medical and Surgical

**Staffed Beds:** 260 **Admissions:** 9723 **Census:** 126 **Outpatient Visits:** 160755 **Births:** 894 **Total Expense ($000):** 164282 **Payroll Expense ($000):** 74080 **Personnel:** 1093

## RAHWAY—Union County

**KINDRED HOSPITAL NEW JERSEY – RAHWAY** See Kindred Hospital–New Jersey Morris County, Dover

✠ **ROBERT WOOD JOHNSON UNIVERSITY HOSPITAL RAHWAY (310024)**, 865 Stone Street, Zip 07065–2797; tel. 732/381–4200, (Total facility includes 24 beds in nursing home–type unit) **A**1 10 **F**3 11 15 17 20 29 30 31 34 35 38 40 46 47 49 50 53 56 57 59 64 65 68 70 74 75 77 78 79 81 82 86 87 93 97 100 101 102 107 108 111 117 118 119 128 129 130 132 134 143 144 146 147 148 **S** Robert Wood Johnson Health System & Network, New Brunswick, NJ
Primary Contact: Kirk C. Tice, President and Chief Executive Officer
CFO: Peter Bihuniak, Vice President Finance
CMO: Radha Vinnakota, M.D., President Medical Staff
CIO: Denine Izzi, Site Manager Information Systems
CHR: Kathryn Tarantino, Vice President Administration
CNO: Lynn Kearney, VP Patient Services & Chief Nursing Officer
Web address: www.rwjuhr.com
**Control:** Other not–for–profit (including NFP Corporation) **Service:** General Medical and Surgical

**Staffed Beds:** 147 **Admissions:** 6597 **Census:** 99 **Outpatient Visits:** 53657 **Births:** 0 **Total Expense ($000):** 99227 **Payroll Expense ($000):** 40970 **Personnel:** 706

**NJ**

---

**Hospital, Medicare Provider Number, Address, Telephone, Approval, Facility, and Physician Codes, Health Care System**

★ American Hospital Association (AHA) membership
□ The Joint Commission accreditation
◇ DNV Healthcare Inc. accreditation
○ Healthcare Facilities Accreditation Program
△ Commission on Accreditation of Rehabilitation Facilities (CARF) accreditation

**RED BANK—Monmouth County**

☒ △ **RIVERVIEW MEDICAL CENTER (310034)**, 1 Riverview Plaza, Zip 07701–1864; tel. 732/741–2700 **A**1 2 7 9 10 **F**3 5 11 13 15 18 20 22 28 29 30 31 38 40 41 44 45 46 47 51 55 56 59 60 61 63 64 65 66 68 70 73 74 75 76 77 78 79 80 81 82 83 84 85 86 87 90 92 93 96 97 98 99 100 101 102 103 104 105 107 108 110 111 114 115 117 119 120 121 123 124 129 130 132 135 144 146 147 148 **P**7 **S** Meridian Health, Wall Township, NJ
Primary Contact: Timothy J. Hogan, FACHE, Regional President
COO: Kelly O'Brien, Vice President Operations
CFO: John Gantner, Executive Vice President Finance
CMO: Joseph Reichman, M.D., Vice President Medical Affairs and Clinical Effectiveness
CIO: Rebecca Weber, Senior Vice President Information Technology
Web address: www.riverviewmedicalcenter.com
**Control:** Other not-for-profit (including NFP Corporation) **Service:** General Medical and Surgical

Staffed Beds: 270 Admissions: 13426 Census: 197 Outpatient Visits: 139476 Births: 1377 Total Expense ($000): 218270 Payroll Expense ($000): 96026 Personnel: 1054

**RIDGEWOOD—Bergen County**

☒ **VALLEY HOSPITAL (310012)**, 223 North Van Dien Avenue, Zip 07450–2726; tel. 201/447–8000 **A**1 2 5 9 10 **F**3 8 11 12 13 15 17 18 19 20 22 24 26 28 29 30 31 32 34 35 36 37 38 40 41 45 46 47 48 49 50 51 52 53 54 55 56 57 58 59 60 61 64 65 66 68 69 70 72 73 74 75 76 77 78 79 80 81 82 84 85 86 87 88 89 91 92 93 94 96 97 100 101 102 103 107 108 109 110 111 112 114 115 116 118 119 120 121 123 124 126 129 130 131 132 134 135 143 145 146 147 148 **P**6
Primary Contact: Audrey Meyers, FACHE, President and Chief Executive Officer
COO: Peter Diestel, Senior Vice President and Chief Operating Officer
CFO: Richard Keenan, Senior Vice President Finance and Chief Financial Officer
CMO: Mitchell Rubinstein, M.D., Vice President Medical Affairs
CIO: Eric R. Carey, Vice President Information Systems and Chief Information Officer
CHR: Russell H. Showers, Vice President Human Resources
CNO: Ann Marie Leichman, R.N., Vice President Patient Care Services and Chief Nursing Officer
Web address: www.valleyhealth.com
**Control:** Other not-for-profit (including NFP Corporation) **Service:** General Medical and Surgical

Staffed Beds: 446 Admissions: 30259 Census: 359 Outpatient Visits: 297899 Births: 3146 Total Expense ($000): 509160 Payroll Expense ($000): 246486 Personnel: 3974

**ROCHELLE PARK—Bergen County**

☒ **SELECT SPECIALTY HOSPITAL–NORTHEAST NEW JERSEY (312019)**, 96 Parkway, Zip 07662–4200; tel. 201/221–2358, (Nonreporting) **A**1 10 **S** Select Medical Corporation, Mechanicsburg, PA
Primary Contact: Barbara E. Hannan, MS, R.N., Chief Executive Officer
Web address: www.selectspecialtyhospitals.com/company/locations/northeastnewjersey.aspx
**Control:** Corporation, Investor–owned, for–profit **Service:** Long–Term Acute Care hospital

Staffed Beds: 59

**SADDLE BROOK—Bergen County**

**KESSLER INSTITUTE FOR REHABILITATION** See Kessler Institute for Rehabilitation, West Orange

**SALEM—Salem County**

☒ **MEMORIAL HOSPITAL OF SALEM COUNTY (310091)**, 310 Woodstown Road, Zip 08079–2080; tel. 856/935–1000, (Nonreporting) **A**1 9 10 **S** Community Health Systems, Inc., Franklin, TN
Primary Contact: Richard Grogan, Chief Executive Officer
CFO: Donald Bevers, Chief Financial Officer
CIO: Brian McCarthy, Director Information Systems
Web address: www.salemhospitalnj.org
**Control:** Corporation, Investor–owned, for–profit **Service:** General Medical and Surgical

Staffed Beds: 110

**SECAUCUS—Hudson County**

**LIBERTYHEALTH–MEADOWLANDS HOSPITAL MEDICAL CENTER** See Meadowlands Hospital Medical Center

☐ ◇ **MEADOWLANDS HOSPITAL MEDICAL CENTER (310118)**, 55 Meadowlands Parkway, Zip 07094–2977; tel. 201/392–3100 **A**1 9 10 21 **F**17 18 29 30 31 34 35 40 45 46 47 48 49 59 64 65 67 70 73 74 76 78 79 81 82 85 87 89 90 107 110 111 113 119 129 130 143 146 147 148 **P**7
Primary Contact: Lynn McVey, President and Chief Executive Officer
COO: Martin W. Baicker, Senior Vice President and Administrator
CFO: Donald Parseghian, Chief Financial Officer
CMO: Kenneth Garay, M.D., Chief Medical Officer
CIO: James Yost, Director Management Information Systems
CHR: Mary Cataudella, Corporate Director Human Resources
Web address: www.meadowlandshospital.org
**Control:** Corporation, Investor–owned, for–profit **Service:** General Medical and Surgical

Staffed Beds: 230 Admissions: 3948 Census: 53 Total Expense ($000): 82768 Payroll Expense ($000): 42120 Personnel: 367

**SOMERS POINT—Atlantic County**

☒ **SHORE MEDICAL CENTER (310047)**, 1 East New York Avenue, Zip 08244–2340; tel. 609/653–3500 **A**1 2 9 10 **F**3 11 13 15 17 18 20 22 28 29 30 31 34 35 36 37 40 44 45 49 50 54 57 59 60 61 64 66 68 70 73 74 75 76 77 78 79 81 82 84 85 86 87 89 92 93 107 108 110 111 114 118 119 120 121 123 129 130 132 135 143 146 147 148
Primary Contact: Ronald W. Johnson, FACHE, President and Chief Executive Officer
CFO: James T. Foley, CPA, Vice President and Chief Financial Officer
CMO: Peter R. Jungblut, M.D., Vice President Medical Affairs and Chief Medical Officer
CMO: Jeanne M. Rowe, M.D., Chief Medical Officer
CIO: Fred Banner, Chief Information Officer
CHR: Alan Beatty, Vice President Human Resources
CNO: Joan Gavin, R.N., Chief Nursing Officer/Vice President, Patient Services
Web address: www.shoremedicalcenter.org
**Control:** Other not-for-profit (including NFP Corporation) **Service:** General Medical and Surgical

Staffed Beds: 198 Admissions: 10697 Census: 123 Outpatient Visits: 104789 Births: 1047 Total Expense ($000): 214043 Payroll Expense ($000): 78842 Personnel: 1669

**SOMERVILLE—Somerset County**

☒ **SOMERSET MEDICAL CENTER (310048)**, 110 Rehill Avenue, Zip 08876–2598; tel. 908/685–2200, (Nonreporting) **A**1 2 3 5 9 10
Primary Contact: Kenneth Bateman, CPA, President and Chief Executive Officer
COO: Maureen Schneider, MSN, Senior Vice President Clinical Program Development and Chief Operating Officer
CFO: James De Rosa, Vice President Finance
CMO: Richard Paris, M.D., Chief Medical Officer
CIO: Dave Dyer, Vice President and Chief Information Officer
CHR: Mary Ann Bross, Vice President Human Resources
Web address: www.smchealthwise.com
**Control:** State–Government, nonfederal **Service:** General Medical and Surgical

Staffed Beds: 250

**STRATFORD—Camden County**

**KENNEDY UNIVERSITY HOSPITAL – STRATFORD** See Kennedy Health System, Cherry Hill

**SUMMIT—Union County**

☒ **OVERLOOK MEDICAL CENTER (310051)**, 99 Beauvoir Avenue, Zip 07901–3533; tel. 908/522–2000 **A**1 2 3 5 8 9 10 13 **F**3 5 6 7 8 9 11 12 13 14 15 17 18 19 20 22 28 29 30 31 32 34 35 36 37 38 39 40 41 42 44 45 46 47 48 49 50 51 52 53 54 55 56 57 58 59 60 61 62 63 64 65 66 68 69 70 71 72 73 74 75 76 77 78 79 81 82 83 84 85 86 87 89 92 93 94 96 97 98 99 100 101 102 103 104 105 107 108 109 110 111 113 114 115 116 117 118 119 120 121 123 124 126 129 130 131 132 134 135 143 144 145 146 147 148 **P**3 5 6 **S** Atlantic Health, Morristown, NJ
Primary Contact: Alan R. Lieber, President
CFO: Kevin Lenahan, Vice President Finance and Chief Financial Officer
CMO: Norman Luka, M.D., Medical Director Clinical Affairs
CIO: Linda Reed, Vice President and Chief Information Officer
CHR: Andrew L. Kovach, Vice President Human Resources and Chief Administrative Officer
CNO: Mary Patricia Sullivan, R.N., Chief Nursing Officer
Web address: www.atlantichealth.org/Overlook
**Control:** Other not-for-profit (including NFP Corporation) **Service:** General Medical and Surgical

Staffed Beds: 428 Admissions: 21437 Census: 288 Outpatient Visits: 213565 Births: 2397 Total Expense ($000): 485285 Payroll Expense ($000): 237480 Personnel: 3263

☐ **SUMMIT OAKS HOSPITAL (314001)**, 19 Prospect Street, Zip 07901–2530; tel. 908/522–7000, (Nonreporting) **A**1 9 10 **S** Universal Health Services, Inc., King of Prussia, PA
Primary Contact: James P. Gallagher, Chief Executive Officer
Web address: www.summitoakshospital.com/
**Control:** Corporation, Investor–owned, for–profit **Service:** Psychiatric

Staffed Beds: 90

*Many Facility Codes have changed. Please refer to the AHA Guide Code Chart.* © 2013 AHA Guide

NJ

**SUSSEX—Sussex County**

**SAINT CLARE'S HOSPITAL/SUSSEX** See Saint Clare's Health System, Denville

**TEANECK—Bergen County**

**HOLY NAME HOSPITAL** See Holy Name Medical Center

⊞ **HOLY NAME MEDICAL CENTER (310008)**, 718 Teaneck Road,
Zip 07666–4281; tel. 201/833–3000 **A**1 2 5 6 9 10 **F**2 3 7 11 12 13 15 18
19 20 22 28 29 30 31 32 34 35 36 37 39 40 44 45 46 47 49 50 51 53 54
55 56 57 58 59 60 62 63 64 65 66 68 70 73 74 75 76 77 78 79 81 82 83
84 85 86 87 89 91 93 94 97 98 100 102 103 107 108 110 111 114 115
116 117 118 119 120 121 123 124 126 129 130 131 132 133 135 143 144
146 147 148 **P**4 5
Primary Contact: Michael Maron, President and Chief Executive Officer
CFO: Joseph M. Lemaire, Executive Vice President and Chief Financial Officer
CMO: Adam D. Jarrett, M.D., Executive Vice President and Chief Medical Officer
CIO: Michael Skvarenina, Assistant Vice President Information Systems
CHR: April Rodgers, Vice President, Human Resources
CNO: Sheryl A. Slonim, Executive Vice President and Chief Nursing Officer
Web address: www.holyname.org
**Control:** Other not–for–profit (including NFP Corporation) **Service:** General
Medical and Surgical

**Staffed Beds:** 318 **Admissions:** 20118 **Census:** 213 **Outpatient Visits:**
360242 **Births:** 1513 **Total Expense ($000):** 287925 **Payroll Expense
($000):** 123555 **Personnel:** 1892

**TINTON FALLS—Monmouth County**

⊞ **REHABILITATION HOSPITAL OF TINTON FALLS (313035)**, 2 Centre Plaza,
Zip 07724–9744; tel. 732/460–5320 **A**1 10 **F**29 64 68 74 75 82 90 93 94 95
96 100 119 148 **S** HEALTHSOUTH Corporation, Birmingham, AL
Primary Contact: Linda A. Savino, MS, Chief Executive Officer
CFO: Lynne Traister, Controller
CMO: Todd Cooperman, M.D., Medical Director
CHR: Anita Saum, Director Human Resources
Web address: www.rehabnj.com
**Control:** Corporation, Investor–owned, for–profit **Service:** Rehabilitation

**Staffed Beds:** 60 **Admissions:** 1307 **Census:** 47 **Outpatient Visits:** 8127
**Births:** 0 **Total Expense ($000):** 16122 **Payroll Expense ($000):** 9948
**Personnel:** 172

**TOMS RIVER—Ocean County**

⊞ **BARNABAS HEALTH BEHAVIORAL HEALTH CENTER (314022)**, (Formerly
Saint Barnabas Behavioral Health Center), 1691 Highway 9, Zip 08755–1245;
tel. 732/914–1688, (Nonreporting) **A**1 9 10 **S** Barnabas Health, West Orange, NJ
Primary Contact: Joe Hicks, President and Chief Executive Officer
Web address: www.barnabashealth.org/hospitals/psychiatric/index.html
**Control:** Other not–for–profit (including NFP Corporation) **Service:** Psychiatric

**Staffed Beds:** 40

⊞ **COMMUNITY MEDICAL CENTER (310041)**, 99 Route 37 West,
Zip 08755–6423; tel. 732/557–8051 **A**1 2 9 10 **F**3 11 12 13 15 17 18 20 22
28 29 30 31 32 34 35 36 38 40 43 44 47 48 49 50 53 54 55 56 57 58 59
60 61 62 63 64 68 69 70 73 74 75 76 77 78 79 81 83 84 85 86 87 89 92
93 96 100 102 107 108 109 110 111 114 115 118 119 120 121 123 124
126 128 129 130 132 133 134 135 143 146 147 148 **P**6 **S** Barnabas Health,
West Orange, NJ
Primary Contact: Stephanie L. Bloom, FACHE, President and Chief Executive
Officer
COO: Frank Gelormini, Chief Operating Officer
CFO: Mark Ostrander, Vice President Financial Services
CMO: John Crisanti, M.D., Vice President Medical Affairs
CIO: Shawn Fitzsimmons, Director Information Technology Services
CHR: Mary Deno, Vice President Human Resources
CNO: Fern Papalia, Vice President, Patient Care Services
Web address: www.barnabashealth.org/hospitals/community_medical/index.html
**Control:** Other not–for–profit (including NFP Corporation) **Service:** General
Medical and Surgical

**Staffed Beds:** 533 **Admissions:** 26682 **Census:** 319 **Outpatient Visits:**
351080 **Births:** 1534 **Total Expense ($000):** 363495 **Payroll Expense
($000):** 149146 **Personnel:** 2385

⊞ **HEALTHSOUTH REHABILITATION HOSPITAL OF TOMS RIVER (313029)**, 14
Hospital Drive, Zip 08755–6470; tel. 732/244–3100 **A**1 10 **F**28 29 64 74 79
90 93 132 **S** HEALTHSOUTH Corporation, Birmingham, AL
Primary Contact: Patricia Ostaszewski, MS, Chief Executive Officer
COO: Patricia Ostaszewski, MS, Chief Executive Officer
CFO: Janet Turso, Controller
CMO: Joseph Stillo, M.D., Medical Director
CIO: Coleen Rossi, Director Quality Services
CHR: Lori Munyan, Director, Human Resources
CNO: Susan Castor, Chief Nursing Officer
Web address: www.rehabnj.com/tomsriver
**Control:** Corporation, Investor–owned, for–profit **Service:** Rehabilitation

**Staffed Beds:** 92 **Admissions:** 3180 **Census:** 97 **Outpatient Visits:** 13042
**Births:** 0 **Total Expense ($000):** 32482 **Payroll Expense ($000):** 19450
**Personnel:** 319

**SAINT BARNABAS BEHAVIORAL HEALTH CENTER** See Barnabas Health
Behavioral Health Center

**TRENTON—Mercer County**

⊞ **CAPITAL HEALTH REGIONAL MEDICAL CENTER (310092)**, 750 Brunswick
Avenue, Zip 08638–4143; tel. 609/394–6000 **A**1 3 5 6 9 10 **F**3 7 11 13 15 18
19 26 27 29 30 31 34 35 39 40 42 43 44 45 46 47 48 50 51 54 57 58 59
60 64 65 66 68 70 72 73 74 75 76 77 78 79 80 81 82 84 85 87 89 90 93
94 96 97 98 99 100 101 102 105 107 108 109 111 114 115 118 119 129
130 132 135 143 144 145 146 147 148 **S** Capital Health, Trenton, NJ
Primary Contact: Al Maghazehe, Ph.D., FACHE, Chief Executive Officer
COO: Larry DiSanto, Executive Vice President and Chief Operating Officer
CFO: Shane Fleming, Chief Financial Officer
CMO: Robert Remstein, D.O., Vice President Medical Affairs
CIO: Eugene Grochala, Vice President Information Systems
CHR: J. Scott Clemmensen, Vice President Human Resources and Leadership
Enhancement
CNO: Eileen M. Horton, Vice President, Patient Services/Chief Nursing Officer
Web address: www.capitalhealth.org
**Control:** Other not–for–profit (including NFP Corporation) **Service:** General
Medical and Surgical

**Staffed Beds:** 271 **Admissions:** 11990 **Census:** 170 **Outpatient Visits:**
185718 **Births:** 404 **Personnel:** 1757

⊞ **ST. FRANCIS MEDICAL CENTER (310021)**, 601 Hamilton Avenue,
Zip 08629–1986; tel. 609/599–5000 **A**1 2 6 9 10 **F**2 3 11 12 15 17 18 20 22
24 26 29 30 31 34 35 40 45 46 48 49 50 56 57 58 59 60 61 62 64 65 66
68 69 70 71 74 75 78 79 81 82 84 85 86 87 92 93 97 98 99 100 101 102
103 104 105 107 108 110 111 114 115 118 119 121 123 124 129 130 132
135 143 144 146 147 148 **P**5 6 **S** Catholic Health East, Newtown Square, PA
Primary Contact: Gerard J. Jablonowski, President and Chief Executive Officer
CFO: Mark Kelly, Vice President Finance
CMO: C. James Romano, M.D., President Medical Staff
CIO: Richard Dowgun, Chief Information Officer
CHR: Laura James, Director Human Resources
Web address: www.stfrancismedical.com
**Control:** Church–operated, Nongovernment, not–for profit **Service:** General
Medical and Surgical

**Staffed Beds:** 163 **Admissions:** 6195 **Census:** 93 **Outpatient Visits:** 95703
**Births:** 0 **Total Expense ($000):** 129191 **Payroll Expense ($000):** 45762
**Personnel:** 955

☐ **TRENTON PSYCHIATRIC HOSPITAL (314013)**, Route 29 and Sullivan Way,
Zip 08628–3425, Mailing Address: P.O. Box 7500, West Trenton,
Zip 08628–0500; tel. 609/633–1500, (Nonreporting) **A**1 10 **S** Division of Mental
Health and Addiction Services, Department of Human Services, State of New
Jersey, Trenton, NJ
Primary Contact: Teresa A. McQuaide, Chief Executive Officer
COO: Christopher Morrison, Deputy Chief Executive Officer
CFO: Joseph Canale, Business Manager
CMO: Lawrence Rossi, M.D., Clinical Director
CIO: Scott Eustace, Director Health Information Technology
CHR: Marybeth Longo, Manager Human Resources
CNO: Colleen Birkhofer, Chief Nursing Officer
Web address: www.state.nj.us/humanservices/dmhs/oshm/tph/
**Control:** State–Government, nonfederal **Service:** Psychiatric

**Staffed Beds:** 392

**TURNERSVILLE—Camden County**

**KENNEDY UNIVERSITY HOSPITAL – WASHINGTON TOWNSHIP** See Kennedy
Health System, Cherry Hill

NJ

---

**Hospital, Medicare Provider Number, Address, Telephone, Approval, Facility, and Physician Codes, Health Care System**

★ American Hospital Association (AHA) membership
☐ The Joint Commission accreditation ◇ DNV Healthcare Inc. accreditation

○ Healthcare Facilities Accreditation Program
△ Commission on Accreditation of Rehabilitation Facilities (CARF) accreditation

## VINELAND—Cumberland County

✠ **HEALTHSOUTH REHABILITATION HOSPITAL OF VINELAND (313036)**, 1237 West Sherman Avenue, Zip 08360–6920; tel. 856/696–7100 **A**1 10 **F**29 34 59 90 94 103 130 132 135 146 148 **S** HEALTHSOUTH Corporation, Birmingham, AL
Primary Contact: Tammy Feuer, Chief Executive Officer
CMO: Eugenio Rocksmith, M.D., Medical Director
CHR: Dawn Pearson, Director Human Resources
Web address: www.healthsouthvineland.com
**Control:** Corporation, Investor–owned, for–profit **Service:** Rehabilitation

> **Staffed Beds:** 41 **Admissions:** 964 **Census:** 36 **Outpatient Visits:** 0 **Births:** 0 **Total Expense ($000):** 11772 **Payroll Expense ($000):** 6769 **Personnel:** 127

★ ◇ **INSPIRA MEDICAL CENTER–VINELAND (310032)**, (Formerly South Jersey Healthcare – Regional Medical Center), 1505 West Sherman Avenue, Zip 08360–6912; tel. 856/641–8000, (Includes BRIDGETON HEALTH CENTER, 333 Irving Avenue, Bridgeton, Zip 08302–2100; tel. 856/575–4500) **A**2 9 10 21 **F**3 8 11 12 13 15 17 18 20 28 29 30 34 35 37 38 40 42 44 49 50 54 57 59 60 64 68 70 72 73 74 75 76 77 78 79 81 82 85 86 87 89 93 98 99 100 101 102 103 104 105 107 108 110 111 114 115 118 119 120 121 123 126 130 131 132 134 144 146 147 148 **P**6 **S** Inspira Health Network, Vineland, NJ
Primary Contact: Chester B. Kaletkowski, President and Chief Executive Officer
COO: Elizabeth Sheridan, Chief Operating Officer
CFO: John A. DiAngelo, Senior Vice President Finance and Chief Financial Officer
CMO: Steven C. Linn, M.D., Chief Medical Officer
CIO: Thomas Pacek, Vice President Information Systems and Chief Information Officer
CHR: Erich Florentine, Chief People Officer
Web address: www.sjhealthcare.net
**Control:** Other not–for–profit (including NFP Corporation) **Service:** General Medical and Surgical

> **Staffed Beds:** 331 **Admissions:** 17962 **Census:** 233 **Outpatient Visits:** 309878 **Births:** 2016 **Total Expense ($000):** 321725 **Payroll Expense ($000):** 135147 **Personnel:** 1527

## VOORHEES—Camden County

★ **VIRTUA VOORHEES (310022)**, 100 Bowman Drive, Zip 08043–9612; tel. 856/325–3000, (Includes VOORHEES PEDIATRIC FACILITY, 1304 Laurel Oak Road, Zip 08043–4310; tel. 888/873–5437) **A**3 5 10 **F**3 11 13 29 30 31 34 35 40 41 45 46 47 48 49 50 55 58 59 64 66 68 70 72 73 74 75 76 78 79 81 82 86 87 88 89 90 92 93 107 108 111 115 116 117 119 126 129 130 143 145 146 147 **S** Virtua Health, Marlton, NJ
Primary Contact: Michael S. Kotzen, Vice President and Chief Operating Officer
COO: Michael S. Kotzen, Vice President and Chief Operating Officer
CFO: Robert Rosvold, Director Finance
CMO: James P. Dwyer, D.O., Executive Vice President and Chief Medical Officer
CIO: Alfred Campanella, Chief Information Officer
Web address: www.virtua.org
**Control:** Other not–for–profit (including NFP Corporation) **Service:** General Medical and Surgical

> **Staffed Beds:** 398 **Admissions:** 21029 **Census:** 248 **Outpatient Visits:** 221889 **Births:** 4774 **Total Expense ($000):** 357660 **Payroll Expense ($000):** 118014 **Personnel:** 1630

## WAYNE—Passaic County

**KINDRED HOSPITAL NEW JERSEY – WAYNE** See Kindred Hospital–New Jersey Morris County, Dover

## WEST ORANGE—Essex County

✠ △ **KESSLER INSTITUTE FOR REHABILITATION (313025)**, 1199 Pleasant Valley Way, Zip 07052–1424; tel. 973/731–3600, (Includes KESSLER INSTITUTE FOR REHABILITATION, 201 Pleasant Hill Road, Chester, Zip 07930–2141; tel. 973/252–6300; Sue Kida, Chief Executive Officer; KESSLER INSTITUTE FOR REHABILITATION, 300 Market Street, Saddle Brook, Zip 07663–5309; tel. 201/368–6000; Philip J. Driscoll, Jr., Chief Executive Officer; KESSLER INSTITUTE FOR REHABILITATION, 1199 Pleasant Valley Way, tel. 973/731–3600; Bonnie Evans, Chief Executive Officer) **A**1 3 5 7 10 **F**29 54 64 90 91 92 93 94 95 96 **S** Select Medical Corporation, Mechanicsburg, PA
Primary Contact: Robert Brehm, Division President
CMO: Bruce M. Gans, M.D., Executive Vice President and Chief Medical Officer
CHR: Ken Caldera, Director Human Resources
Web address: www.kessler–rehab.com
**Control:** Corporation, Investor–owned, for–profit **Service:** Rehabilitation

> **Staffed Beds:** 336 **Admissions:** 6869 **Census:** 300 **Outpatient Visits:** 115191 **Births:** 0 **Personnel:** 725

**KESSLER INSTITUTE FOR REHABILITATION** See Kessler Institute for Rehabilitation

## WESTAMPTON—Burlington County

☐ **HAMPTON BEHAVIORAL HEALTH CENTER (314021)**, 650 Rancocas Road, Zip 08060–5613; tel. 609/267–7000 **A**1 9 10 **F**35 98 99 100 102 103 104 105 130 132 143 **P**6 **S** Universal Health Services, Inc., King of Prussia, PA
Primary Contact: Craig Hilton, Chief Executive Officer
COO: Joanne Aiello, Chief Operating Officer
CFO: Guy DiStefano, Chief Financial Officer
CMO: Charles Trigiani, D.O., Medical Director
CHR: Polly Costantini, Director Human Resources
Web address: www.hamptonhospital.com
**Control:** Corporation, Investor–owned, for–profit **Service:** Psychiatric

> **Staffed Beds:** 110 **Admissions:** 2820 **Census:** 100 **Outpatient Visits:** 15119 **Births:** 0 **Total Expense ($000):** 20299 **Payroll Expense ($000):** 13456 **Personnel:** 236

## WESTWOOD—Bergen County

★ **HACKENSACK UNIVERSITY MEDICAL CENTER AT PASCACK VALLEY (310037)**, (Formerly Pascack Valley Hospital), 250 Old Hook Road, Zip 07675–3123; tel. 201/880–2700, (Nonreporting) **S** LHP Hospital Group, Plano, TX
Primary Contact: Chad Melton, Chief Executive Officer
CFO: Anthony M. Esposito, Jr., CPA, Chief Financial Officer
CNO: Laura Cima, R.N., Chief Nursing Officer
Web address: www.hackensackumcpv.com/
**Control:** Partnership, Investor–owned, for–profit **Service:** General Medical and Surgical

> **Staffed Beds:** 128

## WILLINGBORO—Burlington County

✠ **LOURDES MEDICAL CENTER OF BURLINGTON COUNTY (310061)**, 218–A Sunset Road, Zip 08046–1162; tel. 609/835–2900 **A**1 2 9 10 13 **F**3 5 11 12 15 17 18 29 30 31 34 35 36 38 40 42 44 45 46 47 49 50 55 56 57 59 60 61 64 66 68 70 74 75 78 79 81 82 85 86 87 93 98 100 107 108 109 110 111 114 118 119 129 130 132 135 146 147 148 **S** Catholic Health East, Newtown Square, PA
Primary Contact: Mark Nessel, Executive Vice President and Chief Operating Officer
COO: Robert Ruggero, Senior Vice President Operations
CFO: Michael Hammond, Chief Financial Officer
CMO: Alan R. Pope, M.D., Vice President, Medical Affairs
CIO: Mike Elfert, Director Information Services
CHR: Richard P. Kropp, Vice President Human Resources
CHR: Janet Moran, Vice President Human Resources
CNO: Audrey Jadczak, R.N., Vice President/Chief Nursing Officer
Web address: www.lourdesnet.org
**Control:** Other not–for–profit (including NFP Corporation) **Service:** General Medical and Surgical

> **Staffed Beds:** 154 **Admissions:** 7574 **Census:** 102 **Outpatient Visits:** 112450 **Births:** 0 **Total Expense ($000):** 107800 **Payroll Expense ($000):** 43760 **Personnel:** 737

✠ **LOURDES SPECIALTY HOSPITAL OF SOUTHERN NEW JERSEY (312022)**, 218 Sunset Road, Zip 08046–1110; tel. 609/835–3650, (Nonreporting) **A**1 10 **S** AcuityHealthcare, LP, Charlotte, NC
Primary Contact: Cheri Cowperthwait, R.N., Chief Executive Officer
Web address: www.acuityhealthcarenj.com
**Control:** Corporation, Investor–owned, for–profit **Service:** Long–Term Acute Care hospital

> **Staffed Beds:** 69

## WOODBRIDGE—Middlesex County

**WOODBRIDGE DEVELOPMENT CENTER**, Rahway Avenue, Zip 07095–3697, Mailing Address: P.O. Box 189, Zip 07095–0189; tel. 732/499–5951, (Nonreporting)
Primary Contact: Amy R. Bailon, M.D., Medical Director
Web address: www.state.nj.us/
**Control:** State–Government, nonfederal **Service:** Hospital unit within an institution for the mentally retarded

> **Staffed Beds:** 125

**NJ**

*Many Facility Codes have changed. Please refer to the AHA Guide Code Chart.*
© 2013 AHA Guide

**WOODBURY—Gloucester County**

☒ **INSPIRA MEDICAL CENTER–WOODBURY (310081)**, (Formerly Underwood–Memorial Hospital), 509 North Broad Street, Zip 08096–1697; tel. 856/845–0100 **A**1 3 5 9 10 **F**3 11 13 15 17 18 20 22 28 29 30 34 35 38 39 40 49 50 56 57 58 59 60 61 62 64 66 67 70 73 74 75 76 77 79 80 81 85 86 89 91 93 96 97 98 99 100 102 104 105 107 110 114 115 118 119 129 130 132 135 143 146 147 148 **P**6 **S** Inspira Health Network, Vineland, NJ
Primary Contact: Eileen K. Cardile, R.N., MS, President and Chief Executive Officer
COO: John W. Graham, Executive Vice President and Chief Operating Officer
CFO: John DiAngelo, Executive Vice President and Chief Financial Officer
CIO: Robert Mizia, Director Information Systems and Chief Information Officer
CHR: Robert Manestrina, Vice President Human Resources
Web address: www.umhospital.org
**Control:** Other not–for–profit (including NFP Corporation) **Service:** General Medical and Surgical

**Staffed Beds: 240 Admissions:** 12855 **Census:** 159 **Outpatient Visits:** 122616 **Births:** 888 **Total Expense ($000):** 116653 **Payroll Expense ($000):** 80890 **Personnel:** 1259

**WYCKOFF—Bergen County**

☒ **CHRISTIAN HEALTH CARE CENTER (314019)**, 301 Sicomac Avenue, Zip 07481–2194; tel. 201/848–5200, (Total facility includes 254 beds in nursing home–type unit) **A**1 9 10 **F**10 30 34 56 57 59 64 69 90 98 99 103 104 105 106 125 128 130 132 143 146 148
Primary Contact: Douglas A. Struyk, CPA, President and Chief Executive Officer
COO: Denise Ratcliffe, Executive Vice President and Chief Operating Officer
CFO: Kevin Stagg, Executive Vice President Finance and Chief Financial Officer
CMO: Howard Gilman, M.D., Medical Executive
CIO: Jennifer D'Angelo, Assistant Vice President Information Services
CHR: Bob Zierold, Senior Vice President Human Resources
CNO: Marianne Guerriero, Nurse Executive
Web address: www.chccnj.org
**Control:** Other not–for–profit (including NFP Corporation) **Service:** Psychiatric

**Staffed Beds: 530 Admissions:** 2028 **Census:** 509 **Outpatient Visits:** 46462 **Births:** 0 **Total Expense ($000):** 68355 **Payroll Expense ($000):** 40042 **Personnel:** 1164

NJ

# NEW MEXICO

## ACOMA— County

☐ **ACOMA–CANONCITO–LAGUNA HOSPITAL (320070)**, 80B Veterans Boulevard, Zip 87034, Mailing Address: P.O. Box 130, San Fidel, Zip 87049–0130; tel. 505/552–5300, (Nonreporting) **A**1 10 **S** U. S. Indian Health Service, Rockville, MD
Primary Contact: William Thorne, Jr., Chief Executive Officer
Web address: www.ihs.gov/albuquerque/index.cfm?module=dsp_abq_acoma_canoncito_laguna
**Control:** PHS, Indian Service, Government, federal **Service:** General Medical and Surgical

**Staffed Beds:** 25

## ALAMOGORDO—Otero County

☒ ◇ **GERALD CHAMPION REGIONAL MEDICAL CENTER (320004)**, 2669 North Scenic Drive, Zip 88310–8799; tel. 575/439–6100 **A**1 9 10 20 21 **F**3 8 9 11 13 18 29 30 31 34 35 40 43 45 50 51 56 57 58 59 60 64 70 74 75 76 77 78 79 81 85 86 87 90 92 97 98 101 103 104 105 107 108 111 114 116 117 119 129 130 132 133 142 146 147 **P**6
Primary Contact: Robert J. Heckert, Jr., Chief Executive Officer
CFO: Morgan Hay, Chief Financial Officer
CMO: Arthur Austin, M.D., Vice President Medical Affairs
CIO: Ana Castro, Director Information Services and Clinical Information Services
CHR: Karen O'Brien, Director Human Resources
CNO: Martha C. Gorman, R.N., Vice President of Patient Care Services and Chief Nursing Officer
Web address: www.gcrmc.org
**Control:** Other not–for–profit (including NFP Corporation) **Service:** General Medical and Surgical

**Staffed Beds:** 102 **Admissions:** 3674 **Census:** 39 **Outpatient Visits:** 89009 **Births:** 570 **Total Expense ($000):** 107052 **Payroll Expense ($000):** 39839 **Personnel:** 610

## ALBUQUERQUE—Bernalillo County

☐ **AMG SPECIALTY HOSPITAL–ALBUQUERQUE (322003)**, (Formerly Specialty Hospital of Albuquerque), 235 Elm Street N.E., Zip 87102–3672; tel. 505/842–5550, (Nonreporting) **A**1 9 10 **S** AMG Integrated Healthcare Management, Lafayette, LA
Primary Contact: Elizabeth Rees, Chief Executive Officer
CFO: Julie Lenzo, Director Business Office
CMO: Jeffrey Ross, M.D., Medical Director
CHR: Robin Stendel–Freels, Coordinator Human Resources
Web address: www.amgalbuquerque.com/
**Control:** Partnership, Investor–owned, for–profit **Service:** Long–Term Acute Care hospital

**Staffed Beds:** 24

☒ **HEALTHSOUTH REHABILITATION HOSPITAL (323027)**, 7000 Jefferson Street N.E., Zip 87109–4313; tel. 505/344–9478 **A**1 9 10 **F**28 29 34 35 56 57 59 60 62 64 74 75 77 79 90 91 93 94 95 96 130 132 143 148 **S** HEALTHSOUTH Corporation, Birmingham, AL
Primary Contact: Sylvia K. Kelly, Chief Executive Officer
CFO: Byron Aten, Controller
CMO: Angela Walker, M.D., Medical Director
CHR: Victoria Otero, Director Human Resources
CNO: Veronica Gadomski, R.N., Chief Nursing Officer
Web address: www.healthsouthnewmexico.com
**Control:** Corporation, Investor–owned, for–profit **Service:** Rehabilitation

**Staffed Beds:** 87 **Admissions:** 1628 **Census:** 64 **Outpatient Visits:** 9127 **Births:** 0 **Total Expense ($000):** 19348 **Payroll Expense ($000):** 11893 **Personnel:** 227

☒ **KINDRED HOSPITAL–ALBUQUERQUE (322002)**, 700 High Street N.E., Zip 87102–2565; tel. 505/242–4444, (Nonreporting) **A**1 9 10 **S** Kindred Healthcare, Louisville, KY
Primary Contact: Michael R. Shaw, Chief Executive Officer
CFO: Margaret Wantland, Chief Financial Officer
CMO: Jeffrey Dorf, M.D., Medical Director
CHR: Donald Whitney, Director Human Resources
CNO: Rhonda Lovato, R.N., Chief Clinical Officer
Web address: www.kindredalbuquerque.com/
**Control:** Corporation, Investor–owned, for–profit **Service:** Long–Term Acute Care hospital

**Staffed Beds:** 61

☒ **LOVELACE MEDICAL CENTER (320009)**, 601 Martin Luther King Avenue N.E., Zip 87102–3619; tel. 505/727–8000, (Includes HEART HOSPITAL OF NEW MEXICO, 504 Elm Street, Zip 87102; tel. 505/724–2000; Ronald C. Winger, President), (Nonreporting) **A**1 3 5 9 10 **S** Ardent Health Services, Nashville, TN
Primary Contact: Troy Greer, Chief Executive Officer
COO: Susan K. Rodgers, MSN, Chief Operating Officer
CFO: Gina Anderson, Chief Financial Officer
CFO: Brian Vaughan, Chief Financial Officer
CMO: Jean D. Remillard, M.D., Chief Medical Officer/Chief Quality Officer
CHR: Philip Espinosa, Human Resource Director
CHR: Randy Royster, Vice President Human Resources
CNO: Laurie S. Bigham, R.N., Chief Nursing Officer
Web address: www.lovelace.com/albuquerque–hospital/lovelace–medical–center#.UDZ1laDhf48
**Control:** Corporation, Investor–owned, for–profit **Service:** General Medical and Surgical

**Staffed Beds:** 263

★ △ **LOVELACE REHABILITATION HOSPITAL (323028)**, 505 Elm Street N.E., Zip 87102–2500; tel. 505/727–4700, (Nonreporting) **A**3 5 7 9 10 **S** Ardent Health Services, Nashville, TN
Primary Contact: Derrick Jones, Chief Executive Officer
CFO: Andrea Solin, Chief Financial Officer
CHR: Becky Falance, Director Human Resources
Web address: www.lovelace.com
**Control:** Corporation, Investor–owned, for–profit **Service:** Rehabilitation

**Staffed Beds:** 62

☒ **LOVELACE WESTSIDE HOSPITAL (320074)**, 10501 Golf Course Road N.W., Zip 87114–5000, Mailing Address: P.O. Box 25555, Zip 87125–0555; tel. 505/727–2000 **A**1 3 5 9 10 **F**3 12 13 29 30 39 40 41 42 57 70 76 77 79 81 85 89 93 107 110 111 115 119 130 133 135 146 148 **S** Ardent Health Services, Nashville, TN
Primary Contact: Farron Sneed, FACHE, Chief Executive Officer
COO: Karrie Brazaski, Chief Operating Officer and Chief Nursing Officer
Web address: www.lovelace.com/albuquerque–hospital/lovelace–westside–hospital#.UDZ1t6Dhf48
**Control:** Corporation, Investor–owned, for–profit **Service:** General Medical and Surgical

**Staffed Beds:** 80 **Admissions:** 2550 **Census:** 22 **Outpatient Visits:** 41905 **Births:** 189 **Total Expense ($000):** 51027 **Payroll Expense ($000):** 18645 **Personnel:** 315

☒ **LOVELACE WOMEN'S HOSPITAL (320017)**, 4701 Montgomery Boulevard N.E., Zip 87109–1251, Mailing Address: P.O. Box 25555, Zip 87125–0555; tel. 505/727–7800 **A**1 3 5 9 10 **F**8 11 13 15 29 34 35 40 43 46 49 57 59 64 70 72 73 76 78 79 81 85 89 91 93 107 108 110 111 114 115 116 117 119 126 130 132 146 147 **S** Ardent Health Services, Nashville, TN
Primary Contact: Sheri Milone, Chief Executive Officer and Administrator
COO: Janelle Raborn, Chief Operating Officer
CFO: Joseph Sereno, Chief Financial Officer
CHR: Carol Shelton, Director Human Resources
CNO: Jane Ritter, R.N., Chief Nursing Officer
Web address: www.lovelace.com/albuquerque–hospital/lovelace–womens–hospital#.UDZ17KDhf48
**Control:** Corporation, Investor–owned, for–profit **Service:** General Medical and Surgical

**Staffed Beds:** 78 **Admissions:** 6499 **Census:** 67 **Outpatient Visits:** 140318 **Births:** 3096 **Total Expense ($000):** 87659 **Payroll Expense ($000):** 37665 **Personnel:** 777

☒ **PRESBYTERIAN HOSPITAL (320021)**, 1100 Central Avenue S.E., Zip 87106–4934, Mailing Address: P.O. Box 26666, Zip 87125–6666; tel. 505/841–1234 **A**1 2 3 5 9 10 **F**3 7 8 11 13 14 17 18 19 20 21 22 23 24 25 26 27 29 30 31 35 38 40 44 45 46 47 48 49 51 53 57 59 60 68 70 72 73 74 75 76 77 78 79 81 84 85 86 87 88 89 92 93 96 100 101 107 108 111 113 114 115 118 119 124 126 130 131 132 138 142 144 145 146 147 148 **S** Presbyterian Healthcare Services, Albuquerque, NM
Primary Contact: Sandra C. Podley, Administrator
COO: Clay Holderman, Chief Operating Officer–Central Delivery System
CFO: Paul Briggs, Executive Vice President and Chief Financial Officer
CFO: Donna Garcia, Vice President, Finance
CMO: Jayne McCormick, M.D., Chief Medical Officer CDS
CIO: Lee Marley, VP/Information Services Chief Application Officer
CHR: Lee Patchell, Lead Human Resources Business Partner
CNO: Ann L. Wright, R.N., Assistant Central Delivery System CNO
Web address: www.phs.org
**Control:** Other not–for–profit (including NFP Corporation) **Service:** General Medical and Surgical

**Staffed Beds:** 488 **Admissions:** 32056 **Census:** 381 **Outpatient Visits:** 1344551 **Births:** 4084 **Total Expense ($000):** 779018 **Payroll Expense ($000):** 331983 **Personnel:** 3827

**NM**

*Many Facility Codes have changed. Please refer to the AHA Guide Code Chart.*
© 2013 AHA Guide

★ **PRESBYTERIAN KASEMAN HOSPITAL**, 8300 Constitution Avenue N.E., Zip 87110–7624, Mailing Address: P.O. Box 26666, Zip 87125–6666; tel. 505/291–2000 **A**9 **F**3 5 29 30 31 40 50 53 56 63 64 65 68 75 78 79 81 82 84 85 86 87 93 97 98 99 100 101 102 103 104 105 107 108 111 114 117 118 119 120 121 123 128 129 130 132 134 146 148 **S** Presbyterian Healthcare Services, Albuquerque, NM
Primary Contact: Doyle Boykin, R.N., MSN, Administrator
COO: Paul Briggs, Executive VP/Chief Operating Officer
COO: David R. Scrase, M.D., Executive Senior Vice President and Chief Operating Officer
CFO: Dale Maxwell, Senior VP Chief Financial Officer
CMO: Eddie Benge, M.D., Vice President Medical Staff Affairs
CMO: Jayne McCormick, M.D., Chief Medical Officer CDS
CIO: Lee Marley, VP/Information Services Chief Application Officer
CHR: Cindy McGill, Senior Vice President Human Resources
Web address: www.phs.org
**Control:** Other not–for–profit (including NFP Corporation) **Service:** Surgical

**Staffed Beds: 111 Admissions: 2136 Census: 73 Outpatient Visits: 102710 Births: 0 Total Expense ($000): 86084 Payroll Expense ($000): 34637 Personnel: 479**

△ **TURQUOISE LODGE HOSPITAL**, 5901 Zuni Road S.E., Zip 87108–3073; tel. 505/841–8978, (Nonreporting) **A**7
Primary Contact: Michael Gutierrez, Executive Director
Web address: www.health.state.nm.us
**Control:** State–Government, nonfederal **Service:** Alcoholism and other chemical dependency

**Staffed Beds: 34**

⊞ **UNIVERSITY OF NEW MEXICO HOSPITALS (320001)**, 2211 Lomas Boulevard N.E., Zip 87106–2745; tel. 505/272–2111, (Includes CARRIE TINGLEY HOSPITAL, 1127 University Boulevard N.E., Zip 87102–1715; tel. 505/272–5200; Crystal Frantz, Executive Director; MENTAL HEALTH CENTER, 2600 Marble N.E., Zip 87131–2600; tel. 505/272–2800; UNIVERSITY OF NEW MEXICO CHILDREN'S PSYCHIATRIC HOSPITAL, 1001 Yale Boulevard N.E., Zip 87131 3830; tel. 505/272–2890; UNM CHILDREN'S HOSPITAL, 2211 Lomas Boulevard, N.E., tel. 505/272–2111) **A**1 2 3 5 8 9 10 **F**3 8 9 11 13 15 16 17 18 19 20 21 22 23 24 25 26 27 28 29 30 31 32 34 35 38 40 41 43 44 45 46 47 48 49 50 51 54 56 57 59 60 61 63 64 65 68 70 72 73 74 75 76 77 78 79 81 82 83 84 85 86 87 88 89 90 92 93 94 95 96 97 107 108 109 110 111 114 115 116 117 118 119 121 123 126 129 130 131 132 135 136 138 144 146 147 148 **S** University of New Mexico Hospitals, Albuquerque, NM
Primary Contact: Stephen W. McKernan, Chief Executive Officer
CFO: Ella Watt, Chief Financial Officer
CMO: Robert Katz, M.D., Vice President Clinical Affairs
CIO: Ron Margolis, Chief Information Officer
CHR: Jim Pendergast, Administrator Human Resources
Web address: www.unm.edu
**Control:** State–Government, nonfederal **Service:** General Medical and Surgical

**Staffed Beds: 537 Admissions: 25214 Census: 413 Outpatient Visits: 592980 Births: 3256 Total Expense ($000): 873578 Payroll Expense ($000): 306312 Personnel: 5482**

⊞ △ **VETERANS AFFAIRS MEDICAL CENTER**, 1501 San Pedro S.E., Zip 87108–5153; tel. 505/265–1711, (Nonreporting) **A**1 2 3 5 7 8 **S** Department of Veterans Affairs, Washington, DC
Primary Contact: George Marnell, Director
CFO: Michael McNeill, Chief Financial Management
CMO: Meghan Gerety, M.D., Chief of Staff
CIO: Ronald Ferrell, Chief Information Officer
CHR: Melvin Hooker, Chief Human Resources
Web address: www.southwest.va.gov/albuquerque/
**Control:** Veterans Affairs, Government, federal **Service:** General Medical and Surgical

**Staffed Beds: 281**

### ARTESIA—Eddy County

★ **ARTESIA GENERAL HOSPITAL (320030)**, 702 North 13th Street, Zip 88210–1199; tel. 575/748–3333, (Nonreporting) **A**9 10 20 **S** Community Hospital Corporation, Plano, TX
Primary Contact: Kenneth W. Randall, Chief Executive Officer
CFO: William Zemanek, Assistant Chief Financial Officer
CMO: Joe Salgado, M.D., Chief of Staff
CHR: Dawn Wright, Director Human Resources
Web address: www.artesiageneral.com
**Control:** Other not–for–profit (including NFP Corporation) **Service:** General Medical and Surgical

**Staffed Beds: 43**

### CARLSBAD—Eddy County

⊞ **CARLSBAD MEDICAL CENTER (320063)**, 2430 West Pierce Street, Zip 88220–3597; tel. 575/887–4100, (Nonreporting) **A**1 9 10 **S** Community Health Systems, Inc., Franklin, TN
Primary Contact: Chad Campbell, Chief Executive Officer
CIO: Kenneth Kemp, Director Information Systems
CHR: Christina Beasley, Director Human Resources
Web address: www.carlsbadmedicalcenter.com
**Control:** Corporation, Investor–owned, for–profit **Service:** General Medical and Surgical

**Staffed Beds: 127**

### CLAYTON—Union County

★ **UNION COUNTY GENERAL HOSPITAL (321304)**, 300 Wilson Street, Zip 88415–3304, Mailing Address: P.O. Box 489, Zip 88415–0489; tel. 575/374–2585 **A**9 10 18 **F**3 11 13 29 31 35 40 45 50 57 59 62 64 65 68 70 76 81 82 85 87 89 93 97 102 107 114 119 129 130 133 144 145 148 **S** HealthTech Management Services, Franklin, TN
Primary Contact: Donald Weidemann, Administrator
CFO: Julie Price, Chief Financial Officer
CMO: Daniel Radunsky, M.D., Medical Staff President
CIO: Tim Justice, Chief Information Officer
CHR: Jill Swagerty, Director Human Resources
CNO: Stacye Bradley, R.N., Chief Nursing Officer
Web address: www.unioncountygeneral.com
**Control:** Other not–for–profit (including NFP Corporation) **Service:** General Medical and Surgical

**Staffed Beds: 21 Admissions: 241 Census: 3 Outpatient Visits: 18061 Births: 21 Total Expense ($000): 11514 Payroll Expense ($000): 4315 Personnel: 84**

### CLOVIS—Curry County

⊞ **PLAINS REGIONAL MEDICAL CENTER (320022)**, 2100 Martin Luther King Boulevard, Zip 88101–9412, Mailing Address: P.O. Box 1688, Zip 88102–1688; tel. 575/769–2141 **A**1 9 10 **F**3 8 11 13 15 20 28 29 30 31 35 40 45 47 48 50 51 53 54 62 63 64 68 69 70 75 76 77 78 79 81 82 83 84 85 87 89 93 97 99 100 101 102 103 104 107 111 112 114 115 118 119 123 129 130 135 146 147 148 **P**6 **S** Presbyterian Healthcare Services, Albuquerque, NM
Primary Contact: Hoyt Skabelund, Administrator
CMO: Brian Willmon, M.D., Medical Director
CIO: Hoyt Skabelund, Administrator
CHR: Cindy Duncan, Manager Human Resources
CNO: Terri A. Marney, R.N., Director of Nursing
Web address: www.phs.org
**Control:** Other not–for–profit (including NFP Corporation) **Service:** General Medical and Surgical

**Staffed Beds: 106 Admissions: 5230 Census: 45 Outpatient Visits: 90986 Births: 1558 Total Expense ($000): 88551 Payroll Expense ($000): 32435**

### CROWNPOINT—McKinley County

**U. S. PUBLIC HEALTH SERVICE INDIAN HOSPITAL (320062)**, Route 9 and State Road 371, Zip 87313, Mailing Address: P.O. Box 358, Zip 87313–0358; tel. 505/786–5291, (Nonreporting) **A**10 **S** U. S. Indian Health Service, Rockville, MD
Primary Contact: Virgil Davis, Acting Chief Executive Officer
CFO: Darlene Kirk, Manager Finance
CIO: Jimmy Burbank, Chief Information Officer
CHR: Victoria Pablo, Human Resource Specialist
Web address: www.ihs.gov
**Control:** PHS, Indian Service, Government, federal **Service:** General Medical and Surgical

**Staffed Beds: 12**

### DEMING—Luna County

⊞ **MIMBRES MEMORIAL HOSPITAL (320014)**, 900 West Ash Street, Zip 88030–4098, Mailing Address: P.O. Box 710, Zip 88031–0710; tel. 575/546–2761, (Nonreporting) **A**1 9 20 **S** Community Health Systems, Inc., Franklin, TN
Primary Contact: Steve Westenhofer, Chief Executive Officer
CFO: Suzanne Herbert, Chief Financial Officer
CHR: Johanna Gramer, Director Human Resources
CNO: Colonel Gwenda McClure, USAF, Chief Nursing Officer
Web address: www.mimbresmemorial.com
**Control:** Corporation, Investor–owned, for–profit **Service:** General Medical and Surgical

**Staffed Beds: 75**

**NM**

**Hospital, Medicare Provider Number, Address, Telephone, Approval, Facility, and Physician Codes, Health Care System**

★ American Hospital Association (AHA) membership
□ The Joint Commission accreditation
◇ DNV Healthcare Inc. accreditation
○ Healthcare Facilities Accreditation Program
△ Commission on Accreditation of Rehabilitation Facilities (CARF) accreditation

## ESPANOLA—Rio Arriba County

✠ **ESPANOLA HOSPITAL (320011)**, 1010 Spruce Street, Zip 87532–2746;
tel. 505/753–7111 **A**1 9 10 20 **F**3 7 8 13 15 29 32 34 35 40 45 50 53 57 59
62 70 75 76 79 81 85 93 107 108 110 114 115 118 119 129 146 **P**8
**S** Presbyterian Healthcare Services, Albuquerque, NM
Primary Contact: Brenda Romero, Administrator
Web address: www.phs.org
**Control:** Other not–for–profit (including NFP Corporation) **Service:** General
Medical and Surgical

> **Staffed Beds:** 70 **Admissions:** 2132 **Census:** 20 **Outpatient Visits:** 47370
> **Births:** 278 **Total Expense ($000):** 53245 **Payroll Expense ($000):** 23173
> **Personnel:** 285

## FARMINGTON—San Juan County

✠ ◇ **SAN JUAN REGIONAL MEDICAL CENTER (320005)**, 801 West Maple
Street, Zip 87401–5630; tel. 505/609–2000, (Includes SAN JUAN REGIONAL
MEDICAL CENTER REHABILITATION HOSPITAL, 525 South Schwartz, Zip 87401;
tel. 505/609–2625) **A**1 2 5 9 10 21 **F**3 7 8 11 13 15 18 20 22 26 28 29 30
31 32 34 35 39 40 42 43 47 48 49 50 53 54 57 59 60 64 65 68 70 74 75
76 78 79 81 82 85 86 87 89 90 93 96 97 98 99 100 102 107 108 111 112
114 115 118 119 121 130 132 135 143 144 146 148 **P**5 6
Primary Contact: Rick D. Wallace, FACHE, President and Chief Executive Officer
COO: John Buffington, Chief Operating Officer
CFO: J. Michael Philips, Chief Strategy Officer
CMO: Robert Fabrey, M.D., Chief Medical Officer
CHR: Elizabeth Volkerding, Director Workforce Excellence
Web address: www.sanjuanregional.com
**Control:** Other not–for–profit (including NFP Corporation) **Service:** General
Medical and Surgical

> **Staffed Beds:** 232 **Admissions:** 10834 **Census:** 123 **Outpatient Visits:**
> 161885 **Births:** 1292 **Total Expense ($000):** 246073 **Payroll Expense**
> **($000):** 116423 **Personnel:** 1611

## GALLUP—Mckinley County

✠ **GALLUP INDIAN MEDICAL CENTER (320061)**, 516 East Nizhoni Boulevard,
Zip 87301–5748, Mailing Address: P.O. Box 1337, Zip 87305–1337;
tel. 505/722–1000 **A**1 5 10 **F**3 5 8 15 29 34 35 36 39 40 45 50 54 61 64 65
68 70 75 76 77 79 81 85 87 89 91 93 97 99 101 103 104 107 110 115 119
127 130 132 135 144 146 147 148 **S** U. S. Indian Health Service, Rockville, MD
Primary Contact: Bennie C. Yazzie, Interim Chief Executive Officer
CFO: Agnes Kee, Financial Manager
CMO: Douglas G. Peter, M.D., Chief Medical Officer
CIO: Adrian C. Haven, Site Manager
CHR: Karen Lee, Director Human Resources
Web address: www.ihs.gov/facilitiesservices/areaoffices/navajo/naihs–hcc–gallup.
asp
**Control:** Public Health Service, Government, federal **Service:** General Medical
and Surgical

> **Staffed Beds:** 58 **Admissions:** 982 **Census:** 35 **Outpatient Visits:** 298263
> **Births:** 555

✠ **REHOBOTH MCKINLEY CHRISTIAN HEALTH CARE SERVICES (320038)**,
1901 Red Rock Drive, Zip 87301–5683; tel. 505/863–7000 **A**1 5 9 10 20 **F**3 4
5 11 13 15 28 29 30 32 34 35 39 40 50 57 59 62 63 64 68 75 76 77 79 81
85 89 93 104 107 108 110 111 114 115 119 124 129 130 132 135 146
147 **P**6
Primary Contact: Roger Gleisner, Interim Chief Executive Officer
CFO: Mark Hall, Chief Financial Officer
CMO: Mary L. Poel, M.D., Chief Medical Officer
CIO: Brett Mello, Chief Information Officer
CHR: George Laurin, Interim Chief Human Resources Officer
Web address: www.rmch.org
**Control:** Other not–for–profit (including NFP Corporation) **Service:** General
Medical and Surgical

> **Staffed Beds:** 80 **Admissions:** 3154 **Census:** 36 **Outpatient Visits:** 125365
> **Births:** 505 **Total Expense ($000):** 42350 **Payroll Expense ($000):** 28744
> **Personnel:** 414

## GRANTS—Cibola County

✠ **CIBOLA GENERAL HOSPITAL (321308)**, 1016 East Roosevelt Avenue,
Zip 87020–2118; tel. 505/287–4446 **A**1 9 10 18 20 **F**3 13 15 29 30 34 40
45 46 50 56 57 59 64 65 66 68 70 75 76 77 81 85 93 97 107 113 115 119
127 133 135 147 148 **S** QHR, Brentwood, TN
Primary Contact: Michael Makosky, Chief Executive Officer
CFO: Jeff Rimel, Chief Financial Officer
CIO: Robert Volentine, Director Information Services
CHR: Sheila Cox, Director Human Resources
Web address: www.cibolahospital.com
**Control:** Other not–for–profit (including NFP Corporation) **Service:** General
Medical and Surgical

> **Staffed Beds:** 25 **Admissions:** 957 **Census:** 8 **Outpatient Visits:** 22439
> **Births:** 210 **Total Expense ($000):** 22569 **Payroll Expense ($000):** 10020
> **Personnel:** 163

## HOBBS—Lea County

✠ **LEA REGIONAL MEDICAL CENTER (320065)**, 5419 North Lovington Highway,
Zip 88240–9125, Mailing Address: P.O. Box 3000, Zip 88241–9501;
tel. 575/492–5000, (Nonreporting) **A**1 9 10 20 **S** Community Health Systems,
Inc., Franklin, TN
Primary Contact: Timothy Thornell, FACHE, Chief Executive Officer
CFO: Steven Smith, Chief Financial Officer
CMO: Jesus Fonseca, M.D., Chief of Staff
CIO: Terry Purcell, Director Information Services
CHR: Susan Hayes, Director Human Resources
CNO: Patrick A. Dunn, R.N., Chief Nursing Officer
Web address: www.learegionalmedical.com
**Control:** Corporation, Investor–owned, for–profit **Service:** General Medical and
Surgical

> **Staffed Beds:** 214

## LAS CRUCES—Dona Ana County

☐ **ADVANCED CARE HOSPITAL OF SOUTHERN NEW MEXICO (322004)**, 4451
East Lohman Avenue, Zip 88011–8267; tel. 575/521–6600, (Nonreporting) **A**1 9
10 **S** Ernest Health, Inc., Albuquerque, NM
Primary Contact: Suzanne Quillen, R.N., Chief Executive Officer
Web address: www.achsnm.ernesthealth.com
**Control:** Corporation, Investor–owned, for–profit **Service:** Long–Term Acute Care
hospital

> **Staffed Beds:** 40

✠ **MEMORIAL MEDICAL CENTER (320018)**, 2450 South Telshor Boulevard,
Zip 88011–5076; tel. 575/522–8641 **A**1 9 10 **F**3 8 11 13 15 17 18 20 22 24
26 28 29 30 31 35 39 40 44 45 49 50 51 54 57 59 60 61 62 64 65 68 70
72 74 75 76 78 79 81 85 89 93 97 98 102 103 107 108 111 114 115 118
119 121 122 123 124 130 132 135 147 148 **S** LifePoint Hospitals, Inc.,
Brentwood, TN
Primary Contact: Paul F. Herzog, Chief Executive Officer
COO: Philip Rivera, Chief Operating Officer
CFO: James McGonnell, Chief Financial Officer
CMO: Bruce San Filippo, M.D., Chief Medical Officer
CHR: Laura Pierce, Chief Administrative Officer Human Resources
Web address: www.mmclc.org
**Control:** Corporation, Investor–owned, for–profit **Service:** General Medical and
Surgical

> **Staffed Beds:** 224 **Admissions:** 10858 **Census:** 135 **Outpatient Visits:**
> 182420 **Births:** 1578 **Total Expense ($000):** 177240 **Payroll Expense**
> **($000):** 60384 **Personnel:** 1066

✠ **MESILLA VALLEY HOSPITAL (324010)**, 3751 Del Rey Boulevard,
Zip 88012–8526; tel. 575/382–3500 **A**1 9 10 **F**87 98 99 100 101 102 103
104 106 **S** Universal Health Services, Inc., King of Prussia, PA
Primary Contact: Robert Mansfield, Chief Executive Officer
CFO: Douglas Smith, Chief Financial Officer
CMO: Georgina Herrera, M.D., Medical Director
CHR: Linda Moya, Director Human Resources
Web address: www.mesillavalleyhospital.com
**Control:** Corporation, Investor–owned, for–profit **Service:** Psychiatric

> **Staffed Beds:** 120 **Admissions:** 2151 **Census:** 75 **Outpatient Visits:** 18900
> **Births:** 0 **Total Expense ($000):** 15032 **Payroll Expense ($000):** 7553
> **Personnel:** 174

✠ **MOUNTAINVIEW REGIONAL MEDICAL CENTER (320085)**, 4311 East Lohman
Avenue, Zip 88011–8255; tel. 575/556–7600, (Nonreporting) **A**1 9 10
**S** Community Health Systems, Inc., Franklin, TN
Primary Contact: Denten Park, Chief Executive Officer
CFO: Gene Alexander, Chief Financial Officer
CIO: Donald Harlow, Director of Information Services
CHR: Timothy C. Egan, Director, Human Resources
CNO: Gayle Nash, R.N., Chief Nursing Officer
Web address: www.mountainviewregional.com
**Control:** Corporation, Investor–owned, for–profit **Service:** General Medical and
Surgical

> **Staffed Beds:** 142

✠ **REHABILITATION HOSPITAL OF SOUTHERN NEW MEXICO (323032)**, 4441
East Lohman Avenue, Zip 88011–8267; tel. 575/521–6400, (Nonreporting) **A**1 9
10 **S** Ernest Health, Inc., Albuquerque, NM
Primary Contact: Sabrina Martin, Chief Operating Officer
CFO: Jared Udall, Chief Financial Officer
CMO: Kimberly Encapera, M.D., Medical Director
CIO: Pam Suarez, Director Marketing and Business Development
CHR: Yolanda Mendoza, Director Human Resources
CNO: Yvonne Sandoval, Director of Nursing Operations
Web address: www.rhsnm.ernesthealth.com
**Control:** Corporation, Investor–owned, for–profit **Service:** Rehabilitation

> **Staffed Beds:** 40

**NM**

*Many Facility Codes have changed. Please refer to the AHA Guide Code Chart.*
© 2013 AHA Guide

## LAS VEGAS—San Miguel County

☒ **ALTA VISTA REGIONAL HOSPITAL (320003)**, 104 Legion Drive,
Zip 87701–4804; tel. 505/426–3500, (Nonreporting) **A**1 9 10 20 **S** Community
Health Systems, Inc., Franklin, TN
Primary Contact: Kathleen Cahill, President and Chief Executive Officer
CFO: Leonard Tapia, Chief Financial Officer
CMO: Joseph Brown, M.D., Chief Medical Staff
CIO: Norman Wilder, Director Information Systems
CHR: Barbara Lujan, Director Human Resources
Web address: www.altavistaregionalhospital.com
**Control:** Corporation, Investor–owned, for–profit **Service:** General Medical and
Surgical

**Staffed Beds: 54**

☐ **NEW MEXICO BEHAVIORAL HEALTH INSTITUTE AT LAS VEGAS**, 3695 Hot
Springs Boulevard, Zip 87701–9549; tel. 505/454–2100, (Nonreporting) **A**1 9
Primary Contact: Steve Martinez, Executive Director and Administrator
CFO: Albino Martinez, Director Finance and Budget
Web address: www.health.state.nm.us
**Control:** State–Government, nonfederal **Service:** Psychiatric

**Staffed Beds: 257**

## LOS ALAMOS—Los Alamos County

☒ **LOS ALAMOS MEDICAL CENTER (320033)**, 3917 West Road,
Zip 87544–2293; tel. 505/661–9500, (Nonreporting) **A**1 9 10 20 **S** LifePoint
Hospitals, Inc., Brentwood, TN
Primary Contact: Feliciano Jiron, Chief Executive Officer
CFO: Heather Teter, Chief Financial Officer
CMO: Sara Pasqualoni, M.D., Chief of Staff
CIO: Kevin Vigil, Director Information Systems
CHR: Jacqueline Carroll, Director Human Resources
Web address: www.losalamosmedicalcenter.com
**Control:** Corporation, Investor–owned, for–profit **Service:** General Medical and
Surgical

**Staffed Beds: 38**

## LOVINGTON—Lea County

★ **NOR–LEA GENERAL HOSPITAL (321305)**, 1600 North Main Avenue,
Zip 88260–2871; tel. 575/396–6611, (Nonreporting) **A**9 10 18
Primary Contact: David B. Shaw, Chief Executive Officer and Administrator
COO: Dan Hamilton, Director Inpatient Services
CFO: Allyson Roberts, CPA, Chief Financial Officer
CMO: Jeffrey Nelson, M.D., Chief of Staff
CIO: Brent Kelley, Director Information Technology
CHR: Carol DeArment, Director Human Resources
CNO: Cyndie Cribbs, Director of Nursing
Web address: www.nlgh.org
**Control:** Hospital district or authority, Government, nonfederal **Service:** General
Medical and Surgical

**Staffed Beds: 18**

## MESCALERO—Otero County

☐ **MESCALERO PUBLIC HEALTH SERVICE INDIAN HOSPITAL (320058)**, 318
Abalone Loop, Zip 88340, Mailing Address: Box 210, Zip 88340–0210;
tel. 505/671–4441, (Nonreporting) **A**1 9 10 **S** U. S. Indian Health Service,
Rockville, MD
Primary Contact: Dorlynn Simmons, Chief Executive Officer
CFO: Rainey Enjady, Administrative Officer
CIO: Kathy Murphy, Site Manager
Web address: www.ihs.gov
**Control:** Public Health Service, Government, federal **Service:** General Medical
and Surgical

**Staffed Beds: 13**

## PORTALES—Roosevelt County

**ROOSEVELT GENERAL HOSPITAL (320084)**, 42121 U.S. Highway 70,
Zip 88130, Mailing Address: P.O. Box 868, Zip 88130–0868;
tel. 575/359–1800, (Nonreporting) **A**9 10
Primary Contact: Larry E. Leaming, Ph.D., FACHE, Chief Executive Officer
CFO: Eva Steven, Chief Financial Officer
CMO: Les Donaldson, M.D., Chief of Staff
CHR: Cindy Duncan, Director Human Resources
CNO: Maxine Montano, R.N., Chief Nursing Officer / Director of Patient Care
Web address: www.myrgh.org
**Control:** Hospital district or authority, Government, nonfederal **Service:** General
Medical and Surgical

**Staffed Beds: 22**

## RATON—Colfax County

★ **MINERS' COLFAX MEDICAL CENTER (321307)**, 200 Hospital Drive,
Zip 87740–2099; tel. 575/445–7700, (Includes MINERS' HOSPITAL OF NEW
MEXICO, Hospital Drive, Zip 87740, Mailing Address: Box 1067, Zip 87740;
tel. 505/445–2741), (Nonreporting) **A**9 10 18
Primary Contact: Shawn Lerch, Chief Executive Officer
CFO: Albino Martinez, Director Budget and Finance
CIO: Richard Laner, Jr., Manager Information Systems
CHR: Jamie Johnson, Director Human Resources
Web address: www.minershosp.com
**Control:** County–Government, nonfederal **Service:** General Medical and Surgical

**Staffed Beds: 33**

## RIO RANCHO—Sandoval County

★ **PRESBYTERIAN RUST MEDICAL CENTER**, 2400 Unser Boulevard S.E.,
Zip 87124–4740; tel. 505/253–7878 **A**9 **F**11 13 18 20 29 30 40 50 53 64 68
70 72 73 75 76 79 81 82 87 91 93 107 108 111 115 118 119 130 146
**S** Presbyterian Healthcare Services, Albuquerque, NM
Primary Contact: Jeff McBee, Administrator
Web address: www.phs.org/phs/riorancho/index.htm
**Control:** Other not–for–profit (including NFP Corporation) **Service:** General
Medical and Surgical

**Staffed Beds: 95 Admissions: 5612 Census: 49 Outpatient Visits: 41827
Births: 1066 Total Expense ($000): 88299 Payroll Expense ($000): 30229
Personnel: 488**

◇ **UNM SANDOVAL REGIONAL MEDICAL CENTER (320089)**, 3001 Broadmoor
Boulevard N.E., Zip 87144–2100; tel. 505/994–7000 **A**9 10 21 **S** University of
New Mexico Hospitals, Albuquerque, NM
Primary Contact: Kevin L. Rogols, FACHE, Chief Executive Officer
Web address: www.hospitals.unm.edu/
**Control:** State–Government, nonfederal **Service:** General Medical and Surgical

**Staffed Beds: 72**

## ROSWELL—Chaves County

☒ **EASTERN NEW MEXICO MEDICAL CENTER (320006)**, 405 West Country
Club Road, Zip 88201–5209; tel. 575/622–8170, (Nonreporting) **A**1 3 5 9 10
19 **S** Community Health Systems, Inc., Franklin, TN
Primary Contact: Maridel Acosta, Chief Executive Officer
CFO: Leanne Hacker, Chief Financial Officer
CMO: Jan Hobbs, M.D., Chief Medical Officer
CIO: Deepak Surl, Chief Information Officer
Web address: www.enmmc.com
**Control:** Corporation, Investor–owned, for–profit **Service:** General Medical and
Surgical

**Staffed Beds: 149**

★ **LOVELACE REGIONAL HOSPITAL (320086)**, (Formerly Roswell Regional
Hospital), 117 East 19th Street, Zip 88201–5151; tel. 575/627–7000 **A**9 10 **F**3
13 18 20 24 26 28 29 30 34 35 36 38 40 44 45 48 49 50 54 57 59 68 70
75 76 77 79 81 82 83 84 86 87 89 90 91 93 94 97 107 111 114 117 119
120 121 130 132 135 141 144 146 **P**6 **S** Ardent Health Services, Nashville, TN
Primary Contact: Dawn M. Tschabrun, R.N., Chief Executive Officer
Web address: www.roswellregional.com
**Control:** Corporation, Investor–owned, for–profit **Service:** General Medical and
Surgical

**Staffed Beds: 26 Admissions: 2046 Census: 14 Outpatient Visits: 34544
Births: 947 Total Expense ($000): 24293 Payroll Expense ($000): 11861**

☐ **NEW MEXICO REHABILITATION CENTER (323026)**, 31 Gail Harris Street,
Zip 88203–8190; tel. 575/347–3400, (Includes PECOS VALLEY LODGE, 31 Gail
Harris Avenue, Zip 88201; tel. 505/347–5491), (Nonreporting) **A**1 10
Primary Contact: Genia Devenport, Administrator
COO: Genia Devenport, Administrator
CFO: Janie Davies, Chief Financial Officer
CMO: Evan Nelson, M.D., Medical Director
CHR: Dorie Isler, Director Human Resources
**Control:** State–Government, nonfederal **Service:** Rehabilitation

**Staffed Beds: 41**

**NM**

---

**Hospital, Medicare Provider Number, Address, Telephone, Approval, Facility, and Physician Codes, Health Care System**

★ American Hospital Association (AHA) membership
☐ The Joint Commission accreditation   ◇ DNV Healthcare Inc. accreditation

○ Healthcare Facilities Accreditation Program
△ Commission on Accreditation of Rehabilitation Facilities (CARF) accreditation

## RUIDOSO—Lincoln County

☒ **LINCOLN COUNTY MEDICAL CENTER (321306)**, 211 Sudderth Drive,
Zip 88345–6043, Mailing Address: P.O. Box 8000, Zip 88355–8000;
tel. 575/257–8200 **A**1 9 10 18 **F**7 11 13 15 29 30 35 39 40 45 46 53 56 57
59 64 68 70 76 77 78 81 85 87 91 93 103 107 110 111 115 119 132 135
144 146 148 **P**6 **S** Presbyterian Healthcare Services, Albuquerque, NM
Primary Contact: Alfred Santos, Administrator
CFO: Dudley McCauley, Controller
CMO: Chris Robinson, M.D., Chief of Staff
CHR: Deana Moses, Manager Human Resources
Web address: www.phs.org
**Control:** Other not–for–profit (including NFP Corporation) **Service:** General
Medical and Surgical

> **Staffed Beds:** 25 **Admissions:** 1360 **Census:** 10 **Outpatient Visits:** 44457
> **Births:** 396 **Total Expense ($000):** 35769 **Payroll Expense ($000):** 16798
> **Personnel:** 165

## SANTA FE—Santa Fe County

☒ △ **CHRISTUS ST. VINCENT REGIONAL MEDICAL CENTER (320002)**, 455
St. Michael's Drive, Zip 87505–7663, Mailing Address: P.O. Box 2107,
Zip 87504–2107; tel. 505/983–3361, (Includes CHRISTUS ST. VINCENT
PHYSICIANS MEDICAL CENTER, 2990 Rodeo Park Drive East, Zip 87505;
tel. 505/428–5400; Alex Valdez, JD, President and Chief Executive Officer),
(Nonreporting) **A**1 2 3 5 7 9 10 20 **S** CHRISTUS Health, Irving, TX
Primary Contact: Bruce J. Tassin, President and Chief Executive Officer
COO: Rick Crabtree, Chief Operating Officer
CFO: Rick Doxtator, Chief Financial Officer
CMO: Kevin C. Garrett, M.D., Chief Medical Officer
CHR: Barbara Roe, Vice President and Director Human Resources
Web address: www.stvin.org
**Control:** Other not–for–profit (including NFP Corporation) **Service:** General
Medical and Surgical

> **Staffed Beds:** 195

☐ **PHS SANTA FE INDIAN HOSPITAL (320057)**, 1700 Cerrillos Road,
Zip 87505–3554; tel. 505/988–9821, (Nonreporting) **A**1 5 9 10 **S** U. S. Indian
Health Service, Rockville, MD
Primary Contact: Robert J. Lyon, Chief Executive Officer
CMO: Bret Smoker, M.D., Clinical Director
CIO: Vernita Jones, Site Manager
**Control:** Public Health Service, Government, federal **Service:** General Medical
and Surgical

> **Staffed Beds:** 39

## SANTA ROSA—Guadalupe County

**GUADALUPE COUNTY HOSPITAL (320067)**, 720 Lake Drive,
Zip 88435–2542, Mailing Address: P.O. Box 500, Zip 88435–0500;
tel. 575/472–3417 **A**9 10 20 **F**3 29 34 35 40 57 59 64 65 68 87 107 114
119 130 132 **P**5
Primary Contact: Christina Campos, Administrator
COO: Christina Campos, Administrator
CFO: Bret Goebel, Finance Officer
CMO: Randal Brown, M.D., Chief of Staff
CIO: Kenneth Matthews, Manager Information Technology
CHR: Colleen Gallegos, Director Human Resources
**Control:** County–Government, nonfederal **Service:** General Medical and Surgical

> **Staffed Beds:** 10 **Admissions:** 210 **Census:** 2 **Outpatient Visits:** 5588
> **Births:** 0 **Total Expense ($000):** 6990 **Payroll Expense ($000):** 1421
> **Personnel:** 38

## SANTA TERESA—Dona Ana County

☒ **PEAK BEHAVIORAL HEALTH SERVICES (324012)**, 5065 McNutt Road,
Zip 88008–9442; tel. 575/589–3000, (Nonreporting) **A**1 9 10 **S** Strategic
Behavioral Health, LLC, Memphis, TN
Primary Contact: Jim Shaheen, President
COO: Doug Ginn, Executive Vice President Operations
CFO: Espie Herrara, Chief Financial Officer
CHR: Mayra Lira, Human Resources Specialist
Web address: www.peakbehavioral.com/
**Control:** Corporation, Investor–owned, for–profit **Service:** Psychiatric

> **Staffed Beds:** 120

## SHIPROCK—San Juan County

☒ **NORTHERN NAVAJO MEDICAL CENTER (320059)**, Zip 87420–0160;
tel. 505/368–6001, (Nonreporting) **A**1 5 10 **S** U. S. Indian Health Service,
Rockville, MD
Primary Contact: Fannessa Comer, Chief Executive Officer
CFO: Paulette Chatto, Finance Officer
CMO: Stephen Bowers, M.D., Clinical Director
CIO: Roland Chapman, Chief Information Officer
CHR: Gloria Redhorse–Charley, Director Human Resources
Web address: www.ihs.gov/
**Control:** Public Health Service, Government, federal **Service:** General Medical
and Surgical

> **Staffed Beds:** 62

## SILVER CITY—Grant County

☒ **GILA REGIONAL MEDICAL CENTER (320016)**, 1313 East 32nd Street,
Zip 88061–7251; tel. 575/538–4000 **A**1 9 10 20 **F**3 7 11 13 15 30 31 35 37
40 41 45 50 51 53 57 59 62 63 64 70 73 75 76 78 79 81 85 87 89 93 98
102 103 107 108 111 115 119 120 121 123 129 130 132 148 **P**5
Primary Contact: Brian S. Bentley, Chief Executive Officer
CFO: Craig Stewart, Chief Financial Officer
CIO: David Furnas, Chief Information Officer
CHR: Barbara Barela, Director Human Resources
CNO: Pam Fulks, R.N., Chief Nursing Officer
Web address: www.grmc.org
**Control:** County–Government, nonfederal **Service:** General Medical and Surgical

> **Staffed Beds:** 68 **Admissions:** 2938 **Census:** 25 **Outpatient Visits:** 77350
> **Births:** 406 **Total Expense ($000):** 73502 **Payroll Expense ($000):** 29780
> **Personnel:** 623

## SOCORRO—Socorro County

☒ **SOCORRO GENERAL HOSPITAL (321301)**, 1202 Highway 60 West,
Zip 87801–3914, Mailing Address: P.O. Box 1009, Zip 87801–1009;
tel. 505/835–1140 **A**1 9 10 18 **F**3 8 11 13 15 29 30 34 35 40 45 57 59 62
63 64 68 75 77 81 83 85 91 93 100 103 107 114 130 132 133 134 135
147 **S** Presbyterian Healthcare Services, Albuquerque, NM
Primary Contact: Bo Beames, Administrator
CHR: Pam Miller–Balfour, Director Human Resources
Web address: www.phs.org
**Control:** Other not–for–profit (including NFP Corporation) **Service:** General
Medical and Surgical

> **Staffed Beds:** 24 **Admissions:** 528 **Census:** 4 **Outpatient Visits:** 21359
> **Births:** 137 **Total Expense ($000):** 25309 **Payroll Expense ($000):** 12147

## TAOS—Taos County

★ ◇ **HOLY CROSS HOSPITAL (320013)**, 1397 Weimer Road,
Zip 87571–6253; tel. 575/758–8883 **A**9 10 20 21 **F**11 15 18 29 30 34 35
36 40 43 45 46 50 51 57 59 64 68 70 75 76 81 82 86 89 107 110 114 118
119 127 130 132 135 147 148 **P**8 **S** QHR, Brentwood, TN
Primary Contact: Peter A. Hofstetter, Chief Executive Officer
CFO: Richard Eisenring, Chief Financial Officer
CMO: Loretta Ortiz y Pino, M.D., Chief Medical Officer
CIO: Spencer Hamons, Chief Information Officer
CHR: Lisa Clark, Human Resources Officer
CNO: Mary Anna Abeyta, R.N., Chief Nursing/Clinical Services Officer
Web address: www.taoshospital.org
**Control:** Other not–for–profit (including NFP Corporation) **Service:** General
Medical and Surgical

> **Staffed Beds:** 35 **Admissions:** 2286 **Census:** 21 **Outpatient Visits:** 69404
> **Births:** 240 **Total Expense ($000):** 36407 **Payroll Expense ($000):** 22189
> **Personnel:** 427

## TRUTH OR CONSEQUENCES—Sierra County

★ **SIERRA VISTA HOSPITAL (321300)**, 800 East Ninth Avenue, Zip 87901–1961;
tel. 575/894–2111 **A**9 10 18 **F**7 11 15 16 30 34 40 54 57 59 65 67 93 99
102 104 107 110 127 128 130 133 **P**6
Primary Contact: Domenica Rush, Chief Executive Officer
CFO: Bret Gobel, Chief Financial Officer
CMO: James F. Malcolmson, M.D., Chief of Staff
CIO: Dan Morrell, Manager Information Systems
CHR: Mindee Holguin, Manager Human Resources
Web address: www.svhnm.org
**Control:** City–County, Government, nonfederal **Service:** General Medical and
Surgical

> **Staffed Beds:** 15 **Admissions:** 400 **Census:** 3 **Outpatient Visits:** 21054
> **Births:** 0 **Total Expense ($000):** 13485 **Payroll Expense ($000):** 5981
> **Personnel:** 147

## TUCUMCARI—Quay County

★ **DR. DAN C. TRIGG MEMORIAL HOSPITAL (321302)**, 301 East Miel De Luna
Avenue, Zip 88401–3810, Mailing Address: P.O. Box 608, Zip 88401–0608;
tel. 575/461–7000 **A**9 10 18 **F**3 11 15 29 35 38 40 45 59 62 63 64 65 67
68 81 85 87 90 93 97 99 101 103 104 107 110 114 119 128 130 133 135
146 148 **P**6 **S** Presbyterian Healthcare Services, Albuquerque, NM
Primary Contact: Lance C. Labine, Administrator
Web address: www.phs.org
**Control:** Other not–for–profit (including NFP Corporation) **Service:** General
Medical and Surgical

> **Staffed Beds:** 14 **Admissions:** 269 **Census:** 3 **Outpatient Visits:** 13567
> **Total Expense ($000):** 15817 **Payroll Expense ($000):** 6234 **Personnel:** 89

**NM**

*Many Facility Codes have changed. Please refer to the AHA Guide Code Chart.*
© 2013 AHA Guide

☐ **U. S. PUBLIC HEALTH SERVICE INDIAN HOSPITAL (320060)**, Route 301
North B. Street, Zip 87327, Mailing Address: P.O. Box 467, Zip 87327–0467;
tel. 505/782–4431, (Nonreporting) **A**1 9 10 **S** U. S. Indian Health Service,
Rockville, MD
Primary Contact: Jean Othole, Chief Executive Officer
CFO: Clyde Yatsattie, Administrative Officer
CMO: David Kessler, M.D., Clinical Director
CHR: Cynthia Tsalate, Human Resource Specialist
Web address: www.ihs.gov
**Control:** PHS, Indian Service, Government, federal **Service:** General Medical and
Surgical

**Staffed Beds:** 32

NM

# NEW YORK

## ALBANY—Albany County

✠ **ALBANY MEDICAL CENTER (330013)**, 43 New Scotland Avenue, Zip 12208–3478; tel. 518/262–3125, (Includes ALBANY MEDICAL CENTER SOUTH–CLINICAL CAMPUS, 25 Hackett Boulevard, Zip 12208–3499; tel. 518/242–1200; Timothy W. Duffy, General Director) **A**1 2 3 5 8 9 10 **F**3 6 7 8 11 12 13 15 17 18 19 20 21 22 23 24 25 26 27 28 29 30 31 32 34 35 36 38 39 40 41 43 44 45 46 47 49 50 51 52 53 54 55 56 57 58 59 60 61 64 65 68 70 72 73 74 75 76 77 78 79 81 82 84 85 86 87 88 89 90 92 93 96 98 100 102 103 104 105 107 108 109 110 111 114 115 116 117 118 119 120 121 123 124 126 130 131 132 135 138 142 145 146 148
Primary Contact: James J. Barba, President and Chief Executive Officer
COO: Bernadette R. Pedlow, Senior Vice President Business and Chief Operating Officer
CFO: William C. Hasselbarth, Chief Financial Officer
CMO: Dennis McKenna, M.D., Interim Vice President Medical Affairs
CIO: George Hickman, Executive Vice President and Chief Information Officer
CHR: Catherine Halakan, Senior Vice President
Web address: www.amc.edu
**Control:** Other not–for–profit (including NFP Corporation) **Service:** General Medical and Surgical

**Staffed Beds:** 649 **Admissions:** 32890 **Census:** 547 **Outpatient Visits:** 334168 **Births:** 2076 **Total Expense ($000):** 702823 **Payroll Expense ($000):** 239861 **Personnel:** 5164

★ **ALBANY MEMORIAL HOSPITAL (330003)**, 600 Northern Boulevard, Zip 12204–1083; tel. 518/471–3221, (Nonreporting) **A**5 9 10 **S** Catholic Health East, Newtown Square, PA
Primary Contact: Ann Errichetti, M.D., Chief Executive Officer
COO: Karen Tassey, MS, Chief Operating Officer
CFO: Lori Santos, Vice President Finance
CMO: Daniel C. Silverman, M.D., Senior Vice President Medical Affairs
CIO: Robert J. Duthe, Vice President Corporate Management Information Systems
CHR: Barbara McCandless, Vice President Human Resources, Organization Development
Web address: www.nehealth.com
**Control:** Other not–for–profit (including NFP Corporation) **Service:** General Medical and Surgical

**Staffed Beds:** 165

✠ △ **ALBANY STRATTON VETERANS AFFAIRS MEDICAL CENTER**, 113 Holland Avenue, Zip 12208–3473; tel. 518/626–5000, (Total facility includes 44 beds in nursing home–type unit) **A**1 2 3 5 7 8 9 **F**2 3 4 5 12 15 17 18 20 28 29 30 31 34 35 39 40 45 46 47 50 54 56 57 58 59 60 61 62 63 64 65 68 70 74 75 77 78 79 81 82 83 84 86 87 91 92 93 94 97 98 100 102 103 104 105 106 107 108 109 111 115 119 121 122 128 129 130 132 135 143 146 147 148 **S** Department of Veterans Affairs, Washington, DC
Primary Contact: Linda W. Weiss, MS, FACHE, Director
COO: Donald W. Stuart, Associate Director
CFO: Gerard Scorzelli, Chief Financial Officer
CMO: Lourdes Irizarry, M.D., Chief of Staff
CIO: Mike Mullahey, Operations Manager
CHR: Kenneth Kio, Manager Human Resources
CNO: Deborah Spath, R.N., Associate Director Patient and Nurses Services
Web address: www.albany.va.gov/
**Control:** Veterans Affairs, Government, federal **Service:** General Medical and Surgical

**Staffed Beds:** 150 **Admissions:** 2779 **Census:** 48 **Outpatient Visits:** 332181 **Total Expense ($000):** 225780 **Payroll Expense ($000):** 131657 **Personnel:** 1260

☐ **CAPITAL DISTRICT PSYCHIATRIC CENTER (334046)**, 75 New Scotland Avenue, Zip 12208–3474; tel. 518/447–9611, (Nonreporting) **A**1 3 5 10 **S** New York State Office of Mental Health, Albany, NY
Primary Contact: William Dickson, Acting Executive Director
CMO: Beatrice Kovasznay, M.D., Clinical Director
Web address: www.omh.ny.gov/omhweb/facilities/cdpc/facility.htm
**Control:** State–Government, nonfederal **Service:** Psychiatric

**Staffed Beds:** 200

✠ **ST. PETER'S HOSPITAL (330057)**, 315 South Manning Boulevard, Zip 12208–1789; tel. 518/525–1550, (Nonreporting) **A**1 2 3 5 9 10 **S** Catholic Health East, Newtown Square, PA
Primary Contact: Ann Errichetti, M.D., Chief Executive Officer
CFO: James M. Gavin, Chief Financial Officer
CMO: Robert Cella, M.D., Vice President Medical Affairs
CIO: Jonathan Goldberg, Chief Information Officer
CHR: Judy Gray, Vice President Human Resources
Web address: www.sphcs.org
**Control:** Church–operated, Nongovernment, not–for profit **Service:** General Medical and Surgical

**Staffed Beds:** 487

## ALEXANDRIA BAY—Jefferson County

★ **RIVER HOSPITAL (331309)**, 4 Fuller Street, Zip 13607–1316; tel. 315/482–2511 **A**9 10 18 **F**3 11 15 18 29 34 35 40 45 50 57 59 64 68 81 84 87 93 97 104 105 107 114 119 130 133 135 147
Primary Contact: Ben Moore, III, President and Chief Executive Officer
COO: William Connor, Assistant Administrator and Director Human Resources
CFO: Traci Mintonye, Chief Financial Officer
CMO: Prasad Yitta, M.D., Medical Director
CIO: John Smithers, Network Specialist
CHR: William Connor, Assistant Administrator and Director Human Resources
CNO: Ann Narrow, Director of Nursing
Web address: www.riverhospital.org
**Control:** Other not–for–profit (including NFP Corporation) **Service:** General Medical and Surgical

**Staffed Beds:** 11 **Admissions:** 160 **Census:** 1 **Outpatient Visits:** 38144 **Births:** 0 **Total Expense ($000):** 13184 **Payroll Expense ($000):** 7717 **Personnel:** 139

## AMITYVILLE—Suffolk County

☐ **SOUTH OAKS HOSPITAL (334027)**, 400 Sunrise Highway, Zip 11701–2508; tel. 631/264–4000 **A**1 9 10 **F**4 5 53 98 99 103 104 105 **S** North Shore–Long Island Jewish Health System, Great Neck, NY
Primary Contact: Robert E. Detor, Chief Executive Officer
CFO: Patricia Porter, Chief Financial Officer
CMO: Yogendra Upadhyay, M.D., Senior Vice President Medical Affairs
CHR: Pam Quiroga, Vice President Human Resources
Web address: www.longislandhome.org
**Control:** Other not–for–profit (including NFP Corporation) **Service:** Psychiatric

**Staffed Beds:** 260 **Admissions:** 4233 **Census:** 137 **Outpatient Visits:** 104217 **Births:** 0 **Total Expense ($000):** 49389 **Payroll Expense ($000):** 27477 **Personnel:** 477

## AMSTERDAM—Montgomery County

**ST. MARY'S AMSTERDAM CAMPUS** See St. Mary's Healthcare

✠ △ **ST. MARY'S HEALTHCARE (330047)**, 427 Guy Park Avenue, Zip 12010–1054; tel. 518/842–1900, (Includes ST. MARY'S AMSTERDAM CAMPUS, 4988 State Highway 30, Zip 12010–1699; tel. 518/842–3100), (Total facility includes 160 beds in nursing home–type unit) **A**1 7 9 10 **F**2 3 4 5 8 11 13 15 17 28 29 30 31 34 35 36 38 40 45 49 50 51 54 56 57 59 60 61 65 66 68 70 71 74 75 76 77 78 79 81 82 84 85 86 87 90 93 94 96 97 98 99 100 101 102 103 104 105 106 107 108 110 111 115 118 119 127 128 130 131 132 135 144 145 146 147 **P**6 **S** Ascension Health, Saint Louis, MO
Primary Contact: Victor Giulianelli, FACHE, President and Chief Executive Officer
COO: Scott Bruce, Vice President Operations
CMO: Timothy Shoen, M.D., Vice President Medical Staff Services
CIO: James DeGroff, Director Technology and Network Services
CHR: Beth Case, Vice President Human Resources
Web address: www.smha.org
**Control:** Other not–for–profit (including NFP Corporation) **Service:** General Medical and Surgical

**Staffed Beds:** 290 **Admissions:** 6322 **Census:** 240 **Outpatient Visits:** 405613 **Births:** 473 **Total Expense ($000):** 135698 **Payroll Expense ($000):** 74980 **Personnel:** 1369

## AUBURN—Cayuga County

✠ **AUBURN COMMUNITY HOSPITAL (330235)**, 17 Lansing Street, Zip 13021–1943; tel. 315/255–7011, (Total facility includes 80 beds in nursing home–type unit) **A**1 9 10 **F**1 3 12 13 15 26 28 29 30 34 35 40 45 50 51 54 55 57 59 64 70 76 78 79 81 82 85 89 98 103 107 108 110 111 114 118 129 130 132 135 144 146 147 148
Primary Contact: Scott A. Berlucchi, FACHE, President and Chief Executive Officer
COO: Thomas Filiak, Chief Operating Officer
CFO: John Baran, Chief Financial Officer
CMO: John A. Riccio, M.D., Chief Medical Officer
CIO: Chris Ryan, Chief Information Officer
CHR: Colleen McLaughlin, Director Employee Relations
Web address: www.auburnhospital.org
**Control:** Other not–for–profit (including NFP Corporation) **Service:** General Medical and Surgical

**Staffed Beds:** 179 **Admissions:** 5398 **Census:** 151 **Outpatient Visits:** 152768 **Births:** 451 **Total Expense ($000):** 87369 **Payroll Expense ($000):** 37722 **Personnel:** 630

*Many Facility Codes have changed. Please refer to the AHA Guide Code Chart.* © 2013 AHA Guide

## BATAVIA—Genesee County

☒ **UNITED MEMORIAL MEDICAL CENTER (330073)**, 127 North Street, Zip 14020–1631; tel. 585/343–6030, (Includes UNITED MEMORIAL MEDICAL CENTER–BANK STREET, 127 North Street, Zip 14020–2260; tel. 716/343–3131; UNITED MEMORIAL MEDICAL CENTER–NORTH STREET, 16 Banks Street, Zip 14020–1697; tel. 585/343–6030) **A**1 9 10 **F**3 4 8 13 14 15 17 18 28 29 30 31 34 35 40 43 45 49 50 54 56 57 59 64 70 75 76 77 79 81 82 85 89 93 97 107 111 114 115 119 129 130 131 135 144 146 147 148
Primary Contact: Mark C. Schoell, Chief Executive Officer
CFO: Robert Chiavetta, Vice President Finance
CMO: Michael Merrill, M.D., Interim Vice President Medical Affairs
CIO: Daniel O'Connor, Chief Information Officer
CHR: Sonja Gonyea, Director Human Resources
Web address: www.ummc.org
**Control:** Other not–for–profit (including NFP Corporation) **Service:** General Medical and Surgical

**Staffed Beds:** 131 **Admissions:** 4336 **Census:** 62 **Outpatient Visits:** 230974 **Births:** 653 **Total Expense ($000):** 76304 **Payroll Expense ($000):** 31917 **Personnel:** 667

★ **VETERANS AFFAIRS WESTERN NEW YORK HEALTHCARE SYSTEM–BATAVIA DIVISION**, 222 Richmond Avenue, Zip 14020–1288; tel. 585/297–1000, (Nonreporting) **A**5 9 **S** Department of Veterans Affairs, Washington, DC
Primary Contact: Brian G. Stiller, Director Medical Center
Web address: www.buffalo.va.gov/batavia.asp
**Control:** Veterans Affairs, Government, federal **Service:** General Medical and Surgical

**Staffed Beds:** 128

## BATH—Steuben County

☒ △ **BATH VETERANS AFFAIRS MEDICAL CENTER**, (Formerly Veterans Affairs Medical Center), 76 Veterans Avenue, Zip 14810–0842; tel. 607/664–4000, (Total facility includes 124 beds in nursing home–type unit) **A**1 7 **F**1 3 5 6 7 8 12 16 17 18 20 22 24 26 28 29 30 31 33 34 35 36 38 39 40 50 53 56 57 58 59 61 62 63 64 65 68 70 71 74 75 77 78 79 81 82 83 84 86 87 90 91 92 93 94 97 98 100 101 102 103 104 106 107 111 112 115 116 117 119 126 127 128 129 130 132 135 143 144 146 147 148 **P**6 **S** Department of Veterans Affairs, Washington, DC
Primary Contact: Michael J. Swartz, FACHE, Medical Center Director
COO: David Krueger, Associate Director
CFO: Jill Haynes, Financial Coach
CMO: Felipe Diaz, M.D., Chief of Staff
CIO: Karen Clancy, Manager Information Systems Operations
CHR: Susan DeSalvo, Manager Human Resources
Web address: www.bath.va.gov
**Control:** Veterans Affairs, Government, federal **Service:** General Medical and Surgical

**Staffed Beds:** 371 **Admissions:** 1551 **Census:** 292 **Outpatient Visits:** 164915 **Births:** 0 **Total Expense ($000):** 91829 **Payroll Expense ($000):** 60974 **Personnel:** 704

☒ ◇ **IRA DAVENPORT MEMORIAL HOSPITAL (330144)**, 7571 State Route 54, Zip 14810–9590; tel. 607/776–8500, (Nonreporting) **A**1 9 10 21 **S** Arnot Health, Elmira, NY
Primary Contact: James B. Watson, Chief Operating Officer
CMO: Dennis O'Connor, M.D., Medical Director
CIO: Hendrik Van der Horst, Chief Information Officer
CHR: Marybess Hazlett, Director Human Resources
Web address: www.davenportandtaylor.org
**Control:** Other not–for–profit (including NFP Corporation) **Service:** General Medical and Surgical

**Staffed Beds:** 156

## BAY SHORE—Suffolk County

☒ △ **SOUTHSIDE HOSPITAL (330043)**, 301 East Main Street, Zip 11706–8458; tel. 631/968–3000 **A**1 2 3 5 7 9 10 **F**3 7 11 13 15 17 18 20 22 24 26 28 29 30 31 32 34 35 36 38 40 43 44 45 49 50 54 55 56 57 58 59 60 61 63 64 65 66 68 70 73 74 75 76 77 78 79 81 82 85 86 87 89 90 93 96 97 98 100 101 102 103 107 108 110 111 114 118 119 120 121 123 129 130 131 132 134 135 146 147 148 **P**5 6 **S** North Shore–Long Island Jewish Health System, Great Neck, NY
Primary Contact: Donna Moravick, R.N., MSN, Executive Director
CFO: Robert Power, Associate Executive Director Finance
CMO: Jay Enden, M.D., Medical Director
CIO: Lowney Mincy, Director Information Services
CHR: Anne J. Barrett, Associate Executive Director Human Resources
Web address: www.southsidehospital.org
**Control:** Other not–for–profit (including NFP Corporation) **Service:** General Medical and Surgical

**Staffed Beds:** 300 **Admissions:** 17737 **Census:** 243 **Outpatient Visits:** 152765 **Births:** 2475 **Total Expense ($000):** 377774 **Payroll Expense ($000):** 185632 **Personnel:** 2170

## BELLEROSE—Queens County, See New York City

## BETHPAGE—Nassau County

☐ **ST. JOSEPH HOSPITAL (330332)**, 4295 Hempstead Turnpike, Zip 11714–5769; tel. 516/579–6000 **A**1 9 10 **F**3 8 15 17 18 29 30 34 35 39 40 45 46 49 50 51 56 57 59 60 64 65 68 69 70 74 75 79 81 82 85 86 87 89 93 107 108 110 111 114 119 129 130 131 132 135 146 148 **S** Catholic Health Services of Long Island, Rockville Centre, NY
Primary Contact: Drew Pallas, Executive Vice President and Chief Administrative Officer
CMO: Lawrence A. Reduto, M.D., President and Chief Medical Officer
CIO: Blake Benz, Director Management Information Systems
CHR: Peter Chiacchiaro, Vice President Human Resources
Web address: www.newislandhospital.org
**Control:** Other not–for–profit (including NFP Corporation) **Service:** General Medical and Surgical

**Staffed Beds:** 140 **Admissions:** 6713 **Census:** 95 **Outpatient Visits:** 50679 **Births:** 0 **Total Expense ($000):** 106110 **Payroll Expense ($000):** 45078 **Personnel:** 676

## BINGHAMTON—Broome County

**BINGHAMTON GENERAL HOSPITAL** See United Health Services Hospitals–Binghamton

☐ **GREATER BINGHAMTON HEALTH CENTER (334012)**, 425 Robinson Street, Zip 13904–1735; tel. 607/724–1391, (Nonreporting) **A**1 10 **S** New York State Office of Mental Health, Albany, NY
Primary Contact: Mark Stephany, Executive Director
CFO: Cherry Randall, Business Officer
CIO: Timothy Lauve, Coordinator Mental Health Local Information Systems
CHR: Renee O'Brien, Director Human Resources
Web address: www.omh.ny.gov/omhweb/facilities/bipc/facility.htm
**Control:** State–Government, nonfederal **Service:** Psychiatric

**Staffed Beds:** 115

☒ **OUR LADY OF LOURDES MEMORIAL HOSPITAL (330011)**, 169 Riverside Drive, Zip 13905–4246; tel. 607/798–5111 **A**1 2 9 10 **F**3 11 12 13 15 18 19 28 29 30 32 34 35 36 39 40 44 45 46 47 49 50 51 53 54 56 57 59 60 62 63 64 65 66 68 70 71 74 75 76 77 78 79 81 84 85 86 87 89 93 97 99 100 101 103 104 107 108 110 111 114 115 118 119 120 121 123 124 126 127 129 130 131 132 134 135 143 144 145 146 147 148 **P**6 **S** Ascension Health, Saint Louis, MO
Primary Contact: David Patak, President and Chief Executive Officer
COO: Linda Miller, DNP, R.N., Senior Vice President Operations and Chief Nursing Officer
CFO: Gregg Hayton, Vice President Finance and Chief Financial Officer
CMO: Robert Taylor, III, M.D., Vice President Medical Affairs
CIO: John Laliberte, Assistant Vice President
CHR: Jim Silkworth, Chief Human Resources Officer
Web address: www.lourdes.com
**Control:** Church–operated, Nongovernment, not–for profit **Service:** General Medical and Surgical

**Staffed Beds:** 154 **Admissions:** 10212 **Census:** 114 **Outpatient Visits:** 1464985 **Births:** 1205 **Total Expense ($000):** 280010 **Payroll Expense ($000):** 115125 **Personnel:** 1789

**NY**

**UNITED HEALTH SERVICES HOSPITALS–BINGHAMTON (330394)**, 10–42 Mitchell Avenue, Zip 13903–1678; tel. 607/763–6000, (Includes BINGHAMTON GENERAL HOSPITAL, 10–42 Mitchell Avenue, Zip 13903; tel. 607/762–2200; MEDICENTER, 600 High Avenue, Endicott, Zip 13760; tel. 607/754–7171; WILSON MEMORIAL REGIONAL MEDICAL CENTER, 33–57 Harrison Street, Johnson City, Zip 13790; tel. 607/763–6000) **A**8 9 10 12 13 **F**1 3 4 5 8 11 12 13 15 17 18 20 22 24 26 28 29 30 31 32 33 34 35 37 38 39 40 43 45 46 49 50 51 52 54 57 58 59 60 61 64 65 68 70 72 74 75 76 77 78 79 81 84 85 86 87 89 90 92 93 96 97 98 100 101 102 103 104 107 108 110 114 115 118 119 124 126 127 130 131 132 135 146 147 148 **P**3 **S** United Health Services, Binghamton, NY
Primary Contact: Matthew J. Salanger, President and Chief Executive Officer
Web address: www.uhs.net
**Control:** Other not–for–profit (including NFP Corporation) **Service:** General Medical and Surgical

**Staffed Beds:** 456 **Admissions:** 17281 **Census:** 283 **Outpatient Visits:** 648770 **Births:** 1590 **Total Expense ($000):** 474708 **Payroll Expense ($000):** 184752 **Personnel:** 3308

## BRENTWOOD—Suffolk County

☐ **PILGRIM PSYCHIATRIC CENTER (334013)**, 998 Crooked Hill Road, Zip 11717–1019; tel. 631/761–3500, (Nonreporting) **A**1 10 **S** New York State Office of Mental Health, Albany, NY
Primary Contact: Kathy O'Keefe, Executive Director
CFO: Florence Corwin, Director for Administration
CMO: Inderjit Singh, M.D., Clinical Director
CIO: Douglas Cargonara, Ph.D., Chief Information Officer
CHR: Florence Corwin, Director Administration
Web address: www.omh.ny.gov/omhweb/facilities/pgpc/facility.htm
**Control:** State–Government, nonfederal **Service:** Psychiatric

**Staffed Beds:** 569

## BRONX—Bronx County, See New York City

## BRONXVILLE—Westchester County

✠ **LAWRENCE HOSPITAL CENTER (330061)**, 55 Palmer Avenue, Zip 10708–3403; tel. 914/787–1000 **A**1 2 5 9 10 **F**3 11 12 13 15 18 19 28 29 30 31 34 35 36 40 41 45 46 47 49 50 51 55 57 59 60 62 63 64 65 68 69 70 72 73 74 75 76 77 78 79 81 82 84 85 87 89 91 92 93 94 107 108 110 111 114 115 118 119 129 130 131 132 133 135 141 146 147 148 **P**6
Primary Contact: Edward M. Dinan, President and Chief Executive Officer
COO: James Y. Lee, Executive Vice President and Chief Operating Officer
CFO: Murray Askinazi, Senior Vice President and Chief Financial Officer
CMO: Werner Roeder, M.D., Vice President Medical Affairs
CHR: Tom Mastroianni, Vice President Human Resources
CNO: Rose Ann O'Hare, R.N., Vice President Patient Services
Web address: www.lawrencehealth.org
**Control:** Other not–for–profit (including NFP Corporation) **Service:** General Medical and Surgical

**Staffed Beds:** 187 **Admissions:** 11389 **Census:** 148 **Outpatient Visits:** 164482 **Births:** 1622 **Total Expense ($000):** 187893 **Payroll Expense ($000):** 81374 **Personnel:** 1004

## BROOKLYN—Kings County, See New York City

## BUFFALO—Erie County

**BRYLIN HOSPITALS (334022)**, 1263 Delaware Avenue, Zip 14209–2402; tel. 716/886–8200 **A**9 10 **F**5 29 30 34 35 36 54 56 57 75 86 98 99 101 103 104
Primary Contact: Eric D. Pleskow, President and Chief Executive Officer
CFO: E. Paul Hettich, Chief Financial Officer
CMO: Balvinder Kang, M.D., Medical Director
CIO: Pawel Wieczorek, Director Information Technology
CHR: Jacquelyn Bixler, Vice President Human Resources
Web address: www.brylin.com
**Control:** Corporation, Investor–owned, for–profit **Service:** Psychiatric

**Staffed Beds:** 71 **Admissions:** 1400 **Census:** 44 **Births:** 0 **Total Expense ($000):** 14279 **Payroll Expense ($000):** 9021 **Personnel:** 136

☐ **BUFFALO PSYCHIATRIC CENTER (334052)**, 400 Forest Avenue, Zip 14213–1298; tel. 716/885–2261, (Nonreporting) **A**1 3 5 10 **S** New York State Office of Mental Health, Albany, NY
Primary Contact: Thomas Dodson, Executive Director
COO: Celia Spacone, M.D., Director Operations
CFO: Pamela Esposito, Director Quality Management and Acting Director Facility Administration
CMO: Jeffery Grace, M.D., Clinical Director
CIO: Anne Buchheit, Coordinator Mental Health Local Information Systems
CHR: Charles Siewert, Director Human Resources
Web address: www.omh.ny.gov
**Control:** State–Government, nonfederal **Service:** Psychiatric

**Staffed Beds:** 240

✠ **ERIE COUNTY MEDICAL CENTER (330219)**, 462 Grider Street, Zip 14215–3098; tel. 716/898–3000, (Total facility includes 373 beds in nursing home–type unit) **A**1 3 5 9 10 **F**5 8 11 15 16 18 20 22 24 26 29 30 31 33 34 35 39 40 43 50 53 54 56 58 59 60 61 62 64 65 66 68 70 74 75 77 78 79 81 82 85 87 90 92 93 94 97 98 99 100 102 103 104 107 108 111 115 119 128 130 138 142 146 148 **P**4 5 6
Primary Contact: Jody Lomeo, Chief Executive Officer
COO: Richard C. Cleland, FACHE, Chief Operating Officer
CFO: Michael Sammarco, M.D., Chief Financial Officer
CMO: Brian Murray, M.D., Medical Director
CIO: Leslie Feidt, Chief Information Officer
CHR: Kathleen O'Hara, Vice President Human Resources
Web address: www.ecmc.edu
**Control:** Hospital district or authority, Government, nonfederal **Service:** General Medical and Surgical

**Staffed Beds:** 781 **Admissions:** 16477 **Census:** 789 **Outpatient Visits:** 417866 **Births:** 0 **Total Expense ($000):** 456290 **Payroll Expense ($000):** 157584 **Personnel:** 2700

△ ◇ **KALEIDA HEALTH (330005)**, 100 High Street, Zip 14203–1154; tel. 716/859–5600, (Includes DE GRAFF MEMORIAL HOSPITAL, 445 Tremont Street, North Tonawanda, Zip 14120–0750, Mailing Address: P.O. Box 0750, Zip 14120–0750; tel. 716/694–4500; Tamara Owen, President; MILLARD FILLMORE SUBURBAN HOSPITAL, 1540 Maple Road, Williamsville, Zip 14221; tel. 716/688–3100; WOMEN AND CHILDREN'S HOSPITAL, 219 Bryant Street, Zip 14222–2099; tel. 716/878–7000; Cheryl Klass, President), (Total facility includes 380 beds in nursing home–type unit) **A**3 5 7 10 21 **F**2 3 5 8 9 11 12 13 15 17 18 19 20 21 22 23 24 25 26 28 29 30 31 32 34 35 36 37 39 40 41 43 44 45 46 49 50 51 54 55 57 58 59 60 61 62 63 64 65 66 68 70 71 72 73 74 75 76 77 78 79 81 82 83 84 85 86 87 88 89 90 92 93 94 96 97 98 99 100 101 102 103 104 105 107 108 109 110 111 112 114 115 116 117 118 119 126 128 130 131 132 135 138 143 145 146 147 148 **P**2 4 5 6
Primary Contact: James R. Kaskie, President and Chief Executive Officer
CFO: Joseph Kessler, Executive Vice President and Chief Financial Officer
CMO: Margaret Paroski, M.D., Executive Vice President and Chief Medical Officer
CIO: Francis Meyer, Vice President Information Systems Technology
Web address: www.kaleidahealth.org
**Control:** Other not–for–profit (including NFP Corporation) **Service:** General Medical and Surgical

**Staffed Beds:** 1459 **Admissions:** 59505 **Census:** 1371 **Outpatient Visits:** 452555 **Births:** 5508 **Total Expense ($000):** 1247061 **Payroll Expense ($000):** 516077 **Personnel:** 7453

✠ **MERCY HOSPITAL (330279)**, 565 Abbott Road, Zip 14220–2095; tel. 716/826–7000, (Total facility includes 84 beds in nursing home–type unit) **A**1 3 5 9 10 **F**3 8 13 15 17 18 20 22 24 26 29 30 32 34 35 39 40 42 45 48 49 54 57 59 60 64 65 66 70 72 74 75 76 78 79 81 83 84 85 86 87 89 90 92 93 94 96 97 107 108 110 111 114 115 118 119 126 128 129 130 131 132 146 147 148 **P**5 **S** Catholic Health System, Buffalo, NY
Primary Contact: Charles J. Urlaub, President and Chief Executive Officer
COO: John J. Herman, Chief Operating Officer
CFO: James H. Dunlop, Jr., CPA, Senior Vice President Finance and Chief Financial Officer
CMO: Timothy Gabryel, M.D., Vice President Medical Affairs and Medical Director
CIO: Michael Galang, M.D., Chief Information Officer
CHR: Joseph A. Scrivo, Jr., Director Human Resources
CNO: Kathleen Guarino, R.N., Vice President Patient Care Services
Web address: www.chsbuffalo.org
**Control:** Church–operated, Nongovernment, not–for profit **Service:** General Medical and Surgical

**Staffed Beds:** 438 **Admissions:** 19458 **Census:** 345 **Outpatient Visits:** 377458 **Births:** 2384 **Total Expense ($000):** 334630 **Payroll Expense ($000):** 138276 **Personnel:** 2145

☐ **ROSWELL PARK CANCER INSTITUTE (330354)**, Elm and Carlton Streets, Zip 14263–0001; tel. 716/845–2300 **A**1 2 3 5 8 9 10 **F**3 8 11 14 15 18 29 30 31 32 34 35 38 39 44 45 46 47 49 50 54 55 56 57 58 59 61 63 64 65 66 67 68 70 74 75 77 78 79 81 82 84 85 86 87 89 90 93 94 96 97 98 100 104 107 108 110 111 112 114 115 116 117 118 119 120 121 123 124 126 130 132 135 136 141 145 146 147 148 **P**6
Primary Contact: Donald L. Trump, M.D., President and Chief Executive Officer
COO: Joyce M. Yasko, Ph.D., Chief Operating Officer
CFO: Gregory McDonald, Vice President Finance and Chief Financial Officer
CMO: Judy Smith, M.D., Medical Director
CIO: Kevin Kimball, Vice President Information Technology
CHR: Vicki Garcia, Vice President Human Resources
CNO: Maureen Kelly, R.N., Chief Nursing Officer
Web address: www.roswellpark.org
**Control:** Hospital district or authority, Government, nonfederal **Service:** Cancer

**Staffed Beds:** 123 **Admissions:** 5394 **Census:** 99 **Outpatient Visits:** 201554 **Births:** 0 **Total Expense ($000):** 580506 **Payroll Expense ($000):** 222004 **Personnel:** 3346

*Many Facility Codes have changed. Please refer to the AHA Guide Code Chart.*

⊠ **SISTERS OF CHARITY HOSPITAL OF BUFFALO (330078)**, 2157 Main Street, Zip 14214–2692; tel. 716/862–1000, (Total facility includes 80 beds in nursing home–type unit) **A**1 2 3 5 9 10 12 13 **F**2 3 5 8 12 13 15 17 18 28 29 30 31 32 34 35 39 40 45 47 49 52 54 57 59 60 62 64 65 66 68 70 71 72 73 74 75 76 77 78 79 81 82 84 85 86 87 90 92 93 94 96 97 107 108 110 111 114 115 118 119 128 129 130 131 132 146 147 148 **P**5 **S** Catholic Health System, Buffalo, NY
Primary Contact: Peter U. Bergmann, President and Chief Executive Officer
COO: Matthew Hamp, Chief Operating Officer
CFO: James H. Dunlop, Jr., CPA, Chief Financial Officer
CMO: Nady Shehata, M.D., Vice President Medical Affairs
CIO: Michael Galang, M.D., Chief Information Officer
CHR: David DeLorenzo, Senior Director Human Resources
CNO: Mary E. Dillon, MS, Vice President Patient Care Services
Web address: www.chsbuffalo.org
**Control:** Church–operated, Nongovernment, not–for profit **Service:** General Medical and Surgical

**Staffed Beds:** 467 **Admissions:** 18587 **Census:** 325 **Outpatient Visits:** 669598 **Births:** 3275 **Total Expense ($000):** 252054 **Payroll Expense ($000):** 139149 **Personnel:** 2323

⊠ △ **VETERANS AFFAIRS WESTERN NEW YORK HEALTHCARE SYSTEM–BUFFALO DIVISION**, 3495 Bailey Avenue, Zip 14215–1129; tel. 716/834–9200, (Nonreporting) **A**1 2 3 5 7 8 9 **S** Department of Veterans Affairs, Washington, DC
Primary Contact: Brian G. Stiller, Director Medical Center
CFO: Royce Calhoun, Business Manager
CMO: Miguel Rainstein, M.D., Acting Chief of Staff
CIO: Margaret Owczarzak, Facility Chief Information Officer
Web address: www.buffalo.va.gov/index.asp
**Control:** Veterans Affairs, Government, federal **Service:** General Medical and Surgical

**Staffed Beds:** 113

**WOMEN AND CHILDREN'S HOSPITAL** See KALEIDA Health

**CALLICOON—Sullivan County**

☐ **GROVER M. HERMAN HOSPITAL (331303)**, (Formerly Catskill Regional Medical Center), 8881 Route 97, Zip 12723; tel. 845/887–5530, (Nonreporting) **A**1 9 10 18 **S** Greater Hudson Valley Health System, Middletown, NY
Primary Contact: Chris L. White, Administrator
Web address: www.crmcny.org
**Control:** Other not–for–profit (including NFP Corporation) **Service:** General Medical and Surgical

**Staffed Beds:** 25

**CANANDAIGUA—Ontario County**

★ **CANANDAIGUA VETERANS AFFAIRS MEDICAL CENTER**, (Formerly Veterans Affairs Medical Center), 400 Fort Hill Avenue, Zip 14424–1159; tel. 585/394–2000, (Total facility includes 116 beds in nursing home–type unit) **A**3 5 **F**2 4 5 12 29 30 33 34 35 36 38 39 50 53 54 56 57 59 61 62 63 64 65 68 71 74 75 77 82 83 84 86 87 90 91 93 94 95 96 97 100 101 103 104 106 107 119 127 128 130 132 135 143 146 147 148 **S** Department of Veterans Affairs, Washington, DC
Primary Contact: Craig Howard, Director
CMO: Robert Babcock, M.D., Chief of Staff
CIO: Patricia Simon, Manager Information Systems
Web address: www.canandaigua.va.gov/
**Control:** Veterans Affairs, Government, federal **Service:** General Medical and Surgical

**Staffed Beds:** 196 **Admissions:** 718 **Census:** 181 **Outpatient Visits:** 238914 **Births:** 0 **Total Expense ($000):** 124199 **Payroll Expense ($000):** 93842 **Personnel:** 863

⊠ **F. F. THOMPSON HOSPITAL (330074)**, 350 Parrish Street, Zip 14424–1731; tel. 585/396–6000, (Total facility includes 188 beds in nursing home–type unit) **A**1 9 10 **F**3 11 13 15 18 28 29 30 31 32 34 35 40 45 49 54 57 59 66 70 74 75 76 77 79 81 85 89 93 96 97 107 108 110 111 115 118 119 126 129 130 131 132 135 144 145 146 147 148 **S** University of Rochester Medical Center, Rochester, NY
Primary Contact: Michael Stapleton, R.N., MS, President and Chief Executive Officer
COO: Kurt Koczent, Executive Vice President and Chief Operating Officer
CFO: Mark Prunoske, Chief Financial Officer and Senior Vice President Finance
CMO: Carlos Ortiz, M.D., Senior Vice President Medical Services
CIO: Mark Halladay, Director Information Services
CHR: Jennifer DeVault, Vice President Associate Services
Web address: www.thompsonhealth.com
**Control:** Other not–for–profit (including NFP Corporation) **Service:** General Medical and Surgical

**Staffed Beds:** 214 **Admissions:** 4720 **Census:** 231 **Outpatient Visits:** 1233699 **Births:** 571 **Total Expense ($000):** 110953 **Payroll Expense ($000):** 51327 **Personnel:** 840

**THOMPSON HEALTH** See F. F. Thompson Hospital

**CARMEL—Putnam County**

**ARMS ACRES**, 75 Seminary Hill Road, Zip 10512–1921; tel. 845/225–3400, (Nonreporting) **A**9
Primary Contact: Patrice Wallace–Moore, Chief Executive Officer and Executive Director
CFO: Sultan Niazi, Chief Financial Officer
CMO: Fred Hesse, M.D., Medical Director
CIO: Dolores Watson, Director Health Information Management
CHR: Kim Halpin, Director Human Resources
CNO: Barbara Klein, R.N., Director of Nursing
Web address: www.armsacres.com
**Control:** Corporation, Investor–owned, for–profit **Service:** Alcoholism and other chemical dependency

**Staffed Beds:** 146

⊠ **PUTNAM HOSPITAL CENTER (330273)**, 670 Stoneleigh Avenue, Zip 10512–3997; tel. 845/279–5711 **A**1 2 9 10 **F**3 11 12 13 15 28 29 30 31 32 33 34 35 38 40 49 50 51 54 57 59 60 63 64 68 70 74 75 76 78 79 81 82 85 86 87 89 93 98 99 100 101 102 103 104 105 107 108 111 114 116 117 119 120 121 126 129 130 131 132 135 146 147 148 **S** Health Quest Systems, Inc., LaGrangeville, NY
Primary Contact: Maureen Zipparo, President and Chief Operating Officer
CFO: Anthony Mirdita, Chief Financial Officer
CMO: Ronald Tatelbaum, M.D., Interim Vice President Medical Affairs
CIO: Robert Diamond, Vice President and Chief Information Officer
CHR: Joan L. Calabrese, Director Human Resources
Web address: www.putnamhospital.org
**Control:** Other not–for–profit (including NFP Corporation) **Service:** General Medical and Surgical

**Staffed Beds:** 164 **Admissions:** 6602 **Census:** 90 **Outpatient Visits:** 202050 **Births:** 428 **Total Expense ($000):** 150711 **Payroll Expense ($000):** 49860 **Personnel:** 731

**CARTHAGE—Jefferson County**

☐ ◇ **CARTHAGE AREA HOSPITAL (330263)**, 1001 West Street, Zip 13619–9703; tel. 315/493–1000, (Nonreporting) **A**1 9 10 20 21
Primary Contact: Adel Amir, Interim Chief Executive Officer
COO: Richard Duvall, Director Support Services and Chief Operating Officer
CMO: Mirza Ashraf, M.D., Medical Director
CIO: Skip Edie, Chief Information Officer
CHR: Richard Duvall, Director Support Services and Chief Operating Officer
Web address: www.carthagehospital.com
**Control:** Other not–for–profit (including NFP Corporation) **Service:** General Medical and Surgical

**Staffed Beds:** 78

**CASTLE POINT—Dutchess County**

**VETERAN AFFAIRS HUDSON VALLEY HEALTH CARE SYSTEM–CASTLE POINT DIVISION** See Veterans Affairs Hudson Valley Health Care System–F.D. Roosevelt Hospital, Montrose

**CATSKILL—Greene County**

**KAATERSKILL CARE** See Columbia Memorial Hospital, Hudson

**NY**

---

**Hospital, Medicare Provider Number, Address, Telephone, Approval, Facility, and Physician Codes, Health Care System**

★ American Hospital Association (AHA) membership
☐ The Joint Commission accreditation ◇ DNV Healthcare Inc. accreditation
○ Healthcare Facilities Accreditation Program
△ Commission on Accreditation of Rehabilitation Facilities (CARF) accreditation

## CLIFTON SPRINGS—Ontario County

★ ◇ **CLIFTON SPRINGS HOSPITAL AND CLINIC (330265)**, 2 Coulter Road, Zip 14432–1189; tel. 315/462–9561, (Total facility includes 108 beds in nursing home–type unit) **A**9 10 21 **F**4 5 6 11 15 18 26 28 29 30 31 33 34 35 36 38 40 44 45 46 48 49 50 51 54 55 56 57 59 60 63 64 65 68 70 71 74 75 77 78 79 81 82 83 85 86 87 93 97 98 100 101 102 103 104 106 107 108 110 111 114 117 119 128 130 131 132 135 146 147 148 **P**4 6
Primary Contact: Lewis Zulick, M.D., Chief Executive Officer
CFO: Robert E. Fisher, Chief Financial Officer
CIO: David Markant, Director Information Systems
CHR: Kathy Babb, Manager Human Resources
CNO: Donna P. Smith, R.N., Vice President Patient Care Services and Chief Nursing Officer
Web address: www.cliftonspringshospital.org
**Control:** Other not–for–profit (including NFP Corporation) **Service:** General Medical and Surgical

**Staffed Beds:** 214 **Admissions:** 2770 **Census:** 157 **Outpatient Visits:** 117554 **Births:** 0 **Total Expense ($000):** 60096 **Payroll Expense ($000):** 28644

## COBLESKILL—Schoharie County

✉ **COBLESKILL REGIONAL HOSPITAL (330268)**, 178 Grandview Drive, Zip 12043–5144; tel. 518/254–3456, (Nonreporting) **A**1 9 10 **S** Bassett Healthcare Network, Cooperstown, NY
Primary Contact: Eric H. Stein, FACHE, President and Chief Executive Officer
CFO: Leanna Jensen, Vice President Finance and Chief Financial Officer
CMO: Roy Korn, M.D., Medical Director
CIO: William Mackey, Director Information Systems
Web address: www.cobleskillhospital.org
**Control:** Other not–for–profit (including NFP Corporation) **Service:** General Medical and Surgical

**Staffed Beds:** 40

## COHOES—Albany County

**EDDY COHOES REHABILITATION CENTER (330407)**, 421 West Columbia Street, Zip 12047–2217; tel. 518/237–5630, (Nonreporting)
Primary Contact: Laurie Mante, Administrator and Vice President
Web address: www.nehealth.com/Medical_Care/Eddy_Cohoes_Rehabilitation_Center/
**Control:** Other not–for–profit (including NFP Corporation) **Service:** Rehabilitation

**Staffed Beds:** 37

## COOPERSTOWN—Otsego County

✉ **BASSETT MEDICAL CENTER (330136)**, One Atwell Road, Zip 13326–1394; tel. 607/547–3100 **A**1 2 3 5 8 9 10 **F**3 8 11 12 13 15 18 20 22 24 26 28 29 30 31 32 34 35 38 39 40 43 44 45 48 49 50 51 54 56 57 58 59 60 61 64 65 68 70 71 74 75 76 77 78 79 81 82 84 85 86 87 89 92 93 94 97 98 99 100 101 102 103 104 107 108 109 110 111 114 115 116 117 118 119 120 121 123 124 126 129 130 131 132 134 135 141 142 143 144 146 147 148 **P**6 **S** Bassett Healthcare Network, Cooperstown, NY
Primary Contact: William F. Streck, M.D., President and Chief Executive Officer
COO: Bertine C. McKenna, Ph.D., Executive Vice President and Chief Operating Officer
CFO: Nicholas Nicoletta, Corporate Vice President and Chief Financial Officer
CMO: Gerald D. Groff, M.D., Vice President Medical Affairs
CIO: Scott C. Groom, Vice President Information Services and Chief Information Officer
CHR: Bruce W. Wilhelm, Vice President Human Resources
Web address: www.bassett.org
**Control:** Other not–for–profit (including NFP Corporation) **Service:** General Medical and Surgical

**Staffed Beds:** 164 **Admissions:** 9041 **Census:** 134 **Outpatient Visits:** 667908 **Births:** 832 **Total Expense ($000):** 407003 **Payroll Expense ($000):** 210964 **Personnel:** 3430

## CORNING—Steuben County

✉ **CORNING HOSPITAL (330277)**, 176 Denison Parkway East, Zip 14830–2899; tel. 607/937–7200 **A**1 9 10 **F**3 8 11 13 15 28 29 31 32 34 35 37 38 40 44 45 49 50 53 57 59 64 70 75 76 77 78 79 81 82 87 89 92 93 100 107 108 110 111 115 119 120 121 124 129 130 131 132 135 146 147 148 **S** Guthrie Healthcare System, Sayre, PA
Primary Contact: Shirley P. Magana, R.N., MSN, President and Chief Operating Officer
COO: Shirley P. Magana, R.N., President and Chief Operating Officer
CFO: Francis M. Macafee, Vice President Finance and Chief Financial Officer
CMO: Chris Wentzel, M.D., Interim Medical Director
CIO: Carolyn Handrick, Manager Public Relations
CHR: Laura Manning, Administrative Director
CNO: Debra Raupers, MSN, Chief Nursing Officer
Web address: www.corninghospital.com
**Control:** Other not–for–profit (including NFP Corporation) **Service:** General Medical and Surgical

**Staffed Beds:** 82 **Admissions:** 4265 **Census:** 42 **Outpatient Visits:** 127479 **Births:** 419 **Total Expense ($000):** 72866 **Payroll Expense ($000):** 24532 **Personnel:** 509

## CORNWALL—Orange County

**ST. LUKE'S CORNWALL HOSPITAL – CORNWALL CAMPUS** See St. Luke's Cornwall Hospital, Newburgh

## CORTLAND—Cortland County

✉ **CORTLAND REGIONAL MEDICAL CENTER (330175)**, 134 Homer Avenue, Zip 13045–1206; tel. 607/756–3500, (Total facility includes 82 beds in nursing home–type unit) **A**1 9 10 20 **F**2 3 8 11 13 15 28 29 30 34 35 40 45 49 50 54 56 57 59 62 64 68 70 75 76 77 79 81 82 85 86 87 89 91 93 96 98 100 102 107 108 110 111 114 115 118 119 128 130 131 132 133 135 144 146 147 148 **P**6
Primary Contact: Janice James, Interim Chief Executive Officer
CFO: Denise Wrinn, Vice President Financial Services and Chief Financial Officer
CMO: Robert Karpman, M.D., Vice President Medical Affairs
CIO: Thomas Hallisey, Vice President Information Management
CHR: Jussi Maijala, Vice President Human Resources
CNO: Denise Mironti, Senior Vice President Patient Care Services
Web address: www.cortlandregional.org
**Control:** Other not–for–profit (including NFP Corporation) **Service:** General Medical and Surgical

**Staffed Beds:** 209 **Admissions:** 5278 **Census:** 162 **Outpatient Visits:** 129500 **Births:** 488 **Total Expense ($000):** 86270 **Payroll Expense ($000):** 38317 **Personnel:** 788

## CORTLANDT MANOR—Westchester County

☐ **HUDSON VALLEY HOSPITAL CENTER (330267)**, 1980 Crompond Road, Zip 10567–4182; tel. 914/737–9000 **A**1 9 10 **F**3 9 11 12 13 15 18 28 29 30 31 34 35 40 53 57 59 67 70 72 75 76 77 78 79 81 82 85 86 87 89 93 107 108 110 111 115 119 121 130 132 135 145 146 147 148
Primary Contact: John C. Federspiel, President and Chief Executive Officer
COO: Deborah Neuendorf, Vice President Administration
CFO: Mark Webster, Vice President Finance
CMO: William Higgins, M.D., Vice President Medical Affairs
CIO: Bud Sorbello, Director Management Information Systems
CHR: Jeane L. Costella, Vice President
CNO: Kathleen Webster, R.N., Vice President Patient Services
Web address: www.hvhc.org
**Control:** Other not–for–profit (including NFP Corporation) **Service:** General Medical and Surgical

**Staffed Beds:** 128 **Admissions:** 7090 **Census:** 96 **Outpatient Visits:** 206262 **Births:** 820 **Total Expense ($000):** 155537 **Payroll Expense ($000):** 65994 **Personnel:** 1025

## CUBA—Allegany County

**CUBA MEMORIAL HOSPITAL (331301)**, 140 West Main Street, Zip 14727–1398; tel. 585/968–2000, (Total facility includes 61 beds in nursing home–type unit) **A**9 10 18 **F**3 15 29 35 39 40 57 59 65 83 84 87 93 96 107 119 128 130 132 133 135 144 146 **P**6
Primary Contact: Andrew Boser, Chief Executive Officer
CFO: Jack Ormond, Chief Financial Officer
Web address: www.cubamemorialhospital.com
**Control:** Other not–for–profit (including NFP Corporation) **Service:** General Medical and Surgical

**Staffed Beds:** 81 **Admissions:** 399 **Census:** 66 **Outpatient Visits:** 19142 **Births:** 0 **Total Expense ($000):** 10952 **Payroll Expense ($000):** 5971 **Personnel:** 176

## DANSVILLE—Livingston County

✉ **NICHOLAS H. NOYES MEMORIAL HOSPITAL (330238)**, 111 Clara Barton Street, Zip 14437–9503; tel. 585/335–6001, (Nonreporting) **A**1 9 10
Primary Contact: Amy Pollard, R.N., President and Chief Executive Officer
CFO: Jay T. Maslyn, Chief Financial Officer
CMO: Douglas Mayhle, M.D., Medical Director
CIO: John Dorak, Chief Information Officer
CHR: Jeanine Wilder, Director Human Resources
CNO: Tamara West, R.N., Vice President Patient Care
Web address: www.noyes–health.org
**Control:** Other not–for–profit (including NFP Corporation) **Service:** General Medical and Surgical

**Staffed Beds:** 54

**NY**

*Many Facility Codes have changed. Please refer to the AHA Guide Code Chart.* © 2013 AHA Guide

## DELHI—Delaware County

✠ **O'CONNOR HOSPITAL (331305)**, 460 Andes Road, State Route 28,
Zip 13753–7407; tel. 607/746–0300 **A**1 9 10 18 **F**15 29 34 35 40 45 46 50
56 57 59 64 75 77 79 81 85 86 87 92 93 96 107 110 111 119 130 132 133
135 147 **S** Bassett Healthcare Network, Cooperstown, NY
Primary Contact: Daniel M. Ayres, Chief Executive Officer
CFO: Nicholas Nicoletta, Vice President and Chief Financial Officer
CMO: Alberto Gaitan, M.D., Medical Director
CHR: Barbara Green, Director Human Resources
CNO: Debra Neale, R.N., Chief Nursing Officer
Web address: www.oconnorhosp.org
**Control:** Other not–for–profit (including NFP Corporation) **Service:** General
Medical and Surgical

**Staffed Beds:** 16 **Admissions:** 365 **Census:** 7 **Outpatient Visits:** 32971
**Births:** 0 **Total Expense ($000):** 19021 **Payroll Expense ($000):** 6483
**Personnel:** 151

## DIX HILLS—Suffolk County

☐ **SAGAMORE CHILDREN'S PSYCHIATRIC CENTER**, 197 Half Hollow Road,
Zip 11746–5861; tel. 631/370–1700, (Nonreporting) **A**1 **S** New York State
Office of Mental Health, Albany, NY
Primary Contact: Tom McOlvin, Executive Director
Web address: www.omh.ny.gov
**Control:** State–Government, nonfederal **Service:** Children's hospital psychiatric

**Staffed Beds:** 69

## DUNKIRK—Chautauqua County

✠ ◇ **BROOKS MEMORIAL HOSPITAL (330229)**, 529 Central Avenue,
Zip 14048–2599; tel. 716/366–1111, (Nonreporting) **A**1 9 10 21
Primary Contact: Gary Rhodes, Interim Chief Executive Officer
CFO: Ralph Webdale, Vice President Finance
CIO: Kathy Kucharski, Director Management Information Systems
CHR: Joan VanDette, Vice President Human Resources
Web address: www.brookshospital.org
**Control:** Other not–for–profit (including NFP Corporation) **Service:** General
Medical and Surgical

**Staffed Beds:** 65

## EAST MEADOW—Nassau County

✠ **NASSAU UNIVERSITY MEDICAL CENTER (330027)**, 2201 Hempstead
Turnpike, Zip 11554–1859; tel. 516/572–0123, (Nonreporting) **A**1 3 5 9 10
12 13
Primary Contact: Arthur A. Gianelli, President and Chief Executive Officer
CMO: Steven Walerstein, M.D., Executive Vice President and Medical Director
CIO: Ronald A. Tomo, Vice President and Chief Information Officer
CHR: Maureen Roarty, Vice President Human Resources
Web address: www.nuhealth.net
**Control:** Hospital district or authority, Government, nonfederal **Service:** General
Medical and Surgical

**Staffed Beds:** 1119

## ELIZABETHTOWN—Essex County

✠ **ELIZABETHTOWN COMMUNITY HOSPITAL (331302)**, Park Street,
Zip 12932–0277, Mailing Address: P.O. Box 277, Zip 12932–0277;
tel. 518/873–6377 **A**1 9 10 18 **F**3 7 11 12 15 28 29 30 31 32 34 35 40 45
46 50 53 54 57 59 60 64 65 68 75 77 78 81 85 87 90 93 97 107 110 111
115 119 127 130 132 133 146 147 **P**6
Primary Contact: Rodney C. Boula, Administrator and Chief Executive Officer
COO: Matthew Nolan, Director Facilities and Operations
CFO: Alan Chardavoyne, Controller
CMO: Rob DeMuro, M.D., President Medical Staff
CHR: Michelle Meachem, Director Human Resources
Web address: www.ech.org
**Control:** Other not–for–profit (including NFP Corporation) **Service:** General
Medical and Surgical

**Staffed Beds:** 25 **Admissions:** 495 **Census:** 12 **Outpatient Visits:** 38601
**Births:** 0 **Total Expense ($000):** 18318 **Payroll Expense ($000):** 9626
**Personnel:** 142

## ELLENVILLE—Ulster County

★ **ELLENVILLE REGIONAL HOSPITAL (331310)**, 10 Healthy Way,
Zip 12428–5612; tel. 845/647–6400, (Nonreporting) **A**9 10 18
Primary Contact: Steven L. Kelley, President and Chief Executive Officer
CFO: Patricia Gavis, Chief Financial Officer
CMO: Helen Robinson, Chief Clinical Officer
CIO: Robert Rue, Controller
CHR: Deborah Briggs, Vice President Human Resources, Marketing, Volunteer
Services and Community Relations
Web address: www.ellenvilleregional.org
**Control:** Other not–for–profit (including NFP Corporation) **Service:** General
Medical and Surgical

**Staffed Beds:** 25

## ELMHURST—Queens County, See New York City

## ELMIRA—Chemung County

★ ◇ **ARNOT OGDEN MEDICAL CENTER (330090)**, 600 Roe Avenue,
Zip 14905–1629; tel. 607/737–4100, (Nonreporting) **A**2 6 9 10 21 **S** Arnot
Health, Elmira, NY
Primary Contact: H. Fred Farley, R.N., Ph.D., FACHE, President and Chief
Operating Officer
CFO: Ronald J. Kintz, Vice President and Treasurer
CMO: William Huffner, M.D., Vice President Medical Affairs
CIO: Gregg Martin, Manager Management Information Systems
CHR: Brian Forrest, Director Human Resources
CNO: Mary M. Vosburgh, R.N., Vice President Nursing and Chief Nursing Officer
Web address: www.aomc.org
**Control:** Other not–for–profit (including NFP Corporation) **Service:** General
Medical and Surgical

**Staffed Beds:** 244

☐ **ELMIRA PSYCHIATRIC CENTER (334045)**, 100 Washington Street,
Zip 14901–2898; tel. 607/737–4739 **A**1 10 **F**29 35 39 54 64 98 99 101 103
104 106 132 **P**6 **S** New York State Office of Mental Health, Albany, NY
Primary Contact: Mark Stephany, Executive Director
COO: Shawn Rosno, Deputy Director Operations
CFO: J. Paul Bedzyk, Deputy Director Administration
CMO: Alec Whyte, M.D., Clinical Director
CIO: Edward Lorell, Facility Director Information
CHR: Patricia Santulli, Director Human Resources
Web address: www.omh.ny.gov/omhweb/facilities/elpc/facility.htm
**Control:** State–Government, nonfederal **Service:** Psychiatric

**Staffed Beds:** 100 **Admissions:** 274 **Census:** 87 **Outpatient Visits:** 106868
**Births:** 0 **Total Expense ($000):** 34159 **Payroll Expense ($000):** 20883
**Personnel:** 367

✠ ◇ **ST. JOSEPH'S HOSPITAL (330108)**, 555 St. Joseph's Boulevard,
Zip 14901–3223; tel. 607/733–6541, (Includes TWIN TIERS REHABILITATION
CENTER ), (Total facility includes 71 beds in nursing home–type unit) **A**1 9 10 21
**F**3 4 5 11 15 18 29 30 31 34 35 40 45 46 49 51 57 59 60 64 65 66 70 74
75 78 79 81 82 85 87 90 91 93 96 97 98 102 107 108 111 114 119 128
130 132 135 146 **P**6 **S** Arnot Health, Elmira, NY
Primary Contact: H. Fred Farley, R.N., Ph.D., FACHE, President and Chief
Operating Officer
COO: H. Fred Farley, R.N., President and Chief Operating Officer
CFO: Ronald J. Kintz, Senior Vice President Finance and Chief Financial Officer
CMO: William Huffner, M.D., Chief Medical Officer and Senior Vice President
Medical Affairs
CIO: Gregg Martin, Chief Information Officer
CHR: Brian Forrest, Vice President Human Resources
CNO: Mary M. Vosburgh, R.N., Vice President Nursing and Chief Nursing Officer
Web address: www.stjosephs.org
**Control:** Other not–for–profit (including NFP Corporation) **Service:** General
Medical and Surgical

**Staffed Beds:** 212 **Admissions:** 4824 **Census:** 155 **Outpatient Visits:** 97575
**Total Expense ($000):** 59323 **Payroll Expense ($000):** 23624 **Personnel:**
585

## ENDICOTT—Broome County

**MEDICENTER** See United Health Services Hospitals–Binghamton, Binghamton

## FAR ROCKAWAY—Queens County, See New York City

## FLUSHING—Queens County, See New York City

## FOREST HILLS—Queens County, See New York City

**NY**

---

**Hospital, Medicare Provider Number, Address, Telephone, Approval, Facility, and Physician Codes, Health Care System**

★ American Hospital Association (AHA) membership     ○ Healthcare Facilities Accreditation Program
☐ The Joint Commission accreditation     ◇ DNV Healthcare Inc. accreditation     △ Commission on Accreditation of Rehabilitation Facilities (CARF) accreditation

## FRESH MEADOWS—Queens County

**CORNERSTONE OF MEDICAL ARTS CENTER HOSPITAL**, 159–05 Union Turnpike, Zip 11366–1950; tel. 212/755–0200, (Nonreporting) **A**9
Primary Contact: Norman J. Sokolow, Chairman and Chief Executive Officer
COO: Thomas C. Puzo, President and Chief Operating Officer
CFO: Jeff OniFather, Chief Financial Officer
CMO: Sami Kaddouri, M.D., Medical Director
CHR: Gloria Burtch, Director Human Resources
Web address: www.cornerstoneny.com
**Control:** Corporation, Investor–owned, for–profit **Service:** Alcoholism and other chemical dependency

**Staffed Beds: 162**

## GENEVA—Ontario County

✠ △ **GENEVA GENERAL HOSPITAL (330058)**, 196 North Street, Zip 14456–1694; tel. 315/787–4000 **A**1 7 9 10 **F**3 8 11 13 15 17 18 28 29 30 31 32 34 35 40 45 50 54 57 59 60 61 64 66 69 70 74 75 76 77 78 79 81 85 86 87 90 92 93 96 97 107 108 110 111 115 118 119 129 130 132 135 146 147 **P**6 **S** Finger Lakes Health, Geneva, NY
Primary Contact: Jose Acevedo, M.D., President and Chief Executive Officer
COO: James Hiserodt, Senior Vice President Operations
CFO: Patricia Thompson, Treasurer and Chief Financial Officer
CMO: Jason Feinberg, M.D., Vice President Medical Affairs and Chief Medical Officer
CIO: John Oates, Director Information Systems
CHR: Patrick R. Boyle, Vice President Human Resources
CNO: Eileen Gage, R.N., Vice President Nursing
Web address: www.flhealth.org
**Control:** Other not–for–profit (including NFP Corporation) **Service:** General Medical and Surgical

**Staffed Beds: 132 Admissions: 4256 Census: 51 Outpatient Visits: 457072 Births: 542 Total Expense ($000): 83274 Payroll Expense ($000): 44744 Personnel: 838**

## GLEN COVE—Nassau County

✠ **GLEN COVE HOSPITAL (330181)**, 101 St. Andrews Lane, Zip 11542–2254; tel. 516/674–7300 **A**1 2 3 5 9 10 **F**3 5 8 9 11 12 14 15 17 18 26 28 29 30 31 32 33 34 35 36 38 39 40 43 44 45 46 47 48 49 50 53 54 55 56 57 58 59 60 61 63 64 65 66 68 69 70 74 75 77 78 79 81 82 84 85 86 87 90 92 93 94 96 97 98 100 101 102 103 104 107 108 111 114 117 118 119 121 123 130 131 132 134 135 143 145 146 147 148 **P**5 6 **S** North Shore–Long Island Jewish Health System, Great Neck, NY
Primary Contact: Susan Kwiatek, R.N., Executive Director
COO: Joshua Strugatz, Associate Executive Director Operations
CFO: Michele Frankel, Associate Executive Director Finance
CMO: George Dunn, M.D., Senior Vice President Medical Affairs
CHR: Thomas Salvo, Associate Executive Director Human Resources
CNO: Cathy Sheerin, R.N., Director Patient Care Services
Web address: www.northshorelij.com
**Control:** Other not–for–profit (including NFP Corporation) **Service:** General Medical and Surgical

**Staffed Beds: 235 Admissions: 8998 Census: 163 Outpatient Visits: 84740 Births: 0 Total Expense ($000): 191001 Payroll Expense ($000): 97191 Personnel: 1026**

## GLEN OAKS—Queens County, See New York City

## GLENS FALLS—Warren County

✠ **GLENS FALLS HOSPITAL (330191)**, 100 Park Street, Zip 12801–4413; tel. 518/926–1000 **A**1 2 5 9 10 **F**8 11 13 15 17 18 20 22 28 29 30 31 32 34 35 36 40 45 46 47 49 50 51 54 55 56 58 59 60 64 70 74 75 76 77 78 81 85 87 89 90 92 93 97 98 99 100 102 104 105 107 110 111 114 115 116 117 119 120 121 127 129 130 135 144 145 146 147 148
Primary Contact: Dianne Shugrue, MSN, R.N., President and Chief Executive Officer
COO: Dianne Shugrue, MSN, Senior Vice President Operations and Chief Operating Officer
CFO: Jeffrey S. Treasure, Senior Vice President Finance and Chief Financial Officer
CMO: Robert M. Pickoff, M.D., Vice President Medical Affairs
CIO: Joan McFaul, Vice President Information Technology and Chief Information Officer
CHR: Kathleen Smith, Interim Vice President Human Resources
CNO: Donna Kirker NEA–BC, R.N., Vice President Patient Services and Chief Nursing Officer
Web address: www.glensfallshospital.org
**Control:** Other not–for–profit (including NFP Corporation) **Service:** General Medical and Surgical

**Staffed Beds: 300 Admissions: 15702 Census: 213 Outpatient Visits: 823658 Births: 1393 Total Expense ($000): 301000 Payroll Expense ($000): 139000 Personnel: 2587**

## GLENVILLE—Schenectady County

**CONIFER PARK**, 79 Glenridge Road, Zip 12302–4523; tel. 518/399–6446 **A**9 **F**4 5 29
Primary Contact: Jeanne Gluchowski, Executive Director
COO: Jeanne Gluchowski, Executive Director
CFO: Jason Burczeuski, Controller
CMO: John Melbourne, M.D., Medical Director
CIO: Amy Kentera, Chief Information Officer
CHR: Maureen Fowler, Director Human Resources
Web address: www.libertymgt.com
**Control:** Corporation, Investor–owned, for–profit **Service:** Alcoholism and other chemical dependency

**Staffed Beds: 225 Admissions: 3592 Census: 165 Outpatient Visits: 106443 Births: 0 Total Expense ($000): 20734 Payroll Expense ($000): 13755 Personnel: 331**

## GLOVERSVILLE—Fulton County

✠ ◇ **NATHAN LITTAUER HOSPITAL AND NURSING HOME (330276)**, 99 East State Street, Zip 12078–1203; tel. 518/725–8621, (Total facility includes 84 beds in nursing home–type unit) **A**1 5 9 10 21 **F**3 8 11 13 15 18 28 29 30 31 32 34 35 36 40 45 46 50 53 54 57 59 61 64 65 70 74 75 76 77 78 79 81 82 85 86 87 89 93 97 107 108 110 115 118 119 128 130 131 132 135 145 146 147 **P**6
Primary Contact: Laurence E. Kelly, President and Chief Executive Officer
CFO: Henry Legendziewicz, Senior Vice President and Chief Financial Officer
CMO: Frederick Goldberg, M.D., Vice President Medical Affairs and Chief Medical Officer
CIO: Martin Brown, Vice President Information Services and Chief Information Officer
CHR: Lana Wydra, Vice President Human Resources
CNO: Regina Mulligan, Vice President Nursing
Web address: www.nlh.org
**Control:** Other not–for–profit (including NFP Corporation) **Service:** General Medical and Surgical

**Staffed Beds: 158 Admissions: 3313 Census: 119 Outpatient Visits: 242590 Births: 365 Total Expense ($000): 90858 Payroll Expense ($000): 46504 Personnel: 775**

## GOUVERNEUR—St. Lawrence County

✠ **EDWARD JOHN NOBLE HOSPITAL OF GOUVERNEUR (330177)**, 77 West Barney Street, Zip 13642–1040; tel. 315/287–1000, (Total facility includes 40 beds in nursing home–type unit) (Data for 335 days) **A**1 9 10 20 **F**3 8 11 13 15 29 34 40 41 45 54 57 59 64 70 75 76 77 81 85 86 89 93 97 107 108 111 114 119 127 128 130 133 146 **P**6
Primary Contact: Marlinda L. LaValley, Administrator
CFO: Richard T. Lang, Chief Financial Officer
CMO: Donald Schuessler, M.D., Medical Director
CIO: Linda Fishel, Manager Information Services
CHR: Cathy Chirico, Director Human Resources
Web address: www.ejnoble.com
**Control:** Other not–for–profit (including NFP Corporation) **Service:** General Medical and Surgical

**Staffed Beds: 77 Admissions: 1029 Census: 60 Outpatient Visits: 50626 Births: 92 Total Expense ($000): 22321 Payroll Expense ($000): 10894 Personnel: 180**

## GREENPORT—Suffolk County

✠ **EASTERN LONG ISLAND HOSPITAL (330088)**, 201 Manor Place, Zip 11944–1298; tel. 631/477–1000 **A**1 9 10 **F**3 4 17 18 28 29 34 40 45 47 49 53 56 59 64 65 68 70 74 78 79 81 82 85 93 97 98 100 102 103 106 107 110 111 119 130 132 135 146
Primary Contact: Paul J. Connor, III, President and Chief Executive Officer
CFO: Robert A. Ragona, Vice President Finance
CMO: Lloyd Simon, M.D., Medical Director
CIO: Dan Scotto, Director Data Processing
CHR: August F. Menchini, Director Human Resources
CNO: D. Patricia Pispisa, Vice President Patient Care Services
Web address: www.elih.org
**Control:** Other not–for–profit (including NFP Corporation) **Service:** General Medical and Surgical

**Staffed Beds: 90 Admissions: 3162 Census: 52 Outpatient Visits: 43006 Births: 0 Total Expense ($000): 45281 Payroll Expense ($000): 20160 Personnel: 301**

## HAMILTON—Madison County

✠ **COMMUNITY MEMORIAL HOSPITAL (330249)**, 150 Broad Street, Zip 13346–9518; tel. 315/824–1100, (Nonreporting) **A**1 9 10
Primary Contact: Sean Fadale, President and Chief Executive Officer
CFO: Richard S. Kirby, Executive Vice President and Chief Financial Officer
CMO: Michael S. Jastremski, M.D., Vice President Medical Affairs and Director Emergency Services
Web address: www.communitymemorial.org
**Control:** Other not–for–profit (including NFP Corporation) **Service:** General Medical and Surgical

**Staffed Beds: 72**

*Many Facility Codes have changed. Please refer to the AHA Guide Code Chart.*

© 2013 AHA Guide

## HARRIS—Sullivan County

✠ **CATSKILL REGIONAL MEDICAL CENTER (330386)**, 68 Harris Bushville Road, Zip 12742–5030, Mailing Address: P.O. Box 800, Zip 12742–0800; tel. 845/794–3300, (Total facility includes 64 beds in nursing home–type unit) **A**1 9 10 **F**2 3 4 8 11 13 15 17 18 28 29 30 31 34 35 38 40 42 45 51 54 56 57 59 65 68 70 76 78 79 81 85 86 87 89 93 96 97 98 102 103 107 111 115 119 127 128 130 132 133 146 147 148 **S** Greater Hudson Valley Health System, Middletown, NY
Primary Contact: Gerard Galarneau, M.D., Chief Executive Officer and Chief Medical Officer
CFO: Frank Hemeon, Interim Chief Financial Officer
CMO: Gerard Galarneau, M.D., Chief Executive Officer and Chief Medical Officer
CIO: John Lynch, Vice President Chief Information Officer
CHR: Zigmund Nowicki, Director Human Resources
CNO: Rolland Bojo, R.N., Chief Nursing Officer, Administrator Patient Care and Services
Web address: www.crmcny.org
**Control:** Other not–for–profit (including NFP Corporation) **Service:** General Medical and Surgical

**Staffed Beds:** 196 **Admissions:** 5259 **Census:** 129 **Outpatient Visits:** 107266 **Births:** 726 **Total Expense ($000):** 94908 **Payroll Expense ($000):** 42679 **Personnel:** 720

## HOLLISWOOD—Queens County, See New York City

## HORNELL—Steuben County

✠ **ST. JAMES MERCY HEALTH SYSTEM (330151)**, 411 Canisteo Street, Zip 14843–2197; tel. 607/324–8000, (Total facility includes 120 beds in nursing home–type unit) **A**1 9 10 20 **F**1 2 3 4 5 11 13 15 17 28 29 30 34 35 39 40 43 45 50 54 57 60 65 70 74 75 76 77 78 79 81 85 87 89 91 93 98 99 102 104 107 108 114 118 119 127 128 129 130 132 146 147 **P**1 **S** Catholic Health East, Newtown Square, PA
Primary Contact: Mary E. LaRowe, FACHE, President and Chief Executive Officer
CFO: Jennifer Sullivan, Senior Vice President Finance and Chief Financial Officer
CMO: Bradley Truax, M.D., Senior Vice President Medical Affairs and Chief Medical Officer
CIO: Bonnie Welch, Chief Information Officer
CNO: Patricia Uldrich, R.N., Chief Nursing Officer
Web address: www.stjamesmercy.org
**Control:** Other not–for–profit (including NFP Corporation) **Service:** General Medical and Surgical

**Staffed Beds:** 222 **Admissions:** 3531 **Census:** 162 **Outpatient Visits:** 174327 **Births:** 313 **Total Expense ($000):** 53566 **Payroll Expense ($000):** 25448 **Personnel:** 551

## HUDSON—Columbia County

**COLUMBIA MEMORIAL HOSPITAL (330094)**, 71 Prospect Avenue, Zip 12534–2907; tel. 518/828–7601, (Includes KAATERSKILL CARE, 161 Jefferson Heights, Catskill, Zip 12414; tel. 518/943–6363), (Total facility includes 120 beds in nursing home–type unit) **A**9 10 19 **F**8 11 13 15 18 29 30 34 35 36 37 39 40 45 46 48 49 50 51 53 63 64 68 70 71 74 75 76 77 78 79 81 82 85 86 87 89 92 93 97 98 99 100 102 107 108 110 111 114 115 116 117 119 125 127 128 129 130 131 132 135 144 146 147 **P**6
Primary Contact: Jay P. Cahalan, Chief Executive Officer
CFO: Vincent Dingman, III, Chief Financial Officer
CMO: Norman Chapin, M.D., Medical Director
CIO: Cathleen Crowley, Chief Information Officer
CHR: Ray Jones, Vice President
Web address: www.columbiamemorial.com
**Control:** Other not–for–profit (including NFP Corporation) **Service:** General Medical and Surgical

**Staffed Beds:** 218 **Admissions:** 6428 **Census:** 179 **Outpatient Visits:** 401286 **Births:** 439 **Total Expense ($000):** 142995 **Payroll Expense ($000):** 74237 **Personnel:** 1298

## HUNTINGTON—Suffolk County

✠ **HUNTINGTON HOSPITAL (330045)**, 270 Park Avenue, Zip 11743–2799; tel. 631/351–2200 **A**1 2 9 10 **F**3 11 12 13 15 17 18 20 26 29 30 31 34 35 36 38 40 43 44 45 50 53 54 55 56 57 58 59 60 63 64 65 66 68 69 70 73 74 75 76 78 79 81 82 84 85 86 87 89 93 97 98 100 101 102 103 104 107 108 110 111 114 115 118 119 130 131 132 135 146 147 **P**5 6 **S** North Shore–Long Island Jewish Health System, Great Neck, NY
Primary Contact: Kevin F. Lawlor, President and Chief Executive Officer
COO: Thomas M. Hoeft, Executive Vice President and Chief Operating Officer
CFO: Michael Fagan, Chief Financial Officer
CMO: Michael Grosso, M.D., Senior Vice President Medical Affairs
CIO: Linda Fischer, Director Information Services
CHR: Michael J. Quartier, Vice President Administration and Human Resources
Web address: www.hunthosp.org
**Control:** Other not–for–profit (including NFP Corporation) **Service:** General Medical and Surgical

**Staffed Beds:** 288 **Admissions:** 15869 **Census:** 209 **Outpatient Visits:** 118769 **Births:** 1398 **Total Expense ($000):** 291360 **Payroll Expense ($000):** 138440 **Personnel:** 1664

## IRVING—Chautauqua County

◇ **LAKE SHORE HEALTH CARE CENTER**, 845 Route 5 and 20, Zip 14081–9716; tel. 716/951–7000, (Nonreporting) **A**9 21
Primary Contact: Louis J. Frascella, President and Chief Executive Officer
CMO: James Wild, M.D., Medical Director
CIO: Louis Di Rienzo, Chief Information Officer
CHR: Tracie Luther, Vice President Human Resources
Web address: www.tlchealth.org
**Control:** Other not–for–profit (including NFP Corporation) **Service:** General Medical and Surgical

**Staffed Beds:** 220

## ITHACA—Tompkins County

✠ **CAYUGA MEDICAL CENTER AT ITHACA (330307)**, 101 Dates Drive, Zip 14850–1342; tel. 607/274–4011 **A**1 2 5 9 10 **F**3 8 11 12 13 15 18 20 22 28 29 30 31 34 38 40 41 45 49 51 54 57 59 61 64 70 72 74 75 76 77 78 79 81 82 84 85 86 87 90 93 98 99 100 101 102 103 107 108 110 111 114 115 116 118 119 121 129 130 131 132 133 135 144 145 146 147 148 **P**6
Primary Contact: D. Rob Mackenzie, M.D., President and Chief Executive Officer
COO: D. Rob Mackenzie, M.D., President and Chief Executive Officer
CFO: John Rudd, Chief Financial Officer
CMO: David M. Evelyn, M.D., Vice President Medical Affairs
CIO: Anthony Votaw, Chief Information Officer
CHR: Alan Pedersen, Vice President Human Resources
Web address: www.cayugamed.org
**Control:** Other not–for–profit (including NFP Corporation) **Service:** General Medical and Surgical

**Staffed Beds:** 193 **Admissions:** 6344 **Census:** 81 **Outpatient Visits:** 201283 **Births:** 900 **Total Expense ($000):** 162428 **Payroll Expense ($000):** 60308 **Personnel:** 1157

## JACKSON HEIGHTS—Queens County, See New York City

## JAMAICA—Queens County, See New York City

## JAMESTOWN—Chautauqua County

✠ **WOMAN'S CHRISTIAN ASSOCIATION HOSPITAL (330239)**, 207 Foote Avenue, Zip 14701–7077, Mailing Address: P.O. Box 840, Zip 14702–0840; tel. 716/487–0141 **A**1 2 9 10 **F**4 5 8 11 13 15 18 19 20 28 29 31 34 35 36 40 45 46 57 59 60 64 68 70 74 75 76 77 78 79 81 82 83 84 85 86 87 89 90 92 93 96 98 99 100 101 102 103 104 107 108 111 114 117 119 121 129 130 131 132 135 141 146 147 148
Primary Contact: Betsy T. Wright, President and Chief Executive Officer
CMO: Marlene Garone, M.D., Vice President Medical Affairs and Medical Director
CIO: Keith Robison, Chief Information Officer
CHR: Karen Bohall, Director Human Resources
Web address: www.wcahospital.org
**Control:** Other not–for–profit (including NFP Corporation) **Service:** General Medical and Surgical

**Staffed Beds:** 197 **Admissions:** 7212 **Census:** 109 **Outpatient Visits:** 245000 **Births:** 655 **Total Expense ($000):** 107494 **Payroll Expense ($000):** 43475 **Personnel:** 957

## JOHNSON CITY—Broome County

**WILSON MEMORIAL REGIONAL MEDICAL CENTER** See United Health Services Hospitals–Binghamton, Binghamton

NY

## KATONAH—Westchester County

☐ **FOUR WINDS HOSPITAL (334002)**, 800 Cross River Road, Zip 10536–3549; tel. 914/763–8151, (Nonreporting) **A**1 9 10
Primary Contact: Martin A. Buccolo, Ph.D., Chief Executive Officer
COO: Moira Morrissey, Chief Operating Officer and General Counsel
CFO: Barry S. Weinstein, Chief Financial Officer
CMO: Jonathan Bauman, M.D., Chief Medical Officer
CIO: Barry S. Weinstein, Chief Financial Officer
CHR: Susan Cusano, Director Human Resources
Web address: www.fourwindshospital.com
**Control:** Partnership, Investor–owned, for–profit **Service:** Psychiatric

Staffed Beds: 175

## KENMORE—Erie County

☒ **KENMORE MERCY HOSPITAL (330102)**, 2950 Elmwood Avenue, Zip 14217–1390; tel. 716/447–6100, (Total facility includes 160 beds in nursing home–type unit) **A**1 9 10 **F**3 15 17 18 29 30 31 32 34 35 39 40 45 49 54 57 59 60 64 65 66 68 70 74 75 78 79 81 84 85 86 87 90 92 93 94 96 97 107 108 110 111 114 115 118 119 126 128 129 130 131 132 146 148 **P**5 **S** Catholic Health System, Buffalo, NY
Primary Contact: James M. Millard, President and Chief Executive Officer
COO: Walter Ludwig, Chief Operating Officer
CFO: James H. Dunlop, Jr., CPA, Senior Vice President and Chief Financial Officer
CMO: James Fitzpatrick, M.D., Vice President Medical Affairs
CHR: Pam Nicastro, Director Human Resources
Web address: www.chsbuffalo.org
**Control:** Church–operated, Nongovernment, not–for profit **Service:** General Medical and Surgical

Staffed Beds: 315 Admissions: 9336 Census: 256 Outpatient Visits: 149980 Births: 0 Total Expense ($000): 147217 Payroll Expense ($000): 63720 Personnel: 1017

## KINGSTON—Ulster County

**BENEDICTINE HOSPITAL** See Health Alliance Hospital – Mary's Avenue Campus

☒ **HEALTH ALLIANCE HOSPITAL – BROADWAY CAMPUS (330004)**, (Formerly Kingston Hospital), 396 Broadway, Zip 12401–4692; tel. 845/331–3131 **A**1 9 10 13 19 **F**3 8 11 13 15 18 20 28 29 30 34 35 36 40 45 49 50 54 56 57 59 60 63 64 68 70 74 75 76 77 79 81 82 83 84 85 86 87 92 93 102 107 108 111 114 115 119 130 131 132 135 146 147 148 **S** HealthAlliance of the Hudson Valley, Kingston, NY
Primary Contact: David W. Lundquist, President and Chief Executive Officer
COO: Charles Flinn, Chief Operating Officer
CFO: David Scarpino, Senior Vice President Finance and Chief Financial Officer
CMO: Frank Ehrlich, M.D., Chief Medical Officer
CIO: John Finch, Vice President Information Services
CHR: Greg M. Howard, Director Human Resource
CNO: Kathleen Lunney, R.N., Chief Nursing Officer
Web address: www.kingstonregionalhealth.org
**Control:** Other not–for–profit (including NFP Corporation) **Service:** General Medical and Surgical

Staffed Beds: 150 Admissions: 8892 Census: 111 Outpatient Visits: 116735 Births: 466 Total Expense ($000): 107500 Payroll Expense ($000): 43972 Personnel: 812

☐ **HEALTH ALLIANCE HOSPITAL – MARY'S AVENUE CAMPUS (330224)**, (Formerly Benedictine Hospital), 105 Marys Avenue, Zip 12401–5894; tel. 845/338–2500 **A**1 2 9 10 19 **F**3 4 8 11 15 18 20 29 30 31 34 35 36 45 49 50 54 56 57 59 63 64 66 69 70 74 75 78 79 81 82 83 84 85 86 87 90 98 105 107 108 110 114 119 120 121 123 129 130 131 132 146 147 148 **P**7 **S** HealthAlliance of the Hudson Valley, Kingston, NY
Primary Contact: David W. Lundquist, President and Chief Executive Officer
CFO: David Scarpino, Senior Vice President and Chief Financial Officer
CMO: Rafael Olazagasti, M.D., Vice President Medical Affairs and Network Development
CIO: John Finch, Vice President Corporate Development
CHR: Heidi Rosborough, Manager Human Resources
Web address: www.benedictine.org
**Control:** Church–operated, Nongovernment, not–for profit **Service:** General Medical and Surgical

Staffed Beds: 120 Admissions: 4108 Census: 77 Outpatient Visits: 41309 Births: 0 Total Expense ($000): 66259 Payroll Expense ($000): 25468 Personnel: 554

**KINGSTON HOSPITAL** See Health Alliance Hospital – Broadway Campus

## LEWISTON—Niagara County

☒ **MOUNT ST. MARY'S HOSPITAL AND HEALTH CENTER (330188)**, 5300 Military Road, Zip 14092–1903; tel. 716/297–4800, (Total facility includes 250 beds in nursing home–type unit) **A**1 9 10 **F**3 4 13 15 17 18 28 29 30 35 40 45 49 50 57 60 64 65 66 68 70 74 75 76 77 79 81 82 84 87 92 93 97 107 108 110 111 114 115 119 128 130 131 132 135 143 146 147 148 **P**5 **S** Ascension Health, Saint Louis, MO
Primary Contact: Judith A. Maness, FACHE, President and Chief Executive Officer
COO: Gary Tucker, Senior Vice President Operations and Chief Operating Officer
CFO: Michael F. Ickowski, Vice President Finance and Chief Financial Officer
CMO: Domonic F. Falsetti, M.D., Chief of Staff and Medical Director
CIO: Richard J. Witkowski, Director Management Information Systems
CHR: Deborah J. Serafin, Vice President Human Resources
Web address: www.msmh.org
**Control:** Other not–for–profit (including NFP Corporation) **Service:** General Medical and Surgical

Staffed Beds: 405 Admissions: 6426 Census: 329 Outpatient Visits: 161689 Births: 164 Total Expense ($000): 111088 Payroll Expense ($000): 53865 Personnel: 702

## LITTLE FALLS—Herkimer County

★ **LITTLE FALLS HOSPITAL (331311)**, 140 Burwell Street, Zip 13365–1725; tel. 315/823–1000, (Nonreporting) **A**9 10 18 **S** Bassett Healthcare Network, Cooperstown, NY
Primary Contact: Michael L. Ogden, President and Chief Executive Officer
CFO: James Vielkind, Chief Financial Officer
CMO: Andrew Rauscher, M.D., Medical Director
CIO: Duane Merry, Chief Information Officer
CHR: Jack Fredericks, Vice President Human Resources
Web address: www.lfhny.org
**Control:** Other not–for–profit (including NFP Corporation) **Service:** General Medical and Surgical

Staffed Beds: 59

## LITTLE NECK—Queens County, See New York City

## LOCKPORT—Niagara County

★ **EASTERN NIAGARA HEALTH SYSTEM (330163)**, 521 East Avenue, Zip 14094–3299; tel. 716/514–5700, (Includes EASTERN NIAGARA HOSPITAL INTER–COMMUNITY, 2600 William Street, Newfane, Zip 14108–1093; tel. 716/778–5111; EASTERN NIAGARA HOSPITAL LOCKPORT, 521 East Avenue, tel. 716/514–5700) **A**9 10 **F**3 4 13 15 18 19 28 29 30 31 34 40 45 46 47 48 49 50 51 57 59 60 63 65 68 70 74 75 76 77 79 81 82 83 84 85 87 89 90 93 94 98 99 100 102 107 108 110 111 115 118 119 126 128 130 132 135 144 146 147 148
Primary Contact: Clare A. Haar, Chief Executive Officer
COO: David J. Di Bacco, Chief Operating Officer
CMO: Bruce J. Cusenz, M.D., Medical Director
CHR: Joseph J. DeFazio, Director Human Resources
Web address: www.enhs.org
**Control:** Other not–for–profit (including NFP Corporation) **Service:** General Medical and Surgical

Staffed Beds: 140 Admissions: 6141 Census: 92 Outpatient Visits: 915338 Births: 840 Total Expense ($000): 67915 Payroll Expense ($000): 30643 Personnel: 650

## LONG ISLAND CITY—Queens County, See New York City

## LOWVILLE—Lewis County

☒ **LEWIS COUNTY GENERAL HOSPITAL (330213)**, 7785 North State Street, Zip 13367–1297; tel. 315/376–5200, (Total facility includes 160 beds in nursing home–type unit) **A**1 9 10 20 **F**2 15 29 81 11 13 15 29 30 34 40 45 50 54 56 57 59 70 75 76 77 78 79 81 82 85 86 87 91 93 96 97 107 108 110 111 115 119 124 127 129 130 131 132 133 143 146 147 148 **P**6 8
Primary Contact: Eric Burch, Chief Executive Officer
CMO: Catherine Williams, M.D., Medical Director
CIO: Rob Uttendorfsky, Director Information Management
CHR: Timothy J. Ryan, Jr., Director Human Resources
CNO: David Wood, Director Acute Care Services
Web address: www.lcgh.net
**Control:** County–Government, nonfederal **Service:** General Medical and Surgical

Staffed Beds: 214 Admissions: 1725 Census: 167 Outpatient Visits: 121135 Births: 345 Total Expense ($000): 62242 Payroll Expense ($000): 24719 Personnel: 497

NY

## MALONE—Franklin County

☒ **ALICE HYDE MEDICAL CENTER (330084)**, 133 Park Street, Zip 12953–1243, Mailing Address: P.O. Box 729, Zip 12953–0729; tel. 518/483–3000, (Total facility includes 75 beds in nursing home–type unit) **A**1 9 10 20 **F**3 11 13 15 17 18 28 29 31 34 35 36 39 40 45 50 57 59 60 64 68 70 75 76 77 78 79 81 82 84 85 86 87 90 93 97 107 108 110 111 115 119 121 127 128 129 130 131 132 135 143 146 148 **P**6
Primary Contact: Douglas F. DiVello, President and Chief Executive Officer
CFO: Michael Towle, Vice President Finance
CMO: Leonardo Dishman, M.D., Chief Medical Officer
CIO: Joel Benware, Chief Information Officer
CHR: Emily Campbell, Director Human Resources
CNO: John E. Aufdengarten, R.N., Vice President, Administration
CNO: Linda McClarigan, R.N., Vice President, Patient Care Services
Web address: www.alicehyde.com
**Control:** Other not–for–profit (including NFP Corporation) **Service:** General Medical and Surgical

**Staffed Beds:** 135 **Admissions:** 2703 **Census:** 101 **Outpatient Visits:** 153878 **Births:** 372 **Total Expense ($000):** 68686 **Payroll Expense ($000):** 34089 **Personnel:** 532

## MANHASSET—Nassau County

**MANHASSET AMBULATORY CARE PAVILION** See Long Island Jewish Medical Center, New Hyde Park

☒ **NORTH SHORE UNIVERSITY HOSPITAL (330106)**, 300 Community Drive, Zip 11030–3816; tel. 516/562–0100 **A**1 2 3 5 8 9 10 **F**3 6 7 8 9 11 12 13 14 15 17 18 19 20 21 22 23 24 26 29 30 31 32 34 35 36 37 38 39 40 41 43 44 45 46 47 48 49 50 51 52 53 54 55 56 57 58 59 60 61 62 63 64 65 66 68 69 70 71 72 73 74 75 76 77 78 79 80 81 82 83 84 85 86 87 88 89 91 92 93 94 97 98 99 100 101 102 103 104 107 108 109 110 111 112 113 114 115 116 117 118 119 120 121 123 124 126 129 130 131 132 134 135 136 138 141 142 143 144 145 146 147 148 **P**5 6 **S** North Shore–Long Island Jewish Health System, Great Neck, NY
Primary Contact: Susan Somerville, R.N., Executive Director
CMO: Vicki LoPachin, M.D., Medical Director
CIO: Nympha Meindel, R.N., Chief Information Officer
CHR: Deirdre J. Duke, Associate Executive Director Human Resources
Web address: www.northshorelij.com
**Control:** Other not–for–profit (including NFP Corporation) **Service:** General Medical and Surgical

**Staffed Beds:** 804 **Admissions:** 47220 **Census:** 725 **Outpatient Visits:** 751021 **Births:** 6463 **Total Expense ($000):** 1568039 **Payroll Expense ($000):** 787642 **Personnel:** 14724

## MANHATTAN—New York County, See New York City

## MARCY—Oneida County

☐ **CENTRAL NEW YORK PSYCHIATRIC CENTER**, Zip 13403; tel. 315/765–3600, (Nonreporting) **A**1 **S** New York State Office of Mental Health, Albany, NY
Primary Contact: Maureen Bosco, Executive Director
Web address: www.omh.ny.gov
**Control:** State–Government, nonfederal **Service:** Psychiatric

**Staffed Beds:** 226

## MARGARETVILLE—Delaware County

☐ **MARGARETVILLE HOSPITAL (331304)**, 42084 State Highway 28, Zip 12455–2820; tel. 845/586–2631, (Nonreporting) **A**1 9 10 18 **S** HealthAlliance of the Hudson Valley, Kingston, NY
Primary Contact: Sandra A. Horan, Executive Director
CFO: David Scarpino, Chief Financial Officer
CHR: Linda Mead, Director Human Resources
Web address: www.margaretvillehospital.org
**Control:** Other not–for–profit (including NFP Corporation) **Service:** General Medical and Surgical

**Staffed Beds:** 15

## MASSENA—St. Lawrence County

☒ **MASSENA MEMORIAL HOSPITAL (330223)**, One Hospital Drive, Zip 13662–1097; tel. 315/764–1711 **A**1 9 10 20 **F**3 8 11 13 15 16 17 18 20 29 31 34 35 40 50 51 55 56 57 59 60 64 70 72 73 76 78 80 81 82 85 86 87 88 89 93 97 107 108 109 110 111 114 116 117 118 119 130 132 135 146 147 148 **P**3 6
Primary Contact: Charles F. Fahd, II, Chief Executive Officer
CFO: Sean Curtin, Interim Chief Financial Officer
CMO: Nimesh Desai, M.D., Medical Director
CIO: Jana Grose, Director Management Information Systems
CHR: Jonnie Dorothy, Senior Director Human Resources
CNO: Sue Beaulieu, Chief Nurse Executive
Web address: www.massenahospital.org
**Control:** City–Government, nonfederal **Service:** General Medical and Surgical

**Staffed Beds:** 50 **Admissions:** 2376 **Census:** 25 **Outpatient Visits:** 125209 **Births:** 255 **Total Expense ($000):** 49480 **Payroll Expense ($000):** 22241 **Personnel:** 333

## MEDINA—Orleans County

☒ △ **MEDINA MEMORIAL HOSPITAL (330053)**, 200 Ohio Street, Zip 14103–1095; tel. 585/798–2000, (Nonreporting) **A**1 7 9 10
Primary Contact: Dolores Horvath, Interm Chief Executive Officer
CFO: Raj Mehta, Chief Financial Officer
CMO: Thomas J. Madejski, M.D., President Medical Staff
CHR: Mary Williams, Director Human Resources
Web address: www.medinamemorial.org
**Control:** State–Government, nonfederal **Service:** General Medical and Surgical

**Staffed Beds:** 101

## MIDDLETOWN—Orange County

☒ △ **ORANGE REGIONAL MEDICAL CENTER (330126)**, 707 East Main Street, Zip 10940–2650; tel. 845/333–1000 **A**1 2 7 9 10 **F**3 5 8 11 12 13 15 17 18 19 20 22 26 28 29 30 31 34 35 40 49 51 54 55 57 59 60 64 68 70 72 74 75 76 77 78 79 81 82 83 84 85 86 87 89 90 93 96 98 99 100 101 102 103 104 105 107 108 110 111 114 115 117 118 119 120 121 123 124 129 130 132 135 144 146 147 **S** Greater Hudson Valley Health System, Middletown, NY
Primary Contact: Scott Batulis, President and Chief Executive Officer
COO: Timothy P. Selz, Vice President
CFO: Mitch Amodo, Vice President and Chief Financial Officer
CMO: James Oxley, D.O., Vice President Medical Affairs
CIO: Shafiq Rab, Chief Information Officer
CHR: Deborah Carr, Vice President Human Resources
Web address: www.ormc.org
**Control:** Other not–for–profit (including NFP Corporation) **Service:** General Medical and Surgical

**Staffed Beds:** 301 **Admissions:** 20557 **Census:** 276 **Outpatient Visits:** 163851 **Births:** 1844 **Total Expense ($000):** 359453 **Payroll Expense ($000):** 138634

## MINEOLA—Nassau County

☒ **WINTHROP–UNIVERSITY HOSPITAL (330167)**, 259 First Street, Zip 11501–3957; tel. 516/663–0333, (Includes CHILDREN'S MEDICAL CENTER, 259 First Street, tel. 516/663–0333) **A**1 2 3 5 8 9 10 **F**3 5 6 8 9 11 12 13 14 15 17 18 19 20 22 24 26 28 29 30 31 32 34 35 38 39 40 41 43 44 45 46 47 48 49 50 51 53 54 55 56 57 58 59 60 61 62 63 64 65 66 68 69 70 71 72 73 74 75 76 77 78 79 81 82 84 85 86 87 88 89 92 93 94 97 100 103 107 108 110 111 113 114 115 116 117 118 119 120 121 123 124 126 129 130 131 132 134 135 141 142 145 146 147 148 **P**1 5
Primary Contact: John F. Collins, President and Chief Executive Officer
COO: Garry Schwall, Chief Operating Officer
CFO: Palmira Cataliotti, Vice President, Chief Financial Officer and Treasurer
CMO: Steven Fishbane, M.D., Chief Medical Officer
CIO: Nicholas Casabona, Chief Information Officer
CHR: George P. Rainer, Senior Vice President Human Resources
Web address: www.winthrop.org
**Control:** Other not–for–profit (including NFP Corporation) **Service:** General Medical and Surgical

**Staffed Beds:** 509 **Admissions:** 31237 **Census:** 456 **Outpatient Visits:** 370580 **Births:** 4471 **Total Expense ($000):** 1031000 **Payroll Expense ($000):** 350596 **Personnel:** 6182

**NY**

## MONTOUR FALLS—Schuyler County

☒ **SCHUYLER HOSPITAL (331313)**, 220 Steuben Street, Zip 14865–9709; tel. 607/535–7121, (Total facility includes 120 beds in nursing home–type unit) **A**1 9 10 18 **F**11 12 15 18 29 30 34 35 40 45 57 59 64 70 75 77 81 82 85 93 94 97 107 110 111 114 119 128 129 130 131 133 135 146 147 148 **P**6
Primary Contact: Andrew R. Manzer, President and Chief Executive Officer
CMO: Michael Eisman, M.D., Medical Director
CHR: Troy Preston, Director Human Resources
Web address: www.schuylerhospital.org
**Control:** Other not–for–profit (including NFP Corporation) **Service:** General Medical and Surgical

**Staffed Beds:** 144 **Admissions:** 1049 **Census:** 129 **Outpatient Visits:** 45972 **Births:** 0 **Total Expense ($000):** 30014 **Payroll Expense ($000):** 16161 **Personnel:** 314

## MONTROSE—Westchester County

☒ △ **VETERANS AFFAIRS HUDSON VALLEY HEALTH CARE SYSTEM–F.D. ROOSEVELT HOSPITAL**, 2094 Albany Post Road, Zip 10548–1454, Mailing Address: P.O. Box 100, Zip 10548–0100; tel. 914/737–4400, (Includes VETERAN AFFAIRS HUDSON VALLEY HEALTH CARE SYSTEM–CASTLE POINT DIVISION, Castle Point, Zip 12511–9999; tel. 914/831–2000; VETERANS AFFAIRS HUDSON VALLEY HEALTH CARE SYSTEM–MONTROSE DIVISION, Zip 10548; tel. 914/737–4400), (Nonreporting) **A**1 3 5 7 9 **S** Department of Veterans Affairs, Washington, DC
Primary Contact: Gerald F. Culliton, Director
COO: John M. Grady, Associate Director
CFO: John Walsh, Chief Fiscal Services
CMO: Joanne J. Malina, M.D., Chief of Staff
CIO: Thomas Rooney, Chief Information Resource Management
CHR: Dardanella Russell, Chief Human Resources Management Service
Web address: www.hudsonvalley.va.gov/
**Control:** Veterans Affairs, Government, federal **Service:** Psychiatric

**Staffed Beds:** 383

## MOUNT KISCO—Westchester County

☒ **NORTHERN WESTCHESTER HOSPITAL (330162)**, 400 East Main Street, Zip 10549–3477; tel. 914/666–1200 **A**1 2 5 9 10 **F**3 8 12 13 15 17 18 19 28 29 30 31 32 34 35 36 37 40 43 46 47 48 49 50 54 55 56 57 59 60 61 64 65 68 70 72 73 74 75 76 78 79 81 82 84 85 86 87 89 91 92 93 97 98 99 100 101 102 103 107 108 109 110 111 114 115 119 120 121 123 124 126 129 130 131 132 135 146 147 148
Primary Contact: Joel Seligman, President and Chief Executive Officer
CFO: John Partenza, Vice President and Treasurer
CMO: Marla Koroly, M.D., Chief Medical Officer and Senior Vice President Medical Affairs
CIO: Sue Prince, Director Information Systems
CHR: Kerry Flynn Barrett, Vice President Human Resources
CNO: Lauraine Szekely, R.N., Senior Vice President, Patient Care
Web address: www.nwhc.net
**Control:** Other not–for–profit (including NFP Corporation) **Service:** General Medical and Surgical

**Staffed Beds:** 189 **Admissions:** 9357 **Census:** 122 **Outpatient Visits:** 141372 **Births:** 1593 **Total Expense ($000):** 240608 **Payroll Expense ($000):** 100833 **Personnel:** 1359

## MOUNT VERNON—Westchester County

☐ **MOUNT VERNON HOSPITAL (330086)**, 12 North Seventh Avenue, Zip 10550–2098; tel. 914/664–8000, (Nonreporting) **A**1 3 5 9 10 **S** Sound Shore Health System, New Rochelle, NY
Primary Contact: John R. Spicer, President and Chief Executive Officer
CFO: Albert M. Farina, Chief Financial Officer
CMO: Gary Ishkanian, M.D., Vice President Medical Affairs
CIO: Barbara Cooke, Director Health Information Systems
CHR: Dennis H. Ashley, Vice President Human Resources
Web address: www.sshsw.org
**Control:** Other not–for–profit (including NFP Corporation) **Service:** General Medical and Surgical

**Staffed Beds:** 132

## NEW HAMPTON—Orange County

☐ **MID–HUDSON FORENSIC PSYCHIATRIC CENTER (334061)**, Route 17M, Zip 10958, Mailing Address: P.O. Box 158, Zip 10958–0158; tel. 845/374–8700, (Nonreporting) **A**1 10 **S** New York State Office of Mental Health, Albany, NY
Primary Contact: Peggi Healy, Executive Director
Web address: www.omh.ny.gov
**Control:** State–Government, nonfederal **Service:** Psychiatric

**Staffed Beds:** 268

## NEW HYDE PARK—Queens County, See New York City

## NEW ROCHELLE—Westchester County

☒ **SOUND SHORE MEDICAL CENTER OF WESTCHESTER (330184)**, 16 Guion Place, Zip 10801–5502; tel. 914/632–5000, (Nonreporting) **A**1 2 3 5 9 10 **S** Sound Shore Health System, New Rochelle, NY
Primary Contact: John R. Spicer, President and Chief Executive Officer
COO: John P. Mamangakis, Senior Vice President
CFO: Albert M. Farina, Senior Vice President and Chief Financial Officer
CMO: Richard Barone, M.D., Medical Director
CIO: Barbara Cooke, Director Health Information Systems
CHR: Dennis H. Ashley, Vice President Human Resources
CNO: Pamela M. Dupuis, R.N., Senior Vice President Patient Care Services
Web address: www.sshsw.org
**Control:** Other not–for–profit (including NFP Corporation) **Service:** General Medical and Surgical

**Staffed Beds:** 356

## NEW YORK (Includes all hospitals located within the five boroughs)
**BRONX** - Bronx County (Mailing Address - Bronx)
**BROOKLYN** - Kings County (Mailing Address - Brooklyn)
**MANHATTAN** - New York County (Mailing Address - New York)
**QUEENS** - Queens County (Mailing Addresses - Bellerose, Elmhurst, Far Rockaway, Flushing, Forest Hills, Glen Oaks, Holliswood, Jackson Heights, Jamaica, Little Neck, Long Island City, New Hyde Park, and Queens Village)
**RICHMOND VALLEY** - Richmond County (Mailing Address - Staten Island)

☒ **BELLEVUE HOSPITAL CENTER (330204)**, 462 First Avenue, Zip 10016–9198; tel. 212/562–4141 **A**1 3 5 9 10 **F**3 4 8 12 13 15 17 18 20 22 24 26 28 29 30 31 34 35 36 38 39 40 41 43 44 45 46 48 49 50 52 55 56 57 58 59 60 61 63 64 65 66 68 70 71 72 74 75 76 77 78 79 81 82 84 85 87 88 89 90 91 93 94 96 97 98 99 100 101 102 103 104 105 107 108 110 111 114 115 118 119 130 131 132 134 135 143 144 146 147 148 **S** New York City Health and Hospitals Corporation, New York, NY
Primary Contact: Lynda D. Curtis, Senior Vice President and Executive Director
COO: Steven Alexander, Chief Operating Officer
CFO: Aaron Cohen, Chief Financial Officer
CMO: Nate Link, M.D., Medical Director
CIO: Eli Tarlow, Chief Information Officer
CHR: Howard Kritz, Director Human Resources
CNO: Moftia Aujero, Chief Nurse Executive
Web address: www.nyc.gov/bellevue
**Control:** City–Government, nonfederal **Service:** General Medical and Surgical

**Staffed Beds:** 807 **Admissions:** 29793 **Census:** 686 **Outpatient Visits:** 640373 **Births:** 1674 **Total Expense ($000):** 801624 **Payroll Expense ($000):** 294722 **Personnel:** 4833

☒ **BETH ISRAEL MEDICAL CENTER (330169)**, First Avenue and 16th Street, Zip 10003–3803; tel. 212/420–2000, (Includes BETH ISRAEL MEDICAL CENTER–KINGS HIGHWAY DIVISION, 3201 Kings Highway, Brooklyn, Zip 11234; tel. 718/252–3000), (Total facility includes 28 beds in nursing home–type unit) **A**1 3 5 8 9 10 **F**3 4 5 7 8 9 11 13 14 15 17 18 19 20 22 24 26 28 29 30 31 32 33 34 35 36 38 39 40 41 43 44 45 46 47 48 49 50 51 52 53 54 55 56 57 58 59 60 61 62 64 65 66 68 70 72 74 75 76 77 78 79 80 81 82 83 84 85 86 87 88 89 90 92 93 94 96 97 98 99 100 101 102 103 104 107 108 110 111 114 115 117 118 119 120 121 123 126 128 129 130 131 132 135 141 144 145 146 147 148 **P**5 8 **S** Continuum Health Partners, New York, NY
Primary Contact: Harris M. Nagler, M.D., President
COO: Kevin Molloy, Senior Vice President and Chief Operating Officer
CFO: John Collura, Executive Vice President Financial Services and Chief Financial Officer
CMO: David Bernard, M.D., Chief Medical Officer
CIO: Bonnie Sessa, Vice President and Chief Information Officer
CHR: Marvin Russell, Corporate Senior Vice President Human Resources
Web address: www.bethisraelny.org
**Control:** Other not–for–profit (including NFP Corporation) **Service:** General Medical and Surgical

**Staffed Beds:** 856 **Admissions:** 54882 **Census:** 859 **Outpatient Visits:** 532442 **Births:** 4178 **Total Expense ($000):** 1453623 **Payroll Expense ($000):** 714867 **Personnel:** 8536

☐ **BRONX PSYCHIATRIC CENTER (334053)**, 1500 Waters Place, Bronx, Zip 10461–2796; tel. 718/931–0600, (Nonreporting) **A**1 3 5 10 **S** New York State Office of Mental Health, Albany, NY
Primary Contact: Pamela Turner, Executive Director
CFO: Robert Erway, Director for Administration
Web address: www.omh.ny.gov
**Control:** State–Government, nonfederal **Service:** Psychiatric

**Staffed Beds:** 450

*Many Facility Codes have changed. Please refer to the AHA Guide Code Chart.* © 2013 AHA Guide

☒ **BRONX–LEBANON HOSPITAL CENTER HEALTH CARE SYSTEM (330009)**, 1276 Fulton Avenue, Bronx, Zip 10456–3499; tel. 718/590–1800, (Includes BRONX–LEBANON SPECIAL CARE CENTER, 1265 Fulton Avenue, Zip 10465; tel. 718/579–7000; CONCOURSE DIVISION, 1650 Grand Concourse, Zip 10457; tel. 718/590–1800; FULTON DIVISION, 1276 Fulton Avenue, Zip 10456; tel. 718/590–1800; HIGHBRIDGE WOODYCREST CENTER, 936 Woodycrest Avenue, Zip 10452; tel. 718/293–3200), (Total facility includes 330 beds in nursing home–type unit) **A**1 3 5 8 9 10 **F**2 3 4 5 8 9 11 12 13 15 17 18 19 20 22 26 28 29 30 31 32 34 35 37 38 39 40 41 43 44 45 46 47 48 49 50 51 52 54 55 56 57 58 59 60 61 64 65 66 68 70 71 72 73 74 75 76 77 78 79 81 82 83 84 85 86 87 88 89 91 92 93 94 96 97 98 99 100 101 102 103 104 105 106 107 108 109 110 111 113 114 115 118 119 123 128 129 130 131 132 133 134 135 145 146 147 148 **P**6
Primary Contact: Miguel A. Fuentes, Jr., President and Chief Executive Officer
COO: Steven Anderman, Chief Operating Officer
CFO: Victor DeMarco, Chief Financial Officer
CMO: Milton A. Gumbs, M.D., Vice President and Medical Director
CIO: Ivan Durbak, Chief Information Officer
CHR: Selena Griffin–Mahon, Assistant Vice President Human Resources
Web address: www.bronxcare.org
**Control:** Other not–for–profit (including NFP Corporation) **Service:** General Medical and Surgical

**Staffed Beds:** 923 **Admissions:** 29825 **Census:** 769 **Outpatient Visits:** 992039 **Births:** 2279 **Total Expense ($000):** 701477 **Payroll Expense ($000):** 348496 **Personnel:** 4090

☐ **BROOKDALE HOSPITAL MEDICAL CENTER (330233)**, One Brookdale Plaza, Brooklyn, Zip 11212–3139; tel. 718/240–5000, (Total facility includes 448 beds in nursing home–type unit) **A**1 3 5 9 10 **F**2 3 7 8 10 12 13 14 15 17 18 19 20 22 26 27 29 30 31 32 34 35 38 39 40 41 43 46 49 50 51 54 55 56 57 58 59 60 61 62 63 64 65 66 68 69 70 71 72 73 74 75 76 77 78 79 80 81 82 83 84 85 86 87 88 89 93 94 96 97 98 99 100 101 102 103 104 105 106 107 108 110 111 114 115 119 126 128 129 130 131 132 133 134 135 145 146 147 148 **P**7
Primary Contact: Mark Toney, President and Chief Executive Officer
CFO: Mounir F. Doss, Executive Vice President and Chief Financial Officer
CMO: Richard Fogler, M.D., Chairman Surgery and Chief Medical Officer
CIO: Douglas Thompson, Director Information Systems
CHR: Max Sclair, Vice President Human Resources
Web address: www.brookdalehospital.org
**Control:** Other not–for–profit (including NFP Corporation) **Service:** General Medical and Surgical

**Staffed Beds:** 790 **Admissions:** 17374 **Census:** 735 **Outpatient Visits:** 240000 **Births:** 1400 **Total Expense ($000):** 540573 **Payroll Expense ($000):** 202315 **Personnel:** 2885

☐ **BROOKLYN HOSPITAL CENTER (330056)**, 121 DeKalb Avenue, Brooklyn, Zip 11201–5425; tel. 718/250–8000 **A**1 3 5 8 9 10 **F**3 4 8 12 13 14 15 17 18 20 29 30 31 32 34 35 38 39 40 49 50 51 54 56 57 59 60 61 62 64 65 66 68 70 72 74 75 76 77 78 79 80 81 82 83 84 85 86 87 88 89 90 97 100 102 104 107 108 110 111 114 115 121 123 129 130 131 132 135 143 144 146 147 148 **P**6 **S** New York Presbyterian Healthcare System, New York, NY
Primary Contact: Richard B. Becker, M.D., President, Chief Executive Officer and Interim Chief Medical Officer
COO: W. Trent Crable, Executive Vice President and Chief Operating Officer
CFO: Joseph Guarracino, Senior Vice President and Chief Financial Officer
CIO: Irene Farrelly, Vice President and Chief Information Officer
CHR: Ira Warm, Senior Vice President Human Resources
Web address: www.tbh.org
**Control:** Church–operated, Nongovernment, not–for profit **Service:** General Medical and Surgical

**Staffed Beds:** 312 **Admissions:** 16759 **Census:** 260 **Outpatient Visits:** 265521 **Births:** 2196 **Total Expense ($000):** 380824 **Payroll Expense ($000):** 194649 **Personnel:** 3634

☒ **CALVARY HOSPITAL (332006)**, 1740 Eastchester Road, Bronx, Zip 10461–2392; tel. 718/863–6900 **A**1 9 10 **F**1 29 30 35 39 62 63 64 68 74 78 82 84 87 119 121 130 132 134 146 148 **P**6
Primary Contact: Frank A. Calamari, President and Chief Executive Officer
COO: Richard J. Kutilek, Chief Operating Officer
CFO: Andrew Greco, Chief Financial Officer
CMO: Michael J. Brescia, M.D., Executive Medical Director
CIO: Patrick Martin, Director Information Systems
CHR: Michael T. Troncone, Chief Human Resources Officer
Web address: www.calvaryhospital.org
**Control:** Church–operated, Nongovernment, not–for profit **Service:** Long–Term Acute Care hospital

**Staffed Beds:** 225 **Admissions:** 3033 **Census:** 210 **Outpatient Visits:** 118195 **Births:** 0 **Total Expense ($000):** 134543 **Payroll Expense ($000):** 58569 **Personnel:** 784

☒ △ **COLER–GOLDWATER SPECIALTY HOSPITAL AND NURSING FACILITY (332008)**, One Main Street, Zip 10044–0052; tel. 212/318–8000, (Includes COLER MEMORIAL HOSPITAL, Roosevelt Island, Zip 10044; tel. 212/848–6000; GOLDWATER MEMORIAL HOSPITAL, Franklin D. Roosevelt Island, Zip 10044; tel. 212/318–8000), (Total facility includes 1389 beds in nursing home–type unit) **A**1 3 5 7 10 **F**1 3 11 28 29 30 39 58 61 68 74 75 77 85 87 90 100 103 107 114 119 128 130 132 135 146 148 **P**4 **S** New York City Health and Hospitals Corporation, New York, NY
Primary Contact: Robert Hughes, Executive Director
CFO: Gloria Ranghelli, Deputy Chief Financial Officer
CMO: Yolanda Bruno, M.D., Medical Director
CHR: Howard Kritz, Director
Web address: www.coler–goldwater.org
**Control:** City–Government, nonfederal **Service:** Long–Term Acute Care hospital

**Staffed Beds:** 2016 **Admissions:** 1913 **Census:** 1615 **Outpatient Visits:** 0 **Births:** 0 **Total Expense ($000):** 337606 **Payroll Expense ($000):** 142193 **Personnel:** 2322

**CONCOURSE DIVISION** See Bronx–Lebanon Hospital Center Health Care System, Bronx

☒ **CONEY ISLAND HOSPITAL (330196)**, 2601 Ocean Parkway, Brooklyn, Zip 11235–7795; tel. 718/616–3000 **A**1 3 5 9 10 12 13 **F**3 4 5 8 9 11 13 15 17 18 19 20 28 29 30 31 32 34 35 38 39 40 41 45 46 49 50 51 54 55 56 57 58 59 60 61 64 65 66 68 70 71 73 74 75 76 77 78 79 81 82 83 84 85 87 89 90 91 93 94 96 97 98 99 100 102 103 104 106 107 108 110 111 114 115 118 119 130 132 135 143 146 147 148 **S** New York City Health and Hospitals Corporation, New York, NY
Primary Contact: Arthur Wagner, Senior Vice President and Executive Director
COO: Mary Mong, R.N., Chief Operating Officer
CFO: Paul Pandolfini, Chief Financial Officer
CMO: John Maese, M.D., Chief Medical Officer
CIO: Silvana DeSimone, Chief Information Officer
CHR: Rodney Parker, Senior Associate Executive Director
Web address: www.nyc.gov/html/hhc/html/facilities/coneyisland.shtml
**Control:** City–Government, nonfederal **Service:** General Medical and Surgical

**Staffed Beds:** 371 **Admissions:** 17206 **Census:** 307 **Outpatient Visits:** 369869 **Births:** 1288 **Total Expense ($000):** 395892 **Payroll Expense ($000):** 160549 **Personnel:** 2951

☐ **CREEDMOOR PSYCHIATRIC CENTER (334004)**, 79–25 Winchester Boulevard, Jamaica, Zip 11427–2128; tel. 718/264–3600, (Nonreporting) **A**1 10 **S** New York State Office of Mental Health, Albany, NY
Primary Contact: Ann Marie Barbarotta, Executive Director
CFO: Viodelda Ho–Shing, Deputy Director Administration
CIO: Connie Mitchell, Ph.D., Chief Information Officer
CHR: Rhonda Cicha, Director Human Resources
Web address: www.omh.ny.gov
**Control:** State–Government, nonfederal **Service:** Psychiatric

**Staffed Beds:** 380

☒ **ELMHURST HOSPITAL CENTER (330128)**, 79–01 Broadway, Elmhurst, Zip 11373–1329; tel. 718/334–4000 **A**1 2 3 5 9 10 **F**3 5 8 9 13 14 15 17 18 20 22 26 29 30 31 32 34 35 38 40 41 43 45 49 50 51 53 55 56 57 59 60 61 64 68 70 72 73 74 75 76 77 78 79 81 82 83 84 85 86 87 89 90 92 93 97 98 99 100 101 102 103 104 105 107 108 110 111 115 119 121 126 130 131 132 134 135 143 146 147 **P**6 **S** New York City Health and Hospitals Corporation, New York, NY
Primary Contact: Chris D. Constantino, Executive Director
COO: Wayne Zimmermann, Chief Operating Officer
CFO: Brian Stacey, Chief Financial Officer
CMO: Jasmin Moshirpur, M.D., Dean and Medical Director
CIO: Vincent Smith, Chief Information Officer
CHR: Jeannith Gangemi–Sosa, Associate Executive Director
CNO: Joann Gull, Chief Nursing Officer
Web address: www.nyc.gov/html/hhc/ehc/html/home/home.shtml
**Control:** City–Government, nonfederal **Service:** General Medical and Surgical

**Staffed Beds:** 551 **Admissions:** 24979 **Census:** 455 **Outpatient Visits:** 680798 **Births:** 3362 **Total Expense ($000):** 612745 **Payroll Expense ($000):** 217376 **Personnel:** 3190

**NY**

---

**Hospital, Medicare Provider Number, Address, Telephone, Approval, Facility, and Physician Codes, Health Care System**

★ American Hospital Association (AHA) membership
☐ The Joint Commission accreditation
◇ DNV Healthcare Inc. accreditation
○ Healthcare Facilities Accreditation Program
△ Commission on Accreditation of Rehabilitation Facilities (CARF) accreditation

☐ **FLUSHING HOSPITAL MEDICAL CENTER (330193)**, 4500 Parsons Boulevard, Flushing, Zip 11355–2205; tel. 718/670–5000 **A**1 3 5 9 10 **F**3 4 5 7 8 11 13 15 17 18 29 30 31 32 34 35 36 39 40 41 45 50 56 57 59 60 61 63 64 65 68 70 71 72 74 75 76 77 78 79 81 82 84 85 87 89 91 92 93 97 98 100 101 102 103 104 107 110 111 114 119 130 132 135 146 147 148 **P**5 7
Primary Contact: Bruce J. Flanz, President and Chief Executive Officer
COO: Robert V. Levine, Executive Vice President and Chief Operating Officer
CFO: Mounir F. Doss, Executive Vice President and Chief Financial Officer
CMO: Peter Barra, M.D., Chief Medical Officer
CIO: Tony Gatto, Director Management Information Systems
CHR: Max Sclair, Vice President Human Resources
Web address: www.flushinghospital.org
**Control:** Other not–for–profit (including NFP Corporation) **Service:** General Medical and Surgical

**Staffed Beds:** 293 **Admissions:** 15881 **Census:** 251 **Outpatient Visits:** 147102 **Births:** 2853 **Total Expense ($000):** 270359 **Payroll Expense ($000):** 116822 **Personnel:** 1619

☒ **FOREST HILLS HOSPITAL (330353)**, 102–01 66th Road, Forest Hills, Zip 11375–2029; tel. 718/830–4000 **A**1 2 9 10 **F**3 8 12 13 15 18 29 30 31 34 35 37 38 40 43 45 46 49 50 51 52 55 57 58 59 60 64 65 66 68 70 73 74 75 76 77 78 79 81 82 84 85 86 87 97 100 102 107 111 114 119 124 130 132 135 143 146 147 148 **P**5 6 **S** North Shore–Long Island Jewish Health System, Great Neck, NY
Primary Contact: Rita Mercieca, R.N., Executive Director
COO: Mark J. Solazzo, Senior Vice President and Chief Operating Officer
CFO: Robert S. Shapiro, Senior Vice President and Chief Financial Officer
CMO: Lawrence Smith, M.D., Senior Vice President and Chief Medical Officer
CIO: John Bosco, Vice President and Chief Information Officer
CHR: Joseph Cabral, Senior Vice President and Chief Human Resources Officer
Web address: www.northshorelij.com
**Control:** Other not–for–profit (including NFP Corporation) **Service:** General Medical and Surgical

**Staffed Beds:** 235 **Admissions:** 16760 **Census:** 201 **Outpatient Visits:** 74691 **Births:** 2421 **Total Expense ($000):** 212001 **Payroll Expense ($000):** 104157 **Personnel:** 1248

**FULTON DIVISION** See Bronx–Lebanon Hospital Center Health Care System, Bronx

**GOLDWATER MEMORIAL HOSPITAL** See Coler–Goldwater Specialty Hospital and Nursing Facility

☐ **GRACIE SQUARE HOSPITAL (334048)**, 420 East 76th Street, Zip 10021–3396; tel. 212/988–4400 **A**1 9 10 **F**35 87 98 103 117 130 **S** New York Presbyterian Healthcare System, New York, NY
Primary Contact: Frank Bruno, Chief Executive Officer
Web address: www.nygsh.org
**Control:** Other not–for–profit (including NFP Corporation) **Service:** Psychiatric

**Staffed Beds:** 157 **Admissions:** 2792 **Census:** 155 **Outpatient Visits:** 0 **Births:** 0 **Total Expense ($000):** 38086 **Payroll Expense ($000):** 19619 **Personnel:** 141

☒ △ **HARLEM HOSPITAL CENTER (330240)**, 506 Lenox Avenue, Zip 10037–1802; tel. 212/939–1000, (Includes HARLEM GENERAL CARE UNIT AND HARLEM PSYCHIATRIC UNIT ), (Nonreporting) **A**1 3 5 7 9 10 **S** New York City Health and Hospitals Corporation, New York, NY
Primary Contact: Denise C. Soares, R.N., Executive Director
Web address: www.nyc.gov/html/hhc/harlem
**Control:** City–Government, nonfederal **Service:** General Medical and Surgical

**Staffed Beds:** 272

☐ **HOLLISWOOD HOSPITAL (334055)**, 87–37 Palermo Street, Jamaica, Zip 11423–1209; tel. 718/776–8181, (Nonreporting) **A**1 9 10 **S** Liberty Management Group, Inc.
Primary Contact: Alan Eskenazi, Chief Executive Officer
CMO: Jeffrey Borenstein, M.D., Medical Director
CHR: Dorothy A. Muller, Director Human Resources
Web address: www.holliswoodhospital.com
**Control:** Corporation, Investor–owned, for–profit **Service:** Psychiatric

**Staffed Beds:** 125

☒ **HOSPITAL FOR SPECIAL SURGERY (330270)**, 535 East 70th Street, Zip 10021–4898; tel. 212/606–1000 **A**1 3 5 8 9 10 **F**3 8 9 29 30 32 33 34 35 36 37 38 43 44 50 53 54 56 57 58 59 64 66 68 74 75 77 79 80 81 82 84 85 86 87 89 92 93 94 97 100 107 109 111 114 115 116 117 118 119 121 123 126 130 131 132 134 141 142 146 147 **P**8 **S** New York Presbyterian Healthcare System, New York, NY
Primary Contact: Louis A. Shapiro, President and Chief Executive Officer
COO: Lisa Goldstein, Executive Vice President and Chief Operating Officer
CFO: Stacey Malakoff, Executive Vice President and Chief Financial Officer
CMO: Thomas P. Sculco, M.D., Surgeon–in–Chief and Medical Director
CIO: Jamie Mooney, Vice President and Chief Information Officer
CHR: Bruce Slawitsky, Vice President Human Resources
CNO: Stephanie J. Goldberg, MSN, Senior Vice President and Chief Nursing Officer
Web address: www.hss.edu
**Control:** Other not–for–profit (including NFP Corporation) **Service:** Orthopedic

**Staffed Beds:** 203 **Admissions:** 13945 **Census:** 151 **Outpatient Visits:** 344129 **Births:** 0 **Total Expense ($000):** 727433 **Payroll Expense ($000):** 314570 **Personnel:** 3658

☐ **INTERFAITH MEDICAL CENTER (330397)**, 1545 Atlantic Avenue, Brooklyn, Zip 11213–1122; tel. 718/613–4000, (Nonreporting) **A**1 3 5 9 10
Primary Contact: Laura Gaffney, President and Chief Executive Officer
CFO: Gregg Dixon, CPA, Chief Financial Officer
CMO: Jochanan Weisenfreund, M.D., Senior Vice President Academic and Medical Affairs
CIO: Mark Lederman, Chief Information Officer
CHR: Venra Mathurin, Vice President Human Resources
Web address: www.interfaithmedical.com
**Control:** Other not–for–profit (including NFP Corporation) **Service:** General Medical and Surgical

**Staffed Beds:** 277

**JACK D WEILER HOSPITAL OF ALBERT EINSTEIN COLLEGE OF MEDICINE**
See Montefiore Medical Center, Bronx

☒ **JACOBI MEDICAL CENTER (330127)**, 1400 Pelham Parkway South, Bronx, Zip 10461–1197; tel. 718/918–5000 **A**1 3 5 9 10 **F**3 4 5 8 11 12 13 15 16 17 18 20 26 29 30 31 32 34 35 38 39 40 41 43 44 45 46 47 49 50 51 55 56 57 58 59 60 61 62 64 65 66 70 72 73 74 75 76 77 78 79 80 81 82 84 85 87 88 89 90 92 93 94 96 97 98 99 100 101 102 103 104 107 108 110 111 117 119 130 131 132 134 135 144 146 147 148 **P**6 **S** New York City Health and Hospitals Corporation, New York, NY
Primary Contact: William P. Walsh, Senior Vice President and Executive Director
COO: Christopher Fugazy, Chief Operating Officer
CFO: Kathy Garramone, Chief Financial Officer
CMO: Joseph Skarzynski, M.D., Medical Director
CIO: Diane Carr, Chief Information Officer
CHR: Dolores Leite, Chief Human Resource Executive
CNO: Ellen O'Connor, Chief Nursing Officer
Web address: www.nyc.gov/html/hhc/jacobi/home.html
**Control:** City–Government, nonfederal **Service:** General Medical and Surgical

**Staffed Beds:** 457 **Admissions:** 20053 **Census:** 355 **Outpatient Visits:** 488905 **Births:** 1972 **Total Expense ($000):** 649034 **Payroll Expense ($000):** 244878 **Personnel:** 3755

☒ **JAMAICA HOSPITAL MEDICAL CENTER (330014)**, 8900 Van Wyck Expressway, Jamaica, Zip 11418–2832; tel. 718/206–6000, (Total facility includes 224 beds in nursing home–type unit) **A**1 3 5 9 10 13 **F**1 3 7 11 13 15 17 18 19 20 22 26 29 30 31 34 35 36 39 40 41 43 44 45 49 50 52 53 54 55 56 57 58 59 60 61 62 64 65 66 68 70 71 72 73 74 75 76 77 78 79 80 81 82 83 84 85 86 87 89 90 92 93 94 96 97 98 100 101 102 103 104 107 108 110 111 114 115 118 119 129 130 131 132 134 135 143 144 146 147 **P**5 7 8
Primary Contact: Bruce J. Flanz, President and Chief Executive Officer
CFO: Mounir F. Doss, Executive Vice President and Chief Financial Officer
CMO: Anthony Di Maria, M.D., Medical Director
CIO: Richard Hlavenka, Director Management Information Systems
CHR: Max Sclair, Vice President Human Resources
Web address: www.Jamaicahospital.org
**Control:** Other not–for–profit (including NFP Corporation) **Service:** General Medical and Surgical

**Staffed Beds:** 644 **Admissions:** 23166 **Census:** 548 **Outpatient Visits:** 353025 **Births:** 2128 **Total Expense ($000):** 545374 **Payroll Expense ($000):** 217868 **Personnel:** 3156

☒ △ **JAMES J. PETERS VETERANS AFFAIRS MEDICAL CENTER**, (Formerly Veterans Affairs Medical Center), 130 West Kingsbridge Road, Bronx, Zip 10468–3904; tel. 718/584–9000, (Total facility includes 80 beds in nursing home–type unit) **A**1 2 3 5 7 8 **F**3 5 8 9 11 12 17 18 29 30 31 33 34 35 36 38 39 40 43 44 45 46 47 48 49 50 51 53 54 56 57 59 60 61 62 63 64 65 68 70 74 75 77 78 79 80 81 82 83 84 85 86 87 90 91 92 93 94 95 96 97 98 100 101 102 103 104 107 108 109 111 114 115 118 119 120 123 126 130 131 132 135 143 146 147 148 **S** Department of Veterans Affairs, Washington, DC
Primary Contact: MaryAnn P. Musumeci, Director
CFO: Gregory Angelo, Chief Fiscal Program
CMO: Clive Rosendorff, M.D., Chief Medical Program
CIO: Linda Bund, Chief Information Officer and Director Education
CHR: Peter Tinker, Chief Human Resources Officer
Web address: www.bronx.va.gov/
**Control:** Veterans Affairs, Government, federal **Service:** General Medical and Surgical

**Staffed Beds:** 325 **Admissions:** 4096 **Census:** 108 **Outpatient Visits:** 341868 **Births:** 0 **Total Expense ($000):** 285575 **Payroll Expense ($000):** 142853 **Personnel:** 1959

*Many Facility Codes have changed. Please refer to the AHA Guide Code Chart.*

⊠ **KINGS COUNTY HOSPITAL CENTER (330202)**, 451 Clarkson Avenue, Brooklyn, Zip 11203–2097; tel. 718/245–3131 **A**1 2 3 5 9 10 **F**3 4 5 8 9 11 12 13 15 17 18 19 20 24 26 28 29 30 31 32 34 35 38 39 40 41 43 46 47 49 50 51 52 53 56 57 58 59 60 61 64 65 68 70 71 72 73 74 75 76 77 78 79 81 82 83 84 85 86 87 88 89 90 91 92 93 94 97 98 99 100 101 102 103 104 105 106 107 108 110 111 114 115 116 119 120 121 123 129 130 131 132 134 135 143 144 145 146 147 148 **P**6 **S** New York City Health and Hospitals Corporation, New York, NY
Primary Contact: Ernest Baptiste, Executive Director
COO: Roslyn Weinstein, Chief Operating Officer
CFO: Julian John, Chief Financial Officer
CMO: Abha Agrawal, M.D., Medical Director
CIO: Dino Civan, Chief Information Officer
CHR: Raquel Ayala, Deputy Executive Director Network and Human Resources
Web address: www.nyc.gov/html/hhc/kchc/html/home/home.shtml
**Control:** City–Government, nonfederal **Service:** General Medical and Surgical

**Staffed Beds:** 601 **Admissions:** 25686 **Census:** 512 **Outpatient Visits:** 756819 **Births:** 2478 **Total Expense ($000):** 790956 **Payroll Expense ($000):** 365634 **Personnel:** 5140

☐ **KINGSBORO PSYCHIATRIC CENTER (334058)**, 681 Clarkson Avenue, Brooklyn, Zip 11203–2125; tel. 718/221–7395, (Nonreporting) **A**1 3 5 **S** New York State Office of Mental Health, Albany, NY
Primary Contact: Deborah Parchment, Executive Director
CFO: Yinusa Awolowo, Business Officer
CMO: Jeffery Lucey, M.D., Clinical Director
CIO: George Gavora, Director Program Evaluation
CHR: Geraldine Cody, Director Human Resources
Web address: www.omh.ny.gov/omhweb/facilities/kbpc/facility/htm
**Control:** State–Government, nonfederal **Service:** Psychiatric

**Staffed Beds:** 290

⊠ △ **KINGSBROOK JEWISH MEDICAL CENTER (330201)**, 585 Schenectady Avenue, Brooklyn, Zip 11203–1891; tel. 718/604–5000, (Total facility includes 466 beds in nursing home–type unit) **A**1 3 5 7 9 10 **F**3 8 15 17 18 28 29 30 31 34 35 39 40 45 46 48 49 50 54 56 57 59 60 61 64 65 68 70 74 75 77 78 79 80 81 82 84 85 87 90 91 92 93 94 96 97 98 100 101 103 104 107 108 110 111 114 115 119 128 130 131 135 143 146 147 148
Primary Contact: Linda Brady, M.D., President and Chief Executive Officer
COO: Robert Dubicki, Executive Vice President and Chief Operating Officer
CFO: John Schmitt, Senior Vice President and Chief Financial Officer
CMO: Sibte Burney, M.D., Senior Vice President Medical Affairs and Chief Medical Officer
CIO: Daniel Morreale, Vice President and Chief Information Officer
CHR: John McKeon, Vice President Human Resources
CNO: Jane Lederer, R.N., Vice President and Chief Nursing Officer
Web address: www.kingsbrook.org
**Control:** Other not–for–profit (including NFP Corporation) **Service:** General Medical and Surgical

**Staffed Beds:** 771 **Admissions:** 11894 **Census:** 667 **Outpatient Visits:** 123846 **Births:** 0 **Total Expense ($000):** 270084 **Payroll Expense ($000):** 136823 **Personnel:** 1955

⊠ **LENOX HILL HOSPITAL (330119)**, 100 East 77th Street, Zip 10075–1850; tel. 212/434–2000, (Includes MANHATTAN EYE, EAR AND THROAT HOSPITAL, 210 East 64th Street, Zip 10021–9885; tel. 212/838–9200; Philip P. Rosenthal, Executive Director) **A**1 3 5 8 9 10 **F**7 8 9 11 12 13 14 15 17 18 20 22 24 26 29 30 31 32 34 35 37 38 39 40 43 45 46 47 48 49 50 51 54 55 56 57 58 59 60 61 62 63 64 65 66 68 70 72 74 75 76 77 78 79 81 82 84 85 86 87 89 91 92 93 97 98 99 100 101 102 103 104 105 107 108 111 115 117 118 119 126 130 131 132 135 143 146 147 148 **P**5 6 **S** North Shore–Long Island Jewish Health System, Great Neck, NY
Primary Contact: Dennis Connors, Executive Director
CMO: Marc L. Napp, M.D., Vice President Medical Affairs
CIO: Beth Dituro, Divisional Chief Information Officer
Web address: www.lenoxhillhospital.org
**Control:** Other not–for–profit (including NFP Corporation) **Service:** General Medical and Surgical

**Staffed Beds:** 508 **Admissions:** 29441 **Census:** 386 **Outpatient Visits:** 191110 **Births:** 4400 **Total Expense ($000):** 732529 **Payroll Expense ($000):** 340492 **Personnel:** 3809

⊠ **LINCOLN MEDICAL AND MENTAL HEALTH CENTER (330080)**, 234 East 149th Street, Bronx, Zip 10451–5504; tel. 718/579–5700 **A**1 2 3 5 9 10 **F**3 5 8 11 13 15 18 19 29 30 31 32 34 35 38 39 40 41 43 45 50 55 56 57 58 59 60 61 64 65 66 68 70 71 72 73 74 75 76 77 78 79 81 82 84 85 86 87 88 89 93 97 98 99 100 101 102 103 104 107 108 110 111 114 115 119 121 123 130 132 134 135 143 144 146 147 148 **P**4 **S** New York City Health and Hospitals Corporation, New York, NY
Primary Contact: Milton Nunez, Executive Director
COO: Lauren Johnston, Deputy Executive Director
CFO: Victor Bekker, Chief Financial Officer
CMO: Melissa Schori, M.D., Medical Director
CIO: Maricar Barrameda, Chief Information Officer
CHR: Jeannith Gangemi–Sosa, Senior Associate Executive Director
Web address: www.nyc.gov/html/hhc/lincoln/
**Control:** City–Government, nonfederal **Service:** General Medical and Surgical

**Staffed Beds:** 335 **Admissions:** 21590 **Census:** 248 **Outpatient Visits:** 598936 **Births:** 2264 **Total Expense ($000):** 529173 **Payroll Expense ($000):** 196918 **Personnel:** 3221

⊠ **LONG ISLAND JEWISH MEDICAL CENTER (330195)**, 270–05 76th Avenue, New Hyde Park, Zip 11040–1496; tel. 718/470–7000, (Includes MANHASSET AMBULATORY CARE PAVILION, 1554 Northern Boulevard, Manhasset, Zip 11030; tel. 516/365–2070; STEVEN AND ALEXANDRA COHEN CHILDREN'S MEDICAL CENTER OF NEW YORK, 270–05 76th Avenue, Zip 11040; tel. 718/470–3000; ZUCKER HILLSIDE HOSPITAL, 75–59 263rd Street, Glen Oaks, Zip 11004; tel. 718/470–8000) **A**1 2 3 5 8 9 10 13 **F**2 3 5 6 7 8 9 11 12 13 14 15 17 18 19 20 21 22 23 24 25 26 27 29 30 31 32 34 35 38 39 40 41 43 44 45 46 47 48 49 50 51 53 54 55 56 57 58 59 60 61 62 63 64 65 66 68 70 72 73 74 75 76 77 78 79 81 82 83 84 85 86 87 88 89 92 93 97 98 99 100 101 102 103 104 105 106 107 108 109 110 111 114 115 116 117 118 119 120 121 123 124 126 129 130 131 132 134 135 136 141 142 143 144 145 146 147 148 **P**5 6 **S** North Shore–Long Island Jewish Health System, Great Neck, NY
Primary Contact: Chantal Weinhold, Executive Director
CMO: Jeremy Boal, M.D., Medical Director
CIO: Ty Knox, Chief Information Officer
CHR: Ronald W. Stone, Regional Chief Human Resource Officer
Web address: www.lij.edu
**Control:** Other not–for–profit (including NFP Corporation) **Service:** General Medical and Surgical

**Staffed Beds:** 868 **Admissions:** 48702 **Census:** 799 **Outpatient Visits:** 705603 **Births:** 5957 **Total Expense ($000):** 1566974 **Payroll Expense ($000):** 761182 **Personnel:** 13814

⊠ **LUTHERAN MEDICAL CENTER (330306)**, 150 55th Street, Brooklyn, Zip 11220–2559; tel. 718/630–7000 **A**1 3 5 9 10 13 **F**3 4 5 7 8 11 12 13 14 15 17 18 20 22 28 29 30 31 32 34 35 36 38 39 40 43 44 45 47 49 50 51 54 55 56 57 58 59 60 61 62 64 65 66 68 70 71 72 73 74 75 76 77 78 79 81 82 84 85 86 87 89 90 91 92 93 94 96 97 98 100 101 102 103 104 107 108 110 111 114 115 118 119 121 123 124 125 130 131 132 135 143 146 147 148 **P**6
Primary Contact: Wendy Z. Goldstein, President and Chief Executive Officer
COO: Claudia Caine, Executive Vice President and Chief Operating Officer
CFO: Richard Langfelder, Executive Vice President and Chief Financial Officer
CMO: Beth Raucher, M.D., Senior Vice President and Chief Medical Officer
CIO: Steve Art, Senior Vice President and Chief Information Officer
CHR: Frank Scheets, Senior Vice President
Web address: www.lmcmc.com
**Control:** Church–operated, Nongovernment, not–for profit **Service:** General Medical and Surgical

**Staffed Beds:** 396 **Admissions:** 24748 **Census:** 350 **Outpatient Visits:** 748275 **Births:** 4309 **Total Expense ($000):** 557586 **Payroll Expense ($000):** 265045 **Personnel:** 3804

**NY**

**Hospital, Medicare Provider Number, Address, Telephone, Approval, Facility, and Physician Codes, Health Care System**

★ American Hospital Association (AHA) membership
☐ The Joint Commission accreditation
◇ DNV Healthcare Inc. accreditation
○ Healthcare Facilities Accreditation Program
△ Commission on Accreditation of Rehabilitation Facilities (CARF) accreditation

**MAIMONIDES MEDICAL CENTER (330194)**, 4802 Tenth Avenue, Brooklyn, Zip 11219–2916; tel. 718/283–6000, (Includes MAIMONIDES INFANTS AND CHILDREN'S HOSPITAL OF BROOKLYN, 4802 Tenth Avenue, tel. 718/283–6000) **A**1 2 3 5 8 9 10 12 13 **F**2 3 7 8 9 11 12 13 14 15 17 18 19 20 22 24 26 28 29 30 31 32 34 35 38 39 40 41 44 45 46 47 48 49 50 51 52 54 55 56 57 58 59 60 61 64 65 66 68 70 72 73 74 75 76 77 78 79 81 82 84 85 86 87 88 89 91 92 93 96 97 98 99 100 101 102 103 104 105 107 108 110 111 114 115 116 117 118 119 120 121 123 124 126 129 130 131 132 134 135 145 146 147 148 **P**5 6
Primary Contact: Pamela S. Brier, President and Chief Executive Officer
COO: Mark McDougle, Executive Vice President and Chief Operating Officer
CFO: Robert Naldi, Chief Financial Officer
CMO: Samuel Kopel, M.D., Medical Director
CIO: Walter Fahey, Chief Information Officer
CHR: Marc Leff, Vice President Human Resources
Web address: www.maimonidesmed.org/
**Control:** Other not–for–profit (including NFP Corporation) **Service:** General Medical and Surgical

**Staffed Beds:** 679 **Admissions:** 37766 **Census:** 583 **Outpatient Visits:** 480477 **Births:** 8396 **Total Expense ($000):** 1011582 **Payroll Expense ($000):** 504949 **Personnel:** 5762

**MANHATTAN PSYCHIATRIC CENTER–WARD'S ISLAND (334054)**, 600 East 125th Street, Zip 10035–6000; tel. 646/672–6767, (Nonreporting) **A**1 3 5 10 **S** New York State Office of Mental Health, Albany, NY
Primary Contact: Vinny Miccoli, Executive Director
Web address: www.omh.ny.gov
**Control:** State–Government, nonfederal **Service:** Psychiatric

**Staffed Beds:** 745

**MEMORIAL SLOAN–KETTERING CANCER CENTER (330154)**, 1275 York Avenue, Zip 10065–6007; tel. 212/639–2000 **A**1 2 3 5 8 9 10 **F**3 11 14 15 29 31 32 34 35 36 37 39 44 45 46 47 49 50 54 55 56 57 58 59 60 61 64 66 68 70 74 75 77 78 79 81 82 84 85 86 87 89 92 93 94 96 99 100 103 104 107 108 110 111 112 114 115 116 117 118 119 120 121 123 124 126 130 132 135 136 142 143 144 145 146 147 148 **P**6
Primary Contact: Craig B. Thompson, M.D., President and Chief Executive Officer
COO: John R. Gunn, Executive Vice President and Chief Operating Officer
CFO: Michael Gutnick, Senior Vice President Finance
CMO: Robert E. Wittes, M.D., Physician in Chief
CIO: Patricia Skarulis, Vice President Information Systems
CHR: Dennis Dowdell, Vice President Human Resources
Web address: www.mskcc.org
**Control:** Other not–for–profit (including NFP Corporation) **Service:** Cancer

**Staffed Beds:** 469 **Admissions:** 24597 **Census:** 409 **Outpatient Visits:** 1301286 **Births:** 0 **Total Expense ($000):** 2194757 **Payroll Expense ($000):** 871674 **Personnel:** 12155

**METROPOLITAN HOSPITAL CENTER (330199)**, 1901 First Avenue, Zip 10029–7404; tel. 212/423–6262, (Includes METROPOLITAN GENERAL CARE UNIT, METROPOLITAN DRUG DETOXIFICATION AND METROPOLITAN PSYCHIATRIC UNIT ) **A**1 3 5 9 10 **F**3 4 5 8 9 11 13 15 17 18 19 28 29 30 31 32 34 35 38 39 40 41 43 44 45 46 47 58 59 60 61 64 65 66 68 70 72 73 74 75 76 77 78 79 81 82 83 84 85 87 89 90 92 93 96 97 98 99 100 101 102 103 104 107 108 110 111 115 119 130 132 133 134 135 144 145 146 147 148 **S** New York City Health and Hospitals Corporation, New York, NY
Primary Contact: Meryl Weinberg, Executive Director
COO: Gregory Atwater, Chief Operating Officer
CFO: Elizabeth Guzman, Chief Financial Officer
CMO: Richard Stone, M.D., Medical Director
CIO: Don Lee, Chief Information Officer
CHR: April Alexander, Director Human Resources
Web address: www.nyc.gov/html/hhc/mhc/html/home/home.shtml
**Control:** City–Government, nonfederal **Service:** General Medical and Surgical

**Staffed Beds:** 324 **Admissions:** 13819 **Census:** 235 **Outpatient Visits:** 362936 **Births:** 1225 **Total Expense ($000):** 327223 **Payroll Expense ($000):** 131431 **Personnel:** 2050

**MONTEFIORE MEDICAL CENTER (330059)**, 111 East 210th Street, Bronx, Zip 10467–2401; tel. 718/920–4321, (Includes CHILDREN'S HOSPITAL OF MONTEFIORE, 3415 Bainbridge Avenue, Zip 10467–2403; tel. 718/741–2426; JACK D WEILER HOSPITAL OF ALBERT EINSTEIN COLLEGE OF MEDICINE, 1825 Eastchester Road, Zip 10461–2373; tel. 718/904–2000; MONTEFIORE MEDICAL CENTER – NORTH DIVISION, 600 East 233rd Street, Zip 10466–2697; tel. 718/920–9000) **A**1 2 3 5 8 9 10 **F**3 4 5 6 7 8 9 12 13 14 15 17 18 19 20 21 22 23 24 25 26 27 28 29 30 31 32 34 35 36 37 38 39 40 41 42 43 44 45 46 47 48 49 50 51 52 53 54 55 56 57 58 59 60 61 62 63 64 65 66 68 70 71 72 73 74 75 76 77 78 79 80 81 82 83 84 85 86 87 88 89 90 92 93 94 95 96 97 98 99 100 101 102 103 104 107 108 110 111 114 115 116 117 118 119 120 121 123 124 126 129 130 131 132 134 135 136 137 138 139 141 142 143 144 145 146 147 148 **P**5 6
Primary Contact: Steven M. Safyer, M.D., President and Chief Executive Officer
COO: Robert B. Conaty, Executive Vice President Operations
CFO: Joel A. Perlman, Executive Vice President Finance
CMO: Gary Kalkut, M.D., Senior Vice President and Chief Medical Officer
CIO: Jack Wolf, Vice President Information Systems
Web address: www.montefiore.org
**Control:** Other not–for–profit (including NFP Corporation) **Service:** General Medical and Surgical

**Staffed Beds:** 1469 **Admissions:** 81596 **Census:** 1327 **Outpatient Visits:** 1850311 **Births:** 6507 **Total Expense ($000):** 2983446 **Payroll Expense ($000):** 1384336 **Personnel:** 16848

**MORGAN STANLEY CHILDREN'S HOSPITAL OF NEW YORK–PRESBYTERIAN** See New York–Presbyterian Hospital

△ **MOUNT SINAI HOSPITAL (330024)**, One Gustave L. Levy Place, Zip 10029–6574; tel. 212/241–6500, (Includes KRAVIS CHILDREN'S HOSPITAL, One Gustave L. Levy Pl, Zip 10029, Mailing Address: PO Box 1153, Zip 10002–0916; tel. 800/637–4624) **A**1 3 5 7 8 9 10 **F**3 4 6 7 8 9 11 12 13 14 15 17 18 19 20 21 22 23 24 25 26 27 28 29 30 31 32 34 35 36 37 38 39 40 41 42 43 44 45 46 47 48 49 50 51 52 54 55 56 57 58 59 60 61 63 64 65 66 68 70 71 72 73 74 75 76 77 78 79 80 81 82 83 84 85 86 87 88 89 90 91 92 93 94 95 96 97 98 99 100 101 102 103 104 105 107 108 110 111 114 115 116 117 118 119 120 121 123 124 126 129 130 131 132 134 135 136 137 138 139 141 142 143 144 145 146 147 148 **P**5 6
Primary Contact: David L. Reich, M.D., Interim President
CFO: Donald Scanlon, Chief Financial Officer
CMO: Erin Dupree, M.D., Chief Medical Officer
CIO: Jack Nelson, Senior Vice President and Chief Information Officer
CHR: Jane Maksoud, Senior Vice President Human Resources and Labor Relations
Web address: www.mountsinai.org
**Control:** Other not–for–profit (including NFP Corporation) **Service:** General Medical and Surgical

**Staffed Beds:** 1048 **Admissions:** 53673 **Census:** 868 **Outpatient Visits:** 667614 **Births:** 6506 **Total Expense ($000):** 1545993 **Payroll Expense ($000):** 602590 **Personnel:** 8015

**NEW YORK CITY CHILDREN'S CENTER**, (Formerly Queens Children's Psychiatric Center), 74–03 Commonwealth Boulevard, Jamaica, Zip 11426–1890; tel. 718/264–4506, (Nonreporting) **A**1 **S** New York State Office of Mental Health, Albany, NY
Primary Contact: June DaCosta, Acting Executive Director
CMO: David M. Rube, M.D., Clinical Director
CIO: Ed Yunusov, Coordinator Facility Information Center
Web address: www.omh.ny.gov
**Control:** State–Government, nonfederal **Service:** Children's hospital psychiatric

**Staffed Beds:** 84

**NEW YORK CITY CHILDREN'S CENTER** See Queens Children's Psychiatric Center

**NEW YORK COMMUNITY HOSPITAL (330019)**, 2525 Kings Highway, Brooklyn, Zip 11229–1705; tel. 718/692–5300, (Nonreporting) **A**1 9 10 **S** New York Presbyterian Healthcare System, New York, NY
Primary Contact: Lin H. Mo, President and Chief Executive Officer
COO: Una E. Morrissey, R.N., Senior Vice President, Chief Nursing Officer and Chief Operating Officer
CFO: Leonardo Tamburello, Divisional Chief Financial Officer
CMO: Herbert Rader, M.D., Vice President and Medical Director
CIO: Edward B. Stolyar, D.O., Director Management Information Systems
CHR: Steve Meyers, Director Human Resources
Web address: www.nych.com
**Control:** Other not–for–profit (including NFP Corporation) **Service:** General Medical and Surgical

**Staffed Beds:** 125

NY

*Many Facility Codes have changed. Please refer to the AHA Guide Code Chart.*
© 2013 AHA Guide

⊠ **NEW YORK DOWNTOWN HOSPITAL (330064)**, 170 William Street, Zip 10038–2649; tel. 212/312–5000, (Nonreporting) **A**1 9 10 **S** New York Presbyterian Healthcare System, New York, NY
Primary Contact: Michael Fosina, Senior Vice President and Chief Operating Officer
COO: Anthony Alfano, Senior Vice President and Chief Operating Officer
CMO: Steven G. Friedman, M.D., Interim Chief Medical Officer and Chair, Department of Surgery
CIO: Frank Negro, Interim Chief Information Officer
CHR: Anthony Alfano, Senior Vice President Operations and Chief Human Resources Officer
CNO: Kit Yuen, R.N., Interim Chief Nursing Officer
Web address: www.downtownhospital.org
**Control:** Other not–for–profit (including NFP Corporation) **Service:** General Medical and Surgical

**Staffed Beds:** 128

⊠ **NEW YORK EYE AND EAR INFIRMARY (330100)**, 310 East 14th Street, Zip 10003–4201; tel. 212/979–4000 **A**1 3 5 9 10 **F**11 29 30 34 35 43 44 50 54 57 58 59 64 65 66 68 74 81 82 85 86 91 92 93 94 107 114 119 129 130 132 142 146 **S** Continuum Health Partners, New York, NY
Primary Contact: D. McWilliams Kessler, President and Chief Executive Officer
COO: Allan Fine, Senior Vice President and Chief Strategy and Operations Officer
CFO: Charles Figliozzi, CPA, Vice President and Chief Financial Officer
CMO: J. Robert Rosenthal, M.D., Senior Vice President Medical Affairs
CIO: Don Ushak, Director Information Systems
CHR: Susan Singer, Director Human Resources
Web address: www.nyee.edu
**Control:** Other not–for–profit (including NFP Corporation) **Service:** Eye, ear, nose, and throat

**Staffed Beds:** 32 **Admissions:** 696 **Census:** 4 **Outpatient Visits:** 216180 **Births:** 0 **Total Expense ($000):** 141363 **Payroll Expense ($000):** 59436 **Personnel:** 869

☐ **NEW YORK HOSPITAL QUEENS (330055)**, 56–45 Main Street, Flushing, Zip 11355–5045; tel. 718/670–1231, (Nonreporting) **A**1 2 3 5 9 10 **S** New York Presbyterian Healthcare System, New York, NY
Primary Contact: Stephen S. Mills, President and Chief Executive Officer
COO: John E. Sciortino, Senior Vice President and Chief Operating Officer
CFO: Kevin J. Ward, Vice President and Chief Financial Officer
CMO: Stephen Rimar, M.D., Senior Vice President Medical Affairs
CIO: Thomas Kemp, Chief Information Officer
CHR: Lorraine Orlando, Vice President Human Resources
Web address: www.nyhq.org
**Control:** Other not–for–profit (including NFP Corporation) **Service:** General Medical and Surgical

**Staffed Beds:** 519

⊠ **NEW YORK METHODIST HOSPITAL (330236)**, 506 Sixth Street, Brooklyn, Zip 11215–3609; tel. 718/780–3000 **A**1 2 3 5 8 9 10 **F**8 9 13 14 15 17 18 20 22 24 26 29 30 31 34 35 39 40 41 45 46 49 50 51 52 54 55 56 57 59 61 64 65 68 70 72 74 75 76 77 78 79 81 82 84 85 87 88 89 90 93 95 97 98 107 108 111 114 119 121 124 126 129 130 135 145 146 147 148 **P**6 **S** New York Presbyterian Healthcare System, New York, NY
Primary Contact: Mark J. Mundy, President and Chief Executive Officer
COO: Lauren Yedvab, Senior Vice President
CFO: Edward A. Zaidberg, Senior Vice President Finance
CMO: Stanley Sherbell, M.D., Executive Vice President Medical Affairs
CIO: Joseph Saverese, Director Information Systems
CHR: Dennis Buchanan, Vice President Human Resources
CNO: Rebecca L. Flood, R.N., Senior Vice President Nursing
Web address: www.nym.org
**Control:** Other not–for–profit (including NFP Corporation) **Service:** General Medical and Surgical

**Staffed Beds:** 591 **Admissions:** 34443 **Census:** 521 **Outpatient Visits:** 465068 **Births:** 5689 **Total Expense ($000):** 682399 **Payroll Expense ($000):** 270950 **Personnel:** 3350

☐ **NEW YORK STATE PSYCHIATRIC INSTITUTE (334009)**, 1051 Riverside Drive, Zip 10032–1007; tel. 212/543–5000, (Nonreporting) **A**1 3 5 10 **S** New York State Office of Mental Health, Albany, NY
Primary Contact: Jeffrey A. Lieberman, M.D., Executive Director
COO: Janelle Dierkens, Chief Administration Officer
CFO: Jonathan Segal, Chief Financial Officer
CMO: David Lowenthal, M.D., Clinical Director
CIO: Joseph Grun, Chief Information Officer
CHR: Rebecca Dechabert, Acting Director Personnel
Web address: www.nyspi.org
**Control:** State–Government, nonfederal **Service:** Psychiatric

**Staffed Beds:** 58

⊠ △ **NEW YORK–PRESBYTERIAN HOSPITAL (330101)**, 525 East 68th Street, Zip 10065–4870; tel. 212/746–5454, (Includes MORGAN STANLEY CHILDREN'S HOSPITAL OF NEW YORK–PRESBYTERIAN, 3959 Broadway, Zip 10032–3784; tel. 212/305–2500; NEW YORK–PRESBYTERIAN HOSPITAL, WESTCHESTER DIVISION, 21 Bloomingdale Road, White Plains, Zip 10605; tel. 914/682–9100; NEW YORK–PRESBYTERIAN HOSPITAL/WEILL CORNELL MEDICAL CENTER, 525 East 68th Street, Zip 10021–4885; tel. 212/746–5454; NEW YORK–PRESBYTERIAN/COLUMBIA UNIVERSITY MEDICAL CENTER, 161 Fort Washington Avenue, Zip 10032; tel. 212/305–2500; PAYNE WHITNEY PSYCHIATRIC CLINIC, 525 East 68th Street, Zip 10021; tel. 212/746–3800; PHYLLIS AND DAVID KOMANSKY CENTER FOR CHILDREN'S HEALTH, 525 East 68th Street, tel. 212/746–5454; THE ALLEN PAVILION, 5141 Broadway, Zip 10032; tel. 212/932–5000) **A**1 2 3 5 7 8 9 10 **F**3 4 6 7 9 11 12 13 14 15 16 17 18 19 20 21 22 23 24 25 26 27 28 29 30 31 32 34 35 36 37 38 39 40 41 43 44 45 46 47 48 49 50 51 52 53 54 55 56 57 58 59 60 61 64 65 66 68 70 72 73 74 75 76 77 78 79 80 81 82 84 85 86 87 88 89 90 92 93 94 96 97 98 99 100 101 102 103 104 105 107 108 109 110 111 112 114 115 116 117 118 119 120 121 123 124 126 129 130 131 132 134 135 136 137 138 139 140 141 142 143 144 145 146 147 148 **S** New York Presbyterian Healthcare System, New York, NY
Primary Contact: Steven J. Corwin, M.D., Chief Executive Officer
CFO: Phyllis R. Lantos, Executive Vice President, Chief Financial Officer and Treasurer
CMO: Laura Forese, M.D., Senior Vice President and Chief Medical Officer
CIO: Aurelia Boyer, Senior Vice President and Chief Information Officer
CHR: G. Thomas Ferguson, Senior Vice President and Chief Human Resources Officer
Web address: www.nyp.org
**Control:** Other not–for–profit (including NFP Corporation) **Service:** General Medical and Surgical

**Staffed Beds:** 2262 **Admissions:** 104600 **Census:** 1832 **Outpatient Visits:** 1851689 **Births:** 12758 **Total Expense ($000):** 3653001 **Payroll Expense ($000):** 1756107 **Personnel:** 19264

⊠ **NORTH CENTRAL BRONX HOSPITAL (330385)**, 3424 Kossuth Avenue, Bronx, Zip 10467–2489; tel. 718/519–3500 **A**1 3 5 9 10 **F**3 5 8 11 12 13 15 18 28 29 30 32 34 35 38 39 40 41 43 44 45 46 48 50 51 55 56 57 58 59 60 61 64 65 66 68 70 72 73 74 75 76 77 78 79 80 81 82 84 85 87 92 93 94 96 97 98 99 100 101 102 103 104 105 107 108 110 111 115 119 130 131 132 135 144 146 147 148 **P**6 **S** New York City Health and Hospitals Corporation, New York, NY
Primary Contact: William P. Walsh, Executive Director
COO: Sheldon McLeod, Chief Operating Officer
CFO: Kathy Garramone, Chief Financial Officer
CMO: Joseph Skarzynski, M.D., Medical Director
CIO: Diane Carr, Chief Information Officer
CHR: Dolores Leite, Chief Human Resource Executive
CNO: Elizabeth Gerdts, Chief Nursing Officer
Web address: www.nyc.gov/html/hhc/ncbh/html/home/home.shtml
**Control:** City–Government, nonfederal **Service:** General Medical and Surgical

**Staffed Beds:** 207 **Admissions:** 7498 **Census:** 128 **Outpatient Visits:** 250191 **Births:** 1570 **Total Expense ($000):** 192962 **Payroll Expense ($000):** 75413 **Personnel:** 1249

**NYU HOSPITAL FOR JOINT DISEASES** See NYU Langone Medical Center's Hospital for Joint Diseases

⊠ △ **NYU LANGONE MEDICAL CENTER (330214)**, 550 First Avenue, Zip 10016–6402; tel. 212/263–7300, (Includes NYU CHILDREN'S HOSPITAL, 545 First Avenue, Zip 10016–6401; tel. 212/263–7300; NYU LANGONE MEDICAL CENTER'S HOSPITAL FOR JOINT DISEASES, 301 East 17th Street, Zip 10003–3890; tel. 212/598–6000; David A. Dibner, FACHE, Senior Vice President Hospital Operations and Musculoskeletal Strategic Area; RUSK INSTITUTE, 400 East 34th Street, Zip 10016) **A**1 5 7 8 9 10 **F**3 5 6 8 9 11 12 13 14 15 16 17 24 25 27 28 29 30 31 32 33 34 35 36 37 38 39 40 41 43 44 45 46 47 48 49 50 52 53 54 55 56 57 58 59 60 61 63 64 65 66 68 70 72 73 74 75 76 77 78 79 80 81 82 84 85 86 87 88 89 90 91 92 93 95 96 97 98 99 100 101 102 103 104 107 108 110 111 114 115 116 117 118 119 120 121 123 124 126 129 130 131 132 134 135 136 138 139 141 145 146 147 148 **P**1 5 6
Primary Contact: Robert I. Grossman, M.D., Chief Executive Officer
COO: Bernard Birnbaum, M.D., Senior Vice President, Vice Dean and Chief Hospital Operations
CFO: Michael Burke, Senior Vice President and Corporate Chief Financial Officer
CMO: Robert Press, M.D., Chief Medical Officer
CHR: Nancy Sanchez, Senior Vice President and Vice Dean Human Resources
Web address: www.nyumedicalcenter.org
**Control:** Other not–for–profit (including NFP Corporation) **Service:** General Medical and Surgical

**Staffed Beds:** 791 **Admissions:** 38045 **Census:** 566 **Outpatient Visits:** 753054 **Births:** 4889 **Total Expense ($000):** 1750443 **Payroll Expense ($000):** 669671 **Personnel:** 8731

**PAYNE WHITNEY PSYCHIATRIC CLINIC** See New York–Presbyterian Hospital

**NY**

---

**Hospital, Medicare Provider Number, Address, Telephone, Approval, Facility, and Physician Codes, Health Care System**

★ American Hospital Association (AHA) membership
☐ The Joint Commission accreditation
◇ DNV Healthcare Inc. accreditation
○ Healthcare Facilities Accreditation Program
△ Commission on Accreditation of Rehabilitation Facilities (CARF) accreditation

☒ **QUEENS HOSPITAL CENTER (330231)**, 82–68 164th Street, Jamaica, Zip 11432–1104; tel. 718/883–3000 **A**1 2 3 5 9 10 **F**3 5 8 11 13 14 15 18 29 30 31 32 34 35 38 39 40 45 50 53 54 56 57 59 61 64 68 70 72 73 76 77 78 79 81 83 84 85 87 90 93 97 98 99 100 102 103 104 105 107 111 115 116 119 121 129 130 134 135 146 147 **P**6 **S** New York City Health and Hospitals Corporation, New York, NY
Primary Contact: Julius Wool, Executive Director
COO: Robert Rossdale, Deputy Executive Director
CFO: Brian Stacey, Chief Financial Officer
CMO: Jasmin Moshirpur, M.D., Chief Medical Officer
CIO: Vincent Smith, Chief Information Officer
CHR: Jeannith Gangemi–Sosa, Senior Associate Executive Director
CNO: Joan Gabriele, Deputy Executive Director
Web address: www.nyc.gov/html/hhc/qhc/html/home/home.shtml
**Control:** City–Government, nonfederal **Service:** General Medical and Surgical

**Staffed Beds:** 271 **Admissions:** 13212 **Census:** 234 **Outpatient Visits:** 434518 **Births:** 1900 **Total Expense ($000):** 398444 **Payroll Expense ($000):** 130994 **Personnel:** 1885

☒ **RICHMOND UNIVERSITY MEDICAL CENTER (330028)**, 355 Bard Avenue, Staten Island, Zip 10310–1664; tel. 718/818–1234 **A**1 2 3 5 9 10 **F**3 4 5 7 11 13 14 15 17 18 19 20 26 29 30 31 32 34 35 38 40 47 49 50 55 56 57 58 59 61 64 65 66 68 70 71 72 73 74 75 76 77 78 79 81 82 88 89 92 93 94 98 99 100 101 102 103 104 107 108 109 110 111 114 115 119 129 130 131 132 134 135 143 144 146 147 148 **P**4
Primary Contact: Michael P. Breslin, Interim Chief Executive Officer
CFO: Michael P. Breslin, Chief Financial Officer and Executive Vice President
CMO: Edward Arsura, M.D., Chief Medical Officer
CHR: Patricia Caldari, Vice President
Web address: www.rumcsi.org
**Control:** Other not–for–profit (including NFP Corporation) **Service:** General Medical and Surgical

**Staffed Beds:** 384 **Admissions:** 18013 **Census:** 287 **Outpatient Visits:** 126241 **Births:** 2478 **Total Expense ($000):** 295493 **Payroll Expense ($000):** 144793 **Personnel:** 1840

☐ **ROCKEFELLER UNIVERSITY HOSPITAL (330387)**, 1230 York Avenue, Zip 10065–6399; tel. 212/327–8000, (Nonreporting) **A**1 10
Primary Contact: James G. Krueger, M.D., Ph.D., Chief Executive Officer
CMO: Barbara O'Sullivan, M.D., Medical Director
Web address: www.rucares.org
**Control:** Other not–for–profit (including NFP Corporation) **Service:** Other specialty

**Staffed Beds:** 40

**ROOSEVELT HOSPITAL** See St. Luke's–Roosevelt Hospital Center

☐ **SOUTH BEACH PSYCHIATRIC CENTER (334043)**, 777 Seaview Avenue, Staten Island, Zip 10305–3409; tel. 718/667–2300, (Nonreporting) **A**1 3 5 10 **S** New York State Office of Mental Health, Albany, NY
Primary Contact: Rosanne Gaylor, M.D., Acting Executive Director
CHR: George Bouquio, Director Human Resources
Web address: www.omh.ny.gov/omhweb/facilities/sbpc/facility.htm
**Control:** State–Government, nonfederal **Service:** Psychiatric

**Staffed Beds:** 340

☒ **ST. BARNABAS HOSPITAL (330399)**, 183rd Street & Third Avenue, Bronx, Zip 10457–9998; tel. 718/960–9000, (Nonreporting) **A**1 3 5 6 9 10 12 13
Primary Contact: Scott Cooper, M.D., Chief Executive Officer
COO: Len Walsh, Executive Vice President and Chief Operating Officer
CFO: Todd Gorlewski, Senior Vice President and Chief Financial Officer
CMO: Jerry Balentine, D.O., Executive Vice President and Chief Medical Director
CIO: Noah Caldwell, Senior Vice President and Chief Information Officer
CHR: Marc Wolf, Director Human Resources
CNO: Denise Richardson, R.N., Senior Vice President and Chief Nursing Officer
Web address: www.stbarnabashospital.org
**Control:** Other not–for–profit (including NFP Corporation) **Service:** General Medical and Surgical

**Staffed Beds:** 660

☐ **ST. JOHN'S EPISCOPAL HOSPITAL–SOUTH SHORE (330395)**, 327 Beach 19th Street, Far Rockaway, Zip 11691–4423; tel. 718/869–7000, (Nonreporting) **A**1 3 5 9 10 12 13
Primary Contact: Nelson Toebbe, Chief Executive Officer
COO: Patrick L. Sullivan, Chief Operating Officer
CFO: Kathleen Garcia, Controller
CMO: Raymond Pastore, M.D., Chief Medical Officer
CIO: Michael J. Piro, Chief Information Officer
CHR: Roger Franco, Director Human Resources
Web address: www.ehs.org
**Control:** Church–operated, Nongovernment, not–for profit **Service:** General Medical and Surgical

**Staffed Beds:** 241

☒ **ST. LUKE'S–ROOSEVELT HOSPITAL CENTER (330046)**, 1111 Amsterdam Avenue, Zip 10025–1716; tel. 212/523–4000, (Includes ROOSEVELT HOSPITAL, 1000 Tenth Avenue, Zip 10019; tel. 212/523–5700; ST. LUKE'S HOSPITAL CENTER, 1111 Amsterdam Avenue, Zip 10025; tel. 212/523–4000) **A**1 3 5 8 9 10 **F**3 4 5 7 8 11 12 13 14 15 17 18 20 22 24 26 29 30 31 32 34 35 38 39 40 41 43 44 46 49 50 52 54 55 56 57 58 59 60 61 63 64 65 66 68 70 72 74 75 76 77 78 79 81 82 84 85 86 87 89 90 92 93 94 96 97 98 99 100 101 102 103 104 107 108 110 111 114 115 118 119 120 121 123 124 126 130 131 132 134 135 138 144 145 146 147 148 **P**5 8 **S** Continuum Health Partners, New York, NY
Primary Contact: Frank J. Cracolici, President
COO: Timothy Day, Chief Administrative Officer
CFO: John Collura, Executive Vice President and Chief Financial Officer
CMO: Robert A. Catalano, M.D., Chief Medical Officer
CIO: Mark Moroses, Vice President and Chief Information Officer
CHR: Marvin Russell, Senior Vice President Human Resources
Web address: www.stlukeshospitalnyc.org
**Control:** Other not–for–profit (including NFP Corporation) **Service:** General Medical and Surgical

**Staffed Beds:** 690 **Admissions:** 43525 **Census:** 666 **Outpatient Visits:** 631968 **Births:** 6595 **Total Expense ($000):** 1202504 **Payroll Expense ($000):** 586112 **Personnel:** 6025

☒ △ **STATEN ISLAND UNIVERSITY HOSPITAL (330160)**, 475 Seaview Avenue, Staten Island, Zip 10305–3436; tel. 718/226–9000 **A**1 2 3 5 7 8 9 10 **F**3 4 5 7 8 11 12 13 14 15 16 17 18 19 20 22 24 26 29 30 31 32 34 35 36 38 39 40 41 43 44 45 46 48 49 50 51 52 54 55 56 57 58 59 60 61 63 64 65 66 68 70 72 73 74 75 76 77 78 79 81 82 84 85 86 87 88 89 90 91 92 93 94 95 96 97 98 100 101 102 103 104 105 107 108 110 111 114 115 116 117 118 119 120 121 123 124 126 129 130 132 134 135 145 146 147 148 **P**6 **S** North Shore–Long Island Jewish Health System, Great Neck, NY
Primary Contact: Anthony C. Ferreri, President and Chief Executive Officer
COO: Donna Proske, MS, Executive Vice President, Chief Operating Officer and Chief Nursing Executive
CFO: Thomas Reca, Sr., Senior Vice President Finance and Chief Financial Officer
CMO: Mark Jarrett, M.D., Chief Medical Officer
CIO: Kathy Kania, Chief Information Officer
CHR: Margaret DiAlto, Vice President Human Resources
Web address: www.siuh.edu
**Control:** Other not–for–profit (including NFP Corporation) **Service:** General Medical and Surgical

**Staffed Beds:** 663 **Admissions:** 42575 **Census:** 583 **Outpatient Visits:** 392532 **Births:** 2904 **Total Expense ($000):** 792191 **Payroll Expense ($000):** 401796 **Personnel:** 4967

**STEVEN AND ALEXANDRA COHEN CHILDREN'S MEDICAL CENTER OF NEW YORK** See Long Island Jewish Medical Center, New Hyde Park

☒ **SUNY DOWNSTATE MEDICAL CENTER UNIVERSITY HOSPITAL (330350)**, 445 Lenox Road, Brooklyn, Zip 11203–2017; tel. 718/270–1000, (Includes THE CHILDREN'S HOSPITAL AT SUNY DOWNSTATE, 450 Clarkson Avenue, Zip 11203–2012; tel. 718/270–1625; UNIVERSITY HOSPITAL OF BROOKLYN AT LONG ISLAND COLLEGE HOSPITAL, 339 Hicks Street, Zip 11201–5509; tel. 718/780–1000; George P. Caralis, Interim Chief Executive Officer), (Nonreporting) **A**1 2 3 5 8 9 10
Primary Contact: George P. Caralis, Interim Chief Executive Officer
COO: David Conley, Chief Administrative Officer
CFO: Gerry Dantis, Assistant Vice President Finance
CMO: Michael Lucchesi, M.D., Interim Chief Medical Officer
CIO: Ernest P. Weber, Jr., Interim Chief Information Officer
CHR: Hendrina Goeloe–Alston, Assistant Vice President Personnel
Web address: www.downstate.edu
**Control:** State–Government, nonfederal **Service:** General Medical and Surgical

**Staffed Beds:** 697

**TERENCE CARDINAL COOKE HEALTH CARE CENTER (332022)**, 1249 Fifth Avenue, Zip 10029–4413; tel. 212/360–1000, (Nonreporting) **A**10
Primary Contact: James Karkenny, Chief Executive Officer
Web address: www.tcchcc.org/
**Control:** Church–operated, Nongovernment, not–for profit **Service:** Long–Term Acute Care hospital

**Staffed Beds:** 28

**THE ALLEN PAVILION** See New York–Presbyterian Hospital

**NY**

*Many Facility Codes have changed. Please refer to the AHA Guide Code Chart.*
© 2013 AHA Guide

**THE MOUNT SINAI HOSPITAL OF QUEENS (330258)**, 25–10 30th Avenue, Long Island City, Zip 11102–2448; tel. 718/932–1000 **A**10 **F**3 8 15 18 29 30 31 32 34 35 40 43 45 49 50 54 56 57 59 60 63 64 65 66 68 70 74 75 77 78 79 80 81 82 84 85 86 87 93 97 100 107 111 119 130 135 146 147 148 **P**6
Primary Contact: Caryn A. Schwab, Executive Director
COO: Judy Trilivas, Vice President and Chief Operating Officer
CFO: Salvatore Morello, Vice President Finance
CMO: David M. Nierman, M.D., Vice President and Chief Medical Officer
CIO: Jack Abuin, Director Management Information Systems
CHR: Norma Calame, Director Human Resources
Web address: www.mshq.org
**Control:** Other not–for–profit (including NFP Corporation) **Service:** General Medical and Surgical

| | |
|---|---|
| **Staffed Beds:** 192 **Admissions:** 9860 **Census:** 157 **Outpatient Visits:** 118308 **Births:** 0 **Total Expense ($000):** 147650 **Payroll Expense ($000):** 78031 **Personnel:** 1091 | |

⊠ △ **VETERANS ADMINISTRATION NEW YORK HARBOR HEALTHCARE SYSTEM**, 800 Poly Place, Brooklyn, Zip 11209–7104; tel. 718/630–3500, (Includes VETERANS AFFAIRS MEDICAL CENTER, 423 East 23rd Street, New York, Zip 10010–5050; tel. 212/686–7500), (Total facility includes 179 beds in nursing home–type unit) **A**1 2 3 5 7 8 **F**2 3 4 5 7 8 9 15 17 18 20 22 24 26 28 29 30 31 34 38 39 40 44 45 46 48 49 50 53 54 56 57 59 60 61 62 63 64 65 68 70 74 75 77 78 79 80 81 82 83 84 85 86 87 90 92 93 94 95 96 97 98 100 101 102 103 104 105 106 107 108 110 111 114 115 118 119 120 121 123 124 128 129 130 131 132 135 143 146 147 148 **P**6 **S** Department of Veterans Affairs, Washington, DC
Primary Contact: Martina A. Parauda, Director
CFO: Daniel Downey, Chief Fiscal Service
CIO: Maria Schay, Chief Information Officer
Web address: www.nyharbor.va.gov
**Control:** Veterans Affairs, Government, federal **Service:** General Medical and Surgical

| | |
|---|---|
| **Staffed Beds:** 517 **Admissions:** 9558 **Census:** 378 **Outpatient Visits:** 775199 **Births:** 0 **Total Expense ($000):** 727199 **Payroll Expense ($000):** 313926 **Personnel:** 3829 | |

**VETERANS AFFAIRS MEDICAL CENTER** See James J. Peters Veterans Affairs Medical Center

⊠ **WOODHULL MEDICAL AND MENTAL HEALTH CENTER (330396)**, 760 Broadway, Brooklyn, Zip 11206–5383; tel. 718/963–8000 **A**1 3 5 9 10 **F**3 4 5 8 11 15 29 30 31 34 35 38 39 40 41 43 45 46 48 49 53 54 55 56 57 58 59 60 61 64 65 66 68 70 71 72 73 74 75 76 77 78 79 81 82 83 84 85 86 87 89 93 94 97 98 99 100 101 102 103 104 107 111 119 130 132 135 143 146 147 **P**6 **S** New York City Health and Hospitals Corporation, New York, NY
Primary Contact: George M. Proctor, Senior Vice President and Executive Director
COO: Eve Borzon, R.N., Chief Operating Officer
CMO: Edward Fishkin, M.D., Medical Director
CIO: Cynthia Bianchi, Chief Information Officer
CHR: Yvette Villanueva, Senior Associate Executive Director
Web address: www.nyc.gov/html/hhc
**Control:** City–County, Government, nonfederal **Service:** General Medical and Surgical

| | |
|---|---|
| **Staffed Beds:** 332 **Admissions:** 14036 **Census:** 279 **Outpatient Visits:** 503846 **Births:** 2061 **Total Expense ($000):** 447384 **Payroll Expense ($000):** 160098 **Personnel:** 2571 | |

☐ **WYCKOFF HEIGHTS MEDICAL CENTER (330221)**, 374 Stockholm Street, Brooklyn, Zip 11237–4006; tel. 718/963–7272, (Nonreporting) **A**1 3 5 9 10 12 13
Primary Contact: Ramon J. Rodriguez, President and Chief Executive Officer
COO: Frances Heaney, R.N., Executive Vice President and Chief Operating Officer
CFO: Leon Kozlowski, Vice President Finance and Chief Financial Officer
CMO: Mounzer Tchelebi, M.D., Medical Director
CIO: Cletis Earle, Vice President and Chief Information Officer
CHR: Margaret E. Cornelius, Vice President Human Resources
Web address: www.wyckoffhospital.org
**Control:** Other not–for–profit (including NFP Corporation) **Service:** General Medical and Surgical

| | |
|---|---|
| **Staffed Beds:** 279 | |

**ZUCKER HILLSIDE HOSPITAL** See Long Island Jewish Medical Center, New Hyde Park

**NEWARK—Wayne County**

⊠ **NEWARK–WAYNE COMMUNITY HOSPITAL (330030)**, 1200 Driving Park Avenue, Zip 14513–1057, Mailing Address: P.O. Box 111, Zip 14513–0111; tel. 315/332–2022, (Total facility includes 180 beds in nursing home–type unit) **A**1 9 10 **F**2 3 8 11 13 15 28 29 30 34 35 38 40 43 44 50 54 55 56 57 59 61 64 68 70 74 75 76 77 79 80 81 85 86 87 90 93 97 98 100 102 103 107 110 111 114 118 119 128 130 131 132 135 146 147 148 **P**5 7 **S** Rochester General Health System, Rochester, NY
Primary Contact: Mark F. Klyczek, President and Chief Executive Officer
CFO: Paula Tinch, Interim Chief Financial Officer
CMO: Rob Mayo, M.D., Chief Medical Officer
CIO: Chris Teumer, Vice President and Chief Information Officer
CHR: Janine Schue, Senior Vice President People Resources
CNO: Cheryl Sheridan, R.N., Senior Vice President and Chief Nursing Officer
Web address: www.rochestergeneral.org
**Control:** Other not–for–profit (including NFP Corporation) **Service:** General Medical and Surgical

| | |
|---|---|
| **Staffed Beds:** 270 **Admissions:** 4505 **Census:** 222 **Outpatient Visits:** 148909 **Births:** 397 **Total Expense ($000):** 77984 **Payroll Expense ($000):** 38674 **Personnel:** 669 | |

**NEWBURGH—Orange County**

⊠ **ST. LUKE'S CORNWALL HOSPITAL (330264)**, 70 Dubois Street, Zip 12550–4851; tel. 845/561–4400, (Includes ST. LUKE'S CORNWALL HOSPITAL – CORNWALL CAMPUS, 19 Laurel Avenue, Cornwall, Zip 12518–1499; tel. 845/534–7711; ST. LUKE'S CORNWALL HOSPITAL – NEWBURGH CAMPUS, 70 Dubois Street, Zip 12550–4898; tel. 845/561–4400) **A**1 2 9 10 **F**3 11 13 15 18 20 22 26 28 29 31 34 35 36 37 40 44 46 49 50 51 54 55 57 59 64 70 72 74 75 76 77 78 79 81 82 84 85 86 87 89 93 100 102 107 108 110 114 115 118 119 120 123 124 126 129 130 132 135 146 148 **P**7
Primary Contact: Allan E. Atzrott, FACHE, President and Chief Executive Officer
COO: Robert Ross, Executive Vice President and Chief Operating Officer
CFO: Mary Elizabeth Duffy, Senior Vice President and Chief Financial Officer
CMO: Christine Jelalian, M.D., Medical Director
CIO: Jane Lake, Director Materials Management
CHR: Deborah Turner, Vice President Human Resources
Web address: www.stlukescornwallhospital.org
**Control:** Other not–for–profit (including NFP Corporation) **Service:** General Medical and Surgical

| | |
|---|---|
| **Staffed Beds:** 144 **Admissions:** 10970 **Census:** 133 **Outpatient Visits:** 166923 **Births:** 857 **Total Expense ($000):** 181362 **Payroll Expense ($000):** 73599 **Personnel:** 1044 | |

**NIAGARA FALLS—Niagara County**

**NIAGARA FALLS MEMORIAL MEDICAL CENTER (330065)**, 621 Tenth Street, Zip 14301–1813, Mailing Address: P.O. Box 708, Zip 14302–0708; tel. 716/278–4000, (Nonreporting) **A**3 5 9 10 13
Primary Contact: Joseph A. Ruffolo, President and Chief Executive Officer
CMO: Fatma Patel, M.D., Vice President Medical Affairs
CIO: Diane Martin–Pratt, Director Information Systems
Web address: www.nfmmc.org
**Control:** Other not–for–profit (including NFP Corporation) **Service:** General Medical and Surgical

| | |
|---|---|
| **Staffed Beds:** 288 | |

**NORTH TONAWANDA—Niagara County**

**DE GRAFF MEMORIAL HOSPITAL** See KALEIDA Health, Buffalo

**NORTHPORT—Suffolk County**

⊠ △ **NORTHPORT VETERANS AFFAIRS MEDICAL CENTER**, (Formerly Veterans Affairs Medical Center), 79 Middleville Road, Zip 11768–2200; tel. 631/261–4400, (Total facility includes 170 beds in nursing home–type unit) **A**1 2 3 5 7 8 **F**3 5 8 12 18 20 29 30 31 33 34 35 36 38 39 40 44 45 46 47 49 50 51 53 56 57 58 59 60 61 62 64 65 68 70 71 74 75 77 78 79 81 82 83 84 85 86 87 90 91 92 93 94 95 96 97 98 100 101 102 103 104 105 106 107 108 111 116 118 119 121 122 127 128 129 130 132 133 135 144 146 147 148 **S** Department of Veterans Affairs, Washington, DC
Primary Contact: Philip C. Moschitta, Director
COO: Maria Favale, FACHE, Associate Director
CFO: Mary Pat Hessman, Chief Fiscal
CMO: Edward Mack, M.D., Chief of Staff
CIO: Robert Ziskin, Chief Information Officer
CHR: Edward Yankowski, Chief Human Resources Management Service
CNO: Rosie Chatman, R.N., Associate Director Patient and Nursing Services
Web address: www.northport.va.gov/index.asp
**Control:** Veterans Affairs, Government, federal **Service:** General Medical and Surgical

| | |
|---|---|
| **Staffed Beds:** 502 **Admissions:** 3849 **Census:** 246 **Outpatient Visits:** 577850 **Births:** 0 **Total Expense ($000):** 355405 **Payroll Expense ($000):** 189536 **Personnel:** 1795 | |

**NY**

---

**Hospital, Medicare Provider Number, Address, Telephone, Approval, Facility, and Physician Codes, Health Care System**

★ American Hospital Association (AHA) membership
☐ The Joint Commission accreditation
◇ DNV Healthcare Inc. accreditation
○ Healthcare Facilities Accreditation Program
△ Commission on Accreditation of Rehabilitation Facilities (CARF) accreditation

© 2013 AHA Guide　　*Many Facility Codes have changed. Please refer to the AHA Guide Code Chart.*　　Hospitals **A43**

**NORWICH—Chenango County**

○ **CHENANGO MEMORIAL HOSPITAL (330033)**, 179 North Broad Street, Zip 13815–1097; tel. 607/337–4111, (Nonreporting) **A**9 10 11 **S** United Health Services, Binghamton, NY
Primary Contact: Drake M. Lamen, M.D., President and Chief Executive Officer
COO: Drake M. Lamen, M.D., President and Chief Executive Officer
CFO: Robert R. McCarthy, Vice President Finance and Chief Financial Officer
CMO: Michael F. Trevisani, M.D., Vice President Medical Affairs and Chief Medical Officer
CIO: Tracy McCumber, Manager Information Systems
CHR: Anne L. English, Director Human Resources
CNO: Dru Cavanagh, R.N., Vice President Patient Care Services and Chief Nursing Officer
Web address: www.uhs.net/cmh
**Control:** Other not–for–profit (including NFP Corporation) **Service:** General Medical and Surgical

Staffed Beds: 138

**NYACK—Rockland County**

☐ **NYACK HOSPITAL (330104)**, 160 North Midland Avenue, Zip 10960–1998; tel. 845/348–2000 **A**1 2 5 9 10 **F**4 5 8 11 13 14 15 17 29 30 31 40 43 45 46 49 62 70 72 75 76 77 78 79 81 82 89 93 107 108 111 118 119 129 130 135 146 148 **S** New York Presbyterian Healthcare System, New York, NY
Primary Contact: David H. Freed, President and Chief Executive Officer
CFO: John Burke, Chief Financial Officer
CMO: Michael E. Rader, M.D., Vice President and Medical Director
CIO: John Volanto, Vice President and Chief Information Officer
CHR: Mary K. Shinick, Vice President Human Resources
CNO: Mary Ann Anderson, R.N., Chief Nursing Officer
Web address: www.nyackhospital.org
**Control:** Other not–for–profit (including NFP Corporation) **Service:** General Medical and Surgical

Staffed Beds: 375 Admissions: 16052 Census: 184 Outpatient Visits: 171535 Births: 1714 Total Expense ($000): 207155 Payroll Expense ($000): 97207 Personnel: 1669

**OCEANSIDE—Nassau County**

⊠ **SOUTH NASSAU COMMUNITIES HOSPITAL (330198)**, One Healthy Way, Zip 11572–1551; tel. 516/632–3000 **A**1 2 3 5 9 10 13 **F**3 5 11 12 13 15 17 18 20 22 26 28 29 30 31 34 35 37 38 40 41 43 44 45 46 47 49 50 54 55 56 57 58 59 60 62 64 66 68 69 70 73 74 75 76 77 78 79 81 82 83 84 85 87 89 91 92 93 97 98 99 100 102 103 104 105 107 108 109 110 111 114 115 118 119 120 121 123 124 126 129 130 131 132 135 145 146 148 **P**8
Primary Contact: Richard J. Murphy, President and Chief Executive Officer
COO: Joseph Lamantia, Executive Vice President and Chief Operating Officer
CFO: Mark A. Bogen, Senior Vice President and Chief Financial Officer
CMO: Linda Efferen, M.D., Senior Vice President and Chief Medical Officer
CIO: John Mertz, Chief Information Officer
CHR: Paul Giordano, Vice President Human Resources
CNO: Sue Penque, R.N., Senior Vice President and Chief Nursing Officer
Web address: www.southnassau.org
**Control:** Other not–for–profit (including NFP Corporation) **Service:** General Medical and Surgical

Staffed Beds: 363 Admissions: 20434 Census: 308 Outpatient Visits: 364820 Births: 1691 Total Expense ($000): 396721 Payroll Expense ($000): 187131 Personnel: 2345

**OGDENSBURG—St. Lawrence County**

★ ◇ **CLAXTON–HEPBURN MEDICAL CENTER (330211)**, 214 King Street, Zip 13669–1142; tel. 315/393–3600 **A**2 9 10 20 21 **F**3 11 13 15 28 29 30 31 34 35 36 38 40 44 45 50 51 53 54 56 57 59 60 61 64 70 74 75 76 77 78 79 81 82 85 86 87 90 91 92 93 94 96 97 98 100 101 102 103 104 107 108 110 111 114 118 119 121 123 129 130 131 132 133 135 145 146 147 148 **P**6 7
Primary Contact: Mark Webster, President and Chief Executive Officer
COO: Vicki Perrine, Chief Operating Officer and Vice President Clinical Services
CFO: Kelley Tiernan, Chief Financial Officer
CMO: Gary Hart, M.D., Chief Medical Officer
CIO: James Flood, Director Information Systems
CHR: Lou–Ann McNally, Director Human Resources
CNO: David Ferris, Chief Nursing Officer and Vice President Patient Care Services
Web address: www.claxtonhepburn.org
**Control:** Other not–for–profit (including NFP Corporation) **Service:** General Medical and Surgical

Staffed Beds: 130 Admissions: 3671 Census: 65 Outpatient Visits: 172458
: 340 Total Expense ($000): 92010 Payroll Expense ($000): 42156
el: 610

**NY**

☐ **ST. LAWRENCE PSYCHIATRIC CENTER (334003)**, 1 Chimney Point Drive, Zip 13669–2291; tel. 315/541–2001, (Nonreporting) **A**1 9 10 **S** New York State Office of Mental Health, Albany, NY
Primary Contact: Samua A. Bastien, IV, Ph.D., Executive Director
CFO: Timothy J. Lamitie, Deputy Director Administration
CMO: Harishankar Sanghi, M.D., Clinical Director
CIO: Christopher Ashwood, Coordinator Information Systems
CHR: Geri Koutner–Rausch, Director Human Resources
Web address: www.omh.ny.gov/omhweb/facilities/slpc/facility.htm
**Control:** State–Government, nonfederal **Service:** Psychiatric

Staffed Beds: 146

**OLEAN—Cattaraugus County**

⊠ **OLEAN GENERAL HOSPITAL (330103)**, 515 Main Street, Zip 14760–1513; tel. 716/373–2600 **A**1 3 5 9 10 **F**3 8 11 13 15 17 18 20 22 28 29 30 31 34 35 38 39 40 45 46 47 48 49 50 51 53 54 57 58 59 60 61 62 64 65 70 74 75 76 77 78 79 81 82 83 84 85 86 87 89 92 93 94 97 98 100 101 102 103 107 108 109 110 111 115 116 117 118 119 120 121 123 127 129 130 131 132 133 134 135 143 144 145 146 147 148 **P**6 **S** Upper Allegheny Health System, Olean, NY
Primary Contact: Timothy J. Finan, FACHE, President and Chief Executive Officer
COO: Ronald Mornelli, Senior Vice President Operations and Chief Operating Officer
CFO: Richard G. Braun, Jr., CPA, Senior Vice President and Chief Financial Officer
CMO: William Mills, M.D., Senior Vice President Quality and Professional Affairs
CIO: Jason Yaworsky, Senior Vice President Information Systems and Chief Information Officer
CHR: Timothy M. McNamara, Senior Vice President Human Resources
CNO: Jeff S. Zewe, R.N., Vice President Patient Care Services and Chief Nursing Officer
Web address: www.ogh.org
**Control:** Other not–for–profit (including NFP Corporation) **Service:** General Medical and Surgical

Staffed Beds: 186 Admissions: 6158 Census: 83 Outpatient Visits: 175255 Births: 779 Total Expense ($000): 101519 Payroll Expense ($000): 40567 Personnel: 815

**ONEIDA—Madison County**

⊠ **ONEIDA HEALTHCARE (330115)**, 321 Genesee Street, Zip 13421–2611; tel. 315/363–6000, (Total facility includes 140 beds in nursing home–type unit) **A**1 9 10 **F**3 11 13 15 18 29 34 40 45 49 50 54 57 59 64 65 68 70 74 75 76 77 79 81 86 87 89 92 93 97 107 108 111 115 117 118 119 126 128 129 130 135 146 **P**6
Primary Contact: Gene Morreale, President and Chief Executive Officer
COO: Paul A. Scopac, Vice President of Operations and Chief Operating Officer
CFO: Vincent S. Maneen, Chief Financial Officer
CFO: Dewey R. Rowlands, Vice President Finance and Chief Financial Officer
CMO: Dan J. Vick, M.D., Vice President of Medical Affairs and Chief Medical Officer
CIO: Mary McGuirl, Director Information Systems
CHR: John G. Margo, Vice President Human Resources
CNO: Janis Kohlbrenner, R.N., Vice President Clinical Services and Chief Nursing Officer
Web address: www.oneidahealthcare.org
**Control:** Other not–for–profit (including NFP Corporation) **Service:** General Medical and Surgical

Staffed Beds: 211 Admissions: 3318 Census: 176 Outpatient Visits: 158653 Births: 554 Total Expense ($000): 85572 Payroll Expense ($000): 38292 Personnel: 546

**ONEONTA—Otsego County**

⊠ ◇ **AURELIA OSBORN FOX MEMORIAL HOSPITAL (330085)**, 1 Norton Avenue, Zip 13820–2629; tel. 607/432–2000, (Total facility includes 131 beds in nursing home–type unit) **A**1 9 10 21 **F**2 3 11 13 15 17 26 28 29 30 34 35 39 40 45 46 47 48 50 51 53 54 56 57 59 64 65 68 70 74 75 76 77 81 85 86 87 89 93 96 97 104 107 108 110 111 115 118 119 120 121 123 128 129 130 144 146 147 **P**6 **S** Bassett Healthcare Network, Cooperstown, NY
Primary Contact: John R. Remillard, President
CFO: Mark J. Wright, Vice President Finance
CMO: Benjamin Friedell, Vice President Medical Affairs
CIO: Joseph Phillips, Director Information Systems
CHR: Keith Valk, Vice President Human Resources
CNO: Robbin Scobie, Vice President Nursing
Web address: www.aofoxhospital.com
**Control:** Other not–for–profit (including NFP Corporation) **Service:** General Medical and Surgical

Staffed Beds: 220 Admissions: 3360 Census: 168 Outpatient Visits: 221193 Births: 311 Total Expense ($000): 87783 Payroll Expense ($000): 39144 Personnel: 739

*Many Facility Codes have changed. Please refer to the AHA Guide Code Chart.* © 2013 AHA Guide

## ORANGEBURG—Rockland County

☐ **ROCKLAND CHILDREN'S PSYCHIATRIC CENTER**, 599 Convent Road,
Zip 10962–1162; tel. 845/359–7400, (Nonreporting) **A**1 3 5 **S** New York State
Office of Mental Health, Albany, NY
Primary Contact: Anita Daniels, Executive Director
COO: Kenneth Perrotte, Director Operations
CFO: Peter Gorey, Administrative Coordinator
CMO: Sadhana Sardana, M.D., Clinical Director
CIO: Mary Pivonka, Director Quality Management
Web address: www.omh.ny.gov/
**Control:** State–Government, nonfederal **Service:** Children's hospital psychiatric

**Staffed Beds:** 54

☐ **ROCKLAND PSYCHIATRIC CENTER (334015)**, 140 Old Orangeburg Road,
Zip 10962–1157; tel. 845/359–1000, (Nonreporting) **A**1 3 5 10 **S** New York
State Office of Mental Health, Albany, NY
Primary Contact: Christopher Tavella, Executive Director
Web address: www.omh.ny.gov/
**Control:** State–Government, nonfederal **Service:** Psychiatric

**Staffed Beds:** 525

## OSSINING—Westchester County

**OSSINING CORRECTIONAL FACILITIES HOSPITAL**, 354 Hunter Street,
Zip 10562–5498; tel. 914/941–0108, (Nonreporting)
Primary Contact: John Perilli, M.D., Health Services Director
**Control:** State–Government, nonfederal **Service:** Hospital unit of an institution
(prison hospital, college infimary, etc.)

**Staffed Beds:** 25

**STONY LODGE HOSPITAL (334059)**, 40 Croton Dam Road, Zip 10562–2644,
Mailing Address: P.O. Box 1250, Briarcliff Manor, Zip 10510–0327;
tel. 914/941–7400, (Nonreporting) **A**10
Primary Contact: Kevin F. Czipo, Executive Director and Chief Executive Officer
CMO: Emil R. Pincus, M.D., Medical Director
CHR: Anne Alley, Director Human Resources
Web address: www.stonylodge.com
**Control:** Corporation, Investor–owned, for–profit **Service:** Psychiatric

**Staffed Beds:** 50

## OSWEGO—Oswego County

✠ **OSWEGO HOSPITAL (330218)**, 110 West Sixth Street, Zip 13126–2507;
tel. 315/349–5511 **A**1 9 10 20 **F**3 8 11 13 15 17 28 29 34 38 40 45 46 49
50 57 59 62 64 70 74 75 76 77 79 81 84 85 86 87 89 93 97 98 99 100
101 102 103 104 107 108 110 111 115 118 119 130 131 132 135 144 146
148 **P**6
Primary Contact: Ann C. Gilpin, President and Chief Executive Officer
COO: Nancy Deavers, R.N., Vice President and Chief Operating Officer
CFO: Eric Campbell, Chief Financial Officer
CMO: Renato Mandanas, M.D., Vice President Medical Affairs
CIO: Major Barry Ryle, Chief Information Officer
CNO: Valerie Favata, R.N., Chief Nursing Officer
Web address: www.oswegohealth.org
**Control:** Other not–for–profit (including NFP Corporation) **Service:** General
Medical and Surgical

**Staffed Beds:** 126 **Admissions:** 5523 **Census:** 72 **Outpatient Visits:** 357739
**Births:** 648 **Total Expense ($000):** 100393 **Payroll Expense ($000):** 47902
**Personnel:** 904

## PATCHOGUE—Suffolk County

★ ◇ **BROOKHAVEN MEMORIAL HOSPITAL MEDICAL CENTER (330141)**,
101 Hospital Road, Zip 11772–4897; tel. 631/654–7100, (Nonreporting) **A**9 10
12 13 21
Primary Contact: Richard T. Margulis, President and Chief Executive Officer
COO: Ronald Stephenson, Chief Operating Officer
CFO: Brenda Farrell, Vice President Finance
CMO: Ronald Klein, M.D., Vice President and Chief Medical Officer
CIO: Marc Gibbs, Interim Chief Information Officer
CHR: Susan C. Hever, Director Human Resources
CNO: Kim K. Mendez, Ed.D., Vice President and Chief Nursing Officer
Web address: www.bmhmc.org
**Control:** Other not–for–profit (including NFP Corporation) **Service:** General
Medical and Surgical

**Staffed Beds:** 242

## PENN YAN—Yates County

**SOLDIERS AND SAILORS MEMORIAL HOSPITAL OF YATES COUNTY
(331314)**, 418 North Main Street, Zip 14527–1085; tel. 315/531–2000 **A**9 10
18 **F**2 3 11 15 18 28 29 34 35 38 40 45 54 56 57 59 64 65 66 68 70 75 81
87 93 97 98 100 101 102 103 104 105 106 107 110 114 119 128 130 132
133 135 143 146 147 **P**6 **S** Finger Lakes Health, Geneva, NY
Primary Contact: Jose Acevedo, M.D., President and Chief Executive Officer
COO: Frank Korich, Vice President and Site Administrator
CFO: Patricia Thompson, Treasurer and Chief Financial Officer
CMO: Jason Feinberg, M.D., Vice President Medical Affairs and Chief Medical
Officer
CIO: John Oates, Director Information Systems
CHR: Patrick R. Boyle, Vice President Human Resources
CNO: Eileen Gage, R.N., Vice President Nursing
Web address: www.flhealth.org
**Control:** Other not–for–profit (including NFP Corporation) **Service:** General
Medical and Surgical

**Staffed Beds:** 186 **Admissions:** 1091 **Census:** 154 **Outpatient Visits:**
168868 **Births:** 0 **Total Expense ($000):** 30072 **Payroll Expense ($000):**
15635 **Personnel:** 368

## PLAINVIEW—Nassau County

⊞ **PLAINVIEW HOSPITAL (330331)**, 888 Old Country Road, Zip 11803–4978;
tel. 516/719–3000 **A**1 9 10 12 13 **F**3 9 13 15 17 18 29 30 31 34 35 36 38
40 43 44 45 46 49 50 57 58 59 60 64 65 68 69 70 71 74 75 76 78 79 81
84 85 86 87 97 101 102 107 108 110 111 117 119 130 132 135 146 148
**P**5 6 **S** North Shore–Long Island Jewish Health System, Great Neck, NY
Primary Contact: Michael Fener, Executive Director
CMO: Alan Mensch, M.D., Senior Vice President Medical Affairs
CIO: Nicholas O'Connor, Vice President and Chief Information Officer
Web address: www.northshorelij.com
**Control:** Other not–for–profit (including NFP Corporation) **Service:** General
Medical and Surgical

**Staffed Beds:** 204 **Admissions:** 11384 **Census:** 157 **Outpatient Visits:**
59739 **Births:** 1170 **Total Expense ($000):** 199898 **Payroll Expense
($000):** 97012 **Personnel:** 1156

## PLATTSBURGH—Clinton County

⊞ **CHAMPLAIN VALLEY PHYSICIANS HOSPITAL MEDICAL CENTER (330250)**,
75 Beekman Street, Zip 12901–1438; tel. 518/561–2000, (Total facility includes
90 beds in nursing home–type unit) **A**1 2 9 10 **F**3 7 8 11 13 14 15 17 18 20
22 24 26 28 29 30 31 32 34 35 37 38 39 40 43 44 45 46 49 51 53 54 57
59 60 61 64 65 66 70 74 75 76 77 78 79 81 82 83 84 85 86 87 89 93 94
97 98 99 100 101 102 104 106 107 108 110 111 114 117 118 119 120
121 123 126 128 129 130 131 132 135 144 146 147 148 **P**1 5 7
Primary Contact: Stephens M. Mundy, President and Chief Executive Officer
COO: Debra Donahue, Senior Vice President and Chief Operating Officer
CFO: Joyce Rafferty, Vice President Finance
CMO: Richard Dal Col, Vice President and Chief Medical Officer
CIO: Wouter Rietsema, M.D., Chief Quality and Information Officer
CHR: Michelle Lebeau, Vice President Human Resources
CNO: Debra Donahue, Senior Vice President and Chief Operating Officer
Web address: www.cvph.org
**Control:** Other not–for–profit (including NFP Corporation) **Service:** General
Medical and Surgical

**Staffed Beds:** 341 **Admissions:** 9870 **Census:** 174 **Outpatient Visits:**
341678 **Births:** 895 **Total Expense ($000):** 289061 **Payroll Expense
($000):** 136160 **Personnel:** 1837

## POMONA—Rockland County

☐ **SUMMIT PARK HOSPITAL AND NURSING CARE CENTER (332014)**, 50
Sanatorium Road, Building A., Zip 10970–3555; tel. 845/364–2700,
(Nonreporting) **A**1 9 10
Primary Contact: Richard J. Maloney, M.P.H., Commissioner
COO: Richard J. Maloney, M.P.H., Commissioner
CFO: Chris Kopf, Chief Fiscal Officer
CMO: Paul Mercurio, M.D., Medical Director
CHR: Mary Hagan, Director Human Resources
Web address: www.co.rockland.ny.us
**Control:** County–Government, nonfederal **Service:** Long–Term Acute Care
hospital

**Staffed Beds:** 408

**Hospital, Medicare Provider Number, Address, Telephone, Approval, Facility, and Physician Codes, Health Care System**

★ American Hospital Association (AHA) membership
☐ The Joint Commission accreditation
◇ DNV Healthcare Inc. accreditation
○ Healthcare Facilities Accreditation Program
△ Commission on Accreditation of Rehabilitation Facilities (CARF) accreditation

© 2013 AHA Guide    *Many Facility Codes have changed. Please refer to the AHA Guide Code Chart.*    Hospitals **A439**

**PORT JEFFERSON—Suffolk County**

⌧ **JOHN T. MATHER MEMORIAL HOSPITAL (330185)**, 75 North Country Road,
Zip 11777–2190; tel. 631/473–1320, (Nonreporting) **A**1 2 9 10
Primary Contact: Kenneth D. Roberts, President
COO: Kevin J. Murray, Senior Vice President
CFO: Joseph Wisnoski, Vice President Finance and Chief Financial Officer
CMO: Joan Faro, M.D., Chief Medical Officer
CIO: Thomas Heiman, Assistant Vice President Information Services
CHR: Diane Marotta, Vice President Human Resources
CNO: Marie Mulligan, R.N., Vice President Nursing
Web address: www.matherhospital.com
**Control:** Other not–for–profit (including NFP Corporation) **Service:** General
Medical and Surgical

**Staffed Beds:** 248

☐ △ **ST. CHARLES HOSPITAL (330246)**, 200 Belle Terre Road,
Zip 11777–1928; tel. 631/474–6000 **A**1 2 7 9 10 **F**3 4 8 11 12 13 15 17 18
28 29 30 31 34 35 37 39 40 42 43 44 46 47 49 50 51 54 57 59 60 61 64
65 66 69 70 72 73 74 75 76 77 78 79 80 81 82 84 85 86 87 89 90 91 92
93 94 96 97 100 107 108 109 110 111 114 115 118 119 124 129 130 131
132 135 141 142 146 148 **S** Catholic Health Services of Long Island, Rockville
Centre, NY
Primary Contact: James O'Connor, Executive Vice President and Chief
Administrative Officer
COO: Ronald Weingartner, Chief Operating Officer
CFO: Frank Fox, Vice President Finance and Chief Financial Officer
CIO: Felix Pabon–Ramirez, Chief Information Officer
CHR: Mark Boehrer, Director Human Resources
Web address: www.stcharleshospital.chsli.org
**Control:** Church–operated, Nongovernment, not–for profit **Service:** General
Medical and Surgical

**Staffed Beds:** 231 **Admissions:** 9056 **Census:** 174 **Outpatient Visits:**
150004 **Births:** 1694 **Total Expense ($000):** 170641 **Payroll Expense**
**($000):** 75992 **Personnel:** 972

**PORT JERVIS—Orange County**

⌧ **BON SECOURS COMMUNITY HOSPITAL (330135)**, 160 East Main Street,
Zip 12771–2245, Mailing Address: P.O. Box 1014, Zip 12771–0268;
tel. 845/858–7000, (Nonreporting) **A**1 2 9 10 **S** Bon Secours Health System,
Inc., Marriottsville, MD
Primary Contact: Jeff Reilly, Senior Vice President Operations
COO: Gaynor Rosenstein, Vice President Operations
CMO: Jeffrey Auerbach, D.O., Medical Director
CHR: Kim Hirkaler, Director Human Resources
Web address: www.bonsecourscommunityhosp.org
**Control:** Church–operated, Nongovernment, not–for profit **Service:** General
Medical and Surgical

**Staffed Beds:** 187

**POTSDAM—St. Lawrence County**

★ ◇ **CANTON–POTSDAM HOSPITAL (330197)**, 50 Leroy Street,
Zip 13676–1799; tel. 315/265–3300 **A**9 10 20 21 **F**3 4 5 8 11 13 14 15 18
26 28 29 30 31 34 38 39 40 43 46 54 57 59 64 65 67 68 75 76 77 78 79
81 82 86 87 92 93 95 96 97 98 100 102 104 105 107 108 110 111 115
117 118 119 121 123 127 128 129 130 131 132 133 135 143 145 146 147
148 **P**6
Primary Contact: David B. Acker, FACHE, President and Chief Executive Officer
CFO: Richard Jacobs, Vice President Finance and Chief Financial Officer
CMO: Robert T. Rogers, II, M.D., Medical Director
CIO: Jorge C. Grillo, Chief Information Officer
CHR: A. Jack Davis, Vice President Human Resources
CNO: Cathy Ann Schantz, MSN, Vice President Patient Care Services and Chief
Nursing Officer
Web address: www.cphospital.org
**Control:** Other not–for–profit (including NFP Corporation) **Service:** General
Medical and Surgical

**Staffed Beds:** 94 **Admissions:** 4628 **Census:** 55 **Outpatient Visits:** 220587
**Births:** 252 **Total Expense ($000):** 95768 **Payroll Expense ($000):** 45277
**Personnel:** 759

**POUGHKEEPSIE—Dutchess County**

△ ◇ **SAINT FRANCIS HOSPITAL AND HEALTH CENTERS (330067)**, 241
North Road, Zip 12601–1154; tel. 845/483–5000 **A**2 7 9 10 21 **F**1 3 4 8 11
12 15 16 17 18 20 22 29 30 31 32 34 35 36 37 40 43 45 46 49 50 55 56
57 60 61 62 63 64 65 66 67 68 70 72 73 74 75 76 77 78 79 80 81 82 85
86 87 88 89 90 91 93 98 99 100 101 102 103 104 107 108 111 115 118
119 128 129 130 131 132 133 134 135 144 146 148
Primary Contact: Jason B. Barlow, Interim Chief Executive Officer
CFO: Will de la Pena, Chief Financial Officer
CMO: J. Keith Festa, M.D., Vice President Medical Affairs
CIO: Joseph McCann, Chief Information Officer
CHR: Helen Rinaudo, Vice President Human Resources
CNO: Patricia Nocket, Assistant Vice President Clinical Nursing Services
Web address: www.sfhhc.org
**Control:** Church–operated, Nongovernment, not–for profit **Service:** General
Medical and Surgical

**Staffed Beds:** 322 **Admissions:** 7983 **Census:** 157 **Outpatient Visits:**
226884 **Births:** 0 **Total Expense ($000):** 160815 **Payroll Expense ($000):**
70627 **Personnel:** 1275

⌧ **VASSAR BROTHERS MEDICAL CENTER (330023)**, 45 Reade Place,
Zip 12601–3947; tel. 845/454–8500 **A**1 2 9 10 **F**3 8 11 13 14 15 17 18 20
22 24 26 28 29 30 31 32 34 35 36 39 40 46 49 50 51 54 55 56 57 58 59
60 63 64 66 68 70 72 73 74 75 76 77 78 79 81 82 84 85 86 87 89 93 97
107 108 110 111 114 115 119 120 121 124 126 129 130 132 135 146 147
148 **S** Health Quest Systems, Inc., LaGrangeville, NY
Primary Contact: Janet L. Ready, President and Chief Operating Officer
CFO: Maryann Kepple, Chief Financial Officer
CMO: Stephen A. Katz, M.D., Chief Medical Officer and Senior Vice President
Medical Affairs
CIO: Robert Diamond, Chief Information Officer
CHR: Jeffrey McDonough, Assistant Vice President Human Resources
CNO: Margaret M. Cusumano, R.N., Chief Nursing Officer and Vice President Care
Services
Web address: www.health–quest.org
**Control:** Other not–for–profit (including NFP Corporation) **Service:** General
Medical and Surgical

**Staffed Beds:** 365 **Admissions:** 17947 **Census:** 250 **Outpatient Visits:**
278818 **Births:** 2250 **Total Expense ($000):** 387370 **Payroll Expense**
**($000):** 116668 **Personnel:** 1649

**QUEENS—Queens County, See New York City**

**QUEENS VILLAGE—Queens County, See New York City**

**RHINEBECK—Dutchess County**

⌧ △ **NORTHERN DUTCHESS HOSPITAL (330049)**, 6511 Springbrook Avenue,
Zip 12572–3709, Mailing Address: P.O. Box 5002, Zip 12572–5002;
tel. 845/876–3001 **A**1 7 9 10 **F**3 9 11 13 15 18 28 29 30 34 35 36 37 40 50
53 54 56 57 59 64 68 70 74 75 76 77 79 81 82 85 90 93 107 108 111 114
119 129 130 131 132 146 147 **S** Health Quest Systems, Inc., LaGrangeville, NY
Primary Contact: Tim Cleary, Interim President and Chief Operating Officer
CFO: Alan Mossoff, Chief Financial Officer
CMO: John Sabia, M.D., Medical Director
CIO: Catherine Schuster, Chief Information Officer
CHR: Eileen Miller, Director Human Resources
Web address: www.health–quest.org/home_nd.cfm?id=9
**Control:** Other not–for–profit (including NFP Corporation) **Service:** General
Medical and Surgical

**Staffed Beds:** 68 **Admissions:** 3322 **Census:** 40 **Outpatient Visits:** 93189
**Births:** 877 **Total Expense ($000):** 65655 **Payroll Expense ($000):** 22193
**Personnel:** 380

**RICHMOND VALLEY—Richmond County, See New York City**

**RIVERHEAD—Suffolk County**

☐ **PECONIC BAY MEDICAL CENTER (330107)**, 1300 Roanoke Avenue,
Zip 11901–2031; tel. 631/548–6000, (Nonreporting) **A**1 9 10 12 13
Primary Contact: Andrew J. Mitchell, President and Chief Executive Officer
COO: Ronald McManus, Senior Vice President Clinical Services and Business
Entities
CFO: Michael O'Donnell, Chief Financial Officer
CMO: Richard Kubiak, M.D., Vice President Medical Affairs
CIO: Arthur Crowe, Director Information Systems
CHR: Monica Chestnut–Rauls, Vice President Human Resources
CNO: Gerard Zunno, R.N., Vice President Patient Care Services
Web address: www.pbmchealth.org
**Control:** Other not–for–profit (including NFP Corporation) **Service:** General
Medical and Surgical

**Staffed Beds:** 176

*Many Facility Codes have changed. Please refer to the AHA Guide Code Chart.* © 2013 AHA Guide

## ROCHESTER—Monroe County

☒ **HIGHLAND HOSPITAL OF ROCHESTER (330164)**, 1000 South Avenue, Zip 14620–2733; tel. 585/473–2200 **A**1 3 5 9 10 **F**5 8 12 13 15 18 29 30 31 34 35 37 38 39 40 43 44 45 46 47 49 50 54 55 56 57 59 61 63 64 65 68 70 74 75 76 77 78 79 81 82 83 84 85 86 87 97 100 107 108 109 110 111 112 115 119 120 121 122 123 124 126 130 134 145 146 147 **P**6 **S** University of Rochester Medical Center, Rochester, NY
Primary Contact: Steven I. Goldstein, President and Chief Executive Officer
COO: Cindy Becker, Vice President and Chief Operating Officer
CFO: Leonard J. Shute, Chief Financial Officer
CMO: Raymond Mayewski, M.D., Chief Medical Officer
CIO: D. Jerome Powell, M.D., Chief Information Officer
CHR: Kathleen Gallucci, Chief Human Resources
Web address: www.stronghealth.com
**Control:** Hospital district or authority, Government, nonfederal **Service:** General Medical and Surgical

**Staffed Beds:** 261 **Admissions:** 16193 **Census:** 191 **Outpatient Visits:** 254456 **Births:** 2938 **Total Expense ($000):** 271767 **Payroll Expense ($000):** 129130 **Personnel:** 1860

☒ **ROCHESTER GENERAL HOSPITAL (330125)**, 1425 Portland Avenue, Zip 14621–3099; tel. 585/922–4000 **A**1 2 3 5 9 10 **F**3 5 8 9 11 12 13 14 15 17 18 20 22 24 26 28 29 30 31 32 34 35 36 38 39 40 41 43 44 47 49 50 51 54 55 56 57 58 59 60 61 64 66 68 70 73 74 75 76 77 78 79 80 81 82 84 85 86 87 89 90 92 93 96 97 98 99 100 101 102 103 104 107 108 110 111 114 115 116 118 119 120 121 123 124 126 130 131 132 134 135 145 146 147 148 **P**5 7 **S** Rochester General Health System, Rochester, NY
Primary Contact: Robert Nesselbush, President
CMO: Rob Mayo, M.D., Chief Medical Officer
CHR: Janine Schue, Senior Vice President Human Resources
CNO: Cheryl Sheridan, R.N., Senior Vice President Patient Care Services
Web address: www.rochestergeneral.org
**Control:** Other not–for–profit (including NFP Corporation) **Service:** General Medical and Surgical

**Staffed Beds:** 520 **Admissions:** 30775 **Census:** 445 **Outpatient Visits:** 1456471 **Births:** 2342 **Total Expense ($000):** 714493 **Payroll Expense ($000):** 349083 **Personnel:** 5364

☐ **ROCHESTER PSYCHIATRIC CENTER (334020)**, 1111 Elmwood Avenue, Zip 14620 3005, tel. 585/241 1200, (Nonreporting) **A**1 3 5 10 **S** New York State Office of Mental Health, Albany, NY
Primary Contact: Elizabeth Suhre, Executive Director
COO: Joseph Coffey, Director Facility Administration
CFO: Rosanne Minnis, Business Officer
CMO: Laurence Guttmacher, M.D., Clinical Director
CIO: Stephen Font, Coordinator Information Systems
CHR: Christine Hally, Director Human Resources
Web address: www.omh.ny.gov/omhweb/facilities/ropc/facility.htm
**Control:** State–Government, nonfederal **Service:** Psychiatric

**Staffed Beds:** 180

☒ △ **STRONG MEMORIAL HOSPITAL OF THE UNIVERSITY OF ROCHESTER (330285)**, 601 Elmwood Avenue, Zip 14642–0002; tel. 585/275–2100, (Includes GOLISANO CHILDREN'S HOSPITAL, 601 Elmwood Avenue, Zip 14610; tel. 585/275–2182) **A**1 2 3 5 7 8 9 10 **F**3 5 6 8 9 11 12 13 14 15 16 17 18 19 20 21 22 23 24 25 26 27 28 29 30 31 32 33 34 35 38 39 40 41 43 44 45 46 47 48 49 50 51 52 53 54 55 56 57 58 59 61 63 64 69 70 71 72 73 74 75 76 77 78 79 81 82 83 84 85 86 87 88 89 90 91 92 93 94 96 97 98 99 100 101 102 103 104 105 107 108 110 111 114 115 116 117 118 119 120 121 123 124 126 129 130 131 132 134 135 136 137 138 139 141 142 143 144 146 147 148 **P**6 **S** University of Rochester Medical Center, Rochester, NY
Primary Contact: Steven I. Goldstein, President and Chief Executive Officer
COO: Kathleen M. Parrinello, Ph.D., Chief Operating Officer
CFO: Leonard J. Shute, Chief Financial Officer
CMO: Raymond Mayewski, M.D., Chief Medical Officer
CIO: D. Jerome Powell, M.D., Chief Information Officer
CHR: Charles J. Murphy, Associate Vice President Human Resources
Web address: www.urmc.rochester.edu
**Control:** Other not–for–profit (including NFP Corporation) **Service:** General Medical and Surgical

**Staffed Beds:** 781 **Admissions:** 38423 **Census:** 709 **Outpatient Visits:** 1274690 **Births:** 2854 **Total Expense ($000):** 1083727 **Payroll Expense ($000):** 441938 **Personnel:** 8086

☒ **UNITY HOSPITAL (330226)**, 1555 Long Pond Road, Zip 14626–4182; tel. 585/723–7000, (Total facility includes 120 beds in nursing home–type unit) **A**1 2 3 5 9 10 **F**4 5 8 11 13 18 20 22 26 28 29 30 31 32 34 35 38 39 40 45 46 47 48 49 50 54 56 57 59 60 61 63 64 65 66 68 69 70 71 74 75 76 78 79 80 81 82 84 86 87 90 92 93 96 97 98 99 100 101 102 103 104 105 106 107 119 126 128 129 130 131 132 134 144 146 147 148 **P**6
Primary Contact: Warren Hern, President and Chief Executive Officer
COO: Stewart C. Putnam, Executive Vice President and Chief Operating Officer
CFO: Tom Crilly, Executive Vice President and Chief Financial Officer
CMO: James Haley, M.D., Senior Vice President and Chief Medical Officer
CIO: John Glynn, Senior Vice President and Chief Information Officer
CHR: Maryalice Keller, Vice President Brand and Talent Management
CNO: Jane McCormack, R.N., Vice President, Chief Nursing Officer and Nursing and Patient Care Services
Web address: www.unityhealth.org
**Control:** Other not–for–profit (including NFP Corporation) **Service:** General Medical and Surgical

**Staffed Beds:** 460 **Admissions:** 15584 **Census:** 254 **Outpatient Visits:** 1029969 **Births:** 1472 **Total Expense ($000):** 380441 **Payroll Expense ($000):** 188574 **Personnel:** 3884

## ROCKVILLE CENTRE—Nassau County

☐ **MERCY MEDICAL CENTER (330259)**, 1000 North Village Avenue, Zip 11570–1000; tel. 516/705–2525 **A**1 2 9 10 **F**3 8 12 13 15 29 30 31 34 35 37 40 43 51 55 57 59 60 64 65 68 70 72 74 75 76 77 78 79 81 82 84 85 87 90 92 96 97 98 100 103 104 105 107 108 110 111 114 119 124 130 132 142 143 146 147 **S** Catholic Health Services of Long Island, Rockville Centre, NY
Primary Contact: Aaron Glatt, M.D., Executive Vice President and Chief Administrative Officer
COO: Ronald Steimel, Vice President Administration and Chief Operating Officer
CFO: William C. Armstrong, Senior Vice President and Chief Financial Officer
CMO: John Reilly, M.D., Vice President Medical Affairs and Chief Medical Officer
CIO: Marcy Dunn, Vice President Information Services and Chief Information Officer
CHR: Allison Cianciotto Croyle, Vice President of Human Resources
CNO: Renee Mauriello, R.N., Vice President, Patient Care Services
Web address: www.mercymedicalcenter.chsli.org
**Control:** Church–operated, Nongovernment, not–for profit **Service:** General Medical and Surgical

**Staffed Beds:** 234 **Admissions:** 11267 **Census:** 177 **Outpatient Visits:** 109322 **Births:** 1092 **Personnel:** 1160

## ROME—Oneida County

★ ☐ **ROME MEMORIAL HOSPITAL (330215)**, 1500 North James Street, Zip 13440–2844; tel. 315/338–7000, (Total facility includes 82 beds in nursing home–type unit) **A**9 10 11 **F**3 5 8 13 15 18 26 27 29 30 31 34 35 37 40 46 49 56 57 59 61 64 65 66 70 74 75 76 77 78 79 80 81 84 85 86 87 89 93 97 98 101 102 103 106 107 108 110 111 115 118 119 120 121 123 128 129 130 131 132 135 146 147 148 **P**6
Primary Contact: Basil Ariglio, President and Chief Executive Officer
COO: Raymond Carnevale, Senior Vice President and Chief Operating Officer
CFO: Nicholas Mayhew, Vice President and Chief Financial Officer
CMO: Waleed Albert, M.D., Chief Medical Officer
CIO: Bruce Peterson, Chief Information Officer
CHR: Regina Chambers, Assistant Vice President Human Resource
CNO: Durinda Durr, Vice President and Chief Nursing Officer
Web address: www.romehospital.org
**Control:** Other not–for–profit (including NFP Corporation) **Service:** General Medical and Surgical

**Staffed Beds:** 203 **Admissions:** 5168 **Census:** 136 **Outpatient Visits:** 149156 **Births:** 556 **Total Expense ($000):** 85397 **Payroll Expense ($000):** 39550 **Personnel:** 788

---

**Hospital, Medicare Provider Number, Address, Telephone, Approval, Facility, and Physician Codes, Health Care System**

★ American Hospital Association (AHA) membership
☐ The Joint Commission accreditation
◇ DNV Healthcare Inc. accreditation
○ Healthcare Facilities Accreditation Program
△ Commission on Accreditation of Rehabilitation Facilities (CARF) accreditation

## ROSLYN—Nassau County

⊠ **ST. FRANCIS HOSPITAL (330182)**, 100 Port Washington Boulevard, Zip 11576–1353; tel. 516/562–6000 **A**1 9 10 **F**3 7 11 15 17 18 19 20 21 22 23 24 26 27 28 29 30 31 34 35 36 37 38 39 40 43 44 45 46 47 49 50 53 54 56 57 58 59 60 61 62 63 64 65 66 68 70 71 74 75 77 78 79 80 81 82 84 85 86 87 89 93 94 97 100 102 107 108 109 110 111 114 115 116 117 118 119 124 126 130 131 132 135 141 145 146 147 148 **P**6 **S** Catholic Health Services of Long Island, Rockville Centre, NY
Primary Contact: Ruth Hennessey, Executive Vice President and Chief Administrative Officer
CFO: William C. Armstrong, Vice President and Chief Financial Officer
CMO: Jack Soterakis, M.D., Executive Vice President Medical Affairs
CIO: Marcy Dunn, Vice President Information Services and Chief Information Officer
CHR: Barbara Fierro, Director, Human Resources
CNO: Ann S. Cella, R.N., Senior Vice President, Patient Care Services
Web address: www.stfrancisheartcenter.com/index.html
**Control:** Church–operated, Nongovernment, not–for profit **Service:** General Medical and Surgical

**Staffed Beds:** 306 **Admissions:** 15677 **Census:** 264 **Outpatient Visits:** 180500 **Births:** 0 **Total Expense ($000):** 485414 **Payroll Expense ($000):** 216274 **Personnel:** 2589

## SARANAC LAKE—Franklin County

⊠ ○ **ADIRONDACK MEDICAL CENTER (330079)**, 2233 State Route 86, Zip 12983–5644, Mailing Address: P.O. Box 471, Zip 12983–0471; tel. 518/891–4141, (Total facility includes 194 beds in nursing home–type unit) **A**1 9 10 11 **F**3 8 9 12 13 15 16 18 28 29 30 31 34 35 37 38 39 40 41 42 43 45 46 49 54 56 57 59 60 64 70 71 74 75 76 77 78 79 81 82 84 85 86 89 90 92 93 94 97 98 102 103 104 107 108 110 111 114 116 119 127 128 129 130 131 132 135 146 147 148 **P**1 5 **S** HealthTech Management Services, Franklin, TN
Primary Contact: Chandler M. Ralph, President and Chief Executive Officer
COO: Cynthia McGuire, Chief Operating Officer
CFO: Patrick M. Facteau, Chief Financial Officer
CMO: William Viscardo, M.D., Chief Medical Officer
CHR: MaDena DuChemin, Chief Human Resources Officer
Web address: www.amccares.org
**Control:** Other not–for–profit (including NFP Corporation) **Service:** General Medical and Surgical

**Staffed Beds:** 271 **Admissions:** 3026 **Census:** 207 **Outpatient Visits:** 129261 **Births:** 170 **Total Expense ($000):** 100593 **Payroll Expense ($000):** 45834 **Personnel:** 811

## SARATOGA SPRINGS—Saratoga County

☐ **FOUR WINDS HOSPITAL (334049)**, 30 Crescent Avenue, Zip 12866–5142; tel. 518/584–3600, (Nonreporting) **A**1 9 10
Primary Contact: David J. Woodlock, Administrator
Web address: www.fourwindshospital.com
**Control:** Corporation, Investor–owned, for–profit **Service:** Children's hospital psychiatric

**Staffed Beds:** 83

⊠ **SARATOGA HOSPITAL (330222)**, 211 Church Street, Zip 12866–1003; tel. 518/587–3222, (Total facility includes 36 beds in nursing home–type unit) **A**1 2 5 9 10 **F**3 8 11 12 13 15 17 18 20 26 27 28 29 30 31 34 35 37 38 40 45 47 49 50 54 56 57 59 64 68 70 74 75 76 77 78 79 81 82 85 92 93 94 96 97 98 100 101 102 103 107 108 110 111 114 115 116 117 119 120 121 126 128 130 131 132 135 144 145 146 147 **P**6
Primary Contact: Angelo G. Calbone, President and Chief Executive Officer
CFO: Gary Foster, Vice President and Chief Financial Officer
CMO: Joyce L. Peabody, M.D., Vice President and Chief Medical Officer
CIO: John Mangona, Chief Information Officer and Compliance Officer
CHR: Jeffrey M. Methven, Vice President Ambulatory Services and Chief Human Resources Officer
Web address: www.saratogacare.org
**Control:** Other not–for–profit (including NFP Corporation) **Service:** General Medical and Surgical

**Staffed Beds:** 207 **Admissions:** 8587 **Census:** 165 **Outpatient Visits:** 247121 **Births:** 802 **Total Expense ($000):** 201709 **Payroll Expense ($000):** 90922 **Personnel:** 1635

## SCHENECTADY—Schenectady County

⊠ **ELLIS HOSPITAL (330153)**, 1101 Nott Street, Zip 12308–2425; tel. 518/243–4000, (Includes BELLEVUE WOMAN'S CARE CENTER, 2210 Troy Road, Zip 12309–4797; tel. 518/346–9400; ELLIS HOSPITAL HEALTH CENTER, 600 McClellan Street, Zip 12304–1090; tel. 518/382–2000), (Total facility includes 82 beds in nursing home–type unit) **A**1 3 5 9 10 **F**8 12 13 15 18 20 22 24 26 28 29 30 31 38 39 40 54 60 62 64 65 68 70 72 74 75 76 77 78 79 81 82 83 84 89 93 98 99 100 101 102 103 104 107 108 110 111 114 115 117 119 120 121 126 128 129 130 146 147 148 **P**6
Primary Contact: James W. Connolly, President and Chief Executive Officer
COO: Paul A. Milton, Executive Vice President and Chief Operating Officer
CFO: Daniel Rinaldi, Chief Financial Officer
CMO: David Liebers, M.D., Chief Medical Officer and Vice President Medical Affairs
CIO: David Snyder, Chief Information Officer and Vice President Information Technology
CHR: Joseph Giansante, Vice President Human Resources
Web address: www.ellismedicine.org
**Control:** Other not–for–profit (including NFP Corporation) **Service:** General Medical and Surgical

**Staffed Beds:** 431 **Admissions:** 21418 **Census:** 349 **Outpatient Visits:** 641909 **Births:** 2663 **Total Expense ($000):** 366014 **Payroll Expense ($000):** 188271 **Personnel:** 2795

**ELLIS HOSPITAL HEALTH CENTER** See Ellis Hospital

**ELLIS HOSPITAL MCCLELLAN CAMPUS** See Ellis Hospital Health Center

⊠ △ **SUNNYVIEW REHABILITATION HOSPITAL (330406)**, 1270 Belmont Avenue, Zip 12308–2104; tel. 518/382–4500 **A**1 3 5 7 9 10 **F**3 28 29 53 56 57 59 64 74 79 90 93 94 119 130 132 135 146 **P**5 **S** Catholic Health East, Newtown Square, PA
Primary Contact: Edward Eisenman, Chief Executive Officer
CFO: Kristin Signor, Director Finance
CMO: Lynne T. Nicolson, M.D., Medical Director
CIO: Patrick Clark, Manager Information Technology
CHR: Meghan Glowa, Director Human Resources
Web address: www.sunnyview.org
**Control:** Other not–for–profit (including NFP Corporation) **Service:** Rehabilitation

**Staffed Beds:** 115 **Admissions:** 2601 **Census:** 86 **Outpatient Visits:** 63276 **Births:** 0 **Total Expense ($000):** 44272 **Payroll Expense ($000):** 25903 **Personnel:** 555

## SLEEPY HOLLOW—Westchester County

⊠ **PHELPS MEMORIAL HOSPITAL CENTER (330261)**, 701 North Broadway, Zip 10591–1020; tel. 914/366–3000 **A**1 2 3 5 9 10 **F**3 4 5 8 9 11 13 14 15 17 18 26 27 28 29 30 31 32 34 35 38 39 40 41 43 45 46 47 48 49 50 53 54 55 56 57 58 59 60 61 63 64 65 68 69 70 74 75 76 77 78 79 81 82 84 85 86 87 89 90 91 92 93 94 96 98 100 101 102 103 104 106 107 108 110 111 114 115 118 119 129 130 131 132 135 143 144 145 146 147 148
Primary Contact: Keith F. Safian, President and Chief Executive Officer
COO: Bruce B. Davidow, Senior Vice President and Chief Operating Officer
CFO: Vincent DeSantis, Vice President Finance
CMO: Lawrence L. Faltz, M.D., Senior Vice President Medical Affairs and Medical Director
CHR: Joanne Sturans, Vice President Human Resources
Web address: www.phelpshospital.org
**Control:** Other not–for–profit (including NFP Corporation) **Service:** General Medical and Surgical

**Staffed Beds:** 238 **Admissions:** 7548 **Census:** 136 **Outpatient Visits:** 323525 **Births:** 1070 **Total Expense ($000):** 208662 **Payroll Expense ($000):** 105507 **Personnel:** 1245

## SMITHTOWN—Suffolk County

☐ **ST. CATHERINE OF SIENA MEDICAL CENTER (330401)**, 50 Route 25–A, Zip 11787–1348; tel. 631/862–3000, (Nonreporting) **A**1 9 10 **S** Catholic Health Services of Long Island, Rockville Centre, NY
Primary Contact: Dennis Verzi, Executive Vice President and Chief Administrative Officer
CFO: Dan Macksood, Regional Vice President and Chief Financial Officer
CHR: Danielle A. Robbins, Vice President Human Resources
Web address: www.stcatherinemedicalcenter.org
**Control:** Church–operated, Nongovernment, not–for profit **Service:** General Medical and Surgical

**Staffed Beds:** 535

**NY**

*Many Facility Codes have changed. Please refer to the AHA Guide Code Chart.* © 2013 AHA Guide

## SOUTHAMPTON—Suffolk County

⊠ **SOUTHAMPTON HOSPITAL (330340)**, 240 Meeting House Lane, Zip 11968–5090; tel. 631/726–8200 **A**1 9 10 12 13 **F**3 11 12 13 15 18 29 30 31 34 35 36 40 44 45 46 47 49 54 55 56 57 59 60 61 63 64 65 68 70 74 75 76 77 78 79 81 82 83 84 85 86 87 89 93 94 96 102 107 108 110 111 115 119 127 130 131 132 135 145 146 148 **P**4 6
Primary Contact: Robert S. Chaloner, President and Chief Executive Officer
COO: Frederic Weinbaum, M.D., Executive Vice President Operations and Chief Medical Officer
CFO: Chris Schulteis, Vice President/Chief Financial Officer
CMO: Frederic Weinbaum, M.D., Executive Vice President Operations and Chief Medical Officer
CIO: William Bifulco, Vice President/Chief Information Officer
CNO: Patricia Darcey, R.N., Vice President/Chief Nursing Officer
Web address: www.southamptonhospital.org
**Control:** Other not–for–profit (including NFP Corporation) **Service:** General Medical and Surgical

**Staffed Beds:** 80 **Admissions:** 5587 **Census:** 51 **Outpatient Visits:** 664165 **Births:** 651 **Total Expense ($000):** 118800 **Payroll Expense ($000):** 54123 **Personnel:** 796

## SPRINGVILLE—Erie County

**BERTRAND CHAFFEE HOSPITAL (330111)**, 224 East Main Street, Zip 14141–1497; tel. 716/592–2871, (Nonreporting) **A**9 10
Primary Contact: Nils Gunnersen, Administrator
CMO: J. Matthew Baker, M.D., President Medical Staff
CHR: Mary Beth Brown, Director Human Resources
Web address: www.chaffeehospitalandhome.com
**Control:** Other not–for–profit (including NFP Corporation) **Service:** General Medical and Surgical

**Staffed Beds:** 24

## STAR LAKE—St. Lawrence County

★ **CLIFTON–FINE HOSPITAL (331307)**, Oswegatchie Trail, Zip 13690, Mailing Address: 1014 Oswegatchie Trail, Zip 13690–3143; tel. 315/848–3351, (Nonreporting) **A**9 10 18
Primary Contact: Robert L. Seamon, Chief Executive Officer
CFO: Nancy Russell, Chief Financial Officer
CMO: David Welch, M.D., Medical Director
CIO: Steve Potter, Manager Business and Information Systems
CNO: Michelle Bristol, Director of Nursing
Web address: www.cliftonfinehospital.org
**Control:** Other not–for–profit (including NFP Corporation) **Service:** General Medical and Surgical

**Staffed Beds:** 20

## STATEN ISLAND—Richmond County, See New York City

## STONY BROOK—Suffolk County

⊠ **STONY BROOK UNIVERSITY MEDICAL CENTER (330393)**, State University of New York, Zip 11794–8410; tel. 631/444–1077, (Includes STONY BROOK CHILDREN'S HOSPITAL, 100 Nicolls Road, Zip 11794–0001; tel. 631/444–4000) **A**1 2 3 5 8 9 10 **F**3 6 7 8 9 11 12 13 14 15 16 17 18 19 20 22 24 26 28 29 30 31 32 34 35 36 38 39 40 41 43 44 45 46 47 48 49 50 51 52 54 55 56 57 58 59 60 61 64 65 66 68 70 72 73 74 75 76 77 78 79 81 82 84 85 86 87 88 89 93 96 97 98 99 100 101 102 103 104 105 107 108 110 111 114 115 116 117 118 119 120 121 122 123 124 126 129 130 131 132 134 135 136 138 141 143 145 146 147 148 **P**1 6
Primary Contact: L. Reuven Pasternak, M.D., M.P.H., Vice President for Health System and Chief Executive Officer
COO: Carol Gomes, FACHE, Chief Operating Officer
CFO: Gary E. Bie, Chief Financial Officer
CMO: Todd Griffin, M.D., Chief Medical Officer
CIO: Jane Tsui–Wu, Interim Chief Information Officer
CHR: Elizabeth McCoy, Chief Human Resources Management
Web address: www.stonybrookmedicalcenter.org
**Control:** State–Government, nonfederal **Service:** General Medical and Surgical

**Staffed Beds:** 597 **Admissions:** 32008 **Census:** 521 **Outpatient Visits:** 351770 **Births:** 3042 **Total Expense ($000):** 937857 **Payroll Expense ($000):** 416567 **Personnel:** 4572

## SUFFERN—Rockland County

⊠ **GOOD SAMARITAN HOSPITAL (330158)**, 255 Lafayette Avenue, Zip 10901–4869; tel. 845/368–5000, (Nonreporting) **A**1 2 9 10 **S** Bon Secours Health System, Inc., Marriottsville, MD
Primary Contact: Philip A. Patterson, Chief Executive Officer
COO: Gerry Durney, Chief Operating Officer
CFO: Melinda Hancock, Interim Chief Financial Officer
CMO: Rodney W. Williams, M.D., Vice President Medical Affairs
CIO: Deborah K. Marshall, Vice President Public Relations
CHR: Pamela Tarulli, Senior Vice President Human Resources
Web address: www.goodsamhosp.org
**Control:** Church–operated, Nongovernment, not–for profit **Service:** General Medical and Surgical

**Staffed Beds:** 308

## SYOSSET—Nassau County

★ **SYOSSET HOSPITAL**, 221 Jericho Turnpike, Zip 11791–4515; tel. 516/496–6400 **A**9 **F**3 12 15 18 29 30 34 35 36 38 40 43 44 45 50 57 58 59 64 65 68 70 74 79 81 82 84 85 87 97 98 100 101 102 107 108 119 130 132 135 146 148 **P**5 6 **S** North Shore–Long Island Jewish Health System, Great Neck, NY
Primary Contact: Michael Fener, Executive Director
COO: Mark J. Solazzo, Regional Chief Operating Officer
CFO: Richard Reilly, Deputy Executive Director
CMO: Randolph DiLorenzo, M.D., Medical Director
CHR: Andrew S. Goldberg, Associate Executive Director
Web address: www.northshorelij.com
**Control:** Other not–for–profit (including NFP Corporation) **Service:** General Medical and Surgical

**Staffed Beds:** 72 **Admissions:** 3885 **Census:** 54 **Outpatient Visits:** 37551 **Births:** 0 **Total Expense ($000):** 118506 **Payroll Expense ($000):** 57363 **Personnel:** 603

## SYRACUSE—Onondaga County

**COMMUNITY–GENERAL HOSPITAL OF GREATER SYRACUSE** See Upstate University Hospital at Community General

★ ◇ **CROUSE HOSPITAL (330203)**, 736 Irving Avenue, Zip 13210–1690; tel. 315/470–7111 **A**3 5 9 10 21 **F**3 4 5 8 11 12 13 15 18 19 20 21 22 23 26 27 29 31 34 35 36 37 40 49 50 56 59 60 70 72 74 75 76 77 78 79 81 84 86 87 89 93 96 107 108 110 114 115 116 117 118 119 126 129 130 131 132 135 144 145 146 147 148
Primary Contact: Paul J. Kronenberg, M.D., President and Chief Executive Officer
CFO: Kimberly Boynton, Chief Financial Officer
CMO: Ronald Stahl, M.D., Chief Medical Officer
CHR: John Bergemann, Director Human Resources
Web address: www.crouse.org
**Control:** Other not–for–profit (including NFP Corporation) **Service:** General Medical and Surgical

**Staffed Beds:** 501 **Admissions:** 20958 **Census:** 317 **Outpatient Visits:** 337030 **Births:** 4201 **Total Expense ($000):** 301798 **Payroll Expense ($000):** 159083 **Personnel:** 2255

☐ **RICHARD H. HUTCHINGS PSYCHIATRIC CENTER (334001)**, 620 Madison Street, Zip 13210–2319; tel. 315/426–3632, (Nonreporting) **A**1 3 5 10 **S** New York State Office of Mental Health, Albany, NY
Primary Contact: Colleen A. Sawyer, R.N., MSN, Executive Director
COO: David Peppel, Director Operations
CFO: Robert Stapleton, Director Administration
CMO: Mark Cattalani, M.D., Clinical Director
CIO: Neil Nemi, Administrator Facility Information Center
CHR: Katherine Herron, Director Human Resources
Web address: www.omh.ny.gov
**Control:** State–Government, nonfederal **Service:** Psychiatric

**Staffed Beds:** 131

---

**Hospital, Medicare Provider Number, Address, Telephone, Approval, Facility, and Physician Codes, Health Care System**

★ American Hospital Association (AHA) membership
☐ The Joint Commission accreditation
◇ DNV Healthcare Inc. accreditation
◯ Healthcare Facilities Accreditation Program
△ Commission on Accreditation of Rehabilitation Facilities (CARF) accreditation

© 2013 AHA Guide   *Many Facility Codes have changed. Please refer to the AHA Guide Code Chart.*   Hospitals **A443**

NY

★ ◇ **ST. JOSEPH'S HOSPITAL HEALTH CENTER (330140)**, 301 Prospect Avenue, Zip 13203–1807; tel. 315/448–5111 **A**3 5 9 10 21 **F**2 8 11 12 13 14 15 18 20 22 24 26 28 29 30 31 34 35 38 39 40 45 46 47 48 49 50 53 54 57 58 59 60 62 64 66 68 70 71 72 73 74 75 76 77 78 79 81 82 83 84 87 92 93 94 97 98 99 100 101 102 104 106 107 108 110 114 115 118 119 126 129 130 131 132 135 144 145 146 147 148 **S** Sisters of Saint Francis, Syracuse, NY
Primary Contact: Kathryn H. Ruscitto, President
COO: Mary W. Brown, Senior Vice President Operations
CFO: Michael Shaffer, Vice President Fiscal Services
CMO: Sandra Sulik, M.D., Vice President Medical Affairs
CIO: Charles Fennell, Vice President Information Management
CHR: Frank Panzetta, Director Human Resources
CNO: AnneMarie Czyz, R.N., Vice President for Clinical and Educational Services
Web address: www.sjhsyr.org
**Control:** Other not–for–profit (including NFP Corporation) **Service:** General Medical and Surgical

**Staffed Beds:** 431 **Admissions:** 26254 **Census:** 375 **Outpatient Visits:** 636002 **Births:** 1917 **Total Expense ($000):** 514564 **Payroll Expense ($000):** 227789 **Personnel:** 3471

⊞ △ **SYRACUSE VETERANS AFFAIRS MEDICAL CENTER**, (Formerly Veterans Affairs Medical Center), 800 Irving Avenue, Zip 13210–2716; tel. 315/425–4400, (Total facility includes 50 beds in nursing home–type unit) **A**1 3 5 7 8 **F**2 3 5 8 18 20 22 29 30 31 33 35 36 38 39 40 45 46 49 51 53 54 56 57 58 59 60 61 63 64 70 74 75 77 78 79 80 81 82 84 85 86 87 90 91 93 94 97 98 100 101 102 104 107 108 111 115 119 128 129 130 132 135 143 146 147 148 **P**6 **S** Department of Veterans Affairs, Washington, DC
Primary Contact: James Cody, Director
CFO: Elisabeth Kittell, Chief Financial Officer
CMO: William Marx, M.D., Chief of Staff
CIO: James Nichols, Chief Information Officer
CHR: Mark Antinelli, Manager Human Resources
Web address: www.syracuse.va.gov/
**Control:** Veterans Affairs, Government, federal **Service:** General Medical and Surgical

**Staffed Beds:** 235 **Admissions:** 4797 **Census:** 86 **Outpatient Visits:** 486854 **Births:** 0 **Total Expense ($000):** 277640 **Payroll Expense ($000):** 149428 **Personnel:** 1467

★ ◇ **UPSTATE UNIVERSITY HOSPITAL (330241)**, 750 East Adams Street, Zip 13210–2342; tel. 315/464–5540, (Includes GOLISANO CHILDREN'S HOSPITAL, 750 East Adams Street, tel. 315/464–4570; UPSTATE UNIVERSITY HOSPITAL AT COMMUNITY GENERAL, 4900 Broad Road, Zip 13215–2293; tel. 315/492–5011; Thomas P. Quinn, President and Chief Executive Officer) **A**2 8 9 10 21 **F**3 8 9 12 13 15 16 17 18 19 20 21 22 23 24 25 26 27 28 29 30 31 32 34 35 36 37 38 39 40 41 43 44 45 46 47 48 49 50 51 52 54 55 56 57 58 59 60 61 64 68 70 74 75 76 78 79 81 82 84 85 86 87 88 89 90 92 93 95 96 97 98 99 100 101 102 104 107 108 110 114 115 118 119 120 121 123 124 126 129 130 131 132 134 135 136 138 141 142 145 146 147 148
Primary Contact: John B. McCabe, M.D., Chief Executive Officer
COO: Paul E. Seale, FACHE, Chief Operating Officer
CFO: Stuart M. Wright, CPA, Chief Financial Officer
CMO: David Duggan, M.D., Medical Director
CIO: Terry Wagner, Chief Information Officer
CHR: Eric Frost, Associate Vice President Human Resources
CNO: Katharine Mooney, R.N., Chief Nursing Officer
Web address: www.upstate.edu/hospital
**Control:** State–Government, nonfederal **Service:** General Medical and Surgical

**Staffed Beds:** 554 **Admissions:** 28319 **Census:** 483 **Outpatient Visits:** 622431 **Births:** 917 **Total Expense ($000):** 749040 **Payroll Expense ($000):** 303926 **Personnel:** 4602

**VETERANS AFFAIRS MEDICAL CENTER** See Syracuse Veterans Affairs Medical Center

**TICONDEROGA—Essex County**

★ **MOSES LUDINGTON HOSPITAL (331306)**, 1019 Wicker Street, Zip 12883–1097; tel. 518/585–2831 **A**9 10 18 **F**11 15 28 35 39 40 57 63 64 68 78 79 81 93 107 110 114 119 130 131 132 133 143 146
Primary Contact: William E. Holmes, Chief Executive Officer
CMO: Cornelia Sue Freyhofer, M.D., Medical Director
CIO: Lisa Busby, Manager Information Systems
CHR: Tamara Evens, Director Human Resources
Web address: www.mosesludington.com
**Control:** Other not–for–profit (including NFP Corporation) **Service:** General Medical and Surgical

**Staffed Beds:** 15 **Admissions:** 236 **Census:** 3 **Outpatient Visits:** 24119 **Births:** 0 **Total Expense ($000):** 12085 **Payroll Expense ($000):** 5512 **Personnel:** 125

**NY**

---

**TROY—Rensselaer County**

★ **SAMARITAN HOSPITAL (330180)**, 2215 Burdett Avenue, Zip 12180–2475; tel. 518/271–3300, (Nonreporting) **A**5 9 10 **S** Catholic Health East, Newtown Square, PA
Primary Contact: Norman E. Dascher, Jr., Chief Executive Officer
CFO: Daniel A. Kochie, CPA, Chief Financial Officer
CMO: Daniel C. Silverman, M.D., Chief Medical Officer, Acute Care Troy
CIO: Karen LeBlanc, Director, Applications
CHR: Barbara McCandless, Corporate Vice President Human Resources
CNO: Jacqueline Priore, Chief Nursing Officer
Web address: www.nehealth.com
**Control:** Other not–for–profit (including NFP Corporation) **Service:** General Medical and Surgical

**Staffed Beds:** 134

⊞ **ST. MARY'S HOSPITAL (330232)**, 1300 Massachusetts Avenue, Zip 12180–1695; tel. 518/268–5000, (Includes SETON HEALTH SYSTEM–ST. MARY'S HOSPITAL, 1300 Massachusetts Avenue, Zip 12180; tel. 518/272–5000), (Total facility includes 130 beds in nursing home–type unit) **A**1 9 10 **F**3 4 8 11 12 15 17 18 28 29 30 31 34 35 40 42 45 46 49 50 51 54 55 56 57 58 59 60 61 63 64 65 66 68 74 75 77 78 79 81 82 83 84 85 86 87 93 97 107 108 110 111 114 115 119 128 129 130 131 132 133 135 142 144 145 146 147 148 **S** Catholic Health East, Newtown Square, PA
Primary Contact: Norman E. Dascher, Jr., Executive Vice President
CFO: Scott St George, Senior Vice President and Chief Financial Officer
CMO: Richard Rubin, M.D., Chief Medical Officer
CHR: Kathleen Occhiogrosso, Vice President Human Resources
Web address: www.setonhealth.org
**Control:** Church–operated, Nongovernment, not–for profit **Service:** General Medical and Surgical

**Staffed Beds:** 173 **Admissions:** 5373 **Census:** 84 **Outpatient Visits:** 431370 **Births:** 0 **Total Expense ($000):** 120747 **Payroll Expense ($000):** 61315 **Personnel:** 1117

**UTICA—Oneida County**

★ △ ◇ **FAXTON–ST. LUKE'S HEALTHCARE (330044)**, 1656 Champlin Avenue, Zip 13502–4830, Mailing Address: P.O. Box 479, Zip 13503–0479; tel. 315/624–6000, (Includes FAXTON CAMPUS, 1676 Sunset Avenue, Zip 13502–5475; tel. 315/624–6200; ST. LUKE'S CAMPUS, Zip 13413; tel. 315/624–6000) **A**2 7 9 10 21 **F**3 12 13 15 17 18 20 22 28 29 30 31 32 34 35 39 40 44 45 49 50 53 57 59 60 64 65 67 68 70 73 75 76 77 78 79 81 82 84 89 90 91 92 93 96 97 98 102 107 108 110 111 114 116 117 118 119 120 121 123 124 130 132 135 144 146 147
Primary Contact: Scott H. Perra, President and Chief Executive Officer
COO: Steven J. Brown, Senior Vice President and Chief Operating Officer
CFO: Michael Haile, Senior Vice President and Chief Financial Officer
CMO: Daniel Kopp, M.D., Senior Vice President and Chief Medical Officer
CIO: Kevin Mahoney, Vice President and Chief Information Officer
CHR: Tony Scibelli, Vice President Human Resources and Operations
Web address: www.mvnhealth.com
**Control:** Other not–for–profit (including NFP Corporation) **Service:** General Medical and Surgical

**Staffed Beds:** 319 **Admissions:** 15877 **Census:** 219 **Outpatient Visits:** 478488 **Births:** 2102 **Total Expense ($000):** 288152 **Payroll Expense ($000):** 124431 **Personnel:** 2285

☐ **MOHAWK VALLEY PSYCHIATRIC CENTER (334021)**, 1400 Noyes Street, Zip 13502–3854; tel. 315/738–3800, (Nonreporting) **A**1 10 **S** New York State Office of Mental Health, Albany, NY
Primary Contact: Colleen A. Sawyer, R.N., MSN, Executive Director
Web address: www.omh.ny.gov/omhweb/facilities/mvpc/facility.htm
**Control:** State–Government, nonfederal **Service:** Psychiatric

**Staffed Beds:** 614

★ ◇ **ST. ELIZABETH MEDICAL CENTER (330245)**, 2209 Genesee Street, Zip 13501–5999; tel. 315/798–8100 **A**9 10 12 13 21 **F**3 8 11 15 16 17 18 20 22 24 26 29 30 32 34 36 37 38 40 41 43 47 49 50 54 57 58 59 61 62 64 65 66 68 70 74 75 77 78 79 80 81 85 86 87 89 90 92 93 97 98 100 102 103 107 108 110 114 115 118 119 127 129 130 131 132 146 147 148 **P**6 **S** Sisters of Saint Francis, Syracuse, NY
Primary Contact: Richard H. Ketcham, FACHE, President and Chief Executive Officer
COO: Robert Scholefield, Chief Operating Officer
CFO: Louis Aiello, Chief Financial Officer
CMO: Albert D'Accurzio, M.D., Medical Director
CIO: Robert Gillette, Chief Information Officer
CHR: Patrick Buckley, Vice President Human Resources
CNO: Varinya Sheppard, R.N., Chief Nursing Officer
Web address: www.stemc.org
**Control:** Church–operated, Nongovernment, not–for profit **Service:** General Medical and Surgical

**Staffed Beds:** 181 **Admissions:** 11660 **Census:** 163 **Outpatient Visits:** 473125 **Births:** 0 **Total Expense ($000):** 199913 **Payroll Expense ($000):** 97003 **Personnel:** 1762

**ST. LUKE'S CAMPUS** See Faxton–St. Luke's Healthcare

## VALHALLA—Westchester County

**⊠ BLYTHEDALE CHILDREN'S HOSPITAL (333301)**, 95 Bradhurst Avenue, Zip 10595–1697; tel. 914/592–7555, (Nonreporting) **A**1 9 10
Primary Contact: Larry L. Levine, President and Chief Executive Officer
COO: Maureen Desimone, Chief Operating Officer
CFO: John Canning, Chief Financial Officer
CMO: Joelle Mast, Ph.D., Chief Medical Officer
CHR: Ronald Gallo, Director Human Resources
Web address: www.blythedale.org
**Control:** Other not–for–profit (including NFP Corporation) **Service:** Children's rehabilitation

**Staffed Beds: 92**

**☐ WESTCHESTER MEDICAL CENTER (330234)**, 100 Woods Road, Zip 10595–1530; tel. 914/493–7000, (Includes MARIA FARERI CHILDREN'S HOSPITAL, 95 Grasslands Road, Zip 10595–1652; tel. 866/962–7337) **A**1 2 3 5 8 9 10 **F**3 8 12 13 14 15 16 17 18 19 20 21 22 23 24 25 26 27 28 29 30 31 32 34 35 36 37 38 39 40 41 43 44 45 46 47 48 49 50 52 54 55 56 57 58 59 60 61 64 65 66 68 70 71 72 73 74 75 76 77 78 79 81 82 84 85 86 87 88 89 90 91 92 94 97 98 99 100 101 102 103 104 107 108 110 111 114 115 116 117 118 119 120 121 123 124 126 129 130 131 132 134 135 136 137 138 139 141 142 145 146 147 148 **P**6
Primary Contact: Michael D. Israel, President and Chief Executive Officer
COO: Gary F. Brudnicki, Senior Executive Vice President, Chief Operating Officer and Chief Financial Officer
CFO: Gary F. Brudnicki, Senior Executive Vice President, Chief Operating Officer and Chief Financial Officer
CMO: Renee Garrick, M.D., Chief Medical Officer
CIO: John Moustakakis, Senior Vice President Information Systems and Chief Information Officer
Web address: www.worldclassmedicine.com
**Control:** Hospital district or authority, Government, nonfederal **Service:** General Medical and Surgical

**Staffed Beds: 652 Admissions: 21034 Census: 502 Outpatient Visits:** 140062 **Births:** 821 **Total Expense ($000):** 841193 **Payroll Expense ($000):** 286394 **Personnel:** 2571

## VALLEY STREAM—Nassau County

**⊠ FRANKLIN HOSPITAL (330372)**, 900 Franklin Avenue, Zip 11580–2190; tel. 516/256–6000, (Total facility includes 120 beds in nursing home–type unit) **A**1 2 9 10 **F**2 3 11 12 17 18 26 29 30 31 34 35 40 42 43 45 49 50 56 57 58 59 60 62 63 64 65 68 70 74 75 77 78 79 81 82 83 84 85 86 87 92 94 97 98 100 102 103 107 108 111 114 118 119 128 130 132 135 143 146 148 **P**5 6 **S** North Shore–Long Island Jewish Health System, Great Neck, NY
Primary Contact: Catherine Hottendorf, R.N., MS, Executive Director
COO: Mark J. Solazzo, Executive Vice President and Chief Operating Officer
CFO: Elizabeth Zubko, Associate Executive Director Finance
CMO: Anthony J. Shallash, M.D., Interim Medical Director
CIO: John Bosco, Chief Information Officer
CHR: Karina Norr–McPhillips, Associate Executive Director Human Resources
CNO: Barbara Popkin, R.N., Associate Executive Director Patient Care Services
Web address: www.northshorelij.com
**Control:** Other not–for–profit (including NFP Corporation) **Service:** General Medical and Surgical

**Staffed Beds: 330 Admissions: 12191 Census: 285 Outpatient Visits:** 71442 **Births:** 0 **Total Expense ($000):** 189443 **Payroll Expense ($000):** 92014 **Personnel:** 1219

## WALTON—Delaware County

**DELAWARE VALLEY HOSPITAL (331312)**, 1 Titus Place, Zip 13856–1498; tel. 607/865–2100 **A**9 10 18 **F**3 4 5 15 18 28 29 34 35 36 40 45 50 57 59 64 75 77 81 85 87 89 93 97 107 114 119 130 133 146 **S** United Health Services, Binghamton, NY
Primary Contact: Dru Cavanagh, R.N., President and Chief Executive Officer
CFO: Paul Summers, Chief Financial Officer
CMO: Michael F. Trevisani, M.D., Executive Vice President and Chief Medical Officer
CIO: James Armstrong, Manager Information Technology
CHR: Dru Cavanagh, R.N., President and Chief Executive Officer
CNO: Victoria Conkling, Vice President Chief Nursing Officer
Web address: www.uhs.net
**Control:** Other not–for–profit (including NFP Corporation) **Service:** General Medical and Surgical

**Staffed Beds: 25 Admissions: 647 Census: 11 Outpatient Visits:** 93610 **Births:** 0 **Total Expense ($000):** 15156 **Payroll Expense ($000):** 7966 **Personnel:** 159

## WARSAW—Wyoming County

**☐ WYOMING COUNTY COMMUNITY HOSPITAL (330008)**, 400 North Main Street, Zip 14569–1025; tel. 585/786–8940, (Nonreporting) **A**1 9 10 20
Primary Contact: Donald T. Eichenauer, Chief Executive Officer
COO: Lori Roche, Chief Operating Officer
CFO: Paula Parker, Chief Financial Officer
CMO: Scott Treutlein, M.D., Medical Director
CIO: Jane Beechler, Director Healthcare Information Systems
CHR: Denise M. Morley, Director Human Resources
CNO: Dawn James, Director of Nursing
Web address: www.wcchs.net
**Control:** County–Government, nonfederal **Service:** General Medical and Surgical

**Staffed Beds: 75**

## WARWICK—Orange County

**⊠ ST. ANTHONY COMMUNITY HOSPITAL (330205)**, 15 Maple Avenue, Zip 10990–1028; tel. 845/986–2276, (Nonreporting) **A**1 9 10 **S** Bon Secours Health System, Inc., Marriottsville, MD
Primary Contact: Jeff Reilly, Senior Vice President Operations
Web address: www.stanthonycommunityhosp.org
**Control:** Church–operated, Nongovernment, not–for profit **Service:** General Medical and Surgical

**Staffed Beds: 73**

## WATERTOWN—Jefferson County

**⊠ SAMARITAN MEDICAL CENTER (330157)**, 830 Washington Street, Zip 13601–4034; tel. 315/785–4000 **A**1 9 10 12 13 20 **F**3 5 8 13 15 18 20 29 30 31 35 40 49 51 57 60 64 68 70 73 74 75 76 77 78 79 81 82 87 89 90 93 97 98 99 100 102 103 104 107 108 111 114 116 119 120 121 127 129 130 135 146 147 148 **P**6
Primary Contact: Thomas H. Carman, President and Chief Executive Officer
CFO: Paul Kraeger, Vice President Finance and Chief Financial Officer
CMO: Spencer P. Falcon, M.D., Vice President Medical Affairs
CIO: M. Andrew Short, Vice President Information Services
CHR: Thomas Shatraw, Director Human Resources
Web address: www.samaritanhealth.com
**Control:** Other not–for–profit (including NFP Corporation) **Service:** General Medical and Surgical

**Staffed Beds: 208 Admissions: 9034 Census: 138 Outpatient Visits:** 243427 **Births:** 1752 **Total Expense ($000):** 179823 **Payroll Expense ($000):** 82345 **Personnel:** 1370

## WELLSVILLE—Allegany County

**⊠ JONES MEMORIAL HOSPITAL (330096)**, 191 North Main Street, Zip 14895–1150, Mailing Address: P.O. Box 72, Zip 14895–0072; tel. 585/593–1100 **A**1 9 10 20 **F**3 8 11 13 15 17 28 29 30 31 34 35 36 40 43 57 59 61 64 68 70 75 76 77 78 79 81 82 85 89 93 97 107 110 114 119 129 131 132 133 146 147
Primary Contact: Eva Benedict, President and Chief Executive Officer
CFO: Tracy Gates, Chief Financial Officer
CMO: Frank Edwards, M.D., Medical Director
CIO: Tracy Gates, Chief Financial Officer
CHR: Brenda Sobeck, Director of Human Resources
CNO: Donna Bliven, Vice President Patient Care Services and Chief Nursing Officer
Web address: www.jmhny.org
**Control:** Other not–for–profit (including NFP Corporation) **Service:** General Medical and Surgical

**Staffed Beds: 33 Admissions: 1726 Census: 17 Outpatient Visits:** 98900 **Births:** 271 **Total Expense ($000):** 33662 **Payroll Expense ($000):** 16230 **Personnel:** 327

## WEST HAVERSTRAW—Rockland County

**☐ △ HELEN HAYES HOSPITAL (330405)**, Route 9W, Zip 10993–1127; tel. 845/786–4000, (Nonreporting) **A**1 5 7 10
Primary Contact: Val S. Gray, Chief Executive Officer
COO: Edmund Zybert, Chief Operating Officer
CFO: Richard Buhowski, Chief Financial Officer
CMO: John T. Pellicone, M.D., Medical Director
CIO: Virgil Ennis, Chief Information Officer
CHR: Kathleen Martucci, Director Human Resources
Web address: www.helenhayeshospital.org
**Control:** State–Government, nonfederal **Service:** Rehabilitation

**Staffed Beds: 155**

**NY**

---

**Hospital, Medicare Provider Number, Address, Telephone, Approval, Facility, and Physician Codes, Health Care System**

★ American Hospital Association (AHA) membership
☐ The Joint Commission accreditation
◇ DNV Healthcare Inc. accreditation
○ Healthcare Facilities Accreditation Program
△ Commission on Accreditation of Rehabilitation Facilities (CARF) accreditation

## WEST ISLIP—Suffolk County

⊞ **GOOD SAMARITAN HOSPITAL MEDICAL CENTER (330286)**, 1000 Montauk Highway, Zip 11795–4927; tel. 631/376–3000, (Total facility includes 100 beds in nursing home–type unit) **A**1 2 9 10 12 13 **F**3 8 11 12 13 15 17 18 19 20 22 26 28 29 30 31 32 34 35 40 41 43 44 45 49 50 54 55 56 57 58 59 60 61 62 64 66 68 70 72 73 74 75 76 77 78 79 81 82 83 84 85 87 88 89 91 93 94 97 100 107 108 110 111 114 115 116 117 118 119 120 121 123 124 126 128 129 130 132 135 141 146 147 **P**6 8 **S** Catholic Health Services of Long Island, Rockville Centre, NY
Primary Contact: Nancy B. Simmons, Executive Vice President and Chief Administrative Officer
CFO: Dan Macksood, Regional Senior Vice President and Chief Financial Officer
CMO: Jerome Weiner, M.D., Senior Vice President Medical Affairs
CIO: Marcy Dunn, Vice President Information Services and Chief Information Officer
CHR: Lori Spina, Vice President Human Resources
CNO: Jeanne Dzurenko, R.N., Chief Nursing Officer and Senior Vice President Patient Care
Web address: www.good–samaritan–hospital.org
**Control:** Church–operated, Nongovernment, not–for profit **Service:** General Medical and Surgical

**Staffed Beds:** 447 **Admissions:** 25584 **Census:** 450 **Outpatient Visits:** 387093 **Births:** 2820 **Total Expense ($000):** 564442 **Payroll Expense ($000):** 275079 **Personnel:** 3130

## WEST POINT—Orange County

⊞ **KELLER ARMY COMMUNITY HOSPITAL**, 900 Washington Road, Zip 10996–1197, Mailing Address: U.S. Military Academy, Building 900, Zip 10996–1197; tel. 845/938–5169, (Nonreporting) **A**1 3 5 **S** Department of the Army, Office of the Surgeon General, Falls Church, VA
Primary Contact: Colonel Felicia Pehrson, M.D., Commanding Officer
COO: Lieutenant Colonel Thomas Bell, Deputy Commander Administration
CFO: Russell DeVries, Chief Business Operations
CMO: Lieutenant Colonel Michael Doyle, M.D., Deputy Commander Clinical Services
CIO: Patrick McGuinness, Chief Information Management
CHR: Margaret Greco, Chief Human Resources
Web address: www.kach.amedd.army.mil/
**Control:** Army, Government, federal **Service:** General Medical and Surgical

**Staffed Beds:** 31

## WEST SENECA—Erie County

☐ **WESTERN NEW YORK CHILDREN'S PSYCHIATRIC CENTER**, 1010 East and West Road, Zip 14224–3602; tel. 716/677–7000, (Nonreporting) **A**1 3 5 **S** New York State Office of Mental Health, Albany, NY
Primary Contact: Kathe Hayes, Executive Director
COO: David Privett, Deputy Director
CMO: Patrick Stein, M.D., Clinical Director
CIO: Dan Hrubiak, Associate Computer Program Analyst
CHR: Charles Siewert, Director Human Resources
Web address: www.omh.ny.gov
**Control:** State–Government, nonfederal **Service:** Children's hospital psychiatric

**Staffed Beds:** 46

## WESTFIELD—Chautauqua County

★ **WESTFIELD MEMORIAL HOSPITAL (330166)**, 189 East Main Street, Zip 14787–1195; tel. 716/326–4921, (Nonreporting) **A**9 10 **S** Saint Vincent Health System, Erie, PA
Primary Contact: Scott Whalen, Ph.D., FACHE, President and Chief Executive Officer
COO: Karen Surkala, Vice President
CFO: Henry J. Ward, Vice President and Chief Financial Officer
CMO: Russell Elwell, M.D., Medical Director
CIO: Cindy Harper, Director Information Systems
Web address: www.wmhinc.org
**Control:** Other not–for–profit (including NFP Corporation) **Service:** General Medical and Surgical

**Staffed Beds:** 4

## WHITE PLAINS—Westchester County

⊞ △ **BURKE REHABILITATION HOSPITAL (330404)**, 785 Mamaroneck Avenue, Zip 10605–2523; tel. 914/597–2500, (Nonreporting) **A**1 3 5 7 10
Primary Contact: Mary Beth Walsh, M.D., Chief Executive Officer
COO: Brian M. Swift, Senior Administrator Plant Operations
CFO: John Stewart, Director Finance
CMO: Mary Beth Walsh, M.D., Chief Executive Officer
CIO: Cathy Dwyer, Senior Administrator Information Systems
CHR: Annette Bucci, Senior Administrator Human Resources
CNO: Marie Spencer, Chief Nursing Officer and Senior Administrator
Web address: www.burke.org
**Control:** Other not–for–profit (including NFP Corporation) **Service:** Rehabilitation

**Staffed Beds:** 150

**NEW YORK–PRESBYTERIAN HOSPITAL, WESTCHESTER DIVISION** See New York–Presbyterian Hospital, New York

⊞ **WHITE PLAINS HOSPITAL CENTER (330304)**, 41 East Post Road, Zip 10601–4699; tel. 914/681–0600, (Nonreporting) **A**1 2 5 9 10
Primary Contact: Jon B. Schandler, Chief Executive Officer
COO: Edward F. Leonard, Executive Vice President and Chief Operating Officer
CFO: John Sciurba, Vice President and Chief Financial Officer
CMO: Michael Palumbo, M.D., Executive Vice President and Medical Director
CHR: John Sanchez, Vice President Human Resources
Web address: www.wphospital.org
**Control:** Other not–for–profit (including NFP Corporation) **Service:** General Medical and Surgical

**Staffed Beds:** 292

## WILLIAMSVILLE—Erie County

**MILLARD FILLMORE SUBURBAN HOSPITAL** See KALEIDA Health, Buffalo

## YONKERS—Westchester County

**ANDRUS PAVILION** See St. John's Riverside Hospital

☐ **ST. JOHN'S RIVERSIDE HOSPITAL (330208)**, 967 North Broadway, Zip 10701–1399; tel. 914/964–4444, (Includes ANDRUS PAVILION, 967 North Broadway, tel. 914/964–4444; PARKCARE PAVILION, Two Park Avenue, Zip 10703–3497; tel. 914/964–7300; ST. JOHN'S RIVERSIDE HOSPITAL – DOBBS FERRY PAVILION, 128 Ashford Avenue, Dobbs Ferry, Zip 10522–1896; tel. 914/693–0700), (Total facility includes 120 beds in nursing home–type unit) **A**1 2 9 10 **F**3 4 5 8 11 12 13 15 17 18 29 30 31 34 37 40 45 49 50 57 59 60 61 73 76 77 78 79 81 82 83 84 92 93 107 108 110 111 114 115 119 124 126 128 129 130 143 146 147 148 **P**6
Primary Contact: Ronald Corti, President and Chief Executive Officer
COO: Lynn M. Nelson, R.N., Chief Operating Officer
CFO: Dennis M. Keane, Vice President Finance and Chief Financial Officer
CMO: Paul Antonecchia, M.D., Vice President Medical Affairs
CIO: Peter Weidner, Director Management Information Systems
CHR: Pam La France, Vice President Human Resources
Web address: www.riversidehealth.org
**Control:** Other not–for–profit (including NFP Corporation) **Service:** General Medical and Surgical

**Staffed Beds:** 368 **Admissions:** 19451 **Census:** 288 **Outpatient Visits:** 218837 **Births:** 1440 **Total Expense ($000):** 236627 **Payroll Expense ($000):** 110062 **Personnel:** 2002

⊞ **ST. JOSEPH'S MEDICAL CENTER (330006)**, 127 South Broadway, Zip 10701–4006; tel. 914/378–7000, (Total facility includes 200 beds in nursing home–type unit) **A**1 3 5 9 10 **F**2 3 5 8 11 15 18 29 30 31 32 34 35 39 40 45 46 48 49 54 56 57 58 59 60 61 62 64 65 66 68 70 74 75 77 78 79 80 81 82 84 85 87 89 93 94 97 98 99 100 101 102 103 104 106 107 108 110 111 114 115 118 119 120 121 122 123 125 128 130 131 132 143 145 146 **P**1
Primary Contact: Michael J. Spicer, President and Chief Executive Officer
CFO: James J. Curcuruto, Senior Vice President Finance
CMO: Nicholas De Robertis, M.D., Medical Director
CIO: Deborah Di Bernardo, Chief Information Officer
CHR: Dean Civitello, Vice President Human Resources, Public Relations and Development
CNO: Jeffry E. Foltz, R.N., Vice President for Nursing
Web address: www.saintjosephs.org
**Control:** Other not–for–profit (including NFP Corporation) **Service:** General Medical and Surgical

**Staffed Beds:** 532 **Admissions:** 9226 **Census:** 441 **Outpatient Visits:** 1382035 **Total Expense ($000):** 235612 **Payroll Expense ($000):** 111436 **Personnel:** 1572

*Many Facility Codes have changed. Please refer to the AHA Guide Code Chart.* © 2013 AHA Guide

# NORTH CAROLINA

## AHOSKIE—Hertford County

**VIDANT ROANOKE–CHOWAN HOSPITAL (340099)**, 500 South Academy Street, Zip 27910–3261, Mailing Address: P.O. Box 1385, Zip 27910–1385; tel. 252/209–3000 **A**1 9 10 **F**3 11 13 15 28 29 30 31 34 35 40 43 45 53 56 57 59 64 68 70 75 76 77 78 79 81 82 85 86 87 89 92 93 98 100 101 102 103 107 108 110 111 114 119 129 130 132 146 148 **S** Vidant Health, Greenville, NC
Primary Contact: Susan S. Lassiter, FACHE, President and Chief Executive Officer
CFO: Jon Graham, Chief Financial Officer
CMO: Luis Rodriguez, M.D., Chief of Staff
CHR: Debbie Sisler, Director Human Resources
CNO: Susan Mitchell, Vice President Patient Care Services
Web address: www.vidanthealth.com
**Control:** Other not–for–profit (including NFP Corporation) **Service:** General Medical and Surgical

**Staffed Beds:** 103 **Admissions:** 4729 **Census:** 56 **Outpatient Visits:** 72652 **Births:** 331 **Total Expense ($000):** 78353 **Payroll Expense ($000):** 26583 **Personnel:** 573

## ALBEMARLE—Stanly County

**STANLY REGIONAL MEDICAL CENTER (340119)**, 301 Yadkin Street, Zip 28001–3441, Mailing Address: P.O. Box 1489, Zip 28002–1489; tel. 704/984–4000 **A**1 9 10 **F**3 11 12 13 15 17 20 28 29 30 31 34 35 39 40 45 49 57 59 60 61 62 63 64 68 70 74 75 76 77 78 79 81 82 85 86 89 90 91 93 98 100 101 102 103 107 108 110 111 114 115 119 123 129 130 131 132 146 148 **S** Carolinas HealthCare System, Charlotte, NC
Primary Contact: Alfred P. Taylor, President
COO: Brian Freeman, Vice President of Operations
CFO: Nick Samilo, Vice President Fiscal Services and Chief Financial Officer
CMO: Michael Bohnsack, M.D., Chief of Staff
CIO: Brian Freeman, Vice President of Operations
CHR: Paul Morlock, Vice President Human Resources
CNO: Judy Doran, R.N., Vice President of Hospital Services and Chief Nurse Executive
Web address: www.stanly.org
**Control:** Other not–for–profit (including NFP Corporation) **Service:** General Medical and Surgical

**Staffed Beds:** 104 **Admissions:** 5177 **Census:** 52 **Outpatient Visits:** 83474 **Births:** 617 **Total Expense ($000):** 96683 **Payroll Expense ($000):** 36107 **Personnel:** 868

## ASHEBORO—Randolph County

**RANDOLPH HOSPITAL (340123)**, 364 White Oak Street, Zip 27203–5400, Mailing Address: P.O. Box 1048, Zip 27204–1048; tel. 336/625–5151 **A**1 2 9 10 **F**3 13 15 20 28 29 30 31 34 35 39 40 44 45 48 49 50 57 58 59 61 62 64 65 68 70 71 74 75 76 77 78 79 80 81 84 85 86 87 89 91 92 93 94 95 97 107 109 110 111 114 115 118 119 120 121 123 129 130 131 132 135 146 148 **P**6
Primary Contact: Steven E. Eblin, Chief Executive Officer / President
CMO: Robert Dough, M.D., Chief of Staff
CIO: Angela Burgess, Chief Information Officer
Web address: www.randolphhospital.org
**Control:** Other not–for–profit (including NFP Corporation) **Service:** General Medical and Surgical

**Staffed Beds:** 122 **Admissions:** 5902 **Census:** 61 **Outpatient Visits:** 144646 **Births:** 820 **Total Expense ($000):** 98914 **Payroll Expense ($000):** 42006 **Personnel:** 884

## ASHEVILLE—Buncombe County

★ **ASHEVILLE SPECIALTY HOSPITAL (342017)**, 428 Biltmore Avenue, 4th Floor, Zip 28801–4502; tel. 828/213–5400 **A**10 **F**1 3 29 30 36 77 85 91 148 **S** Mission Health System, Asheville, NC
Primary Contact: Robert C. Desotelle, President and Chief Executive Officer
COO: Michelle Stillman, Director of Care Management
CFO: Gregg Dixon, CPA, Chief Financial Officer
CMO: Joseph Aiello, M.D., Chief of Staff
CIO: Dorothy L. Porter, Director of Compliance/Risk/Quality
CHR: Jennifer Calloway, Human Resources Coordinator
CNO: Wanda Miller, R.N., Director of Clinical Services
Web address: www.missionhospitals.org/acute–care
**Control:** Partnership, Investor–owned, for–profit **Service:** Long–Term Acute Care hospital

**Staffed Beds:** 31 **Admissions:** 363 **Census:** 25 **Outpatient Visits:** 0 **Births:** 0 **Total Expense ($000):** 13172 **Payroll Expense ($000):** 5876 **Personnel:** 116

△ ◇ **CAREPARTNERS HEALTH SERVICES (343025)**, 68 Sweeten Creek Road, Zip 28803–2318, Mailing Address: P.O. Box 15025, Zip 28813–0025; tel. 828/277–4800 **A**1 7 9 10 21 **F**2 29 30 34 36 44 50 56 57 59 62 63 64 68 77 79 82 84 87 90 93 94 120 130 131 132 143 146 148
Primary Contact: Tracy Buchanan, Chief Executive Officer / President
COO: Gary Bowers, Chief Operating Officer
CFO: Diann Bolick, Chief Financial Officer
CIO: Drake Thomas, Chief Information Officer
CHR: Karen Vernon–Young, Vice President Human Resources and Communications
Web address: www.carepartners.org
**Control:** Other not–for–profit (including NFP Corporation) **Service:** Rehabilitation

**Staffed Beds:** 80 **Admissions:** 1299 **Census:** 47 **Outpatient Visits:** 42438 **Births:** 0 **Total Expense ($000):** 19546 **Payroll Expense ($000):** 12602 **Personnel:** 153

**CHARLES GEORGE VETERANS AFFAIRS MEDICAL CENTER**, 1100 Tunnel Road, Zip 28805–2087; tel. 828/298–7911, (Total facility includes 85 beds in nursing home–type unit) **A**1 3 5 **F**3 4 5 12 18 20 22 24 26 28 29 30 31 34 35 36 38 39 40 42 45 49 50 56 57 58 59 61 62 63 64 65 68 70 71 74 75 77 78 79 81 82 83 84 85 86 87 91 92 93 94 97 98 100 101 102 103 104 107 108 111 114 115 119 127 128 130 132 135 145 146 147 148 **P**1 **S** Department of Veterans Affairs, Washington, DC
Primary Contact: Cynthia Breyfogle, Director
CMO: MaryAnn Curl, M.D., Interim Chief of Staff
CIO: Carla McLendon, Director Information Resource Management Services
CHR: Melissa Bragg, Chief Human Resources Management
Web address: www.asheville.va.gov/
**Control:** Veterans Affairs, Government, federal **Service:** General Medical and Surgical

**Staffed Beds:** 257 **Admissions:** 5255 **Census:** 101 **Outpatient Visits:** 395978 **Births:** 0 **Total Expense ($000):** 205653 **Payroll Expense ($000):** 110985 **Personnel:** 1652

**MISSION HOSPITAL (340002)**, 509 Biltmore Avenue, Zip 28801–4690; tel. 828/213–1111, (Includes MEMORIAL MISSION HOSPITAL, 509 Biltmore Avenue, tel. 828/255–4000; MISSION CHILDREN'S HOSPITAL, 509 Biltmore Avenue, Zip 28801–4601; tel. 828/213–1740; ST. JOSEPH'S HOSPITAL, 428 Biltmore Avenue, Zip 28801–9839; tel. 828/255–3100) **A**1 2 3 5 9 10 **F**3 7 8 11 12 13 15 17 18 19 20 22 24 26 28 29 30 31 32 34 35 36 37 39 40 43 44 45 46 47 48 49 50 51 53 54 55 56 57 58 59 60 61 64 65 68 70 71 72 73 74 75 76 77 78 79 80 81 82 84 85 86 87 88 89 91 92 93 95 96 97 98 99 100 101 102 103 104 105 107 108 110 111 114 115 116 117 118 119 120 121 123 124 126 129 130 131 132 134 135 142 143 146 147 148 **S** Mission Health System, Asheville, NC
Primary Contact: Ronald A. Paulus, M.D., President and Chief Executive Officer
COO: Brian W. Aston, Chief Operating Officer
CFO: Charles F. Ayscue, Senior Vice President Finance and Chief Financial Officer
CMO: William Hathaway, M.D., Chief Medical Officer
CIO: D. Arlo Jennings, Ph.D., Chief Information Officer
CHR: Maria Roloff, Vice President Human Resources
Web address: www.missionhospitals.org
**Control:** Other not–for–profit (including NFP Corporation) **Service:** General Medical and Surgical

**Staffed Beds:** 744 **Admissions:** 38131 **Census:** 534 **Outpatient Visits:** 458764 **Births:** 3780 **Total Expense ($000):** 823206 **Payroll Expense ($000):** 376972 **Personnel:** 6201

---

**Hospital, Medicare Provider Number, Address, Telephone, Approval, Facility, and Physician Codes, Health Care System**

★ American Hospital Association (AHA) membership
□ The Joint Commission accreditation
◇ DNV Healthcare Inc. accreditation
○ Healthcare Facilities Accreditation Program
△ Commission on Accreditation of Rehabilitation Facilities (CARF) accreditation

NC

**BELHAVEN—Beaufort County**

★ **VIDANT PUNGO HOSPITAL (341310)**, 202 East Water Street,
Zip 27810–1450; tel. 252/943–2111, (Nonreporting) **A**9 10 18 **S** Vidant Health,
Greenville, NC
Primary Contact: Harvey Case, President
CFO: Gerald Hardison, Director Finance
CMO: Gregory Jones, M.D., Chief of Staff
CIO: Jenny Brown, Director Human Resources and Public Relations
CHR: Jenny Brown, Director Human Resources and Public Relations
Web address: www.vidanthealth.com/vidant/dynamic-detail.aspx?id=11781
**Control:** Other not–for–profit (including NFP Corporation) **Service:** General
Medical and Surgical

Staffed Beds: 35

**BLACK MOUNTAIN—Buncombe County**

**JULIAN F. KEITH ALCOHOL AND DRUG ABUSE TREATMENT CENTER
(344023)**, 201 Tabernacle Road, Zip 28711–2599; tel. 828/669–3400 **A**10 **F**4
29 40 61 68 75 82 86 97 98 100 130 132 135
Primary Contact: W. Douglas Baker, Director
CFO: Jackie Maurer, Fiscal Officer
CMO: Anthony Burnett, M.D., Medical Director
CHR: Faye Hamlin, Manager Human Resources
Web address: www.jfkadatc.net
**Control:** State–Government, nonfederal **Service:** Alcoholism and other chemical
dependency

Staffed Beds: 80 Admissions: 1490 Census: 85 Outpatient Visits: 0 Births:
0

**BLOWING ROCK—Watauga County**

✠ **BLOWING ROCK HOSPITAL (341321)**, 418 Chestnut Street, Zip 28605–0148,
Mailing Address: P.O. Box 148, Zip 28605–0148; tel. 828/295–3136, (Includes
DAVANT REHABILITATION AND EXTENDED CARE CENTER ), (Total facility includes
72 beds in nursing home–type unit) **A**1 9 10 18 **F**39 40 64 75 87 91 93 128
130 133 143 146 148 **S** Appalachian Regional Healthcare System, Boone, NC
Primary Contact: Timothy R. Ford, Chief Executive Officer / President
CFO: Kevin B. May, Chief Financial Officer
CMO: Charles Davant, III, M.D., Chief Medical Officer
CIO: Mike Quinto, Chief Information Officer
CHR: Roxane Greer, Coordinator Human Resources
CNO: Elizabeth Hayes, R.N., Director of Patient Services
Web address: www.https://apprhs.org/locations/blowing-rock-hospital
**Control:** Other not–for–profit (including NFP Corporation) **Service:** General
Medical and Surgical

Staffed Beds: 97 Admissions: 205 Census: 62 Outpatient Visits: 1480
Births: 0 Total Expense ($000): 9313 Payroll Expense ($000): 4161
Personnel: 98

**BOLIVIA—Brunswick County**

✠ **NOVANT HEALTH BRUNSWICK MEDICAL CENTER (340158)**, (Formerly
Brunswick Novant Medical Center), 240 Hospital Drive N.E., Zip 28422–8346;
tel. 910/721–1000 **A**1 9 10 **F**3 11 13 15 18 26 28 29 30 34 35 40 45 46 57
59 64 70 75 76 79 80 81 87 93 96 102 107 108 110 111 114 118 119 126
130 135 146 **S** Novant Health, Winston Salem, NC
Primary Contact: Shelbourn Stevens, President
CFO: Joan Thomas, Chief Financial Officer
CMO: Robert Hassler, M.D., Director Medical Affairs
CIO: Pamela Parrish, Director Information Systems
Web address: www.brunswicknovant.org
**Control:** Other not–for–profit (including NFP Corporation) **Service:** General
Medical and Surgical

Staffed Beds: 60 Admissions: 3847 Census: 37 Outpatient Visits: 117532
Births: 412 Total Expense ($000): 68335 Payroll Expense ($000): 19795
Personnel: 397

**BOONE—Watauga County**

✠ **WATAUGA MEDICAL CENTER (340051)**, 336 Deerfield Road,
Zip 28607–5008, Mailing Address: P.O. Box 2600, Zip 28607–2600;
tel. 828/262–4100 **A**1 2 9 10 **F**3 5 13 15 16 17 18 20 22 26 28 29 30 31 32
34 35 38 40 44 45 46 47 48 49 50 53 54 57 59 62 64 70 72 73 75 76 77
78 80 81 82 84 85 86 87 89 90 91 92 93 96 107 108 110 111 114 115 118
119 120 121 122 123 124 129 130 131 132 135 144 145 146 147 148 **P**6
8 **S** Appalachian Regional Healthcare System, Boone, NC
Primary Contact: Chuck Mantooth, President
CFO: Kevin B. May, Chief Financial Officer
CMO: Herman A. Godwin, Jr., M.D., Senior Vice President and Medical Director
CIO: Mike Quinto, Chief Information Officer
CHR: Amy Crabbe, Senior Vice President Human Resources
CNO: Claire P. Cline, M.P.H., Senior Vice President Patient Care Services/CNO
Web address: www.https://apprhs.org/locations/watauga-medical-center
**Control:** Other not–for–profit (including NFP Corporation) **Service:** General
Medical and Surgical

Staffed Beds: 99 Admissions: 4110 Census: 40 Outpatient Visits: 130370
Births: 516 Total Expense ($000): 104323 Payroll Expense ($000): 37341
Personnel: 676

**BREVARD—Transylvania County**

✠ **TRANSYLVANIA REGIONAL HOSPITAL (341319)**, 260 Hospital Drive,
Zip 28712–3378; tel. 828/884–9111, (Total facility includes 10 beds in nursing
home–type unit) **A**1 9 10 18 **F**2 3 11 13 15 28 29 30 31 34 35 36 40 45 49
53 56 57 59 62 63 64 65 70 76 77 78 79 80 81 85 97 107 110 111 114
119 128 130 131 132 133 146 **P**6 **S** Mission Health System, Asheville, NC
Primary Contact: Robert J. Bednarek, President and Chief Executive Officer
COO: Rebecca W. Carter, MSN, Vice President Patient Care and Chief Operating
Officer
CFO: Marc Nakagawa, Vice President and Chief Financial Officer
CMO: Jim Kelling, M.D., Chief of Staff
CIO: Ed Coye, Director Information Technology
CHR: Mark L. Emory, System Director Human Resources
CNO: Rebecca W. Carter, MSN, Vice President Patient Care and Chief Operating
Officer
Web address: www.trhospital.org
**Control:** Other not–for–profit (including NFP Corporation) **Service:** General
Medical and Surgical

Staffed Beds: 52 Admissions: 1802 Census: 17 Outpatient Visits: 60169
Births: 135 Total Expense ($000): 62856 Payroll Expense ($000): 25721
Personnel: 472

**BRYSON CITY—Swain County**

★ **MEDWEST – SWAIN (341305)**, 45 Plateau Street, Zip 28713–4200;
tel. 828/488–2155 **A**9 10 18 **F**8 11 15 29 30 35 40 44 45 57 59 62 63 68
75 77 81 82 84 85 91 93 107 119 130 133 146 148 **S** MedWest Health
System, Sylva, NC
Primary Contact: Steve Heatherly, Chief Executive Officer
CMO: David Zimmerman, M.D., Chief of Staff
CIO: Dale Chernich, Chief Information Officer
Web address: www.westcare.org
**Control:** Other not–for–profit (including NFP Corporation) **Service:** General
Medical and Surgical

Staffed Beds: 25 Admissions: 422 Census: 4 Outpatient Visits: 30940
Births: 0 Total Expense ($000): 11405 Payroll Expense ($000): 4636
Personnel: 90

**BURGAW—Pender County**

✠ **PENDER MEMORIAL HOSPITAL (341307)**, 507 East Freemont Street,
Zip 28425–5131; tel. 910/259–5451, (Total facility includes 43 beds in nursing
home–type unit) **A**1 9 10 18 **F**3 11 15 29 34 40 45 57 59 62 64 68 81 85 86
87 93 96 107 110 114 119 128 130 133 135 143 146 148 **S** New Hanover
Regional Medical Center, Wilmington, NC
Primary Contact: Ruth Glaser, President
CFO: Chris Riggs, Chief Financial Officer
CMO: Joseph Cooper, M.D., Chief of Staff
CIO: Mark Wilson, Manager Information Systems
CHR: Lori McKoy, Business Partner
CNO: Katherine Haddix–Hill, R.N., Chief Nursing Officer/Chief Operating Officer
Web address: www.pendermemorial.org
**Control:** County–Government, nonfederal **Service:** General Medical and Surgical

Staffed Beds: 68 Admissions: 971 Census: 48 Outpatient Visits: 25016
Births: 0 Total Expense ($000): 18398 Payroll Expense ($000): 7268
Personnel: 233

**BURLINGTON—Alamance County**

✠ **ALAMANCE REGIONAL MEDICAL CENTER (340070)**, 1240 Huffman Mill
Road, Zip 27215–8700, Mailing Address: P.O. Box 202, Zip 27216–0202;
tel. 336/538–7000 **A**1 2 9 10 **F**3 8 9 12 13 15 18 20 22 24 28 29 30 31 32
34 35 36 38 39 40 44 45 46 47 49 50 53 55 56 57 58 59 60 64 68 70 73
74 76 77 78 79 81 82 84 85 86 87 89 91 93 94 96 97 98 100 101 102 103
107 108 110 111 114 117 118 119 120 121 123 130 131 132 135 144 145
146 147 148
Primary Contact: John G. Currin, Jr., President
COO: John G. Currin, Jr., President
CFO: Rex Street, Senior Vice President and Chief Financial Officer
CMO: Andrew Lamb, M.D., Chief of Staff
CIO: Jesse Long, Director Information Technology
CHR: Dick Donahey, Senior Vice President Human Resources
Web address: www.armc.com
**Control:** Other not–for–profit (including NFP Corporation) **Service:** General
Medical and Surgical

Staffed Beds: 218 Admissions: 11703 Census: 132 Outpatient Visits:
180365 Births: 1263 Total Expense ($000): 244503 Payroll Expense
($000): 85532 Personnel: 1752

**BURNSVILLE—Yancey County**

**YANCEY COMMUNITY MEDICAL CENTER (341301)**, 800 Medical Campus
Drive, Zip 28714–9010; tel. 828/682–6136, (Nonreporting) **A**18
Primary Contact: Dena Hensley, Administrator
**Control:** Other not–for–profit (including NFP Corporation) **Service:** General
Medical and Surgical

Staffed Beds: 6

*Many Facility Codes have changed. Please refer to the AHA Guide Code Chart.* © 2013 AHA Guide

## BUTNER—Granville County

☐ **CENTRAL REGIONAL HOSPITAL (344001)**, 300 Veazey Road, Zip 27509–1668; tel. 919/764–2000 **A**1 3 5 10 **F**3 30 39 74 75 98 99 103 106 119 130 143 146 **P**6
Primary Contact: Michael Hennike, Chief Executive Officer
**Control:** State–Government, nonfederal **Service:** Psychiatric

**Staffed Beds: 382 Admissions:** 1592 **Census:** 364 **Outpatient Visits:** 0
**Births:** 0 **Total Expense ($000):** 156722 **Payroll Expense ($000):** 90265
**Personnel:** 2081

☐ **JOHN UMSTEAD HOSPITAL (344004)**, 1003 12th Street, Zip 27509–1626; tel. 919/575–7211, (Includes ALCOHOL AND DRUG ABUSE TREATMENT CENTER, 205 West E Street, Zip 27509; tel. 919/575–7928; Cliff Hood, Director), (Nonreporting) **A**1 3 5 10
Primary Contact: Patricia L. Christian, Ph.D., R.N., Chief Executive Officer
Web address: www.juh.dhhs.state.nc.us
**Control:** State–Government, nonfederal **Service:** Psychiatric

**Staffed Beds:** 514

## CAMP LEJEUNE—Onslow County

☒ **NAVAL HOSPITAL CAMP LEJEUNE**, (Formerly Naval Hospital), 100 Brewster Boulevard, Zip 28547–2538, Mailing Address: P.O. Box 10100, Zip 28547–0100; tel. 910/450–4300, (Nonreporting) **A**1 **S** Bureau of Medicine and Surgery, Department of the Navy, Washington, DC
Primary Contact: Commander Matthew Case, Director Administration
Web address: www.med.navy.mil/sites/nhcl/Pages/default.aspx
**Control:** Navy, Government, federal **Service:** General Medical and Surgical

**Staffed Beds:** 117

## CARY—Wake County

☒ △ **WAKEMED CARY HOSPITAL (340173)**, 1900 Kildaire Farm Road, Zip 27518–6616; tel. 919/350–2300, (Total facility includes 36 beds in nursing home–type unit) **A**1 7 9 10 **F**3 7 11 12 13 15 18 20 22 24 26 28 29 30 31 34 35 40 42 43 44 45 48 49 50 54 57 59 61 64 68 70 72 73 74 75 76 77 79 81 82 85 86 92 93 107 108 111 114 115 118 119 126 128 130 132 146 147 **P**6 **S** WakeMed Health & Hospitals, Raleigh, NC
Primary Contact: David C. Coulter, Senior Vice President and Administrator
CFO: Michael D. DeVaughn, Senior Vice President and Chief Financial Officer
CMO: West Lawson, M.D., Chief Medical Officer
CIO: Denton Arledge, Vice President and Chief Information Officer
CHR: Jeanene R. Martin, M.P.H., Senior Vice President Human Resources
Web address: www.wakemed.org
**Control:** Other not–for–profit (including NFP Corporation) **Service:** General Medical and Surgical

**Staffed Beds: 192 Admissions:** 10201 **Census:** 149 **Outpatient Visits:** 266475 **Births:** 2405 **Total Expense ($000):** 182721 **Payroll Expense ($000):** 63363 **Personnel:** 1047

## CHAPEL HILL—Orange County

☒ △ **UNIVERSITY OF NORTH CAROLINA HOSPITALS (340061)**, 101 Manning Drive, Zip 27514–4220; tel. 919/966–4131, (Includes NORTH CAROLINA CHILDREN'S AND WOMEN'S HOSPITAL ; NORTH CAROLINA CHILDREN'S HOSPITAL, 101 Manning Drive, tel. 919/966–4131; NORTH CAROLINA NEUROSCIENCES HOSPITAL, University Campus, Zip 27514; tel. 919/966–1141) **A**1 2 3 5 7 8 9 10 **F**3 4 5 7 8 9 11 12 13 14 15 16 17 18 19 20 21 22 23 24 25 26 27 28 29 30 31 32 34 35 36 38 39 40 41 43 44 45 46 47 48 49 50 52 53 54 55 56 57 58 59 60 61 62 63 64 65 66 68 70 72 73 74 75 76 77 78 79 80 81 82 84 85 86 87 88 89 90 91 92 93 96 97 98 99 100 101 102 103 104 105 107 108 110 111 114 115 116 117 118 119 120 121 123 124 126 129 130 131 132 134 135 136 137 138 139 140 141 142 143 145 146 147 148 **S** UNC Health Care, Chapel Hill, NC
Primary Contact: Gary L. Park, President
COO: Brian Goldstein, M.D., Executive Vice President and Chief Operating Officer
CFO: Christopher Ellington, Executive Vice President and Chief Financial Officer
CIO: J. P. Kichak, Vice President Information Services
CHR: William Rotella, Vice President Human Resources
Web address: www.unchealthcare.org
**Control:** State–Government, nonfederal **Service:** General Medical and Surgical

**Staffed Beds: 805 Admissions:** 37635 **Census:** 666 **Outpatient Visits:** 971844 **Births:** 3522 **Total Expense ($000):** 1128012 **Payroll Expense ($000):** 474037 **Personnel:** 8174

## CHARLOTTE—Mecklenburg County

☒ **CAROLINAS MEDICAL CENTER (340113)**, 1000 Blythe Boulevard, Zip 28203–5871, Mailing Address: P.O. Box 32861, Zip 28232–2861; tel. 704/355–2000, (Includes LEVINE CHILDREN'S HOSPITAL, 1000 Blythe Boulevard, Zip 28203; tel. 704/381–2000) **A**1 2 3 5 6 8 9 10 **F**3 7 8 12 13 15 17 18 19 20 21 22 23 24 25 26 27 28 29 30 31 32 34 35 36 37 38 39 40 41 42 43 44 45 46 47 48 49 50 52 54 55 56 57 58 59 60 61 62 64 65 66 68 70 71 72 73 74 75 76 77 78 79 80 81 82 83 84 85 86 87 88 89 90 93 96 97 98 99 100 101 102 103 104 105 107 108 109 111 114 115 116 117 118 119 120 121 123 124 126 129 130 131 132 134 135 136 137 138 139 141 142 143 145 146 147 148 **P**6 **S** Carolinas HealthCare System, Charlotte, NC
Primary Contact: Spencer Lilly, President
CFO: Greg A. Gombar, Chief Financial Officer
CMO: Roger A. Ray, M.D., Executive Vice President and Chief Medical Officer
CIO: Craig Richardville, Senior Vice President and Chief Information Officer
CHR: Debra Plousha–Moore, Senior Vice President Human Resources
Web address: www.carolinasmedicalcenter.org
**Control:** Hospital district or authority, Government, nonfederal **Service:** General Medical and Surgical

**Staffed Beds: 874 Admissions:** 50265 **Census:** 789 **Outpatient Visits:** 780787 **Births:** 6071 **Total Expense ($000):** 2049983 **Payroll Expense ($000):** 687609 **Personnel:** 10632

☒ △ **CAROLINAS MEDICAL CENTER–MERCY (340098)**, 2001 Vail Avenue, Zip 28207–1289; tel. 704/304–5000, (Includes CAROLINAS MEDICAL CENTER–PINEVILLE, 10628 Park Road, Zip 28210; tel. 704/543–2000; Christopher R. Hummer, President) **A**1 2 7 9 10 **F**3 4 12 13 18 20 22 24 26 28 29 30 31 34 37 40 42 44 45 49 50 51 57 59 60 64 65 68 70 72 74 75 76 78 79 81 82 84 85 86 87 93 107 108 111 114 115 118 119 126 129 130 145 146 148 **S** Carolinas HealthCare System, Charlotte, NC
Primary Contact: Spencer Lilly, President
COO: Joseph G. Piemont, Executive Vice President and Chief Operating Officer
CFO: Greg A. Gombar, Chief Financial Officer
CMO: Michael Ruhlen, M.D., Chief Medical Officer
CIO: Craig Richardville, Senior Vice President
CHR: Pia Walker, Director Human Resources
Web address: www.carolinashealthcare.org/cmc–mercy
**Control:** Hospital district or authority, Government, nonfederal **Service:** General Medical and Surgical

**Staffed Beds: 348 Admissions:** 18522 **Census:** 213 **Outpatient Visits:** 214015 **Births:** 2769 **Total Expense ($000):** 380106 **Payroll Expense ($000):** 131065 **Personnel:** 2066

☒ **CAROLINAS MEDICAL CENTER–UNIVERSITY (340166)**, 8800 North Tryon Street, Zip 28262–3300, Mailing Address: P.O. Box 560727, Zip 28256–0727; tel. 704/863–6000 **A**1 2 9 10 **F**3 8 13 18 20 26 29 30 31 34 40 42 44 45 46 49 50 51 57 59 60 64 65 68 70 72 74 75 76 78 79 81 82 84 85 86 87 92 93 107 111 114 115 118 119 126 129 130 145 146 148 **S** Carolinas HealthCare System, Charlotte, NC
Primary Contact: William H. Leonard, President
CFO: Greg A. Gombar, Chief Financial Officer
CIO: John Knox, Senior Vice President and Chief Information Officer
Web address: www.carolinashealthcare.org/cmc university
**Control:** Hospital district or authority, Government, nonfederal **Service:** General Medical and Surgical

**Staffed Beds: 94 Admissions:** 5877 **Census:** 58 **Outpatient Visits:** 141422 **Births:** 1401 **Total Expense ($000):** 132992 **Payroll Expense ($000):** 48720 **Personnel:** 771

☒ △ **CAROLINAS REHABILITATION (343026)**, 1100 Blythe Boulevard, Zip 28203–5864; tel. 704/355–4300 **A**1 7 9 10 **F**3 11 29 30 31 64 74 77 79 82 90 91 93 95 129 130 131 132 146 **P**1 **S** Carolinas HealthCare System, Charlotte, NC
Primary Contact: Robert G. Larrison, Jr., President
COO: Todd Bennett, Vice President
CFO: William Hopkins, Director Finance
CMO: William Bockenek, M.D., Medical Director
CIO: Craig Richardville, Chief Information Officer
CNO: Susan Chase, Vice President
Web address: www.carolinashealthcare.org/carolinas–rehab
**Control:** Other not–for–profit (including NFP Corporation) **Service:** Rehabilitation

**Staffed Beds: 169 Admissions:** 2167 **Census:** 119 **Outpatient Visits:** 73572 **Births:** 0 **Total Expense ($000):** 77737 **Payroll Expense ($000):** 35149 **Personnel:** 745

---

**Hospital, Medicare Provider Number, Address, Telephone, Approval, Facility, and Physician Codes, Health Care System**

★ American Hospital Association (AHA) membership
☐ The Joint Commission accreditation
◇ DNV Healthcare Inc. accreditation
○ Healthcare Facilities Accreditation Program
△ Commission on Accreditation of Rehabilitation Facilities (CARF) accreditation

**NC**

⊠ **CAROLINAS SPECIALTY HOSPITAL (342015)**, 2001 Vail Avenue, 7th Floor, Zip 28207–1248; tel. 704/304–6450, (Nonreporting) **A**1 10 **S** AcuityHealthcare, LP, Charlotte, NC
Primary Contact: Daniel C. Dunmyer, Chief Executive Officer
CHR: Doug Gallagher, Director Human Resources
CNO: Teshia Davis, Chief Clinical Officer
Web address: www.cshnc.com
**Control:** Corporation, Investor–owned, for–profit **Service:** Long–Term Acute Care hospital

Staffed Beds: 38

⊠ **NOVANT HEALTH CHARLOTTE ORTHOPAEDIC HOSPITAL (340153)**, (Formerly Presbyterian–Orthopaedic Hospital), 1901 Randolph Road, Zip 28207–1195; tel. 704/316–2000, (Total facility includes 16 beds in nursing home–type unit) **A**1 9 10 **F**3 11 29 30 37 44 50 51 64 68 75 79 81 82 86 87 107 111 118 119 128 130 131 132 146 **S** Novant Health, Winston Salem, NC
Primary Contact: Mike Riley, Senior Vice President and Chief Operating Officer
CFO: Tammy Geist, Chief Financial Officer
CIO: Shelia Cook, Director Information Systems
Web address: www.novanthealth.org
**Control:** Other not–for–profit (including NFP Corporation) **Service:** Orthopedic

Staffed Beds: 80 Admissions: 3674 Census: 39 Outpatient Visits: 23672 Births: 0 Total Expense ($000): 83821 Payroll Expense ($000): 21529 Personnel: 324

⊠ **NOVANT HEALTH PRESBYTERIAN MEDICAL CENTER (340053)**, (Formerly Presbyterian Hospital), 200 Hawthorne Lane, Zip 28204–2528, Mailing Address: P.O. Box 33549, Zip 28233–3549; tel. 704/384–4000, (Includes PRESBYTERIAN HEMBY CHILDREN'S HOSPITAL, 200 Hawthorne Lane, Zip 28204–2515; tel. 704/384–5134) **A**1 2 9 10 **F**3 5 7 8 11 12 13 15 17 18 19 20 22 24 26 28 29 30 31 32 34 35 36 38 40 41 45 46 47 48 49 53 54 55 56 57 58 59 60 61 63 64 65 68 70 71 72 73 74 75 76 77 78 79 81 82 84 85 86 87 88 89 91 92 93 98 99 100 101 102 103 104 105 107 108 111 112 113 114 115 116 117 118 119 120 121 124 126 129 130 132 135 142 143 145 146 147 148 **P**6 **S** Novant Health, Winston Salem, NC
Primary Contact: Harry L. Smith, Jr., President
COO: Amy Vance, Executive Vice President and Chief Operating Officer
CFO: Mark Moyer, Vice President and Chief Financial Officer
CMO: Stephen Wallenhaupt, M.D., Executive Vice President Medical Affairs
CIO: David B. Garrett, Senior Vice President Information Technology
CHR: Janet Smith–Hill, Senior Vice President Human Resources
Web address: www.presbyterian.org
**Control:** Other not–for–profit (including NFP Corporation) **Service:** General Medical and Surgical

Staffed Beds: 595 Admissions: 29657 Census: 446 Outpatient Visits: 394704 Births: 5220 Total Expense ($000): 527035 Payroll Expense ($000): 184548 Personnel: 3098

**CHEROKEE—Swain County**

⊠ **CHEROKEE INDIAN HOSPITAL (340156)**, 1 Hospital Road, Zip 28719; tel. 828/497–9163 **A**1 10 **F**39 40 50 54 59 63 64 65 66 68 75 77 79 82 86 93 97 99 104 107 110 114 119 127 130 131 132 135 **P**6
Primary Contact: Casey Cooper, Chief Executive Officer
COO: Beth Greene, Chief Operating Officer
CFO: Chrissy Arch, Chief Financial Officer
CMO: Michael E. Toedt, M.D., Director Clinical Services
CIO: Anthony Taylor, Manager Information Technology
**Control:** PHS, Indian Service, Government, federal **Service:** General Medical and Surgical

Staffed Beds: 15 Admissions: 862 Census: 9 Outpatient Visits: 151257 Births: 0 Total Expense ($000): 38468 Payroll Expense ($000): 22042 Personnel: 216

**CLINTON—Sampson County**

⊠ **SAMPSON REGIONAL MEDICAL CENTER (340024)**, 607 Beaman Street, Zip 28328–2697, Mailing Address: P.O. Box 260, Zip 28329–0260; tel. 910/592–8511, (Total facility includes 30 beds in nursing home–type unit) **A**1 9 10 **F**3 13 14 15 28 29 30 34 35 40 44 45 46 48 50 53 54 57 59 62 64 65 68 70 76 77 79 81 82 85 87 89 91 93 96 97 107 108 110 111 114 115 118 119 128 129 130 132 135 144 146 **P**6
Primary Contact: David J. Masterson, Chief Executive Officer
COO: Geraldine H. Shipp, Director of Risk Management
CFO: Jerry Heinzman, Senior Vice President and Chief Financial Officer
CMO: Shawn Howerton, M.D., President Medical Staff
CIO: Kelly Lucas, Chief Information Officer
CHR: Michael W. Gilpin, Vice President Human Resources
CNO: Rebecca Willis, Chief Nursing Officer
Web address: www.sampsonrmc.org
**Control:** County–Government, nonfederal **Service:** General Medical and Surgical

Staffed Beds: 105 Admissions: 3449 Census: 52 Outpatient Visits: 73995 Births: 445 Total Expense ($000): 64853 Payroll Expense ($000): 26706 Personnel: 569

**CLYDE—Haywood County**

⊠ **MEDWEST – HAYWOOD (340184)**, 262 Leroy George Drive, Zip 28721–7430; tel. 828/456–7311 **A**1 9 10 **F**3 11 13 15 18 20 28 29 30 31 34 35 38 40 44 45 46 50 51 53 54 57 59 62 63 64 65 68 70 71 74 75 76 77 78 79 81 82 84 85 86 87 93 98 100 101 102 107 108 111 114 118 119 129 130 131 132 144 146 147 148 **P**8 **S** MedWest Health System, Sylva, NC
Primary Contact: Janie Sinacore–Jaberg, R.N., MS, FACHE, Chief Executive Officer
COO: Teresa Reynolds, Chief Operating Officer
CFO: Rose Coyne, Interim CFO
CMO: Tyson Smith, M.D., Chief Medical Officer
CIO: Greg Copen, Chief Information Officer
CHR: Janet Millsaps, Vice President Human Resources
Web address: www.haymed.org
**Control:** Hospital district or authority, Government, nonfederal **Service:** General Medical and Surgical

Staffed Beds: 146 Admissions: 6388 Census: 61 Outpatient Visits: 273367 Births: 356 Total Expense ($000): 113414 Payroll Expense ($000): 51623 Personnel: 854

**COLUMBUS—Polk County**

⊠ **ST. LUKE'S HOSPITAL (341322)**, 101 Hospital Drive, Zip 28722–6418; tel. 828/894–3311 **A**1 9 10 18 **F**3 11 15 29 30 34 35 40 45 56 57 59 64 70 75 77 79 81 85 87 93 98 103 107 108 114 119 130 133 135 146 **P**6 **S** Carolinas HealthCare System, Charlotte, NC
Primary Contact: Kenneth A. Shull, FACHE, Chief Executive Officer
CFO: Christine M. Martin, Chief Financial Officer
CMO: James Holleman, M.D., Chief of Staff
CIO: David Pearson, Chief Information Officer
CHR: Amy Arledge, Vice President Support Services
Web address: www.saintlukeshospital.com
**Control:** Other not–for–profit (including NFP Corporation) **Service:** General Medical and Surgical

Staffed Beds: 35 Admissions: 1586 Census: 23 Outpatient Visits: 22422 Total Expense ($000): 24551 Payroll Expense ($000): 10567 Personnel: 277

**CONCORD—Cabarrus County**

⊠ **CAROLINAS MEDICAL CENTER–NORTHEAST (340001)**, 920 Church Street North, Zip 28025–2983; tel. 704/403–3000 **A**1 2 9 10 **F**3 5 7 8 9 11 12 13 15 17 18 20 22 24 26 28 29 30 31 32 34 35 36 37 38 40 42 43 44 45 49 50 51 53 54 55 56 57 58 59 60 61 63 64 65 68 70 71 72 73 74 75 76 77 78 79 80 81 82 84 85 86 87 88 89 93 97 98 99 100 102 103 104 105 107 108 111 114 115 116 117 118 119 121 123 124 126 129 130 131 132 135 143 145 146 147 148 **P**6 **S** Carolinas HealthCare System, Charlotte, NC
Primary Contact: Phyllis A. Wingate, FACHE, Division President
COO: Bill Hubbard, Vice President, Operations
CFO: James Ramsey, Vice President Finance
CMO: Jean Wright, M.D., Chief Medical Officer
CIO: Keith McNeice, Vice President and Chief Information Officer
CHR: Lesley Chambless, Assistant Vice President Workforce Relations
CNO: Kate Grew, MSN, Vice President/Chief Nurse Executive
Web address: www.carolinashealthcare.org
**Control:** Hospital district or authority, Government, nonfederal **Service:** General Medical and Surgical

Staffed Beds: 450 Admissions: 22420 Census: 274 Outpatient Visits: 536387 Births: 2625 Total Expense ($000): 455509 Payroll Expense ($000): 167776 Personnel: 2892

**DANBURY—Stokes County**

⊠ ◇ **PIONEER COMMUNITY HOSPITAL OF STOKES (341317)**, 1570 Highway 8 and 89 North, Zip 27016, Mailing Address: P.O. Box 10, Zip 27016–0010; tel. 336/593–2831, (Nonreporting) **A**1 9 10 18 21 **S** Pioneer Health Services, Magee, MS
Primary Contact: John Tompkins, Administrator
CMO: Samuel C. Newsome, M.D., President Medical Staff
CHR: Lashaunda Lash, Manager Human Resources
Web address: www.pchstokes.com
**Control:** Corporation, Investor–owned, for–profit **Service:** General Medical and Surgical

Staffed Beds: 25

*Many Facility Codes have changed. Please refer to the AHA Guide Code Chart.*

## DUNN—Harnett County

✠ **HARTNETT HEALTH SYSTEM (340071)**, (Formerly Betsy Johnson Regional Hospital), 800 Tilghman Drive, Zip 28334–5599, Mailing Address: P.O. Box 1706, Zip 28335–1706; tel. 910/892–1000, (Includes CENTRAL HARTNETT HOSPITAL, 215 Brightwater Drive, Lillington, Zip 27546; tel. 910/892–1000) **A**1 9 10 **F**3 11 13 15 18 28 29 30 34 35 39 40 45 50 56 57 59 68 70 73 75 76 77 79 81 82 85 86 87 89 92 93 96 102 107 108 110 111 114 118 119 129 130 135 146 148 **S** WakeMed Health & Hospitals, Raleigh, NC
Primary Contact: Kenneth E. Bryan, FACHE, President and Chief Executive Officer
COO: Kenneth E. Bryan, FACHE, President and Chief Executive Officer
CFO: Robin Nichols, Chief Financial Officer
CMO: Wallace J. Horne, M.D., Vice President Medical Affairs
CIO: Tim Krieger, Director Information Systems
CHR: Sondra Davis, Vice President Human Resources & System Development
Web address: www.myharnetthealth.org/about–hhs/betsy–johnson–hospital/
**Control:** Other not–for–profit (including NFP Corporation) **Service:** General Medical and Surgical

**Staffed Beds:** 82 **Admissions:** 6439 **Census:** 70 **Outpatient Visits:** 93117 **Births:** 675 **Total Expense ($000):** 85479 **Payroll Expense ($000):** 38658 **Personnel:** 723

## DURHAM—Durham County

✠ **DUKE REGIONAL HOSPITAL (340155)**, (Formerly Durham Regional Hospital), 3643 North Roxboro Road, Zip 27704–2763; tel. 919/470–4000 **A**1 3 5 6 9 10 **F**3 8 11 12 13 15 17 18 20 22 24 26 28 29 30 31 34 35 40 44 45 47 50 51 57 58 59 60 64 66 68 70 73 74 75 76 77 78 79 80 81 82 84 85 87 90 96 98 100 102 105 107 108 110 111 115 118 119 120 121 123 124 126 130 131 132 146 147 148 **P**6 **S** Duke University Health System, Durham, NC
Primary Contact: Kerry Watson, President
CFO: Jonathan B. Hoy, Chief Financial Officer
CMO: Lisa C. Pickett, M.D., Chief Medical Officer
CIO: Terry Mears, Director Information Systems
CHR: Richard J. Walsh, Ph.D., Chief Human Resources Officer
Web address: www.durhamregional.org
**Control:** Other not–for–profit (including NFP Corporation) **Service:** General Medical and Surgical

**Staffed Beds:** 194 **Admissions:** 14935 **Census:** 194 **Outpatient Visits:** 126037 **Births:** 2156 **Total Expense ($000):** 264930 **Payroll Expense ($000):** 107526 **Personnel:** 1959

✠ **DUKE UNIVERSITY HOSPITAL (340030)**, 2301 Erwin Road, Zip 27705–4699, Mailing Address: P.O. Box 3708, Zip 27710–3708; tel. 919/684–8111, (Includes DUKE CHILDREN'S HOSPITAL & HEALTH CENTER, 2301 Erwin Road, Zip 27710–0001, Mailing Address: PO Box 3708, Zip 27702; tel. 919/684–8111) **A**1 2 3 5 8 9 10 **F**3 5 6 7 8 9 11 12 13 15 16 17 18 19 20 21 22 23 24 25 26 27 28 29 30 31 32 34 35 36 37 38 39 40 41 43 44 45 46 47 48 49 50 52 53 54 55 56 57 58 59 60 61 62 63 64 65 66 68 70 72 73 74 75 76 77 78 79 80 81 82 84 85 86 87 88 89 91 92 93 94 95 96 97 98 99 100 101 102 103 104 107 108 110 111 114 115 116 117 118 119 120 121 123 124 126 127 129 130 131 132 134 135 136 137 138 139 140 141 142 144 145 146 147 148 **P**1 **S** Duke University Health System, Durham, NC
Primary Contact: Kevin W. Sowers, R.N., MSN, President
CFO: Sabrina Olsen, Chief Financial Officer
CMO: Thomas Owens, M.D., Chief Medical Officer
CIO: Asif Ahmad, Chief Information Officer
CHR: Deborah Page, Chief Human Resources Officer
Web address: www.dukehealth.org
**Control:** Other not–for–profit (including NFP Corporation) **Service:** General Medical and Surgical

**Staffed Beds:** 819 **Admissions:** 37698 **Census:** 667 **Outpatient Visits:** 1234926 **Births:** 3119 **Total Expense ($000):** 1691854 **Payroll Expense ($000):** 581402 **Personnel:** 9424

✠ **DURHAM VETERANS AFFAIRS MEDICAL CENTER**, 508 Fulton Street, Zip 27705–3897; tel. 919/286–0411, (Total facility includes 120 beds in nursing home–type unit) **A**1 3 5 8 **F**3 5 8 10 11 12 15 17 18 20 24 26 28 29 30 31 33 34 35 38 39 40 44 45 46 47 49 50 51 54 56 57 58 59 60 61 63 64 65 66 70 74 75 77 78 79 81 82 83 84 85 86 87 92 93 94 97 98 100 101 102 103 104 107 108 109 110 111 112 114 115 116 117 118 119 120 121 124 126 127 128 129 130 132 135 145 146 147 148 **S** Department of Veterans Affairs, Washington, DC
Primary Contact: DeAnne Seekins, Director
COO: Rudy Klopfer, Associate Director
CFO: David Kuboushek, Chief, Fiscal Service
CMO: John D. Shelburne, M.D., Chief of Staff
CIO: Toby Dickerson, Chief Information Resources Management Services
CIO: Conrad Raber, Chief Information Resources Management Service
CHR: Jerry Freeman, Chief, Human Resources Management Services
CNO: Kathryn M. Ward–Presson, R.N., Associate Director for Patient Care Services
Web address: www.durham.va.gov/
**Control:** Veterans Affairs, Government, federal **Service:** General Medical and Surgical

**Staffed Beds:** 265 **Admissions:** 6880 **Census:** 115 **Outpatient Visits:** 567356 **Births:** 0 **Total Expense ($000):** 488253 **Payroll Expense ($000):** 220820 **Personnel:** 463

☐ **NORTH CAROLINA SPECIALTY HOSPITAL (340049)**, 3916 Ben Franklin Boulevard, Zip 27704–2383; tel. 919/956–9300 **A**1 9 10 **F**3 64 79 81 82 85 86 87 119 126 130 131 135 148 **S** National Surgical Hospitals, Chicago, IL
Primary Contact: Randi L. Shults, Chief Executive Officer
CFO: Bill Wilson, Chief Financial Officer
CMO: Thomas Dimmig, M.D., Medical Director
CHR: Deborah Wheeler, Director Human Resources
CNO: John Medlin, Chief Nursing Officer
Web address: www.ncspecialty.com
**Control:** Partnership, Investor owned, for profit **Service:** General Medical and Surgical

**Staffed Beds:** 18 **Admissions:** 1553 **Census:** 11 **Outpatient Visits:** 11380 **Births:** 0 **Total Expense ($000):** 31932 **Payroll Expense ($000):** 10211 **Personnel:** 189

✠ **SELECT SPECIALTY HOSPITAL–DURHAM (342018)**, 3643 North Roxboro Road, 6th Floor, Zip 27704–2702; tel. 919/470–9137, (Nonreporting) **A**1 10 **S** Select Medical Corporation, Mechanicsburg, PA
Primary Contact: Robert F. Jernigan, Jr., Chief Executive Officer
Web address: www.selectspecialtyhospitals.com/company/locations/durham.aspx
**Control:** Corporation, Investor–owned, for–profit **Service:** Long–Term Acute Care hospital

**Staffed Beds:** 30

## EDEN—Rockingham County

✠ ◇ **MOREHEAD MEMORIAL HOSPITAL (340060)**, 117 East King's Highway, Zip 27288–5201; tel. 336/623–9711, (Total facility includes 121 beds in nursing home–type unit) **A**1 2 9 10 21 **F**3 11 13 15 18 26 28 29 30 31 34 35 36 40 45 47 48 49 50 57 59 64 68 70 73 74 75 76 77 78 79 81 85 87 89 90 93 97 107 108 110 111 114 118 119 122 123 128 129 130 132 135 143 146 147 148 **S** QHR, Brentwood, TN
Primary Contact: Joseph Gilene, Interim Chief Executive Officer
CFO: Dan Elmer, Vice President Finance
CHR: Tom Stevens, Director Personnel
Web address: www.morehead.org
**Control:** Other not–for–profit (including NFP Corporation) **Service:** General Medical and Surgical

**Staffed Beds:** 214 **Admissions:** 5564 **Census:** 167 **Outpatient Visits:** 172953 **Births:** 577 **Total Expense ($000):** 96129 **Payroll Expense ($000):** 43312 **Personnel:** 834

---

**Hospital, Medicare Provider Number, Address, Telephone, Approval, Facility, and Physician Codes, Health Care System**

★ American Hospital Association (AHA) membership
☐ The Joint Commission accreditation ◇ DNV Healthcare Inc. accreditation
○ Healthcare Facilities Accreditation Program
△ Commission on Accreditation of Rehabilitation Facilities (CARF) accreditation

NC

## EDENTON—Chowan County

⊞ **VIDANT CHOWAN HOSPITAL (341318)**, 211 Virginia Road, Zip 27932–9668, Mailing Address: P.O. Box 629, Zip 27932–0629; tel. 252/482–8451 **A**1 9 10 18 **F**3 11 13 15 18 19 28 29 30 31 34 40 45 46 56 57 59 64 70 74 75 76 77 78 79 81 82 85 89 93 107 108 110 111 114 119 130 132 146 147 **S** Vidant Health, Greenville, NC
Primary Contact: Jeffery Dial, Acting Chief Executive Officer
COO: Jeffery Dial, Chief Operating Officer
CFO: Brian Harvill, Vice President Financial Services
CMO: William Hope, IV, M.D., Chief of Medical Staff
CIO: Megan Booth–Mills, Director Planning and Marketing
CHR: Debbie Swicegood, Director Human Resources
CNO: Cindy Coker, M.P.H., Vice President, Patient Care Services
Web address: www.vidanthealth.com
**Control:** Other not–for–profit (including NFP Corporation) **Service:** General Medical and Surgical

**Staffed Beds:** 35 **Admissions:** 1777 **Census:** 32 **Outpatient Visits:** 43051 **Births:** 204 **Total Expense ($000):** 44571 **Payroll Expense ($000):** 18324 **Personnel:** 337

## ELIZABETH CITY—Pasquotank County

⊞ **ALBEMARLE HEALTH (340109)**, 1144 North Road Street, Zip 27909–3473, Mailing Address: P.O. Box 1587, Zip 27906–1587; tel. 252/335–0531 **A**1 9 10 **F**3 13 15 17 18 20 28 29 30 31 34 35 39 40 45 53 57 59 64 68 70 74 75 76 77 78 79 81 84 86 87 92 93 94 107 108 111 115 118 119 121 129 130 132 146 147 148 **S** Vidant Health, Greenville, NC
Primary Contact: Wendell H. Baker, Jr., President
COO: Jan King Robinson, VP, Operations
CFO: Raymond Owings, Vice President Finance
CMO: Daniel S. Terryberry, M.D., Chief Medical Officer
CIO: Steve Clark, Chief Information Officer
CHR: Brenda Rosecrans, Director Human Resources and Education
CNO: Dan Drake, VP, Patient Care Services
Web address: www.albemarlehealth.org
**Control:** Hospital district or authority, Government, nonfederal **Service:** General Medical and Surgical

**Staffed Beds:** 89 **Admissions:** 5043 **Census:** 52 **Outpatient Visits:** 149693 **Births:** 637 **Total Expense ($000):** 106722 **Payroll Expense ($000):** 38358 **Personnel:** 844

## ELIZABETHTOWN—Bladen County

**BLADEN COUNTY HOSPITAL** See Cape Fear Valley – Bladen County Hospital

⊞ **CAPE FEAR VALLEY – BLADEN COUNTY HOSPITAL (341315)**, 501 South Poplar Street, Zip 28337–9375, Mailing Address: P.O. Box 398, Zip 28337–0398; tel. 910/862–5100, (Nonreporting) **A**1 9 10 18 **S** Cape Fear Valley Health System, Fayetteville, NC
Primary Contact: Dan Weatherly, On Site Administrator
CFO: Sandra Williams, Chief Financial Officer
CMO: Pearly Graham Hoskins, M.D., President Medical Staff
CIO: Craig Kellum, Director Management Information Systems
CHR: Ginger Parks, Director Human Resources
Web address: www.bchn.org
**Control:** County–Government, nonfederal **Service:** General Medical and Surgical

**Staffed Beds:** 26

## ELKIN—Surry County

⊞ **HUGH CHATHAM MEMORIAL HOSPITAL (340097)**, 180 Parkwood Drive, Zip 28621–2430, Mailing Address: P.O. Box 560, Zip 28621–0560; tel. 336/527–7000, (Total facility includes 127 beds in nursing home–type unit) **A**1 9 10 **F**3 6 10 11 13 15 28 29 30 34 40 45 57 59 62 63 64 68 70 75 76 79 81 85 87 91 93 96 97 107 108 110 111 114 118 119 120 121 125 127 128 129 130 131 132 133 134 135 146 147 148 **P**6 **S** Alliant Management Services, Louisville, KY
Primary Contact: Michael J. Arno, Interim Chief Executive Officer
CMO: Stephen Isaacs, M.D., Chief of Staff
CIO: Lee Powe, Director Management Information Systems
CHR: Jeff Seaford, Director Human Resources
Web address: www.hughchatham.org
**Control:** Other not–for–profit (including NFP Corporation) **Service:** General Medical and Surgical

**Staffed Beds:** 208 **Admissions:** 5008 **Census:** 150 **Outpatient Visits:** 69290 **Births:** 584 **Total Expense ($000):** 66175 **Payroll Expense ($000):** 24473 **Personnel:** 636

## FAYETTEVILLE—Cumberland County

⊞ △ **CAPE FEAR VALLEY MEDICAL CENTER (340028)**, 1638 Owen Drive, Zip 28304–3431, Mailing Address: P.O. Box 2000, Zip 28302–2000; tel. 910/615–4000, (Includes SOUTHEASTERN REGIONAL REHABILITATION CENTER ; BEHAVIORAL HEALTH CARE OF CAPE FEAR VALLEY HEALTH SYSTEM, 3425 Melrose Road, Zip 28304–1695; tel. 910/609–3000; SOUTHEASTERN REGIONAL REHABILITATION CENTER, 1638 Owen Drive, Zip 28304; tel. 910/609–4000) **A**1 2 3 5 7 9 10 13 **F**1 3 4 5 7 12 13 14 15 17 18 20 22 24 26 28 29 30 31 34 35 38 39 40 41 44 49 53 54 56 57 59 61 64 65 68 70 72 73 74 75 77 78 79 80 81 82 84 86 87 88 90 91 92 93 96 97 98 99 100 101 102 103 104 107 108 109 110 111 114 115 116 117 118 119 120 121 122 123 124 126 127 129 130 132 135 143 144 146 147 148 **P**6 **S** Cape Fear Valley Health System, Fayetteville, NC
Primary Contact: Michael Nagowski, Chief Executive Officer
CFO: Sandra Williams, Chief Financial Officer
CMO: Richard S. Taylor, M.D., Chief Medical Officer
CHR: William B. Pryor, Senior Vice President, Human Resources
Web address: www.capefearvalley.com
**Control:** Other not–for–profit (including NFP Corporation) **Service:** General Medical and Surgical

**Staffed Beds:** 666 **Admissions:** 34002 **Census:** 584 **Outpatient Visits:** 575851 **Births:** 4403 **Total Expense ($000):** 660080 **Payroll Expense ($000):** 304790 **Personnel:** 4777

⊞ **FAYETTEVILLE VETERANS AFFAIRS MEDICAL CENTER**, (Formerly Veterans Affairs Medical Center), 2300 Ramsey Street, Zip 28301–3899; tel. 910/488–2120, (Nonreporting) **A**1 3 5 **S** Department of Veterans Affairs, Washington, DC
Primary Contact: Elizabeth Goolsby, Director
COO: James Galkowski, Associate Director for Operations
CFO: Patrick Bullard, Chief Financial Officer
CMO: Anna B. Teague, M.D., Chief of Staff
CIO: Kenneth Williams, Chief Information Officer
CHR: Joseph Whaley, Chief, Human Resources Management Service
CNO: Joyce Alexander–Hines, R.N., Associate Director, Patient Care Services
Web address: www.fayettevillenc.va.gov
**Control:** Veterans Affairs, Government, federal **Service:** General Medical and Surgical

**Staffed Beds:** 58

☐ **HIGHSMITH–RAINEY SPECIALTY HOSPITAL (342014)**, 150 Robeson Street, Zip 28301–5570; tel. 910/615–1000, (Nonreporting) **A**1 9 10 **S** Cape Fear Valley Health System, Fayetteville, NC
Primary Contact: Kevin Jackson, On Site Administrator
Web address: www.capefearvalley.com
**Control:** Other not–for–profit (including NFP Corporation) **Service:** Long–Term Acute Care hospital

**Staffed Beds:** 133

**VETERANS AFFAIRS MEDICAL CENTER** See Fayetteville Veterans Affairs Medical Center

## FORT BRAGG—Cumberland County

⊞ **WOMACK ARMY MEDICAL CENTER**, Normandy Drive, Zip 28307–5000; tel. 910/907–6000, (Nonreporting) **A**1 3 5 **S** Department of the Army, Office of the Surgeon General, Falls Church, VA
Primary Contact: Colonel Steven Brewster, M.D., Commander
Web address: www.wamc.amedd.army.mil/
**Control:** Army, Government, federal **Service:** General Medical and Surgical

**Staffed Beds:** 156

## FRANKLIN—Macon County

⊞ **ANGEL MEDICAL CENTER (341326)**, 120 Riverview Street, Zip 28734–2612, Mailing Address: P.O. Box 1209, Zip 28744–0569; tel. 828/524–8411 **A**1 9 10 18 **F**3 8 11 13 15 18 28 29 30 31 34 35 36 40 45 49 57 59 62 63 64 65 70 75 76 77 78 79 81 82 84 85 86 87 93 96 107 108 110 111 114 118 119 124 129 131 132 133 135 144 146 147 148 **P**6 **S** Mission Health System, Asheville, NC
Primary Contact: James B. Bross, President and Chief Executive Officer
COO: Martin Wadewitz, Chief Operations Officer/ Vice President, Operations
CFO: Jeff W. Rush, Interim Vice President Finance
CIO: Gary Hanold, Director Management Information Systems
CNO: Sheila C. Price, R.N., Chief Nursing Officer/Vice President of Nursing
Web address: www.angelmed.org
**Control:** Hospital district or authority, Government, nonfederal **Service:** General Medical and Surgical

**Staffed Beds:** 25 **Admissions:** 1557 **Census:** 16 **Outpatient Visits:** 83831 **Births:** 169 **Total Expense ($000):** 44170 **Payroll Expense ($000):** 23236 **Personnel:** 413

**NC**

*Many Facility Codes have changed. Please refer to the AHA Guide Code Chart.*

## GASTONIA—Gaston County

✠ **GASTON MEMORIAL HOSPITAL (340032)**, 2525 Court Drive,
Zip 28054–2140, Mailing Address: P.O. Box 1747, Zip 28053–1747;
tel. 704/834–2000 **A**1 2 9 10 **F**3 13 15 17 18 20 22 24 26 28 29 30 31 34
40 43 44 45 49 50 53 54 57 58 59 60 64 68 70 72 73 74 75 76 78 79 81
82 87 89 91 92 93 94 96 98 99 102 107 108 110 111 114 115 116 117
118 119 120 121 123 124 126 130 132 135 146 147 148
Primary Contact: Douglas R. Luckett, Interim President and Chief Executive Officer
COO: Douglas R. Luckett, Executive Vice President and Chief Operating Officer
CFO: David O'Connor, Executive Vice President and Chief Financial Officer
CIO: Mike Johnson, Assistant Vice President, Chief Information Officer
CHR: Elizabeth McCraw, Vice President, Human Resources
Web address: www.caromont.org
**Control:** Other not–for–profit (including NFP Corporation) **Service:** General
Medical and Surgical

**Staffed Beds:** 394 **Admissions:** 22303 **Census:** 254 **Outpatient Visits:**
324852 **Births:** 2427 **Total Expense ($000):** 341937 **Payroll Expense
($000):** 136123 **Personnel:** 2569

## GOLDSBORO—Wayne County

☐ **CHERRY HOSPITAL (344026)**, 201 Stevens Mill Road, Zip 27530–1057;
tel. 919/731–3200 **A**1 10 **F**30 39 98 99 103 108 146
Primary Contact: J. Luckey Welsh, Jr., Chief Executive Officer
COO: Richard Courliss, Chief Support Services
CFO: Susie Sherrod Sanders, Budget Officer
CMO: Kimberly Johnson, M.D., Clinical Director
CIO: Lisa Pettus, Manager Information Systems
CHR: Angela Crawford, Director Human Resources
Web address: www.cherryhospital.org
**Control:** State–Government, nonfederal **Service:** Psychiatric

**Staffed Beds:** 251 **Admissions:** 1111 **Census:** 165 **Outpatient Visits:** 942
**Births:** 0 **Total Expense ($000):** 53874 **Payroll Expense ($000):** 39603
**Personnel:** 897

✠ **WAYNE MEMORIAL HOSPITAL (340010)**, 2700 Wayne Memorial Drive,
Zip 27534–9494, Mailing Address: P.O. Box 8001, Zip 27533–8001;
tel. 919/736–1110 **A**1 9 10 **F**3 8 13 15 20 22 28 29 30 31 34 35 39 40 47
49 50 57 58 59 60 64 65 68 70 71 73 74 76 77 78 79 81 82 85 86 89 93
96 98 101 102 103 104 107 108 110 111 114 118 119 126 129 130 132
134 135 143 146 147 148 **P**6
Primary Contact: J. William Paugh, FACHE, President and Chief Executive Officer
COO: Thomas A. Bradshaw, Vice President Operations
CFO: Rebecca W. Craig, Vice President and Chief Financial Officer
CIO: Lori Cole, Director Information Management
CHR: Richard K. Rogers, FACHE, Vice President Human Resources
CNO: Shirley S. Harkey, R.N., Vice President, Patient Services
Web address: www.waynehealth.org
**Control:** Other not–for–profit (including NFP Corporation) **Service:** General
Medical and Surgical

**Staffed Beds:** 274 **Admissions:** 10927 **Census:** 134 **Outpatient Visits:**
154091 **Births:** 1468 **Total Expense ($000):** 189928 **Payroll Expense
($000):** 76473 **Personnel:** 1596

## GREENSBORO—Guilford County

✠ △ **CONE HEALTH (340091)**, 1200 North Elm Street, Zip 27401–1020;
tel. 336/832–7000, (Includes ANNIE PENN HOSPITAL, 618 South Main Street,
Reidsville, Zip 27320–5094; tel. 336/951–4000; Mickey Foster, Chief Executive
Officer; BEHAVIORAL HEALTH CENTER, 700 Walter Reed Drive, Zip 27403–1129;
tel. 336/832–9600; Troy Chisolm, President, Behavioral Health Hospital; MOSES
H. CONE MEMORIAL HOSPITAL, 1200 North Elm Street, Zip 27401;
tel. 336/832–7000; Judith A. Schanel, R.N., MSN, FACHE, President; WESLEY
LONG COMMUNITY HOSPITAL, 501 North Elam Avenue, Zip 27403;
tel. 336/832–1000; Paul A. Jeffrey, Vice President and Administrator; WOMEN'S
HOSPITAL OF GREENSBORO, 801 Green Valley Road, Zip 27408;
tel. 336/832–6500), (Total facility includes 92 beds in nursing home–type unit)
**A**1 2 3 5 7 9 10 **F**3 5 7 8 11 12 13 15 17 18 20 22 24 26 28 29 30 31 32
34 35 37 40 41 42 43 44 45 46 47 49 50 54 55 56 57 58 59 60 61 63 64
66 68 70 72 74 75 76 77 78 79 80 81 82 83 84 85 86 87 88 89 90 92 93
95 96 97 98 99 100 101 102 103 104 107 108 110 111 114 115 117 118
119 120 121 122 124 126 128 129 130 131 132 134 135 144 145 146 147
148 **P**6 8 **S** Carolinas HealthCare System, Charlotte, NC
Primary Contact: R. Timothy Rice, Chief Executive Officer
COO: Terry Akin, President and Chief Operating Officer
CFO: Jeffrey Jones, Chief Financial Officer
CMO: William Bowman, M.D., Vice President Medical Affairs
CIO: Steve Horsley, Vice President and Chief Information Officer
CHR: Noel F. Burt, Ph.D., Chief Human Resources Officer
CNO: Theresa M. Brodrick, R.N., Executive Vice President and Chief Nursing
Officer
Web address: www.conehealth.com
**Control:** Other not–for–profit (including NFP Corporation) **Service:** General
Medical and Surgical

**Staffed Beds:** 1018 **Admissions:** 46253 **Census:** 713 **Outpatient Visits:**
705507 **Births:** 6058 **Total Expense ($000):** 1032370 **Payroll Expense
($000):** 423343 **Personnel:** 7561

✠ **KINDRED HOSPITAL–GREENSBORO (342012)**, 2401 Southside Boulevard,
Zip 27406–3311; tel. 336/271–2800, (Total facility includes 23 beds in nursing
home–type unit) **A**1 9 10 **F**1 3 29 30 34 35 45 46 59 61 64 75 77 78 79 81
82 87 94 96 97 100 103 107 128 130 135 145 146 148 **S** Kindred
Healthcare, Louisville, KY
Primary Contact: Derek Murzyn, Chief Executive Officer
CFO: Michael Nelson, Chief Financial Officer
CMO: Percy E. Jones, M.D., Chief of Staff
CIO: Little Shuford, Manager Medical Information
CHR: Michele Roberts, Hospital Recruiter
Web address: www.khgreensboro.com
**Control:** Corporation, Investor–owned, for–profit **Service:** Long–Term Acute Care
hospital

**Staffed Beds:** 101 **Admissions:** 470 **Census:** 54 **Outpatient Visits:** 0 **Births:**
0 **Total Expense ($000):** 28573 **Payroll Expense ($000):** 11442

✠ **SELECT SPECIALTY HOSPITAL–GREENSBORO (342020)**, 1200 North Elm
Street, 5th Floor, Zip 27401–1004; tel. 336/832–8571 **A**1 10 **F**1 3 29 75 77
82 85 86 100 130 148 **S** Select Medical Corporation, Mechanicsburg, PA
Primary Contact: Deana Knight, Chief Executive Officer
CHR: Karen Tracey, Chief Human Resources
CNO: Robin Clark, Chief Nursing Officer
Web address: www.selectspecialtyhospitals.com/company/locations/greensboro.
aspx
**Control:** Corporation, Investor–owned, for–profit **Service:** Long–Term Acute Care
hospital

**Staffed Beds:** 30 **Admissions:** 300 **Census:** 19 **Outpatient Visits:** 0 **Births:**
0

## GREENVILLE—Pitt County

**PITT COUNTY MEMORIAL HOSPITAL** See Vidant Medical Center

NC

✠ △ **VIDANT MEDICAL CENTER (340040)**, 2100 Stantonsburg Road,
Zip 27834–2818, Mailing Address: P.O. Box 6028, Zip 27835–6028;
tel. 252/847–4100, (Includes JAMES AND CONNIE MAYNARD CHILDREN'S
HOSPITAL, 2101 Stantonsburg Road, Zip 27834–2817; tel. 252/847–5712;
UNIVERSITY HEALTH SYSTEMS CHILDREN'S HOSPITAL, 2100 Stantonsburg Road,
Mailing Address: PO Box 6028, Zip 27835–6028; tel. 252/847–4100) **A**1 2 3 5
7 8 9 10 **F**3 7 12 13 14 15 17 18 19 20 21 22 23 24 25 26 27 28 29 30 31
32 34 35 38 40 41 42 43 44 45 46 47 48 49 50 51 52 54 55 56 57 58 59
60 61 64 65 67 68 70 72 73 74 75 76 77 78 79 80 81 82 83 84 85 86 87
88 89 90 92 93 94 95 96 97 98 100 101 102 103 104 107 111 114 115
116 117 118 119 124 126 129 130 131 132 134 135 138 143 145 146 147
148 **P**6 **S** Vidant Health, Greenville, NC
Primary Contact: Stephen Lawler, President
CFO: Jack W. Holsten, Chief Financial Officer
CMO: Ernest Larkin, M.D., Chief Medical Officer
CIO: Stuart James, Chief Information Officer
CHR: Tyree Walker, Chief Human Resources Officer
Web address: www.https://www.vidanthealth.com/
**Control:** Other not–for–profit (including NFP Corporation) **Service:** General
Medical and Surgical

**Staffed Beds:** 875 **Admissions:** 46920 **Census:** 706 **Outpatient Visits:**
384572 **Births:** 3725 **Total Expense ($000):** 982934 **Payroll Expense**
**($000):** 346677 **Personnel:** 7222

**WALTER B. JONES ALCOHOL AND DRUG ABUSE TREATMENT CENTER
(344024)**, 2577 West Fifth Street, Zip 27834–7813; tel. 252/830–3426,
(Nonreporting) **A**10
Primary Contact: Theresa Edmondson, Director
CFO: Tom Basnight, Chief Financial Officer
CMO: Gary Leonhardt, M.D., Clinical Director
Web address: www.ncdhhs.gov
**Control:** State–Government, nonfederal **Service:** Alcoholism and other chemical
dependency

**Staffed Beds:** 80

☐ **SANDHILLS REGIONAL MEDICAL CENTER (340106)**, 1000 West Hamlet
Avenue, Zip 28345–4522, Mailing Address: P.O. Box 1109, Zip 28345–1109;
tel. 910/205–8000 **A**1 9 10 **F**3 7 8 18 29 34 35 40 45 49 57 59 64 70 75 79
81 82 87 98 102 103 104 105 106 107 108 111 114 118 119 130 135 146
**P**6 **S** Health Management Associates, Naples, FL
Primary Contact: Michael H. McNair, Chief Executive Officer
COO: Thomas Roddy, Assistant Administrator
CHR: Jenny La Fave, Director
Web address: www.sandhillsregional.com
**Control:** Corporation, Investor–owned, for–profit **Service:** General Medical and
Surgical

**Staffed Beds:** 64 **Admissions:** 2991 **Census:** 35 **Outpatient Visits:** 14154
**Births:** 0 **Total Expense ($000):** 29892 **Payroll Expense ($000):** 10468
**Personnel:** 158

✠ △ **MARIA PARHAM MEDICAL CENTER (340132)**, 566 Ruin Creek Road,
Zip 27536–2927; tel. 252/438–4143 **A**1 7 9 10 **F**3 11 13 15 18 20 28 29 30
31 34 35 39 40 44 45 46 48 49 50 51 54 57 59 60 62 64 68 70 74 75 76
77 78 79 80 81 82 84 85 86 87 90 92 93 94 96 97 107 108 110 111 114
118 119 120 121 123 129 130 131 132 135 146 147 148 **P**6 **S** Duke
LifePoint Healthcare, Brentwood, TN
Primary Contact: Robert G. Singletary, President and Chief Executive Officer
COO: Jay Kennedy, Chief Operating Officer
CFO: Jim Chatman, Chief Financial Officer
CIO: Randy Williams, Director Management Information Systems
CHR: Tonya A. Jones, Vice President Human Resources
CNO: Cindy Faulkner, Chief Nursing Officer
Web address: www.mariaparham.com
**Control:** Partnership, Investor–owned, for–profit **Service:** General Medical and
Surgical

**Staffed Beds:** 102 **Admissions:** 5598 **Census:** 53 **Outpatient Visits:** 157391
**Births:** 776 **Total Expense ($000):** 87114 **Payroll Expense ($000):** 29895
**Personnel:** 678

✠ ◇ **MARGARET R. PARDEE MEMORIAL HOSPITAL (340017)**, 800 North
Justice Street, Zip 28791–3410; tel. 828/696–1000 **A**1 2 9 10 21 **F**2 3 4 11
13 15 18 22 28 29 30 31 34 35 36 38 39 40 44 45 46 47 48 49 50 56 57
58 59 62 63 65 68 69 70 74 75 76 77 78 79 81 82 85 86 87 89 93 94 97
98 100 101 102 103 104 107 108 110 111 114 115 118 119 121 123 129
130 131 132 135 143 144 146 147 148 **P**6 **S** UNC Health Care, Chapel
Hill, NC
Primary Contact: James M. Kirby, II, President and Chief Executive Officer
CFO: Alan House, Chief Financial Officer
CMO: Robert Kiskaddon, M.D., Chief Medical Officer
CHR: Hope Reynolds, Executive Director Human Resources and Support Services
CNO: Patricia Ashe, R.N., Chief Nursing Officer
Web address: www.pardeehospital.org
**Control:** County–Government, nonfederal **Service:** General Medical and Surgical

**Staffed Beds:** 138 **Admissions:** 7020 **Census:** 71 **Outpatient Visits:** 250283
**Births:** 350 **Total Expense ($000):** 158626 **Payroll Expense ($000):** 55897
**Personnel:** 1040

✠ ○ **PARK RIDGE HEALTH (340023)**, 100 Hospital Drive, Zip 28792–5272;
tel. 828/684–8501 **A**1 2 9 10 11 19 **F**3 11 13 15 18 28 29 30 31 32 34 35
40 43 45 46 47 48 49 50 57 59 62 65 68 70 71 75 76 77 78 79 80 81 82
83 85 87 93 94 98 101 102 103 104 105 107 108 110 111 114 115 118
119 129 130 131 132 135 142 146 147 148 **P**6 **S** Adventist Health System
Sunbelt Health Care Corporation, Altamonte Springs, FL
Primary Contact: Jimm Bunch, President and Chief Executive Officer
CFO: Karsten Randolph, Vice President Finance/Chief Financial Officer
CIO: Lee Strickland, Regional Director Information Technology
CHR: Brandon M. Nudd, Director, Organizational Development
CNO: Craig Lindsey, R.N., Vice President Clinical Services/Chief Nursing Officer
Web address: www.parkridgehealth.org
**Control:** Other not–for–profit (including NFP Corporation) **Service:** General
Medical and Surgical

**Staffed Beds:** 98 **Admissions:** 4283 **Census:** 60 **Outpatient Visits:** 341320
**Births:** 551 **Total Expense ($000):** 116429 **Payroll Expense ($000):** 53041
**Personnel:** 962

✠ △ **CATAWBA VALLEY MEDICAL CENTER (340143)**, 810 Fairgrove Church
Road S.E., Zip 28602–9643; tel. 828/326–3000 **A**1 2 5 7 9 10 **F**3 5 11 12 13
15 18 20 22 26 28 29 30 31 34 35 39 40 44 45 46 47 48 49 50 51 53 54
56 57 59 61 64 65 68 70 71 73 74 75 76 77 78 79 81 82 84 85 86 87 89
90 91 92 93 96 97 98 100 101 102 103 104 107 108 109 110 111 114 115
117 118 119 120 121 122 123 124 126 129 130 131 132 135 143 144 145
146 147 148
Primary Contact: J. Anthony Rose, President and Chief Executive Officer
COO: Scott Echelberger, Vice President, Operations
CFO: David J. Boone, Senior Vice President, Finance
CIO: Jerry Reardon, Director Information Systems
CHR: Phyllis Johnston, Director
CNO: Edward L. Beard, MSN, Senior Vice President, Patient Care Services & CNO
Web address: www.catawbavalleymc.org
**Control:** County–Government, nonfederal **Service:** General Medical and Surgical

**Staffed Beds:** 213 **Admissions:** 10278 **Census:** 127 **Outpatient Visits:**
194890 **Births:** 1836 **Total Expense ($000):** 198579 **Payroll Expense**
**($000):** 84824 **Personnel:** 1326

✠ **FRYE REGIONAL MEDICAL CENTER (340116)**, 420 North Center Street,
Zip 28601–5049; tel. 828/322–6070, (Includes FRYE REGIONAL MEDICAL
CENTER–SOUTH CAMPUS, One Third Avenue N.W., Zip 28601, Mailing Address:
P.O. Box 369, Zip 28603; tel. 704/315–5777) **A**1 2 9 10 **F**11 12 13 15 17 18
20 22 24 26 28 29 30 31 34 35 37 40 45 46 49 54 57 59 64 68 70 72 74
75 76 77 78 79 81 82 85 86 87 89 90 93 96 98 101 103 107 108 110 111
114 115 118 119 126 128 129 130 131 132 144 146 147 148 **P**6 **S** TENET
Healthcare Corporation, Dallas, TX
Primary Contact: Robert Hammond, Interim Chief Executive Officer
COO: Rich Ellis, Chief Operating Officer
CMO: Frank C. Smeeks, M.D., Chief Medical Officer
CHR: Liz Elich, Vice President Human Resources
Web address: www.fryemedctr.com
**Control:** Corporation, Investor–owned, for–profit **Service:** General Medical and
Surgical

**Staffed Beds:** 306 **Admissions:** 11799 **Census:** 170 **Outpatient Visits:**
136377 **Births:** 516 **Personnel:** 1406

**NC**

*Many Facility Codes have changed. Please refer to the AHA Guide Code Chart.* © 2013 AHA Guide

**HIGH POINT—Guilford County**

✠ △ **HIGH POINT REGIONAL HEALTH SYSTEM (340004)**, 601 North Elm Street, Zip 27262–4398, Mailing Address: P.O. Box HP–5, Zip 27261–1899; tel. 336/878–6000 **A**1 2 7 9 10 F3 4 5 7 8 11 12 13 15 17 18 20 22 24 26 28 29 30 31 34 35 40 43 44 45 49 50 51 52 53 54 55 57 58 59 60 62 64 66 68 70 71 73 74 75 76 77 78 79 80 81 82 84 85 86 87 90 93 98 100 101 102 103 104 107 108 109 110 111 114 115 117 119 120 121 123 126 130 131 132 135 144 145 146 147 148 P6 **S** UNC Health Care, Chapel Hill, NC
Primary Contact: Jeffrey S. Miller, President and Chief Executive Officer
COO: Martha Barham, Vice President and Chief Operating Officer
COO: Gregory W. Taylor, M.D., Vice President and Chief Operating Officer
CFO: Kimberly Crews, Vice President Finance and Chief Financial Officer
CMO: L. Dale Williams, M.D., Vice President and Chief Medical Director
CIO: Nancy Waters, Interim Chief Information Officer
CHR: Katherine Burns, Vice President Human Resources
CNO: Tammi Erving–Mengel, Vice President, Chief Nursing Officer
Web address: www.highpointregional.com
**Control:** Other not–for–profit (including NFP Corporation) **Service:** General Medical and Surgical

**Staffed Beds:** 351 **Admissions:** 16516 **Census:** 193 **Outpatient Visits:** 255617 **Births:** 1666 **Total Expense ($000):** 243799 **Payroll Expense ($000):** 91561 **Personnel:** 1687

**HIGHLANDS—Macon County**

✠ **HIGHLANDS–CASHIERS HOSPITAL (341316)**, 190 Hospital Drive, Zip 28741–7600, Mailing Address: P.O. Drawer 190, Zip 28741–0190; tel. 828/526–1200, (Total facility includes 84 beds in nursing home–type unit) **A**1 9 10 18 F1 3 8 11 15 29 30 34 35 40 45 46 49 53 54 56 57 59 75 79 81 82 93 111 112 115 116 118 119 129 130 133 135 146 147 148
Primary Contact: Craig B. James, FACHE, Chief Executive Officer
COO: Frank Leslie, Vice President Operations
CFO: Michael E. Daiken, Chief Financial Officer
CIO: Mike Brown, IT Manager
CHR: Amanda Talley, Human Resources Director
CNO: Eileen Lipham, Chief Nursing Officer
Web address: www.hchospital.org
**Control:** Other not–for–profit (including NFP Corporation) **Service:** General Medical and Surgical

**Staffed Beds:** 108 **Admissions:** 369 **Census:** 62 **Outpatient Visits:** 17873 **Births:** 0 **Total Expense ($000):** 15930 **Payroll Expense ($000):** 10086 **Personnel:** 185

**HUNTERSVILLE—Mecklenburg County**

✠ **NOVANT HEALTH HUNTERSVILLE MEDICAL CENTER (340183)**, (Formerly Presbyterian Hospital Huntersville), 10030 Gilead Road, Zip 28078–7545, Mailing Address: P.O. Box 3508, Zip 28070–3508; tel. 704/316–4000 **A**1 9 10 F8 11 12 13 18 20 26 29 30 31 34 35 40 45 50 57 59 64 68 70 73 75 76 77 78 79 81 82 85 86 87 89 93 96 100 102 107 108 110 111 114 115 118 119 126 129 130 132 135 146 147 **S** Novant Health, Winston Salem, NC
Primary Contact: Tanya S. Blackmon, President
CFO: Jason Yanni, Senior Financial Analyst
CMO: David Cook, M.D., Chief Medical Officer
CIO: Richard B. McKnight, Senior Vice President and Chief Information Officer
CHR: Tracy Craig, Director Human Resources
Web address: www.novanthealth.org
**Control:** Other not–for–profit (including NFP Corporation) **Service:** General Medical and Surgical

**Staffed Beds:** 72 **Admissions:** 5700 **Census:** 56 **Outpatient Visits:** 142033 **Births:** 1031 **Total Expense ($000):** 99232 **Payroll Expense ($000):** 33011 **Personnel:** 547

**JACKSONVILLE—Onslow County**

☐ **BRYNN MARR HOSPITAL (344016)**, 192 Village Drive, Zip 28546–7299; tel. 910/577–1400 **A**1 10 F98 99 102 106 130 P6 **S** Universal Health Services, Inc., King of Prussia, PA
Primary Contact: Jay Kortemeyer, Chief Executive Officer
COO: Cynthia Waun, Chief Operating Officer and Risk Manager
CFO: David Warmerdam, Chief Financial Officer
CMO: Ashraf Mikhail, M.D., Medical Director
CIO: Cynthia Waun, Chief Operating Officer and Risk Manager
CHR: Jeff Nardo, Director Human Resources
Web address: www.brynnmarr.org
**Control:** Corporation, Investor–owned, for–profit **Service:** Psychiatric

**Staffed Beds:** 99 **Admissions:** 1735 **Census:** 90 **Outpatient Visits:** 0 **Births:** 0 **Total Expense ($000):** 14807 **Payroll Expense ($000):** 7177 **Personnel:** 114

**ONSLOW MEMORIAL HOSPITAL (340042)**, 317 Western Boulevard, Zip 28546–6379, Mailing Address: P.O. Box 1358, Zip 28541–1358; tel. 910/577–2345 **A**1 9 10 F3 8 11 13 15 19 20 28 29 34 40 45 46 47 48 49 54 57 59 60 64 68 70 72 73 75 76 77 78 79 81 82 84 85 86 87 89 93 107 108 110 111 117 118 119 126 129 130 131 132 135 146 147 148 P8
Primary Contact: Ed Piper, President and Chief Executive Officer
CFO: Roy Smith, Chief Financial Officer
CMO: Elizabeth D'Angelo, M.D., Chief of Staff
CIO: Christina Feak, Chief Information Officer
CHR: Sue Kegley, Director Human Resources
CNO: Crystal Hayden, R.N., Chief Nursing Officer
Web address: www.onslow.org
**Control:** Hospital district or authority, Government, nonfederal **Service:** General Medical and Surgical

**Staffed Beds:** 144 **Admissions:** 8018 **Census:** 82 **Outpatient Visits:** 137766 **Births:** 1863 **Total Expense ($000):** 136259 **Payroll Expense ($000):** 53119 **Personnel:** 1052

**JEFFERSON—Ashe County**

✠ **ASHE MEMORIAL HOSPITAL (341325)**, 200 Hospital Avenue, Zip 28640–9244; tel. 336/846–7101 **A**1 9 10 18 F3 8 11 13 15 28 30 34 35 40 45 46 48 53 57 59 64 75 76 80 81 85 86 89 93 107 108 110 111 114 118 119 127 130 132 133 135 141 142 146 147
Primary Contact: Laura Lambeth, Chief Executive Officer
COO: Joe Thore, Chief Operating Officer
CFO: Joy McClure, Chief Financial Officer
CMO: Christopher Campbell, M.D., Chief of Staff
CIO: William Baldwin, Chief Information Officer
CHR: Sherry Cox, Chief Human Resources Officer
Web address: www.ashememorial.org
**Control:** Other not–for–profit (including NFP Corporation) **Service:** General Medical and Surgical

**Staffed Beds:** 25 **Admissions:** 1434 **Census:** 35 **Outpatient Visits:** 49546 **Births:** 116 **Total Expense ($000):** 27648 **Payroll Expense ($000):** 12910 **Personnel:** 270

**KENANSVILLE—Duplin County**

✠ **VIDANT DUPLIN HOSPITAL (340120)**, 401 North Main Street, Zip 28349–8801, Mailing Address: P.O. Box 278, Zip 28349–0278; tel. 910/296–0941 **A**1 9 10 F3 11 13 15 18 19 29 30 34 35 39 40 45 56 57 59 68 70 75 76 77 79 81 91 93 97 98 101 102 103 107 108 110 111 115 119 129 130 131 135 146 147 **S** Vidant Health, Greenville, NC
Primary Contact: Jay Briley, President
CFO: Lucinda Crawford, Vice President Financial Services
CMO: Danny Pate, M.D., Chief Medical Staff
CIO: Lucinda Crawford, Vice President Financial Services
CHR: Pansy Chase, Director Human Resources
Web address: www.vidanthealth.com
**Control:** Other not–for–profit (including NFP Corporation) **Service:** General Medical and Surgical

**Staffed Beds:** 74 **Admissions:** 3211 **Census:** 42 **Outpatient Visits:** 44990 **Births:** 533 **Total Expense ($000):** 36924 **Payroll Expense ($000):** 15868 **Personnel:** 388

**KINGS MOUNTAIN—Cleveland County**

✠ **KINGS MOUNTAIN HOSPITAL (340037)**, 706 West King Street, Zip 28086–2708; tel. 980/487–5000 **A**1 9 10 F3 4 15 17 29 30 40 45 46 49 67 70 79 81 82 85 89 93 98 107 111 114 119 130 133 146 148 **S** Carolinas HealthCare System, Charlotte, NC
Primary Contact: Brian Gwyn, President and Chief Executive Officer
COO: Sheri Deshazo, Chief Operating Officer
CFO: Terry Edwards, Controller
CHR: Debra Kale, Director Human Resources
Web address: www.clevelandregional.org/kings–mountain–hospital.html
**Control:** Hospital district or authority, Government, nonfederal **Service:** General Medical and Surgical

**Staffed Beds:** 59 **Admissions:** 2681 **Census:** 41 **Outpatient Visits:** 50408 **Births:** 0 **Total Expense ($000):** 32757 **Payroll Expense ($000):** 14692 **Personnel:** 271

NC

## KINSTON—Lenoir County

**CASWELL CENTER**, 2415 West Vernon Avenue, Zip 28504–3321; tel. 252/208–4000 **F**1 10 11 30 39 67 75 77 90 91 97 128 148 **P**1
Primary Contact: Leon Owens, Director
CFO: Jim Hall, Budget Officer
CMO: Tony Bright, M.D., Administrator Medical Services
CHR: Ken Lafone, Director Human Resources
Web address: www.caswellcenter.org
**Control:** State–Government, nonfederal **Service:** Institution for mental retardation

**Staffed Beds: 365 Admissions: 10 Census: 364 Outpatient Visits: 0 Births:** 0 **Total Expense ($000): 85000 Payroll Expense ($000): 46410**

**LENOIR MEMORIAL HOSPITAL (340027)**, 100 Airport Road, Zip 28501–1634, Mailing Address: P.O. Box 1678, Zip 28503–1678; tel. 252/522–7000, (Total facility includes 26 beds in nursing home–type unit) **A**1 9 10 **F**3 8 11 13 18 20 28 29 30 31 34 35 38 40 43 45 47 48 49 50 53 56 57 59 60 61 64 65 68 70 74 75 76 77 78 79 80 81 82 85 86 87 89 90 93 102 107 108 111 114 115 117 118 119 120 121 123 128 129 130 132 134 135 143 145 146 148
Primary Contact: Gary E. Black, President and Chief Executive Officer
CFO: Sarah Mayo, Vice President Financial and Information Services
CMO: Wayne Jarman, M.D., President Medical Staff
CIO: Karl Vanderstouw, Director Management Information Systems
CHR: Jim Dobbins, Vice President Human Resources
CNO: Rosalind S. McDonald, MSN, Vice President Nursing Services
Web address: www.lenoirmemorial.org
**Control:** Other not–for–profit (including NFP Corporation) **Service:** General Medical and Surgical

**Staffed Beds: 218 Admissions: 7182 Census: 114 Outpatient Visits: 83649 Births: 410 Total Expense ($000): 108491 Payroll Expense ($000): 46257 Personnel: 860**

## LAURINBURG—Scotland County

**SCOTLAND HEALTH CARE SYSTEM (340008)**, 500 Lauchwood Drive, Zip 28352–5599; tel. 910/291–7000, (Total facility includes 50 beds in nursing home–type unit) **A**1 2 9 10 **F**3 11 13 15 18 28 29 31 34 37 40 45 54 57 59 64 66 70 71 73 74 75 76 77 78 79 81 82 85 86 87 89 90 93 96 97 107 110 111 114 115 119 120 121 123 127 128 130 132 135 143 144 145 146 147 148 **P**8 **S** Carolinas HealthCare System, Charlotte, NC
Primary Contact: Gregory C. Wood, President and Chief Executive Officer
CFO: Matthew Pracht, Vice President Finance
CMO: Brian Parkes, M.D., Chief Medical Officer
CIO: Bryan Kincaid, Director Information Systems
CHR: Ann Locklear, Vice President, Human Resources
CNO: Lane Harrington, R.N., Vice President Patient Care Services
Web address: www.scotlandhealth.org
**Control:** Other not–for–profit (including NFP Corporation) **Service:** General Medical and Surgical

**Staffed Beds: 152 Admissions: 6443 Census: 106 Outpatient Visits:** 198035 **Births: 673 Total Expense ($000): 110058 Payroll Expense ($000): 41497 Personnel: 928**

## LENOIR—Caldwell County

**CALDWELL MEMORIAL HOSPITAL (340041)**, 321 Mulberry Street S.W., Zip 28645–5720, Mailing Address: P.O. Box 1890, Zip 28645–1890; tel. 828/757–5100 **A**1 2 9 10 **F**3 8 11 13 15 18 20 28 31 34 35 37 40 45 46 48 49 50 53 54 55 57 59 64 65 70 74 75 76 77 78 79 81 82 85 87 89 93 97 107 108 109 110 111 114 115 118 119 122 123 129 135 144 146 147 148 **P**6
Primary Contact: Laura S. Easton, R.N., President and Chief Executive Officer
CFO: Donald F. Gardner, Vice President Finance/Chief Financial Officer
CMO: Edward Pearce, M.D., Chief of Staff
CIO: Nathan White, Director Information Systems
CHR: Rebecca Smith, Vice President and Chief Operating Officer
CNO: Sharon M. Kimball, R.N., Vice President and Chief Nursing Officer
Web address: www.caldwell–mem.org
**Control:** Other not–for–profit (including NFP Corporation) **Service:** General Medical and Surgical

**Staffed Beds: 74 Admissions: 3835 Census: 52 Outpatient Visits: 53712 Births: 441 Total Expense ($000): 97815 Payroll Expense ($000): 39112 Personnel: 778**

## LEXINGTON—Davidson County

**LEXINGTON MEMORIAL HOSPITAL** See Wake Forest Baptist Health–Lexington Medical Center

**WAKE FOREST BAPTIST HEALTH–LEXINGTON MEDICAL CENTER (340096)**, 250 Hospital Drive, Zip 27292–6728, Mailing Address: P.O. Box 1817, Zip 27293–1817; tel. 336/248–5161 **A**1 9 10 **F**3 11 13 15 17 18 28 29 30 31 32 34 35 40 45 47 50 57 59 64 68 70 74 75 76 77 78 79 80 81 82 85 86 87 89 90 93 107 110 111 115 118 119 124 129 130 131 132 135 144 146 147 148 **P**6 **S** Wake Forest Baptist Health, Winston–Salem, NC
Primary Contact: Steven C. Snelgrove, Chief Executive Officer
CFO: Danny Squires, Vice President and Chief Financial Officer
CMO: Gordon Kammire, M.D., Chief of Staff
CIO: Kevin Buchanan, Chief Information Officer
Web address: www.lexingtonmemorial.com
**Control:** Other not–for–profit (including NFP Corporation) **Service:** General Medical and Surgical

**Staffed Beds: 77 Admissions: 3414 Census: 26 Outpatient Visits: 111436 Births: 630 Total Expense ($000): 61745 Payroll Expense ($000): 27448 Personnel: 570**

## LINCOLNTON—Lincoln County

**CAROLINAS MEDICAL CENTER–LINCOLN (340145)**, 433 McAlister Road, Zip 28092–4147; tel. 980/212–2000 **A**1 9 10 **F**3 8 11 13 15 18 26 27 28 29 30 31 34 35 40 44 45 50 51 54 57 59 64 68 70 73 74 75 76 77 78 79 81 82 84 85 87 91 93 94 96 107 108 111 114 115 118 119 129 130 131 132 135 146 148 **P**6 **S** Carolinas HealthCare System, Charlotte, NC
Primary Contact: Peter W. Acker, President and Chief Executive Officer
COO: Teresa C. Watson, Vice President Administration
CFO: Jarrett Morris, Vice President Finance
CIO: Jarrett Morris, Vice President Finance
CHR: Lesley Chambless, Vice President Human Resources
Web address: www.carolinashealthcare.org/body.cfm?id=7626
**Control:** Hospital district or authority, Government, nonfederal **Service:** General Medical and Surgical

**Staffed Beds: 101 Admissions: 3668 Census: 39 Outpatient Visits: 99863 Births: 392 Total Expense ($000): 84676 Payroll Expense ($000): 33953 Personnel: 597**

## LINVILLE—Avery County

**CHARLES A. CANNON MEMORIAL HOSPITAL (341323)**, 434 Hospital Drive, Zip 28646, Mailing Address: P.O. Box 767, Zip 28646–0767; tel. 828/737–7000 **A**1 9 10 18 **F**3 13 15 18 28 29 30 31 38 40 45 50 68 70 76 77 78 81 85 89 91 93 98 101 102 104 107 114 119 129 130 133 146 **P**8 **S** Appalachian Regional Healthcare System, Boone, NC
Primary Contact: Carmen Lacey, MSN, R.N., President
CFO: Kevin B. May, System Director Finance
CMO: Thomas M. Haizlip, Jr., M.D., Chief of Staff
CIO: Mike Quinto, Chief Information Officer
CHR: Amy Crabbe, Vice President Human Resources
Web address: www.https://apprhs.org/locations/cannon–memorial–hospital
**Control:** Other not–for–profit (including NFP Corporation) **Service:** General Medical and Surgical

**Staffed Beds: 35 Admissions: 1867 Census: 24 Outpatient Visits: 26871 Births: 112 Total Expense ($000): 22270 Payroll Expense ($000): 9553 Personnel: 179**

## LOUISBURG—Franklin County

**NOVANT HEALTH FRANKLIN MEDICAL CENTER (340036)**, (Formerly Franklin Regional Medical Center), 100 Hospital Drive, Zip 27549–2256, Mailing Address: P.O. Box 609, Zip 27549–0609; tel. 919/497–8401 **A**1 9 10 **F**3 11 12 15 18 29 34 40 44 45 49 50 57 59 67 70 74 75 79 80 81 82 85 86 90 107 108 110 111 114 118 119 128 129 130 146 **S** Novant Health, Winston Salem, NC
Primary Contact: Jody Morris, President and Chief Operating Officer
CIO: Kim Webster, Manager Information Systems
CHR: Joanna Holder, Director Human Resources
Web address: www.franklinregional.org
**Control:** Other not–for–profit (including NFP Corporation) **Service:** General Medical and Surgical

**Staffed Beds: 43 Admissions: 1274 Census: 13 Outpatient Visits: 39774 Births: 0 Total Expense ($000): 29855 Payroll Expense ($000): 11115 Personnel: 215**

*Many Facility Codes have changed. Please refer to the AHA Guide Code Chart.*

## LUMBERTON—Robeson County

⊠ **SOUTHEASTERN HEALTH (340050)**, (Formerly Southeastern Regional Medical Center), 300 West 27th Street, Zip 28358–3075, Mailing Address: P.O. Box 1408, Zip 28359–1408; tel. 910/671–5000, (Total facility includes 115 beds in nursing home–type unit) **A**1 2 9 10 **F**3 5 7 9 12 13 17 18 20 22 24 28 29 30 31 34 35 40 45 48 49 50 53 54 57 59 60 61 62 63 64 67 68 70 71 72 73 76 77 78 79 80 81 82 83 84 85 87 89 92 93 98 102 103 107 108 111 113 114 115 118 119 120 121 126 127 128 129 130 131 132 143 144 146 148
Primary Contact: Joann Anderson, President and Chief Executive Officer
CFO: C. Thomas Johnson, III, Vice President Organizational Development and Chief Financial Officer
CMO: Jim Parker, M.D., President Medical Staff
CIO: Eric Harper, Chief Information Officer
CHR: Joseph W. Glezen, M.P.H., Director Human Resources
Web address: www.srmc.org
**Control:** Other not–for–profit (including NFP Corporation) **Service:** General Medical and Surgical

**Staffed Beds:** 385 **Admissions:** 14763 **Census:** 303 **Outpatient Visits:** 391885 **Births:** 1435 **Total Expense ($000):** 239388 **Payroll Expense ($000):** 94067 **Personnel:** 2213

## MARION—Mcdowell County

⊠ **MCDOWELL HOSPITAL (340087)**, 430 Rankin Drive, Zip 28752–6568, Mailing Address: P.O. Box 730, Zip 28752–0730; tel. 828/659–5000 **A**1 9 10 **F**3 11 13 15 28 29 30 31 34 35 39 40 45 54 57 59 64 65 70 76 77 78 79 81 85 87 90 93 107 108 110 111 114 119 127 130 131 132 133 146 148 **P**6 **S** Mission Health System, Asheville, NC
Primary Contact: Lynn Ingram Boggs, Chief Executive Officer
COO: Jason Clapsaddle, Vice President Operations
CFO: Clint Stewart, Vice President Finance/Business Operations
CMO: Robert Morrow, M.D., Chief of Staff
CIO: Andrew Cooper, Manager, Information Services
CHR: Teresa McCarthy, Interim Director Human Resources
CNO: Kathy Hefner, Vice President Clinical Operations
Web address: www.mcdhospital.org
**Control:** Other not–for–profit (including NFP Corporation) **Service:** General Medical and Surgical

**Staffed Beds:** 49 **Admissions:** 2805 **Census:** 17 **Outpatient Visits:** 126356 **Births:** 166 **Total Expense ($000):** 40837 **Payroll Expense ($000):** 19455 **Personnel:** 398

## MATTHEWS—Mecklenburg County

⊠ **NOVANT HEALTH MATTHEWS MEDICAL CENTER (340171)**, (Formerly Presbyterian Hospital Matthews), 1500 Matthews Township Parkway, Zip 28105–4656, Mailing Address: P.O. Box 3310, Zip 28106–3310; tel. 704/384–6500 **A**1 9 10 **F**3 11 12 13 15 18 20 22 26 29 30 31 34 35 36 40 45 49 56 57 59 64 68 70 73 75 76 77 78 79 81 82 84 85 86 87 92 93 107 108 110 111 114 115 118 119 126 129 130 132 145 146 147 148 **S** Novant Health, Winston Salem, NC
Primary Contact: Roland R. Bibeau, FACHE, President
COO: Amy Vance, Executive Vice President and Chief Operating Officer
CFO: Greg Klein, Senior Director Finance
CMO: Thomas Zweng, M.D., Senior Vice President Medical Affairs
CIO: David B. Garrett, Chief Information Officer
CHR: Susan Kennedy, Manager Human Resources
Web address: www.presbyterian.org
**Control:** Other not–for–profit (including NFP Corporation) **Service:** General Medical and Surgical

**Staffed Beds:** 117 **Admissions:** 7942 **Census:** 83 **Outpatient Visits:** 202176 **Births:** 1204 **Total Expense ($000):** 119745 **Payroll Expense ($000):** 40195 **Personnel:** 698

## MOCKSVILLE—Davie County

⊠ **WAKE FOREST BAPTIST HEALTH–DAVIE HOSPITAL (341313)**, 223 Hospital Street, Zip 27028–2038, Mailing Address: P.O. Box 1209, Zip 27028–1209; tel. 336/751–8100 **A**1 9 10 18 **F**3 15 30 34 35 40 59 64 81 82 85 107 114 119 130 133 **S** Wake Forest Baptist Health, Winston–Salem, NC
Primary Contact: Steven C. Snelgrove, Administrator
CFO: Terry R. Bowman, Chief Financial Officer
CMO: Mark Keller, M.D., President Medical Staff
CHR: Linda Pate, Director Human Resources
Web address: www.daviehospital.org
**Control:** Other not–for–profit (including NFP Corporation) **Service:** General Medical and Surgical

**Staffed Beds:** 25 **Admissions:** 252 **Census:** 7 **Outpatient Visits:** 14940 **Births:** 0 **Total Expense ($000):** 10341 **Payroll Expense ($000):** 4217 **Personnel:** 116

## MONROE—Union County

⊠ **CAROLINAS MEDICAL CENTER–UNION (340130)**, 600 Hospital Drive, Zip 28112–6000, Mailing Address: P.O. Box 5003, Zip 28111–5003; tel. 704/283–3100, (Total facility includes 70 beds in nursing home–type unit) **A**1 2 9 10 **F**3 4 5 8 11 13 18 20 26 28 29 30 31 34 35 39 40 42 45 49 56 57 59 62 64 66 67 70 73 74 75 76 77 78 79 81 82 85 86 87 89 93 107 108 111 114 115 118 119 120 121 123 128 129 130 132 135 144 146 147 148 **S** Carolinas HealthCare System, Charlotte, NC
Primary Contact: Michael Lutes, President
CFO: John G. Moore, Vice President and Chief Financial Officer
CMO: Dan Hagler, M.D., Vice President and Chief Medical Officer
CIO: Lisa Sykes, Director Information Services
CHR: Rhonda McFarland, Director Human Resources
Web address: www.carolinashealthcare.org/cmc-uniong
**Control:** Hospital district or authority, Government, nonfederal **Service:** General Medical and Surgical

**Staffed Beds:** 239 **Admissions:** 8732 **Census:** 161 **Outpatient Visits:** 192071 **Births:** 1198 **Total Expense ($000):** 162442 **Payroll Expense ($000):** 65645 **Personnel:** 1195

## MOORESVILLE—Iredell County

☐ **LAKE NORMAN REGIONAL MEDICAL CENTER (340129)**, 171 Fairview Road, Zip 28117–9500, Mailing Address: P.O. Box 3250, Zip 28117–3250; tel. 704/660–4000 **A**1 2 9 10 19 **F**3 8 11 12 13 15 18 20 29 30 31 34 35 37 40 41 45 46 47 48 49 50 51 54 56 57 59 60 61 62 64 65 68 70 72 73 74 75 76 77 78 79 81 82 84 85 86 87 93 96 97 100 107 108 110 111 114 115 117 118 119 126 129 130 131 132 135 145 146 147 148 **S** Health Management Associates, Naples, FL
Primary Contact: Greg Lowe, Chief Executive Officer
CFO: James Stoner, Chief Financial Officer
CHR: Christine McKenzie, Director Human Resources
Web address: www.lnrmc.com
**Control:** Corporation, Investor–owned, for–profit **Service:** General Medical and Surgical

**Staffed Beds:** 100 **Admissions:** 5492 **Census:** 56 **Outpatient Visits:** 54925 **Births:** 919

## MOREHEAD CITY—Carteret County

⊠ **CARTERET GENERAL HOSPITAL (340142)**, 3500 Arendell Street, Zip 28557–2901, Mailing Address: P.O. Box 1619, Zip 28557–1619; tel. 252/808–6000, (Total facility includes 104 beds in nursing home–type unit) **A**1 9 10 **F**3 7 11 12 13 15 18 28 29 30 31 34 35 40 45 46 54 57 59 62 63 64 65 68 70 74 75 76 77 78 79 81 82 84 85 86 87 89 91 92 93 97 107 108 110 111 114 115 118 119 120 121 123 128 129 130 132 135 143 144 145 146 148
Primary Contact: Richard A. Brvenik, FACHE, President
CFO: Joanie King, Chief Financial Officer
CMO: Leon M. Morrison, M.D., Vice President Medical Staff Services
CIO: Kyle Marek, Manager Information Services
CHR: Elizabeth Beswick, Vice President Human Resources and Public Relations
Web address: www.ccgh.org
**Control:** County–Government, nonfederal **Service:** General Medical and Surgical

**Staffed Beds:** 208 **Admissions:** 6117 **Census:** 107 **Outpatient Visits:** 166498 **Births:** 780 **Total Expense ($000):** 116945 **Payroll Expense ($000):** 47561 **Personnel:** 867

## MORGANTON—Burke County

☐ **BROUGHTON HOSPITAL (344025)**, 1000 South Sterling Street, Zip 28655–3999; tel. 828/433–2111 **A**1 5 10 **F**39 87 98 99 103 130 135 146
Primary Contact: George Krebs, M.D., Co–Acting Chief Executive Officer
CFO: Jonathan Berry, Chief Support Services and Chief Financial Officer
CMO: George Krebs, M.D., Chief Medical Officer
CIO: Phil Shirley, Director Information Resource Management
CHR: Mary Ragsdale, Director Human Resources
CNO: Vivian Streater, Chief Nursing Officer and Co–Acting Chief Executive Officer
Web address: www.ncdhhs.gov/dsohf/broughton
**Control:** State–Government, nonfederal **Service:** Psychiatric

**Staffed Beds:** 278 **Admissions:** 919 **Census:** 248 **Outpatient Visits:** 0 **Births:** 0 **Total Expense ($000):** 125945 **Payroll Expense ($000):** 50117 **Personnel:** 1145

---

**Hospital, Medicare Provider Number, Address, Telephone, Approval, Facility, and Physician Codes, Health Care System**

★ American Hospital Association (AHA) membership
☐ The Joint Commission accreditation
◇ DNV Healthcare Inc. accreditation
○ Healthcare Facilities Accreditation Program
△ Commission on Accreditation of Rehabilitation Facilities (CARF) accreditation

⊞ **GRACE HOSPITAL (340075)**, 2201 South Sterling Street, Zip 28655–4058; tel. 828/580–5000 **A**1 2 9 10 **F**3 13 15 18 20 22 29 30 34 35 40 45 50 53 57 59 60 64 68 69 70 71 72 76 77 78 81 82 86 93 96 97 98 105 107 108 110 111 114 115 119 131 146 147 **S** Blue Ridge HealthCare, Morganton, NC
Primary Contact: Kathy C. Bailey, Ph.D., FACHE, President and Chief Executive Officer
CFO: Robert G. Fritts, Chief Financial Officer and Senior Vice President
CMO: Joe Mazzola, D.O., Sr. Vice President Medical Affairs/Chief Quality Officer
CHR: David Shirlen, Vice President Human Resources
CNO: Susan Brown, R.N., Sr. Vice President, Chief Nursing Officer
Web address: www.blueridgehealth.org/grace–hospital.html
**Control:** Other not-for-profit (including NFP Corporation) **Service:** General Medical and Surgical

**Staffed Beds:** 132 **Admissions:** 6219 **Census:** 69 **Outpatient Visits:** 82899 **Births:** 935 **Total Expense ($000):** 109109 **Payroll Expense ($000):** 39935 **Personnel:** 857

### MOUNT AIRY—Surry County

⊞ **NORTHERN HOSPITAL OF SURRY COUNTY (340003)**, 830 Rockford Street, Zip 27030–5365, Mailing Address: P.O. Box 1101, Zip 27030–1101; tel. 336/719–7000, (Total facility includes 33 beds in nursing home–type unit) **A**1 9 10 **F**3 11 13 15 18 29 30 31 34 35 39 40 45 50 51 56 57 59 64 65 70 74 75 76 77 79 80 81 82 85 86 87 93 102 107 108 110 111 114 115 117 118 119 128 129 130 131 132 133 145 146 147 148 **P**6 **S** QHR, Brentwood, TN
Primary Contact: William B. James, FACHE, Chief Executive Officer
CFO: Robert G. Hetrick, Chief Financial Officer
CMO: Scott Corbin, M.D., Chief of Staff
CIO: Robert Hall, Chief Information Officer
CHR: Jeannie Moore, Director Human Resources
CNO: Robin Hodgin, R.N., Chief Administrator of Patient Care Services
Web address: www.northernhospital.com
**Control:** Hospital district or authority, Government, nonfederal **Service:** General Medical and Surgical

**Staffed Beds:** 108 **Admissions:** 4446 **Census:** 72 **Outpatient Visits:** 170550 **Births:** 444 **Total Expense ($000):** 76324 **Payroll Expense ($000):** 31037 **Personnel:** 626

### MURPHY—Cherokee County

⊞ **MURPHY MEDICAL CENTER (340160)**, 3990 U.S. Highway 64 East Alt, Zip 28906–7917; tel. 828/837–8161, (Total facility includes 134 beds in nursing home–type unit) **A**1 9 10 **F**3 6 11 13 15 28 29 30 31 34 35 40 45 49 50 53 54 57 59 62 63 64 67 70 77 78 79 81 93 107 108 110 111 115 119 128 130 131 135 144 146 147 148 **P**6 **S** Carolinas HealthCare System, Charlotte, NC
Primary Contact: Michael Stevenson, Chief Executive Officer
COO: Toni Lovingood, Chief Operating Officer
CFO: Steve Gilgen, Chief Financial Officer
CMO: Jeffrey H. Martin, M.D., Chief of Staff
CIO: Connie Stalcup, Manager Information Systems
CHR: Russ Paine, Human Resources Officer
CNO: Teresa Bowleg, R.N., Chief Nursing Officer
Web address: www.murphymedical.org
**Control:** Other not-for-profit (including NFP Corporation) **Service:** General Medical and Surgical

**Staffed Beds:** 191 **Admissions:** 2284 **Census:** 136 **Outpatient Visits:** 61799 **Births:** 136 **Total Expense ($000):** 58056 **Payroll Expense ($000):** 25341 **Personnel:** 614

### NAGS HEAD—Dare County

⊞ **THE OUTER BANKS HOSPITAL (341324)**, 4800 South Croatan Highway, Zip 27959–9704; tel. 252/449–4511 **A**1 9 10 18 **F**3 13 15 29 30 31 34 35 40 45 50 51 54 56 57 59 64 73 75 77 78 79 81 82 85 87 93 97 100 107 108 109 110 111 115 117 118 119 130 133 135 144 146 **P**5 **S** Vidant Health, Greenville, NC
Primary Contact: Ronald A. Sloan, FACHE, President
CFO: Todd Warlitner, Vice President Business Operations
CMO: Roger Lever, M.D., President Medical Staff
CHR: Mary Kelley, Director Human Resources
CNO: Judy Bruno, R.N., Vice President, Clinical Operations
Web address: www.theouterbankshospital.com
**Control:** Other not-for-profit (including NFP Corporation) **Service:** General Medical and Surgical

**Staffed Beds:** 21 **Admissions:** 1398 **Census:** 7 **Outpatient Visits:** 42726 **Births:** 399 **Total Expense ($000):** 49072 **Payroll Expense ($000):** 16057 **Personnel:** 269

### NEW BERN—Craven County

⊞ △ **CAROLINAEAST HEALTH SYSTEM (340131)**, (Formerly CarolinaEast Medical Center), 2000 Neuse Boulevard, Zip 28560–3499, Mailing Address: P.O. Box 12157, Zip 28561–2157; tel. 252/633–8111 **A**1 2 7 9 10 **F**3 7 11 13 15 17 18 20 22 24 26 28 29 30 31 34 35 40 45 47 48 49 53 54 57 59 60 61 62 64 67 68 70 74 75 76 77 78 79 81 85 87 89 90 92 93 94 96 98 100 101 102 103 104 105 107 108 110 111 113 114 115 116 117 118 119 120 121 123 126 129 130 132 135 143 146 147 148 **P**6
Primary Contact: G. Raymond Leggett, III, President and Chief Executive Officer
COO: Rosanne Leahy, Vice President Nursing Services
CMO: Ronald B. May, M.D., Vice President Medical Affairs
CIO: Tim Ludwig, Vice President Ancillary Services
CHR: Bruce A. Martin, Vice President Human Resources
Web address: www.carolinaeasthealth.com
**Control:** Hospital district or authority, Government, nonfederal **Service:** General Medical and Surgical

**Staffed Beds:** 350 **Admissions:** 13794 **Census:** 163 **Outpatient Visits:** 166240 **Births:** 1355 **Total Expense ($000):** 222548 **Payroll Expense ($000):** 89062 **Personnel:** 1689

### NORTH WILKESBORO—Wilkes County

⊞ **WILKES REGIONAL MEDICAL CENTER (340064)**, 1370 West D Street, Zip 28659–3506, Mailing Address: P.O. Box 609, Zip 28659–0609; tel. 336/651–8100, (Nonreporting) **A**1 9 10 **S** Carolinas HealthCare System, Charlotte, NC
Primary Contact: J. Gene Faile, Chief Executive Officer
CFO: Marlin Markham, Chief Financial Officer
CMO: Ashton Molai, M.D., Chief Medical Officer
CIO: Carl Espenship, Director Facility Services
CHR: Vanya Baker, Director
Web address: www.wilkesregional.org
**Control:** Hospital district or authority, Government, nonfederal **Service:** General Medical and Surgical

**Staffed Beds:** 98

### OXFORD—Granville County

⊞ **GRANVILLE HEALTH SYSTEM (340127)**, 1010 College Street, Zip 27565–2507, Mailing Address: P.O. Box 947, Zip 27565–0947; tel. 919/690–3000, (Total facility includes 80 beds in nursing home–type unit) **A**1 9 10 **F**2 3 7 11 13 15 18 19 29 30 31 34 35 38 39 40 45 50 54 55 56 57 59 64 66 70 75 76 77 78 79 81 82 85 86 93 99 100 101 103 104 107 108 110 111 118 119 124 127 128 129 130 132 133 143 144 146 147 148 **P**3 6 8
Primary Contact: L. Lee Isley, Ph.D., FACHE, Chief Executive Officer
COO: Cristina Rigsbee, Chief Operating Officer
CFO: Jeffrey Armstrong, CPA, Chief Financial Officer
CMO: James Williams, M.D., Chief Medical Staff
CIO: Geoff Tanthorey, Director Information Systems
CHR: Scott C. Thomas, Administrative Director Human Resources/Communication
CNO: Maria Calloway, R.N., Chief Nursing Officer
Web address: www.granvillemedical.com
**Control:** County–Government, nonfederal **Service:** General Medical and Surgical

**Staffed Beds:** 142 **Admissions:** 2262 **Census:** 88 **Outpatient Visits:** 57518 **Births:** 364 **Total Expense ($000):** 56710 **Payroll Expense ($000):** 25491 **Personnel:** 519

### PINEHURST—Moore County

⊞ △ **FIRSTHEALTH MOORE REGIONAL HOSPITAL (340115)**, 155 Memorial Drive, Zip 28374–8710, Mailing Address: P.O. Box 3000, Zip 28374–3000; tel. 910/715–1000 **A**1 2 7 9 10 19 **F**3 4 5 11 12 13 15 17 18 20 22 24 26 28 29 30 31 34 35 40 44 45 46 47 48 49 50 51 53 54 56 57 58 59 60 64 65 68 70 72 74 75 76 77 78 79 81 82 86 87 89 90 93 96 98 99 100 101 102 103 104 105 107 108 111 114 115 118 119 120 121 126 129 130 132 134 135 143 146 147 148 **S** FirstHealth of the Carolinas, Pinehurst, NC
Primary Contact: David J. Kilarski, Chief Executive Officer
COO: Brian Canfield, Chief Operating Officer
CFO: Lynn S. DeJaco, Chief Financial Officer
CMO: John F. Krahnert, M.D., Chief Medical Officer
CIO: David B. Dillehunt, Chief Information Officer
CHR: Daniel F. Biediger, Vice President Human Resources
CNO: Karen Robeano, MS, Chief Nursing Officer and Vice President Patient Care Services
Web address: www.firsthealth.org
**Control:** Other not–for–profit (including NFP Corporation) **Service:** General Medical and Surgical

**Staffed Beds:** 379 **Admissions:** 20878 **Census:** 272 **Outpatient Visits:** 191869 **Births:** 1562 **Total Expense ($000):** 376085 **Payroll Expense ($000):** 131567 **Personnel:** 2665

## PLYMOUTH—Washington County

☒ ◇ **WASHINGTON COUNTY HOSPITAL (341314)**, 958 U.S. Highway 64 East, Zip 27962–9591; tel. 252/793–4135, (Nonreporting) **A1** 9 10 18 21 **S** Rural Community Hospitals of America, Kansas City, MO
Primary Contact: Cameron Highsmith, Chief Executive Officer
CFO: Al Arrowood, Chief Financial Officer
CMO: Robert Venable, M.D., Chief Medical Staff
CIO: Christina Craft, Director Information Systems
CNO: Kimberly Manning, Chief Nursing Officer
**Control:** County–Government, nonfederal **Service:** General Medical and Surgical

**Staffed Beds:** 25

## RALEIGH—Wake County

**CENTRAL PRISON HOSPITAL**, 1300 Western Boulevard, Zip 27606–2148; tel. 919/733–0800, (Nonreporting)
Primary Contact: Thomas J. Hawkins, Administrator
CFO: Annette Goforth, Manager Administrative Services
CMO: Olushola Metiko, M.D., Medical Director
Web address: www.doc.state.nc.us/dop/prisons/central.htm
**Control:** State–Government, nonfederal **Service:** Hospital unit of an institution (prison hospital, college infimary, etc.)

**Staffed Beds:** 230

☒ **DUKE RALEIGH HOSPITAL (340073)**, 3400 Wake Forest Road, Zip 27609–7373, Mailing Address: P.O. Box 28280, Zip 27611–8280; tel. 919/954–3000 **A1** 2 9 10 **F3** 11 12 15 18 20 22 26 28 29 30 31 34 35 36 39 40 44 45 46 47 48 49 50 51 53 55 57 58 59 60 64 68 70 74 75 77 78 79 80 81 82 84 85 87 92 93 96 100 101 102 107 108 110 111 115 117 118 119 120 121 123 126 129 130 131 132 135 146 148 **P6 S** Duke University Health System, Durham, NC
Primary Contact: Richard Gannotta, President
CMO: Ted Kunstling, M.D., Chief Medical Officer
CIO: Janis Curtis, Interim Director Information Technology
CHR: Don Barnes, Chief Human Resources Officer
Web address: www.dukehealthraleigh.org
**Control:** Other not–for–profit (including NFP Corporation) **Service:** General Medical and Surgical

**Staffed Beds:** 148 **Admissions:** 7551 **Census:** 91 **Outpatient Visits:** 145197 **Births:** 0 **Total Expense ($000):** 249792 **Payroll Expense ($000):** 78066 **Personnel:** 1368

☐ **HOLLY HILL HOSPITAL (344014)**, 3019 Falstaff Road, Zip 27610–1812; tel. 919/250–7000 **A1** 10 **F4** 29 38 68 98 99 103 105 **S** Universal Health Services, Inc., King of Prussia, PA
Primary Contact: Michael McDonald, Chief Executive Officer
CFO: Ron Howard, Chief Financial Officer
CMO: Thomas Cornwall, M.D., Medical Director
CHR: Maria Teresa Sulit, Director Human Resources
Web address: www.hollyhillhospital.com
**Control:** Corporation, Investor–owned, for–profit **Service:** Psychiatric

**Staffed Beds:** 168 **Admissions:** 5492 **Census:** 134 **Outpatient Visits:** 2018 **Births:** 0 **Total Expense ($000):** 23456 **Payroll Expense ($000):** 14025 **Personnel:** 259

**LARRY B. ZIEVERINK, SR. ALCOHOLISM TREATMENT CENTER**, 3000 Falstaff Road, Zip 27610–1897; tel. 919/250–1500, (Nonreporting)
Primary Contact: Martin D. Woodward, Director Acute Care Services
COO: Martin D. Woodward, Director Acute Care Services
CFO: Paul Gross, Human Services and Finance Officer
CMO: Enrique Lopez, M.D., Medical Director
CIO: Wil A. Glenn, Director Communications
Web address: www.wakegov.com/county/family/atc
**Control:** County–Government, nonfederal **Service:** Alcoholism and other chemical dependency

**Staffed Beds:** 16

☒ △ **REX HEALTHCARE (340114)**, 4420 Lake Boone Trail, Zip 27607–6599; tel. 919/784–3100, (Total facility includes 227 beds in nursing home–type unit) **A1** 2 3 5 7 9 10 **F3** 7 8 11 12 13 14 15 17 18 20 22 24 26 28 29 30 31 34 35 36 40 44 45 46 47 48 49 50 53 54 56 57 58 59 60 62 64 65 66 68 70 71 73 74 75 76 77 78 79 81 82 84 85 86 87 89 92 93 96 97 100 102 107 108 110 111 114 115 116 117 118 119 120 121 123 126 128 129 130 131 132 135 142 143 144 145 146 147 148 **P6 S** UNC Health Care, Chapel Hill, NC
Primary Contact: David W. Strong, President
COO: Steve W. Burriss, Chief Operating Officer
CFO: Bernadette Spong, Chief Financial Officer
CMO: Linda H. Butler, M.D., Chief Medical Officer
CHR: Sylvia D. Hackett, Vice President Human Resources
CNO: Mary Lou Powell, MSN, Chief Nursing Officer
Web address: www.rexhealth.com
**Control:** Other not–for–profit (including NFP Corporation) **Service:** General Medical and Surgical

**Staffed Beds:** 660 **Admissions:** 27433 **Census:** 485 **Outpatient Visits:** 682844 **Births:** 5505 **Total Expense ($000):** 663403 **Payroll Expense ($000):** 298088 **Personnel:** 4651

☒ △ **WAKEMED RALEIGH CAMPUS (340069)**, 3000 New Bern Avenue, Zip 27610–1295; tel. 919/350–8000, (Total facility includes 19 beds in nursing home–type unit) **A1** 3 5 7 9 10 **F3** 7 8 11 12 13 15 17 18 20 22 24 26 28 29 30 31 32 34 35 37 38 40 41 42 43 44 45 48 49 50 53 54 56 57 58 59 60 61 62 63 64 65 66 68 70 71 72 73 74 75 76 77 78 79 81 85 86 87 88 89 90 92 93 95 96 97 107 108 110 111 114 115 118 119 126 128 130 131 132 135 143 144 146 147 148 **P6 S** WakeMed Health & Hospitals, Raleigh, NC
Primary Contact: William K. Atkinson, II, Ph.D., M.P.H., President and Chief Executive Officer
COO: Thomas Gettinger, Executive Vice President and Chief Operating Officer
CFO: Michael D. DeVaughn, Senior Vice President Finance and Chief Financial Officer
CMO: West Lawson, M.D., Chief Medical Officer
CIO: Denton Arledge, Vice President and Chief Information Officer
CHR: Jeanene R. Martin, M.P.H., Senior Vice President Human Resources
Web address: www.wakemed.org
**Control:** Other not–for–profit (including NFP Corporation) **Service:** General Medical and Surgical

**Staffed Beds:** 651 **Admissions:** 36062 **Census:** 549 **Outpatient Visits:** 1115969 **Births:** 5102 **Total Expense ($000):** 892010 **Payroll Expense ($000):** 432357 **Personnel:** 5902

## REIDSVILLE—Rockingham County

**ANNIE PENN HOSPITAL** See Cone Health, Greensboro

## ROANOKE RAPIDS—Halifax County

☒ **HALIFAX REGIONAL MEDICAL CENTER (340151)**, 250 Smith Church Road, Zip 27870–4914, Mailing Address: P.O. Box 1089, Zip 27870–1089; tel. 252/535–8011 **A1** 9 10 **F3** 11 13 15 18 20 29 31 34 35 38 39 40 45 50 54 57 58 59 60 64 65 66 68 69 70 75 76 77 78 79 81 85 86 91 93 94 97 98 101 102 103 106 107 108 109 110 111 114 119 124 127 129 130 132 135 146 148
Primary Contact: William Mahone, President and Chief Executive Officer
CFO: Sherry Jensen, Chief Financial Officer
CIO: Robert Gordon, Manager Information Systems
CHR: James B. Wood, Chief Human Resources Officer
CNO: Karen Daniels, MSN, Chief Nursing Officer
Web address: www.halifaxmedicalcenter.org
**Control:** Other not–for–profit (including NFP Corporation) **Service:** General Medical and Surgical

**Staffed Beds:** 142 **Admissions:** 6238 **Census:** 88 **Outpatient Visits:** 74637 **Births:** 657 **Total Expense ($000):** 85939 **Payroll Expense ($000):** 35496 **Personnel:** 801

## ROCKINGHAM—Richmond County

★ **FIRSTHEALTH RICHMOND MEMORIAL HOSPITAL (340035)**, 925 Long Drive, Zip 28379–4835; tel. 910/417–3000 **A9 F3** 13 15 18 20 28 29 30 34 35 40 45 46 47 48 49 50 53 57 59 64 70 75 76 77 81 82 85 87 89 92 93 96 107 108 110 111 114 119 120 129 131 132 134 135 145 146 147 148 **S** FirstHealth of the Carolinas, Pinehurst, NC
Primary Contact: John J. Jackson, President
COO: Allison Duckworth, Chief Operating Officer and Chief Nursing Officer
CFO: John D. Price, Chief Financial Officer
CMO: George Bussey, M.D., Chief Medical Officer
Web address: www.firsthealth.org
**Control:** Other not–for–profit (including NFP Corporation) **Service:** General Medical and Surgical

**Staffed Beds:** 91 **Admissions:** 2838 **Census:** 24 **Outpatient Visits:** 61156 **Births:** 346 **Total Expense ($000):** 40755 **Payroll Expense ($000):** 18532 **Personnel:** 331

---

**Hospital, Medicare Provider Number, Address, Telephone, Approval, Facility, and Physician Codes, Health Care System**

★ American Hospital Association (AHA) membership
☐ The Joint Commission accreditation ◇ DNV Healthcare Inc. accreditation

○ Healthcare Facilities Accreditation Program
△ Commission on Accreditation of Rehabilitation Facilities (CARF) accreditation

**NC**

## ROCKY MOUNT—Nash County

☒ **LIFECARE HOSPITALS OF NORTH CAROLINA (342013)**, 1051 Noell Lane, Zip 27804–1761; tel. 252/451–2300 **A**1 10 **F**1 3 18 29 50 74 75 77 79 82 85 119 148 **S** LifeCare Management Services, Plano, TX
Primary Contact: Kevin S. Cooper, R.N., Chief Executive Officer and Administrator
COO: Robyn Perkerson, Chief Clinical Officer
CMO: Daniel Crocker, M.D., Chief Medical Officer
CHR: Vicky Goode, Director Human Resources
CNO: Brandee Chappell, Director of Nursing
Web address: www.lifecare–hospitals.com
**Control:** Corporation, Investor–owned, for–profit **Service:** Long–Term Acute Care hospital

Staffed Beds: 40 Admissions: 487 Census: 39 Outpatient Visits: 0 Births: 0 Total Expense ($000): 17545 Payroll Expense ($000): 7958 Personnel: 150

☐ **NASH HEALTH CARE SYSTEMS (340147)**, 2460 Curtis Ellis Drive, Zip 27804–2237; tel. 252/443–8000 **A**1 2 9 10 **F**3 4 11 12 13 15 18 20 22 28 29 30 31 34 35 38 40 45 47 48 49 50 53 54 57 59 60 63 64 70 73 74 75 76 77 78 79 80 81 82 84 85 86 87 89 90 93 94 96 98 100 101 102 103 104 107 108 110 111 114 117 118 119 121 123 126 129 130 131 132 135 146 147 148 **P**6
Primary Contact: Larry H. Chewning, III, President and Chief Executive Officer
COO: Brad Weisner, Executive Vice President and Chief Operating Officer
CFO: Al Hooks, Senior Vice President and Chief Financial Officer
CMO: David R. Gorby, M.D., Vice President Quality and Patient Safety
CIO: David Hinkle, Senior Vice President and Chief Information Officer
CHR: Cam Blalock, Senior Vice President Corporate Services
CNO: Leslie Hall, R.N., Senior Vice President–Chief Nursing Officer
Web address: www.nhcs.org
**Control:** Hospital district or authority, Government, nonfederal **Service:** General Medical and Surgical

Staffed Beds: 298 Admissions: 12956 Census: 182 Outpatient Visits: 183952 Births: 1172 Total Expense ($000): 218010 Payroll Expense ($000): 91616 Personnel: 1677

## ROXBORO—Person County

☒ **PERSON MEMORIAL HOSPITAL (340159)**, 615 Ridge Road, Zip 27573–4629; tel. 336/599–2121, (Total facility includes 60 beds in nursing home–type unit) **A**1 9 10 **F**3 11 15 28 29 31 34 40 45 57 59 64 70 75 77 78 79 81 85 87 93 96 97 103 104 107 108 110 114 119 128 129 130 132 146 **P**6 **S** Duke LifePoint Healthcare, Brentwood, TN
Primary Contact: Chad Brown, M.P.H., Chief Executive Officer
CFO: Neal Bolton, Chief Financial Officer
CMO: Kenneth Flowe, M.D., Chief Medical Officer
CIO: Cameron Bellamy, CIS Manager
CHR: Mary Drumwright, Director Human Resources
CNO: Jan Ramey, MSN, Chief Nursing Officer
Web address: www.personhospital.com
**Control:** Partnership, Investor–owned, for–profit **Service:** General Medical and Surgical

Staffed Beds: 106 Admissions: 1992 Census: 76 Outpatient Visits: 47078 Births: 0 Total Expense ($000): 38908 Payroll Expense ($000): 12955 Personnel: 291

## RUTHERFORDTON—Rutherford County

☒ **RUTHERFORD REGIONAL HEALTH SYSTEM (340013)**, (Formerly Rutherford Regional Medical Center), 288 South Ridgecrest Avenue, Zip 28139–2838; tel. 828/286–5000 **A**1 2 9 10 19 **F**3 11 13 15 18 19 20 22 28 29 30 31 34 35 40 45 48 49 50 53 57 59 62 64 70 74 75 76 77 78 79 81 82 85 86 87 89 93 97 98 100 101 102 104 106 107 108 110 111 114 115 118 119 130 131 132 135 146 147
Primary Contact: Cindy D. Buck, Chief Executive Officer
CFO: Bob Ellis, Chief Financial Officer
CMO: Dean Backstrom, M.D., Vice President Medical Affairs
CIO: Tommy Finley, Chief Information Officer
CHR: Jim H. Rowell, Vice President Human Resources
Web address: www.rutherfordhosp.org
**Control:** Other not–for–profit (including NFP Corporation) **Service:** General Medical and Surgical

Staffed Beds: 121 Admissions: 5563 Census: 54 Outpatient Visits: 170446 Births: 536 Total Expense ($000): 87278 Payroll Expense ($000): 39448 Personnel: 729

## SALISBURY—Rowan County

☒ **NOVANT HEALTH ROWAN MEDICAL CENTER (340015)**, (Formerly Rowan Regional Medical Center), 612 Mocksville Avenue, Zip 28144–2799; tel. 704/210–5000 **A**1 9 10 **F**3 6 8 11 13 15 17 18 20 22 26 28 29 30 31 32 34 35 37 40 44 45 46 48 49 50 51 53 54 56 57 59 60 61 63 64 70 71 73 74 75 76 77 78 79 81 84 85 86 87 90 91 92 93 94 96 98 100 102 103 107 108 110 111 116 117 118 119 120 121 123 126 130 131 132 135 146 147 148 **P**2 **S** Novant Health, Winston Salem, NC
Primary Contact: Dari Caldwell, R.N., Ph.D., FACHE, President
COO: Sean M. Sanz, Chief Operating Officer
CMO: David N. Smith, M.D., Vice President Medical Affairs
CHR: Jerry Clevenger, Vice President Human Resources
CNO: Katrina King, R.N., Chief Nursing Officer
Web address: www.rowan.org
**Control:** Other not–for–profit (including NFP Corporation) **Service:** General Medical and Surgical

Staffed Beds: 200 Admissions: 9152 Census: 118 Outpatient Visits: 125020 Births: 768 Total Expense ($000): 139433 Payroll Expense ($000): 56959 Personnel: 947

**VETERANS AFFAIRS MEDICAL CENTER** See W. G. (Bill) Heffner Veterans Affairs Medical Center

☒ △ **W. G. (BILL) HEFFNER VETERANS AFFAIRS MEDICAL CENTER**, (Formerly Veterans Affairs Medical Center), 1601 Brenner Avenue, Zip 28144–2559; tel. 704/638–9000, (Nonreporting) **A**1 3 5 7 **S** Department of Veterans Affairs, Washington, DC
Primary Contact: Kaye Green, FACHE, Director
CFO: Steve Patil, Chief Financial Officer
CIO: Deborah Gunn, Chief Information Officer
CHR: Sandra Fischer, Director Human Resources
Web address: www.salisbury.va.gov
**Control:** Veterans Affairs, Government, federal **Service:** Psychiatric

Staffed Beds: 171

## SANFORD—Lee County

☒ **CENTRAL CAROLINA HOSPITAL (340020)**, 1135 Carthage Street, Zip 27330–4162; tel. 919/774–2100, (Nonreporting) **A**1 9 10 **S** TENET Healthcare Corporation, Dallas, TX
Primary Contact: Doug Doris, Chief Executive Officer
COO: David Clay, Chief Operating Officer
CFO: Lyra Howalt, Chief Financial Officer
CMO: David Katzin, M.D., Chief Medical Officer
CIO: Jimmy Whitaker, Director Information Systems
CHR: Joseph F. Eastman, Director Human Resources
CNO: Ursula Lawrence, MSN, Chief Nursing Officer
Web address: www.centralcarolinahosp.com
**Control:** Corporation, Investor–owned, for–profit **Service:** General Medical and Surgical

Staffed Beds: 116

## SCOTLAND NECK—Halifax County

★ **OUR COMMUNITY HOSPITAL (341302)**, 921 Junior High Road, Zip 27874–0405, Mailing Address: Box 405, Zip 27874–0405; tel. 252/826–4144, (Nonreporting) **A**9 10 18
Primary Contact: Thomas K. Majure, Administrator
CFO: Angela Hicks, Controller
CMO: Cornelius Artis, M.D., Chief Medical Officer
CIO: Dana Mobley, Chief Information Officer
CNO: Claudia Giddings, R.N., Chief Nursing Officer
Web address: www.och–bltc.org
**Control:** Other not–for–profit (including NFP Corporation) **Service:** General Medical and Surgical

Staffed Beds: 75

## SHELBY—Cleveland County

☒ **CLEVELAND REGIONAL MEDICAL CENTER (340021)**, 201 East Grover Street, Zip 28150–3917; tel. 704/487–3000, (Total facility includes 120 beds in nursing home–type unit) **A**1 2 9 10 19 **F**1 3 8 11 13 15 18 20 28 29 30 31 32 34 35 38 39 40 43 44 47 48 49 50 51 56 57 59 61 64 65 67 70 74 75 76 77 78 79 80 81 82 85 86 87 89 93 102 106 107 108 110 111 114 115 118 119 121 123 128 130 131 132 135 143 145 146 147 148 **S** Carolinas HealthCare System, Charlotte, NC
Primary Contact: Brian Gwyn, President and Chief Executive Officer
COO: Veronica Poole–Adams, R.N., Vice President, Chief Operating Officer and Chief Nursing Executive
CFO: Rose Coyne, Vice President and Chief Financial Officer
CIO: Craig Richardville, Chief Information Officer
CHR: Debra Kale, Vice President Human Resources
Web address: www.clevelandregional.org
**Control:** Hospital district or authority, Government, nonfederal **Service:** General Medical and Surgical

Staffed Beds: 364 Admissions: 8788 Census: 205 Outpatient Visits: 141301 Births: 1013 Total Expense ($000): 155364 Payroll Expense ($000): 60528 Personnel: 1090

*Many Facility Codes have changed. Please refer to the AHA Guide Code Chart.*   © 2013 AHA Guide

★ **CRAWLEY MEMORIAL HOSPITAL (342019)**, 315 West College Avenue, Zip 28152, Mailing Address: P.O. Box 996, Boiling Springs, Zip 28017–0996; tel. 704/434–9466 **A**10 **F**1 29 85 87 130 148 **S** Carolinas HealthCare System, Charlotte, NC
Primary Contact: Brian Gwyn, President and Chief Executive Officer
CFO: Christine M. Martin, Chief Financial Officer
CMO: Charles M. Tomlinson, M.D., Vice President and Chief Medical Officer
CIO: Theresa Bridges, Chief Information Officer
CHR: Debra Kale, Vice President Human Resources
CNO: Veronica Poole–Adams, R.N., Vice President and Chief Nursing Officer
Web address: www.clevelandcountyhealthcaresystem.com/crawley–memorial.html
**Control:** Other not–for–profit (including NFP Corporation) **Service:** Long–Term Acute Care hospital

**Staffed Beds:** 41 **Admissions:** 166 **Census:** 10 **Outpatient Visits:** 0 **Births:** 0 **Total Expense ($000):** 7261 **Payroll Expense ($000):** 2606 **Personnel:** 57

### SILER CITY—Chatham County

✠ **CHATHAM HOSPITAL (341311)**, 475 Progress Boulevard, Zip 27344–6787, Mailing Address: P.O. Box 649, Zip 27344–0649; tel. 919/799–4000 **A**1 9 10 18 **F**3 15 18 28 29 30 34 35 40 45 57 59 68 70 75 77 81 85 92 93 107 110 111 114 119 130 133 135 146 **S** UNC Health Care, Chapel Hill, NC
Primary Contact: Robert A. Enders, Jr., President
CFO: Brock Simonds, Interim Chief Financial Officer
CMO: James Davis, M.D., Chief Medical Staff
CIO: Louis Manz, Director Information and Communication Services
CHR: Jodie Solow, Director Human Resources
CNO: Linda B. Ellington, R.N., Interim Vice President and Chief Nursing Officer
Web address: www.chathamhospital.org
**Control:** Other not–for–profit (including NFP Corporation) **Service:** General Medical and Surgical

**Staffed Beds:** 25 **Admissions:** 582 **Census:** 6 **Outpatient Visits:** 37643 **Births:** 1 **Total Expense ($000):** 24893 **Payroll Expense ($000):** 8201 **Personnel:** 186

### SMITHFIELD—Johnston County

✠ **JOHNSTON HEALTH (340090)**, 509 North Bright Leaf Boulevard, Zip 27577–4407, Mailing Address: P.O. Box 1376, Zip 27577–1376; tel. 919/934–8171 **A**1 9 10 **F**3 8 11 13 15 17 18 20 26 28 29 30 31 34 35 40 42 45 50 53 54 56 57 59 60 61 62 63 64 68 70 73 74 75 76 79 81 82 85 86 87 89 92 93 97 98 100 107 108 110 111 114 115 119 120 121 122 126 129 130 132 144 146 147 148 **P**6 **S** QHR, Brentwood, TN
Primary Contact: Charles W. Elliott, Jr., Chief Executive Officer
COO: Ruth Marler, Chief Operating Officer/Chief Nursing Officer
CFO: Edward A. Klein, Chief Financial Officer
CIO: Teresa Chappell, Chief Information Officer
CHR: Timothy A. Hays, Vice President Human Resources
CNO: Ruth Marler, Chief Operating Officer/Chief Nursing Officer
Web address: www.johnstonhealth.org
**Control:** Hospital district or authority, Government, nonfederal **Service:** General Medical and Surgical

**Staffed Beds:** 141 **Admissions:** 8762 **Census:** 92 **Outpatient Visits:** 162524 **Births:** 1335 **Total Expense ($000):** 158709 **Payroll Expense ($000):** 61181 **Personnel:** 1118

### SOUTHPORT—Brunswick County

✠ **J. ARTHUR DOSHER MEMORIAL HOSPITAL (341327)**, 924 North Howe Street, Zip 28461–3099; tel. 910/457–3800, (Total facility includes 57 beds in nursing home–type unit) **A**1 9 10 18 **F**3 15 28 30 34 35 40 45 46 47 53 54 57 59 65 68 75 77 79 81 85 92 93 94 107 110 114 119 128 129 130 132 133 143 146
Primary Contact: Thomas R. Siemers, Chief Executive Officer
COO: Lynda Stanley, Senior Vice President and Chief Operating Officer
CFO: Dennis J. Coffey, CPA, Senior Vice President and Chief Financial Officer
CMO: Brad L. Hilaman, M.D., Chief of Staff
CIO: Susan Shomaker, Director Information Management Systems
CHR: Pat Aderhold, Director Human Resources
Web address: www.dosher.org
**Control:** Other not–for–profit (including NFP Corporation) **Service:** General Medical and Surgical

**Staffed Beds:** 82 **Admissions:** 1260 **Census:** 60 **Outpatient Visits:** 57475 **Births:** 0 **Total Expense ($000):** 33851 **Payroll Expense ($000):** 14151 **Personnel:** 290

### SPARTA—Alleghany County

✠ **ALLEGHANY MEMORIAL HOSPITAL (341320)**, 233 Doctors Street, Zip 28675–9247, Mailing Address: P.O. Box 9, Zip 28675–0009; tel. 336/372–5511 **A**1 9 10 18 **F**3 15 29 30 34 35 40 43 45 57 59 64 67 77 79 81 82 87 90 93 97 107 111 119 129 130 131 133 135 146 **S** Alliant Management Services, Louisville, KY
Primary Contact: Wendy Orton, Chief Executive Officer
CFO: Katie Myers, Chief Financial Officer
CMO: Jack Cahn, M.D., Chief Medical Staff
CIO: Darlene Keith, Chief Information Systems
CHR: John Spencer, Director Human Resources
Web address: www.amhsparta.org
**Control:** Other not–for–profit (including NFP Corporation) **Service:** General Medical and Surgical

**Staffed Beds:** 25 **Admissions:** 574 **Census:** 6 **Outpatient Visits:** 26994 **Births:** 0 **Total Expense ($000):** 11273 **Payroll Expense ($000):** 4504 **Personnel:** 139

### SPRUCE PINE—Mitchell County

✠ **BLUE RIDGE REGIONAL HOSPITAL (340011)**, 125 Hospital Drive, Zip 28777–3035, Mailing Address: P.O. Drawer 9, Zip 28777–0009; tel. 828/765–4201 **A**1 9 10 **F**3 13 15 17 28 29 30 31 32 34 35 39 40 43 45 46 50 53 54 57 59 64 66 70 75 76 77 78 79 81 82 85 87 90 93 96 97 107 108 111 114 118 119 127 128 129 130 131 132 133 135 144 145 146 147 148 **P**6 **S** Mission Health System, Asheville, NC
Primary Contact: Oscar K. Weinmeister, III, FACHE, President and Chief Executive Officer
CMO: David Hoeppner, M.D., Chief of Staff
CIO: Pam Blevins, R.N., Director, Clinical Informatics
CHR: Thomas White, Director Human Resources
CNO: A. Jane Edwards, MSN, Vice President, Patient Care Services
Web address: www.spchospital.org
**Control:** Other not–for–profit (including NFP Corporation) **Service:** General Medical and Surgical

**Staffed Beds:** 42 **Admissions:** 2016 **Census:** 17 **Outpatient Visits:** 109238 **Births:** 162 **Total Expense ($000):** 34879 **Payroll Expense ($000):** 17782 **Personnel:** 380

### STATESVILLE—Iredell County

☐ **DAVIS REGIONAL MEDICAL CENTER (340144)**, 218 Old Mocksville Road, Zip 28625–1930, Mailing Address: P.O. Box 1823, Zip 28687–1823; tel. 704/873–0281, (Nonreporting) **A**1 9 10 19 **S** Health Management Associates, Naples, FL
Primary Contact: Vincent T. Cherry, Jr., Chief Executive Officer
CFO: Kyle Johnson, Chief Financial Officer
CMO: Seema Garcha, M.D., Chief of Staff
CIO: Janie Stikeleather, Director Marketing and Community Relations
CHR: Lana Smith, Director Human Resources
Web address: www.davisregional.com
**Control:** Corporation, Investor–owned, for–profit **Service:** General Medical and Surgical

**Staffed Beds:** 131

✠ **IREDELL MEMORIAL HOSPITAL (340039)**, 557 Brookdale Drive, Zip 28677–4107, Mailing Address: P.O. Box 1828, Zip 28687–1828; tel. 704/873–5661, (Total facility includes 48 beds in nursing home–type unit) **A**1 2 9 10 **F**3 11 13 15 17 18 20 22 28 29 30 31 32 34 35 40 41 45 47 49 50 56 57 58 59 60 62 64 68 70 74 75 76 77 78 79 81 82 85 86 87 89 93 97 107 108 111 114 115 117 118 119 120 121 123 128 129 130 132 135 146 147 148 **P**6
Primary Contact: Ed Rush, President and Chief Executive Officer
CFO: Fred W. Karnap, Vice President Finance
CMO: James Bradford, M.D., President Medical Staff
CIO: Myers M. David, Chief Information Officer
CHR: John Green, Vice President Human Resources
Web address: www.iredellmemorial.org
**Control:** Other not–for–profit (including NFP Corporation) **Service:** General Medical and Surgical

**Staffed Beds:** 203 **Admissions:** 8771 **Census:** 132 **Outpatient Visits:** 123397 **Births:** 810 **Total Expense ($000):** 124111 **Payroll Expense ($000):** 55730 **Personnel:** 988

---

**Hospital, Medicare Provider Number, Address, Telephone, Approval, Facility, and Physician Codes, Health Care System**

★ American Hospital Association (AHA) membership
☐ The Joint Commission accreditation
◇ DNV Healthcare Inc. accreditation
○ Healthcare Facilities Accreditation Program
△ Commission on Accreditation of Rehabilitation Facilities (CARF) accreditation

**NC**

## SYLVA—Jackson County

☒ **MEDWEST – HARRIS (340016)**, 68 Hospital Road, Zip 28779–2722;
tel. 828/586–7000 **A**1 9 10 **F**3 7 8 11 13 15 28 29 30 31 34 35 40 46 50 54
62 63 64 68 70 72 75 76 77 78 79 81 82 84 85 86 87 89 93 107 108 110
111 114 119 120 121 129 130 131 135 143 144 146 147 148 **S** MedWest
Health System, Sylva, NC
Primary Contact: Steve Heatherly, Chief Executive Officer
CIO: Dale Chernich, Chief Information Officer
CHR: Janet Millsaps, Chief Human Resources Officer
Web address: www.westcare.org
**Control:** Other not–for–profit (including NFP Corporation) **Service:** General
Medical and Surgical

**Staffed Beds:** 86 **Admissions:** 3592 **Census:** 35 **Outpatient Visits:** 188257
**Births:** 610 **Total Expense ($000):** 97989 **Payroll Expense ($000):** 43956
**Personnel:** 722

## TARBORO—Edgecombe County

☒ △ **VIDANT EDGECOMBE HOSPITAL (340107)**, 111 Hospital Drive,
Zip 27886–2011; tel. 252/641–7700 **A**1 2 7 9 10 **F**3 11 12 13 15 18 28 29
30 31 39 40 45 50 57 59 70 73 75 76 78 79 81 82 85 87 89 90 92 93 96
107 110 111 119 127 130 131 132 135 145 146 **S** Vidant Health,
Greenville, NC
Primary Contact: Patrick Heins, President
CFO: Charles Alford, Vice President Financial Services
CMO: Barry Bunn, M.D., Chief of Staff
CHR: Kadie Moore, Director Human Resources
Web address: www.https://www.vidanthealth.com/edgecombe/default.aspx
**Control:** Other not–for–profit (including NFP Corporation) **Service:** General
Medical and Surgical

**Staffed Beds:** 117 **Admissions:** 4378 **Census:** 47 **Outpatient Visits:** 60436
**Births:** 477 **Total Expense ($000):** 77353 **Payroll Expense ($000):** 25317
**Personnel:** 483

## THOMASVILLE—Davidson County

☒ **NOVANT HEALTH THOMASVILLE MEDICAL CENTER (340085)**, (Formerly
Thomasville Medical Center), 207 Old Lexington Road, Zip 27360–3428, Mailing
Address: P.O. Box 789, Zip 27361–0789; tel. 336/472–2000 **A**1 9 10 **F**13 15
20 28 29 30 34 35 40 45 47 48 56 57 59 64 70 74 75 76 77 79 81 85 86
87 89 93 98 103 104 107 108 111 114 117 118 119 124 129 130 131 132
135 146 147 148 **P**6 **S** Novant Health, Winston Salem, NC
Primary Contact: Kathie A. Johnson, R.N., MS, Ph.D., Chief Executive Officer
CNO: Christina Grabus, R.N., Chief Nursing Officer
Web address: www.thomasvillemedicalcenter.org
**Control:** Other not–for–profit (including NFP Corporation) **Service:** General
Medical and Surgical

**Staffed Beds:** 101 **Admissions:** 4236 **Census:** 61 **Outpatient Visits:** 140512
**Births:** 560 **Total Expense ($000):** 67365 **Payroll Expense ($000):** 25934
**Personnel:** 521

## TROY—Montgomery County

☒ **FIRSTHEALTH MONTGOMERY MEMORIAL HOSPITAL (341303)**, 520 Allen
Street, Zip 27371–2802, Mailing Address: P.O. Box 486, Zip 27371–0486;
tel. 910/572–1301 **A**1 9 10 18 **F**3 11 15 29 30 40 45 59 64 81 85 87 93 97
107 110 114 119 127 129 133 146 **S** FirstHealth of the Carolinas,
Pinehurst, NC
Primary Contact: Beth Walker, R.N., President
CFO: Bryan Hawkins, Controller
CHR: Tina H. Thompson, Coordinator Human Resources
Web address: www.firsthealth.org
**Control:** Other not–for–profit (including NFP Corporation) **Service:** General
Medical and Surgical

**Staffed Beds:** 25 **Admissions:** 291 **Census:** 2 **Outpatient Visits:** 22241
**Births:** 0 **Total Expense ($000):** 11119 **Payroll Expense ($000):** 5709
**Personnel:** 116

## VALDESE—Burke County

☒ **VALDESE GENERAL HOSPITAL (340055)**, 720 Malcolm Boulevard,
Zip 28690–2872, Mailing Address: P.O. Box 700, Zip 28690–0700;
tel. 828/874–2251, (Nonreporting) **A**1 2 9 10 **S** Blue Ridge HealthCare,
Morganton, NC
Primary Contact: Kathy C. Bailey, Ph.D., FACHE, President and Chief Executive
Officer
CFO: Robert G. Fritts, Chief Financial Officer and Senior Vice President
CMO: Dorwyn Croon, M.D., President Medical Staff
CMO: Joe Mazzola, D.O., Sr. Vice President Medical Affairs/Chief Quality Officer
CHR: David Shirlen, Vice President Human Resources
CNO: Susan Brown, R.N., Sr. Vice President, Chief Nursing Officer
Web address: www.blueridgehealth.org
**Control:** Other not–for–profit (including NFP Corporation) **Service:** General
Medical and Surgical

**Staffed Beds:** 155

## WADESBORO—Anson County

☒ **ANSON COMMUNITY HOSPITAL (340084)**, 500 Morven Road,
Zip 28170–2745; tel. 704/694–5131, (Total facility includes 95 beds in nursing
home–type unit) **A**1 9 10 **F**1 4 11 15 16 17 28 29 30 34 35 40 57 59 62 64
65 67 70 71 72 73 77 80 81 86 87 88 89 90 93 97 98 107 110 114 119
128 130 132 133 135 145 146 **S** Carolinas HealthCare System, Charlotte, NC
Primary Contact: Frederick G. Thompson, Ph.D., President
CFO: John G. Moore, Chief Financial Officer
CMO: A. Niazi, M.D., Chief of Staff
CIO: Lisa Sykes, IS/Communications Director
CHR: Sherri McRorie, Director Human Resources
CNO: Paula Stegall, R.N., Chief Nurse Executive
Web address: www.carolinashealthcare.org/anson–community–hospital
**Control:** Hospital district or authority, Government, nonfederal **Service:** General
Medical and Surgical

**Staffed Beds:** 125 **Admissions:** 743 **Census:** 87 **Outpatient Visits:** 25741
**Births:** 0 **Total Expense ($000):** 22534 **Payroll Expense ($000):** 9767
**Personnel:** 238

## WASHINGTON—Beaufort County

**BEAUFORT COUNTY HOSPITAL** See Vidant Beaufort Hospital

☒ **VIDANT BEAUFORT HOSPITAL (340186)**, 628 East 12th Street,
Zip 27889–3409; tel. 252/975–4100 **A**1 9 10 **F**3 5 7 9 13 15 26 27 28 29 30
31 34 35 36 38 40 49 53 57 59 64 65 69 70 75 76 78 79 81 82 85 86 87
93 97 98 99 100 101 102 104 107 108 109 111 115 118 119 129 130 132
135 143 144 145 146 **S** Vidant Health, Greenville, NC
Primary Contact: Harvey Case, President
CMO: Jay Manning, M.D., Chief of Staff
CIO: Amy Boyd, Information Systems Manager
CHR: Penny Coltrain, Director Human Resources
CNO: Lynne Fisher, R.N., Vice President of Patient Care Services
Web address: www.beaufortregionalhealthsystem.org
**Control:** Hospital district or authority, Government, nonfederal **Service:** General
Medical and Surgical

**Staffed Beds:** 95 **Admissions:** 3089 **Census:** 35 **Outpatient Visits:** 81557
**Births:** 343 **Total Expense ($000):** 61023 **Payroll Expense ($000):** 22673
**Personnel:** 475

## WHITEVILLE—Columbus County

☒ **COLUMBUS REGIONAL HEALTHCARE SYSTEM (340068)**, 500 Jefferson
Street, Zip 28472–3634; tel. 910/642–8011 **A**1 9 10 19 **F**3 11 13 15 18 28
29 30 31 34 35 40 45 50 54 57 59 64 70 74 75 76 78 79 81 85 86 87 89
92 93 97 107 108 110 111 119 126 129 130 132 146 **P**6 7 **S** Carolinas
HealthCare System, Charlotte, NC
Primary Contact: Henry Hawthorne, III, President and Chief Executive Officer
COO: A. Todd Howell, Chief Operating Officer
CFO: Carl Biber, Chief Financial Officer
CMO: Craig M. Slater, M.D., Chief Medical Officer
CIO: Lisa Ward, Director Management Information Systems
CHR: Ginger Scott, Vice President Human Resources
Web address: www.crhealthcare.org
**Control:** Hospital district or authority, Government, nonfederal **Service:** General
Medical and Surgical

**Staffed Beds:** 103 **Admissions:** 5195 **Census:** 59 **Outpatient Visits:** 130180
**Births:** 424 **Total Expense ($000):** 71750 **Payroll Expense ($000):** 28736
**Personnel:** 592

## WILLIAMSTON—Martin County

☒ **MARTIN GENERAL HOSPITAL (340133)**, 310 South McCaskey Road,
Zip 27892–2150, Mailing Address: P.O. Box 1128, Zip 27892–1128;
tel. 252/809–6179 **A**1 9 10 **F**3 11 13 15 29 34 35 40 45 50 56 57 59 61 64
65 70 76 77 79 81 82 87 92 93 97 107 111 119 129 133 147 **S** Community
Health Systems, Inc., Franklin, TN
Primary Contact: Jodi Beauregard, Chief Executive Officer
CFO: Craig R. Fichter, Chief Financial Officer
CIO: James Griffin, Manager Information Systems
CHR: Rebecca Edwards, Director Human Resources
CNO: Molly Wells, Chief Nursing Officer
Web address: www.martingeneral.com
**Control:** Corporation, Investor–owned, for–profit **Service:** General Medical and
Surgical

**Staffed Beds:** 49 **Admissions:** 2230 **Census:** 22 **Outpatient Visits:** 47027
**Births:** 172 **Total Expense ($000):** 26777 **Payroll Expense ($000):** 12987
**Personnel:** 243

## WILMINGTON—New Hanover County

☒ △ **NEW HANOVER REGIONAL MEDICAL CENTER (340141)**, 2131 South
17th Street, Zip 28401–7483, Mailing Address: P.O. Box 9000,
Zip 28402–9000; tel. 910/343–7000, (Includes CAPE FEAR HOSPITAL, 5301
Wrightsville Avenue, Zip 28403–6599; tel. 910/452–8100) **A**1 2 3 5 7 9 10 12
13 **F**3 7 8 11 12 13 15 17 18 20 22 24 26 28 29 30 31 34 35 36 37 39 40
43 44 45 46 48 49 50 53 54 56 57 58 59 60 61 64 65 66 68 70 72 73 74
75 76 77 78 79 80 81 82 84 85 86 87 88 89 90 92 93 94 96 97 98 100
101 102 103 107 108 110 111 114 115 117 118 119 120 121 123 126 130
131 132 135 144 146 147 148 **S** New Hanover Regional Medical Center,
Wilmington, NC
Primary Contact: John K. Barto, Jr., President and Chief Executive Officer
CFO: Edwin J. Ollie, Executive Vice President and Chief Financial Officer
CMO: Sam Spicer, M.D., Vice President Medical Affairs
CIO: Avery Cloud, Vice President and Chief Information Officer
CHR: Keith A. Strawn, Vice President Human Resources
Web address: www.nhhn.org
**Control:** County–Government, nonfederal **Service:** General Medical and Surgical

**Staffed Beds:** 678 **Admissions:** 36683 **Census:** 500 **Outpatient Visits:**
332106 **Births:** 3837 **Total Expense ($000):** 649157 **Payroll Expense
($000):** 245201 **Personnel:** 4245

**WILMINGTON TREATMENT CENTER (340168)**, 2520 Troy Drive,
Zip 28401–7643; tel. 910/762–2727 **A**10 **F**4 5 29 54 64 132 **P**6
Primary Contact: Robert Pitts, Executive Director
COO: Paige Bottom, Director Operations
CFO: Virginia Powell, Director Finance
CMO: Patrick Martin, M.D., Medical Director
Web address: www.wilmtreatment.com
**Control:** Corporation, Investor–owned, for–profit **Service:** Alcoholism and other
chemical dependency

**Staffed Beds:** 44 **Admissions:** 931 **Census:** 15 **Outpatient Visits:** 30762
**Total Expense ($000):** 11689 **Payroll Expense ($000):** 3902 **Personnel:**
107

## WILSON—Wilson County

**TRIANGLE EAST NURSING CARE CENTER** See WilMed Nursing Care Center

☒ **WILSON MEDICAL CENTER (340126)**, 1705 Tarboro Street, S.W.,
Zip 27893–3428; tel. 252/399–8040 **A**1 2 9 10 19 **F**3 11 13 15 18 19 20 22
26 28 29 30 31 34 39 40 43 45 47 48 49 57 60 64 70 73 74 75 76 77 78
79 81 82 83 84 85 86 87 89 90 92 93 94 97 98 101 102 103 107 108 110
111 114 115 118 119 120 121 123 127 129 130 132 135 146 148 **P**6
Primary Contact: Richard E. Hudson, FACHE, President and Chief Executive Officer
CFO: Lynn Lambert, Chief Financial Officer
CMO: Rick Guarino, M.D., Vice President Medical Affairs
CIO: Brian Dietrick, Director Information Systems
CHR: Denise O'Hara, Vice President Human Resources
CNO: Catherine A. Rhyne, R.N., Interim Vice President Clinical Services
Web address: www.wilmed.org
**Control:** Other not–for–profit (including NFP Corporation) **Service:** General
Medical and Surgical

**Staffed Beds:** 220 **Admissions:** 7595 **Census:** 90 **Outpatient Visits:** 142983
**Births:** 1034 **Total Expense ($000):** 130766 **Payroll Expense ($000):**
55468 **Personnel:** 1074

## WINDSOR—Bertie County

☒ **VIDANT BERTIE HOSPITAL (341304)**, 1403 South King Street,
Zip 27983–9666, Mailing Address: P.O. Box 40, Zip 27983–0040;
tel. 252/794–6600 **A**1 9 10 18 **F**3 15 29 30 34 35 40 45 57 59 64 77 78 79
81 82 93 94 97 107 110 114 119 127 132 135 146 **S** Vidant Health,
Greenville, NC
Primary Contact: Jeffery Dial, Acting Chief Executive Officer
COO: Jeffery Dial, Chief Operating Officer
CFO: Brian Harvill, Vice President Financial Services
CMO: William Ballance, M.D., Chief of Medical Staff
CIO: Megan Booth-Mills, Director Planning and Marketing
CHR: Mary Beth Hill, Coordinator Human Resources
CNO: Patricia Taylor, Director, Patient Care Services
Web address: www.vidanthealth.com
**Control:** Other not–for–profit (including NFP Corporation) **Service:** General
Medical and Surgical

**Staffed Beds:** 6 **Admissions:** 441 **Census:** 4 **Outpatient Visits:** 23691
**Births:** 0 **Total Expense ($000):** 17562 **Payroll Expense ($000):** 7334
**Personnel:** 124

## WINSTON SALEM—Forsyth County

**BRENNER CHILDREN'S HOSPITAL & HEALTH SERVICES** See Wake Forest
Baptist Medical Center, Winston–Salem

## WINSTON–SALEM—Forsyth County

☒ **NOVANT HEALTH FORSYTH MEDICAL CENTER (340014)**, (Formerly Forsyth
Medical Center), 3333 Silas Creek Parkway, Zip 27103–3090;
tel. 336/718–5000, (Includes KERNERSVILLE MEDICAL CENTER, 2911750
Kernersville Medical Parkway, Kernersville, Zip 27284–2932, Mailing Address:
1750 Kernersville Medical Parkway, Zip 27284–2932; tel. 336/564–4000;
Joanne Allen, R.N., President) **A**1 2 3 5 9 10 **F**3 4 5 7 8 9 10 13 14 17 18 20
22 24 26 28 29 30 31 32 34 35 37 38 40 42 44 45 46 49 50 53 54 56 57
58 59 60 61 64 65 66 67 68 70 71 72 74 75 76 77 78 79 80 81 82 83 84
85 86 87 89 90 93 98 100 101 102 103 104 105 107 108 109 111 112 114
115 116 117 118 119 120 121 123 124 126 128 129 130 131 132 135 143
146 147 148 **P**6 **S** Novant Health, Winston Salem, NC
Primary Contact: Jeffery T. Lindsay, President
COO: Paul Hammes, Senior Vice President and Chief Operating Officer
CMO: Elms Allen, M.D., Senior Vice President Medical Affairs
CIO: David B. Garrett, Chief Information Officer
CHR: Janet Smith-Hill, Senior Vice President Human Resources
Web address: www.forsythmedicalcenter.org
**Control:** Other not–for–profit (including NFP Corporation) **Service:** General
Medical and Surgical

**Staffed Beds:** 672 **Admissions:** 42626 **Census:** 631 **Outpatient Visits:**
385228 **Births:** 6305 **Total Expense ($000):** 657354 **Payroll Expense
($000):** 229100 **Personnel:** 4110

☒ **NOVANT HEALTH MEDICAL PARK HOSPITAL (340148)**, (Formerly Medical
Park Hospital), 1950 South Hawthorne Road, Zip 27103–3993;
tel. 336/718–0600 **A**1 9 10 **F**3 29 35 39 64 68 74 78 79 81 82 85 89 126
130 131 146 **S** Novant Health, Winston Salem, NC
Primary Contact: Teresa Carter, Vice President and Chief Operating Officer
COO: Jeffery T. Lindsay, Executive Vice President and Chief Operating Officer
CMO: Elms Allen, M.D., Senior Vice President Medical Affairs
CHR: Vasilia Perimenis, Vice President Human Resources
Web address: www.novanthealth.org
**Control:** Other not–for–profit (including NFP Corporation) **Service:** General
Medical and Surgical

**Staffed Beds:** 22 **Admissions:** 706 **Census:** 7 **Outpatient Visits:** 38406
**Births:** 0 **Total Expense ($000):** 44354 **Payroll Expense ($000):** 11838
**Personnel:** 203

☐ **OLD VINEYARD BEHAVIORAL HEALTH SERVICES (344007)**, 3637 Old
Vineyard Road, Zip 27104–4842; tel. 336/794–3550 **A**1 10 **F**29 75 87 98 99
101 102 103 104 105 130 **S** Universal Health Services, Inc., King of Prussia, PA
Primary Contact: Kevin Patton, Chief Executive Officer
CFO: Ernest C. Priddy, III, Chief Financial Officer
CMO: Raj Thotakura, M.D., Medical Director
CHR: Jackie Pennino, Director Human Resources
CNO: Carol Fisher, Director of Nursing
Web address: www.oldvineyard.net
**Control:** Corporation, Investor–owned, for–profit **Service:** Psychiatric

**Staffed Beds:** 102 **Admissions:** 3901 **Census:** 90 **Outpatient Visits:** 3740
**Births:** 0 **Total Expense ($000):** 18081 **Payroll Expense ($000):** 9088
**Personnel:** 211

☒ **SELECT SPECIALTY HOSPITAL–WINSTON–SALEM (342016)**, 3333 Silas
Creek Parkway, 6th Floor, Zip 27103–3013; tel. 336/718–6300, (Nonreporting)
**A**1 10 **S** Select Medical Corporation, Mechanicsburg, PA
Primary Contact: Leslie Deane, Chief Executive Officer
CHR: Sherry Meacham, Coordinator Human Resources
Web address: www.selectspecialtyhospitals.com/company/locations/winston–
salem.aspx
**Control:** Corporation, Investor–owned, for–profit **Service:** Long–Term Acute Care
hospital

**Staffed Beds:** 42

⊠ △ **WAKE FOREST BAPTIST MEDICAL CENTER (340047)**, Medical Center Boulevard, Zip 27157–0001; tel. 336/716–2011, (Includes BRENNER CHILDREN'S HOSPITAL & HEALTH SERVICES, Medical Center Boulevard, Winston Salem, Zip 27157, Mailing Address: One Medical Center Boulevard, Zip 27157; tel. 336/716–2255) **A**1 3 5 7 8 9 10 **F**3 5 6 7 8 9 11 12 15 16 17 18 19 20 21 22 23 24 25 26 27 28 29 30 31 32 34 35 36 37 38 39 40 41 43 44 45 46 47 48 49 50 52 53 54 55 56 57 58 59 60 61 64 65 66 67 68 70 71 72 73 74 75 77 78 79 80 81 82 83 84 85 86 87 88 89 90 92 93 96 97 98 99 100 101 102 103 104 107 108 110 111 113 114 115 116 117 118 119 120 121 123 124 126 129 130 131 132 133 134 135 136 137 138 141 142 143 144 145 146 147 148 **P**6 7 **S** Wake Forest Baptist Health, Winston–Salem, NC
Primary Contact: Sanjay K. Saha, Executive Vice President, Operations
CFO: Gina B. Ramsey, Vice President Financial Services and Chief Financial Officer
CMO: Patricia L. Adams, M.D., Chief Professional Services
CIO: Paul M. LoRusso, Vice President Information Services and Chief Information Officer
Web address: www.wfubmc.edu
**Control:** Other not–for–profit (including NFP Corporation) **Service:** General Medical and Surgical

| | |
|---|---|
| **Staffed Beds:** 853 **Admissions:** 38555 **Census:** 657 **Outpatient Visits:** 805593 **Births:** 15 **Total Expense ($000):** 1167730 **Payroll Expense ($000):** 441016 **Personnel:** 8275 | |

**WAKE FOREST UNIVERSITY HEALTH SERVICE (349803)**, Medical Center Boulevard, Zip 27109, Mailing Address: P.O. Box 7386, Zip 27109–7386; tel. 336/758–5937, (Nonreporting) **A**2 10
Primary Contact: Cecil Price, M.D., Director
Web address: www.wfu.edu
**Control:** Other not–for–profit (including NFP Corporation) **Service:** Hospital unit of an institution (prison hospital, college infimary, etc.)

| | |
|---|---|
| **Staffed Beds:** 6 | |

### YADKINVILLE—Yadkin County

**HOOTS MEMORIAL HOSPITAL** See Yadkin Valley Community Hospital

⊠ ◇ **YADKIN VALLEY COMMUNITY HOSPITAL (341308)**, 624 West Main Street, Zip 27055–7804, Mailing Address: P.O. Box 68, Zip 27055–0068; tel. 336/679–2041, (Nonreporting) **A**1 9 10 18 21 **S** Rural Community Hospitals of America, Kansas City, MO
Primary Contact: Shawn Bright, Chief Executive Officer
CFO: Julie Norman, Chief Financial Officer
CHR: Bruce Niemeyer, Director Human Resources
Web address: www.yadkinhospital.com/
**Control:** Other not–for–profit (including NFP Corporation) **Service:** General Medical and Surgical

| | |
|---|---|
| **Staffed Beds:** 22 | |

# NORTH DAKOTA

## ASHLEY—McIntosh County

★ **ASHLEY MEDICAL CENTER (351322)**, 612 North Center Avenue,
Zip 58413–7013, Mailing Address: P.O. Box 450, Zip 58413–0450;
tel. 701/288–3433, (Nonreporting) **A**9 10 18
Primary Contact: Jerry Lepp, Chief Executive Officer
CMO: Udom Tinsa, M.D., Medical Director
Web address: www.amctoday.org
**Control:** Other not–for–profit (including NFP Corporation) **Service:** General
Medical and Surgical

| **Staffed Beds:** 64 |
| --- |

## BELCOURT—Rolette County

☐ **PUBLIC HEALTH SERVICE INDIAN HOSPITAL – QUENTIN N. BURDICK
MEMORIAL HEALTH FACILITY (350063)**, 2 Blocks North of Highway 5,
Zip 58316, Mailing Address: P.O. Box 160, Zip 58316–0160; tel. 701/477–6111
**A**1 3 5 10 **F**7 13 29 39 40 41 64 65 68 76 81 89 93 97 99 102 104 107
108 119 132 135 147 **S** U. S. Indian Health Service, Rockville, MD
Primary Contact: Shelly Harris, Chief Executive Officer
CFO: Peggy Poitra, Financial Management Specialist
CMO: Monica Mayer, M.D., Clinical Director
CIO: Duane Marcellais, Information Technology Specialist
CHR: Donna Belgarde, Human Resources Specialist
Web address: www.ihs.gov
**Control:** PHS, Indian Service, Government, federal **Service:** General Medical and
Surgical

| **Staffed Beds:** 27 **Admissions:** 836 **Census:** 8 **Outpatient Visits:** 75336 |
| --- |
| **Births:** 203 **Total Expense ($000):** 26811 **Payroll Expense ($000):** 20453 |
| **Personnel:** 322 |

## BISMARCK—Burleigh County

⊠ △ **SANFORD BISMARCK (350015)**, (Formerly Sanford Health), 300 North
Seventh Street, Zip 58501–4439, Mailing Address: P.O. Box 5525,
Zip 58506–5525; tel. 701/323–6000, (Total facility includes 18 beds in nursing
home–type unit) (Data for 182 days) **A**1 2 3 5 7 9 10 **F**3 9 11 12 13 15 17 18
20 22 24 26 28 29 30 31 32 33 34 35 36 37 38 40 43 44 45 48 49 50 51
52 53 54 56 57 58 59 60 61 62 63 64 65 69 70 72 73 74 75 76 77 78 79
81 82 85 86 87 88 89 90 91 92 93 96 97 98 99 100 101 102 103 104 105
107 108 110 111 114 115 116 117 118 119 126 128 129 130 131 132 135
138 144 146 147 148 **P**6 **S** Sanford Health, Sioux Falls, SD
Primary Contact: Craig Lambrecht, M.D., President
CFO: Paul Morth, Vice President Finance
CMO: Anthoney M. Tello, M.D., Medical Director
CIO: John Miller, Vice President Information Services
CHR: Scott D. Boehm, Vice President Human Resources
Web address: www.bismarck.sanfordhealth.org/
**Control:** Other not–for–profit (including NFP Corporation) **Service:** General
Medical and Surgical

| **Staffed Beds:** 207 **Admissions:** 5554 **Census:** 143 **Outpatient Visits:** |
| --- |
| 365677 **Births:** 425 **Total Expense ($000):** 161674 **Payroll Expense** |
| **($000):** 86663 **Personnel:** 2555 |

**SANFORD HEALTH** See Sanford Bismarck

⊠ △ **ST. ALEXIUS MEDICAL CENTER (350002)**, 900 East Broadway,
Zip 58501–4586, Mailing Address: P.O. Box 5510, Zip 58506–5510;
tel. 701/530–7000, (Total facility includes 19 beds in nursing home–type unit) **A**1
2 3 5 7 9 10 **F**3 8 9 11 12 13 15 17 18 19 20 21 22 23 24 25 26 28 29 30
32 34 35 38 40 43 49 53 56 57 58 59 60 62 63 64 68 70 72 74 75 76 77
78 79 81 82 85 86 88 89 90 91 92 93 94 98 99 100 101 102 103 104 105
107 110 111 114 117 119 127 128 129 130 131 132 135 145 146 147 148
**P**8 **S** Benedictine Sisters of the Annunciation, Bismarck, ND
Primary Contact: Gary P. Miller, President and Chief Executive Officer
CFO: Gary P. Miller, President and Chief Executive Officer
CMO: Shiraz Hyder, M.D., Director Medical Affairs
CIO: Todd Bortke, Director Information Systems
CHR: Wanda Pfaff, Vice President Human Resources
Web address: www.st.alexius.org
**Control:** Church–operated, Nongovernment, not–for profit **Service:** General
Medical and Surgical

| **Staffed Beds:** 283 **Admissions:** 11333 **Census:** 142 **Outpatient Visits:** |
| --- |
| 234138 **Births:** 1491 **Total Expense ($000):** 246958 **Payroll Expense** |
| **($000):** 117658 **Personnel:** 1977 |

## BOTTINEAU—Bottineau County

**ST. ANDREW'S HEALTH CENTER (351307)**, 316 Ohmer Street,
Zip 58318–1045; tel. 701/228–9300 **A**5 9 10 18 **F**15 28 29 30 34 35 40 45
47 50 56 57 64 75 81 83 87 89 97 107 110 125 127 128 130 131 132 133
135 143 144 146 148 **P**5 **S** Sisters of Mary of the Presentation Health System,
Fargo, ND
Primary Contact: Jodi Atkinson, President and Chief Executive Officer
CHR: Brenda Arneson, Administrative Assistant
Web address: www.standrewshealth.com
**Control:** Church–operated, Nongovernment, not–for profit **Service:** General
Medical and Surgical

| **Staffed Beds:** 25 **Admissions:** 124 **Census:** 1 **Outpatient Visits:** 7516 |
| --- |
| **Births:** 0 **Total Expense ($000):** 6356 **Payroll Expense ($000):** 2537 |
| **Personnel:** 79 |

## BOWMAN—Bowman County

**SOUTHWEST HEALTHCARE SERVICES (351313)**, 802 2nd Street Northwest,
Zip 58623–4483, Mailing Address: P.O. Drawer C, Zip 58623;
tel. 701/523–5265, (Nonreporting) **A**9 10 18
Primary Contact: Becky Hansen, Chief Executive Officer
CFO: Becky Hansen, Chief Financial Officer
Web address: www.swhealthcare.net
**Control:** Other not–for–profit (including NFP Corporation) **Service:** General
Medical and Surgical

| **Staffed Beds:** 89 |
| --- |

## CANDO—Towner County

★ **TOWNER COUNTY MEDICAL CENTER (351331)**, State Highway 281 North,
Zip 58324, Mailing Address: P.O. Box 688, Zip 58324–0688;
tel. 701/968–4411, (Nonreporting) **A**5 9 10 18
Primary Contact: Ivan Mitchell, Chief Executive Officer
CFO: Tammy Larson, Chief Financial Officer
CMO: Russ Petty, M.D., Chief of Staff
CHR: Pat Klingenberg, Director Human Resources
Web address: www.tcmedcenter.org
**Control:** Other not–for–profit (including NFP Corporation) **Service:** General
Medical and Surgical

| **Staffed Beds:** 20 |
| --- |

## CARRINGTON—Foster County

★ **CARRINGTON HEALTH CENTER (351318)**, 800 North Fourth Street,
Zip 58421–1217, Mailing Address: P.O. Box 461, Zip 58421–0461;
tel. 701/652–3141, (Total facility includes 19 beds in nursing home–type unit) **A**5
9 10 18 **F**1 3 4 7 11 12 15 16 17 28 29 30 31 34 35 40 41 43 45 53 56 57
59 64 66 67 68 70 72 73 75 80 81 85 88 89 90 93 98 107 110 114 119
127 128 130 132 133 143 146 148 **P**6 **S** Catholic Health Initiatives,
Englewood, CO
Primary Contact: Mariann Doeling, R.N., President
COO: Brenda Rask, Vice President Operations
CFO: Jennifer Hoornaert, Chief Financial Officer
CMO: Michael J. Page, M.D., Chief Medical Officer
CIO: Keith Stauffer, Regional Chief Information Officer
CHR: Allison Lindgren, Chief Human Resources
CNO: Christine Schroeder, R.N., Chief Nursing Officer
Web address: www.carringtonhealthcenter.org
**Control:** Church–operated, Nongovernment, not–for profit **Service:** General
Medical and Surgical

| **Staffed Beds:** 49 **Admissions:** 494 **Census:** 25 **Outpatient Visits:** 24836 |
| --- |
| **Births:** 0 **Total Expense ($000):** 15027 **Payroll Expense ($000):** 7375 |
| **Personnel:** 144 |

---

**Hospital, Medicare Provider Number, Address, Telephone, Approval, Facility, and Physician Codes, Health Care System**

★ American Hospital Association (AHA) membership
☐ The Joint Commission accreditation
◇ DNV Healthcare Inc. accreditation

○ Healthcare Facilities Accreditation Program
△ Commission on Accreditation of Rehabilitation Facilities (CARF) accreditation

## CAVALIER—Pembina County

★ **PEMBINA COUNTY MEMORIAL HOSPITAL AND WEDGEWOOD MANOR (351319)**, 301 Mountain Street East, Zip 58220–4015, Mailing Address: P.O. Box 380, Zip 58220–0380; tel. 701/265–8461, (Total facility includes 50 beds in nursing home–type unit) **A**5 9 10 18 **F**1 2 3 4 16 17 28 29 31 40 42 43 45 56 59 65 67 68 70 72 73 76 78 80 81 82 84 85 86 87 88 90 93 97 98 107 114 119 127 128 130 131 132 133 135 146 **P**5
Primary Contact: Everett A. Butler, Chief Executive Officer
CMO: K. S. Sumra, M.D., Chief of Staff
CIO: Robert Heidt, Director Information Systems
Web address: www.cavalierhospital.com
**Control:** Other not–for–profit (including NFP Corporation) **Service:** General Medical and Surgical

| | |
|---|---|
| **Staffed Beds:** 74 **Admissions:** 252 **Census:** 51 **Outpatient Visits:** 15207 **Births:** 0 **Total Expense ($000):** 10840 **Payroll Expense ($000):** 3980 **Personnel:** 130 | |

## COOPERSTOWN—Griggs County

**COOPERSTOWN MEDICAL CENTER (351306)**, 1200 Roberts Avenue, Zip 58425–7101; tel. 701/797–2221, (Nonreporting) **A**9 10 18
Primary Contact: Gregory Stomp, Chief Executive Officer
CFO: Ken Smith, Chief Financial Officer
CMO: Jeffrey Peterson, M.D., Medical Director
CHR: Pamela VenHuizen, Chief Human Resources Officer
Web address: www.coopermc.com
**Control:** Other not–for–profit (including NFP Corporation) **Service:** General Medical and Surgical

**Staffed Beds:** 10

## CROSBY—Divide County

**ST. LUKE'S HOSPITAL (351325)**, 702 First Street Southwest, Zip 58730–3329, Mailing Address: P.O. Box 10, Zip 58730–0010; tel. 701/965–6384, (Nonreporting) **A**5 9 10 18
Primary Contact: Leslie O. Urvand, Administrator
Web address: www.dcstlukes.org/
**Control:** Other not–for–profit (including NFP Corporation) **Service:** General Medical and Surgical

**Staffed Beds:** 12

## DEVILS LAKE—Ramsey County

✠ **MERCY HOSPITAL (351333)**, 1031 Seventh Street N.E., Zip 58301–2798; tel. 701/662–2131 **A**1 5 9 10 18 **F**3 11 13 17 28 29 30 34 35 40 43 45 50 53 57 70 75 81 87 93 107 108 111 114 118 119 130 131 132 133 146 148 **S** Catholic Health Initiatives, Englewood, CO
Primary Contact: James L. Marshall, President
CHR: Tanya Knutson, Director Human Resources
Web address: www.mercyhospitaldl.com
**Control:** Other not–for–profit (including NFP Corporation) **Service:** General Medical and Surgical

| | |
|---|---|
| **Staffed Beds:** 25 **Admissions:** 1117 **Census:** 14 **Outpatient Visits:** 23147 **Births:** 316 **Total Expense ($000):** 18507 **Payroll Expense ($000):** 8206 **Personnel:** 154 | |

## DICKINSON—Stark County

✠ **ST. JOSEPH'S HOSPITAL AND HEALTH CENTER (351336)**, 30 Seventh Street West, Zip 58601–4399; tel. 701/456–4000 **A**1 5 9 10 18 **F**3 8 11 13 15 28 29 30 34 35 40 53 57 59 64 70 75 76 79 81 84 85 86 87 89 97 107 108 111 114 119 127 129 130 132 133 146 **S** Catholic Health Initiatives, Englewood, CO
Primary Contact: Reed Reyman, President
CFO: William Schneider, Chief Financial Officer
CMO: Thomas Arnold, M.D., Chief Medical Officer
CHR: Denise Lutz, Chief Human Resources Officer
CNO: Michelle Hinrichs, Chief Nursing Officer
Web address: www.stjoeshospital.org
**Control:** Church–operated, Nongovernment, not–for profit **Service:** General Medical and Surgical

| | |
|---|---|
| **Staffed Beds:** 25 **Admissions:** 1690 **Census:** 14 **Outpatient Visits:** 46203 **Births:** 450 **Total Expense ($000):** 43914 **Payroll Expense ($000):** 18948 **Personnel:** 296 | |

## ELGIN—Grant County

**JACOBSON MEMORIAL HOSPITAL CARE CENTER (351314)**, 601 East Street North, Zip 58533–7105, Mailing Address: P.O. Box 367, Zip 58533–0367; tel. 701/584–2792, (Nonreporting) **A**9 10 18
Primary Contact: Jim Opdahl, Administrator
CFO: Brandon Vaughan, Chief Financial Officer
CMO: Kent Diehl, M.D., Chief of Staff
CHR: Theo Stoller, Director Human Resources
Web address: www.jacobsonhospital.org
**Control:** Other not–for–profit (including NFP Corporation) **Service:** General Medical and Surgical

**Staffed Beds:** 46

## FARGO—Cass County

✠ **ESSENTIA HEALTH FARGO (350070)**, 3000 32nd Avenue South, Zip 58103–6132; tel. 701/364–8000, (Nonreporting) **A**1 2 5 9 10 **S** Essentia Health, Duluth, MN
Primary Contact: Greg Glasner, M.D., Interim President and Chief Executive Officer
CFO: Dennis Fuhrman, Vice President Finance
CMO: Michael Briggs, M.D., Chief Medical Officer
CIO: Ken Gilles, Chief Information Officer
CHR: Keith Wahlund, Vice President Human Resources
Web address: www.essentiahealth.com
**Control:** Other not–for–profit (including NFP Corporation) **Service:** General Medical and Surgical

**Staffed Beds:** 117

✠ **FARGO VETERANS AFFAIRS HEALTH CARE SYSTEM**, (Formerly Veterans Affairs Health Care System), 2101 Elm Street North, Zip 58102–2498; tel. 701/232–3241, (Nonreporting) **A**1 2 3 5 **S** Department of Veterans Affairs, Washington, DC
Primary Contact: Michael J. Murphy, FACHE, Director
COO: Dale DeKrey, MS, Associate Director Operations and Resources
CFO: Roger Sayler, Finance Officer
CMO: J. Brian Hancock, M.D., Chief of Staff
CIO: Raymond Nelson, Acting Chief Information Resource Management
CHR: Jason Wells, Chief Human Resources Management Service
CNO: Julie Bruhn, R.N., Associate Director Patient Care and Nurse Executive
Web address: www.fargo.va.gov/
**Control:** Veterans Affairs, Government, federal **Service:** General Medical and Surgical

**Staffed Beds:** 77

**INNOVIS HEALTH** See Essentia Health Fargo

✠ **KINDRED HOSPITAL FARGO (352004)**, 1720 University Drive South, Zip 58103–4940; tel. 701/241–9099, (Nonreporting) **A**1 9 10 **S** Kindred Healthcare, Louisville, KY
Primary Contact: Custer Huseby, Chief Executive Officer
Web address: www.khfargo.com
**Control:** Corporation, Investor–owned, for–profit **Service:** Long–Term Acute Care hospital

**Staffed Beds:** 31

**MERITCARE MEDICAL CENTER** See Sanford Medical Center Fargo

✠ **PRAIRIE ST. JOHN'S (354004)**, 510 4th Street South, Zip 58103–1914; tel. 701/476–7200 **A**1 9 10 **F**4 5 34 50 54 87 98 99 100 101 102 103 104 105 130 132 134 135 146 **P**6 **S** Universal Health Services, Inc., King of Prussia, PA
Primary Contact: Gregory LaFrancois, Chief Executive Officer
COO: Jennifer Faul, Chief Operating Officer
CFO: Tom Eide, Chief Financial Officer
CMO: Eduardo Meza, M.D., Medical Director
CHR: Michelle A. Parkinson, Director Human Resources
Web address: www.prairie–stjohns.com
**Control:** Partnership, Investor–owned, for–profit **Service:** Psychiatric

| | |
|---|---|
| **Staffed Beds:** 91 **Admissions:** 3180 **Census:** 73 **Outpatient Visits:** 31754 **Births:** 0 **Total Expense ($000):** 24391 **Payroll Expense ($000):** 16167 **Personnel:** 275 | |

✠ △ **SANFORD MEDICAL CENTER FARGO (350011)**, 801 Broadway North, Zip 58102–3641; tel. 701/234–2000, (Includes MERITCARE SOUTH UNIVERSITY, 1720 South University Drive, Zip 58103–4994; tel. 701/280–4100) **A**1 2 3 5 7 8 9 10 **F**3 7 8 9 11 12 13 15 17 18 19 20 21 22 23 24 25 26 27 28 29 30 31 32 33 34 35 36 37 38 39 40 43 44 45 46 47 48 49 50 51 52 53 54 55 56 57 58 59 60 61 62 63 64 65 68 70 71 72 73 74 75 76 78 79 80 81 82 83 84 85 86 87 88 89 90 91 92 93 96 97 98 99 100 101 102 103 104 105 107 111 112 114 115 116 117 118 119 120 121 123 124 126 129 130 131 132 135 138 141 142 143 144 145 146 147 148 **P**6 **S** Sanford Health, Sioux Falls, SD
Primary Contact: Dennis C. Millirons, FACHE, President
COO: Karen A. Tobin, R.N., Chief Operating Officer
CFO: Lisa Carlson, Chief Financial Officer
CMO: Rhonda L. Ketterling, M.D., Chief Medical Officer
CIO: Craig Hewit, Executive Partner Information Technology and Chief Information Officer
Web address: www.sanfordhealth.org
**Control:** Other not–for–profit (including NFP Corporation) **Service:** General Medical and Surgical

| | |
|---|---|
| **Staffed Beds:** 491 **Admissions:** 26687 **Census:** 331 **Outpatient Visits:** 382071 **Births:** 2481 **Total Expense ($000):** 746595 **Payroll Expense ($000):** 186422 **Personnel:** 3814 | |

**TRIUMPH HOSPITAL – FARGO** See Kindred Hospital Fargo

**VETERANS AFFAIRS HEALTH CARE SYSTEM** See Fargo Veterans Affairs Health Care System

*Many Facility Codes have changed. Please refer to the AHA Guide Code Chart.*

© 2013 AHA Guide

## FORT YATES—Sioux County

☐ **U. S. PUBLIC HEALTH SERVICE INDIAN HOSPITAL (350064)**, N 10 North River Road, Zip 58538, Mailing Address: P.O. Box J, Zip 58538; tel. 701/854–3831, (Nonreporting) **A**1 5 9 10 **S** U. S. Indian Health Service, Rockville, MD
Primary Contact: Lisa Guardipee, Director
CFO: William Condon, Deputy Administrative Officer
Web address: www.ihs.gov
**Control:** PHS, Indian Service, Government, federal **Service:** General Medical and Surgical

**Staffed Beds: 12**

## GARRISON—Mclean County

★ **GARRISON MEMORIAL HOSPITAL (351303)**, 407 Third Avenue S.E., Zip 58540–7235; tel. 701/463–2275, (Nonreporting) **A**5 9 10 18 **S** Benedictine Sisters of the Annunciation, Bismarck, ND
Primary Contact: Tod Graeber, Administrator
CMO: Vern Harchenko, M.D., Chief of Staff
CNO: Beth Hetletved, Director of Nurses
Web address: www.garrisonmh.com
**Control:** Other not–for–profit (including NFP Corporation) **Service:** General Medical and Surgical

**Staffed Beds: 22**

## GRAFTON—Walsh County

★ **UNITY MEDICAL CENTER (351320)**, 164 West 13th Street, Zip 58237–1896; tel. 701/352–1620 **A**5 9 10 18 **F**3 11 28 31 34 35 40 42 45 57 59 71 78 81 86 87 107 114 127 128 129 130 132 133 135 143 **P**5
Primary Contact: Everett A. Butler, Chief Executive Officer
CFO: Rachel Ray, Chief Financial Officer
Web address: www.unitymedcenter.com
**Control:** Other not–for–profit (including NFP Corporation) **Service:** General Medical and Surgical

**Staffed Beds: 14 Admissions: 250 Census: 2 Outpatient Visits: 40598 Births: 0 Total Expense ($000): 8509 Payroll Expense ($000): 3891 Personnel: 70**

## GRAND FORKS—Grand Forks County

⌧ △ **ALTRU HEALTH SYSTEM (350019)**, 1200 South Columbia Road, Zip 58201–4036, Mailing Address: P.O. Box 6002, Zip 58206–6002; tel. 701/780–5000, (Includes ALTRU HOSPITAL, 1200 South Columbia Road, Zip 58201; tel. 701/780–5000; ALTRU REHABILITATION CENTER, 1300 South Columbia Road, Zip 58201; tel. 701/780–2311) **A**1 2 3 5 7 9 10 20 **F**3 5 7 8 10 11 12 13 14 15 18 20 22 24 28 29 30 31 32 33 34 35 36 37 38 40 43 44 45 48 49 50 52 53 55 56 57 58 59 60 61 62 63 64 65 68 69 70 71 72 74 75 76 77 78 79 81 82 83 84 85 86 87 90 91 92 93 94 96 97 98 99 100 101 102 103 104 105 107 108 110 111 114 117 119 121 123 124 125 129 130 131 132 135 143 144 145 146 147 148 **P**6
Primary Contact: David R. Molmen, Chief Executive Officer
CFO: Dwight Thompson, Chief Financial Officer
CMO: James Van Looy, M.D., Chief Medical Executive
CIO: Mark Waind, Administrative Director Information Services
CHR: Lee Lindquist, Administrative Director Human Services
Web address: www.altru.org
**Control:** Other not–for–profit (including NFP Corporation) **Service:** General Medical and Surgical

**Staffed Beds: 269 Admissions: 14101 Census: 181 Outpatient Visits: 709322 Births: 1655 Total Expense ($000): 438626 Payroll Expense ($000): 224677 Personnel: 3177**

◇ **RICHARD P. STADTER PSYCHIATRIC CENTER (354005)**, 1451 44th Avenue South, Zip 58201–3434; tel. 701/772–2500 **A**9 10 21 **F**4 5 34 55 56 57 77 87 98 99 101 102 103 105 130 135 148 **P**5
Primary Contact: Thomas Peterson, M.D., Chief Executive Officer
COO: Bonnie Peterson, Chief Operating Officer and Vice President Clinical Services
CFO: Darin Ohe, Chief Financial Officer
CMO: Thomas Peterson, M.D., Chief Executive Officer
CHR: Dan Bjerknes, Director Human Resources
Web address: www.stadtercenter.com
**Control:** Corporation, Investor–owned, for–profit **Service:** Psychiatric

**Staffed Beds: 71 Admissions: 547 Census: 32 Outpatient Visits: 0 Births: 0 Total Expense ($000): 9331 Payroll Expense ($000): 3370 Personnel: 96**

## HARVEY—Wells County

★ **ST. ALOISIUS MEDICAL CENTER (351327)**, 325 East Brewster Street, Zip 58341–1653; tel. 701/324–4651, (Total facility includes 95 beds in nursing home–type unit) **A**5 9 10 18 **F**13 15 28 30 40 45 53 56 57 59 70 76 77 81 85 93 107 110 114 125 128 130 131 132 133 146 147 **S** Sisters of Mary of the Presentation Health System, Fargo, ND
Primary Contact: Rockford Zastoupil, President and Chief Executive Officer
CFO: Sandra Teubner, Chief Financial Officer
Web address: www.staloisius.com
**Control:** Church–operated, Nongovernment, not–for profit **Service:** General Medical and Surgical

**Staffed Beds: 120 Admissions: 579 Census: 95 Outpatient Visits: 8829 Births: 15 Total Expense ($000): 12356 Payroll Expense ($000): 6311 Personnel: 229**

## HAZEN—Mercer County

★ **SAKAKAWEA MEDICAL CENTER (351310)**, 510 Eighth Avenue N.E., Zip 58545–4637; tel. 701/748–2225, (Nonreporting) **A**5 9 10 18
Primary Contact: Darrold Bertsch, Chief Executive Officer
CFO: Renae Snyder, Chief Financial Officer
CHR: Cheryl Axtman, Administrative Assistant
CNO: Marcie Schulz, Director Patient Care
Web address: www.sakmedcenter.com
**Control:** Other not–for–profit (including NFP Corporation) **Service:** General Medical and Surgical

**Staffed Beds: 18**

## HETTINGER—Adams County

**WEST RIVER REGIONAL MEDICAL CENTER (351330)**, 1000 Highway 12, Zip 58639–7530; tel. 701/567–4561, (Nonreporting) **A**5 9 10 18
Primary Contact: James K. Long, CPA, Administrator and Chief Executive Officer
CFO: Karan Ehlers, Chief Financial Officer
CMO: John Joyce, M.D., Chief of Staff
CIO: Julia Guchenour, Manager Information Systems
CHR: Christi Miller, Manager Human Resources
Web address: www.wrhs.com
**Control:** Other not–for–profit (including NFP Corporation) **Service:** General Medical and Surgical

**Staffed Beds: 25**

## HILLSBORO—Traill County

★ **SANFORD HILLSBORO MEDICAL CENTER (351329)**, (Formerly Hillsboro Medical Center), 12 Third Street S.E., Zip 58045–4840, Mailing Address: P.O. Box 609, Zip 58045–0609; tel. 701/636–3200, (Total facility includes 36 beds in nursing home–type unit) **A**5 9 10 18 **F**7 10 11 34 35 40 64 65 68 75 93 103 125 128 130 131 133 143 146 148 **P**6 **S** Sanford Health, Sioux Falls, SD
Primary Contact: Jac McTaggart, Chief Executive Officer
CFO: Darlene Swanson, Business Manager
CMO: Charles J. Breen, M.D., Medical Director
CIO: Darlene Swanson, Business Manager
CHR: Jenny Jacobson, Manager Human Resources
Web address: www.hillsboromedicalcenter.com
**Control:** Other not–for–profit (including NFP Corporation) **Service:** General Medical and Surgical

**Staffed Beds: 52 Admissions: 204 Census: 40 Outpatient Visits: 22500 Births: 0 Total Expense ($000): 5165 Payroll Expense ($000): 2289 Personnel: 68**

## JAMESTOWN—Stutsman County

⌧ **JAMESTOWN REGIONAL MEDICAL CENTER (351335)**, 2422 20th Street S.W., Zip 58401–6201; tel. 701/252–1050 **A**1 5 10 18 **F**3 11 13 15 31 34 35 40 43 45 50 53 57 59 62 63 64 70 75 76 77 79 81 82 84 85 86 87 89 93 107 108 110 111 115 118 119 130 131 132 133 135 146
Primary Contact: Todd R. Hudspeth, President and Chief Executive Officer
CMO: Debra Geier, M.D., President Medical Staff
CIO: Jeremey Schiele, Chief Information Officer
CHR: Ricki Ramlo, Vice President Human Resources
CNO: Cindy Gohner, Vice President Clinical Services
Web address: www.jamestownhospital.com
**Control:** Other not–for–profit (including NFP Corporation) **Service:** General Medical and Surgical

**Staffed Beds: 25 Admissions: 1321 Census: 11 Outpatient Visits: 28916 Births: 345 Total Expense ($000): 34936 Payroll Expense ($000): 14459 Personnel: 282**

☐ **NORTH DAKOTA STATE HOSPITAL (354003)**, 2605 Circle Drive S.E., Zip 58401-6905; tel. 701/253-3964, (Nonreporting) **A**1 5 9 10
Primary Contact: Alex Schweitzer, Superintendent and Chief Executive Officer
CFO: Gene O. Wahl, Chief Financial Officer
Web address: www.nd.gov/
**Control:** State–Government, nonfederal **Service:** Psychiatric

| Staffed Beds: 140 |
|---|

**KENMARE—Ward County**

★ **KENMARE COMMUNITY HOSPITAL (351305)**, 317 First Avenue N.W., Zip 58746-7104, Mailing Address: P.O. Box 697, Zip 58746-0697; tel. 701/385-4296, (Nonreporting) **A**9 10 18
Primary Contact: Margaret Shawn Smothers, Administrator
COO: Bev Heninger, Director Nursing
CFO: Kevin Seehafer, Chief Financial Officer
CMO: Jesse Sabitti, M.D., Chief Medical Officer
CIO: Alan Okerson, Director Information Technology
CHR: Ranae Ehlke, Administrative Secretary and Coordinator Risk Management and Human Resources
Web address: www.kenmarend.net/hospital.htm
**Control:** Corporation, Investor–owned, for–profit **Service:** General Medical and Surgical

| Staffed Beds: 25 |
|---|

**LANGDON—Cavalier County**

★ **CAVALIER COUNTY MEMORIAL HOSPITAL (351323)**, 909 Second Street, Zip 58249-2407; tel. 701/256-6100, (Nonreporting) **A**5 9 10 18
Primary Contact: Lawrence Blue, Administrator and Chief Executive Officer
COO: Lawrence Blue, Administrator and Chief Executive Officer
CFO: Julie Feil, Accountant
CMO: Suresh Patel, M.D., Chief Medical Officer
CIO: Mary Jane Domres, Director Materials Management and Administrator Information Technology
CHR: Andrea Jacobson, Human Resource Officer
Web address: www.cavaliercountyhospital.com
**Control:** Other not–for–profit (including NFP Corporation) **Service:** General Medical and Surgical

| Staffed Beds: 25 |
|---|

**LINTON—Emmons County**

**LINTON HOSPITAL (351328)**, 518 North Broadway, Zip 58552-7308, Mailing Address: P.O. Box 850, Zip 58552-0850; tel. 701/254-4511, (Nonreporting) **A**5 9 10 18
Primary Contact: Robert Black, Chief Executive Officer
CFO: Beverly Vilhauer, Chief Operating Officer and Chief Financial Officer
CMO: Edgar Oliveira, M.D., Chief Medical Staff
CHR: Sue Meidinger, Manager Business Office
Web address: www.lintonhospital.com
**Control:** Other not–for–profit (including NFP Corporation) **Service:** General Medical and Surgical

| Staffed Beds: 14 |
|---|

**LISBON—Ransom County**

★ **LISBON AREA HEALTH SERVICES (351311)**, 905 Main Street, Zip 58054-4334, Mailing Address: P.O. Box 353, Zip 58054-0353; tel. 701/683-5241, (Nonreporting) **A**5 9 10 18 **S** Catholic Health Initiatives, Englewood, CO
Primary Contact: Peggy Larson, R.N., Administrator
COO: Sheri Heinisch, Compliance Officer
CFO: Amber Stowman, Controller
CHR: Janet Froemke, Human Resources Officer
Web address: www.lisbonhospital.com
**Control:** Church–operated, Nongovernment, not–for profit **Service:** General Medical and Surgical

| Staffed Beds: 25 |
|---|

**MANDAN—Morton County**

✉ **KINDRED HOSPITAL–CENTRAL DAKOTAS (352005)**, 1000 18th Street N.W., Zip 58554-1612; tel. 701/667-2000, (Nonreporting) **A**1 9 10 **S** Kindred Healthcare, Louisville, KY
Primary Contact: April Bishop, Chief Executive Officer
Web address: www.khcentraldakotas.com
**Control:** Corporation, Investor–owned, for–profit **Service:** Long–Term Acute Care hospital

| Staffed Beds: 41 |
|---|

**TRIUMPH HOSPITAL – CENTRAL DAKOTAS** See Kindred Hospital–Central Dakotas

**MAYVILLE—Traill County**

**MERITCARE MAYVILLE UNION HOSPITAL** See Sanford Mayville Medical Center

★ **SANFORD MAYVILLE MEDICAL CENTER (351309)**, (Formerly Sanford Medical Center Mayville), 42 Sixth Avenue S.E., Zip 58257-1598; tel. 701/786-3800 **A**5 9 10 18 **F**7 40 43 45 50 65 77 81 93 119 128 129 130 133 147 **S** Sanford Health, Sioux Falls, SD
Primary Contact: Roger Baier, Chief Executive Officer
CMO: James Mehus, M.D., Chief of Staff
Web address: www.unionhospital.com
**Control:** Other not–for–profit (including NFP Corporation) **Service:** General Medical and Surgical

| Staffed Beds: 18 Admissions: 265 Census: 4 Outpatient Visits: 3912 Births: 0 Total Expense ($000): 7375 Payroll Expense ($000): 2794 Personnel: 62 |
|---|

**MCVILLE—Nelson County**

**NELSON COUNTY HEALTH SYSTEM (351308)**, 200 Main Street, Zip 58254, Mailing Address: P.O. Box 367, Zip 58254-0367; tel. 701/322-4328, (Total facility includes 39 beds in nursing home–type unit) **A**9 10 18 **F**10 15 28 29 34 40 59 64 65 107 110 119 127 128 129 130 133 143 **P**8
Primary Contact: Cathy Swenson, Chief Executive Officer
CFO: Steve Forde, Chief Financial Officer
CMO: Erling Martinson, M.D., Medical Director
Web address: www.nelsoncountyhealthsystem.org
**Control:** Other not–for–profit (including NFP Corporation) **Service:** General Medical and Surgical

| Staffed Beds: 58 Admissions: 133 Census: 37 Outpatient Visits: 4059 Births: 0 Total Expense ($000): 5225 Payroll Expense ($000): 2792 Personnel: 29 |
|---|

**MINOT—Ward County**

✉ △ **TRINITY HEALTH (350006)**, One Burdick Expressway West, Zip 58701-4406, Mailing Address: P.O. Box 5020, Zip 58702-5020; tel. 701/857-5000, (Includes TRINITY HOSPITAL–ST. JOSEPH'S, 407 3rd Street S.E., Zip 58702-5001; tel. 701/857-2000), (Nonreporting) **A**1 2 3 5 7 9 10
Primary Contact: John M. Kutch, President
CFO: Kevin Seehafer, Chief Financial Officer
CHR: Paul Simonson, Vice President
Web address: www.trinityhealth.org
**Control:** Other not–for–profit (including NFP Corporation) **Service:** General Medical and Surgical

| Staffed Beds: 584 |
|---|

**NORTHWOOD—Grand Forks County**

**SANFORD NORTHWOOD DEACONESS HEALTH CENTER (351312)**, 4 North Park Street, Zip 58267-4102, Mailing Address: P.O. Box 190, Zip 58267-0190; tel. 701/587-6060, (Nonreporting) **A**5 9 10 18 **S** Sanford Health, Sioux Falls, SD
Primary Contact: Pete Antonson, Chief Executive Officer
CMO: Jon Berg, M.D., Chief of Staff
CIO: Chad Peterson, Chief Information Officer
Web address: www.ndhc.net
**Control:** Church–operated, Nongovernment, not–for profit **Service:** General Medical and Surgical

| Staffed Beds: 73 |
|---|

**OAKES—Dickey County**

★ **OAKES COMMUNITY HOSPITAL (351315)**, 1200 North Seventh Street, Zip 58474-2502; tel. 701/742-3291 **A**5 9 10 18 **F**3 15 28 30 31 40 43 45 50 59 64 68 70 81 82 85 89 107 110 127 130 133 135 **S** Catholic Health Initiatives, Englewood, CO
Primary Contact: Lee Boyles, President
CFO: Becki Thompson, Controller
CMO: Vani Nagala, M.D., Chief Medical Officer
CIO: Terry Engel, Manager Information Technology
CHR: Julie Entzminger, Manager Human Resources
Web address: www.oakeshospital.com
**Control:** Other not–for–profit (including NFP Corporation) **Service:** General Medical and Surgical

| Staffed Beds: 12 Admissions: 517 Census: 6 Outpatient Visits: 10009 Births: 0 Total Expense ($000): 10225 Payroll Expense ($000): 4346 Personnel: 77 |
|---|

*Many Facility Codes have changed. Please refer to the AHA Guide Code Chart.* © 2013 AHA Guide

## PARK RIVER—Walsh County

★ **FIRST CARE HEALTH CENTER (351326)**, 115 Vivian Street, Zip 58270–4540,
Mailing Address: PO Box I., Zip 58270–0708; tel. 701/284–7500 **A**5 9 10 18
**F**11 15 28 29 30 31 34 35 40 45 50 59 64 65 68 77 81 93 104 107 110
111 114 119 127 130 133 **P**6
Primary Contact: Louise Dryburgh, Chief Executive Officer
CFO: Layne Ensrude, Chief Financial Officer
CMO: Olukayode S. Omotunde, M.D., Chief Medical Staff
CNO: Amy Burianek, Director Nurses
Web address: www.firstcarehc.com
**Control:** Other not–for–profit (including NFP Corporation) **Service:** General
Medical and Surgical

**Staffed Beds: 14 Admissions: 308 Census: 5 Outpatient Visits: 29067
Births: 0 Total Expense ($000): 8970 Payroll Expense ($000): 3261
Personnel: 76**

## ROLLA—Rolette County

**PRESENTATION MEDICAL CENTER (351316)**, 213 Second Avenue N.E.,
Zip 58367–7153, Mailing Address: P.O. Box 759, Zip 58367–0759;
tel. 701/477–3161 **A**5 9 10 18 **F**1 3 15 18 28 29 30 31 34 35 40 41 45 50
57 59 64 66 78 81 87 89 91 92 93 94 97 107 110 111 114 119 130 131
133 135 147 148 **P**6 **S** Sisters of Mary of the Presentation Health System,
Fargo, ND
Primary Contact: Mark Kerr, Chief Executive Officer
CFO: Paula Wilkie, Chief Financial Officer
CMO: Norman Gardner, M.D., President Medical Staff
CHR: Holly Cahill, Director Human Resources
Web address: www.pmc-rolla.com
**Control:** Church–operated, Nongovernment, not–for profit **Service:** General
Medical and Surgical

**Staffed Beds: 25 Admissions: 147 Census: 8 Outpatient Visits: 9890
Births: 0 Total Expense ($000): 8490 Payroll Expense ($000): 3440
Personnel: 96**

## RUGBY—Pierce County

★ **HEART OF AMERICA MEDICAL CENTER (351332)**, 800 Main Avenue South,
Zip 58368–2198; tel. 701/776–5261, (Nonreporting) **A**5 9 10 18
Primary Contact: Jeff Lingerfelt, Chief Executive Officer
CFO: Bonnie Kuehnemund, Comptroller
CIO: Jeremy Schonebery, Director Information Technology
Web address: www.hamc.com
**Control:** Other not–for–profit (including NFP Corporation) **Service:** General
Medical and Surgical

**Staffed Beds: 20**

## STANLEY—Mountrail County

★ **MOUNTRAIL COUNTY MEDICAL CENTER (351301)**, 615 6th Street S.E.,
Zip 58784–4444, Mailing Address: P.O. Box 399, Zip 58784–0399;
tel. 701/628–2424 **A**9 10 18 **F**15 40 41 43 45 59 71 77 81 93 97 127 130
133 **P**6
Primary Contact: Doris Brown, Chief Executive Officer
CFO: Scott Sillis, Interim Chief Financial Officer
CMO: Tyrone Langager, M.D., Chief Medical Officer
CIO: Krystle Clark, Director Medical Records
CHR: Linda Halvorson, Director Human Resources
Web address: www.stanleyhealth.org
**Control:** Other not–for–profit (including NFP Corporation) **Service:** General
Medical and Surgical

**Staffed Beds: 11 Admissions: 112 Census: 2 Outpatient Visits: 2146
Births: 0 Total Expense ($000): 4421 Payroll Expense ($000): 944
Personnel: 14**

## TIOGA—Williams County

★ **TIOGA MEDICAL CENTER (351300)**, 810 North Welo Street, Zip 58852–7157,
Mailing Address: P.O. Box 159, Zip 58852–0159; tel. 701/664–3305,
(Nonreporting) **A**3 5 9 10 18
Primary Contact: Randall K. Pederson, Chief Executive Officer
CMO: Swami P. Gade, M.D., Medical Director
CHR: Mary Ann Holm, Office Clerk
Web address: www.tiogahealth.org
**Control:** Other not–for–profit (including NFP Corporation) **Service:** General
Medical and Surgical

**Staffed Beds: 55**

## TURTLE LAKE—McLean County

**COMMUNITY MEMORIAL HOSPITAL (351304)**, 220 Fifth Avenue,
Zip 58575–4005, Mailing Address: P.O. Box 280, Zip 58575–0280;
tel. 701/448–2331, (Nonreporting) **A**9 10 18
Primary Contact: Tod Graeber, Administrator
CFO: Karen Aafedt, Assistant Administrator and Controller
Web address: www.wrtc.com/cullum/hospital
**Control:** Church–operated, Nongovernment, not–for profit **Service:** General
Medical and Surgical

**Staffed Beds: 25**

## VALLEY CITY—Barnes County

★ **MERCY HOSPITAL (351324)**, 570 Chautauqua Boulevard, Zip 58072–3199;
tel. 701/845–6400 **A**5 9 10 18 **F**3 11 28 29 30 32 34 40 43 45 50 64 75 77
81 84 85 86 87 92 93 107 110 114 130 131 132 133 146 **S** Catholic Health
Initiatives, Englewood, CO
Primary Contact: Keith E. Heuser, President
COO: Camille Settelmeyer, Assistant Administrator Clinical Services
CFO: Beth Smith, Controller
CHR: Lesley Erlandson, Human Resources Generalist
Web address: www.mercyhospitalvalleycity.org
**Control:** Church–operated, Nongovernment, not–for profit **Service:** General
Medical and Surgical

**Staffed Beds: 19 Admissions: 545 Census: 9 Outpatient Visits: 15885
Births: 0 Total Expense ($000): 11422 Payroll Expense ($000): 5120
Personnel: 75**

## WATFORD CITY—Mckenzie County

★ **MCKENZIE COUNTY HEALTHCARE SYSTEM (351302)**, 516 North Main
Street, Zip 58854–7310; tel. 701/842–3000 **A**9 10 18 **F**3 11 28 29 34 40 43
50 57 59 64 81 85 93 94 97 107 114 119 127 129 131 133 146
Primary Contact: Daniel R. Kelly, Chief Executive Officer
CFO: Colette Anderson, Manager Finance
CMO: Gary Ramage, M.D., Chief Medical Officer
CIO: Karn Pederson, Manager Health Information Management
CHR: Becky Smith, Manager Human Resources
Web address: www.mckenziehealth.com
**Control:** Other not–for–profit (including NFP Corporation) **Service:** General
Medical and Surgical

**Staffed Beds: 24 Admissions: 185 Census: 2 Outpatient Visits: 12373
Births: 0 Total Expense ($000): 11915 Payroll Expense ($000): 5059
Personnel: 122**

## WILLISTON—Williams County

⊞ **MERCY MEDICAL CENTER (351334)**, 1301 15th Avenue West,
Zip 58801–3896; tel. 701/774–7400 **A**1 5 9 10 18 **F**3 13 15 28 29 30 31 34
40 45 50 57 59 60 64 65 68 70 75 76 77 78 79 81 82 85 91 92 93 97 104
107 108 110 111 114 119 120 121 123 129 130 133 135 146 **S** Catholic
Health Initiatives, Englewood, CO
Primary Contact: Matthew Grimshaw, President
CFO: Kerry Monson, Vice President Finance and Chief Financial Officer
CMO: William Brunsman, M.D., Chief of Staff
CIO: Sean Key, Director Information Technology
CHR: Mary Banta, Director Human Resources
Web address: www.mercy-williston.org
**Control:** Church–operated, Nongovernment, not–for profit **Service:** General
Medical and Surgical

**Staffed Beds: 25 Admissions: 1483 Census: 12 Outpatient Visits: 18803
Births: 560 Total Expense ($000): 51395 Payroll Expense ($000): 23399
Personnel: 382**

## WISHEK—Mcintosh County

★ **WISHEK COMMUNITY HOSPITAL AND CLINICS (351321)**, 1007 Fourth
Avenue South, Zip 58495–7527, Mailing Address: P.O. Box 647,
Zip 58495–0647; tel. 701/452–2326 **A**5 9 10 18 **F**3 7 11 15 17 18 28 29 30
32 34 35 36 40 42 44 50 53 56 57 59 60 62 63 64 65 67 68 75 81 83 87
90 91 92 93 97 107 114 127 128 130 131 133 143 146 147 **P**3 6
Primary Contact: Mark Rinehardt, Chief Executive Officer
CFO: Sahlenia Braun, Chief Financial Officer
CMO: Edgar Oliveira, M.D., Chief of Staff
CIO: Kari Buchholz, Director Health Information Management
CHR: Shar Bauer, Executive Secretary
Web address: www.wishekhospital.com
**Control:** Other not–for–profit (including NFP Corporation) **Service:** General
Medical and Surgical

**Staffed Beds: 17 Admissions: 293 Census: 3 Outpatient Visits: 18331
Births: 0 Total Expense ($000): 6024 Payroll Expense ($000): 2642
Personnel: 75**

---

**Hospital, Medicare Provider Number, Address, Telephone, Approval, Facility, and Physician Codes, Health Care System**

★ American Hospital Association (AHA) membership
☐ The Joint Commission accreditation ◇ DNV Healthcare Inc. accreditation

○ Healthcare Facilities Accreditation Program
△ Commission on Accreditation of Rehabilitation Facilities (CARF) accreditation

# OHIO

## AKRON—Summit County

☒ **AKRON CHILDREN'S HOSPITAL (363303)**, One Perkins Square,
Zip 44308–1062; tel. 330/543–1000 **A**1 2 3 5 8 9 10 13 **F**3 7 11 16 18 19
21 23 25 27 29 30 31 32 33 34 35 36 38 39 40 41 42 43 44 50 54 55 57
58 59 60 61 62 63 64 65 66 68 72 73 74 75 77 78 79 80 81 82 84 85 86
87 88 89 91 92 93 94 96 97 98 99 100 101 102 104 105 107 108 111 112
114 116 117 118 119 129 130 131 132 134 135 136 141 143 144 146
148 **P**6
Primary Contact: William H. Considine, President
COO: Grace Wakulchik, R.N., Chief Operating Officer
CFO: Michael Trainer, Chief Financial Officer
CMO: Michael Bird, M.D., Vice President Medical Services
CIO: Tom Ogg, Vice President Information Services and Chief Information Officer
CHR: Walter Schwoeble, Vice President Human Resources
CNO: Lisa Aurilio, R.N., Vice President Patient Services and Chief Nursing Officer
Web address: www.akronchildrens.org
**Control:** Other not–for–profit (including NFP Corporation) **Service:** Children's
general

> **Staffed Beds:** 372 **Admissions:** 9453 **Census:** 194 **Outpatient Visits:**
> 724395 **Births:** 0 **Total Expense ($000):** 543651 **Payroll Expense ($000):**
> 271660 **Personnel:** 3945

☒ **AKRON GENERAL MEDICAL CENTER (360027)**, 400 Wabash Avenue,
Zip 44307–2433; tel. 330/344–6000 **A**1 2 3 5 8 9 10 **F**3 5 11 12 13 14 15
17 18 20 22 24 26 28 29 30 31 34 35 36 38 39 40 42 43 44 45 46 47 48
49 50 51 52 53 54 55 56 57 58 59 60 61 64 65 66 68 70 71 72 73 74 75
76 77 78 79 80 81 82 84 85 86 87 91 92 93 94 96 97 98 100 101 102 103
104 105 107 108 109 110 111 112 114 115 116 117 118 119 120 121 123
124 126 129 130 131 132 134 135 143 145 146 147 148 **P**6 8 **S** Akron
General Health System, Akron, OH
Primary Contact: Alan Papa, President
CFO: Stephen M. Gary, Senior Vice President and Chief Financial officer
CMO: David Peter, M.D., Senior Vice President Medical Affairs and Chief Medical
Director
CIO: David Fiser, Vice President and Chief Information Officer
CHR: Don Corpora, Executive Vice President and Chief Human Resources Officer
CNO: Beverly Bokovitz, R.N., Senior Vice President and Chief Nursing Officer
Web address: www.akrongeneral.org
**Control:** Other not–for–profit (including NFP Corporation) **Service:** General
Medical and Surgical

> **Staffed Beds:** 498 **Admissions:** 23809 **Census:** 289 **Outpatient Visits:**
> 574621 **Births:** 3244 **Total Expense ($000):** 457457 **Payroll Expense
> ($000):** 189731 **Personnel:** 2944

☒ **SELECT SPECIALTY HOSPITAL–AKRON (362027)**, 200 East Market Street,
Zip 44308–2015; tel. 330/761–7500, (Nonreporting) **A**1 10 **S** Select Medical
Corporation, Mechanicsburg, PA
Primary Contact: Sonda Burns, Chief Executive Officer
Web address: www.selectspecialtyhospitals.com/company/locations/akron.aspx
**Control:** Corporation, Investor–owned, for–profit **Service:** Long–Term Acute Care
hospital

> **Staffed Beds:** 60

**SUMMA AKRON CITY HOSPITAL** See Summa Health System

☒ **SUMMA HEALTH SYSTEM (360020)**, 525 East Market Street,
Zip 44304–1619; tel. 330/375–3000, (Includes SUMMA AKRON CITY HOSPITAL,
525 East Market Street, Zip 44309–2090, Mailing Address: P.O. Box 2090,
Zip 44309–2090; tel. 330/375–3000; SUMMA SAINT THOMAS HOSPITAL, 444
North Main Street, Zip 44310; tel. 330/375–3000) **A**1 2 3 5 8 9 10 **F**1 2 3 4 5
6 8 9 11 12 13 15 17 18 20 22 24 26 28 29 30 31 33 34 35 36 37 38 39
40 41 42 43 44 45 46 47 48 49 50 51 52 53 54 55 56 57 58 59 60 61 62
63 64 65 66 68 70 71 72 74 75 76 77 78 79 80 81 82 83 84 85 86 87 92
93 96 97 98 99 100 101 102 103 104 105 107 108 109 110 111 114 115
116 117 118 119 120 121 123 124 126 129 130 131 132 133 135 144 145
146 147 148 **P**6 8 **S** Summa Health System, Akron, OH
Primary Contact: Thomas J. Strauss, President and Chief Executive Officer
COO: Robert Harrigan, President, Summa Hospitals
CMO: Erik N. Steele, D.O., Senior Vice President and Chief Medical Officer
CIO: Greg Kall, Chief Information Officer
CHR: Kyle Klawitter, Vice President Human Resources
Web address: www.summahealth.org
**Control:** Other not–for–profit (including NFP Corporation) **Service:** General
Medical and Surgical

> **Staffed Beds:** 428 **Admissions:** 31448 **Census:** 396 **Outpatient Visits:**
> 447067 **Births:** 2964 **Total Expense ($000):** 632301 **Payroll Expense
> ($000):** 235613 **Personnel:** 5099

**SUMMA SAINT THOMAS HOSPITAL** See Summa Health System

## ALLIANCE—Stark County

☐ ○ **ALLIANCE COMMUNITY HOSPITAL (360131)**, 200 East State Street,
Zip 44601–4936; tel. 330/596–6000, (Total facility includes 68 beds in nursing
home–type unit) **A**1 2 5 9 10 11 **F**3 8 11 13 15 28 29 30 31 34 35 36 40 45
49 50 51 56 57 59 60 62 63 64 68 69 70 74 75 76 77 79 81 82 85 86 87
90 93 96 98 103 107 108 110 111 115 118 119 128 129 130 132 135 143
146 147 148 **P**5 7 8
Primary Contact: Stanley W. Jonas, Chief Executive Officer
COO: Amy Antonacci, MSN, Vice President Nursing Services
CFO: Dale Wells, Senior Vice President Finance and Operations
CMO: Ashraf Ahmed, M.D., Senior Vice President Physician and Hospital Services
CIO: David W. Shroades, Vice President Technology Services
CHR: Connie Poulton, Vice President Colleague Relations
Web address: www.achosp.org
**Control:** Other not–for–profit (including NFP Corporation) **Service:** General
Medical and Surgical

> **Staffed Beds:** 196 **Admissions:** 3826 **Census:** 107 **Outpatient Visits:**
> 166842 **Births:** 430 **Total Expense ($000):** 86441 **Payroll Expense ($000):**
> 37801 **Personnel:** 794

## AMHERST—Lorain County

☐ **SPECIALTY HOSPITAL OF LORAIN (362025)**, 254 Cleveland Avenue,
Zip 44001–1620; tel. 440/988–6260, (Nonreporting) **A**1 10
Primary Contact: Julia M. Meeks, Chief Operating Officer
**Control:** Other not–for–profit (including NFP Corporation) **Service:** Long–Term
Acute Care hospital

> **Staffed Beds:** 30

## ARCHBOLD—Fulton County

**ARCHBOLD HOSPITAL** See Community Hospitals and Wellness Centers, Bryan

## ASHLAND—Ashland County

☒ **SAMARITAN REGIONAL HEALTH SYSTEM (360002)**, 1025 Center Street,
Zip 44805–4011; tel. 419/289–0491, (Nonreporting) **A**1 5 9 10
Primary Contact: Danny L. Boggs, President and Chief Executive Officer
CFO: Mary Griest, Vice President Finance and Chief Financial Officer
CMO: Philip Myers, M.D., Vice President Medical Affairs
CIO: Alec Williams, Chief Information Officer
CHR: Alyce Legg, Vice President Human Resources
Web address: www.samaritanhospital.org
**Control:** Other not–for–profit (including NFP Corporation) **Service:** General
Medical and Surgical

> **Staffed Beds:** 49

## ASHTABULA—Ashtabula County

☐ **ASHTABULA COUNTY MEDICAL CENTER (360125)**, 2420 Lake Avenue,
Zip 44004–4954; tel. 440/997–2262, (Total facility includes 16 beds in nursing
home–type unit) **A**1 2 5 9 10 20 **F**3 11 13 15 18 20 28 29 30 31 34 35 38 40
45 49 50 51 53 57 59 61 62 63 64 68 70 74 75 76 77 78 79 80 81 82 83
84 85 86 87 89 93 97 98 100 102 103 104 105 107 108 110 111 114 116
117 118 119 128 129 130 131 132 135 146 147 148 **P**4 5 8
Primary Contact: Michael J. Habowski, President and Chief Executive Officer
CFO: Donald L. Kepner, Chief Financial Officer
CMO: Robert Dlwgosh, M.D., Chief of Staff
CIO: Jared Swiger, Director Information Systems
CHR: Robert Sincich, Vice President Human Resources
Web address: www.acmchealth.org
**Control:** Other not–for–profit (including NFP Corporation) **Service:** General
Medical and Surgical

> **Staffed Beds:** 156 **Admissions:** 4947 **Census:** 66 **Outpatient Visits:** 185792
> **Births:** 428 **Total Expense ($000):** 89019 **Payroll Expense ($000):** 40088
> **Personnel:** 685

## ATHENS—Athens County

☐ **APPALACHIAN BEHAVIORAL HEALTHCARE (364015)**, 100 Hospital Drive,
Zip 45701–2301; tel. 740/594–5000, (Nonreporting) **A**1 10 **S** Ohio Department
of Mental Health, Columbus, OH
Primary Contact: Jane E. Krason, R.N., Chief Executive Officer
CMO: Mark F. McGee, M.D., Chief Clinical Officer
CHR: Amy Grover, Director
Web address: www.mh.state.oh.us
**Control:** State–Government, nonfederal **Service:** Psychiatric

> **Staffed Beds:** 224

*Many Facility Codes have changed. Please refer to the AHA Guide Code Chart.* © 2013 AHA Guide

⊞ **O'BLENESS MEMORIAL HOSPITAL (360014)**, 55 Hospital Drive,
Zip 45701–2302; tel. 740/593–5551 **A**1 9 10 12 13 **F**3 13 15 18 20 28 31
34 37 40 44 51 57 59 65 66 68 70 75 76 78 79 80 81 85 93 94 107 108
110 111 115 119 126 130 135 146 148 **P**4 **S** OhioHealth, Columbus, OH
Primary Contact: Greg Long, Chief Executive Officer
CFO: Robert Melaragno, Vice President Finance
CIO: Kristine Barr, Vice President Communication Services
CHR: Sandie Leasure, Senior Vice President Human Resources
Web address: www.obleness.org
**Control:** Other not–for–profit (including NFP Corporation) **Service:** General
Medical and Surgical

**Staffed Beds:** 132 **Admissions:** 2914 **Census:** 23 **Outpatient Visits:** 91119
**Births:** 691 **Total Expense ($000):** 58532 **Payroll Expense ($000):** 30438
**Personnel:** 490

### BARBERTON—Summit County

⊞ **SUMMA BARBERTON CITIZENS HOSPITAL (360019)**, 155 Fifth Street N.E.,
Zip 44203–3332; tel. 330/615–3000 **A**1 2 3 5 9 10 **F**3 8 13 14 15 17 18 20
22 24 26 28 29 30 31 34 35 39 40 44 46 47 48 49 50 51 53 54 56 57 58
59 60 61 63 64 68 70 74 75 76 77 78 79 81 82 83 84 85 86 87 97 98 100
102 103 104 107 108 110 111 113 114 116 117 118 119 128 129 131 132
135 146 147 148 **P**6 8 **S** Summa Health System, Akron, OH
Primary Contact: Thomas DeBord, President
CFO: Charles Alderson, Chief Financial Officer
CMO: Jeffrey Morris, M.D., Medical Director
CIO: David Lynch, Regional Director Information Systems
CHR: Don Argiro, Regional Director Human Resources
CNO: Kathy Jobe, R.N., Chief Nursing Officer and Vice President Patient Care
Services
Web address: www.barbhosp.com
**Control:** Other not–for–profit (including NFP Corporation) **Service:** General
Medical and Surgical

**Staffed Beds:** 202 **Admissions:** 10183 **Census:** 139 **Outpatient Visits:**
417122 **Births:** 625 **Total Expense ($000):** 158982 **Payroll Expense**
**($000):** 56169 **Personnel:** 1107

### BARNESVILLE—Belmont County

⊞ **BARNESVILLE HOSPITAL (361321)**, 639 West Main Street, Zip 43713–1039,
Mailing Address: P.O. Box 309, Zip 43713–0309; tel. 740/425–3941 **A**1 9 10
18 **F**3 11 15 17 28 29 30 31 32 34 35 39 40 41 45 50 57 59 64 65 69 70
74 75 77 78 79 81 85 86 87 89 91 93 107 108 114 119 128 129 130 133
135 145 146 **P**6
Primary Contact: David D. Phillips, Chief Executive Officer and Administrator
CFO: Willie Cooper–Lohr, Chief Financial Officer
CMO: David J. Hilliard, D.O., Chief of Staff
CIO: Tiffany Gramby, Director Health Information Management and Privacy Officer
CHR: Beth K. Brill, Director Human Resources
CNO: Cynthia Touvelle, R.N., Senior Director Care Management and Chief Nursing
Officer
Web address: www.barnesvillehospital.com
**Control:** Other not–for–profit (including NFP Corporation) **Service:** General
Medical and Surgical

**Staffed Beds:** 25 **Admissions:** 1119 **Census:** 12 **Outpatient Visits:** 37056
**Births:** 0 **Total Expense ($000):** 20776 **Payroll Expense ($000):** 8721
**Personnel:** 208

### BATAVIA—Clermont County

⊞ **MERCY HEALTH – CLERMONT HOSPITAL (360236)**, (Formerly Mercy
Hospital Clermont), 3000 Hospital Drive, Zip 45103–1921; tel. 513/732–8200,
(Nonreporting) **A**1 2 9 10 **S** Catholic Health Partners, Cincinnati, OH
Primary Contact: Jeff Graham, Market Leader and President
CFO: Will Woodward, Director Finance
CMO: Howard Bell, M.D., Chief of Staff
CHR: Shelly Sherman, Director Human Resources
Web address: www.e–mercy.com
**Control:** Church–operated, Nongovernment, not–for profit **Service:** General
Medical and Surgical

**Staffed Beds:** 119

### BEACHWOOD—Cuyahoga County

⊞ **UNIVERSITY HOSPITALS AHUJA MEDICAL CENTER (360359)**, 3999
Richmond Road, Zip 44122–6046; tel. 216/593–5500 **A**1 9 10 **F**3 15 18 20 22
24 26 29 30 34 35 36 40 41 42 45 46 47 48 49 50 51 56 57 59 60 61 65
68 70 74 75 77 79 80 81 82 85 87 91 107 108 109 111 115 119 126
130 144 145 146 148 **S** University Hospitals, Cleveland, OH
Primary Contact: Susan V. Juris, President
Web address: www.uhhospitals.org/ahuja/tabid/7051/uhahujamedicalcenter.aspx
**Control:** Other not–for–profit (including NFP Corporation) **Service:** General
Medical and Surgical

**Staffed Beds:** 108 **Admissions:** 5820 **Census:** 64 **Outpatient Visits:** 96540
**Births:** 0 **Total Expense ($000):** 112857 **Payroll Expense ($000):** 34988
**Personnel:** 657

### BEAVERCREEK—Rock County County

★ ○ **SOIN MEDICAL CENTER (360360)**, 3535 Pentagon Boulevard,
Zip 45431–1705; tel. 937/702–4000, (Data for 312 days) **A**9 10 11 **F**3 11 13
18 20 29 30 34 35 38 39 40 43 44 45 46 48 49 50 53 56 57 59 64 68 70
73 75 76 77 79 81 82 85 86 87 102 107 108 111 114 115 116 117 118
119 126 130 132 135 146 147 148 **S** Kettering Health Network, Dayton, OH
Primary Contact: Terry M. Burns, President
CMO: Martha Johnston, M.D., Chief Medical Officer
Web address: www.khnetwork.org/soin
**Control:** Church–operated, Nongovernment, not–for profit **Service:** General
Medical and Surgical

**Staffed Beds:** 71 **Admissions:** 2209 **Census:** 21 **Outpatient Visits:** 26477
**Births:** 187 **Total Expense ($000):** 59815 **Payroll Expense ($000):** 18072
**Personnel:** 364

### BELLAIRE—Belmont County

☐ **BELMONT COMMUNITY HOSPITAL (360153)**, 4697 Harrison Street,
Zip 43906–1338, Mailing Address: P.O. Box 653, Zip 43906–0653;
tel. 740/671–1200, (Nonreporting) **A**1 9 10
Primary Contact: John DeBlasis, Senior Administrator
CFO: James B. Murdy, Chief Financial Officer
CMO: Charles L. Geiger, D.O., Chief of Staff
CHR: Donna Moore, Director Human Resources
Web address: www.wheelinghospital.org/facilities/bch/
**Control:** Other not–for–profit (including NFP Corporation) **Service:** General
Medical and Surgical

**Staffed Beds:** 66

### BELLEFONTAINE—Logan County

⊞ ◇ **MARY RUTAN HOSPITAL (360197)**, 205 Palmer Avenue,
Zip 43311–2281; tel. 937/592–4015 **A**1 3 5 9 10 20 21 **F**3 11 13 14 15 18
20 28 29 30 31 32 34 40 50 54 57 59 64 66 68 70 75 76 77 78 79 81 82
85 86 87 89 107 108 110 111 114 119 129 130 132 133 135 146 147
Primary Contact: Mandy C. Goble, President and Chief Executive Officer
CFO: Ron Carmin, Vice President Fiscal Affairs
CMO: Grant Varian, M.D., Medical Director
CIO: Robert Reynolds, Director Information Systems
CHR: Tim Froebe, Vice President Human Resources
Web address: www.maryrutan.org
**Control:** Other not–for–profit (including NFP Corporation) **Service:** General
Medical and Surgical

**Staffed Beds:** 100 **Admissions:** 1658 **Census:** 14 **Outpatient Visits:** 118294
**Births:** 352 **Total Expense ($000):** 76255 **Payroll Expense ($000):** 28911
**Personnel:** 568

### BELLEVUE—Sandusky County

⊞ **BELLEVUE HOSPITAL (360107)**, 1400 West Main Street, Zip 44811–9088,
Mailing Address: P.O. Box 8004, Zip 44811–8004; tel. 419/483–4040 **A**1 5 9
10 **F**3 11 13 15 28 31 34 35 40 41 46 50 56 57 59 61 62 68 70 74 75 76
77 79 81 82 85 89 93 107 108 110 111 114 118 119 127 129 130 131 132
133 135 143 146 **P**8
Primary Contact: Michael Winthrop, President
CFO: Timothy Buit, Vice President of Finance and Chief Financial Officer
CMO: J. Andrew Huddleston, D.O., President Medical Staff
CIO: Kim Stults, Director Education
CHR: Deborah Ganci, Vice President Human Resources
Web address: www.bellevuehospital.com
**Control:** Other not–for–profit (including NFP Corporation) **Service:** General
Medical and Surgical

**Staffed Beds:** 50 **Admissions:** 1440 **Census:** 13 **Outpatient Visits:** 74696
**Births:** 351 **Total Expense ($000):** 42736 **Payroll Expense ($000):** 16298
**Personnel:** 344

---

**Hospital, Medicare Provider Number, Address, Telephone, Approval, Facility, and Physician Codes, Health Care System**

★ American Hospital Association (AHA) membership
☐ The Joint Commission accreditation
◇ DNV Healthcare Inc. accreditation
○ Healthcare Facilities Accreditation Program
△ Commission on Accreditation of Rehabilitation Facilities (CARF) accreditation

**BLUFFTON—Allen County**

☒ **BLUFFTON HOSPITAL (361322)**, 139 Garau Street, Zip 45817–1027; tel. 419/358–9010 **A**1 9 10 **F**11 13 15 18 40 45 54 57 59 64 70 76 81 82 93 110 114 119 130 135 146 148 **S** Blanchard Valley Health System, Findlay, OH
Primary Contact: William D. Watkins, Chief Administrative Officer
CFO: David Cytlak, Vice President Finance
CMO: William H. Kose, M.D., Vice President Quality and Medical Affairs
CIO: David Cytlak, Vice President Finance
CHR: Ryan Fisher, Director Human Resources
CNO: Barbara J. Pasztor, R.N., Vice President Nursing and Patient Care Services
Web address: www.bvhealthsystem.org/?id=203&sid=1
**Control:** Other not–for–profit (including NFP Corporation) **Service:** General Medical and Surgical

**Staffed Beds:** 25 **Admissions:** 325 **Census:** 2 **Outpatient Visits:** 41410 **Births:** 216 **Total Expense ($000):** 15929 **Payroll Expense ($000):** 8007 **Personnel:** 123

**BOARDMAN—Mahoning County**

☐ **GREENBRIAR REHABILITATION HOSPITAL (363032)**, 8064 South Avenue, Suite One, Zip 44512–6153; tel. 330/726–3700, (Nonreporting) **A**1 9 10
Primary Contact: Daphne Bonner, Administrator
**Control:** Corporation, Investor–owned, for–profit **Service:** Rehabilitation

**Staffed Beds:** 29

**MAHONING VALLEY HOSPITAL** See Vibra Hospital of Mahoning Valley

☒ **ST. ELIZABETH BOARDMAN HEALTH CENTER (360276)**, 8401 Market Street, Zip 44512–6777; tel. 330/729–2929 **A**1 9 10 **F**3 8 11 15 18 29 30 34 35 40 45 46 59 60 67 68 70 74 75 77 78 79 81 82 84 85 87 93 107 108 110 111 114 119 120 121 129 130 131 146 148 **P**3 **S** Catholic Health Partners, Cincinnati, OH
Primary Contact: Eugenia Aubel, President
CFO: Donald E. Kline, Senior Vice President Finance
CMO: Nicholas Kreatsoulas, M.D., Vice President Medical Affairs
CIO: Charles Folkwein, Vice President Ancillary Services
CHR: Molly Seals, Senior Vice President Human Resources and Learning
Web address: www.ehealthconnection.com/regions/youngstown/content/show_facility.asp?facility_id=190
**Control:** Church–operated, Nongovernment, not–for profit **Service:** General Medical and Surgical

**Staffed Beds:** 128 **Admissions:** 8609 **Census:** 97 **Outpatient Visits:** 85613 **Births:** 0 **Total Expense ($000):** 93648 **Payroll Expense ($000):** 30186 **Personnel:** 503

☐ **VIBRA HOSPITAL OF MAHONING VALLEY (362023)**, 8049 South Avenue, Zip 44512–6154; tel. 330/726–5000 **A**1 10 **F**1 3 29 130 148 **S** Vibra Healthcare, Mechanicsburg, PA
Primary Contact: Mary Lou Sankovich, R.N., MSN, Chief Executive Officer and Chief Nursing Officer
Web address: www.mahoningvalleyhospital.com
**Control:** Corporation, Investor–owned, for–profit **Service:** Long–Term Acute Care hospital

**Staffed Beds:** 42 **Admissions:** 803 **Census:** 34 **Outpatient Visits:** 0 **Births:** 0 **Total Expense ($000):** 12150 **Personnel:** 105

**BORDMAN—Mahoning County**

**SELECT SPECIALTY HOSPITAL–YOUNGSTOWN, BOARDMAN CAMPUS** See Select Specialty Hospital–Youngstown, Youngstown

**BOWLING GREEN—Wood County**

☒ **WOOD COUNTY HOSPITAL (360029)**, 950 West Wooster Street, Zip 43402–2603; tel. 419/354–8900 **A**1 3 5 9 10 **F**3 11 12 13 15 17 28 29 30 32 34 35 40 44 45 46 50 57 59 64 65 68 69 70 75 76 77 79 81 82 85 87 89 93 107 108 110 111 114 115 118 119 129 130 131 132 135 144 146 147 148 **P**8
Primary Contact: Stanley R. Korducki, President
COO: Carole Matthews, Vice President Patient Care
CFO: Karol Bortel, Vice President Financial Services
CIO: Joanne White, Chief Information Officer
CHR: Frank Day, Vice President Patient Services
Web address: www.woodcountyhospital.org
**Control:** Other not–for–profit (including NFP Corporation) **Service:** General Medical and Surgical

**Staffed Beds:** 102 **Admissions:** 3442 **Census:** 28 **Outpatient Visits:** 91134 **Births:** 326 **Total Expense ($000):** 73914 **Payroll Expense ($000):** 29832 **Personnel:** 614

**BRYAN—Williams County**

☐ **COMMUNITY HOSPITALS AND WELLNESS CENTERS (360121)**, 433 West High Street, Zip 43506–1679; tel. 419/636–1131, (Includes ARCHBOLD HOSPITAL, 121 Westfield Drive, Archbold, Zip 43502; tel. 419/445–4415; BRYAN HOSPITAL, 433 West High Street, Zip 43506; tel. 419/636–1131; MONTPELIER HOSPITAL, 909 East Snyder Avenue, Montpelier, Zip 43543; tel. 419/485–3154), (Nonreporting) **A**1 2 5 9 10
Primary Contact: Philip L. Ennen, Vice President and Chief Executive Officer
CFO: Leroy P. Feather, Vice President Finance
CIO: Greg Slattery, Vice President Information
CHR: Mary Ann Potts, Director Personnel
Web address: www.chwchospital.com
**Control:** Other not–for–profit (including NFP Corporation) **Service:** General Medical and Surgical

**Staffed Beds:** 113

**BUCYRUS—Crawford County**

☒ ◇ **BUCYRUS COMMUNITY HOSPITAL (361316)**, 629 North Sandusky Avenue, Zip 44820–1821; tel. 419/562–4677 **A**1 5 9 10 18 21 **F**3 11 15 18 28 29 30 31 34 35 45 50 57 59 60 70 74 75 77 78 79 81 82 87 107 108 110 119 124 127 130 131 132 133 146 147 148 **S** Avita Health System, Galion, OH
Primary Contact: Jerome Morasko, Chief Executive Officer
COO: Andy Daniels, Chief Operating Officer
CMO: Michael A. Johnson, M.D., Chief of Staff
CIO: Joann Riedlinger, Vice President Nursing and Manager Information Systems
CHR: Jeanne Perkins, Vice President Nursing and Interim Manager Human Resources
Web address: www.bchonline.org
**Control:** Other not–for–profit (including NFP Corporation) **Service:** General Medical and Surgical

**Staffed Beds:** 25 **Admissions:** 919 **Census:** 10 **Outpatient Visits:** 15806 **Births:** 0 **Total Expense ($000):** 28981 **Payroll Expense ($000):** 10934 **Personnel:** 244

**CADIZ—Harrison County**

☒ **HARRISON COMMUNITY HOSPITAL (361311)**, 951 East Market Street, Zip 43907–9799; tel. 740/942–4631 **A**1 9 10 18 **F**7 11 15 18 28 29 30 31 34 35 40 45 47 50 51 53 57 58 59 62 64 65 68 74 75 77 78 79 81 82 85 86 87 93 97 107 108 110 111 114 119 130 132 133 135 143 146 147 148
Primary Contact: Clifford K. Harmon, Chief Executive Officer
CMO: Isam Tabbah, M.D., Chief of Staff
CHR: Marcella Evans, Director Human Resources
CNO: Elizabeth Kovacs, R.N., Director of Nursing
Web address: www.harrisoncommunity.com
**Control:** Other not–for–profit (including NFP Corporation) **Service:** General Medical and Surgical

**Staffed Beds:** 25 **Admissions:** 411 **Census:** 5 **Outpatient Visits:** 40467 **Births:** 0 **Total Expense ($000):** 16816 **Payroll Expense ($000):** 6844 **Personnel:** 150

**CAMBRIDGE—Guernsey County**

☒ **SOUTHEASTERN OHIO REGIONAL MEDICAL CENTER (360203)**, 1341 North Clark Street, Zip 43725–9614, Mailing Address: P.O. Box 610, Zip 43725–0610; tel. 740/439–8000 **A**1 2 9 10 20 **F**3 7 11 13 15 18 20 28 29 30 31 32 34 35 40 43 46 48 49 51 57 59 60 62 63 64 65 66 70 75 76 77 78 79 81 82 83 84 85 86 87 91 93 96 97 107 108 110 111 114 116 118 119 129 130 131 132 135 144 146 147 148 **P**6 8
Primary Contact: Raymond M. Chorey, President and Chief Executive Officer
CFO: Donald P. Huelskamp, Vice President Finance and Chief Financial Officer
CMO: E. Edwin Conaway, M.D., Vice President Medical Affairs and Chief Medical Officer
CIO: Kevin Ludwigsen, Interim Chief Information Officer
CHR: Ann Rollman, Vice President Human Resources
CNO: Angela S. Long, Vice President Clinical Services and Chief Nursing Officer
Web address: www.seormc.org
**Control:** Other not–for–profit (including NFP Corporation) **Service:** General Medical and Surgical

**Staffed Beds:** 95 **Admissions:** 4301 **Census:** 39 **Outpatient Visits:** 111545 **Births:** 430 **Total Expense ($000):** 72011 **Payroll Expense ($000):** 28461 **Personnel:** 634

**CANAL WINCHESTER—Fairfield County**

☐ **DILEY RIDGE MEDICAL CENTER (360358)**, 7911 Diley Road, Zip 43110–9653; tel. 614/838–7911 **A**1 9 10 **F**3 15 29 30 35 40 50 54 64 68 85 87 107 110 111 114 119 130 147
Primary Contact: Jodi Wilson, Site Administrator
Web address: www.dileyridgemedicalcenter.com
**Control:** Other not–for–profit (including NFP Corporation) **Service:** General Medical and Surgical

**Staffed Beds:** 10 **Admissions:** 25 **Census:** 1 **Outpatient Visits:** 45050 **Births:** 0 **Total Expense ($000):** 10994 **Payroll Expense ($000):** 3827 **Personnel:** 73

*Many Facility Codes have changed. Please refer to the AHA Guide Code Chart.* © 2013 AHA Guide

## CANTON—Stark County

☐ **ACUTE CARE SPECIALTY HOSPITAL OF AULTMAN (362032)**, 2600 Sixth Street, S.W., Zip 44710–1702; tel. 330/363–4000, (Nonreporting) **A**1 10
Primary Contact: Jackie Toth, Administrator
Web address: www.aultman.org
**Control:** Other not–for–profit (including NFP Corporation) **Service:** Long–Term Acute Care hospital

**Staffed Beds:** 30

✠ △ **AULTMAN HOSPITAL (360084)**, 2600 Sixth Street S.W., Zip 44710–1702; tel. 330/452–9911, (Includes AULTMAN HOSPITAL PEDIATRIC SERVICES, 2600 Sixth Street, S.W., tel. 330/363–5455), (Total facility includes 60 beds in nursing home–type unit) (Data for 364 days) **A**1 2 3 5 7 10 13 **F**3 7 8 11 12 13 14 15 17 18 20 22 24 26 28 29 30 31 34 35 39 40 43 44 45 48 49 50 51 53 54 55 56 57 58 59 60 61 62 63 64 68 70 71 72 74 75 76 77 78 79 81 82 83 84 85 86 87 89 90 93 96 97 98 102 103 104 105 106 107 108 109 110 111 114 117 118 119 120 121 123 127 128 129 130 131 132 133 134 135 143 144 145 146 147 148 **P**6 7 **S** Aultman Health Foundation, Canton, OH
Primary Contact: Edward J. Roth, III, President and Chief Executive Officer
COO: Christopher Remark, Chief Operating Officer
CFO: Mark Wright, Vice President
CHR: Sue Olivera, Vice President
Web address: www.aultman.com
**Control:** Other not–for–profit (including NFP Corporation) **Service:** General Medical and Surgical

**Staffed Beds:** 547 **Admissions:** 23983 **Census:** 372 **Outpatient Visits:** 452847 **Births:** 2512 **Total Expense ($000):** 431514 **Payroll Expense ($000):** 178916 **Personnel:** 3291

✠ △ **MERCY MEDICAL CENTER (360070)**, 1320 Mercy Drive N.W., Zip 44708–2641; tel. 330/489–1000 **A**1 2 3 5 7 9 10 **F**3 11 13 15 17 18 20 22 24 26 28 29 30 31 34 35 39 40 43 44 46 48 49 50 51 53 54 57 58 59 60 61 62 63 64 66 68 70 72 74 75 76 77 78 79 80 81 82 84 85 86 87 89 90 91 92 93 96 97 98 100 102 107 108 110 111 114 115 116 117 118 119 120 121 123 126 129 130 131 132 135 143 144 146 147 148 **P**6 7 **S** Sisters of Charity Health System, Cleveland, OH
Primary Contact: Thomas E. Cecconi, President and Chief Executive Officer
COO: David D. Cemate, FACHE, Senior Vice President and Chief Operating Officer
CFO: David K. Stewart, Chief Financial Officer
CMO: David Gormsen, D.O., Chief Medical Officer
CNO: Barbara Yingling, R.N., Vice President and Chief Nursing Officer
Web address: www.cantonmercy.org
**Control:** Other not–for–profit (including NFP Corporation) **Service:** General Medical and Surgical

**Staffed Beds:** 343 **Admissions:** 15102 **Census:** 200 **Outpatient Visits:** 610497 **Births:** 1576 **Total Expense ($000):** 306055 **Payroll Expense ($000):** 117973 **Personnel:** 2242

✠ **SELECT SPECIALTY HOSPITAL–CANTON (362016)**, 1320 Mercy Drive N.W., 7th Floor, Zip 44708–2614; tel. 330/489–8189, (Nonreporting) **A**1 10 **S** Select Medical Corporation, Mechanicsburg, PA
Primary Contact: Dawne Wheeler, Chief Executive Officer
Web address: www.selectspecialtyhospitals.com/company/locations/canton.aspx
**Control:** Corporation, Investor–owned, for–profit **Service:** Long–Term Acute Care hospital

**Staffed Beds:** 30

## CHARDON—Geauga County

☐ **HEATHERHILL CARE COMMUNITIES (362014)**, 12340 Bass Lake Road, Zip 44024–8327; tel. 440/285–4040, (Nonreporting) **A**1 10
Primary Contact: Jim Homa, Chief Executive Officer
COO: Linton Sharpnack, R.N., Director Nursing
CFO: Rebecca Ivcic, Chief Financial Officer
CMO: Donald Goddard, M.D., Chief Medical Officer
CHR: Danialle Lynce, Manager Human Resources
Web address: www.heatherhill.com
**Control:** Other not–for–profit (including NFP Corporation) **Service:** Long–Term Acute Care hospital

**Staffed Beds:** 214

✠ **UNIVERSITY HOSPITALS GEAUGA MEDICAL CENTER (360192)**, 13207 Ravenna Road, Zip 44024–7032; tel. 440/269–6000 **A**1 2 9 10 **F**3 8 11 12 13 14 15 18 20 22 26 28 29 30 31 32 34 35 36 37 38 39 40 41 43 44 47 49 50 51 54 56 57 58 59 60 62 64 65 68 70 74 75 76 77 78 79 81 82 85 86 87 89 91 92 93 96 97 98 100 101 102 103 107 108 110 111 114 115 116 117 118 119 120 121 123 124 129 130 131 132 134 135 143 146 147 148 **S** University Hospitals, Cleveland, OH
Primary Contact: M. Steven Jones, President
COO: M. Steven Jones, President
CFO: Paul Amantea, Director Finance
CMO: David Kosnosky, M.D., Chief Medical Officer
CIO: Lou Ciraldo, Information Services Representative
CHR: Danielle Lynce, Manager Human Resources
CNO: Peggy A. Kuhar, R.N., Chief Nursing Officer
Web address: www.uhhospitals.org/geauga/
**Control:** Other not–for–profit (including NFP Corporation) **Service:** General Medical and Surgical

**Staffed Beds:** 126 **Admissions:** 7698 **Census:** 79 **Outpatient Visits:** 133665 **Births:** 1067 **Total Expense ($000):** 101166 **Payroll Expense ($000):** 34377 **Personnel:** 688

## CHILLICOTHE—Ross County

✠ ◇ **ADENA MEDICAL CENTER (360159)**, (Formerly Adena Health System), 272 Hospital Road, Zip 45601–9031; tel. 740/779–7500 **A**1 2 5 9 10 19 21 **F**3 5 8 13 15 17 18 20 22 24 26 28 29 30 31 32 34 35 38 40 41 42 45 46 49 51 54 56 57 59 60 62 63 64 68 70 71 73 74 75 76 77 78 79 80 81 82 84 85 87 89 92 93 96 97 98 99 100 101 102 104 107 108 110 111 114 115 117 118 119 120 121 123 126 128 129 130 131 132 133 135 144 145 146 147 148 **P**6 **S** Adena Health System, Chillicothe, OH
Primary Contact: Mark H. Shuter, President and Chief Executive Officer
CMO: John Fortney, M.D., Chief Medical Officer
CIO: Mark Moffitt, Chief Information Officer
CHR: Eric Perdue, Chief Human Resource Officer
CNO: Judith Henson, Chief Nursing Officer
Web address: www.adena.org
**Control:** Other not–for–profit (including NFP Corporation) **Service:** General Medical and Surgical

**Staffed Beds:** 279 **Admissions:** 13212 **Census:** 132 **Outpatient Visits:** 477341 **Births:** 1078 **Total Expense ($000):** 402408 **Payroll Expense ($000):** 174181 **Personnel:** 2437

✠ **CHILLICOTHE VETERANS AFFAIRS MEDICAL CENTER**, (Formerly Veterans Affairs Medical Center), 17273 State Route 104, Zip 45601–9718; tel. 740/773–1141, (Total facility includes 162 beds in nursing home–type unit) **A**1 5 **F**3 5 18 29 30 33 34 35 36 38 39 44 45 47 48 50 53 54 56 57 59 61 62 63 64 65 67 74 75 77 79 80 81 82 84 86 87 93 94 96 97 98 100 101 102 103 104 106 107 108 111 115 119 127 128 129 130 132 135 143 144 146 147 148 **P**6 **S** Department of Veterans Affairs, Washington, DC
Primary Contact: Wendy J. Hepker, FACHE, Director
COO: Keith Sullivan, Associate Director
CFO: Rick Deckard, Chief Fiscal Service
CMO: Deborah Meesig, M.D., Chief of Staff
CIO: William Gawler, Chief Information Officer
CHR: Angela Young, Human Resources Officer
Web address: www.chillicothe.va.gov/
**Control:** Veterans Affairs, Government, federal **Service:** General Medical and Surgical

**Staffed Beds:** 297 **Admissions:** 4294 **Census:** 246 **Outpatient Visits:** 329923 **Births:** 0 **Total Expense ($000):** 212260 **Payroll Expense ($000):** 91290 **Personnel:** 1456

**VETERANS AFFAIRS MEDICAL CENTER** See Chillicothe Veterans Affairs Medical Center

**OH**

### CINCINNATI—Hamilton County

☐ **BETHESDA NORTH HOSPITAL (360179)**, 10500 Montgomery Road, Zip 45242–4402; tel. 513/865–1111, (Includes BETHESDA BUTLER COUNTY HOSPITAL, 3125 Hamilton Mason Road, Hamilton, Zip 45011–5307; tel. 513/894–8888; John S. Prout, President and Chief Executive Officer) **A**1 3 5 9 10 **F**3 5 9 11 13 15 17 18 20 22 24 26 28 29 30 31 34 35 36 37 38 39 40 41 42 43 44 45 46 47 48 49 50 53 54 55 56 57 58 59 60 61 63 64 65 66 68 70 71 73 74 75 76 77 78 79 81 82 84 85 86 87 90 91 92 93 94 96 97 100 101 102 104 107 108 110 111 114 115 116 117 118 119 120 121 123 124 126 129 130 131 132 134 135 141 143 144 145 146 147 148 **P**6
Primary Contact: Barb Boyne, Executive Director, Operations
CFO: Craig Rucker, Senior Vice President and Chief Financial Officer
CMO: Georges Feghali, M.D., Senior Vice President Quality and Chief Medical Officer
CIO: Rick Moore, Chief Information Officer
Web address: www.trihealth.com
**Control:** Other not–for–profit (including NFP Corporation) **Service:** General Medical and Surgical

**Staffed Beds:** 375 **Admissions:** 23767 **Census:** 252 **Outpatient Visits:** 277170 **Births:** 4085 **Total Expense ($000):** 418052 **Payroll Expense ($000):** 143363 **Personnel:** 3360

○ **BRIDGEWELL HOSPITAL OF CINCINNATI (364046)**, 5500 Verulam Avenue, Zip 45213–2418; tel. 513/531–6444, (Nonreporting) **A**10 11
Primary Contact: Sharon Wilburn, Chief Operating Officer
CNO: Doug Eppley, Director of Nursing
Web address: www.bridgewellhospitals.com
**Control:** Corporation, Investor–owned, for–profit **Service:** Psychiatric

**Staffed Beds:** 48

⊠ △ **CHRIST HOSPITAL (360163)**, 2139 Auburn Avenue, Zip 45219–2906; tel. 513/585–2000 **A**1 2 3 5 7 9 10 **F**3 6 8 9 11 12 13 15 17 18 20 22 24 26 28 29 30 31 34 35 36 37 38 39 40 44 45 46 47 48 49 50 51 52 53 54 55 56 57 58 59 60 61 64 65 66 68 70 73 74 75 76 77 78 79 80 81 82 83 84 85 86 87 90 92 93 94 96 97 98 99 100 101 102 103 104 107 108 109 110 111 114 115 116 117 118 119 120 121 123 124 126 130 131 132 135 136 138 141 143 144 145 146 147 148 **P**6
Primary Contact: Michael Keating, President and Chief Executive Officer
COO: Victor DiPilla, Vice President and Chief Business Development Officer
CFO: Chris Bergman, Chief Financial Officer
CMO: Bernard B. Gawne, M.D., Vice President and Chief Medical Officer
CIO: Alex Vaillancourt, Chief Information Officer
CHR: Rick Tolson, Chief Administrative Officer and Chief Human Resources Officer
CNO: Deborah Marie Hayes, R.N., Chief Hospital Officer and Chief Nursing Officer
Web address: www.thechristhospital.com
**Control:** Other not–for–profit (including NFP Corporation) **Service:** General Medical and Surgical

**Staffed Beds:** 528 **Admissions:** 24977 **Census:** 306 **Outpatient Visits:** 348249 **Births:** 3047 **Total Expense ($000):** 550381 **Payroll Expense ($000):** 191713 **Personnel:** 2901

⊠ △ **CINCINNATI CHILDREN'S HOSPITAL MEDICAL CENTER (363300)**, 3333 Burnet Avenue, Zip 45229–3039; tel. 513/636–4200, (Includes DIVISION OF ADOLESCENT MEDICINE, CINCINNATI CENTER FOR DEVELOPMENTAL DISORDERS, AND CONVALESCENT HOSPITAL FOR CHILDREN ; CHILDREN'S HOSPITAL, Elland and Bethesda Avenues, Zip 45229) **A**1 2 3 5 7 8 9 10 **F**3 7 9 11 12 17 18 19 20 20 21 25 26 27 28 29 30 31 32 34 35 36 37 38 39 40 41 42 43 44 48 49 50 51 54 55 57 58 59 60 61 62 63 64 65 66 68 72 74 75 77 78 79 81 82 84 85 86 87 88 89 90 91 92 93 94 95 96 97 98 99 100 101 102 104 105 106 107 108 111 112 113 114 115 116 117 118 119 126 129 130 131 132 134 135 136 137 138 139 141 142 144 146 148 **P**1
Primary Contact: Michael Fisher, President and Chief Executive Officer
CFO: Scott J. Hamlin, Chief Financial Officer
CIO: Marianne Speight, Vice President Information System and Chief Information Officer
Web address: www.cincinnatichildrens.org
**Control:** Other not–for–profit (including NFP Corporation) **Service:** Children's general

**Staffed Beds:** 539 **Admissions:** 17078 **Census:** 357 **Outpatient Visits:** 1127780 **Births:** 16 **Total Expense ($000):** 1722990 **Payroll Expense ($000):** 837201 **Personnel:** 12860

⊠ △ **CINCINNATI VETERANS AFFAIRS MEDICAL CENTER**, (Formerly Veterans Affairs Medical Center), 3200 Vine Street, Zip 45220–2288; tel. 513/475–6300, (Total facility includes 62 beds in nursing home–type unit) **A**1 2 3 5 7 8 **F**1 3 4 5 8 12 15 18 20 22 24 26 28 29 30 31 33 34 35 36 37 38 39 40 42 44 45 46 47 48 50 51 53 54 55 56 57 58 59 60 61 63 64 66 70 71 74 75 77 78 79 81 82 83 84 85 86 87 91 92 93 94 97 98 100 101 102 103 104 105 106 107 108 111 114 115 116 117 119 126 127 129 130 132 135 143 144 145 146 147 148 **S** Department of Veterans Affairs, Washington, DC
Primary Contact: Linda D. Smith, FACHE, Director
COO: David Ninneman, Associate Director
CFO: Sandra Selvidge, Chief Fiscal Service
CMO: Robert E. Falcone, M.D., Chief of Staff
CIO: Vique Caro, Chief Information Officer
CHR: Sandra Stenger, Acting Chief Human Resources
CNO: Katheryn Cook, R.N., Nurse Executive
Web address: www.cincinnati.va.gov/
**Control:** Veterans Affairs, Government, federal **Service:** General Medical and Surgical

**Staffed Beds:** 268 **Admissions:** 7362 **Census:** 209 **Outpatient Visits:** 552263 **Births:** 0 **Total Expense ($000):** 361965 **Payroll Expense ($000):** 161222 **Personnel:** 2058

⊠ △ **DRAKE CENTER (362004)**, 151 West Galbraith Road, Zip 45216–1015; tel. 513/418–2500, (Total facility includes 83 beds in nursing home–type unit) **A**1 3 5 7 10 **F**1 3 6 10 11 29 30 34 35 44 50 53 56 57 58 59 64 67 68 74 75 77 80 82 85 86 87 90 91 92 93 94 96 100 107 111 114 119 125 128 130 132 146 148 **P**5 **S** UC Health, Cincinnati, OH
Primary Contact: Debra C. Hampton, Ph.D., Vice President, Administration and Chief Nursing Officer
CFO: Duane Pifko, Interim Director Financial Services
CHR: Sharon Hancock, Director Human Resources
Web address: www.drakecenter.uchealth.com
**Control:** Other not–for–profit (including NFP Corporation) **Service:** Long–Term Acute Care hospital

**Staffed Beds:** 202 **Admissions:** 1642 **Census:** 148 **Outpatient Visits:** 42116 **Births:** 0 **Total Expense ($000):** 66663 **Payroll Expense ($000):** 33151 **Personnel:** 580

☐ **EVENDALE MEDICAL CENTER (360350)**, 3155 Glendale Milford Road, Zip 45241–3134; tel. 513/454–2222, (Nonreporting) **A**1 9 10
Primary Contact: Kelvin Hanger, Chief Executive Officer
Web address: www.evendalemedical.com
**Control:** Other not–for–profit (including NFP Corporation) **Service:** Other specialty

**Staffed Beds:** 29

⊠ △ **GOOD SAMARITAN HOSPITAL (360134)**, 375 Dixmyth Avenue, Zip 45220–2489; tel. 513/862–1400 **A**1 3 5 7 8 9 10 **F**2 3 5 6 9 11 12 13 15 17 18 20 22 24 26 28 29 30 31 34 35 36 37 38 39 40 41 42 44 45 46 47 48 49 50 53 54 55 56 57 58 59 60 61 63 64 65 66 68 70 71 72 74 75 76 77 78 79 81 82 84 85 86 87 90 91 92 93 94 96 97 98 99 100 101 102 103 104 105 106 107 108 110 111 114 115 116 117 118 119 121 123 126 129 130 131 132 134 135 141 143 144 145 146 147 148 **P**6 **S** Catholic Health Initiatives, Englewood, CO
Primary Contact: Jamie Easterling, Executive Director, Operations
COO: Gerald P. Oliphant, Executive Vice President and Chief Operating Officer
CFO: Craig Rucker, Senior Vice President and Chief Financial Officer
CMO: Georges Feghali, M.D., Senior Vice President Quality and Chief Medical Officer
CIO: Rick Moore, Chief Information Officer
CHR: Walter L. McLarty, Chief Human Resources Officer
Web address: www.trihealth.com
**Control:** Church–operated, Nongovernment, not–for profit **Service:** General Medical and Surgical

**Staffed Beds:** 504 **Admissions:** 25828 **Census:** 342 **Outpatient Visits:** 226806 **Births:** 6420 **Total Expense ($000):** 472717 **Payroll Expense ($000):** 165370 **Personnel:** 2971

⊠ **HEALTHSOUTH REHABILITATION HOSPITAL AT DRAKE (363034)**, 151 West Galbraith Road, Zip 45216–1015; tel. 513/418–5600 **A**1 9 10 **F**90 **S** HEALTHSOUTH Corporation, Birmingham, AL
Primary Contact: Brad Kennedy, Chief Executive Officer
CFO: Scott Corder, Controller
CMO: Mark Goddard, M.D., Medical Director
CHR: Jason Sparks, Director, Human Resources
CNO: Kathy McNally, Chief Nursing Officer
Web address: www.healthsouthatdrake.com
**Control:** Corporation, Investor–owned, for–profit **Service:** Rehabilitation

**Staffed Beds:** 40 **Admissions:** 614 **Census:** 27 **Outpatient Visits:** 0 **Births:** 0 **Total Expense ($000):** 9481 **Payroll Expense ($000):** 4994 **Personnel:** 47

*Many Facility Codes have changed. Please refer to the AHA Guide Code Chart.*
© 2013 AHA Guide

⊠ **MERCY HEALTH – ANDERSON HOSPITAL (360001)**, (Formerly Mercy Hospital Anderson), 7500 State Road, Zip 45255–2492; tel. 513/624–4500, (Nonreporting) **A**1 2 9 10 **S** Catholic Health Partners, Cincinnati, OH
Primary Contact: Jeff Graham, Market Leader and President
COO: Gyasi Chisley, Site Administrator and Chief Operating Officer
CFO: Deborah Bloomfield, Chief Financial Officer
CMO: Leonard M. Randolph, Jr., M.D., Senior Vice President and Chief Medical Officer
CIO: Matt Eversole, Regional Vice President Information Services
CHR: Maggie Lund, Divisional Senior Vice President Human Resources
Web address: www.e–mercy.com
**Control:** Church–operated, Nongovernment, not–for profit **Service:** General Medical and Surgical

| **Staffed Beds:** 188 |
| --- |

⊠ **MERCY HEALTH – MT. AIRY HOSPITAL (360234)**, (Formerly Mercy Hospital Mount Airy), 2446 Kipling Avenue, Zip 45239–6650; tel. 513/853–5000 **A**1 2 9 10 **F**3 11 12 15 18 20 28 29 30 31 34 37 40 45 46 49 50 51 56 57 58 59 60 64 68 70 74 75 77 78 79 81 82 84 85 87 90 91 92 98 99 106 107 108 110 111 114 115 116 118 119 130 146 147 148 **S** Catholic Health Partners, Cincinnati, OH
Primary Contact: Michael R. Stephens, Market Leader and President
CMO: Leonard M. Randolph, Jr., M.D., Senior Vice President and Divisional Chief Medical Officer
CIO: Yousuf Ahmad, Divisional Senior Vice President
CHR: Maggie Lund, Regional Vice President Human Resources
Web address: www.e–mercy.com
**Control:** Other not–for–profit (including NFP Corporation) **Service:** General Medical and Surgical

| **Staffed Beds:** 170 **Admissions:** 6463 **Census:** 77 **Outpatient Visits:** 74058 **Births:** 0 **Total Expense ($000):** 81758 **Payroll Expense ($000):** 29055 **Personnel:** 532 |
| --- |

⊠ **MERCY HEALTH – WESTERN HILLS HOSPITAL (360113)**, (Formerly Mercy Hospital Western Hills), 3131 Queen City Avenue, Zip 45238–2396; tel. 513/389–5000 **A**1 2 9 10 **F**3 11 15 18 20 28 29 30 31 34 35 40 42 45 46 47 49 50 53 56 57 58 59 60 62 64 68 70 74 75 77 78 79 81 82 84 85 87 90 92 93 94 98 103 106 107 108 110 111 114 115 118 119 130 146 147 **S** Catholic Health Partners, Cincinnati, OH
Primary Contact: Michael R. Stephens, Market Leader and President
Web address: www.e–mercy.com
**Control:** Other not–for–profit (including NFP Corporation) **Service:** General Medical and Surgical

| **Staffed Beds:** 156 **Admissions:** 6324 **Census:** 68 **Outpatient Visits:** 110372 **Births:** 0 **Total Expense ($000):** 83801 **Payroll Expense ($000):** 31326 **Personnel:** 578 |
| --- |

⊠ **REGENCY HOSPITAL OF CINCINNATI (362034)**, 311 Straight Street, 4th Floor, Zip 45219–1018; tel. 513/559–5957, (Nonreporting) **A**1 10 **S** Select Medical Corporation, Mechanicsburg, PA
Primary Contact: Mark S. Brodeur, FACHE, Chief Executive Officer
CMO: Sunil Dama, M.D., Medical Director
CHR: Elizabeth M. Wilson, Coordinator Human Resources
Web address: www.regencyhospital.com
**Control:** Corporation, Investor–owned, for–profit **Service:** Long–Term Acute Care hospital

| **Staffed Beds:** 31 |
| --- |

⊠ **SELECT SPECIALTY HOSPITAL–CINCINNATI (362019)**, 375 Dixmyth Avenue, Zip 45220–2475; tel. 513/872–4444, (Nonreporting) **A**1 9 10 **S** Select Medical Corporation, Mechanicsburg, PA
Primary Contact: Curtis Ohashi, Chief Executive Officer
Web address: www.selectspecialtyhospitals.com/company/locations/cincinnati.aspx
**Control:** Corporation, Investor–owned, for–profit **Service:** Long–Term Acute Care hospital

| **Staffed Beds:** 35 |
| --- |

☐ **SHRINERS HOSPITALS FOR CHILDREN–CINCINNATI BURNS HOSPITAL (363308)**, 3229 Burnet Avenue, Zip 45229–3095; tel. 513/872–6000, (Nonreporting) **A**1 10 **S** Shriners Hospitals for Children, Tampa, FL
Primary Contact: Tony Lewgood, Interim Administrator
CFO: James Lester, Director Fiscal Services
CMO: Richard J. Kagan, M.D., Chief of Staff
CIO: Mark Washam, Chief Information Officer
CHR: Sally Skillman, Director Human Resources
Web address: www.shrinershospitalsforchildren.org/Hospitals/Locations/Cincinnati.aspx
**Control:** Other not–for–profit (including NFP Corporation) **Service:** Children's other specialty

| **Staffed Beds:** 30 |
| --- |

⊠ **SUMMIT BEHAVIORAL HEALTHCARE (364035)**, 1101 Summit Road, Zip 45237–2652; tel. 513/948–3600 **A**1 10 **F**4 30 39 75 77 87 98 101 103 130 135 146 **S** Ohio Department of Mental Health, Columbus, OH
Primary Contact: Elizabeth Banks, Chief Executive Officer
COO: Jeff Amend, Chief Operating Officer
CFO: Steven Burns, Director Fiscal Services
CMO: Lawrence Ostrowski, M.D., Chief Clinical Officer
CIO: Eric Bradley, Director Computer Information Services
CHR: Rhonda Milton, Director Human Resources
Web address: www.mh.state.oh.us/
**Control:** State–Government, nonfederal **Service:** Psychiatric

| **Staffed Beds:** 291 **Admissions:** 798 **Census:** 256 **Outpatient Visits:** 449 **Births:** 0 **Total Expense ($000):** 46254 **Payroll Expense ($000):** 35914 **Personnel:** 422 |
| --- |

⊠ **THE JEWISH HOSPITAL – MERCY HEALTH (360016)**, (Formerly The Jewish Hospital), 4777 East Galbraith Road, Zip 45236–2725; tel. 513/686–3000 **A**1 2 3 5 9 10 **F**3 11 12 15 18 20 22 24 26 28 29 30 31 32 34 35 37 39 40 41 44 45 46 47 49 50 51 54 58 59 60 64 68 70 74 75 78 79 81 82 84 85 87 93 94 97 100 107 108 109 110 111 115 118 119 120 123 124 126 130 131 132 135 136 143 146 147 **P**6 **S** Catholic Health Partners, Cincinnati, OH
Primary Contact: Steve Holman, Market Leader and President
COO: Jack Hill, Chief Operating Officer and Administrator
Web address: www.jewishhospitalcincinnati.com/
**Control:** Other not–for–profit (including NFP Corporation) **Service:** General Medical and Surgical

| **Staffed Beds:** 209 **Admissions:** 11074 **Census:** 130 **Outpatient Visits:** 129492 **Births:** 0 **Total Expense ($000):** 202030 **Payroll Expense ($000):** 64761 **Personnel:** 1147 |
| --- |

⊠ **UNIVERSITY HOSPITAL (360003)**, 234 Goodman Street, Zip 45219–2316; tel. 513/584–1000 **A**1 2 3 5 8 10 **F**3 6 7 9 11 12 13 15 16 17 18 20 22 24 26 28 29 30 31 34 35 36 37 38 39 40 43 44 45 46 47 48 49 50 51 52 53 54 55 56 57 58 59 60 61 63 64 66 68 70 71 72 74 75 76 77 78 79 80 81 82 84 85 86 87 92 93 97 98 100 101 102 103 104 107 108 110 111 112 114 115 116 117 118 119 120 121 123 124 126 129 130 131 132 134 135 136 138 139 141 142 145 146 147 148 **P**6 **S** UC Health, Cincinnati, OH
Primary Contact: Lee Ann Liska, President and Chief Executive Officer
COO: Nancy Barone, Vice President and Executive Director Operations and Strategic Planning
CFO: Doug Arvin, Vice President Financial Services
CMO: Robert Wones, M.D., Vice President and Associate Chief of Staff
CIO: Jay Brown, Vice President and Chief Information Officer
CHR: Clarence Pauley, Vice President Human Resources
Web address: www.universityhospital.uchealth.com/
**Control:** Other not–for–profit (including NFP Corporation) **Service:** General Medical and Surgical

| **Staffed Beds:** 498 **Admissions:** 31609 **Census:** 429 **Outpatient Visits:** 360482 **Births:** 2555 **Total Expense ($000):** 680891 **Payroll Expense ($000):** 236004 **Personnel:** 4449 |
| --- |

**VETERANS AFFAIRS MEDICAL CENTER** See Cincinnati Veterans Affairs Medical Center

**CIRCLEVILLE—Pickaway County**

⊠ **BERGER HEALTH SYSTEM (360170)**, 600 North Pickaway Street, Zip 43113–1447; tel. 740/474–2126 **A**1 5 9 10 **F**3 13 15 18 22 28 29 30 31 32 34 35 36 40 45 50 54 56 57 59 63 64 65 66 70 75 76 79 81 85 87 90 93 96 107 108 110 111 114 119 124 129 130 131 132 135 146 147 148 Primary Contact: Tim Colburn, President and Chief Executive Officer
CFO: Tom Scherer, Interim Vice President Finance
CMO: Brett Call, D.O., Chief of Staff
CIO: Andy Chileski, Chief Information Officer and Vice President Facilities
CHR: Suzanne Welker, Chief Human Resources Officer and Vice President Marketing Strategy
CNO: Brenda M. Strittmatter, Patient Services Officer
Web address: www.bergerhealth.com
**Control:** City–County, Government, nonfederal **Service:** General Medical and Surgical

| **Staffed Beds:** 82 **Admissions:** 2426 **Census:** 26 **Outpatient Visits:** 108723 **Births:** 385 **Total Expense ($000):** 68258 **Payroll Expense ($000):** 22960 **Personnel:** 452 |
| --- |

**CLEVELAND—Cuyahoga County**

**CLEVELAND CAMPUS** See Northcoast Behavioral Healthcare System, Northfield

---

**Hospital, Medicare Provider Number, Address, Telephone, Approval, Facility, and Physician Codes, Health Care System**

★ American Hospital Association (AHA) membership
☐ The Joint Commission accreditation    ◇ DNV Healthcare Inc. accreditation
○ Healthcare Facilities Accreditation Program
△ Commission on Accreditation of Rehabilitation Facilities (CARF) accreditation

OH

☒ △ **CLEVELAND CLINIC (360180)**, (Formerly Cleveland Clinic Foundation), 9500 Euclid Avenue, Zip 44195–5108; tel. 216/444–2200, (Includes CLEVELAND CLINIC CHILDREN'S HOSPITAL, 9500 Euclid Avenue, Zip 44103; tel. 800/223–2273) **A**1 3 5 7 8 9 10 **F**3 4 5 6 7 8 9 11 12 13 14 15 17 18 19 20 21 22 23 24 25 26 27 28 29 30 31 32 33 34 35 36 37 38 39 40 42 44 45 46 47 48 49 50 51 52 53 54 55 56 57 58 59 60 61 62 63 64 65 66 68 70 71 72 73 74 75 76 77 78 79 80 81 82 83 84 85 86 87 88 89 90 91 92 93 94 96 97 100 101 102 103 104 105 107 108 109 110 111 112 113 114 115 116 117 118 119 120 121 123 124 126 129 130 131 132 134 135 136 137 138 139 140 141 142 143 144 145 146 147 148 **P**6 **S** Cleveland Clinic Health System, Cleveland, OH
Primary Contact: Delos Cosgrove, M.D., President and Chief Executive Officer
CFO: Steven Glass, Chief Financial Officer
CMO: Joseph Hahn, M.D., Chief of Staff
CIO: C. Martin Harris, M.D., Chief Information Officer
CHR: Joseph Patrnchak, Chief Human Resources Officer
Web address: www.clevelandclinic.org
**Control:** Other not–for–profit (including NFP Corporation) **Service:** General Medical and Surgical

**Staffed Beds:** 1268 **Admissions:** 54997 **Census:** 982 **Outpatient Visits:** 4723747 **Births:** 93 **Total Expense ($000):** 4151671 **Payroll Expense ($000):** 2067745 **Personnel:** 27622

☒ △ **CLEVELAND CLINIC CHILDREN'S HOSPITAL FOR REHABILITATION (363304)**, 2801 Martin Luther King Jr. Drive, Zip 44104–3865; tel. 216/448–6400 **A**1 7 9 10 **F**28 29 30 32 34 35 36 50 57 60 68 74 75 80 82 86 89 90 91 93 94 96 100 130 132 143 146 148 **S** Cleveland Clinic Health System, Cleveland, OH
Primary Contact: Michael J. McHugh, M.D., Medical Director
COO: Alec G. Kulik, Administrator
CFO: Debra Nyikes, Director Finance and Chief Financial Officer
CMO: Roberta Bauer, M.D., Acting Chair Medical Staff
CIO: C. Martin Harris, M.D., Chief Information Officer
CHR: Jan Hlahol, Manager Human Resources
Web address: www.my.clevelandclinic.org/childrens–hospital/default.aspx
**Control:** Other not–for–profit (including NFP Corporation) **Service:** Children's rehabilitation

**Staffed Beds:** 25 **Admissions:** 232 **Census:** 16 **Outpatient Visits:** 57250 **Births:** 0 **Total Expense ($000):** 33253 **Payroll Expense ($000):** 18904 **Personnel:** 332

☒ **FAIRVIEW HOSPITAL (360077)**, 18101 Lorain Avenue, Zip 44111–5656; tel. 216/476–7000, (Total facility includes 11 beds in nursing home–type unit) **A**1 2 3 5 9 10 13 **F**3 8 11 13 15 17 18 19 20 22 24 26 28 29 30 31 32 34 35 40 41 43 45 46 49 50 51 53 57 58 59 60 64 65 66 68 69 70 71 72 74 75 76 78 79 81 82 85 86 87 89 92 93 97 98 99 100 102 107 108 110 111 114 115 116 117 118 119 120 121 123 124 126 128 130 131 132 135 143 145 146 147 148 **S** Cleveland Clinic Health System, Cleveland, OH
Primary Contact: Janice Murphy, President
COO: John C. Mills, Senior Vice President Operations
CFO: Ankit Chhabra, Director Finance
CMO: Neil Smith, M.D., Chief Medical Officer
CIO: C. Martin Harris, M.D., Chief Information Officer
CHR: Ann Beatty, Director Human Resources
CNO: Deborah C. Small, R.N., Chief Nursing Officer and Vice President Patient Care Services
Web address: www.fairviewhospital.org
**Control:** Other not–for–profit (including NFP Corporation) **Service:** General Medical and Surgical

**Staffed Beds:** 410 **Admissions:** 20729 **Census:** 262 **Outpatient Visits:** 276622 **Births:** 3953 **Total Expense ($000):** 348563 **Payroll Expense ($000):** 141719 **Personnel:** 2028

☐ **GRACE HOSPITAL (362015)**, 2307 West 14th Street, Zip 44113–3698; tel. 216/687–1500, (Nonreporting) **A**1 10
Primary Contact: Rajive Khanna, Chief Executive Officer
COO: Rajive Khanna, Chief Executive Officer
CMO: John Nickels, M.D., President Medical Staff
CIO: Mary Zimpfer, Vice President Quality Management
Web address: www.gracehospital.org
**Control:** Other not–for–profit (including NFP Corporation) **Service:** Long–Term Acute Care hospital

**Staffed Beds:** 87

**HANNA HOUSE SKILLED NURSING FACILITY** See University Hospitals Case Medical Center

☒ **HILLCREST HOSPITAL (360230)**, 6780 Mayfield Road, Zip 44124–2203; tel. 440/312–4500 **A**1 2 9 10 **F**3 11 13 15 17 18 20 22 24 26 28 29 30 31 34 35 36 37 38 40 41 43 46 49 50 51 53 57 59 60 64 65 68 69 70 72 74 75 76 77 78 79 81 82 84 85 86 89 93 97 100 107 108 110 111 114 115 116 117 119 120 121 126 129 130 131 132 135 143 145 146 147 148 **S** Cleveland Clinic Health System, Cleveland, OH
Primary Contact: Jeffrey A. Leimgruber, President
Web address: www.hillcresthospital.org
**Control:** Other not–for–profit (including NFP Corporation) **Service:** General Medical and Surgical

**Staffed Beds:** 412 **Admissions:** 21966 **Census:** 288 **Outpatient Visits:** 235393 **Births:** 4011 **Total Expense ($000):** 343163 **Payroll Expense ($000):** 129595 **Personnel:** 2114

☒ **KINDRED HOSPITAL CLEVELAND–GATEWAY (362026)**, 2351 East 22nd Street, 7th Floor, Zip 44115–3111; tel. 216/363–2671, (Includes KINDRED HOSPITAL OF CLEVELAND, 11900 Fairhill Road, Zip 44120–1062; tel. 216/983–8030; Steve Jakubcanin, Executive Director), (Nonreporting) **A**1 10 **S** Kindred Healthcare, Louisville, KY
Primary Contact: Ian Cooper, Chief Executive Officer
Web address: www.kindredgateway.com
**Control:** Corporation, Investor–owned, for–profit **Service:** Long–Term Acute Care hospital

**Staffed Beds:** 153

**KINDRED HOSPITAL OF CLEVELAND** See Kindred Hospital Cleveland–Gateway

☒ △ **LOUIS STOKES CLEVELAND VETERANS AFFAIRS MEDICAL CENTER**, (Formerly Veterans Affairs Medical Center), 10701 East Boulevard, Zip 44106–1702; tel. 216/791–3800, (Total facility includes 150 beds in nursing home–type unit) **A**1 2 3 5 7 8 **F**1 2 3 4 5 6 9 11 12 15 17 18 20 22 24 26 28 29 30 31 34 35 36 37 38 39 40 44 46 47 49 50 51 54 56 57 58 59 60 61 62 63 64 65 66 68 70 71 74 75 77 78 79 80 81 82 83 84 85 86 87 90 91 92 93 94 96 97 98 100 101 102 103 104 105 106 107 108 110 111 112 114 115 116 117 118 119 120 121 126 127 128 129 130 132 135 143 144 146 147 148 **S** Department of Veterans Affairs, Washington, DC
Primary Contact: Susan Fuehrer, Director
COO: Sean Nelson, Deputy Director
CFO: Gene DeAngelis, Chief Fiscal Service
CMO: Murray Altose, M.D., Chief of Staff
CIO: Steve Gaj, Facility Chief Information Officer
CHR: Charles Franks, Chief Human Resources
Web address: www.cleveland.va.gov/
**Control:** Veterans Affairs, Government, federal **Service:** General Medical and Surgical

**Staffed Beds:** 585 **Admissions:** 10630 **Census:** 372 **Outpatient Visits:** 1417952 **Births:** 0 **Total Expense ($000):** 842242 **Payroll Expense ($000):** 328943 **Personnel:** 4726

☒ **LUTHERAN HOSPITAL (360087)**, 1730 West 25th Street, Zip 44113–3170; tel. 216/696–4300 **A**1 9 10 **F**3 5 15 29 30 34 35 37 40 50 56 57 58 59 60 65 70 74 75 77 79 81 82 85 86 87 93 98 103 104 105 107 111 114 119 129 130 131 132 135 143 146 148 **S** Cleveland Clinic Health System, Cleveland, OH
Primary Contact: Brian Donley, M.D., President
COO: Kris Bennett, Chief Operating Officer
CFO: Don Urbancsik, Director Finance
CMO: Ronald Golovan, M.D., Vice President Medical Operations
CIO: C. Martin Harris, M.D., Chief Information Officer
CHR: Sheree Laborie, Director Human Resources
CNO: Denise Minor, R.N., Chief Nursing Officer
Web address: www.lutheranhospital.org
**Control:** Other not–for–profit (including NFP Corporation) **Service:** General Medical and Surgical

**Staffed Beds:** 198 **Admissions:** 7111 **Census:** 97 **Outpatient Visits:** 60326 **Births:** 0 **Total Expense ($000):** 97529 **Payroll Expense ($000):** 40158 **Personnel:** 649

☒ △ **METROHEALTH MEDICAL CENTER (360059)**, 2500 MetroHealth Drive, Zip 44109–1998; tel. 216/778–7800, (Total facility includes 141 beds in nursing home–type unit) **A**1 2 3 5 7 8 9 10 13 **F**3 5 6 7 8 9 11 12 13 15 16 17 18 19 20 22 24 26 27 28 29 30 31 32 34 35 36 38 39 40 43 44 45 47 49 50 51 52 53 54 55 56 57 58 59 60 61 63 64 65 66 68 70 71 72 74 75 76 77 78 79 80 81 82 83 84 85 86 87 88 89 90 91 92 93 94 95 96 97 98 99 100 101 102 103 104 105 107 108 110 111 114 115 116 117 118 119 121 123 128 129 130 131 132 134 135 143 144 146 147 148 **P**6
Primary Contact: Akram Boutros, M.D., FACHE, President and Chief Executive Officer
COO: Edward Hills, D.D.S., Interim Chief Operating Officer
CFO: Jeffrey Rooney, Chief Financial Officer
CMO: Alfred Connors, Senior Vice President Medical Affairs and Chief Medical Officer
CIO: James Schlesinger, Interim Chief Information Officer
CHR: Debbie Warman, Vice President Human Resources
CNO: Mavis Bechtle, MSN, Vice President and Chief Nursing Officer
Web address: www.metrohealth.org
**Control:** County–Government, nonfederal **Service:** General Medical and Surgical

**Staffed Beds:** 708 **Admissions:** 26219 **Census:** 493 **Outpatient Visits:** 995281 **Births:** 2876 **Total Expense ($000):** 759787 **Payroll Expense ($000):** 426900 **Personnel:** 5209

**RAINBOW BABIES AND CHILDREN'S HOSPITAL** See University Hospitals Case Medical Center

**REGENCY HOSPITAL CLEVELAND EAST** See Regency Hospital Cleveland East, Warrensville Heights

**SAINT LUKE'S MEDICAL CENTER** See St. Vincent Charity Medical Center

*Many Facility Codes have changed. Please refer to the AHA Guide Code Chart.*
© 2013 AHA Guide

**OH**

☐ **ST. VINCENT CHARITY MEDICAL CENTER (360037)**, 2351 East 22nd Street, Zip 44115–3111; tel. 216/861–6200, (Includes SAINT LUKE'S MEDICAL CENTER, 11311 Shaker Boulevard, Zip 44104–3805; tel. 216/368–7000) **A**1 2 3 5 9 10 **F**3 4 5 12 15 17 18 20 22 24 28 29 30 31 33 34 35 37 39 40 42 45 50 54 56 57 59 60 61 62 64 65 66 68 70 71 74 75 77 78 79 81 82 84 85 86 87 93 97 98 100 102 103 107 108 110 114 118 119 130 146 148 **P**4 **S** Sisters of Charity Health System, Cleveland, OH
Primary Contact: David Perse, M.D., President
COO: Beverly Lozar, Vice President Professional and Support Services
CFO: Matthew Rish, Vice President Finance
CIO: Robin Stursa, Chief Information Officer
CHR: Gary Lazroff, Vice President Human Resources
Web address: www.svch.net
**Control:** Other not–for–profit (including NFP Corporation) **Service:** General Medical and Surgical

**Staffed Beds:** 198 **Admissions:** 8052 **Census:** 110 **Outpatient Visits:** 151555 **Births:** 0 **Total Expense ($000):** 149914 **Payroll Expense ($000):** 59376 **Personnel:** 1100

☒ **UH REGIONAL HOSPITALS (360075)**, 27100 Chardon Road, Zip 44143–1116; tel. 440/585–6500, (Includes UNIVERSITY HOSPITALS BEDFORD MEDICAL CENTER, 44 Blaine Avenue, Zip 44146–2709; tel. 440/735–3900; UNIVERSITY HOSPITALS RICHMOND MEDICAL CENTER, 27100 Chardon Road, tel. 440/585–6500) **A**1 10 12 13 **F**8 14 15 20 29 34 35 40 43 44 49 50 57 59 60 65 66 68 69 70 75 77 79 81 82 86 87 89 93 96 97 107 108 109 110 111 114 116 117 118 119 129 130 132 133 135 143 146 147 148 **S** University Hospitals, Cleveland, OH
Primary Contact: Laurie Delgado, President
CFO: Scott Platz, Director Finance
CMO: Rosemary Leeming, M.D., Chief Medical Officer
CHR: Stephanie W. Neonakis, Manager Human Resources
CNO: Michelle Giltner, Interim Chief Nursing Officer
Web address: www.uhhospitals.org
**Control:** Other not–for–profit (including NFP Corporation) **Service:** General Medical and Surgical

**Staffed Beds:** 109 **Admissions:** 5832 **Census:** 65 **Outpatient Visits:** 166597 **Births:** 0 **Total Expense ($000):** 98942 **Payroll Expense ($000):** 38192 **Personnel:** 731

☒ **UNIVERSITY HOSPITALS CASE MEDICAL CENTER (360137)**, 11100 Euclid Avenue, Zip 44106–1716; tel. 216/844–1000, (Includes ALFRED AND NORMA LERNER TOWER, BOLWELL HEALTH CENTER, HANNA PAVILION, LAKESIDE HOSPITAL, SAMUEL MATHER PAVILION ; HANNA HOUSE SKILLED NURSING FACILITY, 11100 Euclid Avenue, Zip 44106; RAINBOW BABIES AND CHILDREN'S HOSPITAL, 2074 Abington Road, Zip 44106; tel. 216/844–3911; Patricia DePompei, President; UNIVERSITY MACDONALD WOMEN'S HOSPITAL, Abington Road, Zip 44106; Patricia DePompei, President), (Total facility includes 38 beds in nursing home–type unit) **A**1 2 3 5 8 9 10 **F**2 3 5 6 8 9 11 12 13 14 15 17 18 19 20 21 22 23 24 25 26 27 28 29 30 31 32 34 35 36 37 38 39 40 41 42 43 44 45 46 47 48 49 50 51 52 53 54 55 56 57 58 59 60 61 64 65 66 68 70 71 72 73 74 75 76 77 78 79 80 81 82 83 84 85 86 87 88 89 90 91 92 93 94 96 97 98 99 100 101 102 103 104 105 107 108 109 110 111 112 114 115 116 117 118 119 120 121 123 124 126 128 129 130 131 132 134 135 136 137 138 139 140 141 142 143 144 145 146 147 148 **P**6 7 **S** University Hospitals, Cleveland, OH
Primary Contact: Fred C. Rothstein, M.D., President
COO: Ron Dziedzicki, R.N., Chief Support Services Officer
CFO: Sonia Salvino, Vice President Finance
CMO: Michael Anderson, M.D., Chief Medical Officer
CHR: Julie Chester, Director Human Resources
Web address: www.UHhospitals.org
**Control:** Other not–for–profit (including NFP Corporation) **Service:** General Medical and Surgical

**Staffed Beds:** 771 **Admissions:** 45754 **Census:** 653 **Outpatient Visits:** 415640 **Births:** 3715 **Total Expense ($000):** 1128137 **Payroll Expense ($000):** 387833 **Personnel:** 7451

**VETERANS AFFAIRS MEDICAL CENTER** See Louis Stokes Cleveland Veterans Affairs Medical Center

☒ **MERCER HEALTH (360058)**, (Formerly Mercer County Joint Township Community Hospital), 800 West Main Street, Zip 45828–1698; tel. 419/678–2341 **A**1 9 10 **F**7 11 12 13 15 18 28 29 30 31 34 35 40 42 44 45 47 51 54 55 57 59 61 62 64 65 68 75 77 78 79 81 82 85 87 92 93 94 97 107 108 110 111 114 118 119 130 131 132 133 134 135 143 144 145 146 147 148
Primary Contact: Lisa R. Klenke, R.N., Interim Chief Executive Officer
CFO: George Boyles, Vice President Finance and Chief Financial Officer
CMO: Craig Dues, D.O., Chief Medical Officer
CIO: Kyle Rindler, Director Information Systems
CHR: Ed Sweetnich, Vice President Human Resources
CNO: Lisa R. Klenke, R.N., Vice President Patient Care Services
Web address: www.mercer–health.com
**Control:** Hospital district or authority, Government, nonfederal **Service:** General Medical and Surgical

**Staffed Beds:** 60 **Admissions:** 1930 **Census:** 13 **Outpatient Visits:** 41249 **Births:** 341 **Total Expense ($000):** 42804 **Payroll Expense ($000):** 16046 **Personnel:** 385

☒ **JAMES CANCER HOSPITAL AND SOLOVE RESEARCH INSTITUTE (360242)**, 300 West Tenth Avenue, Zip 43210–1280; tel. 614/293–3300 **A**1 2 3 5 8 9 10 **F**3 7 15 29 30 31 32 34 35 36 37 38 39 44 46 47 48 49 50 52 54 55 57 58 59 61 62 64 66 68 70 71 74 75 77 78 79 81 82 84 85 86 87 93 97 100 107 108 110 111 112 114 115 116 117 118 119 120 121 123 124 126 130 132 134 135 136 141 143 144 145 146 147 148 **P**6 **S** Ohio State University Health System, Columbus, OH
Primary Contact: Michael Caligiuri, Chief Executive Officer
COO: Dennis J. Smith, Chief Operating Officer
CFO: Bell Julian, Associate Executive Director and Chief Financial Officer
CIO: Twyla Pohar, Manager Computer Systems
CHR: Jill Hannah, Director Human Resources
Web address: www.jamesline.com
**Control:** State–Government, nonfederal **Service:** Cancer

**Staffed Beds:** 209 **Admissions:** 10243 **Census:** 185 **Outpatient Visits:** 266259 **Births:** 0 **Total Expense ($000):** 553122 **Payroll Expense ($000):** 128829 **Personnel:** 2619

☒ △ **MOUNT CARMEL (360035)**, 793 West State Street, Zip 43222–1551; tel. 614/234–5000, (Includes MOUNT CARMEL EAST HOSPITAL, 6001 East Broad Street, Zip 43213; tel. 614/234–6000; Claus von Zychlin, President; MOUNT CARMEL WEST HOSPITAL, 793 West State Street, Zip 43222; tel. 614/234–5000) **A**1 2 3 5 7 9 10 **F**3 11 12 13 15 17 18 20 22 24 26 29 30 31 34 35 37 40 43 44 45 46 47 48 49 50 51 54 55 57 58 59 61 63 64 65 66 68 70 72 74 75 76 78 79 81 83 84 85 86 87 90 92 96 97 98 100 101 102 103 104 107 108 109 110 111 114 115 116 117 118 119 120 121 123 126 130 131 132 145 146 147 148 **P**6 8 **S** Trinity Health, Livonia, MI
Primary Contact: Sean McKibben, President and Chief Operating Officer
COO: Mary R. Trimmer, Interim Chief Operating Officer
CFO: Keith T. Coleman, Chief Financial Officer
CIO: Cindy Sheets, Chief Information Officer
Web address: www.mountcarmelhealth.com
**Control:** Church–operated, Nongovernment, not–for profit **Service:** General Medical and Surgical

**Staffed Beds:** 738 **Admissions:** 38524 **Census:** 472 **Outpatient Visits:** 421367 **Births:** 3770 **Total Expense ($000):** 636122 **Payroll Expense ($000):** 213752 **Personnel:** 5112

☒ △ **NATIONWIDE CHILDREN'S HOSPITAL (363305)**, 700 Children's Drive, Zip 43205–2664; tel. 614/722–2000 **A**1 3 5 7 8 9 10 **F**3 7 8 12 16 17 18 19 20 21 22 23 24 25 26 27 28 29 30 31 32 34 35 38 39 40 41 43 44 45 48 50 51 53 54 55 57 58 59 60 61 62 63 64 65 66 68 71 72 74 75 77 78 79 81 82 83 84 85 86 87 88 89 90 92 93 94 97 99 100 101 102 104 105 107 108 111 112 114 115 117 118 119 126 127 129 130 131 132 133 134 135 136 137 138 140 141 143 144 146 148 **P**6 8
Primary Contact: Steve Allen, M.D., Chief Executive Officer
COO: Rick Miller, President and Chief Operating Officer
CFO: Tim Robinson, Executive Vice President, Chief Financial and Administrative Officer and Treasurer
CMO: Richard Brilli, M.D., Chief Medical Officer
CIO: Denise Zabawski, Vice President Information Services and Chief Information Officer
CHR: Jose Balderrama, Vice President Human Resources
Web address: www.nationwidechildrens.org
**Control:** Other not–for–profit (including NFP Corporation) **Service:** Children's general

**Staffed Beds:** 508 **Admissions:** 18160 **Census:** 342 **Outpatient Visits:** 1037246 **Births:** 0 **Total Expense ($000):** 788513 **Payroll Expense ($000):** 356947 **Personnel:** 6448

---

**Hospital, Medicare Provider Number, Address, Telephone, Approval, Facility, and Physician Codes, Health Care System**

★ American Hospital Association (AHA) membership
☐ The Joint Commission accreditation
◇ DNV Healthcare Inc. accreditation
○ Healthcare Facilities Accreditation Program
△ Commission on Accreditation of Rehabilitation Facilities (CARF) accreditation

OH

□ **OHIO HOSPITAL FOR CHILD AND ADOLESCENT PSYCHIATRY (364041)**, 880 Greenlawn Avenue, Zip 43223–2616; tel. 614/449–9664 **A**1 9 10 **F**56 64 98 103 105 130 **S** Acadia Healthcare Company, Inc., Franklin, TN
Primary Contact: Roxanne Jividen, Chief Executive Officer
Web address: www.bca-corp.com
**Control:** Corporation, Investor–owned, for–profit **Service:** Psychiatric

**Staffed Beds:** 78 **Admissions:** 2671 **Census:** 67 **Outpatient Visits:** 4192
**Births:** 0 **Total Expense ($000):** 12282 **Payroll Expense ($000):** 6248
**Personnel:** 151

✉ △ **OHIO STATE UNIVERSITY WEXNER MEDICAL CENTER (360085)**, (Formerly Ohio State University Medical Center), 370 West 9th Avenue, Zip 43210–1238; tel. 614/293–8000, (Includes OHIO STATE UNIVERSITY HOSPITALS EAST, 1492 East Broad Street, Zip 43205–1546; tel. 614/257–3000) **A**1 3 5 7 8 10 **F**3 4 5 6 7 8 9 11 12 13 15 16 17 18 20 22 24 26 28 29 30 31 33 34 35 36 37 38 39 40 43 44 45 46 47 48 49 50 51 52 53 54 55 56 57 58 59 60 61 62 64 65 66 68 70 72 73 74 75 76 77 78 79 80 81 82 84 85 86 87 90 91 92 93 94 95 96 97 98 99 100 101 102 103 104 105 107 108 110 111 112 113 114 115 118 119 126 129 130 131 132 134 135 137 138 139 141 142 143 144 145 146 147 148 **P**6 **S** Ohio State University Health System, Columbus, OH
Primary Contact: Steven Gabbe, M.D., Chief Executive Officer
COO: Peter E. Geier, Chief Operating Officer
CFO: Michael Rutherford, Chief Financial Officer
CIO: Herb Smaltz, Chief Information Officer
CHR: Les Ridout, Human Resources Officer
CNO: Jerry A. Mansfield, Ph.D., Chief Nursing Officer
Web address: www.medicalcenter.osu.edu
**Control:** State–Government, nonfederal **Service:** General Medical and Surgical

**Staffed Beds:** 971 **Admissions:** 45927 **Census:** 741 **Outpatient Visits:** 1004467 **Births:** 4054 **Total Expense ($000):** 1300949 **Payroll Expense ($000):** 402773 **Personnel:** 9745

✉ ○ **OHIOHEALTH DOCTORS HOSPITAL (360152)**, (Formerly Doctors Hospital), 5100 West Broad Street, Zip 43228–1607; tel. 614/544–1000 **A**1 2 5 9 10 11 12 13 **F**3 13 15 18 20 22 24 26 28 29 30 34 35 40 42 45 46 47 49 50 57 58 59 64 65 66 68 70 72 74 75 76 77 78 79 81 85 87 93 97 100 107 109 110 111 119 126 130 135 146 147 **P**1 3 5 **S** OhioHealth, Columbus, OH
Primary Contact: Michael L. Reichfield, President
CFO: Troy Hammett, Vice President and Chief Financial Officer
CMO: Dean Colwell, D.O., Vice President Medical Affairs
CIO: Michael Krouse, Chief Information Officer
CHR: David Sullivan, Director Human Resources
Web address: www.ohiohealth.com
**Control:** Church–operated, Nongovernment, not–for profit **Service:** General Medical and Surgical

**Staffed Beds:** 262 **Admissions:** 9316 **Census:** 102 **Outpatient Visits:** 273573 **Births:** 908 **Total Expense ($000):** 208872 **Payroll Expense ($000):** 104515 **Personnel:** 1041

✉ **OHIOHEALTH GRANT MEDICAL CENTER (360017)**, (Formerly Grant Medical Center), 111 South Grant Avenue, Zip 43215–1898; tel. 614/566–9000 **A**1 2 5 8 9 10 **F**3 7 8 9 11 13 15 17 18 20 22 24 26 28 29 30 31 34 35 36 37 40 42 43 45 46 47 48 49 50 53 54 56 57 58 59 60 61 64 66 67 68 70 72 74 75 76 78 79 80 81 82 83 84 85 86 87 97 100 102 107 108 109 110 111 114 115 116 117 119 120 121 123 124 126 129 130 131 132 135 143 144 146 147 148 **P**1 3 5 **S** OhioHealth, Columbus, OH
Primary Contact: Vinson Yates, President
COO: Michael Lawson, Senior Vice President Operations
CMO: Greg Morrison, M.D., Vice President Medical Affairs
CIO: Michael Krouse, Chief Information Officer
CHR: Linda Simpson, Vice President Human Resources
CNO: Donna Hanly, R.N., Senior Vice President and Chief Nursing Officer
Web address: www.ohiohealth.com
**Control:** Church–operated, Nongovernment, not–for profit **Service:** General Medical and Surgical

**Staffed Beds:** 427 **Admissions:** 22280 **Census:** 248 **Outpatient Visits:** 637241 **Births:** 2431 **Total Expense ($000):** 500766 **Payroll Expense ($000):** 232292 **Personnel:** 2279

✉ △ **OHIOHEALTH RIVERSIDE METHODIST HOSPITAL (360006)**, (Formerly Riverside Methodist Hospital), 3535 Olentangy River Road, Zip 43214–3998; tel. 614/566–5000 **A**1 2 3 5 7 8 9 10 **F**3 7 8 11 12 13 14 15 17 18 20 22 24 26 28 29 30 31 33 34 35 36 37 38 39 40 42 43 44 45 46 47 48 50 51 53 54 55 56 57 58 59 60 61 62 63 64 65 66 68 69 70 71 72 74 75 76 77 78 79 80 81 82 83 84 85 86 87 90 91 92 93 94 96 97 98 100 102 103 104 107 110 111 114 115 116 117 119 120 121 123 124 126 130 132 135 143 144 145 146 147 148 **P**1 3 5 **S** OhioHealth, Columbus, OH
Primary Contact: Stephen Markovich, M.D., President
COO: Brian Jepson, Chief Operating Officer
CFO: Peter Bury, Vice President Finance
CMO: Leonard J. Lozada, M.D., Vice President Medical Affairs
CIO: Michael Krouse, Chief Information Officer
CHR: Shereen Solaiman, Vice President Human Resources
Web address: www.ohiohealth.com
**Control:** Church–operated, Nongovernment, not–for profit **Service:** General Medical and Surgical

**Staffed Beds:** 765 **Admissions:** 44665 **Census:** 526 **Outpatient Visits:** 744130 **Births:** 6055 **Total Expense ($000):** 816331 **Payroll Expense ($000):** 339602 **Personnel:** 4582

✉ **REGENCY HOSPITAL OF COLUMBUS (362037)**, 1430 South High Street, Zip 43207–1045; tel. 614/456–0300, (Nonreporting) **A**1 10 **S** Select Medical Corporation, Mechanicsburg, PA
Primary Contact: Lisa J. Pettrey, MSN, R.N., Chief Executive Officer
Web address: www.regencyhospital.com/
**Control:** Corporation, Investor–owned, for–profit **Service:** Long–Term Acute Care hospital

**Staffed Beds:** 43

✉ **SELECT SPECIALTY HOSPITAL–COLUMBUS (362022)**, 1087 Dennison Avenue, Zip 43201–3201; tel. 614/458–9000, (Includes SELECT SPECIALTY HOSPITAL–COLUMBUS, MOUNT CARMEL CAMPUS, 793 West State Street, Zip 43222–1551; tel. 614/234–0950), (Nonreporting) **A**1 10 **S** Select Medical Corporation, Mechanicsburg, PA
Primary Contact: John C. Yanes, Chief Executive Officer
CMO: Victoria Ruff, M.D., Medical Director
CHR: Charles Pankowski, Manager Human Resources
Web address: www.selectspecialtyhospitals.com/company/locations/columbus.aspx
**Control:** Corporation, Investor–owned, for–profit **Service:** Long–Term Acute Care hospital

**Staffed Beds:** 176

**SELECT SPECIALTY HOSPITAL–COLUMBUS, MOUNT CARMEL CAMPUS** See Select Specialty Hospital–Columbus

✉ **TWIN VALLEY BEHAVIORAL HEALTHCARE (364007)**, 2200 West Broad Street, Zip 43223–1297; tel. 614/752–0333 **A**1 10 **F**29 30 39 65 68 87 98 100 101 104 105 130 132 135 146 **S** Ohio Department of Mental Health, Columbus, OH
Primary Contact: Karen Woods–Nyce, Chief Executive Officer
COO: David Blahnik, Chief Operating Officer
CFO: John Eardley, Chief Financial Officer
CMO: R. Alan Freeland, M.D., Chief Clinical Officer
CIO: Missy McGarvey, Director Computer Information Systems
CHR: Marcia McKeen, Director Human Resources
CNO: Michael Breakwell, R.N., Nurse Executive
Web address: www.mh.state.oh.us/ibhs/bhos/tvbh.html
**Control:** State–Government, nonfederal **Service:** Psychiatric

**Staffed Beds:** 248 **Admissions:** 1644 **Census:** 220 **Outpatient Visits:** 0 **Births:** 0 **Total Expense ($000):** 40879 **Payroll Expense ($000):** 28284 **Personnel:** 470

**CONCORD TOWNSHIP—Lake County**

✉ △ **LAKE HEALTH (360098)**, 7590 Auburn Road, Zip 44077–9176; tel. 440/375–8100, (Includes TRIPOINT MEDICAL CENTER, 7950 Auburn Road, Painesville, Zip 44077; Cynthia Moore–Hardy, FACHE, President and Chief Executive Officer) **A**1 7 9 10 **F**3 8 11 13 15 18 20 22 24 26 28 29 30 34 35 40 42 44 45 49 50 51 53 54 56 57 58 59 60 62 63 64 65 68 69 70 73 74 75 76 77 79 81 82 85 86 87 90 93 97 98 100 101 102 103 107 108 110 111 114 116 117 118 119 129 130 131 132 133 135 143 144 146 147 148 **P**1
Primary Contact: Cynthia Moore–Hardy, FACHE, President and Chief Executive Officer
CMO: Theodore Nichols, M.D., Senior Vice President Medical Affairs
CIO: Gerald Peters, Vice President Information Technologies and Chief Information Officer
Web address: www.lhs.net
**Control:** Other not–for–profit (including NFP Corporation) **Service:** General Medical and Surgical

**Staffed Beds:** 357 **Admissions:** 18885 **Census:** 221 **Outpatient Visits:** 470632 **Births:** 1817 **Total Expense ($000):** 316220 **Payroll Expense ($000):** 119120 **Personnel:** 2400

*Many Facility Codes have changed. Please refer to the AHA Guide Code Chart.*
© 2013 AHA Guide

## CONNEAUT—Ashtabula County

☒ **UNIVERSITY HOSPITALS CONNEAUT MEDICAL CENTER (361308)**, 158
West Main Road, Zip 44030–2039; tel. 440/593–1131 **A**1 9 10 18 **F**3 7 11 15
18 28 29 34 35 37 40 51 59 64 70 75 77 78 79 81 82 86 87 93 107 110
111 114 119 130 132 133 135 143 146 147 148 **S** University Hospitals,
Cleveland, OH
Primary Contact: Robert David, President and Chief Executive Officer
COO: Richard Trice, Director Operations
CFO: Wendy Snyder, Director Finance
CMO: Gary Huston, D.O., Chief Medical Officer
CIO: Stephanie Cleversy, Manager Health Information Services
CHR: Barbara Gurto, Manager Human Resources
CNO: Karen McNeil, Chief Nursing Officer
Web address: www.uhhospitals.org
**Control:** Other not–for–profit (including NFP Corporation) **Service:** General
Medical and Surgical

**Staffed Beds:** 25 **Admissions:** 491 **Census:** 6 **Outpatient Visits:** 41475
**Births:** 0 **Total Expense ($000):** 24916 **Payroll Expense ($000):** 9076
**Personnel:** 178

## COSHOCTON—Coshocton County

☐ **COSHOCTON COUNTY MEMORIAL HOSPITAL (360109)**, 1460 Orange
Street, Zip 43812–2229, Mailing Address: P.O. Box 1330, Zip 43812–6330;
tel. 740/622–6411, (Nonreporting) **A**1 5 9 10 20
Primary Contact: Robert Miller, Chief Executive Officer
CFO: Robin Nichols, Chief Financial Officer
CMO: Tammy S. Alverson, M.D., Chief of Staff
CIO: Seth Peterson, Director Information Services
CHR: Rick Davis, Chief Operating Officer and Support Services
Web address: www.ccmh.com
**Control:** Other not–for–profit (including NFP Corporation) **Service:** General
Medical and Surgical

**Staffed Beds:** 56

## CUYAHOGA FALLS—Summit County

**CUYAHOGA FALLS GENERAL HOSPITAL** See Summa Western Reserve Hospital

★ △ **EDWIN SHAW REHAB (360241)**, 330 Broadway Street East,
Zip 44221–3312; tel. 330/436–0910, (Nonreporting) **A**7 9 10 **S** Akron General
Health System, Akron, OH
Primary Contact: Thomas Whelan, President
CFO: Debbie Gorbach, Vice President and Treasurer
CMO: Michael J. Delahanty, D.O., Medical Director
CHR: Heather Sans, Human Resource Generalist
Web address: www.edwinshaw.com
**Control:** County–Government, nonfederal **Service:** Rehabilitation

**Staffed Beds:** 38

○ **SUMMA WESTERN RESERVE HOSPITAL (360150)**, 1900 23rd Street,
Zip 44223–1499; tel. 330/971–7000 **A**9 10 11 12 13 **F**3 18 20 29 30 31 34
35 40 45 47 49 50 51 54 57 58 59 60 63 64 65 66 68 70 74 75 77 78 79
81 82 85 93 96 97 107 108 111 114 119 129 130 135 144 146 148 **P**6 8
**S** Summa Health System, Akron, OH
Primary Contact: Robert Kent, D.O., President and Chief Executive Officer
CFO: Jill Hiner, Vice President and Chief Financial Officer
CMO: Charles Feunning, M.D., President Medical Staff
CHR: Heather Milicevic, Director Human Resources
Web address: www.westernreservehospital.org
**Control:** Partnership, Investor–owned, for–profit **Service:** General Medical and
Surgical

**Staffed Beds:** 57 **Admissions:** 3559 **Census:** 40 **Outpatient Visits:** 119632
**Births:** 0 **Total Expense ($000):** 101682 **Payroll Expense ($000):** 37398
**Personnel:** 817

## DAYTON—Montgomery County

☐ **CHILDREN'S MEDICAL CENTER (363306)**, One Children's Plaza,
Zip 45404–1815; tel. 937/641–3000 **A**1 2 3 5 8 9 10 **F**3 7 11 19 21 29 30
31 32 34 35 39 40 41 43 44 45 50 54 55 57 58 59 60 61 62 63 64 65 66
72 74 75 77 78 79 81 82 84 85 86 87 88 89 93 97 107 111 115 119 129
130 132 134 135 144 146 **P**6
Primary Contact: Deborah A. Feldman, President and Chief Executive Officer
COO: Matthew P. Graybill, Chief Operating Officer
CFO: David T. Miller, Vice President and Chief Financial Officer
CMO: Adam Mezoff, M.D., Vice President and Chief Medical Officer
CIO: Beth Fredette, Chief Information Officer
Web address: www.childrensdayton.org
**Control:** Other not–for–profit (including NFP Corporation) **Service:** Children's
general

**Staffed Beds:** 133 **Admissions:** 6952 **Census:** 79 **Outpatient Visits:** 285814
**Births:** 0 **Total Expense ($000):** 183526 **Payroll Expense ($000):** 80567
**Personnel:** 1584

☐ △ **DAYTON REHABILITATION INSTITUTE (363033)**, One Elizabeth Place,
Zip 45417–3445; tel. 937/424–8200 **A**1 7 10 **F**3 29 90 96 130 148 **S** Reliant
Healthcare Partners, Richardson, TX
Primary Contact: Randy J. Kitchen, Chief Executive Officer
Web address: www.reliantdayton.com
**Control:** Partnership, Investor–owned, for–profit **Service:** Rehabilitation

**Staffed Beds:** 50 **Admissions:** 612 **Census:** 18 **Outpatient Visits:** 0 **Births:**
0 **Total Expense ($000):** 7926 **Payroll Expense ($000):** 3492 **Personnel:**
62

☒ △ **DAYTON VETERANS AFFAIRS MEDICAL CENTER**, (Formerly Veterans
Affairs Medical Center), 4100 West Third Street, Zip 45428–9000;
tel. 937/268–6511, (Total facility includes 225 beds in nursing home–type unit)
**A**1 2 3 5 7 8 **F**2 3 5 18 20 22 28 29 30 31 33 34 35 36 38 39 40 45 46 47
48 49 53 56 57 58 59 60 61 62 63 64 65 68 70 71 74 75 77 78 79 81 82
83 84 85 86 87 91 92 93 94 95 96 97 98 100 101 102 103 104 106 107
108 109 111 112 114 115 116 117 118 119 120 121 122 123 124 127 128
129 130 132 135 144 146 147 148 **S** Department of Veterans Affairs,
Washington, DC
Primary Contact: Glenn A. Costie, FACHE, Director
COO: Terry Taylor, Associate Director
CFO: Lawrence Andrews, Chief Fiscal Services
CMO: William Germann, M.D., Acting Chief of Staff
CIO: Susan Sherer, Chief Information Resource Management
CHR: Jerry A. Erwin, Chief Human Resources Management Service
Web address: www.dayton.va.gov/
**Control:** Veterans Affairs, Government, federal **Service:** General Medical and
Surgical

**Staffed Beds:** 500 **Admissions:** 6228 **Census:** 281 **Outpatient Visits:**
443376 **Births:** 0 **Total Expense ($000):** 332639 **Payroll Expense ($000):**
144530 **Personnel:** 1987

☒ **GOOD SAMARITAN HOSPITAL (360052)**, 2222 Philadelphia Drive,
Zip 45406–1813; tel. 937/734–2612 **A**1 2 3 5 9 10 **F**3 11 13 15 17 18 20 22
24 26 28 29 30 31 36 37 40 44 45 46 49 50 53 54 55 56 58 60 61 64 66
70 73 74 75 76 77 78 79 80 81 82 83 85 86 87 92 93 97 98 100 101 102
103 104 107 108 109 110 111 114 115 118 119 126 129 130 131 132 145
146 148 **P**6 **S** Catholic Health Initiatives, Englewood, CO
Primary Contact: Eloise Broner, President and Chief Executive Officer
CFO: Thomas F. Curtin, Vice President and Chief Financial Officer
CMO: Daniel L. Schoulties, M.D., Vice President Medical Affairs
CIO: Mikki Clancy, Vice President and Chief Information Officer
CHR: William Linesch, Vice President Human Resources
CNO: Mary E. Garman, R.N., Chief Nursing Officer and Vice President Operations
Web address: www.goodsamdayton.com
**Control:** Church–operated, Nongovernment, not–for profit **Service:** General
Medical and Surgical

**Staffed Beds:** 341 **Admissions:** 17226 **Census:** 222 **Outpatient Visits:**
250792 **Births:** 1016 **Total Expense ($000):** 360062 **Payroll Expense**
**($000):** 141165 **Personnel:** 2333

---

**Hospital, Medicare Provider Number, Address, Telephone, Approval, Facility, and Physician Codes, Health Care System**

★ American Hospital Association (AHA) membership
☐ The Joint Commission accreditation ◇ DNV Healthcare Inc. accreditation
○ Healthcare Facilities Accreditation Program
△ Commission on Accreditation of Rehabilitation Facilities (CARF) accreditation

★ ○ △ **GRANDVIEW MEDICAL CENTER (360133)**, 405 Grand Avenue, Zip 45405–4796; tel. 937/226–3200, (Includes SOUTHVIEW HOSPITAL AND FAMILY HEALTH CENTER, 1997 Miamisburg–Centerville Road, Zip 45459–3800; tel. 937/439–6000) **A**7 9 10 11 12 13 **F**3 5 8 11 12 13 15 18 20 22 24 28 29 30 31 34 35 36 38 39 40 42 44 45 47 48 49 50 53 54 57 58 59 60 61 62 65 66 68 70 73 74 75 76 77 78 79 81 82 85 86 87 90 93 96 97 98 100 101 102 103 104 105 107 108 110 111 114 115 116 117 118 119 120 121 123 124 126 129 130 131 132 135 141 144 145 146 147 148 **S** Kettering Health Network, Dayton, OH
Primary Contact: Richard Haas, FACHE, President
CFO: Todd Anderson, Chief Financial Officer
CMO: Tom Hardy, D.O., Vice President Medical Affairs
CHR: Karen Borgert, Vice President Human Resources
Web address: www.khnetwork.org
**Control:** Church–operated, Nongovernment, not–for profit **Service:** General Medical and Surgical

**Staffed Beds:** 284 **Admissions:** 11763 **Census:** 143 **Outpatient Visits:** 300526 **Births:** 1862 **Total Expense ($000):** 297555 **Payroll Expense ($000):** 100243 **Personnel:** 1408

☒ **KINDRED HOSPITAL–DAYTON (362033)**, One Elizabeth Place, 5th Floor, Zip 45417–3445; tel. 937/222–5963, (Nonreporting) **A**1 10 **S** Kindred Healthcare, Louisville, KY
Primary Contact: Lynn Schoen, Chief Executive Officer
CMO: Felipe Rubio, M.D., Medical Director
CNO: Katherine Cass, R.N., Nurse Manager
Web address: www.khdayton.com
**Control:** Corporation, Investor–owned, for–profit **Service:** Long–Term Acute Care hospital

**Staffed Beds:** 67

☒ △ **MIAMI VALLEY HOSPITAL (360051)**, One Wyoming Street, Zip 45409–2793; tel. 937/208–8000 **A**1 2 3 5 7 8 9 10 **F**3 5 12 13 15 16 17 18 20 22 24 26 28 29 30 31 34 35 37 39 40 42 43 44 45 46 47 48 49 50 53 54 55 56 57 58 59 60 61 64 68 70 72 73 74 75 76 78 79 81 82 84 85 86 87 90 91 92 93 96 98 100 101 102 103 104 107 108 110 111 114 115 117 118 119 120 121 123 126 129 130 131 132 134 135 136 138 141 143 145 146 147 148
Primary Contact: Bobbie Gerhart, President and Chief Executive Officer
COO: Micki Clancy, Chief Operating Officer
CFO: Scott Shelton, Executive Vice President and Chief Financial Officer
CHR: William Linesch, Vice President Human Resources
Web address: www.miamivalleyhospital.org
**Control:** Other not–for–profit (including NFP Corporation) **Service:** General Medical and Surgical

**Staffed Beds:** 933 **Admissions:** 41555 **Census:** 558 **Outpatient Visits:** 289762 **Births:** 5099 **Total Expense ($000):** 796623 **Payroll Expense ($000):** 292536 **Personnel:** 5465

**SOUTHVIEW HOSPITAL AND FAMILY HEALTH CENTER** See Grandview Medical Center

☐ **THE MEDICAL CENTER AT ELIZABETH PLACE (360274)**, One Elizabeth Place, Zip 45417–3445; tel. 937/660–3100, (Nonreporting) **A**1 9 10
Primary Contact: Alexander M. Rintoul, Chief Executive Officer
Web address: www.mcep.us
**Control:** Partnership, Investor–owned, for–profit **Service:** General Medical and Surgical

**Staffed Beds:** 26

**VETERANS AFFAIRS MEDICAL CENTER** See Dayton Veterans Affairs Medical Center

**DEFIANCE—Defiance County**

☒ **MERCY HOSPITAL OF DEFIANCE (360270)**, 1404 East Second Street, Zip 43512–2440; tel. 419/782–8444 **A**1 10 **F**3 8 18 29 30 34 35 40 45 57 59 70 75 81 82 85 87 90 129 135 145 **P**8 **S** Catholic Health Partners, Cincinnati, OH
Primary Contact: Sonya Selhorst, Administrator
CFO: Samantha M. Platzke, Senior Vice President Finance and Chief Financial Officer
CMO: William C. Reeves, D.O., Chief of Staff
CHR: Marilyn Reineke, Director Human Resources
Web address: www.ehealthconnection.com/regions/toledo/
**Control:** Church–operated, Nongovernment, not–for profit **Service:** General Medical and Surgical

**Staffed Beds:** 23 **Admissions:** 1359 **Census:** 11 **Outpatient Visits:** 11556 **Births:** 0 **Personnel:** 140

☒ **PROMEDICA DEFIANCE REGIONAL HOSPITAL (361328)**, 1200 Ralston Avenue, Zip 43512–1396; tel. 419/783–6955 **A**1 5 9 10 18 **F**3 11 13 15 18 20 28 31 32 34 40 43 57 59 64 66 68 70 75 76 77 78 79 81 85 86 87 93 98 100 101 102 103 104 105 107 108 110 111 114 118 119 129 130 132 135 144 146 147 148 **S** ProMedica Health System, Toledo, OH
Primary Contact: Gary Cates, President and Chief Executive Officer
CMO: Kermit Erwin, M.D., Medical Director
CIO: Stephanie Sonnenberg, Director Information Management Systems
CHR: Linda Shaffer, Director Human Resources
Web address: www.promedica.org
**Control:** Other not–for–profit (including NFP Corporation) **Service:** General Medical and Surgical

**Staffed Beds:** 35 **Admissions:** 2073 **Census:** 16 **Outpatient Visits:** 72613 **Births:** 583 **Total Expense ($000):** 45054 **Payroll Expense ($000):** 13176

**DELAWARE—Delaware County**

☒ △ **OHIOHEALTH GRADY MEMORIAL HOSPITAL (360210)**, (Formerly Grady Memorial Hospital), 561 West Central Avenue, Zip 43015–1410; tel. 740/615–1000 **A**1 2 7 9 10 **F**3 13 15 18 20 26 28 29 30 31 34 35 39 40 45 46 48 50 54 57 58 59 60 63 64 66 68 70 74 75 76 77 78 79 81 82 85 86 87 92 93 96 97 102 107 108 109 110 111 114 119 124 129 130 131 132 134 135 146 147 148 **P**1 3 5 **S** OhioHealth, Columbus, OH
Primary Contact: Bruce P. Hagen, President
COO: Bob Walsh, R.N., Chief Operating Officer
CFO: David Hensel, Director Financial Operations
CMO: Barbara Evert, M.D., Vice President Medical Affairs
CIO: Michael Krouse, Chief Information Officer Information Services
CHR: Beth Crow, Associate Relations Representative
CNO: Elizabeth A. Biegler, R.N., Chief Nursing Officer
Web address: www.ohiohealth.com
**Control:** Church–operated, Nongovernment, not–for profit **Service:** General Medical and Surgical

**Staffed Beds:** 61 **Admissions:** 2850 **Census:** 27 **Outpatient Visits:** 154178 **Births:** 374 **Total Expense ($000):** 72150 **Payroll Expense ($000):** 30968 **Personnel:** 401

**DENNISON—Tuscarawas County**

☐ **TEN LAKES CENTER (364042)**, 819 North First Street, 3rd Floor, Zip 44621–1003; tel. 740/922–7499, (Nonreporting) **A**1 9 10 **S** Acadia Healthcare Company, Inc., Franklin, TN
Primary Contact: Laura Blackburn, Administrator
Web address: www.tenlakescenter.com/
**Control:** Corporation, Investor–owned, for–profit **Service:** Psychiatric

**Staffed Beds:** 16

☒ **TRINITY HOSPITAL TWIN CITY (361302)**, 819 North First Street, Zip 44621–1098; tel. 740/922–2800 **A**1 9 10 18 **F**11 15 18 28 30 34 35 40 45 50 57 59 64 70 75 77 81 85 86 87 89 93 97 107 114 119 128 129 130 133 146 147 **P**4 **S** Sylvania Franciscan Health, Toledo, OH
Primary Contact: Joseph J. Mitchell, President
CFO: Angela Trammell, Controller
CMO: Jose Martinez, M.D., Chief of Staff
CHR: Lauren Castello, Director Human Resources
Web address: www.trinitytwincity.org
**Control:** Church–operated, Nongovernment, not–for profit **Service:** General Medical and Surgical

**Staffed Beds:** 25 **Admissions:** 506 **Census:** 6 **Outpatient Visits:** 36925 **Births:** 0 **Total Expense ($000):** 20733 **Payroll Expense ($000):** 9918 **Personnel:** 213

**DOVER—Tuscarawas County**

★ ◇ **UNION HOSPITAL (360010)**, 659 Boulevard, Zip 44622–2077; tel. 330/343–3311 **A**5 9 10 19 21 **F**3 8 11 13 14 15 28 29 34 35 40 50 53 57 59 62 64 70 75 76 77 78 79 80 81 82 85 86 89 90 93 107 108 110 111 118 119 120 129 130 131 132 146 148 **P**6 8
Primary Contact: Bruce James, Chief Executive Officer
CFO: Eugene A. Thorn, III, Vice President Finance and Chief Financial Officer
CMO: Thomas J. Kelly, M.P.H., Vice President Medical Affairs
CIO: David Baumgardner, Director Information Management
CHR: Darwin K. Smith, Vice President Human Resources
CNO: Diana Boyd, Vice President Nursing
Web address: www.unionhospital.org
**Control:** Other not–for–profit (including NFP Corporation) **Service:** General Medical and Surgical

**Staffed Beds:** 154 **Admissions:** 5678 **Census:** 59 **Outpatient Visits:** 301812 **Births:** 691 **Total Expense ($000):** 109089 **Payroll Expense ($000):** 44067 **Personnel:** 953

## DUBLIN—Franklin County

⊞ **OHIOHEALTH DUBLIN METHODIST HOSPITAL (360348)**, (Formerly Dublin Methodist Hospital), 7500 Hospital Drive, Zip 43016–8518; tel. 614/544–8000 **A**1 9 10 **F**3 13 15 18 20 22 29 30 34 40 45 46 57 59 62 68 70 76 77 79 81 82 85 87 97 107 110 111 115 119 129 130 131 132 135 144 146 147 148 **P**1 3 5 **S** OhioHealth, Columbus, OH
Primary Contact: Bruce P. Hagen, President
COO: Steve Bunyard, Chief Operating Officer
CFO: Michael Bichimer, Director Financial Operations
CMO: Barbara Evert, M.D., Vice President Medical Affairs
CIO: Michael Krouse, Senior Vice President Chief Information Officer
CHR: Diane Shaub, Director Human Resources
CNO: Elizabeth A. Biegler, R.N., Chief Nursing Officer
Web address: www.ohiohealth.com
**Control:** Church–operated, Nongovernment, not–for profit **Service:** General Medical and Surgical

**Staffed Beds:** 92 **Admissions:** 4772 **Census:** 38 **Outpatient Visits:** 69193 **Births:** 1662 **Total Expense ($000):** 103466 **Payroll Expense ($000):** 37356 **Personnel:** 485

## EAST LIVERPOOL—Columbiana County

⊞ **EAST LIVERPOOL CITY HOSPITAL (360096)**, 425 West Fifth Street, Zip 43920–2498; tel. 330/385–7200, (Nonreporting) **A**1 9 10
Primary Contact: Kenneth Cochran, R.N., FACHE, President and Chief Executive Officer
CFO: Kyle Johnson, Vice President Finance
CMO: Mark Swift, D.O., President Medical Staff
CIO: Frank Mader, Director Information Services
CHR: Pam Smith, Director Human Resources
CNO: Patrick Beaver, R.N., Vice President Patient Care and Chief Nursing Officer
Web address: www.elch.org
**Control:** Other not–for–profit (including NFP Corporation) **Service:** General Medical and Surgical

**Staffed Beds:** 109

## ELYRIA—Lorain County

⊞ **EMH ELYRIA MEDICAL CENTER (360145)**, 630 East River Street, Zip 44035–5902; tel. 440/329–7500 **A**1 2 9 10 **F**3 8 11 12 13 15 17 18 20 22 24 26 28 29 30 31 34 35 37 40 42 50 53 54 57 59 62 64 68 70 73 74 75 76 77 78 79 81 82 85 86 87 89 92 93 94 98 107 108 110 111 114 115 118 119 126 129 130 131 135 146 148 **P**6 7 8
Primary Contact: Donald S. Sheldon, M.D., President and Chief Executive Officer
CFO: James M. Simone, Vice President and Chief Financial Officer
CIO: Char Wray, Vice President Chief Clinical Operations and Chief Information Oficer
CHR: Daniel Miller, Vice President Human Resources
CNO: Jill Cooksey, Vice President Chief Nursing Officer
Web address: www.emh–healthcare.org
**Control:** Other not–for–profit (including NFP Corporation) **Service:** General Medical and Surgical

**Staffed Beds:** 257 **Admissions:** 13782 **Census:** 151 **Outpatient Visits:** 269188 **Births:** 929 **Total Expense ($000):** 192130 **Payroll Expense ($000):** 73441 **Personnel:** 1561

## EUCLID—Cuyahoga County

⊞ △ **EUCLID HOSPITAL (360082)**, 18901 Lake Shore Boulevard, Zip 44119–1090; tel. 216/531–9000, (Total facility includes 40 beds in nursing home–type unit) **A**1 7 10 **F**3 15 17 18 20 26 28 29 30 34 35 39 40 45 49 50 56 57 59 60 64 70 74 75 77 79 81 82 85 87 90 91 93 94 96 98 100 102 103 107 108 111 114 118 119 128 130 131 146 148 **S** Cleveland Clinic Health System, Cleveland, OH
Primary Contact: Mark Froimson, President
COO: Rich Lea, Vice President Operations
CFO: Don Urbancsik, Director Finance
CMO: Marita Volk, M.D., Director Medical Services and Chief of Staff
CHR: Gloria Donnelly, Director Human Resources
Web address: www.euclidhospital.org
**Control:** Other not–for–profit (including NFP Corporation) **Service:** General Medical and Surgical

**Staffed Beds:** 231 **Admissions:** 8242 **Census:** 150 **Outpatient Visits:** 93441 **Births:** 0 **Total Expense ($000):** 116578 **Payroll Expense ($000):** 50047 **Personnel:** 865

## FAIRFIELD—Butler County

⊞ △ **MERCY HEALTH – FAIRFIELD HOSPITAL (360056)**, 3000 Mack Road, Zip 45014–5335; tel. 513/870–7000 **A**1 2 7 9 10 **F**3 8 11 13 15 17 18 20 22 24 28 29 30 31 34 35 40 44 49 50 54 57 59 64 65 68 70 73 74 75 76 77 78 79 81 82 84 85 87 90 93 107 108 110 111 114 115 118 119 126 130 132 135 146 147 148 **S** Catholic Health Partners, Cincinnati, OH
Primary Contact: Thomas S. Urban, Market Leader and President
COO: Patricia Davis–Hagens, R.N., Vice President Operations and Nursing, Chief Operating Officer and Chief Nursing Officer
CFO: Robin Yon, Site Finance Director
CMO: John Kennedy, M.D., Vice President Medical Affairs
CIO: Yousuf Ahmad, Divisional Senior Vice President and Chief Network Transformation Officer
CHR: Maggie Lund, Divisional Senior Vice President Human Resources
CNO: Patricia Davis–Hagens, R.N., Vice President Operations and Nursing, Chief Operating Officer and Chief Nursing Officer
Web address: www.e–mercy.com
**Control:** Church–operated, Nongovernment, not–for profit **Service:** General Medical and Surgical

**Staffed Beds:** 229 **Admissions:** 16533 **Census:** 163 **Outpatient Visits:** 204192 **Births:** 2078 **Total Expense ($000):** 200252 **Payroll Expense ($000):** 67631 **Personnel:** 1307

## FINDLAY—Hancock County

⊞ **BLANCHARD VALLEY HOSPITAL (360095)**, 1900 South Main Street, Zip 45840–1214; tel. 419/423–4500, (Includes BLANCHARD VALLEY HOSPITAL, 1900 South Main Street, Zip 45840; tel. 419/423–4500) **A**1 2 3 5 9 10 19 **F**3 11 13 15 17 18 20 22 24 28 29 30 31 34 35 40 41 42 43 46 48 49 50 59 60 64 70 72 74 76 77 78 79 81 82 83 84 85 86 87 93 94 96 97 98 103 107 108 111 114 116 117 118 119 120 126 129 130 131 132 134 135 146 147 148 **P**5 **S** Blanchard Valley Health System, Findlay, OH
Primary Contact: Scott C. Malaney, President and Chief Executive Officer
COO: Christopher E. Press, FACHE, President, Blanchard Valley Regional Health Center
CFO: David Cytlak, Chief Financial Officer
CMO: William H. Kose, M.D., Senior Vice President Medical Affairs
CHR: Douglas DeFrain, Director Human Resources
Web address: www.bvhealthsystem.org/?id=204&sid=1
**Control:** Other not–for–profit (including NFP Corporation) **Service:** General Medical and Surgical

**Staffed Beds:** 181 **Admissions:** 6768 **Census:** 65 **Outpatient Visits:** 210199 **Births:** 1242 **Total Expense ($000):** 171364 **Payroll Expense ($000):** 72403 **Personnel:** 1091

## FOSTORIA—Hancock County

⊞ **PROMEDICA FOSTORIA COMMUNITY HOSPITAL (361318)**, 501 Van Buren Street, Zip 44830–1534, Mailing Address: P.O. Box 907, Zip 44830–0907; tel. 419/435–7734, (Nonreporting) **A**1 5 9 10 18 **S** ProMedica Health System, Toledo, OH
Primary Contact: Daniel Schwanke, President
COO: Tom Borer, Vice President Operations
CFO: Ken Swint, Vice President Finance and Chief Financial Officer
CMO: Terrence Fondessy, M.D., Vice President Medical Affairs
CIO: David G. Selman, Corporate Vice President Information Resources
CHR: Charles McDowell, Corporate Vice President Human Resources
Web address: www.promedica.org
**Control:** Other not–for–profit (including NFP Corporation) **Service:** General Medical and Surgical

**Staffed Beds:** 25

## FREMONT—Sandusky County

⊞ **MEMORIAL HOSPITAL (360156)**, 715 South Taft Avenue, Zip 43420–3237; tel. 419/332–7321 **A**1 5 9 10 **F**3 11 13 15 28 29 30 34 35 38 40 44 45 46 47 48 50 53 56 57 59 60 61 62 63 64 65 68 69 70 74 75 76 77 79 80 81 82 84 85 86 87 89 91 92 93 96 97 99 100 101 103 104 107 108 110 111 114 115 116 117 119 129 130 131 132 141 142 146 147 148 **P**1 6
Primary Contact: Pamela Jensen, FACHE, President
CFO: Rick Ruppel, Chief Financial Officer
CIO: Dustin Hufford, Chief Information Officer
CHR: Warrenette Parthemore, Director Human Resources
CNO: Jill A. Trosin, R.N., Chief Nursing Officer
Web address: www.memorialhcs.org
**Control:** Other not–for–profit (including NFP Corporation) **Service:** General Medical and Surgical

**Staffed Beds:** 71 **Admissions:** 1976 **Census:** 15 **Outpatient Visits:** 84130 **Births:** 312 **Total Expense ($000):** 65828 **Payroll Expense ($000):** 26595 **Personnel:** 470

---

**Hospital, Medicare Provider Number, Address, Telephone, Approval, Facility, and Physician Codes, Health Care System**

★ American Hospital Association (AHA) membership
☐ The Joint Commission accreditation
◇ DNV Healthcare Inc. accreditation
○ Healthcare Facilities Accreditation Program
△ Commission on Accreditation of Rehabilitation Facilities (CARF) accreditation

**OH**

**PHYSICIAN'S CHOICE HOSPITAL – FREMONT (360356)**, 2390 Enterprise Street, Zip 43420–8507; tel. 567/201–2911, (Nonreporting)
Primary Contact: Jerome McTague, M.D., JD, Administrator and Chief Executive Officer
Web address: www.physicianschoicehospital.com
**Control:** Partnership, Investor–owned, for–profit **Service:** Other specialty

Staffed Beds: 8

---

**GAHANNA—Franklin County**

**THE WOODS AT PARKSIDE (360247)**, 349 Olde Ridenour Road, Zip 43230–2528; tel. 614/471–2552, (Nonreporting) **A**10
Primary Contact: Harry Nguyen, Medical Director
Web address: www.thewoodsatparkside.com
**Control:** Partnership, Investor–owned, for–profit **Service:** Alcoholism and other chemical dependency

Staffed Beds: 50

---

**GALION—Crawford County**

★ ◇ **GALION COMMUNITY HOSPITAL (361325)**, 269 Portland Way South, Zip 44833–2399; tel. 419/468–4841 **A**9 10 18 21 **F**3 11 13 15 18 28 29 30 31 34 35 45 47 50 57 59 60 70 74 75 76 77 78 79 81 82 87 90 107 108 110 111 115 119 127 129 130 131 132 133 146 147 148 **S** Avita Health System, Galion, OH
Primary Contact: Jerome Morasko, President and Chief Executive Officer
CFO: D. Eric Draime, Vice President and Chief Financial Officer
CIO: Andy Daniels, Vice President Non–Clinical Operations and Information Systems
CHR: Traci L. Oswald, Vice President Human Resources
Web address: www.galionhospital.org
**Control:** Other not–for–profit (including NFP Corporation) **Service:** General Medical and Surgical

Staffed Beds: 35 Admissions: 1587 Census: 16 Outpatient Visits: 22451 Births: 350 Total Expense ($000): 64792 Payroll Expense ($000): 29947 Personnel: 534

---

**GALLIPOLIS—Gallia County**

☐ △ **HOLZER MEDICAL CENTER (360054)**, 100 Jackson Pike, Zip 45631–1563; tel. 740/446–5000, (Nonreporting) **A**1 2 5 7 9 10 19
Primary Contact: James R. Phillipe, President
CFO: Kenneth G. Payne, Chief Financial Officer
CMO: John Viall, M.D., Vice President Medical Affairs
CIO: John Allen, Chief Information Officer
CHR: Lisa B. Halley, Vice President Human Resources
Web address: www.holzer.org
**Control:** Other not–for–profit (including NFP Corporation) **Service:** General Medical and Surgical

Staffed Beds: 181

---

**GARFIELD HEIGHTS—Cuyahoga County**

✠ △ **MARYMOUNT HOSPITAL (360143)**, 12300 McCracken Road, Zip 44125–2975; tel. 216/581–0500 **A**1 2 7 10 **F**3 8 11 15 18 28 29 30 31 34 35 38 39 40 42 44 49 50 51 53 54 55 56 57 58 59 60 61 63 64 65 68 69 70 74 75 77 78 79 81 82 85 86 87 93 96 97 98 99 100 101 102 103 104 107 108 110 111 114 116 117 118 119 124 130 131 132 135 143 146 148 **S** Cleveland Clinic Health System, Cleveland, OH
Primary Contact: Joanne Zeroske, President and Chief Executive Officer
COO: William D. Keckan, Chief Operating Officer
CFO: Mike Benich, Controller
CMO: George V. Topalsky, M.D., Vice President Medical Operations
CIO: Ralph A. Cagna, Director Information Technology Operations, Cleveland Clinic Health System South Market
CHR: Doris A. Zajec, Human Resources Business Partner
CNO: Barbara Zinner, Interim Chief Nursing Officer
Web address: www.marymount.org
**Control:** Other not–for–profit (including NFP Corporation) **Service:** General Medical and Surgical

Staffed Beds: 315 Admissions: 11944 Census: 171 Outpatient Visits: 120038 Births: 0 Total Expense ($000): 169429 Payroll Expense ($000): 64834 Personnel: 1032

---

**GENEVA—Ashtabula County**

✠ **UNIVERSITY HOSPITALS GENEVA MEDICAL CENTER (361307)**, 870 West Main Street, Zip 44041–1295; tel. 440/466–1141 **A**1 9 10 18 35 29 34 35 40 46 51 59 64 68 70 75 77 78 79 81 82 86 87 93 107 110 111 114 119 129 130 132 133 135 143 146 147 **S** University Hospitals, Cleveland, OH
Primary Contact: Robert David, President and Chief Executive Officer
CFO: Wendy Snyder, Director Finance
CMO: Amitabh Goel, M.D., Chief Medical Officer
CIO: Stephanie Cleversy, Manager Health Information Systems
CHR: Kate Van Stratton, Manager Human Resources
CNO: Karen McNeil, Chief Nursing Officer
CNO: Richard Trice, Director Operations
Web address: www.uhhs.com
**Control:** Other not–for–profit (including NFP Corporation) **Service:** General Medical and Surgical

Staffed Beds: 25 Admissions: 1272 Census: 13 Outpatient Visits: 72311 Births: 0 Total Expense ($000): 31678 Payroll Expense ($000): 11365 Personnel: 233

---

**GEORGETOWN—Brown County**

☐ **SOUTHWEST REGIONAL MEDICAL CENTER (360116)**, 425 Home Street, Zip 45121–1407; tel. 937/378–7500 **A**1 9 10 **F**3 8 11 15 29 34 35 40 41 45 50 57 59 62 64 65 70 75 77 79 81 83 85 86 87 92 93 97 107 108 110 111 114 119 127 129 130 146 147 148 **P**6
Primary Contact: Michael C. Patterson, Chief Executive Officer
Web address: www.swrmed.org
**Control:** Corporation, Investor–owned, for–profit **Service:** General Medical and Surgical

Staffed Beds: 32 Admissions: 921 Census: 7 Outpatient Visits: 41238 Births: 54 Total Expense ($000): 25152 Payroll Expense ($000): 11768 Personnel: 265

---

**GREEN SPRINGS—Sandusky County**

☐ **ST. FRANCIS HEALTH CARE CENTRE (362007)**, 401 North Broadway, Zip 44836–9653; tel. 419/639–2626, (Nonreporting) **A**1 10
Primary Contact: Kim D. Eicher, Chief Executive Officer
CFO: Douglas Morris, Chief Financial Officer
CMO: John Yuhas, D.O., Medical Director
CHR: Joan E. Schmidt, Director Human Resources
Web address: www.sfhcc.org
**Control:** Church–operated, Nongovernment, not–for profit **Service:** Long–Term Acute Care hospital

Staffed Beds: 186

---

**GREENFIELD—Highland County**

☐ △ ◇ **ADENA GREENFIELD MEDICAL CENTER (361304)**, 550 Mirabeau Street, Zip 45123–1617; tel. 937/981–9400, (Nonreporting) **A**1 7 9 10 18 21 **S** Adena Health System, Chillicothe, OH
Primary Contact: Kathy Dye, Interim Administrator
CFO: Ralph W. Sorrell, Sr., Chief Financial Officer
CIO: Marcus Bost, Director Information Services and Chief Information Officer
CHR: Brandt Lippert, Vice President Human Resources
Web address: www.adena.org
**Control:** Other not–for–profit (including NFP Corporation) **Service:** General Medical and Surgical

Staffed Beds: 25

---

**GREENVILLE—Darke County**

★ ◇ **WAYNE HOSPITAL (360044)**, 835 Sweitzer Street, Zip 45331–1077; tel. 937/548–1141 **A**2 9 10 11 **F**3 8 11 13 15 29 30 31 34 35 39 40 41 45 57 58 59 64 70 75 76 77 78 79 81 83 84 85 86 89 93 107 108 110 111 114 116 117 118 119 129 130 131 132 133 135 146 147 148 **P**1
Primary Contact: Wayne G. Deschambeau, President and Chief Executive Officer
CFO: Dennis Lockard, Vice President Fiscal Services and Chief Financial Officer
CMO: Guillermo Trevino, M.D., President Medical Staff
CIO: Shelton Monger, Director Information Technology
CHR: Peggy Schwartz, Vice President Human Resources
CNO: Kimberlee Freeman, R.N., Vice President Patient Care Services and Chief Nursing Officer
Web address: www.waynehealthcare.org
**Control:** Other not–for–profit (including NFP Corporation) **Service:** General Medical and Surgical

Staffed Beds: 63 Admissions: 2026 Census: 17 Outpatient Visits: 82412 Births: 308 Total Expense ($000): 48644 Payroll Expense ($000): 18748 Personnel: 347

---

## HAMILTON—Butler County

☐ **BETHESDA BUTLER HOSPITAL (360269)**, 3125 Hamilton Mason Road,
Zip 45011–5307; tel. 513/894–8888, (Nonreporting) **A**1 9
Primary Contact: Chuck Brown, Administrator
COO: Mary Ann Gellenbeck, Chief Operating Officer
CFO: Michael L. Griffin, Chief Financial Officer
CHR: Amy Turner, Director Human Resources
Web address: www.bcsurg.com
**Control:** Corporation, Investor–owned, for–profit **Service:** Surgical

**Staffed Beds:** 8

⊞ ○ **FORT HAMILTON HOSPITAL (360132)**, 630 Eaton Avenue,
Zip 45013–2770; tel. 513/867–2000 **A**1 2 9 10 11 **F**3 8 11 13 15 18 20 22
24 28 29 30 31 34 35 40 45 46 50 53 54 59 68 70 73 74 75 76 78 79 81
82 85 86 87 93 98 100 105 107 108 110 111 114 115 116 117 119 120
121 124 129 130 131 135 144 146 147 **S** Kettering Health Network,
Dayton, OH
Primary Contact: Mark T. Smith, JD, CPA, President
CHR: Joseph Geigle, Director Human Resources
Web address: www.khnetwork.org/fort_hamilton
**Control:** Church–operated, Nongovernment, not–for profit **Service:** General
Medical and Surgical

**Staffed Beds:** 194 **Admissions:** 8259 **Census:** 92 **Outpatient Visits:** 107929
**Births:** 669 **Total Expense ($000):** 107314 **Payroll Expense ($000):** 43859
**Personnel:** 744

## HICKSVILLE—Defiance County

⊞ **COMMUNITY MEMORIAL HOSPITAL (361301)**, 208 North Columbus Street,
Zip 43526–1299; tel. 419/542–6692 **A**1 9 10 18 **F**3 8 11 13 15 18 19 28 29
33 34 35 36 40 45 53 57 59 69 70 74 75 76 77 79 81 82 87 89 91 92 93
107 114 119 129 130 131 133 143 146 **P**6
Primary Contact: Melvin H. Fahs, Chief Executive Officer
CFO: Susan Hobeck, Chief Financial Officer
CIO: Chuck Buhlmann, Chief Information Officer
CHR: Michelle Waggoner, Vice President Human Resources and Physician Services
CNO: Jane Zachrich, Chief Nursing Officer
Web address: www.cmhosp.com
**Control:** Hospital district or authority, Government, nonfederal **Service:** General
Medical and Surgical

**Staffed Beds:** 25 **Admissions:** 606 **Census:** 5 **Outpatient Visits:** 137281
**Births:** 118 **Total Expense ($000):** 23806 **Payroll Expense ($000):** 11576
**Personnel:** 221

## HILLSBORO—Highland County

⊞ **HIGHLAND DISTRICT HOSPITAL (361332)**, 1275 North High Street,
Zip 45133–8273; tel. 937/393–6100 **A**1 9 10 18 **F**3 11 13 15 29 30 31 34
35 40 45 47 49 57 59 62 64 74 76 77 78 79 81 85 86 87 92 93 94 96 98
103 107 111 118 119 127 130 131 132 133 135 146 148 **P**3
Primary Contact: James E. Baer, FACHE, President and Chief Executive Officer
CFO: Randal Lennartz, Vice President Finance
CMO: Linda R. Welder, M.D., Chief of Staff
CHR: Julie Pence, Associate Director Human Resources
CNO: Timothy Parry, R.N., Vice President Nursing
Web address: www.hdh.org
**Control:** Hospital district or authority, Government, nonfederal **Service:** General
Medical and Surgical

**Staffed Beds:** 25 **Admissions:** 2181 **Census:** 18 **Outpatient Visits:** 80673
**Births:** 367 **Total Expense ($000):** 37174 **Payroll Expense ($000):** 13467
**Personnel:** 299

## JACKSON—Jackson County

☐ **HOLZER MEDICAL CENTER – JACKSON (361320)**, 500 Burlington Road,
Zip 45640–9360; tel. 740/288–4625 **A**1 9 10 18 **F**3 11 29 30 32 34 35 37
39 40 50 53 56 57 59 70 75 77 79 81 82 85 86 87 93 97 107 108 119 130
133 146 **P**3
Primary Contact: James R. Phillippe, II, President
CFO: Kevin Yeager, Vice President Fiscal Services
CMO: Nimal Dutla, M.D., Chief Medical Staff
CHR: Sandy Carlisle, Manager Human Resources
Web address: www.holzer.org
**Control:** Other not–for–profit (including NFP Corporation) **Service:** General
Medical and Surgical

**Staffed Beds:** 24 **Admissions:** 1237 **Census:** 14 **Outpatient Visits:** 46782
**Births:** 0 **Personnel:** 237

## KENTON—Hardin County

⊞ **HARDIN MEMORIAL HOSPITAL (361315)**, 921 East Franklin Street,
Zip 43326–2099; tel. 419/673–0761 **A**1 9 10 18 **F**11 15 29 30 34 40 45 57
59 61 75 77 78 79 81 86 87 93 97 102 107 108 110 111 114 116 119 129
130 131 132 133 146 147 **S** OhioHealth, Columbus, OH
Primary Contact: Mark R. Seckinger, Administrator and Chief Executive Officer
CFO: Ron Snyder, Chief Financial Officer
Web address: www.hardinmemorial.org
**Control:** Other not–for–profit (including NFP Corporation) **Service:** General
Medical and Surgical

**Staffed Beds:** 25 **Admissions:** 901 **Census:** 10 **Outpatient Visits:** 59334
**Births:** 0 **Total Expense ($000):** 19671 **Payroll Expense ($000):** 8648
**Personnel:** 182

## KETTERING—Montgomery County

⊞ ○ △ **KETTERING MEDICAL CENTER (360079)**, 3535 Southern Boulevard,
Zip 45429–1221; tel. 937/298–4331 **A**1 2 3 5 7 8 10 11 **F**3 5 8 11 12 13 15
17 18 20 22 24 26 28 29 30 31 34 35 38 39 40 42 43 44 45 46 47 48 49
50 51 52 53 54 56 57 58 59 60 61 62 65 66 68 70 71 72 74 75 76 77 78
79 81 82 84 85 86 87 90 92 93 96 97 102 107 108 110 111 114 115 116
117 118 119 120 121 123 124 126 129 130 131 132 135 141 145 146 147
148 **S** Kettering Health Network, Dayton, OH
Primary Contact: Roy G. Chew, Ph.D., President
COO: Chelcia Lambert, Chief Operating Officer and Chief Financial Officer
CFO: Chelcia Lambert, Chief Operating Officer and Chief Financial Officer
CMO: Gregory Wise, M.D., Vice President Medical Affairs
CIO: Jon Russell, Vice President Information Systems
CHR: Beverly Morris, Vice President Human Resources
CNO: Brenda Kuhn, Ph.D., Vice President Patient Care Services
Web address: www.kmcnetwork.org
**Control:** Church–operated, Nongovernment, not–for profit **Service:** General
Medical and Surgical

**Staffed Beds:** 386 **Admissions:** 20198 **Census:** 239 **Outpatient Visits:**
286989 **Births:** 2406 **Total Expense ($000):** 470488 **Payroll Expense**
**($000):** 175959 **Personnel:** 2487

## LAKEWOOD—Cuyahoga County

⊞ △ **LAKEWOOD HOSPITAL (360212)**, 14519 Detroit Avenue,
Zip 44107–4383; tel. 216/521–4200, (Total facility includes 25 beds in nursing
home type unit) **A**1 7 9 10 **F**3 6 13 15 20 22 26 28 29 30 34 35 40 45 46 49
50 56 57 59 60 64 65 68 70 74 75 76 77 79 81 82 85 86 87 90 93 98 100
101 102 103 107 108 111 119 128 130 132 134 143 146 147 148
**S** Cleveland Clinic Health System, Cleveland, OH
Primary Contact: Robert Weil, M.D., President
COO: Shannan Ritchie, Chief Operating Officer
CFO: Ankit Chhabra, Director Finance
CMO: Charles Garven, M.D., Vice President Medical Operations
CIO: C. Martin Harris, M.D., Chief Information Officer
CHR: Sheree Laborie, Director Human Resources
CNO: Mary R. Sauer, R.N., Chief Nursing Officer
Web address: www.lakewoodhospital.org
**Control:** Other not–for–profit (including NFP Corporation) **Service:** General
Medical and Surgical

**Staffed Beds:** 250 **Admissions:** 8647 **Census:** 136 **Outpatient Visits:**
146381 **Births:** 680 **Total Expense ($000):** 138850 **Payroll Expense**
**($000):** 57579 **Personnel:** 837

## LANCASTER—Fairfield County

⊞ △ **FAIRFIELD MEDICAL CENTER (360072)**, 401 North Ewing Street,
Zip 43130–3371; tel. 740/687–8000 **A**1 2 5 7 9 10 13 **F**3 8 9 11 13 15 18
20 22 24 26 28 29 30 31 34 35 38 40 42 44 45 48 49 50 53 54 57 59 64
70 74 75 76 77 78 79 81 82 83 84 85 87 89 93 96 97 98 102 104 107 108
110 111 114 115 116 117 118 119 129 130 131 132 135 145 146 147 148
Primary Contact: Mina H. Ubbing, President and Chief Executive Officer
COO: Howard Sniderman, Chief Operating Officer
CFO: Sky Gettys, Chief Financial Officer
CMO: Steve Cox, M.D., Chief Medical Officer
CIO: Jean Robertson, M.D., Chief Information Officer
CNO: Cynthia Pearsall, Chief Nursing Officer
Web address: www.fmchealth.org
**Control:** Other not–for–profit (including NFP Corporation) **Service:** General
Medical and Surgical

**Staffed Beds:** 222 **Admissions:** 10026 **Census:** 101 **Outpatient Visits:**
270151 **Births:** 1050 **Total Expense ($000):** 199618 **Payroll Expense**
**($000):** 80231 **Personnel:** 1633

**OH**

## LIMA—Allen County

☒ **INSTITUTE FOR ORTHOPAEDIC SURGERY (360263)**, 801 Medical Drive, Suite B., Zip 45804–4030; tel. 419/224–7586, (Nonreporting) **A**1 9 10 **S** Catholic Health Partners, Cincinnati, OH
Primary Contact: Mark McDonald, M.D., President and Chief Executive Officer
CFO: Sally Rhodes, M.D., Administrative Director
CMO: Mark McDonald, M.D., President and Chief Executive Officer
CHR: Pat Farmer, Coordinator Human Resources and Safety Officer
Web address: www.ioshospital.com
**Control:** Partnership, Investor–owned, for–profit **Service:** Orthopedic

Staffed Beds: 3

☒ **KINDRED HOSPITAL LIMA (362020)**, 730 West Market Street, 6th Floor, Zip 45801–4602; tel. 419/224–1888 **A**1 10 **F**1 **S** Kindred Healthcare, Louisville, KY
Primary Contact: Susan Krinke, Chief Executive Officer
Web address: www.khlima.com
**Control:** Corporation, Investor–owned, for–profit **Service:** Long–Term Acute Care hospital

Staffed Beds: 26 Admissions: 339 Census: 25 Outpatient Visits: 0 Births: 0 Total Expense ($000): 12987 Payroll Expense ($000): 5264

☒ △ **LIMA MEMORIAL HEALTH SYSTEM (360009)**, 1001 Bellefontaine Avenue, Zip 45804–2899; tel. 419/228–3335, (Total facility includes 17 beds in nursing home–type unit) **A**1 2 7 9 10 **F**3 11 13 14 15 17 18 20 22 24 28 29 30 31 34 35 36 40 41 42 43 45 46 47 48 49 50 51 54 57 58 59 60 62 63 64 65 68 70 73 74 75 76 77 78 79 81 82 84 85 86 89 90 93 96 107 108 110 111 114 115 118 119 120 121 123 124 126 129 130 131 132 133 135 146 147 148 **P**8
Primary Contact: Michael D. Swick, President and Chief Executive Officer
COO: Robert Armstrong, Senior Vice President and Chief Operating Officer
CFO: Eric Pohjala, Vice President and Chief Financial Officer
CMO: C. Lynn Thompson, M.D., Vice President Medical Affairs
CIO: Cheryl Homan, Administrative Director
CHR: Tillie Schiffler, Director Human Resources
CNO: Ann–Marie J. Pohl, R.N., Vice President and Chief Nursing Officer
Web address: www.limamemorial.org
**Control:** Other not–for–profit (including NFP Corporation) **Service:** General Medical and Surgical

Staffed Beds: 248 Admissions: 7208 Census: 92 Outpatient Visits: 289926 Births: 684 Total Expense ($000): 150672 Payroll Expense ($000): 56980 Personnel: 1022

☐ **OAKWOOD CORRECTIONAL FACILITY**, 3200 North West Street, Zip 45801–2000; tel. 419/225–8052, (Nonreporting) **A**1
Primary Contact: Christopher Yanai, Warden and Chief Executive Officer
CFO: Thomas Ferry, Business Administrator
CHR: Glenda Turner, Director Personnel
Web address: www.drc.state.oh.us/public/ocf.htm
**Control:** State–Government, nonfederal **Service:** Psychiatric

Staffed Beds: 61

☒ △ **ST. RITA'S MEDICAL CENTER (360066)**, 730 West Market Street, Zip 45801–4602; tel. 419/227–3361 **A**1 2 7 9 10 **F**3 4 5 8 9 11 13 15 17 18 20 22 24 26 28 29 30 31 32 34 35 36 39 40 42 43 45 46 47 49 50 53 54 56 57 58 59 60 61 62 63 64 66 68 70 72 73 74 75 76 77 78 79 81 82 84 85 86 87 89 90 92 93 96 98 100 101 102 103 104 107 108 110 111 114 115 116 117 118 119 120 121 126 128 129 130 131 132 135 144 146 147 148 **P**6 8 **S** Catholic Health Partners, Cincinnati, OH
Primary Contact: Robert O. Baxter, President and Chief Executive Officer
COO: Brian Smith, Executive Vice President and Chief Operating Officer
CMO: Herbert Schumm, M.D., Vice President Medical Affairs
CHR: Will Cason, Vice President Human Resources
Web address: www.stritas.org
**Control:** Church–operated, Nongovernment, not–for profit **Service:** General Medical and Surgical

Staffed Beds: 415 Admissions: 19647 Census: 228 Outpatient Visits: 420799 Births: 1497 Total Expense ($000): 341657 Payroll Expense ($000): 116181 Personnel: 2405

**TRIUMPH HOSPITAL LIMA** See Kindred Hospital Lima

## LODI—Medina County

☒ **LODI COMMUNITY HOSPITAL (361303)**, 225 Elyria Street, Zip 44254–1096; tel. 330/948–1222 **A**1 9 10 18 **F**3 11 15 18 26 29 30 34 35 40 45 46 57 59 64 65 69 75 77 79 81 82 93 96 97 107 114 119 128 129 130 132 133 146 **P**1 6 **S** Akron General Health System, Akron, OH
Primary Contact: Thomas Whelan, President
COO: Dana Kocsis, R.N., Vice President Nursing and Operations
CFO: Alan A. Ganci, Director Finance and Controller
CMO: David Peter, M.D., Senior Vice President Medical Affairs and Chief Medical Officer
CIO: Robb Baldauf, Coordinator Information Systems
CHR: Lynn Moraca, Director Human Resources
CNO: Beverly Bokovitz, R.N., Senior Vice President and Chief Nursing Officer
Web address: www.lodihospital.org
**Control:** Other not–for–profit (including NFP Corporation) **Service:** General Medical and Surgical

Staffed Beds: 25 Admissions: 477 Census: 8 Outpatient Visits: 27840 Births: 0 Total Expense ($000): 14026 Payroll Expense ($000): 6411 Personnel: 110

## LOGAN—Hocking County

☒ **HOCKING VALLEY COMMUNITY HOSPITAL (361330)**, 601 State Route 664 North, Zip 43138–8541, Mailing Address: P.O. Box 966, Zip 43138–0966; tel. 740/380–8000, (Total facility includes 18 beds in nursing home–type unit) **A**1 9 10 18 **F**3 8 11 15 28 29 31 34 40 56 57 59 64 70 75 77 78 79 81 85 86 93 98 103 107 111 115 118 119 128 129 130 133 135 144 146 147 148 **P**1 3
Primary Contact: Julie Stuck, R.N., Interim Chief Executive Officer
CFO: Steve Berkhouse, Chief Financial Officer
CMO: Duane Mast, M.D., Medical Director
CIO: John Burgess, Director Information Services
CHR: Robert Schmidt, Director Human Resources
CNO: Julie Stuck, R.N., Vice President Patient Services
Web address: www.hvch.org
**Control:** County–Government, nonfederal **Service:** General Medical and Surgical

Staffed Beds: 53 Admissions: 1416 Census: 30 Outpatient Visits: 75577 Births: 0 Total Expense ($000): 35011 Payroll Expense ($000): 13928 Personnel: 295

## LONDON—Madison County

☒ **MADISON COUNTY HOSPITAL (360189)**, 210 North Main Street, Zip 43140–1115; tel. 740/845–7000 **A**1 9 10 **F**11 13 15 18 29 31 34 35 38 40 45 53 57 59 64 70 75 76 77 78 79 81 82 85 86 87 89 93 94 96 107 108 110 111 114 118 119 129 130 131 132 135 146 147
Primary Contact: Michael Browning, Interim Chief Executive Officer
CFO: Michael Browning, Chief Financial Officer
CMO: Robert Mueller, M.D., Chief of Staff
CIO: Dennis Vogt, Director Information Technology
CHR: Becky Rozell, Chief Human Resources Officer
CNO: Jennifer Piccione, Chief Nursing and Clinical Services Officer
Web address: www.madisoncountyhospital.org
**Control:** Other not–for–profit (including NFP Corporation) **Service:** General Medical and Surgical

Staffed Beds: 55 Admissions: 1116 Census: 11 Outpatient Visits: 37475 Births: 261 Total Expense ($000): 30352 Payroll Expense ($000): 11501 Personnel: 234

## LORAIN—Lorain County

☒ △ **MERCY REGIONAL MEDICAL CENTER (360172)**, 3700 Kolbe Road, Zip 44053–1697; tel. 440/960–4000 **A**1 2 7 9 10 **F**8 11 15 18 20 22 24 26 28 29 30 31 34 35 36 38 39 40 46 50 53 54 56 57 59 61 62 63 64 65 70 74 75 76 77 78 79 81 82 84 85 87 89 90 93 97 98 102 104 105 107 111 114 116 119 120 121 129 130 131 132 135 143 146 147 148 **P**8 **S** Catholic Health Partners, Cincinnati, OH
Primary Contact: Edwin M. Oley, President and Chief Executive Officer
CFO: Gary Wengerd, Vice President Finance and Chief Financial Officer
CMO: Donald Blanford, M.D., Chief Medical Officer
CHR: Sarah Nickell, Vice President Human Resources
Web address: www.community–health–partners.com
**Control:** Church–operated, Nongovernment, not–for profit **Service:** General Medical and Surgical

Staffed Beds: 253 Admissions: 13376 Census: 160 Outpatient Visits: 258662 Births: 857 Total Expense ($000): 198850 Payroll Expense ($000): 73966 Personnel: 1217

## MANSFIELD—Richland County

☒ **KINDRED HOSPITAL OF CENTRAL OHIO (362021)**, 335 Glessner Avenue, 5th Floor, Zip 44903–2269; tel. 419/526–0777, (Nonreporting) **A**1 10 **S** Kindred Healthcare, Louisville, KY
Primary Contact: Vanessa Acevedo, Chief Executive Officer
Web address: www.khcentralohio.com/
**Control:** Corporation, Investor–owned, for–profit **Service:** Long–Term Acute Care hospital

Staffed Beds: 33

*Many Facility Codes have changed. Please refer to the AHA Guide Code Chart.*   © 2013 AHA Guide

☐ **MEDCENTRAL – MANSFIELD HOSPITAL (360118)**, 335 Glessner Avenue, Zip 44903–2265; tel. 419/526–8000, (Includes MANSFIELD HOSPITAL, 335 Glessner Avenue, tel. 419/526–8000) **A**1 2 5 9 10 **F**3 5 8 11 13 15 17 18 20 22 24 26 28 29 30 31 32 34 35 38 39 40 43 44 45 46 47 48 49 50 51 53 54 55 56 57 58 59 61 62 63 64 65 68 70 73 74 75 76 77 78 79 81 82 85 86 87 89 90 92 93 96 98 99 100 101 102 103 104 105 107 108 110 111 114 116 117 118 119 120 121 122 123 124 129 130 131 132 133 135 144 146 147 148 **P**3 **S** MedCentral Health System, Mansfield, OH
Primary Contact: Joe Chamberlain, Chief Operating Officer/Acting Chief Executive Officer
CMO: Terry Weston, M.D., Vice President Physician Services
CIO: Mike Mistretta, Vice President Information Systems and Chief Information Officer
CHR: Beth Hildreth, Vice President Human Resources
Web address: www.medcentral.org
**Control:** Other not–for–profit (including NFP Corporation) **Service:** General Medical and Surgical

**Staffed Beds:** 238 **Admissions:** 11207 **Census:** 141 **Outpatient Visits:** 279551 **Births:** 1006 **Personnel:** 1679

**MARIETTA—Washington County**

★ ○ △ **MARIETTA MEMORIAL HOSPITAL (360147)**, 401 Matthew Street, Zip 45750–1699; tel. 740/374–1400, (Nonreporting) **A**2 5 7 9 10 11
Primary Contact: J. Scott Cantley, President and Chief Executive Officer
CFO: Eric L. Young, Vice President Finance and Chief Financial Officer
CMO: Michael Nill, M.D., President Medical Staff
CIO: Andy Altenburger, Chief Information Officer
CHR: Dee Ann Gehlauf, Senior Vice President Business and Organization Development
Web address: www.mmhospital.org
**Control:** Other not–for–profit (including NFP Corporation) **Service:** General Medical and Surgical

**Staffed Beds:** 152

★ **SELBY GENERAL HOSPITAL (361319)**, 1106 Colegate Drive, Zip 45750–1323; tel. 740/568–2000 **A**9 10 18 **F**3 29 34 35 40 41 45 50 56 57 59 68 69 70 75 77 79 81 82 85 86 87 89 104 107 108 111 114 117 129 130 132 133 135 146 **P**5
Primary Contact: Stephen Smith, Administrator
CFO: Eric L. Young, Chief Financial Officer
CMO: David Spears, D.O., Chief of Staff
CHR: Cindy Hall, Coordinator Human Resources
CNO: Misti Spencer, Director Inpatient Services
Web address: www.selbygeneral.org
**Control:** Other not–for–profit (including NFP Corporation) **Service:** General Medical and Surgical

**Staffed Beds:** 25 **Admissions:** 1283 **Census:** 13 **Outpatient Visits:** 30755 **Births:** 0 **Total Expense ($000):** 28813 **Payroll Expense ($000):** 11616 **Personnel:** 195

**MARION—Marion County**

⊠ △ **OHIOHEALTH MARION GENERAL HOSPITAL (360011)**, (Formerly Marion General Hospital), 1000 McKinley Park Drive, Zip 43302–6397; tel. 740/383–8400, (Nonreporting) **A**1 2 7 9 10 19 **S** OhioHealth, Columbus, OH
Primary Contact: John W. Sanders, President
COO: Joseph Hooper, Vice President Operations
CFO: Steven Brown, Vice President Finance
CMO: Richard Flaksman, M.D., Vice President Medical Affairs
CIO: Chris King, Director Information Services
CHR: Linda Alesi, Director Human Resources
CNO: Eric Wallis, R.N., Vice President Patient Care and Chief Nursing Officer
Web address: www.ohiohealth.com/mariongeneral
**Control:** Other not–for–profit (including NFP Corporation) **Service:** General Medical and Surgical

**Staffed Beds:** 170

**MARTINS FERRY—Belmont County**

☐ **EAST OHIO REGIONAL HOSPITAL (360080)**, 90 North Fourth Street, Zip 43935–1648; tel. 740/633–1100, (Total facility includes 50 beds in nursing home–type unit) **A**1 9 10 **F**3 11 13 15 20 28 29 30 31 34 35 37 40 43 44 45 53 57 59 64 68 70 74 75 76 77 79 81 82 85 87 89 107 108 110 111 114 115 118 119 128 129 130 131 132 133 135 146 148 **P**5 6 **S** Ohio Valley Health Services and Education Corporation, Wheeling, WV
Primary Contact: Michael J. Caruso, President and Chief Executive Officer
COO: Kelly Bettem, Assistant Chief Operating Officer
CFO: Tom Feldman, Chief Financial Officer
CIO: Karen Wayrauch, Interim Director Information Systems
CHR: James R. Stultz, Senior Vice President Human Resources
Web address: www.ovmc–eorh.com
**Control:** Other not–for–profit (including NFP Corporation) **Service:** General Medical and Surgical

**Staffed Beds:** 161 **Admissions:** 3765 **Census:** 73 **Outpatient Visits:** 142407 **Births:** 286 **Total Expense ($000):** 65827 **Payroll Expense ($000):** 24947 **Personnel:** 604

**MARYSVILLE—Union County**

★ ◇ **MEMORIAL HOSPITAL OF UNION COUNTY (360092)**, 500 London Avenue, Zip 43040–1594; tel. 937/644–6115 **A**5 9 10 21 **F**3 11 15 28 29 30 31 32 34 35 40 45 48 49 50 51 53 57 59 62 63 68 69 74 75 76 77 78 79 81 82 85 87 92 93 94 107 108 110 111 114 115 117 118 119 129 130 131 132 135 144 145 146 **P**3
Primary Contact: Olas A. Hubbs, III, FACHE, President and Chief Executive Officer
COO: Laurie A. Whittington, Chief Operating Officer
CFO: Jeffrey Ehlers, Chief Financial Officer
CMO: Matthew Hazelbaker, M.D., President Medical Staff
CIO: Carl Zani, Director Information Systems
CHR: Carman Wirtz, Vice President Human Resources
CNO: Robin Slattman, Chief Nursing Officer
Web address: www.memorialhosp.org
**Control:** County–Government, nonfederal **Service:** General Medical and Surgical

**Staffed Beds:** 56 **Admissions:** 2197 **Census:** 15 **Outpatient Visits:** 105921 **Births:** 549 **Total Expense ($000):** 69573 **Payroll Expense ($000):** 28130 **Personnel:** 477

**MASON—Warren County**

⊞ **LINDNER CENTER OF HOPE (364044)**, 4075 Old Western Row Road, Zip 45040–3104; tel. 513/536–0311 **A**1 9 10 **F**4 29 30 35 53 98 99 101 103 104 105 106 111 130 **P**6
Primary Contact: Paul Keck, M.D., President and Chief Executive Officer
COO: Brian Owens, Chief Operating Officer
CFO: David McAdams, Chief Financial Officer
CIO: Cliff McClintick, Chief Information Officer
CHR: Debbie A. Strawser, Director Human Resources
Web address: www.lindnercenterofhope.org
**Control:** Other not–for–profit (including NFP Corporation) **Service:** Psychiatric

**Staffed Beds:** 48 **Admissions:** 1560 **Census:** 35 **Outpatient Visits:** 10930 **Births:** 0 **Total Expense ($000):** 30161 **Payroll Expense ($000):** 13299 **Personnel:** 219

**MASSILLON—Stark County**

★ ○ △ **AFFINITY MEDICAL CENTER (360151)**, 875 Eighth Street N.E., Zip 44646–8503, Mailing Address: P.O. Box 805, Zip 44648–0805; tel. 330/832–8761, (Nonreporting) **A**7 9 10 11 12 13 **S** Community Health Systems, Inc., Franklin, TN
Primary Contact: Ronald L. Bierman, Chief Executive Officer
CFO: James Hutchinson, CPA, Chief Financial Officer
Web address: www.affinitymedicalcenter.com
**Control:** Corporation, Investor–owned, for–profit **Service:** General Medical and Surgical

**Staffed Beds:** 112

☐ **HEARTLAND BEHAVIORAL HEALTHCARE (364031)**, 3000 Erie Street, Zip 44646–7993, Mailing Address: P.O. Box 540, Zip 44648–0540; tel. 330/833–3135, (Nonreporting) **A**1 5 10 **S** Ohio Department of Mental Health, Columbus, OH
Primary Contact: James Ignelzi, Interim Chief Executive Officer
CFO: Patricia Eddleman, Fiscal Officer
CMO: Steven Thomson, M.D., Medical Director
CIO: Robert Hobart, Director Management Information Systems
CHR: Jerald Wilhite, Administrator Human Resources
Web address: www.mh.state.oh.us/ibhs/bhos/hoh.html
**Control:** State–Government, nonfederal **Service:** Psychiatric

**Staffed Beds:** 130

**OH**

## MAUMEE—Lucas County

☐ **ARROWHEAD BEHAVIORAL HEALTH HOSPITAL (364036)**, 1725 Timber Line Road, Zip 43537–4015; tel. 419/891–9333 **A**1 9 10 **F**4 5 98 101 102 103 104 105 130 **S** Universal Health Services, Inc., King of Prussia, PA
Primary Contact: Ed Speedling, Chief Executive Officer and Managing Director
CFO: Kim Blackwell, Chief Financial Officer
CMO: Siva Yechoor, M.D., Medical Director
CIO: Lynette Box, Director Medical Records
CHR: Eunice Russell, Manager Human Resources
Web address: www.arrowheadbehavioral.com
**Control:** Corporation, Investor–owned, for–profit **Service:** Psychiatric

| | |
|---|---|
| **Staffed Beds:** 42 **Admissions:** 1703 **Census:** 28 **Outpatient Visits:** 12787 **Births:** 0 **Total Expense ($000):** 5401 **Payroll Expense ($000):** 2824 **Personnel:** 61 | |

✠ ◇ **PROMEDICA ST. LUKE'S HOSPITAL (360090)**, 5901 Monclova Road, Zip 43537–1899; tel. 419/893–5911 **A**1 2 3 5 9 10 21 **F**1 3 4 8 11 13 15 16 17 18 20 22 24 26 28 29 30 31 34 35 40 45 46 48 49 56 57 59 64 67 68 70 72 73 74 76 77 78 79 80 81 82 85 86 87 88 89 92 93 98 100 107 108 111 114 118 119 126 128 129 130 131 132 134 135 143 146 147 148 **P**6 8 **S** ProMedica Health System, Toledo, OH
Primary Contact: Daniel L. Wakeman, President
COO: Lori Johnston, Chief Financial Officer and Chief Operating Officer
CFO: Lori Johnston, Chief Financial Officer and Chief Operating Officer
CMO: Stephen Bazeley, M.D., Vice President Medical Affairs
CIO: Patricia Swint, Director Information Technology
CHR: Connie Sessler, Director Human Resources
CNO: Theresa Konwinski, R.N., Vice President Patient Care
Web address: www.stlukeshospital.com
**Control:** Other not–for–profit (including NFP Corporation) **Service:** General Medical and Surgical

| | |
|---|---|
| **Staffed Beds:** 182 **Admissions:** 11194 **Census:** 120 **Outpatient Visits:** 268211 **Births:** 842 **Total Expense ($000):** 165741 **Payroll Expense ($000):** 59799 **Personnel:** 988 | |

## MEDINA—Medina County

✠ **MEDINA HOSPITAL (360091)**, 1000 East Washington Street, Zip 44256–2170; tel. 330/725–1000 **A**1 2 5 9 10 **F**3 7 13 15 16 18 20 28 29 30 31 34 35 40 47 49 50 57 59 60 64 70 74 75 76 77 78 79 81 82 85 86 93 96 107 111 114 117 119 129 130 131 132 133 135 144 146 147 **S** Cleveland Clinic Health System, Cleveland, OH
Primary Contact: Thomas Tulisiak, M.D., President
COO: Vicky Snyder, Chief Operating Officer and Chief Financial Officer
CFO: Vicky Snyder, Chief Operating Officer and Chief Financial Officer
CMO: Rick Shewbridge, M.D., Vice President Medical Operations
CIO: David Ingram, Director Management Information Systems
CHR: Amy Clark, Vice President Human Resources
CNO: Mary Kennedy, R.N., Chief Nursing Officer
Web address: www.medinahospital.org
**Control:** Other not–for–profit (including NFP Corporation) **Service:** General Medical and Surgical

| | |
|---|---|
| **Staffed Beds:** 127 **Admissions:** 6323 **Census:** 69 **Outpatient Visits:** 133497 **Births:** 925 **Total Expense ($000):** 98454 **Payroll Expense ($000):** 41588 **Personnel:** 655 | |

## MIAMISBURG—Montgomery County

✠ **LIFECARE HOSPITAL OF DAYTON (362028)**, 4000 Miamisburg–Centerville Road, Zip 45342–7615; tel. 937/384–8300, (Nonreporting) **A**1 9 10 **S** LifeCare Management Services, Plano, TX
Primary Contact: Russell Dean, Chief Executive Officer
CMO: Richard Gregg, M.D., Medical Director
CHR: Pam Fannin, Coordinator Human Resources
Web address: www.lifecare–hospitals.com
**Control:** Corporation, Investor–owned, for–profit **Service:** Long–Term Acute Care hospital

| | |
|---|---|
| **Staffed Beds:** 44 | |

✠ ◯ **SYCAMORE MEDICAL CENTER (360239)**, 4000 Miamisburg–Centerville Road, Zip 45342–7615; tel. 937/866–0551 **A**1 9 10 11 **F**3 5 8 11 12 15 18 20 28 29 30 31 34 35 36 38 39 40 44 45 47 48 49 50 53 54 56 57 58 59 60 61 64 65 66 68 70 74 75 77 78 79 81 82 84 85 86 87 93 97 98 99 100 101 102 103 104 105 107 108 110 111 114 115 118 119 129 130 131 132 134 135 141 145 146 148 **S** Kettering Health Network, Dayton, OH
Primary Contact: Walter Sackett, President
CMO: Gregory Wise, M.D., Vice President Medical Affairs
CIO: Jon Russell, Chief Information Officer
CHR: Beverly Morris, Vice President Human Resources
Web address: www.khnetwork.org
**Control:** Church–operated, Nongovernment, not–for profit **Service:** General Medical and Surgical

| | |
|---|---|
| **Staffed Beds:** 170 **Admissions:** 7832 **Census:** 90 **Outpatient Visits:** 129805 **Births:** 0 **Total Expense ($000):** 90978 **Payroll Expense ($000):** 37425 **Personnel:** 722 | |

## MIDDLEBURG HEIGHTS—Cuyahoga County

☐ **SOUTHWEST GENERAL HEALTH CENTER (360155)**, 18697 Bagley Road, Zip 44130–3497; tel. 440/816–8000 **A**1 2 5 10 **F**3 5 7 11 13 15 17 18 20 22 24 26 28 29 30 31 32 34 35 36 37 38 39 40 42 43 44 45 49 50 51 53 54 56 57 59 60 62 63 64 65 66 68 70 74 75 76 77 78 79 81 82 84 85 86 87 90 91 92 93 94 98 99 100 101 102 103 104 105 107 108 110 111 114 115 118 119 120 121 123 126 128 129 130 131 132 134 135 143 144 146 147 148 **P**6
Primary Contact: Thomas A. Selden, FACHE, President and Chief Executive Officer
CFO: Mary Ann Freas, Vice President and Chief Financial Officer
CMO: Marilyn McNamara, M.D., Vice President Medical Affairs
CIO: Teresa Rini Barber, Vice President Support Services
CHR: Judy Murphy, Director Human Resources
Web address: www.swgeneral.com
**Control:** Other not–for–profit (including NFP Corporation) **Service:** General Medical and Surgical

| | |
|---|---|
| **Staffed Beds:** 310 **Admissions:** 16000 **Census:** 208 **Outpatient Visits:** 397100 **Births:** 1004 **Total Expense ($000):** 278300 **Payroll Expense ($000):** 104341 **Personnel:** 2019 | |

## MIDDLETOWN—Warren County

☐ △ ◇ **ATRIUM MEDICAL CENTER (360076)**, One Medical Center Drive, Zip 45005–1066; tel. 513/424–2111, (Nonreporting) **A**1 2 7 9 10 21
Primary Contact: Carol Turner, President and Chief Executive Officer
CFO: Tom Maloney, Chief Financial Officer
CMO: Mark Williams, M.D., Chief Medical Officer
CHR: Ted Ripperger, Administrative Director Human Resources
Web address: www.atriummedcenter.org
**Control:** Other not–for–profit (including NFP Corporation) **Service:** General Medical and Surgical

| | |
|---|---|
| **Staffed Beds:** 314 | |

## MILLERSBURG—Holmes County

☐ **POMERENE HOSPITAL (360148)**, 981 Wooster Road, Zip 44654–1094; tel. 330/674–1015 **A**1 9 10 **F**3 11 13 15 29 30 34 35 40 53 55 57 59 68 70 75 76 77 79 81 85 87 89 93 107 108 110 114 118 119 129 130 131 132 135 144 146 148 **P**7
Primary Contact: Tony Snyder, Administrator and Chief Executive Officer
CFO: Jason Justus, Vice President Finance and Chief Financial Officer
CMO: Yasser Omran, M.D., President Medical Staff
CIO: Mark Jacobs, Director Information Services
CHR: Rebecca Ragon, Coordinator Public Relations and Marketing
Web address: www.pomerenehospital.org
**Control:** County–Government, nonfederal **Service:** General Medical and Surgical

| | |
|---|---|
| **Staffed Beds:** 41 **Admissions:** 1457 **Census:** 13 **Outpatient Visits:** 38063 **Births:** 511 **Total Expense ($000):** 26264 **Payroll Expense ($000):** 11041 **Personnel:** 250 | |

## MONTPELIER—Williams County

△ **COMMUNITY HOSPITALS AND WELLNESS CENTERS–MONTPELIER (361327)**, 909 East Snyder Avenue, Zip 43543–1251; tel. 419/385–3154, (Nonreporting) **A**7 9 10 18
Primary Contact: Philip L. Ennen, President and Chief Executive Officer
Web address: www.chwchospital.com
**Control:** Corporation, Investor–owned, for–profit **Service:** General Medical and Surgical

| | |
|---|---|
| **Staffed Beds:** 35 | |

**MONTPELIER HOSPITAL** See Community Hospitals and Wellness Centers, Bryan

## MOUNT GILEAD—Morrow County

✠ **MORROW COUNTY HOSPITAL (361313)**, 651 West Marion Road, Zip 43338–1027; tel. 419/946–5015, (Nonreporting) **A**1 5 9 10 18 **S** OhioHealth, Columbus, OH
Primary Contact: Christopher Truax, Chief Executive Officer
CFO: Joe Schueler, Chief Financial Officer
Web address: www.morrowcountyhospital.com
**Control:** County–Government, nonfederal **Service:** General Medical and Surgical

| | |
|---|---|
| **Staffed Beds:** 53 | |

*Many Facility Codes have changed. Please refer to the AHA Guide Code Chart.*   © 2013 AHA Guide

**OH**

## MOUNT VERNON—Knox County

⊞ **KNOX COMMUNITY HOSPITAL (360040)**, 1330 Coshocton Road,
Zip 43050–1495; tel. 740/393–9000 **A**1 2 9 10 20 **F**3 11 13 15 18 20 22 26
28 29 30 31 34 35 40 44 45 50 53 57 59 64 69 70 75 77 78 79 81 82 83
84 85 86 87 89 93 96 97 107 108 110 111 114 115 116 117 118 119 120
121 129 130 132 144 146 147 **P**6 **S** QHR, Brentwood, TN
Primary Contact: Bruce D. White, Chief Executive Officer
COO: Bruce M. Behner, Chief Operating Officer
CFO: Michael Ambrosiani, Chief Financial Officer
CMO: Judy Schwartz, M.D., Chief Medical Officer
CIO: Kwi Holland, Vice President Information Services
CHR: Lisa Bragg, Vice President Human Resources
CNO: Sandra Beidelschies, MSN, Chief Nursing Officer
Web address: www.knoxcommhosp.org
**Control:** Other not–for–profit (including NFP Corporation) **Service:** General
Medical and Surgical

**Staffed Beds: 87 Admissions: 3132 Census: 28 Outpatient Visits: 125226
Births: 430 Total Expense ($000): 115412 Payroll Expense ($000): 51301
Personnel: 779**

## NAPOLEON—Henry County

⊞ **HENRY COUNTY HOSPITAL (361309)**, 1600 East Riverview Avenue,
Zip 43545–9399; tel. 419/592–4015 **A**1 5 9 10 18 **F**3 5 11 13 15 28 29 31
34 35 36 40 53 57 59 64 65 68 70 75 76 78 79 81 82 85 86 87 93 99 100
101 104 107 108 110 114 119 130 132 133 135 146
Primary Contact: Kimberly Bordenkircher, Chief Executive Officer
COO: Michelle Rychener, Chief Operating Officer
CFO: Mary Clapp, Controller
CHR: Jennifer A. Fisher, Manager Human Resources
CNO: Patricia Frank, Chief Nursing Officer
Web address: www.henrycountyhospital.org
**Control:** Other not–for–profit (including NFP Corporation) **Service:** General
Medical and Surgical

**Staffed Beds: 25 Admissions: 774 Census: 9 Outpatient Visits: 72600
Births: 103 Total Expense ($000): 24680 Payroll Expense ($000): 10009
Personnel: 204**

## NELSONVILLE—Athens County

★ **DOCTORS HOSPITAL NELSONVILLE (361305)**, 1950 Mount Saint Mary Drive,
Zip 45764–1280; tel. 740/753–1931 **A**9 10 18 **F**3 15 29 40 45 50 57 59 64
65 75 81 87 96 97 107 110 114 130 133 148 **P**6 **S** OhioHealth, Columbus, OH
Primary Contact: LaMar L. Wyse, Chief Operating Officer
COO: LaMar L. Wyse, Chief Operating Officer
CFO: Shannon M. Atha, Director Finance
CMO: Marjorie Devol, M.D., Chief of Staff
CIO: Danny Canter, Manager Information Systems
CHR: Terry Wilson, Director Human Resources and Compliance
CNO: Sandy Wood, Director Patient Care Services
Web address: www.ohiohealth.com
**Control:** Other not–for–profit (including NFP Corporation) **Service:** General
Medical and Surgical

**Staffed Beds: 25 Admissions: 503 Census: 7 Outpatient Visits: 33505
Births: 0 Total Expense ($000): 16239 Payroll Expense ($000): 7719
Personnel: 161**

## NEW ALBANY—Franklin County

⊞ **MOUNT CARMEL NEW ALBANY SURGICAL HOSPITAL (360266)**, 7333
Smith's Mill Road, Zip 43054–9291; tel. 614/775–6600 **A**1 9 10 **F**3 29 34 35
44 57 58 59 64 65 68 74 75 79 81 85 86 87 94 107 111 114 146 **P**6 8
**S** Trinity Health, Livonia, MI
Primary Contact: Richard D'Enbeau, Chief Operating Officer
Web address: www.mountcarmelhealth.com
**Control:** Church–operated, Nongovernment, not–for profit **Service:** General
Medical and Surgical

**Staffed Beds: 60 Admissions: 4998 Census: 27 Outpatient Visits: 14602
Births: 0 Total Expense ($000): 88019 Payroll Expense ($000): 12277
Personnel: 236**

## NEWARK—Licking County

☐ **LICKING MEMORIAL HOSPITAL (360218)**, 1320 West Main Street,
Zip 43055–3699; tel. 740/348–4000 **A**1 2 5 9 10 **F**3 4 5 13 15 18 20 22 26
28 29 30 31 32 34 35 40 41 45 49 50 53 57 59 62 64 65 68 70 74 75 76
77 78 79 81 82 84 85 86 87 89 92 93 97 98 100 101 102 104 105 106 107
108 110 111 114 115 118 119 130 132 135 144 146 147 148 **P**6
Primary Contact: Robert A. Montagnese, President and Chief Executive Officer
CFO: Cindy Webster, Vice President Financial Services
CMO: Craig Cairns, M.D., Vice President Medical Affairs
CIO: Sallie Arnett, Vice President Information Systems
CHR: Anne Peterson, Vice President Human Resources and Support Services
Web address: www.lmhealth.org
**Control:** Other not–for–profit (including NFP Corporation) **Service:** General
Medical and Surgical

**Staffed Beds: 199 Admissions: 8103 Census: 66 Outpatient Visits: 283215
Births: 1068 Total Expense ($000): 133955 Payroll Expense ($000):
53965 Personnel: 1220**

⊞ **MEDICAL CENTER OF NEWARK (360347)**, 2000 Tamarack Road,
Zip 43055–1183; tel. 740/522–7800, (Nonreporting) **A**9 10
Primary Contact: Michael Greene, Chief Executive Officer
Web address: www.mcnohio.com
**Control:** Partnership, Investor–owned, for–profit **Service:** General Medical and
Surgical

**Staffed Beds: 20**

## NORTHFIELD—Summit County

☐ **NORTHCOAST BEHAVIORAL HEALTHCARE SYSTEM (364011)**, 1756
Sagamore Road, Zip 44067–1086; tel. 330/467–7131, (Includes CLEVELAND
CAMPUS, 1708 Southpoint Drive, Cleveland, Zip 44109–1999;
tel. 216/787–0500; NORTHFIELD CAMPUS, 1756 Sagamore Road, Zip 44067,
Mailing Address: P.O. Box 305, Zip 44067–0305; tel. 330/467–7131; TOLEDO
CAMPUS, 930 South Detroit Avenue, Toledo, Zip 43614–2701;
tel. 419/381–1881) **A**1 3 10 **F**30 53 65 75 77 82 98 106 130 135 146 **S** Ohio
Department of Mental Health, Columbus, OH
Primary Contact: David Celletti, Chief Executive Officer
CFO: Jeff Comfort, Vice President Administration
CIO: Karl Donenwirth, Vice President Information Services
Web address: www.mh.state.oh.us
**Control:** State–Government, nonfederal **Service:** Psychiatric

**Staffed Beds: 260 Admissions: 1693 Census: 246 Outpatient Visits: 0
Births: 0 Total Expense ($000): 48286 Payroll Expense ($000): 25513
Personnel: 484**

## NORWALK—Huron County

⊞ ○ **FISHER–TITUS MEDICAL CENTER (360065)**, 272 Benedict Avenue,
Zip 44857–2374; tel. 419/668–8101, (Total facility includes 69 beds in nursing
home–type unit) **A**1 2 5 9 10 11 19 **F**3 10 11 13 15 18 20 28 29 31 34 35 36
39 40 43 45 49 50 51 56 57 58 59 62 64 68 70 74 75 76 77 78 79 81 82
85 86 87 92 93 94 96 97 107 108 110 111 115 118 119 126 128 129 130
131 132 135 146 147 148 **P**2 6 7
Primary Contact: Ross A. Matlack, FACHE, President and Chief Executive Officer
COO: Lorna Strayer, Senior Vice President Administration and Business
Development
CFO: Duane L. Woods, Jr., Chief Financial Officer
CMO: Gary L. Moorman, D.O., Vice President Medical Affairs
CIO: John Britton, Director Information Services
CHR: Phillip Annarino, Vice President Human Resources
CNO: Cherie Spragg, R.N., Senior Vice President Nursing Services
Web address: www.fisher-titus.com
**Control:** Other not–for–profit (including NFP Corporation) **Service:** General
Medical and Surgical

**Staffed Beds: 147 Admissions: 4058 Census: 99 Outpatient Visits: 164031
Births: 633 Total Expense ($000): 100621 Payroll Expense ($000): 40585
Personnel: 760**

---

**Hospital, Medicare Provider Number, Address, Telephone, Approval, Facility, and Physician Codes, Health Care System**

★ American Hospital Association (AHA) membership
☐ The Joint Commission accreditation ◇ DNV Healthcare Inc. accreditation
○ Healthcare Facilities Accreditation Program
△ Commission on Accreditation of Rehabilitation Facilities (CARF) accreditation

**OH**

## OBERLIN—Lorain County

✠ **MERCY ALLEN HOSPITAL (361306)**, 200 West Lorain Street, Zip 44074–1077; tel. 440/775–1211 **A**1 9 10 18 **F**3 7 8 11 15 29 30 34 35 40 50 65 69 74 75 79 81 85 87 93 97 107 119 127 129 130 133 146 **S** Catholic Health Partners, Cincinnati, OH
Primary Contact: Susan Bowers, R.N., President and Chief Nursing Officer
CFO: Donald E. Kline, Chief Financial Officer and Vice President Operations
CMO: Eric Jenkins, M.D., Chief of Staff
CIO: Sami Othman, Regional Site Director Information Process Services
CNO: Susan Bowers, R.N., President and Chief Nursing Officer
Web address: www.mercyonline.org/mercy_allen_hospital.aspx
**Control:** Church–operated, Nongovernment, not–for profit **Service:** General Medical and Surgical

**Staffed Beds:** 25 **Admissions:** 937 **Census:** 17 **Outpatient Visits:** 53802 **Births:** 0 **Total Expense ($000):** 21936 **Payroll Expense ($000):** 9256 **Personnel:** 144

## OREGON—Lucas County

✠ △ **MERCY ST. CHARLES HOSPITAL (360081)**, 2600 Navarre Avenue, Zip 43616–3297; tel. 419/696–7200 **A**1 7 9 10 **F**3 11 13 15 17 18 28 29 30 31 34 35 40 43 44 46 48 49 51 53 56 57 59 60 64 66 68 70 71 74 75 76 77 78 79 81 82 85 86 87 90 92 93 94 97 98 100 102 103 107 108 110 111 114 115 116 117 119 123 129 130 132 133 135 146 147 **P**8 **S** Catholic Health Partners, Cincinnati, OH
Primary Contact: Robert E. Gospodarek, President and Chief Executive Officer
COO: Jeffrey Dempsey, Vice President Operations
CFO: Robert Moon, Senior Vice President Northern Region and Chief Financial Officer
CMO: Krishna Ragothaman, M.D., Chief of Staff
CIO: Michael Shork, M.D., Director Information Systems Services
CHR: Gary George, Regional Vice President Human Resources
CNO: Judy Zbierajewski, Chief Nursing Officer and Vice President Patient Care
Web address: www.mercyweb.org
**Control:** Church–operated, Nongovernment, not–for profit **Service:** General Medical and Surgical

**Staffed Beds:** 264 **Admissions:** 10044 **Census:** 148 **Outpatient Visits:** 201850 **Births:** 423 **Personnel:** 949

✠ **PROMEDICA BAY PARK HOSPITAL (360259)**, 2801 Bay Park Drive, Zip 43616–4920; tel. 419/690–7900 **A**1 9 10 **F**3 11 13 15 18 29 30 31 34 35 40 44 45 49 50 51 57 58 59 64 68 70 74 75 76 77 78 79 81 82 85 86 87 92 93 107 108 110 111 114 117 118 119 124 129 130 131 132 135 146 147 148 **S** ProMedica Health System, Toledo, OH
Primary Contact: Holly L. Bristoll, President
CFO: David Brewer, Director Finance
CMO: David Lindstrom, M.D., Vice President Medical Affairs
CIO: David G. Selman, Corporate Vice President Information Resources
CHR: Kara Zimmerly, Manager Human Resources
CNO: Maurine Weis, Vice President Patient Care Service and Chief Nursing Officer
Web address: www.promedica.org
**Control:** Other not–for–profit (including NFP Corporation) **Service:** General Medical and Surgical

**Staffed Beds:** 72 **Admissions:** 3355 **Census:** 35 **Outpatient Visits:** 107448 **Births:** 653 **Total Expense ($000):** 72430 **Payroll Expense ($000):** 22396 **Personnel:** 406

**ST. CHARLES MERCY HOSPITAL** See Mercy St. Charles Hospital

## ORRVILLE—Wayne County

✠ **AULTMAN ORRVILLE HOSPITAL (361323)**, 832 South Main Street, Zip 44667–2208; tel. 330/682–3010 **A**1 9 10 18 **F**3 8 11 13 15 29 30 34 35 40 45 50 51 53 57 59 68 70 75 76 77 79 81 82 85 86 87 93 108 110 111 115 118 119 129 130 131 132 133 135 143 146 147 **P**1 5 **S** Aultman Health Foundation, Canton, OH
Primary Contact: Marchelle Suppan, DPM, President and Chief Executive Officer
COO: Judy Erb, Vice President Patient Care Services and Chief Nursing Officer
CFO: Adam M. Luntz, Vice President Finance and Chief Financial Officer
CIO: Roger Mutchler, Manager Information Technology
CHR: Lori Kotewicz, Supervisor Human Resources
CNO: Judy Erb, Vice President Patient Services and Chief Nursing Officer
Web address: www.aultmanorrville.org
**Control:** Other not–for–profit (including NFP Corporation) **Service:** General Medical and Surgical

**Staffed Beds:** 25 **Admissions:** 790 **Census:** 5 **Outpatient Visits:** 44562 **Births:** 347 **Total Expense ($000):** 15062 **Payroll Expense ($000):** 8907 **Personnel:** 194

## OXFORD—Butler County

★ ○ **MCCULLOUGH–HYDE MEMORIAL HOSPITAL (360046)**, 110 North Poplar Street, Zip 45056–1292; tel. 513/523–2111 **A**9 10 11 **F**3 11 13 15 28 29 30 31 32 34 35 36 40 45 47 49 54 57 59 64 65 69 70 74 75 77 78 79 81 82 85 93 94 107 108 110 111 114 118 119 129 130 131 132 135 143 144 146 147 148
Primary Contact: Bryan D. Hehemann, President and Chief Executive Officer
CFO: John R. Clements, Vice President and Chief Financial Officer
CIO: Kathy Dickman, Director Information Technology
CHR: Dennis Johnson, Director Human Resources
CNO: Pamela Collins, Vice President Chief Patient Services Officer
Web address: www.mhmh.org
**Control:** Other not–for–profit (including NFP Corporation) **Service:** General Medical and Surgical

**Staffed Beds:** 45 **Admissions:** 2384 **Census:** 23 **Outpatient Visits:** 132610 **Births:** 413 **Total Expense ($000):** 55063 **Payroll Expense ($000):** 22359 **Personnel:** 386

## PARMA—Cuyahoga County

✠ △ **PARMA COMMUNITY GENERAL HOSPITAL (360041)**, 7007 Powers Boulevard, Zip 44129–5495; tel. 440/743–3000, (Total facility includes 11 beds in nursing home–type unit) **A**1 2 7 10 **F**2 3 10 11 12 13 15 17 18 20 22 24 26 28 29 30 31 34 35 36 40 44 45 49 50 51 53 55 56 57 58 59 62 63 64 65 68 69 70 71 74 75 76 77 78 79 81 82 85 86 87 90 93 96 98 100 101 103 107 108 111 114 115 116 117 118 119 120 121 126 128 130 131 132 135 143 144 146 147 148 **P**6
Primary Contact: Terrence G. Deis, President and Chief Executive Officer
CFO: Barry L. Franklin, Executive Vice President and Chief Financial Officer
CMO: Dale Cowan, M.D., Vice President Medical Affairs
CIO: Barry L. Franklin, Executive Vice President and Chief Financial Officer
CHR: Ralph Knull, Vice President Human Resources
CNO: Pam Falasco, Vice President, Chief Nursing Officer
Web address: www.parmahospital.org
**Control:** Other not–for–profit (including NFP Corporation) **Service:** General Medical and Surgical

**Staffed Beds:** 278 **Admissions:** 14458 **Census:** 177 **Outpatient Visits:** 225824 **Births:** 493 **Total Expense ($000):** 181083 **Payroll Expense ($000):** 73437 **Personnel:** 1543

## PAULDING—Paulding County

□ **PAULDING COUNTY HOSPITAL (361300)**, 1035 West Wayne Street, Zip 45879–1544; tel. 419/399–4080, (Nonreporting) **A**1 9 10 18
Primary Contact: Gary W. Adkins, Chief Executive Officer
COO: Randy Ruge, Chief Operating Officer
CFO: Rob Goshia, Chief Financial Officer
CMO: Wendell J. Spangler, M.D., Chief of Staff
CIO: Dan Kaufman, Director Information Services
CHR: Melanie Rittenour, Director Human Resources
Web address: www.pauldingcountyhospital.com
**Control:** County–Government, nonfederal **Service:** General Medical and Surgical

**Staffed Beds:** 25

## PORT CLINTON—Ottawa County

✠ **MAGRUDER MEMORIAL HOSPITAL (361314)**, (Formerly H. B. Magruder Memorial Hospital), 615 Fulton Street, Zip 43452–2001; tel. 419/734–3131 **A**1 5 9 10 18 **F**3 11 15 18 28 29 31 34 35 40 44 45 46 48 50 53 57 59 64 65 70 74 75 78 79 81 82 85 86 87 89 93 107 108 110 115 118 119 129 130 131 132 133 135 146 147 148 **P**6 8
Primary Contact: J. Todd Almendinger, President and Chief Executive Officer
CFO: Ronald Weiner, Chief Financial Officer
CMO: Panju Prithviraj, M.D., President Medical Staff
CHR: Jennifer Capizzi, Director Human Resources
Web address: www.magruderhospital.com
**Control:** Other not–for–profit (including NFP Corporation) **Service:** General Medical and Surgical

**Staffed Beds:** 25 **Admissions:** 909 **Census:** 8 **Outpatient Visits:** 91714 **Births:** 0 **Total Expense ($000):** 45859 **Payroll Expense ($000):** 18692 **Personnel:** 352

*Many Facility Codes have changed. Please refer to the AHA Guide Code Chart.*
© 2013 AHA Guide

## PORTSMOUTH—Scioto County

⊠ △ **SOUTHERN OHIO MEDICAL CENTER (360008)**, 1805 27th Street, Zip 45662–2640; tel. 740/356–5000 **A**1 2 5 7 9 10 13 **F**3 11 13 15 17 18 20 22 24 26 28 29 30 31 34 35 37 38 40 41 44 45 46 49 50 53 54 57 59 62 63 64 65 68 70 74 75 76 77 78 79 81 83 84 85 86 87 89 90 92 97 98 100 102 103 104 107 108 109 110 111 114 115 116 117 118 119 120 121 122 123 124 125 129 130 131 132 135 144 145 146 **P**3
Primary Contact: Randal M. Arnett, President and Chief Executive Officer
COO: Claudia L. Burchett, R.N., Vice President Patient Services
CFO: Dean Wray, Vice President Finance
CMO: Kendall Stewart, M.D., Medical Director
CIO: Brent Richard, Administrative Director Information Systems
CHR: Vicki Noel, Vice President Human Resources
Web address: www.somc.org
**Control:** Other not–for–profit (including NFP Corporation) **Service:** General Medical and Surgical

**Staffed Beds:** 245 **Admissions:** 11612 **Census:** 143 **Outpatient Visits:** 271871 **Births:** 1144 **Total Expense ($000):** 237756 **Payroll Expense ($000):** 89822 **Personnel:** 1957

## PROCTORVILLE—Lawrence County

☐ **THREE GABLES SURGERY CENTER (360261)**, 5897 County Road 107, Zip 45669–8852, Mailing Address: P.O. Box 490, Zip, Zip 45669–0490; tel. 740/886–9911 **A**1 9 10 **F**1 3 4 8 16 17 34 45 48 57 59 64 65 67 68 70 72 73 76 79 80 81 82 85 88 89 90 93 98 107 111 114 128 129 **P**8
Primary Contact: Tony Alouise, Chief Executive Officer
Web address: www.threegablessurgery.com
**Control:** Partnership, Investor–owned, for–profit **Service:** General Medical and Surgical

**Staffed Beds:** 8 **Admissions:** 250 **Census:** 1 **Outpatient Visits:** 4868 **Births:** 0 **Total Expense ($000):** 11642 **Payroll Expense ($000):** 3609 **Personnel:** 62

## RAVENNA—Portage County

☐ **ROBINSON MEMORIAL HOSPITAL (360078)**, 6847 North Chestnut Street, Zip 44266–3929, Mailing Address: P.O. Box 1204, Zip 44266–1204; tel. 330/297–0811 **A**1 2 3 5 9 10 **F**3 8 11 13 15 17 18 20 22 26 28 29 30 31 32 34 35 40 43 44 45 47 49 50 51 54 56 57 58 59 61 62 63 64 70 74 75 76 77 78 79 81 82 83 84 85 86 87 92 93 97 100 107 108 110 111 114 115 116 118 119 121 123 129 130 131 132 135 144 145 146 147 148 **P**6 **S** Summa Health System, Akron, OH
Primary Contact: Stephen Colecchi, President and Chief Executive Officer
COO: Richard Clough, Chief Operating Officer
CFO: Carl Ebner, Vice President Finance
CMO: Stephen Francis, M.D., Vice President Medical Affairs
CIO: David Baldwin, Chief Information Officer
CHR: Pamela Mackintosh, Vice President Human Resources
Web address: www.robinsonmemorial.org
**Control:** County–Government, nonfederal **Service:** General Medical and Surgical

**Staffed Beds:** 141 **Admissions:** 8208 **Census:** 84 **Outpatient Visits:** 176903 **Births:** 717

## ROCK CREEK—Ashtabula County

☐ **GLENBEIGH HOSPITAL AND OUTPATIENT CENTERS (360245)**, 2863 Route 45, Zip 44084, Mailing Address: P.O. Box 298, Zip 44084–0298; tel. 440/563–3400 **A**9 10 **F**4 5 29 30 34 36 53 54 57 75 86 87 100 130 132 135 **P**5
Primary Contact: Patricia Weston-Hall, Chief Executive Officer
CFO: Phil Pawlowski, Chief Financial Officer
CIO: Linda Advey, Manager Information Systems
CHR: Shirley Deary, Director Human Resources
Web address: www.glenbeigh.com
**Control:** Other not–for–profit (including NFP Corporation) **Service:** Alcoholism and other chemical dependency

**Staffed Beds:** 114 **Admissions:** 2649 **Census:** 67 **Outpatient Visits:** 79747 **Births:** 0 **Total Expense ($000):** 16810 **Payroll Expense ($000):** 8640 **Personnel:** 255

## SAINT MARYS—Auglaize County

◇ **JOINT TOWNSHIP DISTRICT MEMORIAL HOSPITAL (360032)**, 200 St. Clair Street, Zip 45885–2400; tel. 419/394–3335, (Total facility includes 15 beds in nursing home–type unit) **A**9 10 21 **F**3 7 8 11 12 13 15 28 29 30 31 32 34 35 36 40 41 42 43 51 53 57 59 62 63 64 70 75 76 77 78 79 81 82 83 84 85 87 90 93 97 107 108 110 115 119 128 129 130 131 132 135 143 144 146 147 148
Primary Contact: Kevin W. Harlan, President
CFO: Jeffrey W. Vossler, Vice President Financial Services
CIO: DeWayne Marsee, Director Information Systems
CHR: Art Swain, Vice President Support Services
Web address: www.grandlakehealth.org
**Control:** Other not–for–profit (including NFP Corporation) **Service:** General Medical and Surgical

**Staffed Beds:** 53 **Admissions:** 2033 **Census:** 16 **Outpatient Visits:** 67782 **Births:** 246 **Total Expense ($000):** 63757 **Payroll Expense ($000):** 20527 **Personnel:** 464

## SALEM—Columbiana County

⊠ **SALEM COMMUNITY HOSPITAL (360185)**, 1995 East State Street, Zip 44460–2423; tel. 330/332–1551, (Nonreporting) **A**1 5 9 10
Primary Contact: Steven T. Ruwoldt, Chief Executive Officer
CFO: Mike Giangardella, Vice President Finance and Administration
CMO: Anita Hackstedde, M.D., Vice President Medical Affairs
CIO: Mark L'Italien, Director Information Services
CHR: Barb Hirst, Vice President Human Resources and Chief Nursing Officer
CNO: Barb Hirst, Vice President Human Resources and Chief Nursing Officer
Web address: www.salemhosp.com
**Control:** Other not–for–profit (including NFP Corporation) **Service:** General Medical and Surgical

**Staffed Beds:** 140

## SANDUSKY—Erie County

○ **FIRELANDS REGIONAL HEALTH SYSTEM (360025)**, 1111 Hayes Avenue, Zip 44870–3323; tel. 419/557–7400, (Includes FIRELANDS REGIONAL MEDICAL CENTER – MAIN CAMPUS, 1111 Hayes Avenue, Zip 44870; tel. 419/557–7400; FIRELANDS REGIONAL MEDICAL CENTER SOUTH CAMPUS, 1912 Hayes Avenue, Zip 44870–4736; tel. 419/557–7000), (Nonreporting) **A**2 6 9 10 11 12 13 19
Primary Contact: Martin Tursky, President and Chief Executive Officer
CFO: Daniel J. Moncher, Vice President and Chief Financial Officer
CMO: Brenda Violette, M.D., Director Medical Staff
CIO: Robert Ayres, Director Information Systems
CHR: James Sennish, Vice President Human Resources
Web address: www.firelands.com
**Control:** Other not–for–profit (including NFP Corporation) **Service:** General Medical and Surgical

**Staffed Beds:** 236

## SEAMAN—Adams County

⊠ **ADAMS COUNTY REGIONAL MEDICAL CENTER (361326)**, 230 Medical Center Drive, Zip 45679–8002; tel. 937/386–3400 **A**1 9 10 18 **F**3 11 15 29 30 31 34 35 40 45 47 53 57 59 62 64 65 75 77 78 79 81 85 86 93 104 107 110 111 115 116 119 129 130 131 132 133 148
Primary Contact: Saundra J. Stevens, Chief Executive Officer
CFO: Scott D. Smith, Chief Financial Officer
CHR: Joyce Porter, Chief Human Resources Officer
CNO: Sharon Ashley, MSN, Chief Nursing Officer
Web address: www.acrmc.com
**Control:** County–Government, nonfederal **Service:** General Medical and Surgical

**Staffed Beds:** 25 **Admissions:** 729 **Census:** 7 **Outpatient Visits:** 51106 **Births:** 0 **Total Expense ($000):** 26565 **Payroll Expense ($000):** 9376 **Personnel:** 259

## SHELBY—Richland County

☐ **MEDCENTRAL – SHELBY HOSPITAL (361324)**, 199 West Main Street, Zip 44875–1490; tel. 419/342–5015 **A**1 9 10 18 **F**3 11 13 15 18 29 31 34 35 40 57 59 64 68 69 70 75 76 78 79 81 93 107 114 119 127 130 133 146 **S** MedCentral Health System, Mansfield, OH
Primary Contact: Joe Chamberlain, Acting Chief Executive Officer
Web address: www.medcentral.org/body.cfm?id=153
**Control:** Other not–for–profit (including NFP Corporation) **Service:** General Medical and Surgical

**Staffed Beds:** 25 **Admissions:** 1291 **Census:** 13 **Outpatient Visits:** 36047 **Births:** 162 **Personnel:** 163

---

**Hospital, Medicare Provider Number, Address, Telephone, Approval, Facility, and Physician Codes, Health Care System**

★ American Hospital Association (AHA) membership
☐ The Joint Commission accreditation      ◇ DNV Healthcare Inc. accreditation

○ Healthcare Facilities Accreditation Program
△ Commission on Accreditation of Rehabilitation Facilities (CARF) accreditation

**OH**

## SIDNEY—Shelby County

★ ○ **WILSON MEMORIAL HOSPITAL (360013)**, 915 West Michigan Street, Zip 45365–2491; tel. 937/498–2311 **A**9 10 11 **F**3 11 13 15 20 28 29 30 31 40 45 46 49 56 57 59 62 63 64 68 70 75 76 77 78 79 81 85 86 87 89 93 98 103 107 108 111 118 119 124 129 130 131 132 135 144 146 147 **P**6
Primary Contact: Thomas J. Boecker, President and Chief Executive Officer
COO: Craig Lannoye, Vice President Operations
CFO: Julie Covault, Vice President Finance
CMO: Robert J. McDevitt, M.D., Chief of Staff
CIO: Larry Meyers, Chief Information Officer
CHR: John R. Eve, Vice President Human Resources
CNO: Linda Maurer, Vice President Patient Care Services
Web address: www.wilsonhospital.com
**Control:** Other not–for–profit (including NFP Corporation) **Service:** General Medical and Surgical

**Staffed Beds: 71 Admissions:** 2512 **Census:** 26 **Outpatient Visits:** 182791 **Births:** 790 **Total Expense ($000):** 64112 **Payroll Expense ($000):** 24776 **Personnel:** 636

## SPRINGFIELD—Clark County

☐ **MENTAL HEALTH SERVICES FOR CLARK AND MADISON COUNTIES (364040)**, 1345 North Fountain Boulevard, Zip 45504–1422; tel. 937/399–9500 **A**1 9 10 **F**32 34 35 57 98 99 100 101 102 103 104 105 106 130 132 134 135 **P**6
Primary Contact: James Perry, Chief Executive Officer
Web address: www.mhscc.org
**Control:** Other not–for–profit (including NFP Corporation) **Service:** Psychiatric

**Staffed Beds: 16 Admissions:** 771 **Census:** 12 **Outpatient Visits:** 31925 **Births:** 0 **Total Expense ($000):** 13103 **Payroll Expense ($000):** 8286 **Personnel:** 171

☐ **OHIO VALLEY SURGICAL HOSPITAL (360355)**, (Formerly Ohio Valley Medical Center), 100 West Main Street, Zip 45502–1312; tel. 937/521–3900, (Nonreporting) **A**1 9 10
Primary Contact: Steve Eisentrager, Administrator
Web address: www.myovmc.com/
**Control:** Partnership, Investor–owned, for–profit **Service:** Surgical

**Staffed Beds: 24**

⊠ **SPRINGFIELD REGIONAL MEDICAL CENTER (360086)**, 100 Medical Center Drive, Zip 45504–2687; tel. 937/523–1000, (Includes SPRINGFIELD REGIONAL MEDICAL CENTER – FOUNTAIN CAMPUS, 1343 North Fountain Boulevard, Zip 45501–1380; tel. 937/390–5000) **A**1 2 6 9 10 **F**3 5 8 11 12 13 15 17 18 20 22 24 26 28 29 30 31 34 35 37 40 45 49 51 59 61 63 64 68 70 73 74 75 76 77 78 79 81 82 83 84 85 86 87 89 90 93 107 108 110 111 114 118 119 120 121 126 127 129 130 131 132 135 146 147 148 **P**6 **S** Catholic Health Partners, Cincinnati, OH
Primary Contact: Paul C. Hiltz, FACHE, Market Leader and President
CFO: John F. Dempsey, Vice President and Chief Financial Officer
CIO: Yousuf Ahmad, Chief Information Officer
CHR: Cherie Lamborn, Interim Vice President Human Resources
Web address: www.communityhospital.com
**Control:** Church–operated, Nongovernment, not–for profit **Service:** General Medical and Surgical

**Staffed Beds: 254 Admissions:** 15492 **Census:** 183 **Outpatient Visits:** 306100 **Births:** 1203 **Total Expense ($000):** 221586 **Payroll Expense ($000):** 73459 **Personnel:** 1485

## STEUBENVILLE—Jefferson County

⊠ **ACUITY SPECIALTY HOSPITALS OHIO VALLEY (362035)**, 380 Summit Avenue, 3rd Floor, Zip 43952–2667; tel. 740/283–7600, (Includes ACUITY SPECIALTY HOSPITALS OHIO VALLEY AT BELMONT, 4697 Harrison Street, Bellaire, Zip 43906–1338; tel. 740/671–2086) **A**1 9 10 **F**1 3 29 31 45 58 60 74 75 77 78 79 82 85 86 130 148 **S** AcuityHealthcare, LP, Charlotte, NC
Primary Contact: Judy K. Weaver, MS, Chief Executive Officer
Web address: www.acuityhealthcare.net
**Control:** Individual, Investor–owned, for–profit **Service:** Long–Term Acute Care hospital

**Staffed Beds: 40 Admissions:** 512 **Census:** 36 **Outpatient Visits:** 0 **Births:** 0 **Total Expense ($000):** 16505 **Payroll Expense ($000):** 6769 **Personnel:** 154

☐ **LIFE LINE HOSPITAL (362039)**, 200 School Street, Zip 43953–9610; tel. 740/346–2600, (Nonreporting) **A**1 10
Primary Contact: Susan T. Colpo, Chief Executive Officer
Web address: www.llhospital.com
**Control:** Partnership, Investor–owned, for–profit **Service:** Long–Term Acute Care hospital

**Staffed Beds: 36**

⊠ △ **TRINITY HEALTH SYSTEM (360211)**, 380 Summit Avenue, Zip 43952–2699; tel. 740/283–7000, (Includes TRINITY MEDICAL CENTER EAST, 380 Summit Avenue, tel. 740/283–7000; TRINITY MEDICAL CENTER WEST, 4000 Johnson Road, Zip 43952–2393; tel. 740/264–8000) **A**1 2 6 7 9 10 **F**3 4 5 11 12 13 15 17 18 20 22 24 26 28 29 30 31 32 34 35 38 40 45 46 47 49 51 54 56 57 59 62 64 65 70 74 75 76 77 78 79 81 85 86 87 89 90 92 93 94 96 97 98 99 100 101 102 103 104 105 107 108 110 111 114 115 117 118 119 120 121 123 128 129 130 131 132 135 144 146 147 148 **P**6 **S** Sylvania Franciscan Health, Toledo, OH
Primary Contact: Fred B. Brower, President and Chief Executive Officer
CFO: Elizabeth Allen, Vice President Finance
CMO: Ivan Wright, M.D., Vice President Medical Affairs
CIO: Tom Kiger, Director Information Systems
CHR: Lewis C. Musso, Vice President Human Resources
Web address: www.trinityhealth.com
**Control:** Other not–for–profit (including NFP Corporation) **Service:** General Medical and Surgical

**Staffed Beds: 312 Admissions:** 11002 **Census:** 178 **Outpatient Visits:** 277025 **Births:** 499 **Total Expense ($000):** 194964 **Payroll Expense ($000):** 72692 **Personnel:** 1711

## SYLVANIA—Lucas County

⊠ △ **PROMEDICA FLOWER HOSPITAL (360074)**, 5200 Harroun Road, Zip 43560–2196; tel. 419/824–1444 **A**1 2 3 5 7 9 10 **F**2 3 11 12 13 15 18 24 28 29 30 31 34 35 36 38 40 43 47 48 49 50 57 58 59 60 64 65 67 68 70 75 76 77 78 79 81 82 84 85 86 87 90 91 92 93 94 96 97 98 100 101 102 103 107 108 109 110 111 114 116 117 118 119 120 121 123 124 129 130 131 132 146 147 **S** ProMedica Health System, Toledo, OH
Primary Contact: Alan Sattler, President
CFO: Kathleen S. Hanley, Chief Financial Officer
CMO: John Evanoff, M.D., Vice President Medical Affairs
CIO: Ken Armstrong, Senior Vice President Information
CHR: Arturo Polizzi, Chief Human Resources Officer
CNO: Maurine Weis, Vice President Nursing and Chief Nursing Officer
Web address: www.promedica.org
**Control:** Other not–for–profit (including NFP Corporation) **Service:** General Medical and Surgical

**Staffed Beds: 221 Admissions:** 10084 **Census:** 144 **Outpatient Visits:** 193740 **Births:** 1060 **Total Expense ($000):** 190089 **Payroll Expense ($000):** 64234 **Personnel:** 1319

⊠ **REGENCY HOSPITAL OF TOLEDO (362036)**, 5220 Alexis Road, Zip 43560–2504; tel. 419/318–5700, (Nonreporting) **A**1 3 5 10 **S** Select Medical Corporation, Mechanicsburg, PA
Primary Contact: Diana D. Fisher, Chief Executive Officer
Web address: www.regencyhospital.com
**Control:** Corporation, Investor–owned, for–profit **Service:** Long–Term Acute Care hospital

**Staffed Beds: 35**

## TIFFIN—Seneca County

⊠ **MERCY TIFFIN HOSPITAL (360089)**, 45 St. Lawrence Drive, Zip 44883–8310; tel. 419/455–7000 **A**1 2 5 9 10 **F**3 11 12 13 15 18 19 20 28 29 30 31 34 35 36 40 46 49 50 51 56 57 59 62 64 66 68 70 74 75 76 78 79 81 82 83 84 85 86 87 89 97 107 108 110 111 115 118 119 121 123 124 129 130 132 133 134 135 145 146 147 148 **S** Catholic Health Partners, Cincinnati, OH
Primary Contact: B. Lynn Detterman, Interim President and Chief Executive Officer
CMO: Wesley Hedges, M.D., President Medical Staff
CHR: Diana Olson, Chief Human Resources Officer
Web address: www.mercyweb.org
**Control:** Church–operated, Nongovernment, not–for profit **Service:** General Medical and Surgical

**Staffed Beds: 51 Admissions:** 2046 **Census:** 21 **Outpatient Visits:** 81404 **Births:** 297 **Total Expense ($000):** 55076 **Payroll Expense ($000):** 20475 **Personnel:** 377

## TOLEDO—Lucas County

☐ **ADVANCED SPECIALTY HOSPITAL OF TOLEDO (362038)**, 1015 Garden Lake Parkway, Zip 43614–2779; tel. 419/381–0037 **A**1 10 **F**1 3 29 30 60 74 75 79 82 84 85 94 100 119 130 148
Primary Contact: Salvatore Iweimrin, R.N., Chief Executive Officer
Web address: www.advancedspecialtyhospitals.com
**Control:** Corporation, Investor–owned, for–profit **Service:** Long–Term Acute Care hospital

**Staffed Beds: 25 Admissions:** 335 **Census:** 24 **Outpatient Visits:** 0 **Births:** 0

*Many Facility Codes have changed. Please refer to the AHA Guide Code Chart.*        © 2013 AHA Guide

⊠ **MERCY ST. ANNE HOSPITAL (360262)**, 3404 West Sylvania Avenue, Zip 43623–4467; tel. 419/407–2663 **A**1 2 9 10 **F**3 15 18 29 30 31 34 35 36 38 40 45 46 56 57 59 64 65 68 70 74 75 78 79 81 82 84 85 86 92 97 107 108 110 111 114 116 117 118 119 122 123 129 130 132 135 146 147 **P**8 **S** Catholic Health Partners, Cincinnati, OH
Primary Contact: Bradley J. Bertke, President and Chief Executive Officer
CFO: Robert Moon, Chief Financial Officer
CMO: Herbert Stockard, M.D., Chief Medical Officer
CIO: Rebecca S. Sykes, Chief Information Officer
CHR: Gary George, Regional Vice President Human Resources
CNO: Pamela Kadlick, Vice President Nursing
Web address: www.mercyweb.org
**Control:** Church–operated, Nongovernment, not–for profit **Service:** General Medical and Surgical

**Staffed Beds:** 96 **Admissions:** 4516 **Census:** 48 **Outpatient Visits:** 240528 **Births:** 0 **Personnel:** 572

⊠ ○ **MERCY ST. VINCENT MEDICAL CENTER (360112)**, 2213 Cherry Street, Zip 43608–2691; tel. 419/251–3232, (Includes MERCY CHILDREN'S HOSPITAL, 2213 Cherry Street, tel. 419/251–8000) **A**1 2 3 5 9 10 11 12 13 **F**3 7 8 11 12 13 15 16 17 18 19 20 21 22 23 24 25 26 28 29 30 32 34 35 37 38 40 41 43 44 45 46 48 49 50 51 54 55 56 57 58 59 60 61 64 65 66 68 70 72 74 75 76 77 78 79 81 82 84 85 86 87 88 89 92 93 97 98 103 107 108 110 111 113 114 115 116 118 119 126 129 130 131 132 134 135 141 146 147 **P**8 **S** Catholic Health Partners, Cincinnati, OH
Primary Contact: Kevin S. Cook, President and Chief Executive Officer
CFO: Samantha M. Platzke, Senior Vice President Finance and Chief Financial Officer
CHR: Gary George, Regional Vice President Human Resources
Web address: www.mercyweb.org
**Control:** Church–operated, Nongovernment, not–for profit **Service:** General Medical and Surgical

**Staffed Beds:** 431 **Admissions:** 19330 **Census:** 234 **Outpatient Visits:** 387261 **Births:** 1089 **Personnel:** 2885

□ **NORTHWEST OHIO PSYCHIATRIC HOSPITAL (364014)**, 930 Detroit Avenue, Zip 43614–2701; tel. 419/381–1881 **A**1 10 **F**30 53 75 97 98 106 130 146 **S** Ohio Department of Mental Health, Columbus, OH
Primary Contact: Mychail Scheramic, M.D., Chief Executive Officer
Web address: www.mh.state.oh.us/
**Control:** State–Government, nonfederal **Service:** Psychiatric

**Staffed Beds:** 114 **Admissions:** 400 **Census:** 104 **Outpatient Visits:** 0 **Births:** 0 **Personnel:** 198

⊠ **PROMEDICA TOLEDO HOSPITAL (360068)**, 2142 North Cove Boulevard, Zip 43606–3896; tel. 419/291–4000, (Includes PROMEDICA WILDWOOD ORTHOPAEDIC AND SPINE HOSPITAL, 2901 North Reynolds Road, Zip 43615; tel. 419/578–7700; Holly L. Bristoll, President; TOLEDO CHILDREN'S HOSPITAL, 2142 North Cove Boulevard, Zip 43606), (Total facility includes 25 beds in nursing home–type unit) **A**1 3 5 9 10 13 **F**3 7 8 9 11 12 13 15 17 18 19 20 21 22 23 24 25 26 27 29 30 31 32 34 35 36 38 39 40 43 48 49 50 51 52 53 54 55 57 58 59 60 64 65 67 68 70 71 72 74 75 76 77 78 79 81 82 84 85 86 87 88 89 91 92 93 94 96 97 98 99 100 101 102 104 105 107 108 109 110 111 114 115 118 119 123 126 128 130 131 132 134 135 143 144 146 147 148 **S** ProMedica Health System, Toledo, OH
Primary Contact: Kevin C. Webb, Ph.D., President
COO: Arturo Polizzi, Chief Operating Officer
CFO: Gary Akenberger, Senior Vice President Finance
CMO: Neeraj Kanwal, M.D., Vice President Medical Affairs
CIO: David G. Selman, Chief Information Officer
CHR: Randy Schimmoeller, Vice President Human Resources
Web address: www.promedica.org
**Control:** Other not–for–profit (including NFP Corporation) **Service:** General Medical and Surgical

**Staffed Beds:** 651 **Admissions:** 30881 **Census:** 438 **Outpatient Visits:** 705948 **Births:** 3935 **Total Expense ($000):** 682918 **Payroll Expense ($000):** 220262 **Personnel:** 4288

⊠ △ **THE UNIVERSITY OF TOLEDO MEDICAL CENTER (360048)**, 3000 Arlington Avenue, Zip 43614–2595; tel. 419/383–4000 **A**1 2 3 5 7 8 9 10 **F**3 8 11 15 17 18 20 22 24 26 28 29 30 31 32 34 35 36 37 38 39 40 43 44 45 46 47 49 54 56 57 58 59 60 61 64 65 70 74 75 77 78 79 81 82 84 85 87 89 90 91 92 93 96 97 98 99 100 101 102 103 104 105 107 108 110 111 114 115 118 119 121 124 126 129 130 131 132 134 135 138 146 147 148
Primary Contact: Norma J. Tomlinson, MSN, R.N., FACHE, Associate Vice President and Interim Executive Director
CFO: Daniel Morissette, Senior Vice President Finance and Administration
CMO: Ronald McGinnis, M.D., Medical Director
CIO: Lawrence Burns, Vice President Institutional Advancement
CHR: William Logie, Vice President Human Resources
Web address: www.utoledo.edu
**Control:** State–Government, nonfederal **Service:** General Medical and Surgical

**Staffed Beds:** 244 **Admissions:** 12184 **Census:** 177 **Outpatient Visits:** 263734 **Births:** 0 **Total Expense ($000):** 245941 **Payroll Expense ($000):** 103949 **Personnel:** 2063

**TOLEDO CAMPUS** See Northcoast Behavioral Healthcare System, Northfield

**TROY—Miami County**

□ △ **UPPER VALLEY MEDICAL CENTER (360174)**, 3130 North County Road 25A, Zip 45373–1309; tel. 937/440–4000, (Includes DETTMER HOSPITAL, 3130 North Dixie Highway, Zip 45373–1039; tel. 937/440–7500), (Nonreporting) **A**1 2 5 7 9 10
Primary Contact: Thomas Parker, Chief Executive Officer
CFO: Tim Snider, Senior Vice President and Chief Financial Officer
CMO: Dan Bailey, M.D., Vice President Medical Affairs and Chief Medical Officer
CIO: William Watercutter, Director Management Information System
CHR: Tracy Moser, Director Human Resources
Web address: www.uvmc.com
**Control:** Other not–for–profit (including NFP Corporation) **Service:** General Medical and Surgical

**Staffed Beds:** 168

**UPPER SANDUSKY—Wyandot County**

★ **WYANDOT MEMORIAL HOSPITAL (361329)**, 885 North Sandusky Avenue, Zip 43351–1098; tel. 419/294–4991 **A**9 10 18 **F**3 11 13 15 17 18 28 29 31 34 35 40 45 53 57 59 64 65 74 75 76 77 78 79 81 82 85 86 87 89 92 93 97 107 108 110 111 115 117 118 119 124 129 130 132 133 135 146 148 **P**6
Primary Contact: Joseph A. D'Ettorre, Chief Executive Officer
COO: Ty Shaull, Chief Operating Officer
CFO: Alan H. Yeates, Vice President Fiscal Services
CHR: Vickie Underwood, Director Human Resources
CNO: Marty Gray, R.N., Director of Nursing
Web address: www.wyandotmemorial.org
**Control:** Hospital district or authority, Government, nonfederal **Service:** General Medical and Surgical

**Staffed Beds:** 25 **Admissions:** 936 **Census:** 11 **Outpatient Visits:** 56946 **Births:** 131 **Total Expense ($000):** 29512 **Payroll Expense ($000):** 10337 **Personnel:** 189

**URBANA—Champaign County**

★ **MERCY MEMORIAL HOSPITAL (361312)**, 904 Scioto Street, Zip 43078–2200; tel. 937/653–5231 **A**9 10 18 **F**18 28 29 30 35 40 63 70 79 81 84 85 107 108 111 133 135 146 148 **S** Catholic Health Partners, Cincinnati, OH
Primary Contact: Karen S. Gorby, R.N., MSN, FACHE, Administrator and Chief Nursing Officer
Web address: www.health–partners.org
**Control:** Other not–for–profit (including NFP Corporation) **Service:** General Medical and Surgical

**Staffed Beds:** 8 **Admissions:** 1025 **Census:** 8 **Outpatient Visits:** 42926 **Total Expense ($000):** 19927 **Payroll Expense ($000):** 7404 **Personnel:** 122

**OH**

## VAN WERT—Van Wert County

☒ **VAN WERT COUNTY HOSPITAL (360071)**, 1250 South Washington Street, Zip 45891–2599; tel. 419/238–2390 **A**1 5 9 10 **F**8 13 15 28 31 34 35 39 40 53 54 57 59 70 72 76 79 81 85 89 93 107 108 119 127 129 130 146 **P**7 8
Primary Contact: Mark J. Minick, President and Chief Executive Officer
CFO: Michael T. Holliday, Vice President Fiscal and Administrative Services
CMO: Scott Jarvis, M.D., President Medical Staff
CIO: Jerry Borton, Manager Information
CHR: Joyce Pothast, Vice President Human and Environmental Services
Web address: www.vanwerthospital.org
**Control:** Other not–for–profit (including NFP Corporation) **Service:** General Medical and Surgical

| | |
|---|---|
| **Staffed Beds:** 79 **Admissions:** 1010 **Census:** 10 **Outpatient Visits:** 66667 **Births:** 155 **Total Expense ($000):** 36345 **Payroll Expense ($000):** 11466 **Personnel:** 343 | |

## WADSWORTH—Medina County

☐ **SUMMA WADSWORTH–RITTMAN HOSPITAL (360195)**, 195 Wadsworth Road, Zip 44281–9505; tel. 330/331–1000 **A**1 5 9 10 **F**3 8 11 15 18 29 30 31 34 35 38 40 44 45 46 47 48 49 50 57 59 60 62 64 68 70 74 75 77 78 79 81 82 85 86 87 97 107 108 109 110 111 113 114 119 129 130 131 132 135 143 146 148 **P**6 8 **S** Summa Health System, Akron, OH
Primary Contact: Thomas DeBord, President
CFO: Charles Alderson, Chief Financial Officer
CMO: Jeffrey Morris, M.D., Vice President Medical Affairs
CIO: David Lynch, Regional Director Information Services
CHR: Don Argiro, Regional Director Human Resources
Web address: www.wrhhs.org
**Control:** Other not–for–profit (including NFP Corporation) **Service:** General Medical and Surgical

| | |
|---|---|
| **Staffed Beds:** 50 **Admissions:** 2424 **Census:** 26 **Outpatient Visits:** 90243 **Births:** 0 **Total Expense ($000):** 49517 **Payroll Expense ($000):** 18760 **Personnel:** 414 | |

**WADSWORTH–RITTMAN HOSPITAL** See Summa Wadsworth–Rittman Hospital

## WARREN—Trumbull County

☒ △ **HILLSIDE REHABILITATION HOSPITAL (363026)**, 8747 Squires Lane N.E., Zip 44484–1649; tel. 330/841–3700, (Nonreporting) **A**1 5 7 9 10 **S** Community Health Systems, Inc., Franklin, TN
Primary Contact: Marilyn Titus, Vice President and Chief Operating Officer
CFO: Lisa Medovich, Senior Vice President and Chief Financial Officer
CMO: Cynthia DiMauro, M.D., Medical Director
CIO: Timothy Roe, Chief Information Officer
CHR: Lisa Johnson, Vice President Human Resources
Web address: www.valleycarehealth.net
**Control:** Corporation, Investor–owned, for–profit **Service:** Rehabilitation

| | |
|---|---|
| **Staffed Beds:** 65 | |

☒ ○ **ST. JOSEPH HEALTH CENTER (360161)**, 667 Eastland Avenue S.E., Zip 44484–4531; tel. 330/841–4000 **A**1 9 10 11 12 13 **F**3 5 8 11 12 13 15 28 29 30 31 35 39 40 42 43 44 45 46 50 51 53 54 56 57 59 60 61 64 66 68 69 70 75 76 77 78 79 81 82 85 86 87 89 93 97 107 108 109 111 114 116 117 118 119 120 121 123 126 129 130 132 135 143 144 146 147 148 **P**3 **S** Catholic Health Partners, Cincinnati, OH
Primary Contact: Kathy Cook, R.N., MSN, Interim President
COO: Robert W. Shroder, President and Chief Executive Officer
CFO: Donald E. Kline, Senior Vice President Finance
CMO: Nicholas Kreatsoulas, M.D., Vice President Medical Affairs
CIO: Charles Folkwein, Vice President Ancillary Services
CHR: Molly Seals, Senior Vice President Human Resources and Learning
CNO: Kathy Cook, R.N., Chief Nursing Officer
Web address: www.hmpartners.org
**Control:** Church–operated, Nongovernment, not–for profit **Service:** General Medical and Surgical

| | |
|---|---|
| **Staffed Beds:** 141 **Admissions:** 7849 **Census:** 92 **Outpatient Visits:** 172953 **Births:** 667 **Total Expense ($000):** 126532 **Payroll Expense ($000):** 40283 **Personnel:** 713 | |

☒ **TRUMBULL MEMORIAL HOSPITAL (360055)**, 1350 East Market Street, Zip 44483–6628; tel. 330/841–9011, (Nonreporting) **A**1 2 5 9 10 **S** Community Health Systems, Inc., Franklin, TN
Primary Contact: John Walsh, Interim Chief Executive Officer
CFO: Lisa Medovich, Senior Vice President and Chief Financial Officer
CMO: Thomas L. James, M.D., Senior Vice President and Chief Medical Officer
CIO: Barry Fitts, Chief Information Officer
CHR: Laurie Barber, Director Human Resources
CNO: Joan Darr, R.N., Interim Chief Nursing Officer
Web address: www.valleycarehealth.net
**Control:** Corporation, Investor–owned, for–profit **Service:** General Medical and Surgical

| | |
|---|---|
| **Staffed Beds:** 292 | |

## WARRENSVILLE HEIGHTS—Cuyahoga County

☒ **REGENCY HOSPITAL CLEVELAND EAST (362029)**, 4200 Interchange Corporate Center, Zip 44128–5631; tel. 216/910–3800, (Includes REGENCY HOSPITAL OF AKRON, 155 Fifth Street N.E., Barberton, Zip 44203; tel. 330/615–3792; Timothy Rolsen, Chief Executive Officer; REGENCY HOSPITAL OF CLEVELAND – WEST, 6990 Engle Road, Middleburg Heights, Zip 44130–3420; tel. 440/202–4200; Barbara Wojtala, Chief Executive Officer; REGENCY HOSPITAL OF RAVENNA, 6847 North Chestnut Street, Ravenna, Zip 44266; tel. 330/296–2350; Timothy Rolsen, Chief Executive Officer), (Nonreporting) **A**1 10 **S** Select Medical Corporation, Mechanicsburg, PA
Primary Contact: Scott Williams, Chief Executive Officer
Web address: www.regencyhospital.com/
**Control:** Corporation, Investor–owned, for–profit **Service:** Long–Term Acute Care hospital

| | |
|---|---|
| **Staffed Beds:** 44 | |

☒ ○ **SOUTH POINTE HOSPITAL (360144)**, 20000 Harvard Road, Zip 44122–6805; tel. 216/491–6000 **A**1 2 9 10 11 12 13 **F**11 15 18 20 26 28 29 30 31 34 35 36 38 39 40 42 44 50 51 54 57 58 59 60 61 64 65 66 68 69 70 75 77 78 79 81 82 84 85 86 87 92 93 97 100 102 107 108 110 111 115 117 119 130 131 132 135 143 144 146 148 **S** Cleveland Clinic Health System, Cleveland, OH
Primary Contact: Brian J. Harte, M.D., President
COO: Andrea Jacobs, Chief Operating Officer
CFO: Lindsay Bird, Director Finance
CMO: Arun Gupta, M.D., Vice President Medical Affairs
CIO: Ralph A. Cagna, Director Information Technology
CHR: Doris A. Zajec, Director Human Resources
Web address: www.southpointehospital.org
**Control:** Other not–for–profit (including NFP Corporation) **Service:** General Medical and Surgical

| | |
|---|---|
| **Staffed Beds:** 173 **Admissions:** 7452 **Census:** 100 **Outpatient Visits:** 122420 **Births:** 0 **Total Expense ($000):** 131950 **Payroll Expense ($000):** 52153 **Personnel:** 869 | |

## WASHINGTON COURT HOUSE—Fayette County

☒ **FAYETTE COUNTY MEMORIAL HOSPITAL (361331)**, 1430 Columbus Avenue, Zip 43160–1791; tel. 740/335–1210 **A**1 9 10 18 **F**3 7 11 15 18 29 30 34 35 36 40 45 57 59 64 68 70 74 75 77 79 81 82 85 86 87 89 93 97 102 107 110 114 127 129 130 131 132 133 135 144 146 148 **P**4 **S** Trinity Health, Livonia, MI
Primary Contact: Lyndon J. Christman, President and Chief Executive Officer
COO: Lenora Fitton, D.O., Chief of Staff
CFO: Thomas McDermott, Vice President Finance
CMO: John DesMarais, M.D., Chief Medical Officer
CIO: Bruce Denen, Manager Data Processing
CHR: Earlene Christensen, Director Human Resources
CNO: Beverly Hughes, R.N., Vice President Nursing
Web address: www.fcmh.org
**Control:** County–Government, nonfederal **Service:** General Medical and Surgical

| | |
|---|---|
| **Staffed Beds:** 25 **Admissions:** 1080 **Census:** 14 **Outpatient Visits:** 78497 **Births:** 0 **Total Expense ($000):** 43442 **Payroll Expense ($000):** 20882 **Personnel:** 366 | |

## WAUSEON—Fulton County

☒ **FULTON COUNTY HEALTH CENTER (361333)**, 725 South Shoop Avenue, Zip 43567–1701; tel. 419/335–2015, (Total facility includes 71 beds in nursing home–type unit) **A**1 2 5 9 10 18 **F**3 8 11 13 15 18 20 26 28 29 31 34 40 53 57 59 67 69 70 75 76 77 78 79 81 87 89 93 98 101 102 103 104 105 107 108 111 115 118 119 125 128 129 130 131 132 135 146 148
Primary Contact: Patti Finn, Chief Executive Officer
COO: Patti Finn, Chief Executive Officer
CFO: Darrell Topmiller, Director Finance
CIO: Larry Hefflinger, Director Information Systems
CHR: Kristy Snyder, Director Human Resources
Web address: www.fultoncountyhealthcenter.org
**Control:** Other not–for–profit (including NFP Corporation) **Service:** General Medical and Surgical

| | |
|---|---|
| **Staffed Beds:** 106 **Admissions:** 1746 **Census:** 82 **Outpatient Visits:** 178589 **Births:** 272 **Total Expense ($000):** 59053 **Payroll Expense ($000):** 23530 **Personnel:** 664 | |

## WAVERLY—Pike County

**ADENA PIKE MEDICAL CENTER (361334)**, (Formerly Pike Community Hospital), 100 Dawn Lane, Zip 45690–9138; tel. 740/947–2186, (Nonreporting) **A**9 10 18 **S** Adena Health System, Chillicothe, OH
Primary Contact: Craig E. Solle, Administrator
COO: Tina Perko, Vice President Operations
CFO: Sharon Novak, CPA, Vice President Finance
CHR: Berna Brock, Vice President Human Resources
Web address: www.pikecommunityhospital.org
**Control:** Other not–for–profit (including NFP Corporation) **Service:** General Medical and Surgical

| | |
|---|---|
| **Staffed Beds:** 25 | |

*Many Facility Codes have changed. Please refer to the AHA Guide Code Chart.* © 2013 AHA Guide

## WEST CHESTER—Butler County

☒ **UNIVERSITY POINTE SURGICAL HOSPITAL (360271)**, (Formerly UC Health Surgical Hospital), 7750 University Court, Zip 45069; tel. 513/475–8300 **A**1 10 **F**3 15 64 79 81 82 85 86 107 110 111 115 119 129 147 **S** UC Health, Cincinnati, OH
Primary Contact: Lesley Gilbertson, M.D., Executive and Medical Director
COO: Sara Deem, Director Operations
CFO: Tom Ducro, Chief Financial Officer
CMO: Lesley Gilbertson, M.D., Executive and Medical Director
CIO: Steve Knost, Manager Facilities
CHR: Penny Elder, Manager Human Resources
CNO: Kathy Lipps, Clinical Director
Web address: www.surgicalhospital.uchealth.com
**Control:** Other not–for–profit (including NFP Corporation) **Service:** General Medical and Surgical

**Staffed Beds:** 8 **Admissions:** 44 **Census:** 1 **Outpatient Visits:** 22653 **Births:** 0 **Total Expense ($000):** 11364 **Payroll Expense ($000):** 3658 **Personnel:** 67

☒ **WEST CHESTER HOSPITAL (360354)**, 7700 University Drive, Zip 45069–2505; tel. 513/298–3000 **A**1 10 **F**3 9 12 15 18 20 22 26 28 29 30 31 34 35 37 40 44 45 46 47 48 49 50 51 57 58 59 60 63 64 68 70 74 75 77 78 79 81 82 84 85 86 87 92 107 108 110 111 114 115 116 117 119 126 130 131 132 135 141 145 146 147 148 **P**6 **S** UC Health, Cincinnati, OH
Primary Contact: Kevin Joseph, M.D., Chief Executive Officer
COO: Tom G. Daskalakis, Chief Operating Officer
Web address: www.westchesterhospital.uchealth.com
**Control:** Other not–for–profit (including NFP Corporation) **Service:** General Medical and Surgical

**Staffed Beds:** 126 **Admissions:** 7242 **Census:** 78 **Outpatient Visits:** 75011 **Births:** 1 **Total Expense ($000):** 115044 **Payroll Expense ($000):** 36081 **Personnel:** 658

## WESTERVILLE—Franklin County

☒ **MOUNT CARMEL ST. ANN'S (360012)**, 500 South Cleveland Avenue, Zip 43081–8998; tel. 614/898–4000 **A**1 3 5 9 10 **F**3 11 13 15 18 20 22 26 29 30 31 34 35 37 40 44 45 47 48 49 50 51 54 55 57 58 59 61 63 64 65 66 68 70 74 75 76 78 79 81 83 84 85 86 87 93 94 97 100 101 102 107 108 109 110 111 114 115 118 119 120 121 123 124 126 130 131 132 145 146 147 148 **P**6 8 **S** Trinity Health, Livonia, MI
Primary Contact: Janet Meeks, Chief Operating Officer
Web address: www.mountcarmelhealth.com
**Control:** Church–operated, Nongovernment, not–for profit **Service:** General Medical and Surgical

**Staffed Beds:** 252 **Admissions:** 19187 **Census:** 181 **Outpatient Visits:** 205557 **Births:** 4555 **Total Expense ($000):** 242817 **Payroll Expense ($000):** 86174 **Personnel:** 1654

## WESTLAKE—Cuyahoga County

☐ **ST. JOHN MEDICAL CENTER (360123)**, 29000 Center Ridge Road, Zip 44145–5293; tel. 440/835–8000 **A**1 2 9 10 12 13 **F**3 8 13 15 17 18 20 22 24 26 28 29 30 31 34 35 39 40 43 44 45 47 49 50 51 56 57 59 64 65 68 70 71 74 75 76 78 79 80 81 82 84 85 86 87 89 92 93 100 107 108 110 111 114 115 119 130 132 143 144 146 147 **P**4 **S** Sisters of Charity Health System, Cleveland, OH
Primary Contact: William A. Young, Jr., President and Chief Executive Officer
CFO: Allen R. Tracy, Senior Vice President and Chief Financial Officer
CMO: Michael Dobrovich, M.D., Chief Medical Officer
CIO: James H. Carroll, Chief Information Officer
CHR: Gary Lazroff, Vice President Human Resources
Web address: www.sjws.net
**Control:** Other not–for–profit (including NFP Corporation) **Service:** General Medical and Surgical

**Staffed Beds:** 191 **Admissions:** 11273 **Census:** 105 **Outpatient Visits:** 139484 **Births:** 749 **Total Expense ($000):** 140121 **Payroll Expense ($000):** 55016 **Personnel:** 1058

**ST. JOHN WEST SHORE HOSPITAL** See St. John Medical Center

## WILLARD—Huron County

☒ **MERCY WILLARD HOSPITAL (361310)**, 1100 Neal Zick Road, Zip 44890–9287; tel. 419/964–5000 **A**1 5 9 10 18 **F**3 5 15 18 28 29 30 34 35 40 46 57 59 70 74 75 77 79 81 84 85 87 89 93 107 111 114 117 119 129 130 131 132 133 135 143 145 146 147 **S** Catholic Health Partners, Cincinnati, OH
Primary Contact: B. Lynn Detterman, President and Chief Executive Officer
CFO: Cindy Dennison, Senior Director Rural Division
CMO: David A. Jump, D.O., Chief of Staff
CHR: Diana Olson, Chief Human Resources Officer
CNO: Pamela Napier, R.N., Chief Nursing Officer
Web address: www.mercyweb.org
**Control:** Church–operated, Nongovernment, not–for profit **Service:** General Medical and Surgical

**Staffed Beds:** 20 **Admissions:** 607 **Census:** 9 **Outpatient Visits:** 37892 **Births:** 0 **Total Expense ($000):** 25655 **Payroll Expense ($000):** 8646 **Personnel:** 166

## WILLOUGHBY—Lake County

☐ **WINDSOR–LAURELWOOD CENTER FOR BEHAVIORAL MEDICINE (364029)**, 35900 Euclid Avenue, Zip 44094–4648; tel. 440/953–3000, (Nonreporting) **A**1 9 10 **S** Universal Health Services, Inc., King of Prussia, PA
Primary Contact: Jennifer Wiggins, Interim Chief Executive Officer
CFO: Robin Stough, Chief Financial Officer
CMO: Leonard Barley, M.D., Chief Medical Officer
CIO: Andrew Johnson, Information Technology and Purchasing Officer
CHR: Greg Kennedy, Manager Human Resources
Web address: www.windsorlaurelwood.com
**Control:** Individual, Investor–owned, for–profit **Service:** Psychiatric

**Staffed Beds:** 152

## WILMINGTON—Clinton County

☐ △ **CLINTON MEMORIAL HOSPITAL (360175)**, 610 West Main Street, Zip 45177–2125; tel. 937/382–6611 **A**1 2 3 5 7 9 10 **F**3 11 13 15 18 29 30 31 34 35 36 40 45 50 51 56 59 62 64 70 73 74 75 76 79 81 82 85 86 87 89 90 93 96 97 107 108 111 114 115 119 120 121 124 129 130 131 132 146 148 **S** RegionalCare Hospital Partners, Brentwood, TN
Primary Contact: Mark J. Dooley, Chief Executive Officer
COO: Bradley Mabry, Chief Operating Officer
CHR: Janet M. Blair, Director Human Resources
CNO: Paul C. Poparad, R.N., Chief Nursing Officer
Web address: www.cmhregional.com
**Control:** Corporation, Investor–owned, for–profit **Service:** General Medical and Surgical

**Staffed Beds:** 102 **Admissions:** 4068 **Census:** 34 **Outpatient Visits:** 118904 **Births:** 622 **Total Expense ($000):** 80013 **Payroll Expense ($000):** 27645 **Personnel:** 616

## WOOSTER—Wayne County

☐ △ **WOOSTER COMMUNITY HOSPITAL (360036)**, 1761 Beall Avenue, Zip 44691–2342; tel. 330/263–8100, (Nonreporting) **A**1 2 5 7 9 10 19 **S** QHR, Brentwood, TN
Primary Contact: William E. Sheron, Chief Executive Officer
Web address: www.woosterhospital.org
**Control:** City–Government, nonfederal **Service:** General Medical and Surgical

**Staffed Beds:** 150

## WRIGHT–PATTERSON AFB—Greene County

☒ **WRIGHT PATTERSON MEDICAL CENTER**, 4881 Sugar Maple Drive, Zip 45433–5529; tel. 937/257–9144, (Nonreporting) **A**1 2 3 5 **S** Department of the Air Force, Washington, DC
Primary Contact: Brent Erickson, Administrator
COO: Brent Erickson, Administrator
CFO: Captain Lindsey Wilhardt, Resource Manager Flight Commander
CMO: Colonel William Venanzi, M.D., Chief Medical Officer
CIO: Matt Osborne, Flight Chief Medical Information Systems
CHR: Sharon Stauffer, Chief Civilian Personnel
CNO: Penny Gorsuch, Chief Nursing Officer
Web address: www.wpafb.af.mil/units/wpmc/
**Control:** Air Force, Government, federal **Service:** General Medical and Surgical

**Staffed Beds:** 52

---

**Hospital, Medicare Provider Number, Address, Telephone, Approval, Facility, and Physician Codes, Health Care System**

★ American Hospital Association (AHA) membership
☐ The Joint Commission accreditation ◇ DNV Healthcare Inc. accreditation
○ Healthcare Facilities Accreditation Program
△ Commission on Accreditation of Rehabilitation Facilities (CARF) accreditation

**XENIA—Greene County**

☒ ○ △ **GREENE MEMORIAL HOSPITAL (360026)**, 1141 North Monroe Drive, Zip 45385–1600; tel. 937/352–2000 **A**1 3 5 7 9 10 11 **F**3 11 15 18 28 29 30 31 34 35 38 40 42 43 44 45 46 48 50 53 54 56 57 59 64 68 69 70 74 75 77 78 79 81 82 85 86 87 93 96 102 107 108 110 111 119 129 130 135 144 146 148 **P**3 **S** Kettering Health Network, Dayton, OH
Primary Contact: Terry M. Burns, President
COO: Ron D. Connovich, Vice President
CFO: Steven Chavez, Chief Financial Officer
CMO: Martha Johnston, M.D., Chief Medical Officer
CIO: Jon Russell, Chief Information Officer
CHR: Amanda Koch, Director Human Resources
CNO: Belinda Mallett, R.N., Vice President Patient Care and Clinical Services
Web address: www.greenehealth.org
**Control:** Church–operated, Nongovernment, not–for profit **Service:** General Medical and Surgical

**Staffed Beds:** 58 **Admissions:** 2781 **Census:** 31 **Outpatient Visits:** 90360 **Births:** 0 **Total Expense ($000):** 64742 **Payroll Expense ($000):** 24649 **Personnel:** 374

**YOUNGSTOWN—Trumbull County**

☐ **BELMONT PINES HOSPITAL (364038)**, 615 Churchill–Hubbard Road, Zip 44505–1379; tel. 330/759–2700, (Nonreporting) **A**1 9 10 **S** Universal Health Services, Inc., King of Prussia, PA
Primary Contact: George H. Perry, Ph.D., Chief Executive Officer
CFO: Robin Stough, Chief Financial Officer
CMO: Phillip Maiden, M.D., Medical Director
Web address: www.belmontpines.com
**Control:** Corporation, Investor–owned, for–profit **Service:** Psychiatric

**Staffed Beds:** 46

☒ **NORTHSIDE MEDICAL CENTER (360141)**, 500 Gypsy Lane, Zip 44504–1315; tel. 330/884–1000, (Includes NORTHSIDE MEDICAL CENTER, 500 Gypsy Lane, Zip 44501–0240; tel. 330/747–1444), (Nonreporting) **A**1 2 3 5 8 9 10 **S** Community Health Systems, Inc., Franklin, TN
Primary Contact: Kirk M. Ray, Chief Executive Officer
COO: Michael Seelman, Chief Operating Officer
CFO: Lisa Medovich, Senior Vice President and Chief Financial Officer
CMO: Jay Osborne, M.D., Senior Vice President Medical Affairs
CHR: Lavern H. Carrera, Senior Vice President Human Resources
Web address: www.northsidemedicalcenter.net
**Control:** Corporation, Investor–owned, for–profit **Service:** General Medical and Surgical

**Staffed Beds:** 373

**NORTHSIDE MEDICAL CENTER** See Northside Medical Center

☒ **SELECT SPECIALTY HOSPITAL–YOUNGSTOWN (362024)**, 1044 Belmont Avenue, Zip 44504–1006; tel. 330/480–2349, (Includes SELECT SPECIALTY HOSPITAL–YOUNGSTOWN, BOARDMAN CAMPUS, 8401 Market Street, 7th Floor, Bordman, Zip 44512–6725; Mailing Address: Youngstown, tel. 330/729–1700), (Nonreporting) **A**1 10 **S** Select Medical Corporation, Mechanicsburg, PA
Primary Contact: Sharon Noro, Chief Executive Officer
Web address: www.selectspecialtyhospitals.com/company/locations/youngstown.aspx
**Control:** Corporation, Investor–owned, for–profit **Service:** Long–Term Acute Care hospital

**Staffed Beds:** 51

☒ △ **ST. ELIZABETH HEALTH CENTER (360064)**, 1044 Belmont Avenue, Zip 44504–1096, Mailing Address: P.O. Box 1790, Zip 44501–1790; tel. 330/746–7211 **A**1 3 5 7 9 10 **F**3 7 8 11 12 13 14 15 17 18 20 22 24 26 28 29 30 31 32 34 35 39 40 42 43 44 45 46 49 50 51 53 54 56 57 58 59 60 61 64 66 67 68 69 70 71 74 75 76 77 78 79 81 82 83 84 85 86 87 89 90 93 96 97 98 100 101 102 103 104 106 107 108 109 110 111 114 115 116 117 118 119 120 121 123 124 126 129 130 131 132 135 143 146 147 148 **P**3 **S** Catholic Health Partners, Cincinnati, OH
Primary Contact: Robert W. Shroder, President and Chief Executive Officer
COO: Donald E. Koenig, Jr., Executive Vice President and Chief Operating Officer
CFO: Donald E. Kline, Senior Vice President Finance
CMO: Nicholas Kreatsoulas, M.D., Senior Vice President and Chief Medical Officer
CIO: Charles Folkwein, Senior Vice President Ancillary Services and Information Technology
CHR: Molly Seals, Senior Vice President Human Resources and Learning
Web address: www.hmpartners.org
**Control:** Church–operated, Nongovernment, not–for profit **Service:** General Medical and Surgical

**Staffed Beds:** 429 **Admissions:** 18270 **Census:** 245 **Outpatient Visits:** 285436 **Births:** 1796 **Total Expense ($000):** 287645 **Payroll Expense ($000):** 92036 **Personnel:** 2089

☐ **SURGICAL HOSPITAL AT SOUTHWOODS (360352)**, 7630 Southern Boulevard, Zip 44512–5633; tel. 330/729–8000, (Nonreporting) **A**1 9 10
Primary Contact: Ed Muransky, Owner
Web address: www.surgeryatsouthwoods.com/
**Control:** Individual, Investor–owned, for–profit **Service:** Surgical

**Staffed Beds:** 12

**ZANESVILLE—Muskingum County**

★ ○ △ **GENESIS HEALTHCARE SYSTEM (360039)**, 2951 Maple Avenue, Zip 43701–1406; tel. 740/454–5000, (Includes BETHESDA HOSPITAL, 2951 Maple Avenue, Zip 43701–1465; tel. 614/454–5000; GOOD SAMARITAN MEDICAL AND REHABILITATION CENTER, 800 Forest Avenue, Zip 43701–2881; tel. 614/454–5000) **A**2 5 7 9 10 11 19 **F**3 5 8 11 13 15 17 18 20 22 24 26 28 29 30 31 32 34 35 36 40 43 44 45 46 47 48 50 51 54 58 59 60 63 64 65 68 70 73 74 75 76 77 78 79 80 81 82 83 84 85 86 87 89 90 91 92 93 94 96 98 99 100 101 102 103 104 105 107 108 110 111 114 115 116 117 118 119 120 121 123 124 126 129 130 131 132 135 144 146 147 148 **P**6 8 **S** Franciscan Sisters of Christian Charity Sponsored Ministries, Inc., Manitowoc, WI
Primary Contact: Matthew J. Perry, President and Chief Executive Officer
CFO: Paul Masterson, Chief Financial Officer
CIO: Ed Romito, Director Information Systems
Web address: www.genesishcs.org
**Control:** Other not–for–profit (including NFP Corporation) **Service:** General Medical and Surgical

**Staffed Beds:** 353 **Admissions:** 16584 **Census:** 176 **Outpatient Visits:** 355868 **Births:** 1353 **Total Expense ($000):** 299945 **Payroll Expense ($000):** 116923 **Personnel:** 2777

☒ **SELECT SPECIALTY HOSPITAL–ZANESVILLE (362031)**, 800 Forest Avenue, 6th Floor, Zip 43701–2882; tel. 740/588–7888, (Nonreporting) **A**1 10 **S** Select Medical Corporation, Mechanicsburg, PA
Primary Contact: Linda Supplee, Chief Executive Officer
CMO: Armand Bermudez, M.D., Medical Director
CHR: Jacqueline Nezbeth, Human Resources Officer
CNO: Julie Ross, R.N., Chief Nursing Officer
Web address: www.selectspecialtyhospitals.com/company/locations/zanesville.aspx
**Control:** Corporation, Investor–owned, for–profit **Service:** Long–Term Acute Care hospital

**Staffed Beds:** 35

*Many Facility Codes have changed. Please refer to the AHA Guide Code Chart.* © 2013 AHA Guide

# OKLAHOMA

## ADA—Pontotoc County

✠ **CHICKASAW NATION MEDICAL CENTER (370180)**, 1921 Stonecipher Drive, Zip 74820–3439; tel. 580/436–3980 **A**1 10 **F**3 5 7 8 13 15 18 29 30 34 38 39 40 43 45 50 53 54 57 58 59 60 61 64 65 66 68 69 70 75 76 79 81 82 85 86 87 89 91 92 93 97 99 100 104 107 110 111 114 119 127 130 132 135 143 144 146 147 148
Primary Contact: Judy Goforth Parker, Ph.D., Administrator
CFO: Marty Wafford, Chief Financial Officer
CMO: Richard McClain, M.D., Chief Medical Officer
CIO: Carol McCurdy, Chief Information Officer
CHR: Jalinda Kelley, Director
CNO: Heather Summers, Director
Web address: www.chickasaw.net
**Control:** PHS, Indian Service, Government, federal **Service:** General Medical and Surgical

**Staffed Beds:** 72 **Admissions:** 2732 **Census:** 25 **Outpatient Visits:** 481401 **Births:** 660 **Total Expense ($000):** 130301 **Payroll Expense ($000):** 54024 **Personnel:** 449

☐ **ROLLING HILLS HOSPITAL (374016)**, 1000 Rolling Hills Lane, Zip 74820–9415; tel. 580/436–3600, (Nonreporting) **A**1 9 10 **S** Acadia Healthcare Company, Inc., Franklin, TN
Primary Contact: Selena Stockley, Chief Executive Officer
CMO: Robert Morton, M.D., Medical Director
CIO: Sherry Barnes, Director Health Information and Quality Management
CHR: Timothy Blackwell, Manager Human Resources
Web address: www.rollinghillshospital.com
**Control:** Corporation, Investor–owned, for–profit **Service:** Psychiatric

**Staffed Beds:** 44

✠ △ **VALLEY VIEW REGIONAL HOSPITAL (370020)**, 430 North Monta Vista, Zip 74820–4610; tel. 580/332–2323, (Nonreporting) **A**1 2 7 9 10 **S** Mercy Health, Chesterfield, MO
Primary Contact: W. Kent Rogers, Chief Executive Officer
CFO: Mary Krause, Vice President Finance
CMO: Donald Davies, M.D., Chief of Staff
CHR: Katrina Simpson, Director Human Resources
Web address: www.valleyviewregional.com
**Control:** Other not–for–profit (including NFP Corporation) **Service:** General Medical and Surgical

**Staffed Beds:** 131

## ALTUS—Jackson County

✠ **JACKSON COUNTY MEMORIAL HOSPITAL (370022)**, 1200 East Pecan Street, Zip 73521–6192, Mailing Address: P.O. Box 8190, Zip 73522–8190; tel. 580/379–5000 **A**1 3 5 9 10 **F**3 10 11 13 15 29 30 34 35 40 43 45 49 56 57 59 62 63 64 65 68 70 75 76 77 79 81 85 86 87 93 100 101 103 104 107 110 111 114 119 129 130 132 133 135 145 146 147 148 **P**6
Primary Contact: William G. Wilson, President and Chief Executive Officer
COO: Jim King, Executive Vice President and Chief Operating Officer
CFO: Nancy Davidson, Senior Vice President and Chief Financial Officer
CMO: Melinda Powers, D.O., Chief of Staff
CIO: Dena Daniel, Director Information Systems
CHR: Richard Pope, Vice President Human Resources
CNO: Kay Bolding, R.N., Vice President Patient Care Services and Chief Nursing Officer
Web address: www.jcmh.com
**Control:** Hospital district or authority, Government, nonfederal **Service:** General Medical and Surgical

**Staffed Beds:** 69 **Admissions:** 3551 **Census:** 35 **Outpatient Visits:** 159153 **Births:** 497 **Total Expense ($000):** 68638 **Payroll Expense ($000):** 33264 **Personnel:** 674

## ALVA—Woods County

**SHARE MEDICAL CENTER (370080)**, 800 Share Drive, Zip 73717–3618, Mailing Address: P.O. Box 727, Zip 73717–0727; tel. 580/327–2800, (Total facility includes 65 beds in nursing home–type unit) **A**9 10 20 **F**1 3 15 29 30 34 40 45 57 59 62 63 64 67 69 81 85 87 93 97 100 102 104 107 110 119 129 130 133 146 148
Primary Contact: Kandice K. Allen, R.N., Interim Chief Executive Officer
CFO: Albert Wiss, Chief Financial Officer
CMO: Kirt Bierig, D.O., Chief of Staff
CHR: Kristi Moorman, Supervisor Human Resources
Web address: www.smcok.com
**Control:** Hospital district or authority, Government, nonfederal **Service:** General Medical and Surgical

**Staffed Beds:** 90 **Admissions:** 335 **Census:** 54 **Outpatient Visits:** 18913 **Births:** 0 **Total Expense ($000):** 10967 **Payroll Expense ($000):** 5011 **Personnel:** 168

## ANADARKO—Caddo County

**PHYSICIANS' HOSPITAL IN ANADARKO (371314)**, 1002 Central Boulevard East, Zip 73005–4496; tel. 405/247–2551, (Nonreporting) **A**9 10 18 **S** Southern Plains Medical Group, Oklahoma City, OK
Primary Contact: James L. Clough, Chief Executive Officer
Web address: www.anadarkohospital.com
**Control:** Partnership, Investor–owned, for–profit **Service:** General Medical and Surgical

**Staffed Beds:** 25

## ANTLERS—Pushmataha County

**PUSHMATAHA HOSPITAL & HOME HEALTH (370083)**, 510 East Main Street, Zip 74523–3262, Mailing Address: P.O. Box 518, Zip 74523–0518; tel. 580/298–3341, (Nonreporting) **A**9 10
Primary Contact: Steve Burrage, Interim Chief Executive Officer
CFO: Stephen Poe, Chief Financial Officer
CMO: G. Wayne Flatt, D.O., Chief Medical Director
CHR: Pat McCarty, Director Human Resources
Web address: www.pushhospital.com
**Control:** State–Government, nonfederal **Service:** General Medical and Surgical

**Staffed Beds:** 25

## ARDMORE—Carter County

✠ **MERCY HOSPITAL ARDMORE (370047)**, 1011 14th Avenue N.W., Zip 73401–1828; tel. 580/223–5400 **A**1 9 10 **F**3 8 11 13 15 18 20 22 28 29 30 31 34 40 41 43 45 57 59 62 70 74 76 78 79 81 82 83 84 85 87 89 90 93 107 108 110 111 114 117 118 119 120 121 123 129 130 146 148 **P**6 **S** Mercy Health, Chesterfield, MO
Primary Contact: Daryle Voss, FACHE, President
CFO: Karen Hendren, Vice President of Finance
CMO: Pam Kimbrough, M.D., Vice President Medical Affairs
CHR: Melinda Sharum, Director of Human Resources
CNO: Rhonda Jean Hanan, Vice President of Patient Care
Web address: www.mercyok.net
**Control:** Church–operated, Nongovernment, not–for profit **Service:** General Medical and Surgical

**Staffed Beds:** 190 **Admissions:** 8717 **Census:** 101 **Outpatient Visits:** 147815 **Births:** 896 **Total Expense ($000):** 118484 **Payroll Expense ($000):** 38684 **Personnel:** 776

---

**Hospital, Medicare Provider Number, Address, Telephone, Approval, Facility, and Physician Codes, Health Care System**

★ American Hospital Association (AHA) membership
☐ The Joint Commission accreditation    ◇ DNV Healthcare Inc. accreditation
○ Healthcare Facilities Accreditation Program
△ Commission on Accreditation of Rehabilitation Facilities (CARF) accreditation

**OK**

## ATOKA—Atoka County

★ **ATOKA COUNTY MEDICAL CENTER (371300)**, 1501 South Virginia Avenue, Zip 74525–3233; tel. 580/889–3333 **A**9 10 18 **F**3 34 40 45 53 57 59 64 81 107 114 119 133 146
Primary Contact: Paul Reano, Chief Executive Officer
CFO: Jamie McGaugh, Controller
CMO: Lance Yarbrough, M.D., Chief of Medical Staff
CIO: Chad Henderson, Director Information Systems
CHR: Paula Schalski, Director Human Resources
CNO: Lezley Davidson, Chief Nursing Officer
Web address: www.atokamedicalcenter.org
**Control:** Hospital district or authority, Government, nonfederal **Service:** General Medical and Surgical

> **Staffed Beds:** 25 **Admissions:** 416 **Census:** 6 **Outpatient Visits:** 8437 **Births:** 0 **Total Expense ($000):** 10651 **Payroll Expense ($000):** 5362 **Personnel:** 70

## BARTLESVILLE—Washington County

★ ◇ **JANE PHILLIPS MEDICAL CENTER (370018)**, 3500 East Frank Phillips Boulevard, Zip 74006–2411; tel. 918/333–7200 **A**3 5 9 10 19 21 **F**3 11 13 15 17 18 20 22 24 28 29 30 31 34 35 40 43 46 49 50 51 53 57 58 59 60 61 62 64 68 74 75 76 77 78 79 81 82 84 85 86 87 90 92 93 96 98 102 103 107 111 114 115 116 117 118 119 121 123 127 129 130 131 135 143 145 146 147 148 **P**4 **S** Ascension Health, Saint Louis, MO
Primary Contact: David R. Stire, President and Chief Executive Officer
CFO: Mike Moore, Chief Financial Officer
CIO: Rob Poole, Director
CHR: Jennifer Workman, Director Human Resources
Web address: www.jpmc.org
**Control:** Church–operated, Nongovernment, not–for profit **Service:** General Medical and Surgical

> **Staffed Beds:** 140 **Admissions:** 5954 **Census:** 61 **Outpatient Visits:** 83901 **Births:** 714 **Total Expense ($000):** 101391 **Payroll Expense ($000):** 38466 **Personnel:** 800

## BEAVER—Beaver County

**BEAVER COUNTY MEMORIAL HOSPITAL (371322)**, 212 East Eighth Street, Zip 73932, Mailing Address: P.O. Box 640, Zip 73932–0640; tel. 580/625–4551 **A**9 10 18 **F**7 40 59 127 128 133 **P**6
Primary Contact: Alissa Schlessman, Administrator
Web address: www.beavercountyhospitalauthority.org
**Control:** Hospital district or authority, Government, nonfederal **Service:** General Medical and Surgical

> **Staffed Beds:** 24 **Admissions:** 48 **Census:** 1 **Outpatient Visits:** 4498 **Births:** 0 **Total Expense ($000):** 5184 **Payroll Expense ($000):** 1757 **Personnel:** 54

## BETHANY—Oklahoma County

△ **THE CHILDREN'S CENTER (373302)**, 6800 N.W. 39th Expressway, Zip 73008–2513; tel. 405/789–6711 **A**7 9 10 **F**1 29 39 53 59 75 79 90 91 93 107 130 146 148 **P**6
Primary Contact: Albert Gray, Chief Executive Officer
Web address: www.thechildrens-center.org
**Control:** Other not–for–profit (including NFP Corporation) **Service:** Children's general

> **Staffed Beds:** 120 **Admissions:** 206 **Census:** 105 **Outpatient Visits:** 10100 **Total Expense ($000):** 24797 **Payroll Expense ($000):** 15811 **Personnel:** 416

## BLACKWELL—Kay County

⊞ **INTEGRIS BLACKWELL REGIONAL HOSPITAL (370030)**, (Formerly Blackwell Regional Hospital), 710 South 13th Street, Zip 74631–3700; tel. 580/363–2311, (Data for 275 days) **A**1 9 10 **F**3 15 29 30 34 40 57 59 62 64 65 79 81 107 108 111 119 128 129 130 133 146 **P**5 6 **S** Health Management Associates, Naples, FL
Primary Contact: Julie M. McCormack, Administrator
CFO: Sheryl Schmidtberger, Chief Financial Officer
CMO: Samuel Hague, M.D., Chief of Staff
CHR: Karen Ware, Director Human Resources
Web address: www.integris-health.com
**Control:** Corporation, Investor–owned, for–profit **Service:** General Medical and Surgical

> **Staffed Beds:** 39 **Admissions:** 813 **Census:** 10 **Outpatient Visits:** 14185 **Births:** 0 **Personnel:** 117

## BOISE CITY—Cimarron County

**CIMARRON MEMORIAL HOSPITAL (371307)**, 100 South Ellis Street, Zip 73933; tel. 580/544–2501, (Nonreporting) **A**9 10 18
Primary Contact: Darin A. Janssen, Chief Executive Officer
Web address: www.cimarronmemorialhospital.org
**Control:** County–Government, nonfederal **Service:** General Medical and Surgical

> **Staffed Beds:** 25

## BRISTOW—Creek County

**BRISTOW MEDICAL CENTER (370041)**, 700 West 7th Avenue, Suite 6, Zip 74010–2302; tel. 918/367–2215 **A**9 10 **F**3 8 18 29 34 35 40 41 43 45 56 64 65 66 75 77 79 81 82 89 93 97 107 111 114 119 128 129 133 144 **P**6
Primary Contact: Jan Winter, Chief Executive Officer
CFO: Robin Van Vickle, Chief Financial Officer
Web address: www.bristowmedcenter.com
**Control:** Hospital district or authority, Government, nonfederal **Service:** General Medical and Surgical

> **Staffed Beds:** 30 **Admissions:** 326 **Census:** 3 **Births:** 0

## BROKEN ARROW—Tulsa County

★ ◇ **ST. JOHN BROKEN ARROW (370235)**, 1000 West Boise Circle, Zip 74012–4900; tel. 918/994–8100 **A**9 10 21 **F**3 8 11 14 15 18 29 30 34 35 37 40 45 50 57 59 64 68 74 79 81 84 85 87 89 93 94 107 108 110 111 114 115 119 130 132 135 146 **P**1 5 **S** Ascension Health, Saint Louis, MO
Primary Contact: David L. Phillips, Chief Executive Officer
CFO: Lex S. Anderson, Chief Financial Officer
CMO: Todd Hoffman, M.D., Medical Director
CNO: Martha Mars, R.N., Director of Nursing
Web address: www.stjohnbrokenarrow.com
**Control:** Church–operated, Nongovernment, not–for profit **Service:** General Medical and Surgical

> **Staffed Beds:** 44 **Admissions:** 2632 **Census:** 13 **Outpatient Visits:** 54709 **Births:** 0 **Total Expense ($000):** 57222 **Payroll Expense ($000):** 11610 **Personnel:** 241

## BUFFALO—Harper County

★ **HARPER COUNTY COMMUNITY HOSPITAL (371324)**, Highway 64 North, Zip 73834, Mailing Address: P.O. Box 60, Zip 73834–0060; tel. 580/735–2555 **A**9 10 18 **F**40 68 69 75 81 87 89 93 107 128 133 135 148 **P**6
Primary Contact: Georganna Buss, Chief Executive Officer
CFO: Lisa Oakley, Chief Financial Officer
Web address: www.hcchospital.com/
**Control:** County–Government, nonfederal **Service:** General Medical and Surgical

> **Staffed Beds:** 16 **Admissions:** 188 **Census:** 1 **Births:** 0

## CARNEGIE—Caddo County

★ **CARNEGIE TRI–COUNTY MUNICIPAL HOSPITAL (371334)**, 102 North Broadway, Zip 73015, Mailing Address: P.O. Box 97, Zip 73015–0097; tel. 580/654–1050, (Nonreporting) **A**9 10 18
Primary Contact: Shane Dunning, Administrator
**Control:** City–Government, nonfederal **Service:** General Medical and Surgical

> **Staffed Beds:** 19

## CHEYENNE—Roger Mills County

★ **ROGER MILLS MEMORIAL HOSPITAL (371303)**, Fifth and L. L Males Avenue, Zip 73628; tel. 580/497–3336 **A**9 10 18 **F**3 7 40 57 59 65 107 127 133
Primary Contact: Marilyn Bryan, Administrator
CFO: Lois Wilson, Controller
Web address: www.rogermillsmemorialhospital.com/
**Control:** Hospital district or authority, Government, nonfederal **Service:** General Medical and Surgical

> **Staffed Beds:** 15 **Admissions:** 31 **Census:** 1 **Outpatient Visits:** 3703 **Births:** 0 **Total Expense ($000):** 3581 **Payroll Expense ($000):** 2011 **Personnel:** 49

## CHICKASHA—Grady County

★ **GRADY MEMORIAL HOSPITAL (370054)**, 2220 West Iowa Avenue, Zip 73018–2738; tel. 405/224–2300 **A**5 9 10 19 **F**3 8 11 13 15 17 29 30 34 35 40 43 45 57 59 69 70 73 76 79 81 82 85 89 93 97 107 110 111 114 115 119 127 128 129 130 132 133 144 146 **P**6
Primary Contact: Kean Spellman, Interim Chief Executive Officer
CFO: Linda Hart, Vice President Finance
CMO: Bruce Storms, M.D., Chief of Staff
CIO: Sylvia Ho, Director Information Services
CHR: Steve Hutchens, Vice President General Services
Web address: www.gradymem.org
**Control:** Hospital district or authority, Government, nonfederal **Service:** General Medical and Surgical

> **Staffed Beds:** 52 **Admissions:** 1909 **Census:** 18 **Outpatient Visits:** 93005 **Births:** 287 **Total Expense ($000):** 42201 **Payroll Expense ($000):** 20725 **Personnel:** 359

*Many Facility Codes have changed. Please refer to the AHA Guide Code Chart.* © 2013 AHA Guide

## CLAREMORE—Rogers County

☐ **CLAREMORE INDIAN HOSPITAL (370173)**, 101 South Moore Avenue, Zip 74017–5091; tel. 918/342–6200 **A**1 5 10 **F**3 13 15 39 40 45 59 64 65 68 70 75 76 77 79 81 89 107 115 119 130 135 147 **S** U. S. Indian Health Service, Rockville, MD
Primary Contact: George Valliere, Chief Executive Officer
CFO: LaLana Spears, Supervisor Accounting
CMO: Paul Mobley, D.O., Clinical Director
CIO: David Ponder, Information Technology Officer
CHR: Jamelle King, Director Human Resources
Web address: www.ihs.gov
**Control:** PHS, Indian Service, Government, federal **Service:** General Medical and Surgical

**Staffed Beds:** 44 **Admissions:** 822 **Census:** 8 **Outpatient Visits:** 241403
**Births:** 241 **Personnel:** 378

⊞ **HILLCREST HOSPITAL CLAREMORE (370039)**, 1202 North Muskogee Place, Zip 74017–3036; tel. 918/341–2556 **A**1 9 10 **F**3 11 13 15 18 20 22 26 28 29 30 34 35 37 40 45 49 51 59 64 70 74 76 77 79 81 82 85 86 87 93 98 103 107 108 110 111 119 126 128 129 130 131 133 135 145 146 147 148 **P**6 **S** Ardent Health Services, Nashville, TN
Primary Contact: David Chaussard, Chief Executive Officer
CIO: Celeste Rodden, Chief Information Officer
CHR: Pat Goad, Director Human Resources
CNO: Dava Baldridge, Chief Nursing Officer
Web address: www.hillcrestclaremore.com
**Control:** Corporation, Investor–owned, for–profit **Service:** General Medical and Surgical

**Staffed Beds:** 55 **Admissions:** 3192 **Census:** 31 **Outpatient Visits:** 37895
**Births:** 647 **Total Expense ($000):** 37059 **Payroll Expense ($000):** 14192
**Personnel:** 303

## CLEVELAND—Pawnee County

**CLEVELAND AREA HOSPITAL (371320)**, 1401 West Pawnee Street, Zip 74020–3019; tel. 918/358–2501 **A**9 10 18 **F**11 29 34 35 40 53 57 59 64 77 81 87 89 93 107 110 114 119 130 133 148
Primary Contact: Yonna Creason, R.N., Interim Chief Executive Officer
COO: Yonna Creason, R.N., Chief Operating Officer
CFO: Jon Davis, Chief Financial Officer
CMO: Jason Sims, M.D., Chief Medical Officer
CHR: Sherry Brown, Director Human Resources
Web address: www.clevelandareahospital.com
**Control:** Hospital district or authority, Government, nonfederal **Service:** General Medical and Surgical

**Staffed Beds:** 14 **Admissions:** 496 **Census:** 4 **Outpatient Visits:** 13500
**Births:** 0 **Total Expense ($000):** 11177 **Payroll Expense ($000):** 3592
**Personnel:** 77

## CLINTON—Custer County

⊞ **INTEGRIS CLINTON REGIONAL HOSPITAL (370029)**, 100 North 30th Street, Zip 73601–3117, Mailing Address: P.O. Box 1569, Zip 73601–1569; tel. 580/323–2363, (Data for 275 days) **A**1 9 10 **F**3 11 13 15 29 30 31 34 40 45 59 62 63 68 70 75 76 77 78 81 90 93 96 107 108 111 114 119 121 123 129 130 131 132 133 146 147 148 **P**6 **S** Health Management Associates, Naples, FL
Primary Contact: Darcey O'Brien, Chief Executive Officer
CFO: Richard Foster, Chief Financial Officer
Web address: www.integris-health.com
**Control:** Corporation, Investor–owned, for–profit **Service:** General Medical and Surgical

**Staffed Beds:** 49 **Admissions:** 1209 **Census:** 15 **Outpatient Visits:** 15306
**Births:** 201 **Personnel:** 190

## COALGATE—Coal County

★ **COAL COUNTY GENERAL HOSPITAL (371319)**, 6 North Covington Street, Zip 74538–2002, Mailing Address: P.O. Box 326, Zip 74538–0326; tel. 580/927–2327 **A**10 18 **F**40 57 59 107 114 119 133
Primary Contact: Billy Johnson, Chief Executive Officer
CFO: Jamie Massie, Chief Financial Officer
Web address: www.hillcrest.com
**Control:** Other not–for–profit (including NFP Corporation) **Service:** General Medical and Surgical

**Staffed Beds:** 20 **Admissions:** 811 **Census:** 6 **Outpatient Visits:** 5039
**Births:** 0 **Total Expense ($000):** 4492 **Payroll Expense ($000):** 1955
**Personnel:** 54

## CORDELL—Washita County

★ **CORDELL MEMORIAL HOSPITAL (371325)**, 1220 North Glenn English Street, Zip 73632–2010; tel. 580/832–3339 **A**9 10 18 **F**7 40 57 59 65 89 107 128 133
Primary Contact: Charles H. Greene, Jr., Administrator
CFO: Sue Kelley, Chief Financial Officer
**Control:** City–Government, nonfederal **Service:** General Medical and Surgical

**Staffed Beds:** 25 **Admissions:** 279 **Census:** 3 **Outpatient Visits:** 5980
**Births:** 0 **Total Expense ($000):** 3859 **Payroll Expense ($000):** 1814
**Personnel:** 44

## CUSHING—Payne County

⊞ **HILLCREST HOSPITAL CUSHING (370099)**, (Formerly Cushing Regional Hospital), 1027 East Cherry Street, Zip 74023–4101, Mailing Address: P.O. Box 1409, Zip 74023–1409; tel. 918/225–2915 **A**1 9 10 **F**3 13 15 18 28 29 30 34 35 40 45 50 54 56 57 59 62 64 68 70 75 77 79 81 85 87 93 98 103 104 107 108 110 111 114 127 129 130 132 133 143 146 147 148 **S** Ardent Health Services, Nashville, TN
Primary Contact: Kevin Hawk, Chief Executive Officer
COO: Abigail Kendall, Chief Nursing Officer and Chief Operating Officer
CFO: Brandon Bullard, Chief Financial Officer
Web address: www.hillcrestcushing.com/
**Control:** Corporation, Investor–owned, for–profit **Service:** General Medical and Surgical

**Staffed Beds:** 95 **Admissions:** 1979 **Census:** 23 **Outpatient Visits:** 19946
**Births:** 210 **Total Expense ($000):** 25286 **Payroll Expense ($000):** 11041

## DRUMRIGHT—Creek County

**DRUMRIGHT REGIONAL HOSPITAL (371331)**, 610 West Bypass, Zip 74030–5957; tel. 918/382–2300 **A**9 10 18 **F**3 15 18 29 34 35 40 45 57 59 64 77 79 81 93 107 108 111 116 117 119 127 129 130 133 148 **P**3 6 **S** Rural Community Hospitals of America, Kansas City, MO
Primary Contact: Darrel Morris, Chief Executive Officer
CFO: Mark Conrath, Chief Financial Officer
Web address: www.drumrighthospital.com
**Control:** Corporation, Investor–owned, for–profit **Service:** General Medical and Surgical

**Staffed Beds:** 15 **Admissions:** 644 **Census:** 7 **Outpatient Visits:** 5553
**Births:** 0 **Total Expense ($000):** 8544 **Payroll Expense ($000):** 3990
**Personnel:** 72

## DUNCAN—Stephens County

⊞ △ **DUNCAN REGIONAL HOSPITAL (370023)**, 1407 North Whisenant Drive, Zip 73533–1650, Mailing Address: P.O. Box 2000, Zip 73534–2000; tel. 580/252–5300, (Total facility includes 16 beds in nursing home–type unit) **A**1 5 7 9 10 20 **F**3 11 13 15 18 28 29 30 34 35 40 43 45 50 57 59 62 63 64 70 75 76 77 79 81 85 86 87 90 93 96 98 103 104 107 108 110 111 114 115 119 128 129 130 131 132 141 142 143 145 146 147 148 **P**6
Primary Contact: Jay R. Johnson, FACHE, President and Chief Executive Officer
CFO: Douglas R. Volinski, Vice President and Chief Financial Officer
CIO: Roger Neal, Vice President and Chief Information Officer
CHR: Mark Rhoades, Vice President and Chief Human Resources Officer
CNO: Cindy Rauh, R.N., Vice President and Chief Nursing Officer
Web address: www.duncanregional.com
**Control:** Other not–for–profit (including NFP Corporation) **Service:** General Medical and Surgical

**Staffed Beds:** 117 **Admissions:** 4773 **Census:** 61 **Outpatient Visits:** 73072
**Births:** 531 **Total Expense ($000):** 77907 **Payroll Expense ($000):** 29766
**Personnel:** 793

## DURANT—Bryan County

⊞ **MEDICAL CENTER OF SOUTHEASTERN OKLAHOMA (370014)**, 1800 University Boulevard, Zip 74701–3006, Mailing Address: P.O. Box 1207, Zip 74702–1207; tel. 580/924–3080 **A**1 9 10 13 19 **F**3 11 13 15 17 20 28 29 39 40 45 51 56 59 62 70 74 75 76 79 80 81 85 86 87 89 93 107 108 110 111 115 118 119 126 129 130 135 145 146 147 148 **P**8 **S** Health Management Associates, Naples, FL
Primary Contact: Patricia Dorris, Executive Director
CFO: Cindy Rios, Chief Financial Officer
CMO: Kevin Gordon, M.D., Chief of Staff
CIO: Katy Stinson, Director Information Services
Web address: www.mymcso.com
**Control:** Corporation, Investor–owned, for–profit **Service:** General Medical and Surgical

**Staffed Beds:** 148 **Admissions:** 6636 **Census:** 65 **Outpatient Visits:** 49806
**Births:** 1137 **Personnel:** 418

---

**Hospital, Medicare Provider Number, Address, Telephone, Approval, Facility, and Physician Codes, Health Care System**

★ American Hospital Association (AHA) membership
☐ The Joint Commission accreditation   ◇ DNV Healthcare Inc. accreditation

◯ Healthcare Facilities Accreditation Program
△ Commission on Accreditation of Rehabilitation Facilities (CARF) accreditation

**OK**

### EDMOND—Oklahoma County

☐ **AMG SPECIALTY HOSPITAL–EDMOND (372005)**, (Formerly LTAC of Edmond), 1100 East Ninth Street, Zip 73034–5755; tel. 405/341–8150, (Nonreporting) **A**1 9 10 **S** AMG Integrated Healthcare Management, Lafayette, LA
Primary Contact: Ginger Creech, Chief Executive Officer
CFO: Rowena Davidson, Manager Business Office
CMO: Brian Levy, M.D., Medical Director
CHR: Pam Grimes, Director Human Resources
Web address: www.amgedmond.com/
**Control:** Corporation, Investor–owned, for–profit **Service:** Long–Term Acute Care hospital

| Staffed Beds: 37 |
| --- |

**EDMOND MEDICAL CENTER** See OU Medical Center Edmond

⌧ **INTEGRIS HEALTH EDMOND (370236)**, 4801 Integris Parkway, Zip 73034–8864; tel. 405/657–3000 **A**1 9 10 **F**3 11 13 15 18 26 29 30 34 35 37 40 43 44 45 46 49 50 56 57 59 60 68 70 74 75 76 78 79 81 82 85 87 89 92 93 97 100 102 107 108 110 111 115 119 130 135 146 147 148 **S** INTEGRIS Health, Oklahoma City, OK
Primary Contact: Avilla Williams, MS, President
Web address: www.integrisok.com/edmond
**Control:** Other not–for–profit (including NFP Corporation) **Service:** General Medical and Surgical

| Staffed Beds: 40 Admissions: 750 Census: 6 Outpatient Visits: 12128 Births: 145 Total Expense ($000): 22448 Payroll Expense ($000): 6986 Personnel: 145 |
| --- |

**OU MEDICAL CENTER EDMOND** See OU Medical Center, Oklahoma City

**SUMMIT MEDICAL CENTER (370225)**, 1800 South Renaissance Boulevard, Zip 73013–3023; tel. 405/359–2400, (Nonreporting) **A**9 10
Primary Contact: Curtis Summers, Chief Executive Officer
Web address: www.summitmedcenter.com/
**Control:** Corporation, Investor–owned, for–profit **Service:** Other specialty

| Staffed Beds: 15 |
| --- |

### EL RENO—Canadian County

★ **MERCY HOSPITAL EL RENO (370011)**, 2115 Parkview Drive, Zip 73036–2199, Mailing Address: P.O. Box 129, Zip 73036–0129; tel. 405/262–2640 **A**9 10 **F**3 7 8 29 30 35 40 45 46 50 62 64 65 77 79 81 82 85 93 107 111 114 119 132 135 146 148 **P**6 **S** Mercy Health, Chesterfield, MO
Primary Contact: Doug Danker, Administrator
CMO: Michael Dean Sullivan, M.D., Chief of Staff
CIO: Karen Heldreth, Director Data Processing
CHR: Wendy Ward, Director Human Resources
Web address: www.mercyok.net
**Control:** Church–operated, Nongovernment, not–for profit **Service:** General Medical and Surgical

| Staffed Beds: 48 Admissions: 663 Census: 5 Outpatient Visits: 38955 Births: 22 Total Expense ($000): 12905 Payroll Expense ($000): 6839 Personnel: 121 |
| --- |

**PARKVIEW HOSPITAL** See Mercy Hospital El Reno

### ELK CITY—Beckham County

⌧ **GREAT PLAINS REGIONAL MEDICAL CENTER (370019)**, 1801 West Third Street, Zip 73644–5145, Mailing Address: P.O. Box 2339, Zip 73648–2339; tel. 580/225–2511 **A**1 9 10 **F**3 11 13 15 18 20 22 26 29 30 31 34 35 40 43 44 45 47 50 51 56 57 59 62 64 68 70 75 76 77 78 79 81 82 85 86 87 89 91 93 96 98 100 101 102 107 108 110 111 115 118 119 120 121 123 129 130 131 132 133 135 143 146 147 148
Primary Contact: Don Ikner, Chief Executive Officer
CMO: Craig Phelps, M.D., Chief of Staff
CIO: Terry Davis, Chief Information Officer
CHR: Misty Carter, Director Human Resources
Web address: www.gprmc-ok.com
**Control:** Other not–for–profit (including NFP Corporation) **Service:** General Medical and Surgical

| Staffed Beds: 46 Admissions: 1924 Census: 21 Outpatient Visits: 52903 Births: 415 Total Expense ($000): 44317 Payroll Expense ($000): 16079 Personnel: 336 |
| --- |

### ENID—Garfield County

**INTEGRIS BASS BEHAVIORAL HEALTH SYSTEM** See Integris Bass Meadowlake

⌧ **INTEGRIS BASS BAPTIST HEALTH CENTER (370016)**, 600 South Monroe Street, Zip 73701–7211, Mailing Address: P.O. Box 3168, Zip 73702–3168; tel. 580/233–2300 **A**1 5 9 10 13 19 **F**3 11 13 15 17 18 20 22 24 28 29 30 31 35 40 43 45 49 57 62 68 70 74 75 76 77 78 79 81 85 98 99 103 107 108 111 114 117 118 119 120 121 127 128 129 132 144 146 147 148 **S** INTEGRIS Health, Oklahoma City, OK
Primary Contact: Edward Herrman, R.N., FACHE, President
CFO: Rebecca Tucker, Chief Financial Officer
Web address: www.integris–health.com
**Control:** Other not–for–profit (including NFP Corporation) **Service:** General Medical and Surgical

| Staffed Beds: 167 Admissions: 4919 Census: 95 Outpatient Visits: 62698 Births: 957 Total Expense ($000): 106472 Payroll Expense ($000): 46806 Personnel: 725 |
| --- |

☐ **INTEGRIS BASS PAVILION (372016)**, 401 South Third Street, Zip 73701–5737; tel. 580/249–4260 **A**1 9 10 **F**1 11 29 30 40 43 68 75 77 82 85 93 131 146 148
Primary Contact: Edward Herrman, R.N., FACHE, President
CFO: Rebecca Tucker, Chief Financial Officer
CHR: Tera L. Latta, Director Human Resources
Web address: www.integris–health.com/integris/en–us/locations/bass–enid
**Control:** Other not–for–profit (including NFP Corporation) **Service:** General Medical and Surgical

| Staffed Beds: 24 Admissions: 241 Census: 16 Outpatient Visits: 2252 Births: 0 Total Expense ($000): 8972 Payroll Expense ($000): 3657 Personnel: 63 |
| --- |

☐ △ **ST. MARY'S REGIONAL MEDICAL CENTER (370026)**, 305 South Fifth Street, Zip 73701–5899, Mailing Address: P.O. Box 232, Zip 73702–0232; tel. 580/233–6100 **A**1 5 7 9 10 **F**3 11 18 20 22 26 28 29 30 31 34 35 39 40 43 45 49 51 53 54 57 59 60 64 68 69 70 73 74 75 76 77 78 79 81 82 85 86 87 89 90 92 93 96 100 107 108 110 111 114 115 118 119 128 129 130 131 132 146 147 **S** Universal Health Services, Inc., King of Prussia, PA
Primary Contact: Stanley D. Tatum, FACHE, Chief Executive Officer
CMO: Seth Switzen, M.D., Chief of Staff
CIO: Conrad Ramirez, Director Information Services
CHR: Linda Hoag, Director Human Resources
Web address: www.stmarysregional.com
**Control:** Corporation, Investor–owned, for–profit **Service:** General Medical and Surgical

| Staffed Beds: 166 Admissions: 5667 Census: 82 Outpatient Visits: 72128 Births: 306 Total Expense ($000): 77253 Payroll Expense ($000): 30386 Personnel: 534 |
| --- |

### EUFAULA—Mcintosh County

**EPIC MEDICAL CENTER (370169)**, 1 Hospital Drive, Zip 74432–4010, Mailing Address: P.O. Box 629, Zip 74432–0629; tel. 918/689–2535 **A**9 10 **F**3 34 40 45 81
Primary Contact: Vicki Schaff, Chief Operating Officer
COO: Vicki Schaff, Chief Operating Officer
CFO: Phyllis Eakle, Chief Financial Officer
CMO: Ed Farrow, M.D., Chief Medical Staff
Web address: www.epichealthcare.net
**Control:** Corporation, Investor–owned, for–profit **Service:** General Medical and Surgical

| Staffed Beds: 33 Admissions: 116 Census: 1 Outpatient Visits: 14509 Births: 0 Total Expense ($000): 3150 Payroll Expense ($000): 1785 Personnel: 44 |
| --- |

### FAIRFAX—Osage County

★ **FAIRFAX COMMUNITY HOSPITAL (371318)**, Taft Avenue and Highway 18, Zip 74637–4028, Mailing Address: P.O. Box 219, Zip 74637–0219; tel. 918/642–3291 **A**9 10 18 **F**3 29 40 45 57 81 90 93 107 117 128 129 133 **S** Rural Community Hospitals of America, Kansas City, MO
Primary Contact: Tina Steele, Chief Executive Officer and Chief Financial Officer
COO: Linda Thompson, Chief Operating Officer
CFO: Tina Steele, Chief Executive Officer and Chief Financial Officer
CMO: Arman Janloo, M.D., Chief Medical Staff
CIO: Lisa Drymon, Manager
CHR: Sharon Binkley, Director Human Resources
**Control:** Corporation, Investor–owned, for–profit **Service:** General Medical and Surgical

| Staffed Beds: 15 Admissions: 150 Census: 1 Outpatient Visits: 3330 Births: 0 Total Expense ($000): 4545 Payroll Expense ($000): 2360 Personnel: 42 |
| --- |

**FAIRFAX MEMORIAL HOSPITAL** See Fairfax Community Hospital

*Many Facility Codes have changed. Please refer to the AHA Guide Code Chart.* © 2013 AHA Guide

## FAIRVIEW—Major County

**FAIRVIEW REGIONAL MEDICAL CENTER (371329)**, 523 East State Road, Zip 73737–1453, Mailing Address: P.O. Box 548, Zip 73737–0548; tel. 580/227–3721 **A**9 10 18 **F**3 28 34 40 43 45 57 59 64 65 69 75 77 81 82 84 85 91 93 107 114 127 128 131 133 135 146 **P**6
Primary Contact: Roger Knak, Administrator
CFO: Jamie Eitzen, Chief Financial Officer
CMO: Solomon Ali, M.D., Chief of Staff
CHR: Macky Martin, Director Human Resources
Web address: www.fairviewregional.net
**Control:** Hospital district or authority, Government, nonfederal **Service:** General Medical and Surgical

**Staffed Beds:** 25 **Admissions:** 211 **Census:** 4 **Outpatient Visits:** 10171 **Births:** 0 **Total Expense ($000):** 5842 **Payroll Expense ($000):** 3032 **Personnel:** 86

## FORT SILL—Comanche County

⊠ **REYNOLDS ARMY COMMUNITY HOSPITAL**, 4301 Wilson Street, Zip 73503–4472; tel. 580/558–3000 **A**1 3 5 **F**3 5 7 8 12 13 15 29 30 32 33 34 35 37 38 39 40 43 44 45 50 56 57 59 64 65 68 71 74 75 76 77 79 81 82 85 87 93 96 97 100 101 102 104 107 108 110 111 115 118 119 129 130 131 132 135 143 144 146 147 **S** Department of the Army, Office of the Surgeon General, Falls Church, VA
Primary Contact: Colonel Noel J. Cardenas, FACHE, Commander
CFO: Captain Shelley Mizelle, Chief Resource Management Division
CMO: Colonel Donald Mondragon, M.D., Deputy Commander Clinical Services
CHR: Homer Williams, Chief Civilian Personnel Branch
Web address: www.rach.sill.amedd.army.mil
**Control:** Army, Government, federal **Service:** General Medical and Surgical

**Staffed Beds:** 24 **Admissions:** 2266 **Census:** 13 **Outpatient Visits:** 610169 **Births:** 716 **Total Expense ($000):** 136945 **Payroll Expense ($000):** 47904 **Personnel:** 1074

## FORT SUPPLY— County

**NORTHWEST CENTER FOR BEHAVIORAL HEALTH (374001)**, 1 Mi East Highway 270, Zip 73841; tel. 580/766–2311 **A**10 **F**5 98 102 104 106 **P**6 **S** Oklahoma Department of Mental Health and Substance Abuse Services, Oklahoma City, OK
Primary Contact: Trudy Hoffman, Executive Director
Web address: www.ncbhok.org/
**Control:** State–Government, nonfederal **Service:** Psychiatric

**Staffed Beds:** 28 **Admissions:** 757 **Census:** 24 **Outpatient Visits:** 38000 **Births:** 0 **Total Expense ($000):** 13628 **Payroll Expense ($000):** 7057 **Personnel:** 177

## FREDERICK—Tillman County

★ **MEMORIAL HOSPITAL AND PHYSICIAN GROUP (370051)**, 319 East Josephine Avenue, Zip 73542–2220; tel. 580/335–7565, (Total facility includes 30 beds in nursing home–type unit) **A**9 10 20 **F**11 29 40 59 62 64 67 81 89 93 107 114 119 133 **P**6
Primary Contact: Michael J. Carter, Chief Executive Officer
COO: Cindy Duncan, Chief Operating Officer
Web address: www.frederickhospital.com
**Control:** Hospital district or authority, Government, nonfederal **Service:** General Medical and Surgical

**Staffed Beds:** 55 **Admissions:** 619 **Census:** 35 **Outpatient Visits:** 29936 **Births:** 0 **Total Expense ($000):** 8344 **Payroll Expense ($000):** 3822 **Personnel:** 120

## GROVE—Delaware County

⊠ **INTEGRIS GROVE GENERAL HOSPITAL (370113)**, 1001 East 18th Street, Zip 74344–2907; tel. 918/786–2243 **A**1 9 10 20 **F**3 7 11 13 29 30 40 54 57 62 64 70 77 79 81 85 107 110 111 114 119 125 129 146 147 **S** INTEGRIS Health, Oklahoma City, OK
Primary Contact: Greg Martin, President
CFO: Kevin Cox, Chief Financial Officer
CMO: James Rutter, M.D., Chief of Staff
CHR: Vicki Cossairt, Director Human Resources
CNO: Angela Bidleman, R.N., Chief Nursing Officer
Web address: www.integris-health.com
**Control:** Other not–for–profit (including NFP Corporation) **Service:** General Medical and Surgical

**Staffed Beds:** 58 **Admissions:** 3199 **Census:** 28 **Outpatient Visits:** 53476 **Births:** 366 **Total Expense ($000):** 53893 **Payroll Expense ($000):** 19565 **Personnel:** 289

## GUTHRIE—Logan County

★ **MERCY HOSPITAL LOGAN COUNTY (371317)**, 200 South Academy Road, Zip 73044–8727, Mailing Address: P.O. Box 1017, Zip 73044–1017; tel. 405/282–6700, (Data for 274 days) **A**9 10 18 **F**3 8 11 15 29 30 34 40 49 50 59 62 64 65 79 81 85 93 97 107 110 111 114 119 127 129 130 131 133 146 148 **P**6 **S** Mercy Health, Chesterfield, MO
Primary Contact: Joshua Tucker, Administrator
CMO: Stephen Travis, M.D., Chief of Staff
CHR: Mary Jo Messelt, Director Human Resources
Web address: www.loganmedicalcenter.com
**Control:** Church–operated, Nongovernment, not–for profit **Service:** General Medical and Surgical

**Staffed Beds:** 25 **Admissions:** 667 **Census:** 10 **Outpatient Visits:** 68803 **Births:** 0 **Total Expense ($000):** 14346 **Payroll Expense ($000):** 6803 **Personnel:** 171

## GUYMON—Texas County

★ **MEMORIAL HOSPITAL OF TEXAS COUNTY (370138)**, 520 Medical Drive, Zip 73942–4438; tel. 580/338–6515 **A**9 10 20 **F**3 11 13 15 29 34 40 43 45 57 59 64 65 68 70 75 76 79 81 82 85 89 107 108 110 111 114 119 146 147 **P**6
Primary Contact: John Jones, Interim Chief Executive Officer
CFO: Jamie R. Jacoby, Chief Financial Officer
CNO: John Jones, Chief Nursing Officer
Web address: www.mhtcguymon.org
**Control:** County–Government, nonfederal **Service:** General Medical and Surgical

**Staffed Beds:** 14 **Admissions:** 954 **Census:** 7 **Outpatient Visits:** 45881 **Births:** 309 **Total Expense ($000):** 21510 **Payroll Expense ($000):** 9077 **Personnel:** 207

## HEALDTON—Carter County

★ **MERCY HOSPITAL HEALDTON (371310)**, 918 South 8th Street, Zip 73438–0928, Mailing Address: P.O. Box 928, Zip 73438–0928; tel. 580/229–0701 **A**9 10 18 **F**3 29 30 34 40 64 84 93 107 114 133 146 **P**6 **S** Mercy Health, Chesterfield, MO
Primary Contact: Jeremy A. Jones, Administrator
CMO: Mark Newey, D.O., Chief of Staff
CHR: Melinda Sharum, Director Human Resources
Web address: www.mercyok.com
**Control:** Church–operated, Nongovernment, not–for profit **Service:** General Medical and Surgical

**Staffed Beds:** 22 **Admissions:** 226 **Census:** 5 **Outpatient Visits:** 12170 **Births:** 0 **Total Expense ($000):** 4817 **Payroll Expense ($000):** 2617 **Personnel:** 40

## HENRYETTA—Okmulgee County

★ **HILLCREST HOSPITAL HENRYETTA (370183)**, (Formerly Henryetta Medical Center), Dewey Bartlett & Main Streets, Zip 74437–6820, Mailing Address: P.O. Box 1269, Zip 74437–1269; tel. 918/650–1100 **A**9 10 **F**3 15 29 40 45 54 56 62 64 65 68 79 81 85 87 93 98 102 103 107 111 114 119 128 129 130 133 143 148 **P**6 **S** Ardent Health Services, Nashville, TN
Primary Contact: Dee Renshaw, Chief Executive Officer
CFO: Brandon Bullard, Chief Financial Officer
Web address: www.hillcresthenryetta.com/
**Control:** Corporation, Investor–owned, for–profit **Service:** General Medical and Surgical

**Staffed Beds:** 41 **Admissions:** 1118 **Census:** 18 **Outpatient Visits:** 30767 **Births:** 2 **Total Expense ($000):** 14483 **Payroll Expense ($000):** 7148 **Personnel:** 104

## HOBART—Kiowa County

★ **ELKVIEW GENERAL HOSPITAL (370153)**, 429 West Elm Street, Zip 73651–1615; tel. 580/726–3324 **A**9 10 20 **F**3 15 28 29 31 34 35 40 45 56 59 62 79 81 85 89 93 107 108 110 111 115 118 119 129 133 146 148 **P**6
Primary Contact: Corey Lively, Chief Executive Officer
COO: Harold Moad, Chief Operating Officer
CFO: Lisa Hart, Chief Financial Officer
CMO: Samatha Jackson, M.D., Chief of Staff
CIO: Chris Clark, Chief Technology Officer
CHR: Sharon Moad, Director Personnel
**Control:** Hospital district or authority, Government, nonfederal **Service:** General Medical and Surgical

**Staffed Beds:** 38 **Admissions:** 1251 **Census:** 14 **Outpatient Visits:** 21675 **Births:** 1 **Total Expense ($000):** 14088 **Payroll Expense ($000):** 6853 **Personnel:** 165

---

**Hospital, Medicare Provider Number, Address, Telephone, Approval, Facility, and Physician Codes, Health Care System**

★ American Hospital Association (AHA) membership
□ The Joint Commission accreditation
◇ DNV Healthcare Inc. accreditation
○ Healthcare Facilities Accreditation Program
△ Commission on Accreditation of Rehabilitation Facilities (CARF) accreditation

**OK**

### HOLDENVILLE—Hughes County

★ **HOLDENVILLE GENERAL HOSPITAL (371321)**, 100 McDougal Drive, Zip 74848–2822; tel. 405/379–4200 **A**9 10 18 **F**11 29 30 40 45 51 57 59 64 81 82 93 97 107 111 115 119 127 129 133 135 143 146 148 **P**3 6
Primary Contact: Roberta Jeffrey, Chief Executive Officer
CMO: Tom Osborn, D.O., Chief Medical Staff
CIO: Mike Combs, Manager Information Technology
CHR: Heather Heard, Director Human Resources
CNO: Shirley Orr, R.N., Chief Nursing Officer
Web address: www.holdenvillegeneral.org
**Control:** City–Government, nonfederal **Service:** General Medical and Surgical

| |
|---|
| **Staffed Beds:** 25 **Admissions:** 569 **Census:** 6 **Outpatient Visits:** 28627 **Births:** 0 **Total Expense ($000):** 9096 **Payroll Expense ($000):** 4309 **Personnel:** 116 |

### HOLLIS—Harmon County

★ **HARMON MEMORIAL HOSPITAL (370036)**, 400 East Chestnut Street, Zip 73550–2030, Mailing Address: P.O. Box 791, Zip 73550–0791; tel. 580/688–3363, (Nonreporting) **A**9 10 20
Primary Contact: Sheila Lewis, Administrator
CFO: Willie Mae Copeland, Chief Financial Officer
CMO: Akram Abraham, M.D., Chief of Staff
CHR: Abbey Welch, Director Human Resources
**Control:** Hospital district or authority, Government, nonfederal **Service:** General Medical and Surgical

| |
|---|
| **Staffed Beds:** 72 |

### HUGO—Choctaw County

**CHOCTAW MEMORIAL HOSPITAL (370100)**, 1405 East Kirk Street, Zip 74743–3603; tel. 580/317–9500, (Nonreporting) **A**9 10
Primary Contact: Marcia O'Conner, Chief Executive Officer
CIO: Andy Richmond, Director Information Technology
CHR: Darlene Galyon, Director Human Resources
Web address: www.choctawmemorial.com
**Control:** Hospital district or authority, Government, nonfederal **Service:** General Medical and Surgical

| |
|---|
| **Staffed Beds:** 34 |

**LANE FROST HEALTH AND REHABILITATION CENTER (372017)**, 2815 East Jackson Street, Zip 74743–4250; tel. 580/326–9200, (Nonreporting) **A**10
Primary Contact: Robert F. Berry, Chief Executive Officer
Web address: www.lanefrosthealth.com/
**Control:** Other not–for–profit (including NFP Corporation) **Service:** Long–Term Acute Care hospital

| |
|---|
| **Staffed Beds:** 25 |

### IDABEL—Mccurtain County

★ **MCCURTAIN MEMORIAL HOSPITAL (370048)**, 1301 Lincoln Road, Zip 74745–7341; tel. 580/286–7623 **A**9 10 20 **F**3 11 13 15 28 29 34 40 45 49 53 62 64 70 75 76 81 87 93 98 103 107 110 111 114 119 128 130 133 148 **P**6 8
Primary Contact: Bristol Messer, Chief Executive Officer
CFO: Ray B. Whitmore, Chief Financial Officer
CMO: Michael C. West, M.D., Chief of Staff
CIO: Dana A. Stowell, Chief Information Officer
CHR: Frank Drobil, Director Human Resources
Web address: www.mmhok.com
**Control:** Other not–for–profit (including NFP Corporation) **Service:** General Medical and Surgical

| |
|---|
| **Staffed Beds:** 77 **Admissions:** 1860 **Census:** 21 **Outpatient Visits:** 34631 **Births:** 289 **Total Expense ($000):** 22788 **Payroll Expense ($000):** 10587 **Personnel:** 259 |

### KINGFISHER—Kingfisher County

★ **KINGFISHER REGIONAL HOSPITAL (371313)**, 1000 Kingfisher Regional Hospital Drive, Zip 73750–3528, Mailing Address: P.O. Box 59, Zip 73750–0059; tel. 405/375–3141 **A**9 10 18 **F**3 15 29 40 59 71 81 91 93 107 111 114 119 129 133 146 **S** Mercy Health, Chesterfield, MO
Primary Contact: Bobby Stitt, R.N., Interim Chief Executive Officer
CFO: Amy Harmon, Chief Financial Officer
CMO: Brett Krablin, M.D., Chief of Staff
CIO: Rose Sherwood, Information Technology Specialist
CHR: Carolyn Bjerke, Director Human Resources
Web address: www.kingfisherhospital.com
**Control:** Other not–for–profit (including NFP Corporation) **Service:** General Medical and Surgical

| |
|---|
| **Staffed Beds:** 25 **Admissions:** 526 **Census:** 7 **Outpatient Visits:** 9234 **Births:** 4 **Total Expense ($000):** 15680 **Payroll Expense ($000):** 4552 **Personnel:** 95 |

### LAWTON—Comanche County

⊠ △ **COMANCHE COUNTY MEMORIAL HOSPITAL (370056)**, 3401 West Gore Boulevard, Zip 73505–6332, Mailing Address: P.O. Box 129, Zip 73502–0129; tel. 580/355–8620, (Total facility includes 125 beds in nursing home–type unit) **A**1 2 3 5 7 9 10 **F**3 7 8 11 12 13 15 17 18 20 22 24 26 28 29 30 31 32 34 35 40 43 45 47 48 49 50 51 54 56 57 58 59 62 64 65 66 68 70 74 75 76 77 78 79 80 81 82 84 85 86 90 91 92 93 96 97 98 103 104 107 108 110 111 114 115 117 118 119 120 121 123 124 127 128 129 130 131 132 134 135 143 144 146 147 148 **P**6
Primary Contact: Randall K. Segler, FACHE, Chief Executive Officer
CFO: David Blackmon, Chief Financial Officer
CMO: Richard Campbell, M.D., President Medical Staff
CIO: Ron Noreen, Director Information Services
CHR: Donna Wade, Senior Director Human Resources
Web address: www.ccmhonline.com
**Control:** Hospital district or authority, Government, nonfederal **Service:** General Medical and Surgical

| |
|---|
| **Staffed Beds:** 357 **Admissions:** 10655 **Census:** 247 **Outpatient Visits:** 151794 **Births:** 1099 **Total Expense ($000):** 211365 **Payroll Expense ($000):** 85758 **Personnel:** 1481 |

**JIM TALIAFERRO COMMUNITY MENTAL HEALTH (374008)**, 602 S.W. 37th Street, Zip 73505; tel. 580/248–5780, (Nonreporting) **A**9 10
Primary Contact: Randy May, Interim Executive Director
**Control:** State–Government, nonfederal **Service:** Psychiatric

| |
|---|
| **Staffed Beds:** 26 |

☐ **LAWTON INDIAN HOSPITAL (370170)**, 1515 Lawrie Tatum Road, Zip 73507–3099; tel. 580/353–0350, (Nonreporting) **A**1 10 **S** U. S. Indian Health Service, Rockville, MD
Primary Contact: Greg Ketcher, Administrator
CFO: Sarabeth Sahmaunt, Supervisory Accountant
CMO: Bryce Poolaw, M.D., Clinical Director
CIO: Steve Barse, Chief Information Officer
CHR: Twylla Jimboy, Supervisor Human Resources
Web address: www.ihs.gov
**Control:** PHS, Indian Service, Government, federal **Service:** General Medical and Surgical

| |
|---|
| **Staffed Beds:** 26 |

☐ △ **SOUTHWESTERN MEDICAL CENTER (370097)**, 5602 S.W. Lee Boulevard, Zip 73505–9635; tel. 580/531–4700 **A**1 3 5 7 9 10 **F**3 8 13 29 30 34 38 40 41 43 45 47 49 50 51 57 59 60 65 67 68 70 74 76 77 78 79 81 85 87 89 90 91 92 93 98 99 100 101 102 104 106 107 108 111 114 118 119 120 121 122 123 129 130 131 133 146 147 148 **P**6 8 **S** Capella Healthcare, Franklin, TN
Primary Contact: Stephen O. Hyde, FACHE, Chief Executive Officer
CFO: Lisa Clarke, Interim Chief Financial Officer
CMO: Steve Snell, M.D., Chief of Staff
CIO: Kent Lewis, Director Information Services
CHR: Helen Hooper, Director Human Resources
Web address: www.swmconline.com
**Control:** Corporation, Investor–owned, for–profit **Service:** General Medical and Surgical

| |
|---|
| **Staffed Beds:** 178 **Admissions:** 4518 **Census:** 88 **Outpatient Visits:** 45075 **Births:** 539 **Total Expense ($000):** 52619 **Payroll Expense ($000):** 21534 **Personnel:** 491 |

### LINDSAY—Garvin County

**LINDSAY MUNICIPAL HOSPITAL (370214)**, Highway 19 West, Zip 73052, Mailing Address: P.O. Box 888, Zip 73052–0888; tel. 405/756–1404, (Nonreporting) **A**9 10
Primary Contact: Norma N. Howard, Chief Executive Officer
**Control:** City–Government, nonfederal **Service:** General Medical and Surgical

| |
|---|
| **Staffed Beds:** 26 |

### MADILL—Marshall County

⊠ **INTEGRIS MARSHALL COUNTY MEDICAL CENTER (371326)**, 1 Hospital Drive, Zip 73446, Mailing Address: P.O. Box 827, Zip 73446–0827; tel. 580/795–3384, (Data for 275 days) **A**1 9 10 18 **F**3 11 29 30 34 35 40 43 45 49 59 64 81 87 93 107 114 119 127 130 133 135 146 **S** Health Management Associates, Naples, FL
Primary Contact: Matthew M. Lyden, Chief Executive Officer
CFO: Thomas Briggs, Chief Financial Officer
CMO: Joe Potter, M.D., Chief of Staff
CHR: Lori Friend, Director Human Resources
CNO: Holly Bain, Chief Nursing Officer
Web address: www.integrismarshallcounty.com
**Control:** Corporation, Investor–owned, for–profit **Service:** General Medical and Surgical

| |
|---|
| **Staffed Beds:** 21 **Admissions:** 400 **Census:** 4 **Outpatient Visits:** 10633 **Births:** 0 **Total Expense ($000):** 7843 **Payroll Expense ($000):** 2605 **Personnel:** 116 |

*Many Facility Codes have changed. Please refer to the AHA Guide Code Chart.* © 2013 AHA Guide

**MANGUM—Greer County**

**QUARTZ MOUNTAIN MEDICAL CENTER (371330)**, One Wickersham Drive, Zip 73554–9116, Mailing Address: P.O. Box 280, Zip 73554–0280; tel. 580/782–3353 **A**9 10 18 **F**29 40 41 45 54 57 68 81 82 107 111 119 127 128 129 133 148 **P**6
Primary Contact: Lindsay Crabb, Chief Executive Officer
COO: Danny Avery, Chief Financial Officer and Chief Operating Officer
CIO: Gregg Burnam, Chief Information Officer and Manager Business Office
Web address: www.mangumhealth.com
**Control:** Individual, Investor–owned, for–profit **Service:** General Medical and Surgical

Staffed Beds: 25 Admissions: 167 Census: 2 Outpatient Visits: 8186 Births: 0 Total Expense ($000): 9560 Payroll Expense ($000): 3537 Personnel: 68

**MARIETTA—Love County**

★ **MERCY HEALTH LOVE COUNTY (371306)**, 300 Wanda Street, Zip 73448–1200; tel. 580/276–3347 **A**9 10 18 **F**3 29 34 40 43 50 57 59 84 107 114 119 127 133 135 143 146 148 **S** Mercy Health, Chesterfield, MO
Primary Contact: Richard Barker, Administrator
CMO: J. T. O'Connor, M.D., Medical Director
CIO: Connie Graham, Public Information Officer
Web address: www.mercyhealthlovecounty.com
**Control:** Church–operated, Nongovernment, not–for profit **Service:** General Medical and Surgical

Staffed Beds: 25 Admissions: 369 Census: 8 Outpatient Visits: 30272 Births: 0 Total Expense ($000): 12638 Payroll Expense ($000): 7147 Personnel: 128

**MCALESTER—Pittsburg County**

**CARL ALBERT COMMUNITY MENTAL HEALTH CENTER (374006)**, 1101 East Monroe Avenue, Zip 74501–4826; tel. 918/426–7800, (Nonreporting) **A**10
Primary Contact: Debbie Moran, Executive Director
CFO: Konnie Taylor, Chief Financial Officer
CMO: William Mings, M.D., Medical Director
CHR: Judy Allen, Human Resource Specialist
Web address: www.odmhsas.org
**Control:** State–Government, nonfederal **Service:** Psychiatric

Staffed Beds: 15

★ △ ◇ **MCALESTER REGIONAL HEALTH CENTER (370034)**, One Clark Bass Boulevard, Zip 74501–4267, Mailing Address: P.O. Box 1228, Zip 74502–1228; tel. 918/426–1800 **A**7 9 10 21 **F**2 3 11 13 15 18 20 29 30 34 35 40 43 45 49 50 51 53 54 56 57 59 61 62 64 68 69 70 75 76 77 79 81 82 85 86 90 92 103 104 105 107 109 110 111 114 115 117 118 119 125 127 128 129 130 132 135 144 146 147 148
Primary Contact: David N. Keith, FACHE, President and Chief Executive Officer
CFO: Melissa Walker, Senior Vice President and Chief Financial Officer
CIO: Frank Hilbert, Senior Vice President and Chief Information Officer
CHR: Steven Brooks, Vice President Human Resources
CNO: Danny Hardman, Senior Vice President and Chief Nursing Officer
Web address: www.mrhcok.com
**Control:** City–Government, nonfederal **Service:** General Medical and Surgical

Staffed Beds: 252 Admissions: 4657 Census: 54 Outpatient Visits: 82694 Births: 517 Total Expense ($000): 76016 Payroll Expense ($000): 31282 Personnel: 650

**MIAMI—Ottawa County**

⊠ **INTEGRIS BAPTIST REGIONAL HEALTH CENTER (370004)**, 200 Second Street S.W., Zip 74354–6830, Mailing Address: P.O. Box 1207, Zip 74355–1207; tel. 918/542–6611 **A**1 9 10 20 **F**3 7 11 13 15 18 20 26 28 29 30 34 35 40 43 50 51 56 57 59 62 63 64 66 70 75 76 77 79 81 85 86 89 90 93 98 100 101 102 103 104 105 107 108 111 114 115 119 125 129 130 131 132 135 144 146 147 148 **P**5 7 **S** INTEGRIS Health, Oklahoma City, OK
Primary Contact: Joel A. Hart, FACHE, President
CFO: Amy Marsh, Chief Financial Officer
CMO: Matt Osborn, M.D., Chief of Staff
CHR: Jamil Haynes, Regional Director Human Resources
Web address: www.integris–health.com
**Control:** Other not–for–profit (including NFP Corporation) **Service:** General Medical and Surgical

Staffed Beds: 84 Admissions: 3038 Census: 31 Outpatient Visits: 81903 Births: 373 Total Expense ($000): 52703 Payroll Expense ($000): 23352 Personnel: 364

★ **WILLOW CREST HOSPITAL (374017)**, 130 A Street S.W., Zip 74354–6800; tel. 918/542–1836 **A**9 10 **F**29 75 98 99 101 102 106 130 **P**6
Primary Contact: Anne G. Anthony, FACHE, President and Chief Executive Officer
COO: Steven Goodman, Chief Operating Officer
CFO: Cindy Bell, Director Finance
CMO: Mark Elkington, M.D., Chief Medical Officer
CIO: Steven Goodman, Chief Operating Officer
CHR: Kathy Henderson, Director Human Resources, Media and Public Relations
Web address: www.willowcresthospital.com
**Control:** Corporation, Investor–owned, for–profit **Service:** Children's hospital psychiatric

Staffed Beds: 75 Admissions: 554 Census: 47 Outpatient Visits: 0 Births: 0 Total Expense ($000): 7480 Payroll Expense ($000): 4675 Personnel: 124

**MIDWEST CITY—Oklahoma County**

☐ **MIDWEST REGIONAL MEDICAL CENTER (370094)**, 2825 Parklawn Drive, Zip 73110–4258; tel. 405/610–4411 **A**1 3 5 9 10 **F**3 7 8 11 13 14 15 17 18 20 22 24 28 29 30 31 34 40 43 46 49 50 57 59 70 74 76 77 78 79 81 85 86 87 91 93 98 100 101 102 107 108 110 111 114 115 118 119 126 130 132 143 146 147 **S** Health Management Associates, Naples, FL
Primary Contact: Paul M. Jenson, Chief Executive Officer
CFO: Shea Sutherland, Chief Financial Officer
CMO: Dan Donnell, M.D., Chief of Staff
CHR: Angela C. Giese, Director Human Resources
Web address: www.midwestregional.com
**Control:** Corporation, Investor–owned, for–profit **Service:** General Medical and Surgical

Staffed Beds: 255 Admissions: 11931 Census: 134 Outpatient Visits: 122740 Births: 720 Total Expense ($000): 149982 Payroll Expense ($000): 53027 Personnel: 904

☐ **SPECIALTY HOSPITAL OF MIDWEST CITY (372012)**, 8210 National Avenue, Zip 73110–8518; tel. 405/739–0800 **A**1 9 10 **F**1 3 18 29 34 40 65 75 77 79 85 86 87 135 143 148 **P**5 **S** Encore Healthcare, Columbia, MD
Primary Contact: Chad Lovett, Chief Executive Officer
CFO: Lisa Griffis, Chief Financial Officer and Business Office Manager
Web address: www.encore–healthcare.com/specialty_midwest/index.aspx
**Control:** Partnership, Investor–owned, for–profit **Service:** Long–Term Acute Care hospital

Staffed Beds: 31 Admissions: 279 Census: 21 Outpatient Visits: 0 Births: 0 Total Expense ($000): 9898 Payroll Expense ($000): 3213 Personnel: 72

**MOORE—Cleveland County**

**MOORE MEDICAL CENTER** See Norman Regional Health System, Norman

**MUSKOGEE—Muskogee County**

⊠ △ **JACK C. MONTGOMERY VETERANS AFFAIRS MEDICAL CENTER**, (Formerly Jack C. Montgomery Veteran Affairs Medical Center), 1011 Honor Heights Drive, Zip 74401–1318; tel. 918/577–3000 **A**1 2 5 7 9 **F**3 5 8 12 18 29 30 31 34 35 36 38 39 40 44 45 50 53 54 56 57 58 59 61 63 64 65 70 74 75 77 78 79 81 82 83 84 85 86 87 90 92 93 94 96 97 98 100 101 102 103 104 107 108 114 119 127 130 132 133 135 143 146 147 148 **S** Department of Veterans Affairs, Washington, DC
Primary Contact: James R. Floyd, Director
CFO: Robert Wood, Chief Fiscal Services
CMO: Karen Gribbin, M.D., Chief of Staff
CIO: Gary Duvall, Chief Information Resource Management
CHR: Kay DeCamp, Chief Human Resources Officer
Web address: www.muskogee.va.gov
**Control:** Veterans Affairs, Government, federal **Service:** General Medical and Surgical

Staffed Beds: 83 Admissions: 3900 Census: 60 Births: 0 Total Expense ($000): 242366 Payroll Expense ($000): 84950 Personnel: 1433

**MUSKOGEE COMMUNITY HOSPITAL** See Muskogee Regional Medical Center

**OK**

---

**Hospital, Medicare Provider Number, Address, Telephone, Approval, Facility, and Physician Codes, Health Care System**

★ American Hospital Association (AHA) membership
☐ The Joint Commission accreditation    ◇ DNV Healthcare Inc. accreditation
○ Healthcare Facilities Accreditation Program
△ Commission on Accreditation of Rehabilitation Facilities (CARF) accreditation

☐ **MUSKOGEE REGIONAL MEDICAL CENTER (370025)**, 300 Rockefeller Drive, Zip 74401–5081; tel. 918/682–5501, (Includes MUSKOGEE COMMUNITY HOSPITAL, 2900 North Main Street, Zip 74401–4078; tel. 918/687–7777) **A**1 9 10 19 **F**3 8 11 13 15 18 20 22 29 30 31 35 40 43 45 46 47 48 49 51 53 54 57 59 60 62 64 65 68 70 74 75 76 77 78 79 81 85 86 87 89 90 93 96 98 100 102 105 107 108 110 111 114 115 119 120 121 123 129 130 131 144 146 147 148 **S** Capella Healthcare, Franklin, TN
Primary Contact: Robert B. Wampler, CPA, Interim Chief Executive Officer
COO: Holly Clark, Chief Operating Officer
CFO: Patty Doles, Chief Financial Officer
CHR: Linda Mathis, Director Human Resources
Web address: www.muskogeehealth.com
**Control:** Corporation, Investor–owned, for–profit **Service:** General Medical and Surgical

**Staffed Beds:** 181 **Admissions:** 8559 **Census:** 98 **Outpatient Visits:** 88361 **Births:** 706 **Total Expense ($000):** 83275 **Payroll Expense ($000):** 33764 **Personnel:** 782

**SOLARA HOSPITAL OF MUSKOGEE (372022)**, 351 South 40th Street, Zip 74401–4916; tel. 918/682–6161 **A**9 10 **F**1 3 29 40 77 85 96 130 148 **S** Cornerstone Healthcare Group, Dallas, TX
Primary Contact: Craig Koele, Chief Executive Officer
CMO: David Kyger, M.D., Chief Medical Officer
Web address: www.chghospitals.com/muskogee/
**Control:** Corporation, Investor–owned, for–profit **Service:** Long–Term Acute Care hospital

**Staffed Beds:** 41 **Admissions:** 546 **Census:** 38 **Outpatient Visits:** 4 **Births:** 0 **Total Expense ($000):** 14088 **Payroll Expense ($000):** 5951 **Personnel:** 120

### NORMAN—Cleveland County

☐ **GRIFFIN MEMORIAL HOSPITAL (374000)**, 900 East Main Street, Zip 73071–5305, Mailing Address: P.O. Box 151, Zip 73070–0151; tel. 405/321–4880 **A**1 9 10 **F**40 98 102 103 130 **P**6 **S** Oklahoma Department of Mental Health and Substance Abuse Services, Oklahoma City, OK
Primary Contact: Lawrence Gross, Executive Director
CFO: Bob Mathew, Director Finance
CMO: Stan Ardoin, M.D., Medical Director
Web address: www.odmhsas.org
**Control:** State–Government, nonfederal **Service:** Psychiatric

**Staffed Beds:** 120 **Admissions:** 1761 **Census:** 113 **Outpatient Visits:** 381 **Births:** 0 **Total Expense ($000):** 30795 **Payroll Expense ($000):** 13026 **Personnel:** 382

**J. D. MCCARTY CENTER FOR CHILDREN WITH DEVELOPMENTAL DISABILITIES (373300)**, 2002 East Robinson, Zip 73071–7420; tel. 405/307–2800 **A**10 **F**3 35 64 65 75 77 87 90 91 93 130 135 146
Primary Contact: Vicki Kuerstersteffen, Chief Executive Officer
CFO: Ken Younkin, Comptroller
CMO: Thomas Thurston, M.D., Medical Director
CIO: Joel Mann, Administrator Information Systems
CHR: Debbie Barrett, Director Human Resources
Web address: www.jdmc.org
**Control:** State–Government, nonfederal **Service:** Children's rehabilitation

**Staffed Beds:** 36 **Admissions:** 202 **Census:** 32 **Outpatient Visits:** 8444 **Births:** 0 **Total Expense ($000):** 18723 **Payroll Expense ($000):** 8137 **Personnel:** 225

☒ △ **NORMAN REGIONAL HEALTH SYSTEM (370008)**, 901 North Porter Street, Zip 73071–6482, Mailing Address: P.O. Box 1308, Zip 73070–1308; tel. 405/307–1000, (Includes MOORE MEDICAL CENTER, 700 South Telephone Road, Moore, Zip 73160; tel. 405/793–9355; Ryan Gehris, Chief Administrative Officer; NORMAN REGIONAL HOSPITAL, 901 North Porter Street, Mailing Address: P.O. Box 1308, Zip 73070–1308; tel. 405/307–1000) **A**1 2 7 9 10 **F**3 7 11 12 13 15 17 18 20 22 24 28 29 31 32 34 35 36 37 39 40 42 43 44 45 47 48 49 50 53 54 55 56 57 58 59 63 64 65 70 72 74 75 76 77 78 79 80 81 82 83 84 85 86 87 89 90 93 94 96 97 98 100 101 102 103 104 107 110 111 114 115 117 118 119 120 123 126 127 129 130 131 132 135 143 145 146 147 148 **P**5 6 8
Primary Contact: David D. Whitaker, FACHE, President and Chief Executive Officer
COO: Greg Terrell, Senior Vice President and Chief Operating Officer
CFO: Ken Hopkins, Vice President Finance and Chief Financial Officer
CMO: William McMillan, M.D., Vice President Medical Affairs
CIO: John Meharg, Director Health Information Technology
CHR: Jim Beyer, Director Human Resources
Web address: www.normanregional.com
**Control:** Hospital district or authority, Government, nonfederal **Service:** General Medical and Surgical

**Staffed Beds:** 388 **Admissions:** 17555 **Census:** 200 **Outpatient Visits:** 422256 **Births:** 3006 **Total Expense ($000):** 316980 **Payroll Expense ($000):** 135360 **Personnel:** 2023

☒ **NORMAN SPECIALTY HOSPITAL (372021)**, 1210 West Robinson Street, Zip 73069–7401; tel. 405/321–8824 **A**1 9 10 **F**1 29 30 35 40 60 68 74 75 77 87 91 100 130 148 **P**8
Primary Contact: Talitha Glosemeyer, M.P.H., Administrator
CFO: Stephanie Wortham, Director Financial Services
CMO: Mehan Shahsavari, M.D., Chief of Staff
CHR: Sandy Carroll, Coordinator Human Resources
Web address: www.normanspecialtyhospital.com
**Control:** Individual, Investor–owned, for–profit **Service:** Long–Term Acute Care hospital

**Staffed Beds:** 50 **Admissions:** 489 **Census:** 33 **Outpatient Visits:** 5 **Births:** 0 **Personnel:** 170

### NOWATA—Nowata County

**JANE PHILLIPS NOWATA HEALTH CENTER (371305)**, 237 South Locust Street, Zip 74048–3660, Mailing Address: P.O. Box 426, Zip 74048–0426; tel. 918/273–3102 **A**9 10 18 **F**3 29 34 35 40 50 57 64 68 119 128 133 146 **P**5 **S** Ascension Health, Saint Louis, MO
Primary Contact: Scott Upton, Administrator
CMO: David Caughell, M.D., Chief of Staff
Web address: www.jpmc.org
**Control:** Church–operated, Nongovernment, not–for profit **Service:** General Medical and Surgical

**Staffed Beds:** 13 **Admissions:** 202 **Census:** 5 **Outpatient Visits:** 3199 **Births:** 0 **Total Expense ($000):** 3290 **Payroll Expense ($000):** 1694 **Personnel:** 40

### OKEENE—Blaine County

★ **OKEENE MUNICIPAL HOSPITAL (371327)**, 207 East F Street, Zip 73763–9441, Mailing Address: P.O. Box 489, Zip 73763–0489; tel. 580/822–4417 **A**9 10 18 **F**3 29 34 40 45 50 59 64 68 81 85 93 97 107 111 119 130 132 133 135 146 **P**6
Primary Contact: Shelly Dunham, R.N., Chief Executive Officer
COO: Pat Lorenz, Chief Operating Officer
CFO: Sandra Lamle, Chief Financial Officer
CHR: Barbara Creps, Director Human Resources and Accounting
CNO: Tamara Fischer, Chief Nursing Officer
Web address: www.okeenehospital.com
**Control:** Hospital district or authority, Government, nonfederal **Service:** General Medical and Surgical

**Staffed Beds:** 17 **Admissions:** 262 **Census:** 5 **Outpatient Visits:** 21290 **Births:** 2 **Total Expense ($000):** 5682 **Payroll Expense ($000):** 2454 **Personnel:** 55

### OKEMAH—Okfuskee County

★ ◇ **CREEK NATION COMMUNITY HOSPITAL (371333)**, 309 North 14th Street, Zip 74859–2028; tel. 918/623–1424, (Nonreporting) **A**9 10 18 21
Primary Contact: Judy Aaron, Administrator
COO: Seneca Smith, Chief Operating Officer
CFO: Tyler McIntosh, Chief Financial Officer
CMO: Lawrence Vark, M.D., Chief Medical Officer
CHR: Mickey Romine, Manager
Web address: www.creekhealth.org
**Control:** Other not–for–profit (including NFP Corporation) **Service:** General Medical and Surgical

**Staffed Beds:** 18

### OKLAHOMA CITY—Oklahoma County

☐ **CEDAR RIDGE HOSPITAL (374023)**, 6501 N.E. 50th Street, Zip 73141–9118; tel. 405/605–6111 **A**1 9 10 **F**29 34 56 57 59 71 75 98 99 100 101 102 103 104 106 **P**5 6 **S** Universal Health Services, Inc., King of Prussia, PA
Primary Contact: Kevan Finley, Chief Executive Officer
Web address: www.cedarridgebhs.com
**Control:** Corporation, Investor–owned, for–profit **Service:** Psychiatric

**Staffed Beds:** 116 **Admissions:** 2470 **Census:** 91 **Outpatient Visits:** 0 **Births:** 0 **Total Expense ($000):** 13476 **Payroll Expense ($000):** 6645 **Personnel:** 130

**CHILDREN'S HOSPITAL OF OKLAHOMA** See OU Medical Center

☐ ◇ **COMMUNITY HOSPITAL (370203)**, 3100 S.W. 89th Street, Zip 73159–7900; tel. 405/378–3755, (Nonreporting) **A**1 9 10 21
Primary Contact: Brian L. Clemens, President and Chief Executive Officer
Web address: www.communityhospitalokc.com
**Control:** Corporation, Investor–owned, for–profit **Service:** General Medical and Surgical

**Staffed Beds:** 40

*Many Facility Codes have changed. Please refer to the AHA Guide Code Chart.* © 2013 AHA Guide

OK

✠ △ **DEACONESS HOSPITAL (370032)**, 5501 North Portland Avenue, Zip 73112–2099; tel. 405/604–6000, (Total facility includes 19 beds in nursing home–type unit) **A**1 2 7 9 10 **F**3 8 11 12 13 15 17 18 20 22 24 28 29 30 31 34 35 40 41 43 45 46 47 49 50 52 56 57 59 60 70 72 73 74 75 76 78 79 80 81 83 84 85 86 87 89 90 93 97 98 101 102 103 107 108 109 110 111 114 119 120 126 128 129 130 132 135 146 147 148 **P**8 **S** Community Health Systems, Inc., Franklin, TN
Primary Contact: Cathryn A. Hibbs, FACHE, Chief Executive Officer
COO: Steven Foster, Chief Operating Officer
CFO: Vanessa Kochevar, Chief Financial Officer
CIO: Don Bandy, Director Information Technology
CHR: Ellen Gifford, Director Human Resources
CNO: Jayne Thomas, Chief Nursing Officer
Web address: www.deaconessokc.com
**Control:** Partnership, Investor–owned, for–profit **Service:** General Medical and Surgical

**Staffed Beds:** 273 **Admissions:** 9840 **Census:** 146 **Outpatient Visits:** 72385 **Births:** 1137 **Total Expense ($000):** 130879 **Payroll Expense ($000):** 49897 **Personnel:** 1293

**EVERETT TOWER** See OU Medical Center

✠ △ **INTEGRIS BAPTIST MEDICAL CENTER (370028)**, 3300 N.W. Expressway, Zip 73112–4418; tel. 405/949–3011, (Includes INTEGRIS MENTAL HEALTH SYSTEM–SPENCER, 2601 North Spencer Road, Spencer, Zip 73084–3699, Mailing Address: P.O. Box 11137, Oklahoma City, Zip 73136–0137; tel. 405/717–9800) **A**1 2 3 5 7 9 10 **F**3 8 11 12 13 15 16 17 18 20 22 24 26 28 29 30 31 32 34 35 36 38 39 40 43 44 45 46 49 50 52 54 55 56 57 58 59 60 62 63 68 70 71 72 74 75 76 77 78 79 80 81 82 83 84 85 86 87 88 89 92 93 96 97 98 99 100 101 102 104 106 107 108 110 111 114 115 116 118 119 120 121 123 124 126 129 130 131 132 133 134 135 137 138 139 140 141 142 143 146 147 148 **P**7 **S** INTEGRIS Health, Oklahoma City, OK
Primary Contact: Timothy J. Johnsen, MS, President
CFO: Wentz J. Miller, Jr., Managing Director and Chief Financial Officer
CMO: James P. White, M.D., Chief Medical Officer
CIO: John Delano, Vice President Chief Information Officer
CHR: Robert Quiring, Vice President Human Resources
Web address: www.integrisok.com
**Control:** Other not–for–profit (including NFP Corporation) **Service:** General Medical and Surgical

**Staffed Beds:** 569 **Admissions:** 21895 **Census:** 394 **Outpatient Visits:** 176006 **Births:** 2380 **Total Expense ($000):** 577130 **Payroll Expense ($000):** 197524 **Personnel:** 3724

✠ △ **INTEGRIS SOUTHWEST MEDICAL CENTER (370106)**, 4401 South Western, Zip 73109–3413; tel. 405/636–7000 **A**1 2 7 9 10 13 **F**3 11 13 15 18 20 22 24 28 29 30 31 32 34 35 38 39 40 43 46 47 49 50 57 58 59 60 62 64 68 69 70 74 75 76 77 78 79 80 81 82 85 86 87 90 93 96 100 102 107 108 110 111 114 118 119 120 121 123 124 129 130 131 132 133 134 135 143 144 146 147 148 **P**6 7 **S** INTEGRIS Health, Oklahoma City, OK
Primary Contact: James D. Moore, FACHE, Chief Executive Officer
CFO: Errol Mitchell, Vice President
CIO: John Delano, Vice President and Chief Information Officer
CHR: Lynn Ketch, Director
CNO: David Chansolme, M.D., President of the Medical Staff
Web address: www.integris–health.com
**Control:** Other not–for–profit (including NFP Corporation) **Service:** General Medical and Surgical

**Staffed Beds:** 305 **Admissions:** 12304 **Census:** 186 **Outpatient Visits:** 158545 **Births:** 1035 **Total Expense ($000):** 224901 **Payroll Expense ($000):** 82815 **Personnel:** 1212

✠ **KINDRED HOSPITAL– OKLAHOMA CITY (372004)**, 1407 North Robinson Avenue, Zip 73103–4823; tel. 405/232–8000, (Includes KINDRED HOSPITAL–OKLAHOMA CITY SOUTH, 2129 S.W. 59th Street, Zip 73119; tel. 405/713–5955) **A**1 3 5 9 10 **F**29 40 46 60 68 70 85 87 119 130 145 148 **S** Kindred Healthcare, Louisville, KY
Primary Contact: Mark E. Rogers, Interim Chief Executive Officer
Web address: www.kindredoklahoma.com
**Control:** Corporation, Investor–owned, for–profit **Service:** General Medical and Surgical

**Staffed Beds:** 93 **Admissions:** 790 **Census:** 57 **Outpatient Visits:** 0 **Births:** 0 **Total Expense ($000):** 26079 **Payroll Expense ($000):** 10753 **Personnel:** 211

✠ **LAKESIDE WOMEN'S HOSPITAL (370199)**, 11200 North Portland Avenue, Zip 73120–5045; tel. 405/936–1500 **A**1 9 10 **F**3 12 13 15 30 35 40 45 59 64 73 76 81 85 87 110 119 126 129 132 147 **P**6
Primary Contact: Kelley Brewer, R.N., MSN, Chief Executive Officer
CFO: Darla McCallister, Chief Financial Officer
CMO: Lisa Wasemiller–Smith, M.D., Chief Medical Officer
CHR: Renee Beene, Manager Human Resources
Web address: www.lakeside–wh.net
**Control:** Corporation, Investor–owned, for–profit **Service:** Obstetrics and gynecology

**Staffed Beds:** 23 **Admissions:** 1404 **Census:** 9 **Outpatient Visits:** 2967 **Births:** 1257 **Total Expense ($000):** 20980 **Payroll Expense ($000):** 6830 **Personnel:** 118

**MCBRIDE CLINIC ORTHOPEDIC HOSPITAL (370222)**, 9600 Broadway Extension, Zip 73114–7408; tel. 405/486–2100 **A**9 10 **F**3 29 34 40 64 68 77 79 81 82 85 86 87 91 107 111 114 129 130 131 146 **P**2 6
Primary Contact: Mark Galliart, Chief Executive Officer
COO: Christine H. Weigel, R.N., Clinical Operating Officer
CFO: Annie Bassett, Director Finance
CMO: Thomas Janssen, M.D., Chief of Staff
CIO: Ronnie Green, Director Information Systems
CHR: Cathy Withiam, Director Human Resources
Web address: www.mcbrideclinicorthopedichospital.com
**Control:** Corporation, Investor–owned, for–profit **Service:** Orthopedic

**Staffed Beds:** 75 **Admissions:** 3199 **Census:** 27 **Outpatient Visits:** 152988 **Births:** 0 **Total Expense ($000):** 106319 **Payroll Expense ($000):** 45320 **Personnel:** 644

✠ △ **MERCY HOSPITAL OKLAHOMA CITY (370013)**, 4300 West Memorial Road, Zip 73120–8362; tel. 405/755–1515 **A**1 2 7 9 10 **F**3 11 13 15 28 29 30 31 32 34 35 39 40 41 43 45 49 50 53 55 57 58 59 60 61 62 63 64 65 68 69 70 72 74 75 76 77 78 79 81 82 83 84 85 86 87 89 90 91 92 93 94 96 100 101 107 108 110 111 115 117 118 119 120 121 124 126 129 130 131 132 134 135 143 146 147 148 **P**6 **S** Mercy Health, Chesterfield, MO
Primary Contact: Jim Gebhart, Jr., FACHE, President
COO: Aaron Steffens, Chief Operating Officer
CFO: Jon Vitiello, Chief Financial Officer
CMO: Mark Johnson, M.D., Chief Medical Officer
CIO: Ellen Stephens, Vice President Information Services
CHR: Becky J. Payton, Vice President Human Resources
CNO: Linda T. Fanning, R.N., Chief Nursing Officer
Web address: www.mercyok.net
**Control:** Church–operated, Nongovernment, not–for profit **Service:** General Medical and Surgical

**Staffed Beds:** 369 **Admissions:** 17140 **Census:** 245 **Outpatient Visits:** 390301 **Births:** 3002 **Total Expense ($000):** 312433 **Payroll Expense ($000):** 105945 **Personnel:** 2010

☐ **MERCY REHABILITATION HOSPITAL OKLAHOMA CITY (373033)**, 5401 West Memorial Road, Zip 73142–2026; tel. 405/752–3935, (Nonreporting) **A**1 10 **S** Centerre Healthcare, Brentwood, TN
Primary Contact: Sharon Smeltzer, Chief Executive Officer
**Control:** Partnership, Investor–owned, for–profit **Service:** Rehabilitation

**Staffed Beds:** 50

☐ ◇ **NORTHWEST SURGICAL HOSPITAL (370192)**, 9204 North May Avenue, Zip 73120–4419; tel. 405/848–1918, (Nonreporting) **A**1 9 10 21
Primary Contact: Brian L. Clemens, Chief Executive Officer
CFO: Cindy Thompson, Chief Financial Officer
CMO: Jimmy Conway, M.D., President Medical Staff
Web address: www.nwsurgicalokc.com/
**Control:** Corporation, Investor–owned, for–profit **Service:** Orthopedic

**Staffed Beds:** 9

☐ **OKLAHOMA CENTER FOR ORTHOPEDIC AND MULTI–SPECIALTY SURGERY (370212)**, 8100 South Walker, Suite C., Zip 73139–9402, Mailing Address: P.O. Box 890609, Zip 73189–0609; tel. 405/602–6500 **A**1 9 10 **F**8 29 34 39 40 45 47 48 54 59 64 74 79 81 82 85 86 93 94 97 107 111 131 148 **P**6 **S** United Surgical Partners International, Addison, TX
Primary Contact: Mike Kimzey, Chief Executive Officer and Administrator
CFO: Donna Avant, Chief Financial Officer
CHR: Sherry Wagner, Director Human Resources
Web address: www.ocomhospital.com
**Control:** Partnership, Investor–owned, for–profit **Service:** General Medical and Surgical

**Staffed Beds:** 10 **Admissions:** 570 **Census:** 4 **Outpatient Visits:** 36638 **Births:** 0 **Total Expense ($000):** 36077 **Payroll Expense ($000):** 8766 **Personnel:** 196

---

**Hospital, Medicare Provider Number, Address, Telephone, Approval, Facility, and Physician Codes, Health Care System**

★ American Hospital Association (AHA) membership
☐ The Joint Commission accreditation
◇ DNV Healthcare Inc. accreditation
○ Healthcare Facilities Accreditation Program
△ Commission on Accreditation of Rehabilitation Facilities (CARF) accreditation

© 2013 AHA Guide   *Many Facility Codes have changed. Please refer to the AHA Guide Code Chart.*   Hospitals **A503**

**OK**

✠ △ **OKLAHOMA CITY VETERANS AFFAIRS MEDICAL CENTER**, (Formerly Veterans Affairs Medical Center), 921 N.E. 13th Street, Zip 73104–5028; tel. 405/456–1000 **A**1 2 3 5 7 8 9 **F**2 3 5 6 9 10 12 17 18 20 22 24 26 28 29 30 31 34 35 38 39 40 44 45 47 48 49 50 53 54 56 57 58 59 60 61 62 63 64 65 67 68 70 71 74 75 77 78 79 80 81 82 83 84 85 86 87 90 91 93 94 96 97 98 100 101 102 103 104 105 106 107 111 114 115 116 117 119 130 132 135 143 144 146 147 148 **S** Department of Veterans Affairs, Washington, DC
Primary Contact: Adam C. Walmus, Interim Director
CFO: James Hurst, Chief Fiscal Service
CMO: Mark Huycke, M.D., Chief of Staff
CIO: Lindsay Buell, Chief Information Management Services
CHR: Kyle Inhofe, Chief Human Resources Officer
Web address: www.oklahoma.va.gov
**Control:** Veterans Affairs, Government, federal **Service:** General Medical and Surgical

**Staffed Beds:** 192 **Admissions:** 6875 **Census:** 153 **Outpatient Visits:** 516658 **Births:** 0 **Total Expense ($000):** 304086 **Payroll Expense ($000):** 178197 **Personnel:** 1886

☐ ◇ **OKLAHOMA HEART HOSPITAL (370215)**, 4050 West Memorial Road, Zip 73120–8382; tel. 405/608–3200 **A**1 9 10 21 **F**17 18 20 22 24 26 28 29 30 34 35 40 64 68 74 75 81 86 87 100 102 107 108 116 117 126 146 **P**2
Primary Contact: John Harvey, M.D., President and Chief Executive Officer
COO: Peggy Tipton, Chief Operating Officer and Chief Nursing Officer
CFO: Carol Walker, Chief Financial Officer
CMO: John Harvey, M.D., President and Chief Executive Officer
CIO: Steve Miller, Chief Information Officer
CHR: Katherine Wynn, Director Human Resource
Web address: www.okheart.com
**Control:** Corporation, Investor–owned, for–profit **Service:** Heart

**Staffed Beds:** 99 **Admissions:** 8269 **Census:** 81 **Outpatient Visits:** 286178 **Births:** 0 **Total Expense ($000):** 180096 **Payroll Expense ($000):** 69477 **Personnel:** 1415

☐ ◇ **OKLAHOMA HEART HOSPITAL SOUTH CAMPUS (370234)**, 5200 East I–240 Service Road, Zip 73135; tel. 405/628–6000 **A**1 9 10 21 **F**17 18 20 22 24 26 28 29 30 34 35 40 53 64 68 74 75 81 82 100 107 116 117 146 **P**6
Primary Contact: John Harvey, M.D., President and Chief Executive Officer
Web address: www.okheart.com
**Control:** Corporation, Investor–owned, for–profit **Service:** Heart

**Staffed Beds:** 46 **Admissions:** 4527 **Census:** 41 **Outpatient Visits:** 27868 **Births:** 0 **Total Expense ($000):** 91145 **Payroll Expense ($000):** 27958 **Personnel:** 386

☐ ◇ **OKLAHOMA SPINE HOSPITAL (370206)**, 14101 Parkway Commons Drive, Zip 73134–6012; tel. 405/749–2700, (Nonreporting) **A**1 9 10 21
Primary Contact: Kevin Blaylock, Chief Executive Officer
Web address: www.oklahomaspine.com
**Control:** Corporation, Investor–owned, for–profit **Service:** Other specialty

**Staffed Beds:** 12

**ORTHOPEDIC HOSPITAL (370220)**, 1044 S.W. 44th Street, Suite 620, Zip 73109–3609; tel. 405/631–3085 **A**10 **F**3 40 79 81 82 87 **P**8
Primary Contact: Shaun Beggs, Chief Executive Officer
CFO: Patti Bode, Chief Financial Officer
CMO: Joel L. Frazier, M.D., Medical Director
CIO: Reza Tavasoli, Information Officer
Web address: www.ortho-ok.com
**Control:** Corporation, Investor–owned, for–profit **Service:** Orthopedic

**Staffed Beds:** 8 **Admissions:** 127 **Census:** 1 **Outpatient Visits:** 1040 **Births:** 0 **Total Expense ($000):** 4579 **Payroll Expense ($000):** 2075 **Personnel:** 33

✠ **OU MEDICAL CENTER (370093)**, 1200 Everett Drive, Zip 73104–5047, Mailing Address: P.O. Box 26307, Zip 73126–0307; tel. 405/271–3636, (Includes CHILDREN'S HOSPITAL OF OKLAHOMA, 940 N.E. 13th Street, Zip 73104, Mailing Address: P.O. Box 26307, Zip 73126; tel. 405/271–6165; EVERETT TOWER, 1200 Everett Drive, Zip 73104; tel. 405/271–4700; OU MEDICAL CENTER EDMOND, 1 South Bryant Avenue, Edmond, Zip 73034–6309; tel. 405/341–6100; Jordan Herget, Chief Executive Officer; PRESBYTERIAN TOWER, 700 N.E. 13th Street, Zip 73104–5070; tel. 405/271–5100) **A**1 2 3 5 8 9 10 **F**3 8 11 12 13 15 17 18 19 20 21 22 23 24 25 26 27 28 29 30 31 32 34 35 37 38 39 40 41 43 45 46 47 48 49 50 51 52 55 56 57 58 59 60 61 63 64 65 66 72 73 74 75 76 77 78 79 81 82 83 84 85 86 87 88 89 91 92 93 94 96 97 98 100 102 103 105 107 108 110 111 114 115 116 117 118 119 120 121 123 124 126 129 130 131 132 135 136 138 139 142 144 145 146 147 148 **S** HCA, Nashville, TN
Primary Contact: Charles Spicer, President and Chief Executive Officer
COO: Rebecca Benoit, Chief Operating Officer
CFO: Jim Watson, Chief Financial Officer
CMO: Curt Steinhart, M.D., Chief Medical Officer
CIO: Larry Forsyth, Director Information Services
CHR: Laura Land, Chief Human Resources Officer
Web address: www.oumedicine.com/oumedicalcenter
**Control:** Corporation, Investor–owned, for–profit **Service:** General Medical and Surgical

**Staffed Beds:** 680 **Admissions:** 30560 **Census:** 502 **Outpatient Visits:** 322076 **Births:** 4420 **Total Expense ($000):** 707156 **Payroll Expense ($000):** 199042 **Personnel:** 3775

**PRESBYTERIAN TOWER** See OU Medical Center

✠ **SELECT SPECIALTY HOSPITAL–OKLAHOMA CITY (372009)**, 3524 N.W. 56th Street, Zip 73112–4518; tel. 405/606–6700 **A**1 9 10 **F**1 3 12 29 40 74 75 79 85 87 107 119 130 148 **S** Select Medical Corporation, Mechanicsburg, PA
Primary Contact: Connie Strickland, Chief Executive Officer
Web address: www.selectspecialtyhospitals.com/company/locations/oklahomacity.aspx
**Control:** Corporation, Investor–owned, for–profit **Service:** Long–Term Acute Care hospital

**Staffed Beds:** 72 **Admissions:** 801 **Census:** 57 **Outpatient Visits:** 0 **Births:** 0 **Total Expense ($000):** 25603 **Payroll Expense ($000):** 10490 **Personnel:** 217

✠ △ **ST. ANTHONY HOSPITAL (370037)**, 1000 North Lee Street, Zip 73102–1080, Mailing Address: P.O. Box 205, Zip 73101–0205; tel. 405/272–7000, (Includes BONE AND JOINT HOSPITAL, 1111 North Dewey Avenue, Zip 73103–2609; tel. 405/272–9671; Chad S. Aduddell, President) **A**1 2 3 5 7 9 10 12 13 **F**3 4 5 7 8 11 12 13 15 17 18 20 22 24 28 29 30 31 34 35 36 37 39 40 42 43 45 46 47 48 49 50 54 56 57 59 64 67 70 71 74 76 77 78 79 81 82 84 85 86 87 89 90 91 92 93 96 97 98 99 100 102 103 104 105 106 107 108 109 110 111 112 113 114 115 116 117 119 120 121 123 124 126 127 129 130 131 132 136 138 144 145 146 147 148 **P**2 7 **S** SSM Health Care, Saint Louis, MO
Primary Contact: Michael D. Beaver, President
COO: Marti Jourden, FACHE, Chief Quality Officer
CFO: Shasta Manuel, Executive Director Finance
CMO: Kersey Winfree, M.D., Chief Medical Officer
CIO: Kevin Olson, Director Information Systems
CHR: Cynthia Brundise, Vice President Human Resources
Web address: www.saintsok.com
**Control:** Church–operated, Nongovernment, not–for profit **Service:** General Medical and Surgical

**Staffed Beds:** 524 **Admissions:** 20687 **Census:** 398 **Outpatient Visits:** 255051 **Births:** 1345 **Total Expense ($000):** 430930 **Payroll Expense ($000):** 147852 **Personnel:** 2456

☐ **SURGICAL HOSPITAL OF OKLAHOMA (370201)**, 100 S.E. 59th Street, Zip 73129–3616; tel. 405/634–9300 **A**1 10 **F**3 40 81 129
Primary Contact: Phil Ross, Chief Executive Officer
Web address: www.sh-ok.com
**Control:** Partnership, Investor–owned, for–profit **Service:** General Medical and Surgical

**Staffed Beds:** 12 **Admissions:** 251 **Census:** 2 **Outpatient Visits:** 5331 **Births:** 0 **Total Expense ($000):** 11668 **Payroll Expense ($000):** 3802 **Personnel:** 68

✠ **VALIR REHABILITATION HOSPITAL (373025)**, 700 N.W. Seventh Street, Zip 73102–1212; tel. 405/236–3131 **A**1 10 **F**3 28 29 30 35 40 54 68 75 86 87 90 91 93 96 100 119 143
Primary Contact: Lee Frazier, FACHE, Chief Executive Officer
COO: Ginger Castleberry, Corporate Risk Manager, Quality and Patient Safety
CFO: Scott Brown, Chief Financial Officer
CMO: Tonya Washburn, M.D., Medical Director
CIO: Mark Dickey, Director Business Development
CHR: Bill Turner, Vice President Human Resources
Web address: www.valir.com
**Control:** Corporation, Investor–owned, for–profit **Service:** Rehabilitation

**Staffed Beds:** 45 **Admissions:** 862 **Census:** 27 **Outpatient Visits:** 4750 **Births:** 0 **Total Expense ($000):** 12088 **Payroll Expense ($000):** 6624 **Personnel:** 165

**VETERANS AFFAIRS MEDICAL CENTER** See Oklahoma City Veterans Affairs Medical Center

## OKMULGEE—Okmulgee County

**GEORGE NIGH REHABILITATION CENTER** See George Nigh Rehabilitation Institute

**GEORGE NIGH REHABILITATION INSTITUTE (373026)**, 900 East Airport Road, Zip 74447–9082, Mailing Address: P.O. Box 1118, Zip 74447–1118; tel. 918/756–9211, (Total facility includes 8 beds in nursing home–type unit) **A**10 **F**1 28 29 34 56 57 82 90 93 94 96 128 130 135 143 146 148 **P**5
Primary Contact: Gala McBee, Administrator
CFO: Djogan Djogan, Chief Financial Officer
CHR: Denaye Atwell, Manager Human Resources
Web address: www.gnrc.ouhsc.edu/
**Control:** State–Government, nonfederal **Service:** Rehabilitation

**Staffed Beds:** 38 **Admissions:** 352 **Census:** 14 **Outpatient Visits:** 13944 **Births:** 0 **Total Expense ($000):** 6298 **Payroll Expense ($000):** 5408 **Personnel:** 91

★ **OKMULGEE MEMORIAL HOSPITAL (370057)**, 1401 Morris Drive, Zip 74447–6429, Mailing Address: P.O. Box 1038, Zip 74447–1038; tel. 918/756–4233 **A**9 10 **F**3 11 15 29 30 34 40 43 45 50 56 57 59 62 68 79 81 83 85 87 89 92 93 98 103 106 107 108 115 119 128 130 133 146 **P**6 **S** QHR, Brentwood, TN
Primary Contact: George N. Miller, Jr., Chief Executive Officer
CFO: John W. Crawford, Chief Financial Officer
CMO: Michael Sandlin, M.D., Chief of Staff
CIO: Sharon Riker, Manager Data Processing
CHR: Stacey R. Burton, Director Human Resources
Web address: www.okmulgeehospital.com
**Control:** Other not–for–profit (including NFP Corporation) **Service:** General Medical and Surgical

**Staffed Beds:** 46 **Admissions:** 1098 **Census:** 16 **Outpatient Visits:** 30854 **Births:** 2 **Total Expense ($000):** 17119 **Payroll Expense ($000):** 8505 **Personnel:** 180

## OWASSO—Tulsa County

★ **BAILEY MEDICAL CENTER (370228)**, 10502 North 110th East Avenue, Zip 74055–6655; tel. 918/376–8000 **A**9 10 **F**3 12 13 15 18 29 34 40 45 51 57 70 76 79 81 94 107 108 110 111 115 119 129 132 146 147 **S** Ardent Health Services, Nashville, TN
Primary Contact: Keith Mason, Chief Executive Officer
CFO: Becky Speight, Chief Financial Officer
CHR: Rachel Steward, Manager Human Resources
Web address: www.baileymedicalcenter.com
**Control:** Corporation, Investor–owned, for–profit **Service:** General Medical and Surgical

**Staffed Beds:** 37 **Admissions:** 1259 **Census:** 8 **Outpatient Visits:** 26648 **Births:** 310 **Total Expense ($000):** 28945 **Payroll Expense ($000):** 9855 **Personnel:** 172

★ **ST. JOHN OWASSO (370227)**, 12451 East 100th Street North, Zip 74055–4600; tel. 918/274–5000 **A**9 10 **F**3 11 13 15 18 29 30 34 35 40 45 57 59 64 68 76 79 81 85 87 93 107 108 110 111 114 115 119 130 131 132 146 **P**5 6 **S** Ascension Health, Saint Louis, MO
Primary Contact: David L. Phillips, President and Chief Executive Officer
CFO: Lex S. Anderson, Chief Financial Officer
CMO: Tim Hepner, M.D., Medical Director
CIO: Mike Reeves, Chief Information Officer
CNO: Dan Hall, R.N., Director of Nursing
Web address: www.stjohnowasso.com
**Control:** Church–operated, Nongovernment, not–for profit **Service:** General Medical and Surgical

**Staffed Beds:** 36 **Admissions:** 1807 **Census:** 11 **Outpatient Visits:** 56449 **Births:** 317 **Total Expense ($000):** 29924 **Payroll Expense ($000):** 10383 **Personnel:** 219

## PAULS VALLEY—Garvin County

★ **PAULS VALLEY GENERAL HOSPITAL (370156)**, 100 Valley Drive, Zip 73075–6613, Mailing Address: P.O. Box 368, Zip 73075–0368; tel. 405/238–5501 **A**9 10 20 **F**3 7 8 10 11 13 15 29 30 40 45 46 57 59 62 63 64 65 76 77 81 82 84 87 89 93 107 111 119 129 130 132 133 146 147 148 **P**3
Primary Contact: Bridget Cosby, Chief Executive Officer
CIO: Craig Bowie, Information Technology Manager
CHR: Kari Kuykendall, Human Resources Specialist
CNO: Karla Brown, Interim Chief Nursing Officer
Web address: www.pvgh.net
**Control:** City–Government, nonfederal **Service:** General Medical and Surgical

**Staffed Beds:** 54 **Admissions:** 1011 **Census:** 13 **Outpatient Visits:** 25145 **Births:** 78 **Total Expense ($000):** 17660 **Payroll Expense ($000):** 8234 **Personnel:** 216

## PAWHUSKA—Osage County

**PAWHUSKA HOSPITAL (371309)**, 1101 East 15th Street, Zip 74056–1920; tel. 918/287–3232 **A**9 10 18 **F**3 11 29 34 35 40 50 57 64 68 75 90 93 107 128 133 135 148 **P**1 **S** Ascension Health, Saint Louis, MO
Primary Contact: Karen Arrowsmith, Administrator
CMO: Mike Priest, M.D., Chief of Staff
**Control:** Church–operated, Nongovernment, not–for profit **Service:** General Medical and Surgical

**Staffed Beds:** 27 **Admissions:** 98 **Census:** 3 **Outpatient Visits:** 7647 **Total Expense ($000):** 4231 **Payroll Expense ($000):** 2051 **Personnel:** 49

## PERRY—Noble County

★ **PERRY MEMORIAL HOSPITAL (370139)**, 501 North 14th Street, Zip 73077–5099; tel. 580/336–3541 **A**9 10 20 **F**3 11 15 29 34 40 45 57 59 62 64 79 81 85 93 107 111 114 119 133 146 148 **S** QHR, Brentwood, TN
Primary Contact: Howard D. Turner, Chief Executive Officer
CFO: Terry W. Shambles, Chief Financial Officer
CMO: Michael Hartwig, M.D., Chief of Staff
CHR: Robin Webb, Director Human Resources
Web address: www.pmh–ok.org
**Control:** Hospital district or authority, Government, nonfederal **Service:** General Medical and Surgical

**Staffed Beds:** 26 **Admissions:** 516 **Census:** 9 **Outpatient Visits:** 15590 **Births:** 0 **Total Expense ($000):** 8103 **Payroll Expense ($000):** 3640 **Personnel:** 84

## PONCA CITY—Kay County

⊞ **PONCA CITY MEDICAL CENTER (370006)**, 1900 North 14th Street, Zip 74601–2099; tel. 580/765–3321 **A**1 9 10 19 **F**3 13 15 20 28 29 30 31 34 35 40 43 46 49 51 53 56 57 59 64 65 66 68 69 70 74 75 76 77 78 79 81 82 85 89 90 93 97 107 110 111 114 117 118 119 129 130 131 132 133 135 145 146 147 148 **S** Community Health Systems, Inc., Franklin, TN
Primary Contact: R. Andrew Wachtel, FACHE, Chief Executive Officer
COO: Nikia Beene, Assistant Chief Executive Officer
CFO: Geoff Blomeley, Interim Chief Financial Officer
CIO: Rob Dreussi, Interim Director Information Systems
CHR: Lisa Zaloudek, Chief Human Resources Officer
CNO: Jeanne Stara, R.N., Chief Nursing Officer
Web address: www.poncamedcenter.com
**Control:** Corporation, Investor–owned, for–profit **Service:** General Medical and Surgical

**Staffed Beds:** 72 **Admissions:** 3505 **Census:** 31 **Outpatient Visits:** 67509 **Births:** 651 **Total Expense ($000):** 49753 **Payroll Expense ($000):** 15098 **Personnel:** 357

## POTEAU—Le Flore County

★ **EASTERN OKLAHOMA MEDICAL CENTER (370040)**, 105 Wall Street, Zip 74953–4433, Mailing Address: P.O. Box 1148, Zip 74953–1148; tel. 918/647–8161 **A**9 10 **F**3 4 11 13 15 17 29 40 43 45 50 57 62 68 70 76 81 85 86 89 107 110 111 114 115 116 119 146 **P**4
Primary Contact: Melinda D. Davis, R.N., MSN, Interim Chief Executive Officer
CFO: Nancy Frier, Chief Financial Officer
CMO: Dennis Carter, M.D., Chief of Staff
CIO: Michael C. Huggins, Administrator Network System
CHR: Michele Oglesby, Manager Human Resources
Web address: www.eomchospital.com
**Control:** County–Government, nonfederal **Service:** General Medical and Surgical

**Staffed Beds:** 84 **Admissions:** 2166 **Census:** 27 **Outpatient Visits:** 27615 **Births:** 345 **Total Expense ($000):** 17669 **Payroll Expense ($000):** 8017 **Personnel:** 258

## PRAGUE—Lincoln County

★ **PRAGUE COMMUNITY HOSPITAL (371301)**, 1322 Klabzuba Avenue, Zip 74864–9005, Mailing Address: P.O. Box S., Zip 74864–1090; tel. 405/567–4922 **A**9 10 18 **F**18 29 34 40 43 45 57 59 64 68 70 81 89 93 107 111 119 127 128 129 130 133 148 **P**6 **S** Rural Community Hospitals of America, Kansas City, MO
Primary Contact: Joan Walters, R.N., MSN, Administrator
CFO: Doug Erickson, Chief Financial Officer
CMO: Darryl Jackson, D.O., Chief of Staff
CIO: Rhonda Whitnum, Director Health Improvement Management
CHR: Angie Brezny, Director Human Resources
Web address: www.praguehospital.com
**Control:** Corporation, Investor–owned, for–profit **Service:** General Medical and Surgical

**Staffed Beds:** 19 **Admissions:** 297 **Census:** 3 **Outpatient Visits:** 22084 **Births:** 0 **Total Expense ($000):** 5403 **Payroll Expense ($000):** 3070 **Personnel:** 60

---

**Hospital, Medicare Provider Number, Address, Telephone, Approval, Facility, and Physician Codes, Health Care System**

★ American Hospital Association (AHA) membership
☐ The Joint Commission accreditation
◇ DNV Healthcare Inc. accreditation
○ Healthcare Facilities Accreditation Program
△ Commission on Accreditation of Rehabilitation Facilities (CARF) accreditation

## PRYOR—Mayes County

☒ **INTEGRIS MAYES COUNTY MEDICAL CENTER (370015)**, 111 North Bailey Street, Zip 74361–4201, Mailing Address: P.O. Box 278, Zip 74362–0278; tel. 918/825–1600 **A**1 9 10 **F**3 7 8 11 15 18 29 30 34 35 40 46 47 48 49 57 59 62 63 64 65 68 75 76 77 79 81 87 91 92 93 94 97 107 108 111 119 130 132 133 135 146 **S** Health Management Associates, Naples, FL
Primary Contact: Douglas K. Weaver, FACHE, President
CFO: Kristy McCollough, Assistant Administrator and Chief Financial Officer
CMO: Lora Collier, M.D., Chief Medical Staff
CHR: Jamil Haynes, Director Human Resources
Web address: www.integrismayescounty.com
**Control:** Corporation, Investor–owned, for–profit **Service:** General Medical and Surgical

**Staffed Beds:** 24 **Admissions:** 462 **Census:** 4 **Total Expense ($000):** 17632 **Payroll Expense ($000):** 7132 **Personnel:** 207

## PURCELL—Mcclain County

★ **PURCELL MUNICIPAL HOSPITAL (370158)**, 1500 North Green Avenue, Zip 73080–1699, Mailing Address: P.O. Box 511, Zip 73080–0511; tel. 405/527–6524 **A**9 10 **F**3 11 13 15 18 29 30 35 40 45 48 57 59 64 65 76 77 79 81 82 86 87 89 93 110 114 119 127 130 133 **P**8
Primary Contact: James T. Berry, Chief Executive Officer
COO: Lisa Roberts, Chief Operating Officer
CFO: Jennifer Warren, Chief Financial Officer
CMO: Heather Lynch, M.D., Chief of Staff
CIO: Jennifer Coates, Coordinator Information Technology
CHR: Tara Selfridge, Manager Human Resources
Web address: www.purcellhospital.com
**Control:** City–Government, nonfederal **Service:** General Medical and Surgical

**Staffed Beds:** 30 **Admissions:** 1219 **Census:** 12 **Outpatient Visits:** 45930 **Births:** 37 **Total Expense ($000):** 13987 **Payroll Expense ($000):** 5808 **Personnel:** 150

## SALLISAW—Sequoyah County

**SEQUOYAH MEMORIAL HOSPITAL (370112)**, 213 East Redwood Street, Zip 74955–2811, Mailing Address: P.O. Box 505, Zip 74955–0505; tel. 918/774–1100 **A**9 10 **F**3 11 14 15 18 30 32 34 35 40 43 45 46 50 57 59 60 62 63 64 65 77 81 84 86 87 91 93 107 109 110 111 119 128 129 130 132 133 146 **P**4
Primary Contact: Debra R. Knoke, Chief Executive Officer
COO: Debra R. Knoke, Chief Executive Officer
CFO: Glenn Click, Chief Financial Officer
CMO: William E. Wood, M.D., Chief of Staff
CIO: Gary McClanahan, Chief Information Officer
Web address: www.sequoyahmemorial.com/home.php
**Control:** Hospital district or authority, Government, nonfederal **Service:** General Medical and Surgical

**Staffed Beds:** 26 **Admissions:** 1027 **Census:** 7 **Outpatient Visits:** 20407 **Births:** 1 **Total Expense ($000):** 15079 **Payroll Expense ($000):** 7374 **Personnel:** 213

## SAPULPA—Creek County

★ **ST. JOHN SAPULPA (371312)**, 519 South Division Street, Zip 74066–4501, Mailing Address: P.O. Box 1368, Zip 74067–1368; tel. 918/224–4280, (Nonreporting) **A**9 10 18 **S** Ascension Health, Saint Louis, MO
Primary Contact: Valerie Round, Chief Executive Officer
CMO: Roger D. Wilson, M.D., Medical Director
Web address: www.sjmc.org
**Control:** Church–operated, Nongovernment, not–for profit **Service:** General Medical and Surgical

**Staffed Beds:** 25

## SAYRE—Beckham County

★ **SAYRE MEMORIAL HOSPITAL (370103)**, 911 Hospital Drive, Zip 73662–1206; tel. 580/928–5541 **A**9 10 **F**3 11 29 34 40 45 57 59 62 64 82 93 98 103 104 107 114 119 128 130 133 **P**6 **S** Mercy Health, Chesterfield, MO
Primary Contact: John Lampert, Chief Executive Officer
CFO: Brenda K. Doyel, Chief Financial Officer
Web address: www.sayrehospital.org
**Control:** Hospital district or authority, Government, nonfederal **Service:** General Medical and Surgical

**Staffed Beds:** 25 **Admissions:** 526 **Census:** 10 **Outpatient Visits:** 12078 **Births:** 0 **Total Expense ($000):** 8829 **Payroll Expense ($000):** 4432 **Personnel:** 70

## SEILING—Dewey County

★ **SEILING COMMUNITY HOSPITAL (371332)**, Highway 60 N.E., Zip 73663, Mailing Address: P.O. Box 720, Zip 73663–0720; tel. 580/922–7361 **A**9 10 18 **F**40 41 65 107 111 119 129 133 **P**5 **S** Rural Community Hospitals of America, Kansas City, MO
Primary Contact: Larry Troxell, Chief Executive Officer
CFO: Nancy Freed, Chief Financial Officer
CMO: Kenneth Duffy, M.D., Medical Director
CHR: Sandy Landreth, Director Human Resources
**Control:** Corporation, Investor–owned, for–profit **Service:** General Medical and Surgical

**Staffed Beds:** 18 **Admissions:** 363 **Census:** 5 **Outpatient Visits:** 7329 **Births:** 0 **Total Expense ($000):** 2146 **Payroll Expense ($000):** 1566 **Personnel:** 39

## SEMINOLE—Seminole County

☒ **INTEGRIS SEMINOLE MEDICAL CENTER (370229)**, 2401 Wrangler Boulevard, Zip 74868–1917; tel. 405/303–4000 **A**1 9 10 **F**3 11 15 18 29 30 34 35 40 41 51 57 59 65 68 79 81 82 93 102 107 108 110 111 114 119 130 135 146 148 **P**6 **S** Health Management Associates, Naples, FL
Primary Contact: Jimmy D. Stuart, Chief Executive Officer
CMO: Nikki Chawla, M.D., Medical Director
CHR: Lori Friend, Human Resoures Director
CNO: Barbara Lewis, Chief Nursing Officer
Web address: www.hma.com
**Control:** Corporation, Investor–owned, for–profit **Service:** General Medical and Surgical

**Staffed Beds:** 32 **Admissions:** 370 **Census:** 4 **Outpatient Visits:** 16143 **Births:** 0 **Total Expense ($000):** 8761 **Payroll Expense ($000):** 2872 **Personnel:** 89

## SHATTUCK—Ellis County

★ **NEWMAN MEMORIAL HOSPITAL (370007)**, 905 South Main Street, Zip 73858–9205; tel. 580/938–2551 **A**9 10 20 **F**3 11 13 15 29 30 34 35 39 40 53 59 62 64 65 69 76 81 87 93 104 107 111 115 119 130 133 146 **P**6
Primary Contact: Kevin O'Brien, Interim Chief Executive Officer
COO: Kevin O'Brien, Chief Operating Officer
CMO: Barbara H. Miller, M.D., Chief Medical Officer
CNO: Denise Ketterman, R.N., Chief Nursing Officer
Web address: www.newmanmemorialhospital.org
**Control:** Other not–for–profit (including NFP Corporation) **Service:** General Medical and Surgical

**Staffed Beds:** 27 **Admissions:** 428 **Census:** 3 **Outpatient Visits:** 37067 **Births:** 139 **Total Expense ($000):** 11053 **Payroll Expense ($000):** 3860 **Personnel:** 74

## SHAWNEE—Pottawatomie County

**SOLARA HOSPITAL OF SHAWNEE (372019)**, 1900 Gordon Cooper Drive, 2nd Floor, Zip 74801–8603; tel. 405/395–5800, (Nonreporting) **A**9 10 **S** Cornerstone Healthcare Group, Dallas, TX
Primary Contact: Michael E. Gerten, Chief Executive Officer
COO: Michael E. Gerten, Chief Executive Officer
CMO: Phillip A. Haddad, M.D., Chief Medical Officer
Web address: www.chghospitals.com/shawnee/
**Control:** Corporation, Investor–owned, for–profit **Service:** Long–Term Acute Care hospital

**Staffed Beds:** 34

☒ ◇ **ST. ANTHONY SHAWNEE HOSPITAL (370149)**, 1102 West MacArthur Street, Zip 74804–1744; tel. 405/273–2270, (Data for 184 days) **A**1 2 9 10 19 21 **F**3 11 13 15 18 20 29 30 34 43 45 50 57 59 60 64 65 68 69 70 75 76 77 79 81 82 87 90 93 94 107 110 111 114 119 121 123 129 130 131 132 135 144 146 147 148 **P**6 **S** SSM Health Care, Saint Louis, MO
Primary Contact: Charles E. Skillings, President and Chief Executive Officer
COO: Thomas Keller, Executive Vice President and Chief Operating Officer
CFO: Jennifer Pierce, Administrative Director of Finance
CMO: Gaynell Anderson, M.D., Medical Director
CIO: Linda E. Brown, Vice President of Support Services
CHR: Michael Spears, Vice President of Human Resources
CNO: Angela Mohr, R.N., Vice President of Nursing
Web address: www.stanthonyshawnee.com
**Control:** Other not–for–profit (including NFP Corporation) **Service:** General Medical and Surgical

**Staffed Beds:** 131 **Admissions:** 2424 **Census:** 43 **Outpatient Visits:** 54285 **Births:** 480 **Total Expense ($000):** 34898 **Payroll Expense ($000):** 13742 **Personnel:** 523

**UNITY HEALTH CENTER** See St. Anthony Shawnee Hospital

## SPENCER—Oklahoma County

**INTEGRIS MENTAL HEALTH SYSTEM–SPENCER** See Integris Baptist Medical Center, Oklahoma City

*Many Facility Codes have changed. Please refer to the AHA Guide Code Chart.*

**STIGLER—Haskell County**

**HASKELL COUNTY COMMUNITY HOSPITAL (371335)**, 401 Northwest H Street, Zip 74462–1625, Mailing Address: P.O. Box 728, Zip 74462–0728; tel. 918/967–4682, (Nonreporting) **A**9 10 18 **S** Rural Community Hospitals of America, Kansas City, MO
Primary Contact: Alan Bird, Chief Executive Officer
CMO: Mark McCurry, M.D., Chief of Staff
CIO: Steve Hurst, Information Technology Specialist
Web address: www.haskellhospital.com
**Control:** Corporation, Investor–owned, for–profit **Service:** General Medical and Surgical

Staffed Beds: 32

**HASKELL COUNTY HEALTHCARE SYSTEM** See Haskell County Community Hospital

**STILLWATER—Payne County**

★ △ ◇ **STILLWATER MEDICAL CENTER (370049)**, 1323 West Sixth Avenue, Zip 74074–4399, Mailing Address: P.O. Box 2408, Zip 74076–2408; tel. 405/372–1480 **A**7 9 10 21 **F**3 8 11 13 15 18 20 22 28 29 31 34 35 40 43 45 46 47 48 49 50 51 53 59 62 65 68 69 70 74 75 76 79 81 82 85 87 90 91 93 94 107 108 110 111 115 117 119 126 129 130 132 135 146 147 148 **P**6 7
Primary Contact: Jerry G. Moeller, FACHE, President and Chief Executive Officer
CFO: Alan Lovelace, Vice President and Chief Financial Officer
CMO: Woody Jenkins, M.D., Chief of Medical Staff
CIO: Chris Roark, Chief Information Officer
CHR: Keith Hufnagel, Director Human Resources
CNO: Liz Michael, Vice President Patient Care Services and Chief Nursing Officer
Web address: www.stillwater–medical.org
**Control:** Hospital district or authority, Government, nonfederal **Service:** General Medical and Surgical

Staffed Beds: 87 Admissions: 4698 Census: 48 Outpatient Visits: 119670 Births: 965 Total Expense ($000): 95614 Payroll Expense ($000): 41389 Personnel: 871

**STILWELL—Adair County**

**MEMORIAL HOSPITAL (370178)**, 1401 West Locust, Zip 74960–3275, Mailing Address: P.O. Box 272, Zip 74960–0272; tel. 918/696–3101, (Nonreporting) **A**9 10
Primary Contact: Alan L. Adams, President
Web address: www.stilwellmemorialhospital.com
**Control:** Corporation, Investor–owned, for–profit **Service:** General Medical and Surgical

Staffed Beds: 30

**STROUD—Lincoln County**

**STROUD REGIONAL MEDICAL CENTER (371316)**, Highway 66 West, Zip 74079, Mailing Address: P.O. Box 530, Zip 74079–0530; tel. 918/968–3571 **A**9 10 18 **F**3 8 11 29 30 34 35 40 41 43 45 57 59 64 81 89 107 114 128 129 130 133 **P**5 **S** Southern Plains Medical Group, Oklahoma City, OK
Primary Contact: Regina Peters, Chief Executive Officer
COO: Regina Peters, Chief Executive Officer
CFO: Richard E. Rentsch, President
CMO: Ken Darvin, M.D., Chief of Staff
CIO: Donna Buchanan, Director Nursing
CHR: Leannette Raffety, Administrative Generalist
**Control:** Other not–for–profit (including NFP Corporation) **Service:** General Medical and Surgical

Staffed Beds: 25 Admissions: 371 Census: 4 Outpatient Visits: 10238 Births: 0 Personnel: 58

**SULPHUR—Murray County**

★ **ARBUCKLE MEMORIAL HOSPITAL (371328)**, 2011 West Broadway Street, Zip 73086–4221; tel. 580/622–2161 **A**9 10 18 **F**29 32 40 45 56 57 81 87 93 107 119 129 133 135 148 **P**6 **S** Mercy Health, Chesterfield, MO
Primary Contact: Darin Farrell, Chief Executive Officer
CFO: Denise Hancock, Chief Financial Officer
CMO: Teresa Lynn, D.O., Chief of Staff
CIO: Tiffany Sands, Manager Health Information
CHR: Sallie Tomlinson, Manager Human Resources
Web address: www.arbucklehospital.com/
**Control:** County–Government, nonfederal **Service:** General Medical and Surgical

Staffed Beds: 13 Admissions: 613 Census: 12 Outpatient Visits: 27522 Births: 0 Total Expense ($000): 13295 Payroll Expense ($000): 5653 Personnel: 123

**TAHLEQUAH—Cherokee County**

⊠ ◇ **CHEROKEE NATION W.W. HASTINGS INDIAN HOSPITAL (370171)**, (Formerly William W. Hastings Indian Hospital), 100 South Bliss Avenue, Zip 74464–2512; tel. 918/458–3100, (Nonreporting) **A**1 10 21 **S** U. S. Indian Health Service, Rockville, MD
Primary Contact: Brian Hail, Chief Executive Officer
COO: Mitchell Thornbrugh, Administrative Officer
CMO: Douglas Nolan, M.D., Medical Director
CIO: Mitchell Thornbrugh, Acting Chief Information Officer
CNO: Valerie J. Rogers, Director of Nursing
Web address: www.cherokee.org
**Control:** PHS, Indian Service, Government, federal **Service:** General Medical and Surgical

Staffed Beds: 58

★ **TAHLEQUAH CITY HOSPITAL (370089)**, 1400 East Downing Street, Zip 74464–3324, Mailing Address: P.O. Box 1008, Zip 74465–1008; tel. 918/456–0641 **A**9 10 13 20 **F**3 7 11 13 15 17 18 20 22 24 28 29 30 34 35 39 40 43 45 46 47 49 51 57 59 60 64 68 70 74 75 76 77 78 79 80 81 82 85 87 89 90 93 97 98 103 107 108 110 111 114 115 116 117 119 120 121 123 129 130 135 146 147 148 **P**6
Primary Contact: Brian K. Woodliff, President and Chief Executive Officer
COO: David McClain, Executive Vice President Operations
CFO: Julie Newman, Vice President Finance
CIO: Julie Newman, Vice President Finance
CHR: Phyllis Smith, Vice President Human Resources
Web address: www.tch–ok.org
**Control:** City–Government, nonfederal **Service:** General Medical and Surgical

Staffed Beds: 90 Admissions: 4304 Census: 49 Outpatient Visits: 140445 Births: 403 Total Expense ($000): 70257 Payroll Expense ($000): 24451 Personnel: 686

**TALIHINA—Latimer County**

⊠ **CHOCTAW NATION HEALTH CARE CENTER (370172)**, One Choctaw Way, Zip 74571–2022; tel. 918/567–7000, (Nonreporting) **A**1 10
Primary Contact: Teresa Jackson, Chief Executive Officer
COO: Todd Hallmark, Chief Operating Officer
CMO: Jason Hill, M.D., Chief Medical Officer
CIO: Skip Leader, Chief Information Officer
CHR: Evelyn Jones, Director Human Resources
Web address: www.choctawnationhealth.com
**Control:** Other not–for–profit (including NFP Corporation) **Service:** General Medical and Surgical

Staffed Beds: 37

**TISHOMINGO—Johnston County**

**JOHNSTON MEMORIAL HOSPITAL** See Mercy Hospital Tishomingo

★ **MERCY HOSPITAL TISHOMINGO (371304)**, 1000 South Byrd Street, Zip 73460–3299; tel. 580/371–2327 **A**9 10 18 **F**3 29 40 133 146 **S** Mercy Health, Chesterfield, MO
Primary Contact: Gary Sharum, Administrator
CFO: Lisa Dowling, Manager Finance
CHR: Arlita Hummelke, Manager Human Resources
Web address: www.mercy.net/
**Control:** Church–operated, Nongovernment, not–for profit **Service:** General Medical and Surgical

Staffed Beds: 25 Admissions: 497 Census: 5 Outpatient Visits: 4415 Births: 0 Total Expense ($000): 4991 Payroll Expense ($000): 2580 Personnel: 37

**TULSA—Tulsa County**

**BROOKHAVEN HOSPITAL (374012)**, 201 South Garnett Road, Zip 74128–1805; tel. 918/438–4257 **A**9 10 **F**4 5 29 30 77 98 104 106 130 132
Primary Contact: Rolf B. Gainer, Chief Executive Officer and Administrator
CFO: Kenneth Pierce, Chief Financial Officer
CMO: Mark Gage, D.O., Medical Director
CHR: Mike Atkinson, Director Administrative Services
Web address: www.brookhavenhospital.com
**Control:** Corporation, Investor–owned, for–profit **Service:** Psychiatric

Staffed Beds: 64 Admissions: 1192 Census: 52 Outpatient Visits: 2659 Births: 0 Total Expense ($000): 10369 Payroll Expense ($000): 5808 Personnel: 159

---

**Hospital, Medicare Provider Number, Address, Telephone, Approval, Facility, and Physician Codes, Health Care System**

★ American Hospital Association (AHA) membership
□ The Joint Commission accreditation
◇ DNV Healthcare Inc. accreditation
○ Healthcare Facilities Accreditation Program
△ Commission on Accreditation of Rehabilitation Facilities (CARF) accreditation

**OK**

★ **CONTINUOUS CARE CENTERS OF TULSA (372011)**, 1923 South Utica Avenue, 4 South, Zip 74104–6510; tel. 918/744–3047, (Includes CONTINUOUS CARE CENTERS OF OKLAHOMA, 744 West Ninth Street, 9th Floor, Zip 74127; tel. 918/599–4604) **A**9 10 **F**1 3 29 40 50 65 75 79 82 84 85 87 96 130 148 **P**8
Primary Contact: Raymond L. Replogle, President and Chief Executive Officer
COO: Mike Harris, Chief Operating Officer
CFO: Basil Wyatt, Chief Financial Officer
CMO: Mark Myers, M.D., Chief Medical Officer
CIO: Dana Jetton, Chief Information Officer
CHR: Donna Nagel, Director Human Resources
Web address: www.cccok.com
**Control:** Other not–for–profit (including NFP Corporation) **Service:** General Medical and Surgical

Staffed Beds: 46 Admissions: 345 Census: 25 Outpatient Visits: 0 Births: 0 Total Expense ($000): 14899 Payroll Expense ($000): 5253 Personnel: 57

⊞ **HILLCREST HOSPITAL – SOUTH (370202)**, (Formerly SouthCrest Hospital), 8801 South 101st East Avenue, Zip 74133–5716; tel. 918/294–4000 **A**1 9 10 **F**3 13 15 18 20 22 24 28 29 30 34 40 43 49 51 54 57 59 70 75 76 79 81 85 86 87 93 97 107 108 110 111 114 115 118 119 124 129 130 131 146 147 148 **S** Ardent Health Services, Nashville, TN
Primary Contact: Joseph H. Neely, FACHE, Chief Executive Officer
COO: Kyle McCann, Chief Operating Officer
CFO: Matt Romero, Vice President Finance and Chief Financial Officer
CMO: Gregory R. Pittman, M.D., Chief of Staff
CIO: Frank Evans, Director Information Services
CHR: Rebecca Hert, Director Human Resources
Web address: www.southcresthospital.com
**Control:** Corporation, Investor–owned, for–profit **Service:** General Medical and Surgical

Staffed Beds: 160 Admissions: 7271 Census: 77 Outpatient Visits: 85907 Births: 1625 Total Expense ($000): 102947 Payroll Expense ($000): 32747 Personnel: 558

⊞ **HILLCREST MEDICAL CENTER (370001)**, 1120 South Utica, Zip 74104–4090; tel. 918/579–1000 **A**1 3 5 9 10 **F**3 8 11 13 15 16 17 18 20 22 24 26 28 29 30 31 34 37 39 40 43 45 46 49 50 51 53 56 58 59 60 64 68 70 72 74 76 78 79 80 81 84 85 89 90 93 94 96 98 99 101 102 106 107 108 110 111 112 113 114 115 117 119 120 121 124 126 129 130 145 146 147 148 **S** Ardent Health Services, Nashville, TN
Primary Contact: Jason Fahrlander, FACHE, Chief Executive Officer
COO: Matthew Troup, Chief Operating Officer
CFO: Steve Winegeart, Chief Financial Officer
CMO: Steven Landgarten, M.D., Chief Medical Officer
CHR: Julie Eccleston, Vice President Human Resources
CNO: Kathleen Willis, R.N., Chief Nursing Officer
Web address: www.hillcrest.com
**Control:** Corporation, Investor–owned, for–profit **Service:** General Medical and Surgical

Staffed Beds: 532 Admissions: 23365 Census: 334 Outpatient Visits: 170079 Births: 2904 Total Expense ($000): 379842 Payroll Expense ($000): 125137 Personnel: 1796

⊞ **KINDRED HOSPITAL TULSA (372018)**, 3219 South 79th East Avenue, Zip 74145–1343; tel. 918/663–8183 **A**1 9 10 **F**1 3 29 40 42 60 68 75 87 94 100 107 108 114 130 143 148 **P**8 **S** Kindred Healthcare, Louisville, KY
Primary Contact: Lee A. Simpson, Jr., Chief Executive Officer
CFO: Lee A. Simpson, Jr., Chief Executive Officer
Web address: www.khtulsa.com
**Control:** Corporation, Investor–owned, for–profit **Service:** Long–Term Acute Care hospital

Staffed Beds: 60 Admissions: 504 Census: 35 Outpatient Visits: 5 Births: 0 Total Expense ($000): 16262 Payroll Expense ($000): 7708 Personnel: 134

⊞ **LAUREATE PSYCHIATRIC CLINIC AND HOSPITAL (374020)**, 6655 South Yale Avenue, Zip 74136–3329; tel. 918/481–4000 **A**1 3 5 9 10 **F**4 5 98 100 101 103 104 105 106 146 **P**6 **S** Saint Francis Health System, Tulsa, OK
Primary Contact: William Schloss, Senior Vice President
COO: William Schloss, Senior Vice President
CFO: Barry L. Steichen, Executive Vice President, Chief Administrative Officer and Chief Financial Officer
CMO: Peter P. Aran, M.D., Senior Vice President and Chief Medical Officer
CIO: Mark Stastny, Vice President Information Technology
CHR: Amy B. Adams, Executive Director Human Resources
CNO: Lynn A. Sund, R.N., Senior Vice President, Administrator and Chief Nursing Executive
Web address: www.laureate.com
**Control:** Other not–for–profit (including NFP Corporation) **Service:** Psychiatric

Staffed Beds: 75 Admissions: 3225 Census: 69 Outpatient Visits: 75838 Births: 0 Total Expense ($000): 29529 Payroll Expense ($000): 17637 Personnel: 281

**MEADOWBROOK SPECIALTY HOSPITAL OF TULSA** See Kindred Hospital Tulsa

☐ ○ **OKLAHOMA STATE UNIVERSITY MEDICAL CENTER (370078)**, 744 West Ninth Street, Zip 74127–9020; tel. 918/599–1000 **A**1 9 10 11 12 13 **F**3 8 13 15 18 20 22 24 26 28 29 30 31 34 35 40 43 45 47 49 50 56 57 59 64 65 70 71 72 74 75 76 77 78 79 81 84 85 87 89 92 93 96 97 107 108 110 111 115 119 130 135 146 148 **P**6
Primary Contact: Diane Rafferty, Chief Executive Officer
CFO: Wayne Walthall, Interim Chief Financial Officer
CMO: Damon Baker, D.O., Chief Medical Officer
CHR: Sunny J. Benjamin, Chief Human Resources Officer
Web address: www.osu–medcenter.com
**Control:** City–Government, nonfederal **Service:** General Medical and Surgical

Staffed Beds: 191 Admissions: 6584 Census: 84 Outpatient Visits: 76361 Births: 509 Total Expense ($000): 130002 Payroll Expense ($000): 57184 Personnel: 1239

**OKLAHOMA SURGICAL HOSPITAL (370210)**, 2408 East 81st Street, Suite 300, Zip 74137–4215; tel. 918/477–5000 **A**9 10 **F**3 12 29 30 34 35 40 41 45 49 50 51 64 65 68 74 75 79 81 82 85 86 87 93 94 107 108 111 114 119 126 130 131 **P**2
Primary Contact: Rick Ferguson, Chief Executive Officer
COO: Beverly Pickett, R.N., Chief Nursing Officer
CFO: Dub Cleland, Chief Financial Officer
Web address: www.oklahomasurgicalhospital.com
**Control:** Partnership, Investor–owned, for–profit **Service:** General Medical and Surgical

Staffed Beds: 49 Admissions: 3378 Census: 21 Outpatient Visits: 21121 Births: 0 Total Expense ($000): 70781 Payroll Expense ($000): 16472 Personnel: 397

**PARKSIDE HOSPITAL (374021)**, 1620 East 12th Street, Zip 74120–5407; tel. 918/582–2131 **A**3 5 9 10 **F**3 5 29 35 98 99 102 104 105 106 132 **P**6
Primary Contact: Debra Moore, Chief Executive Officer
CFO: Jim White, Chief Financial Officer
CMO: John White, M.D., Medical Director
CIO: Nita Gould, Director Information Services
CHR: David Patterson, Director Human Resources
Web address: www.parksideinc.org
**Control:** Other not–for–profit (including NFP Corporation) **Service:** Psychiatric

Staffed Beds: 70 Admissions: 2156 Census: 64 Outpatient Visits: 20968 Births: 0 Total Expense ($000): 12346 Payroll Expense ($000): 7839 Personnel: 188

○ **PINNACLE SPECIALTY HOSPITAL (370233)**, 2408 East 81st Street, Suite 600, Zip 74137–4200; tel. 918/392–2780, (Nonreporting) **A**10 11
Primary Contact: Mark Starns, Administrator
Web address: www.pinnaclespecialtyhospital.com/
**Control:** Partnership, Investor–owned, for–profit **Service:** General Medical and Surgical

Staffed Beds: 4

**SAINT FRANCIS HEART HOSPITAL** See Saint Francis Hospital

⊞ **SAINT FRANCIS HOSPITAL (370091)**, 6161 South Yale Avenue, Zip 74136–1902; tel. 918/494–2200, (Includes CHILDREN'S HOSPITAL AT SAINT FRANCIS, 6161 South Yale Avenue, tel. 918/502–6714; SAINT FRANCIS HEART HOSPITAL, 6161 South Yale Avenue, tel. 918/502–2022) **A**1 2 3 5 9 10 **F**3 7 8 11 12 13 15 17 18 19 20 21 22 23 24 25 26 27 28 29 30 31 32 35 37 39 40 41 43 44 45 46 47 49 50 51 54 55 56 57 58 60 61 64 66 68 69 70 72 73 74 75 76 77 78 79 80 81 82 83 84 85 86 87 88 89 90 93 107 108 110 111 112 114 115 116 118 119 120 121 123 124 126 129 130 131 132 135 136 138 141 146 148 **P**6 **S** Saint Francis Health System, Tulsa, OK
Primary Contact: Lynn A. Sund, R.N., MS, Senior Vice President, Administrator and Chief Nursing Executive
COO: Lynn A. Sund, R.N., Senior Vice President, Administrator and Chief Nursing Executive
CFO: Barry L. Steichen, Executive Vice President and Chief Financial Officer
CMO: Peter P. Aran, M.D., Senior Vice President and Chief Medical Officer
CIO: Mark Stastny, Vice President Information Technology
CHR: Amy B. Adams, Executive Director Human Resources
Web address: www.saintfrancis.com
**Control:** Other not–for–profit (including NFP Corporation) **Service:** General Medical and Surgical

Staffed Beds: 774 Admissions: 43593 Census: 596 Outpatient Visits: 353647 Births: 4286 Total Expense ($000): 616691 Payroll Expense ($000): 235815 Personnel: 4776

*Many Facility Codes have changed. Please refer to the AHA Guide Code Chart.* © 2013 AHA Guide

**OK**

✠ **SAINT FRANCIS HOSPITAL SOUTH (370218)**, 10501 East 91St. Streeet, Zip 74133–5790; tel. 918/455–3535 **A**1 9 10 **F**13 15 18 20 22 29 34 40 49 57 64 70 76 79 81 82 92 107 108 110 111 114 115 119 130 146 **P**6 **S** Saint Francis Health System, Tulsa, OK
Primary Contact: David S. Weil, Senior Vice President and Administrator
COO: Barry L. Steichen, Executive Vice President
CFO: Barry L. Steichen, Executive Vice President
CMO: Peter P. Aran, M.D., Senior Vice President and Chief Medical Officer
CIO: Mark Stastny, Vice President Information Technology
CHR: Amy B. Adams, Executive Director Human Resources
CNO: Jimmie Cash, R.N., Executive Director and Patient Care
Web address: www.saintfrancis.com/south/
**Control:** Other not–for–profit (including NFP Corporation) **Service:** General Medical and Surgical

**Staffed Beds: 60 Admissions: 3246 Census: 28 Outpatient Visits:** 65913 **Births:** 1012 **Total Expense ($000):** 48839 **Payroll Expense ($000):** 18581 **Personnel:** 342

✠ **SELECT SPECIALTY HOSPITAL–TULSA MIDTOWN (372007)**, 1125 South Trenton Avenue, 3rd Floor, Zip 74120–5418; tel. 918/579–7300 **A**1 9 10 **F**1 3 29 87 130 148 **S** Select Medical Corporation, Mechanicsburg, PA
Primary Contact: Linda Tiemens, Chief Executive Officer
CFO: Bryon Briggs, Assistant Chief Financial Officer
Web address: www.selectmedical.com
**Control:** Corporation, Investor–owned, for–profit **Service:** Long–Term Acute Care hospital

**Staffed Beds: 56 Admissions: 368 Census: 27 Outpatient Visits:** 0 **Births:** 0 **Total Expense ($000):** 14307 **Payroll Expense ($000):** 5941 **Personnel:** 113

☐ **SHADOW MOUNTAIN BEHAVIORAL HEALTH SYSTEM**, 6262 South Sheridan Road, Zip 74133–4055; tel. 918/492–8200 **A**1 9 **F**40 41 54 59 98 99 101 102 104 106 **P**6 **S** Universal Health Services, Inc., King of Prussia, PA
Primary Contact: Mike Kistler, Chief Executive Officer
CFO: Kirt Penrod, Chief Financial Officer
CMO: Dean Martin, M.D., Medical Director
CHR: Duane Harris, Director Human Resources
Web address: www.shadowmountainbhs.com
**Control:** Corporation, Investor–owned, for–profit **Service:** Children's hospital psychiatric

**Staffed Beds: 202 Admissions: 2109 Census: 187 Outpatient Visits:** 29356 **Births:** 0 **Total Expense ($000):** 32270 **Payroll Expense ($000):** 12705 **Personnel:** 341

☐ **SOUTHWESTERN REGIONAL MEDICAL CENTER (370190)**, 10109 East 79th Street, Zip 74133–4564; tel. 918/286–5000 **A**1 2 10 **F**3 15 29 30 31 33 34 35 36 40 44 45 46 47 49 50 53 58 59 63 64 68 70 74 77 78 81 82 84 85 86 87 93 97 100 104 107 108 109 110 111 114 116 117 118 119 120 121 123 124 129 130 132 135 143 146 148 **P**1 **S** Cancer Treatment Centers of America, Schaumburg, IL
Primary Contact: Steve Mackin, President and Chief Executive Officer
CFO: David Hedges, Chief Financial Officer
CMO: James P. Flynn, M.D., President Medical Staff
CHR: Wendy Whelan, Director Talent
Web address: www.cancercenter.com
**Control:** Corporation, Investor–owned, for–profit **Service:** Cancer

**Staffed Beds: 43 Admissions: 932 Census: 19 Outpatient Visits:** 162979 **Births:** 0 **Personnel:** 804

✠ **ST. JOHN MEDICAL CENTER (370114)**, 1923 South Utica Avenue, Zip 74104–6502; tel. 918/744–2345 **A**1 2 3 5 9 10 **F**3 8 9 11 12 13 14 15 17 18 19 20 22 24 26 28 29 30 31 34 35 37 39 40 43 45 46 47 48 49 50 51 53 54 56 57 58 59 60 61 62 63 64 65 66 68 70 71 72 73 74 75 76 77 78 79 80 81 82 84 85 86 87 88 89 90 93 94 96 97 100 104 107 108 110 111 114 115 116 117 118 119 120 121 123 124 126 129 130 131 132 135 138 141 143 145 146 147 148 **P**6 7 8 **S** Ascension Health, Saint Louis, MO
Primary Contact: Jeffrey D. Nowlin, Vice President, Chief Operating Officer
CFO: Lex S. Anderson, Chief Financial Officer
CMO: William Allred, M.D., Vice President Medical Affairs
CIO: Mike Reeves, Vice President
CHR: Page Bachman, Corporate Vice President
CNO: Pamela Kiser, R.N., Chief Nursing Executive and Vice President of Nursing
Web address: www.sjmc.org
**Control:** Church–operated, Nongovernment, not–for profit **Service:** General Medical and Surgical

**Staffed Beds: 547 Admissions: 28472 Census: 384 Outpatient Visits:** 489608 **Births:** 1948 **Total Expense ($000):** 477197 **Payroll Expense ($000):** 153251 **Personnel:** 3151

✠ **TULSA SPINE AND SPECIALTY HOSPITAL (370216)**, 6901 South Olympia Avenue, Zip 74132–1843; tel. 918/388–5701, (Nonreporting) **A**1 9 10
Primary Contact: Terry L. Woodbeck, Administrator
CFO: Thom Biby, Chief Financial Officer
CMO: David Fell, M.D., Chief Medical Officer
Web address: www.tulsaspinehospital.com
**Control:** Corporation, Investor–owned, for–profit **Service:** General Medical and Surgical

**Staffed Beds:** 21

### VINITA—Craig County

★ **CRAIG GENERAL HOSPITAL (370065)**, 735 North Foreman Street, Zip 74301–1418, Mailing Address: P.O. Box 326, Zip 74301–0326; tel. 918/256–7551 **A**9 10 20 **F**3 11 13 15 29 30 34 35 40 53 56 57 59 64 65 75 76 81 85 93 98 103 104 107 110 111 115 119 127 128 130 132 133 135 146 147 148
Primary Contact: Steven Chase, Chief Executive Officer
CMO: Ed Allensworth, M.D., Medical Director
CHR: Darlene R. Nolte, Chief Human Resource Officer
CNO: Robin Kemp, R.N., Chief Nursing Officer
Web address: www.craiggeneralhospital.com
**Control:** Hospital district or authority, Government, nonfederal **Service:** General Medical and Surgical

**Staffed Beds: 51 Admissions: 1841 Census: 26 Outpatient Visits:** 24791 **Births:** 83 **Total Expense ($000):** 27519 **Payroll Expense ($000):** 10618 **Personnel:** 265

**OKLAHOMA FORENSIC CENTER**, 24800 South 4420 Road, Zip 74301–5544, Mailing Address: P.O. Box 69, Zip 74301–0069; tel. 918/256–7841, (Nonreporting) **S** Oklahoma Department of Mental Health and Substance Abuse Services, Oklahoma City, OK
Primary Contact: Lori Jordan, Chief Executive Officer
CFO: Miriam Harris, Director Finance
CHR: Julie Jacobs, Director Human Resources
**Control:** State–Government, nonfederal **Service:** Psychiatric

**Staffed Beds:** 200

### WAGONER—Wagoner County

**WAGONER COMMUNITY HOSPITAL (370166)**, 1200 West Cherokee Street, Zip 74467–4624, Mailing Address: P.O. Box 407, Zip 74477–0407; tel. 918/485–5514 **A**9 10 **F**3 11 12 15 29 30 34 40 41 45 49 50 56 57 59 64 65 68 70 74 75 79 81 82 85 87 89 98 102 103 104 107 108 114 119 130 135 146 148
Primary Contact: Jimmy Leopard, FACHE, Chief Executive Officer
CFO: Rod Shook, Chief Financial Officer
CMO: John Perry, M.D., Chief of Staff
CHR: Barnetta Pofahl, Director Human Resources
Web address: www.wagonerhospital.com
**Control:** Hospital district or authority, Government, nonfederal **Service:** General Medical and Surgical

**Staffed Beds: 100 Admissions: 2943 Census: 34 Outpatient Visits:** 19491 **Births:** 0 **Total Expense ($000):** 14512 **Payroll Expense ($000):** 7159 **Personnel:** 169

### WATONGA—Blaine County

★ **MERCY HOSPITAL WATONGA (371302)**, (Formerly Watonga Municipal Hospital), 500 North Clarence Nash Boulevard, Zip 73772–2845, Mailing Address: P.O. Box 370, Zip 73772–0370; tel. 580/623–7211 **A**9 10 18 **F**7 11 29 30 40 50 93 107 111 114 119 133 **S** Mercy Health, Chesterfield, MO
Primary Contact: Bobby Stitt, R.N., Administrator
CFO: Gene Kaberline, Chief Financial Officer
CIO: Alisha Glazier, Compliance Officer and Director Health Information Management
CHR: Tim Prepieri, Director Human Resources
Web address: www.mercy.net/watongaok/practice/mercy–hospital–watonga
**Control:** Church–operated, Nongovernment, not–for profit **Service:** General Medical and Surgical

**Staffed Beds: 17 Admissions: 343 Census: 4 Outpatient Visits:** 8108 **Total Expense ($000):** 4821 **Payroll Expense ($000):** 1849 **Personnel:** 46

---

**Hospital, Medicare Provider Number, Address, Telephone, Approval, Facility, and Physician Codes, Health Care System**

★ American Hospital Association (AHA) membership
☐ The Joint Commission accreditation
◇ DNV Healthcare Inc. accreditation
○ Healthcare Facilities Accreditation Program
△ Commission on Accreditation of Rehabilitation Facilities (CARF) accreditation

**WAURIKA—Jefferson County**

★ **JEFFERSON COUNTY HOSPITAL (371311)**, Highway 70 and 81,
Zip 73573–3075, Mailing Address: P.O. Box 90, Zip 73573–0090;
tel. 580/228–2344 **A**9 10 18 **F**11 35 40 107 119 127 133 **P**6
Primary Contact: Jane McDowell, FACHE, Administrator
CFO: Richard Tallon, Chief Financial Officer
CMO: Rob Linzman, D.O., Chief of Staff
CIO: Nikki McGahey, Information Officer
Web address: www.jeffersoncountyhospital.net
**Control:** Hospital district or authority, Government, nonfederal **Service:** General
Medical and Surgical

**Staffed Beds:** 25 **Admissions:** 267 **Census:** 3 **Outpatient Visits:** 11657
**Births:** 0 **Total Expense ($000):** 3144 **Payroll Expense ($000):** 1714
**Personnel:** 40

**WEATHERFORD—Custer County**

★ **WEATHERFORD REGIONAL HOSPITAL (371323)**, 3701 East Main Street,
Zip 73096–3309; tel. 580/772–5551 **A**9 10 18 **F**3 11 13 15 29 34 40 43 45
64 68 75 76 77 81 86 87 93 107 111 115 119 130 133 135 144 146 147
148 **P**6
Primary Contact: Debbie Howe, Chief Executive Officer
CFO: Stephanie Helton, Chief Financial Officer
CMO: Michael Aaron, M.D., Chief of Staff
CIO: Claudia Wright, Director Health Information Management
CHR: Tawnya Paden, Director Human Resources
Web address: www.weatherfordhospital.com
**Control:** Hospital district or authority, Government, nonfederal **Service:** General
Medical and Surgical

**Staffed Beds:** 25 **Admissions:** 824 **Census:** 6 **Outpatient Visits:** 25674
**Births:** 225 **Total Expense ($000):** 18045 **Payroll Expense ($000):** 7255
**Personnel:** 170

**WILBURTON—Latimer County**

**LATIMER COUNTY GENERAL HOSPITAL (370072)**, 806 Highway 2 North,
Zip 74578–3698; tel. 918/465–2391 **A**9 10 **F**3 30 32 35 40 62 65 107 114
119 129 130 146
Primary Contact: Doncie Campagna, Administrator
CMO: Richard Valbuena, M.D., Medical Director
**Control:** County–Government, nonfederal **Service:** General Medical and Surgical

**Staffed Beds:** 33 **Admissions:** 592 **Census:** 4 **Births:** 0

**WOODWARD—Woodward County**

⊞ **WOODWARD REGIONAL HOSPITAL (370002)**, 900 17th Street,
Zip 73801–2448; tel. 580/256–5511 **A**1 9 10 20 **F**13 15 29 30 31 32 34 35
40 43 45 50 57 59 64 68 69 70 75 76 77 79 81 85 93 107 108 110 111
114 119 124 129 130 131 133 135 146 **P**6 **S** Community Health Systems,
Inc., Franklin, TN
Primary Contact: David Wallace, Chief Executive Officer
CFO: Tom Earley, Chief Financial Officer
CIO: Larry Churchill, Director Information Services
CHR: Melinda Brock, Director Human Resources
CNO: Kimberly N. Arnold, R.N., Chief Nursing Officer and Interim Chief Quality
Officer
Web address: www.woodwardhospital.com
**Control:** Corporation, Investor–owned, for–profit **Service:** General Medical and
Surgical

**Staffed Beds:** 40 **Admissions:** 1595 **Census:** 14 **Outpatient Visits:** 38000
**Births:** 267 **Total Expense ($000):** 29036 **Payroll Expense ($000):** 10032
**Personnel:** 202

**YUKON—Canadian County**

⊞ **INTEGRIS CANADIAN VALLEY HOSPITAL (370211)**, 1201 Health Center
Parkway, Zip 73099–6381; tel. 405/717–6800 **A**1 9 10 **F**3 11 13 15 29 30 34
40 45 46 49 57 59 60 64 68 70 76 79 81 87 93 97 107 108 110 111 115
118 119 130 135 144 145 146 148 **S** INTEGRIS Health, Oklahoma City, OK
Primary Contact: Rex Van Meter, President
COO: Cindy White, CPA, Vice President of Operations
CFO: Errol Mitchell, Chief Financial Officer
CHR: Lynn Ketch, Human Resources Recruiter Generalist
CNO: Teresa Gray, Chief Nursing Officer and Assistant Vice President
Web address: www.integris-health.com
**Control:** Other not–for–profit (including NFP Corporation) **Service:** General
Medical and Surgical

**Staffed Beds:** 75 **Admissions:** 2974 **Census:** 27 **Outpatient Visits:** 57811
**Births:** 927 **Total Expense ($000):** 56793 **Payroll Expense ($000):** 23596
**Personnel:** 282

*Many Facility Codes have changed. Please refer to the AHA Guide Code Chart.*   © 2013 AHA Guide

OR

# OREGON

## ALBANY—Linn County

★ ◇ **SAMARITAN ALBANY GENERAL HOSPITAL (380022)**, 1046 West Sixth Avenue, Zip 97321–1999; tel. 541/812–4000 **A**9 10 21 **F**3 5 11 12 13 15 18 28 29 30 31 34 35 36 37 39 40 43 45 47 49 50 53 57 59 61 63 64 67 68 70 72 74 75 76 77 78 79 81 84 85 86 87 89 92 93 97 107 108 110 111 114 117 119 129 130 131 132 135 144 145 146 147 148 **P**6 **S** Samaritan Health Services, Corvallis, OR
Primary Contact: David G. Triebes, Chief Executive Officer
CFO: Daniel B. Smith, Vice President Finance
Web address: www.samhealth.org
**Control:** Other not–for–profit (including NFP Corporation) **Service:** General Medical and Surgical

**Staffed Beds:** 70 **Admissions:** 3366 **Census:** 27 **Outpatient Visits:** 168542 **Births:** 602 **Total Expense ($000):** 127059 **Payroll Expense ($000):** 51218 **Personnel:** 725

## ASHLAND—Jackson County

★ ◇ **ASHLAND COMMUNITY HOSPITAL (380005)**, 280 Maple Street, Zip 97520–1593; tel. 541/201–4000 **A**9 10 21 **F**3 11 13 15 29 30 34 35 36 40 43 48 49 50 54 62 63 64 65 68 70 75 76 79 81 82 84 85 86 87 93 97 107 110 114 119 130 132 145 146 147 148 **P**6 **S** Asante Health System, Medford, OR
Primary Contact: Marvin Haas, Interim Chief Executive Officer
CFO: Arebi Garsa, Chief Financial Officer
CMO: Miriam Soriano, M.D., Chief Medical Staff
CHR: Karen Herwig, Vice President Human Resources
Web address: www.ashlandhospital.org
**Control:** Other not–for–profit (including NFP Corporation) **Service:** General Medical and Surgical

**Staffed Beds:** 36 **Admissions:** 1514 **Census:** 14 **Outpatient Visits:** 58281 **Births:** 362 **Total Expense ($000):** 51840 **Payroll Expense ($000):** 21564 **Personnel:** 300

## ASTORIA—Clatsop County

⊞ **COLUMBIA MEMORIAL HOSPITAL (381320)**, 2111 Exchange Street, Zip 97103–3329; tel. 503/325–4321 **A**1 9 10 18 **F**3 8 11 13 15 18 19 28 29 30 31 34 35 36 40 41 42 43 44 46 50 51 53 57 58 59 62 63 64 68 70 75 76 77 78 79 81 85 86 87 89 93 97 107 108 110 111 114 115 119 130 131 132 134 135 143 144 146 147 148 **P**6
Primary Contact: Erik Thorsen, Chief Executive Officer
CFO: Guy Rivers, Chief Financial Officer
CMO: Hugh Sabahi, M.D., President Professional Staff
CIO: Guy Rivers, Chief Financial Officerr
CHR: Cheryl Martin, Manager Human Resources
CNO: Joe DaFoe, R.N., Chief Clinical Officer
Web address: www.columbiamemorial.org
**Control:** Other not–for–profit (including NFP Corporation) **Service:** General Medical and Surgical

**Staffed Beds:** 25 **Admissions:** 1498 **Census:** 12 **Outpatient Visits:** 119156 **Births:** 338 **Total Expense ($000):** 62404 **Payroll Expense ($000):** 27328 **Personnel:** 432

## BAKER CITY—Baker County

⊞ **SAINT ALPHONSUS MEDICAL CENTER – BAKER CITY (381315)**, 3325 Pocahontas Road, Zip 97814–1464; tel. 541/523–6461, (Total facility includes 30 beds in nursing home–type unit) **A**1 9 10 18 **F**3 11 13 15 29 31 34 35 37 40 43 44 45 57 59 64 67 70 76 77 79 81 82 85 91 93 107 110 115 119 127 128 129 131 133 143 146 147 148 **S** Trinity Health, Livonia, MI
Primary Contact: H. Ray Gibbons, FACHE, Chief Executive Officer
CFO: Robert D. Wehling, Interim Chief Financial Officer
CHR: Jerry Nickell, Vice President Human Resource and Mission
Web address: www.saintalphonsus.org/bakercity
**Control:** Other not–for–profit (including NFP Corporation) **Service:** General Medical and Surgical

**Staffed Beds:** 55 **Admissions:** 1149 **Census:** 37 **Outpatient Visits:** 35219 **Births:** 147 **Total Expense ($000):** 28442 **Payroll Expense ($000):** 12868 **Personnel:** 245

**ST. ELIZABETH HEALTH SERVICES** See Saint Alphonsus Medical Center – Baker City

## BANDON—Coos County

★ **SOUTHERN COOS HOSPITAL AND HEALTH CENTER (381304)**, 900 11th Street S.E., Zip 97411–9114; tel. 541/347–2426 **A**9 10 18 **F**3 15 35 40 45 50 57 65 68 75 81 82 85 87 107 110 114 119 130 132 133 135 148
Primary Contact: Charles W. Johnston, Chief Executive Officer
CFO: Robin Triplett, Chief Financial Officer
CIO: Mandy Calvert, Director of Information Systems
CHR: Cyndy Vollmer, Director of Human Resources
Web address: www.southerncoos.org
**Control:** Hospital district or authority, Government, nonfederal **Service:** General Medical and Surgical

**Staffed Beds:** 19 **Admissions:** 357 **Census:** 4 **Outpatient Visits:** 16067 **Births:** 0 **Total Expense ($000):** 14567 **Payroll Expense ($000):** 6377 **Personnel:** 122

## BEND—Deschutes County

⊞ **ST. CHARLES MEDICAL CENTER – BEND (380047)**, 2500 N.E. Neff Road, Zip 97701–6015; tel. 541/382–4321 **A**1 2 3 5 9 10 19 **F**3 8 11 12 13 14 15 18 19 20 21 22 24 26 28 29 30 31 34 35 36 37 38 40 42 43 45 46 49 50 51 53 54 57 59 60 62 63 64 65 67 68 70 72 74 75 76 77 78 79 81 82 84 85 86 87 89 90 91 92 93 98 99 100 101 102 104 107 108 110 111 114 115 116 117 118 119 120 121 123 124 126 129 130 132 135 136 142 144 146 **S** St. Charles Health System, Inc., Bend, OR
Primary Contact: Jay Henry, Chief Executive Officer
COO: Rick Martin, Vice President of Ancillary and Support Services
CFO: Karen Shepard, Senior Vice President Finance and Chief Financial Officer
CMO: Michel Boileau, M.D., Chief Clinical Officer
CIO: William Winnenberg, Chief Information Officer
CHR: Rebecca Morgan, Senior Director Human Resources
CNO: Timothy D. Eixenberger, R.N., Chief Nursing Officer
Web address: www.scmc.org
**Control:** Other not–for–profit (including NFP Corporation) **Service:** General Medical and Surgical

**Staffed Beds:** 260 **Admissions:** 14478 **Census:** 161 **Outpatient Visits:** 173986 **Births:** 1542 **Total Expense ($000):** 420394 **Payroll Expense ($000):** 161/13 **Personnel:** 2035

## BURNS—Harney County

★ **HARNEY DISTRICT HOSPITAL (381307)**, 557 West Washington Street, Zip 97720–1497; tel. 541/573–7281 **A**9 10 18 **F**3 7 13 15 29 31 34 35 40 43 45 47 54 57 59 64 65 70 71 75 76 78 81 82 85 86 102 107 111 114 119 129 132 133 146 **P**6
Primary Contact: Jim Bishop, Chief Executive Officer
CMO: Kevin Johnston, M.D., Chief Medical Staff
CHR: Sammie Masterson, Chief Human Resources Officer
Web address: www.harneydh.com
**Control:** Hospital district or authority, Government, nonfederal **Service:** General Medical and Surgical

**Staffed Beds:** 20 **Admissions:** 392 **Census:** 4 **Outpatient Visits:** 18127 **Births:** 62 **Total Expense ($000):** 16068 **Payroll Expense ($000):** 6190 **Personnel:** 129

## CLACKAMAS—Clackamas County

⊞ **KAISER PERMANENTE SUNNYSIDE MEDICAL CENTER (380091)**, (Formerly Sunnyside Medical Center), 10180 S.E. Sunnyside Road, Zip 97015–8970; tel. 503/652–2880 **A**1 2 10 **F**3 11 12 13 15 17 18 20 22 24 26 30 31 34 37 40 45 46 47 49 51 60 61 64 68 70 72 74 75 76 77 78 79 81 84 85 86 87 93 94 97 102 107 108 111 114 115 119 130 141 146 147 148 **P**6 **S** Kaiser Foundation Hospitals, Oakland, CA
Primary Contact: Susan Mullaney, Administrator
COO: Gary Petersen, Chief Operating Officer
CFO: Rolf Norman, Chief Financial Officer
CMO: Rick Olson, M.D., Chief of Staff
CIO: Mark A. Burmester, Vice President Strategy and Communications
CHR: Rich Smith, Vice President Human Resources
Web address: www.kaiserpermanente.org
**Control:** Other not–for–profit (including NFP Corporation) **Service:** General Medical and Surgical

**Staffed Beds:** 283 **Admissions:** 19337 **Census:** 190 **Outpatient Visits:** 67066 **Births:** 2102 **Total Expense ($000):** 353721 **Payroll Expense ($000):** 142446 **Personnel:** 2162

---

**OR**

### COOS BAY—Coos County

☒ **BAY AREA HOSPITAL (380090)**, 1775 Thompson Road, Zip 97420–2198;
tel. 541/269–8111 **A**1 2 9 10 **F**3 11 12 13 15 18 28 31 34 35 40 43 45 46
48 50 51 57 59 62 68 70 73 74 75 76 77 78 79 81 82 83 84 85 89 91 92
93 98 99 100 101 102 104 107 108 110 111 114 118 119 120 121 123
129 130 132 135 142 146 148
Primary Contact: Paul Janke, FACHE, President and Chief Executive Officer
COO: Ben Pfau, Chief Facility and Operations Officer
CFO: Sam Patterson, Chief Financial Officer
CMO: Bill Moriarty, M.D., Chief Medical Officer
CIO: Bob Adams, Director Information Services
CHR: Suzie Q. McDaniel, Chief Human Resource Officer
CNO: Lori L. Krenos, R.N., Chief Nursing Officer
Web address: www.bayareahospital.org
**Control:** Hospital district or authority, Government, nonfederal **Service:** General
Medical and Surgical

**Staffed Beds:** 126 **Admissions:** 6005 **Census:** 60 **Outpatient Visits:** 72446
**Births:** 631 **Total Expense ($000):** 122498 **Payroll Expense ($000):** 56965
**Personnel:** 796

### COQUILLE—Coos County

★ **COQUILLE VALLEY HOSPITAL (381312)**, 940 East Fifth Street,
Zip 97423–1699; tel. 541/396–3101 **A**9 10 18 **F**3 11 13 15 29 34 35 40 43
45 50 57 59 62 64 70 75 76 79 81 82 85 86 87 107 110 111 114 118 119
132 133 135 148 **P**6
Primary Contact: Dennis G. Zielinski, Chief Executive Officer and Administrator
CFO: Gail Ludington, Chief Financial Officer
CMO: James Sinnott, M.D., Chief Medical Staff
CIO: Curt Carpenter, Manager Information Technology
CHR: Monte Johnston, Manager Human Resources
Web address: www.cvhospital.org
**Control:** Hospital district or authority, Government, nonfederal **Service:** General
Medical and Surgical

**Staffed Beds:** 25 **Admissions:** 557 **Census:** 5 **Outpatient Visits:** 22494
**Births:** 21 **Total Expense ($000):** 16380 **Payroll Expense ($000):** 6469
**Personnel:** 128

### CORVALLIS—Benton County

★ ◇ **GOOD SAMARITAN REGIONAL MEDICAL CENTER (380014)**, 3600 N.W.
Samaritan Drive, Zip 97330–3737, Mailing Address: P.O. Box 1068,
Zip 97339–1068; tel. 541/768–5111 **A**2 9 10 12 13 19 21 **F**3 5 8 11 12 13
15 18 20 22 24 26 28 29 30 31 34 35 36 37 40 43 46 47 49 50 53 54 57
59 61 62 64 68 70 73 74 76 77 78 79 81 82 84 85 86 87 89 93 97 98 99
100 101 102 104 107 108 110 111 114 115 117 118 119 120 121 123 124
126 129 130 131 132 135 144 145 146 147 148 **P**6 **S** Samaritan Health
Services, Corvallis, OR
Primary Contact: Steven W. Jasperson, Chief Executive Officer
CFO: Daniel B. Smith, Vice President Finance
CIO: Bob Power, Vice President Information Services
CHR: Sheryl Helms, Vice President Human Resources
Web address: www.samhealth.org
**Control:** Other not–for–profit (including NFP Corporation) **Service:** General
Medical and Surgical

**Staffed Beds:** 165 **Admissions:** 9355 **Census:** 110 **Outpatient Visits:**
220619 **Births:** 1073 **Total Expense ($000):** 326995 **Payroll Expense
($000):** 131720 **Personnel:** 1461

### COTTAGE GROVE—Lane County

★ **PEACEHEALTH COTTAGE GROVE COMMUNITY MEDICAL CENTER
(381301)**, (Formerly Cottage Grove Community Hospital), 1515 Village Drive,
Zip 97424–9700; tel. 541/942–0511 **A**9 10 18 **F**3 11 15 29 30 32 34 35 40
50 56 57 58 59 64 65 66 68 75 82 83 84 85 86 87 93 97 107 110 115 119
127 130 132 133 146 147 **P**6 **S** PeaceHealth, Vancouver, WA
Primary Contact: MaryAnne McMurren, R.N., Administrator and Chief Executive
Officer
Web address: www.peacehealth.org
**Control:** Church–operated, Nongovernment, not–for profit **Service:** General
Medical and Surgical

**Staffed Beds:** 14 **Admissions:** 346 **Census:** 3 **Outpatient Visits:** 37842
**Births:** 0 **Total Expense ($000):** 27736 **Payroll Expense ($000):** 9433
**Personnel:** 105

### DALLAS—Polk County

**WEST VALLEY HOSPITAL (381308)**, 525 S.E. Washington Street,
Zip 97338–2834, Mailing Address: P.O. Box 378, Zip 97338–0378;
tel. 503/623–8301 **A**9 10 18 **F**3 11 15 35 40 43 50 59 64 75 79 81 85 93
97 107 108 110 111 114 119 131 132 133 143 146 148 **P**6 **S** Salem Health,
Salem, OR
Primary Contact: Robert C. Brannigan, Administrator
COO: Robert C. Brannigan, Administrator
CFO: Aaron Crane, Chief Financial Officer
CMO: David Holloway, M.D., Chief Medical Officer
CIO: Ken Kudla, Chief Information Officer
CHR: Beverly Bow, Vice President Human Resources
Web address: www.westvalleyhospital.org
**Control:** Other not–for–profit (including NFP Corporation) **Service:** General
Medical and Surgical

**Staffed Beds:** 6 **Admissions:** 162 **Census:** 1 **Outpatient Visits:** 70429 **Total
Expense ($000):** 18973 **Payroll Expense ($000):** 9736 **Personnel:** 105

### ENTERPRISE—Wallowa County

★ **WALLOWA MEMORIAL HOSPITAL (381306)**, 601 Medical Parkway,
Zip 97828–5124; tel. 541/426–3111, (Total facility includes 32 beds in nursing
home–type unit) **A**3 5 9 10 18 **F**3 7 11 13 15 29 30 31 34 35 40 43 45 46 56
57 59 62 64 67 68 75 76 78 79 81 82 85 93 102 107 110 114 119 128 129
131 132 133 135 143 148
Primary Contact: David L. Harman, Chief Executive Officer
CFO: Lexi M. Fields, Chief Financial Officer
CMO: Kirsten Caine, M.D., Chief Medical Staff
CIO: John Straughan, Director Information Technology
CHR: Linda Childers, Director Human Resources
CNO: Jenni Word, Chief Nursing Officer
Web address: www.wchcd.org
**Control:** Hospital district or authority, Government, nonfederal **Service:** General
Medical and Surgical

**Staffed Beds:** 57 **Admissions:** 584 **Census:** 24 **Outpatient Visits:** 18645
**Births:** 42 **Total Expense ($000):** 17137 **Payroll Expense ($000):** 7198
**Personnel:** 121

### EUGENE—Lane County

☒ △ **PEACEHEALTH SACRED HEART MEDICAL CENTER, UNIVERSITY
DISTRICT (380033)**, (Formerly Sacred Heart Medical Center), 1255 Hilyard
Street, Zip 97401–3700, Mailing Address: P.O. Box 10905, Zip 97440–2905;
tel. 541/686–7300 **A**1 7 9 10 **F**29 30 40 43 56 68 90 98 102 146 148 **P**6
**S** PeaceHealth, Vancouver, WA
Primary Contact: John G. Hill, Chief Executive Officer
CFO: Wendy Apland, Interim Chief Financial Officer
CMO: Bill Moshofsky, M.D., Chief of Staff
CIO: Don McMillan, Chief Information Officer
CHR: Craig Mills, Vice President Human Resources
Web address: www.peacehealth.org
**Control:** Church–operated, Nongovernment, not–for profit **Service:** General
Medical and Surgical

**Staffed Beds:** 104 **Admissions:** 2606 **Census:** 53 **Outpatient Visits:** 108998
**Births:** 0 **Total Expense ($000):** 92124 **Payroll Expense ($000):** 41610
**Personnel:** 334

### FLORENCE—Lane County

★ **PEACEHEALTH PEACE HARBOR MEDICAL CENTER (381316)**, (Formerly
Peace Harbor Hospital), 400 Ninth Street, Zip 97439–7398; tel. 541/997–8412
**A**9 10 18 **F**11 13 15 28 29 30 34 35 40 43 45 50 57 59 62 63 64 68 70 76
77 79 81 85 93 97 107 108 110 111 114 118 119 132 133 135 146 147
148 **P**6 **S** PeaceHealth, Vancouver, WA
Primary Contact: Rick Yecny, Chief Executive Officer
CMO: Ron Shearer, M.D., Regional Medical Director
CIO: Ginni Boughal, Director Health Information and Information Technology
CHR: Don Bourland, Vice President Human Resources
Web address: www.peacehealth.org
**Control:** Church–operated, Nongovernment, not–for profit **Service:** General
Medical and Surgical

**Staffed Beds:** 21 **Admissions:** 970 **Census:** 10 **Outpatient Visits:** 98635
**Births:** 59 **Total Expense ($000):** 56997 **Payroll Expense ($000):** 30525
**Personnel:** 375

### FOREST GROVE—Washington County

**TUALITY FOREST GROVE HOSPITAL** See Tuality Healthcare, Hillsboro

*Many Facility Codes have changed. Please refer to the AHA Guide Code Chart.* © 2013 AHA Guide

OR

## GOLD BEACH—Curry County

★ **CURRY GENERAL HOSPITAL (381322)**, 94220 Fourth Street,
Zip 97444–7756; tel. 541/247–6621 **A**9 10 18 **F**3 10 11 13 15 28 29 34 35
40 43 56 57 59 64 65 70 75 76 79 81 82 98 105 107 114 119 127 133 135
144 146 147 148
Primary Contact: Andrew P. Bair, Chief Executive Officer
COO: A. Alexander Gorman, Director Operations
CFO: Mark Sayler, Chief Financial Officer
CIO: Kwang Veloso, Director Information Systems
CHR: Terri Tomberlin, Manager Human Resources
Web address: www.curryhealthnetwork.com
**Control:** Hospital district or authority, Government, nonfederal **Service:** General
Medical and Surgical

**Staffed Beds:** 22 **Admissions:** 711 **Census:** 6 **Outpatient Visits:** 53824
**Births:** 70 **Total Expense ($000):** 24328 **Payroll Expense ($000):** 12038
**Personnel:** 184

## GRANTS PASS—Josephine County

★ ◇ **THREE RIVERS MEDICAL CENTER (380002)**, (Formerly Three Rivers
Community Hospital and Health Center), 500 S.W. Ramsey Avenue,
Zip 97527–5554; tel. 541/472–7000 **A**9 10 21 **F**11 13 15 20 21 22 23 28 29
30 31 34 35 40 43 45 46 50 57 59 64 65 70 75 76 78 81 87 93 102 107
108 110 111 118 119 122 130 132 143 146 147 148 **P**6 **S** Asante Health
System, Medford, OR
Primary Contact: Win Howard, Chief Executive Officer
COO: David Kinyon, Vice President of Operations and Outpatient Services
CMO: Kenneth Lindsey, M.D., Vice President of Medical Affairs
CIO: Mark Hetz, Chief Information Officer
CHR: Gregg Edwards, Chief People Officer
CNO: Kristin Gillen, R.N., Vice President of Patient Care Services
Web address: www.asante.org/trmc/
**Control:** Other not–for–profit (including NFP Corporation) **Service:** General
Medical and Surgical

**Staffed Beds:** 107 **Admissions:** 6798 **Census:** 58 **Outpatient Visits:** 219763
**Births:** 713 **Total Expense ($000):** 127813 **Payroll Expense ($000):** 44030
**Personnel:** 560

## GRESHAM—Multnomah County

⊞ **LEGACY MOUNT HOOD MEDICAL CENTER (380025)**, 24800 S.E. Stark,
Zip 97030–3378; tel. 503/667–1122 **A**1 2 9 10 **F**3 11 13 15 18 20 22 26 28
29 30 31 32 34 35 38 40 44 45 46 49 50 56 57 59 60 64 68 70 74 75 76
77 78 79 81 85 86 87 93 100 101 102 107 108 110 111 114 115 119 120
121 126 129 130 132 146 147 148 **P**8 **S** Legacy Health, Portland, OR
Primary Contact: Gretchen Nichols, R.N., Chief Administrative Officer
COO: Michael Newcomb, D.O., Senior Vice President and Chief Operating Officer
CFO: David Eager, Senior Vice President and Chief Financial Officer
CIO: John Jay Kenagy, Ph.D., Senior Vice President and Chief Information Officer
CHR: Sonja Steves, Senior Vice President Human Resources
CNO: Marcia Soderling, R.N., Hospital Nurse Executive
Web address: www.legacyhealth.org
**Control:** Other not–for–profit (including NFP Corporation) **Service:** General
Medical and Surgical

**Staffed Beds:** 91 **Admissions:** 5410 **Census:** 49 **Outpatient Visits:** 76474
**Births:** 1038 **Total Expense ($000):** 96702 **Payroll Expense ($000):** 35708
**Personnel:** 495

## HEPPNER—Morrow County

**PIONEER MEMORIAL HOSPITAL (381310)**, 564 East Pioneer Drive,
Zip 97836–7318, Mailing Address: P.O. Box 9, Zip 97836–0009;
tel. 541/676–9133 **A**9 10 18 **F**3 7 17 34 35 40 45 50 57 59 62 63 64 66 68
69 75 97 107 119 127 133 143 148 **P**6
Primary Contact: Victor Vander Does, Interim Administrator and Chief Executive
Officer
CFO: Nicole Mahoney, Chief Financial Officer
CIO: Shawn Cutsforth, Information Systems Officer
CHR: Patti Allstott, Administrative Coordinator Human Resources and Grant Writer
Web address: www.morrowcountyhealthdistrict.org
**Control:** Hospital district or authority, Government, nonfederal **Service:** General
Medical and Surgical

**Staffed Beds:** 21 **Admissions:** 68 **Census:** 8 **Outpatient Visits:** 5524 **Births:**
0 **Total Expense ($000):** 7755 **Payroll Expense ($000):** 4277 **Personnel:**
58

## HERMISTON—Umatilla County

★ ◇ **GOOD SHEPHERD HEALTH CARE SYSTEM (381325)**, (Formerly Good
Shepherd Healthcare System), 610 N.W. 11th Street, Zip 97838–6601;
tel. 541/667–3400 **A**9 10 18 21 **F**3 8 13 15 28 29 30 34 35 37 40 43 45 46
50 53 57 59 62 63 64 65 68 70 75 76 77 78 79 81 84 85 86 93 97 107
108 110 111 114 115 119 126 127 130 131 132 135 141 143 146 147 148
**P**3 4 7
Primary Contact: Dennis E. Burke, President and Chief Executive Officer
COO: David T. Hughes, FACHE, Senior Vice President Operations and Chief
Operating Officer
CFO: Jan D. Peter, Vice President Fiscal Services and Chief Financial Officer
CMO: Richard Flaiz, M.D., President Medical Staff
CIO: Rob Rizk, Information Technology Director
CHR: Kelly Sanders, Vice President Human Resources
CNO: Theresa Brock, Vice President Nursing
Web address: www.gshealth.org
**Control:** Other not–for–profit (including NFP Corporation) **Service:** General
Medical and Surgical

**Staffed Beds:** 25 **Admissions:** 1750 **Census:** 14 **Outpatient Visits:** 63668
**Total Expense ($000):** 63182 **Payroll Expense ($000):** 25138 **Personnel:**
376

## HILLSBORO—Washington County

⊞ **TUALITY HEALTHCARE (380021)**, 335 S.E. Eighth Avenue, Zip 97123–4246;
tel. 503/681–1111, (Includes TUALITY COMMUNITY HOSPITAL, 335 S.E. Eighth
Avenue, Zip 97123, Mailing Address: P.O. Box 309, Zip 97123;
tel. 503/681–1111; TUALITY FOREST GROVE HOSPITAL, 1809 Maple Street,
Forest Grove, Zip 97116–1995; tel. 503/357–2173) **A**1 5 9 10 **F**3 11 13 15 17
18 20 22 24 26 28 29 30 31 32 34 35 36 37 40 44 45 47 49 50 53 54 56
57 59 62 64 68 70 71 74 75 76 77 78 79 80 81 82 85 86 87 92 93 97 98
100 103 104 107 108 110 111 114 115 118 119 129 130 131 132 135 143
144 145 146 147 148 **P**1 6
Primary Contact: Richard Stenson, President and Chief Executive Officer
COO: Manuel S. Berman, Administrator and Chief Operating Officer
CFO: Tim Fleischmann, Chief Financial Officer
CMO: Darell Lumaco, M.D., Chief of Staff
CIO: John Stoneburg, Chief Information Officer
CHR: Kathy Ratliffe, Director Human Resources
Web address: www.tuality.org
**Control:** Other not–for–profit (including NFP Corporation) **Service:** General
Medical and Surgical

**Staffed Beds:** 148 **Admissions:** 4854 **Census:** 60 **Outpatient Visits:** 250948
**Births:** 1030 **Total Expense ($000):** 167424 **Payroll Expense ($000):**
77874 **Personnel:** 1133

## HOOD RIVER—Hood River County

⊞ **PROVIDENCE HOOD RIVER MEMORIAL HOSPITAL (381318)**, 811 13th
Street, Zip 97031–1204, Mailing Address: P.O. Box 149, Zip 97031–0055;
tel. 541/386–3911 **A**1 10 18 **F**2 3 5 8 9 10 11 12 13 15 28 29 30 31 34 35
36 40 43 45 47 48 53 54 56 57 59 60 64 65 68 70 71 75 76 77 79 81 85
86 92 97 99 100 101 102 104 107 108 110 111 114 118 119 125 129 132
133 134 135 143 146 147 148 **P**6 **S** Providence Health & Services, Renton, WA
Primary Contact: Edward E. Freysinger, Chief Executive Officer
CFO: Ron Guth, Chief Financial Officer
CHR: Catherine Bourgault, Director Human Resources
Web address: www.providence.org/hoodriver
**Control:** Church–operated, Nongovernment, not–for profit **Service:** General
Medical and Surgical

**Staffed Beds:** 25 **Admissions:** 1661 **Census:** 12 **Outpatient Visits:** 151811
**Births:** 440 **Total Expense ($000):** 65458 **Payroll Expense ($000):** 23722
**Personnel:** 374

## JOHN DAY—Grant County

★ **BLUE MOUNTAIN HOSPITAL (381305)**, 170 Ford Road, Zip 97845–2009;
tel. 541/575–1311, (Total facility includes 48 beds in nursing home–type unit) **A**3
5 9 10 18 **F**2 3 7 8 11 13 15 17 29 30 31 34 35 36 40 41 43 45 56 57 59
62 63 64 67 68 70 75 76 81 82 86 87 89 93 107 110 111 114 119 127 128
130 131 132 133 135 143 144 145 148 **P**6 **S** HealthTech Management
Services, Franklin, TN
Primary Contact: Robert Houser, FACHE, Chief Executive Officer
CFO: Carl J. Flanagan, CPA, Chief Financial Officer
CMO: Keith Thomas, M.D., Chief of Staff
CIO: Marci Brown, Director Information Technology
CHR: Verlene Davis, Director Human Resources
CNO: Les McLeod, Director of Nursing Services
Web address: www.bluemountainhospital.org
**Control:** Hospital district or authority, Government, nonfederal **Service:** General
Medical and Surgical

**Staffed Beds:** 64 **Admissions:** 402 **Census:** 30 **Outpatient Visits:** 24482
**Births:** 42 **Total Expense ($000):** 18057 **Payroll Expense ($000):** 9671
**Personnel:** 158

---

**Hospital, Medicare Provider Number, Address, Telephone, Approval, Facility, and Physician Codes, Health Care System**

★ American Hospital Association (AHA) membership
☐ The Joint Commission accreditation  ◇ DNV Healthcare Inc. accreditation

○ Healthcare Facilities Accreditation Program
△ Commission on Accreditation of Rehabilitation Facilities (CARF) accreditation

OR

### KLAMATH FALLS—Klamath County

★ ◇ **SKY LAKES MEDICAL CENTER (380050)**, 2865 Daggett Avenue, Zip 97601–1106; tel. 541/882–6311 **A**2 3 5 9 10 21 **F**3 8 11 13 15 18 20 22 29 30 31 34 35 37 40 43 44 45 46 47 48 50 51 53 54 56 57 59 61 62 64 68 70 71 74 75 76 77 78 79 81 83 84 85 86 87 93 94 96 97 100 102 107 108 110 111 112 114 115 116 117 118 119 120 121 123 130 131 132 134 135 141 142 145 146 147 148 **P**6
Primary Contact: Paul R. Stewart, President and Chief Executive Officer
CFO: Richard Rico, Vice President and Chief Financial Officer
CMO: Rick Zwartverwer, M.D., Vice President Medical Affairs
CIO: David Chabner, Director Information Services
CHR: Don York, Vice President Human Resources
CNO: Annette E. Cole, R.N., Vice President and Chief Nursing Officer
Web address: www.skylakes.org
**Control:** Other not–for–profit (including NFP Corporation) **Service:** General Medical and Surgical

**Staffed Beds:** 100 **Admissions:** 5584 **Census:** 56 **Outpatient Visits:** 236796 **Births:** 794 **Total Expense ($000):** 155732 **Payroll Expense ($000):** 60099 **Personnel:** 922

### LA GRANDE—Union County

⊠ **GRANDE RONDE HOSPITAL (381321)**, 900 Sunset Drive, Zip 97850–1387, Mailing Address: P.O. Box 3290, Zip 97850–7290; tel. 541/963–8421 **A**1 9 10 18 **F**3 8 11 13 15 17 29 30 31 34 37 39 40 41 43 44 45 50 53 54 57 59 62 63 64 66 70 74 75 76 77 78 79 81 82 85 86 87 89 92 93 96 97 107 108 110 111 114 118 119 128 130 131 132 133 135 144 146 147 148 **P**6
Primary Contact: James A. Mattes, President and Chief Executive Officer
CFO: Wade Weis, Senior Director Finance
CIO: Parhez Sattar, Senior Director Information Technology
CHR: Kristi Puckett, Director Human Resources
Web address: www.grh.org
**Control:** Other not–for–profit (including NFP Corporation) **Service:** General Medical and Surgical

**Staffed Beds:** 25 **Admissions:** 1386 **Census:** 14 **Outpatient Visits:** 80402 **Births:** 270 **Total Expense ($000):** 60622 **Payroll Expense ($000):** 31758 **Personnel:** 397

### LAKEVIEW—Lake County

★ **LAKE DISTRICT HOSPITAL (381309)**, 700 South J Street, Zip 97630–1679; tel. 541/947–2114, (Total facility includes 36 beds in nursing home–type unit) **A**5 9 10 18 **F**13 15 29 30 31 34 35 40 45 46 57 59 62 63 64 67 68 76 78 81 82 85 93 107 111 114 119 128 129 130 132 133 135 144 146 148 **P**4 6
Primary Contact: Charles B. Tveit, Chief Executive Officer
CFO: Ken Landau, Chief Financial Officer
CMO: Stephen Hussey, M.D., Chief of Staff
CHR: Linda Michaelson, Director Human Resources
CNO: Teresa Squires, R.N., Chief Nursing Officer
Web address: www.lakehealthdistrict.org
**Control:** Hospital district or authority, Government, nonfederal **Service:** General Medical and Surgical

**Staffed Beds:** 60 **Admissions:** 498 **Census:** 27 **Outpatient Visits:** 27546 **Births:** 61 **Total Expense ($000):** 19131 **Payroll Expense ($000):** 8102 **Personnel:** 138

### LEBANON—Linn County

★ ◇ **SAMARITAN LEBANON COMMUNITY HOSPITAL (381323)**, 525 North Santiam Highway, Zip 97355–4363, Mailing Address: P.O. Box 739, Zip 97355–0739; tel. 541/258–2101 **A**9 10 18 21 **F**3 11 13 15 28 29 30 31 34 35 40 43 44 45 46 47 50 53 59 60 64 68 70 75 76 78 79 81 82 85 86 87 89 92 93 97 107 108 110 111 114 117 118 119 130 131 132 135 144 146 147 148 **P**6 **S** Samaritan Health Services, Corvallis, OR
Primary Contact: Becky A. Pape, R.N., Chief Executive Officer
CFO: Daniel B. Smith, Vice President Finance
CMO: Alan Blake, M.D., President Medical Staff
CIO: Bob Power, Vice President Information Services
CHR: Connie Erwin, Manager
CNO: Wendie Wunderwald, Vice President Patient Care Services
Web address: www.samhealth.org
**Control:** Other not–for–profit (including NFP Corporation) **Service:** General Medical and Surgical

**Staffed Beds:** 25 **Admissions:** 1786 **Census:** 14 **Outpatient Visits:** 141192 **Births:** 312 **Total Expense ($000):** 79708 **Payroll Expense ($000):** 36438 **Personnel:** 426

### LINCOLN CITY—Lincoln County

★ ◇ **SAMARITAN NORTH LINCOLN HOSPITAL (381302)**, 3043 N.E. 28th Street, Zip 97367–4518, Mailing Address: P.O. Box 767, Zip 97367–0767; tel. 541/994–3661 **A**9 10 18 21 **F**3 8 11 13 15 29 30 31 34 35 40 45 50 51 57 59 62 63 64 68 70 75 76 79 81 84 85 86 87 93 97 107 108 110 111 114 116 117 118 119 127 130 132 133 135 144 146 147 148 **P**6
**S** Samaritan Health Services, Corvallis, OR
Primary Contact: Marty Cahill, Chief Executive Officer
CFO: Kathryn Doksum, Director Finance
CMO: Michael Halferty, M.D., President Medical Staff
CHR: Lauri Bolton, Director Human Resources
Web address: www.samhealth.org
**Control:** Other not–for–profit (including NFP Corporation) **Service:** General Medical and Surgical

**Staffed Beds:** 25 **Admissions:** 1104 **Census:** 8 **Outpatient Visits:** 86021 **Births:** 153 **Total Expense ($000):** 44364 **Payroll Expense ($000):** 22275 **Personnel:** 254

### MADRAS—Jefferson County

★ **ST. CHARLES MADRAS (381324)**, (Formerly Mountain View Hospital District), 470 N.E. A Street, Zip 97741–1844; tel. 541/475–3882 **A**9 10 18 **F**3 13 15 29 30 34 35 37 40 43 45 50 57 59 62 63 64 67 68 70 75 76 77 79 80 81 84 85 87 89 90 98 107 110 115 119 128 130 132 133 135 146 **P**7 **S** St. Charles Health System, Inc., Bend, OR
Primary Contact: Jeanine Gentry, Chief Executive Officer
CFO: Martha Bewley, Chief Financial Officer
CMO: Thomas Manning, M.D., Medical Director
CIO: Burt Ridge, Director of Information Technology
CHR: JoDee Tittle, Director Community and Human Resources
CNO: Christine Gish, R.N., Acute Care Director
Web address: www.mvhd.org
**Control:** Hospital district or authority, Government, nonfederal **Service:** General Medical and Surgical

**Staffed Beds:** 25 **Admissions:** 946 **Census:** 9 **Outpatient Visits:** 25404 **Births:** 171 **Total Expense ($000):** 25314 **Payroll Expense ($000):** 13062 **Personnel:** 214

### MCMINNVILLE—Yamhill County

☐ **WILLAMETTE VALLEY MEDICAL CENTER (380071)**, 2700 S.E. Stratus Avenue, Zip 97128–6255; tel. 503/472–6131 **A**1 2 9 10 **F**3 11 12 13 15 18 20 24 26 27 28 29 30 31 34 35 40 43 46 50 56 57 58 59 60 64 65 70 74 75 76 77 78 79 81 82 84 85 87 92 93 98 103 107 108 110 111 114 115 118 119 120 123 124 129 130 131 132 135 146 147 148 **P**6 **S** Capella Healthcare, Franklin, TN
Primary Contact: Daniel Ordyna, Chief Executive Officer
COO: Frank Almendarez, Chief Operating Officer
CFO: Meredith P. Nelson, Chief Financial Officer
CIO: Diane Farrow, Manager Information Technology and Systems
CHR: Drew Burke, Director Human Resources
Web address: www.wvmcweb.com
**Control:** Corporation, Investor–owned, for–profit **Service:** General Medical and Surgical

**Staffed Beds:** 88 **Admissions:** 4025 **Census:** 35 **Outpatient Visits:** 116964 **Births:** 527 **Total Expense ($000):** 74146 **Payroll Expense ($000):** 26580 **Personnel:** 438

### MEDFORD—Jackson County

⊠ △ **PROVIDENCE MEDFORD MEDICAL CENTER (380075)**, 1111 Crater Lake Avenue, Zip 97504–6241; tel. 541/732–5000 **A**1 2 7 9 10 **F**3 11 13 15 17 18 20 22 29 30 31 32 34 35 40 43 45 49 50 55 56 57 59 61 62 63 64 68 70 74 75 76 77 78 79 81 82 84 85 86 87 90 92 93 96 97 102 107 110 114 115 118 119 120 121 123 124 126 130 132 143 146 147 148 **P**6
**S** Providence Health & Services, Renton, WA
Primary Contact: Thomas S. Hanenburg, Chief Executive
COO: Brian J. Herwig, Chief Operating Officer
CFO: Chris Pizzi, Assistant Administrator Fiscal Services
CHR: Julie Levison, Director Human Resources
CNO: Jane E. Hanson, R.N., Chief Nursing Officer
Web address: www.providence.org
**Control:** Church–operated, Nongovernment, not–for profit **Service:** General Medical and Surgical

**Staffed Beds:** 124 **Admissions:** 6399 **Census:** 68 **Outpatient Visits:** 295634 **Births:** 512 **Total Expense ($000):** 156417 **Payroll Expense ($000):** 57563 **Personnel:** 838

*Many Facility Codes have changed. Please refer to the AHA Guide Code Chart.*   © 2013 AHA Guide

★ ◇ **ROGUE VALLEY MEDICAL CENTER (380018)**, 2825 East Barnett Road, Zip 97504–8332; tel. 541/789–7000 **A**2 9 10 21 **F**11 12 13 15 17 18 19 20 21 22 23 24 25 26 27 28 29 30 31 32 34 35 37 40 43 45 46 50 51 57 58 59 60 63 64 65 70 72 74 75 76 78 79 81 82 84 85 86 87 89 90 93 94 98 100 102 107 108 110 111 112 115 119 120 121 122 126 130 132 143 146 147 148 **P**6 **S** Asante Health System, Medford, OR
Primary Contact: Scott A. Kelly, Chief Executive Officer
COO: Jose Romo, Vice President of Operations
CFO: Mark Collins, Interim Chief Finance Officer
CMO: Jamie Grebosky, M.D., Vice President of Medical Affairs
CIO: Mark Hetz, Chief Information Officer
CHR: Gregg Edwards, Chief People Officer
CNO: Jo Lynn Wallace, Vice President of Nursing
Web address: www.asante.org/rrmc/
**Control:** Other not–for–profit (including NFP Corporation) **Service:** General Medical and Surgical

**Staffed Beds:** 307 **Admissions:** 14510 **Census:** 187 **Outpatient Visits:** 359779 **Births:** 1505 **Total Expense ($000):** 352796 **Payroll Expense ($000):** 106249 **Personnel:** 1410

### MILWAUKIE—Clackamas County

⊠ **PROVIDENCE MILWAUKIE HOSPITAL (380082)**, 10150 S.E. 32nd Avenue, Zip 97222–6516; tel. 503/513–8300 **A**1 3 5 9 10 **F**3 13 15 29 30 34 35 36 40 44 45 46 50 53 54 57 59 63 64 68 70 71 74 75 76 77 79 81 82 84 85 87 89 91 92 93 97 100 105 107 108 111 114 115 119 129 130 131 132 133 135 146 147 148 **P**6 **S** Providence Health & Services, Renton, WA
Primary Contact: Keith Hyde, Chief Executive Officer
CFO: Elizabeth Sublette, Chief Financial Officer
CHR: Joann M. Pfister, Director Human Resources
CNO: Lauren M. Bridge, R.N., Chief Nurse Executive
Web address: www.providence.org
**Control:** Church–operated, Nongovernment, not–for profit **Service:** General Medical and Surgical

**Staffed Beds:** 63 **Admissions:** 3111 **Census:** 25 **Outpatient Visits:** 199659 **Births:** 517 **Total Expense ($000):** 81155 **Payroll Expense ($000):** 28932 **Personnel:** 376

### NEWBERG—Yamhill County

⊠ **PROVIDENCE NEWBERG MEDICAL CENTER (380037)**, 1001 Providence Drive, Zip 97132–7485; tel. 503/537–1555 **A**1 9 10 **F**3 11 13 15 18 20 29 30 34 35 40 45 49 50 57 59 60 64 68 70 75 76 77 79 81 85 87 93 100 107 108 110 111 114 118 119 129 130 132 135 146 147 148 **P**6 **S** Providence Health & Services, Renton, WA
Primary Contact: Lorinda Van Zanten, MSN, Chief Executive Officer
CFO: Jack R. Sumner, Assistant Administrator Finance
CMO: George Weghorst, M.D., Chief Medical Officer
CIO: Laureen O'Brien, Chief Information Officer
CHR: Cheryl Gebhart, Director Human Resources Providence Health Plan and Providence Medical Group
Web address: www.phsor.org
**Control:** Church–operated, Nongovernment, not–for profit **Service:** General Medical and Surgical

**Staffed Beds:** 40 **Admissions:** 2339 **Census:** 19 **Outpatient Visits:** 197192 **Births:** 532 **Total Expense ($000):** 80399 **Payroll Expense ($000):** 25806 **Personnel:** 371

### NEWPORT—Lincoln County

★ ◇ **SAMARITAN PACIFIC COMMUNITIES HOSPITAL (381314)**, 930 S.W. Abbey Street, Zip 97365–4820, Mailing Address: P.O. Box 945, Zip 97365–0072; tel. 541/265–2244 **A**9 10 18 21 **F**3 8 11 13 15 17 28 29 30 31 34 35 40 45 47 50 54 62 63 64 68 70 75 76 77 78 79 81 84 85 87 89 92 93 97 107 110 111 114 119 129 130 132 133 135 144 146 147 148 **P**6 **S** Samaritan Health Services, Corvallis, OR
Primary Contact: David C. Bigelow, PharmD, Chief Executive Officer
CHR: Penny Dunne, R.N., Director Human Resources
Web address: www.samhealth.org
**Control:** Other not–for–profit (including NFP Corporation) **Service:** General Medical and Surgical

**Staffed Beds:** 25 **Admissions:** 1393 **Census:** 11 **Outpatient Visits:** 86176 **Births:** 202 **Total Expense ($000):** 62585 **Payroll Expense ($000):** 28655 **Personnel:** 349

### ONTARIO—Malheur County

**HOLY ROSARY MEDICAL CENTER** See Saint Alphonsus Medical Center – Ontario

⊠ **SAINT ALPHONSUS MEDICAL CENTER – ONTARIO (380052)**, 351 S.W. Ninth Street, Zip 97914–2693; tel. 541/881–7000 **A**1 3 5 9 10 **F**3 11 12 13 15 29 30 32 34 35 40 43 44 45 46 50 51 54 56 57 59 62 63 64 65 66 68 70 75 76 77 79 81 82 87 93 97 107 108 110 114 118 119 129 130 131 132 135 144 146 147 148 **P**6 **S** Trinity Health, Livonia, MI
Primary Contact: Richard L. Palagi, Chief Executive Officer
CFO: Paul Vachek, Vice President of Finance/Operations
CHR: Brenda Munsey, Senior Human Resources Business Partner
CNO: Nancy Greer, R.N., Chief Nursing Officer
Web address: www.holyrosary–ontario.org
**Control:** Church–operated, Nongovernment, not–for profit **Service:** General Medical and Surgical

**Staffed Beds:** 49 **Admissions:** 2741 **Census:** 22 **Outpatient Visits:** 77572 **Births:** 579 **Total Expense ($000):** 60867 **Payroll Expense ($000):** 24831 **Personnel:** 444

### OREGON CITY—Clackamas County

⊠ **PROVIDENCE WILLAMETTE FALLS MEDICAL CENTER (380038)**, 1500 Division Street, Zip 97045–1597; tel. 503/656–1631 **A**1 9 10 **F**13 15 29 30 34 35 36 40 44 45 46 50 53 54 57 59 63 64 68 70 74 75 76 77 78 79 81 82 84 85 87 91 92 93 97 100 107 108 111 114 118 129 130 131 132 133 135 146 147 **P**6 **S** Providence Health & Services, Renton, WA
Primary Contact: Russ Reinhard, Chief Executive
CFO: Elizabeth Sublette, Chief Finance Officer
CMO: Kevin Jamison, M.D., Chief Medical Officer
CHR: Joann M. Pfister, Director Human Resources
Web address: www.providence.org/pwfmc
**Control:** Church–operated, Nongovernment, not–for profit **Service:** General Medical and Surgical

**Staffed Beds:** 89 **Admissions:** 4328 **Census:** 32 **Outpatient Visits:** 152916 **Births:** 965 **Total Expense ($000):** 92072 **Payroll Expense ($000):** 32201 **Personnel:** 408

### PENDLETON—Umatilla County

**BLUE MOUNTAIN RECOVERY CENTER (384011)**, 2600 Westgate, Zip 97801–9604; tel. 541/276–0810, (Nonreporting) **A**10
Primary Contact: Kerry Kelly, Superintendent
COO: Kerry Kelly, Superintendent
CFO: Dan Grant, Manager Business Office
CMO: Peter Davidson, M.D., Chief Medical Officer
CHR: Billy Martin, Human Resource Analyst
**Control:** State–Government, nonfederal **Service:** Psychiatric

**Staffed Beds:** 60

⊠ **ST. ANTHONY HOSPITAL (381319)**, 1601 S.E. Court Avenue, Zip 97801–3217; tel. 541/276–5121, (Nonreporting) **A**1 5 9 10 18 **S** Catholic Health Initiatives, Englewood, CO
Primary Contact: Harold S. Geller, Chief Executive Officer
CFO: Jim Schlenker, Vice President and Chief Financial Officer
CMO: Malcolm Townsley, M.D., Chief of Staff
CHR: Janeen K. Reding, Director Human Resources
Web address: www.sahpendleton.org
**Control:** Church–operated, Nongovernment, not–for profit **Service:** General Medical and Surgical

**Staffed Beds:** 25

### PORTLAND—Multnomah County

⊠ **ADVENTIST MEDICAL CENTER–PORTLAND (380060)**, (Formerly Adventist Medical Center), 10123 S.E. Market Street, Zip 97216–2599; tel. 503/257–2500 **A**1 2 9 10 **F**3 9 11 13 15 17 18 20 22 24 26 28 29 30 31 34 35 36 40 44 45 46 49 53 54 57 58 59 62 63 64 70 71 74 75 76 77 78 79 81 82 83 84 85 86 87 93 97 98 100 102 107 108 110 111 114 115 118 119 120 121 123 126 129 130 131 132 135 144 146 147 148 **P**6 7 **S** Adventist Health, Roseville, CA
Primary Contact: Thomas Russell, President and Chief Executive Officer
COO: Ronald K. Benfield, Chief Operating Officer
CFO: V. Mark Perry, Chief Financial Officer
CMO: Wesley E. Rippey, M.D., Chief Medical Officer
CHR: Shane Voshell, Director Human Resources
CNO: Ellen Tryon, R.N., Chief Nursing Officer
Web address: www.adventisthealthnw.com
**Control:** Church–operated, Nongovernment, not–for profit **Service:** General Medical and Surgical

**Staffed Beds:** 248 **Admissions:** 11659 **Census:** 119 **Outpatient Visits:** 555124 **Births:** 1081 **Total Expense ($000):** 291878 **Payroll Expense ($000):** 121956 **Personnel:** 1515

**OR**

**OR**

☐ **CEDAR HILLS HOSPITAL (384012)**, 10300 S.W. Eastridge Street, Zip 97225–5004; tel. 503/944–5000, (Nonreporting) **A**1 9 10 **S** Universal Health Services, Inc., King of Prussia, PA
Primary Contact: Michael Sherbun, Ph.D., Chief Executive Officer
Web address: www.cedarhillshospital.com
**Control:** Corporation, Investor–owned, for–profit **Service:** Psychiatric

**Staffed Beds:** 78

**DOERNBECHER CHILDREN'S HOSPITAL** See OHSU Hospital

**GOOD SAMARITAN HOSPITAL AND MEDICAL CENTER** See Legacy Good Samaritan Hospital and Medical Center

✠ △ **LEGACY EMANUEL HOSPITAL AND HEALTH CENTER (380007)**, 2801 North Gantenbein Avenue, Zip 97227–1674; tel. 503/413–2200, (Includes RANDALL CHILDREN'S HOSPITAL, 2801 North Gantenbein Avenue, Zip 97227–1623; tel. 503/413–2200) **A**1 2 3 5 7 9 10 **F**3 11 13 15 16 18 19 20 21 22 23 24 25 26 27 29 30 31 32 34 35 38 40 41 43 44 45 46 47 49 50 51 54 56 57 59 60 61 64 65 66 68 70 72 74 75 76 77 78 79 80 81 83 84 85 86 87 88 89 93 97 98 99 100 101 102 105 107 108 110 111 112 114 118 119 126 127 130 132 144 146 147 148 **P**8 **S** Legacy Health, Portland, OR
Primary Contact: Lori Morgan, M.D., Chief Administrative Officer
CFO: Pamela S. Vukovich, Senior Vice President, Chief Financial Officer and Treasurer
CIO: Richard Gibson, Senior Vice President and Chief Information Officer
CHR: Sonja Steves, Senior Vice President Human Resources and Marketing
Web address: www.legacyhealth.org
**Control:** Other not–for–profit (including NFP Corporation) **Service:** General Medical and Surgical

**Staffed Beds:** 419 **Admissions:** 18589 **Census:** 268 **Outpatient Visits:** 532013 **Births:** 1894 **Total Expense ($000):** 573260 **Payroll Expense ($000):** 252949 **Personnel:** 3118

✠ **LEGACY GOOD SAMARITAN HOSPITAL AND MEDICAL CENTER (380017)**, 1015 N.W. 22nd Avenue, Zip 97210–3099; tel. 503/413–7711, (Includes GOOD SAMARITAN HOSPITAL AND MEDICAL CENTER, 1015 N.W. 22nd Avenue, Zip 97210; tel. 503/229–7711; REHABILITATION INSTITUTE OF OREGON, 2010 N.W. Kearney Street, Zip 97209; tel. 503/226–3774) **A**1 2 3 5 9 10 **F**3 8 11 12 13 15 18 20 22 24 26 28 29 30 31 34 35 38 40 44 45 46 47 48 49 50 51 55 56 57 58 59 60 61 64 65 68 70 74 75 76 77 78 79 80 81 82 83 84 85 86 87 90 91 93 94 96 97 98 100 101 102 103 107 110 111 115 116 117 118 119 120 121 123 124 126 129 130 132 135 138 142 145 146 147 148 **P**8 **S** Legacy Health, Portland, OR
Primary Contact: Tony Melaragno, M.D., Chief Administrative Officer
CFO: Pamela S. Vukovich, Senior Vice President, Chief Financial Officer and Treasurer
CIO: C. Matthew Calais, Senior Vice President and Chief Information Officer
CHR: Sonja Steves, Vice President Marketing
Web address: www.legacyhealth.org
**Control:** Other not–for–profit (including NFP Corporation) **Service:** General Medical and Surgical

**Staffed Beds:** 248 **Admissions:** 11870 **Census:** 148 **Outpatient Visits:** 155029 **Births:** 1144 **Total Expense ($000):** 275963 **Payroll Expense ($000):** 101332 **Personnel:** 1356

✠ **OHSU HOSPITAL (380009)**, 3181 S.W. Sam Jackson Park Road, Zip 97239–3098; tel. 503/494–8311, (Includes DOERNBECHER CHILDREN'S HOSPITAL, 3181 S.W. Sam Jackson Park Road, Zip 97201) **A**1 2 3 5 8 9 10 **F**3 5 6 8 9 11 12 13 15 17 18 20 21 22 23 24 25 26 27 28 29 30 31 32 33 34 35 36 37 38 39 40 41 43 44 45 46 47 48 49 50 51 52 53 54 55 56 57 58 59 60 61 64 65 66 68 70 71 72 74 75 76 77 78 79 81 82 83 84 85 86 87 88 89 91 92 93 94 95 97 98 99 100 101 102 103 104 105 106 107 108 109 110 111 112 113 114 115 116 117 118 119 120 121 123 124 126 127 129 130 131 132 134 135 136 137 138 139 141 142 144 145 146 147 148 **P**1
Primary Contact: Peter F. Rapp, Vice President and Executive Director
COO: Cynthia M. Grueber, Chief Operating Officer
CFO: Diana Gernhart, Chief Financial Officer
CMO: Charles M. Kilo, M.D., Chief Medical Officer
CIO: Bridget Haggerty, Chief Information Officer
CHR: Priscilla B. Andres, Director Human Resources
Web address: www.ohsu.edu
**Control:** Hospital district or authority, Government, nonfederal **Service:** General Medical and Surgical

**Staffed Beds:** 522 **Admissions:** 29787 **Census:** 433 **Outpatient Visits:** 735279 **Births:** 2332 **Total Expense ($000):** 1096632 **Payroll Expense ($000):** 392946 **Personnel:** 6369

✠ **PORTLAND VETERANS AFFAIRS MEDICAL CENTER**, (Formerly Veterans Affairs Medical Center), 3710 S.W. U.S. Veterans Hospital Road, Zip 97239–2964, Mailing Address: P.O. Box 1034, Zip 97207–1034; tel. 503/220–8262, (Nonreporting) **A**1 2 3 5 8 **S** Department of Veterans Affairs, Washington, DC
Primary Contact: John E. Patrick, Director
CFO: Annette Barkema, Chief Financial Officer
CMO: Thomas Anderson, M.D., Chief of Staff
CIO: James Horner, Chief Information Officer
CHR: Melody Mikutowski, Chief Human Resources Management
Web address: www.portland.va.gov/
**Control:** Veterans Affairs, Government, federal **Service:** General Medical and Surgical

**Staffed Beds:** 303

✠ **PROVIDENCE PORTLAND MEDICAL CENTER (380061)**, 4805 N.E. Glisan Street, Zip 97213–2933; tel. 503/215–5526 **A**1 2 3 5 9 10 **F**3 4 5 9 13 15 17 18 20 22 24 26 29 30 31 34 35 36 37 38 40 44 45 46 49 50 51 53 54 56 57 58 59 60 61 62 63 64 65 66 68 70 73 74 75 76 77 78 79 81 82 84 85 86 87 90 92 93 97 98 99 100 102 103 104 105 107 108 109 110 111 114 116 117 118 119 121 123 124 126 129 130 131 132 133 135 136 137 145 146 147 148 **P**6 **S** Providence Health & Services, Renton, WA
Primary Contact: Theron Park, Chief Executive Officer
COO: Krista Farnham, Chief Operating Officer
CFO: Eric Olson, Chief Financial Officer
CMO: Robert Wells, M.D., Chief Medical Officer
CIO: Richard Gibson, Chief Information Officer
CHR: Jeannie Mikulic, Director Human Resources
CNO: Mary T. McFadden, MSN, Chief Nurse Executive
Web address: www.providence.org
**Control:** Church–operated, Nongovernment, not–for profit **Service:** General Medical and Surgical

**Staffed Beds:** 426 **Admissions:** 21351 **Census:** 281 **Outpatient Visits:** 1203738 **Births:** 2539 **Total Expense ($000):** 622036 **Payroll Expense ($000):** 210061 **Personnel:** 2629

✠ **PROVIDENCE ST. VINCENT MEDICAL CENTER (380004)**, 9205 S.W. Barnes Road, Zip 97225–6661; tel. 503/216–1234, (Includes CHILDREN AT PROVIDENCE ST. VINCENT, 9205 S.W. Barnes Road, Zip 97225–6603; tel. 503/216–4400) **A**1 2 3 5 9 10 **F**3 5 13 15 17 18 20 22 24 26 28 29 30 31 34 35 36 37 38 40 44 45 46 47 48 49 50 51 53 54 56 57 58 59 60 61 64 65 68 70 72 74 75 76 77 78 79 81 82 83 84 85 86 87 89 91 92 93 97 98 100 102 103 104 105 107 108 109 110 111 112 114 115 116 117 118 119 120 121 123 126 129 130 131 132 133 135 146 147 148 **P**6 **S** Providence Health & Services, Renton, WA
Primary Contact: Janice Burger, Administrator
CFO: William Olson, Director Finance
CIO: Kate Chester, Senior Coordinator Public Relations
Web address: www.providence.org/portland/hospitals
**Control:** Church–operated, Nongovernment, not–for profit **Service:** General Medical and Surgical

**Staffed Beds:** 528 **Admissions:** 28984 **Census:** 339 **Outpatient Visits:** 773771 **Births:** 5135 **Total Expense ($000):** 709179 **Payroll Expense ($000):** 223194 **Personnel:** 2762

**REHABILITATION INSTITUTE OF OREGON** See Legacy Good Samaritan Hospital and Medical Center

☐ **SHRINERS HOSPITALS FOR CHILDREN–PORTLAND (383300)**, (Formerly Shriners Hospitals for Children, Portland), 3101 S.W. Sam Jackson Park Road, Zip 97239–3009; tel. 503/241–5090 **A**1 3 5 10 **F**3 34 35 37 50 58 64 68 75 77 79 81 85 86 87 89 91 93 94 130 131 132 134 146 148 **P**6 **S** Shriners Hospitals for Children, Tampa, FL
Primary Contact: J. Craig Patchin, Administrator
CFO: Mark Knudsen, Director Fiscal Services
CMO: Michael Aiona, M.D., Chief of Staff
CIO: Carl Montante, Director Information Systems and Information Technology
CHR: Rhonda Smith, Director Human Resources
CNO: Suzanne Diers, R.N., Director Patient Care Services
Web address: www.shrinershospitalsforchildren.org/Hospitals/Locations/Portland.aspx
**Control:** Other not–for–profit (including NFP Corporation) **Service:** Children's general

**Staffed Beds:** 8 **Admissions:** 550 **Census:** 6 **Outpatient Visits:** 11268 **Births:** 0 **Personnel:** 222

**VETERANS AFFAIRS MEDICAL CENTER** See Portland Veterans Affairs Medical Center

☐ **VIBRA SPECIALTY HOSPITAL OF PORTLAND (382004)**, 10300 N.E. Hancock Street, Zip 97220–3831; tel. 503/257–5500, (Nonreporting) **A**1 9 10 **S** Vibra Healthcare, Mechanicsburg, PA
Primary Contact: Tina Key, Chief Executive Officer
Web address: www.vibrahealthcare.com
**Control:** Corporation, Investor–owned, for–profit **Service:** Long–Term Acute Care hospital

**Staffed Beds:** 60

**PRINEVILLE—Crook County**

★ **PIONEER MEMORIAL HOSPITAL (381313)**, 1201 N.E. Elm Street,
Zip 97754–1206; tel. 541/447–6254 **A**9 10 18 **F**3 11 15 29 34 35 40 43 45
50 59 63 64 65 70 75 79 81 82 84 85 86 87 89 93 97 100 107 110 115
119 127 130 132 133 135 146 **S** St. Charles Health System, Inc., Bend, OR
Primary Contact: Robert Gomes, Chief Executive Officer
COO: Jim Kirkbride, Director of Support Services
CFO: Karen Shepard, Senior Vice President and Chief Financial Officer
CMO: Michel Boileau, M.D., Chief Clinical Officer
CIO: William Winnenberg, Chief Information Officer
CHR: Rebecca Morgan, Senior Director Human Resources
CNO: Karen Reed, Chief Nursing Officer
Web address: www.stcharleshealthcare.org
**Control:** Other not–for–profit (including NFP Corporation) **Service:** General
Medical and Surgical

**Staffed Beds:** 25 **Admissions:** 695 **Census:** 7 **Outpatient Visits:** 36024
**Births:** 0 **Total Expense ($000):** 21466 **Payroll Expense ($000):** 11178
**Personnel:** 175

**REDMOND—Deschutes County**

✠ **ST. CHARLES MEDICAL CENTER – REDMOND (380040)**, 1253 N.W. Canal
Boulevard, Zip 97756–1395; tel. 541/548–8131 **A**1 9 10 20 **F**3 11 13 29 30
34 40 43 45 47 51 57 59 62 64 68 70 75 76 81 82 84 85 92 93 102 107
108 114 119 130 135 146 148 **P**4 7 **S** St. Charles Health System, Inc.,
Bend, OR
Primary Contact: Robert Gomes, Chief Executive Officer
COO: Jim Kirkbride, Director of Support Services
CFO: Karen Shepard, Senior Vice President Finance and Chief Financial Officer
CMO: Michel Boileau, M.D., Chief Clinical Officer
CIO: William Winnenberg, Chief Information Officer
CHR: Rebecca Morgan, Senior Director Human Resources
CNO: Karen Reed, Interim Chief Nursing Officer
Web address: www.stcharleshealthcare.org
**Control:** Other not–for–profit (including NFP Corporation) **Service:** General
Medical and Surgical

**Staffed Beds:** 48 **Admissions:** 2107 **Census:** 17 **Outpatient Visits:** 61117
**Births:** 358 **Total Expense ($000):** 61097 **Payroll Expense ($000):** 27412
**Personnel:** 353

**REEDSPORT—Douglas County**

**LOWER UMPQUA HOSPITAL DISTRICT (381311)**, 600 Ranch Road,
Zip 97467–1795; tel. 541/271–2171 **A**9 10 18 **F**3 7 11 15 29 34 35 37 40
43 45 46 70 75 77 81 85 87 93 107 108 114 119 127 130 132 133 135
143 **P**6
Primary Contact: Sandra Reese, Administrator
CFO: John Chivers, Chief Financial Officer
CMO: Ronald Vail, M.D., Chief of Staff
CIO: Timothy Picou, Manager Information Technology
Web address: www.lowerumpquahospital.com
**Control:** Hospital district or authority, Government, nonfederal **Service:** General
Medical and Surgical

**Staffed Beds:** 16 **Admissions:** 597 **Census:** 5 **Outpatient Visits:** 21256
**Births:** 0 **Total Expense ($000):** 18919 **Payroll Expense ($000):** 7321
**Personnel:** 130

**ROSEBURG—Douglas County**

✠ **MERCY MEDICAL CENTER (380027)**, 2700 Stewart Parkway,
Zip 97471–1281; tel. 541/673–0611 **A**1 2 9 10 **F**3 8 11 13 15 17 18 19 20
21 22 23 24 25 26 27 28 29 30 31 32 34 35 37 38 40 43 44 45 46 47 48
49 50 51 54 56 57 59 60 61 62 63 64 65 68 70 74 75 76 77 78 79 81 82
84 85 86 87 89 93 96 102 107 108 110 111 114 115 118 119 129 130 132
135 143 146 147 148 **P**6 **S** Catholic Health Initiatives, Englewood, CO
Primary Contact: Kelly C. Morgan, President and Chief Executive Officer
COO: Debbie Boswell, Chief Operating Officer and Chief Nursing Officer
CFO: John Kasberger, Vice President and Chief Financial Officer
CMO: Jason Gray, M.D., Chief Medical Officer
CIO: Kathleen Nickel, Director Communications
CHR: Deb Lightcap, Director Human Resources
CNO: Debbie Boswell, Chief Operating Officer and Chief Nursing Officer
Web address: www.mercyrose.org
**Control:** Church–operated, Nongovernment, not–for profit **Service:** General
Medical and Surgical

**Staffed Beds:** 141 **Admissions:** 7459 **Census:** 76 **Outpatient Visits:** 315675
**Births:** 929 **Total Expense ($000):** 139001 **Payroll Expense ($000):** 53348
**Personnel:** 703

✠ △ **VETERANS AFFAIRS ROSEBURG HEALTHCARE SYSTEM**, 913 N.W.
Garden Valley Boulevard, Zip 97471–6513; tel. 541/440–1000, (Nonreporting)
**A**1 7 **S** Department of Veterans Affairs, Washington, DC
Primary Contact: Carol Bogedain, FACHE, Director
COO: Steven Broskey, Associate Director
CHR: Larry Mentzer, Chief Human Resources Officer
CNO: Sharon Carlson, Executive Assistant to the Director
CNO: Tracy Weistreich, Ph.D., Associate Director Patient Care Services/Nurse
Executive
Web address: www.roseburg.va.gov/
**Control:** Veterans Affairs, Government, federal **Service:** General Medical and
Surgical

**Staffed Beds:** 88

**SALEM—Marion County**

☐ **OREGON STATE HOSPITAL (384008)**, 2600 Center Street N.E.,
Zip 97301–2682; tel. 503/945–2870, (Nonreporting) **A**1 3 5 10
Primary Contact: Greg Roberts, Superintendent
Web address: www.oregon.gov/dhs/mentalhealth/osh/main.shtml
**Control:** State–Government, nonfederal **Service:** Psychiatric

**Staffed Beds:** 638

✠ **SALEM HOSPITAL (380051)**, 665 Winter Street S.E., Zip 97301–3959, Mailing
Address: P.O. Box 14001, Zip 97309–5014; tel. 503/561–5200, (Includes
PSYCHIATRIC MEDICINE CENTER, 1127 Oak Street S.E., Zip 97301, Mailing
Address: P.O. Box 14001, Zip 97309–5014; REGIONAL REHABILITATION
CENTER, 2561 Center Street N.E., Zip 97301, Mailing Address: P.O. Box 14001,
Zip 97309–5014; tel. 503/370–5986) **A**1 2 9 10 **F**3 11 12 13 15 17 18 19 20
22 24 26 28 29 30 31 34 35 36 37 38 40 43 45 46 47 48 49 50 53 54 55
56 57 58 59 64 66 67 68 70 72 74 75 76 77 78 79 81 82 84 85 86 87 89
90 91 92 93 94 95 96 97 98 99 100 102 103 104 105 106 107 108 109
110 111 112 113 114 115 116 117 118 119 120 121 122 123 124 126 129
130 131 132 135 144 145 146 147 148 **P**6 **S** Salem Health, Salem, OR
Primary Contact: Norman F. Gruber, President and Chief Executive Officer
COO: Cheryl R. Nester Wolfe, R.N., Senior Vice President Operations and Chief
Nursing Officer
CFO: Aaron Crane, Chief Financial Officer
CMO: W. David Holloway, M.D., Chief Medical Officer
CIO: Ken Kudla, Chief Information Officer
CHR: Beverly Bow, Vice President Human Resources
Web address: www.salemhospital.org
**Control:** Other not–for–profit (including NFP Corporation) **Service:** General
Medical and Surgical

**Staffed Beds:** 408 **Admissions:** 20719 **Census:** 239 **Outpatient Visits:**
370338 **Births:** 3164 **Total Expense ($000):** 514737 **Payroll Expense
($000):** 218857 **Personnel:** 2939

**SEASIDE—Clatsop County**

✠ **PROVIDENCE SEASIDE HOSPITAL (381303)**, 725 South Wahanna Road,
Zip 97138–7735; tel. 503/717–7000, (Total facility includes 22 beds in nursing
home–type unit) **A**1 9 10 18 **F**12 13 15 30 31 32 34 35 40 45 46 57 59 61 64
65 66 67 68 70 75 76 78 79 81 82 84 85 86 87 92 93 97 104 107 108 110
111 114 119 127 128 132 133 135 143 146 147 148 **P**6 **S** Providence
Health & Services, Renton, WA
Primary Contact: Michael Blauer, Chief Executive Officer
COO: Bonnie Thompson, Chief Operating Officer and Chief Nursing Executive
CFO: Pamela Hayes, Director Finance
CMO: Timothy Opie, M.D., President Professional Staff
CHR: Marti Hanen, Director Human Resources
CNO: Wendy Ackley, Assistant Administrator, Patient Services
CNO: Bonnie Thompson, Chief Operating Officer and Chief Nursing Officer
Web address: www.providence.org
**Control:** Church–operated, Nongovernment, not–for profit **Service:** General
Medical and Surgical

**Staffed Beds:** 47 **Admissions:** 851 **Census:** 27 **Outpatient Visits:** 120355
**Births:** 147 **Total Expense ($000):** 45487 **Payroll Expense ($000):** 21672
**Personnel:** 316

OR

**Hospital, Medicare Provider Number, Address, Telephone, Approval, Facility, and Physician Codes, Health Care System**

★ American Hospital Association (AHA) membership
☐ The Joint Commission accreditation      ◇ DNV Healthcare Inc. accreditation
○ Healthcare Facilities Accreditation Program
△ Commission on Accreditation of Rehabilitation Facilities (CARF) accreditation

**SILVERTON—Marion County**

⊞ **SILVERTON HOSPITAL (380029)**, 342 Fairview Street, Zip 97381–1993;
tel. 503/873–1500 **A**1 9 10 **F**3 11 13 15 20 26 28 29 30 34 35 40 43 47 50
53 54 57 59 64 65 66 68 70 75 76 77 79 81 85 86 87 89 107 108 110 111
114 115 119 124 127 129 130 131 132 133 135 143 144 146 147 148
Primary Contact: Richard M. Cagen, President/Chief Executive Officer
COO: Christine Denning, Chief Operating Officer
COO: Jeffrey D. Lorenz, Vice President Corporate Services
CFO: Jeff Fritsche, Chief Financial Officer
CMO: Frank Lord, M.D., Chief Medical & Quality Officer
CIO: Karen Brady, Chief Information Officer
CHR: Natalie J. Britton, Director Human Resources
CNO: Sue Brody, R.N., Chief Nursing Officer
Web address: www.silvertonhealth.org
**Control:** Other not–for–profit (including NFP Corporation) **Service:** General
Medical and Surgical

**Staffed Beds:** 48 **Admissions:** 3270 **Census:** 24 **Outpatient Visits:** 160391
**Births:** 1614 **Total Expense ($000):** 98607 **Payroll Expense ($000):** 52122
**Personnel:** 726

**SPRINGFIELD—Lane County**

⊞ **MCKENZIE–WILLAMETTE MEDICAL CENTER (380020)**, 1460 G Street,
Zip 97477–4197; tel. 541/726–4400 **A**1 9 10 **F**3 11 13 17 18 20 22 24 28
29 30 31 34 35 39 40 41 43 45 46 47 49 50 57 59 70 73 76 78 79 81 82
85 87 89 93 107 108 111 115 118 119 126 129 130 132 146 147 148 **P**6
**S** Community Health Systems, Inc., Franklin, TN
Primary Contact: Maurine Cate, Chief Executive Officer
COO: Randy Burrows, Director Administrative Services
CFO: Jason McLaughlin, Chief Financial Officer
CIO: Mike Allen, Director Information Technology
CHR: Megan A. O'Leary, Vice President Human Resources and Rehabilitation
Services
Web address: www.mckweb.com
**Control:** Corporation, Investor–owned, for–profit **Service:** General Medical and
Surgical

**Staffed Beds:** 113 **Admissions:** 6310 **Census:** 57 **Outpatient Visits:** 55398
**Births:** 618 **Total Expense ($000):** 113588 **Payroll Expense ($000):** 44710
**Personnel:** 564

⊞ **PEACEHEALTH SACRED HEART MEDICAL CENTER AT RIVERBEND
(380102)**, (Formerly Sacred Heart Medical Center at RiverBend), 3333 Riverbend
Drive, Zip 97477–8800; tel. 541/222–7300 **A**1 9 10 **F**11 12 13 15 18 19 20 21
22 24 25 26 28 29 30 37 40 43 45 46 47 49 51 57 60 64 68 70 72 74 75
76 78 79 81 82 84 85 89 93 102 107 108 111 115 118 119 126 129 130
146 148 **P**6 **S** PeaceHealth, Vancouver, WA
Primary Contact: John G. Hill, Chief Executive Officer
COO: Roger Saydack, Interim Chief Operating Officer
CFO: Wendy Apland, Regional Vice President of Finance/Chief Financial Officer
CIO: Tom Fricks, Interim Senior Vice President of Information Technology
CHR: Craig Mills, Regional Vice President Culture and People
Web address: www.peacehealth.org
**Control:** Church–operated, Nongovernment, not–for profit **Service:** General
Medical and Surgical

**Staffed Beds:** 379 **Admissions:** 23773 **Census:** 271 **Outpatient Visits:**
97208 **Births:** 2808 **Total Expense ($000):** 487131 **Payroll Expense
($000):** 147241 **Personnel:** 2442

**STAYTON—Marion County**

⊞ **SANTIAM MEMORIAL HOSPITAL (380056)**, 1401 North 10th Avenue,
Zip 97383–1399; tel. 503/769–2175 **A**1 9 10 **F**3 7 11 13 15 29 30 40 41 43
50 65 76 81 85 87 89 98 107 111 115 119 128 130 133 135 143 **P**8
Primary Contact: Terry L. Fletchall, Administrator
COO: Maggie Hudson, Director Operations and Financial Services
CFO: Rachael Seeder, Controller
CMO: Thomas VanVeen, M.D., Chief Medical Officer
Web address: www.santiamhospital.com
**Control:** Other not–for–profit (including NFP Corporation) **Service:** General
Medical and Surgical

**Staffed Beds:** 40 **Admissions:** 899 **Census:** 7 **Outpatient Visits:** 34972
**Births:** 155 **Total Expense ($000):** 29932 **Payroll Expense ($000):** 11181
**Personnel:** 246

**THE DALLES—Wasco County**

⊞ △ **MID–COLUMBIA MEDICAL CENTER (380001)**, 1700 East 19th Street,
Zip 97058–3317; tel. 541/296–1111 **A**1 2 7 9 10 **F**3 11 12 13 15 18 28 29
30 31 32 34 35 36 40 41 43 45 46 50 53 57 59 62 65 66 68 70 75 76 77
78 79 81 82 83 84 86 87 89 90 91 92 93 99 100 101 104 107 108 110 111
114 118 119 120 121 123 127 129 130 131 132 133 135 146 147 148 **P**4
Primary Contact: Duane Francis, President and Chief Executive Officer
COO: Randy Skov, Vice President
CFO: Don Arbon, Vice President Finance
CMO: Judy Richardson, M.D., President Medical Staff
CIO: Erick Larson, Vice President and Chief Information Officer
CHR: Christine Espy, Director Human Resources
Web address: www.mcmc.net
**Control:** Other not–for–profit (including NFP Corporation) **Service:** General
Medical and Surgical

**Staffed Beds:** 49 **Admissions:** 2123 **Census:** 18 **Outpatient Visits:** 120597
**Births:** 302 **Total Expense ($000):** 74954 **Payroll Expense ($000):** 38450
**Personnel:** 668

**TILLAMOOK—Tillamook County**

⊞ **TILLAMOOK REGIONAL MEDICAL CENTER (381317)**, 1000 Third Street,
Zip 97141–3430; tel. 503/842–4444 **A**1 9 10 18 **F**2 3 7 13 15 17 18 29 30
31 33 34 35 40 43 45 50 57 59 64 68 75 76 77 78 79 81 85 87 93 94 102
107 108 110 111 115 119 127 130 132 133 135 144 145 146 147 148 **P**6
**S** Adventist Health, Roseville, CA
Primary Contact: Larry Davy, President and Chief Executive Officer
CFO: Walt Larson, Vice President Finance
CMO: Mark Bowman, M.D., Medical Staff President
CNO: Karen Kellar, R.N., Vice President of Patient Care Services
Web address: www.tcgh.com
**Control:** Church–operated, Nongovernment, not–for profit **Service:** General
Medical and Surgical

**Staffed Beds:** 25 **Admissions:** 1218 **Census:** 8 **Outpatient Visits:** 65788
**Births:** 175 **Total Expense ($000):** 53864 **Payroll Expense ($000):** 23216
**Personnel:** 351

**TUALATIN—Clackamas County**

⊞ **LEGACY MERIDIAN PARK HOSPITAL (380089)**, 19300 S.W. 65th Avenue,
Zip 97062–9741; tel. 503/692–1212 **A**1 2 9 10 **F**3 11 13 15 18 20 22 28 29
30 31 32 34 35 38 40 44 45 46 49 50 51 56 57 59 60 64 68 70 74 75 76
77 78 79 80 81 85 86 87 93 107 108 110 111 114 115 116 117 118 119
120 121 126 129 130 132 145 146 147 148 **P**8 **S** Legacy Health,
Portland, OR
Primary Contact: Allyson Anderson, Chief Administrative Officer
COO: Michael Newcomb, D.O., Senior Vice President and Chief Operating Officer
CFO: David Eager, Senior Vice President and Chief Financial Officer
CMO: Lewis Low, M.D., Senior Vice President and Chief Medical Officer
CIO: John Jay Kenagy, Ph.D., Senior Vice President and Chief Information Officer
CHR: Sonja Steves, Vice President Human Resources and Marketing
CNO: Carol Bradley, MSN, Senior Vice President and Chief Nursing Officer
Web address: www.legacyhealth.org
**Control:** Other not–for–profit (including NFP Corporation) **Service:** General
Medical and Surgical

**Staffed Beds:** 130 **Admissions:** 7863 **Census:** 73 **Outpatient Visits:** 99588
**Births:** 894 **Total Expense ($000):** 145528 **Payroll Expense ($000):** 49360
**Personnel:** 673

# PENNSYLVANIA

## ABINGTON—Montgomery County

☒ **ABINGTON MEMORIAL HOSPITAL (390231)**, 1200 Old York Road,
Zip 19001–3720; tel. 215/481–2000 **A**1 2 3 5 6 10 12 13 **F**3 6 8 9 11 12 13
15 17 18 19 20 22 24 26 28 29 30 31 32 34 35 36 37 38 39 40 43 44 45
46 49 50 52 53 54 55 56 57 58 59 60 61 62 63 64 65 66 68 70 72 74 75
76 77 78 79 80 81 82 83 84 85 86 87 89 90 91 92 93 94 96 97 98 99 100
101 102 103 104 107 108 110 111 114 115 118 119 120 121 123 124 126
129 130 131 132 135 146 147 148 **P**6 **S** Abington Health, Abington, PA
Primary Contact: Laurence M. Merlis, President and Chief Executive Officer
COO: Margaret M. McGoldrick, Executive Vice President and Chief Operating
Officer
CFO: Michael Walsh, Senior Vice President Finance and Chief Financial Officer
CMO: John J. Kelly, M.D., Chief of Staff
CIO: Alison Ferren, Vice President Information Technology and Chief Information
Officer
CHR: Meghan Patton, Vice President Human Resources
CNO: Theresa Reilly, R.N., Interim Chief Nursing Officer
Web address: www.amh.org
**Control:** Other not–for–profit (including NFP Corporation) **Service:** General
Medical and Surgical

**Staffed Beds:** 621 **Admissions:** 33564 **Census:** 404 **Outpatient Visits:**
596611 **Births:** 4926 **Total Expense ($000):** 663388 **Payroll Expense
($000):** 315841 **Personnel:** 4033

## ALLENTOWN—Lehigh County

☐ △ **GOOD SHEPHERD REHABILITATION HOSPITAL (393035)**, 850 South 5th
Street, Zip 18103–3308; tel. 610/776–3299 **A**1 3 5 7 9 10 **F**28 29 30 32 34
35 36 53 54 56 57 58 59 64 65 66 68 74 75 77 82 86 87 90 91 92 93 94
95 96 107 111 119 130 131 132 143 146 148 **P**1 **S** Good Shepherd
Rehabilitation Network, Allentown, PA
Primary Contact: John Kristel, President and Chief Executive Officer
CFO: Daniel Confalone, Chief Financial Officer
Web address: www.goodshepherdrehab.org
**Control:** Other not–for–profit (including NFP Corporation) **Service:** Rehabilitation

**Staffed Beds:** 102 **Admissions:** 1895 **Census:** 79 **Outpatient Visits:** 210157
**Births:** 0 **Total Expense ($000):** 76507 **Payroll Expense ($000):** 30613
**Personnel:** 828

☒ **LEHIGH VALLEY HOSPITAL (390133)**, 1200 South Cedar Crest Boulevard,
Zip 18103–6248, Mailing Address: P.O. Box 689, Zip 18105–1556;
tel. 610/402–8000, (Includes LEHIGH VALLEY HEALTH NETWORK PEDIATRICS,
17th and Chew Streets, Zip 18102, Mailing Address: PO Box 7017,
Zip 18105–7017; tel. 610/402–2273) **A**1 2 3 5 8 9 10 **F**3 6 8 9 11 12 13 15
16 17 18 19 20 22 24 26 28 29 30 31 32 33 34 35 36 37 38 39 40 41 43
44 45 46 47 48 49 50 51 53 54 55 56 57 58 59 60 61 62 63 64 66 68 70
71 72 74 76 77 78 79 80 81 84 86 87 88 89 90 92 93 96 97 98 99 100
102 105 106 107 108 110 114 115 118 119 120 121 123 124 128 129
130 131 132 134 135 138 141 142 143 146 147 148 **P**5 6 8 **S** Lehigh Valley
Health Network, Allentown, PA
Primary Contact: Ronald W. Swinfard, M.D., President and Chief Executive Officer
COO: Terry Ann Capuano, R.N., Chief Operating Officer
CIO: Harry Lukens, Senior Vice President and Chief Information Officer
CHR: Mary Kay Grim, Senior Vice President Human Resources
Web address: www.lvhhn.org
**Control:** Other not–for–profit (including NFP Corporation) **Service:** General
Medical and Surgical

**Staffed Beds:** 793 **Admissions:** 44853 **Census:** 657 **Outpatient Visits:**
349175 **Births:** 4106 **Total Expense ($000):** 981833 **Payroll Expense
($000):** 325577 **Personnel:** 6378

☐ △ **SACRED HEART HOSPITAL (390197)**, 421 West Chew Street,
Zip 18102–3490; tel. 610/776–4500, (Total facility includes 20 beds in nursing
home–type unit) **A**1 3 5 7 9 10 13 **F**3 11 12 13 15 18 20 22 24 28 29 30 31
32 34 35 38 39 40 43 45 46 47 49 50 56 57 59 61 62 63 64 66 68 74 75
76 77 78 79 80 81 82 84 85 87 91 92 93 97 98 100 101 102 103 107 108
111 114 119 121 128 129 130 132 135 143 146 147 148 **P**8
Primary Contact: John L. Nespoli, Chief Executive Officer
CMO: Farrokh Sadr, M.D., Chief Medical Officer
CIO: Tracy Burkhart, Vice President Information Services
CHR: Joseph Mikitka, Vice President Human Resources
Web address: www.shh.org
**Control:** Other not–for–profit (including NFP Corporation) **Service:** General
Medical and Surgical

**Staffed Beds:** 130 **Admissions:** 6297 **Census:** 122 **Outpatient Visits:**
165399 **Births:** 360 **Total Expense ($000):** 102000 **Payroll Expense
($000):** 40351 **Personnel:** 876

**ST LUKE'S HOSPITAL – ALLENTOWN CAMPUS** See St. Luke's University
Hospital – Bethlehem Campus, Bethlehem

☐ **SURGICAL SPECIALTY CENTER AT COORDINATED HEALTH (390321)**,
1503 North Cedar Crest Boulevard, Zip 18104–2302; tel. 610/861–8080,
(Nonreporting) **A**1 9 10
Primary Contact: Emil Dilorio, M.D., Chief Executive Officer
Web address: www.coordinatedhealth.com
**Control:** Other not–for–profit (including NFP Corporation) **Service:** Surgical

**Staffed Beds:** 20

☐ **WESTFIELD HOSPITAL (390318)**, 4815 West Tilghman Street,
Zip 18104–9374; tel. 610/973–8400 **A**1 9 10 **F**3 12 18 29 34 35 39 40 45
50 56 57 63 65 68 70 74 75 77 79 81 82 85 86 87 102 107 108 111 114
119 129 130 135 143 146 **P**2 5
Primary Contact: Yasin N. Khan, M.D., Chief Executive Officer
Web address: www.westfieldhospital.com
**Control:** Partnership, Investor–owned, for–profit **Service:** General Medical and
Surgical

**Staffed Beds:** 25 **Admissions:** 717 **Census:** 4 **Outpatient Visits:** 13537
**Births:** 0 **Total Expense ($000):** 12500 **Payroll Expense ($000):** 4000
**Personnel:** 99

## ALTOONA—Blair County

☒ **HEALTHSOUTH REHABILITATION HOSPITAL OF ALTOONA (393040)**, 2005
Valley View Boulevard, Zip 16602–4598; tel. 814/944–3535 **A**1 10 **F**28 29 34
64 74 75 82 90 91 93 94 96 130 131 143 **P**5 **S** HEALTHSOUTH Corporation,
Birmingham, AL
Primary Contact: Scott Filler, Chief Executive Officer
CFO: George Berger, Controller
CMO: Rakesh Patel, D.O., Medical Director
CIO: Kathleen Edwards, Manager Information Systems Operation
CHR: Christine Filer, Director Human Resources
Web address: www.healthsouthaltoona.com
**Control:** Corporation, Investor–owned, for–profit **Service:** Rehabilitation

**Staffed Beds:** 80 **Admissions:** 1842 **Census:** 69 **Outpatient Visits:** 45348
**Births:** 0 **Total Expense ($000):** 26291 **Payroll Expense ($000):** 14489
**Personnel:** 231

☒ **JAMES E. VAN ZANDT VETERANS AFFAIRS MEDICAL CENTER**, 2907
Pleasant Valley Boulevard, Zip 16602–4305; tel. 877/626–2500, (Nonreporting)
**A**1 **S** Department of Veterans Affairs, Washington, DC
Primary Contact: William H. Mills, Director
CFO: Teresa Waksmonski, Chief Fiscal Service
CMO: Santha Kurian, M.D., Chief of Staff
CIO: Shawn Nocita, Chief Information Resource Management
CHR: Nicole Albus, Chief Human Resources
Web address: www.altoona.va.gov/
**Control:** Veterans Affairs, Government, federal **Service:** General Medical and
Surgical

**Staffed Beds:** 68

**PA**

**Hospital, Medicare Provider Number, Address, Telephone, Approval, Facility, and Physician Codes, Health Care System**

★ American Hospital Association (AHA) membership
☐ The Joint Commission accreditation
◇ DNV Healthcare Inc. accreditation
○ Healthcare Facilities Accreditation Program
△ Commission on Accreditation of Rehabilitation Facilities (CARF) accreditation

✦ **UPMC ALTOONA (390073)**, (Formerly Altoona Regional Health System), 620 Howard Avenue, Zip 16601–4804; tel. 814/889–2011 **A**1 2 3 5 9 10 12 13 **F**3 5 8 11 12 13 15 18 20 22 24 26 28 29 30 31 32 34 35 37 38 40 43 45 47 48 49 50 51 54 55 56 57 59 60 64 65 66 68 70 73 74 75 76 77 78 79 81 83 84 85 86 87 89 90 93 98 100 101 102 103 107 108 110 111 114 115 116 117 118 119 120 121 123 124 129 130 131 132 135 146 147 148 **S** UPMC, Pittsburgh, PA
Primary Contact: Gerald Murray, President and Chief Executive Officer
COO: Ron McConnell, Chief Operating Officer
CMO: David Cowger, M.D., Senior Vice President Quality and Medical Affairs and Chief Medical Officer
CIO: Dale Fuller, Vice President and Chief Information Officer
CHR: Gary Naugle, Senior Vice President Human Resources
Web address: www.altoonaregional.org
**Control:** Other not–for–profit (including NFP Corporation) **Service:** General Medical and Surgical

> **Staffed Beds:** 380 **Admissions:** 18260 **Census:** 232 **Outpatient Visits:** 360567 **Births:** 1077 **Total Expense ($000):** 333394 **Payroll Expense ($000):** 133000 **Personnel:** 2089

**UPMC ALTOONA** See Altoona Regional Health System

### AMBLER—Montgomery County

☐ **HORSHAM CLINIC (394034)**, 722 East Butler Pike, Zip 19002–2310; tel. 215/643–7800, (Nonreporting) **A**1 3 5 9 10 **S** Universal Health Services, Inc., King of Prussia, PA
Primary Contact: Phyllis Weisfield, Chief Executive Officer and Managing Director
CFO: Robert Chavez, Chief Financial Officer
CMO: James B. Congdon, M.D., Medical Director
CIO: Suzanne Scholz, Director Medical Records
CHR: Kathleen Nichelson, Director Human Resources
CNO: Linda Starr, Director of Nursing
Web address: www.horshamclinic.com
**Control:** Individual, Investor–owned, for–profit **Service:** Psychiatric

> **Staffed Beds:** 138

### BEAVER—Beaver County

☐ **HERITAGE VALLEY BEAVER (390036)**, 1000 Dutch Ridge Road, Zip 15009–9727; tel. 724/728–7000, (Nonreporting) **A**1 9 10 12 13 **S** Heritage Valley Health System, Beaver, PA
Primary Contact: Norman F. Mitry, President and Chief Executive Officer
COO: Rosemary Nolan, R.N., Chief Operating Officer and Chief Nursing Officer
CFO: Bryan J. Randall, Vice President Finance and Chief Financial Officer
CMO: John Cinicola, M.D., Chief Medical Officer
CIO: David Carleton, Chief Information Officer
CHR: Bruce Edwards, Vice President Human Resources
CNO: Marcia L. Ferrero, MS, Chief Nursing Officer
Web address: www.heritagevalley.org
**Control:** Other not–for–profit (including NFP Corporation) **Service:** General Medical and Surgical

> **Staffed Beds:** 312

✦ **KINDRED HOSPITAL–HERITAGE VALLEY (392043)**, 1000 Dutch Ridge Road, Zip 15009–9727; tel. 724/773–8480, (Nonreporting) **A**1 9 10 **S** Kindred Healthcare, Louisville, KY
Primary Contact: Rodney B. Jones, Administrator
CFO: Kevin Varley, Chief Financial Officer
CMO: Jeffrey Erukhimou, M.D., Medical Director
Web address: www.kindredhospitalhv.com/
**Control:** Corporation, Investor–owned, for–profit **Service:** Long–Term Acute Care hospital

> **Staffed Beds:** 35

### BENSALEM—Bucks County

**LIVENGRIN FOUNDATION**, 4833 Hulmeville Road, Zip 19020–3099; tel. 215/638–5200, (Nonreporting) **A**9
Primary Contact: Richard M. Pine, President and Chief Executive Officer
CFO: James D. Flis, Chief Financial Officer
CMO: William J. Lorman, Ph.D., Clinical Director
CIO: William Miller, Coordinator Management Information Systems
Web address: www.livengrin.org
**Control:** Other not–for–profit (including NFP Corporation) **Service:** Alcoholism and other chemical dependency

> **Staffed Beds:** 76

✦ **ROTHMAN SPECIALTY HOSPITAL (390322)**, 3300 Tillman Drive, Zip 19020–2071; tel. 215/244–7400, (Nonreporting) **A**1 10
Primary Contact: Kelly Doyle, Chief Executive Officer
Web address: www.rothmanspecialtyhospital.com/
**Control:** Partnership, Investor–owned, for–profit **Service:** Surgical

> **Staffed Beds:** 24

### BERWICK—Columbia County

✦ **BERWICK HOSPITAL CENTER (390072)**, 701 East 16th Street, Zip 18603–2397; tel. 570/759–5000, (Total facility includes 240 beds in nursing home–type unit) **A**1 9 10 **F**3 13 15 20 28 29 31 34 39 40 46 56 57 59 62 63 64 70 75 76 77 78 79 81 82 85 93 98 102 103 107 110 111 114 117 119 128 129 130 132 133 146 147 148 **P**6 **S** Community Health Systems, Inc., Franklin, TN
Primary Contact: Ronald R. Beer, Chief Executive Officer
CFO: Jay Graham, Interim Chief Financial Officer
CMO: Frank Giugliano, M.D., Chief of Staff
CHR: Jackie Ridall, Director Human Resources
Web address: www.berwick–hospital.com
**Control:** Corporation, Investor–owned, for–profit **Service:** General Medical and Surgical

> **Staffed Beds:** 341 **Admissions:** 3257 **Census:** 206 **Outpatient Visits:** 91255 **Births:** 96 **Personnel:** 483

### BETHLEHEM—Northampton County

**COORDINATED HEALTH–BETHLEHEM (390314)**, 2310 Highland Avenue, Zip 18020–8920, Mailing Address: 2300 Highland Avenue, Zip 18020; tel. 610/861–8080, (Nonreporting) **A**10
Primary Contact: Mark Holtz, Chief Operating Officer
Web address: www.coordinatedhealth.com
**Control:** Partnership, Investor–owned, for–profit **Service:** General Medical and Surgical

> **Staffed Beds:** 22

☐ △ **GOOD SHEPHERD SPECIALTY HOSPITAL (392033)**, 2545 Schoenersville Road, 3rd Floor, Zip 18017–7300; tel. 484/884–5051 **A**1 7 9 10 **F**1 3 148 **P**5 **S** Good Shepherd Rehabilitation Network, Allentown, PA
Primary Contact: Lisa Marsilio, Vice President and Administrator
Web address: www.goodshepherdrehab.org
**Control:** Other not–for–profit (including NFP Corporation) **Service:** Long–Term Acute Care hospital

> **Staffed Beds:** 32 **Admissions:** 403 **Census:** 28 **Outpatient Visits:** 0 **Births:** 0 **Total Expense ($000):** 15122 **Payroll Expense ($000):** 5266 **Personnel:** 83

✦ **LEHIGH VALLEY HOSPITAL–MUHLENBERG (390263)**, 2545 Schoenersville Road, Zip 18017–7300; tel. 484/884–2201 **A**1 2 9 10 12 13 **F**3 11 12 15 17 18 20 22 24 26 28 29 30 31 34 35 36 37 38 39 40 44 45 49 50 51 53 54 57 58 59 60 62 63 64 65 68 70 74 77 78 79 80 81 82 84 85 86 87 90 92 93 97 102 107 108 110 111 114 115 118 119 120 121 123 124 126 129 130 131 132 134 135 143 146 148 **P**5 6 8 **S** Lehigh Valley Health Network, Allentown, PA
Primary Contact: Ronald W. Swinfard, M.D., President and Chief Executive Officer
COO: Terry Ann Capuano, R.N., Chief Operating Officer
CFO: Edward O'Dea, Chief Financial Officer
CMO: Thomas Whalen, M.D., Chief Medical Officer
CIO: Harry Lukens, Senior Vice President and Chief Information Officer
CHR: Deborah A. Patrick, Vice President Human Resources
CNO: Anne Panik, MS, Senior Vice President Care Services and Chief Nursing Officer
Web address: www.lvhhn.org
**Control:** Other not–for–profit (including NFP Corporation) **Service:** General Medical and Surgical

> **Staffed Beds:** 186 **Admissions:** 10687 **Census:** 140 **Outpatient Visits:** 173175 **Births:** 0 **Total Expense ($000):** 202653 **Payroll Expense ($000):** 74353 **Personnel:** 1331

☐ △ **ST. LUKE'S UNIVERSITY HOSPITAL – BETHLEHEM CAMPUS (390049)**, 801 Ostrum Street, Zip 18015–1065; tel. 610/954–4000, (Includes ST LUKE'S HOSPITAL – ALLENTOWN CAMPUS, 1736 Hamilton Street, Allentown, Zip 18104–5656; tel. 610/770–8300) **A**1 2 3 5 6 7 8 9 10 12 13 **F**3 9 11 12 13 15 17 18 19 20 22 24 26 27 28 29 30 31 32 34 35 36 37 38 39 40 42 43 44 45 46 47 48 49 50 51 52 53 54 55 56 57 58 59 60 61 63 64 65 66 68 70 71 72 73 74 75 76 77 78 79 81 82 84 85 86 87 89 90 92 93 96 97 98 99 100 101 102 103 104 105 107 108 109 110 111 115 117 118 119 120 121 123 124 126 129 130 131 132 134 135 144 145 146 147 148 **P**6 8 **S** St. Luke's University Health Network, Bethlehem, PA
Primary Contact: Richard A. Anderson, President and Chief Executive Officer
COO: Carol Kuplen, R.N., Chief Operating Officer and Chief Nursing Officer
CFO: Tom Lichtenwalner, Vice President Finance
CMO: Jeffrey Jahre, M.D., Vice President Medical and Academic Affairs
CIO: Chad Brisendine, Chief Information Officer
CHR: Robert Zimmel, Senior Vice President Human Resources
Web address: www.slhn–lehighvalley.com
**Control:** Other not–for–profit (including NFP Corporation) **Service:** General Medical and Surgical

> **Staffed Beds:** 572 **Admissions:** 30031 **Census:** 354 **Outpatient Visits:** 1030979 **Births:** 3958 **Total Expense ($000):** 544346 **Payroll Expense ($000):** 228688 **Personnel:** 4054

*Many Facility Codes have changed. Please refer to the AHA Guide Code Chart.*

## BLOOMSBURG—Columbia County

★ **GEISINGER–BLOOMSBURG HOSPITAL (390003)**, 549 Fair Street, Zip 17815–1419; tel. 570/387–2100 **A**9 10 **F**3 11 13 15 18 26 28 29 30 31 34 35 38 40 44 45 50 53 57 59 64 65 68 70 75 76 78 79 81 82 85 87 98 100 102 104 106 107 108 110 111 115 118 119 124 130 146 147 **P**6 **S** Geisinger Health System, Danville, PA
Primary Contact: Lissa Bryan-Smith, Chief Administrative Officer
COO: Joseph M. DeVito, Vice President Finance and Chief Operating Officer
CFO: Joseph M. DeVito, Vice President Finance and Chief Operating Officer
CMO: James Joseph, M.D., President Medical Staff
CIO: Thomas Wray, Director Information
CHR: Mary Lenzini Howe, Vice President Human Resources
Web address: www.bloomhealth.net
**Control:** Other not–for–profit (including NFP Corporation) **Service:** General Medical and Surgical

**Staffed Beds:** 72 **Admissions:** 2244 **Census:** 27 **Outpatient Visits:** 72091 **Births:** 304 **Total Expense ($000):** 39876 **Payroll Expense ($000):** 16672 **Personnel:** 354

## BRADFORD—Mckean County

⊠ **BRADFORD REGIONAL MEDICAL CENTER (390118)**, 116 Interstate Parkway, Zip 16701–1036; tel. 814/368–4143, (Total facility includes 95 beds in nursing home–type unit) **A**1 9 10 **F**3 5 8 11 13 15 18 20 28 29 30 31 34 35 39 40 45 47 49 50 53 56 57 59 62 63 64 65 70 75 76 77 78 79 81 82 83 84 85 86 87 93 94 97 98 100 101 102 103 104 105 107 108 110 111 114 117 118 119 128 129 130 131 132 135 143 144 146 147 148 **P**6 **S** Upper Allegheny Health System, Olean, NY
Primary Contact: Timothy J. Finan, FACHE, President and Chief Executive Officer
COO: David A. Kobis, Senior Vice President and Chief Operating Officer
CFO: Richard G. Braun, Jr., CPA, Senior Vice President and Chief Financial Officer
CMO: William Mills, M.D., Senior Vice President Quality and Professional Affairs
CIO: Jason Yaworsky, Chief Information Officer
CHR: Timothy M. McNamara, Senior Vice President Human Resources
Web address: www.brmc.com
**Control:** Other not–for–profit (including NFP Corporation) **Service:** General Medical and Surgical

**Staffed Beds:** 182 **Admissions:** 3124 **Census:** 122 **Outpatient Visits:** 127434 **Births:** 227 **Total Expense ($000):** 65294 **Payroll Expense ($000):** 28519 **Personnel:** 474

## BRISTOL—Bucks County

☐ **LOWER BUCKS HOSPITAL (390070)**, 501 Bath Road, Zip 19007–3190; tel. 215/785–9200, (Nonreporting) **A**1 9 10
Primary Contact: Peter J. Adamo, Chief Executive Officer
CFO: Michael Olivieri, Chief Financial Officer
CMO: Omid Rowshan, M.D., President Medical Staff
CIO: John McHale, Vice President Management Information Systems
CHR: Kellie Pearson, Director Human Resources
Web address: www.lowerbuckshospital.org
**Control:** Other not–for–profit (including NFP Corporation) **Service:** General Medical and Surgical

**Staffed Beds:** 150

## BROOKVILLE—Jefferson County

**BROOKVILLE HOSPITAL (391312)**, 100 Hospital Road, Zip 15825–1367; tel. 814/849–2312 **A**9 10 18 **F**3 11 15 18 28 29 30 34 35 39 40 45 46 57 59 62 64 65 75 77 79 81 82 85 86 93 98 102 103 104 107 108 110 114 118 119 127 129 130 131 132 133 145 146
Primary Contact: Rose Campbell, R.N., President
CFO: Julie Peer, Vice President Finance
CMO: Timothy Pendleton, M.D., President Medical Staff
CIO: Benjamin Reynolds, Director Information Systems
CHR: Warren Thrush, Coordinator Human Resources
Web address: www.brookvillehospital.org
**Control:** Other not–for–profit (including NFP Corporation) **Service:** General Medical and Surgical

**Staffed Beds:** 35 **Admissions:** 1212 **Census:** 17 **Outpatient Visits:** 82120 **Births:** 0 **Total Expense ($000):** 26185 **Payroll Expense ($000):** 9570 **Personnel:** 240

## BRYN MAWR—Montgomery County

⊠ **BRYN MAWR HOSPITAL (390139)**, 130 South Bryn Mawr Avenue, Zip 19010–3160; tel. 484/337–3000 **A**1 2 3 5 9 10 13 **F**3 5 8 11 12 13 15 17 18 20 22 24 26 28 29 30 31 34 35 36 37 38 40 41 44 45 46 48 49 54 55 57 58 59 65 70 72 74 75 76 78 79 80 81 82 84 85 86 87 89 92 98 100 101 102 103 107 108 109 110 111 114 115 116 117 118 119 120 121 122 123 124 126 129 130 132 135 141 146 147 148 **S** Jefferson Health System, Radnor, PA
Primary Contact: Andrea F. Gilbert, FACHE, President
COO: Andrea F. Gilbert, FACHE, President
CFO: Michael J. Buongiorno, Executive Vice President Finance and Chief Financial Officer
CIO: Karen A. Thomas, Vice President and Chief Information Officer
CHR: Terry Dougherty, Director Human Resources
Web address: www.brynmawrhospital.org
**Control:** Other not–for–profit (including NFP Corporation) **Service:** General Medical and Surgical

**Staffed Beds:** 319 **Admissions:** 17702 **Census:** 195 **Outpatient Visits:** 262476 **Births:** 1801 **Total Expense ($000):** 280748 **Payroll Expense ($000):** 98603 **Personnel:** 1613

## BUTLER—Butler County

★ **BUTLER HEALTH SYSTEM (390168)**, 1 Hospital Way, Zip 16001–4697; tel. 724/283–6666, (Total facility includes 25 beds in nursing home–type unit) **A**2 9 10 **F**3 4 5 12 13 15 18 20 22 24 26 28 29 31 32 35 40 45 57 59 70 74 76 79 81 82 85 87 93 98 100 103 107 108 111 114 118 119 128 129 130 132 135 146 147 148 **P**6
Primary Contact: Ken DeFurio, President and Chief Executive Officer
COO: Stephanie Roskovski, Chief Operating Officer
CFO: Anne Krebs, Chief Financial Officer
CMO: John C. Reefer, M.D., Director
CIO: Chuck Oleson, Chief Information Officer
CHR: Thomas A. Genevro, Vice President Human Resources
CNO: Karen A. Allen, R.N., Chief Nursing Officer
Web address: www.butlerhealthsystem.org
**Control:** Other not–for–profit (including NFP Corporation) **Service:** General Medical and Surgical

**Staffed Beds:** 288 **Admissions:** 12779 **Census:** 180 **Outpatient Visits:** 485176 **Births:** 698 **Total Expense ($000):** 201490 **Payroll Expense ($000):** 75139 **Personnel:** 1418

★ △ **VETERANS AFFAIRS BUTLER HEALTHCARE**, 325 New Castle Road, Zip 16001–2480; tel. 724/287–4781, (Nonreporting) **A**7 **S** Department of Veterans Affairs, Washington, DC
Primary Contact: John Gennaro, FACHE, Director
COO: Richard W. Cotter, Associate Director Operations
CFO: Doug George, Chief Financial Officer
CMO: Timothy R. Burke, M.D., Chief of Staff
CIO: Kirk Hastings, Chief Information Technology
CHR: Michelle Dominski, Human Resources Officer
Web address: www.butler.va.gov
**Control:** Veterans Affairs, Government, federal **Service:** Other specialty

**Staffed Beds:** 126

**VETERANS AFFAIRS MEDICAL CENTER** See Veterans Affairs Butler Healthcare

## CAMP HILL—Cumberland County

⊠ **HOLY SPIRIT HOSPITAL (390004)**, 503 North 21st Street, Zip 17011–2204; tel. 717/763–2100 **A**1 5 9 10 **F**3 8 11 12 13 14 15 17 18 20 22 24 26 28 29 30 31 34 35 37 38 40 44 46 49 50 54 57 58 59 61 62 63 64 65 70 72 73 74 75 76 77 78 79 80 81 82 84 85 86 87 93 94 96 98 99 100 101 102 103 104 105 107 108 110 111 114 115 119 126 129 130 132 134 135 144 145 146 147 148 **P**6
Primary Contact: Sister Romaine Niemeyer, President and Chief Executive Officer
COO: Richard Schaffner, Senior Vice President and Chief Operating Officer
CFO: Manuel J. Evans, Senior Vice President Finance and Chief Financial Officer
CMO: Joseph Torchia, M.D., Senior Vice President Medical Affairs and Chief Medical Officer
CIO: Edith Dees, Vice President Information Services and Chief Information Officer
CHR: William Shartle, Senior Vice President Human Resources
Web address: www.hsh.org
**Control:** Other not–for–profit (including NFP Corporation) **Service:** General Medical and Surgical

**Staffed Beds:** 290 **Admissions:** 15552 **Census:** 186 **Outpatient Visits:** 293177 **Births:** 1206 **Total Expense ($000):** 291881 **Payroll Expense ($000):** 113642 **Personnel:** 2035

---

**Hospital, Medicare Provider Number, Address, Telephone, Approval, Facility, and Physician Codes, Health Care System**

★ American Hospital Association (AHA) membership
☐ The Joint Commission accreditation ◇ DNV Healthcare Inc. accreditation

○ Healthcare Facilities Accreditation Program
△ Commission on Accreditation of Rehabilitation Facilities (CARF) accreditation

PA

**PA**

⊠ **SELECT SPECIALTY HOSPITAL–CENTRAL PENNSYLVANIA (392039)**, 503 North 21st Street, 5th Floor, Zip 17011–2204; tel. 717/972–4575, (Includes SELECT SPECIALTY HOSPITAL–HARRISBURG, 2501 NorthThird Street, Landis Building, Harrisburg, Zip 17110–1904, Mailing Address: 2501 North Third Street, Landis Building, Zip 17110–1904; tel. 717/724–6605; SELECT SPECIALTY HOSPITAL–YORK, 1001 South George Street, York, Zip 17403–3676; tel. 717/851–2661; Marcia Medlin, Chief Executive Officer), (Nonreporting) **A**1 9 10 **S** Select Medical Corporation, Mechanicsburg, PA
Primary Contact: Tom Mullin, Chief Executive Officer
Web address: www.selectspecialtyhospitals.com/company/locations/camphill.aspx
**Control:** Corporation, Investor–owned, for–profit **Service:** Long–Term Acute Care hospital

Staffed Beds: 92

**STATE CORRECTIONAL INSTITUTION AT CAMP HILL**, 2500 Lisburn Road, Zip 17011–8005, Mailing Address: P.O. Box 200, Zip 17001–0200; tel. 717/737–4531, (Nonreporting)
Primary Contact: Kathy Montag, Administrator Health Care
Web address: www.cor.state.pa.us/
**Control:** State–Government, nonfederal **Service:** Other specialty

Staffed Beds: 34

### CANONSBURG—Washington County

⊠ **CANONSBURG GENERAL HOSPITAL (390160)**, 100 Medical Boulevard, Zip 15317–9762; tel. 724/745–6100 **A**1 9 10 **F**3 7 8 11 15 18 29 30 31 32 34 35 40 44 45 46 47 48 49 50 51 54 55 57 59 64 65 66 67 68 70 74 75 78 79 81 82 85 86 87 90 91 92 93 94 97 107 108 110 111 114 118 119 129 130 131 132 134 146 147 **S** West Penn Allegheny Health System, Pittsburgh, PA
Primary Contact: Terry Wiltrout, Chief Executive Officer
COO: Kim Sperring, Chief Operating Officer
CFO: Gene Trout, Chief Financial Officer
CMO: Thomas B. Corkery, D.O., Chief Medical Officer
CIO: David Vincent, Director Information Systems
CHR: Martha L. Clister, Director Human Resources
Web address: www.wpahs.org
**Control:** Other not–for–profit (including NFP Corporation) **Service:** General Medical and Surgical

Staffed Beds: 104 Admissions: 3281 Census: 41 Outpatient Visits: 78790 Births: 0 Total Expense ($000): 52153 Payroll Expense ($000): 19609 Personnel: 419

### CARLISLE—Cumberland County

☐ **CARLISLE REGIONAL MEDICAL CENTER (390058)**, 361 Alexander Spring Road, Zip 17015–6940; tel. 717/249–1212, (Nonreporting) **A**1 9 10 **S** Health Management Associates, Naples, FL
Primary Contact: Rich Newell, Chief Executive Officer
COO: P. Mark Harmon, Chief Operating Officer
CFO: Mike Johnson, Chief Financial Officer
CMO: Howard Alster, M.D., President Medical Staff
CIO: Kemp Beatty, Director Information Management
CNO: Ann Spade, Chief Nursing Executive
Web address: www.carlislermc.com/default.aspx
**Control:** Corporation, Investor–owned, for–profit **Service:** General Medical and Surgical

Staffed Beds: 165

### CENTRE HALL—Centre County

⊠ **MEADOWS PSYCHIATRIC CENTER (394040)**, 132 The Meadows Drive, Zip 16828–9231; tel. 814/364–2161 **A**1 9 10 **F**29 38 54 98 99 102 103 104 105 **P**6 **S** Universal Health Services, Inc., King of Prussia, PA
Primary Contact: Jeffrey Herman, Chief Executive Officer
CMO: Nalin Patel, M.D., Medical Director
CHR: Kimberly J. Tate, Director Human Resources
Web address: www.themeadows.net
**Control:** Corporation, Investor–owned, for–profit **Service:** Psychiatric

Staffed Beds: 107 Admissions: 2439 Census: 88 Outpatient Visits: 0 Births: 0 Personnel: 175

### CHAMBERSBURG—Franklin County

⊠ **CHAMBERSBURG HOSPITAL (390151)**, 112 North Seventh Street, Zip 17201–1720; tel. 717/267–3000 **A**1 2 3 5 9 10 19 **F**3 11 12 13 15 17 18 20 22 28 29 30 31 34 35 36 37 38 39 40 45 49 50 53 54 56 57 59 61 64 65 68 70 74 75 76 77 78 79 81 82 83 84 85 86 87 89 90 91 93 94 95 97 98 99 100 101 102 103 104 107 108 110 111 114 116 117 118 119 120 121 123 126 129 130 131 132 135 144 146 147 148 **P**6 8 **S** Summit Health, Chambersburg, PA
Primary Contact: Patrick W. O'Donnell, CPA, President and Chief Executive Officer
COO: John P. Massimilla, FACHE, Vice President Administration
CFO: Patrick W. O'Donnell, CPA, Senior Vice President and Chief Operating Officer
CMO: Thomas Anderson, M.D., Vice President Medical Affairs
CIO: Michele Zeigler, Vice President and Chief Information Officer
CHR: Louis J. Gregorio, FACHE, Vice President Human Resources
CNO: Sherri Stahl, R.N., Summit Health Vice President for Patient Services
Web address: www.summithealth.org
**Control:** Other not–for–profit (including NFP Corporation) **Service:** General Medical and Surgical

Staffed Beds: 246 Admissions: 12834 Census: 140 Outpatient Visits: 334775 Births: 1377 Total Expense ($000): 226699 Payroll Expense ($000): 101693 Personnel: 1492

### CLARION—Clarion County

★ ○ **CLARION HOSPITAL (390093)**, One Hospital Drive, Zip 16214–8501; tel. 814/226–9500 **A**9 10 11 12 13 **F**3 7 11 13 15 29 30 31 35 40 48 49 51 57 59 64 70 76 77 78 79 81 82 84 85 90 107 108 111 115 119 129 130 132 133 135 145 146 148 **S** QHR, Brentwood, TN
Primary Contact: Byron Quinton, Chief Executive Officer
CFO: Vincent M. Lamorella, Chief Financial Officer
CHR: Michael Wienand, Manager Human Resources
Web address: www.clarionhospital.org
**Control:** Other not–for–profit (including NFP Corporation) **Service:** General Medical and Surgical

Staffed Beds: 77 Admissions: 2413 Census: 25 Outpatient Visits: 155557 Births: 143 Total Expense ($000): 50424 Payroll Expense ($000): 18177 Personnel: 477

⊠ **CLARION PSYCHIATRIC CENTER (394043)**, 2 Hospital Drive, Zip 16214–8502; tel. 814/226–9545 **A**1 9 10 **F**98 99 101 102 105 **P**6 **S** Universal Health Services, Inc., King of Prussia, PA
Primary Contact: Robert Scheffler, Chief Executive Officer
CFO: Shelly Rhoades, Chief Financial Officer
CMO: Maher Ayyash, M.D., Chief Medical Officer
CHR: Dianne C. Bilunka, Director Human Resources
Web address: www.clarioncenter.com
**Control:** Individual, Investor–owned, for–profit **Service:** Psychiatric

Staffed Beds: 74 Admissions: 2064 Census: 65 Outpatient Visits: 0 Births: 0 Total Expense ($000): 7540 Payroll Expense ($000): 4660

### CLARKS SUMMIT—Lackawanna County

☐ **CLARKS SUMMIT STATE HOSPITAL (394012)**, 1451 Hillside Drive, Zip 18411–9504; tel. 570/586–2011 **A**1 10 **F**30 38 39 56 59 65 68 75 77 86 87 98 100 101 102 103 130 132 135 143 146
Primary Contact: Thomas P. Comerford, Jr., Superintendent
COO: Gordon Weber, Chief Operating Officer
CMO: David Waibel, M.D., Medical Director
CHR: William Abda, Chief Human Resources Officer
Web address: www.dpw.state.pa.us/
**Control:** State–Government, nonfederal **Service:** Psychiatric

Staffed Beds: 226 Admissions: 84 Census: 211 Outpatient Visits: 0 Births: 0 Total Expense ($000): 46228 Payroll Expense ($000): 23743 Personnel: 442

### CLEARFIELD—Clearfield County

**CLEARFIELD HOSPITAL (390052)**, 809 Turnpike Avenue, Zip 16830–1232, Mailing Address: P.O. Box 992, Zip 16830–0992; tel. 814/765–5341 **A**9 10 **F**3 8 11 13 15 18 28 29 30 32 34 40 41 44 45 46 50 53 57 62 63 68 70 75 76 77 79 81 84 85 86 87 93 97 98 103 107 108 110 111 115 118 119 129 130 132 133 135 146 148
Primary Contact: Gary Macioce, President and Chief Executive Officer
CFO: Pat Cressley, Vice President and Chief Financial Officer
CMO: Gregory Sheffo, M.D., Chief Medical Officer
CIO: Terry Trinidad, Director Management Information Systems
CHR: Robert J. McKee, Vice President and Chief Human Resources Officer
CNO: Kathy Bedger, Chief Nursing Officer
Web address: www.clearfieldhosp.org
**Control:** Other not–for–profit (including NFP Corporation) **Service:** General Medical and Surgical

Staffed Beds: 96 Admissions: 3061 Census: 37 Outpatient Visits: 208640 Births: 176 Total Expense ($000): 71890 Payroll Expense ($000): 30301 Personnel: 461

## COALDALE—Schuylkill County

☐ **ST. LUKE'S HOSPITAL – MINERS CAMPUS (390183)**, 360 West Ruddle Street, Zip 18218–1027; tel. 570/645–2131, (Total facility includes 48 beds in nursing home–type unit) **A**1 9 10 **F**3 15 18 28 29 31 34 35 40 45 49 50 51 53 54 56 57 59 60 62 64 65 68 70 75 77 78 79 81 85 86 93 107 108 110 111 115 118 119 127 128 129 130 131 132 145 146 148 **P**6 8 **S** St. Luke's University Health Network, Bethlehem, PA
Primary Contact: William E. Moyer, President
COO: Joel Fagerstrom, Executive Vice President and Chief Operating Officer
CFO: Michele Levitz, Director Finance
CMO: Glenn Freed, D.O., Medical Director
CIO: Chad Brisendine, Vice President and Chief Information Officer
CHR: Susan Van Why, Director Human Resources
CNO: Kimberly Sargent, Vice President Patient Services
Web address: www.slhn.org
**Control:** Other not–for–profit (including NFP Corporation) **Service:** General Medical and Surgical

| | |
|---|---|
| **Staffed Beds:** 92 **Admissions:** 1835 **Census:** 63 **Outpatient Visits:** 109226 **Births:** 0 **Total Expense ($000):** 38355 **Payroll Expense ($000):** 17586 **Personnel:** 378 | |

## COATESVILLE—Chester County

⊞ **BRANDYWINE HOSPITAL (390076)**, 201 Reeceville Road, Zip 19320–1536; tel. 610/383–8000, (Nonreporting) **A**1 2 6 9 10 **F**12 14 15 18 20 22 24 26 28 29 31 40 45 49 54 55 59 60 62 64 66 68 74 75 77 78 81 82 85 91 92 93 98 100 102 103 104 107 108 111 114 116 119 124 126 129 130 144 148 **S** Community Health Systems, Inc., Franklin, TN
Primary Contact: Bryan Burklow, Chief Executive Officer
COO: Jill Tillman, Assistant Chief Executive Officer
CFO: Jay Graham, Interim Chief Financial Officer
Web address: www.brandywinehospital.com
**Control:** Corporation, Investor–owned, for–profit **Service:** General Medical and Surgical

| | |
|---|---|
| **Staffed Beds:** 140 **Admissions:** 7422 **Census:** 100 | |

⊞ △ **COATESVILLE VETERANS AFFAIRS MEDICAL CENTER**, (Formerly Veterans Affairs Medical Center), 1400 Black Horse Hill Road, Zip 19320–2040; tel. 610/384–7711, (Nonreporting) **A**1 3 5 7 **S** Department of Veterans Affairs, Washington, DC
Primary Contact: Gary W. Devansky, Director
CFO: Tony Wolfgang, Chief Financial Officer
CMO: James F. Tischler, M.D., Chief of Staff
CIO: Eugene Doria, Chief Information Officer
Web address: www.coatesville.va.gov/
**Control:** Veterans Affairs, Government, federal **Service:** Alcoholism and other chemical dependency

| | |
|---|---|
| **Staffed Beds:** 306 | |

**VETERANS AFFAIRS MEDICAL CENTER** See Coatesville Veterans Affairs Medical Center

## CONNELLSVILLE—Fayette County

**HIGHLANDS HOSPITAL (390184)**, 401 East Murphy Avenue, Zip 15425–2700; tel. 724/628–1500 **A**9 10 **F**3 11 12 15 29 30 34 35 36 39 40 44 45 46 49 50 51 53 54 56 57 59 61 64 65 70 75 77 79 81 82 85 86 87 89 93 98 99 100 101 102 103 107 108 114 119 129 130 132 133 143 146
Primary Contact: Michelle P. Cunningham, Chief Executive Officer
CFO: John Andursky, Chief Financial Officer
CMO: Richard Grimaldi, President Medical Staff
CIO: John Andursky, Chief Financial Officer
CHR: Mary June Krosoff, Chief Human Resources Officer
CNO: Tammy Donaldson, Director of Nursing
Web address: www.highlandshospital.org
**Control:** Other not–for–profit (including NFP Corporation) **Service:** General Medical and Surgical

| | |
|---|---|
| **Staffed Beds:** 71 **Admissions:** 2524 **Census:** 33 **Outpatient Visits:** 59411 **Births:** 0 **Total Expense ($000):** 23274 **Payroll Expense ($000):** 10112 **Personnel:** 263 | |

## CORRY—Erie County

**CORRY MEMORIAL HOSPITAL (391308)**, 612 West Smith Street, Zip 16407–1196; tel. 814/664–4641, (Nonreporting) **A**9 10 18
Primary Contact: Barbara Nichols, R.N., President and Chief Executive Officer
CFO: Michael Heller, Chief Financial Officer
CIO: Ken O'Day, Supervisor Information Systems
CHR: Gary Webb, Director Human Resources
Web address: www.corryhospital.com
**Control:** Other not–for–profit (including NFP Corporation) **Service:** General Medical and Surgical

| | |
|---|---|
| **Staffed Beds:** 25 | |

## COUDERSPORT—Potter County

⊞ **COLE MEMORIAL (391313)**, (Formerly Charles Cole Memorial Hospital), 1001 East Second Street, Zip 16915–8161; tel. 814/274–9300, (Total facility includes 49 beds in nursing home–type unit) **A**1 9 10 18 **F**3 10 11 13 15 28 29 30 31 35 40 45 48 49 53 57 59 62 63 64 70 76 77 78 79 81 82 87 92 93 98 103 107 108 111 114 119 121 127 128 129 130 131 132 133 145 146 147 148 **P**6
Primary Contact: Edward C. Pitchford, President and Chief Executive Officer
COO: Cynthia Hardesty, Vice President and Chief Nursing Executive
CFO: Ron Rapp, Controller
CMO: Michael E. Callahan, M.D., President Medical Staff
CIO: Geoff Mazur, Director Information Technology
CHR: J. Thomas Noe, Director Human Resources
Web address: www.charlescolehospital.com
**Control:** Other not–for–profit (including NFP Corporation) **Service:** General Medical and Surgical

| | |
|---|---|
| **Staffed Beds:** 84 **Admissions:** 1990 **Census:** 70 **Outpatient Visits:** 232603 **Births:** 225 **Total Expense ($000):** 70276 **Payroll Expense ($000):** 23423 **Personnel:** 509 | |

## CRANBERRY—Butler County

**UPMC PASSAVANT CRANBERRY** See UPMC Passavant, Pittsburgh

## DANVILLE—Montour County

☐ **DANVILLE STATE HOSPITAL (394004)**, 200 State Hospital Drive, Zip 17821–9198; tel. 570/271–4500 **A**1 10 **F**30 39 65 75 77 98 106 130 135 146 **P**6
Primary Contact: Theresa Long, Chief Executive Officer
COO: Thomas J. Burk, Chief Operating Officer
CFO: Patricia Riegert, Director Fiscal Services
CMO: Anthony Montecalvo, M.D., Chief Medical Executive
CHR: Thomas J. Burk, Chief Operating Officer
CNO: Brenda Lahout, Chief Nurse Executive
Web address: www.dpw.state.pa.us/foradults/statehospitals/danvillestatehospital/index.htm
**Control:** State–Government, nonfederal **Service:** Psychiatric

| | |
|---|---|
| **Staffed Beds:** 178 **Admissions:** 97 **Census:** 166 **Outpatient Visits:** 0 **Births:** 0 **Total Expense ($000):** 36741 **Payroll Expense ($000):** 20370 **Personnel:** 381 | |

⊞ **GEISINGER HEALTHSOUTH REHABILITATION HOSPITAL (393047)**, 2 Rehab Lane, Zip 17821–8498; tel. 570/271–6733, (Nonreporting) **A**1 9 10 **S** HEALTHSOUTH Corporation, Birmingham, AL
Primary Contact: Lorie Dillon, Chief Executive Officer
CFO: Sally Shipierski, Controller
CMO: Greg Burke, M.D., Medical Director
CHR: Christian Shirley, Director Human Resources
Web address: www.geisingerhealthsouth.com
**Control:** Corporation, Investor–owned, for–profit **Service:** Rehabilitation

| | |
|---|---|
| **Staffed Beds:** 42 | |

⊞ **GEISINGER MEDICAL CENTER (390006)**, 100 North Academy Avenue, Zip 17822–2201; tel. 570/271–6211, (Includes GEISINGER–SHAMOKIN AREA COMMUNITY HOSPITAL, 4200 Hospital Road, Coal Township, Zip 17866–9697; tel. 570/644–4200; Thomas R. Harlow, FACHE, President and Chief Executive Officer), (Total facility includes 15 beds in nursing home–type unit) **A**1 2 3 5 8 9 10 13 19 **F**3 7 8 9 11 12 13 14 15 17 18 19 20 21 22 23 24 25 26 27 28 29 30 31 32 34 35 36 37 38 39 40 43 44 45 46 47 48 49 50 51 52 53 54 55 57 58 59 60 61 64 65 70 71 72 73 74 75 76 77 78 79 80 81 82 84 85 86 87 88 89 93 94 97 98 99 100 101 102 103 104 105 106 107 108 110 111 113 114 115 116 117 118 119 120 121 123 124 126 127 128 129 130 131 132 134 135 136 138 139 141 142 145 146 147 148 **P**6 **S** Geisinger Health System, Danville, PA
Primary Contact: Thomas P. Sokola, Chief Administrative Officer
COO: Frank J. Trembulak, Executive Vice President and Chief Operating Officer
CFO: Kevin F. Brennan, CPA, Executive Vice President and Chief Financial Officer
CIO: Frank Richards, Chief Information Officer
CHR: Richard E. Merkle, Chief Human Resources Officer
Web address: www.geisinger.org
**Control:** Other not–for–profit (including NFP Corporation) **Service:** General Medical and Surgical

| | |
|---|---|
| **Staffed Beds:** 545 **Admissions:** 26686 **Census:** 377 **Outpatient Visits:** 892528 **Births:** 1955 **Total Expense ($000):** 865633 **Payroll Expense ($000):** 237168 **Personnel:** 5754 | |

✠ **SELECT SPECIALTY HOSPITAL–DANVILLE (392047)**, 100 North Academy Avenue, 3rd Floor, Zip 17822–3050; tel. 570/214–9653, (Nonreporting) **A**1 9 10 **S** Select Medical Corporation, Mechanicsburg, PA
Primary Contact: Brian Mann, Chief Executive Officer
Web address: www.selectspecialtyhospitals.com/company/locations/danville.aspx
**Control:** Corporation, Investor–owned, for–profit **Service:** Long–Term Acute Care hospital

> **Staffed Beds:** 30

### DARBY—Delaware County

✠ △ **MERCY FITZGERALD HOSPITAL (390156)**, (Formerly Mercy Catholic Medical Center), 1500 South Lansdowe Avenue, Zip 19023–1200; tel. 610/237–4000, (Includes MERCY FITZGERALD HOSPITAL, 1500 South Lansdowne Avenue, Zip 19023; tel. 610/237–4000; MERCY PHILADELPHIA HOSPITAL, 501 South 54th Street, Philadelphia, Zip 19143; tel. 215/748–9000) **A**1 2 3 7 9 10 12 13 **F**3 4 5 11 12 15 18 20 22 24 26 28 29 30 31 34 35 38 40 45 46 49 50 51 53 54 55 57 58 59 61 64 65 66 69 70 75 77 78 79 81 82 85 86 87 90 91 92 93 96 97 98 100 101 102 103 104 107 108 110 111 114 115 118 119 120 121 123 124 130 132 135 145 146 147 148 **S** Catholic Health East, Newtown Square, PA
Primary Contact: Kathryn Conallen, Chief Executive Officer
COO: Ruth Thomas, Chief Operating Officer
CFO: Don Snenk, Chief Financial Officer
CMO: Jeff Komins, M.D., Chief Medical Officer
CIO: Jeff Byda, Vice President Information Technology
Web address: www.mercyhealth.org
**Control:** Church–operated, Nongovernment, not–for profit **Service:** General Medical and Surgical

> **Staffed Beds:** 391 **Admissions:** 19807 **Census:** 243 **Outpatient Visits:** 215351 **Births:** 0 **Total Expense ($000):** 318186 **Payroll Expense ($000):** 120632 **Personnel:** 2047

### DOWNINGTOWN—Chester County

**ST. JOHN VIANNEY HOSPITAL**, 151 Woodbine Road, Zip 19335–3057; tel. 610/269–2600, (Nonreporting)
Primary Contact: Edward Maguire, Administrator
Web address: www.sjvcenter.org
**Control:** Church–operated, Nongovernment, not–for profit **Service:** Psychiatric

> **Staffed Beds:** 42

### DOYLESTOWN—Bucks County

✠ △ **DOYLESTOWN HOSPITAL (390203)**, 595 West State Street, Zip 18901–2597; tel. 215/345–2200, (Total facility includes 74 beds in nursing home–type unit) **A**1 2 5 7 9 10 **F**3 10 13 15 17 18 20 22 24 26 28 29 30 31 34 35 40 45 49 50 54 56 57 58 59 62 63 64 70 73 74 75 76 77 78 79 81 82 85 86 92 93 94 96 107 108 110 111 114 115 118 119 124 125 126 128 130 131 132 141 146 147 **P**5 6 8
Primary Contact: James L. Brexler, President and Chief Executive Officer
COO: Eleanor Wilson, R.N., Vice President and Chief Operating Officer
CFO: Daniel Upton, Vice President and Chief Financial Officer
CMO: Scott S. Levy, M.D., Vice President and Chief Medical Officer
CIO: Richard Lang, Ed.D., Vice President and Chief Information Officer
CHR: Barbara Hebel, Vice President Human Resources
CNO: Patricia A. Stover, Administrator Nursing
Web address: www.dh.org
**Control:** Other not–for–profit (including NFP Corporation) **Service:** General Medical and Surgical

> **Staffed Beds:** 312 **Admissions:** 12937 **Census:** 205 **Outpatient Visits:** 298682 **Births:** 1243 **Total Expense ($000):** 230162 **Payroll Expense ($000):** 93411 **Personnel:** 1590

☐ **FOUNDATIONS BEHAVIORAL HEALTH (394038)**, 833 East Butler Avenue, Zip 18901–2280; tel. 215/345–0444 **A**1 9 10 **F**98 99 100 101 102 105 106 **S** Universal Health Services, Inc., King of Prussia, PA
Primary Contact: Robert Weinhold, Chief Executive Officer
Web address: www.fbh.com
**Control:** Corporation, Investor–owned, for–profit **Service:** Children's hospital psychiatric

> **Staffed Beds:** 96 **Admissions:** 1057 **Census:** 84 **Outpatient Visits:** 0 **Births:** 0 **Total Expense ($000):** 18474 **Payroll Expense ($000):** 8896 **Personnel:** 264

### DREXEL HILL—Delaware County

✠ **DELAWARE COUNTY MEMORIAL HOSPITAL (390081)**, 501 North Lansdowne Avenue, Zip 19026–1114; tel. 610/284–8100 **A**1 2 3 5 9 10 12 **F**3 7 9 11 13 15 17 18 28 29 30 31 34 35 36 40 43 45 46 49 50 51 55 56 57 58 59 60 61 62 63 64 68 72 74 75 76 77 78 79 81 82 84 85 86 87 90 92 93 94 96 97 100 107 108 109 110 111 114 115 116 117 118 119 120 121 123 129 130 131 132 134 135 143 146 147 148 **P**6 **S** Crozer–Keystone Health System, Springfield, PA
Primary Contact: William McCune, President
CFO: Richard I. Bennett, Senior Vice President and Chief Financial Officer
CMO: Seth Malin, M.D., President Medical and Dental Staff
CIO: Robert E. Wilson, Vice President and Chief Information Officer
Web address: www.crozer.org
**Control:** Other not–for–profit (including NFP Corporation) **Service:** General Medical and Surgical

> **Staffed Beds:** 209 **Admissions:** 9609 **Census:** 122 **Outpatient Visits:** 170849 **Births:** 1742 **Total Expense ($000):** 187165 **Payroll Expense ($000):** 72668 **Personnel:** 870

### DU BOIS—Clearfield County

✠ **DUBOIS REGIONAL MEDICAL CENTER (390086)**, 100 Hospital Avenue, Zip 15801–1440, Mailing Address: P.O. Box 447, Zip 15801–0447; tel. 814/371–2200, (Nonreporting) **A**1 2 9 10 19
Primary Contact: John Sutika, President
CMO: Gary Dugan, M.D., Vice President Medical Affairs
CIO: Thomas Johnson, Manager Management Information Systems
CHR: Robert J. McKee, Vice President Human Resources
Web address: www.drmc.org
**Control:** Other not–for–profit (including NFP Corporation) **Service:** General Medical and Surgical

> **Staffed Beds:** 203

### EAGLEVILLE—Montgomery County

★ **EAGLEVILLE HOSPITAL (390278)**, 100 Eagleville Road, Zip 19403–1829, Mailing Address: P.O. Box 45, Zip 19408–0045; tel. 610/539–6000 **A**5 9 10 **F**4 29 34 35 50 61 68 75 86 98 100 101 103 130 132 134 143 146 147 **P**6
Primary Contact: Maureen King Pollock, Chief Executive Officer
COO: Lois Chepak, R.N., Chief Clinical Officer
CFO: Alfred Salvitti, Chief Financial Officer
CMO: Robert Wilson, D.O., Director Medical Services
CIO: Richard R. Mitchell, Director Information Technology
CHR: Zoe Yousaitis, Director Human Resources
Web address: www.eaglevillehospital.org
**Control:** Other not–for–profit (including NFP Corporation) **Service:** Alcoholism and other chemical dependency

> **Staffed Beds:** 82 **Admissions:** 1964 **Census:** 47 **Outpatient Visits:** 0 **Births:** 0 **Total Expense ($000):** 32533 **Payroll Expense ($000):** 19302 **Personnel:** 365

### EAST NORRITON—Montgomery County

**EINSTEIN MEDICAL CENTER MONTGOMERY (390329)**, 559 West Germantown Pike, Zip 19403–4250; tel. 484/622–1000, (Nonreporting) **A**9 10 **S** Albert Einstein Healthcare Network, Philadelphia, PA
Primary Contact: Beth Duffy, Chief Operating Officer
**Control:** Other not–for–profit (including NFP Corporation) **Service:** General Medical and Surgical

> **Staffed Beds:** 146

### EAST STROUDSBURG—Monroe County

✠ △ **POCONO MEDICAL CENTER (390201)**, 206 East Brown Street, Zip 18301–3006; tel. 570/421–4000 **A**1 2 7 9 10 **F**3 11 12 13 14 15 17 18 20 22 24 26 28 29 30 31 32 34 35 36 38 39 40 43 45 46 48 49 50 54 55 56 57 59 61 64 65 66 70 72 74 75 76 77 78 79 81 82 83 84 85 86 87 89 92 93 97 98 100 101 102 103 107 108 110 111 114 115 116 117 118 119 120 121 123 124 126 130 132 135 144 146 148
Primary Contact: Kathleen E. Kuck, R.N., President and Chief Executive Officer
COO: Jeffrey Snyder, Chief Operating Officer
CFO: Michael Wilk, Senior President Financial Services and Chief Financial Officer
CMO: William K. Cors, M.D., Vice President and Chief Medical Quality Officer
CIO: Joseph Fisne, Vice President and Chief Operating Officer
CHR: Lynn M. Lansdowne, Vice President Human Resources
CNO: Paulette Nish, MSN, Vice President and Chief Nursing Officer
Web address: www.pmchealthsystem.org
**Control:** Other not–for–profit (including NFP Corporation) **Service:** General Medical and Surgical

> **Staffed Beds:** 235 **Admissions:** 11950 **Census:** 147 **Outpatient Visits:** 248089 **Births:** 870 **Total Expense ($000):** 222961 **Payroll Expense ($000):** 90976 **Personnel:** 1501

*Many Facility Codes have changed. Please refer to the AHA Guide Code Chart.* © 2013 AHA Guide

**EASTON—Northampton County**

☒ **EASTON HOSPITAL (390162)**, 250 South 21st Street, Zip 18042–3892; tel. 610/250–4000 **A**1 2 3 5 9 10 **F**3 12 13 15 18 19 20 22 24 26 28 29 30 31 34 35 40 44 45 46 47 48 49 51 54 56 57 58 59 60 61 64 65 66 70 72 74 75 78 79 80 81 82 85 86 87 89 90 92 97 100 107 108 109 110 111 114 115 116 117 119 120 121 123 124 126 129 130 132 135 144 146 147 148 **S** Community Health Systems, Inc., Franklin, TN
Primary Contact: Brian Finestein, Chief Executive Officer
CFO: James Washecka, Chief Financial Officer
CMO: David Lyon, M.D., Chief Medical Officer
CIO: Kenneth Castle, Chief Information Officer
CHR: Lori Ofner, Vice President Human Resources
Web address: www.easton–hospital.com
**Control:** Corporation, Investor–owned, for–profit **Service:** General Medical and Surgical

**Staffed Beds:** 224 **Admissions:** 9140 **Census:** 122 **Outpatient Visits:** 149253 **Births:** 417 **Total Expense ($000):** 148242 **Payroll Expense ($000):** 51875 **Personnel:** 1149

☒ **KINDRED HOSPITAL EASTON (392034)**, 250 South 21st Street, 3rd Floor, Zip 18042–3851; tel. 610/250–4724, (Nonreporting) **A**1 9 10 **S** Kindred Healthcare, Louisville, KY
Primary Contact: Deborah Karn, Chief Executive Officer
Web address: www.kheaston.com/
**Control:** Corporation, Investor–owned, for–profit **Service:** Long–Term Acute Care hospital

**Staffed Beds:** 31

☐ **ST. LUKE'S HOSPITAL – ANDERSON CAMPUS (390326)**, 1872 Riverside Circle, Zip 18045–5669; tel. 484/503–3000, (Data for 233 days) **A**1 9 10 **F**3 11 15 18 20 22 24 26 29 30 31 34 35 38 40 44 45 49 50 51 53 55 57 59 60 63 64 68 70 74 75 77 78 79 81 82 84 85 86 87 93 102 107 108 110 111 115 118 119 120 121 123 124 130 132 146 **P**6 8 **S** St. Luke's University Health Network, Bethlehem, PA
Primary Contact: Edward Nawrocki, President
CMO: Justin P. Psaila, M.D., Vice President Medical Affairs
CNO: Darla Frack, R.N., Chief Nursing Officer
Web address: www.mystlukesonline.org
**Control:** Other not–for–profit (including NFP Corporation) **Service:** General Medical and Surgical

**Staffed Beds:** 57 **Admissions:** 2421 **Census:** 33 **Outpatient Visits:** 48740 **Births:** 0 **Total Expense ($000):** 43370 **Payroll Expense ($000):** 13939 **Personnel:** 331

**TRIUMPH HOSPITAL EASTON** See Kindred Hospital Easton

**ELLWOOD CITY—Lawrence County**

**ELLWOOD CITY HOSPITAL (390008)**, 724 Pershing Street, Zip 16117–1474; tel. 724/752–0081, (Nonreporting) **A**9 10
Primary Contact: Carolyn Izzo, Interim President and Chief Executive Officer
COO: Carolyn Izzo, Senior Vice President and Chief Operating Officer
CFO: Christopher M. Little, Vice President and Chief Financial Officer
CIO: Bryan O'Shaughnessy, Chief Information Officer
CHR: Paul Landman, Director Human Resources
Web address: www.TheEllwoodCityHospital.org
**Control:** Other not–for–profit (including NFP Corporation) **Service:** General Medical and Surgical

**Staffed Beds:** 95

**EPHRATA—Lancaster County**

☐ **EPHRATA COMMUNITY HOSPITAL (390225)**, 169 Martin Avenue, Zip 17522–1724, Mailing Address: P.O. Box 1002, Zip 17522–1002; tel. 717/733–0311 **A**1 2 9 10 **F**11 12 13 15 18 20 28 29 30 31 34 35 36 40 42 49 50 51 54 57 59 60 61 62 64 69 70 72 74 75 76 77 78 79 80 81 82 85 86 87 89 90 97 98 99 100 101 102 103 107 108 111 114 115 118 119 121 129 130 132 135 144 146 147 148 **P**6 8
Primary Contact: John M. Porter, Jr., President and Chief Executive Officer
COO: Robert Graupensperger, Executive Vice President
CFO: John A. Holmes, Chief Financial Officer
CMO: Vincent D. Glielmi, D.O., Senior Vice President Medical Affairs
CIO: John Jabour, Chief Information Officer
CHR: Barbara Mumma, Vice President Human Resources
CNO: Marcia A. Hansen, R.N., Vice President Patient Services and Chief Nursing Officer
Web address: www.ephratahospital.org
**Control:** Other not–for–profit (including NFP Corporation) **Service:** General Medical and Surgical

**Staffed Beds:** 130 **Admissions:** 6307 **Census:** 69 **Outpatient Visits:** 411805 **Births:** 774 **Total Expense ($000):** 209852 **Payroll Expense ($000):** 92287 **Personnel:** 1789

**ERIE—Erie County**

☒ **ERIE VETERANS AFFAIRS MEDICAL CENTER**, (Formerly Veterans Affairs Medical Center), 135 East 38th Street, Zip 16504–1559; tel. 814/860–2576, (Nonreporting) **A**1 **S** Department of Veterans Affairs, Washington, DC
Primary Contact: Michael Adelman, M.D., Director
CFO: Joann Pritchard, Chief Financial Officer
CMO: Anthony Behm, D.O., Chief of Staff
CIO: Sean Rowand, Chief Information Officer
CHR: Lynn Nies, Human Resources Officer
Web address: www.erie.va.gov/
**Control:** Veterans Affairs, Government, federal **Service:** General Medical and Surgical

**Staffed Beds:** 26

**HAMOT MEDICAL CENTER** See UPMC Hamot

☒ **HEALTHSOUTH REHABILITATION HOSPITAL OF ERIE (393046)**, 143 East Second Street, Zip 16507–1501; tel. 814/878–1200 **A**1 9 10 **F**90 91 130 **S** HEALTHSOUTH Corporation, Birmingham, AL
Primary Contact: Lucretia Atti, Chief Executive Officer
CFO: Lori Gibbens, Controller
CMO: Douglas Grisier, D.O., Medical Director
CIO: Sharon Zielinski, Manager Health Information
CHR: William Robinson, Director Human Resources
CNO: Evelyn Armstrong, Chief Nursing Officer
Web address: www.healthsoutherie.com
**Control:** Corporation, Investor–owned, for–profit **Service:** Rehabilitation

**Staffed Beds:** 100 **Admissions:** 1768 **Census:** 66 **Outpatient Visits:** 0 **Births:** 0 **Personnel:** 209

○ **MILLCREEK COMMUNITY HOSPITAL (390198)**, 5515 Peach Street, Zip 16509–2695; tel. 814/864–4031, (Total facility includes 24 beds in nursing home–type unit) **A**9 10 11 12 13 **F**3 4 8 13 15 20 37 40 45 47 50 51 58 64 65 66 68 70 74 75 76 79 80 81 82 85 92 93 98 99 100 102 103 105 107 108 110 111 114 118 119 128 129 130 135 143 146
Primary Contact: Mary L. Eckert, President and Chief Executive Officer
CFO: Richard P. Olinger, Chief Financial Officer
CMO: John J. Kalata, D.O., Chief of Staff
CIO: Cheryl Girardier, Director Information Technology
CHR: Polly Momeyer, Manager Human Resources
CNO: Katie Agresti, R.N., Director Patient Care Services
Web address: www.millcreekcommunityhospital.com
**Control:** Other not–for–profit (including NFP Corporation) **Service:** General Medical and Surgical

**Staffed Beds:** 168 **Admissions:** 5407 **Census:** 84 **Outpatient Visits:** 46211 **Births:** 135 **Total Expense ($000):** 39991 **Payroll Expense ($000):** 20451 **Personnel:** 455

☒ **SAINT VINCENT HOSPITAL (390009)**, (Formerly Saint Vincent Health Center), 232 West 25th Street, Zip 16544–0002; tel. 814/452–5000 **A**1 2 3 5 9 10 12 13 **F**3 5 8 9 11 12 13 15 17 18 20 22 24 26 28 29 30 31 32 33 34 35 36 38 39 40 42 44 45 46 48 49 50 51 53 54 56 57 58 59 60 61 62 63 64 65 66 68 70 72 74 75 76 77 78 79 80 81 82 83 84 85 86 87 89 90 93 96 97 98 100 101 102 103 104 107 108 110 111 114 115 117 118 119 120 121 123 124 126 129 130 131 132 133 135 144 146 147 148 **P**3 6 7 **S** Saint Vincent Health System, Erie, PA
Primary Contact: Scott Whalen, Ph.D., FACHE, President and Chief Executive Officer
COO: Thomas Fucci, Chief Operating Officer
CFO: Al Mansfield, Chief Financial Officer
CMO: Richard Cogley, M.D., Senior Vice President Medical Affairs and Chief Medical Officer
CIO: Richard B. Ong, Chief Information Officer
Web address: www.svhs.org
**Control:** Other not–for–profit (including NFP Corporation) **Service:** General Medical and Surgical

**Staffed Beds:** 486 **Admissions:** 14583 **Census:** 204 **Outpatient Visits:** 172912 **Births:** 1146 **Total Expense ($000):** 254926 **Payroll Expense ($000):** 81100 **Personnel:** 1854

☒ **SELECT SPECIALTY HOSPITAL–ERIE (392037)**, 252 West 11th Street, Zip 16501–1702; tel. 814/874–5300, (Nonreporting) **A**1 9 10 **S** Select Medical Corporation, Mechanicsburg, PA
Primary Contact: Coleen Zimmerman, Interim Chief Executive Officer
Web address: www.selectspecialtyhospitals.com/company/locations/erie.aspx
**Control:** Corporation, Investor–owned, for–profit **Service:** Long–Term Acute Care hospital

**Staffed Beds:** 50

---

**Hospital, Medicare Provider Number, Address, Telephone, Approval, Facility, and Physician Codes, Health Care System**

★ American Hospital Association (AHA) membership
☐ The Joint Commission accreditation
◇ DNV Healthcare Inc. accreditation
○ Healthcare Facilities Accreditation Program
△ Commission on Accreditation of Rehabilitation Facilities (CARF) accreditation

**PA**

☐ **UPMC HAMOT (390063)**, 201 State Street, Zip 16550–0002;
tel. 814/877–6000 **A**1 2 3 5 9 10 13 **F**3 9 11 12 13 15 17 18 20 22 24 26
28 29 30 31 34 35 36 37 38 39 40 43 44 45 46 47 48 49 50 51 56 57 58
59 60 61 62 63 64 65 66 68 70 72 74 75 76 77 78 79 80 81 82 84 85 86
87 89 91 92 93 96 100 107 108 110 111 114 115 118 119 124 126 129
130 131 132 135 141 146 147 148 **P**6 8 **S** UPMC, Pittsburgh, PA
Primary Contact: V. James Fiorenzo, President
COO: David Gibbons, Executive Vice President and Chief Operating Officer
CFO: Stephen M. Danch, Chief Financial Officer
CMO: Richard Long, M.D., Chief Medical Officer
CIO: Joseph Butler, Vice President and Chief Information Officer
CHR: Joseph Butler, Vice President and Chief Information Officer
Web address: www.hamot.org
**Control:** Other not–for–profit (including NFP Corporation) **Service:** General
Medical and Surgical

| | |
|---|---|
| **Staffed Beds:** 373 **Admissions:** 18240 **Census:** 235 **Outpatient Visits:** 340008 **Births:** 1958 **Total Expense ($000):** 316431 **Payroll Expense ($000):** 111670 **Personnel:** 2312 | |

**VETERANS AFFAIRS MEDICAL CENTER** See Erie Veterans Affairs Medical
Center

### EVERETT—Bedford County

☐ **UPMC BEDFORD MEMORIAL (390117)**, 10455 Lincoln Highway,
Zip 15537–7046; tel. 814/623–6161 **A**1 9 10 20 **F**3 8 11 13 15 18 28 29 30
34 35 39 40 41 45 48 50 51 56 57 59 61 64 65 68 70 71 74 75 76 77 78
79 81 85 86 87 89 93 97 102 104 107 108 110 111 114 119 129 130 131
132 133 135 146 147 **S** UPMC, Pittsburgh, PA
Primary Contact: Roger P. Winn, President
CFO: Mario Wilfong, Vice President Finance and Administration
CIO: Mark Wiley, Manager Information Systems Development
CHR: Michelle A. Speck, Vice President Human Resources
CNO: Paula Thomas, R.N., Vice President Patient Services
Web address: www.upmcbedfordmemorial.com
**Control:** Other not–for–profit (including NFP Corporation) **Service:** General
Medical and Surgical

| | |
|---|---|
| **Staffed Beds:** 27 **Admissions:** 1895 **Census:** 13 **Outpatient Visits:** 100810 **Births:** 265 **Total Expense ($000):** 37921 **Payroll Expense ($000):** 14619 **Personnel:** 313 | |

### FARRELL—Mercer County

**SHENANGO VALLEY CAMPUS** See UPMC Horizon, Greenville

### FORT WASHINGTON—Montgomery County

☐ **BROOKE GLEN BEHAVIORAL HOSPITAL (394049)**, 7170 Lafayette Avenue,
Zip 19034–2301; tel. 215/641–5300, (Nonreporting) **A**1 3 5 9 10 **S** Universal
Health Services, Inc., King of Prussia, PA
Primary Contact: Neil Callahan, Chief Executive Officer
COO: William R. Mason, Chief Operating Officer
CFO: Robert Zagerman, Chief Financial Officer
CMO: Chand Nair, M.D., Medical Director
CHR: Dawn Kownacki, Director Human Resources
Web address: www.brookeglenhospital.com
**Control:** Corporation, Investor–owned, for–profit **Service:** Psychiatric

| | |
|---|---|
| **Staffed Beds:** 146 | |

### GETTYSBURG—Adams County

⊠ **GETTYSBURG HOSPITAL (390065)**, 147 Gettys Street, Zip 17325–2534;
tel. 717/334–2121 **A**1 9 10 **F**3 8 11 13 15 18 20 28 29 30 31 35 40 42 45
46 50 54 55 59 60 64 65 68 70 74 75 76 79 81 82 84 85 89 93 102 107
110 111 114 115 118 119 129 130 131 132 134 135 146 147 148 **P**8
**S** WellSpan Health, York, PA
Primary Contact: Jane E. Hyde, President
COO: Joseph H. Edgar, Senior Vice President Operations
CMO: Charles Marley, D.O., Vice President Medical Affairs
CIO: Robin Kimple, Director Information Services
CHR: Kim Brister, Director Human Resources
CNO: Kristen O'Shea, R.N., Vice President Patient Care Services
Web address: www.wellspan.org
**Control:** Other not–for–profit (including NFP Corporation) **Service:** General
Medical and Surgical

| | |
|---|---|
| **Staffed Beds:** 76 **Admissions:** 4323 **Census:** 46 **Outpatient Visits:** 180983 **Births:** 520 **Total Expense ($000):** 118810 **Payroll Expense ($000):** 44693 **Personnel:** 692 | |

### GREENSBURG—Westmoreland County

☐ **EXCELA HEALTH WESTMORELAND HOSPITAL (390145)**, 532 West
Pittsburgh Street, Zip 15601–2282; tel. 724/832–4000 **A**1 9 10 **F**3 5 8 9 11
12 13 15 17 18 20 22 24 26 28 29 30 32 34 35 36 38 40 44 45 47 48 49
50 51 56 57 59 61 64 65 68 70 73 74 75 76 77 78 79 81 82 84 85 86 87
89 90 92 93 96 97 98 100 102 103 104 105 107 108 110 111 114 115
118 119 129 130 131 132 134 135 143 146 147 148 **S** Excela Health,
Greensburg, PA
Primary Contact: Ronald H. Ott, President
COO: Michael D. Busch, Executive Vice President and Chief Operating Officer
CFO: Jeffrey T. Curry, Executive Vice President and Chief Financial Officer
CMO: Jerome Granato, M.D., Senior Vice President and Chief Medical Officer
CIO: David Gawaluck, Vice President and Chief Information Officer
CHR: John Caverno, Chief Human Resources Officer
CNO: Helen K. Burns, Ph.D., Senior Vice President and Chief Nursing Officer
Web address: www.excelahealth.org
**Control:** Other not–for–profit (including NFP Corporation) **Service:** General
Medical and Surgical

| | |
|---|---|
| **Staffed Beds:** 359 **Admissions:** 18326 **Census:** 236 **Outpatient Visits:** 365538 **Births:** 1743 **Total Expense ($000):** 228970 **Payroll Expense ($000):** 92194 **Personnel:** 1903 | |

### GREENVILLE—Mercer County

☐ ○ **UPMC HORIZON (390178)**, 110 North Main Street, Zip 16125–1726;
tel. 724/588–2100, (Includes GREENVILLE CAMPUS, 110 North Main Street,
Zip 16125–1795; tel. 724/588–2100; SHENANGO VALLEY CAMPUS, 2200
Memorial Drive, Farrell, Zip 16121–1398; tel. 724/981–3500), (Total facility
includes 25 beds in nursing home–type unit) **A**1 2 9 10 11 13 **F**3 11 12 13 15
18 20 26 28 29 30 31 32 34 35 39 40 43 44 45 47 49 50 53 54 56 57 59
61 64 65 68 70 74 75 76 77 78 79 81 82 85 86 87 89 90 92 93 97 107
108 110 111 114 115 116 117 118 119 121 123 128 129 130 131 132 133
135 143 146 147 148 **S** UPMC, Pittsburgh, PA
Primary Contact: Donald R. Owrey, President
CFO: David Shulik, Vice President and Chief Financial Officer
CMO: Samuel Daisley, D.O., Vice President Medical Affairs
CHR: Connie Mayle, Vice President Administrative Services
Web address: www.horizon.upmc.com
**Control:** Other not–for–profit (including NFP Corporation) **Service:** General
Medical and Surgical

| | |
|---|---|
| **Staffed Beds:** 184 **Admissions:** 7310 **Census:** 96 **Outpatient Visits:** 210146 **Births:** 759 **Total Expense ($000):** 132194 **Payroll Expense ($000):** 39482 **Personnel:** 737 | |

### GROVE CITY—Mercer County

**GROVE CITY MEDICAL CENTER (390266)**, 631 North Broad Street Extension,
Zip 16127–4603; tel. 724/450–7000, (Total facility includes 20 beds in nursing
home–type unit) **A**9 10 **F**3 13 15 18 20 28 29 31 34 35 40 45 46 50 51 54 57
59 60 62 64 70 75 76 78 79 81 82 87 93 107 108 110 111 115 117 118
119 124 127 128 129 130 132 135 146 147 148 **P**6
Primary Contact: Robert Jackson, Jr., Chief Executive Officer
CFO: David Poland, Vice President Finance
CMO: Armando Sciullo, D.O., Chief of Staff
CIO: Philip Swartwood, Director Information Systems
CHR: Donald Henley, Vice President Human Resources and Social Services
Web address: www.gcmcpa.org
**Control:** Other not–for–profit (including NFP Corporation) **Service:** General
Medical and Surgical

| | |
|---|---|
| **Staffed Beds:** 109 **Admissions:** 2123 **Census:** 30 **Outpatient Visits:** 113617 **Births:** 270 **Total Expense ($000):** 44373 **Payroll Expense ($000):** 17659 **Personnel:** 397 | |

### HANOVER—York County

⊠ **HANOVER HOSPITAL (390233)**, 300 Highland Avenue, Zip 17331–2297;
tel. 717/637–3711 **A**1 9 10 **F**3 7 11 13 15 18 20 28 29 30 31 32 34 35 40
44 45 47 49 50 51 53 54 56 57 59 61 64 65 68 74 75 76 77 78 79 81 84
85 86 87 89 90 93 94 96 107 108 110 111 115 119 129 130 131 132 134
135 143 144 146 147 148
Primary Contact: James Wissler, President and Chief Executive Officer
COO: Michael A. Hockenberry, Vice President Operations
CFO: Michael W. Gaskins, Executive Vice President and Chief Financial Officer
CMO: Michael H. Ader, M.D., Vice President Medical Affairs
CIO: Pamela Owens, Director Health Information Management
CHR: Christine Miller, Vice President Human Resources
CNO: M. Patricia Saunders, R.N., Vice President Nursing
Web address: www.hanoverhospital.org
**Control:** Other not–for–profit (including NFP Corporation) **Service:** General
Medical and Surgical

| | |
|---|---|
| **Staffed Beds:** 106 **Admissions:** 5195 **Census:** 65 **Outpatient Visits:** 235377 **Births:** 588 **Total Expense ($000):** 129641 **Payroll Expense ($000):** 51638 **Personnel:** 998 | |

### HARRISBURG—Dauphin County

**COMMUNITY HOSPITAL** See Pinnacle Health System

□ **PENNSYLVANIA PSYCHIATRIC INSTITUTE (394051)**, (Formerly Pennsylvania Psychiatric Hospital), 2501 North Third Street, Zip 17110–1904; tel. 717/782–6420, (Nonreporting) **A**1 3 5 10
Primary Contact: William Daly, Interim Chief Executive Officer
Web address: www.ppimhs.org/
**Control:** Partnership, Investor–owned, for–profit **Service:** Psychiatric

**Staffed Beds:** 73

□ **PINNACLE HEALTH SYSTEM (390067)**, 111 South Front Street, Zip 17101–2010, Mailing Address: P.O. Box 8700, Zip 17105–8700; tel. 717/782–3131, (Includes COMMUNITY HOSPITAL, 4300 Londonderry Road, Zip 17109–5397, Mailing Address: P.O. Box 3000, Zip 17105–3000; tel. 717/652–3000; HARRISBURG HOSPITAL, 111 South Front Street, Zip 17101–2099; tel. 717/782–3131; POLYCLINIC HOSPITAL, 2501 North Third Street, Zip 17110–1904; tel. 717/782–4141; Roger Longenderfer, M.D., President and Chief Executive Officer) **A**1 2 3 5 8 9 10 12 13 **F**3 7 11 12 13 17 18 20 22 24 26 29 30 31 34 35 36 37 40 42 45 48 49 51 54 55 57 58 59 60 65 68 70 72 74 75 76 77 78 79 81 82 84 85 86 87 89 90 93 95 96 97 107 111 114 115 119 120 121 124 126 130 138 142 146 147 **P**6
Primary Contact: Michael A. Young, FACHE, President and Chief Executive Officer
COO: Philip Guarneschelli, Senior Vice President and Chief Operating Officer
CFO: William H. Pugh, Senior Vice President Corporate Finance and Chief Financial Officer
CMO: Dana Kellis, M.D., Senior Vice President Medical Affairs and Chief Medical Officer
CIO: Steven Roth, Vice President Informatics and Chief Information Officer
CHR: Thomas Kess, Vice President Human Resources
Web address: www.pinnaclehealth.org
**Control:** Other not–for–profit (including NFP Corporation) **Service:** General Medical and Surgical

**Staffed Beds:** 577 **Admissions:** 29962 **Census:** 396 **Outpatient Visits:** 621740 **Births:** 3993 **Personnel:** 4563

**POLYCLINIC HOSPITAL** See Pinnacle Health System

**SELECT SPECIALTY HOSPITAL–HARRISBURG** See Select Specialty Hospital–Central Pennsylvania, Camp Hill

### HASTINGS—Cambria County

★ **CONEMAUGH MINERS MEDICAL CENTER (390130)**, (Formerly Miners Medical Center), 290 Haida Avenue, Zip 16646–5610, Mailing Address: P.O. Box 689, Zip 16646–0689; tel. 814/247–3100 **A**9 10 20 **F**3 15 18 29 30 31 35 36 40 45 48 56 57 59 64 70 75 78 79 81 86 92 93 96 97 102 107 108 110 119 129 130 131 133 144 146 148 **P**8 **S** Conemaugh Health System, Johnstown, PA
Primary Contact: William R. Crowe, President
CFO: Kimberly Semelsberger, Vice President Financial Operations
CIO: James Homerski, Director Information Services
CHR: John Fresh, Vice President Human Resources
Web address: www.minersmedicalcenter.org
**Control:** Other not–for–profit (including NFP Corporation) **Service:** General Medical and Surgical

**Staffed Beds:** 30 **Admissions:** 772 **Census:** 9 **Outpatient Visits:** 55215 **Births:** 1 **Total Expense ($000):** 16949 **Payroll Expense ($000):** 5484 **Personnel:** 125

### HAZLETON—Luzerne County

★ ○ **HAZLETON GENERAL HOSPITAL (390185)**, 700 East Broad Street, Zip 18201–6897; tel. 570/501–4000 **A**9 10 11 **F**3 8 11 12 13 15 28 29 30 31 34 35 40 50 53 54 57 58 59 60 62 64 68 69 70 75 76 77 78 79 81 82 85 86 87 89 90 93 107 108 110 111 114 118 119 124 129 130 131 132 135 143 146 147 148 **P**2
Primary Contact: James Edwards, President
COO: John R. Fletcher, Vice President and Chief Operating Officer
CFO: William Bauer, Vice President Finance and Chief Financial Officer
CMO: Anthony Valente, M.D., Vice President Medical Affairs
CIO: Carl Shoener, Chief Information Officer
CHR: Elizabeth Perrong, Vice President Human Resources
Web address: www.ghha.org
**Control:** Other not–for–profit (including NFP Corporation) **Service:** General Medical and Surgical

**Staffed Beds:** 141 **Admissions:** 6473 **Census:** 85 **Outpatient Visits:** 157406 **Births:** 587 **Total Expense ($000):** 89160 **Payroll Expense ($000):** 39393 **Personnel:** 609

### HERSHEY—Dauphin County

⊠ **PENN STATE MILTON S. HERSHEY MEDICAL CENTER (390256)**, 500 University Drive, Zip 17033–2360, Mailing Address: P.O. Box 850, Zip 17033–0850; tel. 717/531–8521, (Includes PENN STATE CHILDREN'S HOSPITAL, 500 University Drive, tel. 717/531–8521) **A**1 2 3 5 8 9 10 **F**3 5 6 7 8 9 11 12 13 14 15 17 18 19 20 21 22 23 24 25 26 27 28 29 30 31 32 34 35 36 37 38 40 41 43 44 45 46 47 48 49 50 51 52 53 54 55 56 57 58 59 60 61 64 65 66 68 70 72 73 74 75 76 77 78 79 80 81 82 84 85 86 87 88 89 90 91 92 93 96 97 98 99 100 101 102 103 104 105 106 107 108 109 110 111 114 115 116 117 118 119 120 121 123 124 126 129 130 131 132 134 135 136 137 138 139 141 142 143 144 145 146 147 148 **P**6
Primary Contact: Harold L. Paz, M.D., Chief Executive Officer
COO: Robin D. Wittenstein, Ed.D., Director and Chief Operating Officer
CFO: Kevin Haley, Chief Financial Officer
CMO: Carol V. Freer, M.D., Chief Medical Officer
CIO: Thomas Abendroth, M.D., Chief Information Officer
CHR: Charles Wilson, Chief Human Resources Officer
Web address: www.pennstatehershey.org/web/guest/home
**Control:** Other not–for–profit (including NFP Corporation) **Service:** General Medical and Surgical

**Staffed Beds:** 475 **Admissions:** 25615 **Census:** 389 **Outpatient Visits:** 870859 **Births:** 1718 **Total Expense ($000):** 912970 **Payroll Expense ($000):** 343299 **Personnel:** 7398

### HONESDALE—Wayne County

★ **WAYNE MEMORIAL HOSPITAL (390125)**, 601 Park Street, Zip 18431–1498; tel. 570/253–8100 **A**9 10 **F**3 11 13 15 18 28 30 31 34 35 36 37 39 40 45 46 48 49 50 51 53 54 56 57 59 61 62 63 64 65 75 76 77 78 79 81 86 89 90 92 93 99 100 101 102 103 104 107 108 110 111 115 116 117 119 124 129 130 131 132 133 134 135 146 147 148 **P**6
Primary Contact: David L. Hoff, Chief Executive Officer
COO: John D. Conte, Director Facility Services
CFO: Michael J. Clifford, Director Finance
CMO: George Tietjen, M.D., Chief of Staff
CIO: Tom Hoffman, Manager Information Systems
CHR: Elizabeth McDonald, Director Human Resources
Web address: www.wmh.org
**Control:** Other not–for–profit (including NFP Corporation) **Service:** General Medical and Surgical

**Staffed Beds:** 104 **Admissions:** 3469 **Census:** 46 **Outpatient Visits:** 120499 **Births:** 401 **Total Expense ($000):** 65076 **Payroll Expense ($000):** 27906 **Personnel:** 552

### HUMMELSTOWN—Dauphin County

⊠ **PENN STATE HERSHEY REHABILITATION HOSPITAL (393053)**, 1135 Old West Chocolate Avenue, Zip 17036; tel. 717/832–2600, (Nonreporting) **A**1 9 10 **S** Select Medical Corporation, Mechanicsburg, PA
Primary Contact: Scott Guevin, Chief Executive Officer
Web address: www.psh–rehab.com
**Control:** Corporation, Investor–owned, for–profit **Service:** Rehabilitation

**Staffed Beds:** 32

### HUNTINGDON—Huntingdon County

⊠ **J. C. BLAIR MEMORIAL HOSPITAL (390056)**, 1225 Warm Springs Avenue, Zip 16652–2398; tel. 814/643–2290 **A**1 9 10 20 **F**3 11 13 15 18 28 29 34 35 40 45 57 59 64 68 70 75 76 77 79 81 85 86 87 89 96 98 100 102 103 104 105 107 108 110 111 114 117 118 119 129 130 132 133 135 146 147 148
Primary Contact: Lisa Mallon, Chief Executive Officer
CFO: Edward M. Quinn, Interim Chief Financial Officer
CIO: Christine R. Gildea, Director Marketing and Community Relations
CHR: Michael F. Hubert, Vice President Human Resources
CNO: Pam Matthias, Vice President of Patient Care Services
Web address: www.jcblair.org
**Control:** Other not–for–profit (including NFP Corporation) **Service:** General Medical and Surgical

**Staffed Beds:** 69 **Admissions:** 2248 **Census:** 23 **Outpatient Visits:** 99917 **Births:** 217 **Total Expense ($000):** 38054 **Payroll Expense ($000):** 17339 **Personnel:** 317

---

**Hospital, Medicare Provider Number, Address, Telephone, Approval, Facility, and Physician Codes, Health Care System**

★ American Hospital Association (AHA) membership
□ The Joint Commission accreditation
◇ DNV Healthcare Inc. accreditation
○ Healthcare Facilities Accreditation Program
△ Commission on Accreditation of Rehabilitation Facilities (CARF) accreditation

**INDIANA—Indiana County**

★ **INDIANA REGIONAL MEDICAL CENTER (390173)**, 835 Hospital Road, Zip 15701–3629, Mailing Address: P.O. Box 788, Zip 15701–0788; tel. 724/357–7000 **A**2 9 10 20 **F**3 11 15 18 28 29 30 31 32 34 35 40 44 46 47 49 53 56 57 59 64 65 70 71 74 75 76 77 78 79 81 82 83 84 85 87 89 90 91 98 102 103 107 108 111 114 115 118 119 120 121 123 124 129 130 132 144 146 148 **P**4 6
Primary Contact: Stephen A. Wolfe, President and Chief Executive Officer
COO: Dominic Paccapaniccia, Chief Operating Officer
CFO: Robert Gongaware, Senior Vice President Finance
CMO: Bruce A. Bush, M.D., Senior Vice President Medical Affairs
CIO: Wade Patrick, Senior Vice President Information Services
CHR: Matt Reading, Director Human Resources
CNO: Cindy L. Virgil, MSN, Senior Vice President Patient Care Services
Web address: www.indianarmc.org
**Control:** Other not–for–profit (including NFP Corporation) **Service:** General Medical and Surgical

**Staffed Beds:** 164 **Admissions:** 7346 **Census:** 90 **Outpatient Visits:** 250551 **Births:** 610 **Total Expense ($000):** 127622 **Payroll Expense ($000):** 57129 **Personnel:** 945

**JEFFERSON HILLS—Allegheny County**

☐ **JEFFERSON REGIONAL MEDICAL CENTER (390265)**, 565 Coal Valley Road, Zip 15025–3703, Mailing Address: Box 18119, Pittsburgh, Zip 15236–0119; tel. 412/469–5000, (Nonreporting) **A**1 9 10
Primary Contact: John Dempster, President and Chief Executive Officer
COO: Louise Urban, R.N., Executive Vice President and Chief Operating Officer
CFO: Joanne A. Hahey, Senior Vice President and Chief Financial Officer
CMO: Richard F. Collins, M.D., Executive Vice President and Chief Medical Officer
CIO: James Witenske, Chief Information Officer
CHR: Rosanne C. Saunders, Senior Vice President and Chief Human Resources Officer
Web address: www.jeffersonregional.com
**Control:** Other not–for–profit (including NFP Corporation) **Service:** General Medical and Surgical

**Staffed Beds:** 373

**JERSEY SHORE—Lycoming County**

⊞ **JERSEY SHORE HOSPITAL (391300)**, 1020 Thompson Street, Zip 17740–1794; tel. 570/398–0100 **A**1 9 10 18 **F**3 15 18 28 29 30 34 35 40 45 46 47 48 50 57 59 75 77 79 81 82 85 93 107 108 109 110 111 115 119 129 130 131 133 135 144 145 147 148 **P**7 **S** QHR, Brentwood, TN
Primary Contact: Carey W. Plummer, President and Chief Executive Officer
CFO: Mark Rice, CPA, Controller
CMO: Steven E. Katz, M.D., Chief Medical Officer
CIO: Christine Haas, Manager Information Technology
CHR: Trudi Alexander, Director Human Resources
Web address: www.jsh.org
**Control:** Other not–for–profit (including NFP Corporation) **Service:** General Medical and Surgical

**Staffed Beds:** 25 **Admissions:** 902 **Census:** 10 **Outpatient Visits:** 85526 **Births:** 0 **Total Expense ($000):** 28479 **Payroll Expense ($000):** 11538 **Personnel:** 296

**JOHNSTOWN—Cambria County**

⊞ **CONEMAUGH MEMORIAL MEDICAL CENTER (390110)**, (Formerly Memorial Medical Center), 1086 Franklin Street, Zip 15905–4398; tel. 814/534–9000, (Includes GOOD SAMARITAN MEDICAL CENTER, 1020 Franklin Street, Zip 15905–4186; tel. 814/533–1000; MEMORIAL MEDICAL CENTER – LEE CAMPUS, 320 Main Street, Zip 15901–1601; tel. 814/533–0123) **A**1 2 3 5 6 9 10 12 13 **F**3 5 8 11 12 13 14 15 17 18 20 22 24 26 28 29 30 31 32 34 35 40 42 43 44 45 46 49 50 51 53 54 55 56 57 58 59 61 62 63 64 68 70 72 74 75 76 77 78 79 81 82 83 84 85 86 87 89 90 92 93 97 98 99 100 101 103 104 107 108 110 111 114 115 118 119 126 128 129 130 131 132 134 135 145 146 147 148 **S** Conemaugh Health System, Johnstown, PA
Primary Contact: Steven E. Tucker, President
COO: Steven E. Tucker, President
CFO: Edward De Pasquale, Chief Financial Officer
CMO: David J. Carlson, D.O., Chief Medical Officer
CIO: Joseph Dado, Chief Information Officer
CHR: Mary York, Vice President Human Resources
Web address: www.conemaugh.org
**Control:** Other not–for–profit (including NFP Corporation) **Service:** General Medical and Surgical

**Staffed Beds:** 555 **Admissions:** 24262 **Census:** 371 **Outpatient Visits:** 486055 **Births:** 1350 **Total Expense ($000):** 368808 **Payroll Expense ($000):** 151423 **Personnel:** 3356

**MEMORIAL MEDICAL CENTER – LEE CAMPUS** See Conemaugh Memorial Medical Center

⊞ **SELECT SPECIALTY HOSPITAL–JOHNSTOWN (392031)**, 320 Main Street, 3rd Floor, Zip 15901–1601; tel. 814/534–7300, (Nonreporting) **A**1 9 10
**S** Select Medical Corporation, Mechanicsburg, PA
Primary Contact: Kelly Blake, Chief Executive Officer
CMO: Gary Davidson, M.D., Medical Director
Web address: www.selectspecialtyhospitals.com/company/locations/johnstown.aspx
**Control:** Corporation, Investor–owned, for–profit **Service:** Long–Term Acute Care hospital

**Staffed Beds:** 39

**KANE—Mckean County**

**KANE COMMUNITY HOSPITAL (390104)**, 4372 Route 6, Zip 16735–3060; tel. 814/837–8585 **A**9 10 20 **F**3 11 12 15 17 18 28 29 30 31 34 35 40 41 45 46 50 53 57 59 62 64 65 70 75 77 79 81 82 85 89 91 93 107 108 110 111 114 117 118 119 128 129 130 131 132 133 135 145 146 147 **P**4 6
Primary Contact: J. Gary Rhodes, FACHE, Chief Executive Officer
CFO: Angela Hadzega, Chief Financial Officer
CMO: Linda Rettger, M.D., President Medical Staff
CIO: Margaret Twidale, Manager Information Systems
CHR: Marsha Keller, Director Human Resources
CNO: Pam Bray, Director of Nursing and Director Inpatient Services
Web address: www.kanehosp.com
**Control:** Other not–for–profit (including NFP Corporation) **Service:** General Medical and Surgical

**Staffed Beds:** 31 **Admissions:** 903 **Census:** 11 **Outpatient Visits:** 34263 **Births:** 0 **Total Expense ($000):** 17587 **Payroll Expense ($000):** 8665 **Personnel:** 181

**KINGSTON—Luzerne County**

⊞ **FIRST HOSPITAL WYOMING VALLEY (394039)**, 562 Wyoming Avenue, Zip 18704–3721; tel. 570/552–3900 **A**1 9 10 **F**42 98 99 103 105 **P**6
**S** Community Health Systems, Inc., Franklin, TN
Primary Contact: Mark Schor, Chief Executive Officer
COO: Richard Sapolis, Director Clinical Operations
CMO: Steven R. Kafrissen, M.D., Medical Director
Web address: www.firsthospital.net/Pages/home.aspx
**Control:** Corporation, Investor–owned, for–profit **Service:** Psychiatric

**Staffed Beds:** 107 **Admissions:** 3600 **Census:** 91 **Outpatient Visits:** 0 **Births:** 0 **Personnel:** 111

**KITTANNING—Armstrong County**

◇ **ACMH HOSPITAL (390163)**, One Nolte Drive, Zip 16201–7111; tel. 724/543–8500, (Nonreporting) **A**2 9 10 19 21
Primary Contact: John I. Lewis, President and Chief Executive Officer
CFO: Patrick Burns, Vice President Finance
CMO: Harold Altman, M.D., Chief Medical Officer
CIO: Dianne Emminger, Vice President Information Services
CHR: Anne Remaley, Vice President Human Resources
Web address: www.acmh.org
**Control:** Other not–for–profit (including NFP Corporation) **Service:** General Medical and Surgical

**Staffed Beds:** 170

**LANCASTER—Lancaster County**

⊞ **LANCASTER GENERAL HEALTH (390100)**, 555 North Duke Street, Zip 17602–2250, Mailing Address: P.O. Box 3555, Zip 17604–3555; tel. 717/544–5511 **A**1 2 3 5 9 10 **F**3 11 12 13 14 15 17 18 19 20 22 24 26 28 29 30 31 32 34 35 36 37 39 40 43 44 45 46 47 49 50 51 54 55 56 57 58 59 60 61 64 65 66 68 70 72 73 74 75 76 77 78 79 80 81 82 85 86 87 89 91 92 93 96 97 98 100 102 107 108 110 112 114 115 117 118 119 120 121 123 124 126 129 130 132 135 141 142 145 146 147 148 **P**6
Primary Contact: Thomas E. Beeman, Ph.D., FACHE, President and Chief Executive Officer
COO: Marion A. McGowan, Executive Vice President and Chief Operating Officer
CFO: Dennis Roemer, Executive Vice President and Chief Financial Officer
CMO: Lee M. Duke, II, M.D., Senior Vice President and Chief Physician Executive
CIO: Gary Davidson, Senior Vice President and Chief Information Officer
CHR: Regina Mingle, Senior Vice President and Chief Leadership Officer
CNO: Judi Brendle, Vice President Nursing
Web address: www.lancastergeneral.org
**Control:** Other not–for–profit (including NFP Corporation) **Service:** General Medical and Surgical

**Staffed Beds:** 613 **Admissions:** 32815 **Census:** 431 **Outpatient Visits:** 1334989 **Births:** 4320 **Total Expense ($000):** 797016 **Payroll Expense ($000):** 301997 **Personnel:** 4637

*Many Facility Codes have changed. Please refer to the AHA Guide Code Chart.*

© 2013 AHA Guide

PA

PA

☐ **LANCASTER REGIONAL MEDICAL CENTER (390061)**, 250 College Avenue, Zip 17603–3363, Mailing Address: P.O. Box 3434, Zip 17604–3434; tel. 717/291–8211 **A1** 9 10 **F3** 15 18 20 22 24 26 28 29 30 31 34 35 37 40 45 47 48 49 50 51 54 59 64 68 70 74 75 77 78 79 81 82 84 85 87 90 91 92 93 96 98 100 101 102 103 107 108 110 111 114 119 121 126 129 130 131 135 146 **S** Health Management Associates, Naples, FL
Primary Contact: Bob Moore, FACHE, Chief Executive Officer
COO: Deborah J. Willwerth, R.N., Chief Operating Officer
CMO: N. A. Mastropietro, M.D., Medical Director
CHR: Brian Hoffman, Director Human Resources
CNO: Tami L. Johnson, MSN, Chief Nursing Officer
Web address: www.lancasterregional.com
**Control:** Corporation, Investor–owned, for–profit **Service:** General Medical and Surgical

**Staffed Beds:** 150 **Admissions:** 4938 **Census:** 77 **Outpatient Visits:** 91104 **Births:** 0 **Total Expense ($000):** 90018 **Payroll Expense ($000):** 31693 **Personnel:** 560

☐ **LANCASTER REHABILITATION HOSPITAL (393054)**, 675 Good Drive, Zip 17601–2426; tel. 717/406–3000, (Nonreporting) **A1** 10 **S** Centerre Healthcare, Brentwood, TN
Primary Contact: Tammy L. Ober, Chief Executive Officer
CFO: David Stark, Chief Financial Officer
CHR: Lisa Andrews, Director Human Resources
Web address: www.lancastergeneral.org
**Control:** Corporation, Investor–owned, for–profit **Service:** Rehabilitation

**Staffed Beds:** 10

### LANGHORNE—Bucks County

☐ **BARIX CLINICS OF PENNSYLVANIA (390302)**, 280 Middletown Boulevard, Zip 19047–1816; tel. 267/572–3100, (Nonreporting) **A1** 10
Primary Contact: Vivian Costa, Director
Web address: www.barixclinics.com
**Control:** Partnership, Investor–owned, for–profit **Service:** Surgical

**Staffed Beds:** 40

**BUCKS COUNTY CAMPUS** See Aria Health, Philadelphia

☒ **ST. MARY MEDICAL CENTER (390258)**, 1201 Langhorne–Newtown Road, Zip 19047–1201; tel. 215/710–2000 **A1** 2 9 10 **F15** 17 18 20 22 24 26 28 29 30 31 32 34 35 40 41 43 53 55 56 57 58 59 64 70 72 74 75 76 77 78 79 81 82 84 86 87 89 90 91 92 93 94 107 108 110 111 114 115 116 117 118 119 120 121 123 124 129 130 132 135 146 147 148 **S** Catholic Health East, Newtown Square, PA
Primary Contact: Gregory T. Wozniak, President and Chief Executive Officer
COO: Jeffrey N. Yarmel, Chief Operating Officer
CFO: Gail Kosyla, Chief Financial Officer and Vice President Finance
CMO: Joseph Conroy, M.D., Vice President Medical Affairs
CIO: Marian Moran, Chief Information Officer
CHR: Mary Sweeney, Vice President Colleague Services and Development
Web address: www.stmaryhealthcare.org
**Control:** Church–operated, Nongovernment, not–for profit **Service:** General Medical and Surgical

**Staffed Beds:** 320 **Admissions:** 23278 **Census:** 275 **Outpatient Visits:** 293934 **Births:** 2033 **Total Expense ($000):** 371107 **Payroll Expense ($000):** 148414 **Personnel:** 2503

### LANSDALE—Montgomery County

☒ **ABINGTON HEALTH LANSDALE HOSPITAL (390012)**, 100 Medical Campus Drive, Zip 19446–1200; tel. 215/368–2100 **A1** 9 10 **F3** 8 11 15 18 28 29 30 31 34 35 39 40 45 49 50 57 59 64 65 69 70 74 77 78 79 81 82 85 90 93 107 111 114 115 119 129 130 132 146 147 148 **P6 S** Abington Health, Abington, PA
Primary Contact: Gary R. Candia, Ph.D., FACHE, Chief Executive Officer
COO: Katie Farrell, Chief Operating Officer
CFO: Raymond Leichner, Director Finance
CMO: Joseph Kraynak, M.D., Chief Medical Officer
CIO: Joan Lauman, Manager Clinical Systems
CHR: John Clarkin, Director Human Resource
CNO: Nancy Hesse, R.N., Chief Nursing Officer
Web address: www.amh.org/lansdale/index.aspx
**Control:** Other not–for–profit (including NFP Corporation) **Service:** General Medical and Surgical

**Staffed Beds:** 135 **Admissions:** 5532 **Census:** 55 **Outpatient Visits:** 102678 **Births:** 0 **Total Expense ($000):** 73807 **Payroll Expense ($000):** 31898 **Personnel:** 484

### LATROBE—Westmoreland County

☐ **EXCELA LATROBE AREA HOSPITAL (390219)**, One Mellon Way, Zip 15650–1096; tel. 724/537–1000 **A1** 2 3 5 9 10 13 **F3** 8 11 12 15 29 30 34 35 38 40 44 45 48 49 50 51 53 56 57 59 60 64 65 68 70 74 75 77 78 79 81 82 85 86 87 92 93 97 98 99 100 101 104 107 108 110 111 114 115 118 119 126 129 130 132 134 135 143 146 147 148 **P6 S** Excela Health, Greensburg, PA
Primary Contact: Michael D. Busch, Executive Vice President and Chief Operating Officer
COO: Michael D. Busch, Executive Vice President and Chief Operating Officer
COO: Samuel Raneri, Senior Vice President Operations and Business Development
CFO: Jeffrey T. Curry, Executive Vice President and Chief Financial Officer
CMO: Jerome Granato, M.D., Senior Vice President and Chief Medical Officer
CIO: David Gawaluck, Vice President and Chief Information Officer
CHR: John Caverno, Senior Vice President and Chief Human Resource Officer
CNO: Helen K. Burns, Ph.D., Senior Vice President and Chief Nursing Officer
Web address: www.excelahealth.org
**Control:** Other not–for–profit (including NFP Corporation) **Service:** General Medical and Surgical

**Staffed Beds:** 121 **Admissions:** 7540 **Census:** 80 **Outpatient Visits:** 251774 **Births:** 0 **Total Expense ($000):** 117681 **Payroll Expense ($000):** 41398 **Personnel:** 890

☒ **SELECT SPECIALTY HOSPITAL–LAUREL HIGHLANDS (392036)**, One Mellon Way, 3rd Floor, Zip 15650–1197; tel. 724/539–3230, (Nonreporting) **A1** 9 10 **S** Select Medical Corporation, Mechanicsburg, PA
Primary Contact: Laurie Kozorosky, Chief Executive Officer
Web address: www.selectspecialtyhospitals.com/company/locations/laurelhighlands.aspx
**Control:** Corporation, Investor–owned, for–profit **Service:** Long–Term Acute Care hospital

**Staffed Beds:** 40

### LEBANON—Lebanon County

☒ △ **LEBANON VETERANS AFFAIRS MEDICAL CENTER**, (Formerly Veterans Affairs Medical Center), 1700 South Lincoln Avenue, Zip 17042–7529; tel. 717/272–6621, (Nonreporting) **A1** 2 3 5 7 **S** Department of Veterans Affairs, Washington, DC
Primary Contact: Robert W. Callahan, Jr., Director
CFO: John Beistline, Assistant Chief Fiscal
CMO: Kanan Chatterjee, M.D., Chief of Staff
CIO: Debra Stickler, Chief Information Officer
CHR: Raymer Kent, Manager Human Resources
Web address: www.lebanon.va.gov
**Control:** Veterans Affairs, Government, federal **Service:** General Medical and Surgical

**Staffed Beds:** 213

☒ **THE GOOD SAMARITAN HOSPITAL (390066)**, Fourth and Walnut Streets, Zip 17042–1281, Mailing Address: P.O. Box 1281, Zip 17042–1281; tel. 717/270–7500, (Total facility includes 19 beds in nursing home–type unit) **A1** 3 5 9 10 **F3** 8 11 13 14 15 17 18 20 22 24 26 28 29 30 31 34 35 40 45 49 50 51 53 57 59 60 62 63 64 68 70 75 76 77 78 79 80 81 82 84 85 87 89 90 92 93 94 96 97 107 108 110 111 114 118 119 128 129 130 132 135 146 148 **P8**
Primary Contact: Robert J. Longo, FACHE, President and Chief Executive Officer
COO: William Hendrick, Senior Vice President and Chief Operating Officer
CFO: Robert J. Richards, Vice President Finance and Chief Financial Officer
CMO: Robert D. Shaver, M.D., Vice President Medical Affairs
CIO: Louis Eaglehouse, Site Director and Chief Information Officer
CHR: Kimberly Feeman, Vice President Human Resources
Web address: www.gshleb.org
**Control:** Other not–for–profit (including NFP Corporation) **Service:** General Medical and Surgical

**Staffed Beds:** 164 **Admissions:** 8139 **Census:** 111 **Outpatient Visits:** 276694 **Births:** 847 **Total Expense ($000):** 166388 **Payroll Expense ($000):** 57705 **Personnel:** 1238

**VETERANS AFFAIRS MEDICAL CENTER** See Lebanon Veterans Affairs Medical Center

---

**Hospital, Medicare Provider Number, Address, Telephone, Approval, Facility, and Physician Codes, Health Care System**

★ American Hospital Association (AHA) membership
☐ The Joint Commission accreditation
◇ DNV Healthcare Inc. accreditation
○ Healthcare Facilities Accreditation Program
△ Commission on Accreditation of Rehabilitation Facilities (CARF) accreditation

**LEHIGHTON—Carbon County**

☒ △ **GNADEN HUETTEN MEMORIAL HOSPITAL (390194)**, 211 North 12th Street, Zip 18235–1138; tel. 610/377–1300, (Total facility includes 91 beds in nursing home–type unit) **A**1 7 9 10 **F**3 11 15 28 29 30 34 35 40 50 57 59 62 64 65 68 70 74 75 77 79 81 82 85 87 90 93 94 97 98 102 107 111 114 116 117 119 124 128 130 132 133 135 146 147 148 **S** Blue Mountain Health System, Lehighton, PA
Primary Contact: Andrew E. Harris, Chief Executive Officer
CMO: Clement McGinley, M.D., Vice President Medical Affairs
CIO: Maria Nunnes, Director Information Systems
CHR: Terry Purcell, Vice President Support Services and Ambulatory Care
Web address: www.ghmh.org/content/GnadenHuettenMemorialHospital.htm
**Control:** Other not–for–profit (including NFP Corporation) **Service:** General Medical and Surgical

**Staffed Beds:** 181 **Admissions:** 3646 **Census:** 136 **Outpatient Visits:** 49957 **Births:** 0 **Total Expense ($000):** 59122 **Payroll Expense ($000):** 26938 **Personnel:** 622

**LEWISBURG—Union County**

◇ **EVANGELICAL COMMUNITY HOSPITAL (390013)**, One Hospital Drive, Zip 17837–9350; tel. 570/522–2000 **A**9 10 19 21 **F**3 11 12 13 15 18 19 20 22 28 29 30 31 34 35 40 45 48 49 50 51 53 54 57 59 63 64 65 68 74 75 76 77 78 79 81 82 85 86 87 89 90 93 94 96 107 108 110 111 114 115 119 129 130 131 132 135 144 146 148 **P**7
Primary Contact: Michael N. O'Keefe, President and Chief Executive Officer
COO: Kendra A. Aucker, Vice President Operations
CFO: Jim Stopper, Interim Chief Financial Officer
CMO: J. Lawrence Ginsburg, M.D., Vice President Medical Affairs
CIO: Dale Moyer, Vice President Information Systems
CHR: Glenn Eisenhauer, Vice President
Web address: www.evanhospital.com
**Control:** Other not–for–profit (including NFP Corporation) **Service:** General Medical and Surgical

**Staffed Beds:** 127 **Admissions:** 5912 **Census:** 53 **Outpatient Visits:** 230879 **Births:** 985 **Total Expense ($000):** 117655 **Payroll Expense ($000):** 50413 **Personnel:** 1162

**U. S. PENITENTIARY INFIRMARY**, Route 7, Zip 17837–9303; tel. 570/523–1251, (Nonreporting)
Primary Contact: Arnold Reyes, Administrator
**Control:** Department of Justice, Government, federal **Service:** Hospital unit of an institution (prison hospital, college infimary, etc.)

**Staffed Beds:** 17

**LEWISTOWN—Mifflin County**

☒ **LEWISTOWN HOSPITAL (390048)**, 400 Highland Avenue, Zip 17044–1198; tel. 717/248–5411 **A**1 2 5 6 9 10 **F**3 11 12 13 15 17 18 19 28 29 30 31 34 35 40 50 51 57 59 64 68 70 71 74 75 76 78 79 81 82 85 86 89 97 98 100 101 102 103 107 108 110 111 114 116 117 118 119 121 124 129 130 132 135 146 147 148 **P**6
Primary Contact: Kay A. Hamilton, R.N., MS, President and Chief Executive Officer
COO: Kirk E. Thomas, Vice President Operations
CFO: Randy E. Tewksbury, Vice President Finance
CMO: Daniel Reifsnyder, M.D., President Medical and Dental Staff
CIO: Ronald M. Cowan, Vice President Information Systems
CHR: N. Sue Reinke, Vice President Human Resources
Web address: www.lewistownhospital.org
**Control:** Other not–for–profit (including NFP Corporation) **Service:** General Medical and Surgical

**Staffed Beds:** 123 **Admissions:** 4884 **Census:** 52 **Outpatient Visits:** 168465 **Births:** 539 **Total Expense ($000):** 88465 **Payroll Expense ($000):** 36118 **Personnel:** 744

**LITITZ—Lancaster County**

☐ **HEART OF LANCASTER REGIONAL MEDICAL CENTER (390068)**, 1500 Highlands Drive, Zip 17543–7694; tel. 717/625–5000 **A**1 9 10 12 13 **F**3 12 13 15 18 20 26 29 30 31 34 35 44 45 47 49 50 53 54 57 59 60 64 68 70 72 74 75 76 77 79 81 82 85 87 89 93 97 100 102 107 108 110 111 115 118 119 126 130 131 146 147 148 **S** Health Management Associates, Naples, FL
Primary Contact: James Machado, Administrator
CIO: David Fisher, Director Information Systems
Web address: www.heartoflancaster.com
**Control:** Corporation, Investor–owned, for–profit **Service:** General Medical and Surgical

**Staffed Beds:** 148 **Admissions:** 3230 **Census:** 32 **Outpatient Visits:** 67945 **Births:** 827 **Total Expense ($000):** 46683 **Payroll Expense ($000):** 19423 **Personnel:** 288

**LOCK HAVEN—Clinton County**

☒ **LOCK HAVEN HOSPITAL (390071)**, 24 Cree Drive, Zip 17745–2699; tel. 570/893–5000, (Nonreporting) **A**1 9 10 **S** Community Health Systems, Inc., Franklin, TN
Primary Contact: John A. Zidansek, Chief Executive Officer
CFO: Brian Balutanski, CPA, Chief Financial Officer
CMO: Rajesh Patel, M.D., Chief of Staff
CIO: Judy Chapman, Interim Director Information Systems
CHR: Lynn Moon, Director Human Resources
Web address: www.lockhavenhospital.com
**Control:** Corporation, Investor–owned, for–profit **Service:** General Medical and Surgical

**Staffed Beds:** 59

**MALVERN—Chester County**

☒ △ **BRYN MAWR REHABILITATION HOSPITAL (393025)**, 414 Paoli Pike, Zip 19355–3300, Mailing Address: P.O. Box 3007, Zip 19355–0707; tel. 484/596–5400 **A**1 7 9 10 **F**3 11 28 29 30 34 35 36 44 50 57 59 65 75 82 86 87 90 91 92 93 94 95 96 119 130 131 132 134 143 146 **P**5 **S** Jefferson Health System, Radnor, PA
Primary Contact: Donna Phillips, President
CFO: Michael J. Buongiorno, Vice President Finance and Treasurer
CMO: John Kraus, M.D., Chief Medical Officer
CIO: Karen A. Thomas, Chief Information Officer
Web address: www.brynmawrrehab.org
**Control:** Other not–for–profit (including NFP Corporation) **Service:** Rehabilitation

**Staffed Beds:** 148 **Admissions:** 2714 **Census:** 107 **Outpatient Visits:** 55672 **Births:** 0 **Total Expense ($000):** 59183 **Payroll Expense ($000):** 31305 **Personnel:** 508

**DEVEREUX CHILDREN'S BEHAVIORAL HEALTH CENTER**, 655 Sugartown Road, Zip 19355–3303, Mailing Address: P.O. Box 275, Zip 19355–0275; tel. 800/345–1292 **F**29 98 99 106 **P**6 **S** Devereux, Villanova, PA
Primary Contact: David E. Woodwar, Executive Director
COO: Howard Jarden, Ph.D., Assistant Executive Director
CFO: David Schultheis, Chief Financial Officer
CMO: Jacquelyn Zavodnick, M.D., Medical Director
CIO: MaryLou Hettinger, Director Quality Management
CHR: Sean Maher, Director Human Resources
Web address: www.devereux.org
**Control:** Other not–for–profit (including NFP Corporation) **Service:** Children's hospital psychiatric

**Staffed Beds:** 33 **Admissions:** 495 **Census:** 24 **Outpatient Visits:** 0 **Births:** 0 **Total Expense ($000):** 5446 **Payroll Expense ($000):** 3135 **Personnel:** 71

☐ **MALVERN INSTITUTE**, 940 King Road, Zip 19355–3166; tel. 610/647–0330, (Nonreporting) **A**1 9
Primary Contact: Richard Mangano, Administrator and Chief Executive Officer
CFO: Janet Corley, Accountant
Web address: www.malverninstitute.com
**Control:** Corporation, Investor–owned, for–profit **Service:** Alcoholism and other chemical dependency

**Staffed Beds:** 40

**MC CONNELLSBURG—Fulton County**

★ **FULTON COUNTY MEDICAL CENTER (391303)**, 214 Peach Orchard Road, Zip 17233–8559; tel. 717/485–3155, (Total facility includes 67 beds in nursing home–type unit) **A**9 10 18 **F**3 11 12 15 28 29 30 34 40 46 50 57 59 62 64 68 70 75 77 81 87 93 107 111 115 118 119 128 129 130 132 133 135 146 148
Primary Contact: Jason F. Hawkins, President and Chief Executive Officer
COO: William Buterbaugh, Director Support Services
CFO: Deborah A. Shughart, Vice President and Chief Financial Officer
CMO: Sharon E. Martin, M.D., President Medical Staff
CIO: Harold M. Gress, Jr., Manager Management Information Systems
CHR: Cheryl Rose, Human Resources Director
Web address: www.fcmcpa.org
**Control:** Other not–for–profit (including NFP Corporation) **Service:** General Medical and Surgical

**Staffed Beds:** 88 **Admissions:** 949 **Census:** 79 **Outpatient Visits:** 52325 **Births:** 0 **Total Expense ($000):** 32161 **Payroll Expense ($000):** 15100 **Personnel:** 262

## MCKEES ROCKS—Allegheny County

**OHIO VALLEY GENERAL HOSPITAL (390157)**, 25 Heckel Road,
Zip 15136–1694; tel. 412/777–6161 **A**1 6 9 10 **F**3 10 15 18 20 29 30 40 45
46 49 51 59 65 70 74 75 77 79 81 82 85 87 90 92 93 98 103 107 108 111
118 119 129 130 143 146 148 **P**6
Primary Contact: David W. Scott, President and Chief Executive Officer
CFO: Tad Tefera, Vice President Finance
CIO: Lynn Aumer, Director Information Management
CHR: Vicki Mell, Vice President Human Resources and Support Services
CNO: Roni Sue Trischler, Director Nursing Services
Web address: www.ohiovalleyhospital.org
**Control:** Other not–for–profit (including NFP Corporation) **Service:** General
Medical and Surgical

**Staffed Beds:** 138 **Admissions:** 3608 **Census:** 60 **Outpatient Visits:** 122911
**Births:** 0 **Total Expense ($000):** 67828 **Payroll Expense ($000):** 25225
**Personnel:** 448

## MCKEESPORT—Allegheny County

**SELECT SPECIALTY HOSPITAL–MCKEESPORT (392045)**, 1500 Fifth Avenue,
6th Floor, Zip 15132–2422; tel. 412/664–2900 **A**1 9 10 **F**1 3 91 92 97 130
148 **S** Select Medical Corporation, Mechanicsburg, PA
Primary Contact: Dan Butts, Chief Executive Officer
Web address: www.selectspecialtyhospitals.com/company/locations/mckeesport.
aspx
**Control:** Corporation, Investor–owned, for–profit **Service:** Long–Term Acute Care
hospital

**Staffed Beds:** 30 **Admissions:** 296 **Census:** 23 **Outpatient Visits:** 0 **Births:**
0 **Total Expense ($000):** 8350 **Payroll Expense ($000):** 4300 **Personnel:**
76

**UPMC MCKEESPORT (390002)**, 1500 Fifth Avenue, Zip 15132–2422;
tel. 412/664–2000, (Total facility includes 24 beds in nursing home–type unit) **A**1
3 5 9 10 12 13 **F**3 8 11 15 17 18 20 28 29 30 31 32 34 35 37 40 49 50 54
56 57 59 60 61 62 64 65 66 68 70 74 75 77 78 79 81 84 85 86 87 90 93
96 97 98 100 101 102 103 107 111 114 115 118 119 121 128 129 130
131 132 134 135 143 146 147 148 **S** UPMC, Pittsburgh, PA
Primary Contact: Cynthia M. Dorundo, President
COO: Merle Taylor, Vice President Operations
CFO: Christopher Stockhausen, Chief Financial Officer
CMO: R. Curtis Waligura, D.O., Vice President Medical Affairs, Chief Medical
Officer
CIO: Joyce Krut, Vice President Information Systems
CHR: Mark P. Frick, Vice President Human Resources
CNO: Cheryl A. Como, R.N., Vice President Patient Services and Chief Nursing
Officer
Web address: www.mckeesport.upmc.com
**Control:** Other not–for–profit (including NFP Corporation) **Service:** General
Medical and Surgical

**Staffed Beds:** 231 **Admissions:** 10163 **Census:** 166 **Outpatient Visits:**
127270 **Births:** 0 **Total Expense ($000):** 127885 **Payroll Expense ($000):**
63160 **Personnel:** 910

## MEADOWBROOK—Montgomery County

**HOLY REDEEMER HOSPITAL AND MEDICAL CENTER (390097)**, 1648
Huntingdon Pike, Zip 19046–8001; tel. 215/947–3000, (Total facility includes 21
beds in nursing home–type unit) **A**1 2 3 5 9 10 21 **F**3 10 11 13 15 17 18 20
22 29 30 31 34 35 39 40 41 44 45 46 49 50 53 54 55 56 57 58 59 61 62
63 64 69 70 72 74 75 76 77 78 79 81 82 84 85 86 87 92 93 97 98 100
103 107 108 109 110 114 115 117 118 119 120 121 123 128 129 130 131
132 134 135 141 146 147 148
Primary Contact: Michael B. Laign, President and Chief Executive Officer
COO: Michele L. Urofsky, Executive Vice President and Chief Administrative Officer
CFO: Russell R. Wagner, Senior Vice President and Chief Financial Officer
CMO: Anthony V. Coletta, M.D., Executive Vice President and Chief Medical Officer
CIO: Donald F. Friel, Executive Vice President
CHR: Joseph J. Cassidy, Vice President
Web address: www.holyredeemer.com
**Control:** Other not–for–profit (including NFP Corporation) **Service:** General
Medical and Surgical

**Staffed Beds:** 250 **Admissions:** 12244 **Census:** 159 **Outpatient Visits:**
313926 **Births:** 2755 **Total Expense ($000):** 183590 **Payroll Expense
($000):** 75590 **Personnel:** 1380

## MEADVILLE—Crawford County

★ ◇ **MEADVILLE MEDICAL CENTER (390113)**, 751 Liberty Street,
Zip 16335–2559; tel. 814/333–5000, (Total facility includes 32 beds in nursing
home–type unit) **A**2 9 10 12 13 21 **F**3 4 5 11 13 15 18 20 22 28 29 30 31 35
36 38 40 45 46 49 53 57 59 63 64 70 75 76 77 78 79 81 82 85 86 87 89
90 91 93 98 99 103 107 110 111 114 115 118 119 120 128 129 130 131
132 144 146 147 148 **P**6 7
Primary Contact: Philip Pandolph, Chief Executive Officer
CMO: Denise Johnson, M.D., Medical Director
CIO: Mark Mahoney, Manager Information Systems
CHR: Greg Maras, Vice President Human Resources
Web address: www.mmchs.org
**Control:** Other not–for–profit (including NFP Corporation) **Service:** General
Medical and Surgical

**Staffed Beds:** 210 **Admissions:** 7195 **Census:** 111 **Outpatient Visits:**
240955 **Births:** 500 **Total Expense ($000):** 146123 **Payroll Expense
($000):** 54637 **Personnel:** 1079

## MECHANICSBURG—Cumberland County

**HEALTHSOUTH REGIONAL SPECIALTY HOSPITAL** See LifeCare Hospitals of
Mechanicsburg

**HEALTHSOUTH REHABILITATION HOSPITAL OF MECHANICSBURG
(393031)**, 175 Lancaster Boulevard, Zip 17055–3562, Mailing Address: P.O.
Box 2016, Zip 17055–0736; tel. 717/691–3700 **A**1 9 10 **F**28 29 34 54 56 74
77 79 82 90 93 95 96 148 **S** HEALTHSOUTH Corporation, Birmingham, AL
Primary Contact: Mark Freeburn, Chief Executive Officer
CMO: Michael Lupinacci, M.D., Medical Director
CHR: David Staskin, Director Human Resources
Web address: www.healthsouthpa.com
**Control:** Corporation, Investor–owned, for–profit **Service:** Rehabilitation

**Staffed Beds:** 75 **Admissions:** 1469 **Census:** 50 **Outpatient Visits:** 16086
**Births:** 0 **Total Expense ($000):** 19126 **Payroll Expense ($000):** 10402
**Personnel:** 201

**LIFECARE HOSPITALS OF MECHANICSBURG (392038)**, 4950 Wilson Lane,
Zip 17055–4442; tel. 717/697–7706 **A**1 9 10 **F**1 3 29 60 77 91 **P**5 **S** LifeCare
Management Services, Plano, TX
Primary Contact: Nicholas Mezza, Chief Executive Officer
CFO: Jay Shoen, Controller
CHR: David Staskin, Director Human Resources
Web address: www.lifecare–hospitals.com/hospital.php?id=20
**Control:** Corporation, Investor–owned, for–profit **Service:** Long–Term Acute Care
hospital

**Staffed Beds:** 68 **Admissions:** 347 **Census:** 25 **Outpatient Visits:** 0 **Births:**
0 **Total Expense ($000):** 14884 **Payroll Expense ($000):** 5944 **Personnel:**
130

## MEDIA—Delaware County

**RIDDLE HOSPITAL (390222)**, 1068 West Baltimore Pike, Zip 19063–5177;
tel. 484/227–9400, (Total facility includes 23 beds in nursing home–type unit) **A**1
2 9 10 **F**3 7 11 13 15 18 20 22 28 29 31 34 35 40 44 45 49 50 53 54 55
56 57 59 64 65 70 72 74 75 76 78 79 80 81 82 85 86 87 92 93 100 102
107 108 110 111 114 115 117 118 119 129 130 131 132 135 141 143 146
147 **P**5 **S** Jefferson Health System, Radnor, PA
Primary Contact: Gary L. Perecko, President
COO: Jeshahnton Essex, Vice President of Administration
CFO: Ed McKillip, Director of Finance
CMO: Joseph D. Hope, D.O., President Medical Staff
CHR: Mary Louise Ciciretti, Director Human Resources
CNO: Ann Marie T. Brooks, R.N., Vice President, Nursing
Web address: www.riddlehospital.org
**Control:** Other not–for–profit (including NFP Corporation) **Service:** General
Medical and Surgical

**Staffed Beds:** 204 **Admissions:** 10746 **Census:** 130 **Outpatient Visits:**
144860 **Births:** 963 **Total Expense ($000):** 163721 **Payroll Expense
($000):** 61985 **Personnel:** 911

**RIDDLE MEMORIAL HOSPITAL** See Riddle Hospital

### MEYERSDALE—Somerset County

★ **CONEMAUGH MEYERSDALE MEDICAL CENTER (391302)**, (Formerly Meyersdale Medical Center), 200 Hospital Drive, Zip 15552–1249; tel. 814/634–5911 **A**9 10 18 **F**15 18 29 34 40 46 50 57 59 64 75 81 107 114 119 127 130 132 133 146 148 **S** Conemaugh Health System, Johnstown, PA
Primary Contact: Mary L. Libengood, President
CFO: Heather Smith, Director Finance
CMO: Nathan Thomas, M.D., President Medical Staff
Web address: www.conemaugh.org
**Control:** Other not–for–profit (including NFP Corporation) **Service:** General Medical and Surgical

**Staffed Beds:** 20 **Admissions:** 375 **Census:** 5 **Outpatient Visits:** 41409 **Births:** 0 **Total Expense ($000):** 11789 **Payroll Expense ($000):** 4315 **Personnel:** 101

### MONONGAHELA—Washington County

⊞ **MONONGAHELA VALLEY HOSPITAL (390147)**, 1163 Country Club Road, Route 88, Zip 15063–1095; tel. 724/258–1000 **A**1 2 9 10 **F**3 8 9 11 12 15 17 18 20 22 28 29 30 31 32 34 35 39 40 45 48 49 50 51 54 56 57 59 61 64 68 70 74 75 77 78 79 80 81 82 85 86 87 89 90 92 93 96 98 100 101 102 103 107 108 110 114 115 118 119 120 121 123 124 129 130 131 132 134 135 146 147 148 **P**8
Primary Contact: Louis J. Panza, Jr., President and Chief Executive Officer
COO: Patrick J. Alberts, Senior Vice President and Chief Operating Officer
CFO: Daniel F. Simmons, Senior Vice President and Treasurer
CMO: R G Krishnan, M.D., President Medical Staff
CIO: Thomas Lamb, Director Information Systems
CHR: David Clark, Senior Vice President Human Resources
CNO: Mary Lou Murt, R.N., Senior Vice President Nursing
Web address: www.monvalleyhospital.com
**Control:** Other not–for–profit (including NFP Corporation) **Service:** General Medical and Surgical

**Staffed Beds:** 210 **Admissions:** 8172 **Census:** 112 **Outpatient Visits:** 289784 **Births:** 0 **Total Expense ($000):** 123901 **Payroll Expense ($000):** 50645 **Personnel:** 1064

### MONROEVILLE—Allegheny County

⊞ **FORBES REGIONAL HOSPITAL (390267)**, 2570 Haymaker Road, Zip 15146–3513; tel. 412/858–2000 **A**1 2 3 5 9 10 **F**3 7 8 11 13 15 17 18 20 22 24 26 29 30 31 34 35 36 37 40 45 46 49 50 51 55 57 58 59 63 64 65 68 69 70 73 74 75 76 78 79 82 84 85 86 87 89 90 91 98 100 101 102 103 107 108 110 111 115 116 117 119 123 124 126 130 132 146 148 **S** West Penn Allegheny Health System, Pittsburgh, PA
Primary Contact: Reese Jackson, President and Chief Executive Officer
COO: Thomas B. Moser, Chief Operating Officer
CIO: Sharon Lewis, Director Information Systems
CHR: Tanya Ulrich, Director Human Resources
Web address: www.wpahs.org
**Control:** Other not–for–profit (including NFP Corporation) **Service:** General Medical and Surgical

**Staffed Beds:** 350 **Admissions:** 15194 **Census:** 216 **Outpatient Visits:** 129046 **Births:** 857 **Total Expense ($000):** 178861 **Payroll Expense ($000):** 64142 **Personnel:** 1238

⊞ **LIFECARE HOSPITALS OF PITTSBURGH – MONROEVILLE (392041)**, 2380 McGinley Road, Zip 15146–4400; tel. 412/856–2400 **A**1 9 10 **F**29 93 107 **P**5 **S** LifeCare Management Services, Plano, TX
Primary Contact: Richard Pletz, Administrator
CMO: Robert Crossey, D.O., Chief Medical Officer
CIO: Justin Armstrong, Chief Information Officer
CHR: Chelsea Webber, Director Human Resources
Web address: www.lifecare–hospitals.com/hospital.php?id=8
**Control:** Corporation, Investor–owned, for–profit **Service:** Long–Term Acute Care hospital

**Staffed Beds:** 87 **Admissions:** 515 **Census:** 36 **Outpatient Visits:** 4671 **Births:** 0 **Total Expense ($000):** 17487 **Payroll Expense ($000):** 7010 **Personnel:** 143

**UPMC EAST (390528)**, 2775 Mosside Boulevard, Zip 15146–2760; tel. 412/357–3000, (Nonreporting) **A**10 **S** UPMC, Pittsburgh, PA
Primary Contact: Mark Sevco, President
Web address: www.upmc.com/locations/hospitals/east/Pages/default.aspx
**Control:** Other not–for–profit (including NFP Corporation) **Service:** General Medical and Surgical

**Staffed Beds:** 156

### MONTROSE—Susquehanna County

**ENDLESS MOUNTAIN HEALTH SYSTEMS (391306)**, 25 Grow Avenue, Zip 18801–1106; tel. 570/278–3801, (Nonreporting) **A**9 10 18
Primary Contact: Rexford Catlin, Chief Executive Officer
CIO: Gary Passmore, Chief Information Officer
CHR: Paula Anderson, Administrative Director Human Resources
Web address: www.endlesscare.org
**Control:** Other not–for–profit (including NFP Corporation) **Service:** General Medical and Surgical

**Staffed Beds:** 21

### MOUNT GRETNA—Lebanon County

⊠ **PHILHAVEN (394020)**, 283 South Butler Road, Zip 17064–6085, Mailing Address: P.O. Box 550, Zip 17064–0550; tel. 717/273–8871 **A**1 9 10 **F**30 98 99 100 101 102 103 104 105 106 130 146 **P**6
Primary Contact: Phil Hess, Chief Executive Officer
COO: Phil Hess, Chief Executive Officer
CFO: Matt Rogers, Chief Financial Officer
CMO: Francis D. Sparrow, M.D., Medical Director
CIO: Lori Nolt, Director Information Technology
CHR: Denis Orthaus, Director Human Resources
Web address: www.philhaven.com
**Control:** Church–operated, Nongovernment, not–for profit **Service:** Psychiatric

**Staffed Beds:** 97 **Admissions:** 2034 **Census:** 80 **Outpatient Visits:** 84032 **Births:** 0 **Total Expense ($000):** 56275 **Payroll Expense ($000):** 37985 **Personnel:** 922

### MOUNT PLEASANT—Westmoreland County

☐ **EXCELA FRICK HOSPITAL (390217)**, 508 South Church Street, Zip 15666–1790; tel. 724/547–1500 **A**1 9 10 **F**3 8 12 15 29 30 34 35 40 45 49 57 59 64 65 68 70 74 75 77 78 79 81 85 86 87 92 93 96 102 107 108 110 111 114 118 119 129 130 132 135 143 146 148 **S** Excela Health, Greensburg, PA
Primary Contact: Ronald H. Ott, President
COO: Michael D. Busch, Executive Vice President and Chief Operating Officer
CFO: Jeffrey T. Curry, Executive Vice President and Chief Financial Officer
CMO: Jerome Granato, M.D., Senior Vice President and Chief Medical Officer
CIO: David Gawaluck, Vice President and Chief Information Officer
CHR: John Caverno, Chief Human Resources Officer
CNO: Helen K. Burns, Ph.D., Senior Vice President and Chief Nursing Officer
Web address: www.excelahealth.org/PatientsandVisitors/HospitalsFacilities/Hospitals/Frick.aspx
**Control:** Other not–for–profit (including NFP Corporation) **Service:** General Medical and Surgical

**Staffed Beds:** 65 **Admissions:** 3221 **Census:** 37 **Outpatient Visits:** 119617 **Births:** 0 **Total Expense ($000):** 49267 **Payroll Expense ($000):** 17535 **Personnel:** 339

### MUNCY—Lycoming County

★ **MUNCY VALLEY HOSPITAL (391301)**, 215 East Water Street, Zip 17756–8700; tel. 570/546–8282, (Total facility includes 136 beds in nursing home–type unit) **A**9 10 18 **F**6 11 34 40 44 50 56 57 59 64 68 81 86 87 93 107 108 119 128 130 133 144 146 **P**7 **S** Susquehanna Health System, Williamsport, PA
Primary Contact: Ronald J. Reynolds, President
CFO: Charles J. Santangelo, CPA, Executive Vice President and Chief Financial Officer
CMO: George A. Manchester, M.D., Executive Vice President and Chief Medical Officer
CIO: Karen M. Armstrong, FACHE, Senior Vice President and Chief Information Officer
CHR: Christine A. Ballard, Vice President Human Resources
CNO: C. Cynthia Whipple, Administrative Director and Director of Nursing
Web address: www.susquehannahealth.org
**Control:** Other not–for–profit (including NFP Corporation) **Service:** General Medical and Surgical

**Staffed Beds:** 156 **Admissions:** 927 **Census:** 140 **Outpatient Visits:** 29479 **Births:** 0 **Total Expense ($000):** 39144 **Payroll Expense ($000):** 12512 **Personnel:** 266

### NANTICOKE—Luzerne County

★ **SPECIAL CARE HOSPITAL (392025)**, 128 West Washington Street, Zip 18634–3113; tel. 570/735–5000, (Nonreporting) **A**9 10 **S** Community Health Systems, Inc., Franklin, TN
Primary Contact: Robert D. Williams, Chief Executive Officer
CFO: Stephen Franko, Chief Financial Officer
Web address: www.specialcarehospital.net
**Control:** Corporation, Investor–owned, for–profit **Service:** Long–Term Acute Care hospital

**Staffed Beds:** 64

*Many Facility Codes have changed. Please refer to the AHA Guide Code Chart.*

**NATRONA HEIGHTS—Allegheny County**

☒ **ALLEGHENY VALLEY HOSPITAL (390032)**, 1301 Carlisle Street,
Zip 15065–1152; tel. 724/224–5100 **A**1 2 6 9 10 **F**3 11 14 15 17 18 24 28
29 30 31 34 35 38 39 40 44 45 47 49 50 51 54 56 57 58 59 64 65 68 70
74 75 77 78 79 80 81 85 86 87 92 93 96 98 100 101 102 103 107 108 111
114 117 118 119 120 121 123 129 130 132 133 135 143 144 146 147 148
**S** West Penn Allegheny Health System, Pittsburgh, PA
Primary Contact: Ned Laubacher, President and Chief Executive Officer
COO: Michael Harlovic, R.N., Senior Vice President, Chief Operating Officer and
Chief Nursing Officer
CFO: James A. Kanuch, Vice President Finance
CMO: Thomas McClure, M.D., Vice President Medical Affairs and Chief Medical
Officer
CIO: Linda Fergus, Manager Information Technology
CHR: Cindy Moser, Director Human Resources
CNO: Michael Harlovic, R.N., Senior Vice President, Chief Operating Officer and
Chief Nursing Officer
Web address: www.wpahs.org
**Control:** Other not–for–profit (including NFP Corporation) **Service:** General
Medical and Surgical

**Staffed Beds:** 228 **Admissions:** 8572 **Census:** 122 **Outpatient Visits:**
221487 **Births:** 2 **Total Expense ($000):** 113878 **Payroll Expense ($000):**
43148 **Personnel:** 907

**NEW CASTLE—Lawrence County**

☐ **JAMESON HOSPITAL (390016)**, 1211 Wilmington Avenue, Zip 16105–2516;
tel. 724/658–9001, (Total facility includes 20 beds in nursing home–type unit) **A**1
6 9 10 19 **F**3 8 11 12 13 15 18 20 22 28 29 30 31 32 34 35 38 40 44 45
49 50 51 54 56 57 59 63 64 65 68 70 75 76 77 79 81 82 85 86 87 90 93
94 96 98 99 101 102 103 105 107 108 110 111 114 115 118 119 128 129
130 132 135 146 147 **P**7
Primary Contact: Douglas Danko, President and Chief Executive Officer
CFO: James Aubel, Chief Financial Officer
CMO: Mohammad Ali, M.D., President Medical Staff
CIO: Frank Divito, Manager Information Systems
CHR: Neil A. Chessin, Vice President
Web address: www.jamesonhealth.org
**Control:** Other not–for–profit (including NFP Corporation) **Service:** General
Medical and Surgical

**Staffed Beds:** 238 **Admissions:** 9013 **Census:** 116 **Outpatient Visits:**
291576 **Births:** 443 **Total Expense ($000):** 104056 **Payroll Expense
($000):** 45247 **Personnel:** 1019

**NORRISTOWN—Montgomery County**

☒ ○ **MERCY SUBURBAN HOSPITAL (390116)**, 2701 DeKalb Pike,
Zip 19401–1820; tel. 610/278–2000 **A**1 2 9 10 11 12 13 **F**3 12 15 17 18 28
29 30 31 34 40 45 46 50 54 56 57 59 64 70 72 73 74 75 77 78 79 81 82
85 87 89 93 98 103 107 108 110 111 114 115 118 119 120 121 130 132
135 146 147 **S** Catholic Health East, Newtown Square, PA
Primary Contact: Kathryn Conallen, Interim Chief Executive Officer
COO: Carol Fluegge, Chief Operating Officer
CFO: Peter B. Kenniff, CPA, Chief Financial Officer
CMO: Wayne Miller, D.O., Associate Chief Medical Officer
CIO: Michael Yulich, Director Information Services
CHR: Gretchen Pendleton, Chief Human Resources Officer
Web address: www.mercyhealth.org
**Control:** Church–operated, Nongovernment, not–for profit **Service:** General
Medical and Surgical

**Staffed Beds:** 126 **Admissions:** 5194 **Census:** 67 **Outpatient Visits:** 46568
**Births:** 0 **Total Expense ($000):** 111679 **Payroll Expense ($000):** 39450
**Personnel:** 647

☐ **MONTGOMERY COUNTY EMERGENCY SERVICE (394033)**, 50 Beech Drive,
Zip 19403–5421; tel. 610/279–6100 **A**1 9 10 **F**4 5 7 29 35 38 50 64 98 99
100 101 102 103 104 130 **P**6
Primary Contact: Rocio Nell, M.D., Chief Executive Officer
COO: William Myers, Chief Operating Officer
CFO: William Myers, Chief Operating Officer
CHR: Karen Mossop, Director Human Resources
Web address: www.mces.org
**Control:** Other not–for–profit (including NFP Corporation) **Service:** Psychiatric

**Staffed Beds:** 81 **Admissions:** 2454 **Census:** 65 **Outpatient Visits:** 3154
**Births:** 0 **Total Expense ($000):** 16942 **Payroll Expense ($000):** 10770
**Personnel:** 216

☐ **NORRISTOWN STATE HOSPITAL (394001)**, 1001 Sterigere Street,
Zip 19401–5300; tel. 610/270–1000, (Nonreporting) **A**1 3 5 10
Primary Contact: Gerald P. Kent, Chief Executive Officer
COO: Gary Raisner, Chief Operating Officer
CMO: Mia Marcovici, M.D., Chief Medical Officer
CHR: Richard Szczurowski, Director Human Resources
**Control:** State–Government, nonfederal **Service:** Psychiatric

**Staffed Beds:** 394

☐ **VALLEY FORGE MEDICAL CENTER AND HOSPITAL (390272)**, 1033 West
Germantown Pike, Zip 19403–3905; tel. 610/539–8500 **A**1 10 **F**3 4 29 61 68
75 82 100 130 132 148 **P**6
Primary Contact: Marian W. Colcher, President and Chief Executive Officer
CFO: Gregg Y. Slocum, Chief Financial Officer
CMO: Robert E. Colcher, M.D., Medical Director
CHR: Frederick D. Jackes, Assistant Administrator and Director Human Resources
Web address: www.vfmc.net
**Control:** Corporation, Investor–owned, for–profit **Service:** Alcoholism and other
chemical dependency

**Staffed Beds:** 86 **Admissions:** 2477 **Census:** 61 **Outpatient Visits:** 0 **Births:**
0 **Total Expense ($000):** 12113 **Payroll Expense ($000):** 7619 **Personnel:**
166

**OAKDALE—Allegheny County**

☒ **KINDRED HOSPITAL–PITTSBURGH (392028)**, 7777 Steubenville Pike,
Zip 15071–3409; tel. 412/494–5500, (Nonreporting) **A**1 9 10 **S** Kindred
Healthcare, Louisville, KY
Primary Contact: John T. Burton, Administrator
CFO: Kevin Varley, Chief Financial Officer
CMO: Ravi Alagar, M.D., Medical Director
CIO: Kurt Segeleon, Director Health Information Management
CHR: Nancy Smocynski, Director Payroll, Personnel and Human Resources
Web address: www.kindredhospitalpittsburgh.com/
**Control:** Corporation, Investor–owned, for–profit **Service:** Long–Term Acute Care
hospital

**Staffed Beds:** 63

**OREFIELD—Lehigh County**

**KIDSPEACE CHILDREN'S HOSPITAL (394047)**, 5300 Kids Peace Drive,
Zip 18069–2044; tel. 610/799–8800, (Nonreporting) **A**9 10 **F**29 57 59 64 98
99 100 101 102 104 105 106
Primary Contact: William R. Isemann, President and Chief Executive Officer
CFO: Tim Richards, Executive Vice President and Chief Financial Officer
Web address: www.kidspeace.org
**Control:** Other not–for–profit (including NFP Corporation) **Service:** Children's
hospital psychiatric

**Staffed Beds:** 96 **Admissions:** 2240 **Census:** 70 **Births:** 0

**PALMERTON—Carbon County**

☐ **PALMERTON HOSPITAL (390019)**, 135 Lafayette Avenue, Zip 18071–1596;
tel. 610/826–3141 **A**1 9 10 **F**2 3 11 12 15 28 29 34 35 40 44 46 47 49 50
56 57 59 64 65 68 70 74 75 77 79 81 85 86 87 92 93 97 98 102 103 107
108 110 119 129 130 132 135 146 **S** Blue Mountain Health System,
Lehighton, PA
Primary Contact: Andrew E. Harris, Chief Executive Officer
CFO: Andrea Andrae, Chief Financial Officer
CMO: Patrick Hanley, D.O., Interim Vice President Medical Affairs
CIO: Steve Kinkaid, Director Information Systems
CHR: Terry Purcell, Vice President Ambulatory Care and Support Services
Web address: www.ghmh.org/content/palmertoncampus.htm
**Control:** Other not–for–profit (including NFP Corporation) **Service:** General
Medical and Surgical

**Staffed Beds:** 60 **Admissions:** 2032 **Census:** 27 **Outpatient Visits:** 48374
**Births:** 0 **Total Expense ($000):** 29929 **Payroll Expense ($000):** 12715
**Personnel:** 333

---

**Hospital, Medicare Provider Number, Address, Telephone, Approval, Facility, and Physician Codes, Health Care System**

★ American Hospital Association (AHA) membership
☐ The Joint Commission accreditation ◇ DNV Healthcare Inc. accreditation
○ Healthcare Facilities Accreditation Program
△ Commission on Accreditation of Rehabilitation Facilities (CARF) accreditation

## PAOLI—Chester County

☒ **PAOLI HOSPITAL (390153)**, 255 West Lancaster Avenue, Zip 19301–1763;
tel. 484/565–1000 **A**1 2 9 10 **F**3 8 11 13 15 18 20 22 24 26 28 29 30 31 34
35 38 40 43 44 45 46 47 48 49 50 51 54 57 59 60 61 62 63 64 65 66 68
70 72 74 75 76 77 78 79 80 81 82 84 85 86 87 92 93 94 96 97 100 101
102 104 105 107 108 109 110 111 112 114 115 116 117 118 119 120 121
122 123 124 126 129 130 131 132 135 136 141 143 144 146 147 148 **P**5
**S** Jefferson Health System, Radnor, PA
Primary Contact: James Paradis, President
CFO: John Doyle, Vice President Finance
CMO: Donald C. Arthur, M.D., Chief Medical Officer
CIO: Karen A. Thomas, Vice President and Chief Information Officer
CHR: Deborah Fedora, Director Human Resources
CNO: Jan Nash, Ph.D., Vice President Patient Services and Chief Nursing Officer
Web address: www.mainlinehealth.org
**Control:** Other not–for–profit (including NFP Corporation) **Service:** General
Medical and Surgical

| Staffed Beds: 226 Admissions: 14930 Census: 147 Outpatient Visits: |
| 297703 Births: 2396 Total Expense ($000): 225802 Payroll Expense |
| ($000): 76666 Personnel: 1028 |

## PECKVILLE—Lackawanna County

★ **MID–VALLEY HOSPITAL (391311)**, 1400 Main Street, Zip 18452–2009;
tel. 570/383–5500, (Nonreporting) **A**9 10 18 **S** Community Health Systems, Inc.,
Franklin, TN
Primary Contact: Ann Marie Stevens, Chief Executive Officer
CFO: James G. Brittain, Chief Financial Officer
CMO: Rajan Mulloth, M.D., President Medical Staff
CIO: Edward Roman, Chief Information Officer and Chief Privacy Officer
CHR: Michele Dean, Human Resources Specialist
Web address: www.mth.org
**Control:** Corporation, Investor–owned, for–profit **Service:** General Medical and
Surgical

| Staffed Beds: 25 |

## PHILADELPHIA—Philadelphia County

**ALBERT EINSTEIN MEDICAL CENTER** See Einstein Medical Center Philadelphia

☒ △ **ARIA HEALTH (390115)**, 10800 Knights Road, Zip 19114–4200;
tel. 215/612–4000, (Includes BUCKS COUNTY CAMPUS, 380 North Oxford Valley
Road, Langhorne, Zip 19047–8399; tel. 215/949–5000; FRANKFORD CAMPUS,
Frankford Avenue and Wakeling Street, Zip 19124; tel. 215/831–2000) **A**1 3 5 6
7 9 10 12 13 **F**3 5 11 12 14 15 17 18 20 22 24 26 28 29 30 31 32 34 35
36 39 40 43 44 45 46 48 49 53 54 57 59 61 62 64 65 66 68 69 70 74 75
77 78 79 80 81 82 85 86 87 92 93 94 96 97 98 100 101 102 103 104 107
108 110 114 115 116 117 118 119 120 121 123 124 126 127 129 130 131
132 135 143 144 145 146 147 148 **P**6
Primary Contact: Kathleen Kinslow, Ed.D., President and Chief Executive Officer
CFO: Robert J. Crossin, Vice President Finance
CMO: Domenick Bucci, M.D., Medical Director
CIO: Joseph Olszewski, Director Information Services
Web address: www.ariahealth.org
**Control:** Other not–for–profit (including NFP Corporation) **Service:** General
Medical and Surgical

| Staffed Beds: 485 Admissions: 24012 Census: 311 Outpatient Visits: |
| 312616 Births: 0 Total Expense ($000): 388792 Payroll Expense ($000): |
| 166869 Personnel: 2722 |

☐ **BELMONT CENTER FOR COMPREHENSIVE TREATMENT (394023)**, 4200
Monument Road, Zip 19131–1625; tel. 215/877–2000 **A**1 3 5 9 10 **F**5 29 34
58 86 87 98 99 103 104 105 130 146 **P**6 **S** Albert Einstein Healthcare
Network, Philadelphia, PA
Primary Contact: Sharon A. Bergen, Chief Operating Officer
COO: Sharon A. Bergen, Chief Operating Officer
CFO: Guy Romaniello, Director Fiscal Services
CMO: Lawrence A. Real, M.D., Medical Director
CHR: Kymm Steliga, Human Resources Specialist
Web address: www.einstein.edu/locations/belmont–behavioral–health/
**Control:** Other not–for–profit (including NFP Corporation) **Service:** Psychiatric

| Staffed Beds: 147 Admissions: 3675 Census: 131 Outpatient Visits: 68031 |
| Births: 0 Total Expense ($000): 40300 Payroll Expense ($000): 24427 |
| Personnel: 407 |

☒ **CHESTNUT HILL HOSPITAL (390026)**, 8835 Germantown Avenue,
Zip 19118–2718; tel. 215/248–8200, (Nonreporting) **A**1 2 3 5 9 10
**S** Community Health Systems, Inc., Franklin, TN
Primary Contact: John D. Cacciamani, M.D., Chief Executive Officer
COO: Andrew Goldfrach, Assistant Chief Executive Officer
CFO: Debbie Konarski, Chief Financial Officer
CMO: John Scanlon, DPM, Chief Medical Officer
CIO: Beth Crossley, Director Information Systems
CHR: James Como, Director Human Resources
Web address: www.chhealthsystem.com
**Control:** Corporation, Investor–owned, for–profit **Service:** General Medical and
Surgical

| Staffed Beds: 135 |

☐ **CHILDREN'S HOSPITAL OF PHILADELPHIA (393303)**, 3401 Civic Center
Boulevard, Zip 19104–4319; tel. 215/590–1000 **A**1 3 5 8 9 10 **F**3 7 8 11 13
17 18 19 20 21 22 23 24 25 26 27 28 29 30 31 32 35 37 38 39 40 41
43 44 45 46 48 50 53 54 55 57 58 59 60 61 62 64 65 66 68 71 72 74 75
76 77 78 79 81 82 83 84 85 86 87 88 89 90 91 92 93 95 96 97 99 100
101 102 104 107 108 111 112 113 114 115 116 117 118 119 126 129 130
131 132 134 136 137 138 139 140 141 142 144 146 148 **P**6
Primary Contact: Steven M. Altschuler, M.D., President and Chief Executive Officer
COO: Madeline Bell, Executive Vice President and Chief Operating Officer
CFO: Thomas Todorow, Chief Financial Officer
CMO: Michael Apkon, M.D., Senior Vice President and Chief Medical Officer
CIO: Bryan Wolf, M.D., Senior Vice President and Chief Information Officer
CHR: Robert Croner, Executive Vice President and Chief Human Resources Officer
Web address: www.chop.edu
**Control:** Other not–for–profit (including NFP Corporation) **Service:** Children's
general

| Staffed Beds: 480 Admissions: 31262 Census: 413 Outpatient Visits: |
| 1177919 Births: 335 Total Expense ($000): 1477427 Payroll Expense |
| ($000): 684033 Personnel: 9401 |

☐ **EASTERN REGIONAL MEDICAL CENTER (390312)**, 1331 East Wyoming
Avenue, Zip 19124–3808; tel. 800/294–8333, (Nonreporting) **A**1 2 10 **S** Cancer
Treatment Centers of America, Schaumburg, IL
Primary Contact: John McNeil, President and Chief Executive Officer
Web address: www.cancercenter.com
**Control:** Corporation, Investor–owned, for–profit **Service:** Cancer

| Staffed Beds: 22 |

☐ △ **EINSTEIN MEDICAL CENTER PHILADELPHIA (390142)**, 5501 Old York
Road, Zip 19141–3098; tel. 215/456–7890, (Includes EINSTEIN MEDICAL
CENTER ELKINS PARK, 60 East Township Line Road, Elkins Park,
Zip 19027–2220; tel. 215/663–6000; Ruth Lefton, Chief Operating Officer),
(Total facility includes 72 beds in nursing home–type unit) **A**1 2 3 5 7 9 10 12 13
**F**3 8 11 12 13 15 17 18 20 22 24 26 29 30 31 32 34 35 36 39 40 41 43 45
46 47 48 49 50 55 56 57 59 60 61 64 65 66 68 70 72 74 75 76 78 79 81
82 84 85 86 87 90 91 92 93 95 96 97 98 100 103 107 108 110 111 113
114 115 118 119 120 121 123 124 126 128 129 130 131 132 134 135 136
138 139 142 145 146 147 148 **P**6 **S** Albert Einstein Healthcare Network,
Philadelphia, PA
Primary Contact: Barry R. Freedman, President and Chief Executive Officer
COO: A. Susan Bernini, Chief Operating Officer
CIO: Kenneth Levitan, Vice President Information Systems
CHR: Lynne R. Kornblatt, Vice President Human Resources
Web address: www.einstein.edu/locations/einstein–medical–center–philadelphia/
**Control:** Other not–for–profit (including NFP Corporation) **Service:** General
Medical and Surgical

| Staffed Beds: 637 Admissions: 27861 Census: 515 Outpatient Visits: |
| 517283 Births: 3069 Total Expense ($000): 707947 Payroll Expense |
| ($000): 310922 Personnel: 5424 |

☐ **FAIRMOUNT BEHAVIORAL HEALTH SYSTEM (394027)**, 561 Fairthorne
Avenue, Zip 19128–2499; tel. 215/487–4000 **A**1 9 10 **F**4 98 99 102 105 130
**P**6 **S** Universal Health Services, Inc., King of Prussia, PA
Primary Contact: Charles McLister, Chief Executive Officer
COO: Jennifer Riedel, Chief Operating Officer
CFO: Anthony Tortella, Chief Financial Officer
CMO: Silvia Gratz, D.O., Chief Medical Officer
CIO: Anthony Tortella, Chief Financial Officer
CHR: Theresa Mahoney, Director Human Resources
Web address: www.fairmountbhs.com
**Control:** Corporation, Investor–owned, for–profit **Service:** Psychiatric

| Staffed Beds: 239 Admissions: 6210 Census: 215 Outpatient Visits: 8424 |
| Births: 0 Total Expense ($000): 38950 Payroll Expense ($000): 23623 |
| Personnel: 406 |

☒ **FOX CHASE CANCER CENTER–AMERICAN ONCOLOGIC HOSPITAL**
**(390196)**, 333 Cottman Avenue, Zip 19111–2434; tel. 215/728–6900 **A**1 2 3
5 8 9 10 **F**3 8 11 15 29 30 31 34 35 36 45 46 47 49 50 55 57 58 59 60 61
62 64 68 70 71 74 75 77 78 79 81 82 84 85 86 87 93 100 104 107 108
109 110 111 114 115 116 117 118 119 120 121 123 124 126 130 132 135
144 145 146 147 148 **P**6 **S** Temple University Health System, Philadelphia, PA
Primary Contact: Verdi DiSesa, Interim President
COO: Judith Lynn Bachman, Chief Operating Officer
CFO: Joseph Hediger, Chief Financial Officer
CMO: J. Robert Beck, M.D., Chief Medical Officer
CIO: Michael Sweeney, Chief Information Officer
Web address: www.fccc.edu
**Control:** Other not–for–profit (including NFP Corporation) **Service:** General
Medical and Surgical

| Staffed Beds: 64 Admissions: 5187 Census: 62 Outpatient Visits: 94302 |
| Births: 0 Total Expense ($000): 221450 Payroll Expense ($000): 55924 |
| Personnel: 1280 |

*Many Facility Codes have changed. Please refer to the AHA Guide Code Chart.*
© 2013 AHA Guide

**PA**

✠ **FRIENDS HOSPITAL (394008)**, 4641 Roosevelt Boulevard, Zip 19124–2343; tel. 215/831–4600, (Nonreporting) **A**1 3 5 9 10 **S** Universal Health Services, Inc., King of Prussia, PA
Primary Contact: Geoff Botak, Chief Executive Officer
COO: Diane Carugati, Chief Operating Officer
CFO: Alfred P. Salvitti, Chief Financial Officer
CMO: Marc Rothman, M.D., Medical Director
CIO: John Healy, Manager Information Technology
CHR: Paul Cavanaugh, Director Human Resources
Web address: www.friendshospital.com
**Control:** Corporation, Investor–owned, for–profit **Service:** Psychiatric

**Staffed Beds:** 219

☐ **GIRARD MEDICAL CENTER (392026)**, Girard Avenue at Eighth Street, Zip 19122; tel. 215/787–2000, (Nonreporting) **A**1 9
Primary Contact: George J. Walmsley, III, CPA, President and Chief Executive Officer
Web address: www.nphs.com
**Control:** Other not–for–profit (including NFP Corporation) **Service:** Long–Term Acute Care hospital

**Staffed Beds:** 163

✠ **GOOD SHEPHERD PENN PARTNERS SPECIALTY HOSPITAL AT RITTENHOUSE (392050)**, 1800 Lombard Street, Zip 19146–1414; tel. 877/969–7342 **A**1 9 10 **F**1 3 28 29 30 34 57 59 64 77 85 86 87 95 96 130 131 132 135 148 **P**5
Primary Contact: Lisa Marsilio, Executive Director
CFO: Ron Petula, Vice President Finance
CMO: Michael Grippi, M.D., Chief Medical Officer
CHR: Jana Romano, Manager Human Resources
CNO: Julie Galen, R.N., Chief Nursing Officer
Web address: www.phillyrehab.com
**Control:** Other not–for–profit (including NFP Corporation) **Service:** Long–Term Acute Care hospital

**Staffed Beds:** 38 **Admissions:** 320 **Census:** 22 **Outpatient Visits:** 101648 **Births:** 0 **Total Expense ($000):** 33818 **Payroll Expense ($000):** 14850 **Personnel:** 270

✠ **HAHNEMANN UNIVERSITY HOSPITAL (390290)**, Broad and Vine Streets, Zip 19102–1192; tel. 215/762–7000 **A**1 2 3 5 8 9 10 **F**3 8 12 13 14 15 17 18 20 22 24 26 28 29 31 34 35 40 43 45 46 48 49 50 51 56 57 58 59 64 65 70 72 74 75 76 77 78 79 80 81 82 85 87 91 92 97 98 100 102 103 105 107 108 110 111 114 115 118 119 120 121 123 124 126 129 130 131 132 136 137 138 139 142 143 144 147 148 **P**6 **S** TENET Healthcare Corporation, Dallas, TX
Primary Contact: Michael P. Halter, Chief Executive Officer
COO: James B. Burke, Chief Operating Officer
CMO: George Amrom, M.D., Vice President Medical Affairs
CIO: Tom Nataloni, Senior Director Information Technology
CHR: Steven Simmons, Chief Human Resources Officer
CNO: Rosemary Dunn, R.N., Chief Nursing Officer
Web address: www.hahnemannhospital.com
**Control:** Corporation, Investor–owned, for–profit **Service:** General Medical and Surgical

**Staffed Beds:** 496 **Admissions:** 18860 **Census:** 281 **Outpatient Visits:** 111137 **Births:** 2194 **Personnel:** 2534

✠ △ **HOSPITAL OF THE UNIVERSITY OF PENNSYLVANIA (390111)**, 3400 Spruce Street, Zip 19104–4206; tel. 215/662–4000 **A**1 2 3 5 7 8 9 10 **F**3 7 8 9 11 12 13 14 15 17 18 20 21 22 23 24 26 28 29 30 31 34 35 36 37 38 39 40 43 44 45 46 47 48 49 50 51 52 54 55 56 57 58 59 60 61 62 63 64 65 66 68 70 72 73 74 75 76 77 78 79 80 81 82 84 85 86 87 90 91 92 94 96 97 100 101 102 104 107 108 109 110 111 114 115 116 117 118 119 120 121 122 123 124 126 129 130 131 132 134 135 136 137 138 139 140 141 142 143 145 146 147 148 **P**6 **S** University of Pennsylvania Health System, Philadelphia, PA
Primary Contact: Garry L. Scheib, Executive Director
COO: Albert P. Black, Jr., Chief Operating Officer
CFO: Keith Kasper, Chief Financial Officer
CMO: Patrick J. Brennan, M.D., Senior Vice President and Chief Medical Officer
CIO: Michael Restuccia, Chief Information Officer
CHR: Patricia J. Wren, Chief Human Resources Officer
CNO: Victoria L. Rich, Ph.D., Chief Nurse Executive
Web address: www.pennhealth.com
**Control:** Other not–for–profit (including NFP Corporation) **Service:** General Medical and Surgical

**Staffed Beds:** 784 **Admissions:** 37925 **Census:** 682 **Outpatient Visits:** 1148726 **Births:** 4128 **Total Expense ($000):** 2049975 **Payroll Expense ($000):** 767601 **Personnel:** 11690

✠ **JEANES HOSPITAL (390080)**, 7600 Central Avenue, Zip 19111–2499; tel. 215/728–2000 **A**1 5 9 10 **F**3 11 12 15 18 20 22 24 26 28 29 30 31 34 35 40 44 45 56 57 59 60 62 65 68 70 74 75 77 78 79 81 82 85 90 91 92 93 107 108 110 111 114 115 116 117 119 120 124 129 130 132 145 146 147 148 **P**6 **S** Temple University Health System, Philadelphia, PA
Primary Contact: Linda J. Grass, President and Chief Executive Officer
COO: Judith Lynn Bachman, Chief Operating Officer
CFO: Gerald P. Oetzel, Chief Financial Officer
CMO: Andrea C. McCoy, M.D., Chief Medical Officer
CIO: Arthur C. Papacostas, M.D., Vice President and Chief Information Officer
CHR: Elisabeth Donahue, Associate Director Human Resources
Web address: www.jeanes.com
**Control:** Other not–for–profit (including NFP Corporation) **Service:** General Medical and Surgical

**Staffed Beds:** 160 **Admissions:** 8547 **Census:** 107 **Outpatient Visits:** 111270 **Births:** 0 **Total Expense ($000):** 167725 **Payroll Expense ($000):** 62486 **Personnel:** 992

☐ **KENSINGTON HOSPITAL (390025)**, 136 West Diamond Street, Zip 19122–1721; tel. 215/426–8100, (Nonreporting) **A**1 9 10
Primary Contact: Eileen Hause, Chief Executive Officer
CFO: Kenneth Biddle, Controller
CMO: Luis F. Vera, M.D., Medical Director
CHR: Maria Dimichele, Administrative Assistant
CNO: Aleyamma John, R.N., Director of Nursing
**Control:** State–Government, nonfederal **Service:** General Medical and Surgical

**Staffed Beds:** 33

✠ **KINDRED HOSPITAL SOUTH PHILADELPHIA (392046)**, 1930 South Broad Street, Zip 19145–2328; tel. 267/570–5200, (Nonreporting) **A**1 9 10 **S** Kindred Healthcare, Louisville, KY
Primary Contact: Garrett Arneson, Chief Executive Officer
COO: Diane K. White, MSN, Chief Clinical Officer
CFO: Kevin Varley, Chief Financial Officer
CMO: James Dovnarsky, M.D., Director Pulmonary Medical
CHR: Jean Meussner, District Director Human Resources
CNO: Diane K. White, MSN, Chief Clinical Officer
Web address: www.khsouthphilly.com
**Control:** Corporation, Investor–owned, for–profit **Service:** Long–Term Acute Care hospital

**Staffed Beds:** 58

✠ **KINDRED HOSPITAL–PHILADELPHIA (392027)**, 6129 Palmetto Street, Zip 19111–5729; tel. 215/722–8555 **A**1 9 10 **F**3 29 84 130 148 **S** Kindred Healthcare, Louisville, KY
Primary Contact: Margaret M. Murphy, Interim Chief Executive Officer
COO: Sandra Collins, Chief Clinical Officer
CFO: Thomas A. McMullen, Chief Financial Officer
Web address: www.kindredphila.com/
**Control:** Corporation, Investor–owned, for–profit **Service:** Long–Term Acute Care hospital

**Staffed Beds:** 52 **Admissions:** 403 **Census:** 32 **Outpatient Visits:** 0 **Births:** 0 **Total Expense ($000):** 16085 **Payroll Expense ($000):** 8328 **Personnel:** 200

**KIRKBRIDE CENTER (394007)**, 111 North 49th Street, Zip 19139–2718; tel. 215/471–2600, (Nonreporting) **A**10
Primary Contact: Scott Weisenberger, Administrator
Web address: www.kirkbridecenter.com
**Control:** Partnership, Investor–owned, for–profit **Service:** Psychiatric

**Staffed Beds:** 205

✠ △ **MAGEE REHABILITATION HOSPITAL (393038)**, 1513 Race Street, Zip 19102–1177; tel. 215/587–3000 **A**1 3 5 7 9 10 **F**2 29 34 35 50 60 64 68 74 75 77 79 82 86 90 91 92 93 94 95 96 130 132 146 148 **P**6 **S** Jefferson Health System, Radnor, PA
Primary Contact: Jack A. Carroll, Ph.D., President and Chief Executive Officer
CFO: Patricia A. Underwood, Chief Financial Officer
CMO: Guy Fried, M.D., Chief Medical Officer
CHR: Scott Agostini, Director
Web address: www.mageerehab.org
**Control:** Other not–for–profit (including NFP Corporation) **Service:** Rehabilitation

**Staffed Beds:** 96 **Admissions:** 1123 **Census:** 77 **Outpatient Visits:** 56844 **Births:** 0 **Total Expense ($000):** 55836 **Payroll Expense ($000):** 31537 **Personnel:** 489

**MERCY PHILADELPHIA HOSPITAL** See Mercy Fitzgerald Hospital, Darby

**METHODIST HOSPITAL** See Thomas Jefferson University Hospital

**Hospital, Medicare Provider Number, Address, Telephone, Approval, Facility, and Physician Codes, Health Care System**

★ American Hospital Association (AHA) membership
☐ The Joint Commission accreditation
◇ DNV Healthcare Inc. accreditation
○ Healthcare Facilities Accreditation Program
△ Commission on Accreditation of Rehabilitation Facilities (CARF) accreditation

✠ △ **NAZARETH HOSPITAL (390204)**, 2601 Holme Avenue, Zip 19152–2096; tel. 215/335–6000, (Total facility includes 28 beds in nursing home–type unit) **A**1 7 9 10 **F**3 12 15 18 20 22 29 30 31 34 35 37 39 40 45 46 49 50 53 56 57 58 59 64 65 70 74 75 77 78 79 80 81 82 84 85 86 87 90 93 97 100 107 108 110 111 114 115 117 118 119 120 121 128 130 131 132 135 146 147 148 **P**7 **S** Catholic Health East, Newtown Square, PA
Primary Contact: Nancy Cherone, Executive Director and Administrator
CFO: David Wajda, Chief Financial Officer
CMO: James Blute, III, M.D., Chief Medical Officer
CIO: Christine Brutschea, Chief Information Technology
CHR: Mary Ellen Cockerham, Vice President Human Resources
Web address: www.nazarethhospital.org
**Control:** Other not–for–profit (including NFP Corporation) **Service:** General Medical and Surgical

**Staffed Beds:** 231 **Admissions:** 10403 **Census:** 146 **Outpatient Visits:** 150857 **Births:** 0 **Total Expense ($000):** 147656 **Payroll Expense ($000):** 61033 **Personnel:** 1088

○ **NORTH PHILADELPHIA HEALTH SYSTEM (390132)**, 1524 West Girard Avenue, Zip 19130–1613; tel. 215/787–9000, (Includes ST. JOSEPH'S HOSPITAL, Girard Avenue at Sixteenth Street, Zip 19130; tel. 215/787–9000; Catherine Kutzler, R.N., Vice President and Administrator), (Nonreporting) **A**9 10 11
Primary Contact: George J. Walmsley, III, CPA, President and Chief Executive Officer
CFO: Ronald Kaplan, Chief Financial Officer
CIO: Tony Iero, Director Management Information Systems
CHR: James Gloner, Senior Vice President
Web address: www.nphs.com
**Control:** Other not–for–profit (including NFP Corporation) **Service:** General Medical and Surgical

**Staffed Beds:** 315

✠ **PENN PRESBYTERIAN MEDICAL CENTER (390223)**, 51 North 39th Street, Zip 19104–2699; tel. 215/662–8000, (Total facility includes 26 beds in nursing home–type unit) **A**1 2 3 5 9 10 **F**3 4 5 7 9 11 12 15 17 18 20 22 24 26 29 30 31 32 34 35 36 37 39 40 44 45 46 49 50 51 54 56 57 58 59 60 61 62 63 64 65 66 68 70 74 75 77 78 79 81 82 84 85 86 87 92 94 97 98 100 101 104 107 108 109 110 111 114 115 118 119 126 128 130 131 132 134 135 141 142 143 146 147 148 **P**6 **S** University of Pennsylvania Health System, Philadelphia, PA
Primary Contact: Michele M. Volpe, Executive Director and Chief Executive Officer
COO: Robert J. Russell, Associate Executive Director Operations
CFO: Anthony Zumpano, Chief Financial Officer
CMO: Kevin Fosnocht, M.D., Chief Medical Officer and Associate Executive Director
CIO: Theresa Hiltunen, Entity Information Officer
CHR: Gail Kimble, Chief Human Resource Officer
CNO: Michael Becker, R.N., Chief Nursing Officer and Associate Executive Director
Web address: www.pennmedicine.org/pmc/
**Control:** Other not–for–profit (including NFP Corporation) **Service:** General Medical and Surgical

**Staffed Beds:** 331 **Admissions:** 16546 **Census:** 225 **Outpatient Visits:** 170732 **Births:** 0 **Total Expense ($000):** 446917 **Payroll Expense ($000):** 159888 **Personnel:** 1778

✠ **PENNSYLVANIA HOSPITAL (390226)**, 800 Spruce Street, Zip 19107–6192; tel. 215/829–3000, (Total facility includes 21 beds in nursing home–type unit) **A**1 2 3 5 9 10 13 **F**3 8 9 11 12 14 15 17 18 20 22 24 26 29 30 31 34 35 36 37 38 40 44 45 46 50 52 53 54 55 56 57 58 59 60 61 63 64 65 68 70 72 74 75 76 77 78 79 80 81 82 84 85 86 87 97 98 99 100 101 102 103 104 107 108 110 111 114 115 116 117 118 119 120 121 123 124 126 128 130 131 132 134 135 136 141 142 146 147 148 **P**6 **S** University of Pennsylvania Health System, Philadelphia, PA
Primary Contact: R. Michael Buckley, M.D., Executive Director
COO: Deborah L. Staples, Chief Operating Officer
CFO: Frank Anastasi, Chief Financial Officer
CMO: Daniel Feinberg, M.D., Chief Medical Officer
CIO: Linda Sinisi, Intity Information Officer
CHR: Denise Mariotti, Chief Human Resources Officer
Web address: www.pahosp.com
**Control:** Other not–for–profit (including NFP Corporation) **Service:** General Medical and Surgical

**Staffed Beds:** 455 **Admissions:** 22950 **Census:** 325 **Outpatient Visits:** 184551 **Births:** 4843 **Total Expense ($000):** 508336 **Payroll Expense ($000):** 171012 **Personnel:** 2413

✠ △ **PHILADEPHIA VETERANS AFFAIRS MEDICAL CENTER**, (Formerly Veterans Affairs Medical Center), 3900 Woodland Avenue, Zip 19104–4594; tel. 215/823–5800, (Nonreporting) **A**1 2 3 5 7 8 **S** Department of Veterans Affairs, Washington, DC
Primary Contact: Joseph M. Dalpiaz, Director
COO: Jeffrey Beiler, Associate Director
CFO: Graciela McDaniel, Chief Financial Officer
CMO: Dave Oslin, M.D., Chief of Staff
CIO: Adrienne Ficchi, Vice President Information Management
CHR: Gerald Morelli, Director Human Resources
Web address: www.philadelphia.va.gov/
**Control:** Veterans Affairs, Government, federal **Service:** General Medical and Surgical

**Staffed Beds:** 280

☐ **ROXBOROUGH MEMORIAL HOSPITAL (390304)**, 5800 Ridge Avenue, Zip 19128–1737; tel. 215/483–9900, (Nonreporting) **A**1 6 9 10 **S** Prime Healthcare Services, Ontario, CA
Primary Contact: Peter J. Adamo, Chief Executive Officer
CFO: Timothy Richards, Chief Financial Officer
Web address: www.roxboroughmemorial.com
**Control:** Corporation, Investor–owned, for–profit **Service:** General Medical and Surgical

**Staffed Beds:** 137

✠ **SHRINERS HOSPITALS FOR CHILDREN–PHILADELPHIA (393309)**, 3551 North Broad Street, Zip 19140–4160; tel. 215/430–4000 **A**1 3 5 10 **F**29 35 57 58 64 65 68 74 75 77 79 81 82 85 88 89 91 92 93 94 96 119 130 132 133 143 146 **S** Shriners Hospitals for Children, Tampa, FL
Primary Contact: Ernest N. Perilli, Administrator
CFO: Mario Salvati, Director Fiscal Services
CMO: Randal Betz, M.D., Chief of Staff
CIO: Mark Morrison, Director Support Services
CHR: Wanda Amaro, Director Human Resources
Web address: www.shrinershospitalsforchildren.org/Hospitals/Locations/Philadelphia.aspx
**Control:** Other not–for–profit (including NFP Corporation) **Service:** Children's orthopedic

**Staffed Beds:** 39 **Admissions:** 832 **Census:** 13 **Outpatient Visits:** 11614 **Births:** 0 **Personnel:** 281

✠ **ST. CHRISTOPHER'S HOSPITAL FOR CHILDREN (393307)**, 3601 A. Street, Zip 19134–1043; tel. 215/427–5000, (Nonreporting) **A**1 3 5 8 9 10 **S** TENET Healthcare Corporation, Dallas, TX
Primary Contact: Carolyn Jackson, Chief Executive Officer
COO: Maria Scenna, Chief Operating Officer
CFO: Gil Cottle, Chief Financial Officer
CMO: Barbara Hoffman, M.D., Chief Medical Officer
CIO: Robert Taylor, Director Information Services
CHR: Stephen W. Krouse, Chief Human Resource Officer
CNO: Heidi Baur, R.N., Chief Nursing Officer
Web address: www.stchristophershospital.com
**Control:** Corporation, Investor–owned, for–profit **Service:** Children's general

**Staffed Beds:** 181

✠ **TEMPLE UNIVERSITY HOSPITAL (390027)**, 3401 North Broad Street, Zip 19140–5103; tel. 215/707–2000, (Includes TEMPLE UNIVERSITY HOSPITAL – EPISCOPAL DIVISION, 100 East Lehigh Avenue, Zip 19125–1098; tel. 215/427–7000) **A**1 2 3 5 6 8 9 10 **F**1 3 4 8 11 12 13 14 15 16 17 18 20 22 24 26 28 29 30 31 34 35 37 38 40 41 42 43 44 45 46 47 48 49 50 53 54 55 56 57 58 59 60 61 64 67 68 70 72 73 74 75 76 77 78 79 80 81 82 83 84 85 86 87 88 89 90 92 93 94 96 97 98 99 100 101 102 103 104 107 108 109 110 111 114 115 118 119 120 121 123 124 126 129 130 131 132 135 136 137 138 139 140 141 142 146 147 148 **S** Temple University Health System, Philadelphia, PA
Primary Contact: John N. Kastanis, FACHE, Chief Executive Officer
CIO: Arthur C. Papacostas, M.D., Vice President and Chief Information Officer
Web address: www.tuh.templehealth.org/content/default.htm
**Control:** Other not–for–profit (including NFP Corporation) **Service:** General Medical and Surgical

**Staffed Beds:** 728 **Admissions:** 37254 **Census:** 539 **Outpatient Visits:** 331779 **Births:** 3363 **Total Expense ($000):** 786020 **Payroll Expense ($000):** 289970 **Personnel:** 4242

*Many Facility Codes have changed. Please refer to the AHA Guide Code Chart.*
© 2013 AHA Guide

☒ △ **THOMAS JEFFERSON UNIVERSITY HOSPITAL (390174)**, 111 South 11th Street, Zip 19107–5084; tel. 215/955–6000, (Includes METHODIST HOSPITAL, 2301 South Broad Street, Zip 19148; tel. 215/952–9000) **A**1 2 3 5 7 8 9 10 **F**3 5 6 7 8 9 11 12 13 14 15 17 18 20 22 24 26 28 29 30 31 34 35 36 37 38 39 40 43 44 45 46 47 48 49 50 51 52 53 54 55 56 57 58 59 61 64 65 66 68 70 72 73 74 75 76 77 78 79 80 81 82 84 85 86 87 89 90 92 93 94 96 97 98 100 101 102 103 104 107 108 109 110 111 114 115 116 117 118 119 120 121 123 124 126 129 130 131 132 135 136 137 138 139 141 142 143 145 146 147 148 **P**6 8
Primary Contact: David P. McQuaid, FACHE, President
CFO: Neil Lubarsky, Senior Vice President Finance
CMO: Geno Merli, M.D., Chief Medical Officer
CIO: Stephen Tranquillo, Chief Information Officer
CHR: Mary Ellen Keeney, Vice President Human Resources
Web address: www.jeffersonhospital.org
**Control:** Other not–for–profit (including NFP Corporation) **Service:** General Medical and Surgical

**Staffed Beds:** 945 **Admissions:** 47872 **Census:** 701 **Outpatient Visits:** 485356 **Births:** 2041 **Total Expense ($000):** 1447976 **Payroll Expense ($000):** 476562 **Personnel:** 7076

**VETERANS AFFAIRS MEDICAL CENTER** See Philadephia Veterans Affairs Medical Center

### PHOENIXVILLE—Chester County

☒ **PHOENIXVILLE HOSPITAL (390127)**, 140 Nutt Road, Zip 19460–3900, Mailing Address: P.O. Box 3001, Zip 19460–0916; tel. 610/983–1000 **A**1 2 9 10 **F**1 3 4 8 11 12 13 15 16 17 18 20 22 24 26 28 29 31 32 35 38 39 40 45 49 51 56 57 59 61 64 67 69 70 72 73 74 75 76 77 78 79 80 81 82 85 86 87 88 90 93 98 100 102 107 108 111 118 119 128 130 132 134 135 146 147 148 **S** Community Health Systems, Inc., Franklin, TN
Primary Contact: Stephen M. Tullman, Chief Executive Officer
COO: Cheryl Kreider, Chief Operating Officer
CFO: Jacqueline Nalls, Chief Financial Officer
CMO: David Stepansky, M.D., Chief Medical Officer
CIO: Terry Murphy, Director Information Services
CHR: Denise Chiolo, Chief Human Resources Officer
Web address: www.phoenixvillehospital.com
**Control:** Corporation, Investor–owned, for–profit **Service:** General Medical and Surgical

**Staffed Beds:** 118 **Admissions:** 7343 **Census:** 79 **Outpatient Visits:** 117805 **Births:** 900 **Total Expense ($000):** 149735 **Payroll Expense ($000):** 44572 **Personnel:** 723

### PITTSBURGH—Allegheny County

☒ **ALLEGHENY GENERAL HOSPITAL (390050)**, 320 East North Avenue, Zip 15212–4756; tel. 412/359–3131 **A**1 2 3 5 8 9 10 **F**3 7 8 9 11 12 15 17 18 19 20 22 24 26 28 29 30 31 32 34 35 36 38 39 40 41 43 44 45 46 47 48 49 50 51 53 54 55 57 58 59 61 62 63 64 65 66 68 70 74 75 77 78 79 80 81 82 84 85 86 87 88 89 92 93 94 95 96 97 99 100 101 102 103 104 105 107 108 109 110 111 114 115 116 117 118 119 120 121 123 124 126 129 130 131 132 134 135 138 139 140 142 143 145 146 147 148 **P**6 **S** West Penn Allegheny Health System, Pittsburgh, PA
Primary Contact: Judith F. Zedreck, R.N., Interim Chief Executive Officer
COO: Judith F. Zedreck, R.N., Interim Chief Executive Officer
CMO: Tony Farah, M.D., President Medical Staff
CIO: John Foley, Chief Information Officer
CHR: John Lasky, Vice President Human Resources
Web address: www.wpahs.org/locations/allegheny–general–hospital
**Control:** Other not–for–profit (including NFP Corporation) **Service:** General Medical and Surgical

**Staffed Beds:** 381 **Admissions:** 23835 **Census:** 358 **Outpatient Visits:** 417374 **Births:** 0 **Total Expense ($000):** 588676 **Payroll Expense ($000):** 204970 **Personnel:** 3568

☐ **CHILDREN'S HOSPITAL OF PITTSBURGH OF UPMC (393302)**, 4401 Penn Avenue, Zip 15224–1334; tel. 412/692–5325 **A**1 3 5 9 10 **F**3 8 12 17 19 21 22 23 24 25 27 28 29 30 31 32 34 35 39 40 41 43 45 46 49 50 53 54 55 57 59 60 64 66 68 71 72 74 75 77 78 79 81 82 84 86 87 88 89 93 97 100 107 108 109 111 115 116 117 118 119 120 121 123 124 126 129 130 131 132 134 135 136 137 138 139 140 141 142 143 144 146 **S** UPMC, Pittsburgh, PA
Primary Contact: Christopher Gessner, President
COO: Christopher Gessner, President
Web address: www.chp.edu
**Control:** Other not–for–profit (including NFP Corporation) **Service:** Children's general

**Staffed Beds:** 296 **Admissions:** 13804 **Census:** 206 **Outpatient Visits:** 690310 **Births:** 0 **Total Expense ($000):** 459737 **Payroll Expense ($000):** 137239 **Personnel:** 2783

**EYE AND EAR HOSPITAL OF PITTSBURGH** See UPMC Presbyterian Shadyside

☒ **HEALTHSOUTH HARMARVILLE REHABILITATION HOSPITAL (393027)**, Guys Run Road, Zip 15238–0460, Mailing Address: P.O. Box 11460, Zip 15238–0460; tel. 412/828–1300, (Total facility includes 40 beds in nursing home–type unit) **A**1 10 **F**29 30 60 62 64 77 90 93 94 95 96 100 128 132 146 148 **S** HEALTHSOUTH Corporation, Birmingham, AL
Primary Contact: Kenneth J. Anthony, Chief Executive Officer
CFO: Beth Miller, Controller
CMO: Thomas Franz, M.D., Medical Director
CHR: Ethel Black, Director Human Resources
Web address: www.healthsouthharmarville.com
**Control:** Corporation, Investor–owned, for–profit **Service:** Rehabilitation

**Staffed Beds:** 202 **Admissions:** 2493 **Census:** 120 **Outpatient Visits:** 19548 **Births:** 0 **Total Expense ($000):** 31981 **Payroll Expense ($000):** 18678 **Personnel:** 415

☒ **KINDRED HOSPITAL PITTSBURGH–NORTH SHORE (392049)**, 1004 Arch Street, Zip 15212–5235; tel. 412/323–5800, (Nonreporting) **A**1 9 10 **S** Kindred Healthcare, Louisville, KY
Primary Contact: David Johnson, Chief Executive Officer
Web address: www.kindrednorthshore.com/
**Control:** Corporation, Investor–owned, for–profit **Service:** Long–Term Acute Care hospital

**Staffed Beds:** 111

☒ **LIFECARE HOSPITALS OF PITTSBURGH (392024)**, 225 Penn Avenue, Zip 15221–2148; tel. 412/247–2424, (Includes LIFECARE HOSPITALS OF PITTSBURGH – SUBURBAN CAMPUS, 100 South Jackson Avenue, 4th Floor, Zip 15202–3428; Richard Pletz, Administrator), (Total facility includes 40 beds in nursing home–type unit) **A**1 9 10 **F**1 3 29 30 85 87 103 107 114 128 130 146 148 **P**5 **S** LifeCare Management Services, Plano, TX
Primary Contact: Richard Pletz, Administrator
CFO: Nikki Aykul, Manager Business Office
CMO: Steven Sotos, M.D., President Medical Staff
CIO: George Fitzgerald, Regional Director Information Systems
CHR: Robin Arslanpay, Director Human Resources
Web address: www.lifecare–hospitals.com
**Control:** Corporation, Investor–owned, for–profit **Service:** Long–Term Acute Care hospital

**Staffed Beds:** 236 **Admissions:** 2049 **Census:** 137 **Outpatient Visits:** 0 **Births:** 0 **Total Expense ($000):** 53291 **Payroll Expense ($000):** 25014 **Personnel:** 493

☒ **MAGEE–WOMENS HOSPITAL OF UPMC (390114)**, 300 Halket Street, Zip 15213–3108; tel. 412/641–1000, (Total facility includes 20 beds in nursing home–type unit) **A**1 2 3 5 8 9 10 **F**3 11 12 13 15 29 30 31 34 35 40 43 44 45 46 49 52 54 55 56 57 58 59 64 65 66 68 70 72 74 75 76 78 79 80 81 82 84 85 86 87 97 107 108 110 111 115 119 120 121 123 126 130 131 132 134 135 146 147 148 **S** UPMC, Pittsburgh, PA
Primary Contact: Leslie C. Davis, President
CFO: Eileen Simmons, Chief Financial Officer
CMO: Dennis English, M.D., Vice President Medical Affairs
CIO: Lou Baverso, Chief Information Officer
CHR: Kelli Reale, Vice President Human Resources
CNO: Maribeth McLaughlin, R.N., Vice President Patient Care Services
Web address: www.magee.edu
**Control:** Other not–for–profit (including NFP Corporation) **Service:** Obstetrics and gynecology

**Staffed Beds:** 360 **Admissions:** 20510 **Census:** 227 **Outpatient Visits:** 367551 **Births:** 10495 **Total Expense ($000):** 403658 **Payroll Expense ($000):** 107298 **Personnel:** 2152

☒ **SELECT SPECIALTY HOSPITAL–PITTSBURGH/UPMC (392044)**, 200 Lothrop Street, E824, Zip 15213–2536; tel. 412/586–9800 **A**1 9 10 **F**1 3 29 36 65 85 86 87 91 148 **S** Select Medical Corporation, Mechanicsburg, PA
Primary Contact: John St. Leger, Chief Executive Officer
CMO: Michael Donahue, M.D., Medical Director
CHR: Prudence Sloan, Coordinator Human Resources
CNO: Eli Babich, Chief Nursing Officer
Web address: www.selectspecialtyhospitals.com/company/locations/pittsburghupmc.aspx
**Control:** Corporation, Investor–owned, for–profit **Service:** Long–Term Acute Care hospital

**Staffed Beds:** 32 **Admissions:** 276 **Census:** 24 **Outpatient Visits:** 0 **Births:** 0 **Personnel:** 96

---

**Hospital, Medicare Provider Number, Address, Telephone, Approval, Facility, and Physician Codes, Health Care System**

★ American Hospital Association (AHA) membership
☐ The Joint Commission accreditation
◇ DNV Healthcare Inc. accreditation
○ Healthcare Facilities Accreditation Program
△ Commission on Accreditation of Rehabilitation Facilities (CARF) accreditation

**PA**

☐ **SOUTHWOOD PSYCHIATRIC HOSPITAL**, 2575 Boyce Plaza Road, Zip 15241–3925; tel. 412/257–2290, (Nonreporting) **A**1 9 **S** Acadia Healthcare Company, Inc., Franklin, TN
Primary Contact: Stephen J. Quigley, Chief Executive Officer
CFO: Frank Urban, Chief Financial Officer
CMO: Allan W. Clark, M.D., Medical Director
CHR: Erin J. Frohnhofer, Director Human Resources
Web address: www.southwoodhospital.com
**Control:** Corporation, Investor–owned, for–profit **Service:** Children's hospital psychiatric

**Staffed Beds:** 112

✠ **ST. CLAIR MEMORIAL HOSPITAL (390228)**, 1000 Bower Hill Road, Zip 15243–1873; tel. 412/942–4000 **A**1 2 9 10 **F**3 8 12 13 15 17 18 20 22 24 26 28 29 30 31 32 35 38 40 41 44 49 51 53 54 56 60 64 67 70 73 74 75 76 77 78 79 81 82 84 85 86 87 90 92 93 96 98 100 102 105 107 108 110 111 114 115 118 119 126 129 130 131 132 134 135 143 146 147 148
Primary Contact: James M. Collins, President and Chief Executive Officer
COO: Michael J. Flanagan, Senior Vice President and Chief Operating Officer
CFO: Richard C. Chesnos, Senior Vice President Finance and Chief Financial Officer
CMO: G. Alan Yeasted, M.D., Senior Vice President and Chief Medical Officer
CIO: Richard Schaeffer, Vice President Information Systems and Chief Information Officer
CHR: Andrea Kalina, Vice President Human Resources and Organizational Advancement
Web address: www.stclair.org
**Control:** Other not–for–profit (including NFP Corporation) **Service:** General Medical and Surgical

**Staffed Beds:** 315 **Admissions:** 16199 **Census:** 197 **Outpatient Visits:** 342414 **Births:** 1317 **Total Expense ($000):** 219382 **Payroll Expense ($000):** 87923 **Personnel:** 1833

★ **THE CHILDREN'S HOME OF PITTSBURGH (393304)**, 5324 Penn Avenue, Zip 15224–1733; tel. 412/441–4884, (Nonreporting) **A**9 10
Primary Contact: Pamela R. Schanwald, Chief Executive Officer
COO: Kimberly Reblock, M.D., Chief Operating Officer
CFO: Kimberly A. Phillips, Chief Financial Officer
CMO: Frederick C. Sherman, M.D., Chief Medical Officer
Web address: www.childrenshomepgh.org
**Control:** Other not–for–profit (including NFP Corporation) **Service:** Children's general

**Staffed Beds:** 15

★ △ **THE CHILDREN'S INSTITUTE OF PITTSBURGH (393308)**, 1405 Shady Avenue, Zip 15217–1350; tel. 412/420–2400 **A**7 10 **F**3 29 30 34 54 58 59 64 74 75 79 82 85 86 87 90 91 93 96 97 98 99 100 104 107 130 131 132 146 148 **P**6
Primary Contact: David K. Miles, President and Chief Executive Officer
COO: Jane T. Keim, Vice President Operations
CFO: Jody Mulvihill, Vice President Finance
CMO: Maryanne Henderson, D.O., Medical Director
CIO: Sharon Dorogy, Director Health Information Management
CHR: Bob Brown, Director Human Resources
Web address: www.amazingkids.org
**Control:** Other not–for–profit (including NFP Corporation) **Service:** Children's rehabilitation

**Staffed Beds:** 72 **Admissions:** 403 **Census:** 33 **Outpatient Visits:** 50674 **Births:** 0 **Total Expense ($000):** 32321 **Payroll Expense ($000):** 14526 **Personnel:** 309

☐ △ **UPMC MERCY (390028)**, 1400 Locust Street, Zip 15219–5166; tel. 412/232–8111 **A**1 3 5 6 7 9 10 12 13 **F**3 4 8 13 15 16 17 18 19 20 22 24 26 28 29 30 31 32 34 35 36 39 40 43 44 45 54 57 58 59 60 61 62 64 65 66 68 70 72 74 75 76 77 78 79 81 82 84 85 86 87 90 91 92 93 94 95 96 97 98 101 102 107 108 111 114 115 116 118 119 126 129 130 141 142 146 147 148 **P**6 **S** UPMC, Pittsburgh, PA
Primary Contact: Will L. Cook, President
CFO: Jack Gaenzle, Senior Vice President Finance and Administration
CIO: Stephen D. Adams, Executive Vice President and Chief Information Officer
CHR: Kristen Bell, Director Human Resources
Web address: www.upmc.com/HospitalsFacilities/HFHome/Hospitals/Mercy/
**Control:** Other not–for–profit (including NFP Corporation) **Service:** General Medical and Surgical

**Staffed Beds:** 488 **Admissions:** 21886 **Census:** 355 **Outpatient Visits:** 208994 **Births:** 1480 **Total Expense ($000):** 398202 **Payroll Expense ($000):** 124209 **Personnel:** 2333

**UPMC MONTEFIORE** See UPMC Presbyterian Shadyside

☐ **UPMC PASSAVANT (390107)**, 9100 Babcock Boulevard, Zip 15237–5815; tel. 412/367–6700, (Includes UPMC PASSAVANT CRANBERRY, One St. Francis Way, Cranberry, Zip 16066; tel. 724/772–5300; Teresa G. Petrick, President), (Total facility includes 12 beds in nursing home–type unit) **A**1 2 9 10 **F**3 8 11 15 17 18 20 22 24 26 28 29 30 31 34 35 40 46 47 48 49 51 56 57 59 64 65 68 70 74 75 77 78 79 80 81 82 84 85 86 87 90 92 107 108 110 111 114 115 116 117 118 119 120 121 126 128 129 130 132 135 143 145 146 147 148 **S** UPMC, Pittsburgh, PA
Primary Contact: David T. Martin, President
COO: Marcie S. Caplan, Vice President
CFO: Dennis Tomassetti, Chief Financial Officer
CMO: James W. Boyle, M.D., Chief Medical Officer
CIO: Karen Borosky, Vice President and Chief Information Officer
CHR: Gary Mignosna, Vice President Human Resources
Web address: www.upmc.edu/passavant
**Control:** Other not–for–profit (including NFP Corporation) **Service:** General Medical and Surgical

**Staffed Beds:** 424 **Admissions:** 18070 **Census:** 264 **Outpatient Visits:** 296188 **Births:** 0 **Total Expense ($000):** 348648 **Payroll Expense ($000):** 96337 **Personnel:** 1640

☐ **UPMC PRESBYTERIAN SHADYSIDE (390164)**, 200 Lothrop Street, Zip 15213–2536; tel. 412/647–2345, (Includes EYE AND EAR HOSPITAL OF PITTSBURGH, 200 Lothrop Street, Zip 15213–2592; tel. 412/647–2345; UPMC MONTEFIORE, 3459 Fifth Avenue, Zip 15213; tel. 412/647–2345; John Innocenti, Sr., President and Chief Executive Officer; UPMC PRESBYTERIAN HOSPITAL, 200 Lothrop Street, Zip 15213; tel. 412/647–2345; UPMC SHADYSIDE, 5230 Centre Avenue, Zip 15232–1381; tel. 412/623–2121; WESTERN PSYCHIATRIC INSTITUTE AND CLINIC, 3811 O'Hara Street, Zip 15213–2593; tel. 412/624–2100), (Total facility includes 30 beds in nursing home–type unit) **A**1 2 5 6 8 9 10 12 13 **F**2 3 5 6 7 8 9 10 11 12 14 15 18 19 20 22 24 25 26 28 29 30 31 32 33 34 35 36 37 38 39 40 42 43 44 45 46 47 48 49 50 51 52 53 54 55 56 57 58 59 60 61 62 63 64 65 66 68 69 70 71 74 75 77 78 79 80 81 82 83 84 85 86 87 90 91 92 93 94 97 98 99 100 101 102 103 104 105 106 107 108 109 110 111 112 113 114 115 116 117 118 119 120 121 123 124 126 128 129 130 131 132 134 135 136 137 138 139 140 141 142 143 144 145 146 147 148 **P**6 **S** UPMC, Pittsburgh, PA
Primary Contact: John Innocenti, Sr., President and Chief Executive Officer
CMO: Margaret Reidy, M.D., Vice President Medical Affairs
CIO: James Venturella, Chief Information Officer
CHR: Louis Goodman, Vice President Human Resources
Web address: www.upmc.edu
**Control:** Other not–for–profit (including NFP Corporation) **Service:** General Medical and Surgical

**Staffed Beds:** 1528 **Admissions:** 65956 **Census:** 1275 **Outpatient Visits:** 1282310 **Births:** 0 **Total Expense ($000):** 2120298 **Payroll Expense ($000):** 528849 **Personnel:** 15230

☐ **UPMC ST. MARGARET (390102)**, 815 Freeport Road, Zip 15215–3301; tel. 412/784–4000 **A**1 2 3 5 6 9 10 13 **F**3 6 8 9 11 12 15 18 20 29 30 31 34 35 37 40 44 46 49 50 51 54 56 57 58 59 60 61 63 64 65 68 70 74 75 77 78 79 81 82 84 85 86 87 90 94 97 102 103 104 107 108 111 114 115 118 119 121 130 131 132 134 135 146 **S** UPMC, Pittsburgh, PA
Primary Contact: Teresa G. Petrick, President
COO: Douglass Harrison, Vice President Operations
CFO: Thomas M. Newman, Vice President Finance
CMO: John Lagnese, M.D., Vice President Medical Affairs
CIO: Charles M. Rudek, Chief Information Officer
CHR: Tracey Stange Kolo, Vice President Human Resources
CNO: Mary C. Barkhymer, R.N., Vice President Patient Care Services and Chief Nursing Officer
Web address: www.stmargaret.upmc.com
**Control:** Other not–for–profit (including NFP Corporation) **Service:** General Medical and Surgical

**Staffed Beds:** 249 **Admissions:** 14365 **Census:** 197 **Outpatient Visits:** 214451 **Births:** 0 **Total Expense ($000):** 245956 **Payroll Expense ($000):** 77147 **Personnel:** 1333

✠ △ **VETERANS AFFAIRS PITTSBURGH HEALTHCARE SYSTEM**, University Drive, Zip 15240–1001; tel. 412/688–6000, (Includes VETERANS AFFAIRS MEDICAL CENTER, 7180 Highland Drive, Zip 15206–1297; tel. 412/365–4900; VETERANS AFFAIRS MEDICAL CENTER, University Drive C, tel. 412/688–6000), (Nonreporting) **A**1 2 7 8 9 **S** Department of Veterans Affairs, Washington, DC
Primary Contact: Terry Gerigk Wolf, FACHE, Director and Chief Executive Officer
CFO: James Baker, Vice President Business Support Services
CMO: Rajiv Jain, M.D., Chief of Staff
CIO: Dewaine Beard, Chief Information Officer
CHR: Marie Colosimo, Human Resources Officer
Web address: www.pittsburgh.va.gov/
**Control:** Veterans Affairs, Government, federal **Service:** Psychiatric

**Staffed Beds:** 447

*Many Facility Codes have changed. Please refer to the AHA Guide Code Chart.*
© 2013 AHA Guide

☒ **WESTERN PENNSYLVANIA HOSPITAL (390090)**, 4800 Friendship Avenue, Zip 15224–1722; tel. 412/578–5000 **A**1 2 3 5 6 8 9 10 12 13 **F**1 3 4 11 12 13 15 16 17 18 29 30 31 34 35 37 39 40 45 46 49 50 51 54 55 56 57 58 59 63 64 65 67 68 70 72 73 74 75 76 77 78 79 80 81 82 84 85 86 87 88 89 90 91 92 93 94 96 97 98 99 100 101 102 107 108 109 110 111 114 115 116 117 118 119 120 121 123 124 126 128 129 130 131 132 135 136 141 145 146 147 148 **P**6 **S** West Penn Allegheny Health System, Pittsburgh, PA
Primary Contact: Duke Rupert, President and Chief Executive Officer
CFO: James A. Kanuch, Vice President Finance
CMO: Robert Keenan, M.D., Chief Quality Officer
CIO: Joyce Polovich, Manager Information Systems
CHR: Sally Carozza, Director Human Resources
CNO: Paula A. Lacher, MSN, Chief Nursing Officer
Web address: www.wpahs.org
**Control:** Other not–for–profit (including NFP Corporation) **Service:** General Medical and Surgical

**Staffed Beds:** 279 **Admissions:** 6809 **Census:** 113 **Outpatient Visits:** 81436 **Births:** 3027 **Total Expense ($000):** 213395 **Payroll Expense ($000):** 68416 **Personnel:** 1326

**WESTERN PSYCHIATRIC INSTITUTE AND CLINIC** See UPMC Presbyterian Shadyside

### PLEASANT GAP—Centre County

☒ **HEALTHSOUTH NITTANY VALLEY REHABILITATION HOSPITAL (393039)**, 550 West College Avenue, Zip 16823–7401; tel. 814/359–3421, (Nonreporting) **A**1 9 10 **S** HEALTHSOUTH Corporation, Birmingham, AL
Primary Contact: Susan Hartman, Chief Executive Officer
CFO: Kathy Mincin, Controller
CMO: Richard Allatt, M.D., Medical Director
CHR: Jody Hay, Director Human Resources
CNO: Susan Evans, Chief Nursing Officer
Web address: www.nittanyvalleyrehab.com
**Control:** Corporation, Investor–owned, for–profit **Service:** Rehabilitation

**Staffed Beds:** 73

### POTTSTOWN—Montgomery County

☒ **POTTSTOWN MEMORIAL MEDICAL CENTER (390123)**, 1600 East High Street, Zip 19464–5093; tel. 610/327–7000 **A**1 2 9 10 **F**3 13 15 18 29 30 31 34 35 38 40 44 45 49 50 51 54 55 56 57 59 60 64 68 70 74 75 76 77 78 79 81 82 85 89 91 92 93 97 98 100 107 111 116 117 119 124 125 128 131 132 135 146 147 148 **P**6 **S** Community Health Systems, Inc., Franklin, TN
Primary Contact: Sharif Omar, Chief Executive Officer
COO: Sharif Omar, Chief Operating Officer
CFO: Debbie Konarski, Interim Chief Financial Officer
CMO: Richard F. Saylor, M.D., Chief Medical Officer
CIO: Ron Peterson, Chief Information Officer
CHR: Ruta Ore, Director Human Resources
Web address: www.pottstownmemorial.com
**Control:** Corporation, Investor–owned, for–profit **Service:** General Medical and Surgical

**Staffed Beds:** 232 **Admissions:** 9788 **Census:** 124 **Outpatient Visits:** 126497 **Births:** 600 **Total Expense ($000):** 149956 **Payroll Expense ($000):** 57839 **Personnel:** 948

### POTTSVILLE—Schuylkill County

☒ △ **SCHUYLKILL MEDICAL CENTER – EAST NORWEGIAN STREET (390031)**, 700 East Norwegian Street, Zip 17901–2710; tel. 570/621–4000 **A**1 7 9 10 **F**3 5 11 15 18 29 30 31 34 39 40 45 49 56 57 59 64 70 74 75 77 78 79 81 85 86 90 93 98 100 103 107 108 109 110 115 118 119 130 132 135 146 147 148 **P**6 **S** Schuylkill Health System, Pottsville, PA
Primary Contact: John E. Simodejka, President and Chief Executive Officer
CFO: Diane Boris, Vice President and Chief Financial Officer
CMO: Thomas A. Curry, M.D., Vice President Medical Affairs for Clinical Effectiveness and Documentation
CIO: Karen Rarick, Director Information Technology
CHR: Martin Treasure, Director Human Resources
CNO: Darnell F. Furer, MS, Vice President of Patient Care Services
Web address: www.schuylkillhealth.com
**Control:** Other not–for–profit (including NFP Corporation) **Service:** General Medical and Surgical

**Staffed Beds:** 126 **Admissions:** 4744 **Census:** 77 **Outpatient Visits:** 111608 **Births:** 0 **Total Expense ($000):** 61695 **Payroll Expense ($000):** 26572 **Personnel:** 547

☒ **SCHUYLKILL MEDICAL CENTER – SOUTH JACKSON STREET (390030)**, 420 South Jackson Street, Zip 17901–3625; tel. 570/621–5000, (Total facility includes 11 beds in nursing home–type unit) **A**1 6 9 10 19 **F**3 13 15 18 19 28 29 30 32 34 35 38 40 45 49 51 54 55 57 59 62 64 70 74 75 76 77 78 79 81 82 85 86 89 92 93 96 98 99 100 101 102 104 105 107 108 110 111 115 118 119 124 128 129 130 131 132 146 147 **P**6 **S** Schuylkill Health System, Pottsville, PA
Primary Contact: John E. Simodejka, President and Chief Executive Officer
CFO: Diane Boris, Chief Financial Officer
CIO: Karen Rarick, Director Information Systems
CHR: Martin Treasure, Director Human Resources
Web address: www.schuylkillhealth.com
**Control:** Other not–for–profit (including NFP Corporation) **Service:** General Medical and Surgical

**Staffed Beds:** 191 **Admissions:** 6758 **Census:** 101 **Outpatient Visits:** 111647 **Births:** 1047 **Total Expense ($000):** 93497 **Payroll Expense ($000):** 39846 **Personnel:** 773

### PUNXSUTAWNEY—Jefferson County

☒ **PUNXSUTAWNEY AREA HOSPITAL (390199)**, 81 Hillcrest Drive, Zip 15767–2616; tel. 814/938–1800 **A**9 10 **F**3 13 15 18 29 30 34 35 40 45 50 51 57 59 60 61 62 68 70 74 75 76 77 79 81 82 85 86 93 107 108 110 111 114 116 117 118 119 130 132 133 135 146 147 148 **P**6
Primary Contact: Daniel D. Blough, Jr., Chief Executive Officer
CFO: Jack Sisk, Chief Financial Officer
CMO: Dajani Zuhd, M.D., President Medical Staff
CIO: Chuck States, Director Information Systems
CHR: Barbara Kostok, Manager Human Resources
Web address: www.pah.org
**Control:** Other not–for–profit (including NFP Corporation) **Service:** General Medical and Surgical

**Staffed Beds:** 44 **Admissions:** 1758 **Census:** 18 **Outpatient Visits:** 102918 **Total Expense ($000):** 31519 **Payroll Expense ($000):** 16535 **Personnel:** 334

### QUAKERTOWN—Bucks County

☐ **ST. LUKE'S HOSPITAL – QUAKERTOWN CAMPUS (390035)**, 1021 Park Avenue, Zip 18951–1573; tel. 215/538–4500 **A**1 2 9 10 **F**3 11 15 18 28 29 30 31 34 35 38 40 44 45 49 50 51 53 54 56 57 59 60 64 65 66 68 69 70 74 75 77 78 79 81 82 85 86 87 93 98 99 100 102 103 107 108 109 110 111 115 118 119 129 130 132 135 146 147 148 **P**6 8 **S** St. Luke's University Health Network, Bethlehem, PA
Primary Contact: John B. Sylvia, President
CFO: Theresa Corrado, Director Finance
CMO: Thomas Filipowicz, M.D., Medical Director
CIO: Chad Brisendine, Chief Information Officer
CHR: Shelley Maley, Director Human Resources
Web address: www.slhhn.org
**Control:** Other not–for–profit (including NFP Corporation) **Service:** General Medical and Surgical

**Staffed Beds:** 57 **Admissions:** 3226 **Census:** 40 **Outpatient Visits:** 108421 **Births:** 0 **Total Expense ($000):** 50553 **Payroll Expense ($000):** 21596 **Personnel:** 288

### READING—Berks County

☐ **HAVEN BEHAVIORAL HEALTH OF EASTERN PENNSYLVANIA (394052)**, 145 North 6th Street, 3rd Floor, Zip 19601–3096; tel. 610/406–4340, (Nonreporting) **A**1 9 10 **S** Haven Behavioral Healthcare, Nashville, TN
Primary Contact: John Baker, Interim Chief Executive Officer
CMO: Mark Putnam, M.D., Medical Director
CHR: Kathy Copenhaver, Director Human Resources
Web address: www.havenbehavioralhospital.com
**Control:** Corporation, Investor–owned, for–profit **Service:** Psychiatric

**Staffed Beds:** 48

☒ **HEALTHSOUTH READING REHABILITATION HOSPITAL (393026)**, 1623 Morgantown Road, Zip 19607–9455; tel. 610/796–6000, (Nonreporting) **A**1 9 10 **S** HEALTHSOUTH Corporation, Birmingham, AL
Primary Contact: Richard Kruczek, Chief Executive Officer
CFO: Jason Pulaski, Controller
CMO: Patti Brown, M.D., Medical Director
CHR: Edward Werner, Director Human Resources
Web address: www.healthsouthreading.com
**Control:** Corporation, Investor–owned, for–profit **Service:** Rehabilitation

**Staffed Beds:** 60

**PA**

---

**Hospital, Medicare Provider Number, Address, Telephone, Approval, Facility, and Physician Codes, Health Care System**

★ American Hospital Association (AHA) membership
☐ The Joint Commission accreditation
◇ DNV Healthcare Inc. accreditation
○ Healthcare Facilities Accreditation Program
△ Commission on Accreditation of Rehabilitation Facilities (CARF) accreditation

✠ **ST. JOSEPH MEDICAL CENTER (390096)**, 2500 Bernville Road, Zip 19605–9453, Mailing Address: P.O. Box 316, Zip 19603–0316; tel. 610/378–2000, (Includes ST. JOSEPH MEDICAL CENTER–DOWNTOWN READING, 145 North Sixth Street, Zip 19601, Mailing Address: P.O. Box 316, Zip 19603–0316; tel. 610/376–2100) **A**1 2 9 10 12 13 **F**3 15 18 20 22 24 26 28 29 30 31 32 34 35 39 40 44 45 49 50 51 53 54 57 58 59 64 66 68 70 72 74 75 76 77 78 79 81 82 84 85 87 89 93 97 107 108 111 113 114 115 116 117 118 119 120 121 130 131 132 135 144 146 147 148 **P**6 **S** Catholic Health Initiatives, Englewood, CO
Primary Contact: John R. Morahan, FACHE, President and Chief Executive Officer
CFO: Lim David, Vice President Finance and Chief Financial Officer
CMO: Samuel Alfano, D.O., Vice President Medical Affairs
CHR: Scott Mengle, Vice President Human Resources
Web address: www.thefutureofhealthcare.org
**Control:** Church–operated, Nongovernment, not-for profit **Service:** General Medical and Surgical

Staffed Beds: 180 Admissions: 8122 Census: 103 Outpatient Visits: 326550 Births: 718 Total Expense ($000): 201652 Payroll Expense ($000): 64422 Personnel: 1332

### RENOVO—Clinton County

**BUCKTAIL MEDICAL CENTER (391304)**, 1001 Pine Street, Zip 17764–1620; tel. 570/923–1000, (Total facility includes 43 beds in nursing home–type unit) **A**9 10 18 **F**3 7 11 34 40 42 54 59 65 66 69 97 127 128 130 133 143 146
Primary Contact: Thomas Foster, Chief Executive Officer
CFO: Wendy Janerella, Controller
CMO: Alvin Berlot, M.D., Medical Director
Web address: www.bucktailmed.org
**Control:** Other not–for–profit (including NFP Corporation) **Service:** General Medical and Surgical

Staffed Beds: 64 Admissions: 122 Census: 33 Outpatient Visits: 10358 Births: 0 Total Expense ($000): 5871 Payroll Expense ($000): 2754 Personnel: 83

### RIDLEY PARK—Delaware County

**TAYLOR HOSPITAL** See Crozer–Chester Medical Center, Upland

### ROARING SPRING—Blair County

✠ **NASON HOSPITAL (390062)**, 105 Nason Drive, Zip 16673–1202; tel. 814/224–2141 **A**1 9 10 **F**3 11 13 15 29 30 34 35 40 45 51 57 59 62 63 64 68 70 74 75 76 77 79 81 82 85 92 107 108 111 114 119 130 132 135 146 147 148 **P**3
Primary Contact: Garrett W. Hoover, FACHE, President and Chief Executive Officer
CFO: Raymond C. Askey, CPA, Vice President Fiscal Services
CIO: Brian Lilly, Director Information Systems
CHR: Lorie Smith, Director Human Resources
Web address: www.nasonhospital.org
**Control:** Other not–for–profit (including NFP Corporation) **Service:** General Medical and Surgical

Staffed Beds: 45 Admissions: 1932 Census: 19 Outpatient Visits: 106462 Births: 505 Total Expense ($000): 29546 Payroll Expense ($000): 12915 Personnel: 276

### ROYERSFORD—Montgomery County

**PHYSICIANS CARE SURGICAL HOSPITAL (390324)**, 454 Enterprise Drive, Zip 19468–1200; tel. 610/495–3330, (Nonreporting) **A**9 10
Primary Contact: David Orskey, Administrator
Web address: www.phycarehospital.com
**Control:** Partnership, Investor–owned, for–profit **Service:** Surgical

Staffed Beds: 12

### SAINT MARYS—Elk County

★ **ELK REGIONAL HEALTH CENTER (390154)**, 763 Johnsonburg Road, Zip 15857–3498; tel. 814/788–8000, (Total facility includes 138 beds in nursing home–type unit) **A**9 10 20 **F**3 6 11 13 15 20 28 29 30 34 35 40 44 45 56 57 59 70 76 77 79 81 82 85 86 87 89 93 98 100 103 107 110 111 114 119 128 129 130 131 133 135 144 146 147 148
Primary Contact: Gregory P. Bauer, President and Chief Executive Officer
CFO: Laurie MacDonald, Vice President Finance
CMO: David Johe, M.D., President Medical Staff
CIO: Mary Ann Schwabenbauer, Director Information Technology
CHR: Seanna D'Amore, Director Human Resources
Web address: www.elkregional.org
**Control:** Other not–for–profit (including NFP Corporation) **Service:** General Medical and Surgical

Staffed Beds: 218 Admissions: 3347 Census: 161 Outpatient Visits: 175401 Births: 212 Total Expense ($000): 76277 Payroll Expense ($000): 35283 Personnel: 892

### SAYRE—Bradford County

✠ **ROBERT PACKER HOSPITAL (390079)**, 1 Guthrie Square, Zip 18840–1698; tel. 570/888–6666 **A**1 2 3 5 9 10 12 13 19 **F**3 11 12 13 15 17 18 20 22 24 26 28 29 30 31 34 37 38 40 43 45 47 49 50 51 57 58 59 60 61 64 70 73 74 75 76 78 79 81 82 85 86 87 89 92 93 98 99 100 101 102 103 105 107 108 110 111 114 115 116 117 118 119 120 121 123 126 129 130 132 141 142 145 146 148 **S** Guthrie Healthcare System, Sayre, PA
Primary Contact: Marie T. Droege, President
CFO: Minh Dang, Vice President Finance
CMO: Brian Fillipo, M.D., Chief Medical Officer
CIO: Dale Swingle, Vice President Information Services
CHR: Frank Pinkosky, Senior Vice President
CNO: Bonnie J. Onofre, MS, Vice President and Chief Nursing Officer
Web address: www.guthrie.org
**Control:** Other not–for–profit (including NFP Corporation) **Service:** General Medical and Surgical

Staffed Beds: 238 Admissions: 14063 Census: 184 Outpatient Visits: 155846 Births: 755 Total Expense ($000): 248330 Payroll Expense ($000): 70065 Personnel: 1287

### SCRANTON—Lackawanna County

✠ △ **ALLIED SERVICES REHABILITATION HOSPITAL (393030)**, 475 Morgan Highway, Zip 18508–2605, Mailing Address: P.O. Box 1103, Zip 18501–1103; tel. 570/348–1300 **A**1 7 10 **F**11 29 34 53 56 59 64 74 75 77 78 79 86 87 90 91 93 94 96 130 143 146
Primary Contact: Jackie Fletcher–Brozena, Senior Vice President and Chief Operating Officer
CFO: Michael Avvisato, Senior Vice President and Chief Financial Officer
CMO: Gregory Basting, M.D., Vice President Medical Affairs
CIO: John Regula, Chief Information Officer
CHR: Judy P. Oprisko, Chief Human Resources Officer
Web address: www.allied–services.org
**Control:** Other not–for–profit (including NFP Corporation) **Service:** Rehabilitation

Staffed Beds: 117 Admissions: 2125 Census: 58 Outpatient Visits: 75223 Births: 0 Total Expense ($000): 33579 Payroll Expense ($000): 16169 Personnel: 375

**COMMUNITY MEDICAL CENTER HEALTHCARE SYSTEM** See Geisinger–Community Medical Center

✠ **GEISINGER–COMMUNITY MEDICAL CENTER (390001)**, 1800 Mulberry Street, Zip 18510–2369; tel. 570/969–8000 **A**1 3 5 9 10 **F**3 11 15 17 18 20 22 24 26 28 29 30 31 34 35 38 40 42 43 44 45 46 49 50 56 57 58 59 64 68 70 74 75 77 78 79 81 82 85 86 87 89 92 93 97 98 102 103 107 108 109 110 111 114 115 118 119 124 130 132 135 146 147 148 **S** Geisinger Health System, Danville, PA
Primary Contact: Robert P. Steigmeyer, President and Chief Executive Officer
COO: Barbara Bossi, Senior Vice President Operations and Patient Care Services
CFO: Edward Chabalowski, Chief Financial Officer
CHR: Lois Wolfe, Director Human Resources
Web address: www.cmccare.org/
**Control:** Other not–for–profit (including NFP Corporation) **Service:** General Medical and Surgical

Staffed Beds: 248 Admissions: 11390 Census: 148 Outpatient Visits: 94667 Births: 0 Total Expense ($000): 161294 Payroll Expense ($000): 63907 Personnel: 1096

**MERCY HOSPITAL OF SCRANTON** See Regional Hospital of Scranton

✠ △ **MOSES TAYLOR HOSPITAL (390119)**, 700 Quincy Avenue, Zip 18510–1724; tel. 570/340–2100 **A**1 3 5 7 9 10 **F**3 29 30 31 34 40 49 51 56 57 59 60 61 62 64 65 66 68 70 72 74 75 76 77 78 79 81 85 86 87 89 93 98 103 107 108 110 111 114 119 129 130 132 135 146 147 148 **P**6 **S** Community Health Systems, Inc., Franklin, TN
Primary Contact: Justin Davis, Chief Executive Officer
CFO: Thomas Kelly, Jr., Chief Financial Officer
CIO: Edward Roman, Chief Information Officer and Chief Privacy Officer
CHR: Paul Gionfriddo, MS, Vice President Human Resources
Web address: www.mth.org
**Control:** Corporation, Investor–owned, for–profit **Service:** General Medical and Surgical

Staffed Beds: 217 Admissions: 10504 Census: 128 Outpatient Visits: 163344 Births: 2498 Total Expense ($000): 128245 Payroll Expense ($000): 45832 Personnel: 907

✠ △ **REGIONAL HOSPITAL OF SCRANTON (390237)**, 746 Jefferson Avenue, Zip 18510–1624; tel. 570/348–7100, (Nonreporting) **A**1 2 3 5 7 9 10 12 **S** Community Health Systems, Inc., Franklin, TN
Primary Contact: Brooks Turkel, Chief Executive Officer
CFO: Stephen Franko, Vice President Finance and Chief Financial Officer
CMO: Anthony Yanni, M.D., Vice President Medical Affairs
CIO: Jorge Coronel, Chief Information Officer
CHR: Elizabeth Leo, Vice President Human Resources
Web address: www.regionalhospitalofscranton.net
**Control:** Corporation, Investor–owned, for–profit **Service:** General Medical and Surgical

Staffed Beds: 224

*Many Facility Codes have changed. Please refer to the AHA Guide Code Chart.*
© 2013 AHA Guide

PA

PA

## SELLERSVILLE—Bucks County

⊠ **GRAND VIEW HOSPITAL (390057)**, 700 Lawn Avenue, Zip 18960–1548,
Mailing Address: P.O. Box 902, Zip 18960–0902; tel. 215/453–4000 **A**1 2 9 10
**F**3 7 11 13 15 18 19 28 29 31 32 34 40 44 45 49 50 54 56 57 58 59
61 62 63 64 65 68 70 71 72 74 76 77 78 79 81 82 84 85 86 87 89 90 93
96 97 107 108 110 111 114 115 117 118 119 121 123 130 131 132 135
145 146 147 148 **P**6
Primary Contact: Jean Keeler, President and Chief Executive Officer
CFO: Michael Keen, Senior Vice President and Chief Financial Officer
CMO: Jane Ferry, M.D., Vice President Medical Affairs
CIO: Jane Doll Loveless, Vice President Information Services
CNO: Kathleen Burkey, R.N., Vice President of Nursing
Web address: www.gvh.org
**Control:** Other not–for–profit (including NFP Corporation) **Service:** General
Medical and Surgical

**Staffed Beds: 202 Admissions: 9108 Census: 102 Outpatient Visits:**
305487 **Births:** 1587 **Total Expense ($000):** 169049 **Payroll Expense**
**($000):** 85035 **Personnel:** 1427

## SENECA—Venango County

☐ **UPMC NORTHWEST (390091)**, 100 Fairfield Drive, Zip 16346–2130;
tel. 814/676–7600, (Total facility includes 16 beds in nursing home–type unit) **A**1
2 9 10 19 **F**3 6 8 10 11 13 15 18 28 29 30 31 34 35 40 45 47 50 56 57 59
60 62 63 64 68 70 74 75 76 78 79 81 82 83 84 85 86 87 89 90 93 96 97
98 100 101 102 103 107 108 110 111 114 115 118 119 121 128 130 131
132 135 144 145 146 147 148 **S** UPMC, Pittsburgh, PA
Primary Contact: Jason Roeback, President
COO: David J. Patton, Vice President Operations
CFO: W. Roger McCauley, Senior Vice President Administration and Chief Financial
Officer
CMO: John Shonnard, M.D., Medical Director
CHR: Courtney Cox, Vice President Human Resources
Web address: www.upmc.com/locations/hospitals/northwest/Pages/default.aspx
**Control:** Other not–for–profit (including NFP Corporation) **Service:** General
Medical and Surgical

**Staffed Beds: 180 Admissions: 7217 Census: 99 Outpatient Visits:** 172995
**Births:** 496 **Total Expense ($000):** 88785 **Payroll Expense ($000):** 29289
**Personnel:** 624

## SEWICKLEY—Allegheny County

⊠ **HEALTHSOUTH REHABILITATION HOSPITAL (393045)**, 303 Camp Meeting
Road, Zip 15143–8322; tel. 412/741–9500 **A**1 10 **F**29 34 56 57 59 60 64 65
74 75 87 90 91 92 93 95 96 100 132 146 148 **S** HEALTHSOUTH Corporation,
Birmingham, AL
Primary Contact: Leah Laffey, MSN, R.N., Chief Executive Officer
CFO: Daniel A. Vrana, Area Controller
CMO: Shelana Gibbs–McElvy, M.D., Medical Director
CIO: Annette Gratzmiller, Director Information Services
CHR: Melissa Coleman, Director Human Resources
CNO: Al Dunn, Chief Nursing Officer
Web address: www.healthsouthsewickley.com
**Control:** Corporation, Investor–owned, for–profit **Service:** Rehabilitation

**Staffed Beds: 44 Admissions: 805 Census: 33 Outpatient Visits:** 2381
**Births:** 0 **Total Expense ($000):** 9549 **Payroll Expense ($000):** 5231
**Personnel:** 74

☐ **SEWICKLEY VALLEY HOSPITAL, (A DIVISION OF VALLEY MEDICAL**
**FACILITIES) (390037)**, 720 Blackburn Road, Zip 15143–1459;
tel. 412/741–6600, (Nonreporting) **A**1 6 9 10 **S** Heritage Valley Health System,
Beaver, PA
Primary Contact: Norman F. Mitry, President and Chief Executive Officer
COO: Rosemary Nolan, R.N., Chief Operating Officer and Chief Nursing Officer
CFO: Bryan J. Randall, Vice President Finance and Chief Financial Officer
CMO: Oliver Hayes, D.O., Chief Medical Officer
CIO: David Carleton, Chief Information Officer
CHR: Bruce Edwards, Vice President Human Resources
CNO: Linda Homyk, Chief Nursing Officer
Web address: www.heritagevalley.org
**Control:** Other not–for–profit (including NFP Corporation) **Service:** General
Medical and Surgical

**Staffed Beds: 171**

## SHARON—Mercer County

⊠ **SHARON REGIONAL HEALTH SYSTEM (390211)**, 740 East State Street,
Zip 16146–3395; tel. 724/983–3911, (Total facility includes 38 beds in nursing
home–type unit) **A**1 6 9 10 **F**3 5 11 12 13 15 17 18 19 20 22 24 26 28 29 30
31 34 35 38 39 40 44 45 47 48 49 50 51 54 56 57 58 59 60 62 63 64 65
70 73 74 75 76 77 78 79 80 81 82 84 85 86 87 89 90 92 93 96 98 99 100
101 102 103 104 105 107 108 110 111 114 115 118 119 120 121 123 127
128 129 130 131 132 134 135 146 147 148 **P**6 8
Primary Contact: John R. Janoso, President and Chief Executive Officer
CFO: Jeffrey Chrobak, Vice President Finance and Chief Financial Officer
CHR: John Davidson, Vice President Human Resources
Web address: www.sharonregional.com
**Control:** Other not–for–profit (including NFP Corporation) **Service:** General
Medical and Surgical

**Staffed Beds: 256 Admissions: 10255 Census: 146 Outpatient Visits:**
345180 **Births:** 269 **Total Expense ($000):** 187187 **Payroll Expense**
**($000):** 62731 **Personnel:** 1390

## SHICKSHINNY—Luzerne County

**CLEAR BROOK LODGE**, 890 Bethel Road, Zip 18655;
tel. 570/864–3116, (Nonreporting)
Primary Contact: Nicholas Colangelo, Chief Executive Officer
Web address: www.clearbrookinc.com
**Control:** Other not–for–profit (including NFP Corporation) **Service:** Alcoholism and
other chemical dependency

**Staffed Beds: 65**

## SHIPPENSBURG—Franklin County

☐ **ROXBURY TREATMENT CENTER (394050)**, 601 Roxbury Road,
Zip 17257–9302; tel. 800/648–4673, (Nonreporting) **A**1 9 10 **S** Universal Health
Services, Inc., King of Prussia, PA
Primary Contact: Shauna Radzieski, Chief Executive Officer
Web address: www.roxburyhospital.com
**Control:** Corporation, Investor–owned, for–profit **Service:** Psychiatric

**Staffed Beds: 94**

## SOMERSET—Somerset County

★ **SOMERSET HOSPITAL (390039)**, 225 South Center Avenue, Zip 15501–2088;
tel. 814/443–5000 **A**9 10 20 **F**3 8 11 13 15 17 18 20 22 26 28 29 30 32 34
35 40 45 49 50 53 57 59 62 63 64 68 74 76 77 79 80 81 82 85 86 87 89
93 97 98 99 100 103 104 107 108 111 115 119 129 130 131 132 133 135
141 146 147 148
Primary Contact: Ronald Park, Chief Executive Officer
COO: Craig M. Saylor, Vice President and Chief Operating Officer
CIO: Jonathan Bauer, Director Information Services
CHR: Sharon Glover, Director Human Resources
CNO: Bob King, Vice President and Chief Nursing Officer
Web address: www.somersethospital.com
**Control:** Other not–for–profit (including NFP Corporation) **Service:** General
Medical and Surgical

**Staffed Beds: 111 Admissions: 3700 Census: 45 Outpatient Visits:** 148711
**Births:** 345 **Total Expense ($000):** 63742 **Payroll Expense ($000):** 26004
**Personnel:** 623

## SPRINGFIELD—Delaware County

**SPRINGFIELD HOSPITAL** See Crozer–Chester Medical Center, Upland

## STATE COLLEGE—Centre County

⊠ **MOUNT NITTANY MEDICAL CENTER (390268)**, 1800 Park Avenue,
Zip 16803–6797; tel. 814/231–7000 **A**1 2 3 5 9 10 **F**3 7 13 15 17 20 22 28
29 30 31 35 40 51 57 59 64 68 70 73 74 75 76 77 78 79 80 81 82 85 87
89 93 98 100 101 102 107 108 111 114 115 118 119 121 126 129 130
132 135 143 144 146 148
Primary Contact: Steven E. Brown, FACHE, President and Chief Executive Officer
COO: Debra W. Linnes, R.N., Chief Operating Officer
CFO: Richard Wisniewski, Senior Vice President Finance and Chief Financial Officer
CMO: Jeffrey Ratner, M.D., Senior Vice President Medical Affairs
CHR: Jerry Dittmann, Vice President Human Resources
CNO: Janet Schachtner, R.N., Senior Vice President, Patient Care Services
Web address: www.mountnittany.org
**Control:** Other not–for–profit (including NFP Corporation) **Service:** General
Medical and Surgical

**Staffed Beds: 212 Admissions: 11882 Census: 132 Outpatient Visits:**
221781 **Births:** 1340 **Total Expense ($000):** 281448 **Payroll Expense**
**($000):** 115697 **Personnel:** 1309

---

**Hospital, Medicare Provider Number, Address, Telephone, Approval, Facility, and Physician Codes, Health Care System**

★ American Hospital Association (AHA) membership
☐ The Joint Commission accreditation
◇ DNV Healthcare Inc. accreditation
○ Healthcare Facilities Accreditation Program
△ Commission on Accreditation of Rehabilitation Facilities (CARF) accreditation

## SUNBURY—Northumberland County

✉ **SUNBURY COMMUNITY HOSPITAL AND OUTPATIENT CENTER (390084)**,
(Formerly Sunbury Community Hospital), 350 North Eleventh Street,
Zip 17801–1611; tel. 570/286–3333, (Nonreporting) **A**1 9 10 **S** Community
Health Systems, Inc., Franklin, TN
Primary Contact: Jeff Hunt, Chief Executive Officer
CFO: Linda Chen, Chief Financial Officer
CIO: Fax Rector, III, Director Information Technology
CHR: Talia Beatty, Director Human Resources
CNO: Hasan Askari, M.D., Chief of Staff
CNO: Catharine L. Keister, Chief Nursing Officer
Web address: www.sunburyhospital.com
**Control:** Other not–for–profit (including NFP Corporation) **Service:** General
Medical and Surgical

**Staffed Beds:** 76

## SUSQUEHANNA—Susquehanna County

**BARNES–KASSON COUNTY HOSPITAL (391309)**, 2872 Turnpike Street,
Zip 18847–2771; tel. 570/853–3135, (Nonreporting) **A**9 10 18
Primary Contact: Sara F. Adornato, Executive Director
CFO: Sara F. Adornato, Executive Director
CMO: Warren DeWitt, M.D., Chief Medical Officer
CIO: John Sepcoski, Director Information Technology
CHR: William D. Iveson, Jr., Clinical Operations Officer and Director Human
Resources
Web address: www.barnes–kasson.org
**Control:** Other not–for–profit (including NFP Corporation) **Service:** General
Medical and Surgical

**Staffed Beds:** 83

## TITUSVILLE—Crawford County

★ **TITUSVILLE AREA HOSPITAL (390122)**, 406 West Oak Street,
Zip 16354–1404; tel. 814/827–1851, (Nonreporting) **A**9 10 20
Primary Contact: Anthony J. Nasralla, FACHE, President and Chief Executive
Officer
CFO: Paul Mattis, Vice President Finance
CMO: William Sonnenberg, M.D., President Medical Staff
CIO: Deanna Callahan, Director Information Systems
CHR: Jeffrey Saintz, Vice President Human Resources
Web address: www.titusvillehospital.org
**Control:** Other not–for–profit (including NFP Corporation) **Service:** General
Medical and Surgical

**Staffed Beds:** 50

## TORRANCE—Westmoreland County

☐ **TORRANCE STATE HOSPITAL (394026)**, Torrance Road, Zip 15779–0111,
Mailing Address: P.O. Box 111, Zip 15779–0111; tel. 724/459–8000 **A**1 10 **F**39
75 98 130 135 143 146 147 148
Primary Contact: Edna I. McCutcheon, Chief Executive Officer
COO: R. Brad Snyder, Chief Operating Officer
CFO: Michael Yahner, Chief Financial Officer
CMO: Herbert G. Chissell, M.D., Chief Medical Officer
Web address: www.dpw.state.pa.us
**Control:** State–Government, nonfederal **Service:** Psychiatric

**Staffed Beds:** 353 **Admissions:** 402 **Census:** 311 **Outpatient Visits:** 0
**Births:** 0 **Total Expense ($000):** 48898 **Personnel:** 654

## TOWANDA—Bradford County

**MEMORIAL HOSPITAL (390236)**, One Hospital Drive, Zip 18848–9702;
tel. 570/265–2191, (Nonreporting) **A**9 10 **S** QHR, Brentwood, TN
Primary Contact: Gary A. Baker, President
CFO: William K. Rohrbach, Vice President Fiscal Affairs
CMO: Constance Sweet, M.D., President Medical Staff
CHR: Linda Berry, Vice President Human Resources
Web address: www.memorialhospital.org
**Control:** Other not–for–profit (including NFP Corporation) **Service:** General
Medical and Surgical

**Staffed Beds:** 183

## TRANSFER—Mercer County

**EDGEWOOD SURGICAL HOSPITAL (390307)**, 239 Edgewood Drive Extension,
Zip 16154–1817; tel. 724/646–0400, (Nonreporting) **A**9 10
Primary Contact: Michael Torn, Chief Executive Officer
Web address: www.edgewoodsurgical.com
**Control:** Corporation, Investor–owned, for–profit **Service:** Surgical

**Staffed Beds:** 10

## TROY—Bradford County

★ **TROY COMMUNITY HOSPITAL (391305)**, 101 Elmira Street,
Zip 16947–1271; tel. 570/297–2121 **A**9 10 18 **F**3 11 15 28 30 34 40 45 50
57 64 75 81 82 85 87 93 96 107 110 111 119 129 130 133 135 146 148
**S** Guthrie Healthcare System, Sayre, PA
Primary Contact: Staci Covey, R.N., MS, President
CFO: Bernie Smith, Chief Financial Officer
CMO: Vance A. Good, M.D., Chief Medical Staff
CIO: Dale Swingle, Vice President Information Services
CHR: Frank Pinkosky, Senior Vice President
CNO: Lori Barnett, R.N., Chief Nursing Officer
Web address: www.guthrie.org
**Control:** Other not–for–profit (including NFP Corporation) **Service:** General
Medical and Surgical

**Staffed Beds:** 25 **Admissions:** 753 **Census:** 20 **Outpatient Visits:** 29012
**Births:** 0 **Total Expense ($000):** 14077 **Payroll Expense ($000):** 4628
**Personnel:** 107

## TUNKHANNOCK—Wyoming County

✉ **TYLER MEMORIAL HOSPITAL (390192)**, 880 State Road 6 West,
Zip 18657–6149; tel. 570/836–2161, (Nonreporting) **A**1 9 10 **S** Community
Health Systems, Inc., Franklin, TN
Primary Contact: Denise S. Gieski, MS, Chief Executive Officer
CFO: Stephen Franko, Chief Financial Officer
CMO: Brenda Goodrich, D.O., Chief of Staff
Web address: www.tylermemorialhospital.net
**Control:** Corporation, Investor–owned, for–profit **Service:** General Medical and
Surgical

**Staffed Beds:** 58

## TYRONE—Blair County

**TYRONE HOSPITAL (391307)**, 187 Hospital Drive, Zip 16686–1808;
tel. 814/684–1255 **A**9 10 18 **F**3 15 40 75 77 79 81 82 93 107 119 130
133 146
Primary Contact: Stephen Gildea, Chief Executive Officer
CFO: Michael Zenone, Chief Financial Officer
CMO: Jerome DeJulia, M.D., Chief Medical Officer
Web address: www.tyronehospital.org
**Control:** Other not–for–profit (including NFP Corporation) **Service:** General
Medical and Surgical

**Staffed Beds:** 25 **Admissions:** 679 **Census:** 7 **Outpatient Visits:** 30094
**Births:** 0 **Total Expense ($000):** 21632 **Payroll Expense ($000):** 9719
**Personnel:** 184

## UNIONTOWN—Fayette County

✉ **UNIONTOWN HOSPITAL (390041)**, 500 West Berkeley Street,
Zip 15401–5596; tel. 724/430–5000, (Total facility includes 38 beds in nursing
home–type unit) **A**1 9 10 **F**11 13 15 18 20 22 26 28 29 35 40 45 49 51 54 59
64 70 73 74 75 76 78 79 81 84 89 90 92 93 95 96 98 102 103 104 107
108 110 111 114 115 118 119 128 130 132 135 146 148
Primary Contact: Paul Bacharach, President and Chief Executive Officer
CFO: Steven P. Handy, CPA, Senior Vice President, Chief Financial Officer and
Chief Information Officer
CIO: Steven P. Handy, CPA, Senior Vice President, Chief Financial Officer and
Chief Information Officer
CHR: James Proud, Vice President Human Resources and Marketing
CNO: Betty Ann Rock, Vice President Nursing and Chief Nursing Officer
Web address: www.uniontownhospital.com
**Control:** Other not–for–profit (including NFP Corporation) **Service:** General
Medical and Surgical

**Staffed Beds:** 212 **Admissions:** 10807 **Census:** 139 **Outpatient Visits:**
257438 **Births:** 929 **Total Expense ($000):** 126650 **Payroll Expense**
**($000):** 46118 **Personnel:** 1109

## UPLAND—Delaware County

✉ **CROZER–CHESTER MEDICAL CENTER (390180)**, One Medical Center
Boulevard, Zip 19013–3995; tel. 610/447–2000, (Includes SPRINGFIELD
HOSPITAL, 190 West Sproul Road, Springfield, Zip 19064–2097;
tel. 610/328–8700; TAYLOR HOSPITAL, 175 East Chester Pike, Ridley Park,
Zip 19078–2212; tel. 610/595–6000) **A**1 2 3 5 8 10 12 13 **F**2 3 5 6 7 8 11
12 13 14 15 16 17 18 20 22 24 26 28 29 30 31 32 34 35 37 38 40 41 43
44 45 46 49 50 51 52 54 55 56 57 58 59 61 63 64 65 66 68 70 72 74
75 76 77 78 79 81 82 83 84 85 86 87 89 90 92 93 94 96 97 98 99 100
101 102 103 104 105 107 108 109 110 111 114 115 116 117 118 119 120
121 123 124 126 129 130 131 132 134 135 138 143 146 147 148 **P**6
**S** Crozer–Keystone Health System, Springfield, PA
Primary Contact: Patrick J. Gavin, President
CMO: Sat Arora, M.D., President Medical and Dental Staff
CIO: Robert E. Wilson, Vice President and Chief Information Officer
Web address: www.crozer.org
**Control:** Other not–for–profit (including NFP Corporation) **Service:** General
Medical and Surgical

**Staffed Beds:** 472 **Admissions:** 23540 **Census:** 310 **Outpatient Visits:**
445309 **Births:** 1759 **Total Expense ($000):** 541880 **Payroll Expense**
**($000):** 213476 **Personnel:** 2717

PA

**WARREN—Warren County**

☐ **WARREN GENERAL HOSPITAL (390146)**, Two Crescent Park West, Zip 16365–0068, Mailing Address: P.O. Box 68, Zip 16365–0068; tel. 814/723–4973, (Nonreporting) **A**9 10
Primary Contact: John P. Papalia, FACHE, Chief Executive Officer
COO: Randy California, Chief Operating Officer
CFO: Murray S. Marsh, Jr., Chief Financial Officer
CMO: Dale McNett, M.D., Medical Director
CIO: Rick Setili, Manager Information Systems
CHR: Stacy Ryan, Corporate Director Human Resources
CNO: Trudy Bloomquist, Director of Nursing
Web address: www.wgh.org
**Control:** Other not–for–profit (including NFP Corporation) **Service:** General Medical and Surgical

**Staffed Beds:** 105

☐ **WARREN STATE HOSPITAL (394016)**, 33 Main Drive, Zip 16365–5001; tel. 814/723–5500 **A**1 10 **F**4 30 39 50 56 75 77 82 98 100 101 103 128 130 132 135 143 146 **P**1
Primary Contact: Charlotte M. Uber, Chief Executive Officer
COO: Tim Taylor, Chief Operating Officer
CFO: Terry Crambes, Manager Finance
CMO: Asha Prabhu, M.D., Chief Medical Officer
CIO: Karen Byler, Information Technician
CHR: Nancy Saullo, Director Human Resources
Web address: www.dpw.pa.gov
**Control:** State–Government, nonfederal **Service:** Psychiatric

**Staffed Beds:** 190 **Admissions:** 111 **Census:** 168 **Outpatient Visits:** 0 **Births:** 0 **Total Expense ($000):** 41876 **Payroll Expense ($000):** 20843 **Personnel:** 405

**WASHINGTON—Washington County**

☐ **ADVANCED SURGICAL HOSPITAL (390323)**, 100 Trich Drive Suite 1, Zip 15301–5990; tel. 724/884–0710, (Nonreporting) **A**1 10
Primary Contact: Anne S. Hast, R.N., MSN, Chief Executive Officer
Web address: www.ashospital.net
**Control:** Partnership, Investor–owned, for–profit **Service:** Orthopedic

**Staffed Beds:** 14

⊞ **WASHINGTON HOSPITAL (390042)**, 155 Wilson Avenue, Zip 15301–3398; tel. 724/225–7000 **A**1 3 5 6 9 10 13 **F**3 5 11 13 15 18 20 22 24 26 28 29 30 31 32 34 35 36 38 39 40 45 46 49 50 53 54 56 57 59 60 61 63 64 65 70 74 75 76 77 78 79 81 82 83 84 85 86 89 90 91 92 93 94 96 97 98 99 100 101 102 103 107 108 110 111 114 115 119 126 130 131 132 134 135 146 147 148 **P**1 7
Primary Contact: Gary B. Weinstein, President and Chief Executive Officer
COO: Brook Ward, Executive Vice President
CFO: Alisa Rucker, Vice President Finance and Chief Financial Officer
CMO: Paul T. Cullen, M.D., Vice President Medical Affairs
CIO: Rodney Louk, Vice President Information Systems
CHR: Barbara A. McCullough, Vice President Human Resources
CNO: Karen A. Bray, R.N., Vice President Patient Care Services
Web address: www.washingtonhospital.org
**Control:** Other not–for–profit (including NFP Corporation) **Service:** General Medical and Surgical

**Staffed Beds:** 260 **Admissions:** 14795 **Census:** 158 **Outpatient Visits:** 684150 **Births:** 1020 **Total Expense ($000):** 240893 **Payroll Expense ($000):** 99216 **Personnel:** 1600

**WAYNESBORO—Franklin County**

⊞ **WAYNESBORO HOSPITAL (390138)**, 501 East Main Street, Zip 17268–2394; tel. 717/765–4000 **A**1 9 10 **F**3 11 13 15 29 30 34 40 45 49 50 54 57 59 64 65 68 74 75 76 77 79 81 85 86 87 91 92 93 94 107 108 110 111 115 118 119 130 131 132 133 135 146 147 148 **P**8 **S** Summit Health, Chambersburg, PA
Primary Contact: Melissa Dubrow, Chief Operating Officer
COO: Kenneth L. Shur, FACHE, Vice President and Chief Operating Officer
CFO: Patrick W. O'Donnell, CPA, Vice President Finance
CMO: Thomas Anderson, M.D., Vice President Medical Affairs
CIO: Michele Zeigler, Vice President Information Services
CHR: Jennifer Knight, Manager Human Resources
CNO: Jill Keller, R.N., Vice President for Nursing Services, Quality and Risk Management
Web address: www.summithealth.org
**Control:** Other not–for–profit (including NFP Corporation) **Service:** General Medical and Surgical

**Staffed Beds:** 64 **Admissions:** 2672 **Census:** 25 **Outpatient Visits:** 104668 **Births:** 428 **Total Expense ($000):** 57727 **Payroll Expense ($000):** 27019 **Personnel:** 431

**WAYNESBURG—Greene County**

☐ **SOUTHWEST REGIONAL MEDICAL CENTER (390150)**, 350 Bonar Avenue, Zip 15370–1608; tel. 724/627–3101, (Nonreporting) **A**1 9 10 **S** RegionalCare Hospital Partners, Brentwood, TN
Primary Contact: Cynthia Cowie, Chief Executive Officer
COO: Janel Mudry, Chief Operating Officer
CFO: James C. Rutkowski, Chief Financial Officer
CMO: Jamie Boris, M.D., President Medical Staff
CIO: Chris Zaglama, Director Information Services
CHR: Lisa Petro, Director Human Resources
Web address: www.sw–rmc.com
**Control:** Corporation, Investor–owned, for–profit **Service:** General Medical and Surgical

**Staffed Beds:** 77

**WELLSBORO—Tioga County**

⊞ **SOLDIERS AND SAILORS MEMORIAL HOSPITAL (390043)**, 32–36 Central Avenue, Zip 16901–1899; tel. 570/724–1631 **A**1 9 10 20 **F**3 11 13 15 17 28 40 48 49 64 65 70 75 76 79 81 85 93 98 102 103 104 107 108 110 111 115 118 119 129 130 146 **P**7 **S** Susquehanna Health System, Williamsport, PA
Primary Contact: Janie Hilfiger, President
CFO: Ronald Gilbert, Jr., Chief Financial Officer
CMO: Walter Laibinis, M.D., Chief Medical Officer
CIO: Joe Bubacz, Chief Information Officer
CHR: Gene Yajko, Director Human Resources
Web address: www.susquehannahealth.org
**Control:** Other not–for–profit (including NFP Corporation) **Service:** General Medical and Surgical

**Staffed Beds:** 83 **Admissions:** 2512 **Census:** 27 **Outpatient Visits:** 105667 **Births:** 279 **Total Expense ($000):** 45936 **Payroll Expense ($000):** 19060 **Personnel:** 490

**WERNERSVILLE—Berks County**

☐ **WERNERSVILLE STATE HOSPITAL (394014)**, Route 422, Zip 19565–0300, Mailing Address: P.O. Box 300, Zip 19565–0300; tel. 610/678–3411 **A**1 10 **F**30 39 75 77 98 103 130 135 146
Primary Contact: Andrea Kepler, Chief Executive Officer
COO: Cheryl Benson, Chief Operating Officer
CMO: Dale K. Adair, M.D., Chief Medical Officer
CIO: William Edwards, Information Technology Generalist
CHR: Melvin McMinn, Director Human Resources
Web address: www.dpw.state.pa.us/
**Control:** State–Government, nonfederal **Service:** Psychiatric

**Staffed Beds:** 266 **Admissions:** 68 **Census:** 259 **Outpatient Visits:** 0 **Births:** 0 **Total Expense ($000):** 58351 **Payroll Expense ($000):** 26978 **Personnel:** 582

**WEST CHESTER—Chester County**

⊞ **CHESTER COUNTY HOSPITAL (390179)**, 701 East Marshall Street, Zip 19380–4412; tel. 610/431–5000 **A**1 2 3 5 9 10 **F**3 11 13 15 17 18 20 22 24 26 28 29 31 32 34 35 40 41 45 49 50 55 56 57 59 62 63 64 65 68 69 70 72 75 76 77 78 79 81 82 84 85 86 87 89 92 93 97 107 108 110 111 114 115 118 119 121 123 126 130 131 132 134 135 146 147 148 **P**6
Primary Contact: Michael J. Duncan, System Chief Executive Officer
COO: Michael Barber, System Chief Operating Officer
CFO: Kenneth E. Flickinger, System Chief Financial Officer
CMO: Richard D. Donze, D.O., Senior Vice President Medical Affairs
CIO: Karen Pinsky, M.D., Chief Medical Information Officer
CHR: Jacqueline Felicetti, Director Human Resources
CNO: Angela Coladonato, MSN, Chief Nursing Officer
Web address: www.chestercountyhospital.org
**Control:** Other not–for–profit (including NFP Corporation) **Service:** General Medical and Surgical

**Staffed Beds:** 220 **Admissions:** 13534 **Census:** 156 **Outpatient Visits:** 247029 **Births:** 2305 **Total Expense ($000):** 245533 **Payroll Expense ($000):** 99824 **Personnel:** 1556

⊞ **LIFECARE HOSPITALS OF CHESTER COUNTY (392048)**, 400 East Marshall Street, Zip 19380–5412; tel. 484/826–0400, (Nonreporting) **A**1 9 10 **S** LifeCare Management Services, Plano, TX
Primary Contact: Rosalie Cox, Administrator
Web address: www.lifecare–hospitals.com
**Control:** Corporation, Investor–owned, for–profit **Service:** Long–Term Acute Care hospital

**Staffed Beds:** 39

**Hospital, Medicare Provider Number, Address, Telephone, Approval, Facility, and Physician Codes, Health Care System**

★ American Hospital Association (AHA) membership
☐ The Joint Commission accreditation
◇ DNV Healthcare Inc. accreditation
○ Healthcare Facilities Accreditation Program
△ Commission on Accreditation of Rehabilitation Facilities (CARF) accreditation

**PA**

## WEST GROVE—Chester County

✠ **JENNERSVILLE REGIONAL HOSPITAL (390220)**, 1015 West Baltimore Pike, Zip 19390–9459; tel. 610/869–1000 **A**1 2 9 10 **F**3 11 13 15 29 35 40 49 50 51 57 59 70 74 75 76 79 81 82 85 87 92 93 107 108 110 111 115 119 129 130 131 132 133 145 146 147 **P**6 **S** Community Health Systems, Inc., Franklin, TN
Primary Contact: Charles A. Davis, Chief Executive Officer
COO: Matthew Gooch, Chief Operating Officer
CFO: Brent Smith, Chief Financial Officer
CMO: Michael Barkasy, M.D., Chief of Staff
CHR: Nancy Newcomb, Director Human Resources
Web address: www.jennersville.com
**Control:** Corporation, Investor–owned, for–profit **Service:** General Medical and Surgical

**Staffed Beds:** 59 **Admissions:** 3070 **Census:** 32 **Outpatient Visits:** 17847 **Births:** 422 **Total Expense ($000):** 49496 **Payroll Expense ($000):** 18071 **Personnel:** 262

## WEST READING—Berks County

✠ △ **READING HOSPITAL AND MEDICAL CENTER (390044)**, Sixth Avenue and Spruce Street, Zip 19611–1428, Mailing Address: P.O. Box 16052, Zip 19612–6052; tel. 610/988–8000 **A**1 2 3 5 6 7 8 9 10 12 13 **F**3 5 8 11 12 13 15 18 20 22 24 26 28 29 30 31 34 35 37 40 41 42 43 44 45 46 48 49 50 54 56 57 58 59 60 61 64 66 68 70 72 73 74 75 76 77 78 79 81 82 84 85 86 87 89 90 92 93 94 96 97 98 99 100 101 102 103 104 105 106 107 108 110 111 114 115 116 117 118 119 120 121 123 124 125 126 128 129 130 131 132 135 144 146 147 148 **P**6 8
Primary Contact: Clinton Matthews, President and Chief Executive Officer
CFO: Richard W. Jones, Chief Financial Officer
CMO: M. Joseph Grennan, Jr., M.D., Senior Vice President and Chief Medical Officer
CIO: Jayashree Raman, Vice President and Chief Information Officer
CNO: Mary Christine Agnew, R.N., Vice President and Chief Nursing Officer
Web address: www.readinghospital.org
**Control:** Other not–for–profit (including NFP Corporation) **Service:** General Medical and Surgical

**Staffed Beds:** 719 **Admissions:** 30173 **Census:** 467 **Outpatient Visits:** 800971 **Births:** 3666 **Total Expense ($000):** 684368 **Payroll Expense ($000):** 280730 **Personnel:** 4973

## WILKES BARRE—Luzerne County

✠ **GEISINGER WYOMING VALLEY MEDICAL CENTER (390270)**, 1000 East Mountain Boulevard, Zip 18711–0027; tel. 570/808–7300 **A**1 2 3 5 9 10 13 **F**3 7 8 11 12 13 15 17 18 19 20 22 24 25 26 28 29 30 31 32 34 37 39 40 42 43 44 45 46 49 50 54 57 59 64 65 68 70 72 74 75 76 77 78 79 80 81 82 83 84 85 86 87 89 90 92 93 96 100 107 108 111 114 116 117 119 120 121 123 126 129 130 131 132 135 138 142 144 146 147 148 **P**6 **S** Geisinger Health System, Danville, PA
Primary Contact: John J. Buckley, Chief Administrative Officer
CFO: Thomas A. Bielecki, Chief Financial Officer
CMO: Steven Pierdon, M.D., Executive Vice President and Chief Medical Officer
CIO: Frank Richards, Chief Information Officer
CHR: Margaret Heffers, Assistant Vice President Human Resources
Web address: www.geisinger.org
**Control:** Other not–for–profit (including NFP Corporation) **Service:** General Medical and Surgical

**Staffed Beds:** 238 **Admissions:** 13476 **Census:** 173 **Outpatient Visits:** 643737 **Births:** 1469 **Total Expense ($000):** 380122 **Payroll Expense ($000):** 88747 **Personnel:** 1666

✠ **KINDRED HOSPITAL–WYOMING VALLEY (392042)**, 575 North River Street, 7th Floor, Zip 18764–0999; tel. 570/552–7620, (Nonreporting) **A**1 9 10 **S** Kindred Healthcare, Louisville, KY
Primary Contact: Sharon Yurkiewicz, Chief Executive Officer
CFO: Brian Beppler, Controller
CMO: Jon Olenginski, D.O., Medical Director of Hospital Services
CHR: Jean Melissner, District Director of Human Resources
CNO: Lillian Klitsch, R.N., Chief Clinical Officer
Web address: www.kindredhospitalwv.com/
**Control:** Corporation, Investor–owned, for–profit **Service:** Long–Term Acute Care hospital

**Staffed Beds:** 36

## WILKES–BARRE—Luzerne County

**CLEAR BROOK MANOR**, 1100 East Northampton Street, Zip 18702–9803; tel. 570/823–1171, (Nonreporting)
Primary Contact: Robert Piccone, President
Web address: www.clearbrookinc.com
**Control:** Other not–for–profit (including NFP Corporation) **Service:** Alcoholism and other chemical dependency

**Staffed Beds:** 50

✠ △ **JOHN HEINZ INSTITUTE OF REHABILITATION MEDICINE (393036)**, 150 Mundy Street, Zip 18702–6830; tel. 570/826–3800, (Total facility includes 21 beds in nursing home–type unit) **A**1 7 10 **F**3 11 29 30 32 35 54 57 59 62 64 68 75 77 82 86 90 91 92 93 130 131 132 143 146 148
Primary Contact: Jackie Fletcher–Brozena, Senior Vice President and Chief Operating Officer
CFO: Mike Avvisato, Vice President and Chief Financial Officer
CMO: Gregory Basting, M.D., Vice President Medical Affairs
CIO: John Regula, Chief Information Officer
CHR: Susan D. Montross, Vice President Human Resources
Web address: www.allied–services.org
**Control:** Other not–for–profit (including NFP Corporation) **Service:** Rehabilitation

**Staffed Beds:** 71 **Admissions:** 1608 **Census:** 56 **Outpatient Visits:** 104747 **Births:** 0 **Total Expense ($000):** 32447 **Payroll Expense ($000):** 16445 **Personnel:** 381

**VETERANS AFFAIRS MEDICAL CENTER** See Wilkes–Barre Veterans Affairs Medical Center

★ △ **WILKES–BARRE GENERAL HOSPITAL (390137)**, 575 North River Street, Zip 18764–0001; tel. 570/829–8111, (Includes WILKES–BARRE GENERAL HOSPITAL, 575 North River Street, Zip 18764; tel. 570/829–8111) **A**3 5 7 9 10 13 **F**3 4 8 12 13 15 17 18 20 22 24 28 29 30 31 34 37 40 44 45 46 48 49 50 51 53 54 56 57 59 61 64 66 70 73 74 75 76 78 79 81 85 86 87 89 90 93 96 107 108 110 111 112 114 115 116 117 118 119 121 123 126 129 130 132 145 146 147 148 **S** Community Health Systems, Inc., Franklin, TN
Primary Contact: Cornelio R. Catena, President and Chief Executive Officer
COO: Robert P. Hoffman, Vice President and Director Patient Care Services
CFO: Maggie Koehler, Senior Vice President and Chief Financial Officer
CMO: Ragupathy Veluswamy, M.D., Vice President Medical Affairs
CIO: Chris Galanda, Chief Information Officer
CHR: James Carmody, Vice President Human Resources
Web address: www.wvhc.org
**Control:** Corporation, Investor–owned, for–profit **Service:** General Medical and Surgical

**Staffed Beds:** 374 **Admissions:** 17245 **Census:** 238 **Outpatient Visits:** 538513 **Births:** 1114 **Total Expense ($000):** 256587 **Payroll Expense ($000):** 88780 **Personnel:** 1644

✠ △ **WILKES–BARRE VETERANS AFFAIRS MEDICAL CENTER**, (Formerly Veterans Affairs Medical Center), 1111 East End Boulevard, Zip 18711–0030; tel. 570/824–3521, (Total facility includes 105 beds in nursing home–type unit) **A**1 2 3 5 7 9 **F**2 3 5 8 10 11 12 15 18 20 28 29 30 31 34 35 38 39 40 44 45 46 50 53 54 56 57 58 59 60 62 63 64 65 68 70 74 75 77 78 79 81 82 83 84 85 86 87 92 93 94 96 97 98 100 101 102 103 104 107 111 114 115 118 119 128 129 130 132 135 146 147 148 **S** Department of Veterans Affairs, Washington, DC
Primary Contact: Margaret B. Caplan, Director
COO: C. Gene Molino, Associate Director
CFO: Donald E. Foote, Fiscal Officer
CMO: Mirza Z. Ali, M.D., Chief of Staff
CIO: David Longmore, Chief Information Officer
CHR: Dawn P. DeMorrow, Chief Human Resources Service
Web address: www.va.gov/vamcwb
**Control:** Veterans Affairs, Government, federal **Service:** General Medical and Surgical

**Staffed Beds:** 161 **Admissions:** 3603 **Census:** 137 **Outpatient Visits:** 393189 **Births:** 0 **Total Expense ($000):** 250143 **Payroll Expense ($000):** 82718 **Personnel:** 907

**WYOMING VALLEY HEALTH CARE SYSTEM** See Wilkes–Barre General Hospital

## WILLIAMSPORT—Lycoming County

★ **DIVINE PROVIDENCE HOSPITAL (394048)**, 1100 Grampian Boulevard, Zip 17701–1995; tel. 570/326–8000 **A**9 10 **F**10 11 15 31 35 38 44 50 51 53 54 56 59 62 63 64 66 68 75 77 78 79 81 82 83 84 86 87 93 98 99 100 103 107 108 110 111 115 119 120 121 129 130 131 132 134 146 147 148 **P**7 **S** Susquehanna Health System, Williamsport, PA
Primary Contact: Robert E. Kane, Administrator and Chief Executive Officer
COO: Neil G. Armstrong, FACHE, Vice President and Chief Operating Officer
Web address: www.susquehannahealth.org
**Control:** Other not–for–profit (including NFP Corporation) **Service:** Psychiatric

**Staffed Beds:** 31 **Admissions:** 813 **Census:** 18 **Outpatient Visits:** 290564 **Births:** 0 **Total Expense ($000):** 77169 **Payroll Expense ($000):** 19730 **Personnel:** 250

**WILLIAMSPORT HOSPITAL AND MEDICAL CENTER** See Williamsport Regional Medical Center

*Many Facility Codes have changed. Please refer to the AHA Guide Code Chart.*

© 2013 AHA Guide

⊠ △ **WILLIAMSPORT REGIONAL MEDICAL CENTER (390045)**, 700 High Street, Zip 17701–3100; tel. 570/321–1000 **A**1 2 5 7 9 10 13 **F**7 9 11 12 13 15 17 18 20 22 24 26 28 29 30 32 34 35 37 38 40 44 45 46 49 50 52 53 56 57 58 59 60 61 65 68 70 73 74 75 76 77 79 81 85 86 87 89 90 91 92 93 94 96 97 107 108 110 114 115 116 117 118 119 120 121 123 124 126 130 132 134 135 143 144 146 147 **P**7 **S** Susquehanna Health System, Williamsport, PA
Primary Contact: Jan E. Fisher, President
CFO: Charles J. Santangelo, CPA, Executive Vice President and Chief Financial Officer
CMO: George A. Manchester, M.D., Executive Vice President Medical Affairs
CIO: Karen M. Armstrong, FACHE, Senior Vice President and Chief Information Officer
CHR: Christine A. Ballard, Senior Vice President Human Resources
CNO: Susan Duchman, R.N., Vice President and Chief Nursing Officer
**Control:** Other not–for–profit (including NFP Corporation) **Service:** General Medical and Surgical

**Staffed Beds:** 207 **Admissions:** 11561 **Census:** 137 **Outpatient Visits:** 160719 **Births:** 1195 **Total Expense ($000):** 236972 **Payroll Expense ($000):** 83463 **Personnel:** 1291

### WINDBER—Somerset County

★ **WINDBER MEDICAL CENTER (390112)**, 600 Somerset Avenue, Zip 15963–1331; tel. 814/467–3000 **A**9 10 **F**3 12 13 15 18 28 30 32 34 35 36 40 45 53 55 56 57 58 59 62 63 70 75 76 79 81 83 84 85 93 107 110 111 114 117 118 119 127 129 130 131 132 135 146 147
Primary Contact: Barbara J. Cliff, Ph.D., FACHE, President and Chief Executive Officer
CFO: Richard Sukenik, CPA, Vice President Finance and Chief Financial Officer
CIO: Renee Adams, Director Information Technology
CHR: Jamie Brock, Director Human Resources
CNO: Mary Lee Dadey, R.N., Vice President of Nursing
Web address: www.windbercare.org
**Control:** Other not–for–profit (including NFP Corporation) **Service:** General Medical and Surgical

**Staffed Beds:** 53 **Admissions:** 1712 **Census:** 16 **Outpatient Visits:** 111714 **Births:** 268 **Total Expense ($000):** 48346 **Payroll Expense ($000):** 21760 **Personnel:** 445

### WYNNEWOOD—Montgomery County

**LANKENAU HOSPITAL** See Lankenau Medical Center

⊠ **LANKENAU MEDICAL CENTER (390195)**, 100 Lancaster Avenue West, Zip 19096–3411; tel. 484/476–2000, (Total facility includes 22 beds in nursing home–type unit) **A**1 2 3 5 8 10 12 13 **F**3 11 13 15 17 18 20 22 24 26 28 29 30 31 34 35 39 40 43 45 46 47 48 49 50 54 55 56 57 58 59 64 65 66 68 70 72 73 74 75 76 77 78 79 81 82 84 85 86 87 91 92 93 97 107 108 110 111 114 115 119 120 121 123 124 126 128 129 130 131 132 135 138 144 145 146 148 **P**7 **S** Jefferson Health System, Radnor, PA
Primary Contact: Phillip D. Robinson, President
CFO: Michael J. Buongiorno, Vice President Finance
CMO: Thomas G. McCarter, Jr., M.D., Chief Medical Officer
CIO: Karen A. Thomas, Acting Vice President and Chief Information Officer
CHR: Eileen McAnally, Senior Vice President Human Resources
Web address: www.mainlinehealth.org
**Control:** Other not–for–profit (including NFP Corporation) **Service:** General Medical and Surgical

**Staffed Beds:** 339 **Admissions:** 19042 **Census:** 238 **Outpatient Visits:** 305929 **Births:** 2715 **Total Expense ($000):** 355200 **Payroll Expense ($000):** 115849 **Personnel:** 2101

### WYOMISSING—Berks County

☐ **SURGICAL INSTITUTE OF READING (390316)**, 2752 Century Boulevard, Zip 19610–3345; tel. 610/378–8800 **A**1 9 10 **F**3 8 29 45 79 81 82 85 86 107 114
Primary Contact: Debbie Beissel, Administrator
CFO: Cheryl Peterson, Business Office Manager
CHR: Megan Schaffer, Administrative Assistant
Web address: www.sireading.com
**Control:** Partnership, Investor–owned, for–profit **Service:** Surgical

**Staffed Beds:** 15 **Admissions:** 549 **Census:** 4 **Outpatient Visits:** 4676 **Total Expense ($000):** 16500 **Payroll Expense ($000):** 4124 **Personnel:** 79

### YORK—York County

⊠ **HEALTHSOUTH REHABILITATION HOSPITAL OF YORK (393037)**, 1850 Normandie Drive, Zip 17408–1534; tel. 717/767–6941, (Nonreporting) **A**1 9 10 **S** HEALTHSOUTH Corporation, Birmingham, AL
Primary Contact: Steven Alwine, Chief Executive Officer
CFO: Joyce Henry, Controller
CMO: Bruce Sicilia, M.D., Medical Director
CIO: Courtney E. Stoner, Director Marketing Operations
CHR: Sarah Arthur, Director Human Resources
CNO: Julie Scott, Chief Nursing Officer
Web address: www.healthsouthyork.com
**Control:** Corporation, Investor–owned, for–profit **Service:** Rehabilitation

**Staffed Beds:** 90

★ ○ **MEMORIAL HOSPITAL (390101)**, 325 South Belmont Street, Zip 17403–2609, Mailing Address: P.O. Box 15118, Zip 17405–7118; tel. 717/843–8623 **A**9 10 11 12 13 **F**3 7 11 13 15 18 20 22 26 29 30 35 38 40 45 48 54 56 57 58 59 62 63 64 65 66 68 70 75 76 77 78 79 81 85 86 89 92 93 96 108 110 118 119 124 126 129 130 131 132 135 146 **P**6 **S** Community Health Systems, Inc., Franklin, TN
Primary Contact: Sally J. Dixon, President and Chief Executive Officer
CIO: James Mahoney, Chief Information Officer
CHR: Corey Hudak, Director Human Resources
Web address: www.mhyork.org
**Control:** Other not–for–profit (including NFP Corporation) **Service:** General Medical and Surgical

**Staffed Beds:** 100 **Admissions:** 3934 **Census:** 44 **Outpatient Visits:** 119870 **Births:** 591 **Total Expense ($000):** 101258 **Payroll Expense ($000):** 46168 **Personnel:** 656

☐ **OSS ORTHOPAEDIC SPECIALTY HOSPITAL (390325)**, 1861 Powder Mill Road, Zip 17402–4723; tel. 717/718–2000 **A**1 9 10 **F**3 8 29 62 64 79 81 82 85 87 93 94 107 111 119 130 131 135 144 **P**8
Primary Contact: Todd M. Lord, Chief Executive Officer
Web address: www.osshospital.com
**Control:** Partnership, Investor–owned, for–profit **Service:** Orthopedic

**Staffed Beds:** 30 **Admissions:** 1806 **Census:** 10 **Outpatient Visits:** 68714 **Births:** 0 **Total Expense ($000):** 42710 **Payroll Expense ($000):** 14864 **Personnel:** 410

**SELECT SPECIALTY HOSPITAL–YORK** See Select Specialty Hospital–Central Pennsylvania, Camp Hill

⊠ **YORK HOSPITAL (390046)**, 1001 South George Street, Zip 17403–3645; tel. 717/851–2345, (Includes WELLSPAN SURGERY AND REHABILITATION HOSPITAL, 55 Monument Road, Zip 17403–5023; tel. 717/812–6100; Barbara Yarrish, R.N., Vice President, Operations) **A**1 2 3 5 8 9 10 12 13 **F**3 5 7 11 12 13 14 15 17 18 20 22 24 26 28 29 30 31 34 35 39 40 43 44 45 46 48 49 50 54 55 56 57 58 59 60 61 64 65 66 68 70 72 74 75 76 77 78 79 81 82 84 85 86 87 89 92 93 97 98 99 100 101 102 103 104 107 108 110 111 114 115 117 118 119 120 121 123 124 126 129 130 131 132 135 146 147 148 **S** WellSpan Health, York, PA
Primary Contact: Keith Noll, President
COO: Raymond Rosen, FACHE, Vice President Operations
CFO: Michael F. O'Connor, Senior Vice President Finance
CMO: Peter M. Hartmann, M.D., Vice President Medical Affairs
CIO: R. Hal Baker, M.D., Vice President and Chief Information Officer
CHR: Robert J. Batory, Vice President Human Resources
Web address: www.wellspan.org
**Control:** Other not–for–profit (including NFP Corporation) **Service:** General Medical and Surgical

**Staffed Beds:** 552 **Admissions:** 28212 **Census:** 392 **Outpatient Visits:** 880000 **Births:** 2993 **Total Expense ($000):** 720859 **Payroll Expense ($000):** 248140 **Personnel:** 4104

---

**Hospital, Medicare Provider Number, Address, Telephone, Approval, Facility, and Physician Codes, Health Care System**

★ American Hospital Association (AHA) membership
☐ The Joint Commission accreditation
◇ DNV Healthcare Inc. accreditation
○ Healthcare Facilities Accreditation Program
△ Commission on Accreditation of Rehabilitation Facilities (CARF) accreditation

# RHODE ISLAND

## CRANSTON—Providence County

☐ **ELEANOR SLATER HOSPITAL (412001)**, John O. Pastore Center, 111 Howard Avenue, Zip 02920–0269, Mailing Address: P.O. Box 8269, Zip 02920–0269; tel. 401/462–3085, (Nonreporting) **A**1 10
Primary Contact: Paul J. Despres, Chief Executive Officer
CMO: Charlene Tate, M.D., Chief Medical Staff and Clinical Services
Web address: www.bhddh.ri.gov/esh/
**Control:** State–Government, nonfederal **Service:** Long–Term Acute Care hospital

**Staffed Beds:** 495

## EAST PROVIDENCE—Providence County

☐ **EMMA PENDLETON BRADLEY HOSPITAL (414003)**, 1011 Veterans Memorial Parkway, Zip 02915–5099; tel. 401/432–1000, (Nonreporting) **A**1 3 5 9 10 **S** Lifespan Corporation, Providence, RI
Primary Contact: Daniel J. Wall, President and Chief Executive Officer
CFO: Mamie Wakefield, Vice President Finance and Chief Financial Officer
CMO: Henry T. Sachs, III, M.D., Medical Director
CIO: Carole Cotter, Senior Vice President and Chief Information Officer
CHR: Rob Duval, Chief Human Resources Officer
Web address: www.lifespan.org
**Control:** Other not–for–profit (including NFP Corporation) **Service:** Children's hospital psychiatric

**Staffed Beds:** 51

## NEWPORT—Newport County

☐ △ ◇ **NEWPORT HOSPITAL (410006)**, 11 Friendship Street, Zip 02840–2299; tel. 401/846–6400 **A**1 2 7 9 10 21 **F**3 8 11 13 15 28 29 30 31 34 35 40 45 49 51 53 54 56 57 59 60 64 68 70 74 75 76 77 78 79 81 82 85 86 89 90 91 92 93 96 97 98 99 100 102 103 104 105 107 108 110 111 114 118 119 129 130 132 135 146 147 148 **S** Lifespan Corporation, Providence, RI
Primary Contact: August B. Cordeiro, FACHE, President and Chief Executive Officer
CFO: Frank J. Byrne, Director Finance and Treasurer
CMO: Terrence R. McWilliams, M.D., Vice President Medical Affairs
CHR: Barbara J. Arcangeli, Vice President Human Resources
Web address: www.newporthospital.org
**Control:** Other not–for–profit (including NFP Corporation) **Service:** General Medical and Surgical

**Staffed Beds:** 124 **Admissions:** 4589 **Census:** 63 **Outpatient Visits:** 88439 **Births:** 566 **Total Expense ($000):** 101853 **Payroll Expense ($000):** 46019 **Personnel:** 605

## NORTH PROVIDENCE—Providence County

☐ △ **ST. JOSEPH HEALTH SERVICES OF RHODE ISLAND (410005)**, 200 High Service Avenue, Zip 02904–5199; tel. 401/456–3000, (Includes OUR LADY OF FATIMA HOSPITAL, 200 High Service Avenue, Zip 02904; tel. 401/456–3000; ST. JOSEPH HOSPITAL FOR SPECIALTY CARE, 21 Peace Street, Providence, Zip 02907; tel. 401/456–3000), (Nonreporting) **A**1 2 6 7 9 10
Primary Contact: Kenneth H. Belcher, President and Chief Executive Officer
CHR: Darlene Souza, Vice President
Web address: www.saintjosephri.com
**Control:** Other not–for–profit (including NFP Corporation) **Service:** General Medical and Surgical

**Staffed Beds:** 126

## NORTH SMITHFIELD—Providence County

**LANDMARK MEDICAL CENTER–FOGARTY UNIT** See Landmark Medical Center, Woonsocket

☐ **REHABILITATION HOSPITAL OF RHODE ISLAND (413025)**, 116 Eddie Dowling Highway, Zip 02896–7327; tel. 401/766–0800 **A**1 9 10 **F**28 29 35 64 77 82 90 91 92 93 96 130 132 148
Primary Contact: Richard Charest, Chief Executive Officer
COO: Demetra Ouellette, Chief Operating Officer
CFO: Matthew Cotti, Chief Financial Officer
CMO: Jorge Mayoral, M.D., Medical Director
CIO: Colleen Ryan, Chief Information Officer and Vice President Professional Services
CHR: Mona M. Willis, Director Human Resources
Web address: www.rhri.net
**Control:** Partnership, Investor–owned, for–profit **Service:** Rehabilitation

**Staffed Beds:** 40 **Admissions:** 444 **Census:** 17 **Outpatient Visits:** 21158 **Births:** 0 **Total Expense ($000):** 11455

## PAWTUCKET—Providence County

✠ △ **MEMORIAL HOSPITAL OF RHODE ISLAND (410001)**, 111 Brewster Street, Zip 02860–4499; tel. 401/729–2000, (Nonreporting) **A**1 2 3 5 7 8 9 10
Primary Contact: Arthur J. DeBlois, Interim President and Chief Executive Officer
COO: Shelley A. MacDonald Gallagher, R.N., Senior Vice President Operations
CFO: Michael Ryan, Senior Vice President Finance
CMO: Joseph Diaz, M.D., Acting Chief Medical Officer
CIO: Robert Ackerman, Director Information Systems
CHR: Lisa Pratt, Vice President Human Resources
Web address: www.mhri.org
**Control:** Other not–for–profit (including NFP Corporation) **Service:** General Medical and Surgical

**Staffed Beds:** 159

## PROVIDENCE—Providence County

✠ **BUTLER HOSPITAL (414000)**, 345 Blackstone Boulevard, Zip 02906–4829; tel. 401/455–6200 **A**1 3 5 9 10 **F**4 5 29 30 34 35 38 40 44 50 56 57 58 59 68 74 75 77 81 86 87 98 99 101 102 103 104 105 130 132 135 146 147 **P**6 **S** Care New England Health System, Providence, RI
Primary Contact: Patricia R. Recupero, M.D., JD, President and Chief Executive Officer
COO: Walter Dias, Vice President and Chief Operating Officer
CFO: Bonnie Baker, Vice President Finance and Chief Financial Officer
CMO: Steven Rasmussen, M.D., Medical Director
CIO: Cedric T. Priebe, M.D., Vice President and Chief Information Officer
CHR: Timothy Bigelow, Director Human Resources
Web address: www.butler.org
**Control:** Other not–for–profit (including NFP Corporation) **Service:** Psychiatric

**Staffed Beds:** 117 **Admissions:** 5661 **Census:** 122 **Outpatient Visits:** 44722 **Births:** 0 **Total Expense ($000):** 94775 **Payroll Expense ($000):** 48073 **Personnel:** 734

☐ **MIRIAM HOSPITAL (410012)**, 164 Summit Avenue, Zip 02906–2853; tel. 401/793–2500 **A**1 2 3 5 8 9 10 **F**8 11 12 15 17 18 20 22 26 28 29 30 31 34 35 40 45 46 49 50 53 54 56 57 58 59 60 61 64 65 66 68 70 74 75 77 78 79 81 82 84 85 87 92 93 97 100 104 107 108 110 111 114 115 118 119 126 130 132 135 146 147 148 **P**3 5 6 **S** Lifespan Corporation, Providence, RI
Primary Contact: Timothy J. Babineau, M.D., President and Chief Executive Officer
COO: Maria Ducharme, R.N., Interim Chief Nursing Officer
CFO: Mamie Wakefield, Chief Financial Officer
CMO: R. William Corwin, M.D., Vice President and Chief Medical Officer
CIO: Carole Cotter, Vice President and Chief Information Officer
CHR: Nancy McMahon, Vice President Human Resources
Web address: www.lifespan.org
**Control:** Other not–for–profit (including NFP Corporation) **Service:** General Medical and Surgical

**Staffed Beds:** 247 **Admissions:** 15606 **Census:** 173 **Outpatient Visits:** 143663 **Births:** 0 **Total Expense ($000):** 392622 **Payroll Expense ($000):** 162542 **Personnel:** 1918

✠ **PROVIDENCE VETERANS AFFAIRS MEDICAL CENTER**, (Formerly Veterans Affairs Medical Center), 830 Chalkstone Avenue, Zip 02908–4799; tel. 401/273–7100, (Nonreporting) **A**1 2 3 5 **S** Department of Veterans Affairs, Washington, DC
Primary Contact: Vincent Ng, Director
Web address: www.providence.va.gov/
**Control:** Veterans Affairs, Government, federal **Service:** General Medical and Surgical

**Staffed Beds:** 73

☐ **RHODE ISLAND HOSPITAL (410007)**, 593 Eddy Street, Zip 02903–4900; tel. 401/444–4000, (Includes HASBRO CHILDREN'S HOSPITAL, 593 Eddy Street, Zip 02903–4923; tel. 401/444–4000) **A**1 2 3 5 8 9 10 **F**3 6 7 8 11 15 16 17 18 19 20 21 22 23 24 26 29 30 31 32 34 35 38 39 40 41 43 44 45 46 47 48 49 50 51 53 54 55 56 57 58 59 60 61 64 65 66 68 70 74 75 77 78 79 81 82 84 85 86 87 88 89 92 93 94 97 98 99 100 101 102 103 104 105 107 108 110 111 114 115 116 117 118 119 120 121 123 124 129 130 131 132 134 135 138 142 145 146 148 **P**3 5 6 **S** Lifespan Corporation, Providence, RI
Primary Contact: Timothy J. Babineau, M.D., President and Chief Executive Officer
COO: Fredrick Macri, Executive Vice President
CFO: Mamie Wakefield, Senior Vice President and Chief Financial Officer
CMO: John B. Murphy, M.D., Vice President Medical Affairs and Chief Medical Officer
CIO: Carole Cotter, Senior Vice President and Chief Information Officer
CHR: Louis Sperling, Vice President Human Resources
Web address: www.rhodeislandhospital.org/
**Control:** Other not–for–profit (including NFP Corporation) **Service:** General Medical and Surgical

**Staffed Beds:** 645 **Admissions:** 34089 **Census:** 490 **Outpatient Visits:** 357273 **Births:** 0 **Total Expense ($000):** 1026527 **Payroll Expense ($000):** 466956 **Personnel:** 5531

☒ **ROGER WILLIAMS MEDICAL CENTER (410004)**, 825 Chalkstone Avenue, Zip 02908–4735; tel. 401/456–2000, (Nonreporting) **A**1 2 3 5 8 9 10
Primary Contact: Kenneth H. Belcher, President and Chief Executive Officer
CFO: Addy Kane, Chief Financial Officer
CMO: Elaine Jones, M.D., President Medical Staff
CIO: Susan Cerrone Abely, Vice President and Chief Information Officer
Web address: www.rwmc.com
**Control:** Other not–for–profit (including NFP Corporation) **Service:** General Medical and Surgical

**Staffed Beds:** 95

**ST. JOSEPH HOSPITAL FOR SPECIALTY CARE** See St. Joseph Health Services of Rhode Island, North Providence

**VETERANS AFFAIRS MEDICAL CENTER** See Providence Veterans Affairs Medical Center

☒ **WOMEN & INFANTS HOSPITAL OF RHODE ISLAND (410010)**, 101 Dudley Street, Zip 02905–2499; tel. 401/274–1100 **A**1 2 3 5 8 9 10 **F**3 5 11 13 15 29 30 31 33 34 35 36 38 40 44 45 46 50 52 54 55 57 58 59 63 64 65 66 68 71 72 73 75 76 77 78 81 82 84 85 86 87 97 100 101 102 104 105 107 110 111 114 119 126 130 132 134 135 143 146 147 **P**5 6 8 **S** Care New England Health System, Providence, RI
Primary Contact: Constance A. Howes, President and Chief Executive Officer
COO: Mark Marcantano, Executive Vice President and Chief Operating Officer
CMO: Raymond Powrie, M.D., Senior Vice President Quality and Clinical Effectiveness
CIO: Cedric T. Priebe, M.D., Senior Vice President and Chief Information Officer
CHR: Paul F. Heffernan, Vice President Human Resources
CNO: Angelleen Peters–Lewis, R.N., Chief Nurse and Senior Vice President Patient Care
Web address: www.womenandinfants.org
**Control:** Other not–for–profit (including NFP Corporation) **Service:** Obstetrics and gynecology

**Staffed Beds:** 247 **Admissions:** 12658 **Census:** 161 **Outpatient Visits:** 185935 **Births:** 8532 **Total Expense ($000):** 441727 **Payroll Expense ($000):** 192554 **Personnel:** 2109

**WAKEFIELD—Washington County**

☐ **SOUTH COUNTY HOSPITAL (410008)**, 100 Kenyon Avenue, Zip 02879–4299; tel. 401/782–8000 **A**1 2 9 10 **F**1 3 11 13 15 20 28 29 31 34 35 36 37 38 40 45 49 51 53 54 56 57 59 64 65 67 70 74 75 76 77 78 79 81 85 86 87 89 93 98 102 103 104 107 108 110 111 114 119 126 129 130 131 132 133 135 143 144 146 147 148 **P**4 6
Primary Contact: Louis R. Giancola, President and Chief Executive Officer
CFO: Thomas Breen, Vice President and Chief Financial Officer
CMO: Joseph J. O'Neill, M.D., Vice President Medical Affairs
CIO: Gary Croteau, Assistant Vice President and Chief Information Officer
CHR: Maggie Thomas, Vice President Human Resources and Practice Management
Web address: www.schospital.com
**Control:** Other not–for–profit (including NFP Corporation) **Service:** General Medical and Surgical

**Staffed Beds:** 85 **Admissions:** 4401 **Census:** 44 **Outpatient Visits:** 184213 **Births:** 403 **Total Expense ($000):** 114015 **Payroll Expense ($000):** 45435 **Personnel:** 621

**WARWICK—Kent County**

☒ △ **KENT COUNTY MEMORIAL HOSPITAL (410009)**, 455 Tollgate Road, Zip 02886–2770; tel. 401/737–7000 **A**1 2 7 9 10 13 **F**3 11 12 13 15 17 18 20 22 28 29 30 31 32 34 35 36 39 40 41 45 46 47 48 49 50 51 56 57 58 59 60 61 64 65 68 70 73 74 75 76 77 78 79 81 82 85 86 87 89 90 93 96 97 98 100 102 103 107 108 110 111 114 118 119 129 130 131 132 143 146 147 148 **P**6 8 **S** Care New England Health System, Providence, RI
Primary Contact: Sandra L. Coletta, President and Chief Executive Officer
COO: Joseph A. DiPietro, Senior Vice President and Chief Administrative Officer
CFO: Paul Beaudoin, Senior Vice President Finance and Chief Financial Officer
CMO: Michael J. Dacey, M.D., Senior Vice President and Chief Medical Officer
CIO: Cedric T. Priebe, M.D., Senior Vice President and Chief Information Officer
CHR: Marilyn J. Walsh, Vice President Human Resources
CNO: Rene Fischer, R.N., Senior Vice President and Chief Nursing Officer
Web address: www.kentri.org
**Control:** Other not–for–profit (including NFP Corporation) **Service:** General Medical and Surgical

**Staffed Beds:** 306 **Admissions:** 14045 **Census:** 211 **Outpatient Visits:** 222023 **Births:** 991 **Total Expense ($000):** 299211 **Payroll Expense ($000):** 127402 **Personnel:** 1428

**WESTERLY—Washington County**

★ ◇ **WESTERLY HOSPITAL (410013)**, 25 Wells Street, Zip 02891–2934; tel. 401/596–6000, (Nonreporting) **A**2 9 10 21 **S** Lawrence+Memorial Health System, New London, CT
Primary Contact: Bruce D. Cummings, M.D., President and Chief Executive Officer
CFO: James O'Keefe, Chief Financial Officer
CIO: Nancy Barisano, Chief Information Officer
CHR: Jodie Tate, Director Human Resources
Web address: www.westerlyhospital.org
**Control:** Other not–for–profit (including NFP Corporation) **Service:** General Medical and Surgical

**Staffed Beds:** 100

**WOONSOCKET—Providence County**

☐ **LANDMARK MEDICAL CENTER (410011)**, 115 Cass Avenue, Zip 02895–4731; tel. 401/769–4100, (Includes LANDMARK MEDICAL CENTER–FOGARTY UNIT, Eddie Dowling Highway, North Smithfield, Zip 02896; Mailing Address: Woonsocket, tel. 401/766–0800; LANDMARK MEDICAL CENTER–WOONSOCKET UNIT, 115 Cass Avenue, Zip 02895; tel. 401/769–4100) **A**1 2 9 10 **F**3 8 13 15 17 18 20 22 26 28 29 30 31 34 35 40 45 49 50 51 57 59 60 63 64 68 70 71 74 75 76 77 78 79 81 82 84 85 86 98 102 107 108 110 111 114 116 117 119 120 121 130 143 144 146 **P**6
Primary Contact: Richard Charest, President
CFO: Dana Diggins, Chief Financial Officer
CMO: Stanley Balon, M.D., President Medical Staff
CIO: Colleen Ryan, Director Management Information Systems
CHR: Mona M. Willis, Director Human Resources
Web address: www.landmarkmedical.org
**Control:** Other not–for–profit (including NFP Corporation) **Service:** General Medical and Surgical

**Staffed Beds:** 140 **Admissions:** 6549 **Census:** 89 **Outpatient Visits:** 107875 **Births:** 258 **Total Expense ($000):** 116868 **Payroll Expense ($000):** 49296 **Personnel:** 740

**RI**

---

**Hospital, Medicare Provider Number, Address, Telephone, Approval, Facility, and Physician Codes, Health Care System**

★ American Hospital Association (AHA) membership
☐ The Joint Commission accreditation
◇ DNV Healthcare Inc. accreditation
○ Healthcare Facilities Accreditation Program
△ Commission on Accreditation of Rehabilitation Facilities (CARF) accreditation

# SOUTH CAROLINA

**SC**

## ABBEVILLE—Abbeville County

✠ **ABBEVILLE AREA MEDICAL CENTER (421301)**, 420 Thomson Circle,
Zip 29620–5656, Mailing Address: P.O. Box 887, Zip 29620–0887;
tel. 864/366–5011 **A**1 9 10 18 **F**3 15 17 28 29 30 35 40 51 53 56 57 59 62
64 67 70 74 75 77 79 81 85 87 89 90 107 108 110 114 119 127 128 129
130 132 133 135 146 147 148 **S** QHR, Brentwood, TN
Primary Contact: Richard D. Osmus, Chief Executive Officer
CFO: Timothy Wren, Chief Financial Officer
CMO: Michael Turner, M.D., Chief of Staff
CIO: Tim Stewart, Chief Information Officer
CHR: Alice Rigney, Chief Human Resources Officer
Web address: www.abbevilleareamc.com
**Control:** County–Government, nonfederal **Service:** General Medical and Surgical

**Staffed Beds:** 25 **Admissions:** 685 **Census:** 7 **Births:** 0 **Total Expense
($000):** 31375 **Payroll Expense ($000):** 13361 **Personnel:** 306

## AIKEN—Aiken County

☐ **AIKEN REGIONAL MEDICAL CENTERS (420082)**, 302 University Parkway,
Zip 29801–6302; tel. 803/641–5000, (Includes AURORA PAVILION, 655 Medical
Park Drive, Zip 29801; tel. 803/641–5900) **A**1 5 9 10 **F**3 4 5 11 12 15 18 20
22 24 29 30 31 34 35 40 46 49 56 57 58 59 64 70 73 74 76 77 78 79 81
85 86 87 89 98 99 100 101 102 103 104 105 107 108 110 111 114 115
119 121 123 129 130 131 132 135 146 147 148 **S** Universal Health Services,
Inc., King of Prussia, PA
Primary Contact: Carlos Milanes, Chief Executive Officer and Managing Director
COO: Scott Ansede, Chief Operating Officer
Web address: www.aikenregional.com
**Control:** Corporation, Investor–owned, for–profit **Service:** General Medical and
Surgical

**Staffed Beds:** 268 **Admissions:** 12312 **Census:** 173 **Outpatient Visits:**
139467 **Births:** 1140 **Total Expense ($000):** 144471 **Payroll Expense
($000):** 51874 **Personnel:** 851

## ANDERSON—Anderson County

✠ **ANMED HEALTH MEDICAL CENTER (420027)**, 800 North Fant Street,
Zip 29621–5793; tel. 864/512–1000, (Includes ANMED HEALTH WOMEN'S AND
CHILDREN'S HOSPITAL, 2000 East Greenville Street, Zip 29621;
tel. 864/512–1000) **A**1 2 3 5 9 10 **F**3 4 5 11 14 15 17 18 20 22 24 26
28 29 30 31 34 35 37 39 40 43 45 46 48 49 50 51 53 54 56 57 58 59 60
61 62 64 65 68 70 71 73 74 75 76 77 78 79 81 84 85 86 87 89 90 91 97
98 100 101 102 103 104 105 107 108 110 111 114 115 117 118 119 121
123 126 127 129 130 131 132 135 144 146 147 148 **S** AnMed Health,
Anderson, SC
Primary Contact: John A. Miller, Jr., FACHE, Chief Executive Officer
COO: William T. Manson, III, President
CFO: Jerry A. Parrish, Vice President
CMO: Mike Tillirson, D.O., Executive Vice President and Chief Medical Officer
CIO: Kathy Hammond, Director Information Services
CHR: Doug Douglas, Vice President Human Resources
Web address: www.anmedhealth.org
**Control:** Other not–for–profit (including NFP Corporation) **Service:** General
Medical and Surgical

**Staffed Beds:** 322 **Admissions:** 18894 **Census:** 251 **Outpatient Visits:**
699006 **Births:** 1942 **Total Expense ($000):** 416250 **Payroll Expense
($000):** 161080 **Personnel:** 3260

✠ **ANMED HEALTH REHABILITATION HOSPITAL (423029)**, 1 Spring Back Way,
Zip 29621–2676; tel. 864/716–2600, **A**1 10 **F** 3 29 30 56 74 75 79 90 91 95
96 **S** HEALTHSOUTH Corporation, Birmingham, AL
Primary Contact: Michele M. Skripps, R.N., Chief Executive Officer
CFO: Julie Saylors, Controller
CMO: William Vogentiz, M.D., Medical Director
CHR: Tara Myers, Director Human Resources
CNO: Trent Praytor, MSN, Chief Nursing Officer
Web address: www.anmedrehab.com
**Control:** Corporation, Investor–owned, for–profit **Service:** Rehabilitation

**Staffed Beds:** 55 **Admissions:** 1375 **Census:** 46 **Births:** 0 **Total Expense
($000):** 12750 **Payroll Expense ($000):** 7204 **Personnel:** 179

☐ **PATRICK B. HARRIS PSYCHIATRIC HOSPITAL (424011)**, 130 Highway 252,
Zip 29621–5054; tel. 864/231–2600 **A**1 9 10 **F**35 57 86 87 98 100 101 102
103 106 130 143 146
Primary Contact: John Fletcher, Chief Executive Officer
Web address: www.patrickbharrispsychiatrichospital.com/index.htm
**Control:** State–Government, nonfederal **Service:** Psychiatric

**Staffed Beds:** 84 **Admissions:** 465 **Census:** 107 **Outpatient Visits:** 0 **Births:**
0 **Total Expense ($000):** 18615 **Payroll Expense ($000):** 10067
**Personnel:** 291

## BARNWELL—Barnwell County

☐ **BARNWELL COUNTY HOSPITAL (420016)**, 811 Reynolds Road,
Zip 29812–1555; tel. 803/259–1000 **A**1 9 10 20 **F**3 15 29 34 35 40 45 49
57 59 64 65 70 77 81 86 87 89 90 107 108 111 119 127 129 146
Primary Contact: Mary T. Valliant, R.N., MS, Chief Executive Officer
CFO: Troy Pickens, Chief Financial Officer
CMO: Dean Koukos, M.D., Chief Medical Staff
CIO: Randal Padgett, Manager Information Systems
CHR: Sherry Donaldson, Director Human Resources
CNO: Marsha Gantt, Interim Chief Nursing Officer
Web address: www.bchospital.org
**Control:** County–Government, nonfederal **Service:** General Medical and Surgical

**Staffed Beds:** 33 **Admissions:** 744 **Census:** 7 **Births:** 0 **Personnel:** 136

## BEAUFORT—Beaufort County

✠ **BEAUFORT MEMORIAL HOSPITAL (420067)**, 955 Ribaut Road,
Zip 29902–5441; tel. 843/522–5200 **A**1 2 9 10 **F**3 11 12 13 15 18 20 28 29
30 31 32 34 35 40 43 45 49 50 51 53 54 57 59 60 64 65 69 70 71 73 74
75 76 77 78 79 81 85 86 87 89 90 97 98 100 101 102 103 104 107 108
111 115 119 120 121 126 130 132 134 135 145 146 147 **P**6
Primary Contact: Richard Kirk Toomey, FACHE, President and Chief Executive
Officer
CFO: Jeffrey L. White, Senior Vice President and Chief Financial Officer
CMO: James Chadwick Tober, M.D., Chief of Staff
CIO: Edward Ricks, Vice President and Chief Information Officer
CHR: David Homyk, Vice President Human Resources
CNO: Karen Carroll, MSN, Vice President and Chief Nursing Officer
Web address: www.bmhsc.org
**Control:** County–Government, nonfederal **Service:** General Medical and Surgical

**Staffed Beds:** 173 **Admissions:** 10065 **Census:** 111 **Outpatient Visits:**
48023 **Births:** 1617 **Personnel:** 1134

✠ **NAVAL HOSPITAL BEAUFORT**, 1 Pinckney Boulevard, Zip 29902–6122;
tel. 843/228–5301, (Nonreporting) **A**1 5 **S** Bureau of Medicine and Surgery,
Department of the Navy, Washington, DC
Primary Contact: Lieutenant Commander Willie Brown, Director Administration
Web address: www.med.navy.mil/sites/nhbeaufort/Pages/Welcome_Page.aspx
**Control:** Navy, Government, federal **Service:** General Medical and Surgical

**Staffed Beds:** 20

## BENNETTSVILLE—Marlboro County

✠ **MARLBORO PARK HOSPITAL (420054)**, 1138 Cheraw Highway,
Zip 29512–2466; tel. 843/479–2881 **A**1 9 10 **F**3 13 15 17 18 29 34 35 40
45 57 59 64 65 70 75 76 77 79 81 85 87 89 98 103 107 108 119 127
128 130 132 133 135 146 147 **S** Community Health Systems, Inc., Franklin, TN
Primary Contact: Jeff Reece, Chief Executive Officer
CMO: Cindy Crittendon, M.D., Chief of Staff
CIO: Rod McLaurin, Director Information Systems
CHR: Christi Meggs, Director Human Resources
Web address: www.marlboroparkhospital.com
**Control:** Corporation, Investor–owned, for–profit **Service:** General Medical and
Surgical

**Staffed Beds:** 102 **Admissions:** 1617 **Census:** 16 **Births:** 74 **Total Expense
($000):** 26403 **Payroll Expense ($000):** 9948 **Personnel:** 113

## CAMDEN—Kershaw County

✠ **KERSHAWHEALTH (420048)**, 1315 Roberts Street, Zip 29020–3737, Mailing
Address: P.O. Box 7003, Zip 29021–7003; tel. 803/432–4311, (Total facility
includes 96 beds in nursing home–type unit) **A**1 9 10 **F**3 7 11 13 15 20 24 28
29 30 31 35 40 45 46 49 50 51 54 59 61 62 63 64 66 67 68 70 75 76 77
78 79 81 85 86 87 89 90 97 108 110 111 114 115 119 127 128 129 130
143 144 146 147 148
Primary Contact: Donnie J. Weeks, FACHE, President and Chief Executive Officer
COO: Mike Bunch, Executive Vice President, Chief Operating Officer and Chief
Financial Officer
CHR: Angela F. Nettles, Director Human Resources
Web address: www.kershawhealth.com
**Control:** County–Government, nonfederal **Service:** General Medical and Surgical

**Staffed Beds:** 215 **Admissions:** 5509 **Census:** 158 **Outpatient Visits:** 34162
**Births:** 328 **Total Expense ($000):** 109652 **Payroll Expense ($000):** 44359
**Personnel:** 857

*Many Facility Codes have changed. Please refer to the AHA Guide Code Chart.*
© 2013 AHA Guide

## CHARLESTON—Charleston County

⊠ **BON SECOURS ST. FRANCIS XAVIER HOSPITAL (420065)**, (Formerly Bon Secours St. Francis Hospital), 2095 Henry Tecklenburg Drive, Zip 29414–5733; tel. 843/402–1000 **A**1 9 10 **F**3 7 12 13 14 15 20 28 29 30 31 34 35 40 43 45 46 47 48 49 50 51 56 57 59 60 64 68 70 73 74 75 76 77 78 79 80 81 82 84 85 86 87 89 100 107 108 110 111 114 118 119 130 131 132 145 146 147 148 **S** Carolinas HealthCare System, Charlotte, NC
Primary Contact: David L. Dunlap, FACHE, President and Chief Executive Officer
CFO: Bret Johnson, Chief Financial Officer
CMO: Steven D. Shapiro, M.D., Chief Medical Officer
CIO: Michael Taylor, Chief Information Officer
CHR: Doug Harrison, Vice President Human Resources
CNO: Pennie Peralta, R.N., VP, Nursing & Chief Nursing Officer
Web address: www.ropersaintfrancis.com
**Control:** Other not–for–profit (including NFP Corporation) **Service:** General Medical and Surgical

**Staffed Beds:** 179 **Admissions:** 8808 **Census:** 85 **Outpatient Visits:** 157296 **Births:** 1852 **Total Expense ($000):** 147864 **Payroll Expense ($000):** 48613 **Personnel:** 1005

⊠ **HEALTHSOUTH REHABILITATION HOSPITAL OF CHARLESTON (423027)**, 9181 Medcom Street, Zip 29406–9168; tel. 843/820–7777 **A**1 10 **F**9 29 35 54 56 57 64 65 77 82 86 90 95 96 132 143 148 **S** HEALTHSOUTH Corporation, Birmingham, AL
Primary Contact: Troy Powell, Chief Executive Officer
CFO: Beckye Lariviere, Controller
CMO: William Livesay, Jr., D.O., Medical Director
CHR: Donna White, Director Human Resources
Web address: www.healthsouthcharleston.com
**Control:** Corporation, Investor–owned, for–profit **Service:** Rehabilitation

**Staffed Beds:** 49 **Admissions:** 970 **Census:** 35 **Outpatient Visits:** 0 **Births:** 0 **Total Expense ($000):** 13823 **Payroll Expense ($000):** 6330 **Personnel:** 120

⊠ **MUSC MEDICAL CENTER OF MEDICAL UNIVERSITY OF SOUTH CAROLINA (420004)**, 169 Ashley Avenue, Zip 29425–8905; tel. 843/792–2300, (Includes MUSC CHILDREN'S HOSPITAL, 171 Ashley Avenue, Zip 29425–8908; tel. 843/792–1414) **A**1 2 3 5 8 9 10 **F**1 3 4 5 6 7 9 11 12 13 14 15 16 17 18 19 20 21 22 23 24 25 26 27 28 29 30 31 32 34 35 37 38 39 40 41 43 44 45 46 47 48 49 50 51 52 53 54 55 56 57 59 60 61 64 66 67 68 70 71 72 73 74 75 76 77 78 79 80 81 82 84 85 86 87 88 89 92 97 98 99 100 101 102 103 104 105 107 108 109 110 111 114 115 116 117 118 119 120 121 123 124 126 129 130 131 132 134 135 136 137 138 139 140 141 142 144 145 146 147 148
Primary Contact: Patrick J. Cawley, M.D., Vice President of Clinical Operations and Chief Executive Officer
CFO: Lisa P. Montgomery, Administrator Finance and Support Services
CMO: Patrick J. Cawley, M.D., Medical Director
CIO: Frank Clark, Chief Information Officer
CHR: Betts Ellis, Administrator Institutional Relations
Web address: www.muschealth.com
**Control:** State–Government, nonfederal **Service:** General Medical and Surgical

**Staffed Beds:** 725 **Admissions:** 34058 **Census:** 598 **Outpatient Visits:** 941271 **Births:** 2068 **Total Expense ($000):** 1063861 **Payroll Expense ($000):** 385829 **Personnel:** 6512

☐ **PALMETTO LOWCOUNTRY BEHAVIORAL HEALTH (424006)**, 2777 Speissegger Drive, Zip 29405–8229; tel. 843/747–5830, (Total facility includes 32 beds in nursing home–type unit) **A**1 10 **F**4 5 29 64 98 99 101 102 103 104 105 106 130 132 **P**8 **S** Universal Health Services, Inc., King of Prussia, PA
Primary Contact: Shari Baker, Chief Executive Officer
COO: Marc Turner, Chief Operating Officer
CFO: Stan Markowski, Chief Financial Officer
CMO: Steven Lopez, M.D., Chief Medical Officer
CHR: Josh Smith, Vice President Human Resources
Web address: www.palmettobehavioralhealth.com
**Control:** Corporation, Investor–owned, for–profit **Service:** Psychiatric

**Staffed Beds:** 112 **Admissions:** 2632 **Census:** 74 **Births:** 0 **Personnel:** 160

⊠ **RALPH H. JOHNSON VETERANS AFFAIRS MEDICAL CENTER**, 109 Bee Street, Zip 29401–5799; tel. 843/577–5011, (Nonreporting) **A**1 2 3 5 8 **S** Department of Veterans Affairs, Washington, DC
Primary Contact: Carolyn L. Adams, Director
COO: Scott R. Isaacks, Associate Director
CFO: Cassandra Helfer, Chief Financial Officer
CMO: Florence N. Hutchison, M.D., Chief of Staff
CIO: Michael Cortright, Chief Information Officer
CNO: Mary C. Fraggos, R.N., Associate Director of Nursing and Patient Care Services
Web address: www.charleston.va.gov/
**Control:** Veterans Affairs, Government, federal **Service:** General Medical and Surgical

**Staffed Beds:** 98

⊠ △ **ROPER HOSPITAL (420087)**, 316 Calhoun Street, Zip 29401–1125; tel. 843/724–2000 **A**1 2 7 9 10 **F**3 7 8 11 13 14 15 17 18 20 22 24 26 28 29 30 31 34 35 40 42 43 45 49 50 51 54 55 56 57 59 60 61 62 63 64 65 68 69 70 73 74 75 76 77 78 79 80 81 82 84 85 86 87 90 92 96 100 107 108 110 111 114 115 117 118 119 120 121 123 124 126 129 130 131 132 135 136 141 143 144 146 147 148 **S** Carolinas HealthCare System, Charlotte, NC
Primary Contact: David L. Dunlap, FACHE, President and Chief Executive Officer
CFO: Bret Johnson, Chief Financial Officer
CMO: Steven D. Shapiro, M.D., Vice President Medical Affairs
CIO: Michael Taylor, Chief Information Officer
CHR: Doug Harrison, Vice President Human Resources
CHR: Douglas Harrison, Vice President Human Resources
Web address: www.ropersaintfrancis.com
**Control:** Other not–for–profit (including NFP Corporation) **Service:** General Medical and Surgical

**Staffed Beds:** 328 **Admissions:** 15044 **Census:** 217 **Outpatient Visits:** 244982 **Births:** 759 **Total Expense ($000):** 325489 **Payroll Expense ($000):** 108338 **Personnel:** 2180

⊠ **TRIDENT MEDICAL CENTER (420079)**, 9330 Medical Plaza Drive, Zip 29406–9195; tel. 843/797–7000, (Includes MONCKS CORNER MEDICAL CENTER, 401 North Live Oak Drive, Highway 17A, Moncks Corner, Zip 29461–5603; tel. 843/761–8721; SUMMERVILLE MEDICAL CENTER, 295 Midland Parkway, Summerville, Zip 29485–8104; tel. 843/832–5000; Louis Caputo, Chief Executive Officer) **A**1 2 3 5 9 10 **F**3 12 13 15 16 18 20 22 24 26 28 29 30 31 34 35 39 40 42 43 45 46 47 48 49 50 54 55 56 57 59 60 61 64 70 72 73 74 75 76 77 78 79 80 81 85 86 87 89 90 107 108 110 111 114 115 117 118 119 120 121 123 126 130 131 132 135 145 146 147 148 **S** HCA, Nashville, TN
Primary Contact: Todd Gallati, FACHE, President and Chief Executive Officer
CFO: Teresa Finch, Chief Financial Officer
CIO: Susan Murray, Director Information Services
CHR: Joe B. Hill, Jr., Vice President Human Resources
Web address: www.tridenthealthsystem.com
**Control:** Corporation, Investor–owned, for–profit **Service:** General Medical and Surgical

**Staffed Beds:** 403 **Admissions:** 21710 **Census:** 244 **Births:** 2962 **Total Expense ($000):** 301329 **Personnel:** 1455

## CHERAW—Chesterfield County

⊠ **CHESTERFIELD GENERAL HOSPITAL (420062)**, 711 Chesterfield Highway, Zip 29520–7002; tel. 843/537–7881 **A**1 9 10 **F**3 11 13 15 18 19 28 29 30 34 35 40 45 56 57 59 64 65 70 75 76 77 79 81 85 86 87 89 90 97 102 107 108 114 118 119 128 130 132 133 135 146 147 148 **S** Community Health Systems, Inc., Franklin, TN
Primary Contact: Jeff Reece, Chief Executive Officer
CFO: Nathan Crabdree, Chief Financial Officer
CMO: David Bersinger, M.D., Chief of Staff
Web address: www.chesterfieldgeneral.com
**Control:** Corporation, Investor–owned, for–profit **Service:** General Medical and Surgical

**Staffed Beds:** 59 **Admissions:** 2132 **Census:** 20 **Births:** 169 **Total Expense ($000):** 27824 **Payroll Expense ($000):** 10871 **Personnel:** 189

## CHESTER—Chester County

☐ **CHESTER REGIONAL MEDICAL CENTER (420019)**, 1 Medical Park Drive, Zip 29706–9769; tel. 803/581–3151, (Total facility includes 100 beds in nursing home–type unit) **A**1 9 10 **F**1 15 18 20 22 24 28 29 34 35 40 53 56 57 59 64 65 70 75 77 79 81 85 86 87 89 90 107 108 114 119 128 129 130 131 132 135 146 **S** Health Management Associates, Naples, FL
Primary Contact: Page H. Vaughan, Chief Executive Officer
CIO: Rick Lewis, Chief Information Officer
Web address: www.chospital.org
**Control:** Corporation, Investor–owned, for–profit **Service:** General Medical and Surgical

**Staffed Beds:** 136 **Admissions:** 1756 **Census:** 88 **Births:** 0

**SC**

---

**Hospital, Medicare Provider Number, Address, Telephone, Approval, Facility, and Physician Codes, Health Care System**

★ American Hospital Association (AHA) membership
☐ The Joint Commission accreditation
◇ DNV Healthcare Inc. accreditation
○ Healthcare Facilities Accreditation Program
△ Commission on Accreditation of Rehabilitation Facilities (CARF) accreditation

**CLINTON—Laurens County**

✠ **GREENVILLE HEALTH SYSTEM LAURENS COUNTY MEMORIAL HOSPITAL (420038)**, (Formerly Laurens County Health Care System), Highway 76 East, Zip 29325–2331, Mailing Address: P.O. Box 976, Zip 29325–0976; tel. 864/833–9100, (Includes LAURENS COUNTY HOSPITAL, Zip 29325; tel. 803/833–9100), (Total facility includes 14 beds in nursing home–type unit) **A**1 9 10 **F**1 3 11 13 15 17 18 28 29 30 34 35 36 40 46 48 57 59 61 64 70 75 76 77 79 80 81 85 87 89 90 107 108 110 119 128 129 130 132 135 141 146 147 148 **S** Greenville Health System, Greenville, SC
Primary Contact: Richard E. D'Alberto, FACHE, Chief Executive Officer
COO: Kay Swisher, Vice President and Chief Operating Officer
CFO: William Grant, Vice President Fiscal and Support Services
CMO: Mike Wiggins, M.D., Chief of Staff
CIO: Joel Bradley, Director Information Systems
Web address: www.lchcs.org
**Control:** Hospital district or authority, Government, nonfederal **Service:** General Medical and Surgical

**Staffed Beds:** 87 **Admissions:** 3137 **Census:** 41 **Births:** 299 **Total Expense ($000):** 63083 **Payroll Expense ($000):** 24496 **Personnel:** 396

**LAURENS COUNTY HEALTH CARE SYSTEM** See Greenville Health System Laurens County Memorial Hospital

**WHITTEN CENTER**, Highway 76 East, Zip 29325, Mailing Address: P.O. Box 239, Zip 29325–0239; tel. 864/833–2733, (Nonreporting)
Primary Contact: William Killion, Chief Executive Officer
**Control:** State–Government, nonfederal **Service:** Institution for mental retardation

**Staffed Beds:** 22

**COLUMBIA—Richland County**

**EARLE E. MORRIS ALCOHOL AND DRUG TREATMENT CENTER**, 610 Faison Drive, Zip 29203–3218; tel. 803/935–7100 **F**4 29 39 53 61 67 75 98 130 132 146
Primary Contact: George McConnell, Director
Web address: www.state.sc.us/dmh/morris_village/
**Control:** State–Government, nonfederal **Service:** Alcoholism and other chemical dependency

**Staffed Beds:** 107 **Admissions:** 1236 **Census:** 92 **Outpatient Visits:** 0 **Births:** 0 **Personnel:** 87

☐ **G. WERBER BRYAN PSYCHIATRIC HOSPITAL (424005)**, 220 Faison Drive, Zip 29203–3210; tel. 803/935–7146 **A**1 10 **F**4 30 50 74 75 97 98 101 103 130 132 135 146
Primary Contact: Harvey Miller, Director
COO: Jaclyn Upfield, Chief Operating Officer
CIO: Sam Livingston, Information Resource Consultant
CHR: Kim Church, Manager Human Resources
Web address: www.scdmh.org
**Control:** State–Government, nonfederal **Service:** Psychiatric

**Staffed Beds:** 166 **Admissions:** 509 **Census:** 161 **Births:** 0 **Total Expense ($000):** 47553 **Payroll Expense ($000):** 21281 **Personnel:** 279

✠ **HEALTHSOUTH REHABILITATION HOSPITAL OF COLUMBIA (423025)**, (Formerly HEALTHSOUTH Rehabilitation Hospital), 2935 Colonial Drive, Zip 29203–6811; tel. 803/254–7777 **A**1 10 **F**2 29 34 35 54 56 57 59 64 74 75 77 79 86 87 90 91 92 95 96 130 131 132 148 **S** HEALTHSOUTH Corporation, Birmingham, AL
Primary Contact: W. Anthony Jackson, Chief Executive Officer
CFO: Jessica Burriss, Chief Financial Officer
CMO: Devin Troyer, M.D., Medical Director
CHR: Luanne Burton, Director Human Resources
Web address: www.healthsouthcolumbia.com
**Control:** Corporation, Investor–owned, for–profit **Service:** Rehabilitation

**Staffed Beds:** 96 **Admissions:** 1606 **Census:** 59 **Births:** 0 **Total Expense ($000):** 17674 **Payroll Expense ($000):** 9810 **Personnel:** 225

**INTERMEDICAL HOSPITAL OF SOUTH CAROLINA (422006)**, Taylor at Marion Street, Zip 29220, Mailing Address: PO BOX 11069, Zip 29211–1069; tel. 803/296–3757 **A**9 10 **F**1 3 29 34 57 85 130 148
Primary Contact: Armando Colombo, Chief Executive Officer
Web address: www.intermedicalhospital.com
**Control:** Other not–for–profit (including NFP Corporation) **Service:** Long–Term Acute Care hospital

**Staffed Beds:** 35 **Admissions:** 237 **Census:** 20 **Outpatient Visits:** 0 **Births:** 0 **Total Expense ($000):** 9967 **Payroll Expense ($000):** 3041 **Personnel:** 30

✠ **PALMETTO HEALTH BAPTIST (420086)**, Taylor at Marion Street, Zip 29220–0001; tel. 803/296–5010, (Total facility includes 22 beds in nursing home–type unit) **A**1 2 3 5 9 10 **F**1 3 5 11 12 13 15 18 20 29 30 31 34 35 40 45 47 48 49 51 54 57 59 61 62 63 64 68 70 71 72 73 74 75 76 77 78 79 80 81 82 84 85 86 87 89 90 98 99 100 101 102 103 104 105 107 108 110 111 112 114 115 116 117 118 119 124 128 130 132 145 146 147 148 **S** Palmetto Health, Columbia, SC
Primary Contact: James M. Bridges, Executive Vice President and Chief Operating Officer
COO: James M. Bridges, Executive Vice President and Chief Operating Officer
CFO: Paul K. Duane, Chief Financial Officer and Office of Health Reform
CMO: Mark J. Mayson, M.D., Medical Director
CIO: Michelle Edwards, Executive Vice President Information Technology
CHR: Trip Gregory, Senior Vice President Human Resources
Web address: www.palmettohealth.org
**Control:** Other not–for–profit (including NFP Corporation) **Service:** General Medical and Surgical

**Staffed Beds:** 412 **Admissions:** 18222 **Census:** 252 **Outpatient Visits:** 55674 **Births:** 3544 **Total Expense ($000):** 306770 **Payroll Expense ($000):** 123965 **Personnel:** 2071

✠ **PALMETTO HEALTH RICHLAND (420018)**, Five Richland Medical Park Drive, Zip 29203–6897; tel. 803/434–7000, (Includes PALMETTO HEALTH CHILDREN'S HOSPITAL, Five Richland Medical Park Drive, Zip 29203–6863; tel. 803/434–6882) **A**1 2 3 5 8 9 10 **F**2 3 4 5 6 11 13 15 17 18 20 22 24 28 29 30 31 32 34 35 39 40 41 43 45 46 54 55 56 57 59 60 61 64 68 70 72 73 74 75 76 77 78 79 81 86 87 88 89 90 97 98 99 100 101 102 103 104 105 107 108 110 111 114 118 119 121 126 129 130 131 132 134 135 143 146 147 148 **S** Palmetto Health, Columbia, SC
Primary Contact: Stan Hickson, FACHE, Executive Vice President and Chief Operating Officer
CFO: Paul K. Duane, Chief Financial Officer and Office of Health Reform
CMO: Jennifer Risinger, M.D., Chief of Staff
CHR: Trip Gregory, Senior Vice President Human Resources
Web address: www.palmettohealth.org
**Control:** Other not–for–profit (including NFP Corporation) **Service:** General Medical and Surgical

**Staffed Beds:** 674 **Admissions:** 30025 **Census:** 532 **Outpatient Visits:** 449274 **Births:** 2227 **Total Expense ($000):** 639802 **Payroll Expense ($000):** 245409 **Personnel:** 4442

✠ ◇ **PROVIDENCE HOSPITAL (420026)**, 2435 Forest Drive, Zip 29204–2098; tel. 803/865–4500, (Includes PROVIDENCE HOSPITAL NORTHEAST, 120 Gateway Corporate Boulevard, Zip 29203–9611; tel. 803/865–4500; Ryan Hall, Vice President) **A**1 9 10 21 **F**3 8 11 15 17 20 22 24 26 28 29 30 34 35 38 40 44 45 49 50 54 56 57 58 59 61 64 68 70 74 75 77 79 80 81 85 86 87 89 90 92 100 107 108 111 114 118 119 129 130 131 132 141 146 147 148 **P**5 **S** Sisters of Charity Health System, Cleveland, OH
Primary Contact: George A. Zara, President and Chief Executive Officer
COO: W. Carl Martin, Chief Operating Officer
CMO: Wayne Sribnick, M.D., Senior Vice President and Chief Medical Officer
CIO: Lib Cumbee, Director Information Systems
CHR: Richard W. Grooms, Jr., Vice President Human Resources
Web address: www.provhosp.com
**Control:** Church–operated, Nongovernment, not–for profit **Service:** General Medical and Surgical

**Staffed Beds:** 314 **Admissions:** 10707 **Census:** 143 **Births:** 0 **Total Expense ($000):** 231023 **Payroll Expense ($000):** 76310 **Personnel:** 1386

**SOUTH CAROLINA DEPARTMENT OF CORRECTIONS HOSPITAL**, 4344 Broad River Road, Zip 29210–4098; tel. 803/896–8567, (Nonreporting)
Primary Contact: John Solomon, M.D., Director
Web address: www.doc.sc.gov/
**Control:** State–Government, nonfederal **Service:** Hospital unit of an institution (prison hospital, college infirmary, etc.)

**Staffed Beds:** 70

☐ **WILLIAM S. HALL PSYCHIATRIC INSTITUTE (424003)**, 1800 Colonial Drive, Zip 29203–6827; tel. 803/898–1693 **A**1 3 5 10 **F**4 30 74 75 98 99 104 130 146
Primary Contact: Angela Forand, Director
COO: Doug Glover, Controller
CFO: Doug Glover, Controller
CMO: Phyllis Bryant–Mobley, M.D., Director Medical Services
CIO: Mesa Foard, Director Information technology
CHR: Kim Church, Manager Human Resources
Web address: www.scdmh.org
**Control:** State–Government, nonfederal **Service:** Psychiatric

**Staffed Beds:** 38 **Admissions:** 398 **Census:** 30 **Births:** 0 **Total Expense ($000):** 14811 **Payroll Expense ($000):** 9007 **Personnel:** 103

*Many Facility Codes have changed. Please refer to the AHA Guide Code Chart.* © 2013 AHA Guide

⊠ △ **WM. JENNINGS BRYAN DORN VETERANS AFFAIRS MEDICAL CENTER,** 6439 Garners Ferry Road, Zip 29209–1639; tel. 803/776–4000, (Nonreporting) **A**1 2 3 5 7 **S** Department of Veterans Affairs, Washington, DC
Primary Contact: Rebecca J. Wiley, R.N., Director
COO: Rebecca J. Stackhouse, Associate Director
CFO: James Cavanaugh, Chief Finance Officer
CMO: Alfred Boykin, M.D., Chief of Staff
CIO: David C. Owings, Director Information Management Service Line
CHR: Phyllis Jones, Chief Human Resources
Web address: www.columbiasc.va.gov/
**Control:** Veterans Affairs, Government, federal **Service:** General Medical and Surgical

**Staffed Beds:** 216

### CONWAY—Horry County

★ ◇ **CONWAY MEDICAL CENTER (420049),** 300 Singleton Ridge Road, Zip 29526–9142, Mailing Address: P.O. Box 829, Zip 29528–0829; tel. 843/347–7111, (Total facility includes 113 beds in nursing home–type unit) **A**9 10 21 **F**1 3 8 11 12 13 15 18 20 26 28 29 30 34 35 40 45 46 49 50 51 53 57 59 60 61 68 70 71 73 75 76 77 79 81 84 85 86 87 89 90 107 108 110 111 114 115 118 119 128 129 130 132 135 145 146 147 148
Primary Contact: Philip A. Clayton, President and Chief Executive Officer
CFO: Bret Barr, Vice President Fiscal Services
CMO: Preston Strosnider, M.D., Vice President Medical Affairs
CIO: Mickey Waters, Director Information Technology
CHR: Craig Hyman, Vice President Human Resources
Web address: www.conwaymedicalcenter.com
**Control:** Other not–for–profit (including NFP Corporation) **Service:** General Medical and Surgical

**Staffed Beds:** 287 **Admissions:** 7567 **Census:** 190 **Outpatient Visits:** 60643 **Births:** 1257 **Total Expense ($000):** 130710 **Payroll Expense ($000):** 46760 **Personnel:** 1131

☐ **LIGHTHOUSE CARE CENTER OF CONWAY (424002),** 152 Waccamaw Medical Park Drive, Zip 29526–8901; tel. 843/347–8871 **A**1 9 10 **F**1 4 98 101 102 103 106 128 130 **S** Universal Health Services, Inc., King of Prussia, PA
Primary Contact: Thomas L. Ryba, Chief Executive Officer
CFO: Chris Frater, Chief Financial Officer
CMO: William Van Horn, M.D., Medical Director
CIO: Chris Frater, Chief Financial Officer
CHR: Lois Woodall, Director Human Resources
CNO: Penny Muckenfuss, Chief Nursing Officer
Web address: www.lighthousecarecenterofconway.com/
**Control:** Corporation, Investor–owned, for–profit **Service:** Psychiatric

**Staffed Beds:** 72 **Admissions:** 2028 **Census:** 48 **Outpatient Visits:** 0 **Births:** 0 **Personnel:** 115

### DARLINGTON—Darlington County

**MCLEOD MEDICAL CENTER–DARLINGTON** See McLeod Regional Medical Center, Florence

### DILLON—Dillon County

⊠ **MCLEOD MEDICAL CENTER DILLON (420005),** 301 East Jackson Street, Zip 29536–2509, Mailing Address: P.O. Box 1327, Zip 29536–1327; tel. 843/774–4111 **A**1 9 10 **F**3 11 13 15 28 29 30 32 34 35 40 50 57 59 64 68 70 75 76 79 81 82 85 87 89 90 107 111 114 119 130 132 134 135 146 147 148 **P**6 **S** McLeod Health, Florence, SC
Primary Contact: Deborah Locklair, FACHE, Administrator
CFO: Fulton Ervin, Senior Vice President and Chief Financial Officer
CMO: Walter B. Blum, M.D., Chief of Staff
CIO: Jenean Blackmon, Assistant Vice President and Chief Information Officer
CHR: Cynthia Causey, Associate Administrator Human and Mission Services
Web address: www.mcleodhealth.org
**Control:** Other not–for–profit (including NFP Corporation) **Service:** General Medical and Surgical

**Staffed Beds:** 63 **Admissions:** 2747 **Census:** 24 **Outpatient Visits:** 29645 **Births:** 312 **Total Expense ($000):** 37245 **Payroll Expense ($000):** 14864 **Personnel:** 295

### EASLEY—Pickens County

⊠ **BAPTIST EASLEY HOSPITAL (420015),** 200 Fleetwood Drive, Zip 29640–2022, Mailing Address: P.O. Box 2129, Zip 29641–2129; tel. 864/442–7200 **A**1 9 10 **F**3 11 13 15 20 28 29 30 35 39 40 56 57 59 64 70 75 76 79 81 85 86 87 89 107 108 111 114 119 130 132 146 147 148 **P**8 **S** Palmetto Health, Columbia, SC
Primary Contact: Roddey E. Gettys, III, Chief Executive Officer
COO: Roddey E. Gettys, III, Chief Executive Officer
CFO: J. Larry Pope, Vice President Finance
CIO: Cynthia Ellenburg, Director Health Information Services
CHR: Richard B. Posey, Director Human Resources
CNO: Mary Ann Hunter, Director Nursing Services
Web address: www.baptisteasley.org
**Control:** Other not–for–profit (including NFP Corporation) **Service:** General Medical and Surgical

**Staffed Beds:** 89 **Admissions:** 4720 **Census:** 56 **Births:** 468 **Total Expense ($000):** 81193 **Payroll Expense ($000):** 29362 **Personnel:** 703

### EDGEFIELD—Edgefield County

★ **EDGEFIELD COUNTY HOSPITAL (421304),** 300 Ridge Medical Plaza, Zip 29824–4525; tel. 803/637–3174 **A**9 10 18 **F**3 11 34 35 40 45 57 59 65 66 68 75 77 79 81 90 97 107 114 119 127 128 130 132 133 146
Primary Contact: Brandon Clary, Chief Executive Officer
CFO: William Garry, Chief Financial Officer
CMO: W. Hugh Morgan, M.D., Chief Medical Staff
CIO: Faye Burton, Director Health Information Management
CHR: Leslie G. Seigler, Executive Assistant and Coordinator Human Resources
Web address: www.myech.org
**Control:** County–Government, nonfederal **Service:** General Medical and Surgical

**Staffed Beds:** 25 **Admissions:** 409 **Census:** 6 **Births:** 0 **Total Expense ($000):** 12603 **Payroll Expense ($000):** 6336 **Personnel:** 161

### FAIRFAX—Allendale County

★ **ALLENDALE COUNTY HOSPITAL (421300),** 1787 Allendale Fairfax Highway, Zip 29827–9133, Mailing Address: P.O. Box 218, Zip 29827–0218; tel. 803/632–3311, (Total facility includes 44 beds in nursing home–type unit) **A**9 10 18 **F**1 3 15 34 35 40 56 57 59 61 64 67 68 77 87 90 97 107 110 114 119 127 128 130 133 147 **P**6
Primary Contact: M. K. Hiatt, Administrator
Web address: www.allendalecountyhospital.com/
**Control:** County–Government, nonfederal **Service:** General Medical and Surgical

**Staffed Beds:** 69 **Admissions:** 297 **Census:** 42 **Outpatient Visits:** 27050 **Births:** 0 **Total Expense ($000):** 11493 **Payroll Expense ($000):** 6438 **Personnel:** 184

### FLORENCE—Florence County

⊠ △ **CAROLINAS HOSPITAL SYSTEM (420091),** 805 Pamplico Highway, Zip 29505–6050, Mailing Address: P.O. Box 100550, Zip 29502–0550; tel. 843/674–5000, (Total facility includes 24 beds in nursing home–type unit) **A**1 7 9 10 **F**4 5 6 7 8 11 13 15 17 20 22 24 28 29 30 31 34 35 38 40 43 45 53 55 56 57 58 59 60 61 62 63 64 65 68 70 71 72 73 74 75 76 77 78 79 81 82 86 87 88 89 90 97 98 103 104 107 108 110 111 114 115 116 117 119 121 123 128 129 130 131 132 135 143 144 146 147 148 **S** Community Health Systems, Inc., Franklin, TN
Primary Contact: Darcy Craven, Chief Executive Officer
CFO: Steve Embree, Chief Financial Officer
CMO: James Brennan, M.D., Chief of Staff
CIO: Marty Parker, Chief Information Officer
CHR: Tammy Dickerson, Director Human Resources
Web address: www.carolinashospital.com
**Control:** Corporation, Investor–owned, for–profit **Service:** General Medical and Surgical

**Staffed Beds:** 429 **Admissions:** 13440 **Census:** 222 **Births:** 946 **Total Expense ($000):** 179997 **Payroll Expense ($000):** 64922 **Personnel:** 1349

⊠ **HEALTHSOUTH REHABILITATION HOSPITAL (423026),** 900 East Cheves Street, Zip 29506–2704; tel. 843/679–9000 **A**1 10 **F**9 29 34 35 56 57 59 64 75 77 82 86 87 90 91 92 95 96 130 131 132 148 **S** HEALTHSOUTH Corporation, Birmingham, AL
Primary Contact: Jill Strawn, Chief Executive Officer
CFO: Robert Wheeler, Controller
CMO: Adora Matthews, M.D., Medical Director
CHR: Susan Trantham, Director Human Resources
Web address: www.healthsouthflorence.com
**Control:** Corporation, Investor–owned, for–profit **Service:** Rehabilitation

**Staffed Beds:** 88 **Admissions:** 1120 **Census:** 43 **Births:** 0 **Total Expense ($000):** 13279 **Payroll Expense ($000):** 7180 **Personnel:** 160

**SC**

---

**Hospital, Medicare Provider Number, Address, Telephone, Approval, Facility, and Physician Codes, Health Care System**

★ American Hospital Association (AHA) membership
☐ The Joint Commission accreditation  ◇ DNV Healthcare Inc. accreditation
○ Healthcare Facilities Accreditation Program
△ Commission on Accreditation of Rehabilitation Facilities (CARF) accreditation

✠ **MCLEOD REGIONAL MEDICAL CENTER (420051)**, 555 East Cheves Street, Zip 29506–2617, Mailing Address: P.O. Box 100551, Zip 29502–0551; tel. 843/777–2000, (Includes MCLEOD MEDICAL CENTER–DARLINGTON, 701 Cashua Ferry Road, Darlington, Zip 29532–8488, Mailing Address: P.O. Box 1859, Zip 29540; tel. 843/395–1100; Pat Godbold, Administrator) **A**1 2 3 5 9 10 **F**1 3 7 8 11 13 15 17 18 20 22 24 26 28 29 30 31 32 34 35 38 39 40 43 45 46 47 48 49 52 53 54 56 57 58 59 60 61 62 63 64 66 67 68 70 71 72 73 74 75 76 77 78 79 80 81 82 84 85 86 87 88 89 90 92 96 97 98 100 101 102 103 104 107 108 110 111 114 115 116 119 121 127 128 129 130 131 132 133 135 143 145 146 147 148 **P**6 **S** McLeod Health, Florence, SC
Primary Contact: Robert L. Colones, President and Chief Executive Officer
COO: Ronald L. Boring, Senior Vice President and Chief Operating Officer
CFO: Fulton Ervin, Chief Financial Officer
CMO: Alva W. Whitehead, M.D., Vice President Medical Services
CIO: Jenean Blackmon, Associate Vice President and Chief Information Officer
CHR: Jeannette Glenn, Vice President Human Resources, Education and Training
Web address: www.mcleodhealth.org
**Control:** Other not–for–profit (including NFP Corporation) **Service:** General Medical and Surgical

Staffed Beds: 538 **Admissions:** 24707 **Census:** 381 **Births:** 2018 **Total Expense ($000):** 469001 **Payroll Expense ($000):** 165218 **Personnel:** 3056

✠ **REGENCY HOSPITAL OF FLORENCE (422007)**, 121 East Cedar Street, 4th Floor, Zip 29506–2576; tel. 843/661–3499 **A**1 10 **F**1 3 29 34 35 57 58 70 77 80 82 84 85 90 100 130 148 **S** Select Medical Corporation, Mechanicsburg, PA
Primary Contact: Darrell Jones, Chief Executive Officer
COO: Alisa Jett, Director Clinical Services
CMO: Stephen Dersch, M.D., President Medical Staff
CHR: Tina Stokes, Manager Human Resources
CNO: Amy Metz, Chief Nursing Officer
Web address: www.regencyhospital.com
**Control:** Corporation, Investor–owned, for–profit **Service:** Long–Term Acute Care hospital

Staffed Beds: 40 **Admissions:** 428 **Census:** 30 **Outpatient Visits:** 0 **Births:** 0 **Total Expense ($000):** 15014 **Payroll Expense ($000):** 6076 **Personnel:** 127

**FORT JACKSON—Richland County**

✠ **MONCRIEF ARMY COMMUNITY HOSPITAL**, 4500 Stuart Street, Zip 29207–5700; tel. 803/751–2160, (Nonreporting) **A**1 3 5 **S** Department of the Army, Office of the Surgeon General, Falls Church, VA
Primary Contact: Colonel Mark L. Higdon, Commander
CMO: Lieutenant Colonel Larry Andrew, M.D., Deputy Commander Clinical Services
Web address: www.moncrief.amedd.army.mil
**Control:** Army, Government, federal **Service:** General Medical and Surgical

Staffed Beds: 60

**GAFFNEY—Cherokee County**

✠ **NOVANT HEALTH GAFFNEY MEDICAL CENTER (420043)**, (Formerly Upstate Carolina Medical Center), 1530 North Limestone Street, Zip 29340–4738; tel. 864/487–4271 **A**1 9 10 **F**3 11 13 15 18 19 29 35 40 45 46 51 57 59 64 67 70 75 76 79 81 82 85 86 87 89 107 108 110 111 114 119 129 130 135 146 147 148 **S** Novant Health, Winston Salem, NC
Primary Contact: Brian Yates, Administrator
CMO: Steven Lewis, M.D., Chief of Staff
CIO: Richard Bledsoe, Director Information Systems
CHR: Connie Gibson, R.N., Director Human Resources
Web address: www.upstatecarolina.org
**Control:** Other not–for–profit (including NFP Corporation) **Service:** General Medical and Surgical

Staffed Beds: 125 **Admissions:** 2604 **Census:** 28 **Outpatient Visits:** 38518 **Births:** 350 **Personnel:** 318

**GEORGETOWN—Georgetown County**

✠ **GEORGETOWN MEMORIAL HOSPITAL (420020)**, 606 Black River Road, Zip 29440–3368, Mailing Address: Drawer 421718, Zip 29442–4203; tel. 843/527–7000 **A**1 3 5 9 10 19 **F**3 11 12 13 15 17 18 20 22 26 28 29 30 31 32 34 35 39 40 45 50 51 53 54 56 57 59 60 61 64 65 68 70 73 74 75 76 77 78 79 81 82 84 85 86 87 89 90 97 100 102 107 108 109 110 111 115 118 119 130 131 132 135 146 147 148 **S** Georgetown Hospital System, Georgetown, SC
Primary Contact: Bruce P. Bailey, Chief Executive Officer
COO: Gayle L. Resetar, Vice President and Chief Operating Officer
CFO: Terry L. Kiser, Vice President and Chief Financial Officer
CIO: Frank Scafidi, Vice President and Chief Information Officer
CHR: James F. Harper, Vice President and Chief Human Resources Officer
Web address: www.georgetownhospitalsystem.org
**Control:** Other not–for–profit (including NFP Corporation) **Service:** General Medical and Surgical

Staffed Beds: 131 **Admissions:** 4900 **Census:** 51 **Outpatient Visits:** 146329 **Births:** 330 **Total Expense ($000):** 108885 **Payroll Expense ($000):** 43540 **Personnel:** 767

**GREENVILLE—Greenville County**

✠ △ **BON SECOURS ST. FRANCIS HEALTH SYSTEM (420023)**, One St. Francis Drive, Zip 29601–3207; tel. 864/255–1000, (Includes BON SECOURS ST. FRANCIS EASTSIDE, 125 Commonwealth Drive, Zip 29615–4812; tel. 864/675–4000) **A**1 2 7 9 10 **F**3 8 12 13 15 17 18 20 22 24 26 28 29 30 31 34 35 40 44 45 48 49 50 57 59 60 64 68 70 73 74 75 76 77 78 79 80 81 82 84 85 86 87 89 90 93 96 107 108 110 111 114 115 119 126 128 130 131 132 135 136 145 146 147 148 **P**6 **S** Bon Secours Health System, Inc., Marriottsville, MD
Primary Contact: Mark S. Nantz, FACHE, Chief Executive Officer
CFO: Ronnie Hyatt, Senior Vice President Finance and Chief Financial Officer
CMO: Mary Jo Cagle, M.D., Chief Medical Officer
CIO: Rita Hooker, Administrative Director Information Services
CHR: Lisa C. Slayton, Senior Vice President Human Resources
Web address: www.stfrancishealth.org
**Control:** Other not–for–profit (including NFP Corporation) **Service:** General Medical and Surgical

Staffed Beds: 331 **Admissions:** 18935 **Census:** 229 **Births:** 2184 **Total Expense ($000):** 388682 **Payroll Expense ($000):** 132200 **Personnel:** 1746

✠ △ **GREENVILLE MEMORIAL HOSPITAL (420078)**, 701 Grove Road, Zip 29605–4295; tel. 864/455–7000, (Includes CHILDREN'S HOSPITAL, 701 Grove Road, Zip 29605–5611; tel. 864/455–7000; MARSHALL I. PICKENS HOSPITAL, 701 Grove Road, Zip 29605–5601; tel. 864/455–8988; ROGER C. PEACE REHABILITATION HOSPITAL, 701 Grove Road, tel. 864/455–7000), (Total facility includes 44 beds in nursing home–type unit) **A**1 2 3 5 7 8 9 10 **F**1 3 4 5 11 13 15 17 18 19 20 22 24 26 28 29 30 31 34 35 36 38 39 40 41 43 44 45 46 47 48 49 50 52 53 54 56 57 58 59 61 62 64 65 66 68 70 72 73 74 75 76 77 78 79 81 83 84 85 86 87 88 89 90 92 96 97 98 99 100 101 102 103 104 105 106 107 110 111 114 115 118 119 120 121 124 126 128 129 130 132 134 135 136 141 142 145 146 147 148 **P**6 **S** Greenville Health System, Greenville, SC
Primary Contact: Paul F. Johnson, President
CNO: Michelle T. Smith, R.N., Chief Nursing Officer
Web address: www.ghs.org
**Control:** Other not–for–profit (including NFP Corporation) **Service:** General Medical and Surgical

Staffed Beds: 820 **Admissions:** 33432 **Census:** 674 **Outpatient Visits:** 474574 **Births:** 4900 **Total Expense ($000):** 678136 **Payroll Expense ($000):** 212119 **Personnel:** 4515

✠ **PATEWOOD MEMORIAL HOSPITAL (420102)**, 175 Patewood Drive, Zip 29615–3570; tel. 864/797–1000 **A**1 9 10 **F**1 3 11 29 30 37 50 54 64 77 81 85 107 114 119 128 130 146 **P**6 **S** Greenville Health System, Greenville, SC
Primary Contact: Beverly J. Haines, R.N., President
Web address: www.ghs.org/patewood
**Control:** Other not–for–profit (including NFP Corporation) **Service:** Surgical

Staffed Beds: 36 **Admissions:** 1110 **Census:** 7 **Outpatient Visits:** 2505 **Births:** 0 **Total Expense ($000):** 39577 **Payroll Expense ($000):** 9674 **Personnel:** 168

✠ **REGENCY HOSPITAL OF GREENVILLE (422009)**, One St. Francis Drive, 4th Floor, Zip 29601–3955; tel. 864/255–1438 **A**1 10 **F**1 3 29 34 56 57 60 75 77 82 85 86 87 90 130 148 **S** Select Medical Corporation, Mechanicsburg, PA
Primary Contact: Stephanie James, Chief Executive Officer
Web address: www.regencyhospital.com
**Control:** Corporation, Investor–owned, for–profit **Service:** Long–Term Acute Care hospital

Staffed Beds: 32 **Admissions:** 371 **Census:** 27 **Outpatient Visits:** 0 **Births:** 0 **Total Expense ($000):** 14056 **Payroll Expense ($000):** 5352 **Personnel:** 49

☐ **SHRINERS HOSPITALS FOR CHILDREN–GREENVILLE**, 950 West Faris Road, Zip 29605–4277; tel. 864/271–3444 **A**1 3 5 9 **F**29 59 64 68 75 77 79 81 85 87 89 90 128 130 131 146 148 **P**6 **S** Shriners Hospitals for Children, Tampa, FL
Primary Contact: Randall R. Romberger, Administrator
CFO: John Conti, Director Finance
CMO: Peter J. Stasikelis, M.D., Chief of Staff
CHR: Willis E. Tisdale, Director Human Resources
CNO: Ranae M. Thompson, MSN, Director Patient Care Services
Web address: www.shrinershospitalsforchildren.org/Hospitals/Locations/Greenville.aspx
**Control:** Other not–for–profit (including NFP Corporation) **Service:** Children's orthopedic

Staffed Beds: 15 **Admissions:** 287 **Census:** 2 **Outpatient Visits:** 17855 **Births:** 0 **Personnel:** 162

*Many Facility Codes have changed. Please refer to the AHA Guide Code Chart.*   © 2013 AHA Guide

**SC**

## GREENWOOD—Greenwood County

☐ **GREENWOOD REGIONAL REHABILITATION HOSPITAL (423030)**, 1530 Parkway, Zip 29646–4027; tel. 864/330–9070, (Total facility includes 12 beds in nursing home–type unit) **A**1 10 **F**3 29 75 90 128 130 132 143 148 **S** Ernest Health, Inc., Albuquerque, NM
Primary Contact: Kerry A. Trapnell, Chief Executive Officer
Web address: www.grrh.ernesthealth.com
**Control:** Corporation, Investor–owned, for–profit **Service:** Rehabilitation

**Staffed Beds:** 56 **Admissions:** 995 **Census:** 38 **Outpatient Visits:** 0 **Births:** 0 **Personnel:** 143

☒ **SELF REGIONAL HEALTHCARE (420071)**, 1325 Spring Street, Zip 29646–3860; tel. 864/725–4111 **A**1 2 3 5 9 10 **F**3 8 11 13 15 17 18 20 22 24 26 28 29 30 31 32 34 35 39 40 43 49 50 51 53 57 59 60 62 64 68 70 72 73 74 75 76 77 78 79 80 81 82 84 86 87 89 90 97 98 102 107 108 110 111 114 115 117 119 120 121 123 124 129 130 131 132 134 135 144 146 147 148 **P**4 5 7 8
Primary Contact: James A. Pfeiffer, FACHE, President and Chief Executive Officer
COO: Camie Patterson, Senior Vice President and Chief Operating Officer
CFO: Timothy Evans, Vice President and Chief Financial Officer
CMO: F Gregory Mappin, M.D., Vice President Medical Affairs
CIO: Chuck McDevitt, Chief Information Officer
CHR: Michael Dixon, Director Human Resources
Web address: www.selfregional.org
**Control:** County–Government, nonfederal **Service:** General Medical and Surgical

**Staffed Beds:** 294 **Admissions:** 11783 **Census:** 143 **Outpatient Visits:** 59946 **Births:** 1474 **Total Expense ($000):** 288807 **Payroll Expense ($000):** 105543 **Personnel:** 1942

## GREER—Greenville County

☐ **CAROLINA CENTER FOR BEHAVIORAL HEALTH (424010)**, 2700 East Phillips Road, Zip 29650–4816; tel. 864/235–2335 **A**1 9 10 **F**4 5 56 98 99 100 101 102 103 104 105 130 **S** Universal Health Services, Inc., King of Prussia, PA
Primary Contact: John Willingham, Chief Executive Officer and Managing Director
CFO: Jeff Skelton, Chief Financial Officer
CMO: Ralph Castriotta, M.D., Medical Director
CHR: George Hammett, Director Human Resources
Web address: www.thecarolinacenter.com
**Control:** Corporation, Investor–owned, for–profit **Service:** Psychiatric

**Staffed Beds:** 112 **Admissions:** 3275 **Census:** 96 **Outpatient Visits:** 10626 **Births:** 0 **Total Expense ($000):** 20530 **Payroll Expense ($000):** 10227 **Personnel:** 237

☒ **GREER MEMORIAL HOSPITAL (420033)**, 830 South Bumcombe Road, Zip 29650–2400; tel. 864/797–8000, (Includes ROGER HUNTINGTON NURSING CENTER ) **A**1 9 10 **F**1 3 11 13 15 18 29 30 34 40 44 47 49 50 57 59 61 64 65 68 70 76 77 79 81 82 85 86 87 89 107 110 111 114 119 128 129 130 146 147 **P**6 **S** Greenville Health System, Greenville, SC
Primary Contact: John F. Mansure, FACHE, President
Web address: www.ghs.org
**Control:** Other not–for–profit (including NFP Corporation) **Service:** General Medical and Surgical

**Staffed Beds:** 70 **Admissions:** 3468 **Census:** 30 **Outpatient Visits:** 94587 **Births:** 675 **Total Expense ($000):** 66603 **Payroll Expense ($000):** 22604 **Personnel:** 377

☒ **VILLAGE HOSPITAL (420103)**, 250 Westmoreland Road, Zip 29651–9013; tel. 864/530–6000 **A**1 9 10 **F**1 3 11 15 18 29 30 34 35 37 40 45 49 50 54 57 59 64 68 70 74 75 77 79 81 82 84 85 86 87 90 107 108 110 111 114 115 119 128 130 146 **S** Spartanburg Regional Healthcare System, Spartanburg, SC
Primary Contact: Anthony Kouskolekas, President
Web address: www.villageatpelham.com
**Control:** Hospital district or authority, Government, nonfederal **Service:** General Medical and Surgical

**Staffed Beds:** 34 **Admissions:** 1496 **Census:** 14 **Outpatient Visits:** 35373 **Births:** 0 **Total Expense ($000):** 38067 **Payroll Expense ($000):** 12771 **Personnel:** 320

## HARDEEVILLE—Jasper County

☒ **COASTAL CAROLINA HOSPITAL (420101)**, 1000 Medical Center Drive, Zip 29927–3446; tel. 843/784–8000, **A**1 9 10 **F**3 11 15 28 29 30 34 35 40 46 47 48 49 51 57 59 60 64 70 74 75 77 79 81 85 89 107 108 110 111 114 119 127 128 130 131 132 135 146 147 148 **S** TENET Healthcare Corporation, Dallas, TX
Primary Contact: Bradley S. Talbert, FACHE, Chief Executive Officer
CFO: Drew Shea, Chief Financial Officer
CIO: Carnel Aiken, Director Information Systems
CHR: Darlene Nester, Market Chief Human Resources Officer
Web address: www.coastalhospital.com
**Control:** Corporation, Investor–owned, for–profit **Service:** General Medical and Surgical

**Staffed Beds:** 41 **Admissions:** 1780 **Census:** 17 **Outpatient Visits:** 54771 **Births:** 0 **Total Expense ($000):** 32260 **Payroll Expense ($000):** 10740 **Personnel:** 234

## HARTSVILLE—Darlington County

☐ **CAROLINA PINES REGIONAL MEDICAL CENTER (420010)**, 1304 West Bobo Newsom Highway, Zip 29550–4710; tel. 843/339–2100 **A**1 9 10 **F**3 11 13 15 20 28 29 30 34 35 40 43 46 49 57 59 60 64 70 73 74 75 76 79 81 82 85 86 87 89 90 107 108 111 115 118 119 129 130 131 132 146 147 148 **S** Health Management Associates, Naples, FL
Primary Contact: J. Timothy Browne, FACHE, Chief Executive Officer
CFO: Michael Cherry, Chief Financial Officer
CIO: Denise Barefoot, Director Health Information Systems
CHR: Charlotte Adams, Director Associate Resources
Web address: www.cprmc.com
**Control:** Corporation, Investor–owned, for–profit **Service:** General Medical and Surgical

**Staffed Beds:** 116 **Admissions:** 5204 **Census:** 49 **Births:** 593 **Total Expense ($000):** 63467 **Payroll Expense ($000):** 22418 **Personnel:** 289

## HILTON HEAD ISLAND—Beaufort County

☒ **HILTON HEAD HOSPITAL (420080)**, 25 Hospital Center Boulevard, Zip 29926–2738; tel. 843/681–6122 **A**1 9 10 20 **F**3 11 13 15 17 18 20 22 24 26 28 29 30 32 34 35 40 46 47 48 49 50 51 53 54 57 59 60 61 64 65 68 70 74 76 77 78 79 81 84 85 86 89 96 107 110 111 114 115 118 119 130 131 132 135 146 147 148 **S** TENET Healthcare Corporation, Dallas, TX
Primary Contact: Mark T. O'Neil, Jr., President and Chief Executive Officer
CFO: Cassie Ball, Chief Financial Officer
CMO: Glenn Neil Love, M.D., Medical Director
CIO: Stephen Brendler, Director Information Systems
CHR: Darlene Nester, Chief Human Resources Officer
Web address: www.hiltonheadregional.com
**Control:** Partnership, Investor–owned, for–profit **Service:** General Medical and Surgical

**Staffed Beds:** 93 **Admissions:** 5115 **Census:** 51 **Births:** 670 **Total Expense ($000):** 87238 **Payroll Expense ($000):** 22539 **Personnel:** 508

## KINGSTREE—Williamsburg County

☒ **WILLIAMSBURG REGIONAL HOSPITAL (421303)**, 500 Nelson Boulevard, Zip 29556–4027; tel. 843/355–8888 **A**1 9 10 18 **F**3 11 15 28 29 30 31 34 35 40 50 57 59 64 68 70 77 78 79 81 85 86 87 89 90 97 107 108 114 119 127 128 129 130 133 135 146 148
Primary Contact: Sharon Poston, Chief Executive Officer
COO: Dan Harrington, Chief Operating Officer and Director Human Resources
CFO: Judy Gamble, Chief Financial Officer
CMO: Frank Trefney, M.D., Chief Medical Staff
CIO: Jamie Newsom, Director Information Systems
Web address: www.wmbgrh.com/
**Control:** Other not–for–profit (including NFP Corporation) **Service:** General Medical and Surgical

**Staffed Beds:** 25 **Admissions:** 824 **Census:** 11 **Outpatient Visits:** 25697 **Births:** 0 **Personnel:** 150

**SC**

---

**Hospital, Medicare Provider Number, Address, Telephone, Approval, Facility, and Physician Codes, Health Care System**

★ American Hospital Association (AHA) membership
☐ The Joint Commission accreditation
◇ DNV Healthcare Inc. accreditation
○ Healthcare Facilities Accreditation Program
△ Commission on Accreditation of Rehabilitation Facilities (CARF) accreditation

## LAKE CITY—Florence County

★ **LAKE CITY COMMUNITY HOSPITAL (420066)**, 258 North Ron McNair Boulevard, Zip 29560–2462, Mailing Address: P.O. Box 1479, Zip 29560–1479; tel. 843/374–2036 **A**9 10 **F**11 15 28 29 30 34 35 40 50 56 57 59 61 64 69 75 77 79 81 86 90 107 108 111 114 119 127 130 146
Primary Contact: Henry McCutcheon, Jr., Chief Executive Officer
CFO: Henry McCutcheon, Jr., Chief Financial Officer
CMO: Stephen Askins, M.D., Chief of Staff
CIO: Kimberly Glover, Director of Information Systems
CHR: Anne Poston, Director of Human Resources/Compliance
CNO: Renate Browder, R.N., Director of Nursing
Web address: www.lcchospital.org
**Control:** Hospital district or authority, Government, nonfederal **Service:** General Medical and Surgical

**Staffed Beds:** 30 **Admissions:** 874 **Census:** 8 **Outpatient Visits:** 17796 **Births:** 0 **Total Expense ($000):** 16566 **Payroll Expense ($000):** 6423 **Personnel:** 175

## LANCASTER—Lancaster County

✠ **SPRINGS MEMORIAL HOSPITAL (420036)**, 800 West Meeting Street, Zip 29720–2298; tel. 803/286–1214, (Total facility includes 14 beds in nursing home–type unit) **A**1 5 9 10 **F**1 3 8 11 13 15 17 18 20 29 30 31 34 35 40 43 47 48 49 51 57 59 60 62 63 64 68 70 73 74 75 76 78 79 80 81 85 89 90 102 107 108 110 111 114 115 118 119 128 129 132 135 146 147 **S** Community Health Systems, Inc., Franklin, TN
Primary Contact: Janice Dabney, Interim Chief Executive Officer
CFO: Nathan Crabtree, Chief Financial Officer
CMO: Keith Shealy, M.D., Chief of Staff
CIO: Chrys Steele, Director Information Systems
CHR: Trent Elmore, Director Human Resources
Web address: www.springsmemorial.com
**Control:** Corporation, Investor–owned, for–profit **Service:** General Medical and Surgical

**Staffed Beds:** 186 **Admissions:** 7652 **Census:** 94 **Births:** 734 **Total Expense ($000):** 91134 **Payroll Expense ($000):** 29112 **Personnel:** 635

## LORIS—Horry County

✠ **MCLEOD LORIS SEACOAST HOSPITAL (420105)**, 3655 Mitchell Street, Zip 29569–2827; tel. 843/716–7000, (Includes MCLEOD SEACOAST, 4000 Highway 9 East, Little River, Zip 29566–7833; tel. 843/390–8100), (Total facility includes 88 beds in nursing home–type unit) **A**1 9 10 **F**1 3 11 13 15 17 18 20 28 29 30 32 34 35 40 50 53 57 59 60 64 65 68 70 74 75 76 77 79 80 81 82 84 85 86 87 89 90 93 94 96 107 108 110 111 114 115 118 119 128 129 130 131 132 134 135 146 148 **P**6 **S** McLeod Health, Florence, SC
Primary Contact: Edward D. Tinsley, III, Chief Executive Officer
COO: Arnold Green, Senior Vice President and Chief Operating Officer
CFO: Fred O. Todd, Senior Vice President Finance
CMO: James N. Craigie, M.D., Vice President Medical Affairs
CHR: Teresa Pougnaud, Vice President Human Resources
Web address: www.mcleodhealth.org
**Control:** Other not–for–profit (including NFP Corporation) **Service:** General Medical and Surgical

**Staffed Beds:** 243 **Admissions:** 4208 **Census:** 109 **Outpatient Visits:** 111477 **Births:** 408 **Total Expense ($000):** 102087 **Payroll Expense ($000):** 34745 **Personnel:** 682

## MANNING—Clarendon County

✠ ◇ **CLARENDON MEMORIAL HOSPITAL (420069)**, 10 Hospital Street, Zip 29102–3153, Mailing Address: P.O. Box 550, Zip 29102–0550; tel. 803/435–8463 **A**1 9 10 21 **F**1 3 7 11 13 15 28 29 30 35 39 40 45 50 53 54 56 57 59 62 64 65 67 70 75 76 77 79 81 85 89 90 91 96 107 108 110 111 114 118 119 127 128 129 130 132 135 143 146 147
Primary Contact: Edward R. Frye, Jr., Chief Executive Officer
COO: Eleyce Winn, Assistant Administrator
CFO: Richard Stokes, CPA, Chief Financial Officer
CMO: Beryl Bachus Keith, M.D., Chief of Staff
CIO: Pat Kolb, Manager Information Technology
CHR: Gail R. Duke, Director Human Resources
Web address: www.clarendonhealth.com
**Control:** Hospital district or authority, Government, nonfederal **Service:** General Medical and Surgical

**Staffed Beds:** 56 **Admissions:** 2659 **Census:** 29 **Outpatient Visits:** 144475 **Births:** 596 **Total Expense ($000):** 40514 **Payroll Expense ($000):** 17317 **Personnel:** 506

## MOUNT PLEASANT—Charleston County

✠ **EAST COOPER MEDICAL CENTER (420089)**, 2000 Hospital Drive, Zip 29464–3764; tel. 843/881–0100 **A**1 3 5 9 10 **F**3 13 15 18 29 31 34 35 40 43 46 57 59 64 70 73 74 75 76 77 78 79 80 81 82 84 85 86 90 92 107 108 110 111 114 115 119 129 130 131 132 135 146 147 148 **S** TENET Healthcare Corporation, Dallas, TX
Primary Contact: Jason P. Alexander, FACHE, Chief Executive Officer
CFO: Brandon Willams, Chief Financial Officer
CMO: William Stroud, M.D., Physician Advisor
CIO: David Karinshak, Director Information Systems
CHR: Tracy Hunter, Chief Human Resources Officer
CNO: Cathy Landis, R.N., Chief Nursing Officer
Web address: www.eastcoopermedctr.com
**Control:** Corporation, Investor–owned, for–profit **Service:** General Medical and Surgical

**Staffed Beds:** 140 **Admissions:** 4853 **Census:** 41 **Outpatient Visits:** 59002 **Births:** 1415 **Total Expense ($000):** 107500 **Payroll Expense ($000):** 25541 **Personnel:** 442

✠ **MOUNT PLEASANT HOSPITAL (420104)**, 3500 Highway 17 North, Zip 29466–9123, Mailing Address: 3500 North Highway 17, Zip 29466–9123; tel. 843/606–7000 **A**1 9 10 **F**3 7 13 15 29 30 34 40 45 57 68 70 75 76 79 81 84 85 86 87 89 107 108 110 111 115 118 119 129 143 147 148 **S** Carolinas HealthCare System, Charlotte, NC
Primary Contact: John Sullivan, Chief Executive Officer
COO: John Sullivan, Chief Executive Officer
CFO: Bret Johnson, Chief Financial Officer
CMO: Steven D. Shapiro, M.D., Chief Medical Officer
CIO: Michael Taylor, Chief Information Officer
CHR: Doug Harrison, VP of Human Resources
CNO: Diana Topjian, MSN, Vice President and Chief Nursing Executive
Web address: www.mymountpleasanthospital.com
**Control:** Other not–for–profit (including NFP Corporation) **Service:** General Medical and Surgical

**Staffed Beds:** 50 **Admissions:** 1424 **Census:** 11 **Outpatient Visits:** 36081 **Births:** 432 **Total Expense ($000):** 45470 **Payroll Expense ($000):** 12138 **Personnel:** 279

## MT. PLEASANT—Mt. Pleasant County

★ **KINDRED HOSPITAL–CHARLESTON (422005)**, 1200 Hospital Drive, Zip 29464; tel. 843/876–8670 **A**10 **F**1 3 17 29 35 60 70 90 148 **S** Kindred Healthcare, Louisville, KY
Primary Contact: Stephanie Bridges, Interim Chief Executive Officer
CFO: Julia Smith, Chief Financial Officer
CMO: Athena Beldecos, M.D., Medical Director
CHR: Julia Taylor, Area Director Human Resources
Web address: www.khcharleston.com
**Control:** Corporation, Investor–owned, for–profit **Service:** Long–Term Acute Care hospital

**Staffed Beds:** 55 **Admissions:** 251 **Census:** 30 **Total Expense ($000):** 16449 **Payroll Expense ($000):** 7788 **Personnel:** 123

## MULLINS—Marion County

✠ **CAROLINAS HOSPITAL SYSTEM MARION (420055)**, (Formerly Marion Regional Hospital), 2829 East Highway 76, Zip 29574–6035, Mailing Address: P.O. Drawer 1150, Marion, Zip 29571–1150; tel. 843/431–2000, (Total facility includes 92 beds in nursing home–type unit) **A**1 9 10 **F**1 3 13 15 28 29 30 34 40 45 46 51 60 67 70 76 77 79 81 82 85 86 89 90 107 115 119 128 129 130 133 135 146 148 **S** Community Health Systems, Inc., Franklin, TN
Primary Contact: David Cope, Chief Executive Officer
CFO: Alta DuBose, Chief Financial Officer
CMO: Alvin Abinsay, M.D., Chief Medical Staff
CIO: Charlie Grantham, Manager Information Systems
CHR: Kay White, Director Human Resources and Diversity
Web address: www.carolinashospitalmarion.com/Pages/Home.aspx
**Control:** Corporation, Investor–owned, for–profit **Service:** General Medical and Surgical

**Staffed Beds:** 216 **Admissions:** 3280 **Census:** 118 **Outpatient Visits:** 54158 **Births:** 282 **Total Expense ($000):** 61341 **Payroll Expense ($000):** 17806 **Personnel:** 76

**MARION COUNTY MEDICAL CENTER** See Carolinas Hospital System Marion

SC

*Many Facility Codes have changed. Please refer to the AHA Guide Code Chart.*

© 2013 AHA Guide

## MURRELS INLET—Georgetown County

⊠ △ **WACCAMAW COMMUNITY HOSPITAL (420098)**, 4070 Highway 17 Bypass, Zip 29576–5033, Mailing Address: P.O. Drawer 3350, Zip 29576–2673; tel. 843/652–1000 **A**1 2 7 9 10 **F**3 8 11 13 15 17 18 29 30 31 32 35 37 39 40 45 50 51 56 60 61 65 68 70 73 74 75 76 77 78 79 81 82 84 85 86 87 89 90 96 97 100 102 107 108 109 110 111 115 118 119 130 146 147 148 **S** Georgetown Hospital System, Georgetown, SC
Primary Contact: Suzanne Doscher, Vice President Operations
CFO: Terry L. Kiser, Chief Financial Officer
CIO: Frank Scafidi, Chief Information Officer
Web address: www.gmhsc.com
**Control:** Other not–for–profit (including NFP Corporation) **Service:** General Medical and Surgical

**Staffed Beds:** 169 **Admissions:** 8141 **Census:** 105 **Outpatient Visits:** 92139 **Births:** 553 **Total Expense ($000):** 124635 **Payroll Expense ($000):** 32990 **Personnel:** 599

## MYRTLE BEACH—Horry County

⊠ **GRAND STRAND REGIONAL MEDICAL CENTER (420085)**, 809 82nd Parkway, Zip 29572–4607; tel. 843/692–1000 **A**1 2 9 10 **F**3 11 13 15 17 18 20 22 24 26 28 29 30 31 34 35 37 39 40 42 43 46 47 49 50 54 56 57 59 60 64 70 73 74 75 76 77 78 79 81 82 85 86 87 89 90 107 108 110 111 114 115 118 119 126 130 132 135 146 147 **S** HCA, Nashville, TN
Primary Contact: Doug White, Chief Executive Officer
CFO: Turner Wortham, Chief Financial Officer
Web address: www.grandstrandmed.com
**Control:** Corporation, Investor–owned, for–profit **Service:** General Medical and Surgical

**Staffed Beds:** 271 **Admissions:** 16197 **Census:** 197 **Births:** 910 **Personnel:** 1067

## NEWBERRY—Newberry County

⊠ **NEWBERRY COUNTY MEMORIAL HOSPITAL (420053)**, 2669 Kinard Street, Zip 29108–2911, Mailing Address: P.O. Box 497, Zip 29108–0497; tcl. 803/276 7570 **A**1 9 10 20 **F**1 3 7 11 13 15 17 28 29 30 31 32 34 35 40 45 47 53 56 57 59 64 68 70 75 76 77 78 79 81 82 85 86 87 89 90 103 104 107 108 109 110 111 114 119 128 129 130 133 135 143 146 147 148 **P**6 **S** QHR, Brentwood, TN
Primary Contact: Ronald J. Vigus, Chief Executive Officer
CFO: Mike Reynolds, Chief Financial Officer
CMO: Becky White, M.D., Chief of Staff
CIO: David Wolff, Director Information Technology
CHR: Dyan Bowman, Director Human Resources
Web address: www.newberryhospital.org
**Control:** County–Government, nonfederal **Service:** General Medical and Surgical

**Staffed Beds:** 32 **Admissions:** 2250 **Census:** 23 **Outpatient Visits:** 66052 **Births:** 295 **Total Expense ($000):** 45321 **Payroll Expense ($000):** 17783 **Personnel:** 382

## ORANGEBURG—Orangeburg County

⊠ **REGIONAL MEDICAL CENTER (420068)**, 3000 St. Matthews Road, Zip 29118–1442; tel. 803/395–2200 **A**1 2 9 10 19 **F**3 11 13 14 15 17 18 20 28 29 30 31 32 34 35 39 40 43 44 45 46 47 48 50 53 57 58 59 60 61 62 65 68 70 73 74 75 76 77 78 79 81 82 84 85 86 87 89 90 97 98 100 101 102 103 107 108 110 111 114 115 119 121 127 129 130 131 132 134 135 144 146 147 148 **S** QHR, Brentwood, TN
Primary Contact: Thomas C. Dandridge, FACHE, President and Chief Executive Officer
CFO: Cheryl S. Mason, Chief Financial Officer
CIO: Marilyn Tremblay, Chief Information Officer and Vice President
CHR: Howard Harris, Vice President Human Resources
CNO: Julia K. Yawn, MSN, Chief Nursing Officer and Vice President for Patient Care Services
Web address: www.trmchealth.org
**Control:** County–Government, nonfederal **Service:** General Medical and Surgical

**Staffed Beds:** 286 **Admissions:** 11547 **Census:** 165 **Births:** 1136 **Total Expense ($000):** 189725 **Payroll Expense ($000):** 85911 **Personnel:** 1205

☐ **WILLIAM J. MCCORD ADOLESCENT AND TREATMENT CENTER (424013)**, 910 Cook Road, Zip 29118–2124, Mailing Address: P.O. Box 1166, Zip 29116–1166; tel. 803/534–2328 **A**1 10 **F**4 5 34 35 38 57 61 98 99 130 132 134 135
Primary Contact: Michael Dennis, Director
Web address: www.mccordcenter.com
**Control:** Other not–for–profit (including NFP Corporation) **Service:** Psychiatric

**Staffed Beds:** 15 **Admissions:** 114 **Census:** 14 **Outpatient Visits:** 0 **Births:** 0 **Personnel:** 41

## PICKENS—Pickens County

★ ◇ **CANNON MEMORIAL HOSPITAL (420011)**, 123 West G. Acker Drive, Zip 29671–2739, Mailing Address: P.O. Box 188, Zip 29671–0188; tel. 864/878–4791 **A**9 10 21 **F**1 3 11 15 29 34 35 40 50 51 53 56 57 59 61 64 65 75 79 81 85 97 107 108 110 111 114 119 127 128 130 146 **P**8 **S** Carolinas HealthCare System, Charlotte, NC
Primary Contact: Norman G. Rentz, President and Chief Executive Officer
CFO: Mary F. Arnette, Chief Financial Officer
CMO: Daniel J. Dahlhausen, M.D., President of Medical Staff/Chief Medical Officer
CIO: Kimi Stanley, Director of Information Services
CHR: Lisa G. Bryant, Director Human Resources
CNO: Donna K. Anderson, R.N., Chief Nursing Officer
Web address: www.cannonhospital.org
**Control:** Other not–for–profit (including NFP Corporation) **Service:** General Medical and Surgical

**Staffed Beds:** 38 **Admissions:** 884 **Census:** 10 **Outpatient Visits:** 38417 **Births:** 0 **Personnel:** 246

## ROCK HILL—York County

⊠ **HEALTHSOUTH REHABILITATION HOSPITAL (423028)**, 1795 Dr. Frank Gaston Boulevard, Zip 29732–1190; tel. 803/326–3500 **A**1 10 **F**29 56 58 64 75 90 95 130 **S** HEALTHSOUTH Corporation, Birmingham, AL
Web address: www.healthsouthrockhill.com
**Control:** Corporation, Investor–owned, for–profit **Service:** Rehabilitation

**Staffed Beds:** 50 **Admissions:** 1271 **Census:** 40 **Outpatient Visits:** 0 **Births:** 0 **Personnel:** 84

⊠ **PIEDMONT MEDICAL CENTER (420002)**, 222 Herlong Avenue, Zip 29732; tel. 803/329–1234 **A**1 2 9 10 **F**3 7 11 13 15 17 18 20 22 24 28 29 30 31 34 35 40 43 45 49 50 57 59 60 64 70 73 74 75 76 77 78 79 81 82 85 86 89 90 91 98 100 102 107 108 110 111 114 115 118 119 130 132 135 146 147 148 **S** TENET Healthcare Corporation, Dallas, TX
Primary Contact: William Masterton, Chief Executive Officer
COO: Claudia Douglass, Chief Operating Officer
CFO: Jay M. Pennisson, Chief Financial Officer
CIO: Joel Dean, Director Information Services
CHR: Donald L. Currier, Vice President Human Resources
CNO: Mary Kaye Halterman, R.N., Chief Nursing Officer
Web address: www.piedmontmedicalcenter.com
**Control:** Corporation, Investor–owned, for–profit **Service:** General Medical and Surgical

**Staffed Beds:** 280 **Admissions:** 14577 **Census:** 184 **Births:** 1934 **Total Expense ($000):** 206031 **Payroll Expense ($000):** 67031 **Personnel:** 1491

## SENECA—Oconee County

⊠ **OCONEE MEDICAL CENTER (420009)**, 298 Memorial Drive, Zip 29672–9499; tel. 864/882–3351, (Includes LILA DOYLE NURSING CARE FACILITY ), (Total facility includes 120 beds in nursing home–type unit) **A**1 9 10 **F**3 7 11 13 15 20 28 29 30 31 34 35 40 54 56 57 59 61 62 63 64 67 70 71 74 75 76 77 78 79 81 82 85 86 87 89 90 97 100 107 108 114 119 128 130 132 135 143 146 148 **P**8
Primary Contact: Jeanne L. Ward, Ed.D., R.N., President and Chief Executive Officer
COO: Hunter Kome, Chief Operating Officer
CFO: Kevin Herbert, Chief Financial Officer
CMO: Conrad K. Shuler, M.D., Chief Medical Officer
CIO: Jay Hansen, Director Information Services
CHR: Thomas C. Conley, Vice President Human Resources
CNO: Pat J. Smith, Vice President Nursing
Web address: www.oconeemed.org
**Control:** Other not–for–profit (including NFP Corporation) **Service:** General Medical and Surgical

**Staffed Beds:** 248 **Admissions:** 7175 **Census:** 183 **Personnel:** 877

## SIMPSONVILLE—Greenville County

⊠ **HILLCREST MEMORIAL HOSPITAL (420037)**, 729 S.E. Main Street, Zip 29681–3280; tel. 864/454–6100 **A**1 9 10 **F**1 3 11 12 15 18 29 30 35 37 40 44 45 50 57 59 64 68 70 79 81 85 86 90 107 110 111 114 119 128 129 130 132 135 146 **P**6 **S** Greenville Health System, Greenville, SC
Primary Contact: Eric Bour, M.D., President
CFO: Pam DeVore, Financial Manager
Web address: www.ghs.org
**Control:** Other not–for–profit (including NFP Corporation) **Service:** General Medical and Surgical

**Staffed Beds:** 36 **Admissions:** 1756 **Census:** 16 **Outpatient Visits:** 62070 **Births:** 0 **Total Expense ($000):** 45806 **Payroll Expense ($000):** 14253 **Personnel:** 222

**SC**

---

**Hospital, Medicare Provider Number, Address, Telephone, Approval, Facility, and Physician Codes, Health Care System**

★ American Hospital Association (AHA) membership
☐ The Joint Commission accreditation
◇ DNV Healthcare Inc. accreditation
○ Healthcare Facilities Accreditation Program
△ Commission on Accreditation of Rehabilitation Facilities (CARF) accreditation

## SPARTANBURG—Spartanburg County

✠ △ **MARY BLACK MEMORIAL HOSPITAL (420083)**, 1700 Skylyn Drive, Zip 29307–1061, Mailing Address: P.O. Box 3217, Zip 29304–3217; tel. 864/573–3000 **A**1 3 5 7 9 10 **F**3 11 13 15 18 19 20 29 31 34 35 37 40 45 46 47 49 50 54 57 59 64 70 73 75 76 77 78 79 80 87 89 90 98 103 107 108 109 110 111 114 115 118 119 124 126 130 131 141 142 146 147 148 **S** Community Health Systems, Inc., Franklin, TN
Primary Contact: Douglas J. Moyer, Chief Executive Officer
COO: Brandon Downey, Chief Operating Officer
CFO: Richard A. Meyer, Chief Financial Officer
CIO: Jeff Nash, Director Information Technology and Services
CHR: Amy Martin, Director Human Resources
Web address: www.maryblackhealthsystem.com
**Control:** Corporation, Investor–owned, for–profit **Service:** General Medical and Surgical

> **Staffed Beds:** 181 **Admissions:** 7120 **Census:** 92 **Outpatient Visits:** 52176 **Births:** 932 **Personnel:** 806

✠ **SPARTANBURG HOSPITAL FOR RESTORATIVE CARE (422004)**, 389 Serpentine Drive, Zip 29303–3026; tel. 864/560–3280, (Total facility includes 25 beds in nursing home–type unit) **A**1 10 **F**1 29 30 31 35 57 59 60 68 70 75 77 79 82 84 85 87 90 119 128 130 148 **S** Spartanburg Regional Healthcare System, Spartanburg, SC
Primary Contact: Anita M. Butler, Chief Executive Officer
Web address: www.srhs.com
**Control:** Hospital district or authority, Government, nonfederal **Service:** Long–Term Acute Care hospital

> **Staffed Beds:** 116 **Admissions:** 866 **Census:** 50 **Outpatient Visits:** 0 **Births:** 0 **Total Expense ($000):** 22361 **Payroll Expense ($000):** 11188 **Personnel:** 75

★ **SPARTANBURG REGIONAL MEDICAL CENTER (420007)**, 101 East Wood Street, Zip 29303–3040; tel. 864/560–6000 **A**2 3 5 9 10 13 **F**3 7 11 12 13 15 17 18 20 22 24 26 28 29 30 31 34 35 36 37 38 39 40 43 45 46 47 48 49 50 53 54 56 57 58 59 60 61 62 63 64 65 66 68 70 71 72 73 74 75 76 77 78 79 81 82 83 84 85 86 87 88 89 90 97 98 99 100 101 102 103 104 105 107 108 110 111 114 115 117 118 119 120 121 123 124 126 129 130 131 132 135 143 144 145 146 147 148 **S** Spartanburg Regional Healthcare System, Spartanburg, SC
Primary Contact: Bruce Holstien, President and Chief Executive Officer
CMO: Robert Flandry, M.D., Vice President and Chief Medical Officer
CHR: Kathy Sinclair, Vice President Human Resources
Web address: www.spartanburgregional.com
**Control:** Hospital district or authority, Government, nonfederal **Service:** General Medical and Surgical

> **Staffed Beds:** 514 **Admissions:** 26522 **Census:** 409 **Births:** 2765 **Total Expense ($000):** 548651 **Payroll Expense ($000):** 173236 **Personnel:** 3913

## SUMTER—Sumter County

✠ **TUOMEY HEALTHCARE SYSTEM (420070)**, 129 North Washington Street, Zip 29150–4983; tel. 803/774–9000, (Total facility includes 18 beds in nursing home–type unit) **A**1 9 10 **F**1 3 13 15 20 28 29 30 31 32 34 35 40 45 51 54 56 59 60 62 63 64 68 70 73 75 76 77 78 79 81 85 86 87 89 90 102 107 108 110 111 114 117 119 121 128 129 130 131 132 135 146 147 148 **P**6
Primary Contact: Jay Cox, FACHE, President and Chief Executive Officer
COO: Gregg Martin, Senior Vice President and Chief Operating Officer
CFO: Mark Lovell, Vice President and Chief Financial Officer
CMO: Gene Dickerson, M.D., Vice President Medical Affairs
CIO: Cheryl Martin, Chief Information Officer
CHR: Letitia Pringle–Miller, Administrative Director
CNO: Terrie Carlton, R.N., Vice President & Chief Nursing Officer
Web address: www.tuomey.com
**Control:** Other not–for–profit (including NFP Corporation) **Service:** General Medical and Surgical

> **Staffed Beds:** 270 **Admissions:** 5117 **Census:** 114 **Outpatient Visits:** 132503 **Births:** 1374 **Personnel:** 1482

## TRAVELERS REST—Greenville County

✠ **NORTH GREENVILLE HOSPITAL (422008)**, 807 North Main Street, Zip 29690–1551; tel. 864/455–9206 **A**1 10 **F**1 3 15 29 30 34 35 40 44 50 58 64 68 75 79 85 86 87 107 110 111 114 128 130 146 148 **P**6
Primary Contact: Michael Batchelor, President
CFO: Juan Fernandez, Director of Campus Operations
CMO: Kyle Meade, M.D., Medical Director
CHR: Carol Bish, Human Resources Coordinator
CNO: Marian Crawford, Director of Patient Care Services
Web address: www.ghs.org
**Control:** Other not–for–profit (including NFP Corporation) **Service:** Long–Term Acute Care hospital

> **Staffed Beds:** 21 **Admissions:** 266 **Census:** 24 **Outpatient Visits:** 37327 **Births:** 0 **Total Expense ($000):** 25138 **Payroll Expense ($000):** 8610 **Personnel:** 147

☐ **SPRINGBROOK BEHAVIORAL HEALTH SYSTEM (424007)**, One Havenwood Lane, Zip 29690–9447, Mailing Address: P.O. Box 1005, Zip 29690–1005; tel. 864/834–8013, (Total facility includes 68 beds in nursing home–type unit) **A**1 9 10 **F**98 99 104
Primary Contact: Mike Rowley, Chief Executive Officer
CFO: Bart Bennett, Chief Financial Officer
CMO: April Richardson, M.D., Medical Director
CIO: Lateka Benson, Manager Health Information
CHR: Steve Ivester, Director Human Resources
CNO: Francine Lopomo, R.N., Director of Nursing
Web address: www.springbrookbehavioral.com
**Control:** Corporation, Investor–owned, for–profit **Service:** Psychiatric

> **Staffed Beds:** 96 **Admissions:** 696 **Census:** 80 **Outpatient Visits:** 2136 **Births:** 0 **Personnel:** 233

## UNION—Union County

☐ **WALLACE THOMSON HOSPITAL (420039)**, 322 West South Street, Zip 29379–2857, Mailing Address: P.O. Box 789, Zip 29379–0789; tel. 864/427–0351, (Total facility includes 113 beds in nursing home–type unit) **A**1 9 10 **F**1 3 7 13 15 29 34 35 40 57 59 64 69 70 75 76 79 81 82 86 87 89 107 111 119 129 130 135 146 147
Primary Contact: Paul R. Newhouse, Chief Executive Officer
CFO: Jeff W. Rush, Chief Financial Officer
CIO: Billy Helmandollar, Director Information Services
CHR: Michelle Helton, Director Human Resources
Web address: www.wallacethomson.com
**Control:** Hospital district or authority, Government, nonfederal **Service:** General Medical and Surgical

> **Staffed Beds:** 171 **Admissions:** 2707 **Census:** 139 **Outpatient Visits:** 34423 **Births:** 66 **Personnel:** 280

## VARNVILLE—Hampton County

★ **HAMPTON REGIONAL MEDICAL CENTER (420072)**, 503 Carolina Avenue West, Zip 29944–4735, Mailing Address: P.O. Box 338, Zip 29944–0338; tel. 803/943–2771 **A**9 10 20 **F**15 17 18 24 28 29 34 35 40 57 59 64 67 70 77 79 81 90 107 108 110 111 114 119 127 128 129 130 133 146
Primary Contact: Dave H. Hamill, President and Chief Executive Officer
Web address: www.hamptonregional.com
**Control:** Other not–for–profit (including NFP Corporation) **Service:** General Medical and Surgical

> **Staffed Beds:** 32 **Admissions:** 709 **Census:** 7 **Births:** 0 **Total Expense ($000):** 19180 **Payroll Expense ($000):** 7811 **Personnel:** 177

## WALTERBORO—Colleton County

✠ **COLLETON MEDICAL CENTER (420030)**, 501 Robertson Boulevard, Zip 29488–5714; tel. 843/782–2000 **A**1 9 10 20 **F**3 11 13 15 18 26 29 30 32 34 35 36 40 45 47 49 56 57 59 60 64 65 68 70 75 76 77 79 81 82 85 86 87 89 90 96 98 102 107 108 110 111 114 119 129 130 131 132 146 147 148 **P**5 **S** HCA, Nashville, TN
Primary Contact: Brad Griffin, Chief Executive Officer
COO: Tony Taylor, Vice President Operations
CFO: Ronnie Midgett, Chief Financial Officer
CMO: Kim Rakes–Stephens, M.D., Chief Medical Staff
CHR: Alysia Price, Director Human Resources
Web address: www.colletonmedical.com
**Control:** Corporation, Investor–owned, for–profit **Service:** General Medical and Surgical

> **Staffed Beds:** 131 **Admissions:** 4922 **Census:** 64 **Outpatient Visits:** 30688 **Births:** 333 **Total Expense ($000):** 60087 **Payroll Expense ($000):** 20383 **Personnel:** 387

## WEST COLUMBIA—Lexington County

★ ◇ **LEXINGTON MEDICAL CENTER (420073)**, 2720 Sunset Boulevard, Zip 29169–4810; tel. 803/791–2000 **A**2 9 10 21 **F**3 8 11 12 13 15 18 20 22 24 28 29 30 31 32 34 35 38 39 40 43 44 45 49 50 53 54 57 58 59 61 64 68 70 72 73 74 75 76 77 78 79 80 81 85 86 87 89 90 92 107 108 110 111 114 115 118 119 120 121 123 127 129 130 131 132 135 141 142 144 145 146 147 148 **P**6
Primary Contact: Michael J. Biediger, FACHE, President and Chief Executive Officer
COO: Tod Augsburger, Senior Vice President and Chief Operating Officer
CFO: Melinda Kruzner, Chief Financial Officer
CMO: Brent Powers, M.D., Vice President/Chief Medical Officer
CIO: Kathleen R. Herald, Vice President and Chief Information Officer
CHR: Kathy A. Howell, Vice President Human Resources
CNO: Cindy Rohman, R.N., Vice President/Chief Nursing Officer
Web address: www.lexmed.com
**Control:** Hospital district or authority, Government, nonfederal **Service:** General Medical and Surgical

> **Staffed Beds:** 390 **Admissions:** 23340 **Census:** 281 **Outpatient Visits:** 122133 **Births:** 3460 **Total Expense ($000):** 426417 **Payroll Expense ($000):** 168691 **Personnel:** 3182

*Many Facility Codes have changed. Please refer to the AHA Guide Code Chart.*

☐ **THREE RIVERS BEHAVIORAL HEALTH (424008)**, 2900 Sunset Boulevard, Zip 29169–3422; tel. 803/796–9911, (Total facility includes 20 beds in nursing home–type unit) **A**1 9 10 **F**4 5 35 98 99 100 101 103 104 105 106 **S** Universal Health Services, Inc., King of Prussia, PA
Primary Contact: Elyssia Lowe, Chief Executive Officer
CFO: Christopher Jensen, Chief Financial Officer
CMO: Cheryl Dodds, M.D., Medical Director
CHR: Nita Sundberg, Director Human Resources
CNO: Regena Sellers, Chief Nursing Officer
Web address: www.threeriversbehavioral.org
**Control:** Corporation, Investor–owned, for–profit **Service:** Psychiatric

**Staffed Beds:** 118 **Admissions:** 2733 **Census:** 93 **Outpatient Visits:** 0
**Births:** 0 **Total Expense ($000):** 14118 **Payroll Expense ($000):** 7623
**Personnel:** 101

### WINNSBORO—Fairfield County

☐ **FAIRFIELD MEMORIAL HOSPITAL (421302)**, 102 U.S. Highway 321 By–Pass N., Zip 29180–9251, Mailing Address: P.O. Box 620, Zip 29180–0620; tel. 803/635–5548 **A**1 5 9 10 18 **F**3 11 15 18 28 29 30 34 35 40 50 56 57 59 62 63 64 65 68 75 77 78 86 87 90 102 107 108 111 114 119 127 128 129 130 132 133 146 148
Primary Contact: Michael Williams, FACHE, Administrator
CFO: Anne Bass, Chief Financial Officer
CMO: Larry D. Cantey, M.D., Chief Medical Officer
CIO: Reynolds Searle, Director Information Systems
CHR: Shawna Martin Lyde, Director Human Resources
Web address: www.fairfieldmemorial.com
**Control:** County–Government, nonfederal **Service:** General Medical and Surgical

**Staffed Beds:** 25 **Admissions:** 509 **Census:** 9 **Births:** 0 **Personnel:** 139

**SC**

---

**Hospital, Medicare Provider Number, Address, Telephone, Approval, Facility, and Physician Codes, Health Care System**

★ American Hospital Association (AHA) membership
☐ The Joint Commission accreditation
◇ DNV Healthcare Inc. accreditation
○ Healthcare Facilities Accreditation Program
△ Commission on Accreditation of Rehabilitation Facilities (CARF) accreditation

# SOUTH DAKOTA

## ABERDEEN—Brown County

★ △ **AVERA ST. LUKE'S HOSPITAL (430014)**, 305 South State Street, Zip 57401–4527; tel. 605/622–5000, (Total facility includes 137 beds in nursing home–type unit) **A**2 7 9 10 20 **F**2 3 5 7 10 11 13 15 17 18 20 22 28 29 30 31 32 34 35 36 39 40 45 46 48 56 57 59 60 61 62 63 64 70 71 74 75 76 77 78 79 81 82 84 85 86 87 89 90 92 93 96 97 98 99 100 101 102 103 104 107 108 110 111 114 115 118 119 120 121 123 125 127 128 129 130 131 132 133 135 146 147 148 **P**6 **S** Avera Health, Sioux Falls, SD
Primary Contact: Todd Forkel, President and Chief Executive Officer
COO: K. C. DeBoer, Vice President
CFO: Geoff Durst, Vice President Finance
CMO: John Fritz, D.O., Vice President Medical Affairs
CIO: Julie Kusler, Manager Information Services
CHR: Mary Davis, Vice President
Web address: www.avera.org/st-lukes-hospital/
**Control:** Church–operated, Nongovernment, not–for profit **Service:** General Medical and Surgical

| Staffed Beds: 270 Admissions: 5963 Census: 203 Outpatient Visits: 255085 Births: 702 Total Expense ($000): 158741 Payroll Expense ($000): 80113 Personnel: 1202 |

**DAKOTA PLAINS SURGICAL CENTER (430092)**, 701 8th Avenue N.W., Suite C., Zip 57401–1865; tel. 605/225–3300, (Nonreporting) **A**9 10
Primary Contact: Charles Livingston, Administrator
**Control:** Corporation, Investor–owned, for–profit **Service:** Surgical

| Staffed Beds: 15 |

★ **SANFORD ABERDEEN MEDICAL CENTER (430097)**, (Formerly Sanford Medical Center Aberdeen), 2905 3rd Avenue S.E., Zip 57401–5420; tel. 605/725–1700, (Nonreporting) **A**9 10 **S** Sanford Health, Sioux Falls, SD
Primary Contact: Gordon Larson, Chief Executive Officer
Web address: www.sanfordaberdeen.org/
**Control:** Other not–for–profit (including NFP Corporation) **Service:** General Medical and Surgical

| Staffed Beds: 48 |

## ARMOUR—Douglas County

**DOUGLAS COUNTY MEMORIAL HOSPITAL (431305)**, 708 Eighth Street, Zip 57313–2102; tel. 605/724–2159 **A**9 10 18 **F**3 7 10 13 15 28 31 34 35 40 45 53 57 59 62 64 65 69 76 77 81 93 107 119 127 133 **P**6
Primary Contact: Heath Brouwer, Administrator
CFO: Dorothy Spease, Manager Business Office
Web address: www.dcmhsd.org
**Control:** Other not–for–profit (including NFP Corporation) **Service:** General Medical and Surgical

| Staffed Beds: 11 Admissions: 195 Census: 2 Outpatient Visits: 8782 Births: 29 Total Expense ($000): 7763 Payroll Expense ($000): 3302 Personnel: 72 |

## BOWDLE— County

★ **BOWDLE HOSPITAL (431318)**, 8001 West Fifth Street, Zip 57428, Mailing Address: P.O. Box 556, Zip 57428–0556; tel. 605/285–6146, (Total facility includes 36 beds in nursing home–type unit) **A**9 10 18 **F**2 7 10 28 40 43 45 53 59 65 127 128 133
Primary Contact: Sandy Schlechter, Chief Executive Officer
CMO: Janice Lumnitz, M.D., Chief of Staff
CIO: Kim Miller, Chief Information Officer
Web address: www.bowdlehc.com
**Control:** City–Government, nonfederal **Service:** General Medical and Surgical

| Staffed Beds: 48 Admissions: 204 Census: 34 Outpatient Visits: 4037 Births: 0 Total Expense ($000): 3460 Payroll Expense ($000): 2363 Personnel: 79 |

## BRITTON—Marshall County

★ **MARSHALL COUNTY HEALTHCARE CENTER AVERA (431312)**, 413 Ninth Street, Zip 57430–2274; tel. 605/448–2253 **A**9 10 18 **F**10 11 28 29 34 35 40 41 53 57 59 62 64 65 77 86 87 133 146 **P**5 **S** Avera Health, Sioux Falls, SD
Primary Contact: Nick Fosness, Chief Executive Officer
Web address: www.avera.org
**Control:** Other not–for–profit (including NFP Corporation) **Service:** General Medical and Surgical

| Staffed Beds: 18 Admissions: 251 Census: 4 Outpatient Visits: 5695 Births: 0 Total Expense ($000): 5294 Payroll Expense ($000): 2400 Personnel: 65 |

## BROOKINGS—Brookings County

★ **BROOKINGS HEALTH SYSTEM (430008)**, 300 22nd Avenue, Zip 57006–2496; tel. 605/696–9000, (Total facility includes 79 beds in nursing home–type unit) **A**9 10 20 **F**3 7 11 13 28 29 30 31 32 34 35 40 43 45 57 59 62 63 64 69 70 75 76 77 81 84 85 87 89 93 96 102 107 111 114 118 119 125 126 127 128 129 130 132 133 146 147 148
Primary Contact: Jason R. Merkley, Chief Executive Officer
CMO: Merritt Warren, M.D., Medical Director and Chief of Staff
CHR: September Bessler, Manager Human Resources
CNO: Tammy Hillestad, Chief Nursing Officer
Web address: www.brookingshealth.org
**Control:** City–Government, nonfederal **Service:** General Medical and Surgical

| Staffed Beds: 128 Admissions: 1113 Census: 81 Outpatient Visits: 10522 Births: 248 Total Expense ($000): 33737 Payroll Expense ($000): 16364 Personnel: 337 |

## BURKE—Gregory County

★ **COMMUNITY MEMORIAL HOSPITAL (431309)**, 809 Jackson Street, Zip 57523–2065, Mailing Address: P.O. Box 319, Zip 57523–0319; tel. 605/775–2621 **A**9 10 18 **F**3 11 28 31 34 40 57 59 64 65 67 87 97 107 114 127 128 133 **S** Sanford Health, Sioux Falls, SD
Primary Contact: Jim Frank, Chief Executive Officer
CMO: Teresa Marts, M.D., Chief Medical Staff
CHR: Tami Lyon, Director Human Resources
Web address: www.sanfordhealth.org
**Control:** Other not–for–profit (including NFP Corporation) **Service:** General Medical and Surgical

| Staffed Beds: 16 Admissions: 175 Census: 6 Outpatient Visits: 2100 Births: 0 Total Expense ($000): 4241 Payroll Expense ($000): 1976 Personnel: 54 |

## CANTON—Lincoln County

★ **SANFORD CANTON–INWOOD MEDICAL CENTER (431333)**, 440 North Hiawatha Drive, Zip 57013–5800; tel. 605/764–1400 **A**9 10 18 **F**10 15 28 40 45 59 64 71 77 81 93 107 127 130 133 **S** Sanford Health, Sioux Falls, SD
Primary Contact: Scott C. Larson, Chief Executive Officer
CFO: Paul Gerhart, Chief Financial Officer
Web address: www.sanfordcantoninwood.org
**Control:** Other not–for–profit (including NFP Corporation) **Service:** General Medical and Surgical

| Staffed Beds: 16 Admissions: 207 Census: 2 Outpatient Visits: 19654 Births: 0 Total Expense ($000): 5817 Payroll Expense ($000): 2670 Personnel: 75 |

## CHAMBERLAIN—Brule County

★ **SANFORD CHAMBERLAIN MEDICAL CENTER (431329)**, (Formerly Sanford Medical Center Chamberlain), 300 South Byron Boulevard, Zip 57325–9741; tel. 605/234–5511, (Total facility includes 44 beds in nursing home–type unit) **A**9 10 18 **F**3 8 13 15 18 19 28 29 31 34 35 40 43 50 57 59 68 70 75 76 77 78 81 85 86 87 89 93 100 101 102 103 107 110 114 119 130 131 133 146 148 **P**6 **S** Sanford Health, Sioux Falls, SD
Primary Contact: Erica Peterson, Chief Executive Officer
CFO: Erica Peterson, Chief Financial Officer
CMO: John Jones, M.D., Chief Medical Staff
CHR: Dorothy Hieb, Director Human Resources
CNO: Sarah Talbott, Chief Nursing Officer
Web address: www.sanfordmiddakota.org
**Control:** Other not–for–profit (including NFP Corporation) **Service:** General Medical and Surgical

| Staffed Beds: 69 Admissions: 451 Census: 48 Outpatient Visits: 21644 Births: 92 Total Expense ($000): 19062 Payroll Expense ($000): 8818 Personnel: 158 |

**SANFORD MID DAKOTA MEDICAL CENTER** See Sanford Chamberlain Medical Center

*Many Facility Codes have changed. Please refer to the AHA Guide Code Chart.*   © 2013 AHA Guide

## CLEAR LAKE—Deuel County

★ **SANFORD CLEAR LAKE MEDICAL CENTER (431307)**, (Formerly Sanford Deuel County Medical Center), 701 Third Avenue South, Zip 57226–2016; tel. 605/874–2141 **A**9 10 18 **F**3 28 29 34 35 40 45 50 53 57 59 62 64 65 68 81 86 87 92 97 107 119 127 128 133 135 144 147 148 **P**6 **S** Sanford Health, Sioux Falls, SD
Primary Contact: Lori Sisk, R.N., Chief Executive Officer
CFO: Allison Nelson, Chief Financial Officer
CMO: Terrance Smith, M.D., Chairman Medical Staff
CNO: Michelle Skillings, Chief Nursing Officer
Web address: www.sanforddeuelcounty.org
**Control:** Other not–for–profit (including NFP Corporation) **Service:** General Medical and Surgical

**Staffed Beds:** 10 **Admissions:** 208 **Census:** 3 **Outpatient Visits:** 16175 **Births:** 0 **Total Expense ($000):** 5553 **Payroll Expense ($000):** 2751 **Personnel:** 79

## CUSTER—Custer County

★ **CUSTER REGIONAL HOSPITAL (431323)**, 1039 Montgomery Street, Zip 57730–1397; tel. 605/673–2229, (Nonreporting) **A**9 10 18 **S** Regional Health, Rapid City, SD
Primary Contact: Veronica Schmidt, Chief Executive Officer
Web address: www.regionalhealth.com
**Control:** Other not–for–profit (including NFP Corporation) **Service:** General Medical and Surgical

**Staffed Beds:** 87

## DAKOTA DUNES—Union County

**SIOUXLAND SURGERY CENTER (430089)**, 600 North Sioux Point Road, Zip 57049–5000; tel. 605/232–3332, (Nonreporting) **A**9 10
Primary Contact: Greg Miner, Administrator
Web address: www.siouxlandsurg.com/
**Control:** Corporation, Investor–owned, for–profit **Service:** Other specialty

**Staffed Beds:** 40

## DE SMET—Kingsbury County

★ **AVERA DE SMET MEMORIAL HOSPITAL (431332)**, 306 Prairie Avenue S.W., Zip 57231–2285, Mailing Address: P.O. Box 160, Zip 57231–0160; tel. 605/854–3329 **A**9 10 18 **F**3 15 28 34 35 40 59 68 93 107 133 **P**6 **S** Avera Health, Sioux Falls, SD
Primary Contact: Janice Schardin, R.N., MS, Administrator and Chief Executive Officer
Web address: www.desmetmemorial.org
**Control:** Other not–for–profit (including NFP Corporation) **Service:** General Medical and Surgical

**Staffed Beds:** 14 **Admissions:** 53 **Census:** 1 **Outpatient Visits:** 11591 **Births:** 0 **Total Expense ($000):** 3486 **Payroll Expense ($000):** 1499 **Personnel:** 23

## DEADWOOD—Lawrence County

★ **LEAD–DEADWOOD REGIONAL HOSPITAL (431320)**, 61 Charles Street, Zip 57732–1303; tel. 605/722–6101 **A**9 10 18 **F**3 7 15 28 29 30 31 34 40 43 59 64 65 67 68 69 70 77 78 81 85 87 93 107 114 115 117 119 120 121 128 132 133 148 **S** Regional Health, Rapid City, SD
Primary Contact: Sherry Bea Smith, R.N., Chief Executive Officer
CFO: Sherry Bea Smith, R.N., Chief Executive Officer and Chief Financial Officer
CMO: Elizabeth Sayler, M.D., Chief of Staff
CHR: Kathryn L. Shockey, Director Human Resources
Web address: www.regionalhealth.com
**Control:** State–Government, nonfederal **Service:** General Medical and Surgical

**Staffed Beds:** 18 **Admissions:** 302 **Census:** 5 **Outpatient Visits:** 12998 **Births:** 0 **Total Expense ($000):** 8437 **Payroll Expense ($000):** 4031 **Personnel:** 78

## DELL RAPIDS—Minnehaha County

**AVERA DELLS AREA HEALTH CENTER** See Avera Dells Area Hospital

---

★ **AVERA DELLS AREA HOSPITAL (431331)**, 909 North Iowa Avenue, Zip 57022–1231; tel. 605/428–5431 **A**9 10 18 **F**3 11 15 28 34 35 40 45 53 57 59 64 65 75 81 86 92 93 97 107 110 128 132 133 146 148 **P**6 **S** Avera Health, Sioux Falls, SD
Primary Contact: Lindsay Flannery, R.N., Administrator and Chief Executive Officer
CFO: Kory Holt, Division Controller Network Operations
CMO: Matt Herber, M.D., Chief of Staff
CIO: Thelma Haak, Manager Health Information
CHR: Dawn Ingalls, Regional Manager Human Resources
CNO: Karla Carstensen, Director Patient Care
Web address: www.www1.avera.org/amck/regionalfacilities/dellsareahealth/index.aspx
**Control:** Other not–for–profit (including NFP Corporation) **Service:** General Medical and Surgical

**Staffed Beds:** 23 **Admissions:** 316 **Census:** 4 **Outpatient Visits:** 17509 **Births:** 0 **Total Expense ($000):** 5187 **Payroll Expense ($000):** 2029 **Personnel:** 50

## EAGLE BUTTE—Dewey County

**U. S. PUBLIC HEALTH SERVICE INDIAN HOSPITAL (430083)**, 317 Main Street, Zip 57625–1012, Mailing Address: P.O. Box 1012, Zip 57625–1012; tel. 605/964–7724, (Nonreporting) **A**10 **S** U. S. Indian Health Service, Rockville, MD
Primary Contact: Charlene Red Thunder, Chief Executive Officer
CFO: Lisa Deal, Budget Analyst
Web address: www.ihs.gov
**Control:** Public Health Service, Government, federal **Service:** General Medical and Surgical

**Staffed Beds:** 11

## EUREKA—Mcpherson County

★ **EUREKA COMMUNITY HEALTH SERVICES AVERA (431308)**, 410 Ninth Street, Zip 57437–2182, Mailing Address: P.O. Box 517, Zip 57437–0517; tel. 605/284–2661 **A**9 10 18 **F**10 28 35 40 45 59 62 65 77 81 93 133 **S** Avera Health, Sioux Falls, SD
Primary Contact: Carmen Weber, Interim Administrator
CFO: Joyce Schwingler, Chief Financial Officer
Web address: www.avera.org
**Control:** Other not–for–profit (including NFP Corporation) **Service:** General Medical and Surgical

**Staffed Beds:** 6 **Admissions:** 99 **Census:** 1 **Outpatient Visits:** 6006 **Births:** 0 **Total Expense ($000):** 222254 **Payroll Expense ($000):** 911 **Personnel:** 32

## FAULKTON—Faulk County

**FAULKTON AREA MEDICAL CENTER (431301)**, 1300 Oak Street, Zip 57438–2149, Mailing Address: P.O. Box 100, Zip 57438–0100; tel. 605/598–6263 **A**9 10 18 **F**3 17 28 29 40 45 57 59 77 93 97 107 127 133 **P**5
Primary Contact: Jay A. Jahnig, Chief Executive Officer
COO: Jay A. Jahnig, Chief Executive Officer
CFO: Susan Miller, Financial Administrator
CMO: K. A. Bartholomew, M.D., Medical Director
CIO: Cheryl Arthurs, Health Information Transcriptionist
CHR: Susan Miller, Financial Administrator
Web address: www.faulktonmedical.org
**Control:** Other not–for–profit (including NFP Corporation) **Service:** General Medical and Surgical

**Staffed Beds:** 12 **Admissions:** 355 **Census:** 5 **Outpatient Visits:** 13424 **Births:** 0 **Total Expense ($000):** 7698 **Payroll Expense ($000):** 3308 **Personnel:** 73

## FLANDREAU—Moody County

★ **AVERA FLANDREAU HOSPITAL (431310)**, 214 North Prairie Street, Zip 57028–1243; tel. 605/997–2433 **A**9 10 18 **F**3 28 34 35 40 45 57 59 64 65 75 81 86 92 93 97 107 119 127 128 132 133 146 148 **P**6 **S** Avera Health, Sioux Falls, SD
Primary Contact: Lindsay Flannery, R.N., Administrator and Chief Executive Officer
CFO: Kory Holt, Division Controller Network Operations
CMO: Gary Bruning, M.D., President Medical Staff
CIO: Brittney Luze, Director Health Information
CHR: Mona Schafer, Regional Manager Human Resources
Web address: www.flandreaumedical.org
**Control:** Other not–for–profit (including NFP Corporation) **Service:** General Medical and Surgical

**Staffed Beds:** 18 **Admissions:** 125 **Census:** 1 **Outpatient Visits:** 13590 **Births:** 0 **Total Expense ($000):** 4529 **Payroll Expense ($000):** 1842 **Personnel:** 47

**SD**

---

**Hospital, Medicare Provider Number, Address, Telephone, Approval, Facility, and Physician Codes, Health Care System**

★ American Hospital Association (AHA) membership
□ The Joint Commission accreditation
◇ DNV Healthcare Inc. accreditation
○ Healthcare Facilities Accreditation Program
△ Commission on Accreditation of Rehabilitation Facilities (CARF) accreditation

AVERA FLANDREAU MEDICAL CENTER See Avera Flandreau Hospital

## FORT MEADE—Meade County

⊠  △  **VETERANS AFFAIRS BLACK HILLS HEALTH CARE SYSTEM**, 113 Comanche Road, Zip 57741–1099; tel. 605/347–2511, (Includes VETERANS AFFAIRS MEDICAL CENTER, 500 North Fifth Street, Hot Springs, Zip 57747; tel. 605/745–2052), (Nonreporting) **A**1 5 7 9 **S** Department of Veterans Affairs, Washington, DC
Primary Contact: Stephen R. DiStasio, Director
CFO: Bill Gambill, Chief Financial Officer
CHR: Marg McCaleb, Chief Human Resources Management
Web address: www.blackhills.va.gov/
**Control:** Veterans Affairs, Government, federal **Service:** General Medical and Surgical

**Staffed Beds:** 308

## FREEMAN—Hutchinson County

★  **FREEMAN REGIONAL HEALTH SERVICES (431313)**, 510 East Eighth Street, Zip 57029–2086, Mailing Address: P.O. Box 370, Zip 57029–0370; tel. 605/925–4000, (Total facility includes 56 beds in nursing home–type unit) **A**9 10 18 **F**2 3 6 11 15 28 30 31 34 35 40 45 49 56 57 59 64 65 68 69 70 75 77 79 81 82 86 89 90 93 107 114 119 125 127 128 130 132 133 143 146 **P**6
Primary Contact: Daniel Gran, Chief Executive Officer
CFO: Neil Frizzell, Chief Financial Officer
Web address: www.freemanregional.com
**Control:** Other not–for–profit (including NFP Corporation) **Service:** General Medical and Surgical

**Staffed Beds:** 81 **Admissions:** 262 **Census:** 55 **Outpatient Visits:** 10038 **Births:** 0 **Total Expense ($000):** 9072 **Payroll Expense ($000):** 3979 **Personnel:** 113

## GETTYSBURG—Potter County

★  **AVERA GETTYSBURG HOSPITAL (431302)**, (Formerly Gettysburg Memorial Hospital), 606 East Garfield Avenue, Zip 57442–1398; tel. 605/765–2480, (Total facility includes 50 beds in nursing home–type unit) **A**9 10 18 **F**3 6 11 28 29 30 34 35 36 40 50 59 64 67 75 77 79 81 82 86 87 93 107 125 128 130 132 133 146 **S** Avera Health, Sioux Falls, SD
Primary Contact: Mark Schmidt, President and Chief Executive Officer
Web address: www.st-marys.com
**Control:** Church–operated, Nongovernment, not–for profit **Service:** General Medical and Surgical

**Staffed Beds:** 60 **Admissions:** 98 **Census:** 48 **Outpatient Visits:** 6250 **Births:** 0 **Total Expense ($000):** 5546 **Payroll Expense ($000):** 2590 **Personnel:** 72

## GREGORY—Gregory County

★  **AVERA GREGORY HOSPITAL (431338)**, 400 Park Avenue, Zip 57533–1302, Mailing Address: P.O. Box 408, Zip 57533–0408; tel. 605/835–8394, (Total facility includes 42 beds in nursing home–type unit) **A**9 10 18 **F**3 13 15 17 28 29 30 31 34 35 40 43 45 56 57 59 60 70 75 76 77 78 79 81 82 86 87 89 107 110 128 129 130 131 132 133 143 147 **S** Avera Health, Sioux Falls, SD
Primary Contact: Anthony Timanus, Chief Executive Officer
CFO: Trish Keiser, Comptroller
CMO: Rich Kafka, M.D., Chief Medical Officer
CIO: Justin Keegan, Director Support Services
CHR: Carol Postulka, Administrative Coordinator
Web address: www.gregoryhealthcare.org
**Control:** Church–operated, Nongovernment, not–for profit **Service:** General Medical and Surgical

**Staffed Beds:** 67 **Admissions:** 661 **Census:** 44 **Outpatient Visits:** 16338 **Births:** 5 **Total Expense ($000):** 12892 **Payroll Expense ($000):** 5747 **Personnel:** 128

## HOT SPRINGS—Fall River County

★  **FALL RIVER HOSPITAL (431322)**, 1201 Highway 71 South, Zip 57747–8800; tel. 605/745–3159, (Includes CASTLE MANOR ) **A**9 10 18 **F**3 28 34 40 43 45 56 57 59 64 65 74 77 79 81 93 102 107 114 119 127 128 129 131 132 133 146 148 **P**6
Primary Contact: Tricia Uhlir, Chief Executive Officer
CFO: Jesse Naze, Chief Financial Officer
CMO: Heather Preuss, M.D., Medical Director
CHR: Cindy Trent, Manager Personnel
Web address: www.fallriverhealthservices.com
**Control:** Other not–for–profit (including NFP Corporation) **Service:** General Medical and Surgical

**Staffed Beds:** 25 **Admissions:** 331 **Census:** 8 **Outpatient Visits:** 18751 **Births:** 0 **Total Expense ($000):** 11886 **Payroll Expense ($000):** 4748 **Personnel:** 95

VETERANS AFFAIRS MEDICAL CENTER See Veterans Affairs Black Hills Health Care System, Fort Meade

## HURON—Beadle County

★  **HURON REGIONAL MEDICAL CENTER (431335)**, 172 Fourth Street S.E., Zip 57350–2590; tel. 605/353–6200 **A**9 10 18 **F**3 11 13 14 15 28 29 30 31 34 35 40 41 43 45 57 59 60 62 63 64 68 70 75 76 77 78 79 81 85 86 93 102 107 108 110 111 115 118 119 130 132 133 146 148 **P**6 **S** QHR, Brentwood, TN
Primary Contact: John L. Single, Chief Executive Officer
CFO: Marcia Zwanziger, Vice President Finance
CMO: Cy Haatvedt, M.D., Chief of Staff
CHR: Rhonda Hanson, Director Human Resources
CNO: Gail Robeson, Vice President Patient Services
Web address: www.huronregional.org
**Control:** Other not–for–profit (including NFP Corporation) **Service:** General Medical and Surgical

**Staffed Beds:** 25 **Admissions:** 1316 **Census:** 13 **Outpatient Visits:** 64417 **Births:** 313 **Total Expense ($000):** 30067 **Payroll Expense ($000):** 13769 **Personnel:** 237

## MADISON—Lake County

★  **MADISON COMMUNITY HOSPITAL (431300)**, 917 North Washington Avenue, Zip 57042–1696; tel. 605/256–6551 **A**9 10 18 **F**7 11 13 15 28 31 34 35 40 41 43 57 59 62 64 70 75 76 77 81 82 85 89 93 107 110 114 119 129 132 133 135 143 145 146 148 **P**5
Primary Contact: Tamara Miller, R.N., Administrator
CFO: Teresa Mallett, Chief Financial Officer
CNO: Charlotte Charles, Director Acute Patient Services
Web address: www.madisonhospital.com
**Control:** Other not–for–profit (including NFP Corporation) **Service:** General Medical and Surgical

**Staffed Beds:** 25 **Admissions:** 529 **Census:** 7 **Outpatient Visits:** 27589 **Births:** 45 **Total Expense ($000):** 12945 **Payroll Expense ($000):** 6109 **Personnel:** 134

## MARTIN—Bennett County

**BENNETT COUNTY HOSPITAL AND NURSING HOME (431314)**, (Critical Access Hospital), 102 Major Allen Street, Zip 57551–6005, Mailing Address: P.O. Box 70, Zip 57551–0070; tel. 605/685–6622, (Total facility includes 42 beds in nursing home–type unit) **A**9 10 18 **F**7 10 28 29 30 34 35 40 50 53 57 59 62 65 66 67 68 84 92 93 130 131 133 143 148
Primary Contact: Ethel Frein, Chief Executive Officer
CFO: Jean Kirk, Chief Financial Officer
CMO: Peter Knowles–Smith, M.D., Medical Director
CIO: Jean Kirk, Chief Financial Officer
CHR: T. J. Porter, Director Human Resources
Web address: www.bennettcountyhospital.com/
**Control:** Other not–for–profit (including NFP Corporation) **Service:** Other specialty

**Staffed Beds:** 53 **Admissions:** 214 **Census:** 38 **Outpatient Visits:** 50346 **Births:** 1 **Total Expense ($000):** 5562 **Payroll Expense ($000):** 3455 **Personnel:** 95

## MILBANK—Grant County

★  **MILBANK AREA HOSPITAL AVERA (431326)**, 901 East Virgil Avenue, Zip 57252–2124; tel. 605/432–4538, (Includes ST. WILLIAM HOME FOR THE AGED ), (Nonreporting) **A**9 10 18 **S** Avera Health, Sioux Falls, SD
Primary Contact: Natalie Gauer, Administrator
CMO: Kevin Bjordahl, M.D., Chief Medical Officer
CHR: Mona Schafer, Regional Manager Human Resources
Web address: www.averamilbank.org
**Control:** Other not–for–profit (including NFP Corporation) **Service:** General Medical and Surgical

**Staffed Beds:** 25

## MILLER—Hand County

★  **AVERA HAND COUNTY MEMORIAL HOSPITAL (431337)**, (Formerly Avera Hand County Memorial Hospital & Clinic), 300 West Fifth Street, Zip 57362–1238; tel. 605/853–2421 **A**9 10 18 **F**8 11 15 17 28 29 34 35 40 42 43 45 46 50 56 57 59 64 74 77 79 81 86 87 93 107 114 119 128 129 132 133 146 148 **P**5 **S** Avera Health, Sioux Falls, SD
Primary Contact: Bryan Breitling, Administrator
CFO: Debbie Pullman, Director Finance
CMO: Joel Huber, M.D., Chief of Staff
CIO: Janice Purrington, Coordinator Medical Records
CNO: Vicki Hasart, Nurse Manager
Web address: www.avera.org
**Control:** Other not–for–profit (including NFP Corporation) **Service:** General Medical and Surgical

**Staffed Beds:** 16 **Admissions:** 352 **Census:** 4 **Outpatient Visits:** 13959 **Total Expense ($000):** 5748 **Payroll Expense ($000):** 2752 **Personnel:** 45

*Many Facility Codes have changed. Please refer to the AHA Guide Code Chart.*    © 2013 AHA Guide

**SD**

**MITCHELL—Davison County**

☒ **AVERA QUEEN OF PEACE HOSPITAL (430013)**, 525 North Foster,
Zip 57301–2999; tel. 605/995–2000, (Total facility includes 111 beds in nursing
home–type unit) **A**1 2 9 10 **F**3 10 12 13 15 28 29 30 31 34 35 39 40 43 48
50 53 56 57 59 62 63 64 65 69 70 71 75 76 77 78 79 81 82 84 85 86 89
93 94 96 102 107 110 111 114 116 118 119 121 123 125 127 128 129
130 131 132 133 135 144 146 147 148 **P**6 **S** Avera Health, Sioux Falls, SD
Primary Contact: Thomas A. Clark, President and Chief Executive Officer
CFO: Will Flett, Senior Vice President Finance and Chief Financial Officer
CMO: Jennifer Tegethoff, M.D., President Medical Staff
CIO: Patti Brooks, Director Information Systems
CHR: Rita Lemon, Director Human Resources
Web address: www.averaqueenofpeace.org
**Control:** Church–operated, Nongovernment, not–for profit **Service:** General
Medical and Surgical

| | |
|---|---|
| **Staffed Beds:** 196 **Admissions:** 2664 **Census:** 130 **Outpatient Visits:** 113742 **Births:** 486 **Total Expense ($000):** 77128 **Payroll Expense ($000):** 38550 **Personnel:** 654 | |

**MOBRIDGE—Walworth County**

★ **MOBRIDGE REGIONAL HOSPITAL (431325)**, 1401 Tenth Avenue West,
Zip 57601–1106, Mailing Address: P.O. Box 580, Zip 57601–0580;
tel. 605/845–3692 **A**9 10 18 **F**3 7 8 10 11 13 15 17 28 31 34 35 40 43 45
56 57 59 62 64 65 67 70 75 76 81 89 93 97 107 110 114 119 125 127 128
129 130 133 **P**6
Primary Contact: Angelia K. Svihovec, Chief Executive Officer
CFO: Renae Tisdall, Chief Financial Officer
CMO: Travis Henderson, M.D., Chief of Staff
CIO: Brian Schaefbauer, Director Information Technology
CHR: Keri Wientjes, Director Human Resources
Web address: www.mobridgehospital.org
**Control:** Other not–for–profit (including NFP Corporation) **Service:** General
Medical and Surgical

| | |
|---|---|
| **Staffed Beds:** 25 **Admissions:** 775 **Census:** 7 **Outpatient Visits:** 32223 **Births:** 53 **Total Expense ($000):** 14229 **Payroll Expense ($000):** 7202 **Personnel:** 139 | |

**PARKSTON—Hutchinson County**

★ **AVERA ST. BENEDICT HEALTH CENTER (431330)**, (Formerly Avera St.
Benedict Hospital), 401 West Glynn Drive, Zip 57366–9605; tel. 605/928–3311,
(Total facility includes 75 beds in nursing home–type unit) **A**9 10 18 **F**2 3 8 10
13 15 28 29 30 31 32 34 35 38 40 45 53 56 57 59 64 65 69 75 76 81 82
83 85 86 87 89 107 110 111 114 116 119 128 129 130 131 132 133 135
146 148 **P**6 **S** Avera Health, Sioux Falls, SD
Primary Contact: Gale N. Walker, President and Chief Executive Officer
CFO: Rita Blasius, Assistant Administrator and Chief Financial Officer
CMO: Jason Wickersham, M.D., Chief of Staff
CIO: Adam Popp, Director Information Systems
CHR: Phyllis Ehler, Director Human Resources
CNO: Denise Muntefering, Vice President Patient Care Services
Web address: www.averastbenedict.com
**Control:** Church–operated, Nongovernment, not–for profit **Service:** General
Medical and Surgical

| | |
|---|---|
| **Staffed Beds:** 100 **Admissions:** 513 **Census:** 78 **Outpatient Visits:** 20775 **Births:** 42 **Total Expense ($000):** 16416 **Payroll Expense ($000):** 8498 **Personnel:** 163 | |

**PHILIP—Haakon County**

**HANS P. PETERSON MEMORIAL HOSPITAL** See Philip Health Services

★ **PHILIP HEALTH SERVICES (431319)**, 503 West Pine Street, Zip 57567–3300,
Mailing Address: P.O. Box 790, Zip 57567–0790; tel. 605/859–2511, (Total
facility includes 30 beds in nursing home–type unit) **A**9 10 18 **F**10 11 40 57 59
62 85 93 107 114 119 125 127 128 130 131 133 148 **P**6 **S** Regional Health,
Rapid City, SD
Primary Contact: Kent Olson, Administrator and Chief Executive Officer
**Control:** Other not–for–profit (including NFP Corporation) **Service:** General
Medical and Surgical

| | |
|---|---|
| **Staffed Beds:** 48 **Admissions:** 253 **Census:** 31 **Outpatient Visits:** 9000 **Births:** 1 **Total Expense ($000):** 7869 **Payroll Expense ($000):** 4398 **Personnel:** 126 | |

**PIERRE—Hughes County**

☒ **AVERA ST. MARY'S HOSPITAL (430015)**, (Formerly St. Mary's Healthcare
Center), 801 East Sioux Avenue, Zip 57501–3323; tel. 605/224–3100, (Total
facility includes 90 beds in nursing home–type unit) **A**1 9 10 20 **F**2 3 8 13 15 28
29 30 31 34 38 40 41 43 45 48 49 50 51 59 60 64 68 70 71 76 77 78 79
81 82 83 84 85 87 93 96 97 107 110 111 114 119 125 128 129 130 132
133 135 146 148 **P**5 **S** Avera Health, Sioux Falls, SD
Primary Contact: Joseph Messmer, Interim Chief Executive Officer
CFO: Tom Wagner, Interim Vice President Finance
CMO: Denise Hanisch, M.D., Chief of Staff
CIO: Jamie Raske, Information Technology Lead
CHR: Paul Marso, Vice President Human Resources
Web address: www.avera.org/st–marys–pierre/
**Control:** Other not–for–profit (including NFP Corporation) **Service:** General
Medical and Surgical

| | |
|---|---|
| **Staffed Beds:** 164 **Admissions:** 1910 **Census:** 83 **Outpatient Visits:** 49043 **Births:** 427 **Total Expense ($000):** 45354 **Payroll Expense ($000):** 16983 **Personnel:** 336 | |

**PINE RIDGE—Shannon County**

**U. S. PUBLIC HEALTH SERVICE INDIAN HOSPITAL (430081)**, East Highway
18, Zip 57770, Mailing Address: P.O. Box 1201, Zip 57770–1201;
tel. 605/867–5131, (Nonreporting) **A**10 **S** U. S. Indian Health Service,
Rockville, MD
Primary Contact: William Pourier, Service Unit Director
CFO: Sophia Conny, Deputy Administrative Officer
CMO: Jan Colton, M.D., Acting Clinical Director
CHR: Annabelle Blackbear, Human Resources Specialist
Web address: www.ihs.gov
**Control:** Public Health Service, Government, federal **Service:** General Medical
and Surgical

| | |
|---|---|
| **Staffed Beds:** 45 | |

**PLATTE—Charles Mix County**

★ **PLATTE HEALTH CENTER AVERA (431306)**, 601 East Seventh,
Zip 57369–2123, Mailing Address: P.O. Box 200, Zip 57369–0200;
tel. 605/337–3364, (Nonreporting) **A**9 10 18 **S** Avera Health, Sioux Falls, SD
Primary Contact: Mark Burket, Chief Executive Officer
CFO: Jerry Hoffman, Chief Financial Officer
Web address: www.phcavera.org
**Control:** Other not–for–profit (including NFP Corporation) **Service:** General
Medical and Surgical

| | |
|---|---|
| **Staffed Beds:** 65 | |

**RAPID CITY—Pennington County**

**BLACK HILLS SURGERY CENTER (430091)**, 216 Anamaria Drive,
Zip 57701–7366, Mailing Address: 1868 Lombardy Drive, Zip 57703–4130;
tel. 605/721–4900, (Nonreporting) **A**9 10
Primary Contact: Franklin Shobe, Administrator and Chief Executive Officer
Web address: www.bhsc.com
**Control:** Partnership, Investor–owned, for–profit **Service:** General Medical and
Surgical

| | |
|---|---|
| **Staffed Beds:** 26 | |

**INDIAN HEALTH SERVICE HOSPITAL (430082)**, 3200 Canyon Lake Drive,
Zip 57702–8197; tel. 605/355–2280 **A**10 **F**3 4 5 15 29 34 35 39 40 50 53
59 64 65 89 97 98 100 111 119 130 135 **S** U. S. Indian Health Service,
Rockville, MD
Primary Contact: Helen Thompson, Interim Director
CFO: Helen Thompson, Administrative Officer
Web address: www.ihs.gov
**Control:** PHS, Indian Service, Government, federal **Service:** General Medical and
Surgical

| | |
|---|---|
| **Staffed Beds:** 9 **Admissions:** 54 **Census:** 1 **Outpatient Visits:** 130247 **Births:** 0 **Personnel:** 243 | |

SD

---

**Hospital, Medicare Provider Number, Address, Telephone, Approval, Facility, and Physician Codes, Health Care System**

★ American Hospital Association (AHA) membership
☐ The Joint Commission accreditation    ◇ DNV Healthcare Inc. accreditation

○ Healthcare Facilities Accreditation Program
△ Commission on Accreditation of Rehabilitation Facilities (CARF) accreditation

☒ △ **RAPID CITY REGIONAL HOSPITAL (430077)**, 353 Fairmont Boulevard, Zip 57701–7393, Mailing Address: P.O. Box 6000, Zip 57709–6000; tel. 605/719–1000 **A**1 3 5 7 9 10 **F**3 5 11 12 13 15 17 18 20 22 24 26 28 29 30 31 34 35 36 38 40 43 44 45 46 47 48 49 51 56 57 58 59 60 62 63 64 65 66 68 70 72 73 74 75 76 77 78 79 80 81 82 84 85 86 87 88 89 90 92 93 98 99 100 101 102 104 107 108 110 111 115 119 120 121 122 123 124 129 130 131 132 135 141 143 146 148 **P**1 5 6 **S** Regional Health, Rapid City, SD
Primary Contact: Timothy H. Sughrue, Chief Executive Officer
CFO: Mark Thompson, Vice President Financial Services
CMO: Robert Allen, M.D., Vice President Medical Affairs
CIO: Richard Latuchie, Vice President Business Development
CHR: Robert McGlone, Vice President Human Resources
CNO: Rita K. Haxton, R.N., Vice President Patient Care Nursing
Web address: www.rcrh.org
**Control:** Other not–for–profit (including NFP Corporation) **Service:** General Medical and Surgical

**Staffed Beds:** 394 **Admissions:** 17674 **Census:** 280 **Outpatient Visits:** 193374 **Births:** 2336 **Total Expense ($000):** 264798 **Payroll Expense ($000):** 154753 **Personnel:** 2843

**SAME DAY SURGERY CENTER (430093)**, 651 Cathedral Drive, Zip 57701–7368; tel. 605/719–5000, (Nonreporting) **A**9 10
Primary Contact: Doris Fritts, R.N., Executive Director
Web address: www.samedaysurgerycenter.org
**Control:** Corporation, Investor–owned, for–profit **Service:** Surgical

**Staffed Beds:** 8

### REDFIELD—Spink County

**COMMUNITY MEMORIAL HOSPITAL (431316)**, 110 West Tenth Avenue, Zip 57469–1520, Mailing Address: P.O. Box 420, Zip 57469–0420; tel. 605/472–1110 **A**9 10 18 **F**7 8 11 17 28 34 35 40 45 53 56 57 59 62 64 65 77 81 84 85 89 93 97 107 114 119 127 128 130 131 132 133 146 **P**6
Primary Contact: Nicholas R. Brandner, Chief Executive Officer
Web address: www.redfield–sd.com/hospital.html
**Control:** City–Government, nonfederal **Service:** General Medical and Surgical

**Staffed Beds:** 23 **Admissions:** 315 **Census:** 6 **Outpatient Visits:** 18069 **Births:** 0 **Total Expense ($000):** 10653 **Payroll Expense ($000):** 5063 **Personnel:** 109

### ROSEBUD—Todd County

**U. S. PUBLIC HEALTH SERVICE INDIAN HOSPITAL (430084)**, Highway 18, Soldier Creek Road, Zip 57570; tel. 605/747–2231, (Nonreporting) **A**10 **S** U. S. Indian Health Service, Rockville, MD
Primary Contact: Sophie M. Two Hawk, Chief Executive Officer
COO: Romeo Vivit, Chief Surgeon
CMO: Valerie Parker, M.D., Clinical Director
CHR: Michelle Zephier, Human Resource Specialist
Web address: www.ihs.gov
**Control:** PHS, Indian Service, Government, federal **Service:** General Medical and Surgical

**Staffed Beds:** 35

### SCOTLAND—Bon Homme County

★ **LANDMANN–JUNGMAN MEMORIAL HOSPITAL AVERA (431317)**, 600 Billars Street, Zip 57059–2026; tel. 605/583–2226, (Nonreporting) **A**9 10 18 **S** Avera Health, Sioux Falls, SD
Primary Contact: Lee Baldwin, Administrator and Chief Executive Officer
CFO: Darcy Kepplinger, Manager Business Office
Web address: www.ljmh.org
**Control:** Other not–for–profit (including NFP Corporation) **Service:** General Medical and Surgical

**Staffed Beds:** 19

### SIOUX FALLS—Lincoln County

☐ **AVERA HEART HOSPITAL OF SOUTH DAKOTA (430095)**, 4500 West 69th Street, Zip 57108–8148; tel. 605/977–7000 **A**1 9 10 **F**3 11 17 18 20 22 24 26 28 29 30 34 35 40 45 57 59 60 68 71 74 79 81 82 84 85 87 99 100 107 108 111 115 118 119 121 124 130 132 135 146 148 **P**2 **S** Avera Health, Sioux Falls, SD
Primary Contact: Jon Soderholm, President
CFO: Jean White, Vice President Finance
Web address: www.southdakotaheart.com
**Control:** Corporation, Investor–owned, for–profit **Service:** Heart

**Staffed Beds:** 53 **Admissions:** 2802 **Census:** 27 **Outpatient Visits:** 5902 **Births:** 0 **Personnel:** 338

☒ △ **AVERA McKENNAN HOSPITAL AND UNIVERSITY HEALTH CENTER (430016)**, 800 East 21st Street, Zip 57105–1096, Mailing Address: P.O. Box 5045, Zip 57117–5045; tel. 605/322–8000, (Includes AVERA CHILDREN'S HOSPITAL, 800 East 21st Street, Zip 57105–1016, Mailing Address: PO Box 5045, Zip 57117–5045; tel. 605/322–5437), (Total facility includes 90 beds in nursing home–type unit) **A**1 2 3 5 7 8 9 10 **F**3 5 7 8 10 11 12 13 15 18 19 20 21 22 23 24 29 30 32 34 35 36 38 39 40 41 43 44 46 49 50 53 54 55 56 57 58 59 60 61 63 64 65 66 67 68 70 71 72 74 75 76 77 78 79 81 82 84 85 86 87 88 89 90 92 93 94 96 97 98 99 100 101 102 103 104 105 107 108 110 111 114 115 116 117 118 119 120 121 123 124 125 126 128 129 130 131 132 134 135 136 138 141 142 143 144 145 146 147 148 **P**6 **S** Avera Health, Sioux Falls, SD
Primary Contact: David Kapaska, D.O., Regional President
COO: Judy Blauwet, M.P.H., Senior Vice President Operations and Chief Nursing Officer
CFO: Julie Norton, Chief Financial Officer
CIO: Kristin Gross, Director Information Technology Center
CHR: Bill McLean, Senior Vice President Human Resources
Web address: www.averamckennan.org
**Control:** Church–operated, Nongovernment, not–for profit **Service:** General Medical and Surgical

**Staffed Beds:** 403 **Admissions:** 20637 **Census:** 290 **Outpatient Visits:** 218990 **Births:** 1960 **Total Expense ($000):** 624856 **Payroll Expense ($000):** 300062 **Personnel:** 3628

**CHILDRENS CARE HOSPITAL AND SCHOOL (433300)**, 2501 West 26th Street, Zip 57105–2498; tel. 605/782–2300, (Nonreporting) **A**9 10
Primary Contact: David A. Timpe, Interim President and Chief Executive Officer
CFO: John Clark, Chief Financial Officer
CMO: Christiane Maroun, M.D., Chief of Staff
CHR: Tiffany Reilly, Director Human Resources
Web address: www.cchs.org
**Control:** Other not–for–profit (including NFP Corporation) **Service:** Children's rehabilitation

**Staffed Beds:** 114

☒ △ **SANFORD USD MEDICAL CENTER (430027)**, 1305 West 18th Street, Zip 57105–0496, Mailing Address: P.O. Box 5039, Zip 57117–5039; tel. 605/333–1000, (Includes SANFORD CHILDREN'S HOSPITAL, 1600 West 22nd Street, Zip 57105, Mailing Address: PO Box 5039, Zip 57117–5039; tel. 605/333–1000) **A**1 2 3 5 7 8 9 10 **F**3 7 8 9 11 12 13 14 15 17 18 19 20 21 22 23 24 25 26 27 28 29 30 31 32 34 35 36 37 38 40 43 44 45 46 48 49 50 51 52 53 54 55 56 57 58 59 60 61 63 64 65 70 71 72 73 74 75 76 77 78 79 80 81 82 83 84 85 86 87 88 89 90 91 92 93 94 96 97 99 100 101 107 108 110 111 114 115 116 117 118 119 120 121 123 124 126 129 130 131 132 134 135 138 141 142 143 146 147 148 **P**6 **S** Sanford Health, Sioux Falls, SD
Primary Contact: Paul D. Hanson, President
COO: Randy Bury, Chief Operating Officer
CFO: Jeff Sandene, Chief Finance
CMO: Ken Aspaas, M.D., Chief Medical Officer
CIO: Arlyn Broekhuis, Vice President and Chief Information Officer
CHR: Evan Burkett, Chief Human Resource Officer
Web address: www.sanfordhealth.org
**Control:** Other not–for–profit (including NFP Corporation) **Service:** General Medical and Surgical

**Staffed Beds:** 511 **Admissions:** 26215 **Census:** 313 **Outpatient Visits:** 394764 **Births:** 3101 **Total Expense ($000):** 521205 **Payroll Expense ($000):** 204380 **Personnel:** 4666

☒ **SELECT SPECIALTY HOSPITAL–SIOUX FALLS (432002)**, 1305 West 18th Street, Zip 57105–0401; tel. 605/322–3500, (Nonreporting) **A**1 9 10 **S** Select Medical Corporation, Mechanicsburg, PA
Primary Contact: Carol Ulmer, Chief Executive Officer
Web address: www.selectspecialtyhospitals.com/company/locations/siouxfalls.aspx
**Control:** Corporation, Investor–owned, for–profit **Service:** Long–Term Acute Care hospital

**Staffed Beds:** 21

**SIOUX FALLS SPECIALTY HOSPITAL (430090)**, (Formerly Sioux Falls Surgical Center), 910 East 20th Street, Zip 57105–1012; tel. 605/334–6730 **A**9 10 **F**39 45 49 51 59 74 77 79 81 82 97 111 131 **P**5
Primary Contact: Donald A. Schellpfeffer, M.D., Chief Executive Officer
CFO: Kyle Goldammer, Chief Financial Officer
CMO: Donald A. Schellpfeffer, M.D., Medical Director
Web address: www.sfsurgical.com
**Control:** Partnership, Investor–owned, for–profit **Service:** Orthopedic

**Staffed Beds:** 35 **Admissions:** 13778 **Census:** 8 **Outpatient Visits:** 12503 **Births:** 0 **Total Expense ($000):** 44175 **Payroll Expense ($000):** 10476 **Personnel:** 212

**SD**

✠ **SIOUX FALLS VETERANS AFFAIRS HEALTH CARE SYSTEM**, 2501 West 22nd Street, Zip 57105–1305, Mailing Address: P.O. Box 5046, Zip 57117–5046; tel. 605/336–3230, (Total facility includes 58 beds in nursing home–type unit) **A**1 3 5 9 **F**1 5 12 18 20 28 29 30 31 35 38 39 40 45 50 56 58 59 60 61 62 64 65 70 74 75 77 78 79 81 82 84 85 86 87 93 94 97 98 100 102 103 104 105 107 108 111 119 127 129 130 135 143 146 147 **P**6 **S** Department of Veterans Affairs, Washington, DC
Primary Contact: Sandra Horsman, Acting Medical Center Director
COO: Sara Ackert, Associate Director
CFO: Daniel Hubbard, Chief Financial Officer
CMO: Victor Waters, M.D., Chief of Staff
CIO: Eric Heiser, Chief Information Resource Management
CHR: Betsy Geiver, Chief Human Resources Officer
Web address: www.siouxfalls.va.gov
**Control:** Veterans Affairs, Government, federal **Service:** General Medical and Surgical

**Staffed Beds:** 98 **Admissions:** 2551 **Census:** 81 **Outpatient Visits:** 278678
**Births:** 0 **Personnel:** 877

## SISSETON—Roberts County

★ **COTEAU DES PRAIRIES HOSPITAL (431339)**, 205 Orchard Drive, Zip 57262–2398; tel. 605/698–7647 **A**9 10 18 **F**13 28 31 34 35 40 53 57 59 62 64 70 75 76 77 81 86 89 90 93 107 119 127 133 **P**6
Primary Contact: Dan C. Ellis, Chief Executive Officer
Web address: www.cdphospital.com
**Control:** Other not–for–profit (including NFP Corporation) **Service:** General Medical and Surgical

**Staffed Beds:** 25 **Admissions:** 504 **Census:** 3 **Outpatient Visits:** 42589
**Births:** 150 **Total Expense ($000):** 12163 **Payroll Expense ($000):** 5798
**Personnel:** 120

## SPEARFISH—Lawrence County

★ **SPEARFISH REGIONAL HOSPITAL (430048)**, 1440 North Main Street, Zip 57783–1504; tel. 605/644–4000 **A**9 10 20 **F**3 11 13 15 28 29 31 34 40 43 45 57 59 62 63 70 75 76 79 81 84 85 89 93 97 107 108 110 111 114 119 128 129 130 132 133 135 146 147 148 **P**6 **S** Regional Health, Rapid City, SD
Primary Contact: Larry W. Veitz, Chief Executive Officer
Web address: www.regionalhealth.com
**Control:** Other not–for–profit (including NFP Corporation) **Service:** General Medical and Surgical

**Staffed Beds:** 34 **Admissions:** 1545 **Census:** 12 **Outpatient Visits:** 32880
**Births:** 419 **Total Expense ($000):** 28229 **Payroll Expense ($000):** 11788
**Personnel:** 212

★ **SPEARFISH REGIONAL SURGERY CENTER (430094)**, 1316 North 10th Street, Zip 57783–1530; tel. 605/642–3113, (Nonreporting) **A**9 10
Primary Contact: Michael DeLano, Administrator
COO: Matthew Long, Chief Operating Officer
CFO: Jeff Roehrich, Chief Financial Officer
CMO: Richard Keim, M.D., Chief Medical Officer
CIO: Bill Stoeckman, Chief Information Officer
CHR: Pat Akin, Chief Human Resource Officer
CNO: Peggy O'Sullivan, Director Patient Services
Web address: www.rcrh.org
**Control:** Other not–for–profit (including NFP Corporation) **Service:** Surgical

**Staffed Beds:** 4

## STURGIS—Meade County

★ **STURGIS REGIONAL HOSPITAL (431321)**, 949 Harmon Street, Zip 57785–2452; tel. 605/720–2400, (Total facility includes 84 beds in nursing home–type unit) **A**9 10 18 **F**11 15 28 29 40 46 77 81 82 93 107 110 111 114 119 128 132 133 148 **S** Regional Health, Rapid City, SD
Primary Contact: Van D. Hyde, MS, Chief Executive Officer
CFO: Jodie Mitchell, Facility Financial Director
CMO: Constance Stock, M.D., Chief of Staff
CHR: Ginger Chord, Coordinator Human Resources
Web address: www.regionalhealth.com/Our–Locations/Regional–Hospitals/Sturgis–Regional–Hospital.aspx
**Control:** Other not–for–profit (including NFP Corporation) **Service:** General Medical and Surgical

**Staffed Beds:** 109 **Admissions:** 670 **Census:** 92 **Outpatient Visits:** 9821
**Births:** 0 **Total Expense ($000):** 15297 **Payroll Expense ($000):** 7847
**Personnel:** 168

## TYNDALL—Bon Homme County

★ **ST. MICHAEL'S HOSPITAL AVERA (431327)**, 410 West 16th Avenue, Zip 57066–2318; tel. 605/589–3341 **A**9 10 18 **F**3 15 28 31 34 40 45 53 57 59 64 65 67 70 75 77 81 86 89 92 93 94 107 110 114 119 127 128 129 131 133 148 **P**6 **S** Avera Health, Sioux Falls, SD
Primary Contact: Carol Deurmier, Chief Executive Officer
CFO: Lisa Ronke, Director Finance
CMO: Herbert A. Saloum, M.D., Medical Director
Web address: www.stmichaels–bhfp.org
**Control:** Church–operated, Nongovernment, not–for profit **Service:** General Medical and Surgical

**Staffed Beds:** 25 **Admissions:** 188 **Census:** 9 **Outpatient Visits:** 10203
**Births:** 0 **Total Expense ($000):** 8091 **Payroll Expense ($000):** 3246
**Personnel:** 64

## VERMILLION—Clay County

★ **SANFORD VERMILLION MEDICAL CENTER (431336)**, 20 South Plum Street, Zip 57069–3346; tel. 605/624–2611, (Total facility includes 66 beds in nursing home–type unit) **A**9 10 18 **F**15 29 35 40 43 59 67 81 91 92 93 97 107 116 119 129 130 131 132 133 135 **P**8 **S** Sanford Health, Sioux Falls, SD
Primary Contact: Timothy J. Tracy, Chief Executive Officer
CFO: Valerie Osterberg, Chief Financial Officer
CMO: Roy Mortinsen, M.D., Chief of Staff
CIO: Mary C. Merrigan, Manager Public Relations
CHR: Cindy Benzel, Manager Human Resources
CNO: Jeff Berens, MS, Chief Nursing Officer
Web address: www.sanfordvermillion.org
**Control:** Other not–for–profit (including NFP Corporation) **Service:** General Medical and Surgical

**Staffed Beds:** 114 **Admissions:** 538 **Census:** 69 **Outpatient Visits:** 37533
**Births:** 95 **Total Expense ($000):** 18429 **Payroll Expense ($000):** 7355
**Personnel:** 146

## VIBORG—Turner County

★ **PIONEER MEMORIAL HOSPITAL AND HEALTH SERVICES (431328)**, 315 North Washington Street, Zip 57070–2002, Mailing Address: P.O. Box 368, Zip 57070–0368; tel. 605/326–5161, (Total facility includes 52 beds in nursing home–type unit) **A**9 10 18 **F**6 10 15 28 30 34 40 43 45 53 56 57 59 63 65 69 75 79 81 87 97 107 111 119 125 127 128 130 132 133 **P**6 **S** Sanford Health, Sioux Falls, SD
Primary Contact: Thomas V. Richter, Chief Executive Officer
CFO: Anne Christiansen, Chief Financial Officer
CMO: Curtis Mark, M.D., Chief Medical Officer
Web address: www.pioneermemorial.org
**Control:** Other not–for–profit (including NFP Corporation) **Service:** General Medical and Surgical

**Staffed Beds:** 64 **Admissions:** 146 **Census:** 48 **Outpatient Visits:** 29415
**Births:** 0 **Total Expense ($000):** 12581 **Payroll Expense ($000):** 6584
**Personnel:** 149

## WAGNER—Charles Mix County

★ **WAGNER COMMUNITY MEMORIAL HOSPITAL AVERA (431315)**, 513 Third Street S.W., Zip 57380–9675, Mailing Address: P.O. Box 280, Zip 57380–0280; tel. 605/384–3611 **A**9 10 18 **F**3 11 15 17 18 28 31 34 40 43 45 57 59 64 67 70 75 77 81 93 97 107 110 114 119 125 128 130 133 148 **P**6 **S** Avera Health, Sioux Falls, SD
Primary Contact: Bryan Slaba, Chief Executive Officer
CFO: Lisa Weisser, Supervisor Finance
CIO: Mark VanRavenswaay, Coordinator Information Systems
CHR: Marcia Podzimek, Chief Human Resources Officer
Web address: www.avera.org/wagnerhospital
**Control:** Other not–for–profit (including NFP Corporation) **Service:** General Medical and Surgical

**Staffed Beds:** 20 **Admissions:** 299 **Census:** 2 **Outpatient Visits:** 9603
**Births:** 0 **Total Expense ($000):** 8068 **Payroll Expense ($000):** 3377
**Personnel:** 64

**SD**

---

**Hospital, Medicare Provider Number, Address, Telephone, Approval, Facility, and Physician Codes, Health Care System**

★ American Hospital Association (AHA) membership
☐ The Joint Commission accreditation      ◇ DNV Healthcare Inc. accreditation
○ Healthcare Facilities Accreditation Program
△ Commission on Accreditation of Rehabilitation Facilities (CARF) accreditation

## WATERTOWN—Codington County

★ **PRAIRIE LAKES HEALTHCARE SYSTEM (430005)**, 401 9th Avenue N.W., Zip 57201–1548, Mailing Address: P.O. Box 1210, Zip 57201–6210; tel. 605/882–7000 **A**9 10 20 **F**3 8 12 13 18 20 22 28 29 30 31 34 35 38 40 43 50 57 58 59 60 62 63 76 77 78 79 80 81 82 83 84 85 87 89 93 107 108 111 114 119 120 121 123 124 130 132 133 146 147 148
Primary Contact: Jill Fuller, R.N., Ph.D., President and Chief Executive Officer
COO: Traci Rabine, Vice President Clinic Operations
CFO: Adam Paul, Chief Financial Officer
CMO: Jon McAreavey, M.D., Chief Medical Staff
CIO: Grant Tillett, Chief Information Officer
CHR: Nathan Lake, Vice President Human Resources
CNO: Shelly Turbak, R.N., Chief Nursing Officer
Web address: www.prairielakes.com
**Control:** Other not–for–profit (including NFP Corporation) **Service:** General Medical and Surgical

**Staffed Beds:** 81 **Admissions:** 3424 **Census:** 31 **Outpatient Visits:** 81216 **Births:** 619 **Total Expense ($000):** 66110 **Payroll Expense ($000):** 28266 **Personnel:** 469

## WEBSTER—Day County

★ **SANFORD WEBSTER MEDICAL CENTER (431311)**, (Formerly Sanford Medical Center Webster), 1401 West 1st Street, Zip 57274–1054, Mailing Address: P.O. Box 489, Zip 57274–0489; tel. 605/345–3336, (Nonreporting) **A**9 10 18 **S** Sanford Health, Sioux Falls, SD
Primary Contact: David Rogers, Chief Executive Officer
CFO: Sheryl L. Pappas, Chief Financial Officer
Web address: www.sanfordhealth.org
**Control:** Other not–for–profit (including NFP Corporation) **Service:** General Medical and Surgical

**Staffed Beds:** 20

## WESSINGTON SPRINGS—Jerauld County

★ **AVERA WESKOTA MEMORIAL HOSPITAL (431324)**, 604 First Street N.E., Zip 57382–2166; tel. 605/539–1201 **A**9 10 18 **F**3 15 28 31 35 40 53 57 59 64 75 77 81 85 93 107 114 119 128 130 131 132 133 **P**5 **S** Avera Health, Sioux Falls, SD
Primary Contact: Gaea Blue, Administrator and Chief Executive Officer
CFO: Linda Jager, Director Finance
CMO: Thomas Dean, M.D., Chief of Staff
CNO: JoAnn Hettinger, R.N., Director of Patient Care Services
Web address: www.averaweskota.org
**Control:** Other not–for–profit (including NFP Corporation) **Service:** General Medical and Surgical

**Staffed Beds:** 23 **Admissions:** 145 **Census:** 3 **Outpatient Visits:** 6254 **Births:** 0 **Total Expense ($000):** 4102 **Payroll Expense ($000):** 1726 **Personnel:** 31

## WINNER—Tripp County

★ **WINNER REGIONAL HEALTHCARE CENTER (431334)**, 745 East Eighth Street, Zip 57580–2631; tel. 605/842–7100, (Total facility includes 70 beds in nursing home–type unit) **A**9 10 18 **F**13 15 17 28 31 34 35 40 47 56 57 59 62 64 65 68 75 76 79 81 85 87 107 108 115 119 127 128 131 132 133 148 **P**3 5 **S** Sanford Health, Sioux Falls, SD
Primary Contact: Kevin Coffey, Chief Executive Officer
CFO: Phil Husher, Chief Financial Officer
CMO: Thomas Kosina, M.D., Chief of Staff
CHR: Karleen Flakus, Director Human Resources
Web address: www.winnerregional.org
**Control:** Other not–for–profit (including NFP Corporation) **Service:** General Medical and Surgical

**Staffed Beds:** 104 **Admissions:** 743 **Census:** 70 **Outpatient Visits:** 6671 **Births:** 153 **Total Expense ($000):** 20065 **Payroll Expense ($000):** 8454 **Personnel:** 224

## YANKTON—Yankton County

⊠ **AVERA SACRED HEART HOSPITAL (430012)**, 501 Summit Avenue, Zip 57078–3855; tel. 605/668–8000, (Total facility includes 187 beds in nursing home–type unit) **A**1 2 5 9 10 **F**2 3 6 8 10 13 15 18 20 28 29 30 34 35 40 45 46 47 48 51 53 57 59 60 62 63 64 68 70 73 76 77 78 79 81 82 84 85 86 89 90 93 96 107 108 110 111 115 118 119 120 121 123 128 129 130 132 133 146 148 **S** Avera Health, Sioux Falls, SD
Primary Contact: Pamela J. Rezac, Regional President
COO: Douglas R. Ekeren, Vice President Planning and Development
CFO: Jamie Schaefer, Vice President Finance
CMO: Barry A. Graham, M.D., Vice President Medical Affairs
CIO: Kathy Quinlivan, Director Management Information Systems
CHR: Kimberly Jensen, Vice President Human Resources
CNO: Barbara R. Larson, R.N., Vice President Patient Care Services
Web address: www.averasacredheart.com
**Control:** Church–operated, Nongovernment, not–for profit **Service:** General Medical and Surgical

**Staffed Beds:** 293 **Admissions:** 3942 **Census:** 221 **Outpatient Visits:** 93924 **Births:** 574 **Total Expense ($000):** 91877 **Payroll Expense ($000):** 41518 **Personnel:** 624

---

**LEWIS AND CLARK SPECIALTY HOSPITAL (430096)**, 2601 Fox Run Parkway, Zip 57078–5341; tel. 605/665–5100, (Nonreporting) **A**9 10
Primary Contact: Michelle J. Jordan, Administrator
CFO: Terry Steichen, Business Officer
CHR: Elizabeth Steichen, Human Resources
Web address: www.lewisandclarkspecialty.com
**Control:** Corporation, Investor–owned, for–profit **Service:** Other specialty

**Staffed Beds:** 6

**SD**

# TENNESSEE

## ASHLAND CITY—Cheatham County

⊠ **TRISTAR ASHLAND CITY (441311)**, (Formerly Tristar Ashland City Medical Center), 313 North Main Street, Zip 37015–1347; tel. 615/792–3030 **A**1 9 10 18 **F**3 15 29 30 40 45 81 93 107 111 119 130 133 **S** HCA, Nashville, TN
Primary Contact: Darrell White, R.N., Administrator/Chief Nursing Officer
COO: Micki J. Slingerland, Chief Operating Officer
CFO: David A. Summers, Chief Financial Officer
CMO: F. J. Campbell, M.D., Chief Medical Officer
CIO: David Archer, Director Information Systems
CNO: Darrell White, R.N., Administrator/Chief Nursing Officer
Web address: www.tristarcentennial.com
**Control:** Corporation, Investor–owned, for–profit **Service:** General Medical and Surgical

**Staffed Beds:** 12 **Admissions:** 194 **Census:** 4 **Outpatient Visits:** 20798
**Births:** 0 **Total Expense ($000):** 9664 **Payroll Expense ($000):** 3492
**Personnel:** 53

## ATHENS—Mcminn County

⊠ **ATHENS REGIONAL MEDICAL CENTER (440068)**, 1114 West Madison Avenue, Zip 37303–4150, Mailing Address: P.O. Box 250, Zip 37371–0250; tel. 423/745–1411 **A**1 9 10 **F**3 11 13 15 28 29 30 31 34 35 37 40 41 43 44 45 46 48 50 51 54 57 59 61 64 65 68 70 73 74 75 76 77 78 79 81 84 85 86 87 89 90 93 102 107 108 110 111 114 115 116 117 118 119 126 129 130 132 133 135 146 147 148 **S** LifePoint Hospitals, Inc., Brentwood, TN
Primary Contact: John R. Workman, Chief Executive Officer
CFO: David Alley, Chief Financial Officer
CNO: Margie Brusseau, R.N., Chief Nursing Officer
Web address: www.athensrmc.com
**Control:** Corporation, Investor–owned, for–profit **Service:** General Medical and Surgical

**Staffed Beds:** 63 **Admissions:** 2327 **Census:** 23 **Outpatient Visits:** 83798
**Births:** 412 **Total Expense ($000):** 32563 **Payroll Expense ($000):** 13795
**Personnel:** 331

## BARTLETT—Shelby County

⊠ **SAINT FRANCIS HOSPITAL–BARTLETT (440228)**, 2986 Kate Bond Road, Zip 38133–4003; tel. 901/820–7000 **A**1 9 10 **F**3 11 13 15 18 20 22 29 30 31 34 35 40 43 44 45 47 48 49 50 54 57 59 60 64 68 70 72 74 75 76 77 78 79 81 85 86 87 93 107 108 110 111 115 119 130 131 146 147 148 **S** TENET Healthcare Corporation, Dallas, TX
Primary Contact: Jeremy Clark, Chief Executive Officer
COO: Gwen Bonner, Chief Operating Officer
CMO: Thomas W. Ratliff, M.D., President Medical Staff
CIO: Mike Hadley, Director Information Systems
CHR: Deb Lollar, Director Human Resources
Web address: www.saintfrancisbartlett.com
**Control:** Corporation, Investor–owned, for–profit **Service:** General Medical and Surgical

**Staffed Beds:** 156 **Admissions:** 6553 **Census:** 94 **Outpatient Visits:** 64289
**Births:** 710 **Total Expense ($000):** 84269 **Payroll Expense ($000):** 31914
**Personnel:** 450

## BOLIVAR—Hardeman County

⊠ **BOLIVAR GENERAL HOSPITAL (440181)**, 650 Nuckolls Road, Zip 38008–1532, Mailing Address: P.O. Box 509, Zip 38008–0509; tel. 731/658–3100 **A**1 9 10 **F**3 15 29 30 35 40 44 45 57 59 64 75 81 87 93 107 119 130 132 133 146 **S** West Tennessee Healthcare, Jackson, TN
Primary Contact: Ruby Kirby, Administrator
CFO: Terry Swindell, Controller
CMO: Suara Rahaman, M.D., Chief Medical Staff
CNO: Angela Lacy, Director of Nursing
Web address: www.wth.net
**Control:** Hospital district or authority, Government, nonfederal **Service:** General Medical and Surgical

**Staffed Beds:** 23 **Admissions:** 309 **Census:** 2 **Outpatient Visits:** 15822
**Births:** 2 **Total Expense ($000):** 6821 **Payroll Expense ($000):** 2914
**Personnel:** 68

☐ **WESTERN MENTAL HEALTH INSTITUTE (444008)**, 11100 Old Highway 64, West, Zip 38008–1554; tel. 731/228–2000, (Nonreporting) **A**1 10
Primary Contact: Roger Pursley, Chief Executive Officer
CFO: Richard Taylor, Chief Financial Officer
CMO: Doug King, M.D., Director Clinical Services
CIO: Earl Bates, Director Information Technology
CHR: Barry Young, Director Human Resources
**Control:** State–Government, nonfederal **Service:** Psychiatric

**Staffed Beds:** 247

## BRISTOL—Sullivan County

⊠ **SELECT SPECIALTY HOSPITAL–TRI CITIES (442016)**, (Formerly Select Specialty Hospital–Tricities), One Medical Park Boulevard, 5th Floor, Zip 37620–8964; tel. 423/844–5900, (Nonreporting) **A**1 9 10 **S** Select Medical Corporation, Mechanicsburg, PA
Primary Contact: Eric Carroll, Chief Executive Officer
CMO: John Byers, M.D., Medical Director
CHR: William G. Ison, Human Resources Manager
CNO: Jeffrey Radford, Chief Nursing Officer
Web address: www.selectspecialtyhospitals.com/company/locations/tricities.aspx
**Control:** Corporation, Investor–owned, for–profit **Service:** Long–Term Acute Care hospital

**Staffed Beds:** 33

⊠ **WELLMONT BRISTOL REGIONAL MEDICAL CENTER (440012)**, 1 Medical Park Boulevard, Zip 37620–7430; tel. 423/844–1121 **A**1 2 3 5 9 10 **F**3 8 11 12 13 15 17 18 20 22 24 28 29 30 31 34 35 37 38 39 40 43 46 47 49 50 51 54 56 57 58 59 60 61 62 63 64 67 70 73 74 75 76 77 78 79 80 81 82 83 84 85 86 87 89 90 91 92 93 94 96 97 98 99 100 101 102 103 104 106 107 108 110 111 114 115 118 119 120 121 123 124 126 129 130 131 132 135 145 146 147 148 **P**5 8 **S** Wellmont Health System, Kingsport, TN
Primary Contact: Greg Neal, Interim Chief Executive Officer
COO: Brad H. Price, Chief Operating Officer
CIO: Kent Petty, System Chief Information Officer
CHR: Hamlin J. Wilson, Senior Vice President Human Resources
CNO: Penny Miller, Vice President of Patient Care Services
Web address: www.wellmont.org
**Control:** Other not–for–profit (including NFP Corporation) **Service:** General Medical and Surgical

**Staffed Beds:** 348 **Admissions:** 16134 **Census:** 199 **Outpatient Visits:** 154293 **Births:** 858 **Total Expense ($000):** 213748 **Payroll Expense ($000):** 70082 **Personnel:** 1636

## BROWNSVILLE—Haywood County

⊠ **HAYWOOD PARK COMMUNITY HOSPITAL (440174)**, 2545 North Washington Avenue, Zip 38012–1610; tel. 731/772–4110 **A**1 9 10 **F**15 29 40 45 64 81 87 93 107 111 114 119 129 133 145 146 **S** Community Health Systems, Inc., Franklin, TN
Primary Contact: Joel Southern, R.N., MSN, Interim Chief Executive Officer
CFO: Richard Read, Chief Financial Officer
CMO: Daniel Cofie, M.D., Chief of Staff
CHR: Phyllis Cozart, Director Human Resources
Web address: www.haywoodparkcommunity.com
**Control:** Corporation, Investor–owned, for–profit **Service:** General Medical and Surgical

**Staffed Beds:** 36 **Admissions:** 594 **Census:** 4 **Outpatient Visits:** 10026
**Births:** 0 **Total Expense ($000):** 8734 **Payroll Expense ($000):** 3727
**Personnel:** 68

---

**Hospital, Medicare Provider Number, Address, Telephone, Approval, Facility, and Physician Codes, Health Care System**

★ American Hospital Association (AHA) membership
☐ The Joint Commission accreditation   ◇ DNV Healthcare Inc. accreditation
○ Healthcare Facilities Accreditation Program
△ Commission on Accreditation of Rehabilitation Facilities (CARF) accreditation

## CAMDEN—Benton County

☒ **CAMDEN GENERAL HOSPITAL (441316)**, 175 Hospital Drive,
Zip 38320–1617; tel. 731/584–6135 **A**1 9 10 18 **F**3 15 29 30 35 40 44 57
59 64 75 79 81 85 87 93 107 111 119 130 132 133 146 **S** West Tennessee
Healthcare, Jackson, TN
Primary Contact: Denny R. Smith, Administrator
COO: James E. Ross, Chief Operating Officer
CFO: Terry Swindell, Chief Financial Officer
CMO: Jon R. Winter, D.O., Chief of Staff
CIO: Jeff Frieling, Vice President Information Systems
CHR: Barry Phillips, Executive Director Human Resources
Web address: www.wth.net
**Control:** Hospital district or authority, Government, nonfederal **Service:** General
Medical and Surgical

**Staffed Beds:** 12 **Admissions:** 360 **Census:** 5 **Outpatient Visits:** 14401
**Births:** 1 **Total Expense ($000):** 6891 **Payroll Expense ($000):** 2848
**Personnel:** 71

## CARTHAGE—Smith County

☒ **RIVERVIEW REGIONAL MEDICAL CENTER (441307)**, (Formerly Riverview
Regional Medical Center North), 158 Hospital Drive, Zip 37030–1096;
tel. 615/735–1560, (Nonreporting) **A**1 9 10 **S** LifePoint Hospitals, Inc.,
Brentwood, TN
Primary Contact: Rod Harkleroad, R.N., Interim Administrator
CHR: Gina Anderson, Human Resources Officer
CNO: Kathy Lewis, Chief Nursing Officer and Vice President Clinical Services
Web address: www.myriverviewmedical.com/
**Control:** Corporation, Investor–owned, for–profit **Service:** General Medical and
Surgical

**Staffed Beds:** 63

## CELINA—Clay County

☐ **CUMBERLAND RIVER HOSPITAL (440141)**, 100 Old Jefferson Street,
Zip 38551–4040, Mailing Address: P. O. Box 427, Zip 38551–0427;
tel. 931/243–3581, (Nonreporting) **A**1 9 10
Primary Contact: Andrea Rich–McLerran, Chief Executive Officer
CFO: Tricia Strong, Chief Financial Officer
CMO: Roberto Mauricio, M.D., Chief of Staff
CIO: Margie Boone, Registered Health Information Technician
CHR: Susan Renodin Deaton, Chief Human Resources Officer
Web address: www.cumberlandriverhospital.com
**Control:** Corporation, Investor–owned, for–profit **Service:** General Medical and
Surgical

**Staffed Beds:** 34

## CENTERVILLE—Hickman County

☒ **SAINT THOMAS HICKMAN HOSPITAL (441300)**, (Formerly Hickman
Community Hospital), 135 East Swan Street, Zip 37033–1417;
tel. 931/729–4271, (Total facility includes 40 beds in nursing home–type unit) **A**1
9 10 18 **F**29 30 34 35 40 41 45 56 57 59 62 64 65 67 77 81 86 87 89 90
93 104 107 119 127 128 130 133 135 148 **P**6 **S** Ascension Health, Saint
Louis, MO
Primary Contact: Jack M. Keller, Administrator
COO: Jack M. Keller, Administrator
CFO: Craig Sullivan, Chief Financial Officer
CMO: Marek Durakiewicz, M.D., Chief of Staff
CIO: Kevin Campbell, Administrator Compliance and Mission
CHR: Dorothy Yokley, Assistant Administrator
Web address: www.hickmanhospital.com
**Control:** Other not–for–profit (including NFP Corporation) **Service:** General
Medical and Surgical

**Staffed Beds:** 65 **Admissions:** 369 **Census:** 31 **Outpatient Visits:** 12189
**Births:** 0 **Total Expense ($000):** 14830 **Payroll Expense ($000):** 7034
**Personnel:** 101

## CHATTANOOGA—Hamilton County

☒ **ERLANGER MEDICAL CENTER (440104)**, 632 Morrison Springs Road,
Zip 37415–3402; tel. 423/778–7000, (Includes ERLANGER EAST HOSPITAL,
1755 Gunbarrel Road, Zip 37421; tel. 423/778–8700; Teresa Radeker,
Administrator; ERLANGER NORTH HOSPITAL, 632 Morrison Springs Road,
Zip 37415; tel. 615/778–3300; T. C. THOMPSON CHILDREN'S HOSPITAL, 910
Blackford Street, Zip 37403; tel. 615/778–6011; Cynthia Rhodes, Administrator;
WILLIE D. MILLER EYE CENTER, 975 East Third Street, Zip 37403;
tel. 615/778–6011) **A**1 2 3 5 8 9 10 **F**3 11 12 13 14 15 17 18 19 20 21 22
23 24 25 26 27 28 29 30 31 32 34 35 37 38 39 40 41 43 44 45 47 49 50
54 55 57 59 60 61 64 68 70 72 74 75 76 77 78 79 80 81 82 85 86 87 88
89 93 96 97 98 103 107 108 110 111 114 115 118 119 120 121 124 126
129 130 131 132 138 144 145 146 147 148 **S** Erlanger Health System,
Chattanooga, TN
Primary Contact: Kevin M. Spiegel, FACHE, Chief Executive Officer
CFO: J. Britton Tabor, Senior VP and Chief Financial Officer
CMO: Cy Huffman, M.D., Chief Medical Officer
CIO: Laurene Vamprine, Senior Vice President Information Systems
CHR: Gregg Gentry, Senior Vice President Human Resources
Web address: www.erlanger.org
**Control:** Hospital district or authority, Government, nonfederal **Service:** General
Medical and Surgical

**Staffed Beds:** 540 **Admissions:** 28773 **Census:** 383 **Outpatient Visits:**
271622 **Births:** 5345 **Total Expense ($000):** 638222 **Payroll Expense
($000):** 241629 **Personnel:** 3923

**ERLANGER WOMEN'S EAST HOSPITAL** See Erlanger East Hospital

☒ **HEALTHSOUTH CHATTANOOGA REHABILITATION HOSPITAL (440162)**,
2412 McCallie Avenue, Zip 37404–3398; tel. 423/698–0221 **A**1 10 **F**29 34 59
90 92 95 96 132 146 148 **S** HEALTHSOUTH Corporation, Birmingham, AL
Primary Contact: Scott Rowe, Chief Executive Officer
COO: Scott Rowe, Chief Executive Officer
CFO: Karen Klassen, Controller
CMO: Amjad Munir, M.D., Medical Director
CIO: Denise Smith, Director Health Information
CHR: Deborah Hersom, Director Human Resources
CNO: Michelle Cowart, R.N., Chief Nursing Officer
Web address: www.healthsouthchattanooga.com
**Control:** Corporation, Investor–owned, for–profit **Service:** Rehabilitation

**Staffed Beds:** 46 **Admissions:** 1009 **Census:** 35 **Outpatient Visits:** 0 **Births:**
0 **Total Expense ($000):** 10550 **Payroll Expense ($000):** 5964 **Personnel:**
97

☒ **KINDRED HOSPITAL–CHATTANOOGA (442007)**, 709 Walnut Street,
Zip 37402–1916; tel. 423/266–7721, (Nonreporting) **A**1 9 10 **S** Kindred
Healthcare, Louisville, KY
Primary Contact: William J. Bryant, Chief Executive Officer
COO: Rick Rheinheimer, Chief Clinical Officer
CFO: Julia Smith, Chief Financial Officer
CMO: Randy Heisser, M.D., Medical Director
CHR: Kellie McCampbell, Coordinator Human Resources
Web address: www.kindredchattanooga.com/
**Control:** Corporation, Investor–owned, for–profit **Service:** Long–Term Acute Care
hospital

**Staffed Beds:** 44

☒ **MEMORIAL HEALTH CARE SYSTEM (440091)**, 2525 De Sales Avenue,
Zip 37404–1161; tel. 423/495–2525, (Includes MEMORIAL HOSPITAL HIXSON,
2051 Hamill Road, Hixson, Zip 37343–4026; tel. 423/495–7100), (Nonreporting)
**A**1 2 3 5 9 10 **S** Catholic Health Initiatives, Englewood, CO
Primary Contact: James M. Hobson, President and Chief Executive Officer
COO: Debra L. Moore, Senior Vice President
CFO: David Winchester, Interim President and Chief Financial Officer
CMO: S. Gale Fellowes, M.D., Chief Medical Officer
CIO: David Peterson, Regional Chief Information Officer
CHR: Brad W. Pope, Vice President Human Resources
Web address: www.memorial.org
**Control:** Church–operated, Nongovernment, not–for profit **Service:** General
Medical and Surgical

**Staffed Beds:** 336

☐ **MOCCASIN BEND MENTAL HEALTH INSTITUTE (444002)**, 100 Moccasin
Bend Road, Zip 37405–4415; tel. 423/265–2271 **A**1 10 **F**30 34 50 56 57 59
65 75 77 86 87 98 100 101 102 103 130 132 135 143 146
Primary Contact: William L. Ventress, Chief Executive Officer
COO: Rob Cotterman, Assistant Superintendent Program Services
CMO: Terry R. Holmes, M.D., Clinical Director
CIO: Mickey Williams, Manager Information Technology
CHR: Cynthia Honeycutt, Director Human Resources
Web address: www.state.tn.us/mental/mhs/mbhmhi/moc.htm
**Control:** State–Government, nonfederal **Service:** Psychiatric

**Staffed Beds:** 150 **Admissions:** 2340 **Census:** 104 **Outpatient Visits:** 0
**Births:** 0 **Total Expense ($000):** 24010 **Payroll Expense ($000):** 13389
**Personnel:** 351

*Many Facility Codes have changed. Please refer to the AHA Guide Code Chart.*  © 2013 AHA Guide

**TN**

✖ **PARKRIDGE MEDICAL CENTER (440156)**, 2333 McCallie Avenue,
Zip 37404–3258; tel. 423/698–6061, (Includes EAST RIDGE HOSPITAL, 941
Spring Creek Road, East Ridge, Zip 37412, Mailing Address: P.O. Box 91229,
Zip 37412–6229; tel. 423/855–3500; Jarrett B. Millsaps, Jr., FACHE, Chief
Executive Officer; PARKRIDGE EAST HOSPITAL, 941 Spring Creek Road,
Zip 37412–3909; tel. 423/894–7870; Jarrett B. Millsaps, Jr., FACHE, Chief
Executive Officer; PARKRIDGE VALLEY HOSPTIAL, 2200 Morris Hill Road,
Zip 37421; tel. 423/894–4220) **A**1 2 3 5 9 10 **F**3 5 13 15 18 20 22 24 26 28
29 30 31 39 40 45 46 49 51 56 57 58 59 60 70 72 75 76 77 78 79 81 85
90 93 98 99 103 104 105 106 107 108 110 111 114 115 119 121 126 129
130 131 146 148 **S** HCA, Nashville, TN
Primary Contact: Darrell W. Moore, Chief Executive Officer
COO: Jim L. Coleman, Jr., Chief Operating Officer
CIO: Paul Marsh, Director Information Systems
CHR: Carole Hoffman, Vice President
Web address: www.parkridgemedicalcenter.com
**Control:** Corporation, Investor–owned, for–profit **Service:** General Medical and
Surgical

**Staffed Beds:** 433 **Admissions:** 15440 **Census:** 263 **Outpatient Visits:**
148300 **Births:** 1577 **Total Expense ($000):** 199113 **Payroll Expense
($000):** 76781 **Personnel:** 1568

✖ △ **SISKIN HOSPITAL FOR PHYSICAL REHABILITATION (443025)**, One
Siskin Plaza, Zip 37403–1306; tel. 423/634–1200, (Total facility includes 29
beds in nursing home–type unit) **A**1 7 10 **F**29 35 53 54 59 64 75 77 82 90 93
95 128 130 132 146 148 **P**4
Primary Contact: Robert P. Main, President and Chief Executive Officer
COO: Linda Knudson Lind, Senior Vice President and Chief Operating Officer
CFO: Carol Arnhart, Controller and Chief Financial Officer
CMO: David N. Bowers, M.D., Medical Director
CIO: Baret H. Avery, Chief Information Officer
CHR: M. Debby Barker, Director Human Resources
CNO: Karla Woodby, R.N., Director of Nursing
Web address: www.siskinrehab.org
**Control:** Other not for profit (including NFP Corporation) **Service:** Rehabilitation

**Staffed Beds:** 109 **Admissions:** 1974 **Census:** 69 **Outpatient Visits:** 33417
**Births:** 0 **Total Expense ($000):** 27206 **Payroll Expense ($000):** 14452
**Personnel:** 271

**T. C. THOMPSON CHILDREN'S HOSPITAL** See Erlanger Medical Center

**WILLIE D. MILLER EYE CENTER** See Erlanger Medical Center

### CLARKSVILLE—Montgomery County

**BEHAVIORAL HEALTHCARE CENTER AT CLARKSVILLE (444019)**, 930
Professional Park Drive, Zip 37040–5136; tel. 931/538–6420, (Nonreporting)
**A**10 **S** Tennessee Health Management, Parsons, TN
Primary Contact: Jennifer Robinson, Administrator
CMO: Michael McGhee, M.D., Medical Director
CNO: Chrissy Myers, R.N., Director of Nursing
Web address: www.bhcclarksville.com
**Control:** Partnership, Investor–owned, for–profit **Service:** Psychiatric

**Staffed Beds:** 26

✖ **GATEWAY MEDICAL CENTER (440035)**, 651 Dunlop Lane, Zip 37040–5015,
Mailing Address: P.O. Box 31629, Zip 37040–0028; tel. 931/502–1000,
(Nonreporting) **A**1 2 9 10 **S** Community Health Systems, Inc., Franklin, TN
Primary Contact: Mark A. Marsh, Chief Executive Officer
COO: Corey Ewing, Chief Operating Officer
CFO: Scott Pfister, Chief Financial Officer
CMO: Thomas L. Ely, D.O., Chief Medical Officer
CIO: Frank Ruotolo, Chief Information Officer
CHR: Richard H. Johnson, Director Human Resources
Web address: www.ghsystem.com
**Control:** Partnership, Investor–owned, for–profit **Service:** General Medical and
Surgical

**Staffed Beds:** 247

### CLEVELAND—Bradley County

✖ **SKYRIDGE MEDICAL CENTER (440185)**, 2305 Chambliss Avenue N.W.,
Zip 37311–3847, Mailing Address: P.O. Box 3060, Zip 37320–3060;
tel. 423/559–6000, (Includes SKYRIDGE MEDICAL CENTER – WESTSIDE
CAMPUS, 2800 Westside Drive N.W., Zip 37312–3599; tel. 423/339–4100; R.
Coleman Foss, Chief Executive Officer), (Nonreporting) **A**1 9 10 **S** Community
Health Systems, Inc., Franklin, TN
Primary Contact: R. Coleman Foss, Chief Executive Officer
COO: Bernadette De Prez, Chief Operating Officer
CFO: Bill Ziesmer, Chief Financial Officer
CMO: Stephen Jackson, M.D., Chief of Staff
CHR: Kristine Godfrey, Director Human Resources
Web address: www.skyridgemedicalcenter.net
**Control:** Corporation, Investor–owned, for–profit **Service:** General Medical and
Surgical

**Staffed Beds:** 208

### COLLIERVILLE—Shelby County

★ **BAPTIST MEMORIAL HOSPITAL–COLLIERVILLE (440217)**, 1500 West Poplar
Avenue, Zip 38017–0601; tel. 901/861–9400 **A**5 9 **F**3 7 8 12 15 18 19 20 21
22 23 24 25 26 27 28 29 30 31 32 34 35 36 37 38 40 41 45 46 47 48 49
52 53 54 55 56 57 58 59 60 61 62 63 64 65 66 68 70 71 74 75 77 78 79
81 82 83 84 85 86 87 92 93 96 107 108 109 110 111 112 113 114 115
116 117 118 119 120 121 123 124 126 129 130 132 135 136 137 143 144
145 146 147 148 **S** Baptist Memorial Health Care Corporation, Memphis, TN
Primary Contact: Kyle E. Armstrong, Administrator and Chief Executive Officer
CFO: Terri Seago, Chief Financial Officer
CIO: Doug Reiselt, Vice President and Chief Information Officer
CHR: Brenda Johnson, Director Human Resources
Web address: www.baptistonline.org/collierville/
**Control:** Other not-for-profit (including NFP Corporation) **Service:** General
Medical and Surgical

**Staffed Beds:** 61 **Admissions:** 2451 **Census:** 26 **Outpatient Visits:** 31687
**Births:** 0 **Total Expense ($000):** 55670 **Payroll Expense ($000):** 18151
**Personnel:** 339

### COLUMBIA—Maury County

**BEHAVIORAL HEALTHCARE CENTER AT COLUMBIA (444021)**, 1400
Rosewood Drive, Zip 38401–4878; tel. 931/388–6573, (Nonreporting) **A**10
**S** Tennessee Health Management, Parsons, TN
Primary Contact: Paula Chennault, Administrator
CMO: Rodney Poling, M.D., Medical Director
CNO: Betsy Ladner, Director of Nursing
Web address: www.bhccolumbia.com
**Control:** Partnership, Investor–owned, for–profit **Service:** Psychiatric

**Staffed Beds:** 68

✖ **MAURY REGIONAL HOSPITAL (440073)**, 1224 Trotwood Avenue,
Zip 38401–4802; tel. 931/381–1111, (Total facility includes 17 beds in nursing
home–type unit) **A**1 2 9 10 19 **F**7 8 11 13 15 17 18 20 22 24 28 29 30 31 34
35 40 44 45 46 48 50 51 54 57 59 60 62 64 68 70 73 74 75 76 77 78 79
80 81 85 86 87 89 93 97 107 108 111 114 116 117 118 119 121 123 128
129 130 131 132 135 144 146 147 148 **S** Maury Regional Health System,
Columbia, TN
Primary Contact: H. Alan Watson, FACHE, Chief Executive Officer
COO: Paul Betz, FACHE, Chief Operating Officer and Senior Vice President
CFO: Nick Swift, Chief Financial Officer
CMO: Chris Edwards, M.D., Chief Medical Officer
CIO: Jim Parcel, Director Information Technology
CHR: Kaye Brewer, Director Human Resources
CNO: Deborah Lumpkins, MSN, Chief Nursing Officer
Web address: www.mauryregional.com
**Control:** County–Government, nonfederal **Service:** General Medical and Surgical

**Staffed Beds:** 232 **Admissions:** 12670 **Census:** 135 **Outpatient Visits:**
228729 **Births:** 1462 **Total Expense ($000):** 254972 **Payroll Expense
($000):** 94678 **Personnel:** 1566

**TN**

---

**Hospital, Medicare Provider Number, Address, Telephone, Approval, Facility, and Physician Codes, Health Care System**

★ American Hospital Association (AHA) membership
☐ The Joint Commission accreditation
◇ DNV Healthcare Inc. accreditation
○ Healthcare Facilities Accreditation Program
△ Commission on Accreditation of Rehabilitation Facilities (CARF) accreditation

© 2013 AHA Guide   *Many Facility Codes have changed. Please refer to the AHA Guide Code Chart.*   Hospitals **A567**

## COOKEVILLE—Putnam County

⊠ **COOKEVILLE REGIONAL MEDICAL CENTER (440059)**, 1 Medical Center Boulevard, Zip 38501–4294, Mailing Address: P.O. Box 340, Zip 38503–0340; tel. 931/528–2541 **A**1 2 9 10 19 **F**3 8 11 12 13 15 17 18 20 22 24 26 28 29 30 31 34 35 40 44 45 49 50 51 54 56 57 59 62 64 65 68 70 73 74 75 76 77 78 79 81 85 86 87 89 90 93 96 107 108 110 111 114 115 117 118 119 120 121 123 126 129 130 132 135 146 147 **P**7
Primary Contact: Paul Korth, Chief Executive Officer
CFO: Paul Korth, Chief Financial Officer
CMO: Jeffrey J. Gleason, M.D., Chief Medical Officer
CIO: Les Bernstein, Director Information Systems
CHR: Angel Lewis, Senior Vice President Administration
CNO: Linda Crawford, R.N., Chief Nursing Officer
Web address: www.crmchealth.org
**Control:** Hospital district or authority, Government, nonfederal **Service:** General Medical and Surgical

**Staffed Beds:** 267 **Admissions:** 13075 **Census:** 164 **Outpatient Visits:** 190296 **Births:** 1497 **Total Expense ($000):** 228372 **Payroll Expense ($000):** 86191 **Personnel:** 1777

◇ **TEN BROECK TENNESSEE TREATMENT FACILITY (444022)**, 1 Medical Center Boulevard, 5 West, Zip 38501; tel. 931/783–2570, (Nonreporting) **A**21 **S** United Medical Corporation, Windermere, FL
Primary Contact: Matthew Quinn, Executive Director
Web address: www.tenbroeck.com
**Control:** Corporation, Investor–owned, for–profit **Service:** General Medical and Surgical

**Staffed Beds:** 32

## COPPERHILL—Polk County

☐ **COPPER BASIN MEDICAL CENTER (441315)**, 144 Medical Center Drive, Zip 37317–5005, Mailing Address: P.O. Box 990, Zip 37317–0990; tel. 423/496–5511, (Nonreporting) **A**1 9 10 18
Primary Contact: Alexander B. Altman, III, Chief Executive Officer and Chief Financial Officer
CFO: Alexander B. Altman, III, Chief Executive Officer and Chief Financial Officer
CMO: Allen Uhlik, M.D., Chief of Staff
CIO: Matt Deal, Director Maintenance
CHR: Kathy Pack, Manager Human Resources
Web address: www.copperbasin.org
**Control:** Other not–for–profit (including NFP Corporation) **Service:** General Medical and Surgical

**Staffed Beds:** 25

## COVINGTON—Tipton County

⊠ **BAPTIST MEMORIAL HOSPITAL–TIPTON (440131)**, 1995 Highway 51 South, Zip 38019–3635; tel. 901/476–2621 **A**1 9 10 **F**3 11 15 29 30 31 34 35 40 45 55 57 58 59 65 70 74 75 76 77 78 79 81 85 87 89 93 100 107 108 110 111 114 117 119 120 121 129 130 132 135 146 148 **P**6 **S** Baptist Memorial Health Care Corporation, Memphis, TN
Primary Contact: Jamie Rodgers, Chief Executive Officer and Administrator
CFO: Monique Hart, Chief Financial Officer
CMO: James W. Martin, D.D.S., Chief of Staff
CHR: Myra Cousar, Director Human Resources
Web address: www.baptistonline.org/tipton/
**Control:** Other not–for–profit (including NFP Corporation) **Service:** General Medical and Surgical

**Staffed Beds:** 44 **Admissions:** 1441 **Census:** 12 **Outpatient Visits:** 50897 **Births:** 448 **Total Expense ($000):** 70877 **Payroll Expense ($000):** 14604 **Personnel:** 271

## CROSSVILLE—Cumberland County

⊠ **CUMBERLAND MEDICAL CENTER (440009)**, 421 South Main Street, Zip 38555–5031; tel. 931/484–9511 **A**1 2 9 10 20 **F**3 8 11 13 15 18 20 28 29 30 31 34 35 40 41 45 47 48 49 51 53 57 59 62 68 70 74 75 76 77 78 79 81 85 86 87 89 90 93 97 107 108 110 111 114 119 129 130 132 135 146 148
Primary Contact: Edwin S. Anderson, Chief Executive Officer
COO: Larry E. Moore, Executive Vice President/Chief Operating Officer/Chief Financial Officer
CFO: Larry E. Moore, Executive Vice President/Chief Operating Officer/Chief Financial Officer
CIO: Joe Lowe, Director Management Information Systems
CHR: Sally Cooney, Director Human Resources
CNO: Perri Lynn Capps, Chief Nursing Officer
Web address: www.cmchealthcare.org
**Control:** Other not–for–profit (including NFP Corporation) **Service:** General Medical and Surgical

**Staffed Beds:** 118 **Admissions:** 5491 **Census:** 61 **Outpatient Visits:** 97033 **Births:** 679 **Total Expense ($000):** 96581 **Payroll Expense ($000):** 41063 **Personnel:** 903

## DAYTON—Rhea County

⊠ **RHEA MEDICAL CENTER (441310)**, 9400 Rhea County Highway, Zip 37321–7922; tel. 423/775–1121, (Nonreporting) **A**1 9 10 18 **S** QHR, Brentwood, TN
Primary Contact: Kennedy L. Croom, Jr., Administrator and Chief Executive Officer
CFO: Harv Sanders, Chief Financial Officer
CMO: Chetan Shah, M.D., Chief of Staff
CHR: Peri Meadows, Director Human Resources
Web address: www.rheamedical.org
**Control:** County–Government, nonfederal **Service:** General Medical and Surgical

**Staffed Beds:** 25

## DICKSON—Dickson County

⊠ **TRISTAR HORIZON MEDICAL CENTER (440046)**, (Formerly Horizon Medical Center), 111 Highway 70 East, Zip 37055–2080; tel. 615/446–0446, (Nonreporting) **A**1 2 9 10 **S** HCA, Nashville, TN
Primary Contact: John A. Marshall, Chief Executive Officer
CFO: Clarence Gray, Chief Financial Officer
CIO: Rick Stoker, Director Management Information Systems
CHR: Sheila Kight, Director Human Resources
CNO: Gina Bullington, Chief Nursing Officer
Web address: www.horizonmedicalcenter.com
**Control:** Corporation, Investor–owned, for–profit **Service:** General Medical and Surgical

**Staffed Beds:** 130

## DYERSBURG—Dyer County

⊠ **DYERSBURG REGIONAL MEDICAL CENTER (440072)**, 400 East Tickle Street, Zip 38024–3120; tel. 731/285–2410 **A**1 9 10 20 **F**7 8 13 15 18 20 29 39 40 45 46 47 48 49 50 51 57 59 60 70 75 76 77 79 81 82 85 87 89 92 93 97 107 108 109 110 111 114 115 119 120 121 127 129 131 133 145 146 147 148 **P**4 5 6 **S** Community Health Systems, Inc., Franklin, TN
Primary Contact: Ben Youree, Chief Executive Officer
CFO: Meredith Malone, Chief Financial Officer
CMO: Darren Johnson, M.D., Chief of Staff
CIO: Russ Shephard, Senior Systems Analyst
CHR: Beverly Ray, Director Human Resources
CNO: Marye Elliott, Chief Nursing Officer
Web address: www.dyersburgregionalmc.com
**Control:** Corporation, Investor–owned, for–profit **Service:** General Medical and Surgical

**Staffed Beds:** 120 **Admissions:** 4492 **Census:** 34 **Outpatient Visits:** 62727 **Births:** 484 **Total Expense ($000):** 46951 **Payroll Expense ($000):** 18478 **Personnel:** 532

## EAST RIDGE—Hamilton County

**EAST RIDGE HOSPITAL** See Parkridge Medical Center, Chattanooga

## ELIZABETHTON—Carter County

☐ **SYCAMORE SHOALS HOSPITAL (440018)**, 1501 West Elk Avenue, Zip 37643–2874; tel. 423/542–1300 **A**1 9 10 **F**3 11 13 15 29 30 35 40 44 50 53 56 57 59 62 64 68 70 74 76 77 78 79 81 86 87 93 98 103 107 108 111 114 119 129 130 132 135 146 147 **P**6 8 **S** Mountain States Health Alliance, Johnson City, TN
Primary Contact: Dwayne Taylor, Chief Executive Officer
COO: Melanie Stanton, R.N., Chief Nursing Officer
CFO: Bradley Logan, Chief Financial Officer
CMO: Morris H. Seligman, M.D., Chief Medical Officer and Chief Medical Information Officer
CIO: Paul Merrywell, Chief Information Officer
CHR: Sharon Sheppard, Manager Human Resources
Web address: www.msha.com
**Control:** Other not–for–profit (including NFP Corporation) **Service:** General Medical and Surgical

**Staffed Beds:** 79 **Admissions:** 3673 **Census:** 42 **Outpatient Visits:** 71804 **Births:** 435 **Total Expense ($000):** 41131 **Payroll Expense ($000):** 18093 **Personnel:** 307

## ERIN—Houston County

⊠ **HOUSTON COUNTY COMMUNITY HOSPITAL (441312)**, (Formerly Patients' Choice Medical Center of Erin), 5001 East Main Street, Zip 37061–4115, Mailing Address: P.O. Box 489, Zip 37061–0489; tel. 931/289–4211, (Nonreporting) **A**1 9 10 18
Primary Contact: Gladys Anderson, Interim CEO
CFO: Shannon Allison, Chief Financial Officer
CMO: Erin Chambers, M.D., Chief Medical Officer
CHR: Reta Brady, Administrative Assistant and Manager Human Resources
Web address: www.pcmc–erintn.com/
**Control:** Corporation, Investor–owned, for–profit **Service:** General Medical and Surgical

**Staffed Beds:** 25

**PATIENTS CHOICE MEDICAL CENTER OF ERIN** See Houston County Community Hospital

*Many Facility Codes have changed. Please refer to the AHA Guide Code Chart.*
© 2013 AHA Guide

TN

## ERWIN—Unicoi County

☒ **UNICOI COUNTY MEMORIAL HOSPITAL (440001)**, 100 Greenway Circle, Zip 37650–2196, Mailing Address: P.O. Box 802, Zip 37650–0802; tel. 423/743–3141, (Total facility includes 46 beds in nursing home–type unit) **A**1 9 10 **F**1 15 26 29 40 57 62 70 79 81 93 107 110 111 114 119 129 130 131 **P**6
Primary Contact: Jim S. Pate, President and Chief Executive Officer
CFO: Toni Buchanan, Chief Financial Officer
CMO: Charles Miller, D.O., Chief of Staff
CIO: Spencer Levleit, Director Information Technology
CHR: Susan Broyles, Director Human Resources and Safety
Web address: www.ucmhnet.org
**Control:** Other not–for–profit (including NFP Corporation) **Service:** General Medical and Surgical

**Staffed Beds:** 71 **Admissions:** 1070 **Census:** 59 **Outpatient Visits:** 31330 **Births:** 0 **Total Expense ($000):** 20224 **Payroll Expense ($000):** 7400 **Personnel:** 155

## ETOWAH—Mcminn County

☒ **WOODS MEMORIAL HOSPITAL (440054)**, 886 Highway 411 North, Zip 37331–1912; tel. 423/263–3600, (Total facility includes 88 beds in nursing home–type unit) (Data for 184 days) **A**1 9 10 **F**3 8 11 14 28 29 30 34 35 40 41 50 51 56 57 59 61 64 65 67 68 70 75 77 79 80 81 84 85 90 93 102 103 107 108 111 118 119 128 130 133 146 148 **S** LifePoint Hospitals, Inc., Brentwood, TN
Primary Contact: John R. Workman, Chief Executive Officer
CMO: Charles B. Cox, M.D., Chief of Staff
Web address: www.woodshospital.org
**Control:** Corporation, Investor–owned, for–profit **Service:** General Medical and Surgical

**Staffed Beds:** 140 **Admissions:** 702 **Census:** 52 **Outpatient Visits:** 14933 **Births:** 0 **Total Expense ($000):** 11349 **Payroll Expense ($000):** 1876 **Personnel:** 303

## FAYETTEVILLE—Lincoln County

☒ **LINCOLN COUNTY HEALTH SYSTEM (440102)**, 106 Medical Center Boulevard, Zip 37334–2684; tel. 931/438–1100, (Total facility includes 264 beds in nursing home–type unit) **A**1 9 10 **F**2 3 7 10 11 13 15 18 29 30 34 35 40 45 50 53 56 57 59 62 63 64 67 68 70 74 75 76 77 79 81 85 93 98 103 104 107 108 110 111 114 118 119 128 129 132 143 146 148 **P**6 **S** QHR, Brentwood, TN
Primary Contact: Jamie W. Guin, Jr., Chief Executive Officer
CFO: David Groce, Associate Administrator and Chief Financial Officer
CMO: Linda Jackson, M.D., Chief of Staff
CHR: Wendy Nogler, Director Human Resources
Web address: www.lchealthsystem.com
**Control:** County–Government, nonfederal **Service:** General Medical and Surgical

**Staffed Beds:** 323 **Admissions:** 2286 **Census:** 229 **Outpatient Visits:** 46281 **Births:** 290 **Total Expense ($000):** 42375 **Payroll Expense ($000):** 20265 **Personnel:** 544

## FRANKLIN—Williamson County

☐ **ROLLING HILLS HOSPITAL (444007)**, 2014 Quail Hollow Circle, Zip 37067–5967; tel. 615/628–5700, (Nonreporting) **A**1 10 **S** Universal Health Services, Inc., King of Prussia, PA
Primary Contact: Laurel Roberts, R.N., Interim Chief Executive Officer
Web address: www.rollinghillshospital.org/
**Control:** Corporation, Investor–owned, for–profit **Service:** Psychiatric

**Staffed Beds:** 80

☐ **WILLIAMSON MEDICAL CENTER (440029)**, 4321 Carothers Parkway, Zip 37067–8542; tel. 615/435–5000 **A**1 2 9 10 **F**3 7 11 13 15 17 18 20 22 28 29 30 31 34 35 40 43 45 49 54 57 59 64 67 70 72 74 75 76 78 79 80 81 85 86 87 93 97 102 107 108 110 111 114 115 118 119 124 126 129 130 132 135 146 148 **P**6 8
Primary Contact: Donald Webb, Chief Executive Officer
COO: Julie Miller, Chief Operating Officer
CMO: Starling C. Evins, M.D., Chief of Staff
CIO: Steve Dycus, Director Marketing and Public Relations
CHR: Phyllis Molyneux, Associate Administrator Human Resources and Education
Web address: www.williamsonmedicalcenter.org
**Control:** County–Government, nonfederal **Service:** General Medical and Surgical

**Staffed Beds:** 185 **Admissions:** 9600 **Census:** 97 **Outpatient Visits:** 103871 **Births:** 1403 **Total Expense ($000):** 145296 **Payroll Expense ($000):** 62888 **Personnel:** 1050

## GALLATIN—Sumner County

☒ **SUMNER REGIONAL MEDICAL CENTER (440003)**, 555 Hartsville Pike, Zip 37066–2400, Mailing Address: P.O. Box 1558, Zip 37066–1558; tel. 615/452–4210, (Nonreporting) **A**1 2 9 10 **S** LifePoint Hospitals, Inc., Brentwood, TN
Primary Contact: Susan M. Peach, R.N., R.N., Chief Executive Officer
CFO: David Wilhoite, CPA, Senior Vice President Finance and Chief Financial Officer
CIO: David Young, Vice President External Operations
Web address: www.mysumnermedical.com
**Control:** Corporation, Investor–owned, for–profit **Service:** General Medical and Surgical

**Staffed Beds:** 145

## GERMANTOWN—Shelby County

☒ △ **BAPTIST REHABILITATION–GERMANTOWN (440147)**, 2100 Exeter Road, Zip 38138–3978; tel. 901/757–1350, (Total facility includes 18 beds in nursing home–type unit) **A**1 7 9 10 **F**3 29 30 34 35 54 57 59 64 68 75 77 79 86 87 90 91 92 93 96 107 111 114 119 128 130 131 132 143 146 148 **S** Baptist Memorial Health Care Corporation, Memphis, TN
Primary Contact: Brian Hogan, Chief Executive Officer and Administrator
CMO: Sunita Jain, M.D., Chief Medical Officer
CNO: Brian Hogan, Chief Executive Officer
Web address: www.baptistonline.org/germantown/
**Control:** Other not–for–profit (including NFP Corporation) **Service:** Rehabilitation

**Staffed Beds:** 68 **Admissions:** 1035 **Census:** 37 **Outpatient Visits:** 11703 **Births:** 0 **Total Expense ($000):** 24633 **Payroll Expense ($000):** 12140 **Personnel:** 218

**METHODIST LE BONHEUR GERMANTOWN HOSPITAL** See Methodist Healthcare Memphis Hospitals, Memphis

## GREENEVILLE—Greene County

☒ **LAUGHLIN MEMORIAL HOSPITAL (440025)**, 1420 Tusculum Boulevard, Zip 37745–5825; tel. 423/787–5000, (Total facility includes 90 beds in nursing home–type unit) **A**1 2 9 10 19 **F**3 11 12 13 15 18 20 28 29 31 34 35 37 40 45 46 47 48 49 50 56 57 59 62 64 68 70 73 74 75 76 77 78 79 81 85 86 87 89 93 97 107 108 110 111 114 115 118 119 121 123 128 129 130 131 132 134 135 146 147 148
Primary Contact: Charles H. Whitfield, Jr., President and Chief Executive Officer
CFO: Mark Compton, Chief Financial Officer
CIO: Andrea Neas, Health Information Management Director
CHR: Robert Roark, Director Human Resources
CNO: Brenda Cannon, R.N., Director of Nursing
Web address: www.laughlinmemorial.org
**Control:** Other not–for–profit (including NFP Corporation) **Service:** General Medical and Surgical

**Staffed Beds:** 224 **Admissions:** 3753 **Census:** 123 **Outpatient Visits:** 99513 **Births:** 233 **Total Expense ($000):** 73878 **Payroll Expense ($000):** 30945 **Personnel:** 622

☒ **TAKOMA REGIONAL HOSPITAL (440050)**, 401 Takoma Avenue, Zip 37743–4647; tel. 423/639–3151 **A**1 9 10 **F**3 11 13 15 29 30 40 45 57 70 75 76 81 87 89 90 93 98 103 107 108 110 111 119 131 144 148 **S** Adventist Health System Sunbelt Health Care Corporation, Altamonte Springs, FL
Primary Contact: Daniel Wolcott, President
CFO: Steven Miller, Chief Financial Officer
CMO: Frederick Myers, M.D., Chief Medical Officer
CHR: Jack Lister, Director Human Resources
Web address: www.takoma.org
**Control:** Church–operated, Nongovernment, not–for profit **Service:** General Medical and Surgical

**Staffed Beds:** 100 **Admissions:** 2360 **Census:** 29 **Outpatient Visits:** 181256 **Births:** 300 **Total Expense ($000):** 49706 **Payroll Expense ($000):** 21729 **Personnel:** 433

## HARRIMAN—Roane County

☒ **ROANE MEDICAL CENTER (440031)**, 412 Devonia Street, Zip 37748–2009, Mailing Address: P.O. Box 489, Zip 37748–0489; tel. 865/882–1323, (Nonreporting) **A**1 9 10 **S** Covenant Health, Knoxville, TN
Primary Contact: Gaye Jolly, FACHE, President/Chief Administrative Officer
CFO: Janice Bardill, Chief Financial Officer
CIO: Mike Ward, Senior Vice President Chief Information Officer
CHR: Mary Elena Burns, Director Human Resources
CNO: Lynda L. Sallee, R.N., Chief Nursing Officer
Web address: www.roanemedical.com
**Control:** Other not–for–profit (including NFP Corporation) **Service:** General Medical and Surgical

**Staffed Beds:** 36

**TN**

---

**Hospital, Medicare Provider Number, Address, Telephone, Approval, Facility, and Physician Codes, Health Care System**

★ American Hospital Association (AHA) membership
☐ The Joint Commission accreditation
◇ DNV Healthcare Inc. accreditation
○ Healthcare Facilities Accreditation Program
△ Commission on Accreditation of Rehabilitation Facilities (CARF) accreditation

## HARTSVILLE—Trousdale County

⊠ **TROUSDALE MEDICAL CENTER (441301)**, 500 Church Street, Zip 37074–1744; tel. 615/374–2221, (Nonreporting) **A**1 9 10 18 **S** LifePoint Hospitals, Inc., Brentwood, TN
Primary Contact: William D. Mize, Interim Chief Executive Officer
COO: William D. Mize, Chief Operating Officer
CFO: David Wilhoite, CPA, Senior Vice President Finance and Chief Financial Officer
CIO: David Young, Senior Vice President Planning and Technology
CHR: Amy Overstreet, Director Human Resources
Web address: www.mytrousdalemedical.com
**Control:** Corporation, Investor–owned, for–profit **Service:** General Medical and Surgical

Staffed Beds: 25

## HENDERSONVILLE—Sumner County

⊠ **TRISTAR HENDERSONVILLE MEDICAL CENTER (440194)**, (Formerly Hendersonville Medical Center), 355 New Shackle Island Road, Zip 37075–2479; tel. 615/338–1000, (Nonreporting) **A**1 9 10 **S** HCA, Nashville, TN
Primary Contact: Regina Bartlett, Chief Executive Officer
COO: Kenneth C. Donahey, Chief Operating Officer
CFO: Michael Morrison, Chief Financial Officer
CMO: Randy Howard, M.D., Chief of Staff
CIO: Hal Schultheis, Director Information Systems
CHR: Jennifer Burden, Vice President Human Resources
CNO: Lisa Gann, R.N., Chief Nursing Officer
Web address: www.hendersonvillemedicalcenter.com
**Control:** Corporation, Investor–owned, for–profit **Service:** General Medical and Surgical

Staffed Beds: 81

## HERMITAGE—Davidson County

⊠ **TRISTAR SUMMIT MEDICAL CENTER (440150)**, (Formerly Summit Medical Center), 5655 Frist Boulevard, Zip 37076–2053; tel. 615/316–3000 **A**1 2 9 10 **F**3 11 13 15 18 20 22 26 28 29 30 31 34 35 37 38 39 40 43 45 46 47 48 49 50 53 56 57 59 61 64 70 72 74 75 76 77 78 79 80 81 82 85 87 89 93 98 100 102 107 108 110 111 114 115 118 119 121 123 124 126 129 130 131 135 145 146 147 148 **P**6 **S** HCA, Nashville, TN
Primary Contact: Jeffrey T. Whitehorn, Chief Executive Officer
COO: Greg Caples, Chief Operating Officer
CFO: Timothy Stanfill, Chief Financial Officer
Web address: www.summitmedctr.com
**Control:** Corporation, Investor–owned, for–profit **Service:** General Medical and Surgical

Staffed Beds: 188 Admissions: 10737 Census: 117 Outpatient Visits: 116858 Births: 1124 Total Expense ($000): 120857 Payroll Expense ($000): 44152 Personnel: 698

## HUMBOLDT—Gibson County

⊠ **HUMBOLDT GENERAL HOSPITAL (440115)**, 3525 Chere Carol Road, Zip 38343–3638; tel. 731/784–2321 **A**1 9 10 **F**3 29 30 35 40 44 57 59 64 68 75 81 85 87 93 107 119 130 132 133 146 **S** West Tennessee Healthcare, Jackson, TN
Primary Contact: Sherry Scruggs, Administrator
CFO: Terry Swindell, Chief Financial Officer
CMO: R. Louis Murphy, M.D., Chief of Staff
CNO: Mitzie Taylor, Interim Director of Nursing
Web address: www.wth.net
**Control:** Hospital district or authority, Government, nonfederal **Service:** General Medical and Surgical

Staffed Beds: 30 Admissions: 492 Census: 6 Outpatient Visits: 14447 Births: 1 Total Expense ($000): 7752 Payroll Expense ($000): 3164 Personnel: 78

## HUNTINGDON—Carroll County

⊠ **BAPTIST MEMORIAL HOSPITAL–HUNTINGDON (440016)**, 631 R.B. Wilson Drive, Zip 38344–1727; tel. 731/986–4461 **A**1 9 10 **F**3 7 15 28 29 30 34 35 40 50 57 59 61 62 63 64 65 68 70 75 77 79 81 82 85 86 87 93 102 107 111 114 118 119 130 131 132 133 135 145 146 148 **S** Baptist Memorial Health Care Corporation, Memphis, TN
Primary Contact: Susan M. Breeden, Administrator and Chief Executive Officer
CFO: Sharron Holland, Chief Financial Officer
CHR: Kim King, Director Human Resources and Public Relations
Web address: www.baptistonline.org/huntingdon/
**Control:** Other not–for–profit (including NFP Corporation) **Service:** General Medical and Surgical

Staffed Beds: 33 Admissions: 547 Census: 8 Outpatient Visits: 17263 Births: 0 Total Expense ($000): 16305 Payroll Expense ($000): 6311 Personnel: 156

## JACKSON—Madison County

⊠ △ **JACKSON–MADISON COUNTY GENERAL HOSPITAL (440002)**, 620 Skyline Drive, Zip 38301–3923; tel. 731/541–5000 **A**1 2 3 5 7 9 10 19 **F**3 7 8 11 13 15 17 18 20 22 24 26 28 29 30 31 34 35 40 44 45 46 47 48 49 51 56 57 58 59 60 63 64 65 68 70 72 74 75 76 77 78 79 80 81 82 83 84 85 86 87 88 89 90 92 93 94 96 97 107 108 110 111 112 115 116 117 118 119 120 121 124 126 129 130 131 132 135 145 146 147 148 **P**5 8 **S** West Tennessee Healthcare, Jackson, TN
Primary Contact: Bobby Arnold, President and Chief Executive Officer
COO: James E. Ross, Vice President and Chief Operating Officer
CFO: Jeff Blankenship, CPA, Vice President and Chief Financial Officer
CMO: Richard Wagner, M.D., Chief of Staff
CIO: Jeff Frieling, Vice President and Chief Information Officer
CHR: Wendie Carlson, Vice President, Human Resources
CNO: Tina Prescott, Vice President, Hospital Services
Web address: www.wth.org
**Control:** Hospital district or authority, Government, nonfederal **Service:** General Medical and Surgical

Staffed Beds: 601 Admissions: 28090 Census: 414 Outpatient Visits: 178703 Births: 2783 Total Expense ($000): 475891 Payroll Expense ($000): 181252 Personnel: 3819

★ **PATHWAYS OF TENNESSEE (444010)**, 238 Summar Drive, Zip 38301–3906; tel. 731/541–8200 **A**10 **F**4 5 29 35 38 44 57 59 98 99 100 101 102 103 104 132 134 **S** West Tennessee Healthcare, Jackson, TN
Primary Contact: Pam Henson, Executive Director
CMO: Doug King, M.D., Medical Director
CIO: Jeff Frieling, Chief Information Officer
CHR: Barry Phillips, Director Human Resources
Web address: www.wth.net
**Control:** Hospital district or authority, Government, nonfederal **Service:** Psychiatric

Staffed Beds: 25 Admissions: 590 Census: 8 Outpatient Visits: 142913 Births: 0 Total Expense ($000): 17164 Payroll Expense ($000): 9362 Personnel: 235

⊠ **REGIONAL HOSPITAL OF JACKSON (440189)**, 367 Hospital Boulevard, Zip 38305–2080; tel. 731/661–2000 **A**1 9 10 **F**13 15 18 20 22 28 29 30 31 34 35 39 40 45 49 50 51 56 57 59 60 62 64 68 70 74 75 76 77 78 79 81 82 89 90 92 93 97 107 108 110 111 112 114 115 119 129 130 132 146 147 **S** Community Health Systems, Inc., Franklin, TN
Primary Contact: Dale Humphrey, Interim Chief Executive Officer
COO: Dale Humphrey, Chief Operating Officer
CFO: Richard Read, Chief Financial Officer
CMO: Michael Saridakis, M.D., Physician Adviser
CIO: Jimmy Anderson, Director of Information Systems
CHR: Barbara Euler, Director Human Resources
CNO: Jan Zimmer, R.N., Chief Nursing Officer
Web address: www.regionalhospitaljackson.com/Pages/Home.aspx
**Control:** Corporation, Investor–owned, for–profit **Service:** General Medical and Surgical

Staffed Beds: 129 Admissions: 6429 Census: 79 Outpatient Visits: 74266 Births: 575 Personnel: 650

## JAMESTOWN—Fentress County

☐ **JAMESTOWN REGIONAL MEDICAL CENTER (440083)**, 436 Central Avenue West, Zip 38556–3031, Mailing Address: P.O. Box 1500, Zip 38556–1500; tel. 931/879–8171, (Nonreporting) **A**1 9 10 20 **S** Health Management Associates, Naples, FL
Primary Contact: Kimberly L. Anthony, Chief Executive Officer
CMO: Mark Hendrixson, M.D., Chief Medical Officer
CIO: Rick Smith, Director Information Systems
CHR: Shelia Russell, Director Human Resources
Web address: www.jamestownregional.org
**Control:** Corporation, Investor–owned, for–profit **Service:** General Medical and Surgical

Staffed Beds: 85

## JASPER—Marion County

☐ **GRANDVIEW MEDICAL CENTER (440064)**, 1000 Highway 28, Zip 37347–3638; tel. 423/837–9500, (Nonreporting) **A**1 9 10 **S** Capella Healthcare, Franklin, TN
Primary Contact: Bruce A. Baldwin, Chief Executive Officer
CFO: Debbie Hennessee, Chief Financial Officer
Web address: www.grandviewhospital.com
**Control:** Corporation, Investor–owned, for–profit **Service:** General Medical and Surgical

Staffed Beds: 68

## JEFFERSON CITY—Jefferson County

**ST. MARY'S JEFFERSON MEMORIAL HOSPITAL** See Tennova–Jefferson Memorial Hospital

⊠ **TENNOVA–JEFFERSON MEMORIAL HOSPITAL (440056)**, (Formerly Jefferson Memorial Hospital), 110 Hospital Drive, Zip 37760–5281; tel. 865/471–2500, (Nonreporting) **A**1 9 10 **S** Health Management Associates, Naples, FL
Primary Contact: Colin McRae, Chief Executive Officer
CFO: Roseann M. Devault, Chief Financial Officer
CMO: Richard Carter, M.D., Chief of Staff
CNO: Carol C. Wolfenbarger, R.N., Chief Nursing Officer
Web address: www.tennova.com/
**Control:** Corporation, Investor–owned, for–profit **Service:** General Medical and Surgical

| Staffed Beds: 54 |
|---|

### JELLICO—Campbell County

⊠ **JELLICO COMMUNITY HOSPITAL (440180)**, 188 Hospital Lane, Zip 37762–4400; tel. 423/784–7252 **A**1 9 10 **F**3 7 11 13 15 29 30 34 35 40 43 44 48 50 53 54 57 59 62 64 65 68 70 75 76 77 81 85 86 87 93 97 107 108 110 111 114 119 130 131 132 133 134 135 143 146 148 **P**6 **S** Adventist Health System Sunbelt Health Care Corporation, Altamonte Springs, FL
Primary Contact: Erik Wangsness, Chief Executive Officer
COO: Pamela Hodge, R.N., Chief Nursing Officer and Coordinator Performance Improvement
CFO: William Villegas, Chief Financial Officer
CMO: Geogy Thomas, M.D., Chief of Staff
CIO: Derek Brown, Chief Information Officer
CHR: Vince Vannett, Director Human Resources
Web address: www.jellicohospital.com
**Control:** Other not–for–profit (including NFP Corporation) **Service:** General Medical and Surgical

| Staffed Beds: 31 Admissions: 1602 Census: 13 Outpatient Visits: 42744 Births: 151 Total Expense ($000): 29511 Payroll Expense ($000): 9602 Personnel: 259 |
|---|

### JOHNSON CITY—Washington County

⊠ **FRANKLIN WOODS COMMUNITY HOSPITAL (440184)**, 300 MedTech Parkway, Zip 37604–2277; tel. 423/302–1000 **A**1 9 10 **F**2 3 13 29 30 35 40 43 44 50 56 59 68 70 74 76 77 79 81 86 87 93 97 107 108 111 114 118 119 126 130 143 146 **P**6 8 **S** Mountain States Health Alliance, Johnson City, TN
Primary Contact: Tony Benton, Chief Executive Officer
CFO: Bradley Logan, Chief Financial Officer
CHR: Brooke Graham, Human Resources Manager
CNO: Rhonda Mann, Chief Nursing Officer
Web address: www.msha.com
**Control:** Other not–for–profit (including NFP Corporation) **Service:** General Medical and Surgical

| Staffed Beds: 80 Admissions: 4379 Census: 62 Outpatient Visits: 42024 Births: 876 Total Expense ($000): 50303 Payroll Expense ($000): 19012 Personnel: 354 |
|---|

⊠ **JOHNSON CITY MEDICAL CENTER (440063)**, 400 North State of Franklin Road, Zip 37604–6094; tel. 423/431–6111, (Includes NISWONGER CHILDREN'S HOSPITAL, 400 North State Of Franklin Road, Zip 37604–6035; tel. 423/431–6111; QUILLEN REHABILITATION HOSPITAL, 2511 Wesley Street, Zip 37601–1723; tel. 423/283–0700; Ann Fleming, Senior Vice President; WOODRIDGE HOSPITAL, 403 State of Franklin Road, Zip 37604–6034; tel. 423/431–7111; Grace Pereira, Interim Chief Executive Officer), (Total facility includes 13 beds in nursing home–type unit) **A**1 2 3 5 8 9 10 **F**3 7 8 11 12 13 15 17 18 19 20 21 22 23 24 25 26 28 29 30 31 32 34 35 39 40 41 43 44 46 47 48 49 50 51 53 54 55 56 57 58 59 60 61 62 63 64 68 70 72 74 75 76 77 78 79 81 82 84 85 86 87 88 89 93 97 100 102 107 108 111 115 117 118 119 121 123 124 126 128 129 130 131 132 134 135 143 146 147 148 **P**6 8 **S** Mountain States Health Alliance, Johnson City, TN
Primary Contact: David E. Nicely, Chief Executive Officer
CFO: Shane Hilton, Vice President and Chief Financial Officer
CHR: Jamie Parsons, Vice President Human Resources
Web address: www.msha.com
**Control:** Other not–for–profit (including NFP Corporation) **Service:** General Medical and Surgical

| Staffed Beds: 514 Admissions: 26026 Census: 363 Outpatient Visits: 258575 Births: 1040 Total Expense ($000): 384876 Payroll Expense ($000): 132385 Personnel: 2444 |
|---|

**NORTH SIDE HOSPITAL** See Franklin Woods Community Hospital

### KINGSPORT—Sullivan County

⊠ **HEALTHSOUTH REHABILITATION HOSPITAL (443027)**, 113 Cassel Drive, Zip 37660–3775; tel. 423/246–7240, (Nonreporting) **A**1 10 **S** HEALTHSOUTH Corporation, Birmingham, AL
Primary Contact: Susan Glenn, Chief Executive Officer
CFO: Natalie Tilson, Controller
CMO: James P. Little, M.D., Medical Director
CIO: Natalie Tilson, Controller
CHR: Joyce Jones, Director Human Resources
Web address: www.healthsouthkingsport.com
**Control:** Corporation, Investor–owned, for–profit **Service:** Rehabilitation

| Staffed Beds: 50 |
|---|

☐ **INDIAN PATH MEDICAL CENTER (440176)**, 2000 Brookside Drive, Zip 37660–4627; tel. 423/857–7000, (Total facility includes 22 beds in nursing home–type unit) **A**1 9 10 **F**3 5 8 11 13 15 18 20 29 30 31 35 38 40 49 50 51 56 57 59 60 64 68 70 73 74 75 76 77 78 79 81 86 87 93 97 100 101 102 103 104 105 107 108 111 114 118 119 123 128 129 130 131 132 146 147 148 **P**6 8 **S** Mountain States Health Alliance, Johnson City, TN
Primary Contact: Monty E. McLaurin, President and Chief Executive Officer
CFO: Pat Hale, Chief Financial Officer
CMO: Frank Lauro, M.D., Chief Medical Officer
CIO: Matthew Grissinger, Site Manager Information Systems
CHR: Kevin M. Smith, Director Human Resources
CNO: Susan Fannon, Chief Nursing Officer
Web address: www.msha.com
**Control:** Other not–for–profit (including NFP Corporation) **Service:** General Medical and Surgical

| Staffed Beds: 189 Admissions: 6801 Census: 83 Outpatient Visits: 148114 Births: 879 Total Expense ($000): 90729 Payroll Expense ($000): 33842 Personnel: 610 |
|---|

⊠ **WELLMONT HOLSTON VALLEY MEDICAL CENTER (440017)**, 130 West Ravine Street, Zip 37660–3837, Mailing Address: P.O. Box 238, Zip 37662–0238; tel. 423/224–4000, (Nonreporting) **A**1 2 3 5 9 10 **S** Wellmont Health System, Kingsport, TN
Primary Contact: Virginia Frank, President and Chief Executive Officer
COO: Troy Clark, Chief Operating Officer
CFO: Brad H. Price, Vice President Finance and Operations
CMO: J. Dale Sargent, M.D., Chief Medical Officer
CIO: Kent Petty, Chief Information Officer
CHR: Hamlin J. Wilson, Senior Vice President Human Resources
Web address: www.wellmont.org
**Control:** Other not–for–profit (including NFP Corporation) **Service:** General Medical and Surgical

| Staffed Beds: 345 |
|---|

### KNOXVILLE—Knox County

☐ **EAST TENNESSEE CHILDREN'S HOSPITAL (443303)**, 2018 Clinch Avenue, Zip 37916–2393, Mailing Address: P.O. Box 15010, Zip 37901–5010; tel. 865/541–8000, (Nonreporting) **A**1 3 5 6 9 10
Primary Contact: Keith D. Goodwin, President and Chief Executive Officer
COO: Rudolph McKinley, Jr., Vice President Operations and Chief Operating Officer
CFO: Zane Goodrich, Vice President Finance
CMO: Joe Childs, M.D., Vice President Medical Services
CIO: John Hanks, Director Information Systems
CHR: Sue Wilburn, Vice President Human Resources and Organizational Development
CNO: Laura P. Barnes, MSN, Vice President Patient Care Services and Chief Nursing Officer
Web address: www.etch.com
**Control:** Other not–for–profit (including NFP Corporation) **Service:** Children's general

| Staffed Beds: 152 |
|---|

⊠ △ **FORT SANDERS REGIONAL MEDICAL CENTER (440125)**, 1901 West Clinch Avenue, Zip 37916–2307; tel. 865/541–1111, (Nonreporting) **A**1 2 7 9 10 **S** Covenant Health, Knoxville, TN
Primary Contact: Keith Altshuler, President and Chief Administrative Officer
CHR: Gina Kinkaid, Director Human Resources
Web address: www.covenanthealth.com
**Control:** Other not–for–profit (including NFP Corporation) **Service:** General Medical and Surgical

| Staffed Beds: 402 |
|---|

**TN**

---

**Hospital, Medicare Provider Number, Address, Telephone, Approval, Facility, and Physician Codes, Health Care System**

★ American Hospital Association (AHA) membership
☐ The Joint Commission accreditation
◇ DNV Healthcare Inc. accreditation
○ Healthcare Facilities Accreditation Program
△ Commission on Accreditation of Rehabilitation Facilities (CARF) accreditation

✠ **PARKWEST MEDICAL CENTER (440173)**, 9352 Park West Boulevard, Zip 37923–4325, Mailing Address: P.O. Box 22993, Zip 37933–0993; tel. 865/373–1000 **A**1 2 9 10 **F**17 28 29 30 31 40 45 46 47 48 49 58 59 70 74 75 76 77 78 79 81 82 84 98 102 103 107 108 110 111 114 115 116 117 118 119 126 141 142 **S** Covenant Health, Knoxville, TN
Primary Contact: Rick Lassiter, President and Chief Administrative Officer
COO: Emlyn Cobble, Vice President and Chief Support Officer
CFO: Scott Hamilton, Vice President and Chief Financial Officer
CHR: Randall Carr, Director Human Resources
CNO: Diane Oliver, R.N., Chief Nursing Officer
Web address: www.yesparkwest.com
**Control:** Other not–for–profit (including NFP Corporation) **Service:** General Medical and Surgical

**Staffed Beds:** 297 **Admissions:** 16303 **Census:** 205 **Outpatient Visits:** 152555 **Births:** 1614

✠ △ **PHYSICIANS REGIONAL MEDICAL CENTER (440120)**, 900 East Oak Hill Avenue, Zip 37917–4556; tel. 865/545–8000, (Includes NORTH KNOXVILLE MEDICAL CENTER, 7565 Dannaher Way, Powell, Zip 37849–4029; tel. 865/859–7000; Rob Followell, Chief Executive Officer) **A**1 2 7 9 10 **F**8 13 15 17 18 20 22 24 26 28 29 30 31 34 35 40 49 51 53 54 56 57 59 60 61 62 63 64 70 73 74 75 76 77 78 79 80 81 82 83 84 85 86 87 90 92 93 96 98 100 103 105 107 108 110 111 114 115 117 118 119 120 121 123 124 126 128 129 130 131 132 146 147 148 **S** Health Management Associates, Naples, FL
Primary Contact: Karen Metz, Chief Executive Officer
CFO: Rhonda Maynard, Chief Financial Officer
CIO: Tom Lakins, Director Information Systems
CHR: Marty Margetts, Senior Vice President Human Resources
Web address: www.hma.com/content/physicians–regional–medical–center
**Control:** Corporation, Investor–owned, for–profit **Service:** General Medical and Surgical

**Staffed Beds:** 233 **Admissions:** 15580 **Census:** 205 **Outpatient Visits:** 191248 **Births:** 1466 **Total Expense ($000):** 250499 **Payroll Expense ($000):** 65748 **Personnel:** 1311

✠ **SELECT SPECIALTY HOSPITAL–KNOXVILLE (442012)**, 1901 Clinch Avenue, 4th Floor West, Zip 37916–2307; tel. 865/541–2615, (Nonreporting) **A**1 9 10 **S** Select Medical Corporation, Mechanicsburg, PA
Primary Contact: Vanda Scott, Chief Executive Officer
COO: Steve Plumlee, Chief Operating Officer
CFO: Mike Gillis, Controller
CMO: Brantly Burns, M.D., Medical Director
CIO: Vanda Scott, Chief Executive Officer
CHR: Hanna Bacon, Administrative Assistant/Human Resources Coordinator
CNO: Rick McVey, Chief Nursing Officer
Web address: www.selectspecialtyhospitals.com/company/locations/knoxville.aspx
**Control:** Corporation, Investor–owned, for–profit **Service:** Long–Term Acute Care hospital

**Staffed Beds:** 35

✠ **SELECT SPECIALTY HOSPITAL–NORTH KNOXVILLE (442015)**, 900 East Oak Hill Avenue, 4th Floor, Zip 37917–4505; tel. 865/541–2615, (Nonreporting) **A**1 9 10 **S** Select Medical Corporation, Mechanicsburg, PA
Primary Contact: Steve Plumlee, Chief Executive Officer
COO: Steve Plumlee, Chief Operating Officer
CFO: Mike Gillis, Controller
CMO: Jeff Summers, M.D., Medical Director
CHR: Jennifer Martin, Administrative Assistant/Human Resources Coordinator
CNO: Nancy Johnson, Chief Nursing Officer
Web address: www.selectspecialtyhospitals.com/company/locations/northknoxville.aspx
**Control:** Corporation, Investor–owned, for–profit **Service:** Long–Term Acute Care hospital

**Staffed Beds:** 33

✠ **TURKEY CREEK MEDICAL CENTER (440226)**, 10820 Parkside Drive, Zip 37934–1956; tel. 865/218–7094, (Nonreporting) **A**1 **S** Health Management Associates, Naples, FL
Primary Contact: Lance Jones, Chief Executive Officer
COO: Brad Stockton, Chief Operating Officer
CFO: Mike Stephens, Chief Financial Officer
CHR: Laura Pender, Human Resources Site Manager
Web address: www.hma.com/content/turkey–creek–medical–center
**Control:** Corporation, Investor–owned, for–profit **Service:** General Medical and Surgical

**Staffed Beds:** 101

✠ **UNIVERSITY OF TENNESSEE MEDICAL CENTER (440015)**, 1924 Alcoa Highway, Zip 37920–6900; tel. 865/305–9000 **A**1 2 3 5 8 9 10 13 **F**3 8 11 12 13 15 17 18 19 20 21 22 23 24 25 26 27 28 29 30 31 34 35 36 39 40 43 44 45 46 47 48 49 50 51 53 54 55 56 57 58 59 60 61 62 63 64 68 70 71 72 74 75 76 77 78 79 81 82 84 85 86 87 88 91 92 93 94 96 97 100 107 108 109 110 111 114 115 116 117 118 119 120 121 123 124 126 129 130 131 132 135 138 141 142 144 145 146 147 148 **P**6
Primary Contact: Joseph Landsman, President and Chief Executive Officer
COO: David Hall, Senior Vice President and Chief Operating Officer
CFO: Thomas Fisher, Senior Vice President and Chief Financial Officer
CMO: John W. Lacey, III, M.D., Senior Vice President and Chief Medical Officer
CIO: Douglas Fain, Director Computer Services
CHR: Betty Gissel, Vice President Human Resources
CNO: Janell Cecil, R.N., Senior Vice President and Chief Nursing Officer
Web address: www.utmedicalcenter.org
**Control:** Other not–for–profit (including NFP Corporation) **Service:** General Medical and Surgical

**Staffed Beds:** 536 **Admissions:** 23907 **Census:** 373 **Outpatient Visits:** 215984 **Births:** 3123 **Total Expense ($000):** 567827 **Payroll Expense ($000):** 204110 **Personnel:** 3212

**LA FOLLETTE—Campbell County**

✠ **LAFOLLETTE MEDICAL CENTER (440033)**, 923 East Central Avenue, Zip 37766–2768, Mailing Address: P.O. Box 1301, Zip 37766–1301; tel. 423/907–1200, (Nonreporting) **A**1 9 10 **S** Health Management Associates, Naples, FL
Primary Contact: Mark Cain, Chief Executive Officer
COO: Sara Heatherly–Lloyd, Chief Operating Officer
CFO: Glenn McGuire, Chief Financial Officer
CMO: Michael Hill, M.D., Chief of Staff
CIO: Doug Kibler, Management Information Systems Specialist
CHR: Bess Stout, Director Human Resources
Web address: www.hma.com
**Control:** Corporation, Investor–owned, for–profit **Service:** General Medical and Surgical

**Staffed Beds:** 164

**LAFAYETTE—Macon County**

✠ ◇ **MACON COUNTY GENERAL HOSPITAL (441305)**, 204 Medical Drive, Zip 37083–1799, Mailing Address: P.O. Box 378, Zip 37083–0378; tel. 615/666–2147 **A**1 9 10 18 21 **F**3 15 18 29 30 34 35 40 57 59 65 75 77 81 86 93 107 114 119 128 130 132 133 146 **S** QHR, Brentwood, TN
Primary Contact: Dennis A. Wolford, FACHE, Chief Executive Officer
CFO: Thomas J. Kidd, Assistant Administrator and Chief Financial Officer
Web address: www.mcgh.net
**Control:** Other not–for–profit (including NFP Corporation) **Service:** General Medical and Surgical

**Staffed Beds:** 25 **Admissions:** 946 **Census:** 10 **Outpatient Visits:** 23636 **Births:** 2

**LAWRENCEBURG—Lawrence County**

✠ **CROCKETT HOSPITAL (440175)**, 1607 South Locust Avenue, Zip 38464–4011, Mailing Address: P.O. Box 847, Zip 38464–0847; tel. 931/762–6571, (Nonreporting) **A**1 9 10 **S** LifePoint Hospitals, Inc., Brentwood, TN
Primary Contact: Jeff Noblin, FACHE, Chief Executive Officer
CFO: Kristie Taylor, Chief Financial Officer
CIO: Jason Weaver, Director Information Systems
CHR: Robert Augustin, Director Human Resources
CNO: Carol Laird, R.N., Chief Nursing Officer
Web address: www.crocketthospital.com
**Control:** Corporation, Investor–owned, for–profit **Service:** General Medical and Surgical

**Staffed Beds:** 90

**LEBANON—Wilson County**

☐ **UNIVERSITY MEDICAL CENTER (440193)**, 1411 Baddour Parkway, Zip 37087–2513; tel. 615/444–8262, (Includes MCFARLAND SPECIALTY HOSPITAL, 500 Park Avenue, Zip 37087–3720; tel. 615/449–0500), (Nonreporting) **A**1 5 9 10 **S** Health Management Associates, Naples, FL
Primary Contact: Matthew T. Caldwell, Chief Executive Officer
CMO: Andrew Jordan, M.D., Chief of Staff
CIO: Adrian Fung, Director Information Systems
Web address: www.universitymedicalcenter.com
**Control:** Corporation, Investor–owned, for–profit **Service:** General Medical and Surgical

**Staffed Beds:** 245

TN

## LENOIR CITY—Loudon County

⊞ **FORT LOUDOUN MEDICAL CENTER (440110)**, 550 Fort Loudoun Medical Center Drive, Zip 37772–5673; tel. 865/271–6000 **A**1 9 10 **F**3 11 15 18 28 29 30 34 35 40 45 50 57 59 65 68 70 77 79 81 85 93 102 107 108 110 111 114 118 119 130 135 146 148 **S** Covenant Health, Knoxville, TN
Primary Contact: Jeffrey Feike, President and Chief Administrative Officer
CNO: Teresa Gomez, Chief Nursing Officer
Web address: www.covenanthealth.com
**Control:** Other not–for–profit (including NFP Corporation) **Service:** General Medical and Surgical

**Staffed Beds:** 30 **Admissions:** 1713 **Census:** 17 **Outpatient Visits:** 73102 **Births:** 0 **Total Expense ($000):** 27190 **Payroll Expense ($000):** 10991 **Personnel:** 215

## LEWISBURG—Marshall County

⊞ **MARSHALL MEDICAL CENTER (441309)**, 1080 North Ellington Parkway, Zip 37091–2227, Mailing Address: P.O. Box 1609, Zip 37091–1609; tel. 931/359–6241 **A**1 9 10 18 **F**3 11 15 29 30 34 40 45 50 56 57 59 68 75 77 81 92 93 108 110 111 114 119 129 131 133 135 146 **S** Maury Regional Health System, Columbia, TN
Primary Contact: Phyllis Brown, Chief Executive Officer
CFO: Kyle Jones, Controller
CMO: Tim Nash, M.D., Chief of Staff
CHR: Joyce Gentile, Human Resource Benefits Specialist
Web address: www.mauryregional.com
**Control:** County–Government, nonfederal **Service:** General Medical and Surgical

**Staffed Beds:** 12 **Admissions:** 219 **Census:** 2 **Outpatient Visits:** 41368 **Births:** 0 **Total Expense ($000):** 13008 **Payroll Expense ($000):** 6068 **Personnel:** 138

## LEXINGTON—Henderson County

⊞ **HENDERSON COUNTY COMMUNITY HOSPITAL (440008)**, 200 West Church Street, Zip 38351–2038; tel. 731/968–3646, (Nonreporting) **A**1 9 10 **S** Community Health Systems, Inc., Franklin, TN
Primary Contact: David Henry, Chief Executive Officer
CFO: Leonard Binkley, Jr., Interim Chief Financial Officer
CHR: John Degi, Director Human Resources
Web address: www.hendersoncchospital.com
**Control:** Corporation, Investor–owned, for–profit **Service:** General Medical and Surgical

**Staffed Beds:** 36

## LINDEN—Perry County

**PERRY COMMUNITY HOSPITAL (440040)**, 2718 Squirrel Hollow Drive, Zip 37096–3526; tel. 931/589–2121, (Nonreporting) **A**9 10
Primary Contact: John B. Avery, III, Administrator
**Control:** Other not–for–profit (including NFP Corporation) **Service:** General Medical and Surgical

**Staffed Beds:** 53

## LIVINGSTON—Overton County

⊞ **LIVINGSTON REGIONAL HOSPITAL (440187)**, 315 Oak Street, Zip 38570–1728, Mailing Address: P.O. Box 550, Zip 38570–0550; tel. 931/823–5611, (Nonreporting) **A**1 9 10 **S** LifePoint Hospitals, Inc., Brentwood, TN
Primary Contact: Michael J. Meadows, Chief Executive Officer
COO: Michelle Watson, Chief Operating Officer and Chief Nursing Officer
CFO: Joseph Ross, Chief Financial Officer
CMO: Trueman Smith, M.D., Chief Medical Officer
CIO: Joseph Ross, Chief Financial Officer
CHR: Valerie Guimaraes, Director Human Resources
Web address: www.livingstonregionalhospital.com
**Control:** Corporation, Investor–owned, for–profit **Service:** General Medical and Surgical

**Staffed Beds:** 82

## LOUISVILLE—Blount County

**PENINSULA HOSPITAL**, 2347 Jones Bend Road, Zip 37777–5213, Mailing Address: P.O. Box 2000, Zip 37777–2000; tel. 865/970–9800, (Nonreporting)
Primary Contact: Jeffrey N. Dice, Vice President Behavioral Health
CFO: Sonja Jones, Chief Financial Officer
CMO: Kris Houser, M.D., Medical Director
CIO: Roger Ricker, Director Marketing and Public Relations
CHR: Angie Montgomery, Director Human Resources
Web address: www.peninsula–hospital.org
**Control:** Other not–for–profit (including NFP Corporation) **Service:** Psychiatric

**Staffed Beds:** 141

## MADISON—Davidson County

★ **TRISTAR SKYLINE MADISON CAMPUS (440135)**, (Formerly Skyline Madison Campus), 500 Hospital Drive, Zip 37115–5032; tel. 615/769–5000, (Nonreporting) **A**9 **S** HCA, Nashville, TN
Primary Contact: Steve Otto, Chief Executive Officer
COO: Jill Howard, R.N., Chief Operating Officer
CFO: Bradley Schultz, Chief Financial Officer
CMO: Christopher Colburn, M.D., Chief Medical Officer
CHR: Andy Hooper, Director Human Resources
CNO: Laurie Turner, Chief Nursing Officer
Web address: www.skylinemadison.com
**Control:** Corporation, Investor–owned, for–profit **Service:** General Medical and Surgical

**Staffed Beds:** 284

## MANCHESTER—Coffee County

**MEDICAL CENTER OF MANCHESTER (441308)**, 481 Interstate Drive, Zip 37355–3108, Mailing Address: P.O. Box 1409, Zip 37349–4409; tel. 931/728–6354, (Nonreporting) **A**9 10 18
Primary Contact: Robert J. Couch, Chief Executive Officer
CMO: W. D. Daniel, D.O., Chief of Staff
CHR: Shelly Turner, Chief Clinical Services Officer
**Control:** Corporation, Investor–owned, for–profit **Service:** General Medical and Surgical

**Staffed Beds:** 25

**UNITED REGIONAL MEDICAL CENTER (440007)**, 1001 McArthur Drive, Zip 37355–2455, Mailing Address: P.O. Box 1079, Zip 37349–1079; tel. 931/728–3586, (Nonreporting) **A**9 10
Primary Contact: Martha Logan, Chief Executive Officer
CFO: Pam Jernigan, Chief Financial Officer
CMO: Gary Bryant, M.D., Chief of Staff
CIO: Matt Burks, Director Information Technology
CHR: Nolan Hayes, Director Human Resources
Web address: www.urmchealthcare.com
**Control:** Corporation, Investor–owned, for–profit **Service:** General Medical and Surgical

**Staffed Beds:** 36

## MARTIN—Weakley County

★ **BEHAVIORAL HEALTHCARE CENTER AT MARTIN (444005)**, 458 Hannings Lane, Zip 38237–3308; tel. 731/588–2830, (Nonreporting) **A**10 **S** Tennessee Health Management, Parsons, TN
Primary Contact: Carrie Brawley, Administrator
Web address: www.tnhealthmanagement.com/BHC/martin/
**Control:** Partnership, Investor–owned, for–profit **Service:** Psychiatric

**Staffed Beds:** 16

⊞ **HEALTHSOUTH CANE CREEK REHABILITATION HOSPITAL (443030)**, 180 Mt Pelia Road, Zip 38237–3812; tel. 731/587–4231 **A**1 10 **F**34 56 57 74 75 79 90 91 94 95 96 128 148 **S** HEALTHSOUTH Corporation, Birmingham, AL
Primary Contact: Eric Garrard, Chief Executive Officer
CFO: Bethany Smith, Controller
CMO: William Eason, M.D., Medical Director
CIO: Jan Trowhill, Director Health Information Management Systems
CHR: Sharon Shihady, Director Human Resources
Web address: www.healthsouthcanecreek.com
**Control:** Corporation, Investor–owned, for–profit **Service:** Rehabilitation

**Staffed Beds:** 40 **Admissions:** 804 **Census:** 28 **Outpatient Visits:** 0 **Births:** 0 **Total Expense ($000):** 7995 **Payroll Expense ($000):** 4505 **Personnel:** 102

⊞ **VOLUNTEER COMMUNITY HOSPITAL (440061)**, 161 Mount Pelia Road, Zip 38237–3811; tel. 731/587–4261, (Nonreporting) **A**1 9 10 **S** Community Health Systems, Inc., Franklin, TN
Primary Contact: Darrell Blaylock, Chief Executive Officer
CFO: Jason Draper, Chief Financial Officer
CMO: Elizabeth Lund, M.D., Chief of Staff
CHR: Tammie Bell, Director Human Resources
CNO: Donna Barfield, Chief Nursing Officer
Web address: www.volunteercommunityhospital.com
**Control:** Corporation, Investor–owned, for–profit **Service:** General Medical and Surgical

**Staffed Beds:** 65

TN

---

**Hospital, Medicare Provider Number, Address, Telephone, Approval, Facility, and Physician Codes, Health Care System**

★ American Hospital Association (AHA) membership
☐ The Joint Commission accreditation   ◇ DNV Healthcare Inc. accreditation
◯ Healthcare Facilities Accreditation Program
△ Commission on Accreditation of Rehabilitation Facilities (CARF) accreditation

## MARYVILLE—Blount County

⊠ **BLOUNT MEMORIAL HOSPITAL (440011)**, 907 East Lamar Alexander Parkway, Zip 37804–5016; tel. 865/983–7211, (Total facility includes 76 beds in nursing home–type unit) **A**1 2 9 10 **F**3 4 10 11 12 13 15 17 18 20 22 26 28 29 30 31 32 35 38 40 43 45 46 49 53 54 56 57 59 62 63 64 67 68 70 74 75 76 77 78 79 80 81 82 84 85 86 87 90 93 96 97 98 99 100 101 102 103 104 105 107 108 110 111 114 115 116 117 118 119 120 121 122 123 125 126 128 129 130 131 132 134 135 146 147 148 **P**6 7
Primary Contact: Don Heinemann, Administrator and Chief Executive Officer
CFO: Jonathan Smith, Chief Financial Officer, Assistant Administrator
CMO: G. Harold Naramore, M.D., Chief Medical Officer and In house Legal Counsel
CIO: Clay Puckett, Assistant Administrator and Chief Information Officer
CHR: Chris Wilkes, MS, Director Human Resources
CNO: Sonya Newman, R.N., Chief Nursing Officer
Web address: www.blountmemorial.org
**Control:** County–Government, nonfederal **Service:** General Medical and Surgical

**Staffed Beds:** 314 **Admissions:** 12902 **Census:** 210 **Outpatient Visits:** 185992 **Births:** 748 **Total Expense ($000):** 187276 **Payroll Expense ($000):** 84662 **Personnel:** 2026

## MC MINNVILLE—Warren County

☐ **RIVER PARK HOSPITAL (440151)**, 1559 Sparta Street, Zip 37110–1316; tel. 931/815–4000 **A**1 9 10 **F**8 11 13 15 18 28 29 30 34 35 40 50 51 57 59 64 70 74 75 76 79 80 81 89 90 93 107 110 111 114 115 119 129 146 148 **P**6 **S** Capella Healthcare, Franklin, TN
Primary Contact: Timothy W. McGill, Chief Executive Officer
COO: Joseph Mazzo, Chief Financial Officer
CFO: Christina Patterson, Chief Financial Officer
CMO: Randal D. Rampp, M.D., Chief Medical Officer
CIO: Jeff Johnson, Director Information Systems
CHR: Deeann Johnson, Director Human Resources
Web address: www.riverparkhospital.com
**Control:** Corporation, Investor–owned, for–profit **Service:** General Medical and Surgical

**Staffed Beds:** 85 **Admissions:** 3263 **Census:** 32 **Outpatient Visits:** 33268 **Births:** 480 **Total Expense ($000):** 38804 **Payroll Expense ($000):** 15346 **Personnel:** 326

## MCKENZIE—Carroll County

⊠ **MCKENZIE REGIONAL HOSPITAL (440182)**, 161 Hospital Drive, Zip 38201–1636; tel. 731/352–5344 **A**1 9 10 **F**3 29 40 53 76 81 85 89 93 107 119 131 133 146 **S** Community Health Systems, Inc., Franklin, TN
Primary Contact: Michael G. Morrical, Chief Executive Officer
CFO: Kevin Harvey, Chief Financial Officer
CHR: Joyce Hamilton, Director Human Resources
Web address: www.mckenzieregionalhospital.com
**Control:** Corporation, Investor–owned, for–profit **Service:** General Medical and Surgical

**Staffed Beds:** 35 **Admissions:** 1382 **Census:** 10 **Outpatient Visits:** 14055 **Births:** 393 **Total Expense ($000):** 12252 **Payroll Expense ($000):** 5476 **Personnel:** 111

## MEMPHIS—Shelby County

⊠ **BAPTIST MEMORIAL HOSPITAL – MEMPHIS (440048)**, 6019 Walnut Grove Road, Zip 38120–2173; tel. 901/226–5000, (Total facility includes 32 beds in nursing home–type unit) **A**1 2 3 5 9 10 **F**3 7 8 12 15 17 18 19 20 21 22 24 26 28 29 30 31 32 34 35 36 37 38 40 41 45 46 47 48 49 52 53 54 55 56 57 58 59 60 61 62 63 64 65 66 68 70 71 74 75 77 78 79 80 81 82 83 84 85 86 87 92 93 96 107 108 109 110 111 112 113 114 115 116 117 118 119 120 121 123 124 126 128 129 130 132 135 136 137 143 144 145 146 147 148 **S** Baptist Memorial Health Care Corporation, Memphis, TN
Primary Contact: Derick Ziegler, Administrator and Chief Executive Officer
CFO: Cyndi Pittman, Chief Financial Officer
CMO: Christian C. Patrick, M.D., Chief Medical Officer
CIO: Doug Reiselt, Vice President and Chief Information Officer
CHR: Jerry Barbaree, Director Human Resources
CNO: Becky Hunter, R.N., Chief Nursing Officer
Web address: www.baptistonline.org/memphis/
**Control:** Other not–for–profit (including NFP Corporation) **Service:** General Medical and Surgical

**Staffed Beds:** 605 **Admissions:** 25997 **Census:** 496 **Outpatient Visits:** 63410 **Births:** 0 **Total Expense ($000):** 507767 **Payroll Expense ($000):** 162716 **Personnel:** 3077

★ **BAPTIST MEMORIAL HOSPITAL FOR WOMEN (440222)**, 6225 Humphreys Boulevard, Zip 38120–2373; tel. 901/227–9000 **A**9 **F**3 7 8 12 13 15 18 19 20 21 22 23 24 25 26 27 28 29 30 31 32 34 35 36 37 38 41 45 46 47 48 49 52 53 54 55 56 57 58 59 60 61 62 63 64 65 66 68 70 71 72 73 74 75 76 77 78 79 81 82 83 84 85 86 87 89 92 93 96 107 108 109 110 111 112 113 114 115 116 117 118 119 120 121 123 124 126 129 130 132 135 136 137 143 144 145 146 147 148 **S** Baptist Memorial Health Care Corporation, Memphis, TN
Primary Contact: Anita Vaughn, Administrator and Chief Executive Officer
CFO: Margaret Williams, Chief Financial Officer
CMO: Melrose Blackett, M.D., President Medical Staff
CIO: Cindy Beard, Assistant Administrator
CHR: Karen Ingram, Director Human Resources
CNO: Carol Thetford, Chief Nursing Officer
Web address: www.baptistonline.org/womens/
**Control:** Other not–for–profit (including NFP Corporation) **Service:** Obstetrics and gynecology

**Staffed Beds:** 140 **Admissions:** 6806 **Census:** 74 **Outpatient Visits:** 43614 **Births:** 5307 **Total Expense ($000):** 77058 **Payroll Expense ($000):** 32090 **Personnel:** 576

⊠ **BAPTIST MEMORIAL RESTORATIVE CARE HOSPITAL (442010)**, 6019 Walnut Grove Road, Zip 38120–2113; tel. 901/226–1400 **A**1 9 10 **F**1 3 29 68 75 130 148 **S** Baptist Memorial Health Care Corporation, Memphis, TN
Primary Contact: Janice Hill, R.N., Administrator
Web address: www.baptistonline.org/restorative–care/
**Control:** Other not–for–profit (including NFP Corporation) **Service:** Long–Term Acute Care hospital

**Staffed Beds:** 30 **Admissions:** 249 **Census:** 24 **Outpatient Visits:** 0 **Births:** 0 **Total Expense ($000):** 14844 **Payroll Expense ($000):** 4976 **Personnel:** 95

☐ **DELTA MEDICAL CENTER (440159)**, 3000 Getwell Road, Zip 38118–2299; tel. 901/369–8100, (Nonreporting) **A**1 9 10 **S** Acadia Healthcare Company, Inc., Franklin, TN
Primary Contact: William Patterson, Chief Executive Officer
CFO: Joy Fergie, Chief Financial Officer
CFO: Glen Roberts, Chief Financial Officer
CMO: David Richardson, M.D., Chief of Staff
CIO: Patrick Duffee, Director Medical Information Systems
CHR: Karyn Erickson, Director Human Resources
Web address: www.deltamedcenter.com
**Control:** Corporation, Investor–owned, for–profit **Service:** General Medical and Surgical

**Staffed Beds:** 170

⊠ **HEALTHSOUTH REHABILITATION HOSPITAL MEMPHIS–NORTH (443031)**, (Formerly HEALTHSOUTH Rehabilitation Hospital), 4100 Austin Peay Highway, Zip 38128–2502; tel. 901/213–5400 **A**1 10 **F**28 29 30 90 **S** HEALTHSOUTH Corporation, Birmingham, AL
Primary Contact: Marcia Taylor, Chief Executive Officer
CFO: Valerie Jones, Chief Financial Officer
CMO: Donald Sullivan, M.D., Medical Director
CHR: Adrienne Huntley, Director, Human Resources
CNO: Charlotte Boyce, Chief Nursing Officer
Web address: www.healthsouthnorthmemphis.com
**Control:** Corporation, Investor–owned, for–profit **Service:** Rehabilitation

**Staffed Beds:** 40 **Admissions:** 1135 **Census:** 39 **Outpatient Visits:** 0 **Births:** 0 **Total Expense ($000):** 9837 **Payroll Expense ($000):** 5857 **Personnel:** 94

⊠ **HEALTHSOUTH REHABILITATION HOSPITAL OF MEMPHIS (443029)**, 1282 Union Avenue, Zip 38104–3414; tel. 901/722–2000 **A**1 3 5 10 **F**3 28 29 30 34 60 75 87 90 93 95 96 **S** HEALTHSOUTH Corporation, Birmingham, AL
Primary Contact: Michael L. Pierce, Chief Executive Officer
CFO: Valerie Jones, Chief Financial Officer
CMO: Dale Cunningham, M.D., Medical Director
CHR: Sandra Milburn, Director Human Resources
CNO: Jennifer Ferrell, Chief Nursing Officer
Web address: www.healthsouthmemphis.com
**Control:** Partnership, Investor–owned, for–profit **Service:** Rehabilitation

**Staffed Beds:** 72 **Admissions:** 1612 **Census:** 58 **Outpatient Visits:** 7872 **Births:** 0 **Total Expense ($000):** 17710 **Payroll Expense ($000):** 9206 **Personnel:** 202

☐ **LAKESIDE BEHAVIORAL HEALTH SYSTEM (444004)**, 2911 Brunswick Road, Zip 38133–4199; tel. 901/377–4700 **A**1 10 **F**4 5 38 98 99 100 101 102 103 104 105 106 **S** Universal Health Services, Inc., King of Prussia, PA
Primary Contact: Joy Golden, Chief Executive Officer
CFO: Felicia Swauncy, Chief Financial Officer
CMO: C. Hal Brunt, M.D., Medical Director
CIO: Kevin Pendleton, Chief Information Technology
CHR: James Miller, Director Human Resources
Web address: www.lakesidebhs.com
**Control:** Corporation, Investor–owned, for–profit **Service:** Psychiatric

**Staffed Beds:** 311 **Admissions:** 6606 **Census:** 174 **Outpatient Visits:** 21510 **Births:** 0 **Total Expense ($000):** 28952 **Payroll Expense ($000):** 15317 **Personnel:** 374

*Many Facility Codes have changed. Please refer to the AHA Guide Code Chart.*   © 2013 AHA Guide

**LE BONHEUR CHILDREN'S HOSPITAL** See Methodist Healthcare Memphis Hospitals

☐ **MEMPHIS MENTAL HEALTH INSTITUTE (444001)**, 865 Poplar Avenue, Zip 38105–4608, Mailing Address: P.O. Box 40966, Zip 38174–0966; tel. 901/577–1800 **A**1 3 5 10 **F**3 50 86 87 98 101 103 130 146 **P**6
Primary Contact: Lisa Daniel, Interim Chief Executive Officer
COO: Clyde Slate, Assistant Superintendent Administrative Services
CFO: Linda White, Director Fiscal Services
CMO: Kayla Fisher, M.D., Medical Director
CHR: Randy Durham, Director Personnel
Web address: www.tn.gov/mental/mhs/mhs2.html
**Control:** State–Government, nonfederal **Service:** Psychiatric

**Staffed Beds: 75 Admissions: 1440 Census: 59 Outpatient Visits:** 0 **Births:** 0 **Total Expense ($000):** 19547 **Payroll Expense ($000):** 10542 **Personnel:** 218

☒ △ **MEMPHIS VETERANS AFFAIRS MEDICAL CENTER**, (Formerly Veterans Affairs Medical Center), 1030 Jefferson Avenue, Zip 38104–2193; tel. 901/523–8990 **A**1 3 5 7 8 **F**3 4 5 8 9 15 17 18 20 22 24 26 28 29 30 31 34 35 38 39 40 42 45 46 47 49 50 51 56 58 60 61 62 64 65 67 70 74 75 77 78 79 80 81 82 83 84 85 86 87 90 93 94 97 98 100 101 102 103 104 105 106 107 108 111 114 115 117 118 119 122 127 129 130 132 135 146 147 148 **S** Department of Veterans Affairs, Washington, DC
Primary Contact: C. Diane Knight, M.D., Interim Director and Chief Executive Officer
COO: Marlin Angell, Associate Director
CMO: Margarethe Hagemann, M.D., Chief of Staff
CIO: Jenny Pangle, Chief Officer Information and Technology
CHR: Brenda Cabunoc, Chief Human Resource Management Services
Web address: www.memphis.va.gov/
**Control:** Veterans Affairs, Government, federal **Service:** General Medical and Surgical

**Staffed Beds: 262 Admissions: 7331 Census: 180 Outpatient Visits:** 678663 **Births:** 0 **Personnel:** 2189

☐ **METHODIST EXTENDED CARE HOSPITAL (442013)**, 225 South Claybrook Street, Zip 38104–3537; tel. 901/516–2152 **A**1 10 **F**1 3 29 30 75 130 132 148 **S** Methodist Le Bonheur Healthcare, Memphis, TN
Primary Contact: Sandra Bailey–DeLeeuw, Chief Executive Officer
COO: Sandra Hugueley, Assistant Administrator and Chief Nursing Officer
CFO: Kris Sanders, Chief Financial Officer
CMO: Hany Mounir Habashy, M.D., Chief Medical Director
CHR: Tina Sims, Director Human Resources
CNO: Sandra Hugueley, Assistant Administrator and Chief Nursing Officer
Web address: www.methodisthealth.org
**Control:** Other not–for–profit (including NFP Corporation) **Service:** Long–Term Acute Care hospital

**Staffed Beds: 36 Admissions: 434 Census: 30 Outpatient Visits:** 0 **Births:** 0 **Total Expense ($000):** 15032 **Payroll Expense ($000):** 6940 **Personnel:** 141

☐ **METHODIST HEALTHCARE MEMPHIS HOSPITALS (440049)**, 1265 Union Avenue, Zip 38104–3415; tel. 901/516–7000, (Includes LE BONHEUR CHILDREN'S HOSPITAL, 50 North Dunlap Street, Zip 38103; tel. 901/287–5437; Meri Armour, Chief Executive Officer; METHODIST HEALTHCARE–NORTH HOSPITAL, 3960 New Covington Pike, Zip 38128; tel. 901/384–5389; METHODIST HEALTHCARE–SOUTH HOSPITAL, 1300 Wesley Drive, Zip 38116; tel. 901/516–3081; James L. Robinson, III, PsyD, Chief Executive Officer; METHODIST LE BONHEUR GERMANTOWN HOSPITAL, 7691 Poplar Avenue, Germantown, Zip 38138; tel. 901/516–6000; William A. Kenley, Chief Executive Officer), (Total facility includes 20 beds in nursing home–type unit) **A**1 2 3 5 8 9 10 **F**3 7 8 11 12 13 15 17 18 19 20 21 22 23 24 25 26 27 28 29 30 31 32 34 35 37 38 39 40 41 43 44 45 46 47 48 49 50 54 55 56 57 60 61 64 65 66 68 70 71 72 73 74 75 76 77 78 79 80 81 82 84 85 86 87 88 89 92 93 94 96 97 98 99 100 101 102 103 104 105 107 108 110 111 112 113 114 115 116 117 118 119 120 121 123 124 126 128 129 130 131 132 134 135 136 138 139 141 142 143 144 146 147 148 **P**5 6 8 **S** Methodist Le Bonheur Healthcare, Memphis, TN
Primary Contact: James R. Carter, Jr., Interim Chief Executive Officer
COO: James R. Carter, Jr., Chief Operating Officer
CFO: Chris J. McLean, Chief Financial Officer
CMO: Robin Womeodu, M.D., Chief Medical Officer
CIO: Andy Fowler, Senior Vice President Information Systems
CHR: Carol Ross–Spang, Senior Vice President
Web address: www.methodisthealth.org
**Control:** Other not–for–profit (including NFP Corporation) **Service:** General Medical and Surgical

**Staffed Beds: 1324 Admissions: 62362 Census: 958 Outpatient Visits:** 578477 **Births:** 4911 **Total Expense ($000):** 1278804 **Payroll Expense ($000):** 437220 **Personnel:** 9504

☒ **REGIONAL MEDICAL CENTER AT MEMPHIS (440152)**, 877 Jefferson Avenue, Zip 38103–2897; tel. 901/545–7100, (Nonreporting) **A**1 3 5 8 9 10
Primary Contact: Reginald W. Coopwood, M.D., President and Chief Executive Officer
COO: Rob Sumter, Executive Vice President and Chief Operating Officer
CFO: Rick Wagers, Senior Executive Vice President and Chief Financial Officer
CMO: Jack D. McCue, M.D., Senior Vice President and Interim Chief Medical Officer
CHR: Fred Boyd, Interim Vice President Human Resources
Web address: www.the–med.org
**Control:** Other not–for–profit (including NFP Corporation) **Service:** General Medical and Surgical

**Staffed Beds: 325**

☒ **SAINT FRANCIS HOSPITAL (440183)**, 5959 Park Avenue, Zip 38119–5198, Mailing Address: P.O. Box 171808, Zip 38187–1808; tel. 901/765–1000 **A**1 2 3 5 9 10 **F**3 8 11 12 13 15 17 18 20 22 24 26 28 29 30 31 34 35 38 39 40 44 45 46 47 48 49 50 51 54 56 57 58 59 64 68 70 72 74 75 76 77 78 79 81 82 84 85 86 87 90 93 96 97 98 99 100 101 102 103 104 107 108 110 111 114 115 116 117 118 119 121 123 124 126 129 130 131 132 143 146 147 148 **P**5 6 8 **S** TENET Healthcare Corporation, Dallas, TX
Primary Contact: David L. Archer, Chief Executive Officer
COO: Audrey Gregory, R.N., Chief Operating Officer
CFO: Bradley Robertson, Chief Financial Officer
CMO: Michael Lachina, M.D., Chief Medical Officer
CIO: Mike Hadley, Chief Information Officer
CHR: Everett Liddell, Vice President Human Resources
Web address: www.saintfrancishosp.com
**Control:** Corporation, Investor–owned, for–profit **Service:** General Medical and Surgical

**Staffed Beds: 511 Admissions: 14295 Census: 234 Outpatient Visits:** 118109 **Births:** 1525 **Total Expense ($000):** 240207 **Payroll Expense ($000):** 75920 **Personnel:** 1352

☒ **SELECT SPECIALTY HOSPITAL–MEMPHIS (442014)**, 5959 Park Avenue, 12th Floor, Zip 38119–5200; tel. 901/765–1245, (Nonreporting) **A**1 9 10 **S** Select Medical Corporation, Mechanicsburg, PA
Primary Contact: Kris Kitzke, Chief Executive Officer
Web address: www.selectspecialtyhospitals.com/company/locations/memphis.aspx
**Control:** Corporation, Investor–owned, for–profit **Service:** Long–Term Acute Care hospital

**Staffed Beds: 38**

☒ **ST. JUDE CHILDREN'S RESEARCH HOSPITAL (443302)**, 262 Danny Thomas Place, Zip 38105–3678; tel. 901/595–3300, (Nonreporting) **A**1 3 5 9 10
Primary Contact: William E. Evans, PharmD, Director
CFO: Mike Canarios, Vice President and Chief Financial Officer
CMO: Joseph Laver, M.D., Executive Vice President and Chief Medical Officer
CIO: Clayton Naeve, Vice President and Chief Information Officer
CHR: Mary Anna Quinn, Vice President
Web address: www.stjude.org
**Control:** Other not–for–profit (including NFP Corporation) **Service:** Children's other specialty

**Staffed Beds: 56**

**VETERANS AFFAIRS MEDICAL CENTER** See Memphis Veterans Affairs Medical Center

### MILAN—Gibson County

☒ **MILAN GENERAL HOSPITAL (440060)**, 4039 Highland Street, Zip 38358–3483; tel. 731/686–1591 **A**1 9 10 **F**3 15 29 30 35 40 44 45 57 59 64 68 70 81 85 87 107 119 130 132 133 146 **S** West Tennessee Healthcare, Jackson, TN
Primary Contact: Sherry Scruggs, Administrator
CMO: Kenneth Tozier, M.D., Chief of Surgery
CNO: Linda Wheelock, Director of Nursing
Web address: www.wth.org
**Control:** Hospital district or authority, Government, nonfederal **Service:** General Medical and Surgical

**Staffed Beds: 28 Admissions: 319 Census: 5 Outpatient Visits:** 12752 **Births:** 0 **Total Expense ($000):** 7894 **Payroll Expense ($000):** 3122 **Personnel:** 68

TN

**Hospital, Medicare Provider Number, Address, Telephone, Approval, Facility, and Physician Codes, Health Care System**

★ American Hospital Association (AHA) membership
☐ The Joint Commission accreditation
◇ DNV Healthcare Inc. accreditation
○ Healthcare Facilities Accreditation Program
△ Commission on Accreditation of Rehabilitation Facilities (CARF) accreditation

© 2013 AHA Guide    *Many Facility Codes have changed. Please refer to the AHA Guide Code Chart.*    Hospitals **A575**

## MORRISTOWN—Hamblen County

☒ **LAKEWAY REGIONAL HOSPITAL (440067)**, 726 McFarland Street, Zip 37814–3990; tel. 423/586–2302, (Nonreporting) **A**1 9 10 19 **S** Community Health Systems, Inc., Franklin, TN
Primary Contact: Priscilla Millis, Chief Executive Officer
CMO: Paul Cardali, M.D., Chief of Staff
CHR: Deirdre Helton, Director Human Resources
Web address: www.lakewayregionalhospital.com
**Control:** Corporation, Investor–owned, for–profit **Service:** General Medical and Surgical

**Staffed Beds:** 135

☒ **MORRISTOWN–HAMBLEN HEALTHCARE SYSTEM (440030)**, 908 West Fourth North Street, Zip 37814–3894, Mailing Address: P.O. Box 1178, Zip 37816–1178; tel. 423/586–4231 **A**1 9 10 **F**2 3 11 13 15 18 19 20 22 26 28 29 30 31 34 35 39 40 41 45 46 49 50 56 57 59 60 67 74 76 78 79 81 85 93 98 102 103 105 107 108 110 111 114 117 118 119 121 129 141 142 146 147 148 **P**6 7 **S** Covenant Health, Knoxville, TN
Primary Contact: Gordon Lintz, Chief Administrative Officer
CFO: James Alwell, Interim Vice President and Chief Financial Officer
CIO: Tim Krieger, Director Information Systems
CHR: Derek Winkle, Director Human Resources
Web address: www.mhhs1.org
**Control:** Other not–for–profit (including NFP Corporation) **Service:** General Medical and Surgical

**Staffed Beds:** 147 **Admissions:** 6680 **Census:** 69 **Outpatient Visits:** 91184 **Births:** 832 **Total Expense ($000):** 80618 **Payroll Expense ($000):** 30201 **Personnel:** 614

## MOUNTAIN CITY—Johnson County

★ **JOHNSON COUNTY COMMUNITY HOSPITAL (441304)**, 1901 South Shady Street, Zip 37683–2271; tel. 423/727–1100 **A**5 9 10 18 **F**3 15 28 30 35 40 44 50 68 86 93 97 107 **P**6 8 **S** Mountain States Health Alliance, Johnson City, TN
Primary Contact: Lisa Heaton, Assistant Vice President/Administrator and Chief Nursing Officer
Web address: www.msha.com
**Control:** Other not–for–profit (including NFP Corporation) **Service:** General Medical and Surgical

**Staffed Beds:** 2 **Admissions:** 26 **Census:** 1 **Outpatient Visits:** 38930 **Births:** 0 **Total Expense ($000):** 8092 **Payroll Expense ($000):** 3939 **Personnel:** 57

## MOUNTAIN HOME— County

☒ **JAMES H. QUILLEN VETERANS AFFAIRS MEDICAL CENTER**, Corner of Lamont & Veterans Way, Zip 37684, Mailing Address: P.O. Box 4000, Zip 37684–4000; tel. 423/926–1171, (Total facility includes 78 beds in nursing home–type unit) **A**1 2 3 5 **F**1 3 4 5 9 11 12 18 19 21 29 30 31 33 34 35 36 38 39 40 44 45 48 50 51 53 54 55 56 57 59 60 61 62 63 64 65 66 68 70 74 75 77 78 79 80 81 82 83 84 85 86 87 91 92 93 94 96 97 98 100 101 102 103 104 105 106 107 108 109 111 114 115 118 119 120 121 123 127 128 129 130 132 133 135 143 144 146 147 148 **P**6 **S** Department of Veterans Affairs, Washington, DC
Primary Contact: Charlene S. Ehret, FACHE, Director
CFO: Brian P. Fuchs, Chief Fiscal Service
CMO: David Reagan, M.D., Chief of Staff
CIO: Karen Perry, Chief Information Resource Management Services
CHR: Patsy Fish, Chief Human Resources Management
Web address: www.mountainhome.va.gov/
**Control:** Veterans Affairs, Government, federal **Service:** General Medical and Surgical

**Staffed Beds:** 98 **Admissions:** 5598 **Census:** 79 **Outpatient Visits:** 60634 **Births:** 0 **Total Expense ($000):** 344520 **Payroll Expense ($000):** 143501 **Personnel:** 2125

## MURFREESBORO—Rutherford County

**ALVIN C. YORK CAMPUS** See Tennessee Valley Healthcare System, Nashville

☒ **SAINT THOMAS RUTHERFORD HOSPITAL (440053)**, (Formerly Middle Tennessee Medical Center), 1700 Medical Center Parkway, Zip 37129–2245; tel. 615/396–4100, (Nonreporting) **A**1 3 5 9 10 **S** Ascension Health, Saint Louis, MO
Primary Contact: Gordon B. Ferguson, President and Chief Executive Officer
COO: Elizabeth Lemons, Chief Operating Officer
CFO: Martha Tolbert Rowland, Vice President Finance
CMO: Andy Brown, M.D., Vice President Medical Affairs
CIO: Dan West, Director Information Technology Systems
CHR: Carol Bragdon, Director Human Resources
Web address: www.mtmc.org
**Control:** Church–operated, Nongovernment, not–for profit **Service:** General Medical and Surgical

**Staffed Beds:** 286

**TRUSTPOINT HOSPITAL (440231)**, 1009 North Thompson Lane, Zip 37129–4351; tel. 615/867–1111, (Nonreporting) **A**10 **S** Polaris Hospital Company, Brentwood, TN
Primary Contact: Anita Peterson, Chief Executive Officer
Web address: www.trustpointhospital.com
**Control:** Partnership, Investor–owned, for–profit **Service:** Rehabilitation

**Staffed Beds:** 60

## NASHVILLE—Davidson County

**BAPTIST HOSPITAL** See Saint Thomas Midtown

**CENTENNIAL MEDICAL CENTER** See Tristar Centennial Medical Center

**CENTER FOR SPINAL SURGERY** See Saint Thomas Hospital for Spinal Surgery

☒ **KINDRED HOSPITAL–NASHVILLE (442006)**, 1412 County Hospital Road, Zip 37218–3007; tel. 615/687–2600, (Nonreporting) **A**1 10 **S** Kindred Healthcare, Louisville, KY
Primary Contact: William P. Macri, Chief Executive Officer
CFO: Philip L. Jones, Chief Financial Officer
CMO: Clyde Heflin, M.D., Chief Medical Officer
CHR: Robyn Dunman, Coordinator Human Resources
Web address: www.khnashville.com/
**Control:** Corporation, Investor–owned, for–profit **Service:** Long–Term Acute Care hospital

**Staffed Beds:** 58

☐ **MIDDLE TENNESSEE MENTAL HEALTH INSTITUTE (444014)**, 221 Stewarts Ferry Pike, Zip 37214–3325; tel. 615/902–7535 **A**1 3 5 10 **F**30 75 98 101 102 103 106
Primary Contact: Candace L. Gilligan, Chief Executive Officer
CFO: Mark Stanley, Director Fiscal Services
CMO: Mohammad S. Jahan, M.D., Clinical Director
CHR: Margie Dunn, Director Human Resources
Web address: www.tn.gov/mental/mhs/mhs2.html
**Control:** State–Government, nonfederal **Service:** Psychiatric

**Staffed Beds:** 195 **Admissions:** 2881 **Census:** 166 **Outpatient Visits:** 0 **Births:** 0 **Total Expense ($000):** 35534 **Payroll Expense ($000):** 22556 **Personnel:** 570

**MONROE CARELL JR. CHILDREN'S HOSPITAL AT VANDERBILT** See Vanderbilt Hospital and Clinics

☐ **NASHVILLE GENERAL HOSPITAL (440111)**, 1818 Albion Street, Zip 37208–2918; tel. 615/341–4000 **A**1 2 3 5 9 10 **F**15 18 20 29 30 31 34 35 40 58 59 60 64 66 70 72 75 76 77 78 79 81 86 91 93 107 111 114 115 119 146
Primary Contact: Jason E. Boyd, FACHE, Interim Chief Executive Officer
COO: Jason E. Boyd, FACHE, Chief Operating Officer
CHR: Diana Wohlfardt, Director Human Resources
Web address: www.nashvilleha.org
**Control:** Hospital district or authority, Government, nonfederal **Service:** General Medical and Surgical

**Staffed Beds:** 116 **Admissions:** 4053 **Census:** 47 **Outpatient Visits:** 112958 **Births:** 689 **Total Expense ($000):** 103275 **Payroll Expense ($000):** 32183

☒ **SAINT THOMAS HOSPITAL FOR SPINAL SURGERY (440218)**, (Formerly Center for Spinal Surgery), 2011 Murphy Avenue, Suite 400, Zip 37203–2065; tel. 615/341–7500, (Nonreporting) **A**1 9 10 **S** Ascension Health, Saint Louis, MO
Primary Contact: Kathy Watson, R.N., Administrator and Chief Nursing Officer
CFO: Angie Crow, Financial Director
CMO: Everette Howell, M.D., Chief Medical Officer
Web address: www.centerforspinalsurgery.com
**Control:** Partnership, Investor–owned, for–profit **Service:** General Medical and Surgical

**Staffed Beds:** 23

☒ **SAINT THOMAS MIDTOWN HOSPITAL (440133)**, (Formerly Baptist Hospital), 2000 Church Street, Zip 37236–0002; tel. 615/284–5555, (Nonreporting) **A**1 3 5 9 10 **S** Ascension Health, Saint Louis, MO
Primary Contact: Bernard Sherry, President and Chief Executive Officer
COO: Renee A. Kessler, Chief Operating Officer
CFO: Carrie Teaford, Vice President Finance
CMO: William Thompson, M.D., Chief Medical Officer
CIO: Jim Drew, Chief Information Officer
CHR: Martha Underwood, Chief Human Resources Officer
Web address: www.baptisthospital.com
**Control:** Other not–for–profit (including NFP Corporation) **Service:** General Medical and Surgical

**Staffed Beds:** 425

*Many Facility Codes have changed. Please refer to the AHA Guide Code Chart.*

© 2013 AHA Guide

✠ **SAINT THOMAS WEST HOSPITAL (440082)**, (Formerly Saint Thomas Hospital), 4220 Harding Road, Zip 37205–2095, Mailing Address: P.O. Box 380, Zip 37202–0380; tel. 615/222-2111, (Nonreporting) **A**1 2 3 5 9 10 **S** Ascension Health, Saint Louis, MO
Primary Contact: Dawn Rudolph, Chief Executive Officer
COO: Don King, Chief Operating Officer
CFO: Lisa Davis, Vice President Finance
CMO: Dale Batchelor, M.D., Chief Medical Officer
CIO: Chris Young, Vice President and Chief Information Officer
Web address: www.stthomas.org
**Control:** Church–operated, Nongovernment, not–for profit **Service:** General Medical and Surgical

**Staffed Beds:** 395

✠ **SELECT SPECIALTY HOSPITAL–NASHVILLE (442011)**, 2000 Hayes Street, Zip 37203–2318; tel. 615/284-4599, (Nonreporting) **A**1 9 10 **S** Select Medical Corporation, Mechanicsburg, PA
Primary Contact: Michael McAlister, Chief Executive Officer
CNO: Karen Cagle, Chief Nursing Officer
Web address: www.selectspecialtyhospitals.com/company/locations/nashville.aspx
**Control:** Corporation, Investor–owned, for–profit **Service:** Long–Term Acute Care hospital

**Staffed Beds:** 47

✠ **TENNESSEE VALLEY HEALTHCARE SYSTEM**, (Formerly Veterans Affairs Tennessee Valley Healthcare System), 1310 24th Avenue South, Zip 37212–2637; tel. 615/327-4751, (Includes ALVIN C. YORK CAMPUS, 3400 Lebanon Pike, Murfreesboro, Zip 37129–1236; tel. 615/867-6000; NASHVILLE CAMPUS, 1310 24th Avenue South, tel. 615/327-4751), (Total facility includes 238 beds in nursing home–type unit) **A**1 3 5 8 **F**1 3 4 5 12 15 17 18 20 22 24 26 28 30 31 39 40 45 54 56 57 58 60 62 63 64 70 74 75 77 78 79 81 82 83 84 87 90 91 92 93 94 97 98 100 102 103 104 107 108 110 111 116 119 129 130 135 136 142 143 146 147 **S** Department of Veterans Affairs, Washington, DC
Primary Contact: Juan A. Morales, R.N., MSN, Health System Director
COO: Gary D. Trende, FACHE, Chief Operating Officer
CFO: Jim A. Hayes, Chief Fiscal Service
CMO: Michael Doukas, Chief of Staff
CHR: Shirley F. Pettite, Chief, Human Resources
Web address: www.tennesseevalley.va.gov
**Control:** Veterans Affairs, Government, federal **Service:** General Medical and Surgical

**Staffed Beds:** 520 **Admissions:** 12273 **Census:** 431 **Outpatient Visits:** 866154 **Births:** 0 **Total Expense ($000):** 497166 **Payroll Expense ($000):** 317104 **Personnel:** 2444

✠ **TRISTAR CENTENNIAL MEDICAL CENTER (440161)**, 2300 Patterson Street, Zip 37203–1528; tel. 615/342-1000, (Includes TRISTAR CENTENNIAL WOMEN'S & CHILDREN'S, 2221 Murphy Avenue, Zip 37203; tel. 615/342-1000) **A**1 2 3 5 9 10 **F**3 5 12 13 15 17 18 20 22 24 26 28 29 30 31 35 40 41 42 46 47 49 50 51 53 54 56 59 60 64 68 70 71 72 73 74 75 76 77 78 79 81 82 85 86 87 88 89 93 98 100 102 103 104 105 107 108 110 111 114 115 117 118 119 121 124 126 129 130 132 136 138 146 147 148 **S** HCA, Nashville, TN
Primary Contact: Heather J. Rohan, Chief Executive Officer
COO: Micki J. Slingerland, Chief Operating Officer
CFO: David A. Summers, Chief Financial Officer
CMO: Ravi Chari, M.D., Chief Medical Officer
CHR: Patricia Knight, Vice President Human Resources
CHR: Leigh Mangum, Vice President Human Resources
Web address: www.tristarcentennial.com
**Control:** Corporation, Investor–owned, for–profit **Service:** General Medical and Surgical

**Staffed Beds:** 641 **Admissions:** 25830 **Census:** 404 **Outpatient Visits:** 165406 **Births:** 2998 **Total Expense ($000):** 471939 **Payroll Expense ($000):** 138101 **Personnel:** 2246

✠ △ **TRISTAR SKYLINE MEDICAL CENTER (440006)**, (Formerly Skyline Medical Center), 3441 Dickerson Pike, Zip 37207–2539; tel. 615/769-2000, (Nonreporting) **A**1 2 7 9 10 **S** HCA, Nashville, TN
Primary Contact: Steve Otto, Chief Executive Officer
CFO: Bradley Schultz, Chief Financial Officer
CMO: Christopher Colburn, M.D., Chief Medical Officer
CHR: Andy Hooper, Director Human Resources
CNO: Laurie Turner, Chief Nursing Officer
Web address: www.skylinemedicalcenter.com
**Control:** Corporation, Investor–owned, for–profit **Service:** General Medical and Surgical

**Staffed Beds:** 295

✠ **TRISTAR SOUTHERN HILLS MEDICAL CENTER (440197)**, (Formerly Southern Hills Medical Center), 391 Wallace Road, Zip 37211–4859; tel. 615/781-4000, (Nonreporting) **A**1 2 9 10 **S** HCA, Nashville, TN
Primary Contact: Thomas H. Ozburn, Chief Executive Officer
COO: Richard Tumlin, Chief Operating Officer
CFO: John Porada, Chief Financial Officer
CMO: Robert McCain, M.D., Chief of Staff
CIO: Ronnie Gannon, Director Information Services
CHR: Gary Briggs, Director Human Resources
CNO: Brenda C. Logan, R.N., Chief Nursing Officer
Web address: www.southernhills.com
**Control:** Corporation, Investor–owned, for–profit **Service:** General Medical and Surgical

**Staffed Beds:** 101

✠ **VANDERBILT HOSPITAL AND CLINICS (440039)**, 1211 22nd Avenue North, Zip 37232–2102; tel. 615/322-5000, (Includes MONROE CARELL JR. CHILDREN'S HOSPITAL AT VANDERBILT, 2200 Children's Way, Zip 37232; tel. 615/936-1000; Luke Gregory, Chief Executive Officer; VANDERBILT PSYCHIATRIC HOSPITAL, 1601 23rd Avenue South, Zip 37212–3198; tel. 615/320-7770) **A**1 2 3 5 8 9 10 **F**2 3 4 5 6 7 8 9 11 12 13 15 16 17 18 19 20 21 22 23 24 25 26 27 28 29 30 31 32 34 35 36 37 38 39 40 41 42 43 44 45 46 47 48 49 50 51 52 53 54 55 56 57 58 59 60 61 62 63 64 65 66 68 70 71 72 73 74 75 76 77 78 79 80 81 82 84 85 86 87 88 89 90 91 92 93 94 95 96 97 98 99 100 101 102 103 104 105 106 107 108 109 110 111 114 115 116 117 118 119 120 121 123 124 126 129 130 131 132 134 135 136 137 138 139 140 141 142 143 144 146 147 148 **P**1 5 6 7 **S** Vanderbilt Health, Nashville, TN
Primary Contact: David R. Posch, Chief Executive Officer
CFO: Warren E. Beck, Associate Vice Chancellor Health Affairs and Senior Vice President Finance
CMO: Paul Sternberg, M.D., Professor and Chairman
CIO: William Stead, Associate Vice Chancellor for Health Affairs, Director Informatics Center and Chief Strategy and Information Officer
CHR: Lenon J. Coleman, Interim Chief Human Resources Officer
Web address: www.mc.vanderbilt.edu
**Control:** Other not–for–profit (including NFP Corporation) **Service:** General Medical and Surgical

**Staffed Beds:** 966 **Admissions:** 50240 **Census:** 757 **Outpatient Visits:** 1939477 **Births:** 4194 **Total Expense ($000):** 1835269 **Payroll Expense ($000):** 631307 **Personnel:** 13097

**VANDERBILT PSYCHIATRIC HOSPITAL** See Vanderbilt Hospital and Clinics

✠ **VANDERBILT STALLWORTH REHABILITATION HOSPITAL (443028)**, 2201 Childrens Way, Zip 37212–3165; tel. 615/320-7600 **A**1 5 9 10 **F**28 29 56 57 59 68 74 75 87 90 91 94 95 96 132 148 **P**8 **S** HEALTHSOUTH Corporation, Birmingham, AL
Primary Contact: Susan Heath, Chief Executive Officer
CFO: Peggy Belyeu, Controller
CMO: Bob Coxe, M.D., Medical Director
CHR: Ruth Beasley, Director Human Resources
Web address: www.vanderbiltstallworthrehab.com
**Control:** Partnership, Investor–owned, for–profit **Service:** Rehabilitation

**Staffed Beds:** 80 **Admissions:** 1620 **Census:** 63 **Outpatient Visits:** 0 **Births:** 0 **Total Expense ($000):** 21767 **Payroll Expense ($000):** 11434 **Personnel:** 199

**VETERANS AFFAIRS TENNESSEE VALLEY HEALTHCARE SYSTEM** See Tennessee Valley Healthcare System

## NEWPORT—Cocke County

**BAPTIST HOSPITAL OF COCKE COUNTY** See Newport Medical Center

✠ **NEWPORT MEDICAL CENTER (440153)**, 435 Second Street, Zip 37821–3799; tel. 423/625-2200, (Nonreporting) **A**1 9 10 **S** Health Management Associates, Naples, FL
Primary Contact: Spencer Thomas, Chief Executive Officer
CFO: Jon Richards, Chief Financial Officer
CMO: Larry Mathers, M.D., Chief of Staff
CNO: Tonia Hale, Chief Nursing Officer
Web address: www.tennova.com
**Control:** Corporation, Investor–owned, for–profit **Service:** General Medical and Surgical

**Staffed Beds:** 47

**TN**

**Hospital, Medicare Provider Number, Address, Telephone, Approval, Facility, and Physician Codes, Health Care System**

★ American Hospital Association (AHA) membership
☐ The Joint Commission accreditation
◇ DNV Healthcare Inc. accreditation
○ Healthcare Facilities Accreditation Program
△ Commission on Accreditation of Rehabilitation Facilities (CARF) accreditation

## OAK RIDGE—Anderson County

✠ **METHODIST MEDICAL CENTER OF OAK RIDGE (440034)**, 990 Oak Ridge Turnpike, Zip 37830–6976, Mailing Address: P.O. Box 2529, Zip 37831–2529; tel. 865/835–1000 **A**1 2 9 10 **F**3 11 13 15 17 18 20 22 24 26 28 29 30 31 34 35 37 40 45 48 49 51 57 59 60 61 64 65 68 70 74 75 76 77 78 79 82 85 87 92 93 102 107 108 110 111 114 115 116 117 118 119 120 121 123 124 126 129 130 132 135 141 142 146 148 **S** Covenant Health, Knoxville, TN
Primary Contact: Michael Belbeck, President and Chief Administrative Officer
COO: Connie Martin, Vice President and Chief Support Officer
CFO: Julie Utterback, Vice President and Chief Financial Officer
CIO: Mike Ward, Senior Vice President, Chief Information Officer, Covenant
CHR: Rick Akens, Director Human Resources
CNO: Sue Harris, Vice President and Chief Nursing Officer
Web address: www.mmcoakridge.com
**Control:** Other not–for–profit (including NFP Corporation) **Service:** General Medical and Surgical

**Staffed Beds:** 255 **Admissions:** 11026 **Census:** 132 **Outpatient Visits:** 165847 **Births:** 673 **Total Expense ($000):** 160302 **Payroll Expense ($000):** 54089 **Personnel:** 975

**RIDGEVIEW PSYCHIATRIC HOSPITAL AND CENTER (444003)**, 240 West Tyrone Road, Zip 37830–6571; tel. 865/482–1076, (Nonreporting) **A**10
Primary Contact: Robert J. Benning, Chief Executive Officer
COO: Brian Buuck, Chief Operating Officer
CFO: Mary Claire Duff, CPA, Chief Financial Officer
CMO: Renu Bhateja, M.D., President Medical Staff
CHR: Julie M. Wright, Director Human Resources
Web address: www.ridgewresources.com
**Control:** Other not–for–profit (including NFP Corporation) **Service:** Psychiatric

**Staffed Beds:** 20

## PARIS—Henry County

✠ **HENRY COUNTY MEDICAL CENTER (440132)**, 301 Tyson Avenue, Zip 38242–4544, Mailing Address: P.O. Box 1030, Zip 38242–1030; tel. 731/642–1220, (Total facility includes 150 beds in nursing home–type unit) **A**1 9 10 **F**3 7 8 11 13 15 18 20 28 29 30 31 32 34 35 39 40 51 53 57 59 62 63 64 65 67 68 70 71 76 77 78 79 81 82 85 86 87 89 93 98 102 103 107 108 110 111 114 118 119 121 126 128 129 130 131 132 133 135 146 148 **P**6
Primary Contact: Thomas H. Gee, Administrator
CFO: Lisa Casteel, Chief Financial Officer/Assistant Administrator
CIO: Pam Ridley, Director Information Systems
CHR: Edwin L. Ledden, Human Resources Director/Assistant Administrator
CNO: Stephen O'Neal, R.N., Chief Nursing Officer
Web address: www.hcmc–tn.org
**Control:** Hospital district or authority, Government, nonfederal **Service:** General Medical and Surgical

**Staffed Beds:** 251 **Admissions:** 4088 **Census:** 172 **Outpatient Visits:** 78785 **Births:** 343 **Total Expense ($000):** 71497 **Payroll Expense ($000):** 29848 **Personnel:** 682

## PARSONS—Decatur County

☐ **DECATUR COUNTY GENERAL HOSPITAL (440070)**, 969 Tennessee Avenue South, Zip 38363–3700, Mailing Address: P.O. Box 250, Zip 38363–0250; tel. 731/847–3031, (Nonreporting) **A**1 9 10
Primary Contact: Scott Barber, Chief Executive Officer
CFO: Donna Hayes, Controller
CMO: Tom Hamilton, M.D., Chief of Staff
CHR: Shelley Bartholomew, Director Human Resources
Web address: www.dcgh.org
**Control:** County–Government, nonfederal **Service:** General Medical and Surgical

**Staffed Beds:** 40

## PIKEVILLE—Bledsoe County

☐ **ERLANGER BLEDSOE HOSPITAL (441306)**, 71 Wheeler Avenue, Zip 37367, Mailing Address: P.O. Box 699, Zip 37367–0699; tel. 423/447–2112 **A**1 9 10 18 **F**3 15 18 40 50 54 56 57 59 64 65 86 93 107 110 119 130 133 **S** Erlanger Health System, Chattanooga, TN
Primary Contact: Stephanie Boynton, Administrator
CMO: Arturo L. Quito, M.D., Chief of Staff
CIO: Debbie Rains, Coordinator Health Information Management
CHR: Patsy Brown, Site Coordinator Human Resources
Web address: www.erlanger.org
**Control:** Hospital district or authority, Government, nonfederal **Service:** General Medical and Surgical

**Staffed Beds:** 25 **Admissions:** 214 **Census:** 8 **Outpatient Visits:** 13766 **Births:** 0 **Total Expense ($000):** 10481 **Payroll Expense ($000):** 3568 **Personnel:** 66

## POWELL—Knox County

**MERCY MEDICAL CENTER NORTH** See North Knoxville Medical Center

## PULASKI—Giles County

✠ **HILLSIDE HOSPITAL (440020)**, 1265 East College Street, Zip 38478–4541; tel. 931/363–7531, (Nonreporting) **A**1 9 10 **S** LifePoint Hospitals, Inc., Brentwood, TN
Primary Contact: Jeff Jennings, FACHE, Chief Executive Officer
CFO: Donald Gavin, Chief Financial Officer
CMO: J. Michael Windland, M.D., Chief of Staff
CIO: Mitzi Foster, Director of Information Services
CHR: Jane Petty, Director Human Resources
CNO: Sherry Sands, R.N., Chief Nursing Officer
Web address: www.hillsidehospital.com
**Control:** Corporation, Investor–owned, for–profit **Service:** General Medical and Surgical

**Staffed Beds:** 50

## RIPLEY—Lauderdale County

✠ ◇ **LAUDERDALE COMMUNITY HOSPITAL (441314)**, 326 Asbury Avenue, Zip 38063–5577; tel. 731/221–2200 **A**1 9 10 18 21 **F**1 3 11 15 28 29 30 34 35 40 45 57 59 64 74 75 77 79 81 85 87 89 93 107 114 119 130 132 133 134 135 146 148 **S** Rural Community Hospitals of America, Kansas City, MO
Primary Contact: Scott Tongate, Chief Executive Officer
CFO: Jim Sneed, Chief Financial Officer
CMO: Syed A. Zaidi, M.D., Chief of Staff
CIO: Jim Vaden, Director Information Systems
CHR: Gail Henderson, Manager Human Resources
Web address: www.lauderdalehospital.com/
**Control:** Corporation, Investor–owned, for–profit **Service:** General Medical and Surgical

**Staffed Beds:** 25 **Admissions:** 535 **Census:** 8 **Outpatient Visits:** 18447 **Births:** 0 **Total Expense ($000):** 13413 **Payroll Expense ($000):** 5842 **Personnel:** 141

## ROGERSVILLE—Hawkins County

✠ **WELLMONT HAWKINS COUNTY MEMORIAL HOSPITAL (440032)**, 851 Locust Street, Zip 37857–2407, Mailing Address: P.O. Box 130, Zip 37857–0130; tel. 423/921–7000, (Nonreporting) **A**1 5 9 10 **S** Wellmont Health System, Kingsport, TN
Primary Contact: Fred L. Pelle, FACHE, Interim Chief Executive Officer
CFO: Dale Poe, Chief Financial Officer
CHR: Robin Poteete, Manager Human Resources
Web address: www.wellmont.org
**Control:** Other not–for–profit (including NFP Corporation) **Service:** General Medical and Surgical

**Staffed Beds:** 50

## SAVANNAH—Hardin County

✠ **HARDIN MEDICAL CENTER (440109)**, 935 Wayne Road, Zip 38372–1904; tel. 731/926–8000, (Total facility includes 73 beds in nursing home–type unit) **A**1 9 10 **F**2 3 7 11 13 15 18 19 28 29 31 34 40 45 46 57 59 65 69 75 76 77 78 79 80 81 89 91 92 93 107 108 110 111 115 119 128 129 130 131 133 144 148
Primary Contact: Nicholas P. Lewis, Chief Executive Officer
CFO: Mike Harbor, Chief Financial Officer
CMO: Gilbert M. Thayer, M.D., Chief Medical Staff
CIO: Jacob Bomar, Director Information Technology
CHR: Jimmy Davis, Director Human Resources
CNO: Jennifer Nelson, Director of Nursing
Web address: www.hardinmedicalcenter.org
**Control:** County–Government, nonfederal **Service:** General Medical and Surgical

**Staffed Beds:** 122 **Admissions:** 1806 **Census:** 82 **Outpatient Visits:** 70223 **Births:** 338 **Total Expense ($000):** 36721 **Payroll Expense ($000):** 17181 **Personnel:** 350

## SELMER—Mcnairy County

✠ **MCNAIRY REGIONAL HOSPITAL (440051)**, 705 East Poplar Avenue, Zip 38375–1828; tel. 731/645–3221, (Nonreporting) **A**1 9 10 **S** Community Health Systems, Inc., Franklin, TN
Primary Contact: Pamela W. Roberts, Chief Executive Officer
CFO: Meredith Jones, Chief Financial Officer
CMO: Ryan Bartz, D.O., Chief of Staff
CHR: Linda Durham, Director Human Resources
Web address: www.mcnairyregionalhospital.com
**Control:** Other not–for–profit (including NFP Corporation) **Service:** General Medical and Surgical

**Staffed Beds:** 45

**TN**

*Many Facility Codes have changed. Please refer to the AHA Guide Code Chart.*

## SEVIERVILLE—Sevier County

☒ **LECONTE MEDICAL CENTER (440081)**, 742 Middle Creek Road, Zip 37862–5019, Mailing Address: P.O. Box 8005, Zip 37864–8005; tel. 865/446–7000, (Total facility includes 54 beds in nursing home–type unit) **A**1 5 9 10 **F**3 11 13 15 18 20 28 29 30 31 34 35 40 45 50 51 53 57 59 61 64 67 68 70 75 76 77 78 79 81 85 87 93 107 110 111 114 119 128 130 131 135 146 147 **S** Covenant Health, Knoxville, TN
Primary Contact: Ellen Wilhoit, President and Chief Administrative Officer
COO: Rick Carringer, Vice President Finance and Support Services
CFO: Rick Carringer, Vice President Finance and Support Services
CMO: Curtis Burke, M.D., Chief of Staff
CIO: Amanda Brabson, Director Marketing and Public Relations
CHR: Steve Bramble, Director Human Resources
Web address: www.lecontemedicalcenter.com
**Control:** Other not–for–profit (including NFP Corporation) **Service:** General Medical and Surgical

**Staffed Beds:** 123 **Admissions:** 4185 **Census:** 78 **Outpatient Visits:** 120137 **Births:** 943 **Total Expense ($000):** 62021 **Payroll Expense ($000):** 22737 **Personnel:** 452

## SEWANEE—Franklin County

**EMERALD–HODGSON HOSPITAL** See Southern Tennessee Medical Center, Winchester

## SHELBYVILLE—Bedford County

☒ **HERITAGE MEDICAL CENTER (440137)**, 2835 Highway 231 North, Zip 37160–7327; tel. 931/685–5433, (Nonreporting) **A**1 9 10 **S** Community Health Systems, Inc., Franklin, TN
Primary Contact: David V. Bunch, Chief Executive Officer
CFO: Jon Baker, Chief Financial Officer
CIO: John F. Bryant, Director Information Services
CHR: Rob Thorne, Director of Human Resources
CNO: Pat Sweeton, Chief Nursing Officer
Web address: www.heritagemedicalcenter.com
**Control:** County–Government, nonfederal **Service:** General Medical and Surgical

**Staffed Beds:** 70

## SMITHVILLE—Dekalb County

☐ **DEKALB COMMUNITY HOSPITAL (440148)**, 520 West Main Street, Zip 37166–1138, Mailing Address: P.O. Box 640, Zip 37166–0640; tel. 615/215–5000 **A**1 9 10 **F**3 8 15 29 31 34 35 40 41 45 46 47 50 57 70 74 75 78 79 81 82 85 87 89 93 94 107 108 111 114 119 129 133 **S** Capella Healthcare, Franklin, TN
Primary Contact: Susan Conley, Chief Executive Officer
CMO: Hugh Don Cripps, M.D., Chief of Staff
CHR: Gingie Braswell, Director Human Resources
CNO: Kimberly Frazier, Chief Nursing Officer
Web address: www.dekalbcommunityhospital.com
**Control:** Corporation, Investor–owned, for–profit **Service:** General Medical and Surgical

**Staffed Beds:** 56 **Admissions:** 1136 **Census:** 11 **Outpatient Visits:** 7674 **Births:** 2 **Total Expense ($000):** 13124 **Payroll Expense ($000):** 6673 **Personnel:** 132

## SMYRNA—Rutherford County

☒ **TRISTAR STONECREST MEDICAL CENTER (440227)**, (Formerly StoneCrest Medical Center), 200 StoneCrest Boulevard, Zip 37167–6810; tel. 615/768–2000, (Nonreporting) **A**1 2 9 10 **S** HCA, Nashville, TN
Primary Contact: Mark E. Sims, Chief Executive Officer
COO: Zachary McCluskey, Chief Operating Officer
CFO: Joseph E. Bowman, Chief Financial Officer
CMO: Corbi Milligan, M.D., Chief of Staff
CHR: Cynthia Adams, Vice President Human Resources
CNO: Cynthia S. Stroburg, Chief Nursing Officer
Web address: www.stonecrestmedical.com
**Control:** Corporation, Investor–owned, for–profit **Service:** General Medical and Surgical

**Staffed Beds:** 101

## SNEEDVILLE—Hancock County

★ **WELLMONT HANCOCK COUNTY HOSPITAL (441313)**, 1519 Main Street, Zip 37869–3657; tel. 423/733–5000, (Nonreporting) **A**9 10 18 **S** Wellmont Health System, Kingsport, TN
Primary Contact: Fred L. Pelle, FACHE, Interim Chief Executive Officer
COO: Tracey Moffatt, Chief Operating Officer
CFO: Dale Poe, Chief Financial Officer
CMO: J. Dale Sargent, M.D., Chief Medical Officer
CIO: Kent Petty, Chief Information Officer
CHR: Robin Poteete, Manager Human Resources
Web address: www.wellmont.org/Hospitals/Hancock–County–Hospital.aspx
**Control:** Other not–for–profit (including NFP Corporation) **Service:** General Medical and Surgical

**Staffed Beds:** 10

## SOMERVILLE—Fayette County

☐ **METHODIST HEALTHCARE–FAYETTE HOSPITAL (440168)**, 214 Lakeview Drive, Zip 38068–9737; tel. 901/516–4000 **A**1 9 10 **F**3 15 29 34 35 40 45 57 59 64 65 75 81 85 87 93 107 114 119 133 146 148 **S** Methodist Le Bonheur Healthcare, Memphis, TN
Primary Contact: William A. Kenley, Chief Executive Officer
CFO: Jane George, Controller
CMO: Barton Thrasher, M.D., Chief of Staff
CHR: Joanell West, Human Resources Generalist
Web address: www.methodisthealth.org
**Control:** Other not–for–profit (including NFP Corporation) **Service:** General Medical and Surgical

**Staffed Beds:** 10 **Admissions:** 212 **Census:** 2 **Outpatient Visits:** 12610 **Births:** 0 **Total Expense ($000):** 8636 **Payroll Expense ($000):** 3873 **Personnel:** 94

## SPARTA—White County

☐ **HIGHLANDS MEDICAL CENTER (440192)**, 401 Sewell Road, Zip 38583–1299; tel. 931/738–9211, (Nonreporting) **A**1 9 10 **S** Capella Healthcare, Franklin, TN
Primary Contact: William Little, Chief Executive Officer
CFO: Tim Lynch, Interim Chief Financial Officer
CMO: Ronald Cunliffe, D.O., Chief of Staff
CIO: Glenn Wade, Director Information Systems
CHR: Kent Frisbee, Director Human Resources
Web address: www.whitecountyhospital.com
**Control:** Corporation, Investor–owned, for–profit **Service:** General Medical and Surgical

**Staffed Beds:** 44

## SPRINGFIELD—Robertson County

☒ **NORTHCREST MEDICAL CENTER (440065)**, 100 North Crest Drive, Zip 37172–3961; tel. 615/384–2411, (Nonreporting) **A**1 9 10
Primary Contact: Scott Raynes, President and Chief Executive Officer
COO: Randy Mills, Vice President Operations and Business Development
CFO: James A. Schmidt, Chief Financial Officer
CMO: Jonathan Kroser, M.D., Chief of Staff
CIO: Randy Davis, Chief Information Officer
CHR: Amber King, Director Human Resources
Web address: www.northcrest.com
**Control:** Other not–for–profit (including NFP Corporation) **Service:** General Medical and Surgical

**Staffed Beds:** 81

## SWEETWATER—Monroe County

☒ **SWEETWATER HOSPITAL (440084)**, 304 Wright Street, Zip 37874–2823; tel. 865/213–8200, (Nonreporting) **A**1 9 10
Primary Contact: Scott Bowman, Administrator
Web address: www.sweetwaterhospital.org
**Control:** Other not–for–profit (including NFP Corporation) **Service:** General Medical and Surgical

**Staffed Beds:** 59

## TAZEWELL—Claiborne County

☒ **CLAIBORNE COUNTY HOSPITAL (440057)**, 1850 Old Knoxville Road, Zip 37879–3625; tel. 423/626–4211, (Nonreporting) **A**1 9 10 20
Primary Contact: Tim S. Brown, Chief Executive Officer
CFO: Tracee McFarland, Chief Financial Officer
CHR: Susan Stone, Director Human Resources
Web address: www.claibornehospital.org
**Control:** County–Government, nonfederal **Service:** General Medical and Surgical

**Staffed Beds:** 62

**TN**

---

**Hospital, Medicare Provider Number, Address, Telephone, Approval, Facility, and Physician Codes, Health Care System**

★ American Hospital Association (AHA) membership
☐ The Joint Commission accreditation    ◇ DNV Healthcare Inc. accreditation
○ Healthcare Facilities Accreditation Program
△ Commission on Accreditation of Rehabilitation Facilities (CARF) accreditation

**TRENTON—Gibson County**

☒ **GIBSON GENERAL HOSPITAL (440047)**, 200 Hospital Drive, Zip 38382–3324;
tel. 731/855–7900 **A**1 9 10 **F**3 29 30 35 40 44 57 59 64 68 75 81 87 93
107 119 130 132 133 146 **S** West Tennessee Healthcare, Jackson, TN
Primary Contact: Sherry Scruggs, Administrator
CFO: Terry Swindell, Controller
CMO: Thomas Nelson, M.D., Director Emergency Room
CHR: Judy Hime, Director Human Resources
CNO: Rebecca Neely, R.N., Director of Nursing
Web address: www.wth.net
**Control:** Hospital district or authority, Government, nonfederal **Service:** General
Medical and Surgical

**Staffed Beds: 32 Admissions: 336 Census: 3 Outpatient Visits: 10909
Births: 2 Total Expense ($000): 6718 Payroll Expense ($000): 2968
Personnel: 72**

**TULLAHOMA—Coffee County**

☐ **HARTON REGIONAL MEDICAL CENTER (440144)**, 1801 North Jackson
Street, Zip 37388–8259; tel. 931/393–3000, (Nonreporting) **A**1 9 10 19
**S** Health Management Associates, Naples, FL
Primary Contact: William R. Spray, Chief Executive Officer
COO: Tracy Byers, Chief Operating Officer
CFO: Shaun Adams, Chief Financial Officer
CMO: Michael Tepedino, M.D., Chief of Staff
CIO: Donald Cooper, Director Information Systems
CHR: Lenore Blackwell, Director Human Resources
Web address: www.hartonmedicalcenter.com
**Control:** Corporation, Investor–owned, for–profit **Service:** Rehabilitation

**Staffed Beds: 104**

**UNION CITY—Obion County**

☒ **BAPTIST MEMORIAL HOSPITAL–UNION CITY (440130)**, 1201 Bishop Street,
Zip 38261–5403, Mailing Address: P.O. Box 310, Zip 38281–0310;
tel. 731/885–2410 **A**1 9 10 **F**4 5 7 11 13 15 18 20 26 29 30 34 35 40 45 48
50 51 53 57 58 59 63 64 70 75 76 79 80 81 82 84 85 86 87 89 91 93 98
99 100 101 102 104 105 107 108 109 110 111 115 118 119 124 130 132
135 146 **P**3 **S** Baptist Memorial Health Care Corporation, Memphis, TN
Primary Contact: Barry Bondurant, Administrator and Chief Executive Officer
CFO: Mike Perryman, Chief Financial Officer
CMO: James Batey, M.D., President Medical Staff
CIO: David Mercer, Coordinator Information Systems
CHR: Nicky Thomas, Director Human Resources
Web address: www.baptistonline.org/union–city/
**Control:** Other not–for–profit (including NFP Corporation) **Service:** General
Medical and Surgical

**Staffed Beds: 85 Admissions: 2749 Census: 27 Outpatient Visits: 43602
Births: 290 Total Expense ($000): 42222 Payroll Expense ($000): 15893
Personnel: 346**

**WAVERLY—Humphreys County**

**THREE RIVERS HOSPITAL (441303)**, 451 Highway 13 South,
Zip 37185–2109, Mailing Address: P.O. Box 437, Zip 37185–0437;
tel. 931/296–4203 **A**9 10 18 **F**3 15 29 34 40 45 57 59 64 81 91 103 107
114 119 130 133 135 148
Primary Contact: Freda Russell, Interim Chief Executive Officer
CFO: Sandra Patrick, Chief Financial Officer
CMO: Patrick J. Murphy, M.D., Chief of Staff
CHR: Linda Rawlings, Director Human Resources and Personnel
Web address: www.threerivershospital.org
**Control:** Other not–for–profit (including NFP Corporation) **Service:** General
Medical and Surgical

**Staffed Beds: 25 Admissions: 487 Census: 5 Outpatient Visits: 23909
Births: 1 Total Expense ($000): 8456 Payroll Expense ($000): 3773
Personnel: 104**

**WAYNESBORO—Wayne County**

☒ **WAYNE MEDICAL CENTER (440010)**, 103 J. V. Mangubat Drive,
Zip 38485–2440, Mailing Address: P.O. Box 580, Zip 38485–0580;
tel. 931/722–5411, (Nonreporting) **A**1 9 10 20 **S** Maury Regional Health System,
Columbia, TN
Primary Contact: Harley Smith, Chief Executive Officer
CFO: Michael A. Sears, Chief Financial Officer
CMO: Esmeraldo Herrera, M.D., Chief of Staff
CHR: Vicki Petty, Manager Human Resources
Web address: www.mauryregional.com
**Control:** Other not–for–profit (including NFP Corporation) **Service:** General
Medical and Surgical

**Staffed Beds: 78**

**WINCHESTER—Franklin County**

☒ **SOUTHERN TENNESSEE MEDICAL CENTER (440058)**, 185 Hospital Road,
Zip 37398–2404; tel. 931/967–8200, (Includes EMERALD–HODGSON HOSPITAL,
1260 University Avenue, Sewanee, Zip 37375–2303; tel. 931/598–5691; Ralph
Underwood, Administrator), (Total facility includes 46 beds in nursing home–type
unit) **A**1 9 10 **F**3 13 15 17 18 20 28 29 34 38 40 42 45 46 48 56 57 59 70
74 75 76 77 79 81 85 86 87 90 93 98 103 107 108 110 111 114 119 128
129 130 131 135 146 147 148 **S** LifePoint Hospitals, Inc., Brentwood, TN
Primary Contact: J. Phillip Young, FACHE, Chief Executive Officer
COO: Heather L. Harper, Chief Operating Officer
CFO: Steve Moore, Chief Financial Officer
CIO: James Payne, Director Information Systems
CHR: Linda Tipps, Director Human Resources
Web address: www.southerntennessee.com
**Control:** Corporation, Investor–owned, for–profit **Service:** General Medical and
Surgical

**Staffed Beds: 188 Admissions: 5453 Census: 83 Outpatient Visits: 77198
Births: 358 Total Expense ($000): 62663 Payroll Expense ($000): 28127
Personnel: 462**

**WOODBURY—Cannon County**

☐ **STONES RIVER HOSPITAL (440200)**, 324 Doolittle Road, Zip 37190–1139;
tel. 615/563–4001, (Nonreporting) **A**1 9 10 **S** Capella Healthcare, Franklin, TN
Primary Contact: Susan Conley, Chief Executive Officer
CMO: J. C. Wall, M.D., Chief of Staff
CHR: Brian Woods, Director Human Resources
CNO: Kimberly Frazier, Chief Nursing Officer
Web address: www.stonesriverhospital.com
**Control:** Corporation, Investor–owned, for–profit **Service:** General Medical and
Surgical

**Staffed Beds: 60**

*Many Facility Codes have changed. Please refer to the AHA Guide Code Chart.* © 2013 AHA Guide

**TN**

# TEXAS

## ABILENE—Taylor County

✠ **ABILENE REGIONAL MEDICAL CENTER (450558)**, 6250 U.S. Highway 83, Zip 79606–5299; tel. 325/428–1000, (Total facility includes 25 beds in nursing home–type unit) **A**1 9 10 **F**8 11 13 15 17 18 20 22 24 26 28 29 30 31 34 35 40 41 43 46 49 50 51 53 56 57 59 64 68 70 72 75 76 77 78 79 81 85 86 87 89 93 107 108 110 111 114 115 118 119 128 130 132 135 146 147 148 **P**3 **S** Community Health Systems, Inc., Franklin, TN
Primary Contact: Michael D. Murphy, Chief Executive Officer
COO: Jeremy Riney, Chief Operating Officer
CFO: Ron Bennett, Chief Financial Officer
CMO: LaNoard Bayouth, M.D., Chief of Staff
CIO: Dennis Newquist, Director Information Systems
CHR: John J. Jeziorske, Director Human Resources
CNO: Jessica Kiehle, R.N., Chief Nursing Officer
Web address: www.abileneregional.com
**Control:** Corporation, Investor–owned, for–profit **Service:** General Medical and Surgical

**Staffed Beds:** 205 **Admissions:** 7388 **Census:** 86 **Outpatient Visits:** 71418 **Births:** 1376 **Total Expense ($000):** 91254 **Payroll Expense ($000):** 35942 **Personnel:** 621

✠ **ACADIA ABILENE HOSPITAL (454098)**, 4225 Woods Place, Zip 79602–7991, Mailing Address: P.O. Box 5559, Zip 79608–5559; tel. 325/698–6600 **A**1 9 10 **F**4 5 29 34 54 56 57 64 86 87 98 99 101 103 104 105 130 **P**4 **S** Acadia Healthcare Company, Inc., Franklin, TN
Primary Contact: Chris Perkins, Chief Executive Officer
Web address: www.acadiaabilene.com
**Control:** Corporation, Investor–owned, for–profit **Service:** Psychiatric

**Staffed Beds:** 92 **Admissions:** 2062 **Census:** 54 **Outpatient Visits:** 8673 **Births:** 0 **Total Expense ($000):** 10344 **Payroll Expense ($000):** 4769 **Personnel:** 122

**HENDRICK CENTER FOR EXTENDED CARE (452029)**, 1900 Pine Street, Zip 79601–2432; tel. 325/670–2384 **A**10 **F**1 29 31 68 85 130
Primary Contact: Tim Riley, Vice President
**Control:** Church–operated, Nongovernment, not–for profit **Service:** Long–Term Acute Care hospital

**Staffed Beds:** 19 **Admissions:** 210 **Census:** 17 **Outpatient Visits:** 0 **Births:** 0 **Total Expense ($000):** 5822 **Payroll Expense ($000):** 1787 **Personnel:** 35

✠ **HENDRICK HEALTH SYSTEM (450229)**, 1900 Pine Street, Zip 79601–2432; tel. 325/670–2000, (Total facility includes 20 beds in nursing home–type unit) **A**1 9 10 **F**3 11 12 13 14 15 17 18 20 22 24 26 28 29 30 31 32 34 35 36 39 40 43 44 45 48 49 50 51 53 56 57 59 60 61 62 64 68 70 73 74 75 76 77 78 79 80 81 85 86 87 88 89 90 92 93 96 97 102 107 108 110 111 114 115 118 119 121 123 128 129 130 131 132 135 143 146 147 148 **P**8
Primary Contact: Tim Lancaster, FACHE, President and Chief Executive Officer
CFO: Stephen Kimmel, Senior Vice President and Chief Financial Officer
CMO: Steve Faehnle, M.D., Vice President Medical Affairs
Web address: www.ehendrick.org
**Control:** Church–operated, Nongovernment, not–for profit **Service:** General Medical and Surgical

**Staffed Beds:** 369 **Admissions:** 15601 **Census:** 232 **Outpatient Visits:** 272839 **Births:** 1372 **Total Expense ($000):** 270259 **Payroll Expense ($000):** 100083 **Personnel:** 1895

☐ **RELIANT REHABILITATION HOSPITAL ABILENE (673039)**, 6401 Directors Parkway, Zip 79606–5869; tel. 325/691–1600 **A**1 9 10 **F**3 29 90 93 96 130 148 **S** Reliant Healthcare Partners, Richardson, TX
Primary Contact: Lisa M. Nelson, R.N., MS, Chief Executive Officer
Web address: www.reliantabilene.com
**Control:** Partnership, Investor–owned, for–profit **Service:** Rehabilitation

**Staffed Beds:** 30 **Admissions:** 527 **Census:** 14 **Outpatient Visits:** 371 **Births:** 0 **Total Expense ($000):** 6822 **Payroll Expense ($000):** 2479 **Personnel:** 49

## ADDISON—Dallas County

◇ **METHODIST HOSPITAL FOR SURGERY (670073)**, 17101 North Dallas Parkway, Zip 75001–7103; tel. 469/248–3900 **A**9 10 21 **F**3 29 30 35 40 64 70 81 93 107 111 112 119 130 146 **P**2 **S** Methodist Health System, Dallas, TX
Primary Contact: Chris Shoup, President
CFO: Jade Andrews, Chief Financial Officer
CMO: Rajiv Pandit, M.D., Medical Director
CIO: Ronda Kirk Johnson, Manager Health Information Management
CNO: Patti Griffith, R.N., Chief Nursing Officer
Web address: www.methodisthospitalforsurgery.com/
**Control:** Corporation, Investor–owned, for–profit **Service:** Surgical

**Staffed Beds:** 32 **Admissions:** 2128 **Census:** 14 **Outpatient Visits:** 6833 **Births:** 0 **Total Expense ($000):** 74394 **Payroll Expense ($000):** 11610 **Personnel:** 179

## ALICE—Jim Wells County

✠ **CHRISTUS SPOHN HOSPITAL ALICE (450828)**, 2500 East Main Street, Zip 78332–4169; tel. 361/661–8000 **A**1 9 10 20 **F**3 11 13 15 18 20 22 28 29 30 35 39 40 42 43 45 46 49 50 57 59 68 70 75 76 77 79 81 85 86 87 89 93 97 98 100 101 102 103 107 108 111 114 119 127 130 146 148 **P**8 **S** CHRISTUS Health, Irving, TX
Primary Contact: Steven G. Daniel, Senior Vice President and Chief Operating Officer
CFO: Michael Guajardo, Director Finance
CMO: Alejandro Lopez, Jr., M.D., Chief of Staff
CIO: Jean Deanoglis, Director Management Information Systems
CHR: Emily Diaz–Lopez, Director Human Resources
Web address: www.christusspohn.org/locations_alice.htm
**Control:** Church–operated, Nongovernment, not–for profit **Service:** General Medical and Surgical

**Staffed Beds:** 115 **Admissions:** 3884 **Census:** 39 **Outpatient Visits:** 54302 **Births:** 506 **Total Expense ($000):** 45254 **Payroll Expense ($000):** 18476 **Personnel:** 244

## ALLEN—Collin County

✠ **TEXAS HEALTH PRESBYTERIAN HOSPITAL ALLEN (450840)**, 1105 Central Expressway North, Zip 75013–6103; tel. 972/747–1000 **A**1 9 10 **F**3 13 15 28 29 30 34 35 38 40 47 49 51 54 55 57 59 64 65 70 73 74 75 76 79 81 89 93 107 110 111 114 115 118 119 126 129 130 132 135 146 147 148 **S** Texas Health Resources, Arlington, TX
Primary Contact: Jeff Reecer, President
CFO: Dan Rich, Director Finance
CMO: Bob Schwab, M.D., Chief Medical Officer
CHR: Sharon Chisholm, Director Human Resources
CNO: Jane Cook, R.N., Chief Nursing Officer
Web address: www.texashealth.org
**Control:** Other not–for–profit (including NFP Corporation) **Service:** General Medical and Surgical

**Staffed Beds:** 73 **Admissions:** 4154 **Census:** 36 **Outpatient Visits:** 54536 **Births:** 983 **Total Expense ($000):** 79316 **Payroll Expense ($000):** 27901 **Personnel:** 310

☐ **TWIN CREEKS REHABILITATION HOSPITAL (673025)**, 1001 Raintree Circle, Zip 75013–4912; tel. 972/908–2015 **A**1 9 10 **F**3 28 29 30 34 40 56 59 60 74 75 79 87 90 91 94 96 100 130 132 146 148
Primary Contact: Amy Shope, Chief Executive Officer
Web address: www.twincreekshosp.com/
**Control:** Partnership, Investor–owned, for–profit **Service:** Rehabilitation

**Staffed Beds:** 39 **Admissions:** 583 **Census:** 17 **Outpatient Visits:** 3 **Births:** 0 **Total Expense ($000):** 8386 **Payroll Expense ($000):** 3765 **Personnel:** 118

TX

## ALPINE—Brewster County

☒ **BIG BEND REGIONAL MEDICAL CENTER (451378)**, 2600 Highway 118 North, Zip 79830–2002; tel. 432/837–3447 **A**1 9 10 18 **F**3 29 30 34 35 40 43 45 49 57 59 64 68 70 75 76 81 85 93 107 119 132 133 146 147 148 **P**6 **S** Community Health Systems, Inc., Franklin, TN
Primary Contact: Michael J. Ellis, Chief Executive Officer
Web address: www.bigbendhealthcare.com
**Control:** Corporation, Investor–owned, for–profit **Service:** General Medical and Surgical

**Staffed Beds:** 25 **Admissions:** 902 **Census:** 7 **Outpatient Visits:** 12117 **Births:** 170 **Total Expense ($000):** 18925 **Payroll Expense ($000):** 6046 **Personnel:** 95

## ALVIN—Brazoria County

**ALVIN DIAGNOSTIC AND URGENT CARE CENTER** See Clear Lake Regional Medical Center, Webster

## AMARILLO—Potter County

☒ **AMARILLO VETERANS AFFAIRS HEALTH CARE SYSTEM**, 6010 West Amarillo Boulevard, Zip 79106–1992; tel. 806/355–9703, (Nonreporting) **A**1 2 3 5 9 **S** Department of Veterans Affairs, Washington, DC
Primary Contact: Andrew Welch, Director
COO: Lance Robinson, Associate Director
CMO: James Gray, M.D., Chief Medical Service
CIO: Modesto Baca, Chief Information Officer
CHR: Ken Creamer, Chief Human Resource
Web address: www.amarillo.va.gov/
**Control:** Veterans Affairs, Government, federal **Service:** General Medical and Surgical

**Staffed Beds:** 55

☒ ◇ **BAPTIST ST. ANTHONY HEALTH SYSTEM (450231)**, 1600 Wallace Boulevard, Zip 79106–1799; tel. 806/212–2000 **A**1 2 3 5 9 10 21 **F**3 7 8 11 12 13 15 17 18 19 20 22 24 26 28 29 30 31 34 35 40 45 46 48 49 51 53 54 57 59 62 63 64 70 72 74 75 76 77 78 79 81 82 85 86 87 88 89 90 91 93 96 107 108 110 111 114 115 117 119 126 129 130 131 145 146 147 148
Primary Contact: Bob Williams, President and Chief Executive Officer
COO: Michael Cruz, Vice President Operations
CFO: Brian Walton, Vice President and Chief Financial Officer
CHR: Cheryl L. Jones, Director Human Resources and Organizational Development
CNO: Belinda D. Gibson, R.N., Vice President Patient Services
Web address: www.bsahs.org
**Control:** Church–operated, Nongovernment, not–for profit **Service:** General Medical and Surgical

**Staffed Beds:** 445 **Admissions:** 20957 **Census:** 264 **Outpatient Visits:** 162592 **Births:** 2325 **Total Expense ($000):** 279707 **Payroll Expense ($000):** 95200 **Personnel:** 2498

☒ **KINDRED HOSPITAL–AMARILLO (452060)**, 7501 Wallace Boulevard, Zip 79124–2150; tel. 806/467–7000 **A**1 9 10 **F**1 3 29 34 35 45 46 50 56 57 59 60 61 70 74 75 77 79 82 84 85 86 87 91 96 107 114 130 148 **P**8 **S** Kindred Healthcare, Louisville, KY
Primary Contact: Kay E. Peck, Ph.D., Chief Executive Officer
COO: Kay E. Peck, Ph.D., Chief Executive Officer
CFO: Carlene Wright, Chief Financial Officer
CMO: Pablo Rodrigues, M.D., Medical Director
CNO: Melany McCarty, R.N., Chief Clinical Officer
Web address: www.khamarillo.com/
**Control:** Corporation, Investor–owned, for–profit **Service:** Long–Term Acute Care hospital

**Staffed Beds:** 72 **Admissions:** 821 **Census:** 58 **Outpatient Visits:** 0 **Births:** 0 **Total Expense ($000):** 25643 **Payroll Expense ($000):** 9693 **Personnel:** 210

☒ **KINDRED REHABILITATION HOSPITAL AMARILLO (453096)**, (Formerly Kindred Rehabilitation Hospital), 7200 West 9th Avenue, Zip 79106–1703; tel. 806/468–2900 **A**1 10 **F**3 29 56 60 75 77 82 87 90 91 96 130 143 148 **S** Kindred Healthcare, Louisville, KY
Primary Contact: Kay E. Peck, Ph.D., Chief Executive Officer
Web address: www.khrehabamarillo.com/
**Control:** Corporation, Investor–owned, for–profit **Service:** Rehabilitation

**Staffed Beds:** 44 **Admissions:** 695 **Census:** 22 **Outpatient Visits:** 0 **Births:** 0 **Total Expense ($000):** 9375 **Payroll Expense ($000):** 3883 **Personnel:** 114

☒ **NORTHWEST TEXAS HEALTHCARE SYSTEM (450209)**, 1501 South Coulter Avenue, Zip 79106–1770, Mailing Address: P.O. Box 1110, Zip 79105–1110; tel. 806/354–1000, (Includes CHILDREN'S HOSPITAL, 1501 South Coulter Street, tel. 806/354–1000; PSYCHIATRIC PAVILION, 7201 Evans, Zip 79106) **A**1 2 3 5 9 10 **F**3 4 5 11 13 15 17 18 20 22 24 25 26 28 29 30 31 32 34 35 37 38 39 40 43 44 45 46 48 49 50 54 56 57 59 60 61 64 66 68 70 72 74 75 76 77 78 79 81 84 86 87 88 89 92 93 94 97 98 99 100 101 102 103 104 105 107 108 110 111 114 118 119 130 132 135 146 147 148 **P**6 **S** Universal Health Services, Inc., King of Prussia, PA
Primary Contact: Mark W. Crawford, Chief Executive Officer
COO: Sharon Oxendale, Chief Operating Officer
CFO: Raymond Grenier, Chief Financial Officer
CMO: Nathan Goldstein, III, M.D., Chief Medical Officer
CIO: Sam Mason, Director Management Information Systems
CHR: Charlyn Snow, Director Human Resources
Web address: www.nwtexashealthcare.com
**Control:** Corporation, Investor–owned, for–profit **Service:** General Medical and Surgical

**Staffed Beds:** 431 **Admissions:** 19835 **Census:** 252 **Outpatient Visits:** 242286 **Births:** 2497 **Total Expense ($000):** 256026 **Payroll Expense ($000):** 84611 **Personnel:** 1563

**NORTHWEST TEXAS SURGERY CENTER (450796)**, 3501 South Soncy Road Suite 118, Zip 79119–6405; tel. 806/359–7999 **A**10 **F**26 39 40 58 68 79 81 82 85 93 126 131
Primary Contact: Clay Weiss, Administrator
**Control:** Corporation, Investor–owned, for–profit **Service:** General Medical and Surgical

**Staffed Beds:** 4 **Admissions:** 127 **Census:** 1 **Outpatient Visits:** 4700 **Births:** 0 **Total Expense ($000):** 8883 **Payroll Expense ($000):** 2996 **Personnel:** 48

**PHYSICIANS SURGICAL HOSPITAL – PANHANDLE CAMPUS**, 7100 West 9th Avenue, Zip 79106–1704; tel. 806/212–0247, (Nonreporting)
Primary Contact: Brad McCall, President and Chief Executive Officer
CFO: Whitt Holder, Chief Financial Officer
CNO: Debbie Inman, Chief Nursing Officer
Web address: www.physurg.com/
**Control:** Partnership, Investor–owned, for–profit **Service:** General Medical and Surgical

**Staffed Beds:** 11

**PHYSICIANS SURGICAL HOSPITAL – QUAIL CREEK (450875)**, 6819 Plum Creek, Zip 79124–1602; tel. 806/354–6100 **A**9 10 **F**29 30 40 44 50 68 75 79 81 85 89 130 135
Primary Contact: Brad McCall, President and Chief Executive Officer
CFO: Whitt Holder, Chief Financial Officer
CNO: Debbie Inman, Chief Nursing Officer
Web address: www.physurg.com
**Control:** Corporation, Investor–owned, for–profit **Service:** Surgical

**Staffed Beds:** 39 **Admissions:** 1490 **Census:** 8 **Outpatient Visits:** 12714 **Births:** 0 **Total Expense ($000):** 35876 **Payroll Expense ($000):** 9011 **Personnel:** 155

☐ **PLUM CREEK SPECIALTY HOSPITAL (452066)**, 5601 Plum Creek Drive, Zip 79124–1801; tel. 806/351–1000 **A**1 9 10 **F**1 3 29 75 85 148 **S** Encore Healthcare, Columbia, MD
Primary Contact: Billy Blasingame, Chief Executive Officer
Web address: www.specialtyhospital–plumcreek.net
**Control:** Corporation, Investor–owned, for–profit **Service:** Long–Term Acute Care hospital

**Staffed Beds:** 47 **Admissions:** 248 **Census:** 18 **Outpatient Visits:** 0 **Births:** 0 **Total Expense ($000):** 6282 **Payroll Expense ($000):** 2809 **Personnel:** 66

**SPECIALTY HOSPITAL AT PLUM CREEK** See Plum Creek Specialty Hospital

## ANAHUAC—Chambers County

★ **CHAMBERS COUNTY PUBLIC HOSPITAL DISTRICT 1 (451320)**, 200 Hospital Drive, Zip 77514, Mailing Address: P.O. Box 398, Zip 77514–0398; tel. 409/267–3143 **A**9 10 18 **F**3 8 11 29 34 35 40 43 45 47 50 53 54 56 57 59 64 70 80 81 86 87 88 89 93 107 111 114 119 128 130 133 146 **P**3
Primary Contact: Steven Gularte, Chief Executive Officer
CFO: Theresa Cheaney, Controller
CMO: Leonidas Andres, M.D., Chief of Staff
CNO: Christi Morris, Director of Nursing
Web address: www.chambershealth.org
**Control:** Hospital district or authority, Government, nonfederal **Service:** General Medical and Surgical

**Staffed Beds:** 14 **Admissions:** 221 **Census:** 2 **Outpatient Visits:** 36132 **Births:** 0 **Total Expense ($000):** 11275 **Payroll Expense ($000):** 5020 **Personnel:** 103

*Many Facility Codes have changed. Please refer to the AHA Guide Code Chart.*
© 2013 AHA Guide

**TX**

## ANDREWS—Andrews County

⊠ ◇ **PERMIAN REGIONAL MEDICAL CENTER (450144)**, Northeast By–Pass, Zip 79714, Mailing Address: P.O. Box 2108, Zip 79714–2108; tel. 432/523–2200 **A**1 9 10 20 21 **F**3 11 13 15 29 34 35 36 38 40 43 44 50 53 56 57 59 62 64 68 70 73 75 76 77 81 82 84 85 86 87 89 93 97 107 108 110 111 115 119 127 129 130 131 132 133 135 144 145 146 148 **P**6 7
Primary Contact: Russell Tippin, Chief Executive Officer and Administrator
CFO: Sandra Cox, Controller
CIO: Dan Smart, Chief Information Management Officer
CHR: Pam McCormick, Director Human Resources
Web address: www.permianregional.com
**Control:** Hospital district or authority, Government, nonfederal **Service:** General Medical and Surgical

**Staffed Beds: 44 Admissions: 753 Census: 7 Outpatient Visits:** 30216
**Births: 306 Total Expense ($000): 32059 Payroll Expense ($000):** 15556
**Personnel: 260**

## ANGLETON—Brazoria County

⊠ **ANGLETON DANBURY MEDICAL CENTER (450591)**, 132 East Hospital Drive, Zip 77515–4197; tel. 979/849–7721 **A**1 9 10 **F**3 11 13 15 18 28 29 30 34 35 36 40 43 45 46 49 53 57 59 64 65 68 70 74 75 76 77 79 81 85 86 87 89 91 93 107 108 111 114 115 119 130 132 135 146 **P**1
Primary Contact: David A. Bleakney, Chief Executive Officer and Administrator
CFO: William D. Garwood, III, Associate Administrator and Chief Financial Officer
CMO: Craig L. McDonald, M.D., Chief Medical Officer
CHR: Paula Tobon–Stevens, Associate Administrator
CNO: Rose McCullough, R.N., Associate Administrator Patient Care and Chief Nursing Officer
Web address: www.admc.org
**Control:** Hospital district or authority, Government, nonfederal **Service:** General Medical and Surgical

**Staffed Beds: 51 Admissions: 3454 Census: 22 Outpatient Visits:** 41898
**Births: 376 Total Expense ($000): 22446 Payroll Expense ($000):** 12046
**Personnel: 219**

## ANSON—Jones County

★ **ANSON GENERAL HOSPITAL (450078)**, 101 Avenue J, Zip 79501–2198; tel. 325/823–3231 **A**9 10 **F**7 11 29 40 45 62 75 77 81 89 107 127 133 **P**8
Primary Contact: Pamela Gonzales, Chief Operating Officer
CFO: Rick McDonald, Chief Financial Officer
CIO: Lynna B. Cox, Director Health Information Services
**Control:** City–Government, nonfederal **Service:** General Medical and Surgical

**Staffed Beds: 30 Admissions: 327 Census: 6 Outpatient Visits:** 7349
**Births: 0 Total Expense ($000): 7209 Payroll Expense ($000):** 3619
**Personnel: 122**

## ARANSAS PASS—San Patricio County

**CARE REGIONAL MEDICAL CENTER (450605)**, 1711 West Wheeler Avenue, Zip 78336–4536; tel. 361/758–8585 **A**9 10 **F**3 4 11 15 18 29 34 35 40 44 45 50 56 57 59 64 65 68 70 75 77 78 79 81 85 86 87 90 93 97 98 101 102 103 107 108 111 114 119 130 132 133 143 146 148
Primary Contact: Sunil Reddy, Chief Executive Officer
CHR: Sherry Gwynn, Administrative Director Human Resources
Web address: www.crmctx.com
**Control:** Corporation, Investor–owned, for–profit **Service:** General Medical and Surgical

**Staffed Beds: 54 Admissions: 1317 Census: 17 Outpatient Visits:** 26015
**Births: 0 Total Expense ($000): 12119 Payroll Expense ($000):** 6078
**Personnel: 166**

**NORTH BAY HOSPITAL** See Care Regional Medical Center

## ARLINGTON—Tarrant County

**ARLINGTON REHABILITATION HOSPITAL** See Kindred Rehabilitation Hospital Arlington

☐ **BAYLOR ORTHOPEDIC AND SPINE HOSPITAL AT ARLINGTON (670067)**, 707 Highlander Boulevard, Zip 76015–4319; tel. 817/583–7100 **A**1 9 10 **F**3 29 40 42 75 79 81 82 85 86 107 111 114
Primary Contact: Allan Beck, Chief Executive Officer
Web address: www.baylorarlington.com/
**Control:** Partnership, Investor–owned, for–profit **Service:** General Medical and Surgical

**Staffed Beds: 24 Admissions: 998 Census: 6 Outpatient Visits:** 5707
**Births: 0 Total Expense ($000): 32018 Payroll Expense ($000):** 6102
**Personnel: 89**

⊠ **HEALTHSOUTH REHABILITATION HOSPITAL OF ARLINGTON (453040)**, 3200 Matlock Road, Zip 76015–2911; tel. 817/468–4000 **A**1 9 10 **F**3 29 64 74 75 77 79 90 91 93 94 95 96 130 131 **S** HEALTHSOUTH Corporation, Birmingham, AL
Primary Contact: Mark S. Deno, Chief Executive Officer
CFO: Kathy Dickerson, Chief Financial Officer
CMO: Rizwan Shah, M.D., Medical Director
CHR: Nancy Rosiles, Coordinator Human Resources
Web address: www.healthsoutharlington.com
**Control:** Corporation, Investor–owned, for–profit **Service:** Rehabilitation

**Staffed Beds: 85 Admissions: 1649 Census: 57 Outpatient Visits:** 7292
**Births: 0 Total Expense ($000): 24240 Payroll Expense ($000):** 11353
**Personnel: 218**

⊠ **KINDRED HOSPITAL TARRANT COUNTY–ARLINGTON (452028)**, 1000 North Cooper Street, Zip 76011–5540; tel. 817/548–3400 **A**1 9 10 **F**1 3 29 30 40 56 57 77 80 82 93 130 148 **S** Kindred Healthcare, Louisville, KY
Primary Contact: Christina Richard, Administrator
CFO: Jennifer Penland, Controller
CMO: Bernard A. McGowen, M.D., Medical Director
Web address: www.kindredhospitalarl.com/
**Control:** Corporation, Investor–owned, for–profit **Service:** Long–Term Acute Care hospital

**Staffed Beds: 78 Admissions: 578 Census: 41 Outpatient Visits:** 361
**Births: 0 Total Expense ($000): 20632 Payroll Expense ($000):** 8163
**Personnel: 153**

⊠ △ **KINDRED REHABILITATION HOSPITAL ARLINGTON (453094)**, 2601 West Randol Mill Road, Zip 76012–4289; tel. 817/804–4400 **A**1 7 9 10 **F**3 29 34 57 59 74 75 86 87 90 94 96 130 132 146 148 **S** Kindred Healthcare, Louisville, KY
Primary Contact: Seth A. Sauve, FACHE, Chief Executive Officer
CFO: Jennifer Penland, Controller
CNO: Katherine Kreis, Chief Clinical Officer
Web address: www.khrehabarlington.com
**Control:** Corporation, Investor–owned, for–profit **Service:** Rehabilitation

**Staffed Beds: 24 Admissions: 569 Census: 18 Outpatient Visits: 0 Births:
0 Total Expense ($000): 6264 Payroll Expense ($000): 3977 Personnel:
62**

⊠ **MEDICAL CENTER OF ARLINGTON (450675)**, 3301 Matlock Road, Zip 76015–2998; tel. 817/465–3241 **A**1 2 9 10 **F**3 11 12 13 15 17 18 20 22 24 26 28 29 31 34 35 39 40 43 45 46 47 48 49 50 56 57 59 64 68 70 72 73 74 75 76 78 79 81 82 85 86 87 92 93 107 108 110 111 114 115 118 119 126 130 131 132 135 145 146 147 148 **S** HCA, Nashville, TN
Primary Contact: Winston Borland, FACHE, President and Chief Executive Officer
COO: LaSharndra Barbarin, Chief Operating Officer
CFO: Jeff Ardemagni, Chief Financial Officer
CMO: Randy Davidson, M.D., Chief of Staff
CIO: Basil Holloway, Director Information Services
CHR: Jerry L. McMorrough, Vice President Human Resources
CNO: Omar Pineda, R.N., Chief Nursing Officer
Web address: www.medicalcenterarlington.com
**Control:** Corporation, Investor–owned, for–profit **Service:** General Medical and Surgical

**Staffed Beds: 284 Admissions: 14103 Census: 190 Outpatient Visits:** 92131 **Births: 4028 Total Expense ($000): 177695 Payroll Expense ($000): 68754 Personnel: 981**

☐ **MILLWOOD HOSPITAL (454012)**, 1011 North Cooper Street, Zip 76011–5517; tel. 817/261–3121 **A**1 9 10 **F**4 5 29 30 35 54 56 71 87 98 99 100 101 102 103 104 105 130 132 **S** Universal Health Services, Inc., King of Prussia, PA
Primary Contact: Rick Paczkowski, Chief Executive Officer
CFO: Jeff Epperson, Chief Financial Officer
CMO: Ernest Brownlee, M.D., Medical Director
CIO: Linda Jones, Director Medical Records
CHR: Shirley Spurlock, Director Human Resources
Web address: www.millwoodhospital.com
**Control:** Partnership, Investor–owned, for–profit **Service:** Psychiatric

**Staffed Beds: 122 Admissions: 4371 Census: 93 Outpatient Visits:** 25548
**Births: 0 Total Expense ($000): 23708 Payroll Expense ($000):** 10167
**Personnel: 251**

☐ **SUNDANCE HOSPITAL (454113)**, 7000 U.S. Highway 287 South, Zip 76001; tel. 817/583–8080 **A**1 9 10 **F**98 99 101 102 103
Primary Contact: Jimmye Lou Cockrell, Chief Executive Officer
Web address: www.sundancehealthcare.com
**Control:** Corporation, Investor–owned, for–profit **Service:** Psychiatric

**Staffed Beds: 56 Admissions: 1954 Census: 38 Outpatient Visits: 0 Births:
0 Total Expense ($000): 8504 Payroll Expense ($000): 4843 Personnel:
123**

---

**Hospital, Medicare Provider Number, Address, Telephone, Approval, Facility, and Physician Codes, Health Care System**

★ American Hospital Association (AHA) membership
☐ The Joint Commission accreditation    ◇ DNV Healthcare Inc. accreditation
○ Healthcare Facilities Accreditation Program
△ Commission on Accreditation of Rehabilitation Facilities (CARF) accreditation

**TX**

⊞ **TEXAS HEALTH ARLINGTON MEMORIAL HOSPITAL (450064)**, 800 West Randol Mill Road, Zip 76012–2503; tel. 817/548–6100 **A**1 2 9 10 **F**3 11 12 13 15 18 26 28 29 30 31 34 35 37 40 45 46 47 48 49 51 53 54 57 59 63 64 65 68 70 72 74 75 76 77 78 79 81 82 85 86 87 93 100 107 108 110 111 114 115 118 119 123 124 126 130 132 135 136 145 146 147 148 **S** Texas Health Resources, Arlington, TX
Primary Contact: Kirk King, FACHE, President
COO: Sandra L. Harris, R.N., Senior Vice President and Chief Operating Officer
CMO: Robert N. Cluck, M.D., Vice President and Medical Director
CHR: Yvonne Kyler, Director Human Resources
Web address: www.arlingtonmemorial.org
**Control:** Other not–for–profit (including NFP Corporation) **Service:** General Medical and Surgical

**Staffed Beds:** 289 **Admissions:** 13085 **Census:** 176 **Outpatient Visits:** 108536 **Births:** 1832 **Total Expense ($000):** 226571 **Payroll Expense ($000):** 91916 **Personnel:** 1453

☐ **TEXAS HEALTH HEART & VASCULAR HOSPITAL ARLINGTON (670071)**, 811 Wright Street, Zip 76012–4708; tel. 817/960–3500 **A**1 9 10 **F**3 17 18 20 22 24 26 29 30 60 64 65 68 81 85
Primary Contact: Baron L. Hamman, M.D., President
Web address: www.texashealthheartandvascular.org/
**Control:** Partnership, Investor–owned, for–profit **Service:** Heart

**Staffed Beds:** 48 **Admissions:** 1266 **Census:** 15 **Outpatient Visits:** 2484 **Births:** 0 **Total Expense ($000):** 42206 **Payroll Expense ($000):** 8193 **Personnel:** 113

⊞ **USMD HOSPITAL AT ARLINGTON (450872)**, 801 West Interstate 20, Zip 76017–5851; tel. 817/472–3400 **A**1 9 10 **F**3 12 29 34 35 39 40 45 49 50 51 57 58 59 64 70 74 75 78 79 81 82 85 87 92 107 108 111 114 119 124 126 132 **S** USMD Inc., Irving, TX
Primary Contact: Marcia Crim, R.N., MSN, Chief Executive Officer
COO: Marcia Crim, R.N., Chief Nursing Officer and Chief Operating Officer
CFO: Gordon Davis, Vice President Finance
CMO: James Ward, M.D., President Medical Staff
CIO: Bob Rick, Vice President Information Technology
CHR: Alex Stefanowicz, Vice President Human Resources
Web address: www.usmdarlington.com
**Control:** Partnership, Investor–owned, for–profit **Service:** General Medical and Surgical

**Staffed Beds:** 34 **Admissions:** 1772 **Census:** 13 **Outpatient Visits:** 35869 **Births:** 0 **Total Expense ($000):** 69478 **Payroll Expense ($000):** 15383 **Personnel:** 307

**ASPERMONT—Stonewall County**

**STONEWALL MEMORIAL HOSPITAL (451318)**, 821 North Broadway, Zip 79502–2029, Mailing Address: P.O. Box C, Zip 79502–0902; tel. 940/989–3551 **A**9 10 18 **F**3 29 34 35 40 41 56 57 59 64 93 97 103 107 114 119 127 128 133 148 **P**5
Primary Contact: Andy Kolb, Chief Executive Officer
CFO: Debra Meador, Assistant Administrator
CMO: Daniel Hadzie, M.D., Chief of Staff
Web address: www.smhdhealth.org/
**Control:** Hospital district or authority, Government, nonfederal **Service:** General Medical and Surgical

**Staffed Beds:** 12 **Admissions:** 186 **Census:** 1 **Outpatient Visits:** 10683 **Births:** 0 **Total Expense ($000):** 6338 **Payroll Expense ($000):** 3652 **Personnel:** 52

**ATHENS—Henderson County**

⊞ **EAST TEXAS MEDICAL CENTER ATHENS (450389)**, 2000 South Palestine Street, Zip 75751–5610; tel. 903/676–1000 **A**1 9 10 **F**3 11 13 15 18 20 26 29 40 42 43 45 49 50 51 57 64 65 66 70 74 75 76 77 78 79 81 85 86 89 107 108 110 111 114 115 119 130 132 145 **P**7 **S** East Texas Medical Center Regional Healthcare System, Tyler, TX
Primary Contact: Patrick L. Wallace, Administrator
CFO: David A. Travis, Chief Financial Officer
CHR: Jennifer Rummel, Director Human Resources
Web address: www.etmc.org
**Control:** Other not–for–profit (including NFP Corporation) **Service:** General Medical and Surgical

**Staffed Beds:** 127 **Admissions:** 6752 **Census:** 63 **Outpatient Visits:** 100578 **Births:** 803 **Total Expense ($000):** 69036 **Payroll Expense ($000):** 22971 **Personnel:** 451

**ATLANTA—Cass County**

★ **CHRISTUS ST. MICHAEL HOSPITAL–ATLANTA (450615)**, 1007 South William Street, Zip 75551–3245; tel. 903/799–3000 **A**9 10 **F**3 11 15 29 30 34 35 40 43 45 53 57 59 62 64 68 70 75 77 81 87 91 93 107 110 111 114 119 129 130 132 146 **P**8
Primary Contact: Deborah Robison, R.N., Chief Executive Officer and Administrator
CFO: Jackie Rainey, Assistant Administrator and Controller
CIO: Rick Mauldin, Director Information Services
CHR: Debra Embry, Associate Administrator Employee Services
Web address: www.atlantamemorial.com
**Control:** Hospital district or authority, Government, nonfederal **Service:** General Medical and Surgical

**Staffed Beds:** 29 **Admissions:** 760 **Census:** 8 **Outpatient Visits:** 25997 **Births:** 0 **Total Expense ($000):** 11638 **Payroll Expense ($000):** 6308 **Personnel:** 133

**AUBREY—Denton County**

◇ **BAYLOR EMERGENCY MEDICAL CENTER AT AUBREY (670062)**, 26791 Highway 380, Zip 76227; tel. 972/347–2525 **A**9 10 21 **F**3 29 40 75 87 107 119 **P**5 **S** Emerus, The Woodlands, TX
Primary Contact: John Wood, Chief Executive Officer
Web address: www.emerus.com
**Control:** Partnership, Investor–owned, for–profit **Service:** General Medical and Surgical

**Staffed Beds:** 8 **Admissions:** 100 **Census:** 1 **Outpatient Visits:** 8631 **Births:** 0 **Total Expense ($000):** 5320 **Payroll Expense ($000):** 2150 **Personnel:** 28

**AUSTIN—Travis County**

☐ **AUSTIN LAKES HOSPITAL (454069)**, 1025 East 32nd Street, Zip 78705–2714; tel. 512/544–5253 **A**1 5 9 10 **F**98 104 105 130 **S** Universal Health Services, Inc., King of Prussia, PA
Primary Contact: Jennifer Miller, Chief Executive Officer
Web address: www.austinlakeshospital.com
**Control:** Corporation, Investor–owned, for–profit **Service:** Psychiatric

**Staffed Beds:** 58 **Admissions:** 3031 **Census:** 54 **Outpatient Visits:** 8329 **Births:** 0 **Total Expense ($000):** 11212 **Payroll Expense ($000):** 6389 **Personnel:** 174

☐ **AUSTIN STATE HOSPITAL (454084)**, 4110 Guadalupe Street, Zip 78751–4296; tel. 512/452–0381 **A**1 3 5 10 **F**29 30 39 40 50 56 59 65 68 75 82 86 98 99 101 103 130 132 143 146 **P**1 **S** Texas Department of State Health Services, Austin, TX
Primary Contact: Cathy Nottebart, Acting Superintendent
CMO: Ross Taylor, M.D., Clinical Director
CIO: Cindy Reed, Director Community Relations
Web address: www.dshs.state.tx.us/mhhospitals/austinsh/default.shtm
**Control:** State–Government, nonfederal **Service:** Psychiatric

**Staffed Beds:** 314 **Admissions:** 3642 **Census:** 273 **Outpatient Visits:** 0 **Births:** 0 **Total Expense ($000):** 66664 **Payroll Expense ($000):** 35642 **Personnel:** 856

☐ **AUSTIN SURGICAL HOSPITAL (450871)**, 3003 Bee Caves Road, Zip 78746–5542; tel. 512/314–3800 **A**1 9 10 **F**3 29 37 40 51 59 64 65 68 70 77 79 81 82 85 107 111 119 148 **P**2
Primary Contact: Gregg Magers, Chief Executive Officer
CFO: Lawrence Oldham, Chief Financial Officer
CMO: Brannon Smoot, M.D., Medical Director
CHR: Marilyn Jennings, Director Human Resources
Web address: www.austinsurgicalhospital.com
**Control:** Partnership, Investor–owned, for–profit **Service:** Orthopedic

**Staffed Beds:** 23 **Admissions:** 914 **Census:** 6 **Outpatient Visits:** 6696 **Births:** 0 **Total Expense ($000):** 22374 **Payroll Expense ($000):** 6599 **Personnel:** 101

⊞ **CENTRAL TEXAS REHABILITATION HOSPITAL (673027)**, 700 West 45th Street, Zip 78751–2800; tel. 512/407–2111 **A**1 9 10 **F**3 29 59 74 79 82 90 91 96 130 132 148 **S** Kindred Healthcare, Louisville, KY
Primary Contact: Peggy Barrett, R.N., Chief Executive Officer
CFO: Tracey Allen, Controller
CMO: Mary Ann Gonzales, M.D., Medical Director
CIO: Peggy Barrett, R.N., Chief Executive Officer
CHR: Liza Cuero, Coordinator Human Resources
CNO: Kerry Radcliffe, JD, Chief Nursing Officer
Web address: www.khrehabcentraltexas.com/
**Control:** Partnership, Investor–owned, for–profit **Service:** Rehabilitation

**Staffed Beds:** 50 **Admissions:** 754 **Census:** 27 **Outpatient Visits:** 0 **Births:** 0 **Total Expense ($000):** 13221 **Payroll Expense ($000):** 5543 **Personnel:** 106

**TX**

☐ **CORNERSTONE HOSPITAL OF AUSTIN (452034)**, 4207 Burnet Road,
Zip 78756–3396; tel. 512/706–1900, (Includes CORNERSTONE HOSPITAL OF
AUSTIN, 1005 East 32nd Street, Zip 78705; tel. 512/867–5822; Edward J.
Sherwood, M.D., Chief Executive Officer) **A**1 9 10 **F**1 3 29 30 75 77 87 91 148
**S** Cornerstone Healthcare Group, Dallas, TX
Primary Contact: Laura Sims, Chief Executive Officer
CFO: Gregory Taylor, Chief Financial Officer
CMO: David Pohl, M.D., Chief of Staff
Web address: www.chghospitals.com/austin/
**Control:** Corporation, Investor–owned, for–profit **Service:** Long–Term Acute Care
hospital

**Staffed Beds:** 64 **Admissions:** 705 **Census:** 49 **Outpatient Visits:** 0 **Births:**
0 **Total Expense ($000):** 19441 **Payroll Expense ($000):** 8810 **Personnel:**
209

⊠ **DELL CHILDREN'S MEDICAL CENTER OF CENTRAL TEXAS (453310)**, 4900
Mueller Boulevard, Zip 78723–3079; tel. 512/324–0000 **A**1 3 5 9 10 **F**3 11 19
21 23 25 27 29 30 31 32 34 35 39 40 41 43 44 46 49 50 54 58 59 61 64
65 68 71 72 74 75 77 78 79 80 81 82 83 84 85 86 87 88 89 93 100 104
107 111 112 114 115 118 119 126 129 130 131 132 135 143 146 148 **P**3
8 **S** Ascension Health, Saint Louis, MO
Primary Contact: Mark W. Shen, M.D., Chief Executive Officer
Web address: www.dellchildrens.net
**Control:** Church–operated, Nongovernment, not–for profit **Service:** Children's
general

**Staffed Beds:** 176 **Admissions:** 8268 **Census:** 102 **Outpatient Visits:**
410843 **Births:** 0 **Total Expense ($000):** 335669 **Payroll Expense ($000):**
161725 **Personnel:** 2293

⊠ **HEALTHSOUTH REHABILITATION HOSPITAL OF AUSTIN (453044)**, 1215
Red River Street, Zip 78701–1921; tel. 512/474–5700 **A**1 9 10 **F**29 56 62 74
75 77 79 86 87 90 91 148 **S** HEALTHSOUTH Corporation, Birmingham, AL
Primary Contact: Duke Saldivar, FACHE, Chief Executive Officer
CFO: Pamela McLaughlin, Chief Financial Officer
CMO: Maria E. Arizmendez, M.D., Executive Medical Director
CHR: Debbie Belcher, Director Human Resources
CNO: Mary Ann Lee, Chief Nursing Officer
Web address: www.healthsouthaustin.com
**Control:** Corporation, Investor–owned, for–profit **Service:** Rehabilitation

**Staffed Beds:** 40 **Admissions:** 791 **Census:** 29 **Outpatient Visits:** 17786
**Births:** 0 **Total Expense ($000):** 15084 **Payroll Expense ($000):** 7558
**Personnel:** 122

☐ **NORTHWEST HILLS SURGICAL HOSPITAL (450808)**, 6818 Austin Center
Boulevard, Suite 100, Zip 78731–3199; tel. 512/346–1994 **A**1 9 10 **F**40 45 64
79 81
Primary Contact: Angie Kauffman, R.N., MSN, Acting Administrator and Director of
Nursing
CFO: Jenny Salome, Chief Financial Officer and Assistant Administrator
Web address: www.northwesthillssurgical.com
**Control:** Partnership, Investor–owned, for–profit **Service:** General Medical and
Surgical

**Staffed Beds:** 8 **Admissions:** 507 **Census:** 2 **Outpatient Visits:** 9392 **Births:**
0 **Total Expense ($000):** 21451 **Payroll Expense ($000):** 4301 **Personnel:**
85

☐ **RELIANT AUSTIN (673054)**, 330 West Ben White Boulevard, Zip 78704;
tel. 512/730–4800, (Data for 186 days) **A**1 9 10 **F**3 29 90 93 96 130 148
Primary Contact: Jack Boggess, Chief Executive Officer
CNO: Vidette J. Forbes, R.N., Chief Nursing Officer and Chief Operating Officer
Web address: www.reliantaustin.com
**Control:** Partnership, Investor–owned, for–profit **Service:** Rehabilitation

**Staffed Beds:** 60 **Admissions:** 361 **Census:** 19 **Outpatient Visits:** 52 **Births:**
0 **Total Expense ($000):** 5909 **Payroll Expense ($000):** 2621 **Personnel:**
62

⊠ **SETON MEDICAL CENTER AUSTIN (450056)**, 1201 West 38th Street,
Zip 78705–1006; tel. 512/324–1000 **A**1 2 3 5 9 10 **F**3 11 12 13 15 18 20 22
24 26 28 29 30 31 34 35 37 40 43 44 45 46 49 50 57 58 59 60 61 64 68
70 72 74 75 76 77 78 79 81 82 84 85 86 87 93 107 108 111 114 115 119
130 131 132 135 137 146 148 **P**3 8 **S** Ascension Health, Saint Louis, MO
Primary Contact: Gregory Hartman, President and Chief Executive Officer
COO: Charlotte Thrasher, Vice President and Chief Operating Officer
CFO: Douglas D. Waite, Chief Financial Officer
CMO: Carol Wratten, M.D., Vice President Medical Affairs
CIO: Gerry Lewis, Chief Information Officer
CHR: Fenorris Pearson, Chief Human Resources Officer
CNO: Angela Stalbaum, R.N., Chief Nursing Officer
Web address: www.seton.net
**Control:** Church–operated, Nongovernment, not–for profit **Service:** General
Medical and Surgical

**Staffed Beds:** 425 **Admissions:** 21357 **Census:** 275 **Outpatient Visits:**
81784 **Births:** 3667 **Total Expense ($000):** 347847 **Payroll Expense
($000):** 145788 **Personnel:** 2406

⊠ **SETON NORTHWEST HOSPITAL (450867)**, 11113 Research Boulevard,
Zip 78759–5236; tel. 512/324–6000 **A**1 2 3 5 9 10 **F**3 11 12 13 15 18 29 30
31 34 35 36 37 40 43 44 45 47 49 50 51 57 59 64 68 70 72 74 75 76 77
78 79 81 85 86 87 93 107 111 114 119 129 130 131 132 135 146 148 **P**3
8 **S** Ascension Health, Saint Louis, MO
Primary Contact: Michelle Robertson, R.N., President and Chief Executive Officer
CFO: Douglas D. Waite, Chief Financial Officer
CMO: Ed LeBlanc, M.D., Vice President Medical Affairs
CIO: Gerry Lewis, Chief Information Officer
CHR: Trennis Jones, Senior Vice President and Chief Administrative Officer
Web address: www.seton.net
**Control:** Church–operated, Nongovernment, not–for profit **Service:** General
Medical and Surgical

**Staffed Beds:** 121 **Admissions:** 4846 **Census:** 45 **Outpatient Visits:** 58956
**Births:** 903 **Total Expense ($000):** 71723 **Payroll Expense ($000):** 37098
**Personnel:** 520

⊠ **SETON SHOAL CREEK HOSPITAL (454029)**, 3501 Mills Avenue,
Zip 78731–6391; tel. 512/324–2000 **A**1 3 5 9 10 **F**4 5 29 30 34 68 72 86 87
88 98 99 100 101 103 104 130 132 135 146 **P**3 8 **S** Ascension Health, Saint
Louis, MO
Primary Contact: Alan Isaacson, Vice President and Chief Operating Officer
COO: Alan Isaacson, Vice President and Chief Operating Officer
CFO: Douglas D. Waite, Chief Financial Officer
CMO: Kari Wolfe, M.D., Medical Director
CIO: Gerry Lewis, Chief Information Officer
CHR: Thomas Wilken, Vice President Human Resources
Web address: www.seton.net
**Control:** Church–operated, Nongovernment, not–for profit **Service:** Psychiatric

**Staffed Beds:** 92 **Admissions:** 4695 **Census:** 65 **Outpatient Visits:** 23267
**Births:** 0 **Total Expense ($000):** 23618 **Payroll Expense ($000):** 15569
**Personnel:** 307

⊠ **SETON SOUTHWEST HEALTHCARE CENTER (450865)**, 7900 F. M. 1826,
Zip 78737–1407; tel. 512/324–9000 **A**1 9 10 **F**3 11 13 15 29 30 34 35 36
40 43 44 45 50 57 59 64 68 71 75 76 79 81 82 85 87 93 107 111 115 119
129 130 131 132 135 146 **P**3 8 **S** Ascension Health, Saint Louis, MO
Primary Contact: Mary Faria, FACHE, Administrator
Web address: www.seton.net
**Control:** Church–operated, Nongovernment, not–for profit **Service:** General
Medical and Surgical

**Staffed Beds:** 17 **Admissions:** 1449 **Census:** 10 **Outpatient Visits:** 30042
**Births:** 826 **Total Expense ($000):** 27652 **Payroll Expense ($000):** 14221
**Personnel:** 225

**TX**

☒ ◇ **ST. DAVID'S MEDICAL CENTER (450431)**, 919 East 32nd Street, Zip 78705–2709, Mailing Address: P.O. Box 4039, Zip 78765–4039; tel. 512/476–7111, (Includes HEART HOSPITAL OF AUSTIN, 3801 North Lamar Boulevard, Zip 78756–4080; tel. 512/407–7000; David Laird, Chief Executive Officer; ST. DAVID'S GEORGETOWN HOSPITAL, 2000 Scenic Drive, Georgetown, Zip 78626–7726; tel. 512/943–3000; Hugh Brown, Chief Executive Officer) **A**1 2 3 5 9 10 21 **F**3 8 11 12 13 15 17 18 20 22 24 26 28 29 30 31 34 35 37 39 40 43 45 46 47 48 49 53 56 57 58 59 61 64 68 70 72 73 74 75 76 77 78 79 80 81 85 86 87 89 90 93 107 108 109 110 111 114 115 116 119 126 130 131 132 135 146 147 148 **S** HCA, Nashville, TN
Primary Contact: Donald H. Wilkerson, Chief Executive Officer
CFO: Cindy Brouillette, Chief Financial Officer
CMO: John Marietta, M.D., Chief Medical Officer
CIO: Debi Castleberry, Director Information System
CHR: De De Juel, Director Human Resources
Web address: www.stdavids.com
**Control:** Other not–for–profit (including NFP Corporation) **Service:** General Medical and Surgical

**Staffed Beds: 484 Admissions:** 24326 **Census:** 317 **Outpatient Visits:** 169398 **Births:** 5586 **Total Expense ($000):** 380026 **Payroll Expense ($000):** 133324 **Personnel:** 2442

☒ **ST. DAVID'S NORTH AUSTIN MEDICAL CENTER (450809)**, 12221 North MoPac Expressway, Zip 78758–2496; tel. 512/901–1000 **A**1 3 10 **F**3 11 12 13 15 18 20 22 24 26 28 29 30 31 34 35 37 39 40 42 43 45 47 49 53 54 56 57 59 64 70 72 73 74 75 76 77 78 79 81 82 84 85 86 87 90 93 107 108 111 114 115 118 119 126 130 131 132 138 144 145 146 147 148 **S** HCA, Nashville, TN
Primary Contact: Allen Harrison, Chief Executive Officer
COO: Sheri Dube, Chief Operating Officer
CFO: Cindy Sexton, Chief Financial Officer
CMO: Kenneth W. Mitchell, M.D., Medical Director
CIO: Marshall Pearson, Director Management Information Systems
CHR: Julie Hajek, Director Human Resources
Web address: www.northaustin.com
**Control:** Other not–for–profit (including NFP Corporation) **Service:** General Medical and Surgical

**Staffed Beds: 332 Admissions:** 17433 **Census:** 243 **Outpatient Visits:** 137328 **Births:** 5874 **Total Expense ($000):** 229317 **Payroll Expense ($000):** 78994 **Personnel:** 1259

☒ **ST. DAVID'S REHABILITATION CENTER (453038)**, 1005 East 32nd Street, Zip 78705–2713, Mailing Address: P.O. Box 4270, Zip 78765–4270; tel. 512/544–5100 **A**1 3 5 9 10 **F**29 30 35 36 64 77 90 93 96 131 132 148 **S** HCA, Nashville, TN
Primary Contact: Diane Owens, Administrator
CFO: Cindy Brouillette, Chief Financial Officer
CMO: John Marietta, M.D., Chief Medical Officer
CIO: Debi Castleberry, Director Information System
CHR: De De Juel, Director Human Resources
Web address: www.stdavidsrehab.com/home.aspx
**Control:** Other not–for–profit (including NFP Corporation) **Service:** Rehabilitation

**Staffed Beds: 64 Admissions:** 1407 **Census:** 56 **Outpatient Visits:** 33753 **Births:** 0 **Total Expense ($000):** 25990 **Payroll Expense ($000):** 12434 **Personnel:** 211

☒ **ST. DAVID'S SOUTH AUSTIN MEDICAL CENTER (450713)**, 901 West Ben White Boulevard, Zip 78704–6903; tel. 512/447–2211 **A**1 2 3 5 9 10 **F**3 11 12 13 15 17 18 20 22 24 26 28 29 30 31 34 35 40 41 44 45 47 48 49 54 56 57 59 64 70 73 74 75 76 77 78 79 81 82 85 87 93 107 108 110 111 114 115 118 119 126 129 130 132 144 146 147 148 **P**7 8 **S** HCA, Nashville, TN
Primary Contact: Todd E. Steward, Chief Executive Officer
COO: Brett Matens, Chief Operating Officer
CFO: Wesley D. Fountain, Chief Financial Officer
CMO: Albert Gros, M.D., Chief Medical Officer
CIO: Richard Lear, Director Information Systems
CHR: Lisa Talbot, Director Human Resources
CNO: Sally A. Gillam, R.N., Chief Nursing Officer
Web address: www.southaustinmc.com
**Control:** Other not–for–profit (including NFP Corporation) **Service:** General Medical and Surgical

**Staffed Beds: 233 Admissions:** 14129 **Census:** 181 **Outpatient Visits:** 140275 **Births:** 1509 **Total Expense ($000):** 170941 **Payroll Expense ($000):** 63967 **Personnel:** 1057

☒ △ **TEXAS NEROREHAB CENTER (452038)**, 1106 West Dittmar, Zip 78745–6328, Mailing Address: P.O. Box 150459, Zip 78715–0459; tel. 512/444–4835 **A**1 7 9 10 **F**1 10 29 43 54 74 75 79 93 108 130 148 **P**5 **S** Universal Health Services, Inc., King of Prussia, PA
Primary Contact: Edgar E. Prettyman, PsyD, Chief Executive Officer
COO: Omar Correa, Chief Operating Officer
CFO: Omar Correa, Chief Financial Officer
CMO: James Boysen, M.D., Executive Medical Director
CHR: Colleen Lewis, Director Human Resources
Web address: www.texasneurorehab.com
**Control:** Partnership, Investor–owned, for–profit **Service:** Long–Term Acute Care hospital

**Staffed Beds: 47 Admissions:** 470 **Census:** 42 **Outpatient Visits:** 4539 **Births:** 0 **Total Expense ($000):** 12120 **Payroll Expense ($000):** 7134 **Personnel:** 319

**TEXAS STAR RECOVERY (454111)**, 1106 West Dittmar Road, Zip 78745–6328; tel. 512/462–6729, (Nonreporting) **A**10
Primary Contact: Edgar E. Prettyman, PsyD, Chief Executive Officer
Web address: www.texasstarrecovery.com
**Control:** Partnership, Investor–owned, for–profit **Service:** Psychiatric

**Staffed Beds: 28**

**THE HOSPITAL AT WESTLAKE MEDICAL CENTER (670006)**, 5656 Bee Caves Road, Zip 78746–5280; tel. 512/327–0000 **A**9 10 **F**3 18 20 22 24 26 28 29 37 39 40 45 51 53 58 64 68 70 75 77 79 81 82 85 93 96 107 108 111 114 118 119 126 129 130 131 135 148
Primary Contact: Rip Miller, Chief Executive Officer
CFO: Julie Churchill, Director Financial Services
CMO: Tom Burns, M.D., Chief of Staff
CHR: Kellie Bryson, Director Human Resources
Web address: www.westlakemedical.com
**Control:** Partnership, Investor–owned, for–profit **Service:** General Medical and Surgical

**Staffed Beds: 23 Admissions:** 1012 **Census:** 8 **Outpatient Visits:** 10822 **Births:** 0 **Total Expense ($000):** 29430 **Payroll Expense ($000):** 11221 **Personnel:** 181

☒ **UNIVERSITY MEDICAL CENTER AT BRACKENRIDGE (450124)**, 601 East 15th Street, Zip 78701–1996; tel. 512/324–7000 **A**1 3 5 9 10 **F**3 11 13 15 18 20 22 24 26 29 30 31 34 35 37 39 40 43 44 45 47 49 55 57 58 59 60 64 65 66 68 70 71 72 74 75 76 77 78 79 81 82 84 85 87 93 97 104 107 108 110 111 114 115 118 119 124 130 132 135 143 146 148 **P**3 8 **S** Ascension Health, Saint Louis, MO
Primary Contact: Gregory Hartman, President and Chief Executive Officer
COO: Kate Henderson, Vice President and Chief Operating Officer
CFO: Douglas D. Waite, Chief Financial Officer
CMO: Jim Lindsey, M.D., Senior Vice President Medical Affairs
CIO: Gerry Lewis, Chief Information Officer
CHR: Fenorris Pearson, Chief Human Resources Officer
CNO: Michelle Ryerson, Chief Nursing Officer
Web address: www.seton.net
**Control:** Church–operated, Nongovernment, not–for profit **Service:** General Medical and Surgical

**Staffed Beds: 244 Admissions:** 14206 **Census:** 177 **Outpatient Visits:** 532451 **Births:** 2003 **Total Expense ($000):** 468984 **Payroll Expense ($000):** 243169 **Personnel:** 3123

**AZLE—Tarrant County**

☒ **TEXAS HEALTH HARRIS METHODIST HOSPITAL AZLE (450419)**, 108 Denver Trail, Zip 76020–3614; tel. 817/444–8600 **A**1 9 10 **F**3 11 15 29 30 34 35 40 43 45 57 59 63 64 65 70 75 77 79 81 82 85 93 107 110 114 119 130 131 135 146 147 148 **S** Texas Health Resources, Arlington, TX
Primary Contact: Bob S. Ellzey, FACHE, President
CFO: Brian Blessing, Chief Financial Officer
CMO: Kristi Kuenstler, M.D., Chief of Staff
CIO: Edward Marx, Vice President and Chief Information Officer
CHR: Cindy Bierbrauer, Director Human Resources
CNO: Valarie Gilbert, R.N., Chief Nursing Officer
Web address: www.texashealth.org/Azle
**Control:** Other not–for–profit (including NFP Corporation) **Service:** General Medical and Surgical

**Staffed Beds: 31 Admissions:** 1615 **Census:** 14 **Outpatient Visits:** 35840 **Births:** 2 **Total Expense ($000):** 30112 **Payroll Expense ($000):** 14139 **Personnel:** 213

**TX**

## BALLINGER—Runnels County

**BALLINGER MEMORIAL HOSPITAL (451310)**, 608 Avenue B,
Zip 76821–2499, Mailing Address: P.O. Box 617, Zip 76821–0617;
tel. 325/365–2531 **A**9 10 18 **F**3 7 11 28 32 34 40 43 50 53 54 56 57 59 64
65 68 75 77 87 93 107 114 127 130 133 135 143 147 148 **P**5
Primary Contact: Grady Hooper, Chief Executive Officer
CFO: Josilyn Peterson, Chief Financial Officer
CHR: Roselyn Hudgens, Director Human Resources
Web address: www.ballingerhospital.org
**Control:** Hospital district or authority, Government, nonfederal **Service:** General
Medical and Surgical

**Staffed Beds:** 16 **Admissions:** 172 **Census:** 3 **Outpatient Visits:** 19406
**Births:** 0 **Total Expense ($000):** 7259 **Payroll Expense ($000):** 3057
**Personnel:** 78

## BAY CITY—Matagorda County

⊠ **MATAGORDA REGIONAL MEDICAL CENTER (450465)**, 104 7th Street,
Zip 77414–4853; tel. 979/245–6383 **A**1 9 10 20 **F**3 11 13 15 18 20 22 28
29 30 32 34 38 39 40 43 46 47 50 51 53 56 57 59 64 65 66 68 70 75 76
77 79 81 82 85 86 89 93 98 103 107 108 110 111 114 119 130 132 135
146 147 148 **S** QHR, Brentwood, TN
Primary Contact: Steven L. Smith, Chief Executive Officer
CFO: Bryan Prochnow, Chief Financial Officer
CIO: Mary Ann Cervantes, District Director Management Information Systems
CHR: Cindy Krebs, District Director Human Resources
CNO: Kim Pierson, R.N., Chief Nursing Officer
Web address: www.matagordaregional.org
**Control:** Hospital district or authority, Government, nonfederal **Service:** General
Medical and Surgical

**Staffed Beds:** 58 **Admissions:** 2589 **Census:** 30 **Outpatient Visits:** 38626
**Births:** 381 **Total Expense ($000):** 61070 **Payroll Expense ($000):** 17428
**Personnel:** 291

## BAYTOWN—Harris County

★ ◇ **SAN JACINTO METHODIST HOSPITAL (450424)**, 4401 Garth Road,
Zip 77521–2122; tel. 281/420–8600, (Includes SAN JACINTO METHODIST
HOSPITAL – ALEXANDER, 1700 James Bowie Drive, Zip 77520–3386;
tel. 281/420–6100), (Total facility includes 30 beds in nursing home–type unit)
**A**2 9 10 13 21 **F**3 8 11 12 13 15 18 20 22 24 26 28 29 30 31 34 35 38 40
44 48 49 50 53 57 59 61 64 65 70 73 74 75 76 77 78 79 80 81 82 85 86
87 90 91 93 97 98 102 103 107 108 110 111 114 115 116 117 118 119
120 121 123 124 126 128 129 130 132 145 146 147 148 **P**3 **S** The
Methodist Hospital System, Houston, TX
Primary Contact: Donna Gares, R.N., President and Chief Executive Officer
CFO: Jonathan Sturgis, Chief Financial Officer
CMO: Bruce Kennedy, M.D., Chief Medical Officer
CHR: Sherri Davis–Sampson, Director Human Resources
Web address: www.methodisthealth.com
**Control:** Other not–for–profit (including NFP Corporation) **Service:** General
Medical and Surgical

**Staffed Beds:** 275 **Admissions:** 12242 **Census:** 168 **Outpatient Visits:**
122133 **Births:** 1542 **Total Expense ($000):** 189092 **Payroll Expense**
**($000):** 79838 **Personnel:** 1363

## BEAUMONT—Jefferson County

★ ◇ **BAPTIST HOSPITALS OF SOUTHEAST TEXAS (450346)**, 3080 College
Street, Zip 77701–4689, Mailing Address: P.O. Box 1591, Zip 77704–1591;
tel. 409/212–5000, (Includes BAPTIST HOSPITALS OF SOUTHEAST TEXAS
FANNIN BEHAVIORAL HEALTH CENTER, 3250 Fannin Street, Zip 77701;
tel. 409/212–7000) **A**2 9 10 21 **F**3 4 5 11 13 15 17 18 20 22 24 26 28 29
30 31 34 35 37 40 45 48 49 51 55 57 59 60 64 70 72 73 74 75 76 77 78
79 81 84 85 86 87 88 89 90 93 94 96 98 99 100 101 102 103 105 107 108
110 111 114 115 117 118 119 120 121 123 124 130 132 135 144 146 147
148 **P**6 **S** Community Hospital Corporation, Plano, TX
Primary Contact: David N. Parmer, Chief Executive Officer
COO: Guy Giesecke, Chief Operations Officer
CFO: Gary Troutman, CPA, Chief Financial Officer
CIO: Troy Napier, Chief Information Officer
CHR: Jennifer Barroeta, Chief Human Resources Officer
Web address: www.bhset.net
**Control:** Other not–for–profit (including NFP Corporation) **Service:** General
Medical and Surgical

**Staffed Beds:** 376 **Admissions:** 17113 **Census:** 215 **Outpatient Visits:**
136381 **Births:** 1627 **Total Expense ($000):** 192656 **Payroll Expense**
**($000):** 76035 **Personnel:** 1318

**BEAUMONT BONE AND JOINT INSTITUTE (670007)**, 3650 Laurel Street,
Zip 77707–2216; tel. 409/838–0346 **A**9 10 **F**3 40 79 81 131 141
Primary Contact: Duane N. Hill, Chief Executive Officer
Web address: www.orthodoc.aaos.org/bbji/
**Control:** Partnership, Investor–owned, for–profit **Service:** General Medical and
Surgical

**Staffed Beds:** 6 **Admissions:** 31 **Census:** 1 **Outpatient Visits:** 4976 **Births:**
0 **Total Expense ($000):** 6680 **Payroll Expense ($000):** 1851 **Personnel:**
47

⊠ **CHRISTUS HOSPITAL–ST. ELIZABETH (450034)**, 2830 Calder Avenue,
Zip 77702–1809, Mailing Address: P.O. Box 5405, Zip 77726–5405;
tel. 409/892–7171, (Includes CHRISTUS HOSPITAL–ST. MARY, 3600 Gates
Boulevard, Port Arthur, Zip 77642–3601, Mailing Address: P.O. Box 3696,
Zip 77643–3696; tel. 409/985–7431; Wayne Moore, Administrator) **A**1 2 9 10
**F**3 11 13 15 17 18 20 22 24 26 28 29 30 31 34 35 36 38 40 43 44 49 50
51 53 54 57 59 60 64 70 72 74 75 76 77 78 79 81 82 83 85 86 87 88 89
93 94 107 108 111 114 118 119 124 129 130 132 144 146 147 148 **P**4 8
**S** CHRISTUS Health, Irving, TX
Primary Contact: Paul Trevino, Administrator
CFO: Shawn Adams, Assistant Administrator Finance
CMO: Rick Tyler, M.D., Vice President Medical Affairs
CIO: Robert Jacobs, Regional Director Information Management
CHR: Charles Foster, Regional Director Human Resources
Web address: www.christushospital.org
**Control:** Church–operated, Nongovernment, not–for profit **Service:** General
Medical and Surgical

**Staffed Beds:** 448 **Admissions:** 20537 **Census:** 264 **Outpatient Visits:**
345945 **Births:** 1897 **Total Expense ($000):** 344961 **Payroll Expense**
**($000):** 109937 **Personnel:** 1715

⊠ **DUBUIS HOSPITAL OF BEAUMONT (452042)**, 2830 Calder Avenue, 4th Floor,
Zip 77702–1809; tel. 409/899–8154 **A**1 9 10 **F**1 3 18 29 30 31 35 130 148
**P**5 **S** Dubuis Health System, Houston, TX
Primary Contact: Jeffrey Livingston, Administrator
Web address: www.dubuis.org/BeaumontandPortArthurSystem–
CHRISTUSDubuisHospitalofBeaumont
**Control:** Church–operated, Nongovernment, not–for profit **Service:** Long–Term
Acute Care hospital

**Staffed Beds:** 51 **Admissions:** 584 **Census:** 43 **Outpatient Visits:** 0 **Births:**
0 **Total Expense ($000):** 17337 **Payroll Expense ($000):** 6706 **Personnel:**
108

**HARBOR HOSPITAL OF SOUTHEAST TEXAS (452093)**, 860 South 8th Street,
Zip 77701–4626; tel. 409/840–3200 **A**9 10 **F**1 3 29 30 35 45 85 130 148
Primary Contact: Thomas P. Harlan, Chief Executive Officer
Web address: www.communityhospitalcorp.com
**Control:** Partnership, Investor–owned, for–profit **Service:** Long–Term Acute Care
hospital

**Staffed Beds:** 30 **Admissions:** 350 **Census:** 24 **Outpatient Visits:** 0 **Births:**
0 **Total Expense ($000):** 11420 **Payroll Expense ($000):** 5371 **Personnel:**
121

⊠ **HEALTHSOUTH REHABILITATION HOSPITAL OF BEAUMONT (453048)**,
3340 Plaza 10 Boulevard, Zip 77707–2551; tel. 409/835–0835 **A**1 9 10 **F**3 28
29 30 62 64 74 75 77 79 87 90 91 93 95 96 130 131 132 148
**S** HEALTHSOUTH Corporation, Birmingham, AL
Primary Contact: H. J. Gaspard, Chief Executive Officer
CFO: David Pipkins, Controller
CMO: Linda C. Smith, M.D., Medical Director
CHR: Joanna Donica, Director Human Resource
CNO: Sandy Irvin, Chief Nursing Officer
Web address: www.healthsouthbeaumont.com
**Control:** Corporation, Investor–owned, for–profit **Service:** Rehabilitation

**Staffed Beds:** 61 **Admissions:** 651 **Census:** 23 **Outpatient Visits:** 6964
**Births:** 0 **Total Expense ($000):** 10567 **Payroll Expense ($000):** 5470
**Personnel:** 109

**MEMORIAL HERMANN BAPTIST FANNIN BEHAVIORAL HEALTH CENTER**
See Baptist Hospitals of Southeast Texas Fannin Behavioral Health Center

**TX**

---

**Hospital, Medicare Provider Number, Address, Telephone, Approval, Facility, and Physician Codes, Health Care System**

★ American Hospital Association (AHA) membership
□ The Joint Commission accreditation
◇ DNV Healthcare Inc. accreditation
○ Healthcare Facilities Accreditation Program
△ Commission on Accreditation of Rehabilitation Facilities (CARF) accreditation

**BEDFORD—Tarrant County**

☐ **RELIANT REHABILITATION HOSPITAL MID–CITIES (673044)**, 2304 State Highway 121, Zip 76021–5985; tel. 817/684–2000 **A**1 9 10 **F**3 29 90 93 96 148
Primary Contact: Robert M. Smart, Chief Executive Officer
CFO: Mary Mwaniki, Chief Financial Officer
CMO: Toni Willis, M.D., Medical Director
CHR: Christie Moore, Director Human Resources
Web address: www.relianthcp.com
**Control:** Partnership, Investor–owned, for–profit **Service:** Rehabilitation

Staffed Beds: 60 Admissions: 1177 Census: 35 Outpatient Visits: 2922 Births: 0 Total Expense ($000): 14591 Payroll Expense ($000): 6691 Personnel: 134

☒ **TEXAS HEALTH HARRIS METHODIST HOSPITAL HURST–EULESS–BEDFORD (450639)**, 1600 Hospital Parkway, Zip 76022–6913, Mailing Address: P.O. Box 669, Zip 76095–0669; tel. 817/685–4000, (Includes HARRIS METHODIST–SPRINGWOOD, 1608 Hospital Parkway, Zip 76022; tel. 817/355–7700) **A**1 2 9 10 **F**5 9 11 12 13 15 18 20 22 24 26 28 29 30 31 34 35 40 43 47 49 50 53 60 64 70 72 74 75 76 78 79 80 81 82 86 87 93 99 100 101 102 103 104 105 106 107 108 111 114 118 119 126 130 131 132 134 135 146 147 148 **S** Texas Health Resources, Arlington, TX
Primary Contact: Deborah Paganelli, President
COO: Alice Landers, Administrative Director Operations
CFO: Shelly Miland, Vice President Finance and Chief Financial Officer
CMO: Bob Nowland, M.D., Chief of Staff
CHR: Dale Smith, Director Human Resources
Web address: www.texashealth.org
**Control:** Other not–for–profit (including NFP Corporation) **Service:** General Medical and Surgical

Staffed Beds: 213 Admissions: 15417 Census: 191 Outpatient Visits: 88899 Births: 1980 Total Expense ($000): 226767 Payroll Expense ($000): 94552 Personnel: 1370

**BEEVILLE—Bee County**

☒ **CHRISTUS SPOHN HOSPITAL BEEVILLE (450082)**, 1500 East Houston Street, Zip 78102–5312; tel. 361/354–2000 **A**1 9 10 20 **F**3 11 13 15 29 30 32 34 35 40 43 45 50 57 59 60 64 70 72 74 75 76 77 79 81 83 87 93 97 107 108 111 119 130 132 146 147 148 **P**8 **S** CHRISTUS Health, Irving, TX
Primary Contact: Raymond Ramos, Vice President and Chief Executive Officer
Web address: www.christusspohn.org
**Control:** Church–operated, Nongovernment, not–for profit **Service:** General Medical and Surgical

Staffed Beds: 49 Admissions: 1985 Census: 18 Outpatient Visits: 42910 Births: 385 Total Expense ($000): 30991 Payroll Expense ($000): 12032 Personnel: 158

**BELLAIRE—Harris County**

◇ **FIRST STREET HOSPITAL (670029)**, 4801 Bissonnet, Zip 77401–4028; tel. 713/275–1111 **A**9 10 21 **F**3 12 29 37 40 42 45 64 68 79 81 85 87 107 111 114 119 126 130
Primary Contact: Sharon McDonough, Chief Executive Officer
Web address: www.firststreethospital.com
**Control:** Corporation, Investor–owned, for–profit **Service:** General Medical and Surgical

Staffed Beds: 19 Admissions: 518 Census: 2 Outpatient Visits: 10452 Births: 0 Total Expense ($000): 33446 Payroll Expense ($000): 6179 Personnel: 138

☐ **HOUSTON ORTHOPEDIC AND SPINE HOSPITAL (670012)**, 5410 West Loop South, Zip 77401–2103; tel. 713/314–4500 **A**1 9 10 **F**1 3 4 8 16 17 29 37 40 64 67 70 72 73 74 79 80 81 82 85 88 89 90 91 93 98 107 111 114 119 128 130 131 **S** Foundation Surgical Hospital Affiliates, Oklahoma City, OK
Primary Contact: Andrew Knizley, Chief Executive Officer
CMO: L. V. Ansell, M.D., Medical Director
Web address: www.foundationsurgicalhospital.com
**Control:** Partnership, Investor–owned, for–profit **Service:** Surgical

Staffed Beds: 64 Admissions: 2205 Census: 17 Outpatient Visits: 11178 Births: 0 Total Expense ($000): 65044 Payroll Expense ($000): 16018 Personnel: 242

**BELLVILLE—Austin County**

☒ **BELLVILLE ST. JOSEPH HEALTH CENTER (450253)**, (Formerly Bellville General Hospital), 44 North Cummings Street, Zip 77418–1347; tel. 979/413–7400 **A**1 9 10 **F**3 11 15 29 40 43 45 50 57 59 64 65 68 75 81 107 111 114 119 127 130 133 146
Primary Contact: Michael E. Zilm, Interim Chief Executive Officer and Administrator
CMO: Christophe Gay, M.D., Chief of Staff
CHR: Jacqueline McEuen, Coordinator Human Resources
Web address: www.bellvillehospital.com
**Control:** Other not–for–profit (including NFP Corporation) **Service:** General Medical and Surgical

Staffed Beds: 23 Admissions: 434 Census: 4 Outpatient Visits: 64955 Births: 0 Total Expense ($000): 10389 Payroll Expense ($000): 3935 Personnel: 85

**BELTON—Bell County**

☐ **CEDAR CREST HOSPITAL AND RESIDENTIAL TREATMENT CENTER (454114)**, (Formerly Cedar Crest Hospital), 3500 I–35 South, Zip 76513; tel. 254/939–2100 **A**1 9 10 **F**29 34 35 59 68 86 87 98 99 100 101 103 104 105 106 130 143 **P**4 **S** Acadia Healthcare Company, Inc., Franklin, TN
Primary Contact: Ingrid Whittle, Chief Executive Officer
CFO: Barry Combs, Chief Financial Officer
CMO: Karen Brooks, M.D., Medical Director
CIO: Melanie Orsag, Director Health Information Services
CHR: Jackie Burk, Director Human Resources
Web address: www.cedarcresthospital.com
**Control:** Corporation, Investor–owned, for–profit **Service:** Psychiatric

Staffed Beds: 70 Admissions: 1716 Census: 38 Outpatient Visits: 2326 Births: 0 Total Expense ($000): 7694 Payroll Expense ($000): 3886 Personnel: 124

**BIG LAKE—Reagan County**

★ **REAGAN MEMORIAL HOSPITAL (451301)**, 805 North Main Street, Zip 76932–3999; tel. 325/884–2561 **A**9 10 18 **F**3 40 43 53 57 89 93 107 114 128 130 133 **P**5
Primary Contact: John R. Perushek, Chief Executive Officer
CMO: Joseph Sudolcan, M.D., Medical Director
**Control:** Hospital district or authority, Government, nonfederal **Service:** General Medical and Surgical

Staffed Beds: 7 Admissions: 22 Census: 1 Outpatient Visits: 3917 Births: 0 Total Expense ($000): 7576 Payroll Expense ($000): 3087 Personnel: 40

**BIG SPRING—Howard County**

☐ **BIG SPRING STATE HOSPITAL (454000)**, 1901 North Highway 87, Zip 79720–0283; tel. 432/267–8216 **A**1 3 5 10 **F**30 56 59 68 75 77 86 87 98 101 103 106 130 132 135 146 **P**6 **S** Texas Department of State Health Services, Austin, TX
Primary Contact: Edward Moughon, Superintendent
CFO: Adrienne Bides, Assistant Chief Financial Officer and Budget Analyst
CMO: Ba Han, M.D., Clinical Director
CIO: Elizabeth Correa, Director Information Management
CHR: Lorie Couch, Assistant Superintendent
CNO: Stormy Ward, Chief Nurse Executive
Web address: www.dshs.state.tx.us/mhhospitals/BigSpringSH/default.shtm
**Control:** State–Government, nonfederal **Service:** Psychiatric

Staffed Beds: 200 Admissions: 761 Census: 190 Outpatient Visits: 0 Births: 0 Total Expense ($000): 39113 Payroll Expense ($000): 20943 Personnel: 557

☒ **SCENIC MOUNTAIN MEDICAL CENTER (450653)**, 1601 West 11th Place, Zip 79720–4198; tel. 432/263–1211 **A**1 9 10 20 **F**3 11 13 15 20 29 30 34 39 40 43 45 51 57 59 64 65 68 69 70 75 76 77 79 81 85 87 89 93 94 107 110 111 114 119 129 130 133 146 147 148 **P**6 **S** Community Health Systems, Inc., Franklin, TN
Primary Contact: Larry Rodgers, Chief Executive Officer
CFO: John Irby, Chief Financial Officer
CMO: Steve Saeed Ahmed, M.D., Chief of Staff
CIO: Gene Mills, Director Information Technology
CHR: Dwight Linton, Director Human Resources
CNO: Judy Roever, MSN, Chief Nursing Officer
Web address: www.smmccares.com
**Control:** Corporation, Investor–owned, for–profit **Service:** General Medical and Surgical

Staffed Beds: 75 Admissions: 2853 Census: 26 Outpatient Visits: 28544 Births: 246 Total Expense ($000): 38500 Payroll Expense ($000): 14090 Personnel: 246

☒ **WEST TEXAS VETERANS AFFAIRS HEALTH CARE SYSTEM**, 300 Veterans Boulevard, Zip 79720–5500; Mailing Address: Big Springs, tel. 432/263–7361, (Nonreporting) **A**1 3 5 9 **S** Department of Veterans Affairs, Washington, DC
Primary Contact: Daniel L. Marsh, Director
CFO: Ray Olivas, Chief Fiscal Service
CMO: Martin Schnier, D.O., Chief of Staff
CIO: Mike McKinley, Information Security Officer
CHR: Anna Osborne, Chief Human Resources Management Service
Web address: www.bigspring.va.gov/about/
**Control:** Veterans Affairs, Government, federal **Service:** General Medical and Surgical

Staffed Beds: 149

*Many Facility Codes have changed. Please refer to the AHA Guide Code Chart.*

TX

## BONHAM—Fannin County

☐ ◇ **RED RIVER REGIONAL HOSPITAL (451370)**, 504 Lipscomb Boulevard, Zip 75418–4096, Mailing Address: P.O. Box C., Zip 75418–0180; tel. 903/583–8585 **A**1 9 10 18 21 **F**3 11 15 28 29 30 34 35 40 46 50 57 59 64 65 70 75 81 87 93 107 108 110 111 118 119 130 133 135 146
Primary Contact: David Conejo, Chief Executive Officer
CFO: Jay Hodges, Chief Financial Officer
CMO: Michael Brown, D.O., Chief of Staff
CIO: Jack Farguson, Director Information Technology
CHR: Brenda Bagley, Director Human Resources
CNO: William Kiefer, Chief Nursing Officer
Web address: www.redriverregional.com/
**Control:** Partnership, Investor–owned, for–profit **Service:** General Medical and Surgical

**Staffed Beds:** 25 **Admissions:** 881 **Census:** 10 **Outpatient Visits:** 12136 **Births:** 0 **Total Expense ($000):** 13322 **Payroll Expense ($000):** 5600 **Personnel:** 119

**SAM RAYBURN MEMORIAL VETERANS CENTER** See Veterans Affairs North Texas Health Care System, Dallas

## BORGER—Hutchinson County

**GOLDEN PLAINS COMMUNITY HOSPITAL (451369)**, 100 Medical Drive, Zip 79007–7579; tel. 806/273–1100 **A**9 10 18 **F**11 13 15 29 30 34 35 40 43 45 50 54 57 59 62 64 65 66 68 70 75 76 77 79 81 85 86 87 93 107 108 115 119 127 130 131 132 133 146 147 148 **P**6
Primary Contact: Charlie Slaton, Interim Chief Executive Officer
COO: Melody Henderson, R.N., Chief Operating Officer and Chief Nursing Officer
CFO: Dennis P. Kilday, Chief Financial Officer
CMO: Bard Rogers, M.D., Chief of Staff
CHR: Sally Mason, Director Human Resources
Web address: www.goldenplains.org
**Control:** Corporation, Investor–owned, for–profit **Service:** General Medical and Surgical

**Staffed Beds:** 25 **Admissions:** 815 **Census:** 7 **Outpatient Visits:** 49927 **Births:** 202 **Total Expense ($000):** 23867 **Payroll Expense ($000):** 7528 **Personnel:** 172

## BOWIE—Montague County

★ **BOWIE MEMORIAL HOSPITAL (450497)**, 705 East Greenwood Avenue, Zip 76230–3199; tel. 940/872–1126 **A**9 10 **F**3 10 11 15 28 29 40 43 45 53 57 62 63 64 70 75 81 82 84 93 103 107 115 119 129 130 131 132 133 148 **P**4
Primary Contact: C. Lynn Heller, Interim Chief Executive Officer
CFO: Terri Wallace, Controller
CMO: Doug Hodde, M.D., Chief of Staff
CIO: Randell Cox, Director Data Processing
CHR: Mary Bates, Director Human Resources
CNO: Pam Alexander, R.N., Chief Nursing Officer
Web address: www.bowiememorial.com
**Control:** Hospital district or authority, Government, nonfederal **Service:** General Medical and Surgical

**Staffed Beds:** 44 **Admissions:** 685 **Census:** 12 **Outpatient Visits:** 31049 **Births:** 0 **Total Expense ($000):** 10666 **Payroll Expense ($000):** 5708 **Personnel:** 183

## BRADY—Mcculloch County

**HEART OF TEXAS MEMORIAL HOSPITAL (451348)**, 2008 Nine Road, Zip 76825–7210, Mailing Address: P.O. Box 1150, Zip 76825–1150; tel. 325/597–2901 **A**9 10 18 **F**11 15 28 40 43 45 64 81 93 107 111 114 119 127 133 **P**4
Primary Contact: Tim Jones, Chief Executive Officer
CFO: Brad Burnett, Chief Financial Officer
CMO: Pete Castro, D.O., Chief of Staff
**Control:** Other not–for–profit (including NFP Corporation) **Service:** General Medical and Surgical

**Staffed Beds:** 25 **Admissions:** 383 **Census:** 4 **Outpatient Visits:** 29595 **Births:** 0 **Total Expense ($000):** 9916 **Payroll Expense ($000):** 3386 **Personnel:** 80

## BRECKENRIDGE—Stephens County

**STEPHENS MEMORIAL HOSPITAL (450498)**, 200 South Geneva Street, Zip 76424–4799; tel. 254/559–2242 **A**9 10 20 **F**3 7 8 11 15 28 30 34 35 40 43 45 50 53 56 57 59 63 64 68 69 81 85 87 89 93 97 103 107 114 130 133 146
Primary Contact: Ernest R. Parisi, Interim Chief Executive Officer and Administrator
CMO: Dwight J. Nichols, M.D., Chief of Staff
CIO: Bobby Thompson, Director Information Technology
CHR: Michelle Funderburg, Director Human Resources
Web address: www.smhtx.com
**Control:** County–Government, nonfederal **Service:** General Medical and Surgical

**Staffed Beds:** 21 **Admissions:** 485 **Census:** 5 **Outpatient Visits:** 18140 **Births:** 0 **Total Expense ($000):** 12893 **Payroll Expense ($000):** 4725 **Personnel:** 110

## BRENHAM—Washington County

⊠ **SCOTT & WHITE HOSPITAL – BRENHAM (450187)**, 700 Medical Parkway, Zip 77833–5498; tel. 979/836–6173 **A**1 9 10 **F**3 11 13 29 30 32 34 35 40 43 44 50 51 53 56 57 59 64 65 70 75 76 77 78 79 80 81 85 86 87 93 107 108 110 114 119 127 129 130 132 133 135 146 **P**6 **S** Scott & White Healthcare, Temple, TX
Primary Contact: Michael Pittman, Chief Executive Officer
CFO: Jane Wellmann, Chief Financial Officer
CMO: Donald Draehn, M.D., Chief of Staff
CIO: Sharon Schwartz, Director Medical Records
CHR: Bob Schubert, Director Human Resources
Web address: www.swbrenham.org
**Control:** Other not–for–profit (including NFP Corporation) **Service:** General Medical and Surgical

**Staffed Beds:** 60 **Admissions:** 1674 **Census:** 16 **Outpatient Visits:** 35817 **Births:** 282 **Total Expense ($000):** 28952 **Payroll Expense ($000):** 12854 **Personnel:** 268

## BRIDGEPORT—Wise County

◇ **NORTH TEXAS COMMUNITY HOSPITAL (670052)**, 1905 Doctors Hospital Drive, Zip 76426–2260; tel. 940/683–0300 **A**9 10 21 **F**3 11 13 18 19 29 30 34 40 45 51 57 59 64 68 70 75 76 79 81 85 93 107 108 111 115 118 119 121 129 130 135 146 147
Primary Contact: Max L. Ludeke, FACHE, Chief Executive Officer
Web address: www.ntchospital.org
**Control:** Other not–for–profit (including NFP Corporation) **Service:** General Medical and Surgical

**Staffed Beds:** 21 **Admissions:** 906 **Census:** 8 **Outpatient Visits:** 19442 **Births:** 229 **Total Expense ($000):** 26377 **Payroll Expense ($000):** 7891 **Personnel:** 175

## BROWNFIELD—Terry County

★ **BROWNFIELD REGIONAL MEDICAL CENTER (450399)**, 705 East Felt Street, Zip 79316–3439; tel. 806/637–3551 **A**9 10 20 **F**3 7 13 28 29 30 34 40 43 45 50 53 57 59 62 64 65 68 75 76 80 81 85 86 87 89 90 93 97 102 107 119 127 130 135 148 **P**4
Primary Contact: Mike Click, Administrator
CFO: Josh Savage, Chief Financial Officer
CIO: Sheryl Holcombe, Administrative Assistant
CHR: Avis DePoyster, Director Human Resources
CNO: Melissa Richolson, R.N., Director of Nursing
Web address: www.brownfield–rmc.org
**Control:** Hospital district or authority, Government, nonfederal **Service:** General Medical and Surgical

**Staffed Beds:** 26 **Admissions:** 706 **Census:** 6 **Outpatient Visits:** 54296 **Births:** 113 **Total Expense ($000):** 14854 **Payroll Expense ($000):** 6314 **Personnel:** 194

## BROWNSVILLE—Cameron County

☐ **BROWNSVILLE DOCTORS HOSPITAL (450841)**, 4750 North Expressway, Zip 78526–4120; tel. 956/554–2000, (Nonreporting) **A**1 10
Primary Contact: Natalie Shafer, Chief Executive Officer
CFO: Rusty Young, Chief Financial Officer
CMO: Manuel G. Guajardo, M.D., Medical Director
CIO: Rusty Young, Chief Financial Officer
CHR: Eddie Melendez, Director Human Resources
**Control:** Corporation, Investor–owned, for–profit **Service:** General Medical and Surgical

**Staffed Beds:** 56

**TX**

**Hospital, Medicare Provider Number, Address, Telephone, Approval, Facility, and Physician Codes, Health Care System**

★ American Hospital Association (AHA) membership
☐ The Joint Commission accreditation   ◇ DNV Healthcare Inc. accreditation
○ Healthcare Facilities Accreditation Program
△ Commission on Accreditation of Rehabilitation Facilities (CARF) accreditation

☐ **SOUTH TEXAS REHABILITATION HOSPITAL (453092)**, 425 East Alton Gloor Boulevard, Zip 78526–3361; tel. 956/554–6000 **A**1 9 10 **F**3 28 29 34 35 59 64 75 77 86 87 90 93 94 96 130 132 148 **P**6 **S** Ernest Health, Inc., Albuquerque, NM
Primary Contact: Jessie Eason Smedley, Chief Executive Officer
COO: Mary Valdez, Chief Operating Officer
CFO: Sue Thomsen, Chief Financial Officer
CMO: Christopher Wilson, M.D., Inpatient Medical Director
CIO: Deborah Alcocer, Chief Information Officer
CHR: Tony Rodriguez, Director Human Resources
CNO: Cheryl Sexton, Director Nursing Operations
Web address: www.strh.ernesthealth.com
**Control:** Partnership, Investor–owned, for–profit **Service:** Rehabilitation

> **Staffed Beds:** 40 **Admissions:** 843 **Census:** 33 **Outpatient Visits:** 4937 **Births:** 0 **Total Expense ($000):** 14169 **Payroll Expense ($000):** 6458 **Personnel:** 117

⊠ **VALLEY BAPTIST MEDICAL CENTER–BROWNSVILLE (450028)**, 1040 West Jefferson Street, Zip 78520–6338, Mailing Address: P.O. Box 3590, Zip 78523–3590; tel. 956/698–5400, (Total facility includes 11 beds in nursing home–type unit) (Data for 304 days) **A**1 9 10 **F**3 11 12 13 15 18 20 22 24 26 28 29 30 34 35 39 40 43 44 45 49 50 54 56 57 59 60 63 64 65 70 72 73 74 75 76 77 79 81 82 85 86 87 89 93 98 100 101 102 103 104 105 106 107 109 110 111 112 114 115 119 128 129 130 132 146 147 148 **P**8 **S** Vanguard Health Systems, Nashville, TN
Primary Contact: Leslie Bingham, Senior Vice President and Chief Executive Officer
COO: Matthew M. Stone, Chief Operating Officer
CFO: Harvey Torres, Chief Financial Officer
CMO: Jose L. Ayala, M.D., Chief Medical Officer
CIO: Carlos Morales, Manager Data Processing
CHR: Irma L. Pye, Chief Human Resource Officer
CNO: Aniceta Mendoza, R.N., Chief Nursing Officer
Web address: www.valleybaptist.net/brownsville/index.htm
**Control:** Corporation, Investor–owned, for–profit **Service:** General Medical and Surgical

> **Staffed Beds:** 240 **Admissions:** 7971 **Census:** 133 **Outpatient Visits:** 47665 **Births:** 1328 **Total Expense ($000):** 117567 **Payroll Expense ($000):** 35278 **Personnel:** 502

⊠ **VALLEY REGIONAL MEDICAL CENTER (450662)**, 100A Alton Gloor Boulevard, Zip 78526–3354, Mailing Address: P.O. Box 3710, Zip 78523–3710; tel. 956/350–7101 **A**1 9 10 **F**3 11 13 15 18 20 22 24 26 29 30 31 32 34 35 39 40 43 44 45 47 49 50 53 57 59 60 61 64 65 68 70 72 73 74 75 76 77 78 79 81 82 84 85 86 87 89 93 107 108 110 111 115 118 119 124 130 132 135 143 146 147 148 **P**7 **S** HCA, Nashville, TN
Primary Contact: Susan Andrews, Chief Executive Officer
COO: Steven C. Hoelscher, Chief Operating Officer
CFO: Marcia Patterson, Chief Financial Officer
CHR: Margie Salazar, Director Human Resources
CNO: Holley Tyler, R.N., Chief Nursing Officer
Web address: www.valleyregionalmedicalcenter.com
**Control:** Partnership, Investor–owned, for–profit **Service:** General Medical and Surgical

> **Staffed Beds:** 214 **Admissions:** 9868 **Census:** 117 **Outpatient Visits:** 66234 **Births:** 2492 **Total Expense ($000):** 129935 **Payroll Expense ($000):** 44119 **Personnel:** 683

**BROWNWOOD—Brown County**

⊠ **BROWNWOOD REGIONAL MEDICAL CENTER (450587)**, 1501 Burnet Drive, Zip 76801–8520, Mailing Address: P.O. Box 760, Zip 76804–0760; tel. 325/646–8541, (Total facility includes 20 beds in nursing home–type unit) **A**1 9 10 20 **F**3 11 13 15 18 20 26 28 29 30 31 35 39 40 45 48 49 50 51 53 54 56 57 59 64 68 70 74 75 76 77 78 79 81 82 85 86 87 93 97 107 108 111 114 119 121 123 128 129 130 132 146 147 148 **P**3 8 **S** Community Health Systems, Inc., Franklin, TN
Primary Contact: Claude E. Camp, III, Chief Executive Officer
CFO: John D. Montois, Chief Financial Officer
CMO: Dan Locker, M.D., Chief of Staff
CIO: Jay Smith, Director Information Systems
CHR: Mikeana Bailey, Director Human Resources
CNO: Michael Cadoret, R.N., Chief Nursing Officer
Web address: www.brmc–cares.com
**Control:** Partnership, Investor–owned, for–profit **Service:** General Medical and Surgical

> **Staffed Beds:** 168 **Admissions:** 5365 **Census:** 64 **Outpatient Visits:** 67480 **Births:** 674 **Total Expense ($000):** 75966 **Payroll Expense ($000):** 24076 **Personnel:** 501

**BRYAN—Brazos County**

⊠ **CHRISTUS DUBUIS HOSPITAL OF BRYAN (452113)**, 1600 Joseph Drive, 2nd Floor, Zip 77802–1502; tel. 979/821–5000 **A**1 9 10 **F**1 3 29 30 34 75 80 82 85 86 87 91 130 148 **P**8 **S** Dubuis Health System, Houston, TX
Primary Contact: Judy Wolfe, Chief Executive Officer
Web address: www.dubuis.org/CHRISTUSDubuisHospitalofBryan
**Control:** Church–operated, Nongovernment, not–for profit **Service:** Long–Term Acute Care hospital

> **Staffed Beds:** 30 **Admissions:** 208 **Census:** 14 **Outpatient Visits:** 0 **Births:** 0 **Total Expense ($000):** 6718 **Payroll Expense ($000):** 2546 **Personnel:** 47

⊠ **ST. JOSEPH REGIONAL HEALTH CENTER (450011)**, 2801 Franciscan Drive, Zip 77802–2599; tel. 979/776–3777 **A**1 2 3 5 9 10 **F**3 7 11 12 13 15 17 18 20 22 24 28 29 30 31 32 34 35 37 40 42 43 44 45 46 48 49 50 53 54 57 59 64 65 68 70 74 75 76 77 78 79 80 81 84 85 86 87 89 90 93 96 107 110 111 114 118 119 121 123 124 126 127 129 130 131 132 135 143 144 146 148 **S** Sylvania Franciscan Health, Toledo, OH
Primary Contact: Kathleen R. Krusie, FACHE, Chief Executive Officer
CFO: Lisa McNair, CPA, Senior Vice President and Chief Financial Officer
CMO: Mark Montgomery, M.D., Vice President Quality and Medical Affairs
CIO: John Phillips, Vice President Information Services
CHR: Michael G. Costa, Vice President Human Resources
Web address: www.st–joseph.org
**Control:** Church–operated, Nongovernment, not–for profit **Service:** General Medical and Surgical

> **Staffed Beds:** 232 **Admissions:** 16524 **Census:** 181 **Outpatient Visits:** 332150 **Births:** 1731 **Total Expense ($000):** 253728 **Payroll Expense ($000):** 90789 **Personnel:** 1630

☐ **THE PHYSICIANS CENTRE HOSPITAL (450834)**, 3131 University Drive East, Zip 77802–3473; tel. 979/731–3100 **A**1 9 10 **F**3 12 15 29 34 35 40 44 45 50 51 59 64 68 74 75 79 81 82 85 86 87 89 107 111 114 119 130 131 132 135
Primary Contact: Kori Rich, Chief Executive Officer
CIO: Shawn Clark, Director Information Systems
CHR: LeeAnn Ford, Director Human Resources and Imaging
Web address: www.thephysicianscentre.com
**Control:** Corporation, Investor–owned, for–profit **Service:** General Medical and Surgical

> **Staffed Beds:** 16 **Admissions:** 362 **Census:** 2 **Outpatient Visits:** 9540 **Births:** 0 **Total Expense ($000):** 14477 **Payroll Expense ($000):** 4063 **Personnel:** 111

**BURNET—Burnet County**

⊠ **SETON HIGHLAND LAKES (451365)**, 3201 South Water Street, Zip 78611–4510, Mailing Address: P.O. Box 1219, Zip 78611–7219; tel. 512/715–3000 **A**1 9 10 18 **F**3 11 15 18 28 29 30 34 35 40 43 44 50 57 59 62 63 64 65 66 68 70 71 74 75 77 78 79 81 82 84 85 86 87 91 92 93 97 107 110 111 115 119 127 130 132 133 135 146 148 **P**3 8 **S** Ascension Health, Saint Louis, MO
Primary Contact: Michelle Robertson, R.N., President and Chief Executive Officer
CFO: Douglas D. Waite, Senior Vice President and Chief Financial Officer
CIO: Gerry Lewis, Chief Information Officer
Web address: www.seton.net
**Control:** Church–operated, Nongovernment, not–for profit **Service:** General Medical and Surgical

> **Staffed Beds:** 25 **Admissions:** 1434 **Census:** 12 **Outpatient Visits:** 104455 **Births:** 0 **Total Expense ($000):** 41323 **Payroll Expense ($000):** 20659 **Personnel:** 361

**CALDWELL—Burleson County**

⊠ **BURLESON ST. JOSEPH HEALTH CENTER (451305)**, 1101 Woodson Drive, Zip 77836–1052, Mailing Address: P.O. Box 360, Zip 77836–0360; tel. 979/567–3245 **A**1 9 10 18 **F**3 7 11 14 29 30 34 35 40 43 57 59 64 68 84 93 107 114 130 133 143 **P**6 **S** Sylvania Franciscan Health, Toledo, OH
Primary Contact: John Hughson, Administrator
CFO: Lisa McNair, CPA, Senior Vice President and Chief Financial Officer
CMO: Kristel Leubner, D.O., Chief of Staff
CHR: Michael G. Costa, Vice President Human Resources
Web address: www.st–joseph.org/
**Control:** Church–operated, Nongovernment, not–for profit **Service:** General Medical and Surgical

> **Staffed Beds:** 25 **Admissions:** 263 **Census:** 4 **Outpatient Visits:** 17230 **Births:** 0 **Total Expense ($000):** 8726 **Payroll Expense ($000):** 4061 **Personnel:** 72

**TX**

*Many Facility Codes have changed. Please refer to the AHA Guide Code Chart.*

## CAMERON—Milam County

**CENTRAL TEXAS HOSPITAL (450770)**, 806 North Crockett Avenue, Zip 76520–2553, Mailing Address: P.O. Box 947, Zip 76520–0947; tel. 254/697–6591, (Nonreporting) **A**9 10
Primary Contact: Tariq Mahmood, Chief Executive Officer
CFO: Joe White, Chief Financial Officer
Web address: www.centexhospital.com
**Control:** Corporation, Investor–owned, for–profit **Service:** General Medical and Surgical

**Staffed Beds:** 34

## CANADIAN—Hemphill County

**HEMPHILL COUNTY HOSPITAL (450578)**, 1020 South Fourth Street, Zip 79014–3315; tel. 806/323–6422 **A**9 10 20 **F**2 7 29 35 40 45 56 57 62 63 64 68 69 87 89 93 97 102 107 108 130 133 146 148
Primary Contact: Christy Francis, Administrator
Web address: www.hchdst.org
**Control:** Hospital district or authority, Government, nonfederal **Service:** General Medical and Surgical

**Staffed Beds:** 19 **Admissions:** 205 **Census:** 3 **Outpatient Visits:** 13250 **Births:** 0 **Total Expense ($000):** 7871 **Payroll Expense ($000):** 3519 **Personnel:** 75

## CARRIZO SPRINGS—Dimmit County

**DIMMIT REGIONAL HOSPITAL (450620)**, (Formerly Dimmit County Memorial Hospital), 704 Hospital Drive, Zip 78834–3836, Mailing Address: P.O. Box 1016, Zip 78834–7016; tel. 830/876–2424 **A**9 10 20 **F**11 13 40 43 45 57 62 64 70 76 81 87 89 93 107 115 119
Primary Contact: Ernest Flores, Jr., Chief Executive Officer and Administrator
CFO: Alma Melendez, Controller
Web address: www.dcmhospital.org
**Control:** Other not–for–profit (including NFP Corporation) **Service:** General Medical and Surgical

**Staffed Beds:** 35 **Admissions:** 1074 **Census:** 8 **Outpatient Visits:** 20410 **Births:** 253 **Total Expense ($000):** 16489 **Payroll Expense ($000):** 5104 **Personnel:** 156

## CARROLLTON—Denton County

⊞ **BAYLOR MEDICAL CENTER AT CARROLLTON (450730)**, 4343 North Josey Lane, Zip 75010–4691; tel. 972/492–1010 **A**1 9 10 **F**3 11 12 13 15 18 20 29 30 31 35 40 48 49 50 52 54 55 56 57 59 64 70 72 73 74 75 76 77 78 79 81 82 84 85 86 87 93 107 108 111 114 115 119 129 130 131 132 135 146 147 148
Primary Contact: Michael Sanborn, MS, FACHE, President
CFO: James McNatt, Chief Financial Officer
CIO: Paul Ratcliff, Director Information Services
CHR: Sheila K. Richards, Director Human Resources
CNO: Barbara Vaughn, Chief Nursing Officer
Web address: www.baylorhealth.com
**Control:** Corporation, Investor–owned, for–profit **Service:** General Medical and Surgical

**Staffed Beds:** 115 **Admissions:** 6139 **Census:** 67 **Outpatient Visits:** 65158 **Births:** 1429 **Total Expense ($000):** 110708 **Payroll Expense ($000):** 41068 **Personnel:** 583

☐ **CARROLLTON SPRINGS (454119)**, 2225 Parker Road, Zip 75010–4711; tel. 972/242–4114, (Data for 342 days) **A**1 9 10 **F**4 98 102 103 104 105
Primary Contact: William W. Brattvet, Chief Executive Officer
Web address: www.carrolltonsprings.com
**Control:** Corporation, Investor–owned, for–profit **Service:** Psychiatric

**Staffed Beds:** 45 **Admissions:** 668 **Census:** 14 **Outpatient Visits:** 2734 **Births:** 0 **Total Expense ($000):** 6865 **Payroll Expense ($000):** 3595 **Personnel:** 93

⊞ **SELECT SPECIALTY HOSPITAL–DALLAS (452022)**, 2329 West Parker Road, Zip 75010–4713; tel. 469/892–1400 **A**1 9 10 **F**1 3 29 40 56 74 75 77 85 91 107 114 130 148 **S** Select Medical Corporation, Mechanicsburg, PA
Primary Contact: Barbara Mobley, Chief Executive Officer
Web address: www.selectspecialtyhospitals.com/company/locations/dallas.aspx
**Control:** Corporation, Investor–owned, for–profit **Service:** Long–Term Acute Care hospital

**Staffed Beds:** 60 **Admissions:** 486 **Census:** 37 **Outpatient Visits:** 0 **Births:** 0 **Total Expense ($000):** 20633 **Payroll Expense ($000):** 8752 **Personnel:** 182

## CARTHAGE—Panola County

⊞ **EAST TEXAS MEDICAL CENTER CARTHAGE (450210)**, 409 Cottage Road, Zip 75633–1466, Mailing Address: P.O. Box 549, Zip 75633–0549; tel. 903/693–3841 **A**1 9 10 20 **F**3 8 11 15 28 29 30 34 35 40 43 45 50 57 59 64 65 75 81 85 107 108 110 111 115 119 127 129 145 146 **S** East Texas Medical Center Regional Healthcare System, Tyler, TX
Primary Contact: Gary Mikeal Hudson, Administrator
COO: Gary Mikeal Hudson, Administrator
CFO: Phillip A. Caron, Chief Financial Officer
CMO: Gerald Akpassa, M.D., Chief of Staff
CIO: Renee Lawhorn, Director Medical Records
CHR: Amber Cox, Director Human Resources
CNO: Judy Peterson, R.N., Chief Nursing Officer
Web address: www.etmc.org
**Control:** Other not–for–profit (including NFP Corporation) **Service:** General Medical and Surgical

**Staffed Beds:** 23 **Admissions:** 1015 **Census:** 7 **Outpatient Visits:** 75997 **Births:** 26 **Total Expense ($000):** 20375 **Payroll Expense ($000):** 7450 **Personnel:** 172

## CEDAR PARK—Williamson County

⊞ **CEDAR PARK REGIONAL MEDICAL CENTER (670043)**, 1401 Medical Parkway, Zip 78613–7763; tel. 512/528–7000 **A**1 5 9 10 **F**3 12 13 15 18 20 29 34 35 40 45 47 49 50 54 57 59 64 68 70 73 75 76 77 78 79 81 82 85 87 93 107 108 110 111 115 119 126 132 135 146 147 148 **P**6 **S** Community Health Systems, Inc., Franklin, TN
Primary Contact: Brad D. Holland, Chief Executive Officer
COO: Jeremy Barclay, Chief Operating Officer
CFO: Erich Wallschlaeger, Chief Financial Officer
CIO: Brad Hoar, Director Information and Technology
CHR: Amy D. Reeves, Director Human Resources
Web address: www.cedarparkregional.com
**Control:** Corporation, Investor–owned, for–profit **Service:** General Medical and Surgical

**Staffed Beds:** 85 **Admissions:** 3926 **Census:** 32 **Outpatient Visits:** 37981 **Births:** 865 **Total Expense ($000):** 67625 **Payroll Expense ($000):** 22381 **Personnel:** 370

## CHANNELVIEW—Harris County

⊞ **KINDRED HOSPITAL EAST HOUSTON (452075)**, 15101 East Freeway, Zip 77530–4104; tel. 832/200–5500, (Includes KINDRED HOSPITAL BAYTOWN, 1700 James Bowie Drive, 3rd Floor, Baytown, Zip 77520; tel. 281/420–7800; Angel Gradney, Chief Executive Officer) **A**1 9 10 **F**1 3 29 45 57 64 75 77 81 85 93 96 107 130 148 **S** Kindred Healthcare, Louisville, KY
Primary Contact: Angel Gradney, Chief Executive Officer
Web address: www.kheasthouston.com
**Control:** Corporation, Investor–owned, for–profit **Service:** Long–Term Acute Care hospital

**Staffed Beds:** 230 **Admissions:** 2153 **Census:** 150 **Outpatient Visits:** 4530 **Births:** 0 **Total Expense ($000):** 84351 **Payroll Expense ($000):** 29879 **Personnel:** 494

## CHILDRESS—Childress County

★ **CHILDRESS REGIONAL MEDICAL CENTER (450369)**, Highway 83 North, Zip 79201–5800, Mailing Address: P.O. Box 1030, Zip 79201–1030; tel. 940/937–6371 **A**9 10 20 **F**7 8 13 15 29 32 34 35 40 43 45 50 56 57 59 60 61 62 63 64 65 66 76 79 81 91 92 93 107 111 119 127 129 130 133
Primary Contact: John Henderson, Chief Executive Officer
COO: Holly Holcomb, R.N., Chief Operating Officer
CFO: Kathy McLain, Chief Financial Officer
CMO: Steve Carter, M.D., Chief of Staff
CIO: Holly Holcomb, R.N., Chie Operating Officer
CHR: Gayle Cannon, Director Human Resources
CNO: Sulynn Mester, R.N., Chief Nursing Officer
Web address: www.childresshospital.com
**Control:** Hospital district or authority, Government, nonfederal **Service:** General Medical and Surgical

**Staffed Beds:** 39 **Admissions:** 1170 **Census:** 9 **Outpatient Visits:** 89008 **Births:** 247 **Total Expense ($000):** 22615 **Payroll Expense ($000):** 9362 **Personnel:** 256

---

**Hospital, Medicare Provider Number, Address, Telephone, Approval, Facility, and Physician Codes, Health Care System**

★ American Hospital Association (AHA) membership
☐ The Joint Commission accreditation
◇ DNV Healthcare Inc. accreditation
○ Healthcare Facilities Accreditation Program
△ Commission on Accreditation of Rehabilitation Facilities (CARF) accreditation

TX

## CHILLICOTHE—Hardeman County

★ **CHILLICOTHE HOSPITAL DISTRICT (451326)**, 303 Avenue I, Zip 79225, Mailing Address: P.O. Box 370, Zip 79225–0370; tel. 940/852–5131 **A**9 10 18 **F**29 34 40 43 45 57 59 69 89 132 133 **P**5
Primary Contact: Linda Hall, Administrator and Chief Executive Officer
CFO: Linda Hall, Administrator and Chief Executive Officer
CMO: Weldon Glidden, M.D., Chief of Staff
CIO: Kathy Busby, Medical Record Technician
CHR: Linda Hall, Administrator and Chief Executive Officer
Web address: www.chillicothehospital.org
**Control:** Hospital district or authority, Government, nonfederal **Service:** General Medical and Surgical

**Staffed Beds:** 13 **Admissions:** 66 **Census:** 1 **Outpatient Visits:** 5351 **Births:** 0 **Total Expense ($000):** 2007 **Payroll Expense ($000):** 1217 **Personnel:** 24

## CLARKSVILLE—Red River County

★ **EAST TEXAS MEDICAL CENTER CLARKSVILLE (450188)**, 3000 West Main Street, Zip 75426–3371, Mailing Address: P.O. Box 1270, Zip 75426–1270; tel. 903/427–6400 **A**9 10 **F**11 17 26 29 34 39 40 43 44 45 54 56 57 59 64 68 75 81 85 86 87 107 108 115 118 119 127 129 130 135 145 146 **P**8 **S** East Texas Medical Center Regional Healthcare System, Tyler, TX
Primary Contact: Matthew Wylie, Administrator
CFO: James Hines, Chief Financial Officer
CMO: Ravi K. Sreerama, M.D., Chief of Staff
CIO: James Hines, Chief Financial Officer
CHR: Susan Hill, Director Human Resources
Web address: www.etmc.org
**Control:** Other not–for–profit (including NFP Corporation) **Service:** General Medical and Surgical

**Staffed Beds:** 36 **Admissions:** 1134 **Census:** 11 **Outpatient Visits:** 15207 **Births:** 0 **Total Expense ($000):** 11741 **Payroll Expense ($000):** 4503 **Personnel:** 96

## CLEBURNE—Johnson County

⊞ **TEXAS HEALTH HARRIS METHODIST HOSPITAL CLEBURNE (450148)**, 201 Walls Drive, Zip 76033–4007; tel. 817/641–2551 **A**1 9 10 **F**3 11 13 15 29 32 34 35 40 43 44 45 46 49 50 51 56 57 59 64 65 68 70 75 76 77 79 81 85 89 93 107 108 110 114 119 124 129 130 146 148 **P**6 **S** Texas Health Resources, Arlington, TX
Primary Contact: Blake Kretz, President
CFO: Vicki L. Galati, Director Finance
CHR: Shelly Allain, Director
CNO: Lorrie Normand, R.N., Chief Nursing Officer
Web address: www.texashealth.org
**Control:** Other not–for–profit (including NFP Corporation) **Service:** General Medical and Surgical

**Staffed Beds:** 85 **Admissions:** 3664 **Census:** 36 **Outpatient Visits:** 46816 **Births:** 498 **Total Expense ($000):** 58846 **Payroll Expense ($000):** 23526 **Personnel:** 284

## CLEVELAND—Liberty County

☐ **CLEVELAND REGIONAL MEDICAL CENTER (450296)**, 300 East Crockett Street, Zip 77327–4062, Mailing Address: P.O. Box 1688, Zip 77328–1688; tel. 281/593–1811 **A**1 9 10 **F**3 11 13 15 18 29 30 34 35 40 41 43 50 57 59 62 64 68 70 74 75 76 77 79 81 85 87 92 107 108 114 119 130 132 133 146 **P**6
Primary Contact: Charles Fulner, Chief Executive Officer
Web address: www.clevelandregionalmedicalcenter.com
**Control:** Partnership, Investor–owned, for–profit **Service:** General Medical and Surgical

**Staffed Beds:** 98 **Admissions:** 2108 **Census:** 19 **Outpatient Visits:** 26702 **Births:** 449 **Total Expense ($000):** 20489 **Payroll Expense ($000):** 12471 **Personnel:** 238

**DOCTORS DIAGNOSTIC HOSPITAL (670018)**, 1017 South Travis Street, Zip 77327–5152; tel. 281/622–2900, (Nonreporting) **A**9 10
Primary Contact: Don Vickers, Chief Executive Officer
Web address: www.ddhclv.com
**Control:** Corporation, Investor–owned, for–profit **Service:** General Medical and Surgical

**Staffed Beds:** 4

## CLIFTON—Bosque County

★ **GOODALL–WITCHER HEALTHCARE (450052)**, 101 South Avenue T, Zip 76634–1897, Mailing Address: P.O. Box 549, Zip 76634–0549; tel. 254/675–8322 **A**9 10 20 **F**3 11 13 15 29 30 34 35 36 40 43 45 53 57 59 62 64 65 68 76 77 81 93 107 108 114 119 127 130 133 146 147 148 **P**3
Primary Contact: Adam Willmann, President and Chief Executive Officer
CMO: Kevin Blanton, D.O., Chief of Staff
CHR: Jennie Oldham, Director Human Resources
Web address: www.gwhf.org
**Control:** Other not–for–profit (including NFP Corporation) **Service:** General Medical and Surgical

**Staffed Beds:** 33 **Admissions:** 617 **Census:** 8 **Outpatient Visits:** 37663 **Births:** 73 **Total Expense ($000):** 15697 **Payroll Expense ($000):** 6762 **Personnel:** 175

## COLEMAN—Coleman County

★ **COLEMAN COUNTY MEDICAL CENTER (451347)**, 310 South Pecos Street, Zip 76834–4159; tel. 325/625–2135 **A**9 10 18 **F**7 8 11 13 29 40 77 81 107 114 128 133 **P**5 **S** Preferred Management Corporation, Shawnee, OK
Primary Contact: Michael W. Pruitt, Administrator and Chief Executive Officer
CMO: Paul Reynolds, M.D., Medical Director
CIO: Raul Hurtado, Chief Information Officer
CHR: Sue Titsworth, Director Human Resources
CNO: Melissa Ereman, R.N., Chief Nursing Officer
Web address: www.colemantexas.org/hospital.html
**Control:** Hospital district or authority, Government, nonfederal **Service:** General Medical and Surgical

**Staffed Beds:** 25 **Admissions:** 339 **Census:** 4 **Outpatient Visits:** 2790 **Births:** 18 **Total Expense ($000):** 5676 **Payroll Expense ($000):** 2507 **Personnel:** 118

## COLLEGE STATION—Brazos County

⊞ **COLLEGE STATION MEDICAL CENTER (450299)**, 1604 Rock Prairie Road, Zip 77845–8345, Mailing Address: P.O. Box 10000, Zip 77842–3500; tel. 979/764–5100 **A**1 2 3 5 9 10 **F**3 11 13 15 18 20 22 24 26 28 29 30 31 34 40 43 45 46 49 53 57 61 70 72 74 76 77 78 79 81 82 84 85 87 89 90 91 93 107 108 111 113 115 118 119 126 127 129 130 131 132 135 146 147 148 **P**7 **S** Community Health Systems, Inc., Franklin, TN
Primary Contact: Thomas W. Jackson, Chief Executive Officer
CFO: Wayne Colson, Chief Financial Officer
CHR: Sharon Bond, Director Human Resources
Web address: www.csmedcenter.com
**Control:** Corporation, Investor–owned, for–profit **Service:** General Medical and Surgical

**Staffed Beds:** 167 **Admissions:** 6529 **Census:** 63 **Outpatient Visits:** 58689 **Births:** 1651 **Total Expense ($000):** 122334 **Payroll Expense ($000):** 47844 **Personnel:** 788

## COLORADO CITY—Mitchell County

★ **MITCHELL COUNTY HOSPITAL (451342)**, 997 West Interstate 20, Zip 79512–2685; tel. 325/728–3431 **A**9 10 18 **F**3 7 11 28 29 40 43 45 50 57 59 64 68 81 93 107 119 133 146 **P**6
Primary Contact: Robbie Dewberry, Chief Executive Officer
CFO: Joe Wright, Chief Financial Officer
CMO: Dee A. Roach, M.D., Chief of Staff
CIO: Randy Myers, Chief Information Officer, Information Technology
CHR: Deana Overton, Director Human Resources
CNO: Donna Goebel, M.D., Chief Nursing Officer
Web address: www.mitchellcountyhospital.com
**Control:** Hospital district or authority, Government, nonfederal **Service:** General Medical and Surgical

**Staffed Beds:** 25 **Admissions:** 1206 **Census:** 16 **Outpatient Visits:** 43115 **Total Expense ($000):** 11168 **Payroll Expense ($000):** 7056 **Personnel:** 199

## COLUMBUS—Colorado County

★ **COLUMBUS COMMUNITY HOSPITAL (450370)**, 110 Shult Drive, Zip 78934–3010; tel. 979/732–2371 **A**5 6 9 10 **F**3 11 13 15 29 31 35 40 43 56 57 62 68 76 79 81 89 107 110 111 114 119 127 130 133 135
Primary Contact: Robert Thomas, Chief Executive Officer and Administrator
CFO: Regina Wicke, Chief Financial Officer
CMO: David Wilkinson, M.D., Chief of Staff
CIO: Regina Wicke, Chief Financial Officer
CHR: Janie Hammonds, Human Resources Officer
Web address: www.columbusch.com
**Control:** Other not–for–profit (including NFP Corporation) **Service:** General Medical and Surgical

**Staffed Beds:** 40 **Admissions:** 1113 **Census:** 11 **Outpatient Visits:** 67488 **Births:** 207 **Total Expense ($000):** 22072 **Payroll Expense ($000):** 7640 **Personnel:** 151

TX

*Many Facility Codes have changed. Please refer to the AHA Guide Code Chart.*

© 2013 AHA Guide

## COMANCHE—Comanche County

★ **COMANCHE COUNTY MEDICAL CENTER (451382)**, 10201 Highway 16, Zip 76442–4462; tel. 254/879–4900 **A**9 10 18 20 **F**8 11 15 28 29 30 40 43 45 49 50 57 59 64 65 68 70 75 77 79 81 87 93 107 111 115 119 127 129 130 132 133 135 143 145 146 148 **P**4
Primary Contact: Kevin Storey, Chief Executive Officer
CMO: Todd Davis, D.O., Chief of Staff
CIO: Ismelda Garza, Director Information Systems
CHR: Peggy Jordan, Director Human Resources
CNO: Mona Sloan, Chief Nursing Officer
Web address: www.comanchecmc.org
**Control:** Other not–for–profit (including NFP Corporation) **Service:** General Medical and Surgical

**Staffed Beds:** 25 **Admissions:** 646 **Census:** 8 **Outpatient Visits:** 20729 **Births:** 0 **Total Expense ($000):** 18983 **Payroll Expense ($000):** 6663 **Personnel:** 160

## COMMERCE—Hunt County

☒ **HUNT REGIONAL COMMUNITY HOSPITAL (451321)**, 2900 Sterling Hart Drive, Zip 75428–3912; tel. 903/886–3161 **A**1 9 10 18 **F**3 11 29 30 40 41 43 57 75 85 87 93 105 107 114 119 130 133 135 146 **S** Hunt Regional Healthcare, Greenville, TX
Primary Contact: Michael R. Klepin, Administrator
COO: John Heatherly, Assistant Administrator Support Services
CFO: Jeri Rich, Assistant Administrator and Chief Financial Officer
CMO: Richard Selvaggi, M.D., Chief of Staff
CIO: Joe Hartley, Director Information Systems
CHR: Stacey Lane, Director Human Resources
Web address: www.huntregional.org
**Control:** Hospital district or authority, Government, nonfederal **Service:** General Medical and Surgical

**Staffed Beds:** 15 **Admissions:** 252 **Census:** 4 **Outpatient Visits:** 8285 **Births:** 0 **Total Expense ($000):** 8359 **Payroll Expense ($000):** 2819 **Personnel:** 44

## CONROE—Montgomery County

☐ **ASPIRE BEHAVIORAL HEALTH OF CONROE (454112)**, 2006 South Loop 336 West, Suite 500, Zip 77304–3315; tel. 936/647–3500 **A**1 9 10 **F**3 5 34 40 56 57 59 64 78 98 102 103 104 105 116 117 118 121 122 130
Primary Contact: Brian Neal, Chief Executive Officer
Web address: www.aspirebhc.com/
**Control:** Partnership, Investor–owned, for–profit **Service:** Psychiatric

**Staffed Beds:** 28 **Admissions:** 618 **Census:** 16 **Outpatient Visits:** 1206 **Births:** 0 **Total Expense ($000):** 3280 **Payroll Expense ($000):** 2543 **Personnel:** 55

☒ **CONROE REGIONAL MEDICAL CENTER (450222)**, 504 Medical Boulevard, Zip 77304, Mailing Address: P.O. Box 1538, Zip 77305–1538; tel. 936/539–1111 **A**1 9 10 13 **F**3 11 12 13 15 17 18 20 22 24 26 28 29 31 34 35 40 41 43 45 46 53 54 57 59 64 68 70 72 73 74 75 76 78 79 81 82 85 86 89 91 93 107 108 111 114 115 118 119 121 124 129 130 132 135 146 147 148 **P**7 **S** HCA, Nashville, TN
Primary Contact: Thomas A. Holt, Interim Chief Executive Officer
CFO: Thomas A. Holt, Chief Financial Officer
CIO: Daniel Andresen, Director Information Services
CHR: Diana Howell, Director Human Resources
Web address: www.conroeregional.com/
**Control:** Partnership, Investor–owned, for–profit **Service:** General Medical and Surgical

**Staffed Beds:** 292 **Admissions:** 14296 **Census:** 197 **Outpatient Visits:** 113034 **Births:** 789 **Total Expense ($000):** 203591 **Payroll Expense ($000):** 69262 **Personnel:** 969

☒ **HEALTHSOUTH REHABILITATION HOSPITAL OF NORTH HOUSTON (453059)**, 18550 'IH' 45 South, Zip 77384; tel. 281/364–2000 **A**1 10 **F**3 29 35 44 57 59 62 64 68 75 77 79 82 86 87 90 91 93 130 132 148 **S** HEALTHSOUTH Corporation, Birmingham, AL
Primary Contact: Krista Uselman, Chief Executive Officer
CMO: Ben Agana, M.D., Medical Director
CHR: Valerie Wells, Manager Human Resources
Web address: www.healthsouth.com
**Control:** Corporation, Investor–owned, for–profit **Service:** Rehabilitation

**Staffed Beds:** 84 **Admissions:** 1127 **Census:** 40 **Outpatient Visits:** 15110 **Births:** 0 **Total Expense ($000):** 17130 **Payroll Expense ($000):** 8780 **Personnel:** 107

☐ **SOLARA HOSPITAL CONROE (452107)**, 1500 Grand Lake Drive, Zip 77304–2891; tel. 936/523–1800 **A**1 9 10 **F**1 3 29 34 39 40 74 75 79 85 86 87 91 130 148 **S** Cornerstone Healthcare Group, Dallas, TX
Primary Contact: Steve Hockert, Chief Executive Officer
Web address: www.chghospitals.com/conroe/
**Control:** Partnership, Investor–owned, for–profit **Service:** Long–Term Acute Care hospital

**Staffed Beds:** 41 **Admissions:** 543 **Census:** 37 **Outpatient Visits:** 13 **Births:** 0 **Total Expense ($000):** 17107 **Payroll Expense ($000):** 6566 **Personnel:** 114

## CORINTH—Denton County

☐ ◇ **ATRIUM MEDICAL CENTER OF CORINTH (452111)**, 3305 Corinth Parkway, Zip 76208–5380; tel. 940/270–4100 **A**1 9 10 21 **F**1 3 28 29 40 45 47 60 64 68 70 75 77 86 87 96 107 111 114 119 148 **P**2
Primary Contact: Dorothy J. Elford, Chief Executive Officer
COO: Kathy Mason, Chief Operating Officer
CFO: Melissa Dovel, Manager Human Resources
CFO: Anbu Nachimuthu, Chief Financial Officer
CMO: Jalil Kahn, M.D., Chief of Staff
CIO: Wendy Keller, Director Health Information Management
CNO: Michelle Gray, Nurse Executive
Web address: www.atriumhealthcare.net
**Control:** Corporation, Investor–owned, for–profit **Service:** Long–Term Acute Care hospital

**Staffed Beds:** 57 **Admissions:** 607 **Census:** 43 **Outpatient Visits:** 2908 **Births:** 0 **Total Expense ($000):** 24506 **Payroll Expense ($000):** 11119 **Personnel:** 185

## CORPUS CHRISTI—Nueces County

☒ △ **CHRISTUS SPOHN HOSPITAL CORPUS CHRISTI MEMORIAL (450046)**, 2606 Hospital Boulevard, Zip 78405–1804, Mailing Address: P.O. Box 5280, Zip 78465–5280; tel. 361/902–4000, (Includes CHRISTUS SPOHN HOSPITAL CORPUS CHRISTI SHORELINE, 600 Elizabeth Street, Zip 78404–2235; tel. 361/881–3000; Paul Gaden, Chief Executive Officer; CHRISTUS SPOHN HOSPITAL CORPUS CHRISTUS SOUTH, 5950 Saratoga, Zip 78414–4100; tel. 361/985–5000), (Total facility includes 24 beds in nursing home–type unit) **A**1 2 3 5 7 9 10 **F**3 8 11 13 15 17 18 20 22 24 26 28 29 30 34 35 37 38 39 40 43 45 46 47 48 49 50 51 53 54 56 57 58 59 60 64 66 68 70 72 73 74 75 76 77 78 79 81 85 86 87 90 93 96 97 98 99 100 101 102 103 107 108 111 114 115 118 119 120 121 123 126 127 128 130 146 147 148 **P**8 **S** CHRISTUS Health, Irving, TX
Primary Contact: Paul Gaden, Vice President and Chief Operating Officer
CFO: Scott Merryman, Chief Financial Officer
CMO: Richard Davis, M.D., Regional Chief Medical Officer
CHR: Mary LaFrancois, Vice President Human Resources
Web address: www.christusspohn.org
**Control:** Church–operated, Nongovernment, not–for profit **Service:** General Medical and Surgical

**Staffed Beds:** 783 **Admissions:** 35207 **Census:** 528 **Outpatient Visits:** 300942 **Births:** 2811 **Total Expense ($000):** 523394 **Payroll Expense ($000):** 190615 **Personnel:** 2870

☒ **CORPUS CHRISTI MEDICAL CENTER (450788)**, 3315 South Alameda Street, Zip 78411–1883, Mailing Address: P.O. Box 8991, Zip 78468–8991; tel. 361/761–1400, (Includes BAYVIEW BEHAVIORAL HOSPITAL, 6629 Wooldridge Road, Zip 78414; tel. 361/986–9444; Jamie Molbert, Associate Administrator; CORPUS CHRISTI MEDICAL CENTER BAY AREA, 7101 South Padre Island Drive, Zip 78412–4999; tel. 361/985–1200) **A**1 9 10 12 13 **F**3 11 12 13 15 17 18 20 22 24 26 28 29 30 31 34 35 37 38 40 42 44 47 49 50 53 57 58 59 64 68 70 72 73 74 75 76 77 78 79 81 85 86 87 90 93 97 98 99 100 101 102 103 104 107 108 110 111 114 115 118 119 120 121 126 130 131 132 146 147 **P**3 8 **S** HCA, Nashville, TN
Primary Contact: Jay Woodall, Chief Executive Officer
CFO: Chris Nicosia, Chief Financial Officer
CMO: Scott McKinstry, M.D., Chief of Staff
CIO: Sharon Orton, Director Information Services and Technology
CHR: Michael Conwill, Director Human Resources
Web address: www.ccmedicalcenter.com
**Control:** Partnership, Investor–owned, for–profit **Service:** General Medical and Surgical

**Staffed Beds:** 421 **Admissions:** 18069 **Census:** 231 **Outpatient Visits:** 108394 **Births:** 3919 **Total Expense ($000):** 231999 **Payroll Expense ($000):** 79793 **Personnel:** 1524

⌧ **DRISCOLL CHILDREN'S HOSPITAL (453301)**, 3533 South Alameda Street, Zip 78411–1785, Mailing Address: P.O. Box 6530, Zip 78466–6530; tel. 361/694–5000 **A**1 3 5 9 10 13 **F**3 7 11 12 19 21 23 25 27 29 30 31 32 34 35 38 39 40 41 43 44 50 54 55 57 58 59 60 61 64 65 68 72 74 75 77 78 79 81 82 85 86 87 88 89 92 93 97 99 104 107 108 111 115 118 119 130 132 134 138 143 144 146 148
Primary Contact: Steve Woerner, President and Chief Executive Officer
COO: Donna Quinn, Vice President Operations and Quality
CFO: Eric Hamon, Chief Financial Officer
CIO: Miguel Perez, Director Information Systems
CHR: Bill Larsen, Vice President Human Resources
Web address: www.driscollchildrens.org
**Control:** Other not–for–profit (including NFP Corporation) **Service:** Children's general

**Staffed Beds:** 162 **Admissions:** 4334 **Census:** 66 **Outpatient Visits:** 123504 **Births:** 0 **Total Expense ($000):** 140122 **Payroll Expense ($000):** 78609 **Personnel:** 1677

⌧ **DUBUIS HOSPITAL OF CORPUS CHRISTI (452086)**, 600 Elizabeth Street, 3rd Floor, Zip 78404–2235; tel. 361/881–3223 **A**1 9 10 **F**1 3 29 30 31 75 85 87 148 **P**5 **S** Dubuis Health System, Houston, TX
Primary Contact: Diane Kaiser, Administrator
Web address: www.dubuis.org/DubuisHospitalofCorpusChristi
**Control:** Church–operated, Nongovernment, not–for profit **Service:** Long–Term Acute Care hospital

**Staffed Beds:** 22 **Admissions:** 242 **Census:** 18 **Outpatient Visits:** 0 **Births:** 0 **Total Expense ($000):** 8347 **Payroll Expense ($000):** 3487 **Personnel:** 55

⌧ **KINDRED HOSPITAL–CORPUS CHRISTI (452092)**, 6226 Saratoga Boulevard, Zip 78414–3421; tel. 361/986–1600 **A**1 9 10 **F**1 3 29 30 34 35 45 57 59 60 61 64 70 74 75 77 79 82 85 86 87 93 97 100 107 130 146 148 **S** Kindred Healthcare, Louisville, KY
Primary Contact: Diana Schultz, Chief Executive Officer
CFO: Eva De La Paz, Chief Financial Officer
CMO: Salim Surani, M.D., Medical Director
CHR: Kasey Parkey, Coordinator Payroll and Benefits
Web address: www.khcorpuschristi.com/
**Control:** Corporation, Investor–owned, for–profit **Service:** Long–Term Acute Care hospital

**Staffed Beds:** 68 **Admissions:** 570 **Census:** 39 **Outpatient Visits:** 663 **Births:** 0 **Total Expense ($000):** 16745 **Payroll Expense ($000):** 7530 **Personnel:** 139

▢ **SOUTH TEXAS SURGICAL HOSPITAL (670061)**, 6130 Parkway Drive, Zip 78414–2455; tel. 361/993–2000 **A**1 9 10 **F**3 29 40 45 54 64 68 75 79 81 82 85 119 130 **S** National Surgical Hospitals, Chicago, IL
Primary Contact: James Murphy, Chief Executive Officer
Web address: www.nshinc.com
**Control:** Partnership, Investor–owned, for–profit **Service:** General Medical and Surgical

**Staffed Beds:** 20 **Admissions:** 975 **Census:** 9 **Outpatient Visits:** 3950 **Births:** 0 **Total Expense ($000):** 25254 **Payroll Expense ($000):** 5740 **Personnel:** 125

**CORSICANA—Navarro County**

⌧ **NAVARRO REGIONAL HOSPITAL (450447)**, 3201 West State Highway 22, Zip 75110–2469; tel. 903/654–6800 **A**1 9 10 19 **F**3 11 13 14 15 18 29 30 34 35 39 40 43 45 47 49 50 51 57 59 60 64 68 70 75 76 79 81 82 85 93 107 108 110 111 114 119 129 132 135 146 148 **P**7 **S** Community Health Systems, Inc., Franklin, TN
Primary Contact: Xavier Villarreal, Chief Executive Officer
CFO: Marco Rodriguez, Chief Financial Officer
CIO: Marco Rodriguez, Chief Financial Officer
CHR: Linda Gould, Director Human Resources
Web address: www.navarrohospital.com
**Control:** Partnership, Investor–owned, for–profit **Service:** General Medical and Surgical

**Staffed Beds:** 148 **Admissions:** 3562 **Census:** 31 **Outpatient Visits:** 41755 **Births:** 479 **Total Expense ($000):** 42006 **Payroll Expense ($000):** 15134 **Personnel:** 267

**CRANE—Crane County**

★ **CRANE MEMORIAL HOSPITAL (451353)**, 1310 South Alford Street, Zip 79731–3899; tel. 432/558–3555 **A**9 10 18 **F**3 29 32 34 40 57 59 64 65 68 75 81 86 97 107 119 127 133 145 147 148 **P**6
Primary Contact: Dianne Yeager, Chief Executive Officer
CMO: Jay Sigel, M.D., Chief Medical Staff
Web address: www.cranememorial.org
**Control:** Hospital district or authority, Government, nonfederal **Service:** General Medical and Surgical

**Staffed Beds:** 25 **Admissions:** 177 **Census:** 2 **Outpatient Visits:** 12112 **Births:** 0 **Total Expense ($000):** 3715 **Payroll Expense ($000):** 2186 **Personnel:** 44

**CROCKETT—Houston County**

⌧ **EAST TEXAS MEDICAL CENTER CROCKETT (450580)**, 1100 Loop 304 East, Zip 75835–1810; tel. 936/546–3862 **A**1 9 10 20 **F**3 11 13 15 28 29 32 35 40 43 46 50 54 57 58 59 61 64 70 75 76 81 87 97 107 108 111 114 118 119 129 133 146 **P**7 **S** East Texas Medical Center Regional Healthcare System, Tyler, TX
Primary Contact: Terry Cutler, Administrator and Chief Executive Officer
Web address: www.etmc.org
**Control:** Other not–for–profit (including NFP Corporation) **Service:** General Medical and Surgical

**Staffed Beds:** 49 **Admissions:** 1713 **Census:** 17 **Outpatient Visits:** 65642 **Births:** 227 **Total Expense ($000):** 20256 **Payroll Expense ($000):** 8065 **Personnel:** 153

**CROSBYTON—Crosby County**

**CROSBYTON CLINIC HOSPITAL (451345)**, 710 West Main Street, Zip 79322–2143; tel. 806/675–2382 **A**9 10 18 **F**7 29 34 40 50 57 59 63 64 68 87 93 111 119 125 127 130 133 148 **P**6
Primary Contact: Debra Miller, Administrator
CFO: Cherie Parkhill, Chief Financial Officer
CMO: Steve B. Alley, M.D., Chief of Staff
CHR: Jane Wheeless, Director Human Resources
CNO: Anna Bradford, R.N., Chief Nursing Officer
Web address: www.crosbytonclinichospital.com
**Control:** Other not–for–profit (including NFP Corporation) **Service:** General Medical and Surgical

**Staffed Beds:** 25 **Admissions:** 317 **Census:** 4 **Outpatient Visits:** 17296 **Births:** 0 **Total Expense ($000):** 5093 **Payroll Expense ($000):** 2522 **Personnel:** 71

**CUERO—Dewitt County**

★ **CUERO COMMUNITY HOSPITAL (450597)**, 2550 North Esplanade Street, Zip 77954–4716; tel. 361/275–6191 **A**9 10 **F**3 7 11 13 15 29 34 40 43 45 57 59 62 64 68 70 75 76 77 79 81 85 86 93 103 107 108 111 115 118 119 129 130 131
Primary Contact: Darryl Stefka, Administrator
CFO: Greg Pritchett, Controller
CIO: Arthur Mueller, Director Management Information Systems
CHR: Wanda Kolodziejcyk, Director Human Resources
Web address: www.cuerohosp.org
**Control:** Hospital district or authority, Government, nonfederal **Service:** General Medical and Surgical

**Staffed Beds:** 35 **Admissions:** 1437 **Census:** 14 **Outpatient Visits:** 138899 **Births:** 61 **Total Expense ($000):** 27414 **Payroll Expense ($000):** 11636 **Personnel:** 323

**CYPRESS—Harris County**

▢ ◇ **LONE STAR BEHAVIORAL HEALTH (454118)**, 16303 Grant Road, Zip 77429–1253; tel. 281/516–6200 **A**1 9 10 21 **F**98 104 105 **P**5
Primary Contact: Nathan Daniel Ingram, Chief Executive Officer and Owner
Web address: www.lonestarbehavioralhealth.com
**Control:** Partnership, Investor–owned, for–profit **Service:** Psychiatric

**Staffed Beds:** 24 **Admissions:** 358 **Census:** 8 **Outpatient Visits:** 0 **Births:** 0 **Total Expense ($000):** 4085 **Payroll Expense ($000):** 2449 **Personnel:** 91

▢ **NORTH CYPRESS MEDICAL CENTER (670024)**, 21214 Northwest Freeway, Zip 77429–3373; tel. 832/912–3500 **A**1 9 10 **F**3 8 12 15 18 20 22 24 26 28 29 31 34 35 36 37 39 40 42 44 45 46 47 48 49 50 51 57 59 60 64 70 74 75 77 78 79 81 82 85 86 87 93 96 107 108 109 110 111 114 115 116 117 118 119 120 121 123 124 129 130 131 132 146 148
Primary Contact: Robert Behar, M.D., Chief Executive Officer
Web address: www.ncmc–hospital.com
**Control:** Partnership, Investor–owned, for–profit **Service:** General Medical and Surgical

**Staffed Beds:** 139 **Admissions:** 8035 **Census:** 105 **Outpatient Visits:** 212149 **Births:** 0 **Total Expense ($000):** 217742 **Payroll Expense ($000):** 70712 **Personnel:** 1293

**DALHART—Hartley County**

**COON MEMORIAL HOSPITAL AND HOME (451331)**, 1411 Denver Avenue, Zip 79022–4809, Mailing Address: P.O. Box 2014, Zip 79022–6014; tel. 806/244–4571 **A**9 10 18 **F**3 7 10 11 13 30 34 35 40 43 45 50 53 57 59 62 63 64 65 68 69 71 76 77 79 81 82 83 85 87 89 90 93 97 103 107 114 119 125 127 131 133 143 144 146 148 **P**5
Primary Contact: Leroy Schaffner, Chief Executive Officer
CFO: Donny Pettit, Chief Financial Officer
CMO: Randy Herring, M.D., Chief of Staff
CIO: Joshua Gray, Director Information Technology
CHR: Dee Dawn McCormick, Director Personnel and Human Resources
Web address: www.coonmemorial.org
**Control:** Hospital district or authority, Government, nonfederal **Service:** General Medical and Surgical

**Staffed Beds:** 21 **Admissions:** 465 **Census:** 4 **Outpatient Visits:** 14818 **Births:** 108 **Total Expense ($000):** 23631 **Payroll Expense ($000):** 8291 **Personnel:** 170

*Many Facility Codes have changed. Please refer to the AHA Guide Code Chart.* © 2013 AHA Guide

**TX**

**DALLAS—Dallas County**

**A. WEBB ROBERTS HOSPITAL** See Baylor University Medical Center

⊠ △ **BAYLOR INSTITUTE FOR REHABILITATION (453036)**, 909 North Washington Avenue, Zip 75246–1520; tel. 214/820–9300 **A**1 7 9 10 **F**3 29 30 35 44 62 64 65 68 74 77 85 86 87 90 92 93 94 96 130 131 132 135 143 148 **S** Baylor Health Care System, Dallas, TX
Primary Contact: Jon C. Skinner, President
COO: Fabian Polo, Chief Operating Officer
CFO: Ted Bolcavage, Vice President and Division Controller
CMO: Amy Wilson, M.D., Medical Director
CIO: Brian Rusignuolo, Senior Vice President Information Services
CHR: Karen Hill, Director Human Resources
CNO: Beth Hudson, Chief Nursing Officer
Web address: www.baylorhealth.com/PhysiciansLocations/BIR/Pages/Default.aspx
**Control:** Partnership, Investor–owned, for–profit **Service:** Rehabilitation

**Staffed Beds:** 78 **Admissions:** 1505 **Census:** 75 **Outpatient Visits:** 3874 **Births:** 0 **Total Expense ($000):** 67221 **Payroll Expense ($000):** 46605 **Personnel:** 309

☐ **BAYLOR JACK AND JANE HAMILTON HEART AND VASCULAR HOSPITAL (450851)**, 621 North Hall Street, Zip 75226–1339; tel. 214/820–0600 **A**1 5 9 10 **F**3 11 18 20 21 22 26 28 29 30 34 35 57 58 59 64 68 75 81 85 86 87 93 96 100 107 115 119 132 135
Primary Contact: Nancy Vish, Ph.D., President
CFO: Julius Wicke, III, Vice President Finance and Hospital Financial Officer
CMO: Kevin Wheelan, M.D., Medical Director
CHR: Kim Krause, Director Human Resources
Web address: www.baylorhearthospital.com
**Control:** Partnership, Investor–owned, for–profit **Service:** General Medical and Surgical

**Staffed Beds:** 64 **Admissions:** 2080 **Census:** 18 **Outpatient Visits:** 20552 **Births:** 0 **Total Expense ($000):** 78711 **Payroll Expense ($000):** 21837 **Personnel:** 290

⊠ **BAYLOR MEDICAL CENTER AT UPTOWN (450422)**, 2727 East Lemmon Avenue, Zip 75204–2895; tel. 214/443–3000 **A**1 9 10 **F**29 40 68 79 81 82 85 107 111 **S** United Surgical Partners International, Addison, TX
Primary Contact: Matt Chance, Chief Executive Officer
CFO: Colene Fielding, Manager Business Office
CMO: Mark Armstrong, M.D., Medical Director
CIO: Javier Vela, Director Information Technology
CHR: Emalie Sanchez, Director Human Resources
CNO: Verette Neeb, R.N., Chief Nursing Officer
Web address: www.bmcuptown.com
**Control:** Partnership, Investor–owned, for–profit **Service:** General Medical and Surgical

**Staffed Beds:** 24 **Admissions:** 1103 **Census:** 6 **Outpatient Visits:** 7192 **Births:** 0 **Total Expense ($000):** 37545 **Payroll Expense ($000):** 8504 **Personnel:** 201

⊠ **BAYLOR SPECIALTY HOSPITAL (452017)**, 3504 Swiss Avenue, Zip 75204–6224; tel. 214/820–9700 **A**1 9 10 **F**1 30 50 75 77 85 93 130 148 **S** Baylor Health Care System, Dallas, TX
Primary Contact: Elizabeth Youngblood, President
CFO: Clint Stapp, Vice President
CMO: Michael Highbaugh, M.D., Medical Director
CHR: Stacie Roberts, Coordinator Human Resources
CNO: Kelli Terpstra, R.N., Chief Nursing Officer
Web address: www.baylorhealth.com/PhysiciansLocations/BSH/Pages/Default.aspx
**Control:** Other not–for–profit (including NFP Corporation) **Service:** Long–Term Acute Care hospital

**Staffed Beds:** 61 **Admissions:** 604 **Census:** 45 **Outpatient Visits:** 0 **Births:** 0 **Total Expense ($000):** 28050 **Payroll Expense ($000):** 10909 **Personnel:** 168

⊠ **BAYLOR UNIVERSITY MEDICAL CENTER (450021)**, 3500 Gaston Avenue, Zip 75246–2088; tel. 214/820–0111, (Includes A. WEBB ROBERTS HOSPITAL, Zip 75246; ERIK AND MARGARET JONSSON HOSPITAL, Zip 75246; GEORGE W. TRUETT MEMORIAL HOSPITAL, 3500 Gaston Avenue, Zip 75246; KARL AND ESTHER HOBLITZELLE MEMORIAL HOSPITAL, 3500 Gaston Avenue, Zip 75246) **A**1 2 3 5 8 9 10 **F**3 6 11 12 13 14 15 17 18 20 22 24 26 28 29 30 31 34 35 36 37 38 39 40 43 44 45 46 47 48 49 50 51 54 55 56 57 58 59 60 61 63 64 65 66 68 70 72 74 75 76 78 79 80 81 82 84 85 86 87 90 91 92 94 95 96 97 102 107 108 110 111 112 114 115 116 117 118 119 120 121 123 124 126 129 130 132 135 136 137 138 139 140 141 142 143 144 145 146 147 148 **S** Baylor Health Care System, Dallas, TX
Primary Contact: John B. McWhorter, III, President
COO: Doug Lawson, Chief Operating Officer
CFO: Jay Whitfield, Chief Financial Officer
CMO: Irving Prengler, M.D., Vice President Medical Staff Affairs
CHR: Queen Greene, Director Human Resources
Web address: www.baylorhealth.com/PhysiciansLocations/Dallas/Pages/Default.aspx
**Control:** Other not–for–profit (including NFP Corporation) **Service:** General Medical and Surgical

**Staffed Beds:** 876 **Admissions:** 36241 **Census:** 631 **Outpatient Visits:** 279109 **Births:** 4408 **Total Expense ($000):** 876844 **Payroll Expense ($000):** 302709 **Personnel:** 3835

⊠ **CHILDREN'S MEDICAL CENTER OF DALLAS (453302)**, 1935 Medical District Drive, Zip 75235; tel. 214/456–7000 **A**1 3 5 8 9 10 **F**3 7 8 11 12 17 19 21 23 25 27 29 30 31 32 34 35 38 39 40 41 43 44 45 46 47 48 49 50 51 54 55 57 58 59 60 61 62 64 65 66 68 72 74 75 77 78 79 81 82 84 85 86 87 88 89 91 92 93 94 97 98 99 100 101 102 104 105 106 107 108 111 114 116 117 118 119 126 127 129 130 131 132 134 136 137 138 139 140 141 142 143 144 145 146 148
Primary Contact: Christopher J. Durovich, President and Chief Executive Officer
COO: Douglas G. Hock, Senior Vice President Operations
CFO: Ray R. Dziesinski, Senior Vice President and Chief Financial Officer
CMO: Julio Perez–Foutan, M.D., Executive Vice President Medical Affairs
CIO: Pamela Arora, Vice President Information Systems
CHR: Jim Herring, Senior Vice President
Web address: www.childrens.com
**Control:** Other not–for–profit (including NFP Corporation) **Service:** Children's general

**Staffed Beds:** 410 **Admissions:** 28289 **Census:** 281 **Outpatient Visits:** 551543 **Births:** 0 **Total Expense ($000):** 925169 **Payroll Expense ($000):** 399686 **Personnel:** 5208

☐ **DALLAS MEDICAL CENTER (450379)**, Seven Medical Parkway, Zip 75234–7823, Mailing Address: P.O. Box 819094, Zip 75381–9094; tel. 972/247–1000 **A**1 10 **F**3 12 15 18 20 22 26 29 34 40 44 45 49 56 57 59 68 70 74 75 77 78 79 81 82 84 85 86 93 97 107 108 111 114 119 130 131 132 141 142 146 147 148 **S** Prime Healthcare Services, Ontario, CA
Primary Contact: Raji Kumar, Chief Executive Officer
CFO: Karen Bomersbach, Chief Financial Officer
CIO: Mary Jo Tallant–Ball, Director Health Information Systems
CHR: Stephanie S. Talley, Associate Administrator and Director Human Resources
Web address: www.dallasmedcenter.com
**Control:** Corporation, Investor–owned, for–profit **Service:** General Medical and Surgical

**Staffed Beds:** 78 **Admissions:** 1997 **Census:** 30 **Outpatient Visits:** 39942 **Births:** 0 **Total Expense ($000):** 46442 **Payroll Expense ($000):** 16909 **Personnel:** 295

⊠ **DOCTORS HOSPITAL AT WHITE ROCK LAKE (450678)**, 9440 Poppy Drive, Zip 75218–3694; tel. 214/324–6100 **A**1 9 10 **F**3 8 11 12 13 15 17 18 20 22 24 26 28 29 30 31 34 35 37 40 45 47 49 50 53 56 57 59 64 68 70 72 73 74 75 76 77 78 79 81 82 85 93 107 108 110 111 115 119 124 129 130 132 135 146 147 148 **S** TENET Healthcare Corporation, Dallas, TX
Primary Contact: Jaikumar Krishnaswamy, Chief Executive Officer
COO: Charles Williams, Chief Operating Officer
CFO: Roger D. Hutchins, Chief Financial Officer
CMO: Robert S. Hendler, M.D., Chief Medical Officer
CIO: Clarence McCullough, Director Information Systems
CHR: Marlene R. Urbach, Chief Human Resources Officer
CNO: Denise Krajewski, R.N., Chief Nursing Officer
Web address: www.doctorshospitaldallas.com
**Control:** Partnership, Investor–owned, for–profit **Service:** General Medical and Surgical

**Staffed Beds:** 153 **Admissions:** 7441 **Census:** 79 **Outpatient Visits:** 67731 **Births:** 1126 **Total Expense ($000):** 115125 **Payroll Expense ($000):** 35285 **Personnel:** 537

**TX**

---

**Hospital, Medicare Provider Number, Address, Telephone, Approval, Facility, and Physician Codes, Health Care System**

★ American Hospital Association (AHA) membership
☐ The Joint Commission accreditation   ◇ DNV Healthcare Inc. accreditation
○ Healthcare Facilities Accreditation Program
△ Commission on Accreditation of Rehabilitation Facilities (CARF) accreditation

○ **FOREST PARK MEDICAL CENTER (670057)**, 11990 North Central Expressway, Zip 75243–3714; tel. 972/234–1900 **A**9 11 **F**3 12 29 35 37 40 45 47 49 64 68 70 75 77 79 81 82 85 87 107 111 115 119 126 130 132 **P**8
Primary Contact: Cindy Bledsoe, Chief Executive Officer
Web address: www.forestparkmc.com/
**Control:** Partnership, Investor–owned, for–profit **Service:** General Medical and Surgical

**Staffed Beds:** 84 **Admissions:** 5051 **Census:** 29 **Outpatient Visits:** 13896 **Births:** 0 **Total Expense ($000):** 188106 **Payroll Expense ($000):** 29941 **Personnel:** 423

**GLOBALREHAB HOSPITAL – DALLAS (673033)**, 1340 Empire Central Drive, Zip 75247–4022; tel. 214/879–7300 **A**10 **F**3 28 29 30 68 75 90 91 96 100 130 148 **S** GLOBALREHAB, Dallas, TX
Primary Contact: David Smith, Chief Executive Officer
Web address: www.globalrehabhospitals.com
**Control:** Partnership, Investor–owned, for–profit **Service:** Rehabilitation

**Staffed Beds:** 42 **Admissions:** 747 **Census:** 29 **Outpatient Visits:** 0 **Births:** 0 **Total Expense ($000):** 13901 **Payroll Expense ($000):** 7423 **Personnel:** 96

✠ **GREEN OAKS HOSPITAL (454094)**, 7808 Clodus Fields Drive, Zip 75251–2206; tel. 972/991–9504 **A**1 9 10 **F**4 5 29 54 87 98 99 102 103 104 105 130 132 **P**5 **S** HCA, Nashville, TN
Primary Contact: Thomas M. Collins, President, Chairman and Chief Executive Officer
COO: Pam Whitley, R.N., Chief Operating Officer and Chief Nursing Officer
CFO: Scott Cook, Chief Financial Officer
CMO: Joel Holiner, M.D., Executive Medical Director
CIO: Chebon Bravo, Director Information Systems
CHR: Kevin Adkins, Director Human Resources
Web address: www.greenoakspsych.com
**Control:** Corporation, Investor–owned, for–profit **Service:** Psychiatric

**Staffed Beds:** 106 **Admissions:** 4749 **Census:** 104 **Outpatient Visits:** 32811 **Births:** 0 **Total Expense ($000):** 33421 **Payroll Expense ($000):** 18501 **Personnel:** 343

✠ **KINDRED HOSPITAL DALLAS CENTRAL (452108)**, 8050 Meadows Road, Zip 75231–3406; tel. 469/232–6500 **A**1 9 10 **F**1 3 29 75 77 85 87 96 107 114 148 **P**8 **S** Kindred Healthcare, Louisville, KY
Primary Contact: Justin Smith, Chief Executive Officer
CFO: Joni Gonzalez, Controller
CNO: Jackie Gordon, Chief Clinical Officer
Web address: www.khdallascentral.com/
**Control:** Corporation, Investor–owned, for–profit **Service:** Long–Term Acute Care hospital

**Staffed Beds:** 60 **Admissions:** 448 **Census:** 33 **Outpatient Visits:** 240 **Births:** 0 **Total Expense ($000):** 23548 **Payroll Expense ($000):** 8380 **Personnel:** 125

**KINDRED HOSPITAL DALLAS–WALNUT HILL** See Kindred Hospital–Dallas

✠ **KINDRED HOSPITAL–DALLAS (452015)**, 9525 Greenville Avenue, Zip 75243–4116; tel. 214/355–2600, (Includes KINDRED HOSPITAL DALLAS–WALNUT HILL, 8200 Walnut Hill Lane, Zip 75231; tel. 214/345–6500) **A**1 9 10 **F**1 3 29 40 70 107 130 148 **S** Kindred Healthcare, Louisville, KY
Primary Contact: Ellen Shankles, Chief Executive Officer
CFO: Jean McDowell, Chief Financial Officer
Web address: www.khdallas.com
**Control:** Partnership, Investor–owned, for–profit **Service:** Long–Term Acute Care hospital

**Staffed Beds:** 50 **Admissions:** 410 **Census:** 30 **Outpatient Visits:** 0 **Births:** 0 **Total Expense ($000):** 19615 **Payroll Expense ($000):** 7250 **Personnel:** 132

✠ **KINDRED HOSPITAL–WHITE ROCK (452071)**, 9440 Poppy Drive, 5th Floor, Zip 75218–3652; tel. 214/324–6562 **A**1 9 10 **F**1 29 85 86 87 130 148 **P**5 **S** Kindred Healthcare, Louisville, KY
Primary Contact: Kelly Bailey, R.N., MSN, Interim Administrator
COO: Kim Chipman, Chief Clinical Officer
CFO: Jennifer Penland, Controller
CMO: Mark Ferris, M.D., Medical Director
CNO: Brenda Perez, R.N., Chief Clinical Officer
Web address: www.khwhiterock.com
**Control:** Corporation, Investor–owned, for–profit **Service:** Long–Term Acute Care hospital

**Staffed Beds:** 25 **Admissions:** 287 **Census:** 20 **Outpatient Visits:** 0 **Births:** 0 **Total Expense ($000):** 10728 **Payroll Expense ($000):** 4553 **Personnel:** 72

✠ **LIFECARE HOSPITALS OF DALLAS (452044)**, 1950 Record Crossing Road, Zip 75235–6223; tel. 214/640–9600 **A**1 9 10 **F**1 3 26 29 45 64 75 77 119 148 **S** LifeCare Management Services, Plano, TX
Primary Contact: Jay Lindsey, Chief Executive Officer
CFO: Karin Bradford, Chief Financial Officer
CHR: Cathy Greenwood, Manager Human Resources
Web address: www.lifecare–hospitals.com/hospital/dallas
**Control:** Corporation, Investor–owned, for–profit **Service:** Long–Term Acute Care hospital

**Staffed Beds:** 60 **Admissions:** 627 **Census:** 44 **Outpatient Visits:** 2759 **Births:** 0 **Total Expense ($000):** 23594 **Payroll Expense ($000):** 9583 **Personnel:** 127

**MARY SHIELS HOSPITAL** See Baylor Medical Center at Uptown

✠ **MEDICAL CITY DALLAS HOSPITAL (450647)**, 7777 Forest Lane, Zip 75230–2598; tel. 972/566–7000, (Includes MEDICAL CITY CHILDREN'S HOSPITAL, 7777 Forest Lane, Zip 75230–2505; tel. 972/566–7000) **A**1 2 3 5 9 10 **F**3 8 11 12 13 15 17 18 19 20 21 22 23 24 25 26 27 28 29 30 31 34 35 37 40 41 44 45 46 47 49 50 51 55 56 57 58 59 60 63 64 65 68 70 72 73 74 75 76 77 78 79 81 82 84 85 86 87 88 89 93 97 105 107 108 110 111 114 115 116 117 118 119 126 129 130 132 135 136 137 138 141 142 143 144 146 147 148 **P**6 7 **S** HCA, Nashville, TN
Primary Contact: Erol R. Akdamar, President and Chief Executive Officer
CFO: Mark Atchley, Vice President and Chief Financial Officer
CMO: Mark Hebert, M.D., President Medical Staff
CIO: Troy Sypien, Director Information Technology and Systems
CHR: Jenifer K. Tertel, Director Human Resources
Web address: www.medicalcityhospital.com
**Control:** Corporation, Investor–owned, for–profit **Service:** General Medical and Surgical

**Staffed Beds:** 540 **Admissions:** 24555 **Census:** 373 **Outpatient Visits:** 170366 **Births:** 3263 **Total Expense ($000):** 419408 **Payroll Expense ($000):** 162809 **Personnel:** 2090

✠ **METHODIST CHARLTON MEDICAL CENTER (450723)**, 3500 West Wheatland Road, Zip 75237–3460, Mailing Address: P.O. Box 225357, Zip 75222–5357; tel. 214/947–7777 **A**1 9 10 13 **F**3 11 13 15 20 22 29 30 31 34 35 40 46 47 49 50 53 58 59 60 64 68 70 74 76 78 79 81 82 84 85 86 87 97 107 108 111 114 118 119 130 131 132 146 148 **P**1 7 **S** Methodist Health System, Dallas, TX
Primary Contact: Jonathan S. Davis, FACHE, President
COO: Pamela Stoyanoff, Executive Vice President and Chief Operating Officer
CFO: Michael J. Schaefer, Executive Vice President and Chief Financial Officer
CIO: Pamela McNutt, Vice President Information Systems
CHR: Deanna Kenard, Senior Vice President Human Resources
CNO: Fran Laukaitis, R.N., Vice President Nursing
Web address: www.methodisthealthsystem.org/charlton
**Control:** Other not–for–profit (including NFP Corporation) **Service:** General Medical and Surgical

**Staffed Beds:** 265 **Admissions:** 13155 **Census:** 182 **Outpatient Visits:** 161221 **Births:** 1836 **Total Expense ($000):** 194513 **Payroll Expense ($000):** 91914 **Personnel:** 1421

✠ **METHODIST DALLAS MEDICAL CENTER (450051)**, 1441 North Beckley Avenue, Zip 75203–1201, Mailing Address: P.O. Box 655999, Zip 75265–5999; tel. 214/947–8181 **A**1 2 3 5 8 9 10 **F**3 11 12 13 15 17 18 20 22 24 28 29 30 31 34 35 37 40 43 45 46 47 48 49 50 53 54 58 59 60 64 66 68 70 72 74 76 78 79 81 82 84 85 87 92 93 97 107 108 110 111 118 119 126 130 132 138 139 142 146 148 **P**1 7 **S** Methodist Health System, Dallas, TX
Primary Contact: Laura Irvine, President
COO: Pamela Stoyanoff, Executive Vice President and Chief Operating Officer
CFO: Randy Walker, Vice President
CIO: Pamela McNutt, Senior Vice President and Chief Information Officer
CHR: Jackie Middleton, Vice President Human Resources
Web address: www.methodisthealthsystem.org/Dallas
**Control:** Other not–for–profit (including NFP Corporation) **Service:** General Medical and Surgical

**Staffed Beds:** 409 **Admissions:** 18512 **Census:** 269 **Outpatient Visits:** 162879 **Births:** 3489 **Total Expense ($000):** 342906 **Payroll Expense ($000):** 144466 **Personnel:** 2287

□ **METHODIST REHABILITATION HOSPITAL (673031)**, 3020 West Wheatland Road, Zip 75237–3537; tel. 972/708–8604 **A**1 9 10 **F**29 30 60 90 91 93 96 **S** Methodist Health System, Dallas, TX
Primary Contact: Lyndell H. Weaks, Chief Executive Officer
Web address: www.methodist–rehab.com
**Control:** Partnership, Investor–owned, for–profit **Service:** Rehabilitation

**Staffed Beds:** 40 **Admissions:** 936 **Census:** 32 **Outpatient Visits:** 12149 **Births:** 0 **Total Expense ($000):** 15093 **Payroll Expense ($000):** 7819 **Personnel:** 147

*Many Facility Codes have changed. Please refer to the AHA Guide Code Chart.*
© 2013 AHA Guide

**TX**

☐ **NORTH CENTRAL SURGICAL CENTER (670049)**, 9301 North Central Expressway, Suite 100, Zip 75231–0802; tel. 214/265–2810 **A**1 9 10 **F**3 40 45 79 81 82 85 107 111 114 115 119
Primary Contact: Suzanne Greever, Chief Executive Officer
COO: Keli Odom, Chief Operating Officer
CFO: Lisa Gildon, Chief Financial Officer
CMO: Stuart Simon, M.D., Medical Director
Web address: www.northcentral–sc.com/
**Control:** Partnership, Investor–owned, for–profit **Service:** Surgical

**Staffed Beds:** 23 **Admissions:** 964 **Census:** 6 **Outpatient Visits:** 20734 **Births:** 0 **Total Expense ($000):** 54557 **Payroll Expense ($000):** 13006 **Personnel:** 276

⊠ **OUR CHILDREN'S HOUSE AT BAYLOR (453308)**, 1208 North Hall Street, Zip 75204; tel. 214/820–9838 **A**1 3 5 9 10 **F**3 29 30 32 34 35 39 50 54 58 59 74 75 81 85 86 87 89 90 93 129 130 132 146 148 **S** Baylor Health Care System, Dallas, TX
Primary Contact: Elizabeth Youngblood, President
CMO: Andrew Gelfand, M.D., Medical Director
CHR: Stacie Roberts, Coordinator Human Resources
CNO: Kelli Terpstra, R.N., Chief Nursing Officer
Web address: www.baylorhealth.com/PhysiciansLocations/OCH/Pages/Default. aspx
**Control:** Other not–for–profit (including NFP Corporation) **Service:** Children's general

**Staffed Beds:** 54 **Admissions:** 350 **Census:** 19 **Outpatient Visits:** 122735 **Births:** 0 **Total Expense ($000):** 33704 **Payroll Expense ($000):** 17126 **Personnel:** 280

⊠ **PARKLAND HEALTH & HOSPITAL SYSTEM (450015)**, 5201 Harry Hines Boulevard, Zip 75235–7708; tel. 214/590–8000 **A**1 2 3 5 8 9 10 **F**3 8 9 11 12 13 15 16 17 18 20 22 26 28 29 30 31 34 35 38 39 40 43 46 47 48 49 50 51 54 55 56 57 58 59 60 61 64 65 66 68 70 71 72 74 75 76 77 78 79 81 82 84 85 86 87 90 91 92 93 94 97 98 99 100 101 102 103 104 107 108 110 111 112 115 118 119 129 130 131 132 134 135 138 141 143 144 146 147 148 **P**1
Primary Contact: Robert L. Smith, Interim Chief Executive Officer
CIO: Jack Kowitt, Senior Vice President and Chief Information Officer
CNO: Mary K. Eagen, R.N., Executive Vice President, Chief Nursing Officer
Web address: www.parklandhospital.com
**Control:** Hospital district or authority, Government, nonfederal **Service:** General Medical and Surgical

**Staffed Beds:** 769 **Admissions:** 37515 **Census:** 563 **Outpatient Visits:** 1221433 **Births:** 11348 **Total Expense ($000):** 1687609 **Payroll Expense ($000):** 588808 **Personnel:** 9635

☐ **PINE CREEK MEDICAL CENTER (450894)**, 9032 Harry Hines Boulevard, Zip 75235–1720; tel. 214/231–2273 **A**1 9 10 **F**3 12 29 30 34 40 42 45 49 51 64 79 81 82 85 93 107 111 114
Primary Contact: Corazon Ramirez, M.D., Chief Executive Officer
CFO: Michael Conroy, Chief Financial Officer
CIO: Kevin Carney, Senior Information Systems Analyst
Web address: www.pinecreekmedicalcenter.com
**Control:** Partnership, Investor–owned, for–profit **Service:** General Medical and Surgical

**Staffed Beds:** 18 **Admissions:** 1177 **Census:** 7 **Outpatient Visits:** 5936 **Births:** 0 **Total Expense ($000):** 47758 **Payroll Expense ($000):** 9339 **Personnel:** 141

☐ **RELIANT REHABILITATION HOSPITAL DALLAS (673043)**, 7930 Northaven Road, Zip 75230–3331; tel. 214/706–8200 **A**1 9 10 **F**3 29 90 93 96 130 148
Primary Contact: Randy Penny, Chief Executive Officer
CFO: Mary Mwaniki, Chief Financial Officer
CMO: Anna Freed–Sigurdsson, M.D., Medical Director
CIO: James E. King, Corporate Director Information Technology
CHR: Ieesha Cannida, Director Human Resources
CNO: Nancy Faas, R.N., Chief Nursing Officer
Web address: www.relianthcp.com
**Control:** Partnership, Investor–owned, for–profit **Service:** Rehabilitation

**Staffed Beds:** 60 **Admissions:** 803 **Census:** 25 **Outpatient Visits:** 3229 **Births:** 0 **Total Expense ($000):** 12303 **Payroll Expense ($000):** 5123 **Personnel:** 113

⊠ **SELECT SPECIALTY HOSPITAL–SOUTH DALLAS (452078)**, 3500 West Wheatland Road, 4th Floor, Zip 75237–3460; tel. 972/780–6500 **A**1 9 10 **F**1 3 29 40 85 107 130 148 **S** Select Medical Corporation, Mechanicsburg, PA
Primary Contact: Richard Knowland, Chief Executive Officer
Web address: www.selectspecialtyhospitals.com/company/locations/southdallas. aspx
**Control:** Corporation, Investor–owned, for–profit **Service:** Long–Term Acute Care hospital

**Staffed Beds:** 69 **Admissions:** 370 **Census:** 26 **Outpatient Visits:** 0 **Births:** 0 **Total Expense ($000):** 15790 **Payroll Expense ($000):** 5867 **Personnel:** 138

**SOUTH HAMPTON COMMUNITY HOSPITAL (670002)**, 2929 South Hampton Road, Zip 75224–3026; tel. 214/623–4400, (Nonreporting) **A**9 10
Primary Contact: Steven Walker, Chief Executive Officer
Web address: www.shchospital.com
**Control:** Partnership, Investor–owned, for–profit **Service:** General Medical and Surgical

**Staffed Beds:** 90

⊠ △ **TEXAS HEALTH PRESBYTERIAN HOSPITAL DALLAS (450462)**, 8200 Walnut Hill Lane, Zip 75231–4426; tel. 214/345–6789 **A**1 2 3 5 7 9 10 **F**3 5 11 12 13 15 17 18 20 22 24 26 28 29 30 31 34 35 36 37 38 40 44 45 46 47 49 50 51 52 53 54 55 56 57 58 59 60 61 63 64 65 66 68 70 72 74 75 76 77 78 79 81 82 85 86 87 90 91 92 93 94 95 96 97 98 100 101 102 103 104 105 107 108 110 111 112 114 115 118 119 124 126 129 130 131 132 135 143 144 146 147 148 **P**6 **S** Texas Health Resources, Arlington, TX
Primary Contact: Britt Berrett, President
COO: James A. Berg, Senior Vice President and Chief Quality Officer
CFO: Sherry Mercer, Interim Vice President Finance
CMO: Mark Lester, M.D., Vice President and Chief Quality Officer
CHR: Connie Wright, Director Human Resources
CNO: Cole Edmonson, R.N., Vice President and Chief Nursing Officer
Web address: www.texashealth.org
**Control:** Other not–for–profit (including NFP Corporation) **Service:** General Medical and Surgical

**Staffed Beds:** 609 **Admissions:** 27244 **Census:** 411 **Outpatient Visits:** 411922 **Births:** 5282 **Total Expense ($000):** 550129 **Payroll Expense ($000):** 190303 **Personnel:** 2610

☐ **TEXAS INSTITUTE FOR SURGERY AT TEXAS HEALTH PRESBYTERIAN DALLAS (450889)**, 7115 Greenville Avenue, Zip 75231–5100; tel. 214/647–5300 **A**1 9 10 **F**40 51 64 79 81 82 107 129 **P**2
Primary Contact: David Helfer, President
CFO: Andrew Summers, Vice President Business Operations
CMO: Presley Mock, M.D., Chief of Staff
CHR: Jack Martin, Director Human Resources
CNO: Joy Dier, R.N., Vice President Clinical Services and Chief Nursing Officer
Web address: www.texasinstituteforsurgery.com
**Control:** Partnership, Investor–owned, for–profit **Service:** General Medical and Surgical

**Staffed Beds:** 9 **Admissions:** 80 **Census:** 1 **Outpatient Visits:** 12028 **Births:** 0 **Total Expense ($000):** 41007 **Payroll Expense ($000):** 9633 **Personnel:** 171

⊠ **TEXAS SCOTTISH RITE HOSPITAL FOR CHILDREN (453314)**, 2222 Welborn Street, Zip 75219–3924, Mailing Address: P.O. Box 190567, Zip 75219–0567; tel. 214/559–5000 **A**1 3 5 **F**3 9 11 29 30 34 35 39 50 53 58 64 68 74 75 77 79 81 85 86 87 89 92 94 107 111 115 119 130 132 143 146 148 **P**6
Primary Contact: Robert L. Walker, President and Chief Executive Officer
CFO: Sharon Ellis, Senior Vice President and Chief Financial Officer
CMO: Daniel J. Sucado, M.D., Chief of Staff
CIO: Hunt Gregg, Director Information Systems
CHR: James D. Sturgis, Associate Administrator
CNO: Debbie Sayles, R.N., Vice President and Chief Nursing Officer
Web address: www.tsrhc.org
**Control:** Other not–for–profit (including NFP Corporation) **Service:** Children's orthopedic

**Staffed Beds:** 52 **Admissions:** 1753 **Census:** 20 **Outpatient Visits:** 38844 **Births:** 0 **Total Expense ($000):** 104697 **Payroll Expense ($000):** 51300 **Personnel:** 774

TX

---

**Hospital, Medicare Provider Number, Address, Telephone, Approval, Facility, and Physician Codes, Health Care System**

★ American Hospital Association (AHA) membership
☐ The Joint Commission accreditation  ◇ DNV Healthcare Inc. accreditation
○ Healthcare Facilities Accreditation Program
△ Commission on Accreditation of Rehabilitation Facilities (CARF) accreditation

☐ **TEXAS SPECIALTY HOSPITAL AT DALLAS (452067)**, 7955 Harry Hines Boulevard, Zip 75235–3305; tel. 214/637–0000 **A**1 9 10 **F**1 3 29 30 75 85 87 148 **S** Fundamental Long Term Care Holdings, LLC, Sparks Glencoe, MD
Primary Contact: Scott Athans, Chief Executive Officer
CFO: Diana B. Smith, Chief Financial Officer
CMO: Gary E. Goff, M.D., Medical Director
CHR: Ginger Davenport, Director Human Resources
Web address: www.texasspecialtydallas.com/index.html
**Control:** Corporation, Investor–owned, for–profit **Service:** Long–Term Acute Care hospital

**Staffed Beds:** 62 **Admissions:** 176 **Census:** 13 **Outpatient Visits:** 0 **Births:** 0 **Total Expense ($000):** 4401 **Payroll Expense ($000):** 2772 **Personnel:** 49

☐ **TIMBERLAWN MENTAL HEALTH SYSTEM (454081)**, 4600 Samuell Boulevard, Zip 75228–6800; tel. 214/381–7181 **A**1 9 10 **F**4 5 54 56 59 64 87 98 99 100 101 102 103 104 105 130 132 143 **S** Universal Health Services, Inc., King of Prussia, PA
Primary Contact: Craig Nuckles, Chief Executive Officer and Regional Vice President
CFO: Lori Verbeke, Chief Financial Officer
CMO: John Pascoe, M.D., Executive Medical Director
CIO: Angela L. Pruitt, Director Health Information Management and Quality Improvement
CHR: Winnie Boehnke, Director Human Resources
Web address: www.timberlawn.com
**Control:** Corporation, Investor–owned, for–profit **Service:** Psychiatric

**Staffed Beds:** 144 **Admissions:** 5972 **Census:** 119 **Outpatient Visits:** 16019 **Births:** 0 **Total Expense ($000):** 21880 **Payroll Expense ($000):** 10561 **Personnel:** 249

⊠ △ **UNIVERSITY OF TEXAS SOUTHWESTERN MEDICAL CENTER (450766)**, 5323 Harry Hines Boulevard, Zip 75390–9265; tel. 214/645–5555, (Includes UNIVERSITY OF TEXAS SOUTHWESTERN MEDICAL CENTER – ST. PAUL, 5909 Harry Hines Boulevard, Zip 75390–9200; tel. 214/645–5555; UNIVERSITY OF TEXAS SOUTHWESTERN MEDICAL CENTER – ZALE LIPSHY, 5151 Harry Hines Boulevard, tel. 214/645–5555; Daniel Podolsky, M.D., President) **A**1 2 3 5 7 8 9 10 **F**3 6 7 8 9 11 12 13 15 17 18 20 22 24 26 28 29 30 31 34 35 36 38 39 40 44 45 46 47 48 49 50 52 53 54 55 56 57 58 59 60 61 62 64 65 66 68 70 71 72 74 75 76 77 78 79 80 81 82 84 85 86 87 90 91 92 93 94 95 96 97 98 99 100 101 102 103 104 107 108 109 110 111 114 115 116 117 118 119 120 121 123 124 126 129 130 131 132 135 136 137 138 139 140 141 142 143 145 146 147 148 **P**5 6
Primary Contact: John Warner, M.D., Chief Executive Officer
CMO: Steven Leach, M.D., Chief Medical Officer
CIO: Suresh Gunasekaran, Assistant Vice President Information Resources
CHR: William Behrendt, Ph.D., Vice President Human Resources
Web address: www.utsouthwestern.edu
**Control:** State–Government, nonfederal **Service:** General Medical and Surgical

**Staffed Beds:** 459 **Admissions:** 21112 **Census:** 346 **Outpatient Visits:** 348615 **Births:** 1430 **Total Expense ($000):** 659282 **Payroll Expense ($000):** 206706 **Personnel:** 3121

⊠ △ **VETERANS AFFAIRS NORTH TEXAS HEALTH CARE SYSTEM**, 4500 South Lancaster Road, Zip 75216–7167; tel. 214/742–8387, (Includes SAM RAYBURN MEMORIAL VETERANS CENTER, 1201 East Ninth Street, Bonham, Zip 75418–4091; tel. 903/583–2111), (Nonreporting) **A**1 2 3 5 7 9 **S** Department of Veterans Affairs, Washington, DC
Primary Contact: Jeffrey Milligan, Director
CFO: Garry Martin, Chief Fiscal
CIO: Lucy Rogers, Chief Information Resource Management Systems
Web address: www.northtexas.va.gov/
**Control:** Veterans Affairs, Government, federal **Service:** General Medical and Surgical

**Staffed Beds:** 875

⊠ **WISE REGIONAL HEALTH SYSTEM (450271)**, 2000 South FM 51, Zip 76234–3702; tel. 940/627–5921 **A**1 2 9 10 **F**3 11 12 13 15 17 18 20 22 24 26 28 29 30 31 32 34 40 43 45 47 49 51 53 54 56 57 59 60 64 70 74 75 76 77 78 79 81 85 87 89 90 93 96 97 98 101 104 107 108 110 111 114 115 116 118 119 129 130 131 132 135 147 148 **P**7
Primary Contact: Stephen M. Summers, CPA, FACHE, Chief Executive Officer
COO: Leon Fuqua, Chief Operating Officer
CFO: Jim Eaton, Chief Financial Officer
CMO: Jason Schuh, M.D., Chief of Staff
CIO: Joe Arispie, Director Information Systems
CHR: Mike McQuiston, Director Human Resources
CNO: Sue Sewell, Chief Nursing Officer
Web address: www.wiseregional.com
**Control:** Hospital district or authority, Government, nonfederal **Service:** General Medical and Surgical

**Staffed Beds:** 133 **Admissions:** 4815 **Census:** 59 **Outpatient Visits:** 187205 **Births:** 504 **Total Expense ($000):** 127724 **Payroll Expense ($000):** 43368 **Personnel:** 1072

⊠ **VAL VERDE REGIONAL MEDICAL CENTER (450154)**, 801 Bedell Avenue, Zip 78840–4112, Mailing Address: P.O. Box 1527, Zip 78841–1527; tel. 830/775–8566 **A**1 9 10 20 **F**3 7 11 13 15 18 20 29 30 34 35 40 43 46 48 54 57 59 63 73 75 76 77 79 81 82 84 85 87 89 93 96 107 108 110 111 114 119 129 131 132 133 146 147
Primary Contact: Marc Strode, Chief Executive Officer
CFO: Tom Grimert, Chief Financial Officer
CMO: Mustafa Salama, M.D., Chief of Staff
CIO: Mark Moore, Director Information Technology
CHR: John Furman, Director Human Resources
CNO: Victoria Barnthouse, R.N., Chief Nursing Officer
Web address: www.vvrmc.org
**Control:** Hospital district or authority, Government, nonfederal **Service:** General Medical and Surgical

**Staffed Beds:** 80 **Admissions:** 3333 **Census:** 29 **Outpatient Visits:** 53794 **Births:** 927 **Total Expense ($000):** 45939 **Payroll Expense ($000):** 18497 **Personnel:** 413

☐ **TEXOMA MEDICAL CENTER (450324)**, 5016 South U.S. Highway 75, Zip 75020–4584, Mailing Address: P.O. Box 890, Zip 75021–0890; tel. 903/416–4000 **A**1 9 10 **F**3 11 12 13 15 17 18 20 22 24 28 29 30 31 34 40 41 43 45 46 47 49 50 53 54 57 59 62 64 70 74 75 76 77 78 79 81 85 86 87 89 90 93 96 98 99 100 101 102 103 104 105 107 108 110 111 115 119 126 129 130 132 144 145 146 147 148 **P**6 7 **S** Universal Health Services, Inc., King of Prussia, PA
Primary Contact: Ronald T. Seal, Chief Executive Officer
COO: Justin Kendrick, Chief Operating Officer
CFO: Bobby Pruiett, Chief Financial Officer
CMO: Robert Sanders, M.D., Chief Medical Officer
CHR: Minnie Burkhardt, Associate Administrator
Web address: www.texomamedicalcenter.net
**Control:** Corporation, Investor–owned, for–profit **Service:** General Medical and Surgical

**Staffed Beds:** 251 **Admissions:** 11025 **Census:** 162 **Outpatient Visits:** 80325 **Births:** 979 **Total Expense ($000):** 159752 **Payroll Expense ($000):** 58185 **Personnel:** 1253

⊠ **DENTON REGIONAL MEDICAL CENTER (450634)**, 3535 South 1–35 East, Zip 76210; tel. 940/384–3535 **A**1 9 10 **F**3 12 13 18 20 22 24 26 28 29 30 34 35 40 43 45 46 47 49 50 57 59 64 66 68 69 70 73 74 75 76 77 79 81 82 84 85 86 87 93 95 96 107 108 111 114 118 119 126 130 132 135 144 146 147 148 **S** HCA, Nashville, TN
Primary Contact: Caleb F. O'Rear, Chief Executive Officer
COO: Jeffrey T. Lawrence, Chief Operating Officer
CMO: Filippo Masciarelli, M.D., Chief of Staff
CHR: Jenna Sutherland, Manager Human Resources
Web address: www.dentonregional.com
**Control:** Partnership, Investor–owned, for–profit **Service:** General Medical and Surgical

**Staffed Beds:** 208 **Admissions:** 10259 **Census:** 118 **Outpatient Visits:** 101493 **Births:** 908 **Total Expense ($000):** 127116 **Payroll Expense ($000):** 50784 **Personnel:** 729

☐ **INTEGRITY TRANSITIONAL HOSPITAL (452109)**, 2813 South Mayhill Road, Zip 76208–5910; tel. 940/320–2300 **A**1 9 10 **F**1 3 29 40 42 77 84 86 87 91 130 148 **P**5
Primary Contact: Ben Patton, Chief Executive Officer
Web address: www.ithdenton.com
**Control:** Partnership, Investor–owned, for–profit **Service:** General Medical and Surgical

**Staffed Beds:** 54 **Admissions:** 543 **Census:** 22 **Outpatient Visits:** 0 **Births:** 0 **Total Expense ($000):** 12504 **Payroll Expense ($000):** 4735 **Personnel:** 79

☐ **MAYHILL HOSPITAL (670010)**, 2809 South Mayhill Road, Zip 76208–5910; tel. 940/239–3000 **A**1 9 10 **F**4 29 40 56 82 98 102 103 104 130 **S** Universal Health Services, Inc., King of Prussia, PA
Primary Contact: Linda S. Hayes, MSN, Chief Executive Officer
CFO: Lori Davis, Chief Financial Officer
CMO: Gary Watts, M.D., Chief Medical Officer
CIO: Darla Powell, Administrative Assistant
CHR: Kashion Lewis, Director Human Resources
Web address: www.mayhillhospital.com
**Control:** Partnership, Investor–owned, for–profit **Service:** Psychiatric

**Staffed Beds:** 59 **Admissions:** 1349 **Census:** 40 **Outpatient Visits:** 1538 **Births:** 0 **Total Expense ($000):** 8303 **Payroll Expense ($000):** 3960 **Personnel:** 78

**TX**

*Many Facility Codes have changed. Please refer to the AHA Guide Code Chart.* © 2013 AHA Guide

◇ **NORTH TEXAS HOSPITAL (450893)**, 2801 South Mayhill Road,
Zip 76208–5910; tel. 940/220–0600, (Nonreporting) **A**9 10 21 **S** Cirrus Health,
Dallas, TX
Primary Contact: Travis W. Roderick, Chief Executive Officer
Web address: www.northtexashospital.com
**Control:** Partnership, Investor–owned, for–profit **Service:** General Medical and
Surgical

**Staffed Beds:** 16

⊠ **SELECT REHABILITATION HOSPITAL OF DENTON (673036)**, 2620 Scripture
Street, Zip 76201–4315; tel. 940/297–6500 **A**1 9 10 **F**3 29 40 60 64 68 74
75 77 79 86 87 90 93 96 135 148 **P**6 **S** Select Medical Corporation,
Mechanicsburg, PA
Primary Contact: Michelle Powell, Chief Executive Officer
CFO: Doug Selsor, Director Finance
CHR: Patsy Martin, Manager Human Resources
CNO: Lee Ann Elliott, R.N., Director of Nursing
Web address: www.selectrehab–denton.com/
**Control:** Corporation, Investor–owned, for–profit **Service:** Rehabilitation

**Staffed Beds:** 44 **Admissions:** 833 **Census:** 29 **Outpatient Visits:** 3890
**Births:** 0 **Total Expense ($000):** 12707 **Payroll Expense ($000):** 7812
**Personnel:** 99

⊠ **TEXAS HEALTH PRESBYTERIAN HOSPITAL DENTON (450743)**, 3000 North
I–35, Zip 76201–5119; tel. 940/898–7000 **A**1 9 10 **F**3 11 12 13 15 18 20 22
24 26 28 29 30 31 34 35 40 45 46 48 49 57 59 70 72 74 75 76 78 79 81
82 85 86 89 93 107 108 110 111 114 115 118 119 126 129 130 131 132
135 145 146 147 148 **S** Texas Health Resources, Arlington, TX
Primary Contact: Stan C. Morton, FACHE, President
COO: Jeff Reecer, Chief Operating Officer
CFO: David B. Meltzer, Chief Financial Officer
CMO: Bob Schwab, M.D., Chief Quality Officer
CIO: Elizabeth Long, Communication and Public Relations Specialist
CHR: Donna Coleman, Director Human Resources
CNO: Deborah Bostic, R.N., Chief Nursing Officer
Web address: www.dentonhospital.com
**Control:** Other not–for–profit (including NFP Corporation) **Service:** General
Medical and Surgical

**Staffed Beds:** 208 **Admissions:** 10078 **Census:** 128 **Outpatient Visits:**
61524 **Births:** 1865 **Total Expense ($000):** 154526 **Payroll Expense
($000):** 58091 **Personnel:** 844

⊠ **UNIVERSITY BEHAVIORAL HEALTH OF DENTON (454104)**, 2026 West
University Drive, Zip 76201–0644; tel. 940/320–8100 **A**1 9 10 **F**4 5 54 98 100
102 103 104 105 **S** Universal Health Services, Inc., King of Prussia, PA
Primary Contact: Susan M. Young, Chief Executive Officer
CFO: Cathi Ledet, Comptroller
CMO: Atique Khan, M.D., Medical Director
CIO: Elizabeth Pratt, Director Health Information Management
CHR: Russell Allison, Human Resources Representative
CNO: Patricia Brewer, Chief Nursing Officer
Web address: www.ubhdenton.net
**Control:** Partnership, Investor–owned, for–profit **Service:** Psychiatric

**Staffed Beds:** 104 **Admissions:** 3246 **Census:** 90 **Outpatient Visits:** 12277
**Births:** 0 **Total Expense ($000):** 15639 **Payroll Expense ($000):** 9590
**Personnel:** 220

### DENVER CITY—Yoakum County

★ **YOAKUM COUNTY HOSPITAL (451308)**, 412 Mustang Avenue,
Zip 79323–2762, Mailing Address: P.O. Box 1130, Zip 79323–1130;
tel. 806/592–2121 **A**9 10 18 **F**3 11 13 28 29 34 35 40 43 50 53 59 60 62
64 76 81 87 89 93 107 115 119 127 129 133 **P**6
Primary Contact: Chris Ekrem, Chief Executive Officer
CFO: Suann Parrish, Chief Financial Officer
CMO: Dan Khan, M.D., Chief Medical Officer
CIO: Todd Carrillo, Chief Information Officer
CHR: Teresa Howard, Manager Human Resources
Web address: www.ych.us
**Control:** County–Government, nonfederal **Service:** General Medical and Surgical

**Staffed Beds:** 22 **Admissions:** 586 **Census:** 7 **Outpatient Visits:** 47159
**Births:** 122 **Total Expense ($000):** 20395 **Payroll Expense ($000):** 7258
**Personnel:** 167

### DESOTO—Dallas County

☐ **HICKORY TRAIL HOSPITAL (454065)**, 2000 Old Hickory Trail,
Zip 75115–2242; tel. 972/298–7323 **A**1 9 10 **F**4 5 29 38 98 99 103 104 105
130 **S** Universal Health Services, Inc., King of Prussia, PA
Primary Contact: Lance Folske, Chief Executive Officer
CFO: Terri Logsdon, Chief Financial Officer
CMO: Manoochehr Khatami, M.D., Medical Director
CHR: Sarah Warren, Coordinator Human Resources
Web address: www.hickorytrail.com
**Control:** Corporation, Investor–owned, for–profit **Service:** Psychiatric

**Staffed Beds:** 86 **Admissions:** 2936 **Census:** 65 **Outpatient Visits:** 8054
**Births:** 0 **Total Expense ($000):** 12291 **Payroll Expense ($000):** 7544
**Personnel:** 226

☐ **VIBRA SPECIALTY HOSPITAL OF DALLAS (452097)**, 2700 Walker Way,
Zip 75115–2088; tel. 214/638–1500, (Nonreporting) **A**1 10 **S** Vibra Healthcare,
Mechanicsburg, PA
Primary Contact: Greg Floyd, Chief Executive Officer
CFO: Donald Trimble, CPA, Chief Financial Officer
CMO: Lauren McDonald, M.D., Medical Director and Medical Staff President
CHR: Tim Lozier, Director Human Resources
Web address: www.vibrahealthcare.com
**Control:** Corporation, Investor–owned, for–profit **Service:** Long–Term Acute Care
hospital

**Staffed Beds:** 60

### DILLEY—Frio County

☐ **COMMUNITY GENERAL HOSPITAL (450813)**, 230 West Miller,
Zip 78017–3818; tel. 830/965–2003, (Nonreporting) **A**1 9 10
Primary Contact: Syed Parvez, M.D., Administrator
**Control:** Corporation, Investor–owned, for–profit **Service:** General Medical and
Surgical

**Staffed Beds:** 18

### DIMMITT—Castro County

★ **PLAINS MEMORIAL HOSPITAL (451350)**, 310 West Halsell Street,
Zip 79027–1846, Mailing Address: P.O. Box 278, Zip 79027–0278;
tel. 806/647–2191 **A**9 10 18 **F**7 32 34 35 40 43 53 57 59 64 65 69 75 77
81 82 85 86 87 93 97 107 114 115 119 127 130 133 135 148 **P**6
Primary Contact: Linda Rasor, R.N., Chief Executive Officer
CFO: Terri Martinez, Chief Financial Officer
CMO: Gary R. Hardee, M.D., Medical Director
CIO: Terry Young, Chief Information Officer
CHR: Debbie Underwood, Manager Human Resources
CNO: Renee Castillo, Chief Nursing Officer
Web address: www.plainsmemorial.com
**Control:** Hospital district or authority, Government, nonfederal **Service:** General
Medical and Surgical

**Staffed Beds:** 25 **Admissions:** 256 **Census:** 4 **Outpatient Visits:** 16168
**Births:** 0 **Total Expense ($000):** 5715 **Payroll Expense ($000):** 3675
**Personnel:** 95

### DUMAS—Moore County

☐ **MOORE COUNTY HOSPITAL DISTRICT (450221)**, 224 East Second Street,
Zip 79029–3808; tel. 806/935–7171 **A**1 9 10 20 **F**3 7 11 13 15 28 34 35 39
40 43 46 50 51 57 59 62 63 70 75 76 77 79 81 85 86 89 91 93 107 111
115 119 130 131 132 133 146 147 148
Primary Contact: Jeff Turner, FACHE, Chief Executive Officer
COO: Yvonne Blue, Chief Operations Officer
CFO: John E. Bailey, Chief Financial Officer
CHR: Ashleigh Wiswell, Director Human Resources
CNO: Stacey Cropley, M.D., Chief Nursing Officer
Web address: www.mchd.net
**Control:** Hospital district or authority, Government, nonfederal **Service:** General
Medical and Surgical

**Staffed Beds:** 47 **Admissions:** 1024 **Census:** 8 **Outpatient Visits:** 17964
**Births:** 204 **Total Expense ($000):** 24019 **Payroll Expense ($000):** 12401
**Personnel:** 302

**TX**

| Hospital, Medicare Provider Number, Address, Telephone, Approval, Facility, and Physician Codes, Health Care System |
|---|
| ★ American Hospital Association (AHA) membership  ☐ The Joint Commission accreditation  ◇ DNV Healthcare Inc. accreditation  ○ Healthcare Facilities Accreditation Program  △ Commission on Accreditation of Rehabilitation Facilities (CARF) accreditation |

**EAGLE LAKE—Colorado County**

★ **RICE MEDICAL CENTER (451312)**, 600 South Austin Road, Zip 77434–3298, Mailing Address: P.O. Box 277, Zip 77434–0277; tel. 979/234–5571 **A**9 10 18 **F**11 13 15 29 40 43 57 59 64 65 70 76 79 81 107 119 127 133 **P**6
Primary Contact: James D. Janek, Chief Executive Officer
CFO: Noble Anderson, Director Patient Financial Services
CMO: Ray Cantu, D.O., Chief of Staff
CHR: Darilyn Henderson, Human Resources Officer
Web address: www.ricemedicalcenter.net/
**Control:** Corporation, Investor–owned, for–profit **Service:** General Medical and Surgical

**Staffed Beds:** 15 **Admissions:** 256 **Census:** 3 **Outpatient Visits:** 25053 **Births:** 39 **Total Expense ($000):** 11019 **Payroll Expense ($000):** 3256 **Personnel:** 122

**EAGLE PASS—Maverick County**

☐ **FORT DUNCAN REGIONAL MEDICAL CENTER (450092)**, 3333 North Foster Maldonado Boulevard, Zip 78852–5893; tel. 830/773–5321 **A**1 9 10 20 **F**3 13 15 29 35 40 43 46 57 59 60 64 65 68 70 75 76 77 79 81 86 87 89 90 93 107 110 111 114 119 129 130 146 147 148 **S** Universal Health Services, Inc., King of Prussia, PA
Primary Contact: Richard Prati, Chief Executive Officer
COO: Richard Prati, Chief Executive Officer
CFO: Joel Morales, Chief Financial Officer
CMO: David Land, D.O., Chief Medical Staff
CIO: Tony Hernandez, Director Information Technology
CHR: Daisy Rodriquez, Director Human Resources
CNO: Wilma Carbonel Mason, Chief Nursing Officer
Web address: www.fortduncanmedicalcenter.com
**Control:** Corporation, Investor–owned, for–profit **Service:** General Medical and Surgical

**Staffed Beds:** 101 **Admissions:** 5200 **Census:** 60 **Outpatient Visits:** 42395 **Births:** 1189 **Total Expense ($000):** 46148 **Payroll Expense ($000):** 20480 **Personnel:** 386

**EASTLAND—Eastland County**

★ **EASTLAND MEMORIAL HOSPITAL (450411)**, 304 South Daugherty Street, Zip 76448–2609, Mailing Address: P.O. Box 897, Zip 76448–0897; tel. 254/629–2601 **A**9 10 20 **F**7 11 15 28 30 34 40 43 45 49 50 53 56 57 59 64 65 68 75 81 85 86 87 93 107 111 114 119 130 131 146 148
Primary Contact: Ted Matthews, Chief Executive Officer
CFO: Jamie Hayden, Chief Financial Officer
CHR: Leisha Hodges, Human Resources Officer
Web address: www.eastlandmemorial.com
**Control:** Hospital district or authority, Government, nonfederal **Service:** General Medical and Surgical

**Staffed Beds:** 36 **Admissions:** 929 **Census:** 11 **Outpatient Visits:** 22322 **Births:** 0 **Total Expense ($000):** 12149 **Payroll Expense ($000):** 5809 **Personnel:** 151

**EDEN—Concho County**

**CONCHO COUNTY HOSPITAL (451325)**, 614 Eaker Street, Zip 76837–0359, Mailing Address: P.O. Box 987, Zip 76837–0987; tel. 325/869–5911 **A**9 10 18 **F**3 40 43 50 57 59 68 77 87 107 133 146
Primary Contact: Dudley R. White, Administrator and Chief Executive Officer
CFO: Melanie Lozano, Chief Financial Officer
Web address: www.conchocountyhospital.com
**Control:** Hospital district or authority, Government, nonfederal **Service:** General Medical and Surgical

**Staffed Beds:** 16 **Admissions:** 100 **Census:** 1 **Outpatient Visits:** 4488 **Births:** 1 **Total Expense ($000):** 3966 **Payroll Expense ($000):** 1575 **Personnel:** 30

**EDINBURG—Hidalgo County**

☒ **CORNERSTONE REGIONAL HOSPITAL (450825)**, 2302 Cornerstone Boulevard, Zip 78539–8471; tel. 956/618–4444 **A**1 9 10 **F**3 8 29 35 37 39 40 45 46 51 57 64 74 79 81 82 85 87 119 **S** Universal Health Services, Inc., King of Prussia, PA
Primary Contact: Roxanna M. Godinez, Chief Executive Officer
CFO: Janie Alvarez, Accounting Director
CMO: Omar Gomez, M.D., Chief of Staff
CHR: Erika Betancourt, Coordinator Human Resources
CNO: Roxanne Reyes, Director of Nursing
Web address: www.southtexashealthsystem.com/Facilities/Cornerstone–Regional–Hospital
**Control:** Partnership, Investor–owned, for–profit **Service:** General Medical and Surgical

**Staffed Beds:** 14 **Admissions:** 395 **Census:** 3 **Outpatient Visits:** 2315 **Births:** 0 **Total Expense ($000):** 11045 **Payroll Expense ($000):** 2669 **Personnel:** 60

☐ **DOCTOR'S HOSPITAL AT RENAISSANCE (450869)**, 5501 South McColl Road, Zip 78539–9152; tel. 956/362–7360 **A**1 9 10 **F**3 12 13 15 17 18 20 22 24 26 28 29 30 31 34 35 38 39 40 45 46 47 49 50 51 57 58 59 60 64 65 70 72 73 74 75 76 77 78 79 81 82 84 85 87 88 89 90 93 96 98 99 100 101 102 103 107 108 110 111 112 113 114 115 116 117 118 119 120 121 123 124 126 130 132 145 146 147 148 **P**3 8
Primary Contact: Lawrence Gelman, M.D., Chief Executive Officer
COO: Marissa Castaneda, Chief Operating Officer and Director Marketing
CFO: Susan S. Turley, Chief Financial Officer
Web address: www.dhr–rgv.com
**Control:** Partnership, Investor–owned, for–profit **Service:** General Medical and Surgical

**Staffed Beds:** 513 **Admissions:** 29756 **Census:** 358 **Outpatient Visits:** 188430 **Births:** 8983 **Total Expense ($000):** 316796 **Payroll Expense ($000):** 140913 **Personnel:** 2988

☐ **SOUTH TEXAS HEALTH SYSTEM (450119)**, 1102 West Trenton Road, Zip 78539–9105; tel. 956/388–6000, (Includes EDINBURG CHILDREN'S HOSPITAL, 1400 West Trenton Road, Zip 78539; tel. 956/388–8000; EDINBURG REGIONAL MEDICAL CENTER, 1102 West Trenton Road, Zip 78539–6199; tel. 956/388–6000; MCALLEN HEART HOSPITAL, 1900 South D. Street, McAllen, Zip 78503; tel. 956/994–2000; MCALLEN MEDICAL CENTER, 301 West Expressway 83, McAllen, Zip 78503–3045; tel. 956/632–4000; SOUTH TEXAS BEHAVIORAL HEALTH CENTER, 2101 West Trenton Road, Zip 78539; tel. 956/388–1300; Joe Rodriguez, Chief Executive Officer) **A**1 9 10 **F**3 4 11 12 13 15 17 18 20 22 24 26 29 30 31 34 35 37 38 39 40 41 43 45 46 47 48 49 50 53 57 59 60 68 70 72 74 75 76 77 78 79 81 85 86 87 88 89 90 96 98 99 100 101 102 103 104 107 108 110 111 114 115 119 129 130 135 138 146 148 **P**6 8 **S** Universal Health Services, Inc., King of Prussia, PA
Primary Contact: Joe Rodriguez, Chief Executive Officer
COO: Mike Adams, Chief Operating Officer
CMO: Humberto Hidalgo, M.D., Chief of Staff
CIO: Rosie L. Mendiola, Director Information Systems
CHR: Cindi Mistrot, Associate Administrator
Web address: www.southtexashealthsystem.com
**Control:** Partnership, Investor–owned, for–profit **Service:** General Medical and Surgical

**Staffed Beds:** 775 **Admissions:** 23211 **Census:** 307 **Outpatient Visits:** 102400 **Births:** 1250 **Total Expense ($000):** 397569 **Payroll Expense ($000):** 98348 **Personnel:** 1834

**EDNA—Jackson County**

★ **JACKSON COUNTY HOSPITAL DISTRICT (451363)**, 1013 South Wells Street, Zip 77957–4098; tel. 361/782–7800 **A**9 10 18 **F**7 15 34 40 43 45 50 56 57 59 62 64 65 68 75 81 87 93 103 104 107 110 111 114 119 127 129 130 131 133 146 148 **P**8
Primary Contact: Bill Jones, Chief Executive Officer
CFO: Lance Smiga, Chief Financial Officer
CMO: Deepinder Judge, M.D., Chief of Staff
CIO: Robert Castillo, Director Profesional Services
CIO: Donna Coleman, Director Professional Services
CHR: Donna Coleman, Coordinator Human Resources
CNO: Tammy Zajicek, Director of Nursing
Web address: www.jchd.org
**Control:** Hospital district or authority, Government, nonfederal **Service:** General Medical and Surgical

**Staffed Beds:** 25 **Admissions:** 455 **Census:** 4 **Outpatient Visits:** 15935 **Births:** 0 **Total Expense ($000):** 17988 **Payroll Expense ($000):** 5867 **Personnel:** 136

**EL CAMPO—Wharton County**

**EL CAMPO MEMORIAL HOSPITAL (450694)**, 303 Sandy Corner Road, Zip 77437–9535; tel. 979/543–6251, (Data for 152 days) **A**9 10 **F**3 11 15 29 34 35 40 45 56 57 59 60 62 64 68 70 75 77 79 81 85 86 93 97 107 108 110 111 114 119 127 129 130 131 132 133 148 **P**6
Primary Contact: Tisha Zalman, Chief Executive Officer
CFO: Gwynn Wigginton, Controller
CMO: Patrick Johnson, D.O., Chief of Staff
CHR: Pat Trigg, Coordinator Personnel and Credentialing
CNO: Desiree Vrazel, Director of Nurses
Web address: www.ecmh.org
**Control:** Other not–for–profit (including NFP Corporation) **Service:** General Medical and Surgical

**Staffed Beds:** 26 **Admissions:** 233 **Census:** 7 **Outpatient Visits:** 23076 **Births:** 0 **Total Expense ($000):** 8778 **Payroll Expense ($000):** 2859 **Personnel:** 123

**EL PASO—El Paso County**

**EAST EL PASO PHYSICIANS MEDICAL CENTER** See Foundation Surgical Hospital of El Paso

**TX**

*Many Facility Codes have changed. Please refer to the AHA Guide Code Chart.*
© 2013 AHA Guide

☐ **EL PASO CHILDREN'S HOSPITAL (453313)**, 4845 Alameda Avenue, Zip 79905–2705; tel. 915/298–5444, (Data for 228 days) **A**1 3 5 9 10 **F**3 11 29 31 40 41 44 45 46 47 48 49 50 58 64 65 72 73 74 75 78 79 81 82 85 86 87 88 89 93 96 111 119 130 146 148 **P**6
Primary Contact: Lawrence Duncan, Chief Executive Officer
COO: Elias Armendariz, Vice President Operations
CFO: David Mier, Chief Financial Officer
CMO: Bradley Fuhrman, M.D., Physician in Chief
CIO: Janina Prada, Director Information Technology
CHR: Natalia Chaparro, Manager Human Resources
CNO: Paul Ocon, R.N., Chief Nursing Officer
Web address: www.elpasochildrens.org
**Control:** Other not–for–profit (including NFP Corporation) **Service:** Children's general

**Staffed Beds:** 122 **Admissions:** 2405 **Census:** 56 **Outpatient Visits:** 19309 **Births:** 0 **Total Expense ($000):** 57239 **Payroll Expense ($000):** 17415 **Personnel:** 446

☐ **EL PASO LTAC HOSPITAL (452103)**, 1221 North Cotton Street, 3rd Floor, Zip 79902–3015; tel. 915/496–9687 **A**9 10 **F**1 3 29 30 34 57 60 75 77 82 84 85 86 87 91 100 103 119 130 148
Primary Contact: Evelyn G. Stewart, Chief Executive Officer
**Control:** Partnership, Investor–owned, for–profit **Service:** Long–Term Acute Care hospital

**Staffed Beds:** 33 **Admissions:** 260 **Census:** 19 **Outpatient Visits:** 0 **Births:** 0 **Total Expense ($000):** 7162 **Payroll Expense ($000):** 2751 **Personnel:** 69

☐ **EL PASO PSYCHIATRIC CENTER (454100)**, 4615 Alameda Avenue, Zip 79905–2702; tel. 915/532–2202 **A**1 3 5 9 10 **F**29 98 99 103 130 135 **P**6 **S** Texas Department of State Health Services, Austin, TX
Primary Contact: Zulema Carrillo, Superintendent
CFO: David Osterhout, Assistant Superintendent and Chief Financial Officer
CMO: Nicolas Baida–Fragoso, M.D., Clinical Director
Web address: www.dshs.state.tx.us/mhhospitals/ElPasoPC/default.shtm
**Control:** State–Government, nonfederal **Service:** Psychiatric

**Staffed Beds:** 77 **Admissions:** 1055 **Census:** 70 **Outpatient Visits:** 0 **Births:** 0 **Total Expense ($000):** 18527 **Payroll Expense ($000):** 9545 **Personnel:** 246

☐ **EL PASO SPECIALTY HOSPITAL (450845)**, 1755 Curie Drive, Zip 79902–2919; tel. 915/544–3636 **A**1 9 10 **F**3 29 34 35 40 59 64 68 75 79 81 82 85 87 107 130 131 148 **S** National Surgical Hospitals, Chicago, IL
Primary Contact: James Wilcox, Chief Executive Officer
CFO: Greg Watters, Chief Financial Officer
CMO: David Mansfield, M.D., Chief of Staff
CNO: Anne Harvey, MSN, Chief Nursing Officer
Web address: www.elpasospecialtyhospital.com
**Control:** Partnership, Investor–owned, for–profit **Service:** Orthopedic

**Staffed Beds:** 27 **Admissions:** 875 **Census:** 6 **Outpatient Visits:** 16280 **Births:** 0 **Total Expense ($000):** 28058 **Payroll Expense ($000):** 6331 **Personnel:** 154

☐ ◇ **FOUNDATION SURGICAL HOSPITAL OF EL PASO (450877)**, (Formerly East El Paso Physicians Medical Center), 1416 George Dieter Drive, Zip 79936–7601; tel. 915/598–4240 **A**1 9 10 21 **F**3 29 40 45 49 79 81 82 85 86 107 111 114 119 **S** Foundation Surgical Hospital Affiliates, Oklahoma City, OK
Primary Contact: Marta Contreras, Chief Nursing Officer and Chief Operating Officer
COO: Marta Contreras, Chief Nursing Officer and Chief Operating Officer
CFO: Scott Banks, Chief Financial Officer
CIO: Louie Aguilera, Director Information Technology
CHR: Grace Beltran, Director Human Resources
CNO: Marta Contreras, Chief Nursing Officer and Chief Operating Officer
Web address: www.physiciansmedcenter.com
**Control:** Partnership, Investor–owned, for–profit **Service:** Surgical

**Staffed Beds:** 20 **Admissions:** 827 **Census:** 8 **Outpatient Visits:** 40236 **Births:** 0 **Total Expense ($000):** 32036 **Payroll Expense ($000):** 7226 **Personnel:** 197

☐ △ **HIGHLANDS REGIONAL REHABILITATION HOSPITAL (453086)**, 1395 George Dieter Drive, Zip 79936–7410; tel. 915/298–7222 **A**1 7 9 10 **F**3 29 30 34 57 59 64 74 75 79 86 87 90 93 96 100 130 132 143 146 148
Primary Contact: Helen Carmona, Acting Chief Executive Officer
Web address: www.highlandsrehab.com
**Control:** Partnership, Investor–owned, for–profit **Service:** Rehabilitation

**Staffed Beds:** 41 **Admissions:** 845 **Census:** 26 **Outpatient Visits:** 5315 **Births:** 0 **Total Expense ($000):** 12839 **Payroll Expense ($000):** 5506 **Personnel:** 117

⊠ **KINDRED HOSPITAL EL PASO (452079)**, 1740 Curie Drive, Zip 79902–2901; tel. 915/351–9044 **A**1 9 10 **F**1 3 29 30 34 75 77 87 130 148 **S** Kindred Healthcare, Louisville, KY
Primary Contact: Aleen D. Arabit, Chief Executive Officer
CFO: Michael Smesny, Chief Financial Officer
CMO: Mauricio Jimenez, M.D., Chief Medical Officer
CHR: Laura Anchondo, Administrator Human Resources
Web address: www.khelpaso.com
**Control:** Corporation, Investor–owned, for–profit **Service:** Long–Term Acute Care hospital

**Staffed Beds:** 62 **Admissions:** 746 **Census:** 49 **Outpatient Visits:** 640 **Births:** 0 **Total Expense ($000):** 18755 **Payroll Expense ($000):** 8446 **Personnel:** 116

⊠ △ **LAS PALMAS MEDICAL CENTER (450107)**, (Formerly Las Palmas Del Sol Healthcare), 1801 North Oregon Street, Zip 79902–3591; tel. 915/521–1200, (Includes DEL SOL MEDICAL CENTER, 10301 West Gateway Boulevard, Zip 79925–7798; tel. 915/595–9000; Jacob Cintron, FACHE, Chief Executive Officer; LAS PALMAS REHABILITATION HOSPITAL, 300 Waymore Drive, Zip 79902–1628; tel. 915/577–2600) **A**1 3 5 7 9 10 **F**1 3 5 9 10 11 12 13 15 16 17 18 20 22 24 28 29 30 31 34 35 36 40 43 46 50 51 53 54 56 57 59 61 64 65 68 70 72 73 74 75 76 77 78 79 81 86 87 88 89 90 93 107 108 111 115 118 119 121 130 131 132 138 142 146 147 148 **S** HCA, Nashville, TN
Primary Contact: Hank Hernandez, Chief Executive Officer
COO: Don Karl, Chief Operating Officer
Web address: www.laspalmashealth.com
**Control:** Partnership, Investor–owned, for–profit **Service:** General Medical and Surgical

**Staffed Beds:** 570 **Admissions:** 28255 **Census:** 374 **Outpatient Visits:** 236386 **Births:** 4805 **Total Expense ($000):** 349343 **Payroll Expense ($000):** 126486 **Personnel:** 2150

☐ **MESA HILLS SPECIALTY HOSPITAL (452035)**, 2311 North Oregon Street, Zip 79902–3216; tel. 915/545–1823, (Nonreporting) **A**1 9 10 **S** Encore Healthcare, Columbia, MD
Primary Contact: Jesus Ruiz, Chief Executive Officer
COO: Elena Pino, Chief Operating Officer and Chief Nursing Officer
CFO: Priscilla Carter, Chief Financial Officer
Web address: www.encore–healthcare.com/mesa_hills/index.aspx
**Control:** Corporation, Investor–owned, for–profit **Service:** Long–Term Acute Care hospital

**Staffed Beds:** 32

⊠ **PROVIDENCE MEMORIAL HOSPITAL (450002)**, 2001 North Oregon Street, Zip 79902–3368; tel. 915/577–6011, (Includes CHILDREN'S HOSPITAL AT PROVIDENCE, 2001 North Oregon Street, Zip 79902–3320; tel. 915/577–7746) **A**1 9 10 **F**3 11 12 13 14 15 17 18 19 20 21 22 23 24 25 29 30 31 32 34 35 40 41 42 43 44 45 46 49 50 51 54 55 57 59 63 64 65 70 72 73 74 75 76 77 78 79 81 82 84 85 87 88 89 91 92 93 107 108 110 111 114 118 119 126 129 130 132 134 135 145 146 147 148 **P**1 **S** TENET Healthcare Corporation, Dallas, TX
Primary Contact: J. Eric Evans, Chief Executive Officer
CFO: Charles Hondley, Chief Financial Officer
CIO: Ray Davis, Administrative Director
CHR: Mark Thomasson, Vice President Human Resources
Web address: www.sphn.com
**Control:** Partnership, Investor–owned, for–profit **Service:** General Medical and Surgical

**Staffed Beds:** 359 **Admissions:** 17647 **Census:** 206 **Outpatient Visits:** 180108 **Births:** 3831 **Total Expense ($000):** 227654 **Payroll Expense ($000):** 76962 **Personnel:** 1338

⊠ **SIERRA MEDICAL CENTER (450668)**, 1625 Medical Center Drive, Zip 79902–5044; tel. 915/747–4000 **A**1 5 9 10 **F**3 8 11 13 15 17 18 20 22 24 26 29 30 31 34 35 37 40 43 44 45 46 47 48 49 50 54 55 57 58 59 60 61 64 68 70 72 74 75 76 77 78 79 81 82 85 86 107 108 110 111 114 115 119 120 124 126 130 132 134 144 145 146 147 148 **P**1 **S** TENET Healthcare Corporation, Dallas, TX
Primary Contact: J. Eric Evans, Chief Executive Officer
COO: Enrique Gallegos, Chief Operating Officer
CFO: David Byrd, Chief Financial Officer
CIO: Ray Davis, Administrative Director Information Systems
CHR: Linda Wallace, Director Human Resources
CNO: Katherine Doll, R.N., Chief Nursing Officer
Web address: www.sphn.com
**Control:** Partnership, Investor–owned, for–profit **Service:** General Medical and Surgical

**Staffed Beds:** 334 **Admissions:** 10971 **Census:** 139 **Outpatient Visits:** 104675 **Births:** 1967 **Total Expense ($000):** 149277 **Payroll Expense ($000):** 58735 **Personnel:** 818

**TX**

---

**Hospital, Medicare Provider Number, Address, Telephone, Approval, Facility, and Physician Codes, Health Care System**

★ American Hospital Association (AHA) membership
☐ The Joint Commission accreditation
◇ DNV Healthcare Inc. accreditation
○ Healthcare Facilities Accreditation Program
△ Commission on Accreditation of Rehabilitation Facilities (CARF) accreditation

✠ **SIERRA PROVIDENCE EAST MEDICAL CENTER (670047)**, 3280 Joe Battle Boulevard, Zip 79938–2622; tel. 915/832–2000 **A**1 2 5 9 10 **F**3 13 15 18 20 22 26 29 30 31 34 35 40 45 46 47 49 50 57 59 60 63 64 68 70 72 73 74 75 76 77 79 81 85 86 87 93 107 108 111 115 119 130 134 146 148 **P**4 **S** TENET Healthcare Corporation, Dallas, TX
Primary Contact: Sally A. Deitch, MSN, R.N., Chief Executive Officer
COO: Lauren Morton, Chief Operating Officer
CFO: Brandon May, Chief Financial Officer
Web address: www.sphn.com
**Control:** Individual, Investor–owned, for–profit **Service:** General Medical and Surgical

**Staffed Beds:** 110 **Admissions:** 7592 **Census:** 88 **Outpatient Visits:** 73696 **Births:** 1609 **Total Expense ($000):** 114566 **Payroll Expense ($000):** 34267 **Personnel:** 561

**TRIUMPH HOSPITAL EL PASO** See Kindred Hospital El Paso

☐ **UNIVERSITY BEHAVIORAL HEALTH OF EL PASO (454109)**, 1900 Denver Avenue, Zip 79902–3008; tel. 915/544–4000, (Nonreporting) **A**1 3 5 9 10 **S** Universal Health Services, Inc., King of Prussia, PA
Primary Contact: David Morris, Chief Executive Officer
Web address: www.ubhelpaso.com/
**Control:** Corporation, Investor–owned, for–profit **Service:** Psychiatric

**Staffed Beds:** 163

✠ **UNIVERSITY MEDICAL CENTER OF EL PASO (450024)**, 4815 Alameda Avenue, Zip 79905–2794, Mailing Address: P.O. Box 20009, Zip 79998–0009; tel. 915/544–1200 **A**1 2 3 5 8 9 10 **F**3 8 11 13 15 17 18 20 22 24 26 28 29 30 31 34 35 37 40 43 45 46 47 48 49 50 51 53 54 56 57 59 60 61 64 65 68 70 74 75 76 77 79 81 82 85 86 87 92 93 94 97 100 102 107 108 110 111 114 118 119 126 127 130 134 143 144 145 146 147 148 **P**6
Primary Contact: James N. Valenti, FACHE, President and Chief Executive Officer
COO: James N. Valenti, FACHE, President and Chief Executive Officer
CMO: Carmela Morales, M.D., Chief of Staff
CIO: Janina Prada, Director Information Services
CHR: Gilbert Blancas, Director Human Resources
Web address: www.thomasoncares.org
**Control:** Hospital district or authority, Government, nonfederal **Service:** General Medical and Surgical

**Staffed Beds:** 242 **Admissions:** 14925 **Census:** 183 **Outpatient Visits:** 668466 **Births:** 3452 **Total Expense ($000):** 449089 **Payroll Expense ($000):** 116539 **Personnel:** 2132

✠ **WILLIAM BEAUMONT ARMY MEDICAL CENTER**, 5005 North Piedras Street, Zip 79920–5001; tel. 915/742–2121, (Nonreporting) **A**1 2 3 5 9 **S** Department of the Army, Office of the Surgeon General, Falls Church, VA
Primary Contact: Colonel Michael S. Heimall, Commander
CIO: Major Rion Koon, Chief Information Management Division
Web address: www.wbamc.amedd.army.mil
**Control:** Army, Government, federal **Service:** General Medical and Surgical

**Staffed Beds:** 209

**ELDORADO—Schleicher County**

★ **SCHLEICHER COUNTY MEDICAL CENTER (451304)**, 400 West Murchison, Zip 76936, Mailing Address: P.O. Box V., Zip 76936–1246; tel. 325/853–2507 **A**9 10 18 **F**11 18 34 40 57 59 64 65 66 68 93 107 127 128 133 **S** Preferred Management Corporation, Shawnee, OK
Primary Contact: Paul Burke, Administrator
CFO: Larry Stephens, Chief Financial Officer
CMO: Gordy Day, M.D., Medical Director
CHR: Beverly Minor, Chief Human Resources
Web address: www.scmc.us
**Control:** Corporation, Investor–owned, for–profit **Service:** General Medical and Surgical

**Staffed Beds:** 14 **Admissions:** 86 **Census:** 1 **Outpatient Visits:** 8428 **Births:** 0 **Total Expense ($000):** 4395 **Payroll Expense ($000):** 2085 **Personnel:** 44

**ELECTRA—Wichita County**

★ **ELECTRA MEMORIAL HOSPITAL (451343)**, 1207 South Bailey Street, Zip 76360–3221, Mailing Address: P.O. Box 1112, Zip 76360–1112; tel. 940/495–3981 **A**9 10 18 **F**3 7 11 32 40 43 50 53 56 57 59 62 64 65 66 75 77 93 97 107 114 119 129 130 131 133 144 147 148
Primary Contact: Jan A. Reed, CPA, Administrator and Chief Executive Officer
CFO: Rebecca McCain, Chief Financial Officer and Assistant Administrator
CIO: Brandon Huffstutler, Chief Information Officer
CNO: Kim Gilbert, R.N., Chief Nursing Officer
Web address: www.electrahospital.com
**Control:** Hospital district or authority, Government, nonfederal **Service:** General Medical and Surgical

**Staffed Beds:** 19 **Admissions:** 390 **Census:** 5 **Outpatient Visits:** 20796 **Births:** 0 **Total Expense ($000):** 8944 **Payroll Expense ($000):** 5016 **Personnel:** 106

**ENNIS—Ellis County**

✠ **ENNIS REGIONAL MEDICAL CENTER (450833)**, 2201 West Lampasas Street, Zip 75119–5644; tel. 972/875–0900 **A**1 9 10 **F**3 11 13 15 18 29 34 40 43 45 50 51 57 59 70 76 77 79 81 82 85 93 94 107 110 111 115 119 146 **S** LifePoint Hospitals, Inc., Brentwood, TN
Primary Contact: Kevin Zachary, Chief Executive Officer
CFO: Jack Wilcox, Chief Financial Officer
CMO: Ralph W. Blair, Jr., M.D., Chief of Staff
CHR: James Dopson, Director Human Resources
Web address: www.ennisregional.com
**Control:** Partnership, Investor–owned, for–profit **Service:** General Medical and Surgical

**Staffed Beds:** 58 **Admissions:** 2133 **Census:** 16 **Outpatient Visits:** 32346 **Births:** 642 **Total Expense ($000):** 24713 **Payroll Expense ($000):** 10318 **Personnel:** 186

**FAIRFIELD—Freestone County**

★ **EAST TEXAS MEDICAL CENTER FAIRFIELD (450658)**, 125 Newman Street, Zip 75840–1499; tel. 903/389–2121 **A**9 10 20 **F**15 28 40 57 59 75 81 82 107 115 119 127 130 132 133 **P**7 **S** East Texas Medical Center Regional Healthcare System, Tyler, TX
Primary Contact: Ruth Cook, Administrator
CFO: David A. Travis, Chief Financial Officer
CMO: J. Michael Orms, M.D., Chief of Staff
CHR: Jennifer Rummel, Director Human Resources
Web address: www.etmc.org
**Control:** Other not–for–profit (including NFP Corporation) **Service:** General Medical and Surgical

**Staffed Beds:** 20 **Admissions:** 508 **Census:** 4 **Outpatient Visits:** 40463 **Births:** 0 **Total Expense ($000):** 11449 **Payroll Expense ($000):** 3865 **Personnel:** 91

**FLORESVILLE—Wilson County**

**CONNALLY MEDICAL CENTER (450108)**, 499 10th Street, Zip 78114–3175; tel. 830/393–1300 **A**9 10 **F**3 15 18 29 34 35 40 43 45 47 54 57 59 62 64 70 75 81 82 85 86 87 107 111 114 119 130 132 133 146 148 **P**4
Primary Contact: Jerome M. Brooks, Chief Executive Officer
COO: Thomas Repino, Executive Director Ancillary Services
CIO: Kim Schultz, Manager Information
CHR: Dane Bonecutter, Director Human Resources
CNO: Celeste Brizzee, Chief Nursing Officer
Web address: www.connallymmc.org
**Control:** Hospital district or authority, Government, nonfederal **Service:** General Medical and Surgical

**Staffed Beds:** 17 **Admissions:** 1075 **Census:** 10 **Outpatient Visits:** 61500 **Births:** 2 **Total Expense ($000):** 21025 **Payroll Expense ($000):** 7233 **Personnel:** 209

**FLOWER MOUND—Denton County**

◇ **CONTINUUM REHABILITATION HOSPITAL OF NORTH TEXAS (673047)**, 3100 Peters Colony Road, Zip 75022–2949; tel. 214/513–0310, (Total facility includes 12 beds in nursing home–type unit) **A**9 10 21 **F**3 34 57 59 64 90 93 96 128 130
Primary Contact: Patrick Lee, Chief Executive Officer
Web address: www.continuumhs.com
**Control:** Individual, Investor–owned, for–profit **Service:** Rehabilitation

**Staffed Beds:** 41 **Admissions:** 379 **Census:** 11 **Outpatient Visits:** 5874 **Births:** 0 **Total Expense ($000):** 8181 **Payroll Expense ($000):** 3875 **Personnel:** 77

☐ ◇ **TEXAS HEALTH PRESBYTERIAN HOSPITAL FLOWER MOUND (670068)**, 4400 Long Prairie Road, Zip 75028–1892; tel. 469/322–7000 **A**1 9 10 21 **F**3 13 15 18 20 29 30 31 40 45 49 57 70 73 74 76 77 78 79 81 85 107 108 110 111 115 119 126 130 146 147
Primary Contact: Spencer Turner, Chief Executive Officer
COO: Shelley R. Tobey, R.N., Chief Operating Officer and Chief Nursing Officer
CFO: Tom Howard, Chief Financial Officer
CHR: Nicole Schweigert, Director Human Resources
CNO: Shelley R. Tobey, R.N., Chief Operating Officer and Chief Nursing Officer
Web address: www.phfmtexas.com/
**Control:** Partnership, Investor–owned, for–profit **Service:** General Medical and Surgical

**Staffed Beds:** 85 **Admissions:** 3645 **Census:** 39 **Outpatient Visits:** 27377 **Births:** 1047 **Total Expense ($000):** 75044 **Payroll Expense ($000):** 24762 **Personnel:** 418

**TX**

*Many Facility Codes have changed. Please refer to the AHA Guide Code Chart.* © 2013 AHA Guide

**FORT HOOD—Bell County**

⊠ **CARL R. DARNALL ARMY MEDICAL CENTER**, 36000 Darnall Loop,
Zip 76544–5095; tel. 254/288–8000, (Nonreporting) **A**1 2 3 5 9 **S** Department
of the Army, Office of the Surgeon General, Falls Church, VA
Primary Contact: Colonel Patrick D. Sargent, Commander
CFO: Major David Rollins, Chief Resource Management
CMO: Colonel Kimberly Kesling, Deputy Commander Clinical Service
CHR: Charles Burton, Chief Human Resources
Web address: www.crdamc.amedd.army.mil
**Control:** Army, Government, federal **Service:** General Medical and Surgical

Staffed Beds: 109

**FORT SAM HOUSTON—Bexar County**

**BROOKE ARMY MEDICAL CENTER** See San Antonio Military Medical Center

⊠ **SAN ANTONIO MILITARY MEDICAL CENTER**, 3851 Roger Brookes Drive,
Zip 78234–4501; tel. 210/916–4141, (Nonreporting) **A**1 2 3 5 9 **S** Department
of the Army, Office of the Surgeon General, Falls Church, VA
Primary Contact: Major General M. Ted Wong, Commanding General
CFO: Lieutenant Colonel Derrick Flowers, Chief Resource Management Division
CMO: Colonel Joseph P. Chozinski, M.D., Deputy Commander Clinical Services
CIO: Lieutenant Colonel David Broyhill, Chief Information Management
CHR: Rose Juarez, Chief Civilian Personnel Branch
CNO: Colonel Sheri Howell, Deputy Commander Nursing
Web address: www.bamc.amedd.army.mil
**Control:** Army, Government, federal **Service:** General Medical and Surgical

Staffed Beds: 226

**FORT STOCKTON—Pecos County**

★ **PECOS COUNTY MEMORIAL HOSPITAL (450178)**, 387 West I. H–10,
Zip 79735–8912, Mailing Address: P.O. Box 1648, Zip 79735–1648;
tel. 432/336–2004 **A**9 10 20 **F**3 11 13 28 29 30 32 34 35 40 43 53 57 59
62 63 64 65 75 76 81 93 107 111 119 127 129 130 146 **P**5 6
Primary Contact: Jim Horton, Chief Executive Officer
CFO: Leticia Fox, Chief Financial Officer
CMO: Larry Boyd, M.D., Chief of Staff
CHR: Malissa Trevino, Director Human Resources
CNO: Gina Kalka, R.N., Chief Nursing Officer
Web address: www.pcmhfs.com
**Control:** County–Government, nonfederal **Service:** General Medical and Surgical

Staffed Beds: 27 Admissions: 1489 Census: 12 Outpatient Visits: 67775
Births: 154 Total Expense ($000): 24548 Payroll Expense ($000): 10593
Personnel: 259

**FORT WORTH—Tarrant County**

⊠ **BAYLOR ALL SAINTS MEDICAL CENTER AT FORT WORTH (450137)**, 1400
Eighth Avenue, Zip 76104–4192; tel. 817/926–2544 **A**1 2 9 10 **F**3 11 12 13
15 17 18 20 22 24 26 28 29 30 31 34 35 36 38 40 45 46 47 49 53 54 59
64 68 70 72 73 74 75 76 77 78 79 80 81 82 84 86 87 90 93 96 97 98 100
101 102 103 104 105 107 108 111 114 115 119 124 126 130 131 132 135
138 139 142 146 147 148 **S** Baylor Health Care System, Dallas, TX
Primary Contact: David G. Klein, M.D., Interim President
COO: David G. Klein, M.D., Chief Operating Officer
CFO: Preshie Wilson, Vice President Finance
CIO: Sandy Vaughn, Director Information Services
CHR: Julie Strittmatter, Director Human Resources
Web address: www.baylorhealth.com/PhysiciansLocations/AllSaints/Pages/
Default.aspx
**Control:** Other not–for–profit (including NFP Corporation) **Service:** General
Medical and Surgical

Staffed Beds: 395 Admissions: 19770 Census: 244 Outpatient Visits:
103330 Births: 5653 Total Expense ($000): 362371 Payroll Expense
($000): 124885 Personnel: 1556

☐ **BAYLOR SURGICAL HOSPITAL AT FORT WORTH (450880)**, 750 12th
Avenue, Zip 76104–2517; tel. 817/334–5050 **A**1 9 10 **F**3 29 40 45 51 64 65
75 77 79 81 82 85 86 87 107 111 114 119 130 141
Primary Contact: Roger Rhodes, Chief Executive Officer
Web address: www.mcsh–hospital.com
**Control:** Partnership, Investor–owned, for–profit **Service:** General Medical and
Surgical

Staffed Beds: 22 Admissions: 1103 Census: 8 Outpatient Visits: 11051
Births: 0 Total Expense ($000): 54339 Payroll Expense ($000): 9450
Personnel: 180

⊠ **COOK CHILDREN'S MEDICAL CENTER (453300)**, 801 Seventh Avenue,
Zip 76104–2796; tel. 682/885–4000 **A**1 3 5 9 10 **F**3 7 8 19 21 23 25 27 29
30 31 32 34 35 38 39 40 41 43 44 45 48 50 51 54 55 57 58 59 60 61 64
68 72 74 75 77 78 79 80 81 82 84 85 86 87 88 89 90 93 97 98 99 100
101 102 104 105 106 107 108 111 112 113 114 118 119 129 130 131 132
134 136 138 143 146 **P**6
Primary Contact: Rick W. Merrill, President and Chief Executive Officer
CFO: Richard P. Goode, Chief Financial Officer
CMO: James C. Cunningham, M.D., Chief Medical Officer
CIO: Theresa Meadows, Chief Information Officer
CHR: Frank J. Rossi, Senior Vice President Human Resources
CNO: Paula J. Webb, R.N., Chief Nursing Officer
Web address: www.cookchildrens.org
**Control:** Other not–for–profit (including NFP Corporation) **Service:** Children's
general

Staffed Beds: 329 Admissions: 11352 Census: 216 Outpatient Visits:
315537 Births: 0 Total Expense ($000): 585950 Payroll Expense ($000):
206296 Personnel: 3435

**GLOBALREHAB HOSPITAL – FORT WORTH (673035)**, 6601 Harris Parkway,
Zip 76132–6108; tel. 817/433–9600 **A**10 **F**3 28 29 30 75 90 130
**S** GLOBALREHAB, Dallas, TX
Web address: www.globalrehabhospitals.com
**Control:** Partnership, Investor–owned, for–profit **Service:** Rehabilitation

Staffed Beds: 42 Admissions: 937 Census: 33 Outpatient Visits: 270
Births: 0 Total Expense ($000): 14266 Payroll Expense ($000): 7782
Personnel: 112

⊠ **HEALTHSOUTH REHABILITATION HOSPITAL OF FORT WORTH (453041)**,
1212 West Lancaster Avenue, Zip 76102–4510; tel. 817/870–2336 **A**1 9 10 **F**3
29 30 64 74 75 77 79 82 86 90 91 95 96 100 130 131 148 **S** HEALTHSOUTH
Corporation, Birmingham, AL
Primary Contact: Trent Pierce, R.N., Chief Executive Officer
CFO: Sherry Hapney, Chief Financial Officer
CMO: Patrick Donovan, M.D., Director Medical Staff
CHR: Tara Kleas, Director Human Resources
Web address: www.healthsouthfortworth.com
**Control:** Corporation, Investor–owned, for–profit **Service:** Rehabilitation

Staffed Beds: 60 Admissions: 1048 Census: 38 Outpatient Visits: 594
Births: 0 Total Expense ($000): 12326 Payroll Expense ($000): 7290
Personnel: 148

⊠ **HEALTHSOUTH REHABILITATION HOSPITAL–CITYVIEW (453042)**, 6701
Oakmont Boulevard, Zip 76132–2957; tel. 817/370–4700 **A**1 9 10 **F**3 29 30 62
68 77 82 90 91 93 94 95 96 118 130 148 **S** HEALTHSOUTH Corporation,
Birmingham, AL
Primary Contact: Deborah Hopps, Chief Executive Officer
Web address: www.healthsouthcityview.com
**Control:** Corporation, Investor–owned, for–profit **Service:** Rehabilitation

Staffed Beds: 62 Admissions: 1037 Census: 38 Outpatient Visits: 8934
Births: 0 Total Expense ($000): 14767 Payroll Expense ($000): 8640
Personnel: 152

⊠ **HUGULEY MEMORIAL MEDICAL CENTER (450677)**, 11801 South Freeway,
Zip 76028–7021, Mailing Address: P.O. Box 6337, Zip 76115–0337;
tel. 817/293–9110 **A**1 10 **F**3 5 8 13 15 17 18 20 22 24 28 29 30 31 32 34
35 38 40 44 49 51 53 54 56 57 59 60 64 68 70 71 75 76 77 78 79 80 81
82 85 86 87 89 93 98 100 101 102 103 104 105 107 108 110 111 114 118
119 120 121 130 132 135 146 147 148 **S** Adventist Health System Sunbelt
Health Care Corporation, Altamonte Springs, FL
Primary Contact: Kenneth A. Finch, President and Chief Executive Officer
CFO: Penny Johnson, Chief Financial Officer
CMO: Edward Laue, M.D., Chief Medical Officer
CIO: David Smith, Manager Data Center
CHR: Laura Fisher, Director Human Resources
CNO: Tammy Collier, Vice President Patient Services
Web address: www.huguley.org
**Control:** Church–operated, Nongovernment, not–for profit **Service:** General
Medical and Surgical

Staffed Beds: 192 Admissions: 9397 Census: 108 Outpatient Visits:
141169 Births: 1066 Total Expense ($000): 142295 Payroll Expense
($000): 53505 Personnel: 990

**JOHN PETER SMITH HOSPITAL** See JPS Health Network

---

**Hospital, Medicare Provider Number, Address, Telephone, Approval, Facility, and Physician Codes, Health Care System**

★ American Hospital Association (AHA) membership
☐ The Joint Commission accreditation ◇ DNV Healthcare Inc. accreditation
○ Healthcare Facilities Accreditation Program
△ Commission on Accreditation of Rehabilitation Facilities (CARF) accreditation

★ **JPS HEALTH NETWORK (450039)**, 1500 South Main Street, Zip 76104–4917; tel. 817/921–3431, (Includes JOHN PETER SMITH HOSPITAL, 1500 South Main Street, Zip 76104; tel. 817/921–3431; TRINITY SPRINGS PAVILION, 1500 South Main Street, tel. 817/927–3636; Lily Wong, Director Psychiatry), (Total facility includes 15 beds in nursing home–type unit) **A**2 3 5 8 9 10 **F**3 8 11 13 15 17 18 20 22 24 26 28 29 30 31 32 34 35 36 37 38 39 40 43 44 45 49 50 54 55 56 57 58 59 60 61 64 65 66 68 70 72 74 75 76 77 78 79 80 81 82 85 86 87 89 91 92 93 97 98 99 100 101 102 103 104 107 108 110 111 114 115 118 119 120 121 123 124 126 128 130 131 132 134 135 142 143 144 146 147 148 **P**3
Primary Contact: Robert Earley, President and Chief Executive Officer
COO: Bill Whitman, Chief Operating Officer
CFO: David Salsberry, Chief Financial Officer
CMO: Gary Floyd, M.D., Executive Vice President Medical Affairs and Chief Medical Officer
CIO: James Pennington, Chief Information Officer
CHR: Rose Thomason, Interim Vice President Human Resources
Web address: www.jpshealthnet.org
**Control:** Hospital district or authority, Government, nonfederal **Service:** General Medical and Surgical

**Staffed Beds:** 517 **Admissions:** 26619 **Census:** 384 **Outpatient Visits:** 977034 **Births:** 5138 **Total Expense ($000):** 667132 **Payroll Expense ($000):** 252353 **Personnel:** 4284

⊠ **KINDRED HOSPITAL TARRANT COUNTY–FORT WORTH SOUTHWEST (452088)**, 7800 Oakmont Boulevard, Zip 76132–4299; tel. 817/346–0094 **A**1 9 10 **F**1 3 28 29 107 130 135 148 **S** Kindred Healthcare, Louisville, KY
Primary Contact: Anna Rojas, Chief Executive Officer
CFO: Amy Skelton, Chief Financial Officer
CMO: Henry Cunningham, M.D., President Medical Staff
CHR: Kay Lanam, Coordinator Human Resources
CNO: Mary Edobor, Chief Clinical Officer
Web address: www.kindredhospitalfwsw.com/
**Control:** Corporation, Investor–owned, for–profit **Service:** Long–Term Acute Care hospital

**Staffed Beds:** 78 **Admissions:** 944 **Census:** 61 **Outpatient Visits:** 212 **Births:** 0 **Total Expense ($000):** 27096 **Payroll Expense ($000):** 10762 **Personnel:** 183

⊠ **KINDRED HOSPITAL–FORT WORTH (452088)**, 815 Eighth Avenue, Zip 76104–2609; tel. 817/332–4812 **A**1 9 10 **F**3 29 46 48 60 70 77 79 82 85 107 114 130 148 **S** Kindred Healthcare, Louisville, KY
Primary Contact: Angela Harris, Chief Executive Officer
CFO: Susan Popp, Controller
CMO: Stuart McDonald, M.D., President Medical Staff
CIO: Norma Warner, Area Director Health Information Management
CHR: Nicole Newpower, Coordinator Human Resources
Web address: www.kindredfortworth.com/
**Control:** Corporation, Investor–owned, for–profit **Service:** Long–Term Acute Care hospital

**Staffed Beds:** 54 **Admissions:** 617 **Census:** 43 **Outpatient Visits:** 0 **Births:** 0 **Total Expense ($000):** 21880 **Payroll Expense ($000):** 8883 **Personnel:** 166

⊠ **PLAZA MEDICAL CENTER OF FORT WORTH (450672)**, 900 Eighth Avenue, Zip 76104–3902; tel. 817/336–2100 **A**1 2 9 10 12 13 **F**3 11 12 17 18 20 22 24 26 28 29 30 31 34 35 36 37 40 45 47 48 49 50 57 58 59 68 70 74 75 77 78 79 80 81 85 87 91 93 96 107 108 111 115 117 118 119 129 130 132 136 138 145 146 148 **P**8 **S** HCA, Nashville, TN
Primary Contact: Clay Franklin, Chief Executive Officer
COO: Gregory Haralson, Chief Operating Officer
CFO: Elia Stokes, Chief Financial Officer
CMO: Amir Malik, M.D., Cardiologist
CIO: Kelley Fredrickson, Director Information Services
CHR: Cyndi Roberts, Director Human Resources
Web address: www.plazamedicalcenter.com
**Control:** Partnership, Investor–owned, for–profit **Service:** General Medical and Surgical

**Staffed Beds:** 217 **Admissions:** 11356 **Census:** 153 **Outpatient Visits:** 37887 **Births:** 0 **Total Expense ($000):** 174795 **Payroll Expense ($000):** 59431 **Personnel:** 770

⊠ **REGENCY HOSPITAL OF FORT WORTH (452099)**, 6801 Oakmont Boulevard, Zip 76132–3918; tel. 817/840–2500 **A**1 9 10 **F**1 3 29 45 75 77 85 86 87 130 148 **P**5 **S** Select Medical Corporation, Mechanicsburg, PA
Primary Contact: Brad Ervin, Chief Executive Officer
Web address: www.regencyhospital.com
**Control:** Corporation, Investor–owned, for–profit **Service:** Long–Term Acute Care hospital

**Staffed Beds:** 44 **Admissions:** 407 **Census:** 30 **Outpatient Visits:** 0 **Births:** 0 **Total Expense ($000):** 16368 **Payroll Expense ($000):** 6963 **Personnel:** 117

⊠ **TEXAS HEALTH HARRIS METHODIST HOSPITAL ALLIANCE**, 10864 Texas Health Trail, Zip 76244–4897; tel. 682/212–2000, (Nonreporting) **A**1 9 **S** Texas Health Resources, Arlington, TX
Primary Contact: Winjie Tang Miao, President
**Control:** Other not–for–profit (including NFP Corporation) **Service:** General Medical and Surgical

**Staffed Beds:** 50

⊠ △ **TEXAS HEALTH HARRIS METHODIST HOSPITAL FORT WORTH (450135)**, 1301 Pennsylvania Avenue, Zip 76104–2122; tel. 817/250–2000 **A**1 2 7 9 10 **F**3 8 11 12 13 15 17 18 20 22 24 26 28 29 30 31 34 35 36 40 42 43 45 46 47 48 49 50 52 53 54 55 56 57 58 59 60 64 68 70 71 72 74 75 76 77 78 79 81 83 84 85 86 87 93 95 96 100 107 108 110 111 114 115 116 117 118 119 124 126 130 131 132 135 138 145 146 147 148 **S** Texas Health Resources, Arlington, TX
Primary Contact: Lillie Biggins, R.N., President
CFO: Richard Humphrey, Vice President Finance
CMO: Harold Berenzweig, M.D., Vice President Medical and Information Management
CHR: Joseph Condon, Director Human Resources
CNO: Lillie Biggins, R.N., President
CNO: Elaine Nelson, R.N., Chief Nursing Officer
Web address: www.texashealth.org
**Control:** Other not–for–profit (including NFP Corporation) **Service:** General Medical and Surgical

**Staffed Beds:** 635 **Admissions:** 35061 **Census:** 497 **Outpatient Visits:** 176301 **Births:** 3380 **Total Expense ($000):** 654300 **Payroll Expense ($000):** 237505 **Personnel:** 3890

⊠ **TEXAS HEALTH HARRIS METHODIST HOSPITAL SOUTHWEST FORT WORTH (450779)**, 6100 Harris Parkway, Zip 76132–4199; tel. 817/433–5000 **A**1 9 10 **F**3 11 13 15 18 20 29 30 34 35 38 40 45 46 47 49 50 59 64 68 70 72 74 75 76 77 78 79 81 82 84 85 86 87 93 102 107 108 110 111 114 118 119 126 129 130 146 147 **S** Texas Health Resources, Arlington, TX
Primary Contact: Joseph DeLeon, President
COO: Allen Tseng, Administrative Director
CMO: Robert Lilli, M.D., Chief of Staff
CHR: Jody Thomas, Director Human Resources
Web address: www.texashealth.org
**Control:** Church–operated, Nongovernment, not–for profit **Service:** General Medical and Surgical

**Staffed Beds:** 151 **Admissions:** 10851 **Census:** 110 **Outpatient Visits:** 93038 **Births:** 3119 **Total Expense ($000):** 148918 **Payroll Expense ($000):** 56557 **Personnel:** 756

⊠ **TEXAS HEALTH SPECIALTY HOSPITAL (452018)**, 1301 Pennsylvania Avenue, 4th Floor, Zip 76104–2190; tel. 817/250–5500 **A**1 9 10 **F**1 3 44 87 130 148 **P**7 **S** Texas Health Resources, Arlington, TX
Primary Contact: Susan Louise Baldwin, R.N., FACHE, President and Chief Nursing Officer
CFO: Vicki L. Galati, Chief Financial Officer
CMO: John Pender, M.D., Medical Director
CHR: Kathy Hardcastle, Manager Human Resources
CNO: Susan Louise Baldwin, R.N., President and Chief Nursing Officer
Web address: www.texashealth.org
**Control:** Church–operated, Nongovernment, not–for profit **Service:** Long–Term Acute Care hospital

**Staffed Beds:** 10 **Admissions:** 102 **Census:** 8 **Outpatient Visits:** 0 **Births:** 0 **Total Expense ($000):** 6619 **Payroll Expense ($000):** 2872 **Personnel:** 41

☐ △ **TEXAS REHABILITATION HOSPITAL OF FORT WORTH (673048)**, 425 Alabama Avenue, Zip 76104–1022; tel. 817/820–3400 **A**1 7 9 10 **F**3 29 74 79 90 91 96 130 132 148 **S** Centerre Healthcare, Brentwood, TN
Primary Contact: Russell Bailey, Chief Executive Officer
Web address: www.texasrehabhospital.com/
**Control:** Corporation, Investor–owned, for–profit **Service:** Rehabilitation

**Staffed Beds:** 50 **Admissions:** 1123 **Census:** 44 **Outpatient Visits:** 0 **Births:** 0 **Total Expense ($000):** 16310 **Payroll Expense ($000):** 8230 **Personnel:** 137

☐ **USMD HOSPITAL AT FORT WORTH (670046)**, 5900 Dirks Road, Zip 76132–5473; tel. 817/433–9100 **A**1 9 10 **F**3 29 39 40 51 64 68 81 85 89 107 114 119 130 **S** USMD Inc., Irving, TX
Primary Contact: Stephanie Atkins–Guidry, Administrator
CHR: Alex Stefanowicz, Vice President Human Resources
CNO: Stephanie Atkins–Guidry, Administrator and Chief Nursing Officer
Web address: www.usmdfortworth.com/
**Control:** Partnership, Investor–owned, for–profit **Service:** Surgical

**Staffed Beds:** 8 **Admissions:** 472 **Census:** 3 **Outpatient Visits:** 5407 **Births:** 0 **Total Expense ($000):** 29994 **Payroll Expense ($000):** 4377 **Personnel:** 101

*Many Facility Codes have changed. Please refer to the AHA Guide Code Chart.*

© 2013 AHA Guide

**TX**

## FREDERICKSBURG—Gillespie County

☒ **HILL COUNTRY MEMORIAL HOSPITAL (450604)**, 1020 South State Highway 16, Zip 78624-4471, Mailing Address: P.O. Box 835, Zip 78624-0835; tel. 830/997-4353 **A**1 9 10 20 **F**3 11 13 15 20 28 29 30 31 32 34 35 37 40 43 45 49 50 51 53 57 59 62 63 64 68 70 74 75 76 77 78 79 81 82 84 85 86 87 90 93 96 107 108 110 111 114 118 119 124 129 130 131 132 133 135 146 148 **P**8
Primary Contact: Jayne E. Pope, Chief Executive Officer
COO: Debbye Wallace, Chief Operating Officer
CFO: Mark Jones, Chief Financial Officer
CMO: Jose A. Lopez, M.D., Chief of Staff
CIO: Holly Schmidt, Chief Information Officer
CHR: Erin Cates, Director Human Resources
Web address: www.hcmhs.org
**Control:** Other not-for-profit (including NFP Corporation) **Service:** General Medical and Surgical

**Staffed Beds:** 57 **Admissions:** 2826 **Census:** 27 **Outpatient Visits:** 76296 **Births:** 493 **Total Expense ($000):** 61470 **Payroll Expense ($000):** 26024 **Personnel:** 544

## FRIONA—Parmer County

**PARMER COUNTY COMMUNITY HOSPITAL** See Parmer Medical Center

**PARMER MEDICAL CENTER (451300)**, 1307 Cleveland Avenue, Zip 79035-1121; tel. 806/250-2754 **A**9 10 18 **F**30 34 40 43 57 64 75 77 89 93 107 119 130 133 148 **S** Preferred Management Corporation, Shawnee, OK
Primary Contact: Gayla Quillin, Administrator
Web address: www.parmermedicalcenter.com
**Control:** Other not-for-profit (including NFP Corporation) **Service:** General Medical and Surgical

**Staffed Beds:** 15 **Admissions:** 160 **Census:** 4 **Outpatient Visits:** 13108 **Births:** 0 **Total Expense ($000):** 8072 **Payroll Expense ($000):** 2836 **Personnel:** 70

## FRISCO—Collin County

☐ **BAYLOR INSTITUTE FOR REHABILITATION AT FRISCO (673046)**, 2990 Legacy Drive, Zip 75034-6066; tel. 469/888-5100 **A**1 9 10 **F**29 30 34 36 75 90 91 93 96 130 132 148
Primary Contact: Mark D. Boles, Chief Executive Officer
Web address: www.baylorhealth.com/bir
**Control:** Partnership, Investor-owned, for-profit **Service:** Rehabilitation

**Staffed Beds:** 44 **Admissions:** 748 **Census:** 28 **Outpatient Visits:** 5365 **Births:** 0 **Total Expense ($000):** 15181 **Payroll Expense ($000):** 7838 **Personnel:** 114

☐ **BAYLOR MEDICAL CENTER AT FRISCO (450853)**, 5601 Warren Parkway, Zip 75034-4069; tel. 214/407-5000 **A**1 9 10 **F**3 13 29 34 40 51 54 57 64 68 72 74 75 76 79 81 85 87 107 111 114 119 144 **S** United Surgical Partners International, Addison, TX
Primary Contact: William A. Keaton, Chief Executive Officer
CFO: Kevin Coats, Chief Financial Officer
CMO: Jimmy Laferney, M.D., Vice President Medical Staff Affairs
CIO: Steve Young, Director Information Systems
CHR: Margaret Garcia, Manager Human Resources
CNO: Randi Elliott MSN, Chief Nursing Officer
Web address: www.bmcf.com
**Control:** Partnership, Investor-owned, for-profit **Service:** General Medical and Surgical

**Staffed Beds:** 68 **Admissions:** 4492 **Census:** 39 **Outpatient Visits:** 29540 **Births:** 2561 **Total Expense ($000):** 115487 **Payroll Expense ($000):** 37424 **Personnel:** 549

☒ **CENTENNIAL MEDICAL CENTER (450885)**, 12505 Lebanon Road, Zip 75035-8298; tel. 972/963-3333 **A**1 9 10 **F**3 8 13 15 18 20 22 24 29 31 34 35 40 45 46 47 48 49 50 51 57 59 70 72 74 76 78 79 81 85 86 89 93 97 107 108 110 111 114 115 119 124 130 131 146 147 148 **S** TENET Healthcare Corporation, Dallas, TX
Primary Contact: Joe D. Thomason, Chief Executive Officer
COO: Reed Hammond, Chief Operating Officer
CFO: Blaise Bondi, Chief Financial Officer
CMO: Robert S. Hendler, M.D., Regional Chief Medical Officer
CIO: Dianne Yarborough, Director of Information Technology
CHR: Stephanie S. Talley, Director Human Resources
CNO: Calee Travis, R.N., Chief Nursing Officer
Web address: www.centennialmedcenter.com
**Control:** Corporation, Investor-owned, for-profit **Service:** General Medical and Surgical

**Staffed Beds:** 118 **Admissions:** 4890 **Census:** 59 **Outpatient Visits:** 38659 **Births:** 900 **Total Expense ($000):** 81996 **Payroll Expense ($000):** 28756 **Personnel:** 522

○ **FOREST PARK MEDICAL CENTER FRISCO**, 5500 Frisco Square Boulevard, Zip 75034-3305; tel. 214/618-0500, (Nonreporting) **A**11
Primary Contact: Julie A. Camp, R.N., Chief Executive Officer
Web address: www.forestparkfrisco.com/default.aspx
**Control:** Corporation, Investor-owned, for-profit **Service:** Surgical

**Staffed Beds:** 30

## GAINESVILLE—Cooke County

★ **NORTH TEXAS MEDICAL CENTER (450090)**, 1900 Hospital Boulevard, Zip 76240-2002; tel. 940/665-1751 **A**9 10 20 **F**3 11 13 15 28 29 30 34 35 40 43 45 50 59 60 62 64 68 70 75 76 77 79 81 82 85 87 93 104 107 108 110 111 115 118 119 127 130 132 133 146 147
Primary Contact: Randy B. Bacus, FACHE, Chief Executive Officer
CFO: Kelly Hayes, Chief Financial Officer
CHR: Teresa Krebs, Director Human Resources
Web address: www.ntmconline.net
**Control:** Hospital district or authority, Government, nonfederal **Service:** General Medical and Surgical

**Staffed Beds:** 48 **Admissions:** 1689 **Census:** 16 **Outpatient Visits:** 46782 **Births:** 355 **Total Expense ($000):** 34893 **Payroll Expense ($000):** 13892 **Personnel:** 266

## GALVESTON—Galveston County

☐ **SHRINERS HOSPITALS FOR CHILDREN–GALVESTON BURNS HOSPITAL (453311)**, (Burn Care), 815 Market Street, Zip 77550-2725; tel. 409/770-6600 **A**1 3 5 10 **F**3 11 16 29 30 32 34 35 38 64 68 75 77 81 82 85 86 93 99 100 101 104 119 130 132 146 148 **S** Shriners Hospitals for Children, Tampa, FL
Primary Contact: David A. Ferrell, Regional Administrator
COO: Mary Jaco, R.N., Director Patient Care Services and Chief Operating Officer
CFO: Lona Pope, Director Financial Services
CMO: David N. Herndon, M.D., Chief of Staff
CHR: Lynn Clements, Director Human Resources
CNO: Mary Jaco, R.N., Director Patient Care Services and Chief Operating Officer
Web address: www.shrinershospitalsforchildren.org/Hospitals/Locations/Galveston.aspx
**Control:** Other not-for-profit (including NFP Corporation) **Service:** Children's other specialty

**Staffed Beds:** 15 **Admissions:** 205 **Census:** 8 **Outpatient Visits:** 9592 **Births:** 0 **Total Expense ($000):** 29947 **Payroll Expense ($000):** 11491 **Personnel:** 193

☒ **UNIVERSITY OF TEXAS MEDICAL BRANCH HOSPITALS (450018)**, 301 University Boulevard, Zip 77555-0128; tel. 409/772-1011 **A**1 2 5 8 9 10 13 **F**3 8 11 12 13 14 15 16 17 18 19 20 21 22 23 24 25 26 28 29 30 34 35 36 38 40 41 43 44 45 46 49 50 51 52 53 54 55 56 57 58 59 60 61 64 65 66 68 70 71 72 73 74 75 76 77 78 79 81 82 84 85 86 87 88 89 90 93 94 96 97 99 100 101 102 103 104 107 108 110 111 114 115 117 118 119 120 121 123 124 126 129 130 131 132 134 135 137 138 139 140 141 142 143 144 145 146 147 148 **P**6 **S** University of Texas System, Austin, TX
Primary Contact: Donna K. Sollenberger, Executive Vice President and Chief Executive Officer
COO: Deb McGrew, Chief Operating Officer
CFO: William Elger, Executive Vice President and Chief Business and Finance Officer
CMO: Steve Quach, M.D., Chief Medical Officer
CIO: Ralph Farr, Chief Information Officer
CHR: Ronald McKinley, Ph.D., Vice President Human Resources and Employee Services
CNO: David R. Marshall, JD, Chief Nursing and Patient Care Services Officer
Web address: www.utmb.edu
**Control:** State-Government, nonfederal **Service:** General Medical and Surgical

**Staffed Beds:** 380 **Admissions:** 23250 **Census:** 310 **Outpatient Visits:** 681100 **Births:** 5684 **Total Expense ($000):** 601519 **Payroll Expense ($000):** 223278 **Personnel:** 3480

TX

**Hospital, Medicare Provider Number, Address, Telephone, Approval, Facility, and Physician Codes, Health Care System**

★ American Hospital Association (AHA) membership
☐ The Joint Commission accreditation
◇ DNV Healthcare Inc. accreditation
○ Healthcare Facilities Accreditation Program
△ Commission on Accreditation of Rehabilitation Facilities (CARF) accreditation

© 2013 AHA Guide    *Many Facility Codes have changed. Please refer to the AHA Guide Code Chart.*    Hospitals **A605**

## GARLAND—Dallas County

✉ **BAYLOR MEDICAL CENTER AT GARLAND (450280)**, 2300 Marie Curie Drive, Zip 75042–5706; tel. 972/487–5000 **A**1 2 3 5 9 10 **F**3 11 13 15 18 20 22 24 26 28 29 30 34 35 40 45 47 50 54 57 59 60 64 65 66 70 72 74 75 76 77 78 79 81 82 84 85 86 87 90 93 94 107 108 110 111 114 118 119 129 130 132 135 145 146 147 148 **S** Baylor Health Care System, Dallas, TX
Primary Contact: Thomas J. Trenary, President
COO: Janice L. Walker, R.N., Chief Nursing Officer and Chief Operating Officer
CFO: Robert Knowlton, Vice President and Chief Financial Officer
CMO: Steven Arze, M.D., Chief Medical Officer and Vice President Medical Affiars
CIO: Michael Larsen, Director Information Systems
CHR: Laura Settles, Director Human Resources
CNO: Janice L. Walker, R.N., Chief Nursing Officer and Chief Operating Officer
Web address: www.baylorhealth.com/PhysiciansLocations/Garland/Pages/Default.aspx
**Control:** Other not–for–profit (including NFP Corporation) **Service:** General Medical and Surgical

**Staffed Beds:** 240 **Admissions:** 10177 **Census:** 125 **Outpatient Visits:** 122143 **Births:** 1255 **Total Expense ($000):** 209182 **Payroll Expense ($000):** 70734 **Personnel:** 981

## GATESVILLE—Coryell County

☐ **CORYELL MEMORIAL HOSPITAL (451379)**, 1507 West Main Street, Zip 76528–1098; tel. 254/865–8251 **A**1 9 10 18 **F**3 7 10 11 15 18 20 28 40 43 50 53 57 62 65 70 81 82 87 93 97 107 111 115 119 125 127 129 130 133 **P**6
Primary Contact: David Byrom, Chief Executive Officer
COO: David Byrom, Chief Executive Officer
CFO: Carol Jones, Controller and Manager Business Office
CMO: J D Sheffield, D.O., President Medical Staff
CIO: Mike Huckabee, Network Administrator
CHR: Paula Smithhart, Director Human Resources
CNO: Jeanne Griffith, Chief Nursing Officer
Web address: www.cmhos.org
**Control:** Hospital district or authority, Government, nonfederal **Service:** General Medical and Surgical

**Staffed Beds:** 25 **Admissions:** 599 **Census:** 6 **Outpatient Visits:** 43725 **Births:** 0 **Total Expense ($000):** 22228 **Payroll Expense ($000):** 10185 **Personnel:** 312

## GILMER—Upshur County

★ **EAST TEXAS MEDICAL CENTER–GILMER (450884)**, 712 North Wood Street, Zip 75644–1751; tel. 903/841–7100 **A**9 10 **F**3 11 29 30 40 43 50 57 59 68 85 87 97 107 108 111 115 119 127 **P**6 **S** East Texas Medical Center Regional Healthcare System, Tyler, TX
Primary Contact: Jorge E. Leal, Administrator
CFO: Thomas O'Gorman, Jr., Chief Financial Officer
CHR: William Henry, Director Human Resources
CNO: Miguel Casas, R.N., Chief Nursing Officer
Web address: www.etmc.org
**Control:** Other not–for–profit (including NFP Corporation) **Service:** General Medical and Surgical

**Staffed Beds:** 35 **Admissions:** 618 **Census:** 6 **Outpatient Visits:** 26766 **Births:** 0 **Total Expense ($000):** 10683 **Payroll Expense ($000):** 3932 **Personnel:** 81

## GLEN ROSE—Somervell County

✉ **GLEN ROSE MEDICAL CENTER (450451)**, 1021 Holden Street, Zip 76043–4937, Mailing Address: P.O. Box 2099, Zip 76043–2099; tel. 254/897–2215, (Total facility includes 118 beds in nursing home–type unit) **A**1 9 10 **F**2 15 29 34 40 43 45 48 51 56 57 59 65 79 81 93 103 104 107 108 110 111 119 127 129 130 132 133 143 146 **P**7
Primary Contact: Ray Reynolds, Chief Executive Officer
COO: Mo S. Sheldon, Chief Operating Officer
CFO: Michael Honea, Chief Financial Officer
CHR: LaDonna Green, Director Human Resources
CNO: Lisa McClammy, Chief Nursing Officer
Web address: www.glenrosemedicalcenter.com
**Control:** Hospital district or authority, Government, nonfederal **Service:** General Medical and Surgical

**Staffed Beds:** 134 **Admissions:** 985 **Census:** 102 **Outpatient Visits:** 151924 **Births:** 0 **Total Expense ($000):** 19343 **Payroll Expense ($000):** 8695 **Personnel:** 137

## GONZALES—Gonzales County

★ **MEMORIAL HOSPITAL (450235)**, 1110 Sarah Dewitt Drive, Zip 78629–3311, Mailing Address: P.O. Box 587, Zip 78629–0587; tel. 830/672–7581 **A**9 10 **F**3 11 13 15 29 30 34 35 40 43 53 57 59 62 64 65 68 70 75 76 77 81 85 87 93 97 107 111 115 119 127 129 130 132 133 148 **S** QHR, Brentwood, TN
Primary Contact: Charles Norris, Chief Executive Officer
CFO: Patty Stewart, Chief Financial Officer
CMO: Commie Hisey, D.O., Chief of Staff
CHR: Joni Leland, Director Human Resources
Web address: www.gonzaleshealthcare.com
**Control:** Hospital district or authority, Government, nonfederal **Service:** General Medical and Surgical

**Staffed Beds:** 32 **Admissions:** 1006 **Census:** 8 **Outpatient Visits:** 63190 **Births:** 190 **Total Expense ($000):** 25050 **Payroll Expense ($000):** 9619 **Personnel:** 225

## GRAHAM—Young County

★ **GRAHAM REGIONAL MEDICAL CENTER (450085)**, 1301 Montgomery Road, Zip 76450–4240, Mailing Address: P.O. Box 1390, Zip 76450–1390; tel. 940/549–3400 **A**9 10 20 **F**7 11 13 15 28 29 40 43 53 57 59 62 63 70 75 76 79 81 85 89 93 104 107 111 115 119 127 130 133 135 **P**5
Primary Contact: Steve L. Hartgraves, Chief Executive Officer
CFO: Bonnie Blevins, Chief Financial Officer
CIO: Jeff Clark, Director Information Systems
CHR: Judy Guinn, Chief Human Resources Officer
Web address: www.grahamrmc.com
**Control:** City–Government, nonfederal **Service:** General Medical and Surgical

**Staffed Beds:** 37 **Admissions:** 1005 **Census:** 9 **Outpatient Visits:** 49728 **Births:** 228 **Total Expense ($000):** 22511 **Payroll Expense ($000):** 9376 **Personnel:** 200

## GRANBURY—Hood County

✉ **LAKE GRANBURY MEDICAL CENTER (450596)**, 1310 Paluxy Road, Zip 76048–5655; tel. 817/573–2273 **A**1 9 10 **F**3 8 11 12 13 15 18 20 22 26 28 29 30 34 37 40 43 45 49 53 57 59 64 70 74 75 76 77 79 81 82 85 86 93 107 108 110 111 114 118 119 126 129 133 135 146 147 **S** Community Health Systems, Inc., Franklin, TN
Primary Contact: Derrick Cuenca, Chief Executive Officer
CFO: Noe Gutierrez, Chief Financial Officer
CIO: Kevin Myers, Director Information Systems
CHR: Vanessa Anyaso, Director Human Resources
CNO: Shirley A. Graves, R.N., Chief Nursing Officer
Web address: www.lakegranburymedicalcenter.com
**Control:** Corporation, Investor–owned, for–profit **Service:** General Medical and Surgical

**Staffed Beds:** 83 **Admissions:** 2437 **Census:** 19 **Outpatient Visits:** 53806 **Births:** 513 **Total Expense ($000):** 46597 **Payroll Expense ($000):** 16661 **Personnel:** 310

## GRAND PRAIRIE—Dallas County

◇ **TEXAS GENERAL HOSPITAL (670083)**, 2709 Hospital Boulevard, Zip 75051–1017; tel. 469/999–0000 **A**10 21 **F**8 12 18 20 22 34 35 40 45 49 50 57 59 64 70 79 81 82 85 107 108 111 115 119
Primary Contact: Suleman Hashmi, President and Chief Executive Officer
Web address: www.texasgeneralhospital.com
**Control:** Partnership, Investor–owned, for–profit **Service:** General Medical and Surgical

**Staffed Beds:** 10 **Admissions:** 178 **Census:** 1 **Outpatient Visits:** 5038 **Births:** 0 **Total Expense ($000):** 18737 **Payroll Expense ($000):** 4037 **Personnel:** 127

## GRAND SALINE—Van Zandt County

**COZBY–GERMANY HOSPITAL (450283)**, 707 North Waldrip Street, Zip 75140–1555; tel. 903/962–4242, (Nonreporting) **A**9 10 20
Primary Contact: Laura Wiggins, Chief Executive Officer
CMO: Irfan Rana, M.D., Chief of Staff
CIO: Suzi Walker, Manager Business Office
CHR: Lee Anne Sanders, Director Human Resources
**Control:** Other not–for–profit (including NFP Corporation) **Service:** General Medical and Surgical

**Staffed Beds:** 24

*Many Facility Codes have changed. Please refer to the AHA Guide Code Chart.*   © 2013 AHA Guide

## GRAPEVINE—Tarrant County

⊠ **BAYLOR REGIONAL MEDICAL CENTER AT GRAPEVINE (450563)**, 1650 West College Street, Zip 76051–3565; tel. 817/481–1588 **A**1 2 9 10 **F**3 11 12 13 15 18 20 22 24 26 28 29 30 31 34 35 40 45 46 47 48 49 56 57 59 61 64 65 70 72 74 75 76 77 78 79 80 81 82 86 87 107 108 110 111 114 115 119 126 129 130 131 132 135 145 146 147 **S** Baylor Health Care System, Dallas, TX
Primary Contact: Steven R. Newton, President
COO: Chris York, FACHE, Chief Operating Officer
CFO: Preshie Wilson, Vice President Finance Services
CMO: Thomas Purgett, M.D., Chief Medical Staff
CIO: David Krzjci, Director Information Systems
CHR: Donna Stark, Director Human Resources
Web address: www.https://www.baylorhealth.com/PhysiciansLocations/Grapevine/Pages/Default.aspx
**Control:** Other not–for–profit (including NFP Corporation) **Service:** General Medical and Surgical

**Staffed Beds:** 269 **Admissions:** 12596 **Census:** 157 **Outpatient Visits:** 88820 **Births:** 2875 **Total Expense ($000):** 205349 **Payroll Expense ($000):** 76265 **Personnel:** 1041

☐ **ETHICUS HOSPITAL – GRAPEVINE (452110)**, 4201 William D. Tate Avenue, Zip 76051–5736; tel. 817/288–1300 **A**1 9 10 **F**1 3 29 30 40 60 64 68 74 75 77 85 87 93 94 96 107 119 130 148
Primary Contact: Robbye N. Dubois, Chief Executive Officer
Web address: www.ethicusgrapevine.com
**Control:** Partnership, Investor–owned, for–profit **Service:** Long–Term Acute Care hospital

**Staffed Beds:** 48 **Admissions:** 508 **Census:** 43 **Outpatient Visits:** 39 **Births:** 0 **Total Expense ($000):** 26071 **Payroll Expense ($000):** 11825 **Personnel:** 157

## GREENVILLE—Hunt County

☐ **GLEN OAKS HOSPITAL (454050)**, 301 Division Street, Zip 75401–4101; tel. 903/454–6000 **A**1 9 10 **F**4 5 29 34 40 68 98 99 100 101 102 103 104 105 **S** Universal Health Services, Inc., King of Prussia, PA
Primary Contact: Joel Klein, Chief Executive Officer and Managing Director
CFO: Lowell K. Hudson, Chief Financial Officer
CMO: David Lucas, R.N., Director of Nursing
CMO: Satish Narayan, M.D., Medical Director
CHR: Joe Carson, Director Human Resources
Web address: www.glenoakshospital.com
**Control:** Corporation, Investor–owned, for–profit **Service:** Psychiatric

**Staffed Beds:** 54 **Admissions:** 1630 **Census:** 39 **Outpatient Visits:** 5860 **Births:** 0 **Total Expense ($000):** 7471 **Payroll Expense ($000):** 3889 **Personnel:** 94

⊠ **HUNT REGIONAL MEDICAL CENTER (450352)**, (Formerly Hunt Memorial Hospital District), 4215 Joe Ramsey Boulevard, Zip 75401–7899, Mailing Address: P.O. Box 1059, Zip 75403–1059; tel. 903/408–5000, (Includes HUNT REGIONAL MEDICAL CENTER, 4215 Joe Ramsey Boulevard, Zip 75403–1059, Mailing Address: Drawer 1059, Zip 75403–1059; tel. 903/408–5000), (Nonreporting) **A**1 9 10 **S** Hunt Regional Healthcare, Greenville, TX
Primary Contact: Richard Carter, District Chief Executive Officer
COO: Michael R. Klepin, Administrator
CFO: Jeri Rich, Assistant Administrator and Chief Financial Officer
CMO: James H. Sandin, M.D., Assistant Administrator Medical Affairs
CIO: Joe Hartley, Director Information Systems
CHR: John Heatherly, Assistant Administrator Support Services
Web address: www.huntregional.org
**Control:** Hospital district or authority, Government, nonfederal **Service:** General Medical and Surgical

**Staffed Beds:** 206

## GROESBECK—Limestone County

★ **LIMESTONE MEDICAL CENTER (451303)**, 701 Mcclintic Drive, Zip 76642–2128; tel. 254/729–3281 **A**9 10 18 **F**3 7 11 28 32 34 35 40 41 43 45 57 64 65 75 77 84 85 90 93 96 97 104 107 114 127 129 130 133 135 146 148
Primary Contact: Larry Price, Chief Executive Officer
CFO: Mike Williams, Accountant
CIO: Byong Lee, Manager Information Technology and PACS Administrator
CHR: Jean Koester, Manager Human Resources
CNO: Jean Wragge, Director of Nurses
Web address: www.lmchospital.com
**Control:** Hospital district or authority, Government, nonfederal **Service:** General Medical and Surgical

**Staffed Beds:** 20 **Admissions:** 417 **Census:** 6 **Outpatient Visits:** 19124 **Births:** 0 **Total Expense ($000):** 16606 **Payroll Expense ($000):** 7136 **Personnel:** 191

## HALLETTSVILLE—Lavaca County

**LAVACA MEDICAL CENTER (451376)**, 1400 North Texana Street, Zip 77964–2099; tel. 361/798–3671 **A**9 10 18 **F**3 11 15 29 34 40 41 43 45 47 53 56 57 59 64 65 68 75 77 81 85 86 87 93 107 108 110 111 114 119 127 133 135 146 148
Primary Contact: James Vanek, Chief Executive Officer
**Control:** Hospital district or authority, Government, nonfederal **Service:** General Medical and Surgical

**Staffed Beds:** 25 **Admissions:** 635 **Census:** 7 **Outpatient Visits:** 27228 **Births:** 0 **Total Expense ($000):** 14583 **Payroll Expense ($000):** 5422 **Personnel:** 130

## HAMILTON—Hamilton County

★ **HAMILTON GENERAL HOSPITAL (450754)**, 400 North Brown Street, Zip 76531–1518; tel. 254/386–1600 **A**9 10 20 **F**3 7 11 15 28 29 34 40 43 44 45 50 53 56 57 59 64 68 79 80 81 82 85 86 93 97 103 104 107 110 114 127 130 132
Primary Contact: Michele Cathey, Administrator and Chief Executive Officer
CFO: Brenda Denison, Chief Financial Officer
CIO: Chad Reinert, Director Information Technology
CHR: Emily Dossey, Director Human Resources
CNO: Debra Martin, Director of Nursing
Web address: www.hamiltonhospital.org
**Control:** Hospital district or authority, Government, nonfederal **Service:** General Medical and Surgical

**Staffed Beds:** 42 **Admissions:** 1553 **Census:** 15 **Outpatient Visits:** 95987 **Births:** 0 **Total Expense ($000):** 19409 **Payroll Expense ($000):** 7532 **Personnel:** 201

## HAMLIN—Jones County

**HAMLIN MEMORIAL HOSPITAL (450243)**, 632 Northwest Second Street, Zip 79520–3831, Mailing Address: P.O. Box 400, Zip 79520–0400; tel. 325/576–3646 **A**9 10 **F**3 7 11 28 29 40 43 64 68 69 107 133 135 146 148 **P**5
Primary Contact: Brian Roland, Chief Executive Officer
CMO: Krishna Sunkavalle, M.D., Chief Medical Officer
**Control:** Hospital district or authority, Government, nonfederal **Service:** General Medical and Surgical

**Staffed Beds:** 23 **Admissions:** 151 **Census:** 2 **Outpatient Visits:** 4034 **Births:** 0 **Total Expense ($000):** 2985 **Payroll Expense ($000):** 1757 **Personnel:** 65

## HARKER HEIGHTS—Bell County

⊠ **SETON MEDICAL CENTER HARKER HEIGHTS (670080)**, 850 West Central Texas Expressway, Zip 76548–1890; tel. 254/690–0900, (Data for 197 days) **A**1 9 10 **F**3 13 15 18 20 22 26 29 30 34 35 40 45 49 50 51 56 57 59 60 64 70 74 75 76 77 79 81 82 91 97 107 108 110 111 115 119 129 135 146 147 148 **P**3 **S** LHP Hospital Group, Plano, TX
Primary Contact: Matt T. Maxfield, FACHE, Chief Executive Officer
CFO: John K. Sharp, Chief Financial Officer
CHR: Mona Tucker, Director Human Resources
CNO: Pamela Craig, R.N., Chief Nursing Officer
Web address: www.setonharkerheights.net
**Control:** Partnership, Investor–owned, for–profit **Service:** General Medical and Surgical

**Staffed Beds:** 83 **Admissions:** 1406 **Census:** 23 **Outpatient Visits:** 21599 **Births:** 294 **Total Expense ($000):** 37771 **Payroll Expense ($000):** 14391 **Personnel:** 376

## HARLINGEN—Cameron County

⊠ **HARLINGEN MEDICAL CENTER (450855)**, 5501 South Expressway 77, Zip 78550–3213; tel. 956/365–1000 **A**1 9 10 **F**3 12 13 15 17 18 20 22 24 29 30 40 43 49 50 51 57 59 64 68 70 74 75 76 79 81 85 86 89 107 108 110 111 114 115 118 119 129 130 146 147 148 **S** Prime Healthcare Services, Ontario, CA
Primary Contact: Brenda Ivory, Chief Executive Officer
CFO: Harvey Torres, Vice President Finance and Chief Financial Officer
CMO: Hugo Blake, M.D., Chief Medical Staff
CHR: Diane Elizondo, Director Human Resources
Web address: www.harlingenmedicalcenter.com
**Control:** Partnership, Investor–owned, for–profit **Service:** General Medical and Surgical

**Staffed Beds:** 88 **Admissions:** 5705 **Census:** 49 **Outpatient Visits:** 55301 **Births:** 913 **Total Expense ($000):** 68623 **Payroll Expense ($000):** 27594 **Personnel:** 477

---

**Hospital, Medicare Provider Number, Address, Telephone, Approval, Facility, and Physician Codes, Health Care System**

★ American Hospital Association (AHA) membership
☐ The Joint Commission accreditation
◇ DNV Healthcare Inc. accreditation
○ Healthcare Facilities Accreditation Program
△ Commission on Accreditation of Rehabilitation Facilities (CARF) accreditation

☐ **RIO GRANDE STATE CENTER/SOUTH TEXAS HEALTH CARE SYSTEM (454088)**, 1401 South Rangerville Road, Zip 78552-7638; tel. 956/364-8000, (Includes RIO GRANDE STATE CENTER, 1401 South Rangerville Road, tel. 956/364-8000; SOUTH TEXAS HEALTH CARE SYSTEM, 1401 Rangerville Road, Zip 78552-7609; tel. 956/364-8000) **A**1 10 **F**30 53 54 57 65 66 68 75 87 97 98 101 107 119 130 132 135 143 146 147 **P**6 **S** Texas Department of State Health Services, Austin, TX
Primary Contact: Sonia Hernandez-Keeble, Superintendent
CFO: Tom Garza, Director Fiscal and Support
CMO: David Moron, M.D., Clinical Director
CIO: Blas Ortiz, Jr., Assistant Superintendent and Public Information Officer
CHR: Irma Garcia, Job Coordinator
Web address: www.dshs.state.tx.us/mhhospitals/RioGrandeSC/default.shtm
**Control:** State-Government, nonfederal **Service:** Psychiatric

**Staffed Beds:** 128 **Admissions:** 1125 **Census:** 52 **Outpatient Visits:** 39929 **Births:** 0 **Total Expense ($000):** 14684 **Payroll Expense ($000):** 7735 **Personnel:** 564

**SOLARA HOSPITAL HARLINGEN (452101)**, 508 Victoria Lane, Zip 78550-3225; tel. 956/425-9600, (Includes SOLARA HOSPITAL – BROWNSVILLE CAMPUS, 333 Lorenaly Drive, Brownsville, Zip 78526-4333; tel. 956/546-0808) **A**9 10 **F**1 3 29 30 35 40 57 75 85 86 130 148 **S** Cornerstone Healthcare Group, Dallas, TX
Primary Contact: Cary L. Montalvo, Chief Executive Officer
CFO: Laura Nowell, Vice President Accounting and Finance
CMO: Ann B. McCracken, M.D., President Medical Staff
CIO: Adam Davis, Chief Information Officer
CHR: Lydia Cantu-Lopez, Human Resources Representative
Web address: www.chghospitals.com/harlingen/
**Control:** Partnership, Investor-owned, for-profit **Service:** Long-Term Acute Care hospital

**Staffed Beds:** 82 **Admissions:** 832 **Census:** 55 **Outpatient Visits:** 0 **Births:** 0 **Total Expense ($000):** 25318 **Payroll Expense ($000):** 10136 **Personnel:** 189

☒ **VALLEY BAPTIST MEDICAL CENTER–HARLINGEN (450033)**, 2101 Pease Street, Zip 78550-8307, Mailing Address: P.O. Drawer 2588, Zip 78551-2588; tel. 956/389-1100, (Data for 304 days) **A**1 3 5 9 10 **F**3 11 12 13 14 15 17 18 20 22 24 26 28 29 30 31 34 35 39 40 43 44 45 46 47 48 49 50 51 54 56 57 59 60 63 64 65 68 70 71 72 73 74 75 76 77 78 79 81 82 84 85 86 87 88 89 90 91 92 93 94 100 103 104 107 108 110 111 112 114 115 119 126 129 130 132 144 146 147 148 **P**8 **S** Vanguard Health Systems, Nashville, TN
Primary Contact: Todd Mann, Senior Vice President and Chief Executive Officer
CHR: Irma L. Pye, Senior Vice President and Chief Human Resource Officer
CNO: Stephen Hill, Vice President and Chief Nursing Officer
Web address: www.valleybaptist.net/harlingen/index.htm
**Control:** Corporation, Investor-owned, for-profit **Service:** General Medical and Surgical

**Staffed Beds:** 417 **Admissions:** 14898 **Census:** 236 **Outpatient Visits:** 81402 **Births:** 1589 **Total Expense ($000):** 249575 **Payroll Expense ($000):** 67767 **Personnel:** 909

**HASKELL—Haskell County**

**HASKELL MEMORIAL HOSPITAL (451341)**, 1 North Avenue N, Zip 79521-5499, Mailing Address: P.O. Box 1117, Zip 79521-1117; tel. 940/864-2621 **A**9 10 18 **F**11 28 29 34 35 40 45 56 57 59 68 75 77 86 87 93 130 131 133 146 **P**1
Primary Contact: Fran McCown, Administrator
CHR: Emily Moore, Director Human Resources and Information Technology
CNO: Charlotte Welch, Chief Nursing Officer
**Control:** Hospital district or authority, Government, nonfederal **Service:** General Medical and Surgical

**Staffed Beds:** 15 **Admissions:** 333 **Census:** 4 **Outpatient Visits:** 7659 **Births:** 0 **Total Expense ($000):** 4362 **Payroll Expense ($000):** 1978 **Personnel:** 61

**HEMPHILL—Sabine County**

☒ **SABINE COUNTY HOSPITAL (451361)**, Highway 83 West, Zip 75948, Mailing Address: P.O. Box 750, Zip 75948-0750; tel. 409/787-3300 **A**1 9 10 18 **F**34 35 40 43 50 57 59 64 68 75 83 84 91 92 93 94 107 114 119 127 132 133 **S** Preferred Management Corporation, Shawnee, OK
Primary Contact: Diana Taylor, Administrator
COO: Deanna Lathrop, Assistant Administrator
CFO: Cindy Erickson, Chief Financial Officer
CMO: Grover C. Winslow, M.D., Chief of Staff
CIO: Margaret Moore, Manager Business Office
Web address: www.sabinecountyhospital.com/
**Control:** Corporation, Investor-owned, for-profit **Service:** General Medical and Surgical

**Staffed Beds:** 25 **Admissions:** 428 **Census:** 5 **Outpatient Visits:** 16168 **Births:** 0 **Total Expense ($000):** 7893 **Payroll Expense ($000):** 2885 **Personnel:** 75

**HENDERSON—Rusk County**

☒ **EAST TEXAS MEDICAL CENTER HENDERSON (450475)**, 300 Wilson Street, Zip 75652-5956; tel. 903/657-7541 **A**1 9 10 **F**3 8 11 13 15 28 29 30 34 35 37 40 43 45 50 57 59 64 65 70 75 76 79 81 85 107 108 110 111 115 119 127 129 133 145 146 147 148 **S** East Texas Medical Center Regional Healthcare System, Tyler, TX
Primary Contact: Mark Leitner, Chief Executive Officer
CFO: Phillip A. Caron, Chief Financial Officer
CHR: William Henry, Director Human Resources
Web address: www.etmc.org/etmchenderson/
**Control:** Other not-for-profit (including NFP Corporation) **Service:** General Medical and Surgical

**Staffed Beds:** 47 **Admissions:** 1602 **Census:** 15 **Outpatient Visits:** 46152 **Births:** 235 **Total Expense ($000):** 25782 **Payroll Expense ($000):** 8861 **Personnel:** 178

**HENRIETTA—Clay County**

**CLAY COUNTY MEMORIAL HOSPITAL (451362)**, 310 West South Street, Zip 76365-3346; tel. 940/538-5621 **A**9 10 18 **F**7 8 11 28 34 35 40 50 53 57 62 68 80 81 90 93 107 111 119 130 132 133 148 **P**5
Primary Contact: Jeff Huskey, Chief Executive Officer and Administrator
COO: Michael Clark, Director Operations
CFO: Debra Haehn, Chief Financial Officer
CMO: Mitchell Wolfe, M.D., Chief of Staff
CIO: Larry Evangelista, Supervisor Information Technology
CHR: Linda Burleson, Administrative Secretary
Web address: www.ccmhospital.com
**Control:** County-Government, nonfederal **Service:** General Medical and Surgical

**Staffed Beds:** 25 **Admissions:** 248 **Census:** 4 **Outpatient Visits:** 7505 **Births:** 0 **Total Expense ($000):** 5071 **Payroll Expense ($000):** 2702 **Personnel:** 78

**HEREFORD—Deaf Smith County**

**HEREFORD REGIONAL MEDICAL CENTER (450155)**, 540 West 15th Street, Zip 79045-2820; tel. 806/364-2141 **A**9 10 **F**3 7 11 13 15 29 35 40 43 50 57 59 62 65 70 76 77 81 85 93 107 111 114 119 127 130 133 147 **P**5
Primary Contact: Nathan A. Flood, Chief Executive Officer
COO: Meri Killingsworth, Chief Operating Officer
CFO: Greg Reinart, Chief Financial Officer
Web address: www.herefordregional.com
**Control:** Hospital district or authority, Government, nonfederal **Service:** General Medical and Surgical

**Staffed Beds:** 39 **Admissions:** 777 **Census:** 6 **Outpatient Visits:** 68536 **Births:** 304 **Total Expense ($000):** 20757 **Payroll Expense ($000):** 7713 **Personnel:** 146

**HILLSBORO—Hill County**

☒ **HILL REGIONAL HOSPITAL (450192)**, 101 Circle Drive, Zip 76645-2670; tel. 254/580-8500 **A**1 9 10 **F**3 13 15 17 18 19 29 34 35 40 43 45 50 57 59 64 65 68 70 75 76 77 78 79 81 82 86 87 88 89 93 107 114 118 119 133 146 147 **S** Community Health Systems, Inc., Franklin, TN
Primary Contact: Jan McClure, Chief Executive Officer
CFO: Judy Culp, Chief Financial Officer
CHR: Becky Hale, Director Human Resources
Web address: www.chs.net
**Control:** Corporation, Investor-owned, for-profit **Service:** General Medical and Surgical

**Staffed Beds:** 66 **Admissions:** 1674 **Census:** 13 **Outpatient Visits:** 21791 **Births:** 245 **Total Expense ($000):** 28838 **Payroll Expense ($000):** 8714 **Personnel:** 189

**HONDO—Medina County**

**MEDINA COMMUNITY HOSPITAL** See Medina Regional Hospital

**MEDINA REGIONAL HOSPITAL (451330)**, 3100 Avenue E., Zip 78861-3599; tel. 830/426-7700 **A**9 10 18 **F**3 11 13 15 29 34 35 40 43 45 50 57 59 64 76 81 87 93 97 107 111 114 119 127 133 146 **P**4
Primary Contact: Janice Simons, FACHE, Chief Executive Officer
COO: Dale Semar, Controller
CFO: Kevin Frosch, Chief Financial Officer
CMO: John Meyer, M.D., Chief of Staff
CIO: Michael Smith, Director Support Services and Information Technology
CHR: Sharon Garcia, Human Resources Representative
Web address: www.medinahospital.net
**Control:** Hospital district or authority, Government, nonfederal **Service:** General Medical and Surgical

**Staffed Beds:** 25 **Admissions:** 865 **Census:** 12 **Outpatient Visits:** 96444 **Births:** 154 **Total Expense ($000):** 20101 **Payroll Expense ($000):** 8033 **Personnel:** 198

**TX**

*Many Facility Codes have changed. Please refer to the AHA Guide Code Chart.*
© 2013 AHA Guide

**HOUSTON—Harris County**

☐ **BEHAVIORAL HOSPITAL OF BELLAIRE (454107)**, 5314 Dashwood Drive, Zip 77081–4603; tel. 713/600–9500, (Nonreporting) **A**1 9 10 **S** Universal Health Services, Inc., King of Prussia, PA
Primary Contact: John Nekic, Chief Executive Officer
Web address: www.bhbhospital.com
**Control:** Corporation, Investor–owned, for–profit **Service:** Psychiatric

Staffed Beds: 70

**BEN TAUB GENERAL HOSPITAL** See Harris Health System

**CAMBRIDGE HOSPITAL IN HOUSTON (454120)**, 7601 Fannin Street, Zip 77054–1905; tel. 713/795–5025, (Data for 90 days) **A**9 10 **F**4 40 44 53 56 74 86 87 98 99 100 101 102 103 130 132 135 **P**8
Primary Contact: Trey Miller, Chief Executive Officer
Web address: www.cambridgehospitalhouston.com
**Control:** Corporation, Investor–owned, for–profit **Service:** Psychiatric

Staffed Beds: 50 Admissions: 36 Census: 2 Outpatient Visits: 0 Births: 0 Total Expense ($000): 331 Payroll Expense ($000): 252 Personnel: 28

**CHILDREN'S MEMORIAL HERMANN HOSPITAL** See Memorial Hermann – Texas Medical Center

**CORNERSTONE HOSPITAL OF HOUSTON – BELLAIRE (452032)**, 5314 Dashwood, Zip 77081–4603; tel. 713/295–5300, (Includes CORNERSTONE HOSPITAL OF HOUSTON AT CLEARLAKE, 709 Medical Center Boulevard, Webster, Zip 77598; tel. 281/332–3322; James Camp, R.N., Regional Chief Executive Officer, Houston Market) **A**9 10 **F**1 3 29 56 85 86 87 91 130 148 **S** Cornerstone Healthcare Group, Dallas, TX
Primary Contact: James Camp, R.N., Chief Executive Officer
CFO: A. Shane Wells, Chief Financial Officer
CMO: Mark Barlow, M.D., Chief Medical Officer and President Medical Staff
CIO: Kent Chambless, Chief Information Officer
CHR: Margaret Blunt, Director Human Resources
Web address: www.chghospitals.com
**Control:** Partnership, Investor–owned, for–profit **Service:** Long–Term Acute Care hospital

Staffed Beds: 134 Admissions: 1260 Census: 88 Outpatient Visits: 0 Births: 0 Total Expense ($000): 40496 Payroll Expense ($000): 15735 Personnel: 374

⊠ **CORNERSTONE HOSPITAL–MEDICAL CENTER OF HOUSTON (452055)**, (Formerly Cornerstone Hospital of South Houston), 2001 Hermann Park Drive, Zip 77004; tel. 713/756–8660 **A**1 10 **F**1 3 29 65 68 77 85 86 87 119 130 148 **S** Cornerstone Healthcare Group, Dallas, TX
Primary Contact: James Camp, R.N., Chief Executive Officer
Web address: www.chghospitals.com
**Control:** Corporation, Investor–owned, for–profit **Service:** Long–Term Acute Care hospital

Staffed Beds: 30 Admissions: 224 Census: 15 Outpatient Visits: 0 Births: 0 Total Expense ($000): 8523 Payroll Expense ($000): 3657 Personnel: 76

☐ **CYPRESS CREEK HOSPITAL (454108)**, 17750 Cali Drive, Zip 77090–2700; tel. 281/586–7600 **A**1 9 10 **F**4 5 29 30 64 87 98 99 100 102 104 105 130 132 **S** Universal Health Services, Inc., King of Prussia, PA
Primary Contact: Brian Brooker, Chief Executive Officer
CFO: Carol Neilson–Beale, Chief Financial Officer
CMO: Marshall Lucas, M.D., Medical Director
CHR: Brenda Dominguez, Director Human Resources
CNO: Shazetta Richardson, Director of Nursing
Web address: www.cypresscreekhospital.com
**Control:** Corporation, Investor–owned, for–profit **Service:** Psychiatric

Staffed Beds: 96 Admissions: 4146 Census: 87 Outpatient Visits: 6821 Births: 0 Total Expense ($000): 22564 Payroll Expense ($000): 10905 Personnel: 206

⊠ **CYPRESS FAIRBANKS MEDICAL CENTER (450716)**, 10655 Steepletop Drive, Zip 77065–4297; tel. 281/890–4285 **A**1 9 10 **F**3 11 12 13 15 18 20 22 24 28 29 30 31 34 40 42 45 46 47 49 50 53 57 59 64 70 72 74 75 76 77 78 79 81 82 85 87 89 93 107 108 110 111 114 115 118 119 120 121 129 130 131 132 144 145 146 147 148 **P**8 **S** TENET Healthcare Corporation, Dallas, TX
Primary Contact: Terry J. Wheeler, Chief Executive Officer
COO: Collin LeMaistre, Chief Operating Officer
CFO: James Wright, M.D., Chief Financial Officer
CMO: Marcus Barnett, M.D., Chief of Staff
CIO: Donna Cain, Director Information Systems Department
CHR: Lorinnsa Bridges Kee, Director Human Resource
Web address: www.cyfairhospital.com
**Control:** Corporation, Investor–owned, for–profit **Service:** General Medical and Surgical

Staffed Beds: 181 Admissions: 8551 Census: 90 Outpatient Visits: 104588 Births: 2860 Total Expense ($000): 147427 Payroll Expense ($000): 45405 Personnel: 723

☐ **DOCTOR'S HOSPITAL – TIDWELL (450803)**, 510 West Tidwell Road, Zip 77091–4399; tel. 713/691–1111, (Includes DOCTORS HOSPITAL PARKWAY, 233 West Parker Road, Zip 77076–2999; tel. 281/765–2600) **A**1 9 10 **F**40 43 70 107 111 114 119 148
Primary Contact: Michael R. Bullard, Chief Executive Officer
COO: Farida Moeen, M.D., Chief Operating Officer
CFO: Theresa Eatherly, Chief Financial Officer
CMO: Cesar Ortega, M.D., Chief of Staff
CIO: Dell Davis, Director Information Systems
CHR: Carolyn Washington, Director of Human Resources
Web address: www.dhthou.com/
**Control:** Partnership, Investor–owned, for–profit **Service:** General Medical and Surgical

Staffed Beds: 89 Admissions: 4110 Census: 39 Outpatient Visits: 22154 Births: 1223 Total Expense ($000): 40817 Payroll Expense ($000): 18082 Personnel: 317

**DUBUIS HOSPITAL OF HOUSTON** See Cornerstone Hospital–Medical Center of Houston

⊠ △ **HARRIS HEALTH SYSTEM (450289)**, (Formerly Harris County Hospital District), 2525 Holly Hall Street, Zip 77054–4108, Mailing Address: P.O. Box 66769, Zip 77266–6769; tel. 713/566–6403, (Includes BEN TAUB GENERAL HOSPITAL, 1504 Taub Loop, Zip 77030; tel. 713/873–2300; LYNDON B JOHNSON GENERAL HOSPITAL, 5656 Kelley, Zip 77026; tel. 713/566–5000; Jesse Lee Tucker, Administrator; QUENTIN MEASE HOSPITAL, 3601 North MacGregor, Zip 77004; tel. 713/873–3700; Jeffrey Webster, Administrator), (Total facility includes 24 beds in nursing home–type unit) **A**1 2 3 5 7 8 9 10 **F**3 5 7 13 15 17 18 20 22 24 26 29 30 31 32 34 35 39 40 43 45 46 49 50 51 54 55 56 57 58 59 60 61 64 65 68 70 71 72 73 74 75 76 77 78 79 81 82 84 87 89 90 91 92 93 94 97 98 99 100 101 102 103 104 107 110 111 112 114 115 118 119 120 121 124 128 129 130 132 134 135 143 144 145 146 147 148 **P**6
Primary Contact: David S. Lopez, FACHE, President and Chief Executive Officer
COO: George V. Masi, Chief Operating Officer
CFO: Michael Norby, Interim Chief Financial Officer
CMO: Fred Sutton, M.D., Chief Medical Officer
CIO: Tim Tindle, Chief Information Officer
CHR: Lou Gould, Vice President Human Resources
Web address: www.hchdonline.com
**Control:** Hospital district or authority, Government, nonfederal **Service:** General Medical and Surgical

Staffed Beds: 813 Admissions: 35343 Census: 548 Outpatient Visits: 1718731 Births: 6643 Total Expense ($000): 1087217 Payroll Expense ($000): 463785 Personnel: 6817

☐ ◇ **HEALTHBRIDGE CHILDREN'S HOSPITAL OF HOUSTON (453309)**, 2929 Woodland Park Drive, Zip 77082–2687; tel. 281/293–7774 **A**1 9 10 21 **F**3 29 74 75 79 85 87 89 93 100 130 146 148 **S** Nexus Health Systems, Houston, TX
Primary Contact: Joseph Rafferty, Chief Executive Officer
CMO: Robert Yetman, M.D., Medical Director
CHR: Guy Murdock, Vice President Human Resources
Web address: www.healthbridgehouston.com/
**Control:** Partnership, Investor–owned, for–profit **Service:** Children's general

Staffed Beds: 40 Admissions: 291 Census: 26 Outpatient Visits: 663 Births: 0 Total Expense ($000): 12558 Payroll Expense ($000): 5259 Personnel: 104

**TX**

---

**Hospital, Medicare Provider Number, Address, Telephone, Approval, Facility, and Physician Codes, Health Care System**

★ American Hospital Association (AHA) membership
☐ The Joint Commission accreditation
◇ DNV Healthcare Inc. accreditation
○ Healthcare Facilities Accreditation Program
△ Commission on Accreditation of Rehabilitation Facilities (CARF) accreditation

✠ **HEALTHSOUTH REHABILITATION HOSPITAL OF CYPRESS (673050)**, 13031 Wortham Center Drive, Zip 77065–5662; tel. 832/280–2500 **A**1 10 **F**3 29 34 57 60 62 64 68 75 77 87 90 91 93 94 95 96 100 130 132 146 148 **S** HEALTHSOUTH Corporation, Birmingham, AL
Primary Contact: Sheila A. Kramer, Chief Executive Officer
CFO: Kathryn Brigaitis, Controller
CMO: Ignazio LaChina, M.D., Medical Director
CHR: Kelly McGuire, Director Human Resources
CNO: Cynthia Jolivette, Chief Nursing Officer
Web address: www.healthsouthcypress.com
**Control:** Corporation, Investor–owned, for–profit **Service:** Rehabilitation

**Staffed Beds:** 40 **Admissions:** 916 **Census:** 30 **Outpatient Visits:** 1847 **Births:** 0 **Total Expense ($000):** 12270 **Payroll Expense ($000):** 6305 **Personnel:** 128

☐ **HOUSTON HOSPITAL FOR SPECIALIZED SURGERY (450797)**, 5445 La Branch Street, Zip 77004–6835; tel. 713/528–6800 **A**1 3 5 9 10 **F**3 8 40 45 46 47 48 49 79 81 82
Primary Contact: Gary Williams, Administrator
CFO: Deborah Jones, Controller
Web address: www.scasurgery.com
**Control:** Partnership, Investor–owned, for–profit **Service:** General Medical and Surgical

**Staffed Beds:** 7 **Admissions:** 172 **Census:** 1 **Outpatient Visits:** 5290 **Births:** 0 **Total Expense ($000):** 14554 **Payroll Expense ($000):** 3975 **Personnel:** 77

✠ **HOUSTON NORTHWEST MEDICAL CENTER (450638)**, 710 FM 1960 Road West, Zip 77090–3402; tel. 281/440–1000 **A**1 2 3 5 9 10 **F**3 8 11 12 13 15 18 20 22 24 26 28 29 30 31 34 40 42 43 45 46 49 50 54 59 64 65 70 72 74 75 77 78 79 81 82 84 85 87 89 91 92 93 96 102 107 108 109 110 111 112 113 114 115 116 117 118 119 126 129 130 132 135 144 145 146 147 148 **S** TENET Healthcare Corporation, Dallas, TX
Primary Contact: Linda Mercier, R.N., MSN, Chief Executive Officer
COO: Juan Fresquez, Chief Operating Officer
CFO: Bryan Forry, Chief Financial Officer
CIO: Terry Janis, Director Information Systems
CHR: Melanie R. Webb, Director Human Resources
CNO: Terry D. Kirk, R.N., Chief Nursing Officer
Web address: www.hnmc.com
**Control:** Partnership, Investor–owned, for–profit **Service:** General Medical and Surgical

**Staffed Beds:** 339 **Admissions:** 15805 **Census:** 192 **Outpatient Visits:** 139773 **Births:** 2950 **Total Expense ($000):** 283550 **Payroll Expense ($000):** 82697 **Personnel:** 1299

☐ **INTRACARE NORTH HOSPITAL (454083)**, 1120 Cypress Station Drive, Zip 77090–3031; tel. 281/893–7200 **A**1 9 10 **F**5 98 99 100 101 103 104 105
Primary Contact: Rob Yates, Chief Executive Officer
CFO: Fred Chan, Chief Financial Officer
CMO: Javier Ruiz, M.D., Medical Director
Web address: www.intracare.org
**Control:** Other not–for–profit (including NFP Corporation) **Service:** Psychiatric

**Staffed Beds:** 68 **Admissions:** 3006 **Census:** 58 **Outpatient Visits:** 50299 **Births:** 0 **Total Expense ($000):** 15457 **Payroll Expense ($000):** 8195 **Personnel:** 249

✠ **KINDRED HOSPITAL MIDTOWN (452027)**, 105 Drew Avenue, Zip 77006–1527; tel. 713/529–8922 **A**1 9 10 **F**1 3 29 75 77 85 87 96 130 148 **S** Kindred Healthcare, Louisville, KY
Primary Contact: Robert Stein, Chief Executive Officer
Web address: www.khmidtown.com
**Control:** Corporation, Investor–owned, for–profit **Service:** Long–Term Acute Care hospital

**Staffed Beds:** 40 **Admissions:** 174 **Census:** 15 **Outpatient Visits:** 0 **Births:** 0 **Total Expense ($000):** 8603 **Payroll Expense ($000):** 3855 **Personnel:** 88

✠ **KINDRED HOSPITAL NORTH HOUSTON (452074)**, 7407 North Freeway, Zip 77076–1314; tel. 832/200–6000, (Includes KINDRED HOSPITAL SPRING, 205 Hollow Tree Lane, Zip 77090; tel. 832/249–2700; Eric Cantrell, Chief Executive Officer; TRIUMPH HOSPITAL WEST HOUSTON, 8850 Long Point Road, 6th Floor, Zip 77055; tel. 713/365–7800) **A**1 9 10 **F**1 3 18 29 30 31 42 45 49 60 64 70 74 75 78 79 84 85 86 87 91 93 94 107 119 130 148 **S** Kindred Healthcare, Louisville, KY
Primary Contact: Larkin Virden, Interim Chief Executive Officer
COO: Erin O'Malley, M.D., Chief Clinical Officer
CFO: Terry Hohmann, Chief Financial Officer
CMO: Erin O'Malley, M.D., Chief Clinical Officer
CIO: William Elsesser, Director Professional Relations
CHR: Charles Lopez, Director Human Resources
Web address: www.khnorthhouston.com
**Control:** Partnership, Investor–owned, for–profit **Service:** Long–Term Acute Care hospital

**Staffed Beds:** 288 **Admissions:** 2512 **Census:** 172 **Outpatient Visits:** 1004 **Births:** 0 **Total Expense ($000):** 102809 **Payroll Expense ($000):** 35989 **Personnel:** 583

✠ **KINDRED HOSPITAL–HOUSTON (452023)**, 6441 Main Street, Zip 77030–1596; tel. 713/790–0500 **A**1 5 9 10 **F**1 3 29 30 31 70 75 77 85 107 130 148 **S** Kindred Healthcare, Louisville, KY
Primary Contact: Robert Stein, Chief Executive Officer
CFO: Sara Langlitz, Controller
Web address: www.khhouston.com/
**Control:** Corporation, Investor–owned, for–profit **Service:** Long–Term Acute Care hospital

**Staffed Beds:** 105 **Admissions:** 1025 **Census:** 80 **Outpatient Visits:** 0 **Births:** 0 **Total Expense ($000):** 37988 **Payroll Expense ($000):** 16116 **Personnel:** 220

✠ **KINDRED HOSPITAL–HOUSTON NORTHWEST (452039)**, 11297 Fallbrook Drive, Zip 77065–4292; tel. 281/897–8114 **A**1 9 10 **F**1 3 29 57 64 70 77 87 107 114 130 148 **P**5 **S** Kindred Healthcare, Louisville, KY
Primary Contact: Mary Anne Craig, Chief Executive Officer
Web address: www.khhoustonnw.com/
**Control:** Corporation, Investor–owned, for–profit **Service:** Long–Term Acute Care hospital

**Staffed Beds:** 84 **Admissions:** 794 **Census:** 56 **Outpatient Visits:** 369 **Births:** 0 **Total Expense ($000):** 30413 **Payroll Expense ($000):** 11822 **Personnel:** 179

**LYNDON B JOHNSON GENERAL HOSPITAL** See Harris Health System

✠ **MEMORIAL HERMANN – TEXAS MEDICAL CENTER (450068)**, 6411 Fannin Street, Zip 77030–1501; tel. 713/704–4000, (Includes CHILDREN'S MEMORIAL HERMANN HOSPITAL, 6411 Fannin, Zip 77030; tel. 713/704–5437), (Total facility includes 8 beds in nursing home–type unit) **A**1 2 3 5 8 9 10 **F**3 7 12 13 15 16 17 18 19 20 21 22 23 24 25 26 27 28 29 30 31 32 34 35 36 37 40 41 43 44 45 46 47 48 49 50 51 55 56 57 58 59 60 61 64 68 70 72 73 74 75 76 77 78 79 81 82 84 85 86 87 88 89 90 91 92 93 96 97 100 102 107 108 109 110 111 113 114 115 116 117 118 119 120 121 123 124 126 128 129 130 131 132 135 138 139 141 142 144 146 147 148 **P**1 5 6 **S** Memorial Hermann Healthcare System, Houston, TX
Primary Contact: Craig Cordola, Chief Executive Officer
COO: Tom Flanagan, Chief Operating Officer
CFO: William Pack, Chief Financial Officer
CMO: Jeffrey Katz, M.D., Chief Medical Officer
CIO: David Bradshaw, Chief Information Officer
CHR: Vivian Kardow, Chief Human Resources Officer
Web address: www.mhhs.org
**Control:** Other not–for–profit (including NFP Corporation) **Service:** General Medical and Surgical

**Staffed Beds:** 897 **Admissions:** 33283 **Census:** 591 **Outpatient Visits:** 166028 **Births:** 4378 **Total Expense ($000):** 941303 **Payroll Expense ($000):** 283165 **Personnel:** 3974

✠ **MEMORIAL HERMANN MEMORIAL CITY MEDICAL CENTER (450610)**, 921 Gessner Road, Zip 77024–2501; tel. 713/242–3000 **A**1 2 9 10 **F**3 12 13 15 18 20 22 24 26 28 29 30 31 34 35 37 40 41 43 45 46 49 51 56 57 59 60 65 70 72 74 75 76 77 78 79 80 81 82 84 85 87 89 107 108 110 111 114 115 117 118 119 120 121 123 124 126 129 130 131 132 135 146 147 148 **P**1 5 6 **S** Memorial Hermann Healthcare System, Houston, TX
Primary Contact: Keith N. Alexander, Chief Executive Officer
COO: James Witt, Chief Operations Officer
CFO: Lisa Kendler, Chief Financial Officer
CMO: Donald Gibson, M.D., Chief Medical Officer
CIO: David Bradshaw, Chief Information, Planning and Marketing Officer
CHR: Suzanne S. Meier, System Director, Compensation and Human Resources Technology
CNO: Dan Kelly, R.N., Chief Nursing Officer
Web address: www.memorialhermann.org
**Control:** Other not–for–profit (including NFP Corporation) **Service:** General Medical and Surgical

**Staffed Beds:** 383 **Admissions:** 18533 **Census:** 214 **Outpatient Visits:** 223283 **Births:** 2992 **Total Expense ($000):** 366919 **Payroll Expense ($000):** 100083 **Personnel:** 1256

**TX**

✉ **MEMORIAL HERMANN NORTHWEST HOSPITAL (450184)**, 1635 North Loop West, Zip 77008–1532; tel. 713/867–3380, (Includes MEMORIAL HERMANN SOUTHEAST HOSPITAL, 11800 Astoria Boulevard, Zip 77089–6041; tel. 281/929–6100; Erin Asprec, Chief Executive Officer; MEMORIAL HERMANN SOUTHWEST HOSPITAL, 7600 Beechnut, Zip 77074–1850; tel. 713/456–5000; George Gaston, Chief Executive Officer; MEMORIAL HERMANN THE WOODLANDS HOSPITAL, 9250 Pinecroft Drive, The Woodlands, Zip 77380–3225; tel. 281/364–2300) **A**1 2 3 5 9 10 **F**3 8 9 11 12 13 15 17 18 20 22 24 26 28 29 30 31 34 35 36 37 40 41 42 43 44 45 46 47 48 49 50 51 53 54 55 56 57 58 59 60 61 62 63 64 65 68 69 70 71 72 73 74 75 76 77 78 79 80 81 82 83 84 85 86 87 89 90 91 92 93 96 97 98 100 101 102 103 107 108 109 110 111 114 115 116 117 118 119 120 121 123 124 126 127 129 130 131 132 135 143 146 147 148 **P**1 5 6 **S** Memorial Hermann Healthcare System, Houston, TX
Primary Contact: Gary Kerr, Chief Executive Officer
CFO: Roger Faculak, Chief Financial Officer
CMO: Maurice Leibman, M.D., Chief Medical Officer
CIO: David Bradshaw, Chief Information Officer
CHR: Terry Henske, Director Human Resources
Web address: www.mhbh.org
**Control:** Other not–for–profit (including NFP Corporation) **Service:** General Medical and Surgical

**Staffed Beds:** 1180 **Admissions:** 54659 **Census:** 692 **Outpatient Visits:** 471025 **Births:** 11306 **Total Expense ($000):** 930099 **Payroll Expense ($000):** 323504 **Personnel:** 4426

**MEMORIAL HERMANN SOUTHEAST HOSPITAL** See Memorial Hermann Northwest Hospital

**MEMORIAL HERMANN SOUTHWEST HOSPITAL** See Memorial Hermann Northwest Hospital

☐ **MENNINGER CLINIC**, 12301 Main Street, Zip 77035–6207, Mailing Address: 2801 Gessner, Zip 77080–2503; tel. 713/275–5000 **A**1 3 5 **F**30 98 99 101 106 130 132
Primary Contact: Ian Aitken, President and Chief Executive Officer
COO: Shawna Morris, Senior Vice President Operations and Chief Operating Officer
CFO: Kenneth Klein, CPA, Senior Vice President Finance and Chief Financial Officer
CMO: John M. Oldham, M.D., Senior Vice President and Chief of Staff
CIO: Kenneth Klein, CPA, Senior Vice President Finance and Chief Financial Officer
CHR: Shawna Morris, Senior Vice President Operations and Chief Operating Officer
Web address: www.menningerclinic.com
**Control:** Other not–for–profit (including NFP Corporation) **Service:** Psychiatric

**Staffed Beds:** 102 **Admissions:** 768 **Census:** 78 **Outpatient Visits:** 0 **Births:** 0 **Total Expense ($000):** 40603 **Payroll Expense ($000):** 16910 **Personnel:** 287

★ ◇ **METHODIST WEST HOUSTON HOSPITAL (670077)**, 18500 Katy Freeway, Zip 77094–1110; tel. 832/522–1000 **A**3 5 9 10 21 **F**3 12 13 15 18 20 22 24 26 28 29 30 31 34 35 40 45 49 50 51 57 59 60 63 64 68 70 72 74 75 76 78 79 81 82 84 85 87 91 92 93 107 108 109 110 111 114 115 119 120 121 123 124 126 130 131 132 135 146 147 **P**1 **S** The Methodist Hospital System, Houston, TX
Primary Contact: Wayne M. Voss, Chief Executive Officer
Web address: www.methodisthealth.com
**Control:** Other not–for–profit (including NFP Corporation) **Service:** General Medical and Surgical

**Staffed Beds:** 126 **Admissions:** 6238 **Census:** 63 **Outpatient Visits:** 63038 **Births:** 1435 **Total Expense ($000):** 115281 **Payroll Expense ($000):** 40946 **Personnel:** 781

✉ **METHODIST WILLOWBROOK HOSPITAL (450844)**, 18220 Tomball Parkway, Zip 77070–4347; tel. 281/477–1000 **A**1 3 5 9 10 **F**3 8 12 13 15 17 18 20 22 24 26 28 29 30 31 34 35 36 37 40 44 45 49 53 57 59 64 65 70 72 73 74 75 76 77 78 79 81 85 86 87 93 96 107 108 110 111 114 115 119 120 121 123 124 126 130 131 132 135 146 147 148 **S** The Methodist Hospital System, Houston, TX
Primary Contact: Beryl O. Ramsey, FACHE, Chief Executive Officer
CHR: Sherene Thompson, Director Human Resources
Web address: www.methodisthealth.com
**Control:** Other not–for–profit (including NFP Corporation) **Service:** General Medical and Surgical

**Staffed Beds:** 241 **Admissions:** 13596 **Census:** 153 **Outpatient Visits:** 133213 **Births:** 3112 **Total Expense ($000):** 212796 **Payroll Expense ($000):** 81553 **Personnel:** 1368

✉ △ **MICHAEL E. DEBAKEY VETERANS AFFAIRS MEDICAL CENTER**, 2002 Holcombe Boulevard, Zip 77030–4298; tel. 713/791–1414, (Nonreporting) **A**1 2 3 5 7 8 9 **S** Department of Veterans Affairs, Washington, DC
Primary Contact: Adam C. Walmus, Director
COO: Francisco Vazquez, Associate Director
CFO: Alisa Cooper, Manager Financial Resources
CMO: Jagadeesh S. Kalavar, M.D., Chief of Staff
CIO: Kevin Lenamond, Information Management Service Line Executive
CHR: Kathy Salazar, Manager Human Resources
Web address: www.houston.va.gov
**Control:** Veterans Affairs, Government, federal **Service:** General Medical and Surgical

**Staffed Beds:** 479

✉ **PARK PLAZA HOSPITAL (450659)**, 1313 Hermann Drive, Zip 77004–7092; tel. 713/527–5000 **A**1 2 9 10 **F**3 12 13 15 18 20 22 29 31 34 35 40 45 49 50 56 57 59 60 70 73 74 76 78 79 81 85 92 107 108 110 111 114 115 118 119 120 121 123 129 130 132 146 147 148 **S** TENET Healthcare Corporation, Dallas, TX
Primary Contact: John Tressa, R.N., MSN, Chief Executive Officer
COO: Mary Jo Goodman, Chief Operating Officer
CFO: Wayne Gordon, Chief Financial Officer
CMO: Robert Brown, M.D., Chief Medical Officer
CIO: Terry Janis, Assistant Vice President
CHR: Melanie R. Webb, Chief Human Resources Officer
CNO: Martha M. Smith, R.N., Chief Nursing Officer
Web address: www.parkplazahospital.com
**Control:** Partnership, Investor–owned, for–profit **Service:** General Medical and Surgical

**Staffed Beds:** 208 **Admissions:** 5381 **Census:** 74 **Outpatient Visits:** 43569 **Births:** 727 **Total Expense ($000):** 98774 **Payroll Expense ($000):** 35171 **Personnel:** 576

✉ **PLAZA SPECIALTY HOSPITAL (452046)**, 1300 Binz, Zip 77004–7016; tel. 713/285–1000 **A**1 9 10 **F**1 3 29 31 56 63 68 70 75 77 78 82 84 85 87 130 148 **P**8 **S** TENET Healthcare Corporation, Dallas, TX
Primary Contact: Steven Barr, R.N., MSN, Chief Executive Officer
CFO: Charles R. Handley, Chief Financial Officer
CMO: Wasae S. Tabibi, M.D., President Medical Staff
CIO: Steve Peacock, Assistant Vice President
Web address: www.plazaspecialtyhospital.com
**Control:** Corporation, Investor–owned, for–profit **Service:** Long–Term Acute Care hospital

**Staffed Beds:** 39 **Admissions:** 336 **Census:** 27 **Outpatient Visits:** 0 **Births:** 0 **Total Expense ($000):** 21964 **Payroll Expense ($000):** 5592 **Personnel:** 80

**QUENTIN MEASE HOSPITAL** See Harris Health System

☐ **RELIANT NORTHWEST HOUSTON (673052)**, 20180 Chasewood Park Drive, Zip 77070–1436; tel. 281/205–5100, (Data for 232 days) **A**1 9 10 **F**3 29 65 74 79 86 90 93 96 130 148
Primary Contact: Jeff Crawford, Chief Executive Officer
CNO: Stanley F. Kiebzak, R.N., Chief Nursing Officer
Web address: www.reliantnwhouston.com
**Control:** Partnership, Investor–owned, for–profit **Service:** Rehabilitation

**Staffed Beds:** 60 **Admissions:** 440 **Census:** 20 **Outpatient Visits:** 253 **Births:** 0 **Total Expense ($000):** 6134 **Personnel:** 77

**RENAISSANCE HOSPITAL – HOUSTON** See St. Anthony's Hospital

☐ **RIVERSIDE GENERAL HOSPITAL (450446)**, 3204 Ennis Street, Zip 77004–3299; tel. 713/526–2441 **A**1 10 **F**4 5 29 35 40 43 57 61 80 98 99 100 101 105 130 132 146 **P**5
Primary Contact: Earnest Gibson, III, Administrator
CFO: Manny Ignacio, Controller
Web address: www.riversidegeneral.org
**Control:** Other not–for–profit (including NFP Corporation) **Service:** Psychiatric

**Staffed Beds:** 88 **Admissions:** 1149 **Census:** 28 **Outpatient Visits:** 3090 **Births:** 0 **Total Expense ($000):** 20688 **Payroll Expense ($000):** 8295 **Personnel:** 172

TX

**⊠ SELECT SPECIALTY HOSPITAL–HOUSTON HEIGHTS (452049)**, (Formerly Select Specialty Hospital–Houston), 1917 Ashland Street, Zip 77008–3994; tel. 713/861–6161, (Includes SELECT SPECIALTY HOSPITAL–HOUSTON MEDICAL CENTER, 2130 West Holcombe, Zip 77030–1502; tel. 713/218–2300; Michael A. Anaya, FACHE, Chief Executive Officer; SELECT SPECIALTY HOSPITAL–HOUSTON WEST, 9430 Old Katy Road, Zip 77055; tel. 713/984–2273; Mitali Paul, Chief Executive Officer) **A**1 9 10 **F**1 3 29 34 40 45 50 57 59 60 64 70 81 85 87 91 130 148 **S** Select Medical Corporation, Mechanicsburg, PA
Primary Contact: Naman Mahajan, Chief Executive Officer
CFO: Traci Jameson, Manager Finance
CMO: Chi C. Mao, M.D., Medical Director
CHR: Pamela Simpson, Director Human Resources
Web address: www.selectspecialtyhospitals.com/company/locations/houstonheights.aspx
**Control:** Partnership, Investor–owned, for–profit **Service:** Long–Term Acute Care hospital

**Staffed Beds:** 300 **Admissions:** 1773 **Census:** 134 **Outpatient Visits:** 1846 **Births:** 0 **Total Expense ($000):** 75104 **Payroll Expense ($000):** 32047 **Personnel:** 573

**SELECT SPECIALTY HOSPITAL–HOUSTON MEDICAL CENTER** See Select Specialty Hospital–Houston Heights

**SELECT SPECIALTY HOSPITAL–HOUSTON WEST** See Select Specialty Hospital–Houston Heights

**☐ SHRINERS HOSPITALS FOR CHILDREN–HOUSTON (453312)**, 6977 Main Street, Zip 77030–3701; tel. 713/797–1616 **A**1 3 5 10 **F**3 29 30 35 50 64 66 68 74 75 77 79 81 86 87 89 93 94 96 130 131 132 134 143 146 148 **P**6 **S** Shriners Hospitals for Children, Tampa, FL
Primary Contact: David A. Ferrell, Regional Administrator
COO: Cathy Moniaci, Chief Operating Officer
CFO: Lona Pope, Director Fiscal Services
CMO: Douglas A. Barnes, M.D., Chief of Staff
CHR: Lynn Clements, Director Human Resources
Web address: www.shrinershospitalsforchildren.org/Hospitals/Locations/Houston.aspx
**Control:** Other not–for–profit (including NFP Corporation) **Service:** Children's orthopedic

**Staffed Beds:** 40 **Admissions:** 278 **Census:** 2 **Outpatient Visits:** 11246 **Births:** 0 **Total Expense ($000):** 24051 **Payroll Expense ($000):** 11841 **Personnel:** 165

**☐ SPRING BRANCH MEDICAL CENTER (450630)**, 8850 Long Point Road, Zip 77055–3082; tel. 713/467–6555, (Nonreporting) **A**1 5
Primary Contact: Marty McVey, Chief Executive Officer
Web address: www.springbranchmedical.com
**Control:** Individual, Investor–owned, for–profit **Service:** General Medical and Surgical

**Staffed Beds:** 36

**◇ ST. ANTHONY'S HOSPITAL (450795)**, 2807 Little York Road, Zip 77093–3495; tel. 713/697–7777 **A**9 10 21 **F**12 18 20 21 22 23 24 29 40 64 65 67 68 70 75 79 81 87 90 91 94 98 99 105 107 114 119 129 130
Primary Contact: Jason LeDay, Chief Executive Officer
COO: Nora Peralta, Chief Nursing Officer
CFO: John Lucia, Chief Financial Officer
CMO: Rafael Borges, M.D., Chief of Staff
CIO: Bill DuBrul, Director Information Technology
CHR: Cathy McCue, Director Human Resources
Web address: www.stanthonyshouston.com
**Control:** Individual, Investor–owned, for–profit **Service:** General Medical and Surgical

**Staffed Beds:** 39 **Admissions:** 1230 **Census:** 12 **Outpatient Visits:** 17750 **Births:** 0 **Total Expense ($000):** 23040 **Payroll Expense ($000):** 9846 **Personnel:** 179

**☐ ◇ ST. JOSEPH MEDICAL CENTER (450035)**, 1401 St. Joseph Parkway, Zip 77002–8301; tel. 713/757–1000, (Total facility includes 18 beds in nursing home–type unit) **A**1 3 5 9 10 21 **F**3 11 12 13 15 18 20 22 24 26 29 30 31 34 35 40 43 49 50 51 53 55 57 58 59 60 64 68 70 72 74 75 76 77 78 79 81 82 84 85 86 87 90 93 94 97 99 100 101 102 103 107 108 111 114 115 116 117 118 119 121 124 128 129 130 131 132 135 143 144 146 147 148 **P**8 **S** IASIS Healthcare, Franklin, TN
Primary Contact: Patrick J. Mathews, Chief Executive Officer and Chief Financial Officer
COO: Laura Fortin, Chief Operating Officer
CFO: Patrick J. Mathews, Chief Executive Officer and Chief Financial Officer
CIO: Robin Brown, Chief Information Officer and Compliance Officer
CHR: Kris Clatanoff, Director Human Resources
Web address: www.sjmctx.com
**Control:** Partnership, Investor–owned, for–profit **Service:** General Medical and Surgical

**Staffed Beds:** 384 **Admissions:** 16493 **Census:** 232 **Outpatient Visits:** 120795 **Births:** 4618 **Total Expense ($000):** 217900 **Payroll Expense ($000):** 85861 **Personnel:** 1374

**⊠ ◇ ST. LUKE'S EPISCOPAL HOSPITAL (450193)**, 6720 Bertner Avenue, Zip 77030–2697, Mailing Address: P.O. Box 20269, Zip 77225–0269; tel. 832/355–1000 **A**1 2 3 5 8 9 10 21 **F**3 11 12 13 14 15 17 18 20 22 24 26 28 29 30 31 34 35 36 37 39 40 42 44 45 46 47 48 49 50 51 54 56 57 58 59 60 61 63 64 65 66 68 70 74 75 76 77 78 79 81 82 84 85 86 87 90 92 96 97 100 107 108 110 111 112 114 115 118 119 120 121 123 124 126 129 130 131 132 135 137 138 139 140 141 142 145 146 147 148 **P**5 6 8 **S** Catholic Health Initiatives, Englewood, CO
Primary Contact: Margaret M. Van Bree, Dr.PH, Chief Executive Officer
CFO: William Brosius, Vice President and Chief Financial Officer
CMO: T. Pinckney McIlwain, M.D., Vice President Quality and Performance Improvement
CIO: James Albin, Chief Information Officer
CHR: Susan Bailey–Newell, Vice President Human Resources
CNO: Karen K. Myers, MSN, Vice President and Chief Nursing Officer
Web address: www.stlukestexas.com
**Control:** Church–operated, Nongovernment, not–for profit **Service:** General Medical and Surgical

**Staffed Beds:** 690 **Admissions:** 28653 **Census:** 499 **Outpatient Visits:** 275102 **Births:** 729 **Total Expense ($000):** 755097 **Payroll Expense ($000):** 295123 **Personnel:** 3462

**★ ◇ ST. LUKE'S HOSPITAL AT THE VINTAGE (670075)**, 20171 Chasewood Park Drive, Zip 77070–1437; tel. 832/534–5000 **A**9 10 21 **F**3 11 12 13 15 18 20 22 24 26 29 30 34 35 40 42 45 49 50 57 59 60 64 65 68 70 72 75 76 77 79 81 82 87 107 108 110 111 114 115 118 119 130 146 147 **P**5 **S** Catholic Health Initiatives, Englewood, CO
Primary Contact: Norman F. Stephens, Chief Executive Officer
Web address: www.stlukesvintage.com/
**Control:** Corporation, Investor–owned, for–profit **Service:** General Medical and Surgical

**Staffed Beds:** 78 **Admissions:** 3188 **Census:** 35 **Outpatient Visits:** 25684 **Births:** 448 **Total Expense ($000):** 60551 **Payroll Expense ($000):** 24856 **Personnel:** 376

**☐ TEXAS CHILDREN'S HOSPITAL (453304)**, 6621 Fannin Street, Zip 77030–2399, Mailing Address: Box 300630, Zip 77230–0630; tel. 832/824–1000, (Includes TEXAS CHILDREN'S HOSPITAL WEST CAMPUS, 18200 Katy Freeway, Zip 77094–1285; tel. 832/227–1000) **A**1 3 5 8 9 10 **F**3 7 11 12 13 17 19 21 23 25 27 29 30 31 32 34 35 38 39 40 41 43 48 49 50 52 55 57 58 59 60 61 64 65 68 71 72 73 74 75 76 77 78 79 80 81 84 85 86 87 88 89 90 92 93 94 95 96 97 99 100 101 104 107 108 111 114 115 118 119 129 130 131 132 134 136 137 138 139 140 143 144 146 147 148 Primary Contact: Mark A. Wallace, President and Chief Executive Officer
COO: Randall P. Wright, Executive Vice President and Chief Operating Officer
CFO: Benjamin B. Melson, CPA, Executive Vice President and Chief Financial Officer
CMO: Mark W. Kline, M.D., Physician in Chief
CHR: Linda W. Aldred, Senior Vice President
Web address: www.texaschildrenshospital.org
**Control:** Other not–for–profit (including NFP Corporation) **Service:** Children's general

**Staffed Beds:** 595 **Admissions:** 25966 **Census:** 436 **Outpatient Visits:** 1877687 **Births:** 2184 **Total Expense ($000):** 1211041 **Payroll Expense ($000):** 489529 **Personnel:** 5316

**⊠ TEXAS ORTHOPEDIC HOSPITAL (450804)**, 7401 South Main Street, Zip 77030–4509; tel. 713/799–8600 **A**1 3 5 9 10 **F**3 29 30 40 59 64 68 70 79 81 82 85 86 87 90 93 94 97 107 111 115 119 146 **S** HCA, Nashville, TN
Primary Contact: Trent Lind, Chief Executive Officer
CFO: Blair Callaway, Chief Financial Officer
CMO: James B. Bennett, M.D., Chief of Staff
CNO: Troy Sarver, Chief Nursing Officer
Web address: www.texasorthopedic.com
**Control:** Partnership, Investor–owned, for–profit **Service:** Orthopedic

**Staffed Beds:** 49 **Admissions:** 2812 **Census:** 22 **Outpatient Visits:** 36044 **Births:** 0 **Total Expense ($000):** 67649 **Payroll Expense ($000):** 21890 **Personnel:** 349

**☐ TEXAS SPECIALTY HOSPITAL AT HOUSTON (452043)**, 6160 South Loop East, Zip 77087–1010; tel. 713/640–2400 **A**1 9 10 **F**1 3 4 29 30 67 70 75 77 85 87 90 98 128 130 148 **S** Fundamental Long Term Care Holdings, LLC, Sparks Glencoe, MD
Primary Contact: Michael Higginbotham, Chief Executive Officer
CFO: Betty Priestley, Manager Business Office
CMO: Alfred Louis, M.D., Chief Medical Staff
CHR: Laura Garza, Director Human Resources
Web address: www.thicare.com
**Control:** Corporation, Investor–owned, for–profit **Service:** Long–Term Acute Care hospital

**Staffed Beds:** 25 **Admissions:** 285 **Census:** 18 **Outpatient Visits:** 0 **Births:** 0 **Total Expense ($000):** 10338 **Payroll Expense ($000):** 3437 **Personnel:** 56

*Many Facility Codes have changed. Please refer to the AHA Guide Code Chart.*     © 2013 AHA Guide

✠ △ ◇ **THE METHODIST HOSPITAL (450358)**, 6565 Fannin Street,
Zip 77030–2707; tel. 713/790–3311, (Total facility includes 25 beds in nursing
home–type unit) **A**1 2 3 5 7 8 9 10 21 **F**3 6 8 9 11 12 13 14 15 17 18 20 22
24 26 28 29 30 31 33 34 35 36 37 39 40 41 42 44 45 46 47 48 49 50 51
53 54 55 56 57 58 59 60 61 63 64 65 67 68 70 72 73 74 75 76 77 78 79
81 82 83 84 85 86 87 90 92 93 94 96 97 98 100 101 102 103 104 105 107
108 110 111 112 114 115 116 117 118 119 120 121 122 123 124 126 128
129 130 131 132 135 136 137 138 139 140 141 142 143 145 146 147 148
**P**8 **S** The Methodist Hospital System, Houston, TX
Primary Contact: Roberta Schwartz, Executive Vice President
CMO: Dirk Sostman, M.D., Executive Vice President, Chief Medical Officer and
Chief Academic Officer
CIO: Timothy L. Thompson, Sr., Senior Vice President and Chief Information
Officer
CHR: Lauren P. Rykert, Senior Vice President
Web address: www.methodisthealth.com
**Control:** Other not–for–profit (including NFP Corporation) **Service:** General
Medical and Surgical

**Staffed Beds:** 839 **Admissions:** 35542 **Census:** 619 **Outpatient Visits:**
345925 **Births:** 1064 **Total Expense ($000):** 1189887 **Payroll Expense**
**($000):** 339114 **Personnel:** 6102

✠ **THE WOMAN'S HOSPITAL OF TEXAS (450674)**, 7600 Fannin Street,
Zip 77054–1906; tel. 713/790–1234 **A**1 3 5 9 10 **F**3 7 13 15 29 30 34 40 46
50 53 58 68 70 72 73 75 76 77 81 85 86 87 93 107 108 110 111 118 119
126 130 132 146 147 **S** HCA, Nashville, TN
Primary Contact: Linda B. Russell, Chief Executive Officer
COO: Eric Evans, Chief Operating Officer
CFO: Scott Bentley, Chief Financial Officer
CMO: Eberhard Lotze, M.D., Chief Medical Officer
CIO: Emily Le, Director Information Technology and Services
CHR: Arnita Crawford, Director Human Resources
CNO: Andrea Harrow, Chief Nursing Officer
Web address: www.womanshospital.com
**Control:** Partnership, Investor–owned, for–profit **Service:** Obstetrics and
gynecology

**Staffed Beds:** 367 **Admissions:** 14371 **Census:** 222 **Outpatient Visits:**
57079 **Births:** 10144 **Total Expense ($000):** 168727 **Payroll Expense**
**($000):** 85348 **Personnel:** 1103

✠ △ **TIRR MEMORIAL HERMANN (453025)**, 1333 Moursund Street,
Zip 77030–3405; tel. 713/799–5000 **A**1 3 5 7 9 10 **F**11 29 30 34 35 44 50
52 54 58 59 60 64 68 74 75 77 79 82 86 87 90 91 93 95 96 97 100 104
107 114 119 130 131 132 146 148 **P**1 5 6 **S** Memorial Hermann
Healthcare System, Houston, TX
Primary Contact: Carl E. Josehart, Chief Executive Officer
COO: Mary Ann Euliarte, R.N., Chief Operating Officer and Chief Nursing Officer
CFO: William Pack, Chief Financial Officer
CMO: Gerard E. Francisco, M.D., Chief Medical Officer
CIO: Gina Tripp, Director Information Systems
CHR: Vivian Kardow, Chief Human Resources Officer
CNO: Mary Ann Euliarte, R.N., Chief Operating Officer and Chief Nursing Officer
Web address: www.memorialhermann.org/locations/tirr.html
**Control:** Other not–for–profit (including NFP Corporation) **Service:** Rehabilitation

**Staffed Beds:** 119 **Admissions:** 1133 **Census:** 88 **Outpatient Visits:** 15513
**Births:** 0 **Total Expense ($000):** 74264 **Payroll Expense ($000):** 37677
**Personnel:** 570

**TOPS SURGICAL SPECIALTY HOSPITAL (450774)**, 17080 Red Oak Drive,
Zip 77090–2602; tel. 281/539–2900 **A**9 10 **F**3 15 29 37 39 40 45 51 64 68
79 81 85 91 107 110 111 114 119 142 **P**2 **S** United Surgical Partners
International, Addison, TX
Primary Contact: Samuel H. Rossmann, Chief Executive Officer
CFO: Daniel Smith, Chief Financial Officer
CMO: Thomas Barton, M.D., Medical Director
CIO: Maud Jones, Manager Medical Records
CHR: Ashley Monzingo, Human Resources, Accounts Payable and Payroll
CNO: Andrea Wappelhorst, Chief Nursing Officer
Web address: www.tops–hospital.com
**Control:** Partnership, Investor–owned, for–profit **Service:** General Medical and
Surgical

**Staffed Beds:** 15 **Admissions:** 642 **Census:** 4 **Outpatient Visits:** 40869
**Births:** 0 **Total Expense ($000):** 27865 **Payroll Expense ($000):** 7712
**Personnel:** 186

☐ **UNIVERSITY GENERAL HOSPITAL (670019)**, 7501 Fannin Street,
Zip 77054–1938; tel. 713/375–7000 **A**1 9 10 **F**3 8 12 18 20 22 29 40 45 49
54 57 59 67 70 75 79 81 82 85 86 107 108 111 114 119 130 132 148
Primary Contact: Charles D. Schuetz, Chief Executive Officer
Web address: www.ughospital.com
**Control:** Partnership, Investor–owned, for–profit **Service:** General Medical and
Surgical

**Staffed Beds:** 69 **Admissions:** 3462 **Census:** 36 **Outpatient Visits:** 24915
**Births:** 0 **Total Expense ($000):** 68214 **Payroll Expense ($000):** 22271
**Personnel:** 509

✠ **UNIVERSITY OF TEXAS HARRIS COUNTY PSYCHIATRIC CENTER (454076)**,
2800 South MacGregor Way, Zip 77021–1000, Mailing Address: P.O. Box
20249, Zip 77225–0249; tel. 713/741–7870 **A**1 5 9 10 **F**29 30 34 35 57 58
68 75 86 87 98 99 100 101 103 106 130 146 **P**6 **S** University of Texas
System, Austin, TX
Primary Contact: Jair C. Soares, M.D., Executive Director
COO: Stephen Glazier, Chief Operating Officer
CFO: Lois K. Pierson, Chief Financial Officer
CMO: R. Andrew Harper, M.D., Medical Director
CIO: Geri Konigsberg, Director Public Information
CHR: Karla T. Crabtree, Director Personnel Systems
CNO: Margaret Pung, R.N., Chief Nursing Officer
Web address: www.hcpc.uth.tmc.edu
**Control:** State–Government, nonfederal **Service:** Psychiatric

**Staffed Beds:** 181 **Admissions:** 7159 **Census:** 182 **Outpatient Visits:** 0
**Births:** 0 **Total Expense ($000):** 40402 **Payroll Expense ($000):** 25420
**Personnel:** 446

✠ **UNIVERSITY OF TEXAS M.D. ANDERSON CANCER CENTER (450076)**,
1515 Holcombe Boulevard, Box 91, Zip 77030–4000; tel. 713/792–2121 **A**1 2
3 5 8 9 10 **F**3 8 11 14 15 18 20 29 30 31 32 34 35 36 37 38 39 40 44 45
46 47 48 49 50 54 55 57 58 59 60 63 64 66 68 70 71 74 75 77 78 79 80
81 82 83 84 85 86 87 88 89 92 93 96 97 99 100 101 102 104 107 108 110
111 112 114 115 116 117 118 119 120 121 122 123 124 126 129 130 132
134 135 136 141 145 146 147 148 **P**6 **S** University of Texas System,
Austin, TX
Primary Contact: Ronald A. DePinho, M.D., President
CFO: Dwain Morris, Vice President and Chief Financial Officer
CMO: Thomas Burke, M.D., Executive Vice President and Physician–in–Chief
CIO: Keith Perry, Associate Vice President and Deputy Chief Information Officer
CHR: Shibu Varghese, Vice President Human Resources
CNO: Barbara L. Summers, Ph.D., Vice President Nursing Practice and Chief
Nursing Officer
Web address: www.mdanderson.org
**Control:** State–Government, nonfederal **Service:** Cancer

**Staffed Beds:** 631 **Admissions:** 26726 **Census:** 524 **Outpatient Visits:**
1291770 **Births:** 0 **Total Expense ($000):** 3406308 **Payroll Expense**
**($000):** 1529081 **Personnel:** 18776

☐ **VICTORY MEDICAL CENTER HOUSTON (670081)**, 2001 Hermann Drive,
Zip 77004–7643; tel. 713/285–5500 **A**1 10 **F**29 40 81 107 119 **S** Victory
Healthcare, The Woodlands, TX
Primary Contact: Luis Garcia, Chief Executive Officer
Web address: www.victory–healthcare.com
**Control:** Hospital district or authority, Government, nonfederal **Service:** Surgical

**Staffed Beds:** 25 **Admissions:** 476 **Census:** 2 **Outpatient Visits:** 1702
**Births:** 0 **Total Expense ($000):** 34756 **Payroll Expense ($000):** 5345
**Personnel:** 75

✠ **WEST HOUSTON MEDICAL CENTER (450644)**, 12141 Richmond Avenue,
Zip 77082–2499; tel. 281/558–3444 **A**1 9 10 **F**3 11 12 13 15 18 20 22 24
26 28 29 30 31 39 40 42 45 46 47 48 49 50 51 56 57 59 60 64 70 73 74
75 76 77 78 79 80 81 82 85 90 93 96 98 102 103 107 110 111 115 116
117 118 119 121 124 129 130 132 145 146 147 148 **S** HCA, Nashville, TN
Primary Contact: Todd Caliva, Chief Executive Officer
CFO: Stanley K. Nord, Chief Financial Officer
CMO: Magdy Rizk, M.D., Chief of Staff
CIO: Sergio Almeida, Director Information Systems
CHR: Carol Melville, Director Human Resources
Web address: www.westhoustonmedical.com
**Control:** Partnership, Investor–owned, for–profit **Service:** General Medical and
Surgical

**Staffed Beds:** 238 **Admissions:** 11601 **Census:** 162 **Outpatient Visits:**
111858 **Births:** 2372 **Total Expense ($000):** 139868 **Payroll Expense**
**($000):** 63946 **Personnel:** 897

**TX**

---

**Hospital, Medicare Provider Number, Address, Telephone, Approval, Facility, and Physician Codes, Health Care System**

★ American Hospital Association (AHA) membership
☐ The Joint Commission accreditation
◇ DNV Healthcare Inc. accreditation
○ Healthcare Facilities Accreditation Program
△ Commission on Accreditation of Rehabilitation Facilities (CARF) accreditation

☐ **WEST OAKS HOSPITAL (454026)**, 6500 Hornwood Drive, Zip 77074–5095; tel. 713/995–0909 **A**1 3 5 9 10 **F**5 29 54 56 64 68 98 99 100 101 103 104 105 132 **S** Universal Health Services, Inc., King of Prussia, PA
Primary Contact: Greg Drummond, Chief Executive Officer
CFO: Christy Amy, Chief Financial Officer
CMO: George Santos, M.D., Executive Medical Director
CHR: Janice Webster, Director Human Resources
Web address: www.westoakshospital.com
**Control:** Corporation, Investor–owned, for–profit **Service:** Psychiatric

**Staffed Beds:** 144 **Admissions:** 6506 **Census:** 120 **Outpatient Visits:** 27920 **Births:** 0 **Total Expense ($000):** 25103 **Payroll Expense ($000):** 14736 **Personnel:** 253

◇ **WESTBURY COMMUNITY HOSPITAL (670072)**, 5556 Gasmer Drive, Zip 77035–4502; tel. 713/422–2625 **A**9 10 21 **F**3 29 35 38 64 68 98 99 100 101 102 103 104 105 130
Primary Contact: Tim C. Simmons, Chief Executive Officer
Web address: www.westburyhospital.com
**Control:** Corporation, Investor–owned, for–profit **Service:** Psychiatric

**Staffed Beds:** 85 **Admissions:** 2455 **Census:** 51 **Outpatient Visits:** 67592 **Births:** 0 **Total Expense ($000):** 22920 **Payroll Expense ($000):** 11633 **Personnel:** 219

### HUMBLE—Harris County

✠ **HEALTHSOUTH REHABILITATION HOSPITAL (453029)**, 19002 McKay Drive, Zip 77338–5701; tel. 281/446–6148 **A**1 9 10 **F**29 56 64 75 77 82 86 87 90 91 92 93 95 96 130 132 143 148 **S** HEALTHSOUTH Corporation, Birmingham, AL
Primary Contact: Angela L. Simmons, Chief Executive Officer
CFO: Sheila Shepard, Accounting Manager
CMO: Emile Mathurin, Jr., M.D., Medical Director
CHR: Christy Dixon, Chief Human Resources Officer
CNO: Anita L. Marban, R.N., Chief Nursing Officer
Web address: www.healthsouthhumble.com
**Control:** Corporation, Investor–owned, for–profit **Service:** Rehabilitation

**Staffed Beds:** 60 **Admissions:** 1032 **Census:** 40 **Outpatient Visits:** 7821 **Births:** 0 **Total Expense ($000):** 14042 **Payroll Expense ($000):** 7916 **Personnel:** 149

✠ **ICON HOSPITAL (452112)**, 19211 McKay Boulevard, Zip 77338–5502; tel. 281/883–5500 **A**1 9 10 **F**1 3 29 40 77 81 85 91 130 135 148 **S** AcuityHealthcare, LP, Charlotte, NC
Primary Contact: Hilda Long, Chief Executive Officer
Web address: www.acuityhealthcare.net
**Control:** Corporation, Investor–owned, for–profit **Service:** Long–Term Acute Care hospital

**Staffed Beds:** 42 **Admissions:** 580 **Census:** 40 **Outpatient Visits:** 150 **Births:** 0 **Total Expense ($000):** 20595 **Payroll Expense ($000):** 9235 **Personnel:** 163

✠ **KINDRED REHABILITATION HOSPITAL NORTHEAST HOUSTON (673051)**, 18839 McKay Road, Zip 77338–5721; tel. 281/964–6600, (Data for 330 days) **A**1 9 10 **F**29 40 64 77 90 91 93 130 148 **S** Kindred Healthcare, Louisville, KY
Primary Contact: Jeffrey Smith, Chief Executive Officer
Web address: www.khrehabnortheasthouston.com
**Control:** Corporation, Investor–owned, for–profit **Service:** Rehabilitation

**Staffed Beds:** 46 **Admissions:** 431 **Census:** 16 **Outpatient Visits:** 303 **Births:** 0 **Total Expense ($000):** 10813 **Payroll Expense ($000):** 4006 **Personnel:** 96

✠ **MEMORIAL HERMANN NORTHEAST (450684)**, 18951 North Memorial Drive, Zip 77338–4297; tel. 281/540–7700 **A**1 2 9 10 **F**3 11 12 13 15 18 20 22 24 26 29 30 31 34 35 36 37 40 45 46 49 53 54 56 57 59 64 70 72 73 74 75 76 77 78 79 80 81 85 86 87 93 107 108 109 110 111 114 115 119 120 121 123 129 130 132 135 146 147 148 **P**1 5 6 **S** Memorial Hermann Healthcare System, Houston, TX
Primary Contact: Louis G. Smith, Jr., Chief Executive Officer
COO: Louis G. Smith, Jr., Chief Executive Officer
CMO: Susan Curling, M.D., Chief Medical Officer
CHR: Stephanie Foster, Director Human Resources
Web address: www.memorialhermann.org
**Control:** Other not–for–profit (including NFP Corporation) **Service:** General Medical and Surgical

**Staffed Beds:** 227 **Admissions:** 9977 **Census:** 121 **Outpatient Visits:** 93724 **Births:** 1151 **Total Expense ($000):** 158462 **Payroll Expense ($000):** 54677 **Personnel:** 731

### HUNTSVILLE—Walker County

✠ **HUNTSVILLE MEMORIAL HOSPITAL (450347)**, 110 Memorial Hospital Drive, Zip 77340–4940, Mailing Address: P.O. Box 4001, Zip 77342–4001; tel. 936/291–3411 **A**1 9 10 **F**3 5 8 11 13 15 26 28 29 31 32 34 35 39 40 43 45 46 50 53 54 56 57 59 62 64 65 66 68 70 75 76 77 78 79 81 82 85 86 87 89 90 91 92 93 97 100 101 103 107 108 110 111 114 115 118 119 127 130 131 132 135 141 142 146 147 148
Primary Contact: Shannon Brown, Chief Executive Officer
COO: Tripp Montalbo, Chief Operating Officer
CFO: Dale Dodds, Interim Chief Financial Officer
CIO: John Heeman, Director Information Systems
CHR: Diane L. Stevens, MS, Director Human Resources and Compliance Officer
Web address: www.huntsvillememorial.com
**Control:** Other not–for–profit (including NFP Corporation) **Service:** General Medical and Surgical

**Staffed Beds:** 97 **Admissions:** 3505 **Census:** 38 **Outpatient Visits:** 101182 **Births:** 460 **Total Expense ($000):** 68336 **Payroll Expense ($000):** 30583 **Personnel:** 442

### HURST—Tarrant County

☐ **COOK CHILDREN'S NORTHEAST HOSPITAL (670045)**, 6316 Precinct Line Road, Zip 76054–2766; tel. 817/605–2500 **A**1 9 10 **F**3 39 40 41 45 48 64 68 79 81 85 89 107 111 114 119 144
Primary Contact: Jan Milligan, Administrator
Web address: www.cookchildrens.org/AboutUs/Companies/Pages/NortheastHospital.aspx
**Control:** Corporation, Investor–owned, for–profit **Service:** Children's general

**Staffed Beds:** 3 **Admissions:** 21 **Census:** 1 **Outpatient Visits:** 58974 **Births:** 0 **Total Expense ($000):** 23819 **Payroll Expense ($000):** 8461 **Personnel:** 163

☐ **VICTORY MEDICAL CENTER MID–CITIES (450886)**, (Formerly Southwest Surgical Hospital), 1612 Hurst Town Center Drive, Zip 76054–6236; tel. 817/345–4100, (Nonreporting) **A**1 9 10 **S** Victory Healthcare, The Woodlands, TX
Primary Contact: Barbara Millwood, Chief Executive Officer
CFO: Michelle Brost, Financial Officer
CMO: Dale Brancel, D.O., Chief of Staff
CHR: Donna Irvin, Director Human Resources
Web address: www.victory–healthcare.com
**Control:** Partnership, Investor–owned, for–profit **Service:** Surgical

**Staffed Beds:** 23

### IRAAN—Pecos County

**IRAAN GENERAL HOSPITAL (451307)**, 600 349 North, Zip 79744, Mailing Address: P.O. Box 665, Zip 79744–0665; tel. 432/639–2871 **A**9 10 18 **F**28 40 43 56 57 59 64 65 75 86 93 104 107 119 127 130 133
Primary Contact: Teresa Callahan, R.N., MSN, Chief Executive Officer
CFO: Tami Burks, Chief Fiscal Services
CMO: Robert W. Garcia, M.D., Chief Medical Officer
CHR: Cathy Tucker, Director Human Resources
Web address: www.igh-hospital.com
**Control:** Hospital district or authority, Government, nonfederal **Service:** General Medical and Surgical

**Staffed Beds:** 13 **Admissions:** 25 **Census:** 1 **Outpatient Visits:** 16178 **Births:** 0 **Total Expense ($000):** 6265 **Payroll Expense ($000):** 2581 **Personnel:** 47

### IRVING—Dallas County

✠ **BAYLOR MEDICAL CENTER AT IRVING (450079)**, 1901 North MacArthur Boulevard, Zip 75061–2220; tel. 972/579–8100 **A**1 2 9 10 **F**3 11 12 13 15 17 18 20 22 24 26 28 29 30 31 34 35 40 45 46 47 49 54 55 57 58 59 64 65 70 73 74 75 76 77 78 79 80 81 82 84 85 86 87 90 93 94 100 107 108 110 111 114 115 116 117 118 119 120 121 122 126 129 130 141 143 146 147 148 **S** Baylor Health Care System, Dallas, TX
Primary Contact: Cindy K. Schamp, President
COO: Brenda K. Blain, MSN, Chief Nursing Officer and Chief Operating Officer
CFO: Lucy Catala, Vice President Finance
CMO: Jeffrey Embrey, M.D., Vice President Medical Affairs
CHR: Lisa Seay, Director Human Resources
CNO: Brenda K. Blain, MSN, Chief Nursing Officer and Chief Operating Officer
Web address: www.baylorhealth.com/PhysiciansLocations/Irving/Pages/Default.aspx
**Control:** Other not–for–profit (including NFP Corporation) **Service:** General Medical and Surgical

**Staffed Beds:** 231 **Admissions:** 9772 **Census:** 122 **Outpatient Visits:** 107513 **Births:** 1981 **Total Expense ($000):** 185288 **Payroll Expense ($000):** 68225 **Personnel:** 913

*Many Facility Codes have changed. Please refer to the AHA Guide Code Chart.* © 2013 AHA Guide

**TX**

☐ **IRVING COPPELL SURGICAL HOSPITAL (450874)**, 400 West Interstate 635, Zip 75063; tel. 972/868–4000 **A**1 9 10 **F**3 40 51 64 68 75 79 81 85 87 100 107 111 114 119 **P**2 **S** United Surgical Partners International, Addison, TX
Primary Contact: Deonna Unell, Chief Executive Officer
CFO: Gabrielle Holland, Chief Financial Officer
CMO: Scott McGraw, M.D., Medical Director
Web address: www.ic-sh.com
**Control:** Partnership, Investor–owned, for–profit **Service:** General Medical and Surgical

**Staffed Beds:** 12 **Admissions:** 505 **Census:** 2 **Outpatient Visits:** 9182 **Births:** 0 **Total Expense ($000):** 32838 **Payroll Expense ($000):** 6166 **Personnel:** 104

☒ **LAS COLINAS MEDICAL CENTER (450822)**, 6800 North MacArthur Boulevard, Zip 75039–2422; tel. 972/969–2000 **A**1 9 10 **F**3 8 13 15 18 20 22 24 28 29 30 31 34 35 40 43 45 46 47 48 49 50 57 59 60 64 68 70 72 73 74 75 76 77 78 79 81 87 93 100 102 107 108 110 111 114 118 119 126 129 130 132 147 148 **S** HCA, Nashville, TN
Primary Contact: Daniela Decell, Chief Executive Officer
COO: Chip Zahn, Chief Operating Officer
CFO: Nick Galt, Chief Financial Officer
Web address: www.lascolinasmedical.com
**Control:** Corporation, Investor–owned, for–profit **Service:** General Medical and Surgical

**Staffed Beds:** 90 **Admissions:** 5186 **Census:** 47 **Outpatient Visits:** 55015 **Births:** 1792 **Total Expense ($000):** 62269 **Payroll Expense ($000):** 24535 **Personnel:** 379

### JACKSBORO—Jack County

**FAITH COMMUNITY HOSPITAL (450241)**, 717 Magnolia Street, Zip 76458–1111; tel. 940/567–6633 **A**9 10 20 **F**7 11 28 35 40 43 57 77 93 107 119 127 130 133 **P**6
Primary Contact: Frank Beaman, Administrator
CFO: James Bartlett, Chief Financial Officer
CMO: S. Jamal, M.D., Medical Director
CIO: Bradlee Landis, Chief Information Officer
CHR: James Bartlett, Human Resources
CNO: Joy Henry, R.N., Director Nurses
Web address: www.faithcommunityhospital.com
**Control:** Hospital district or authority, Government, nonfederal **Service:** General Medical and Surgical

**Staffed Beds:** 17 **Admissions:** 391 **Census:** 3 **Outpatient Visits:** 18186 **Births:** 0 **Total Expense ($000):** 6729 **Payroll Expense ($000):** 3194 **Personnel:** 94

### JACKSONVILLE—Cherokee County

☒ **EAST TEXAS MEDICAL CENTER JACKSONVILLE (450194)**, 501 South Ragsdale Street, Zip 75766–2413; tel. 903/541–5000 **A**1 9 10 20 **F**3 8 11 13 15 18 20 26 29 31 34 35 37 39 40 43 45 50 57 59 64 65 70 75 76 79 81 82 85 97 107 108 110 111 115 119 127 129 145 146 147 148 **S** East Texas Medical Center Regional Healthcare System, Tyler, TX
Primary Contact: Jack R. Endres, Administrator
CFO: Phillip A. Caron, Chief Financial Officer
CMO: Lucia Williams, M.D., Chief of Staff
CHR: Elysia Epperson, Director Human Resources
CNO: Jana Bateman, R.N., Chief Nursing Officer
Web address: www.etmc.org
**Control:** Other not–for–profit (including NFP Corporation) **Service:** General Medical and Surgical

**Staffed Beds:** 38 **Admissions:** 1955 **Census:** 18 **Outpatient Visits:** 62590 **Births:** 436 **Total Expense ($000):** 40677 **Payroll Expense ($000):** 10939 **Personnel:** 201

☒ **MOTHER FRANCES HOSPITAL – JACKSONVILLE (451319)**, 2026 South Jackson, Zip 75766–5822; tel. 903/541–4500 **A**1 9 10 18 **F**3 8 15 18 28 29 30 32 34 35 40 43 45 50 53 56 57 59 64 65 68 77 79 81 82 85 93 97 107 108 110 111 114 119 129 130 145 147 **P**5 6 7 8 **S** Trinity Mother Frances Hospitals and Clinics, Tyler, TX
Primary Contact: Thomas N. Cammack, Jr., Chief Administrative Officer
COO: Michael Lewis, Chief Operating Officer
CFO: William L. Bellenfant, Chief Financial Officer
CMO: Matthew Vierkant, M.D., President Medical Staff
CIO: Lee Portwood, Chief Information Officer
CHR: Davlin King, Team Leader Human Resources
Web address: www.tmfhs.org/jacksonville
**Control:** Other not–for–profit (including NFP Corporation) **Service:** General Medical and Surgical

**Staffed Beds:** 21 **Admissions:** 1026 **Census:** 8 **Outpatient Visits:** 72367 **Births:** 0 **Total Expense ($000):** 29480 **Payroll Expense ($000):** 7788 **Personnel:** 133

### JASPER—Jasper County

☒ **CHRISTUS JASPER MEMORIAL HOSPITAL (450573)**, 1275 Marvin Hancock Drive, Zip 75951–4995; tel. 409/384–5461 **A**1 9 10 **F**3 11 13 15 29 30 34 40 43 50 51 57 59 64 70 76 77 79 81 83 89 90 107 111 119 127 130 135 146 **P**8 **S** CHRISTUS Health, Irving, TX
Primary Contact: Deborah Mecom, R.N., Administrator
COO: Mark Durand, Assistant Administrator Operations
CFO: Libby Lewis, Chief Financial Officer
CIO: Robert Jacobs, Regional Information Management Executive
CHR: Kay Powell, Director Human Resources
CNO: Rebecca Firmin, R.N., Chief Nursing Officer
Web address: www.christusjasper.org
**Control:** Church–operated, Nongovernment, not–for profit **Service:** General Medical and Surgical

**Staffed Beds:** 50 **Admissions:** 1880 **Census:** 17 **Outpatient Visits:** 76345 **Births:** 392 **Total Expense ($000):** 26561 **Payroll Expense ($000):** 11199 **Personnel:** 227

### JOURDANTON—Atascosa County

☒ **SOUTH TEXAS REGIONAL MEDICAL CENTER (450165)**, 1905 Highway 97 East, Zip 78026–1504; tel. 830/769–3515 **A**1 9 10 20 **F**3 11 13 15 18 20 28 29 30 34 35 39 40 43 45 57 59 64 68 70 75 76 77 79 81 82 85 93 107 108 110 111 114 119 127 129 130 132 133 146 147 148 **P**6 **S** Community Health Systems, Inc., Franklin, TN
Primary Contact: James R. Resendez, Chief Executive Officer
CFO: Gary Redmon, Chief Financial Officer
CMO: Edward Blackmon, M.D., Chief of Staff
CIO: Rita S. Castillo, R.N., Chief Quality Officer
CHR: Carrie Steinle, Chief Human Resources
CNO: Shelly Farrow, R.N., Chief Nursing Officer
Web address: www.strmc.com
**Control:** Corporation, Investor–owned, for–profit **Service:** General Medical and Surgical

**Staffed Beds:** 67 **Admissions:** 1859 **Census:** 18 **Outpatient Visits:** 43879 **Births:** 264 **Total Expense ($000):** 340340 **Payroll Expense ($000):** 13966 **Personnel:** 242

### JUNCTION—Kimble County

★ **KIMBLE HOSPITAL (451306)**, 349 Reid Road, Zip 76849–3049; tel. 325/446–3321 **A**9 10 18 **F**3 29 34 35 40 41 43 57 59 66 93 107 119 127 133 **S** Preferred Management Corporation, Shawnee, OK
Primary Contact: Steve Bowen, Administrator
COO: Teena Hagood, Chief Nursing Officer
CFO: Larry Stephens, Chief Financial Officer
CMO: Ben Udall, M.D., Chief of Staff
CIO: Anna Henry, Chief Information Officer
CHR: Hope Lamb, Manager Human Resources
Web address: www.kimblehospital.org/
**Control:** Corporation, Investor–owned, for–profit **Service:** General Medical and Surgical

**Staffed Beds:** 15 **Admissions:** 252 **Census:** 2 **Outpatient Visits:** 16178 **Births:** 0 **Total Expense ($000):** 6550 **Payroll Expense ($000):** 2795 **Personnel:** 66

### KATY—Harris County

☒ **CHRISTUS ST. CATHERINE HOSPITAL (450832)**, 701 Fry Road, Zip 77450–2255; tel. 281/599–5700 **A**1 2 9 10 **F**3 11 12 13 15 17 18 29 30 34 35 40 54 57 59 61 64 69 70 75 76 77 78 79 81 82 84 86 87 89 90 93 107 108 110 111 114 115 117 119 124 129 130 131 132 135 146 147 148 **S** CHRISTUS Health, Irving, TX
Primary Contact: Gene B. Wright, Interim Chief Executive Officer
CFO: Nancy Brock, Chief Financial Officer
CHR: James A. Fitch, Director Human Resources
Web address: www.christusstcatherine.org
**Control:** Church–operated, Nongovernment, not–for profit **Service:** General Medical and Surgical

**Staffed Beds:** 102 **Admissions:** 6507 **Census:** 53 **Outpatient Visits:** 67696 **Births:** 1130 **Total Expense ($000):** 91982 **Payroll Expense ($000):** 31939 **Personnel:** 487

TX

**Hospital, Medicare Provider Number, Address, Telephone, Approval, Facility, and Physician Codes, Health Care System**

★ American Hospital Association (AHA) membership
☐ The Joint Commission accreditation
◇ DNV Healthcare Inc. accreditation
○ Healthcare Facilities Accreditation Program
△ Commission on Accreditation of Rehabilitation Facilities (CARF) accreditation

© 2013 AHA Guide *Many Facility Codes have changed. Please refer to the AHA Guide Code Chart.* Hospitals **A615**

✠ **MEMORIAL HERMANN KATY HOSPITAL (450847)**, 23900 Katy Freeway, Zip 77494–1323; tel. 281/644–7000 **A**1 9 10 **F**3 8 11 13 15 29 30 35 39 40 43 45 46 49 50 57 59 61 64 65 68 69 70 73 74 75 76 77 79 81 85 89 93 102 107 108 111 114 118 119 130 131 132 146 147 **P**1 5 6 **S** Memorial Hermann Healthcare System, Houston, TX
Primary Contact: Brian S. Barbe, Chief Executive Officer
CFO: Linda Kulhanek, Chief Financial Officer
Web address: www.memorialhermann.org/locations/katy/
**Control:** Other not–for–profit (including NFP Corporation) **Service:** General Medical and Surgical

**Staffed Beds:** 142 **Admissions:** 8946 **Census:** 87 **Outpatient Visits:** 80801 **Births:** 2385 **Total Expense ($000):** 134349 **Payroll Expense ($000):** 47408 **Personnel:** 607

✠ **MEMORIAL HERMANN REHABILITATION HOSPITAL – KATY (673038)**, 21720 Kingsland Boulevard, Zip 77450–2550; tel. 281/579–5555 **A**1 9 10 **F**3 29 64 79 90 92 93 107 111 114 119 130 131 148 **P**1 5 6 **S** Memorial Hermann Healthcare System, Houston, TX
Primary Contact: Noelle Lopez, Executive Director
CMO: Mukesh Mehta, M.D., Chief Medical Officer
CMO: Tanya Phillips, R.N., Director Patient Care
CHR: Everitt Lang, Consultant Human Resources and Organizational Development
Web address: www.memorialhermann.com
**Control:** Partnership, Investor–owned, for–profit **Service:** Rehabilitation

**Staffed Beds:** 35 **Admissions:** 792 **Census:** 29 **Outpatient Visits:** 9829 **Births:** 0 **Total Expense ($000):** 19515 **Payroll Expense ($000):** 7594 **Personnel:** 109

### KAUFMAN—Kaufman County

✠ **TEXAS HEALTH PRESBYTERIAN HOSPITAL KAUFMAN (450292)**, 850 Ed Hall Drive, Zip 75142–1861, Mailing Address: P.O. Box 1108, Zip 75142–5401; tel. 972/932–7200 **A**1 9 10 **F**3 11 13 15 29 30 34 35 40 43 45 50 53 57 59 65 68 70 75 76 79 81 85 86 87 93 102 107 108 111 114 118 119 130 132 135 146 148 **P**5 **S** Texas Health Resources, Arlington, TX
Primary Contact: Patsy Youngs, President
CMO: Prabha Mohan, M.D., President Medical Staff
CHR: Carolyn Whitehurst, Director Human Resources
Web address: www.texashealth.org/Kaufman
**Control:** Other not–for–profit (including NFP Corporation) **Service:** General Medical and Surgical

**Staffed Beds:** 68 **Admissions:** 2145 **Census:** 18 **Outpatient Visits:** 69105 **Births:** 307 **Total Expense ($000):** 32193 **Payroll Expense ($000):** 12889 **Personnel:** 286

### KENEDY—Karnes County

★ **OTTO KAISER MEMORIAL HOSPITAL (451364)**, 3349 South Highway 181, Zip 78119–5247; tel. 830/583–3401 **A**9 10 18 **F**3 11 15 29 30 34 40 45 46 57 62 64 68 77 81 93 107 111 114 119 133 135 148 **P**8
Primary Contact: David Lee, Interim Chief Executive Officer
CFO: David Lee, Chief Financial Officer
CIO: Shaneece Pieprzyca, Director Information Technology
CHR: Christina Benavides, Director Employee Services
CNO: Audrey Cortez, Chief Nursing Officer
Web address: www.okmh.org/
**Control:** Hospital district or authority, Government, nonfederal **Service:** General Medical and Surgical

**Staffed Beds:** 25 **Admissions:** 463 **Census:** 8 **Outpatient Visits:** 24140 **Births:** 0 **Total Expense ($000):** 13196 **Payroll Expense ($000):** 5496 **Personnel:** 134

### KERMIT—Winkler County

**WINKLER COUNTY MEMORIAL HOSPITAL (451314)**, 821 Jeffee Drive, Zip 79745–4696, Mailing Address: P.O. Box H., Zip 79745–6008; tel. 432/586–5864 **A**9 10 18 **F**3 32 34 36 40 57 59 64 65 69 93 97 107 114 119 127 133
Primary Contact: William E. Ernst, Administrator
CFO: Wannah Hartley, Controller
CMO: K. Pham, M.D., Chief of Staff
CIO: Keith Palmer, Assistant Administrator
**Control:** County–Government, nonfederal **Service:** General Medical and Surgical

**Staffed Beds:** 19 **Admissions:** 336 **Census:** 2 **Outpatient Visits:** 8096 **Births:** 0 **Total Expense ($000):** 10192 **Payroll Expense ($000):** 3023 **Personnel:** 69

### KERRVILLE—Kerr County

**KERRVILLE DIVISION** See South Texas Veterans Health Care System, San Antonio

□ **KERRVILLE STATE HOSPITAL (454014)**, 721 Thompson Drive, Zip 78028–5154; tel. 830/896–2211 **A**1 3 5 10 **F**11 30 34 39 44 50 56 65 68 75 86 87 97 98 101 103 130 132 135 146 **S** Texas Department of State Health Services, Austin, TX
Primary Contact: Leigh Ann Fitzpatrick, Superintendent
CMO: Janet E. True, M.D., Clinical Director
Web address: www.dshs.state.tx.us/mhhospitals/KerrvilleSH/default.shtm
**Control:** State–Government, nonfederal **Service:** Psychiatric

**Staffed Beds:** 202 **Admissions:** 82 **Census:** 187 **Outpatient Visits:** 0 **Births:** 0 **Total Expense ($000):** 36230 **Payroll Expense ($000):** 20326 **Personnel:** 536

✠ **PETERSON REGIONAL MEDICAL CENTER (450007)**, 551 Hill Country Drive, Zip 78028–6085; tel. 830/896–4200 **A**1 9 10 **F**3 8 11 13 15 18 20 26 29 30 31 34 35 39 40 44 45 49 54 57 59 62 63 64 65 68 70 74 75 76 77 78 79 80 81 82 84 85 86 87 90 93 96 100 107 108 110 111 114 119 126 130 131 132 135 145 146 147 148 **P**1 6
Primary Contact: James Patrick Murray, FACHE, Chief Executive Officer
COO: Stephen Pautler, FACHE, Chief Operating Officer
CFO: Julie Johnson, Chief Financial Officer
CMO: Tyson Hale, M.D., Chief of Staff
CIO: Richard Cruthirds, Director Information Systems
CHR: Buddy Volpe, Director Human Resources
CNO: Kaeli Dressler, R.N., Chief Nursing Officer
Web address: www.petersonrmc.com
**Control:** Other not–for–profit (including NFP Corporation) **Service:** General Medical and Surgical

**Staffed Beds:** 124 **Admissions:** 4795 **Census:** 60 **Outpatient Visits:** 147184 **Births:** 368 **Total Expense ($000):** 99949 **Payroll Expense ($000):** 38524 **Personnel:** 755

### KILGORE—Gregg County

◇ **ALLEGIANCE SPECIALTY HOSPITAL OF KILGORE (450488)**, 1612 South Henderson Boulevard, Zip 75662–3594; tel. 903/984–3505 **A**9 10 21 **F**3 29 34 35 56 57 59 98 101 103 104 130 **S** Allegiance Health Management, Shreveport, LA
Primary Contact: Sherry Bustin, Chief Executive Officer
CHR: Becky Wilson, Manager Human Resources
Web address: www.ahmgt.com
**Control:** Corporation, Investor–owned, for–profit **Service:** Psychiatric

**Staffed Beds:** 60 **Admissions:** 593 **Census:** 19 **Outpatient Visits:** 23178 **Births:** 0 **Total Expense ($000):** 8688 **Payroll Expense ($000):** 3617 **Personnel:** 94

### KILLEEN—Bell County

✠ **METROPLEX ADVENTIST HOSPITAL (450152)**, 2201 South Clear Creek Road, Zip 76549–4110; tel. 254/526–7523 **A**1 9 10 **F**3 8 11 12 13 15 18 20 22 26 28 29 30 34 35 39 40 46 48 49 54 57 59 62 65 68 70 71 75 76 77 78 79 81 82 85 86 87 89 93 98 99 100 101 102 103 104 105 107 108 111 114 115 118 119 129 130 131 132 135 146 147 148 **P**8 **S** Adventist Health System Sunbelt Health Care Corporation, Altamonte Springs, FL
Primary Contact: Carlyle L. E. Walton, Chief Executive Officer
CFO: Penny Johnson, Chief Financial Officer
CMO: Frederick Barnett, M.D., Chief of Staff
CIO: Dale Koebnick, Director Management Information Systems and Patient Access
CHR: Brenda Coley, Executive Director
Web address: www.mplex.org
**Control:** Church–operated, Nongovernment, not–for profit **Service:** General Medical and Surgical

**Staffed Beds:** 177 **Admissions:** 7879 **Census:** 76 **Outpatient Visits:** 118595 **Births:** 1537 **Total Expense ($000):** 110165 **Payroll Expense ($000):** 45525 **Personnel:** 1049

### KINGSVILLE—Kleberg County

✠ **CHRISTUS SPOHN HOSPITAL KLEBERG (450163)**, 1311 General Cavazos Boulevard, Zip 78363–7130; tel. 361/595–1661 **A**1 9 10 20 **F**3 11 13 15 29 30 34 35 40 43 53 54 57 59 64 65 70 74 75 76 77 81 85 86 87 89 93 102 107 108 110 111 119 130 146 **S** CHRISTUS Health, Irving, TX
Primary Contact: Steven G. Daniel, Interim Vice President and Chief Operating Officer
CFO: Lauralinda Moore, Manager Finance
CHR: Candace Jefferson, Manager Human Resources
Web address: www.christusspohn.org
**Control:** Church–operated, Nongovernment, not–for profit **Service:** General Medical and Surgical

**Staffed Beds:** 79 **Admissions:** 4113 **Census:** 51 **Outpatient Visits:** 46621 **Births:** 311 **Total Expense ($000):** 39897 **Payroll Expense ($000):** 18239 **Personnel:** 255

*Many Facility Codes have changed. Please refer to the AHA Guide Code Chart.*   © 2013 AHA Guide

**TX**

## KINGWOOD—Harris County

☒ **KINGWOOD MEDICAL CENTER (450775)**, 22999 U.S. Highway 59 North, Zip 77339; tel. 281/348–8000 **A1** 9 10 **F3** 11 13 15 18 20 22 24 26 28 29 30 34 35 40 42 49 50 51 56 57 59 60 61 64 68 70 72 74 75 76 77 78 79 81 82 84 85 87 89 90 92 97 102 107 108 110 111 114 115 119 124 126 129 130 132 143 144 146 147 148 **P7 S** HCA, Nashville, TN
Primary Contact: Melinda Stephenson, Chief Executive Officer
COO: Megan Marietta, Chief Operating Officer
CFO: Daniel E. Davis, Chief Financial Officer
CMO: J. Mario Villafani, M.D., Chief of Staff
Web address: www.kingwoodmedical.com
**Control:** Corporation, Investor–owned, for–profit **Service:** General Medical and Surgical

**Staffed Beds:** 262 **Admissions:** 14502 **Census:** 195 **Outpatient Visits:** 94911 **Births:** 2533 **Total Expense ($000):** 161078 **Payroll Expense ($000):** 63238 **Personnel:** 772

☐ **KINGWOOD PINES HOSPITAL (454103)**, 2001 Ladbrook Drive, Zip 77339–3004; tel. 281/358–1495 **A1** 9 10 **F4** 5 29 75 86 87 98 99 101 103 104 105 130 132 **S** Universal Health Services, Inc., King of Prussia, PA
Primary Contact: James Burroughs, Chief Executive Officer
CFO: Richard Kurzenberger, Chief Financial Officer
CMO: Gary E. Miller, M.D., Medical Director
CHR: Adrienne Livingston, Director Human Resources
Web address: www.kingwoodpines.com
**Control:** Corporation, Investor–owned, for–profit **Service:** Psychiatric

**Staffed Beds:** 116 **Admissions:** 3758 **Census:** 79 **Outpatient Visits:** 3301 **Births:** 0 **Total Expense ($000):** 19604 **Payroll Expense ($000):** 9300 **Personnel:** 200

**KINGWOOD SPECIALTY HOSPITAL** See Memorial Hermann Surgical Hospital Kingwood

☐ **MEMORIAL HERMANN SURGICAL HOSPITAL KINGWOOD (670005)**, 300 Kingwood Medical Drive, Zip 77339–6400; tel. 281/312–4000 **A1** 9 10 **F3** 40 45 51 64 68 79 81 82 85 86 87
Primary Contact: Marc Celia, R.N., MS, FACHE, Chief Executive Officer
Web address: www.memorialhermannkingwood.com
**Control:** Corporation, Investor–owned, for–profit **Service:** General Medical and Surgical

**Staffed Beds:** 10 **Admissions:** 162 **Census:** 1 **Outpatient Visits:** 5479 **Births:** 0 **Total Expense ($000):** 16596 **Payroll Expense ($000):** 3825 **Personnel:** 95

## KNOX CITY—Knox County

**KNOX COUNTY HOSPITAL (450746)**, 701 South Fifth Street, Zip 79529–2107, Mailing Address: P.O. Box 608, Zip 79529–0608; tel. 940/657–3535 **A9** 10 20 **F7** 11 28 40 43 57 59 62 127 133 **P6**
Primary Contact: Stephan A. Kuehler, Administrator
CFO: Dan Offutt, Manager Finance
CMO: Shirley Barretto, M.D., Chief of Staff
CIO: Sue Marion, Manager Business Office
Web address: www.knoxcountyhospital–texas.com
**Control:** Hospital district or authority, Government, nonfederal **Service:** General Medical and Surgical

**Staffed Beds:** 14 **Admissions:** 127 **Census:** 1 **Outpatient Visits:** 37091 **Births:** 0 **Total Expense ($000):** 6159 **Payroll Expense ($000):** 2419 **Personnel:** 78

## KYLE—Hays County

☒ **SETON MEDICAL CENTER HAYS (670056)**, 6001 Kyle Parkway, Zip 78640–6112, Mailing Address: 6001 Kyle Prkway, Zip 78640–6112; tel. 512/504–5000 **A1** 3 5 9 10 **F3** 11 13 15 18 20 22 24 28 29 30 31 34 35 40 43 44 45 46 49 50 57 60 64 68 70 72 74 75 76 77 78 79 81 82 85 87 107 108 110 111 114 115 118 119 129 130 131 135 146 148 **P3** 8 **S** Ascension Health, Saint Louis, MO
Primary Contact: John C. Brindley, FACHE, President and Chief Executive Officer
COO: Herbert A. Dyer, Vice President and Project Executive
Web address: www.seton.net/locations/seton_medical_center_hays/
**Control:** Church–operated, Nongovernment, not–for profit **Service:** General Medical and Surgical

**Staffed Beds:** 83 **Admissions:** 5359 **Census:** 62 **Outpatient Visits:** 45478 **Births:** 692 **Total Expense ($000):** 90961 **Payroll Expense ($000):** 42415 **Personnel:** 683

## LA GRANGE—Fayette County

★ **ST. MARK'S MEDICAL CENTER (670004)**, One St. Mark's Place, Zip 78945; tel. 979/242–2200 **A3** 5 9 10 **F3** 8 11 12 13 15 17 29 30 34 40 43 45 50 56 57 59 68 70 74 75 76 79 81 82 84 85 87 89 93 107 110 111 114 119 128 129 130 133 145 146 147 **P6 S** Community Hospital Corporation, Plano, TX
Primary Contact: Shane Kernell, Chief Executive Officer
COO: Carol Drozd, Chief Operating Officer
CFO: Dennis Boyd, Chief Financial Officer
CMO: Russell Juno, M.D., Chief of Staff
CHR: Tammy Oehlke, Director Human Resources
Web address: www.smmctx.org
**Control:** Other not–for–profit (including NFP Corporation) **Service:** General Medical and Surgical

**Staffed Beds:** 44 **Admissions:** 1971 **Census:** 20 **Outpatient Visits:** 51316 **Births:** 277 **Total Expense ($000):** 26203 **Payroll Expense ($000):** 9205 **Personnel:** 176

## LAKE JACKSON—Brazoria County

☒ **BRAZOSPORT REGIONAL HEALTH SYSTEM (450072)**, 100 Medical Drive, Zip 77566–5674; tel. 979/297–4411 **A1** 2 9 10 **F3** 11 12 13 15 18 20 22 28 29 30 31 34 37 40 41 43 45 47 49 50 51 57 59 60 62 64 65 68 70 74 75 76 77 78 79 81 82 85 86 87 89 90 91 93 94 107 108 110 111 114 117 118 119 120 121 123 129 130 132 146 147 148 **P8 S** QHR, Brentwood, TN
Primary Contact: Al Guevara, FACHE, President and Chief Executive Officer
CFO: Chuck Jeffress, Vice President Fiscal Services
CMO: Adam Corley, M.D., Chief of Staff
CIO: Todd Edwards, Director Information Management Systems
CHR: Christopher Calia, Director Human Resources
Web address: www.brhstx.org
**Control:** Other not–for–profit (including NFP Corporation) **Service:** General Medical and Surgical

**Staffed Beds:** 103 **Admissions:** 5087 **Census:** 52 **Outpatient Visits:** 131011 **Births:** 709 **Total Expense ($000):** 72870 **Payroll Expense ($000):** 29179 **Personnel:** 552

## LAKEWAY—Travis County

**LAKEWAY REGIONAL MEDICAL CENTER (670079)**, 100 Medical Parkway, Zip 78738–5621; tel. 512/571–5000, (Data for 259 days) **A9** 10 **F3** 13 15 17 18 20 22 24 26 29 30 31 34 40 41 43 45 46 49 50 51 54 57 59 60 64 65 68 70 72 74 75 76 77 78 79 81 82 85 86 87 93 94 96 97 100 102 107 108 110 111 115 116 117 118 119 129 130 143 145 146 147 148 **P7**
Primary Contact: David Kreye, Chief Executive Officer
Web address: www.lakewayregional.com
**Control:** Corporation, Investor–owned, for–profit **Service:** General Medical and Surgical

**Staffed Beds:** 41 **Admissions:** 1216 **Census:** 15 **Outpatient Visits:** 7688 **Births:** 115 **Total Expense ($000):** 47431 **Payroll Expense ($000):** 10936 **Personnel:** 333

## LAMESA—Dawson County

**MEDICAL ARTS HOSPITAL (450489)**, 2200 North Bryan Avenue, Zip 79331–2451; tel. 806/872–2183 **A9** 10 20 **F3** 11 13 28 29 30 35 40 43 45 50 57 59 62 64 75 76 81 87 93 97 107 111 114 119 127 130 133 146 148 **P6**
Primary Contact: Letha Hughes, Chief Executive Officer
CFO: Steve Brock, Chief Financial Officer
CMO: Fidel Ogeda, M.D., Chief of Staff
CHR: Jo Beth Smith, Director Human Resources
Web address: www.medicalartshospital.org
**Control:** Hospital district or authority, Government, nonfederal **Service:** General Medical and Surgical

**Staffed Beds:** 22 **Admissions:** 501 **Census:** 7 **Outpatient Visits:** 83253 **Births:** 92 **Total Expense ($000):** 25943 **Payroll Expense ($000):** 7452 **Personnel:** 211

**TX**

---

**Hospital, Medicare Provider Number, Address, Telephone, Approval, Facility, and Physician Codes, Health Care System**

★ American Hospital Association (AHA) membership
☐ The Joint Commission accreditation
◇ DNV Healthcare Inc. accreditation
○ Healthcare Facilities Accreditation Program
△ Commission on Accreditation of Rehabilitation Facilities (CARF) accreditation

## LAMPASAS—Lampasas County

✠ **ROLLINS–BROOK COMMUNITY HOSPITAL (451323)**, 608 North Key Avenue, Zip 76550–1106, Mailing Address: P.O. Box 589, Zip 76550–0032; tel. 512/556–3682 **A**1 9 10 18 **F**3 15 29 30 35 40 57 59 61 75 77 81 87 93 107 111 114 119 130 132 133 146 148 **P**8 **S** Adventist Health System Sunbelt Health Care Corporation, Altamonte Springs, FL
Primary Contact: Carlyle L. E. Walton, President and Chief Executive Officer
CFO: Janice Hagensicker, Chief Financial Officer
CHR: Brenda Coley, Executive Director
Web address: www.mplex.org
**Control:** Church–operated, Nongovernment, not–for profit **Service:** General Medical and Surgical

**Staffed Beds:** 35 **Admissions:** 674 **Census:** 9 **Outpatient Visits:** 17360 **Births:** 0 **Total Expense ($000):** 13369 **Payroll Expense ($000):** 4575 **Personnel:** 129

## LAREDO—Webb County

☐ **DOCTORS HOSPITAL OF LAREDO (450643)**, 10700 McPherson Road, Zip 78045–6268; tel. 956/523–2000 **A**1 2 9 10 **F**3 11 12 13 15 18 20 22 26 29 30 31 32 34 37 39 40 43 45 48 49 50 54 57 59 60 63 64 70 71 72 74 75 76 77 78 79 81 85 87 89 90 91 93 107 108 111 114 121 129 130 132 146 **P**5 **S** Universal Health Services, Inc., King of Prussia, PA
Primary Contact: Rene Lopez, Chief Executive Officer
COO: Eladio Montalvo, Chief Operating Officer
CFO: Dinah Gonzalez, Chief Financial Officer
CMO: Juan F. Montalvo, M.D., Chief of Staff
CIO: Maribel Mata, Director Information Services
CHR: Roseann Figueroa, Director Human Resources
Web address: www.doctorshosplaredo.com
**Control:** Partnership, Investor–owned, for–profit **Service:** General Medical and Surgical

**Staffed Beds:** 183 **Admissions:** 8532 **Census:** 98 **Outpatient Visits:** 96738 **Births:** 2637 **Total Expense ($000):** 103121 **Payroll Expense ($000):** 34525 **Personnel:** 644

✠ **LAREDO MEDICAL CENTER (450029)**, 1700 East Saunders Avenue, Zip 78041–5474, Mailing Address: P.O. Box 2068, Zip 78044–2068; tel. 956/796–5000, (Total facility includes 18 beds in nursing home–type unit) **A**1 9 10 **F**3 8 11 12 13 15 18 20 22 24 26 28 29 30 31 32 34 35 36 37 40 43 45 46 49 50 51 53 54 56 57 59 60 64 68 70 72 74 75 76 77 78 79 81 85 86 87 89 90 91 92 93 96 107 108 110 111 114 119 120 121 123 128 129 132 135 146 147 148 **S** Community Health Systems, Inc., Franklin, TN
Primary Contact: Timothy E. Schmidt, Chief Executive Officer
COO: John E. Ulbricht, Chief Operating Officer
CFO: Ed Romero, Chief Financial Officer
CIO: Joe Rivera, Chief Information Technology Officer
CHR: Michael W. Hartley, Director Human Resources
Web address: www.laredomedical.com
**Control:** Corporation, Investor–owned, for–profit **Service:** General Medical and Surgical

**Staffed Beds:** 326 **Admissions:** 16773 **Census:** 230 **Outpatient Visits:** 176217 **Births:** 3391 **Total Expense ($000):** 257245 **Payroll Expense ($000):** 54723 **Personnel:** 1325

☐ **LAREDO SPECIALTY HOSPITAL (452096)**, 2005 Bustamente Street, Zip 78041–5470; tel. 956/753–5353 **A**1 10 **F**3 29 30 53 70 75 77 85 86 87 91 96 130 148 **S** Ernest Health, Inc., Albuquerque, NM
Primary Contact: Mario Rodriguez, Chief Executive Officer
COO: Bernadette Hernandez, R.N., Chief Operating Officer
CFO: Robert Voss, Chief Financial Officer
CMO: Marisa Guerrero, Director Human Resources
CMO: Benson Huang, M.D., Medical Director
CNO: Bernadette Hernandez, R.N., Chief Operating Officer and Chief Nursing Officer
Web address: www.lsh.ernesthealth.com
**Control:** Partnership, Investor–owned, for–profit **Service:** General Medical and Surgical

**Staffed Beds:** 60 **Admissions:** 491 **Census:** 34 **Outpatient Visits:** 0 **Births:** 0 **Total Expense ($000):** 17537 **Payroll Expense ($000):** 6321 **Personnel:** 135

## LEAGUE CITY—Galveston County

☐ **DEVEREUX TEXAS TREATMENT NETWORK (454085)**, 1150 Devereux Drive, Zip 77573–2043; tel. 281/335–1000 **A**1 9 10 **F**4 5 29 32 35 38 43 53 54 59 64 75 86 87 98 99 100 101 102 104 105 106 130 132 134 **S** Devereux, Villanova, PA
Primary Contact: Pamela E. Helm, Executive Director
Web address: www.devereux.org
**Control:** Other not–for–profit (including NFP Corporation) **Service:** Children's hospital psychiatric

**Staffed Beds:** 60 **Admissions:** 492 **Census:** 63 **Outpatient Visits:** 5266 **Births:** 0 **Total Expense ($000):** 11940 **Payroll Expense ($000):** 4027 **Personnel:** 89

## LEVELLAND—Hockley County

★ **COVENANT HOSPITAL–LEVELLAND (450755)**, 1900 South College Avenue, Zip 79336–6508; tel. 806/894–4963 **A**9 10 **F**11 13 15 29 30 34 40 43 45 50 54 57 59 64 65 68 75 76 77 81 82 85 86 87 89 90 91 93 97 107 111 119 127 130 133 146 **P**4 **S** Covenant Health System, Lubbock, TX
Primary Contact: Alan N. King, FACHE, Interim Chief Executive Officer
CFO: John Dolan, Chief Financial Officer
CMO: Stephanie Kubacak, M.D., Chief of Staff
CIO: Kevin Elmore, Chief Information Officer
CHR: Kathy McDonald, Director Personnel
Web address: www.covenanthospitallevelland.com/
**Control:** Church–operated, Nongovernment, not–for profit **Service:** General Medical and Surgical

**Staffed Beds:** 22 **Admissions:** 1067 **Census:** 10 **Outpatient Visits:** 35265 **Births:** 257 **Total Expense ($000):** 19990 **Payroll Expense ($000):** 7886 **Personnel:** 241

## LEWISVILLE—Denton County

✠ **MEDICAL CENTER OF LEWISVILLE (450669)**, 500 West Main, Zip 75057–3699; tel. 972/420–1000 **A**1 9 10 **F**3 13 15 18 20 22 24 26 28 29 30 31 34 35 40 42 46 49 57 59 68 70 72 74 75 76 78 79 81 85 87 89 90 93 96 107 108 110 111 114 118 119 129 130 131 132 135 146 147 148 **P**5 **S** HCA, Nashville, TN
Primary Contact: Ashley McClellan, Chief Executive Officer
COO: James G. Russell, Chief Operating Officer
CFO: Lisa Brodbeck, Chief Financial Officer
CIO: Shirley Archambeault, Chief Information Officer
CHR: Dara Biegert, Vice President Human Resources
CNO: Lynn O'Neill, R.N., Chief Nursing Officer
Web address: www.lewisvillemedical.com
**Control:** Corporation, Investor–owned, for–profit **Service:** General Medical and Surgical

**Staffed Beds:** 166 **Admissions:** 7676 **Census:** 88 **Outpatient Visits:** 65901 **Births:** 1408 **Total Expense ($000):** 121993 **Payroll Expense ($000):** 45310 **Personnel:** 670

## LIBERTY—Liberty County

☐ **LIBERTY DAYTON REGIONAL MEDICAL CENTER (451375)**, 1353 North Travis, Zip 77575–3549; tel. 936/336–7316 **A**1 9 10 18 **F**3 29 40 45 56 64 81 85 107 115 128 130 133
Primary Contact: James E. Koulovatos, Chief Executive Officer
CFO: Hal Mayo, Chief Financial Officer
CMO: Don Callens, M.D., Chief Medical Officer
CNO: Mark Nichols, R.N., Director of Nurses
Web address: www.libertydaytonrmc.com
**Control:** Hospital district or authority, Government, nonfederal **Service:** General Medical and Surgical

**Staffed Beds:** 17 **Admissions:** 370 **Census:** 3 **Outpatient Visits:** 15178 **Births:** 0 **Total Expense ($000):** 7430 **Payroll Expense ($000):** 3151 **Personnel:** 70

## LINDEN—Cass County

★ **GOOD SHEPHERD MEDICAL CENTER–LINDEN (451302)**, 404 North Kaufman Street, Zip 75563–5234; tel. 903/756–5561 **A**9 10 18 **F**3 11 28 29 30 34 40 43 45 49 50 57 64 68 75 77 81 85 87 93 94 97 102 107 108 110 113 114 119 127 130 131 132 133 135 143 146 148 **P**8 **S** Good Shepherd Health System, Longview, TX
Primary Contact: Carla Roadcap, R.N., MSN, Chief Executive Officer
CMO: Donald Simmons, M.D., Chief Medical Staff
Web address: www.gsmclinden.org
**Control:** Other not–for–profit (including NFP Corporation) **Service:** General Medical and Surgical

**Staffed Beds:** 25 **Admissions:** 401 **Census:** 4 **Outpatient Visits:** 30273 **Births:** 0 **Total Expense ($000):** 11702 **Payroll Expense ($000):** 4021 **Personnel:** 81

## LITTLEFIELD—Lamb County

★ **LAMB HEALTHCARE CENTER (450698)**, 1500 South Sunset, Zip 79339–4899; tel. 806/385–6411 **A**9 10 20 **F**3 29 35 40 43 45 57 59 64 66 75 76 81 86 87 89 107 114 119 127 132 133 134 147 **P**6
Primary Contact: Jo Nell Wischkaemper, Administrator and Chief Executive Officer
CFO: Cindy Klein, Chief Financial Officer
CMO: Isabel Molina, M.D., Chief Medical Officer
CHR: Joan Williams, Administrative Assistant/Human Resources
CNO: Justin Johnson, R.N., Chief Nursing Officer
**Control:** County–Government, nonfederal **Service:** General Medical and Surgical

**Staffed Beds:** 41 **Admissions:** 439 **Census:** 7 **Outpatient Visits:** 22163 **Births:** 97 **Total Expense ($000):** 10648 **Payroll Expense ($000):** 4114 **Personnel:** 131

*Many Facility Codes have changed. Please refer to the AHA Guide Code Chart.*
© 2013 AHA Guide

## LIVINGSTON—Polk County

☐ **MEMORIAL MEDICAL CENTER – LIVINGSTON (450395)**, 1717 Highway 59 Bypass, Zip 77351–1257, Mailing Address: P.O. Box 1257, Zip 77351–0022; tel. 936/329–8700 **A**1 9 10 **F**3 11 13 15 29 34 35 40 43 45 46 50 57 59 62 64 68 70 74 75 76 79 81 85 87 89 107 108 110 111 114 119 129 130 132 146 **S** Memorial Health System of East Texas, Lufkin, TX
Primary Contact: Earl Denning, Interim Administrator
CFO: Kristi Gay, Chief Financial Officer
CMO: C. K. Mani, M.D., Chief of Staff
CHR: Ray G. Grossman, Vice President Human Resources
Web address: www.memorialhealth.org
**Control:** Other not–for–profit (including NFP Corporation) **Service:** General Medical and Surgical

**Staffed Beds:** 66 **Admissions:** 2523 **Census:** 26 **Outpatient Visits:** 51636 **Births:** 329 **Total Expense ($000):** 42094 **Payroll Expense ($000):** 16880 **Personnel:** 233

## LLANO—Llano County

★ **SCOTT & WHITE HOSPITAL – LLANO (450219)**, 200 West Ollie Street, Zip 78643–2628; tel. 325/247–5040 **A**5 9 10 20 **F**3 7 11 12 13 15 32 34 35 40 43 45 57 59 62 75 76 77 81 85 87 93 107 114 119 127 129 130 135 146 **P**6 **S** Scott & White Healthcare, Temple, TX
Primary Contact: Kevin Leeper, Chief Executive Officer
COO: Linda Meredith, MSN, Chief Operating Officer
CFO: Jason Cole, Director Finance
CMO: Kim Russell, M.D., Chief of Staff
CIO: Rodney Lott, Director Management Information Systems and Facility Operations
CHR: Pearl Oestreich, Director Human Resources
CNO: Reta Hunt, Director of Nursing
Web address: www.llanomemorial.org
**Control:** Other not–for–profit (including NFP Corporation) **Service:** General Medical and Surgical

**Staffed Beds:** 17 **Admissions:** 848 **Census:** 6 **Outpatient Visits:** 106359 **Births:** 235 **Total Expense ($000):** 26697 **Payroll Expense ($000):** 11563 **Personnel:** 214

## LOCKNEY—Floyd County

★ **W. J. MANGOLD MEMORIAL HOSPITAL (451337)**, 320 North Main Street, Zip 79241–0037, Mailing Address: Box 37, Zip 79241–0037; tel. 806/652–3373, (Nonreporting) **A**9 10 18
Primary Contact: Larry Mullins, Chief Executive Officer
CFO: Sharon Hunt, Chief Financial Officer
CMO: Kevin T. Stennett, M.D., Chief of Staff
CIO: Sam Vanderbeek, Chief Information Officer
CHR: Janice Yearwood, Director Human Resources
CNO: Billie Hendrix, R.N., Director of Nursing
Web address: www.mangoldmemorial.org
**Control:** Hospital district or authority, Government, nonfederal **Service:** General Medical and Surgical

**Staffed Beds:** 25

## LONGVIEW—Gregg County

☐ **AUDUBON BEHAVIORAL HEALTHCARE OF LONGVIEW (454117)**, 615 Clinic Drive, Zip 75605–5172; tel. 903/212–3105 **A**1 10 **F**29 35 38 56 74 75 98 100 101 102 103 104 130 **P**6 **S** Audubon Behavioral Healthcare, Longview, TX
Primary Contact: Lauren Weber, Administrator
Web address: www.audubonbehavioral.com
**Control:** Individual, Investor–owned, for–profit **Service:** Psychiatric

**Staffed Beds:** 24 **Admissions:** 303 **Census:** 13 **Outpatient Visits:** 810 **Births:** 0 **Total Expense ($000):** 4942 **Payroll Expense ($000):** 2303 **Personnel:** 92

☐ **BEHAVIORAL HOSPITAL OF LONGVIEW (454105)**, 22 Bermuda Lane, Zip 75605–2902; tel. 903/291–3456 **A**1 9 10 **F**29 98 100 101 130 **P**6
Primary Contact: David King, Administrator
Web address: www.longviewhospital.com
**Control:** Corporation, Investor–owned, for–profit **Service:** Psychiatric

**Staffed Beds:** 60 **Admissions:** 807 **Census:** 35 **Outpatient Visits:** 0 **Births:** 0 **Total Expense ($000):** 7780 **Payroll Expense ($000):** 3965 **Personnel:** 95

⊞ △ **GOOD SHEPHERD MEDICAL CENTER (450037)**, 700 East Marshall Avenue, Zip 75601–5580; tel. 903/315–2000 **A**1 7 9 10 **F**3 7 11 13 15 18 20 22 24 26 28 29 30 31 32 33 34 35 37 40 42 43 45 46 49 50 51 53 54 56 57 59 60 61 63 64 68 70 71 72 73 74 75 76 77 78 79 80 81 82 85 86 87 89 90 92 93 97 102 107 108 111 114 115 118 119 129 130 131 132 135 143 144 146 147 148 **P**8 **S** Good Shepherd Health System, Longview, TX
Primary Contact: Steve Altmiller, President and Chief Executive Officer
CFO: Patricia Keel, Chief Financial Officer
CIO: Ralph Holcomb, Chief Information Officer
CHR: Sandie Feriggno, Vice President Human Resources
Web address: www.gsmc.org
**Control:** Other not–for–profit (including NFP Corporation) **Service:** General Medical and Surgical

**Staffed Beds:** 399 **Admissions:** 19796 **Census:** 260 **Outpatient Visits:** 163544 **Births:** 2521 **Total Expense ($000):** 278049 **Payroll Expense ($000):** 99165 **Personnel:** 1883

⊞ **LONGVIEW REGIONAL MEDICAL CENTER (450702)**, 2901 North Fourth Street, Zip 75605–5191, Mailing Address: P.O. Box 14000, Zip 75607–4000; tel. 903/758–1818, (Total facility includes 15 beds in nursing home–type unit) **A**1 9 10 **F**3 8 11 12 13 17 18 20 22 24 28 29 30 31 34 37 40 43 45 46 47 49 50 57 59 61 64 65 67 70 74 75 76 78 79 81 84 85 86 87 89 107 108 111 114 115 118 119 126 128 130 146 148 **P**8 **S** Community Health Systems, Inc., Franklin, TN
Primary Contact: Jim R. Kendrick, Chief Executive Officer
COO: Jill Bayless–Berney, MSN, Chief Operating Officer
CFO: Todd Johnson, Chief Financial Officer
CMO: Alan Cowan, M.D., Chief of Staff
CIO: Keith Jarvis, Director Information Systems
CHR: Terry Hardan, Director Human Resources
CNO: Stephanie Foster, MSN, Chief Nursing Officer
Web address: www.longviewregional.com
**Control:** Corporation, Investor–owned, for–profit **Service:** General Medical and Surgical

**Staffed Beds:** 127 **Admissions:** 6512 **Census:** 72 **Outpatient Visits:** 73696 **Births:** 1007 **Total Expense ($000):** 99023 **Payroll Expense ($000):** 37532 **Personnel:** 760

⊞ **SELECT SPECIALTY HOSPITAL–LONGVIEW (452087)**, 700 East Marshall Avenue, 1st Floor, Zip 75601–5580; tel. 903/315–1100 **A**1 9 10 **F**1 3 28 29 40 75 77 85 91 92 130 148 **S** Select Medical Corporation, Mechanicsburg, PA
Primary Contact: Dennis Baker, Chief Executive Officer
Web address: www.selectspecialtyhospitals.com/company/locations/longview.aspx
**Control:** Corporation, Investor–owned, for–profit **Service:** Long–Term Acute Care hospital

**Staffed Beds:** 32 **Admissions:** 418 **Census:** 31 **Outpatient Visits:** 0 **Births:** 0 **Total Expense ($000):** 14323 **Payroll Expense ($000):** 6153 **Personnel:** 107

## LUBBOCK—Lubbock County

⊞ **COVENANT CHILDREN'S HOSPITAL (453306)**, 4015 22nd Place, Zip 79410; tel. 806/725–1011 **A**1 3 5 9 10 **F**3 19 21 23 25 27 30 31 32 40 41 43 50 59 72 73 81 89 **P**8 **S** Covenant Health System, Lubbock, TX
Primary Contact: Christopher J. Dougherty, Chief Executive Officer
CMO: Scott Robins, M.D., Chief Medical Officer
CIO: Jim Reid, Vice President and Chief Information Officer
CHR: Rodney Cates, Senior Vice President Human Resources
Web address: www.covenanthealth.org/About–Us/Facilities/Childrens–Hospital.aspx
**Control:** Other not–for–profit (including NFP Corporation) **Service:** Children's general

**Staffed Beds:** 73 **Admissions:** 2519 **Census:** 48 **Outpatient Visits:** 32263 **Births:** 0 **Total Expense ($000):** 57332 **Payroll Expense ($000):** 19609 **Personnel:** 204

**TX**

✠ **COVENANT MEDICAL CENTER (450040)**, 3615 19th Street,
Zip 79410–1203, Mailing Address: P.O. Box 1201, Zip 79408–1201;
tel. 806/725–0000, (Includes COVENANT MEDICAL CENTER–LAKESIDE, 4000
24th Street, Zip 79410–1894; tel. 806/725–0000) **A**1 2 3 5 6 9 10 **F**5 7 12 13
15 17 18 20 22 24 26 28 29 30 31 34 35 39 40 43 46 47 48 49 50 51 53
54 55 57 58 59 60 61 63 64 65 68 70 71 74 75 76 77 78 79 80 81 82 83
84 85 86 87 90 91 93 94 96 98 102 105 107 108 109 111 114 115 116
117 119 120 121 123 129 130 131 132 135 143 144 146 147 148 **P**6 8
**S** Covenant Health System, Lubbock, TX
Primary Contact: Richard H. Parks, FACHE, President and Chief Executive Officer
CFO: John A. Grigson, Senior Vice President and Chief Financial Officer
CMO: Scott Robins, M.D., Chief Medical Officer
CIO: Jim Reid, Vice President and Chief Information Officer
CHR: Rodney Cates, Senior Vice President Human Resources
Web address: www.covenanthealth.org
**Control:** Other not–for–profit (including NFP Corporation) **Service:** General
Medical and Surgical

**Staffed Beds: 646 Admissions: 28995 Census: 371 Outpatient Visits:**
357676 **Births: 2722 Total Expense ($000): 376037 Payroll Expense**
**($000): 147520 Personnel: 3121**

**COVENANT SPECIALTY HOSPITAL (452102)**, 3815 20th Street,
Zip 79410–1235; tel. 806/725–9200 **A**10 **F**1 3 29 30 31 60 63 68 75 77 78
79 87 119 130 143 148 **S** Covenant Health System, Lubbock, TX
Primary Contact: Walt Cathey, Chief Operating Officer
Web address: www.covenanthealth.org/view/Facilities/Specialty_Hospital
**Control:** Partnership, Investor–owned, for–profit **Service:** Long–Term Acute Care
hospital

**Staffed Beds: 56 Admissions: 483 Census: 33 Outpatient Visits: 0 Births:**
0 **Total Expense ($000): 11938 Payroll Expense ($000): 6023 Personnel:**
118

□ **GRACE MEDICAL CENTER (450162)**, 2412 50th Street, Zip 79412–2494;
tel. 806/788–4100 **A**1 3 5 9 10 **F**3 8 11 12 15 29 34 35 40 44 45 47 49 51
59 64 70 75 79 81 82 85 87 102 107 108 109 110 111 114 115 119
146 **P**6
Primary Contact: Charley O. Trimble, Chief Executive Officer
CMO: Howard Beck, M.D., Chief of Staff
CIO: Jason Derouen, Director Management Information Systems
CHR: Sally Charles, Coordinator Human Resources
Web address: www.gracehealthsystem.com
**Control:** Partnership, Investor–owned, for–profit **Service:** General Medical and
Surgical

**Staffed Beds: 59 Admissions: 980 Census: 7 Outpatient Visits: 63088**
**Births: 0 Total Expense ($000): 34678 Payroll Expense ($000): 8219**
**Personnel: 212**

□ **LLANO SPECIALTY HOSPITAL OF LUBBOCK (452050)**, 1409 9th Street,
Zip 79401–2601; tel. 806/767–9133 **A**1 9 10 **F**1 12 29 60 65 75 91 92 107
119 130 143 148 **S** Fundamental Long Term Care Holdings, LLC, Sparks
Glencoe, MD
Primary Contact: Dennis Fleenor, R.N., Chief Executive Officer
CFO: Robert Stanley, Chief Financial Officer
CMO: Enrique Rodriguez, M.D., Medical Director
CHR: Jerrie Yoakum, Director Human Resources
CNO: Charalene Ruble, Chief Nursing Officer
Web address: www.fundltc.com/Healthcare%20Facility%20Locator/facility_page.
aspx?locationID=190
**Control:** Corporation, Investor–owned, for–profit **Service:** Long–Term Acute Care
hospital

**Staffed Beds: 30 Admissions: 79 Census: 5 Outpatient Visits: 0 Births: 0**
**Total Expense ($000): 3282 Payroll Expense ($000): 1405 Personnel: 31**

**LUBBOCK HEART HOSPITAL (450876)**, 4810 North Loop 289,
Zip 79416–3025; tel. 806/687–7777 **A**3 5 9 10 **F**3 17 18 20 22 24 26 29 40
45 59 79 81 83 107 108 115 119 148
Primary Contact: Roy C. Vinson, Chief Executive Officer
Web address: www.lubbockhearthospital.com
**Control:** Partnership, Investor–owned, for–profit **Service:** General Medical and
Surgical

**Staffed Beds: 74 Admissions: 3312 Census: 32 Outpatient Visits: 11756**
**Births: 0 Total Expense ($000): 50386 Payroll Expense ($000): 16462**
**Personnel: 320**

□ **SUNRISE CANYON HOSPITAL (454093)**, 1602 10th Street, Zip 79401–3924,
Mailing Address: P.O. Box 2828, Zip 79408–2828; tel. 806/740–1407 **A**1 10
**F**86 98 101 103 130 143
Primary Contact: Leonard Valderaz, Administrator
CFO: Beth Lawson, Chief Financial Officer and Director Governmental Affairs
CMO: Marsha Spalding, M.D., Medical Director
CIO: Tim Carroll, Chief Information Officer
CHR: Barbara McCann, Director Human Resources
Web address: www.lrl.mhmr.state.tx.us
**Control:** Other not–for–profit (including NFP Corporation) **Service:** Psychiatric

**Staffed Beds: 30 Admissions: 532 Census: 20 Outpatient Visits: 0 Births:**
0 **Total Expense ($000): 4741 Payroll Expense ($000): 1991 Personnel:**
36

□ **TEXAS SPECIALTY HOSPITAL AT LUBBOCK (452116)**, 4302 Princeton
Street, Zip 79415–1304; tel. 806/723–8700 **A**1 9 10 **F**1 3 12 29 60 92 148
**S** Fundamental Long Term Care Holdings, LLC, Sparks Glencoe, MD
Primary Contact: Deanna Graves, Chief Executive Officer
CFO: Robert Stanley, Chief Financial Officer
CNO: Jennifer Reeves, Chief Nursing Officer
**Control:** Corporation, Investor–owned, for–profit **Service:** Long–Term Acute Care
hospital

**Staffed Beds: 37 Admissions: 421 Census: 30 Outpatient Visits: 0 Births:**
0 **Total Expense ($000): 10275 Payroll Expense ($000): 3699 Personnel:**
81

□ **TRUSTPOINT HOSPITAL (670050)**, 4302 Princeton Street, Zip 79415–1304;
tel. 806/749–2222 **A**1 3 5 9 10 **F**3 29 34 35 40 56 57 64 68 74 75 77 79 85
86 87 90 91 93 94 96 98 103 130 135 148 **S** Polaris Hospital Company,
Brentwood, TN
Primary Contact: Craig Bragg, Chief Executive Officer
Web address: www.trustpointhospital.com/
**Control:** Partnership, Investor–owned, for–profit **Service:** Rehabilitation

**Staffed Beds: 64 Admissions: 1333 Census: 49 Outpatient Visits: 9 Births:**
0 **Total Expense ($000): 18451 Payroll Expense ($000): 7439 Personnel:**
185

✠ **UNIVERSITY MEDICAL CENTER (450686)**, 602 Indiana Avenue,
Zip 79415–3364, Mailing Address: P.O. Box 5980, Zip 79408–5980;
tel. 806/775–8200 **A**1 2 3 5 8 9 10 **F**3 7 8 11 12 13 15 16 17 18 19 20 22
24 26 27 28 29 30 31 34 35 40 41 43 46 47 48 49 50 54 57 58 59 60
62 64 65 66 68 70 72 74 75 76 77 78 79 81 83 84 85 86 87 88 89 93 94
96 97 107 108 110 111 114 115 116 118 119 120 121 123 124 130 131
132 136 141 142 144 146 147 148
Primary Contact: David G. Allison, President and Chief Executive Officer
COO: Mark Funderburk, Executive Vice President and Administrator
CFO: Jeff Dane, Executive Vice President and Chief Financial Officer
CIO: Bill Eubanks, Senior Vice President and Chief Information Officer
CHR: Adrienne Cozart, Vice President Human Resources
Web address: www.umchealthsystem.com
**Control:** Hospital district or authority, Government, nonfederal **Service:** General
Medical and Surgical

**Staffed Beds: 402 Admissions: 25135 Census: 292 Outpatient Visits:**
261403 **Births: 2420 Total Expense ($000): 351034 Payroll Expense**
**($000): 151154 Personnel: 2519**

**LUFKIN—Angelina County**

□ **AUDUBON BEHAVIORAL HEALTHCARE OF LUFKIN (454116)**, 302 Gobblers
Knob, Zip 75904–5419; tel. 936/632–2276 **A**1 10 **F**6 29 56 74 75 98 100
101 102 103 104 130 **P**6 **S** Audubon Behavioral Healthcare, Longview, TX
Primary Contact: Karen Parker, Administrator
Web address: www.audubonbehavioral.com
**Control:** Individual, Investor–owned, for–profit **Service:** Psychiatric

**Staffed Beds: 24 Admissions: 308 Census: 12 Outpatient Visits: 3004**
**Births: 0 Total Expense ($000): 4899 Payroll Expense ($000): 1966**
**Personnel: 86**

✠ **MEMORIAL MEDICAL CENTER – LUFKIN (450211)**, 1201 West Frank Avenue,
Zip 75904–3357, Mailing Address: P.O. Box 1447, Zip 75902–1447;
tel. 936/634–8111 **A**1 2 9 10 19 **F**3 11 12 13 14 15 17 18 20 21 22 23 24
26 28 29 30 31 34 35 37 38 40 44 45 46 47 48 49 50 51 56 57 59 60 61
62 63 64 68 70 71 73 74 75 76 77 78 79 81 82 83 84 85 86 87 90 91 92
93 97 100 101 102 107 108 110 111 112 114 115 116 117 119 121 126
129 130 132 135 143 144 146 147 148 **P**7 **S** Memorial Health System of East
Texas, Lufkin, TX
Primary Contact: Gary N. Looper, Chief Executive Officer
CFO: Kristi Gay, Chief Financial Officer
CHR: Tanya Tyler, Vice President Human Resources
Web address: www.memorialhealth.us/centers/lufkin
**Control:** Other not–for–profit (including NFP Corporation) **Service:** General
Medical and Surgical

**Staffed Beds: 217 Admissions: 7728 Census: 98 Outpatient Visits: 142627**
**Births: 611 Total Expense ($000): 127019 Payroll Expense ($000): 37342**
**Personnel: 809**

**MEMORIAL SPECIALTY HOSPITAL (452031)**, 1201 West Frank Avenue,
Zip 75904–3357; tel. 936/639–7975 **A**9 10 **F**1 3 29 31 50 61 68 74 75 85
86 130 145 **S** Memorial Health System of East Texas, Lufkin, TX
Primary Contact: Leslie Leach, Administrator
CFO: Kristi Gay, Chief Financial Officer
CMO: David Todd, M.D., President Medical Staff
CHR: Tanya Tyler, Vice President Human Resources
Web address: www.memorialhealth.org
**Control:** Other not–for–profit (including NFP Corporation) **Service:** Long–Term
Acute Care hospital

**Staffed Beds: 26 Admissions: 293 Census: 22 Outpatient Visits: 0 Births:**
0 **Total Expense ($000): 8471 Payroll Expense ($000): 4279 Personnel:**
54

*Many Facility Codes have changed. Please refer to the AHA Guide Code Chart.*
© 2013 AHA Guide

**TX**

✠ **WOODLAND HEIGHTS MEDICAL CENTER (450484)**, 505 South John Redditt Drive, Zip 75904–3157, Mailing Address: P.O. Box 150610, Zip 75904; tel. 936/634–8311, (Total facility includes 15 beds in nursing home–type unit) **A**1 9 10 19 **F**3 8 11 12 13 15 17 18 20 22 24 26 28 29 30 34 35 40 41 46 49 50 51 53 57 59 64 68 70 74 75 76 77 78 79 81 82 85 86 87 93 102 107 108 111 114 115 118 119 128 129 130 131 146 147 148 **S** Community Health Systems, Inc., Franklin, TN
Primary Contact: Casey Robertson, Chief Executive Officer
COO: Lance Beus, Chief Operating Officer
CFO: Sam Minkowitz, Chief Financial Officer
CMO: Kevin L. Hudson, D.O., Chief of Staff
CIO: Kalvin Buckley, Director Information Systems
CHR: Sally McKinney, Director Human Resources
CNO: Cathy L. Busbee, Chief Nursing Officer
Web address: www.woodlandheights.net
**Control:** Partnership, Investor–owned, for–profit **Service:** General Medical and Surgical

**Staffed Beds:** 115 **Admissions:** 5000 **Census:** 62 **Outpatient Visits:** 45375 **Births:** 721 **Total Expense ($000):** 68300 **Payroll Expense ($000):** 28270 **Personnel:** 522

**LULING—Caldwell County**

✠ **SETON EDGAR B. DAVIS HOSPITAL (451371)**, 130 Hays Street, Zip 78648–3207; tel. 830/875–7000 **A**1 9 10 18 **F**3 11 15 18 29 30 35 40 43 44 45 50 56 68 71 75 79 81 84 85 87 93 97 103 107 111 114 119 127 130 133 135 143 146 **P**3 8 **S** Ascension Health, Saint Louis, MO
Primary Contact: Apryl Haynes, R.N., Vice President, Chief Operating Officer, Chief Nursing Officer and Administrator
CFO: Douglas D. Waite, Chief Financial Officer
CMO: Martin E. Weiner, M.D., Chief of Staff
CIO: Gerry Lewis, Chief Information Officer
CHR: Cheryl Williams, Director Human Resources
CNO: Apryl Haynes, R.N., Vice President, Chief Operating Officer, Chief Nursing Officer and Administrator
Web address: www.seton.net/locations/edgar_davis/
**Control:** Church–operated, Nongovernment, not–for profit **Service:** General Medical and Surgical

**Staffed Beds:** 25 **Admissions:** 1295 **Census:** 14 **Outpatient Visits:** 66756 **Births:** 0 **Total Expense ($000):** 24578 **Payroll Expense ($000):** 13514 **Personnel:** 253

☐ **WARM SPRINGS SPECIALTY HOSPITAL (452062)**, 200 Memorial Drive, Zip 78648–3213; tel. 830/875–8400 **A**1 9 10 **F**1 3 29 53 64 93 96 130 133 **S** Post Acute Medical, LLC, Camp Hill, PA
Primary Contact: Jason Carter, Chief Executive Officer
CFO: James Asberry, Chief Financial Officer
Web address: www.warmsprings.org
**Control:** Partnership, Investor–owned, for–profit **Service:** Long–Term Acute Care hospital

**Staffed Beds:** 34 **Admissions:** 424 **Census:** 32 **Outpatient Visits:** 12191 **Births:** 0 **Total Expense ($000):** 15334 **Payroll Expense ($000):** 6382 **Personnel:** 139

**MADISONVILLE—Madison County**

✠ **MADISON ST. JOSEPH HEALTH CENTER (451316)**, 100 West Cross Street, Zip 77864–2432, Mailing Address: Box 698, Zip 77864–0698; tel. 936/348–2631 **A**1 9 10 18 **F**3 7 11 15 30 40 43 57 59 64 68 75 82 93 107 108 110 119 130 133 135 146 148 **S** Sylvania Franciscan Health, Toledo, OH
Primary Contact: Reed Edmundson, Administrator
COO: Reed Edmundson, Administrator
CFO: Bruce Thacker, Controller
CMO: Grover Hubley, M.D., President Medical Staff
CIO: Jana Ard, R.N., Director Clinical Resource Management
CHR: Doni Roper, Director Human Resources
Web address: www.st–joseph.org
**Control:** Church–operated, Nongovernment, not–for profit **Service:** General Medical and Surgical

**Staffed Beds:** 25 **Admissions:** 409 **Census:** 8 **Outpatient Visits:** 20904 **Births:** 0 **Total Expense ($000):** 10136 **Payroll Expense ($000):** 4978 **Personnel:** 94

**MANSFIELD—Tarrant County**

✠ **KINDRED HOSPITAL–MANSFIELD (452019)**, 1802 Highway 157 North, Zip 76063–3923; tel. 817/473–6101 **A**1 9 10 **F**1 3 29 30 45 46 60 70 75 81 82 85 130 132 148 **S** Kindred Healthcare, Louisville, KY
Primary Contact: Susan Schaetti, Administrator
CFO: Judy Baker, Chief Financial Officer
Web address: www.kindredmansfield.com
**Control:** Corporation, Investor–owned, for–profit **Service:** Long–Term Acute Care hospital

**Staffed Beds:** 55 **Admissions:** 364 **Census:** 24 **Outpatient Visits:** 144 **Births:** 0 **Total Expense ($000):** 12280 **Payroll Expense ($000):** 5911 **Personnel:** 95

✠ **METHODIST MANSFIELD MEDICAL CENTER (670023)**, 2700 East Broad Street, Zip 76063–5899; tel. 682/622–2000 **A**1 9 10 **F**3 11 13 15 18 20 22 29 30 31 34 35 37 40 46 48 49 50 58 59 60 68 70 71 74 76 78 79 81 82 84 85 87 93 97 107 108 110 111 115 118 119 130 132 146 **P**1 7 **S** Methodist Health System, Dallas, TX
Primary Contact: John E. Phillips, FACHE, President
CFO: Jary Ganshe, Chief Financial Officer
CMO: Adam L. Myers, Chief Medical Officer
CIO: Pamela McNutt, Senior Vice President and Chief Information Officer
CHR: Judy K. Laister, Director, Human Resources
CNO: Jeanne Reeves, Chief Nursing Officer
Web address: www.methodisthealthsystem.org/mansfield
**Control:** Other not–for–profit (including NFP Corporation) **Service:** General Medical and Surgical

**Staffed Beds:** 161 **Admissions:** 8252 **Census:** 100 **Outpatient Visits:** 77153 **Births:** 1966 **Total Expense ($000):** 107414 **Payroll Expense ($000):** 50096 **Personnel:** 725

**MARLIN—Falls County**

★ **FALLS COMMUNITY HOSPITAL AND CLINIC (450348)**, 322 Coleman Street, Zip 76661–2358, Mailing Address: P.O. Box 60, Zip 76661–0060; tel. 254/803–3561 **A**9 10 20 **F**3 11 32 33 34 35 36 40 43 45 53 56 57 59 64 65 66 68 75 82 87 91 93 97 99 103 104 107 114 127 129 131 133 135 146 148
Primary Contact: Willis L. Reese, Administrator
COO: Julie Sharp, Chief Operations Officer
CFO: Willis L. Reese, Administrator
CMO: James Scott Crockett, M.D., Chief of Staff
CIO: Julie Sharp, Chief Operations Officer
CHR: Peggy Polster, Manager Personnel and Administrative Assistant
Web address: www.fallshospital.com
**Control:** Other not–for–profit (including NFP Corporation) **Service:** General Medical and Surgical

**Staffed Beds:** 32 **Admissions:** 635 **Census:** 6 **Outpatient Visits:** 69982 **Births:** 0 **Total Expense ($000):** 19758 **Payroll Expense ($000):** 6302 **Personnel:** 167

**MARSHALL—Harrison County**

☐ **GOOD SHEPHERD MEDICAL CENTER–MARSHALL (450032)**, 811 South Washington Avenue, Zip 75670–5336, Mailing Address: P.O. Box 1599, Zip 75671–1599; tel. 903/927–6000 **A**1 9 10 **F**3 11 13 15 18 28 29 30 34 35 40 43 49 50 53 54 57 59 60 64 65 68 70 75 77 79 80 81 86 87 89 90 93 97 102 103 107 110 111 115 119 127 129 130 131 132 145 146 147 148 **P**7 8 **S** Good Shepherd Health System, Longview, TX
Primary Contact: Russell J. Collier, FACHE, President and Chief Executive Officer
COO: Ray Delk, FACHE, Vice President Operations
CFO: Patricia Keel, Chief Financial Officer
CMO: John McDonald, D.O., President and Chief of Medical Staff
CIO: Walter Grimes, Director Information Technology
CHR: Ginger Garrett, Regional Director Human Resources
CNO: Paula Brandon, MSN, Vice President Patient Care Services
Web address: www.gsmcmarshall.org
**Control:** Other not–for–profit (including NFP Corporation) **Service:** General Medical and Surgical

**Staffed Beds:** 142 **Admissions:** 4934 **Census:** 42 **Outpatient Visits:** 94674 **Births:** 544 **Total Expense ($000):** 65242 **Payroll Expense ($000):** 19541 **Personnel:** 411

**MCALLEN—Hidalgo County**

**LIFECARE HOSPITALS OF SOUTH TEXAS–MCALLEN** See Lifecare Hospitals of South Texas–North McAllen

**TX**

---

**Hospital, Medicare Provider Number, Address, Telephone, Approval, Facility, and Physician Codes, Health Care System**

★ American Hospital Association (AHA) membership
☐ The Joint Commission accreditation
◇ DNV Healthcare Inc. accreditation
○ Healthcare Facilities Accreditation Program
∧ Commission on Accreditation of Rehabilitation Facilities (CARF) accreditation

✠ **LIFECARE HOSPITALS OF SOUTH TEXAS–NORTH MCALLEN (452063)**,
5101 North Jackson, Zip 78504–6343; tel. 956/926–7000, (Includes LIFECARE
HOSPITALS OF SOUTH TEXAS–MCALLEN, 2001 South M Street, Zip 78503;
tel. 956/688–4300) **A**1 9 10 **F**1 3 29 57 75 77 84 85 87 148 **S** LifeCare
Management Services, Plano, TX
Primary Contact: Michelle Lozano, Chief Executive Officer
Web address: www.lifecare–hospitals.com/hospital/southtexas
**Control:** Corporation, Investor–owned, for–profit **Service:** Long–Term Acute Care
hospital

**Staffed Beds:** 84 **Admissions:** 824 **Census:** 62 **Outpatient Visits:** 0 **Births:**
0 **Total Expense ($000):** 26026 **Payroll Expense ($000):** 11096
**Personnel:** 200

✠ **RIO GRANDE REGIONAL HOSPITAL (450711)**, 101 East Ridge Road,
Zip 78503–1299; tel. 956/632–6000 **A**1 3 5 9 10 **F**3 8 11 12 13 15 18 19 20
21 22 23 24 25 26 27 29 30 31 34 35 39 40 42 43 45 46 49 50 54 56 57
59 60 64 68 70 71 72 73 74 75 76 78 79 81 85 87 88 89 93 107 108 110
111 114 118 119 130 132 146 147 148 **P**7 **S** HCA, Nashville, TN
Primary Contact: Cristina Rivera, Chief Executive Officer
COO: David Elgarico, Chief Operating Officer
CFO: William Saller, Chief Financial Officer
CIO: Carlos Leal, Chief Information Officer
CHR: Marjorie Whittemore, Director Human Resources
Web address: www.riohealth.com
**Control:** Partnership, Investor–owned, for–profit **Service:** General Medical and
Surgical

**Staffed Beds:** 320 **Admissions:** 15501 **Census:** 177 **Outpatient Visits:**
83264 **Births:** 2893 **Total Expense ($000):** 133213 **Payroll Expense
($000):** 58723 **Personnel:** 949

☐ **SOLARA HOSPITAL MCALLEN (452095)**, 301 West Expressway 83,
Zip 78503–3045; tel. 956/632–4880 **A**1 9 10 **F**1 3 29 56 70 75 82 87 91
148 **P**5 **S** Cornerstone Healthcare Group, Dallas, TX
Primary Contact: Jose Huerta, Chief Executive Officer
Web address: www.chghospitals.com/mcallen/
**Control:** Corporation, Investor–owned, for–profit **Service:** Long–Term Acute Care
hospital

**Staffed Beds:** 78 **Admissions:** 748 **Census:** 52 **Outpatient Visits:** 0 **Births:**
0 **Total Expense ($000):** 20338 **Payroll Expense ($000):** 9258 **Personnel:**
161

### MCCAMEY—Upton County

★ **MCCAMEY COUNTY HOSPITAL DISTRICT (451309)**, 2500 Highway 305
South, Zip 79752, Mailing Address: P.O. Box 1200, Zip 79752–1200;
tel. 432/652–8626, (Total facility includes 30 beds in nursing home–type unit) **A**9
10 18 **F**3 40 53 59 64 65 66 93 127 128 133
Primary Contact: Jaime Ramirez, Chief Executive Officer
COO: Tana Robertson, Chief Operating Officer
CFO: Judith Gulihur, Director Human Resources and Chief Financial Officer
CMO: Ramon Domingo, M.D., Chief of Staff
CIO: Larry Rollins, Supervisor Information Technology
CHR: Judith Gulihur, Director Human Resources and Chief Financial Officer
CNO: Cheryl Roberts, Chief Nursing Officer
Web address: www.mccameyhospital.org
**Control:** Hospital district or authority, Government, nonfederal **Service:** General
Medical and Surgical

**Staffed Beds:** 44 **Admissions:** 89 **Census:** 26 **Outpatient Visits:** 7851
**Births:** 0 **Total Expense ($000):** 8207 **Payroll Expense ($000):** 4361
**Personnel:** 68

### MCKINNEY—Collin County

✠ **BAYLOR MEDICAL CENTER AT MCKINNEY (670082)**, 5252 West University
Drive, Zip 75071–7822; tel. 469/764–1000, (Nonreporting) **A**1 9 10 **S** Baylor
Health Care System, Dallas, TX
Primary Contact: Scott Peek, FACHE, President
COO: Melissa Winter, R.N., Chief Operating Officer and Chief Nursing Officer
CFO: Steve Roussel, Chief Financial Officer
CNO: Melissa Winter, R.N., Chief Operating Officer and Chief Nursing Officer
Web address: www.baylorhealth.com/PhysiciansLocations/McKinney/Pages/
Default.aspx
**Control:** Other not–for–profit (including NFP Corporation) **Service:** General
Medical and Surgical

**Staffed Beds:** 95

✠ **MEDICAL CENTER OF MCKINNEY (450403)**, 4500 Medical Center Drive,
Zip 75069–1650; tel. 972/547–8000, (Includes WYSONG CAMPUS, 130 South
Central Expressway, Zip 75070; tel. 972/548–5300) **A**1 9 10 **F**3 4 11 13 15 18
20 22 24 26 28 29 30 34 37 40 45 49 56 57 59 60 64 68 70 74 75 76 77
78 79 81 82 85 87 90 91 92 93 94 96 97 98 102 103 107 108 109 110 111
114 115 119 126 129 130 131 132 146 147 148 **S** HCA, Nashville, TN
Primary Contact: Ernest C. Lynch, III, Chief Executive Officer
COO: LaSharndra Barbarin, Chief Operating Officer
CFO: Dwayne Ray, Chief Financial Officer
CIO: Kevin Fletcher, Director Information Systems
CHR: Senta Miles, Director Human Resources
CNO: Kimberly Kay Hatchel, Chief Nursing Officer
Web address: www.medicalcenterofmckinney.com
**Control:** Partnership, Investor–owned, for–profit **Service:** General Medical and
Surgical

**Staffed Beds:** 217 **Admissions:** 11726 **Census:** 167 **Outpatient Visits:**
67401 **Births:** 859 **Total Expense ($000):** 122965 **Payroll Expense ($000):**
53369 **Personnel:** 812

☐ **METHODIST MCKINNEY HOSPITAL (670069)**, 8000 West Eldorado Parkway,
Zip 75070–5940; tel. 972/569–2700 **A**1 9 10 **F**3 15 29 34 40 45 51 70 75
79 81 82 85 93 107 111 119 130 **S** Methodist Health System, Dallas, TX
Primary Contact: Joseph Minissale, President
CFO: Rebecca Chaisson, Interim Chief Financial Officer
CHR: Rory Money, Manager Human Resources
Web address: www.methodistmckinneyhospital.com
**Control:** Partnership, Investor–owned, for–profit **Service:** General Medical and
Surgical

**Staffed Beds:** 23 **Admissions:** 593 **Census:** 4 **Outpatient Visits:** 13116
**Births:** 0 **Total Expense ($000):** 32895 **Payroll Expense ($000):** 6058
**Personnel:** 94

◇ **THE HOSPITAL AT CRAIG RANCH (670063)**, 6045 Alma Road,
Zip 75070–2188; tel. 469/854–8000, (Nonreporting) **A**10 21
Primary Contact: Glenda Mendoza, Chief Executive Officer and Chief Nursing
Executive
Web address: www.hospitalcraigranch.com
**Control:** Corporation, Investor–owned, for–profit **Service:** Surgical

**Staffed Beds:** 24

### MESQUITE—Dallas County

☐ **DALLAS REGIONAL MEDICAL CENTER (450688)**, 1011 North Galloway
Avenue, Zip 75149–2433; tel. 214/320–7000 **A**1 9 10 **F**3 12 15 18 20 22 24
26 29 30 34 35 40 43 46 47 49 50 54 56 57 59 64 68 70 74 75 79 80 81
85 86 87 97 107 108 110 111 114 119 126 130 131 135 146 148 **S** Health
Management Associates, Naples, FL
Primary Contact: Derrick Yu, Interim Chief Executive Officer
CFO: Gene Winters, Chief Financial Officer
CMO: Srinivas Gunukula, M.D., Chief of Staff
CNO: Tina Pollock, R.N., Chief Nursing Officer
Web address: www.dallasregionalmedicalcenter.com
**Control:** Corporation, Investor–owned, for–profit **Service:** General Medical and
Surgical

**Staffed Beds:** 85 **Admissions:** 4602 **Census:** 51 **Outpatient Visits:** 65023
**Births:** 0 **Total Expense ($000):** 71306 **Payroll Expense ($000):** 24638
**Personnel:** 407

☐ **MESQUITE REHABILITATION INSTITUTE (673045)**, (Formerly Mesquite
Rehabilitation Hospital), 1023 North Belt Line Road, Zip 75149–1788;
tel. 972/216–2400 **A**1 9 10 **F**3 28 29 30 34 35 57 59 64 82 90 91 93 96
148 **S** Ernest Health, Inc., Albuquerque, NM
Primary Contact: Brian Abraham, Chief Operating Officer
Web address: www.mesquiterehab.ernesthealth.com/
**Control:** Corporation, Investor–owned, for–profit **Service:** Rehabilitation

**Staffed Beds:** 20 **Admissions:** 419 **Census:** 15 **Outpatient Visits:** 1894
**Births:** 0 **Total Expense ($000):** 5452 **Payroll Expense ($000):** 3111
**Personnel:** 45

☐ **MESQUITE SPECIALTY HOSPITAL (452100)**, 1024 North Galloway Avenue,
Zip 75149–2434; tel. 972/216–2300 **A**1 9 10 **F**1 3 29 74 75 77 79 85 87
130 135 148 **S** Ernest Health, Inc., Albuquerque, NM
Primary Contact: Louis Bradley, Chief Operating Officer
Web address: www.msh.ernesthealth.com
**Control:** Partnership, Investor–owned, for–profit **Service:** Long–Term Acute Care
hospital

**Staffed Beds:** 40 **Admissions:** 447 **Census:** 34 **Outpatient Visits:** 0 **Births:**
0 **Total Expense ($000):** 15607 **Payroll Expense ($000):** 7395 **Personnel:**
129

**TX**

*Many Facility Codes have changed. Please refer to the AHA Guide Code Chart.*
© 2013 AHA Guide

## MEXIA—Limestone County

✠ **PARKVIEW REGIONAL HOSPITAL (450400)**, 600 South Bonham, Zip 76667–3603; tel. 254/562–0408 **A**1 9 10 20 **F**3 11 15 29 30 34 35 40 43 45 51 53 56 57 59 64 65 70 75 77 78 79 81 85 86 87 93 97 98 103 107 108 110 111 114 119 127 130 132 133 146 **P**5 6 **S** LifePoint Hospitals, Inc., Brentwood, TN
Primary Contact: Kevin Zachary, Chief Executive Officer
CFO: Michael Herr, Chief Financial Officer
CMO: Greg Newman, M.D., Chief of Staff
Web address: www.parkviewregional.com
**Control:** Partnership, Investor–owned, for–profit **Service:** General Medical and Surgical

**Staffed Beds:** 58 **Admissions:** 955 **Census:** 12 **Outpatient Visits:** 21292 **Births:** 0 **Total Expense ($000):** 16417 **Payroll Expense ($000):** 7902 **Personnel:** 178

## MIDLAND—Midland County

☐ **BCA PERMIAN BASIN (454110)**, 3300 South FM 1788, Zip 79706–2601; tel. 432/561–5915, (Nonreporting) **A**1 9 10
Primary Contact: John Flanagan, Chief Executive Officer
Web address: www.bcapermianbasin.com/
**Control:** Corporation, Investor–owned, for–profit **Service:** Psychiatric

**Staffed Beds:** 64

◇ **BEHAVIORAL HEALTH CENTER OF THE PERMIAN BASIN (454110)**, (Formerly Allegiance Specialty Hospital Permian Basin), 3300 South FM 1788, Zip 79706–2601; tel. 432/561–5915 **A**10 21 **F**34 56 57 64 68 98 101 103 104 130 132 135 **S** Allegiance Health Management, Shreveport, LA
Primary Contact: Cheryl Rayl, Chief Executive Officer
Web address: www.ahmgt.com
**Control:** Corporation, Investor–owned, for–profit **Service:** Psychiatric

**Staffed Beds:** 48 **Admissions:** 713 **Census:** 23 **Outpatient Visits:** 11282 **Births:** 0 **Total Expense ($000):** 9478 **Payroll Expense ($000):** 3959 **Personnel:** 92

✠ **HEALTHSOUTH REHABILITATION HOSPITAL MIDLAND–ODESSA (453057)**, 1800 Heritage Boulevard, Zip 79707–9750; tel. 432/520–1600, (Nonreporting) **A**1 5 9 10 **S** HEALTHSOUTH Corporation, Birmingham, AL
Primary Contact: Christopher Wortham, Chief Executive Officer
CFO: Nichole Dykes, Chief Financial Officer and Controller
CMO: Mark A. Fredrickson, M.D., Medical Director
CHR: Tina Parker, Director Human Resources
Web address: www.healthsouthmidland.com
**Control:** Corporation, Investor–owned, for–profit **Service:** Rehabilitation

**Staffed Beds:** 60

★ ◇ **MIDLAND MEMORIAL HOSPITAL (450133)**, 400 Rosalind Redfern Grover Parkway, Zip 79701–6499; tel. 432/221–1111, (Includes MIDLAND MEMORIAL HOSPITAL, 4214 Andrews Highway, Zip 79703–4822; tel. 432/685–1584) **A**2 3 5 9 10 21 **F**3 8 11 13 15 17 18 20 22 24 28 29 30 31 32 34 35 40 45 49 50 54 57 59 61 64 68 70 73 74 75 76 77 78 79 80 81 82 83 84 85 86 87 88 89 93 97 107 108 111 114 115 116 117 118 119 124 126 129 130 131 132 135 145 146 147 148 **P**8
Primary Contact: Russell Meyers, President and Chief Executive Officer
COO: Stephen Bowerman, Chief Financial Officer
CFO: Lawrence A. Sanz, Senior Vice President Finance and Chief Financial Officer
CIO: David Whiles, Director Health Information Systems
CHR: Cori Hyatt, Director Human Resources
Web address: www.midland–memorial.com
**Control:** Hospital district or authority, Government, nonfederal **Service:** General Medical and Surgical

**Staffed Beds:** 229 **Admissions:** 10542 **Census:** 128 **Outpatient Visits:** 147894 **Births:** 2104 **Total Expense ($000):** 249619 **Payroll Expense ($000):** 83668 **Personnel:** 1470

✠ **SELECT SPECIALTY HOSPITAL–MIDLAND (452084)**, 4214 Andrews Highway, 3rd Floor, Zip 79703–4811; tel. 432/522–3364 **A**1 9 10 **F**1 3 28 29 91 148 **S** Select Medical Corporation, Mechanicsburg, PA
Primary Contact: Connie K. Siffring, Chief Executive Officer
Web address: www.selectspecialtyhospitals.com/company/locations/midland.aspx
**Control:** Corporation, Investor–owned, for–profit **Service:** Long–Term Acute Care hospital

**Staffed Beds:** 29 **Admissions:** 294 **Census:** 21 **Outpatient Visits:** 0 **Births:** 0 **Total Expense ($000):** 8723 **Payroll Expense ($000):** 4113 **Personnel:** 65

## MINERAL WELLS—Palo Pinto County

✠ **PALO PINTO GENERAL HOSPITAL (450565)**, 400 S.W. 25th Avenue, Zip 76067–8246; tel. 940/328–6403 **A**1 9 10 **F**11 13 15 17 18 28 29 32 34 40 43 46 51 53 54 57 59 62 63 64 65 66 68 69 71 74 75 76 77 78 79 81 84 86 87 91 93 107 108 111 114 119 127 129 130 131 133 135 146 147 **P**1
Primary Contact: Harris W. Brooks, Administrator and Chief Executive Officer
CFO: Dee Waldow, Chief Financial Officer
CMO: Patrick Hisel, M.D., Chief of Staff
CHR: Mary B. Braddock, Director Human Resources
CNO: Cheryl Kirby, Chief Nursing Officer
Web address: www.ppgh.com
**Control:** Hospital district or authority, Government, nonfederal **Service:** General Medical and Surgical

**Staffed Beds:** 42 **Admissions:** 1846 **Census:** 15 **Outpatient Visits:** 155061 **Births:** 381 **Total Expense ($000):** 34717 **Payroll Expense ($000):** 16198 **Personnel:** 297

## MISSION—Hidalgo County

✠ △ **MISSION REGIONAL MEDICAL CENTER (450176)**, 900 South Bryan Road, Zip 78572–6613; tel. 956/323–9103 **A**1 7 9 10 **F**3 11 12 13 15 18 20 22 29 30 31 34 35 40 43 45 46 49 50 51 57 59 60 64 65 66 68 70 72 74 75 76 77 79 81 85 87 89 90 93 96 107 108 110 111 115 119 130 132 146 147 148 **P**8
Primary Contact: Javier Iruegas, FACHE, Chief Executive Officer
COO: Carlos Trevino, Chief Operating Officer
CFO: Timothy J. McVey, Chief Financial Officer
CHR: Susan Willars, Vice President Human Resources
Web address: www.missionrmc.org
**Control:** Other not–for–profit (including NFP Corporation) **Service:** General Medical and Surgical

**Staffed Beds:** 245 **Admissions:** 10674 **Census:** 145 **Outpatient Visits:** 73785 **Births:** 2271 **Total Expense ($000):** 113246 **Payroll Expense ($000):** 56080 **Personnel:** 1046

## MONAHANS—Ward County

**WARD MEMORIAL HOSPITAL (451373)**, 406 South Gary Street, Zip 79756–4798, Mailing Address: P.O. Box 40, Zip 79756–0040; tel. 432/943–2511 **A**9 10 18 **F**3 11 40 42 43 45 64 65 66 81 82 89 93 107 114 119 127 131 133 148 **P**6
Primary Contact: Padraic White, Administrator, Chief Executive Officer and Chief Financial Officer
CFO: Leticia Rodriguez, Controller
CHR: Donna Lemon, Director Human Resources
Web address: www.wardmemorial.org
**Control:** County–Government, nonfederal **Service:** General Medical and Surgical

**Staffed Beds:** 25 **Admissions:** 405 **Census:** 4 **Births:** 0 **Total Expense ($000):** 9926 **Payroll Expense ($000):** 4833

## MORTON—Cochran County

**COCHRAN MEMORIAL HOSPITAL (451366)**, 201 East Grant Street, Zip 79346–3444; tel. 806/266–5565 **A**9 10 18 **F**34 40 57 59 65 127 **P**5 6
Primary Contact: Larry Turney, Administrator
CHR: Niona Tunney, Director Human Resources
**Control:** Hospital district or authority, Government, nonfederal **Service:** General Medical and Surgical

**Staffed Beds:** 13 **Admissions:** 24 **Census:** 1 **Outpatient Visits:** 5835 **Births:** 0 **Total Expense ($000):** 3556 **Payroll Expense ($000):** 1716 **Personnel:** 45

## MOUNT PLEASANT—Titus County

✠ **TITUS REGIONAL MEDICAL CENTER (450080)**, 2001 North Jefferson Avenue, Zip 75455–2398; tel. 903/577–6000, (Total facility includes 7 beds in nursing home–type unit) **A**1 9 10 19 **F**3 7 11 12 13 15 18 19 20 24 26 28 29 30 34 35 39 40 43 45 47 50 51 53 54 56 57 58 59 64 68 70 73 74 75 76 78 79 81 82 85 89 90 93 97 98 103 108 110 111 114 115 117 118 119 121 123 127 128 129 130 132 135 147 148
Primary Contact: Ronald D. Davis, Chief Executive Officer
CFO: Terry Scoggin, Chief Financial Officer
CMO: Chris Burling, M.D., Chief of Staff
CIO: Kevin Harris, Director Information Systems
CHR: Tony Piazza, Director Human Resources
CNO: Carol Slider, Chief Nursing Officer
Web address: www.titusregional.com
**Control:** Hospital district or authority, Government, nonfederal **Service:** General Medical and Surgical

**Staffed Beds:** 92 **Admissions:** 4717 **Census:** 51 **Outpatient Visits:** 216346 **Births:** 1042 **Total Expense ($000):** 68462 **Payroll Expense ($000):** 26932 **Personnel:** 588

**TX**

---

**Hospital, Medicare Provider Number, Address, Telephone, Approval, Facility, and Physician Codes, Health Care System**

★ American Hospital Association (AHA) membership
☐ The Joint Commission accreditation ◇ DNV Healthcare Inc. accreditation
○ Healthcare Facilities Accreditation Program
△ Commission on Accreditation of Rehabilitation Facilities (CARF) accreditation

## MOUNT VERNON—Franklin County

★ **EAST TEXAS MEDICAL CENTER–MOUNT VERNON (450373)**, 500 Highway 37 South, Zip 75457–6550, Mailing Address: P.O. Box 477, Zip 75457–0477; tel. 903/537–8000 **A**9 10 **F**3 29 34 35 40 43 50 57 63 64 65 68 75 82 84 85 86 87 97 102 107 114 119 127 **P**7 **S** East Texas Medical Center Regional Healthcare System, Tyler, TX
Primary Contact: Jamie–Crystal Wylie, Chief Executive Officer
CFO: Margaret Haak–Muse, Chief Financial Officer and Assistant Administrator
CMO: Michael Walker, D.O., Chief of Staff
CHR: Kathy Shelton, Director Human Resources
Web address: www.etmc.org/etmcmountvernon/
**Control:** Other not–for–profit (including NFP Corporation) **Service:** General Medical and Surgical

**Staffed Beds:** 30 **Admissions:** 475 **Census:** 4 **Outpatient Visits:** 17805 **Births:** 0 **Total Expense ($000):** 6821 **Payroll Expense ($000):** 2528 **Personnel:** 53

## MUENSTER—Cooke County

**MUENSTER MEMORIAL HOSPITAL (451335)**, 605 North Maple Street, Zip 76252–2424, Mailing Address: P.O. Box 370, Zip 76252–0370; tel. 940/759–2271 **A**9 10 18 **F**11 35 40 43 45 53 57 59 62 64 65 75 77 81 93 107 114 119 127 130 133 146 **P**8
Primary Contact: Michael Kent, Chief Executive Officer
CFO: Richard Teeter, Chief Financial Officer
CMO: J. Stephen Jones, M.D., Chief of Staff
CIO: Sheri Hutchins, Director Health Information Management
**Control:** Hospital district or authority, Government, nonfederal **Service:** General Medical and Surgical

**Staffed Beds:** 18 **Admissions:** 319 **Census:** 8 **Outpatient Visits:** 5165 **Births:** 0 **Total Expense ($000):** 9016 **Payroll Expense ($000):** 4175 **Personnel:** 104

## MULESHOE—Bailey County

★ **MULESHOE AREA MEDICAL CENTER (451372)**, 708 South First Street, Zip 79347–3627; tel. 806/272–4524 **A**9 10 18 **F**3 8 11 29 34 35 40 43 45 50 59 64 65 68 69 75 77 81 93 107 114 119 127 130 133
Primary Contact: David Burke, Administrator and Chief Executive Officer
CMO: Bruce Purdy, M.D., Chief of Staff
CHR: Suzanne Nichols, Director Human Resources
Web address: www.mahdtx.org
**Control:** Hospital district or authority, Government, nonfederal **Service:** General Medical and Surgical

**Staffed Beds:** 25 **Admissions:** 540 **Census:** 7 **Outpatient Visits:** 28275 **Births:** 0 **Total Expense ($000):** 9521 **Payroll Expense ($000):** 3259 **Personnel:** 118

## NACOGDOCHES—Nacogdoches County

✠ **NACOGDOCHES MEDICAL CENTER (450656)**, 4920 N.E. Stallings Drive, Zip 75965–1200; tel. 936/569–9481 **A**1 2 9 10 19 **F**11 13 15 18 20 22 24 26 29 31 34 35 39 40 43 45 46 49 51 56 57 59 60 64 70 74 75 76 78 79 81 82 85 86 87 93 107 108 110 111 115 118 119 121 123 129 130 131 132 135 146 147 148 **S** TENET Healthcare Corporation, Dallas, TX
Primary Contact: Gary L. Stokes, Chief Executive Officer
COO: Collin LeMaistre, Chief Operating Officer
CFO: Rhonda Rogers, Chief Financial Officer
CMO: James M. Randle, M.D., Chief of Staff
CIO: Teresa Simon, Director Information Systems
CHR: Teresa Farrell, Chief Human Resources Officer
CNO: Ed Price, R.N., Chief Clinical Officer
Web address: www.nacmedicalcenter.com
**Control:** Partnership, Investor–owned, for–profit **Service:** General Medical and Surgical

**Staffed Beds:** 109 **Admissions:** 4293 **Census:** 41 **Outpatient Visits:** 43307 **Births:** 648 **Total Expense ($000):** 52596 **Payroll Expense ($000):** 18903 **Personnel:** 342

☐ **NACOGDOCHES MEMORIAL HOSPITAL (450508)**, 1204 North Mound Street, Zip 75961–4061; tel. 936/564–4611 **A**1 9 10 19 **F**3 7 11 13 15 18 20 22 24 26 28 29 30 31 34 35 40 43 46 47 49 50 57 59 61 64 68 70 74 76 77 78 79 80 81 85 86 89 90 93 96 107 108 110 111 114 118 119 126 129 130 132 146 147 148
Primary Contact: Jane Ann Bridges, Acting Administrator
CFO: Jane Ann Bridges, Chief Financial Officer
CNO: Beth Knight, Chief Nursing Officer
Web address: www.nacmem.org
**Control:** Hospital district or authority, Government, nonfederal **Service:** General Medical and Surgical

**Staffed Beds:** 118 **Admissions:** 5344 **Census:** 76 **Outpatient Visits:** 70169 **Births:** 779 **Total Expense ($000):** 89692 **Payroll Expense ($000):** 32492 **Personnel:** 713

## NASSAU BAY—Harris County

✠ **CHRISTUS ST. JOHN HOSPITAL (450709)**, 18300 St. John Drive, Zip 77058–6302; tel. 281/333–5503 **A**1 2 3 5 10 **F**3 8 11 13 15 18 20 22 24 26 28 29 30 34 35 40 44 45 49 51 53 54 57 59 60 62 63 64 65 66 68 69 70 71 73 74 75 76 77 78 79 81 82 83 84 85 86 87 93 107 108 110 111 114 115 119 130 131 132 146 147 148 **P**8 **S** CHRISTUS Health, Irving, TX
Primary Contact: Thomas Permetti, Regional Chief Operating Officer and Administrator
COO: Nancy Pittman, MS, Chief Operating Officer and Chief Nursing Executive
CFO: David Witt, Chief Financial Officer
CMO: Harold Gottlieb, M.D., Medical Director
CHR: Charles Foster, Region Vice President Human Resources
CNO: Nancy Pittman, MS, Chief Operating Officer and Chief Nursing Officer
Web address: www.christusstjohn.org
**Control:** Other not–for–profit (including NFP Corporation) **Service:** General Medical and Surgical

**Staffed Beds:** 121 **Admissions:** 6618 **Census:** 73 **Outpatient Visits:** 137420 **Births:** 637 **Total Expense ($000):** 101432 **Payroll Expense ($000):** 39551 **Personnel:** 564

## NAVASOTA—Grimes County

✠ **GRIMES ST. JOSEPH HEALTH CENTER (451322)**, 210 South Judson Street, Zip 77868–3704; tel. 936/825–6585 **A**1 9 10 18 **F**3 29 34 40 43 57 59 75 77 81 93 107 111 119 130 132 133 135 146 **S** Sylvania Franciscan Health, Toledo, OH
Primary Contact: Reed Edmundson, Interim Administrator
COO: Kathleen R. Krusie, FACHE, Chief Executive Officer
CFO: Lisa McNair, CPA, Senior Vice President and Chief Financial Officer
CMO: Jamie Benton, M.D., Chief of Staff
CIO: Mike Russo, Vice President Information Systems
CHR: Michael G. Costa, Director Human Resources
Web address: www.st–joseph.org
**Control:** Church–operated, Nongovernment, not–for profit **Service:** General Medical and Surgical

**Staffed Beds:** 18 **Admissions:** 462 **Census:** 7 **Outpatient Visits:** 18142 **Births:** 0 **Total Expense ($000):** 9371 **Payroll Expense ($000):** 4553 **Personnel:** 90

## NEDERLAND—Jefferson County

**MID–JEFFERSON EXTENDED CARE HOSPITAL (452083)**, (Formerly Promise Specialty Hospital of Southeast Texas), 2600 Highway 365, Zip 77627–6237; tel. 409/726–8700 **A**9 10 **F**1 3 29 30 34 35 40 70 74 75 77 79 85 130 148
Primary Contact: Mark Rice, Administrator
COO: Wade K. Lester, Chief Nursing and Operations Officer
Web address: www.midjeffextendedcare.com/index.php
**Control:** Corporation, Investor–owned, for–profit **Service:** Long–Term Acute Care hospital

**Staffed Beds:** 48 **Admissions:** 386 **Census:** 26 **Outpatient Visits:** 0 **Births:** 0 **Total Expense ($000):** 11851 **Payroll Expense ($000):** 5217 **Personnel:** 112

## NEW BRAUNFELS—Comal County

**GULF STATES LONG TERM ACUTE CARE OF NEW BRAUNFELS** See Warm Springs Specialty Hospital of New Braunfels

☐ **NEW BRAUNFELS REGIONAL REHABILITATION HOSPITAL (673049)**, 2041 Sundance Parkway, Zip 78130–2779; tel. 830/625–6700 **A**1 9 10 **F**29 34 57 64 90 91 93 130 132 148 **S** Ernest Health, Inc., Albuquerque, NM
Primary Contact: Jennifer Malatek, Chief Executive Officer
CFO: Robert Voss, Chief Financial Officer
CMO: Maria R. Lomba, Medical Director
CHR: Laura Granger, Director, Human Resources
CNO: Denise Benningfield–Crelia, Director, Nursing Operations
Web address: www.nbrrh.ernesthealth.com
**Control:** Corporation, Investor–owned, for–profit **Service:** Rehabilitation

**Staffed Beds:** 40 **Admissions:** 592 **Census:** 26 **Outpatient Visits:** 3717 **Births:** 0 **Total Expense ($000):** 10772 **Payroll Expense ($000):** 5291 **Personnel:** 103

☐ **WARM SPRINGS SPECIALTY HOSPITAL OF NEW BRAUNFELS (452106)**, (Formerly Hill Country Specialty Hospital), 1445 Hanz Drive, Zip 78130–2567; tel. 830/627–7600 **A**1 9 10 **F**1 3 29 30 34 35 85 130 148
Primary Contact: Shayne Goode, Administrator
Web address: www.warmsprings.org/locations/hos/h1/
**Control:** Partnership, Investor–owned, for–profit **Service:** Long–Term Acute Care hospital

**Staffed Beds:** 40 **Admissions:** 402 **Census:** 29 **Outpatient Visits:** 0 **Births:** 0 **Total Expense ($000):** 12829 **Payroll Expense ($000):** 5295 **Personnel:** 96

TX

## NOCONA—Montague County

**NOCONA GENERAL HOSPITAL (450641)**, 100 Park Road, Zip 76255–3616; tel. 940/825–3235 **A**9 10 **F**7 11 28 29 30 34 35 40 43 50 53 57 59 62 64 75 81 82 86 87 93 97 107 108 114 119 130 133 146 148 **P**5
Primary Contact: Lance Meekins, Administrator
CFO: Lance Meekins, Administrator
CMO: Chance Dingler, M.D., Chief Medical Officer
CHR: Paula Monkres, Administrative Assistant and Director Human Resources
Web address: www.noconageneral.com/
**Control:** Hospital district or authority, Government, nonfederal **Service:** General Medical and Surgical

**Staffed Beds:** 25 **Admissions:** 635 **Census:** 8 **Outpatient Visits:** 13513 **Births:** 0 **Total Expense ($000):** 7461 **Payroll Expense ($000):** 3966 **Personnel:** 104

## NORTH RICHLAND HILLS—Tarrant County

⌧ **NORTH HILLS HOSPITAL (450087)**, 4401 Booth Calloway Road, Zip 76180–7399; tel. 817/255–1000 **A**1 9 10 **F**3 8 12 13 15 17 18 20 22 24 28 29 30 31 34 37 40 42 45 49 53 56 57 59 64 70 74 75 76 77 78 79 81 85 86 87 93 107 108 110 111 115 118 119 126 130 132 135 146 147 148 **P**3 **S** HCA, Nashville, TN
Primary Contact: Randy Moresi, Chief Executive Officer
COO: Jay Duty, Chief Operating Officer
CFO: William Saller, Chief Financial Officer
CMO: Richard Scriven, M.D., Chief of Staff
CIO: Ruben Castro, Associate Administrator and Facility Information Security Officer
CHR: Cynthia Dang, Vice President Human Resources
Web address: www.northhillshospital.com
**Control:** Partnership, Investor–owned, for–profit **Service:** General Medical and Surgical

**Staffed Beds:** 176 **Admissions:** 7931 **Census:** 92 **Outpatient Visits:** 94885 **Births:** 776 **Total Expense ($000):** 114238 **Payroll Expense ($000):** 44768 **Personnel:** 627

## ODESSA—Ector County

☐ **BASIN HEALTHCARE CENTER (670066)**, 900 East 4th Street, Zip 79761–5255; tel. 432/362–9900 **A**1 9 10 **F**3 29 39 40 45 64 68 81 82 85 98 107 111 114 119
Primary Contact: Gail Knous, Interim Administrator
CFO: Carl J. Flanagan, CPA, Chief Financial Officer
CMO: Richard Bartlett, M.D., Chief Medical Officer
CIO: Carl J. Flanagan, CPA, Chief Financial Officer
CHR: Gail Knous, Chief Executive Officer and Chief Compliance Officer
Web address: www.bhcodessa.com/
**Control:** Corporation, Investor–owned, for–profit **Service:** General Medical and Surgical

**Staffed Beds:** 14 **Admissions:** 424 **Census:** 2 **Outpatient Visits:** 14602 **Births:** 0 **Total Expense ($000):** 12970 **Payroll Expense ($000):** 3866 **Personnel:** 95

⌧ **MEDICAL CENTER HEALTH SYSTEM (450132)**, 500 West Fourth Street, Zip 79761–5059, Mailing Address: P.O. Drawer 7239, Zip 79760–7239; tel. 432/640–4000 **A**1 2 3 5 8 9 10 **F**3 8 11 12 13 15 17 18 20 22 24 26 28 29 30 31 34 35 39 40 43 46 47 48 49 50 53 54 57 59 64 65 66 68 70 71 72 74 75 76 77 78 79 81 85 87 89 90 93 107 111 114 115 116 117 118 119 126 129 130 131 132 135 144 146 147 148 **P**6 8
Primary Contact: William W. Webster, FACHE, Chief Executive Officer
COO: Tony Ruiz, Chief Operating Officer
CFO: Jon Riggs, Chief Financial Officer
CMO: Bruce Becker, M.D., Chief Medical Officer
CIO: Gary Barnes, Chief Information Officer
CHR: Robbi Banks, Executive Director Human Resources
CNO: Marlene McAllister, R.N., Chief Nursing Officer
Web address: www.mchodessa.com
**Control:** Hospital district or authority, Government, nonfederal **Service:** General Medical and Surgical

**Staffed Beds:** 326 **Admissions:** 13658 **Census:** 181 **Outpatient Visits:** 286011 **Births:** 1502 **Total Expense ($000):** 232175 **Payroll Expense ($000):** 84317 **Personnel:** 1532

**MEDICAL CENTER HOSPITAL** See Medical Center Health System

◇ **ODESSA REGIONAL MEDICAL CENTER (450661)**, 520 East Sixth Street, Zip 79761–4565, Mailing Address: P.O. Box 4859, Zip 79760–4859; tel. 432/582–8000 **A**5 9 10 21 **F**3 12 13 15 17 18 20 22 23 24 25 29 34 35 40 43 46 49 50 51 52 55 57 59 60 64 72 74 75 76 79 80 81 82 85 86 87 89 90 91 107 108 111 115 119 124 130 132 146 147 148 **P**8 **S** IASIS Healthcare, Franklin, TN
Primary Contact: Stacey L. Gerig, Chief Executive Officer
CFO: Michael Metts, Chief Financial Officer
CHR: Jill Sparkman, Director Human Resources
Web address: www.odessaregionalmedicalcenter.com
**Control:** Partnership, Investor–owned, for–profit **Service:** General Medical and Surgical

**Staffed Beds:** 230 **Admissions:** 6743 **Census:** 94 **Outpatient Visits:** 45374 **Births:** 2474 **Total Expense ($000):** 141328 **Payroll Expense ($000):** 35863 **Personnel:** 614

## OLNEY—Young County

★ **HAMILTON HOSPITAL (451354)**, 901 West Hamilton Street, Zip 76374–1725, Mailing Address: P.O. Box 158, Zip 76374–0158; tel. 940/564–5521 **A**9 10 18 **F**7 11 13 28 29 30 34 40 43 53 57 76 77 81 86 89 93 107 114 119 127 133 146 148
Primary Contact: Michael H. Huff, Chief Executive Officer
CMO: Mark L. Mankins, M.D., Chief of Staff
Web address: www.olneyhamiltonhospital.com
**Control:** Hospital district or authority, Government, nonfederal **Service:** General Medical and Surgical

**Staffed Beds:** 25 **Admissions:** 692 **Census:** 9 **Outpatient Visits:** 13184 **Births:** 26 **Total Expense ($000):** 10409 **Payroll Expense ($000):** 4758 **Personnel:** 118

## ORANGE—Orange County

★ ◇ **BAPTIST ORANGE HOSPITAL (450005)**, 608 Strickland Drive, Zip 77630–4717; tel. 409/883–9361 **A**9 10 21 **F**3 13 15 18 29 30 34 35 40 45 57 59 64 70 75 76 79 81 85 89 93 107 108 111 115 118 119 130 146 147 **S** Community Hospital Corporation, Plano, TX
Primary Contact: Jarren Garrett, Chief Administrative Officer
CFO: Gary Troutman, CPA, Chief Financial Officer
CMO: James B. Jones, M.D., Chief of Staff
CIO: William Toon, Director
CHR: Jennifer Barroeta, Chief Human Resources Officer
Web address: www.bhset.net
**Control:** Other not–for–profit (including NFP Corporation) **Service:** General Medical and Surgical

**Staffed Beds:** 40 **Admissions:** 2050 **Census:** 19 **Outpatient Visits:** 35700 **Births:** 317 **Total Expense ($000):** 31210 **Payroll Expense ($000):** 9483 **Personnel:** 183

**MEMORIAL HERMANN BAPTIST ORANGE HOSPITAL** See Baptist Orange Hospital

## PALACIOS—Matagorda County

**PALACIOS COMMUNITY MEDICAL CENTER (451332)**, 311 Green Street, Zip 77465–3213; tel. 361/972–2511 **A**9 10 18 **F**3 11 34 40 50 54 57 87 107 114 119 127 132 133 148
Primary Contact: Don Bates, Chief Executive Officer
CFO: Cherri Waites, Chief Financial Officer
CIO: Lisa Henderson, Administrative Assistant
CHR: Lisa Henderson, Administrative Assistant
Web address: www.palacioshospital.com
**Control:** Other not–for–profit (including NFP Corporation) **Service:** General Medical and Surgical

**Staffed Beds:** 11 **Admissions:** 325 **Census:** 2 **Outpatient Visits:** 8249 **Births:** 0 **Total Expense ($000):** 5428 **Payroll Expense ($000):** 2626 **Personnel:** 48

## PALESTINE—Anderson County

⌧ **PALESTINE REGIONAL MEDICAL CENTER (453089)**, (Formerly Palestine Regional Rehabilitation Center), 4000 South Loop 256, Zip 75801–8467, Mailing Address: P.O. Box 4070, Zip 75802–4070; tel. 903/731–5100, (Nonreporting) **A**1 **S** LifePoint Hospitals, Inc., Brentwood, TN
Primary Contact: Alan E. George, Chief Executive Officer
CHR: Rhonda Beard, Director Human Resources
Web address: www.palestineregional.com
**Control:** Corporation, Investor–owned, for–profit **Service:** Rehabilitation

**Staffed Beds:** 12

**TX**

---

**Hospital, Medicare Provider Number, Address, Telephone, Approval, Facility, and Physician Codes, Health Care System**

★ American Hospital Association (AHA) membership
☐ The Joint Commission accreditation ◇ DNV Healthcare Inc. accreditation
○ Healthcare Facilities Accreditation Program
△ Commission on Accreditation of Rehabilitation Facilities (CARF) accreditation

★ **PALESTINE REGIONAL MEDICAL CENTER–EAST (450747)**, 2900 South Loop 256, Zip 75801–6958; tel. 903/731–1000 **A**9 10 20 **F**3 7 11 13 15 18 20 22 26 28 29 30 34 40 43 44 47 48 49 50 51 56 57 59 63 70 76 79 81 82 85 86 87 89 90 93 96 97 98 100 101 102 103 104 107 108 110 111 114 118 119 129 130 131 133 143 146 147 148 **S** LifePoint Hospitals, Inc., Brentwood, TN
Primary Contact: Alan E. George, Chief Executive Officer
CFO: Louis D. Ferguson, Chief Financial Officer
CIO: Rebecca Chou, Director Information Systems
CHR: Rhonda Beard, Director Human Resources
Web address: www.palestineregional.com
**Control:** Partnership, Investor–owned, for–profit **Service:** General Medical and Surgical

**Staffed Beds:** 113 **Admissions:** 6167 **Census:** 64 **Outpatient Visits:** 67633 **Births:** 776 **Total Expense ($000):** 51841 **Payroll Expense ($000):** 25813 **Personnel:** 502

### PAMPA—Gray County

⊠ **PAMPA REGIONAL MEDICAL CENTER (450099)**, One Medical Plaza, Zip 79065; tel. 806/665–3721, (Nonreporting) **A**1 9 10 20 **S** Prime Healthcare Services, Ontario, CA
Primary Contact: Brad S. Morse, Chief Executive Officer
CFO: Paul Christenson, Chief Financial Officer
CMO: David Hampton, M.D., Chief Medical Staff
CIO: Joy Patton, Chief Information Services
CHR: Debbie Dixon, Director Human Resources
CNO: Catherine Kenney, Chief Nursing Officer
Web address: www.prmctx.com
**Control:** Partnership, Investor–owned, for–profit **Service:** General Medical and Surgical

**Staffed Beds:** 32

### PARIS—Lamar County

⊠ **DUBUIS HOSPITAL OF PARIS (452082)**, 865 Deshong Drive, 5th Floor, Zip 75460–9313; tel. 903/782–2961 **A**1 9 10 **F**1 3 29 30 85 148 **S** Dubuis Health System, Houston, TX
Primary Contact: Kathie Reese, Administrator
CMO: James E. Gulde, M.D., Medical Director
CNO: Janice Cochran, R.N., Director of Patient Care
Web address: www.dubuis.org/CHRISTUSDubuisHospitalofParis
**Control:** Church–operated, Nongovernment, not–for profit **Service:** Long–Term Acute Care hospital

**Staffed Beds:** 25 **Admissions:** 187 **Census:** 13 **Outpatient Visits:** 0 **Births:** 0 **Total Expense ($000):** 5428 **Payroll Expense ($000):** 1892 **Personnel:** 34

☐ **PARIS REGIONAL MEDICAL CENTER (450196)**, 820 Clarksville Street, Zip 75460–6027, Mailing Address: P.O. Box 9070, Zip 75461–9070; tel. 903/785–4521, (Includes PARIS REGIONAL MEDICAL CENTER, 865 Deshong Drive, Zip 75462–2097; tel. 903/737–1111; PARIS REGIONAL MEDICAL CENTER–SOUTH CAMPUS, 820 Clarksville Street, Zip 75460–9070, Mailing Address: P.O. Box 9070, Zip 75461–9070; tel. 903/785–4521) **A**1 9 10 19 **F**3 8 11 13 15 17 18 20 22 24 26 28 29 30 31 34 35 36 39 40 45 49 50 51 55 57 59 60 64 65 66 68 70 72 74 75 76 77 78 79 81 82 85 86 87 89 90 91 93 97 98 102 103 107 108 111 115 119 127 130 132 135 144 145 146 147 148 **P**5 **S** RegionalCare Hospital Partners, Brentwood, TN
Primary Contact: Stephen Grubbs, Chief Executive Officer
CFO: Ken Miller, Chief Financial Officer
CMO: Richard Bercher, M.D., Chief Medical Officer
CHR: Cheryl Perry, Director Human Resources
Web address: www.parisrmc.com
**Control:** Partnership, Investor–owned, for–profit **Service:** General Medical and Surgical

**Staffed Beds:** 192 **Admissions:** 7620 **Census:** 95 **Outpatient Visits:** 86258 **Births:** 664 **Total Expense ($000):** 91952 **Payroll Expense ($000):** 31957 **Personnel:** 673

### PASADENA—Harris County

⊠ **BAYSHORE MEDICAL CENTER (450097)**, 4000 Spencer Highway, Zip 77504–1202; tel. 713/359–2000, (Includes EAST HOUSTON REGIONAL MEDICAL CENTER, 13111 East Freeway, Houston, Zip 77015–5820; tel. 713/393–2000; Alice G. Adams, R.N., Chief Executive Officer) **A**1 2 3 5 9 10 **F**3 8 12 13 15 17 18 20 22 24 26 28 29 31 34 35 39 40 41 42 43 47 49 51 55 56 57 59 60 64 70 72 74 75 76 77 78 79 81 82 84 86 89 90 91 93 98 100 102 103 107 108 111 114 115 116 117 118 119 120 121 123 129 130 131 144 146 147 148 **S** HCA, Nashville, TN
Primary Contact: Jeanna Barnard, Chief Executive Officer
CFO: John Armour, Chief Financial Officer
CMO: Harold Walton, M.D., Chief of Staff
CIO: Clifford Ferguson, Director Information Technology and Systems
Web address: www.bayshoremedical.com
**Control:** Partnership, Investor–owned, for–profit **Service:** General Medical and Surgical

**Staffed Beds:** 476 **Admissions:** 20110 **Census:** 264 **Outpatient Visits:** 187222 **Births:** 3832 **Total Expense ($000):** 172557 **Payroll Expense ($000):** 98000 **Personnel:** 1477

★ **KINDRED HOSPITAL–BAY AREA**, 4801 East Sam Houston Parkway South, Zip 77505–3955; tel. 281/991–5463 **A**9 **F**1 3 29 30 34 45 46 47 60 64 70 77 93 107 114 130 132 146 148 **S** Kindred Healthcare, Louisville, KY
Primary Contact: Laura Cedillo–Rodriguez, Chief Executive Officer
CHR: Nellie Moen, Coordinator Human Resources
Web address: www.khbayareahouston.com/
**Control:** Corporation, Investor–owned, for–profit **Service:** Long–Term Acute Care hospital

**Staffed Beds:** 74 **Admissions:** 995 **Census:** 70 **Outpatient Visits:** 45 **Births:** 0 **Total Expense ($000):** 27362 **Payroll Expense ($000):** 13243 **Personnel:** 172

**PATIENTS MEDICAL CENTER** See St. Luke's Patients Medical Center

◇ **PRISTINE HOSPITAL OF PASADENA (670084)**, 1004 Seymour Street, Zip 77506–2637; tel. 832/581–3275, (Nonreporting) **A**21
Primary Contact: David B. Dale, III, Chief Executive Officer
Web address: www.pristinehealthcare.com
**Control:** Partnership, Investor–owned, for–profit **Service:** General Medical and Surgical

**Staffed Beds:** 32

★ ◇ **ST. LUKE'S PATIENTS MEDICAL CENTER (670031)**, 4600 East Sam Houston Parkway South, Zip 77505–3948; tel. 713/948–7000, (Nonreporting) **A**9 10 21 **S** Catholic Health Initiatives, Englewood, CO
Primary Contact: William Simmons, Chief Executive Officer
Web address: www.stlukestexas.com
**Control:** Corporation, Investor–owned, for–profit **Service:** General Medical and Surgical

**Staffed Beds:** 61

◯ **SURGERY SPECIALTY HOSPITALS OF AMERICA (450831)**, 4301B Vista Road, Zip 77504; tel. 713/378–3000 **A**10 11 **F**3 12 29 40 45 68 70 75 79 81 85 107 119 129 132 **P**8
Primary Contact: Dana Drummond, Chief Nursing Officer and Administrator
Web address: www.backsurgeryhouston.com/
**Control:** Partnership, Investor–owned, for–profit **Service:** General Medical and Surgical

**Staffed Beds:** 37 **Admissions:** 166 **Census:** 1 **Outpatient Visits:** 1385 **Births:** 0 **Total Expense ($000):** 13449 **Payroll Expense ($000):** 3272 **Personnel:** 88

### PEARSALL—Frio County

★ **FRIO REGIONAL HOSPITAL (450293)**, 200 South I. H. 35, Zip 78061–3998; tel. 830/334–3617 **A**9 10 **F**3 8 15 29 35 40 43 45 53 59 62 64 68 76 77 81 87 93 107 114 119 130 148 **P**6
Primary Contact: Michael S. Thompson, Chief Executive Officer
CFO: Rhett D. Fricke, Chief Financial Officer
CMO: Oscar Garza, M.D., Chief of Medical Staff
CIO: Jacob Flores, Chief Information Officer
CHR: Amparo Garcia, Administrative Assistant
CNO: Louisa Martinez, Director of Nursing
Web address: www.frioregionalhospital.com
**Control:** Other not–for–profit (including NFP Corporation) **Service:** General Medical and Surgical

**Staffed Beds:** 22 **Admissions:** 407 **Census:** 3 **Outpatient Visits:** 17663 **Births:** 131 **Total Expense ($000):** 10576 **Payroll Expense ($000):** 3953 **Personnel:** 104

### PECOS—Reeves County

**REEVES COUNTY HOSPITAL (451377)**, 2323 Texas Street, Zip 79772–7338; tel. 432/447–3551 **A**9 10 18 **F**3 11 13 35 40 43 57 60 64 68 70 76 81 87 89 93 107 114 119 127 130 131 133 146 147 148
Primary Contact: Albert LaRochelle, Chief Executive Officer
CFO: Frank Seals, Chief Financial Officer
CMO: W. J. Bang, M.D., Chief of Staff
CHR: Nadine Smith, Director Human Resources
Web address: www.reevescountyhospital.com
**Control:** Hospital district or authority, Government, nonfederal **Service:** General Medical and Surgical

**Staffed Beds:** 25 **Admissions:** 852 **Census:** 11 **Outpatient Visits:** 45973 **Births:** 80 **Total Expense ($000):** 19626 **Payroll Expense ($000):** 7379 **Personnel:** 169

**TX**

*Many Facility Codes have changed. Please refer to the AHA Guide Code Chart.* © 2013 AHA Guide

## PERRYTON—Ochiltree County

**OCHILTREE GENERAL HOSPITAL (451359)**, 3101 Garrett Drive, Zip 79070–5323; tel. 806/435–3606 **A**9 10 18 **F**10 11 13 15 30 35 40 43 57 59 62 63 64 69 76 81 85 89 93 107 108 114 119 127 130 133 143 146 147 **P**1
Primary Contact: Jeff Barnhart, Chief Executive Officer
CFO: Debbie Blodgett, Director of Fiscal Services
CIO: Dyan Harrison, Manager Health Information
CNO: Judy Russell, Director of Nurses
Web address: www.ochiltreehospital.com
**Control:** Hospital district or authority, Government, nonfederal **Service:** General Medical and Surgical

**Staffed Beds:** 25 **Admissions:** 761 **Census:** 9 **Outpatient Visits:** 32787 **Births:** 168 **Total Expense ($000):** 13199 **Payroll Expense ($000):** 5860 **Personnel:** 168

## PITTSBURG—Camp County

★ **EAST TEXAS MEDICAL CENTER PITTSBURG (451367)**, 2701 Highway 271 North, Zip 75686–1032; tel. 903/946–5000 **A**9 10 18 **F**3 11 12 28 29 35 40 43 45 50 53 57 59 64 68 70 75 77 81 85 87 89 92 93 97 104 107 108 111 115 119 127 129 130 133 **P**6 **S** East Texas Medical Center Regional Healthcare System, Tyler, TX
Primary Contact: Jorge E. Leal, Chief Executive Officer
CFO: Steve Miller, Chief Financial Officer
CMO: W. R. Christensen, M.D., Chief of Staff
CIO: Paula Anthony, Vice President Information Services
CHR: Kathy Shelton, Director Human Resources
CNO: Casey Mayben, Chief Nursing Officer
Web address: www.etmc.org/newpittsburg.htm
**Control:** Other not–for–profit (including NFP Corporation) **Service:** General Medical and Surgical

**Staffed Beds:** 25 **Admissions:** 1129 **Census:** 12 **Outpatient Visits:** 79816 **Births:** 0 **Total Expense ($000):** 28708 **Payroll Expense ($000):** 9209 **Personnel:** 196

## PLAINVIEW—Hale County

**ALLEGIANCE BEHAVIORAL HEALTH CENTER OF PLAINVIEW (454101)**, 2601 Dimmit Road, 4th Floor, Zip 79072–1833; tel. 806/296–9191 **A**10 **F**29 35 56 64 98 101 103 104 **S** Allegiance Health Management, Shreveport, LA
Primary Contact: Glenn G. Hoffman, MS, Chief Executive Officer
COO: Don Cameron, Chief Operating Officer
CFO: Jim Turgeon, Vice President Finance
CMO: Victor A. Gutierrez, M.D., Medical Director
CIO: Richard Merk, Executive Vice President
CHR: Rob Lindsey, Jr., Vice President Human Resources
Web address: www.ahmgt.com
**Control:** Corporation, Investor–owned, for–profit **Service:** Psychiatric

**Staffed Beds:** 20 **Admissions:** 261 **Census:** 11 **Outpatient Visits:** 34743 **Births:** 0 **Total Expense ($000):** 4962 **Payroll Expense ($000):** 1961 **Personnel:** 33

⊠ **COVENANT HOSPITAL PLAINVIEW (450539)**, 2601 Dimmitt Road, Zip 79072–1833; tel. 806/296–5531 **A**1 9 10 20 **F**3 11 13 15 29 30 32 34 35 40 43 44 50 51 54 56 57 59 61 64 65 68 70 75 76 77 79 81 85 86 87 93 97 107 108 114 118 119 127 129 130 131 132 133 134 146 148 **S** Covenant Health System, Lubbock, TX
Primary Contact: Alan N. King, FACHE, Chief Executive Officer
COO: Mike McNutt, Assistant Administrator
CFO: Clay Taylor, Chief Financial Officer
CMO: Sergio Lara, M.D., Chief Medical Officer
CIO: Tim Branch, Manager Information Technology
Web address: www.covenantplainview.org
**Control:** Church–operated, Nongovernment, not–for profit **Service:** General Medical and Surgical

**Staffed Beds:** 68 **Admissions:** 2119 **Census:** 17 **Outpatient Visits:** 90544 **Births:** 548 **Total Expense ($000):** 30563 **Payroll Expense ($000):** 10382 **Personnel:** 298

## PLANO—Collin County

⊠ **BAYLOR REGIONAL MEDICAL CENTER AT PLANO (450890)**, 4700 Alliance Boulevard, Zip 75093–5323; tel. 469/814–2000 **A**1 2 9 10 **F**3 12 15 29 30 34 35 40 45 46 47 49 54 57 58 59 64 70 74 75 77 78 79 80 81 82 84 85 86 87 107 108 110 111 114 118 119 126 129 130 131 132 145 146 147 148 **S** Baylor Health Care System, Dallas, TX
Primary Contact: Jerri Garison, R.N., President
COO: Ellen Pitcher, MSN, Chief Operating Officer and Chief Nursing Officer
CFO: Deanne Kindered, Vice President Finance
CMO: Bradley M. Leonard, M.D., Vice President Medical Affairs
CHR: Tamara DeFer, Director Human Resources
Web address: www.baylorhealth.com/PhysiciansLocations/Plano/Pages/Default.aspx
**Control:** Other not–for–profit (including NFP Corporation) **Service:** General Medical and Surgical

**Staffed Beds:** 160 **Admissions:** 5788 **Census:** 83 **Outpatient Visits:** 59329 **Births:** 0 **Total Expense ($000):** 159567 **Payroll Expense ($000):** 50005 **Personnel:** 694

⊠ **HEALTHSOUTH PLANO REHABILITATION HOSPITAL (453047)**, 2800 West 15th Street, Zip 75075–7526; tel. 972/612–9000 **A**1 9 10 **F**34 57 59 62 90 93 95 96 100 129 130 132 148 **S** HEALTHSOUTH Corporation, Birmingham, AL
Primary Contact: Jennifer Lynn Brewer, Chief Executive Officer
CFO: Catrina Madkins, Controller and Chief Financial Officer
CMO: Omar Colon, M.D., Medical Director
Web address: www.healthsouthplano.com
**Control:** Corporation, Investor–owned, for–profit **Service:** Rehabilitation

**Staffed Beds:** 83 **Admissions:** 1393 **Census:** 51 **Outpatient Visits:** 10923 **Births:** 0 **Total Expense ($000):** 18921 **Payroll Expense ($000):** 10657 **Personnel:** 233

⊠ **MEDICAL CENTER OF PLANO (450651)**, 3901 West 15th Street, Zip 75075–7738; tel. 972/596–6800 **A**1 2 9 10 **F**3 11 12 13 15 18 20 22 24 26 28 29 30 31 34 35 40 43 45 46 48 49 51 53 54 55 57 58 59 60 64 70 72 74 75 76 78 79 81 82 84 85 86 87 89 93 107 108 110 111 112 114 115 117 118 119 124 126 129 130 132 135 145 146 147 148 **P**5 **S** HCA, Nashville, TN
Primary Contact: Troy Villarreal, Chief Executive Officer
COO: Glenn Wallace, Chief Operating Officer
CFO: W. Patrick Whitmore, Chief Financial Officer
CMO: Ann Arnold, M.D., Medical Director
CIO: Michael Gfeller, Director Information Systems
CHR: Shanna Warren, Director Human Resources
Web address: www.medicalcenterplano.com
**Control:** Partnership, Investor–owned, for–profit **Service:** General Medical and Surgical

**Staffed Beds:** 309 **Admissions:** 17766 **Census:** 245 **Outpatient Visits:** 116974 **Births:** 2299 **Total Expense ($000):** 250989 **Payroll Expense ($000):** 91376 **Personnel:** 1279

☐ **PLANO SPECIALTY HOSPITAL (452054)**, 1621 Coit Road, Zip 75075–6141; tel. 972/758–5200 **A**1 9 10 **F**1 3 29 45 75 82 84 85 86 87 96 130 135 148 **S** Encore Healthcare, Columbia, MD
Primary Contact: Jerry Amato, Chief Executive Officer
CFO: Deanna Lankford, Business Office Manager
CHR: Robbie McCranie, Director Human Resources
Web address: www.encore–healthcare.com/plano/index.aspx
**Control:** Corporation, Investor–owned, for–profit **Service:** Long–Term Acute Care hospital

**Staffed Beds:** 43 **Admissions:** 310 **Census:** 22 **Outpatient Visits:** 0 **Births:** 0 **Total Expense ($000):** 10040 **Payroll Expense ($000):** 3886 **Personnel:** 89

☐ **TEXAS HEALTH CENTER FOR DIAGNOSTIC & SURGERY (450891)**, 6020 West Parker Road, Zip 75093–8171; tel. 972/403–2700 **A**1 2 9 10 **F**3 29 40 42 45 54 64 79 81 82 85 87 107 111 114 119 129
Primary Contact: Larry Robertson, President
CFO: Douglas Browning, Chief Financial Officer
CHR: Cookie Tedder, Human Resources Manager
CNO: Ellen Baldwin, R.N., Chief Nursing Officer
Web address: www.thcds.com
**Control:** Partnership, Investor–owned, for–profit **Service:** General Medical and Surgical

**Staffed Beds:** 18 **Admissions:** 711 **Census:** 4 **Outpatient Visits:** 18333 **Births:** 0 **Total Expense ($000):** 49666 **Payroll Expense ($000):** 10371 **Personnel:** 154

TX

---

**Hospital, Medicare Provider Number, Address, Telephone, Approval, Facility, and Physician Codes, Health Care System**

★ American Hospital Association (AHA) membership
☐ The Joint Commission accreditation    ◇ DNV Healthcare Inc. accreditation
○ Healthcare Facilities Accreditation Program
△ Commission on Accreditation of Rehabilitation Facilities (CARF) accreditation

✠ **TEXAS HEALTH PRESBYTERIAN HOSPITAL PLANO (450771)**, 6200 West Parker Road, Zip 75093-8185; tel. 972/981-8000 **A**1 9 10 **F**3 12 13 15 18 20 22 24 26 29 30 31 32 34 35 37 38 40 43 44 45 46 48 49 50 52 54 55 57 58 59 60 64 65 68 70 72 74 75 76 77 78 79 81 85 86 87 89 93 107 108 110 111 114 115 118 119 126 130 132 135 145 146 147 148 **P**8 **S** Texas Health Resources, Arlington, TX
Primary Contact: Mike Evans, R.N., MS, President
CFO: Brian Craft, Vice President and Chief Financial Officer
CMO: Dean Cione, M.D., President Medical Staff
CIO: Susan Anderson, Director Information Systems
CHR: Angela Noel, Administrative Director Human Resources
CNO: Raymond Kelly, R.N., Chief Nursing Officer
Web address: www.texashealth.org
**Control:** Other not-for-profit (including NFP Corporation) **Service:** General Medical and Surgical

**Staffed Beds:** 338 **Admissions:** 15468 **Census:** 215 **Outpatient Visits:** 86357 **Births:** 3922 **Total Expense ($000):** 272400 **Payroll Expense ($000):** 92086 **Personnel:** 1161

☐ **THE HEART HOSPITAL BAYLOR PLANO (670025)**, 1100 Allied Drive, Zip 75093-5348; tel. 469/814-3278 **A**1 9 10 **F**3 18 20 22 24 26 28 29 30 34 40 54 57 64 75 78 79 81 82 84 85 86 87 91 92 93 94 95 96 97 107 108 110 111 112 114 115 116 117 118 119 120 121 123 124 126 130 146 147
Primary Contact: Mark Valentine, President
CFO: Bryan Nichols, Chief Financial Officer
CMO: Trent Pettijohn, M.D., Chief Medical Officer
CIO: Nayan Patel, Director Information Systems
CHR: Michael Ramey, Director Human Resources
CNO: Susan Moats, R.N., Vice President of Patient Care Services and Chief Nursing Officer
Web address: www.thehearthospital.com
**Control:** Partnership, Investor-owned, for-profit **Service:** General Medical and Surgical

**Staffed Beds:** 122 **Admissions:** 3450 **Census:** 52 **Outpatient Visits:** 18322 **Births:** 0 **Total Expense ($000):** 148937 **Payroll Expense ($000):** 44252 **Personnel:** 600

### PORT ARTHUR—Jefferson County

★ **CHRISTUS DUBUIS HOSPITAL OF PORT ARTHUR**, 3600 Gates Boulevard, Zip 77642-3858; tel. 409/989-5300, (Nonreporting) **A**9 **S** Dubuis Health System, Houston, TX
Primary Contact: Jeffrey Livingston, Administrator
Web address: www.dubuis.org/CHRISTUSDubuisHospitalofPortArthur
**Control:** Church-operated, Nongovernment, not-for profit **Service:** Other specialty

**Staffed Beds:** 15

**DUBUIS HOSPITAL OF PORT ARTHUR** See Christus Dubuis Hospital of Port Arthur

◇ **THE MEDICAL CENTER OF SOUTHEAST TEXAS (450518)**, 2555 Jimmy Johnson Boulevard, Zip 77640-2007; tel. 409/724-7389 **A**9 10 21 **F**3 8 11 13 15 17 18 20 22 24 28 29 30 34 44 45 47 49 50 56 57 59 64 72 74 76 77 78 79 81 82 85 86 87 89 90 91 92 93 94 98 101 102 103 104 105 107 108 110 111 114 115 119 129 130 132 135 148 **P**2 **S** IASIS Healthcare, Franklin, TN
Primary Contact: Matthew S. Roberts, Chief Executive Officer
COO: Chris McMahon, Chief Operating Officer
CFO: William Whiddon, Chief Financial Officer
CMO: Nidal Buheis, M.D., Chief of Staff
CIO: Bryan Hebert, Director Information Systems
CHR: Carol Hebert, Director Human Resources
Web address: www.medicalcentersetexas.com
**Control:** Partnership, Investor-owned, for-profit **Service:** General Medical and Surgical

**Staffed Beds:** 185 **Admissions:** 7997 **Census:** 97 **Outpatient Visits:** 56155 **Births:** 1320 **Total Expense ($000):** 102126 **Payroll Expense ($000):** 37017 **Personnel:** 717

### PORT LAVACA—Calhoun County

★ **MEMORIAL MEDICAL CENTER (451356)**, 815 North Virginia Street, Zip 77979-3025, Mailing Address: P.O. Box 25, Zip 77979-0025; tel. 361/552-6713 **A**9 10 18 **F**3 11 13 15 18 29 30 32 34 35 40 43 44 45 46 49 50 57 59 64 65 68 70 75 76 77 78 79 81 84 85 86 87 93 107 108 111 115 118 119 129 130 132 133 134 135 146 147 148
Primary Contact: Jason Anglin, Chief Executive Officer
CFO: Rick Hart, Chief Financial Officer
CMO: John B. Wright, M.D., Chief of Staff
CIO: Genevieve Sutherland, Health Information Management Director
CHR: Laurie Harvey, Administrative Officer
CNO: Amy Day, Chief Nursing Officer
Web address: www.mmcportlavaca.com
**Control:** County-Government, nonfederal **Service:** General Medical and Surgical

**Staffed Beds:** 25 **Admissions:** 1272 **Census:** 15 **Outpatient Visits:** 29058 **Births:** 111 **Total Expense ($000):** 20598 **Payroll Expense ($000):** 7947 **Personnel:** 167

### QUANAH—Hardeman County

**HARDEMAN COUNTY MEMORIAL HOSPITAL (451352)**, 402 Mercer Street, Zip 79252-4026, Mailing Address: P.O. Box 90, Zip 79252-0090; tel. 940/663-2795, (Nonreporting) **A**9 10 18
Primary Contact: Carol Lively, Chief Executive Officer
CFO: Butch Hall, Chief Financial Officer
CMO: Kevin Lane, D.O., Chief of Staff
Web address: www.quanahnet.comhospitalnavbarframe.htm
**Control:** Hospital district or authority, Government, nonfederal **Service:** General Medical and Surgical

**Staffed Beds:** 18

### QUITMAN—Wood County

★ **EAST TEXAS MEDICAL CENTER-QUITMAN (451380)**, 117 Winnsboro Street, Zip 75783-2144, Mailing Address: P.O. Box 1000, Zip 75783-1000; tel. 903/763-6300 **A**9 10 18 **F**3 11 15 29 30 35 40 43 45 50 57 59 64 65 68 79 81 85 87 107 108 110 115 119 127 129 130 133 **P**7 **S** East Texas Medical Center Regional Healthcare System, Tyler, TX
Primary Contact: Warren Robicheaux, Administrator
CFO: Tania LeMons, Assistant Chief Financial Officer
CMO: Norman Hicks, M.D., Chief Medical Staff
CHR: Alyssa Johnson, Director Human Resources
CNO: Teresa Meeks, Chief Nursing Officer
Web address: www.etmc.org/etmcquitman/
**Control:** Other not-for-profit (including NFP Corporation) **Service:** General Medical and Surgical

**Staffed Beds:** 25 **Admissions:** 902 **Census:** 10 **Outpatient Visits:** 36826 **Births:** 0 **Total Expense ($000):** 13781 **Payroll Expense ($000):** 5554 **Personnel:** 115

### RANKIN—Upton County

★ **RANKIN HOSPITAL DISTRICT (451329)**, 1105 Elizabeth Street, Zip 79778, Mailing Address: P.O. Box 327, Zip 79778-0327; tel. 432/693-2443 **A**9 10 18 **F**35 40 59 64 65 68 89 93 97
Primary Contact: Tommy Johnson, Chief Executive Officer
CFO: Tami Burks, Comptroller
CMO: Thomas J. Curvin, M.D., Chief of Staff
**Control:** Hospital district or authority, Government, nonfederal **Service:** General Medical and Surgical

**Staffed Beds:** 10 **Admissions:** 44 **Census:** 1 **Outpatient Visits:** 2745 **Births:** 0 **Personnel:** 43

### REFUGIO—Refugio County

**REFUGIO COUNTY MEMORIAL HOSPITAL (451317)**, 107 Swift Street, Zip 78377-2425; tel. 361/526-2321 **A**9 10 18 **F**3 7 29 40 43 57 61 64 75 81 86 87 93 97 107 119 127 133 **P**6
Primary Contact: Louis R. Willeke, Administrator
Web address: www.refugiohospital.com/
**Control:** Hospital district or authority, Government, nonfederal **Service:** General Medical and Surgical

**Staffed Beds:** 20 **Admissions:** 118 **Census:** 2 **Outpatient Visits:** 25391 **Births:** 0 **Total Expense ($000):** 8424 **Payroll Expense ($000):** 4798 **Personnel:** 124

### RICHARDSON—Dallas County

✠ **METHODIST RICHARDSON MEDICAL CENTER (450537)**, 401 West Campbell Road, Zip 75080-3416; tel. 972/498-4000 **A**1 2 9 10 **F**3 4 5 11 13 15 17 18 20 22 24 29 30 31 34 35 38 40 42 46 49 54 55 56 57 59 64 65 68 70 74 75 76 77 78 79 81 82 85 86 87 93 97 98 100 101 102 103 104 105 107 108 109 110 111 112 115 116 117 119 120 121 123 124 126 129 130 131 132 135 146 147 148 **P**1 7 **S** Methodist Health System, Dallas, TX
Primary Contact: E. Kenneth Hutchenrider, President
CFO: Bob Simpson, Vice President Finance
CIO: Terri Morris, Manager Information Systems
CHR: Shannan Gulbis, Director Human Resources
Web address: www.richardsonregional.com
**Control:** Other not-for-profit (including NFP Corporation) **Service:** General Medical and Surgical

**Staffed Beds:** 160 **Admissions:** 5569 **Census:** 72 **Outpatient Visits:** 77901 **Total Expense ($000):** 114315 **Payroll Expense ($000):** 51086 **Personnel:** 547

✠ **RELIANT REHABILITATION HOSPITAL NORTH TEXAS (673029)**, 3351 Waterview Parkway, Zip 75080-1449; tel. 972/398-5700 **A**1 9 10 **F**3 29 90 93 96 148 **S** Reliant Healthcare Partners, Richardson, TX
Primary Contact: Jim Ransom, Chief Executive Officer
CFO: Mary Mwaniki, Chief Financial Officer
CMO: Richard Jones, M.D., Medical Director
Web address: www.relianthcp.com
**Control:** Partnership, Investor-owned, for-profit **Service:** Rehabilitation

**Staffed Beds:** 50 **Admissions:** 1220 **Census:** 42 **Outpatient Visits:** 10297 **Births:** 0 **Total Expense ($000):** 15459 **Payroll Expense ($000):** 7847 **Personnel:** 159

*Many Facility Codes have changed. Please refer to the AHA Guide Code Chart.*    © 2013 AHA Guide

## RICHMOND—Fort Bend County

☐ △ **OAKBEND MEDICAL CENTER (450330)**, 1705 Jackson Street,
Zip 77469–3289; tel. 281/341–3000, (Total facility includes 26 beds in nursing
home–type unit) **A**1 7 9 10 **F**3 11 13 15 18 20 22 24 26 29 30 31 34 35 40
42 43 45 46 47 49 50 56 57 59 64 65 70 72 74 75 76 78 79 81 82 85 87
89 93 98 102 103 107 108 109 110 111 114 118 119 128 129 130 132
146 147 148 **P**6
Primary Contact: Joe Freudenberger, Chief Executive Officer
CFO: James R. Shallock, Chief Financial Officer
CMO: Douglas Thibodeaux, M.D., Chief Medical Officer
CHR: Nancy Retzlaff, Director Human Resources
Web address: www.oakbendmedcenter.org
**Control:** Hospital district or authority, Government, nonfederal **Service:** General
Medical and Surgical

**Staffed Beds:** 195 **Admissions:** 5987 **Census:** 78 **Outpatient Visits:** 59575
**Births:** 1460 **Total Expense ($000):** 81848 **Payroll Expense ($000):** 27411
**Personnel:** 677

## RIO GRANDE CITY—Starr County

★ **STARR COUNTY MEMORIAL HOSPITAL (450654)**, 2753 Hospital Court,
Zip 78582–6859, Mailing Address: P.O. Box 78, Zip 78582–0078;
tel. 956/487–5561 **A**9 10 20 **F**7 11 13 15 29 30 34 40 43 45 46 50 57 59
64 65 66 68 75 76 79 80 81 89 107 110 111 114 119 127 130 135
145 148
Primary Contact: Thalia H. Munoz, R.N., MS, Hospital Administrator
CFO: Rafael Olivares, Controller
Web address: www.starrcountyhospital.com
**Control:** Hospital district or authority, Government, nonfederal **Service:** General
Medical and Surgical

**Staffed Beds:** 47 **Admissions:** 1884 **Census:** 18 **Outpatient Visits:** 55091
**Births:** 320 **Total Expense ($000):** 25662 **Payroll Expense ($000):** 11719
**Personnel:** 259

## ROCKDALE—Milam County

◇ **LITTLE RIVER HEALTHCARE (451357)**, (Formerly Little River Medical Center),
1700 Brazos Street, Zip 76567–2517, Mailing Address: Drawer 1010,
Zip 76567–1010; tel. 512/446–4500 **A**9 10 18 21 **F**11 15 18 20 22 26 28 29
40 64 65 68 75 77 79 81 82 83 84 85 87 93 96 97 107 108 110 111 114
119 127 130 131 133 148
Primary Contact: Jeffrey Madison, Chief Executive Officer
CMO: John Weed, III, M.D., Medical Director
CHR: Crystal Foley, Director Human Resources
Web address: www.lrhealthcare.com
**Control:** Corporation, Investor–owned, for–profit **Service:** General Medical and
Surgical

**Staffed Beds:** 21 **Admissions:** 451 **Census:** 9 **Outpatient Visits:** 38175
**Births:** 2 **Total Expense ($000):** 29608 **Payroll Expense ($000):** 10385
**Personnel:** 226

## ROCKWALL—Rockwall County

☒ **TEXAS HEALTH PRESBYTERIAN HOSPITAL OF ROCKWALL (670044)**,
(Formerly Presbyterian Hospital of Rockwall), 3150 Horizon Road,
Zip 75032–7805; tel. 469/698–1000 **A**1 9 10 **F**3 12 13 15 29 30 40 45 46
47 49 50 54 67 68 70 75 76 77 79 81 85 87 93 107 108 110 111 115 119
130 146 147 148
Primary Contact: Cindy Paris, R.N., President
Web address: www.phrtexas.com
**Control:** Corporation, Investor–owned, for–profit **Service:** General Medical and
Surgical

**Staffed Beds:** 50 **Admissions:** 3605 **Census:** 33 **Outpatient Visits:** 44019
**Births:** 775 **Total Expense ($000):** 76495 **Payroll Expense ($000):** 26197
**Personnel:** 456

## ROTAN—Fisher County

**FISHER COUNTY HOSPITAL DISTRICT (451313)**, 774 State Highway 70
North, Zip 79546–6918, Mailing Address: P.O. Drawer F, Zip 79546–4019;
tel. 325/735–2256 **A**9 10 18 **F**7 28 32 34 35 40 43 50 53 56 57 59 64 66
75 93 97 107 119 127 133 **P**6
Primary Contact: Steve Lefevre, Chief Executive Officer and Administrator
CFO: Debbie Hull, Chief Financial Officer
CMO: C. M. Callan, M.D., Chief of Staff
Web address: www.fishercountyhospital.com
**Control:** Hospital district or authority, Government, nonfederal **Service:** General
Medical and Surgical

**Staffed Beds:** 10 **Admissions:** 104 **Census:** 2 **Outpatient Visits:** 18572
**Births:** 1 **Total Expense ($000):** 7620 **Payroll Expense ($000):** 3360
**Personnel:** 72

## ROUND ROCK—Williamson County

☐ **RELIANT REHABILITATION HOSPITAL CENTRAL TEXAS (673032)**, 1400
Hester's Crossing, Zip 78681–8025; tel. 512/244–4400, (Total facility includes
25 beds in nursing home–type unit) **A**1 9 10 **F**3 29 90 93 96 128 130 148
**S** Reliant Healthcare Partners, Richardson, TX
Primary Contact: Eric Mueller, Chief Executive Officer
CNO: Vidette J. Forbes, R.N., Chief Nursing Officer and Chief Operating officer
Web address: www.reliantcentraltx.com/
**Control:** Partnership, Investor–owned, for–profit **Service:** Rehabilitation

**Staffed Beds:** 75 **Admissions:** 1665 **Census:** 56 **Outpatient Visits:** 7770
**Births:** 0 **Total Expense ($000):** 17412 **Payroll Expense ($000):** 8296
**Personnel:** 133

☒ **SCOTT & WHITE HOSPITAL AT ROUND ROCK (670034)**, 300 University
Boulevard, Zip 78665–1032; tel. 512/509–0200 **A**1 5 9 10 **F**3 13 15 18 20 22
26 28 29 30 31 34 35 40 43 45 46 47 49 51 52 54 59 60 64 68 70 74 75
76 78 79 81 82 85 87 93 97 99 100 104 107 110 111 115 116 119 130
131 144 146 147 148 **P**6 **S** Scott & White Healthcare, Temple, TX
Primary Contact: Ernest L. Bovio, Jr., Chief Executive Officer
CFO: Jason Cole, Senior Director Finance
CMO: Bud Chumbley, M.D., Chief Medical Officer
CHR: Brenda Cox, Director Human Resources
Web address: www.scottandwhite.org
**Control:** Other not–for–profit (including NFP Corporation) **Service:** General
Medical and Surgical

**Staffed Beds:** 84 **Admissions:** 4420 **Census:** 43 **Outpatient Visits:** 355661
**Births:** 618 **Total Expense ($000):** 115331 **Payroll Expense ($000):** 38071
**Personnel:** 873

☒ **SETON MEDICAL CENTER WILLIAMSON (670041)**, 201 Seton Parkway,
Zip 78665–8000; tel. 512/324–4000 **A**1 5 9 10 **F**3 11 12 13 15 18 20 22 24
26 28 29 30 31 34 35 37 40 43 44 45 46 49 50 51 53 54 57 58 59 60 64
68 70 72 74 75 76 77 78 79 81 82 84 85 86 87 93 96 107 108 110 111
114 115 119 124 126 130 131 132 135 146 147 148 **P**3 8 **S** Ascension
Health, Saint Louis, MO
Primary Contact: Michelle Robertson, R.N., President and Chief Executive Officer
CFO: Douglas D. Waite, Senior Vice President and Chief Financial Officer
CMO: Hugh V. Gilmore, M.D., Vice President Medical Affairs
CIO: Gerry Lewis, Chief Information Officer
CHR: Thomas Wilken, Vice President Human Resources
Web address: www.seton.net/williamson
**Control:** Church–operated, Nongovernment, not–for profit **Service:** General
Medical and Surgical

**Staffed Beds:** 143 **Admissions:** 7653 **Census:** 86 **Outpatient Visits:** 62275
**Births:** 1068 **Total Expense ($000):** 139114 **Payroll Expense ($000):**
58069 **Personnel:** 945

☒ **ST. DAVID'S ROUND ROCK MEDICAL CENTER (450718)**, 2400 Round Rock
Avenue, Zip 78681–4097; tel. 512/341–1000 **A**1 2 5 9 10 **F**3 11 13 15 18 22
24 26 28 29 30 31 34 35 40 43 47 49 57 59 64 70 73 74 75 76 77 78 79
80 81 84 85 86 87 90 93 107 108 110 111 114 115 119 129 130 132 144
146 147 148 **P**7 8 **S** HCA, Nashville, TN
Primary Contact: Deborah L. Ryle, Administrator and Chief Executive Officer
COO: Tad Hatton, Chief Operating Officer
CFO: Cindy Sexton, Chief Financial Officer
CMO: David Martin, M.D., Vice President Medical Staff Affairs
CHR: Amy Noak, Director Human Resources
Web address: www.stdavids.com
**Control:** Other not–for–profit (including NFP Corporation) **Service:** General
Medical and Surgical

**Staffed Beds:** 156 **Admissions:** 9440 **Census:** 89 **Outpatient Visits:** 70728
**Births:** 1860 **Total Expense ($000):** 111992 **Payroll Expense ($000):**
38877 **Personnel:** 610

**Hospital, Medicare Provider Number, Address, Telephone, Approval, Facility, and Physician Codes, Health Care System**

★ American Hospital Association (AHA) membership
☐ The Joint Commission accreditation
◇ DNV Healthcare Inc. accreditation
○ Healthcare Facilities Accreditation Program
△ Commission on Accreditation of Rehabilitation Facilities (CARF) accreditation

## ROWLETT—Rockwall County

☒ **LAKE POINTE MEDICAL CENTER (450742)**, 6800 Scenic Drive, Zip 75088–4552, Mailing Address: P.O. Box 1550, Zip 75030–1550; tel. 972/412–2273 **A**1 9 10 **F**3 12 13 15 18 20 22 24 28 29 30 34 35 40 42 45 46 49 50 53 54 57 59 60 64 65 70 72 73 74 75 76 77 78 79 81 82 85 86 87 93 107 108 110 111 114 115 118 119 120 121 126 129 130 131 132 144 146 147 148 **S** TENET Healthcare Corporation, Dallas, TX
Primary Contact: Brett D. Lee, Chief Executive Officer
COO: Debbie A. Moeller, R.N., Chief Operating Officer
CFO: Becky Speight, Chief Financial Officer
CMO: Larry Dencklau, D.O., Chief of Staff
CIO: Mark Slater, Director Information Systems
CHR: David Olmstead, Associate Administrator and Director Human Resources
CNO: Patti Gilliano, Chief Nursing Officer
Web address: www.lakepointemedical.com
**Control:** Corporation, Investor–owned, for–profit **Service:** General Medical and Surgical

**Staffed Beds:** 112 **Admissions:** 6847 **Census:** 63 **Outpatient Visits:** 80189 **Births:** 1387 **Total Expense ($000):** 82503 **Payroll Expense ($000):** 30527 **Personnel:** 548

## RUSK—Cherokee County

☐ **RUSK STATE HOSPITAL (454009)**, 805 North Dickinson, Zip 75785–2333, Mailing Address: P.O. Box 318, Zip 75785–0318; tel. 903/683–3421 **A**1 10 **F**3 30 39 44 50 68 75 86 87 98 103 106 130 135 146 148 **P**6 **S** Texas Department of State Health Services, Austin, TX
Primary Contact: Brenda Slaton, Administrator
COO: Lynda Roberson, Senior Program Director
CFO: Frances Long, Chief Financial Officer
CMO: Douglas Johnson, M.D., Clinical Director
CIO: Glenda Bruce, Director Community Relations
Web address: www.dshs.state.tx.us/mhhospitals/RuskSH/default.shtm
**Control:** State–Government, nonfederal **Service:** Psychiatric

**Staffed Beds:** 330 **Admissions:** 780 **Census:** 304 **Outpatient Visits:** 0 **Births:** 0 **Total Expense ($000):** 57262 **Payroll Expense ($000):** 31420 **Personnel:** 949

## SAN ANGELO—Tom Green County

☐ **RIVER CREST HOSPITAL (454064)**, 1636 Hunters Glen Road, Zip 76901–5016; tel. 325/949–5722 **A**1 9 10 **F**4 29 87 98 99 100 101 102 104 105 130 132 **S** Universal Health Services, Inc., King of Prussia, PA
Primary Contact: Shelah Adams, Chief Executive Officer
CFO: Frank Urban, Chief Financial Officer
CMO: John Crowley, M.D., Medical Director
CHR: Brenda Coats, Director Human Resources
Web address: www.rivercresthospital.com
**Control:** Corporation, Investor–owned, for–profit **Service:** Psychiatric

**Staffed Beds:** 80 **Admissions:** 1869 **Census:** 43 **Outpatient Visits:** 3664 **Births:** 0 **Total Expense ($000):** 9004 **Payroll Expense ($000):** 4454 **Personnel:** 135

☒ △ **SAN ANGELO COMMUNITY MEDICAL CENTER (450340)**, 3501 Knickerbocker Road, Zip 76904–7698; tel. 325/949–9511 **A**1 2 7 9 10 **F**3 8 11 13 15 18 20 22 24 28 29 30 31 34 37 40 43 45 49 51 53 54 57 59 60 63 64 68 70 72 74 75 76 77 78 79 81 82 85 89 90 93 107 108 110 111 118 119 129 130 131 135 144 145 146 148 **P**8 **S** Community Health Systems, Inc., Franklin, TN
Primary Contact: Eric Becker, Chief Executive Officer
CFO: Richard Ervin, Chief Financial Officer
CHR: Lisa Bibb, Director Human Resources
Web address: www.sacmc.com
**Control:** Partnership, Investor–owned, for–profit **Service:** General Medical and Surgical

**Staffed Beds:** 131 **Admissions:** 5239 **Census:** 61 **Outpatient Visits:** 78809 **Births:** 853 **Total Expense ($000):** 77011 **Payroll Expense ($000):** 31324 **Personnel:** 588

☒ △ **SHANNON MEDICAL CENTER (450571)**, 120 East Harris Street, Zip 76903–5976, Mailing Address: P.O. Box 1879, Zip 76902–1879; tel. 325/653–6741, (Includes SHANNON MEDICAL CENTER– ST. JOHN'S CAMPUS, 2018 Pulliam Street, Zip 76905–5197; tel. 915/659–7100), (Total facility includes 24 beds in nursing home–type unit) **A**1 2 3 5 7 9 10 **F**3 7 8 11 13 15 18 20 22 24 26 28 29 30 31 32 34 35 37 38 40 43 45 49 50 51 53 54 56 57 58 59 60 61 62 64 68 70 72 73 74 75 76 77 78 79 80 81 82 84 85 86 87 89 90 92 93 94 96 98 100 101 102 103 107 108 110 111 114 115 117 119 128 129 130 132 145 146 147 148 **P**6
Primary Contact: Bryan Horner, President and Chief Executive Officer
CFO: Shane Plymell, Chief Financial Officer
CMO: Irvin Zeitler, D.O., Vice President Medical Affairs
CIO: Tom Perkins, Chief Information Officer
CHR: Teresa Morgan, Assistant Vice President Human Resources
Web address: www.shannonhealth.com
**Control:** Other not–for–profit (including NFP Corporation) **Service:** General Medical and Surgical

**Staffed Beds:** 282 **Admissions:** 11684 **Census:** 154 **Outpatient Visits:** 113662 **Births:** 1048 **Total Expense ($000):** 192879 **Payroll Expense ($000):** 72939 **Personnel:** 1470

## SAN ANTONIO—Bexar County

☒ **ACUITY HOSPITAL OF SOUTH TEXAS (452040)**, 718 Lexington Avenue, Zip 78212–4768; tel. 210/572–4600 **A**1 9 10 **F**1 3 29 45 85 87 91 107 119 148 **S** AcuityHealthcare, LP, Charlotte, NC
Primary Contact: Kris Karns, Ph.D., FACHE, Chief Executive Officer
CFO: Wayne Hegwood, Chief Financial Officer
CFO: Lydia Washington, Controller
CMO: Lovelesh Manocha, M.D., Chief Medical Officer
CHR: Yolanda Ochoa, Director Human Resources
CNO: Emilie Kilpatrick, Chief Clinical Officer
Web address: www.acuityhealthcare.net
**Control:** Corporation, Investor–owned, for–profit **Service:** Long–Term Acute Care hospital

**Staffed Beds:** 30 **Admissions:** 315 **Census:** 23 **Outpatient Visits:** 0 **Births:** 0 **Personnel:** 93

◇ **BAPTIST EMERGENCY HOSPITAL (670078)**, 16088 San Pedro, Zip 78232–2249; tel. 210/402–4092 **A**10 21 **F**3 40 41 42 75 107 108 **P**5
Primary Contact: Laura Salgado, Administrator
Web address: www.baptistemergencyhospital.com
**Control:** Corporation, Investor–owned, for–profit **Service:** General Medical and Surgical

**Staffed Beds:** 26 **Admissions:** 199 **Census:** 1 **Outpatient Visits:** 16194 **Births:** 0 **Total Expense ($000):** 8381 **Payroll Expense ($000):** 2842 **Personnel:** 80

☒ △ **BAPTIST MEDICAL CENTER (450058)**, (Formerly Baptist Health System), 111 Dallas Street, Zip 78205–1230; tel. 210/297–7000, (Includes MISSION TRAIL BAPTIST HOSPITAL, 3333 Research Plaza, Zip 78235–5154; tel. 210/297–3000; Andrew M. Harris, Chief Executive Officer; NORTH CENTRAL BAPTIST HOSPITAL, 520 Madison Oak Drive, Zip 78258–3912; tel. 210/297–4000; NORTHEAST BAPTIST HOSPITAL, 8811 Village Drive, Zip 78217–5440; tel. 210/297–2000; Matthew Stone, Chief Executive Officer; ST. LUKE'S BAPTIST HOSPITAL, 7930 Floyd Curl Drive, Zip 78229–0100; tel. 210/297–5000; John E. Knox, FACHE, Chief Executive Officer) **A**1 2 3 5 7 9 10 **F**1 3 11 12 13 14 15 17 18 19 20 22 24 26 28 29 30 31 35 37 38 40 41 42 43 44 45 46 47 50 54 55 56 57 59 60 64 65 68 70 72 73 74 75 76 77 78 79 80 81 82 85 86 87 88 89 90 91 92 93 95 96 98 101 102 103 107 108 111 114 115 116 117 119 124 126 129 130 132 135 145 146 147 148 **P**8 **S** Vanguard Health Systems, Nashville, TN
Primary Contact: David S. Goldberg, President
COO: Philip J. Noel, III, Assistant Administrator and Chief Operating Officer
CFO: Linda Kirks, Chief Financial Officer
CIO: Gary Davis, Vice President Information Systems
CHR: Sarah Spinharney, Senior Vice President
Web address: www.baptisthealthsystem.com
**Control:** Partnership, Investor–owned, for–profit **Service:** General Medical and Surgical

**Staffed Beds:** 1527 **Admissions:** 64784 **Census:** 761 **Outpatient Visits:** 301046 **Births:** 10763 **Total Expense ($000):** 761444 **Payroll Expense ($000):** 302765 **Personnel:** 5711

☒ **CHRISTUS SANTA ROSA HEALTH SYSTEM (450237)**, (Formerly CHRISTUS Santa Rosa Health Care), 333 North Santa Rosa Street, Zip 78207–3108; tel. 210/704–4184, (Includes CHILDREN'S HOSPITAL OF SANTA ROSA, 333 North Santa Rosa Street, Zip 78207; tel. 210/704–2011; Marcy Doderer, Vice President and Administrator; CHRISTUS SANTA ROSA HOSPITAL – NEW BRAUNFELS, 600 North Union Avenue, New Braunfels, Zip 78130–4191; tel. 830/606–9111; Jim D. Wesson, Vice President and Administrator; CHRISTUS SANTA ROSA REHABILITATION HOSPITAL, 2827 Babcock Road, Zip 78229–4813; tel. 210/705–6300) **A**1 3 5 9 10 **F**3 8 11 12 13 15 18 19 20 21 22 23 24 25 26 27 28 29 30 32 34 35 37 39 40 41 42 43 45 46 48 49 54 55 56 57 58 59 60 63 64 65 67 70 71 72 73 74 75 76 77 78 79 80 81 82 84 85 86 87 88 89 90 93 96 97 104 107 108 110 111 114 115 117 118 119 126 129 130 132 134 137 138 139 140 142 146 147 **P**6 **S** CHRISTUS Health, Irving, TX
Primary Contact: Patrick Brian Carrier, President and Chief Executive Officer
COO: Val Baciarelli, Chief Operating Officer
CFO: Shawn Barnett, Vice President and Chief Financial Officer
CMO: James C. Martin, M.D., Vice President and Chief Medical Officer
CIO: Steve Martin, Chief Information Officer
CHR: Fernando Fleites, Vice President Human Resources
Web address: www.christussantarosa.org
**Control:** Church–operated, Nongovernment, not–for profit **Service:** General Medical and Surgical

**Staffed Beds:** 766 **Admissions:** 31167 **Census:** 442 **Outpatient Visits:** 400017 **Births:** 3517 **Total Expense ($000):** 591041 **Payroll Expense ($000):** 199825 **Personnel:** 3037

☐ **CLARITY CHILD GUIDANCE CENTER**, 8535 Tom Slick, Zip 78229–3363;
tel. 210/616–0300 **A**1 3 5 9 **F**29 41 98 99 101 102 104 105 106 130
Primary Contact: Frederick W. Hines, President and Chief Executive Officer
CFO: Michael Bernick, Vice President Finance
CMO: Graham Rogeness, M.D., Medical Director
CHR: Gina Massey, Vice President Human Resources
Web address: www.claritycgc.org
**Control:** Other not–for–profit (including NFP Corporation) **Service:** Children's
hospital psychiatric

**Staffed Beds:** 52 **Admissions:** 1532 **Census:** 44 **Outpatient Visits:** 15890
**Births:** 0 **Total Expense ($000):** 15814 **Payroll Expense ($000):** 9695
**Personnel:** 226

☐ ◇ **FOUNDATION SURGICAL HOSPITAL OF SAN ANTONIO (670054)**, 9522
Huebner Road, Zip 78240–1548; tel. 210/478–5400 **A**1 9 10 21 **F**3 12 29 30
35 37 40 44 45 51 53 68 74 75 77 79 81 85 86 87 107 114 119 129 130
132 135 148 **S** Foundation Surgical Hospital Affiliates, Oklahoma City, OK
Primary Contact: Robert Trussell, Chief Executive Officer
CFO: Scott Banks, Chief Financial Officer
Web address: www.fshsanantonio.com/bariatric–foundation–surgical.html
**Control:** Corporation, Investor–owned, for–profit **Service:** Surgical

**Staffed Beds:** 20 **Admissions:** 9367 **Census:** 7 **Outpatient Visits:** 2045
**Births:** 0 **Total Expense ($000):** 29396 **Payroll Expense ($000):** 5542
**Personnel:** 99

○ **GLOBALREHAB HOSPITAL – SAN ANTONIO (673040)**, 19126 Stonehue
Road, Zip 78258–3490; tel. 210/482–3400 **A**9 10 11 **F**3 29 75 90 96 130
148 **S** GLOBALREHAB, Dallas, TX
Primary Contact: Edward L. Dyer, Chief Executive Officer
Web address: www.globalrehabhospitals.com
**Control:** Partnership, Investor–owned, for–profit **Service:** Rehabilitation

**Staffed Beds:** 42 **Admissions:** 762 **Census:** 27 **Outpatient Visits:** 0 **Births:**
0 **Total Expense ($000):** 13183 **Payroll Expense ($000):** 6128 **Personnel:**
108

⊠ **HEALTHSOUTH REHABILITATION INSTITUTE OF SAN ANTONIO (453031)**,
9119 Cinnamon Hill, Zip 78240–5401; tel. 210/691–0737 **A**1 9 10 **F**29 62 64
75 90 91 93 94 96 130 132 148 **P**5 **S** HEALTHSOUTH Corporation,
Birmingham, AL
Primary Contact: Scott Butcher, Chief Executive Officer
CFO: Larry Spriggs, Controller
CMO: Richard Senelick, M.D., Medical Director
CHR: Vanessa Tejada, Manager Human Resources
Web address: www.hsriosa.com
**Control:** Corporation, Investor–owned, for–profit **Service:** Rehabilitation

**Staffed Beds:** 96 **Admissions:** 1193 **Census:** 55 **Outpatient Visits:** 10475
**Births:** 0 **Total Expense ($000):** 20617 **Payroll Expense ($000):** 10551
**Personnel:** 191

⊠ **KINDRED HOSPITAL–SAN ANTONIO (452016)**, 3636 Medical Drive,
Zip 78229–2183; tel. 210/616–0616 **A**1 9 10 **F**1 3 29 30 70 85 87 107 130
148 **S** Kindred Healthcare, Louisville, KY
Primary Contact: Katherine Eskew, Chief Executive Officer
CFO: Erin Russell, Controller
CMO: Charles Duncan, M.D., Medical Director
CHR: Brian Mosley, Coordinator Human Resources and Payroll Benefits
Web address: www.khsanantonio.com/
**Control:** Corporation, Investor–owned, for–profit **Service:** Long–Term Acute Care
hospital

**Staffed Beds:** 59 **Admissions:** 427 **Census:** 30 **Outpatient Visits:** 140
**Births:** 0 **Total Expense ($000):** 19173 **Payroll Expense ($000):** 7072
**Personnel:** 114

⊠ **LAUREL RIDGE TREATMENT CENTER (454060)**, 17720 Corporate Woods
Drive, Zip 78259–3500; tel. 210/491–9400 **A**1 3 5 9 10 **F**5 29 35 38 75 77
98 99 100 101 103 105 106 130 132 **S** Universal Health Services, Inc., King of
Prussia, PA
Primary Contact: Jacob Cuellar, M.D., Chief Executive Officer
COO: Shawn Owens, Chief Operating Officer
CFO: Linda Maenius, Chief Financial Officer
CMO: Benigno J. Fernandez, M.D., Executive Medical Director
CHR: Brenda Frederick, Director Human Resources
CNO: Kathy Rosetta, Chief Nursing Officer
Web address: www.laurelridgetc.com
**Control:** Partnership, Investor–owned, for–profit **Service:** Psychiatric

**Staffed Beds:** 208 **Admissions:** 6118 **Census:** 169 **Outpatient Visits:** 17986
**Births:** 0 **Total Expense ($000):** 45527 **Payroll Expense ($000):** 18744
**Personnel:** 332

⊠ **LIFECARE HOSPITALS OF SAN ANTONIO (452059)**, 8902 Floyd Curl Drive,
Zip 78240–1681; tel. 210/690–7000 **A**1 9 10 **F**1 3 29 45 75 77 85 86 87 96
97 107 114 130 148 **S** LifeCare Management Services, Plano, TX
Primary Contact: Randell G. Stokes, Chief Executive Officer
CMO: Randall C. Bell, M.D., Medical Director
CIO: Mike Wattenbarger, Chief Information Officer
Web address: www.lifecare–hospitals.com
**Control:** Corporation, Investor–owned, for–profit **Service:** Long–Term Acute Care
hospital

**Staffed Beds:** 62 **Admissions:** 602 **Census:** 55 **Outpatient Visits:** 0 **Births:**
0 **Total Expense ($000):** 26773 **Payroll Expense ($000):** 12351
**Personnel:** 240

⊠ **METHODIST AMBULATORY SURGERY HOSPITAL (450780)**, 9150 Huebner
Road, Suite 100, Zip 78240–1545; tel. 210/575–5000 **A**1 9 10 **F**3 29 40 68
79 81 85 87 **P**8 **S** HCA, Nashville, TN
Primary Contact: Elaine F. Morris, Chief Executive Officer
CFO: Tim Carr, Chief Financial Officer
CHR: Barry Burns, Vice President
CNO: Cathy Bump, R.N., Chief Nursing Officer
Web address: www.sahealth.com
**Control:** Partnership, Investor–owned, for–profit **Service:** General Medical and
Surgical

**Staffed Beds:** 23 **Admissions:** 732 **Census:** 5 **Outpatient Visits:** 7819
**Births:** 0 **Total Expense ($000):** 23262 **Payroll Expense ($000):** 6705
**Personnel:** 116

⊠ **METHODIST HOSPITAL (450388)**, 7700 Floyd Curl Drive, Zip 78229–3993;
tel. 210/575–4000, (Includes METHODIST CHILDREN'S HOSPITAL OF SOUTH
TEXAS, 7700 Floyd Curl Drive, Zip 78229–3383; tel. 210/575–7000; Mark
McLoone, Chief Executive Officer; METHODIST SPECIALTY AND TRANSPLANT
HOSPITAL, 8026 Floyd Curl Drive, Zip 78229–3915; tel. 210/575–4000;
METHODIST TEXSAN HOSPITAL, 6700 IH–10 West, Zip 78201;
tel. 210/736–6700; Ashley S. Hixon, Interim Chief Executive Officer;
METROPOLITAN METHODIST HOSPITAL, 1310 McCullough Avenue,
Zip 78212–2617; tel. 210/757–2200; Gregory A. Seiler, Chief Executive Officer;
NORTHEAST METHODIST HOSPITAL, 12412 Judson Road, Live Oak,
Zip 78233–3255; tel. 210/650–4949) **A**1 2 3 5 9 10 **F**3 4 5 8 11 12 13 15 17
18 19 20 21 22 23 24 25 26 27 28 29 30 31 34 35 38 40 41 42 43 44 45
46 47 48 49 51 53 54 56 57 58 59 60 64 65 68 70 72 74 75 76 77 78 79
80 81 82 84 85 86 87 88 89 90 93 95 96 98 100 101 102 103 104 105 107
108 111 114 115 119 121 124 126 127 128 129 130 132 135 136 137 138 139
142 143 145 146 147 148 **P**7 **S** HCA, Nashville, TN
Primary Contact: Gay Nord, Chief Executive Officer
CFO: Nancy Meadows, Chief Financial Officer
CMO: Russell Woodward, M.D., Chief Medical Officer
CIO: Eddie Cuellar, Vice President Information Systems
CHR: Nancy Edgar, Vice President Human Resources
Web address: www.sahealth.com
**Control:** Partnership, Investor–owned, for–profit **Service:** General Medical and
Surgical

**Staffed Beds:** 1604 **Admissions:** 77058 **Census:** 1036 **Outpatient Visits:**
445521 **Births:** 9041 **Total Expense ($000):** 1182866 **Payroll Expense
($000):** 350727 **Personnel:** 5813

⊠ **METHODIST STONE OAK HOSPITAL (670055)**, 1139 East Sonterra
Boulevard, Zip 78258–4347; tel. 210/638–2100 **A**1 9 10 **F**3 13 15 18 20 22
24 29 30 31 34 38 40 44 45 46 47 49 57 59 60 64 65 68 70 72 74 75 76
77 78 79 80 81 82 85 86 87 107 108 111 115 118 119 126 130 145 146
147 **S** HCA, Nashville, TN
Primary Contact: Dean M. Alexander, Chief Executive Officer
COO: Patricia Burns, Chief Operating Officer/Ethics and Compliance Officer
CFO: Stephanie Parker, Chief Financial Officer
CNO: Eileen Huss, Chief Nursing Officer
Web address: www.stoneoakhealth.com
**Control:** Partnership, Investor–owned, for–profit **Service:** General Medical and
Surgical

**Staffed Beds:** 140 **Admissions:** 7937 **Census:** 84 **Outpatient Visits:** 36646
**Births:** 1053 **Total Expense ($000):** 112722 **Payroll Expense ($000):**
31778 **Personnel:** 448

---

**Hospital, Medicare Provider Number, Address, Telephone, Approval, Facility, and Physician Codes, Health Care System**

★ American Hospital Association (AHA) membership  ○ Healthcare Facilities Accreditation Program
☐ The Joint Commission accreditation  ◇ DNV Healthcare Inc. accreditation  △ Commission on Accreditation of Rehabilitation Facilities (CARF) accreditation

TX

☐ **NIX HEALTH CARE SYSTEM (450130)**, 414 Navarro Street, Zip 78205–2516; tel. 210/271–1800, (Data for 243 days) **A**1 3 5 9 10 **F**3 5 12 15 18 20 22 24 26 29 30 31 35 40 44 45 49 56 57 59 60 62 64 68 70 74 75 78 79 81 82 85 87 90 93 97 98 99 103 107 108 110 111 114 118 119 129 130 132 142 143 146 147 148
Primary Contact: John F. Strieby, Chief Executive Officer
COO: Thomas Klawiter, Senior Vice President and Chief Operating Officer
CFO: Lester Surrock, Chief Financial Officer
CMO: Lisa A. Davis, M.D., Chief of Staff
CIO: Steve Kinkaid, Vice President Technology
CHR: Richard Lance, Vice President Human Resources
Web address: www.nixhealth.com
**Control:** Corporation, Investor–owned, for–profit **Service:** General Medical and Surgical

| | |
|---|---|
| **Staffed Beds:** 173 **Admissions:** 5160 **Census:** 113 **Outpatient Visits:** 87686 **Births:** 0 **Total Expense ($000):** 54978 **Payroll Expense ($000):** 22633 **Personnel:** 737 | |

☐ **PROMISE HOSPITAL OF SAN ANTONIO (452090)**, 7400 Barlite Boulevard, 2nd Floor, Zip 78224–1308; tel. 210/921–3550, (Nonreporting) **A**1 9 10 **S** Promise Healthcare, Boca Raton, FL
Primary Contact: Karen Pitcher, Vice President and Chief Executive Officer
CHR: Margaret Silva, Executive Assistant and Coordinator Human Resources
CNO: Sharon Schirmer, R.N., Chief Clinical Officer
Web address: www.promise–sanantonio.com
**Control:** Corporation, Investor–owned, for–profit **Service:** Long–Term Acute Care hospital

| |
|---|
| **Staffed Beds:** 26 |

☐ **SAN ANTONIO STATE HOSPITAL (454011)**, 6711 South New Braunfels, Suite 100, Zip 78223–3006; tel. 210/531–7711 **A**1 5 10 **F**30 39 53 56 57 59 68 75 77 86 87 91 98 99 100 101 103 106 130 132 135 146 **P**1 **S** Texas Department of State Health Services, Austin, TX
Primary Contact: Robert C. Arizpe, Superintendent
CFO: Janie Rabago, Chief Accountant
CMO: Terresa Stallworth, M.D., Clinical Director
CIO: Chris Stanush, Director Information Management
CHR: Renee Bourland, Human Resources Specialist
CNO: Maria DC Ostrander, R.N., Chief Nurse Executive
Web address: www.dshs.state.tx.us/mhhospitals/SanAntonioSH/default.shtm
**Control:** State–Government, nonfederal **Service:** Psychiatric

| |
|---|
| **Staffed Beds:** 302 **Admissions:** 1897 **Census:** 268 **Outpatient Visits:** 0 **Births:** 0 **Total Expense ($000):** 61003 **Payroll Expense ($000):** 33217 **Personnel:** 836 |

☒ **SELECT SPECIALTY HOSPITAL–SAN ANTONIO (452073)**, 111 Dallas Street, 4th Floor, Zip 78205–1201; tel. 210/297–7185 **A**1 9 10 **F**1 29 148 **P**8 **S** Select Medical Corporation, Mechanicsburg, PA
Primary Contact: Sean Stricker, Chief Executive Officer
Web address: www.selectspecialtyhospitals.com/company/locations/sanantonio.aspx
**Control:** Corporation, Investor–owned, for–profit **Service:** Long–Term Acute Care hospital

| |
|---|
| **Staffed Beds:** 44 **Admissions:** 498 **Census:** 39 **Outpatient Visits:** 0 **Births:** 0 **Total Expense ($000):** 19904 **Payroll Expense ($000):** 7270 **Personnel:** 133 |

☐ **SOUTH TEXAS SPINE AND SURGICAL HOSPITAL (450856)**, 18600 Hardy Oak Boulevard, Zip 78258–4206; tel. 210/507–4090 **A**1 5 9 10 **F**3 29 40 41 64 75 77 79 81 85 86 87 89 **S** National Surgical Hospitals, Chicago, IL
Primary Contact: Debbie Kelly, Chief Executive Officer
CFO: Sylvia Garcia, Chief Accounting Officer
CHR: Sally Hall, Manager Human Resources
Web address: www.southtexassurgical.com
**Control:** Partnership, Investor–owned, for–profit **Service:** General Medical and Surgical

| |
|---|
| **Staffed Beds:** 30 **Admissions:** 1070 **Census:** 7 **Outpatient Visits:** 2212 **Births:** 0 **Total Expense ($000):** 25019 **Payroll Expense ($000):** 5453 **Personnel:** 95 |

☒ △ **SOUTH TEXAS VETERANS HEALTH CARE SYSTEM**, 7400 Merton Minter Boulevard, Zip 78229–4404; tel. 210/617–5300, (Includes KERRVILLE DIVISION, 3600 Memorial Boulevard, Kerrville, Zip 78028; tel. 210/896–2020; SAN ANTONIO DIVISION, 7400 Merton Minter Boulevard, Zip 78284–5799; tel. 210/617–5300), (Nonreporting) **A**1 3 5 7 8 **S** Department of Veterans Affairs, Washington, DC
Primary Contact: Marie L. Weldon, FACHE, Director
CFO: I. M. Rachal, Chief Fiscal Service
CMO: Richard Bauer, M.D., Chief of Staff
CIO: Simon Willett, Director Administrative Operations
CHR: Leslie Cruthirds, Chief Human Resource Management Service
Web address: www.southtexas.va.gov/
**Control:** Veterans Affairs, Government, federal **Service:** General Medical and Surgical

| |
|---|
| **Staffed Beds:** 838 |

◇ **SOUTHWEST GENERAL HOSPITAL (450697)**, 7400 Barlite Boulevard, Zip 78224–1399; tel. 210/921–2000 **A**9 10 21 **F**3 12 13 15 18 20 22 24 26 29 30 35 37 40 43 44 45 46 49 50 51 56 57 59 60 64 65 70 72 74 75 76 77 78 79 80 81 85 87 90 93 98 100 102 103 105 107 108 110 111 114 115 119 126 129 130 132 135 146 147 148 **S** IASIS Healthcare, Franklin, TN
Primary Contact: P. Craig Desmond, Chief Executive Officer
COO: Trey Klawiter, Chief Operating Officer
CFO: Joe Sereno, Interim Chief Financial Officer
CMO: Damaso Oliva, M.D., Chief Medical Officer
CIO: Sam Sowder, Director Information Systems
CHR: Christina Rivera, Director Human Resources
Web address: www.swgeneralhospital.com
**Control:** Corporation, Investor–owned, for–profit **Service:** General Medical and Surgical

| |
|---|
| **Staffed Beds:** 265 **Admissions:** 9787 **Census:** 130 **Outpatient Visits:** 81950 **Births:** 1742 **Total Expense ($000):** 109851 **Payroll Expense ($000):** 42673 **Personnel:** 612 |

**ST. LUKE'S BAPTIST HOSPITAL** See Baptist Medical Center

☐ **TEXAS CENTER FOR INFECTIOUS DISEASE (452033)**, 2303 S.E. Military Drive, Zip 78223–3597; tel. 210/534–8857 **A**1 10 **F**1 3 29 30 50 53 54 61 64 68 75 87 130 132 135 143 146 **P**4 6 **S** Texas Department of State Health Services, Austin, TX
Primary Contact: James N. Elkins, FACHE, Superintendent
COO: Peggy Perry, Assistant Director
CFO: Glenda Armstrong–Huff, Assistant Superintendent
CMO: David Griffith, M.D., Medical Director
CIO: Andre Avant, Facility Automation Manager
CHR: Gerald Shackelford, Staff Support Specialist
CNO: Rebecca Sanchez, R.N., Director of Nursing
Web address: www.dshs.state.tx.us/tcid/default.shtm
**Control:** State–Government, nonfederal **Service:** Tuberculosis and other respiratory diseases

| |
|---|
| **Staffed Beds:** 42 **Admissions:** 81 **Census:** 41 **Outpatient Visits:** 642 **Births:** 0 **Total Expense ($000):** 13009 **Payroll Expense ($000):** 5975 **Personnel:** 170 |

☒ **UNIVERSITY HEALTH SYSTEM (450213)**, 4502 Medical Drive, Zip 78229–4493; tel. 210/358–4000, (Includes UNIVERSITY HEALTH CENTER – DOWNTOWN, 4502 Medical Drive, tel. 210/358–3400; UNIVERSITY HOSPITAL, 4502 Medical Drive, tel. 210/358–4000) **A**1 2 3 5 8 9 10 **F**3 4 7 11 13 14 15 16 17 18 20 22 24 26 28 29 30 31 32 34 35 38 40 41 43 44 45 46 47 48 49 50 51 52 53 54 55 56 57 58 59 61 64 65 66 68 70 72 73 74 75 76 77 78 79 80 81 82 83 84 85 86 87 88 89 90 92 93 96 98 100 101 102 107 109 110 111 115 118 119 124 126 129 130 132 135 138 139 140 141 142 143 144 145 146 147 148 **P**6
Primary Contact: George B. Hernandez, Jr., President and Chief Executive Officer
COO: Chris Vasquez, Executive Vice President and Chief Operating Officer
CFO: Peggy Deming, Executive Vice President and Chief Financial Officer
CIO: Bill Phillips, Vice President Information Services
CHR: Theresa Scepanski, Vice President People and Organizational Development
Web address: www.universityhealthsystem.com
**Control:** Hospital district or authority, Government, nonfederal **Service:** General Medical and Surgical

| |
|---|
| **Staffed Beds:** 378 **Admissions:** 21214 **Census:** 348 **Outpatient Visits:** 2120528 **Births:** 2763 **Total Expense ($000):** 942347 **Payroll Expense ($000):** 264378 **Personnel:** 5460 |

☐ **VICTORY MEDICAL CENTER – SAN ANTONIO (670021)**, 4243 East Southcross Boulevard, Zip 78222–3727; tel. 210/368–7400 **A**1 10 **F**3 12 29 40 45 75 79 81 82 86 132 **S** Victory Healthcare, The Woodlands, TX
Primary Contact: Alex Garcia, Chief Executive Officer
COO: Leroy Bernal, Chief Operating Officer
Web address: www.victory–healthcare.com/san–antonio–location/
**Control:** Corporation, Investor–owned, for–profit **Service:** Surgical

| |
|---|
| **Staffed Beds:** 9 **Admissions:** 186 **Census:** 2 **Outpatient Visits:** 1063 **Births:** 0 **Total Expense ($000):** 36195 **Payroll Expense ($000):** 4082 **Personnel:** 112 |

☐ **WARM SPRINGS REHABILITATION HOSPITAL (453035)**, 5101 Medical Drive, Zip 78229–4801; tel. 210/616–0100, (Total facility includes 4 beds in nursing home–type unit) **A**1 3 5 9 10 **F**3 11 29 30 57 64 68 74 75 79 82 90 91 93 94 96 128 130 132 146 148 **S** Post Acute Medical, LLC, Camp Hill, PA
Primary Contact: Steve Flaherty, Chief Executive Officer
CFO: James Asberry, Chief Financial Officer
CMO: Alex Willingham, M.D., Medical Director
CIO: Rick Marek, Vice President Medical Information Systems
CHR: Waynea Finley, System Director Human Resources
Web address: www.warmsprings.org
**Control:** Partnership, Investor–owned, for–profit **Service:** Rehabilitation

| |
|---|
| **Staffed Beds:** 138 **Admissions:** 2025 **Census:** 73 **Outpatient Visits:** 31603 **Births:** 0 **Total Expense ($000):** 37057 **Payroll Expense ($000):** 17487 **Personnel:** 382 |

**TX**

*Many Facility Codes have changed. Please refer to the AHA Guide Code Chart.* © 2013 AHA Guide

## SAN AUGUSTINE—San Augustine County

**MEMORIAL MEDICAL CENTER – SAN AUGUSTINE (451360)**, 511 East Hospital Street, Zip 75972–2121, Mailing Address: P.O. Box 658, Zip 75972–0658; tel. 936/275–3446 **A**9 10 18 **F**29 35 40 57 59 64 102 107 119 132 133 **S** Memorial Health System of East Texas, Lufkin, TX
Primary Contact: Darlene Williams, R.N., Administrator
CFO: Kristi Gay, Chief Financial Officer
Web address: www.memorialhealth.org
**Control:** Other not–for–profit (including NFP Corporation) **Service:** General Medical and Surgical

**Staffed Beds:** 18 **Admissions:** 370 **Census:** 3 **Outpatient Visits:** 13692
**Births:** 0 **Total Expense ($000):** 5713 **Payroll Expense ($000):** 2884
**Personnel:** 51

## SAN MARCOS—Hays County

✠ **CENTRAL TEXAS MEDICAL CENTER (450272)**, 1301 Wonder World Drive, Zip 78666–7544; tel. 512/353–8979 **A**1 9 10 **F**3 11 13 15 18 20 29 30 32 34 35 39 40 43 44 45 49 50 51 56 57 59 60 62 63 64 65 68 70 72 75 76 77 79 80 81 82 85 86 87 92 93 94 107 108 109 110 111 114 116 117 118 119 126 129 130 131 132 146 147 148 **P**6 8 **S** Adventist Health System Sunbelt Health Care Corporation, Altamonte Springs, FL
Primary Contact: Sam Huenergardt, President and Chief Executive Officer
CFO: Jesse Sutton, Chief Financial Officer
CHR: Debbie D. Cox, Administrative Director Human Resources
CNO: Lana Cameron, Chief Nursing Officer
Web address: www.ctmc.org
**Control:** Church–operated, Nongovernment, not–for profit **Service:** General Medical and Surgical

**Staffed Beds:** 140 **Admissions:** 4265 **Census:** 38 **Outpatient Visits:** 69167
**Births:** 1013 **Total Expense ($000):** 76517 **Payroll Expense ($000):** 28190
**Personnel:** 541

## SEGUIN—Guadalupe County

✠ **GUADALUPE REGIONAL MEDICAL CENTER (450104)**, 1215 East Court Street, Zip 78155–5189; tel. 830/379–2411 **A**1 9 10 **F**3 5 11 13 15 18 20 28 29 30 31 34 40 43 45 46 49 50 51 53 56 57 59 60 62 63 64 68 70 74 75 76 77 78 79 81 82 85 86 87 90 93 96 103 104 107 108 110 111 112 114 118 119 129 130 132 143 145 146 148 **P**1
Primary Contact: Robert Haynes, FACHE, Chief Executive Officer
COO: Michelle Rumbaut, Chief Operating Officer
CFO: Penny Wallace, Chief Financial Officer
CMO: Steve White, M.D., Chief Medical Officer
CIO: Steve Ratliff, Director Information
CHR: Fay Bennett, Director Human Resources
CNO: Daphne Blake, Chief Nursing Officer
Web address: www.grmedcenter.com
**Control:** City–County, Government, nonfederal **Service:** General Medical and Surgical

**Staffed Beds:** 90 **Admissions:** 4507 **Census:** 45 **Outpatient Visits:** 132626
**Births:** 708 **Total Expense ($000):** 85927 **Payroll Expense ($000):** 31419
**Personnel:** 648

## SEMINOLE—Gaines County

★ **MEMORIAL HOSPITAL (451358)**, 209 N.W. Eighth Street, Zip 79360–3447; tel. 432/758–5811 **A**9 10 18 **F**3 10 11 13 28 29 30 32 34 35 40 43 45 53 56 57 59 62 63 64 65 75 76 81 87 93 97 102 107 114 119 130 131 132 133 143 146 147 148
Primary Contact: Betsy Briscoe, Chief Executive Officer
CFO: Traci Anderson, Chief Financial Officer
CMO: Jean–Pierre Letellier, M.D., Chief of Staff
Web address: www.seminolehospitaldistrict.com
**Control:** Hospital district or authority, Government, nonfederal **Service:** General Medical and Surgical

**Staffed Beds:** 25 **Admissions:** 771 **Census:** 9 **Outpatient Visits:** 64490
**Births:** 180 **Total Expense ($000):** 27853 **Payroll Expense ($000):** 6806
**Personnel:** 175

## SEYMOUR—Baylor County

**SEYMOUR HOSPITAL (450586)**, 200 Stadium Drive, Zip 76380–2344; tel. 940/889–5572 **A**9 10 20 **F**2 3 7 11 13 14 28 29 34 36 40 43 45 50 53 56 57 59 62 64 65 66 68 70 75 76 81 85 86 87 93 94 100 102 103 104 107 119 127 130 133 135 146 147 148 **P**1
Primary Contact: Leslie Hardin, Chief Executive Officer and Chief Financial Officer
CFO: Leslie Hardin, Chief Executive Officer and Chief Financial Officer
CMO: Richard Niles, M.D., Chief of Staff
CHR: Linda Moore, Manager Human Resources
Web address: www.seymourhospital.com/
**Control:** Hospital district or authority, Government, nonfederal **Service:** General Medical and Surgical

**Staffed Beds:** 38 **Admissions:** 613 **Census:** 8 **Outpatient Visits:** 30958
**Births:** 43 **Total Expense ($000):** 10638 **Payroll Expense ($000):** 4674
**Personnel:** 117

## SHAMROCK—Wheeler County

**SHAMROCK GENERAL HOSPITAL (451340)**, 1000 South Main Street, Zip 79079–2896, Mailing Address: P. O. Box 511, Zip 79079–0511; tel. 806/256–2114 **A**9 10 18 **F**7 11 29 32 34 40 43 63 65 68 93 107 119 127 130 133 **P**4
Primary Contact: Wiley M. Fires, Administrator
CFO: Wiley M. Fires, Administrator
CHR: Cecille Williams, Assistant Administrator
**Control:** Hospital district or authority, Government, nonfederal **Service:** General Medical and Surgical

**Staffed Beds:** 13 **Admissions:** 78 **Census:** 1 **Outpatient Visits:** 12814
**Births:** 0 **Total Expense ($000):** 4957 **Payroll Expense ($000):** 2599
**Personnel:** 73

## SHENANDOAH—Montgomery County

☐ ◇ **NEXUS SPECIALTY HOSPITAL**, 123 Vision Park Boulevard, Zip 77384–3001; tel. 281/364–0317 **A**1 9 21 **F**1 3 70 74 75 77 82 84 85 91 92 93 100 101 107 119 130 132 135 148 **S** Nexus Health Systems, Houston, TX
Primary Contact: Erin Cassidy, Chief Executive Officer
COO: Guido J. Cubellis, Chief Operating Officer
CFO: Julia Hatton, Chief Financial Officer
CMO: Ather Siddiqi, M.D., Medical Director
CIO: Deepak Chaudhry, Vice President Information Technology
CHR: Guy Murdock, Vice President Human Resources
CNO: Natalie Munoz, Director of Clinical Services
Web address: www.nexusspecialty.com
**Control:** Partnership, Investor–owned, for–profit **Service:** Long–Term Acute Care hospital

**Staffed Beds:** 75 **Admissions:** 765 **Census:** 53 **Outpatient Visits:** 432
**Births:** 0 **Total Expense ($000):** 26943 **Payroll Expense ($000):** 11548
**Personnel:** 237

☐ **RELIANT REHABILITATION HOSPITAL NORTH HOUSTON (673034)**, 117 Vision Park Boulevard, Zip 77384–3001; tel. 936/444–1700 **A**1 9 10 **F**3 29 65 90 93 96 130 148 **S** Reliant Healthcare Partners, Richardson, TX
Primary Contact: Abraham Sims, Chief Executive Officer
CFO: Terri Weiss, Chief Financial Officer
Web address: www.reliantnorthhouston.com/
**Control:** Partnership, Investor–owned, for–profit **Service:** Rehabilitation

**Staffed Beds:** 60 **Admissions:** 1748 **Census:** 50 **Outpatient Visits:** 11649
**Births:** 0 **Total Expense ($000):** 18236 **Payroll Expense ($000):** 9002
**Personnel:** 158

## SHERMAN—Grayson County

◇ **CARRUS REHABILITATION HOSPITAL (673041)**, 1810 West U.S. Highway 82, Suite 100, Zip 75092–7069; tel. 903/870–2600 **A**9 10 21 **F**3 29 40 41 44 65 74 75 77 79 85 86 87 90 91 96 130 **P**4 **S** Carrus Hospitals, Sherman, TX
Primary Contact: Ronald E. Dorris, Chief Executive Officer
Web address: www.carrushospital.com
**Control:** Corporation, Investor–owned, for–profit **Service:** Rehabilitation

**Staffed Beds:** 24 **Admissions:** 497 **Census:** 16 **Outpatient Visits:** 0 **Births:** 0 **Total Expense ($000):** 5844 **Payroll Expense ($000):** 2927 **Personnel:** 36

---

Hospital, Medicare Provider Number, Address, Telephone, Approval, Facility, and Physician Codes, Health Care System

★ American Hospital Association (AHA) membership
☐ The Joint Commission accreditation ◇ DNV Healthcare Inc. accreditation
○ Healthcare Facilities Accreditation Program
△ Commission on Accreditation of Rehabilitation Facilities (CARF) accreditation

TX

◇ **CARRUS SPECIALTY HOSPITAL (452041)**, 1810 West U.S. Highway 82, Zip 75092–7069; tel. 903/870–2600 **A9** 10 21 **F1** 3 29 40 41 44 56 65 74 75 77 78 79 83 85 86 87 91 107 114 129 130 148 **P4 S** Carrus Hospitals, Sherman, TX
Primary Contact: Ronald E. Dorris, Chief Executive Officer
CFO: Michael Exline, Chief Financial Officer
CHR: Diane Swenson, Director of Staff Services and Chief Nursing Officer
CNO: Diane Swenson, Director of Staff Services and Chief Nursing Officer
Web address: www.carrushospital.com
**Control:** Corporation, Investor–owned, for–profit **Service:** Long–Term Acute Care hospital

**Staffed Beds:** 16 **Admissions:** 170 **Census:** 12 **Outpatient Visits:** 2493 **Births:** 0 **Total Expense ($000):** 7691 **Payroll Expense ($000):** 3126 **Personnel:** 62

◇ **HERITAGE PARK SURGICAL HOSPITAL (670076)**, 3601 North Calais Street, Zip 75090–1785; tel. 903/870–0999 **A9** 10 21 **F3** 8 29 34 35 39 40 46 49 51 54 57 68 79 81 82 85 86 87 107 111 114 119 131 **P8 S** Foundation Surgical Hospital Affiliates, Oklahoma City, OK
Primary Contact: Raymond Ford, Chief Executive Officer
CFO: Scott Banks, Chief Financial Officer
Web address: www.heritageparksurgicalhospital.com
**Control:** Corporation, Investor–owned, for–profit **Service:** General Medical and Surgical

**Staffed Beds:** 12 **Admissions:** 281 **Census:** 2 **Outpatient Visits:** 28963 **Births:** 0 **Total Expense ($000):** 22954 **Payroll Expense ($000):** 6945 **Personnel:** 150

**LIFE CENTER SPECIALTY HOSPITAL (673037)**, 1111 Gallagher Drive, Zip 75090–1713; tel. 903/870–7000, (Nonreporting) **A9** 10
Primary Contact: Janis Thompson, Chief Executive Officer
Web address: www.lifecenterhospital.org
**Control:** Other not–for–profit (including NFP Corporation) **Service:** Other specialty

**Staffed Beds:** 59

✠ **TEXAS HEALTH PRESBYTERIAN HOSPITAL–WNJ (450469)**, 500 North Highland Avenue, Zip 75092–7354; tel. 903/870–4611 **A1** 9 10 **F3** 11 13 15 17 18 20 22 24 26 28 29 30 31 35 40 41 45 49 53 54 56 57 58 59 61 64 70 74 76 77 78 79 80 81 84 86 87 89 93 96 98 100 103 106 107 108 111 118 119 129 130 132 146 147 148 **S** LHP Hospital Group, Plano, TX
Primary Contact: Vance V. Reynolds, FACHE, CPA, Chief Executive Officer
CFO: Mitch Mulvehill, Senior Vice President and Chief Financial Officer
CMO: Gary Marlow, M.D., President Medical Staff
CIO: Tom Fitzgerald, Manager Information Technology Service Delivery
CHR: Linda Creswell, Director Human Resources
Web address: www.wnj.org
**Control:** Partnership, Investor–owned, for–profit **Service:** General Medical and Surgical

**Staffed Beds:** 235 **Admissions:** 6793 **Census:** 86 **Outpatient Visits:** 48764 **Births:** 511 **Total Expense ($000):** 101968 **Payroll Expense ($000):** 35000 **Personnel:** 479

**WILSON N. JONES MEDICAL CENTER** See Texas Health Presbyterian Hospital–WNJ

## SMITHVILLE—Bastrop County

★ **SETON SMITHVILLE REGIONAL HOSPITAL (450143)**, 800 East Highway 71, Zip 78957–1730; tel. 512/237–3214 **A9** 10 **F3** 11 15 29 34 40 43 53 57 62 64 68 77 79 81 87 93 107 108 110 111 114 119 146 148 **P3** 8 **S** Ascension Health, Saint Louis, MO
Primary Contact: Noralene Corder, Interim Senior Vice President and Chief Operating Officer
CFO: Noralene Corder, Chief Financial Officer
CHR: Debbie Adkins, Director Human Resources
Web address: www.srhnet.org
**Control:** Hospital district or authority, Government, nonfederal **Service:** General Medical and Surgical

**Staffed Beds:** 10 **Admissions:** 660 **Census:** 5 **Outpatient Visits:** 42616 **Births:** 0 **Total Expense ($000):** 19512 **Payroll Expense ($000):** 10562 **Personnel:** 200

## SNYDER—Scurry County

**COGDELL MEMORIAL HOSPITAL (450073)**, 1700 Cogdell Boulevard, Zip 79549–6198; tel. 325/573–6374 **A9** 10 20 **F8** 11 13 15 18 19 29 30 34 40 43 45 46 47 48 49 50 53 56 57 59 62 64 65 68 75 76 77 79 81 85 86 87 91 92 93 97 107 108 111 115 119 127 130 131 132 133 145 146 147 148 **P6**
Primary Contact: William W. Weldon, Ph.D., Interim Chief Executive Officer
CFO: John Everett, Chief Financial Officer
CMO: Robert Rakov, M.D., Chief Medical Officer
CHR: Linda Warren, Director Human Resources
Web address: www.cogdellhospital.com
**Control:** Hospital district or authority, Government, nonfederal **Service:** General Medical and Surgical

**Staffed Beds:** 49 **Admissions:** 703 **Census:** 7 **Outpatient Visits:** 54500 **Births:** 184 **Total Expense ($000):** 22778 **Payroll Expense ($000):** 7758 **Personnel:** 195

## SONORA—Sutton County

★ **LILLIAN M. HUDSPETH MEMORIAL HOSPITAL (451324)**, 308 Hudspeth Avenue, Zip 76950–8003, Mailing Address: P.O. Box 455, Zip 76950–0455; tel. 325/387–2521 **A9** 10 18 **F3** 7 11 12 15 18 28 29 30 32 34 35 40 43 44 45 50 53 57 59 64 65 66 68 74 75 79 86 87 89 90 93 96 97 107 110 111 115 119 127 131 132 133 134 135 147 148
Primary Contact: Robert A. Pascasio, FACHE, Chief Executive Officer
CFO: Michelle Schaefer, Chief Financial Officer
CMO: Kristy Edwards, M.D., Chief Medical Officer
CNO: Jon–Michael Parker, R.N., Chief Nursing Officer
Web address: www.sonora–hospital.org
**Control:** Hospital district or authority, Government, nonfederal **Service:** General Medical and Surgical

**Staffed Beds:** 12 **Admissions:** 237 **Census:** 2 **Outpatient Visits:** 8927 **Births:** 0 **Total Expense ($000):** 8425 **Payroll Expense ($000):** 3908 **Personnel:** 77

## SOUTHLAKE—Tarrant County

□ **TEXAS HEALTH HARRIS METHODIST HOSPITAL SOUTHLAKE (450888)**, 1545 East Southlake Boulevard, Zip 76092–6422; tel. 817/748–8700 **A1** 9 10 **F3** 29 30 40 64 74 79 81 85 107 111 113 114 119 130 146 **P2**
Primary Contact: Traci Bernard, President
CFO: Gorman Warren, Chief Financial Officer
CMO: David Taunton, M.D., Chief of Staff
CHR: Kenneth Drinkwater, Director Human Resources
Web address: www.texashealthsouthlake.com
**Control:** Corporation, Investor–owned, for–profit **Service:** General Medical and Surgical

**Staffed Beds:** 18 **Admissions:** 949 **Census:** 7 **Outpatient Visits:** 12531 **Births:** 0 **Total Expense ($000):** 50004 **Payroll Expense ($000):** 11442 **Personnel:** 133

## SPEARMAN—Hansford County

★ **HANSFORD HOSPITAL (451344)**, 707 South Roland Street, Zip 79081–3441; tel. 806/659–2535 **A9** 10 18 **F**11 31 32 34 40 43 56 57 59 62 63 64 65 68 69 78 93 107 127 130 133 **P6**
Primary Contact: Jonathan D. Bailey, Chief Executive Officer and Administrator
CFO: Scott Beedy, Chief Financial Officer
CMO: Mark Garnett, M.D., Chief of Staff
CHR: Jackie Nelson, Director Human Resources
Web address: www.hchd.net
**Control:** Hospital district or authority, Government, nonfederal **Service:** General Medical and Surgical

**Staffed Beds:** 14 **Admissions:** 181 **Census:** 2 **Outpatient Visits:** 23166 **Births:** 0 **Total Expense ($000):** 8893 **Payroll Expense ($000):** 3496 **Personnel:** 82

## SPRING—Montgomery County

**NEXUS SPECIALTY HOSPITAL THE WOODLANDS (452057)**, 9182 Six Pines Drive, Zip 77380–3670; tel. 281/364–0317, (Nonreporting) **A**10
Primary Contact: Erin Cassidy, Chief Executive Officer
COO: Guido J. Cubellis, Chief Operating Officer
CFO: Julia Hatton, Chief Financial Officer
CMO: Ather Siddiqi, M.D., Medical Director
CIO: Deepak Chaudhry, Vice President Informatin Technology
CHR: Guy Murdock, Vice President Human Resources
CNO: Natalie Munoz, Director of Clinical Services
Web address: www.nexusspecialty.com
**Control:** Partnership, Investor–owned, for–profit **Service:** Long–Term Acute Care hospital

**Staffed Beds:** 21

## STAFFORD—Fort Bend County

◇ **ATRIUM MEDICAL CENTER (452114)**, 11929 West Airport Boulevard, Zip 77477–2451; tel. 281/207–8200 **A9** 10 21 **F1** 3 29 45 46 56 60 83 85 105 107 114 119 148
Primary Contact: Danny Cox, Chief Executive Officer
Web address: www.atriummedicalcenter.com
**Control:** Partnership, Investor–owned, for–profit **Service:** Long–Term Acute Care hospital

**Staffed Beds:** 68 **Admissions:** 600 **Census:** 38 **Outpatient Visits:** 11981 **Births:** 0 **Total Expense ($000):** 20665 **Payroll Expense ($000):** 9199 **Personnel:** 185

*Many Facility Codes have changed. Please refer to the AHA Guide Code Chart.*

© 2013 AHA Guide

**TX**

## STAMFORD—Jones County

**STAMFORD MEMORIAL HOSPITAL (450306)**, 1601 Columbia Street, Zip 79553–6863, Mailing Address: P.O. Box 911, Zip 79553–0911; tel. 325/773–2725 **A**9 10 **F**1 10 11 28 30 34 35 36 40 41 43 50 53 57 59 62 64 65 67 68 81 89 93 127 128 133 146 148 **P**4
Primary Contact: Richard G. DeFoore, FACHE, Chief Executive Officer
CFO: Elizabeth Miller, CPA, Chief Financial Officer
CMO: Michael Hart, M.D., Medical Director
CIO: Birgitta Neal, Data Entry and Information Technologist
CHR: Cheryl Hertel, Coordinator Human Resources
Web address: www.stamfordhosp.com/
**Control:** Hospital district or authority, Government, nonfederal **Service:** General Medical and Surgical

**Staffed Beds:** 25 **Admissions:** 260 **Census:** 3 **Outpatient Visits:** 24200 **Births:** 0 **Total Expense ($000):** 8966 **Payroll Expense ($000):** 4484 **Personnel:** 158

## STANTON—Martin County

**MARTIN COUNTY HOSPITAL DISTRICT (451333)**, 600 Interstate 20E, Zip 79782, Mailing Address: P.O. Box 640, Zip 79782–0640; tel. 432/756–3345 **A**9 10 18 **F**7 40 43 57 62 76 81 89 91 93 107 119 127 133
Primary Contact: Paul McKinney, Administrator
CFO: Alison Israel, Controller
**Control:** Hospital district or authority, Government, nonfederal **Service:** General Medical and Surgical

**Staffed Beds:** 20 **Admissions:** 68 **Census:** 1 **Outpatient Visits:** 9947 **Births:** 0 **Total Expense ($000):** 9572 **Payroll Expense ($000):** 3807 **Personnel:** 85

## STEPHENVILLE—Erath County

**TEXAS HEALTH HARRIS METHODIST HOSPITAL STEPHENVILLE (450351)**, 411 North Belknap Street, Zip 76401–3415; tel. 254/965–1500 **A**1 9 10 20 **F**3 8 13 15 29 30 34 35 39 40 41 43 45 50 51 57 59 65 68 70 75 76 77 79 81 82 86 89 93 94 108 111 114 118 119 129 130 135 145 146 147 148 **S** Texas Health Resources, Arlington, TX
Primary Contact: Christopher Leu, President
CFO: Carol Cross, Chief Financial Officer
CMO: Jeffrey Edwards, M.D., Chief of Staff
CHR: Kimberly Leondar, Director Human Resources
Web address: www.texashealth.org/landing.cfm?id=108
**Control:** Other not–for–profit (including NFP Corporation) **Service:** General Medical and Surgical

**Staffed Beds:** 54 **Admissions:** 1918 **Census:** 16 **Outpatient Visits:** 32580 **Births:** 450 **Total Expense ($000):** 37779 **Payroll Expense ($000):** 14829 **Personnel:** 194

## SUGAR LAND—Fort Bend County

◇ **EMERUS (670058)**, 16000 Southwest Freeway, Suite 100, Zip 77479–2674; tel. 281/277–0911 **A**10 21 **F**3 40 75 107 114 119 **P**5 **S** Emerus, The Woodlands, TX
Primary Contact: Mike Kohler, Chief Executive Officer
Web address: www.emerus.com
**Control:** Corporation, Investor–owned, for–profit **Service:** General Medical and Surgical

**Staffed Beds:** 7 **Admissions:** 108 **Census:** 1 **Outpatient Visits:** 8999 **Births:** 0 **Total Expense ($000):** 5397 **Payroll Expense ($000):** 1983 **Personnel:** 30

✠ **HEALTHSOUTH SUGAR LAND REHABILITATION HOSPITAL (673042)**, 1325 Highway 6, Zip 77478–4906; tel. 281/276–7574 **A**1 9 10 **F**3 29 34 75 87 90 95 96 130 132 146 148 **S** HEALTHSOUTH Corporation, Birmingham, AL
Primary Contact: Nicholas Hardin, Chief Executive Officer
Web address: www.healthsouthsugarland.com
**Control:** Corporation, Investor–owned, for–profit **Service:** Rehabilitation

**Staffed Beds:** 50 **Admissions:** 1059 **Census:** 37 **Outpatient Visits:** 0 **Births:** 0 **Total Expense ($000):** 15455 **Payroll Expense ($000):** 7255 **Personnel:** 154

✠ **KINDRED HOSPITAL SUGAR LAND (452080)**, 1550 First Colony Boulevard, Zip 77479–4000; tel. 281/275–6000 **A**1 9 10 **F**1 3 29 31 35 45 57 65 75 77 85 87 91 107 130 148 **S** Kindred Healthcare, Louisville, KY
Primary Contact: Lorene Perona, Chief Executive Officer
COO: Roberta Consolver, Chief Clinical Officer
CFO: Steven Bryan, Chief Financial Officer
CMO: Subodh Bhuchar, M.D., Chief of Staff
CIO: Artie Dmello, Director Case Management
CHR: Craig King, Coordinator Human Resources
Web address: www.khsugarland.com
**Control:** Corporation, Investor–owned, for–profit **Service:** Long–Term Acute Care hospital

**Staffed Beds:** 171 **Admissions:** 1979 **Census:** 140 **Outpatient Visits:** 577 **Births:** 0 **Total Expense ($000):** 74136 **Payroll Expense ($000):** 26926 **Personnel:** 439

✠ **MEMORIAL HERMANN SUGAR LAND HOSPITAL (450848)**, 17500 West Grand Parkway South, Zip 77479–2562; tel. 281/725–5000 **A**1 3 5 9 10 **F**3 8 13 14 15 20 22 29 30 34 35 36 37 39 40 41 43 44 45 46 47 48 49 50 51 53 54 55 56 57 59 60 62 63 64 68 70 72 74 75 76 77 78 79 81 82 85 86 87 89 91 92 93 97 107 108 109 110 111 112 114 116 117 119 124 129 130 131 146 147 148 **P**1 5 6 **S** Memorial Hermann Healthcare System, Houston, TX
Primary Contact: Gregory Haralson, Chief Executive Officer
CFO: Lisa Kendler, Chief Financial Officer
CMO: William Riley, Jr., M.D., Chief of Staff
CHR: Robert Blake, Chief Human Resources Officer Southwest Market
Web address: www.memorialhermann.org
**Control:** Other not–for–profit (including NFP Corporation) **Service:** General Medical and Surgical

**Staffed Beds:** 77 **Admissions:** 4261 **Census:** 39 **Outpatient Visits:** 62631 **Births:** 1085 **Total Expense ($000):** 85560 **Payroll Expense ($000):** 27103 **Personnel:** 306

✠ ◇ **METHODIST SUGAR LAND HOSPITAL (450820)**, 16655 S.W. Freeway, Zip 77479–2329; tel. 281/274–7000 **A**1 9 10 21 **F**3 12 13 15 18 20 22 24 26 29 30 31 33 34 35 36 37 39 40 41 44 45 47 49 50 51 53 57 58 59 60 64 65 68 70 73 74 75 76 77 78 79 81 82 85 86 87 92 93 96 102 107 108 110 111 114 115 119 120 121 123 124 126 130 131 132 135 146 147 148 **S** The Methodist Hospital System, Houston, TX
Primary Contact: Christopher Siebenaler, Chief Executive Officer
CFO: Lowell Stanton, Chief Financial Officer
CMO: Jeffrey Jackson, M.D., Medical Director
CHR: Luis Mario Garcia, Jr., Director Human Resources
Web address: www.methodisthealth.com
**Control:** Other not–for–profit (including NFP Corporation) **Service:** General Medical and Surgical

**Staffed Beds:** 235 **Admissions:** 13132 **Census:** 148 **Outpatient Visits:** 157766 **Births:** 2699 **Total Expense ($000):** 229084 **Payroll Expense ($000):** 81301 **Personnel:** 1508

✠ ◇ **ST. LUKE'S SUGAR LAND HOSPITAL (670053)**, 1317 Lake Pointe Parkway, Zip 77478–3997; tel. 281/637–7000 **A**1 9 10 21 **F**3 15 18 20 22 26 29 30 34 35 37 39 40 41 44 45 46 49 50 57 60 64 68 70 72 74 75 76 79 81 82 85 107 108 110 111 115 119 129 130 146 147 148 **P**5 **S** Catholic Health Initiatives, Englewood, CO
Primary Contact: Robert A. Heifner, Chief Executive Officer
Web address: www.stlukessugarland.com
**Control:** Church–operated, Nongovernment, not–for profit **Service:** General Medical and Surgical

**Staffed Beds:** 58 **Admissions:** 3317 **Census:** 36 **Outpatient Visits:** 23252 **Births:** 39 **Total Expense ($000):** 65125 **Payroll Expense ($000):** 19535 **Personnel:** 294

**SUGAR LAND REHABILITATION HOSPITAL** See HEALTHSOUTH Sugar Land Rehabilitation Hospital

□ **SUGAR LAND SURGICAL HOSPITAL (450860)**, 16906 Southwest Freeway, Zip 77479–2350; tel. 281/243–1000 **A**1 9 10 **F**3 29 40 45 59 64 75 79 81 82 85 86 87 89 92 111 119 130 **P**2 **S** United Surgical Partners International, Addison, TX
Primary Contact: Daniel Smith, Interim Chief Executive Officer
CFO: Raquel Hebert, Business Manager
CMO: Ken Thomson, M.D., Medical Director
Web address: www.sugarlandsurgicalhospital.com/
**Control:** Partnership, Investor–owned, for–profit **Service:** General Medical and Surgical

**Staffed Beds:** 6 **Admissions:** 326 **Census:** 2 **Outpatient Visits:** 7296 **Births:** 0 **Total Expense ($000):** 23040 **Payroll Expense ($000):** 5442 **Personnel:** 157

**TRIUMPH HOSPITAL SOUTHWEST** See Kindred Hospital Sugar Land

**TX**

---

**Hospital, Medicare Provider Number, Address, Telephone, Approval, Facility, and Physician Codes, Health Care System**

★ American Hospital Association (AHA) membership
□ The Joint Commission accreditation
◇ DNV Healthcare Inc. accreditation
○ Healthcare Facilities Accreditation Program
△ Commission on Accreditation of Rehabilitation Facilities (CARF) accreditation

## SULPHUR SPRINGS—Hopkins County

★ **HOPKINS COUNTY MEMORIAL HOSPITAL (450236)**, 115 Airport Road, Zip 75482–2105; tel. 903/885–7671 **A**9 10 **F**1 7 11 13 15 28 29 34 35 40 43 56 59 63 70 73 74 76 80 81 93 96 107 108 110 111 118 119 127 130 146 **P**6
Primary Contact: Michael McAndrew, Chief Executive Officer
COO: Donna Geiken Wallace, Chief Operating Officer and Chief Financial Officer
CFO: Donna Geiken Wallace, Chief Operating Officer and Chief Financial Officer
CMO: Sherri Barclay, M.D., Chief Medical Staff
CIO: Brandon Gauntt, Director Information Systems
CHR: Donna Rudzik, Director Human Resources
CNO: Terri Bunch, R.N., Chief Nursing Officer
Web address: www.hcmh.com
**Control:** Hospital district or authority, Government, nonfederal **Service:** General Medical and Surgical

| | |
|---|---|
| **Staffed Beds:** 50 **Admissions:** 3613 **Census:** 33 **Outpatient Visits:** 70350 **Births:** 826 **Total Expense ($000):** 56585 **Payroll Expense ($000):** 18273 **Personnel:** 449 | |

## SUNNYVALE—Dallas County

☐ **TEXAS REGIONAL MEDICAL CENTER AT SUNNYVALE (670060)**, (Formerly Texas Regional Medical Center), 231 South Collins Road, Zip 75182–4624; tel. 972/892–3000 **A**1 9 10 **F**3 13 15 18 20 22 24 29 34 35 40 45 49 57 59 64 70 74 75 76 79 80 81 82 85 87 107 108 110 111 114 115 119 130 135 146 147 148 **P**8
Primary Contact: Stephen Garrison, Interim Chief Executive Officer
CFO: Ben Dunford, Chief Financial Officer
Web address: www.texasregionalmedicalcenter.com
**Control:** Partnership, Investor–owned, for–profit **Service:** General Medical and Surgical

| | |
|---|---|
| **Staffed Beds:** 70 **Admissions:** 4505 **Census:** 48 **Outpatient Visits:** 35193 **Births:** 1218 **Total Expense ($000):** 72814 **Payroll Expense ($000):** 24159 **Personnel:** 365 | |

## SWEENY—Brazoria County

**SWEENY COMMUNITY HOSPITAL (451311)**, 305 North McKinney Street, Zip 77480–2895; tel. 979/548–1500 **A**9 10 18 **F**3 7 10 11 15 29 34 35 40 43 45 53 56 57 59 65 69 70 75 81 85 93 103 104 107 110 114 119 130 132 133 143 145 148
Primary Contact: William H. Barnes, Administrator
CFO: Hong Wade, Chief Financial Officer
CMO: Fabio Aglieco, D.O., Chief of Staff
CIO: Stuart Butler, Director Information Technology
CHR: Grace Baty, Director Human Resources
Web address: www.sweenyhospital.org
**Control:** Hospital district or authority, Government, nonfederal **Service:** General Medical and Surgical

| | |
|---|---|
| **Staffed Beds:** 14 **Admissions:** 256 **Census:** 2 **Outpatient Visits:** 17514 **Births:** 0 **Total Expense ($000):** 11431 **Payroll Expense ($000):** 6292 **Personnel:** 161 | |

## SWEETWATER—Nolan County

☒ **ROLLING PLAINS MEMORIAL HOSPITAL (450055)**, 200 East Arizona Street, Zip 79556–7199, Mailing Address: P.O. Box 690, Zip 79556–0690; tel. 325/235–1701 **A**1 9 10 20 **F**3 11 13 15 28 29 34 35 40 43 59 62 70 76 81 85 89 93 97 107 108 110 114 119 130 132 133 135 146 **P**6
Primary Contact: Donna Boatright, MSN, Administrator
CFO: Rhonda Guelker, Senior Director Finance
CMO: Frederick Kassis, M.D., Chief of Staff
CHR: Gay Nell Cherry, Director Human Resources
Web address: www.rpmh.net
**Control:** Hospital district or authority, Government, nonfederal **Service:** General Medical and Surgical

| | |
|---|---|
| **Staffed Beds:** 52 **Admissions:** 1141 **Census:** 14 **Outpatient Visits:** 81144 **Births:** 153 **Total Expense ($000):** 23193 **Payroll Expense ($000):** 11593 **Personnel:** 256 | |

## TAHOKA—Lynn County

★ **LYNN COUNTY HOSPITAL DISTRICT (451351)**, 2600 Lockwood, Zip 79373–4118, Mailing Address: Box 1310, Zip 79373–1310; tel. 806/998–4533 **A**9 10 18 **F**3 7 10 13 29 32 34 35 40 43 44 53 54 56 57 59 64 65 66 75 76 86 89 93 97 107 133 147 148 **P**5
Primary Contact: Stace D. Holland, Chief Executive Officer
CFO: Donna Raindl, Manager Business Office
CMO: Donald Freitag, M.D., Chief Medical Officer
CIO: Tim Pledger, Director Information Technology
CHR: Amy Schuknecht, Manager Human Resources
Web address: www.lchdhealthcare.org
**Control:** Hospital district or authority, Government, nonfederal **Service:** General Medical and Surgical

| | |
|---|---|
| **Staffed Beds:** 24 **Admissions:** 139 **Census:** 4 **Births:** 0 **Total Expense ($000):** 5523 **Payroll Expense ($000):** 2739 **Personnel:** 99 | |

## TAYLOR—Williamson County

**JOHNS COMMUNITY HOSPITAL** See Scott & White Hospital – Taylor

☒ **SCOTT & WHITE HOSPITAL – TAYLOR (451374)**, 305 Mallard Lane, Zip 76574–1208; tel. 512/352–7611 **A**1 9 10 18 **F**3 11 15 18 29 34 40 41 43 45 57 59 62 64 81 85 86 93 97 107 108 110 114 119 129 130 132 133 148 **P**6 **S** Scott & White Healthcare, Temple, TX
Primary Contact: Kevin E. Smith, Acting Administrator and Chief Operating Officer
CIO: Tim Tarbell, Assistant Administrator Support Services
Web address: www.swtaylor.org
**Control:** Other not–for–profit (including NFP Corporation) **Service:** General Medical and Surgical

| | |
|---|---|
| **Staffed Beds:** 23 **Admissions:** 518 **Census:** 10 **Outpatient Visits:** 13879 **Births:** 0 **Total Expense ($000):** 13888 **Payroll Expense ($000):** 6450 **Personnel:** 155 | |

## TEMPLE—Bell County

☒ △ **CENTRAL TEXAS VETERANS HEALTHCARE SYSTEM**, 1901 Veterans Memorial Drive, Zip 76504–7493; tel. 254/778–4811, (Includes OLIN E. TEAGUE VETERANS' CENTER, 1901 South First Street, Zip 76504; tel. 817/778–4811; WACO VETERANS AFFAIRS HOSPITAL, 4800 Memorial Drive, Waco, Zip 76711–1397; tel. 254/752–6581), (Nonreporting) **A**1 2 3 5 7 8 9
**S** Department of Veterans Affairs, Washington, DC
Primary Contact: Thomas C. Smith, III, FACHE, Director
COO: Russell E. Lloyd, Associate Director Resources
CFO: Amy Maynard, Acting Chief Finance Service
CMO: William F. Harper, M.D., Chief of Staff
CIO: Sandra Wright, Acting Chief Information Technology Services
CHR: James Basso, Chief Human Resources Officer
Web address: www.centraltexas.va.gov/
**Control:** Veterans Affairs, Government, federal **Service:** General Medical and Surgical

| | |
|---|---|
| **Staffed Beds:** 1532 | |

**MCLANE CHILDREN'S HOSPITAL SCOTT & WHITE** See Scott and White Memorial Hospital

**OLIN E. TEAGUE VETERANS' CENTER** See Central Texas Veterans Healthcare System

★ **SCOTT AND WHITE CONTINUING CARE HOSPITAL (452105)**, 546 North Kegley Road, Zip 76502–4069; tel. 254/215–0900 **A**9 **F**1 3 29 30 35 50 60 65 68 107 119 130 148 **S** Scott & White Healthcare, Temple, TX
Primary Contact: Kimberly K. Langston, R.N., Chief Executive Officer
CMO: David P. Ciceri, M.D., Chief Medical Officer
CNO: Cindy Linck, R.N., Chief Nursing Officer
Web address: www.sw.org/location/temple–cch
**Control:** Other not–for–profit (including NFP Corporation) **Service:** Long–Term Acute Care hospital

| | |
|---|---|
| **Staffed Beds:** 50 **Admissions:** 425 **Census:** 36 **Outpatient Visits:** 0 **Births:** 0 **Total Expense ($000):** 19523 **Payroll Expense ($000):** 8365 **Personnel:** 126 | |

☒ **SCOTT AND WHITE MEMORIAL HOSPITAL (450054)**, 2401 South 31st Street, Zip 76508–0002; tel. 254/724–2111, (Includes MCLANE CHILDREN'S HOSPITAL SCOTT & WHITE, 2401 South 31st Street, Zip 76508–0001; tel. 877/724–5437; John Boyd, III, M.D., Chief Executive Officer and Chief Medical Officer; MCLANE CHILDREN'S HOSPITAL SCOTT & WHITE, 1901 S.W. H. K. Dodgen Loop, Zip 76502–1896; tel. 254/771–8600; John Boyd, III, M.D., Chief Executive Officer), (Total facility includes 49 beds in nursing home–type unit) **A**1 2 3 5 8 9 10 **F**3 5 7 9 11 12 13 14 15 17 18 19 20 21 22 24 26 27 28 29 30 31 32 34 35 36 37 38 39 40 43 44 45 46 47 48 49 50 51 52 54 55 56 57 58 59 60 61 62 63 64 65 68 70 72 73 74 75 76 77 78 79 81 82 84 85 86 87 88 89 91 92 93 96 97 98 100 102 103 104 105 107 108 110 111 113 114 115 116 117 118 119 120 121 123 124 126 128 129 130 131 132 134 135 136 137 138 139 141 142 144 145 146 147 148 **P**6 **S** Scott & White Healthcare, Temple, TX
Primary Contact: Shahin Motakef, Chief Executive Officer
CIO: William McCombs, III, Ph.D., Chief Information Officer
Web address: www.sw.org/location/temple–hospital
**Control:** Other not–for–profit (including NFP Corporation) **Service:** General Medical and Surgical

| | |
|---|---|
| **Staffed Beds:** 638 **Admissions:** 32278 **Census:** 445 **Outpatient Visits:** 1459187 **Births:** 2891 **Total Expense ($000):** 768849 **Payroll Expense ($000):** 320309 **Personnel:** 6466 | |

*Many Facility Codes have changed. Please refer to the AHA Guide Code Chart.* © 2013 AHA Guide

## TERRELL—Kaufman County

☐ **TERRELL STATE HOSPITAL (454006)**, 1200 East Brin Street, Zip 75160–2938, Mailing Address: P.O. Box 70, Zip 75160–9000; tel. 972/524–6452 **A**1 5 9 10 **F**30 34 39 57 68 75 86 87 98 99 100 101 103 130 132 135 146 **P**6 **S** Texas Department of State Health Services, Austin, TX
Primary Contact: Joe Finch, PsyD, Superintendent
CFO: Mike Verseckes, Financial Officer
CMO: Anthony Claxton, M.D., Clinical Director
CIO: Lisa Knox, Manager Facility Automation
Web address: www.dshs.state.tx.us/mhhospitals/terrellsh
**Control:** State–Government, nonfederal **Service:** Psychiatric

**Staffed Beds:** 316 **Admissions:** 2466 **Census:** 304 **Outpatient Visits:** 0 **Births:** 0 **Total Expense ($000):** 60758 **Payroll Expense ($000):** 35703 **Personnel:** 874

## TEXARKANA—Bowie County

⊞ **CHRISTUS ST. MICHAEL HEALTH SYSTEM (450801)**, 2600 St. Michael Drive, Zip 75503–5220; tel. 903/614–1000 **A**1 2 9 10 **F**3 11 13 15 17 18 20 22 24 29 30 31 34 35 40 41 43 45 49 51 53 55 56 57 59 60 64 65 68 70 71 72 74 75 76 77 78 79 80 81 82 84 85 86 87 89 92 97 107 108 109 110 111 114 115 118 119 120 121 122 123 124 126 129 130 131 132 135 143 144 146 147 148 **P**8 **S** CHRISTUS Health, Irving, TX
Primary Contact: Chris Karam, President and Chief Executive Officer
CFO: Shawn Barnett, Vice President and Chief Financial Officer
CMO: Mike Finley, M.D., Chief Medical Officer
CIO: Alana Higgins, Regional Information Management Executive
CHR: Pam Kennedy, Vice President Regional Human Resources and Organizational Department
Web address: www.christusstmichael.org
**Control:** Church–operated, Nongovernment, not–for profit **Service:** General Medical and Surgical

**Staffed Beds:** 312 **Admissions:** 14750 **Census:** 167 **Outpatient Visits:** 155798 **Births:** 1490 **Total Expense ($000):** 212983 **Payroll Expense ($000):** 66984 **Personnel:** 1479

⊞ △ **CHRISTUS ST. MICHAEL REHABILITATION HOSPITAL (453065)**, 2400 St. Michael Drive, Zip 75503–2374; tel. 903/614–4000 **A**1 7 9 10 **F**3 11 18 28 29 30 34 35 57 59 65 68 75 77 79 82 87 90 93 96 132 135 143 148 **S** CHRISTUS Health, Irving, TX
Primary Contact: Aloma Gender, R.N., MSN, Administrator and Chief Nursing Officer
COO: Jason Rounds, Chief Operating Officer
CFO: Glen Boles, Vice President and Chief Financial Officer
CMO: Richard Sharp, M.D., Medical Director
CIO: Alana Higgins, Regional Information Management Executive
CHR: Karen Williams, Director Human Resources
CNO: Aloma Gender, R.N., Administrator and Chief Nursing Officer
Web address: www.christusstmichael.org/rehab
**Control:** Church–operated, Nongovernment, not–for profit **Service:** Rehabilitation

**Staffed Beds:** 50 **Admissions:** 1207 **Census:** 36 **Outpatient Visits:** 44521 **Births:** 0 **Total Expense ($000):** 20747 **Payroll Expense ($000):** 9386 **Personnel:** 179

⊞ **DUBUIS HOSPITAL OF TEXARKANA (452061)**, 2400 St. Michael Drive, 2nd Floor, Zip 75503–2372; tel. 903/614–7600 **A**1 9 10 **F**1 3 29 77 82 84 86 87 130 148 **S** Dubuis Health System, Houston, TX
Primary Contact: Holly Powell, Administrator
Web address: www.dubuis.org/DubuisHospitalofTexarkanaSystem
**Control:** Church–operated, Nongovernment, not–for profit **Service:** Long–Term Acute Care hospital

**Staffed Beds:** 49 **Admissions:** 463 **Census:** 32 **Outpatient Visits:** 0 **Births:** 0 **Total Expense ($000):** 12963 **Payroll Expense ($000):** 4921 **Personnel:** 93

⊞ **HEALTHSOUTH REHABILITATION HOSPITAL OF TEXARKANA (453053)**, 515 West 12th Street, Zip 75501–4416; tel. 903/793–0088 **A**1 9 10 **F**3 28 29 62 64 74 77 79 90 91 93 95 96 130 131 132 143 148 **P**5 **S** HEALTHSOUTH Corporation, Birmingham, AL
Primary Contact: Jerry Jasper, Chief Executive Officer
CFO: Phylis Buck, Controller
CMO: Mark A. Wren, M.D., Medical Director
CHR: Ann R. Clapp, Director Human Resources
Web address: www.healthsouthtexarkana.com
**Control:** Corporation, Investor–owned, for–profit **Service:** Rehabilitation

**Staffed Beds:** 60 **Admissions:** 954 **Census:** 36 **Outpatient Visits:** 11498 **Births:** 0 **Total Expense ($000):** 11147 **Payroll Expense ($000):** 6682 **Personnel:** 144

☐ **WADLEY REGIONAL MEDICAL CENTER (450200)**, 1000 Pine Street, Zip 75501–5170; tel. 903/798–8000 **A**1 9 10 **F**3 11 12 13 15 18 20 22 24 28 29 30 31 34 35 40 43 45 49 50 56 57 59 60 61 64 65 70 71 73 74 75 76 77 78 79 81 82 85 86 87 89 98 103 107 108 110 111 114 115 119 126 130 132 146 147 148 **P**2 8 **S** IASIS Healthcare, Franklin, TN
Primary Contact: Thomas D. Gilbert, FACHE, Chief Executive Officer
CMO: G. Peter Dingeldein, M.D., Chief Medical Officer
CHR: Debby Butler, Director Human Resources
Web address: www.wadleyhealth.com
**Control:** Corporation, Investor–owned, for–profit **Service:** General Medical and Surgical

**Staffed Beds:** 177 **Admissions:** 7414 **Census:** 86 **Outpatient Visits:** 85296 **Births:** 1307 **Total Expense ($000):** 93472 **Payroll Expense ($000):** 32454 **Personnel:** 687

## THE WOODLANDS—Montgomery County

**MEMORIAL HERMANN THE WOODLANDS HOSPITAL** See Memorial Hermann Northwest Hospital, Houston

★ ◇ **ST. LUKE'S LAKESIDE HOSPITAL (670059)**, 17400 St. Luke's Way, Zip 77384–8036; tel. 936/266–9000 **A**9 10 21 **F**3 18 20 22 26 29 30 34 35 40 50 57 59 64 68 75 79 81 87 94 107 111 115 119 130 131 135 **P**5 **S** Catholic Health Initiatives, Englewood, CO
Primary Contact: Debra F. Sukin, Chief Executive Officer
COO: Blake Sims, Director, Operations
CFO: Mary Sue Lipham, Chief Financial Officer
CMO: A. Brant Lipscomb, M.D., Chief of Medical Staff
CIO: James Albin, Chief Information Officer
CHR: Debra Roberts, Director of Human Resources
CNO: Diane Freeman, R.N., Assistant Vice President and Chief Nursing Officer
Web address: www.stlukeslakeside.com/
**Control:** Corporation, Investor–owned, for–profit **Service:** General Medical and Surgical

**Staffed Beds:** 30 **Admissions:** 747 **Census:** 5 **Outpatient Visits:** 11318 **Births:** 0 **Total Expense ($000):** 40212 **Payroll Expense ($000):** 7221 **Personnel:** 131

⊞ ◇ **ST. LUKE'S THE WOODLANDS HOSPITAL (450862)**, 17200 St. Luke's Way, Zip 77384–8007; tel. 936/266–2000 **A**1 9 10 21 **F**3 11 12 13 15 18 20 22 24 26 29 30 34 35 38 40 41 45 49 50 57 58 59 64 68 70 72 74 75 76 78 79 81 82 85 86 87 89 93 107 108 109 110 111 114 118 119 124 126 129 130 131 135 145 146 147 148 **P**5 6 **S** Catholic Health Initiatives, Englewood, CO
Primary Contact: Debra F. Sukin, Chief Executive Officer
CFO: Mary Sue Lipham, Controller
CMO: Jefy Mathew, M.D., Chief of Staff
Web address: www.stlukeswoodlands.com
**Control:** Church–operated, Nongovernment, not–for profit **Service:** General Medical and Surgical

**Staffed Beds:** 154 **Admissions:** 10074 **Census:** 108 **Outpatient Visits:** 62285 **Births:** 1969 **Total Expense ($000):** 138288 **Payroll Expense ($000):** 47708 **Personnel:** 863

## THROCKMORTON—Throckmorton County

★ **THROCKMORTON COUNTY MEMORIAL HOSPITAL (451339)**, 802 North Minter Street, Zip 76483–5357, Mailing Address: P.O. Box 729, Zip 76483–0729; tel. 940/849–2151, (Nonreporting) **A**9 10 18
Primary Contact: Robert Carruthers, Chief Executive Officer
CFO: Silvia A. Tipton, Chief Financial Officer and Director Human Resources
CMO: Craig Beasley, M.D., Chief of Staff and Medical Officer
CIO: Amber Myer, Director Medical Records
CHR: Silvia A. Tipton, Chief Financial Officer and Director Human Resources
**Control:** County–Government, nonfederal **Service:** General Medical and Surgical

**Staffed Beds:** 14

**TX**

---

**Hospital, Medicare Provider Number, Address, Telephone, Approval, Facility, and Physician Codes, Health Care System**

★ American Hospital Association (AHA) membership
☐ The Joint Commission accreditation
◇ DNV Healthcare Inc. accreditation
○ Healthcare Facilities Accreditation Program
△ Commission on Accreditation of Rehabilitation Facilities (CARF) accreditation

**TOMBALL—Harris County**

⊞ ◇ **TOMBALL REGIONAL MEDICAL CENTER (450670)**, 605 Holderrieth Street, Zip 77375–6445, Mailing Address: P.O. Box 889, Zip 77377–0889; tel. 281/401–7500, (Total facility includes 17 beds in nursing home–type unit) **A**1 9 10 21 **F**3 8 13 15 17 18 20 22 24 26 28 29 30 34 40 44 45 46 47 48 49 50 51 53 54 57 59 60 64 70 72 74 75 76 78 79 80 81 82 85 86 87 89 90 91 94 96 98 102 103 107 108 110 111 114 115 119 120 121 123 124 126 128 129 130 131 132 146 148 **S** Community Health Systems, Inc., Franklin, TN
Primary Contact: Bud Wethington, Chief Executive Officer
COO: Keith Barber, CPA, Chief Operating Officer and Chief Financial Officer
CFO: Keith Barber, CPA, Chief Operating Officer and Chief Financial Officer
CMO: Rodney Light, M.D., Chief Medical Officer
CIO: Marlene Pezzia, Director
CHR: Marcia Moore, Vice President
Web address: www.tomballregionalmedicalcenter.com
**Control:** Corporation, Investor–owned, for–profit **Service:** General Medical and Surgical

**Staffed Beds:** 289 **Admissions:** 10039 **Census:** 149 **Outpatient Visits:** 78351 **Births:** 658 **Total Expense ($000):** 163783 **Payroll Expense ($000):** 60017 **Personnel:** 988

**TRINITY—Trinity County**

★ **EAST TEXAS MEDICAL CENTER TRINITY (450749)**, 317 Prospect Drive, Zip 75862–6202, Mailing Address: P.O. Box 3169, Zip 75862–3169; tel. 936/744–1100 **A**9 10 **F**11 29 40 43 45 64 81 97 107 114 115 119 127 146 **P**7 **S** East Texas Medical Center Regional Healthcare System, Tyler, TX
Primary Contact: Brett Kirkham, Administrator
CFO: Jerry A. Dominguez, CPA, Chief Financial Officer
CMO: David Mandel, M.D., Chief of Staff
CHR: Kathy Turner, Director Human Resources
Web address: www.etmc.org
**Control:** Other not–for–profit (including NFP Corporation) **Service:** General Medical and Surgical

**Staffed Beds:** 22 **Admissions:** 632 **Census:** 7 **Outpatient Visits:** 35012 **Births:** 0 **Total Expense ($000):** 11817 **Payroll Expense ($000):** 3565 **Personnel:** 58

**TROPHY CLUB—Denton County**

☐ **BAYLOR MEDICAL CENTER AT TROPHY CLUB (450883)**, 2850 East State Highway 114, Zip 76262–5302; tel. 817/837–4600 **A**1 9 10 **F**3 12 29 40 64 70 75 79 81 85 87 107 108 111 114 118 121 123 141 **S** Cirrus Health, Dallas, TX
Primary Contact: Melanie Chick, Chief Executive Officer
CFO: Jonathan Saunders, Chief Financial Officer
CMO: Mike Stanton, D.O., Medical Director
CIO: Scot Bradford, Chief Information Officer
CNO: Tina Huddleston, Chief Nursing Officer
Web address: www.tc–mc.com
**Control:** Partnership, Investor–owned, for–profit **Service:** General Medical and Surgical

**Staffed Beds:** 20 **Admissions:** 662 **Census:** 3 **Outpatient Visits:** 6803 **Births:** 0 **Total Expense ($000):** 31778 **Payroll Expense ($000):** 7532 **Personnel:** 153

**TULIA—Swisher County**

**SWISHER MEMORIAL HOSPITAL DISTRICT (451349)**, 539 Southeast Second, Zip 79088–2400, Mailing Address: P.O. Box 808, Zip 79088–0808; tel. 806/995–3581 **A**9 10 18 **F**3 7 10 11 29 34 35 40 43 50 53 57 59 62 64 68 93 107 114 127 130 133 **P**4
Primary Contact: Ryan Barnard, Chief Executive Officer
CFO: Connie Wilhelm, Chief Financial Officer
CIO: Brad Roberts, Network Administrator
Web address: www.swisherhospital.com
**Control:** Other not–for–profit (including NFP Corporation) **Service:** General Medical and Surgical

**Staffed Beds:** 20 **Admissions:** 252 **Census:** 2 **Outpatient Visits:** 25362 **Births:** 0 **Total Expense ($000):** 8852 **Payroll Expense ($000):** 3607 **Personnel:** 93

**TYLER—Smith County**

⊞ △ **EAST TEXAS MEDICAL CENTER REHABILITATION HOSPITAL (453072)**, (Formerly East Texas Medical Center Rehabilitation Center), 701 Olympic Plaza Circle, Zip 75701–1950, Mailing Address: P.O. Box 7530, Zip 75711–7530; tel. 903/596–3000 **A**1 7 9 10 **F**3 28 29 30 34 53 57 75 86 90 91 93 96 130 131 132 148 **S** East Texas Medical Center Regional Healthcare System, Tyler, TX
Primary Contact: Eddie L. Howard, Vice President and Chief Operating Officer
CFO: James Blanton, Chief Financial Officer
CMO: Jerry Schwarzbach, M.D., Medical Director
CIO: Paula Anthony, Vice President Information Services
CHR: Mike Gray, Corporate Vice President Human Resources
Web address: www.etmc.org
**Control:** Other not–for–profit (including NFP Corporation) **Service:** Rehabilitation

**Staffed Beds:** 49 **Admissions:** 1039 **Census:** 36 **Outpatient Visits:** 72293 **Births:** 0 **Total Expense ($000):** 26212 **Payroll Expense ($000):** 11744 **Personnel:** 193

⊞ **EAST TEXAS MEDICAL CENTER SPECIALTY HOSPITAL (452051)**, 1000 South Beckham, 5th Floor, Zip 75701–1908, Mailing Address: P.O. Box 7018, Zip 75711–7018; tel. 903/596–3600 **A**1 9 10 **F**1 3 29 30 75 84 130 148 **S** East Texas Medical Center Regional Healthcare System, Tyler, TX
Primary Contact: Eddie L. Howard, Vice President and Chief Operating Officer
CFO: James Blanton, Chief Financial Officer
CMO: J. David Johnson, M.D., Chief of Staff
CIO: Paula Anthony, Vice President Information Services
CHR: Mike Gray, Corporate Vice President Human Resources
Web address: www.etmc.org
**Control:** Other not–for–profit (including NFP Corporation) **Service:** Long–Term Acute Care hospital

**Staffed Beds:** 36 **Admissions:** 387 **Census:** 31 **Outpatient Visits:** 0 **Births:** 0 **Total Expense ($000):** 15411 **Payroll Expense ($000):** 4764 **Personnel:** 80

⊞ **EAST TEXAS MEDICAL CENTER TYLER (450083)**, 1000 South Beckham Street, Zip 75701–1908, Mailing Address: Box 6400, Zip 75711–6400; tel. 903/597–0351, (Includes EAST TEXAS MEDICAL CENTER BEHAVIORAL HEALTH CENTER, 4101 University Boulevard, Zip 75701–6600; tel. 903/566–8668; Jerry W. Echols, Administrator and Chief Executive Officer) **A**1 2 3 5 9 10 **F**3 5 8 11 12 13 15 17 18 20 22 24 26 28 29 30 31 35 37 38 40 42 43 44 45 46 47 48 49 51 54 56 58 59 60 61 64 65 68 70 71 73 74 75 76 78 79 80 81 82 84 85 86 87 89 93 98 99 100 101 102 103 104 105 107 110 111 115 117 118 119 120 121 123 124 126 129 130 132 138 141 145 146 147 148 **S** East Texas Medical Center Regional Healthcare System, Tyler, TX
Primary Contact: Robert B. Evans, Administrator and Chief Executive Officer
CFO: Byron Hale, Chief Financial Officer
CMO: John Andrews, M.D., Chief of Staff
CIO: Paula Anthony, Vice President Information Services
CHR: Mike Gray, Corporate Vice President Human Resources
Web address: www.etmc.org
**Control:** Other not–for–profit (including NFP Corporation) **Service:** General Medical and Surgical

**Staffed Beds:** 450 **Admissions:** 20846 **Census:** 324 **Outpatient Visits:** 138999 **Births:** 807 **Total Expense ($000):** 388667 **Payroll Expense ($000):** 127350 **Personnel:** 2996

⊞ **MOTHER FRANCES HOSPITAL – TYLER (450102)**, 800 East Dawson Street, Zip 75701–2036; tel. 903/593–8441, (Includes LOUIS & PEACHES OWEN HEART HOSPITAL, 703 South Fleishel Avenue, Zip 75701–2015; tel. 903/606–3000; John McGreevy, Chief Executive Officer) **A**1 2 9 10 **F**3 7 8 11 12 13 15 17 18 19 20 22 24 26 28 29 30 31 32 34 37 40 43 45 46 47 48 49 50 51 53 54 55 59 60 64 66 68 70 72 73 74 75 76 77 78 79 80 81 82 83 84 85 86 87 89 93 102 107 108 110 111 114 115 119 124 126 127 129 130 131 132 134 144 146 147 148 **P**5 6 7 8 **S** Trinity Mother Frances Hospitals and Clinics, Tyler, TX
Primary Contact: Laura Owen, Senior Vice President and Chief Executive Officer
CFO: Joyce Hester, CPA, Senior Vice President and Chief Financial Officer
CMO: Barbara Allen, M.D., Vice President Medical Affairs
CIO: Jeff Pearson, Vice President and Chief Information Officer
CHR: Randy Perdue, Assistant Vice President
CHR: Thomas Wilken, Senior Vice President and Chief Human Resources Officer
CNO: Robert Rose, R.N., Senior Vice President/System Chief Nursing Offcer
Web address: www.tmfhs.org
**Control:** Other not–for–profit (including NFP Corporation) **Service:** General Medical and Surgical

**Staffed Beds:** 392 **Admissions:** 23699 **Census:** 297 **Outpatient Visits:** 532316 **Births:** 2535 **Total Expense ($000):** 449065 **Payroll Expense ($000):** 141558 **Personnel:** 2681

☐ **TEXAS SPINE & JOINT HOSPITAL (450864)**, 1814 Roseland Boulevard, Suite 100, Zip 75701–4262; tel. 903/525–3300 **A**1 10 **F**8 29 39 40 77 79 81 82 85 107 111 114 119
Primary Contact: Tony Wahl, Chief Executive Officer
CFO: Greg Cummings, Chief Financial Officer
CMO: Duane Lee Griffith, M.D., Chief of Staff
CNO: Deborah Pelton, R.N., Chief Nursing Officer
Web address: www.tsjh.org
**Control:** Partnership, Investor–owned, for–profit **Service:** Orthopedic

**Staffed Beds:** 20 **Admissions:** 1447 **Census:** 9 **Outpatient Visits:** 17339 **Births:** 0 **Total Expense ($000):** 54639 **Payroll Expense ($000):** 12119 **Personnel:** 278

⊞ **TRINITY MOTHER FRANCES REHABILITATION HOSPITAL (453056)**, 3131 Troup Highway, Zip 75701–8352; tel. 903/510–7000 **A**1 9 10 **F**3 9 28 29 56 62 64 74 75 77 79 82 87 90 91 93 95 96 130 131 132 143 147 148 **S** HEALTHSOUTH Corporation, Birmingham, AL
Primary Contact: Sharla Anderson, Chief Executive Officer
CFO: Michael G. Treadway, Controller
CMO: Bradley Merritt, M.D., Medical Director
Web address: www.tmfrehabhospital.com
**Control:** Partnership, Investor–owned, for–profit **Service:** Rehabilitation

**Staffed Beds:** 74 **Admissions:** 1702 **Census:** 58 **Outpatient Visits:** 17415 **Births:** 0 **Total Expense ($000):** 18316 **Payroll Expense ($000):** 10327 **Personnel:** 191

**TX**

**TYLER CONTINUECARE HOSPITAL AT MOTHER FRANCES (452091)**, 800 East Dawson, 4th Floor, Zip 75701–2036; tel. 903/531–4080 **A**9 10 **F**1 3 29 34 59 74 75 77 85 86 87 130 135 148 **P**4 **S** Trinity Mother Frances Hospitals and Clinics, Tyler, TX
Primary Contact: Stephanie Hyde, Chief Executive Officer
Web address: www.continuecare.org
**Control:** Other not–for–profit (including NFP Corporation) **Service:** Long–Term Acute Care hospital

**Staffed Beds:** 51 **Admissions:** 676 **Census:** 48 **Outpatient Visits:** 0 **Births:** 0 **Total Expense ($000):** 21786 **Payroll Expense ($000):** 8436 **Personnel:** 134

✠ **UNIVERSITY OF TEXAS HEALTH SCIENCE CENTER AT TYLER (450690)**, 11937 Highway 271, Zip 75708–3154; tel. 903/877–7777 **A**1 5 9 10 **F**3 8 11 15 18 20 22 24 26 28 29 30 31 32 34 35 40 43 45 46 47 48 49 50 53 55 56 57 58 59 64 65 68 70 74 75 77 78 79 81 85 86 87 93 97 107 108 110 111 114 118 119 120 121 123 124 129 130 135 146 147 148 **P**6 **S** University of Texas System, Austin, TX
Primary Contact: Kirk A. Calhoun, M.D., President
CFO: Vernon Moore, Chief Business and Finance
CMO: David Coultas, M.D., Vice President Clinical Affairs
CIO: Vernon Moore, Chief Business and Finance
CHR: Georgia Melton, Associate Vice President Human Resources
Web address: www.uthct.edu
**Control:** State–Government, nonfederal **Service:** General Medical and Surgical

**Staffed Beds:** 116 **Admissions:** 1709 **Census:** 21 **Outpatient Visits:** 207310 **Births:** 0 **Total Expense ($000):** 121615 **Payroll Expense ($000):** 56417 **Personnel:** 849

### UVALDE—Uvalde County

✠ **UVALDE COUNTY HOSPITAL AUTHORITY (450177)**, 1025 Garner Field Road, Zip 78801–4809; tel. 830/278–6251 **A**1 9 10 20 **F**3 11 13 15 17 18 29 30 39 40 43 45 50 56 57 59 63 64 68 70 76 81 85 86 87 89 90 93 104 107 108 111 115 119 127 130 132 133 146 147 148 **P**3
Primary Contact: James E. Buckner, Jr., FACHE, Administrator
CFO: Valerie Lopez, CPA, Controller
CMO: Clifford White, M.D., Chief of Staff
CIO: Carolina Velasquez, Chief Information Officer
CHR: Charla Carter, Director Human Resources
CNO: Jeanne E. Leake, R.N., Chief Nursing Officer
Web address: www.umhtx.org
**Control:** Hospital district or authority, Government, nonfederal **Service:** General Medical and Surgical

**Staffed Beds:** 48 **Admissions:** 1830 **Census:** 19 **Outpatient Visits:** 63110 **Births:** 376 **Total Expense ($000):** 47278 **Payroll Expense ($000):** 20008 **Personnel:** 404

### VAN HORN—Culberson County

★ **CULBERSON HOSPITAL (451338)**, Eisenhower–Farm Market Road 2185, Zip 79855, Mailing Address: P.O. Box 609, Zip 79855–0609; tel. 432/283–2760 **A**9 10 18 **F**3 7 34 40 43 57 59 65 66 68 93 107 114 119 127 133 148 **P**6 **S** Preferred Management Corporation, Shawnee, OK
Primary Contact: Jared Chanski, Administrator
CMO: John A. Thomas, M.D., Chief Medical Staff
Web address: www.culbersonhospital.org
**Control:** Corporation, Investor–owned, for–profit **Service:** General Medical and Surgical

**Staffed Beds:** 14 **Admissions:** 106 **Census:** 2 **Outpatient Visits:** 9604 **Births:** 0 **Total Expense ($000):** 5644 **Payroll Expense ($000):** 2405 **Personnel:** 57

### VERNON—Wilbarger County

☐ **NORTH TEXAS STATE HOSPITAL**, Highway 70 Northwest, Zip 76384, Mailing Address: P.O. Box 2231, Zip 76385–2231; tel. 940/552–9901 **A**1 **F**11 30 39 44 56 57 68 75 86 87 96 98 99 103 130 132 135 146 **P**6 **S** Texas Department of State Health Services, Austin, TX
Primary Contact: James E. Smith, Superintendent
CFO: William Lowery, Financial Officer
CIO: Crystal Dennstedt, Information Officer
Web address: www.dshs.state.tx.us/mhhospitals/NorthTexasSH/default.shtm
**Control:** State–Government, nonfederal **Service:** Psychiatric

**Staffed Beds:** 640 **Admissions:** 2247 **Census:** 581 **Outpatient Visits:** 0 **Births:** 0 **Total Expense ($000):** 114589 **Payroll Expense ($000):** 66194 **Personnel:** 2017

**WILBARGER GENERAL HOSPITAL (450584)**, 920 Hillcrest Drive, Zip 76384–3196; tel. 940/552–9351 **A**9 10 20 **F**3 11 15 29 34 35 40 43 45 54 56 57 60 62 75 81 85 86 87 93 98 101 103 104 107 111 115 119 124 127 130 132 133 143 146 148
Primary Contact: Jonathon Voelkel, Chief Executive Officer
CFO: Richard Thieman, Chief Financial Officer
CIO: Ed Nary, Director Information Technology and Chief Compliance Officer
CHR: Cathie Bristo, Director Human Resources
Web address: www.wghospital.com
**Control:** Hospital district or authority, Government, nonfederal **Service:** General Medical and Surgical

**Staffed Beds:** 27 **Admissions:** 657 **Census:** 10 **Outpatient Visits:** 20072 **Births:** 0 **Total Expense ($000):** 18974 **Payroll Expense ($000):** 9671 **Personnel:** 229

### VICTORIA—Victoria County

★ ◇ **CITIZENS MEDICAL CENTER (450023)**, 2701 Hospital Drive, Zip 77901–5749; tel. 361/573–9181, (Total facility includes 20 beds in nursing home–type unit) **A**2 9 10 21 **F**1 3 4 8 11 12 13 15 16 17 18 20 22 24 28 29 30 31 34 35 38 40 41 43 49 50 51 53 54 56 57 59 62 64 65 66 67 70 72 73 74 75 76 77 78 79 80 81 84 85 86 87 88 89 90 93 94 97 98 100 101 102 103 105 107 108 109 111 114 115 116 117 118 119 120 121 127 128 130 131 132 135 144 146 147 148 **P**6
Primary Contact: David P. Brown, Administrator
CFO: Phillip Hacker, Chief Financial Officer
CHR: Jim Heger, Director Human Resources
CNO: Lynne Voskamp, Chief Nursing Officer
Web address: www.citizensmedicalcenter.org
**Control:** County–Government, nonfederal **Service:** General Medical and Surgical

**Staffed Beds:** 296 **Admissions:** 8237 **Census:** 114 **Outpatient Visits:** 86668 **Births:** 833 **Total Expense ($000):** 132465 **Payroll Expense ($000):** 58964 **Personnel:** 1080

✠ **DETAR HEALTHCARE SYSTEM (450147)**, 506 East San Antonio Street, Zip 77901–6060, Mailing Address: P.O. Box 2089, Zip 77902–2089; tel. 361/575–7441, (Includes DETAR HOSPITAL NORTH, 101 Medical Drive, Zip 77904–3198; tel. 361/573–6100; William R. Blanchard, Chief Executive Officer), (Total facility includes 16 beds in nursing home–type unit) **A**1 9 10 **F**3 12 13 15 18 20 22 24 28 29 30 31 39 40 41 43 47 49 51 53 56 64 70 72 74 75 76 77 78 79 81 82 85 86 87 89 90 91 93 98 100 101 103 107 108 110 111 114 118 119 126 128 130 132 146 147 148 **P**3 5 8 **S** Community Health Systems, Inc., Franklin, TN
Primary Contact: William R. Blanchard, Chief Executive Officer
CFO: Donald E. Hagan, Chief Financial Officer
CMO: James R. Brand, M.D., Chief of Staff
CIO: Kim Tompkins, Director Information Services
CHR: Kristina Elsik, Director Human Resources
Web address: www.detar.com
**Control:** Corporation, Investor–owned, for–profit **Service:** General Medical and Surgical

**Staffed Beds:** 222 **Admissions:** 9051 **Census:** 113 **Outpatient Visits:** 82990 **Births:** 1366 **Total Expense ($000):** 104821 **Payroll Expense ($000):** 45486 **Personnel:** 870

✠ **KINDRED HOSPITAL VICTORIA (452056)**, 506 East San Antonio Street, 3rd Floor, Zip 77901–6060; tel. 361/575–1445 **A**1 9 10 **F**1 3 29 30 31 82 85 86 87 97 130 148 **S** Kindred Healthcare, Louisville, KY
Primary Contact: Portlyn Brogger, Chief Executive Officer
CHR: Rachel Reeves, Manager Human Resources
Web address: www.khvictoria.com
**Control:** Corporation, Investor–owned, for–profit **Service:** Long–Term Acute Care hospital

**Staffed Beds:** 23 **Admissions:** 307 **Census:** 22 **Outpatient Visits:** 0 **Births:** 0 **Total Expense ($000):** 9864 **Payroll Expense ($000):** 3882 **Personnel:** 61

☐ **WARM SPRINGS SPECIALTY HOSPITAL OF VICTORIA (452094)**, 102 Medical Drive, Zip 77904–3101; tel. 361/576–6200 **A**1 9 10 **F**1 3 29 75 77 85 93 94 96 148 **S** Post Acute Medical, LLC, Camp Hill, PA
Primary Contact: Brian Holt, Chief Executive Officer
CFO: James Asberry, Chief Financial Officer
CMO: Behram Khan, M.D., Medical Director
CHR: Waynea Finley, Corporate Director Human Resources
Web address: www.warmsprings.org
**Control:** Partnership, Investor–owned, for–profit **Service:** Long–Term Acute Care hospital

**Staffed Beds:** 26 **Admissions:** 350 **Census:** 25 **Outpatient Visits:** 8657 **Births:** 0 **Total Expense ($000):** 12858 **Payroll Expense ($000):** 5295 **Personnel:** 110

**TX**

---

**Hospital, Medicare Provider Number, Address, Telephone, Approval, Facility, and Physician Codes, Health Care System**

★ American Hospital Association (AHA) membership
☐ The Joint Commission accreditation
◇ DNV Healthcare Inc. accreditation
○ Healthcare Facilities Accreditation Program
△ Commission on Accreditation of Rehabilitation Facilities (CARF) accreditation

## WACO—Mclennan County

△ **HILLCREST BAPTIST MEDICAL CENTER (450101)**, 100 Hillcrest Medical Boulevard, Zip 76712–8897, Mailing Address: P.O. Box 21146, Zip 76702–1146; tel. 254/202–2000, (Includes HILLCREST BAPTIST MEDICAL CENTER – HERRING AVENUE CAMPUS, 3000 HERRING AVENUE, ZIP 76708 ), (Total facility includes 20 beds in nursing home–type unit) **A**1 2 3 5 7 9 10 **F**3 11 13 15 18 20 22 24 26 28 29 30 31 34 40 42 43 44 45 46 47 49 50 51 53 54 56 57 59 60 61 64 68 70 72 74 75 76 78 79 81 82 84 85 86 87 89 90 93 96 97 107 108 110 111 113 114 115 116 117 118 119 128 129 130 131 132 134 135 145 146 147 148 **P**6 **S** Scott & White Healthcare, Temple, TX
Primary Contact: Glenn A. Robinson, Chief Executive Officer
CFO: Richard Perkins, Chief Financial Officer
CMO: J. E. Morrison, M.D., Chief Medical Officer
CIO: Richard Warren, Chief Information Officer
CNO: Marcy Weber, R.N., Chief Nursing Officer
Web address: www.hillcrest.net
**Control:** Other not–for–profit (including NFP Corporation) **Service:** General Medical and Surgical

> **Staffed Beds:** 262 **Admissions:** 13211 **Census:** 168 **Outpatient Visits:** 156244 **Births:** 2754 **Total Expense ($000):** 182415 **Payroll Expense ($000):** 66500 **Personnel:** 1312

**PROVIDENCE HEALTH CENTER (450042)**, 6901 Medical Parkway, Zip 76712–7998, Mailing Address: P.O. Box 2589, Zip 76702–2589; tel. 254/751–4764, (Includes DEPAUL CENTER, 301 Londonderry Drive, Zip 76712; tel. 254/776–5970; Keith Hopkins, Vice President), (Total facility includes 341 beds in nursing home–type unit) **A**1 2 3 5 9 10 **F**2 3 4 5 6 8 9 10 11 12 13 15 18 20 22 24 26 28 29 30 31 34 35 38 40 41 44 45 46 48 49 50 53 54 56 57 58 59 61 62 64 67 68 70 74 75 76 77 78 79 81 82 84 85 86 87 89 93 97 98 99 100 101 102 103 104 105 107 108 110 114 115 119 125 128 130 132 135 144 146 147 148 **P**5 6 **S** Ascension Health, Saint Louis, MO
Primary Contact: Brett A. Esrock, President and Chief Executive Officer
CFO: Karen K. Richardson, Senior Vice President and Chief Financial Officer
CMO: T. Marc Barrett, M.D., Senior Vice President Medical Affairs
CIO: Jay Scherler, Director Information Systems and Vice President Business Services
CHR: Chuck Sivess, Vice President Human Resources
CNO: Annette Ayers, R.N., Senior Vice President and Chief Nursing Officer
Web address: www.providence.net
**Control:** Church–operated, Nongovernment, not–for profit **Service:** General Medical and Surgical

> **Staffed Beds:** 647 **Admissions:** 18204 **Census:** 497 **Outpatient Visits:** 380278 **Births:** 1539 **Total Expense ($000):** 272300 **Payroll Expense ($000):** 114672 **Personnel:** 2017

**WACO VETERANS AFFAIRS HOSPITAL** See Central Texas Veterans Healthcare System, Temple

## WAXAHACHIE—Ellis County

**BAYLOR MEDICAL CENTER AT WAXAHACHIE (450372)**, 1405 West Jefferson Street, Zip 75165–2275; tel. 972/923–7000 **A**1 2 9 10 **F**3 11 12 15 28 29 30 34 35 40 41 53 57 59 64 65 68 70 71 74 75 77 78 79 81 82 84 85 93 107 108 110 111 114 119 124 129 130 135 147 148 **S** Baylor Health Care System, Dallas, TX
Primary Contact: Jay Fox, President
COO: Cindy Murray, R.N., Chief Nursing Officer and Chief Operating Officer
CFO: Steve Roussel, Vice President Finance
CMO: Valerie Goman, M.D., President Medical Staff
CIO: Gary Beazley, Coordinator Information Systems
CHR: Marcos Ramirez, Manager Human Resources
Web address: www.baylorhealth.com/PhysiciansLocations/Waxahachie/Pages/Default.aspx
**Control:** Other not–for–profit (including NFP Corporation) **Service:** General Medical and Surgical

> **Staffed Beds:** 54 **Admissions:** 2641 **Census:** 30 **Outpatient Visits:** 67001 **Births:** 0 **Total Expense ($000):** 61800 **Payroll Expense ($000):** 23399 **Personnel:** 322

## WEATHERFORD—Parker County

**WEATHERFORD REGIONAL MEDICAL CENTER (450203)**, 713 East Anderson Street, Zip 76086–5705; tel. 817/596–8751 **A**1 9 10 **F**3 13 17 18 20 28 29 31 34 35 40 43 49 57 59 68 70 75 76 77 78 79 81 82 85 89 93 107 111 114 115 119 130 132 133 135 144 146 148 **P**8 **S** Community Health Systems, Inc., Franklin, TN
Primary Contact: David Orcutt, Chief Executive Officer
COO: Benjamin Casmer, Assistant Chief Executive Officer
CFO: Nancy Cooke, Chief Financial Officer
CMO: Scott Walker, M.D., Chief Medical Staff
CIO: Merri Roy, Director Information Services
CHR: Kristin Lawyer, Director Human Resources
CNO: Donna Boone, R.N., Chief Nursing Officer
Web address: www.weatherfordregional.com
**Control:** Corporation, Investor–owned, for–profit **Service:** General Medical and Surgical

> **Staffed Beds:** 86 **Admissions:** 4591 **Census:** 44 **Outpatient Visits:** 60622 **Births:** 550 **Total Expense ($000):** 66410 **Payroll Expense ($000):** 21066 **Personnel:** 424

## WEBSTER—Harris County

**CLEAR LAKE REGIONAL MEDICAL CENTER (450617)**, 500 Medical Center Boulevard, Zip 77598–4220; tel. 281/332–2511, (Includes ALVIN DIAGNOSTIC AND URGENT CARE CENTER, 301 Medic Lane, Alvin, Zip 77511–5597; tel. 281/331–6141; MAINLAND MEDICAL CENTER, 6801 E F Lowry Expressway, Texas City, Zip 77591; tel. 409/938–5000; Michael Ehrat, Chief Executive Officer) **A**1 3 5 9 10 **F**3 11 13 15 17 18 20 22 24 26 28 29 30 31 34 35 40 41 42 44 45 46 47 49 50 51 54 56 57 59 60 64 70 72 74 75 76 77 78 79 81 83 85 86 87 88 89 90 93 96 98 100 101 103 104 107 108 110 111 114 115 118 119 124 126 129 130 132 135 146 147 148 **S** HCA, Nashville, TN
Primary Contact: Stephen K. Jones, Jr., FACHE, Chief Executive Officer
CFO: Jeff Sliwinski, Chief Financial Officer
CMO: Richard Marietta, M.D., Medical Director
CIO: Ley Samson, Director Management Information Systems
CHR: Brad Horst, Director Human Resources
Web address: www.clearlakermc.com
**Control:** Partnership, Investor–owned, for–profit **Service:** General Medical and Surgical

> **Staffed Beds:** 655 **Admissions:** 29831 **Census:** 403 **Outpatient Visits:** 207557 **Births:** 4174 **Total Expense ($000):** 378495 **Payroll Expense ($000):** 159025 **Personnel:** 2148

**CLEAR LAKE REHABILITATION HOSPITAL** See Kindred Rehabilitation Hospital Clear Lake

◇ **HOUSTON PHYSICIANS HOSPITAL (670008)**, 333 North Texas Avenue, Zip 77598–4966; tel. 281/557–5620 **A**5 9 10 21 **F**3 29 40 51 64 68 74 79 81 82 85 86 91 93 107 111 114 141
Primary Contact: Michele Dionne, Chief Executive Officer
Web address: www.houstonphysianshospital.com
**Control:** Corporation, Investor–owned, for–profit **Service:** General Medical and Surgical

> **Staffed Beds:** 21 **Admissions:** 622 **Census:** 3 **Outpatient Visits:** 11681 **Births:** 0 **Total Expense ($000):** 37514 **Payroll Expense ($000):** 8246 **Personnel:** 151

**KINDRED REHABILITATION HOSPITAL CLEAR LAKE (453052)**, 655 East Medical Center Boulevard, Zip 77598–4328; tel. 281/286–1500 **A**1 9 10 **F**3 29 64 74 75 79 90 93 95 130 131 132 143 146 148 **S** Kindred Healthcare, Louisville, KY
Primary Contact: Dale R. Mulder, Chief Executive Officer
CFO: Barbara Franco, Chief Financial Officer
CMO: Michael Rosenblatt, M.D., Medical Director
CIO: Barbara Franco, Chief Financial Officer
CHR: Dalia Nandin, Manager Human Resources
Web address: www.khrehabclearlake.com/
**Control:** Corporation, Investor–owned, for–profit **Service:** Rehabilitation

> **Staffed Beds:** 60 **Admissions:** 1049 **Census:** 39 **Outpatient Visits:** 7048 **Births:** 0 **Total Expense ($000):** 16373 **Payroll Expense ($000):** 7787 **Personnel:** 158

## WELLINGTON—Collingsworth County

**COLLINGSWORTH GENERAL HOSPITAL (451355)**, 1013 15th Street, Zip 79095–3703, Mailing Address: P.O. Box 1112, Zip 79095–1112; tel. 806/447–2521 **A**9 10 18 **F**3 16 36 40 43 57 59 68 93 97 107 114 127 133 **S** Preferred Management Corporation, Shawnee, OK
Primary Contact: Candy Powell, Administrator
CFO: Larry Stephens, Chief Financial Officer
CMO: David E. Haacke, M.D., Chief of Staff
CIO: Thomas T. Ng, Chief Information Officer
CHR: Christie O'Rear, Human Resources Officer
Web address: www.collingsworthgeneral.net
**Control:** Corporation, Investor–owned, for–profit **Service:** General Medical and Surgical

> **Staffed Beds:** 13 **Admissions:** 337 **Census:** 4 **Outpatient Visits:** 12667 **Births:** 0 **Total Expense ($000):** 5976 **Payroll Expense ($000):** 2389 **Personnel:** 59

**TX**

*Many Facility Codes have changed. Please refer to the AHA Guide Code Chart.* © 2013 AHA Guide

## WESLACO—Hidalgo County

✠ **KNAPP MEDICAL CENTER (450128)**, 1401 East Eighth Street,
Zip 78596–6640, Mailing Address: P.O. Box 1110, Zip 78599–1110;
tel. 956/968–8567 **A**1 9 10 **F**3 8 11 12 13 15 18 20 22 29 30 31 34 35 39
40 43 44 46 49 50 51 56 57 59 60 63 64 70 73 74 75 76 77 78 79 81 82
84 85 86 87 89 93 107 108 110 111 114 115 119 130 131 132 134 135
141 142 143 146 147 148 **P**8
Primary Contact: William D. Adams, Chief Executive Officer
CIO: Gary Light, Chief Information Officer
CHR: Emmett Craig, Chief Human Resources Officer
Web address: www.knappmed.org
**Control:** Other not–for–profit (including NFP Corporation) **Service:** General
Medical and Surgical

| | |
|---|---|
| **Staffed Beds:** 202 **Admissions:** 10395 **Census:** 98 **Outpatient Visits:** 75234 **Births:** 1840 **Total Expense ($000):** 101571 **Payroll Expense ($000):** 42232 **Personnel:** 831 | |

△ **WESLACO REHABILITATION HOSPITAL (453091)**, 906 South James Street,
Zip 78596–9840; tel. 956/969–2222 **A**7 9 10 **F**3 29 30 90 130
Primary Contact: Maggie E. Barreiro, Administrator
CFO: Leo Dan Perez, Controller
CMO: Pedro McDougal, M.D., Medical Director
CHR: Debbie Pendleton, Human Resources Specialist
CNO: Rita Mata–Guerrero, Nurse Director
Web address: www.weslacorehabhospital.com
**Control:** Partnership, Investor–owned, for–profit **Service:** Rehabilitation

| | |
|---|---|
| **Staffed Beds:** 32 **Admissions:** 554 **Census:** 19 **Outpatient Visits:** 0 **Births:** 0 **Total Expense ($000):** 7246 **Payroll Expense ($000):** 4988 **Personnel:** 84 | |

## WHARTON—Wharton County

☐ **GULF COAST MEDICAL CENTER (450214)**, 10141 Highway 59,
Zip 77488–3004; tel. 979/282–6100 **A**1 9 10 **F**11 18 20 22 29 40 43 49 64
70 76 77 78 79 81 82 93 98 103 104 107 108 114 118 119 121 129 130
146 148
Primary Contact: Ermanno Mariani, Interim Chief Executive Officer
CFO: Gary Williams, Chief Financial Officer
CHR: Loretta Flynn, Director Human Resources
Web address: www.gulfcoastmedical.com
**Control:** Partnership, Investor–owned, for–profit **Service:** General Medical and
Surgical

| | |
|---|---|
| **Staffed Beds:** 129 **Admissions:** 1420 **Census:** 18 **Outpatient Visits:** 24162 **Births:** 254 **Total Expense ($000):** 25808 **Payroll Expense ($000):** 10058 **Personnel:** 162 | |

## WHEELER—Wheeler County

★ **PARKVIEW HOSPITAL (451334)**, 1000 Sweetwater Street, Zip 79096–2421,
Mailing Address: P.O. Box 1030, Zip 79096–1030; tel. 806/826–5581 **A**9 10 18
**F**3 7 10 40 43 59 62 65 68 89 93 107 114 128 130 133 148
Primary Contact: Monica Kidd, R.N., MSN, Interim Administrator
CIO: Ann Fagan Cook, Chief Information Officer
Web address: www.parkviewhosp.org
**Control:** Hospital district or authority, Government, nonfederal **Service:** General
Medical and Surgical

| | |
|---|---|
| **Staffed Beds:** 16 **Admissions:** 234 **Census:** 3 **Outpatient Visits:** 2675 **Births:** 0 **Total Expense ($000):** 6997 **Payroll Expense ($000):** 3103 **Personnel:** 95 | |

## WHITNEY—Hill County

**LAKE WHITNEY MEDICAL CENTER (450270)**, 200 North San Jacinto Street,
Zip 76692–2388, Mailing Address: P.O. Box 458, Zip 76692–0458;
tel. 254/694–3165 **A**9 10 **F**3 7 11 35 40 41 56 62 64 65 68 87 89 102 107
114 127 130 133 146 148 **P**5 6
Primary Contact: Ruth Ann Crow, Administrator
COO: Tariq Mahmood, Chief Executive Officer
CFO: Joe White, Chief Financial Officer
CMO: Aman Ali Shah, M.D., Chief Medical Staff
CIO: Patricia Daniel, Chief Information Officer
CHR: Darleen Towers, Director Human Resources
Web address: www.lakewhitneychamber.com/lake–whitney–medical–center.html
**Control:** Corporation, Investor–owned, for–profit **Service:** General Medical and
Surgical

| | |
|---|---|
| **Staffed Beds:** 25 **Admissions:** 979 **Census:** 8 **Outpatient Visits:** 6280 **Births:** 0 **Personnel:** 94 | |

## WICHITA FALLS—Wichita County

✠ **HEALTHSOUTH REHABILITATION HOSPITAL–WICHITA FALLS (453054)**,
3901 Armory Road, Zip 76302–2204; tel. 940/720–5700 **A**1 9 10 **F**3 28 29 44
50 53 62 64 68 74 75 77 79 82 86 87 90 91 92 93 95 96 132 143 146 148
**S** HEALTHSOUTH Corporation, Birmingham, AL
Primary Contact: Michael L. Bullitt, Chief Executive Officer
CFO: Tom Box, CPA, Chief Financial Officer
CMO: Virgil Frardo, M.D., Medical Director
CIO: Mary Walker, Manager Information Technology
CHR: Kathleen Pirtle, Director Human Resources
CNO: Karla Dwyer, R.N., Chief Nursing Officer
Web address: www.healthsouthwichitafalls.com
**Control:** Partnership, Investor–owned, for–profit **Service:** Rehabilitation

| | |
|---|---|
| **Staffed Beds:** 63 **Admissions:** 1309 **Census:** 46 **Outpatient Visits:** 11477 **Births:** 0 **Total Expense ($000):** 14679 **Payroll Expense ($000):** 7987 **Personnel:** 169 | |

☐ **KELL WEST REGIONAL HOSPITAL (450827)**, 5420 Kell West Boulevard,
Zip 76310–1610; tel. 940/692–5888 **A**1 9 10 **F**3 31 39 40 49 50 51 74 75
78 79 81 82 85 87 91 93 107 108 111 114 119 129 130 **P**5
Primary Contact: Jerry Myers, M.D., Chief Executive Officer
CFO: Fran Lindemann, Director Finance
Web address: www.kellwest.com
**Control:** Partnership, Investor–owned, for–profit **Service:** General Medical and
Surgical

| | |
|---|---|
| **Staffed Beds:** 41 **Admissions:** 914 **Census:** 9 **Outpatient Visits:** 28770 **Births:** 0 **Total Expense ($000):** 31023 **Payroll Expense ($000):** 8987 **Personnel:** 230 | |

☐ **NORTH TEXAS STATE HOSPITAL, WICHITA FALLS CAMPUS (454008)**,
6515 Lake Road, Zip 76308–5419, Mailing Address: Box 300, Zip 76307–0300;
tel. 940/692–1220, (Nonreporting) **A**1 5 10
Primary Contact: James E. Smith, Superintendent
CFO: Bill Lowery, Chief Financial Officer
CMO: Lauren Parsons, M.D., Clinical Director
CIO: Crystal Dennstedt, Chief Information Officer
Web address: www.mhmr.state.tx.us
**Control:** State–Government, nonfederal **Service:** Psychiatric

| | |
|---|---|
| **Staffed Beds:** 381 | |

☐ **RED RIVER HOSPITAL (454018)**, 1505 Eighth Street, Zip 76301–3106;
tel. 940/322–3171 **A**1 9 10 **F**4 5 29 75 86 87 98 99 101 102 103 104 105
130 132 **S** Acadia Healthcare Company, Inc., Franklin, TN
Primary Contact: Rob Marsh, Chief Executive Officer
CFO: Lee Mitchell, Chief Financial Officer
CMO: Harvey C. Martin, M.D., Medical Director
CIO: Fay Helton, Director Medical Records
CHR: Tracy Fehr, Executive Assistant and Director Human Resources
CNO: Amy Frate, Director of Nursing
Web address: www.redriverhospital.com
**Control:** Corporation, Investor–owned, for–profit **Service:** Psychiatric

| | |
|---|---|
| **Staffed Beds:** 74 **Admissions:** 1730 **Census:** 61 **Outpatient Visits:** 371 **Births:** 0 **Total Expense ($000):** 9193 **Payroll Expense ($000):** 5620 **Personnel:** 202 | |

☐ **TEXAS SPECIALTY HOSPITAL AT WICHITA FALLS (452068)**, 1103 Grace
Street, Zip 76301–4414; tel. 940/720–6633 **A**1 9 10 **F**1 3 29 30 31 56 75 77
82 85 86 87 91 100 130 143 148 **S** Fundamental Long Term Care Holdings,
LLC, Sparks Glencoe, MD
Primary Contact: Delnita Bray, Administrator
CFO: Debbie Herder, Controller
CMO: Robert McBroom, M.D., Medical Director
CIO: Gail McIlroy, Director Medical Records
CNO: Deanna Dowling, R.N., Chief Nursing Officer
**Control:** Corporation, Investor–owned, for–profit **Service:** Long–Term Acute Care
hospital

| | |
|---|---|
| **Staffed Beds:** 31 **Admissions:** 235 **Census:** 20 **Outpatient Visits:** 0 **Births:** 0 **Total Expense ($000):** 6321 **Payroll Expense ($000):** 2252 **Personnel:** 56 | |

**TX**

---

**Hospital, Medicare Provider Number, Address, Telephone, Approval, Facility, and Physician Codes, Health Care System**

★ American Hospital Association (AHA) membership
☐ The Joint Commission accreditation
◇ DNV Healthcare Inc. accreditation
○ Healthcare Facilities Accreditation Program
△ Commission on Accreditation of Rehabilitation Facilities (CARF) accreditation

✠ **UNITED REGIONAL HEALTH CARE SYSTEM (450010)**, 1600 11th Street,
Zip 76301–4300; tel. 940/764–7000, (Includes UNITED REGIONAL HEALTH
CARE SYSTEM–EIGHTH STREET CAMPUS, 1600 Eighth Street, Zip 76301–3164;
UNITED REGIONAL HEALTH CARE SYSTEM–ELEVENTH STREET CAMPUS, 1600
11th Street, Zip 76301–9988; tel. 940/764–0055) **A**1 2 3 5 9 10 **F**3 11 12 13
15 17 18 20 21 22 24 26 28 29 30 31 32 34 35 37 39 40 43 44 45 46 47
48 49 50 51 53 57 59 60 61 64 65 68 70 73 74 75 76 77 78 79 80 81 82
84 85 86 87 89 92 93 102 107 110 111 114 115 116 117 118 119 126 130
131 132 134 146 147 148 **P**3
Primary Contact: Phyllis A. Cowling, CPA, President and Chief Executive Officer
COO: Nancy Townley, R.N., Senior Vice President Operations
CFO: Robert M. Pert, Vice President Finance and Chief Financial Officer
CMO: Scott Hoyer, M.D., Vice President Quality and Chief Medical Officer
CIO: Jerry Marshall, Director Information Systems
CHR: Kristi Faulkner, Director Human Resources
Web address: www.urhcs.org
**Control:** Other not–for–profit (including NFP Corporation) **Service:** General
Medical and Surgical

**Staffed Beds:** 303 **Admissions:** 15084 **Census:** 167 **Outpatient Visits:**
139346 **Births:** 2188 **Total Expense ($000):** 253551 **Payroll Expense
($000):** 105335 **Personnel:** 1736

### WINNIE—Chambers County

**WINNIE COMMUNITY HOSPITAL (451328)**, 538 Broadway, Zip 77665–7600,
Mailing Address: P.O. Box 1249, Zip 77665–1249; tel. 409/296–6000 **A**9 10 18
**F**3 29 34 40 59 65 107 127 133 146 **P**6
Primary Contact: Daniel Yancy, Administrator and Chief Executive Officer
CFO: Julie Harris, Chief Financial Officer
CMO: Leonidas Andres, M.D., Chief of Staff
CHR: Anha Simon, Director Human Resources
Web address: www.winniehospital.com
**Control:** Partnership, Investor–owned, for–profit **Service:** General Medical and
Surgical

**Staffed Beds:** 25 **Admissions:** 501 **Census:** 4 **Outpatient Visits:** 25311
**Births:** 1 **Total Expense ($000):** 7826 **Payroll Expense ($000):** 3482
**Personnel:** 75

### WINNSBORO—Wood County

✠ **MOTHER FRANCES HOSPITAL – WINNSBORO (451381)**, 719 West Coke
Road, Zip 75494–3011, Mailing Address: P.O. Box 628, Zip 75494–0628;
tel. 903/342–5227 **A**1 9 10 18 **F**3 15 18 29 30 34 40 43 45 56 57 59 64 68
70 75 79 81 82 85 87 93 98 100 101 103 104 107 110 114 127 129 130
131 132 133 146 148 **P**5 6 7 8 **S** Trinity Mother Frances Hospitals and Clinics,
Tyler, TX
Primary Contact: Janet E. Coates, R.N., President and Chief Executive Officer
CFO: Glenn Peltier, Chief Financial Officer
CNO: Kevin Jablonski, Chief Nursing Officer
Web address: www.tmfhs.org
**Control:** Other not–for–profit (including NFP Corporation) **Service:** General
Medical and Surgical

**Staffed Beds:** 35 **Admissions:** 746 **Census:** 11 **Outpatient Visits:** 16952
**Births:** 0 **Total Expense ($000):** 19569 **Payroll Expense ($000):** 6191
**Personnel:** 101

**TEXAS HEALTH PRESBYTERIAN HOSPITAL WINNSBORO** See Mother Frances
Hospital – Winnsboro

### WINTERS—Runnels County

**NORTH RUNNELS HOSPITAL (451315)**, 7821 East Highway 53, Zip 79567,
Mailing Address: P.O. Box 185, Zip 79567–0185; tel. 325/754–5551 **A**9 10 18
**F**7 11 40 57 59 62 65 66 68 97 119 127 133 **P**5
Primary Contact: Sidney Tucker, Chief Executive Officer
CFO: Judy Espitia, Chief Financial Officer
CMO: Sarah Endicott, M.D., Chief of Staff
**Control:** Hospital district or authority, Government, nonfederal **Service:** General
Medical and Surgical

**Staffed Beds:** 21 **Admissions:** 231 **Census:** 2 **Outpatient Visits:** 4102
**Births:** 0 **Total Expense ($000):** 4263 **Payroll Expense ($000):** 2250
**Personnel:** 48

### WOODVILLE—Tyler County

★ **TYLER COUNTY HOSPITAL (450460)**, 1100 West Bluff Street,
Zip 75979–4799, Mailing Address: P.O. Box 549, Zip 75979–0549;
tel. 409/283–8141 **A**9 10 20 **F**3 11 30 35 40 43 46 57 59 64 81 107 114
119 127 146 **P**5
Primary Contact: Sandra Gayle Wright, R.N., Ed.D., Chief Executive Officer
CFO: Tom Letz, Interim Assistant Administrator, Chief Financial Officer and
Controller
CMO: James Brown, M.D., President
CIO: Rachel Haygood, Director Information Technology
CHR: Jan Thomsen, Director Human Resources
CNO: Sondra Wilson, R.N., Chief Nursing Officer
Web address: www.tchospital.us
**Control:** Hospital district or authority, Government, nonfederal **Service:** General
Medical and Surgical

**Staffed Beds:** 25 **Admissions:** 633 **Census:** 6 **Outpatient Visits:** 21389
**Births:** 0 **Total Expense ($000):** 12331 **Payroll Expense ($000):** 4526
**Personnel:** 129

### YOAKUM—Lavaca County

★ **YOAKUM COMMUNITY HOSPITAL (451346)**, 1200 Carl Ramert Drive,
Zip 77995–4868, Mailing Address: P.O. Box 753, Zip 77995–0753;
tel. 361/293–2321 **A**9 10 18 **F**3 11 13 15 29 34 35 40 43 56 57 59 64 70
76 79 81 85 86 93 107 108 111 114 119 129 132 133 134 146 148
**S** Community Hospital Corporation, Plano, TX
Primary Contact: Karen Barber, Chief Executive Officer
CFO: Robert Foret, Chief Financial Officer
CMO: Timothy Wagner, M.D., Chief Medical Staff
CHR: Karen Roznovsky, Director Human Resources
Web address: www.yoakumhospital.org
**Control:** Other not–for–profit (including NFP Corporation) **Service:** General
Medical and Surgical

**Staffed Beds:** 25 **Admissions:** 1080 **Census:** 14 **Outpatient Visits:** 19787
**Births:** 65 **Total Expense ($000):** 14747 **Payroll Expense ($000):** 6216
**Personnel:** 105

**TX**

*Many Facility Codes have changed. Please refer to the AHA Guide Code Chart.*

# UTAH

## AMERICAN FORK—Utah County

⊠ **AMERICAN FORK HOSPITAL (460023)**, 170 North 1100 East,
Zip 84003–2096; tel. 801/855–3300 **A**1 10 **F**3 13 15 29 31 32 34 38 39 40
43 44 45 48 54 57 59 62 64 70 72 75 76 77 78 81 82 85 86 87 89 107
110 111 114 116 117 119 123 128 130 131 132 134 144 146 147 148
**S** Intermountain Healthcare, Inc., Salt Lake City, UT
Primary Contact: Michael R. Olson, Administrator
CFO: Rod Lisonbee, Chief Financial Officer
CMO: Paul H. Robinson, M.D., Medical Director
CIO: Mary Gathers, Manager Information Systems
CHR: Nathan Bigler, Regional Director Human Resources
CNO: Lori Bertelsen, R.N., Nursing Administrator
Web address: www.intermountainhealthcare.org
**Control:** Other not–for–profit (including NFP Corporation) **Service:** General
Medical and Surgical

**Staffed Beds:** 88 **Admissions:** 6637 **Census:** 51 **Outpatient Visits:** 169415
**Births:** 3040 **Total Expense ($000):** 94162 **Payroll Expense ($000):** 31260
**Personnel:** 652

## BEAVER—Beaver County

**BEAVER VALLEY HOSPITAL (460035)**, 1109 North 100 West, Zip 84713,
Mailing Address: P.O. Box 1670, Zip 84713–1670; tel. 435/438–2531,
(Nonreporting) **A**9 10 20
Primary Contact: Craig Val Davidson, Chief Executive Officer and Administrator
Web address: www.beaverutah.net
**Control:** City–Government, nonfederal **Service:** General Medical and Surgical

**Staffed Beds:** 49

## BLANDING—San Juan County

☐ **BLUE MOUNTAIN HOSPITAL (461310)**, 802 South 200 West,
Zip 84511–3910; tel. 435/678–3993, (Nonreporting) **A**1 9 10 18
Primary Contact: Donna Singer, Chief Executive Officer
COO: Donna Jensen, Director Clinical Services
CFO: Jeremy Lyman, Chief Financial Director
CMO: L. Val Jones, M.D., Medical Director
CIO: Billy Xaochay, Manager Information Technology
CHR: Gail M. Northern, Director Human Resources
Web address: www.bmhutah.com
**Control:** Other not–for–profit (including NFP Corporation) **Service:** General
Medical and Surgical

**Staffed Beds:** 11

## BOUNTIFUL—Davis County

⊠ **LAKEVIEW HOSPITAL (460042)**, 630 East Medical Drive, Zip 84010–4908;
tel. 801/299–2200, (Nonreporting) **A**1 9 10 **S** HCA, Nashville, TN
Primary Contact: Rand Kerr, Chief Executive Officer
COO: Troy Wood, Chief Operating Officer
CFO: Wayne Dalton, Chief Financial Officer
CMO: Scott H. West, M.D., Chief Medical Officer
CIO: Eric Peterson, Director Information Technology
CHR: Julie Isom, Director Human Resources
CNO: Marilyn Mariani, R.N., Chief Nursing Officer
Web address: www.lakeviewhospital.com
**Control:** Corporation, Investor–owned, for–profit **Service:** General Medical and
Surgical

**Staffed Beds:** 116

**SOUTH DAVIS COMMUNITY HOSPITAL (462003)**, 401 South 400 East,
Zip 84010–4933; tel. 801/295–2361, (Nonreporting) **A**9 10
Primary Contact: David Bland, Chief Executive Officer
CFO: Daniel J. Foster, Chief Financial Officer
CMO: Scott Southworth, M.D., Medical Director
CHR: Jamey Sulser, Director Human Resources
Web address: www.sdch.com
**Control:** Other not–for–profit (including NFP Corporation) **Service:** Long–Term
Acute Care hospital

**Staffed Beds:** 176

## BRIGHAM CITY—Box Elder County

⊠ **BRIGHAM CITY COMMUNITY HOSPITAL (460017)**, 950 South Medical Drive,
Zip 84302–4724; tel. 435/734–9471, (Nonreporting) **A**1 9 10 **S** HCA,
Nashville, TN
Primary Contact: Richard Spuhler, Chief Executive Officer
CMO: Carey Lloyd, M.D., Chief Medical Officer
CIO: Steve Reichard, Manager Information Systems
CHR: Kathy Worley, Director Human Resources
Web address: www.brighamcityhospital.com
**Control:** Corporation, Investor–owned, for–profit **Service:** General Medical and
Surgical

**Staffed Beds:** 39

## CEDAR CITY—Iron County

⊠ **VALLEY VIEW MEDICAL CENTER (460007)**, 1303 North Main Street,
Zip 84721–9746; tel. 435/868–5000, (Nonreporting) **A**1 9 10 20
**S** Intermountain Healthcare, Inc., Salt Lake City, UT
Primary Contact: Jason Wilson, Administrator
CFO: Reed Sargent, Assistant Administrator Finance
Web address: www.ihc.com
**Control:** Other not–for–profit (including NFP Corporation) **Service:** General
Medical and Surgical

**Staffed Beds:** 48

## DELTA—Millard County

★ **DELTA COMMUNITY MEDICAL CENTER (461300)**, 126 South White Sage
Avenue, Zip 84624–8937; tel. 435/864–5591 **A**9 10 18 **F**3 8 11 13 15 31 34
40 41 42 45 54 57 59 68 75 76 81 82 86 87 89 107 110 114 128 133 145
146 147 148 **P**5 **S** Intermountain Healthcare, Inc., Salt Lake City, UT
Primary Contact: James E. Beckstrand, Administrator
CFO: Chris Thompson, Chief Financial Officer
Web address: www.ihc.com
**Control:** Other not–for–profit (including NFP Corporation) **Service:** General
Medical and Surgical

**Staffed Beds:** 18 **Admissions:** 274 **Census:** 2 **Outpatient Visits:** 17779
**Births:** 89 **Total Expense ($000):** 7551 **Payroll Expense ($000):** 2731
**Personnel:** 48

## FILLMORE—Millard County

★ **FILLMORE COMMUNITY MEDICAL CENTER (461301)**, 674 South Highway
99, Zip 84631–5013; tel. 435/743–5591 **A**9 10 18 **F**3 8 11 13 15 29 31 34
38 40 41 50 56 57 59 62 63 64 67 68 75 76 81 82 86 87 89 93 107 110
119 128 133 145 146 147 148 **S** Intermountain Healthcare, Inc., Salt Lake
City, UT
Primary Contact: James E. Beckstrand, Administrator
CFO: Chris Thompson, Chief Financial Officer
Web address: www.ihc.com
**Control:** Other not–for–profit (including NFP Corporation) **Service:** General
Medical and Surgical

**Staffed Beds:** 19 **Admissions:** 209 **Census:** 12 **Outpatient Visits:** 11365
**Births:** 43 **Total Expense ($000):** 6795 **Payroll Expense ($000):** 2553
**Personnel:** 46

## GUNNISON—Sanpete County

★ **GUNNISON VALLEY HOSPITAL (461306)**, 64 East 100 North, Zip 84634,
Mailing Address: P.O. Box 759, Zip 84634–0759; tel. 435/528–7246 **A**9 10 18
**F**7 11 13 15 18 34 35 40 56 57 59 62 63 64 65 76 78 79 81 82 85 97 107
115 119 129 130 133 146 147 148 **P**6
Primary Contact: Mark F. Dalley, Administrator
CFO: Brian Murray, Chief Financial Officer
CIO: Mike Ryan, Director of Information Services
CHR: Liz Brown, Manager Human Resources
CNO: Brenda Bartholomew, Chief Nursing Officer
Web address: www.gvhospital.org
**Control:** County–Government, nonfederal **Service:** General Medical and Surgical

**Staffed Beds:** 25 **Admissions:** 804 **Census:** 9 **Outpatient Visits:** 31204
**Births:** 152 **Total Expense ($000):** 16578 **Payroll Expense ($000):** 6995
**Personnel:** 173

UT

---

**Hospital, Medicare Provider Number, Address, Telephone, Approval, Facility, and Physician Codes, Health Care System**

★ American Hospital Association (AHA) membership ◯ Healthcare Facilities Accreditation Program
☐ The Joint Commission accreditation ◇ DNV Healthcare Inc. accreditation △ Commission on Accreditation of Rehabilitation Facilities (CARF) accreditation

## HEBER CITY—Wasatch County

★ **HEBER VALLEY MEDICAL CENTER (461307)**, 1485 South Highway 40, Zip 84032–3522; tel. 435/654–2500, (Total facility includes 5 beds in nursing home–type unit) **A**9 10 18 **F**3 4 13 15 29 35 40 45 50 56 57 59 64 68 75 76 77 79 81 82 85 86 87 97 107 108 114 119 120 128 129 130 133 135 146 147 **P**5 6 **S** Intermountain Healthcare, Inc., Salt Lake City, UT
Primary Contact: Shawn Morrow, Administrator
Web address: www.ihc.com
**Control:** Other not–for–profit (including NFP Corporation) **Service:** General Medical and Surgical

**Staffed Beds:** 19 **Admissions:** 385 **Census:** 5 **Births:** 136 **Total Expense ($000):** 16026 **Payroll Expense ($000):** 6051

## KANAB—Kane County

**KANE COUNTY HOSPITAL (461309)**, 355 North Main Street, Zip 84741–3260; tel. 435/644–5811, (Nonreporting) **A**9 10 18
Primary Contact: Sherrie Pandya, Administrator
CFO: Stephen Howells, Chief Financial Officer
CMO: Darin Ott, D.O., Chief of Staff
CHR: Laurali Noteman, Director Human Resources
Web address: www.kanecountyhospital.net
**Control:** Hospital district or authority, Government, nonfederal **Service:** General Medical and Surgical

**Staffed Beds:** 25

## LAYTON—Davis County

◇ **DAVIS HOSPITAL AND MEDICAL CENTER (460041)**, 1600 West Antelope Drive, Zip 84041–1142; tel. 801/807–1000 **A**9 10 21 **F**3 11 12 13 15 17 18 20 22 26 28 29 31 34 35 40 45 46 47 48 49 55 57 59 64 65 68 70 72 73 74 75 76 77 78 79 81 82 85 86 87 89 90 93 94 98 102 105 107 108 109 110 111 114 115 116 117 119 120 129 130 146 147 148 **S** IASIS Healthcare, Franklin, TN
Primary Contact: Michael E. Jensen, Chief Executive Officer
CFO: Jared Spackman, Chief Financial Officer
CMO: Shay Holley, M.D., President Medical Staff
CIO: Shane Williams, Director Information Systems
CHR: Kevin Mansfield, Director Human Resources
Web address: www.davishospital.com
**Control:** Corporation, Investor–owned, for–profit **Service:** General Medical and Surgical

**Staffed Beds:** 200 **Admissions:** 6005 **Census:** 57 **Outpatient Visits:** 141703 **Births:** 1785 **Personnel:** 615

## LOGAN—Cache County

⊞ **LOGAN REGIONAL HOSPITAL (460015)**, 1400 North 500 East, Zip 84341–2455; tel. 435/716–1000, (Total facility includes 10 beds in nursing home–type unit) **A**1 9 10 **F**3 8 11 13 14 15 18 20 22 28 29 31 32 34 35 36 37 40 43 45 46 49 50 51 57 59 60 64 66 68 70 72 74 75 76 77 78 79 81 82 85 86 87 89 91 93 97 98 99 100 101 102 103 104 105 107 108 109 110 111 114 115 119 120 121 123 128 129 130 131 132 135 146 147 148 **P**6 **S** Intermountain Healthcare, Inc., Salt Lake City, UT
Primary Contact: Michael A. Clark, Administrator and Chief Executive Officer
COO: Brandon McBride, Operations Officer
CFO: Alan Robinson, Chief Financial Officer
CMO: Todd A. Brown, M.D., Medical Director
CIO: Dave Felts, Chief Information Systems
CHR: Jolene Clonts, Director Human Resources
CNO: Neil C. Perkes, Operations Officer
Web address: www.loganregionalhospital.org
**Control:** Other not–for–profit (including NFP Corporation) **Service:** General Medical and Surgical

**Staffed Beds:** 135 **Admissions:** 7321 **Census:** 58 **Outpatient Visits:** 292680 **Births:** 2670 **Total Expense ($000):** 123610 **Payroll Expense ($000):** 41902 **Personnel:** 839

## MILFORD—Beaver County

★ **MILFORD VALLEY MEMORIAL HOSPITAL (461305)**, 451 North Main Street, Zip 84751–0640, Mailing Address: P.O. Box 640, Zip 84751–0640; tel. 435/387–2411, (Nonreporting) **A**9 10 18
Primary Contact: Craig Val Davidson, Chief Executive Officer
**Control:** Hospital district or authority, Government, nonfederal **Service:** General Medical and Surgical

**Staffed Beds:** 25

## MOAB—Grand County

★ **MOAB REGIONAL HOSPITAL (461302)**, 450 West Williams Way, Zip 84532–2065, Mailing Address: P.O. Box 998, Zip 84532–0998; tel. 435/719–3500, (Nonreporting) **A**9 10 18
Primary Contact: Robert Austin, Chief Executive Officer
COO: Vicki Gigliotti, Chief Clinical Officer
CFO: Craig M. Daniels, Chief Financial Officer
CMO: Kathy Williams, M.D., Chief Medical Staff
CIO: Mike Foster, Manager Information Systems
CHR: Dianne H. Hanson, Director Human Resources
Web address: www.amhmoab.org
**Control:** Other not–for–profit (including NFP Corporation) **Service:** General Medical and Surgical

**Staffed Beds:** 17

## MONTICELLO—San Juan County

**SAN JUAN HOSPITAL (461308)**, 380 West 100 North, Zip 84535, Mailing Address: P.O. Box 308, Zip 84535–0308; tel. 435/587–2116, (Nonreporting) **A**9 10 18
Primary Contact: Phillip W. Lowe, Chief Executive Officer
CFO: Lyman Duncan, Chief Financial Officer
CMO: James Redd, M.D., Chief Medical Officer
Web address: www.sanjuanhealthservices.org/
**Control:** County–Government, nonfederal **Service:** General Medical and Surgical

**Staffed Beds:** 25

## MOUNT PLEASANT—Sanpete County

★ **SANPETE VALLEY HOSPITAL (461303)**, 1100 South Medical Drive, Zip 84647–2222; tel. 435/462–2441, (Nonreporting) **A**9 10 18 **S** Intermountain Healthcare, Inc., Salt Lake City, UT
Primary Contact: Mark L. Allen, FACHE, Administrator
CFO: Chris Thompson, Chief Financial Officer
CMO: Michael Frischknecht, M.D., President Medical Staff
CIO: Michael Ence, Computer Specialist
CHR: Heather Hafen, Manager Human Resources
CNO: Ryan Robison, Nursing Administrator
Web address: www.intermountainhealthcare.com
**Control:** Other not–for–profit (including NFP Corporation) **Service:** General Medical and Surgical

**Staffed Beds:** 19

## MURRAY—Salt Lake County

☐ △ **INTERMOUNTAIN MEDICAL CENTER (460010)**, 5121 South Cottonwood Street, Zip 84107–5701; tel. 801/507–7000 **A**1 2 3 5 7 10 **F**3 7 8 12 13 15 17 18 20 22 24 26 28 29 30 31 34 35 37 38 39 40 43 44 45 46 47 48 49 50 51 52 53 54 55 56 57 58 59 60 61 63 64 68 70 72 74 75 76 77 78 79 81 82 84 85 86 87 90 91 92 93 94 95 96 97 100 102 107 108 109 110 111 112 114 115 116 117 118 119 120 121 122 123 124 126 129 130 131 132 137 138 139 141 142 146 147 148 **P**6 **S** Intermountain Healthcare, Inc., Salt Lake City, UT
Primary Contact: David Grauer, Chief Executive Officer and Administrator
COO: Kelly L. Duffin, Operations Officer
CFO: Jeff Jensen, Finance Officer
CMO: William L. Hamilton, M.D., Urban Central Region Medical Director
CIO: David Baird, Director of Information Systems
CHR: Nate Miller, Human Resources Manager
CNO: Suzanne P. Anderson, Nurse Administrator
Web address: www.intermountainhealthcare.org
**Control:** Other not–for–profit (including NFP Corporation) **Service:** General Medical and Surgical

**Staffed Beds:** 452 **Admissions:** 26668 **Census:** 314 **Outpatient Visits:** 637580 **Births:** 4604 **Total Expense ($000):** 676219 **Payroll Expense ($000):** 213131 **Personnel:** 3818

⊞ **THE ORTHOPEDIC SPECIALTY HOSPITAL (460049)**, 5848 South 300 East, Zip 84107–6121; tel. 801/314–4100 **A**1 10 **F**3 9 29 32 34 35 37 53 57 58 59 68 74 75 77 79 81 85 86 87 91 93 94 107 111 114 119 130 131 134 135 146 **S** Intermountain Healthcare, Inc., Salt Lake City, UT
Primary Contact: Barbara Ohm, Administrator
CFO: Ronald Jensen, Manager Finance
CMO: Jon Sundin, M.D., Medical Director
CIO: David Baird, Chief Information Officer
CHR: Tina Tasso, Manager Human Resources
Web address: www.intermountainhealthcare.org
**Control:** Other not–for–profit (including NFP Corporation) **Service:** Orthopedic

**Staffed Beds:** 36 **Admissions:** 1834 **Census:** 12 **Outpatient Visits:** 222512 **Births:** 0 **Total Expense ($000):** 61062 **Payroll Expense ($000):** 16995 **Personnel:** 350

*Many Facility Codes have changed. Please refer to the AHA Guide Code Chart.* © 2013 AHA Guide

## NEPHI—Juab County

★ **CENTRAL VALLEY MEDICAL CENTER (461304)**, 48 West 1500 North, Zip 84648–8900; tel. 435/623–3000, (Nonreporting) **A**9 10 18 **S** Rural Health Group, Nephi, UT
Primary Contact: Mark R. Stoddard, President
COO: John E. Gledhill, Chief Operating Officer
CFO: Brent Davis, Chief Financial Officer
CMO: James Rosenbeck, D.O., Chief of Staff
CIO: Ken Richens, Chief Information Officer
CHR: Brian Allsop, Director Human Resources
Web address: www.cvmed.net
**Control:** Other not-for-profit (including NFP Corporation) **Service:** General Medical and Surgical

**Staffed Beds:** 25

## NORTH LOGAN—Cache County

☐ **CACHE VALLEY SPECIALTY HOSPITAL (460054)**, 2380 North 400 East, Zip 84341–6000; tel. 435/713–9700, (Nonreporting) **A**1 10 **S** National Surgical Hospitals, Chicago, IL
Primary Contact: John C. Worley, III, Chief Executive Officer
CFO: David S. Geary, Chief Financial Officer
CMO: Brian Nelson, M.D., Chief Medical Officer
Web address: www.cvsh.com
**Control:** Corporation, Investor-owned, for-profit **Service:** General Medical and Surgical

**Staffed Beds:** 15

## OGDEN—Weber County

⊠ **MCKAY–DEE HOSPITAL CENTER (460004)**, 4401 Harrison Boulevard, Zip 84403–3195; tel. 801/387–2800 **A**1 2 10 **F**3 8 11 12 13 15 17 18 20 22 24 26 28 29 30 31 34 35 38 40 43 44 45 46 49 50 51 53 54 55 57 58 59 60 61 64 65 66 67 68 70 72 74 75 76 77 78 79 81 82 84 85 86 87 89 90 91 93 97 98 99 100 101 102 103 104 105 106 107 108 110 111 114 115 116 117 119 120 121 123 126 129 130 131 132 134 135 144 146 147 148 **P**6 **S** Intermountain Healthcare, Inc., Salt Lake City, UT
Primary Contact: Timothy T. Pehrson, Chief Executive Officer
CFO: Doug Smith, Chief Financial Officer
CMO: Christine Nefcy, M.D., Chief Medical Officer
CIO: Mary Gathers, Director Information Systems
CHR: Karen Burnett, Regional Director Human Resources
CNO: Bonnie Jacklin, R.N., Chief Nursing Officer
Web address: www.mckay-dee.org
**Control:** Other not-for-profit (including NFP Corporation) **Service:** General Medical and Surgical

**Staffed Beds:** 310 **Admissions:** 19306 **Census:** 187 **Outpatient Visits:** 257736 **Births:** 3994 **Total Expense ($000):** 342378 **Payroll Expense ($000):** 106576 **Personnel:** 2105

⊠ **OGDEN REGIONAL MEDICAL CENTER (460005)**, 5475 South 500 East, Zip 84405–6905; tel. 801/479–2111, (Nonreporting) **A**1 9 10 **S** HCA, Nashville, TN
Primary Contact: Mark B. Adams, Chief Executive Officer
COO: Scott Davis, Chief Operating Officer
CFO: Judd Taylor, Chief Financial Officer
CMO: William Sheffield, M.D., President
CIO: Eric Peterson, Director
CHR: Chris Bissenden, Director Human Resources
CNO: Elizabeth B. Later, R.N., Chief Nursing Officer
Web address: www.ogdenregional.com
**Control:** Corporation, Investor-owned, for-profit **Service:** General Medical and Surgical

**Staffed Beds:** 167

## OREM—Utah County

⊠ **OREM COMMUNITY HOSPITAL (460043)**, 331 North 400 West, Zip 84057–1999; tel. 801/224–4080 **A**1 10 **F**3 11 13 15 29 32 35 38 39 40 43 44 54 59 64 68 75 76 81 82 86 87 93 97 107 111 119 132 135 146 **S** Intermountain Healthcare, Inc., Salt Lake City, UT
Primary Contact: Steven Badger, R.N., FACHE, Administrator
CFO: Rod Lisonbee, Chief Financial Officer
CMO: Neil Whitaker, M.D., Chief Medical Director
CIO: Diane Rindlisbacher, Manager Information Systems
CHR: Pamela S. Niece, Director Human Resources
Web address: www.intermountainhealthcare.org
**Control:** Other not-for-profit (including NFP Corporation) **Service:** General Medical and Surgical

**Staffed Beds:** 18 **Admissions:** 1276 **Census:** 7 **Outpatient Visits:** 48007 **Births:** 1177 **Total Expense ($000):** 23000 **Payroll Expense ($000):** 8577 **Personnel:** 195

⊠ **TIMPANOGOS REGIONAL HOSPITAL (460052)**, 750 West 800 North, Zip 84057–3660; tel. 801/714–6000, (Nonreporting) **A**1 9 10 **S** HCA, Nashville, TN
Primary Contact: Keith D. Tintle, Chief Executive Officer
COO: Kyle Brostrom, Chief Operating Officer
CFO: Zandra Anderson, Chief Financial Officer
CMO: David K. Anderson, M.D., Chief of Staff
CIO: Richard Neilson, Director of Information Services
CHR: Kelly Brimhall, Director of Human Resources
CNO: Sandy Ewell, Chief Nursing Officer
Web address: www.timpanogosregionalhospital.com
**Control:** Corporation, Investor-owned, for-profit **Service:** General Medical and Surgical

**Staffed Beds:** 117

## PANGUITCH—Garfield County

★ **GARFIELD MEMORIAL HOSPITAL AND CLINICS (460033)**, 200 North 400 East, Zip 84759, Mailing Address: P.O. Box 389, Zip 84759–0389; tel. 435/676–8811, (Total facility includes 27 beds in nursing home–type unit) **A**9 10 20 **F**2 13 15 28 29 32 34 35 40 45 56 57 59 64 65 67 75 76 81 82 87 97 107 110 119 127 128 129 130 132 133 148 **P**6 **S** Intermountain Healthcare, Inc., Salt Lake City, UT
Primary Contact: Alberto Vasquez, Administrator
CFO: Reed Sargent, Assistant Administrator Finance
Web address: www.ihc.com/hospitals/garfield
**Control:** Other not-for-profit (including NFP Corporation) **Service:** General Medical and Surgical

**Staffed Beds:** 41 **Admissions:** 366 **Census:** 30 **Outpatient Visits:** 34903 **Births:** 29 **Total Expense ($000):** 9694 **Payroll Expense ($000):** 4978 **Personnel:** 109

## PARK CITY—Summit County

⊠ **PARK CITY MEDICAL CENTER (460057)**, 900 Round Valley Drive, Zip 84060–7552; tel. 435/658–7000 **A**1 9 10 **F**3 13 15 18 29 34 35 36 38 40 43 45 48 50 51 53 57 59 65 68 74 75 76 79 81 82 85 87 89 93 96 102 107 108 110 111 115 119 129 130 131 135 146 147 **P**6 **S** Intermountain Healthcare, Inc., Salt Lake City, UT
Primary Contact: Si William Hutt, Chief Executive Officer
CFO: Craig Mills, Senior Financial Advisor
CMO: Wain Allen, M.D., Medical Director
CHR: Bruce Dent, Director Human Resources
CNO: Dan Davis, R.N., Nurse Administrator
Web address: www.intermountainhealthcare.org
**Control:** Other not-for-profit (including NFP Corporation) **Service:** General Medical and Surgical

**Staffed Beds:** 26 **Admissions:** 1285 **Census:** 8 **Outpatient Visits:** 82719 **Births:** 289 **Total Expense ($000):** 53114 **Payroll Expense ($000):** 16907 **Personnel:** 294

## PAYSON—Utah County

⊠ **MOUNTAIN VIEW HOSPITAL (460013)**, 1000 East 100 North, Zip 84651–1600; tel. 801/465–7000, (Nonreporting) **A**1 9 10 **S** HCA, Nashville, TN
Primary Contact: Kevin Johnson, Chief Executive Officer
COO: Kimball Anderson, FACHE, Chief Operating Officer
COO: Ric Johnson, Associate Administrator
CFO: Steven R. Schramm, Chief Financial Officer
CMO: Elizabeth Dayton, M.D., Chief Medical Staff
CIO: Cindy Mecham, Health Information Director
CHR: Wally Trotter, Director Human Resources
CNO: Lisa Taylor, Director of Nursing
Web address: www.mvhpayson.com
**Control:** Corporation, Investor-owned, for-profit **Service:** General Medical and Surgical

**Staffed Beds:** 114

## PRICE—Carbon County

⊠ **CASTLEVIEW HOSPITAL (460011)**, 300 North Hospital Drive, Zip 84501–4200; tel. 435/637–4800, (Nonreporting) **A**1 9 10 20 **S** LifePoint Hospitals, Inc., Brentwood, TN
Primary Contact: Mark Holyoak, Chief Executive Officer
CFO: Ryan Moynier, Chief Financial Officer
CMO: Karen M. Radley, M.D., Chief of Staff
CIO: Keenan Johnson, Director Information Systems
CHR: Misty Birch, Director Human Resources
CNO: Terri Watkins, R.N., Chief Nursing Officer
Web address: www.castleviewhospital.net
**Control:** Corporation, Investor-owned, for-profit **Service:** General Medical and Surgical

**Staffed Beds:** 49

UT

---

**Hospital, Medicare Provider Number, Address, Telephone, Approval, Facility, and Physician Codes, Health Care System**

★ American Hospital Association (AHA) membership
☐ The Joint Commission accreditation
◇ DNV Healthcare Inc. accreditation
○ Healthcare Facilities Accreditation Program
△ Commission on Accreditation of Rehabilitation Facilities (CARF) accreditation

## PROVO—Utah County

☐ **UTAH STATE HOSPITAL (464001)**, 1300 East Center Street, Zip 84606–3554, Mailing Address: P.O. Box 270, Zip 84603–0270; tel. 801/344–4400 **A**1 10 **F**30 34 56 75 77 86 87 91 98 99 100 101 103 130 135 143 146 **P**6
Primary Contact: Dallas Earnshaw, Superintendent
COO: Dallas Earnshaw, Superintendent
CFO: Robert Burton, Manager Finance
CMO: Richard Spencer, M.D., Clinical Director
CIO: Jill Hill, Director Information Technology
CHR: David Gardner, Manager Human Resources
Web address: www.ush.utah.gov
**Control:** State–Government, nonfederal **Service:** Psychiatric

**Staffed Beds:** 329 **Admissions:** 388 **Census:** 285 **Outpatient Visits:** 0
**Births:** 0 **Total Expense ($000):** 51734 **Payroll Expense ($000):** 22035
**Personnel:** 697

⊞ △ **UTAH VALLEY REGIONAL MEDICAL CENTER (460001)**, 1034 North 500 West, Zip 84604–3337; tel. 801/357–7850 **A**1 2 7 10 **F**3 11 13 15 17 18 20 21 22 23 24 25 28 29 30 31 32 34 35 38 39 40 43 44 45 48 49 50 51 53 54 56 57 58 59 60 61 62 63 64 68 69 70 72 74 75 76 77 78 81 82 84 85 86 87 88 89 90 91 92 93 94 97 98 99 100 101 102 103 104 105 107 108 110 111 114 115 116 117 118 119 121 123 129 130 131 132 133 134 144 146 147 148 **P**6 **S** Intermountain Healthcare, Inc., Salt Lake City, UT
Primary Contact: Steve Smoot, Administrator
CFO: Rod Lisonbee, Chief Financial Officer
CIO: Mary Gathers, Director Information Systems
CHR: Nathan Bigler, Regional Director Human Resources
CNO: Lisa A. Paletta, R.N., Chief Nursing Officer
Web address: www.utahvalleyregional.org
**Control:** Other not–for–profit (including NFP Corporation) **Service:** General Medical and Surgical

**Staffed Beds:** 367 **Admissions:** 20400 **Census:** 239 **Outpatient Visits:** 335193 **Births:** 4186 **Total Expense ($000):** 375813 **Payroll Expense ($000):** 133361 **Personnel:** 2795

☐ **UTAH VALLEY SPECIALTY HOSPITAL (462005)**, 306 River Bend Lane, Zip 84604–5625; tel. 801/226–8880, (Nonreporting) **A**1 9 10 **S** Ernest Health, Inc., Albuquerque, NM
Primary Contact: Marie Prothero, R.N., MSN, Chief Executive Officer
Web address: www.uvsh.ernesthealth.com
**Control:** Corporation, Investor–owned, for–profit **Service:** Long–Term Acute Care hospital

**Staffed Beds:** 40

## RICHFIELD—Sevier County

⊞ **SEVIER VALLEY MEDICAL CENTER (460026)**, 1000 North Main Street, Zip 84701–1857; tel. 435/896–8271, (Nonreporting) **A**1 9 10 20 **S** Intermountain Healthcare, Inc., Salt Lake City, UT
Primary Contact: Gary E. Beck, Administrator
CFO: Chris Thompson, Chief Financial Officer
CHR: Katey Nelson, Director Human Resources
Web address: www.intermountain.com
**Control:** Other not–for–profit (including NFP Corporation) **Service:** General Medical and Surgical

**Staffed Beds:** 27

## RIVERTON—Salt Lake County

⊞ **RIVERTON HOSPITAL (460058)**, 3741 West 12600 South, Zip 84065–7215; tel. 801/285–4000 **A**1 9 10 **F**3 13 15 29 31 34 39 40 43 44 45 46 47 48 49 50 51 57 59 64 68 70 76 78 79 81 85 86 87 89 91 93 94 97 107 108 110 111 114 115 118 119 129 130 131 146 147 148 **S** Intermountain Healthcare, Inc., Salt Lake City, UT
Primary Contact: Blair Kent, Administrator
Web address: www.intermountainhealthcare.org/
**Control:** Other not–for–profit (including NFP Corporation) **Service:** General Medical and Surgical

**Staffed Beds:** 92 **Admissions:** 4932 **Census:** 31 **Outpatient Visits:** 120925 **Births:** 2321 **Total Expense ($000):** 74077 **Payroll Expense ($000):** 22369 **Personnel:** 435

## ROOSEVELT—Duchesne County

★ **UINTAH BASIN MEDICAL CENTER (460019)**, 250 West 300 North, 75–2, Zip 84066–2336; tel. 435/722–6163, (Total facility includes 90 beds in nursing home–type unit) **A**9 10 20 **F**6 7 11 13 15 17 35 40 43 45 50 52 53 54 57 59 60 62 63 70 73 76 77 79 81 82 84 85 87 89 93 107 110 111 114 118 119 128 129 130 131 132 135 144 146 147 148 **P**7
Primary Contact: Bradley D. LeBaron, FACHE, President and Chief Executive Officer
CFO: Brent Hales, Chief Financial Officer
CMO: Gary B. White, M.D., Chief Medical Staff
CHR: Randall Bennett, Assistant Administrator
Web address: www.ubmc.org
**Control:** Other not–for–profit (including NFP Corporation) **Service:** General Medical and Surgical

**Staffed Beds:** 124 **Admissions:** 1997 **Census:** 86 **Outpatient Visits:** 61804 **Births:** 595 **Total Expense ($000):** 61033 **Payroll Expense ($000):** 20305 **Personnel:** 510

## SAINT GEORGE—Washington County

⊞ △ **DIXIE REGIONAL MEDICAL CENTER (460021)**, 1380 East Medical Center Drive, Zip 84790–2123; tel. 435/251–1000, (Includes DIXIE REGIONAL MEDICAL CENTER, 544 South 400 East, St. George, Zip 84770) **A**1 2 7 9 10 **F**3 7 11 12 13 15 18 19 20 21 22 23 24 25 28 29 31 34 35 38 40 43 45 46 50 53 54 57 59 64 67 68 70 72 74 75 76 77 78 79 80 81 82 83 84 85 89 90 93 98 102 107 108 110 111 114 115 117 119 120 121 127 129 130 131 132 135 146 147 148 **P**5 **S** Intermountain Healthcare, Inc., Salt Lake City, UT
Primary Contact: Terri Kane, Chief Executive Officer
CFO: Mary Hatch, Chief Financial Officer
CMO: Steven Van Norman, M.D., Medical Director
CIO: Lance Bedingfield, Director Information Services
Web address: www.intermountainhealthcare.org
**Control:** Other not–for–profit (including NFP Corporation) **Service:** General Medical and Surgical

**Staffed Beds:** 261 **Admissions:** 15467 **Census:** 143 **Outpatient Visits:** 456342 **Births:** 2276 **Total Expense ($000):** 324824 **Payroll Expense ($000):** 93466 **Personnel:** 1831

## SALT LAKE CITY—Salt Lake County

⊞ **LDS HOSPITAL (460006)**, Eighth Avenue and C Street, Zip 84143–0001; tel. 801/408–1100 **A**1 3 5 10 **F**3 4 5 7 8 12 13 15 18 28 29 30 31 34 35 38 39 40 43 44 45 46 48 50 51 52 53 54 55 56 57 58 59 60 61 63 64 65 66 68 70 73 74 75 76 77 78 79 81 84 85 86 87 91 92 93 94 98 100 101 102 103 104 105 107 108 109 110 111 114 115 117 119 120 121 129 130 131 132 136 146 147 148 **S** Intermountain Healthcare, Inc., Salt Lake City, UT
Primary Contact: Jim Sheets, Chief Executive Officer and Administrator
COO: David Gardiner, Operations Officer
CFO: Dave M. Larsen, Chief Financial Officer
CMO: William L. Hamilton, M.D., Chief Medical Officer
CIO: David Baird, Chief Information Officer
CHR: Pamela S. Niece, Chief Human Resources Officer
CNO: Todd Neubert, Nurse Administrator
Web address: www.intermountainhealthcare.org
**Control:** Other not–for–profit (including NFP Corporation) **Service:** General Medical and Surgical

**Staffed Beds:** 241 **Admissions:** 9728 **Census:** 111 **Outpatient Visits:** 250805 **Births:** 2480 **Total Expense ($000):** 222106 **Payroll Expense ($000):** 68953 **Personnel:** 1214

⊞ **MARIAN CENTER (464012)**, 451 East Bishop Federal Lane, Zip 84115–2357; tel. 801/487–7557, (Nonreporting) **A**1 10
Primary Contact: Gina Hallam, Administrator
Web address: www.stjosephvilla.com
**Control:** Partnership, Investor–owned, for–profit **Service:** Psychiatric

**Staffed Beds:** 14

⊞ **PRIMARY CHILDREN'S MEDICAL CENTER (463301)**, 100 North Mario Capecchi Drive, Zip 84113–1100; tel. 801/662–1000 **A**1 3 5 9 10 **F**3 4 5 8 9 11 17 19 21 23 25 27 29 30 31 32 34 35 36 38 39 40 41 43 44 45 48 49 50 54 55 57 58 59 60 61 63 64 65 68 72 74 75 77 78 79 81 82 84 85 86 87 88 89 90 92 93 96 98 99 100 101 102 104 105 106 107 108 111 113 114 115 116 117 118 119 124 130 131 132 134 135 136 137 138 139 141 142 146 148 **S** Intermountain Healthcare, Inc., Salt Lake City, UT
Primary Contact: Katy Welkie, R.N., Chief Executive Officer
CFO: Jeremiah Radandt, Chief Financial Officer
CMO: Ed Clark, M.D., Chief Medical Officer
CIO: Joe Hales, Director Information Systems
CHR: Albert Bennett Buckworth, Director Human Resources
CNO: Judy Geiger, R.N., Chief Nursing Officer
Web address: www.intermountainhealthcare.org
**Control:** Other not–for–profit (including NFP Corporation) **Service:** Children's general

**Staffed Beds:** 289 **Admissions:** 14456 **Census:** 188 **Outpatient Visits:** 370455 **Births:** 0 **Total Expense ($000):** 387761 **Payroll Expense ($000):** 144468 **Personnel:** 2701

*Many Facility Codes have changed. Please refer to the AHA Guide Code Chart.* © 2013 AHA Guide

UT

**PROMISE SPECIALTY HOSPITAL OF SALT LAKE (462004)**, 8th Avenue and C Street, Zip 84143; tel. 801/350–4110, (Nonreporting) **A**9 10 **S** Promise Healthcare, Boca Raton, FL
Primary Contact: Linda Hook, Chief Executive Officer
Web address: www.promise–saltlake.com
**Control:** Corporation, Investor–owned, for–profit **Service:** Long–Term Acute Care hospital

Staffed Beds: 32

☐ **SALT LAKE BEHAVIORAL HEALTH (464013)**, 3802 South 700 East, Zip 84106–1182; tel. 801/264–6000 **A**1 9 10 **F**5 98 99 103 104 105 **P**6 **S** Universal Health Services, Inc., King of Prussia, PA
Primary Contact: Melissa Eckstein, Chief Executive Officer
Web address: www.saltlakebehavioralhealth.com
**Control:** Corporation, Investor–owned, for–profit **Service:** Psychiatric

Staffed Beds: 118 Admissions: 1999 Census: 69

☐ ◇ **SALT LAKE REGIONAL MEDICAL CENTER (460003)**, 1050 East South Temple, Zip 84102–1507; tel. 801/350–4111, (Nonreporting) **A**1 3 5 9 10 21 **S** IASIS Healthcare, Franklin, TN
Primary Contact: Jeff Frandsen, Chief Executive Officer
CFO: Steven Payne, Chief Financial Officer
CMO: Wanda Updike, M.D., Chief of Staff
CIO: Mark Runyan, Director Information Services
CHR: Carolyn Livingston, Director Human Resources
Web address: www.saltlakeregional.com
**Control:** Corporation, Investor–owned, for–profit **Service:** General Medical and Surgical

Staffed Beds: 132

☐ **SHRINERS HOSPITALS FOR CHILDREN–SALT LAKE CITY (463302)**, (Formerly Shriners Hospitals for Children–Intermountain), Fairfax Road & Virginia Street, Zip 84103–4399; tel. 801/536–3500, (Nonreporting) **A**1 3 5 10 **S** Shriners Hospitals for Children, Tampa, FL
Primary Contact: Kevin Martin, M.P.H., R.N., M.P.H., Administrator
CFO: Randy Lindberg, Director Fiscal Services
CMO: Jacques D'Astous, M.D., Chief of Staff
CIO: Mike Allen, Director Information Technology
CHR: Russ Crockett, Director Human Resources
Web address: www.shrinershospitalsforchildren.org/Hospitals/Locations/SaltLakeCity.aspx
**Control:** Other not–for–profit (including NFP Corporation) **Service:** Children's orthopedic

Staffed Beds: 40

⊞ **ST. MARK'S HOSPITAL (460047)**, 1200 East 3900 South, Zip 84124–1390; tel. 801/268–7111, (Nonreporting) **A**1 9 10 **S** HCA, Nashville, TN
Primary Contact: Steven B. Bateman, Chief Executive Officer
COO: Matt Dixon, Chief Operating Officer
CFO: Bryan McKinley, Chief Financial Officer
CMO: J. Eric Vanderhooft, M.D., President Medical Staff
CIO: Jesse Trujillo, Chief Information Officer
CHR: Robyn Opheikens, Assistant Administrator Human Resources
Web address: www.stmarkshospital.com
**Control:** Corporation, Investor–owned, for–profit **Service:** General Medical and Surgical

Staffed Beds: 317

⊞ △ ◇ **UNIVERSITY OF UTAH HEALTH CARE – HOSPITAL AND CLINICS (460009)**, 50 North Medical Drive, Zip 84132–0002; tel. 801/587–3572 **A**1 3 5 7 8 9 10 21 **F**3 6 7 8 9 11 12 13 15 16 17 18 20 22 24 26 28 29 30 31 33 34 35 36 37 38 39 40 42 43 44 45 46 47 48 49 50 51 52 53 54 55 56 57 58 59 60 61 62 64 65 68 70 71 72 73 74 75 76 77 78 79 80 81 82 83 84 85 86 87 89 90 91 92 93 94 95 96 97 98 100 101 102 103 104 107 108 109 110 111 112 113 114 115 116 117 118 119 120 121 123 124 126 129 130 131 132 134 135 136 137 138 139 140 141 142 143 144 145 146 147 148 **P**1
Primary Contact: David Entwistle, Chief Executive Officer
COO: Quinn McKenna, Chief Operating Officer
CFO: Gordon Crabtree, Chief Financial Officer
CMO: Thomas Miller, M.D., Medical Director
CIO: James Turnbull, Chief Information Officer
CHR: Sherri Hollingsworth, Chief Human Resources Officer
CNO: Margaret Pearce, R.N., Chief Nursing Officer
Web address: www.uuhsc.utah.edu
**Control:** State–Government, nonfederal **Service:** General Medical and Surgical

Staffed Beds: 526 Admissions: 22831 Census: 364 Outpatient Visits: 1335670 Births: 3701 Total Expense ($000): 919714 Payroll Expense ($000): 335164 Personnel: 6290

☐ ◇ **UNIVERSITY OF UTAH NEUROPSYCHIATRIC INSTITUTE (464009)**, 501 South Chipeta Way, Zip 84108–1222; tel. 801/583–2500, (Nonreporting) **A**1 3 5 9 10 21
Primary Contact: Ross Van Vranken, Executive Director
CFO: Becky Schaefer, Chief Financial Officer
CMO: Michael Lowry, M.D., Medical Director
Web address: www.med.utah.edu/uni
**Control:** State–Government, nonfederal **Service:** Psychiatric

Staffed Beds: 90

⊞ △ **VETERANS AFFAIRS SALT LAKE CITY HEALTH CARE SYSTEM**, 500 Foothill Drive, Zip 84148–0002; tel. 801/582–1565, (Nonreporting) **A**1 3 5 7 **S** Department of Veterans Affairs, Washington, DC
Primary Contact: Steven W. Young, Director
COO: Roy Hawkins, Acting Associate Director
CFO: Val Martin, Director Financial Management Services Center
CMO: Ronald J. Gebhart, M.D., Chief of Staff
CIO: Lisa Leonelis, Chief Information Officer
CHR: Lisa Porter, Director Human Resources, Leadership and Education
Web address: www.saltlakecity.va.gov/
**Control:** Veterans Affairs, Government, federal **Service:** General Medical and Surgical

Staffed Beds: 121

### SANDY—Salt Lake County

⊞ **ALTA VIEW HOSPITAL (460044)**, 9660 South 1300 East, Zip 84094–3793; tel. 801/501–2600 **A**1 10 **F**3 8 12 13 15 29 34 35 38 39 40 44 45 46 47 48 49 50 53 54 56 57 59 64 68 70 75 76 77 81 85 86 87 92 93 102 107 108 110 111 115 119 129 130 131 132 135 146 147 **S** Intermountain Healthcare, Inc., Salt Lake City, UT
Primary Contact: Bryan L. Johnson, Administrator
CFO: Todd Sanders, Manager Finance
CHR: Diane Holman, Manager Human Resources
Web address: www.intermountainhealthcare.org
**Control:** Other not–for–profit (including NFP Corporation) **Service:** General Medical and Surgical

Staffed Beds: 71 Admissions: 3721 Census: 26 Outpatient Visits: 140078 Births: 1343 Total Expense ($000): 84626 Payroll Expense ($000): 24642 Personnel: 456

⊞ **HEALTHSOUTH REHABILITATION HOSPITAL OF UTAH (463025)**, 8074 South 1300 East, Zip 84094–0743; tel. 801/561–3400, (Nonreporting) **A**1 10 **S** HEALTHSOUTH Corporation, Birmingham, AL
Primary Contact: Philip Eaton, Chief Executive Officer and Administrator
CFO: Daren Woolstenhulme, Chief Financial Officer
CMO: Joseph VickRoy, M.D., Medical Director
CHR: Troy Jensen, Director Human Resources
Web address: www.healthsouthutah.com
**Control:** Corporation, Investor–owned, for–profit **Service:** Rehabilitation

Staffed Beds: 105

### TOOELE—Tooele County

⊞ **MOUNTAIN WEST MEDICAL CENTER (460014)**, 2055 North Main Street, Zip 84074–9819; tel. 435/843–3600, (Nonreporting) **A**1 9 10 **S** Community Health Systems, Inc., Franklin, TN
Primary Contact: Tim Moran, Interim Chief Executive Officer
CMO: James Antinori, M.D., Chief of Staff
CHR: James Glade, Director Human Resources
Web address: www.mountainwestmc.com
**Control:** Corporation, Investor–owned, for–profit **Service:** General Medical and Surgical

Staffed Beds: 31

### TREMONTON—Box Elder County

★ **BEAR RIVER VALLEY HOSPITAL (460039)**, 905 North 1000 West, Zip 84337–2497; tel. 435/207–4500, (Nonreporting) **A**9 10 **S** Intermountain Healthcare, Inc., Salt Lake City, UT
Primary Contact: Eric Packer, Administrator
CHR: Joy Sadler, Director Human Resources
Web address: www.intermountainhealthcare.org/hospitals/bearriver
**Control:** Other not–for–profit (including NFP Corporation) **Service:** General Medical and Surgical

Staffed Beds: 14

**UT**

---

**Hospital, Medicare Provider Number, Address, Telephone, Approval, Facility, and Physician Codes, Health Care System**

| | | |
|---|---|---|
| ★ American Hospital Association (AHA) membership | ○ Healthcare Facilities Accreditation Program | |
| ☐ The Joint Commission accreditation | ◇ DNV Healthcare Inc. accreditation | △ Commission on Accreditation of Rehabilitation Facilities (CARF) accreditation |

### VERNAL—Uintah County

⊠ **ASHLEY REGIONAL MEDICAL CENTER (460030)**, 150 West 100 North,
Zip 84078–2036; tel. 435/789–3342, (Nonreporting) **A**1 9 10 20 **S** LifePoint
Hospitals, Inc., Brentwood, TN
Primary Contact: Ben Cluff, Chief Executive Officer
COO: Ryan Thornton, Chief Clinical Officer
CFO: Chad Labrum, Chief Financial Officer
CMO: Daniel Kwak, M.D., Chief of Staff
CIO: Mark Rich, Director Information Services
CHR: Deena Mansfield, Director Human Resources
Web address: www.ashleyregional.com
**Control:** Corporation, Investor–owned, for–profit **Service:** General Medical and
Surgical

**Staffed Beds:** 39

### WEST JORDAN—Salt Lake County

☐ ◇ **JORDAN VALLEY MEDICAL CENTER (460051)**, 3580 West 9000 South,
Zip 84088–8812; tel. 801/561–8888, (Nonreporting) **A**1 9 10 21 **S** IASIS
Healthcare, Franklin, TN
Primary Contact: Steven Anderson, Chief Executive Officer
COO: Jon Butterfield, Chief Operating Officer
CFO: Kurt Shipley, Chief Financial Officer
CMO: B. Dee Allred, M.D., President Medical Staff
Web address: www.jordanvalleymc.com
**Control:** Partnership, Investor–owned, for–profit **Service:** General Medical and
Surgical

**Staffed Beds:** 183

### WEST VALLEY CITY—Salt Lake County

**PIONEER VALLEY HOSPITAL**, 3460 South Pioneer Parkway, Zip 84120–2049;
tel. 801/964–3100, (Nonreporting) **S** IASIS Healthcare, Franklin, TN
Primary Contact: Steven Anderson, Chief Executive Officer
COO: Jon Butterfield, Chief Operating Officer
CFO: Kurt Shipley, Chief Financial Officer
CMO: B. Dee Allred, M.D., President Medical Staff
CIO: Jodi DeJong, Director Marketing
Web address: www.pioneervalleyhospital.com
**Control:** Corporation, Investor–owned, for–profit **Service:** General Medical and
Surgical

**Staffed Beds:** 101

UT

# VERMONT

## BENNINGTON—Bennington County

⊠ **SOUTHWESTERN VERMONT MEDICAL CENTER (470012)**, 100 Hospital Drive, Zip 05201–5004; tel. 802/442–6361 **A**1 2 9 10 **F**11 13 15 18 28 29 30 31 34 40 43 45 49 60 62 63 68 70 77 78 79 81 84 85 87 107 108 110 115 119 120 121 129 130 135 145 146 147 148 **P**8
Primary Contact: Thomas A. Dee, Chief Executive Officer
CFO: Stephen D. Majetich, CPA, Chief Financial Officer
CMO: Trey Dobson, M.D., Chief Medical Officer
CIO: Richard Ogilvie, Chief Information Officer
CHR: Rudolph D. Weaver, Vice President Human Resources
CNO: Carol Conroy, R.N., Chief Nursing Officer
Web address: www.svhealthcare.org
**Control:** Other not–for–profit (including NFP Corporation) **Service:** General Medical and Surgical

> **Staffed Beds:** 77 **Admissions:** 3836 **Census:** 38 **Outpatient Visits:** 266751 **Births:** 413 **Total Expense ($000):** 136499 **Payroll Expense ($000):** 58446 **Personnel:** 583

## BERLIN—Washington County

⊠ **CENTRAL VERMONT MEDICAL CENTER (470001)**, 130 Fisher Road, Zip 05602–9516, Mailing Address: P.O. Box 547, Barre, Zip 05641–0547; tel. 802/371–4100, (Total facility includes 153 beds in nursing home–type unit) **A**1 2 9 10 **F**3 8 11 13 15 28 29 30 31 34 35 36 40 43 44 45 46 49 50 51 52 53 57 58 59 64 65 70 74 75 76 77 78 81 82 84 85 87 93 94 96 97 98 99 100 102 103 104 107 108 110 111 114 115 116 117 118 119 130 131 132 135 143 146 147 148 **P**6 8
Primary Contact: Judith C. Tartaglia, President and Chief Executive Officer
COO: Nancy Lothian, Chief Operating Officer and Chief Information Officer
CFO: Cheyenne Follard, Chief Financial Officer
CMO: Philip Brown, D.O., Vice President Medical Affairs
CIO: Nancy Lothian, Chief Operating Officer and Chief Information Officer
CHR: Robert Patterson, Vice President Human Resources and Rehabilitation Services
CNO: Alison White, R.N., Vice President Nursing and Quality
Web address: www.cvmc.org/
**Control:** Other not–for–profit (including NFP Corporation) **Service:** General Medical and Surgical

> **Staffed Beds:** 248 **Admissions:** 3520 **Census:** 178 **Outpatient Visits:** 273745 **Births:** 382 **Total Expense ($000):** 119301 **Payroll Expense ($000):** 52366

## BRATTLEBORO—Windham County

★ **BRATTLEBORO MEMORIAL HOSPITAL (470011)**, 17 Belmont Avenue, Zip 05301–3498; tel. 802/257–0341 **A**9 10 **F**3 8 11 13 14 15 17 18 28 29 30 31 34 35 39 40 45 49 51 53 55 57 59 64 68 70 74 75 76 77 78 79 81 85 87 93 107 108 110 114 118 119 130 131 132 135 146 147 148
Primary Contact: Steven R. Gordon, President and Chief Executive Officer
CFO: Michael Rogers, Vice President Fiscal Services
CMO: David Albright, M.D., Chief Medical Officer
CIO: Jonathan Farina, Chief Information Officer
CHR: Robin R. Heald, Director Human Resources
CHR: Michael Kelliher, Vice President Human Resources
CNO: Mary Urquhart, Vice President Patient Care
Web address: www.bmhvt.org
**Control:** Other not–for–profit (including NFP Corporation) **Service:** General Medical and Surgical

> **Staffed Beds:** 32 **Admissions:** 1687 **Census:** 16 **Outpatient Visits:** 76084 **Births:** 364 **Total Expense ($000):** 69188 **Payroll Expense ($000):** 27854 **Personnel:** 343

⊠ **BRATTLEBORO RETREAT (474001)**, Anna Marsh Lane, Zip 05301, Mailing Address: P.O. Box 803, Zip 05302–0803; tel. 802/257–7785 **A**1 5 9 10 **F**29 34 35 50 68 98 99 100 101 102 103 104 105 106
Primary Contact: Robert E. Simpson, Jr., M.P.H., President and Chief Executive Officer
CFO: John E. Blaha, Vice President Finance and Chief Financial Officer
CMO: Frederick Engstrom, M.D., Medical Director
CHR: Kathleen Brooks, Director Human Resources
Web address: www.brattlbororetreat.org
**Control:** Other not–for–profit (including NFP Corporation) **Service:** Psychiatric

> **Staffed Beds:** 108 **Admissions:** 3026 **Census:** 91 **Outpatient Visits:** 32543 **Births:** 0 **Total Expense ($000):** 55010 **Payroll Expense ($000):** 35656 **Personnel:** 492

## BURLINGTON—Chittenden County

⊠ **FLETCHER ALLEN HEALTH CARE (470003)**, 111 Colchester Avenue, Zip 05401–1473; tel. 802/847–0000, (Includes FANNY ALLEN CAMPUS, 101 College Parkway, Colchester, Zip 05446–3035; tel. 802/655–1234; MEDICAL CENTER HOSPITAL CAMPUS, Colchester Avenue, Zip 05401; tel. 802/847–2345; VERMONT CHILDREN'S HOSPITAL, 111 Colchester Avenue, tel. 802/847–0000) **A**1 2 3 5 8 9 10 **F**3 4 5 6 7 9 11 12 13 15 16 17 18 19 20 21 22 23 24 25 26 28 29 30 31 32 34 35 36 37 39 40 43 44 45 46 47 48 49 50 51 52 54 55 56 57 58 59 60 61 63 64 65 66 68 70 72 73 74 75 76 77 78 79 81 82 84 85 86 87 88 89 90 91 92 93 94 96 97 98 99 100 101 102 103 104 105 107 108 110 111 114 115 116 117 118 119 120 121 123 124 126 129 130 131 132 135 136 138 141 142 143 144 145 146 147 148 **P**6
Primary Contact: John R. Brumsted, M.D., President and Chief Executive Officer
COO: Sandra L. Felis, R.N., Senior Vice President Patient Care Services and Chief Nursing Officer
CFO: Roger Deshaies, Chief Financial Officer
CMO: Stephen Leffler, Chief Medical Officer
CIO: Charles H. Podesta, Vice President Information Services
CHR: Paul Macuga, Chief Human Resources Officer
Web address: www.fletcherallen.org
**Control:** Other not–for–profit (including NFP Corporation) **Service:** General Medical and Surgical

> **Staffed Beds:** 419 **Admissions:** 20491 **Census:** 315 **Outpatient Visits:** 1336088 **Births:** 2224 **Total Expense ($000):** 904316 **Payroll Expense ($000):** 441356 **Personnel:** 6084

## MIDDLEBURY—Addison County

⊠ **PORTER MEDICAL CENTER (471307)**, 115 Porter Drive, Zip 05753–8423; tel. 802/388–4701 **A**1 9 10 18 **F**3 8 11 13 15 18 26 29 40 43 45 50 59 64 68 70 75 76 79 81 85 86 93 97 107 108 111 114 115 119 130 133 146 **P**6
Primary Contact: James L. Daily, President
CFO: Marilyn A. Olejnik, Vice President Finance
CMO: Mike Kiernan, M.D., President Medical Staff
CIO: Denis Mailloux, Chief Information Officer
CHR: Dan Arseneau, Vice President Human Resources
CNO: Patricia Jannene, Vice President Patient Care Services
Web address: www.portermedical.org
**Control:** Other not–for–profit (including NFP Corporation) **Service:** General Medical and Surgical

> **Staffed Beds:** 25 **Admissions:** 1581 **Census:** 14 **Outpatient Visits:** 88931 **Births:** 338 **Total Expense ($000):** 68411

## MORRISVILLE—Lamoille County

★ **COPLEY HOSPITAL (471305)**, 528 Washington Highway, Zip 05661–8973; tel. 802/888–8888 **A**9 10 18 **F**13 15 18 28 29 30 31 34 35 39 40 58 59 64 65 70 74 75 76 77 78 79 81 85 86 93 107 110 111 119 129 130 131 133 135 146 147
Primary Contact: Melvyn Patashnick, President and Chief Executive Officer
COO: Greg Ward, Vice President Operations
CFO: Rassoul Rangaviz, Chief Financial Officer
CMO: Joel Silverstein, M.D., Chief Medical Officer
CIO: Greg Ward, Vice President Operations
CHR: April E. Tuck, Vice President Human Resources and Compliance
CNO: Jina Cate, Interim Chief Nursing Officer
Web address: www.copleyvt.org
**Control:** Other not–for–profit (including NFP Corporation) **Service:** General Medical and Surgical

> **Staffed Beds:** 25 **Admissions:** 1619 **Census:** 14 **Outpatient Visits:** 71694 **Births:** 193 **Total Expense ($000):** 52253 **Payroll Expense ($000):** 25946 **Personnel:** 328

**VT**

---

**Hospital, Medicare Provider Number, Address, Telephone, Approval, Facility, and Physician Codes, Health Care System**

★ American Hospital Association (AHA) membership
□ The Joint Commission accreditation
◇ DNV Healthcare Inc. accreditation
○ Healthcare Facilities Accreditation Program
△ Commission on Accreditation of Rehabilitation Facilities (CARF) accreditation

### NEWPORT—Orleans County

★ **NORTH COUNTRY HOSPITAL AND HEALTH CENTER (471304)**, 189 Prouty Drive, Zip 05855–9326; tel. 802/334–7331 **A**9 10 18 **F**11 13 15 28 30 31 34 40 45 53 70 74 75 76 77 78 79 81 82 84 89 93 104 107 108 110 111 114 118 119 127 129 130 131 133 135 146 148
Primary Contact: Claudio D. Fort, President and Chief Executive Officer
CFO: Andre Bissonnette, Vice President Finance
CMO: Marc Bouchard, M.D., President Medical Staff
CIO: Ervin Goodwin, Manager Information Services
CHR: William Perket, Vice President Human Resources
CNO: Sheryl M. Washburn, MSN, Vice President Patient Care Services
Web address: www.nchsi.org
**Control:** Other not–for–profit (including NFP Corporation) **Service:** General Medical and Surgical

**Staffed Beds:** 25 **Admissions:** 1493 **Census:** 15 **Outpatient Visits:** 77650 **Births:** 220 **Total Expense ($000):** 77874 **Payroll Expense ($000):** 35017 **Personnel:** 471

### RANDOLPH—Orange County

★ **GIFFORD MEDICAL CENTER (471301)**, 44 South Main Street, Zip 05060–1381, Mailing Address: P.O. Box 2000, Zip 05060–2000; tel. 802/728–7000, (Nonreporting) **A**2 9 10 18
Primary Contact: Joseph L. Woodin, President and Chief Executive Officer
CFO: Jeff Hebert, Interim Vice President Finance
CMO: Joshua Plavin, M.D., Medical Director Medicine Division
CIO: Sean Patrick, Director Information Systems
CHR: Janice Davis, Interim Director Human Resources
CNO: Linda Minsinger, Vice President Hospital Division
Web address: www.giffordmed.org
**Control:** Other not–for–profit (including NFP Corporation) **Service:** General Medical and Surgical

**Staffed Beds:** 82

### RUTLAND—Rutland County

⌧ **RUTLAND REGIONAL MEDICAL CENTER (470005)**, 160 Allen Street, Zip 05701–4595; tel. 802/775–7111 **A**1 2 9 10 **F**13 15 18 20 22 23 24 28 29 31 34 36 38 40 45 47 48 49 51 55 57 59 61 64 65 70 76 77 78 79 81 82 83 84 85 87 90 92 93 94 98 100 101 102 103 104 107 108 111 115 116 117 118 119 128 129 130 132 133 135 146 147 148
Primary Contact: Thomas W. Huebner, President
CFO: Ed Ogorzalek, Chief Financial Officer
CIO: John Kijewski, Vice President and Chief Information Officer
Web address: www.rrmc.org
**Control:** Other not–for–profit (including NFP Corporation) **Service:** General Medical and Surgical

**Staffed Beds:** 139 **Admissions:** 6257 **Census:** 89 **Outpatient Visits:** 192628 **Births:** 280 **Total Expense ($000):** 197474 **Payroll Expense ($000):** 69162 **Personnel:** 1106

### SAINT ALBANS—Franklin County

⌧ **NORTHWESTERN MEDICAL CENTER (470024)**, 133 Fairfield Street, Zip 05478–1726; tel. 802/524–5911, (Nonreporting) **A**1 2 9 10 20 **S** QHR, Brentwood, TN
Primary Contact: Jill Berry Bowen, President and Chief Executive Officer
CFO: Ted D. Sirotta, Chief Financial Officer
CIO: Stephen C. Stata, Interim Chief Technology Officer
CHR: Mary Lou Beaulieu, Director Human Resources and Compliance Officer
Web address: www.northwesternmedicalcenter.org
**Control:** Other not–for–profit (including NFP Corporation) **Service:** General Medical and Surgical

**Staffed Beds:** 20

### SAINT JOHNSBURY—Caledonia County

★ **NORTHEASTERN VERMONT REGIONAL HOSPITAL (471303)**, 1315 Hospital Drive, Zip 05819–9210, Mailing Address: PO Box 905, Zip 05819–0905; tel. 802/748–8141 **A**9 10 18 **F**3 11 13 15 18 26 28 29 30 34 35 40 44 45 50 51 59 64 68 70 74 75 76 77 79 81 84 86 87 89 93 107 108 110 111 115 118 119 127 129 130 131 132 133 135 146 147 **P**6
Primary Contact: Paul R. Bengtson, Chief Executive Officer
CFO: Robert Hersey, Chief Financial Officer
CIO: Andrea Lott, Vice President Information Services
CHR: Betty Ann Gwatkin, Vice President Human Resources
CNO: Veronica T. Hychalk, MSN, Vice President Professional Services
Web address: www.nvrh.org
**Control:** Other not–for–profit (including NFP Corporation) **Service:** General Medical and Surgical

**Staffed Beds:** 25 **Admissions:** 1416 **Census:** 13 **Outpatient Visits:** 155338 **Births:** 210 **Total Expense ($000):** 59073 **Payroll Expense ($000):** 26844 **Personnel:** 351

### SPRINGFIELD—Windsor County

**SPRINGFIELD HOSPITAL (471306)**, 25 Ridgewood Road, Zip 05156–3050, Mailing Address: P.O. Box 2003, Zip 05156–2003; tel. 802/885–2151, (Nonreporting) **A**9 10 18
Primary Contact: Glenn D. Cordner, Chief Executive Officer
CFO: Laverne Lindamood, Director Finance
CMO: Mark C. Hamilton, M.D., President Medical Staff
Web address: www.springfieldhospital.org
**Control:** Other not–for–profit (including NFP Corporation) **Service:** General Medical and Surgical

**Staffed Beds:** 35

### TOWNSHEND—Windham County

★ **GRACE COTTAGE HOSPITAL (471300)**, 185 Grafton Road, Zip 05353–0216, Mailing Address: P.O. Box 216, Zip 05353–0216; tel. 802/365–7357 **A**9 10 18 **F**3 11 29 30 34 40 50 53 56 57 59 64 68 75 77 85 87 93 97 102 104 107 114 119 127 128 130 131 132 133 135 146 148 **P**6
Primary Contact: Margaret S. Cleary, Interim Chief Executive Officer
CFO: Stephen A. Brown, Chief Financial Officer
CMO: Timothy Shafer, M.D., Medical Director
CIO: Tony Marques, Director Information Systems
CHR: Christopher J. Lackney, Director Human Resources
CNO: Jeanne M. Fortier, R.N., Vice President Patient Care Services
Web address: www.gracecottage.org
**Control:** Other not–for–profit (including NFP Corporation) **Service:** General Medical and Surgical

**Staffed Beds:** 19 **Admissions:** 473 **Census:** 12 **Outpatient Visits:** 42382 **Births:** 0 **Total Expense ($000):** 18017 **Payroll Expense ($000):** 10206 **Personnel:** 151

### WHITE RIVER JUNCTION—Windsor County

⌧ **WHITE RIVER JUNCTION VETERANS AFFAIRS MEDICAL CENTER**, (Formerly Veterans Affairs Medical Center), 215 North Main Street, Zip 05009–0001; tel. 802/295–9363 **A**1 3 5 8 **F**3 5 8 9 12 18 20 29 31 34 35 36 38 39 40 44 45 46 49 50 53 54 56 57 58 59 60 61 62 63 64 65 70 74 75 77 78 79 81 82 84 85 86 87 93 94 95 96 97 98 100 101 102 103 104 105 107 108 111 115 118 119 127 130 132 135 141 143 144 146 147 148 **P**1 6
**S** Department of Veterans Affairs, Washington, DC
Primary Contact: Marc Levenson, M.D., Acting Director
CFO: Joan Wilmot, Chief Finance Officer
CMO: Melanie Thompson, M.D., Acting Chief of Staff
CIO: Matthew Rafus, Chief Information Officer
CHR: Barbara Nadeau, Chief Human Resources Management Service
Web address: www.whiteriver.va.gov/
**Control:** Veterans Affairs, Government, federal **Service:** General Medical and Surgical

**Staffed Beds:** 60 **Admissions:** 2969 **Census:** 40 **Outpatient Visits:** 369540 **Births:** 0 **Total Expense ($000):** 166523 **Payroll Expense ($000):** 68506 **Personnel:** 898

### WINDSOR—Windsor County

★ **MT. ASCUTNEY HOSPITAL AND HEALTH CENTER (471302)**, 289 County Road, Zip 05089–9000; tel. 802/674–6711, (Total facility includes 25 beds in nursing home–type unit) **A**9 10 18 **F**3 8 10 11 15 28 29 30 31 32 34 35 36 40 41 44 45 49 50 54 56 57 59 63 64 65 66 68 69 70 71 75 77 78 79 81 82 84 85 86 87 90 91 92 93 94 96 97 100 104 107 110 111 114 119 125 128 130 131 132 133 134 135 143 146 148 **P**6
Primary Contact: Kevin Donovan, Chief Executive Officer
COO: Paul Calandrella, Chief Operating Officer
CMO: Catherine Schneider, M.D., Chief Medical Officer
CIO: Brenna Heighes, Manager Information Technology
CHR: Jean Martaniuk, Director Human Resources
CNO: Jill Lord, MS, Director Patient Care Services
Web address: www.mtascutneyhospital.org
**Control:** Other not–for–profit (including NFP Corporation) **Service:** General Medical and Surgical

**Staffed Beds:** 60 **Admissions:** 1018 **Census:** 49 **Outpatient Visits:** 90339 **Births:** 0 **Total Expense ($000):** 47854 **Payroll Expense ($000):** 22040 **Personnel:** 459

VT

*Many Facility Codes have changed. Please refer to the AHA Guide Code Chart.*
© 2013 AHA Guide

# VIRGINIA

## ABINGDON—Washington County

✠ **JOHNSTON MEMORIAL HOSPITAL (490053)**, 16000 Johnston Memorial Drive, Zip 24211–7659; tel. 276/676–7000 **A**1 2 9 10 **F**3 11 13 14 15 34 35 37 40 49 50 51 54 57 59 61 62 64 68 70 74 75 76 77 78 79 81 82 85 86 87 93 103 107 108 110 111 114 115 118 119 121 123 130 131 132 135 146 147 148 **P**6 8 **S** Mountain States Health Alliance, Johnson City, TN
Primary Contact: Sean S. McMurray, FACHE, Vice President and Chief Executive Officer
CFO: Timothy Evans, Chief Financial Officer
CFO: John Jeter, Assistant Administrator and Chief Financial Officer
CIO: Jackson Dale, Director Management Information Services
CHR: Jackie G. Phipps, Director Human Resources
Web address: www.jmh.org
**Control:** Other not–for–profit (including NFP Corporation) **Service:** General Medical and Surgical

> **Staffed Beds:** 116 **Admissions:** 7135 **Census:** 70 **Outpatient Visits:** 121885
> **Births:** 783 **Total Expense ($000):** 113908 **Payroll Expense ($000):** 36595
> **Personnel:** 741

## ALDIE—Loudoun County

★ **HEALTHSOUTH REHABILITATION HOSPITAL OF NORTHERN VIRGINIA (493033)**, 24430 Millstream Drive, Zip 20105–3098; tel. 703/957–2000 **A**10 **F**29 34 35 57 64 68 75 77 90 93 95 96 132 148 **S** HEALTHSOUTH Corporation, Birmingham, AL
Primary Contact: Gary J. Herbek, Chief Executive Officer
Web address: www.healthsouthnorthernvirginia.com
**Control:** Corporation, Investor–owned, for–profit **Service:** Rehabilitation

> **Staffed Beds:** 40 **Admissions:** 992 **Census:** 37 **Outpatient Visits:** 890
> **Births:** 0 **Total Expense ($000):** 12746 **Payroll Expense ($000):** 7974
> **Personnel:** 136

## ALEXANDRIA—Alexandria City County

✠ **INOVA ALEXANDRIA HOSPITAL (490040)**, 4320 Seminary Road, Zip 22304–1535; tel. 703/504–3167 **A**1 2 5 9 10 **F**3 11 13 14 15 17 18 20 22 24 26 28 29 30 31 34 35 38 39 40 42 44 45 48 49 50 51 54 55 57 59 60 61 63 64 65 66 68 69 70 72 74 75 76 77 78 79 80 81 82 84 85 86 87 89 92 93 100 101 102 107 108 110 111 114 115 117 118 119 120 121 123 124 129 130 131 132 135 145 146 147 148 **P**6 **S** Inova Health System, Falls Church, VA
Primary Contact: Christine Candio, Chief Executive Officer
CFO: Todd Lockcuff, Chief Financial Officer
CMO: John R. Audett, M.D., Chief Medical Officer
CIO: Geoffrey Brown, Senior Vice President Information Services
CHR: Hugo Aguas, Vice President Human Resources
CNO: Mary Dixon, R.N., Chief Nursing Executive
Web address: www.inova.org
**Control:** Other not–for–profit (including NFP Corporation) **Service:** General Medical and Surgical

> **Staffed Beds:** 334 **Admissions:** 16195 **Census:** 203 **Outpatient Visits:** 254177 **Births:** 3789 **Total Expense ($000):** 284985 **Payroll Expense ($000):** 107610 **Personnel:** 1636

✠ △ **INOVA MOUNT VERNON HOSPITAL (490122)**, 2501 Parker's Lane, Zip 22306–3209; tel. 703/664–7000 **A**1 2 3 5 7 9 10 **F**3 5 11 14 15 18 26 28 29 30 31 34 35 37 38 39 40 44 45 48 49 50 51 55 57 58 59 60 61 63 64 65 66 68 69 70 74 75 77 78 79 80 81 82 84 85 86 87 90 91 92 93 94 96 98 100 101 102 103 104 105 107 108 110 111 114 115 118 119 130 131 132 135 145 146 148 **S** Inova Health System, Falls Church, VA
Primary Contact: Barbara J. Doyle, R.N., MS, Senior Vice President and Chief Executive Officer
CFO: Tammy Razmic, Associate Administrator Finance and Chief Financial Officer
CHR: Bev Sugar, Associate Administrator and Director Human Resources
Web address: www.inova.org
**Control:** Other not–for–profit (including NFP Corporation) **Service:** General Medical and Surgical

> **Staffed Beds:** 237 **Admissions:** 8364 **Census:** 137 **Outpatient Visits:** 78545
> **Births:** 0 **Total Expense ($000):** 158912 **Payroll Expense ($000):** 59581
> **Personnel:** 894

## ARLINGTON—Arlington County

**CAPITAL HOSPICE (490129)**, 4715 15th Street North, Zip 22205–2640; tel. 703/538–2065, (Nonreporting) **A**3 10
Primary Contact: Malene S. Davis, R.N., President and Chief Executive Officer
CFO: David Schwind, Chief Financial Officer
CIO: Diane Rigsby, Chief Information Officer
Web address: www.capitalhospice.org
**Control:** Other not–for–profit (including NFP Corporation) **Service:** Other specialty

> **Staffed Beds:** 15

✠ △ **VIRGINIA HOSPITAL CENTER – ARLINGTON (490050)**, 1701 North George Mason Drive, Zip 22205–3698; tel. 703/558–5000 **A**1 2 3 5 7 9 10 **F**3 4 5 8 11 12 13 15 17 18 20 22 24 26 28 29 30 31 34 35 37 38 40 45 46 47 48 49 50 51 54 57 59 60 61 62 64 65 66 68 70 72 73 74 75 76 78 79 81 85 86 87 89 90 92 93 94 95 96 97 98 100 102 103 104 105 107 110 111 114 115 116 117 118 119 120 121 123 124 126 129 130 132 135 144 145 146 147 148 **P**6
Primary Contact: James B. Cole, Chief Executive Officer
COO: Carl Bahnlein, Executive Vice President and Chief Operating Officer
CFO: Robin Norman, Senior Vice President and Chief Financial Officer
CMO: Jeffrey P. DiLisi, Vice President and Chief Medical Officer
CIO: David Crutchfield, Vice President and Chief Information Officer
CHR: Michael Malone, Vice President and Chief Human Resources Officer
CNO: Darlene Vrotsos, R.N., Vice President and Chief Nursing Officer
Web address: www.virginiahospitalcenter.com
**Control:** Other not–for–profit (including NFP Corporation) **Service:** General Medical and Surgical

> **Staffed Beds:** 357 **Admissions:** 21358 **Census:** 245 **Outpatient Visits:** 327725 **Births:** 4646 **Total Expense ($000):** 334370 **Payroll Expense ($000):** 134678 **Personnel:** 2071

## BEDFORD—Bedford City County

✠ **BEDFORD MEMORIAL HOSPITAL (490088)**, 1613 Oakwood Street, Zip 24523–1213, Mailing Address: P.O. Box 688, Zip 24523–0688; tel. 540/586–2441, (Total facility includes 111 beds in nursing home–type unit) **A**1 9 10 **F**2 3 11 15 18 19 28 29 30 34 35 40 53 57 59 63 67 70 81 84 85 93 97 107 119 128 129 130 134 143 145 146 148 **S** Carilion Clinic, Roanoke, VA
Primary Contact: Patti Jurkus, Vice President, Regional Hospital
CFO: Donald E. Lorton, Executive Vice President
CMO: E. Allen Joslyn, M.D., Chief Medical Officer
Web address: www.bmhva.com
**Control:** Other not–for–profit (including NFP Corporation) **Service:** General Medical and Surgical

> **Staffed Beds:** 124 **Admissions:** 1872 **Census:** 112 **Outpatient Visits:** 25863
> **Births:** 0 **Total Expense ($000):** 32439 **Payroll Expense ($000):** 13833
> **Personnel:** 307

## BIG STONE GAP—Wise County

✠ **WELLMONT LONESOME PINE HOSPITAL (490114)**, 1990 Holton Avenue East, Zip 24219–3350; tel. 276/523–3111 **A**1 9 10 13 **F**3 11 13 15 18 29 30 31 34 35 40 49 50 57 59 63 68 70 76 77 78 79 81 85 87 89 93 97 107 111 116 117 118 119 120 121 130 146 **S** Wellmont Health System, Kingsport, TN
Primary Contact: Fred L. Pelle, FACHE, Interim President and Chief Executive Officer
CMO: Michael Vacco, M.D., Chief Medical Officer
CHR: Bobby Collins, Director Human Resources
CNO: Lori B. Cole, R.N., Vice President Care Services
Web address: www.wellmont.org
**Control:** Other not–for–profit (including NFP Corporation) **Service:** General Medical and Surgical

> **Staffed Beds:** 60 **Admissions:** 1955 **Census:** 16 **Outpatient Visits:** 35006
> **Births:** 206 **Total Expense ($000):** 36859 **Payroll Expense ($000):** 9248
> **Personnel:** 196

**VA**

---

**Hospital, Medicare Provider Number, Address, Telephone, Approval, Facility, and Physician Codes, Health Care System**

★ American Hospital Association (AHA) membership
□ The Joint Commission accreditation
◇ DNV Healthcare Inc. accreditation
○ Healthcare Facilities Accreditation Program
△ Commission on Accreditation of Rehabilitation Facilities (CARF) accreditation

**BLACKSBURG—Montgomery County**

✠ **LEWISGALE HOSPITAL MONTGOMERY (490110)**, (Formerly Montgomery Regional Hospital), 3700 South Main Street, Zip 24060–7081, Mailing Address: P.O. Box 90004, Zip 24062–9004; tel. 540/951–1111, (Nonreporting) **A**1 9 10 12 13 **S** HCA, Nashville, TN
Primary Contact: Alan J. Fabian, Chief Executive Officer
COO: David Cashwell, Chief Operating Officer
CFO: Timothy W. Haasken, Chief Financial Officer
CMO: C. Y. Davis, M.D., Chief Medical Officer
CHR: Kristie Walker, Director Human Resources
Web address: www.mrhospital.com
**Control:** Corporation, Investor–owned, for–profit **Service:** General Medical and Surgical

Staffed Beds: 103

**BRISTOL—Bristol City County**

✠ **REHABILITATION HOSPITAL OF SOUTHWEST VIRGINIA (493034)**, 103 North Street, Zip 24201–3201; tel. 276/642–7900, (Nonreporting) **A**1 10 **S** HEALTHSOUTH Corporation, Birmingham, AL
Primary Contact: Georgeanne Cole, Chief Executive Officer
Web address: www.rehabilitationhospitalsswvirginia.com
**Control:** Corporation, Investor–owned, for–profit **Service:** Rehabilitation

Staffed Beds: 25

**BURKEVILLE—Nottoway County**

☐ **PIEDMONT GERIATRIC HOSPITAL (490134)**, 5001 East Patrick Henry Highway, Zip 23922–3460, Mailing Address: P.O. Box 427, Zip 23922–0427; tel. 434/767–4401, (Nonreporting) **A**1 9 10 **S** Virginia Department of Mental Health, Richmond, VA
Primary Contact: Stephen M. Herrick, Ph.D., Director
CFO: James G. Ayers, Chief Financial Officer
CMO: Hugo Falcon, M.D., Director Medical Services
CHR: Michael Wimsatt, Director Human Resources
Web address: www.pgh.dmhmrsas.virginia.gov
**Control:** State–Government, nonfederal **Service:** Other specialty

Staffed Beds: 150

**CATAWBA—Roanoke County**

☐ **CATAWBA HOSPITAL (490135)**, 5525 Catawba Hospital Drive, Zip 24070–2115, Mailing Address: P.O. Box 200, Zip 24070–0200; tel. 540/375–4200 **A**1 9 10 **F**29 30 35 38 39 44 50 68 75 77 98 103 130 146 **P**6 **S** Virginia Department of Mental Health, Richmond, VA
Primary Contact: Walton F. Mitchell, III, Director
COO: Charles Law, Chief Operating Officer
CFO: Cecil Hardin, CPA, Chief Financial Officer
CMO: Yad Jabbarpour, M.D., Chief of Staff
CIO: Charles Law, Chief Operating Officer
CHR: Patricia Ebbett, Chief Human Resources Officer
Web address: www.catawba.dmhmrsas.virginia.gov
**Control:** State–Government, nonfederal **Service:** Psychiatric

Staffed Beds: 110 Admissions: 309 Census: 93 Outpatient Visits: 0 Births: 0 Total Expense ($000): 19374 Payroll Expense ($000): 11811 Personnel: 264

**CHARLOTTESVILLE—Charlottesville City County**

✠ ◇ **MARTHA JEFFERSON HOSPITAL (490077)**, 500 Martha Jefferson Drive, Zip 22911–4668; tel. 434/654–7000 **A**1 2 3 5 9 10 21 **F**3 8 12 13 15 18 20 22 26 28 29 30 31 34 35 36 40 42 45 46 48 49 50 52 54 57 59 64 68 70 74 75 76 78 79 81 82 84 85 86 87 89 92 93 94 97 98 107 108 110 111 114 115 118 119 120 121 123 124 129 130 132 135 145 146 147 148 **P**1 **S** Sentara Healthcare, Norfolk, VA
Primary Contact: James E. Haden, President and Chief Executive Officer
COO: Elliot H. Kuida, Vice President and Chief Operating Officer
CFO: J. Michael Burris, Vice President Corporate Services and Chief Financial Officer
CMO: F. Michael Ashby, M.D., Vice President and Medical Director
CIO: Marijo Lecker, Vice President
CHR: Susan M. Cabell–Mains, Vice President Administration
Web address: www.marthajefferson.org
**Control:** Other not–for–profit (including NFP Corporation) **Service:** General Medical and Surgical

Staffed Beds: 139 Admissions: 11046 Census: 98 Outpatient Visits: 438221 Births: 1759 Total Expense ($000): 226820 Payroll Expense ($000): 97481 Personnel: 1497

**TRANSITIONAL CARE HOSPITAL (492011)**, 2965 Ivy Road (250 West), Zip 22903–9330; tel. 434/924–7897 **A**10 **F**1 3 29 77 85 94 114 130 146 148 **P**3 **S** UVA Health System, Charlottesville, VA
Primary Contact: Michelle Hereford, Administrator
Web address: www.uvahealth.com/services/transitional–care–hospital
**Control:** State–Government, nonfederal **Service:** Long–Term Acute Care hospital

Staffed Beds: 40 Admissions: 222 Census: 16 Outpatient Visits: 0 Births: 0 Total Expense ($000): 14126 Payroll Expense ($000): 4702 Personnel: 77

✠ △ **UNIVERSITY OF VIRGINIA MEDICAL CENTER (490009)**, 1215 Lee Street, Zip 22908–0001, Mailing Address: P.O. Box 800809, Zip 22908–0809; tel. 434/924–0211, (Includes UNIVERSITY OF VIRGINIA CHILDREN'S HOSPITAL, PO Box 800566, Zip 22901; tel. 434/982–4453) **A**1 2 3 5 7 8 9 10 **F**3 4 5 6 7 8 9 11 12 13 15 16 17 18 19 20 21 22 23 24 25 26 27 28 29 30 31 32 34 35 36 37 38 39 40 41 43 44 45 46 47 48 49 50 51 52 54 55 56 57 58 59 60 61 62 64 65 66 68 70 71 72 73 74 75 76 77 78 79 80 81 82 83 84 85 86 87 88 89 90 91 92 93 94 97 98 99 100 101 102 103 104 107 108 110 111 112 114 115 116 117 118 119 120 121 123 124 126 129 130 131 132 134 135 136 137 138 139 140 141 142 143 145 146 147 148 **P**3 4 **S** UVA Health System, Charlottesville, VA
Primary Contact: R. Edward Howell, Vice President and Chief Executive Officer
COO: Robert Cofield, Dr.PH, Chief Operating Officer and Associate Vice President
CFO: Larry Fitzgerald, Chief Financial Officer
CMO: Jonathon D. Truwit, M.D., Chief Medical Officer
CIO: Barbara Baldwin, Chief Information Officer
CHR: John Boswell, Associate Chief Human Resources
Web address: www.healthsystem.virginia.edu
**Control:** State–Government, nonfederal **Service:** General Medical and Surgical

Staffed Beds: 565 Admissions: 28639 Census: 453 Outpatient Visits: 1702522 Births: 1570 Total Expense ($000): 1071260 Payroll Expense ($000): 384072 Personnel: 6445

✠ **UVA–HEALTHSOUTH REHABILITATION HOSPITAL (493029)**, 515 Ray C. Hunt Drive, Zip 22903–2981; tel. 434/244–2000 **A**1 3 5 10 **F**29 64 74 77 82 90 93 94 131 **S** HEALTHSOUTH Corporation, Birmingham, AL
Primary Contact: Thomas J. Cook, Chief Executive Officer
Web address: www.uvahealthsouth.com
**Control:** Corporation, Investor–owned, for–profit **Service:** Rehabilitation

Staffed Beds: 50 Admissions: 1083 Census: 38 Outpatient Visits: 24870 Births: 0 Total Expense ($000): 19581 Payroll Expense ($000): 12585 Personnel: 213

**CHESAPEAKE—Chesapeake City County**

✠ **CHESAPEAKE REGIONAL MEDICAL CENTER (490120)**, 736 Battlefield Boulevard North, Zip 23320–4941, Mailing Address: P.O. Box 2028, Zip 23327–2028; tel. 757/312–8121 **A**1 2 9 10 **F**3 6 8 10 11 12 13 15 18 20 22 26 28 29 30 31 34 35 40 44 45 46 49 50 53 54 57 58 59 61 62 63 64 65 66 68 69 70 71 73 74 75 76 77 78 79 81 84 85 86 87 89 91 93 100 101 102 103 107 108 110 111 114 115 118 119 120 121 123 129 130 132 135 141 142 143 146 147 148 **P**6
Primary Contact: Peter F. Bastone, Chief Executive Officer
COO: Robert Guanci, Chief Operating Officer
CFO: Michael Corcoran, Chief Financial Officer
CMO: Cynthia Romero, M.D., Chief Medical Officer
CIO: Ken Deans, Chief Information Officer
Web address: www.chesapeakeregional.com
**Control:** Hospital district or authority, Government, nonfederal **Service:** General Medical and Surgical

Staffed Beds: 310 Admissions: 14424 Census: 186 Outpatient Visits: 189302 Births: 2700 Total Expense ($000): 240451 Payroll Expense ($000): 98631 Personnel: 1759

**CHRISTIANSBURG—Montgomery County**

✠ **CARILION NEW RIVER VALLEY MEDICAL CENTER (490042)**, 2900 Lamb Circle, Zip 24073–6344, Mailing Address: P.O. Box 5, Radford, Zip 24143–0005; tel. 540/731–2000 **A**1 9 10 19 **F**3 5 12 13 15 18 28 29 30 31 34 35 40 43 45 47 48 49 50 51 57 59 62 63 64 68 70 74 75 76 77 79 81 84 85 86 87 89 93 96 98 99 102 103 104 105 107 108 110 111 114 115 117 119 126 129 130 135 146 147 148 **S** Carilion Clinic, Roanoke, VA
Primary Contact: John S. Piatkowski, M.D., Vice President, Regional Hospital
CFO: Rob Vaughan, Chief Financial Officer
CMO: Dennis Means, M.D., Vice President Medical Affairs
CIO: Daniel Borchi, Chief Information Officer
CHR: Patti Jurkus, Director Human Resources
Web address: www.carilionclinic.org/Carilion/cnrv
**Control:** Other not–for–profit (including NFP Corporation) **Service:** General Medical and Surgical

Staffed Beds: 146 Admissions: 7915 Census: 82 Outpatient Visits: 89843 Births: 1235 Total Expense ($000): 128431 Payroll Expense ($000): 47957 Personnel: 820

**CLINTWOOD—Dickenson County**

**DICKENSON COMMUNITY HOSPITAL (491303)**, 312 Hospital Drive, Zip 24228, Mailing Address: P.O. Box 1440, Zip 24228–1440; tel. 276/926–0300 **A**9 10 18 **F**3 11 29 30 40 50 57 64 68 75 85 86 97 107 119 130 133 146 **P**6 8 **S** Mountain States Health Alliance, Johnson City, TN
Primary Contact: Mark T. Leonard, Chief Executive Officer
CFO: Stephen Sawyer, Chief Financial Officer
CMO: Erin Mullins, D.O., Chief Medical Staff
CHR: Valeri J. Colyer, Director Human Resources
Web address: www.msha.com/dch
**Control:** Other not–for–profit (including NFP Corporation) **Service:** General Medical and Surgical

Staffed Beds: 2 Admissions: 11 Census: 1 Outpatient Visits: 21106 Births: 0 Total Expense ($000): 5558 Payroll Expense ($000): 2595 Personnel: 37

**VA**

## CULPEPER—Culpeper County

⊞ **CULPEPER REGIONAL HOSPITAL (490019)**, 501 Sunset Lane, Zip 22701–3917, Mailing Address: P.O. Box 592, Zip 22701–0500; tel. 540/829–4100 **A**1 3 5 9 10 **F**3 7 8 11 15 18 28 29 30 34 35 36 37 38 40 45 50 54 57 59 64 68 70 74 75 76 77 78 79 81 82 85 87 93 97 102 107 108 110 111 114 119 120 121 123 130 132 133 135 143 146 148 **P**6 8
Primary Contact: H. Lee Kirk, Jr., FACHE, President and Chief Executive Officer
COO: Greg Napps, Vice President Operations and Chief Operating Officer
CFO: Samuel Morgan, Senior Vice President Financial Operations
CMO: Ralph DeSimone, M.D., President Medical Staff
CIO: Brian Rock, Director Information Systems
CHR: Susan Edwards, Vice President Human Resources
CNO: Janice Suter, R.N., Vice President Services and Chief Nursing Officer
Web address: www.culpeperhealth.org
**Control:** Other not–for–profit (including NFP Corporation) **Service:** General Medical and Surgical

**Staffed Beds:** 68 **Admissions:** 3155 **Census:** 31 **Outpatient Visits:** 64395 **Births:** 383 **Total Expense ($000):** 67604 **Payroll Expense ($000):** 29365 **Personnel:** 583

## DANVILLE—Danville City County

⊞ **DANVILLE REGIONAL MEDICAL CENTER (490075)**, 142 South Main Street, Zip 24541–2922; tel. 434/799–2100, (Nonreporting) **A**1 2 6 9 10 12 13 **S** LifePoint Hospitals, Inc., Brentwood, TN
Primary Contact: Eric Deaton, Chief Executive Officer
CFO: Mark T. Anderson, Chief Financial Officer
CMO: James F. Starling, M.D., Chief Medical Officer
CIO: David Cartwright, Director Management Information Systems
Web address: www.danvilleregional.org
**Control:** Other not–for–profit (including NFP Corporation) **Service:** General Medical and Surgical

**Staffed Beds:** 151

☐ **SOUTHERN VIRGINIA MENTAL HEALTH INSTITUTE (494017)**, 382 Taylor Drive, Zip 24541–4023; tel. 434/799–6220 **A**1 9 10 **F**34 50 57 68 75 77 86 87 98 101 102 130 132 146 **P**6 **S** Virginia Department of Mental Health, Richmond, VA
Primary Contact: David M. Lyon, Director
CFO: Wade Hopkins, Administrator
CMO: B. R. Ashby, Jr., M.D., President and Chief Executive Officer
CIO: Bracken Jones, Director Information Technology
CHR: Pauline Wasiuk, Director Human Resources
Web address: www.svmhi.dmhmrsas.virginia.gov
**Control:** State–Government, nonfederal **Service:** Psychiatric

**Staffed Beds:** 72 **Admissions:** 287 **Census:** 71 **Outpatient Visits:** 0 **Births:** 0 **Total Expense ($000):** 12685 **Payroll Expense ($000):** 7417

## EMPORIA—Emporia City County

⊞ **SOUTHERN VIRGINIA REGIONAL MEDICAL CENTER (490097)**, 727 North Main Street, Zip 23847–1274; tel. 434/348–4400 **A**1 9 10 **F**3 11 15 26 28 29 30 31 39 40 45 49 57 59 62 64 70 77 78 79 81 82 85 89 93 98 103 107 115 119 124 129 130 133 146 148 **S** Community Health Systems, Inc., Franklin, TN
Primary Contact: Eric Lachance, Chief Executive Officer
CFO: Kevin Cargill, Chief Financial Officer
CMO: Michael S. Anderson, M.D., Chief of Staff
CIO: Brian Hopkins, Director Management Information Systems
CHR: Becky Parrish, Director Human Resources
CNO: Linda Burnette, R.N., Chief Nursing Officer
Web address: www.svrmc.com
**Control:** Corporation, Investor–owned, for–profit **Service:** General Medical and Surgical

**Staffed Beds:** 80 **Admissions:** 2429 **Census:** 33 **Outpatient Visits:** 23722 **Births:** 0 **Total Expense ($000):** 34542 **Payroll Expense ($000):** 11676 **Personnel:** 261

## FAIRFAX—Fairfax County

⊞ **INOVA FAIR OAKS HOSPITAL (490101)**, 3600 Joseph Siewick Drive, Zip 22033–1798; tel. 703/391–3600 **A**1 2 3 5 9 10 **F**3 11 12 13 14 15 18 29 30 31 32 34 35 37 38 39 40 44 45 47 48 49 50 51 54 55 57 59 60 61 63 64 65 66 68 69 70 72 74 75 76 77 78 79 80 81 82 84 85 86 87 89 92 93 100 101 102 107 108 110 111 114 115 118 119 126 129 130 131 132 135 145 146 147 148 **S** Inova Health System, Falls Church, VA
Primary Contact: John L. Fitzgerald, Chief Executive Officer
CFO: Bill Bane, Assistant Vice President and Chief Financial Officer
CMO: G. Michael Lynch, M.D., Chief Medical Officer
CIO: Geoffrey Brown, Chief Information Officer
CHR: Jennifer Gertenbach, Director Human Resources
Web address: www.inova.org
**Control:** Other not–for–profit (including NFP Corporation) **Service:** General Medical and Surgical

**Staffed Beds:** 196 **Admissions:** 13188 **Census:** 123 **Outpatient Visits:** 122213 **Births:** 3649 **Total Expense ($000):** 221564 **Payroll Expense ($000):** 72527 **Personnel:** 948

## FALLS CHURCH—Fairfax County

⊞ **DOMINION HOSPITAL (494023)**, 2960 Sleepy Hollow Road, Zip 22044–2030; tel. 703/536–2000, (Nonreporting) **A**1 9 10 **S** HCA, Nashville, TN
Primary Contact: Cynthia A. Meyer, Interim Chief Executive Officer
CFO: Edward R. Stojakovich, Chief Financial Officer
CMO: Gary Litovitz, M.D., Medical Director
CIO: Leslie Gilliam, Director Health Information Management
CHR: Lesley Channell, Assistant Vice President Human Resources
CNO: Mark Phillips, Chief Nursing Officer
Web address: www.dominionhospital.com
**Control:** Corporation, Investor–owned, for–profit **Service:** Psychiatric

**Staffed Beds:** 94

⊞ **INOVA FAIRFAX HOSPITAL (490063)**, 3300 Gallows Road, Zip 22042–3300; tel. 703/776–4001, (Includes INOVA FAIRFAX HOSPITAL FOR CHILDREN, 3300 Gallows Road, Zip 22042–3307; tel. 703/776–4002) **A**1 2 3 5 8 9 10 **F**3 4 5 6 8 11 12 13 14 15 17 18 19 20 21 22 23 24 25 26 27 28 29 30 31 34 35 36 37 38 39 40 41 42 43 44 45 46 47 48 49 50 51 54 55 56 57 58 59 60 61 63 64 65 66 68 69 70 71 72 74 75 76 77 78 79 80 81 82 83 84 85 86 87 88 89 92 93 94 96 97 98 99 100 101 102 103 104 105 107 108 109 110 111 114 115 118 119 120 121 123 124 126 130 131 132 134 135 136 137 138 140 141 142 145 146 147 148 **P**6 **S** Inova Health System, Falls Church, VA
Primary Contact: Patrick Christiansen, Ph.D., Chief Executive Officer
CFO: Ronald Ewald, Chief Financial Officer
CMO: Joseph Hallal, M.D., Chief Medical Officer
CIO: Geoffrey Brown, Vice President Information Systems
CHR: Ken Hull, Director Human Resources
Web address: www.inova.org
**Control:** Other not–for–profit (including NFP Corporation) **Service:** General Medical and Surgical

**Staffed Beds:** 926 **Admissions:** 47442 **Census:** 673 **Outpatient Visits:** 344089 **Births:** 9964 **Total Expense ($000):** 1073031 **Payroll Expense ($000):** 399393 **Personnel:** 5295

☐ **NORTHERN VIRGINIA MENTAL HEALTH INSTITUTE (494010)**, 3302 Gallows Road, Zip 22042–3398; tel. 703/207–7110 **A**1 3 5 9 10 **F**11 29 30 35 44 50 59 68 75 77 87 98 101 130 132 **S** Virginia Department of Mental Health, Richmond, VA
Primary Contact: R. Maximilien del Rio, M.D., Facility Director
CFO: Anne Baxter, Director Fiscal Services
CMO: R. Maximilien del Rio, M.D., Medical Director
CHR: Betsy Thompson, Director Human Resources
Web address: www.nvmhi.dmhmrsas.virginia.gov
**Control:** State–Government, nonfederal **Service:** Psychiatric

**Staffed Beds:** 123 **Admissions:** 763 **Census:** 114 **Outpatient Visits:** 0 **Births:** 0 **Total Expense ($000):** 22965 **Payroll Expense ($000):** 16122 **Personnel:** 294

## FARMVILLE—Prince Edward County

⊞ **CENTRA SOUTHSIDE COMMUNITY HOSPITAL (490090)**, 800 Oak Street, Zip 23901–1199; tel. 434/392–8811 **A**1 5 9 10 20 **F**3 11 13 15 28 29 30 34 35 40 44 45 49 50 57 59 62 64 70 75 76 77 79 81 85 86 87 89 93 107 108 110 115 118 119 129 130 132 133 146 147 148 **P**6 **S** Centra Health, Inc., Lynchburg, VA
Primary Contact: William L. Bass, Jr., Vice President and Chief Executive Officer
Web address: www.sch.centrahealth.com/
**Control:** Other not–for–profit (including NFP Corporation) **Service:** General Medical and Surgical

**Staffed Beds:** 86 **Admissions:** 4439 **Census:** 36 **Outpatient Visits:** 111331 **Births:** 462 **Total Expense ($000):** 64013 **Payroll Expense ($000):** 30018 **Personnel:** 455

**VA**

---

**Hospital, Medicare Provider Number, Address, Telephone, Approval, Facility, and Physician Codes, Health Care System**

★ American Hospital Association (AHA) membership
☐ The Joint Commission accreditation ◇ DNV Healthcare Inc. accreditation
○ Healthcare Facilities Accreditation Program
△ Commission on Accreditation of Rehabilitation Facilities (CARF) accreditation

**SOUTHSIDE COMMUNITY HOSPITAL** See Centra Southside Community Hospital

### FISHERSVILLE—Augusta County

☒ **AUGUSTA HEALTH (490018)**, 78 Medical Center Drive, Zip 22939–2332, Mailing Address: P.O. Box 1000, Zip 22939–1000; tel. 540/932–4000 **A**1 2 3 5 9 10 **F**3 5 7 11 13 15 18 20 22 28 29 30 31 34 35 36 39 40 45 46 48 49 50 51 53 54 56 57 58 59 61 62 63 64 66 68 70 74 75 76 77 78 79 81 82 85 86 87 89 90 91 92 93 96 97 98 100 101 102 103 104 107 108 110 111 114 115 118 119 120 121 123 128 129 130 131 132 135 144 145 146 147 148 **P**6
Primary Contact: Mary N. Mannix, FACHE, President and Chief Executive Officer
CFO: John R. Heider, Vice President Finance
CMO: Fred Castello, M.D., Chief Medical Officer
CIO: Velma Carroll, Chief Information Officer
CHR: Sue Krzastek, Vice President Human Resources
Web address: www.augustahealth.com
**Control:** Other not–for–profit (including NFP Corporation) **Service:** General Medical and Surgical

**Staffed Beds:** 224 **Admissions:** 11173 **Census:** 127 **Outpatient Visits:** 584516 **Births:** 1153 **Total Expense ($000):** 245034 **Payroll Expense ($000):** 102571 **Personnel:** 1941

**WOODROW WILSON REHABILITATION CENTER**, Zip 22939–1500; tel. 540/332–7000, (Nonreporting) **A**5
Primary Contact: Richard Luck, Ed.D., Facility Director
COO: Richard Luck, Ed.D., Facility Director
CFO: Ernie Steidle, Chief Operating Officer
CMO: Mammen Mathew, M.D., Chief Rehabilitation Medicine
CIO: Keith Burt, Director Marketing
CHR: Debbie Mitchell, Director Human Resources
Web address: www.wwrc.net
**Control:** State–Government, nonfederal **Service:** Rehabilitation

**Staffed Beds:** 30

### FORT BELVOIR—Fairfax County

☒ **FORT BELVOIR COMMUNITY HOSPITAL**, (Formerly DeWitt Army Community Hospital), 9300 Dewitt Loop, Zip 22060–5285; tel. 703/805–0510, (Nonreporting) **A**1 3 5 9 **S** Department of the Army, Office of the Surgeon General, Falls Church, VA
Primary Contact: Colonel Susan Annicelli, Commander
CMO: Lieutenant Colonel Mark D. Harris, Deputy Commander Clinical Services
CIO: Terrance Branch, Chief Information Management
Web address: www.fbch.capmed.mil/SitePages/Home.aspx
**Control:** Army, Government, federal **Service:** General Medical and Surgical

**Staffed Beds:** 46

### FRANKLIN—Franklin City County

☒ **SOUTHAMPTON MEMORIAL HOSPITAL (490092)**, 100 Fairview Drive, Zip 23851–1238, Mailing Address: P.O. Box 817, Zip 23851–0817; tel. 757/569–6100, (Nonreporting) **A**1 9 10 20 **S** Community Health Systems, Inc., Franklin, TN
Primary Contact: Phil A. Wright, II, Chief Executive Officer
CFO: Steve Ramey, Chief Financial Officer
CMO: Daniel Peak, M.D., Chief Medical Staff
CHR: E. Al Parrish, Director Human Resources
Web address: www.smhfranklin.com
**Control:** Corporation, Investor–owned, for–profit **Service:** General Medical and Surgical

**Staffed Beds:** 72

### FREDERICKSBURG—Fredericksburg City County

☒ **HEALTHSOUTH REHABILITATION HOSPITAL OF FREDERICKSBURG (493032)**, 300 Park Hill Drive, Zip 22401–3387; tel. 540/368–7300, (Nonreporting) **A**1 10 **S** HEALTHSOUTH Corporation, Birmingham, AL
Primary Contact: Donna Z. Phillips, M.D., Chief Executive Officer
Web address: www.fredericksburgrehabhospital.com
**Control:** Corporation, Investor–owned, for–profit **Service:** Rehabilitation

**Staffed Beds:** 40

☒ **MARY WASHINGTON HOSPITAL (490022)**, 1001 Sam Perry Boulevard, Zip 22401–3354; tel. 540/741–1100 **A**1 2 9 10 **F**3 5 13 15 18 20 22 24 26 28 29 30 31 34 35 40 42 43 44 45 46 48 49 50 54 57 58 59 61 62 64 68 70 74 75 76 77 78 79 81 84 85 86 87 89 92 93 96 98 99 100 101 102 104 105 107 108 111 114 115 118 119 120 121 124 126 129 130 131 132 135 146 147 148 **P**6 **S** Mary Washington Healthcare, Fredericksburg, VA
Primary Contact: Fred M. Rankin, III, President and Chief Executive Officer
COO: Walter J. Kiwall, Executive Vice President and Chief Operating Officer
CFO: Sean Barden, Executive Vice President and Chief Financial Officer
CMO: J. Thomas Ryan, M.D., Executive Vice President and Chief Medical Officer
CHR: Kathryn S. Wall, Executive Vice President Human Resources and Organizational Development
Web address: www.marywashingtonhealthcare.com/locations/mary–washington–hospital
**Control:** Other not–for–profit (including NFP Corporation) **Service:** General Medical and Surgical

**Staffed Beds:** 437 **Admissions:** 23294 **Census:** 290 **Outpatient Visits:** 361074 **Births:** 2893 **Total Expense ($000):** 402546 **Payroll Expense ($000):** 136477 **Personnel:** 2258

**SNOWDEN AT FREDERICKSBURG**, 1200 Sam Perry Boulevard, Zip 22401–4456; tel. 540/741–3900, (Nonreporting) **A**9
Primary Contact: Charles Scercy, Chief Executive Officer
Web address: www.snowdenmentalhealth.com
**Control:** Other not–for–profit (including NFP Corporation) **Service:** Psychiatric

**Staffed Beds:** 30

☒ **SPOTSYLVANIA REGIONAL MEDICAL CENTER (490141)**, 4600 Spotsylvania Parkway, Zip 22408–7762; tel. 540/834–1500, (Nonreporting) **A**1 9 10 **S** HCA, Nashville, TN
Primary Contact: Timothy C. Tobin, FACHE, President and Chief Executive Officer
COO: Terika Richardson, M.P.H., Associate Administrator
CFO: Sean Thomson, CPA, Chief Financial Officer
Web address: www.spotsrmc.com
**Control:** Corporation, Investor–owned, for–profit **Service:** General Medical and Surgical

**Staffed Beds:** 100

### FRONT ROYAL—Warren County

☒ **WARREN MEMORIAL HOSPITAL (490033)**, 1000 North Shenandoah Avenue, Zip 22630–3598; tel. 540/636–0300, (Total facility includes 120 beds in nursing home–type unit) **A**1 9 10 13 **F**3 11 13 15 28 29 30 34 35 36 40 50 53 54 56 57 59 64 65 67 70 75 76 77 79 81 82 85 86 87 93 96 107 108 111 114 118 119 128 130 132 135 144 146 147 148 **P**6 **S** Valley Health System, Winchester, VA
Primary Contact: Patrick B. Nolan, President and Chief Executive Officer
CFO: Phillip Graybeal, Chief Financial Officer
CMO: Robert Meltvedt, Jr., M.D., Vice President Medical Affairs
Web address: www.valleyhealthlink.com/WMH
**Control:** Other not–for–profit (including NFP Corporation) **Service:** General Medical and Surgical

**Staffed Beds:** 166 **Admissions:** 2045 **Census:** 140 **Outpatient Visits:** 112193 **Births:** 384 **Total Expense ($000):** 63878 **Payroll Expense ($000):** 23583 **Personnel:** 437

### GALAX—Galax City County

☒ **TWIN COUNTY REGIONAL HOSPITAL (490115)**, 200 Hospital Drive, Zip 24333–2227; tel. 276/236–8181 **A**1 9 10 20 **F**3 9 13 14 15 28 29 30 31 32 34 35 40 45 50 51 53 57 62 63 64 65 68 70 75 76 77 78 79 81 85 87 89 93 94 98 100 101 102 103 104 107 108 111 114 118 119 127 129 130 132 133 135 146 147 148 **P**5 8 **S** Duke LifePoint Healthcare, Brentwood, TN
Primary Contact: Jon D. Applebaum, Chief Executive Officer
COO: David Southerland, Chief Operating Officer
CFO: Stephanie Bryant, Chief Financial Officer
CIO: Jack Roberts, Director Information Systems
CHR: Kay P. Cochran, Director Human Resources
CNO: Joan Martin, R.N., Chief Nursing Officer
Web address: www.tcrh.org
**Control:** Partnership, Investor–owned, for–profit **Service:** General Medical and Surgical

**Staffed Beds:** 86 **Admissions:** 3608 **Census:** 39 **Outpatient Visits:** 71055 **Births:** 324 **Total Expense ($000):** 46129 **Payroll Expense ($000):** 19620 **Personnel:** 536

**VA**

## GLOUCESTER—Gloucester County

☒ **RIVERSIDE WALTER REED HOSPITAL (490130)**, 7519 Hospital Drive, Zip 23061–4178, Mailing Address: P.O. Box 1130, Zip 23061–1130; tel. 804/693–8800 **A**1 2 9 10 **F**3 11 15 28 29 35 40 43 44 45 49 50 51 57 59 63 64 70 75 77 79 81 85 86 87 92 93 107 108 110 111 114 118 119 120 121 123 130 132 146 **P**6 **S** Riverside Health System, Newport News, VA
Primary Contact: Megan Kleckner, Vice President and Administrator
CHR: Kent Taylor, Director Human Resources
Web address: www.riversideonline.com
**Control:** Other not–for–profit (including NFP Corporation) **Service:** General Medical and Surgical

**Staffed Beds:** 32 **Admissions:** 2886 **Census:** 31 **Outpatient Visits:** 110932 **Births:** 0 **Total Expense ($000):** 53026 **Payroll Expense ($000):** 16094 **Personnel:** 300

## GRUNDY—Buchanan County

☒ **BUCHANAN GENERAL HOSPITAL (490127)**, 1535 Slate Creek Road, Zip 24614–6974; tel. 276/935–1000 **A**1 9 10 20 **F**3 15 18 29 34 35 40 41 45 57 59 62 64 68 70 81 85 87 93 107 108 115 119 130 132 135 146
Primary Contact: Robert D. Ruchti, Chief Executive Officer
CFO: Kim Boyd, Chief Financial Officer
CIO: Rita Ramey, Director Information Systems
CHR: Wanda Stiltner, Director Human Resources
CNO: Patty Dorton, Director of Nursing
Web address: www.bgh.org
**Control:** Other not–for–profit (including NFP Corporation) **Service:** General Medical and Surgical

**Staffed Beds:** 49 **Admissions:** 1480 **Census:** 16 **Outpatient Visits:** 30859 **Births:** 0 **Total Expense ($000):** 21761 **Payroll Expense ($000):** 9548 **Personnel:** 216

## HAMPTON—Hampton City County

☒ △ **HAMPTON VETERANS AFFAIRS MEDICAL CENTER**, (Formerly Veterans Affairs Medical Center), 100 Emancipation Drive, Zip 23667–0001; tel. 757/722–9961, (Nonreporting) **A**1 3 5 7 **S** Department of Veterans Affairs, Washington, DC
Primary Contact: Benita K. Stoddard, FACHE, Acting Director
COO: Lorraine B. Price, Associate Director
CFO: Terry Grew, Chief Business Office
CMO: Val Gibberman, M.D., Acting Chief of Staff
CIO: Cary Parks, Chief Information Resource Management
Web address: www.hampton.va.gov/
**Control:** Veterans Affairs, Government, federal **Service:** General Medical and Surgical

**Staffed Beds:** 395

☐ **RIVERSIDE BEHAVIORAL HEALTH CENTER (494001)**, 2244 Executive Drive, Zip 23666–2430; tel. 757/827–1001, (Nonreporting) **A**1 5 9 10 **S** Riverside Health System, Newport News, VA
Primary Contact: Debra Campbell, R.N., Administrator
COO: William B. Downey, Chief Operating Officer
CMO: Phillip Schlobohm, M.D., Executive Medical Director
CHR: Amy Barrack, Director Human Resources
Web address: www.riversideonline.com
**Control:** Other not–for–profit (including NFP Corporation) **Service:** Psychiatric

**Staffed Beds:** 136

☒ ◇ **SENTARA CAREPLEX HOSPITAL (490093)**, 3000 Coliseum Drive, Zip 23666–5963; tel. 757/736–1000 **A**1 2 3 5 9 10 21 **F**3 8 11 12 15 18 20 22 26 28 29 30 31 34 35 36 37 39 40 41 42 43 44 45 47 49 50 53 54 57 58 59 60 61 63 64 65 68 70 71 74 75 77 78 79 80 81 82 83 84 86 87 92 93 94 96 97 100 107 108 110 111 114 116 117 118 119 120 121 123 129 130 131 132 144 146 147 148 **S** Sentara Healthcare, Norfolk, VA
Primary Contact: Debra A. Flores, R.N., MS, President and Administrator
COO: Chet Hart, Vice President Operations
CFO: Cheryl Larner, Chief Financial Officer
CMO: Arthur Greene, M.D., Vice President Medical Affairs
CIO: Thomas Ewing, Director Information Technology
CHR: David Kidd, Manager Human Resources
Web address: www.sentara.com
**Control:** Other not–for–profit (including NFP Corporation) **Service:** General Medical and Surgical

**Staffed Beds:** 148 **Admissions:** 9389 **Census:** 122 **Outpatient Visits:** 389085 **Births:** 0 **Total Expense ($000):** 224345 **Payroll Expense ($000):** 73583 **Personnel:** 1148

☒ **U. S. AIR FORCE HOSPITAL**, 77 Nealy Avenue, Zip 23665–2040; tel. 757/764–6969, (Nonreporting) **A**1 **S** Department of the Air Force, Washington, DC
Primary Contact: Colonel Eric Stone, Commander
COO: Colonel Jerome Wizda, Commander
CFO: Major Travis Ingrodi, Flight Commander Resource Management
CMO: Colonel Paul Gourley, M.D., Chief Hospital Services
CIO: Lieutenant Elliot Blackman, Chief Information Management and Technology
CHR: Michael Dietz, Chief Hospital Administration
Web address: www.jble.af.mil
**Control:** Air Force, Government, federal **Service:** General Medical and Surgical

**Staffed Beds:** 65

## HARRISONBURG—Harrisonburg City County

☒ ◇ **ROCKINGHAM MEMORIAL HOSPITAL (490004)**, 2010 Health Campus Drive, Zip 22801–3293; tel. 540/689–1000 **A**1 2 5 9 10 21 **F**3 5 8 11 12 13 15 17 18 20 22 24 26 28 29 30 31 32 34 35 36 40 44 45 49 50 53 54 55 56 57 59 62 63 64 68 70 71 73 74 76 77 78 79 81 82 84 85 86 87 89 93 97 98 99 102 104 105 107 108 110 111 114 115 118 119 120 121 129 130 131 132 135 145 146 147 **P**6 8 **S** Sentara Healthcare, Norfolk, VA
Primary Contact: James D. Krauss, President
COO: Richard L. Haushalter, Senior Vice President Operations and Chief Operating Officer
CFO: J. Michael Burris, Chief Financial Officer
CMO: Dale Carroll, M.D., Senior Vice President Medical Affairs and Performance Improvement
CIO: Mike Rozmus, Director Information Systems
CHR: Mark Zimmerman, Vice President Human Resources Development and Support Services
CNO: Donna S. Hahn, R.N., Vice President Acute Care and Chief Nurse Executive
Web address: www.rmhonline.com
**Control:** Other not–for–profit (including NFP Corporation) **Service:** General Medical and Surgical

**Staffed Beds:** 238 **Admissions:** 14034 **Census:** 147 **Outpatient Visits:** 371436 **Births:** 1725 **Total Expense ($000):** 324055 **Payroll Expense ($000):** 136321 **Personnel:** 2322

## HOPEWELL—Hopewell City County

☒ **JOHN RANDOLPH MEDICAL CENTER (490020)**, 411 West Randolph Road, Zip 23860–2938; tel. 804/541–1600 **A**1 2 9 10 **F**3 5 11 15 17 18 20 28 29 30 31 34 38 40 44 45 49 50 51 54 57 59 61 64 70 74 75 77 78 79 81 85 86 87 92 93 96 98 100 101 102 103 105 106 107 108 114 115 118 119 130 131 132 135 144 146 148 **P**6 **S** HCA, Nashville, TN
Primary Contact: Suzanne B. Jackson, FACHE, Chief Executive Officer
CFO: Chigger Bynum, Chief Financial Officer
CHR: MaDena DuChemin, Assistant Administrator Human Resources
Web address: www.johnrandolphmed.com
**Control:** Corporation, Investor–owned, for–profit **Service:** General Medical and Surgical

**Staffed Beds:** 118 **Admissions:** 5099 **Census:** 76 **Outpatient Visits:** 66281 **Births:** 0 **Personnel:** 463

## HOT SPRINGS—Bath County

☒ **BATH COMMUNITY HOSPITAL (491300)**, 83 Park Drive, Zip 24445–2788, Mailing Address: P.O. Box Z., Zip 24445–0750; tel. 540/839–7000 **A**1 9 10 18 **F**3 7 15 28 30 35 40 45 49 50 53 57 59 64 75 77 79 81 92 93 94 102 107 111 119 127 128 129 130 131 133 135 143
Primary Contact: Jason Paret, Chief Executive Officer
COO: Mitzi Grey, Chief Operating Officer
CMO: James Redington, M.D., Chief of Staff
CIO: Tracy Bartley, Manager Information Technology
CHR: Patricia Foutz, Director Human Resources
CNO: Kyna Moore, R.N., Director of Nursing
Web address: www.bcchospital.org
**Control:** Other not–for–profit (including NFP Corporation) **Service:** General Medical and Surgical

**Staffed Beds:** 25 **Admissions:** 492 **Census:** 8 **Outpatient Visits:** 14603 **Births:** 0 **Total Expense ($000):** 14408 **Payroll Expense ($000):** 6634 **Personnel:** 142

## KILMARNOCK—Lancaster County

☒ **RAPPAHANNOCK GENERAL HOSPITAL (490123)**, 101 Harris Drive, Zip 22482–3880, Mailing Address: P.O. Box 1449, Zip 22482–1449; tel. 804/435–8000, (Nonreporting) **A**1 9 10 20
Primary Contact: James M. Holmes, Jr., President and Chief Executive Officer
Web address: www.rgh–hospital.com
**Control:** Other not–for–profit (including NFP Corporation) **Service:** General Medical and Surgical

**Staffed Beds:** 76

VA

---

**Hospital, Medicare Provider Number, Address, Telephone, Approval, Facility, and Physician Codes, Health Care System**

★ American Hospital Association (AHA) membership
☐ The Joint Commission accreditation
◇ DNV Healthcare Inc. accreditation
○ Healthcare Facilities Accreditation Program
△ Commission on Accreditation of Rehabilitation Facilities (CARF) accreditation

## LEBANON—Russell County

☐ **RUSSELL COUNTY MEDICAL CENTER (490002)**, 58 Carroll Street, Zip 24266, Mailing Address: P.O. Box 3600, Zip 24266–0200; tel. 276/883–8000 **A**1 9 10 **F**3 11 15 29 30 35 38 40 50 54 56 57 59 62 63 64 68 70 75 81 82 84 85 93 97 98 100 102 103 104 107 108 111 114 118 119 130 132 133 146 148 **P**6 8 **S** Mountain States Health Alliance, Johnson City, TN
Primary Contact: Stephen K. Givens, Assistant Vice President and Administrator
CMO: Louis Dizon, M.D., Chief of Staff
CHR: Phyllis Kiser, Director Human Resources
Web address: www.msha.com/rcmc
**Control:** Other not–for–profit (including NFP Corporation) **Service:** General Medical and Surgical

| | |
|---|---|
| **Staffed Beds:** 78 **Admissions:** 2876 **Census:** 34 **Outpatient Visits:** 31476 **Births:** 0 **Total Expense ($000):** 25927 **Payroll Expense ($000):** 10464 **Personnel:** 206 | |

## LEESBURG—Loudoun County

✠ **INOVA LOUDOUN HOSPITAL (490043)**, 44045 Riverside Parkway, Zip 20176–5101, Mailing Address: P.O. Box 6000, Zip 20177–0600; tel. 703/858–6000, (Total facility includes 100 beds in nursing home–type unit) **A**1 2 5 9 10 **F**3 5 11 13 14 15 18 20 22 26 28 29 30 31 34 35 37 38 39 40 41 42 44 45 48 49 50 54 55 57 59 60 61 63 64 65 66 67 68 69 70 71 72 74 75 76 77 78 79 80 81 82 84 85 86 87 89 92 93 96 98 100 101 102 103 104 105 107 108 110 111 114 115 118 119 120 121 123 126 128 130 131 132 135 145 146 147 148 **P**6 **S** Inova Health System, Falls Church, VA
Primary Contact: Patrick Walters, Interim Chief Executive Officer
COO: Susan Carroll, Chief Operating Officer
CFO: Glenn Zirbser, Chief Financial Officer
CMO: Christopher Chiantella, M.D., Chief of Staff
CIO: Nancy Mengel, Director Information Technology
CHR: Sarah Pavik, Director Human Resources and Guest Services
Web address: www.inova.org
**Control:** Other not–for–profit (including NFP Corporation) **Service:** General Medical and Surgical

| | |
|---|---|
| **Staffed Beds:** 290 **Admissions:** 12141 **Census:** 218 **Outpatient Visits:** 167573 **Births:** 2688 **Total Expense ($000):** 219086 **Payroll Expense ($000):** 84936 **Personnel:** 1311 | |

## LEXINGTON—Lexington City County

✠ **CARILION STONEWALL JACKSON HOSPITAL (491304)**, 1 Health Circle, Zip 24450–2492; tel. 540/458–3300 **A**1 9 10 18 **F**3 7 8 11 15 18 28 29 34 35 40 45 48 49 50 53 56 57 59 62 65 70 75 77 79 81 85 86 87 93 107 108 110 111 115 119 129 130 132 133 135 146 148 **S** Carilion Clinic, Roanoke, VA
Primary Contact: Charles E. Carr, Vice President, Regional Hospital
CMO: Lyle McClung, M.D., Chief of Staff
Web address: www.carilionclinic.org/Carilion/csjh
**Control:** Other not–for–profit (including NFP Corporation) **Service:** General Medical and Surgical

| | |
|---|---|
| **Staffed Beds:** 17 **Admissions:** 1394 **Census:** 14 **Outpatient Visits:** 30346 **Births:** 0 **Total Expense ($000):** 27644 **Payroll Expense ($000):** 10275 **Personnel:** 198 | |

## LOW MOOR—Alleghany County

✠ **LEWISGALE HOSPITAL ALLEGHANY (490126)**, One ARH Lane, Zip 24457, Mailing Address: P.O. Box 7, Zip 24457–0007; tel. 540/862–6011, (Nonreporting) **A**1 9 10 20 **S** HCA, Nashville, TN
Primary Contact: Greg T. Madsen, Chief Executive Officer
CMO: Michele Ballou, M.D., Chief Medical Staff
CIO: Jeffrey Steelman, Director Information Systems
CHR: Bernard M. Campbell, Administrator Human Resources
CNO: Robin Broughman, R.N., Chief Nursing Officer
Web address: www.alleghanyregional.com
**Control:** Corporation, Investor–owned, for–profit **Service:** General Medical and Surgical

| | |
|---|---|
| **Staffed Beds:** 146 | |

## LURAY—Page County

✠ **PAGE MEMORIAL HOSPITAL (491307)**, 200 Memorial Drive, Zip 22835–1005; tel. 540/743–4561 **A**1 9 10 18 **F**3 7 8 11 15 29 30 34 35 40 43 53 56 57 59 60 64 66 68 74 75 77 79 81 85 90 93 107 108 110 111 114 119 127 128 129 133 143 146 **P**2 **S** Valley Health System, Winchester, VA
Primary Contact: N. Travis Clark, President
CFO: Phillip Graybeal, Chief Financial Officer
Web address: www.valleyhealthlink.com/page
**Control:** Other not–for–profit (including NFP Corporation) **Service:** General Medical and Surgical

| | |
|---|---|
| **Staffed Beds:** 25 **Admissions:** 699 **Census:** 6 **Outpatient Visits:** 110263 **Births:** 0 **Total Expense ($000):** 23019 **Payroll Expense ($000):** 11186 **Personnel:** 175 | |

## LYNCHBURG—Lynchburg City County

**CENTER FOR RESTORATIVE CARE AND REHABILITATION (492010)**, 3300 Rivermont Avenue, Zip 24503–2030; tel. 434/200–1799, (Nonreporting) **A**10
Primary Contact: Kay Bowling, Chief Executive Officer
**Control:** Partnership, Investor–owned, for–profit **Service:** Long–Term Acute Care hospital

| | |
|---|---|
| **Staffed Beds:** 36 | |

**CENTRA HEALTH** See Centra Lynchburg General Hospital

✠ **CENTRA LYNCHBURG GENERAL HOSPITAL (490021)**, 1920 Atherholt Road, Zip 24501–1104; tel. 434/200–4700, (Includes LYNCHBURG GENERAL HOSPITAL, 1901 Tate Springs Road, Zip 24501–1167; tel. 434/200–3000; VIRGINIA BAPTIST HOSPITAL, 3300 Rivermont Avenue, Zip 24503–2053; tel. 434/200–4000), (Total facility includes 447 beds in nursing home–type unit) **A**1 2 3 5 6 9 10 **F**1 2 3 5 7 10 11 13 15 17 18 19 20 22 24 26 28 29 30 31 34 35 37 38 40 43 44 45 46 47 48 49 50 53 54 55 56 57 59 60 61 62 63 64 67 68 70 71 72 74 75 76 77 78 79 80 81 82 84 85 86 87 89 90 93 94 98 99 100 101 102 103 104 105 106 107 108 109 110 111 114 115 117 118 119 120 121 123 124 125 126 127 128 129 130 132 135 143 144 146 147 148 **P**7 **S** Centra Health, Inc., Lynchburg, VA
Primary Contact: E. W. Tibbs, President and Chief Executive Officer
CFO: Lewis C. Addison, Senior Vice President and Chief Financial Officer
CMO: Chalmers Nunn, M.D., Chief Medical Officer and Senior Vice President
CIO: Ben Clark, Vice President and Chief Information Officer
CHR: Jan Walker, Director Human Resources
Web address: www.centrahealth.com
**Control:** Other not–for–profit (including NFP Corporation) **Service:** General Medical and Surgical

| | |
|---|---|
| **Staffed Beds:** 1081 **Admissions:** 31057 **Census:** 787 **Outpatient Visits:** 483587 **Births:** 2536 **Total Expense ($000):** 579680 **Payroll Expense ($000):** 262340 **Personnel:** 4341 | |

## MADISON HEIGHTS—Amherst County

**CENTRAL VIRGINIA TRAINING CENTER (490108)**, 210 East Colony Road, Zip 24572–2005, Mailing Address: P.O. Box 1098, Lynchburg, Zip 24505–1098; tel. 434/947–6326, (Nonreporting) **A**10 **S** Virginia Department of Mental Health, Richmond, VA
Primary Contact: Denise D. Micheletti, R.N., Director
COO: Denise D. Micheletti, R.N., Director
CFO: Charles Felmlee, Assistant Director Fiscal Services
CMO: Balraj Bawa, M.D., Assistant Director Medical Services
CHR: Burchkhard Blob, Manager Human Resources
Web address: www.cvtc.dmhmrsas.virginia.gov/
**Control:** State–Government, nonfederal **Service:** Institution for mental retardation

| | |
|---|---|
| **Staffed Beds:** 1112 | |

## MANASSAS—Manassas City County

✠ **NOVANT HEALTH PRINCE WILLIAM MEDICAL CENTER (490045)**, (Formerly Prince William Hospital), 8700 Sudley Road, Zip 20110–4418, Mailing Address: P.O. Box 2610, Zip 20108–0867; tel. 703/369–8000 **A**1 2 9 10 **F**3 5 8 10 11 13 15 18 19 20 22 26 28 29 30 31 32 34 35 36 38 39 40 42 44 45 49 50 51 53 54 57 59 64 65 68 70 72 74 75 76 77 78 79 81 82 84 85 86 87 89 93 97 98 99 100 102 103 104 107 110 111 114 115 118 119 126 129 130 132 134 135 146 147 148 **P**6 **S** Novant Health, Winston Salem, NC
Primary Contact: Melissa Robson, President
COO: Melissa Robson, President
CFO: Robert Riley, Chief Financial Officer
CMO: S. Marc Krenytzky, M.D., Vice President Medical Affairs
CHR: Tracy Bowers, Director Human Resources
CNO: Bebe Holt, Vice President and Chief Nursing Officer
Web address: www.pwhs.org
**Control:** Other not–for–profit (including NFP Corporation) **Service:** General Medical and Surgical

| | |
|---|---|
| **Staffed Beds:** 168 **Admissions:** 10840 **Census:** 108 **Outpatient Visits:** 214352 **Births:** 2137 **Total Expense ($000):** 155098 **Payroll Expense ($000):** 72695 **Personnel:** 938 | |

## MARION—Smyth County

☐ **SMYTH COUNTY COMMUNITY HOSPITAL (490038)**, 245 Medical Park Drive, Zip 24354, Mailing Address: P.O. Box 880, Zip 24354–0880; tel. 276/378–1000, (Total facility includes 109 beds in nursing home–type unit) **A**1 9 10 **F**2 3 10 11 15 28 29 30 34 40 46 47 48 56 57 59 62 64 65 67 68 70 75 77 79 81 82 84 85 87 90 93 97 107 111 119 128 130 132 133 135 146 148 **P**6 8 **S** Mountain States Health Alliance, Johnson City, TN
Primary Contact: Lindy P. White, President and Chief Executive Officer
Web address: www.msha.com/scch
**Control:** Other not–for–profit (including NFP Corporation) **Service:** General Medical and Surgical

| | |
|---|---|
| **Staffed Beds:** 153 **Admissions:** 2242 **Census:** 120 **Outpatient Visits:** 66962 **Births:** 0 **Total Expense ($000):** 44049 **Payroll Expense ($000):** 17860 **Personnel:** 325 | |

*Many Facility Codes have changed. Please refer to the AHA Guide Code Chart.* © 2013 AHA Guide

☐ **SOUTHWESTERN VIRGINIA MENTAL HEALTH INSTITUTE (490105)**, 340 Bagley Circle, Zip 24354–3390; tel. 276/783–1200, (Nonreporting) **A**1 9 10 **S** Virginia Department of Mental Health, Richmond, VA
Primary Contact: Cynthia McClaskey, Ph.D., Director
CIO: Kim Ratliff, Director Health Information Management
Web address: www.swvmhi.dmhmrsas.virginia.gov/
**Control:** State–Government, nonfederal **Service:** Psychiatric

**Staffed Beds:** 266

### MARTINSVILLE—Martinsville City County

⊠ **MEMORIAL HOSPITAL (490079)**, 320 Hospital Drive, Zip 24112–1981, Mailing Address: P.O. Box 4788, Zip 24115–4788; tel. 276/666–7200, (Nonreporting) **A**1 2 9 10 19 **S** LifePoint Hospitals, Inc., Brentwood, TN
Primary Contact: Grady W. Philips, III, Chief Executive Officer
COO: John Maxwell, Chief Operating Officer
CFO: Brandy Hanners, Chief Financial Officer
CIO: Jeff Butker, Chief Information Officer
CHR: Sherry Schofield, Director Human Resources
CNO: Michael Pittman, Chief Nursing Officer
Web address: www.martinsvillehospital.com
**Control:** Corporation, Investor–owned, for–profit **Service:** General Medical and Surgical

**Staffed Beds:** 220

### MECHANICSVILLE—Hanover County

⊠ **BON SECOURS MEMORIAL REGIONAL MEDICAL CENTER (490069)**, 8260 Atlee Road, Zip 23116–1844; tel. 804/764–6000, (Nonreporting) **A**1 2 5 9 10 **S** Bon Secours Health System, Inc., Marriottsville, MD
Primary Contact: Michael Robinson, Chief Executive Officer
CFO: Peter Gallagher, Vice President and Chief Financial Officer
CMO: Roger Cappello, M.D., Vice President Medical Affairs
Web address: www.bonsecours.com
**Control:** Church–operated, Nongovernment, not–for profit **Service:** General Medical and Surgical

**Staffed Beds:** 225

⊠ **SHELTERING ARMS REHABILITATION HOSPITAL (493025)**, 8254 Atlee Road, Zip 23116–1844; tel. 804/764–7055 **A**1 10 **F**29 30 34 53 54 57 59 64 68 75 77 79 82 86 87 90 91 92 93 95 96 130 131 132 143 146 148 **P**6
Primary Contact: James E. Sok, FACHE, President and Chief Executive Officer
COO: Michael J. McDonnell, Vice President and Chief Operating Officer
CFO: Michael E. Dacus, Vice President and Chief Financial Officer
CMO: Hillary Hawkins, M.D., Medical Director
CHR: Ellen B. Vance, Chief Human Resource Officer
CNO: Cheryl D. Lee, R.N., Vice President and Chief Nursing Executive Inpatient
Web address: www.shelteringarms.com
**Control:** Other not–for–profit (including NFP Corporation) **Service:** Rehabilitation

**Staffed Beds:** 68 **Admissions:** 1668 **Census:** 58 **Outpatient Visits:** 79333 **Births:** 0 **Total Expense ($000):** 55579 **Payroll Expense ($000):** 31601 **Personnel:** 458

### MIDLOTHIAN—Chesterfield County

⊠ **BON SECOURS ST. FRANCIS MEDICAL CENTER (490136)**, 13710 St. Francis Boulevard, Zip 23114–3267; tel. 804/594–7300, (Nonreporting) **A**1 2 9 10 **S** Bon Secours Health System, Inc., Marriottsville, MD
Primary Contact: Mark M. Gordon, Executive Vice President
COO: Peter J. Bernard, Chief Executive Officer
CFO: Peter Gallagher, Chief Financial Officer
CIO: Mike Lokie, Project Director
CHR: Paul Catucci, Administrative Director Human Resources
Web address: www.bonsecours.com/sfmc/default.asp
**Control:** Other not–for–profit (including NFP Corporation) **Service:** General Medical and Surgical

**Staffed Beds:** 130

☐ **SHELTERING ARMS HOSPITAL SOUTH (493030)**, 13700 St. Francis Boulevard, Suite 400, Zip 23114–3222; tel. 804/764–1000, (Nonreporting) **A**1 10
Primary Contact: James E. Sok, FACHE, President and Chief Executive Officer
COO: Michael J. McDonnell, Vice President and Chief Operations Officer
CFO: Michael E. Dacus, Vice President and Chief Financial Officer
CMO: Timothy Silver, M.D., Medical Director
CHR: Ellen B. Vance, Vice President Human Resources
CNO: Cheryl D. Lee, R.N., Vice President Patient Care Services, Chief Executive Nurse and Compliance Officer
Web address: www.shelteringarms.com
**Control:** Other not–for–profit (including NFP Corporation) **Service:** Rehabilitation

**Staffed Beds:** 28

### NASSAWADOX—Northampton County

☐ **RIVERSIDE SHORE MEMORIAL HOSPITAL (490037)**, 9507 Hospital Avenue, Zip 23413–1821, Mailing Address: P.O. Box 17, Zip 23413–0017; tel. 757/414–8000, (Total facility includes 13 beds in nursing home–type unit) **A**1 2 9 10 20 **F**2 3 11 15 28 29 30 31 34 40 45 50 62 70 75 76 77 78 79 81 82 85 93 102 103 105 107 110 111 118 119 128 129 130 132 133 135 146 148 **P**6 **S** Riverside Health System, Newport News, VA
Primary Contact: Susan McAndrews, R.N., Administrator
CFO: Wade Broughman, Chief Financial Officer
CMO: Charles Goldstein, M.D., President Medical Staff
CIO: Rob Gayman, Director Information Systems
CHR: Nicole Miller, Director Human Resources
Web address: www.shorehealthservices.org
**Control:** Other not–for–profit (including NFP Corporation) **Service:** General Medical and Surgical

**Staffed Beds:** 51 **Admissions:** 3573 **Census:** 38 **Outpatient Visits:** 83936 **Births:** 401 **Total Expense ($000):** 61999 **Payroll Expense ($000):** 20070 **Personnel:** 294

**SHORE MEMORIAL HOSPITAL** See Riverside Shore Memorial Hospital

### NEW KENT—New Kent County

☐ **CUMBERLAND HOSPITAL (493300)**, 9407 Cumberland Road, Zip 23124–2029; tel. 804/966–2242, (Nonreporting) **A**1 10 **S** Universal Health Services, Inc., King of Prussia, PA
Primary Contact: Patrice Gay Brooks, Chief Executive Officer
CFO: Joanne Rial, Chief Financial Officer
CMO: Daniel N. Davidow, M.D., Medical Director
CIO: Towanda Brown, Director Standards and Regulatory Compliance
CHR: Lauren Bonner, Director Human Resources
Web address: www.cumberlandhospital.com
**Control:** Corporation, Investor–owned, for–profit **Service:** Children's rehabilitation

**Staffed Beds:** 132

### NEWPORT NEWS—Newport News City County

☐ **HAMPTON ROADS SPECIALTY HOSPITAL (492008)**, 245 Chesapeake Avenue, Zip 23607–6038; tel. 757/534–5000, (Nonreporting) **A**1 10 **S** Riverside Health System, Newport News, VA
Primary Contact: Courtney Detwiler, R.N., Administrator
Web address: www.hamptonroadsspecialtyhospital.com
**Control:** Other not–for–profit (including NFP Corporation) **Service:** Long–Term Acute Care hospital

**Staffed Beds:** 25

**KEYSTONE NEWPORT NEWS**, 17579 Warwick Boulevard, Zip 23603–1343; tel. 757/888–0400, (Nonreporting)
Primary Contact: Paul Kirkham, Chief Executive Officer
Web address: www.keystonenewportnews.com
**Control:** Corporation, Investor–owned, for–profit **Service:** Psychiatric

**Staffed Beds:** 68

⊠ **MARY IMMACULATE HOSPITAL (490041)**, 2 Bernardine Drive, Zip 23602–4499; tel. 757/886–6000, (Includes ST. FRANCIS NURSING CENTER ), (Total facility includes 115 beds in nursing home–type unit) **A**1 9 10 **F**3 5 11 12 13 15 18 20 22 24 26 28 29 30 31 32 34 35 36 38 40 44 45 46 50 51 57 59 61 63 64 67 68 70 71 73 74 75 76 77 78 79 81 82 84 85 86 87 91 93 102 107 108 111 114 118 119 130 131 132 143 145 146 147 148 **P**6 **S** Bon Secours Health System, Inc., Marriottsville, MD
Primary Contact: Patricia L. Robertson, Executive Vice President
COO: Darlene Stephenson, Vice President Operations
CIO: Terri Spence, Vice President Information Services
CHR: John Mashinski, Vice President Human Resources
Web address: www.bonsecourshamptonroads.com
**Control:** Other not–for–profit (including NFP Corporation) **Service:** General Medical and Surgical

**Staffed Beds:** 232 **Admissions:** 9074 **Census:** 177 **Outpatient Visits:** 71632 **Births:** 1612 **Total Expense ($000):** 157565 **Payroll Expense ($000):** 44373 **Personnel:** 762

**VA**

---

☐ **RIVERSIDE REGIONAL MEDICAL CENTER (490052)**, 500 J. Clyde Morris Boulevard, Zip 23601–1929; tel. 757/594–2000, (Includes RIVERSIDE PSYCHIATRIC INSTITUTE ) **A**1 2 3 5 6 9 10 13 **F**3 11 12 13 15 17 18 20 22 24 26 28 29 30 31 32 35 38 39 40 44 45 49 50 51 54 55 56 57 58 59 60 61 62 63 64 70 72 74 75 76 77 78 79 81 82 85 86 87 89 92 93 97 107 108 110 111 114 115 116 117 118 119 120 121 123 124 126 129 130 132 141 142 144 146 147 148 **P**6 **S** Riverside Health System, Newport News, VA
Primary Contact: Patrick Parcells, Senior Vice President and Administrator
COO: William B. Downey, Chief Operating Officer
CFO: Wade Broughman, Executive Vice President and Chief Financial Officer
CMO: Barry L. Gross, M.D., Executive Vice President and Chief Medical Officer
CIO: John T. Stanley, Vice President Planning and Information Systems
CHR: Larry Boyles, Senior Vice President
Web address: www.riverside–online.com
**Control:** Other not–for–profit (including NFP Corporation) **Service:** General Medical and Surgical

**Staffed Beds:** 199 **Admissions:** 17063 **Census:** 198 **Outpatient Visits:** 437198 **Births:** 2708 **Total Expense ($000):** 451725 **Payroll Expense ($000):** 156453 **Personnel:** 1271

☒ △ **RIVERSIDE REHABILITATION INSTITUTE (493027)**, 245 Chesapeake Avenue, Zip 23607–6038; tel. 757/928–8000 **A**1 7 10 **F**3 29 30 57 64 77 82 87 90 91 93 94 96 130 132 146 **P**6 **S** Riverside Health System, Newport News, VA
Primary Contact: Edward Heckler, Administrator
COO: William B. Downey, President and Chief Executive Officer
CFO: Wade Broughman, Executive Vice President and Chief Financial Officer
CMO: C. Renee Moss, M.D., Chief Medical Officer
CIO: John T. Stanley, Vice President Planning and Information Systems
CHR: Ashleigh Andrews, Manager Human Resources
CNO: Debbie Outlaw, R.N., Director Patient Care Services
Web address: www.riverside–online.com
**Control:** Other not–for–profit (including NFP Corporation) **Service:** Rehabilitation

**Staffed Beds:** 32 **Admissions:** 824 **Census:** 33 **Outpatient Visits:** 11743 **Births:** 0 **Total Expense ($000):** 13867 **Payroll Expense ($000):** 8059 **Personnel:** 135

### NORFOLK—Norfolk City County

☒ **BON SECOURS–DEPAUL MEDICAL CENTER (490011)**, 150 Kingsley Lane, Zip 23505–4650; tel. 757/889–5000, (Total facility includes 24 beds in nursing home–type unit) **A**1 2 3 5 9 10 **F**3 11 13 15 18 20 22 29 30 31 34 35 40 44 45 46 50 51 56 57 59 61 64 68 70 71 74 75 76 78 79 81 82 84 85 86 87 93 97 102 107 108 110 111 114 115 117 119 120 121 128 129 130 131 132 143 145 146 147 148 **P**6 **S** Bon Secours Health System, Inc., Marriottsville, MD
Primary Contact: John E. Barrett, III, Chief Executive Officer
COO: David P. Setchel, Vice President Operations
CIO: Lynne Zultanky, Director Corporate Communications and Media Relations
CHR: John Mashinski, Senior Vice President Human Resources
Web address: www.bonsecourshamptonroads.com
**Control:** Other not–for–profit (including NFP Corporation) **Service:** General Medical and Surgical

**Staffed Beds:** 204 **Admissions:** 7689 **Census:** 103 **Outpatient Visits:** 142009 **Births:** 1215 **Total Expense ($000):** 165645 **Payroll Expense ($000):** 51918 **Personnel:** 905

☐ **CHILDREN'S HOSPITAL OF THE KING'S DAUGHTERS (493301)**, 601 Children's Lane, Zip 23507–1910; tel. 757/668–7000 **A**1 3 5 9 10 **F**3 7 8 9 12 16 17 19 21 23 25 27 29 30 34 35 39 40 41 44 45 48 49 50 54 55 57 58 59 60 61 64 65 66 68 72 73 74 75 77 78 79 80 81 82 84 85 86 87 88 89 90 91 92 93 94 97 99 100 102 107 108 111 115 118 119 129 130 131 132 134 138 145 146 148 **P**8
Primary Contact: James D. Dahling, President and Chief Executive Officer
CFO: Dennis Ryan, Senior Vice President and Chief Financial Officer
CMO: Arno Zaritsky, M.D., Senior Vice President Clinical Services
CIO: Deborah Barnes, Vice President and Chief Information Officer
CHR: David Bowers, Vice President Human Resources and Support Services
CNO: Jo–Ann Burke, R.N., Vice President Patient Care Services
Web address: www.chkd.org
**Control:** Other not–for–profit (including NFP Corporation) **Service:** Children's general

**Staffed Beds:** 206 **Admissions:** 5399 **Census:** 133 **Outpatient Visits:** 216765 **Births:** 0 **Total Expense ($000):** 264796 **Payroll Expense ($000):** 114960 **Personnel:** 2248

**HOSPITAL FOR EXTENDED RECOVERY (492007)**, 600 Gresham Drive, Suite 700, Zip 23507–1904; tel. 757/388–1700, (Nonreporting) **A**9 10
Primary Contact: Linda B. O'Neil, R.N., Chief Executive Officer
**Control:** Other not–for–profit (including NFP Corporation) **Service:** Long–Term Acute Care hospital

**Staffed Beds:** 35

**KEMPSVILLE CENTER FOR BEHAVIORAL HEALTH**, 860 Kempsville Road, Zip 23502–3980; tel. 757/461–4565, (Nonreporting)
Primary Contact: Matt Ours, Chief Executive Officer
**Control:** Corporation, Investor–owned, for–profit **Service:** Psychiatric

**Staffed Beds:** 77

**LAKE TAYLOR TRANSITIONAL CARE HOSPITAL (492001)**, 1309 Kempsville Road, Zip 23502–2286; tel. 757/461–5001, (Nonreporting) **A**3 5 10
Primary Contact: Thomas J. Orsini, President and Chief Executive Officer
CFO: Robert W. Fogg, Director Finance
CMO: Antoine A. Arrage, M.D., Director Medical Services
CIO: Mark Davis, Director Information Systems
CHR: LeeAnn Lowman, Director Human Resources
Web address: www.laketaylor.org
**Control:** Hospital district or authority, Government, nonfederal **Service:** Long–Term Acute Care hospital

**Staffed Beds:** 293

☒ ◇ **SENTARA LEIGH HOSPITAL (490046)**, 830 Kempsville Road, Zip 23502–3920; tel. 757/261–6000 **A**1 2 3 5 9 10 21 **F**3 8 9 11 13 15 18 20 22 26 28 29 30 31 34 35 36 38 39 40 43 44 45 46 47 48 49 50 51 54 57 58 59 60 61 63 64 68 70 71 74 75 76 77 78 79 81 82 84 85 86 87 92 93 94 96 97 100 102 107 108 110 111 114 119 126 130 131 132 141 144 145 146 147 148 **P**6 **S** Sentara Healthcare, Norfolk, VA
Primary Contact: Teresa L. Edwards, Vice President and Administrator
COO: Howard P. Kern, President and Chief Operating Officer
CFO: Robert Broermann, Senior Vice President and Chief Financial Officer
CIO: Bert Reese, Chief Information Officer
CHR: Michael V. Taylor, Senior Vice President Human Resources
Web address: www.sentara.com
**Control:** Other not–for–profit (including NFP Corporation) **Service:** General Medical and Surgical

**Staffed Beds:** 231 **Admissions:** 14556 **Census:** 174 **Outpatient Visits:** 422634 **Births:** 1960 **Total Expense ($000):** 232136 **Payroll Expense ($000):** 84556 **Personnel:** 1220

☒ ◇ **SENTARA NORFOLK GENERAL HOSPITAL (490007)**, 600 Gresham Drive, Zip 23507–1904; tel. 757/388–3000 **A**1 2 3 5 6 9 10 21 **F**3 7 11 12 13 15 16 17 18 20 22 24 26 28 29 30 31 34 35 36 38 39 40 41 43 44 45 46 47 48 49 50 51 54 56 57 58 59 60 61 65 66 68 70 71 72 74 75 76 77 78 79 81 82 84 85 86 87 90 93 94 97 98 100 101 102 103 105 107 108 110 111 114 115 116 117 118 119 120 121 123 124 126 129 130 131 132 135 136 137 138 141 142 144 146 147 148 **P**6 **S** Sentara Healthcare, Norfolk, VA
Primary Contact: Kurt T. Hofelich, President
CFO: Robert Broermann, Senior Vice President and Chief Financial Officer
CIO: Bert Reese, Chief Information Officer
Web address: www.sentara.com
**Control:** Other not–for–profit (including NFP Corporation) **Service:** General Medical and Surgical

**Staffed Beds:** 495 **Admissions:** 25494 **Census:** 401 **Outpatient Visits:** 628817 **Births:** 2730 **Total Expense ($000):** 641892 **Payroll Expense ($000):** 202152 **Personnel:** 3310

### NORTON—Norton City County

☒ **MOUNTAIN VIEW REGIONAL MEDICAL CENTER (490027)**, 310 Third Street N.E., Zip 24273–1137; tel. 276/679–9100, (Total facility includes 44 beds in nursing home–type unit) **A**1 9 **F**3 11 15 18 28 29 30 34 35 40 48 49 50 57 59 63 68 70 77 79 81 85 87 92 93 97 107 111 115 117 118 119 129 130 131 146 **S** Wellmont Health System, Kingsport, TN
Primary Contact: Fred L. Pelle, FACHE, Interim President and Chief Executive Officer
CMO: Souhail Shamiyeh, M.D., Chief of Staff
CHR: Lori B. Cole, R.N., Vice President Patient Care Services
CHR: Bobby Collins, Director Human Resources
Web address: www.wellmont.org
**Control:** Other not–for–profit (including NFP Corporation) **Service:** General Medical and Surgical

**Staffed Beds:** 118 **Admissions:** 1653 **Census:** 51 **Outpatient Visits:** 39926 **Births:** 0 **Total Expense ($000):** 28694 **Payroll Expense ($000):** 8066 **Personnel:** 211

○ △ **NORTON COMMUNITY HOSPITAL (490001)**, 100 15th Street N.W., Zip 24273–1616; tel. 276/679–9600 **A**7 9 10 11 13 **F**3 11 12 13 15 28 29 30 32 34 35 36 38 40 50 51 53 54 56 57 59 62 64 65 68 70 75 76 77 79 81 82 85 86 87 90 93 97 107 111 114 118 119 129 130 131 132 133 134 135 146 147 148 **P**6 8 **S** Mountain States Health Alliance, Johnson City, TN
Primary Contact: Mark T. Leonard, Chief Executive Officer
CFO: Stephen Sawyer, Chief Financial Officer
CMO: Allen Mullens, M.D., Chief Medical Staff
CIO: Judy Lawson, Director Information Services
CHR: Valeri J. Colyer, Director Human Resources
Web address: www.msha.com/nch
**Control:** Other not–for–profit (including NFP Corporation) **Service:** General Medical and Surgical

**Staffed Beds:** 50 **Admissions:** 4145 **Census:** 36 **Outpatient Visits:** 81450 **Births:** 306 **Total Expense ($000):** 47674 **Payroll Expense ($000):** 20001 **Personnel:** 345

**VA**

## PEARISBURG—Giles County

⊠ **CARILION GILES COMMUNITY HOSPITAL (491302)**, 159 Hartley Way,
Zip 24134–2471; tel. 540/921–6000 **A**1 9 10 18 **F**3 11 15 28 29 34 35 40
45 50 57 59 64 65 68 70 75 77 79 81 82 85 86 87 90 93 96 107 108 110
111 115 119 128 130 133 135 146 147 **S** Carilion Clinic, Roanoke, VA
Primary Contact: James E. Tyler, Vice President, Regional Hospital
CMO: John Tamminen, M.D., President Medical Staff
CHR: Carrie Boggess, Human Resource Generalist
Web address: www.carilionclinic.org/Carilion/cgch
**Control:** Other not–for–profit (including NFP Corporation) **Service:** General
Medical and Surgical

| | |
|---|---|
| **Staffed Beds:** 25 **Admissions:** 1217 **Census:** 15 **Outpatient Visits:** 25082 **Births:** 0 **Total Expense ($000):** 24938 **Payroll Expense ($000):** 9166 **Personnel:** 176 | |

## PENNINGTON GAP—Lee County

⊠ **LEE REGIONAL MEDICAL CENTER (490012)**, 1800 Combs Road,
Zip 24277–1808, Mailing Address: P.O. Box 589, Zip 24277–0589;
tel. 276/546–1440 **A**1 9 10 **F**3 11 15 29 30 34 35 40 45 50 57 59 64 68 70
81 87 93 107 108 111 114 118 119 129 130 148 **S** Wellmont Health System,
Kingsport, TN
Primary Contact: Fred L. Pelle, FACHE, Interim President and Chief Executive
Officer
Web address: www.wellmont.org/Hospitals/Lee–Regional–Medical–Center.aspx
**Control:** Other not–for–profit (including NFP Corporation) **Service:** General
Medical and Surgical

| | |
|---|---|
| **Staffed Beds:** 27 **Admissions:** 1884 **Census:** 19 **Outpatient Visits:** 37707 **Total Expense ($000):** 22487 **Payroll Expense ($000):** 7082 **Personnel:** 171 | |

## PETERSBURG—Petersburg City County

☐ **CENTRAL STATE HOSPITAL**, 26317 West Washington Street, Zip 23803–2727,
Mailing Address: P.O. Box 4030, Zip 23803–0030; tel. 804/524–7000 **A**1 9 **F**30
77 87 98 102 106 130 143 **P**6 **S** Virginia Department of Mental Health,
Richmond, VA
Primary Contact: Charles M. Davis, M.D., Ph.D., Director
CMO: Ronald O. Forbes, M.D., Medical Director
CHR: Tracy Salisbury, Director Human Resources
Web address: www.csh.dmhmrsas.virginia.gov
**Control:** State–Government, nonfederal **Service:** Psychiatric

| | |
|---|---|
| **Staffed Beds:** 277 **Admissions:** 546 **Census:** 227 **Outpatient Visits:** 0 **Births:** 0 **Total Expense ($000):** 47146 **Payroll Expense ($000):** 31320 **Personnel:** 724 | |

⊠ **HEALTHSOUTH REHABILITATION HOSPITAL OF PETERSBURG (493031)**, 95
Pinehill Boulevard, Zip 23805–9233; tel. 804/504–8100 **A**1 10 **F**28 29 60 82
90 91 93 94 148 **P**5 **S** HEALTHSOUTH Corporation, Birmingham, AL
Web address: www.healthsouthpetersburg.com
**Control:** Corporation, Investor–owned, for–profit **Service:** Rehabilitation

| | |
|---|---|
| **Staffed Beds:** 53 **Admissions:** 1305 **Census:** 48 **Outpatient Visits:** 1193 **Births:** 0 **Total Expense ($000):** 16170 **Payroll Expense ($000):** 9208 **Personnel:** 134 | |

☐ **HIRAM W. DAVIS MEDICAL CENTER (490104)**, 26317 West Washington
Street, Zip 23803–2727, Mailing Address: P.O. Box 4030, Zip 23803–0030;
tel. 804/524–7344, (Nonreporting) **A**1 10 **S** Virginia Department of Mental
Health, Richmond, VA
Primary Contact: Bill Hawkins, Director
COO: Brenda Buenvenida, Facility Administrator
CFO: Bob Kaufman, Fiscal Officer
CHR: Tracy Salisbury, Director Human Resources
**Control:** State–Government, nonfederal **Service:** Other specialty

| | |
|---|---|
| **Staffed Beds:** 10 | |

⊠ **POPLAR SPRINGS HOSPITAL (494022)**, 350 Poplar Drive, Zip 23805–9367;
tel. 804/733–6874, (Nonreporting) **A**1 9 10 **S** Universal Health Services, Inc.,
King of Prussia, PA
Primary Contact: Richard Clark, Chief Executive Officer
COO: Kate McBride, Chief Operating Officer
CFO: Bettie Hill, Chief Financial Officer
CMO: Thresa Simon, M.D., Medical Director
CHR: Morris Mitchell, Director Human Resources
Web address: www.poplarsprings.com
**Control:** Corporation, Investor–owned, for–profit **Service:** Psychiatric

| | |
|---|---|
| **Staffed Beds:** 183 | |

⊠ **SOUTHSIDE REGIONAL MEDICAL CENTER (490067)**, 200 Medical Park
Boulevard, Zip 23805–9274; tel. 804/765–5000 **A**1 2 6 9 10 **F**3 11 12 13 15
18 20 22 26 28 29 30 31 34 35 40 43 45 46 48 49 50 54 56 57 59 60 64
70 72 74 75 76 77 78 79 81 82 85 86 87 89 93 96 97 98 101 102 104 105
107 108 110 111 114 115 118 119 121 124 130 131 132 135 146 147 148
**P**6 **S** Community Health Systems, Inc., Franklin, TN
Primary Contact: Michael Yungmann, Chief Executive Officer
CFO: Charles Coder, Chief Financial Officer
CMO: Boyd Wickizer, Jr., M.D., Chief Medical Officer
CHR: Irene Buskey, Director Human Resources
Web address: www.srmconline.com
**Control:** Corporation, Investor–owned, for–profit **Service:** General Medical and
Surgical

| | |
|---|---|
| **Staffed Beds:** 300 **Admissions:** 13232 **Census:** 175 **Outpatient Visits:** 191047 **Births:** 1330 **Total Expense ($000):** 148559 **Payroll Expense ($000):** 76321 **Personnel:** 1398 | |

## PORTSMOUTH—Portsmouth City County

⊠ △ **BON SECOURS MARYVIEW MEDICAL CENTER (490017)**, 3636 High
Street, Zip 23707–3270; tel. 757/398–2200, (Total facility includes 120 beds in
nursing home–type unit) **A**1 2 3 5 7 9 10 **F**3 4 5 11 12 13 15 17 18 20 22 24
26 28 29 30 31 34 35 36 38 40 42 44 45 46 50 51 54 57 59 61 62 63 64
66 67 68 70 71 74 75 76 77 78 79 81 82 84 85 86 87 90 91 93 96 97 98
99 100 101 102 103 104 105 106 107 108 110 111 114 115 118 119 121
126 128 129 130 131 132 134 135 143 145 146 147 **P**6 **S** Bon Secours
Health System, Inc., Marriottsville, MD
Primary Contact: Joseph M. Oddis, Chief Executive Officer
CFO: Ernest C. Padden, Chief Financial Officer
CMO: Warren Austin, M.D., Vice President Medical Affairs
CIO: Terri Spence, Chief Information Officer
CHR: Vickie Humphries, Director Human Resources
CNO: Leana Fox, MSN, Interim Chief Nurse Executive
Web address: www.bonsecourshamptonroads.com
**Control:** Other not–for–profit (including NFP Corporation) **Service:** General
Medical and Surgical

| | |
|---|---|
| **Staffed Beds:** 466 **Admissions:** 12972 **Census:** 284 **Outpatient Visits:** 376211 **Births:** 1031 **Total Expense ($000):** 294589 **Payroll Expense ($000):** 104517 **Personnel:** 2189 | |

⊠ **NAVAL MEDICAL CENTER**, 620 John Paul Jones Circle, Zip 23708–2197;
tel. 757/953–0700, (Nonreporting) **A**1 2 3 5 **S** Bureau of Medicine and Surgery,
Department of the Navy, Washington, DC
Primary Contact: Captain David Collins, Director Administration
COO: Captain David Collins, Director Administration
CFO: Commander Carlos J. Martinez, Director Resource Management
CMO: Commander Thomas Mooney, M.D., President Executive Committee Medical
Staff
CIO: Lieutenant Colonel Karen Albany, Chief Information Officer
CHR: Jane Ackiss, Site Manager Human Resources
Web address: www.nmcphc.med.navy.mil/
**Control:** Navy, Government, federal **Service:** General Medical and Surgical

| | |
|---|---|
| **Staffed Beds:** 274 | |

## PULASKI—Pulaski County

⊠ **LEWISGALE HOSPITAL AT PULASKI (490116)**, 2400 Lee Highway,
Zip 24301–2326, Mailing Address: P.O. Box 759, Zip 24301–0759;
tel. 540/994–8100, (Nonreporting) **A**1 2 9 10 **S** HCA, Nashville, TN
Primary Contact: Mark Nichols, FACHE, Chief Executive Officer
CMO: Stuart Goldstein, D.O., Chief of Staff
CIO: Dan Cheverton, Director Information Systems
CHR: Jana Beckner, Director Human Resources
Web address: www.pch–va.com/
**Control:** Corporation, Investor–owned, for–profit **Service:** General Medical and
Surgical

| | |
|---|---|
| **Staffed Beds:** 54 | |

## RESTON—Fairfax County

⊠ **RESTON HOSPITAL CENTER (490107)**, 1850 Town Center Parkway,
Zip 20190–3219; tel. 703/689–9000, (Nonreporting) **A**1 2 9 10 **S** HCA,
Nashville, TN
Primary Contact: John A. Deardorff, Chief Executive Officer
COO: Jane Raymond, Vice President and Chief Operating Officer
CFO: Edward R. Stojakovich, Chief Financial Officer
CMO: Walter R. Zolkiwsky, M.D., Vice President Medical Affairs
CIO: Paresh Shah, Director Information Systems
CHR: Lesley Channell, Assistant Vice President Human Resources
CNO: Cynthia Glover, R.N., Chief Nursing Officer
Web address: www.restonhospital.com
**Control:** Corporation, Investor–owned, for–profit **Service:** General Medical and
Surgical

| | |
|---|---|
| **Staffed Beds:** 187 | |

**VA**

| Hospital, Medicare Provider Number, Address, Telephone, Approval, Facility, and Physician Codes, Health Care System | |
|---|---|
| ★ American Hospital Association (AHA) membership | ○ Healthcare Facilities Accreditation Program |
| ☐ The Joint Commission accreditation ◇ DNV Healthcare Inc. accreditation | △ Commission on Accreditation of Rehabilitation Facilities (CARF) accreditation |

## RICHLANDS—Tazewell County

✠ **CLINCH VALLEY MEDICAL CENTER (490060)**, 6801 Governor G. C. Peery Highway, Zip 24641–2194; tel. 276/596–6000, (Total facility includes 14 beds in nursing home–type unit) **A**1 9 10 **F**3 13 14 15 17 18 19 20 22 28 29 30 31 34 35 39 40 41 45 49 56 57 59 64 70 74 75 76 77 78 79 81 85 86 87 89 93 94 97 107 108 110 111 114 115 118 119 120 121 128 129 130 132 134 135 143 146 147 148 **S** LifePoint Hospitals, Inc., Brentwood, TN
Primary Contact: Peter Mulkey, Chief Executive Officer
CFO: Bob Barrett, Chief Financial Officer
CMO: Larry Mitchell, M.D., Chief of Staff
CIO: Chris Perkins, Director Information Services
CHR: John Knowles, Director Human Resources
Web address: www.clinchvalleymedicalcenter.com
**Control:** Corporation, Investor–owned, for–profit **Service:** General Medical and Surgical

**Staffed Beds:** 111 **Admissions:** 4918 **Census:** 53 **Outpatient Visits:** 63463 **Births:** 411 **Personnel:** 456

## RICHMOND—Henrico County

✠ **BON SECOURS ST. MARY'S HOSPITAL (490059)**, 5801 Bremo Road, Zip 23226–1907; tel. 804/285–2011, (Includes BON SECOURS ST. MARY'S CHILDREN'S SERVICES, 5801 Bremo Road, tel. 804/285–2011) **A**1 2 3 5 9 10 **F**3 8 11 12 13 15 17 18 20 22 24 26 28 29 30 31 34 36 37 40 41 44 45 46 47 49 50 51 56 57 59 60 63 64 70 72 73 74 75 76 78 79 80 81 82 84 85 86 87 88 89 98 102 103 107 108 110 111 114 115 116 117 118 119 120 121 123 124 126 131 132 145 146 147 148 **P**6 8 **S** Bon Secours Health System, Inc., Marriottsville, MD
Primary Contact: Toni R. Ardabell, R.N., Chief Executive Officer
COO: Thomas L. Koenig, Vice President and Chief Operating Officer
CFO: Peter Gallagher, Chief Financial Officer
CMO: Mark Bladergroen, M.D., Vice President Medical Affairs
CIO: Jeff Burke, Chief Information Officer
CHR: Paul Catucci, Director Human Resources
Web address: www.bonsecours.com
**Control:** Church–operated, Nongovernment, not–for profit **Service:** General Medical and Surgical

**Staffed Beds:** 391 **Admissions:** 21446 **Census:** 258 **Outpatient Visits:** 157969 **Births:** 1962 **Total Expense ($000):** 428690 **Payroll Expense ($000):** 139137 **Personnel:** 1926

✠ **BON SECOURS–RICHMOND COMMUNITY HOSPITAL (490094)**, 1500 North 28th Street, Zip 23223–5396, Mailing Address: P.O. Box 27184, Zip 23261–7184; tel. 804/225–1700, (Nonreporting) **A**1 6 9 10 **S** Bon Secours Health System, Inc., Marriottsville, MD
Primary Contact: Michael Robinson, Executive Vice President and Administrator
CFO: Peter Gallagher, Senior Vice President and Chief Financial Officer
CIO: Jeff Burke, Chief Information Officer
CHR: Shelia White, Director Human Resources
Web address: www.bonsecours.com
**Control:** Church–operated, Nongovernment, not–for profit **Service:** General Medical and Surgical

**Staffed Beds:** 101

★ **CHILDREN'S HOSPITAL OF RICHMOND AT VCU–BROOK ROAD CAMPUS (493302)**, (Formerly Children's Hospital of Richmond), 2924 Brook Road, Zip 23220–1298; tel. 804/321–7474, (Nonreporting) **A**3 5 9 10
Primary Contact: Leslie G. Wyatt, Senior Vice President Children's Services and Executive Director
COO: Leslie G. Wyatt, Senior Vice President Children's Services and Executive Director
CFO: James A. Deyarmin, Controller
CMO: Eugene A. Monasterio, M.D., Medical Director
CIO: Greg Friedman, Director Information Technology
CHR: Karen A. Bennett, Vice President Human Resources and Compliance
CNO: Sharon Darby, R.N., Vice President, Clinical Operations
Web address: www.chrichmond.org
**Control:** Other not–for–profit (including NFP Corporation) **Service:** Children's rehabilitation

**Staffed Beds:** 36

✠ **CJW MEDICAL CENTER (490112)**, 7101 Jahnke Road, Zip 23225–4044; tel. 804/320–3911, (Includes CHIPPENHAM MEDICAL CENTER, 7101 Jahnke Road, Zip 23225; tel. 804/320–3911; JOHNSTON–WILLIS HOSPITAL, 1401 Johnston–Willis Drive, Zip 23235; tel. 804/330–2000) **A**1 2 3 5 9 10 **F**3 4 13 15 17 18 19 20 22 24 26 28 29 30 31 34 37 38 40 41 43 45 46 47 49 50 51 52 56 57 59 60 64 65 68 70 72 73 74 75 76 77 78 79 80 81 82 84 85 86 87 88 89 90 96 98 99 100 101 102 103 105 107 108 110 111 114 115 117 118 119 120 121 123 124 126 127 129 130 131 132 133 135 146 147 148 **S** HCA, Nashville, TN
Primary Contact: Tim McManus, Interim Chief Executive Officer
COO: Betsy Blair, R.N., Chief Operating Officer
CFO: Lynn Strader, Chief Financial Officer
CMO: Georgean DeBlois, M.D., Chairman Medical Staff
CIO: Tracy Hechler, Healthcare Director Information Services
CHR: Kris Lukish, Human Resources Officer
Web address: www.cjwmedical.com
**Control:** Corporation, Investor–owned, for–profit **Service:** General Medical and Surgical

**Staffed Beds:** 627 **Admissions:** 33233 **Census:** 486 **Outpatient Visits:** 309112 **Births:** 2998

**HALLMARK YOUTHCARE – RICHMOND**, 12800 West Creek Parkway, Zip 23238–1116; tel. 804/784–2200, (Nonreporting)
Primary Contact: A. Scott Cork, Chief Executive Officer
Web address: www.hallmarkyouthcare.org
**Control:** State–Government, nonfederal **Service:** Children's hospital psychiatric

**Staffed Beds:** 84

✠ **HEALTHSOUTH REHABILITATION HOSPITAL OF VIRGINIA (493028)**, 5700 Fitzhugh Avenue, Zip 23226–1800; tel. 804/288–5700, (Nonreporting) **A**1 9 10 **S** HEALTHSOUTH Corporation, Birmingham, AL
Primary Contact: Tonya Ferguson, Interim Chief Executive Officer
CFO: Alan M. Phillips, Controller
CMO: Roger Giordano, M.D., Medical Director
CIO: Faye Encke, Director Information Management
CHR: Tonya Ferguson, Director Human Resources
CNO: Michelle Anthony, Chief Nursing Officer
Web address: www.healthsouthrichmond.com
**Control:** Corporation, Investor–owned, for–profit **Service:** Rehabilitation

**Staffed Beds:** 40

✠ **HENRICO DOCTORS' HOSPITAL (490118)**, 1602 Skipwith Road, Zip 23229–5205; tel. 804/289–4500, (Includes HENRICO DOCTORS' HOSPITAL – FOREST, 1602 Skipwith Road, Zip 23229–5298; tel. 804/289–4500; HENRICO DOCTORS' HOSPITAL – PARHAM, 7700 East Parham Road, Zip 23294–4301; tel. 804/747–5600; Lisa R. Valentine, Interim Chief Executive Officer; HENRICO DOCTORS' HOSPITAL – RETREAT CAMPUS, 2621 Grove Avenue, Zip 23220–4308; tel. 804/254–5100; Lisa R. Valentine, Interim Chief Executive Officer), (Nonreporting) **A**1 2 9 10 **S** HCA, Nashville, TN
Primary Contact: Lisa R. Valentine, Interim Chief Executive Officer
COO: Lisa R. Valentine, Chief Operating Officer
CFO: Christopher Denton, Chief Financial Officer
CIO: Daniel Patton, Director Information Systems
CHR: Steven Burgess, Administrator Human Resources
Web address: www.henricodoctorshospital.com
**Control:** Corporation, Investor–owned, for–profit **Service:** General Medical and Surgical

**Staffed Beds:** 488

✠ △ **HUNTER HOLMES MCGUIRE VETERANS AFFAIRS MEDICAL CENTER**, 1201 Broad Rock Boulevard, Zip 23249–0002; tel. 804/675–5000, (Total facility includes 98 beds in nursing home–type unit) **A**1 2 3 5 7 8 **F**3 4 5 7 8 11 12 15 17 18 20 22 24 26 28 29 30 31 34 35 36 38 39 40 44 45 46 47 48 49 50 51 53 54 56 57 58 59 60 62 63 64 65 66 68 70 71 74 75 77 78 79 81 82 83 84 85 86 87 90 91 92 93 94 95 96 97 98 100 102 103 104 107 108 110 111 115 116 117 118 119 120 121 124 126 127 128 129 130 132 135 137 145 146 147 148 **P**6 **S** Department of Veterans Affairs, Washington, DC
Primary Contact: David P. Budinger, Interim Director
COO: David P. Budinger, Associate Director
CFO: Roger T. Vergne, Chief Fiscal Service
CMO: Judy Brannen, M.D., Interim Chief of Staff
CIO: David Dahlstrand, Associate Chief of Staff Information Technology
CHR: Heather Moody, Chief Human Resource Management
Web address: www.richmond.va.gov/
**Control:** Veterans Affairs, Government, federal **Service:** General Medical and Surgical

**Staffed Beds:** 427 **Admissions:** 8163 **Census:** 246 **Outpatient Visits:** 517092 **Births:** 0 **Total Expense ($000):** 417611 **Payroll Expense ($000):** 195224 **Personnel:** 2439

**JOHNSTON–WILLIS HOSPITAL** See CJW Medical Center

✠ **KINDRED HOSPITAL RICHMOND (492009)**, 2220 Edward Holland Drive, Zip 23230–2519; tel. 804/678–7000, (Nonreporting) **A**1 10 **S** Kindred Healthcare, Louisville, KY
Primary Contact: Barbara L. Callaghan, Interim Chief Executive Officer
Web address: www.kindredrichmond.com/
**Control:** Corporation, Investor–owned, for–profit **Service:** Long–Term Acute Care hospital

**Staffed Beds:** 60

*Many Facility Codes have changed. Please refer to the AHA Guide Code Chart.*  © 2013 AHA Guide

⊞ **VCU HEALTH SYSTEM (490032)**, 1250 East Marshall Street,
Zip 23298–5051, Mailing Address: P.O. Box 980510, Zip 23298–0510;
tel. 804/828–9000, (Includes VCU HEALTH SYSTEM CHILDREN'S MEDICAL
CENTER, 1001 East Marshall Street, Zip 23219–1918, Mailing Address: PO Box
980646, Zip 23298–0646; tel. 804/828–9602) **A**1 3 5 8 9 10 **F**2 3 4 6 8 9 11
12 13 15 16 17 18 19 20 21 22 23 24 25 26 27 28 29 30 31 32 34 35 36
37 38 39 40 41 43 44 45 46 47 48 49 50 51 52 54 55 56 57 58 59 60 61
62 64 66 68 70 71 72 73 74 75 76 78 79 80 81 82 83 84 85 86 87 88 89
90 92 93 95 96 97 98 99 100 101 102 103 104 105 107 108 109 110 111
114 115 116 117 118 119 120 121 123 124 126 129 130 131 132 134 135
136 137 138 139 141 142 143 144 145 146 147 148 **P**6
Primary Contact: John Duval, Chief Executive Officer
COO: Deborah W. Davis, Chief Operating Officer
CFO: Dominic J. Pulco, Executive Vice President Finance and Chief Financial
Officer
CMO: Ron Clark, M.D., Vice President Clinical Activities and Chief Medical Officer
CIO: Richard Pollack, Vice President Information Services
CHR: Maria Curran, Vice President Human Resources
Web address: www.vcuhealth.org
**Control:** Hospital district or authority, Government, nonfederal **Service:** General
Medical and Surgical

**Staffed Beds:** 755 **Admissions:** 31143 **Census:** 562 **Outpatient Visits:**
651560 **Births:** 2239 **Total Expense ($000):** 986720 **Payroll Expense
($000):** 364558 **Personnel:** 6979

### ROANOKE—Roanoke County

⊞ **CARILION MEDICAL CENTER (490024)**, Belleview at Jefferson Street,
Zip 24014, Mailing Address: P.O. Box 13367, Zip 24033–3367;
tel. 540/981–7000, (Includes CARILION CLINIC CHILDREN'S HOSPITAL, 1906
Belleview Avenue, S.E., Zip 24014–1838; tel. 540/981–7000; CARILION
ROANOKE COMMUNITY HOSPITAL, 101 Elm Avenue S.E., Zip 24013–2230,
Mailing Address: P.O. Box 12946, Zip 24029–2946; tel. 540/985–8000;
ROANOKE MEMORIAL REHABILITATION CENTER, South Jefferson and McClanahan
Streets, Mailing Address: P.O. Box 13367, Zip 24033; tel. 703/342–4541) **A**1 2
3 5 8 9 10 12 13 **F**3 5 7 8 9 11 12 13 15 17 18 19 20 22 24 26 28 29 30
31 32 33 34 35 36 37 38 39 40 41 42 43 44 45 46 47 48 49 50 51 52 53
54 55 56 57 58 59 60 61 62 63 64 65 66 68 70 71 72 73 74 75 76 77 78
79 81 82 83 84 85 86 87 88 89 90 92 93 96 97 98 99 100 101 102 103
104 106 107 108 110 111 113 114 115 117 118 119 120 121 123 124 126
129 130 131 132 134 135 143 144 146 147 148 **P**6 **S** Carilion Clinic,
Roanoke, VA
Primary Contact: Nancy Howell Agee, President and Chief Executive Officer
CFO: Donald E. Lorton, Executive Vice President and Chief Financial Officer
CMO: Mark D. Werner, M.D., Executive Vice President and Chief Medical Officer
CIO: Daniel Barchi, Senior Vice President and Chief Information Officer
CHR: Jeanne S. Armentrout, Vice President Human Resources
Web address: www.carilionclinic.org
**Control:** Other not–for–profit (including NFP Corporation) **Service:** General
Medical and Surgical

**Staffed Beds:** 624 **Admissions:** 36005 **Census:** 500 **Outpatient Visits:**
227662 **Births:** 3282 **Total Expense ($000):** 885265 **Payroll Expense
($000):** 394450 **Personnel:** 5660

### ROCKY MOUNT—Franklin County

⊞ **CARILION FRANKLIN MEMORIAL HOSPITAL (490089)**, 180 Floyd Avenue,
Zip 24151–1389; tel. 540/483–5277 **A**1 9 10 **F**11 15 18 28 29 30 34 35 40
45 50 59 62 63 68 70 75 77 81 84 85 93 96 107 110 115 119 130 132 135
146 **S** Carilion Clinic, Roanoke, VA
Primary Contact: William D. Jacobsen, Vice President, Regional Hospital
Web address: www.carilionclinic.org/Carilion/Franklin+Memorial+Hospital
**Control:** Other not–for–profit (including NFP Corporation) **Service:** General
Medical and Surgical

**Staffed Beds:** 32 **Admissions:** 1597 **Census:** 14 **Outpatient Visits:** 40212
**Births:** 0 **Total Expense ($000):** 32502 **Payroll Expense ($000):** 12925
**Personnel:** 240

### SALEM—Salem City County

⊞ **LEWIS–GALE MEDICAL CENTER (490048)**, 1900 Electric Road,
Zip 24153–7494; tel. 540/776–4000, (Includes LEWIS–GALE PAVILION, 1902
Braeburn Drive, Zip 24153–7391; tel. 703/772–2800), (Nonreporting) **A**1 2 9 10
**S** HCA, Nashville, TN
Primary Contact: Victor Giovanetti, President and Chief Executive Officer
COO: Charlotte C. Tyson, Chief Operating Officer
CFO: Angela D. Reynolds, Chief Financial Officer
CMO: Joseph Nelson, M.D., President Medical Staff
CIO: Beth Cole, Director Information Services
CHR: Dale Beaudoin, Vice President Human Resources
Web address: www.lewis–gale.com
**Control:** Corporation, Investor–owned, for–profit **Service:** General Medical and
Surgical

**Staffed Beds:** 521

⊞ **SALEM VETERANS AFFAIRS MEDICAL CENTER**, (Formerly Veterans Affairs
Medical Center), 1970 Roanoke Boulevard, Zip 24153–6478;
tel. 540/982–2463, (Total facility includes 60 beds in nursing home–type unit)
(Data for 364 days) **A**1 2 3 5 8 **F**1 3 4 5 6 8 17 18 20 22 29 30 31 34 35 36
38 39 40 45 50 53 54 56 57 58 59 64 65 67 70 74 75 77 78
79 81 82 83 84 85 86 87 90 91 92 93 94 97 98 100 101 102 103 104 105
106 107 108 109 111 114 115 116 117 119 127 128 129 130 132 135 143
144 145 146 147 148 **P**6 **S** Department of Veterans Affairs, Washington, DC
Primary Contact: Miguel H. LaPuz, M.D., Director
CFO: Codie Walker, Chief Financial Officer
CMO: Maureen McCarthy, M.D., Chief of Staff
CIO: Sharon Collins, Chief Information Officer
CHR: Timothy McGuigan, Chief Human Resources
Web address: www.salem.va.gov
**Control:** Veterans Affairs, Government, federal **Service:** General Medical and
Surgical

**Staffed Beds:** 200 **Admissions:** 2800 **Census:** 181 **Outpatient Visits:**
600000 **Births:** 0 **Total Expense ($000):** 222000 **Payroll Expense ($000):**
222000 **Personnel:** 2049

### SOUTH BOSTON—Halifax County

⊞ **HALIFAX REGIONAL HEALTH SYSTEM (490013)**, 2204 Wilborn Avenue,
Zip 24592–1638; tel. 434/517–3100, (Total facility includes 348 beds in nursing
home–type unit) **A**1 9 10 **F**3 13 14 15 17 18 20 28 29 30 31 35 36 38 40 44
45 46 47 48 57 60 62 63 64 65 67 68 70 74 75 76 77 78 79 81 82 84 85
86 87 89 92 93 94 96 97 100 101 102 103 104 107 108 110 111 114 115
116 117 118 119 127 128 129 130 131 132 135 146 147 148 **P**1 7
Primary Contact: Chris A. Lumsden, Chief Executive Officer
COO: Thomas S. Kluge, Chief Operating Officer
CFO: Stewart R. Nelson, Chief Financial Officer
CMO: James H. Priest, D.D.S., Chief Medical Officer
CIO: William Zirkle, Manager Information Systems
CHR: Catherine Howard, Director Human Resources
CNO: Patricia F. Thomas, Chief Nursing Officer
Web address: www.hrhs.org
**Control:** Other not–for–profit (including NFP Corporation) **Service:** General
Medical and Surgical

**Staffed Beds:** 438 **Admissions:** 4402 **Census:** 382 **Outpatient Visits:** 75498
**Births:** 414 **Total Expense ($000):** 115264 **Payroll Expense ($000):** 48753
**Personnel:** 673

### SOUTH HILL—Mecklenburg County

⊞ **COMMUNITY MEMORIAL HEALTHCENTER (490098)**, 125 Buena Vista Circle,
Zip 23970–1431, Mailing Address: P.O. Box 90, Zip 23970–0090;
tel. 434/447–3151, (Total facility includes 110 beds in nursing home–type unit)
**A**1 9 10 20 **F**3 11 15 18 28 29 30 31 34 35 39 40 45 46 49 50 53 54 56 57
59 61 62 63 64 65 70 74 75 77 78 79 81 82 84 85 86 87 93 96 97 107
108 110 111 114 118 119 127 130 131 132 133 135 146 147 148 **P**8
Primary Contact: W. Scott Burnette, President and Chief Executive Officer
COO: Edward M. Brandenburg, FACHE, Vice President Professional Services
CFO: Kenneth Libby, Vice President Finance
CMO: Anthony Adams, M.D., Chief of Staff
CIO: Mark Clemmons, Director Information Systems
CHR: Maria Stephens, PHR, Director Human Resources, Education and
Occupational Health and Wellness
Web address: www.cmh–sh.org
**Control:** Other not–for–profit (including NFP Corporation) **Service:** General
Medical and Surgical

**Staffed Beds:** 178 **Admissions:** 4461 **Census:** 169 **Outpatient Visits:**
135222 **Births:** 206 **Total Expense ($000):** 74891 **Payroll Expense ($000):**
34885 **Personnel:** 656

### STAFFORD—Stafford County

⊞ **STAFFORD HOSPITAL (490140)**, 101 Hospital Center Boulevard,
Zip 22554–6200; tel. 540/741–9000 **A**1 9 10 **F**3 13 15 18 20 22 29 30 31
34 35 40 44 45 46 48 49 50 55 57 59 60 61 64 68 70 74 75 76 77 78 79
81 85 86 87 93 96 107 108 111 115 118 119 120 131 132 146 **P**6 **S** Mary
Washington Healthcare, Fredericksburg, VA
Primary Contact: Fred M. Rankin, III, President and Chief Executive Officer
COO: Walter J. Kiwall, Executive Vice President and Chief Operating Officer
CFO: Sean Barden, Executive Vice President and Chief Financial Officer
CMO: J. Thomas Ryan, M.D., Executive Vice President and Chief Medical Officer
CIO: Joyce Hanscome, Senior Vice President and Chief Information Officer
CHR: Kathryn S. Wall, Executive Vice President Human Resources and
Organizational Development
CNO: Marianna Bedway, R.N., Senior Vice President and Chief Nursing Officer
Web address: www.mwhc.com
**Control:** Other not–for–profit (including NFP Corporation) **Service:** General
Medical and Surgical

**Staffed Beds:** 100 **Admissions:** 3459 **Census:** 34 **Outpatient Visits:** 70696
**Births:** 546 **Total Expense ($000):** 75668 **Payroll Expense ($000):** 25042
**Personnel:** 377

**VA**

---

**Hospital, Medicare Provider Number, Address, Telephone, Approval, Facility, and Physician Codes, Health Care System**

★ American Hospital Association (AHA) membership
☐ The Joint Commission accreditation
◇ DNV Healthcare Inc. accreditation
○ Healthcare Facilities Accreditation Program
△ Commission on Accreditation of Rehabilitation Facilities (CARF) accreditation

## STAUNTON—Staunton City County

**COMMONWEALTH CENTER FOR CHILDREN AND ADOLESCENTS**, 1355 Richmond Road, Zip 24401–9146, Mailing Address: Box 4000, Zip 24402–4000; tel. 540/332–2100, (Nonreporting) **A**3 5 9 **S** Virginia Department of Mental Health, Richmond, VA
Primary Contact: William J. Tuell, MSN, Facility Director
Web address: www.ccca.dbhds.virginia.gov
**Control:** State–Government, nonfederal **Service:** Children's other specialty

| Staffed Beds: 60 |
|---|

☐ **WESTERN STATE HOSPITAL (490106)**, 1301 Richmond Avenue, Zip 24401–9146, Mailing Address: P.O. Box 2500, Zip 24402–2500; tel. 540/332–8000, (Nonreporting) **A**1 3 5 9 10 **S** Virginia Department of Mental Health, Richmond, VA
Primary Contact: Jack W. Barber, M.D., Director
CFO: David Mawyer, Chief Financial Officer
CMO: Mary Clare Smith, M.D., Medical Director
CIO: Sharon Johnson, Director Health Information Management
CHR: Kimberly Harman, Regional Manager Human Resources
Web address: www.dbhds.virginia.gov
**Control:** State–Government, nonfederal **Service:** Psychiatric

| Staffed Beds: 260 |
|---|

## STUART—Patrick County

★ ◇ **PIONEER COMMUNITY HOSPITAL OF PATRICK COUNTY (491306)**, 18688 Jeb Stuart Highway, Zip 24171–1559; tel. 276/694–3151, (Nonreporting) **A**9 10 18 21 **S** Pioneer Health Services, Magee, MS
Primary Contact: Jeanette Filpi, Chief Executive Officer
CFO: Julie Gieger, Chief Financial Officer
CMO: Nicholas Kipreos, M.D., Chief Medical Staff
CIO: Eddie Pope, Director Information Systems
CHR: Donn Paul, Vice President Human Resources
Web address: www.phscorporate.com
**Control:** Corporation, Investor–owned, for–profit **Service:** General Medical and Surgical

| Staffed Beds: 25 |
|---|

## SUFFOLK—Suffolk City County

⊠ ◇ **SENTARA OBICI HOSPITAL (490044)**, 2800 Godwin Boulevard, Zip 23434–8038; tel. 757/934–4000 **A**1 3 5 9 10 21 **F**3 11 15 18 20 22 26 28 29 30 35 36 37 40 41 42 45 47 48 50 51 54 56 57 58 59 64 68 70 73 74 75 76 77 78 79 81 85 86 87 92 93 94 96 97 98 107 108 110 114 116 117 118 120 121 123 129 130 131 132 144 146 147 148 **S** Sentara Healthcare, Norfolk, VA
Primary Contact: Steve Julian, M.D., President
CFO: Mike Mounie, Director Finance
CMO: Steve Julian, M.D., Vice President Medical Affairs
CIO: Alice Oxton, Director Information Technology
CHR: Deborah Ferguson, Human Resources Consultant
Web address: www.sentara.com
**Control:** Other not–for–profit (including NFP Corporation) **Service:** General Medical and Surgical

| Staffed Beds: 168 Admissions: 8841 Census: 100 Outpatient Visits: 266822 Births: 1233 Total Expense ($000): 167478 Payroll Expense ($000): 59741 Personnel: 960 |
|---|

## TAPPAHANNOCK—Essex County

☐ **RIVERSIDE TAPPAHANNOCK HOSPITAL (490084)**, 618 Hospital Road, Zip 22560–5000; tel. 804/443–3311 **A**1 9 10 20 **F**3 11 15 29 31 34 35 38 40 43 44 45 49 50 51 56 57 59 62 63 64 70 75 77 78 79 81 82 85 86 87 92 93 97 107 108 111 114 116 117 118 119 130 131 132 133 135 146 148 **P**6 **S** Riverside Health System, Newport News, VA
Primary Contact: Elizabeth J. Martin, Vice President and Administrator
COO: Elizabeth J. Martin, Vice President and Administrator
CFO: Jeri Sibley, Director Revenue Cycle
CMO: Reginald Mason, M.D., President Medical Staff
CHR: Jaime Cook, Director Human Resources
Web address: www.riverside-online.com
**Control:** Other not–for–profit (including NFP Corporation) **Service:** General Medical and Surgical

| Staffed Beds: 16 Admissions: 1709 Census: 14 Outpatient Visits: 65090 Births: 0 Total Expense ($000): 43837 Payroll Expense ($000): 12592 Personnel: 187 |
|---|

## TAZEWELL—Tazewell County

⊠ **CARILION TAZEWELL COMMUNITY HOSPITAL (490117)**, 141 Ben Bolt Avenue, Zip 24651–9700; tel. 276/988–8700 **A**1 9 10 **F**3 11 15 29 30 34 39 40 44 45 50 59 62 64 68 75 79 81 85 87 107 111 114 119 133 135 146 **S** Carilion Clinic, Roanoke, VA
Primary Contact: John S. Piatkowski, M.D., Vice President, Regional Hospital
CMO: Kerry Moore, M.D., Chief of Staff
CHR: Carrie Boggess, Human Resources Generalist
Web address: www.carilionclinic.org/Carilion/Carilion+Tazewell+Community+Hospital
**Control:** Other not–for–profit (including NFP Corporation) **Service:** General Medical and Surgical

| Staffed Beds: 12 Admissions: 704 Census: 6 Outpatient Visits: 14943 Births: 0 Total Expense ($000): 11811 Payroll Expense ($000): 4220 Personnel: 93 |
|---|

## VIRGINIA BEACH—Virginia Beach City County

⊠ ◇ **SENTARA PRINCESS ANNE HOSPITAL (490119)**, 2025 Glenn Mitchell Drive, Zip 23456–0178; tel. 757/507–1000 **A**1 3 5 9 10 21 **F**3 11 13 15 18 20 22 26 29 30 31 34 35 36 38 40 41 43 44 45 46 47 49 50 54 57 58 59 60 61 64 65 68 70 71 72 73 74 75 76 77 78 79 81 82 83 84 85 86 87 92 93 94 96 97 100 102 107 108 110 111 114 115 118 119 129 130 131 132 144 145 146 147 148 **S** Sentara Healthcare, Norfolk, VA
Primary Contact: Stephen D. Porter, President
COO: Howard P. Kern, Chief Operating Officer
CFO: Robert Broermann, Senior Vice President and Chief Financial Officer
CMO: Victor Sonnino, M.D., Vice President Medical Affairs
CIO: Bert Reese, Chief Information Officer
CHR: Michael V. Taylor, Vice President Human Resources
CNO: Grace Myers, MSN, Vice President, Nurse Executive
Web address: www.sentara.com
**Control:** Other not–for–profit (including NFP Corporation) **Service:** General Medical and Surgical

| Staffed Beds: 160 Admissions: 9927 Census: 118 Outpatient Visits: 266822 Births: 2546 Total Expense ($000): 185629 Payroll Expense ($000): 64855 Personnel: 968 |
|---|

⊠ ◇ **SENTARA VIRGINIA BEACH GENERAL HOSPITAL (490057)**, 1060 First Colonial Road, Zip 23454–3002; tel. 757/395–8000 **A**1 2 3 5 9 10 21 **F**3 11 15 17 18 20 22 24 26 28 29 30 31 34 36 37 38 39 40 41 42 43 44 45 46 47 49 50 51 53 54 57 58 59 60 61 63 64 65 68 70 74 75 77 78 79 80 81 82 84 85 86 87 90 92 93 94 96 97 100 102 107 108 109 110 111 114 115 118 119 120 121 123 126 129 130 131 132 141 142 144 145 146 147 148 **S** Sentara Healthcare, Norfolk, VA
Primary Contact: Elwood Bernard Boone, III, FACHE, President
COO: Joanne Inman, Vice President Operations
CFO: Marley Nacey, Director Finance
CMO: Thomas B. Thames, M.D., Vice President Medical Affairs
CHR: Michelle Meekins, Manager Human Resources
CNO: Peggy Braun, R.N., Vice President Patient Care Services and Chief Nurse Executive
Web address: www.sentara.com
**Control:** Other not–for–profit (including NFP Corporation) **Service:** General Medical and Surgical

| Staffed Beds: 265 Admissions: 12304 Census: 185 Outpatient Visits: 349364 Births: 0 Total Expense ($000): 253295 Payroll Expense ($000): 88083 Personnel: 1292 |
|---|

☐ **VIRGINIA BEACH PSYCHIATRIC CENTER (494025)**, 1100 First Colonial Road, Zip 23454–2403; tel. 757/496–6000, (Nonreporting) **A**1 9 10 **S** Universal Health Services, Inc., King of Prussia, PA
Primary Contact: Frank Gallagher, Chief Executive Officer
Web address: www.absfirst.com
**Control:** Corporation, Investor–owned, for–profit **Service:** Psychiatric

| Staffed Beds: 100 |
|---|

## WARRENTON—Fauquier County

⊠ △ **FAUQUIER HOSPITAL (490023)**, 500 Hospital Drive, Zip 20186–3099; tel. 540/316–5000 **A**1 7 9 10 **F**3 11 13 15 18 28 29 30 31 32 34 35 36 37 40 45 47 48 49 53 57 59 62 64 70 74 75 76 77 78 79 81 85 86 87 93 107 108 110 111 114 117 118 119 129 130 131 132 135 146 148
Primary Contact: Rodger H. Baker, President and Chief Executive Officer
CFO: Lionel J. Phillips, Vice President Financial Services
CMO: Anhtai H. Nguyen, M.D., Vice President Medical Affairs and Chief Medical Officer
CIO: Donna Staton, Chief Information Officer
CHR: Katy Reeves, Vice President Human Resources
CNO: Linda Sharkey, R.N., Vice President Patient Care Services and Chief Nurse Executive
Web address: www.fauquierhospital.org
**Control:** Other not–for–profit (including NFP Corporation) **Service:** General Medical and Surgical

| Staffed Beds: 86 Admissions: 5128 Census: 55 Outpatient Visits: 121687 Births: 808 Total Expense ($000): 123390 Payroll Expense ($000): 51172 Personnel: 781 |
|---|

**VA**

*Many Facility Codes have changed. Please refer to the AHA Guide Code Chart.*   © 2013 AHA Guide

## WILLIAMSBURG—James City County

☐ **EASTERN STATE HOSPITAL (490109)**, 4601 Ironbound Road,
Zip 23188–2652; tel. 757/253–5161, (Nonreporting) **A**1 3 5 9 10 **S** Virginia
Department of Mental Health, Richmond, VA
Primary Contact: John M. Favret, Director
CFO: E. Clifford Love, Director Fiscal Services
CMO: Guillermo Schrader, M.D., Acting Medical Director
CIO: Barbara Lambert, Director Healthcare Compliance
CHR: Edie Rogan, Manager Human Resources
Web address: www.esh.dmhmrsas.virginia.gov/
**Control:** State–Government, nonfederal **Service:** Psychiatric

**Staffed Beds:** 334

**RIVERSIDE DOCTORS' HOSPITAL (490143)**, 1500 Commonwealth Avenue,
Zip 23185–5229; tel. 757/585–2200, (Nonreporting) **S** Riverside Health System,
Newport News, VA
Primary Contact: Steve C. McCary, Administrator
CNO: Arlene Messina, R.N., Director of Nursing
Web address: www.riversideonline.com
**Control:** Other not–for–profit (including NFP Corporation) **Service:** General
Medical and Surgical

**Staffed Beds:** 40

★ ◇ **SENTARA WILLIAMSBURG REGIONAL MEDICAL CENTER (490066)**,
100 Sentara Circle, Zip 23188–5713; tel. 757/984–6000 **A**2 9 10 21 **F**3 8 11
13 15 18 20 22 26 28 29 30 31 34 35 36 37 39 40 41 44 45 46 48 49 50
51 54 56 57 58 59 60 63 64 65 68 70 74 75 76 77 78 79 81 82 83 84 85
86 87 89 90 92 93 94 96 97 100 102 103 104 107 108 110 111 114 115
116 117 118 119 129 130 131 132 135 144 146 147 148 **S** Sentara
Healthcare, Norfolk, VA
Primary Contact: Robert L. Graves, President
CFO: Andreas Roehrle, Director Finance
CMO: Joe Rubbins, M.D., Vice President Medical Affairs
CIO: Mike Freeman, Director Information Technology
CHR: Lois B. Demerich, Director Human Resources
CNO: Donna Wilmoth, Vice President Patient Care Services and Chief Nursing
Officer
Web address: www.sentara.com
**Control:** Other not–for–profit (including NFP Corporation) **Service:** General
Medical and Surgical

**Staffed Beds:** 145 **Admissions:** 7996 **Census:** 97 **Outpatient Visits:** 228654
**Births:** 941 **Total Expense ($000):** 105500 **Payroll Expense ($000):** 50933
**Personnel:** 734

## WINCHESTER—Winchester City County

⊠ △ **WINCHESTER MEDICAL CENTER (490005)**, 1840 Amherst Street,
Zip 22601–2808, Mailing Address: P.O. Box 3340, Zip 22604–2540;
tel. 540/536–8000 **A**1 2 3 5 7 9 10 19 **F**3 5 11 12 13 15 17 18 20 22 24 26
28 29 30 31 32 34 35 38 39 40 41 43 44 45 47 49 50 51 54 56 57 58 59
61 62 64 65 68 70 71 72 74 75 76 77 78 79 80 81 82 84 85 86 87 89 90
91 92 93 97 98 100 101 102 103 107 108 110 111 114 115 116 117 118
119 120 121 123 124 129 130 131 132 135 136 146 147 148 **P**5 **S** Valley
Health System, Winchester, VA
Primary Contact: Mark H. Merrill, Interim Chief Executive Officer
CFO: Robert Amos, Vice President and Chief Financial Officer
CMO: Nicolas Restrepo, M.D., Vice President Medical Affairs
CIO: Joan Roscoe, Chief Information Officer
CHR: Elizabeth Savage–Tracy, Vice President and Human Resources Officer
Web address: www.valleyhealthlink.com/WMC
**Control:** Other not–for–profit (including NFP Corporation) **Service:** General
Medical and Surgical

**Staffed Beds:** 475 **Admissions:** 24287 **Census:** 328 **Outpatient Visits:**
433564 **Births:** 2303 **Total Expense ($000):** 451010 **Payroll Expense
($000):** 148138 **Personnel:** 2546

## WOODBRIDGE—Prince William County

⊠ ◇ **SENTARA NORTHERN VIRGINIA MEDICAL CENTER (490113)**, 2300
Opitz Boulevard, Zip 22191–3399; tel. 703/523–1000 **A**1 2 9 10 21 **F**3 7 8 11
12 13 15 18 20 22 28 29 30 31 34 35 40 41 42 45 49 51 54 57 59 60 63
65 68 70 71 74 75 76 77 78 79 80 81 82 84 85 87 89 97 102 107 108 110
111 114 115 119 121 126 129 130 132 135 144 145 146 147 148
**S** Sentara Healthcare, Norfolk, VA
Primary Contact: Megan R. Perry, Corporate Vice President and President
COO: Valerie E. Keane, FACHE, Vice President Operations
CFO: Nathan VanGenderen, Chief Financial Officer
CMO: David M. Schwartz, D.O., Vice President, Medical Affairs
CIO: Thomas Ewing, Director Information Technology
CHR: Brett Willsie, Vice President Human Resources
CNO: Patricia Hill, Senior Director Nurse Executive
Web address: www.sentara.com/northernvirginia
**Control:** Other not–for–profit (including NFP Corporation) **Service:** General
Medical and Surgical

**Staffed Beds:** 172 **Admissions:** 10553 **Census:** 108 **Outpatient Visits:**
284654 **Births:** 1964 **Total Expense ($000):** 183987 **Payroll Expense
($000):** 62508 **Personnel:** 1049

## WOODSTOCK—Shenandoah County

⊠ **SHENANDOAH MEMORIAL HOSPITAL (491305)**, 759 South Main Street,
Zip 22664–1127; tel. 540/459–1100 **A**1 9 10 18 **F**3 11 15 28 29 30 35 40
45 50 53 57 59 64 65 68 69 70 75 77 79 81 82 87 92 93 97 107 108 110
114 118 119 130 132 133 135 146 148 **S** Valley Health System,
Winchester, VA
Primary Contact: Floyd Heater, President
CFO: Virginia Kilmer, Chief Financial Officer
CMO: Donald Jansen, M.D., Vice President Medical Affairs
CMO: James Kleinschmidt, M.D., Vice President Medical Affairs
CIO: Joan Roscoe, Chief Information Officer
CHR: Charles E. Walton, Corporate Director Human Resources
CNO: Lisa Stokes, R.N., Vice President Patient Care Services
Web address: www.valleyhealthlink.com/shenandoah
**Control:** Other not–for–profit (including NFP Corporation) **Service:** General
Medical and Surgical

**Staffed Beds:** 25 **Admissions:** 1835 **Census:** 16 **Outpatient Visits:** 98039
**Births:** 0 **Total Expense ($000):** 46516 **Payroll Expense ($000):** 15298
**Personnel:** 279

## WYTHEVILLE—Wythe County

⊠ **WYTHE COUNTY COMMUNITY HOSPITAL (490111)**, 600 West Ridge Road,
Zip 24382–1099; tel. 276/228–0200, (Nonreporting) **A**1 2 9 10 20 **S** LifePoint
Hospitals, Inc., Brentwood, TN
Primary Contact: Timothy A. Bess, Chief Executive Officer
CFO: John D. White, Chief Financial Officer
CMO: George Farrell, M.D., Chief of Staff
CIO: Andrea Harless, Director Information Services
CHR: Dale Clark, Assistant Administrator and Director Human Resources
CNO: Theresa Dix, R.N., Chief Nursing Officer
Web address: www.wcch.org
**Control:** Corporation, Investor–owned, for–profit **Service:** General Medical and
Surgical

**Staffed Beds:** 90

VA

---

**Hospital, Medicare Provider Number, Address, Telephone, Approval, Facility, and Physician Codes, Health Care System**

★ American Hospital Association (AHA) membership
☐ The Joint Commission accreditation
◇ DNV Healthcare Inc. accreditation
○ Healthcare Facilities Accreditation Program
△ Commission on Accreditation of Rehabilitation Facilities (CARF) accreditation

# WASHINGTON

### ABERDEEN—Grays Harbor County

☐ **GRAYS HARBOR COMMUNITY HOSPITAL (500031)**, 915 Anderson Drive, Zip 98520–1097; tel. 360/532–8330, (Nonreporting) **A**1 9 10 20
Primary Contact: Tom Jensen, Chief Executive Officer
COO: Thomas Hightower, R.N., Chief Operating Officer
CFO: Tim Howden, Interim Chief Financial Officer
CMO: Bill Hofmann, M.D., Chief Medical Staff
CIO: Scott Quigley, Director Information Services
CHR: Julie Feller, Director Human Resources
Web address: www.ghchwa.org
**Control:** Other not–for–profit (including NFP Corporation) **Service:** General Medical and Surgical

**Staffed Beds:** 200

### ANACORTES—Skagit County

★ ◇ **ISLAND HOSPITAL (500007)**, 1211 24th Street, Zip 98221–2562; tel. 360/299–1300 **A**2 9 10 21 **F**3 7 8 11 13 15 28 29 30 31 34 35 40 43 45 50 53 57 59 62 64 70 75 76 77 78 79 81 82 85 86 89 93 99 100 102 104 107 108 110 111 114 115 116 119 127 129 130 132 134 135 146 147 148 **P**6 8
Primary Contact: Vincent Oliver, Administrator
CFO: Peter Swanson, Assistant Administrator Fiscal Services
CMO: Linda Brown, M.D., Chief of Staff
CIO: Tom Bluhm, Director Information Systems
CHR: Carolyn J. Tucker, Director Human Resources
Web address: www.islandhospital.org
**Control:** Hospital district or authority, Government, nonfederal **Service:** General Medical and Surgical

**Staffed Beds:** 43 **Admissions:** 3029 **Census:** 27 **Outpatient Visits:** 197857 **Births:** 368 **Total Expense ($000):** 84952 **Payroll Expense ($000):** 35469 **Personnel:** 436

### ARLINGTON—Snohomish County

◇ **CASCADE VALLEY HOSPITAL AND CLINICS (500060)**, 330 South Stillaguamish Avenue, Zip 98223–1642; tel. 360/435–2133, (Nonreporting) **A**9 10 21
Primary Contact: W. Clark Jones, Administrator
CFO: Ardis Schmiege, Chief Financial Officer
CMO: Ross Hartling, M.D., President Medical Staff
CIO: Heather Logan, Assistant Administrator Diagnostic and Support Services
CHR: Connie L. DiGregorio, Assistant Administrator
Web address: www.cascadevalley.org
**Control:** Hospital district or authority, Government, nonfederal **Service:** General Medical and Surgical

**Staffed Beds:** 48

### AUBURN—King County

☐ △ **MULTICARE AUBURN MEDICAL CENTER (500015)**, (Formerly Auburn Regional Medical Center), 202 North Division, Plaza One, Zip 98001–4908; tel. 253/833–7711, (Nonreporting) **A**1 7 9 10 **S** MultiCare Health System, Tacoma, WA
Primary Contact: David Nicewonger, Chief Operating Officer
COO: David Nicewonger, Chief Operating Officer
Web address: www.auburnregional.com
**Control:** Corporation, Investor–owned, for–profit **Service:** General Medical and Surgical

**Staffed Beds:** 120

### BELLEVUE—King County

⊞ **OVERLAKE HOSPITAL MEDICAL CENTER (500051)**, 1035 116th Avenue N.E., Zip 98004–4604; tel. 425/688–5000 **A**1 2 9 10 **F**3 11 12 13 15 17 18 20 22 24 26 29 30 31 34 35 40 43 44 45 46 48 49 56 57 58 59 64 68 70 72 74 75 76 77 78 79 81 84 85 86 87 91 92 93 97 98 100 102 104 105 107 108 110 111 114 115 116 117 118 119 120 121 123 124 126 130 132 134 144 145 146 147 148 **P**6
Primary Contact: Craig L. Hendrickson, President and Chief Executive Officer
COO: David W. Schultz, FACHE, Executive Vice President and Chief Operating Officer
CFO: Gary McLaughlin, Vice President Finance and Chief Financial Officer
CMO: Alan Ertle, M.D., Chief Medical Officer
CIO: Jody Albright, Vice President Information Services and Chief Information Officer
CHR: Lisa Brock, Vice President Human Resources
CNO: Kristine F. Becker, R.N., Interim Chief Nursing Officer/Director of Cardiac Nursing and Nursing Resources
Web address: www.overlakehospital.org
**Control:** Other not–for–profit (including NFP Corporation) **Service:** General Medical and Surgical

**Staffed Beds:** 286 **Admissions:** 19937 **Census:** 187 **Outpatient Visits:** 255867 **Births:** 3982 **Total Expense ($000):** 394914 **Payroll Expense ($000):** 169271 **Personnel:** 1925

### BELLINGHAM—Whatcom County

⊞ △ **PEACEHEALTH ST. JOSEPH MEDICAL CENTER (500030)**, 2901 Squalicum Parkway, Zip 98225–1851; tel. 360/734–5400, (Nonreporting) **A**1 2 5 7 9 10 **S** PeaceHealth, Vancouver, WA
Primary Contact: Nancy Steiger, R.N., Chief Executive Officer and Chief Mission Officer
COO: Stephen R. Omta, Chief Operating Officer
CFO: Dale Zender, Regional Vice President Finance and Chief Financial Officer
CMO: Chris Sprowl, M.D., Vice President
CIO: Marc Pierson, M.D., Vice President Clinical Information and Quality
CHR: Cindy C. Klein, Vice President Human Resources
Web address: www.peacehealth.org
**Control:** Church–operated, Nongovernment, not–for profit **Service:** General Medical and Surgical

**Staffed Beds:** 253

**ST. JOSEPH HOSPITAL** See PeaceHealth St. Joseph Medical Center

### BREMERTON—Kitsap County

⊞ **HARRISON MEDICAL CENTER (500039)**, 2520 Cherry Avenue, Zip 98310–4229; tel. 360/744–3911, (Nonreporting) **A**1 2 9 10
Primary Contact: Scott W. Bosch, FACHE, President and Chief Executive Officer
COO: Patricia Cochrell, R.N., Executive Vice President, Chief Clinical and Operating Officer
CFO: Forrest Ehlinger, Vice President and Chief Financial Officer
CMO: Gordon N. Cromwell, M.D., Chief Medical Officer
CIO: Adar Palis, Executive Vice President and Chief Administrative & Operating Officer
CHR: Marie LaMarche, Executive Director, Human Resources, Organizational Development, Employee Health
Web address: www.harrisonmedical.org
**Control:** Other not–for–profit (including NFP Corporation) **Service:** General Medical and Surgical

**Staffed Beds:** 262

⊞ **NAVAL HOSPITAL BREMERTON**, One Boone Road, Zip 98312–1898; tel. 360/475–4000 **A**1 3 5 **F**3 5 8 13 15 18 29 30 32 33 34 35 38 39 40 43 45 46 50 53 54 57 58 59 64 65 70 74 75 76 77 79 81 82 85 86 87 92 93 97 99 100 101 104 107 108 110 111 114 115 119 130 131 132 134 135 146 147 **S** Bureau of Medicine and Surgery, Department of the Navy, Washington, DC
Primary Contact: Commander Brendan Melody, Director Administration
CFO: Judith Hogan, Comptroller and Director Resources and Logistics
CIO: Patrick Flaherty, Director Management Information
Web address: www.med.navy.mil/sites/nhbrem/Pages/default.aspx
**Control:** Navy, Government, federal **Service:** General Medical and Surgical

**Staffed Beds:** 40 **Admissions:** 2164 **Census:** 13 **Outpatient Visits:** 322823 **Births:** 813 **Personnel:** 1435

**WA**

*Many Facility Codes have changed. Please refer to the AHA Guide Code Chart.* © 2013 AHA Guide

## BREWSTER—Okanogan County

**THREE RIVERS HOSPITAL (501324)**, (Formerly Okanogan Douglas District Hospital), 507 Hospital Way, Zip 98812–0577, Mailing Address: P.O. Box 577, Zip 98812–0577; tel. 509/689–2517, (Nonreporting) **A**9 10 18
Primary Contact: O. E. Hufnagel, Chief Executive Officer
COO: Sandy Sylvester, Chief Operating Officer
CFO: Jennifer Munson, Chief Financial Officer
CMO: Eric Haeger, M.D., President Medical Staff
CIO: Christopher Freel, Chief Information Technologist
CHR: Anita Fisk, Director Human Resources
Web address: www.oddh.org
**Control:** Hospital district or authority, Government, nonfederal **Service:** General Medical and Surgical

**Staffed Beds:** 20

## BURIEN—King County

☒ △ **HIGHLINE MEDICAL CENTER (500011)**, 16251 Sylvester Road S.W., Zip 98166–3052; tel. 206/244–9970, (Includes HIGHLINE SPECIALTY CENTER, 12844 MILITARY ROAD FORK, TUKWILA, ZIP 98168; MARK BENEDUM, ADMINISTRATOR ), (Nonreporting) **A**1 2 7 9 10
Primary Contact: Mark Benedum, Chief Executive Officer
COO: Bud Musselman, Chief Operating Officer and Chief Financial Officer
CFO: Bud Musselman, Chief Operating Officer and Chief Financial Officer
CIO: Matt Crockett, Assistant Administrator and Chief Information Officer
CHR: Rozanne Martin, Assistant Administrator Human Resources
Web address: www.hchnet.org
**Control:** Other not–for–profit (including NFP Corporation) **Service:** General Medical and Surgical

**Staffed Beds:** 179

## CENTRALIA—Lewis County

☒ **PROVIDENCE CENTRALIA HOSPITAL (500019)**, 914 South Scheuber Road, Zip 98531–9027; tel. 360/736–2803 **A**1 9 10 20 **F**5 8 11 13 15 30 31 32 34 35 40 43 48 57 58 59 64 67 68 70 75 76 77 78 79 81 86 87 90 93 102 107 108 110 111 114 116 117 118 119 129 130 131 132 146 147 148 **P**6 **S** Providence Health & Services, Renton, WA
Primary Contact: Cindy Mayo, R.N., FACHE, Chief Executive
COO: Dennis Mesaros, Chief Operating Officer
CFO: Denise Marroni, Chief Financial Officer
CMO: Kevin Caserta, M.D., Chief Medical Officer
CIO: Kerry Miles, Site Director
CHR: Susan Meenk, Vice President Service Area
CNO: Jeanell Rasmussen, R.N., Vice President/Chief Nursing Officer
Web address: www.providence.org
**Control:** Church–operated, Nongovernment, not–for profit **Service:** General Medical and Surgical

**Staffed Beds:** 96 **Admissions:** 5140 **Census:** 52 **Outpatient Visits:** 217986 **Births:** 622 **Total Expense ($000):** 134048 **Payroll Expense ($000):** 44762 **Personnel:** 585

## CHELAN—Chelan County

★ **LAKE CHELAN COMMUNITY HOSPITAL (501334)**, 503 East Highland Avenue, Zip 98816–8631, Mailing Address: P.O. Box 908, Zip 98816–0908; tel. 509/682–3300 **A**9 10 18 **F**4 5 7 8 11 13 15 18 29 30 34 35 36 38 39 40 41 43 44 45 50 56 57 59 62 63 64 65 66 68 71 75 76 77 79 81 84 85 86 87 91 92 93 94 96 99 100 101 102 103 104 106 107 108 110 111 119 125 130 131 132 133 135 143 146 147 148 **P**6
Primary Contact: Kevin Abel, Chief Executive Officer
COO: Brad Hankins, Chief Operating Quality Officer
CFO: Robert Wiegenstein, Chief Financial Officer
CIO: Ross Hurd, Chief Information Officer
CHR: DeLynn K. Cook, Director Human Resources
CNO: Carol N. Velasquez, CENP, R.N., Chief Nursing Officer
Web address: www.lakechelancommunityhospital.com
**Control:** Hospital district or authority, Government, nonfederal **Service:** General Medical and Surgical

**Staffed Beds:** 25 **Admissions:** 766 **Census:** 16 **Outpatient Visits:** 21295 **Births:** 104 **Total Expense ($000):** 20681 **Payroll Expense ($000):** 12145 **Personnel:** 198

## CHEWELAH—Stevens County

☒ **PROVIDENCE ST. JOSEPH'S HOSPITAL (501309)**, 500 East Webster Street, Zip 99109–9523; tel. 509/935–8211, (Total facility includes 40 beds in nursing home–type unit) **A**1 9 10 18 **F**3 8 10 11 13 15 29 30 34 35 40 43 44 45 57 59 65 75 79 81 82 84 87 91 93 107 114 119 128 133 146 148 **P**6 **S** Providence Health & Services, Renton, WA
Primary Contact: Robert D. Campbell, Jr., President and Chief Executive
CFO: Chris Hargis, Chief Financial Officer
CHR: Linda Grittner, Director Human Resources
Web address: www.sjhospital.org
**Control:** Church–operated, Nongovernment, not–for profit **Service:** General Medical and Surgical

**Staffed Beds:** 65 **Admissions:** 512 **Census:** 45 **Outpatient Visits:** 17957 **Births:** 42 **Total Expense ($000):** 19926 **Payroll Expense ($000):** 8608 **Personnel:** 134

## CLARKSTON—Asotin County

☒ **TRI–STATE MEMORIAL HOSPITAL (501332)**, 1221 Highland Avenue, Zip 99403–2829, Mailing Address: P.O. Box 189, Zip 99403–0189; tel. 509/758–5511, (Nonreporting) **A**1 9 10 18
Primary Contact: Donald Wee, Chief Executive Officer
CFO: Alex Town, Chief Financial Officer
CMO: Don Greggain, M.D., Physician Network Director
CIO: Joleen Carper, Director Quality and Risk
CHR: Mark Brigham, Human Resources Officer
CNO: Rhonda Mason, Director of Patient Care Services
Web address: www.tristatehospital.org
**Control:** Other not–for–profit (including NFP Corporation) **Service:** General Medical and Surgical

**Staffed Beds:** 35

## COLFAX—Whitman County

★ **WHITMAN HOSPITAL AND MEDICAL CENTER (501327)**, 1200 West Fairview Street, Zip 99111–9579; tel. 509/397–3435 **A**9 10 18 **F**29 30 34 35 40 45 59 64 65 68 69 76 77 79 81 85 93 107 110 111 119 130 133 135 148 **S** Providence Health & Services, Renton, WA
Primary Contact: Deborah Glass, MS, R.N., Chief Executive Officer
CFO: Jim Heilsberg, Chief Financial Officer and Chief Information Officer
CMO: Nathan Ullrich, M.D., Chief Medical Officer
CIO: Jim Heilsberg, Chief Financial Officer and Chief Information Officer
CHR: Michelle Ellis, Director Human Resources
CNO: Denise Fowler, R.N., Chief Clinical Officer
Web address: www.whitmanhospital.com
**Control:** Hospital district or authority, Government, nonfederal **Service:** General Medical and Surgical

**Staffed Beds:** 25 **Admissions:** 550 **Census:** 6 **Outpatient Visits:** 15954 **Births:** 44 **Total Expense ($000):** 22180 **Payroll Expense ($000):** 8832 **Personnel:** 174

## COLVILLE—Stevens County

☒ **PROVIDENCE MOUNT CARMEL HOSPITAL (501326)**, 982 East Columbia Avenue, Zip 99114–3352; tel. 509/685–5100 **A**1 9 10 18 **F**3 11 13 15 29 30 34 40 43 44 45 57 59 64 70 75 76 77 79 81 82 84 85 86 87 93 107 108 115 118 119 123 129 131 132 133 135 146 148 **P**6 **S** Providence Health & Services, Renton, WA
Primary Contact: Robert D. Campbell, Jr., Chief Executive
COO: Robert D. Campbell, Jr., President, Chief Executive and Chief Operating Officer
CFO: Chris Hargis, Chief Financial Officer
CMO: Mehrdad Farahmand, M.D., Chief Medical Officer
CIO: Theron DePaulo, Manager Information Systems
CHR: Linda Grittner, Vice President Human Resources
CNO: Deborah Watson, Vice President, Patient Care Services
Web address: www.mtcarmelhospital.org
**Control:** Church–operated, Nongovernment, not–for profit **Service:** General Medical and Surgical

**Staffed Beds:** 25 **Admissions:** 1186 **Census:** 11 **Outpatient Visits:** 30978 **Births:** 216 **Total Expense ($000):** 35441 **Payroll Expense ($000):** 13137 **Personnel:** 274

**WA**

---

**Hospital, Medicare Provider Number, Address, Telephone, Approval, Facility, and Physician Codes, Health Care System**

★ American Hospital Association (AHA) membership
☐ The Joint Commission accreditation
◇ DNV Healthcare Inc. accreditation
○ Healthcare Facilities Accreditation Program
△ Commission on Accreditation of Rehabilitation Facilities (CARF) accreditation

### COUPEVILLE—Island County

★ **WHIDBEY GENERAL HOSPITAL (501339)**, 101 North Main Street,
Zip 98239–3413; tel. 360/678–5151, (Nonreporting) **A**2 9 10 18
Primary Contact: Tom Tomasino, Administrator and Chief Executive Officer
COO: Hank Hanigan, Chief Operating Officer
CMO: Gabe Barrio, M.D., Chief of Staff
CHR: Carolyn Pape, Director Human Resources
CNO: Linda Stephens Gipson, MSN, Chief Nursing Officer
Web address: www.whidbeygen.org
**Control:** Hospital district or authority, Government, nonfederal **Service:** General Medical and Surgical

**Staffed Beds:** 25

### DAVENPORT—Lincoln County

★ **LINCOLN HOSPITAL (501305)**, 10 Nicholls Street, Zip 99122–9729;
tel. 509/725–7101, (Nonreporting) **A**9 10 18
Primary Contact: Thomas J. Martin, Administrator
CFO: Tyson Lacy, Chief Financial Officer
CMO: Ralph Monteagudo, M.D., Chief of Staff
CIO: Elliott Donson, Chief Information Specialist
CHR: Janelle Hiccox, Director Human Resources
Web address: www.lincolnhospital.org
**Control:** Hospital district or authority, Government, nonfederal **Service:** General Medical and Surgical

**Staffed Beds:** 60

### DAYTON—Columbia County

**DAYTON GENERAL HOSPITAL (501302)**, 1012 South Third Street,
Zip 99328–1696; tel. 509/382–2531, (Nonreporting) **A**9 10 18
Primary Contact: Dale E. Polla, Chief Executive Officer
CFO: Gary Schroeder, Chief Financial Officer
CHR: Kari Newman, Director Human Resources
Web address: www.cchd–wa.org
**Control:** County–Government, nonfederal **Service:** General Medical and Surgical

**Staffed Beds:** 59

### EDMONDS—Snohomish County

**STEVENS HEALTHCARE** See Swedish/Edmonds

⊞ **SWEDISH/EDMONDS (500026)**, 21601 76th Avenue West, Zip 98026–7506;
tel. 425/640–4000, (Nonreporting) **A**1 2 9 10 **S** Swedish Health Services,
Seattle, WA
Primary Contact: David E. Jaffe, Chief Executive
CMO: Tim Roddy, M.D., Vice President Medical Affairs
CIO: Robert Pageler, Director Information Services
CHR: Steven Losleben, Vice President Human Resources
Web address: www.swedish.org
**Control:** Other not–for–profit (including NFP Corporation) **Service:** General Medical and Surgical

**Staffed Beds:** 161

### ELLENSBURG—Kittitas County

★ **KITTITAS VALLEY COMMUNITY HOSPITAL (501333)**, 603 South Chestnut
Street, Zip 98926–3875; tel. 509/962–7302, (Nonreporting) **A**9 10 18
Primary Contact: Paul E. Nurick, Chief Executive Officer
CFO: Libby Allgood, Chief Financial Officer
Web address: www.kvch.com
**Control:** Hospital district or authority, Government, nonfederal **Service:** General Medical and Surgical

**Staffed Beds:** 25

### ENUMCLAW—King County

★ **ST. ELIZABETH HOSPITAL (501335)**, 1455 Battersby Avenue,
Zip 98022–3634, Mailing Address: P.O. Box 218, Zip 98022–0218;
tel. 360/284–4171, (Nonreporting) **A**9 10 18 **S** Catholic Health Initiatives,
Englewood, CO
Primary Contact: Donna Russell–Cook, President
COO: Joseph Wilczek, Chief Executive Officer
CFO: Philip Hjembo, Chief Financial Officer
CHR: Jerilyn Ray, Manager Human Resources
Web address: www.fhshealth.org
**Control:** Church–operated, Nongovernment, not–for profit **Service:** General Medical and Surgical

**Staffed Beds:** 25

### EPHRATA—Grant County

★ **COLUMBIA BASIN HOSPITAL (501317)**, 200 Nat Washington Way,
Zip 98823–1982; tel. 509/754–4631, (Nonreporting) **A**9 10 18
Primary Contact: Rosalinda Kibby, Acting Chief Executive Officer
CFO: Rhonda Handley, Chief Financial Officer
CMO: Lowell C. Allred, M.D., Chief of Staff
CHR: Suzanne Little, Human Resources Specialist
Web address: www.columbiabasinhospital.org
**Control:** Hospital district or authority, Government, nonfederal **Service:** General Medical and Surgical

**Staffed Beds:** 25

### EVERETT—Snohomish County

⊞ △ **PROVIDENCE REGIONAL MEDICAL CENTER EVERETT (500014)**, 1321
Colby Avenue, Zip 98201–1665, Mailing Address: P.O. Box 1147,
Zip 98206–1147; tel. 425/261–2000, (Includes PROVIDENCE EVERETT MEDICAL
CENTER – COLBY CAMPUS, 1321 Colby Avenue, Zip 98206, Mailing Address:
P.O. Box 1147, Zip 98206; tel. 425/261–2000; PROVIDENCE EVERETT MEDICAL
CENTER – PACIFIC CAMPUS, Pacific and Nassau Streets, Zip 98201, Mailing
Address: P.O. Box 1067, Zip 98206–1067; tel. 206/258–7123) **A**1 2 3 5 7 9
10 **F**3 4 5 8 11 12 13 15 17 18 20 22 24 26 28 29 30 31 32 34 35 36 38
40 43 44 45 46 47 48 49 50 53 54 55 56 57 58 59 60 61 64 65 66 68 70
72 73 74 75 76 77 78 79 80 81 82 83 84 85 86 87 89 90 93 97 107 108
109 111 114 115 116 117 118 119 120 121 123 124 126 129 130 131 132
135 144 146 147 148 **P**6 8 **S** Providence Health & Services, Renton, WA
Primary Contact: Preston M. Simmons, Chief Executive Officer
CFO: Todd Hofheins, Chief Financial Officer
CMO: Lawrence Schecter, M.D., Chief Medical Officer
CHR: Bob Sampson, Vice President Human Resources
Web address: www.providence.org
**Control:** Church–operated, Nongovernment, not–for profit **Service:** General Medical and Surgical

**Staffed Beds:** 491 **Admissions:** 29547 **Census:** 320 **Outpatient Visits:** 574673 **Births:** 4351 **Total Expense ($000):** 615439 **Payroll Expense ($000):** 227905 **Personnel:** 3641

### FEDERAL WAY—King County

⊞ **ST. FRANCIS HOSPITAL (500141)**, 34515 Ninth Avenue South,
Zip 98003–6799; tel. 253/944–8100, (Nonreporting) **A**1 9 10 **S** Catholic Health Initiatives, Englewood, CO
Primary Contact: Anthony McLean, President
CFO: Mike Fitzgerald, Chief Financial Officer
CMO: Mark C. Adams, M.D., Chief Medical Officer
CIO: Bruce Elkington, Regional Chief Information Officer
CHR: David C. Lawson, Senior Vice President Human Resources
CNO: Laurie Brown, R.N., Chief Nursing Officer
Web address: www.fhshealth.org
**Control:** Church–operated, Nongovernment, not–for profit **Service:** General Medical and Surgical

**Staffed Beds:** 120

### FORKS—Clallam County

**FORKS COMMUNITY HOSPITAL (501325)**, 530 Bogachiel Way,
Zip 98331–9120; tel. 360/374–6271, (Nonreporting) **A**9 10 18
Primary Contact: Camille Scott, Chief Executive Officer
COO: John Sherrett, Chief Financial Officer and Chief Operating Officer
CFO: John Sherrett, Chief Financial Officer and Chief Operating Officer
CIO: Andrea Perkins–Peppers, Manager Information Services
CHR: Geoff Roach, Director Human Resources
Web address: www.forkshospital.org
**Control:** Hospital district or authority, Government, nonfederal **Service:** General Medical and Surgical

**Staffed Beds:** 45

### FRIDAY HARBOR—San Juan County

◇ **PEACEHEALTH PEACE ISLAND MEDICAL CENTER (500153)**, 1117 Spring
Street, Zip 98250–9782; tel. 360/378–2141, (Nonreporting) **A**9 21
**S** PeaceHealth, Vancouver, WA
Primary Contact: James R. Barnhart, Chief Administrator Officer
Web address: www.peacehealth.org
**Control:** Church–operated, Nongovernment, not–for profit **Service:** General Medical and Surgical

**Staffed Beds:** 10

### GIG HARBOR—Pierce County

⊞ **ST. ANTHONY HOSPITAL (500151)**, 11567 Canterwood Boulevard N.W.,
Zip 98332–5812; tel. 253/530–2000, (Nonreporting) **A**1 9 10 **S** Catholic Health Initiatives, Englewood, CO
Primary Contact: Kurt Schley, President
Web address: www.fhshealth.org/
**Control:** Church–operated, Nongovernment, not–for profit **Service:** General Medical and Surgical

**Staffed Beds:** 80

**WA**

## GOLDENDALE—Klickitat County

★ **KLICKITAT VALLEY HEALTH (501316)**, 310 South Roosevelt Avenue,
Zip 98620–9201; tel. 509/773–4022 **A**9 10 18 **F**3 7 8 15 18 29 30 34 35 40
43 45 47 59 62 63 64 65 68 75 77 81 83 84 85 97 107 111 119 127 128
130 133 135 144 146 148
Primary Contact: John R. White, Chief Executive Officer and Superintendent
CFO: Leslie Hiebert, Chief Financial Officer
CMO: Anh Nguyen, M.D., Chief of Staff
CIO: Jonathan Hatfield, Supervisor Information Technology
CHR: Charis Weis, Director Human Resources
CNO: Karen Warren, Chief Nursing Officer
Web address: www.kvhealth.net
**Control:** Hospital district or authority, Government, nonfederal **Service:** General
Medical and Surgical

**Staffed Beds:** 17 **Admissions:** 200 **Census:** 5 **Outpatient Visits:** 4342
**Births:** 0 **Total Expense ($000):** 18214 **Payroll Expense ($000):** 8613
**Personnel:** 177

## GRAND COULEE—Grant County

**COULEE COMMUNITY HOSPITAL** See Coulee Medical Center

**COULEE MEDICAL CENTER (501308)**, 411 Fortuyn Road, Zip 99133–8718;
tel. 509/633–1753, (Nonreporting) **A**9 10 18
Primary Contact: J. Scott Graham, Chief Executive Officer and Superintendent
COO: Alan Wagner, Chief Operating Officer
CFO: Debbie Bigelow, Chief Financial Officer
CMO: Jacob Chaffee, M.D., Chief Medical Officer
CHR: Julie D. Bjorklund, Director Human Resources
Web address: www.cmccares.org
**Control:** Hospital district or authority, Government, nonfederal **Service:** General
Medical and Surgical

**Staffed Beds:** 25

## ILWACO—Pacific County

★ **OCEAN BEACH HOSPITAL (501314)**, 174 First Avenue North,
Zip 98624–9137, Mailing Address: P.O. Box H., Zip 98624–0258;
tel. 360/642–3181 **A**9 10 18 **F**3 11 15 28 29 30 31 34 35 40 43 45 57 59
68 75 77 78 79 81 85 86 87 97 107 111 114 119 127 130 132 133 135
147 **P**6
Primary Contact: Kendall Sawa, R.N., Chief Executive Officer
CMO: Randy Ensminger, M.D., Chief Medical Officer
CIO: Julie P. Oakes, R.N., Manager Risk and Quality
CHR: Kary Holloway, Director Human Resources
Web address: www.oceanbeachhospital.net
**Control:** Hospital district or authority, Government, nonfederal **Service:** General
Medical and Surgical

**Staffed Beds:** 15 **Admissions:** 457 **Census:** 5 **Outpatient Visits:** 29660
**Births:** 0 **Total Expense ($000):** 16404 **Payroll Expense ($000):** 9156
**Personnel:** 44

## ISSAQUAH—King County

★ ◇ **SWEDISH/ISSAQUAH (500152)**, 751 N.E. Blakely Drive, Zip 98029–6201;
tel. 425/313–4000, (Nonreporting) **A**9 10 21 **S** Swedish Health Services,
Seattle, WA
Primary Contact: Chuck Salmon, Chief Executive
Web address: www.swedish.org/issaquah
**Control:** Other not–for–profit (including NFP Corporation) **Service:** General
Medical and Surgical

**Staffed Beds:** 49

## KENNEWICK—Benton County

⊠ **KENNEWICK GENERAL HOSPITAL (500053)**, 900 South Auburn Street,
Zip 99336–5621, Mailing Address: P.O. Box 6128, Zip 99336–0128;
tel. 509/586–6111, (Nonreporting) **A**1 2 9 10
Primary Contact: Glen Marshall, Chief Executive Officer
CFO: Gerald Paule, Chief Financial Officer
CFO: Gerald Paule, Chief Financial Officer
CMO: James Newman, M.D., President Medical Staff
CIO: Michael Cloutier, Director Information Services
CHR: Russ Keefer, Chief Human Resources Officer
Web address: www.kennewickgeneral.com
**Control:** Hospital district or authority, Government, nonfederal **Service:** General
Medical and Surgical

**Staffed Beds:** 111

## KIRKLAND—King County

**EVERGREEN HEALTHCARE** See EvergreenHealth

⊠ **EVERGREENHEALTH (500124)**, (Formerly Evergreen Hospital Medical Center),
12040 N.E. 128th Street, Zip 98034–3013; tel. 425/899–1000 **A**1 2 5 9 10 **F**3
8 11 12 13 15 18 20 22 28 29 30 34 35 37 38 40 42 43 44 46 49 50 51 53
54 55 56 57 58 59 62 63 64 65 68 70 71 72 73 74 75 76 78 79 80 81 82
84 85 86 87 89 90 92 93 95 96 97 103 107 108 110 111 114 115 119 120
121 123 124 126 129 130 131 132 135 144 146 147 148 **P**4 6
Primary Contact: Robert H. Malte, Chief Executive Officer
COO: David S. Danielson, Senior Vice President Operations
CFO: Chrissy Yamada, CPA, Senior Vice President Finance
CMO: Mitch Weinberg, M.D., Chief of Staff
CIO: Tom Martin, Vice President and Chief Information Officer
Web address: www.evergreenhealthcare.org
**Control:** Hospital district or authority, Government, nonfederal **Service:** General
Medical and Surgical

**Staffed Beds:** 293 **Admissions:** 15288 **Census:** 140 **Outpatient Visits:**
517537 **Births:** 4503 **Total Expense ($000):** 445465 **Payroll Expense
($000):** 220174 **Personnel:** 2761

☐ **FAIRFAX HOSPITAL (504002)**, 10200 N.E. 132nd Street, Zip 98034–2899;
tel. 425/821–2000, (Nonreporting) **A**1 9 10 **S** Universal Health Services, Inc.,
King of Prussia, PA
Primary Contact: Ron Escarda, Chief Executive Officer
COO: Michael Uradnik, Chief Operating Officer
CFO: Pam Rhoads, Chief Financial Officer
CMO: William Adams, M.D., Medical Director
CHR: Anne Schreiber, Manager Human Resources
Web address: www.fairfaxhospital.com
**Control:** Corporation, Investor–owned, for–profit **Service:** Psychiatric

**Staffed Beds:** 95

## LAKEWOOD—Pierce County

⊠ △ **ST. CLARE HOSPITAL (500021)**, 11315 Bridgeport Way S.W.,
Zip 98499–3004; tel. 253/588–1711, (Nonreporting) **A**1 7 9 10 **S** Catholic
Health Initiatives, Englewood, CO
Primary Contact: Kathy Bressler, President
COO: Kathy Bressler, President
CFO: Mike Fitzgerald, Chief Financial Officer
CIO: Bruce Elkington, Regional Chief Information Officer
CHR: David C. Lawson, Senior Vice President Human Resources
Web address: www.fhshealth.org
**Control:** Church–operated, Nongovernment, not–for profit **Service:** General
Medical and Surgical

**Staffed Beds:** 104

## LEAVENWORTH—Chelan County

★ **CASCADE MEDICAL CENTER (501313)**, 817 Commercial Street,
Zip 98826–1316, Mailing Address: P.O. Box 330, Zip 98826–0330;
tel. 509/548–5815 **A**9 10 18 **F**3 7 15 30 34 40 43 45 59 63 64 65 68 77 93
97 104 107 110 114 127 130 131 133 148 **P**6
Primary Contact: Diane Blake, Chief Executive Officer
CMO: John Deliduka, M.D., Chief Medical Officer
CHR: Lance Heise, Director Human Resources
CNO: Julie Meredith, Acting Chief Nursing Officer
Web address: www.cascademedical.org
**Control:** Hospital district or authority, Government, nonfederal **Service:** General
Medical and Surgical

**Staffed Beds:** 9 **Admissions:** 280 **Census:** 4 **Outpatient Visits:** 54591
**Births:** 0 **Total Expense ($000):** 13154 **Payroll Expense ($000):** 6832
**Personnel:** 92

## LONGVIEW—Cowlitz County

⊠ **PEACEHEALTH ST. JOHN MEDICAL CENTER (500041)**, 1615 Delaware
Street, Zip 98632–2367, Mailing Address: P.O. Box 3002, Zip 98632–0302;
tel. 360/414–2000, (Nonreporting) **A**1 2 9 10 **S** PeaceHealth, Vancouver, WA
Primary Contact: Sy Johnson, Chief Executive Officer and Chief Mission Officer
Web address: www.peacehealth.org
**Control:** Church–operated, Nongovernment, not–for profit **Service:** General
Medical and Surgical

**Staffed Beds:** 202

**WA**

---

| Hospital, Medicare Provider Number, Address, Telephone, Approval, Facility, and Physician Codes, Health Care System |
| --- |

★ American Hospital Association (AHA) membership  ○ Healthcare Facilities Accreditation Program
☐ The Joint Commission accreditation  ◇ DNV Healthcare Inc. accreditation  △ Commission on Accreditation of Rehabilitation Facilities (CARF) accreditation

## MCCLEARY—Grays Harbor County

**SUMMIT PACIFIC MEDICAL CENTER (501304)**, (Formerly Mark Reed Health Care District), 322 South Birch Street, Zip 98557–9522; tel. 360/346–2222, (Nonreporting) **A**9 10 18
Primary Contact: Renee K. Jensen, Chief Executive Officer
CFO: Ronald Hulscher, Chief Financial Officer
CMO: Patrick Ogilvie, M.D., Chief Medical Officer
CIO: Chayne King, Contracted Manager Information Technology
CHR: Mindy Portchy, Manager Human Resources
Web address: www.markreed.org
**Control:** Corporation, Investor–owned, for–profit **Service:** General Medical and Surgical

**Staffed Beds:** 6

## MEDICAL LAKE—Spokane County

□ **EASTERN STATE HOSPITAL (504004)**, Maple Street, Zip 99022–0045, Mailing Address: P.O. Box 800, Zip 99022–0800; tel. 509/565–4705, (Nonreporting) **A**1 9 10
Primary Contact: Harold E. Wilson, Chief Executive Officer
Web address: www.www1.dsgs.wa.gov/mentalhealth/eshfaqs.shtml
**Control:** State–Government, nonfederal **Service:** Psychiatric

**Staffed Beds:** 319

## MONROE—Snohomish County

⊞ ◇ **VALLEY GENERAL HOSPITAL (500084)**, 14701 179th S.E., Zip 98272–1108, Mailing Address: P.O. Box 646, Zip 98272–0646; tel. 360/794–7497, (Nonreporting) **A**1 2 9 10 21
Primary Contact: Eric Jensen, Chief Executive Officer
CFO: John Beltz, Chief Financial Officer
CIO: Kathy Nelson, Director Marketing and Strategic Planning
CHR: Joan Catlett, Director Human Resources
Web address: www.valleygeneral.com
**Control:** Hospital district or authority, Government, nonfederal **Service:** General Medical and Surgical

**Staffed Beds:** 68

## MORTON—Lewis County

★ **MORTON GENERAL HOSPITAL (501319)**, 521 Adams Avenue, Zip 98356–9323, Mailing Address: P.O. Box 1138, Zip 98356–0019; tel. 360/496–5112 **A**9 10 18 **F**3 8 13 40 45 81 85 93 107 110 111 119 127 129 147 148
Primary Contact: Ron DeArth, Chief Executive Director
CFO: Tim Cournyer, Chief Financial Officer
CHR: Shannon Kelly, Director Human Resources
Web address: www.mortongeneral.org
**Control:** Hospital district or authority, Government, nonfederal **Service:** General Medical and Surgical

**Staffed Beds:** 25 **Admissions:** 357 **Census:** 17 **Outpatient Visits:** 27705 **Births:** 16 **Total Expense ($000):** 22118 **Payroll Expense ($000):** 10901 **Personnel:** 187

## MOSES LAKE—Grant County

★ **SAMARITAN HEALTHCARE (500033)**, 801 East Wheeler Road, Zip 98837–1899; tel. 509/765–5606, (Nonreporting) **A**5 9 10 20
Primary Contact: Thomas R. Thompson, Chief Executive Officer
COO: Tom Legel, Chief Financial Officer and Chief Operating Officer
CFO: Tom Legel, Chief Financial Officer and Chief Operating Officer
CMO: James Irwin, M.D., Chief Medical Officer
CHR: Lisa A. McDaniel, Director Human Resources
CNO: Kathryn E. Trumbull, R.N., Chief Nursing Officer and Vice President Patient Care Services
Web address: www.samaritanhealthcare.com
**Control:** Hospital district or authority, Government, nonfederal **Service:** General Medical and Surgical

**Staffed Beds:** 47

## MOUNT VERNON—Skagit County

★ ◇ **SKAGIT VALLEY HOSPITAL (500003)**, 1415 East Kincaid Street, Zip 98274–4126, Mailing Address: P.O. Box 1376, Zip 98273–1376; tel. 360/424–4111 **A**2 5 9 10 19 21 **F**3 8 11 13 18 20 22 26 28 29 30 31 32 34 35 36 40 43 46 47 48 49 51 54 56 58 59 60 62 63 64 65 68 70 73 74 75 76 77 78 79 80 81 84 85 86 87 89 90 92 93 97 98 100 101 102 103 107 108 111 114 116 117 118 119 120 127 129 130 144 146 147 148 **P**6
Primary Contact: Gregg A. Davidson, FACHE, Chief Executive Officer
COO: Michael T. Liepman, Chief Operating Officer
CFO: Thomas Litaker, Chief Financial Officer
CMO: Richard Abbott, M.D., Medical Advisor Quality Improvement
CIO: Doug Riley, Director Information Services
CHR: Deborah Martin, Assistant Administrator
CNO: Jan Iverson, R.N., Chief Nursing Officer
Web address: www.skagitvalleyhospital.org
**Control:** Hospital district or authority, Government, nonfederal **Service:** General Medical and Surgical

**Staffed Beds:** 137 **Admissions:** 7889 **Census:** 82 **Outpatient Visits:** 412936 **Births:** 1135 **Total Expense ($000):** 238972 **Payroll Expense ($000):** 99075 **Personnel:** 1190

## NEWPORT—Pend Oreille County

**NEWPORT HOSPITAL AND HEALTH SERVICES (501310)**, 714 West Pine Street, Zip 99156–9046; tel. 509/447–2441, (Nonreporting) **A**9 10 18
Primary Contact: Thomas W. Wilbur, Chief Executive Officer and Superintendent
COO: Ginny Monroe, Chief Operating Officer
CFO: Kim Manus, Chief Financial Officer
CMO: Sara Ragsdale, D.O., Chief Medical Staff
CIO: Kim Manus, Chief Financial Officer
CHR: Roger Rasmussen, Chief Administrative Officer
Web address: www.phd1.org
**Control:** Hospital district or authority, Government, nonfederal **Service:** General Medical and Surgical

**Staffed Beds:** 70

## OAK HARBOR—Island County

⊞ **NAVAL HOSPITAL OAK HARBOR**, (Formerly Naval Hospital), 3475 North Saratoga Street, Zip 98278–8800; tel. 360/257–9500, (Nonreporting) **A**1 **S** Bureau of Medicine and Surgery, Department of the Navy, Washington, DC
Primary Contact: Lieutenant Commander Chris Morrison
CFO: Lieutenant Gerald Hall, Director Resource Management
CMO: Commander Stephen Cooley, M.D., Chairman Executive Committee Medical Staff
CIO: Gregory Carruth, Head Information Management
CHR: Kathy Vass, Head Human Resources
Web address: www.med.navy.mil/sites/nhoh/Pages/default.aspx
**Control:** Navy, Government, federal **Service:** General Medical and Surgical

**Staffed Beds:** 29

## ODESSA—Lincoln County

**ODESSA MEMORIAL HEALTHCARE CENTER (501307)**, 502 East Amende Drive, Zip 99159–7003, Mailing Address: P.O. Box 368, Zip 99159–0368; tel. 509/982–2611, (Nonreporting) **A**9 10 18
Primary Contact: Gary L. DelForge, Administrator
COO: Alyssa Oestreich, Chief Operating Officer
CFO: Annette Edwards, Chief Financial Officer
CMO: Linda J. Powel, M.D., Medical Director
CHR: Julie Wehr, Director Human Resources
Web address: www.omhc.org
**Control:** Hospital district or authority, Government, nonfederal **Service:** General Medical and Surgical

**Staffed Beds:** 25

## OLYMPIA—Thurston County

□ **CAPITAL MEDICAL CENTER (500139)**, 3900 Capital Mall Drive S.W., Zip 98502–5026, Mailing Address: P.O. Box 19002, Zip 98507–0013; tel. 360/754–5858, (Nonreporting) **A**1 9 10 **S** Capella Healthcare, Franklin, TN
Primary Contact: Jim Geist, Chief Executive Officer
CFO: Brian Anderson, Chief Financial Officer
CMO: Rojesh Sharangpani, M.D., Chief of Staff
CIO: Renee Crotty, Coordinator Marketing and Public Relations
CHR: Dana Vandewege, Director Human Resources
Web address: www.capitalmedical.com
**Control:** Partnership, Investor–owned, for–profit **Service:** General Medical and Surgical

**Staffed Beds:** 110

*Many Facility Codes have changed. Please refer to the AHA Guide Code Chart.* © 2013 AHA Guide

☒ △ **PROVIDENCE ST. PETER HOSPITAL (500024)**, 413 Lilly Road N.E.,
Zip 98506–5166; tel. 360/491–9480 **A**1 7 9 10 **F**3 4 5 11 12 13 15 17 18 20
22 24 26 28 29 30 34 35 36 38 40 43 44 45 46 48 49 51 53 56 57 58 59
60 61 64 66 70 73 74 75 76 77 78 79 81 83 84 85 86 87 89 90 91 92 93
94 97 98 99 100 101 102 104 105 107 108 111 114 118 119 129 130 131
132 134 135 143 146 147 148 **P**6 **S** Providence Health & Services, Renton, WA
Primary Contact: Medrice Coluccio, R.N., Chief Executive Officer
COO: Paul G. Wilkinson, Chief Operating Officer
CFO: Thomas Risse, Chief Financial Officer
CMO: Mike Matlock, M.D., Chief Medical Officer
CIO: Kerry Miles, Chief Information Officer
CHR: Susan Meenk, Vice President Service Area
Web address: www.providence.org/swsa/facilities/st_peter_hospital
**Control:** Church–operated, Nongovernment, not–for profit **Service:** General
Medical and Surgical

**Staffed Beds:** 369 **Admissions:** 21783 **Census:** 263 **Outpatient Visits:**
280060 **Births:** 2165 **Total Expense ($000):** 374906 **Payroll Expense
($000):** 132329 **Personnel:** 1900

### OMAK—Okanogan County

**MID–VALLEY HOSPITAL (501328)**, 810 Jasmine, Zip 98841–9578, Mailing
Address: P.O. Box 793, Zip 98841–0793; tel. 509/826–1760, (Nonreporting) **A**9
10 18
Primary Contact: Michael D. Billing, Administrator
CFO: Scott Attridge, Controller
CMO: David Bradford, M.D., Chief Medical Officer
CIO: Kelly Cariker, Manager
CHR: Randy Coffell, Manager Human Resources
Web address: www.mvhealth.org
**Control:** Hospital district or authority, Government, nonfederal **Service:** General
Medical and Surgical

**Staffed Beds:** 30

### OTHELLO—Adams County

★ **OTHELLO COMMUNITY HOSPITAL (501318)**, 315 North 14th Avenue,
Zip 99344–1297; tel. 509/488–2636, (Nonreporting) **A**9 10 18
CFO: Mark Bunch, Director Finance
CHR: Cheryl Olson, Chief Human Resources Officer
Web address: www.othellocommunityhospital.org
**Control:** Hospital district or authority, Government, nonfederal **Service:** General
Medical and Surgical

**Staffed Beds:** 25

### PASCO—Franklin County

☒ △ **LOURDES MEDICAL CENTER (501337)**, 520 North Fourth Avenue,
Zip 99301–5257, Mailing Address: P.O. Box 2568, Zip 99302–2568;
tel. 509/547–7704, (Nonreporting) **A**1 7 9 10 18 **S** Ascension Health, Saint
Louis, MO
Primary Contact: John Serle, FACHE, President and Chief Executive Officer
COO: Janet Wright, R.N., Vice President Patient Care Executive
CFO: Frank Becker, Chief Financial Officer
CIO: Vern Turney, Director Information Technology
Web address: www.lourdeshealth.net
**Control:** Church–operated, Nongovernment, not–for profit **Service:** General
Medical and Surgical

**Staffed Beds:** 35

### POMEROY—Garfield County

★ **GARFIELD COUNTY PUBLIC HOSPITAL DISTRICT (501301)**, 66 North 6th
Street, Zip 99347–9705; tel. 509/843–1591, (Nonreporting) **A**9 10 18
Primary Contact: Andrew Craigie, Chief Executive Officer
CFO: Andrew Craigie, Chief Executive Officer
CMO: Glenn Houser, M.D., Chief Medical Officer
CIO: Nevelyn Schooler, Health Information Manager
CHR: Alicia Scharnhorst, Human Resources and Business Office Manager
CNO: Susan Morrow, R.N., Chief Nursing Officer
Web address: www.garfieldcountyphd.org
**Control:** Hospital district or authority, Government, nonfederal **Service:** General
Medical and Surgical

**Staffed Beds:** 40

### PORT ANGELES—Clallam County

☒ **OLYMPIC MEDICAL CENTER (500072)**, 939 Caroline Street,
Zip 98362–3997; tel. 360/417–7000, (Nonreporting) **A**1 2 5 9 10
Primary Contact: Eric Lewis, Chief Executive Officer
CFO: Julie Rukstad, Chief Financial Officer
CMO: R. Scott Kennedy, M.D., Assistant Administrator and Chief Medical Officer
CIO: Linda Brown, Chief Information Officer
CHR: Richard Neuman, Assistant Administrator and Chief Human Resources
Officer
Web address: www.olympicmedical.org
**Control:** Hospital district or authority, Government, nonfederal **Service:** General
Medical and Surgical

**Staffed Beds:** 78

### PORT TOWNSEND—Jefferson County

★ ◇ **JEFFERSON HEALTHCARE (501323)**, 834 Sheridan Street,
Zip 98368–2443; tel. 360/385–2200, (Nonreporting) **A**9 10 18 21
Primary Contact: Mike Glenn, Administrator and Chief Executive Officer
COO: Paula Dowdle, Chief Operating Officer
CFO: Hilary Whittington, Chief Financial Officer
CMO: Joe Mattern, M.D., Chief Medical Officer
CHR: Heather Bailey, Chief Human Resources Officer
CNO: Joyce Cardinal, Chief Nursing Executive
Web address: www.jeffersonhealthcare.org
**Control:** Hospital district or authority, Government, nonfederal **Service:** General
Medical and Surgical

**Staffed Beds:** 25

### PROSSER—Benton County

★ **PMH MEDICAL CENTER (501312)**, (Formerly Prosser Memorial Hospital), 723
Memorial Street, Zip 99350–1593; tel. 509/786–2222, (Nonreporting) **A**9 10 18
Primary Contact: Julie Petersen, Chief Executive Officer
CFO: Tim Cooper, Chief Financial Officer
CIO: Dan Harter, Manager Information Systems
Web address: www.pmhmedicalcenter.com/
**Control:** Hospital district or authority, Government, nonfederal **Service:** General
Medical and Surgical

**Staffed Beds:** 25

### PULLMAN—Whitman County

☐ **PULLMAN REGIONAL HOSPITAL (501331)**, 835 S.E. Bishop Boulevard,
Zip 99163–5512; tel. 509/332–2541 **A**1 9 10 18 **F**3 13 15 28 29 30 34 35
36 37 38 40 43 44 45 47 50 51 53 55 57 59 64 68 70 74 75 76 77 78 79
81 86 87 89 93 98 101 102 104 105 107 108 110 111 114 118 119 126
129 130 131 132 133 144 146 **P**4 6
Primary Contact: Scott K. Adams, Chief Executive Officer
CFO: Steven Febus, Chief Financial Officer
CMO: Richard Caggiano, M.D., Chief Medical Officer
CHR: Bernadette Berney, Director Human Resources
Web address: www.pullmanhospital.org
**Control:** Hospital district or authority, Government, nonfederal **Service:** General
Medical and Surgical

**Staffed Beds:** 25 **Admissions:** 1306 **Census:** 11 **Outpatient Visits:** 66234
**Births:** 453 **Total Expense ($000):** 47380 **Payroll Expense ($000):** 22861
**Personnel:** 327

### PUYALLUP—Pierce County

**GOOD SAMARITAN COMMUNITY HEALTHCARE** See MultiCare Good Samaritan
Hospital

☐ △ **MULTICARE GOOD SAMARITAN HOSPITAL (500079)**, 407 14th Avenue
S.E., Zip 98372–3770, Mailing Address: P.O. Box 1247, Zip 98371–0192;
tel. 253/697–4000 **A**1 2 7 9 10 **F**3 8 11 18 20 22 24 28 29 30 31 34
35 38 40 41 43 45 47 48 50 51 55 56 57 58 59 61 64 65 66 68 70 73 74
75 76 78 79 81 82 84 85 87 89 90 91 92 93 94 96 97 99 100 101 102 103
104 106 107 108 111 114 115 117 118 119 126 129 130 132 146 147 148
**S** MultiCare Health System, Tacoma, WA
Primary Contact: Glenn Kasman, President
CFO: Kim Lintott, Vice President
CMO: J. D. Fitz, M.D., Vice President Medical Affairs
CIO: Florence Chang, Senior Vice President, Clinical Support Services and Chief
Information Officer
CHR: Sarah Horsman, Vice President Human Resources
Web address: www.goodsamhealth.org
**Control:** Other not–for–profit (including NFP Corporation) **Service:** General
Medical and Surgical

**Staffed Beds:** 265 **Admissions:** 18753 **Census:** 193 **Outpatient Visits:**
116230 **Births:** 2284 **Total Expense ($000):** 357471 **Payroll Expense
($000):** 128438 **Personnel:** 1647

**WA**

---

**Hospital, Medicare Provider Number, Address, Telephone, Approval, Facility, and Physician Codes, Health Care System**

★ American Hospital Association (AHA) membership  ○ Healthcare Facilities Accreditation Program
☐ The Joint Commission accreditation  ◇ DNV Healthcare Inc. accreditation  △ Commission on Accreditation of Rehabilitation Facilities (CARF) accreditation

## QUINCY—Grant County

★ **QUINCY VALLEY MEDICAL CENTER (501320)**, 908 10th Avenue S.W., Zip 98848–1376; tel. 509/787–3531, (Nonreporting) **A**9 10 18
Primary Contact: Mehdi Merred, Chief Executive Officer
CFO: Dean Taplett, Controller
CMO: Mark Vance, M.D., Chief Medical Officer
CIO: Ruth Vance, Director Information Systems
CHR: Alene Walker, Director Human Resources
Web address: www.quincyhospital.org
**Control:** County–Government, nonfederal **Service:** General Medical and Surgical

**Staffed Beds:** 47

## RENTON—King County

☒ **UW MEDICINE/VALLEY MEDICAL CENTER (500088)**, (Formerly Valley Medical Center), 400 South 43rd Street, Zip 98055–5714; tel. 425/228–3450 **A**1 2 3 5 9 10 **F**3 8 11 13 15 18 19 20 22 26 28 29 30 31 32 34 35 36 37 38 40 43 44 45 48 49 50 51 53 54 55 57 58 59 60 64 65 66 68 70 72 74 75 76 77 78 79 81 82 84 85 86 87 89 91 92 93 94 96 97 100 101 102 104 107 110 114 115 118 119 120 121 123 124 126 129 130 131 132 135 144 146 147 148 **P**6 **S** UW Medicine, Seattle, WA
Primary Contact: Richard D. Roodman, Chief Executive Officer
COO: Paul Hayes, Executive Vice President and Chief Operating Officer
CFO: Larry Smith, Senior Vice President and Chief Financial Officer
CMO: Kathryn Beattie, M.D., Senior Vice President and Chief Medical Officer
CIO: Rand Strobel, Vice President Information Technology
CHR: Barbara Mitchell, Senior Vice President Marketing and Human Resources
CNO: Scott Alleman, Senior Vice President Patient Care Services and Chief Nursing Officer
Web address: www.valleymed.org
**Control:** Hospital district or authority, Government, nonfederal **Service:** General Medical and Surgical

**Staffed Beds:** 174 **Admissions:** 16842 **Census:** 172 **Outpatient Visits:** 621006 **Births:** 3964 **Total Expense ($000):** 437252 **Payroll Expense ($000):** 194316 **Personnel:** 2458

## REPUBLIC—Ferry County

★ **FERRY COUNTY MEMORIAL HOSPITAL (501322)**, 36 Klondike Road, Zip 99166–9701; tel. 509/775–3333, (Nonreporting) **A**9 10 18
Primary Contact: Gary W. Robertson, Chief Executive Officer
CFO: Kelly Leslie, Chief Financial Officer
CMO: Farhad H. Alrashedy, M.D., Chief Medical Officer
CIO: James Davidson, Director of Information Services
CHR: Michelle Loftis, Human Resources Officer
CNO: Thomas Durham, Chief Nursing Officer
Web address: www.fcphd.org
**Control:** Hospital district or authority, Government, nonfederal **Service:** General Medical and Surgical

**Staffed Beds:** 25

## RICHLAND—Benton County

☒ △ **KADLEC REGIONAL MEDICAL CENTER (500058)**, (Formerly Kadlec Medical Center), 888 Swift Boulevard, Zip 99352–3514; tel. 509/946–4611 **A**1 2 7 9 10 **F**3 11 13 15 18 20 22 24 26 28 29 30 31 34 36 40 43 46 47 48 49 50 51 54 55 57 59 64 68 70 72 75 76 77 78 79 81 82 85 86 87 89 90 93 96 97 107 108 110 111 114 115 116 117 118 119 130 146 148 **S** QHR, Brentwood, TN
Primary Contact: Rand J. Wortman, Chief Executive Officer
COO: Lane A. Savitch, President
CFO: Julie Meek, Vice President Finance
CMO: Wassim Khawandi, M.D., Chief of Staff
CIO: David Roach, Vice President Information Systems
CHR: Jeff Clark, Vice President Human Resources
CNO: Kirk Harper, R.N., Vice President, Nursing
Web address: www.kadlecmed.org
**Control:** Other not–for–profit (including NFP Corporation) **Service:** General Medical and Surgical

**Staffed Beds:** 249 **Admissions:** 14655 **Census:** 161 **Outpatient Visits:** 225669 **Births:** 2574 **Total Expense ($000):** 289076 **Payroll Expense ($000):** 110547 **Personnel:** 1750

★ **LOURDES COUNSELING CENTER (504008)**, 1175 Carondelet Drive, Zip 99354–3300; tel. 509/943–9104, (Nonreporting) **A**9 10 **S** Ascension Health, Saint Louis, MO
Primary Contact: Barbara Mead, Executive Director
CFO: Frank Becker, Chief Financial Officer
CIO: Vern Turney, Director Information Services
CHR: Craig K. Pearsall, Director Human Resources
Web address: www.lourdeshealth.net
**Control:** Church–operated, Nongovernment, not–for profit **Service:** Psychiatric

**Staffed Beds:** 20

## RITZVILLE—Adams County

★ **EAST ADAMS RURAL HOSPITAL (501311)**, 903 South Adams Street, Zip 99169–2298; tel. 509/659–1200, (Nonreporting) **A**9 10 18
Primary Contact: Gary Bostrom, Chief Executive Officer and Chief Executive Financial Officer
CFO: Gary Bostrom, Chief Executive Officer and Chief Executive Financial Officer
CMO: Jill Jenkins, M.D., Chief of Staff
CIO: Kellie Ottmar, Manager Information Services
CHR: Leslie Lzicar, Director Human Resources
CHR: Dina McBride, Executive Assistant and Human Resources Director
CNO: Brenda Herr, Chief Nursing Officer
Web address: www.earh.com
**Control:** Hospital district or authority, Government, nonfederal **Service:** General Medical and Surgical

**Staffed Beds:** 10

## SEATTLE—King County

◇ **GROUP HEALTH COOPERATIVE CENTRAL HOSPITAL (500052)**, 201 16th Avenue East, Zip 98112–5226; tel. 206/326–6300, (Nonreporting) **A**3 5 9 10 21
Primary Contact: Jane Hutcheson, Administrator and Director Clinical Operations
Web address: www.https://www.ghc.org
**Control:** Corporation, Investor–owned, for–profit **Service:** General Medical and Surgical

**Staffed Beds:** 306

☒ **KINDRED HOSPITAL SEATTLE–NORTHGATE (502002)**, 10631 8th Avenue N.E., Zip 98125–7213; tel. 206/364–2050, (Includes KINDRED HOSPITAL SEATTLE–FIRST HILL, 1334 Terry Avenue, Zip 98101–2747; tel. 206/682–2661; Lourene Money, Interim Chief Executive Officer), (Nonreporting) **A**1 9 10 **S** Kindred Healthcare, Louisville, KY
Primary Contact: Lauren Suarez, Chief Executive Officer
CFO: David Stob, Chief Financial Officer
Web address: www.kindredhospitalseattle.com/
**Control:** Corporation, Investor–owned, for–profit **Service:** Long–Term Acute Care hospital

**Staffed Beds:** 42

☐ **NAVOS (504009)**, 2600 S.W. Holden Street, Zip 98126–3505; tel. 206/933–7199, (Nonreporting) **A**1 9 10
Primary Contact: David Johnson, Chief Executive Officer
COO: Jerry Scott, Chief Operating Officer
CFO: Jerry Scott, Chief Operating Officer
CMO: Samir Aziz, M.D., Inpatient Medical Director
CIO: Jeff Coleman, Manager Information Systems
CHR: Judi Mitchell, Vice President Human Resources
Web address: www.navos.org
**Control:** Other not–for–profit (including NFP Corporation) **Service:** Psychiatric

**Staffed Beds:** 69

☒ **REGIONAL HOSPITAL FOR RESPIRATORY AND COMPLEX CARE (502001)**, 12844 Military Road South, Zip 98168–3045; tel. 206/248–4548 **A**1 10 **F**1 29 30 50 85 87 130 148 **P**1 4 5
Primary Contact: Anne McBride, Chief Executive Officer
CMO: Embra Roper, Chief Medical Officer
CHR: Valerie Albano, Director, Human Resources
Web address: www.regionalhospital.org
**Control:** Other not–for–profit (including NFP Corporation) **Service:** Long–Term Acute Care hospital

**Staffed Beds:** 31 **Admissions:** 209 **Census:** 19 **Outpatient Visits:** 0 **Births:** 0 **Total Expense ($000):** 17213 **Personnel:** 67

**SCHICK SHADEL HOSPITAL**, 12101 Ambaum Boulevard S.W., Zip 98146–2651, Mailing Address: P.O. Box 48149, Zip 98148–0149; tel. 206/244–8100, (Nonreporting) **A**9
Primary Contact: Elaine Oksendahl, Administrator
CFO: Scott Miller, Chief Financial Officer
CMO: Ron Merchant, M.D., Medical Director
CIO: Henry Brown, Director Plant Operations and Information Technology
CHR: Janet Sill–Leahy, Manager Human Resources
Web address: www.schickshadel.com
**Control:** Corporation, Investor–owned, for–profit **Service:** Alcoholism and other chemical dependency

**Staffed Beds:** 48

**WA**

*Many Facility Codes have changed. Please refer to the AHA Guide Code Chart.* © 2013 AHA Guide

☐ **SEATTLE CANCER CARE ALLIANCE (500138)**, 825 Eastlake Avenue East, Zip 98109–4405, Mailing Address: P.O. Box 19023, Zip 98109–1023; tel. 206/288–1400 **A**1 9 10 **F**3 8 15 30 31 34 39 45 46 47 55 58 59 68 71 75 78 80 84 86 87 107 108 110 111 114 115 116 117 118 119 120 121 123 130 132 135 136 143 146 147
Primary Contact: Norm Hubbard, Executive Vice President
COO: Madeline Buelt, Vice President Operations
CFO: Jonathan Tingstad, Vice President and Chief Financial Officer
CMO: Marc Stewart, M.D., Vice President and Medical Director
CIO: David Ackerson, Chief Information Officer
CHR: Han Nachtrieb, Vice President Human Resources
Web address: www.seattlecca.org
**Control:** Other not–for–profit (including NFP Corporation) **Service:** Cancer

**Staffed Beds: 20 Admissions: 571 Census: 17 Outpatient Visits: 72300 Births: 0 Total Expense ($000): 324716 Payroll Expense ($000): 68583 Personnel: 983**

☐ △ **SEATTLE CHILDREN'S HOSPITAL (503300)**, 4800 Sand Point Way N.E., Zip 98105–3901, Mailing Address: P.O. Box 5371, Zip 98145–5005; tel. 206/987–2000, (Nonreporting) **A**1 2 3 5 7 9 10
Primary Contact: Thomas N. Hansen, M.D., Chief Executive Officer
COO: Patrick J. Hagan, President and Chief Operating Officer
CFO: Kelly Wallace, Senior Vice President and Chief Financial Officer
CMO: David Fisher, M.D., Senior Vice President and Medical Director
CIO: Wes Wright, Senior Vice President and Chief Information Officer
CHR: Steven Hurwitz, Vice President Human Resources
Web address: www.seattlechildrens.org
**Control:** Other not–for–profit (including NFP Corporation) **Service:** Children's general

**Staffed Beds: 250**

☒ △ **SWEDISH MEDICAL CENTER–CHERRY HILL CAMPUS (500025)**, 500 17th Avenue, Zip 98122–5711; tel. 206/320–2000, (Nonreporting) **A**1 2 3 5 7 9 10 **S** Swedish Health Services, Seattle, WA
Primary Contact: Rayburn Lewis, M.D., Executive
CFO: Jeffrey Veilleux, Senior Vice President and Chief Financial Officer
CMO: John Vassall, M.D., Chief Medical Officer
CIO: Janice Newell, Chief Information Officer
Web address: www.swedish.org
**Control:** Other not–for–profit (including NFP Corporation) **Service:** General Medical and Surgical

**Staffed Beds: 198**

☒ **SWEDISH MEDICAL CENTER–FIRST HILL (500027)**, 747 Broadway, Zip 98122–4307; tel. 206/386–6000, (Includes SWEDISH MEDICAL CENTER–BALLARD, 5300 Tallman Avenue N.W., Zip 98107–3932; tel. 206/782–2700; Jennifer Graves, R.N., MS, Chief Executive), (Nonreporting) **A**1 2 3 5 9 10 **S** Swedish Health Services, Seattle, WA
Primary Contact: Todd Strumwasser, M.D., Chief Executive
CFO: Jeffrey Veilleux, Executive Vice President and Chief Financial Officer
CMO: John Vassall, M.D., Chief Medical Officer
CIO: Janice Newell, Chief Information Officer
Web address: www.swedish.org
**Control:** Other not–for–profit (including NFP Corporation) **Service:** General Medical and Surgical

**Staffed Beds: 620**

☒ △ **UNIVERSITY OF WASHINGTON MEDICAL CENTER (500008)**, 1959 N.E. Pacific Street, Zip 98195–6151; tel. 206/598–3300 **A**1 2 3 5 7 8 9 10 **F**3 8 9 11 12 13 15 16 17 18 20 22 24 25 26 28 29 30 31 34 35 36 39 40 43 44 45 46 47 48 49 50 51 52 54 55 56 57 58 59 60 61 64 65 68 70 72 74 75 76 77 78 79 80 81 82 84 85 86 87 88 89 90 91 92 93 94 95 96 97 98 100 101 102 103 104 106 107 108 110 111 113 114 115 116 117 118 119 120 121 123 124 126 130 132 136 137 138 139 140 141 142 144 145 146 147 148 **P**6 **S** UW Medicine, Seattle, WA
Primary Contact: Stephen P. Zieniewicz, FACHE, Executive Director
CFO: Lori J. Mitchell, Chief Financial Officer
CMO: Tom Staiger, M.D., Medical Director
CHR: Jennifer J. Petritz, Director Human Resources
CNO: Grace E. Parker, R.N., Interim Chief Nursing Officer
Web address: www.uwmedicine.org/Patient–Care/Locations/UWMC/Pages/default.aspx
**Control:** State–Government, nonfederal **Service:** General Medical and Surgical

**Staffed Beds: 450 Admissions: 17915 Census: 330 Outpatient Visits: 331650 Births: 1950 Total Expense ($000): 853721 Payroll Expense ($000): 315065 Personnel: 5057**

☒ △ **UW MEDICINE/HARBORVIEW MEDICAL CENTER (500064)**, (Formerly Harborview Medical Center), 325 Ninth Avenue, Zip 98104–2499, Mailing Address: P.O. Box 359717, Zip 98195–9717; tel. 206/744–3000 **A**1 3 5 7 8 9 10 **F**3 5 16 17 18 20 22 26 29 30 31 34 35 36 37 38 40 43 45 46 50 56 58 59 60 61 64 65 66 68 70 72 73 74 75 77 78 79 80 81 82 84 85 86 87 88 89 90 91 92 93 94 96 97 98 100 101 102 103 104 105 107 108 111 114 115 117 118 119 124 126 129 130 131 132 135 146 148 **P**6 **S** UW Medicine, Seattle, WA
Primary Contact: Eileen Whalen, R.N., Executive Director
CFO: Kera Rabbit, Assistant Administrator, Finance
CMO: J. Richard Goss, M.D., Medical Director
CIO: James Fine, M.D., Chief Information Officer
CHR: Nicki McCraw, Assistant Vice President Human Resources
CNO: Darcy Jaffe, R.N., Interim Chief Nursing Officer
Web address: www.uwmedicine.org/Patient–Care/Locations/HMC/Pages/default.aspx
**Control:** County–Government, nonfederal **Service:** General Medical and Surgical

**Staffed Beds: 413 Admissions: 19094 Census: 369 Outpatient Visits: 346338 Births: 0 Total Expense ($000): 762490 Payroll Expense ($000): 350212 Personnel: 5245**

☒ △ **UW MEDICINE/NORTHWEST HOSPITAL & MEDICAL CENTER (500001)**, (Formerly Northwest Hospital & Medical Center), 1550 North 115th Street, Zip 98133–8401; tel. 206/364–0500, (Nonreporting) **A**1 2 3 5 7 9 10 **S** UW Medicine, Seattle, WA
Primary Contact: Cynthia Hecker, Executive Director
CFO: Bruce Ferguson, Vice President and Chief Financial Officer
CMO: Greg Schroedl, M.D., Vice President, Medical and Chief Medical Officer
CIO: Eric Neil, Interim Chief Information Officer
CHR: Linda Olmstead, Director, Human Resources
CNO: Gayle Ward, R.N., Vice President and Chief Nursing Officer
Web address: www.uwmedicine.org/Patient–Care/Locations/nwh/Pages/default.aspx
**Control:** Other not–for–profit (including NFP Corporation) **Service:** General Medical and Surgical

**Staffed Beds: 176**

☒ △ **VETERANS AFFAIRS PUGET SOUND HEALTH CARE SYSTEM**, 1660 South Columbian Way, Zip 98108–1597; tel. 206/762–1010, (Includes VETERANS AFFAIRS PUGET SOUND HEALTH CARE SYSTEM–AMERICAN LAKE DIVISION, Tacoma, Zip 98493; tel. 253/582–8440), (Nonreporting) **A**1 2 3 5 7 8 9 **S** Department of Veterans Affairs, Washington, DC
Primary Contact: David A. Elizalde, Director
CFO: Kenneth J. Hudson, Chief Financial Officer
CMO: Gordon Starkebaum, M.D., Chief of Staff
CIO: Glenn Zwinger, Manager Information Systems Services
Web address: www.pugetsound.va.gov/
**Control:** Veterans Affairs, Government, federal **Service:** General Medical and Surgical

**Staffed Beds: 358**

☒ △ **VIRGINIA MASON MEDICAL CENTER (500005)**, 1100 Ninth Avenue, Zip 98101–2756, Mailing Address: P.O. Box 900, Zip 98111–0900; tel. 206/223 6600, (Total facility includes 35 beds in nursing home–type unit) **A**1 2 3 5 7 8 9 10 **F**2 3 5 6 8 9 12 15 17 18 20 22 24 26 28 29 30 31 32 34 35 36 37 38 39 40 44 45 46 47 48 49 50 51 54 55 56 57 58 59 60 61 63 64 65 66 68 70 71 74 75 77 78 79 81 82 83 84 85 86 87 90 91 92 93 94 96 97 100 101 102 103 104 105 107 108 110 111 114 115 116 117 118 119 120 121 123 126 128 129 130 131 132 135 136 138 141 142 143 145 146 147 148 **P**6
Primary Contact: Gary Kaplan, M.D., FACHE, Chairman and Chief Executive Officer
COO: Sarah Patterson, Executive Vice President and Chief Operating Officer
CFO: Sue Anderson, Senior Vice President, Chief Financial Officer and Chief Information Officer
CMO: Andrew Jacobs, M.D., Chief Medical Officer
CIO: Sue Anderson, Senior Vice President, Chief Financial Officer and Chief Information Officer
CHR: Kathy J. Shingleton, Ed.D., Vice President, Human Resources
CNO: Charleen Tachibana, R.N., Senior Vice President and Hospital Administrator
Web address: www.vmmc.org
**Control:** Other not–for–profit (including NFP Corporation) **Service:** General Medical and Surgical

**Staffed Beds: 291 Admissions: 16539 Census: 239 Outpatient Visits: 885507 Births: 0 Total Expense ($000): 909834 Payroll Expense ($000): 456805 Personnel: 5044**

**WA**

---

**Hospital, Medicare Provider Number, Address, Telephone, Approval, Facility, and Physician Codes, Health Care System**

★ American Hospital Association (AHA) membership
☐ The Joint Commission accreditation
◇ DNV Healthcare Inc. accreditation
○ Healthcare Facilities Accreditation Program
△ Commission on Accreditation of Rehabilitation Facilities (CARF) accreditation

## SEDRO WOOLLEY—Skagit County

**UNITED GENERAL HOSPITAL (501329)**, 2000 Hospital Drive, Zip 98284–4327; tel. 360/856–6021 **A**1 2 9 10 18 **F**3 11 15 29 30 31 34 35 40 43 45 50 53 57 59 64 68 70 75 77 78 79 81 85 89 92 93 107 108 110 111 114 118 119 120 121 123 129 130 133 134 135 143 146 **P**6
Primary Contact: Gregory C. Reed, FACHE, Chief Executive Officer
CFO: Michael W. Bonthuis, Chief Financial Officer
CMO: Randy Anderson, DPM, Chief Medical Officer
CHR: Tracie Skrinde, Director Human Resources
Web address: www.unitedgeneral.org
**Control:** Hospital district or authority, Government, nonfederal **Service:** General Medical and Surgical

**Staffed Beds:** 25 **Admissions:** 811 **Census:** 6 **Outpatient Visits:** 92638 **Births:** 1 **Total Expense ($000):** 43279 **Payroll Expense ($000):** 17770 **Personnel:** 263

## SHELTON—Mason County

**MASON GENERAL HOSPITAL (501336)**, 901 Mountain View Drive, Zip 98584–4401, Mailing Address: P.O. Box 1668, Zip 98584–5001; tel. 360/426–1611, (Nonreporting) **A**1 9 10 18
Primary Contact: G. Robert Appel, Chief Executive Officer
COO: Eileen Branscome, Chief Operating Officer
CFO: Merle Brandt, Chief Financial Officer
CMO: Dean Gushee, M.D., Medical Director
CIO: Tom Hornburg, Director Information Systems
CHR: Claudia Hawley, Director Human Resources
Web address: www.masongeneral.com
**Control:** Hospital district or authority, Government, nonfederal **Service:** General Medical and Surgical

**Staffed Beds:** 25

## SNOQUALMIE—King County

**SNOQUALMIE VALLEY HOSPITAL (501338)**, 9575 Ethan Wade Way S.E., Zip 98065–9577, Mailing Address: P.O. Box 2021, Zip 98065–2021; tel. 425/831–2300, (Nonreporting) **A**9 10 18
Primary Contact: Rodger McCollum, Chief Executive Officer
Web address: www.snoqualmiehospital.org/
**Control:** Hospital district or authority, Government, nonfederal **Service:** General Medical and Surgical

**Staffed Beds:** 18

## SOUTH BEND—Pacific County

**WILLAPA HARBOR HOSPITAL (501303)**, 800 Alder Street, Zip 98586–4900, Mailing Address: P.O. Box 438, Zip 98586–0438; tel. 360/875–5526, (Nonreporting) **A**9 10 18
Primary Contact: Carole Halsan, R.N., Chief Executive Officer
CFO: Terry Stone, Chief Financial Officer and Chief Information Officer
CIO: Terry Stone, Chief Financial Officer and Chief Information Officer
CHR: Krisy L. Funkhouser, Manager Human Resources
Web address: www.willapaharborhospital.com
**Control:** Hospital district or authority, Government, nonfederal **Service:** General Medical and Surgical

**Staffed Beds:** 15

## SPOKANE—Spokane County

**DEACONESS HOSPITAL (500044)**, (Formerly Deaconess Medical Center), 800 West Fifth Avenue, Zip 99204–2803, Mailing Address: P.O. Box 248, Zip 99210–0248; tel. 509/458–5800, (Nonreporting) **A**1 2 3 5 9 10 **S** Community Health Systems, Inc., Franklin, TN
Primary Contact: Rodney Schumacher, Interim Chief Executive Officer
CFO: Garman E. Lutz, Chief Financial Officer
CIO: Paul Fitzpatrick, Manager Information Technology
Web address: www.deaconess–spokane.org
**Control:** Other not–for–profit (including NFP Corporation) **Service:** General Medical and Surgical

**Staffed Beds:** 388

**PROVIDENCE HOLY FAMILY HOSPITAL (500077)**, 5633 North Lidgerwood Street, Zip 99208–1224; tel. 509/482–0111 **A**1 2 5 9 10 **F**3 4 8 11 12 13 15 18 20 22 29 30 31 34 35 37 38 39 40 41 43 45 46 47 48 49 50 53 56 57 58 59 60 61 64 68 70 73 74 75 76 77 78 79 81 82 84 85 86 87 89 92 100 107 108 121 123 129 130 131 132 135 143 145 146 147 148 **P**6 **S** Providence Health & Services, Renton, WA
Primary Contact: Elaine Couture, R.N., Chief Executive
COO: Cathy J. Simchuk, Chief Operating Officer
CMO: Jeff Collins, M.D., Chief Medical Officer
CIO: Mark Vogelsang, Director Information Services
CHR: Patrick M. Clarry, Vice President Human Resources
Web address: www.providence.org
**Control:** Church–operated, Nongovernment, not–for profit **Service:** General Medical and Surgical

**Staffed Beds:** 180 **Admissions:** 9265 **Census:** 97 **Outpatient Visits:** 112241 **Births:** 1273 **Total Expense ($000):** 167230 **Payroll Expense ($000):** 54843 **Personnel:** 825

**PROVIDENCE SACRED HEART MEDICAL CENTER & CHILDREN'S HOSPITAL (500054)**, 101 West Eighth Avenue, Zip 99204–2364, Mailing Address: P.O. Box 2555, Zip 99220–2555; tel. 509/474–3131, (Includes SACRED HEART CHILDREN'S HOSPITAL, 101 West Eight Avenue, Zip 99204–2307, Mailing Address: PO Box 2555, Zip 99220–2555; tel. 509/474–4841) **A**1 2 3 5 9 10 **F**3 8 9 11 13 15 16 17 18 19 20 21 22 23 24 25 26 27 28 29 30 31 35 36 37 40 41 42 43 45 46 47 48 49 50 56 57 58 64 68 70 72 74 75 76 78 79 81 82 83 84 85 86 87 88 89 92 98 99 100 102 103 104 105 106 107 108 110 111 114 115 118 119 120 121 123 124 126 130 132 137 138 141 145 146 147 148 **P**6 **S** Providence Health & Services, Renton, WA
Primary Contact: Elaine Couture, R.N., Chief Executive
CMO: Jeff Collins, M.D., Chief Medical Officer
CHR: Patrick Clary, Vice President Human Resources
Web address: www.shmc.org
**Control:** Church–operated, Nongovernment, not–for profit **Service:** General Medical and Surgical

**Staffed Beds:** 642 **Admissions:** 28319 **Census:** 395 **Outpatient Visits:** 173850 **Births:** 2982 **Total Expense ($000):** 695166 **Payroll Expense ($000):** 246008 **Personnel:** 3113

**SHRINERS HOSPITALS FOR CHILDREN–SPOKANE (503302)**, 911 West Fifth Avenue, Zip 99204–2901, Mailing Address: P.O. Box 2472, Zip 99210–2472; tel. 509/455–7844, (Nonreporting) **A**1 9 10 **S** Shriners Hospitals for Children, Tampa, FL
Primary Contact: J. Craig Patchin, Interim Administrator
CFO: Monica Hickman, Director Fiscal Services
CMO: Paul Caskey, M.D., Chief of Staff
CHR: Russ Crockett, Director Human Resources
CNO: Lynda Vilanova, Director Patient Care Services
Web address: www.shrinershospitalsforchildren.org/Hospitals/Locations/Spokane.aspx
**Control:** Other not–for–profit (including NFP Corporation) **Service:** Children's orthopedic

**Staffed Beds:** 30

**SPOKANE VETERANS AFFAIRS MEDICAL CENTER**, (Formerly Veterans Affairs Medical Center), 4815 North Assembly Street, Zip 99205–6197; tel. 509/434–7000, (Nonreporting) **A**1 5 9 **S** Department of Veterans Affairs, Washington, DC
Primary Contact: Sandy J. Nielsen, Director
COO: Cheryl L. Wood, Chief Engineering and Technology
CFO: Michael Gathman, Chief Financial Officer
CMO: Nirmala Rozario, M.D., Chief of Staff
CIO: Rob Fortenberry, Chief Information Officer
CHR: Jacqueline Ross, Chief Human Resources Officer
Web address: www.spokane.va.gov/
**Control:** Veterans Affairs, Government, federal **Service:** General Medical and Surgical

**Staffed Beds:** 70

△ **ST. LUKE'S REHABILITATION INSTITUTE (503025)**, 711 South Cowley Street, Zip 99202–1388; tel. 509/473–6000 **A**1 7 9 10 **F**28 29 30 43 50 58 64 68 74 75 77 79 82 86 87 90 91 92 93 94 95 96 130 131 132 146 **P**6
Primary Contact: Thomas M. Fritz, Chief Executive Officer
COO: Ulrike Berzau, FACHE, Administrator
CFO: John D. Craig, Chief Financial Officer
CMO: Stefan Humphries, M.D., Medical Director
CIO: Fred Galusha, Chief Information Officer
CHR: Phyllis Gabel, Chief Human Resource Officer
CNO: Ginger Cohen, Chief Nurse Executive
Web address: www.st–lukes.org
**Control:** Other not–for–profit (including NFP Corporation) **Service:** Rehabilitation

**Staffed Beds:** 72 **Admissions:** 1527 **Census:** 59 **Outpatient Visits:** 64840 **Births:** 0 **Total Expense ($000):** 37155 **Payroll Expense ($000):** 21772 **Personnel:** 473

**VETERANS AFFAIRS MEDICAL CENTER** See Spokane Veterans Affairs Medical Center

## SPOKANE VALLEY—Spokane County

**VALLEY HOSPITAL (500119)**, (Formerly Valley Hospital and Medical Center), 12606 East Mission Avenue, Zip 99216–1090; tel. 509/924–6650 **A**1 2 9 10 **F**15 18 29 30 31 34 40 43 45 49 50 60 64 68 70 74 75 76 77 78 79 81 85 87 107 111 114 119 146 147 148 **S** Community Health Systems, Inc., Franklin, TN
Primary Contact: Dennis Barts, Chief Executive Officer
COO: David Martin, Assistant Administrator
CFO: Justin Voelker, Chief Financial Officer
CMO: Robert Hartman, M.D., Vice President Medical Affairs
CNO: Carol Torpey, Chief Nursing Officer
Web address: www.valleyhospital.org
**Control:** Corporation, Investor–owned, for–profit **Service:** General Medical and Surgical

**Staffed Beds:** 123 **Admissions:** 6357 **Census:** 64 **Outpatient Visits:** 66256 **Births:** 622 **Total Expense ($000):** 93342 **Payroll Expense ($000):** 40941 **Personnel:** 546

**WA**

*Many Facility Codes have changed. Please refer to the AHA Guide Code Chart.* © 2013 AHA Guide

**SUNNYSIDE—Yakima County**

★ **SUNNYSIDE COMMUNITY HOSPITAL (501330)**, 1016 Tacoma Avenue, Zip 98944–2263, Mailing Address: P.O. Box 719, Zip 98944–0719; tel. 509/837–1500 **A**9 10 18 **F**3 13 15 18 26 29 30 32 34 35 40 43 45 46 50 55 56 57 59 64 65 68 70 75 77 79 81 82 85 86 87 97 107 108 110 111 114 119 127 130 131 133 146 147 148 **S** HealthTech Management Services, Franklin, TN
Primary Contact: John Gallagher, Chief Executive Officer
CFO: Martha Rodriguez, Chief Financial Officer
CMO: Coke R. Smith, M.D., Medical Director
CIO: Salvador Betancourt, Manager Information Systems
CHR: Lisa Garcia, Director Human Resources
Web address: www.sunnysidehospital.com
**Control:** Other not–for–profit (including NFP Corporation) **Service:** General Medical and Surgical

**Staffed Beds:** 25 **Admissions:** 1368 **Census:** 10 **Outpatient Visits:** 61007 **Births:** 514 **Total Expense ($000):** 45292 **Payroll Expense ($000):** 22025 **Personnel:** 315

**TACOMA—Pierce County**

**ALLENMORE HOSPITAL** See MultiCare Tacoma General Hospital

⊠ **MADIGAN HEALTHCARE SYSTEM**, Fitzsimmons Drive, Building 9040, Zip 98431–1100; tel. 253/968–1110 **A**1 2 3 5 **F**3 7 8 11 12 14 15 17 18 19 20 21 22 24 26 27 28 29 30 31 32 33 34 35 36 38 39 40 41 43 44 45 46 48 49 50 51 52 54 55 56 57 58 59 60 61 65 68 70 72 73 74 75 76 77 78 79 80 81 82 84 85 86 87 88 89 91 92 93 94 96 97 98 99 100 101 102 103 104 107 108 110 111 114 117 118 119 120 121 123 126 127 129 130 131 132 134 135 144 146 147 148 **S** Department of the Army, Office of the Surgeon General, Falls Church, VA
Primary Contact: Colonel Dallas Homas, Commander
COO: Colonel R. Neal David, Administrator and Chief of Staff
CFO: Lieutenant Colonel Bryan Longmuir, Chief Resource Management
CIO: Lieutenant Colonel Andrew Smith, Chief Information Management
CHR: David Aiken, Chief Human Resources Officer
Web address: www.mamc.amedd.army.mil
**Control:** Army, Government, federal **Service:** General Medical and Surgical

**Staffed Beds:** 227 **Admissions:** 15735 **Census:** 99 **Outpatient Visits:** 1286057 **Births:** 2738 **Total Expense ($000):** 540334 **Payroll Expense ($000):** 241368 **Personnel:** 4451

☐ **MULTICARE MARY BRIDGE CHILDREN'S HOSPITAL AND HEALTH CENTER (503301)**, 317 Martin Luther King Jr. Way, Zip 98405–4234, Mailing Address: P.O. Box 5299, Zip 98415–0299; tel. 253/403–1400 **A**1 9 10 **F**3 7 8 12 19 21 23 25 27 29 30 31 32 34 35 40 41 43 48 50 54 55 57 58 59 62 63 64 65 66 71 74 75 78 79 81 82 84 85 86 87 88 89 91 93 94 97 99 104 107 108 109 110 111 114 115 116 117 119 120 121 123 124 129 130 131 132 134 135 143 144 146 148 **S** MultiCare Health System, Tacoma, WA
Primary Contact: Mady Murrey, R.N., Chief Operating Officer
CFO: Vince Schmitz, Senior Vice President and Chief Financial Officer
CMO: Lester Reed, M.D., Vice President Medical Affairs and Acute Care
CIO: Florence Chang, Senior Vice President, Clinical Support Services and Chief Information Officer
CHR: Sarah Horsman, Senior Vice President Human Potential
Web address: www.multicare.org/marybridge
**Control:** Other not–for–profit (including NFP Corporation) **Service:** Children's general

**Staffed Beds:** 72 **Admissions:** 4426 **Census:** 38 **Outpatient Visits:** 37324 **Births:** 0 **Total Expense ($000):** 157899 **Payroll Expense ($000):** 54353 **Personnel:** 476

⊠ **MULTICARE TACOMA GENERAL HOSPITAL (500129)**, 315 Martin Luther King Jr. Way, Zip 98405–4234, Mailing Address: P.O. Box 5299, Zip 98415–0299; tel. 253/403–1000, (Includes ALLENMORE HOSPITAL, South 19th and Union Avenue, Zip 98405, Mailing Address: P.O. Box 11414, Zip 98411–0414; tel. 253/403–2323) **A**1 2 9 10 **F**2 3 8 13 15 17 18 19 20 21 22 23 24 25 26 27 28 29 30 31 34 35 38 39 40 44 45 46 47 48 49 50 51 54 55 57 58 59 62 63 64 65 70 71 72 73 74 75 76 77 78 79 80 81 82 83 84 85 86 87 91 92 93 94 97 102 107 108 109 110 111 114 115 116 117 119 120 121 123 124 126 127 129 130 131 132 135 144 146 147 148 **S** MultiCare Health System, Tacoma, WA
Primary Contact: Diane E. Cecchettini, R.N., President and Chief Executive Officer
CFO: Vince Schmitz, Senior Vice President and Chief Financial Officer
CMO: Lester Reed, M.D., Vice President Medical Affairs and Acute Care
CIO: Florence Chang, Senior Vice President, Clinical Support Services and Chief Information Officer
CHR: Sarah Horsman, Senior Vice President Human Potential
Web address: www.multicare.org
**Control:** Other not–for–profit (including NFP Corporation) **Service:** General Medical and Surgical

**Staffed Beds:** 402 **Admissions:** 18739 **Census:** 218 **Outpatient Visits:** 213919 **Births:** 3033 **Total Expense ($000):** 595602 **Payroll Expense ($000):** 209601 **Personnel:** 2139

⊠ △ **ST. JOSEPH MEDICAL CENTER (500108)**, 1717 South J Street, Zip 98405–3004, Mailing Address: P.O. Box 2197, Zip 98401–2197; tel. 253/426–4101, (Nonreporting) **A**1 2 7 9 10 **S** Catholic Health Initiatives, Englewood, CO
Primary Contact: Syd Bersante, President
COO: Syd Bersante, President
CFO: Mike Fitzgerald, Chief Financial Officer
CMO: Gregory Semerdjian, M.D., Senior Vice President Medical Affairs
CIO: Bruce Elkington, Vice President Information Technology
CHR: David C. Lawson, Senior Vice President Human Resources
Web address: www.fhshealth.org
**Control:** Church–operated, Nongovernment, not–for profit **Service:** General Medical and Surgical

**Staffed Beds:** 363

**VETERANS AFFAIRS PUGET SOUND HEALTH CARE SYSTEM–AMERICAN LAKE DIVISION** See Veterans Affairs Puget Sound Health Care System, Seattle

**WESTERN STATE HOSPITAL (504003)**, 9601 Steilacoom Boulevard S.W., Zip 98498–7213; tel. 253/582–8900, (Nonreporting) **A**5 9 10
Primary Contact: Jess Jamieson, Chief Executive Officer
COO: Dale Thompson, Chief Operating Officer
CFO: Charm Reimer, Chief Financial Officer
CMO: John Chiles, M.D., Medical Director
CHR: Lori Manning, Administrator Human Resources
Web address: www.dshs.wa.gov/mentalhealth/wsh.shtml
**Control:** State–Government, nonfederal **Service:** Psychiatric

**Staffed Beds:** 867

**TONASKET—Okanogan County**

★ **NORTH VALLEY HOSPITAL (501321)**, 203 South Western Avenue, Zip 98855–8803; tel. 509/486–2151, (Nonreporting) **A**9 10 18
Primary Contact: Linda Michel, Administrator
COO: Marcia Naillon, Chief Operating Officer and Administrative Registered Nurse
CFO: Bomi Bharucha, Chief Financial Officer
CMO: Theresa M. DiCroce, M.D., Chief Medical Staff
CIO: John Boyd, Manager Information Systems
CHR: Jan Gonzales, Director Human Resources
Web address: www.nvhospital.org
**Control:** Hospital district or authority, Government, nonfederal **Service:** General Medical and Surgical

**Staffed Beds:** 85

**TOPPENISH—Yakima County**

☐ **TOPPENISH COMMUNITY HOSPITAL (500037)**, 502 West Fourth Avenue, Zip 98948–1616, Mailing Address: P.O. Box 672, Zip 98948–0672; tel. 509/865–3105, (Nonreporting) **A**1 9 10 **S** Health Management Associates, Naples, FL
Primary Contact: Albert Pilkington, III, Chief Executive Officer
CFO: Curtis Herrin, Chief Financial Officer
CHR: Rosa Solorzano, Interim Director Human Resources
Web address: www.toppenishhospital.com
**Control:** Corporation, Investor–owned, for–profit **Service:** General Medical and Surgical

**Staffed Beds:** 63

**VANCOUVER—Clark County**

**LEGACY SALMON CREEK HOSPITAL** See Legacy Salmon Creek Medical Center

⊠ **LEGACY SALMON CREEK MEDICAL CENTER (500150)**, 2211 N.E. 139th Street, Zip 98686–2742; tel. 360/487–1000 **A**1 2 9 10 **F**3 11 13 15 18 20 26 28 29 30 31 32 34 35 38 39 40 44 45 46 47 50 51 57 59 60 64 65 68 70 72 74 75 76 77 78 79 80 81 82 84 85 87 89 93 96 97 101 107 108 110 111 114 116 117 118 119 120 121 126 129 130 132 146 147 148 **P**8 **S** Legacy Health, Portland, OR
Primary Contact: Jonathan Avery, Chief Administrative Officer
COO: Michael Newcomb, D.O., Senior Vice President and Chief Operating Officer
CFO: David Eager, Senior Vice President and Chief Financial Officer
CMO: Lewis Low, M.D., Senior Vice President and Chief Medical Officer
CHR: Sonja Steves, Senior Vice President Human Resources
CNO: Carol Bradley, MSN, Senior Vice President and Chief Nursing Officer
Web address: www.legacyhealth.org
**Control:** Other not–for–profit (including NFP Corporation) **Service:** General Medical and Surgical

**Staffed Beds:** 194 **Admissions:** 11164 **Census:** 106 **Outpatient Visits:** 187731 **Births:** 2232 **Total Expense ($000):** 191631 **Payroll Expense ($000):** 102122 **Personnel:** 1425

**WA**

---

**Hospital, Medicare Provider Number, Address, Telephone, Approval, Facility, and Physician Codes, Health Care System**

★ American Hospital Association (AHA) membership
☐ The Joint Commission accreditation
◇ DNV Healthcare Inc. accreditation
○ Healthcare Facilities Accreditation Program
△ Commission on Accreditation of Rehabilitation Facilities (CARF) accreditation

⊠ △ **PEACEHEALTH SOUTHWEST MEDICAL CENTER (500050)**, 400 N.E.
Mother Joseph Place, Zip 98664–3200, Mailing Address: P.O. Box 1600,
Zip 98668–1600; tel. 360/256–2000, (Includes VANCOUVER MEMORIAL
CAMPUS, 3400 Main Street, Zip 98663; tel. 206/696–5000), (Nonreporting) **A**1
2 3 5 7 9 10 **S** PeaceHealth, Vancouver, WA
Primary Contact: Joseph M. Kortum, President and Chief Mission Officer
COO: Rainy Atkins, Chief Operating Officer and Administrator
CMO: Alden Roberts, M.D., Chief Medical Officer
CIO: Petra Knowles, R.N., Chief Information Officer
CHR: Cheri Meyerhofer, Vice President Human Resources
Web address: www.swmedicalcenter.org
**Control:** Other not–for–profit (including NFP Corporation) **Service:** General
Medical and Surgical

> **Staffed Beds:** 450

**SOUTHWEST WASHINGTON MEDICAL CENTER** See PeaceHealth Southwest
Medical Center

### WALLA WALLA—Walla Walla County

★ **JONATHAN M. WAINWRIGHT MEMORIAL VETERANS AFFAIRS MEDICAL
CENTER**, 77 Wainwright Drive, Zip 99362–3994; tel. 509/525–5200,
(Nonreporting) **A**9 **S** Department of Veterans Affairs, Washington, DC
Primary Contact: Brian W. Westfield, MSN, Director
COO: Brian W. Westfield, MSN, Director
CFO: Debra Pearson, Chief Financial Officer
CMO: Charles Beleny, D.O., Chief of Stafff
CIO: Gary Ramer, Manager Information Management
CHR: Mary C. Lee, Manager Human Resources
CNO: Diana Nelson, R.N., Associate Director for Patient Care Services/Nurse
Executive
Web address: www.wallawalla.va.gov
**Control:** Veterans Affairs, Government, federal **Service:** General Medical and
Surgical

> **Staffed Beds:** 14

⊠ △ **PROVIDENCE ST. MARY MEDICAL CENTER (500002)**, 401 West Poplar
Street, Zip 99362–2846, Mailing Address: P.O. Box 1477, Zip 99362–0312;
tel. 509/525–3320 **A**1 2 7 9 10 19 **F**3 8 11 13 15 16 17 20 28 34 35
40 43 45 46 49 57 58 59 60 62 64 65 68 70 73 74 75 76 77 78 79 81 82
84 85 87 89 90 93 96 107 108 109 110 111 112 113 114 115 116 118 119
121 123 129 130 132 135 144 146 147 148 **P**6 **S** Providence Health &
Services, Renton, WA
Primary Contact: Steven A. Burdick, Chief Executive Officer
COO: Susan Blackburn, Chief Operating Officer
CFO: Michael Parenteau, Chief Financial Officer
CMO: Tim Davidson, M.D., Chief Executive Physician Services
CIO: Martin Manny, Director, I.S.
CNO: Yvonne M. Strader, Chief Nursing Officer
Web address: www.smmc.com
**Control:** Church–operated, Nongovernment, not–for profit **Service:** General
Medical and Surgical

> **Staffed Beds:** 79 **Admissions:** 4026 **Census:** 39 **Outpatient Visits:** 115005
> **Births:** 565 **Total Expense ($000):** 153098 **Payroll Expense ($000):** 59157
> **Personnel:** 755

**STATE PENITENTIARY HOSPITAL**, 1313 North 13th Street, Zip 99362–8817;
tel. 509/525–3610, (Nonreporting)
Primary Contact: Pat Rima, Health Care Manager
**Control:** State–Government, nonfederal **Service:** Hospital unit of an institution
(prison hospital, college infirmary, etc.)

> **Staffed Beds:** 36

⊠ **WALLA WALLA GENERAL HOSPITAL (500049)**, 1025 South Second Avenue,
Zip 99362–4116, Mailing Address: P.O. Box 1398, Zip 99362–0309;
tel. 509/525–0480 **A**1 9 10 **F**13 15 20 28 29 30 34 35 40 43 45 49 52 56
57 59 62 64 68 69 70 73 74 75 76 79 81 83 85 87 89 93 97 107 110 111
115 119 127 129 130 132 133 135 146 147 **S** Adventist Health, Roseville, CA
Primary Contact: Monty E. Knittel, President and Chief Executive Officer
CFO: Duane Meidinger, Vice President Finance
CIO: Gary Dietz, Director Information Technology Services
CHR: Barbara Blood, Director Human Resources
Web address: www.wwgh.com
**Control:** Church–operated, Nongovernment, not–for profit **Service:** General
Medical and Surgical

> **Staffed Beds:** 37 **Admissions:** 1504 **Census:** 11 **Outpatient Visits:** 42187
> **Births:** 281

### WENATCHEE—Chelan County

⊠ **CENTRAL WASHINGTON HOSPITAL (500016)**, 1201 South Miller Street,
Zip 98801–3201, Mailing Address: P.O. Box 1887, Zip 98807–1887;
tel. 509/662–1511 **A**1 9 10 13 19 **F**3 13 15 17 20 22 24 26 28 29 30 34 35
39 40 43 46 55 57 59 60 62 63 64 68 69 70 74 75 76 77 78 79 81 82 85
86 87 89 93 97 107 110 111 114 115 119 128 130 146 147 148 **P**6
Primary Contact: John B. Hamilton, FACHE, Interim President and Chief Executive
Officer
COO: John B. Hamilton, FACHE, Executive Vice President and Chief Operating
Officer
CFO: Steven R. Jacobs, Chief Financial Officer
CHR: Jack Powers, Director Human Resources
Web address: www.cwhs.com
**Control:** Other not–for–profit (including NFP Corporation) **Service:** General
Medical and Surgical

> **Staffed Beds:** 198 **Admissions:** 9912 **Census:** 96 **Outpatient Visits:** 153974
> **Births:** 1276 **Total Expense ($000):** 199513 **Payroll Expense ($000):**
> 86204

△ **WENATCHEE VALLEY MEDICAL CENTER (500148)**, (Formerly Wenatchee
Valley Hospital), 820 North Chelan Avenue, Zip 98801–2028; tel. 509/663–8711
**A**2 7 9 10 **F**29 31 34 40 45 46 58 59 64 65 68 75 77 78 79 81 82 84 85 87
90 93 96 97 100 107 108 110 111 114 117 119 120 121 126 127 129 130
131 132 135 143 144 145 147 148 **P**8
Primary Contact: Shaun Koos, Administrator
COO: Kevin Gilbert, R.N., Director Surgical and Operations
CFO: John Doyle, Chief Financial Officer
CMO: Stuart Freed, M.D., Medical Director
CIO: Joe Janda, Chief Information Officer
CHR: Alan Patterson, Director Human Resources
Web address: www.wvmedical.com
**Control:** Corporation, Investor–owned, for–profit **Service:** Surgical

> **Staffed Beds:** 20 **Admissions:** 949 **Census:** 9

### WHITE SALMON—Klickitat County

**SKYLINE HOSPITAL (501315)**, 211 Skyline Drive, Zip 98672–1918, Mailing
Address: P.O. Box 99, Zip 98672–0099; tel. 509/493–1101 **A**9 10 18 **F**17 34
40 43 57 64 67 81 89 93 97 107 114 119 128 131 133 145 146 **P**5
Primary Contact: Robert P. Kimmes, Chief Executive Officer
CFO: Brenda Schneider, Chief Financial Officer
CMO: Cynthia Horton, M.D., Chief Medical Officer
CHR: Robin Loomis, Manager Human Resources
Web address: www.skylinehospital.com
**Control:** Hospital district or authority, Government, nonfederal **Service:** General
Medical and Surgical

> **Staffed Beds:** 25 **Admissions:** 372 **Census:** 4 **Outpatient Visits:** 21018
> **Births:** 17 **Total Expense ($000):** 18629 **Payroll Expense ($000):** 8710
> **Personnel:** 133

### YAKIMA—Yakima County

☐ △ **YAKIMA REGIONAL MEDICAL AND CARDIAC CENTER (500012)**, 110
South Ninth Avenue, Zip 98902–3315; tel. 509/575–5000, (Nonreporting) **A**1 2
7 9 10 **S** Health Management Associates, Naples, FL
Primary Contact: Richard H. Robinson, Chief Executive Officer
CFO: Curtis Herrin, Chief Financial Officer
CMO: Albert Brady, M.D., Chief of Staff
Web address: www.yakimaregional.net
**Control:** Corporation, Investor–owned, for–profit **Service:** General Medical and
Surgical

> **Staffed Beds:** 214

⊠ **YAKIMA VALLEY MEMORIAL HOSPITAL (500036)**, 2811 Tieton Drive,
Zip 98902–3761; tel. 509/575–8000 **A**1 2 3 5 9 10 **F**3 8 11 13 15 17 18 20
22 26 28 29 30 31 32 34 35 36 40 41 42 43 44 45 46 47 49 50 51 55 57
59 60 62 63 65 68 70 72 73 74 75 76 77 78 79 81 82 84 85 86 87 89 92
93 96 98 100 102 104 107 108 110 111 114 116 117 119 120 121 123
124 129 130 131 132 135 144 146 147 148 **P**4 6 7
Primary Contact: Richard W. Linneweh, Jr., President and Chief Executive Officer
COO: Russ Myers, Senior Vice President and Chief Operating Officer
CFO: Scott Olander, Vice President and Chief Financial Officer
CMO: Gregory D. Sawyer, M.D., Vice President Physician Practices
CIO: Jeff Yamada, Assistant Vice President
CHR: Teresa Pritchard, Vice President
Web address: www.yakimamemorial.org
**Control:** Other not–for–profit (including NFP Corporation) **Service:** General
Medical and Surgical

> **Staffed Beds:** 226 **Admissions:** 14272 **Census:** 144 **Outpatient Visits:**
> 444405 **Births:** 2897 **Total Expense ($000):** 312602 **Payroll Expense**
> **($000):** 111876 **Personnel:** 1892

**WA**

*Many Facility Codes have changed. Please refer to the AHA Guide Code Chart.*

© 2013 AHA Guide

# WEST VIRGINIA

### BECKLEY—Raleigh County

☐ **BECKLEY ARH HOSPITAL (510062)**, 306 Stanaford Road, Zip 25801–3142; tel. 304/255–3000 **A**1 9 10 **F**3 11 15 17 18 20 28 29 30 31 34 35 38 39 40 43 44 45 46 47 48 49 50 51 54 57 59 60 61 62 64 65 70 74 75 77 78 79 81 82 85 86 87 89 90 93 97 98 99 100 101 102 103 107 108 110 111 115 116 118 119 129 130 146 148 **P**6 **S** Appalachian Regional Healthcare, Inc., Lexington, KY
Primary Contact: Rocco K. Massey, Community Chief Executive Officer
CMO: Prakash Puranik, M.D., Chief of Staff
CHR: Sue Thomas, Manager Human Resources
Web address: www.arh.org
**Control:** Other not–for–profit (including NFP Corporation) **Service:** General Medical and Surgical

**Staffed Beds:** 169 **Admissions:** 7587 **Census:** 121 **Outpatient Visits:** 75872 **Births:** 0 **Total Expense ($000):** 83314 **Payroll Expense ($000):** 26352 **Personnel:** 513

⊠ **BECKLEY VETERANS AFFAIRS MEDICAL CENTER**, (Formerly Veterans Affairs Medical Center), 200 Veterans Avenue, Zip 25801–6499; tel. 304/255–2121, (Nonreporting) **A**1 **S** Department of Veterans Affairs, Washington, DC
Primary Contact: Karin L. McGraw, MSN, FACHE, Director
CFO: Chris Raines, Chief Fiscal Services
Web address: www.beckley.va.gov/
**Control:** Veterans Affairs, Government, federal **Service:** General Medical and Surgical

**Staffed Beds:** 40

⊠ **RALEIGH GENERAL HOSPITAL (510070)**, 1710 Harper Road, Zip 25801–3397; tel. 304/256–4100 **A**1 9 10 19 **F**3 13 15 17 18 20 22 29 30 34 35 40 43 49 57 59 60 64 70 75 76 78 79 81 85 87 89 93 107 110 111 114 115 117 119 126 130 131 132 146 147 **S** LifePoint Hospitals, Inc., Brentwood, TN
Primary Contact: David B. Darden, Chief Executive Officer
COO: Reba Celsor, Chief Operating Officer
CFO: Tom Thompson, Vice President and Chief Financial Officer
CMO: Michael Kelly, M.D., President Medical Staff
CIO: Kevin Sexton, Director Information Systems
CHR: Matthew Hess, Director Human Resources
Web address: www.raleighgeneral.com
**Control:** Corporation, Investor–owned, for–profit **Service:** General Medical and Surgical

**Staffed Beds:** 229 **Admissions:** 12053 **Census:** 150 **Outpatient Visits:** 107946 **Births:** 1429 **Total Expense ($000):** 125644 **Payroll Expense ($000):** 48380 **Personnel:** 965

### BERKELEY SPRINGS—Morgan County

★ **WAR MEMORIAL HOSPITAL (511309)**, One Healthy Way, Zip 25411–7463; tel. 304/258–1234, (Total facility includes 16 beds in nursing home–type unit) **A**9 10 18 **F**3 11 15 28 29 34 35 40 45 50 53 54 57 59 64 65 77 79 81 85 86 93 97 107 119 129 130 133 **P**6 **S** Valley Health System, Winchester, VA
Primary Contact: Neil R. McLaughlin, R.N., President
CFO: Christine Lowman, Vice President Finance
Web address: www.valleyhealthlink.com/war
**Control:** Other not–for–profit (including NFP Corporation) **Service:** General Medical and Surgical

**Staffed Beds:** 41 **Admissions:** 447 **Census:** 25 **Outpatient Visits:** 38268 **Births:** 0 **Total Expense ($000):** 18549 **Payroll Expense ($000):** 7958 **Personnel:** 148

### BLUEFIELD—Mercer County

⊠ **BLUEFIELD REGIONAL MEDICAL CENTER (510071)**, 500 Cherry Street, Zip 24701–3390; tel. 304/327–1100 **A**1 9 10 12 13 19 **F**3 8 13 15 17 18 20 22 28 29 30 31 34 40 43 45 46 47 49 50 56 57 59 60 64 68 70 74 75 76 77 78 79 81 85 86 89 96 107 108 110 115 118 119 121 124 127 129 130 132 144 146 147 **P**8 **S** Community Health Systems, Inc., Franklin, TN
Primary Contact: William Hawley, Chief Executive Officer
CMO: Joel Shor, M.D., Chief of Staff
CIO: Rose Lasker, Director Information Services
CHR: Sandee Cheynet, Vice President Administrative Services
Web address: www.bluefield.org
**Control:** Corporation, Investor–owned, for–profit **Service:** General Medical and Surgical

**Staffed Beds:** 240 **Admissions:** 4808 **Census:** 53 **Outpatient Visits:** 75210 **Births:** 656 **Total Expense ($000):** 78443 **Payroll Expense ($000):** 25388 **Personnel:** 536

### BRIDGEPORT—Harrison County

⊠ **UNITED HOSPITAL CENTER (510006)**, 327 Medical Park Drive, Zip 26330–9006; tel. 681/342–1000 **A**1 2 3 5 9 10 12 13 **F**3 5 11 13 15 17 18 20 22 28 29 30 31 34 36 38 39 40 45 46 48 49 51 54 57 58 59 60 62 63 64 65 68 70 74 75 76 77 78 79 81 82 84 85 86 87 89 93 97 98 99 100 101 102 103 104 107 108 109 110 111 114 115 116 117 118 119 120 121 123 126 128 129 130 131 132 146 148 **P**6 8 **S** West Virginia United Health System, Fairmont, WV
Primary Contact: Bruce C. Carter, President and Chief Executive Officer
COO: Michael Tillman, Vice President Patient Services and Chief Operating Officer
CFO: Douglas Coffman, Vice President and Chief Financial Officer
CMO: Eric Radcliffe, M.D., Medical Director
CIO: Brian Cottrill, Chief Information Officer
CHR: Timothy M. Allen, Vice President Human Resources
Web address: www.uhcwv.org
**Control:** Other not–for–profit (including NFP Corporation) **Service:** General Medical and Surgical

**Staffed Beds:** 264 **Admissions:** 12810 **Census:** 185 **Outpatient Visits:** 412876 **Births:** 969 **Total Expense ($000):** 243063 **Payroll Expense ($000):** 89725 **Personnel:** 1689

### BUCKEYE—Pocahontas County

★ **POCAHONTAS MEMORIAL HOSPITAL (511314)**, Zip 24924; tel. 304/799–7400 **A**9 10 18 **F**2 3 7 11 29 30 34 35 40 43 56 57 59 64 65 68 86 87 93 97 107 108 119 127 128 130 132 133 135 144 146
Primary Contact: Barbara Lay, Chief Executive Officer
COO: Terry Wagner, R.N., Chief Operating Officer
CFO: Chad Carpenter, Chief Financial Officer
CMO: Frank Puckett, M.D., Chief Medical Officer
CIO: Aaron Vaughan, Coordinator Information Systems
CHR: Melissa Kane, Coordinator Human Resources
CNO: Kerrie Ridgeway, R.N., Chief Nursing Officer
Web address: www.pmhwv.org/
**Control:** County–Government, nonfederal **Service:** General Medical and Surgical

**Staffed Beds:** 25 **Admissions:** 401 **Census:** 5 **Outpatient Visits:** 15194 **Births:** 3 **Total Expense ($000):** 10053 **Payroll Expense ($000):** 4434

### BUCKHANNON—Upshur County

⊠ **ST. JOSEPH'S HOSPITAL OF BUCKHANNON (510053)**, 1 Amalia Drive, Zip 26201–2276; tel. 304/473–2000, (Total facility includes 16 beds in nursing home–type unit) **A**1 9 10 **F**3 11 13 15 18 28 29 30 31 34 35 40 43 44 45 50 57 59 62 63 64 65 70 75 76 79 81 84 85 87 89 107 110 114 119 128 129 130 132 133 135 144 146 **P**6 **S** Pallottine Health Services, Huntington, WV
Primary Contact: Sue E. Johnson–Phillippe, President and Chief Executive Officer
CFO: Renee Hofer, Senior Vice President Fiscal Services
CMO: J. Michael Rollins, M.D., Chief of Staff
CIO: Brian Williams, Director Information Systems
CHR: Anissa Hite–Davis, Vice President Human Resources
CNO: Anna Shreves, Vice President Patient Care Services
Web address: www.stj.net
**Control:** Other not–for–profit (including NFP Corporation) **Service:** General Medical and Surgical

**Staffed Beds:** 69 **Admissions:** 1506 **Census:** 30 **Outpatient Visits:** 99058 **Births:** 299 **Total Expense ($000):** 40669 **Payroll Expense ($000):** 19021 **Personnel:** 338

WV

---

**Hospital, Medicare Provider Number, Address, Telephone, Approval, Facility, and Physician Codes, Health Care System**

★ American Hospital Association (AHA) membership
☐ The Joint Commission accreditation
◇ DNV Healthcare Inc. accreditation
○ Healthcare Facilities Accreditation Program
△ Commission on Accreditation of Rehabilitation Facilities (CARF) accreditation

## CHARLESTON—Kanawha County

☒ △ **CHARLESTON AREA MEDICAL CENTER (510022)**, 501 Morris Street, Zip 25301–1300, Mailing Address: P.O. Box 1547, Zip 25326–1547; tel. 304/388–5432, (Includes GENERAL HOSPITAL, 501 Morris Street, Zip 25301, Mailing Address: Box 1393, Zip 25325; tel. 304/388–5432; Michael D. Williams, Vice President and Administrator; MEMORIAL HOSPITAL, 3200 MacCorkle Avenue S.E., Zip 25304; tel. 304/388–5973; WOMEN AND CHILDREN'S HOSPITAL, 800 Pennsylvania Avenue, Zip 25302, Mailing Address: P.O. Box 6669, Zip 25362; tel. 304/388–5432; Andrew Weber, Vice President and Administrator) **A**1 2 3 5 7 8 9 10 12 13 **F**3 8 11 12 13 15 17 18 19 20 22 24 26 28 29 30 31 32 34 35 38 40 41 43 44 45 46 47 48 49 50 51 52 54 55 56 57 59 60 61 64 65 68 70 72 74 75 76 77 78 79 81 82 84 85 86 88 89 90 92 93 94 96 97 98 99 100 101 102 103 104 107 108 110 111 114 115 116 117 118 119 124 126 129 130 131 132 134 135 138 141 143 144 145 146 147 148 **P**6 **S** Charleston Area Medical Center Health System, Inc., Charleston, WV
Primary Contact: David L. Ramsey, President and Chief Executive Officer
COO: Glenn Crotty, Jr., M.D., Executive Vice President and Chief Operating Officer
CFO: Larry C. Hudson, Executive Vice President and Chief Financial Officer
CMO: Elizabeth L. Spangler, M.D., Vice President Medical Affairs
CIO: Lynn Brookshire, Vice President Information Services and Chief Information Officer
Web address: www.camc.org
**Control:** Other not–for–profit (including NFP Corporation) **Service:** General Medical and Surgical

**Staffed Beds: 795 Admissions: 36050 Census: 533 Outpatient Visits:** 554628 **Births: 2765 Total Expense ($000): 761809 Payroll Expense ($000): 267878 Personnel:** 5650

☐ **EYE AND EAR CLINIC OF CHARLESTON (510059)**, 1306 Kanawha Boulevard East, Zip 25301–3001, Mailing Address: P.O. Box 2271, Zip 25328–2271; tel. 304/343–4371 **A**1 10 **F**39 45 64 79 81 89 111 119 141
Primary Contact: Christina Arvon, Administrator and Chief Executive Officer
CMO: James W. Candill, M.D., President Medical Staff
Web address: www.eyeandearclinicwv.org
**Control:** Corporation, Investor–owned, for–profit **Service:** General Medical and Surgical

**Staffed Beds: 21 Admissions: 1 Census: 1 Outpatient Visits:** 11907 **Births: 0 Total Expense ($000): 12094 Payroll Expense ($000): 4271 Personnel:** 121

**GENERAL HOSPITAL** See Charleston Area Medical Center

☒ **HIGHLAND HOSPITAL (514001)**, 300 56th Street S.E., Zip 25304–2361, Mailing Address: P.O. Box 4107, Zip 25364–4107; tel. 304/926–1600 **A**1 9 10 **F**29 35 57 75 98 99 101 105 130 **P**6
Primary Contact: James H. Dissen, Interim President and Chief Executive Officer
COO: Lisa Layden, Chief Operating Officer
CFO: Lisa Layden, Director of Finance
CMO: Charles Weise, M.D., Medical Director
CIO: Pearl McWatters, Director Information Services
CHR: Susan Bayles, Director Human Resources
CNO: Carla Hall, Director of Nursing
Web address: www.highlandhosp.com
**Control:** Other not–for–profit (including NFP Corporation) **Service:** Psychiatric

**Staffed Beds: 80 Admissions: 1262 Census: 40 Outpatient Visits:** 1705 **Births: 0 Total Expense ($000): 11514 Payroll Expense ($000): 6535 Personnel:** 258

**MEMORIAL HOSPITAL** See Charleston Area Medical Center

☒ **SAINT FRANCIS HOSPITAL (510031)**, 333 Laidley Street, Zip 25301–1628, Mailing Address: P.O. Box 471, Zip 25322–0471; tel. 304/347–6500, (Total facility includes 29 beds in nursing home–type unit) **A**1 9 10 **F**3 11 15 18 20 22 29 30 34 40 46 48 49 51 57 59 60 64 68 69 70 74 75 79 81 82 84 86 87 93 97 107 108 110 111 115 116 119 128 130 131 135 143 145 146 147 148 **P**5 **S** Thomas Health System, Inc., South Charleston, WV
Primary Contact: Stephen P. Dexter, President and Chief Executive Officer
COO: Daniel Lauffer, FACHE, Executive Vice President and Chief Operating Officer
CFO: Charles O. Covert, Chief Financial Officer
CMO: Paul Legg, M.D., President Medical Staff
CIO: Jeremy Taylor, Director Information Services
CHR: Marybeth Smith, Director Human Resources
CNO: Rebecca Brannon, R.N., Chief Nursing Officer
Web address: www.stfrancishospital.com
**Control:** Other not–for–profit (including NFP Corporation) **Service:** General Medical and Surgical

**Staffed Beds: 119 Admissions: 3909 Census: 57 Outpatient Visits:** 90947 **Births: 0 Total Expense ($000): 99140 Payroll Expense ($000): 31249 Personnel:** 670

☒ **SELECT SPECIALTY HOSPITAL–CHARLESTON (512002)**, 333 Laidley Street, 3rd Floor East, Zip 25301–1614; tel. 304/720–7234 **A**1 9 10 **F**1 29 74 75 79 85 130 148 **S** Select Medical Corporation, Mechanicsburg, PA
Primary Contact: Frank Weber, Chief Executive Officer
CHR: Sabrina White, Coordinator Human Resources
Web address: www.selectspecialtyhospitals.com/company/locations/charleston. aspx
**Control:** Corporation, Investor–owned, for–profit **Service:** Long–Term Acute Care hospital

**Staffed Beds: 32 Admissions: 394 Census: 30 Outpatient Visits:** 0 **Births:** 0 **Total Expense ($000): 15719 Payroll Expense ($000): 5681 Personnel:** 104

**WOMEN AND CHILDREN'S HOSPITAL** See Charleston Area Medical Center

## CLARKSBURG—Harrison County

☒ **LOUIS A. JOHNSON VETERANS AFFAIRS MEDICAL CENTER**, 1 Medical Center Drive, Zip 26301–4199; tel. 304/623–3461, (Nonreporting) **A**1 3 5 **S** Department of Veterans Affairs, Washington, DC
Primary Contact: Beth Brown, Director
CMO: Glenn R. Snider, M.D., Chief of Staff
CIO: Michael Matthey, Facility Chief Information Officer
CHR: Ian Jacobs, Chief, Human Resource Management Service
Web address: www.clarksburg.va.gov
**Control:** Veterans Affairs, Government, federal **Service:** General Medical and Surgical

**Staffed Beds: 71**

## ELKINS—Randolph County

☒ **DAVIS MEMORIAL HOSPITAL (510030)**, Gorman Avenue and Reed Street, Zip 26241, Mailing Address: P.O. Box 1484, Zip 26241–1484; tel. 304/636–3300 **A**1 2 9 10 20 **F**11 13 15 20 28 29 30 31 34 35 40 49 50 51 54 57 59 64 68 69 70 71 74 75 76 77 78 79 81 82 85 86 87 89 92 93 107 108 109 110 111 115 116 117 118 119 121 123 129 130 132 135 146 147 148 **P**8 **S** Davis Health System, Elkins, WV
Primary Contact: Mark Doak, President and Chief Executive Officer
COO: D. Parker Haddix, Chief Operating Officer
CFO: Rebecca J. Hammer, Chief Financial Officer
CMO: Nitesh Ratnakar, M.D., Chief Medical Officer
CHR: Judith L. Williams, Director Human Resources
Web address: www.davishealthsystem.com
**Control:** Other not–for–profit (including NFP Corporation) **Service:** General Medical and Surgical

**Staffed Beds: 90 Admissions: 4401 Census: 42 Outpatient Visits:** 138513 **Births: 368 Total Expense ($000): 85732 Payroll Expense ($000): 33956 Personnel:** 593

## FAIRMONT—Marion County

☒ **FAIRMONT GENERAL HOSPITAL (510047)**, 1325 Locust Avenue, Zip 26554–1435; tel. 304/367–7100 **A**1 2 9 10 19 **F**3 5 11 12 13 15 18 20 28 29 30 31 34 35 38 39 40 43 44 45 48 49 50 51 53 54 56 57 59 61 62 64 65 68 69 70 74 75 76 78 79 81 84 85 86 87 89 92 96 98 99 100 101 102 103 104 107 108 111 114 115 116 117 118 119 129 130 131 132 134 135 146 147 148 **P**6 7
Primary Contact: Robert C. Marquardt, FACHE, President and Chief Executive Officer
CFO: Daniel Honerbrink, Vice President Finance and Chief Financial Officer
CMO: Wes Steele, M.D., Chief of Staff
CIO: Mike Wooddell, Director Information Services
CHR: Jim Harris, Vice President Human Resources
CNO: Margaret C. Coster, R.N., Vice President Patient Services
Web address: www.fghi.org
**Control:** Other not–for–profit (including NFP Corporation) **Service:** General Medical and Surgical

**Staffed Beds: 140 Admissions: 4348 Census: 69 Outpatient Visits:** 172674 **Births: 373 Total Expense ($000): 77363 Payroll Expense ($000): 27420 Personnel:** 635

## GASSAWAY—Braxton County

★ **BRAXTON COUNTY MEMORIAL HOSPITAL (511308)**, 100 Hoylman Drive, Zip 26624–9318; tel. 304/364–5156 **A**9 10 18 **F**1 3 4 8 11 15 30 32 34 35 40 43 45 57 59 62 64 67 75 81 89 90 97 98 107 108 114 116 127 128 130 133 146 147 **P**6
Primary Contact: Ben Vincent, FACHE, Chief Executive Officer
CFO: Kimber Knight, Chief Financial Officer
CMO: Russell L. Stewart, M.D., Chief Medical Officer
Web address: www.braxtonmemorial.org
**Control:** Other not–for–profit (including NFP Corporation) **Service:** General Medical and Surgical

**Staffed Beds: 25 Admissions: 272 Census: 2 Outpatient Visits:** 41343 **Births: 0 Total Expense ($000): 14505 Payroll Expense ($000): 6532 Personnel:** 161

**WV**

*Many Facility Codes have changed. Please refer to the AHA Guide Code Chart.*   © 2013 AHA Guide

## GLEN DALE—Marshall County

⊠ **REYNOLDS MEMORIAL HOSPITAL (510013)**, 800 Wheeling Avenue, Zip 26038–1697; tel. 304/845–3211, (Total facility includes 20 beds in nursing home–type unit) **A**1 9 10 **F**3 11 13 15 18 20 28 30 34 39 40 43 53 56 57 59 62 64 65 70 74 75 76 77 78 79 80 81 82 84 85 86 89 92 93 107 108 110 111 114 118 119 128 130 132 135 146 148 **P**8
Primary Contact: Jay E. Prager, Chief Executive Officer
CFO: William Robert Hunt, Chief Financial Officer
CMO: David F. Hess, M.D., President Medical Staff
CIO: Warren Kelley, Chief Information Officer
CHR: R. Craig Madden, Director Employee Relations
CNO: Carol R. Miller, R.N., Chief Nursing Officer
Web address: www.reynoldsmemorial.com
**Control:** Other not–for–profit (including NFP Corporation) **Service:** General Medical and Surgical

**Staffed Beds:** 99 **Admissions:** 2550 **Census:** 41 **Outpatient Visits:** 84750 **Births:** 129 **Total Expense ($000):** 36445 **Payroll Expense ($000):** 17448 **Personnel:** 359

## GRAFTON—Taylor County

**GRAFTON CITY HOSPITAL (511307)**, 500 Market Street, Zip 26354–1187; tel. 304/265–0400, (Total facility includes 76 beds in nursing home–type unit) **A**9 10 18 **F**11 15 29 30 31 32 34 35 39 40 43 53 54 56 57 59 61 64 65 67 75 77 78 79 81 83 84 86 87 91 93 97 100 101 102 103 104 105 107 108 111 114 119 127 128 130 131 132 133 134 135 144 146 147 148 **P**6
Primary Contact: Patrick Shaw, Chief Executive Officer
CFO: Susie Higgins, Chief Financial Officer
CFO: Brian Kelbaugh, Chief Financial Officer
CMO: Christopher Villaraza, II, M.D., Chief Medical Staff
CIO: Ann Rexroad, Director Information Technology
CHR: Missey Kimbrew, Director Human Resources
CNO: Violet Shaw, R.N., Director of Nursing
Web address: www.graftonhospital.com
**Control:** City–Government, nonfederal **Service:** General Medical and Surgical

**Staffed Beds:** 101 **Admissions:** 616 **Census:** 75 **Outpatient Visits:** 49914 **Births:** 0 **Total Expense ($000):** 17686 **Payroll Expense ($000):** 10103 **Personnel:** 304

## GRANTSVILLE—Calhoun County

★ **MINNIE HAMILTON HEALTHCARE CENTER (511303)**, 186 Hospital Drive, Zip 26147–7100; tel. 304/354–9244, (Total facility includes 24 beds in nursing home–type unit) **A**9 10 18 **F**3 7 11 15 29 30 32 34 35 36 39 40 41 44 50 53 56 57 59 61 64 65 66 68 75 82 84 86 87 93 97 99 101 107 108 119 127 130 132 133 134 135 143 144 146 147 148 **P**6
Primary Contact: Steve Whited, Chief Executive Officer
CFO: Edward Lawaty, Chief Financial Officer
CMO: Suresh Balasubramony, M.D., Chief Medical Officer
CIO: Brent Barr, Chief Information Officer
CHR: Sheila Gherke, Director Human Resources
CNO: Kim Houchin, Chief Nursing Officer
Web address: www.mhhcc.com
**Control:** Other not–for–profit (including NFP Corporation) **Service:** General Medical and Surgical

**Staffed Beds:** 42 **Admissions:** 291 **Census:** 28 **Outpatient Visits:** 64249 **Births:** 0 **Total Expense ($000):** 16711 **Payroll Expense ($000):** 10105 **Personnel:** 261

## HINTON—Summers County

☐ **SUMMERS COUNTY ARH HOSPITAL (511310)**, Terrace Street, Zip 25951–2407, Mailing Address: Drawer 940, Zip 25951–0940; tel. 304/466–1000 **A**1 9 10 18 **F**11 15 29 30 32 34 35 40 43 44 50 54 57 59 62 64 65 71 81 82 86 87 90 97 107 114 119 127 130 133 146 147 148 **P**6 **S** Appalachian Regional Healthcare, Inc., Lexington, KY
Primary Contact: Wesley Dangerfield, Community Chief Executive Officer
CFO: Ryan St. John, Assistant Administrator
CMO: Ajay Anand, M.D., President Medical Staff
CIO: Polly Bentley, Chief Information Officer
CHR: Nancy Whitlock, Manager Human Resources
Web address: www.arh.org
**Control:** Other not–for–profit (including NFP Corporation) **Service:** General Medical and Surgical

**Staffed Beds:** 25 **Admissions:** 664 **Census:** 9 **Outpatient Visits:** 24597 **Births:** 0 **Total Expense ($000):** 15400 **Payroll Expense ($000):** 5190 **Personnel:** 119

## HUNTINGTON—Cabell County

⊠ **CABELL HUNTINGTON HOSPITAL (510055)**, 1340 Hal Greer Boulevard, Zip 25701–0195; tel. 304/526–2000, (Includes HOOPS FAMILY CHILDREN'S HOSPITAL, 1340 Hal Greer Boulevard, Zip 25701–3800; tel. 304/526–2000), (Total facility includes 15 beds in nursing home–type unit) **A**1 2 3 5 9 10 12 13 **F**3 7 11 12 13 15 16 17 18 19 20 26 28 29 30 31 32 34 35 37 38 39 40 41 43 44 45 46 48 49 50 51 52 54 55 56 57 58 59 60 61 62 64 65 66 70 72 73 74 75 76 77 78 79 81 82 84 85 86 87 88 89 92 93 94 96 97 107 108 110 111 114 115 117 118 119 120 121 123 126 128 129 130 131 132 134 135 144 145 146 147 148 **P**8
Primary Contact: Brent A. Marsteller, President and Chief Executive Officer
COO: Glen A. Washington, Senior Vice President and Chief Operating Officer
CFO: David M. Ward, Senior Vice President and Chief Financial Officer
CMO: Hoyt J. Burdick, M.D., Vice President Medical Affairs
CHR: Barry Tourigny, Vice President Human Resources and Organizational Development
Web address: www.cabellhuntington.org
**Control:** Other not–for–profit (including NFP Corporation) **Service:** General Medical and Surgical

**Staffed Beds:** 303 **Admissions:** 25151 **Census:** 225 **Outpatient Visits:** 472951 **Births:** 2533 **Total Expense ($000):** 367023 **Payroll Expense ($000):** 125505 **Personnel:** 2065

☐ **CORNERSTONE HOSPITAL OF HUNTINGTON (512003)**, 2900 First Avenue, Two East, Zip 25702–1241; tel. 304/399–2600 **A**1 9 10 **F**1 3 29 30 65 85 135 148 **S** Cornerstone Healthcare Group, Dallas, TX
Primary Contact: Cynthia Isaacs, Chief Executive Officer
CFO: Frank Carter, Chief Financial Officer
CMO: William Beam, M.D., Chief of Staff
Web address: www.chghospitals.com
**Control:** Other, Government, federal **Service:** Long–Term Acute Care hospital

**Staffed Beds:** 28 **Admissions:** 349 **Census:** 24 **Outpatient Visits:** 0 **Births:** 0 **Total Expense ($000):** 11362

⊠ **HEALTHSOUTH HUNTINGTON REHABILITATION HOSPITAL (513028)**, 6900 West Country Club Drive, Zip 25705–2000; tel. 304/733–1060 **A**1 10 **F**29 90 95 96 146 **S** HEALTHSOUTH Corporation, Birmingham, AL
Primary Contact: Michael E. Zuliani, Chief Executive Officer
CHR: Chad Bailey, Director of Human Resources
Web address: www.healthsouthhuntington.com
**Control:** Corporation, Investor–owned, for–profit **Service:** Rehabilitation

**Staffed Beds:** 52 **Admissions:** 1129 **Census:** 42 **Outpatient Visits:** 0 **Births:** 0 **Total Expense ($000):** 11583 **Payroll Expense ($000):** 6452 **Personnel:** 145

⊠ **HUNTINGTON VETERANS AFFAIRS MEDICAL CENTER**, (Formerly Veterans Affairs Medical Center), 1540 Spring Valley Drive, Zip 25704–9300; tel. 304/429–6741, (Nonreporting) **A**1 3 5 **S** Department of Veterans Affairs, Washington, DC
Primary Contact: Edward H. Seiler, Director
CIO: Gary Henderson, Chief Information Resources Management Services
Web address: www.huntington.va.gov/
**Control:** Veterans Affairs, Government, federal **Service:** General Medical and Surgical

**Staffed Beds:** 80

☐ **MILDRED MITCHELL–BATEMAN HOSPITAL (514009)**, 1530 Norway Avenue, Zip 25705–1358, Mailing Address: P.O. Box 448, Zip 25709–0448; tel. 304/525–7801 **A**1 9 10 **F**11 29 30 86 87 98 99 105 130 135 146 **P**6
Primary Contact: Mary Beth Carlisle, Chief Executive Officer
COO: Mary Beth Carlisle, Chief Executive Officer
CFO: James Spencer, Chief Financial Officer
CMO: Shahid Masood, M.D., Clinical Director
CIO: Elias Majdalani, Director Management Information Systems
CHR: Kieth Anne Worden, Director Human Resources
Web address: www.batemanhospital.org
**Control:** State–Government, nonfederal **Service:** Psychiatric

**Staffed Beds:** 110 **Admissions:** 578 **Census:** 108 **Outpatient Visits:** 0 **Births:** 0 **Total Expense ($000):** 33668 **Payroll Expense ($000):** 14162 **Personnel:** 393

WV

---

**Hospital, Medicare Provider Number, Address, Telephone, Approval, Facility, and Physician Codes, Health Care System**

★ American Hospital Association (AHA) membership
☐ The Joint Commission accreditation
◇ DNV Healthcare Inc. accreditation
○ Healthcare Facilities Accreditation Program
△ Commission on Accreditation of Rehabilitation Facilities (CARF) accreditation

☐ **RIVER PARK HOSPITAL (514008)**, 1230 Sixth Avenue, Zip 25701–2312, Mailing Address: P.O. Box 1875, Zip 25719–1875; tel. 304/526–9111 **A**1 9 10 **F**29 34 35 38 40 56 98 99 100 101 102 103 106 130 143 **S** Universal Health Services, Inc., King of Prussia, PA
Primary Contact: Terry A. Stephens, Chief Executive Officer
CFO: Steve Kuhn, Chief Financial Officer
CMO: David J. Humphreys, M.D., Medical Director
CIO: Tony Radenheimer, Network Administrator
CHR: Mary Stratton, Director Human Resources
CNO: Charles Christopher Whitt, Chief Nursing Officer
Web address: www.riverparkhospital.net
**Control:** Corporation, Investor–owned, for–profit **Service:** Psychiatric

**Staffed Beds:** 167 **Admissions:** 1549 **Census:** 135 **Outpatient Visits:** 0 **Births:** 0 **Total Expense ($000):** 18550 **Payroll Expense ($000):** 10646 **Personnel:** 288

✠ **ST. MARY'S MEDICAL CENTER (510007)**, 2900 First Avenue, Zip 25702–1272; tel. 304/526–1234, (Total facility includes 19 beds in nursing home–type unit) **A**1 2 3 5 9 10 **F**3 9 11 12 13 15 17 18 20 22 24 26 28 29 30 31 32 34 35 36 40 42 43 44 45 46 47 48 49 50 53 55 57 58 59 60 62 64 65 66 67 68 70 73 74 75 76 77 78 79 81 82 85 86 87 89 92 93 96 97 98 100 101 102 103 107 108 110 111 114 115 118 119 120 121 123 124 126 128 129 130 132 133 135 145 146 147 148 **P**8 **S** Pallottine Health Services, Huntington, WV
Primary Contact: Michael G. Sellards, President and Chief Executive Officer
COO: Todd Campbell, Senior Vice President and Chief Operating Officer
CFO: Angela Swearingen, Vice President Finance
CMO: Ernest Lee Taylor, M.D., Vice President Medical Affairs
CHR: Susan Beth Robinson, Vice President Human Resources
CNO: Elizabeth Bosley, R.N., Vice President Patient Services
Web address: www.st–marys.org
**Control:** Church–operated, Nongovernment, not–for profit **Service:** General Medical and Surgical

**Staffed Beds:** 375 **Admissions:** 19082 **Census:** 273 **Outpatient Visits:** 261256 **Births:** 419 **Total Expense ($000):** 339184 **Payroll Expense ($000):** 113642 **Personnel:** 2226

**HURRICANE—Putnam County**

✠ **CAMC TEAYS VALLEY HOSPITAL (510085)**, 1400 Hospital Drive, Zip 25526–9202; tel. 304/757–1700 **A**1 9 10 **F**3 11 15 28 29 34 35 39 40 45 46 47 50 54 56 57 59 64 65 70 74 75 77 79 81 82 85 87 93 97 100 102 107 108 110 111 115 118 119 130 131 132 135 145 146 148 **S** Charleston Area Medical Center Health System, Inc., Charleston, WV
Primary Contact: Randall H. Hodges, President and Chief Executive Officer
CFO: Larry C. Hudson, Executive Vice President and Chief Financial Officer
CMO: Elizabeth L. Spangler, M.D., Vice President Medical Affairs and Chief Medical Officer
CIO: Lynn Brookshire, Vice President Information Services and Chief Information Officer
CNO: Mary Beth Mullins, Associate Administrator and Chief Nursing Officer
Web address: www.camc.org
**Control:** Other not–for–profit (including NFP Corporation) **Service:** General Medical and Surgical

**Staffed Beds:** 70 **Admissions:** 2525 **Census:** 36 **Outpatient Visits:** 85520 **Births:** 0 **Total Expense ($000):** 52406 **Payroll Expense ($000):** 17550 **Personnel:** 337

**KEYSER—Mineral County**

☐ **POTOMAC VALLEY HOSPITAL (511315)**, 100 Pin Oak Lane, Zip 26726–5908; tel. 304/597–3500 **A**1 9 10 18 **F**3 15 18 28 29 30 34 40 45 57 59 63 64 70 75 79 81 85 87 93 107 108 110 111 114 119 127 128 130 132 133 135 146 **S** Mid Atlantic Health Management, Inc., Stevensville, MD
Primary Contact: Linda K. Shroyer, Administrator
CFO: Marian Cardwell, Chief Financial Officer
Web address: www.potomacvalleyhospital.com
**Control:** Corporation, Investor–owned, for–profit **Service:** General Medical and Surgical

**Staffed Beds:** 25 **Admissions:** 799 **Census:** 9 **Outpatient Visits:** 49439 **Births:** 0 **Total Expense ($000):** 22515 **Payroll Expense ($000):** 7011 **Personnel:** 202

**KINGWOOD—Preston County**

★ **PRESTON MEMORIAL HOSPITAL (511312)**, 300 South Price Street, Zip 26537–1495; tel. 304/329–1400 **A**9 10 18 **F**3 11 12 13 15 18 29 30 34 35 40 43 45 47 48 53 57 59 64 65 74 75 76 77 79 81 93 107 108 111 114 119 129 132 133 135 146 147
Primary Contact: Melissa Lockwood, Chief Executive Officer
CFO: Robert W. Milvet, Jr., Chief Financial Officer
CIO: Beth Horne, System Administrator Information Technology
CHR: Michele Batiste, Director Human Resources
Web address: www.prestonmemorial.org
**Control:** Other not–for–profit (including NFP Corporation) **Service:** General Medical and Surgical

**Staffed Beds:** 25 **Admissions:** 724 **Census:** 8 **Outpatient Visits:** 53062 **Births:** 0 **Total Expense ($000):** 23405 **Payroll Expense ($000):** 11082 **Personnel:** 290

**LOGAN—Logan County**

✠ **LOGAN REGIONAL MEDICAL CENTER (510048)**, 20 Hospital Drive, Zip 25601–3452; tel. 304/831–1101 **A**1 9 10 20 **F**3 11 13 15 18 20 28 29 31 34 35 40 43 45 49 51 54 57 59 64 65 70 74 75 76 77 78 79 81 86 87 89 90 92 93 97 107 108 110 111 114 115 117 118 119 129 130 133 135 146 147 **P**6 **S** LifePoint Hospitals, Inc., Brentwood, TN
Primary Contact: John E. Walker, FACHE, Chief Executive Officer
COO: Timothy Harclerode, R.N., Chief Operating Officer
CFO: Tim Matney, Chief Financial Officer
CIO: Barry Hensley, Director Information Systems
CHR: Janet Wold, Director Human Resources
CNO: Aphreikah DuHaney, R.N., Chief Nursing Officer
Web address: www.loganregionalmedicalcenter.com
**Control:** Corporation, Investor–owned, for–profit **Service:** General Medical and Surgical

**Staffed Beds:** 129 **Admissions:** 5721 **Census:** 75 **Outpatient Visits:** 98075 **Births:** 305 **Total Expense ($000):** 80405 **Payroll Expense ($000):** 25543 **Personnel:** 608

**MADISON—Boone County**

✠ **BOONE MEMORIAL HOSPITAL (511313)**, 701 Madison Avenue, Zip 25130–1699; tel. 304/369–1230 **A**1 9 10 18 **F**3 11 15 28 34 35 40 43 45 50 53 54 57 59 64 65 75 77 81 87 97 107 108 111 119 127 128 129 130 131 133 135 146 147
Primary Contact: Tommy H. Mullins, Administrator
COO: Tommy H. Mullins, Administrator
CFO: Randy Foxx, Chief Financial Officer
CMO: Ziad Chanaa, M.D., Chief of Staff
CIO: Susan Shreve, Executive Director Information Technology
CHR: Sheliah Cook, Director Human Resources
Web address: www.bmh.org
**Control:** County–Government, nonfederal **Service:** General Medical and Surgical

**Staffed Beds:** 25 **Admissions:** 488 **Census:** 9 **Outpatient Visits:** 54165 **Births:** 0 **Total Expense ($000):** 19243 **Payroll Expense ($000):** 6797 **Personnel:** 202

**MARTINSBURG—Berkeley County**

✠ **BERKELEY MEDICAL CENTER (510008)**, (Formerly City Hospital), 2500 Hospital Drive, Zip 25401–3402, Mailing Address: P.O. Box 1418, Zip 25402–1418; tel. 304/264–1000 **A**1 2 3 5 9 10 **F**3 11 12 13 15 18 20 21 22 28 29 30 31 34 35 38 40 43 44 45 49 51 53 57 59 62 64 70 74 76 77 78 79 81 82 85 86 87 89 92 93 98 102 103 107 108 110 111 115 118 119 124 129 130 131 132 135 145 146 147 148 **S** West Virginia United Health System, Fairmont, WV
Primary Contact: Anthony Zelenka, Chief Administrative Officer
CFO: Christopher D. Knight, Chief Financial Officer
Web address: www.cityhospital.org
**Control:** Other not–for–profit (including NFP Corporation) **Service:** General Medical and Surgical

**Staffed Beds:** 166 **Admissions:** 8074 **Census:** 94 **Outpatient Visits:** 208196 **Births:** 931 **Total Expense ($000):** 134207 **Payroll Expense ($000):** 52948 **Personnel:** 854

✠ △ **MARTINSBURG VETERANS AFFAIRS MEDICAL CENTER**, (Formerly Veterans Affairs Medical Center), 510 Butler Avenue, Zip 25405–9990; tel. 304/263–0811, (Nonreporting) **A**1 3 5 7 9 **S** Department of Veterans Affairs, Washington, DC
Primary Contact: Ann Brown, Director
COO: Timothy J. Cooke, Associate Medical Center Director
CFO: Eric C. Sorenson, Chief Fiscal Office
CMO: Jonathan Fierer, M.D., Chief of Staff
CIO: Mary Ann Creel, Chief Information Resource Management
CHR: George Pearson, Chief Human Resources Management Office
CNO: Susan George, R.N., Associate Director Patient Care Services
Web address: www.martinsburg.va.gov/
**Control:** Veterans Affairs, Government, federal **Service:** General Medical and Surgical

**Staffed Beds:** 246

**MONTGOMERY—Fayette County**

✠ **MONTGOMERY GENERAL HOSPITAL (511318)**, 401 Sixth Avenue, Zip 25136–2116, Mailing Address: P.O. Box 270, Zip 25136–0270; tel. 304/442–5151, (Total facility includes 44 beds in nursing home–type unit) **A**1 9 10 18 **F**3 11 15 29 30 34 35 40 45 49 53 57 59 64 67 77 81 87 93 97 107 111 114 119 128 129 130 131 133 135 146 147 148 **P**6 8
Primary Contact: Vickie Gay, Chief Executive Officer
CFO: Sherri Murray, Chief Financial Officer
CMO: Traci Acklin, M.D., Chief of Staff
CIO: Denzil Blevins, Director Information Systems
CHR: Kelly D. Frye, Director Human Resources
Web address: www.mghwv.com
**Control:** Other not–for–profit (including NFP Corporation) **Service:** General Medical and Surgical

**Staffed Beds:** 69 **Admissions:** 755 **Census:** 42 **Outpatient Visits:** 61227 **Births:** 0 **Total Expense ($000):** 23978 **Payroll Expense ($000):** 10129 **Personnel:** 217

*Many Facility Codes have changed. Please refer to the AHA Guide Code Chart.* © 2013 AHA Guide

**MORGANTOWN—Monongalia County**

**CHESTNUT RIDGE HOSPITAL** See West Virginia University Hospitals

☒ **HEALTHSOUTH MOUNTAINVIEW REGIONAL REHABILITATION HOSPITAL (513030)**, 1160 Van Voorhis Road, Zip 26505–3437; tel. 304/598–1100 **A**1 3 5 10 **F**3 29 57 64 74 75 77 86 90 93 94 95 96 130 131 132 135 148 **S** HEALTHSOUTH Corporation, Birmingham, AL
Primary Contact: Vickie Demers, Chief Executive Officer
CFO: Jason Gizzi, Controller
CMO: Russell Biundo, M.D., Medical Director
CIO: Robin Wherry, Risk Manager and Director Quality Assurance and Health Information Management
CHR: Joseph Huffman, Director Human Resources
Web address: www.healthsouthmountainview.com
**Control:** Corporation, Investor–owned, for–profit **Service:** Rehabilitation

Staffed Beds: 80 Admissions: 1739 Census: 66 Outpatient Visits: 8302 Births: 0 Total Expense ($000): 21081 Payroll Expense ($000): 11176 Personnel: 275

☒ **MONONGALIA GENERAL HOSPITAL (510024)**, 1200 J. D. Anderson Drive, Zip 26505–3486; tel. 304/598–1200 **A**1 9 10 19 **F**3 13 15 17 18 20 22 24 26 28 29 30 31 32 34 35 36 40 43 45 46 49 50 51 54 57 59 60 63 64 65 68 70 74 75 76 77 78 79 81 82 84 85 86 87 89 97 107 108 111 114 115 116 118 119 129 130 132 135 144 145 146 147 148 **P**6 8
Primary Contact: Darryl L. Duncan, President and Chief Executive Officer
COO: Linda Neu Ollis, FACHE, Chief Operating Officer
CFO: Daris Rosencrance, Chief Financial Officer
CMO: Mike Ferrebee, M.D., Vice President Medical Affairs
CIO: Linda Allen, Vice President Quality and Information Systems
CHR: Melissa Shreves, Director Human Resources
Web address: www.mongeneral.com
**Control:** Other not–for–profit (including NFP Corporation) **Service:** General Medical and Surgical

Staffed Beds: 175 Admissions: 9621 Census: 104 Outpatient Visits: 165186 Births: 998 Total Expense ($000): 200059 Payroll Expense ($000): 67346 Personnel: 1258

☒ **WEST VIRGINIA UNIVERSITY HOSPITALS (510001)**, 1 Medical Center Drive, Zip 26506–4749; tel. 304/598–4000, (Includes CHESTNUT RIDGE HOSPITAL, 930 Chestnut Ridge Road, Zip 26505–2854; tel. 304/293–4000; WEST VIRGINIA UNIVERSITY CHILDREN'S HOSPITAL, Medical Center Drive, Zip 26506–8111; tel. 800/982–6277), (Total facility includes 1 beds in nursing home–type unit) **A**1 3 5 8 9 10 12 13 19 **F**3 4 5 9 11 12 13 15 17 18 19 20 21 22 23 24 25 26 27 28 29 30 31 35 36 37 38 39 40 43 45 46 47 48 49 50 51 54 55 56 57 59 60 61 64 68 70 72 74 75 76 77 78 79 80 81 82 84 85 86 87 88 89 92 98 99 100 101 102 103 105 106 107 108 110 111 114 115 118 119 120 121 123 124 126 129 130 132 136 141 145 146 147 148 **P**6 **S** West Virginia United Health System, Fairmont, WV
Primary Contact: Bruce McClymonds, President and Chief Executive Officer
CFO: Mary Jo Shahan, Vice President and Chief Financial Officer
CMO: Michelle Nuss, M.D., Chief Medical Officer
CIO: Rich King, Vice President Information Technology
CHR: Charlotte Bennett, Vice President Human Resources
Web address: www.health.wvu.edu
**Control:** Other not–for–profit (including NFP Corporation) **Service:** General Medical and Surgical

Staffed Beds: 512 Admissions: 26313 Census: 417 Outpatient Visits: 643219 Births: 1375 Total Expense ($000): 643162 Payroll Expense ($000): 231054 Personnel: 4621

**NEW MARTINSVILLE—Wetzel County**

☒ **WETZEL COUNTY HOSPITAL (510072)**, 3 East Benjamin Drive, Zip 26155–2758; tel. 304/455–8000 **A**1 9 10 20 **F**3 15 28 30 31 34 40 43 45 57 59 64 65 70 75 77 81 85 93 94 107 108 114 118 119 127 130 132 133 135 146 148 **P**6
Primary Contact: Brian K. Felici, Chief Executive Officer
CFO: Edwin Szewczyk, Chief Financial Officer
CMO: Donald A. Blum, M.D., Chief of Staff
CIO: Amy Frazier, Supervisor Management Information Systems
CHR: Sarah Boley, Director Human Resources
Web address: www.wetzelcountyhospital.org
**Control:** County–Government, nonfederal **Service:** General Medical and Surgical

Staffed Beds: 44 Admissions: 1133 Census: 15 Outpatient Visits: 89859 Births: 2 Total Expense ($000): 24238 Payroll Expense ($000): 9961 Personnel: 269

**OAK HILL—Fayette County**

☒ **PLATEAU MEDICAL CENTER (511317)**, 430 Main Street, Zip 25901–3455; tel. 304/469–8600 **A**1 9 10 18 **F**3 8 15 18 29 30 34 35 40 45 46 50 57 59 64 68 70 75 77 79 81 85 87 91 93 97 107 108 110 111 114 119 146 **S** Community Health Systems, Inc., Franklin, TN
Primary Contact: Chad Hatfield, Chief Executive Officer
CFO: Heather Hylton, Chief Financial Officer
CMO: Ryan Newell, M.D., Chief of Staff
CIO: Steve Bowen, Director Information Systems
CHR: Tammie Miller, Director Marketing and Public Relations
Web address: www.plateaumedicalcenter.com
**Control:** Corporation, Investor–owned, for–profit **Service:** General Medical and Surgical

Staffed Beds: 25 Admissions: 1554 Census: 17 Outpatient Visits: 43206 Births: 0 Total Expense ($000): 30406 Payroll Expense ($000): 13193 Personnel: 216

**PARKERSBURG—Wood County**

☒ **CAMDEN CLARK MEDICAL CENTER (510058)**, 800 Garfield Avenue, Zip 26101–5378, Mailing Address: P.O. Box 718, Zip 26102–0718; tel. 304/424–2111, (Includes ST. JOSEPH'S HOSPITAL, 1824 Murdoch Avenue, Zip 26101–3246, Mailing Address: P.O. Box 327, Zip 26102–0327; tel. 304/424–4111), (Total facility includes 25 beds in nursing home–type unit) **A**1 9 10 13 **F**3 7 8 11 12 13 15 17 18 20 22 24 28 29 30 31 34 35 40 43 45 49 50 51 53 54 57 58 59 64 65 66 68 70 71 74 75 76 78 79 81 84 85 86 87 89 92 97 98 100 101 102 107 108 110 111 114 115 116 117 118 119 120 121 123 124 128 130 132 135 145 146 147 148 **P**6 8 **S** West Virginia United Health System, Fairmont, WV
Primary Contact: Michael A. King, FACHE, President and Chief Executive Officer
CFO: Allen R. Butcher, Vice President Finance
CMO: Edwin Boso, M.D., President Medical Staff
CIO: Josh Woods, Director Information Systems
CHR: Tom Heller, Vice President Human Resources
CNO: Sherry Simmons, Vice President Patient Care Services and Chief Nursing Officer
Web address: www.camdenclark.org
**Control:** Other not–for–profit (including NFP Corporation) **Service:** General Medical and Surgical

Staffed Beds: 428 Admissions: 15241 Census: 204 Outpatient Visits: 311932 Births: 1563 Total Expense ($000): 234787 Payroll Expense ($000): 77173 Personnel: 1764

☒ **HEALTHSOUTH WESTERN HILLS REHABILITATION HOSPITAL (513027)**, 3 Western Hills Drive, Zip 26105–8122; tel. 304/420–1300 **A**1 10 **F**29 54 57 64 90 93 94 95 96 130 146 **S** HEALTHSOUTH Corporation, Birmingham, AL
Primary Contact: Alvin R. Lawson, JD, FACHE, Chief Executive Officer
CFO: Jessica Walkup, Controller
CMO: Kalapala Rao, M.D., Medical Director
CHR: Candace Ross, Coordinator Human Resources
CNO: Jean Francis, Chief Nursing Officer
Web address: www.healthsouthwesternhills.com
**Control:** Corporation, Investor–owned, for–profit **Service:** Rehabilitation

Staffed Beds: 50 Admissions: 1110 Census: 38 Outpatient Visits: 10423 Births: 0 Total Expense ($000): 12879 Payroll Expense ($000): 6189 Personnel: 137

**PETERSBURG—Grant County**

★ **GRANT MEMORIAL HOSPITAL (511316)**, 117 Hospital Drive, Zip 26847–9566, Mailing Address: P.O. Box 1019, Zip 26847–1019; tel. 304/257–1026, (Total facility includes 20 beds in nursing home–type unit) **A**9 10 18 **F**3 11 13 15 28 29 30 31 34 35 40 45 50 53 57 59 62 63 64 65 67 68 70 75 76 77 79 81 82 84 85 86 87 91 93 107 108 114 118 119 128 130 132 133 146 147 **P**6
Primary Contact: Mary Beth Barr, R.N., Chief Executive Officer
COO: Mary Beth Barr, R.N., Chief Executive Officer
CFO: Joe Barnes, Chief Financial Officer
CMO: Fernando Indacochea, M.D., Chief of Staff
CIO: Derek Nesselrodt, Director Information Systems
CHR: Ronnie Arbaugh, Director Human Resources
CNO: Kimberly Linville, Chief Nursing Officer
Web address: www.grantmemorial.com
**Control:** County–Government, nonfederal **Service:** General Medical and Surgical

Staffed Beds: 45 Admissions: 1491 Census: 16 Outpatient Visits: 50024 Births: 241 Total Expense ($000): 30433 Payroll Expense ($000): 10173 Personnel: 288

**WV**

---

**Hospital, Medicare Provider Number, Address, Telephone, Approval, Facility, and Physician Codes, Health Care System**

★ American Hospital Association (AHA) membership
☐ The Joint Commission accreditation
◇ DNV Healthcare Inc. accreditation
○ Healthcare Facilities Accreditation Program
△ Commission on Accreditation of Rehabilitation Facilities (CARF) accreditation

## PHILIPPI—Barbour County

★ **BROADDUS HOSPITAL (511300)**, 1 Healthcare Drive, Zip 26416–9405, Mailing Address: P.O. Box 930, Zip 26416–0930; tel. 304/457–1760, (Total facility includes 60 beds in nursing home–type unit) **A**9 10 18 **F**3 15 29 30 34 35 40 57 59 64 65 75 85 87 107 110 114 119 128 130 133 143 146 **S** Davis Health System, Elkins, WV
Primary Contact: Jeffrey A. Powelson, Chief Executive Officer
CFO: Cathy Kalar, Chief Financial Officer
CHR: Penny D. Brown, Human Resource Representative
Web address: www.davishealthsystem.org/
**Control:** Other not–for–profit (including NFP Corporation) **Service:** General Medical and Surgical

**Staffed Beds:** 72 **Admissions:** 344 **Census:** 64 **Outpatient Visits:** 22995 **Births:** 0 **Total Expense ($000):** 14830 **Payroll Expense ($000):** 6315 **Personnel:** 151

## POINT PLEASANT—Mason County

☒ **PLEASANT VALLEY HOSPITAL (510012)**, 2520 Valley Drive, Zip 25550–2031; tel. 304/675–4340, (Total facility includes 100 beds in nursing home–type unit) **A**1 9 10 **F**3 11 13 15 17 18 28 29 30 33 34 35 39 40 43 48 50 53 56 57 59 62 63 68 70 74 75 76 77 78 79 81 85 86 87 89 93 107 108 110 111 114 115 118 119 128 129 130 131 132 143 144 146 147 148 **P**6
Primary Contact: Larry Unroe, Interim Chief Executive Officer
COO: William A. Barker, Jr., Vice President Administration
CFO: Richard Hogan, Chief Financial Officer
CMO: Agnes Enrico–Simon, M.D., President Medical Staff
CIO: Paula Brooker, Director Information Services
CHR: David A. Brown, Director Human Resources and Corporate Compliance
CNO: Amber Findley, Senior Director Nursing Services and NRC Administrator
Web address: www.pvalley.org
**Control:** Other not–for–profit (including NFP Corporation) **Service:** General Medical and Surgical

**Staffed Beds:** 201 **Admissions:** 2838 **Census:** 115 **Outpatient Visits:** 213479 **Births:** 200 **Total Expense ($000):** 64017 **Payroll Expense ($000):** 28297 **Personnel:** 649

## PRINCETON—Mercer County

☒ **HEALTHSOUTH SOUTHERN HILLS REHABILITATION HOSPITAL (513026)**, 120 Twelfth Street, Zip 24740–2352; tel. 304/487–8000 **A**1 10 **F**29 56 57 59 60 64 74 75 77 79 87 90 93 94 130 132 148 **S** HEALTHSOUTH Corporation, Birmingham, AL
Primary Contact: Robert Williams, Chief Executive Officer
CFO: Melinda Fanning, Chief Financial Officer and Controller
CMO: Robert Walker, M.D., Medical Director
CIO: Brian Bales, Director Plant Operations
CHR: Jan Thibodeau, Director Human Resources
Web address: www.healthsouthsouthernhills.com
**Control:** Corporation, Investor–owned, for–profit **Service:** Rehabilitation

**Staffed Beds:** 42 **Admissions:** 863 **Census:** 27 **Outpatient Visits:** 3429 **Births:** 0 **Personnel:** 117

☒ **PRINCETON COMMUNITY HOSPITAL (510046)**, 122 12th Street, Zip 24740–2352, Mailing Address: P.O. Box 1369, Zip 24740–1369; tel. 304/487–7000 **A**1 2 9 10 19 **F**3 11 12 13 15 17 29 30 31 32 34 35 39 40 44 45 46 48 49 50 51 53 57 59 64 65 70 74 75 76 77 78 79 81 85 86 87 89 93 98 100 101 102 103 104 107 108 110 111 114 115 118 119 127 129 130 131 132 135 141 142 144 146 147 **P**1
Primary Contact: Wayne B. Griffith, FACHE, Chief Executive Officer
COO: Jeffrey Lilley, CPA, Vice President Operations
CFO: Frank J. Sinicrope, Jr., Vice President Financial Services
CMO: Phil Branson, M.D., President Medical Staff
CIO: Stephen A. Curry, Director Information Services
CHR: Heather Poff, Director Human Resources
CNO: Rose Morgan, R.N., Vice President Patient Care Services
Web address: www.pchonline.org
**Control:** City–Government, nonfederal **Service:** General Medical and Surgical

**Staffed Beds:** 230 **Admissions:** 8687 **Census:** 113 **Outpatient Visits:** 199180 **Births:** 667 **Total Expense ($000):** 115962 **Payroll Expense ($000):** 41829 **Personnel:** 985

## RANSON—Jefferson County

☒ **JEFFERSON MEDICAL CENTER (511319)**, (Formerly Jefferson Memorial Hospital), 300 South Preston Street, Zip 25438–1631; tel. 304/728–1600 **A**1 3 5 9 10 18 **F**3 11 13 15 29 30 34 35 38 40 43 44 45 57 59 64 70 74 75 76 77 79 81 82 85 86 87 92 93 107 108 110 111 115 118 119 129 130 132 135 146 147 148 **S** West Virginia United Health System, Fairmont, WV
Primary Contact: Christina D. Coad, Ph.D., Chief Administrative Officer
CFO: Christopher D. Knight, Vice President Finance
CMO: Robert Jones, III, M.D., President Medical Staff
CIO: Todd Smoot, Chief Information Officer
CHR: Christina D. Coad, Ph.D., Interim Vice President Human Resources
Web address: www.jeffmem.com
**Control:** Other not–for–profit (including NFP Corporation) **Service:** General Medical and Surgical

**Staffed Beds:** 25 **Admissions:** 1606 **Census:** 13 **Outpatient Visits:** 75634 **Births:** 280 **Total Expense ($000):** 41466 **Payroll Expense ($000):** 17234 **Personnel:** 262

## RIPLEY—Jackson County

☐ **JACKSON GENERAL HOSPITAL (511320)**, 122 Pinnell Street, Zip 25271–9101, Mailing Address: P.O. Box 720, Zip 25271–0720; tel. 304/372–2731 **A**1 9 10 **F**3 11 15 17 29 30 34 35 40 50 57 59 64 68 75 79 81 85 93 107 114 119 127 128 132 133 **P**6
Primary Contact: Stephanie McCoy, President and Chief Executive Officer
CFO: Angela Frame, Chief Financial Officer
CMO: James G. Gaal, M.D., Chief of Medical Staff
CIO: John Manley, Director Information Systems
CHR: Jeffrey Tabor, Director Human Resources
Web address: www.jacksongeneral.com
**Control:** Other not–for–profit (including NFP Corporation) **Service:** General Medical and Surgical

**Staffed Beds:** 36 **Admissions:** 1186 **Census:** 14 **Outpatient Visits:** 43618 **Births:** 0 **Total Expense ($000):** 22577 **Payroll Expense ($000):** 11103 **Personnel:** 239

## ROMNEY—Hampshire County

☒ **HAMPSHIRE MEMORIAL HOSPITAL (511311)**, 363 Sunrise Boulevard, Zip 26757–4607; tel. 304/822–4561, (Total facility includes 36 beds in nursing home–type unit) **A**1 9 10 18 **F**3 15 29 30 40 45 54 59 64 65 71 77 79 81 85 93 107 119 127 128 129 130 133 148 **P**6 **S** Valley Health System, Winchester, VA
Primary Contact: Neil R. McLaughlin, R.N., Interim President
CFO: Christine Lowman, Vice President Finance
CMO: Vijay K. Chowdhary, M.D., Medical Director
CHR: Cindy Combs, Supervisor Human Resources
CNO: Gena Swisher, Vice President Nursing
Web address: www.valleyhealthlink.com/hampshire
**Control:** Other not–for–profit (including NFP Corporation) **Service:** General Medical and Surgical

**Staffed Beds:** 44 **Admissions:** 475 **Census:** 38 **Outpatient Visits:** 44295 **Births:** 0 **Total Expense ($000):** 21298 **Payroll Expense ($000):** 7775 **Personnel:** 162

## RONCEVERTE—Greenbrier County

★ ○ **GREENBRIER VALLEY MEDICAL CENTER (510002)**, 202 Maplewood Avenue, Zip 24970–1334, Mailing Address: P.O. Box 497, Zip 24970–0497; tel. 304/647–4411 **A**9 10 11 12 13 **F**8 13 15 18 20 29 31 34 40 45 49 51 57 59 60 68 70 74 75 76 78 79 81 85 86 87 89 107 108 110 111 114 116 119 120 129 133 135 146 148 **P**6 **S** Community Health Systems, Inc., Franklin, TN
Primary Contact: Paul Storey, Chief Executive Officer
CFO: Paige Adkins, Chief Financial Officer
CMO: Patrick Ryan, M.D., Chief of Staff
CIO: Karen Hoylman, Director Information Systems
CHR: Melissa Wickline, Director Marketing
CNO: Charlene Warren, R.N., Chief Nursing Officer
Web address: www.gvmc.com
**Control:** Corporation, Investor–owned, for–profit **Service:** General Medical and Surgical

**Staffed Beds:** 113 **Admissions:** 4081 **Census:** 41 **Outpatient Visits:** 55429 **Births:** 614 **Total Expense ($000):** 49470 **Payroll Expense ($000):** 19978 **Personnel:** 465

*Many Facility Codes have changed. Please refer to the AHA Guide Code Chart.*

© 2013 AHA Guide

## SISTERSVILLE—Tyler County

★ **SISTERSVILLE GENERAL HOSPITAL (511304)**, 314 South Wells Street, Zip 26175–1098; tel. 304/652–2611 **A**9 10 18 **F**3 7 11 15 28 29 30 32 35 40 43 50 53 57 59 63 64 65 79 83 84 87 93 97 107 119 127 129 130 132 133 135 146 147 148 **P**6
Primary Contact: John May, Chief Executive Officer
COO: Mike Hall, Risk Manager
CFO: Pat Burdette, Chief Financial Officer
CMO: Ramon Fagundo, M.D., Chief of Staff
CHR: Mary Beth Neff, Director Human Resources
Web address: www.sistersvillehospital.com
**Control:** City–Government, nonfederal **Service:** General Medical and Surgical

**Staffed Beds:** 12 **Admissions:** 189 **Census:** 1 **Outpatient Visits:** 16405 **Births:** 0 **Total Expense ($000):** 10496 **Payroll Expense ($000):** 5754 **Personnel:** 163

## SOUTH CHARLESTON—Kanawha County

✠ **THOMAS MEMORIAL HOSPITAL (510029)**, 4605 MacCorkle Avenue S.W., Zip 25309–1398; tel. 304/766–3600 **A**1 3 5 9 10 **F**3 5 8 11 13 15 17 18 20 22 29 30 31 32 34 35 38 40 43 45 46 47 48 49 50 53 54 57 59 60 62 64 65 68 69 70 72 74 75 76 77 78 79 81 84 85 86 87 89 92 93 98 99 100 101 102 103 104 105 107 108 110 111 114 115 118 119 120 121 123 124 126 129 130 131 132 143 144 146 147 **S** Thomas Health System, Inc., South Charleston, WV
Primary Contact: Stephen P. Dexter, President and Chief Executive Officer
COO: Daniel Lauffer, FACHE, Senior Vice President and Chief Operating Officer
CFO: Charles O. Covert, Vice President Finance
CIO: Charles O. Covert, Vice President Finance
CHR: Marybeth Smith, Director Human Resources
CNO: Rebecca Brannon, R.N., Vice President Patient Services
Web address: www.thomaswv.org
**Control:** Other not–for–profit (including NFP Corporation) **Service:** General Medical and Surgical

**Staffed Beds:** 215 **Admissions:** 9407 **Census:** 128 **Outpatient Visits:** 189724 **Births:** 1063 **Total Expense ($000):** 160488 **Payroll Expense ($000):** 54450 **Personnel:** 990

## SPENCER—Roane County

✠ **ROANE GENERAL HOSPITAL (511306)**, 200 Hospital Drive, Zip 25276–1050; tel. 304/927–4444, (Total facility includes 35 beds in nursing home–type unit) **A**1 9 10 18 **F**1 3 15 28 29 34 40 43 45 53 57 59 64 65 67 81 89 90 93 97 107 108 119 127 128 130 133 144 148 **P**6
Primary Contact: Douglas E. Bentz, Chief Executive Officer
CFO: Louise Ward, Vice President Financial and Support Services
CMO: Brent Watson, M.D., Chief Medical Staff
CIO: Tony Keaton, Director Information Systems
CHR: Jeff Beane, Director Human Resources
Web address: www.roanegeneralhospital.com
**Control:** Other not–for–profit (including NFP Corporation) **Service:** General Medical and Surgical

**Staffed Beds:** 60 **Admissions:** 485 **Census:** 42 **Outpatient Visits:** 66184 **Births:** 0 **Total Expense ($000):** 26107 **Payroll Expense ($000):** 11490 **Personnel:** 260

## SUMMERSVILLE—Nicholas County

✠ **SUMMERSVILLE REGIONAL MEDICAL CENTER (510082)**, 400 Fairview Heights Road, Zip 26651–9308; tel. 304/872–2891, (Total facility includes 52 beds in nursing home–type unit) **A**1 9 10 **F**1 3 13 15 28 30 34 35 40 43 57 59 64 65 67 68 70 75 76 77 79 81 83 84 85 89 91 93 97 107 108 110 111 115 119 127 128 129 130 131 133 135 146 147 148
Primary Contact: Deborah A. Hill, R.N., FACHE, Chief Executive Officer
CFO: Dora Douglas, Chief Financial Officer
CMO: Robert Fleer, M.D., Chief of Staff
CIO: Mike Ellison, Information Systems Lead
CHR: David M. Henderson, Director Human Resources
Web address: www.summersvillememorial.org
**Control:** City–Government, nonfederal **Service:** General Medical and Surgical

**Staffed Beds:** 105 **Admissions:** 1629 **Census:** 83 **Outpatient Visits:** 120969 **Births:** 288 **Total Expense ($000):** 41470 **Payroll Expense ($000):** 22871 **Personnel:** 486

## WEBSTER SPRINGS—Webster County

★ **WEBSTER COUNTY MEMORIAL HOSPITAL (511301)**, 324 Miller Mountain Drive, Zip 26288–1087, Mailing Address: P.O. Box 312, Zip 26288–0312; tel. 304/847–5682 **A**9 10 18 **F**7 15 28 30 34 35 40 57 59 64 75 87 93 97 107 114 119 127 130 133 135 146 147 148 **P**6
Primary Contact: Annette M. Keenan, Chief Executive Officer
CMO: Robert Mace, M.D., Chief of Staff
CIO: Margaret W. Short, Coordinator Information Technology
CHR: Deborah Bragg, Director Human Resources
Web address: www.wcmhwv.com
**Control:** Other not–for–profit (including NFP Corporation) **Service:** General Medical and Surgical

**Staffed Beds:** 15 **Admissions:** 189 **Census:** 2 **Outpatient Visits:** 54450 **Births:** 1 **Total Expense ($000):** 10872 **Payroll Expense ($000):** 6132 **Personnel:** 129

## WEIRTON—Brooke County

✠ **WEIRTON MEDICAL CENTER (510023)**, 601 Colliers Way, Zip 26062–5091; tel. 304/797–6000, (Total facility includes 33 beds in nursing home–type unit) **A**1 9 10 **F**3 5 9 11 13 15 17 18 20 22 26 29 30 32 34 35 37 39 40 41 43 45 46 47 48 49 50 51 53 54 56 57 59 60 61 62 64 68 70 74 75 76 77 78 79 81 82 85 86 89 92 93 96 97 98 99 100 101 102 103 104 105 106 107 108 110 111 114 115 116 118 119 124 126 128 129 130 131 132 135 143 145 146 147 148 **P**6
Primary Contact: Charles M. O'Brien, Jr., President and Chief Executive Officer
CFO: Robert A. Frank, Chief Financial Officer
CIO: Richard Lucas, Director Information Services
CHR: Jennifer Anderson, Director Human Resources
Web address: www.weirtonmedical.com
**Control:** Other not–for–profit (including NFP Corporation) **Service:** General Medical and Surgical

**Staffed Beds:** 168 **Admissions:** 6017 **Census:** 87 **Outpatient Visits:** 185959 **Births:** 393 **Total Expense ($000):** 91592 **Payroll Expense ($000):** 38331 **Personnel:** 855

## WELCH—Mcdowell County

**WELCH COMMUNITY HOSPITAL (510086)**, 454 McDowell Street, Zip 24801–2097; tel. 304/436–8461, (Total facility includes 59 beds in nursing home–type unit) **A**9 10 20 **F**3 13 15 29 35 40 45 50 57 59 64 65 66 67 68 70 75 76 81 86 87 97 107 110 114 119 127 130 135 146 147 148 **P**6
Primary Contact: Walter J. Garrett, Chief Executive Officer
CFO: Johnny Brant, Chief Financial Officer
CMO: Chandra Sharma, M.D., Chief of Staff
CIO: Thaddeus Robinson, Chief Information Officer
CHR: Diana Blankenship, Director Human Resources
**Control:** State–Government, nonfederal **Service:** General Medical and Surgical

**Staffed Beds:** 108 **Admissions:** 851 **Census:** 56 **Outpatient Visits:** 34622 **Births:** 54 **Total Expense ($000):** 28171 **Payroll Expense ($000):** 9837 **Personnel:** 316

## WESTON—Lewis County

✠ **STONEWALL JACKSON MEMORIAL HOSPITAL (510038)**, 230 Hospital Plaza, Zip 26452–8558; tel. 304/269–8000 **A**1 9 10 **F**3 11 13 15 28 29 30 31 35 40 43 45 48 50 56 57 59 62 64 68 70 75 76 79 81 85 86 87 93 94 97 107 108 111 114 118 119 129 130 131 132 133 135 145 146 147 148 **P**8
Primary Contact: Avah Stalnaker, Chief Executive Officer
COO: Kevin P. Stalnaker, CPA, Chief Operating Officer
CFO: Dodie Arbogest, Chief Financial Officer
CMO: John Wyllie, M.D., President Medical Staff
CIO: Kay Butcher, Director Health Information Management
CHR: Rhonda M. Hager, Director Human Resources
CNO: Carole Norton, R.N., Chief Nursing Officer
Web address: www.stonewallhospital.com
**Control:** Other not–for–profit (including NFP Corporation) **Service:** General Medical and Surgical

**Staffed Beds:** 70 **Admissions:** 2611 **Census:** 26 **Outpatient Visits:** 83989 **Births:** 310 **Total Expense ($000):** 40600 **Payroll Expense ($000):** 21567 **Personnel:** 422

**WV**

---

**Hospital, Medicare Provider Number, Address, Telephone, Approval, Facility, and Physician Codes, Health Care System**

★ American Hospital Association (AHA) membership
☐ The Joint Commission accreditation
◇ DNV Healthcare Inc. accreditation
○ Healthcare Facilities Accreditation Program
△ Commission on Accreditation of Rehabilitation Facilities (CARF) accreditation

☐ **WILLIAM R. SHARPE, JR. HOSPITAL (514010)**, 936 Sharpe Hospital Road,
Zip 26452–8550; tel. 304/269–1210 **A**1 5 9 10 **F**11 30 53 56 86 87 98 100
101 103 130 132 143 146 **P**6
Primary Contact: Parker Haddix, Chief Executive Officer
COO: Terry L. Small, Assistant Chief Executive Officer
CFO: Tammy Keough, Chief Financial Officer
CMO: Robert Keefover, M.D., Chief Medical Officer
CIO: Pam Lewis, Chief Compliance Officer
Web address: www.wvdhhr.org/sharpe
**Control:** State–Government, nonfederal **Service:** Psychiatric

**Staffed Beds:** 150 **Admissions:** 567 **Census:** 150 **Outpatient Visits:** 0
**Births:** 0 **Total Expense ($000):** 44082 **Payroll Expense ($000):** 14240
**Personnel:** 457

### WHEELING—Ohio County

☐ ○ **OHIO VALLEY MEDICAL CENTER (510039)**, 2000 Eoff Street,
Zip 26003–3870; tel. 304/234–0123 **A**1 2 5 9 10 11 12 13 **F**3 5 9 11 13 15
17 18 20 28 29 30 31 34 35 38 39 40 43 44 48 49 50 51 53 55 56 57 58
59 60 61 64 65 68 70 74 75 76 77 78 79 81 82 84 85 86 87 89 93 97 98
99 100 101 102 103 104 105 107 108 111 114 115 116 117 119 121 123
129 130 131 132 134 135 146 147 148 **P**6 **S** Ohio Valley Health Services and
Education Corporation, Wheeling, WV
Primary Contact: Michael J. Caruso, President and Chief Executive Officer
CFO: David T. Baranik, Senior Vice President and Chief Financial Officer
CIO: Robert Panichi, Chief Information Officer
CHR: James R. Stultz, Senior Vice President Human Resources
Web address: www.ovmc–eorh.com
**Control:** Other not–for–profit (including NFP Corporation) **Service:** General
Medical and Surgical

**Staffed Beds:** 185 **Admissions:** 6485 **Census:** 91 **Outpatient Visits:** 143143
**Births:** 276 **Total Expense ($000):** 96738 **Payroll Expense ($000):** 37633
**Personnel:** 816

★ **PETERSON REHABILITATION HOSPITAL (513025)**, Homestead Avenue,
Zip 26003; tel. 304/234–0500, (Total facility includes 150 beds in nursing
home–type unit) **A**10 **F**29 34 56 57 59 75 77 86 87 90 93 96 128 130 131
132 143 148
Primary Contact: Barbara Sisarcick, Administrator
COO: Tom Barr, Director Operational Support Services
CFO: Tammy Parasida, Manager Business Office
CMO: William Mercer, M.D., Director
CIO: Jolene Nagle, Director Medical Records
CHR: Annie Barton, Director Human Resources
Web address: www.weat.com/site6/
**Control:** Corporation, Investor–owned, for–profit **Service:** Rehabilitation

**Staffed Beds:** 172 **Admissions:** 754 **Census:** 153 **Outpatient Visits:** 3001
**Births:** 0 **Total Expense ($000):** 18857 **Payroll Expense ($000):** 5741
**Personnel:** 147

☐ **WHEELING HOSPITAL (510050)**, 1 Medical Park, Zip 26003–6379;
tel. 304/243–3000, (Total facility includes 24 beds in nursing home–type unit) **A**1
2 9 10 13 **F**3 11 13 15 17 18 20 22 24 26 28 29 30 31 32 34 35 36 40 43
44 45 49 50 53 54 57 58 59 61 62 64 66 70 74 75 76 77 78 79 81 85 86
87 89 92 93 94 96 97 99 107 108 110 114 115 117 118 119 120 121 123
128 129 130 131 132 135 143 146 147 148 **P**5
Primary Contact: Ronald L. Violi, Chief Executive Officer
CMO: Angelo Georges, M.D., President Medical and Dental Staff
CIO: David Rapp, Chief Information Officer
CHR: Susan Falbo, Vice President Human Resources
Web address: www.wheelinghospital.org
**Control:** Other not–for–profit (including NFP Corporation) **Service:** General
Medical and Surgical

**Staffed Beds:** 247 **Admissions:** 10285 **Census:** 132 **Outpatient Visits:**
531267 **Births:** 1205 **Total Expense ($000):** 262132 **Payroll Expense
($000):** 112847 **Personnel:** 2577

### WILLIAMSON—Mingo County

☐ **WILLIAMSON MEMORIAL HOSPITAL (510077)**, 859 Alderson Street,
Zip 25661–3215, Mailing Address: P.O. Box 1980, Zip 25661–1980;
tel. 304/235–2500 **A**1 9 10 **F**3 13 15 18 20 26 28 29 30 34 40 45 49 50 51
57 59 61 65 70 74 75 76 77 79 81 87 91 93 107 108 114 119 130 131 135
146 **P**6 **S** Health Management Associates, Naples, FL
Primary Contact: David Pryor, Chief Executive Officer
CMO: Manuel Angco, M.D., Chief of Staff
CHR: Tina Jackson, Manager Human Resources
Web address: www.williamsonmemorial.net
**Control:** Corporation, Investor–owned, for–profit **Service:** General Medical and
Surgical

**Staffed Beds:** 76 **Admissions:** 2225 **Census:** 18 **Outpatient Visits:** 33187
**Births:** 103 **Total Expense ($000):** 27870 **Payroll Expense ($000):** 9594
**Personnel:** 222

**WV**

*Many Facility Codes have changed. Please refer to the AHA Guide Code Chart.*     © 2013 AHA Guide

# WISCONSIN

## AMERY—Polk County

★ **AMERY REGIONAL MEDICAL CENTER (521308)**, 265 Griffin Street East, Zip 54001–1439; tel. 715/268–8000 **A**9 10 18 **F**11 13 15 28 29 34 36 40 43 53 54 56 64 75 76 77 78 80 81 82 86 87 89 93 98 100 101 102 103 104 105 107 111 119 130 131 144 **P**6 **S** QHR, Brentwood, TN
Primary Contact: Michael Karuschak, Jr., Chief Executive Officer
CFO: Scott D. Edin, Chief Financial Officer
CMO: James Quenan, M.D., Chief Medical Officer
CIO: Bill Lehner, Director Management Information Systems
CHR: Joanne Jackson, Administrator Human Resources, Community Relations and Quality Improvement
Web address: www.amerymedicalcenter.org
**Control:** Other not–for–profit (including NFP Corporation) **Service:** General Medical and Surgical

**Staffed Beds:** 15 **Admissions:** 1162 **Census:** 16 **Outpatient Visits:** 106688 **Births:** 152 **Total Expense ($000):** 51096 **Payroll Expense ($000):** 17669 **Personnel:** 320

## ANTIGO—Langlade County

☐ **LANGLADE HOSPITAL (521350)**, (Formerly Langlade Memorial Hospital), 112 East Fifth Avenue, Zip 54409–2796; tel. 715/623–2331, (Total facility includes 56 beds in nursing home–type unit) **A**1 5 9 10 18 **F**2 3 10 11 13 15 28 29 30 31 34 40 43 44 45 53 54 56 57 59 60 63 64 65 68 69 70 74 75 76 77 78 81 82 84 85 86 87 89 92 93 96 107 108 109 110 111 114 116 118 119 120 121 123 124 125 130 131 132 133 144
Primary Contact: David R. Schneider, Executive Director
CFO: Pat Tincher, Director Finance
CMO: Noel Deep, M.D., Chief Medical Staff
CHR: Janelle Markgraf, Director Human Resources
Web address: www.langladehospital.org
**Control:** Church–operated, Nongovernment, not–for profit **Service:** General Medical and Surgical

**Staffed Beds:** 81 **Admissions:** 1081 **Census:** 66 **Outpatient Visits:** 114939 **Births:** 201 **Total Expense ($000):** 65965 **Payroll Expense ($000):** 29452 **Personnel:** 406

## APPLETON—Outagamie County

☐ **APPLETON MEDICAL CENTER (520160)**, 1818 North Meade Street, Zip 54911–3496; tel. 920/731–4101 **A**1 3 5 9 10 **F**3 4 8 9 11 13 15 17 18 19 20 21 22 23 24 25 26 28 29 30 31 32 34 35 36 37 39 40 43 44 45 46 49 50 51 53 55 56 59 60 64 68 69 70 74 75 76 78 79 80 81 82 84 85 86 87 88 89 93 107 108 110 111 114 116 117 118 119 121 123 124 130 132 135 143 144 146 147 148 **P**1 6 **S** ThedaCare, Inc., Appleton, WI
Primary Contact: Kim Barnas, Senior Vice President
COO: Matthew Furlan, Chief Operating Officer
CFO: Tim Olson, Senior Vice President Finance
CMO: Gregory L. Long, M.D., Chief Medical Officer
CIO: Keith Livingston, Senior Vice President and Chief Information Officer
CHR: Roberta Chapman, Manager Human Resources
Web address: www.thedacare.org
**Control:** Other not–for–profit (including NFP Corporation) **Service:** General Medical and Surgical

**Staffed Beds:** 147 **Admissions:** 8101 **Census:** 85 **Outpatient Visits:** 123596 **Births:** 1218 **Total Expense ($000):** 207260 **Payroll Expense ($000):** 83942 **Personnel:** 1148

⊠ **ST. ELIZABETH HOSPITAL (520009)**, 1506 South Oneida Street, Zip 54915–1305; tel. 920/738–2000 **A**1 2 3 5 9 10 **F**3 4 5 6 9 11 13 15 17 18 20 22 24 26 28 29 30 31 32 35 36 37 40 43 44 45 46 47 48 49 50 56 59 66 68 69 70 72 74 75 76 77 78 79 80 81 82 84 85 86 87 88 89 93 94 97 98 99 100 102 103 104 105 106 107 108 110 111 114 115 117 118 119 120 121 123 124 126 129 130 131 132 135 144 145 146 147 148
Primary Contact: Travis Andersen, President
COO: Travis Andersen, President
CFO: Jeff Badger, Chief Financial Officer
CMO: Lawrence Donatelle, M.D., Vice President Medical Affairs
CIO: Will Weider, Chief Information Officer
CHR: Vince Gallucci, Senior Vice President Human Resources
Web address: www.affinityhealth.org
**Control:** Church–operated, Nongovernment, not–for profit **Service:** General Medical and Surgical

**Staffed Beds:** 206 **Admissions:** 7901 **Census:** 91 **Outpatient Visits:** 151722 **Births:** 1135 **Total Expense ($000):** 150746 **Payroll Expense ($000):** 57726 **Personnel:** 609

## ASHLAND—Ashland County

⊠ **MEMORIAL MEDICAL CENTER – ASHLAND (521359)**, 1615 Maple Lane, Zip 54806–3689; tel. 715/685–5500 **A**1 9 10 18 **F**3 5 13 15 28 30 34 39 40 43 45 48 49 57 59 64 65 68 75 76 79 81 85 86 93 94 96 98 99 100 101 102 104 105 107 108 110 111 115 118 119 130 132 135 144 146 148
Primary Contact: Daniel J. Hymans, President
COO: Daniel H. Adams, Vice President and Chief Operating Officer
CFO: Les Whiteaker, Vice President and Chief Financial Officer
CMO: Donald Patton, Medical Staff President
CIO: Todd Reynolds, Chief Information Officer
CHR: Diane Lulich, Director Human Resources
CNO: Kathryn Tuttle, Clinical Director of Nursing
Web address: www.ashlandmmc.com
**Control:** Other not–for–profit (including NFP Corporation) **Service:** General Medical and Surgical

**Staffed Beds:** 35 **Admissions:** 1724 **Census:** 14 **Outpatient Visits:** 45531 **Births:** 254 **Total Expense ($000):** 49084 **Payroll Expense ($000):** 21551 **Personnel:** 350

## BALDWIN—St. Croix County

★ **BALDWIN AREA MEDICAL CENTER (521347)**, 730 10th Avenue, Zip 54002–9416; tel. 715/684–3311 **A**9 10 18 **F**3 8 11 13 15 17 28 29 31 32 34 36 40 43 45 48 50 53 57 59 64 70 75 76 77 78 79 80 81 83 84 85 86 87 89 90 91 93 97 107 108 110 111 115 119 127 129 130 131 132 133 135 143 144 145 146 148 **P**6
Primary Contact: Alison Page, Chief Executive Officer
CFO: Brian A. Lovdahl, Chief Financial Officer
CMO: Joel Stoeckeler, M.D., Chief of Staff
CIO: Scott Swedien, Director Information Services
CHR: Trudy Acterhof, Director Human Resources
Web address: www.baldwinhospital.com
**Control:** Other not–for–profit (including NFP Corporation) **Service:** General Medical and Surgical

**Staffed Beds:** 25 **Admissions:** 632 **Census:** 5 **Outpatient Visits:** 33428 **Births:** 51 **Total Expense ($000):** 27947 **Payroll Expense ($000):** 12077 **Personnel:** 210

## BARABOO—Sauk County

⊠ **ST. CLARE HOSPITAL (520057)**, (Formerly St. Clare Hospital and Health Services), 707 14th Street, Zip 53913–1597; tel. 608/356–1400 **A**1 3 5 10 **F**5 8 11 12 13 15 28 29 30 31 34 35 36 38 40 45 46 50 56 57 59 60 64 69 70 75 76 77 78 79 81 82 84 85 86 93 97 107 108 115 116 118 119 121 129 130 131 132 135 144 146 **S** SSM Health Care, Saint Louis, MO
Primary Contact: Sandra L. Anderson, President
COO: Laura Jelle, Executive Vice President and Chief Operating Officer
CFO: Troy Walker, Director Finance
CMO: Maureen Murphy, M.D., Director of Medical Affairs
CIO: Alan Steevens, Director Information Management
CHR: Jason Stelzer, Director Human Resources
CNO: Alice Facey, Vice President of Patient Care Services
Web address: www.stclare.com
**Control:** Church–operated, Nongovernment, not–for profit **Service:** General Medical and Surgical

**Staffed Beds:** 60 **Admissions:** 2580 **Census:** 18 **Outpatient Visits:** 83606 **Births:** 279 **Total Expense ($000):** 56514 **Payroll Expense ($000):** 21748 **Personnel:** 304

WI

---

**Hospital, Medicare Provider Number, Address, Telephone, Approval, Facility, and Physician Codes, Health Care System**

★ American Hospital Association (AHA) membership
☐ The Joint Commission accreditation
◇ DNV Healthcare Inc. accreditation
○ Healthcare Facilities Accreditation Program
△ Commission on Accreditation of Rehabilitation Facilities (CARF) accreditation

## BARRON—Barron County

☐ **MAYO CLINIC HEALTH SYSTEM – NORTHLAND IN BARRON (521315)**, 1222 Woodland Avenue, Zip 54812–1798; tel. 715/537–3186, (Total facility includes 20 beds in nursing home–type unit) **A**1 9 10 18 **F**3 7 10 13 15 18 28 29 30 31 32 34 35 36 40 43 44 45 50 56 57 59 64 65 67 68 69 75 76 77 78 79 80 81 84 85 86 87 89 90 93 97 107 110 114 115 127 128 130 131 132 133 135 144 145 146 147 148 **P**6 **S** Mayo Clinic Health System, Rochester, MN
Primary Contact: Maurita Sullivan, Administrator
COO: Karolyn Bartlett, Assistant Administrator
CFO: Kristy Hanson, Chief Financial Officer
CMO: Richard Nagler, M.D., Chief of Staff
CIO: Brian Foster, Vice President
Web address: www.luthermidelfortnorthland.org
**Control:** Other not–for–profit (including NFP Corporation) **Service:** General Medical and Surgical

**Staffed Beds:** 38 **Admissions:** 812 **Census:** 29 **Outpatient Visits:** 147008
**Births:** 103 **Total Expense ($000):** 52716 **Payroll Expense ($000):** 23416
**Personnel:** 398

## BEAVER DAM—Dodge County

☒ **BEAVER DAM COMMUNITY HOSPITALS (520076)**, 707 South University Avenue, Zip 53916–3089; tel. 920/887–7181, (Total facility includes 123 beds in nursing home–type unit) **A**1 9 10 19 **F**3 6 8 10 11 13 15 17 18 26 28 29 31 34 36 37 40 43 44 45 47 53 56 57 59 62 63 64 65 69 70 74 75 76 77 78 79 80 81 82 85 86 87 89 90 94 96 97 107 108 110 111 114 115 118 119 128 129 130 131 132 135 143 144 146 147 148 **P**6
Primary Contact: Kimberly J. Miller, FACHE, Chief Executive Officer
COO: David Corso, Chief Operating Officer
CFO: Donna Hutchinson, Chief Financial Officer
CMO: Richard Tovar, M.D., Chief of Staff
CHR: Bridget Sheridan, Chief Human Resources Officer
CNO: Mike Murphy, Chief Patient Care Officer
Web address: www.bdch.com
**Control:** Other not–for–profit (including NFP Corporation) **Service:** General Medical and Surgical

**Staffed Beds:** 173 **Admissions:** 2437 **Census:** 133 **Outpatient Visits:** 99090
**Births:** 354 **Total Expense ($000):** 79126 **Payroll Expense ($000):** 24441
**Personnel:** 508

## BELOIT—Rock County

☐ **BELOIT HEALTH SYSTEM (520100)**, 1969 West Hart Road, Zip 53511–2299; tel. 608/364–5011 **A**1 9 10 **F**5 6 8 9 10 11 12 13 15 17 18 20 22 24 26 28 29 31 34 35 36 40 43 47 49 50 51 53 54 56 57 58 59 60 62 68 70 74 75 76 77 78 79 80 81 82 85 86 87 89 93 97 99 100 101 102 103 104 108 110 111 114 115 116 117 118 119 129 130 131 132 144 146 147 148 **P**8
Primary Contact: Timothy M. McKevett, President
CFO: William E. Groeper, Vice President Finance
CMO: Leland From, M.D., Vice President Medical Affairs
CHR: Kristinn P. Armann, Vice President Human Resources
Web address: www.beloithealthsystem.org
**Control:** Other not–for–profit (including NFP Corporation) **Service:** General Medical and Surgical

**Staffed Beds:** 103 **Admissions:** 3995 **Census:** 45 **Outpatient Visits:** 350106
**Births:** 632 **Total Expense ($000):** 185707 **Payroll Expense ($000):** 82131
**Personnel:** 1178

## BERLIN—Green Lake County

☐ **BERLIN MEMORIAL HOSPITAL (521355)**, 225 Memorial Drive, Zip 54923–1295; tel. 920/361–1313, (Includes JULIETTE MANOR NURSING HOME, COMMUNITY CLINICS ), (Total facility includes 54 beds in nursing home–type unit) **A**1 9 10 18 **F**10 11 13 15 17 28 29 34 40 43 51 54 56 62 64 69 70 75 76 77 78 80 81 82 86 88 89 93 107 108 111 116 119 125 128 130 131 144 147
Primary Contact: John Feeney, President and Chief Executive Officer
CFO: Thomas P. Krystowiak, Vice President Finance
CIO: Greg Beltran, Director Information Technology
Web address: www.chnwi.org
**Control:** Other not–for–profit (including NFP Corporation) **Service:** General Medical and Surgical

**Staffed Beds:** 75 **Admissions:** 1995 **Census:** 66 **Outpatient Visits:** 63166
**Births:** 188 **Total Expense ($000):** 67209 **Payroll Expense ($000):** 32691
**Personnel:** 316

## BLACK RIVER FALLS—Jackson County

☐ **BLACK RIVER MEMORIAL HOSPITAL (521333)**, 711 West Adams Street, Zip 54615–9113; tel. 715/284–5361 **A**1 9 10 18 **F**3 8 11 13 29 30 40 50 53 56 57 62 63 65 69 75 76 77 79 80 81 85 86 87 89 90 93 107 111 112 115 116 118 119 129 130 131 132 133 135 144 146 148
Primary Contact: Mary Beth White–Jacobs, R.N., President and Chief Executive Officer
CFO: Robert Daley, Vice President Fiscal and Information Technology Services
CMO: Jerome Kitowski, M.D., Chief of Staff
CIO: Robert Daley, Vice President Fiscal and Information Technology Services
CHR: Holly Winn, Vice President Human Resources and Ancillary Services
CNO: Melissa Bergerson, R.N., BSN, Vice President Patient Care Services
Web address: www.brmh.net
**Control:** Other not–for–profit (including NFP Corporation) **Service:** General Medical and Surgical

**Staffed Beds:** 25 **Admissions:** 903 **Census:** 7 **Outpatient Visits:** 19332
**Births:** 155 **Total Expense ($000):** 36649 **Payroll Expense ($000):** 15604
**Personnel:** 267

## BLOOMER—Chippewa County

☐ **MAYO CLINIC HEALTH SYSTEM – CHIPPEWA VALLEY IN BLOOMER (521314)**, 1501 Thompson Street, Zip 54724–1299; tel. 715/568–2000, (Total facility includes 30 beds in nursing home–type unit) **A**1 9 10 18 **F**3 15 18 28 29 30 31 32 34 35 40 43 44 45 50 53 54 56 57 59 64 65 68 75 77 78 80 81 84 85 86 87 90 93 96 97 107 110 114 119 128 130 132 133 135 144 146 147 148 **P**6 **S** Mayo Clinic Health System, Rochester, MN
Primary Contact: Edward A. Wittrock, Vice President Regional System
COO: Jennifer Abernathy, Assistant Administrator
CFO: Michele Eberle, Assistant Administrator
CHR: Sandra Moore, Director Human Resources
Web address: www.bloomermedicalcenter.org
**Control:** Other not–for–profit (including NFP Corporation) **Service:** General Medical and Surgical

**Staffed Beds:** 55 **Admissions:** 514 **Census:** 41 **Outpatient Visits:** 67101
**Births:** 0 **Total Expense ($000):** 34437 **Payroll Expense ($000):** 16294
**Personnel:** 256

## BOSCOBEL—Grant County

**BOSCOBEL AREA HEALTH CARE (521344)**, 205 Parker Street, Zip 53805–1698; tel. 608/375–4112 **A**9 10 18 **F**3 8 11 13 15 28 29 34 38 40 43 45 54 56 57 59 64 70 75 76 77 78 80 81 82 86 87 89 90 91 93 96 97 101 102 107 110 111 114 119 127 129 130 131 132 133 135 144 148 **P**6
Primary Contact: David Hartberg, Administrator
CFO: Rita Moore, Director Finance
CMO: Thomas Pelz, M.D., Chief of Staff
CIO: Mathew Young, Manager Information Systems
CHR: Dennis Carpenter, Director Human Resources
Web address: www.boscobelhealth.com
**Control:** Other not–for–profit (including NFP Corporation) **Service:** General Medical and Surgical

**Staffed Beds:** 25 **Admissions:** 366 **Census:** 4 **Outpatient Visits:** 12399
**Births:** 24 **Total Expense ($000):** 14023 **Payroll Expense ($000):** 5384
**Personnel:** 100

## BROOKFIELD—Waukesha County

☒ **WHEATON FRANCISCAN HEALTHCARE – ELMBROOK MEMORIAL (520170)**, 19333 West North Avenue, Zip 53045–4198; tel. 262/785–2000 **A**1 2 9 **F**3 4 8 11 12 13 15 17 18 20 22 24 28 29 30 31 34 35 36 40 43 44 47 49 50 54 56 58 59 64 68 70 72 74 75 76 77 78 79 80 81 82 84 85 86 87 89 90 91 93 96 97 99 100 107 108 109 110 111 112 114 115 117 118 119 120 121 123 126 130 131 133 135 143 144 145 146 147 148 **S** Wheaton Franciscan Healthcare, Wheaton, IL
Primary Contact: Debra K. Standridge, President
CFO: Michael Petitt, Director of Finance
CMO: Rita Hanson, M.D., Vice President Medical Affairs
CHR: Christopher Morris, Director Human Resources
CNO: Sharon Baughman, Vice President Patient Services and Chief Nursing Officer
Web address: www.wfhealthcare.org
**Control:** Church–operated, Nongovernment, not–for profit **Service:** General Medical and Surgical

**Staffed Beds:** 100 **Admissions:** 5101 **Census:** 54 **Outpatient Visits:** 74585
**Births:** 456 **Total Expense ($000):** 117544 **Payroll Expense ($000):** 33937
**Personnel:** 458

**WI**

*Many Facility Codes have changed. Please refer to the AHA Guide Code Chart.*   © 2013 AHA Guide

## BURLINGTON—Racine County

✠ **AURORA MEMORIAL HOSPITAL OF BURLINGTON (520059)**, 252 McHenry Street, Zip 53105–1828; tel. 262/767–6000 **A**1 2 9 10 **F**3 11 13 15 17 18 20 29 30 31 34 35 36 40 43 44 45 46 47 48 49 50 51 53 56 57 58 59 64 65 68 70 74 75 76 79 80 81 82 84 85 86 87 89 93 94 96 100 107 108 110 111 114 116 118 119 129 130 131 132 135 146 148 **P**6 **S** Aurora Health Care, Milwaukee, WI
Primary Contact: Vicki Lewis, R.N., MS, FACHE, Vice President and Chief Administrative Officer
CFO: Stuart Arnett, Vice President Finance and Chief Financial Officer
CIO: Jean Chase, Regional Manager Information Services
CHR: Gene Krauklis, Regional Vice President Human Resources
Web address: www.aurorahealthcare.org
**Control:** Other not–for–profit (including NFP Corporation) **Service:** General Medical and Surgical

**Staffed Beds:** 65 **Admissions:** 2901 **Census:** 26 **Outpatient Visits:** 67085 **Births:** 269 **Total Expense ($000):** 63768 **Payroll Expense ($000):** 24872 **Personnel:** 446

## CHILTON—Calumet County

☐ **CALUMET MEDICAL CENTER (521317)**, 614 Memorial Drive, Zip 53014–1597; tel. 920/849–2386 **A**1 9 10 18 **F**3 7 15 28 29 34 35 40 43 45 56 57 59 64 65 75 77 78 79 80 81 82 85 86 87 89 92 93 97 102 107 110 114 119 126 127 129 130 131 132 133 144 145 146 147 148 **S** Ascension Health, Saint Louis, MO
Primary Contact: Timothy Richman, President
CFO: Jeff Badger, Chief Financial Officer
CMO: Mark Kehrberg, M.D., Chief Medical Officer
CIO: Will Weider, Chief Information Officer
Web address: www.affinityhealth.org
**Control:** Other not–for–profit (including NFP Corporation) **Service:** General Medical and Surgical

**Staffed Beds:** 15 **Admissions:** 546 **Census:** 6 **Outpatient Visits:** 35008 **Births:** 0 **Total Expense ($000):** 20605 **Payroll Expense ($000):** 8726 **Personnel:** 129

## CHIPPEWA FALLS—Chippewa County

✠ **ST. JOSEPH'S HOSPITAL (520017)**, 2661 County Highway I, Zip 54729–1498; tel. 715/723–1811 **A**1 9 10 **F**3 4 5 13 15 17 28 29 30 34 35 38 39 40 43 45 50 56 57 59 62 63 64 65 68 69 70 71 74 75 76 77 79 80 81 82 84 86 87 88 89 92 93 100 101 102 104 105 106 107 110 111 114 119 129 130 132 135 144 146 147 148 **P**6 **S** Hospital Sisters Health System, Springfield, IL
Primary Contact: Joan Coffman, President and Chief Executive Officer
CFO: Steve Palecek, Divisional Director of Financial Services
CMO: Humayun Khan, M.D., Chief Medical Officer
CIO: Kevin Groskreutz, Chief Information Systems
CHR: Kim Entenmann, Director People Services
Web address: www.stjoeschipfalls.com
**Control:** Other not–for–profit (including NFP Corporation) **Service:** General Medical and Surgical

**Staffed Beds:** 102 **Admissions:** 3279 **Census:** 36 **Outpatient Visits:** 80835 **Births:** 460 **Total Expense ($000):** 62841 **Payroll Expense ($000):** 27134 **Personnel:** 375

## COLUMBUS—Columbia County

✠ **COLUMBUS COMMUNITY HOSPITAL (521338)**, 1515 Park Avenue, Zip 53925–2402; tel. 920/623–2200 **A**1 9 10 18 **F**3 8 13 15 16 17 18 28 29 34 40 45 51 56 57 64 70 75 76 77 78 79 80 81 85 86 88 89 91 93 96 107 110 114 118 119 129 130 132 133 135 144 146 147
Primary Contact: John D. Russell, President and Chief Executive Officer
CFO: Phillip Roberts, Vice President Finance and Chief Financial Officer
CMO: Gary Galvin, M.D., Chief of Staff
CIO: Phillip Roberts, Vice President Finance and Chief Financial Officer
CHR: Ann Roundy, Vice President Employee Services
CNO: Jamie Hendrix, Vice President Patient Care Services
Web address: www.cch–inc.com
**Control:** Other not–for–profit (including NFP Corporation) **Service:** General Medical and Surgical

**Staffed Beds:** 25 **Admissions:** 756 **Census:** 9 **Outpatient Visits:** 31905 **Births:** 59 **Total Expense ($000):** 26999 **Payroll Expense ($000):** 10505 **Personnel:** 143

## CUBA CITY—Grant County

**SOUTHWEST HEALTH CENTER NURSING HOME** See Southwest Health Center, Platteville

## CUDAHY—Milwaukee County

**AURORA ST. LUKE'S SOUTH SHORE** See Aurora St. Luke's Medical Center, Milwaukee

## CUMBERLAND—Barron County

☐ **CUMBERLAND MEMORIAL HOSPITAL (521353)**, 1110 Seventh Avenue, Zip 54829–9138; tel. 715/822–2741, (Total facility includes 50 beds in nursing home–type unit) **A**1 9 10 18 **F**11 13 28 29 34 40 43 53 56 75 76 77 81 82 86 87 89 93 98 102 103 104 107 125 128 130 131 144 **P**8
Primary Contact: Michael Gutsch, Chief Executive Officer
CFO: Angela Martens, Controller
CMO: Kenneth Garrison, M.D., Chief of Staff
CHR: Hilary Butzler, Director Human Resources
Web address: www.cumberlandhealthcare.com
**Control:** Other not–for–profit (including NFP Corporation) **Service:** General Medical and Surgical

**Staffed Beds:** 85 **Admissions:** 1143 **Census:** 52 **Outpatient Visits:** 10057 **Births:** 36 **Total Expense ($000):** 16720 **Payroll Expense ($000):** 7769 **Personnel:** 141

## DARLINGTON—Lafayette County

**MEMORIAL HOSPITAL OF LAFAYETTE COUNTY (521312)**, 800 Clay Street, Zip 53530–1228, Mailing Address: P.O. Box 70, Zip 53530–0070; tel. 608/776–4466 **A**9 10 18 **F**1 3 11 13 15 18 26 28 29 32 35 40 43 45 46 47 48 54 56 57 60 64 68 74 75 76 79 80 81 82 86 89 90 93 102 105 107 111 116 117 119 130 131 133 144
Primary Contact: Sherry Kudronowicz, Administrator
CFO: Marie Wamsley, Chief Financial Officer
Web address: www.memorialhospitaloflafayettecounty.org
**Control:** County–Government, nonfederal **Service:** General Medical and Surgical

**Staffed Beds:** 23 **Admissions:** 400 **Census:** 5 **Outpatient Visits:** 19517 **Births:** 45 **Total Expense ($000):** 12482 **Payroll Expense ($000):** 3555 **Personnel:** 91

## DODGEVILLE—Iowa County

✠ **UPLAND HILLS HEALTH (521352)**, 800 Compassion Way, Zip 53533–1956, Mailing Address: P.O. Box 800, Zip 53533–0800; tel. 608/930–8000, (Total facility includes 44 beds in nursing home–type unit) **A**1 9 10 18 **F**3 8 11 13 15 17 28 29 31 32 34 35 36 40 43 53 54 56 57 59 60 62 63 64 67 70 75 76 77 78 80 81 82 85 86 87 88 89 90 93 97 107 114 119 128 129 130 131 132 133 144 146 147 148 **P**6
Primary Contact: Phyllis Fritsch, Administrator
COO: Steve McCarthy, Assistant Administrator Business Operations
CFO: Karl Pustina, Assistant Administrator Finance
CIO: Karen Thuli, Coordinator Information Systems
CHR: Troy Marx, Director Human Resources
Web address: www.uplandhillshealth.org
**Control:** Other not–for–profit (including NFP Corporation) **Service:** General Medical and Surgical

**Staffed Beds:** 69 **Admissions:** 1128 **Census:** 51 **Outpatient Visits:** 49859 **Births:** 277 **Total Expense ($000):** 36685 **Payroll Expense ($000):** 15759 **Personnel:** 250

## DURAND—Pepin County

★ **CHIPPEWA VALLEY HOSPITAL AND OAKVIEW CARE CENTER (521307)**, 1220 Third Avenue West, Zip 54736–1600, Mailing Address: P.O. Box 224, Zip 54736–0224; tel. 715/672–4211, (Total facility includes 50 beds in nursing home–type unit) **A**9 10 18 **F**3 15 18 19 25 28 29 30 40 45 56 59 65 68 69 75 79 81 86 87 97 107 114 128 129 130 132 133 **S** Adventist Health System Sunbelt Health Care Corporation, Altamonte Springs, FL
Primary Contact: Douglas R. Peterson, President and Chief Executive Officer
Web address: www.chippewavalleyhospital.com/
**Control:** Church–operated, Nongovernment, not–for profit **Service:** General Medical and Surgical

**Staffed Beds:** 75 **Admissions:** 418 **Census:** 53 **Outpatient Visits:** 32908 **Births:** 0 **Total Expense ($000):** 15466 **Payroll Expense ($000):** 6377 **Personnel:** 92

WI

**Hospital, Medicare Provider Number, Address, Telephone, Approval, Facility, and Physician Codes, Health Care System**

★ American Hospital Association (AHA) membership
☐ The Joint Commission accreditation
◇ DNV Healthcare Inc. accreditation
○ Healthcare Facilities Accreditation Program
△ Commission on Accreditation of Rehabilitation Facilities (CARF) accreditation

## EAGLE RIVER—Vilas County

★ **MINISTRY EAGLE RIVER MEMORIAL HOSPITAL (521300)**, (Formerly Eagle River Memorial Hospital), 201 Hospital Road, Zip 54521–8835; tel. 715/479–7411 **A**9 10 18 **F**3 11 15 28 29 30 35 40 44 45 50 59 64 68 75 80 81 82 84 85 86 89 93 96 107 108 110 114 119 130 133 146 148 **S** Ascension Health, Saint Louis, MO
Primary Contact: Sheila Clough, President
COO: Sheila Clough, President
CFO: Cathy Bukowski, Regional Chief Financial Officer
CMO: Richard Brodhead, M.D., President Medical Staff
CIO: Will Weider, Chief Information Officer
CHR: Michelle Cornelius, Director Human Resources for Northern Region
Web address: www.ministryhealth.org
**Control:** Church–operated, Nongovernment, not–for profit **Service:** General Medical and Surgical

**Staffed Beds:** 12 **Admissions:** 428 **Census:** 4 **Outpatient Visits:** 19315 **Births:** 1 **Total Expense ($000):** 15324 **Payroll Expense ($000):** 6683 **Personnel:** 119

## EAU CLAIRE—Eau Claire County

☐ **MAYO CLINIC HEALTH SYSTEM IN EAU CLAIRE (520070)**, 1221 Whipple Street, Zip 54703–5270, Mailing Address: P.O. Box 5, Zip 54702–0005; tel. 715/838–3311 **A**1 2 3 5 9 10 **F**3 4 5 8 12 13 15 17 18 20 22 24 26 28 29 30 31 32 34 35 36 37 40 43 44 45 46 48 49 50 53 54 57 58 59 60 64 65 68 70 71 72 74 75 76 78 79 80 81 82 84 85 86 87 89 90 92 93 96 97 98 99 100 101 102 103 105 107 108 110 111 114 115 118 119 120 121 124 126 129 130 132 135 144 145 146 147 148 **P**6 **S** Mayo Clinic Health System, Rochester, MN
Primary Contact: Randall L. Linton, M.D., President and Chief Executive Officer
COO: John M. Dickey, Chief Administrative Officer
CFO: Paul Bammel, Vice President
CIO: Brian Foster, Chief Information Officer
CHR: Blythe Loyd, Vice President
Web address: www.mhs.mayo.edu
**Control:** Other not–for–profit (including NFP Corporation) **Service:** General Medical and Surgical

**Staffed Beds:** 204 **Admissions:** 11094 **Census:** 126 **Outpatient Visits:** 163107 **Births:** 1066 **Total Expense ($000):** 231593 **Payroll Expense ($000):** 92233 **Personnel:** 1723

☐ **OAKLEAF SURGICAL HOSPITAL (520196)**, 3802 West Oakwood Mall Drive, Zip 54701–3016; tel. 715/831–8130 **A**1 9 10 **F**3 37 45 47 48 51 64 75 79 80 81 82 85 119 130 **S** National Surgical Hospitals, Chicago, IL
Primary Contact: Anne Hargrave–Thomas, Chief Executive Officer
Web address: www.oakleafmedical.com
**Control:** Corporation, Investor–owned, for–profit **Service:** General Medical and Surgical

**Staffed Beds:** 13 **Admissions:** 510 **Census:** 4 **Outpatient Visits:** 8676 **Births:** 0 **Total Expense ($000):** 27041 **Payroll Expense ($000):** 8391 **Personnel:** 123

✉ △ **SACRED HEART HOSPITAL (520013)**, 900 West Clairemont Avenue, Zip 54701–6122; tel. 715/717–4121 **A**1 2 3 5 7 9 10 **F**3 6 8 11 12 13 15 17 18 20 22 24 28 29 30 32 34 35 38 39 40 41 43 44 45 46 47 48 49 50 53 56 57 59 60 64 68 69 70 72 74 75 76 78 79 80 81 82 84 85 86 87 88 89 90 92 93 94 96 97 98 99 100 101 102 103 104 107 108 110 111 112 114 116 117 118 119 120 121 123 124 126 129 130 132 135 141 142 144 145 146 147 148 **P**6 **S** Hospital Sisters Health System, Springfield, IL
Primary Contact: Julie Manas, President and Chief Executive Officer
COO: Faye L. Deich, R.N., Chief Operating Officer
CFO: Steve Palecek, Controller
CMO: Humayun Khan, M.D., Chief Medical Officer
CIO: Kevin Groskreutz, Chief Information Officer
CHR: Craig Brenholt, Division Director Human Resources
CNO: Amy L. Dwyer, R.N., Chief Nursing Officer
Web address: www.sacredhearteauclaire.org
**Control:** Other not–for–profit (including NFP Corporation) **Service:** General Medical and Surgical

**Staffed Beds:** 212 **Admissions:** 10125 **Census:** 129 **Outpatient Visits:** 113448 **Births:** 905 **Total Expense ($000):** 187333 **Payroll Expense ($000):** 70068 **Personnel:** 1143

## EDGERTON—Rock County

★ **EDGERTON HOSPITAL AND HEALTH SERVICES (521319)**, 11101 North Sherman Road, Zip 53534–9002; tel. 608/884–3441 **A**9 10 18 **F**11 15 28 34 40 43 64 75 77 81 86 90 93 107 108 111 119 130 144 **P**6
Primary Contact: James O. Pernau, Chief Executive Officer
CFO: Charles Roader, Vice President Finance
CMO: William West, M.D., Chief of Staff
CIO: Sheryl Rucker, Chief Information Officer
CHR: Brad Olm, Director Human Resources
Web address: www.edgertonhospital.com
**Control:** Other not–for–profit (including NFP Corporation) **Service:** General Medical and Surgical

**Staffed Beds:** 18 **Admissions:** 428 **Census:** 9 **Outpatient Visits:** 19742 **Births:** 0 **Total Expense ($000):** 19408 **Payroll Expense ($000):** 7771 **Personnel:** 123

## ELKHORN—Walworth County

✉ △ **AURORA LAKELAND MEDICAL CENTER (520102)**, W3985 County Road NN, Zip 53121–4389; tel. 262/741–2000 **A**1 2 7 9 10 **F**3 11 13 15 17 18 20 26 29 30 34 35 36 39 40 43 44 45 46 47 48 49 50 51 56 57 58 59 64 65 68 70 74 75 76 78 79 80 81 82 84 85 86 87 89 90 93 94 96 100 107 108 109 110 111 115 116 118 119 130 131 132 134 135 146 148 **P**6 **S** Aurora Health Care, Milwaukee, WI
Primary Contact: Vicki Lewis, R.N., MS, FACHE, President
CFO: Stuart Arnett, Regional Vice President Finance
CMO: Greg Gerber, M.D., Chief Medical Officer
CIO: Jean Chase, Regional Manager Information Services
CHR: Gene Krauklis, Regional Vice President Human Resources
Web address: www.aurorahealthcare.org
**Control:** Other not–for–profit (including NFP Corporation) **Service:** General Medical and Surgical

**Staffed Beds:** 75 **Admissions:** 2967 **Census:** 30 **Outpatient Visits:** 77106 **Births:** 567 **Total Expense ($000):** 66464 **Payroll Expense ($000):** 22153 **Personnel:** 405

## FOND DU LAC—Fond Du Lac County

✉ △ **AGNESIAN HEALTHCARE (520088)**, 430 East Division Street, Zip 54935–4560, Mailing Address: P.O. Box 385, Zip 54936–0385; tel. 920/929–2300 **A**1 2 7 9 10 20 **F**2 3 5 6 11 13 15 18 20 22 24 26 28 29 30 31 34 35 36 38 40 43 44 48 49 50 51 53 54 55 56 59 62 63 64 66 67 68 69 71 74 75 76 77 78 79 80 81 82 83 84 85 86 87 90 93 97 98 99 100 101 102 103 104 105 106 107 108 109 110 111 114 115 117 118 119 120 121 123 124 126 129 130 131 132 134 135 143 144 146 147 148 **P**3 6
Primary Contact: Steven N. Little, President and Chief Executive Officer
COO: James Mugan, Senior Vice President for Clincial Services and Chief Operating Officer
CFO: Bonnie Schmitz, Vice President and Chief Financial Officer
CMO: Derek Colmenares, Chief Medical Officer
CIO: Nancy Birschbach, Assistant Vice President Information Services
CHR: Sue Edminster, Vice President Human Resources
Web address: www.agnesian.com
**Control:** Church–operated, Nongovernment, not–for profit **Service:** General Medical and Surgical

**Staffed Beds:** 174 **Admissions:** 6066 **Census:** 73 **Outpatient Visits:** 695694 **Births:** 843 **Total Expense ($000):** 284455 **Payroll Expense ($000):** 98677 **Personnel:** 1151

**FOND DU LAC COUNTY MENTAL HEALTH CENTER (524025)**, 459 East First Street, Zip 54935–4599; tel. 920/929–3571 **A**10 **F**4 38 98 99 102 103 130 **P**6
Primary Contact: Don Stout, Administrator
Web address: www.fdlco.wi.gov
**Control:** County–Government, nonfederal **Service:** Psychiatric

**Staffed Beds:** 25 **Admissions:** 998 **Census:** 13 **Outpatient Visits:** 573 **Births:** 0 **Total Expense ($000):** 3646 **Payroll Expense ($000):** 2013 **Personnel:** 44

## FORT ATKINSON—Jefferson County

✉ **FORT HEALTHCARE (520071)**, 611 East Sherman Avenue, Zip 53538–1998; tel. 920/568–5000 **A**1 9 10 **F**3 11 12 13 15 28 29 34 35 40 53 56 57 59 62 68 75 76 77 79 80 81 85 86 87 89 90 93 94 96 107 108 110 111 115 118 119 129 130 132 135 144 145 146 147 **P**1 5
Primary Contact: Michael S. Wallace, President and Chief Executive Officer
CFO: James J. Nelson, Senior Vice President Finance and Strategic Planning
CIO: James E. Dahl, Chief Information Officer
CHR: Nancy Alstad, Director Human Resources
CNO: Renee Clark, R.N., Vice President Nursing Services and Performance Improvement
Web address: www.forthealthcare.com
**Control:** Other not–for–profit (including NFP Corporation) **Service:** General Medical and Surgical

**Staffed Beds:** 72 **Admissions:** 3067 **Census:** 20 **Outpatient Visits:** 299204 **Births:** 469 **Total Expense ($000):** 124639 **Payroll Expense ($000):** 41348 **Personnel:** 585

## FRANKLIN—Milwaukee County

✉ **MIDWEST ORTHOPEDIC SPECIALTY HOSPITAL (520205)**, 10101 South 27th Street, 2nd Floor, Zip 53132–7209; tel. 414/817–5800 **A**1 9 10 **F**3 29 30 34 50 57 68 79 81 82 85 86 130 131 **S** Wheaton Franciscan Healthcare, Wheaton, IL
Primary Contact: Daniel Mattes, Chief Executive Officer
Web address: www.mymosh.com/
**Control:** Partnership, Investor–owned, for–profit **Service:** General Medical and Surgical

**Staffed Beds:** 16 **Admissions:** 1433 **Census:** 10 **Outpatient Visits:** 8047 **Births:** 0 **Total Expense ($000):** 37973 **Payroll Expense ($000):** 5966 **Personnel:** 103

*Many Facility Codes have changed. Please refer to the AHA Guide Code Chart.*
© 2013 AHA Guide

⊠ **WHEATON FRANCISCAN HEALTHCARE – FRANKLIN (520204)**, 10101 South 27th Street, Zip 53132–7209; tel. 414/325–4700 **A**1 9 10 **F**3 15 18 29 30 34 35 40 47 49 50 57 64 68 70 74 75 77 79 81 82 84 85 86 87 92 93 107 108 110 111 115 119 130 131 144 145 146 147 148 **S** Wheaton Franciscan Healthcare, Wheaton, IL
Primary Contact: Daniel Mattes, President
Web address: www.mywheaton.org/
**Control:** Church–operated, Nongovernment, not–for profit **Service:** General Medical and Surgical

**Staffed Beds:** 24 **Admissions:** 1718 **Census:** 16 **Outpatient Visits:** 70327
**Births:** 0 **Total Expense ($000):** 49872 **Payroll Expense ($000):** 17272
**Personnel:** 300

### FRIENDSHIP—Adams County

**MOUNDVIEW MEMORIAL HOSPITAL & CLINICS (521309)**, 402 West Lake Street, Zip 53934–9699, Mailing Address: P.O. Box 40, Zip 53934–0040; tel. 608/339–3331 **A**9 10 18 **F**6 11 15 28 29 34 36 40 43 56 64 77 81 82 86 87 93 107 111 118 119 130 144 **P**5 6
Primary Contact: Jeremy Normington–Slay, FACHE, Chief Executive Officer
Web address: www.moundview.org
**Control:** Other not–for–profit (including NFP Corporation) **Service:** General Medical and Surgical

**Staffed Beds:** 25 **Admissions:** 207 **Census:** 3 **Outpatient Visits:** 22958
**Births:** 0 **Total Expense ($000):** 14493 **Payroll Expense ($000):** 6172
**Personnel:** 97

### GRAFTON—Ozaukee County

⊠ **AURORA MEDICAL CENTER GRAFTON (520207)**, 975 Port Washington Road, Zip 53024–9201; tel. 262/329–1000 **A**1 9 10 **F**3 6 8 13 15 17 18 20 22 24 26 28 29 30 31 36 40 43 44 45 46 48 49 50 51 53 54 56 64 65 68 69 70 72 74 75 76 78 79 80 81 82 85 86 87 89 91 93 96 107 108 109 110 111 114 115 116 117 118 119 120 121 123 126 130 131 146 148 **P**6 **S** Aurora Health Care, Milwaukee, WI
Primary Contact: Michael J. Laird, FACHE, President
CMO: William Ebinger, M.D., President and Chief of Staff
Web address: www.aurorahealthcare.org
**Control:** Other not–for–profit (including NFP Corporation) **Service:** General Medical and Surgical

**Staffed Beds:** 96 **Admissions:** 5961 **Census:** 58 **Outpatient Visits:** 70603
**Births:** 648 **Total Expense ($000):** 129303 **Payroll Expense ($000):** 39365
**Personnel:** 736

### GRANTSBURG—Burnett County

★ **BURNETT MEDICAL CENTER (521331)**, 257 West St. George Avenue, Zip 54840–7827; tel. 715/463–5353, (Total facility includes 50 beds in nursing home–type unit) **A**9 10 18 **F**2 3 13 15 28 29 31 35 40 45 56 57 59 64 67 68 75 76 77 78 80 81 85 86 87 89 90 93 97 107 114 127 128 130 131 132 133 135 144 148 **P**6
Primary Contact: Gordon Lewis, Chief Executive Officer
CFO: Charles J. Faught, Chief Financial Officer
CMO: Hans Rechsteiner, M.D., Chief of Staff
CIO: Andy Douglas, Manager Information Technology
CHR: Sandy Hinrichs, Director Human Resources
Web address: www.burnettmedicalcenter.com
**Control:** Other not–for–profit (including NFP Corporation) **Service:** General Medical and Surgical

**Staffed Beds:** 67 **Admissions:** 538 **Census:** 54 **Outpatient Visits:** 33486
**Births:** 43 **Total Expense ($000):** 16081 **Payroll Expense ($000):** 7034
**Personnel:** 131

### GREEN BAY—Brown County

⊠ △ **AURORA BAYCARE MEDICAL CENTER (520193)**, 2845 Greenbrier Road, Zip 54311–6519, Mailing Address: P.O. Box 8900, Zip 54308–8900; tel. 920/288–8000 **A**1 2 7 9 10 **F**3 8 12 13 15 17 18 20 22 24 26 28 29 30 31 34 35 36 40 43 44 45 46 47 48 49 50 53 54 57 58 59 64 65 70 72 74 75 76 78 79 80 81 82 85 86 87 89 90 93 94 96 107 108 109 110 111 114 115 116 117 118 119 120 121 123 124 126 129 130 131 132 135 144 146 147 148 **P**6 **S** Aurora Health Care, Milwaukee, WI
Primary Contact: Daniel T. Meyer, President
COO: Daniel T. Meyer, President
CFO: Sandra Ewald, Vice President Finance
CMO: Brian Johnson, M.D., Chief of Staff
CIO: Chuck Geurts, Manager Management Information Services
CHR: Elizabeth A. Kirby, Director Human Resources
CNO: Heather Schroeder, R.N., Chief Nurse Executive and Vice President of Nursing
Web address: www.aurorabaycare.com
**Control:** Partnership, Investor–owned, for–profit **Service:** General Medical and Surgical

**Staffed Beds:** 167 **Admissions:** 7925 **Census:** 89 **Outpatient Visits:** 195724
**Births:** 1556 **Total Expense ($000):** 214629 **Payroll Expense ($000):** 67543 **Personnel:** 1192

⊠ ◇ **BELLIN MEMORIAL HOSPITAL (520049)**, 744 South Webster Avenue, Zip 54301–3581, Mailing Address: P.O. Box 23400, Zip 54305–3400; tel. 920/433–3500 **A**1 9 10 21 **F**3 12 13 15 17 18 20 22 24 26 28 29 30 31 36 40 41 43 45 46 47 49 51 53 54 57 58 59 62 64 74 75 76 77 78 79 80 81 82 84 85 86 87 89 90 92 94 108 110 111 115 116 118 119 126 129 130 131 135 144 146 148 **P**6 8
Primary Contact: George Kerwin, President
CFO: Jim Dietsche, Chief Financial Officer
CMO: Christopher Watson, M.D., Chief Medical Officer
CIO: Jacquelyn Hunt, Vice President Clinical Support and Information Services
CHR: Ken Peters, Director Human Resources Management
Web address: www.bellin.org
**Control:** Church–operated, Nongovernment, not–for profit **Service:** General Medical and Surgical

**Staffed Beds:** 238 **Admissions:** 8413 **Census:** 85 **Outpatient Visits:** 661338
**Births:** 1267 **Total Expense ($000):** 341941 **Payroll Expense ($000):** 157196 **Personnel:** 2180

☐ ◇ **BELLIN PSYCHIATRIC CENTER (524038)**, 301 East St. Joseph Street, Zip 54305–3725, Mailing Address: P.O. Box 23725, Zip 54305–3725; tel. 920/433–3630 **A**1 9 10 21 **F**4 5 6 29 34 36 38 53 54 56 64 75 86 87 98 99 100 101 102 103 104 105 130 **P**2 6
Primary Contact: Sharla Baenen, President
CFO: Kevin McGurk, Controller
CMO: Anthony Marchlewski, M.D., President Medical and Psychological Staff
CIO: Randy Ronsman, Director Information Services
CHR: Ken Peters, Director Human Resources
Web address: www.bellin.org
**Control:** Church–operated, Nongovernment, not–for profit **Service:** Psychiatric

**Staffed Beds:** 53 **Admissions:** 1882 **Census:** 20 **Outpatient Visits:** 65394
**Births:** 0 **Total Expense ($000):** 18033 **Payroll Expense ($000):** 11636
**Personnel:** 139

**BROWN COUNTY COMMUNITY TREATMENT CENTER (524014)**, 3150 Gershwin Drive, Zip 54311–5899; tel. 920/391–4700 **A**10 **F**98 102 130
Primary Contact: Mary Johnson, Administrator
CFO: Margaret Hoff, Account Manager
CMO: Yogesh Pareek, M.D., Clinical Director
CIO: Linda Turner, Manager Health Information Management
CHR: Debbie Klarkowski, Manager Human Resources
Web address: www.co.brown.wi.us/
**Control:** County–Government, nonfederal **Service:** Psychiatric

**Staffed Beds:** 10 **Admissions:** 1498 **Census:** 16 **Outpatient Visits:** 2888
**Births:** 0 **Total Expense ($000):** 5347 **Payroll Expense ($000):** 2835
**Personnel:** 77

**BROWN COUNTY HUMAN SERVICES MENTAL HEALTH CENTER** See Brown County Community Treatment Center

**WI**

---

✠ **ST. MARY'S HOSPITAL MEDICAL CENTER (520097)**, 1726 Shawano Avenue, Zip 54303–3282; tel. 920/498–4200 **A1** 9 10 **F3** 13 15 17 18 20 22 26 28 29 30 31 34 35 39 40 43 44 45 46 47 48 49 50 51 53 55 57 59 64 65 68 69 70 74 75 76 77 78 79 80 81 82 84 85 86 87 92 93 94 96 102 107 108 110 111 114 115 116 117 118 119 130 132 143 145 146 147 148 **P2 S** Hospital Sisters Health System, Springfield, IL
Primary Contact: Therese B. Pandl, President and Chief Executive Officer
COO: Lawrence J. Connors, Chief Operating Officer
CFO: Greg Simia, Chief Financial Officer
CIO: Tanya Townsend, Chief Information Officer
CHR: Christine Jensema, Chief People Officer
CNO: Paula Hafeman, R.N., Chief Nursing Officer
Web address: www.stmgb.org
**Control:** Church–operated, Nongovernment, not–for profit **Service:** General Medical and Surgical

Staffed Beds: 83 Admissions: 4744 Census: 42 Outpatient Visits: 108029 Births: 659 Total Expense ($000): 109870 Payroll Expense ($000): 35313 Personnel: 389

✠ **ST. VINCENT HOSPITAL (520075)**, 835 South Van Buren Street, Zip 54301–3526, Mailing Address: P.O. Box 13508, Zip 54307–3508; tel. 920/433–0111 **A1** 2 9 10 **F3** 9 11 12 13 15 17 18 19 20 22 24 28 29 30 31 34 35 36 39 40 43 44 45 49 50 51 56 57 58 59 60 62 64 65 68 70 72 74 75 76 77 78 79 80 81 83 84 85 86 88 89 90 91 92 93 94 96 107 108 110 111 114 115 116 117 118 119 120 121 123 124 126 129 130 132 135 143 144 146 147 148 **P2** 6 **S** Hospital Sisters Health System, Springfield, IL
Primary Contact: Therese B. Pandl, President and Chief Executive Officer
COO: Lawrence J. Connors, Chief Operating Officer
CFO: Kelly Gigot, Assistant Administrator and Chief Financial Officer
CIO: Tanya Townsend, Chief Information Officer
CHR: Christine Jensema, Chief People Officer
CNO: Paula Hafeman, R.N., Chief Nursing Officer
Web address: www.stvincenthospital.org
**Control:** Church–operated, Nongovernment, not–for profit **Service:** General Medical and Surgical

Staffed Beds: 255 Admissions: 10083 Census: 131 Outpatient Visits: 135587 Births: 922 Total Expense ($000): 242682 Payroll Expense ($000): 85032 Personnel: 1291

### GREENFIELD—Milwaukee County

✠ **KINDRED HOSPITAL–MILWAUKEE (522004)**, 5017 South 110Th Street, Zip 53228–3131; tel. 414/427–8282 **A1** 9 10 **F1** 3 29 56 65 75 80 85 86 87 90 96 100 130 **S** Kindred Healthcare, Louisville, KY
Primary Contact: Jeff Cellucci, Interim Chief Executive Officer
COO: Christine Ninu, Chief Clinical Officer
CMO: Alok Goyal, M.D., Medical Director
Web address: www.khmilwaukee.com/
**Control:** Corporation, Investor–owned, for–profit **Service:** Long–Term Acute Care hospital

Staffed Beds: 56 Admissions: 391 Census: 30 Outpatient Visits: 0 Births: 0 Total Expense ($000): 16852 Payroll Expense ($000): 6335 Personnel: 130

### HARTFORD—Washington County

✠ **AURORA MEDICAL CENTER OF WASHINGTON COUNTY (520038)**, 1032 East Sumner Street, Zip 53027–1698; tel. 262/673–2300 **A1** 2 9 10 **F2** 3 8 11 15 17 28 29 30 32 34 35 37 39 40 43 44 46 47 48 49 50 53 54 56 57 58 59 60 64 65 68 70 74 75 76 79 80 81 82 84 85 87 89 90 93 97 107 111 118 119 129 130 131 132 133 134 135 143 146 148 **P6 S** Aurora Health Care, Milwaukee, WI
Primary Contact: Michael J. Laird, FACHE, President
CMO: Scott Moretti, M.D., Chief of Staff
CIO: John Sipek, Supervisor Client Services
CNO: Jeff Euclide, R.N., Chief Nursing Officer
Web address: www.aurorahealthcare.org
**Control:** Other not–for–profit (including NFP Corporation) **Service:** General Medical and Surgical

Staffed Beds: 39 Admissions: 1926 Census: 18 Outpatient Visits: 68045 Births: 117 Total Expense ($000): 47480 Payroll Expense ($000): 17338 Personnel: 284

### HAYWARD—Sawyer County

★ **HAYWARD AREA MEMORIAL HOSPITAL AND NURSING HOME (521336)**, 11040 North State Road 77, Zip 54843–6391; tel. 715/934–4321, (Total facility includes 67 beds in nursing home–type unit) **A9** 10 18 **F10** 11 13 15 34 40 43 51 64 75 76 78 81 82 86 93 107 119 128 130
Primary Contact: Timothy M. Gullingsrud, Chief Executive Officer
COO: Brad Zeller, Vice President Operations
CHR: Rose Gates, Director Human Resources
Web address: www.hamhnh.com
**Control:** Other not–for–profit (including NFP Corporation) **Service:** General Medical and Surgical

Staffed Beds: 75 Admissions: 1003 Census: 72 Outpatient Visits: 21986 Births: 150 Total Expense ($000): 30680 Payroll Expense ($000): 12430 Personnel: 168

### HILLSBORO—Vernon County

★ **ST. JOSEPH'S HEALTH SERVICES–GUNDERSEN LUTHERAN (521304)**, (Formerly St. Joseph's Health Services), 400 Water Avenue, Zip 54634–9054, Mailing Address: P.O. Box 527, Zip 54634–0527; tel. 608/489–8000 **A9** 10 18 **F3** 8 11 15 28 29 30 32 33 34 40 43 50 53 54 56 57 59 64 69 75 77 80 81 82 85 86 87 89 90 93 97 107 110 117 127 129 130 131 133 135 144 146 147 148
Primary Contact: Debra Smith, Chief Executive Officer
CFO: Pamela DeWitt, Chief Financial Officer
CMO: William Cooke, M.D., Chief of Staff
CHR: Kristie McCoic, Clinic Operations Officer and Director Human Resources
CNO: Mary Brueggeman, Vice President Clinical Services
Web address: www.stjhealthcare.org
**Control:** Other not–for–profit (including NFP Corporation) **Service:** General Medical and Surgical

Staffed Beds: 15 Admissions: 287 Census: 4 Outpatient Visits: 30558 Births: 0 Total Expense ($000): 16093 Payroll Expense ($000): 6081 Personnel: 122

### HUDSON—St. Croix County

☐ **HUDSON HOSPITAL AND CLINICS (521335)**, (Formerly Hudson Hospital), 405 Stageline Road, Zip 54016–7848; tel. 715/531–6000 **A1** 9 10 18 **F3** 5 13 15 28 29 30 31 34 35 36 37 38 40 43 44 45 46 50 53 56 57 59 64 68 74 75 76 77 78 79 80 81 85 86 87 89 93 94 96 97 107 108 110 111 115 117 119 129 130 132 133 135 146 148 **P2**
Primary Contact: Marian M. Furlong, R.N., Chief Executive Officer
CFO: Sheila R. Proehl, Chief Financial Officer
CMO: Mark Stannard, M.D., Chief of Staff
CIO: Sheila R. Proehl, Chief Financial Officer
CHR: Brenda L. Creighton, Director Human Resources
Web address: www.hudsonhospital.org
**Control:** Other not–for–profit (including NFP Corporation) **Service:** General Medical and Surgical

Staffed Beds: 19 Admissions: 1654 Census: 13 Outpatient Visits: 43232 Births: 646 Total Expense ($000): 48276 Payroll Expense ($000): 17940 Personnel: 245

### JANESVILLE—Rock County

✠ **MERCY HOSPITAL AND TRAUMA CENTER (520066)**, 1000 Mineral Point Avenue, Zip 53548–2982, Mailing Address: P.O. Box 5003, Zip 53547–5003; tel. 608/756–6000, (Nonreporting) **A1** 2 9 10 **S** Mercy Health System, Janesville, WI
Primary Contact: Javon R. Bea, President and Chief Executive Officer
CFO: John Cook, Vice President and Chief Financial Officer
CHR: Kathy Harris, Vice President
Web address: www.mercyhealthsystem.org
**Control:** Other not–for–profit (including NFP Corporation) **Service:** General Medical and Surgical

Staffed Beds: 148

★ **ST. MARY'S JANESVILLE HOSPITAL (520208)**, 3400 East Racine Steeet, Zip 53546–2344; tel. 608/373–8000 **A10 F3** 8 11 13 28 29 30 34 35 38 40 44 45 46 47 49 50 57 59 65 68 70 74 75 76 77 79 80 81 82 84 85 86 87 89 90 93 107 108 111 119 129 130 132 135 146 **S** SSM Health Care, Saint Louis, MO
Primary Contact: Kerry Swanson, President
Web address: www.stmarysjanesville.com
**Control:** Church–operated, Nongovernment, not–for profit **Service:** General Medical and Surgical

Staffed Beds: 50 Admissions: 2809 Census: 25 Outpatient Visits: 20651 Births: 378 Total Expense ($000): 56005 Payroll Expense ($000): 18227 Personnel: 212

### KENOSHA—Kenosha County

✠ **AURORA MEDICAL CENTER (520189)**, 10400 South 75th Street, Zip 53142–7884; tel. 262/948–5600 **A1** 2 9 10 **F3** 8 11 13 15 17 18 20 28 29 30 34 35 36 39 40 43 44 45 46 47 48 49 50 51 54 57 59 64 68 70 74 75 76 79 80 81 82 84 85 86 87 89 93 94 96 100 107 108 110 111 114 115 116 117 118 119 120 121 123 129 130 131 132 135 146 148 **P6 S** Aurora Health Care, Milwaukee, WI
Primary Contact: Christine K. Olson, R.N., MSN, FACHE, President
COO: Christine K. Olson, R.N., Chief Administrative Officer and Chief Nursing Executive
CFO: David Yeager, Vice President Finance
CMO: James Santarelli, M.D., President Medical Staff
CIO: Jean Chase, Regional Manager Information Services
CHR: Gene Krauklis, Regional Vice President Human Resources
CNO: Connie Yuska, R.N., Chief Nursing Officer
Web address: www.aurorahealthcare.org
**Control:** Other not–for–profit (including NFP Corporation) **Service:** General Medical and Surgical

Staffed Beds: 73 Admissions: 4753 Census: 46 Outpatient Visits: 145277 Births: 860 Total Expense ($000): 104722 Payroll Expense ($000): 33009 Personnel: 613

WI

☐ **UNITED HEALTH SYSTEM–KENOSHA CAMPUS (520021)**, 6308 Eighth Avenue, Zip 53143–5082; tel. 262/656–2011, (Includes UNITED HOSPITAL SYSTEM ST. CATHERINES MEDICAL CENTER CAMPUS, 9555 76th Street, Pleasant Prarie) **A**1 2 9 10 **F**1 11 12 13 15 17 20 22 24 28 29 34 40 43 51 53 60 64 70 72 75 76 77 78 80 81 86 87 89 90 93 100 102 107 108 111 118 119 130 131 144 147 **P**6
Primary Contact: Richard O. Schmidt, Jr., President and Chief Executive Officer
Web address: www.unitedhospitalsystem.org/
**Control:** Other not–for–profit (including NFP Corporation) **Service:** General Medical and Surgical

**Staffed Beds: 247 Admissions: 9410 Census: 108 Outpatient Visits: 390618 Births: 1007 Total Expense ($000): 260008 Payroll Expense ($000): 114330 Personnel: 1735**

### LA CROSSE—La Crosse County

☒ △ **GUNDERSEN LUTHERAN MEDICAL CENTER (520087)**, 1900 South Avenue, Zip 54601–5467; tel. 608/782–7300 **A**1 2 3 5 7 8 9 10 **F**3 4 5 9 11 18 19 20 22 24 28 29 30 31 32 35 36 38 40 43 45 46 47 48 49 50 51 56 60 61 63 68 72 74 76 78 79 80 81 82 83 85 86 87 88 89 90 91 92 93 94 96 97 98 99 100 101 102 103 104 105 110 114 115 117 120 121 123 124 126 129 130 134 144 145 146 147 148
Primary Contact: Jeffrey E. Thompson, M.D., Chief Executive Officer
COO: Kathy Klock, R.N., Senior Vice President Clinical Operations and Human Resources
CFO: Gordon Edwards, Chief Financial Officer
CMO: Julio J. Bird, M.D., Chief Medical Officer
CIO: Deb Rislow, Chief Information Officer
CHR: Kathy Klock, R.N., Senior Vice President Clinical Operations and Human Resources
Web address: www.gundluth.org
**Control:** Other not–for–profit (including NFP Corporation) **Service:** General Medical and Surgical

**Staffed Beds: 254 Admissions: 13455 Census: 155 Outpatient Visits: 308823 Births: 1335 Total Expense ($000): 311535 Payroll Expense ($000): 96960 Personnel: 1405**

☐ **MAYO CLINIC HEALTH SYSTEM – FRANCISCAN HEALTHCARE IN LA CROSSE (520004)**, 700 West Avenue South, Zip 54601–4783; tel. 608/785–0940 **A**1 2 3 5 9 10 **F**1 3 4 5 6 8 9 11 13 15 16 17 18 19 20 21 22 23 25 26 27 28 29 30 31 32 34 35 36 40 42 43 50 52 53 54 55 56 57 58 59 61 64 65 66 68 69 70 71 72 74 75 76 77 78 79 80 81 82 84 86 87 88 89 90 93 94 97 98 99 100 101 102 103 104 105 107 108 110 111 114 115 117 118 119 120 121 123 124 127 129 130 131 132 134 135 143 144 145 146 147 148 **S** Mayo Clinic Health System, Rochester, MN
Primary Contact: Timothy J. Johnson, President and Chief Executive Officer
COO: Ronald R. Paczkowski, Executive Vice President
CFO: Tom Tiggelaar, Vice President Finance
CMO: P. Stephen Shultz, M.D., Vice President Medical Affairs
CIO: Daniel Schaefer, Vice President Information Services
Web address: www.franciscanskemp.org
**Control:** Church–operated, Nongovernment, not–for profit **Service:** General Medical and Surgical

**Staffed Beds: 155 Admissions: 8078 Census: 81 Outpatient Visits: 86647 Births: 976 Total Expense ($000): 189641 Payroll Expense ($000): 76318 Personnel: 1503**

### LADYSMITH—Rusk County

★ **RUSK COUNTY MEMORIAL HOSPITAL AND NURSING HOME (521328)**, 900 College Avenue West, Zip 54848–2116; tel. 715/532–5561, (Total facility includes 50 beds in nursing home–type unit) **A**9 10 18 **F**3 13 15 28 29 30 40 43 45 47 53 56 57 59 64 68 70 76 77 81 85 89 90 93 107 110 111 115 117 128 130 133 144 146
Primary Contact: Charisse S. Oland, FACHE, Chief Executive Officer
CFO: Judith Strop, Director Finance
CMO: John Ziemer, M.D., Chief of Staff
CHR: Rita Telitz, Director Human Resources
Web address: www.ruskhospital.org
**Control:** County–Government, nonfederal **Service:** General Medical and Surgical

**Staffed Beds: 75 Admissions: 542 Census: 50 Outpatient Visits: 31706 Births: 47 Total Expense ($000): 16960 Payroll Expense ($000): 6477 Personnel: 105**

### LAKE GENEVA—Walworth County

**MERCY WALWORTH HOSPITAL AND MEDICAL CENTER (521357)**, N2950 State Road 67, Zip 53147–2655; tel. 262/245–0535 **A**9 10 18 **F**3 5 9 11 13 15 18 26 29 30 31 34 35 40 44 45 50 54 55 57 59 64 65 70 74 75 76 77 78 79 81 82 85 86 92 93 94 96 97 100 101 103 104 107 108 110 111 114 118 119 130 131 132 135 144 146 148 **P**6 **S** Mercy Health System, Janesville, WI
Primary Contact: Jennifer Hallatt, Chief Operating Officer
Web address: www.mercyhealthsystem.org
**Control:** Other not–for–profit (including NFP Corporation) **Service:** General Medical and Surgical

**Staffed Beds: 15 Admissions: 870 Census: 7 Outpatient Visits: 121921 Births: 110 Total Expense ($000): 57511 Payroll Expense ($000): 12102 Personnel: 265**

### LANCASTER—Grant County

☒ **GRANT REGIONAL HEALTH CENTER (521322)**, 507 South Monroe Street, Zip 53813–2054; tel. 608/723–2143 **A**1 9 10 18 **F**3 8 11 13 15 28 29 34 35 36 40 43 53 56 57 59 64 68 69 75 76 77 78 80 81 82 84 85 86 87 89 90 93 107 110 114 119 129 130 131 132 133 135 144 146 148 **P**6 **S** HealthTech Management Services, Franklin, TN
Primary Contact: Nicole Clapp, R.N., MSN, FACHE, President and Chief Executive Officer
CFO: Barbara Tabor, Chief Financial Officer
CMO: Eric Slane, M.D., Chief of Staff
CMO: Robert Smith, M.D., Chief of Staff
CIO: Kevin Ruchti, Coordinator Information Systems
CHR: Stacy L. Martin, Director Human Resources
CNO: Jennifer Rutkowski, R.N., Vice President Professional Services
Web address: www.grantregional.com
**Control:** Other not–for–profit (including NFP Corporation) **Service:** General Medical and Surgical

**Staffed Beds: 8 Admissions: 632 Census: 5 Outpatient Visits: 24519 Births: 162 Total Expense ($000): 18055 Payroll Expense ($000): 8030 Personnel: 125**

### MADISON—Dane County

☐ **MENDOTA MENTAL HEALTH INSTITUTE (524008)**, 301 Troy Drive, Zip 53704–1599; tel. 608/301–1000 **A**1 3 5 9 10 **F**6 29 30 38 39 56 68 75 82 86 87 98 99 100 101 103 104 105 130 **P**6
Primary Contact: Greg Van Rybroek, Chief Executive Officer
CFO: Stacie Schiereck, Manager Business Office
CMO: Kenneth Casimir, M.D., Medical Director
Web address: www.dhfs.state.wi.us
**Control:** State–Government, nonfederal **Service:** Psychiatric

**Staffed Beds: 234 Admissions: 709 Census: 222 Outpatient Visits: 18613 Births: 0 Total Expense ($000): 63939 Payroll Expense ($000): 35879 Personnel: 674**

☒ △ **MERITER HOSPITAL (520089)**, 202 South Park Street, Zip 53715–1507; tel. 608/417–6000 **A**1 3 5 7 9 10 **F**3 4 5 9 11 12 13 15 17 18 20 22 24 26 28 29 30 31 32 34 35 36 37 39 40 41 43 45 46 48 49 50 53 56 57 58 59 64 65 66 68 70 71 72 74 75 76 78 79 80 81 84 85 86 87 89 90 92 93 97 98 99 100 101 102 103 104 105 106 107 108 111 115 117 118 119 126 130 132 135 145 146 147 148 **P**6
Primary Contact: James L. Woodward, President and Chief Executive Officer
CFO: Linda Hoff, Executive Vice President and Chief Financial Officer
CMO: Geoff Priest, M.D., Chief Medical Officer
CIO: Kerra Guffey, Chief Information Officer
CHR: Tamara L. Saunaitis, Chief Human Resources Officer
CNO: Pat Grunwald, MSN, Chief Nursing Officer
Web address: www.meriter.com
**Control:** Other not–for–profit (including NFP Corporation) **Service:** General Medical and Surgical

**Staffed Beds: 315 Admissions: 17181 Census: 190 Outpatient Visits: 181926 Births: 3772 Total Expense ($000): 413356 Payroll Expense ($000): 184544 Personnel: 2324**

☒ **SELECT SPECIALTY HOSPITAL–MADISON (522008)**, 801 Braxton Place, 2nd Floor, Zip 53715–1415; tel. 608/260–2700 **A**1 10 **F**1 3 12 18 22 29 60 74 75 77 80 86 90 107 148 **P**8 **S** Select Medical Corporation, Mechanicsburg, PA
Primary Contact: Raymond F. Carnevale, Chief Executive Officer
Web address: www.selectspecialtyhospitals.com/company/locations/madison.aspx
**Control:** Corporation, Investor–owned, for–profit **Service:** Long–Term Acute Care hospital

**Staffed Beds: 58 Admissions: 483 Census: 44 Outpatient Visits: 0 Births: 0 Total Expense ($000): 26894 Payroll Expense ($000): 10174 Personnel: 170**

**WI**

---

**Hospital, Medicare Provider Number, Address, Telephone, Approval, Facility, and Physician Codes, Health Care System**

★ American Hospital Association (AHA) membership
☐ The Joint Commission accreditation
◇ DNV Healthcare Inc. accreditation
◯ Healthcare Facilities Accreditation Program
△ Commission on Accreditation of Rehabilitation Facilities (CARF) accreditation

☒ **ST. MARY'S HOSPITAL (520083)**, 700 South Park Street, Zip 53715–1830; tel. 608/251–6100 **A**1 3 5 10 **F**7 11 12 13 17 20 22 24 28 29 34 38 40 43 60 70 72 75 76 78 80 81 82 86 87 88 89 93 98 100 101 103 107 108 119 130 144 **S** SSM Health Care, Saint Louis, MO
Primary Contact: Frank D. Byrne, M.D., President
COO: Kristin McManmon, Chief Operating Officer
CFO: Charlie Johnson, Vice President Finance and Chief Financial Officer
CMO: John Butler, M.D., Vice President Medical Affairs
CIO: Major Dave Lundal, Vice President and Regional Chief Information Officer
CHR: Craig Brenholt, Director Human Resources
Web address: www.stmarysmadison.com
**Control:** Other not–for–profit (including NFP Corporation) **Service:** General Medical and Surgical

> **Staffed Beds:** 361 **Admissions:** 20688 **Census:** 234 **Outpatient Visits:** 133449 **Births:** 3363 **Total Expense ($000):** 378673 **Payroll Expense ($000):** 141001 **Personnel:** 1920

☒ △ **UNIVERSITY OF WISCONSIN HOSPITAL AND CLINICS (520098)**, 600 Highland Avenue, Zip 53792–0002; tel. 608/263–6400, (Includes UNIVERSITY OF WISCONSIN CHILDREN'S HOSPITAL ; AMERICAN FAMILY CHILDREN'S HOSPITAL, 1675 Highland Avenue, Zip 53705; tel. 608/890–5437) **A**1 3 5 7 8 9 10 13 **F**3 5 6 8 9 12 15 16 17 18 19 20 21 22 23 24 25 26 27 28 29 30 31 32 34 35 36 37 39 40 43 44 45 46 47 48 49 50 51 52 54 55 56 57 58 59 60 61 62 64 68 70 71 74 75 77 78 79 80 81 82 83 84 85 86 87 88 89 90 92 93 94 96 97 98 100 102 103 104 107 108 109 110 111 112 114 115 116 117 118 119 120 121 123 124 126 129 130 132 134 135 136 137 138 139 140 141 142 143 145 146 147 148 **P**3
Primary Contact: Donna Katen–Bahensky, President and Chief Executive Officer
COO: Ron Sliwinski, Chief Operations Officer
CFO: Michael D. Buhl, Senior Vice President and Chief Financial Officer
CMO: Carl J. Getto, M.D., Senior Vice President Medical Affairs and Associate Dean Hospital Affairs
CIO: Michael Sauk, Chief Information Officer
CHR: Janice K. Bultema, MSN, Senior Vice President Human Resources
Web address: www.uwhospital.org
**Control:** Other not–for–profit (including NFP Corporation) **Service:** General Medical and Surgical

> **Staffed Beds:** 530 **Admissions:** 27325 **Census:** 380 **Outpatient Visits:** 950718 **Births:** 0 **Total Expense ($000):** 1118387 **Payroll Expense ($000):** 404138 **Personnel:** 6750

☒ △ **WILLIAM S. MIDDLETON MEMORIAL VETERANS HOSPITAL**, 2500 Overlook Terrace, Zip 53705–2286; tel. 608/256–1901, (Nonreporting) **A**1 3 5 7 **S** Department of Veterans Affairs, Washington, DC
Primary Contact: Judy McKee, FACHE, Director
COO: Allen R. Ackers, Associate Director
CFO: Abraham Rabinowitz, Assistant Finance Officer
CMO: Alan J. Bridges, M.D., Chief of Staff
CIO: Randall Margenau, Chief Information Officer
CHR: Stuart Souders, Coordinator Human Resources
Web address: www.madison.va.gov
**Control:** Veterans Affairs, Government, federal **Service:** General Medical and Surgical

> **Staffed Beds:** 87

### MANITOWOC—Manitowoc County

☒ **HOLY FAMILY MEMORIAL (520107)**, (Formerly Holy Family Memorial Medical Center), 2300 Western Avenue, Zip 54220–3712, Mailing Address: P.O. Box 1450, Zip 54221–1450; tel. 920/320–2011 **A**1 2 9 10 **F**3 4 5 8 11 13 15 17 20 22 28 29 30 31 34 36 40 43 45 46 47 48 49 50 51 53 54 56 57 58 59 62 63 64 65 68 70 71 74 75 76 77 78 79 80 81 82 84 85 86 89 93 97 99 100 101 102 103 104 107 108 110 111 115 116 118 119 121 129 130 131 132 135 144 146 147 148 **P**6 8 **S** Franciscan Sisters of Christian Charity Sponsored Ministries, Inc., Manitowoc, WI
Primary Contact: Mark P. Herzog, President and Chief Executive Officer
CFO: Patricia Huettl, Vice President Finance and Chief Financial Officer
CMO: Steve Driggers, M.D., Chief Medical Officer
CIO: Theron Pappas, Director Management Information Systems
CHR: Laura M. Fielding, Administrative Director Organizational Development
CNO: Marcia Donlon, Chief Nursing Officer
Web address: www.hfmhealth.org
**Control:** Church–operated, Nongovernment, not–for profit **Service:** General Medical and Surgical

> **Staffed Beds:** 62 **Admissions:** 2770 **Census:** 25 **Outpatient Visits:** 293652 **Births:** 225 **Total Expense ($000):** 127340 **Payroll Expense ($000):** 64064 **Personnel:** 741

### MARINETTE—Marinette County

☒ **BAY AREA MEDICAL CENTER (520113)**, 3100 Shore Drive, Zip 54143–4242; tel. 715/735–6621 **A**1 9 10 20 **F**3 7 11 13 15 17 18 20 22 28 29 30 31 34 40 43 45 48 50 55 57 59 60 64 68 70 74 75 76 77 78 79 80 81 85 86 87 89 93 107 108 110 111 114 119 129 130 131 146 147 148
Primary Contact: Edward A. Harding, FACHE, President and Chief Executive Officer
COO: Bernie VanCourt, Chief Operating Officer
CFO: Dan Carlson, Chief Financial Officer
CMO: Richard Stein, M.D., Chief Medical Officer
CIO: Pete Eisenzoph, Director Information Technology
CHR: Ken Joyner, Vice President of Employee Services
CNO: Rooney Freimund, R.N., Chief Nurse Executive
Web address: www.bamc.org
**Control:** Other not–for–profit (including NFP Corporation) **Service:** General Medical and Surgical

> **Staffed Beds:** 44 **Admissions:** 3966 **Census:** 41 **Outpatient Visits:** 64819 **Births:** 342 **Total Expense ($000):** 111511 **Payroll Expense ($000):** 47446 **Personnel:** 591

### MARSHFIELD—Wood County

☒ △ **MINISTRY SAINT JOSEPH'S HOSPITAL (520037)**, (Formerly Saint Joseph's Hospital), 611 St. Joseph Avenue, Zip 54449–1898; tel. 715/387–1713, (Includes SAINT JOSEPH'S CHILDEN'S HOSPITAL, 611 Saint Joseph Avenue, Zip 54449–1832; tel. 715/387–1713) **A**1 2 3 5 7 9 10 20 **F**3 4 5 6 7 9 11 12 13 16 17 18 19 20 22 24 26 27 28 29 30 31 34 35 36 38 39 40 43 44 49 50 56 57 59 61 64 68 69 70 72 74 75 76 77 78 79 80 81 82 83 84 85 86 87 88 89 90 93 96 98 100 101 102 103 108 111 112 116 117 118 119 120 121 123 124 126 130 132 135 136 144 146 147 148 **P**6 **S** Ascension Health, Saint Louis, MO
Primary Contact: Brian Kief, President and Chief Executive Officer
CFO: John Skaden, Chief Financial Officer
CMO: Peter Stamas, M.D., Vice President Medical Affairs
CIO: Will Weider, Chief Information Officer
CHR: Layton Anderson, Regional Director Human Resources
Web address: www.stjosephs–marshfield.org
**Control:** Church–operated, Nongovernment, not–for profit **Service:** General Medical and Surgical

> **Staffed Beds:** 319 **Admissions:** 17582 **Census:** 245 **Outpatient Visits:** 54629 **Births:** 938 **Total Expense ($000):** 312910 **Payroll Expense ($000):** 100193 **Personnel:** 1562

**NORWOOD HEALTH CENTER (524019)**, 1600 North Chestnut Avenue, Zip 54449–1499; tel. 715/384–2188, (Total facility includes 24 beds in nursing home–type unit) **A**9 10 **F**3 4 30 34 98 99 100 101 102 103 128 130 143 146 148 **P**6
Primary Contact: Rhonda Kozik, Administrator
CFO: Jo Timmerman, Manager Accounting
CHR: Larry Shear, Administrative Assistant
Web address: www.co.wood.wi.us/norwood/index.htm
**Control:** County–Government, nonfederal **Service:** Psychiatric

> **Staffed Beds:** 40 **Admissions:** 715 **Census:** 32 **Outpatient Visits:** 0 **Births:** 0 **Total Expense ($000):** 3702 **Payroll Expense ($000):** 1555 **Personnel:** 40

### MAUSTON—Juneau County

☐ **MILE BLUFF MEDICAL CENTER (520109)**, 1050 Division Street, Zip 53948–1997; tel. 608/847–6161, (Total facility includes 132 beds in nursing home–type unit) **A**1 9 10 20 **F**3 10 11 13 15 28 29 30 31 34 35 36 40 43 44 45 46 50 52 56 57 59 60 62 64 65 68 69 71 75 76 77 78 79 80 81 82 85 86 87 92 93 94 96 97 99 100 101 103 104 107 108 111 112 114 117 118 119 125 127 128 129 130 131 132 135 143 144 145 146 148
Primary Contact: James M. O'Keefe, President and Chief Executive Officer
Web address: www.milebluff.com
**Control:** Other not–for–profit (including NFP Corporation) **Service:** General Medical and Surgical

> **Staffed Beds:** 157 **Admissions:** 1539 **Census:** 137 **Outpatient Visits:** 123887 **Births:** 213 **Total Expense ($000):** 52083 **Payroll Expense ($000):** 26514 **Personnel:** 357

**WI**

*Many Facility Codes have changed. Please refer to the AHA Guide Code Chart.*  © 2013 AHA Guide

## MEDFORD—Taylor County

☒ **MEMORIAL HEALTH CENTER (521324)**, 135 South Gibson Street, Zip 54451–1696; tel. 715/748–8100, (Includes MEMORIAL NURSING HOME ), (Total facility includes 109 beds in nursing home–type unit) **A**1 9 10 18 **F**1 3 10 11 13 15 28 29 31 34 35 36 43 45 50 53 57 59 60 64 68 75 76 77 78 81 82 86 87 89 90 93 97 107 109 110 111 112 115 116 117 118 119 125 127 128 129 130 131 132 133 144 146 147 **S** Aspirus, Inc., Wausau, WI
Primary Contact: Gregory A. Olson, President and Chief Executive Officer
COO: Kaaron Keene, Vice President Patient Care Services
CFO: Lori Peck, Vice President Finance
CMO: Alecia Hylton, M.D., Chief of Staff
CIO: Helen Volger, Director of Information Services
CHR: Angela Hupf, Vice President Human Resources and Community Relations
CNO: Kaaron Keene, Vice President Patient Care Services
Web address: www.memhc.com
**Control:** Other not–for–profit (including NFP Corporation) **Service:** General Medical and Surgical

**Staffed Beds:** 124 **Admissions:** 813 **Census:** 99 **Outpatient Visits:** 67649 **Births:** 207 **Total Expense ($000):** 45814 **Payroll Expense ($000):** 22173 **Personnel:** 362

## MENOMONEE FALLS—Waukesha County

☒ △ **COMMUNITY MEMORIAL HOSPITAL (520103)**, W180 N8085 Town Hall Road, Zip 53051–3518, Mailing Address: P.O. Box 408, Zip 53052–0408; tel. 262/251–1000 **A**1 2 3 5 7 9 10 **F**3 4 5 11 12 13 15 17 18 20 22 24 26 28 29 30 31 34 35 36 38 39 40 43 44 45 46 47 48 49 50 51 55 56 57 58 59 60 64 65 66 70 72 75 76 77 78 79 80 81 82 83 84 85 86 87 88 89 90 92 93 94 96 98 100 101 102 103 104 105 106 107 108 110 111 115 116 117 118 119 120 121 123 126 129 130 131 132 135 145 146 147 148 **P**5 6
Primary Contact: Dennis Pollard, President
CFO: Thomas Knoll, Site Director Finance
CMO: David Goldberg, M.D., Vice President Medical Affairs
CIO: Robert DeGrand, Chief Information Officer
CHR: Allen Keith, Senior Vice President and Chief Human Resources Officer
CNO: Teri Lux, R.N., Vice President Patient Care Services and Chief Nursing Officer
Web address: www.communitymemorial.com
**Control:** Other not–for–profit (including NFP Corporation) **Service:** General Medical and Surgical

**Staffed Beds:** 194 **Admissions:** 8835 **Census:** 111 **Outpatient Visits:** 96213 **Births:** 933 **Total Expense ($000):** 157556 **Payroll Expense ($000):** 59418 **Personnel:** 954

## MENOMONIE—Dunn County

☐ **MAYO CLINIC HEALTH SYSTEM – RED CEDAR IN MENOMONIE (521340)**, 2321 Stout Road, Zip 54751–2397; tel. 715/235–5531 **A**1 5 9 10 18 **F**6 11 13 15 17 28 34 36 40 43 52 54 55 56 64 70 75 76 77 80 81 82 86 87 89 90 93 99 100 101 102 103 104 107 108 111 119 125 130 131 144 147 **S** Mayo Clinic Health System, Rochester, MN
Primary Contact: Steven Lindberg, Chief Administrative Officer
CFO: Jeanie Lubinsky, Chief Financial Officer
CMO: Mark Deyo Svendsen, M.D., Medical Director
CIO: Frank Wrogg, Director Information Technology
CHR: Leann Wurtzel, Director Human Resources
Web address: www.rcmc–mhs.org
**Control:** Other not–for–profit (including NFP Corporation) **Service:** General Medical and Surgical

**Staffed Beds:** 25 **Admissions:** 1641 **Census:** 16 **Outpatient Visits:** 37611 **Births:** 315 **Total Expense ($000):** 79662 **Payroll Expense ($000):** 39600 **Personnel:** 643

**RED CEDAR MEDICAL CENTER–MAYO HEALTH SYSTEM** See Mayo Clinic Health System – Red Cedar in Menomonie

## MEQUON—Ozaukee County

**COLUMBIA CENTER (520195)**, 13125 North Port Washington Road, Zip 53097–2416; tel. 262/243–7408 **A**9 10 **F**3 8 13 34 35 64 71 76 81 85 86 87 104 133
Primary Contact: Candy J. Casey, R.N., MS, President and Chief Executive Officer
CMO: Robert Stumpf, M.D., President Medical Staff
Web address: www.columbiacenter.org
**Control:** Other not–for–profit (including NFP Corporation) **Service:** General Medical and Surgical

**Staffed Beds:** 6 **Admissions:** 574 **Census:** 4 **Outpatient Visits:** 245 **Births:** 569 **Total Expense ($000):** 7362 **Payroll Expense ($000):** 3136 **Personnel:** 54

☒ **COLUMBIA ST. MARY'S OZAUKEE HOSPITAL (520027)**, 13111 North Port Washington Road, Zip 53097–2416; tel. 262/243–7300 **A**1 2 9 10 **F**4 5 9 15 17 20 22 24 28 29 34 36 38 40 43 51 53 54 56 64 70 75 77 78 80 81 86 89 90 93 98 100 102 103 107 108 111 116 118 119 130 144 147 **P**6
**S** Ascension Health, Saint Louis, MO
Primary Contact: Mark R. Taylor, FACHE, President and Chief Executive Officer
CFO: Rhonda Anderson, Executive Vice President Finance and Chief Financial Officer
CMO: David Shapiro, M.D., Vice President Medical Affairs and Chief Medical Officer
CIO: Mary Paul, Chief Information Officer
CHR: Cheryl Hill, Vice President Human Resources
Web address: www.columbia–stmarys.org
**Control:** Church–operated, Nongovernment, not–for profit **Service:** General Medical and Surgical

**Staffed Beds:** 102 **Admissions:** 5000 **Census:** 57 **Outpatient Visits:** 117238 **Births:** 0 **Total Expense ($000):** 157394 **Payroll Expense ($000):** 5306/ **Personnel:** 579

## MERRILL—Lincoln County

**GOOD SAMARITAN HEALTH CENTER OF MERRILL** See Ministry Good Samaritan Health Center

☒ **MINISTRY GOOD SAMARITAN HEALTH CENTER (521339)**, 601 South Center Avenue, Zip 54452–3404; tel. 715/536–5511 **A**1 9 10 18 **F**3 15 28 29 30 31 34 40 43 45 50 56 60 64 75 78 79 80 81 82 85 86 87 89 93 107 108 111 114 118 119 130 132 133 144 146 147 **S** Ascension Health, Saint Louis, MO
Primary Contact: Mary T. Krueger, President
CFO: David Jirovec, Director Finance
CHR: Nancy Kwiesielewicz, Human Resources Manager
CNO: Kristine McGarigle, R.N., Vice President Patient Care
Web address: www.ministryhealth.org
**Control:** Church–operated, Nongovernment, not–for profit **Service:** General Medical and Surgical

**Staffed Beds:** 16 **Admissions:** 554 **Census:** 5 **Outpatient Visits:** 28976 **Births:** 0 **Total Expense ($000):** 24563 **Payroll Expense ($000):** 11872 **Personnel:** 126

## MILWAUKEE—Milwaukee County

★ △ **AURORA SINAI MEDICAL CENTER (520064)**, 945 North 12th Street, Zip 53233–1337, Mailing Address: P.O. Box 342, Zip 53201–0342; tel. 414/219–2000 **A**2 3 5 7 8 9 **F**1 3 5 6 8 11 12 13 15 17 18 20 22 24 28 29 30 31 34 35 36 38 40 42 43 44 49 50 51 54 55 56 57 59 64 65 68 70 72 75 76 77 78 79 80 81 82 84 85 86 87 89 90 93 96 100 102 103 104 107 108 110 111 114 116 117 118 119 123 129 130 131 132 135 143 144 146 147 148 **P**6 **S** Aurora Health Care, Milwaukee, WI
Primary Contact: George Hinton, Administrator
CFO: Kevin Jones, Director Finance
Web address: www.aurorahealthcare.org
**Control:** Other not–for–profit (including NFP Corporation) **Service:** General Medical and Surgical

**Staffed Beds:** 177 **Admissions:** 8306 **Census:** 101 **Outpatient Visits:** 241432 **Births:** 2295 **Total Expense ($000):** 206961 **Payroll Expense ($000):** 62358 **Personnel:** 979

☒ △ **AURORA ST. LUKE'S MEDICAL CENTER (520138)**, 2900 West Oklahoma Avenue, Zip 53215–4330, Mailing Address: P.O. Box 2901, Zip 53201–2901; tel. 414/649–6000, (Includes AURORA ST. LUKE'S SOUTH SHORE, 5900 South Lake Drive, Cudahy, Zip 53110–8903; tel. 414/769–9000) **A**1 2 3 5 7 8 9 10 **F**1 2 3 4 5 6 8 11 12 15 17 18 20 22 24 26 28 29 30 31 34 35 36 37 38 40 42 43 44 45 46 47 49 50 51 54 56 57 58 59 64 65 66 68 69 70 72 74 75 78 79 80 81 82 84 85 86 87 89 90 93 94 96 97 98 100 101 102 103 104 105 107 108 109 110 111 114 115 116 117 118 119 120 121 123 124 126 129 130 132 135 136 137 138 139 140 142 143 144 145 146 147 148 **P**6
**S** Aurora Health Care, Milwaukee, WI
Primary Contact: Dennis B. Potts, President
COO: Sue Ela, Executive Vice President and Chief Operating Officer
CMO: Bruce L. Van Cleave, M.D., Senior Vice President and Chief Medical Officer
CIO: Philip Loftus, Ph.D., Vice President and Chief Information Officer
CHR: Dwight Morgan, Vice President Human Resources
Web address: www.aurorahealthcare.org
**Control:** Other not–for–profit (including NFP Corporation) **Service:** General Medical and Surgical

**Staffed Beds:** 680 **Admissions:** 36208 **Census:** 544 **Outpatient Visits:** 511490 **Births:** 0 **Total Expense ($000):** 917299 **Payroll Expense ($000):** 277234 **Personnel:** 4598

**WI**

---

**Hospital, Medicare Provider Number, Address, Telephone, Approval, Facility, and Physician Codes, Health Care System**

★ American Hospital Association (AHA) membership
☐ The Joint Commission accreditation
◇ DNV Healthcare Inc. accreditation
◯ Healthcare Facilities Accreditation Program
△ Commission on Accreditation of Rehabilitation Facilities (CARF) accreditation

✠ **CHILDREN'S HOSPITAL OF WISCONSIN (523300)**, 9000 West Wisconsin Avenue, Zip 53226–4810, Mailing Address: P.O. Box 1997, Zip 53201–1997; tel. 414/266–2000 **A**1 3 5 8 9 10 **F**7 9 12 17 20 22 24 28 29 34 36 38 40 43 51 60 61 64 72 75 77 78 81 82 87 88 89 93 99 100 102 104 107 108 111 116 119 130 131 137 138 140 141 144 **S** Children's Hospital and Health System, Milwaukee, WI
Primary Contact: Peggy N. Troy, President and Chief Executive Officer
COO: Cinthia S. Christensen, JD, Executive Vice President and Chief Operating Officer
CMO: Michael Gutzeit, M.D., Chief Medical Officer
CIO: Michael Jones, Vice President and Chief Information Officer
CHR: Peggy Niemer, Vice President Human Resources
Web address: www.chw.org
**Control:** Other not–for–profit (including NFP Corporation) **Service:** Children's general

Staffed Beds: 296 Admissions: 24085 Census: 232 Outpatient Visits: 371782 Births: 0 Total Expense ($000): 503032 Payroll Expense ($000): 158255 Personnel: 2534

✠ △ **CLEMENT J. ZABLOCKI VETERANS AFFAIRS MEDICAL CENTER**, 5000 West National Avenue, Zip 53295–0001; tel. 414/384–2000, (Nonreporting) **A**1 2 3 5 7 **S** Department of Veterans Affairs, Washington, DC
Primary Contact: Robert H. Beller, FACHE, Director
COO: Larry L. Berkeley, Associate Director
CFO: John La Sota, Assistant Finance Officer
CMO: Michael Erdmann, M.D., Chief of Staff
CIO: Bryan Vail, Chief Information Officer
CHR: Wayne Davis, Chief Human Resources
Web address: www.milwaukee.va.gov/
**Control:** Veterans Affairs, Government, federal **Service:** General Medical and Surgical

Staffed Beds: 637

✠ **COLUMBIA ST. MARY'S HOSPITAL MILWAUKEE (520051)**, 2301 North Lake Drive, Zip 53211–4508; tel. 414/291–1000, (Includes COLUMBIA ST. MARY'S COLUMBIA HOSPITAL, 2025 East Newport Avenue, Zip 53211–2990; tel. 414/961–3300; COLUMBIA ST. MARY'S MILWAUKEE HOSPITAL, 2323 North Lake Drive, Zip 53211–9682, Mailing Address: P.O. Box 503, Zip 53201–0503; tel. 414/291–1000) **A**1 2 3 5 7 **F**4 9 12 13 15 16 17 20 22 24 28 29 34 36 38 40 43 51 53 54 56 64 70 72 75 76 77 78 87 89 90 100 102 103 107 108 111 116 118 119 130 141 144 147 **P**6 **S** Ascension Health, Saint Louis, MO
Primary Contact: Mark R. Taylor, FACHE, President and Chief Executive Officer
CFO: Rhonda Anderson, Executive Vice President Finance and Chief Financial Officer
CMO: David Shapiro, M.D., Vice President Medical Affairs and Chief Medical Officer
CIO: Mary Paul, Chief Information Officer
CHR: Cheryl Hill, Vice President Human Resources
Web address: www.columbia–stmarys.org
**Control:** Church–operated, Nongovernment, not–for profit **Service:** General Medical and Surgical

Staffed Beds: 324 Admissions: 12852 Census: 162 Outpatient Visits: 248229 Births: 3016 Total Expense ($000): 447679 Payroll Expense ($000): 168544 Personnel: 1633

✠ △ **FROEDTERT MEMORIAL LUTHERAN HOSPITAL (520177)**, 9200 West Wisconsin Avenue, Zip 53226–3596, Mailing Address: P.O. Box 26099, Zip 53226–0099; tel. 414/805–3000 **A**1 2 3 5 7 **F**4 8 11 12 13 15 17 18 20 22 24 26 29 30 31 34 35 38 40 43 44 45 46 47 48 49 50 51 52 55 56 57 58 59 60 64 68 70 74 75 76 77 78 79 80 81 84 85 86 87 90 91 92 93 94 96 97 98 100 107 108 110 111 113 114 115 116 117 118 119 120 121 123 124 126 129 130 131 132 134 135 136 137 138 139 140 141 144 145 146 147 148 **P**5 6
Primary Contact: Catherine A. Jacobson, President and Chief Executive Officer
COO: Catherine Buck, Executive Vice President Operations
CFO: Jeffrey Van De Kreeke, Senior Vice President Finance
CMO: Andrew J. Norton, M.D., Senior Vice President Medical Affairs
CIO: Robert DeGrand, Chief Information Officer
Web address: www.froedtert.com
**Control:** Other not–for–profit (including NFP Corporation) **Service:** General Medical and Surgical

Staffed Beds: 500 Admissions: 27610 Census: 389 Outpatient Visits: 665597 Births: 1942 Total Expense ($000): 887693 Payroll Expense ($000): 252284 Personnel: 4391

★ **MILWAUKEE COUNTY BEHAVIORAL HEALTH DIVISION (524001)**, 9455 Watertown Plank Road, Zip 53226–3559; tel. 414/257–6995, (Total facility includes 72 beds in nursing home–type unit) **A**3 5 10 **F**30 42 44 66 67 71 75 77 87 98 99 100 102 103 104 105 128 130 146 **P**3 6
Primary Contact: Paula A. Lucey, MSN, R.N., Administrator
CFO: Michael Kreuser, Director Fiscal Services
CMO: Thomas Harding, M.D., Medical Director
CIO: William Borja, Chief Information Officer
Web address: www.milwaukeecounty.org
**Control:** County–Government, nonfederal **Service:** Psychiatric

Staffed Beds: 180 Admissions: 2825 Census: 204 Outpatient Visits: 14734 Births: 0 Total Expense ($000): 152560 Payroll Expense ($000): 32793 Personnel: 570

**ORTHOPAEDIC HOSPITAL OF WISCONSIN – GLENDALE (520194)**, 475 West River Woods Parkway, Zip 53212–1081; tel. 414/961–6800 **A**9 10 **F**3 29 38 53 64 79 80 81 82 85 86 93 94 107 111 112 114 119 130 131 135
Primary Contact: Brian J. Cramer, Chief Executive Officer
CFO: Tom Swiderski, Chief Financial Officer
CMO: Rory Wright, M.D., President Medical Staff
CIO: Todd Heikkinen, Director Rehabilitation Services
Web address: www.ohow.org
**Control:** Partnership, Investor–owned, for–profit **Service:** General Medical and Surgical

Staffed Beds: 30 Admissions: 1049 Census: 8 Outpatient Visits: 28868 Births: 0 Total Expense ($000): 34650 Payroll Expense ($000): 10007 Personnel: 157

✠ △ **SACRED HEART REHABILITATION INSTITUTE (523025)**, 2025 East Newport Avenue, Zip 53211–2906; tel. 414/298–6700 **A**1 7 9 10 **F**9 29 34 54 56 64 75 77 86 90 93 100 102 103 130 131 **P**6 **S** Ascension Health, Saint Louis, MO
Primary Contact: Allan M. Spooner, President
CFO: Rhonda Anderson, Executive Vice President Finance and Chief Financial Officer
CMO: David Shapiro, M.D., Vice President Medical Affairs and Chief Medical Officer
CIO: Mary Paul, Vice President and Chief Information Officer
CHR: Cheryl Hill, Vice President Human Resources
Web address: www.columbia–stmarys.com
**Control:** Church–operated, Nongovernment, not–for profit **Service:** Rehabilitation

Staffed Beds: 20 Admissions: 388 Census: 17 Outpatient Visits: 11499 Births: 0 Total Expense ($000): 12595 Payroll Expense ($000): 5609 Personnel: 90

✠ **SELECT SPECIALTY HOSPITAL–MILWAUKEE (522006)**, 8901 West Lincoln Avenue, 2nd Floor, Zip 53227–2409; tel. 414/328–7700 **A**1 9 10 **F**1 3 17 29 30 36 38 39 56 70 71 74 75 77 78 79 80 82 87 90 100 103 118 130 148 **S** Select Medical Corporation, Mechanicsburg, PA
Primary Contact: Richard Keddington, Chief Executive Officer
CMO: Matt Mathai, M.D., Medical Director
CHR: Chris Froh, Senior Coordinator Human Resources
CNO: Jane Cerra, Market Nurse Executive and Chief Nursing Officer
Web address: www.selectspecialtyhospitals.com/company/locations/milwaukee.aspx
**Control:** Corporation, Investor–owned, for–profit **Service:** Long–Term Acute Care hospital

Staffed Beds: 34 Admissions: 408 Census: 31 Outpatient Visits: 0 Births: 0 Total Expense ($000): 16872 Payroll Expense ($000): 5538 Personnel: 99

✠ **WHEATON FRANCISCAN HEALTHCARE – ST. FRANCIS (520078)**, 3237 South 16th Street, Zip 53215–4592; tel. 414/647–5000 **A**1 2 9 10 **F**3 9 13 15 18 20 22 24 26 28 29 30 31 32 34 35 36 38 40 46 47 48 49 50 54 56 57 59 64 68 72 74 75 76 77 78 79 80 81 82 83 84 85 86 87 93 97 98 100 101 102 103 104 105 106 107 108 109 110 111 112 113 114 115 118 119 120 121 122 123 129 130 131 132 135 144 146 147 148 **S** Wheaton Franciscan Healthcare, Wheaton, IL
Primary Contact: Daniel Mattes, President
CFO: Aaron Bridgeland, Director Finance
CIO: Gregory Smith, Senior Vice President and Chief Information Officer
CHR: Robert Bauer, Vice President Human Resources
Web address: www.mywheaton.org
**Control:** Church–operated, Nongovernment, not–for profit **Service:** General Medical and Surgical

Staffed Beds: 164 Admissions: 8002 Census: 106 Outpatient Visits: 149589 Births: 926 Total Expense ($000): 156052 Payroll Expense ($000): 57051 Personnel: 883

✠ **WHEATON FRANCISCAN HEALTHCARE – ST. JOSEPH'S (520136)**, 5000 West Chambers Street, Zip 53210–1650; tel. 414/447–2000 **A**1 2 3 5 9 10 **F**3 8 11 13 15 17 18 20 22 24 26 28 29 30 31 33 35 37 39 40 42 43 45 46 48 49 53 54 56 64 70 72 74 75 76 77 78 79 80 81 82 83 84 85 87 89 90 91 92 93 94 96 97 107 108 110 111 112 114 115 116 117 118 119 121 123 124 129 130 131 143 144 145 146 147 148 **P**6 **S** Wheaton Franciscan Healthcare, Wheaton, IL
Primary Contact: Debra K. Standridge, President
CFO: Michael Petitt, Director of Finance
CMO: Rita Hanson, M.D., Vice President Medical Affairs
CIO: Dawn Hansen, Regional Director Information Services
CHR: Christopher Morris, Vice President Human Resources
CNO: Sharon Baughman, Vice President Patient Services and Chief Nursing Officer
Web address: www.mywheaton.org/stjoseph
**Control:** Church–operated, Nongovernment, not–for profit **Service:** General Medical and Surgical

Staffed Beds: 346 Admissions: 11808 Census: 149 Outpatient Visits: 414850 Births: 2653 Total Expense ($000): 275215 Payroll Expense ($000): 94947 Personnel: 1565

**WI**

*Many Facility Codes have changed. Please refer to the AHA Guide Code Chart.*
© 2013 AHA Guide

## MONROE—Green County

☐ **MONROE CLINIC (520028)**, 515 22nd Avenue, Zip 53566–1598;
tel. 608/324–1000 **A**1 9 10 **F**3 5 6 8 9 11 13 15 17 18 20 22 26 28 30 31
32 34 35 36 37 38 40 43 44 45 46 49 50 55 56 57 59 62 63 65 68 70 74
75 76 77 79 80 81 84 85 86 87 89 90 93 97 99 100 101 102 103 104 107
108 110 111 112 115 117 119 126 129 130 131 132 135 144 145 146 147
148 **P**6
Primary Contact: Michael B. Sanders, President and Chief Executive Officer
CFO: Julie Wilke, Vice President and Chief Financial Officer
CMO: Mark Thompson, M.D., Chief Medical Officer
CIO: Carrie Blum, Director Information Systems
CHR: Jane Monahan, Director Human Resources
Web address: www.monroeclinic.org
**Control:** Other not–for–profit (including NFP Corporation) **Service:** General
Medical and Surgical

**Staffed Beds:** 50 **Admissions:** 2965 **Census:** 28 **Outpatient Visits:** 263140
**Births:** 462 **Total Expense ($000):** 160112 **Payroll Expense ($000):** 76275
**Personnel:** 1035

## NEENAH—Winnebago County

☐ **CHILDREN'S HOSPITAL OF WISCONSIN–FOX VALLEY (523302)**, 130
Second Avenue, 3rd Floor South, Zip 54956–2883; tel. 920/969–7900 **A**1 9 10
**F**7 29 34 38 72 75 86 89 93 99 101 104 130 **P**6 **S** Children's Hospital and
Health System, Milwaukee, WI
Primary Contact: Peggy N. Troy, President and Chief Executive Officer
COO: Tim Klunk, Executive Director
CMO: Paul Myers, M.D., Neonatologist and Chief Medical Officer
Web address: www.chw.org
**Control:** Other not–for–profit (including NFP Corporation) **Service:** Children's
general

**Staffed Beds:** 42 **Admissions:** 1284 **Census:** 17 **Outpatient Visits:** 12666
**Births:** 0 **Total Expense ($000):** 21613 **Payroll Expense ($000):** 7980
**Personnel:** 113

☐ △ **THEDA CLARK MEDICAL CENTER (520045)**, 130 Second Street,
Zip 54956–2883, Mailing Address: P.O. Box 2021, Zip 54957–2021;
tel. 920/729–3100 **A**1 2 7 9 10 **F**3 4 5 7 8 9 11 12 13 15 17 18 19 20 21 22
23 25 28 29 30 31 32 34 35 36 39 40 43 44 45 46 47 48 49 50 51 53 55
56 59 60 64 68 69 70 74 75 76 78 79 80 82 84 85 86 87 88 90 93 98 99
101 102 103 104 105 106 107 108 110 111 112 114 115 118 119 126 130
132 134 135 144 146 147 148 **P**1 6 **S** ThedaCare, Inc., Appleton, WI
Primary Contact: Kim Barnas, Senior Vice President
COO: Matthew Furlan, Chief Operating Officer
CFO: Tim Olson, Senior Vice President Finance
CIO: Keith Livingston, Senior Vice President and Chief Information Officer
CHR: Maureen Pistone, Senior Vice President Human Resources
CNO: Jill Case–Wirth, Vice President and Chief Nursing Officer
Web address: www.thedacare.org
**Control:** Other not–for–profit (including NFP Corporation) **Service:** General
Medical and Surgical

**Staffed Beds:** 147 **Admissions:** 7915 **Census:** 81 **Outpatient Visits:** 92558
**Births:** 1286 **Total Expense ($000):** 156772 **Payroll Expense ($000):**
60524 **Personnel:** 891

## NEILLSVILLE—Clark County

**MEMORIAL MEDICAL CENTER – NEILLSVILLE (521323)**, 216 Sunset Place,
Zip 54456–1799; tel. 715/743–3101, (Includes NEILLSVILLE MEMORIAL HOME )
**A**9 10 18 **F**6 10 11 13 15 28 34 40 43 56 62 64 75 76 77 80 81 82 86 89
107 108 119 130 131 144 147 **P**2 6
Primary Contact: Bobbe L. Teigen, FACHE, Chief Executive Officer
CFO: Kelly Moen, Chief Financial Officer
CMO: Timothy Meyer, M.D., Chief of Staff
CIO: Travis Obrycki, Director Information Systems
CHR: Tamie Zarak, Director Human Resources
Web address: www.mmcneillsville.com
**Control:** Other not–for–profit (including NFP Corporation) **Service:** General
Medical and Surgical

**Staffed Beds:** 5 **Admissions:** 355 **Census:** 2 **Outpatient Visits:** 13315
**Births:** 50 **Total Expense ($000):** 22231 **Payroll Expense ($000):** 11668
**Personnel:** 245

## NEW LONDON—Outagamie County

☐ **NEW LONDON FAMILY MEDICAL CENTER (521326)**, 1405 Mill Street,
Zip 54961–2155, Mailing Address: P.O. Box 307, Zip 54961–0307;
tel. 920/531–2000 **A**1 9 10 18 **F**3 7 8 11 13 15 28 29 30 34 35 40 43 45 47
56 57 59 64 65 66 75 76 79 80 81 82 85 86 87 89 90 91 92 93 96 97 107
108 109 110 114 117 119 131 132 133 141 143 146 148 **S** ThedaCare, Inc.,
Appleton, WI
Primary Contact: William Schmidt, President and Chief Executive Officer
CFO: Gina Moon, Vice President Finance
CMO: Paul Hoell, M.D., President Medical Staff
Web address: www.thedacare.org
**Control:** Other not–for–profit (including NFP Corporation) **Service:** General
Medical and Surgical

**Staffed Beds:** 25 **Admissions:** 917 **Census:** 12 **Outpatient Visits:** 30312
**Births:** 115 **Total Expense ($000):** 24299 **Payroll Expense ($000):** 11777
**Personnel:** 166

## NEW RICHMOND—St. Croix County

★ **WESTFIELDS HOSPITAL (521345)**, 535 Hospital Road, Zip 54017–1449;
tel. 715/243–2600 **A**9 10 18 **F**1 3 13 15 18 26 27 28 29 30 34 38 40 42 43
45 46 50 56 57 59 64 65 66 70 71 74 75 76 77 78 79 80 81 82 86 87 89
90 93 104 107 110 112 114 117 119 129 130 131 132 133 146 148
**P**5 **S** HealthPartners, Bloomington, MN
Primary Contact: Steven Massey, President and Chief Executive Officer
CFO: Jason J. Luhrs, Vice President Fiscal Services
CMO: David O. DeGear, M.D., Vice President Medical Affairs
CIO: Patrice P. Wolff, Director Information Services
CHR: Chad P. Engstrom, Director Human Resources
Web address: www.westfieldshospital.com
**Control:** Other not–for–profit (including NFP Corporation) **Service:** General
Medical and Surgical

**Staffed Beds:** 25 **Admissions:** 853 **Census:** 8 **Outpatient Visits:** 34089
**Births:** 105 **Total Expense ($000):** 30810 **Payroll Expense ($000):** 11875
**Personnel:** 179

## OCONOMOWOC—Waukesha County

☒ **OCONOMOWOC MEMORIAL HOSPITAL (520062)**, 791 Summit Avenue,
Zip 53066–3896; tel. 262/569–9400 **A**1 2 9 10 **F**3 11 13 15 18 20 22 28 29
30 31 35 37 40 45 46 47 48 49 64 74 75 76 78 79 80 81 82 84 85 87 89
93 107 108 110 111 114 115 118 119 120 121 126 130 132 135 146 147
148 **S** ProHealth Care, Inc., Waukesha, WI
Primary Contact: John R. Robertstad, FACHE, President
COO: Mary Jo O'Malley, R.N., Vice President Diagnostics and Support Services
CFO: Nan Nelson, Chief Financial Officer
CMO: Brian Lipman, M.D., Medical Director and Medical Staff Services
CIO: Christine Bessler, Vice President Information Services
CHR: Edward Malindzak, Chief Human Resources Officer
CNO: Catherine Rapp, R.N., Vice President Nursing
Web address: www.prohealthcare.org/locations/locations–v2–detail/?id=1123
**Control:** Other not–for–profit (including NFP Corporation) **Service:** General
Medical and Surgical

**Staffed Beds:** 76 **Admissions:** 3252 **Census:** 27 **Outpatient Visits:** 69125
**Births:** 396 **Total Expense ($000):** 90190 **Payroll Expense ($000):** 22807
**Personnel:** 360

☒ **ROGERS MEMORIAL HOSPITAL (524018)**, 34700 Valley Road,
Zip 53066–4599; tel. 262/646–4411 **A**1 3 5 9 10 **F**3 5 29 30 35 38 42 57 58
59 75 86 87 98 99 100 101 102 103 104 105 106 130 132 134
Primary Contact: Patrick T. Hammer, President and Chief Executive Officer
COO: Paul A. Mueller, Chief Operating Officer
CFO: Gerald A. Noll, Chief Financial Officer
CMO: Peter M. Lake, M.D., Chief Medical Officer
CIO: Wayne Mattson, Management Information Systems Specialist
CHR: Renee A. Patterson, Vice President Employment and Training Services
CNO: Teresa L. Schultz, R.N., Vice President of Patient Care
Web address: www.rogershospital.org
**Control:** Other not–for–profit (including NFP Corporation) **Service:** Psychiatric

**Staffed Beds:** 58 **Admissions:** 1858 **Census:** 32 **Outpatient Visits:** 41917
**Births:** 0 **Total Expense ($000):** 40919 **Payroll Expense ($000):** 21732
**Personnel:** 413

**WI**

---

**Hospital, Medicare Provider Number, Address, Telephone, Approval, Facility, and Physician Codes, Health Care System**

★ American Hospital Association (AHA) membership
☐ The Joint Commission accreditation
◇ DNV Healthcare Inc. accreditation
○ Healthcare Facilities Accreditation Program
△ Commission on Accreditation of Rehabilitation Facilities (CARF) accreditation

### OCONTO—Oconto County

◇ **BELLIN HEALTH OCONTO HOSPITAL (521356)**, (Formerly Oconto Hospital & Medical Center), 820 Arbutus Avenue, Zip 54153–2004, Mailing Address: P.O. Box 357, Zip 54153–0357; tel. 920/835–1100 **A**9 10 18 21 **F**3 29 40 43 62 65 97 104 107 115 119 127 129 133 144 **P**8
Primary Contact: Laura Cormier, Director
Web address: www.bellin.org/facilities_amenities/oconto_hospital_medical_center/
**Control:** Other not–for–profit (including NFP Corporation) **Service:** General Medical and Surgical

**Staffed Beds:** 10 **Admissions:** 56 **Census:** 1 **Outpatient Visits:** 7182 **Births:** 0 **Total Expense ($000):** 5579 **Payroll Expense ($000):** 2579 **Personnel:** 54

### OCONTO FALLS—Oconto County

★ **COMMUNITY MEMORIAL HOSPITAL (521310)**, 855 South Main Street, Zip 54154–1296; tel. 920/846–3444 **A**9 10 18 **F**3 11 15 18 28 29 40 43 45 56 57 59 64 65 75 76 77 79 80 81 85 86 87 89 90 93 94 97 107 108 110 111 112 114 119 127 132 133 144 146 147 **P**5 6
Primary Contact: Daniel DeGroot, Chief Executive Officer
CFO: Michele Miller–Campbell, Chief Financial Officer
CMO: Judith Bowers, D.O., Chief of Staff
CIO: Jared Alfson, Chief Information Officer
CHR: Trisha Brown, Director Human Resources
CNO: Kay Kuchta, R.N., Chief Nursing Officer
Web address: www.cmhospital.org
**Control:** Other not–for–profit (including NFP Corporation) **Service:** General Medical and Surgical

**Staffed Beds:** 13 **Admissions:** 893 **Census:** 10 **Outpatient Visits:** 63079 **Births:** 70 **Total Expense ($000):** 34962 **Payroll Expense ($000):** 15292 **Personnel:** 227

### OSCEOLA—Polk County

**OSCEOLA MEDICAL CENTER (521318)**, 2600 65th Avenue, Zip 54020–4370, Mailing Address: P.O. Box 218, Zip 54020–0218; tel. 715/294–2111 **A**9 10 18 **F**3 8 11 13 15 18 26 28 29 30 31 32 33 34 35 40 43 45 46 47 48 49 50 53 56 57 58 59 64 65 68 70 74 75 76 77 78 79 81 86 87 89 91 93 97 107 110 111 112 114 115 117 119 127 129 132 133 144 146 148 **P**6
Primary Contact: Jeffrey K. Meyer, Chief Executive Officer
CMO: Rob Dybvig, M.D., Chief Medical Officer
CIO: Shawn Kammerud, Manager Information Services
CHR: Margie Evenson, Manager Human Resources
Web address: www.osceolamedicalcenter.com
**Control:** Other not–for–profit (including NFP Corporation) **Service:** General Medical and Surgical

**Staffed Beds:** 18 **Admissions:** 619 **Census:** 5 **Outpatient Visits:** 3095 **Births:** 81 **Total Expense ($000):** 28459 **Payroll Expense ($000):** 10129 **Personnel:** 220

### OSHKOSH—Winnebago County

⌧ **AURORA MEDICAL CENTER OF OSHKOSH (520198)**, 855 North Westhaven Drive, Zip 54904–7668; tel. 920/456–6000 **A**1 2 9 10 **F**3 8 11 12 13 15 17 18 20 22 26 29 30 31 34 40 41 43 45 46 47 48 49 50 53 54 56 64 70 71 74 75 76 79 80 81 82 85 86 87 89 92 93 94 97 107 108 110 111 114 115 118 119 120 121 123 124 129 130 131 145 146 147 148 **P**6 **S** Aurora Health Care, Milwaukee, WI
Primary Contact: Jeffrey Bard, President
CFO: Sandra Ewald, Vice President Finance
CMO: Bruce L. Van Cleave, M.D., Senior Vice President and Chief Medical Officer
CIO: Philip Loftus, Ph.D., Vice President and Chief Information Officer
CHR: Linda Mingus, Director Human Resources
CNO: Mary Beth Kingston, R.N., Executive Vice President and Chief Nursing Officer
Web address: www.aurorahealthcare.com
**Control:** Other not–for–profit (including NFP Corporation) **Service:** General Medical and Surgical

**Staffed Beds:** 61 **Admissions:** 2974 **Census:** 26 **Outpatient Visits:** 97929 **Births:** 663 **Total Expense ($000):** 82678 **Payroll Expense ($000):** 25815 **Personnel:** 483

□ △ **MERCY MEDICAL CENTER (520048)**, 500 South Oakwood Road, Zip 54904–7944, Mailing Address: P.O. Box 3370, Zip 54903–3370; tel. 920/223–2000 **A**1 2 7 9 10 **F**3 4 5 11 13 15 16 17 18 20 22 26 28 29 30 31 34 35 38 39 40 43 44 46 47 48 49 50 51 53 56 57 59 64 65 67 68 70 75 76 78 80 81 82 86 87 88 89 90 92 93 96 98 103 104 107 108 110 111 112 114 117 118 119 120 121 122 123 129 130 131 132 134 144 146 147 148 **S** Ascension Health, Saint Louis, MO
Primary Contact: William Calhoun, President
CFO: Jeff Badger, Chief Financial Officer
CMO: Mark W. Kehrberg, M.D., Senior Vice President and Chief Medical Officer
CIO: Will Weider, Chief Information Officer
CHR: Vince Gallucci, Senior Vice President Human Resources
Web address: www.affinityhealth.org
**Control:** Church–operated, Nongovernment, not–for profit **Service:** General Medical and Surgical

**Staffed Beds:** 137 **Admissions:** 5756 **Census:** 66 **Outpatient Visits:** 93368 **Births:** 658 **Total Expense ($000):** 107328 **Payroll Expense ($000):** 40670 **Personnel:** 542

### OSSEO—Trempealeau County

□ **MAYO CLINIC HEALTH SYSTEM – OAKRIDGE IN OSSEO (521302)**, 13025 Eighth Street, Zip 54758–7634, Mailing Address: P.O. Box 70, Zip 54758–0070; tel. 715/597–3121, (Total facility includes 35 beds in nursing home–type unit) **A**1 9 10 18 **F**3 7 10 15 18 26 28 29 32 34 35 40 43 44 56 59 64 65 68 75 77 80 84 85 86 87 90 93 97 107 110 114 125 128 130 132 133 135 143 144 146 148 **P**6 **S** Mayo Clinic Health System, Rochester, MN
Primary Contact: Dean Eide, Vice President
CFO: Nancy Steig, Director Fiscal Services
CHR: Rhonda Wilson, Director Human Resources
Web address: www.mayoclinichealthsystem.org/locations/osseo
**Control:** Other not–for–profit (including NFP Corporation) **Service:** General Medical and Surgical

**Staffed Beds:** 39 **Admissions:** 394 **Census:** 40 **Outpatient Visits:** 37436 **Births:** 0 **Total Expense ($000):** 17916 **Payroll Expense ($000):** 9998 **Personnel:** 182

### PARK FALLS—Price County

★ **FLAMBEAU HOSPITAL (521325)**, 98 Sherry Avenue, Zip 54552–1467, Mailing Address: P.O. Box 310, Zip 54552–0310; tel. 715/762–2484 **A**9 10 18 **F**3 8 11 14 15 17 28 29 30 31 34 35 40 44 45 50 53 56 57 59 62 63 64 65 68 69 70 75 77 79 80 81 82 84 85 86 87 89 90 93 96 97 107 108 110 115 119 130 131 132 133 143 144 146 148 **S** Ascension Health, Saint Louis, MO
Primary Contact: David A. Grundstrom, Chief Administrative Officer
CFO: James R. Braun, Chief Financial Officer
CMO: Amil Chauhan, M.D., Chief of Staff
CHR: Barb Michalski, Manager Human Resources
CNO: Elizabeth Schreiber, R.N., Director Patient Care Services
Web address: www.flambeauhospital.org
**Control:** Other not–for–profit (including NFP Corporation) **Service:** General Medical and Surgical

**Staffed Beds:** 25 **Admissions:** 666 **Census:** 6 **Outpatient Visits:** 28038 **Births:** 0 **Total Expense ($000):** 18936 **Payroll Expense ($000):** 8038 **Personnel:** 168

### PEWAUKEE—Waukesha County

⌧ **LIFECARE HOSPITALS OF WISCONSIN (522007)**, 2400 Golf Road, Zip 53072–5590; tel. 262/524–2600 **A**1 9 10 **F**1 3 29 68 86 130 143 148 **P**5 **S** LifeCare Management Services, Plano, TX
Primary Contact: Jevne Conover, Administrator
CFO: Susan Stermer, Director Finance
CMO: John Daniels, M.D., Medical Director
CHR: Jill Schuetz, Director Human Resources
Web address: www.lifecare–hospitals.com
**Control:** Corporation, Investor–owned, for–profit **Service:** Long–Term Acute Care hospital

**Staffed Beds:** 34 **Admissions:** 328 **Census:** 30 **Outpatient Visits:** 0 **Births:** 0 **Total Expense ($000):** 19436 **Payroll Expense ($000):** 8215 **Personnel:** 113

**WI**

*Many Facility Codes have changed. Please refer to the AHA Guide Code Chart.* © 2013 AHA Guide

## PLATTEVILLE—Grant County

✠ **SOUTHWEST HEALTH CENTER (521354)**, 1400 Eastside Road, Zip 53818–9800; tel. 608/348–2331, (Includes SOUTHWEST HEALTH CENTER NURSING HOME, 808 South Washington Street, Cuba City, Zip 53807; tel. 608/744–2161), (Total facility includes 84 beds in nursing home–type unit) **A**1 9 10 18 **F**2 3 6 8 13 15 28 29 31 34 40 43 45 46 47 48 49 50 56 57 59 64 68 74 75 76 77 79 81 82 83 84 85 86 87 93 96 97 98 100 101 102 103 104 105 106 107 110 112 115 117 119 128 129 130 132 133 143 144 146 148
Primary Contact: Dan D. Rohrbach, President and Chief Executive Officer
CFO: Matthew Streeter, Chief Financial Officer
CMO: Kevin Carr, M.D., Chief of Staff
CHR: Tammy Nelson, Manager Human Resources
Web address: www.southwesthealth.org
**Control:** Other not–for–profit (including NFP Corporation) **Service:** General Medical and Surgical

> **Staffed Beds:** 119 **Admissions:** 919 **Census:** 86 **Outpatient Visits:** 38819 **Births:** 148 **Total Expense ($000):** 30258 **Payroll Expense ($000):** 11729 **Personnel:** 184

## PLEASANT PRAIRIE—Kenosha County

★ **UNITED HOSPITAL SYSTEM, ST. CATHERINE'S MEDICAL CENTER CAMPUS**, 9555 76th Street, Zip 53158–1984; tel. 262/656–2011, (Nonreporting) **A**2 9 **S** Wheaton Franciscan Healthcare, Wheaton, IL
Primary Contact: Richard O. Schmidt, Jr., President and Chief Executive Officer
Web address: www.uhsi.org
**Control:** Other not–for–profit (including NFP Corporation) **Service:** General Medical and Surgical

> **Staffed Beds:** 202

## PORTAGE—Columbia County

☐ **DIVINE SAVIOR HEALTHCARE (520041)**, 2817 New Pinery Road, Zip 53901–9240, Mailing Address: P.O. Box 387, Zip 53901–0387; tel. 608/742–4131, (Total facility includes 123 beds in nursing home–type unit) **A**1 9 10 **F**3 4 7 11 12 13 15 28 30 31 34 35 36 40 43 44 45 50 54 55 57 59 60 62 64 68 69 70 74 75 76 77 78 79 80 81 82 85 86 87 89 90 91 92 93 94 96 97 107 108 110 111 115 117 118 119 128 129 130 131 132 133 143 144 145 146 147 148 **P**6
Primary Contact: Michael Decker, President and Chief Executive Officer
CFO: Marlin Pete Nelson, Vice President Fiscal Services
CMO: Elizabeth Strabel, M.D., Chief Medical Staff
CHR: Carol J. Bank, Vice President Human Resources
Web address: www.dshealthcare.com
**Control:** Church–operated, Nongovernment, not–for profit **Service:** General Medical and Surgical

> **Staffed Beds:** 133 **Admissions:** 2379 **Census:** 116 **Outpatient Visits:** 151580 **Births:** 245 **Total Expense ($000):** 67273 **Payroll Expense ($000):** 32946 **Personnel:** 557

## PRAIRIE DU CHIEN—Crawford County

✠ **PRAIRIE DU CHIEN MEMORIAL HOSPITAL (521330)**, 705 East Taylor Street, Zip 53821–2196; tel. 608/357–2000 **A**1 9 10 18 **F**10 11 13 15 17 28 29 34 35 36 40 53 56 59 62 63 64 68 69 70 75 76 77 80 81 82 84 86 87 93 107 108 110 115 119 129 130 131 132 133 134 144 146 147 148
Primary Contact: William P. Sexton, Chief Executive Officer
CFO: Dave Breitbach, Chief Financial Officer
CIO: John Daane, Information Systems Officer
CHR: Laurie Hampton, Director Human Resources
Web address: www.pdcmemorialhospital.org
**Control:** Other not–for–profit (including NFP Corporation) **Service:** General Medical and Surgical

> **Staffed Beds:** 16 **Admissions:** 1024 **Census:** 14 **Outpatient Visits:** 10503 **Births:** 117 **Total Expense ($000):** 30166 **Payroll Expense ($000):** 14633 **Personnel:** 256

## PRAIRIE DU SAC—Sauk County

★ ○ **SAUK PRAIRIE MEMORIAL HOSPITAL & CLINICS (520095)**, 80 First Street, Zip 53578–1599; tel. 608/643–3311 **A**9 10 11 **F**1 3 11 13 15 29 32 34 35 36 40 43 45 47 48 53 54 56 57 58 59 64 69 75 76 78 79 80 81 82 83 84 85 86 93 96 97 107 108 118 119 124 127 129 130 131 132 133 135 144 146 148 **P**7
Primary Contact: Larry Schroeder, Chief Executive Officer
CFO: Carol May, Chief Financial Officer, Vice President Finance and Operations
CMO: John McAuliffe, M.D., Medical Director
CIO: Marybeth Bay, Director Information Technology
CHR: Robbi Eccher, Vice President Human Resources
CNO: Margaret Sheeks, R.N., Vice President, Patient Services
Web address: www.spmh.org
**Control:** Other not–for–profit (including NFP Corporation) **Service:** General Medical and Surgical

> **Staffed Beds:** 36 **Admissions:** 1777 **Census:** 11 **Outpatient Visits:** 69831 **Births:** 281 **Total Expense ($000):** 58545 **Payroll Expense ($000):** 26314 **Personnel:** 396

## RACINE—Racine County

✠ △ **WHEATON FRANCISCAN HEALTHCARE – ALL SAINTS (520096)**, 3801 Spring Street, Zip 53405–1690; tel. 262/687–4011, (Total facility includes 50 beds in nursing home–type unit) **A**1 2 7 9 10 **F**3 4 5 6 13 15 17 18 20 22 24 26 28 29 30 31 33 34 35 38 40 43 44 45 46 48 49 50 51 53 55 56 57 58 59 64 65 68 70 72 74 75 76 77 78 79 80 81 85 86 87 89 90 91 92 93 96 97 98 99 100 101 102 103 104 105 107 108 110 111 112 115 116 118 119 120 121 123 124 128 129 130 131 132 134 135 146 147 148 **P**6 **S** Wheaton Franciscan Healthcare, Wheaton, IL
Primary Contact: Susan Boland, President and Chief Executive Officer
CFO: Jeanne Gramza, Director Finance
CMO: Jerry Hardacre, M.D., Chief of Staff
CIO: Joanne Bisterfeldt, Chief Information Officer
CHR: Mary Jo Wodicka, Vice President Human Resources
CNO: Mary Elizabeth Ouimet, MSN, Senior Vice President and Chief Nursing Officer
Web address: www.allsaintshealth.com
**Control:** Church–operated, Nongovernment, not–for profit **Service:** General Medical and Surgical

> **Staffed Beds:** 385 **Admissions:** 15697 **Census:** 252 **Outpatient Visits:** 449138 **Births:** 1768 **Total Expense ($000):** 346976 **Payroll Expense ($000):** 124987 **Personnel:** 2469

## REEDSBURG—Sauk County

✠ **REEDSBURG AREA MEDICAL CENTER (521351)**, 2000 North Dewey Street, Zip 53959–1097; tel. 608/524–6487 **A**1 9 10 18 **F**3 8 11 13 15 17 26 28 29 30 31 34 35 40 41 43 45 53 54 57 59 64 68 70 75 76 77 78 79 80 81 82 85 86 87 88 89 93 96 97 107 111 117 129 130 131 132 133 135 144 146 147 148 **P**6
Primary Contact: Robert Van Meeteren, President and Chief Executive Officer
CFO: Joe Svetlik, Vice President Finance
CHR: Dale Turner, Vice President Human Resources
Web address: www.ramchealth.com
**Control:** Other not–for–profit (including NFP Corporation) **Service:** General Medical and Surgical

> **Staffed Beds:** 25 **Admissions:** 1483 **Census:** 14 **Outpatient Visits:** 56237 **Births:** 247 **Total Expense ($000):** 43715 **Payroll Expense ($000):** 17722 **Personnel:** 365

## RHINELANDER—Oneida County

✠ **MINISTRY SAINT MARY'S HOSPITALS (520019)**, (Formerly Sacred Heart–St. Mary's Hospitals), 2251 North Shore Drive, Zip 54501–6710; tel. 715/361–2000, (Includes ST. MARY'S HOSPITAL, 1044 Kabel Avenue, Zip 54501; tel. 715/369–6600) **A**1 9 10 20 **F**3 4 5 13 15 28 29 30 31 34 35 36 40 44 45 49 50 54 57 59 64 65 68 69 75 76 77 78 79 80 81 82 84 85 86 87 89 91 92 93 94 96 98 99 100 101 103 104 107 108 109 110 111 112 115 116 117 119 130 131 132 144 146 148 **S** Ascension Health, Saint Louis, MO
Primary Contact: Monica Hilt, President and Chief Operating Officer
COO: William A. Erickson, Vice President and Chief Operating Officer
CFO: Cathy Bukowski, Regional Chief Financial Officer
CMO: Shishir Sheth, M.D., President Medical Staff
CIO: Howard Dobizl, Director Information Services for the Northern Region
CHR: Michelle Cornelius, Director Human Resources for the Northern Region
Web address: www.ministryhealth.org
**Control:** Church–operated, Nongovernment, not–for profit **Service:** General Medical and Surgical

> **Staffed Beds:** 67 **Admissions:** 3409 **Census:** 30 **Outpatient Visits:** 92627 **Births:** 369 **Total Expense ($000):** 117264 **Payroll Expense ($000):** 59077 **Personnel:** 618

**WI**

---

**Hospital, Medicare Provider Number, Address, Telephone, Approval, Facility, and Physician Codes, Health Care System**

★ American Hospital Association (AHA) membership
☐ The Joint Commission accreditation
◇ DNV Healthcare Inc. accreditation
○ Healthcare Facilities Accreditation Program
△ Commission on Accreditation of Rehabilitation Facilities (CARF) accreditation

## RICE LAKE—Barron County

☒ **LAKEVIEW MEDICAL CENTER (520011)**, 1700 West Stout Street,
Zip 54868–5000; tel. 715/234–1515 **A**1 9 10 20 **F**7 11 13 15 28 29 34 36
40 43 51 53 54 56 60 62 63 64 69 70 75 76 77 78 80 81 82 86 87 89 93
107 111 119 130 144 147
Primary Contact: Edward H. Wolf, President and Chief Executive Officer
COO: Cindy Arts–Strenke, Chief Operating Officer and Chief Nursing Officer
CFO: Jacqueline Klein, Chief Financial Officer
CMO: John L. Olson, M.D., Medical Director
CIO: Brad Gerrits, Director Information Systems
CHR: Kathy Mitchell, Director Human Resources
Web address: www.lakeviewmedical.com
**Control:** Other not–for–profit (including NFP Corporation) **Service:** General
Medical and Surgical

**Staffed Beds:** 40 **Admissions:** 2359 **Census:** 18 **Outpatient Visits:** 142134
**Births:** 488 **Total Expense ($000):** 60430 **Payroll Expense ($000):** 23418
**Personnel:** 421

## RICHLAND CENTER—Richland County

☐ **RICHLAND HOSPITAL (521341)**, 333 East Second Street, Zip 53581–1914;
tel. 608/647–6321 **A**1 9 10 18 **F**8 11 12 13 15 18 28 30 31 34 35 40 43 45
46 50 56 57 58 59 64 65 66 68 70 74 76 78 79 80 81 85 86 89 93 97 107
110 112 115 119 127 129 130 131 132 133 143 144 146 148
Primary Contact: Michael Delfs, Chief Executive Officer
CFO: Karen Traynor, Chief Financial Officer
CMO: Kay M. Balink, M.D., Chief of Staff
CIO: Jerry Cooper, Manager Data Processing
CHR: Rhonda Sutton, Director Human Resources
Web address: www.richlandhospital.com
**Control:** Other not–for–profit (including NFP Corporation) **Service:** General
Medical and Surgical

**Staffed Beds:** 25 **Admissions:** 1234 **Census:** 11 **Outpatient Visits:** 35988
**Births:** 169 **Total Expense ($000):** 33252 **Payroll Expense ($000):** 14838
**Personnel:** 257

## RIPON—Fond Du Lac County

☐ **RIPON MEDICAL CENTER (521321)**, 933 Newbury Street, Zip 54971–1798,
Mailing Address: P.O. Box 390, Zip 54971–0390; tel. 920/748–3101 **A**1 9 10
18 **F**3 8 11 15 17 26 28 29 30 32 34 35 36 37 40 43 45 46 49 53 55 57 59
68 69 70 74 75 77 79 80 81 82 85 86 87 88 89 93 94 96 97 106 107 109
110 114 119 130 131 132 133 135 144 146 147 148 **P**6
Primary Contact: Katherine Vergos, Chief Operating Officer
CFO: Bobbie Pollesch, Chief Financial Officer
CIO: Wayne Johnston, Director Information Systems
CHR: Sarah Brus, Director Human Resources
Web address: www.riponmedicalcenter.com
**Control:** Other not–for–profit (including NFP Corporation) **Service:** General
Medical and Surgical

**Staffed Beds:** 25 **Admissions:** 673 **Census:** 8 **Outpatient Visits:** 32708
**Births:** 0 **Total Expense ($000):** 22627 **Payroll Expense ($000):** 9111
**Personnel:** 114

## RIVER FALLS—St. Croix County

☒ **RIVER FALLS AREA HOSPITAL (521349)**, 1629 East Division Street,
Zip 54022–1571; tel. 715/425–6155 **A**1 2 9 10 18 **F**3 8 11 14 15 18 28 29
31 34 35 40 43 44 45 50 53 59 64 65 68 74 76 77 78 79 80 81 82 83 85
86 87 89 90 91 93 94 96 107 114 117 119 126 129 130 131 133 143 146
147 148 **S** Allina Health, Minneapolis, MN
Primary Contact: David R. Miller, President
COO: William Frommelt, Director Operations and Finance
CFO: William Frommelt, Director Operations and Finance
CHR: Kristen Novak, Manager Human Resources
Web address: www.allina.com
**Control:** Other not–for–profit (including NFP Corporation) **Service:** General
Medical and Surgical

**Staffed Beds:** 16 **Admissions:** 1136 **Census:** 9 **Outpatient Visits:** 21300
**Births:** 212 **Total Expense ($000):** 35870 **Payroll Expense ($000):** 12688
**Personnel:** 142

## SHAWANO—Shawano County

☒ **SHAWANO MEDICAL CENTER (521346)**, 309 North Bartlette Street,
Zip 54166–2127; tel. 715/526–2111 **A**1 9 10 18 **F**3 11 13 18 28 29 31 34
35 39 40 45 46 50 53 56 57 59 64 65 68 74 75 76 77 79 80 81 82 84 85
86 87 90 93 94 97 102 107 108 111 114 119 129 131 132 133 135 142
143 146 148 **P**5 **S** ThedaCare, Inc., Appleton, WI
Primary Contact: Dorothy Erdmann, Chief Executive Officer
CFO: Kenneth Monger, Chief Financial Officer
CMO: Amy Slagle, M.D., President Medical Staff, Menominee Tribal Clinic
CIO: Jennifer Quinn, Quality and Safety Coordinator
CHR: Mark Gabavics, Director Human Resources
Web address: www.shawanomed.org
**Control:** Other not–for–profit (including NFP Corporation) **Service:** General
Medical and Surgical

**Staffed Beds:** 25 **Admissions:** 1658 **Census:** 12 **Outpatient Visits:** 35561
**Births:** 306 **Total Expense ($000):** 35411 **Payroll Expense ($000):** 16452
**Personnel:** 220

## SHEBOYGAN—Sheboygan County

☒ **AURORA SHEBOYGAN MEMORIAL MEDICAL CENTER (520035)**, 2629 North
Seventh Street, Zip 53083–4998; tel. 920/451–5000 **A**1 2 9 10 **F**3 4 8 13 17
18 20 22 26 28 29 31 34 35 36 40 41 43 44 45 49 50 53 54 56 57 59 64
65 68 70 72 74 75 76 78 79 80 81 82 85 86 87 89 93 94 96 98 99 100
102 103 107 108 111 112 114 115 118 119 120 121 123 129 130 131 132
135 146 147 148 **P**6 **S** Aurora Health Care, Milwaukee, WI
Primary Contact: David Graebner, President
CFO: Laura Sellmann, Director Finance
CMO: James Hoell, M.D., President Medical Staff
CIO: Steve Serketich, Manager Information Services
CHR: Jennifer Vogel, Director Human Resources
CNO: Kathy Becker, Chief Nursing Officer
Web address: www.aurorahealthcare.org
**Control:** Other not–for–profit (including NFP Corporation) **Service:** General
Medical and Surgical

**Staffed Beds:** 134 **Admissions:** 5487 **Census:** 52 **Outpatient Visits:** 88840
**Births:** 905 **Total Expense ($000):** 104708 **Payroll Expense ($000):** 31620
**Personnel:** 564

☒ **ST. NICHOLAS HOSPITAL (520044)**, 3100 Superior Avenue, Zip 53081–1948;
tel. 920/459–8300 **A**1 2 9 10 **F**3 11 13 15 17 18 20 22 26 28 29 30 31 34
35 36 38 39 40 43 47 49 50 53 57 59 60 62 63 64 65 68 70 71 74 75 76
79 80 81 84 86 87 89 90 93 96 107 108 110 111 114 116 118 119 120
121 123 129 130 132 146 **P**2 5 **S** Hospital Sisters Health System,
Springfield, IL
Primary Contact: Andrew Bagnall, President and Chief Executive Officer
CFO: Pamela Ott, Financial Site Manager
CMO: Gregory Gross, M.D., President Medical Staff
CIO: Karen Held, Site Coordinator Information Technology
CHR: Barbara Hamann, Manager People Services
CNO: Debra Frenn, Chief Nursing Officer
Web address: www.stnicholashospital.org
**Control:** Church–operated, Nongovernment, not–for profit **Service:** General
Medical and Surgical

**Staffed Beds:** 55 **Admissions:** 2786 **Census:** 25 **Outpatient Visits:** 72651
**Births:** 318 **Total Expense ($000):** 64278 **Payroll Expense ($000):** 19807
**Personnel:** 295

## SHELL LAKE—Washburn County

☐ **INDIANHEAD MEDICAL CENTER (521342)**, 113 Fourth Avenue,
Zip 54871–4457, Mailing Address: P.O. Box 300, Zip 54871–0300;
tel. 715/468–7833 **A**1 9 10 18 **F**3 15 17 18 26 28 31 34 35 40 43 45 47 48
56 57 59 62 64 65 70 76 79 80 81 83 84 85 86 89 93 94 97 107 114 119
127 130 133 144 148 **P**5 **S** Mid Atlantic Health Management, Inc.,
Stevensville, MD
Primary Contact: Paul Naglosky, Administrator
CFO: Michael Elliott, Controller
CMO: Allan Haesemeyer, M.D., Chief of Staff
CHR: Gwen Nielsen, Manager Human Resources
Web address: www.indianheadmedicalcenter.com
**Control:** Corporation, Investor–owned, for–profit **Service:** General Medical and
Surgical

**Staffed Beds:** 25 **Admissions:** 441 **Census:** 4 **Outpatient Visits:** 8860
**Births:** 8 **Total Expense ($000):** 6705 **Payroll Expense ($000):** 2690
**Personnel:** 65

## SPARTA—Monroe County

☐ **MAYO CLINIC HEALTH SYSTEM – FRANCISCAN HEALTHCARE IN SPARTA
(521305)**, 310 West Main Street, Zip 54656–2171; tel. 608/269–2132 **A**1 9
10 18 **F**5 11 15 28 29 30 34 35 40 42 43 53 56 57 59 64 65 66 68 75 77
80 81 86 87 93 97 107 108 119 127 130 132 133 143 144 146 **P**2 **S** Mayo
Clinic Health System, Rochester, MN
Primary Contact: Kimberly Hawthorne, Administrator
CMO: Tracy Warsing, M.D., Site Leader Chief of Staff
Web address: www.mayohealthsystem.com
**Control:** Church–operated, Nongovernment, not–for profit **Service:** General
Medical and Surgical

**Staffed Beds:** 13 **Admissions:** 338 **Census:** 6 **Outpatient Visits:** 21868
**Births:** 0 **Total Expense ($000):** 13325 **Payroll Expense ($000):** 6965
**Personnel:** 111

## SPOONER—Washburn County

★ **SPOONER HEALTH SYSTEM (521332)**, 819 Ash Street, Zip 54801–1299;
tel. 715/635–2111 **A**9 10 18 **F**3 13 15 17 29 31 34 35 40 45 50 56 57 59
62 63 64 65 68 70 76 78 80 81 85 86 87 89 90 93 107 111 115 119 130
132 133 135 146 148 **S** HealthTech Management Services, Franklin, TN
Primary Contact: Michael Schafer, Chief Executive Officer and Administrator
CFO: Rebecca Busch, Chief Financial Officer
CHR: Cindy Rouzer, Director Human Resources
Web address: www.spoonerhealthsystem.com
**Control:** Other not–for–profit (including NFP Corporation) **Service:** General
Medical and Surgical

**Staffed Beds:** 25 **Admissions:** 763 **Census:** 30 **Outpatient Visits:** 17132
**Births:** 57 **Total Expense ($000):** 15471 **Payroll Expense ($000):** 6806
**Personnel:** 106

WI

*Many Facility Codes have changed. Please refer to the AHA Guide Code Chart.*
© 2013 AHA Guide

**ST. CROIX FALLS—Polk County**

**ST. CROIX REGIONAL MEDICAL CENTER (521337)**, 235 State Street, Zip 54024–4117; tel. 715/483–3261 **A**9 10 18 **F**3 6 8 11 13 15 18 26 28 29 31 32 34 35 36 40 41 43 45 48 50 51 55 56 57 64 65 66 70 74 75 76 77 78 79 80 81 82 83 85 86 87 92 93 94 97 99 100 101 104 107 108 110 111 114 116 117 118 119 127 129 131 132 133 135 146 148 **P**5 6
Primary Contact: Dave Dobosenski, Chief Executive Officer
CFO: John Tremble, Chief Financial Officer
CMO: William Beyer, M.D., Chief Medical Officer
CIO: Brent McCurdy, Director Management Information
CHR: Lee Ann Vitalis, Executive Director Human Resources
Web address: www.scrmc.org
**Control:** Other not–for–profit (including NFP Corporation) **Service:** General Medical and Surgical

**Staffed Beds: 25 Admissions: 1652 Census: 13 Outpatient Visits: 178242 Births: 279 Total Expense ($000): 60116 Payroll Expense ($000): 20901 Personnel: 388**

**STANLEY—Chippewa County**

★ **MINISTRY OUR LADY OF VICTORY HOSPITAL (521311)**, (Formerly Our Lady of Victory Hospital), 1120 Pine Street, Zip 54768–1297; tel. 715/644–5571 **A**9 10 18 **F**3 15 28 29 30 34 35 40 43 45 50 59 65 75 76 77 80 81 84 85 86 87 89 90 93 94 96 97 107 109 110 114 127 130 131 133 144 146 **P**6 **S** Ascension Health, Saint Louis, MO
Primary Contact: Cynthia Eichman, President
CFO: Terri Lewandowski, Director Financial Services
Web address: www.ministryhealth.org
**Control:** Other not–for–profit (including NFP Corporation) **Service:** General Medical and Surgical

**Staffed Beds: 4 Admissions: 355 Census: 6 Outpatient Visits: 33863 Births: 0 Total Expense ($000): 20387 Payroll Expense ($000): 8337 Personnel: 105**

**STEVENS POINT—Portage County**

⊞ **MINISTRY SAINT MICHAEL'S HOSPITAL (520002)**, 900 Illinois Avenue, Zip 54481–3196; tel. 715/346–5000 **A**1 9 10 19 **F**3 4 5 12 13 15 17 20 28 29 30 34 35 39 40 41 43 44 45 47 48 50 51 56 57 59 64 65 68 70 72 74 75 76 77 79 80 81 82 84 85 86 87 88 89 93 94 98 99 100 101 102 103 104 105 106 107 108 110 111 114 116 118 119 120 121 129 130 131 132 135 144 146 147 148 **S** Ascension Health, Saint Louis, MO
Primary Contact: Jeffrey L. Martin, President
CFO: William J. Hinner, Vice President Financial Analysis and Planning
CIO: Will Weider, Chief Information Officer
CHR: Cheryl F. Zima, Vice President Human Resources
Web address: www.ministryhealth.org/SMH/home.nws
**Control:** Church–operated, Nongovernment, not–for profit **Service:** General Medical and Surgical

**Staffed Beds: 51 Admissions: 4651 Census: 45 Outpatient Visits: 320860 Births: 512 Total Expense ($000): 163183 Payroll Expense ($000): 84174 Personnel: 644**

**SAINT MICHAEL'S HOSPITAL** See Ministry Saint Michael's Hospital

**STOUGHTON—Dane County**

☐ **STOUGHTON HOSPITAL ASSOCIATION (521343)**, 900 Ridge Street, Zip 53589–1864; tel. 608/873–6611 **A**1 9 10 18 **F**3 4 6 8 14 15 28 29 34 35 36 40 41 43 45 53 54 56 57 59 62 64 65 70 75 77 80 81 85 86 89 90 91 93 96 97 98 100 102 103 107 110 115 117 129 130 131 132 133 135 144 146 147 148
Primary Contact: Terrence Brenny, President and Chief Executive Officer
CFO: Karen Myers, Vice President Financial Services
CMO: Guirish Agni, M.D., Chief of Staff
CIO: Karen Myers, Vice President Financial Services
CHR: Christopher Schmitz, Director Human Resources
Web address: www.stoughtonhospital.com
**Control:** Other not–for–profit (including NFP Corporation) **Service:** General Medical and Surgical

**Staffed Beds: 32 Admissions: 1046 Census: 17 Outpatient Visits: 53086 Births: 0 Total Expense ($000): 36349 Payroll Expense ($000): 15406 Personnel: 267**

**STURGEON BAY—Door County**

**DOOR COUNTY MEMORIAL HOSPITAL** See Ministry Door County Medical Center

⊞ **MINISTRY DOOR COUNTY MEDICAL CENTER (521358)**, 323 South 18th Avenue, Zip 54235–1495; tel. 920/743–5566, (Total facility includes 30 beds in nursing home–type unit) **A**1 9 10 18 **F**2 3 11 13 15 17 28 29 30 31 32 34 35 36 39 40 43 55 56 57 59 61 64 65 66 68 70 75 76 77 78 79 80 81 82 84 85 86 87 89 90 93 107 108 110 111 114 117 118 119 127 128 129 130 132 133 135 144 145 147 148 **P**6 **S** Ascension Health, Saint Louis, MO
Primary Contact: Gerald M. Worrick, President and Chief Executive Officer
CFO: Robert C. Scieszinski, Vice President Finance
CIO: Mary Lopas, Chief Information Officer
CHR: Kelli Bowling, Chief Culture Officer
CNO: Jody Boes, Vice President Patient Care Services
Web address: www.ministryhealth.org
**Control:** Church–operated, Nongovernment, not–for profit **Service:** General Medical and Surgical

**Staffed Beds: 55 Admissions: 1487 Census: 39 Outpatient Visits: 87282 Births: 115 Total Expense ($000): 65224 Payroll Expense ($000): 32985 Personnel: 478**

**SUMMIT—Waukesha County**

⊞ **AURORA MEDICAL CENTER SUMMIT (520206)**, 36500 Aurora Drive, Zip 53066–4899; tel. 262/434–1000 **A**1 2 9 10 **F**3 8 11 12 13 15 17 18 20 22 24 26 28 29 30 34 36 37 39 40 44 45 46 47 48 49 50 53 54 59 64 68 70 72 74 75 76 79 80 81 82 85 86 87 89 90 92 93 94 96 107 108 110 111 112 115 116 117 118 119 121 123 124 126 129 130 131 132 146 147 148 **P**6 **S** Aurora Health Care, Milwaukee, WI
Primary Contact: Daniel J. Bonk, Chief Executive Officer
Web address: www.aurorahealthcare.org
**Control:** Other not–for–profit (including NFP Corporation) **Service:** General Medical and Surgical

**Staffed Beds: 75 Admissions: 2691 Census: 28 Outpatient Visits: 77116 Births: 446 Total Expense ($000): 91131 Payroll Expense ($000): 28678 Personnel: 528**

**SUPERIOR—Douglas County**

⊞ **ESSENTIA HEALTH ST. MARY'S HOSPITAL OF SUPERIOR (521329)**, 3500 Tower Avenue, Zip 54880–5395; tel. 715/817–7000 **A**1 9 10 18 **F**3 11 15 28 29 30 40 56 59 65 75 77 78 80 81 82 86 87 90 93 96 97 107 110 119 130 133 135 142 146 148 **P**6 **S** Essentia Health, Duluth, MN
Primary Contact: Terry Jacobson, Administrator and Chief Executive Officer
Web address: www.essentiahealth.org/StMarysHospitalSuperior/FindaClinic/Essentia–Health–St–Marys–HospitalSuperior—61.aspx
**Control:** Other not–for–profit (including NFP Corporation) **Service:** General Medical and Surgical

**Staffed Beds: 25 Admissions: 537 Census: 10 Outpatient Visits: 21429 Births: 0 Total Expense ($000): 33838 Payroll Expense ($000): 15113 Personnel: 195**

**TOMAH—Monroe County**

⊞ **TOMAH MEMORIAL HOSPITAL (521320)**, 321 Butts Avenue, Zip 54660–1412; tel. 608/372–2181 **A**1 9 10 18 **F**3 11 12 13 28 30 31 34 35 40 43 57 59 63 64 76 77 79 80 81 82 84 85 86 87 89 90 93 107 111 114 119 129 130 132 133 135 144 **P**5 **S** HealthTech Management Services, Franklin, TN
Primary Contact: Philip J. Stuart, Administrator and Chief Executive Officer
CFO: Joseph Zeps, Vice President Finance
CIO: LaVonne Smith, Director Health Information Technology
CHR: Brenda Reinert, Director Human Resources
CNO: Evie Chapman, Chief Nursing Officer
Web address: www.tomahhospital.org
**Control:** Other not–for–profit (including NFP Corporation) **Service:** General Medical and Surgical

**Staffed Beds: 25 Admissions: 995 Census: 8 Outpatient Visits: 21849 Births: 324 Total Expense ($000): 33289 Payroll Expense ($000): 13997 Personnel: 227**

⊞ △ **TOMAH VETERANS AFFAIRS MEDICAL CENTER**, (Formerly Veterans Affairs Medical Center), 500 East Veterans Street, Zip 54660–3105; tel. 608/372–3971, (Nonreporting) **A**1 7 **S** Department of Veterans Affairs, Washington, DC
Primary Contact: Mario DeSanctis, FACHE, Director
CFO: Jane Mashak–Ekern, Fiscal Officer
CMO: David Houlihan, M.D., Chief of Staff
CIO: Mary Monroe, Chief Information Officer
Web address: www.tomah.va.gov
**Control:** Veterans Affairs, Government, federal **Service:** General Medical and Surgical

**Staffed Beds: 71**

WI

---

## TOMAHAWK—Lincoln County

**MINISTRY SACRED HEART HOSPITAL (521313)**, (Formerly Sacred Heart Hospital), 401 West Mohawk Drive, Zip 54487–2274; tel. 715/453–7700 **A**9 10 18 **F**15 28 29 30 34 35 36 40 44 45 49 50 56 57 59 64 65 68 75 77 80 81 84 86 87 89 91 92 93 96 100 101 104 107 109 115 119 130 131 133 146 **S** Ascension Health, Saint Louis, MO
Primary Contact: Monica Hilt, President
Web address: www.ministryhealth.org
**Control:** Church–operated, Nongovernment, not–for profit **Service:** General Medical and Surgical

**Staffed Beds:** 6 **Admissions:** 336 **Census:** 3 **Outpatient Visits:** 10595 **Births:** 0 **Total Expense ($000):** 13698 **Payroll Expense ($000):** 7879 **Personnel:** 87

## TWO RIVERS—Manitowoc County

☒ **AURORA MEDICAL CENTER – MANITOWOC COUNTY (520034)**, 5000 Memorial Drive, Zip 54241–3900; tel. 920/794–5000 **A**1 2 9 10 **F**3 11 13 28 29 30 31 34 35 36 37 40 43 44 45 47 48 49 50 54 56 57 59 64 75 76 78 79 80 81 82 85 86 87 89 93 94 107 108 111 114 119 121 123 129 130 132 133 134 135 143 146 147 148 **P**6 **S** Aurora Health Care, Milwaukee, WI
Primary Contact: Cathie A. Kocourek, President
COO: Carrie L. Penovich, Director Clinical and Support Services
CFO: Sandra Ewald, Vice President Finance
CMO: Paul Mihalakakos, M.D., Chief of Staff
CIO: Philip Loftus, Ph.D., Chief Information Officer
CHR: Stacie A. Schneider, Director Human Resources
CNO: Betsy Benz, R.N., Chief Nursing Officer
Web address: www.aurorahealthcare.org
**Control:** Other not–for–profit (including NFP Corporation) **Service:** General Medical and Surgical

**Staffed Beds:** 65 **Admissions:** 2242 **Census:** 19 **Outpatient Visits:** 53033 **Births:** 410 **Total Expense ($000):** 49854 **Payroll Expense ($000):** 16084 **Personnel:** 320

## VIROQUA—Vernon County

**VERNON MEMORIAL HEALTHCARE (521348)**, 507 South Main Street, Zip 54665–2096; tel. 608/637–2101 **A**9 10 18 **F**3 5 13 15 28 29 34 35 36 37 40 43 45 53 56 57 59 62 63 75 76 77 80 81 82 86 87 89 93 107 110 114 127 130 131 132 133 135 144 146 148 **P**2 6
Primary Contact: Kyle Bakkum, Chief Executive Officer and Administrator
COO: Kristy Wiltrout, R.N., Chief Operating Officer
CFO: Mary Koenig, Chief Financial Officer
CIO: Julie Steiner, Manager Marketing and Public Relations
CHR: Kay Starr, Manager Human Resources
Web address: www.vmh.org
**Control:** Other not–for–profit (including NFP Corporation) **Service:** General Medical and Surgical

**Staffed Beds:** 11 **Admissions:** 1351 **Census:** 10 **Outpatient Visits:** 127736 **Births:** 171 **Total Expense ($000):** 58637 **Payroll Expense ($000):** 23532 **Personnel:** 360

## WATERFORD—Racine County

☐ **LAKEVIEW SPECIALTY HOSPITAL AND REHABILITATION CENTER (522005)**, 1701 Sharp Road, Zip 53185–5214; tel. 262/534–7297 **A**1 9 10 **F**1 12 28 29 34 36 38 53 62 64 75 82 86 87 90 93 99 100 101 104 130 **P**6
Primary Contact: Robyn Rushing, Administrator
Web address: www.lakeviewsystem.com
**Control:** Corporation, Investor–owned, for–profit **Service:** Long–Term Acute Care hospital

**Staffed Beds:** 39 **Admissions:** 269 **Census:** 27 **Outpatient Visits:** 4435 **Births:** 0 **Total Expense ($000):** 16340 **Payroll Expense ($000):** 7326 **Personnel:** 172

## WATERTOWN—Dodge County

☒ **WATERTOWN REGIONAL MEDICAL CENTER (520116)**, 125 Hospital Drive, Zip 53098–3303; tel. 920/261–4210 **A**1 9 10 **F**3 10 11 13 15 18 20 22 26 28 29 34 35 36 40 53 54 56 57 59 64 65 68 69 71 74 75 76 77 78 79 80 81 82 86 87 89 90 93 104 107 108 111 112 115 118 119 125 129 130 131 132 135 144 146 147 148 **P**8
Primary Contact: John P. Kosanovich, President
COO: John P. Kosanovich, President
CFO: John Graf, Senior Vice President
CMO: Jeff Meade, M.D., Chief Medical Officer
CIO: Jennifer Laughlin, Vice President and Chief Information Officer
CHR: Duane Floyd, Vice President Human Resources and Professional Services
CNO: Jacklynn Lesniak, R.N., Vice President Patient Services
Web address: www.uwphwatertown.com
**Control:** Other not–for–profit (including NFP Corporation) **Service:** General Medical and Surgical

**Staffed Beds:** 55 **Admissions:** 1961 **Census:** 18 **Outpatient Visits:** 203583 **Births:** 257 **Total Expense ($000):** 95776 **Payroll Expense ($000):** 41693 **Personnel:** 595

## WAUKESHA—Waukesha County

☐ **REHABILITATION HOSPITAL OF WISCONSIN (523027)**, 1625 Coldwater Creek Drive, Zip 53188–8028; tel. 262/521–8800 **A**1 9 10 **F**29 34 64 75 86 90 93 99 103 130 **S** Centerre Healthcare, Brentwood, TN
Primary Contact: Anne E. Jurenec, Chief Executive Officer
CFO: Mary Reeves, Controller
CMO: Yechiel Kleen, M.D., Medical Director
CHR: Annette Hahn, Director Human Resources
Web address: www.rehabhospitalwi.com
**Control:** Partnership, Investor–owned, for–profit **Service:** Rehabilitation

**Staffed Beds:** 40 **Admissions:** 717 **Census:** 29 **Outpatient Visits:** 5142 **Births:** 0 **Total Expense ($000):** 12969 **Payroll Expense ($000):** 6334 **Personnel:** 112

**WAUKESHA COUNTY MENTAL HEALTH CENTER (524026)**, 2501 Airport Road, Zip 53188; tel. 262/548–7950 **A**10 **F**4 98 130
Primary Contact: Michele A. Cusatis, Ph.D., Administrator
Web address: www.waukeshacounty.gov/
**Control:** County–Government, nonfederal **Service:** Psychiatric

**Staffed Beds:** 28 **Admissions:** 901 **Census:** 16 **Outpatient Visits:** 0 **Births:** 0 **Total Expense ($000):** 6239 **Payroll Expense ($000):** 3180 **Personnel:** 52

☒ **WAUKESHA MEMORIAL HOSPITAL (520008)**, 725 American Avenue, Zip 53188–5099; tel. 262/928–1000 **A**1 2 3 5 9 10 **F**3 4 5 6 11 12 13 15 18 20 22 24 26 28 29 30 31 32 34 35 37 40 44 45 46 47 49 50 56 57 58 59 64 68 72 74 75 76 78 79 80 81 82 84 85 87 89 93 97 98 100 101 102 103 105 107 108 110 111 114 115 116 117 118 119 120 121 123 124 126 129 130 132 135 143 146 147 148 **S** ProHealth Care, Inc., Waukesha, WI
Primary Contact: John R. Robertstad, FACHE, President
CFO: Nan Nelson, Vice President Finance
CMO: James D. Gardner, M.D., Vice President and Chief Medical Officer
CIO: Rodney Dykehouse, Senior Vice President Information Services
CHR: Nadine T. Guirl, Senior Vice President Human Resources
Web address: www.prohealthcare.org/locations/locations–v2–detail/?id=1119
**Control:** Other not–for–profit (including NFP Corporation) **Service:** General Medical and Surgical

**Staffed Beds:** 317 **Admissions:** 15832 **Census:** 177 **Outpatient Visits:** 267691 **Births:** 1818 **Total Expense ($000):** 380190 **Payroll Expense ($000):** 105923 **Personnel:** 1813

## WAUPACA—Waupaca County

☐ **RIVERSIDE MEDICAL CENTER (521334)**, 800 Riverside Drive, Zip 54981–1999; tel. 715/258–1000 **A**1 9 10 18 **F**3 8 11 13 17 28 29 34 35 40 45 57 59 64 68 70 76 78 80 81 82 86 87 88 89 90 97 107 111 112 115 119 130 133 144 146 147 148 **S** ThedaCare, Inc., Appleton, WI
Primary Contact: Craig A. Kantos, Chief Executive Officer
CFO: Kerry Lee Blanke, Director Financial Services
CMO: James Williams, M.D., Chief of Staff
CHR: Kevin Gossens, Director Human Resources
Web address: www.riversidemedical.org
**Control:** Other not–for–profit (including NFP Corporation) **Service:** General Medical and Surgical

**Staffed Beds:** 25 **Admissions:** 1052 **Census:** 10 **Outpatient Visits:** 49446 **Births:** 161 **Total Expense ($000):** 29502 **Payroll Expense ($000):** 15607 **Personnel:** 228

## WAUPUN—Dodge County

☐ **WAUPUN MEMORIAL HOSPITAL (521327)**, 620 West Brown Street, Zip 53963–1799; tel. 920/324–5581 **A**1 9 10 18 **F**3 11 13 15 28 29 31 34 35 36 40 43 44 50 51 57 59 60 66 68 69 70 71 74 75 76 77 79 81 82 84 85 86 87 93 97 107 108 109 110 114 118 119 130 131 132 133 134 143 144 146 147 148 **P**6
Primary Contact: DeAnn Thurmer, Chief Operating Officer
CFO: Bonnie Schmitz, Chief Financial Officer
Web address: www.agnesian.com
**Control:** Church–operated, Nongovernment, not–for profit **Service:** General Medical and Surgical

**Staffed Beds:** 25 **Admissions:** 1044 **Census:** 10 **Outpatient Visits:** 57441 **Births:** 129 **Total Expense ($000):** 32677 **Payroll Expense ($000):** 12886 **Personnel:** 175

**WI**

*Many Facility Codes have changed. Please refer to the AHA Guide Code Chart.*
© 2013 AHA Guide

## WAUSAU—Marathon County

☒ △ **ASPIRUS WAUSAU HOSPITAL (520030)**, 333 Pine Ridge Boulevard, Zip 54401–4187; tel. 715/847–2121 **A**1 2 3 5 7 9 10 **F**3 5 6 7 8 11 12 13 15 17 18 20 22 24 26 28 29 30 31 34 35 36 39 40 43 44 45 46 47 48 49 50 51 54 55 56 58 59 60 62 63 64 65 68 69 70 71 72 74 75 76 78 79 80 81 82 83 84 85 86 87 89 90 92 93 96 97 100 102 103 104 107 108 110 111 114 115 116 117 118 119 120 121 123 124 126 129 130 132 135 143 144 146 147 148 **P**8 **S** Aspirus, Inc., Wausau, WI
Primary Contact: Marita Hattem, Interim President and Chief Operating Officer
COO: Marita Hattem, Interim President and Chief Operating Officer
CFO: Sidney C. Sczygelski, Senior Vice President Finance and Chief Financial Officer
CHR: Roger V. Lucas, Vice President, Human Resources
Web address: www.aspirus.org
**Control:** Other not–for–profit (including NFP Corporation) **Service:** General Medical and Surgical

| | |
|---|---|
| **Staffed Beds:** 257 **Admissions:** 13130 **Census:** 141 **Outpatient Visits:** 107742 **Births:** 1329 **Total Expense ($000):** 324196 **Payroll Expense ($000):** 108530 **Personnel:** 2134 | |

**NORTH CENTRAL HEALTH CARE (524017)**, 1100 Lake View Drive, Zip 54403–6785; tel. 715/848–4600, (Total facility includes 239 beds in nursing home–type unit) **A**9 10 **F**3 4 5 6 29 38 56 75 86 93 98 99 100 101 102 103 104 105 106 128
Primary Contact: Gary Bezucha, FACHE, Chief Executive Officer
CFO: Brenda Glodowski, Chief Financial Officer
CHR: Chad Bastable, Director Human Resources
Web address: www.norcen.org
**Control:** County–Government, nonfederal **Service:** Psychiatric

| | |
|---|---|
| **Staffed Beds:** 247 **Admissions:** 1221 **Census:** 257 **Outpatient Visits:** 190633 **Births:** 0 **Total Expense ($000):** 27660 **Payroll Expense ($000):** 15906 **Personnel:** 234 | |

**NORTH CENTRAL HEALTH CARE FACILITIES** See North Central Health Care

## WAUWATOSA—Milwaukee County

☒ **AURORA PSYCHIATRIC HOSPITAL (524000)**, 1220 Dewey Avenue, Zip 53213–2598; tel. 414/454–6600 **A**1 9 10 **F**4 5 30 35 38 44 50 54 59 64 68 75 86 87 98 99 100 101 102 104 105 106 130 132 135 **P**6 **S** Aurora Health Care, Milwaukee, WI
Primary Contact: Peter Carlson, Administrator
CFO: David Yeager, Senior Vice President Finance
CMO: Anthony Meyer, M.D., Medical Director
CIO: Philip Loftus, Ph.D., Vice President and Chief Information Officer
CHR: Barbara Molthen, Director Human Resources
CNO: Jamie Lewiston, R.N., Chief Nursing Officer
Web address: www.aurorahealthcare.org
**Control:** Other not–for–profit (including NFP Corporation) **Service:** Psychiatric

| | |
|---|---|
| **Staffed Beds:** 78 **Admissions:** 3218 **Census:** 44 **Outpatient Visits:** 14806 **Births:** 0 **Total Expense ($000):** 23827 **Payroll Expense ($000):** 12271 **Personnel:** 242 | |

★ **WHEATON FRANCISCAN HEALTHCARE – THE WISCONSIN HEART HOSPITAL (520199)**, 10000 West Bluemound Road, Zip 53226–4321; tel. 414/778–7800, **A**9 **F**3 17 20 22 24 29 34 37 40 43 45 47 48 64 75 77 79 81 85 86 107 108 118 119 130 **S** Wheaton Franciscan Healthcare, Wheaton, IL
Primary Contact: Debra K. Standridge, President
CFO: Michael Petitt, Director of Finance
CMO: Rita Hanson, M.D., Vice President Medical Affairs
CIO: Gregory Smith, Senior Vice President and Chief Information Officer
CHR: Christopher Morris, Director Human Resources
CNO: Sharon Baughman, Vice President Patient Services and Chief Nursing Officer
Web address: www.mywheaton.org/hearthospital
**Control:** Church–operated, Nongovernment, not–for profit **Service:** Heart

| | |
|---|---|
| **Staffed Beds:** 30 **Admissions:** 1635 **Census:** 14 **Outpatient Visits:** 11524 **Births:** 0 **Total Expense ($000):** 45750 **Payroll Expense ($000):** 10854 **Personnel:** 143 | |

## WEST ALLIS—Milwaukee County

☒ △ **AURORA WEST ALLIS MEDICAL CENTER (520139)**, 8901 West Lincoln Avenue, Zip 53227–2409, Mailing Address: P.O. Box 27901, Zip 53227–0901; tel. 414/328–6000 **A**1 2 7 9 10 **F**2 3 8 11 12 13 15 29 30 31 34 35 37 38 40 43 44 45 49 50 52 54 55 56 57 59 64 65 68 70 72 74 75 76 78 79 80 81 82 84 85 86 87 91 93 94 95 96 107 108 110 111 114 115 116 118 119 120 121 123 126 130 132 135 146 147 148 **P**6 **S** Aurora Health Care, Milwaukee, WI
Primary Contact: Richard A. Kellar, President
CFO: Chris Hemmer, Director Finance
CIO: Philip Loftus, Ph.D., Chief Information Officer
CHR: Shannon Christenson, Director Human Resources
CHR: Mindy Necci, Director Human Resources
CNO: Diane Strack, R.N., Chief Nursing Officer
Web address: www.aurorahealthcare.org
**Control:** Other not–for–profit (including NFP Corporation) **Service:** General Medical and Surgical

| | |
|---|---|
| **Staffed Beds:** 220 **Admissions:** 12878 **Census:** 146 **Outpatient Visits:** 132716 **Births:** 3331 **Total Expense ($000):** 192266 **Payroll Expense ($000):** 61237 **Personnel:** 1090 | |

## WEST BEND—Washington County

☒ **ST. JOSEPH'S COMMUNITY HOSPITAL OF WEST BEND (520063)**, 3200 Pleasant Valley Road, Zip 53095–9274; tel. 262/334–5533 **A**1 2 9 10 **F**3 4 13 15 17 28 29 30 31 34 35 40 43 44 45 46 47 48 49 50 51 57 59 63 64 68 70 74 75 76 77 78 79 80 81 85 86 87 89 100 101 107 108 110 111 114 115 118 119 120 121 129 130 132 135 146 147 148
Primary Contact: Allen Ericson, President
CFO: Mike Malzewski, Chief Financial Officer
CMO: Patrick Gardner, M.D., Vice President Medical Affairs
CHR: Deb Lauenstein, Director Human Resources and Marketing
Web address: www.stjosephswbclinic.com
**Control:** Other not–for–profit (including NFP Corporation) **Service:** General Medical and Surgical

| | |
|---|---|
| **Staffed Beds:** 78 **Admissions:** 3672 **Census:** 41 **Outpatient Visits:** 79479 **Births:** 650 **Total Expense ($000):** 81580 **Payroll Expense ($000):** 27309 **Personnel:** 397 | |

## WESTON—Marathon County

☒ **MINISTRY SAINT CLARE'S HOSPITAL (520202)**, (Formerly Saint Clare's Hospital), 3400 Ministry Parkway, Zip 54476–5220; tel. 715/393–3000 **A**1 9 10 **F**3 11 13 17 18 20 22 24 26 29 30 31 34 35 37 40 43 44 50 51 57 59 64 68 70 72 74 75 76 78 79 80 81 82 85 86 87 89 130 132 135 143 146 148 **P**6 **S** Ascension Health, Saint Louis, MO
Primary Contact: Mary T. Krueger, President
CFO: Charlotte Esselman, Director Finance
CMO: Larry T. Hegland, M.D., Chief Medical Officer
CIO: Stacy Marver, Director Information Technology
CHR: Nancy Kwiesielewicz, Human Resources Manager
CNO: Kristine McGarigle, R.N., Vice President Patient Care
Web address: www.ministryhealth.org
**Control:** Church–operated, Nongovernment, not–for profit **Service:** General Medical and Surgical

| | |
|---|---|
| **Staffed Beds:** 69 **Admissions:** 5459 **Census:** 47 **Outpatient Visits:** 17835 **Births:** 665 **Total Expense ($000):** 96821 **Payroll Expense ($000):** 30530 **Personnel:** 397 | |

## WHITEHALL—Trempealeau County

★ **GUNDERSEN TRI–COUNTY HOSPITAL AND CLINICS (521316)**, (Formerly Tri–County Memorial Hospital), 18601 Lincoln Street, Zip 54773–8605; tel. 715/538–4361, (Total facility includes 62 beds in nursing home–type unit) **A**9 10 18 **F**7 10 11 28 34 40 43 53 56 64 69 75 78 81 86 90 93 107 108 128 130 144
Primary Contact: Brian Theiler, President and Chief Executive Officer
COO: Brian Theiler, President and Chief Executive Officer
CFO: Patti Dockendorff, Director Finance
CMO: Smita Rajasekaran, M.D., Chief Medical Officer
CIO: John Waldera, Director Information Technology
CHR: Jill Wesener Dieck, Director Human Resources
CNO: Emily Anderson, Director of Nursing Emergency Room
Web address: www.tricountymemorial.org/index.html
**Control:** Other not–for–profit (including NFP Corporation) **Service:** General Medical and Surgical

| | |
|---|---|
| **Staffed Beds:** 65 **Admissions:** 473 **Census:** 61 **Outpatient Visits:** 20721 **Births:** 0 **Total Expense ($000):** 11083 **Payroll Expense ($000):** 4220 **Personnel:** 111 | |

**WI**

---

**Hospital, Medicare Provider Number, Address, Telephone, Approval, Facility, and Physician Codes, Health Care System**

★ American Hospital Association (AHA) membership
☐ The Joint Commission accreditation
◇ DNV Healthcare Inc. accreditation
○ Healthcare Facilities Accreditation Program
△ Commission on Accreditation of Rehabilitation Facilities (CARF) accreditation

### WILD ROSE—Waushara County

**WILD ROSE COMMUNITY MEMORIAL HOSPITAL (521303)**, 601 Grove
Avenue, Zip 54984–6903, Mailing Address: P.O. Box 243, Zip 54984–0243;
tel. 920/622–3257 **A**9 10 18 **F**10 11 15 28 29 34 40 43 56 64 75 77 80 81
86 87 89 90 93 99 100 101 102 103 104 107 111 119 131 144 147 **P**7
Primary Contact: Donald Caves, President
CFO: Thomas P. Krystowiak, Vice President Finance
CMO: Reginaldo Arboleda, M.D., Chief of Staff
CHR: Karen M. West, Administrator Support Services
Web address: www.wildrosehospital.org
**Control:** Other not–for–profit (including NFP Corporation) **Service:** General
Medical and Surgical

**Staffed Beds:** 25 **Admissions:** 529 **Census:** 10 **Outpatient Visits:** 17073
**Births:** 0 **Total Expense ($000):** 13099 **Payroll Expense ($000):** 4864
**Personnel:** 124

### WINNEBAGO—Winnebago County

☐ **WINNEBAGO MENTAL HEALTH INSTITUTE (524002)**, 1300 South Drive,
Zip 54985, Mailing Address: Box 9, Zip 54985–0009; tel. 920/235–4910 **A**1 9
10 **F**3 4 5 29 30 39 75 82 87 92 98 99 103 130 143 146 **P**7
Primary Contact: Thomas Speech, M.D., Director
CMO: Randy Kerswill, M.D., Medical Director
CIO: Greg Schneider, Director Information Technology
CHR: Frances Dujon–Reynolds, Director Human Resources
Web address: www.dhfs.state.wi.us/mh_winnebago
**Control:** State–Government, nonfederal **Service:** Psychiatric

**Staffed Beds:** 169 **Admissions:** 1626 **Census:** 171 **Outpatient Visits:** 0
**Births:** 0 **Total Expense ($000):** 51628 **Payroll Expense ($000):** 29190
**Personnel:** 655

### WISCONSIN RAPIDS—Wood County

⌧ **RIVERVIEW HOSPITAL ASSOCIATION (520033)**, 410 Dewey Street,
Zip 54494–4715, Mailing Address: P.O. Box 8080, Zip 54495–8080;
tel. 715/423–6060 **A**1 9 10 **F**3 4 8 13 14 15 17 28 30 31 34 35 39 40 43 45
56 59 64 65 68 69 70 74 75 76 77 78 79 80 81 84 85 86 88 89 90 93 97
98 100 107 108 110 111 115 117 118 119 120 121 124 129 130 131 132
135 146
Primary Contact: Celse A. Berard, President
CFO: Michael Bovee, Vice President Finance
CMO: Timothy K. Huebner, M.D., President Medical Affairs
CIO: Marjorie Tell, Vice President Information Technology
CHR: Tom Hunsberger, Vice President Human Resources
Web address: www.riverviewhospital.org
**Control:** Other not–for–profit (including NFP Corporation) **Service:** General
Medical and Surgical

**Staffed Beds:** 69 **Admissions:** 2905 **Census:** 25 **Outpatient Visits:** 55679
**Births:** 458 **Total Expense ($000):** 81401 **Payroll Expense ($000):** 31879
**Personnel:** 518

### WOODRUFF—Oneida County

⌧ **HOWARD YOUNG MEDICAL CENTER (520091)**, 240 Maple Street,
Zip 54568–9190, Mailing Address: P.O. Box 470, Zip 54568–0470;
tel. 715/356–8000 **A**1 9 10 20 **F**3 11 13 15 28 29 30 35 40 43 44 45 50 57
64 68 75 76 77 80 81 82 84 85 86 87 88 89 93 96 107 108 110 114 119
126 129 130 133 146 148 **P**6 **S** Ascension Health, Saint Louis, MO
Primary Contact: Sheila Clough, President
CFO: Cathy Bukowski, Chief Financial Officer
CIO: Howard Dobizl, Director Information Technology Services
CHR: Michelle Cornelius, Director Human Resources
Web address: www.ministryhealth.org
**Control:** Church–operated, Nongovernment, not–for profit **Service:** General
Medical and Surgical

**Staffed Beds:** 35 **Admissions:** 3017 **Census:** 29 **Outpatient Visits:** 39683
**Births:** 304 **Total Expense ($000):** 53876 **Payroll Expense ($000):** 23961
**Personnel:** 405

WI

*Many Facility Codes have changed. Please refer to the AHA Guide Code Chart.*

© 2013 AHA Guide

# WYOMING

## AFTON—Lincoln County

★ **STAR VALLEY MEDICAL CENTER (531313)**, 901 Adams Street,
Zip 83110–9621, Mailing Address: P.O. Box 579, Zip 83110–0579;
tel. 307/885–5800, (Total facility includes 24 beds in nursing home–type unit) **A**9
10 18 **F**3 7 11 12 13 15 29 31 34 40 43 45 57 59 64 65 67 74 75 76 77 78
79 81 82 85 86 87 89 97 102 107 110 111 114 118 119 128 129 130 131
132 133 135 144 146 147 148 **P**6
Primary Contact: Charlie A. Button, President and Chief Executive Officer
CMO: David Shrader, M.D., Chief of Staff
CIO: Denise Wheeler, Chief Information Officer
CHR: Joel Johnson, Director Human Resources
CNO: Mike Kentner, Director of Nursing
Web address: www.svmcwy.org
**Control:** Hospital district or authority, Government, nonfederal **Service:** General
Medical and Surgical

**Staffed Beds:** 44 **Admissions:** 690 **Census:** 28 **Outpatient Visits:** 21612
**Births:** 99 **Total Expense ($000):** 24385 **Payroll Expense ($000):** 11566
**Personnel:** 212

## BASIN—Big Horn County

**SOUTH BIG HORN COUNTY HOSPITAL (531301)**, 388 South U.S. Highway
20, Zip 82410–8902; tel. 307/568–3311, (Total facility includes 37 beds in
nursing home–type unit) **A**9 10 18 **F**1 32 34 35 40 56 57 59 64 82 93 97 107
110 119 127 128 130 133 **P**4
Primary Contact: Jackie Claudson, Administrator
Web address: www.midwayclinic.com
**Control:** Hospital district or authority, Government, nonfederal **Service:** General
Medical and Surgical

**Staffed Beds:** 43 **Admissions:** 143 **Census:** 30 **Outpatient Visits:** 1202
**Births:** 1 **Total Expense ($000):** 5955 **Payroll Expense ($000):** 2237
**Personnel:** 92

## BUFFALO—Johnson County

★ **JOHNSON COUNTY HEALTHCARE CENTER (531308)**, 497 West Lott Street,
Zip 82834–1691; tel. 307/684–5521, (Total facility includes 50 beds in nursing
home–type unit) **A**9 10 18 **F**6 11 13 15 28 31 40 57 62 63 67 70 76 78 79 81
89 93 107 119 130 133
Primary Contact: Sandy Ward, Administrator
CFO: Sandy Ward, Administrator
CMO: Brian Darnell, D.O., Chief of Staff
CIO: Laurie Hansen, Director Administrative Services
CHR: Karen Ferguson, Director Human Resources
CNO: Mary Whaley, Director of Acute Care
Web address: www.jchealthcare.com
**Control:** Hospital district or authority, Government, nonfederal **Service:** General
Medical and Surgical

**Staffed Beds:** 75 **Admissions:** 412 **Census:** 43 **Outpatient Visits:** 18329
**Births:** 38 **Total Expense ($000):** 17315 **Payroll Expense ($000):** 8568
**Personnel:** 169

## CASPER—Natrona County

☐ **ELKHORN VALLEY REHABILITATION HOSPITAL (533027)**, 5715 East 2nd
Street, Zip 82609–4322; tel. 307/265–0005, (Nonreporting) **A**1 10 **S** Ernest
Health, Inc., Albuquerque, NM
Primary Contact: Michael Phillips, Chief Executive Officer
Web address: www.evrh.ernesthealth.com/
**Control:** Corporation, Investor–owned, for–profit **Service:** Rehabilitation

**Staffed Beds:** 40

○ **MOUNTAIN VIEW REGIONAL HOSPITAL (530033)**, 6550 East Second Street,
Zip 82609–4321, Mailing Address: P.O. Box 51888, Zip 82605–1888;
tel. 307/995–8100, (Nonreporting) **A**10 11 **S** National Surgical Hospitals,
Chicago, IL
Primary Contact: Jeff Van Horn, Chief Executive Officer
Web address: www.mountainviewregionalhospital.com
**Control:** Partnership, Investor–owned, for–profit **Service:** Surgical

**Staffed Beds:** 23

☐ **WYOMING BEHAVIORAL INSTITUTE (534004)**, 2521 East 15th Street,
Zip 82609–4126; tel. 307/237–7444 **A**1 10 **F**34 56 57 59 98 99 100 101 102
103 104 105 130 **S** Universal Health Services, Inc., King of Prussia, PA
Primary Contact: Joseph Gallagher, Chief Executive Officer
CFO: Carmel Bickford, Chief Financial Officer
CMO: Steven Brown, M.D., Medical Director
CHR: Jon Barra, Director Human Resources
Web address: www.wbihelp.com
**Control:** Corporation, Investor–owned, for–profit **Service:** Psychiatric

**Staffed Beds:** 130 **Admissions:** 1877 **Census:** 55 **Births:** 0

⊞ **WYOMING MEDICAL CENTER (530012)**, 1233 East Second Street,
Zip 82601–2988; tel. 307/577–7201 **A**1 9 10 20 **F**3 7 11 12 13 18 20 22 24
28 29 30 31 34 35 40 41 43 45 46 48 49 50 51 57 59 60 61 68 70 74 76
79 81 82 85 86 87 89 97 102 107 108 111 114 118 119 120 121 123 124
126 129 130 132 135 144 146 147 148 **P**6
Primary Contact: Vickie L. Diamond, R.N., MS, President and Chief Executive
Officer
COO: Julie Cann–Taylor, R.N., Chief Operating Officer, Senior Vice President
Patient Care Services and Chief Nursing Officer
CFO: Don Claunch, Senior Vice President, Chief Financial Officer
CMO: Carol M. Solie, M.D., Chief Medical Officer
CIO: Tom Schoenig, Chief Information Officer
CHR: Matt Kaiser, Vice President of Employee Services
CNO: Julie Cann–Taylor, R.N., Chief Operating Officer, Senior Vice President
Patient Care Services and Chief Nursing Officer
Web address: www.wmcnet.org
**Control:** Other not–for–profit (including NFP Corporation) **Service:** General
Medical and Surgical

**Staffed Beds:** 192 **Admissions:** 8826 **Census:** 93 **Outpatient Visits:** 81728
**Births:** 1061 **Total Expense ($000):** 189678 **Payroll Expense ($000):**
64548 **Personnel:** 1019

## CHEYENNE—Laramie County

⊞ △ **CHEYENNE REGIONAL MEDICAL CENTER (530014)**, 214 East 23rd
Street, Zip 82001–3790; tel. 307/634–2273 **A**1 2 7 9 10 20 **F**2 3 4 5 11 12
13 15 18 20 22 24 26 28 29 30 31 34 35 37 38 40 43 46 47 48 49 51 53
57 59 60 62 63 64 65 68 70 72 73 74 75 76 77 78 79 81 82 83 84 85 86
87 89 90 93 94 98 99 100 101 102 103 104 105 107 108 110 111 114 116
118 119 120 121 123 124 128 129 130 131 132 135 143 144 146 147 148
**P**6 7
Primary Contact: John Lucas, M.D., Chief Executive Officer
COO: Paul Panico, Chief Operating Officer
CFO: Kimberly Webb, Chief Financial Officer
CMO: David Lind, M.D., Interim Chief Medical Officer
CHR: Carlene B. Crall, Chief Human Resources Officer
Web address: www.crmcwy.org
**Control:** County–Government, nonfederal **Service:** General Medical and Surgical

**Staffed Beds:** 222 **Admissions:** 10351 **Census:** 132 **Outpatient Visits:**
198935 **Births:** 1145 **Total Expense ($000):** 231342 **Payroll Expense
($000):** 99435 **Personnel:** 1885

⊞ **CHEYENNE VETERANS AFFAIRS MEDICAL CENTER**, (Formerly Veterans
Affairs Medical Center), 2360 East Pershing Boulevard, Zip 82001–5392;
tel. 307/778–7550, (Nonreporting) **A**1 9 **S** Department of Veterans Affairs,
Washington, DC
Primary Contact: Cynthia McCormack, MS, Director
CFO: Melvin Cranford, Chief Fiscal Services
CMO: Roger Johnson, M.D., Chief of Staff
CIO: Liz McCulloch, Chief Information Resource Management Systems
CHR: Ron Lester, Chief Human Resources
Web address: www.cheyenne.va.gov/
**Control:** Veterans Affairs, Government, federal **Service:** General Medical and
Surgical

**Staffed Beds:** 21

---

**Hospital, Medicare Provider Number, Address, Telephone, Approval, Facility, and Physician Codes, Health Care System**

★ American Hospital Association (AHA) membership
☐ The Joint Commission accreditation   ◇ DNV Healthcare Inc. accreditation

○ Healthcare Facilities Accreditation Program
△ Commission on Accreditation of Rehabilitation Facilities (CARF) accreditation

WY

© 2013 AHA Guide    *Many Facility Codes have changed. Please refer to the AHA Guide Code Chart.*    Hospitals **A701**

## CODY—Park County

★ **WEST PARK HOSPITAL (531312)**, 707 Sheridan Avenue, Zip 82414–3409;
tel. 307/527–7501, (Total facility includes 97 beds in nursing home–type unit) **A**9
10 18 **F**3 4 5 6 7 11 13 15 18 26 28 29 30 31 34 35 36 38 39 40 42 45 46
56 57 59 60 62 63 64 65 68 70 75 76 78 79 81 82 84 85 86 93 97 99 102
103 104 105 107 108 110 111 114 119 120 128 130 131 132 133 135 144
145 146 147 148 **S** QHR, Brentwood, TN
Primary Contact: Douglas A. McMillan, Administrator and Chief Executive Officer
CFO: Patrick G. McConnell, Chief Financial Officer
CHR: Dick Smith, Director Human Resources
Web address: www.westparkhospital.org
**Control:** Hospital district or authority, Government, nonfederal **Service:** General
Medical and Surgical

**Staffed Beds:** 140 **Admissions:** 1494 **Census:** 88 **Outpatient Visits:** 61426
**Births:** 246 **Total Expense ($000):** 60487 **Payroll Expense ($000):** 26428
**Personnel:** 391

## DOUGLAS—Converse County

★ **MEMORIAL HOSPITAL OF CONVERSE COUNTY (531302)**, 111 South Fifth
Street, Zip 82633–2434, Mailing Address: P.O. Box 1450, Zip 82633–1450;
tel. 307/358–2122 **A**10 18 **F**3 7 8 13 15 28 29 32 34 35 40 43 45 46 50 57
59 64 70 75 76 79 81 82 85 86 87 94 107 110 115 119 127 129 133 135
144 146 147 148 **P**6
Primary Contact: Ryan K. Smith, Chief Executive Officer
CFO: Curtis R. Dugger, Chief Financial Officer
CMO: Jonathan L. Grosdidier, M.D., Chief of Staff
CIO: Dave Patterson, Information Systems Manager
CHR: Linda York, Manager Human Resources
Web address: www.conversehospital.com
**Control:** County–Government, nonfederal **Service:** General Medical and Surgical

**Staffed Beds:** 25 **Admissions:** 722 **Census:** 6 **Outpatient Visits:** 31058
**Births:** 123 **Total Expense ($000):** 35426 **Payroll Expense ($000):** 15729
**Personnel:** 326

## EVANSTON—Uinta County

✉ **EVANSTON REGIONAL HOSPITAL (530032)**, 190 Arrowhead Drive,
Zip 82930–9266; tel. 307/789–3636 **A**1 9 10 20 **F**3 11 15 29 34 35 40 43
45 48 60 65 70 74 75 76 77 79 81 82 85 86 87 89 93 107 108 111 114
119 128 129 133 134 146 **P**6 **S** Community Health Systems, Inc., Franklin, TN
Primary Contact: George Winn, Chief Executive Officer
CFO: Gary Karg, Interim Chief Financial Officer
CHR: Joshua Jones, Director of Human Resources
CNO: Darin Linford, R.N., Chief Nursing Officer
Web address: www.evanstonregionalhospital.com
**Control:** Corporation, Investor–owned, for–profit **Service:** General Medical and
Surgical

**Staffed Beds:** 42 **Admissions:** 999 **Census:** 6 **Outpatient Visits:** 25658
**Births:** 298 **Total Expense ($000):** 25320 **Payroll Expense ($000):** 10995
**Personnel:** 193

△ **WYOMING STATE HOSPITAL (534001)**, 830 Highway 150 South,
Zip 82931–5341, Mailing Address: P.O. Box 177, Zip 82931–0177;
tel. 307/789–3464 **A**7 9 10 **F**29 30 50 75 77 87 98 100 101 102 103 130
132 135 143 **P**6
Primary Contact: William J. Sexton, Administrator
CFO: Paul Mullenax, Business Manager
CIO: Steve Baldwin, Manager Information Technology
Web address: www.health.wyo.gov/statehospital/index.html
**Control:** State–Government, nonfederal **Service:** Psychiatric

**Staffed Beds:** 183 **Admissions:** 207 **Census:** 80 **Births:** 0 **Personnel:** 401

## GILLETTE—Campbell County

★ ◇ **CAMPBELL COUNTY MEMORIAL HOSPITAL (530002)**, 501 South Burma
Avenue, Zip 82716–3426, Mailing Address: P.O. Box 3011, Zip 82717–3011;
tel. 307/682–8811, (Total facility includes 143 beds in nursing home–type unit)
**A**9 10 20 21 **F**3 5 6 7 11 13 15 28 29 30 31 34 35 38 40 43 45 51 53 54
56 59 60 62 63 64 65 66 68 69 70 71 73 75 76 77 78 79 81 82 84 85 86
87 88 93 94 96 97 98 99 100 101 102 103 104 105 107 108 109 110 111
114 115 116 118 119 120 121 125 129 130 131 132 133 134 135 143 144
146 147 148 **P**6
Primary Contact: Robert A. Morasko, Chief Executive Officer
COO: Andy Fitzgerald, Executive Vice President
CFO: Andy Fitzgerald, Executive Vice President
CIO: Stevan Bailey, Manager Information Systems
CHR: John A. Fitch, Vice President Human Resources
Web address: www.ccmh.net
**Control:** Hospital district or authority, Government, nonfederal **Service:** General
Medical and Surgical

**Staffed Beds:** 215 **Admissions:** 3496 **Census:** 140 **Outpatient Visits:**
232013 **Births:** 790 **Total Expense ($000):** 122784 **Payroll Expense
($000):** 64818 **Personnel:** 963

## JACKSON—Teton County

⊠ **ST. JOHN'S MEDICAL CENTER AND LIVING CENTER (530015)**, 625 East
Broadway Street, Zip 83001–8642, Mailing Address: P.O. Box 428,
Zip 83001–0428; tel. 307/733–3636, (Total facility includes 60 beds in nursing
home–type unit) **A**1 9 10 20 **F**3 11 13 15 29 30 31 34 35 40 43 44 45 46 51
53 54 57 59 62 63 67 68 70 74 75 76 77 78 81 82 84 86 87 97 107 108
110 111 115 119 129 130 132 133 135 144 145 146 148 **P**5
Primary Contact: Lou Hochheiser, Chief Executive Officer
COO: Gary Tauner, Chief Operating Officer
CFO: John Kren, Chief Financial Officer
CIO: David Witton, Manager Information Systems
CNO: Lynn Kirman, R.N., Chief Nursing Officer
Web address: www.tetonhospital.org
**Control:** Hospital district or authority, Government, nonfederal **Service:** General
Medical and Surgical

**Staffed Beds:** 100 **Admissions:** 2106 **Census:** 66 **Outpatient Visits:** 70880
**Births:** 432 **Total Expense ($000):** 72626 **Payroll Expense ($000):** 28887
**Personnel:** 442

## KEMMERER—Lincoln County

★ **SOUTH LINCOLN MEDICAL CENTER (531315)**, 711 Onyx Street,
Zip 83101–3214; tel. 307/877–4401, (Total facility includes 24 beds in nursing
home–type unit) **A**9 10 18 **F**3 7 13 15 32 34 35 40 43 57 59 65 68 75 76 77
79 81 93 97 107 111 114 119 128 129 130 133 135 146 148 **P**6
Primary Contact: Eric Boley, Administrator and Chief Executive Officer
COO: Lou Ann Carmichael, Director Operations
CFO: Curtis Nielson, Director Finance
CMO: G. Christopher Krell, M.D., Chief of Staff
CIO: Kristin Housley, Chief Management Information Systems
CHR: Armand Drummond, Manager Human Resources
Web address: www.southlincolnmedical.com
**Control:** Hospital district or authority, Government, nonfederal **Service:** General
Medical and Surgical

**Staffed Beds:** 40 **Admissions:** 122 **Census:** 23 **Outpatient Visits:** 24563
**Births:** 39 **Total Expense ($000):** 12837 **Payroll Expense ($000):** 6591
**Personnel:** 134

## LANDER—Fremont County

⊠ **LANDER REGIONAL HOSPITAL (530010)**, 1320 Bishop Randall Drive,
Zip 82520–3996; tel. 307/332–4420 **A**1 9 10 20 **F**3 11 13 15 28 29 30 34
35 39 40 43 57 59 70 74 76 77 79 80 81 85 87 90 91 93 96 98 103 106
107 108 110 111 114 119 128 130 131 133 135 147 **P**5 **S** LifePoint
Hospitals, Inc., Brentwood, TN
Primary Contact: Stephen M. Erixon, Chief Executive Officer
CFO: Ann Huhnke, Chief Financial Officer
CMO: Brian Gee, M.D., Director Emergency Services
CIO: Keith Blair, M.D., Manager Information Systems
CHR: Janet Morgan, Manager Human Resources
Web address: www.landerhospital.com
**Control:** Corporation, Investor–owned, for–profit **Service:** General Medical and
Surgical

**Staffed Beds:** 89 **Admissions:** 2143 **Census:** 25 **Outpatient Visits:** 35226
**Births:** 274 **Total Expense ($000):** 32411 **Payroll Expense ($000):** 11629
**Personnel:** 225

## LARAMIE—Albany County

⊠ **IVINSON MEMORIAL HOSPITAL (530025)**, 255 North 30th Street,
Zip 82072–5140; tel. 307/742–2141, (Total facility includes 9 beds in nursing
home–type unit) **A**1 10 20 **F**11 13 15 28 29 30 31 34 38 40 45 50 56 57 59
60 64 70 73 75 76 77 78 79 81 85 89 98 99 102 107 108 111 115 119 121
128 129 130 132 133 146 147 **P**8
Primary Contact: Karl Vilums, Interim Chief Executive Officer
COO: Linda Mink, R.N., Vice President Clinical Service Line Development and
Quality
CFO: Karl Vilums, Chief Financial Officer
CMO: Debra Anderson, M.D., Chief of Staff
CIO: Brandon Lewis, Director of Information Technology
CHR: Holly Zajic, Vice President Human Resources and Physician Services
CNO: Sharon Gern, R.N., Chief Nursing Officer
Web address: www.ivinsonhospital.org
**Control:** Hospital district or authority, Government, nonfederal **Service:** General
Medical and Surgical

**Staffed Beds:** 99 **Admissions:** 2263 **Census:** 21 **Outpatient Visits:** 41277
**Births:** 417 **Total Expense ($000):** 60244 **Payroll Expense ($000):** 22612
**Personnel:** 376

**WY**

*Many Facility Codes have changed. Please refer to the AHA Guide Code Chart.*
© 2013 AHA Guide

## LOVELL—Big Horn County

★ **NORTH BIG HORN HOSPITAL DISTRICT (531309)**, 1115 Lane 12, Zip 82431–9537; tel. 307/548–5203, (Total facility includes 85 beds in nursing home–type unit) **A**9 10 18 **F**3 6 7 10 15 28 29 34 40 41 45 56 57 59 62 64 65 66 68 75 77 79 81 85 86 87 93 97 107 114 119 127 130 131 132 133 143 146 147 148 **P**6
Primary Contact: Rick Schroeder, Chief Executive Officer
CFO: Daphne Hartman, Chief Financial Officer
CMO: Troy J. Caldwell, M.D., Chief of Staff
CIO: Eileen Fink, Health Information Officer
CHR: Barbara Shumway, Director Human Resources
CNO: Tina Toner, Director of Nursing
Web address: www.nbhh.com
**Control:** Hospital district or authority, Government, nonfederal **Service:** General Medical and Surgical

**Staffed Beds:** 100 **Admissions:** 313 **Census:** 80 **Outpatient Visits:** 20241 **Births:** 0 **Total Expense ($000):** 14392 **Payroll Expense ($000):** 8263 **Personnel:** 173

## LUSK—Niobrara County

**NIOBRARA HEALTH AND LIFE CENTER (531314)**, 921 Ballencee Avenue, Zip 82225, Mailing Address: P.O. Box 780, Zip 82225–0780; tel. 307/334–4000, (Nonreporting) **A**9 10 18
Primary Contact: Gary R. Poquette, FACHE, Chief Executive Officer
Web address: www.niobrarahospital.com
**Control:** Hospital district or authority, Government, nonfederal **Service:** General Medical and Surgical

**Staffed Beds:** 24

## NEWCASTLE—Weston County

★ **WESTON COUNTY HEALTH SERVICES (531303)**, 1124 Washington Boulevard, Zip 82701–2972; tel. 307/746–4491, (Total facility includes 54 beds in nursing home–type unit) **A**9 10 18 **F**28 29 40 41 56 57 59 62 64 77 91 93 107 119 130 133 **S** Regional Health, Rapid City, SD
Primary Contact: Maureen K. Cadwell, Chief Executive Officer
CFO: Lynn Moller, Chief Financial Officer
CMO: Chuck Franklin, M.D., Chief Medical Staff
CIO: Keith Gaudsmith, Information Technology Officer
CHR: Julie A. Sindlinger, Director of Human Resources
Web address: www.wchs–wy.org
**Control:** Hospital district or authority, Government, nonfederal **Service:** General Medical and Surgical

**Staffed Beds:** 75 **Admissions:** 248 **Census:** 59 **Outpatient Visits:** 9218 **Births:** 0 **Total Expense ($000):** 10462 **Payroll Expense ($000):** 5049 **Personnel:** 134

## POWELL—Park County

★ **POWELL VALLEY HEALTHCARE (531310)**, 777 Avenue H, Zip 82435–2296; tel. 307/754–2267, (Total facility includes 100 beds in nursing home–type unit) **A**9 10 18 **F**3 6 7 10 11 13 15 18 28 29 34 35 36 40 43 45 56 57 59 62 63 64 70 76 79 81 82 85 87 107 110 111 115 119 128 130 131 132 133 135 144 146 147 148 **P**1 **S** HealthTech Management Services, Franklin, TN
Primary Contact: Bill D. Patten, Chief Executive Officer
CFO: Sandra Ehman, CPA, Chief Financial Officer
CMO: Valerie Lengfelder, M.D., Chief of Staff
CIO: Joshua Baxter, Director, Information Systems
CHR: Cassie Tinsley, Director, Human Resources
CNO: Arleen Campeau, R.N., Vice President of Patient Care Services, Chief Nursing Officer
Web address: www.pvhc.org
**Control:** Other not–for–profit (including NFP Corporation) **Service:** General Medical and Surgical

**Staffed Beds:** 125 **Admissions:** 837 **Census:** 97 **Outpatient Visits:** 30433 **Births:** 185 **Total Expense ($000):** 43452 **Payroll Expense ($000):** 22434 **Personnel:** 331

## RAWLINS—Carbon County

★ **MEMORIAL HOSPITAL OF CARBON COUNTY (531316)**, 2221 West Elm Street, Zip 82301–5108, Mailing Address: P.O. Box 460, Zip 82301–0460; tel. 307/324–2221 **A**9 10 18 **F**3 7 11 13 15 18 28 29 31 34 35 39 40 45 50 57 59 65 68 70 76 79 81 85 90 93 105 107 110 111 114 119 129 130 133 135 146 147 148 **S** QHR, Brentwood, TN
Primary Contact: Ned Hill, Chief Executive Officer
CFO: David Pike, Interim Chief Financial Officer
CMO: Duane E. Abels, M.D., Chief of Staff
CHR: Beverly Young, Director Human Resources
Web address: www.imhcc.com
**Control:** County–Government, nonfederal **Service:** General Medical and Surgical

**Staffed Beds:** 25 **Admissions:** 632 **Census:** 5 **Outpatient Visits:** 15242 **Births:** 96 **Total Expense ($000):** 21464 **Payroll Expense ($000):** 10416 **Personnel:** 153

## RIVERTON—Fremont County

⊞ **RIVERTON MEMORIAL HOSPITAL (530008)**, 2100 West Sunset Drive, Zip 82501–2274; tel. 307/856–4161 **A**1 9 10 20 **F**3 11 12 13 15 29 31 34 35 40 43 45 46 47 48 49 50 51 57 59 64 70 74 75 76 77 78 79 81 85 87 107 108 110 111 114 119 129 130 131 132 133 145 147 **P**7 **S** LifePoint Hospitals, Inc., Brentwood, TN
Primary Contact: Stephen M. Erixon, Interim Chief Executive Officer
CFO: Susan Goetzinger, Chief Financial Officer
CMO: Cielette Karn, M.D., Chief of Staff
CIO: Linda Tice, Director Information Systems
CHR: Dawn Nelson, Director Human Resources
Web address: www.riverton–hospital.com
**Control:** Corporation, Investor–owned, for–profit **Service:** General Medical and Surgical

**Staffed Beds:** 37 **Admissions:** 1508 **Census:** 11 **Outpatient Visits:** 19003 **Births:** 306 **Total Expense ($000):** 25731 **Payroll Expense ($000):** 9811 **Personnel:** 169

## ROCK SPRINGS—Sweetwater County

⊞ **MEMORIAL HOSPITAL OF SWEETWATER COUNTY (530011)**, 1200 College Drive, Zip 82901–5868, Mailing Address: P.O. Box 1359, Zip 82902–1359; tel. 307/362–3711 **A**1 9 10 20 **F**3 8 11 13 15 28 29 30 31 34 35 40 43 48 57 59 60 70 75 76 77 78 79 81 82 87 93 97 100 102 103 104 105 107 110 111 115 116 118 119 129 130 135 146
Primary Contact: Gerard D. Klein, Chief Executive Officer
CFO: Irene Richardson, Chief Financial Officer
CMO: Richard Clark, M.D., President, Medical Staff
CHR: Charles Frye, Director Human Resources
CNO: Deborah L. Gaspar, R.N., Chief Nursing Officer
Web address: www.sweetwatermedicalcenter.com
**Control:** County–Government, nonfederal **Service:** General Medical and Surgical

**Staffed Beds:** 58 **Admissions:** 2035 **Census:** 15 **Outpatient Visits:** 102363 **Births:** 462 **Total Expense ($000):** 53467 **Payroll Expense ($000):** 22328 **Personnel:** 375

## SHERIDAN—Sheridan County

☐ **SHERIDAN MEMORIAL HOSPITAL (530006)**, 1401 West Fifth Street, Zip 82801–2799; tel. 307/672–1000, (Nonreporting) **A**1 9 10 20
Primary Contact: Michael McCafferty, Chief Executive Officer
CFO: Ed Johlman, Chief Financial Officer
CMO: Brad Hanebrink, D.O., Chief of Staff
CIO: Nyle Morgan, Chief Information Officer
CHR: Len Gross, Director Human Resources
Web address: www.sheridanhospital.org
**Control:** County–Government, nonfederal **Service:** General Medical and Surgical

**Staffed Beds:** 72

⊞ △ **SHERIDAN VETERANS AFFAIRS MEDICAL CENTER**, (Formerly Veterans Affairs Medical Center), 1898 Fort Road, Zip 82801–8320; tel. 307/672–3473, (Total facility includes 40 beds in nursing home–type unit) **A**1 7 9 **F**1 3 4 5 29 30 31 34 35 38 39 45 48 53 54 56 57 59 61 62 63 64 65 71 74 75 77 78 82 83 84 85 86 87 93 94 96 97 98 100 101 102 103 104 105 106 107 111 115 119 127 129 130 132 135 143 144 146 147 148 **P**6 **S** Department of Veterans Affairs, Washington, DC
Primary Contact: Debra L. Hirschman, R.N., MSN, Director
COO: Michele Beach, Associate Director
CFO: Donna Fuerstenberg, Fiscal Chief
CMO: Wendell Robison, M.D., Chief of Staff
CIO: Cynthia Sostrom, Chief Information Officer
CHR: James Hardin, Human Resources Officer
Web address: www.sheridan.va.gov/
**Control:** Veterans Affairs, Government, federal **Service:** Psychiatric

**Staffed Beds:** 185 **Admissions:** 1854 **Census:** 170 **Outpatient Visits:** 133615 **Births:** 0 **Personnel:** 563

---

**Hospital, Medicare Provider Number, Address, Telephone, Approval, Facility, and Physician Codes, Health Care System**

★ American Hospital Association (AHA) membership
☐ The Joint Commission accreditation
◇ DNV Healthcare Inc. accreditation
○ Healthcare Facilities Accreditation Program
△ Commission on Accreditation of Rehabilitation Facilities (CARF) accreditation

WY

## SUNDANCE—Crook County

★ **CROOK COUNTY MEDICAL SERVICES DISTRICT (531311)**, 713 Oak Street,
Zip 82729, Mailing Address: P.O. Box 517, Zip 82729–0517;
tel. 307/283–3501, (Total facility includes 32 beds in nursing home–type unit) **A**9
10 18 **F**7 29 40 53 56 57 59 62 67 82 97 128 130 133 143 **S** Regional
Health, Rapid City, SD
Primary Contact: Jan VanBeek, Chief Executive Officer
CFO: Betty Meyers, Chief Financial Officer
CMO: Jeremi Villano, M.D., Chief of Staff
CHR: Patricia Feist, Manager Human Resources
Web address: www.crookcountymedical.com
**Control:** Hospital district or authority, Government, nonfederal **Service:** General
Medical and Surgical

**Staffed Beds:** 48 **Admissions:** 91 **Census:** 29 **Outpatient Visits:** 9788
**Births:** 0 **Total Expense ($000):** 6839 **Payroll Expense ($000):** 4298
**Personnel:** 101

## THERMOPOLIS—Hot Springs County

★ **HOT SPRINGS COUNTY MEMORIAL HOSPITAL (531304)**, 150 East Arapahoe
Street, Zip 82443–2498; tel. 307/864–3121 **A**10 18 **F**3 11 13 15 28 29 31 34
40 43 45 64 75 76 78 79 81 82 85 86 89 107 108 110 111 115 119 127
129 130 133 145 146 **S** HealthTech Management Services, Franklin, TN
Primary Contact: Robin Roling, President and Chief Executive Officer
CFO: Shelly Larson, Chief Financial Officer
CIO: Tim Knight, Director Information Technology
CHR: Patti Jeunehomme, Director Human Resources
Web address: www.hscmh.org
**Control:** County–Government, nonfederal **Service:** General Medical and Surgical

**Staffed Beds:** 25 **Admissions:** 472 **Census:** 5 **Outpatient Visits:** 18013
**Births:** 64 **Total Expense ($000):** 13871 **Payroll Expense ($000):** 5296
**Personnel:** 86

## TORRINGTON—Goshen County

★ **COMMUNITY HOSPITAL (531307)**, 2000 Campbell Drive, Zip 82240–1597;
tel. 307/532–4181 **A**9 10 18 **F**3 8 11 13 15 29 30 35 36 40 42 43 45 46 57
59 64 68 70 75 77 79 81 84 87 107 119 128 129 130 131 132 133 135
145 146 **P**6 **S** Banner Health, Phoenix, AZ
Primary Contact: Vincent B. DiFranco, Chief Executive Officer
CMO: Bonnie Randolph, M.D., Chief of Staff
CIO: Rod Miller, Chief Information Technology
CHR: Sandy Dugger, Director Human Resources
Web address: www.bannerhealth.com/Locations/Wyoming/Community+Hospital/
**Control:** Other not–for–profit (including NFP Corporation) **Service:** General
Medical and Surgical

**Staffed Beds:** 25 **Admissions:** 714 **Census:** 8 **Outpatient Visits:** 35021
**Births:** 65 **Total Expense ($000):** 17878 **Payroll Expense ($000):** 7132
**Personnel:** 135

## WHEATLAND—Platte County

⊞ **PLATTE COUNTY MEMORIAL HOSPITAL (531305)**, 201 14th Street,
Zip 82201–3201, Mailing Address: P.O. Box 848, Zip 82201–0848;
tel. 307/322–3636 **A**1 9 10 18 **F**3 13 15 29 30 40 43 46 47 48 49 59 64 70
75 76 81 107 110 114 119 128 129 130 132 133 **S** Banner Health,
Phoenix, AZ
Primary Contact: Shelby Nelson, Chief Executive Officer
CFO: Stephanie Kaul, Chief Financial Officer
CMO: Ty Battershell, M.D., Chief of Staff
CIO: Robin Wood, Director Information Systems
CHR: Sandy Dugger, Chief Human Resources Officer
Web address: www.bannerhealth.com/Locations/Wyoming/Platte+County+
Memorial+Hospital
**Control:** Other not–for–profit (including NFP Corporation) **Service:** General
Medical and Surgical

**Staffed Beds:** 25 **Admissions:** 480 **Census:** 3 **Outpatient Visits:** 21121
**Births:** 75 **Total Expense ($000):** 14094 **Payroll Expense ($000):** 6051
**Personnel:** 111

## WORLAND—Washakie County

★ **WASHAKIE MEDICAL CENTER (531306)**, 400 South 15th Street,
Zip 82401–3531, Mailing Address: P.O. Box 700, Zip 82401–0700;
tel. 307/347–3221 **A**9 10 18 **F**3 11 13 15 28 29 31 34 35 40 43 45 57 59
64 68 70 75 76 77 79 81 82 85 87 89 93 97 107 110 111 114 119 129 131
133 135 145 146 148 **P**6 **S** Banner Health, Phoenix, AZ
Primary Contact: Margie Molitor, R.N., Chief Executive Officer
CFO: Jennifer Montgomery, Chief Financial Officer
CMO: Ryan Clifford, M.D., Chief of Staff
CHR: Jerry Clipp, Manager Human Resources
Web address: www.washakiemedicalcenter.com
**Control:** Other not–for–profit (including NFP Corporation) **Service:** General
Medical and Surgical

**Staffed Beds:** 25 **Admissions:** 890 **Census:** 9 **Outpatient Visits:** 33723
**Births:** 50 **Total Expense ($000):** 17181 **Payroll Expense ($000):** 7543
**Personnel:** 116

WY

*Many Facility Codes have changed. Please refer to the AHA Guide Code Chart.*
© 2013 AHA Guide

# Hospitals in Areas Associated with the United States, by Area

## AMERICAN SAMOA

### PAGO PAGO— County

**LYNDON B. JOHNSON TROPICAL MEDICAL CENTER (640001)**, Faga'alu Village, Zip 96799, Mailing Address: P.O. Box LBJ, Zip 96799; tel. 684/633–1222, (Nonreporting) **A**10
Primary Contact: Patricia Tindall, Chief Executive Officer
Web address: www.asmca.org
**Control:** State–Government, nonfederal **Service:** General Medical and Surgical

Staffed Beds: 125

## GUAM

### AGANA—Guam County

☒ **U. S. NAVAL HOSPITAL GUAM**, (Formerly U. S. Naval Hospital), Zip 96910; Mailing Address: FPO, AP, tel. 671/344–9340, (Nonreporting) **A**1 **S** Bureau of Medicine and Surgery, Department of the Navy, Washington, DC
Primary Contact: Lieutenant Commander Rona Green
Web address: www.med.navy.mil/sites/usnhguam/Pages/default.aspx
**Control:** Navy, Government, federal **Service:** General Medical and Surgical

Staffed Beds: 55

### TAMUNING—Guam County

☒ **GUAM MEMORIAL HOSPITAL AUTHORITY (650001)**, 850 Governor Carlos G. Camacho Road, Zip 96913; tel. 671/647–2108, (Nonreporting) **A**1 10
Primary Contact: Joseph P. Verga, FACHE, Chief Executive Officer
CFO: Jun Infante, Acting Chief Financial Officer
CFO: Alan Ulrich, Chief Financial Officer
CMO: James J. Stadler, M.D., Associate Administrator Medical Services
CIO: Vince Quichocho, Manager Information Systems
CHR: Elizabeth Claros, Administrator Personnel Services
Web address: www.gmha.org
**Control:** Hospital district or authority, Government, nonfederal **Service:** General Medical and Surgical

Staffed Beds: 104

## MARSHALL ISLANDS

### KWAJALEIN ISLAND— County

**KWAJALEIN HOSPITAL**, U.S. Army Kwajalein Atoll, Zip 96960, Mailing Address: Box 1702, APO, AP, Zip 96555–5000; tel. 805/355–2225, (Nonreporting) **S** Department of the Army, Office of the Surgeon General, Falls Church, VA
Primary Contact: Elaine McMahon, Administrator
**Control:** Army, Government, federal **Service:** General Medical and Surgical

Staffed Beds: 14

## NORTHERN MARIANA ISLANDS

### SAIPAN— County

**COMMONWEALTH HEALTH CENTER (660001)**, Navy Hill Road, Zip 96950, Mailing Address: P.O. Box 409, Zip 96950; tel. 670/234–8950, (Nonreporting) **A**10
Primary Contact: Joseph C. Santos, M.P.H., Deputy Secretary for Hospital Administration
Web address: www.dphsaipan.com
**Control:** Corporation, Investor–owned, for–profit **Service:** Other specialty

Staffed Beds: 86

## PUERTO RICO

### AGUADILLA—Aguadilla County

☒ **HOSPITAL BUEN SAMARITANO (400079)**, Carr #2 Km 141–1 Avenue Severiano Cuevas, Zip 00603, Mailing Address: P.O. Box 4055, Zip 00605–4055; tel. 787/658–0000, (Nonreporting) **A**1 5 9 10
Primary Contact: Elyonel Ponton Cruz, Executive Director
CFO: Luis J. Torres Rodriguez, Finance Director
CFO: Taira Valentin, Interim Director Finance
CMO: Arturo Cedeno Llorens, M.D., Medical Director
CHR: Jose Garcia Rivera, Director Human Resources
CNO: Eneida Alicea Perez, Interim Nursing Director
Web address: www.hbspr.org
**Control:** Other not–for–profit (including NFP Corporation) **Service:** General Medical and Surgical

Staffed Beds: 154

### AIBONITO—Aibonito County

☒ **CENTRO DE SALUD CONDUCTUAL MENONITA–CIMA (404009)**, Carretera Estatal 14 Interior, Zip 00705, Mailing Address: CIMA Calle Sargento Gerardo Santiago, Zip 00705; tel. 787/714–2462 **A**1 9 10 **F**77 98 102 104 105 130 135
Primary Contact: Pedro Melendez, Administrator
**Control:** Other not–for–profit (including NFP Corporation) **Service:** Psychiatric

Staffed Beds: 20 Admissions: 3897 Census: 17 Outpatient Visits: 2089 Births: 0 Total Expense ($000): 4991 Payroll Expense ($000): 2036 Personnel: 108

☒ **MENNONITE GENERAL HOSPITAL (400018)**, Calle Jose C. Vasquez, Zip 00705, Mailing Address: P.O. Box 373130, Cayey, Zip 00737–3130; tel. 787/535–1001 **A**1 9 10 **F**13 15 29 30 31 34 35 40 41 42 46 47 57 59 63 64 65 68 70 74 75 76 78 79 81 82 89 107 111 114 115 119 143 144 145 146 147 148
Primary Contact: Pedro Melendez, Administrator
COO: Marta R Mercado Suro, Chief Operating Officer
CFO: Jose E. Solivan, Chief Financial Officer
CMO: Victor Hernandez Miranda, M.D., Chief of Staff
CIO: Daniza Morales, Manager Information System
CHR: Evelyn Padilla Ortiz, Director Human Resources
Web address: www.hospitalmenonita.com
**Control:** Other not–for–profit (including NFP Corporation) **Service:** General Medical and Surgical

Staffed Beds: 116 Admissions: 8260 Census: 96 Outpatient Visits: 66257 Births: 693 Total Expense ($000): 65939 Payroll Expense ($000): 22279 Personnel: 812

---

**Hospital, Medicare Provider Number, Address, Telephone, Approval, Facility, and Physician Codes, Health Care System**

★ American Hospital Association (AHA) membership
☐ The Joint Commission accreditation

○ American Osteopathic Association (AOA) accreditation
△ Commission on Accreditation of Rehabilitation Facilities (CARF) accreditation

---

### ARECIBO—Arecibo County

✉ **HOSPITAL DR. CAYETANO COLL Y TOSTE (400087)**, 129 San Luis Avenue, Zip 00612, Mailing Address: P.O. Box 659, Zip 00613; tel. 787/650–7272, (Nonreporting) **A**1 9 10
Primary Contact: Homar Perez, Chief Executive Officer and Vice President Administration
COO: Maritza Rodriguez, Chief Financial Officer
CFO: Luis Curbelo, Director Finance
CMO: Ada S. Miranda, M.D., Medical Director
CHR: Carmen Sanchez, Director Human Resources
Web address: www.cayetano@xsn.net
**Control:** Corporation, Investor–owned, for–profit **Service:** General Medical and Surgical

Staffed Beds: 188

★ **HOSPITAL METROPOLITANO DR. SUSONI (400117)**, 55 Nicomedes Rivera Street, Zip 00612, Mailing Address: P.O. Box 145200, Zip 00614; tel. 787/650–1030, (Nonreporting) **A**9 10
Primary Contact: Luis Z. Allende Ruiz, Executive Director
CFO: Vivian Aceuedo, CPA, Chief Financial Director
CMO: Ada S. Miranda, M.D., Medical Director
CIO: Mayra Montano, Director Information Systems
CHR: Patria Nieves, Director
**Control:** Corporation, Investor–owned, for–profit **Service:** General Medical and Surgical

Staffed Beds: 138

### ARROYO—Arroyo County

★ **LAFAYETTE HOSPITAL (400026)**, Central Lafayette, Zip 00714, Mailing Address: P.O. Box 207, Zip 00714; tel. 787/839–3232, (Nonreporting) **A**9 10
Primary Contact: Ruth M. Ortiz Vargas, Administrator
CMO: Jose L. Pimentel Fernandez, Medical Director
**Control:** Corporation, Investor–owned, for–profit **Service:** General Medical and Surgical

Staffed Beds: 38

### BAYAMON—Bayamon County

★ **DOCTOR'S CENTER OF BAYAMON (400102)**, Extension Hermanas Davila, Zip 00960, Mailing Address: P.O. Box 2957, Zip 00960; tel. 787/622–5420, (Nonreporting) **A**10
Primary Contact: Carlos Blanco, M.D., Administrator
**Control:** Corporation, Investor–owned, for–profit **Service:** General Medical and Surgical

Staffed Beds: 91

✉ **HOSPITAL HERMANOS MELENDEZ (400032)**, Route 2, KM 11–7, Zip 00960, Mailing Address: P.O. Box 306, Zip 00960; tel. 787/620–8181, (Nonreporting) **A**1 9 10
Primary Contact: Maria T. Machado, Administrator
CFO: Luz D. Medina, Controller
CMO: Norma Ortiz, M.D., Medical Director
CIO: Leticia Santana, Administrator Medical Records
Web address: www.hospitalhermanosmelendez.net
**Control:** Corporation, Investor–owned, for–profit **Service:** General Medical and Surgical

Staffed Beds: 211

✉ **HOSPITAL SAN PABLO (400109)**, Calle Santa Cruz 70, Zip 00961–7020, Mailing Address: P.O. Box 236, Zip 00960–0236; tel. 787/740–4747, (Nonreporting) **A**1 3 5 9 10
Primary Contact: Jose E. Carballo, Chief Executive Officer and Managing Director
Web address: www.sanpablo.com
**Control:** Corporation, Investor–owned, for–profit **Service:** General Medical and Surgical

Staffed Beds: 410

✉ **HOSPITAL UNIVERSITARIO DR. RAMON RUIZ ARNAU (400105)**, Avenue Laurel, Santa Juanita, Zip 00956; tel. 787/787–5151, (Nonreporting) **A**1 3 5 10 **S** Puerto Rico Department of Health, San Juan, PR
Primary Contact: Humberto M. Monserrate, Chief Executive Officer
CFO: Elsie Morales, Chief Financial Officer
CMO: Hector Cintron Principe, M.D., Director
CIO: Irma Duprey, Administrator Medical Records
CHR: Aurea De Leon, Chief Human Resources Officer
**Control:** State–Government, nonfederal **Service:** General Medical and Surgical

Staffed Beds: 102

### CABO ROJO—Cabo Rojo County

★ **HOSPITAL PSIQUIATRICO METROPOLITANO (404007)**, 108 Munoz Rivera Street, Zip 00623–4060, Mailing Address: P.O. Box 910, Zip 00623–0910; tel. 787/851–2025, (Nonreporting) **A**9 10
Primary Contact: Elizabeth De Santiago, Director
**Control:** Other not–for–profit (including NFP Corporation) **Service:** General Medical and Surgical

Staffed Beds: 39

### CAGUAS—Caguas County

✉ **HOSPITAL INTERAMERICANO DE MEDICINA AVANZADA (400120)**, Avenida Luis Munoz Marin, Zip 00726, Mailing Address: P.O. Box 4980, Zip 00726; tel. 787/653–3434, (Nonreporting) **A**1 5 9 10
Primary Contact: Carlos M. Pineiro, President
CFO: Luis A. Arroyo, Chief Financial Officer
CIO: Fernando Mora, Vice President Management Information Systems
**Control:** Partnership, Investor–owned, for–profit **Service:** General Medical and Surgical

Staffed Beds: 300

### CAROLINA—Carolina County

✉ **HOSPITAL DE LA UNIVERSIDAD DE PUERTO RICO/DR. FEDERICO TRILLA (400112)**, 65th Infanteria, KM 8 3, Zip 00984, Mailing Address: P.O. Box 6021, Zip 00984; tel. 787/757–1800 **A**1 3 5 9 10 **F**3 8 11 12 15 29 30 34 38 39 40 45 50 56 64 70 72 73 74 75 76 78 79 80 81 87 89 91 93 94 96 97 98 99 100 101 102 103 104 105 107 108 110 111 119 130 145 146 148
Primary Contact: Domingo Nevarez, Chief Executive Officer
COO: Diraida Maldonado, Administrator
CFO: Yolanda Quinonez, Chief Financial Officer
CMO: Marina Roman, M.D., Medical Director
CIO: Francisco Perez, Manager Management Information Systems
CHR: Betzaida Jimenez, Director Human Resources
Web address: www.hospitalupr.org
**Control:** State–Government, nonfederal **Service:** General Medical and Surgical

Staffed Beds: 250 Admissions: 10405 Census: 166 Outpatient Visits: 64127 Births: 1227 Total Expense ($000): 31949 Payroll Expense ($000): 13579 Personnel: 662

### CASTANER—Lares County

★ **CASTANER GENERAL HOSPITAL (400010)**, KM 64–2, Route 135, Zip 00631, Mailing Address: P.O. Box 1003, Zip 00631; tel. 787/829–5010, (Nonreporting) **A**3 5 10
Primary Contact: Domingo Monroig, Administrator
COO: Agustin Ponce, Supervisor Maintenance
CFO: Ernesto Montes, Director Finance
CMO: Jose O. Rodriguez, M.D., Medical Director
CIO: Domingo Monroig, Administrator
CHR: Nydimar Salcedo, Chief Human Resources Officer
**Control:** Other not–for–profit (including NFP Corporation) **Service:** General Medical and Surgical

Staffed Beds: 24

### CAYEY—Cayey County

✉ **HOSPITAL MENONITA DE CAYEY (400013)**, 4 H. Mendoza Street, Zip 00736–3801, Mailing Address: P.O. Box 373130, Zip 00737–3130; tel. 787/263–1001 **A**1 9 10 **F**12 13 15 18 20 22 26 29 30 40 41 42 45 61 65 70 72 73 75 76 78 79 81 89 107 111 114 115 116 117 130 146 148
Primary Contact: Pedro Melendez, Administrator
COO: Leda Marta R Mercado, Chief Operating Officer
CFO: Jose E. Solivan, Chief Financial Officer
CMO: Luis J Rodriquez Saenz, M.D., Medical Director
CIO: Daniza Morales, Chief Information Officer
CHR: Evelyn Padilla Ortiz, Director Human Resources
Web address: www.hospitalmenonita.com
**Control:** Other not–for–profit (including NFP Corporation) **Service:** General Medical and Surgical

Staffed Beds: 208 Admissions: 9848 Census: 136 Outpatient Visits: 50679 Births: 1184 Personnel: 565

### CIDRA—Cidra County

✉ **FIRST HOSPITAL PANAMERICANO (404004)**, State Road 787 KM 1 5, Zip 00739, Mailing Address: P.O. Box 1400, Zip 00739; tel. 787/739–5555, (Nonreporting) **A**1 3 5 9 10 **S** Universal Health Services, Inc., King of Prussia, PA
Primary Contact: Astro Munoz, Executive Director
COO: Tim McCarthy, President Puerto Rico Division
CFO: Gabriel Rivera, Controller
CMO: Ramon Parrilla, M.D., Chief Medical Officer
CIO: Carlos Nunez, Director Management Information Systems
CHR: Shirley Ayala, Director Human Resources
Web address: www.hospitalpanamericano.com
**Control:** Corporation, Investor–owned, for–profit **Service:** Psychiatric

Staffed Beds: 153

## COTO LAUREL—Ponce County

★ **HOSPITAL SAN CRISTOBAL (400113)**, 506 Carr Road, Zip 00780;
tel. 787/848–2100, (Nonreporting) **A**3 5 9 10
Primary Contact: Pedro L. Benetti–Loyola, Administrator
COO: Pedro L. Benetti–Loyola, Senior Executive and Vice President
CFO: Marian Collazo, Director Finance
CMO: Ramon Rodriguez Rivas, M.D., Medical Director
CIO: Ramon Acevedo, Supervisor Information Systems
CHR: Candie Rodriguez, Director Human Resources
Web address: www.hospitalsancristobal.com
**Control:** Corporation, Investor–owned, for–profit **Service:** Other specialty

Staffed Beds: 103

## FAJARDO—Fajardo County

★ **CARIBBEAN MEDICAL CENTER (400131)**, 151 Avenue Osvaldo Molina,
Zip 00738–4013, Mailing Address: Call Box 70006, Zip 00738–7006;
tel. 787/801–0081, (Nonreporting) **A**9 10
Primary Contact: Eduardo Sotomayor, Administrator
CMO: Miguel Rodriguez, Medical Director
**Control:** Other not–for–profit (including NFP Corporation) **Service:** General
Medical and Surgical

Staffed Beds: 39

⊞ **HOSPITAL SAN PABLO DEL ESTE (400125)**, Avenida General Valero, 404,
Zip 00738, Mailing Address: P.O. Box 1028, Zip 00738–1028;
tel. 787/863–0505 **A**1 9 10 **F**3 29 30 31 34 35 40 41 45 46 48 49 56 57 70
72 73 75 76 78 79 80 81 82 87 89 93 107 111 119 130 133 146 148 **P**6
Primary Contact: Aixa Irizarry, Executive Director
CFO: Luis A. Arroyo, Chief Financial Officer
CMO: Manuel Navas, M.D., Medical Director
CHR: Vilma Rodriguez, Director Human Resources
Web address: www.sanpablo.com
**Control:** Corporation, Investor–owned, for–profit **Service:** General Medical and
Surgical

Staffed Beds: 145 Admissions: 5281 Census: 82 Outpatient Visits: 29923
Births: 713

## GUAYAMA—Guayama County

⊞ **HOSPITAL EPISCOPAL SAN LUCAS GUAYAMA (400048)**, Avenue Pedro
Albesus, Zip 00784, Mailing Address: PO Box 10011, Zip 00785–1006;
tel. 787/864–4300, (Nonreporting) **A**1 3 5 9 10
Primary Contact: Arnaldo Rodriguez, President and Chief Executive Officer
COO: Wilfredo Rabelo, Chief Operating Officer
CFO: Carlos Porrata, CPA, Chief Financial Officer
CMO: Gerson Jimenez, M.D., Medical Director
CHR: Ivette Lacot, Director Human Resources
**Control:** Church–operated, Nongovernment, not–for profit **Service:** General
Medical and Surgical

Staffed Beds: 115

★ **HOSPITAL SANTA ROSA (400009)**, Veterans Avenue, Zip 00784, Mailing
Address: P.O. Box 10008, Zip 00785; tel. 787/864–0101 **A**9 10 **F**18 40 45 46
70 76 81 89 107 111 119
Primary Contact: Gloria Diaz, Executive Director
CFO: Edwin De Jesus, Comptroller
CMO: Joaquin Pales, President
CIO: Waleska Rolon, Manager
**Control:** Other not–for–profit (including NFP Corporation) **Service:** General
Medical and Surgical

Staffed Beds: 86 Admissions: 3243 Census: 31 Outpatient Visits: 23172
Births: 185 Total Expense ($000): 13474 Payroll Expense ($000): 3705
Personnel: 198

## GUAYNABO—Guaynabo County

**PROFESSIONAL HOSPITAL GUAYNABO (400122)**, Carretera 199 Km 1.2
Avenue, Zip 00969, Mailing Address: PO Box 1609, Zip 00970;
tel. 787/708–6560, (Nonreporting) **A**10
Primary Contact: Leonardo Valentin, Chief Executive Officer
Web address: www.professionalhospital.com
**Control:** Other not–for–profit (including NFP Corporation) **Service:** Psychiatric

Staffed Beds: 54

## HATO REY—San Juan County, See San Juan

## HUMACAO—Humacao County

**HOSPITAL DR. DOMINGUEZ** See Hospital Oriente

⊞ **HOSPITAL HMA DE HUMACAO (400005)**, 3 Font Martelo Street,
Zip 00791–3342, Mailing Address: P.O. Box 639, Zip 00792–0639;
tel. 787/656–2424, (Nonreporting) **A**1 9 10
Primary Contact: Aixa Irizarry, Executive Director
COO: Carlos M. Pineiro, President
CFO: Luis A. Arroyo, Chief Financial Officer
CMO: Francisco R. Carballo, M.D., Medical Director
CIO: Giovanni Piereschi, Vice President Management Information Systems
CHR: Iris Abreu, Supervisor Human Resources
**Control:** Corporation, Investor–owned, for–profit **Service:** General Medical and
Surgical

Staffed Beds: 64

★ **HOSPITAL ORIENTE (400011)**, 300 Font Martelo Street, Zip 00791–3230,
Mailing Address: P.O. Box 699, Zip 00792–0699; tel. 787/852–0505,
(Nonreporting) **A**9 10
Primary Contact: Miguel A. Solivan, Administrator
CFO: Ivonne Rivera, Director Finance
CMO: Carmelo Herrero, M.D., Medical Director
CHR: Ivonne Lopez, Director Human Resources
**Control:** Corporation, Investor–owned, for–profit **Service:** General Medical and
Surgical

Staffed Beds: 71

★ **RYDER MEMORIAL HOSPITAL (400007)**, 355 Font Martelo Street,
Zip 00791–3249, Mailing Address: P.O. Box 859, Zip 00792–0859;
tel. 787/852–0768, (Nonreporting) **A**9 10
Primary Contact: Jose R. Feliciano, Chief Executive Officer
COO: Nemuel O. Artiles, FACHE, Administrator
CFO: Jose O. Ortiz, Chief Financial Officer
CMO: Raul Ramos Pereira, M.D., Medical Director
CIO: Joseph V. Cruz, Chief Information Officer
CHR: Maria Figueroa, Director Human Resources
Web address: www.hryder@prtc.net
**Control:** Other not–for–profit (including NFP Corporation) **Service:** General
Medical and Surgical

Staffed Beds: 227

## MANATI—Manati County

⊞ **DOCTORS CENTER (400118)**, KM 47–7, Zip 00674, Mailing Address: P.O. Box
30532, Zip 00674; tel. 787/854–3322, (Nonreporting) **A**1 9 10
Primary Contact: Carlos Blanco, M.D., Administrator
**Control:** Corporation, Investor–owned, for–profit **Service:** General Medical and
Surgical

Staffed Beds: 150

★ **HEALTHSOUTH HOSPITAL OF MANATI (403026)**, Carretera 2, Kilometro 47
7, Zip 00674; tel. 787/621–3800, (Nonreporting) **A**9 10 **S** HEALTHSOUTH
Corporation, Birmingham, AL
Primary Contact: Enrique A. Vicens–Rivera, Jr., JD, Chief Executive Officer
CFO: Jesus M. Corazon, Controller
CMO: Jamie L. Marrero, M.D., Medical Director
CHR: Erika Landrau, Human Resources Coordinator
CNO: Evelyn Diaz, R.N., Chief Nursing Officer
Web address: www.healthsouth.com
**Control:** Corporation, Investor–owned, for–profit **Service:** Rehabilitation

Staffed Beds: 40

⊞ **HOSPITAL MANATI MEDICAL CENTER (400114)**, Calle Hernandez, Carrion
668, Zip 00674, Mailing Address: P.O. Box 1142, Zip 00674–1142;
tel. 787/621–3700 **A**1 3 5 9 10 **F**3 8 13 14 15 18 20 24 29 30 40 41 42 45
46 49 60 64 74 75 76 80 81 86 89 92 93 107 112 119 130 146 **P**8
Primary Contact: Jorge Galva, Executive Director
CFO: Noriselle Rivera–Pol, Vice President Finance
CMO: Luis R. Rosa–Toledo, M.D., Medical Director
CIO: Alberto Medina, Information Technology Senior Consultant
CHR: Nilda Paravisini, Director Human Resources
Web address: www.manatimedical.com
**Control:** Corporation, Investor–owned, for–profit **Service:** General Medical and
Surgical

Staffed Beds: 235 Admissions: 16111 Census: 216 Outpatient Visits:
56310 Births: 1504 Personnel: 1422

---

**Hospital, Medicare Provider Number, Address, Telephone, Approval, Facility, and Physician Codes, Health Care System**

★ American Hospital Association (AHA) membership
☐ The Joint Commission accreditation
◇ DNV Healthcare Inc. accreditation
○ Healthcare Facilities Accreditation Program
△ Commission on Accreditation of Rehabilitation Facilities (CARF) accreditation

**MAYAGUEZ—Mayaguez County**

☒ **BELLA VISTA HOSPITAL (400014)**, State Road 349, Zip 00680, Mailing Address: P.O. Box 1750, Zip 00681; tel. 787/834–6000, (Nonreporting) **A**1 3 5 9 10
Primary Contact: Jesus Nieves, Chief Executive Officer
CFO: Enrique Rivera, Chief Financial Officer
CMO: Miguel Cruz, M.D., Medical Director
CHR: Benjamin Astacio, Director Human Resources
Web address: www.bvhpr.org
**Control:** Church–operated, Nongovernment, not–for profit **Service:** General Medical and Surgical

| Staffed Beds: 157 |
|---|

☒ **DR. RAMON E. BETANCES HOSPITAL–MAYAGUEZ MEDICAL CENTER BRANCH (400103)**, 410 Hostos Avenue, Zip 00680–1501, Mailing Address: P.O. Box 600, Zip 00681–0600; tel. 787/652–9200, (Nonreporting) **A**1 3 5 9 10
Primary Contact: Jaime Maestre, Chief Executive Officer
CMO: Milton D. Carrero, M.D., Medical Director
CHR: Betsmari Medina, Director Human Resources
**Control:** State–Government, nonfederal **Service:** General Medical and Surgical

| Staffed Beds: 181 |
|---|

★ **HOSPITAL PEREA (400123)**, 15 Basora Street, Zip 00681, Mailing Address: P.O. Box 170, Zip 00681; tel. 787/834–0101, (Nonreporting) **A**10 **S** United Medical Corporation, Windermere, FL
Primary Contact: Marco Reyes Concepcion, Executive Director
CFO: Joannie Garcia, CPA, Director Finance
CMO: Humberto Olivencia, M.D., Medical Director
Web address: www.paviahealth.com/perea_hospital.htm
**Control:** Corporation, Investor–owned, for–profit **Service:** General Medical and Surgical

| Staffed Beds: 103 |
|---|

**MOCA—Moca County**

★ **HOSPITAL SAN CARLOS BORROMEO (400111)**, 550 Concepcion Vera Ayala, Zip 00676; tel. 787/877–8000 **A**9 10 **F**8 15 29 30 34 40 45 65 70 74 75 76 79 81 89 107 111 115 119 130 133 145 146 148 **P**8
Primary Contact: Rosaida M. Crespo, Executive Director
COO: Rosaida M. Crespo, Executive Director
CFO: Irma Cabrera, Finance Director
CMO: Erick Nieves, M.D., Medical Director
CIO: Jose Nieves, Director Information Systems
CHR: Migdalia Ortiz, Director Human Resources
CNO: Luz M. Velez, Director–Administration of Nursing Services
Web address: www.hscbpr.org
**Control:** Other not–for–profit (including NFP Corporation) **Service:** General Medical and Surgical

| Staffed Beds: 106 Admissions: 5115 Census: 72 Outpatient Visits: 33372 Births: 630 Total Expense ($000): 24435 Payroll Expense ($000): 8520 Personnel: 419 |
|---|

**PONCE—Ponce County**

☒ **DR. PILA'S HOSPITAL (400003)**, Avenida Las Americas, Zip 00731, Mailing Address: P.O. Box 1910, Zip 00733–1910; tel. 787/848–5600, (Nonreporting) **A**1 3 5 9 10
Primary Contact: Rafael Alvarado, Chief Executive Officer
Web address: www.drpila.com
**Control:** Other not–for–profit (including NFP Corporation) **Service:** General Medical and Surgical

| Staffed Beds: 115 |
|---|

☒ **HOSPITAL DE DAMAS (400022)**, Ponce by Pass, Zip 00731; tel. 787/840–8686, (Total facility includes 22 beds in nursing home–type unit) **A**1 3 5 9 10 **F**3 13 14 17 18 20 22 24 29 30 40 45 47 49 62 67 70 72 76 80 81 88 89 107 114 115 119 128 129 130 146 **P**8
Primary Contact: Edwin Sueiro, Administrator
CMO: Pedro Benitez, M.D., Medical Director
CIO: Bienvenido Ortiz, Coordinator Information Systems
CHR: Gilberto Cuevas, Director Human Resources
Web address: www.hospitaldamas.com
**Control:** Other not–for–profit (including NFP Corporation) **Service:** General Medical and Surgical

| Staffed Beds: 251 Admissions: 12416 Census: 178 Outpatient Visits: 46983 Births: 1531 Total Expense ($000): 75698 Payroll Expense ($000): 25423 Personnel: 830 |
|---|

☒ **HOSPITAL ONCOLOGICO ANDRES GRILLASCA (400028)**, Centro Medico De Ponce, Zip 00733, Mailing Address: P.O. Box 331324, Zip 00733–1324; tel. 787/848–0800, (Nonreporting) **A**1 3 5 9
Primary Contact: Manuel J. Vazquez, Executive Administrator
CMO: Roberto Velasquez, M.D., Medical Director
CIO: Maria T. Teissonniere, Director Public Relations
CHR: Carlos T. Santiago, Director Human Resources
**Control:** Other not–for–profit (including NFP Corporation) **Service:** Cancer

| Staffed Beds: 49 |
|---|

☒ **ST. LUKE'S EPISCOPAL HOSPITAL (400044)**, 917 Tito Castro Avenue, Zip 00731–4717, Mailing Address: P.O. Box 336810, Zip 00733–6810; tel. 787/844–2080 **A**1 3 5 9 10 **F**7 13 17 18 20 22 24 26 30 40 41 46 49 51 57 64 67 70 72 73 75 76 79 81 82 85 87 88 89 92 93 107 111 114 115 119 130 144 145 147 148
Primary Contact: Julio Colon, Interim President and Chief Executive Officer
CFO: Julio Colon, Chief Financial Officer
CMO: Jenaro Scarano, M.D., Medical Director
CHR: Juan Salazar, Director Human Resources
Web address: www.sanlucaspr.com
**Control:** Church–operated, Nongovernment, not–for profit **Service:** General Medical and Surgical

| Staffed Beds: 334 Admissions: 16731 Census: 248 Outpatient Visits: 85955 Births: 1970 Total Expense ($000): 115118 Payroll Expense ($000): 31781 Personnel: 1187 |
|---|

**RIO PIEDRAS—San Juan County, See San Juan**

**SAN GERMAN—San German County**

☒ **HOSPITAL DE LA CONCEPCION (400021)**, Carr 2, Km 173, Bo Cain Alto, Zip 00683–3920, Mailing Address: P.O. Box 285, Zip 00683–0285; tel. 787/892–1860, (Nonreporting) **A**1 3 5 9 10
Primary Contact: Felicita Bonilla, Administrator
CFO: Lizmari Calderon, Director Finance
CMO: Ivan Acosta, M.D., Medical Director
CIO: Aaron Mendez, Director Management Information Systems
CHR: Jorge Rodriguez Diaz, Director Human Resources
Web address: www.hospitalconcepcion.org
**Control:** Church–operated, Nongovernment, not–for profit **Service:** General Medical and Surgical

| Staffed Beds: 167 |
|---|

★ **HOSPITAL METROPOLITANO SAN GERMAN (400126)**, Calle Javilla Al Costado Parque de Bombas, Zip 00683; tel. 787/892–5300, (Nonreporting) **A**9 10
Primary Contact: Jorge Martinez, Chief Executive Officer
**Control:** Corporation, Investor–owned, for–profit **Service:** Other specialty

| Staffed Beds: 40 |
|---|

**SAN JUAN—San Juan County**
**(Mailing Addresses - Hato Rey, Rio Piedras)**

☒ **ASHFORD PRESBYTERIAN COMMUNITY HOSPITAL (400001)**, 1451 Avenue Ashford, Zip 00907–1511, Mailing Address: P.O. Box 9020032, Zip 00902–0032; tel. 787/721–2160 **A**1 9 10 **F**2 3 13 15 18 30 40 41 45 46 53 59 65 70 72 76 79 80 81 82 87 88 89 93 97 107 110 111 114 119 130 131 146 147 148 **P**5
Primary Contact: Pedro J. Gonzalez, FACHE, Chief Executive Officer
COO: Obdulia Medina, MSN, Associate Director for Administrative Support, Clinical Management and Ambulatory Care
CFO: Milagros Ortiz, CPA, Chief Financial Officer
CMO: Francisco de Torres, M.D., Medical Director
CIO: Gerald Lopez, Chief Information Officer
CHR: Irma Carrillo, Director Human Resources
CNO: Itza Soto, MSN, Nursing Executive
Web address: www.presbypr.com
**Control:** Other not–for–profit (including NFP Corporation) **Service:** General Medical and Surgical

| Staffed Beds: 195 Admissions: 10947 Census: 147 Outpatient Visits: 59948 Births: 3404 Total Expense ($000): 71416 Payroll Expense ($000): 25864 Personnel: 820 |
|---|

☒ **AUXILIO MUTUO HOSPITAL (400016)**, Ponce De Leon Avenue, Zip 00918–1000, Mailing Address: P.O. Box 191227, Zip 00919–1227; tel. 787/758–2000, (Nonreporting) **A**1 3 5 9 10
Primary Contact: Jorge L. Matta Serrano, Administrator
COO: Carmen Martin, Associate Administrator
CFO: Maria L. Marti, Director Fiscal Services
CMO: Jose Isado, M.D., Medical Director
CIO: Edgardo Rodriguez, Director Management Information Systems
CHR: Maria Vega, Director Human Resources
Web address: www.auxiliomutuo.com
**Control:** Other not–for–profit (including NFP Corporation) **Service:** General Medical and Surgical

| Staffed Beds: 483 |
|---|

*Many Facility Codes have changed. Please refer to the AHA Guide Code Chart.*   © 2013 AHA Guide

⌖ **CARDIOVASCULAR CENTER OF PUERTO RICO AND THE CARIBBEAN (400124)**, Americo Miranda Centro Medico, Zip 00936, Mailing Address: P.O. Box 366528, Zip 00936–6528; tel. 787/754–8500, (Nonreporting) **A**1 3 5 10 **S** Puerto Rico Department of Health, San Juan, PR
Primary Contact: Waleska Crespo, Executive Director
COO: Wilfredo Rabelo Millan, Chief Operating Officer
CFO: Arthur J. Fernandez del Valle, Chief Financial Officer
CMO: Jose E. Novoa Loyola, M.D., Medical Director
CIO: Eugenio Torres Ayala, Director Information Systems
CHR: Myriam T. Rodriguez Schmidt, Director Human Resources
CNO: Pedro Laureano Cantre, Chief Nursing Officer
Web address: www.cardiovascular.gobierno.pr
**Control:** State–Government, nonfederal **Service:** General Medical and Surgical

**Staffed Beds: 146**

★ **DOCTORS' CENTER HOSPITAL SAN JUAN (400006)**, 1395 San Rafael Street, Zip 00909–2518, Mailing Address: Box 11338, Santurce Station, Zip 00910–3428; tel. 787/999–7620 **A**9 10 **F**40 45 46 70 74 76 81 89 107 108 119 130 148
Primary Contact: Norma Marrero, Executive Administrator
COO: Norma Marrero, Executive Administrator
CFO: Alejandro Santiago, Director Finance
CMO: Ubaldo Santiago, M.D., Chairman
CIO: Luis Alicea, Chief Informaton Officer
CHR: Carmen Perez, Director Human Resources
CNO: Lesbia Lopez, Chief Nursing Officer
Web address: www.tuhospitalfamiliar.com
**Control:** Corporation, Investor–owned, for–profit **Service:** General Medical and Surgical

**Staffed Beds: 125 Admissions: 5262 Census: 90 Outpatient Visits: 22966 Births: 851 Total Expense ($000): 15093 Payroll Expense ($000): 7922 Personnel: 224**

**HEALTHSOUTH REHABILITATION HOSPITAL OF SAN JUAN** See

⌖ **HOSPITAL DEL MAESTRO (400004)**, 550 Sergio Cuevas, Zip 00918–3741, Mailing Address: P.O. Box 364708, Zip 00936–4708; tel. 787/758–8383, (Nonreporting) **A**1 9 10
Primary Contact: Tania Conde–Sterling, Executive Director
CFO: Marisol Vargas, Director Finance
CMO: Jose Montalvo, M.D., Medical Director
CIO: Laura Rodriguez, Director Medical Records
CHR: Orlando Santiago, Human Resources Officer
**Control:** Corporation, Investor–owned, for–profit **Service:** General Medical and Surgical

**Staffed Beds: 250**

⌖ **HOSPITAL METROPOLITAN (400106)**, 1785 Carr 21, Zip 00921–3399, Mailing Address: P.O. Box 11981, Zip 00922; tel. 787/782–9999 **A**1 9 10 **F**3 8 15 18 19 29 30 31 34 40 41 42 45 46 47 49 59 60 65 67 68 70 74 75 78 79 81 86 87 89 94 107 108 110 111 115 118 119 120 121 130 143 144 145 146 148 **P**8
Primary Contact: Jose Rosado, Chief Executive Officer
CFO: Maritza Rodriguez, Chief Financial Officer
CMO: Maria de los Angeles Correa, M.D., Medical Director
CIO: Manuel Santiago, Chief Information Officer
**Control:** Corporation, Investor–owned, for–profit **Service:** General Medical and Surgical

**Staffed Beds: 127 Admissions: 6379 Census: 96 Outpatient Visits: 36798 Births: 0 Total Expense ($000): 32050 Payroll Expense ($000): 11662**

⌖ **HOSPITAL PAVIA–HATO REY (400128)**, 435 Ponce De Leon Avenue, Zip 00917–3428; tel. 787/641–2323, (Nonreporting) **A**1 3 5 9 10 **S** United Medical Corporation, Windermere, FL
Primary Contact: Luis R. Allende Ruiz, Executive Director
Web address: www.paviahealth.com
**Control:** Corporation, Investor–owned, for–profit **Service:** General Medical and Surgical

**Staffed Beds: 180**

⌖ **HOSPITAL PAVIA–SANTURCE (400019)**, 1462 Asia Street, Zip 00909–2143, Mailing Address: Box 11137, Santurce Station, Zip 00910–1137; tel. 787/727–6060 **A**1 10 **F**8 11 17 18 20 22 24 26 30 34 37 38 40 47 48 49 56 57 58 59 60 65 70 73 74 75 76 79 82 85 87 92 107 108 109 111 112 114 115 119 130 143 148 **S** United Medical Corporation, Windermere, FL
Primary Contact: Jose Luis Rodriguez, Chief Executive Officer
CFO: Francisco Espina, Director Finance
Web address: www.paviahealth.com
**Control:** Corporation, Investor–owned, for–profit **Service:** General Medical and Surgical

**Staffed Beds: 215 Admissions: 9712 Census: 172 Outpatient Visits: 29379 Births: 937 Total Expense ($000): 73140 Payroll Expense ($000): 2663**

⌖ **HOSPITAL SAN FRANCISCO (400098)**, 371 Avenida De Diego, Zip 00923–1711, Mailing Address: P.O. Box 29025, Zip 00929–0025; tel. 787/767–5100, (Nonreporting) **A**1 10
Primary Contact: Marcos Aguila, Chief Executive Officer
CFO: Lizzette Rodriguez, Director Finance
CMO: Hector L. Cotto, M.D., Medical Director
CIO: Deborah Nieves, Director Management Information Systems
CHR: Sugehi Santiago, Director
Web address: www.sanpablo.com
**Control:** Corporation, Investor–owned, for–profit **Service:** General Medical and Surgical

**Staffed Beds: 150**

★ **HOSPITAL SAN GERARDO (400121)**, 138 Avenue Winston Churchill, Zip 00926–6013; tel. 787/761–8383, (Nonreporting) **A**9 10
Primary Contact: Henry Ruberte, Administrator
**Control:** Other not–for–profit (including NFP Corporation) **Service:** Chronic disease

**Staffed Beds: 60**

⌖ **I. GONZALEZ MARTINEZ ONCOLOGIC HOSPITAL (400012)**, Puerto Rico Medical Center, Hato Rey, Zip 00935, Mailing Address: P.O. Box 191811, Zip 00919–1811; tel. 787/765–2382, (Nonreporting) **A**1 2 3 5 10
Primary Contact: Jorge De Jesus, Executive Director
COO: Felix Ortiz, Administrator
CFO: Yolanda Quinones, Director Finance
CMO: Carlos Chevere, M.D., Medical Director
CHR: Luz Maria Hernandez, Director Human Resources
**Control:** Other not–for–profit (including NFP Corporation) **Service:** General Medical and Surgical

**Staffed Beds: 47**

★ **INDUSTRIAL HOSPITAL**, Puerto Rico Medical Center, Zip 00936, Mailing Address: P.O. Box 365028, Zip 00936; tel. 787/764–3660 **A**9 **F**3 8 16 18 36 40 64 73 74 75 77 79 81 82 90 93 94 96 104 130 148
Primary Contact: Jorge Garcia Ortiz, Executive Director
CFO: Robert Bernier Casanova, Chief Financial Officer
CMO: Carmen Carrasquillo, M.D., Medical Director
CHR: Sonia M. Lebron, Human Resources Specialist
**Control:** State–Government, nonfederal **Service:** General Medical and Surgical

**Staffed Beds: 108 Admissions: 2075 Census: 47 Outpatient Visits: 49144 Births: 0 Total Expense ($000): 67616 Personnel: 540**

⌖ **SAN JORGE CHILDREN'S HOSPITAL**, 252 San Jorge Street, Santurce, Zip 00912–3310; tel. 787/727–1000, (Nonreporting) **A**1 3 5 9 **S** United Medical Corporation, Windermere, FL
Primary Contact: Domingo Cruz, Senior Vice President Operations
CFO: Jose Marrero, Director Finance
CMO: Luis Clavell, M.D., Medical Director
CIO: Rogelio Caballero, Chief Information Systems
CHR: Odette Burgos, Supervisor Human Resources
CNO: Leticia Fuentes, Nursing Director
Web address: www.sanjorgechildrenshospital.com
**Control:** Corporation, Investor–owned, for–profit **Service:** Children's general

**Staffed Beds: 125**

⌖ **SAN JUAN CAPESTRANO HOSPITAL (404005)**, Rural Route 2, Box 11, Zip 00926; tel. 787/625–2900 **A**1 9 10 **F**2 4 5 29 30 38 75 98 99 100 101 102 103 104 105 106 130 132 **P**8
Primary Contact: Laura Vargas, Chief Executive Officer and Managing Director
CFO: Julia Cruz, Chief Financial Officer
CMO: Jose' Alonso, M.D., Medical Director
CIO: Ana Morandeira, Director Marketing
CHR: Luis Rivera, Director Human Resources
Web address: www.sjcapestrano.com
**Control:** Corporation, Investor–owned, for–profit **Service:** Psychiatric

**Staffed Beds: 108 Admissions: 4236 Census: 85 Outpatient Visits: 31656 Births: 0 Total Expense ($000): 16066 Payroll Expense ($000): 6487 Personnel: 257**

⌖ **SAN JUAN CITY HOSPITAL (400015)**, Puerto Rico Medical Center, Zip 00928, Mailing Address: PMB 79, P.O. Box 70344, Zip 00936–8344; tel. 787/766–2222, (Nonreporting) **A**1 3 5 10
Primary Contact: Myrna Boissen, Executive Director
COO: Norma Marcano, Chief Operating Officer
CFO: Jaime Rodriguez, Chief Financial Officer
CMO: Raul Reyes, M.D., Medical Director
CIO: Gustavo Mesa, Chief Information Officer
CHR: Jose Garcia, Chief Human Resources Officer
Web address: www.massalud.com
**Control:** City–Government, nonfederal **Service:** General Medical and Surgical

**Staffed Beds: 267**

---

★ **STATE PSYCHIATRIC HOSPITAL (404006)**, Monacillos Avenue, Zip 00936,
Mailing Address: Call Box 2100, Caparra Heights Station, Zip 00922–2100;
tel. 787/766–4646, (Nonreporting) **A**3 5
Primary Contact: Jimmy Rivera Viana, Executive Director
CMO: Brunilda Vazquez, Medical Director
CHR: Idalia Garcia, Chief Human Resources Officer
**Control:** State–Government, nonfederal **Service:** Psychiatric

Staffed Beds: 153

★ **UNIVERSITY HOSPITAL (400061)**, Nineyas 869 Rio Piedras, Zip 00922,
Mailing Address: P.O. Box 2116, Zip 00922; tel. 787/754–0101, (Nonreporting)
**A**3 5 9 10 **S** Puerto Rico Department of Health, San Juan, PR
Primary Contact: Jorge Matta Gonzalez, Executive Director
CFO: Janet Baez, Director
CMO: Ricardo Moscoso, M.D., Medical Director
CIO: Josue Martinez, Coordinator Information Systems
CHR: Wanda Maldonado, Director Human Resources
**Control:** State–Government, nonfederal **Service:** General Medical and Surgical

Staffed Beds: 262

⊠ **UNIVERSITY PEDIATRIC HOSPITAL (403301)**, Barrio Monacenno, Carretera
22, Rio Piedras, Zip 00935, Mailing Address: P.O. Box 191079, San Juan,
Zip 00910–1070; tel. 787/777–3535, (Nonreporting) **A**1 3 5 9 10 **S** Puerto Rico
Department of Health, San Juan, PR
Primary Contact: Gloria Hernandez, Executive Director
CMO: Myrna Quinones Feliciano, M.D., Medical Director
**Control:** State–Government, nonfederal **Service:** Children's general

Staffed Beds: 145

⊠ △ **VETERANS AFFAIRS CARIBBEAN HEALTHCARE SYSTEM**, (Formerly
Veterans Affairs Medical Center), 10 Casia Street, Zip 00921–3201;
tel. 787/641–7582, (Nonreporting) **A**1 2 3 5 7 9 **S** Department of Veterans
Affairs, Washington, DC
Primary Contact: Wanda Mims, Director
CFO: Ricardo Ochoa, Chief Fiscal Officer
CMO: Sandra C. Gracia, M.D., Chief of Staff
CIO: Manuel Negron, Chief Information Technology Service
CHR: Damaris Tosado, Manager Human Resources
Web address: www.caribbean.va.gov/
**Control:** Veterans Affairs, Government, federal **Service:** General Medical and
Surgical

Staffed Beds: 330

### VEGA BAJA—Vega Alta County

★ **WILMA N. VAZQUEZ MEDICAL CENTER (400115)**, KM 39 1/2 Road 2, Call
Box 7001, Zip 00694; tel. 787/858–1580, (Total facility includes 20 beds in
nursing home–type unit) **A**9 10 **F**2 3 8 13 18 29 30 35 40 41 60 64 65 70 75
77 78 79 81 82 87 89 91 93 94 96 107 119 128 130 146 148 **P**5 6
Primary Contact: Ramon J. Vilar, Administrator
COO: Jose O. Pabon, Director Operations
CFO: Youdie Reynolds–Gossette, Controller
CMO: Jorge Feria, M.D., President Medical Staff
CIO: Miguel Aponte, Supervisor Management Information Systems
CHR: Aymette Garcia, Manager Human Resources
**Control:** Corporation, Investor–owned, for–profit **Service:** General Medical and
Surgical

Staffed Beds: 150 **Admissions:** 4147 **Census:** 76 **Outpatient Visits:** 24023
**Births:** 0

### YAUCO—Yauco County

⊠ **HOSPITAL METROPOLITANO DR. TITO MATTEI (400110)**, Carretera 128 KM
1, Zip 00698, Mailing Address: P.O. Box 5643, Zip 00698; tel. 787/856–1000,
(Nonreporting) **A**1 5 9 10
Primary Contact: Astrid J. Abreu, Chief Executive Officer
CFO: Elizabeth Gonzalez, Chief Financial Officer
CMO: Manuel Ramirez Soto, M.D., Medical Director
CIO: Edson Ortiz, Chief Information Officer
CHR: Nannete Acosta, Director Human Resources
Web address: www.hmyauco.com
**Control:** Corporation, Investor–owned, for–profit **Service:** General Medical and
Surgical

Staffed Beds: 105

# VIRGIN ISLANDS

### CHRISTIANSTED—St. Croix County

⊠ **GOVERNOR JUAN F. LOUIS HOSPITAL (480002)**, 4007 Estate Diamond Ruby,
Zip 00820–4421; tel. 340/778–6311, (Nonreporting) **A**1 9 10
Primary Contact: Darice S. Plaskett, R.N., FACHE, Interim Chief Executive Officer
CFO: Rosalie Javois, Chief Financial Officer
CMO: Robert Centeno, M.D., Chief Medical Officer
CIO: Reuben D. Molloy, Chief Information Officer
CHR: Joan Jean–Baptiste, Vice President Human Resources
Web address: www.jflusvi.org
**Control:** State–Government, nonfederal **Service:** General Medical and Surgical

Staffed Beds: 108

### SAINT THOMAS—St. Thomas County

⊠ **SCHNEIDER REGIONAL MEDICAL CENTER (480001)**, 9048 Sugar Estate,
Charlotte Amalie, Zip 00802; tel. 340/776–8311, (Nonreporting) **A**1 10
Primary Contact: Bernard Wheatley, FACHE, Chief Executive Officer
CMO: Thelma Ruth Watson, M.D., Medical Director
CIO: J. C. Creque, Director Management Information Systems
CHR: Marlene J. Adams, Director Human Resources
Web address: www.rlshospital.org
**Control:** State–Government, nonfederal **Service:** General Medical and Surgical

Staffed Beds: 123

*Many Facility Codes have changed. Please refer to the AHA Guide Code Chart.* © 2013 AHA Guide

## GERMANY

**Heidelberg:** ★ Heidelberg Army Community Hospital, APO, CMR 242, AE 09042

**Landstuhl:** ★ Landstuhl Army Regional Medical Center, APO, CMR 402, AE 09180

**Wuerzburg:** ★ Wuerzburg Army Community Hospital, APO, USAMEDDAC Wuerzburg, Ut 26610, AE 09244

## ITALY

**Naples:** ★ U. S. Naval Hospital, FPO, none, AE 09619

## SPAIN

**Rota:** ★ U. S. Naval Hospital, Rota, FPO, PSC 819, Box 18, AE 09645–2500

## JAPAN

**Yokosuka:** ★ U. S. Naval Hospital, FPO, Box 1487, AP 96350

## SOUTH KOREA

**Seoul:** ★ Brian Allgood Army Community Hospital, APO, 121st General Hospital, AP 96205

**Yongsan: Medcom 18th Commander, Facilities Division Eamc L EM, APO, AP 96205**

## TAIWAN

**Taipei:** ★ U. S. Naval Hospital Taipei, No 300 Shin–Pai Road, Sec 2

# Notes

# Notes

# Notes

# Notes

# Notes

# Notes

# Indexes

Indexes

This section is an index of all hospitals in alphabetical order by hospital name, followed by the city, state, and page reference to the hospital's listing in Section A.

## A

AMG SPECIALTY HOSPITAL – BOGALUSA, BOGALUSA, LOUISIANA (see LSU BOGALUSA MEDICAL CENTER), p. A264
AMG SPECIALTY HOSPITAL – MUNCIE, MUNCIE, IN, p. A210
AMG SPECIALTY HOSPITAL–ALBUQUERQUE, ALBUQUERQUE, NM, p. A414
AMG SPECIALTY HOSPITAL–DENHAM SPRINGS, DENHAM SPRINGS, LA, p. A266
AMG SPECIALTY HOSPITAL–EDMOND, EDMOND, OK, p. A498
AMG SPECIALTY HOSPITAL–FELICIANA, CLINTON, LA, p. A265
AMG SPECIALTY HOSPITAL–GREENWOOD, GREENWOOD, MS, p. A347
AMG SPECIALTY HOSPITAL–HOUMA, HOUMA, LA, p. A268
AMG SPECIALTY HOSPITAL–LAFAYETTE, LAFAYETTE, LA, p. A270
AMG SPECIALTY HOSPITAL–SLIDELL, SLIDELL, LA, p. A278
AMG SPECIALTY HOSPITAL–WICHITA, WICHITA, KS, p. A246
ANAHEIM REGIONAL MEDICAL CENTER, ANAHEIM, CA, p. A52
ANCHOR HOSPITAL, ATLANTA, GA, p. A145
ANCORA PSYCHIATRIC HOSPITAL, HAMMONTON, NJ, p. A404
ANDALUSIA REGIONAL HOSPITAL, ANDALUSIA, AL, p. A15
ANDERSON COUNTY HOSPITAL, GARNETT, KS, p. A234
ANDERSON HOSPITAL, MARYVILLE, IL, p. A187
ANDERSON REGIONAL MEDICAL CENTER, MERIDIAN, MS, p. A351
ANDERSON REGIONAL MEDICAL CENTER–SOUTH CAMPUS, MERIDIAN, MS, p. A351
ANDREW MCFARLAND MENTAL HEALTH CENTER, SPRINGFIELD, IL, p. A195
ANDROSCOGGIN VALLEY HOSPITAL, BERLIN, NH, p. A397
ANDRUS PAVILION, YONKERS, NEW YORK (see ST. JOHN'S RIVERSIDE HOSPITAL), p. A446
ANGEL MEDICAL CENTER, FRANKLIN, NC, p. A452
ANGLETON DANBURY MEDICAL CENTER, ANGLETON, TX, p. A583
ANIMAS SURGICAL HOSPITAL, DURANGO, CO, p. A100
ANMED HEALTH MEDICAL CENTER, ANDERSON, SC, p. A548
ANMED HEALTH REHABILITATION HOSPITAL, ANDERSON, SC, p. A548
ANMED HEALTH WOMEN'S AND CHILDREN'S HOSPITAL, ANDERSON, SOUTH CAROLINA (see ANMED HEALTH MEDICAL CENTER), p. A548
ANN & ROBERT H. LURIE CHILDREN'S HOSPITAL OF CHICAGO, CHICAGO, IL, p. A176
ANNA JAQUES HOSPITAL, NEWBURYPORT, MA, p. A302
ANNE ARUNDEL MEDICAL CENTER, ANNAPOLIS, MD, p. A287
ANNIE JEFFREY MEMORIAL COUNTY HEALTH CENTER, OSCEOLA, NE, p. A388
ANNIE PENN HOSPITAL, REIDSVILLE, NORTH CAROLINA (see CONE HEALTH), p. A453
ANOKA–METROPOLITAN REGIONAL TREATMENT CENTER, ANOKA, MN, p. A328
ANSON COMMUNITY HOSPITAL, WADESBORO, NC, p. A462
ANSON GENERAL HOSPITAL, ANSON, TX, p. A583
ANTELOPE MEMORIAL HOSPITAL, NELIGH, NE, p. A386
ANTELOPE VALLEY HOSPITAL, LANCASTER, CA, p. A66
ANTHONY MEDICAL CENTER, ANTHONY, KS, p. A231
APPALACHIAN BEHAVIORAL HEALTHCARE, ATHENS, OH, p. A470
APPLETON AREA HEALTH SERVICES, APPLETON, MN, p. A328
APPLETON MEDICAL CENTER, APPLETON, WI, p. A683
APPLING HEALTHCARE SYSTEM, BAXLEY, GA, p. A148
ARBOUR H. R. I. HOSPITAL, BROOKLINE, MA, p. A298
ARBOUR HOSPITAL, BOSTON, MA, p. A295
ARBOUR–FULLER HOSPITAL, ATTLEBORO, MA, p. A295
ARBUCKLE MEMORIAL HOSPITAL, SULPHUR, OK, p. A507
ARCHBOLD HOSPITAL, ARCHBOLD, OHIO (see COMMUNITY HOSPITALS AND WELLNESS CENTERS), p. A472
ARIA HEALTH, PHILADELPHIA, PA, p. A534
ARIZONA CHILDREN'S CENTER, PHOENIX, ARIZONA (see MARICOPA INTEGRATED HEALTH SYSTEM), p. A34
ARIZONA HEART HOSPITAL, PHOENIX, ARIZONA (see PHOENIX BAPTIST HOSPITAL), p. A35
ARIZONA ORTHOPEDIC SURGICAL HOSPITAL, CHANDLER, AZ, p. A30
ARIZONA SPINE AND JOINT HOSPITAL, MESA, AZ, p. A32
ARIZONA STATE HOSPITAL, PHOENIX, AZ, p. A34
ARKANSAS CHILDREN'S HOSPITAL, LITTLE ROCK, AR, p. A46
ARKANSAS DEPARTMENT OF CORRECTION HOSPITAL, PINE BLUFF, AR, p. A49
ARKANSAS HEART HOSPITAL, LITTLE ROCK, AR, p. A46
ARKANSAS METHODIST MEDICAL CENTER, PARAGOULD, AR, p. A49
ARKANSAS STATE HOSPITAL, LITTLE ROCK, AR, p. A46
ARKANSAS SURGICAL HOSPITAL, NORTH LITTLE ROCK, AR, p. A48
ARKANSAS VALLEY REGIONAL MEDICAL CENTER, LA JUNTA, CO, p. A103
ARMS ACRES, CARMEL, NY, p. A423
ARNOLD PALMER CHILDREN'S HOSPITAL, ORLANDO, FLORIDA (see ORLANDO REGIONAL MEDICAL CENTER), p. A135

ARNOT OGDEN MEDICAL CENTER, ELMIRA, NY, p. A425
AROOSTOOK HEALTH CENTER, MARS HILL, MAINE (see THE AROOSTOOK MEDICAL CENTER), p. A285
ARROWHEAD BEHAVIORAL HEALTH HOSPITAL, MAUMEE, OH, p. A486
ARROWHEAD HOSPITAL, GLENDALE, AZ, p. A31
ARROWHEAD REGIONAL MEDICAL CENTER, COLTON, CA, p. A57
ARROYO GRANDE COMMUNITY HOSPITAL, ARROYO GRANDE, CA, p. A53
ARTESIA GENERAL HOSPITAL, ARTESIA, NM, p. A415
ARTHUR R. GOULD MEMORIAL HOSPITAL, PRESQUE ISLE, MAINE (see THE AROOSTOOK MEDICAL CENTER), p. A285
ASCENSION GONZALES REHABILITATION HOSPITAL, GONZALES, LA, p. A267
ASHE MEMORIAL HOSPITAL, JEFFERSON, NC, p. A455
ASHEVILLE SPECIALTY HOSPITAL, ASHEVILLE, NC, p. A447
ASHFORD PRESBYTERIAN COMMUNITY HOSPITAL, SAN JUAN, PR, p. A708
ASHLAND COMMUNITY HOSPITAL, ASHLAND, OR, p. A511
ASHLAND HEALTH CENTER, ASHLAND, KS, p. A231
ASHLEY COUNTY MEDICAL CENTER, CROSSETT, AR, p. A42
ASHLEY MEDICAL CENTER, ASHLEY, ND, p. A465
ASHLEY REGIONAL MEDICAL CENTER, VERNAL, UT, p. A648
ASHTABULA COUNTY MEDICAL CENTER, ASHTABULA, OH, p. A470
ASPEN VALLEY HOSPITAL DISTRICT, ASPEN, CO, p. A97
ASPIRE BEHAVIORAL HEALTH OF CONROE, CONROE, TX, p. A593
ASPIRUS GRAND VIEW HOSPITAL, IRONWOOD, MI, p. A317
ASPIRUS KEWEENAW HOSPITAL, LAURIUM, MI, p. A319
ASPIRUS ONTONAGON HOSPITAL, ONTONAGON, MI, p. A321
ASPIRUS WAUSAU HOSPITAL, WAUSAU, WI, p. A699
ASSUMPTION COMMUNITY HOSPITAL, NAPOLEONVILLE, LA, p. A274
ATASCADERO STATE HOSPITAL, ATASCADERO, CA, p. A53
ATCHISON HOSPITAL, ATCHISON, KS, p. A231
ATHENS REGIONAL MEDICAL CENTER, ATHENS, GA, p. A145
ATHENS REGIONAL MEDICAL CENTER, ATHENS, TN, p. A565
ATHENS–LIMESTONE HOSPITAL, ATHENS, AL, p. A16
ATHOL MEMORIAL HOSPITAL, ATHOL, MA, p. A295
ATLANTA MEDICAL CENTER, ATLANTA, GA, p. A146
ATLANTA MEDICAL CENTER – SOUTH CAMPUS, ATLANTA, GA, p. A146
ATLANTA VETERANS AFFAIRS MEDICAL CENTER, DECATUR, GA, p. A151
ATLANTIC GENERAL HOSPITAL, BERLIN, MD, p. A289
ATLANTIC SHORES HOSPITAL, FORT LAUDERDALE, FL, p. A123
ATLANTICARE REGIONAL MEDICAL CENTER, ATLANTIC CITY, NJ, p. A401
ATLANTICARE REGIONAL MEDICAL CENTER–MAINLAND DIVISION, POMONA, NEW JERSEY (see ATLANTICARE REGIONAL MEDICAL CENTER), p. A401
ATMORE COMMUNITY HOSPITAL, ATMORE, AL, p. A16
ATOKA COUNTY MEDICAL CENTER, ATOKA, OK, p. A496
ATRIUM MEDICAL CENTER, MIDDLETOWN, OH, p. A486
ATRIUM MEDICAL CENTER, STAFFORD, TX, p. A634
ATRIUM MEDICAL CENTER OF CORINTH, CORINTH, TX, p. A593
AUBURN COMMUNITY HOSPITAL, AUBURN, NY, p. A420
AUDRAIN MEDICAL CENTER, MEXICO, MO, p. A366
AUDUBON BEHAVIORAL HEALTHCARE OF LONGVIEW, LONGVIEW, TX, p. A619
AUDUBON BEHAVIORAL HEALTHCARE OF LUFKIN, LUFKIN, TX, p. A620
AUDUBON COUNTY MEMORIAL HOSPITAL, AUDUBON, IA, p. A216
AUGUSTA HEALTH, FISHERSVILLE, VA, p. A654
AULTMAN HOSPITAL, CANTON, OH, p. A473
AULTMAN HOSPITAL PEDIATRIC SERVICES, CANTON, OHIO (see AULTMAN HOSPITAL), p. A473
AULTMAN ORRVILLE HOSPITAL, ORRVILLE, OH, p. A488
AURELIA OSBORN FOX MEMORIAL HOSPITAL, ONEONTA, NY, p. A438
AURORA BAYCARE MEDICAL CENTER, GREEN BAY, WI, p. A687
AURORA BEHAVIORAL HEALTH CARE, SAN DIEGO, CA, p. A85
AURORA CHARTER OAK HOSPITAL, COVINA, CA, p. A58
AURORA CHICAGO LAKESHORE HOSPITAL, CHICAGO, IL, p. A176
AURORA LAKELAND MEDICAL CENTER, ELKHORN, WI, p. A686
AURORA LAS ENCINAS HOSPITAL, PASADENA, CA, p. A79
AURORA MEDICAL CENTER, KENOSHA, WI, p. A688
AURORA MEDICAL CENTER – MANITOWOC COUNTY, TWO RIVERS, WI, p. A698
AURORA MEDICAL CENTER GRAFTON, GRAFTON, WI, p. A687
AURORA MEDICAL CENTER OF OSHKOSH, OSHKOSH, WI, p. A694
AURORA MEDICAL CENTER OF WASHINGTON COUNTY, HARTFORD, WI, p. A688
AURORA MEDICAL CENTER SUMMIT, SUMMIT, WI, p. A697

AURORA MEMORIAL HOSPITAL OF BURLINGTON, BURLINGTON, WI, p. A685
AURORA PAVILION, AIKEN, SOUTH CAROLINA (see AIKEN REGIONAL MEDICAL CENTERS), p. A548
AURORA PHOENIX HOSPITAL, GLENDALE, AZ, p. A32
AURORA PSYCHIATRIC HOSPITAL, WAUWATOSA, WI, p. A699
AURORA SHEBOYGAN MEMORIAL MEDICAL CENTER, SHEBOYGAN, WI, p. A696
AURORA SINAI MEDICAL CENTER, MILWAUKEE, WI, p. A691
AURORA ST. LUKE'S MEDICAL CENTER, MILWAUKEE, WI, p. A691
AURORA ST. LUKE'S SOUTH SHORE, CUDAHY, WISCONSIN (see AURORA ST. LUKE'S MEDICAL CENTER), p. A691
AURORA TEMPE HOSPITAL, TEMPE, AZ, p. A38
AURORA VISTA DEL MAR HOSPITAL, VENTURA, CA, p. A94
AURORA WEST ALLIS MEDICAL CENTER, WEST ALLIS, WI, p. A699
AUSTEN RIGGS CENTER, STOCKBRIDGE, MA, p. A305
AUSTIN LAKES HOSPITAL, AUSTIN, TX, p. A584
AUSTIN STATE HOSPITAL, AUSTIN, TX, p. A584
AUSTIN SURGICAL HOSPITAL, AUSTIN, TX, p. A584
AUXILIO MUTUO HOSPITAL, SAN JUAN, PR, p. A708
AVENTURA HOSPITAL AND MEDICAL CENTER, AVENTURA, FL, p. A118
AVERA CHILDREN'S HOSPITAL, SIOUX FALLS, SOUTH DAKOTA (see AVERA MCKENNAN HOSPITAL AND UNIVERSITY HEALTH CENTER), p. A562
AVERA CREIGHTON HOSPITAL, CREIGHTON, NE, p. A383
AVERA DE SMET MEMORIAL HOSPITAL, DE SMET, SD, p. A559
AVERA DELLS AREA HOSPITAL, DELL RAPIDS, SD, p. A559
AVERA FLANDREAU HOSPITAL, FLANDREAU, SD, p. A559
AVERA GETTYSBURG HOSPITAL, GETTYSBURG, SD, p. A560
AVERA GREGORY HOSPITAL, GREGORY, SD, p. A560
AVERA HAND COUNTY MEMORIAL HOSPITAL, MILLER, SD, p. A560
AVERA HEART HOSPITAL OF SOUTH DAKOTA, SIOUX FALLS, SD, p. A562
AVERA HOLY FAMILY HOSPITAL, ESTHERVILLE, IA, p. A221
AVERA MARSHALL REGIONAL MEDICAL CENTER, MARSHALL, MN, p. A335
AVERA MCKENNAN HOSPITAL AND UNIVERSITY HEALTH CENTER, SIOUX FALLS, SD, p. A562
AVERA QUEEN OF PEACE HOSPITAL, MITCHELL, SD, p. A561
AVERA SACRED HEART HOSPITAL, YANKTON, SD, p. A564
AVERA ST. ANTHONY'S HOSPITAL, O'NEILL, NE, p. A386
AVERA ST. BENEDICT HEALTH CENTER, PARKSTON, SD, p. A561
AVERA ST. LUKE'S HOSPITAL, ABERDEEN, SD, p. A558
AVERA ST. MARY'S HOSPITAL, PIERRE, SD, p. A561
AVERA WESKOTA MEMORIAL HOSPITAL, WESSINGTON SPRINGS, SD, p. A564
AVISTA ADVENTIST HOSPITAL, LOUISVILLE, CO, p. A104
AVOYELLES HOSPITAL, MARKSVILLE, LA, p. A273

# B

BACHARACH INSTITUTE FOR REHABILITATION, POMONA, NJ, p. A409
BACON COUNTY HOSPITAL AND HEALTH SYSTEM, ALMA, GA, p. A145
BAILEY MEDICAL CENTER, OWASSO, OK, p. A505
BAKERSFIELD HEART HOSPITAL, BAKERSFIELD, CA, p. A53
BAKERSFIELD MEMORIAL HOSPITAL, BAKERSFIELD, CA, p. A53
BALDPATE HOSPITAL, HAVERHILL, MA, p. A300
BALDWIN AREA MEDICAL CENTER, BALDWIN, WI, p. A683
BALLARD REHABILITATION HOSPITAL, SAN BERNARDINO, CA, p. A84
BALLINGER MEMORIAL HOSPITAL, BALLINGER, TX, p. A587
BALTIMORE WASHINGTON MEDICAL CENTER, GLEN BURNIE, MD, p. A292
BANNER BAYWOOD MEDICAL CENTER, MESA, AZ, p. A32
BANNER BEHAVIORAL HEALTH CENTER–THUNDERBIRD CAMPUS, GLENDALE, ARIZONA (see BANNER THUNDERBIRD MEDICAL CENTER), p. A32
BANNER BEHAVIORAL HEALTH HOSPITAL – SCOTTSDALE, SCOTTSDALE, AZ, p. A37
BANNER BOSWELL MEDICAL CENTER, SUN CITY, AZ, p. A38
BANNER CHURCHILL COMMUNITY HOSPITAL, FALLON, NV, p. A391
BANNER DEL E. WEBB MEDICAL CENTER, SUN CITY WEST, AZ, p. A38
BANNER DESERT MEDICAL CENTER, MESA, AZ, p. A33
BANNER ESTRELLA MEDICAL CENTER, PHOENIX, AZ, p. A34
BANNER GATEWAY MEDICAL CENTER, GILBERT, AZ, p. A31
BANNER GOLDFIELD MEDICAL CENTER, APACHE JUNCTION, AZ, p. A30

BANNER GOOD SAMARITAN MEDICAL CENTER, PHOENIX, AZ, p. A34

BANNER HEART HOSPITAL, MESA, AZ, p. A33

BANNER IRONWOOD MEDICAL CENTER, SAN TAN VALLEY, AZ, p. A36

BANNER LASSEN MEDICAL CENTER, SUSANVILLE, CA, p. A92

BANNER THUNDERBIRD MEDICAL CENTER, GLENDALE, AZ, p. A32

BAPTIST CHILDREN'S HOSPITAL, MIAMI, FLORIDA (see BAPTIST HEALTH SOUTH FLORIDA, BAPTIST HOSPITAL OF MIAMI), p. A131

BAPTIST EASLEY HOSPITAL, EASLEY, SC, p. A551

BAPTIST EMERGENCY HOSPITAL, SAN ANTONIO, TX, p. A630

BAPTIST HEALTH CORBIN, CORBIN, KY, p. A249

BAPTIST HEALTH EXTENDED CARE HOSPITAL, LITTLE ROCK, AR, p. A46

BAPTIST HEALTH LA GRANGE, LA GRANGE, KY, p. A253

BAPTIST HEALTH LEXINGTON, LEXINGTON, KY, p. A253

BAPTIST HEALTH LOUISVILLE, LOUISVILLE, KY, p. A255

BAPTIST HEALTH MADISONVILLE, MADISONVILLE, KY, p. A257

BAPTIST HEALTH MEDICAL CENTER – NORTH LITTLE ROCK, NORTH LITTLE ROCK, AR, p. A48

BAPTIST HEALTH MEDICAL CENTER–ARKADELPHIA, ARKADELPHIA, AR, p. A41

BAPTIST HEALTH MEDICAL CENTER–HEBER SPRINGS, HEBER SPRINGS, AR, p. A44

BAPTIST HEALTH MEDICAL CENTER–LITTLE ROCK, LITTLE ROCK, AR, p. A46

BAPTIST HEALTH MEDICAL CENTER–STUTTGART, STUTTGART, AR, p. A50

BAPTIST HEALTH PADUCAH, PADUCAH, KY, p. A259

BAPTIST HEALTH REHABILITATION INSTITUTE, LITTLE ROCK, AR, p. A46

BAPTIST HEALTH RICHMOND, RICHMOND, KY, p. A260

BAPTIST HEALTH SOUTH FLORIDA, BAPTIST HOSPITAL OF MIAMI, MIAMI, FL, p. A131

BAPTIST HEALTH SOUTH FLORIDA, DOCTORS HOSPITAL, CORAL GABLES, FL, p. A121

BAPTIST HEALTH SOUTH FLORIDA, HOMESTEAD HOSPITAL, HOMESTEAD, FL, p. A125

BAPTIST HEALTH SOUTH FLORIDA, MARINERS HOSPITAL, TAVERNIER, FL, p. A142

BAPTIST HEALTH SOUTH FLORIDA, SOUTH MIAMI HOSPITAL, MIAMI, FL, p. A131

BAPTIST HEALTH SOUTH FLORIDA, WEST KENDALL BAPTIST HOSPITAL, MIAMI, FL, p. A131

BAPTIST HOSPITAL, PENSACOLA, FL, p. A136

BAPTIST HOSPITALS OF SOUTHEAST TEXAS, BEAUMONT, TX, p. A587

BAPTIST HOSPITALS OF SOUTHEAST TEXAS FANNIN BEHAVIORAL HEALTH CENTER, BEAUMONT, TEXAS (see BAPTIST HOSPITALS OF SOUTHEAST TEXAS), p. A587

BAPTIST MEDICAL CENTER, SAN ANTONIO, TX, p. A630

BAPTIST MEDICAL CENTER BEACHES, JACKSONVILLE BEACH, FL, p. A127

BAPTIST MEDICAL CENTER EAST, MONTGOMERY, AL, p. A23

BAPTIST MEDICAL CENTER JACKSONVILLE, JACKSONVILLE, FL, p. A126

BAPTIST MEDICAL CENTER LEAKE, CARTHAGE, MS, p. A345

BAPTIST MEDICAL CENTER NASSAU, FERNANDINA BEACH, FL, p. A123

BAPTIST MEDICAL CENTER SOUTH, JACKSONVILLE, FLORIDA (see BAPTIST MEDICAL CENTER JACKSONVILLE), p. A126

BAPTIST MEDICAL CENTER SOUTH, MONTGOMERY, AL, p. A23

BAPTIST MEMORIAL HOSPITAL – MEMPHIS, MEMPHIS, TN, p. A574

BAPTIST MEMORIAL HOSPITAL FOR WOMEN, MEMPHIS, TN, p. A574

BAPTIST MEMORIAL HOSPITAL–BOONEVILLE, BOONEVILLE, MS, p. A345

BAPTIST MEMORIAL HOSPITAL–COLLIERVILLE, COLLIERVILLE, TN, p. A567

BAPTIST MEMORIAL HOSPITAL–DESOTO, SOUTHAVEN, MS, p. A354

BAPTIST MEMORIAL HOSPITAL–GOLDEN TRIANGLE, COLUMBUS, MS, p. A346

BAPTIST MEMORIAL HOSPITAL–HUNTINGDON, HUNTINGDON, TN, p. A570

BAPTIST MEMORIAL HOSPITAL–NORTH MISSISSIPPI, OXFORD, MS, p. A352

BAPTIST MEMORIAL HOSPITAL–TIPTON, COVINGTON, TN, p. A568

BAPTIST MEMORIAL HOSPITAL–UNION CITY, UNION CITY, TN, p. A580

BAPTIST MEMORIAL HOSPITAL–UNION COUNTY, NEW ALBANY, MS, p. A352

BAPTIST MEMORIAL RESTORATIVE CARE HOSPITAL, MEMPHIS, TN, p. A574

BAPTIST ORANGE HOSPITAL, ORANGE, TX, p. A625

BAPTIST REHABILITATION–GERMANTOWN, GERMANTOWN, TN, p. A569

BAPTIST ST. ANTHONY HEALTH SYSTEM, AMARILLO, TX, p. A582

BARAGA COUNTY MEMORIAL HOSPITAL, L'ANSE, MI, p. A318

BARBARA BUSH CHILDREN'S HOSPITAL, PORTLAND, MAINE (see MAINE MEDICAL CENTER), p. A284

BARIX CLINICS OF PENNSYLVANIA, LANGHORNE, PA, p. A529

BARLOW RESPIRATORY HOSPITAL, LOS ANGELES, CA, p. A68

BARNABAS HEALTH BEHAVIORAL HEALTH CENTER, TOMS RIVER, NJ, p. A411

BARNES–JEWISH HOSPITAL, SAINT LOUIS, MO, p. A369

BARNES–JEWISH ST. PETERS HOSPITAL, SAINT PETERS, MO, p. A371

BARNES–JEWISH WEST COUNTY HOSPITAL, SAINT LOUIS, MO, p. A369

BARNES–KASSON COUNTY HOSPITAL, SUSQUEHANNA, PA, p. A542

BARNESVILLE HOSPITAL, BARNESVILLE, OH, p. A471

BARNWELL COUNTY HOSPITAL, BARNWELL, SC, p. A548

BARRETT HOSPITAL & HEALTHCARE, DILLON, MT, p. A375

BARROW REGIONAL MEDICAL CENTER, WINDER, GA, p. A163

BARSTOW COMMUNITY HOSPITAL, BARSTOW, CA, p. A54

BARTLETT REGIONAL HOSPITAL, JUNEAU, AK, p. A28

BARTON COUNTY MEMORIAL HOSPITAL, LAMAR, MO, p. A364

BARTON MEMORIAL HOSPITAL, SOUTH LAKE TAHOE, CA, p. A91

BARTOW REGIONAL MEDICAL CENTER, BARTOW, FL, p. A118

BASCOM PALMER EYE INSTITUTE–ANNE BATES LEACH EYE HOSPITAL, MIAMI, FL, p. A131

BASIN HEALTHCARE CENTER, ODESSA, TX, p. A625

BASSETT ARMY COMMUNITY HOSPITAL, FORT WAINWRIGHT, AK, p. A28

BASSETT MEDICAL CENTER, COOPERSTOWN, NY, p. A424

BASTROP REHABILITATION HOSPITAL, BASTROP, LA, p. A262

BATES COUNTY MEMORIAL HOSPITAL, BUTLER, MO, p. A357

BATESVILLE SPECIALTY HOSPITAL, BATESVILLE, MS, p. A344

BATH COMMUNITY HOSPITAL, HOT SPRINGS, VA, p. A655

BATH VETERANS AFFAIRS MEDICAL CENTER, BATH, NY, p. A421

BATON ROUGE GENERAL MEDICAL CENTER, BATON ROUGE, LA, p. A263

BATON ROUGE GENERAL MEDICAL CENTER–BLUEBONNET, BATON ROUGE, LOUISIANA (see BATON ROUGE GENERAL MEDICAL CENTER), p. A263

BATON ROUGE REHABILITATION HOSPITAL, BATON ROUGE, LA, p. A263

BATTLE CREEK VETERANS AFFAIRS MEDICAL CENTER, BATTLE CREEK, MI, p. A309

BATTLE MOUNTAIN GENERAL HOSPITAL, BATTLE MOUNTAIN, NV, p. A391

BAUM HARMON MERCY HOSPITAL, PRIMGHAR, IA, p. A227

BAXTER REGIONAL MEDICAL CENTER, MOUNTAIN HOME, AR, p. A48

BAY AREA HOSPITAL, COOS BAY, OR, p. A512

BAY AREA MEDICAL CENTER, MARINETTE, WI, p. A690

BAY MEDICAL CENTER SACRED HEART, PANAMA CITY, FL, p. A136

BAY PINES VETERANS AFFAIRS MEDICAL CENTER, BAY PINES, FL, p. A118

BAY REGIONAL MEDICAL CENTER–WEST CAMPUS, BAY CITY, MICHIGAN (see MCLAREN BAY REGION), p. A309

BAYCARE ALLIANT HOSPITAL, DUNEDIN, FL, p. A122

BAYFRONT HEALTH BROOKSVILLE, BROOKSVILLE, FL, p. A119

BAYFRONT HEALTH DADE CITY, DADE CITY, FL, p. A121

BAYFRONT HEALTH PORT CHARLOTTE, PORT CHARLOTTE, FL, p. A137

BAYFRONT HEALTH PUNTA GORDA, PUNTA GORDA, FL, p. A138

BAYFRONT HEALTH ST. PETERSBURG, SAINT PETERSBURG, FL, p. A138

BAYHEALTH MEDICAL CENTER, DOVER, DE, p. A114

BAYHEALTH MEDICAL CENTER AT KENT GENERAL, DOVER, DELAWARE (see BAYHEALTH MEDICAL CENTER), p. A114

BAYHEALTH MEDICAL CENTER, MILFORD MEMORIAL HOSPITAL, MILFORD, DELAWARE (see BAYHEALTH MEDICAL CENTER), p. A114

BAYLOR ALL SAINTS MEDICAL CENTER AT FORT WORTH, FORT WORTH, TX, p. A603

BAYLOR EMERGENCY MEDICAL CENTER AT AUBREY, AUBREY, TX, p. A584

BAYLOR INSTITUTE FOR REHABILITATION, DALLAS, TX, p. A595

BAYLOR INSTITUTE FOR REHABILITATION AT FRISCO, FRISCO, TX, p. A605

BAYLOR JACK AND JANE HAMILTON HEART AND VASCULAR HOSPITAL, DALLAS, TX, p. A595

BAYLOR MEDICAL CENTER AT CARROLLTON, CARROLLTON, TX, p. A591

BAYLOR MEDICAL CENTER AT FRISCO, FRISCO, TX, p. A605

BAYLOR MEDICAL CENTER AT GARLAND, GARLAND, TX, p. A606

BAYLOR MEDICAL CENTER AT IRVING, IRVING, TX, p. A614

BAYLOR MEDICAL CENTER AT MCKINNEY, MCKINNEY, TX, p. A622

BAYLOR MEDICAL CENTER AT TROPHY CLUB, TROPHY CLUB, TX, p. A638

BAYLOR MEDICAL CENTER AT UPTOWN, DALLAS, TX, p. A595

BAYLOR MEDICAL CENTER AT WAXAHACHIE, WAXAHACHIE, TX, p. A640

BAYLOR ORTHOPEDIC AND SPINE HOSPITAL AT ARLINGTON, ARLINGTON, TX, p. A583

BAYLOR REGIONAL MEDICAL CENTER AT GRAPEVINE, GRAPEVINE, TX, p. A607

BAYLOR REGIONAL MEDICAL CENTER AT PLANO, PLANO, TX, p. A627

BAYLOR SPECIALTY HOSPITAL, DALLAS, TX, p. A595

BAYLOR SURGICAL HOSPITAL AT FORT WORTH, FORT WORTH, TX, p. A603

BAYLOR UNIVERSITY MEDICAL CENTER, DALLAS, TX, p. A595

BAYNE–JONES ARMY COMMUNITY HOSPITAL, FORT POLK, LA, p. A267

BAYONNE MEDICAL CENTER, BAYONNE, NJ, p. A401

BAYPOINTE BEHAVIORAL HEALTH, MOBILE, AL, p. A22

BAYSHORE COMMUNITY HOSPITAL, HOLMDEL, NJ, p. A405

BAYSHORE MEDICAL CENTER, PASADENA, TX, p. A626

BAYSTATE CHILDREN'S HOSPITAL, SPRINGFIELD, MASSACHUSETTS (see BAYSTATE MEDICAL CENTER), p. A305

BAYSTATE FRANKLIN MEDICAL CENTER, GREENFIELD, MA, p. A300

BAYSTATE MARY LANE HOSPITAL, WARE, MA, p. A306

BAYSTATE MEDICAL CENTER, SPRINGFIELD, MA, p. A305

BAYVIEW BEHAVIORAL HEALTH CAMPUS, CHULA VISTA, CALIFORNIA (see PARADISE VALLEY HOSPITAL), p. A76

BAYVIEW BEHAVIORAL HOSPITAL, CORPUS CHRISTI, TEXAS (see CORPUS CHRISTI MEDICAL CENTER), p. A593

BCA PERMIAN BASIN, MIDLAND, TX, p. A623

BEACHAM MEMORIAL HOSPITAL, MAGNOLIA, MS, p. A350

BEACON BEHAVIORAL HOSPITAL – NEW ORLEANS, NEW ORLEANS, LA, p. A275

BEACON CHILDREN'S HOSPITAL, LUVERNE, AL, p. A22

BEAR LAKE MEMORIAL HOSPITAL, MONTPELIER, ID, p. A170

BEAR RIVER VALLEY HOSPITAL, TREMONTON, UT, p. A647

BEAR VALLEY COMMUNITY HOSPITAL, BIG BEAR LAKE, CA, p. A55

BEARTOOTH BILLINGS CLINIC, RED LODGE, MT, p. A379

BEATRICE COMMUNITY HOSPITAL AND HEALTH CENTER, BEATRICE, NE, p. A382

BEAUFORT MEMORIAL HOSPITAL, BEAUFORT, SC, p. A548

BEAUMONT BONE AND JOINT INSTITUTE, BEAUMONT, TX, p. A587

BEAUMONT CHILDREN'S HOSPITAL, ROYAL OAK, MICHIGAN (see BEAUMONT HOSPITAL – ROYAL OAK), p. A323

BEAUMONT HOSPITAL – ROYAL OAK, ROYAL OAK, MI, p. A323

BEAUMONT HOSPITAL – TROY, TROY, MI, p. A326

BEAUMONT HOSPITAL GROSSE POINTE, GROSSE POINTE, MI, p. A316

BEAUREGARD MEMORIAL HOSPITAL, DE RIDDER, LA, p. A266

BEAVER COUNTY MEMORIAL HOSPITAL, BEAVER, OK, p. A496

BEAVER DAM COMMUNITY HOSPITALS, BEAVER DAM, WI, p. A684

BEAVER VALLEY HOSPITAL, BEAVER, UT, p. A643

BECKLEY ARH HOSPITAL, BECKLEY, WV, p. A675

BECKLEY VETERANS AFFAIRS MEDICAL CENTER, BECKLEY, WV, p. A675

BEDFORD MEMORIAL HOSPITAL, BEDFORD, VA, p. A651

BEEBE MEDICAL CENTER, LEWES, DE, p. A114

BEHAVIORAL CENTER OF MICHIGAN, WARREN, MI, p. A326

BEHAVIORAL HEALTH CENTER, WINFIELD, ILLINOIS (see CENTRAL DUPAGE HOSPITAL), p. A197

BEHAVIORAL HEALTH CENTER, GREENSBORO, NORTH CAROLINA (see CONE HEALTH), p. A453

BEHAVIORAL HEALTH CENTER OF THE PERMIAN BASIN, MIDLAND, TX, p. A623

BEHAVIORAL HEALTHCARE CENTER AT CLARKSVILLE, CLARKSVILLE, TN, p. A567

BEHAVIORAL HEALTHCARE CENTER AT COLUMBIA, COLUMBIA, TN, p. A567

BEHAVIORAL HEALTHCARE CENTER AT HUNTSVILLE, HUNTSVILLE, AL, p. A21

BEHAVIORAL HEALTHCARE CENTER AT MARTIN, MARTIN, TN, p. A573

BEHAVIORAL HOSPITAL OF BELLAIRE, HOUSTON, TX, p. A609

BEHAVIORAL HOSPITAL OF LONGVIEW, LONGVIEW, TX, p. A619

BELL HOSPITAL, ISHPEMING, MI, p. A317

BELLA VISTA HOSPITAL, MAYAGUEZ, PR, p. A708

BELLEVUE HOSPITAL, BELLEVUE, OH, p. A471

BELLEVUE HOSPITAL CENTER, NEW YORK, NY, p. A430

BELLEVUE MEDICAL CENTER, BELLEVUE, NE, p. A382

BROWARD HEALTH MEDICAL CENTER, FORT LAUDERDALE, FL, p. A123
BROWARD HEALTH NORTH, DEERFIELD BEACH, FL, p. A122
BROWN COUNTY COMMUNITY TREATMENT CENTER, GREEN BAY, WI, p. A687
BROWN COUNTY HOSPITAL, AINSWORTH, NE, p. A381
BROWNFIELD REGIONAL MEDICAL CENTER, BROWNFIELD, TX, p. A589
BROWNSVILLE DOCTORS HOSPITAL, BROWNSVILLE, TX, p. A589
BROWNWOOD REGIONAL MEDICAL CENTER, BROWNWOOD, TX, p. A590
BRYAN HOSPITAL, BRYAN, OHIO (see COMMUNITY HOSPITALS AND WELLNESS CENTERS), p. A472
BRYAN MEDICAL CENTER, LINCOLN, NE, p. A385
BRYAN MEDICAL CENTER–EAST, LINCOLN, NEBRASKA (see BRYAN MEDICAL CENTER), p. A385
BRYAN MEDICAL CENTER–WEST, LINCOLN, NEBRASKA (see BRYAN MEDICAL CENTER), p. A385
BRYAN W. WHITFIELD MEMORIAL HOSPITAL, DEMOPOLIS, AL, p. A19
BRYCE HOSPITAL, TUSCALOOSA, AL, p. A25
BRYLIN HOSPITALS, BUFFALO, NY, p. A422
BRYN MAWR HOSPITAL, BRYN MAWR, PA, p. A521
BRYN MAWR REHABILITATION HOSPITAL, MALVERN, PA, p. A530
BRYNN MARR HOSPITAL, JACKSONVILLE, NC, p. A455
BUCHANAN COUNTY HEALTH CENTER, INDEPENDENCE, IA, p. A223
BUCHANAN GENERAL HOSPITAL, GRUNDY, VA, p. A655
BUCKS COUNTY CAMPUS, LANGHORNE, PENNSYLVANIA (see ARIA HEALTH), p. A534
BUCKTAIL MEDICAL CENTER, RENOVO, PA, p. A540
BUCYRUS COMMUNITY HOSPITAL, BUCYRUS, OH, p. A472
BUENA VISTA REGIONAL MEDICAL CENTER, STORM LAKE, IA, p. A229
BUFFALO HOSPITAL, BUFFALO, MN, p. A330
BUFFALO PSYCHIATRIC CENTER, BUFFALO, NY, p. A422
BULLOCK COUNTY HOSPITAL, UNION SPRINGS, AL, p. A26
BUNKIE GENERAL HOSPITAL, BUNKIE, LA, p. A265
BURGESS HEALTH CENTER, ONAWA, IA, p. A226
BURKE MEDICAL CENTER, WAYNESBORO, GA, p. A162
BURKE REHABILITATION HOSPITAL, WHITE PLAINS, NY, p. A446
BURLESON ST. JOSEPH HEALTH CENTER, CALDWELL, TX, p. A590
BURNETT MEDICAL CENTER, GRANTSBURG, WI, p. A687
BUTLER COUNTY HEALTH CARE CENTER, DAVID CITY, NE, p. A383
BUTLER HEALTH SYSTEM, BUTLER, PA, p. A521
BUTLER HOSPITAL, PROVIDENCE, RI, p. A546
BYRD REGIONAL HOSPITAL, LEESVILLE, LA, p. A272

# C

C.S. MOTT CHILDREN'S HOSPITAL, ANN ARBOR, MICHIGAN (see UNIVERSITY OF MICHIGAN HOSPITALS AND HEALTH CENTERS), p. A308
CABELL HUNTINGTON HOSPITAL, HUNTINGTON, WV, p. A677
CACHE VALLEY SPECIALTY HOSPITAL, NORTH LOGAN, UT, p. A645
CALAIS REGIONAL HOSPITAL, CALAIS, ME, p. A282
CALCASIEU OAKS GERIATRIC PSYCHIATRIC HOSPITAL, LAKE CHARLES, LA, p. A271
CALDWELL MEDICAL CENTER, PRINCETON, KY, p. A259
CALDWELL MEMORIAL HOSPITAL, COLUMBIA, LA, p. A265
CALDWELL MEMORIAL HOSPITAL, LENOIR, NC, p. A456
CALHOUN HEALTH SERVICES, CALHOUN CITY, MS, p. A345
CALHOUN–LIBERTY HOSPITAL, BLOUNTSTOWN, FL, p. A118
CALIFORNIA HOSPITAL MEDICAL CENTER, LOS ANGELES, CA, p. A68
CALIFORNIA MEDICAL FACILITY, VACAVILLE, CA, p. A94
CALIFORNIA MENS COLONY HOSPITAL, SAN LUIS OBISPO, CA, p. A88
CALIFORNIA PACIFIC MEDICAL CENTER, SAN FRANCISCO, CA, p. A86
CALIFORNIA PACIFIC MEDICAL CENTER–DAVIES CAMPUS, SAN FRANCISCO, CALIFORNIA (see CALIFORNIA PACIFIC MEDICAL CENTER), p. A86
CALLAWAY COMMUNITY HOSPITAL, FULTON, MO, p. A361
CALLAWAY DISTRICT HOSPITAL, CALLAWAY, NE, p. A382
CALUMET MEDICAL CENTER, CHILTON, WI, p. A685
CALVARY HOSPITAL,, NY, p. A431
CALVERT MEMORIAL HOSPITAL, PRINCE FREDERICK, MD, p. A293
CAMBRIDGE HEALTH ALLIANCE, CAMBRIDGE, MA, p. A299
CAMBRIDGE HOSPITAL, CAMBRIDGE, MASSACHUSETTS (see CAMBRIDGE HEALTH ALLIANCE), p. A299

CAMBRIDGE HOSPITAL IN HOUSTON, HOUSTON, TX, p. A609
CAMBRIDGE MEDICAL CENTER, CAMBRIDGE, MN, p. A330
CAMC TEAYS VALLEY HOSPITAL, HURRICANE, WV, p. A678
CAMDEN CLARK MEDICAL CENTER, PARKERSBURG, WV, p. A679
CAMDEN COUNTY HEALTH SERVICES CENTER, BLACKWOOD, NJ, p. A401
CAMDEN GENERAL HOSPITAL, CAMDEN, TN, p. A566
CAMERON MEMORIAL COMMUNITY HOSPITAL, ANGOLA, IN, p. A198
CAMERON REGIONAL MEDICAL CENTER, CAMERON, MO, p. A357
CAMPBELL COUNTY MEMORIAL HOSPITAL, GILLETTE, WY, p. A702
CAMPBELLTON GRACEVILLE HOSPITAL, GRACEVILLE, FL, p. A124
CANANDAIGUA VETERANS AFFAIRS MEDICAL CENTER, CANANDAIGUA, NY, p. A423
CANDLER COUNTY HOSPITAL, METTER, GA, p. A157
CANDLER HOSPITAL, SAVANNAH, GA, p. A159
CANNON MEMORIAL HOSPITAL, PICKENS, SC, p. A555
CANONSBURG GENERAL HOSPITAL, CANONSBURG, PA, p. A522
CANTON–POTSDAM HOSPITAL, POTSDAM, NY, p. A440
CANYON RIDGE HOSPITAL, CHINO, CA, p. A56
CAPE COD & ISLAND COMMUNITY MENTAL HEALTH CENTER, POCASSET, MA, p. A304
CAPE COD HOSPITAL, HYANNIS, MA, p. A301
CAPE CORAL HOSPITAL, CAPE CORAL, FL, p. A120
CAPE FEAR HOSPITAL, WILMINGTON, NORTH CAROLINA (see NEW HANOVER REGIONAL MEDICAL CENTER), p. A463
CAPE FEAR VALLEY – BLADEN COUNTY HOSPITAL, ELIZABETHTOWN, NC, p. A452
CAPE FEAR VALLEY MEDICAL CENTER, FAYETTEVILLE, NC, p. A452
CAPE REGIONAL MEDICAL CENTER, CAPE MAY COURT HOUSE, NJ, p. A402
CAPITAL DISTRICT PSYCHIATRIC CENTER, ALBANY, NY, p. A420
CAPITAL HEALTH MEDICAL CENTER–HOPEWELL, PENNINGTON, NJ, p. A408
CAPITAL HEALTH REGIONAL MEDICAL CENTER, TRENTON, NJ, p. A411
CAPITAL HOSPICE, ARLINGTON, VA, p. A651
CAPITAL MEDICAL CENTER, OLYMPIA, WA, p. A668
CAPITAL REGION MEDICAL CENTER, JEFFERSON CITY, MO, p. A362
CAPITAL REGIONAL MEDICAL CENTER, TALLAHASSEE, FL, p. A140
CAPTAIN JAMES A. LOVELL FEDERAL HEALTH CARE CENTER, NORTH CHICAGO, IL, p. A190
CARDINAL HILL REHABILITATION HOSPITAL, LEXINGTON, KY, p. A254
CARDIOVASCULAR CENTER OF PUERTO RICO AND THE CARIBBEAN, SAN JUAN, PR, p. A709
CARDON CHILDREN'S MEDICAL CENTER, MESA, ARIZONA (see BANNER DESERT MEDICAL CENTER), p. A33
CARE ONE AT RARITAN BAY MEDICAL CENTER, PERTH AMBOY, NJ, p. A408
CARE REGIONAL MEDICAL CENTER, ARANSAS PASS, TX, p. A583
CARELINK OF JACKSON, JACKSON, MI, p. A317
CAREPARTNERS HEALTH SERVICES, ASHEVILLE, NC, p. A447
CARIBBEAN MEDICAL CENTER, FAJARDO, PR, p. A707
CARIBOU MEMORIAL HOSPITAL AND LIVING CENTER, SODA SPRINGS, ID, p. A172
CARILION CLINIC CHILDREN'S HOSPITAL, ROANOKE, VIRGINIA (see CARILION MEDICAL CENTER), p. A661
CARILION FRANKLIN MEMORIAL HOSPITAL, ROCKY MOUNT, VA, p. A661
CARILION GILES COMMUNITY HOSPITAL, PEARISBURG, VA, p. A659
CARILION MEDICAL CENTER, ROANOKE, VA, p. A661
CARILION NEW RIVER VALLEY MEDICAL CENTER, CHRISTIANSBURG, VA, p. A652
CARILION ROANOKE COMMUNITY HOSPITAL, ROANOKE, VIRGINIA (see CARILION MEDICAL CENTER), p. A661
CARILION STONEWALL JACKSON HOSPITAL, LEXINGTON, VA, p. A656
CARILION TAZEWELL COMMUNITY HOSPITAL, TAZEWELL, VA, p. A662
CARL ALBERT COMMUNITY MENTAL HEALTH CENTER, MCALESTER, OK, p. A501
CARL R. DARNALL ARMY MEDICAL CENTER, FORT HOOD, TX, p. A603
CARL VINSON VETERANS AFFAIRS MEDICAL CENTER, DUBLIN, GA, p. A152
CARLE FOUNDATION HOSPITAL, URBANA, IL, p. A196
CARLINVILLE AREA HOSPITAL, CARLINVILLE, IL, p. A175
CARLISLE REGIONAL MEDICAL CENTER, CARLISLE, PA, p. A522

CARLSBAD MEDICAL CENTER, CARLSBAD, NM, p. A415
CARNEGIE TRI–COUNTY MUNICIPAL HOSPITAL, CARNEGIE, OK, p. A496
CARNEY HOSPITAL, BOSTON, MA, p. A296
CARO CENTER, CARO, MI, p. A310
CARO COMMUNITY HOSPITAL, CARO, MI, p. A310
CAROLINA CENTER FOR BEHAVIORAL HEALTH, GREER, SC, p. A553
CAROLINA PINES REGIONAL MEDICAL CENTER, HARTSVILLE, SC, p. A553
CAROLINAEAST HEALTH SYSTEM, NEW BERN, NC, p. A458
CAROLINAS HOSPITAL SYSTEM, FLORENCE, SC, p. A551
CAROLINAS HOSPITAL SYSTEM MARION, MULLINS, SC, p. A554
CAROLINAS MEDICAL CENTER, CHARLOTTE, NC, p. A449
CAROLINAS MEDICAL CENTER–LINCOLN, LINCOLNTON, NC, p. A456
CAROLINAS MEDICAL CENTER–MERCY, CHARLOTTE, NC, p. A449
CAROLINAS MEDICAL CENTER–NORTHEAST, CONCORD, NC, p. A450
CAROLINAS MEDICAL CENTER–PINEVILLE, CHARLOTTE, NORTH CAROLINA (see CAROLINAS MEDICAL CENTER–MERCY), p. A449
CAROLINAS MEDICAL CENTER–UNION, MONROE, NC, p. A457
CAROLINAS MEDICAL CENTER–UNIVERSITY, CHARLOTTE, NC, p. A449
CAROLINAS REHABILITATION, CHARLOTTE, NC, p. A449
CAROLINAS SPECIALTY HOSPITAL, CHARLOTTE, NC, p. A450
CARONDELET HOLY CROSS HOSPITAL, NOGALES, AZ, p. A33
CARONDELET ST. JOSEPH'S HOSPITAL, TUCSON, AZ, p. A38
CARONDELET ST. MARY'S HOSPITAL, TUCSON, AZ, p. A38
CARRIE TINGLEY HOSPITAL, ALBUQUERQUE, NEW MEXICO (see UNIVERSITY OF NEW MEXICO HOSPITALS), p. A415
CARRIER CLINIC, BELLE MEAD, NJ, p. A401
CARRINGTON HEALTH CENTER, CARRINGTON, ND, p. A465
CARROLL COUNTY MEMORIAL HOSPITAL, CARROLLTON, KY, p. A249
CARROLL COUNTY MEMORIAL HOSPITAL, CARROLLTON, MO, p. A358
CARROLL HOSPITAL CENTER, WESTMINSTER, MD, p. A294
CARROLLTON SPRINGS, CARROLLTON, TX, p. A591
CARRUS REHABILITATION HOSPITAL, SHERMAN, TX, p. A633
CARRUS SPECIALTY HOSPITAL, SHERMAN, TX, p. A634
CARSON CITY HOSPITAL, CARSON CITY, MI, p. A310
CARSON TAHOE CONTINUING CARE HOSPITAL, CARSON CITY, NV, p. A391
CARSON TAHOE REGIONAL HEALTHCARE, CARSON CITY, NV, p. A391
CARSON VALLEY MEDICAL CENTER, GARDNERVILLE, NV, p. A391
CARTERET GENERAL HOSPITAL, MOREHEAD CITY, NC, p. A457
CARTERSVILLE MEDICAL CENTER, CARTERSVILLE, GA, p. A149
CARTHAGE AREA HOSPITAL, CARTHAGE, NY, p. A423
CARY MEDICAL CENTER, CARIBOU, ME, p. A282
CASA COLINA HOSPITAL FOR REHABILITATIVE MEDICINE, POMONA, CA, p. A80
CASA GRANDE REGIONAL MEDICAL CENTER, CASA GRANDE, AZ, p. A30
CASCADE MEDICAL CENTER, CASCADE, ID, p. A168
CASCADE MEDICAL CENTER, LEAVENWORTH, WA, p. A667
CASCADE VALLEY HOSPITAL AND CLINICS, ARLINGTON, WA, p. A664
CASEY COUNTY HOSPITAL, LIBERTY, KY, p. A255
CASS COUNTY MEMORIAL HOSPITAL, ATLANTIC, IA, p. A216
CASS REGIONAL MEDICAL CENTER, HARRISONVILLE, MO, p. A361
CASSIA REGIONAL MEDICAL CENTER, BURLEY, ID, p. A168
CASTANER GENERAL HOSPITAL, CASTANER, PR, p. A706
CASTLE MANOR (see FALL RIVER HOSPITAL), p. A560
CASTLE MEDICAL CENTER, KAILUA, HI, p. A165
CASTLEVIEW HOSPITAL, PRICE, UT, p. A645
CASWELL CENTER, KINSTON, NC, p. A456
CATALINA ISLAND MEDICAL CENTER, AVALON, CA, p. A53
CATAWBA HOSPITAL, CATAWBA, VA, p. A652
CATAWBA VALLEY MEDICAL CENTER, HICKORY, NC, p. A454
CATHOLIC MEDICAL CENTER, MANCHESTER, NH, p. A399
CATSKILL REGIONAL MEDICAL CENTER, HARRIS, NY, p. A427
CAVALIER COUNTY MEMORIAL HOSPITAL, LANGDON, ND, p. A468
CAVERNA MEMORIAL HOSPITAL, HORSE CAVE, KY, p. A253
CAYUGA MEDICAL CENTER AT ITHACA, ITHACA, NY, p. A427
CCC AT PINEVIEW HOSPITAL, LAKESIDE, AZ, p. A32
CEDAR COUNTY MEMORIAL HOSPITAL, EL DORADO SPRINGS, MO, p. A360
CEDAR CREST HOSPITAL AND RESIDENTIAL TREATMENT CENTER, BELTON, TX, p. A588
CEDAR HILLS HOSPITAL, PORTLAND, OR, p. A516
CEDAR PARK REGIONAL MEDICAL CENTER, CEDAR PARK, TX, p. A591
CEDAR RIDGE HOSPITAL, OKLAHOMA CITY, OK, p. A502

CHINLE COMPREHENSIVE HEALTH CARE FACILITY, CHINLE, AZ, p. A30

CHINO VALLEY MEDICAL CENTER, CHINO, CA, p. A56

CHIPPENHAM MEDICAL CENTER, RICHMOND, VIRGINIA (see CJW MEDICAL CENTER), p. A660

CHIPPEWA COUNTY–MONTEVIDEO HOSPITAL, MONTEVIDEO, MN, p. A336

CHIPPEWA VALLEY HOSPITAL AND OAKVIEW CARE CENTER, DURAND, WI, p. A685

CHOATE MENTAL HEALTH CENTER, ANNA, IL, p. A173

CHOCTAW GENERAL HOSPITAL, BUTLER, AL, p. A18

CHOCTAW HEALTH CENTER, PHILADELPHIA, MS, p. A352

CHOCTAW MEMORIAL HOSPITAL, HUGO, OK, p. A500

CHOCTAW NATION HEALTH CARE CENTER, TALIHINA, OK, p. A507

CHRIS EVERT CHILDRENS HOSPITAL, FORT LAUDERDALE, FLORIDA (see BROWARD HEALTH MEDICAL CENTER), p. A123

CHRIST HOSPITAL, JERSEY CITY, NJ, p. A405

CHRIST HOSPITAL, CINCINNATI, OH, p. A474

CHRISTIAN HEALTH CARE CENTER, WYCKOFF, NJ, p. A413

CHRISTIAN HOSPITAL, SAINT LOUIS, MO, p. A369

CHRISTIANA CARE HEALTH SYSTEM, NEWARK, DE, p. A114

CHRISTIANA HOSPITAL, WILMINGTON, DELAWARE (see CHRISTIANA CARE HEALTH SYSTEM), p. A114

CHRISTUS COUSHATTA HEALTH CARE CENTER, COUSHATTA, LA, p. A265

CHRISTUS DUBUIS HOSPITAL OF BRYAN, BRYAN, TX, p. A590

CHRISTUS DUBUIS HOSPITAL OF PORT ARTHUR, PORT ARTHUR, TX, p. A628

CHRISTUS HIGHLAND MEDICAL CENTER, SHREVEPORT, LOUISIANA (see CHRISTUS SCHUMPERT MEDICAL CENTER), p. A278

CHRISTUS HOSPITAL–ST. ELIZABETH, BEAUMONT, TX, p. A587

CHRISTUS HOSPITAL–ST. MARY, PORT ARTHUR, TEXAS (see CHRISTUS HOSPITAL–ST. ELIZABETH), p. A587

CHRISTUS JASPER MEMORIAL HOSPITAL, JASPER, TX, p. A615

CHRISTUS SANTA ROSA HEALTH SYSTEM, SAN ANTONIO, TX, p. A630

CHRISTUS SANTA ROSA HOSPITAL – NEW BRAUNFELS, NEW BRAUNFELS, TEXAS (see CHRISTUS SANTA ROSA HEALTH SYSTEM), p. A630

CHRISTUS SANTA ROSA REHABILITATION HOSPITAL, SAN ANTONIO, TEXAS (see CHRISTUS SANTA ROSA HEALTH SYSTEM), p. A630

CHRISTUS SCHUMPERT MEDICAL CENTER, SHREVEPORT, LA, p. A278

CHRISTUS SCHUMPERT MEDICAL CENTER, SHREVEPORT, LOUISIANA (see CHRISTUS SCHUMPERT MEDICAL CENTER), p. A278

CHRISTUS SCHUMPERT SUTTON CHILDREN'S MEDICAL CENTER, SHREVEPORT, LOUISIANA (see CHRISTUS SCHUMPERT MEDICAL CENTER), p. A278

CHRISTUS SPOHN HOSPITAL ALICE, ALICE, TX, p. A581

CHRISTUS SPOHN HOSPITAL BEEVILLE, BEEVILLE, TX, p. A588

CHRISTUS SPOHN HOSPITAL CORPUS CHRISTI MEMORIAL, CORPUS CHRISTI, TX, p. A593

CHRISTUS SPOHN HOSPITAL CORPUS CHRISTI SHORELINE, CORPUS CHRISTI, TEXAS (see CHRISTUS SPOHN HOSPITAL CORPUS CHRISTI MEMORIAL), p. A593

CHRISTUS SPOHN HOSPITAL CORPUS CHRISTUS SOUTH, CORPUS CHRISTI, TEXAS (see CHRISTUS SPOHN HOSPITAL CORPUS CHRISTI MEMORIAL), p. A593

CHRISTUS SPOHN HOSPITAL KLEBERG, KINGSVILLE, TX, p. A616

CHRISTUS ST. CATHERINE HOSPITAL, KATY, TX, p. A615

CHRISTUS ST. FRANCES CABRINI HOSPITAL, ALEXANDRIA, LA, p. A262

CHRISTUS ST. JOHN HOSPITAL, NASSAU BAY, TX, p. A624

CHRISTUS ST. MICHAEL HEALTH SYSTEM, TEXARKANA, TX, p. A637

CHRISTUS ST. MICHAEL HOSPITAL–ATLANTA, ATLANTA, TX, p. A584

CHRISTUS ST. MICHAEL REHABILITATION HOSPITAL, TEXARKANA, TX, p. A637

CHRISTUS ST. PATRICK HOSPITAL OF LAKE CHARLES, LAKE CHARLES, LA, p. A271

CHRISTUS ST. VINCENT PHYSICIANS MEDICAL CENTER, SANTA FE, NEW MEXICO (see CHRISTUS ST. VINCENT REGIONAL MEDICAL CENTER), p. A418

CHRISTUS ST. VINCENT REGIONAL MEDICAL CENTER, SANTA FE, NM, p. A418

CIBOLA GENERAL HOSPITAL, GRANTS, NM, p. A416

CIMARRON MEMORIAL HOSPITAL, BOISE CITY, OK, p. A496

CINCINNATI CHILDREN'S HOSPITAL MEDICAL CENTER, CINCINNATI, OH, p. A474

CINCINNATI VETERANS AFFAIRS MEDICAL CENTER, CINCINNATI, OH, p. A474

CIRCLES OF CARE, MELBOURNE, FL, p. A130

CITIZENS BAPTIST MEDICAL CENTER, TALLADEGA, AL, p. A25

CITIZENS MEDICAL CENTER, COLBY, KS, p. A232

CITIZENS MEDICAL CENTER, COLUMBIA, LA, p. A265

CITIZENS MEDICAL CENTER, VICTORIA, TX, p. A639

CITIZENS MEMORIAL HOSPITAL, BOLIVAR, MO, p. A356

CITRUS MEMORIAL HEALTH SYSTEM, INVERNESS, FL, p. A126

CITRUS VALLEY MEDICAL CENTER, COVINA, CA, p. A58

CITRUS VALLEY MEDICAL CENTER–INTER–COMMUNITY CAMPUS, COVINA, CALIFORNIA (see CITRUS VALLEY MEDICAL CENTER), p. A58

CITRUS VALLEY MEDICAL CENTER–QUEEN OF THE VALLEY CAMPUS, WEST COVINA, CALIFORNIA (see CITRUS VALLEY MEDICAL CENTER), p. A58

CITY OF HOPE'S HELFORD CLINICAL RESEARCH HOSPITAL, DUARTE, CA, p. A59

CJW MEDICAL CENTER, RICHMOND, VA, p. A660

CLAIBORNE COUNTY HOSPITAL, TAZEWELL, TN, p. A579

CLARA BARTON HOSPITAL, HOISINGTON, KS, p. A235

CLARA MAASS MEDICAL CENTER, BELLEVILLE, NJ, p. A401

CLAREMORE INDIAN HOSPITAL, CLAREMORE, OK, p. A497

CLARENDON MEMORIAL HOSPITAL, MANNING, SC, p. A554

CLARINDA REGIONAL HEALTH CENTER, CLARINDA, IA, p. A218

CLARION HOSPITAL, CLARION, PA, p. A522

CLARION PSYCHIATRIC CENTER, CLARION, PA, p. A522

CLARITY CHILD GUIDANCE CENTER, SAN ANTONIO, TX, p. A631

CLARK FORK VALLEY HOSPITAL, PLAINS, MT, p. A378

CLARK MEMORIAL HOSPITAL, JEFFERSONVILLE, IN, p. A207

CLARK REGIONAL MEDICAL CENTER, WINCHESTER, KY, p. A261

CLARKE COUNTY HOSPITAL, OSCEOLA, IA, p. A226

CLARKS SUMMIT STATE HOSPITAL, CLARKS SUMMIT, PA, p. A522

CLAXTON–HEPBURN MEDICAL CENTER, OGDENSBURG, NY, p. A438

CLAY COUNTY HOSPITAL, ASHLAND, AL, p. A15

CLAY COUNTY HOSPITAL, FLORA, IL, p. A182

CLAY COUNTY MEDICAL CENTER, CLAY CENTER, KS, p. A232

CLAY COUNTY MEMORIAL HOSPITAL, HENRIETTA, TX, p. A608

CLEAR BROOK LODGE, SHICKSHINNY, PA, p. A541

CLEAR BROOK MANOR, WILKES–BARRE, PA, p. A544

CLEAR LAKE REGIONAL MEDICAL CENTER, WEBSTER, TX, p. A640

CLEARFIELD HOSPITAL, CLEARFIELD, PA, p. A522

CLEARVIEW REGIONAL MEDICAL CENTER, MONROE, GA, p. A157

CLEARWATER VALLEY HOSPITAL AND CLINICS, OROFINO, ID, p. A170

CLEMENT J. ZABLOCKI VETERANS AFFAIRS MEDICAL CENTER, MILWAUKEE, WI, p. A692

CLEO WALLACE CENTERS HOSPITAL, WESTMINSTER, CO, p. A106

CLEVELAND AREA HOSPITAL, CLEVELAND, OK, p. A497

CLEVELAND CAMPUS, CLEVELAND, OHIO (see NORTHCOAST BEHAVIORAL HEALTHCARE SYSTEM), p. A487

CLEVELAND CLINIC, CLEVELAND, OH, p. A476

CLEVELAND CLINIC CHILDREN'S HOSPITAL, CLEVELAND, OHIO (see CLEVELAND CLINIC), p. A476

CLEVELAND CLINIC CHILDREN'S HOSPITAL FOR REHABILITATION, CLEVELAND, OH, p. A476

CLEVELAND CLINIC FLORIDA, WESTON, FL, p. A144

CLEVELAND REGIONAL MEDICAL CENTER, SHELBY, NC, p. A460

CLEVELAND REGIONAL MEDICAL CENTER, CLEVELAND, TX, p. A592

CLIFTON SPRINGS HOSPITAL AND CLINIC, CLIFTON SPRINGS, NY, p. A424

CLIFTON T. PERKINS HOSPITAL CENTER, JESSUP, MD, p. A292

CLIFTON–FINE HOSPITAL, STAR LAKE, NY, p. A443

CLINCH MEMORIAL HOSPITAL, HOMERVILLE, GA, p. A155

CLINCH VALLEY MEDICAL CENTER, RICHLANDS, VA, p. A660

CLINTON COUNTY HOSPITAL, ALBANY, KY, p. A248

CLINTON HOSPITAL, CLINTON, MA, p. A299

CLINTON MEMORIAL HOSPITAL, WILMINGTON, OH, p. A493

CLOUD COUNTY HEALTH CENTER, CONCORDIA, KS, p. A232

CLOVIS COMMUNITY MEDICAL CENTER, CLOVIS, CA, p. A56

COAL COUNTY GENERAL HOSPITAL, COALGATE, OK, p. A497

COALINGA REGIONAL MEDICAL CENTER, COALINGA, CA, p. A57

COAST PLAZA HOSPITAL, NORWALK, CA, p. A76

COASTAL CAROLINA HOSPITAL, HARDEEVILLE, SC, p. A553

COASTAL COMMUNITIES HOSPITAL, SANTA ANA, CA, p. A89

COASTAL HARBOR TREATMENT CENTER, SAVANNAH, GA, p. A159

COATESVILLE VETERANS AFFAIRS MEDICAL CENTER, COATESVILLE, PA, p. A523

COBLESKILL REGIONAL HOSPITAL, COBLESKILL, NY, p. A424

COBRE VALLEY REGIONAL MEDICAL CENTER, GLOBE, AZ, p. A32

COCHRAN MEMORIAL HOSPITAL, MORTON, TX, p. A623

COFFEE REGIONAL MEDICAL CENTER, DOUGLAS, GA, p. A152

COFFEY COUNTY HOSPITAL, BURLINGTON, KS, p. A232

COFFEYVILLE REGIONAL MEDICAL CENTER, COFFEYVILLE, KS, p. A232

COGDELL MEMORIAL HOSPITAL, SNYDER, TX, p. A634

COLE MEMORIAL, COUDERSPORT, PA, p. A523

COLEMAN COUNTY MEDICAL CENTER, COLEMAN, TX, p. A592

COLER MEMORIAL HOSPITAL, NEW YORK, NEW YORK (see COLER–GOLDWATER SPECIALTY HOSPITAL AND NURSING FACILITY), p. A431

COLER–GOLDWATER SPECIALTY HOSPITAL AND NURSING FACILITY, NEW YORK, NY, p. A431

COLISEUM CENTER FOR BEHAVIORAL HEALTH, MACON, GA, p. A156

COLISEUM MEDICAL CENTERS, MACON, GA, p. A156

COLISEUM NORTHSIDE HOSPITAL, MACON, GA, p. A156

COLLEGE HOSPITAL, CERRITOS, CA, p. A56

COLLEGE HOSPITAL COSTA MESA, COSTA MESA, CA, p. A57

COLLEGE STATION MEDICAL CENTER, COLLEGE STATION, TX, p. A592

COLLETON MEDICAL CENTER, WALTERBORO, SC, p. A556

COLLINGSWORTH GENERAL HOSPITAL, WELLINGTON, TX, p. A640

COLMERY–O'NEIL VETERANS AFFAIRS MEDICAL CENTER, TOPEKA, KANSAS (see VETERANS AFFAIRS EASTERN KANSAS HEALTH CARE SYSTEM), p. A245

COLONEL FLORENCE A. BLANCHFIELD ARMY COMMUNITY HOSPITAL, FORT CAMPBELL, KY, p. A251

COLORADO ACUTE LONG TERM HOSPITAL, DENVER, CO, p. A99

COLORADO MENTAL HEALTH INSTITUTE AT FORT LOGAN, DENVER, CO, p. A99

COLORADO MENTAL HEALTH INSTITUTE AT PUEBLO, PUEBLO, CO, p. A105

COLORADO PLAINS MEDICAL CENTER, FORT MORGAN, CO, p. A101

COLORADO RIVER MEDICAL CENTER, NEEDLES, CA, p. A76

COLORADO WEST PSYCHIATRIC HOSPITAL, GRAND JUNCTION, CO, p. A101

COLQUITT REGIONAL MEDICAL CENTER, MOULTRIE, GA, p. A158

COLUMBIA BASIN HOSPITAL, EPHRATA, WA, p. A666

COLUMBIA CENTER, MEQUON, WI, p. A691

COLUMBIA MEMORIAL HOSPITAL, HUDSON, NY, p. A427

COLUMBIA MEMORIAL HOSPITAL, ASTORIA, OR, p. A511

COLUMBIA ST. MARY'S COLUMBIA HOSPITAL, MILWAUKEE, WISCONSIN (see COLUMBIA ST. MARY'S HOSPITAL MILWAUKEE), p. A692

COLUMBIA ST. MARY'S HOSPITAL MILWAUKEE, MILWAUKEE, WI, p. A692

COLUMBIA ST. MARY'S MILWAUKEE HOSPITAL, MILWAUKEE, WISCONSIN (see COLUMBIA ST. MARY'S HOSPITAL MILWAUKEE), p. A692

COLUMBIA ST. MARY'S OZAUKEE HOSPITAL, MEQUON, WI, p. A691

COLUMBUS COMMUNITY HOSPITAL, COLUMBUS, NE, p. A382

COLUMBUS COMMUNITY HOSPITAL, COLUMBUS, TX, p. A592

COLUMBUS COMMUNITY HOSPITAL, COLUMBUS, WI, p. A685

COLUMBUS REGIONAL HEALTHCARE SYSTEM, WHITEVILLE, NC, p. A462

COLUMBUS REGIONAL HOSPITAL, COLUMBUS, IN, p. A200

COLUMBUS SPECIALTY HOSPITAL, COLUMBUS, GA, p. A150

COLUSA REGIONAL MEDICAL CENTER, COLUSA, CA, p. A57

COMANCHE COUNTY HOSPITAL, COLDWATER, KS, p. A232

COMANCHE COUNTY MEDICAL CENTER, COMANCHE, TX, p. A593

COMANCHE COUNTY MEMORIAL HOSPITAL, LAWTON, OK, p. A500

COMMONWEALTH CENTER FOR CHILDREN AND ADOLESCENTS, STAUNTON, VA, p. A662

COMMONWEALTH HEALTH CENTER, SAIPAN, MP, p. A705

COMMONWEALTH REGIONAL SPECIALTY HOSPITAL, BOWLING GREEN, KY, p. A248

COMMUNITY BEHAVIORAL HEALTH CENTER, FRESNO, CA, p. A61

COMMUNITY BEHAVIORAL HEALTH HOSPITAL – ALEXANDRIA, ALEXANDRIA, MN, p. A328

COMMUNITY BEHAVIORAL HEALTH HOSPITAL – ANNANDALE, ANNANDALE, MN, p. A328

COMMUNITY BEHAVIORAL HEALTH HOSPITAL – BAXTER, BAXTER, MN, p. A329

COMMUNITY BEHAVIORAL HEALTH HOSPITAL – BEMIDJI, BEMIDJI, MN, p. A329

COMMUNITY BEHAVIORAL HEALTH HOSPITAL – FERGUS FALLS, FERGUS FALLS, MN, p. A332

COMMUNITY BEHAVIORAL HEALTH HOSPITAL – ROCHESTER, ROCHESTER, MN, p. A339

COMMUNITY BEHAVIORAL HEALTH HOSPITAL – ST. PETER, SAINT PETER, MN, p. A340

COMMUNITY CARE HOSPITAL, NEW ORLEANS, LA, p. A275

COMMUNITY GENERAL HEALTH CENTER, FORT FAIRFIELD, MAINE (see THE AROOSTOOK MEDICAL CENTER), p. A285

COMMUNITY GENERAL HOSPITAL, DILLEY, TX, p. A599
COMMUNITY HEALTH CENTER OF BRANCH COUNTY, COLDWATER, MI, p. A311
COMMUNITY HEALTHCARE SYSTEM, ONAGA, KS, p. A241
COMMUNITY HEART AND VASCULAR HOSPITAL, INDIANAPOLIS, IN, p. A205
COMMUNITY HOSPITAL, TALLASSEE, AL, p. A25
COMMUNITY HOSPITAL, GRAND JUNCTION, CO, p. A101
COMMUNITY HOSPITAL, MUNSTER, IN, p. A211
COMMUNITY HOSPITAL, MCCOOK, NE, p. A386
COMMUNITY HOSPITAL, OKLAHOMA CITY, OK, p. A502
COMMUNITY HOSPITAL, TORRINGTON, WY, p. A704
COMMUNITY HOSPITAL, HARRISBURG, Pennsylvania (see PINNACLE HEALTH SYSTEM), p. A527
COMMUNITY HOSPITAL EAST, INDIANAPOLIS, IN, p. A205
COMMUNITY HOSPITAL NORTH, INDIANAPOLIS, IN, p. A205
COMMUNITY HOSPITAL OF ANACONDA, ANACONDA, MT, p. A374
COMMUNITY HOSPITAL OF ANDERSON AND MADISON COUNTY, ANDERSON, IN, p. A198
COMMUNITY HOSPITAL OF BREMEN, BREMEN, IN, p. A199
COMMUNITY HOSPITAL OF HUNTINGTON PARK, HUNTINGTON PARK, CA, p. A64
COMMUNITY HOSPITAL OF LONG BEACH, LONG BEACH, CA, p. A67
COMMUNITY HOSPITAL OF SAN BERNARDINO, SAN BERNARDINO, CA, p. A84
COMMUNITY HOSPITAL OF THE MONTEREY PENINSULA, MONTEREY, CA, p. A75
COMMUNITY HOSPITAL SOUTH, INDIANAPOLIS, IN, p. A205
COMMUNITY HOSPITAL–FAIRFAX, FAIRFAX, MO, p. A360
COMMUNITY HOSPITALS AND WELLNESS CENTERS, BRYAN, OH, p. A472
COMMUNITY HOSPITALS AND WELLNESS CENTERS–MONTPELIER, MONTPELIER, OH, p. A486
COMMUNITY HOWARD REGIONAL HOSPITAL, KOKOMO, IN, p. A207
COMMUNITY HOWARD SPECIALTY HOSPITAL, KOKOMO, IN, p. A207
COMMUNITY MEDICAL CENTER, MISSOULA, MT, p. A378
COMMUNITY MEDICAL CENTER, FALLS CITY, NE, p. A383
COMMUNITY MEDICAL CENTER, TOMS RIVER, NJ, p. A411
COMMUNITY MEDICAL CENTER OF IZARD COUNTY, CALICO ROCK, AR, p. A41
COMMUNITY MEMORIAL HEALTH SYSTEM, VENTURA, CA, p. A94
COMMUNITY MEMORIAL HEALTHCARE, MARYSVILLE, KS, p. A239
COMMUNITY MEMORIAL HEALTHCENTER, SOUTH HILL, VA, p. A661
COMMUNITY MEMORIAL HOSPITAL, VENTURA, CALIFORNIA (see COMMUNITY MEMORIAL HEALTH SYSTEM), p. A94
COMMUNITY MEMORIAL HOSPITAL, STAUNTON, IL, p. A195
COMMUNITY MEMORIAL HOSPITAL, SUMNER, IA, p. A229
COMMUNITY MEMORIAL HOSPITAL, CLOQUET, MN, p. A330
COMMUNITY MEMORIAL HOSPITAL, SYRACUSE, NE, p. A390
COMMUNITY MEMORIAL HOSPITAL, HAMILTON, NY, p. A426
COMMUNITY MEMORIAL HOSPITAL, TURTLE LAKE, ND, p. A469
COMMUNITY MEMORIAL HOSPITAL, HICKSVILLE, OH, p. A483
COMMUNITY MEMORIAL HOSPITAL, BURKE, SD, p. A558
COMMUNITY MEMORIAL HOSPITAL, REDFIELD, SD, p. A562
COMMUNITY MEMORIAL HOSPITAL, MENOMONEE FALLS, WI, p. A691
COMMUNITY MEMORIAL HOSPITAL, OCONTO FALLS, WI, p. A694
COMMUNITY MENTAL HEALTH CENTER, LAWRENCEBURG, IN, p. A208
COMMUNITY REGIONAL MEDICAL CENTER, FRESNO, CA, p. A61
COMMUNITY SPECIALTY HOSPITAL, LAFAYETTE, LA, p. A270
COMMUNITY WESTVIEW HOSPITAL, INDIANAPOLIS, IN, p. A205
COMPASS BEHAVIORAL CENTER OF CROWLEY, CROWLEY, LA, p. A266
COMPASS BEHAVIORAL CENTER OF HOUMA, INC., HOUMA, LA, p. A268
COMPLEX CARE HOSPITAL AT RIDGELAKE, SARASOTA, FL, p. A139
COMPLEX CARE HOSPITAL AT TENAYA, LAS VEGAS, NV, p. A392
COMPLEX CARE HOSPITAL OF IDAHO, MERIDIAN, ID, p. A170
CONCHO COUNTY HOSPITAL, EDEN, TX, p. A600
CONCORD HOSPITAL, CONCORD, NH, p. A397
CONCOURSE DIVISION,, NEW YORK (see BRONX–LEBANON HOSPITAL CENTER HEALTH CARE SYSTEM), p. A431
CONE HEALTH, GREENSBORO, NC, p. A453
CONEJOS COUNTY HOSPITAL, LA JARA, CO, p. A102
CONEMAUGH MEMORIAL MEDICAL CENTER, JOHNSTOWN, PA, p. A528
CONEMAUGH MEYERSDALE MEDICAL CENTER, MEYERSDALE, PA, p. A532

CONEMAUGH MINERS MEDICAL CENTER, HASTINGS, PA, p. A527
CONEY ISLAND HOSPITAL,, NY, p. A431
CONIFER PARK, GLENVILLE, NY, p. A426
CONNALLY MEDICAL CENTER, FLORESVILLE, TX, p. A602
CONNECTICUT CHILDREN'S MEDICAL CENTER, HARTFORD, CT, p. A109
CONNECTICUT DEPARTMENT OF CORRECTION'S HOSPITAL, SOMERS, CT, p. A111
CONNECTICUT MENTAL HEALTH CENTER, NEW HAVEN, CT, p. A110
CONNECTICUT VALLEY HOSPITAL, MIDDLETOWN, CT, p. A110
CONROE REGIONAL MEDICAL CENTER, CONROE, TX, p. A593
CONTINUING CARE HOSPITAL, LEXINGTON, KY, p. A254
CONTINUING CARE HOSPITAL AT ST. LUKE'S, CEDAR RAPIDS, IA, p. A217
CONTINUOUS CARE CENTERS OF OKLAHOMA, TULSA, OKLAHOMA (see CONTINUOUS CARE CENTERS OF TULSA), p. A508
CONTINUOUS CARE CENTERS OF TULSA, TULSA, OK, p. A508
CONTINUUM REHABILITATION HOSPITAL OF NORTH TEXAS, FLOWER MOUND, TX, p. A602
CONTRA COSTA REGIONAL MEDICAL CENTER, MARTINEZ, CA, p. A73
CONWAY MEDICAL CENTER, CONWAY, SC, p. A551
CONWAY REGIONAL MEDICAL CENTER, CONWAY, AR, p. A42
CONWAY REGIONAL REHAB HOSPITAL, CONWAY, AR, p. A42
COOK CHILDREN'S MEDICAL CENTER, FORT WORTH, TX, p. A603
COOK CHILDREN'S NORTHEAST HOSPITAL, HURST, TX, p. A614
COOK COUNTY NORTH SHORE HOSPITAL, GRAND MARAIS, MN, p. A333
COOK HOSPITAL AND CONVALESCENT NURSING CARE UNIT, COOK, MN, p. A330
COOK MEDICAL CENTER–A CAMPUS OF TIFT REGIONAL MEDICAL CENTER, ADEL, GA, p. A145
COOKEVILLE REGIONAL MEDICAL CENTER, COOKEVILLE, TN, p. A568
COOLEY DICKINSON HOSPITAL, NORTHAMPTON, MA, p. A303
COON MEMORIAL HOSPITAL AND HOME, DALHART, TX, p. A594
COOPER COUNTY MEMORIAL HOSPITAL, BOONVILLE, MO, p. A357
COOPER HEALTH SYSTEM, CAMDEN, NJ, p. A402
COOPERSTOWN MEDICAL CENTER, COOPERSTOWN, ND, p. A466
COORDINATED HEALTH–BETHLEHEM, BETHLEHEM, PA, p. A520
COOSA VALLEY MEDICAL CENTER, SYLACAUGA, AL, p. A25
COPLEY HOSPITAL, MORRISVILLE, VT, p. A649
COPPER BASIN MEDICAL CENTER, COPPERHILL, TN, p. A568
COPPER QUEEN COMMUNITY HOSPITAL, BISBEE, AZ, p. A30
COQUILLE VALLEY HOSPITAL, COQUILLE, OR, p. A512
CORAL GABLES HOSPITAL, CORAL GABLES, FL, p. A121
CORCORAN DISTRICT HOSPITAL, CORCORAN, CA, p. A57
CORDELL MEMORIAL HOSPITAL, CORDELL, OK, p. A497
CORDOVA COMMUNITY MEDICAL CENTER, CORDOVA, AK, p. A27
CORNERSTONE HOSPITAL OF AUSTIN, AUSTIN, TX, p. A585
CORNERSTONE HOSPITAL OF AUSTIN, AUSTIN, TEXAS (see CORNERSTONE HOSPITAL OF AUSTIN), p. A585
CORNERSTONE HOSPITAL OF BOSSIER CITY, BOSSIER CITY, LA, p. A264
CORNERSTONE HOSPITAL OF HOUSTON – BELLAIRE, HOUSTON, TX, p. A609
CORNERSTONE HOSPITAL OF HOUSTON AT CLEARLAKE, WEBSTER, TEXAS (see CORNERSTONE HOSPITAL OF HOUSTON – BELLAIRE), p. A609
CORNERSTONE HOSPITAL OF HUNTINGTON, HUNTINGTON, WV, p. A677
CORNERSTONE HOSPITAL OF NORTH LITTLE ROCK, JACKSONVILLE, AR, p. A45
CORNERSTONE HOSPITAL OF SOUTHEAST ARIZONA, TUCSON, AZ, p. A38
CORNERSTONE HOSPITAL OF SOUTHWEST LOUISIANA, SULPHUR, LA, p. A279
CORNERSTONE HOSPITAL–MEDICAL CENTER OF HOUSTON, HOUSTON, TX, p. A609
CORNERSTONE HOSPITAL–WEST MONROE, WEST MONROE, LA, p. A280
CORNERSTONE OF MEDICAL ARTS CENTER HOSPITAL, FRESH MEADOWS, NY, p. A426
CORNERSTONE REGIONAL HOSPITAL, EDINBURG, TX, p. A600
CORNING HOSPITAL, CORNING, NY, p. A424
CORONA REGIONAL MEDICAL CENTER, CORONA, CA, p. A57
CORONA REGIONAL MEDICAL CENTER–REHABILITATION, CORONA, CALIFORNIA (see CORONA REGIONAL MEDICAL CENTER), p. A57

CORPUS CHRISTI MEDICAL CENTER, CORPUS CHRISTI, TX, p. A593
CORPUS CHRISTI MEDICAL CENTER BAY AREA, CORPUS CHRISTI, TEXAS (see CORPUS CHRISTI MEDICAL CENTER), p. A593
CORRY MEMORIAL HOSPITAL, CORRY, PA, p. A523
CORTLAND REGIONAL MEDICAL CENTER, CORTLAND, NY, p. A424
CORYELL MEMORIAL HOSPITAL, GATESVILLE, TX, p. A606
COSHOCTON COUNTY MEMORIAL HOSPITAL, COSHOCTON, OH, p. A479
COTEAU DES PRAIRIES HOSPITAL, SISSETON, SD, p. A563
COTTAGE CHILDREN'S HOSPITAL, SANTA BARBARA, CALIFORNIA (see SANTA BARBARA COTTAGE HOSPITAL), p. A89
COTTAGE HOSPITAL, WOODSVILLE, NH, p. A400
COTTAGE REHABILITATION HOSPITAL, SANTA BARBARA, CALIFORNIA (see SANTA BARBARA COTTAGE HOSPITAL), p. A89
COULEE MEDICAL CENTER, GRAND COULEE, WA, p. A667
COVENANT CHILDREN'S HOSPITAL, LUBBOCK, TX, p. A619
COVENANT HOSPITAL PLAINVIEW, PLAINVIEW, TX, p. A627
COVENANT HOSPITAL–LEVELLAND, LEVELLAND, TX, p. A618
COVENANT MEDICAL CENTER, WATERLOO, IA, p. A229
COVENANT MEDICAL CENTER, SAGINAW, MI, p. A323
COVENANT MEDICAL CENTER, LUBBOCK, TX, p. A620
COVENANT MEDICAL CENTER–COOPER, SAGINAW, MICHIGAN (see COVENANT MEDICAL CENTER), p. A323
COVENANT MEDICAL CENTER–HARRISON, SAGINAW, MICHIGAN (see COVENANT MEDICAL CENTER), p. A323
COVENANT MEDICAL CENTER–LAKESIDE, LUBBOCK, TEXAS (see COVENANT MEDICAL CENTER), p. A620
COVENANT SPECIALTY HOSPITAL, LUBBOCK, TX, p. A620
COVINGTON COUNTY HOSPITAL, COLLINS, MS, p. A346
COX MEDICAL CENTER BRANSON, BRANSON, MO, p. A357
COX MONETT, MONETT, MO, p. A366
COZAD COMMUNITY HOSPITAL, COZAD, NE, p. A382
COZBY–GERMANY HOSPITAL, GRAND SALINE, TX, p. A606
CRAIG GENERAL HOSPITAL, VINITA, OK, p. A509
CRAIG HOSPITAL, ENGLEWOOD, CO, p. A100
CRANE MEMORIAL HOSPITAL, CRANE, TX, p. A594
CRAWFORD COUNTY MEMORIAL HOSPITAL, DENISON, IA, p. A220
CRAWFORD MEMORIAL HOSPITAL, ROBINSON, IL, p. A193
CRAWLEY MEMORIAL HOSPITAL, SHELBY, NC, p. A461
CREEDMOOR PSYCHIATRIC CENTER,, NY, p. A431
CREEK NATION COMMUNITY HOSPITAL, OKEMAH, OK, p. A502
CRENSHAW COMMUNITY HOSPITAL, LUVERNE, AL, p. A22
CRESTWOOD MEDICAL CENTER, HUNTSVILLE, AL, p. A21
CRETE AREA MEDICAL CENTER, CRETE, NE, p. A383
CRISP REGIONAL HOSPITAL, CORDELE, GA, p. A151
CRITTENDEN COUNTY HOSPITAL, MARION, KY, p. A257
CRITTENDEN REGIONAL HOSPITAL, WEST MEMPHIS, AR, p. A51
CRITTENTON CHILDREN'S CENTER, KANSAS CITY, MO, p. A362
CRITTENTON HOSPITAL MEDICAL CENTER, ROCHESTER, MI, p. A322
CROCKETT HOSPITAL, LAWRENCEBURG, TN, p. A572
CROOK COUNTY MEDICAL SERVICES DISTRICT, SUNDANCE, WY, p. A704
CROSBYTON CLINIC HOSPITAL, CROSBYTON, TX, p. A594
CROSSGATES RIVER OAKS HOSPITAL, BRANDON, MS, p. A345
CROSSRIDGE COMMUNITY HOSPITAL, WYNNE, AR, p. A51
CROSSROADS COMMUNITY HOSPITAL, MOUNT VERNON, IL, p. A189
CROSSROADS REGIONAL HOSPITAL, ALEXANDRIA, LA, p. A262
CROTCHED MOUNTAIN REHABILITATION CENTER, GREENFIELD, NH, p. A398
CROUSE HOSPITAL, SYRACUSE, NY, p. A443
CROW/NORTHERN CHEYENNE HOSPITAL, CROW AGENCY, MT, p. A375
CROWLEY REHABILITATION HOSPITAL, CROWLEY, LA, p. A266
CROZER–CHESTER MEDICAL CENTER, UPLAND, PA, p. A542
CUBA MEMORIAL HOSPITAL, CUBA, NY, p. A424
CUERO COMMUNITY HOSPITAL, CUERO, TX, p. A594
CULBERSON HOSPITAL, VAN HORN, TX, p. A639
CULLMAN REGIONAL MEDICAL CENTER, CULLMAN, AL, p. A18
CULPEPER REGIONAL HOSPITAL, CULPEPER, VA, p. A653
CULPEPER COUNTY HOSPITAL, BURKESVILLE, KY, p. A249
CUMBERLAND HALL HOSPITAL, HOPKINSVILLE, KY, p. A252
CUMBERLAND HOSPITAL, NEW KENT, VA, p. A657
CUMBERLAND MEDICAL CENTER, CROSSVILLE, TN, p. A568
CUMBERLAND MEMORIAL HOSPITAL, CUMBERLAND, WI, p. A685
CUMBERLAND RIVER HOSPITAL, CELINA, TN, p. A566
CURRY GENERAL HOSPITAL, GOLD BEACH, OR, p. A513
CUSTER REGIONAL HOSPITAL, CUSTER, SD, p. A559
CUYUNA REGIONAL MEDICAL CENTER, CROSBY, MN, p. A331
CYPRESS CREEK HOSPITAL, HOUSTON, TX, p. A609
CYPRESS FAIRBANKS MEDICAL CENTER, HOUSTON, TX, p. A609

CYPRESS POINTE HOSPITAL EAST, SLIDELL, LA, p. A278
CYPRESS POINTE SURGICAL HOSPITAL, HAMMOND, LA, p. A268

# D

D. W. MCMILLAN MEMORIAL HOSPITAL, BREWTON, AL, p. A18
DAHL MEMORIAL HEALTHCARE ASSOCIATION, EKALAKA, MT, p. A375
DAKOTA PLAINS SURGICAL CENTER, ABERDEEN, SD, p. A558
DALE MEDICAL CENTER, OZARK, AL, p. A24
DALLAS COUNTY HOSPITAL, PERRY, IA, p. A227
DALLAS COUNTY MEDICAL CENTER, FORDYCE, AR, p. A44
DALLAS MEDICAL CENTER, DALLAS, TX, p. A595
DALLAS REGIONAL MEDICAL CENTER, MESQUITE, TX, p. A622
DAMERON HOSPITAL, STOCKTON, CA, p. A91
DANA–FARBER CANCER INSTITUTE, BOSTON, MA, p. A296
DANBURY HOSPITAL, DANBURY, CT, p. A108
DANIELS MEMORIAL HEALTHCARE CENTER, SCOBEY, MT, p. A379
DANVILLE REGIONAL MEDICAL CENTER, DANVILLE, VA, p. A653
DANVILLE STATE HOSPITAL, DANVILLE, PA, p. A523
DARTMOUTH–HITCHCOCK MEDICAL CENTER, LEBANON, NH, p. A398
DAUTERIVE HOSPITAL, NEW IBERIA, LA, p. A275
DAVANT REHABILITATION AND EXTENDED CARE CENTER (see BLOWING ROCK HOSPITAL), p. A448
DAVID GRANT MEDICAL CENTER, TRAVIS AFB, CA, p. A93
DAVIESS COMMUNITY HOSPITAL, WASHINGTON, IN, p. A214
DAVIS COUNTY HOSPITAL, BLOOMFIELD, IA, p. A217
DAVIS HOSPITAL AND MEDICAL CENTER, LAYTON, UT, p. A644
DAVIS MEMORIAL HOSPITAL, ELKINS, WV, p. A676
DAVIS REGIONAL MEDICAL CENTER, STATESVILLE, NC, p. A461
DAY KIMBALL HOSPITAL, PUTNAM, CT, p. A111
DAYTON GENERAL HOSPITAL, DAYTON, WA, p. A666
DAYTON REHABILITATION INSTITUTE, DAYTON, OH, p. A479
DAYTON VETERANS AFFAIRS MEDICAL CENTER, DAYTON, OH, p. A479
DCH REGIONAL MEDICAL CENTER, TUSCALOOSA, AL, p. A26
DE GRAFF MEMORIAL HOSPITAL, NORTH TONAWANDA, NEW YORK (see KALEIDA HEALTH), p. A422
DE POO HOSPITAL, KEY WEST, FLORIDA (see LOWER KEYS MEDICAL CENTER), p. A127
DE QUEEN MEDICAL CENTER, DE QUEEN, AR, p. A42
DE SOTO REGIONAL HEALTH SYSTEM, MANSFIELD, LA, p. A273
DEACONESS CROSS POINTE CENTER, EVANSVILLE, INDIANA (see DEACONESS HOSPITAL), p. A202
DEACONESS HOSPITAL, EVANSVILLE, IN, p. A202
DEACONESS HOSPITAL, OKLAHOMA CITY, OK, p. A503
DEACONESS HOSPITAL, SPOKANE, WA, p. A672
DEARBORN COUNTY HOSPITAL, LAWRENCEBURG, IN, p. A208
DEBORAH HEART AND LUNG CENTER, BROWNS MILLS, NJ, p. A402
DECATUR COUNTY GENERAL HOSPITAL, PARSONS, TN, p. A578
DECATUR COUNTY HOSPITAL, LEON, IA, p. A224
DECATUR COUNTY HOSPITAL AND CEDAR LIVING CENTER, OBERLIN, KS, p. A241
DECATUR COUNTY MEMORIAL HOSPITAL, GREENSBURG, IN, p. A204
DECATUR GENERAL HOSPITAL, DECATUR, AL, p. A18
DECATUR GENERAL HOSPITAL–WEST, DECATUR, ALABAMA (see DECATUR GENERAL HOSPITAL), p. A18
DECATUR MEMORIAL HOSPITAL, DECATUR, IL, p. A180
DECATUR MORGAN HOSPITAL, DECATUR, AL, p. A19
DECKERVILLE COMMUNITY HOSPITAL, DECKERVILLE, MI, p. A311
DEER LODGE MEDICAL CENTER, DEER LODGE, MT, p. A375
DEER'S HEAD HOSPITAL CENTER, SALISBURY, MD, p. A294
DEKALB COMMUNITY HOSPITAL, SMITHVILLE, TN, p. A579
DEKALB HEALTH, AUBURN, IN, p. A198
DEKALB MEDICAL AT DOWNTOWN DECATUR, DECATUR, GA, p. A152
DEKALB MEDICAL AT HILLANDALE, LITHONIA, GA, p. A156
DEKALB MEDICAL AT NORTH DECATUR, DECATUR, GA, p. A152
DEKALB REGIONAL MEDICAL CENTER, FORT PAYNE, AL, p. A20
DEL AMO HOSPITAL, TORRANCE, CA, p. A92
DEL SOL MEDICAL CENTER, EL PASO, TEXAS (see LAS PALMAS MEDICAL CENTER), p. A601
DELANO REGIONAL MEDICAL CENTER, DELANO, CA, p. A58
DELAWARE COUNTY MEMORIAL HOSPITAL, DREXEL HILL, PA, p. A524
DELAWARE PSYCHIATRIC CENTER, NEW CASTLE, DE, p. A114
DELAWARE VALLEY HOSPITAL, WALTON, NY, p. A445
DELL CHILDREN'S MEDICAL CENTER OF CENTRAL TEXAS, AUSTIN, TX, p. A585

DELNOR HOSPITAL, GENEVA, IL, p. A183
DELRAY MEDICAL CENTER, DELRAY BEACH, FL, p. A122
DELTA COMMUNITY MEDICAL CENTER, DELTA, UT, p. A643
DELTA COUNTY MEMORIAL HOSPITAL, DELTA, CO, p. A99
DELTA MEDICAL CENTER, MEMPHIS, TN, p. A574
DELTA MEMORIAL HOSPITAL, DUMAS, AR, p. A43
DELTA REGIONAL MEDICAL CENTER, GREENVILLE, MS, p. A347
DENTON REGIONAL MEDICAL CENTER, DENTON, TX, p. A598
DENVER HEALTH MEDICAL CENTER, DENVER, CO, p. A99
DEPAUL CENTER, WACO, TEXAS (see PROVIDENCE HEALTH CENTER), p. A640
DEQUINCY MEMORIAL HOSPITAL, DEQUINCY, LA, p. A266
DES MOINES DIVISION, DES MOINES, IOWA (see VETERANS AFFAIRS CENTRAL IOWA HEALTH CARE SYSTEM), p. A220
DES PERES HOSPITAL, SAINT LOUIS, MO, p. A369
DESERT REGIONAL MEDICAL CENTER, PALM SPRINGS, CA, p. A78
DESERT SPRINGS HOSPITAL MEDICAL CENTER, LAS VEGAS, NV, p. A392
DESERT VALLEY HOSPITAL, VICTORVILLE, CA, p. A95
DESERT VIEW HOSPITAL, PAHRUMP, NV, p. A394
DESERT WILLOW TREATMENT CENTER, LAS VEGAS, NV, p. A392
DESOTO MEMORIAL HOSPITAL, ARCADIA, FL, p. A118
DETAR HEALTHCARE SYSTEM, VICTORIA, TX, p. A639
DETAR HOSPITAL NORTH, VICTORIA, TEXAS (see DETAR HEALTHCARE SYSTEM), p. A639
DETROIT RECEIVING HOSPITAL/UNIVERSITY HEALTH CENTER, DETROIT, MI, p. A311
DETTMER HOSPITAL, TROY, OHIO (see UPPER VALLEY MEDICAL CENTER), p. A491
DEVEREUX CHILDREN'S BEHAVIORAL HEALTH CENTER, MALVERN, PA, p. A530
DEVEREUX GEORGIA TREATMENT NETWORK, KENNESAW, GA, p. A155
DEVEREUX HOSPITAL AND CHILDREN'S CENTER OF FLORIDA, MELBOURNE, FL, p. A130
DEVEREUX TEXAS TREATMENT NETWORK, LEAGUE CITY, TX, p. A618
DEWITT HOSPITAL, DE WITT, AR, p. A42
DIAMOND CHILDREN'S HOSPITAL, TUCSON, ARIZONA (see UNIVERSITY OF ARIZONA MEDICAL CENTER – UNIVERSITY CAMPUS), p. A39
DICKENSON COMMUNITY HOSPITAL, CLINTWOOD, VA, p. A652
DICKINSON COUNTY HEALTHCARE SYSTEM, IRON MOUNTAIN, MI, p. A317
DILEY RIDGE MEDICAL CENTER, CANAL WINCHESTER, OH, p. A472
DIMMIT REGIONAL HOSPITAL, CARRIZO SPRINGS, TX, p. A591
DISNEY CHILDREN'S HOSPITAL, ORLANDO, FLORIDA (see FLORIDA HOSPITAL), p. A135
DISTRICT ONE HOSPITAL, FARIBAULT, MN, p. A332
DIVINE PROVIDENCE HOSPITAL, WILLIAMSPORT, PA, p. A544
DIVINE SAVIOR HEALTHCARE, PORTAGE, WI, p. A695
DIVISION OF ADOLESCENT MEDICINE, CINCINNATI CENTER FOR DEVELOPMENTAL DISORDERS, AND CONVALESCENT HOSPITAL FOR CHILDREN, CHILDREN'S HOSPITAL, CINCINNATI, OHIO (see CINCINNATI CHILDREN'S HOSPITAL MEDICAL CENTER), p. A474
DIXIE REGIONAL MEDICAL CENTER, SAINT GEORGE, UT, p. A646
DIXIE REGIONAL MEDICAL CENTER, ST. GEORGE, UTAH (see DIXIE REGIONAL MEDICAL CENTER), p. A646
DMC HURON VALLEY–SINAI HOSPITAL, COMMERCE TOWNSHIP, MI, p. A311
DMC SURGERY HOSPITAL, MADISON HEIGHTS, MICHIGAN (see HARPER UNIVERSITY HOSPITAL/HUTZEL WOMEN'S HOSPITAL), p. A312
DOCTOR'S CENTER OF BAYAMON, BAYAMON, PR, p. A706
DOCTOR'S HOSPITAL, LEAWOOD, KS, p. A238
DOCTOR'S HOSPITAL – TIDWELL, HOUSTON, TX, p. A609
DOCTOR'S HOSPITAL AND NEUROMUSCULAR CENTER, BREMEN, IN, p. A199
DOCTOR'S HOSPITAL AT RENAISSANCE, EDINBURG, TX, p. A600
DOCTOR'S HOSPITAL OF DEER CREEK, LEESVILLE, LA, p. A272
DOCTOR'S MEMORIAL HOSPITAL, PERRY, FL, p. A137
DOCTORS CENTER, MANATI, PR, p. A707
DOCTORS COMMUNITY HOSPITAL, LANHAM, MD, p. A292
DOCTORS DIAGNOSTIC HOSPITAL, CLEVELAND, TX, p. A592
DOCTORS HOSPITAL, AUGUSTA, GA, p. A147
DOCTORS HOSPITAL AT WHITE ROCK LAKE, DALLAS, TX, p. A595
DOCTORS HOSPITAL NELSONVILLE, NELSONVILLE, OH, p. A487
DOCTORS HOSPITAL OF COLUMBUS, COLUMBUS, GA, p. A150
DOCTORS HOSPITAL OF JEFFERSON, METAIRIE, LOUISIANA (see EAST JEFFERSON GENERAL HOSPITAL), p. A273
DOCTORS HOSPITAL OF LAREDO, LAREDO, TX, p. A618
DOCTORS HOSPITAL OF MANTECA, MANTECA, CA, p. A73

DOCTORS HOSPITAL OF SARASOTA, SARASOTA, FL, p. A139
DOCTORS HOSPITAL OF WEST COVINA, WEST COVINA, CA, p. A95
DOCTORS HOSPITAL PARKWAY, HOUSTON, TEXAS (see DOCTOR'S HOSPITAL – TIDWELL), p. A609
DOCTORS MEDICAL CENTER, MODESTO, CA, p. A74
DOCTORS MEDICAL CENTER–SAN PABLO CAMPUS, SAN PABLO, CA, p. A88
DOCTORS MEMORIAL HOSPITAL, BONIFAY, FL, p. A119
DOCTORS' CENTER HOSPITAL SAN JUAN, SAN JUAN, PR, p. A709
DOCTORS' HOSPITAL OF MICHIGAN, PONTIAC, MI, p. A322
DODGE COUNTY HOSPITAL, EASTMAN, GA, p. A153
DOERNBECHER CHILDREN'S HOSPITAL, PORTLAND, OREGON (see OHSU HOSPITAL), p. A516
DOMINICAN HOSPITAL, SANTA CRUZ, CA, p. A90
DOMINION HOSPITAL, FALLS CHURCH, VA, p. A653
DONALSONVILLE HOSPITAL, DONALSONVILLE, GA, p. A152
DORCHESTER GENERAL HOSPITAL, CAMBRIDGE, MD, p. A290
DORMINY MEDICAL CENTER, FITZGERALD, GA, p. A153
DOROTHEA DIX PSYCHIATRIC CENTER, BANGOR, ME, p. A281
DOUGLAS COUNTY COMMUNITY MENTAL HEALTH CENTER, OMAHA, NE, p. A388
DOUGLAS COUNTY HOSPITAL, ALEXANDRIA, MN, p. A328
DOUGLAS COUNTY MEMORIAL HOSPITAL, ARMOUR, SD, p. A558
DOVER BEHAVIORAL HEALTH SYSTEM, DOVER, DE, p. A114
DOWN EAST COMMUNITY HOSPITAL, MACHIAS, ME, p. A284
DOWNEY REGIONAL MEDICAL CENTER, DOWNEY, CA, p. A58
DOYLESTOWN HOSPITAL, DOYLESTOWN, PA, p. A524
DR. DAN C. TRIGG MEMORIAL HOSPITAL, TUCUMCARI, NM, p. A418
DR. J. CORRIGAN MENTAL HEALTH CENTER, FALL RIVER, MA, p. A299
DR. JOHN WARNER HOSPITAL, CLINTON, IL, p. A180
DR. PILA'S HOSPITAL, PONCE, PR, p. A708
DR. RAMON E. BETANCES HOSPITAL–MAYAGUEZ MEDICAL CENTER BRANCH, MAYAGUEZ, PR, p. A708
DR. SOLOMON CARTER FULLER MENTAL HEALTH CENTER, BOSTON, MA, p. A296
DRAKE CENTER, CINCINNATI, OH, p. A474
DREW MEMORIAL HOSPITAL, MONTICELLO, AR, p. A47
DRISCOLL CHILDREN'S HOSPITAL, CORPUS CHRISTI, TX, p. A594
DRUMRIGHT REGIONAL HOSPITAL, DRUMRIGHT, OK, p. A497
DUANE L. WATERS HOSPITAL, JACKSON, MI, p. A317
DUBOIS REGIONAL MEDICAL CENTER, DU BOIS, PA, p. A524
DUBUIS HOSPITAL OF ALEXANDRIA, ALEXANDRIA, LA, p. A262
DUBUIS HOSPITAL OF BEAUMONT, BEAUMONT, TX, p. A587
DUBUIS HOSPITAL OF CORPUS CHRISTI, CORPUS CHRISTI, TX, p. A594
DUBUIS HOSPITAL OF LAKE CHARLES, LAKE CHARLES, LA, p. A271
DUBUIS HOSPITAL OF PARIS, PARIS, TX, p. A626
DUBUIS HOSPITAL OF SHREVEPORT, SHREVEPORT, LA, p. A278
DUBUIS HOSPITAL OF TEXARKANA, TEXARKANA, TX, p. A637
DUKE CHILDREN'S HOSPITAL & HEALTH CENTER, DURHAM, NORTH CAROLINA (see DUKE UNIVERSITY HOSPITAL), p. A451
DUKE RALEIGH HOSPITAL, RALEIGH, NC, p. A459
DUKE REGIONAL HOSPITAL, DURHAM, NC, p. A451
DUKE UNIVERSITY HOSPITAL, DURHAM, NC, p. A451
DUKES MEMORIAL HOSPITAL, PERU, IN, p. A212
DUNCAN REGIONAL HOSPITAL, DUNCAN, OK, p. A497
DUNDY COUNTY HOSPITAL, BENKELMAN, NE, p. A382
DUPONT HOSPITAL, FORT WAYNE, IN, p. A202
DURHAM VETERANS AFFAIRS MEDICAL CENTER, DURHAM, NC, p. A451
DWIGHT D. EISENHOWER VETERANS AFFAIRS MEDICAL CENTER, LEAVENWORTH, KANSAS (see VETERANS AFFAIRS EASTERN KANSAS HEALTH CARE SYSTEM), p. A245
DWIGHT DAVID EISENHOWER ARMY MEDICAL CENTER, FORT GORDON, GA, p. A154
DYERSBURG REGIONAL MEDICAL CENTER, DYERSBURG, TN, p. A568

# E

E. A. CONWAY MEDICAL CENTER, MONROE, LA, p. A274
EAGLEVILLE HOSPITAL, EAGLEVILLE, PA, p. A524
EARLE E. MORRIS ALCOHOL AND DRUG TREATMENT CENTER, COLUMBIA, SC, p. A550
EAST ADAMS RURAL HOSPITAL, RITZVILLE, WA, p. A670
EAST ALABAMA MEDICAL CENTER, OPELIKA, AL, p. A24
EAST CAMPUS, NORFOLK, NEBRASKA (see FAITH REGIONAL HEALTH SERVICES), p. A386

EAST CARROLL PARISH HOSPITAL, LAKE PROVIDENCE, LA, p. A272
EAST CENTRAL REGIONAL HOSPITAL, AUGUSTA, GA, p. A147
EAST CENTRAL REGIONAL HOSPITAL, GRACEWOOD, GEORGIA (see EAST CENTRAL REGIONAL HOSPITAL), p. A147
EAST COOPER MEDICAL CENTER, MOUNT PLEASANT, SC, p. A554
EAST GEORGIA REGIONAL MEDICAL CENTER, STATESBORO, GA, p. A160
EAST HOUSTON REGIONAL MEDICAL CENTER, HOUSTON, TEXAS (see BAYSHORE MEDICAL CENTER), p. A626
EAST JEFFERSON GENERAL HOSPITAL, METAIRIE, LA, p. A273
EAST LIVERPOOL CITY HOSPITAL, EAST LIVERPOOL, OH, p. A481
EAST LOS ANGELES DOCTORS HOSPITAL, LOS ANGELES, CA, p. A68
EAST MISSISSIPPI STATE HOSPITAL, MERIDIAN, MS, p. A351
EAST MORGAN COUNTY HOSPITAL, BRUSH, CO, p. A98
EAST MOUNTAIN HOSPITAL, BELLE MEAD, NJ, p. A401
EAST OHIO REGIONAL HOSPITAL, MARTINS FERRY, OH, p. A485
EAST ORANGE DIVISION, EAST ORANGE, NEW JERSEY (see VETERANS AFFAIRS NEW JERSEY HEALTH CARE SYSTEM), p. A403
EAST ORANGE GENERAL HOSPITAL, EAST ORANGE, NJ, p. A403
EAST RIDGE HOSPITAL, EAST RIDGE, TENNESSEE (see PARKRIDGE MEDICAL CENTER), p. A567
EAST TENNESSEE CHILDREN'S HOSPITAL, KNOXVILLE, TN, p. A571
EAST TEXAS MEDICAL CENTER ATHENS, ATHENS, TX, p. A584
EAST TEXAS MEDICAL CENTER BEHAVIORAL HEALTH CENTER, TYLER, TEXAS (see EAST TEXAS MEDICAL CENTER TYLER), p. A638
EAST TEXAS MEDICAL CENTER CARTHAGE, CARTHAGE, TX, p. A591
EAST TEXAS MEDICAL CENTER CLARKSVILLE, CLARKSVILLE, TX, p. A592
EAST TEXAS MEDICAL CENTER CROCKETT, CROCKETT, TX, p. A594
EAST TEXAS MEDICAL CENTER FAIRFIELD, FAIRFIELD, TX, p. A602
EAST TEXAS MEDICAL CENTER HENDERSON, HENDERSON, TX, p. A608
EAST TEXAS MEDICAL CENTER JACKSONVILLE, JACKSONVILLE, TX, p. A615
EAST TEXAS MEDICAL CENTER PITTSBURG, PITTSBURG, TX, p. A627
EAST TEXAS MEDICAL CENTER REHABILITATION HOSPITAL, TYLER, TX, p. A638
EAST TEXAS MEDICAL CENTER SPECIALTY HOSPITAL, TYLER, TX, p. A638
EAST TEXAS MEDICAL CENTER TRINITY, TRINITY, TX, p. A638
EAST TEXAS MEDICAL CENTER TYLER, TYLER, TX, p. A638
EAST TEXAS MEDICAL CENTER-GILMER, GILMER, TX, p. A606
EAST TEXAS MEDICAL CENTER-MOUNT VERNON, MOUNT VERNON, TX, p. A624
EAST TEXAS MEDICAL CENTER-QUITMAN, QUITMAN, TX, p. A628
EAST VALLEY HOSPITAL MEDICAL CENTER, GLENDORA, CA, p. A63
EASTERN IDAHO REGIONAL MEDICAL CENTER, IDAHO FALLS, ID, p. A169
EASTERN LONG ISLAND HOSPITAL, GREENPORT, NY, p. A426
EASTERN LOUISIANA MENTAL HEALTH SYSTEM, JACKSON, LA, p. A269
EASTERN MAINE MEDICAL CENTER, BANGOR, ME, p. A281
EASTERN NEW MEXICO MEDICAL CENTER, ROSWELL, NM, p. A417
EASTERN NIAGARA HEALTH SYSTEM, LOCKPORT, NY, p. A428
EASTERN NIAGARA HOSPITAL INTER-COMMUNITY, NEWFANE, NEW YORK (see EASTERN NIAGARA HEALTH SYSTEM), p. A428
EASTERN NIAGARA HOSPITAL LOCKPORT, LOCKPORT, NEW YORK (see EASTERN NIAGARA HEALTH SYSTEM), p. A428
EASTERN OKLAHOMA MEDICAL CENTER, POTEAU, OK, p. A505
EASTERN PLUMAS HEALTH CARE DISTRICT, PORTOLA, CA, p. A80
EASTERN REGIONAL MEDICAL CENTER, PHILADELPHIA, PA, p. A534
EASTERN SHORE HOSPITAL CENTER, CAMBRIDGE, MD, p. A290
EASTERN STATE HOSPITAL, LEXINGTON, KY, p. A254
EASTERN STATE HOSPITAL, WILLIAMSBURG, VA, p. A663
EASTERN STATE HOSPITAL, MEDICAL LAKE, WA, p. A668
EASTLAND MEMORIAL HOSPITAL, EASTLAND, TX, p. A600
EASTON HOSPITAL, EASTON, PA, p. A525
EASTPOINTE HOSPITAL, DAPHNE, AL, p. A18
EASTSIDE MEDICAL CENTER, SNELLVILLE, GA, p. A160
EASTSIDE PSYCHIATRIC HOSPITAL, TALLAHASSEE, FL, p. A140
EATON RAPIDS MEDICAL CENTER, EATON RAPIDS, MI, p. A313

ED FRASER MEMORIAL HOSPITAL AND BAKER COMMUNITY HEALTH CENTER, MACCLENNY, FL, p. A129
EDDY COHOES REHABILITATION CENTER, COHOES, NY, p. A424
EDEN MEDICAL CENTER, CASTRO VALLEY, CA, p. A56
EDGEFIELD COUNTY HOSPITAL, EDGEFIELD, SC, p. A551
EDGERTON HOSPITAL AND HEALTH SERVICES, EDGERTON, WI, p. A686
EDGEWOOD SURGICAL HOSPITAL, TRANSFER, PA, p. A542
EDINBURG CHILDREN'S HOSPITAL, EDINBURG, TEXAS (see SOUTH TEXAS HEALTH SYSTEM), p. A600
EDINBURG REGIONAL MEDICAL CENTER, EDINBURG, TEXAS (see SOUTH TEXAS HEALTH SYSTEM), p. A600
EDITH NOURSE ROGERS MEMORIAL VETERANS HOSPITAL, BEDFORD, MA, p. A295
EDWARD HINES, JR. VETERANS AFFAIRS HOSPITAL, HINES, IL, p. A185
EDWARD HOSPITAL, NAPERVILLE, IL, p. A189
EDWARD JOHN NOBLE HOSPITAL OF GOUVERNEUR, GOUVERNEUR, NY, p. A426
EDWARD WHITE HOSPITAL, SAINT PETERSBURG, FL, p. A139
EDWARDS COUNTY HOSPITAL AND HEALTHCARE CENTER, KINSLEY, KS, p. A237
EDWIN SHAW REHAB, CUYAHOGA FALLS, OH, p. A479
EFFINGHAM HOSPITAL, SPRINGFIELD, GA, p. A160
EINSTEIN MEDICAL CENTER ELKINS PARK, ELKINS PARK, PENNSYLVANIA (see EINSTEIN MEDICAL CENTER PHILADELPHIA), p. A534
EINSTEIN MEDICAL CENTER MONTGOMERY, EAST NORRITON, PA, p. A524
EINSTEIN MEDICAL CENTER PHILADELPHIA, PHILADELPHIA, PA, p. A534
EISENHOWER MEDICAL CENTER, RANCHO MIRAGE, CA, p. A81
EL CAMINO HOSPITAL, MOUNTAIN VIEW, CA, p. A75
EL CAMINO HOSPITAL LOS GATOS, LOS GATOS, CALIFORNIA (see EL CAMINO HOSPITAL), p. A75
EL CAMPO MEMORIAL HOSPITAL, EL CAMPO, TX, p. A600
EL CENTRO REGIONAL MEDICAL CENTER, EL CENTRO, CA, p. A59
EL PASO CHILDREN'S HOSPITAL, EL PASO, TX, p. A601
EL PASO LTAC HOSPITAL, EL PASO, TX, p. A601
EL PASO PSYCHIATRIC CENTER, EL PASO, TX, p. A601
EL PASO SPECIALTY HOSPITAL, EL PASO, TX, p. A601
ELBERT MEMORIAL HOSPITAL, ELBERTON, GA, p. A153
ELEANOR SLATER HOSPITAL, CRANSTON, RI, p. A546
ELECTRA MEMORIAL HOSPITAL, ELECTRA, TX, p. A602
ELGIN MENTAL HEALTH CENTER, ELGIN, IL, p. A181
ELIZA COFFEE MEMORIAL HOSPITAL, FLORENCE, AL, p. A20
ELIZABETHTOWN COMMUNITY HOSPITAL, ELIZABETHTOWN, NY, p. A425
ELK REGIONAL HEALTH CENTER, SAINT MARYS, PA, p. A540
ELKHART GENERAL HEALTHCARE SYSTEM, ELKHART, IN, p. A201
ELKHORN VALLEY REHABILITATION HOSPITAL, CASPER, WY, p. A701
ELKS REHAB HOSPITAL, BOISE, ID, p. A167
ELKVIEW GENERAL HOSPITAL, HOBART, OK, p. A499
ELLENVILLE REGIONAL HOSPITAL, ELLENVILLE, NY, p. A425
ELLETT MEMORIAL HOSPITAL, APPLETON CITY, MO, p. A356
ELLINWOOD DISTRICT HOSPITAL, ELLINWOOD, KS, p. A233
ELLIOT HOSPITAL, MANCHESTER, NH, p. A399
ELLIS FISCHEL CANCER CENTER, COLUMBIA, MISSOURI (see UNIVERSITY OF MISSOURI HOSPITALS AND CLINICS), p. A359
ELLIS HOSPITAL, SCHENECTADY, NY, p. A442
ELLIS HOSPITAL HEALTH CENTER, SCHENECTADY, NEW YORK (see ELLIS HOSPITAL), p. A442
ELLSWORTH COUNTY MEDICAL CENTER, ELLSWORTH, KS, p. A233
ELLSWORTH MUNICIPAL HOSPITAL, IOWA FALLS, IA, p. A223
ELLWOOD CITY HOSPITAL, ELLWOOD CITY, PA, p. A525
ELMHURST HOSPITAL CENTER,, NY, p. A431
ELMHURST MEMORIAL HOSPITAL,, IL, p. A182
ELMIRA PSYCHIATRIC CENTER, ELMIRA, NY, p. A425
ELMORE COMMUNITY HOSPITAL, WETUMPKA, AL, p. A26
ELY-BLOOMENSON COMMUNITY HOSPITAL, ELY, MN, p. A332
EMANUEL MEDICAL CENTER, TURLOCK, CA, p. A93
EMANUEL MEDICAL CENTER, SWAINSBORO, GA, p. A161
EMERALD COAST BEHAVIORAL HOSPITAL, PANAMA CITY, FL, p. A136
EMERALD-HODGSON HOSPITAL, SEWANEE, TENNESSEE (see SOUTHERN TENNESSEE MEDICAL CENTER), p. A580
EMERSON HOSPITAL, CONCORD, MA, p. A299
EMERUS, SUGAR LAND, TX, p. A635
EMH ELYRIA MEDICAL CENTER, ELYRIA, OH, p. A481
EMMA PENDLETON BRADLEY HOSPITAL, EAST PROVIDENCE, RI, p. A546
EMORY JOHNS CREEK HOSPITAL, JOHNS CREEK, GA, p. A155
EMORY UNIVERSITY HOSPITAL, ATLANTA, GA, p. A146
EMORY UNIVERSITY HOSPITAL MIDTOWN, ATLANTA, GA, p. A146

EMORY UNIVERSITY ORTHOPAEDIC AND SPINE HOSPITAL, TUCKER, GEORGIA (see EMORY UNIVERSITY HOSPITAL), p. A146
EMORY-ADVENTIST HOSPITAL, SMYRNA, GA, p. A160
ENCINO HOSPITAL MEDICAL CENTER,, CA, p. A68
ENDLESS MOUNTAIN HEALTH SYSTEMS, MONTROSE, PA, p. A532
ENGLEWOOD COMMUNITY HOSPITAL, ENGLEWOOD, FL, p. A123
ENGLEWOOD HOSPITAL AND MEDICAL CENTER, ENGLEWOOD, NJ, p. A404
ENLOE MEDICAL CENTER, CHICO, CA, p. A56
ENLOE MEDICAL CENTER-COHASSET, CHICO, CALIFORNIA (see ENLOE MEDICAL CENTER), p. A56
ENNIS REGIONAL MEDICAL CENTER, ENNIS, TX, p. A602
EPHRAIM MCDOWELL FORT LOGAN HOSPITAL, STANFORD, KY, p. A260
EPHRAIM MCDOWELL REGIONAL MEDICAL CENTER, DANVILLE, KY, p. A250
EPHRATA COMMUNITY HOSPITAL, EPHRATA, PA, p. A525
EPIC MEDICAL CENTER, EUFAULA, OK, p. A498
ERIE COUNTY MEDICAL CENTER, BUFFALO, NY, p. A422
ERIE VETERANS AFFAIRS MEDICAL CENTER, ERIE, PA, p. A525
ERIK AND MARGARET JONSSON HOSPITAL, DALLAS, TEXAS (see BAYLOR UNIVERSITY MEDICAL CENTER), p. A595
ERLANGER AT HUTCHESON, FORT OGLETHORPE, GA, p. A154
ERLANGER BLEDSOE HOSPITAL, PIKEVILLE, TN, p. A578
ERLANGER EAST HOSPITAL, CHATTANOOGA, TENNESSEE (see ERLANGER MEDICAL CENTER), p. A566
ERLANGER MEDICAL CENTER, CHATTANOOGA, TN, p. A566
ERLANGER NORTH HOSPITAL, CHATTANOOGA, TENNESSEE (see ERLANGER MEDICAL CENTER), p. A566
ESPANOLA HOSPITAL, ESPANOLA, NM, p. A416
ESSENTIA HEALTH ADA, ADA, MN, p. A328
ESSENTIA HEALTH DULUTH, DULUTH, MN, p. A331
ESSENTIA HEALTH FARGO, FARGO, ND, p. A466
ESSENTIA HEALTH FOSSTON, FOSSTON, MN, p. A332
ESSENTIA HEALTH NORTHERN PINES, AURORA, MN, p. A328
ESSENTIA HEALTH SANDSTONE, SANDSTONE, MN, p. A340
ESSENTIA HEALTH ST. JOSEPH'S MEDICAL CENTER, BRAINERD, MN, p. A329
ESSENTIA HEALTH ST. MARY'S HOSPITAL – DETROIT LAKES, DETROIT LAKES, MN, p. A331
ESSENTIA HEALTH ST. MARY'S HOSPITAL OF SUPERIOR, SUPERIOR, WI, p. A697
ESSENTIA HEALTH ST. MARY'S MEDICAL CENTER, DULUTH, MN, p. A331
ESSENTIA HEALTH-DEER RIVER, DEER RIVER, MN, p. A331
ESSENTIA HEALTH-HOLY TRINITY HOSPITAL, GRACEVILLE, MN, p. A333
ESSENTIA HEALTH-VIRGINIA, VIRGINIA, MN, p. A342
ESSEX COUNTY HOSPITAL CENTER, CEDAR GROVE, NJ, p. A402
ESTES PARK MEDICAL CENTER, ESTES PARK, CO, p. A101
ETHICUS HOSPITAL – GRAPEVINE, GRAPEVINE, TX, p. A607
EUCLID HOSPITAL, EUCLID, OH, p. A481
EUNICE EXTENDED CARE HOSPITAL, EUNICE, LOUISIANA (see LOUISIANA EXTENDED CARE HOSPITAL OF LAFAYETTE), p. A271
EUREKA COMMUNITY HEALTH SERVICES AVERA, EUREKA, SD, p. A559
EUREKA SPRINGS HOSPITAL, EUREKA SPRINGS, AR, p. A43
EVANGELICAL COMMUNITY HOSPITAL, LEWISBURG, PA, p. A530
EVANGELINE EXTENDED CARE HOSPITAL-MAMOU, MAMOU, LOUISIANA (see ST. LANDRY EXTENDED CARE HOSPITAL), p. A276
EVANS MEMORIAL HOSPITAL, CLAXTON, GA, p. A150
EVANS U. S. ARMY COMMUNITY HOSPITAL, FORT CARSON, CO, p. A101
EVANSTON REGIONAL HOSPITAL, EVANSTON, WY, p. A702
EVANSVILLE PSYCHIATRIC CHILDREN CENTER, EVANSVILLE, IN, p. A202
EVANSVILLE STATE HOSPITAL, EVANSVILLE, IN, p. A202
EVENDALE MEDICAL CENTER, CINCINNATI, OH, p. A474
EVERETT TOWER, OKLAHOMA CITY, OKLAHOMA (see OU MEDICAL CENTER), p. A504
EVERGREEN MEDICAL CENTER, EVERGREEN, AL, p. A20
EVERGREENHEALTH, KIRKLAND, WA, p. A667
EXCELA FRICK HOSPITAL, MOUNT PLEASANT, PA, p. A532
EXCELA HEALTH WESTMORELAND HOSPITAL, GREENSBURG, PA, p. A526
EXCELA LATROBE AREA HOSPITAL, LATROBE, PA, p. A529
EXCELSIOR SPRINGS HOSPITAL, EXCELSIOR SPRINGS, MO, p. A360
EXEMPLA GOOD SAMARITAN MEDICAL CENTER, LAFAYETTE, CO, p. A103
EXEMPLA LUTHERAN MEDICAL CENTER, WHEAT RIDGE, CO, p. A107
EXEMPLA SAINT JOSEPH HOSPITAL, DENVER, CO, p. A99

EXEMPLA WEST PINES, WHEAT RIDGE, COLORADO (see EXEMPLA LUTHERAN MEDICAL CENTER), p. A107
EXETER HOSPITAL, EXETER, NH, p. A398
EXTENDED CARE OF SOUTHWEST LOUISIANA, LAKE CHARLES, LA, p. A272
EYE AND EAR CLINIC OF CHARLESTON, CHARLESTON, WV, p. A676
EYE AND EAR HOSPITAL OF PITTSBURGH, PITTSBURGH, PENNSYLVANIA (see UPMC PRESBYTERIAN SHADYSIDE), p. A538

# F

F. F. THOMPSON HOSPITAL, CANANDAIGUA, NY, p. A423
F. W. HUSTON MEDICAL CENTER, WINCHESTER, KS, p. A247
FAIR OAKS (see GREENVILLE REGIONAL HOSPITAL), p. A184
FAIR OAKS PAVILION, DELRAY BEACH, FLORIDA (see DELRAY MEDICAL CENTER), p. A122
FAIRBANKS, INDIANAPOLIS, IN, p. A205
FAIRBANKS MEMORIAL HOSPITAL, FAIRBANKS, AK, p. A28
FAIRCHILD MEDICAL CENTER, YREKA, CA, p. A96
FAIRFAX COMMUNITY HOSPITAL, FAIRFAX, OK, p. A498
FAIRFAX HOSPITAL, KIRKLAND, WA, p. A667
FAIRFIELD MEDICAL CENTER, LANCASTER, OH, p. A483
FAIRFIELD MEMORIAL HOSPITAL, FAIRFIELD, IL, p. A182
FAIRFIELD MEMORIAL HOSPITAL, WINNSBORO, SC, p. A557
FAIRLAWN REHABILITATION HOSPITAL, WORCESTER, MA, p. A306
FAIRMONT GENERAL HOSPITAL, FAIRMONT, WV, p. A676
FAIRMOUNT BEHAVIORAL HEALTH SYSTEM, PHILADELPHIA, PA, p. A534
FAIRVIEW HOSPITAL, GREAT BARRINGTON, MA, p. A300
FAIRVIEW HOSPITAL, CLEVELAND, OH, p. A476
FAIRVIEW LAKES HEALTH SERVICES, WYOMING, MN, p. A343
FAIRVIEW NORTHLAND MEDICAL CENTER, PRINCETON, MN, p. A338
FAIRVIEW PARK HOSPITAL, DUBLIN, GA, p. A152
FAIRVIEW REGIONAL MEDICAL CENTER, FAIRVIEW, OK, p. A499
FAIRVIEW RIDGES HOSPITAL, BURNSVILLE, MN, p. A330
FAIRVIEW RIVERSIDE HOSPITAL, MINNEAPOLIS, MINNESOTA (see UNIVERSITY OF MINNESOTA MEDICAL CENTER, FAIRVIEW), p. A336
FAIRVIEW SOUTHDALE HOSPITAL, EDINA, MN, p. A332
FAIRWAY MEDICAL CENTER, COVINGTON, LA, p. A265
FAITH COMMUNITY HOSPITAL, JACKSBORO, TX, p. A615
FAITH REGIONAL HEALTH SERVICES, NORFOLK, NE, p. A386
FALL RIVER HOSPITAL, HOT SPRINGS, SD, p. A560
FALLBROOK HOSPITAL, FALLBROOK, CA, p. A60
FALLON MEDICAL COMPLEX, BAKER, MT, p. A374
FALLS COMMUNITY HOSPITAL AND CLINIC, MARLIN, TX, p. A621
FALMOUTH HOSPITAL, FALMOUTH, MA, p. A300
FAMILY HEALTH WEST, FRUITA, CO, p. A101
FANNIN REGIONAL HOSPITAL, BLUE RIDGE, GA, p. A148
FANNY ALLEN CAMPUS, COLCHESTER, VERMONT (see FLETCHER ALLEN HEALTH CARE), p. A649
FARGO VETERANS AFFAIRS HEALTH CARE SYSTEM, FARGO, ND, p. A466
FAULKTON AREA MEDICAL CENTER, FAULKTON, SD, p. A559
FAUQUIER HOSPITAL, WARRENTON, VA, p. A662
FAWCETT MEMORIAL HOSPITAL, PORT CHARLOTTE, FL, p. A137
FAXTON CAMPUS, UTICA, NEW YORK (see FAXTON–ST. LUKE'S HEALTHCARE), p. A444
FAXTON–ST. LUKE'S HEALTHCARE, UTICA, NY, p. A444
FAYETTE COUNTY HOSPITAL, VANDALIA, IL, p. A196
FAYETTE COUNTY MEMORIAL HOSPITAL, WASHINGTON COURT HOUSE, OH, p. A492
FAYETTE MEDICAL CENTER, FAYETTE, AL, p. A20
FAYETTE REGIONAL HEALTH SYSTEM, CONNERSVILLE, IN, p. A200
FAYETTEVILLE VETERANS AFFAIRS MEDICAL CENTER, FAYETTEVILLE, NC, p. A452
FEATHER RIVER HOSPITAL, PARADISE, CA, p. A79
FEDERAL CORRECTIONAL INSTITUTE HOSPITAL, LITTLETON, CO, p. A103
FEDERAL MEDICAL CENTER, LEXINGTON, KY, p. A254
FERRELL HOSPITAL, ELDORADO, IL, p. A181
FERRY COUNTY MEMORIAL HOSPITAL, REPUBLIC, WA, p. A670
FHN MEMORIAL HOSPITAL, FREEPORT, IL, p. A183
FIELD MEMORIAL COMMUNITY HOSPITAL, CENTREVILLE, MS, p. A345
FIELDSTONE CENTER, BATTLE CREEK, MICHIGAN (see BRONSON BATTLE CREEK), p. A309
FILLMORE COMMUNITY MEDICAL CENTER, FILLMORE, UT, p. A643
FILLMORE COUNTY HOSPITAL, GENEVA, NE, p. A383

FIRELANDS REGIONAL HEALTH SYSTEM, SANDUSKY, OH, p. A489
FIRELANDS REGIONAL MEDICAL CENTER – MAIN CAMPUS, SANDUSKY, OHIO (see FIRELANDS REGIONAL HEALTH SYSTEM), p. A489
FIRELANDS REGIONAL MEDICAL CENTER SOUTH CAMPUS, SANDUSKY, OHIO (see FIRELANDS REGIONAL HEALTH SYSTEM), p. A489
FIRST CARE HEALTH CENTER, PARK RIVER, ND, p. A469
FIRST HOSPITAL PANAMERICANO, CIDRA, PR, p. A706
FIRST HOSPITAL WYOMING VALLEY, KINGSTON, PA, p. A528
FIRST STREET HOSPITAL, BELLAIRE, TX, p. A588
FIRSTHEALTH MONTGOMERY MEMORIAL HOSPITAL, TROY, NC, p. A462
FIRSTHEALTH MOORE REGIONAL HOSPITAL, PINEHURST, NC, p. A458
FIRSTHEALTH RICHMOND MEMORIAL HOSPITAL, ROCKINGHAM, NC, p. A459
FIRSTLIGHT HEALTH SYSTEM, MORA, MN, p. A337
FISHER COUNTY HOSPITAL DISTRICT, ROTAN, TX, p. A629
FISHER–TITUS MEDICAL CENTER, NORWALK, OH, p. A487
FISHERMEN'S HOSPITAL, MARATHON, FL, p. A129
FITZGIBBON HOSPITAL, MARSHALL, MO, p. A365
FIVE RIVERS MEDICAL CENTER, POCAHONTAS, AR, p. A49
FLAGET MEMORIAL HOSPITAL, BARDSTOWN, KY, p. A248
FLAGLER HOSPITAL, SAINT AUGUSTINE, FL, p. A138
FLAGSTAFF MEDICAL CENTER, FLAGSTAFF, AZ, p. A31
FLAMBEAU HOSPITAL, PARK FALLS, WI, p. A694
FLEMING COUNTY HOSPITAL, FLEMINGSBURG, KY, p. A250
FLETCHER ALLEN HEALTH CARE, BURLINGTON, VT, p. A649
FLINT RIVER COMMUNITY HOSPITAL, MONTEZUMA, GA, p. A157
FLORALA MEMORIAL HOSPITAL, FLORALA, AL, p. A20
FLORENCE HOSPITAL AT ANTHEM, FLORENCE, AZ, p. A31
FLORIDA HOSPITAL, ORLANDO, FL, p. A135
FLORIDA HOSPITAL AT CONNERTON LONG TERM ACUTE CARE, LAND O'LAKES, FL, p. A128
FLORIDA HOSPITAL CELEBRATION HEALTH, CELEBRATION, FLORIDA (see FLORIDA HOSPITAL), p. A135
FLORIDA HOSPITAL DELAND, DELAND, FL, p. A122
FLORIDA HOSPITAL EAST ORLANDO, ORLANDO, FLORIDA (see FLORIDA HOSPITAL), p. A135
FLORIDA HOSPITAL FISH MEMORIAL, ORANGE CITY, FL, p. A134
FLORIDA HOSPITAL HEARTLAND MEDICAL CENTER, SEBRING, FL, p. A140
FLORIDA HOSPITAL KISSIMMEE, KISSIMMEE, FLORIDA (see FLORIDA HOSPITAL), p. A135
FLORIDA HOSPITAL MEMORIAL MEDICAL CENTER, DAYTONA BEACH, FL, p. A122
FLORIDA HOSPITAL NORTH PINELLAS, TARPON SPRINGS, FL, p. A142
FLORIDA HOSPITAL TAMPA, TAMPA, FL, p. A141
FLORIDA HOSPITAL WATERMAN, TAVARES, FL, p. A142
FLORIDA HOSPITAL WAUCHULA, WAUCHULA, FL, p. A143
FLORIDA HOSPITAL WESLEY CHAPEL, WESLEY CHAPEL, FL, p. A143
FLORIDA HOSPITAL ZEPHYRHILLS, ZEPHYRHILLS, FL, p. A144
FLORIDA HOSPITAL–ALTAMONTE, ALTAMONTE SPRINGS, FLORIDA (see FLORIDA HOSPITAL), p. A135
FLORIDA HOSPITAL–APOPKA, APOPKA, FLORIDA (see FLORIDA HOSPITAL), p. A135
FLORIDA HOSPITAL–CARROLLWOOD, TAMPA, FL, p. A141
FLORIDA HOSPITAL–FLAGLER, PALM COAST, FL, p. A136
FLORIDA HOSPITAL–OCEANSIDE, ORMOND BEACH, FLORIDA (see FLORIDA HOSPITAL MEMORIAL MEDICAL CENTER), p. A122
FLORIDA STATE HOSPITAL, CHATTAHOOCHEE, FL, p. A120
FLOWERS HOSPITAL, DOTHAN, AL, p. A19
FLOYD COUNTY MEDICAL CENTER, CHARLES CITY, IA, p. A218
FLOYD MEDICAL CENTER, ROME, GA, p. A159
FLOYD MEMORIAL HOSPITAL AND HEALTH SERVICES, NEW ALBANY, IN, p. A211
FLOYD VALLEY HOSPITAL, LE MARS, IA, p. A224
FLUSHING HOSPITAL MEDICAL CENTER,, NY, p. A432
FOND DU LAC COUNTY MENTAL HEALTH CENTER, FOND DU LAC, WI, p. A686
FOOTHILL PRESBYTERIAN HOSPITAL, GLENDORA, CA, p. A63
FORBES REGIONAL HOSPITAL, MONROEVILLE, PA, p. A532
FOREST HEALTH MEDICAL CENTER, YPSILANTI, MI, p. A327
FOREST HILLS HOSPITAL,, NY, p. A432
FOREST PARK MEDICAL CENTER, DALLAS, TX, p. A596
FOREST PARK MEDICAL CENTER FRISCO, FRISCO, TX, p. A605
FOREST VIEW PSYCHIATRIC HOSPITAL, GRAND RAPIDS, MI, p. A314
FORKS COMMUNITY HOSPITAL, FORKS, WA, p. A666
FORREST CITY MEDICAL CENTER, FORREST CITY, AR, p. A44
FORREST GENERAL HOSPITAL, HATTIESBURG, MS, p. A347
FORT BELKNAP U. S. PUBLIC HEALTH SERVICE INDIAN HOSPITAL, HARLEM, MT, p. A377

FORT BELVOIR COMMUNITY HOSPITAL, FORT BELVOIR, VA, p. A654
FORT DEFIANCE INDIAN HEALTH SERVICE HOSPITAL, FORT DEFIANCE, AZ, p. A31
FORT DUNCAN REGIONAL MEDICAL CENTER, EAGLE PASS, TX, p. A600
FORT HAMILTON HOSPITAL, HAMILTON, OH, p. A483
FORT HEALTHCARE, FORT ATKINSON, WI, p. A686
FORT LAUDERDALE HOSPITAL, FORT LAUDERDALE, FL, p. A123
FORT LOUDOUN MEDICAL CENTER, LENOIR CITY, TN, p. A573
FORT MADISON COMMUNITY HOSPITAL, FORT MADISON, IA, p. A221
FORT SANDERS REGIONAL MEDICAL CENTER, KNOXVILLE, TN, p. A571
FORT WALTON BEACH MEDICAL CENTER, FORT WALTON BEACH, FL, p. A124
FORT WASHINGTON MEDICAL CENTER, FORT WASHINGTON, MD, p. A291
FOUNDATION SURGICAL HOSPITAL OF EL PASO, EL PASO, TX, p. A601
FOUNDATION SURGICAL HOSPITAL OF SAN ANTONIO, SAN ANTONIO, TX, p. A631
FOUNDATIONS BEHAVIORAL HEALTH, DOYLESTOWN, PA, p. A524
FOUNTAIN VALLEY REGIONAL HOSPITAL AND MEDICAL CENTER, FOUNTAIN VALLEY, CA, p. A60
FOUR COUNTY COUNSELING CENTER, LOGANSPORT, IN, p. A209
FOUR WINDS HOSPITAL, KATONAH, NY, p. A428
FOUR WINDS HOSPITAL, SARATOGA SPRINGS, NY, p. A442
FOX CHASE CANCER CENTER–AMERICAN ONCOLOGIC HOSPITAL, PHILADELPHIA, PA, p. A534
FRAMINGHAM UNION HOSPITAL, FRAMINGHAM, MASSACHUSETTS (see METROWEST MEDICAL CENTER), p. A300
FRANCES MAHON DEACONESS HOSPITAL, GLASGOW, MT, p. A376
FRANCISCAN HOSPITAL FOR CHILDREN, BOSTON, MA, p. A296
FRANCISCAN PHYSICIANS HOSPITAL, MUNSTER, IN, p. A211
FRANCISCAN ST. ANTHONY HEALTH – CROWN POINT, CROWN POINT, IN, p. A201
FRANCISCAN ST. ANTHONY HEALTH – MICHIGAN CITY, MICHIGAN CITY, IN, p. A210
FRANCISCAN ST. ELIZABETH HEALTH – CRAWFORDSVILLE, CRAWFORDSVILLE, IN, p. A200
FRANCISCAN ST. ELIZABETH HEALTH – LAFAYETTE CENTRAL, LAFAYETTE, IN, p. A208
FRANCISCAN ST. ELIZABETH HEALTH – LAFAYETTE EAST, LAFAYETTE, IN, p. A208
FRANCISCAN ST. FRANCIS HEALTH – INDIANAPOLIS, INDIANAPOLIS, IN, p. A205
FRANCISCAN ST. FRANCIS HEALTH – MOORESVILLE, MOORESVILLE, IN, p. A210
FRANCISCAN ST. FRANCIS HEALTH–CARMEL, CARMEL, IN, p. A199
FRANCISCAN ST. JAMES HOSPITAL AND HEALTH CENTERS, OLYMPIA FIELDS, IL, p. A191
FRANCISCAN ST. MARGARET HEALTH – DYER, DYER, INDIANA (see FRANCISCAN ST. MARGARET HEALTH – HAMMOND), p. A204
FRANCISCAN ST. MARGARET HEALTH – HAMMOND, HAMMOND, IN, p. A204
FRANK R. HOWARD MEMORIAL HOSPITAL, WILLITS, CA, p. A96
FRANKFORD CAMPUS, PHILADELPHIA, PENNSYLVANIA (see ARIA HEALTH), p. A534
FRANKFORT REGIONAL MEDICAL CENTER, FRANKFORT, KY, p. A251
FRANKLIN COUNTY MEDICAL CENTER, PRESTON, ID, p. A171
FRANKLIN COUNTY MEMORIAL HOSPITAL, MEADVILLE, MS, p. A350
FRANKLIN COUNTY MEMORIAL HOSPITAL, FRANKLIN, NE, p. A383
FRANKLIN FOUNDATION HOSPITAL, FRANKLIN, LA, p. A267
FRANKLIN GENERAL HOSPITAL, HAMPTON, IA, p. A222
FRANKLIN HOSPITAL, VALLEY STREAM, NY, p. A445
FRANKLIN HOSPITAL DISTRICT, BENTON, IL, p. A174
FRANKLIN MEDICAL CENTER, WINNSBORO, LA, p. A280
FRANKLIN MEMORIAL HOSPITAL, FARMINGTON, ME, p. A283
FRANKLIN REGIONAL HOSPITAL, FRANKLIN, NH, p. A398
FRANKLIN WOODS COMMUNITY HOSPITAL, JOHNSON CITY, TN, p. A571
FRAZIER REHAB INSTITUTE, LOUISVILLE, KY, p. A255
FREDERICK MEMORIAL HOSPITAL, FREDERICK, MD, p. A291
FREDONIA REGIONAL HOSPITAL, FREDONIA, KS, p. A234
FREEMAN HOSPITAL EAST, JOPLIN, MISSOURI (see FREEMAN HOSPITAL WEST), p. A362
FREEMAN HOSPITAL WEST, JOPLIN, MO, p. A362
FREEMAN NEOSHO HOSPITAL, NEOSHO, MO, p. A366
FREEMAN REGIONAL HEALTH SERVICES, FREEMAN, SD, p. A560

# G

GRANITE FALLS MUNICIPAL HOSPITAL AND MANOR, GRANITE FALLS, MN, p. A333
GRANT MEMORIAL HOSPITAL, PETERSBURG, WV, p. A679
GRANT REGIONAL HEALTH CENTER, LANCASTER, WI, p. A689
GRANT–BLACKFORD MENTAL HEALTH CENTER, MARION, IN, p. A209
GRANVILLE HEALTH SYSTEM, OXFORD, NC, p. A458
GRAYS HARBOR COMMUNITY HOSPITAL, ABERDEEN, WA, p. A664
GREAT BEND REGIONAL HOSPITAL, GREAT BEND, KS, p. A234
GREAT FALLS CLINIC MEDICAL CENTER, GREAT FALLS, MT, p. A376
GREAT LAKES SPECIALTY HOSPITAL–GRAND RAPIDS CAMPUS, GRAND RAPIDS, MI, p. A315
GREAT LAKES SPECIALTY HOSPITAL–MUSKEGON, MUSKEGON, MI, p. A320
GREAT PLAINS REGIONAL MEDICAL CENTER, NORTH PLATTE, NE, p. A386
GREAT PLAINS REGIONAL MEDICAL CENTER, ELK CITY, OK, p. A498
GREAT RIVER MEDICAL CENTER, BLYTHEVILLE, AR, p. A41
GREAT RIVER MEDICAL CENTER, WEST BURLINGTON, IA, p. A230
GREATER BALTIMORE MEDICAL CENTER, BALTIMORE, MD, p. A287
GREATER BINGHAMTON HEALTH CENTER, BINGHAMTON, NY, p. A421
GREATER EL MONTE COMMUNITY HOSPITAL, SOUTH EL MONTE, CA, p. A91
GREATER REGIONAL MEDICAL CENTER, CRESTON, IA, p. A219
GREELEY COUNTY HEALTH SERVICES, TRIBUNE, KS, p. A245
GREEN CLINIC SURGICAL HOSPITAL, RUSTON, LA, p. A277
GREEN OAKS HOSPITAL, DALLAS, TX, p. A596
GREENBRIAR REHABILITATION HOSPITAL, BOARDMAN, OH, p. A472
GREENBRIER HOSPITAL, COVINGTON, LA, p. A265
GREENBRIER VALLEY MEDICAL CENTER, RONCEVERTE, WV, p. A680
GREENE COUNTY GENERAL HOSPITAL, LINTON, IN, p. A209
GREENE COUNTY HOSPITAL, EUTAW, AL, p. A19
GREENE COUNTY HOSPITAL, LEAKESVILLE, MS, p. A349
GREENE COUNTY MEDICAL CENTER, JEFFERSON, IA, p. A223
GREENE MEMORIAL HOSPITAL, XENIA, OH, p. A494
GREENLEAF CENTER, VALDOSTA, GEORGIA (see SOUTH GEORGIA MEDICAL CENTER), p. A162
GREENVILLE CAMPUS, GREENVILLE, PENNSYLVANIA (see UPMC HORIZON), p. A526
GREENVILLE HEALTH SYSTEM LAURENS COUNTY MEMORIAL HOSPITAL, CLINTON, SC, p. A550
GREENVILLE MEMORIAL HOSPITAL, GREENVILLE, SC, p. A552
GREENVILLE REGIONAL HOSPITAL, GREENVILLE, IL, p. A184
GREENWICH HOSPITAL, GREENWICH, CT, p. A109
GREENWOOD COUNTY HOSPITAL, EUREKA, KS, p. A233
GREENWOOD LEFLORE HOSPITAL, GREENWOOD, MS, p. A347
GREENWOOD REGIONAL REHABILITATION HOSPITAL, GREENWOOD, SC, p. A553
GREER MEMORIAL HOSPITAL, GREER, SC, p. A553
GRENADA LAKE MEDICAL CENTER, GRENADA, MS, p. A347
GREYSTONE PARK PSYCHIATRIC HOSPITAL, MORRIS PLAINS, NJ, p. A406
GRIFFIN HOSPITAL, DERBY, CT, p. A108
GRIFFIN MEMORIAL HOSPITAL, NORMAN, OK, p. A502
GRIMES ST. JOSEPH HEALTH CENTER, NAVASOTA, TX, p. A624
GRINNELL REGIONAL MEDICAL CENTER, GRINNELL, IA, p. A222
GRISELL MEMORIAL HOSPITAL DISTRICT ONE, RANSOM, KS, p. A243
GRITMAN MEDICAL CENTER, MOSCOW, ID, p. A170
GROUP HEALTH COOPERATIVE CENTRAL HOSPITAL, SEATTLE, WA, p. A670
GROVE CITY MEDICAL CENTER, GROVE CITY, PA, p. A526
GROVE HILL MEMORIAL HOSPITAL, GROVE HILL, AL, p. A21
GROVER C. DILS MEDICAL CENTER, CALIENTE, NV, p. A391
GROVER M. HERMAN HOSPITAL, CALLICOON, NY, p. A423
GRUNDY COUNTY MEMORIAL HOSPITAL, GRUNDY CENTER, IA, p. A222
GUADALUPE COUNTY HOSPITAL, SANTA ROSA, NM, p. A418
GUADALUPE REGIONAL MEDICAL CENTER, SEGUIN, TX, p. A633
GUAM MEMORIAL HOSPITAL AUTHORITY, TAMUNING, GU, p. A705
GUIDANCE CENTER, FLAGSTAFF, AZ, p. A31
GULF BREEZE HOSPITAL, GULF BREEZE, FL, p. A125
GULF COAST MEDICAL CENTER, FORT MYERS, FL, p. A124
GULF COAST MEDICAL CENTER, PANAMA CITY, FL, p. A136
GULF COAST MEDICAL CENTER, WHARTON, TX, p. A641
GUNDERSEN LUTHERAN MEDICAL CENTER, LA CROSSE, WI, p. A689
GUNDERSEN TRI–COUNTY HOSPITAL AND CLINICS, WHITEHALL, WI, p. A699
GUNNISON VALLEY HOSPITAL, GUNNISON, CO, p. A102

GUNNISON VALLEY HOSPITAL, GUNNISON, UT, p. A643
GUTHRIE COUNTY HOSPITAL, GUTHRIE CENTER, IA, p. A222
GUTTENBERG MUNICIPAL HOSPITAL, GUTTENBERG, IA, p. A222
GWINNETT HOSPITAL SYSTEM, LAWRENCEVILLE, GA, p. A156
GWINNETT MEDICAL CENTER, LAWRENCEVILLE, GEORGIA (see GWINNETT HOSPITAL SYSTEM), p. A156
GWINNETT MEDICAL CENTER–DULUTH, DULUTH, GEORGIA (see GWINNETT HOSPITAL SYSTEM), p. A156

# H

H. C. WATKINS MEMORIAL HOSPITAL, QUITMAN, MS, p. A353
H. DOUGLAS SINGER MENTAL HEALTH AND DEVELOPMENTAL CENTER, ROCKFORD, IL, p. A193
H. LEE MOFFITT CANCER CENTER AND RESEARCH INSTITUTE, TAMPA, FL, p. A141
H.S.C. MEDICAL CENTER, MALVERN, AR, p. A47
HABERSHAM MEDICAL CENTER, DEMOREST, GA, p. A152
HACKENSACK UNIVERSITY MEDICAL CENTER, HACKENSACK, NJ, p. A404
HACKENSACK UNIVERSITY MEDICAL CENTER AT PASCACK VALLEY, WESTWOOD, NJ, p. A412
HACKENSACK UNIVERSITY MEDICAL CENTER MOUNTAINSIDE, MONTCLAIR, NJ, p. A406
HACKETTSTOWN REGIONAL MEDICAL CENTER, HACKETTSTOWN, NJ, p. A404
HAHNEMANN CAMPUS, WORCESTER, MASSACHUSETTS (see UMASS MEMORIAL MEDICAL CENTER), p. A307
HAHNEMANN UNIVERSITY HOSPITAL, PHILADELPHIA, PA, p. A535
HALE COUNTY HOSPITAL, GREENSBORO, AL, p. A21
HALE HO'OLA HAMAKUA, HONOKAA, HI, p. A164
HALIFAX BEHAVIORAL SERVICES, DAYTONA BEACH, FLORIDA (see HALIFAX HEALTH MEDICAL CENTER OF DAYTONA BEACH), p. A122
HALIFAX HEALTH MEDICAL CENTER OF DAYTONA BEACH, DAYTONA BEACH, FL, p. A122
HALIFAX HEALTH MEDICAL CENTER OF PORT ORANGE, PORT ORANGE, FLORIDA (see HALIFAX HEALTH MEDICAL CENTER OF DAYTONA BEACH), p. A122
HALIFAX REGIONAL HEALTH SYSTEM, SOUTH BOSTON, VA, p. A661
HALIFAX REGIONAL MEDICAL CENTER, ROANOKE RAPIDS, NC, p. A459
HALLMARK HEALTH SYSTEM, MELROSE, MA, p. A302
HALLMARK YOUTHCARE – RICHMOND, RICHMOND, VA, p. A660
HAMILTON CENTER, TERRE HAUTE, IN, p. A213
HAMILTON COUNTY HOSPITAL, SYRACUSE, KS, p. A244
HAMILTON GENERAL HOSPITAL, HAMILTON, TX, p. A607
HAMILTON HOSPITAL, OLNEY, TX, p. A625
HAMILTON MEDICAL CENTER, DALTON, GA, p. A151
HAMILTON MEMORIAL HOSPITAL DISTRICT, MCLEANSBORO, IL, p. A188
HAMLIN MEMORIAL HOSPITAL, HAMLIN, TX, p. A607
HAMMOND–HENRY HOSPITAL, GENESEO, IL, p. A183
HAMPSHIRE MEMORIAL HOSPITAL, ROMNEY, WV, p. A680
HAMPSTEAD HOSPITAL, HAMPSTEAD, NH, p. A398
HAMPTON BEHAVIORAL HEALTH CENTER, WESTAMPTON, NJ, p. A412
HAMPTON REGIONAL MEDICAL CENTER, VARNVILLE, SC, p. A556
HAMPTON ROADS SPECIALTY HOSPITAL, NEWPORT NEWS, VA, p. A657
HAMPTON VETERANS AFFAIRS MEDICAL CENTER, HAMPTON, VA, p. A655
HANCOCK COUNTY HEALTH SYSTEM, BRITT, IA, p. A217
HANCOCK MEDICAL CENTER, BAY SAINT LOUIS, MS, p. A344
HANCOCK REGIONAL HOSPITAL, GREENFIELD, IN, p. A204
HANNIBAL REGIONAL HOSPITAL, HANNIBAL, MO, p. A361
HANOVER HOSPITAL, HANOVER, KS, p. A234
HANOVER HOSPITAL, HANOVER, PA, p. A526
HANSFORD HOSPITAL, SPEARMAN, TX, p. A634
HARBOR BEACH COMMUNITY HOSPITAL, HARBOR BEACH, MI, p. A316
HARBOR HOSPITAL OF SOUTHEAST TEXAS, BEAUMONT, TX, p. A587
HARBOR OAKS HOSPITAL, NEW BALTIMORE, MI, p. A321
HARDEMAN COUNTY MEMORIAL HOSPITAL, QUANAH, TX, p. A628
HARDIN COUNTY GENERAL HOSPITAL, ROSICLARE, IL, p. A194
HARDIN MEDICAL CENTER, SAVANNAH, TN, p. A578
HARDIN MEMORIAL HOSPITAL, ELIZABETHTOWN, KY, p. A250
HARDIN MEMORIAL HOSPITAL, KENTON, OH, p. A483
HARDTNER MEDICAL CENTER, OLLA, LA, p. A276
HARDY WILSON MEMORIAL HOSPITAL, HAZLEHURST, MS, p. A348

HARFORD MEMORIAL HOSPITAL, HAVRE DE GRACE, MD, p. A292
HARLAN ARH HOSPITAL, HARLAN, KY, p. A252
HARLAN COUNTY HEALTH SYSTEM, ALMA, NE, p. A381
HARLEM GENERAL CARE UNIT AND HARLEM PSYCHIATRIC UNIT (see HARLEM HOSPITAL CENTER), p. A432
HARLEM HOSPITAL CENTER, NEW YORK, NY, p. A432
HARLINGEN MEDICAL CENTER, HARLINGEN, TX, p. A607
HARMON MEDICAL AND REHABILITATION HOSPITAL, LAS VEGAS, NV, p. A392
HARMON MEMORIAL HOSPITAL, HOLLIS, OK, p. A500
HARNEY DISTRICT HOSPITAL, BURNS, OR, p. A511
HARPER COUNTY COMMUNITY HOSPITAL, BUFFALO, OK, p. A496
HARPER HOSPITAL DISTRICT FIVE, HARPER, KS, p. A235
HARPER UNIVERSITY HOSPITAL/HUTZEL WOMEN'S HOSPITAL, DETROIT, MI, p. A312
HARRINGTON MEMORIAL HOSPITAL, SOUTHBRIDGE, MA, p. A304
HARRIS HEALTH SYSTEM, HOUSTON, TX, p. A609
HARRIS HOSPITAL, NEWPORT, AR, p. A48
HARRIS METHODIST–SPRINGWOOD, BEDFORD, TEXAS (see TEXAS HEALTH HARRIS METHODIST HOSPITAL HURST–EULESS–BEDFORD), p. A588
HARRISBURG HOSPITAL, HARRISBURG, PENNSYLVANIA (see PINNACLE HEALTH SYSTEM), p. A527
HARRISBURG MEDICAL CENTER, HARRISBURG, IL, p. A184
HARRISON COMMUNITY HOSPITAL, CADIZ, OH, p. A472
HARRISON COUNTY COMMUNITY HOSPITAL, BETHANY, MO, p. A356
HARRISON COUNTY HOSPITAL, CORYDON, IN, p. A200
HARRISON MEDICAL CENTER, BREMERTON, WA, p. A664
HARRISON MEMORIAL HOSPITAL, CYNTHIANA, KY, p. A250
HARRY S. TRUMAN MEMORIAL VETERANS HOSPITAL, COLUMBIA, MO, p. A359
HARSHA BEHAVIORAL CENTER, TERRE HAUTE, IN, p. A214
HARTFORD HOSPITAL, HARTFORD, CT, p. A109
HARTGROVE HOSPITAL, CHICAGO, IL, p. A176
HARTNETT HEALTH SYSTEM, DUNN, NC, p. A451
HARTON REGIONAL MEDICAL CENTER, TULLAHOMA, TN, p. A580
HASBRO CHILDREN'S HOSPITAL, PROVIDENCE, RHODE ISLAND (see RHODE ISLAND HOSPITAL), p. A547
HASKELL COUNTY COMMUNITY HOSPITAL, STIGLER, OK, p. A507
HASKELL MEMORIAL HOSPITAL, HASKELL, TX, p. A608
HASTINGS REGIONAL CENTER, HASTINGS, NE, p. A384
HAVASU REGIONAL MEDICAL CENTER, LAKE HAVASU CITY, AZ, p. A32
HAVEN BEHAVIORAL HEALTH OF EASTERN PENNSYLVANIA, READING, PA, p. A539
HAVEN BEHAVIORAL SENIOR CARE OF NORTH DENVER, THORNTON, CO, p. A106
HAVEN BEHAVIORAL WAR HEROES HOSPITAL, PUEBLO, CO, p. A105
HAVEN SENIOR HORIZONS, PHOENIX, AZ, p. A34
HAVENWYCK HOSPITAL, AUBURN HILLS, MI, p. A308
HAWAII STATE HOSPITAL, KANEOHE, HI, p. A165
HAWARDEN REGIONAL HEALTHCARE, HAWARDEN, IA, p. A222
HAWTHORN CENTER, NORTHVILLE, MI, p. A321
HAWTHORN CHILDREN PSYCHIATRIC HOSPITAL, SAINT LOUIS, MO, p. A369
HAXTUN HOSPITAL DISTRICT, HAXTUN, CO, p. A102
HAYES GREEN BEACH MEMORIAL HOSPITAL, CHARLOTTE, MI, p. A310
HAYS MEDICAL CENTER, HAYS, KS, p. A235
HAYWARD AREA MEMORIAL HOSPITAL AND NURSING HOME, HAYWARD, WI, p. A688
HAYWOOD PARK COMMUNITY HOSPITAL, BROWNSVILLE, TN, p. A565
HAZARD ARH REGIONAL MEDICAL CENTER, HAZARD, KY, p. A252
HAZEL HAWKINS MEMORIAL HOSPITAL, HOLLISTER, CA, p. A64
HAZLETON GENERAL HOSPITAL, HAZLETON, PA, p. A527
HCMC DEPARTMENT OF PEDIATRICS, MINNEAPOLIS, MINNESOTA (see HENNEPIN COUNTY MEDICAL CENTER), p. A336
HEALDSBURG DISTRICT HOSPITAL, HEALDSBURG, CA, p. A64
HEALTH ALLIANCE HOSPITAL – BROADWAY CAMPUS, KINGSTON, NY, p. A428
HEALTH ALLIANCE HOSPITAL – MARY'S AVENUE CAMPUS, KINGSTON, NY, p. A428
HEALTH ALLIANCE HOSPITALS, LEOMINSTER, MA, p. A301
HEALTH CENTRAL, OCOEE, FL, p. A134
HEALTH FIRST CAPE CANAVERAL HOSPITAL, COCOA BEACH, FL, p. A121
HEALTH FIRST HOLMES REGIONAL MEDICAL CENTER, MELBOURNE, FL, p. A130
HEALTH FIRST PALM BAY HOSPITAL, MELBOURNE, FL, p. A130
HEALTH FIRST VIERA HOSPITAL, MELBOURNE, FL, p. A130

HEALTHBRIDGE CHILDREN'S HOSPITAL OF HOUSTON, HOUSTON, TX, p. A609

HEALTHBRIDGE CHILDRENS REHABILITATION HOSPITAL, ORANGE, CA, p. A78

HEALTHMARK REGIONAL MEDICAL CENTER, DEFUNIAK SPRINGS, FL, p. A122

HEALTHPARK, OWENSBORO, KENTUCKY (see OWENSBORO HEALTH REGIONAL HOSPITAL), p. A258

HEALTHPARK HOSPITAL, HOT SPRINGS NATIONAL PARK, ARKANSAS (see MERCY HOSPITAL HOT SPRINGS), p. A45

HEALTHPARK MEDICAL CENTER, FORT MYERS, FLORIDA (see LEE MEMORIAL HOSPITAL), p. A124

HEALTHSOURCE SAGINAW, SAGINAW, MI, p. A323

HEALTHSOUTH BAKERSFIELD REHABILITATION HOSPITAL, BAKERSFIELD, CA, p. A54

HEALTHSOUTH CANE CREEK REHABILITATION HOSPITAL, MARTIN, TN, p. A573

HEALTHSOUTH CHATTANOOGA REHABILITATION HOSPITAL, CHATTANOOGA, TN, p. A566

HEALTHSOUTH CHESAPEAKE REHABILITATION HOSPITAL, SALISBURY, MD, p. A294

HEALTHSOUTH DEACONESS REHABILITATION HOSPITAL, EVANSVILLE, IN, p. A202

HEALTHSOUTH DESERT CANYON REHABILITATION HOSPITAL, LAS VEGAS, NV, p. A392

HEALTHSOUTH EAST VALLEY REHABILITATION HOSPITAL, MESA, AZ, p. A33

HEALTHSOUTH EMERALD COAST REHABILITATION HOSPITAL, PANAMA CITY, FL, p. A136

HEALTHSOUTH HARMARVILLE REHABILITATION HOSPITAL, PITTSBURGH, PA, p. A537

HEALTHSOUTH HOSPITAL OF MANATI, MANATI, PR, p. A707

HEALTHSOUTH HUNTINGTON REHABILITATION HOSPITAL, HUNTINGTON, WV, p. A677

HEALTHSOUTH LAKESHORE REHABILITATION HOSPITAL, BIRMINGHAM, AL, p. A16

HEALTHSOUTH LAKEVIEW REHABILITATION HOSPITAL, ELIZABETHTOWN, KY, p. A250

HEALTHSOUTH MOUNTAINVIEW REGIONAL REHABILITATION HOSPITAL, MORGANTOWN, WV, p. A679

HEALTHSOUTH NITTANY VALLEY REHABILITATION HOSPITAL, PLEASANT GAP, PA, p. A539

HEALTHSOUTH NORTHERN KENTUCKY REHABILITATION HOSPITAL, EDGEWOOD, KY, p. A250

HEALTHSOUTH PLANO REHABILITATION HOSPITAL, PLANO, TX, p. A627

HEALTHSOUTH READING REHABILITATION HOSPITAL, READING, PA, p. A539

HEALTHSOUTH REHABILITATION HOSPITAL, DOTHAN, AL, p. A19

HEALTHSOUTH REHABILITATION HOSPITAL, FAYETTEVILLE, AR, p. A43

HEALTHSOUTH REHABILITATION HOSPITAL, LARGO, FL, p. A128

HEALTHSOUTH REHABILITATION HOSPITAL, CONCORD, NH, p. A397

HEALTHSOUTH REHABILITATION HOSPITAL, ALBUQUERQUE, NM, p. A414

HEALTHSOUTH REHABILITATION HOSPITAL, SEWICKLEY, PA, p. A541

HEALTHSOUTH REHABILITATION HOSPITAL, FLORENCE, SC, p. A551

HEALTHSOUTH REHABILITATION HOSPITAL, ROCK HILL, SC, p. A555

HEALTHSOUTH REHABILITATION HOSPITAL, KINGSPORT, TN, p. A571

HEALTHSOUTH REHABILITATION HOSPITAL, HUMBLE, TX, p. A614

HEALTHSOUTH REHABILITATION HOSPITAL – HENDERSON, HENDERSON, NV, p. A392

HEALTHSOUTH REHABILITATION HOSPITAL AT DRAKE, CINCINNATI, OH, p. A474

HEALTHSOUTH REHABILITATION HOSPITAL MEMPHIS–NORTH, MEMPHIS, TN, p. A574

HEALTHSOUTH REHABILITATION HOSPITAL MIDLAND–ODESSA, MIDLAND, TX, p. A623

HEALTHSOUTH REHABILITATION HOSPITAL OF ALEXANDRIA, ALEXANDRIA, LA, p. A262

HEALTHSOUTH REHABILITATION HOSPITAL OF ALTOONA, ALTOONA, PA, p. A519

HEALTHSOUTH REHABILITATION HOSPITAL OF ARLINGTON, ARLINGTON, TX, p. A583

HEALTHSOUTH REHABILITATION HOSPITAL OF AUSTIN, AUSTIN, TX, p. A585

HEALTHSOUTH REHABILITATION HOSPITAL OF BEAUMONT, BEAUMONT, TX, p. A587

HEALTHSOUTH REHABILITATION HOSPITAL OF CHARLESTON, CHARLESTON, SC, p. A549

HEALTHSOUTH REHABILITATION HOSPITAL OF COLORADO SPRINGS, COLORADO SPRINGS, CO, p. A98

HEALTHSOUTH REHABILITATION HOSPITAL OF COLUMBIA, COLUMBIA, SC, p. A550

HEALTHSOUTH REHABILITATION HOSPITAL OF CYPRESS, HOUSTON, TX, p. A610

HEALTHSOUTH REHABILITATION HOSPITAL OF ERIE, ERIE, PA, p. A525

HEALTHSOUTH REHABILITATION HOSPITAL OF FORT SMITH, FORT SMITH, AR, p. A44

HEALTHSOUTH REHABILITATION HOSPITAL OF FORT WORTH, FORT WORTH, TX, p. A603

HEALTHSOUTH REHABILITATION HOSPITAL OF FREDERICKSBURG, FREDERICKSBURG, VA, p. A654

HEALTHSOUTH REHABILITATION HOSPITAL OF JONESBORO, JONESBORO, AR, p. A45

HEALTHSOUTH REHABILITATION HOSPITAL OF MECHANICSBURG, MECHANICSBURG, PA, p. A531

HEALTHSOUTH REHABILITATION HOSPITAL OF MEMPHIS, MEMPHIS, TN, p. A574

HEALTHSOUTH REHABILITATION HOSPITAL OF MIAMI, MIAMI, FL, p. A131

HEALTHSOUTH REHABILITATION HOSPITAL OF MONTGOMERY, MONTGOMERY, AL, p. A23

HEALTHSOUTH REHABILITATION HOSPITAL OF NORTH ALABAMA, HUNTSVILLE, AL, p. A21

HEALTHSOUTH REHABILITATION HOSPITAL OF NORTH HOUSTON, CONROE, TX, p. A593

HEALTHSOUTH REHABILITATION HOSPITAL OF NORTHERN VIRGINIA, ALDIE, VA, p. A651

HEALTHSOUTH REHABILITATION HOSPITAL OF OCALA, OCALA, FL, p. A134

HEALTHSOUTH REHABILITATION HOSPITAL OF PETERSBURG, PETERSBURG, VA, p. A659

HEALTHSOUTH REHABILITATION HOSPITAL OF SARASOTA, SARASOTA, FL, p. A139

HEALTHSOUTH REHABILITATION HOSPITAL OF SOUTHERN ARIZONA, TUCSON, AZ, p. A38

HEALTHSOUTH REHABILITATION HOSPITAL OF SPRING HILL, BROOKSVILLE, FL, p. A120

HEALTHSOUTH REHABILITATION HOSPITAL OF TALLAHASSEE, TALLAHASSEE, FL, p. A140

HEALTHSOUTH REHABILITATION HOSPITAL OF TEXARKANA, TEXARKANA, TX, p. A637

HEALTHSOUTH REHABILITATION HOSPITAL OF TOMS RIVER, TOMS RIVER, NJ, p. A411

HEALTHSOUTH REHABILITATION HOSPITAL OF UTAH, SANDY, UT, p. A647

HEALTHSOUTH REHABILITATION HOSPITAL OF VINELAND, VINELAND, NJ, p. A412

HEALTHSOUTH REHABILITATION HOSPITAL OF VIRGINIA, RICHMOND, VA, p. A660

HEALTHSOUTH REHABILITATION HOSPITAL OF WESTERN MASSACHUSETTS, LUDLOW, MA, p. A301

HEALTHSOUTH REHABILITATION HOSPITAL OF YORK, YORK, PA, p. A545

HEALTHSOUTH REHABILITATION HOSPITAL–CITYVIEW, FORT WORTH, TX, p. A603

HEALTHSOUTH REHABILITATION HOSPITAL–LAS VEGAS, LAS VEGAS, NV, p. A392

HEALTHSOUTH REHABILITATION HOSPITAL–WICHITA FALLS, WICHITA FALLS, TX, p. A641

HEALTHSOUTH REHABILITATION INSTITUTE OF SAN ANTONIO, SAN ANTONIO, TX, p. A631

HEALTHSOUTH REHABILITATION INSTITUTE OF TUCSON, TUCSON, AZ, p. A38

HEALTHSOUTH REHABILITATION OF GADSDEN, GADSDEN, AL, p. A20

HEALTHSOUTH SCOTTSDALE REHABILITATION HOSPITAL, SCOTTSDALE, AZ, p. A37

HEALTHSOUTH SEA PINES REHABILITATION HOSPITAL, MELBOURNE, FL, p. A130

HEALTHSOUTH SOUTHERN HILLS REHABILITATION HOSPITAL, PRINCETON, WV, p. A680

HEALTHSOUTH SUGAR LAND REHABILITATION HOSPITAL, SUGAR LAND, TX, p. A635

HEALTHSOUTH SUNRISE REHABILITATION HOSPITAL, FORT LAUDERDALE, FL, p. A123

HEALTHSOUTH TREASURE COAST REHABILITATION HOSPITAL, VERO BEACH, FL, p. A143

HEALTHSOUTH TUSTIN REHABILITATION HOSPITAL, TUSTIN, CA, p. A93

HEALTHSOUTH VALLEY OF THE SUN REHABILITATION HOSPITAL, GLENDALE, AZ, p. A32

HEALTHSOUTH WALTON REHABILITATION HOSPITAL, AUGUSTA, GA, p. A148

HEALTHSOUTH WESTERN HILLS REHABILITATION HOSPITAL, PARKERSBURG, WV, p. A679

HEART HOSPITAL OF AUSTIN, AUSTIN, TEXAS (see ST. DAVID'S MEDICAL CENTER), p. A586

HEART HOSPITAL OF LAFAYETTE, LAFAYETTE, LA, p. A270

HEART HOSPITAL OF NEW MEXICO, ALBUQUERQUE, NEW MEXICO (see LOVELACE MEDICAL CENTER), p. A414

HEART OF AMERICA MEDICAL CENTER, RUGBY, ND, p. A469

HEART OF FLORIDA REGIONAL MEDICAL CENTER, DAVENPORT, FL, p. A121

HEART OF LANCASTER REGIONAL MEDICAL CENTER, LITITZ, PA, p. A530

HEART OF TEXAS MEMORIAL HOSPITAL, BRADY, TX, p. A589

HEART OF THE ROCKIES REGIONAL MEDICAL CENTER, SALIDA, CO, p. A105

HEARTLAND BEHAVIORAL HEALTH SERVICES, NEVADA, MO, p. A366

HEARTLAND BEHAVIORAL HEALTHCARE, MASSILLON, OH, p. A485

HEARTLAND LONG TERM ACUTE CARE HOSPITAL, SAINT JOSEPH, MO, p. A368

HEARTLAND REGIONAL MEDICAL CENTER, MARION, IL, p. A187

HEARTLAND REGIONAL MEDICAL CENTER, SAINT JOSEPH, MO, p. A369

HEARTLAND SURGICAL SPECIALTY HOSPITAL, OVERLAND PARK, KS, p. A241

HEATHERHILL CARE COMMUNITIES, CHARDON, OH, p. A473

HEBER VALLEY MEDICAL CENTER, HEBER CITY, UT, p. A644

HEBREW REHABILITATION CENTER, BOSTON, MA, p. A297

HEDRICK MEDICAL CENTER, CHILLICOTHE, MO, p. A358

HEGG MEMORIAL HEALTH CENTER AVERA, ROCK VALLEY, IA, p. A227

HELEN DEVOS CHILDREN'S HOSPITAL, GRAND RAPIDS, MICHIGAN (see SPECTRUM HEALTH – GRAND RAPIDS), p. A315

HELEN HAYES HOSPITAL, WEST HAVERSTRAW, NY, p. A445

HELEN KELLER HOSPITAL, SHEFFIELD, AL, p. A25

HELEN NEWBERRY JOY HOSPITAL, NEWBERRY, MI, p. A321

HELEN NEWBERRY JOY HOSPITAL ANNEX (see HELEN NEWBERRY JOY HOSPITAL), p. A321

HELENA REGIONAL MEDICAL CENTER, HELENA, AR, p. A44

HEMET VALLEY MEDICAL CENTER, HEMET, CA, p. A64

HEMPHILL COUNTY HOSPITAL, CANADIAN, TX, p. A591

HENDERSON COUNTY COMMUNITY HOSPITAL, LEXINGTON, TN, p. A573

HENDERSON HEALTH CARE SERVICES, HENDERSON, NE, p. A384

HENDRICK CENTER FOR EXTENDED CARE, ABILENE, TX, p. A581

HENDRICK HEALTH SYSTEM, ABILENE, TX, p. A581

HENDRICKS COMMUNITY HOSPITAL, HENDRICKS, MN, p. A333

HENDRICKS REGIONAL HEALTH, DANVILLE, IN, p. A201

HENDRY REGIONAL MEDICAL CENTER, CLEWISTON, FL, p. A120

HENNEPIN COUNTY MEDICAL CENTER, MINNEAPOLIS, MN, p. A336

HENRICO DOCTORS' HOSPITAL, RICHMOND, VA, p. A660

HENRICO DOCTORS' HOSPITAL – FOREST, RICHMOND, VIRGINIA (see HENRICO DOCTORS' HOSPITAL), p. A660

HENRICO DOCTORS' HOSPITAL – PARHAM, RICHMOND, VIRGINIA (see HENRICO DOCTORS' HOSPITAL), p. A660

HENRICO DOCTORS' HOSPITAL – RETREAT CAMPUS, RICHMOND, VIRGINIA (see HENRICO DOCTORS' HOSPITAL), p. A660

HENRIETTA D. GOODALL HOSPITAL, SANFORD, ME, p. A285

HENRY COUNTY HEALTH CENTER, MOUNT PLEASANT, IA, p. A225

HENRY COUNTY HOSPITAL, NEW CASTLE, IN, p. A211

HENRY COUNTY HOSPITAL, NAPOLEON, OH, p. A487

HENRY COUNTY MEDICAL CENTER, PARIS, TN, p. A578

HENRY FORD HOSPITAL, DETROIT, MI, p. A312

HENRY FORD KINGSWOOD HOSPITAL, FERNDALE, MI, p. A313

HENRY FORD MACOMB HOSPITAL – MOUNT CLEMENS CAMPUS, MOUNT CLEMENS, MICHIGAN (see HENRY FORD MACOMB HOSPITALS), p. A311

HENRY FORD MACOMB HOSPITALS, CLINTON TOWNSHIP, MI, p. A311

HENRY FORD WEST BLOOMFIELD HOSPITAL, WEST BLOOMFIELD, MI, p. A326

HENRY FORD WYANDOTTE HOSPITAL, WYANDOTTE, MI, p. A327

HENRY MAYO NEWHALL MEMORIAL HOSPITAL, VALENCIA, CA, p. A94

HENRY MEDICAL CENTER, STOCKBRIDGE, GA, p. A161

HEREFORD REGIONAL MEDICAL CENTER, HEREFORD, TX, p. A608

HERINGTON MUNICIPAL HOSPITAL, HERINGTON, KS, p. A235

HERITAGE MEDICAL CENTER, SHELBYVILLE, TN, p. A579

HERITAGE OAKS HOSPITAL, SACRAMENTO, CA, p. A83

HERITAGE PARK SURGICAL HOSPITAL, SHERMAN, TX, p. A634

HERITAGE VALLEY BEAVER, BEAVER, PA, p. A520

HERMANN AREA DISTRICT HOSPITAL, HERMANN, MO, p. A361

HERRIN HOSPITAL, HERRIN, IL, p. A184

HEYWOOD HOSPITAL, GARDNER, MA, p. A300

HI–DESERT MEDICAL CENTER, JOSHUA TREE, CA, p. A64

HIALEAH HOSPITAL, HIALEAH, FL, p. A125
HIAWATHA COMMUNITY HOSPITAL, HIAWATHA, KS, p. A235
HICKORY TRAIL HOSPITAL, DESOTO, TX, p. A599
HIGGINS GENERAL HOSPITAL, BREMEN, GA, p. A148
HIGH POINT REGIONAL HEALTH SYSTEM, HIGH POINT, NC, p. A455
HIGHBRIDGE WOODYCREST CENTER,, NEW YORK (see BRONX–LEBANON HOSPITAL CENTER HEALTH CARE SYSTEM), p. A431
HIGHLAND COMMUNITY HOSPITAL, PICAYUNE, MS, p. A352
HIGHLAND DISTRICT HOSPITAL, HILLSBORO, OH, p. A483
HIGHLAND HOSPITAL, CHARLESTON, WV, p. A676
HIGHLAND HOSPITAL OF ROCHESTER, ROCHESTER, NY, p. A441
HIGHLAND PARK HOSPITAL, MIAMI, FLORIDA (see JACKSON HEALTH SYSTEM), p. A131
HIGHLANDS BEHAVIORAL HEALTH SYSTEM, LITTLETON, CO, p. A103
HIGHLANDS HOSPITAL, CONNELLSVILLE, PA, p. A523
HIGHLANDS MEDICAL CENTER, SCOTTSBORO, AL, p. A25
HIGHLANDS MEDICAL CENTER, SPARTA, TN, p. A579
HIGHLANDS REGIONAL MEDICAL CENTER, SEBRING, FL, p. A140
HIGHLANDS REGIONAL MEDICAL CENTER, PRESTONSBURG, KY, p. A259
HIGHLANDS REGIONAL REHABILITATION HOSPITAL, EL PASO, TX, p. A601
HIGHLANDS–CASHIERS HOSPITAL, HIGHLANDS, NC, p. A455
HIGHLINE MEDICAL CENTER, BURIEN, WA, p. A665
HIGHLINE SPECIALTY CENTER, 12844 MILITARY ROAD FORK, TUKWILA, ZIP 98168; MARK BENEDUM, ADMINISTRATOR (see HIGHLINE MEDICAL CENTER), p. A665
HIGHSMITH–RAINEY SPECIALTY HOSPITAL, FAYETTEVILLE, NC, p. A452
HILL COUNTRY MEMORIAL HOSPITAL, FREDERICKSBURG, TX, p. A605
HILL CREST BEHAVIORAL HEALTH SERVICES, BIRMINGHAM, AL, p. A16
HILL HOSPITAL OF SUMTER COUNTY, YORK, AL, p. A26
HILL REGIONAL HOSPITAL, HILLSBORO, TX, p. A608
HILLCREST BAPTIST MEDICAL CENTER, WACO, TX, p. A640
HILLCREST BAPTIST MEDICAL CENTER – HERRING AVENUE CAMPUS, 3000 HERRING AVENUE, ZIP 76708 (see HILLCREST BAPTIST MEDICAL CENTER), p. A640
HILLCREST HOSPITAL, PITTSFIELD, MASSACHUSETTS (see BERKSHIRE MEDICAL CENTER), p. A304
HILLCREST HOSPITAL, CLEVELAND, OH, p. A476
HILLCREST HOSPITAL – SOUTH, TULSA, OK, p. A508
HILLCREST HOSPITAL CLAREMORE, CLAREMORE, OK, p. A497
HILLCREST HOSPITAL CUSHING, CUSHING, OK, p. A497
HILLCREST HOSPITAL HENRYETTA, HENRYETTA, OK, p. A499
HILLCREST MEDICAL CENTER, TULSA, OK, p. A508
HILLCREST MEMORIAL HOSPITAL, SIMPSONVILLE, SC, p. A555
HILLS & DALES GENERAL HOSPITAL, CASS CITY, MI, p. A310
HILLSBORO AREA HOSPITAL, HILLSBORO, IL, p. A185
HILLSBORO COMMUNITY HOSPITAL, HILLSBORO, KS, p. A235
HILLSDALE COMMUNITY HEALTH CENTER, HILLSDALE, MI, p. A316
HILLSIDE HOSPITAL, PULASKI, TN, p. A578
HILLSIDE REHABILITATION HOSPITAL, WARREN, OH, p. A492
HILO MEDICAL CENTER, HILO, HI, p. A164
HILTON HEAD HOSPITAL, HILTON HEAD ISLAND, SC, p. A553
HIND GENERAL HOSPITAL, HOBART, IN, p. A204
HIRAM W. DAVIS MEDICAL CENTER, PETERSBURG, VA, p. A659
HOAG HOSPITAL IRVINE, IRVINE, CALIFORNIA (see HOAG MEMORIAL HOSPITAL PRESBYTERIAN), p. A76
HOAG MEMORIAL HOSPITAL PRESBYTERIAN, NEWPORT BEACH, CA, p. A76
HOAG ORTHOPEDIC INSTITUTE, IRVINE, CA, p. A64
HOBOKEN UNIVERSITY MEDICAL CENTER, HOBOKEN, NJ, p. A405
HOCKING VALLEY COMMUNITY HOSPITAL, LOGAN, OH, p. A484
HODGEMAN COUNTY HEALTH CENTER, JETMORE, KS, p. A236
HOLDENVILLE GENERAL HOSPITAL, HOLDENVILLE, OK, p. A500
HOLLAND HOSPITAL, HOLLAND, MI, p. A316
HOLLISWOOD HOSPITAL,, NY, p. A432
HOLLY HILL HOSPITAL, RALEIGH, NC, p. A459
HOLLYWOOD COMMUNITY HOSPITAL, LOS ANGELES, CA, p. A69
HOLLYWOOD COMMUNITY HOSPITAL OF VAN NUYS,, CALIFORNIA (see HOLLYWOOD COMMUNITY HOSPITAL), p. A69
HOLLYWOOD PAVILION,, FL, p. A125
HOLLYWOOD PRESBYTERIAN MEDICAL CENTER, LOS ANGELES, CA, p. A69
HOLMES COUNTY HOSPITAL AND CLINICS, LEXINGTON, MS, p. A350
HOLTON COMMUNITY HOSPITAL, HOLTON, KS, p. A235
HOLTZ CHILDREN'S HOSPITAL, MIAMI, FLORIDA (see JACKSON HEALTH SYSTEM), p. A131

HOLY CROSS HOSPITAL, FORT LAUDERDALE, FL, p. A123
HOLY CROSS HOSPITAL, CHICAGO, IL, p. A176
HOLY CROSS HOSPITAL, SILVER SPRING, MD, p. A294
HOLY CROSS HOSPITAL, TAOS, NM, p. A418
HOLY FAMILY HOSPITAL AND MEDICAL CENTER, METHUEN, MA, p. A302
HOLY FAMILY MEMORIAL, MANITOWOC, WI, p. A690
HOLY NAME MEDICAL CENTER, TEANECK, NJ, p. A411
HOLY REDEEMER HOSPITAL AND MEDICAL CENTER, MEADOWBROOK, PA, p. A531
HOLY ROSARY HEALTHCARE, MILES CITY, MT, p. A378
HOLY SPIRIT HOSPITAL, CAMP HILL, PA, p. A521
HOLYOKE MEDICAL CENTER, HOLYOKE, MA, p. A300
HOLZER MEDICAL CENTER, GALLIPOLIS, OH, p. A482
HOLZER MEDICAL CENTER – JACKSON, JACKSON, OH, p. A483
HOMER MEMORIAL HOSPITAL, HOMER, LA, p. A268
HOOD MEMORIAL HOSPITAL, AMITE, LA, p. A262
HOOPESTON REGIONAL HEALTH CENTER, HOOPESTON, IL, p. A185
HOOPS FAMILY CHILDREN'S HOSPITAL, HUNTINGTON, WEST VIRGINIA (see CABELL HUNTINGTON HOSPITAL), p. A677
HOPEDALE MEDICAL COMPLEX, HOPEDALE, IL, p. A185
HOPI HEALTH CARE CENTER, KEAMS CANYON, AZ, p. A32
HOPKINS COUNTY MEMORIAL HOSPITAL, SULPHUR SPRINGS, TX, p. A636
HORIZON SPECIALTY HOSPITAL, LAS VEGAS, NV, p. A393
HORN MEMORIAL HOSPITAL, IDA GROVE, IA, p. A223
HORSHAM CLINIC, AMBLER, PA, p. A520
HORTON COMMUNITY HOSPITAL, HORTON, KS, p. A235
HOSPITAL BUEN SAMARITANO, AGUADILLA, PR, p. A705
HOSPITAL DE DAMAS, PONCE, PR, p. A708
HOSPITAL DE LA CONCEPCION, SAN GERMAN, PR, p. A708
HOSPITAL DE LA UNIVERSIDAD DE PUERTO RICO/DR. FEDERICO TRILLA, CAROLINA, PR, p. A706
HOSPITAL DEL MAESTRO, SAN JUAN, PR, p. A709
HOSPITAL DR. CAYETANO COLL Y TOSTE, ARECIBO, PR, p. A706
HOSPITAL EPISCOPAL SAN LUCAS GUAYAMA, GUAYAMA, PR, p. A707
HOSPITAL FOR EXTENDED RECOVERY, NORFOLK, VA, p. A658
HOSPITAL FOR SPECIAL CARE, NEW BRITAIN, CT, p. A110
HOSPITAL FOR SPECIAL SURGERY, NEW YORK, NY, p. A432
HOSPITAL HERMANOS MELENDEZ, BAYAMON, PR, p. A706
HOSPITAL HMA DE HUMACAO, HUMACAO, PR, p. A707
HOSPITAL INTERAMERICANO DE MEDICINA AVANZADA, CAGUAS, PR, p. A706
HOSPITAL MANATI MEDICAL CENTER, MANATI, PR, p. A707
HOSPITAL MENONITA DE CAYEY, CAYEY, PR, p. A706
HOSPITAL METROPOLITAN, SAN JUAN, PR, p. A709
HOSPITAL METROPOLITANO DR. SUSONI, ARECIBO, PR, p. A706
HOSPITAL METROPOLITANO DR. TITO MATTEI, YAUCO, PR, p. A710
HOSPITAL METROPOLITANO SAN GERMAN, SAN GERMAN, PR, p. A708
HOSPITAL OF THE UNIVERSITY OF PENNSYLVANIA, PHILADELPHIA, PA, p. A535
HOSPITAL ONCOLOGICO ANDRES GRILLASCA, PONCE, PR, p. A708
HOSPITAL ORIENTE, HUMACAO, PR, p. A707
HOSPITAL PAVIA–HATO REY, SAN JUAN, PR, p. A709
HOSPITAL PAVIA–SANTURCE, SAN JUAN, PR, p. A709
HOSPITAL PEREA, MAYAGUEZ, PR, p. A708
HOSPITAL PSIQUIATRICO METROPOLITANO, CABO ROJO, PR, p. A706
HOSPITAL SAN CARLOS BORROMEO, MOCA, PR, p. A708
HOSPITAL SAN CRISTOBAL, COTO LAUREL, PR, p. A707
HOSPITAL SAN FRANCISCO, SAN JUAN, PR, p. A709
HOSPITAL SAN GERARDO, SAN JUAN, PR, p. A709
HOSPITAL SAN PABLO, BAYAMON, PR, p. A706
HOSPITAL SAN PABLO DEL ESTE, FAJARDO, PR, p. A707
HOSPITAL SANTA ROSA, GUAYAMA, PR, p. A707
HOSPITAL UNIVERSITARIO DR. RAMON RUIZ ARNAU, BAYAMON, PR, p. A706
HOT SPRINGS COUNTY MEMORIAL HOSPITAL, THERMOPOLIS, WY, p. A704
HOULTON REGIONAL HOSPITAL, HOULTON, ME, p. A283
HOUSTON COUNTY COMMUNITY HOSPITAL, ERIN, TN, p. A568
HOUSTON HOSPITAL FOR SPECIALIZED SURGERY, HOUSTON, TX, p. A610
HOUSTON MEDICAL CENTER, WARNER ROBINS, GA, p. A162
HOUSTON NORTHWEST MEDICAL CENTER, HOUSTON, TX, p. A610
HOUSTON ORTHOPEDIC AND SPINE HOSPITAL, BELLAIRE, TX, p. A588
HOUSTON PHYSICIANS HOSPITAL, WEBSTER, TX, p. A640
HOWARD A. RUSK REHABILITATION CENTER, COLUMBIA, MO, p. A359
HOWARD COUNTY GENERAL HOSPITAL, COLUMBIA, MD, p. A291

HOWARD COUNTY MEDICAL CENTER, SAINT PAUL, NE, p. A389
HOWARD MEMORIAL HOSPITAL, NASHVILLE, AR, p. A48
HOWARD UNIVERSITY HOSPITAL, WASHINGTON, DC, p. A116
HOWARD YOUNG MEDICAL CENTER, WOODRUFF, WI, p. A700
HUDSON HOSPITAL AND CLINICS, HUDSON, WI, p. A688
HUDSON VALLEY HOSPITAL CENTER, CORTLANDT MANOR, NY, p. A424
HUEY P. LONG MEDICAL CENTER, PINEVILLE, LA, p. A277
HUGGINS HOSPITAL, WOLFEBORO, NH, p. A400
HUGH CHATHAM MEMORIAL HOSPITAL, ELKIN, NC, p. A452
HUGHSTON HOSPITAL, COLUMBUS, GA, p. A150
HUGULEY MEMORIAL MEDICAL CENTER, FORT WORTH, TX, p. A603
HUHUKAM MEMORIAL HOSPITAL, SACATON, AZ, p. A36
HUMBOLDT COUNTY MEMORIAL HOSPITAL, HUMBOLDT, IA, p. A222
HUMBOLDT GENERAL HOSPITAL, WINNEMUCCA, NV, p. A396
HUMBOLDT GENERAL HOSPITAL, HUMBOLDT, TN, p. A570
HUNT REGIONAL COMMUNITY HOSPITAL, COMMERCE, TX, p. A593
HUNT REGIONAL MEDICAL CENTER, GREENVILLE, TX, p. A607
HUNT REGIONAL MEDICAL CENTER, GREENVILLE, TEXAS (see HUNT REGIONAL MEDICAL CENTER), p. A607
HUNTER HOLMES MCGUIRE VETERANS AFFAIRS MEDICAL CENTER, RICHMOND, VA, p. A660
HUNTERDON MEDICAL CENTER, FLEMINGTON, NJ, p. A404
HUNTINGTON BEACH HOSPITAL, HUNTINGTON BEACH, CA, p. A64
HUNTINGTON HOSPITAL, HUNTINGTON, NY, p. A427
HUNTINGTON MEMORIAL HOSPITAL, PASADENA, CA, p. A79
HUNTINGTON VETERANS AFFAIRS MEDICAL CENTER, HUNTINGTON, WV, p. A677
HUNTSVILLE HOSPITAL, HUNTSVILLE, AL, p. A21
HUNTSVILLE HOSPITAL FOR WOMEN AND CHILDREN, HUNTSVILLE, ALABAMA (see HUNTSVILLE HOSPITAL), p. A21
HUNTSVILLE MEMORIAL HOSPITAL, HUNTSVILLE, TX, p. A614
HURLEY CHILDREN'S HOSPITAL, FLINT, MICHIGAN (see HURLEY MEDICAL CENTER), p. A313
HURLEY MEDICAL CENTER, FLINT, MI, p. A313
HURON MEDICAL CENTER, BAD AXE, MI, p. A308
HURON REGIONAL MEDICAL CENTER, HURON, SD, p. A560
HUTCHINSON HEALTH, HUTCHINSON, MN, p. A334
HUTCHINSON REGIONAL MEDICAL CENTER, HUTCHINSON, KS, p. A236
HUTZEL HOSPITAL, DETROIT, MICHIGAN (see HARPER UNIVERSITY HOSPITAL/HUTZEL WOMEN'S HOSPITAL), p. A312

# I

I-70 COMMUNITY HOSPITAL, SWEET SPRINGS, MO, p. A372
I. GONZALEZ MARTINEZ ONCOLOGIC HOSPITAL,, PR, p. A709
IBERIA EXTENDED CARE HOSPITAL, NEW IBERIA, LOUISIANA (see LOUISIANA EXTENDED CARE HOSPITAL OF LAFAYETTE), p. A271
IBERIA MEDICAL CENTER, NEW IBERIA, LA, p. A275
IBERIA REHABILITATION HOSPITAL, NEW IBERIA, LA, p. A275
ICON HOSPITAL, HUMBLE, TX, p. A614
ILLINI COMMUNITY HOSPITAL, PITTSFIELD, IL, p. A192
ILLINOIS VALLEY COMMUNITY HOSPITAL, PERU, IL, p. A192
INCLINE VILLAGE COMMUNITY HOSPITAL, INCLINE VILLAGE, NV, p. A392
INDIAN HEALTH SERVICE HOSPITAL, RAPID CITY, SD, p. A561
INDIAN PATH MEDICAL CENTER, KINGSPORT, TN, p. A571
INDIAN RIVER MEDICAL CENTER, VERO BEACH, FL, p. A143
INDIANA ORTHOPAEDIC HOSPITAL, INDIANAPOLIS, IN, p. A205
INDIANA REGIONAL MEDICAL CENTER, INDIANA, PA, p. A528
INDIANA UNIVERSITY HEALTH ARNETT HOSPITAL, LAFAYETTE, IN, p. A208
INDIANA UNIVERSITY HEALTH BALL MEMORIAL HOSPITAL, MUNCIE, IN, p. A210
INDIANA UNIVERSITY HEALTH BEDFORD HOSPITAL, BEDFORD, IN, p. A198
INDIANA UNIVERSITY HEALTH BLACKFORD HOSPITAL, HARTFORD CITY, IN, p. A204
INDIANA UNIVERSITY HEALTH BLOOMINGTON HOSPITAL, BLOOMINGTON, IN, p. A199
INDIANA UNIVERSITY HEALTH GOSHEN HOSPITAL, GOSHEN, IN, p. A203
INDIANA UNIVERSITY HEALTH LA PORTE HOSPITAL, LA PORTE, IN, p. A208
INDIANA UNIVERSITY HEALTH METHODIST HOSPITAL, INDIANAPOLIS, INDIANA (see INDIANA UNIVERSITY HEALTH UNIVERSITY HOSPITAL), p. A205
INDIANA UNIVERSITY HEALTH MORGAN HOSPITAL, MARTINSVILLE, IN, p. A209

INDIANA UNIVERSITY HEALTH NORTH HOSPITAL, CARMEL, IN, p. A200
INDIANA UNIVERSITY HEALTH PAOLI HOSPITAL, PAOLI, IN, p. A212
INDIANA UNIVERSITY HEALTH STARKE HOSPITAL, KNOX, IN, p. A207
INDIANA UNIVERSITY HEALTH TIPTON HOSPITAL, TIPTON, IN, p. A214
INDIANA UNIVERSITY HEALTH UNIVERSITY HOSPITAL, INDIANAPOLIS, IN, p. A205
INDIANA UNIVERSITY HEALTH WEST HOSPITAL, AVON, IN, p. A198
INDIANA UNIVERSITY HEALTH WHITE MEMORIAL HOSPITAL, MONTICELLO, IN, p. A210
INDIANA UNIVERSITY HOSPITAL, INDIANAPOLIS, INDIANA (see INDIANA UNIVERSITY HEALTH UNIVERSITY HOSPITAL), p. A205
INDIANHEAD MEDICAL CENTER, SHELL LAKE, WI, p. A696
INDUSTRIAL HOSPITAL, SAN JUAN, PR, p. A709
INFIRMARY LONG TERM ACUTE CARE HOSPITAL, MOBILE, AL, p. A22
INGALLS MEMORIAL HOSPITAL, HARVEY, IL, p. A184
INGHAM REGIONAL MEDICAL CENTER, GREENLAWN CAMPUS, LANSING, MICHIGAN (see MCLAREN GREATER LANSING), p. A318
INLAND HOSPITAL, WATERVILLE, ME, p. A285
INLAND VALLEY MEDICAL CENTER, WILDOMAR, CALIFORNIA (see SOUTHWEST HEALTHCARE SYSTEM), p. A76
INOVA ALEXANDRIA HOSPITAL, ALEXANDRIA, VA, p. A651
INOVA FAIR OAKS HOSPITAL, FAIRFAX, VA, p. A653
INOVA FAIRFAX HOSPITAL, FALLS CHURCH, VA, p. A653
INOVA FAIRFAX HOSPITAL FOR CHILDREN, FALLS CHURCH, VIRGINIA (see INOVA FAIRFAX HOSPITAL), p. A653
INOVA LOUDOUN HOSPITAL, LEESBURG, VA, p. A656
INOVA MOUNT VERNON HOSPITAL, ALEXANDRIA, VA, p. A651
INSPIRA MEDICAL CENTER-ELMER, ELMER, NJ, p. A404
INSPIRA MEDICAL CENTER-VINELAND, VINELAND, NJ, p. A412
INSPIRA MEDICAL CENTER-WOODBURY, WOODBURY, NJ, p. A413
INSTITUTE FOR ORTHOPAEDIC SURGERY, LIMA, OH, p. A484
INSTITUTE OF LIVING, HARTFORD, CONNECTICUT (see HARTFORD HOSPITAL), p. A109
INTEGRIS BAPTIST MEDICAL CENTER, OKLAHOMA CITY, OK, p. A503
INTEGRIS BAPTIST REGIONAL HEALTH CENTER, MIAMI, OK, p. A501
INTEGRIS BASS BAPTIST HEALTH CENTER, ENID, OK, p. A498
INTEGRIS BASS PAVILION, ENID, OK, p. A498
INTEGRIS BLACKWELL REGIONAL HOSPITAL, BLACKWELL, OK, p. A496
INTEGRIS CANADIAN VALLEY HOSPITAL, YUKON, OK, p. A510
INTEGRIS CLINTON REGIONAL HOSPITAL, CLINTON, OK, p. A497
INTEGRIS GROVE GENERAL HOSPITAL, GROVE, OK, p. A499
INTEGRIS HEALTH EDMOND, EDMOND, OK, p. A498
INTEGRIS MARSHALL COUNTY MEDICAL CENTER, MADILL, OK, p. A500
INTEGRIS MAYES COUNTY MEDICAL CENTER, PRYOR, OK, p. A506
INTEGRIS MENTAL HEALTH SYSTEM-SPENCER, SPENCER, OKLAHOMA (see INTEGRIS BAPTIST MEDICAL CENTER), p. A503
INTEGRIS SEMINOLE MEDICAL CENTER, SEMINOLE, OK, p. A506
INTEGRIS SOUTHWEST MEDICAL CENTER, OKLAHOMA CITY, OK, p. A503
INTEGRITY TRANSITIONAL HOSPITAL, DENTON, TX, p. A598
INTERFAITH MEDICAL CENTER,, NY, p. A432
INTERIM LSU PUBLIC HOSPITAL, NEW ORLEANS, LA, p. A275
INTERMEDICAL HOSPITAL OF SOUTH CAROLINA, COLUMBIA, SC, p. A550
INTERMOUNTAIN HOSPITAL, BOISE, ID, p. A167
INTERMOUNTAIN MEDICAL CENTER, MURRAY, UT, p. A644
INTRACARE NORTH HOSPITAL, HOUSTON, TX, p. A610
IOWA CITY VETERANS AFFAIRS HEALTH CARE SYSTEM, IOWA CITY, IA, p. A223
IOWA MEDICAL AND CLASSIFICATION CENTER, OAKDALE, IA, p. A226
IOWA METHODIST MEDICAL CENTER, DES MOINES, IA, p. A220
IOWA SPECIALTY HOSPITAL, BELMOND, IA, p. B74
IOWA SPECIALTY HOSPITAL-BELMOND, BELMOND, IA, p. A216, B74
IOWA SPECIALTY HOSPITAL-CLARION, CLARION, IA, p. A218, B74
IRA DAVENPORT MEMORIAL HOSPITAL, BATH, NY, p. A421
IRAAN GENERAL HOSPITAL, IRAAN, TX, p. A614
IREDELL MEMORIAL HOSPITAL, STATESVILLE, NC, p. A461
IRELAND ARMY COMMUNITY HOSPITAL, FORT KNOX, KY, p. A251
IRON COUNTY HOSPITAL, PILOT KNOB, MO, p. A367

IROQUOIS MEMORIAL HOSPITAL AND RESIDENT HOME, WATSEKA, IL, p. A196
IRVING COPPELL SURGICAL HOSPITAL, IRVING, TX, p. A615
IRWIN ARMY COMMUNITY HOSPITAL, JUNCTION CITY, KS, p. A236
IRWIN COUNTY HOSPITAL, OCILLA, GA, p. A158
ISHAM HEALTH CENTER, ANDOVER, MA, p. A295
ISLAND HOSPITAL, ANACORTES, WA, p. A664
IU HEALTH SAXONY HOSPITAL, FISHERS, INDIANA (see INDIANA UNIVERSITY HEALTH UNIVERSITY HOSPITAL), p. A205
IVINSON MEMORIAL HOSPITAL, LARAMIE, WY, p. A702

# J

J. ARTHUR DOSHER MEMORIAL HOSPITAL, SOUTHPORT, NC, p. A461
J. C. BLAIR MEMORIAL HOSPITAL, HUNTINGDON, PA, p. A527
J. D. MCCARTY CENTER FOR CHILDREN WITH DEVELOPMENTAL DISABILITIES, NORMAN, OK, p. A502
J. F. K. MEDICAL CENTER, ATLANTIS, FL, p. A118
J. PAUL JONES HOSPITAL, CAMDEN, AL, p. A18
JACK C. MONTGOMERY VETERANS AFFAIRS MEDICAL CENTER, MUSKOGEE, OK, p. A501
JACK D WEILER HOSPITAL OF ALBERT EINSTEIN COLLEGE OF MEDICINE,, NEW YORK (see MONTEFIORE MEDICAL CENTER), p. A434
JACK HUGHSTON MEMORIAL HOSPITAL, PHENIX CITY, AL, p. A24
JACKSON COUNTY HOSPITAL DISTRICT, EDNA, TX, p. A600
JACKSON COUNTY MEMORIAL HOSPITAL, ALTUS, OK, p. A495
JACKSON COUNTY REGIONAL HEALTH CENTER, MAQUOKETA, IA, p. A224
JACKSON GENERAL HOSPITAL, RIPLEY, WV, p. A680
JACKSON HEALTH SYSTEM, MIAMI, FL, p. A131
JACKSON HOSPITAL, MARIANNA, FL, p. A130
JACKSON HOSPITAL AND CLINIC, MONTGOMERY, AL, p. A23
JACKSON MEDICAL CENTER, JACKSON, AL, p. A22
JACKSON MEMORIAL HOSPITAL, MIAMI, FLORIDA (see JACKSON HEALTH SYSTEM), p. A131
JACKSON NORTH MEDICAL CENTER, NORTH MIAMI BEACH, FLORIDA (see JACKSON HEALTH SYSTEM), p. A131
JACKSON PARISH HOSPITAL, JONESBORO, LA, p. A269
JACKSON PARK HOSPITAL AND MEDICAL CENTER, CHICAGO, IL, p. A177
JACKSON PURCHASE MEDICAL CENTER, MAYFIELD, KY, p. A257
JACKSON SOUTH COMMUNITY HOSPITAL, MIAMI, FLORIDA (see JACKSON HEALTH SYSTEM), p. A131
JACKSON-MADISON COUNTY GENERAL HOSPITAL, JACKSON, TN, p. A570
JACKSONVILLE MEDICAL CENTER, JACKSONVILLE, AL, p. A22
JACOBI MEDICAL CENTER,, NY, p. A432
JACOBSON MEMORIAL HOSPITAL CARE CENTER, ELGIN, ND, p. A466
JAMAICA HOSPITAL MEDICAL CENTER,, NY, p. A432
JAMES A. HALEY VETERANS' HOSPITAL, TAMPA, FL, p. A141
JAMES AND CONNIE MAYNARD CHILDREN'S HOSPITAL, GREENVILLE, NORTH CAROLINA (see VIDANT MEDICAL CENTER), p. A454
JAMES B. HAGGIN MEMORIAL HOSPITAL, HARRODSBURG, KY, p. A252
JAMES CANCER HOSPITAL AND SOLOVE RESEARCH INSTITUTE, COLUMBUS, OH, p. A477
JAMES E. VAN ZANDT VETERANS AFFAIRS MEDICAL CENTER, ALTOONA, PA, p. A519
JAMES H. QUILLEN VETERANS AFFAIRS MEDICAL CENTER, MOUNTAIN HOME, TN, p. A576
JAMES J. PETERS VETERANS AFFAIRS MEDICAL CENTER,, NY, p. A432
JAMESON HOSPITAL, NEW CASTLE, PA, p. A533
JAMESTOWN REGIONAL MEDICAL CENTER, JAMESTOWN, ND, p. A467
JAMESTOWN REGIONAL MEDICAL CENTER, JAMESTOWN, TN, p. A570
JANE PHILLIPS MEDICAL CENTER, BARTLESVILLE, OK, p. A496
JANE PHILLIPS NOWATA HEALTH CENTER, NOWATA, OK, p. A502
JANE TODD CRAWFORD HOSPITAL, GREENSBURG, KY, p. A251
JASPER COUNTY HOSPITAL, RENSSELAER, IN, p. A212
JASPER COUNTY NURSING HOME (see JASPER GENERAL HOSPITAL), p. A344
JASPER GENERAL HOSPITAL, BAY SPRINGS, MS, p. A344
JASPER MEMORIAL HOSPITAL, MONTICELLO, GA, p. A157
JAY COUNTY HOSPITAL, PORTLAND, IN, p. A212
JAY HOSPITAL, JAY, FL, p. A127
JEANES HOSPITAL, PHILADELPHIA, PA, p. A535
JEFF DAVIS HOSPITAL, HAZLEHURST, GA, p. A154

JEFFERSON COMMUNITY HEALTH CENTER, FAIRBURY, NE, p. A383
JEFFERSON COUNTY HEALTH CENTER, FAIRFIELD, IA, p. A221
JEFFERSON COUNTY HOSPITAL, FAYETTE, MS, p. A346
JEFFERSON COUNTY HOSPITAL, WAURIKA, OK, p. A510
JEFFERSON DAVIS COMMUNITY HOSPITAL, PRENTISS, MS, p. A353
JEFFERSON HEALTHCARE, PORT TOWNSEND, WA, p. A669
JEFFERSON HOSPITAL, LOUISVILLE, GA, p. A156
JEFFERSON MEDICAL CENTER, RANSON, WV, p. A680
JEFFERSON REGIONAL MEDICAL CENTER, PINE BLUFF, AR, p. A49
JEFFERSON REGIONAL MEDICAL CENTER, JEFFERSON HILLS, PA, p. A528
JELLICO COMMUNITY HOSPITAL, JELLICO, TN, p. A571
JENKINS COUNTY HOSPITAL, MILLEN, GA, p. A157
JENNERSVILLE REGIONAL HOSPITAL, WEST GROVE, PA, p. A544
JENNIE M. MELHAM MEMORIAL MEDICAL CENTER, BROKEN BOW, NE, p. A382
JENNIE STUART MEDICAL CENTER, HOPKINSVILLE, KY, p. A252
JENNINGS AMERICAN LEGION HOSPITAL, JENNINGS, LA, p. A269
JENNINGS SENIOR CARE HOSPITAL, JENNINGS, LA, p. A269
JEROLD PHELPS COMMUNITY HOSPITAL, GARBERVILLE, CA, p. A62
JEROME GOLDEN CENTER FOR BEHAVIORAL HEALTH, INC., WEST PALM BEACH, FL, p. A143
JERSEY COMMUNITY HOSPITAL, JERSEYVILLE, IL, p. A186
JERSEY SHORE HOSPITAL, JERSEY SHORE, PA, p. A528
JERSEY SHORE UNIVERSITY MEDICAL CENTER, NEPTUNE, NJ, p. A407
JESSE BROWN VETERANS AFFAIRS MEDICAL CENTER, CHICAGO, IL, p. A177
JEWELL COUNTY HOSPITAL, MANKATO, KS, p. A239
JEWISH HOME OF SAN FRANCISCO, SAN FRANCISCO, CA, p. A86
JEWISH HOSPITAL, LOUISVILLE, KY, p. A255
JEWISH HOSPITAL-SHELBYVILLE, SHELBYVILLE, KY, p. A260
JFK JOHNSON REHABILITATION INSTITUTE, EDISON, NJ, p. A403
JFK MEDICAL CENTER, EDISON, NJ, p. A403
JIM TALIAFERRO COMMUNITY MENTAL HEALTH, LAWTON, OK, p. A500
JOE DIMAGGIO CHILDREN'S HOSPITAL,, FLORIDA (see MEMORIAL REGIONAL HOSPITAL SOUTH), p. A125
JOHN C. FREMONT HEALTHCARE DISTRICT, MARIPOSA, CA, p. A73
JOHN C. LINCOLN DEER VALLEY HOSPITAL, PHOENIX, AZ, p. A34
JOHN C. LINCOLN NORTH MOUNTAIN HOSPITAL, PHOENIX, AZ, p. A34
JOHN C. STENNIS MEMORIAL HOSPITAL, DE KALB, MS, p. A346
JOHN D. ARCHBOLD MEMORIAL HOSPITAL, THOMASVILLE, GA, p. A161
JOHN D. DINGELL VETERANS AFFAIRS MEDICAL CENTER, DETROIT, MI, p. A312
JOHN F. KENNEDY MEMORIAL HOSPITAL, INDIO, CA, p. A64
JOHN H. STROGER JR. HOSPITAL OF COOK COUNTY, CHICAGO, IL, p. A177
JOHN HEINZ INSTITUTE OF REHABILITATION MEDICINE, WILKES-BARRE, PA, p. A544
JOHN J. MADDEN MENTAL HEALTH CENTER, HINES, IL, p. A185
JOHN J. PERSHING VETERANS AFFAIRS MEDICAL CENTER, POPLAR BLUFF, MO, p. A367
JOHN MUIR BEHAVIORAL HEALTH CENTER, CONCORD, CA, p. A57
JOHN MUIR MEDICAL CENTER, CONCORD, CONCORD, CA, p. A57
JOHN MUIR MEDICAL CENTER, WALNUT CREEK, WALNUT CREEK, CA, p. A95
JOHN PETER SMITH HOSPITAL, FORT WORTH, TEXAS (see JPS HEALTH NETWORK), p. A604
JOHN RANDOLPH MEDICAL CENTER, HOPEWELL, VA, p. A655
JOHN STODDARD CANCER CENTER, DES MOINES, IOWA (see IOWA METHODIST MEDICAL CENTER), p. A220
JOHN T. MATHER MEMORIAL HOSPITAL, PORT JEFFERSON, NY, p. A440
JOHN UMSTEAD HOSPITAL, BUTNER, NC, p. A449
JOHNS HOPKINS BAYVIEW MEDICAL CENTER, BALTIMORE, MD, p. A287
JOHNS HOPKINS CHILDREN'S CENTER, BALTIMORE, MARYLAND (see JOHNS HOPKINS HOSPITAL), p. A287
JOHNS HOPKINS HOSPITAL, BALTIMORE, MD, p. A287
JOHNSON CITY MEDICAL CENTER, JOHNSON CITY, TN, p. A571
JOHNSON COUNTY COMMUNITY HOSPITAL, MOUNTAIN CITY, TN, p. A576

JOHNSON COUNTY HEALTHCARE CENTER, BUFFALO, WY, p. A701
JOHNSON COUNTY HOSPITAL, TECUMSEH, NE, p. A390
JOHNSON MEMORIAL HEALTH SERVICES, DAWSON, MN, p. A331
JOHNSON MEMORIAL HOSPITAL, STAFFORD SPRINGS, CT, p. A112
JOHNSON MEMORIAL HOSPITAL, FRANKLIN, IN, p. A203
JOHNSON REGIONAL MEDICAL CENTER, CLARKSVILLE, AR, p. A42
JOHNSON–MATHERS NURSING HOME (see NICHOLAS COUNTY HOSPITAL), p. A249
JOHNSTON HEALTH, SMITHFIELD, NC, p. A461
JOHNSTON MEMORIAL HOSPITAL, ABINGDON, VA, p. A651
JOHNSTON R. BOWMAN HEALTH CENTER, CHICAGO, ILLINOIS (see RUSH UNIVERSITY MEDICAL CENTER), p. A179
JOHNSTON–WILLIS HOSPITAL, RICHMOND, VIRGINIA (see CJW MEDICAL CENTER), p. A660
JOINT TOWNSHIP DISTRICT MEMORIAL HOSPITAL, SAINT MARYS, OH, p. A489
JONATHAN M. WAINWRIGHT MEMORIAL VETERANS AFFAIRS MEDICAL CENTER, WALLA WALLA, WA, p. A674
JONES MEMORIAL HOSPITAL, WELLSVILLE, NY, p. A445
JONES REGIONAL MEDICAL CENTER, ANAMOSA, IA, p. A216
JORDAN HOSPITAL, PLYMOUTH, MA, p. A304
JORDAN VALLEY MEDICAL CENTER, WEST JORDAN, UT, p. A648
JOYCE EISENBERG–KEEFER MEDICAL CENTER, RESEDA, CA, p. A82
JPS HEALTH NETWORK, FORT WORTH, TX, p. A604
JULIAN F. KEITH ALCOHOL AND DRUG ABUSE TREATMENT CENTER, BLACK MOUNTAIN, NC, p. A448
JULIETTE MANOR NURSING HOME, COMMUNITY CLINICS (see BERLIN MEMORIAL HOSPITAL), p. A684
JUPITER MEDICAL CENTER, JUPITER, FL, p. A127

# K

K. HOVNANIAN CHILDREN'S HOSPITAL, NEPTUNE, NEW JERSEY (see JERSEY SHORE UNIVERSITY MEDICAL CENTER), p. A407
KAATERSKILL CARE, CATSKILL, NEW YORK (see COLUMBIA MEMORIAL HOSPITAL), p. A427
KADLEC REGIONAL MEDICAL CENTER, RICHLAND, WA, p. A670
KAHI MOHALA BEHAVIORAL HEALTH, EWA BEACH, HI, p. A164
KAHUKU MEDICAL CENTER, KAHUKU, HI, p. A165
KAISER FOUNDATION HOSPITAL, MARTINEZ, CALIFORNIA (see KAISER PERMANENTE WALNUT CREEK MEDICAL CENTER), p. A95
KAISER FOUNDATION MENTAL HEALTH CENTER, LOS ANGELES, CALIFORNIA (see KAISER PERMANENTE LOS ANGELES MEDICAL CENTER), p. A69
KAISER PERMANENTE ANAHEIM MEDICAL CENTER, ANAHEIM, CA, p. A52
KAISER PERMANENTE ANTIOCH MEDICAL CENTER, ANTIOCH, CA, p. A52
KAISER PERMANENTE BALDWIN PARK MEDICAL CENTER, BALDWIN PARK, CA, p. A54
KAISER PERMANENTE DOWNEY MEDICAL CENTER, DOWNEY, CA, p. A58
KAISER PERMANENTE FONTANA MEDICAL CENTER, FONTANA, CA, p. A60
KAISER PERMANENTE FRESNO MEDICAL CENTER, FRESNO, CA, p. A61
KAISER PERMANENTE HAYWARD MEDICAL CENTER, HAYWARD, CA, p. A63
KAISER PERMANENTE LOS ANGELES MEDICAL CENTER, LOS ANGELES, CA, p. A69
KAISER PERMANENTE MANTECA MEDICAL CENTER, MANTECA, CA, p. A73
KAISER PERMANENTE MEDICAL CENTER, HONOLULU, HI, p. A164
KAISER PERMANENTE MORENO VALLEY MEDICAL CENTER, MORENO VALLEY, CA, p. A75
KAISER PERMANENTE OAKLAND MEDICAL CENTER, OAKLAND, CA, p. A77
KAISER PERMANENTE PANORAMA CITY MEDICAL CENTER,, CA, p. A69
KAISER PERMANENTE REDWOOD CITY MEDICAL CENTER, REDWOOD CITY, CA, p. A82
KAISER PERMANENTE RIVERSIDE MEDICAL CENTER, RIVERSIDE, CA, p. A82
KAISER PERMANENTE ROSEVILLE MEDICAL CENTER, ROSEVILLE, CA, p. A83
KAISER PERMANENTE SACRAMENTO MEDICAL CENTER, SACRAMENTO, CA, p. A83
KAISER PERMANENTE SAN DIEGO MEDICAL CENTER, SAN DIEGO, CA, p. A85

KAISER PERMANENTE SAN FRANCISCO MEDICAL CENTER, SAN FRANCISCO, CA, p. A86
KAISER PERMANENTE SAN JOSE MEDICAL CENTER, SAN JOSE, CA, p. A87
KAISER PERMANENTE SAN RAFAEL MEDICAL CENTER, SAN RAFAEL, CA, p. A89
KAISER PERMANENTE SANTA CLARA MEDICAL CENTER, SANTA CLARA, CA, p. A89
KAISER PERMANENTE SANTA ROSA MEDICAL CENTER, SANTA ROSA, CA, p. A90
KAISER PERMANENTE SOUTH BAY MEDICAL CENTER,, CA, p. A69
KAISER PERMANENTE SOUTH SACRAMENTO MEDICAL CENTER, SACRAMENTO, CA, p. A83
KAISER PERMANENTE SOUTH SAN FRANCISCO, SOUTH SAN FRANCISCO, CA, p. A91
KAISER PERMANENTE SUNNYSIDE MEDICAL CENTER, CLACKAMAS, OR, p. A511
KAISER PERMANENTE VACAVILLE MEDICAL CENTER, VACAVILLE, CA, p. A94
KAISER PERMANENTE VALLEJO MEDICAL CENTER, VALLEJO, CA, p. A94
KAISER PERMANENTE WALNUT CREEK MEDICAL CENTER, WALNUT CREEK, CA, p. A95
KAISER PERMANENTE WEST LOS ANGELES MEDICAL CENTER, LOS ANGELES, CA, p. A69
KAISER PERMANENTE WOODLAND HILLS MEDICAL CENTER,, CA, p. A69
KALAMAZOO PSYCHIATRIC HOSPITAL, KALAMAZOO, MI, p. A318
KALEIDA HEALTH, BUFFALO, NY, p. A422
KALISPELL REGIONAL MEDICAL CENTER, KALISPELL, MT, p. A377
KALKASKA MEMORIAL HEALTH CENTER, KALKASKA, MI, p. A318
KANE COMMUNITY HOSPITAL, KANE, PA, p. A528
KANE COUNTY HOSPITAL, KANAB, UT, p. A644
KANSAS CITY ORTHOPAEDIC INSTITUTE, LEAWOOD, KS, p. A238
KANSAS CITY VETERANS AFFAIRS MEDICAL CENTER, KANSAS CITY, MO, p. A363
KANSAS HEART HOSPITAL, WICHITA, KS, p. A246
KANSAS MEDICAL CENTER, ANDOVER, KS, p. A231
KANSAS NEUROLOGICAL INSTITUTE, TOPEKA, KS, p. A244
KANSAS REHABILITATION HOSPITAL, TOPEKA, KS, p. A245
KANSAS SPINE HOSPITAL, WICHITA, KS, p. A246
KANSAS SURGERY AND RECOVERY CENTER, WICHITA, KS, p. A246
KAPIOLANI MEDICAL CENTER FOR WOMEN & CHILDREN, HONOLULU, HI, p. A164
KARL AND ESTHER HOBLITZELLE MEMORIAL HOSPITAL, DALLAS, TEXAS (see BAYLOR UNIVERSITY MEDICAL CENTER), p. A595
KARMANOS CANCER CENTER, DETROIT, MI, p. A312
KATHERINE SHAW BETHEA HOSPITAL, DIXON, IL, p. A181
KAU HOSPITAL, PAHALA, HI, p. A166
KAUAI VETERANS MEMORIAL HOSPITAL, WAIMEA, HI, p. A166
KAWEAH DELTA MEDICAL CENTER, VISALIA, CA, p. A95
KEARNEY COUNTY HEALTH SERVICES, MINDEN, NE, p. A386
KEARNY COUNTY HOSPITAL, LAKIN, KS, p. A237
KECK HOSPITAL OF USC, LOS ANGELES, CA, p. A70
KEDREN COMMUNITY MENTAL HEALTH CENTER, LOS ANGELES, CA, p. A70
KEEFE MEMORIAL HOSPITAL, CHEYENNE WELLS, CO, p. A98
KELL WEST REGIONAL HOSPITAL, WICHITA FALLS, TX, p. A641
KELLER ARMY COMMUNITY HOSPITAL, WEST POINT, NY, p. A446
KEMPSVILLE CENTER FOR BEHAVIORAL HEALTH, NORFOLK, VA, p. A658
KENDALL REGIONAL MEDICAL CENTER, MIAMI, FL, p. A131
KENMARE COMMUNITY HOSPITAL, KENMARE, ND, p. A468
KENMORE MERCY HOSPITAL, KENMORE, NY, p. A428
KENNEDY HEALTH SYSTEM, CHERRY HILL, NJ, p. A402
KENNEDY KRIEGER INSTITUTE, BALTIMORE, MD, p. A287
KENNEDY UNIVERSITY HOSPITAL – STRATFORD, STRATFORD, NEW JERSEY (see KENNEDY HEALTH SYSTEM), p. A402
KENNEDY UNIVERSITY HOSPITAL – WASHINGTON TOWNSHIP, TURNERSVILLE, NEW JERSEY (see KENNEDY HEALTH SYSTEM), p. A402
KENNEWICK GENERAL HOSPITAL, KENNEWICK, WA, p. A667
KENSINGTON HOSPITAL, PHILADELPHIA, PA, p. A535
KENT COUNTY MEMORIAL HOSPITAL, WARWICK, RI, p. A547
KENTFIELD REHABILITATION AND SPECIALTY HOSPITAL, KENTFIELD, CA, p. A65
KENTUCKIANA MEDICAL CENTER, CLARKSVILLE, IN, p. A200
KENTUCKY CHILDREN'S HOSPITAL, LEXINGTON, KENTUCKY (see UNIVERSITY OF KENTUCKY ALBERT B. CHANDLER HOSPITAL), p. A254
KENTUCKY RIVER MEDICAL CENTER, JACKSON, KY, p. A253
KEOKUK AREA HOSPITAL, KEOKUK, IA, p. A224

KEOKUK COUNTY HEALTH CENTER, SIGOURNEY, IA, p. A228
KERN MEDICAL CENTER, BAKERSFIELD, CA, p. A54
KERN VALLEY HEALTHCARE DISTRICT, LAKE ISABELLA, CA, p. A66
KERNAN ORTHOPAEDICS AND REHABILITATION, BALTIMORE, MD, p. A287
KERNERSVILLE MEDICAL CENTER, KERNERSVILLE, NORTH CAROLINA (see NOVANT HEALTH FORSYTH MEDICAL CENTER), p. A463
KERRVILLE DIVISION, KERRVILLE, TEXAS (see SOUTH TEXAS VETERANS HEALTH CARE SYSTEM), p. A632
KERRVILLE STATE HOSPITAL, KERRVILLE, TX, p. A616
KERSHAWHEALTH, CAMDEN, SC, p. A548
KESSLER INSTITUTE FOR REHABILITATION, WEST ORANGE, NJ, p. A412
KESSLER INSTITUTE FOR REHABILITATION, CHESTER, NEW JERSEY (see KESSLER INSTITUTE FOR REHABILITATION), p. A412
KESSLER INSTITUTE FOR REHABILITATION, SADDLE BROOK, NEW JERSEY (see KESSLER INSTITUTE FOR REHABILITATION), p. A412
KESSLER INSTITUTE FOR REHABILITATION, WEST ORANGE, NEW JERSEY (see KESSLER INSTITUTE FOR REHABILITATION), p. A412
KETTERING MEDICAL CENTER, KETTERING, OH, p. A483
KEWANEE HOSPITAL, KEWANEE, IL, p. A186
KEYSTONE NEWPORT NEWS, NEWPORT NEWS, VA, p. A657
KIDSPEACE CHILDREN'S HOSPITAL, OREFIELD, PA, p. A533
KILMICHAEL HOSPITAL, KILMICHAEL, MS, p. A349
KIMBALL HEALTH SERVICES, KIMBALL, NE, p. A385
KIMBALL MEDICAL CENTER, LAKEWOOD, NJ, p. A405
KIMBALL–RIDGE CENTER, WATERLOO, IOWA (see COVENANT MEDICAL CENTER), p. A229
KIMBLE HOSPITAL, JUNCTION, TX, p. A615
KINDRED CHICAGO LAKESHORE, CHICAGO, ILLINOIS (see KINDRED CHICAGO–CENTRAL HOSPITAL), p. A177
KINDRED CHICAGO–CENTRAL HOSPITAL, CHICAGO, IL, p. A177
KINDRED HOSPITAL ARIZONA–NORTHWEST PHOENIX, PEORIA, ARIZONA (see KINDRED HOSPITAL ARIZONA–PHOENIX), p. A34
KINDRED HOSPITAL ARIZONA–PHOENIX, PHOENIX, AZ, p. A34
KINDRED HOSPITAL BAY AREA–TAMPA, TAMPA, FL, p. A141
KINDRED HOSPITAL BAYTOWN, BAYTOWN, TEXAS (see KINDRED HOSPITAL EAST HOUSTON), p. A591
KINDRED HOSPITAL BOSTON–NORTH SHORE, PEABODY, MA, p. A303
KINDRED HOSPITAL CHICAGO NORTH, CHICAGO, ILLINOIS (see KINDRED CHICAGO–CENTRAL HOSPITAL), p. A177
KINDRED HOSPITAL CHICAGO–NORTHLAKE, NORTHLAKE, IL, p. A190
KINDRED HOSPITAL CLEVELAND–GATEWAY, CLEVELAND, OH, p. A476
KINDRED HOSPITAL DALLAS CENTRAL, DALLAS, TX, p. A596
KINDRED HOSPITAL DALLAS–WALNUT HILL, DALLAS, TEXAS (see KINDRED HOSPITAL–DALLAS), p. A596
KINDRED HOSPITAL DETROIT, DETROIT, MI, p. A312
KINDRED HOSPITAL EAST HOUSTON, CHANNELVIEW, TX, p. A591
KINDRED HOSPITAL EASTON, EASTON, PA, p. A525
KINDRED HOSPITAL EL PASO, EL PASO, TX, p. A601
KINDRED HOSPITAL FARGO, FARGO, ND, p. A466
KINDRED HOSPITAL INDIANAPOLIS SOUTH, GREENWOOD, IN, p. A204
KINDRED HOSPITAL KANSAS CITY, KANSAS CITY, MO, p. A363
KINDRED HOSPITAL LAFAYETTE, LAFAYETTE, LA, p. A270
KINDRED HOSPITAL LAS VEGAS, DESERT SPRINGS CAMPUS, LAS VEGAS, NEVADA (see KINDRED HOSPITAL LAS VEGAS–SAHARA), p. A393
KINDRED HOSPITAL LAS VEGAS–SAHARA, LAS VEGAS, NV, p. A393
KINDRED HOSPITAL LIMA, LIMA, OH, p. A484
KINDRED HOSPITAL LOUISVILLE AT JEWISH HOSPITAL, LOUISVILLE, KENTUCKY (see KINDRED HOSPITAL–LOUISVILLE), p. A255
KINDRED HOSPITAL MELBOURNE, MELBOURNE, FL, p. A130
KINDRED HOSPITAL MIDTOWN, HOUSTON, TX, p. A610
KINDRED HOSPITAL NEW JERSEY – RAHWAY, RAHWAY, NEW JERSEY (see KINDRED HOSPITAL–NEW JERSEY MORRIS COUNTY), p. A403
KINDRED HOSPITAL NEW JERSEY – WAYNE, WAYNE, NEW JERSEY (see KINDRED HOSPITAL–NEW JERSEY MORRIS COUNTY), p. A403
KINDRED HOSPITAL NORTH FLORIDA, GREEN COVE SPRINGS, FL, p. A125
KINDRED HOSPITAL NORTH HOUSTON, HOUSTON, TX, p. A610
KINDRED HOSPITAL NORTHEAST–STOUGHTON, STOUGHTON, MA, p. A305
KINDRED HOSPITAL NORTHLAND, KANSAS CITY, MO, p. A363
KINDRED HOSPITAL NORTHWEST INDIANA, HAMMOND, IN, p. A204

## L

## M

METHODIST HOSPITAL, HENDERSON, KY, p. A252
METHODIST HOSPITAL, SAN ANTONIO, TX, p. A631
METHODIST HOSPITAL, PHILADELPHIA, PENNSYLVANIA (*see* THOMAS JEFFERSON UNIVERSITY HOSPITAL), p. A537
METHODIST HOSPITAL FOR SURGERY, ADDISON, TX, p. A581
METHODIST HOSPITAL OF CHICAGO, CHICAGO, IL, p. A177
METHODIST HOSPITAL OF SACRAMENTO, SACRAMENTO, CA, p. A83
METHODIST HOSPITAL OF SOUTHERN CALIFORNIA, ARCADIA, CA, p. A53
METHODIST HOSPITAL UNION COUNTY, MORGANFIELD, KY, p. A258
METHODIST HOSPITALS, GARY, IN, p. A203
METHODIST JENNIE EDMUNDSON HOSPITAL, COUNCIL BLUFFS, IA, p. A219
METHODIST LE BONHEUR GERMANTOWN HOSPITAL, GERMANTOWN, TENNESSEE (*see* METHODIST HEALTHCARE MEMPHIS HOSPITALS), p. A575
METHODIST MANSFIELD MEDICAL CENTER, MANSFIELD, TX, p. A621
METHODIST MCKINNEY HOSPITAL, MCKINNEY, TX, p. A622
METHODIST MEDICAL CENTER OF OAK RIDGE, OAK RIDGE, TN, p. A578
METHODIST REHABILITATION CENTER, JACKSON, MS, p. A348
METHODIST REHABILITATION HOSPITAL, DALLAS, TX, p. A596
METHODIST RICHARDSON MEDICAL CENTER, RICHARDSON, TX, p. A628
METHODIST SPECIALTY AND TRANSPLANT HOSPITAL, SAN ANTONIO, TEXAS (*see* METHODIST HOSPITAL), p. A631
METHODIST STONE OAK HOSPITAL, SAN ANTONIO, TX, p. A631
METHODIST SUGAR LAND HOSPITAL, SUGAR LAND, TX, p. A635
METHODIST TEXSAN HOSPITAL, SAN ANTONIO, TEXAS (*see* METHODIST HOSPITAL), p. A631
METHODIST WEST HOSPITAL, WEST DES MOINES, IOWA (*see* IOWA METHODIST MEDICAL CENTER), p. A220
METHODIST WEST HOUSTON HOSPITAL, HOUSTON, TX, p. A611
METHODIST WILLOWBROOK HOSPITAL, HOUSTON, TX, p. A611
METHODIST WOMEN'S HOSPITAL, ELKHORN, NEBRASKA (*see* NEBRASKA METHODIST HOSPITAL), p. A388
METRO HEALTH HOSPITAL, WYOMING, MI, p. A327
METROHEALTH MEDICAL CENTER, CLEVELAND, OH, p. A476
METROPLEX ADVENTIST HOSPITAL, KILLEEN, TX, p. A616
METROPOLITAN GENERAL CARE UNIT, METROPOLITAN DRUG DETOXIFICATION AND METROPOLITAN PSYCHIATRIC UNIT (*see* METROPOLITAN HOSPITAL CENTER), p. A434
METROPOLITAN HOSPITAL CENTER, NEW YORK, NY, p. A434
METROPOLITAN HOSPITAL OF MIAMI, MIAMI, FL, p. A131
METROPOLITAN METHODIST HOSPITAL, SAN ANTONIO, TEXAS (*see* METHODIST HOSPITAL), p. A631
METROPOLITAN ST. LOUIS PSYCHIATRIC CENTER, SAINT LOUIS, MO, p. A370
METROPOLITAN STATE HOSPITAL, NORWALK, CA, p. A76
METROSOUTH MEDICAL CENTER, BLUE ISLAND, IL, p. A174
METROWEST MEDICAL CENTER, FRAMINGHAM, MA, p. A300
MIAMI CHILDREN'S HOSPITAL, MIAMI, FL, p. A132
MIAMI COUNTY MEDICAL CENTER, PAOLA, KS, p. A242
MIAMI HEART CAMPUS AT MOUNT SINAI MEDICAL CENTER, MIAMI BEACH, FLORIDA (*see* MOUNT SINAI MEDICAL CENTER), p. A133
MIAMI JEWISH HOME AND HOSPITAL FOR AGED, MIAMI, FL, p. A132
MIAMI VALLEY HOSPITAL, DAYTON, OH, p. A480
MIAMI VETERANS AFFAIRS HEALTHCARE SYSTEM, MIAMI, FL, p. A132
MICHAEL E. DEBAKEY VETERANS AFFAIRS MEDICAL CENTER, HOUSTON, TX, p. A611
MICHIANA BEHAVIORAL HEALTH CENTER, PLYMOUTH, IN, p. A212
MID COAST HOSPITAL, BRUNSWICK, ME, p. A282
MID–AMERICA REHABILITATION HOSPITAL, SHAWNEE MISSION, KS, p. A244
MID–COLUMBIA MEDICAL CENTER, THE DALLES, OR, p. A518
MID–HUDSON FORENSIC PSYCHIATRIC CENTER, NEW HAMPTON, NY, p. A430
MID–JEFFERSON EXTENDED CARE HOSPITAL, NEDERLAND, TX, p. A624
MID–VALLEY HOSPITAL, PECKVILLE, PA, p. A534
MID–VALLEY HOSPITAL, OMAK, WA, p. A669
MIDDLE PARK MEDICAL CENTER, KREMMLING, CO, p. A102
MIDDLE TENNESSEE MENTAL HEALTH INSTITUTE, NASHVILLE, TN, p. A576
MIDDLESBORO ARH HOSPITAL, MIDDLESBORO, KY, p. A257
MIDDLESEX HOSPITAL, MIDDLETOWN, CT, p. A110
MIDLAND MEMORIAL HOSPITAL, MIDLAND, TX, p. A623
MIDLAND MEMORIAL HOSPITAL, MIDLAND, TEXAS (*see* MIDLAND MEMORIAL HOSPITAL), p. A623
MIDMICHIGAN MEDICAL CENTER–CLARE, CLARE, MI, p. A310

MIDMICHIGAN MEDICAL CENTER–GLADWIN, GLADWIN, MI, p. A314
MIDMICHIGAN MEDICAL CENTER–GRATIOT, ALMA, MI, p. A308
MIDMICHIGAN MEDICAL CENTER–MIDLAND, MIDLAND, MI, p. A320
MIDSTATE MEDICAL CENTER, MERIDEN, CT, p. A109
MIDWEST MEDICAL CENTER, GALENA, IL, p. A183
MIDWEST ORTHOPEDIC SPECIALTY HOSPITAL, FRANKLIN, WI, p. A686
MIDWEST REGIONAL MEDICAL CENTER, MIDWEST CITY, OK, p. A501
MIDWEST SURGICAL HOSPITAL, OMAHA, NE, p. A388
MIDWESTERN REGIONAL MEDICAL CENTER, ZION, IL, p. A197
MIKE O'CALLAGHAN FEDERAL HOSPITAL, NELLIS AFB, NV, p. A394
MILAN GENERAL HOSPITAL, MILAN, TN, p. A575
MILBANK AREA HOSPITAL AVERA, MILBANK, SD, p. A560
MILDRED MITCHELL–BATEMAN HOSPITAL, HUNTINGTON, WV, p. A677
MILE BLUFF MEDICAL CENTER, MAUSTON, WI, p. A690
MILES MEMORIAL HOSPITAL, DAMARISCOTTA, ME, p. A283
MILFORD HOSPITAL, MILFORD, CT, p. A110
MILFORD REGIONAL MEDICAL CENTER, MILFORD, MA, p. A302
MILFORD VALLEY MEMORIAL HOSPITAL, MILFORD, UT, p. A644
MILLARD FILLMORE SUBURBAN HOSPITAL, WILLIAMSVILLE, NEW YORK (*see* KALEIDA HEALTH), p. A422
MILLCREEK COMMUNITY HOSPITAL, ERIE, PA, p. A525
MILLE LACS HEALTH SYSTEM, ONAMIA, MN, p. A337
MILLER CHILDREN'S HOSPITAL, LONG BEACH, CA, p. A67
MILLER COUNTY HOSPITAL, COLQUITT, GA, p. A150
MILLINOCKET REGIONAL HOSPITAL, MILLINOCKET, ME, p. A284
MILLS HOSPITAL, SAN MATEO, CALIFORNIA (*see* MILLS–PENINSULA HEALTH SERVICES), p. A55
MILLS–PENINSULA HEALTH SERVICES, BURLINGAME, CA, p. A55
MILLWOOD HOSPITAL, ARLINGTON, TX, p. A583
MILWAUKEE COUNTY BEHAVIORAL HEALTH DIVISION, MILWAUKEE, WI, p. A692
MIMBRES MEMORIAL HOSPITAL, DEMING, NM, p. A415
MINDEN MEDICAL CENTER, MINDEN, LA, p. A274
MINERAL AREA REGIONAL MEDICAL CENTER, FARMINGTON, MO, p. A360
MINERAL COMMUNITY HOSPITAL, SUPERIOR, MT, p. A380
MINERS' COLFAX MEDICAL CENTER, RATON, NM, p. A417
MINERS' HOSPITAL OF NEW MEXICO, RATON, NEW MEXICO (*see* MINERS' COLFAX MEDICAL CENTER), p. A417
MINIDOKA MEMORIAL HOSPITAL, RUPERT, ID, p. A171
MINIMALLY INVASIVE SURGERY CENTER, LENEXA, KS, p. A238
MINISTRY DOOR COUNTY MEDICAL CENTER, STURGEON BAY, WI, p. A697
MINISTRY EAGLE RIVER MEMORIAL HOSPITAL, EAGLE RIVER, WI, p. A686
MINISTRY GOOD SAMARITAN HEALTH CENTER, MERRILL, WI, p. A691
MINISTRY OUR LADY OF VICTORY HOSPITAL, STANLEY, WI, p. A697
MINISTRY SACRED HEART HOSPITAL, TOMAHAWK, WI, p. A698
MINISTRY SAINT CLARE'S HOSPITAL, WESTON, WI, p. A699
MINISTRY SAINT JOSEPH'S HOSPITAL, MARSHFIELD, WI, p. A690
MINISTRY SAINT MARY'S HOSPITALS, RHINELANDER, WI, p. A695
MINISTRY SAINT MICHAEL'S HOSPITAL, STEVENS POINT, WI, p. A697
MINNEAPOLIS VETERANS AFFAIRS HEALTH CARE SYSTEM, MINNEAPOLIS, MN, p. A336
MINNEOLA DISTRICT HOSPITAL, MINNEOLA, KS, p. A240
MINNESOTA NEUROREHABILITATION HOSPITAL, BRAINERD, MN, p. A329
MINNESOTA VALLEY HEALTH CENTER, LE SUEUR, MN, p. A334
MINNIE HAMILTON HEALTHCARE CENTER, GRANTSVILLE, WV, p. A677
MIRACLE MILE MEDICAL CENTER, LOS ANGELES, CA, p. A70
MIRIAM HOSPITAL, PROVIDENCE, RI, p. A546
MISSION CHILDREN'S HOSPITAL, ASHEVILLE, NORTH CAROLINA (*see* MISSION HOSPITAL), p. A447
MISSION COMMUNITY HOSPITAL,, CA, p. A70
MISSION HOSPITAL, MISSION VIEJO, CA, p. A74
MISSION HOSPITAL, ASHEVILLE, NC, p. A447
MISSION HOSPITAL LAGUNA BEACH, LAGUNA BEACH, CALIFORNIA (*see* MISSION HOSPITAL), p. A74
MISSION REGIONAL MEDICAL CENTER, MISSION, TX, p. A623
MISSION TRAIL BAPTIST HOSPITAL, SAN ANTONIO, TEXAS (*see* BAPTIST MEDICAL CENTER), p. A630
MISSISSIPPI BAPTIST MEDICAL CENTER, JACKSON, MS, p. A348
MISSISSIPPI HOSPITAL FOR RESTORATIVE CARE, JACKSON, MS, p. A349
MISSISSIPPI STATE HOSPITAL, WHITFIELD, MS, p. A355

MISSOURI BAPTIST MEDICAL CENTER, SAINT LOUIS, MO, p. A370
MISSOURI BAPTIST SULLIVAN HOSPITAL, SULLIVAN, MO, p. A372
MISSOURI DELTA MEDICAL CENTER, SIKESTON, MO, p. A371
MISSOURI REHABILITATION CENTER, MOUNT VERNON, MO, p. A366
MISSOURI RIVER MEDICAL CENTER, FORT BENTON, MT, p. A376
MITCHELL COUNTY HOSPITAL, CAMILLA, GA, p. A149
MITCHELL COUNTY HOSPITAL, COLORADO CITY, TX, p. A592
MITCHELL COUNTY HOSPITAL HEALTH SYSTEMS, BELOIT, KS, p. A232
MITCHELL COUNTY REGIONAL HEALTH CENTER, OSAGE, IA, p. A226
MIZELL MEMORIAL HOSPITAL, OPP, AL, p. A24
MMO REHABILITATION AND WELLNESS CENTER, PLAQUEMINE, LA, p. A277
MMO WESTEND HOSPITAL, JENNINGS, LA, p. A269
MOAB REGIONAL HOSPITAL, MOAB, UT, p. A644
MOBERLY REGIONAL MEDICAL CENTER, MOBERLY, MO, p. A366
MOBILE INFIRMARY MEDICAL CENTER, MOBILE, AL, p. A22
MOBRIDGE REGIONAL HOSPITAL, MOBRIDGE, SD, p. A561
MOCCASIN BEND MENTAL HEALTH INSTITUTE, CHATTANOOGA, TN, p. A566
MODESTO MEDICAL CENTER, MODESTO, CALIFORNIA (*see* KAISER PERMANENTE MANTECA MEDICAL CENTER), p. A73
MODOC MEDICAL CENTER, ALTURAS, CA, p. A52
MOHAWK VALLEY PSYCHIATRIC CENTER, UTICA, NY, p. A444
MOLOKAI GENERAL HOSPITAL, KAUNAKAKAI, HI, p. A166
MONADNOCK COMMUNITY HOSPITAL, PETERBOROUGH, NH, p. A400
MONCKS CORNER MEDICAL CENTER, MONCKS CORNER, SOUTH CAROLINA (*see* TRIDENT MEDICAL CENTER), p. A549
MONCRIEF ARMY COMMUNITY HOSPITAL, FORT JACKSON, SC, p. A552
MONMOUTH MEDICAL CENTER, LONG BRANCH, NJ, p. A406
MONONGAHELA VALLEY HOSPITAL, MONONGAHELA, PA, p. A532
MONONGALIA GENERAL HOSPITAL, MORGANTOWN, WV, p. A679
MONROE CARELL JR. CHILDREN'S HOSPITAL AT VANDERBILT, NASHVILLE, TENNESSEE (*see* VANDERBILT HOSPITAL AND CLINICS), p. A577
MONROE CLINIC, MONROE, WI, p. A693
MONROE COUNTY HOSPITAL, MONROEVILLE, AL, p. A23
MONROE COUNTY HOSPITAL, FORSYTH, GA, p. A153
MONROE COUNTY HOSPITAL, ALBIA, IA, p. A216
MONROE COUNTY MEDICAL CENTER, TOMPKINSVILLE, KY, p. A260
MONROE HOSPITAL, BLOOMINGTON, IN, p. A199
MONROE SURGICAL HOSPITAL, MONROE, LA, p. A274
MONROVIA MEMORIAL HOSPITAL, MONROVIA, CA, p. A74
MONTANA STATE HOSPITAL, WARM SPRINGS, MT, p. A380
MONTCLAIR HOSPITAL MEDICAL CENTER, MONTCLAIR, CA, p. A74
MONTEFIORE MEDICAL CENTER,, NY, p. A434
MONTEFIORE MEDICAL CENTER – NORTH DIVISION,, NEW YORK (*see* MONTEFIORE MEDICAL CENTER), p. A434
MONTEREY PARK HOSPITAL, MONTEREY PARK, CA, p. A75
MONTEVISTA HOSPITAL, LAS VEGAS, NV, p. A393
MONTFORT JONES MEMORIAL HOSPITAL, KOSCIUSKO, MS, p. A349
MONTGOMERY COUNTY EMERGENCY SERVICE, NORRISTOWN, PA, p. A533
MONTGOMERY COUNTY MEMORIAL HOSPITAL, RED OAK, IA, p. A227
MONTGOMERY DIVISION, MONTGOMERY, ALABAMA (*see* CENTRAL ALABAMA VETERANS HEALTH CARE SYSTEM), p. A23
MONTGOMERY GENERAL HOSPITAL, MONTGOMERY, WV, p. A678
MONTPELIER HOSPITAL, MONTPELIER, OHIO (*see* COMMUNITY HOSPITALS AND WELLNESS CENTERS), p. A472
MONTROSE MEMORIAL HOSPITAL, MONTROSE, CO, p. A104
MOORE COUNTY HOSPITAL DISTRICT, DUMAS, TX, p. A599
MOORE MEDICAL CENTER, MOORE, OKLAHOMA (*see* NORMAN REGIONAL HEALTH SYSTEM), p. A502
MOREHEAD MEMORIAL HOSPITAL, EDEN, NC, p. A451
MOREHOUSE GENERAL HOSPITAL, BASTROP, LA, p. A263
MORGAN COUNTY ARH HOSPITAL, WEST LIBERTY, KY, p. A261
MORGAN MEMORIAL HOSPITAL, MADISON, GA, p. A157
MORGAN STANLEY CHILDREN'S HOSPITAL OF NEW YORK–PRESBYTERIAN, NEW YORK, NEW YORK (*see* NEW YORK–PRESBYTERIAN HOSPITAL), p. A435
MORRILL COUNTY COMMUNITY HOSPITAL, BRIDGEPORT, NE, p. A382
MORRIS COUNTY HOSPITAL, COUNCIL GROVE, KS, p. A233

MORRIS HOSPITAL & HEALTHCARE CENTERS, MORRIS, IL, p. A189

MORRISON COMMUNITY HOSPITAL, MORRISON, IL, p. A189

MORRISTOWN MEDICAL CENTER, MORRISTOWN, NJ, p. A406

MORRISTOWN–HAMBLEN HEALTHCARE SYSTEM, MORRISTOWN, TN, p. A576

MORROW COUNTY HOSPITAL, MOUNT GILEAD, OH, p. A486

MORTON COUNTY HEALTH SYSTEM, ELKHART, KS, p. A233

MORTON GENERAL HOSPITAL, MORTON, WA, p. A668

MORTON HOSPITAL AND MEDICAL CENTER, TAUNTON, MA, p. A305

MORTON PLANT HOSPITAL, CLEARWATER, FL, p. A120

MORTON PLANT NORTH BAY HOSPITAL, NEW PORT RICHEY, FL, p. A133

MOSES H. CONE MEMORIAL HOSPITAL, GREENSBORO, NORTH CAROLINA (see CONE HEALTH), p. A453

MOSES LUDINGTON HOSPITAL, TICONDEROGA, NY, p. A444

MOSES TAYLOR HOSPITAL, SCRANTON, PA, p. A540

MOTHER FRANCES HOSPITAL – JACKSONVILLE, JACKSONVILLE, TX, p. A615

MOTHER FRANCES HOSPITAL – TYLER, TYLER, TX, p. A638

MOTHER FRANCES HOSPITAL – WINNSBORO, WINNSBORO, TX, p. A642

MOTION PICTURE AND TELEVISION FUND HOSPITAL AND RESIDENTIAL SERVICES,, CA, p. A70

MOUNDVIEW MEMORIAL HOSPITAL & CLINICS, FRIENDSHIP, WI, p. A687

MOUNT AUBURN HOSPITAL, CAMBRIDGE, MA, p. A299

MOUNT CARMEL, COLUMBUS, OH, p. A477

MOUNT CARMEL EAST HOSPITAL, COLUMBUS, OHIO (see MOUNT CARMEL), p. A477

MOUNT CARMEL NEW ALBANY SURGICAL HOSPITAL, NEW ALBANY, OH, p. A487

MOUNT CARMEL ST. ANN'S, WESTERVILLE, OH, p. A493

MOUNT CARMEL WEST HOSPITAL, COLUMBUS, OHIO (see MOUNT CARMEL), p. A477

MOUNT DESERT ISLAND HOSPITAL, BAR HARBOR, ME, p. A281

MOUNT GRANT GENERAL HOSPITAL, HAWTHORNE, NV, p. A392

MOUNT NITTANY MEDICAL CENTER, STATE COLLEGE, PA, p. A541

MOUNT PLEASANT HOSPITAL, MOUNT PLEASANT, SC, p. A554

MOUNT SINAI HOSPITAL, CHICAGO, IL, p. A177

MOUNT SINAI HOSPITAL, NEW YORK, NY, p. A434

MOUNT SINAI MEDICAL CENTER, MIAMI BEACH, FL, p. A133

MOUNT SINAI REHABILITATION HOSPITAL, HARTFORD, CT, p. A109

MOUNT ST. MARY'S HOSPITAL AND HEALTH CENTER, LEWISTON, NY, p. A428

MOUNT VERNON HOSPITAL, MOUNT VERNON, NY, p. A430

MOUNTAIN CREST HOSPITAL, FORT COLLINS, COLORADO (see POUDRE VALLEY HOSPITAL), p. A101

MOUNTAIN LAKES MEDICAL CENTER, CLAYTON, GA, p. A150

MOUNTAIN RIVER BIRTHING AND SURGERY CENTER, BLACKFOOT, ID, p. A167

MOUNTAIN VALLEY REGIONAL REHABILITATION HOSPITAL, PRESCOTT VALLEY, AZ, p. A36

MOUNTAIN VIEW HOSPITAL, GADSDEN, AL, p. A20

MOUNTAIN VIEW HOSPITAL, IDAHO FALLS, ID, p. A169

MOUNTAIN VIEW HOSPITAL, PAYSON, UT, p. A645

MOUNTAIN VIEW REGIONAL HOSPITAL, CASPER, WY, p. A701

MOUNTAIN VIEW REGIONAL MEDICAL CENTER, NORTON, VA, p. A658

MOUNTAIN VISTA MEDICAL CENTER, MESA, AZ, p. A33

MOUNTAIN WEST MEDICAL CENTER, TOOELE, UT, p. A647

MOUNTAINVIEW HOSPITAL, LAS VEGAS, NV, p. A393

MOUNTAINVIEW MEDICAL CENTER, WHITE SULPHUR SPRINGS, MT, p. A380

MOUNTAINVIEW REGIONAL MEDICAL CENTER, LAS CRUCES, NM, p. A416

MOUNTRAIL COUNTY MEDICAL CENTER, STANLEY, ND, p. A469

MT. ASCUTNEY HOSPITAL AND HEALTH CENTER, WINDSOR, VT, p. A650

MT. GRAHAM REGIONAL MEDICAL CENTER, SAFFORD, AZ, p. A36

MT. SAN RAFAEL HOSPITAL, TRINIDAD, CO, p. A106

MT. WASHINGTON PEDIATRIC HOSPITAL, BALTIMORE, MD, p. A288

MUENSTER MEMORIAL HOSPITAL, MUENSTER, TX, p. A624

MUHLENBERG COMMUNITY HOSPITAL, GREENVILLE, KY, p. A252

MULESHOE AREA MEDICAL CENTER, MULESHOE, TX, p. A624

MULTICARE AUBURN MEDICAL CENTER, AUBURN, WA, p. A664

MULTICARE GOOD SAMARITAN HOSPITAL, PUYALLUP, WA, p. A669

MULTICARE MARY BRIDGE CHILDREN'S HOSPITAL AND HEALTH CENTER, TACOMA, WA, p. A673

MULTICARE TACOMA GENERAL HOSPITAL, TACOMA, WA, p. A673

MUNCY VALLEY HOSPITAL, MUNCY, PA, p. A532

---

MUNISING MEMORIAL HOSPITAL, MUNISING, MI, p. A320

MUNROE REGIONAL MEDICAL CENTER, OCALA, FL, p. A134

MUNSON MEDICAL CENTER, TRAVERSE CITY, MI, p. A325

MURPHY MEDICAL CENTER, MURPHY, NC, p. A458

MURRAY COUNTY MEDICAL CENTER, SLAYTON, MN, p. A341

MURRAY MEDICAL CENTER, CHATSWORTH, GA, p. A149

MURRAY–CALLOWAY COUNTY HOSPITAL, MURRAY, KY, p. A258

MUSC CHILDREN'S HOSPITAL, CHARLESTON, SOUTH CAROLINA (see MUSC MEDICAL CENTER OF MEDICAL UNIVERSITY OF SOUTH CAROLINA), p. A549

MUSC MEDICAL CENTER OF MEDICAL UNIVERSITY OF SOUTH CAROLINA, CHARLESTON, SC, p. A549

MUSKOGEE COMMUNITY HOSPITAL, MUSKOGEE, OKLAHOMA (see MUSKOGEE REGIONAL MEDICAL CENTER), p. A502

MUSKOGEE REGIONAL MEDICAL CENTER, MUSKOGEE, OK, p. A502

MYRTUE MEDICAL CENTER, HARLAN, IA, p. A222

# N

NACOGDOCHES MEDICAL CENTER, NACOGDOCHES, TX, p. A624

NACOGDOCHES MEMORIAL HOSPITAL, NACOGDOCHES, TX, p. A624

NANTICOKE MEMORIAL HOSPITAL, SEAFORD, DE, p. A114

NANTUCKET COTTAGE HOSPITAL, NANTUCKET, MA, p. A302

NAPA STATE HOSPITAL, NAPA, CA, p. A76

NASH HEALTH CARE SYSTEMS, ROCKY MOUNT, NC, p. A460

NASHOBA VALLEY MEDICAL CENTER, AYER, MA, p. A295

NASHVILLE CAMPUS, NASHVILLE, TENNESSEE (see TENNESSEE VALLEY HEALTHCARE SYSTEM), p. A577

NASHVILLE GENERAL HOSPITAL, NASHVILLE, TN, p. A576

NASON HOSPITAL, ROARING SPRING, PA, p. A540

NASSAU UNIVERSITY MEDICAL CENTER, EAST MEADOW, NY, p. A425

NATCHAUG HOSPITAL, MANSFIELD CENTER, CT, p. A109

NATCHEZ COMMUNITY HOSPITAL, NATCHEZ, MS, p. A351

NATCHEZ REGIONAL MEDICAL CENTER, NATCHEZ, MS, p. A351

NATCHITOCHES REGIONAL MEDICAL CENTER, NATCHITOCHES, LA, p. A274

NATHAN LITTAUER HOSPITAL AND NURSING HOME, GLOVERSVILLE, NY, p. A426

NATIONAL INSTITUTES OF HEALTH CLINICAL CENTER, BETHESDA, MD, p. A290

NATIONAL JEWISH HEALTH, DENVER, CO, p. A99

NATIONAL PARK MEDICAL CENTER, HOT SPRINGS, AR, p. A45

NATIONWIDE CHILDREN'S HOSPITAL, COLUMBUS, OH, p. A477

NATIVIDAD MEDICAL CENTER, SALINAS, CA, p. A84

NAVAL HOSPITAL, LEMOORE, CA, p. A66

NAVAL HOSPITAL BEAUFORT, BEAUFORT, SC, p. A548

NAVAL HOSPITAL BREMERTON, BREMERTON, WA, p. A664

NAVAL HOSPITAL CAMP LEJEUNE, CAMP LEJEUNE, NC, p. A449

NAVAL HOSPITAL CAMP PENDLETON, CAMP PENDLETON, CA, p. A55

NAVAL HOSPITAL JACKSONVILLE, JACKSONVILLE, FL, p. A126

NAVAL HOSPITAL OAK HARBOR, OAK HARBOR, WA, p. A668

NAVAL HOSPITAL PENSACOLA, PENSACOLA, FL, p. A136

NAVAL MEDICAL CENTER, PORTSMOUTH, VA, p. A659

NAVAL MEDICAL CENTER SAN DIEGO, SAN DIEGO, CA, p. A85

NAVARRO REGIONAL HOSPITAL, CORSICANA, TX, p. A594

NAVOS, SEATTLE, WA, p. A670

NAZARETH HOSPITAL, PHILADELPHIA, PA, p. A536

NCH DOWNTOWN NAPLES HOSPITAL, NAPLES, FL, p. A133

NCH NORTH NAPLES HOSPITAL, NAPLES, FLORIDA (see NCH DOWNTOWN NAPLES HOSPITAL), p. A133

NEA BAPTIST MEMORIAL HOSPITAL, JONESBORO, AR, p. A45

NEBRASKA HEART HOSPITAL, LINCOLN, NE, p. A385

NEBRASKA MEDICAL CENTER, OMAHA, NE, p. A388

NEBRASKA METHODIST HOSPITAL, OMAHA, NE, p. A388

NEBRASKA ORTHOPAEDIC HOSPITAL, OMAHA, NE, p. A388

NEBRASKA PENAL AND CORRECTIONAL HOSPITAL, LINCOLN, NE, p. A385

NEBRASKA SPINE HOSPITAL, OMAHA, NE, p. A388

NEILLSVILLE MEMORIAL HOME (see MEMORIAL MEDICAL CENTER – NEILLSVILLE), p. A693

NELSON COUNTY HEALTH SYSTEM, MCVILLE, ND, p. A468

NEMAHA COUNTY HOSPITAL, AUBURN, NE, p. A381

NEMAHA VALLEY COMMUNITY HOSPITAL, SENECA, KS, p. A244

NEMOURS CHILDREN'S HOSPITAL, ORLANDO, FL, p. A135

NEOSHO MEMORIAL REGIONAL MEDICAL CENTER, CHANUTE, KS, p. A232

NESHOBA COUNTY GENERAL HOSPITAL, PHILADELPHIA, MS, p. A352

NESS COUNTY HOSPITAL, NESS CITY, KS, p. A240

NEUROMEDICAL CENTER REHABILITATION HOSPITAL, BATON ROUGE, LA, p. A263

---

NEVADA REGIONAL MEDICAL CENTER, NEVADA, MO, p. A367

NEW BEDFORD REHABILITATION HOSPITAL, NEW BEDFORD, MA, p. A302

NEW BRAUNFELS REGIONAL REHABILITATION HOSPITAL, NEW BRAUNFELS, TX, p. A624

NEW BRITAIN GENERAL, NEW BRITAIN, CONNECTICUT (see THE HOSPITAL OF CENTRAL CONNECTICUT), p. A110

NEW ENGLAND BAPTIST HOSPITAL, BOSTON, MA, p. A297

NEW ENGLAND REHABILITATION HOSPITAL, WOBURN, MA, p. A306

NEW ENGLAND REHABILITATION HOSPITAL OF PORTLAND, PORTLAND, ME, p. A285

NEW ENGLAND SINAI HOSPITAL AND REHABILITATION CENTER, STOUGHTON, MA, p. A305

NEW HAMPSHIRE HOSPITAL, CONCORD, NH, p. A397

NEW HANOVER REGIONAL MEDICAL CENTER, WILMINGTON, NC, p. A463

NEW HORIZONS HEALTH SYSTEMS, OWENTON, KY, p. A258

NEW LONDON FAMILY MEDICAL CENTER, NEW LONDON, WI, p. A693

NEW LONDON HOSPITAL, NEW LONDON, NH, p. A399

NEW MEXICO BEHAVIORAL HEALTH INSTITUTE AT LAS VEGAS, LAS VEGAS, NM, p. A417

NEW MEXICO REHABILITATION CENTER, ROSWELL, NM, p. A417

NEW MILFORD HOSPITAL, NEW MILFORD, CT, p. A111

NEW ULM MEDICAL CENTER, NEW ULM, MN, p. A337

NEW YORK CITY CHILDREN'S CENTER,, NY, p. A434

NEW YORK COMMUNITY HOSPITAL,, NY, p. A434

NEW YORK DOWNTOWN HOSPITAL, NEW YORK, NY, p. A435

NEW YORK EYE AND EAR INFIRMARY, NEW YORK, NY, p. A435

NEW YORK HOSPITAL QUEENS,, NY, p. A435

NEW YORK METHODIST HOSPITAL,, NY, p. A435

NEW YORK STATE PSYCHIATRIC INSTITUTE, NEW YORK, NY, p. A435

NEW YORK–PRESBYTERIAN HOSPITAL, NEW YORK, NY, p. A435

NEW YORK–PRESBYTERIAN HOSPITAL, WESTCHESTER DIVISION, WHITE PLAINS, NEW YORK (see NEW YORK–PRESBYTERIAN HOSPITAL), p. A435

NEW YORK–PRESBYTERIAN HOSPITAL/WEILL CORNELL MEDICAL CENTER, NEW YORK, NEW YORK (see NEW YORK–PRESBYTERIAN HOSPITAL), p. A435

NEW YORK–PRESBYTERIAN/COLUMBIA UNIVERSITY MEDICAL CENTER, NEW YORK, NEW YORK (see NEW YORK–PRESBYTERIAN HOSPITAL), p. A435

NEWARK BETH ISRAEL MEDICAL CENTER, NEWARK, NJ, p. A407

NEWARK–WAYNE COMMUNITY HOSPITAL, NEWARK, NY, p. A437

NEWBERRY COUNTY MEMORIAL HOSPITAL, NEWBERRY, SC, p. A555

NEWMAN MEMORIAL HOSPITAL, SHATTUCK, OK, p. A506

NEWMAN REGIONAL HEALTH, EMPORIA, KS, p. A233

NEWPORT BAY HOSPITAL, NEWPORT BEACH, CA, p. A76

NEWPORT HOSPITAL, NEWPORT, RI, p. A546

NEWPORT HOSPITAL AND HEALTH SERVICES, NEWPORT, WA, p. A668

NEWPORT MEDICAL CENTER, NEWPORT, TN, p. A577

NEWPORT SPECIALTY HOSPITAL, TUSTIN, CA, p. A93

NEWTON MEDICAL CENTER, COVINGTON, GA, p. A151

NEWTON MEDICAL CENTER, NEWTON, KS, p. A240

NEWTON MEDICAL CENTER, NEWTON, NJ, p. A408

NEWTON–WELLESLEY HOSPITAL, NEWTON LOWER FALLS, MA, p. A303

NEXUS SPECIALTY HOSPITAL, SHENANDOAH, TX, p. A633

NEXUS SPECIALTY HOSPITAL THE WOODLANDS, SPRING, TX, p. A634

NIAGARA FALLS MEMORIAL MEDICAL CENTER, NIAGARA FALLS, NY, p. A437

NICHOLAS COUNTY HOSPITAL, CARLISLE, KY, p. A249

NICHOLAS H. NOYES MEMORIAL HOSPITAL, DANSVILLE, NY, p. A424

NIOBRARA HEALTH AND LIFE CENTER, LUSK, WY, p. A703

NIOBRARA VALLEY HOSPITAL, LYNCH, NE, p. A386

NISWONGER CHILDREN'S HOSPITAL, JOHNSON CITY, TENNESSEE (see JOHNSON CITY MEDICAL CENTER), p. A571

NIX HEALTH CARE SYSTEM, SAN ANTONIO, TX, p. A632

NOBLE HOSPITAL, WESTFIELD, MA, p. A306

NOCONA GENERAL HOSPITAL, NOCONA, TX, p. A625

NOLAND HOSPITAL ANNISTON, ANNISTON, AL, p. A15

NOLAND HOSPITAL BIRMINGHAM, BIRMINGHAM, AL, p. A16

NOLAND HOSPITAL DOTHAN, DOTHAN, AL, p. A19

NOLAND HOSPITAL MONTGOMERY, MONTGOMERY, AL, p. A23

NOLAND HOSPITAL SHELBY, ALABASTER, AL, p. A15

NOLAND HOSPITAL TUSCALOOSA, TUSCALOOSA, AL, p. A26

NOR–LEA GENERAL HOSPITAL, LOVINGTON, NM, p. A417

NORFOLK REGIONAL CENTER, NORFOLK, NE, p. A386

NORMAN REGIONAL HEALTH SYSTEM, NORMAN, OK, p. A502

NORMAN REGIONAL HOSPITAL, NORMAN, OKLAHOMA (see NORMAN REGIONAL HEALTH SYSTEM), p. A502
NORMAN SPECIALTY HOSPITAL, NORMAN, OK, p. A502
NORRISTOWN STATE HOSPITAL, NORRISTOWN, PA, p. A533
NORTH ADAMS REGIONAL HOSPITAL, NORTH ADAMS, MA, p. A303
NORTH ALABAMA REGIONAL HOSPITAL, DECATUR, AL, p. A19
NORTH ARKANSAS REGIONAL MEDICAL CENTER, HARRISON, AR, p. A44
NORTH BALDWIN INFIRMARY, BAY MINETTE, AL, p. A16
NORTH BIG HORN HOSPITAL DISTRICT, LOVELL, WY, p. A703
NORTH CADDO MEDICAL CENTER, VIVIAN, LA, p. A280
NORTH CANYON MEDICAL CENTER, GOODING, ID, p. A169
NORTH CAROLINA CHILDREN'S AND WOMEN'S HOSPITAL, NORTH CAROLINA CHILDREN'S HOSPITAL, CHAPEL HILL, NORTH CAROLINA (see UNIVERSITY OF NORTH CAROLINA HOSPITALS), p. A449
NORTH CAROLINA NEUROSCIENCES HOSPITAL, CHAPEL HILL, NORTH CAROLINA (see UNIVERSITY OF NORTH CAROLINA HOSPITALS), p. A449
NORTH CAROLINA SPECIALTY HOSPITAL, DURHAM, NC, p. A451
NORTH CENTRAL BAPTIST HOSPITAL, SAN ANTONIO, TEXAS (see BAPTIST MEDICAL CENTER), p. A630
NORTH CENTRAL BRONX HOSPITAL,, NY, p. A435
NORTH CENTRAL HEALTH CARE, WAUSAU, WI, p. A699
NORTH CENTRAL SURGICAL CENTER, DALLAS, TX, p. A597
NORTH COLORADO MEDICAL CENTER, GREELEY, CO, p. A102
NORTH COUNTRY HOSPITAL AND HEALTH CENTER, NEWPORT, VT, p. A650
NORTH CYPRESS MEDICAL CENTER, CYPRESS, TX, p. A594
NORTH DAKOTA STATE HOSPITAL, JAMESTOWN, ND, p. A468
NORTH FLORIDA REGIONAL MEDICAL CENTER, GAINESVILLE, FL, p. A124
NORTH FULTON REGIONAL HOSPITAL, ROSWELL, GA, p. A159
NORTH GEORGIA MEDICAL CENTER, ELLIJAY, GA, p. A153
NORTH GREENVILLE HOSPITAL, TRAVELERS REST, SC, p. A556
NORTH HAWAII COMMUNITY HOSPITAL, KAMUELA, HI, p. A165
NORTH HILLS HOSPITAL, NORTH RICHLAND HILLS, TX, p. A625
NORTH IDAHO BEHAVIORAL HEALTH, DIVISION OF KOOTENAI MEDICAL CENTER, COEUR D'ALENE, IDAHO (see KOOTENAI MEDICAL CENTER), p. A168
NORTH KANSAS CITY HOSPITAL, NORTH KANSAS CITY, MO, p. A367
NORTH KNOXVILLE MEDICAL CENTER, POWELL, TENNESSEE (see PHYSICIANS REGIONAL MEDICAL CENTER), p. A572
NORTH LITTLE ROCK DIVISION, NORTH LITTLE ROCK, ARKANSAS (see CENTRAL ARKANSAS VETERANS HEALTHCARE SYSTEM), p. A46
NORTH MEMORIAL MEDICAL CENTER, ROBBINSDALE, MN, p. A338
NORTH METRO MEDICAL CENTER, JACKSONVILLE, AR, p. A45
NORTH MISSISSIPPI MEDICAL CENTER – TUPELO, TUPELO, MS, p. A354
NORTH MISSISSIPPI MEDICAL CENTER–EUPORA, EUPORA, MS, p. A346
NORTH MISSISSIPPI MEDICAL CENTER–HAMILTON, HAMILTON, AL, p. A21
NORTH MISSISSIPPI MEDICAL CENTER–IUKA, IUKA, MS, p. A348
NORTH MISSISSIPPI MEDICAL CENTER–PONTOTOC HOSPITAL AND NURSING HOME, PONTOTOC, MS, p. A352
NORTH MISSISSIPPI MEDICAL CENTER–WEST POINT, WEST POINT, MS, p. A355
NORTH MISSISSIPPI STATE HOSPITAL, TUPELO, MS, p. A354
NORTH OAK REGIONAL MEDICAL CENTER, SENATOBIA, MS, p. A353
NORTH OAKS MEDICAL CENTER, HAMMOND, LA, p. A268
NORTH OAKS REHABILITATION HOSPITAL, HAMMOND, LA, p. A268
NORTH OKALOOSA MEDICAL CENTER, CRESTVIEW, FL, p. A121
NORTH OTTAWA COMMUNITY HOSPITAL, GRAND HAVEN, MI, p. A314
NORTH PHILADELPHIA HEALTH SYSTEM, PHILADELPHIA, PA, p. A536
NORTH RUNNELS HOSPITAL, WINTERS, TX, p. A642
NORTH SHORE MEDICAL CENTER, MIAMI, FL, p. A132
NORTH SHORE MEDICAL CENTER, SALEM, MA, p. A304
NORTH SHORE MEDICAL CENTER, FLORIDA MEDICAL CENTER CAMPUS, FORT LAUDERDALE, FL, p. A123
NORTH SHORE UNIVERSITY HOSPITAL, MANHASSET, NY, p. A429
NORTH STAR BEHAVIORAL HEALTH, ANCHORAGE, ALASKA (see NORTH STAR BEHAVIORAL HEALTH SYSTEM), p. A27
NORTH STAR BEHAVIORAL HEALTH SYSTEM, ANCHORAGE, AK, p. A27
NORTH SUBURBAN MEDICAL CENTER, THORNTON, CO, p. A106
NORTH SUNFLOWER MEDICAL CENTER, RULEVILLE, MS, p. A353

NORTH TEXAS COMMUNITY HOSPITAL, BRIDGEPORT, TX, p. A589
NORTH TEXAS HOSPITAL, DENTON, TX, p. A599
NORTH TEXAS MEDICAL CENTER, GAINESVILLE, TX, p. A605
NORTH TEXAS STATE HOSPITAL, VERNON, TX, p. A639
NORTH TEXAS STATE HOSPITAL, WICHITA FALLS CAMPUS, WICHITA FALLS, TX, p. A641
NORTH VALLEY HEALTH CENTER, WARREN, MN, p. A342
NORTH VALLEY HOSPITAL, WHITEFISH, MT, p. A380
NORTH VALLEY HOSPITAL, TONASKET, WA, p. A673
NORTH VISTA HOSPITAL, NORTH LAS VEGAS, NV, p. A394
NORTHBAY MEDICAL CENTER, FAIRFIELD, CA, p. A59
NORTHBAY VACAVALLEY HOSPITAL, VACAVILLE, CALIFORNIA (see NORTHBAY MEDICAL CENTER), p. A59
NORTHCOAST BEHAVIORAL HEALTHCARE SYSTEM, NORTHFIELD, OH, p. A487
NORTHCREST MEDICAL CENTER, SPRINGFIELD, TN, p. A579
NORTHEAST ALABAMA REGIONAL MEDICAL CENTER, ANNISTON, AL, p. A15
NORTHEAST BAPTIST HOSPITAL, SAN ANTONIO, TEXAS (see BAPTIST MEDICAL CENTER), p. A630
NORTHEAST GEORGIA MEDICAL CENTER, GAINESVILLE, GA, p. A154
NORTHEAST METHODIST HOSPITAL, LIVE OAK, TEXAS (see METHODIST HOSPITAL), p. A631
NORTHEAST REGIONAL MEDICAL CENTER, KIRKSVILLE, MO, p. A364
NORTHEAST REHABILITATION HOSPITAL, SALEM, NH, p. A400
NORTHEASTERN CENTER, AUBURN, IN, p. A198
NORTHEASTERN NEVADA REGIONAL HOSPITAL, ELKO, NV, p. A391
NORTHEASTERN VERMONT REGIONAL HOSPITAL, SAINT JOHNSBURY, VT, p. A650
NORTHERN ARIZONA VETERANS AFFAIRS HEALTH CARE SYSTEM, PRESCOTT, AZ, p. A36
NORTHERN COCHISE COMMUNITY HOSPITAL, WILLCOX, AZ, p. A39
NORTHERN COLORADO LONG TERM ACUTE HOSPITAL, JOHNSTOWN, CO, p. A102
NORTHERN COLORADO REHABILITATION HOSPITAL, JOHNSTOWN, CO, p. A102
NORTHERN DUTCHESS HOSPITAL, RHINEBECK, NY, p. A440
NORTHERN HOSPITAL OF SURRY COUNTY, MOUNT AIRY, NC, p. A458
NORTHERN IDAHO ADVANCED CARE HOSPITAL, POST FALLS, ID, p. A171
NORTHERN INYO HOSPITAL, BISHOP, CA, p. A55
NORTHERN LOUISIANA MEDICAL CENTER, RUSTON, LA, p. A277
NORTHERN MAINE MEDICAL CENTER, FORT KENT, ME, p. A283
NORTHERN MONTANA HOSPITAL, HAVRE, MT, p. A377
NORTHERN NAVAJO MEDICAL CENTER, SHIPROCK, NM, p. A418
NORTHERN NEVADA ADULT MENTAL HEALTH SERVICES, SPARKS, NV, p. A395
NORTHERN NEVADA MEDICAL CENTER, SPARKS, NV, p. A396
NORTHERN ROCKIES MEDICAL CENTER, CUT BANK, MT, p. A375
NORTHERN VIRGINIA MENTAL HEALTH INSTITUTE, FALLS CHURCH, VA, p. A653
NORTHERN WESTCHESTER HOSPITAL, MOUNT KISCO, NY, p. A430
NORTHFIELD CAMPUS, NORTHFIELD, OHIO (see NORTHCOAST BEHAVIORAL HEALTHCARE SYSTEM), p. A487
NORTHFIELD HOSPITAL, NORTHFIELD, MN, p. A337
NORTHKEY COMMUNITY CARE, COVINGTON, KY, p. A250
NORTHLAKE BEHAVIORAL HOSPITAL, MANDEVILLE, LA, p. A273
NORTHPORT MEDICAL CENTER, NORTHPORT, AL, p. A24
NORTHPORT VETERANS AFFAIRS MEDICAL CENTER, NORTHPORT, NY, p. A437
NORTHRIDGE HOSPITAL MEDICAL CENTER–ROSCOE BOULEVARD CAMPUS,, CA, p. A70
NORTHRIDGE MEDICAL CENTER, COMMERCE, GA, p. A150
NORTHSHORE GLENBROOK HOSPITAL, GLENVIEW, ILLINOIS (see NORTHSHORE UNIVERSITY HEALTH SYSTEM EVANSTON HOSPITAL), p. A182
NORTHSHORE HIGHLAND PARK HOSPITAL, HIGHLAND PARK, ILLINOIS (see NORTHSHORE UNIVERSITY HEALTH SYSTEM EVANSTON HOSPITAL), p. A182
NORTHSHORE SPECIALTY HOSPITAL, COVINGTON, LA, p. A266
NORTHSHORE UNIVERSITY HEALTH SYSTEM EVANSTON HOSPITAL, EVANSTON, IL, p. A182
NORTHSHORE UNIVERSITY HEALTH SYSTEM SKOKIE HOSPITAL, SKOKIE, IL, p. A194
NORTHSIDE HOSPITAL, ATLANTA, GA, p. A146
NORTHSIDE HOSPITAL AND HEART INSTITUTE, SAINT PETERSBURG, FL, p. A139
NORTHSIDE HOSPITAL–CHEROKEE, CANTON, GA, p. A149
NORTHSIDE HOSPITAL–FORSYTH, CUMMING, GA, p. A151
NORTHSIDE MEDICAL CENTER, YOUNGSTOWN, OH, p. A494

NORTHSIDE MEDICAL CENTER, YOUNGSTOWN, OHIO (see NORTHSIDE MEDICAL CENTER), p. A494
NORTHSTAR HEALTH SYSTEM, IRON RIVER, MI, p. A317
NORTHWEST CENTER FOR BEHAVIORAL HEALTH, FORT SUPPLY, OK, p. A499
NORTHWEST COMMUNITY HOSPITAL, ARLINGTON HEIGHTS, IL, p. A173
NORTHWEST FLORIDA COMMUNITY HOSPITAL, CHIPLEY, FL, p. A120
NORTHWEST HILLS SURGICAL HOSPITAL, AUSTIN, TX, p. A585
NORTHWEST HOSPITAL, RANDALLSTOWN, MD, p. A293
NORTHWEST MEDICAL CENTER, WINFIELD, AL, p. A26
NORTHWEST MEDICAL CENTER, TUCSON, AZ, p. A39
NORTHWEST MEDICAL CENTER, SPRINGDALE, AR, p. A50
NORTHWEST MEDICAL CENTER, MARGATE, FL, p. A130
NORTHWEST MEDICAL CENTER, ALBANY, MO, p. A356
NORTHWEST MEDICAL CENTER – BENTONVILLE, BENTONVILLE, ARKANSAS (see NORTHWEST MEDICAL CENTER), p. A50
NORTHWEST MISSISSIPPI REGIONAL MEDICAL CENTER, CLARKSDALE, MS, p. A345
NORTHWEST MISSOURI PSYCHIATRIC REHABILITATION CENTER, SAINT JOSEPH, MO, p. A369
NORTHWEST OHIO PSYCHIATRIC HOSPITAL, TOLEDO, OH, p. A491
NORTHWEST SPECIALTY HOSPITAL, POST FALLS, ID, p. A171
NORTHWEST SURGICAL HOSPITAL, OKLAHOMA CITY, OK, p. A503
NORTHWEST TEXAS HEALTHCARE SYSTEM, AMARILLO, TX, p. A582
NORTHWEST TEXAS SURGERY CENTER, AMARILLO, TX, p. A582
NORTHWESTERN LAKE FOREST HOSPITAL, LAKE FOREST, IL, p. A186
NORTHWESTERN MEDICAL CENTER, SAINT ALBANS, VT, p. A650
NORTHWESTERN MEMORIAL HOSPITAL, CHICAGO, IL, p. A178
NORTON AUDUBON HOSPITAL, LOUISVILLE, KY, p. A256
NORTON BROWNSBORO HOSPITAL, LOUISVILLE, KY, p. A256
NORTON COMMUNITY HOSPITAL, NORTON, VA, p. A658
NORTON COUNTY HOSPITAL, NORTON, KS, p. A240
NORTON HEALTHCARE PAVILION, LOUISVILLE, KENTUCKY (see NORTON HOSPITAL), p. A256
NORTON HOSPITAL, LOUISVILLE, KY, p. A256
NORTON SOUND REGIONAL HOSPITAL, NOME, AK, p. A28
NORTON SUBURBAN HOSPITAL, LOUISVILLE, KY, p. A256
NORWALK HOSPITAL, NORWALK, CT, p. A111
NORWEGIAN AMERICAN HOSPITAL, CHICAGO, IL, p. A178
NORWOOD HEALTH CENTER, MARSHFIELD, WI, p. A690
NORWOOD HOSPITAL, NORWOOD, MA, p. A303
NOVANT HEALTH BRUNSWICK MEDICAL CENTER, BOLIVIA, NC, p. A448
NOVANT HEALTH CHARLOTTE ORTHOPAEDIC HOSPITAL, CHARLOTTE, NC, p. A450
NOVANT HEALTH FORSYTH MEDICAL CENTER, WINSTON–SALEM, NC, p. A463
NOVANT HEALTH FRANKLIN MEDICAL CENTER, LOUISBURG, NC, p. A456
NOVANT HEALTH GAFFNEY MEDICAL CENTER, GAFFNEY, SC, p. A552
NOVANT HEALTH HUNTERSVILLE MEDICAL CENTER, HUNTERSVILLE, NC, p. A455
NOVANT HEALTH MATTHEWS MEDICAL CENTER, MATTHEWS, NC, p. A457
NOVANT HEALTH MEDICAL PARK HOSPITAL, WINSTON–SALEM, NC, p. A463
NOVANT HEALTH PRESBYTERIAN MEDICAL CENTER, CHARLOTTE, NC, p. A450
NOVANT HEALTH PRINCE WILLIAM MEDICAL CENTER, MANASSAS, VA, p. A656
NOVANT HEALTH ROWAN MEDICAL CENTER, SALISBURY, NC, p. A460
NOVANT HEALTH THOMASVILLE MEDICAL CENTER, THOMASVILLE, NC, p. A462
NOVATO COMMUNITY HOSPITAL, NOVATO, CA, p. A76
NOXUBEE GENERAL HOSPITAL, MACON, MS, p. A350
NYACK HOSPITAL, NYACK, NY, p. A438
NYE REGIONAL MEDICAL CENTER, TONOPAH, NV, p. A396
NYU CHILDREN'S HOSPITAL, NEW YORK, NEW YORK (see NYU LANGONE MEDICAL CENTER), p. A435
NYU LANGONE MEDICAL CENTER, NEW YORK, NY, p. A435
NYU LANGONE MEDICAL CENTER'S HOSPITAL FOR JOINT DISEASES, NEW YORK, NEW YORK (see NYU LANGONE MEDICAL CENTER), p. A435

PALM SPRINGS GENERAL HOSPITAL, HIALEAH, FL, p. A125
PALMDALE REGIONAL MEDICAL CENTER, PALMDALE, CA, p. A78
PALMER LUTHERAN HEALTH CENTER, WEST UNION, IA, p. A230
PALMERTON HOSPITAL, PALMERTON, PA, p. A533
PALMETTO GENERAL HOSPITAL, HIALEAH, FL, p. A125
PALMETTO HEALTH BAPTIST, COLUMBIA, SC, p. A550
PALMETTO HEALTH CHILDREN'S HOSPITAL, COLUMBIA, SOUTH CAROLINA (see PALMETTO HEALTH RICHLAND), p. A550
PALMETTO HEALTH RICHLAND, COLUMBIA, SC, p. A550
PALMETTO LOWCOUNTRY BEHAVIORAL HEALTH, CHARLESTON, SC, p. A549
PALMS OF PASADENA HOSPITAL, SAINT PETERSBURG, FL, p. A139
PALMS WEST HOSPITAL, LOXAHATCHEE, FL, p. A129
PALO ALTO COUNTY HEALTH SYSTEM, EMMETSBURG, IA, p. A221
PALO ALTO DIVISION, PALO ALTO, CALIFORNIA (see VETERANS AFFAIRS PALO ALTO HEALTH CARE SYSTEM), p. A79
PALO PINTO GENERAL HOSPITAL, MINERAL WELLS, TX, p. A623
PALO VERDE HOSPITAL, BLYTHE, CA, p. A55
PALO VERDE MENTAL HEALTH SERVICES, TUCSON, ARIZONA (see TMC HEALTHCARE), p. A39
PALOMAR MEDICAL CENTER, ESCONDIDO, CA, p. A59
PALOS COMMUNITY HOSPITAL, PALOS HEIGHTS, IL, p. A191
PAMPA REGIONAL MEDICAL CENTER, PAMPA, TX, p. A626
PANA COMMUNITY HOSPITAL, PANA, IL, p. A191
PAOLI HOSPITAL, PAOLI, PA, p. A534
PARADISE VALLEY HOSPITAL, PHOENIX, AZ, p. A35
PARADISE VALLEY HOSPITAL, NATIONAL CITY, CA, p. A76
PARIS COMMUNITY HOSPITAL, PARIS, IL, p. A191
PARIS REGIONAL MEDICAL CENTER, PARIS, TX, p. A626
PARIS REGIONAL MEDICAL CENTER, PARIS, TEXAS (see PARIS REGIONAL MEDICAL CENTER), p. A626
PARIS REGIONAL MEDICAL CENTER–SOUTH CAMPUS, PARIS, TEXAS (see PARIS REGIONAL MEDICAL CENTER), p. A626
PARK CITY MEDICAL CENTER, PARK CITY, UT, p. A645
PARK NICOLLET METHODIST HOSPITAL, SAINT LOUIS PARK, MN, p. A339
PARK PLACE SURGICAL HOSPITAL, LAFAYETTE, LA, p. A271
PARK PLAZA HOSPITAL, HOUSTON, TX, p. A611
PARK RIDGE HEALTH, HENDERSONVILLE, NC, p. A454
PARK ROYAL HOSPITAL, FORT MYERS, FL, p. A124
PARKCARE PAVILION, YONKERS, NEW YORK (see ST. JOHN'S RIVERSIDE HOSPITAL), p. A446
PARKER ADVENTIST HOSPITAL, PARKER, CO, p. A105
PARKLAND HEALTH & HOSPITAL SYSTEM, DALLAS, TX, p. A597
PARKLAND HEALTH CENTER, FARMINGTON, MO, p. A360
PARKLAND HEALTH CENTER–BONNE TERRE, BONNE TERRE, MO, p. A356
PARKLAND MEDICAL CENTER, DERRY, NH, p. A397
PARKRIDGE EAST HOSPITAL, CHATTANOOGA, TENNESSEE (see PARKRIDGE MEDICAL CENTER), p. A567
PARKRIDGE MEDICAL CENTER, CHATTANOOGA, TN, p. A567
PARKRIDGE VALLEY HOSPTIAL, CHATTANOOGA, TENNESSEE (see PARKRIDGE MEDICAL CENTER), p. A567
PARKSIDE HOSPITAL, TULSA, OK, p. A508
PARKVIEW ORTHO HOSPITAL, FORT WAYNE, IN, p. A202
PARKVIEW ADVENTIST MEDICAL CENTER, BRUNSWICK, ME, p. A282
PARKVIEW COMMUNITY HOSPITAL MEDICAL CENTER, RIVERSIDE, CA, p. A82
PARKVIEW HOSPITAL, WHEELER, TX, p. A641
PARKVIEW HUNTINGTON HOSPITAL, HUNTINGTON, IN, p. A205
PARKVIEW LAGRANGE HOSPITAL, LAGRANGE, IN, p. A208
PARKVIEW MEDICAL CENTER, PUEBLO, CO, p. A105
PARKVIEW NOBLE HOSPITAL, KENDALLVILLE, IN, p. A207
PARKVIEW REGIONAL HOSPITAL, MEXIA, TX, p. A623
PARKVIEW REGIONAL MEDICAL CENTER, FORT WAYNE, IN, p. A202
PARKVIEW WHITLEY HOSPITAL, COLUMBIA CITY, IN, p. A200
PARKWAY REGIONAL HOSPITAL, FULTON, KY, p. A251
PARKWEST MEDICAL CENTER, KNOXVILLE, TN, p. A572
PARKWOOD BEHAVIORAL HEALTH SYSTEM, OLIVE BRANCH, MS, p. A352
PARMA COMMUNITY GENERAL HOSPITAL, PARMA, OH, p. A488
PARMER MEDICAL CENTER, FRIONA, TX, p. A605
PARRISH MEDICAL CENTER, TITUSVILLE, FL, p. A143
PARSONS STATE HOSPITAL AND TRAINING CENTER, PARSONS, KS, p. A242
PASSAVANT AREA HOSPITAL, JACKSONVILLE, IL, p. A186
PATEWOOD MEMORIAL HOSPITAL, GREENVILLE, SC, p. A552
PATHWAY REHABILITATION HOSPITAL, BOSSIER CITY, LA, p. A264
PATHWAYS OF TENNESSEE, JACKSON, TN, p. A570
PATHWAYS TREATMENT CENTER, KALISPELL, MONTANA (see KALISPELL REGIONAL MEDICAL CENTER), p. A377

PATIENT'S CHOICE MEDICAL CENTER OF CLAIBORNE COUNTY, PORT GIBSON, MS, p. A353
PATIENT'S CHOICE MEDICAL CENTER OF HUMPHREYS COUNTY, BELZONI, MS, p. A344
PATIENTS CHOICE MEDICAL CENTER OF SMITH COUNTY, RALEIGH, MS, p. A353
PATIENTS' HOSPITAL OF REDDING, REDDING, CA, p. A81
PATRICK B. HARRIS PSYCHIATRIC HOSPITAL, ANDERSON, SC, p. A548
PATTON STATE HOSPITAL, PATTON, CA, p. A79
PAUL B. HALL REGIONAL MEDICAL CENTER, PAINTSVILLE, KY, p. A259
PAUL OLIVER MEMORIAL HOSPITAL, FRANKFORT, MI, p. A314
PAULDING COUNTY HOSPITAL, PAULDING, OH, p. A488
PAULS VALLEY GENERAL HOSPITAL, PAULS VALLEY, OK, p. A505
PAWHUSKA HOSPITAL, PAWHUSKA, OK, p. A505
PAWNEE COUNTY MEMORIAL HOSPITAL AND RURAL HEALTH CLINIC, PAWNEE CITY, NE, p. A389
PAWNEE VALLEY COMMUNITY HOSPITAL, LARNED, KS, p. A238
PAYNE WHITNEY PSYCHIATRIC CLINIC, NEW YORK, NEW YORK (see NEW YORK–PRESBYTERIAN HOSPITAL), p. A435
PAYNESVILLE AREA HEALTH CARE SYSTEM, PAYNESVILLE, MN, p. A338
PAYSON REGIONAL MEDICAL CENTER, PAYSON, AZ, p. A34
PEACEHEALTH COTTAGE GROVE COMMUNITY MEDICAL CENTER, COTTAGE GROVE, OR, p. A512
PEACEHEALTH KETCHIKAN MEDICAL CENTER, KETCHIKAN, AK, p. A28
PEACEHEALTH PEACE HARBOR MEDICAL CENTER, FLORENCE, OR, p. A512
PEACEHEALTH PEACE ISLAND MEDICAL CENTER, FRIDAY HARBOR, WA, p. A666
PEACEHEALTH SACRED HEART MEDICAL CENTER AT RIVERBEND, SPRINGFIELD, OR, p. A518
PEACEHEALTH SACRED HEART MEDICAL CENTER, UNIVERSITY DISTRICT, EUGENE, OR, p. A512
PEACEHEALTH SOUTHWEST MEDICAL CENTER, VANCOUVER, WA, p. A674
PEACEHEALTH ST. JOHN MEDICAL CENTER, LONGVIEW, WA, p. A667
PEACEHEALTH ST. JOSEPH MEDICAL CENTER, BELLINGHAM, WA, p. A664
PEACH REGIONAL MEDICAL CENTER, FORT VALLEY, GA, p. A154
PEACHFORD BEHAVIORAL HEALTH SYSTEM, ATLANTA, GA, p. A146
PEAK BEHAVIORAL HEALTH SERVICES, SANTA TERESA, NM, p. A418
PEAK VIEW BEHAVIORAL HEALTH, COLORADO SPRINGS, CO, p. A98
PEARL RIVER COUNTY HOSPITAL, POPLARVILLE, MS, p. A353
PECONIC BAY MEDICAL CENTER, RIVERHEAD, NY, p. A440
PECOS COUNTY MEMORIAL HOSPITAL, FORT STOCKTON, TX, p. A603
PECOS VALLEY LODGE, ROSWELL, NEW MEXICO (see NEW MEXICO REHABILITATION CENTER), p. A417
PEKIN HOSPITAL, PEKIN, IL, p. A191
PELLA REGIONAL HEALTH CENTER, PELLA, IA, p. A227
PEMBINA COUNTY MEMORIAL HOSPITAL AND WEDGEWOOD MANOR, CAVALIER, ND, p. A466
PEMBROKE HOSPITAL, PEMBROKE, MA, p. A303
PEMISCOT MEMORIAL HEALTH SYSTEM, HAYTI, MO, p. A361
PEN BAY MEDICAL CENTER, ROCKPORT, ME, p. A285
PENDER COMMUNITY HOSPITAL, PENDER, NE, p. A389
PENDER MEMORIAL HOSPITAL, BURGAW, NC, p. A448
PENINSULA HOSPITAL, BURLINGAME, CALIFORNIA (see MILLS–PENINSULA HEALTH SERVICES), p. A55
PENINSULA HOSPITAL, LOUISVILLE, TN, p. A573
PENINSULA REGIONAL MEDICAL CENTER, SALISBURY, MD, p. A294
PENN PRESBYTERIAN MEDICAL CENTER, PHILADELPHIA, PA, p. A536
PENN STATE CHILDREN'S HOSPITAL, HERSHEY, PENNSYLVANIA (see PENN STATE MILTON S. HERSHEY MEDICAL CENTER), p. A527
PENN STATE HERSHEY REHABILITATION HOSPITAL, HUMMELSTOWN, PA, p. A527
PENN STATE MILTON S. HERSHEY MEDICAL CENTER, HERSHEY, PA, p. A527
PENNOCK HOSPITAL, HASTINGS, MI, p. A316
PENNSYLVANIA HOSPITAL, PHILADELPHIA, PA, p. A536
PENNSYLVANIA PSYCHIATRIC INSTITUTE, HARRISBURG, PA, p. A527
PENOBSCOT VALLEY HOSPITAL, LINCOLN, ME, p. A284
PENROSE HOSPITAL, COLORADO SPRINGS, COLORADO (see PENROSE–ST. FRANCIS HEALTH SERVICES), p. A98
PENROSE–ST. FRANCIS HEALTH SERVICES, COLORADO SPRINGS, CO, p. A98
PERHAM HEALTH, PERHAM, MN, p. A338

PERKINS COUNTY HEALTH SERVICES, GRANT, NE, p. A384
PERMIAN REGIONAL MEDICAL CENTER, ANDREWS, TX, p. A583
PERRY COMMUNITY HOSPITAL, LINDEN, TN, p. A573
PERRY COUNTY GENERAL HOSPITAL, RICHTON, MS, p. A353
PERRY COUNTY MEMORIAL HOSPITAL, TELL CITY, IN, p. A213
PERRY COUNTY MEMORIAL HOSPITAL, PERRYVILLE, MO, p. A367
PERRY HOSPITAL, PERRY, GA, p. A158
PERRY MEMORIAL HOSPITAL, PRINCETON, IL, p. A192
PERRY MEMORIAL HOSPITAL, PERRY, OK, p. A505
PERSHING GENERAL HOSPITAL, LOVELOCK, NV, p. A394
PERSON MEMORIAL HOSPITAL, ROXBORO, NC, p. A460
PERTH AMBOY DIVISION, PERTH AMBOY, NEW JERSEY (see RARITAN BAY MEDICAL CENTER), p. A409
PETALUMA VALLEY HOSPITAL, PETALUMA, CA, p. A79
PETERSBURG MEDICAL CENTER, PETERSBURG, AK, p. A29
PETERSON REGIONAL MEDICAL CENTER, KERRVILLE, TX, p. A616
PETERSON REHABILITATION HOSPITAL, WHEELING, WV, p. A682
PEYTON MANNING CHILDREN'S HOSPITAL, INDIANAPOLIS, INDIANA (see ST. VINCENT INDIANAPOLIS HOSPITAL), p. A206
PEYTON MANNING CHILDREN'S HOSPITAL AT ST. VINCENT, INDIANAPOLIS, INDIANA (see ST. VINCENT INDIANAPOLIS HOSPITAL), p. A206
PHELPS COUNTY REGIONAL MEDICAL CENTER, ROLLA, MO, p. A368
PHELPS MEMORIAL HEALTH CENTER, HOLDREGE, NE, p. A384
PHELPS MEMORIAL HOSPITAL CENTER, SLEEPY HOLLOW, NY, p. A442
PHILADEPHIA VETERANS AFFAIRS MEDICAL CENTER, PHILADELPHIA, PA, p. A536
PHILHAVEN, MOUNT GRETNA, PA, p. A532
PHILIP HEALTH SERVICES, PHILIP, SD, p. A561
PHILLIPS COUNTY HOSPITAL, PHILLIPSBURG, KS, p. A242
PHILLIPS COUNTY HOSPITAL, MALTA, MT, p. A378
PHILLIPS EYE INSTITUTE, MINNEAPOLIS, MN, p. A336
PHOEBE NORTH, ALBANY, GA, p. A145
PHOEBE PUTNEY MEMORIAL HOSPITAL, ALBANY, GA, p. A145
PHOEBE SUMTER MEDICAL CENTER, AMERICUS, GA, p. A145
PHOEBE WORTH MEDICAL CENTER, SYLVESTER, GA, p. A161
PHOENIX BAPTIST HOSPITAL, PHOENIX, AZ, p. A35
PHOENIX BEHAVIORAL HOSPITAL, RAYNE, LA, p. A277
PHOENIX CHILDREN'S HOSPITAL, PHOENIX, AZ, p. A35
PHOENIX VETERANS AFFAIRS HEALTH CARE SYSTEM, PHOENIX, AZ, p. A35
PHOENIXVILLE HOSPITAL, PHOENIXVILLE, PA, p. A537
PHS SANTA FE INDIAN HOSPITAL, SANTA FE, NM, p. A418
PHYLLIS AND DAVID KOMANSKY CENTER FOR CHILDREN'S HEALTH, NEW YORK, NEW YORK (see NEW YORK–PRESBYTERIAN HOSPITAL), p. A435
PHYSICIAN'S CHOICE HOSPITAL – FREMONT, FREMONT, OH, p. A482
PHYSICIANS BEHAVIORAL HOSPITAL, SHREVEPORT, LA, p. A278
PHYSICIANS CARE SURGICAL HOSPITAL, ROYERSFORD, PA, p. A540
PHYSICIANS MEDICAL CENTER, HOUMA, LA, p. A268
PHYSICIANS REGIONAL MEDICAL CENTER, KNOXVILLE, TN, p. A572
PHYSICIANS REGIONAL MEDICAL CENTER, NAPLES, FLORIDA (see PHYSICIANS REGIONAL MEDICAL CENTER – PINE RIDGE), p. A133
PHYSICIANS REGIONAL MEDICAL CENTER – PINE RIDGE, NAPLES, FL, p. A133
PHYSICIANS SURGICAL HOSPITAL – PANHANDLE CAMPUS, AMARILLO, TX, p. A582
PHYSICIANS SURGICAL HOSPITAL – QUAIL CREEK, AMARILLO, TX, p. A582
PHYSICIANS' HOSPITAL IN ANADARKO, ANADARKO, OK, p. A495
PHYSICIANS' MEDICAL CENTER, NEW ALBANY, IN, p. A211
PHYSICIANS' SPECIALTY HOSPITAL, FAYETTEVILLE, AR, p. A43
PICKENS COUNTY MEDICAL CENTER, CARROLLTON, AL, p. A18
PIEDMONT FAYETTE HOSPITAL, FAYETTEVILLE, GA, p. A153
PIEDMONT GERIATRIC HOSPITAL, BURKEVILLE, VA, p. A652
PIEDMONT HOSPITAL, ATLANTA, GA, p. A147
PIEDMONT MEDICAL CENTER, ROCK HILL, SC, p. A555
PIEDMONT MOUNTAINSIDE HOSPITAL, JASPER, GA, p. A155
PIEDMONT NEWNAN HOSPITAL, NEWNAN, GA, p. A158
PIGGOTT COMMUNITY HOSPITAL, PIGGOTT, AR, p. A49
PIKE COUNTY MEMORIAL HOSPITAL, LOUISIANA, MO, p. A365
PIKES PEAK REGIONAL HOSPITAL, WOODLAND PARK, CO, p. A107
PIKEVILLE MEDICAL CENTER, PIKEVILLE, KY, p. A259
PILGRIM PSYCHIATRIC CENTER, BRENTWOOD, NY, p. A422
PINCKNEYVILLE COMMUNITY HOSPITAL, PINCKNEYVILLE, IL, p. A192
PINE CREEK MEDICAL CENTER, DALLAS, TX, p. A597

PSYCHIATRIC PAVILION, AMARILLO, TEXAS (see NORTHWEST TEXAS HEALTHCARE SYSTEM), p. A582
PUBLIC HEALTH SERVICE INDIAN HOSPITAL – QUENTIN N. BURDICK MEMORIAL HEALTH FACILITY, BELCOURT, ND, p. A465
PULASKI MEMORIAL HOSPITAL, WINAMAC, IN, p. A215
PULLMAN REGIONAL HOSPITAL, PULLMAN, WA, p. A669
PUNXSUTAWNEY AREA HOSPITAL, PUNXSUTAWNEY, PA, p. A539
PURCELL MUNICIPAL HOSPITAL, PURCELL, OK, p. A506
PUSHMATAHA HOSPITAL & HOME HEALTH, ANTLERS, OK, p. A495
PUTNAM COMMUNITY MEDICAL CENTER, PALATKA, FL, p. A135
PUTNAM COUNTY HOSPITAL, GREENCASTLE, IN, p. A204
PUTNAM COUNTY MEMORIAL HOSPITAL, UNIONVILLE, MO, p. A373
PUTNAM GENERAL HOSPITAL, EATONTON, GA, p. A153
PUTNAM HOSPITAL CENTER, CARMEL, NY, p. A423

# Q

QUARTZ MOUNTAIN MEDICAL CENTER, MANGUM, OK, p. A501
QUEEN OF THE VALLEY MEDICAL CENTER, NAPA, CA, p. A76
QUEEN'S MEDICAL CENTER, HONOLULU, HI, p. A165
QUEENS HOSPITAL CENTER,, NY, p. A436
QUENTIN MEASE HOSPITAL, HOUSTON, TEXAS (see HARRIS HEALTH SYSTEM), p. A609
QUILLEN REHABILITATION HOSPITAL, JOHNSON CITY, TENNESSEE (see JOHNSON CITY MEDICAL CENTER), p. A571
QUINCY MEDICAL CENTER, QUINCY, MA, p. A304
QUINCY VALLEY MEDICAL CENTER, QUINCY, WA, p. A670
QUITMAN COUNTY HOSPITAL, MARKS, MS, p. A350

# R

RADIUS SPECIALTY HOSPITAL BOSTON, BOSTON, MA, p. A297
RADY CHILDREN'S HOSPITAL – SAN DIEGO, SAN DIEGO, CA, p. A85
RAINBOW MENTAL HEALTH FACILITY, KANSAS CITY, KS, p. A237
RAINY LAKE MEDICAL CENTER, INTERNATIONAL FALLS, MN, p. A334
RALEIGH GENERAL HOSPITAL, BECKLEY, WV, p. A675
RALPH H. JOHNSON VETERANS AFFAIRS MEDICAL CENTER, CHARLESTON, SC, p. A549
RANCHO LOS AMIGOS NATIONAL REHABILITATION CENTER, DOWNEY, CA, p. A58
RANCHO SPRINGS MEDICAL CENTER, MURRIETA, CALIFORNIA (see SOUTHWEST HEALTHCARE SYSTEM), p. A76
RANDALL CHILDREN'S HOSPITAL, PORTLAND, OREGON (see LEGACY EMANUEL HOSPITAL AND HEALTH CENTER), p. A516
RANDOLPH HOSPITAL, ASHEBORO, NC, p. A447
RANGE REGIONAL HEALTH SERVICES, HIBBING, MN, p. A334
RANGELY DISTRICT HOSPITAL, RANGELY, CO, p. A105
RANKEN JORDAN – A PEDIATRIC SPECIALTY HOSPITAL, MARYLAND HEIGHTS, MO, p. A365
RANKIN HOSPITAL DISTRICT, RANKIN, TX, p. A628
RANSOM MEMORIAL HOSPITAL, OTTAWA, KS, p. A241
RAPID CITY REGIONAL HOSPITAL, RAPID CITY, SD, p. A562
RAPIDES REGIONAL MEDICAL CENTER, ALEXANDRIA, LA, p. A262
RAPPAHANNOCK GENERAL HOSPITAL, KILMARNOCK, VA, p. A655
RARITAN BAY MEDICAL CENTER, PERTH AMBOY, NJ, p. A409
RAULERSON HOSPITAL, OKEECHOBEE, FL, p. A134
RAWLINS COUNTY HEALTH CENTER, ATWOOD, KS, p. A231
RAY COUNTY MEMORIAL HOSPITAL, RICHMOND, MO, p. A368
RAYMOND BLANK MEMORIAL HOSPITAL FOR CHILDREN, DES MOINES, IOWA (see IOWA METHODIST MEDICAL CENTER), p. A220
RC HOSPITAL AND CLINICS, OLIVIA, MN, p. A337
READING HOSPITAL AND MEDICAL CENTER, WEST READING, PA, p. A544
REAGAN MEMORIAL HOSPITAL, BIG LAKE, TX, p. A588
RECEPTION AND MEDICAL CENTER, LAKE BUTLER, FL, p. A128
RED BAY HOSPITAL, RED BAY, AL, p. A25
RED BUD REGIONAL HOSPITAL, RED BUD, IL, p. A193
RED RIVER BEHAVIORAL CENTER, BOSSIER CITY, LA, p. A264
RED RIVER HOSPITAL, WICHITA FALLS, TX, p. A641
RED RIVER REGIONAL HOSPITAL, BONHAM, TX, p. A589
RED ROCK BEHAVIORAL HOSPITAL, LAS VEGAS, NV, p. A393

REDINGTON–FAIRVIEW GENERAL HOSPITAL, SKOWHEGAN, ME, p. A285
REDLANDS COMMUNITY HOSPITAL, REDLANDS, CA, p. A82
REDMOND REGIONAL MEDICAL CENTER, ROME, GA, p. A159
REDWOOD AREA HOSPITAL, REDWOOD FALLS, MN, p. A338
REDWOOD MEMORIAL HOSPITAL, FORTUNA, CA, p. A60
REEDSBURG AREA MEDICAL CENTER, REEDSBURG, WI, p. A695
REEVES COUNTY HOSPITAL, PECOS, TX, p. A626
REEVES MEMORIAL MEDICAL CENTER, BERNICE, LA, p. A264
REFUGIO COUNTY MEMORIAL HOSPITAL, REFUGIO, TX, p. A628
REGENCY HOSPITAL CLEVELAND EAST, WARRENSVILLE HEIGHTS, OH, p. A492
REGENCY HOSPITAL OF AKRON, BARBERTON, OHIO (see REGENCY HOSPITAL CLEVELAND EAST), p. A492
REGENCY HOSPITAL OF CENTRAL GEORGIA, MACON, GA, p. A156
REGENCY HOSPITAL OF CINCINNATI, CINCINNATI, OH, p. A475
REGENCY HOSPITAL OF CLEVELAND – WEST, MIDDLEBURG HEIGHTS, OHIO (see REGENCY HOSPITAL CLEVELAND EAST), p. A492
REGENCY HOSPITAL OF COLUMBUS, COLUMBUS, OH, p. A478
REGENCY HOSPITAL OF COVINGTON, COVINGTON, LA, p. A266
REGENCY HOSPITAL OF FLORENCE, FLORENCE, SC, p. A552
REGENCY HOSPITAL OF FORT WORTH, FORT WORTH, TX, p. A604
REGENCY HOSPITAL OF GREENVILLE, GREENVILLE, SC, p. A552
REGENCY HOSPITAL OF HATTIESBURG, HATTIESBURG, MS, p. A348
REGENCY HOSPITAL OF JACKSON, JACKSON, MS, p. A349
REGENCY HOSPITAL OF MERIDIAN, MERIDIAN, MS, p. A351
REGENCY HOSPITAL OF MINNEAPOLIS, GOLDEN VALLEY, MN, p. A333
REGENCY HOSPITAL OF NORTHWEST ARKANSAS, FAYETTEVILLE, AR, p. A43
REGENCY HOSPITAL OF NORTHWEST ARKANSAS – SPRINGDALE, SPRINGDALE, ARKANSAS (see REGENCY HOSPITAL OF NORTHWEST ARKANSAS), p. A43
REGENCY HOSPITAL OF NORTHWEST INDIANA, EAST CHICAGO, IN, p. A201
REGENCY HOSPITAL OF PORTER COUNTY, PORTAGE, INDIANA (see REGENCY HOSPITAL OF NORTHWEST INDIANA), p. A201
REGENCY HOSPITAL OF RAVENNA, RAVENNA, OHIO (see REGENCY HOSPITAL CLEVELAND EAST), p. A492
REGENCY HOSPITAL OF SOUTH ATLANTA, EAST POINT, GA, p. A153
REGENCY HOSPITAL OF TOLEDO, SYLVANIA, OH, p. A490
REGINA MEDICAL CENTER, HASTINGS, MN, p. A333
REGIONAL HEALTH SERVICES OF HOWARD COUNTY, CRESCO, IA, p. A219
REGIONAL HOSPITAL FOR RESPIRATORY AND COMPLEX CARE, SEATTLE, WA, p. A670
REGIONAL HOSPITAL OF JACKSON, JACKSON, TN, p. A570
REGIONAL HOSPITAL OF SCRANTON, SCRANTON, PA, p. A540
REGIONAL MEDICAL CENTER, MANCHESTER, IA, p. A224
REGIONAL MEDICAL CENTER, ORANGEBURG, SC, p. A555
REGIONAL MEDICAL CENTER AT MEMPHIS, MEMPHIS, TN, p. A575
REGIONAL MEDICAL CENTER OF ACADIANA, LAFAYETTE, LA, p. A271
REGIONAL MEDICAL CENTER OF SAN JOSE, SAN JOSE, CA, p. A88
REGIONAL MEDICAL CENTER–BAYONET POINT, HUDSON, FL, p. A126
REGIONAL MENTAL HEALTH CENTER, MERRILLVILLE, IN, p. A210
REGIONAL REHABILITATION CENTER, SALEM, OREGON (see SALEM HOSPITAL), p. A517
REGIONAL REHABILITATION HOSPITAL, PHENIX CITY, AL, p. A24
REGIONAL WEST MEDICAL CENTER, SCOTTSBLUFF, NE, p. A389
REGIONS HOSPITAL, SAINT PAUL, MN, p. A340
REHABILITATION HOSPITAL OF FORT WAYNE, FORT WAYNE, IN, p. A203
REHABILITATION HOSPITAL OF INDIANA, INDIANAPOLIS, IN, p. A206
REHABILITATION HOSPITAL OF JENNINGS, JENNINGS, LA, p. A269
REHABILITATION HOSPITAL OF RHODE ISLAND, NORTH SMITHFIELD, RI, p. A546
REHABILITATION HOSPITAL OF SOUTHERN NEW MEXICO, LAS CRUCES, NM, p. A416
REHABILITATION HOSPITAL OF SOUTHWEST VIRGINIA, BRISTOL, VA, p. A652
REHABILITATION HOSPITAL OF THE PACIFIC, HONOLULU, HI, p. A165
REHABILITATION HOSPITAL OF TINTON FALLS, TINTON FALLS, NJ, p. A411

REHABILITATION HOSPITAL OF WISCONSIN, WAUKESHA, WI, p. A698
REHABILITATION INSTITUTE AT THE MOUNT KEMBLE DIVISION, GORYEB CHILDREN'S HOSPITAL, MORRISTOWN, NEW JERSEY (see MORRISTOWN MEDICAL CENTER), p. A406
REHABILITATION INSTITUTE OF CHICAGO, CHICAGO, IL, p. A178
REHABILITATION INSTITUTE OF MICHIGAN, DETROIT, MI, p. A312
REHABILITATION INSTITUTE OF OREGON, PORTLAND, OREGON (see LEGACY GOOD SAMARITAN HOSPITAL AND MEDICAL CENTER), p. A516
REHABILITATION INSTITUTE OF WEST FLORIDA, PENSACOLA, FLORIDA (see WEST FLORIDA HOSPITAL), p. A137
REHOBOTH MCKINLEY CHRISTIAN HEALTH CARE SERVICES, GALLUP, NM, p. A416
REID HOSPITAL AND HEALTH CARE SERVICES, RICHMOND, IN, p. A212
REISCH MEMORIAL NURSING HOME (see THOMAS H. BOYD MEMORIAL HOSPITAL), p. A175
RELIANT AUSTIN, AUSTIN, TX, p. A585
RELIANT NORTHWEST HOUSTON, HOUSTON, TX, p. A611
RELIANT REHABILITATION HOSPITAL ABILENE, ABILENE, TX, p. A581
RELIANT REHABILITATION HOSPITAL CENTRAL TEXAS, ROUND ROCK, TX, p. A629
RELIANT REHABILITATION HOSPITAL DALLAS, DALLAS, TX, p. A597
RELIANT REHABILITATION HOSPITAL MID–CITIES, BEDFORD, TX, p. A588
RELIANT REHABILITATION HOSPITAL NORTH HOUSTON, SHENANDOAH, TX, p. A633
RELIANT REHABILITATION HOSPITAL NORTH TEXAS, RICHARDSON, TX, p. A628
RENOWN CHILDREN'S HOSPITAL, RENO, NEVADA (see RENOWN REGIONAL MEDICAL CENTER), p. A395
RENOWN REGIONAL MEDICAL CENTER, RENO, NV, p. A395
RENOWN REHABILITATION HOSPITAL, RENO, NV, p. A395
RENOWN SOUTH MEADOWS MEDICAL CENTER, RENO, NV, p. A395
REPUBLIC COUNTY HOSPITAL, BELLEVILLE, KS, p. A231
RESEARCH MEDICAL CENTER, KANSAS CITY, MO, p. A363
RESEARCH PSYCHIATRIC CENTER, KANSAS CITY, MO, p. A363
RESTON HOSPITAL CENTER, RESTON, VA, p. A659
RESTORA HOSPITAL OF MESA, MESA, AZ, p. A33
RESTORA HOSPITAL OF SUN CITY, SUN CITY, AZ, p. A38
REX HEALTHCARE, RALEIGH, NC, p. A459
REYNOLDS ARMY COMMUNITY HOSPITAL, FORT SILL, OK, p. A499
REYNOLDS MEMORIAL HOSPITAL, GLEN DALE, WV, p. A677
RHEA MEDICAL CENTER, DAYTON, TN, p. A568
RHODE ISLAND HOSPITAL, PROVIDENCE, RI, p. A547
RICE COUNTY DISTRICT HOSPITAL, LYONS, KS, p. A239
RICE MEDICAL CENTER, EAGLE LAKE, TX, p. A600
RICE MEMORIAL HOSPITAL, WILLMAR, MN, p. A343
RICHARD H. HUTCHINGS PSYCHIATRIC CENTER, SYRACUSE, NY, p. A443
RICHARD H. YOUNG HOSPITAL, KEARNEY, NEBRASKA (see GOOD SAMARITAN HOSPITAL), p. A385
RICHARD L. ROUDEBUSH VETERANS AFFAIRS MEDICAL CENTER, INDIANAPOLIS, IN, p. A206
RICHARD P. STADTER PSYCHIATRIC CENTER, GRAND FORKS, ND, p. A467
RICHARDSON MEDICAL CENTER, RAYVILLE, LA, p. A277
RICHLAND HOSPITAL, RICHLAND CENTER, WI, p. A696
RICHLAND MEMORIAL HOSPITAL, OLNEY, IL, p. A191
RICHLAND PARISH HOSPITAL, DELHI, LA, p. A266
RICHMOND MEDICAL CENTER, RICHMOND, CALIFORNIA (see KAISER PERMANENTE OAKLAND MEDICAL CENTER), p. A77
RICHMOND STATE HOSPITAL, RICHMOND, IN, p. A212
RICHMOND UNIVERSITY MEDICAL CENTER,, NY, p. A436
RIDDLE HOSPITAL, MEDIA, PA, p. A531
RIDGE BEHAVIORAL HEALTH SYSTEM, LEXINGTON, KY, p. A254
RIDGECREST REGIONAL HOSPITAL, RIDGECREST, CA, p. A82
RIDGEVIEW INSTITUTE, SMYRNA, GA, p. A160
RIDGEVIEW MEDICAL CENTER, WACONIA, MN, p. A342
RIDGEVIEW PSYCHIATRIC HOSPITAL AND CENTER, OAK RIDGE, TN, p. A578
RILEY HOSPITAL FOR CHILDREN AT INDIANA UNIVERSITY HEALTH, INDIANAPOLIS, INDIANA (see INDIANA UNIVERSITY HEALTH UNIVERSITY HOSPITAL), p. A205
RINGGOLD COUNTY HOSPITAL, MOUNT AYR, IA, p. A225
RIO GRANDE HOSPITAL, DEL NORTE, CO, p. A99
RIO GRANDE REGIONAL HOSPITAL, MCALLEN, TX, p. A622
RIO GRANDE STATE CENTER, HARLINGEN, TEXAS (see RIO GRANDE STATE CENTER/SOUTH TEXAS HEALTH CARE SYSTEM), p. A608
RIO GRANDE STATE CENTER/SOUTH TEXAS HEALTH CARE SYSTEM, HARLINGEN, TX, p. A608
RIPON MEDICAL CENTER, RIPON, WI, p. A696

# S

SEATTLE CHILDREN'S HOSPITAL, SEATTLE, WA, p. A671
SEBASTIAN RIVER MEDICAL CENTER, SEBASTIAN, FL, p. A140
SEBASTICOOK VALLEY HEALTH, PITTSFIELD, ME, p. A284
SEDAN CITY HOSPITAL, SEDAN, KS, p. A244
SEDGWICK COUNTY HEALTH CENTER, JULESBURG, CO, p. A102
SEILING COMMUNITY HOSPITAL, SEILING, OK, p. A506
SELBY GENERAL HOSPITAL, MARIETTA, OH, p. A485
SELECT LONG TERM CARE HOSPITAL – COLORADO SPRINGS, COLORADO SPRINGS, CO, p. A98
SELECT REHABILITATION HOSPITAL OF DENTON, DENTON, TX, p. A599
SELECT SPECIALTY HOSPITAL DENVER SOUTH, DENVER, COLORADO (see SELECT SPECIALTY HOSPITAL–DENVER), p. A100
SELECT SPECIALTY HOSPITAL–AKRON, AKRON, OH, p. A470
SELECT SPECIALTY HOSPITAL–ANN ARBOR, YPSILANTI, MI, p. A327
SELECT SPECIALTY HOSPITAL–ATLANTA, ATLANTA, GA, p. A147
SELECT SPECIALTY HOSPITAL–AUGUSTA, AUGUSTA, GA, p. A148
SELECT SPECIALTY HOSPITAL–BATTLE CREEK, BATTLE CREEK, MI, p. A309
SELECT SPECIALTY HOSPITAL–BEECH GROVE, INDIANAPOLIS, IN, p. A206
SELECT SPECIALTY HOSPITAL–BIRMINGHAM, BIRMINGHAM, AL, p. A17
SELECT SPECIALTY HOSPITAL–CANTON, CANTON, OH, p. A473
SELECT SPECIALTY HOSPITAL–CENTRAL PENNSYLVANIA, CAMP HILL, PA, p. A522
SELECT SPECIALTY HOSPITAL–CHARLESTON, CHARLESTON, WV, p. A676
SELECT SPECIALTY HOSPITAL–CINCINNATI, CINCINNATI, OH, p. A475
SELECT SPECIALTY HOSPITAL–COLUMBUS, COLUMBUS, OH, p. A478
SELECT SPECIALTY HOSPITAL–COLUMBUS, MOUNT CARMEL CAMPUS, COLUMBUS, OHIO (see SELECT SPECIALTY HOSPITAL–COLUMBUS), p. A478
SELECT SPECIALTY HOSPITAL–DALLAS, CARROLLTON, TX, p. A591
SELECT SPECIALTY HOSPITAL–DANVILLE, DANVILLE, PA, p. A524
SELECT SPECIALTY HOSPITAL–DENVER, DENVER, CO, p. A100
SELECT SPECIALTY HOSPITAL–DOWNRIVER, TAYLOR, MI, p. A325
SELECT SPECIALTY HOSPITAL–DURHAM, DURHAM, NC, p. A451
SELECT SPECIALTY HOSPITAL–ERIE, ERIE, PA, p. A525
SELECT SPECIALTY HOSPITAL–EVANSVILLE, EVANSVILLE, IN, p. A202
SELECT SPECIALTY HOSPITAL–FLINT, FLINT, MI, p. A314
SELECT SPECIALTY HOSPITAL–FORT SMITH, FORT SMITH, AR, p. A44
SELECT SPECIALTY HOSPITAL–FORT WAYNE, FORT WAYNE, IN, p. A203
SELECT SPECIALTY HOSPITAL–GAINESVILLE, GAINESVILLE, FL, p. A124
SELECT SPECIALTY HOSPITAL–GREENSBORO, GREENSBORO, NC, p. A453
SELECT SPECIALTY HOSPITAL–GROSSE POINTE, GROSSE POINTE, MI, p. A316
SELECT SPECIALTY HOSPITAL–GULF COAST, GULFPORT, MS, p. A347
SELECT SPECIALTY HOSPITAL–HARRISBURG, HARRISBURG, PENNSYLVANIA (see SELECT SPECIALTY HOSPITAL–CENTRAL PENNSYLVANIA), p. A522
SELECT SPECIALTY HOSPITAL–HOUSTON HEIGHTS, HOUSTON, TX, p. A612
SELECT SPECIALTY HOSPITAL–HOUSTON MEDICAL CENTER, HOUSTON, TEXAS (see SELECT SPECIALTY HOSPITAL–HOUSTON HEIGHTS), p. A612
SELECT SPECIALTY HOSPITAL–HOUSTON WEST, HOUSTON, TEXAS (see SELECT SPECIALTY HOSPITAL–HOUSTON HEIGHTS), p. A612
SELECT SPECIALTY HOSPITAL–JACKSON, JACKSON, MS, p. A349
SELECT SPECIALTY HOSPITAL–JOHNSTOWN, JOHNSTOWN, PA, p. A528
SELECT SPECIALTY HOSPITAL–KANSAS CITY, KANSAS CITY, KS, p. A237
SELECT SPECIALTY HOSPITAL–KNOXVILLE, KNOXVILLE, TN, p. A572
SELECT SPECIALTY HOSPITAL–LAUREL HIGHLANDS, LATROBE, PA, p. A529
SELECT SPECIALTY HOSPITAL–LEXINGTON, LEXINGTON, KY, p. A254
SELECT SPECIALTY HOSPITAL–LITTLE ROCK, LITTLE ROCK, AR, p. A46

SELECT SPECIALTY HOSPITAL–LONGVIEW, LONGVIEW, TX, p. A619
SELECT SPECIALTY HOSPITAL–MACOMB COUNTY, MOUNT CLEMENS, MI, p. A320
SELECT SPECIALTY HOSPITAL–MADISON, MADISON, WI, p. A689
SELECT SPECIALTY HOSPITAL–MCKEESPORT, MCKEESPORT, PA, p. A531
SELECT SPECIALTY HOSPITAL–MEMPHIS, MEMPHIS, TN, p. A575
SELECT SPECIALTY HOSPITAL–MIAMI, MIAMI, FL, p. A132
SELECT SPECIALTY HOSPITAL–MIDLAND, MIDLAND, TX, p. A623
SELECT SPECIALTY HOSPITAL–MILWAUKEE, MILWAUKEE, WI, p. A692
SELECT SPECIALTY HOSPITAL–NASHVILLE, NASHVILLE, TN, p. A577
SELECT SPECIALTY HOSPITAL–NORTH KNOXVILLE, KNOXVILLE, TN, p. A572
SELECT SPECIALTY HOSPITAL–NORTHEAST NEW JERSEY, ROCHELLE PARK, NJ, p. A410
SELECT SPECIALTY HOSPITAL–NORTHERN KENTUCKY, FORT THOMAS, KY, p. A251
SELECT SPECIALTY HOSPITAL–NORTHWEST DETROIT, DETROIT, MI, p. A312
SELECT SPECIALTY HOSPITAL–OKLAHOMA CITY, OKLAHOMA CITY, OK, p. A504
SELECT SPECIALTY HOSPITAL–OMAHA, OMAHA, NE, p. A388
SELECT SPECIALTY HOSPITAL–ORLANDO, ORLANDO, FL, p. A135
SELECT SPECIALTY HOSPITAL–ORLANDO SOUTH, ORLANDO, FLORIDA (see SELECT SPECIALTY HOSPITAL–ORLANDO), p. A135
SELECT SPECIALTY HOSPITAL–PALM BEACH, LAKE WORTH, FL, p. A128
SELECT SPECIALTY HOSPITAL–PANAMA CITY, PANAMA CITY, FL, p. A136
SELECT SPECIALTY HOSPITAL–PENSACOLA, PENSACOLA, FL, p. A137
SELECT SPECIALTY HOSPITAL–PHOENIX, PHOENIX, AZ, p. A35
SELECT SPECIALTY HOSPITAL–PHOENIX DOWNTOWN, PHOENIX, ARIZONA (see SELECT SPECIALTY HOSPITAL–SCOTTSDALE), p. A37
SELECT SPECIALTY HOSPITAL–PITTSBURGH/UPMC, PITTSBURGH, PA, p. A537
SELECT SPECIALTY HOSPITAL–PONTIAC, PONTIAC, MI, p. A322
SELECT SPECIALTY HOSPITAL–QUAD CITIES, DAVENPORT, IA, p. A219
SELECT SPECIALTY HOSPITAL–SAGINAW, SAGINAW, MI, p. A323
SELECT SPECIALTY HOSPITAL–SAN ANTONIO, SAN ANTONIO, TX, p. A632
SELECT SPECIALTY HOSPITAL–SAVANNAH, SAVANNAH, GA, p. A160
SELECT SPECIALTY HOSPITAL–SCOTTSDALE, SCOTTSDALE, AZ, p. A37
SELECT SPECIALTY HOSPITAL–SIOUX FALLS, SIOUX FALLS, SD, p. A562
SELECT SPECIALTY HOSPITAL–SOUTH DALLAS, DALLAS, TX, p. A597
SELECT SPECIALTY HOSPITAL–SPRINGFIELD, SPRINGFIELD, MO, p. A372
SELECT SPECIALTY HOSPITAL–ST. LOUIS, SAINT CHARLES, MO, p. A368
SELECT SPECIALTY HOSPITAL–TALLAHASSEE, TALLAHASSEE, FL, p. A141
SELECT SPECIALTY HOSPITAL–TOPEKA, TOPEKA, KS, p. A245
SELECT SPECIALTY HOSPITAL–TRI CITIES, BRISTOL, TN, p. A565
SELECT SPECIALTY HOSPITAL–TULSA MIDTOWN, TULSA, OK, p. A509
SELECT SPECIALTY HOSPITAL–WESTERN MISSOURI, KANSAS CITY, MO, p. A363
SELECT SPECIALTY HOSPITAL–WICHITA, WICHITA, KS, p. A246
SELECT SPECIALTY HOSPITAL–WILMINGTON, WILMINGTON, DE, p. A115
SELECT SPECIALTY HOSPITAL–WINSTON–SALEM, WINSTON–SALEM, NC, p. A463
SELECT SPECIALTY HOSPITAL–YORK, YORK, PENNSYLVANIA (see SELECT SPECIALTY HOSPITAL–CENTRAL PENNSYLVANIA), p. A522
SELECT SPECIALTY HOSPITAL–YOUNGSTOWN, YOUNGSTOWN, OH, p. A494
SELECT SPECIALTY HOSPITAL–YOUNGSTOWN, BOARDMAN CAMPUS, BORDMAN, OHIO (see SELECT SPECIALTY HOSPITAL–YOUNGSTOWN), p. A494
SELECT SPECIALTY HOSPITAL–ZANESVILLE, ZANESVILLE, OH, p. A494
SELF REGIONAL HEALTHCARE, GREENWOOD, SC, p. A553

SEMPERVIRENS PSYCHIATRIC HEALTH FACILITY, EUREKA, CA, p. A59
SENECA HEALTHCARE DISTRICT, CHESTER, CA, p. A56
SENIOR HAVEN CONVALESCENT NURSING CENTER (see SANFORD CANBY MEDICAL CENTER), p. A330
SENTARA CAREPLEX HOSPITAL, HAMPTON, VA, p. A655
SENTARA LEIGH HOSPITAL, NORFOLK, VA, p. A658
SENTARA NORFOLK GENERAL HOSPITAL, NORFOLK, VA, p. A658
SENTARA NORTHERN VIRGINIA MEDICAL CENTER, WOODBRIDGE, VA, p. A663
SENTARA OBICI HOSPITAL, SUFFOLK, VA, p. A662
SENTARA PRINCESS ANNE HOSPITAL, VIRGINIA BEACH, VA, p. A662
SENTARA VIRGINIA BEACH GENERAL HOSPITAL, VIRGINIA BEACH, VA, p. A662
SENTARA WILLIAMSBURG REGIONAL MEDICAL CENTER, WILLIAMSBURG, VA, p. A663
SEQUOIA HOSPITAL, REDWOOD CITY, CA, p. A82
SEQUOYAH MEMORIAL HOSPITAL, SALLISAW, OK, p. A506
SERENITY SPRINGS SPECIALTY HOSPITAL, FARMERVILLE, LA, p. A266
SETON EDGAR B. DAVIS HOSPITAL, LULING, TX, p. A621
SETON HEALTH SYSTEM–ST. MARY'S HOSPITAL, TROY, NEW YORK (see ST. MARY'S HOSPITAL), p. A444
SETON HIGHLAND LAKES, BURNET, TX, p. A590
SETON MEDICAL CENTER, DALY CITY, CA, p. A58
SETON MEDICAL CENTER AUSTIN, AUSTIN, TX, p. A585
SETON MEDICAL CENTER HARKER HEIGHTS, HARKER HEIGHTS, TX, p. A607
SETON MEDICAL CENTER HAYS, KYLE, TX, p. A617
SETON MEDICAL CENTER WILLIAMSON, ROUND ROCK, TX, p. A629
SETON NORTHWEST HOSPITAL, AUSTIN, TX, p. A585
SETON SHOAL CREEK HOSPITAL, AUSTIN, TX, p. A585
SETON SMITHVILLE REGIONAL HOSPITAL, SMITHVILLE, TX, p. A634
SETON SOUTHWEST HEALTHCARE CENTER, AUSTIN, TX, p. A585
SEVEN HILLS BEHAVIORAL INSTITUTE, HENDERSON, NV, p. A392
SEVEN RIVERS REGIONAL MEDICAL CENTER, CRYSTAL RIVER, FL, p. A121
SEVIER VALLEY MEDICAL CENTER, RICHFIELD, UT, p. A646
SEWICKLEY VALLEY HOSPITAL, (A DIVISION OF VALLEY MEDICAL FACILITIES), SEWICKLEY, PA, p. A541
SEYMOUR HOSPITAL, SEYMOUR, TX, p. A633
SHADOW MOUNTAIN BEHAVIORAL HEALTH SYSTEM, TULSA, OK, p. A509
SHADY GROVE ADVENTIST HOSPITAL, ROCKVILLE, MD, p. A294
SHAMROCK GENERAL HOSPITAL, SHAMROCK, TX, p. A633
SHANDS AT THE UNIVERSITY OF FLORIDA, GAINESVILLE, FL, p. A124
SHANDS CANCER HOSPITAL, GAINESVILLE, FLORIDA (see SHANDS AT THE UNIVERSITY OF FLORIDA), p. A124
SHANDS HOSPITAL FOR CHILDREN, GAINESVILLE, FLORIDA (see SHANDS AT THE UNIVERSITY OF FLORIDA), p. A124
SHANDS JACKSONVILLE MEDICAL CENTER, JACKSONVILLE, FL, p. A126
SHANDS LAKE SHORE REGIONAL MEDICAL CENTER, LAKE CITY, FL, p. A128
SHANDS LIVE OAK REGIONAL MEDICAL CENTER, LIVE OAK, FL, p. A129
SHANDS REHAB HOSPITAL, GAINESVILLE, FLORIDA (see SHANDS AT THE UNIVERSITY OF FLORIDA), p. A124
SHANDS STARKE REGIONAL MEDICAL CENTER, STARKE, FL, p. A140
SHANDS VISTA, GAINESVILLE, FLORIDA (see SHANDS AT THE UNIVERSITY OF FLORIDA), p. A124
SHANNON MEDICAL CENTER, SAN ANGELO, TX, p. A630
SHANNON MEDICAL CENTER– ST. JOHN'S CAMPUS, SAN ANGELO, TEXAS (see SHANNON MEDICAL CENTER), p. A630
SHARE MEDICAL CENTER, ALVA, OK, p. A495
SHARKEY–ISSAQUENA COMMUNITY HOSPITAL, ROLLING FORK, MS, p. A353
SHARON HOSPITAL, SHARON, CT, p. A111
SHARON REGIONAL HEALTH SYSTEM, SHARON, PA, p. A541
SHARP CHULA VISTA MEDICAL CENTER, CHULA VISTA, CA, p. A56
SHARP CORONADO HOSPITAL AND HEALTHCARE CENTER, CORONADO, CA, p. A57
SHARP GROSSMONT HOSPITAL, LA MESA, CA, p. A65
SHARP MCDONALD CENTER, SAN DIEGO, CALIFORNIA (see SHARP MESA VISTA HOSPITAL), p. A86
SHARP MEMORIAL HOSPITAL, SAN DIEGO, CA, p. A85
SHARP MESA VISTA HOSPITAL, SAN DIEGO, CA, p. A86
SHASTA REGIONAL MEDICAL CENTER, REDDING, CA, p. A81
SHAWANO MEDICAL CENTER, SHAWANO, WI, p. A696
SHAWNEE MISSION MEDICAL CENTER, SHAWNEE MISSION, KS, p. A244

ST. LUKE'S–ROOSEVELT HOSPITAL CENTER, NEW YORK, NY, p. A436
ST. MARGARET'S HOSPITAL, SPRING VALLEY, IL, p. A195
ST. MARK'S HOSPITAL, SALT LAKE CITY, UT, p. A647
ST. MARK'S MEDICAL CENTER, LA GRANGE, TX, p. A617
ST. MARTIN HOSPITAL, BREAUX BRIDGE, LA, p. A264
ST. MARY MEDICAL CENTER, LONG BEACH, CA, p. A67
ST. MARY MEDICAL CENTER, HOBART, IN, p. A204
ST. MARY MEDICAL CENTER, LANGHORNE, PA, p. A529
ST. MARY MERCY HOSPITAL, LIVONIA, MI, p. A319
ST. MARY'S WARRICK HOSPITAL, BOONVILLE, IN, p. A199
ST. MARY'S AMSTERDAM CAMPUS, AMSTERDAM, NEW YORK (see ST. MARY'S HEALTHCARE), p. A420
ST. MARY'S CHILDREN'S HOSPITAL, DULUTH, MINNESOTA (see ESSENTIA HEALTH ST. MARY'S MEDICAL CENTER), p. A331
ST. MARY'S COMMUNITY HOSPITAL, NEBRASKA CITY, NE, p. A386
ST. MARY'S GOOD SAMARITAN HOSPITAL, GREENSBORO, GA, p. A154
ST. MARY'S HEALTH CARE SYSTEM, ATHENS, GA, p. A145
ST. MARY'S HEALTHCARE, AMSTERDAM, NY, p. A420
ST. MARY'S HOSPITAL, RHINELANDER, WISCONSIN (see MINISTRY SAINT MARY'S HOSPITALS), p. A695
ST. MARY'S HOSPITAL, COTTONWOOD, ID, p. A168
ST. MARY'S HOSPITAL, CENTRALIA, IL, p. A175
ST. MARY'S HOSPITAL, DECATUR, IL, p. A180
ST. MARY'S HOSPITAL, STREATOR, IL, p. A196
ST. MARY'S HOSPITAL, PASSAIC, NJ, p. A408
ST. MARY'S HOSPITAL, TROY, NY, p. A444
ST. MARY'S HOSPITAL, MADISON, WI, p. A690
ST. MARY'S HOSPITAL AND MEDICAL CENTER, GRAND JUNCTION, CO, p. A102
ST. MARY'S HOSPITAL AND REHABILITATION CENTER, MINNEAPOLIS, MINNESOTA (see UNIVERSITY OF MINNESOTA MEDICAL CENTER, FAIRVIEW), p. A336
ST. MARY'S HOSPITAL MEDICAL CENTER, GREEN BAY, WI, p. A688
ST. MARY'S JANESVILLE HOSPITAL, JANESVILLE, WI, p. A688
ST. MARY'S MEDICAL CENTER, SAN FRANCISCO, CA, p. A87
ST. MARY'S MEDICAL CENTER, WEST PALM BEACH, FL, p. A143
ST. MARY'S MEDICAL CENTER, BLUE SPRINGS, MO, p. A356
ST. MARY'S MEDICAL CENTER, HUNTINGTON, WV, p. A678
ST. MARY'S MEDICAL CENTER OF EVANSVILLE, EVANSVILLE, IN, p. A202
ST. MARY'S OF MICHIGAN, SAGINAW, MI, p. A323
ST. MARY'S OF MICHIGAN STANDISH HOSPITAL, STANDISH, MI, p. A325
ST. MARY'S REGIONAL MEDICAL CENTER, LEWISTON, ME, p. A284
ST. MARY'S REGIONAL MEDICAL CENTER, ENID, OK, p. A498
ST. MARY–CORWIN MEDICAL CENTER, PUEBLO, CO, p. A105
ST. MARYS HEALTH CENTER, JEFFERSON CITY, MO, p. A362
ST. MICHAEL'S HOSPITAL AVERA, TYNDALL, SD, p. A563
ST. NICHOLAS HOSPITAL, SHEBOYGAN, WI, p. A696
ST. PATRICK HOSPITAL, MISSOULA, MT, p. A378
ST. PETER'S HOSPITAL, HELENA, MT, p. A377
ST. PETER'S HOSPITAL, ALBANY, NY, p. A420
ST. PETERSBURG GENERAL HOSPITAL, SAINT PETERSBURG, FL, p. A139
ST. RITA'S MEDICAL CENTER, LIMA, OH, p. A484
ST. ROSE DOMINICAN HOSPITALS – ROSE DE LIMA CAMPUS, HENDERSON, NV, p. A392
ST. ROSE DOMINICAN HOSPITALS – SAN MARTIN CAMPUS, LAS VEGAS, NV, p. A393
ST. ROSE DOMINICAN HOSPITALS – SIENA CAMPUS, HENDERSON, NV, p. A392
ST. ROSE HOSPITAL, HAYWARD, CA, p. A64
ST. TAMMANY PARISH HOSPITAL, COVINGTON, LA, p. A266
ST. THERESA SPECIALTY HOSPITAL, METAIRIE, LA, p. A273
ST. THOMAS MORE HOSPITAL, CANON CITY, CO, p. A98
ST. VINCENT ANDERSON REGIONAL HOSPITAL, ANDERSON, IN, p. A198
ST. VINCENT CARMEL HOSPITAL, CARMEL, IN, p. A200
ST. VINCENT CHARITY MEDICAL CENTER, CLEVELAND, OH, p. A477
ST. VINCENT CLAY HOSPITAL, BRAZIL, IN, p. A199
ST. VINCENT DOCTORS HOSPITAL, LITTLE ROCK, ARKANSAS (see ST. VINCENT INFIRMARY MEDICAL CENTER), p. A47
ST. VINCENT DUNN HOSPITAL, BEDFORD, IN, p. A198
ST. VINCENT FRANKFORT HOSPITAL, FRANKFORT, IN, p. A203
ST. VINCENT GENERAL HOSPITAL DISTRICT, LEADVILLE, CO, p. A103
ST. VINCENT HEALTHCARE, BILLINGS, MT, p. A374
ST. VINCENT HEART CENTER OF INDIANA, INDIANAPOLIS, IN, p. A206
ST. VINCENT HOSPITAL, GREEN BAY, WI, p. A688
ST. VINCENT INDIANAPOLIS HOSPITAL, INDIANAPOLIS, IN, p. A206

ST. VINCENT INFIRMARY MEDICAL CENTER, LITTLE ROCK, AR, p. A47
ST. VINCENT JENNINGS HOSPITAL, NORTH VERNON, IN, p. A212
ST. VINCENT MEDICAL CENTER, LOS ANGELES, CA, p. A72
ST. VINCENT MEDICAL CENTER–NORTH, SHERWOOD, AR, p. A50
ST. VINCENT MERCY HOSPITAL, ELWOOD, IN, p. A201
ST. VINCENT MORRILTON, MORRILTON, AR, p. A47
ST. VINCENT RANDOLPH HOSPITAL, WINCHESTER, IN, p. A215
ST. VINCENT REHABILITATION HOSPITAL, SHERWOOD, AR, p. A50
ST. VINCENT SALEM HOSPITAL, SALEM, IN, p. A213
ST. VINCENT SETON SPECIALTY HOSPITAL, INDIANAPOLIS, IN, p. A206
ST. VINCENT SETON SPECIALTY HOSPITAL, LAFAYETTE, IN, p. A208
ST. VINCENT STRESS CENTER, INDIANAPOLIS, INDIANA (see ST. VINCENT INDIANAPOLIS HOSPITAL), p. A206
ST. VINCENT WILLIAMSPORT HOSPITAL, WILLIAMSPORT, IN, p. A215
ST. VINCENT WOMEN'S HOSPITAL, INDIANAPOLIS, INDIANA (see ST. VINCENT INDIANAPOLIS HOSPITAL), p. A206
ST. VINCENT'S BEHAVIORAL HEALTH, WESTPORT, CONNECTICUT (see ST. VINCENT'S MEDICAL CENTER), p. A108
ST. VINCENT'S BIRMINGHAM, BIRMINGHAM, AL, p. A17
ST. VINCENT'S BLOUNT, ONEONTA, AL, p. A24
ST. VINCENT'S EAST, BIRMINGHAM, AL, p. A17
ST. VINCENT'S MEDICAL CENTER, BRIDGEPORT, CT, p. A108
ST. VINCENT'S MEDICAL CENTER RIVERSIDE, JACKSONVILLE, FL, p. A127
ST. VINCENT'S MEDICAL CENTER SOUTHSIDE, JACKSONVILLE, FL, p. A127
ST. VINCENT'S ST. CLAIR, PELL CITY, AL, p. A24
ST. WILLIAM HOME FOR THE AGED (see MILBANK AREA HOSPITAL AVERA), p. A560
STAFFORD COUNTY HOSPITAL, STAFFORD, KS, p. A244
STAFFORD HOSPITAL, STAFFORD, VA, p. A661
STAMFORD HOSPITAL, STAMFORD, CT, p. A112
STAMFORD MEMORIAL HOSPITAL, STAMFORD, TX, p. A635
STANFORD HOSPITAL AND CLINICS, PALO ALTO, CA, p. A79
STANISLAUS SURGICAL HOSPITAL, MODESTO, CA, p. A74
STANLY REGIONAL MEDICAL CENTER, ALBEMARLE, NC, p. A447
STANTON COUNTY HOSPITAL, JOHNSON, KS, p. A236
STAR VALLEY MEDICAL CENTER, AFTON, WY, p. A701
STARR COUNTY MEMORIAL HOSPITAL, RIO GRANDE CITY, TX, p. A629
STATE CORRECTIONAL INSTITUTION AT CAMP HILL, CAMP HILL, PA, p. A522
STATE HOSPITAL NORTH, OROFINO, ID, p. A170
STATE HOSPITAL SOUTH, BLACKFOOT, ID, p. A167
STATE PENITENTIARY HOSPITAL, WALLA WALLA, WA, p. A674
STATE PSYCHIATRIC HOSPITAL, SAN JUAN, PR, p. A710
STATE PSYCHIATRIC HOSPITAL, IOWA CITY, IOWA (see UNIVERSITY OF IOWA HOSPITALS AND CLINICS), p. A223
STATEN ISLAND UNIVERSITY HOSPITAL,, NY, p. A436
STE. GENEVIEVE COUNTY MEMORIAL HOSPITAL, STE. GENEVIEVE, MO, p. A372
STEELE MEMORIAL MEDICAL CENTER, SALMON, ID, p. A171
STEPHENS COUNTY HOSPITAL, TOCCOA, GA, p. A162
STEPHENS MEMORIAL HOSPITAL, NORWAY, ME, p. A284
STEPHENS MEMORIAL HOSPITAL, BRECKENRIDGE, TX, p. A589
STERLING REGIONAL MEDCENTER, STERLING, CO, p. A106
STERLINGTON REHABILITATION HOSPITAL, STERLINGTON, LA, p. A279
STEVEN AND ALEXANDRA COHEN CHILDREN'S MEDICAL CENTER OF NEW YORK,, NEW YORK (see LONG ISLAND JEWISH MEDICAL CENTER), p. A433
STEVENS COMMUNITY MEDICAL CENTER, MORRIS, MN, p. A337
STEVENS COUNTY HOSPITAL, HUGOTON, KS, p. A236
STEWART & LYNDA RESNICK NEUROPSYCHIATRIC HOSPITAL AT UCLA, LOS ANGELES, CA, p. A72
STEWART MEMORIAL COMMUNITY HOSPITAL, LAKE CITY, IA, p. A224
STILLWATER COMMUNITY HOSPITAL, COLUMBUS, MT, p. A375
STILLWATER MEDICAL CENTER, STILLWATER, OK, p. A507
STONE COUNTY HOSPITAL, WIGGINS, MS, p. A355
STONE COUNTY MEDICAL CENTER, MOUNTAIN VIEW, AR, p. A48
STONE INSTITUTE OF PSYCHIATRY, CHICAGO, ILLINOIS (see NORTHWESTERN MEMORIAL HOSPITAL), p. A178
STONECREST CENTER, DETROIT, MI, p. A312
STONES RIVER HOSPITAL, WOODBURY, TN, p. A580
STONEWALL JACKSON MEMORIAL HOSPITAL, WESTON, WV, p. A681
STONEWALL MEMORIAL HOSPITAL, ASPERMONT, TX, p. A584

STONY BROOK CHILDREN'S HOSPITAL, STONY BROOK, NEW YORK (see STONY BROOK UNIVERSITY MEDICAL CENTER), p. A443
STONY BROOK UNIVERSITY MEDICAL CENTER, STONY BROOK, NY, p. A443
STONY LODGE HOSPITAL, OSSINING, NY, p. A439
STORMONT–VAIL HEALTHCARE, TOPEKA, KS, p. A245
STORY COUNTY MEDICAL CENTER, NEVADA, IA, p. A225
STOUGHTON HOSPITAL ASSOCIATION, STOUGHTON, WI, p. A697
STRAITH HOSPITAL FOR SPECIAL SURGERY, SOUTHFIELD, MI, p. A324
STRAUB CLINIC & HOSPITAL, HONOLULU, HI, p. A165
STREAMWOOD BEHAVIORAL HEALTH CENTER, STREAMWOOD, IL, p. A195
STRINGFELLOW MEMORIAL HOSPITAL, ANNISTON, AL, p. A15
STRONG MEMORIAL HOSPITAL OF THE UNIVERSITY OF ROCHESTER, ROCHESTER, NY, p. A441
STROUD REGIONAL MEDICAL CENTER, STROUD, OK, p. A507
STS. MARY & ELIZABETH HOSPITAL, LOUISVILLE, KY, p. A256
STURDY MEMORIAL HOSPITAL, ATTLEBORO, MA, p. A295
STURGIS HOSPITAL, STURGIS, MI, p. A325
STURGIS REGIONAL HOSPITAL, STURGIS, SD, p. A563
SUBURBAN HOSPITAL, BETHESDA, MD, p. A290
SUGAR LAND SURGICAL HOSPITAL, SUGAR LAND, TX, p. A635
SULLIVAN COUNTY COMMUNITY HOSPITAL, SULLIVAN, IN, p. A213
SULLIVAN COUNTY MEMORIAL HOSPITAL, MILAN, MO, p. A366
SUMMA AKRON CITY HOSPITAL, AKRON, OHIO (see SUMMA HEALTH SYSTEM), p. A470
SUMMA BARBERTON CITIZENS HOSPITAL, BARBERTON, OH, p. A471
SUMMA HEALTH SYSTEM, AKRON, OH, p. A470
SUMMA SAINT THOMAS HOSPITAL, AKRON, OHIO (see SUMMA HEALTH SYSTEM), p. A470
SUMMA WADSWORTH–RITTMAN HOSPITAL, WADSWORTH, OH, p. A492
SUMMA WESTERN RESERVE HOSPITAL, CUYAHOGA FALLS, OH, p. A479
SUMMERLIN HOSPITAL MEDICAL CENTER, LAS VEGAS, NV, p. A394
SUMMERS COUNTY ARH HOSPITAL, HINTON, WV, p. A677
SUMMERSVILLE REGIONAL MEDICAL CENTER, SUMMERSVILLE, WV, p. A681
SUMMERVILLE MEDICAL CENTER, SUMMERVILLE, SOUTH CAROLINA (see TRIDENT MEDICAL CENTER), p. A549
SUMMIT BEHAVIORAL HEALTHCARE, CINCINNATI, OH, p. A475
SUMMIT HEALTHCARE REGIONAL MEDICAL CENTER, SHOW LOW, AZ, p. A37
SUMMIT MEDICAL CENTER, VAN BUREN, AR, p. A50
SUMMIT MEDICAL CENTER, EDMOND, OK, p. A498
SUMMIT OAKS HOSPITAL, SUMMIT, NJ, p. A410
SUMMIT PACIFIC MEDICAL CENTER, MCCLEARY, WA, p. A668
SUMMIT PARK HOSPITAL AND NURSING CARE CENTER, POMONA, NY, p. A439
SUMMIT SURGICAL, LLC, HUTCHINSON, KS, p. A236
SUMMITRIDGE HOSPITAL, LAWRENCEVILLE, GA, p. A156
SUMNER COUNTY HOSPITAL DISTRICT ONE, CALDWELL, KS, p. A232
SUMNER REGIONAL MEDICAL CENTER, WELLINGTON, KS, p. A246
SUMNER REGIONAL MEDICAL CENTER, GALLATIN, TN, p. A569
SUN COAST HOSPITAL, LARGO, FL, p. A129
SUNBURY COMMUNITY HOSPITAL AND OUTPATIENT CENTER, SUNBURY, PA, p. A542
SUNDANCE HOSPITAL, ARLINGTON, TX, p. A583
SUNNYSIDE COMMUNITY HOSPITAL, SUNNYSIDE, WA, p. A673
SUNNYVIEW REHABILITATION HOSPITAL, SCHENECTADY, NY, p. A442
SUNRISE CANYON HOSPITAL, LUBBOCK, TX, p. A620
SUNRISE CHILDREN'S HOSPITAL (see SUNRISE HOSPITAL AND MEDICAL CENTER), p. A394
SUNRISE HOSPITAL AND MEDICAL CENTER, LAS VEGAS, NV, p. A394
SUNY DOWNSTATE MEDICAL CENTER UNIVERSITY HOSPITAL,, NY, p. A436
SURGERY SPECIALTY HOSPITALS OF AMERICA, PASADENA, TX, p. A626
SURGICAL HOSPITAL AT SOUTHWOODS, YOUNGSTOWN, OH, p. A494
SURGICAL HOSPITAL OF JONESBORO, JONESBORO, AR, p. A45
SURGICAL HOSPITAL OF OKLAHOMA, OKLAHOMA CITY, OK, p. A504
SURGICAL INSTITUTE OF READING, WYOMISSING, PA, p. A545
SURGICAL SPECIALTY CENTER AT COORDINATED HEALTH, ALLENTOWN, PA, p. A519
SURGICAL SPECIALTY CENTER OF BATON ROUGE, BATON ROUGE, LA, p. A264
SURGICAL SPECIALTY HOSPITAL OF ARIZONA, PHOENIX, AZ, p. A35

SURPRISE VALLEY HEALTHCARE DISTRICT, CEDARVILLE, CA, p. A56

SUSAN B. ALLEN MEMORIAL HOSPITAL, EL DORADO, KS, p. A233

SUTTER AMADOR HOSPITAL, JACKSON, CA, p. A64

SUTTER AUBURN FAITH HOSPITAL, AUBURN, CA, p. A53

SUTTER CENTER FOR PSYCHIATRY, SACRAMENTO, CA, p. A84

SUTTER CHILDREN'S CENTER, SACRAMENTO, CALIFORNIA (see SUTTER MEDICAL CENTER, SACRAMENTO), p. A84

SUTTER COAST HOSPITAL, CRESCENT CITY, CA, p. A58

SUTTER DAVIS HOSPITAL, DAVIS, CA, p. A58

SUTTER DELTA MEDICAL CENTER, ANTIOCH, CA, p. A52

SUTTER GENERAL HOSPITAL, SACRAMENTO, CALIFORNIA (see SUTTER MEDICAL CENTER, SACRAMENTO), p. A84

SUTTER LAKESIDE HOSPITAL, LAKEPORT, CA, p. A66

SUTTER MATERNITY AND SURGERY CENTER OF SANTA CRUZ, SANTA CRUZ, CA, p. A90

SUTTER MEDICAL CENTER OF SANTA ROSA, CHANATE CAMPUS, SANTA ROSA, CA, p. A90

SUTTER MEDICAL CENTER, SACRAMENTO, SACRAMENTO, CA, p. A84

SUTTER ROSEVILLE MEDICAL CENTER, ROSEVILLE, CA, p. A83

SUTTER SOLANO MEDICAL CENTER, VALLEJO, CA, p. A94

SUTTER SURGICAL HOSPITAL – NORTH VALLEY, YUBA CITY, CA, p. A96

SUTTER TRACY COMMUNITY HOSPITAL, TRACY, CA, p. A93

SWEDISH COVENANT HOSPITAL, CHICAGO, IL, p. A179

SWEDISH MEDICAL CENTER, ENGLEWOOD, CO, p. A100

SWEDISH MEDICAL CENTER–BALLARD, SEATTLE, WASHINGTON (see SWEDISH MEDICAL CENTER–FIRST HILL), p. A671

SWEDISH MEDICAL CENTER–CHERRY HILL CAMPUS, SEATTLE, WA, p. A671

SWEDISH MEDICAL CENTER–FIRST HILL, SEATTLE, WA, p. A671

SWEDISH/EDMONDS, EDMONDS, WA, p. A666

SWEDISH/ISSAQUAH, ISSAQUAH, WA, p. A667

SWEDISHAMERICAN HOSPITAL, ROCKFORD, IL, p. A194

SWEENY COMMUNITY HOSPITAL, SWEENY, TX, p. A636

SWEETWATER HOSPITAL, SWEETWATER, TN, p. A579

SWIFT COUNTY–BENSON HOSPITAL, BENSON, MN, p. A329

SWISHER MEMORIAL HOSPITAL DISTRICT, TULIA, TX, p. A638

SYCAMORE MEDICAL CENTER, MIAMISBURG, OH, p. A486

SYCAMORE SHOALS HOSPITAL, ELIZABETHTON, TN, p. A568

SYCAMORE SPRINGS HOSPITAL, LAFAYETTE, IN, p. A208

SYLVAN GROVE HOSPITAL, JACKSON, GA, p. A155

SYOSSET HOSPITAL, SYOSSET, NY, p. A443

SYRACUSE VETERANS AFFAIRS MEDICAL CENTER, SYRACUSE, NY, p. A444

SYRINGA HOSPITAL AND CLINICS, GRANGEVILLE, ID, p. A169

# T

T. C. THOMPSON CHILDREN'S HOSPITAL, CHATTANOOGA, TENNESSEE (see ERLANGER MEDICAL CENTER), p. A566

T. J. SAMSON COMMUNITY HOSPITAL, GLASGOW, KY, p. A251

TAHLEQUAH CITY HOSPITAL, TAHLEQUAH, OK, p. A507

TAHOE FOREST HOSPITAL DISTRICT, TRUCKEE, CA, p. A93

TAHOE PACIFIC HOSPITALS, RENO, NV, p. A395

TAHOE PACIFIC HOSPITALS – WEST, RENO, NEVADA (see TAHOE PACIFIC HOSPITALS), p. A395

TAKOMA REGIONAL HOSPITAL, GREENEVILLE, TN, p. A569

TALLAHASSEE MEMORIAL HEALTHCARE, TALLAHASSEE, FL, p. A141

TALLAHATCHIE GENERAL HOSPITAL, CHARLESTON, MS, p. A345

TAMPA GENERAL HOSPITAL, TAMPA, FL, p. A142

TAMPA GENERAL HOSPITAL CHILDREN'S MEDICAL CENTER, TAMPA, FLORIDA (see TAMPA GENERAL HOSPITAL), p. A142

TANNER MEDICAL CENTER–CARROLLTON, CARROLLTON, GA, p. A149

TANNER MEDICAL CENTER–VILLA RICA, VILLA RICA, GA, p. A162

TAUNTON STATE HOSPITAL, TAUNTON, MA, p. A305

TAYLOR HARDIN SECURE MEDICAL FACILITY, TUSCALOOSA, AL, p. A26

TAYLOR HOSPITAL, RIDLEY PARK, PENNSYLVANIA (see CROZER–CHESTER MEDICAL CENTER), p. A542

TAYLOR REGIONAL HOSPITAL, HAWKINSVILLE, GA, p. A154

TAYLOR REGIONAL HOSPITAL, CAMPBELLSVILLE, KY, p. A249

TAYLORVILLE MEMORIAL HOSPITAL, TAYLORVILLE, IL, p. A196

TECHE REGIONAL MEDICAL CENTER, MORGAN CITY, LA, p. A274

TEHACHAPI VALLEY HEALTHCARE DISTRICT, TEHACHAPI, CA, p. A92

TELECARE HERITAGE PSYCHIATRIC HEALTH CENTER, OAKLAND, CA, p. A77

TEMPE ST. LUKE'S HOSPITAL, TEMPE, ARIZONA (see ST. LUKE'S MEDICAL CENTER), p. A35

TEMPLE COMMUNITY HOSPITAL, LOS ANGELES, CA, p. A72

TEMPLE UNIVERSITY HOSPITAL, PHILADELPHIA, PA, p. A536

TEMPLE UNIVERSITY HOSPITAL – EPISCOPAL DIVISION, PHILADELPHIA, PENNSYLVANIA (see TEMPLE UNIVERSITY HOSPITAL), p. A536

TEN BROECK TENNESSEE TREATMENT FACILITY, COOKEVILLE, TN, p. A568

TEN LAKES CENTER, DENNISON, OH, p. A480

TENNESSEE VALLEY HEALTHCARE SYSTEM, NASHVILLE, TN, p. A577

TENNOVA–JEFFERSON MEMORIAL HOSPITAL, JEFFERSON CITY, TN, p. A571

TERENCE CARDINAL COOKE HEALTH CARE CENTER, NEW YORK, NY, p. A436

TERRE HAUTE REGIONAL HOSPITAL, TERRE HAUTE, IN, p. A214

TERREBONNE GENERAL MEDICAL CENTER, HOUMA, LA, p. A268

TERRELL STATE HOSPITAL, TERRELL, TX, p. A637

TETON MEDICAL CENTER, CHOTEAU, MT, p. A375

TETON VALLEY HEALTH CARE, DRIGGS, ID, p. A169

TEWKSBURY HOSPITAL, TEWKSBURY, MA, p. A305

TEXAS CENTER FOR INFECTIOUS DISEASE, SAN ANTONIO, TX, p. A632

TEXAS CHILDREN'S HOSPITAL, HOUSTON, TX, p. A612

TEXAS CHILDREN'S HOSPITAL WEST CAMPUS, HOUSTON, TEXAS (see TEXAS CHILDREN'S HOSPITAL), p. A612

TEXAS COUNTY MEMORIAL HOSPITAL, HOUSTON, MO, p. A361

TEXAS GENERAL HOSPITAL, GRAND PRAIRIE, TX, p. A606

TEXAS HEALTH ARLINGTON MEMORIAL HOSPITAL, ARLINGTON, TX, p. A584

TEXAS HEALTH CENTER FOR DIAGNOSTIC & SURGERY, PLANO, TX, p. A627

TEXAS HEALTH HARRIS METHODIST HOSPITAL ALLIANCE, FORT WORTH, TX, p. A604

TEXAS HEALTH HARRIS METHODIST HOSPITAL AZLE, AZLE, TX, p. A586

TEXAS HEALTH HARRIS METHODIST HOSPITAL CLEBURNE, CLEBURNE, TX, p. A592

TEXAS HEALTH HARRIS METHODIST HOSPITAL FORT WORTH, FORT WORTH, TX, p. A604

TEXAS HEALTH HARRIS METHODIST HOSPITAL HURST–EULESS–BEDFORD, BEDFORD, TX, p. A588

TEXAS HEALTH HARRIS METHODIST HOSPITAL SOUTHLAKE, SOUTHLAKE, TX, p. A634

TEXAS HEALTH HARRIS METHODIST HOSPITAL SOUTHWEST FORT WORTH, FORT WORTH, TX, p. A604

TEXAS HEALTH HARRIS METHODIST HOSPITAL STEPHENVILLE, STEPHENVILLE, TX, p. A635

TEXAS HEALTH HEART & VASCULAR HOSPITAL ARLINGTON, ARLINGTON, TX, p. A584

TEXAS HEALTH PRESBYTERIAN HOSPITAL ALLEN, ALLEN, TX, p. A581

TEXAS HEALTH PRESBYTERIAN HOSPITAL DALLAS, DALLAS, TX, p. A597

TEXAS HEALTH PRESBYTERIAN HOSPITAL DENTON, DENTON, TX, p. A599

TEXAS HEALTH PRESBYTERIAN HOSPITAL FLOWER MOUND, FLOWER MOUND, TX, p. A602

TEXAS HEALTH PRESBYTERIAN HOSPITAL KAUFMAN, KAUFMAN, TX, p. A616

TEXAS HEALTH PRESBYTERIAN HOSPITAL OF ROCKWALL, ROCKWALL, TX, p. A629

TEXAS HEALTH PRESBYTERIAN HOSPITAL PLANO, PLANO, TX, p. A628

TEXAS HEALTH PRESBYTERIAN HOSPITAL–WNJ, SHERMAN, TX, p. A634

TEXAS HEALTH SPECIALTY HOSPITAL, FORT WORTH, TX, p. A604

TEXAS INSTITUTE FOR SURGERY AT TEXAS HEALTH PRESBYTERIAN DALLAS, DALLAS, TX, p. A597

TEXAS NEUROREHAB CENTER, AUSTIN, TX, p. A586

TEXAS ORTHOPEDIC HOSPITAL, HOUSTON, TX, p. A612

TEXAS REGIONAL MEDICAL CENTER AT SUNNYVALE, SUNNYVALE, TX, p. A636

TEXAS REHABILITATION HOSPITAL OF FORT WORTH, FORT WORTH, TX, p. A604

TEXAS SCOTTISH RITE HOSPITAL FOR CHILDREN, DALLAS, TX, p. A597

TEXAS SPECIALTY HOSPITAL AT DALLAS, DALLAS, TX, p. A598

TEXAS SPECIALTY HOSPITAL AT HOUSTON, HOUSTON, TX, p. A612

TEXAS SPECIALTY HOSPITAL AT LUBBOCK, LUBBOCK, TX, p. A620

TEXAS SPECIALTY HOSPITAL AT WICHITA FALLS, WICHITA FALLS, TX, p. A641

TEXAS SPINE & JOINT HOSPITAL, TYLER, TX, p. A638

TEXAS STAR RECOVERY, AUSTIN, TX, p. A586

TEXOMA MEDICAL CENTER, DENISON, TX, p. A598

THAYER COUNTY HEALTH SERVICES, HEBRON, NE, p. A384

THE ACADIA HOSPITAL, BANGOR, ME, p. A281

THE ALLEN PAVILION, NEW YORK, NEW YORK (see NEW YORK–PRESBYTERIAN HOSPITAL), p. A435

THE AROOSTOOK MEDICAL CENTER, PRESQUE ISLE, ME, p. A285

THE BRIDGEWAY, NORTH LITTLE ROCK, AR, p. A48

THE BROOK AT DUPONT, LOUISVILLE, KY, p. A256

THE BROOK HOSPITAL – KMI, LOUISVILLE, KY, p. A256

THE CHARLOTTE HUNGERFORD HOSPITAL, TORRINGTON, CT, p. A112

THE CHILDREN'S CENTER, BETHANY, OK, p. A496

THE CHILDREN'S CENTER AT WESLEY, WICHITA, KANSAS (see WESLEY MEDICAL CENTER), p. A247

THE CHILDREN'S HOME OF PITTSBURGH, PITTSBURGH, PA, p. A538

THE CHILDREN'S HOSPITAL AT SAINT PETER'S UNIVERSITY, NEW BRUNSWICK, NEW JERSEY (see SAINT PETER'S UNIVERSITY HOSPITAL), p. A407

THE CHILDREN'S HOSPITAL AT SUNY DOWNSTATE,, NEW YORK (see SUNY DOWNSTATE MEDICAL CENTER UNIVERSITY HOSPITAL), p. A436

THE CHILDREN'S HOSPITAL OF ALABAMA, BIRMINGHAM, AL, p. A17

THE CHILDREN'S INSTITUTE OF PITTSBURGH, PITTSBURGH, PA, p. A538

THE CONNECTICUT HOSPICE, BRANFORD, CT, p. A108

THE GOOD SAMARITAN HOSPITAL, LEBANON, PA, p. A529

THE HEALTHCENTER, KALISPELL, MT, p. A377

THE HEART HOSPITAL AT DEACONESS GATEWAY, NEWBURGH, IN, p. A211

THE HEART HOSPITAL BAYLOR PLANO, PLANO, TX, p. A628

THE HOSPITAL AT CRAIG RANCH, MCKINNEY, TX, p. A622

THE HOSPITAL AT HEBREW HEALTH CARE, WEST HARTFORD, CT, p. A112

THE HOSPITAL AT WESTLAKE MEDICAL CENTER, AUSTIN, TX, p. A586

THE HOSPITAL OF CENTRAL CONNECTICUT, NEW BRITAIN, CT, p. A110

THE HSC PEDIATRIC CENTER, WASHINGTON, DC, p. A117

THE JEWISH HOSPITAL – MERCY HEALTH, CINCINNATI, OH, p. A475

THE JOSEPH M. SANZARI CHILDREN'S HOSPITAL, HACKENSACK, NEW JERSEY (see HACKENSACK UNIVERSITY MEDICAL CENTER), p. A404

THE KING'S DAUGHTERS HOSPITAL, GREENVILLE, MISSISSIPPI (see DELTA REGIONAL MEDICAL CENTER), p. A347

THE MEDICAL CENTER, COLUMBUS, GA, p. A150

THE MEDICAL CENTER AT ELIZABETH PLACE, DAYTON, OH, p. A480

THE MEDICAL CENTER OF SOUTHEAST TEXAS, PORT ARTHUR, TX, p. A628

THE METHODIST HOSPITAL, HOUSTON, TX, p. A613

THE MOUNT SINAI HOSPITAL OF QUEENS,, NY, p. A437

THE NEUROMEDICAL CENTER SURGICAL HOSPITAL, BATON ROUGE, LA, p. A264

THE ORTHOPEDIC SPECIALTY HOSPITAL, MURRAY, UT, p. A644

THE OUTER BANKS HOSPITAL, NAGS HEAD, NC, p. A458

THE PAVILION, CHAMPAIGN, IL, p. A176

THE PAVILION, PENSACOLA, FLORIDA (see WEST FLORIDA HOSPITAL), p. A137

THE PHYSICIANS CENTRE HOSPITAL, BRYAN, TX, p. A590

THE REHABILITATION HOSPITAL, FORT MYERS, FLORIDA (see LEE MEMORIAL HOSPITAL), p. A124

THE REHABILITATION INSTITUTE OF ST. LOUIS, SAINT LOUIS, MO, p. A371

THE UNIVERSITY OF KANSAS HOSPITAL, KANSAS CITY, KS, p. A237

THE UNIVERSITY OF TOLEDO MEDICAL CENTER, TOLEDO, OH, p. A491

THE VILLAGES HEALTH SYSTEM, THE VILLAGES, FL, p. A142

THE VINES, OCALA, FL, p. A134

THE WILLIAM W. BACKUS HOSPITAL, NORWICH, CT, p. A111

THE WOMAN'S HOSPITAL OF TEXAS, HOUSTON, TX, p. A613

THE WOMEN'S HOSPITAL, NEWBURGH, IN, p. A211

THE WOODS AT PARKSIDE, GAHANNA, OH, p. A482

THEDA CLARK MEDICAL CENTER, NEENAH, WI, p. A693

THIBODAUX REGIONAL MEDICAL CENTER, THIBODAUX, LA, p. A279

THOMAS B. FINAN CENTER, CUMBERLAND, MD, p. A291

THOMAS H. BOYD MEMORIAL HOSPITAL, CARROLLTON, IL, p. A175

THOMAS HOSPITAL, FAIRHOPE, AL, p. A20

THOMAS JEFFERSON UNIVERSITY HOSPITAL, PHILADELPHIA, PA, p. A537

THOMAS MEMORIAL HOSPITAL, SOUTH CHARLESTON, WV, p. A681

THOREK MEMORIAL HOSPITAL, CHICAGO, IL, p. A179

THOUSAND OAKS SURGICAL HOSPITAL, THOUSAND OAKS, CA, p. A92

## V

# W

# Y

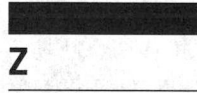

# Z

This section is an index of the key health care professionals for the hospitals and/or health care systems listed in this publication. The index is in alphabetical order, by individual, followed by the title, institutional affiliation, city, state and page reference to the hospital and/or health care system listing in section A and/or B.

# A

AAFEDT, Karen, Assistant Administrator and Controller, Community Memorial Hospital, Turtle Lake, ND, p. A469

AAGARD, Kim, Chief Financial Officer, Tri-County Hospital, Wadena, MN, p. A342

AARON, Judy, Administrator, Creek Nation Community Hospital, Okemah, OK, p. A502

AARON, Michael, M.D. Chief of Staff, Weatherford Regional Hospital, Weatherford, OK, p. A510

AASVED, Craig E., Chief Operating Officer, St. Patrick Hospital, Missoula, MT, p. A378

ABAD, Ann, Vice President Operations, Barnes-Jewish St. Peters Hospital, Saint Peters, MO, p. A371

ABADIER, Ralph, M.D. Chief of Staff, Citrus Memorial Health System, Inverness, FL, p. A126

ABAIR, Cynthia, Associate Director, Veterans Affairs San Diego Healthcare System, San Diego, CA, p. A86

ABARICIA, Eduardo, Director Information Technology, Northwest Missouri Psychiatric Rehabilitation Center, Saint Joseph, MO, p. A369

ABBATE, Richard, Director Human Resources, Sutter Lakeside Hospital, Lakeport, CA, p. A66

ABBEN, Richard, M.D. Chief of Staff, Terrebonne General Medical Center, Houma, LA, p. A268

ABBOTT, Jody, Senior Vice President and Chief Operating Officer, North Kansas City Hospital, North Kansas City, MO, p. A367

ABBOTT, Peggy, President and Chief Executive Officer, Ouachita County Medical Center, Camden, AR, p. A42

ABBOTT, Richard, M.D. Medical Advisor Quality Improvement, Skagit Valley Hospital, Mount Vernon, WA, p. A668

ABDA, William, Chief Human Resources Officer, Clarks Summit State Hospital, Clarks Summit, PA, p. A522

ABE, John, M.D. Chief of Staff, Saint Joseph - London, London, KY, p. A255

ABEL, Barbara J., Vice President Human Resources, Heart of the Rockies Regional Medical Center, Salida, CO, p. A105

ABEL, Douglas A., Chief Information Officer, Anne Arundel Medical Center, Annapolis, MD, p. A287

ABEL, Kevin, Chief Executive Officer, Lake Chelan Community Hospital, Chelan, WA, p. A665

ABEL, Stacy L., Director Human Resources, Craig Hospital, Englewood, CO, p. A100

ABELS, Duane E., M.D. Chief of Staff, Memorial Hospital of Carbon County, Rawlins, WY, p. A703

ABELSON, David, M.D., President and Chief Executive Officer, Park Nicollet Methodist Hospital, Saint Louis Park, MN, p. A339

ABELY, Susan Cerrone, Vice President and Chief Information Officer, Roger Williams Medical Center, Providence, RI, p. A547

ABENDROTH, Thomas, M.D. Chief Information Officer, Penn State Milton S. Hershey Medical Center, Hershey, PA, p. A527

ABERCROMBIE, David, Chief Executive Officer, Madison County Memorial Hospital, Madison, FL, p. A129

ABERNATHY, Jennifer, Assistant Administrator, Mayo Clinic Health System - Chippewa Valley in Bloomer, Bloomer, WI, p. A684

ABERNETHY, Linda O., R.N., Superintendent, Dorothea Dix Psychiatric Center, Bangor, ME, p. A281

ABEYTA, Mary Anna, R.N. Chief Nursing/Clinical Services Officer, Holy Cross Hospital, Taos, NM, p. A418

ABINSAY, Alvin, M.D. Chief Medical Staff, Carolinas Hospital System Marion, Mullins, SC, p. A554

ABNEY, Stuart, Controller, Jasper Memorial Hospital, Monticello, GA, p. A157

ABOUD, Al, Chief Financial Officer, East Orange General Hospital, East Orange, NJ, p. A403

ABRAHAM, Akram, M.D. Chief of Staff, Harmon Memorial Hospital, Hollis, OK, p. A500

ABRAHAM, Brian, Chief Operating Officer, Mesquite Rehabilitation Institute, Mesquite, TX, p. A622

ABRAHAMY, Ran, M.D. Chief of Staff, University Hospital and Medical Center, Tamarac, FL, p. A141

ABRAMOVICH, Mark, M.D. Chief of Staff, Flaget Memorial Hospital, Bardstown, KY, p. A248

ABRAMOVITZ, Alan L., Director Human Resources, Saint Luke's North Hospital - Barry Road, Kansas City, MO, p. A363

ABRAMS, David, Vice President Human Resources, North Memorial Medical Center, Robbinsdale, MN, p. A338

ABREU, John, Interim Chief executive Officer, Portneuf Medical Center, Pocatello, ID, p. A171

ABRINA, Sofia
Administrator and Chief Nursing Officer, Garden Grove Hospital and Medical Center, Garden Grove, CA, p. A62
Administrator and Chief Nursing Officer, Huntington Beach Hospital, Huntington Beach, CA, p. A64

ABROMOVICH, Sari, Chief Executive Officer, Harbor Oaks Hospital, New Baltimore, MI, p. A321

ABRUTZ Jr., Joseph F., Administrator, Cameron Regional Medical Center, Cameron, MO, p. A357

ABSHIRE, Allen, Director Information Services, CHRISTUS St. Patrick Hospital of Lake Charles, Lake Charles, LA, p. A271

ABUIN, Jack, Director Management Information Systems, The Mount Sinai Hospital of Queens,, NY, p. A437

ACCASHIAN, Chris, Chief Executive Officer, Parkland Medical Center, Derry, NH, p. A397

ACETO, Anthony, Vice President Human Resources, Norwalk Hospital, Norwalk, CT, p. A111

ACEVEDO, Jose, M.D.,
President and Chief Executive Officer, Geneva General Hospital, Geneva, NY, p. A426
President and Chief Executive Officer, Soldiers and Sailors Memorial Hospital of Yates County, Penn Yan, NY, p. A439

ACEVEDO, Vanessa, Chief Executive Officer, Kindred Hospital of Central Ohio, Mansfield, OH, p. A484

ACEVEDO, Vivian, Chief Financial Officer, Metropolitan Hospital of Miami, Miami, FL, p. A131

ACHAMALLAH, Nagui, M.D. Chief of Staff, John Muir Behavioral Health Center, Concord, CA, p. A57

ACHBER, Linda, Director Clinical Services, Aurora Behavioral Health Care, San Diego, CA, p. A85

ACHTER, Dick, Chief Financial Officer, Barrett Hospital & HealthCare, Dillon, MT, p. A375

ACHTERHOFF, Shari, R.N. Chief Nursing Officer, Murray County Medical Center, Slayton, MN, p. A341

ACKELSON, Rocky, Director Information Services, Arkansas Valley Regional Medical Center, La Junta, CO, p. A103

ACKER, Carmen, Chief Financial Officer, Morton Hospital and Medical Center, Taunton, MA, p. A305

ACKER, David B., FACHE, President and Chief Executive Officer, Canton-Potsdam Hospital, Potsdam, NY, p. A440

ACKER, Peter W., President and Chief Executive Officer, Carolinas Medical Center-Lincoln, Lincolnton, NC, p. A456

ACKERMAN, Robert, Director Information Systems, Memorial Hospital of Rhode Island, Pawtucket, RI, p. A546

ACKERMAN, Sigurd H., M.D., President and Chief Executive Officer, Silver Hill Hospital, New Canaan, CT, p. A110

ACKERS, Allen R., Associate Director, William S. Middleton Memorial Veterans Hospital, Madison, WI, p. A690

ACKERSON, David, Chief Information Officer, Seattle Cancer Care Alliance, Seattle, WA, p. A671

ACKERT, Sara, Associate Director, Sioux Falls Veterans Affairs Health Care System, Sioux Falls, SD, p. A563

ACKISS, Jane, Site Manager Human Resources, Naval Medical Center, Portsmouth, VA, p. A659

ACKLAND, Jeanne, Director of Finance, Fillmore County Hospital, Geneva, NE, p. A383

ACKLEY, Michael, Chief Financial Officer, Kentucky River Medical Center, Jackson, KY, p. A253

ACKLEY, Wendy, Assistant Administrator, Patient Services, Providence Seaside Hospital, Seaside, OR, p. A517

ACKLIN, Traci, M.D. Chief of Staff, Montgomery General Hospital, Montgomery, WV, p. A678

ACKMAN, Jeffrey D., M.D. Chief of Staff, Shriners Hospitals for Children-Chicago, Chicago, IL, p. A179

ACKMAN, Laura, Chief Operating Officer and Administrator, Essentia Health Northern Pines, Aurora, MN, p. A328

ACOSTA, Louis, M.D. Chief of Staff, Silver Lake Medical Center, Los Angeles, CA, p. A71

ACOSTA, Maridel, Chief Executive Officer, Eastern New Mexico Medical Center, Roswell, NM, p. A417

ACOSTA-CARLSON, Francisca, M.D. Chief of Staff, Lexington Regional Health Center, Lexington, NE, p. A385

ACREE, Charis, Senior Vice President, West Georgia Health, La Grange, GA, p. A155

ACTERHOF, Trudy, Director Human Resources, Baldwin Area Medical Center, Baldwin, WI, p. A683

ADAIR, Dale K., M.D. Chief Medical Officer, Wernersville State Hospital, Wernersville, PA, p. A543

ADAM, Sheryl, Chief Financial Officer, Hanover Hospital, Hanover, KS, p. A234

ADAMO, James D., M.D. Medical Director, Harbor Oaks Hospital, New Baltimore, MI, p. A321

ADAMO, Peter J.
Chief Executive Officer, Lower Bucks Hospital, Bristol, PA, p. A521
Chief Executive Officer, Roxborough Memorial Hospital, Philadelphia, PA, p. A536

ADAMS, Alan L., President, Memorial Hospital, Stilwell, OK, p. A507

ADAMS, Amy B.
Executive Director Human Resources, Laureate Psychiatric Clinic and Hospital, Tulsa, OK, p. A508
Executive Director Human Resources, Saint Francis Hospital, Tulsa, OK, p. A508
Executive Director Human Resources, Saint Francis Hospital South, Tulsa, OK, p. A509

ADAMS, Angela C., Director Human Resources, St. Mary's Good Samaritan Hospital, Greensboro, GA, p. A154

ADAMS, Anthony, M.D. Chief of Staff, Community Memorial Healthcenter, South Hill, VA, p. A661

ADAMS, Bob, Director Information Services, Bay Area Hospital, Coos Bay, OR, p. A512

ADAMS, Brian, Chief Executive Officer, Florida Hospital Wesley Chapel, Wesley Chapel, FL, p. A143

ADAMS, Carla A., Chief Operating Officer, French Hospital Medical Center, San Luis Obispo, CA, p. A88

ADAMS, Carolyn L., Director, Ralph H. Johnson Veterans Affairs Medical Center, Charleston, SC, p. A549

ADAMS, Charlotte, Director Associate Resources, Carolina Pines Regional Medical Center, Hartsville, SC, p. A553

ADAMS, Chris, Vice President Operations, Good Samaritan Regional Health Center, Mount Vernon, IL, p. A189

ADAMS, Chris, M.D. Physician, Rangely District Hospital, Rangely, CO, p. A105

ADAMS, Cynthia, Vice President Human Resources, TriStar StoneCrest Medical Center, Smyrna, TN, p. A579

ADAMS, Daniel H., Vice President and Chief Operating Officer, Memorial Medical Center - Ashland, Ashland, WI, p. A683

ADAMS, Dian, R.N. Chief Nursing Officer, Good Samaritan Hospital, San Jose, CA, p. A87

ADAMS, Diane, Director Business Services, Temple Community Hospital, Los Angeles, CA, p. A72

ADAMS, Earl, Chief Information Officer, Indiana University Health La Porte Hospital, La Porte, IN, p. A208

ADAMS, Essie, Director of Nursing, Kedren Community Mental Health Center, Los Angeles, CA, p. A70

ADAMS, Gini, Director Employee and Public Relations, Yuma District Hospital, Yuma, CO, p. A107

ADAMS, Jennifer B., Chief Operating Officer and Chief Financial Officer, Lake City Medical Center, Lake City, FL, p. A128

ADAMS, Jo, Director Human Resources, Donalsonville Hospital, Donalsonville, GA, p. A152

ADAMS, Karen, Vice President Human Resources, Baxter Regional Medical Center, Mountain Home, AR, p. A48

ADAMS, Kelly H., Chief Executive Officer, Desert View Hospital, Pahrump, NV, p. A394

ADAMS, Liz, Manager Informatics, The Women's Hospital, Newburgh, IN, p. A211

ADAMS, Mark A., President and Chief Executive Officer, Methodist Rehabilitation Center, Jackson, MS, p. A348

ADAMS, Mark B., Chief Executive Officer, Ogden Regional Medical Center, Ogden, UT, p. A645

ADAMS, Mark C., M.D. Chief Medical Officer, St. Francis Hospital, Federal Way, WA, p. A666

ADAMS, Mary Jane, R.N. Senior Vice President and Chief Nursing Officer, University of Louisville Hospital, Louisville, KY, p. A256

ADAMS, Mike, M.D. Chief Medical Officer, Gateway Regional Medical Center, Granite City, IL, p. A184

ADAMS, Mike, Chief Operating Officer, South Texas Health System, Edinburg, TX, p. A600

ADAMS, Nancy D., R.N. Senior Vice President and Chief Nurse Executive, Western Maryland Regional Medical Center, Cumberland, MD, p. A291

ADAMS, Norma, Director Human Resources, Southern Regional Medical Center, Riverdale, GA, p. A159

ADAMS, Patricia L., M.D. Chief Professional Services, Wake Forest Baptist Medical Center, Winston–Salem, NC, p. A464

ADAMS, Patsy, Director Human Resources, Redmond Regional Medical Center, Rome, GA, p. A159

ADAMS, Renee, Director Information Technology, Windber Medical Center, Windber, PA, p. A545

ADAMS, Robert H., Vice President Operations, Jersey Shore University Medical Center, Neptune, NJ, p. A407

ADAMS, Robin, Director Human Resources, Reeves Memorial Medical Center, Bernice, LA, p. A264

ADAMS, Scott K., Chief Executive Officer, Pullman Regional Hospital, Pullman, WA, p. A669

ADAMS, Shaun, Chief Financial Officer, Harton Regional Medical Center, Tullahoma, TN, p. A580

ADAMS, Shawn, Assistant Administrator Finance, CHRISTUS Hospital–St. Elizabeth, Beaumont, TX, p. A587

ADAMS, Shelah, Chief Executive Officer, River Crest Hospital, San Angelo, TX, p. A630

ADAMS, Stanley
Chief Financial Officer, Banner Baywood Medical Center, Mesa, AZ, p. A32
Chief Financial Officer, Banner Heart Hospital, Mesa, AZ, p. A33

ADAMS, Stephen D., Executive Vice President and Chief Information Officer, UPMC Mercy, Pittsburgh, PA, p. A538

ADAMS, William, M.D. Medical Director, Fairfax Hospital, Kirkland, WA, p. A667

ADAMS, William D., Chief Executive Officer, Knapp Medical Center, Weslaco, TX, p. A641

ADAMSKI, Joseph, Chief Nursing Officer, HEALTHSOUTH Rehabilitation Hospital, Concord, NH, p. A397

ADAMSON, James, Chief Executive Officer, Mountain View Hospital, Idaho Falls, ID, p. A169

ADAMSON, Nancy, R.N. Chief Nursing Officer, Banner Estrella Medical Center, Phoenix, AZ, p. A34

ADAMSON, Paula, Manager Human Resources, Cleveland Clinic Florida, Weston, FL, p. A144

ADCOCK, D. W., M.D. Medical Director, Colquitt Regional Medical Center, Moultrie, GA, p. A158

ADCOCK, William, Chief Financial Officer, Union General Hospital, Farmerville, LA, p. A267

ADDISON, Holland M., M.D. Medical Director, Mississippi Hospital for Restorative Care, Jackson, MS, p. A349

ADDISON, Lewis C., Senior Vice President and Chief Financial Officer, Centra Lynchburg General Hospital, Lynchburg, VA, p. A656

ADDO–SAMUELS, Deborah, Senior Vice President and Chief Operating Officer, Meritus Medical Center, Hagerstown, MD, p. A292

ADELMAN, Michael, M.D., Director, Erie Veterans Affairs Medical Center, Erie, PA, p. A525

ADEMA, Carolyn, Senior Vice President Human Resources, North Oaks Medical Center, Hammond, LA, p. A268

ADER, Michael H., M.D. Vice President Medical Affairs, Hanover Hospital, Hanover, PA, p. A526

ADERHOLD, Pat, Director Human Resources, J. Arthur Dosher Memorial Hospital, Southport, NC, p. A461

ADERHOLDT, Elizabeth, President, Genesys Regional Medical Center, Grand Blanc, MI, p. A314

ADHAMI, Shawn, M.D. Chief of Staff, Monterey Park Hospital, Monterey Park, CA, p. A75

ADKINS, Debbie, Director Human Resources, Seton Smithville Regional Hospital, Smithville, TX, p. A634

ADKINS, Gary W., Chief Executive Officer, Paulding County Hospital, Paulding, OH, p. A488

ADKINS, Jo, Chief Executive Officer, West Valley Hospital, Goodyear, AZ, p. A32

ADKINS, John, Vice President and Chief Information Officer, St. Joseph's Hospital, Savannah, GA, p. A160

ADKINS, Kevin, Director Human Resources, Green Oaks Hospital, Dallas, TX, p. A596

ADKINS, Paige, Chief Financial Officer, Greenbrier Valley Medical Center, Ronceverte, WV, p. A680

ADKINS, Raymond, Chief Information Officer, Peninsula Regional Medical Center, Salisbury, MD, p. A294

ADKINSON, Jessica, Administrator, MMO WestEnd Hospital, Jennings, LA, p. A269

ADLER, Josh, M.D. Interim Co–Chief Medical Officer, UCSF Medical Center, San Francisco, CA, p. A87

ADLER, Linda, Administrator, Florida Hospital Wauchula, Wauchula, FL, p. A143

ADLER, Maurita, Director Information Services, Gottlieb Memorial Hospital, Melrose Park, IL, p. A188

ADLER–MARKS, Cathy
Director Information Technology, Vista Medical Center East, Waukegan, IL, p. A196
Director Information Technology, Vista Medical Center West, Waukegan, IL, p. A196

ADORNATO, Sara F., Executive Director, Barnes–Kasson County Hospital, Susquehanna, PA, p. A542

ADRIAANSE, Steven W., Vice President and Chief Human Resources Officer, Tallahassee Memorial HealthCare, Tallahassee, FL, p. A141

ADRIAN, Cheri D., Director Human Resources, St. Margaret's Hospital, Spring Valley, IL, p. A195

ADVEY, Linda, Manager Information Systems, Glenbeigh Hospital and Outpatient Centers, Rock Creek, OH, p. A489

AEA, Richard, Director Human Resources, Wahiawa General Hospital, Wahiawa, HI, p. A166

AFLAK, Ziba, Chief Financial Officer, Kindred Hospital–San Francisco Bay Area, San Leandro, CA, p. A88

AGANA, Ben, M.D. Medical Director, HEALTHSOUTH Rehabilitation Hospital of North Houston, Conroe, TX, p. A593

AGAPITO, Arnold, M.D. President Medical Staff, Shelby Memorial Hospital, Shelbyville, IL, p. A194

AGBA, C. Okey, Senior Vice President, Chief Financial Officer and Treasurer, Tufts Medical Center, Boston, MA, p. A297

AGEE, Nancy Howell, President and Chief Executive Officer, Carilion Medical Center, Roanoke, VA, p. A661

AGLIECO, Fabio, D.O. Chief of Staff, Sweeny Community Hospital, Sweeny, TX, p. A636

AGLOINGA, Roy, Chief Administrative Officer, Norton Sound Regional Hospital, Nome, AK, p. A28

AGNEW, Claire, Chief Financial Officer, Banner Gateway Medical Center, Gilbert, AZ, p. A31

AGNEW, Mary Christine, R.N. Vice President and Chief Nursing Officer, Reading Hospital and Medical Center, West Reading, PA, p. A544

AGNI, Guirish, M.D. Chief of Staff, Stoughton Hospital Association, Stoughton, WI, p. A697

AGOSTINI, Scott, Director, Magee Rehabilitation Hospital, Philadelphia, PA, p. A535

AGRAWAL, Abha, M.D. Medical Director, Kings County Hospital Center,, NY, p. A433

AGRESTI, Katie, R.N. Director Patient Care Services, Millcreek Community Hospital, Erie, PA, p. A525

AGUAS, Hugo, Vice President Human Resources, Inova Alexandria Hospital, Alexandria, VA, p. A651

AGUIAR–OLSEN, Rinely, M.D. Medical Director, Yuma Rehabilitation Hospital, Yuma, AZ, p. A40

AGUILAR, Abram, M.D. Chief Medical Officer, Northwest Medical Center, Tucson, AZ, p. A39

AGUILERA, Louie, Director Information Technology, Foundation Surgical Hospital of El Paso, El Paso, TX, p. A601

AHEARN, Patrick, Senior Vice President Finance and Administrative Services, Saint Barnabas Medical Center, Livingston, NJ, p. A405

AHL, Dennis, Director Information Technology, Jefferson Community Health Center, Fairbury, NE, p. A383

AHMAD, Asif, Chief Information Officer, Duke University Hospital, Durham, NC, p. A451

AHMAD, Yousuf
Divisional Senior Vice President and Chief Network Transformation Officer, Mercy Health – Fairfield Hospital, Fairfield, OH, p. A481
Divisional Senior Vice President, Mercy Health – Mt. Airy Hospital, Cincinnati, OH, p. A475
Chief Information Officer, Springfield Regional Medical Center, Springfield, OH, p. A490

AHMED, Ashraf, M.D. Senior Vice President Physician and Hospital Services, Alliance Community Hospital, Alliance, OH, p. A470

AHMED, Mohammed Shafeeq, M.D. Chief Operating Officer and Chief Medical Officer, Baystate Mary Lane Hospital, Ware, MA, p. A306

AHMED, Steve Saeed, M.D. Chief of Staff, Scenic Mountain Medical Center, Big Spring, TX, p. A588

AHNER, Dawn, Chief Financial Officer, Renown Rehabilitation Hospital, Reno, NV, p. A395

AHNQUIST, Gary, M.D. President Medical Staff, Ephraim McDowell Regional Medical Center, Danville, KY, p. A250

AHRENDSEN, Jon, M.D. Chief of Staff, Iowa Specialty Hospital–Clarion, Clarion, IA, p. A218

AHRENS, C. Todd, President and Chief Executive Officer, Hannibal Regional Hospital, Hannibal, MO, p. A361

AIELLO, Joanne, Chief Operating Officer, Hampton Behavioral Health Center, Westampton, NJ, p. A412

AIELLO, Joseph, M.D. Chief of Staff, Asheville Specialty Hospital, Asheville, NC, p. A447

AIELLO, Louis, Chief Financial Officer, St. Elizabeth Medical Center, Utica, NY, p. A444

AIKEN, Carnel, Director Information Systems, Coastal Carolina Hospital, Hardeeville, SC, p. A553

AIKEN, David, Chief Human Resources Officer, Madigan Healthcare System, Tacoma, WA, p. A673

AIKEN, Richard, M.D. Vice President and Medical Director, Lakeland Behavioral Health System, Springfield, MO, p. A372

AILANI, Rajesh, M.D. Chief Medical Staff, Bert Fish Medical Center, New Smyrna Beach, FL, p. A133

AINSLEY, Howard N., Regional Chief Executive Officer, Hilo Medical Center, Hilo, HI, p. A164

AIONA, Michael, M.D. Chief of Staff, Shriners Hospitals for Children–Portland, Portland, OR, p. A516

AIRHART, Steven, Chief Executive Officer, Hartgrove Hospital, Chicago, IL, p. A176

AIROSUS, Diane, Chief Financial Officer, Pembroke Hospital, Pembroke, MA, p. A303

AISEN, Mindy, M.D. Chief Medical Officer, Rancho Los Amigos National Rehabilitation Center, Downey, CA, p. A58

AISENBREY, Lisa, Administrator Human Resources and Support Services, Sidney Health Center, Sidney, MT, p. A380

AITKEN, Ian, President and Chief Executive Officer, Menninger Clinic, Houston, TX, p. A611

AITTAMA, Craig
Chief Financial Officer, Aspirus Keweenaw Hospital, Laurium, MI, p. A319
Chief Financial Officer, Aspirus Ontonagon Hospital, Ontonagon, MI, p. A321

AJANAH, Muhammed, M.D. Clinical Director, Clifton T. Perkins Hospital Center, Jessup, MD, p. A292

AKAKA, Gerard, M.D. Vice President Medical Affairs, Queen's Medical Center, Honolulu, HI, p. A165

AKBARIAN, M., M.D. Medical Director, Kindred Hospital Boston–North Shore, Peabody, MA, p. A303

AKDAMAR, Erol R., President and Chief Executive Officer, Medical City Dallas Hospital, Dallas, TX, p. A596

AKENBERGER, Gary, Senior Vice President Finance, ProMedica Toledo Hospital, Toledo, OH, p. A491

AKENS, Rick, Director Human Resources, Methodist Medical Center of Oak Ridge, Oak Ridge, TN, p. A578

AKHRAS, Omar, M.D. Chief of Staff, Putnam General Hospital, Eatonton, GA, p. A153

AKIN, Pat, Chief Human Resource Officer, Spearfish Regional Surgery Center, Spearfish, SD, p. A563

AKIN, Terry, President and Chief Operating Officer, Cone Health, Greensboro, NC, p. A453

AKINTEWE, Janice, Director Information Technology, United Medical Center, Washington, DC, p. A117

AKO, Julie-Beth, Director, Systems Services, Hilo Medical Center, Hilo, HI, p. A164

AKPASSA, Gerald, M.D. Chief of Staff, East Texas Medical Center Carthage, Carthage, TX, p. A591

AL–HASHMI, Samer, M.D. Chief Medical Staff, Stevens County Hospital, Hugoton, KS, p. A236

AL–KHOURI, Samir, M.D. Medical Director, Specialty Hospital of Washington–Hadley, Washington, DC, p. A117

ALAGAR, Ravi, M.D. Medical Director, Kindred Hospital–Pittsburgh, Oakdale, PA, p. A533

ALBAN, John, Interim Director Information Systems, Advocate Illinois Masonic Medical Center, Chicago, IL, p. A176

ALBANO, Valerie, Director, Human Resources, Regional Hospital for Respiratory and Complex Care, Seattle, WA, p. A670

ALBANY, Karen, Chief Information Officer, Naval Medical Center, Portsmouth, VA, p. A659

ALBARANO, Francis G., Administrator, St. Vincent Randolph Hospital, Winchester, IN, p. A215

ALBAUGH, Jolene, R.N. Vice President and Chief Nursing Officer, Adventist Bolingbrook Hospital, Bolingbrook, IL, p. A175

ALBAUGH, Rick, Manager Information Services, Southwest Regional Rehabilitation Center, Battle Creek, MI, p. A309

ALBERG, Ellen, Director Human Resources, Johnson Memorial Health Services, Dawson, MN, p. A331

ALBERT, James, Chief Information Officer, Jordan Hospital, Plymouth, MA, p. A304

ALBERT, Kristine, Personnel Officer, Riverview Psychiatric Center, Augusta, ME, p. A281

ALBERT, Waleed, M.D. Chief Medical Officer, Rome Memorial Hospital, Rome, NY, p. A441

ALBERTI, Harry, M.D. Chief Medical Officer and Vice President Medical Affairs, Verde Valley Medical Center, Cottonwood, AZ, p. A30

ALBERTO, Carl M., Vice President Finance and Chief Financial Officer, St. Luke's Hospital – Warren Campus, Phillipsburg, NJ, p. A409

ALBERTS, Patrick J., Senior Vice President and Chief Operating Officer, Monongahela Valley Hospital, Monongahela, PA, p. A532

ALBERTS, W. Michael, M.D. Vice President Medical Affairs, H. Lee Moffitt Cancer Center and Research Institute, Tampa, FL, p. A141

ALLIES, Karla, Director Human Resources, Rosebud Health Care Center, Forsyth, MT, p. A376

ALLISON, David G., President and Chief Executive Officer, University Medical Center, Lubbock, TX, p. A620

ALLISON, Russell, Human Resources Representative, University Behavioral Health of Denton, Denton, TX, p. A599

ALLISON, Shannon, Chief Financial Officer, Houston County Community Hospital, Erin, TN, p. A568

ALLISON, Steve, Director Human Resources, Logan County Hospital, Oakley, KS, p. A240

ALLMAN, Rex, M.D. President Medical Staff, Pulaski Memorial Hospital, Winamac, IN, p. A215

ALLORE, Gary
Chief Financial Officer, Mercy Health Partners, Hackley Campus, Muskegon, MI, p. A320
Chief Financial Officer, Mercy Health Partners, Mercy Campus, Muskegon, MI, p. A321

ALLOWAY, Cindy
President, Alegent Creighton Health Lakeside Hospital, Omaha, NE, p. A387
President, Alegent Creighton Health Midlands Hospital, Papillion, NE, p. A389

ALLPHIN, Allan, M.D. Chief of Staff, Mercy Hospital Springfield, Springfield, MO, p. A372

ALLRED, Al W., Chief Financial Officer, Bert Fish Medical Center, New Smyrna Beach, FL, p. A133

ALLRED, B. Dee, M.D
President Medical Staff, Jordan Valley Medical Center, West Jordan, UT, p. A648
President Medical Staff, Pioneer Valley Hospital, West Valley City, UT, p. A648

ALLRED, Kyla, Manager Human Resources, Bartlett Regional Hospital, Juneau, AK, p. A28

ALLRED, Lowell C., M.D. Chief of Staff, Columbia Basin Hospital, Ephrata, WA, p. A666

ALLRED, Russ, Manager Information Systems, Shoshone Medical Center, Kellogg, ID, p. A169

ALLRED, William, M.D. Vice President Medical Affairs, St. John Medical Center, Tulsa, OK, p. A509

ALLSOP, Brian, Director Human Resources, Central Valley Medical Center, Nephi, UT, p. A645

ALLSTOTT, Patti, Administrative Coordinator Human Resources and Grant Writer, Pioneer Memorial Hospital, Heppner, OR, p. A513

ALLUMS, Allyson, Director Medical Records, North Caddo Medical Center, Vivian, LA, p. A280

ALLVIN, Patricia, Account Executive Information Technology, San Luis Valley Regional Medical Center, Alamosa, CO, p. A97

ALMAUHY, Deborah, R.N. Chief Nursing Officer, Rockdale Medical Center, Conyers, GA, p. A151

ALMEIDA, Sergio, Director Information Systems, West Houston Medical Center, Houston, TX, p. A613

ALMENDAREZ, Frank, Chief Operating Officer, Willamette Valley Medical Center, McMinnville, OR, p. A514

ALMENDINGER, J. Todd, President and Chief Executive Officer, Magruder Memorial Hospital, Port Clinton, OH, p. A488

ALO, Kathleen, R.N. Chief Nursing Officer, Mammoth Hospital, Mammoth Lakes, CA, p. A73

ALONSO, Nancy, Vice President Human Resources, Vista Medical Center East, Waukegan, IL, p. A196

ALONZO, Patti, Manager Human Resources, Pacifica Hospital of the Valley,, CA, p. A71

ALOUISE, Tony, Chief Executive Officer, Three Gables Surgery Center, Proctorville, OH, p. A489

ALPERT, Jeffrey, M.D. Medical Director, Wichita County Health Center, Leoti, KS, p. A238

ALPERT, Len, Director Human Resources, Hollywood Pavilion,, FL, p. A125

ALRASHEDY, Farhad H., M.D. Chief Medical Officer, Ferry County Memorial Hospital, Republic, WA, p. A670

ALREDGE, Will, Administrator, Genesis Behavioral Hospital, Breaux Bridge, LA, p. A264

ALSLEBEN, Tony, Director Information Technology, Glencoe Regional Health Services, Glencoe, MN, p. A332

ALSTAD, Nancy, Director Human Resources, Fort HealthCare, Fort Atkinson, WI, p. A686

ALSTER, Howard, M.D. President Medical Staff, Carlisle Regional Medical Center, Carlisle, PA, p. A522

ALSTON, Shawanza L., Administrator, Ascension Gonzales Rehabilitation Hospital, Gonzales, LA, p. A267

ALT, Melinda, Chief Financial Officer, Guthrie County Hospital, Guthrie Center, IA, p. A222

ALTEBARMAKIAN, Varouj, M.D. Physician in Chief, Kaiser Permanente Fresno Medical Center, Fresno, CA, p. A61

ALTENBURGER, Andy, Chief Information Officer, Marietta Memorial Hospital, Marietta, OH, p. A485

ALTMAN, III, Alexander B., Chief Executive Officer and Chief Financial Officer, Copper Basin Medical Center, Copperhill, TN, p. A568

ALTMAN, Brett, Clinical Operations Officer, Skiff Medical Center, Newton, IA, p. A226

ALTMAN, Harold, M.D. Chief Medical Officer, ACMH Hospital, Kittanning, PA, p. A528

ALTMILLER, Steve, President and Chief Executive Officer, Good Shepherd Medical Center, Longview, TX, p. A619

ALTOE, Ann, Senior Director Information Systems and Security Officer, Alfred I. duPont Hospital for Children, Wilmington, DE, p. A114

ALTOM, Andy, Chief Executive Officer, Methodist Behavioral Hospital of Arkansas, Maumelle, AR, p. A47

ALTON, Guy, Chief Financial Officer, St. Bernard Hospital and Health Care Center, Chicago, IL, p. A179

ALTOSE, Murray, M.D. Chief of Staff, Louis Stokes Cleveland Veterans Affairs Medical Center, Cleveland, OH, p. A476

ALTSCHULER, Steven M., M.D., President and Chief Executive Officer, Children's Hospital of Philadelphia, Philadelphia, PA, p. A534

ALTSHULER, Keith, President and Chief Administrative Officer, Fort Sanders Regional Medical Center, Knoxville, TN, p. A571

ALVARADO, Ramona, Interim Manager Human Resources, Adventist Medical Center–Reedley, Reedley, CA, p. A82

ALVAREZ, Dena C., R.N. COO & Chief Compliance Officer, Brodstone Memorial Hospital, Superior, NE, p. A390

ALVAREZ, Janie, Accounting Director, Cornerstone Regional Hospital, Edinburg, TX, p. A600

ALVAREZ, Jose, M.D. Chief Medical Staff, Circles of Care, Melbourne, FL, p. A130

ALVAREZ, Maria Charlotte, M.D. Chief of Staff, Sheridan Community Hospital, Sheridan, MI, p. A324

ALVAREZ, Mike, M.D. Chief Medical Officer, Dauterive Hospital, New Iberia, LA, p. A275

ALVAREZ, Valerie, Executive Assistant, Adventist Medical Center–Reedley, Reedley, CA, p. A82

ALVERSON, Tammy S., M.D. Chief of Staff, Coshocton County Memorial Hospital, Coshocton, OH, p. A479

ALVES, Richard, Chief Financial Officer, Kaiser Permanente Fresno Medical Center, Fresno, CA, p. A61

ALVEY, Raymond, Chief Financial Officer, Saint Louis University Hospital, Saint Louis, MO, p. A370

ALVIS, Darlene, Chief Human Resources Officer, McKee Medical Center, Loveland, CO, p. A104

ALWARD, Dale, Chief Executive Officer, Englewood Community Hospital, Englewood, FL, p. A123

ALWELL, James, Interim Vice President and Chief Financial Officer, Morristown–Hamblen Healthcare System, Morristown, TN, p. A576

ALWINE, Steven, Chief Executive Officer, HEALTHSOUTH Rehabilitation Hospital of York, York, PA, p. A545

AMANTEA, Paul, Director Finance, University Hospitals Geauga Medical Center, Chardon, OH, p. A473

AMAR Jr., Eugene, Administrator, Kohala Hospital, Kohala, HI, p. A166

AMARO, Wanda, Director Human Resources, Shriners Hospitals for Children–Philadelphia, Philadelphia, PA, p. A536

AMATO, Jerry, Chief Executive Officer, Plano Specialty Hospital, Plano, TX, p. A627

AMATO, Joe, Interim Chief Financial Officer, DeSoto Memorial Hospital, Arcadia, FL, p. A118

AMBACHER, Linda, Interim Chief Nursing Officer, Hackettstown Regional Medical Center, Hackettstown, NJ, p. A404

AMBROSIANI, Michael, Chief Financial Officer, Knox Community Hospital, Mount Vernon, OH, p. A487

AMEEN, David J., President and Chief Executive Officer, Logansport Memorial Hospital, Logansport, IN, p. A209

AMEND, Jeff, Chief Operating Officer, Summit Behavioral Healthcare, Cincinnati, OH, p. A475

AMERSON, Jeff, Director Information System, West Florida Hospital, Pensacola, FL, p. A137

AMES, Julie
Chief Information Officer, RML Specialty Hospital, Chicago, IL, p. A178
Chief Information Officer, RML Specialty Hospital, Hinsdale, IL, p. A185

AMEY, Mark, Chief Information Officer, Keck Hospital of USC, Los Angeles, CA, p. A70

AMIN, Yogesh, M.D. Medical Director, Select Specialty Hospital–Fort Wayne, Fort Wayne, IN, p. A203

AMIR, Adel, Interim Chief Executive Officer, Carthage Area Hospital, Carthage, NY, p. A423

AMIZICH, Tammy, Chief Nursing Executive, Washington County Hospital, Nashville, IL, p. A190

AMMONS, Donna, Director Human Resources, East Jefferson General Hospital, Metairie, LA, p. A273

AMMONS, Eric, President, Mercy Hospital Jefferson, Crystal City, MO, p. A359

AMODO, Mitch, Vice President and Chief Financial Officer, Orange Regional Medical Center, Middletown, NY, p. A429

AMONS, Gene, Administrator, Oceans Behavioral Hospital of Alexandria, Alexandria, LA, p. A262

AMOROSE, Carl, Vice President Finance, Norton Hospital, Louisville, KY, p. A256

AMOS, John, COO East Campus, Yavapai Regional Medical Center – East, Prescott Valley, AZ, p. A36

AMOS, Robert, Vice President and Chief Financial Officer, Winchester Medical Center, Winchester, VA, p. A663

AMROM, George, M.D. Vice President Medical Affairs, Hahnemann University Hospital, Philadelphia, PA, p. A535

AMSTUTZ, Terry L., FACHE, Vice President and Administrator, Baptist Health Medical Center–Stuttgart, Stuttgart, AR, p. A50

AMUNDSON, David H., Chief Financial Officer, FirstLight Health System, Mora, MN, p. A337

AMY, Christy, Chief Financial Officer, West Oaks Hospital, Houston, TX, p. A614

AMYX, Maleigha, Chief Information Officer, Rockcastle Regional Hospital and Respiratory Care Center, Mount Vernon, KY, p. A258

ANAND, Ajay, M.D. President Medical Staff, Summers County ARH Hospital, Hinton, WV, p. A677

ANASTASI, Frank, Chief Financial Officer, Pennsylvania Hospital, Philadelphia, PA, p. A536

ANASTASIO, Lance W., President, Winter Haven Hospital, Winter Haven, FL, p. A144

ANCHONDO, Laura, Administrator Human Resources, Kindred Hospital El Paso, El Paso, TX, p. A601

ANDERMAN, Steven, Chief Operating Officer, Bronx–Lebanon Hospital Center Health Care System,, NY, p. A431

ANDERS, Jr., James M., Administrator and Chief Operating Officer, Kennedy Krieger Institute, Baltimore, MD, p. A287

ANDERS, Robert, Chief Financial Officer, Ouachita County Medical Center, Camden, AR, p. A42

ANDERSEN, Mark, Senior Vice President Information Systems and Chief Information Officer, Yale–New Haven Hospital, New Haven, CT, p. A110

ANDERSEN, Sue
Chief Financial Officer, French Hospital Medical Center, San Luis Obispo, CA, p. A88
Chief Financial Officer, Marian Medical Center, Santa Maria, CA, p. A90

ANDERSEN, Travis, President, St. Elizabeth Hospital, Appleton, WI, p. A683

ANDERSEN, Wendy, Director Human Resources, Eastern Idaho Regional Medical Center, Idaho Falls, ID, p. A169

ANDERSON, A. Elizabeth, Administrator, University of South Alabama Medical Center, Mobile, AL, p. A23

ANDERSON, Allyson, Chief Administrative Officer, Legacy Meridian Park Hospital, Tualatin, OR, p. A518

ANDERSON, Angie, Director Information Technology, Crawford County Memorial Hospital, Denison, IA, p. A220

ANDERSON, Barbara, Chief Financial Officer, Stanton County Hospital, Johnson, KS, p. A236

ANDERSON, Brad, Chief Financial Officer, Community Memorial Hospital, Cloquet, MN, p. A330

ANDERSON, Brian, Chief Financial Officer, Capital Medical Center, Olympia, WA, p. A668

ANDERSON, Cherri, Chief Nursing Officer, Banner Behavioral Health Hospital – Scottsdale, Scottsdale, AZ, p. A37

ANDERSON, Chris, Chief Executive Officer, Singing River Health System, Pascagoula, MS, p. A352

ANDERSON, Colette, Manager Finance, McKenzie County Healthcare System, Watford City, ND, p. A469

ANDERSON, Craig, Director Management Information Systems, River Bend Hospital, West Lafayette, IN, p. A215

ANDERSON, Cy, M.D. Chief of Staff, Newman Regional Health, Emporia, KS, p. A233

ANDERSON, Darla, Chief Financial Officer, Sibley Medical Center, Arlington, MN, p. A328

ANDERSON, David, M.D. Medical Director, Heartland Surgical Specialty Hospital, Overland Park, KS, p. A241

ANDERSON, David, Chief Executive Officer, Jackson Purchase Medical Center, Mayfield, KY, p. A257

ANDERSON, David E., Ph.D. Chief Operating Officer, Sierra Tucson, Tucson, AZ, p. A39

ANDERSON, David K., M.D. Chief of Staff, Timpanogos Regional Hospital, Orem, UT, p. A645

ANDERSON, David W., Executive Vice President Human Resources and Chief Compliance Officer, WellStar Kennestone Hospital, Marietta, GA, p. A157

ANDERSON, Debra, M.D. Chief of Staff, Ivinson Memorial Hospital, Laramie, WY, p. A702

ANDERSON, Dianne J., R.N., President and Chief Executive Officer, Lawrence General Hospital, Lawrence, MA, p. A301

ANDERSON, Donna K., R.N. Chief Nursing Officer, Cannon Memorial Hospital, Pickens, SC, p. A555

ANDERSON, Duke, President and Chief Executive Officer, Hillsdale Community Health Center, Hillsdale, MI, p. A316

ANDERSON, Edward, Chief Financial Officer, Johnson Regional Medical Center, Clarksville, AR, p. A42

ANDERSON, Edwin S., Chief Executive Officer, Cumberland Medical Center, Crossville, TN, p. A568

ANDERSON, Emily, Director of Nursing Emergency Room, Gundersen Tri–County Hospital and Clinics, Whitehall, WI, p. A699

ANDERSON, Jr., Gail, M.D. Chief Medical Officer, LAC–Harbor–University of California at Los Angeles Medical Center, Torrance, CA, p. A92

ANDERSON, Gaynell, M.D. Medical Director, St. Anthony Shawnee Hospital, Shawnee, OK, p. A506

ANDERSON, Gina
Chief Financial Officer, Lovelace Medical Center, Albuquerque, NM, p. A414
Human Resources Officer, Riverview Regional Medical Center, Carthage, TN, p. A566

ANDERSON, Gladys, Interim CEO, Houston County Community Hospital, Erin, TN, p. A568

ANDERSON, Greg E.
Chief Financial Officer, Emory University Hospital Midtown, Atlanta, GA, p. A146
Chief Financial Officer, Wesley Woods Geriatric Hospital of Emory University, Atlanta, GA, p. A147

ANDERSON, Heidi, Human Resources Specialist, State Hospital South, Blackfoot, ID, p. A167

ANDERSON, J. Bryant, Administrator and Chief Executive Officer, Anthony Medical Center, Anthony, KS, p. A231

ANDERSON, JaNelle, Director, Mary Greeley Medical Center, Ames, IA, p. A216

ANDERSON, Jason, Chief Financial Officer, Mackinac Straits Health System, Saint Ignace, MI, p. A323

ANDERSON, Jennifer, Director Human Resources, Weirton Medical Center, Weirton, WV, p. A681

ANDERSON, Jimmy, Director of Information Systems, Regional Hospital of Jackson, Jackson, TN, p. A570

ANDERSON, Joann, President and Chief Executive Officer, Southeastern Health, Lumberton, NC, p. A457

ANDERSON, John D., FACHE, Administrator, Marshall Medical Center South, Boaz, AL, p. A17

ANDERSON, Jonathon, Director Information Technology and Telecommunications, Fresno Heart and Surgical Hospital, Fresno, CA, p. A61

ANDERSON, Kenneth, M.D. Vice President and Chief Medical Officer, Baptist Health Louisville, Louisville, KY, p. A255

ANDERSON, Kevin, Director Information Technology, CGH Medical Center, Sterling, IL, p. A195

ANDERSON, Kimball, FACHE Chief Operating Officer, Mountain View Hospital, Payson, UT, p. A645

ANDERSON, Kimball, FACHE, Chief Executive Officer, Southern Hills Hospital and Medical Center, Las Vegas, NV, p. A393

ANDERSON, Larry B., Chief Executive Officer, Tri–City Medical Center, Oceanside, CA, p. A77

ANDERSON, Layton, Regional Director Human Resources, Ministry Saint Joseph's Hospital, Marshfield, WI, p. A690

ANDERSON, Lex S.
Chief Financial Officer, St. John Broken Arrow, Broken Arrow, OK, p. A496
Chief Financial Officer, St. John Medical Center, Tulsa, OK, p. A509
Chief Financial Officer, St. John Owasso, Owasso, OK, p. A505

ANDERSON, Libby, Chief Financial Officer, Satanta District Hospital, Satanta, KS, p. A244

ANDERSON, Lisa K., Vice President Finance, Unity Hospital, Fridley, MN, p. A332

ANDERSON, Lucia E., Senior Vice President Nursing and Chief Nurse Executive, Lake Region Healthcare, Fergus Falls, MN, p. A332

ANDERSON, Mark, Chief Financial Officer, Lane Regional Medical Center, Zachary, LA, p. A280

ANDERSON, Mark T., Chief Financial Officer, Danville Regional Medical Center, Danville, VA, p. A653

ANDERSON, Mary, R.N. Chief Nursing Officer, East Georgia Regional Medical Center, Statesboro, GA, p. A160

ANDERSON, Mary Ann, R.N. Chief Nursing Officer, Nyack Hospital, Nyack, NY, p. A438

ANDERSON, Matthew, Director Human Resources, Mesa View Regional Hospital, Mesquite, NV, p. A394

ANDERSON, Michael, M.D. Chief Medical Officer, University Hospitals Case Medical Center, Cleveland, OH, p. A477

ANDERSON, Michael S., M.D. Chief of Staff, Southern Virginia Regional Medical Center, Emporia, VA, p. A653

ANDERSON, Mike, Chief Financial Officer, Skiff Medical Center, Newton, IA, p. A226

ANDERSON, Noble, Director Patient Financial Services, Rice Medical Center, Eagle Lake, TX, p. A600

ANDERSON, Patrick, Chief Information Officer, Memorial Medical Center, Modesto, CA, p. A74

ANDERSON, Paula, Administrative Director Human Resources, Endless Mountain Health Systems, Montrose, PA, p. A532

ANDERSON, Randy, DPM Chief Medical Officer, United General Hospital, Sedro Woolley, WA, p. A672

ANDERSON, Rhonda
Executive Vice President Finance and Chief Financial Officer, Columbia St. Mary's Hospital Milwaukee, Milwaukee, WI, p. A692
Executive Vice President Finance and Chief Financial Officer, Columbia St. Mary's Ozaukee Hospital, Mequon, WI, p. A691
Executive Vice President Finance and Chief Financial Officer, Sacred Heart Rehabilitation Institute, Milwaukee, WI, p. A692

ANDERSON, Richard A., President and Chief Executive Officer, St. Luke's University Hospital – Bethlehem Campus, Bethlehem, PA, p. A520

ANDERSON, Rick, M.D. Senior Vice President Medical Affairs and Chief Medical Officer, UnityPoint Health – Methodist, Peoria, IL, p. A192

ANDERSON, Robert C., Interim Chief Financial Officer, Alameda Hospital, Alameda, CA, p. A52

ANDERSON, Roland, M.D., Medical Director, Arkansas Department of Correction Hospital, Pine Bluff, AR, p. A49

ANDERSON, Sandra L., President, St. Clare Hospital, Baraboo, WI, p. A683

ANDERSON, Sharla, Chief Executive Officer, Trinity Mother Frances Rehabilitation Hospital, Tyler, TX, p. A638

ANDERSON, Shawn, Chief Operating Officer, Cary Medical Center, Caribou, ME, p. A282

ANDERSON, Stephanie, Senior Vice President, Finance and Administration, Woman's Hospital, Baton Rouge, LA, p. A264

ANDERSON, Steve, Chief Financial Officer, Community Health Center of Branch County, Coldwater, MI, p. A311

ANDERSON, Steven
Chief Executive Officer, Jordan Valley Medical Center, West Jordan, UT, p. A648
Chief Executive Officer, Pioneer Valley Hospital, West Valley City, UT, p. A648

ANDERSON, Sue, Senior Vice President, Chief Financial Officer and Chief Information Officer, Virginia Mason Medical Center, Seattle, WA, p. A671

ANDERSON, Susan, Director Information Systems, Texas Health Presbyterian Hospital Plano, Plano, TX, p. A628

ANDERSON, Suzanne P., Nurse Administrator, Intermountain Medical Center, Murray, UT, p. A644

ANDERSON, Thomas, M.D
Vice President Medical Affairs, Chambersburg Hospital, Chambersburg, PA, p. A522
Chief of Staff, Portland Veterans Affairs Medical Center, Portland, OR, p. A516
Vice President Medical Affairs, Waynesboro Hospital, Waynesboro, PA, p. A543

ANDERSON, Todd, Chief Financial Officer, Grandview Medical Center, Dayton, OH, p. A480

ANDERSON, Traci, Chief Financial Officer, Memorial Hospital, Seminole, TX, p. A633

ANDERSON, William, M.D. Medical Director, Rosebud Health Care Center, Forsyth, MT, p. A376

ANDERSON, Zandra, Chief Financial Officer, Timpanogos Regional Hospital, Orem, UT, p. A645

ANDERT, Nancy, Director Human Resources, Murray County Medical Center, Slayton, MN, p. A341

ANDERTON, Beth, Vice President Human Resources, Ferrell Hospital, Eldorado, IL, p. A181

ANDRADA, Sally, Chief Information Officer, Los Alamitos Medical Center, Los Alamitos, CA, p. A68

ANDRAE, Andrea, Chief Financial Officer, Palmerton Hospital, Palmerton, PA, p. A533

ANDREAS, Lori, Director Patient Care Services, Johnson Memorial Health Services, Dawson, MN, p. A331

ANDREASEN, Raymond, M.D. Chief Medical Officer–Inpatient, California Medical Facility, Vacaville, CA, p. A94

ANDRES, Dale, D.O. Senior Vice President Medical Affairs, Mercy Medical Center–Des Moines, Des Moines, IA, p. A220

ANDRES, Leonidas, M.D
Chief of Staff, Chambers County Public Hospital District 1, Anahuac, TX, p. A582
Chief of Staff, Winnie Community Hospital, Winnie, TX, p. A642

ANDRES, Priscilla B., Director Human Resources, OHSU Hospital, Portland, OR, p. A516

ANDRESEN, Daniel, Director Information Services, Conroe Regional Medical Center, Conroe, TX, p. A593

ANDREW, Larry, M.D. Deputy Commander Clinical Services, Moncrief Army Community Hospital, Fort Jackson, SC, p. A552

ANDREW, Mark, M.D. Chief of Staff, Van Diest Medical Center, Webster City, IA, p. A230

ANDREWS, Ashleigh, Manager Human Resources, Riverside Rehabilitation Institute, Newport News, VA, p. A658

ANDREWS, Callie, Chief Operating Officer, Eastside Medical Center, Snellville, GA, p. A160

ANDREWS, Carolle, Interim Chief Human Resources Officer, University of Connecticut Health Center, John Dempsey Hospital, Farmington, CT, p. A108

ANDREWS, David, Manager Information Systems, Chicot Memorial Medical Center, Lake Village, AR, p. A46

ANDREWS, Jade, Chief Financial Officer, Methodist Hospital for Surgery, Addison, TX, p. A581

ANDREWS, Jim, Chief Financial Officer, North Okaloosa Medical Center, Crestview, FL, p. A121

ANDREWS, John, M.D. Chief of Staff, East Texas Medical Center Tyler, Tyler, TX, p. A638

ANDREWS, Laurie, Chief Human Resources Officer, Memorial Community Health, Aurora, NE, p. A381

ANDREWS, Lawrence, Chief Fiscal Services, Dayton Veterans Affairs Medical Center, Dayton, OH, p. A479

ANDREWS, Lisa, Director Human Resources, Lancaster Rehabilitation Hospital, Lancaster, PA, p. A529

ANDREWS, Maria, MS, Director, Tuscaloosa Veterans Affairs Medical Center, Tuscaloosa, AL, p. A26

ANDREWS, Mike, Assistant Administrator and Chief Operating Officer, OCH Regional Medical Center, Starkville, MS, p. A354

ANDREWS, Paul
Chief Executive Officer, The Brook at Dupont, Louisville, KY, p. A256
Chief Executive Officer, The Brook Hospital – KMI, Louisville, KY, p. A256

ANDREWS, Rebecca, Chief Financial Officer, Vibra Hospital of Northern California, Redding, CA, p. A81

ANDREWS, Steve, Chief Financial Officer, Three Rivers Health, Three Rivers, MI, p. A325

ANDREWS, Susan, Chief Executive Officer, Valley Regional Medical Center, Brownsville, TX, p. A590

ANDRITSCH, Scott, Vice President and Chief Financial Officer, Indiana University Health Morgan Hospital, Martinsville, IN, p. A209

ANDRO, Ronald J., Senior Vice President and Chief Operating Officer, Baltimore Washington Medical Center, Glen Burnie, MD, p. A292

ANDRUS, Jonathon, Chief Executive Officer, Fairchild Medical Center, Yreka, CA, p. A96

ANDRUS, Michael G., Administrator and Chief Executive Officer, Franklin County Medical Center, Preston, ID, p. A171

ANDRUS, Terry W., President, East Alabama Medical Center, Opelika, AL, p. A24

ANDURSKY, John, Chief Financial Officer, Highlands Hospital, Connellsville, PA, p. A523

ANFINSON, Julie, Director Human Resources, Mercy Medical Center–Sioux City, Sioux City, IA, p. A228

ANGCO, Manuel, M.D. Chief of Staff, Williamson Memorial Hospital, Williamson, WV, p. A682

ANGELL, Marlin, Associate Director, Memphis Veterans Affairs Medical Center, Memphis, TN, p. A575

ANGELL, Troy, Director Human Resources, Two Rivers Behavioral Health System, Kansas City, MO, p. A364

ANGELO, Gregory, Chief Fiscal Program, James J. Peters Veterans Affairs Medical Center,, NY, p. A432

ANGLE, Gregory R., President and Chief Executive Officer, Los Robles Hospital and Medical Center, Thousand Oaks, CA, p. A92

ANGLE, James L., FACHE, Chief Executive Officer, St. Luke's Magic Valley Medical Center, Twin Falls, ID, p. A172

ANGLIN, Jason, Chief Executive Officer, Memorial Medical Center, Port Lavaca, TX, p. A628

ANGUIANO, Francisco, M.D. Chief of Staff, Sharp Chula Vista Medical Center, Chula Vista, CA, p. A56

ANKIN, Michael G., M.D
Vice President Medical Affairs & Chief Medical Officer, Northwestern Lake Forest Hospital, Lake Forest, IL, p. A186
Vice President Medical Affairs & Chief Medical Officer, Northwestern Memorial Hospital, Chicago, IL, p. A178

ANMUTH, Craig, M.D. Medical Director, Bacharach Institute for Rehabilitation, Pomona, NJ, p. A409

ANNARINO, Phillip, Vice President Human Resources, Fisher–Titus Medical Center, Norwalk, OH, p. A487

ANNECHARICO, Mary Alice
Chief Information Officer, Henry Ford Hospital, Detroit, MI, p. A312
Senior VP and CIO, Henry Ford Health System, Henry Ford Wyandotte Hospital, Wyandotte, MI, p. A327

ANNESSER, Sue
Director Information Technology, Freeman Hospital West, Joplin, MO, p. A362
Director Information Systems, Freeman Neosho Hospital, Neosho, MO, p. A366

ANNICELLI, Susan, Commander, Fort Belvoir Community Hospital, Fort Belvoir, VA, p. A654

ANNIS, Donald E., Chief Executive Officer, Crawford Memorial Hospital, Robinson, IL, p. A193

ANOTHAYANONTHA, Aaron, Chief Executive Officer, Kindred Hospital Kansas City, Kansas City, MO, p. A363

ANSEDE, Scott, Chief Operating Officer, Aiken Regional Medical Centers, Aiken, SC, p. A548

ANSELL, David A., M.D. Vice President and Chief Medical Officer, Rush University Medical Center, Chicago, IL, p. A179

ANSELL, L. V., M.D. Medical Director, Houston Orthopedic and Spine Hospital, Bellaire, TX, p. A588

ANSELN, Bernadean, Chief Executive Officer, Southeast Health Center of Reynolds County, Ellington, MO, p. A360

ANSI, Azena, Manager Health Information Management, Horizon Specialty Hospital, Las Vegas, NV, p. A393

ANSLEY, Pamela, Director Finance, Sutter Center for Psychiatry, Sacramento, CA, p. A84

ANTCZAK, Kenneth
    Vice President Human Resources, St. Joseph Mercy Livingston Hospital, Howell, MI, p. A316
    Vice President Human Resources, St. Mary Mercy Hospital, Livonia, MI, p. A319

ANTES, John, President, Missouri Baptist Medical Center, Saint Louis, MO, p. A370

ANTHONY, Anne G., FACHE, President and Chief Executive Officer, Willow Crest Hospital, Miami, OK, p. A501

ANTHONY, Jean, Chief Operating Officer and Vice President Patient Services, Hills & Dales General Hospital, Cass City, MI, p. A310

ANTHONY, Kenneth J., Chief Executive Officer, HEALTHSOUTH Harmarville Rehabilitation Hospital, Pittsburgh, PA, p. A537

ANTHONY, Kimberly L., Chief Executive Officer, Jamestown Regional Medical Center, Jamestown, TN, p. A570

ANTHONY, Mark, Executive Vice President and Chief Operating Officer, Borgess Medical Center, Kalamazoo, MI, p. A317

ANTHONY, Michelle, Chief Nursing Officer, HEALTHSOUTH Rehabilitation Hospital of Virginia, Richmond, VA, p. A660

ANTHONY, Paula
    Vice President Information Services, East Texas Medical Center Pittsburg, Pittsburg, TX, p. A627
    Vice President Information Services, East Texas Medical Center Rehabilitation Hospital, Tyler, TX, p. A638
    Vice President Information Services, East Texas Medical Center Specialty Hospital, Tyler, TX, p. A638
    Vice President Information Services, East Texas Medical Center Tyler, Tyler, TX, p. A638

ANTHONY, Sharon, Chief Executive Officer, Select Specialty Hospital–Phoenix, Phoenix, AZ, p. A35

ANTINELLI, Mark, Manager Human Resources, Syracuse Veterans Affairs Medical Center, Syracuse, NY, p. A444

ANTINORI, James, M.D. Chief of Staff, Mountain West Medical Center, Tooele, UT, p. A647

ANTON, Lourdes, Director Human Resources, Palm Springs General Hospital, Hialeah, FL, p. A125

ANTONACCI, Amy, MSN Vice President Nursing Services, Alliance Community Hospital, Alliance, OH, p. A470

ANTONECCHIA, Paul, M.D. Vice President Medical Affairs, St. John's Riverside Hospital, Yonkers, NY, p. A446

ANTONSON, Pete, Chief Executive Officer, Sanford Northwood Deaconess Health Center, Northwood, ND, p. A468

ANTONUCCI, Lawrence, M.D
    Chief Operating Officer, Cape Coral Hospital, Cape Coral, FL, p. A120
    Chief Operating Officer, Gulf Coast Medical Center, Fort Myers, FL, p. A124
    Chief Operating Officer, Lee Memorial Hospital, Fort Myers, FL, p. A124

ANUSZKIEWICZ, Dawn, Chief Executive Officer, Ochsner Baptist Medical Center, New Orleans, LA, p. A275

ANWAR, Muhammad, M.D. Chief Medical Officer, Encino Hospital Medical Center,, CA, p. A68

ANYASO, Vanessa, Director Human Resources, Lake Granbury Medical Center, Granbury, TX, p. A606

ANZEVENO, Jim, Chief Information Officer, Brigham and Women's Faulkner Hospital, Boston, MA, p. A296

APKON, Michael, M.D. Senior Vice President and Chief Medical Officer, Children's Hospital of Philadelphia, Philadelphia, PA, p. A534

APLAND, Wendy
    Regional Vice President of Finance/Chief Financial Officer, PeaceHealth Sacred Heart Medical Center at RiverBend, Springfield, OR, p. A518
    Interim Chief Financial Officer, PeaceHealth Sacred Heart Medical Center, University District, Eugene, OR, p. A512

APOLIONA, Nicole, M.D. Medical Director, Kula Hospital, Kula, HI, p. A166

APPEL, G. Robert, Chief Executive Officer, Mason General Hospital, Shelton, WA, p. A672

APPENHEIMER, Tim, M.D. Vice President and Chief Medical Officer, Katherine Shaw Bethea Hospital, Dixon, IL, p. A181

APPLE, Donald L., Chief Financial Officer, St. Vincent Anderson Regional Hospital, Anderson, IN, p. A198

APPLEBAUM, Jon D., Chief Executive Officer, Twin County Regional Hospital, Galax, VA, p. A654

APPLEGATE, Mary Jane, Chief Nursing Officer, Knoxville Hospital & Clinics, Knoxville, IA, p. A224

APPLING, J. Scott, M.D. Chief of Staff, Rush County Memorial Hospital, La Crosse, KS, p. A237

APRILE, Patricia, Chief Executive Officer, Henrietta D. Goodall Hospital, Sanford, ME, p. A285

AQUILINA, Joanne, Vice President Finance and Chief Financial Officer, Bethesda Memorial Hospital, Boynton Beach, FL, p. A119

ARABIT, Aleen D., Chief Executive Officer, Kindred Hospital El Paso, El Paso, TX, p. A601

ARAD, Lana, Chief Financial Officer, MountainView Hospital, Las Vegas, NV, p. A393

ARAIR, Sohaib, M.D. Chairman of Medical Staff, Pioneer Community Hospital of Newton, Newton, MS, p. A352

ARAKELIAN, Armen, Chief Information Officer, Nashoba Valley Medical Center, Ayer, MA, p. A295

ARAMBULA, Frank, Chief Financial Officer, Arrowhead Regional Medical Center, Colton, CA, p. A57

ARAN, Lana, Chief Financial Officer, Good Samaritan Hospital, San Jose, CA, p. A87

ARAN, Peter P., M.D
    Senior Vice President and Chief Medical Officer, Laureate Psychiatric Clinic and Hospital, Tulsa, OK, p. A508
    Senior Vice President and Chief Medical Officer, Saint Francis Hospital, Tulsa, OK, p. A508
    Senior Vice President and Chief Medical Officer, Saint Francis Hospital South, Tulsa, OK, p. A509

ARANDA, Brenda, Director Communications and Government Relations, Advocate Trinity Hospital, Chicago, IL, p. A176

ARANIO, Lani, Regional Director Human Resources, Samuel Mahelona Memorial Hospital, Kapaa, HI, p. A165

ARATOW, Michael, M.D. Chief Information Officer, San Mateo Medical Center, San Mateo, CA, p. A88

ARBACH, Joan M., Interim President, Phillips Eye Institute, Minneapolis, MN, p. A336

ARBAUGH, Ronnie, Director Human Resources, Grant Memorial Hospital, Petersburg, WV, p. A679

ARBOGEST, Dodie, Chief Financial Officer, Stonewall Jackson Memorial Hospital, Weston, WV, p. A681

ARBOLEDA, Reginaldo, M.D. Chief of Staff, Wild Rose Community Memorial Hospital, Wild Rose, WI, p. A700

ARBON, Don, Vice President Finance, Mid–Columbia Medical Center, The Dalles, OR, p. A518

ARBONEAUX, Jane, Chief Financial Officer, Prevost Memorial Hospital, Donaldsonville, LA, p. A266

ARBONEAUX, Wayne M., Chief Executive Officer, Assumption Community Hospital, Napoleonville, LA, p. A274

ARBUTHNOT, Rena, Director Human Resources, Shriners Hospitals for Children–Shreveport, Shreveport, LA, p. A278

ARCANGELI, Barbara J., Vice President Human Resources, Newport Hospital, Newport, RI, p. A546

ARCENEAUX, Susan, R.N. Coordinator Information Technology, Leonard J. Chabert Medical Center, Houma, LA, p. A268

ARCH, Chrissy, Chief Financial Officer, Cherokee Indian Hospital, Cherokee, NC, p. A450

ARCH, John K., FACHE, Administrator, Boys Town National Research Hospital, Omaha, NE, p. A387

ARCHAMBEAULT, Shirley, Chief Information Officer, Medical Center of Lewisville, Lewisville, TX, p. A618

ARCHER, David, Director Information Systems, Tristar Ashland City, Ashland City, TN, p. A565

ARCHER, David L., Chief Executive Officer, Saint Francis Hospital, Memphis, TN, p. A575

ARCHER, Doug, Assistant Administrator, Sutter Tracy Community Hospital, Tracy, CA, p. A93

ARCHER, Joe, Chief Information Officer, Victor Valley Community Hospital, Victorville, CA, p. A95

ARCHER, Kenneth W., Chief Executive Officer, Saunders Medical Center, Wahoo, NE, p. A390

ARCHER, Martha, Director Human Resources, St. Francis Hospital and Health Services, Maryville, MO, p. A365

ARCHER–DUSTE, Helen, Chief Operating Officer, Kaiser Permanente San Francisco Medical Center, San Francisco, CA, p. A86

ARCHEY, Eugene, Chief Information Technology, Veterans Affairs Greater Los Angeles Healthcare System, Los Angeles, CA, p. A72

ARCHIBOLD, Robert, Director, Human Resources, St. Anthony North Hospital, Westminster, CO, p. A106

ARCIDI, Alfred J., M.D.,
    Senior Vice President, Whittier Rehabilitation Hospital, Bradford, MA, p. A297
    Senior Vice President, Whittier Rehabilitation Hospital, Westborough, MA, p. A306

ARCIDI, Alfred L., M.D., Chief Executive Officer, Whittier Pavilion, Haverhill, MA, p. A300

ARD, Jana, R.N. Director Clinical Resource Management, Madison St. Joseph Health Center, Madisonville, TX, p. A621

ARDABELL, Toni R., R.N., Chief Executive Officer, Bon Secours St. Mary's Hospital, Richmond, VA, p. A660

ARDEMAGNI, Jeff, Chief Financial Officer, Medical Center of Arlington, Arlington, TX, p. A583

ARDOIN, Candice, Director Human Resources, Dauterive Hospital, New Iberia, LA, p. A275

ARDOIN, Stan, M.D. Medical Director, Griffin Memorial Hospital, Norman, OK, p. A502

ARGIRO, Don
    Regional Director Human Resources, Summa Barberton Citizens Hospital, Barberton, OH, p. A471
    Regional Director Human Resources, Summa Wadsworth–Rittman Hospital, Wadsworth, OH, p. A492

ARIGLIO, Basil, President and Chief Executive Officer, Rome Memorial Hospital, Rome, NY, p. A441

ARISMENDI, Nicholas, Chief Operating Officer, Dameron Hospital, Stockton, CA, p. A91

ARISPIE, Joe, Director Information Systems, Wise Regional Health System, Decatur, TX, p. A598

ARIZMENDEZ, Maria E., M.D. Executive Medical Director, HEALTHSOUTH Rehabilitation Hospital of Austin, Austin, TX, p. A585

ARIZPE, Robert C., Superintendent, San Antonio State Hospital, San Antonio, TX, p. A632

ARKFELD, Diane, R.N. Director of Nursing, Crawford County Memorial Hospital, Denison, IA, p. A220

ARLEDGE, Amy, Vice President Support Services, St. Luke's Hospital, Columbus, NC, p. A450

ARLEDGE, Denton
    Vice President and Chief Information Officer, WakeMed Cary Hospital, Cary, NC, p. A449
    Vice President and Chief Information Officer, WakeMed Raleigh Campus, Raleigh, NC, p. A459

ARMADA, Anthony A., President, Advocate Lutheran General Hospital, Park Ridge, IL, p. A191

ARMANN, Kristinn P., Vice President Human Resources, Beloit Health System, Beloit, WI, p. A684

ARMENDARIZ, Elias, Vice President Operations, El Paso Children's Hospital, El Paso, TX, p. A601

ARMENTROUT, Jeanne S., Vice President Human Resources, Carilion Medical Center, Roanoke, VA, p. A661

ARMISTEAD, Russell, Chief Executive Officer, Shands Jacksonville Medical Center, Jacksonville, FL, p. A126

ARMOUR, John, Chief Financial Officer, Bayshore Medical Center, Pasadena, TX, p. A626

ARMSTRONG, Alan, M.D. Chief Medical Officer, Pine Rest Christian Mental Health Services, Grand Rapids, MI, p. A315

ARMSTRONG, Deborah
    Chief Executive Officer, Rockdale Medical Center, Conyers, GA, p. A151
    Chief Financial Officer, St. Joseph Mercy Port Huron, Port Huron, MI, p. A322

ARMSTRONG, Evelyn, Chief Nursing Officer, HEALTHSOUTH Rehabilitation Hospital of Erie, Erie, PA, p. A525

ARMSTRONG, Gary, Executive Vice President, Methodist Rehabilitation Center, Jackson, MS, p. A348

ARMSTRONG, James, Manager Information Technology, Delaware Valley Hospital, Walton, NY, p. A445

ARMSTRONG, Jeffrey, CPA Chief Financial Officer, Granville Health System, Oxford, NC, p. A458

ARMSTRONG, Jeremy, FACHE, Chief Executive Officer, St. Luke Hospital and Living Center, Marion, KS, p. A239

ARMSTRONG, Justin, Chief Information Officer, LifeCare Hospitals of Pittsburgh – Monroeville, Monroeville, PA, p. A532

ARMSTRONG, Karen M., FACH
    Senior Vice President and Chief Information Officer, Muncy Valley Hospital, Muncy, PA, p. A532
    Senior Vice President and Chief Information Officer, Williamsport Regional Medical Center, Williamsport, PA, p. A545

ARMSTRONG, Ken, Senior Vice President Information, ProMedica Flower Hospital, Sylvania, OH, p. A490

ARMSTRONG, Kim, Chief Financial Officer, Windom Area Hospital, Windom, MN, p. A343

ARMSTRONG, Kyle E., Administrator and Chief Executive Officer, Baptist Memorial Hospital–Collierville, Collierville, TN, p. A567

ARMSTRONG, Marcus, Chief Financial Officer, Carson Valley Medical Center, Gardnerville, NV, p. A391

ARMSTRONG, Mark, M.D. Medical Director, Baylor Medical Center at Uptown, Dallas, TX, p. A595

ARMSTRONG, Mark, Chief Operating Officer, UK HealthCare Good Samaritan Hospital, Lexington, KY, p. A254

ARMSTRONG, Neil G., FACHE Vice President and Chief Operating Officer, Divine Providence Hospital, Williamsport, PA, p. A544

ARMSTRONG, Phyllis, R.N. Interim Chief Nursing Officer, Desert Valley Hospital, Victorville, CA, p. A95

ARMSTRONG, Robert, Senior Vice President and Chief Operating Officer, Lima Memorial Health System, Lima, OH, p. A484

ARMSTRONG, Roger, Vice President Finance and Chief Financial Officer, Proctor Hospital, Peoria, IL, p. A192

ARMSTRONG, Sandra, Chief Information Officer, University of Connecticut Health Center, John Dempsey Hospital, Farmington, CT, p. A108

ARMSTRONG, William C.
Senior Vice President and Chief Financial Officer, Mercy Medical Center, Rockville Centre, NY, p. A441
Vice President and Chief Financial Officer, St. Francis Hospital, Roslyn, NY, p. A442

ARMSTRONG–HUFF, Glenda, Assistant Superintendent, Texas Center for Infectious Disease, San Antonio, TX, p. A632

ARNAU, Barbara, R.N. Chief Nursing Officer, Chestatee Regional Hospital, Dahlonega, GA, p. A151

ARNDELL, Scott, Chief Financial Officer, Twin Lakes Regional Medical Center, Leitchfield, KY, p. A253

ARNESON, Brenda, Administrative Assistant, St. Andrew's Health Center, Bottineau, ND, p. A465

ARNESON, Garrett, Chief Executive Officer, Kindred Hospital South Philadelphia, Philadelphia, PA, p. A535

ARNETT, Gayle, President and Chief Executive Officer, Susan B. Allen Memorial Hospital, El Dorado, KS, p. A233

ARNETT, Peg, Interim Vice President of Nursing, Heart of the Rockies Regional Medical Center, Salida, CO, p. A105

ARNETT, Randal M., President and Chief Executive Officer, Southern Ohio Medical Center, Portsmouth, OH, p. A489

ARNETT, Sallie, Vice President Information Systems, Licking Memorial Hospital, Newark, OH, p. A487

ARNETT, Stuart
Regional Vice President Finance, Aurora Lakeland Medical Center, Elkhorn, WI, p. A686
Vice President Finance and Chief Financial Officer, Aurora Memorial Hospital of Burlington, Burlington, WI, p. A685

ARNETTE, Mary F., Chief Financial Officer, Cannon Memorial Hospital, Pickens, SC, p. A555

ARNHART, Carol, Controller and Chief Financial Officer, Siskin Hospital for Physical Rehabilitation, Chattanooga, TN, p. A567

ARNO, Michael J., Interim Chief Executive Officer, Hugh Chatham Memorial Hospital, Elkin, NC, p. A452

ARNOLD, Ann, M.D. Medical Director, Medical Center of Plano, Plano, TX, p. A627

ARNOLD, Bill, Chief Operating Officer, Monmouth Medical Center, Long Branch, NJ, p. A406

ARNOLD, Bobby, President and Chief Executive Officer, Jackson–Madison County General Hospital, Jackson, TN, p. A570

ARNOLD, Kevin, President and Chief Executive Officer, Southwest Regional Rehabilitation Center, Battle Creek, MI, p. A309

ARNOLD, Kimberly N., R.N. Chief Nursing Officer and Interim Chief Quality Officer, Woodward Regional Hospital, Woodward, OK, p. A510

ARNOLD, Leslie, Chief Executive Officer, St. Vincent Morrilton, Morrilton, AR, p. A47

ARNOLD, Mary, Interim Vice President Human Resources, St. John's Hospital, Saint Paul, MN, p. A340

ARNOLD, Pauline, MSN Chief Nursing and Quality Officer, Indiana University Health La Porte Hospital, La Porte, IN, p. A208

ARNOLD, Thomas, Chief Financial Officer, Piedmont Hospital, Atlanta, GA, p. A147

ARNOLD, Thomas, M.D. Chief Medical Officer, St. Joseph's Hospital and Health Center, Dickinson, ND, p. A466

ARNOLD, W. Douglas, President and Chief Executive Officer, Helen Keller Hospital, Sheffield, AL, p. A25

ARNOW, Debbie, R.N. VP Patient Care & Chief Nursing Officer, Children's Hospital and Medical Center, Omaha, NE, p. A387

ARNSTON, Hanz, R.N., Chief Executive Officer, Garfield County Health Center, Jordan, MT, p. A377

AROCHO, Jacqueline, Administrator, BayCare Alliant Hospital, Dunedin, FL, p. A122

ARONS, Bernard, M.D. Director Medical Affairs, St. Elizabeths Hospital, Washington, DC, p. A117

ARORA, Pamela, Vice President Information Systems, Children's Medical Center of Dallas, Dallas, TX, p. A595

ARORA, Sat, M.D. President Medical and Dental Staff, Crozer–Chester Medical Center, Upland, PA, p. A542

ARRAGE, Antoine A., M.D. Director Medical Services, Lake Taylor Transitional Care Hospital, Norfolk, VA, p. A658

ARRIGONI, Tammy, Human Resources Lead, Woodwinds Health Campus, Woodbury, MN, p. A343

ARROWOOD, Al, Chief Financial Officer, Washington County Hospital, Plymouth, NC, p. A459

ARROWSMITH, Karen, Administrator, Pawhuska Hospital, Pawhuska, OK, p. A505

ARSENAULT, Donna, Director Human Resources, Baystate Mary Lane Hospital, Ware, MA, p. A306

ARSENAULT, Lisa, Director Human Resources, Millinocket Regional Hospital, Millinocket, ME, p. A284

ARSENEAU, Dan, Vice President Human Resources, Porter Medical Center, Middlebury, VT, p. A649

ARSLANI, Adem, Director Information Systems, Advocate Good Shepherd Hospital, Barrington, IL, p. A174

ARSLANPAY, Robin, Director Human Resources, LifeCare Hospitals of Pittsburgh, Pittsburgh, PA, p. A537

ARSURA, Edward, M.D. Chief Medical Officer, Richmond University Medical Center,, NY, p. A436

ART, Steve, Senior Vice President and Chief Information Officer, Lutheran Medical Center,, NY, p. A433

ARTHERHOLT, William, M.D. Chief of Staff, Montgomery County Memorial Hospital, Red Oak, IA, p. A227

ARTHUR, Donald C., M.D. Chief Medical Officer, Paoli Hospital, Paoli, PA, p. A534

ARTHUR, John, Chief Financial Officer, St. Vincent Randolph Hospital, Winchester, IN, p. A215

ARTHUR, Rita K., Director Human Resources, Littleton Adventist Hospital, Littleton, CO, p. A103

ARTHUR, Sarah, Director Human Resources, HEALTHSOUTH Rehabilitation Hospital of York, York, PA, p. A545

ARTHUR, Tanya, Chief Information Officer, Good Samaritan Hospital, Kearney, NE, p. A385

ARTHURS, Cheryl, Health Information Transcriptionist, Faulkton Area Medical Center, Faulkton, SD, p. A559

ARTIS, Cornelius, M.D. Chief Medical Officer, Our Community Hospital, Scotland Neck, NC, p. A460

ARTS–STRENKE, Cindy, Chief Operating Officer and Chief Nursing Officer, Lakeview Medical Center, Rice Lake, WI, p. A696

ARUNAMATA, Peti, Interim Area Director Information Technology, Kaiser Permanente San Francisco Medical Center, San Francisco, CA, p. A86

ARVIN, Doug, Vice President Financial Services, University Hospital, Cincinnati, OH, p. A475

ARVIN, Jon A., M.D. Chief Medical Officer, Rockcastle Regional Hospital and Respiratory Care Center, Mount Vernon, KY, p. A258

ARVON, Christina, Administrator and Chief Executive Officer, Eye and Ear Clinic of Charleston, Charleston, WV, p. A676

ARZE, Steven, M.D. Chief Medical Officer and Vice President Medical Affiars, Baylor Medical Center at Garland, Garland, TX, p. A606

ASADA, Bonnie, Director of Nursing, Alvarado Parkway Institute Behavioral Health System, La Mesa, CA, p. A65

ASAFTEI, Laura, Administrative Director, Florida Hospital Zephyrhills, Zephyrhills, FL, p. A144

ASAOKA, Danny, Executive Director Information Systems, Long Beach Memorial Medical Center, Long Beach, CA, p. A67

ASBECK, Lynn, Manager Business Office, Missouri River Medical Center, Fort Benton, MT, p. A376

ASBERRY, James
Chief Financial Officer, Warm Springs Rehabilitation Hospital, San Antonio, TX, p. A632
Chief Financial Officer, Warm Springs Specialty Hospital, Luling, TX, p. A621
Chief Financial Officer, Warm Springs Specialty Hospital of Victoria, Victoria, TX, p. A639

ASCHOFF, Jodi, Chief Financial Officer, Osmond General Hospital, Osmond, NE, p. A388

ASH, Richard M., Chief Executive Officer, Ortonville Area Health Services, Ortonville, MN, p. A337

ASH, Sharon, Vice President Finance, Mercy Hospital Berryville, Berryville, AR, p. A41

ASHBY, Jr., B. R., M.D. President and Chief Executive Officer, Southern Virginia Mental Health Institute, Danville, VA, p. A653

ASHBY, F. Michael, M.D. Vice President and Medical Director, Martha Jefferson Hospital, Charlottesville, VA, p. A652

ASHBY, Fred, Director Information Technology, Fort Washington Medical Center, Fort Washington, MD, p. A291

ASHBY, Pamela, Vice President Human Resources, MedStar National Rehabilitation Hospital, Washington, DC, p. A116

ASHCOM, Thomas L., Ph.D., Chief Executive Officer, Kansas Heart Hospital, Wichita, KS, p. A246

ASHCRAFT, Kim, Director Human Resources, Cooper County Memorial Hospital, Boonville, MO, p. A357

ASHCRAFT, Steven F.
Superintendent, Osawatomie State Hospital, Osawatomie, KS, p. A241
Superintendent, Rainbow Mental Health Facility, Kansas City, KS, p. A237

ASHE, Patricia, R.N. Chief Nursing Officer, Margaret R. Pardee Memorial Hospital, Hendersonville, NC, p. A454

ASHENFELTER, Kathy, Chief Financial Officer, Swedish Medical Center, Englewood, CO, p. A100

ASHFORD, Michael, Administrator, DeQuincy Memorial Hospital, DeQuincy, LA, p. A266

ASHKAR, Ziad, M.D. Chief Medical Officer, Lafayette General Medical Center, Lafayette, LA, p. A271

ASHLEY, Clint, Director, South Mississippi State Hospital, Purvis, MS, p. A353

ASHLEY, Dennis H.
Vice President Human Resources, Mount Vernon Hospital, Mount Vernon, NY, p. A430
Vice President Human Resources, Sound Shore Medical Center of Westchester, New Rochelle, NY, p. A430

ASHLEY, Sharon, MSN Chief Nursing Officer, Adams County Regional Medical Center, Seaman, OH, p. A489

ASHLEY, Stanley, M.D. Chief Medical Officer, Brigham and Women's Hospital, Boston, MA, p. A296

ASHMENT, Kerry, Chief Executive Officer, Advanced Care Hospital of Montana, Billings, MT, p. A374

ASHRAF, Mirza, M.D. Medical Director, Carthage Area Hospital, Carthage, NY, p. A423

ASHWOOD, Christopher, Coordinator Information Systems, St. Lawrence Psychiatric Center, Ogdensburg, NY, p. A438

ASHWORTH, Fred, Chief Financial Officer, Venice Regional Medical Center, Venice, FL, p. A143

ASK, Rachel K., Supervisor Human Resources, Sanford Rock Rapids Medical Center, Rock Rapids, IA, p. A227

ASKARI, Hasan, M.D. Chief of Staff, Sunbury Community Hospital and Outpatient Center, Sunbury, PA, p. A542

ASKEW, Pam, R.N. Vice President Patient Care Services, Trinity Muscatine, Muscatine, IA, p. A225

ASKEY, Raymond C., CPA Vice President Fiscal Services, Nason Hospital, Roaring Spring, PA, p. A540

ASKIE, Charity L., Director Finance, Sage Memorial Hospital, Ganado, AZ, p. A31

ASKINAZI, Murray, Senior Vice President and Chief Financial Officer, Lawrence Hospital Center, Bronxville, NY, p. A422

ASKINS, Stephen, M.D. Chief of Staff, Lake City Community Hospital, Lake City, SC, p. A554

ASPAAS, Ken, M.D. Chief Medical Officer, Sanford USD Medical Center, Sioux Falls, SD, p. A562

ASPER, Mirelis, Human Resources Generalist, Metropolitan Hospital of Miami, Miami, FL, p. A131

ASSAAD, Haney, Chief of Staff, North Ottawa Community Hospital, Grand Haven, MI, p. A314

ASSESSOR, Peggy, Director Information Services, St. Joseph Mercy Port Huron, Port Huron, MI, p. A322

ASTON, Brian W., Chief Operating Officer, Mission Hospital, Asheville, NC, p. A447

ASTRAN, Melinda, M.D. Chief of Staff, La Paz Regional Hospital, Parker, AZ, p. A33

ATCHLEY, Mark, Vice President and Chief Financial Officer, Medical City Dallas Hospital, Dallas, TX, p. A596

ATEIA, Nashat, M.D. Chief of Staff, Doctors Hospital of West Covina, West Covina, CA, p. A95

ATEN, Byron, Controller, HEALTHSOUTH Rehabilitation Hospital, Albuquerque, NM, p. A414

ATHA, Shannon M., Director Finance, Doctors Hospital Nelsonville, Nelsonville, OH, p. A487

ATHANS, Scott, Chief Executive Officer, Texas Specialty Hospital at Dallas, Dallas, TX, p. A598

ATHENAIS, Dierdre, Director Human Resources, Colusa Regional Medical Center, Colusa, CA, p. A57

ATIENZA, Terry S., Director, Grand Junction Veterans Affairs Medical Center, Grand Junction, CO, p. A102

ATKIN, Suzanne, M.D. Chief of Staff and Associate Dean Clinical Affairs, University of Medicine and Dentistry of New Jersey–University Hospital, Newark, NJ, p. A407

ATKINS, James, Chief Operating Officer, Rockdale Medical Center, Conyers, GA, p. A151

ATKINS, Jim, Director Employee Services, Elks Rehab Hospital, Boise, ID, p. A167

ATKINS, Melissa, CPA, Chief Executive Officer, Graham County Hospital, Hill City, KS, p. A235

ATKINS, Rainy, Chief Operating Officer and Administrator, PeaceHealth Southwest Medical Center, Vancouver, WA, p. A674

ATKINS, Stephen R., M.D. Medical Director, Southwest Connecticut Mental Health System, Bridgeport, CT, p. A108

ATKINS–GUIDRY, Stephanie, Administrator, USMD Hospital at Fort Worth, Fort Worth, TX, p. A604

ATKINSON, Chris, Director of Human Resources, Ochsner Medical Center–Baton Rouge, Baton Rouge, LA, p. A263

ATKINSON, James, M.D. Medical Director, Santa Monica–UCLA Medical Center and Orthopaedic Hospital, Santa Monica, CA, p. A90

ATKINSON, Jodi, President and Chief Executive Officer, St. Andrew's Health Center, Bottineau, ND, p. A465

ATKINSON, Mike, Director Administrative Services, Brookhaven Hospital, Tulsa, OK, p. A507

ATKINSON II, William K., M.P.H., President and Chief Executive Officer, WakeMed Raleigh Campus, Raleigh, NC, p. A459

ATTEBURY, Mary, Chief Operating Officer, Northwest Missouri Psychiatric Rehabilitation Center, Saint Joseph, MO, p. A369

ATTI, Lucretia, Chief Executive Officer, HEALTHSOUTH Rehabilitation Hospital of Erie, Erie, PA, p. A525

ATTRIDGE, Scott, Controller, Mid–Valley Hospital, Omak, WA, p. A669

ATTY, James, Chief Executive Officer, Humboldt County Memorial Hospital, Humboldt, IA, p. A222

ATWAL, Money, Chief Financial Officer, Hilo Medical Center, Hilo, HI, p. A164

ATWATER, Gregory, Chief Operating Officer, Metropolitan Hospital Center, New York, NY, p. A434

ATWELL, Denaye, Manager Human Resources, George Nigh Rehabilitation Institute, Okmulgee, OK, p. A505

ATWOOD, Julie, Director Human Resources, San Bernardino Mountains Community Hospital District, Lake Arrowhead, CA, p. A66

ATWOOD, Sheila, R.N. Chief Operating Officer, Kalkaska Memorial Health Center, Kalkaska, MI, p. A318

ATZROTT, Allan E., FACHE, President and Chief Executive Officer, St. Luke's Cornwall Hospital, Newburgh, NY, p. A437

AUBEL, Eugenia, President, St. Elizabeth Boardman Health Center, Boardman, OH, p. A472

AUBEL, James, Chief Financial Officer, Jameson Hospital, New Castle, PA, p. A533

AUBRY, Michael, Director Information Systems, Adventist Medical Center – Hanford, Hanford, CA, p. A63

AUBUT, Richard H., R.N., President and Chief Executive Officer, South Shore Hospital, South Weymouth, MA, p. A304

AUCKER, Kendra A., Vice President Operations, Evangelical Community Hospital, Lewisburg, PA, p. A530

AUDETT, John R., M.D. Chief Medical Officer, Inova Alexandria Hospital, Alexandria, VA, p. A651

AUDIRSCH, Lanell, Administrative Assistant, North Caddo Medical Center, Vivian, LA, p. A280

AUER, Kenneth E., Director Human Resources, Unity Hospital, Fridley, MN, p. A332

AUERBACH, Jeffrey, D.O. Medical Director, Bon Secours Community Hospital, Port Jervis, NY, p. A440

AUERBACH, Lorraine P., President and Chief Executive Officer, Dameron Hospital, Stockton, CA, p. A91

AUFDENGARTEN, John E., R.N. Vice President, Administration, Alice Hyde Medical Center, Malone, NY, p. A429

AUFDERHEIDE, Allen D., Chief Executive Officer, Callaway Community Hospital, Fulton, MO, p. A361

AUGSBURGER, Marc, President and Chief Executive Officer, Caro Community Hospital, Caro, MI, p. A310

AUGSBURGER, Tod, Senior Vice President and Chief Operating Officer, Lexington Medical Center, West Columbia, SC, p. A556

AUGUSTIN, Robert, Director Human Resources, Crockett Hospital, Lawrenceburg, TN, p. A572

AUGUSTIN, III, W. Walter, CPA Vice President Financial Services and Chief Financial Officer, Kernan Orthopaedics and Rehabilitation, Baltimore, MD, p. A287

AUGUSTYNIAK, Becky, Director Human Resources, Hughston Hospital, Columbus, GA, p. A150

AUJERO, Moftia, Chief Nurse Executive, Bellevue Hospital Center, New York, NY, p. A430

AUMER, Lynn, Director Information Management, Ohio Valley General Hospital, McKees Rocks, PA, p. A531

AUNAN, II, Milton E., CPA Vice President and Chief Financial Officer, UnityPoint Health St. Luke's, Cedar Rapids, IA, p. A217

AURILIO, Lisa, R.N. Vice President Patient Services and Chief Nursing Officer, Akron Children's Hospital, Akron, OH, p. A470

AUSMAN, Dan F., President and Chief Executive Officer, Methodist Hospital of Southern California, Arcadia, CA, p. A53

AUSTELLI, Oscar, Chief Information Officer, LAC/University of Southern California Medical Center, Los Angeles, CA, p. A70

AUSTEN, Terry L., Senior Vice President and Area Manager, Kaiser Permanente San Jose Medical Center, San Jose, CA, p. A87

AUSTIN, Arthur, M.D. Vice President Medical Affairs, Gerald Champion Regional Medical Center, Alamogordo, NM, p. A414

AUSTIN, Cheryse, Vice President Patient Care Services and Chief Nursing Officer, Casa Grande Regional Medical Center, Casa Grande, AZ, p. A30

AUSTIN, Cynthia, Manager Health Information Management, Murray Medical Center, Chatsworth, GA, p. A149

AUSTIN, Dan, Manager Data Processing, Ashley County Medical Center, Crossett, AR, p. A42

AUSTIN, Debbie W., R.N. Vice President Patient Care Services, P & S Surgical Hospital, Monroe, LA, p. A274

AUSTIN, James D., FACHE,
Administrator, Kalkaska Memorial Health Center, Kalkaska, MI, p. A318
Administrator, Paul Oliver Memorial Hospital, Frankfort, MI, p. A314

AUSTIN, John, M.D. Director Medical Staff, Aspirus Ontonagon Hospital, Ontonagon, MI, p. A321

AUSTIN, Judy, Director Human Resources, Campbellton Graceville Hospital, Graceville, FL, p. A124

AUSTIN, Laura, Chief Financial Officer and Chief Operating Officer, Community Hospital of Anaconda, Anaconda, MT, p. A374

AUSTIN, Lori, Director Human Resources, Troy Regional Medical Center, Troy, AL, p. A25

AUSTIN, Robert, Chief Executive Officer, Moab Regional Hospital, Moab, UT, p. A644

AUSTIN, Warren, M.D. Vice President Medical Affairs, Bon Secours Maryview Medical Center, Portsmouth, VA, p. A659

AUSTIN–MOORE, Gale, Director Area Technology, Kaiser Permanente Vallejo Medical Center, Vallejo, CA, p. A94

AUTRY, Brennan, Director Administration, Robert E. Bush Naval Hospital, Twentynine Palms, CA, p. A93

AUWARTER, Tim, Interim President and Chief Executive Officer, Faith Regional Health Services, Norfolk, NE, p. A386

AVANT, Andre, Facility Automation Manager, Texas Center for Infectious Disease, San Antonio, TX, p. A632

AVANT, Donna, Chief Financial Officer, Oklahoma Center for Orthopedic and Multi–Specialty Surgery, Oklahoma City, OK, p. A503

AVATO, Rich, Director, St. Mary's Medical Center, West Palm Beach, FL, p. A143

AVENEL, William, Assistant Vice President Information Services, Medical Center of Central Georgia, Macon, GA, p. A156

AVERETT, Elaine, Chief Financial Officer, Grove Hill Memorial Hospital, Grove Hill, AL, p. A21

AVERILL, Clark, Director Information Technology, St. Luke's Hospital, Duluth, MN, p. A331

AVERNA, Russell, Director Human Resources, Spaulding Rehabilitation Hospital, Boston, MA, p. A297

AVERY, Baret H., Chief Information Officer, Siskin Hospital for Physical Rehabilitation, Chattanooga, TN, p. A567

AVERY, Danny, Chief Financial Officer and Chief Operating Officer, Quartz Mountain Medical Center, Mangum, OK, p. A501

AVERY, Donald R., FACHE, President and Chief Executive Officer, Fairview Park Hospital, Dublin, GA, p. A152

AVERY III, John B., Administrator, Perry Community Hospital, Linden, TN, p. A573

AVERY, Jonathan, Chief Administrative Officer, Legacy Salmon Creek Medical Center, Vancouver, WA, p. A673

AVILA, Daniel, Director Human Resources, St. Cloud Regional Medical Center, Saint Cloud, FL, p. A138

AVVISATO, Michael, Senior Vice President and Chief Financial Officer, Allied Services Rehabilitation Hospital, Scranton, PA, p. A540

AVVISATO, Mike, Vice President and Chief Financial Officer, John Heinz Institute of Rehabilitation Medicine, Wilkes–Barre, PA, p. A544

AWAN, Naveed, FACHE, Chief Executive Officer, St. Helena Parish Hospital, Greensburg, LA, p. A267

AWOLOWO, Yinusa, Business Officer, Kingsboro Psychiatric Center,, NY, p. A433

AXTMAN, Cheryl, Administrative Assistant, Sakakawea Medical Center, Hazen, ND, p. A467

AYALA, Jose L., M.D. Chief Medical Officer, Valley Baptist Medical Center–Brownsville, Brownsville, TX, p. A590

AYALA, Lisa, R.N. Director Human Resources, Specialty Hospital Jacksonville, Jacksonville, FL, p. A127

AYALA, Raquel, Deputy Executive Director Network and Human Resources, Kings County Hospital Center,, NY, p. A433

AYCOCK, Jean, President and Chief Executive Officer, Oconee Regional Medical Center, Milledgeville, GA, p. A157

AYERS, Annette, R.N. Senior Vice President and Chief Nursing Officer, Providence Health Center, Waco, TX, p. A640

AYERS, James G., Chief Financial Officer, Piedmont Geriatric Hospital, Burkeville, VA, p. A652

AYKUL, Nikki, Manager Business Office, LifeCare Hospitals of Pittsburgh, Pittsburgh, PA, p. A537

AYOUB, John J., FACHE, Chief Executive Officer, Melissa Memorial Hospital, Holyoke, CO, p. A102

AYRES, Daniel M., Chief Executive Officer, O'Connor Hospital, Delhi, NY, p. A425

AYRES, Robert, Director Information Systems, Firelands Regional Health System, Sandusky, OH, p. A489

AYRES, Shane, Chief Financial Officer, Sanford Wheaton Medical Center, Wheaton, MN, p. A342

AYSCUE, Charles F., Senior Vice President Finance and Chief Financial Officer, Mission Hospital, Asheville, NC, p. A447

AYYASH, Maher, M.D. Chief Medical Officer, Clarion Psychiatric Center, Clarion, PA, p. A522

AZCONA, Alain, Director Business Development, Aurora Behavioral Health Care, San Diego, CA, p. A85

AZEVEDO, Michael, M.D. Medical Director, San Joaquin Valley Rehabilitation Hospital, Fresno, CA, p. A62

AZIZ, Samir, M.D. Inpatient Medical Director, Navos, Seattle, WA, p. A670

# B

BAADE, Leigh, Director Human Resources, New England Rehabilitation Hospital of Portland, Portland, ME, p. A285

BAAS, Dina, Director Financial Services, Orange City Area Health System, Orange City, IA, p. A226

BABAKANIAN, Ed, Chief Information Officer, UC San Diego Health System, San Diego, CA, p. A86

BABB, Cindy, Executive Director Human Resources and Organizational Effectiveness, St. Joseph Hospital and Health Center, Kokomo, IN, p. A207

BABB, Daniel R., Chief Executive Officer, Oakland Regional Hospital, Southfield, MI, p. A324

BABB, Donald J., Chief Executive Officer, Citizens Memorial Hospital, Bolivar, MO, p. A356

BABB, Kathy, Manager Human Resources, Clifton Springs Hospital and Clinic, Clifton Springs, NY, p. A424

BABCOCK, Daniel, Chief Executive Officer, Marlette Regional Hospital, Marlette, MI, p. A319

BABCOCK, Kimberly, Administrator Human Resources, Kalkaska Memorial Health Center, Kalkaska, MI, p. A318

BABCOCK, Robert, M.D. Chief of Staff, Canandaigua Veterans Affairs Medical Center, Canandaigua, NY, p. A423

BABICH, Eli, Chief Nursing Officer, Select Specialty Hospital–Pittsburgh/UPMC, Pittsburgh, PA, p. A537

BABIN, Beth, Vice President Human Resources, Tulane Medical Center, New Orleans, LA, p. A276

BABINEAU, Timothy J., M.D.,
President and Chief Executive Officer, Miriam Hospital, Providence, RI, p. A546
President and Chief Executive Officer, Rhode Island Hospital, Providence, RI, p. A547

BABUSCIO, Cathy, Director Human Resources, Mat–Su Regional Medical Center, Palmer, AK, p. A28

BACA, Modesto, Chief Information Officer, Amarillo Veterans Affairs Health Care System, Amarillo, TX, p. A582

BACH, Dawn M., MS Chief Clinical Officer, Buena Vista Regional Medical Center, Storm Lake, IA, p. A229

BACHARACH, Paul, President and Chief Executive Officer, Uniontown Hospital, Uniontown, PA, p. A542

BACHE–WIIG, Ben, M.D., President, Abbott Northwestern Hospital, Minneapolis, MN, p. A335

BACHELDOR, H. Lee, D.O. Medical Director, St. John River District Hospital, East China, MI, p. A313

BACHENBERG, Timothy, M.D. Chief Medical Officer, Madelia Community Hospital, Madelia, MN, p. A335

BACHER, Beth, Chief Executive Officer, HEALTHSOUTH Valley of the Sun Rehabilitation Hospital, Glendale, AZ, p. A32

BACHETTI, Kathleen, Director Human Resources, Shriners Hospitals for Children–Springfield, Springfield, MA, p. A305

BACHMAN, Judith Lynn
Chief Operating Officer, Fox Chase Cancer Center–American Oncologic Hospital, Philadelphia, PA, p. A534
Chief Operating Officer, Jeanes Hospital, Philadelphia, PA, p. A535

BACHMAN, Page, Corporate Vice President, St. John Medical Center, Tulsa, OK, p. A509

BACHMAN, Robert J., Chief Operating Officer, Emory University Hospital, Atlanta, GA, p. A146

BACHUS KEITH, Beryl, M.D. Chief of Staff, Clarendon Memorial Hospital, Manning, SC, p. A554

BACIARELLI, Val, Chief Operating Officer, CHRISTUS Santa Rosa Health System, San Antonio, TX, p. A630

BACK, Barbara, Manager Human Resources, Encino Hospital Medical Center,, CA, p. A68

BACKS, Craig, M.D. Medical Director, St. John's Hospital, Springfield, IL, p. A195

BACKSTROM, Dean, M.D. Vice President Medical Affairs, Rutherford Regional Health System, Rutherfordton, NC, p. A460

BACON, Hanna, Administrative Assistant/Human Resources Coordinator, Select Specialty Hospital–Knoxville, Knoxville, TN, p. A572

BACON, James S., Director Team Resources, St. Anthony's Hospital, Saint Petersburg, FL, p. A139

BACON, Ken J., President and Chief Executive Officer, Shawnee Mission Medical Center, Shawnee Mission, KS, p. A244

BACON, William, M.D. Chief of Staff, Fleming County Hospital, Flemingsburg, KY, p. A250

BACUS, Randy B., FACHE, Chief Executive Officer, North Texas Medical Center, Gainesville, TX, p. A605

BADALIAN, B. Joseph, President and Chief Executive Officer, Lakewood Regional Medical Center, Lakewood, CA, p. A66

BADEN, Robert M., Chief Financial Officer, Lompoc Valley Medical Center, Lompoc, CA, p. A67

BAKER, W. Douglas, Director, Julian F. Keith Alcohol and Drug Abuse Treatment Center, Black Mountain, NC, p. A448

BAKER Jr., Wendell H., President, Albemarle Health, Elizabeth City, NC, p. A452

BAKICH, Sandy, Director Information Management, Delano Regional Medical Center, Delano, CA, p. A58

BAKKEN, Mary, Executive Vice President and Chief Operating Officer, Silver Cross Hospital, New Lenox, IL, p. A190

BAKKUM, Kyle, Chief Executive Officer and Administrator, Vernon Memorial Healthcare, Viroqua, WI, p. A698

BALASUBRAMONY, Suresh, M.D. Chief Medical Officer, Minnie Hamilton HealthCare Center, Grantsville, WV, p. A677

BALAZY, Thomas E., M.D. Medical Director, Craig Hospital, Englewood, CO, p. A100

BALCAVAGE, Thomas, Vice President Information Systems and Chief Information Officer, Kennedy Health System, Cherry Hill, NJ, p. A402

BALCH, Jackson, IT Director, Garden Park Medical Center, Gulfport, MS, p. A347

BALCITIS, Judith, MS Vice President, Nursing and Chief Nursing Officer, Advocate Sherman Hospital, Elgin, IL, p. A181

BALDAUF, Robb, Coordinator Information Systems, Lodi Community Hospital, Lodi, OH, p. A484

BALDERRAMA, Jose, Vice President Human Resources, Nationwide Children's Hospital, Columbus, OH, p. A477

BALDRIDGE, Dava, Chief Nursing Officer, Hillcrest Hospital Claremore, Claremore, OK, p. A497

BALDWIN, Barbara, Chief Information Officer, University of Virginia Medical Center, Charlottesville, VA, p. A652

BALDWIN, Bruce A., Chief Executive Officer, Grandview Medical Center, Jasper, TN, p. A570

BALDWIN, Christopher, Vice President Information Systems, Southcoast Hospitals Group, Fall River, MA, p. A300

BALDWIN, David, Chief Information Officer, Robinson Memorial Hospital, Ravenna, OH, p. A489

BALDWIN, Ellen, R.N. Chief Nursing Officer, Texas Health Center for Diagnostic & Surgery, Plano, TX, p. A627

BALDWIN, Gilda, Chief Executive Officer, Westchester General Hospital, Miami, FL, p. A132

BALDWIN, Lee, Administrator and Chief Executive Officer, Landmann–Jungman Memorial Hospital Avera, Scotland, SD, p. A562

BALDWIN, Nathan, M.D. President Medical Staff, Baptist Memorial Hospital–Booneville, Booneville, MS, p. A345

BALDWIN, Steve
Vice President Finance, Willough Healthcare System, Naples, FL, p. A133
Manager Information Technology, Wyoming State Hospital, Evanston, WY, p. A702

BALDWIN, Susan Louise, FACHE, President and Chief Nursing Officer, Texas Health Specialty Hospital, Fort Worth, TX, p. A604

BALDWIN, William, Chief Information Officer, Ashe Memorial Hospital, Jefferson, NC, p. A455

BALENTINE, Jerry, D.O. Executive Vice President and Chief Medical Director, St. Barnabas Hospital,, NY, p. A436

BALES, Brian, Director Plant Operations, HEALTHSOUTH Southern Hills Rehabilitation Hospital, Princeton, WV, p. A680

BALFOUR, Ann M., R.N., President, St. Joseph Health System, Tawas City, MI, p. A325

BALINK, Kay M., M.D. Chief of Staff, Richland Hospital, Richland Center, WI, p. A696

BALKO, Tom, Manager Information Systems, Redwood Area Hospital, Redwood Falls, MN, p. A338

BALL, Cassie, Chief Financial Officer, Hilton Head Hospital, Hilton Head Island, SC, p. A553

BALL, Charlie, Chief Operating Officer, Specialty Rehabilitation Hospital, Coushatta, LA, p. A265

BALL, Jim, Chief Operating Officer, St. Catherine's Rehabilitation Hospital, North Miami, FL, p. A134

BALL, Kristie, Director of Nursing, William Newton Hospital, Winfield, KS, p. A247

BALLANCE, William, M.D. Chief of Medical Staff, Vidant Bertie Hospital, Windsor, NC, p. A463

BALLARD, Christine A.
Vice President Human Resources, Muncy Valley Hospital, Muncy, PA, p. A532
Senior Vice President Human Resources, Williamsport Regional Medical Center, Williamsport, PA, p. A545

BALLARD, Lorraine L., Director Human Resources, St. Helena Parish Hospital, Greensburg, LA, p. A267

BALLARD, Richard R., Administrator, University of Miami Hospital and Clinics, Miami, FL, p. A132

BALLESTERO, Susan, Vice President Human Resources, Saint Peter's University Hospital, New Brunswick, NJ, p. A407

BALLOU, Michele, M.D. Chief Medical Staff, LewisGale Hospital Alleghany, Low Moor, VA, p. A656

BALON, Stanley, M.D. President Medical Staff, Landmark Medical Center, Woonsocket, RI, p. A547

BALSANO, Tony, Vice President Finance, Saint Francis Medical Center, Cape Girardeau, MO, p. A358

BALSANO, Brian, CPA Chief Financial Officer, Lock Haven Hospital, Lock Haven, PA, p. A530

BALZANO, Janice, Chief Operating Officer, Brandon Regional Hospital, Brandon, FL, p. A119

BAMMEL, Paul, Vice President, Mayo Clinic Health System in Eau Claire, Eau Claire, WI, p. A686

BANAS, Thomas, Chief Medical Officer, Rehabilitation Hospital of Fort Wayne, Fort Wayne, IN, p. A203

BANBURY, Brian, Director Site Information Systems, Advocate Christ Medical Center, Oak Lawn, IL, p. A190

BANCO, Leonard, M.D. Senior Vice President and Chief Medical Officer, Bristol Hospital, Bristol, CT, p. A108

BANDA, Venkat, M.D. President Medical Staff, Promise Hospital of Baton Rouge – Ochsner Campus, Baton Rouge, LA, p. A263

BANDY, Don, Director Information Technology, Deaconess Hospital, Oklahoma City, OK, p. A503

BANDY, P. Ross, M.D. Chief Medical Officer and Chief of Staff, Levi Hospital, Hot Springs National Park, AR, p. A45

BANE, Bill, Assistant Vice President and Chief Financial Officer, Inova Fair Oaks Hospital, Fairfax, VA, p. A653

BANG, W. J., M.D. Chief of Staff, Reeves County Hospital, Pecos, TX, p. A626

BANIGAN, Elisa, Chief Financial Officer, Huhukam Memorial Hospital, Sacaton, AZ, p. A36

BANK, Carol J., Vice President Human Resources, Divine Savior Healthcare, Portage, WI, p. A695

BANKO, Peter D., FACHE, President and Chief Executive Officer, St. Vincent Infirmary Medical Center, Little Rock, AR, p. A47

BANKS, Chester, Director Human Resources, East Orange General Hospital, East Orange, NJ, p. A403

BANKS, Elizabeth, Chief Executive Officer, Summit Behavioral Healthcare, Cincinnati, OH, p. A475

BANKS, Maureen, MS,
President, Spaulding Hospital for Continuing Medical Care North Shore, Salem, MA, p. A304
President, Spaulding Hospital for Continuing Medical Care Cambridge, Cambridge, MA, p. A299

BANKS, Maureen, R.N. Chief Operating Officer, Spaulding Rehabilitation Hospital, Boston, MA, p. A297

BANKS, Maureen, MS, President and Chief Executive Officer, Spaulding Rehabilitation Hospital Cape Cod, East Sandwich, MA, p. A299

BANKS, Robbi, Executive Director Human Resources, Medical Center Health System, Odessa, TX, p. A625

BANKS, Ronni, Administrator, RiverCrest Specialty Hospital, Mishawaka, IN, p. A210

BANKS, Scott
Chief Financial Officer, Foundation Surgical Hospital of El Paso, El Paso, TX, p. A601
Chief Financial Officer, Foundation Surgical Hospital of San Antonio, San Antonio, TX, p. A631
Chief Financial Officer, Heritage Park Surgical Hospital, Sherman, TX, p. A634

BANKS, Walter, Director Human Resources, Baptist Memorial Hospital–Desoto, Southaven, MS, p. A354

BANKTSON, Julie, Manager Human Resources, Paul Oliver Memorial Hospital, Frankfort, MI, p. A314

BANNER, Fred, Chief Information Officer, Shore Medical Center, Somers Point, NJ, p. A410

BANOS, Edward D., Chief Operating Officer, Marquette General Health System, Marquette, MI, p. A319

BANSBACH, Steven, M.D. Medical Director, Thousand Oaks Surgical Hospital, Thousand Oaks, CA, p. A92

BANTA, Mary, Director Human Resources, Mercy Medical Center, Williston, ND, p. A469

BANUELOS, Jr., Alfonso F., M.D. Chief Medical Officer, Santa Clara Valley Medical Center, San Jose, CA, p. A88

BAPTISTE, Ernest, Executive Director, Kings County Hospital Center,, NY, p. A433

BARABANI, Paul, Superintendent, Soldiers' Home in Holyoke, Holyoke, MA, p. A301

BARAN, John, Chief Financial Officer, Auburn Community Hospital, Auburn, NY, p. A420

BARANIK, David T., Senior Vice President and Chief Financial Officer, Ohio Valley Medical Center, Wheeling, WV, p. A682

BARANSKI, David J., Vice President Human Resources, Phoebe Putney Memorial Hospital, Albany, GA, p. A145

BARANSKI, Kenneth, Chief Financial Officer, Hills & Dales General Hospital, Cass City, MI, p. A310

BARBA, James J., President and Chief Executive Officer, Albany Medical Center, Albany, NY, p. A420

BARBADIAN, John, Vice President Human Resources, Tulare Regional Medical Center, Tulare, CA, p. A93

BARBAGLIA, J. Joseph, Vice President Financial Services, Columbus Community Hospital, Columbus, NE, p. A382

BARBAREE, Jerry, Director Human Resources, Baptist Memorial Hospital – Memphis, Memphis, TN, p. A574

BARBARIN, LaSharndra
Chief Operating Officer, Medical Center of Arlington, Arlington, TX, p. A583
Chief Operating Officer, Medical Center of McKinney, McKinney, TX, p. A622

BARBAROTTA, Ann Marie, Executive Director, Creedmoor Psychiatric Center,, NY, p. A431

BARBE, Brian S., Chief Executive Officer, Memorial Hermann Katy Hospital, Katy, TX, p. A616

BARBER, Chris B., FACHE, President and Chief Executive Officer, St. Bernards Medical Center, Jonesboro, AR, p. A45

BARBER, Eric A., Chief Executive Officer, Northeast Regional Medical Center, Kirksville, MO, p. A364

BARBER, Jack W., M.D., Director, Western State Hospital, Staunton, VA, p. A662

BARBER, Jeffrey B., FACHE, President and Chief Executive Officer, Owensboro Health Regional Hospital, Owensboro, KY, p. A258

BARBER, Karen, Chief Executive Officer, Yoakum Community Hospital, Yoakum, TX, p. A642

BARBER, Keith, CPA Chief Operating Officer and Chief Financial Officer, Tomball Regional Medical Center, Tomball, TX, p. A638

BARBER, Laurie, Director Human Resources, Trumbull Memorial Hospital, Warren, OH, p. A492

BARBER, Michael, System Chief Operating Officer, Chester County Hospital, West Chester, PA, p. A543

BARBER, Scott, Chief Executive Officer, Decatur County General Hospital, Parsons, TN, p. A578

BARBER, Teresa Rini, Vice President Support Services, Southwest General Health Center, Middleburg Heights, OH, p. A486

BARBER, Wendi, Vice President Finance, Castle Medical Center, Kailua, HI, p. A165

BARBINI, Gerald J., President and Chief Executive Officer, Allegan General Hospital, Allegan, MI, p. A308

BARBO, Steve, R.N., Administrator, Citizens Medical Center, Columbia, LA, p. A265

BARBOSA, Robert, D.O. Chief Medical Officer, Oakland Regional Hospital, Southfield, MI, p. A324

BARBUAT, James P., Chief Financial Officer, Heart Hospital of Lafayette, Lafayette, LA, p. A270

BARCA, Robin
Chief Operating Officer, Baptist Medical Center East, Montgomery, AL, p. A23
Chief Executive Officer, Baptist Medical Center South, Montgomery, AL, p. A23
Chief Executive Officer, Baptist Medical Center South, Montgomery, AL, p. A23

BARCHI, Daniel
Senior Vice President, Technical Services and Chief Information Officer, Bridgeport Hospital, Bridgeport, CT, p. A108
Senior Vice President and Chief Information Officer, Carilion Medical Center, Roanoke, VA, p. A661

BARCLAY, Duane, D.O
Chief Medical Officer, DeKalb Medical at Hillandale, Lithonia, GA, p. A156
Vice President Physician Support Services, DeKalb Medical at North Decatur, Decatur, GA, p. A152

BARCLAY, Emily, Vice President Human Resources, Dana–Farber Cancer Institute, Boston, MA, p. A296

BARCLAY, Jeremy, Chief Operating Officer, Cedar Park Regional Medical Center, Cedar Park, TX, p. A591

BARCLAY, Rick, Vice President Support Services, Mercy Hospital Rogers, Rogers, AR, p. A49

BARCLAY, Sherri, M.D. Chief Medical Staff, Hopkins County Memorial Hospital, Sulphur Springs, TX, p. A636

BARCLIFT, Larry, Chief Financial Officer, Yuma Rehabilitation Hospital, Yuma, AZ, p. A40

BARD, Jeffrey, President, Aurora Medical Center of Oshkosh, Oshkosh, WI, p. A694

BARDEN, Sean
Executive Vice President and Chief Financial Officer, Mary Washington Hospital, Fredericksburg, VA, p. A654
Executive Vice President and Chief Financial Officer, Stafford Hospital, Stafford, VA, p. A661

BARDIER, Catherine, Senior Director Human Resources, New London Hospital, New London, NH, p. A399

BARDILL, Janice, Chief Financial Officer, Roane Medical Center, Harriman, TN, p. A569

BARDWELL, Carol A., R.N. Chief Nurse Executive, Martha's Vineyard Hospital, Oak Bluffs, MA, p. A303

BARDWELL, Jean, Vice President and Chief Financial Officer, Ranken Jordan – A Pediatric Specialty Hospital, Maryland Heights, MO, p. A365

BARDWELL, Sheila, Director Information Systems, Baptist Memorial Hospital–Golden Triangle, Columbus, MS, p. A346

BARDWELL, Tom, Vice President Human Resources, Hills & Dales General Hospital, Cass City, MI, p. A310

BAREFOOT, Denise, Director Health Information Systems, Carolina Pines Regional Medical Center, Hartsville, SC, p. A553

BAREIS, Charles, M.D. Medical Director, UnityHealth MacNeal Hospital, Berwyn, IL, p. A174

BARELA, Barbara, Director Human Resources, Gila Regional Medical Center, Silver City, NM, p. A418

BARFIELD, Deirdre, M.D. Vice President Medical Affairs and Chief Medical Officer, CHRISTUS Schumpert Medical Center, Shreveport, LA, p. A278

BARFIELD, Donna, Chief Nursing Officer, Volunteer Community Hospital, Martin, TN, p. A573

BARGER, Pamela, R.N., Interim Administrator, Community Behavioral Health Hospital – Annandale, Annandale, MN, . p. A328

BARGINERE, Cynthia, MSN Vice President Clinical Nursing and Chief Nursing Officer, Rush University Medical Center, Chicago, IL, p. A179

BARHAM, Martha, Vice President and Chief Operating Officer, High Point Regional Health System, High Point, NC, p. A455

BARIOLA, Christopher L.
Chief Executive Officer, Eureka Springs Hospital, Eureka Springs, AR, p. A43
Chief Executive Officer, River Valley Medical Center, Dardanelle, AR, p. A42

BARISANO, Nancy, Chief Information Officer, Westerly Hospital, Westerly, RI, p. A547

BARKASY, Michael, M.D. Chief of Staff, Jennersville Regional Hospital, West Grove, PA, p. A544

BARKEMA, Annette, Chief Financial Officer, Portland Veterans Affairs Medical Center, Portland, OR, p. A516

BARKER, Alanna, Director Human Resources, Washington County Hospital, Nashville, IL, p. A190

BARKER, Jaime, M.D. Medical Director, Manatee Palms Youth Services, Bradenton, FL, p. A119

BARKER, James, President, West Shore Medical Center, Manistee, MI, p. A319

BARKER, Jason, Chief Executive Officer, St. Vincent Healthcare, Billings, MT, p. A374

BARKER, Karen
Vice President and Chief Information Officer, Levindale Hebrew Geriatric Center and Hospital, Baltimore, MD, p. A288
Vice President and Chief Information Officer, Northwest Hospital, Randallstown, MD, p. A293
Vice President and Chief Information Officer, Sinai Hospital of Baltimore, Baltimore, MD, p. A289

BARKER, Kathryn L., Chief Human Resources Management, Veterans Health Care System of the Ozarks, Fayetteville, AR, p. A43

BARKER, Larry
Chief Operating Officer, Clearwater Valley Hospital and Clinics, Orofino, ID, p. A170
Chief Operating Officer, St. Mary's Hospital, Cottonwood, ID, p. A168

BARKER, Louise, R.N., Chief Executive Officer, Central Louisiana Surgical Hospital, Alexandria, LA, p. A262

BARKER, M. Debby, Director Human Resources, Siskin Hospital for Physical Rehabilitation, Chattanooga, TN, p. A567

BARKER, Richard, Administrator, Mercy Health Love County, Marietta, OK, p. A501

BARKER, Russell
Community Chief Executive Officer, McDowell ARH Hospital, McDowell, KY, p. A257
Chief Information Officer, U. S. Public Health Service Indian Hospital–Whiteriver, Whiteriver, AZ, p. A39

BARKER, Thomas, Director Information, Southeast Health Center of Reynolds County, Ellington, MO, p. A360

BARKER, Jr., William A., Vice President Administration, Pleasant Valley Hospital, Point Pleasant, WV, p. A680

BARKHYMER, Mary C., R.N. Vice President Patient Care Services and Chief Nursing Officer, UPMC St. Margaret, Pittsburgh, PA, p. A538

BARKMAN, H. William, M.D. Chief of Staff, The University of Kansas Hospital, Kansas City, KS, p. A237

BARKSDALE, Vickie, Manager Human Resources, North Oak Regional Medical Center, Senatobia, MS, p. A353

BARLEY, Leonard, M.D. Chief Medical Officer, Windsor–Laurelwood Center for Behavioral Medicine, Willoughby, OH, p. A493

BARLEY, Tammy, Director Human Resources, HEALTHSOUTH Rehabilitation Hospital of Jonesboro, Jonesboro, AR, p. A45

BARLOW, Christopher, Chief Executive Officer, Horton Community Hospital, Horton, KS, p. A235

BARLOW, Jason B., Interim Chief Executive Officer, Saint Francis Hospital and Health Centers, Poughkeepsie, NY, p. A440

BARLOW, Mark, M.D. Chief Medical Officer and President Medical Staff, Cornerstone Hospital of Houston – Bellaire, Houston, TX, p. A609

BARNARD, David, M.D. Medical Director, Huey P. Long Medical Center, Pineville, LA, p. A277

BARNARD, Dawn, Administrator, Minnesota Neurorehabilitation Hospital, Brainerd, MN, p. A329

BARNARD, Jeanna, Chief Executive Officer, Bayshore Medical Center, Pasadena, TX, p. A626

BARNARD, Ryan, Chief Executive Officer, Swisher Memorial Hospital District, Tulia, TX, p. A638

BARNAS, Kim
Senior Vice President, Appleton Medical Center, Appleton, WI, p. A683
Senior Vice President, Theda Clark Medical Center, Neenah, WI, p. A693

BARNCORD, Sharon
Business Partner Human Resources, Kaiser Permanente Redwood City Medical Center, Redwood City, CA, p. A82
Human Resource Business Partner, Kaiser Permanente South San Francisco, South San Francisco, CA, p. A91

BARNES, Betty, Director Human Resources, Maryville Behavioral Health Hospital, Des Plaines, IL, p. A181

BARNES, Chenell, Administrator, Specialty Rehabilitation Hospital of Luling, Luling, LA, p. A272

BARNES, Deborah, Vice President and Chief Information Officer, Children's Hospital of The King's Daughters, Norfolk, VA, p. A658

BARNES, Don, Chief Human Resources Officer, Duke Raleigh Hospital, Raleigh, NC, p. A459

BARNES, Douglas A., M.D. Chief of Staff, Shriners Hospitals for Children–Houston, Houston, TX, p. A612

BARNES, Gary, Chief Information Officer, Medical Center Health System, Odessa, TX, p. A625

BARNES, George, M.D. Medical Director, Lakeview Regional Medical Center, Covington, LA, p. A265

BARNES, Gloria V., Assistant Vice President Patient Care Services, Southeastern Regional Medical Center, Newnan, GA, p. A158

BARNES, Jacqueline, Manager Health Information, Select Specialty Hospital–Jackson, Jackson, MS, p. A349

BARNES, Jeff, Director of Information Technology, Girard Medical Center, Girard, KS, p. A234

BARNES, Joe, Chief Financial Officer, Grant Memorial Hospital, Petersburg, WV, p. A679

BARNES, Larry, Vice President Information Technology, Salina Regional Health Center, Salina, KS, p. A243

BARNES, Laura P., MSN Vice President Patient Care Services and Chief Nursing Officer, East Tennessee Children's Hospital, Knoxville, TN, p. A571

BARNES, Mary Ann, Senior Vice President and Executive Director, Kaiser Permanente San Diego Medical Center, San Diego, CA, p. A85

BARNES, Maryann, MS Vice President and Chief Nursing Officer East Region, St. John Hospital and Medical Center, Detroit, MI, p. A312

BARNES, Michael, Chief Information Officer, North Valley Hospital, Whitefish, MT, p. A380

BARNES, P. Marie, Director, Human Resources, North Mississippi Medical Center–Pontotoc Hospital and Nursing Home, Pontotoc, MS, p. A352

BARNES, Sherry, Director Health Information and Quality Management, Rolling Hills Hospital, Ada, OK, p. A495

BARNES, Sheryl L., MSN Senior Director Clinical Services, Mercy Medical Center – West Lakes, West Des Moines, IA, p. A230

BARNES, William H., Administrator, Sweeny Community Hospital, Sweeny, TX, p. A636

BARNETT, Frederick, M.D. Chief of Staff, Metroplex Adventist Hospital, Killeen, TX, p. A616

BARNETT, Julia, Chief Nursing Officer, Fannin Regional Hospital, Blue Ridge, GA, p. A148

BARNETT, Lori, R.N. Chief Nursing Officer, Troy Community Hospital, Troy, PA, p. A542

BARNETT, Marcus, M.D. Chief of Staff, Cypress Fairbanks Medical Center, Houston, TX, p. A609

BARNETT, Shawn
Vice President and Chief Financial Officer, CHRISTUS Santa Rosa Health System, San Antonio, TX, p. A630
Vice President and Chief Financial Officer, CHRISTUS St. Michael Health System, Texarkana, TX, p. A637

BARNETT, Steve, MS, President and Chief Executive Officer, McKenzie Health System, Sandusky, MI, p. A324

BARNETT, Timothy
Chief Executive Officer, Yavapai Regional Medical Center – East, Prescott Valley, AZ, p. A36
President and Chief Executive Officer, Yavapai Regional Medical Center, Prescott, AZ, p. A36

BARNHARDT, Bonnie, Executive Director Human Resources, Minnesota Valley Health Center, Le Sueur, MN, p. A334

BARNHART, David, Director Information Systems, Wuesthoff Medical Center – Rockledge, Rockledge, FL, p. A138

BARNHART, J. T., Chief Executive Officer, Clearview Regional Medical Center, Monroe, GA, p. A157

BARNHART, James R., Chief Administrator Officer, PeaceHealth Peace Island Medical Center, Friday Harbor, WA, p. A666

BARNHART, Jeff, Chief Executive Officer, Ochiltree General Hospital, Perryton, TX, p. A627

BARNHART, Rodger, Chief Executive Officer, Ashland Health Center, Ashland, KS, p. A231

BARNTHOUSE, Victoria, R.N. Chief Nursing Officer, Val Verde Regional Medical Center, Del Rio, TX, p. A598

BAROCO, Paul T., M.D. Chief Medical Officer, Sacred Heart Hospital of Pensacola, Pensacola, FL, p. A137

BARONE, Charles, M.D. Vice President Medical Affairs, Children's Hospital of Michigan, Detroit, MI, p. A311

BARONE, Nancy, Vice President and Executive Director Operations and Strategic Planning, University Hospital, Cincinnati, OH, p. A475

BARONE, Richard, M.D. Medical Director, Sound Shore Medical Center of Westchester, New Rochelle, NY, p. A430

BARR, Brant, M.D. Chief Medical Officer, District One Hospital, Faribault, MN, p. A332

BARR, Brent, Chief Information Officer, Minnie Hamilton HealthCare Center, Grantsville, WV, p. A677

BARR, Bret, Vice President Fiscal Services, Conway Medical Center, Conway, SC, p. A551

BARR, Catherine, Senior Vice President and President, Bethesda Hospital, Bethesda Hospital, Saint Paul, MN, p. A340

BARR, Kristine, Vice President Communication Services, O'Bleness Memorial Hospital, Athens, OH, p. A471

BARR, Mary Beth, R.N., Chief Executive Officer, Grant Memorial Hospital, Petersburg, WV, p. A679

BARR, Steven, MSN, Chief Executive Officer, Plaza Specialty Hospital, Houston, TX, p. A611

BARR, Tamara, Human Resources Generalist, St. Vincent's St. Clair, Pell City, AL, p. A24

BARR, Tom, Director Operational Support Services, Peterson Rehabilitation Hospital, Wheeling, WV, p. A682

BARR, Vivian C.
Director Human Resources, Higgins General Hospital, Bremen, GA, p. A148
Director Human Resources, Tanner Medical Center–Carrollton, Carrollton, GA, p. A149

BARRA, Jon, Director Human Resources, Wyoming Behavioral Institute, Casper, WY, p. A701

BARRA, Peter, M.D. Chief Medical Officer, Flushing Hospital Medical Center,, NY, p. A432

BARRACK, Amy, Director Human Resources, Riverside Behavioral Health Center, Hampton, VA, p. A655

BARRACO, Dennis, D.O. Medical Director, Wickenburg Community Hospital, Wickenburg, AZ, p. A39

BARRAMEDA, Maricar, Chief Information Officer, Lincoln Medical and Mental Health Center,, NY, p. A433

BARRAN, Peter, M.D. Chief of Staff, Pondera Medical Center, Conrad, MT, p. A375

BARREIRO, Maggie E., Administrator, Weslaco Rehabilitation Hospital, Weslaco, TX, p. A641

BARRERA, Diahann, Chief Financial Officer, Willow Springs Center, Reno, NV, p. A395

BARRERA, Edward, Director Communications, Encino Hospital Medical Center,, CA, p. A68

BARRETO, Marcelino, M.D. Chief Medical Staff, MidMichigan Medical Center–Gladwin, Gladwin, MI, p. A314

BARRETT, Anne J., Associate Executive Director Human Resources, Southside Hospital, Bay Shore, NY, p. A421

BARRETT, Bob, Chief Financial Officer, Clinch Valley Medical Center, Richlands, VA, p. A660

BARRETT, Cindy, Administrative Assistant, Patton State Hospital, Patton, CA, p. A79

BARRETT, Debbie, Director Human Resources, J. D. McCarty Center for Children With Developmental Disabilities, Norman, OK, p. A502

BARRETT, Douglas T., Senior Vice President Human Resources, Masonicare Health Center, Wallingford, CT, p. A112

BARRETT Jr., James W., Chief Executive Officer, Richardson Medical Center, Rayville, LA, p. A277

BARRETT, Janet, R.N. Chief Nurse Executive, Massac Memorial Hospital, Metropolis, IL, p. A188

BARRETT, Jason P., Chief Operating Officer, Flagler Hospital, Saint Augustine, FL, p. A138

BARRETT III, John E., Chief Executive Officer, Bon Secours–DePaul Medical Center, Norfolk, VA, p. A658

BARRETT, Kerry Flynn, Vice President Human Resources, Northern Westchester Hospital, Mount Kisco, NY, p. A430

BARRETT, Linda, Vice President of Information Services, Community Hospital of Bremen, Bremen, IN, p. A199

BARRETT, Peggy, R.N., Chief Executive Officer, Central Texas Rehabilitation Hospital, Austin, TX, p. A584

BARRETT, T. Marc, M.D. Senior Vice President Medical Affairs, Providence Health Center, Waco, TX, p. A640

BARRETTO, Shirley, M.D. Chief of Staff, Knox County Hospital, Knox City, TX, p. A617

BARRICK, Lisa, Controller, HEALTHSOUTH Scottsdale Rehabilitation Hospital, Scottsdale, AZ, p. A37

BARRILLEAUX, Scott G., FACHE, Chief Executive Officer, Madison Parish Hospital, Tallulah, LA, p. A279

BARRIO, Gabe, M.D. Chief of Staff, Whidbey General Hospital, Coupeville, WA, p. A666

BARROCAS, Albert, M.D. Chief Medical Officer, Atlanta Medical Center – South Campus, Atlanta, GA, p. A146

BARROETA, Jennifer
Chief Human Resources Officer, Baptist Hospitals of Southeast Texas, Beaumont, TX, p. A587
Chief Human Resources Officer, Baptist Orange Hospital, Orange, TX, p. A625

BARRON, Bill, M.D. Chief Medical Officer, University of California, Irvine Healthcare, Orange, CA, p. A78

BARRON, Lee, Chief Executive Officer, Southern Inyo Healthcare District, Lone Pine, CA, p. A67

BARRON, Steven R., President and Senior Vice President Operations Dignity Health Southern California East Service Area, St. Bernardine Medical Center, San Bernardino, CA, p. A84

BARROW, Robert, Chief Executive Officer, Doctors' Hospital of Michigan, Pontiac, MI, p. A322

BARROW II, William F., President and Chief Executive Officer, Our Lady of Lourdes Regional Medical Center, Lafayette, LA, p. A271

BARROWS, Cheryl, Vice President Human Resources, Sturdy Memorial Hospital, Attleboro, MA, p. A295

BARRY, Thomas, Chief Executive Officer, Pulaski Memorial Hospital, Winamac, IN, p. A215

BARSE, Steve, Chief Information Officer, Lawton Indian Hospital, Lawton, OK, p. A500

BARSOM, Michael, M.D., Executive Director, Metropolitan State Hospital, Norwalk, CA, p. A76

BARSTAD, Stacy
Chief Executive Officer, Sanford Tracy Medical Center, Tracy, MN, p. A341
Chief Executive Officer, Sanford Westbrook Medical Center, Westbrook, MN, p. A342

BARTAL, Ely, M.D., Chief Executive Officer, Kansas Surgery and Recovery Center, Wichita, KS, p. A246

BARTELS, Jennifer, Director Human Resources, Pawnee County Memorial Hospital and Rural Health Clinic, Pawnee City, NE, p. A389

BARTH, Tara, Chief Nursing Officer, Palo Verde Hospital, Blythe, CA, p. A55

BARTHEL, Gayle, Coordinator Human Resources, Select Specialty Hospital–Flint, Flint, MI, p. A314

BARTHOLOMEW, Brenda, Chief Nursing Officer, Gunnison Valley Hospital, Gunnison, UT, p. A643

BARTHOLOMEW, K. A., M.D. Medical Director, Faulkton Area Medical Center, Faulkton, SD, p. A559

BARTHOLOMEW, Shelley, Director Human Resources, Decatur County General Hospital, Parsons, TN, p. A578

BARTILSON, Jim, Manager Information Systems, South Peninsula Hospital, Homer, AK, p. A28

BARTINGALE, Robert, Administrator, Mayo Clinic Health System in Fairmont, Fairmont, MN, p. A332

BARTLETT, James, Chief Financial Officer, Faith Community Hospital, Jacksboro, TX, p. A615

BARTLETT, Karolyn, Assistant Administrator, Mayo Clinic Health System – Northland in Barron, Barron, WI, p. A684

BARTLETT, Regina, Chief Executive Officer, TriStar Hendersonville Medical Center, Hendersonville, TN, p. A570

BARTLETT, Richard, M.D. Chief Medical Officer, Basin Healthcare Center, Odessa, TX, p. A625

BARTLETT, Roderick, M.D. President Medical Staff, Hannibal Regional Hospital, Hannibal, MO, p. A361

BARTLETT, Ronald E., Chief Financial Officer, Boston Medical Center, Boston, MA, p. A296

BARTLETT, Taci, Chief Financial Officer, Gothenburg Memorial Hospital, Gothenburg, NE, p. A384

BARTLETT III, Thomas G., Administrator, Laird Hospital, Union, MS, p. A354

BARTLEY, Tracy, Manager Information Technology, Bath Community Hospital, Hot Springs, VA, p. A655

BARTO Jr., John K., President and Chief Executive Officer, New Hanover Regional Medical Center, Wilmington, NC, p. A463

BARTON, Annie, Director Human Resources, Peterson Rehabilitation Hospital, Wheeling, WV, p. A682

BARTON, Charles, Business Manager, Southwestern State Hospital, Thomasville, GA, p. A161

BARTON, Gratia, Chief Financial Officer, Sequoia Hospital, Redwood City, CA, p. A82

BARTON, Larry O., FACHE, President, Baptist Health Paducah, Paducah, KY, p. A259

BARTON, Rod, Administrator, Cassia Regional Medical Center, Burley, ID, p. A168

BARTON, Thomas, M.D. Medical Director, TOPS Surgical Specialty Hospital, Houston, TX, p. A613

BARTON, Wendy, Manager Business Office, Fredonia Regional Hospital, Fredonia, KS, p. A234

BARTOS, John M., Chief Executive Officer, Marcus Daly Memorial Hospital, Hamilton, MT, p. A376

BARTRUFF, Craig, M.D. Medical Director, Gothenburg Memorial Hospital, Gothenburg, NE, p. A384

BARTS, Dennis
Chief Executive Officer, Avista Adventist Hospital, Louisville, CO, p. A104
Chief Executive Officer, Valley Hospital, Spokane Valley, WA, p. A672

BARTZ, Daniel R., CPA Chief Financial Officer, Warren Memorial Hospital, Friend, NE, p. A383

BARTZ, Ryan, D.O. Chief of Staff, McNairy Regional Hospital, Selmer, TN, p. A578

BARWICK, Kim, Vice President Human Resources, Anthony Medical Center, Anthony, KS, p. A231

BARWIS, Kurt A., FACHE, President and Chief Executive Officer, Bristol Hospital, Bristol, CT, p. A108

BASCOM, Steven, M.D. Chief Medical Officer, Guthrie County Hospital, Guthrie Center, IA, p. A222

BASEY, Marjorie, Chief Financial Officer, Rehabilitation Hospital of Indiana, Indianapolis, IN, p. A206

BASNIGHT, Tom, Chief Financial Officer, Walter B. Jones Alcohol and Drug Abuse Treatment Center, Greenville, NC, p. A454

BASS, Anne, Chief Financial Officer, Fairfield Memorial Hospital, Winnsboro, SC, p. A557

BASS, G. Michael, President and Chief Executive Officer, Piedmont Newnan Hospital, Newnan, GA, p. A158

BASS, Gordon B., Chief Operating Officer, Ann & Robert H. Lurie Children's Hospital of Chicago, Chicago, IL, p. A176

BASS, Louis A., Vice President Finance, Northeast Alabama Regional Medical Center, Anniston, AL, p. A15

BASS, Sonya, MS Chief Nursing Officer, Colorado Plains Medical Center, Fort Morgan, CO, p. A101

BASS Jr., William L., Vice President and Chief Executive Officer, Centra Southside Community Hospital, Farmville, VA, p. A653

BASSETT, Annie, Director Finance, McBride Clinic Orthopedic Hospital, Oklahoma City, OK, p. A503

BASSETT, Eugene, President and Chief Executive Officer, Methodist Hospital of Sacramento, Sacramento, CA, p. A83

BASSETT, Kimberly S., R.N., President, Morton Hospital and Medical Center, Taunton, MA, p. A305

BASSO, James, Chief Human Resources Officer, Central Texas Veterans Healthcare System, Temple, TX, p. A636

BASSO, Marty, Senior Vice President Finance, Suburban Hospital, Bethesda, MD, p. A290

BASTABLE, Chad, Director Human Resources, North Central Health Care, Wausau, WI, p. A699

BASTIANELLO, Carol, Director Employee Services, NORTHSTAR Health System, Iron River, MI, p. A317

BASTIEN IV, Samua A., Ph.D., Executive Director, St. Lawrence Psychiatric Center, Ogdensburg, NY, p. A438

BASTING, Gregory, M.D
Vice President Medical Affairs, Allied Services Rehabilitation Hospital, Scranton, PA, p. A540
Vice President Medical Affairs, John Heinz Institute of Rehabilitation Medicine, Wilkes–Barre, PA, p. A544

BASTONE, Peter F., Chief Executive Officer, Chesapeake Regional Medical Center, Chesapeake, VA, p. A652

BATA, Katie, Vice President Human Resources, Advocate Sherman Hospital, Elgin, IL, p. A181

BATAL, Lucille M., Administrator, Baldpate Hospital, Haverhill, MA, p. A300

BATCHELOR, Dale, M.D. Chief Medical Officer, Saint Thomas West Hospital, Nashville, TN, p. A577

BATCHELOR, Daniela, Director Human Resources, Springhill Memorial Hospital, Mobile, AL, p. A22

BATCHELOR, Diana, Chief Nursing Officer, UnityPoint Health Finley, Dubuque, IA, p. A221

BATCHELOR, Michael, President, North Greenville Hospital, Travelers Rest, SC, p. A556

BATEMAN, Bryan S., Chief Executive Officer, Women and Children's Hospital, Lake Charles, LA, p. A272

BATEMAN, Jana, R.N. Chief Nursing Officer, East Texas Medical Center Jacksonville, Jacksonville, TX, p. A615

BATEMAN, Kenneth, CPA, President and Chief Executive Officer, Somerset Medical Center, Somerville, NJ, p. A410

BATEMAN, Mark T., Interim Chief Operating Officer, Saint Agnes Medical Center, Fresno, CA, p. A61

BATEMAN, Steven B., Chief Executive Officer, St. Mark's Hospital, Salt Lake City, UT, p. A647

BATES, Don
Chief Executive Officer, Palacios Community Medical Center, Palacios, TX, p. A625
Chief Executive Officer, Trego County–Lemke Memorial Hospital, Wakeeney, KS, p. A245

BATES, Earl, Director Information Technology, Western Mental Health Institute, Bolivar, TN, p. A565

BATES, Juanita Ann, Administrator, St. Charles Specialty Rehabilitation Hospital, Luling, LA, p. A272

BATES, Mary, Director Human Resources, Bowie Memorial Hospital, Bowie, TX, p. A589

BATES, Peter, M.D. Vice President Medical Affairs and Chief Medical Officer, Maine Medical Center, Portland, ME, p. A284

BATES, Robert A., Executive Director Finance and Chief Financial Officer, St. Vincent Carmel Hospital, Carmel, IN, p. A200

BATEY, James, M.D. President Medical Staff, Baptist Memorial Hospital–Union City, Union City, TN, p. A580

BATH, Jeffrey, M.D. President Medical Staff, North Adams Regional Hospital, North Adams, MA, p. A303

BATISTA, David J., Chief Executive Officer, Garfield Medical Center, Monterey Park, CA, p. A75

BATISTE, Michele, Director Human Resources, Preston Memorial Hospital, Kingwood, WV, p. A678

BATORY, Robert J., Vice President Human Resources, York Hospital, York, PA, p. A545

BATSHAW, Mark L., M.D. Interim Chief Medical Officer and Chief Academic Officer, Children's National Medical Center, Washington, DC, p. A116

BATTERSHELL, Ty, M.D. Chief of Staff, Platte County Memorial Hospital, Wheatland, WY, p. A704

BATTERTON, Owen A., M.D. Chief of Staff, Greene County General Hospital, Linton, IN, p. A209

BATTISTA, Donald P., President and Chief Executive Officer, Garrett County Memorial Hospital, Oakland, MD, p. A293

BATTISTA, Edward, Vice President Human Resources, West Hills Hospital and Medical Center,, CA, p. A72

BATTLE, Joe, Interim Director, G.V. (Sonny) Montgomery Veterans Affairs Medical Center, Jackson, MS, p. A348

BATTLES, Ruth, Administrative Director Human Resources, Corona Regional Medical Center, Corona, CA, p. A57

BATTY, Jill I., Chief Financial Officer, Cheshire Medical Center, Keene, NH, p. A398

BATTY, Mark, Chief Executive Officer, Rochelle Community Hospital, Rochelle, IL, p. A193

BATULIS, Scott, President and Chief Executive Officer, Orange Regional Medical Center, Middletown, NY, p. A429

BATY, Grace, Director Human Resources, Sweeny Community Hospital, Sweeny, TX, p. A636

BAUER, Brian, Chief Executive Officer, Lutheran Hospital of Indiana, Fort Wayne, IN, p. A202

BAUER, Gregory P., President and Chief Executive Officer, Elk Regional Health Center, Saint Marys, PA, p. A540

BAUER, Jonathan, Director Information Services, Somerset Hospital, Somerset, PA, p. A541

BAUER, Kyle, Chief Financial Officer, Cuyuna Regional Medical Center, Crosby, MN, p. A331

BAUER, Richard, M.D. Chief of Staff, South Texas Veterans Health Care System, San Antonio, TX, p. A632

BAUER, Robert, Vice President Human Resources, Wheaton Franciscan Healthcare – St. Francis, Milwaukee, WI, p. A692

BAUER, Roberta, M.D. Acting Chair Medical Staff, Cleveland Clinic Children's Hospital for Rehabilitation, Cleveland, OH, p. A476

BAUER, Roger, M.D. Chief Medical Officer, Swift County–Benson Hospital, Benson, MN, p. A329

BAUER, Sandra A., Director Human Resources, Jefferson Community Health Center, Fairbury, NE, p. A383

BAUER, Shar, Executive Secretary, Wishek Community Hospital and Clinics, Wishek, ND, p. A469

BAUER, Tracy, Chief Executive Officer, Midwest Medical Center, Galena, IL, p. A183

BAUER, William, Vice President Finance and Chief Financial Officer, Hazleton General Hospital, Hazleton, PA, p. A527

BAUER, William, M.D. Medical Director, Montevista Hospital, Las Vegas, NV, p. A393

BAUGHMAN, Sharon
Vice President Patient Services and Chief Nursing Officer, Wheaton Franciscan Healthcare – Elmbrook Memorial, Brookfield, WI, p. A684
Vice President Patient Services and Chief Nursing Officer, Wheaton Franciscan Healthcare – St. Joseph's, Milwaukee, WI, p. A692
Vice President Patient Services and Chief Nursing Officer, Wheaton Franciscan Healthcare – The Wisconsin Heart Hospital, Wauwatosa, WI, p. A699

BAUM, Judy, Chief Executive Officer, Mountain Valley Regional Rehabilitation Hospital, Prescott Valley, AZ, p. A36

BAUMAN, Jonathan, M.D. Chief Medical Officer, Four Winds Hospital, Katonah, NY, p. A428

BAUMEIER, Mark, M.D. Chief of Staff, St. Joseph Mercy Livingston Hospital, Howell, MI, p. A316

BAUMERT, Steven P., President and Chief Executive Officer, Methodist Jennie Edmundson Hospital, Council Bluffs, IA, p. A219

BAUMGARDNER, Brian, Chief Executive Officer, West Florida Hospital, Pensacola, FL, p. A137

BAUMGARDNER, Charles J., Vice President Corporate Operations, Psychiatric Institute of Washington, Washington, DC, p. A117

BAUMGARDNER, David, Director Information Management, Union Hospital, Dover, OH, p. A480

BAUMGARTNER, David, M.D. Vice President Medical Affairs, Saint Mary's Health Care, Grand Rapids, MI, p. A315

BAUMGARTNER, Jennifer, Chief Information Officer, Perkins County Health Services, Grant, NE, p. A384

BAUMGARTNER, Michael A., President, St. Francis Regional Medical Center, Shakopee, MN, p. A341

BAUNCHALK, James M., Deputy Chief Clinical Services, Dwight David Eisenhower Army Medical Center, Fort Gordon, GA, p. A154

BAUR, Heidi, R.N. Chief Nursing Officer, St. Christopher's Hospital for Children, Philadelphia, PA, p. A536

BAUTISTA, Veronica, Chief Financial Officer, Memorial Regional Hospital South,, FL, p. A125

BAVERSO, Lou, Chief Information Officer, Magee–Womens Hospital of UPMC, Pittsburgh, PA, p. A537

BAW, Joseph, Director Human Resources, Riveredge Hospital, Forest Park, IL, p. A182

BAWA, Balraj, M.D. Assistant Director Medical Services, Central Virginia Training Center, Madison Heights, VA, p. A656

BAXTER, Anne, Director Fiscal Services, Northern Virginia Mental Health Institute, Falls Church, VA, p. A653

BAXTER, Greg, M.D. Vice President Medical Affairs, Elliot Hospital, Manchester, NH, p. A399

BAXTER, Joshua, Director, Information Systems, Powell Valley Healthcare, Powell, WY, p. A703

BAXTER, Michael T., Chief Executive Officer, Parkview Medical Center, Pueblo, CO, p. A105

BAXTER, Robert O., President and Chief Executive Officer, St. Rita's Medical Center, Lima, OH, p. A484

BAY, Marybeth, Director Information Technology, Sauk Prairie Memorial Hospital & Clinics, Prairie Du Sac, WI, p. A695

BAY, Shelley, Chief Financial Officer, Fayette County Hospital, Vandalia, IL, p. A196

BAYER, Allison, Executive Vice President and Chief Operating Officer, Cambridge Health Alliance, Cambridge, MA, p. A299

BAYLES, Susan, Director Human Resources, Highland Hospital, Charleston, WV, p. A676

BAYLESS, Betsey, President and Chief Executive Officer, Maricopa Integrated Health System, Phoenix, AZ, p. A34

BAYLESS, Victoria, President and Chief Executive Officer, Anne Arundel Medical Center, Annapolis, MD, p. A287

BAYLESS–BERNEY, Jill, MSN Chief Operating Officer, Longview Regional Medical Center, Longview, TX, p. A619

BAYOUTH, LaNoard, M.D. Chief of Staff, Abilene Regional Medical Center, Abilene, TX, p. A581

BAYUS, Robin, Chief Financial Officer, Rancho Los Amigos National Rehabilitation Center, Downey, CA, p. A58

BAZELEY, Stephen, M.D. Vice President Medical Affairs, ProMedica St. Luke's Hospital, Maumee, OH, p. A486

BEA, Javon R., President and Chief Executive Officer, Mercy Hospital and Trauma Center, Janesville, WI, p. A688

BEACH, David, Vice President Human Resources, Spectrum Health – Grand Rapids, Grand Rapids, MI, p. A315

BEACH, Karrie, Director Human Resources, Community Memorial Hospital, Syracuse, NE, p. A390

BEACH, Michele, Associate Director, Sheridan Veterans Affairs Medical Center, Sheridan, WY, p. A703

BEADMAN, Cindi, Director Medical Records, Harper Hospital District Five, Harper, KS, p. A235

BEALE, George L., M.D. Director Medical Staff, Clay County Hospital, Ashland, AL, p. A15

BEALER, Ruth, Director Human Resources, Great Bend Regional Hospital, Great Bend, KS, p. A234

BEALER, Shirley, Medical Center Director, Overton Brooks Veterans Affairs Medical Center, Shreveport, LA, p. A278

BEAM, William, M.D. Chief of Staff, Cornerstone Hospital of Huntington, Huntington, WV, p. A677

BEAMAN, Frank, Administrator, Faith Community Hospital, Jacksboro, TX, p. A615

BEAMAN, John, Senior Vice President and Chief Financial Officer, Simi Valley Hospital and Health Care Services, Simi Valley, CA, p. A91

BEAMES, Bo, Administrator, Socorro General Hospital, Socorro, NM, p. A418

BEANE, Jeff, Director Human Resources, Roane General Hospital, Spencer, WV, p. A681

BEAR, Lawrence P., Administrator and Chief Executive Officer, Jersey Community Hospital, Jerseyville, IL, p. A186

BEARB, April, Administrator, Jennings Senior Care Hospital, Jennings, LA, p. A269

BEARD, Bradley, President, Fairview Southdale Hospital, Edina, MN, p. A332

BEARD, Cindy, Assistant Administrator, Baptist Memorial Hospital for Women, Memphis, TN, p. A574

BEARD, Dewaine, Chief Information Officer, Veterans Affairs Pittsburgh Healthcare System, Pittsburgh, PA, p. A538

BEARD, Edward L., MSN Senior Vice President, Patient Care Services & CNO, Catawba Valley Medical Center, Hickory, NC, p. A454

BEARD, Gerald C., Chief Operating Officer, Healthmark Regional Medical Center, DeFuniak Springs, FL, p. A122

BEARD, Joan, Chief Nursing Officer, Northwest Florida Community Hospital, Chipley, FL, p. A120

BEARD, Pat, Director Human Resources, Clinton County Hospital, Albany, KY, p. A248

BEARD, Raleigh, Chief Fiscal Services, Edward Hines, Jr. Veterans Affairs Hospital, Hines, IL, p. A185

BEARD, Rhonda
Director Human Resources, Palestine Regional Medical Center, Palestine, TX, p. A625
Director Human Resources, Palestine Regional Medical Center–East, Palestine, TX, p. A626

BEARD, Scott, M.D. Chief of Staff, Nevada Regional Medical Center, Nevada, MO, p. A367

BEASLEY, Christina, Director Human Resources, Carlsbad Medical Center, Carlsbad, NM, p. A415

BEASLEY, Craig, M.D. Chief of Staff and Medical Officer, Throckmorton County Memorial Hospital, Throckmorton, TX, p. A637

BEASLEY, Jared, Interim President, Indiana University Health Starke Hospital, Knox, IN, p. A207

BEASLEY, Leslie, Director Human Resources, Temple Community Hospital, Los Angeles, CA, p. A72

BEASLEY, Ruth, Director Human Resources, Vanderbilt Stallworth Rehabilitation Hospital, Nashville, TN, p. A577

BEASLEY, Tareka, Director Human Resources, RiverWoods Behavioral Health System, Riverdale, GA, p. A158

BEATTIE, Kathryn, M.D. Senior Vice President and Chief Medical Officer, UW Medicine/Valley Medical Center, Renton, WA, p. A670

BEATTIE, Mac, Computer Network Specialist, Deer's Head Hospital Center, Salisbury, MD, p. A294

BEATTY, Alan, Vice President Human Resources, Shore Medical Center, Somers Point, NJ, p. A410

BEATTY, Ann, Director Human Resources, Fairview Hospital, Cleveland, OH, p. A476

BEATTY, James R., Chief Operating Officer, Rapides Regional Medical Center, Alexandria, LA, p. A262

BEATTY, John, Vice President Human Resources, Barnes–Jewish Hospital, Saint Louis, MO, p. A369

BEATTY, Kemp, Director Information Management, Carlisle Regional Medical Center, Carlisle, PA, p. A522

BEATTY, Talia, Director Human Resources, Sunbury Community Hospital and Outpatient Center, Sunbury, PA, p. A542

BEATY, Holly, Chief Financial Officer, South Central Kansas Medical Center, Arkansas City, KS, p. A231

BEATY, Ralph E.
Chief Executive Officer, Great River Medical Center, Blytheville, AR, p. A41
Chief Executive Officer, South Mississippi County Regional Medical Center, Osceola, AR, p. A48

BEATY, Ryan D., President and Chief Executive Officer, Citrus Memorial Health System, Inverness, FL, p. A126

BEAUBIEN, Troy, Director Information Services, Manatee Memorial Hospital, Bradenton, FL, p. A119

BEAUDOIN, Dale, Vice President Human Resources, Lewis–Gale Medical Center, Salem, VA, p. A661

BEAUDOIN, Paul, Senior Vice President Finance and Chief Financial Officer, Kent County Memorial Hospital, Warwick, RI, p. A547

BEAUDRY, Lisa, M.P.H. Director, Patient Care, Baystate Mary Lane Hospital, Ware, MA, p. A306

BEAULAC, Gary, Chief Operating Officer, Henry Ford Macomb Hospitals, Clinton Township, MI, p. A311

BEAULIEU, Mary Lou, Director Human Resources and Compliance Officer, Northwestern Medical Center, Saint Albans, VT, p. A650

BEAULIEU, Sue, Chief Nurse Executive, Massena Memorial Hospital, Massena, NY, p. A429

BEAUPRE, Paul, M.D., Chief Executive Officer, Good Samaritan Hospital, San Jose, CA, p. A87

BEAUREGARD, Jodi, Chief Executive Officer, Martin General Hospital, Williamston, NC, p. A462

BEAUVAIS, Richard E., Ph.D., Chief Executive Officer, Wellspring Foundation, Bethlehem, CT, p. A108

BEAVER, Michael D., President, St. Anthony Hospital, Oklahoma City, OK, p. A504

BEAVER, Patrick, R.N. Vice President Patient Care and Chief Nursing Officer, East Liverpool City Hospital, East Liverpool, OH, p. A481

BEAVER, Randy, Chief Information Officer, Palo Alto County Health System, Emmetsburg, IA, p. A221

BEAZLEY, Gary, Coordinator Information Systems, Baylor Medical Center at Waxahachie, Waxahachie, TX, p. A640

BEBEE, Beldia, Acting Chief Financial Officer, Huey P. Long Medical Center, Pineville, LA, p. A277

BEBOW, Gary, FACHE, Administrator and Chief Executive Officer, White River Medical Center, Batesville, AR, p. A41

BECHTLE, Mavis, MSN Vice President and Chief Nursing Officer, MetroHealth Medical Center, Cleveland, OH, p. A476

BECK, Allan, Chief Executive Officer, Baylor Orthopedic and Spine Hospital at Arlington, Arlington, TX, p. A583

BECK, Ann, Vice President Finance, Carson Tahoe Regional Healthcare, Carson City, NV, p. A391

BECK, David, Chief Operating Officer and Director Human Resources, Lane Regional Medical Center, Zachary, LA, p. A280

BECK, Gary E., Administrator, Sevier Valley Medical Center, Richfield, UT, p. A646

BECK, Howard, M.D. Chief of Staff, Grace Medical Center, Lubbock, TX, p. A620

BECK, J. Christopher, D.O. President Medical Staff, Aspen Valley Hospital District, Aspen, CO, p. A97

BECK, J. Robert, M.D. Chief Medical Officer, Fox Chase Cancer Center–American Oncologic Hospital, Philadelphia, PA, p. A534

BECK, Joyce
Interim Chief Executive Officer, St. Vincent General Hospital District, Leadville, CO, p. A103
Administrator, Thayer County Health Services, Hebron, NE, p. A384

BECK, Walter G., Chief Executive Officer, Modoc Medical Center, Alturas, CA, p. A52

BECK, Warren E., Associate Vice Chancellor Health Affairs and Senior Vice President Finance, Vanderbilt Hospital and Clinics, Nashville, TN, p. A577

BECKER, Bernard H., Vice President and Chief Human Resources Officer, Stormont–Vail HealthCare, Topeka, KS, p. A245

BECKER, Bruce, M.D. Chief Medical Officer, Medical Center Health System, Odessa, TX, p. A625

BECKER, Bryan, Interim Chief Executive Officer, University of Illinois Hospital & Health Sciences System, Chicago, IL, p. A180

BECKER, Cindy, Vice President and Chief Operating Officer, Highland Hospital of Rochester, Rochester, NY, p. A441

BECKER, Eric, Chief Executive Officer, San Angelo Community Medical Center, San Angelo, TX, p. A630

BECKER, Frank
Chief Financial Officer, Lourdes Counseling Center, Richland, WA, p. A670
Chief Financial Officer, Lourdes Medical Center, Pasco, WA, p. A669

BECKER, Kathleen R., JD, President, SSM St. Mary's Health Center, Saint Louis, MO, p. A370

BECKER, Kathy, Chief Nursing Officer, Aurora Sheboygan Memorial Medical Center, Sheboygan, WI, p. A696

BECKER, Kelly, Administrative Coordinator Human Resources, Select Specialty Hospital–Beech Grove, Indianapolis, IN, p. A206

BECKER, Kristine F., R.N. Interim Chief Nursing Officer/Director of Cardiac Nursing and Nursing Resources, Overlake Hospital Medical Center, Bellevue, WA, p. A664

BECKER, Michael, R.N. Chief Nursing Officer and Associate Executive Director, Penn Presbyterian Medical Center, Philadelphia, PA, p. A536

BECKER, Preston, Chief Financial Officer, Kewanee Hospital, Kewanee, IL, p. A186

BECKER, Ralph W., Chief Financial Officer, MidState Medical Center, Meriden, CT, p. A109

BECKER, Richard B., M.D., President, Chief Executive Officer and Interim Chief Medical Officer, Brooklyn Hospital Center,, NY, p. A431

BECKES, Hap, Director Information Systems, Sullivan County Community Hospital, Sullivan, IN, p. A213

BECKETT, Jason, Director Information Services, San Dimas Community Hospital, San Dimas, CA, p. A86

BECKHAM, Steve, Director Human Resources, Magee General Hospital, Magee, MS, p. A350

BECKMANN, Enrique, Ph.D., President and Chief Executive Officer, MetroSouth Medical Center, Blue Island, IL, p. A174

BECKMANN, Gregory, Finance Controller, Avera Creighton Hospital, Creighton, NE, p. A383

BECKNER, Jana, Director Human Resources, LewisGale Hospital at Pulaski, Pulaski, VA, p. A659

BECKSTRAND, James E.
Administrator, Delta Community Medical Center, Delta, UT, p. A643
Administrator, Fillmore Community Medical Center, Fillmore, UT, p. A643

BECKSVOORT, Jennifer F., Senior Human Resource Business Partner, Spectrum Health Zeeland Community Hospital, Zeeland, MI, p. A327

BEDARD, Lori, Chief Executive Officer, HEALTHSOUTH Rehabilitation Hospital of Spring Hill, Brooksville, FL, p. A120

BEDDOE, Chris, Chief Executive Officer, Sabine Medical Center, Many, LA, p. A273

BEDFORD, Jeff, Executive Vice President and Chief Financial Officer, Woman's Hospital, Flowood, MS, p. A346

BEDFORD, Tim, Chief Executive Officer, Emerald Coast Behavioral Hospital, Panama City, FL, p. A136

BEDGER, Kathy, Chief Nursing Officer, Clearfield Hospital, Clearfield, PA, p. A522

BEDINGFIELD, Lance, Director Information Services, Dixie Regional Medical Center, Saint George, UT, p. A646

BEDNAREK, Robert J., President and Chief Executive Officer, Transylvania Regional Hospital, Brevard, NC, p. A448

BEDWAY, Marianna, R.N. Senior Vice President and Chief Nursing Officer, Stafford Hospital, Stafford, VA, p. A661

BEDZYK, J. Paul, Deputy Director Administration, Elmira Psychiatric Center, Elmira, NY, p. A425

BEEBY, Lori, Director Information Systems, Community Hospital, McCook, NE, p. A386

BEECHLER, Jane, Director Healthcare Information Systems, Wyoming County Community Hospital, Warsaw, NY, p. A445

BEED, Donna E., Division Chief Information Management, Tripler Army Medical Center, Honolulu, HI, p. A165

BEEDLE, Chester, Chief Financial Officer, Kern Valley Healthcare District, Lake Isabella, CA, p. A66

BEEDY, Scott, Chief Financial Officer, Hansford Hospital, Spearman, TX, p. A634

BEEG, Gregg, Chief Financial Officer, McLaren Central Michigan, Mount Pleasant, MI, p. A320

BEEHLER, Darryl, D.O. Chief of Staff, St. Joseph's Area Health Services, Park Rapids, MN, p. A338

BEEMAN, Michael, Chief Financial Officer, Deckerville Community Hospital, Deckerville, MI, p. A311

BEEMAN, Thomas E., FACHE, President and Chief Executive Officer, Lancaster General Health, Lancaster, PA, p. A528

BEENE, Nikia, Assistant Chief Executive Officer, Ponca City Medical Center, Ponca City, OK, p. A505

BEENE, Renee, Manager Human Resources, Lakeside Women's Hospital, Oklahoma City, OK, p. A503

BEER, Ronald R., Chief Executive Officer, Berwick Hospital Center, Berwick, PA, p. A520

BEERY, Kristin, Executive Assistant and Director Human Resources, Rangely District Hospital, Rangely, CO, p. A105

BEESON, John C., M.D. Vice President Medical Affairs, St. Mary's Hospital and Medical Center, Grand Junction, CO, p. A102

BEGALSKE, Kathy, Chief Nursing Officer, Palmer Lutheran Health Center, West Union, IA, p. A230

BEGGANE, Thomas, Manager Human Resources, LAC–Olive View–UCLA Medical Center,, CA, p. A70

BEGGS, Shaun, Chief Executive Officer, Orthopedic Hospital, Oklahoma City, OK, p. A504

BEGIN, James, Director Information Technology, Golden Valley Memorial Healthcare, Clinton, MO, p. A359

BEGLEY, Bruce D., Executive Director, Methodist Hospital, Henderson, KY, p. A252

BEGUIN, Shelley, Director Human Resources, Gordon Memorial Hospital, Gordon, NE, p. A384

BEHAR, Robert, M.D., Chief Executive Officer, North Cypress Medical Center, Cypress, TX, p. A594

BEHM, Anthony, D.O. Chief of Staff, Erie Veterans Affairs Medical Center, Erie, PA, p. A525

BEHM, Richard, Director Information Technology, Camden County Health Services Center, Blackwood, NJ, p. A401

BEHNE, Carl P., Administrator and Chief Executive Officer, Greene County Medical Center, Jefferson, IA, p. A223

BEHNER, Bruce M., Chief Operating Officer, Knox Community Hospital, Mount Vernon, OH, p. A487

BEHNKEN, Nick, Supervisor Information Technology, Red Bud Regional Hospital, Red Bud, IL, p. A193

BEHRENDT, William, Ph.D. Vice President Human Resources, University of Texas Southwestern Medical Center, Dallas, TX, p. A598

BEHRENS, Karen, Director Technology Services, Perry Memorial Hospital, Princeton, IL, p. A192

BEIDELSCHIES, Sandra, MSN Chief Nursing Officer, Knox Community Hospital, Mount Vernon, OH, p. A487

BEIERMAN, Jennifer, Director Human Resources, Boone County Health Center, Albion, NE, p. A381

BEILER, Jeffrey, Associate Director, Philadephia Veterans Affairs Medical Center, Philadelphia, PA, p. A536

BEINDIT, Dawn, Director Work Life Services, St. John River District Hospital, East China, MI, p. A313

BEIRNE, Frank T.
Senior Vice President and Area Manager, Kaiser Permanente Redwood City Medical Center, Redwood City, CA, p. A82
Senior Vice President and Area Manager, Kaiser Permanente South San Francisco, South San Francisco, CA, p. A91

BEISSEL, Debbie, Administrator, Surgical Institute of Reading, Wyomissing, PA, p. A545

BEISTLINE, John, Assistant Chief Fiscal, Lebanon Veterans Affairs Medical Center, Lebanon, PA, p. A529

BEISWENGER, Joel, Chief Executive Officer, Tri–County Hospital, Wadena, MN, p. A342

BEITCHER, Bob, Interim Chief Executive Officer, Motion Picture and Television Fund Hospital and Residential Services,, CA, p. A70

BEITER, Amy, M.D., President and Chief Executive Officer, Carondelet St. Mary's Hospital, Tucson, AZ, p. A38

BEITER, Donna M., MSN, Director, Veterans Affairs Greater Los Angeles Healthcare System, Los Angeles, CA, p. A72

BEITING, Mark, Vice President Human Resources, Alta Bates Summit Medical Center – Summit Campus, Oakland, CA, p. A77

BEITZEL, Earl, Vice President Finance, Mercy Hospital, Coon Rapids, MN, p. A330

BEITZEL, Mark, Director Information Systems, Advocate Lutheran General Hospital, Park Ridge, IL, p. A191

BEJARINO, Paul, M.D. Chief of Staff, Oro Valley Hospital, Oro Valley, AZ, p. A33

BEKES, Carolyn, M.D. Chief Medical Officer, Cooper Health System, Camden, NJ, p. A402

BEKKER, Victor, Chief Financial Officer, Lincoln Medical and Mental Health Center,, NY, p. A433

BELAIR, Norman, Chief Financial Officer and Vice President Finance, Southern Maine Medical Center, Biddeford, ME, p. A282

BELBECK, Michael, President and Chief Administrative Officer, Methodist Medical Center of Oak Ridge, Oak Ridge, TN, p. A578

BELCHER, Debbie, Director Human Resources, HEALTHSOUTH Rehabilitation Hospital of Austin, Austin, TX, p. A585

BELCHER, Kenneth H.
President and Chief Executive Officer, Roger Williams Medical Center, Providence, RI, p. A547
President and Chief Executive Officer, St. Joseph Health Services of Rhode Island, North Providence, RI, p. A546

BELDECOS, Athena, M.D. Medical Director, Kindred Hospital–Charleston, Mt. Pleasant, SC, p. A554

BELENY, Charles, D.O. Chief of Staff, Jonathan M. Wainwright Memorial Veterans Affairs Medical Center, Walla Walla, WA, p. A674

BELETE, Frey, Controller, Boulder City Hospital, Boulder City, NV, p. A391

BELGARDE, Donna, Human Resources Specialist, Public Health Service Indian Hospital – Quentin N. Burdick Memorial Health Facility, Belcourt, ND, p. A465

BELHASEN, F. K., M.D. Medical Director, Paul B. Hall Regional Medical Center, Paintsville, KY, p. A259

BELKOSKI, David, Executive Vice President and Chief Financial Officer, University Hospital, Augusta, GA, p. A148

BELL, Brian, Associate Administrator and Chief Operating Officer, National Park Medical Center, Hot Springs, AR, p. A45

BELL, Cindy, Director Finance, Willow Crest Hospital, Miami, OK, p. A501

BELL, David C., Chief Executive Officer, Havenwyck Hospital, Auburn Hills, MI, p. A308

BELL, Gordon, M.D. Chief of Staff, Frances Mahon Deaconess Hospital, Glasgow, MT, p. A376

BELL, Heath
Chief Information Officer, Kishwaukee Hospital, DeKalb, IL, p. A180
Chief Information Officer, Valley West Hospital, Sandwich, IL, p. A194

BELL, Howard, M.D. Chief of Staff, Mercy Health – Clermont Hospital, Batavia, OH, p. A471

BELL, Keith, M.D. Chief of Staff, Conway Regional Medical Center, Conway, AR, p. A42

BELL, Kristen, Director Human Resources, UPMC Mercy, Pittsburgh, PA, p. A538

BELL, Madeline, Executive Vice President and Chief Operating Officer, Children's Hospital of Philadelphia, Philadelphia, PA, p. A534

BELL, Pamela, R.N., President and Chief Executive Officer, Presence Holy Family Medical Center, Des Plaines, IL, p. A181

BELL, Randall C., M.D. Medical Director, LifeCare Hospitals of San Antonio, San Antonio, TX, p. A631

BELL, Roderick, Chief Financial Officer, College Hospital, Cerritos, CA, p. A56

BELL, Rodric, M.D. Medical Director, HEALTHSOUTH Tustin Rehabilitation Hospital, Tustin, CA, p. A93

BELL, Jr., Sammie, Chief Financial Officer, Tallahatchie General Hospital, Charleston, MS, p. A345

BELL, Sonja, Coordinator Human Resources, Sedgwick County Health Center, Julesburg, CO, p. A102

BELL, Stuart, M.D. Vice President Medical Affairs, MedStar Union Memorial Hospital, Baltimore, MD, p. A288

BELL, Talana, Chief Financial Officer, Flowers Hospital, Dothan, AL, p. A19

BELL, Tammie, Director Human Resources, Volunteer Community Hospital, Martin, TN, p. A573

BELL, Tanya, Public Information Officer, Penrose–St. Francis Health Services, Colorado Springs, CO, p. A98

BELL, Thomas, Deputy Commander Administration, Keller Army Community Hospital, West Point, NY, p. A446

BELL, W. Scot, M.D. Chief Medical Officer, Rush Foundation Hospital, Meridian, MS, p. A351

BELLAMY, Cameron, CIS Manager, Person Memorial Hospital, Roxboro, NC, p. A460

BELLAND, Patrick, Vice President Operations, Unity Hospital, Fridley, MN, p. A332

BELLEAU, Christopher, M.D. Medical Director, Sage Rehabilitation Hospital, Baton Rouge, LA, p. A264

BELLEAU, Donella, Director Human Resources, Graham County Hospital, Hill City, KS, p. A235

BELLENFANT, William L., Chief Financial Officer, Mother Frances Hospital – Jacksonville, Jacksonville, TX, p. A615

BELLER, Robert H., FACHE, Director, Clement J. Zablocki Veterans Affairs Medical Center, Milwaukee, WI, p. A692

BELLEY, Maureen, Director Information Services, Lowell General Hospital, Lowell, MA, p. A301

BELMONT, James, Associate Director, Northern Arizona Veterans Affairs Health Care System, Prescott, AZ, p. A36

BELMONT, Terry A., Chief Executive Officer, University of California, Irvine Healthcare, Orange, CA, p. A78

BELSKI, Krystyna, M.D. Chief of Staff, Oak Valley Hospital District, Oakdale, CA, p. A77

BELT, Katrina, Chief Financial Officer, Baptist Medical Center East, Montgomery, AL, p. A23

BELTRAN, Grace, Director Human Resources, Foundation Surgical Hospital of El Paso, El Paso, TX, p. A601

BELTRAN, Greg, Director Information Technology, Berlin Memorial Hospital, Berlin, WI, p. A684

BELTZ, John, Chief Financial Officer, Valley General Hospital, Monroe, WA, p. A668

BELYEU, Peggy, Controller, Vanderbilt Stallworth Rehabilitation Hospital, Nashville, TN, p. A577

BELZER, Michael, M.D. Medical Director, Hennepin County Medical Center, Minneapolis, MN, p. A336

BEMENT, Douglas J., Chief Financial Officer, Kosciusko Community Hospital, Warsaw, IN, p. A214

BEN, Gary, Administrator, Choctaw Health Center, Philadelphia, MS, p. A352

BENAVIDES, Christina, Director Employee Services, Otto Kaiser Memorial Hospital, Kenedy, TX, p. A616

BENCOMO, Dionisio, Chief Executive Officer, Select Specialty Hospital–Miami, Miami, FL, p. A132

BENDER, Brad, M.D. Chief of Staff, Malcom Randall Veterans Affairs Medical Center, Gainesville, FL, p. A124

BENDER, Janette, Chief Financial Officer, Arkansas Valley Regional Medical Center, La Junta, CO, p. A103

BENDER, Ron, Chief Executive Officer, Clay County Medical Center, Clay Center, KS, p. A232

BENDER, Roxanna, Interim Administrator, Bryce Hospital, Tuscaloosa, AL, p. A25

BENDER, Steve, Chief Financial Officer, Wuesthoff Medical Center – Melbourne, Melbourne, FL, p. A130

BENDINELLI, Emily, Interim Director of Nurses, Ashley County Medical Center, Crossett, AR, p. A42

BENEDI, Hector, Coordinator Information Systems, Psychiatric Institute of Washington, Washington, DC, p. A117

BENEDICT, Eva, President and Chief Executive Officer, Jones Memorial Hospital, Wellsville, NY, p. A445

BENEDICT, Joy M., Director Human Resources, Baptist Health Richmond, Richmond, KY, p. A260

BENEDUM, Mark, Chief Executive Officer, Highline Medical Center, Burien, WA, p. A665

BENEFIELD, Marlene, Director Human Resources, Cherokee Medical Center, Centre, AL, p. A18

BENFIELD, Ronald K., Chief Operating Officer, Adventist Medical Center–Portland, Portland, OR, p. A515

BENGE, Eddie, M.D. Vice President Medical Staff Affairs, Presbyterian Kaseman Hospital, Albuquerque, NM, p. A415

BENGSTON, Jennifer, M.D. Chief Medical Officer, Valley County Health System, Ord, NE, p. A388

BENGTSON, Paul R., Chief Executive Officer, Northeastern Vermont Regional Hospital, Saint Johnsbury, VT, p. A650

BENICH, Mike, Controller, Marymount Hospital, Garfield Heights, OH, p. A482

BENINK, Eric, M.D. Vice President and Chief Medical Officer, OSF Saint Anthony Medical Center, Rockford, IL, p. A193

BENJAMIN, Christian, MC, Commander, Mike O'Callaghan Federal Hospital, Nellis AFB, NV, p. A394

BENJAMIN, Sunny J., Chief Human Resources Officer, Oklahoma State University Medical Center, Tulsa, OK, p. A508

BENJAMIN, Susan, Chief Financial Officer, Lake View Memorial Hospital, Two Harbors, MN, p. A342

BENNER, Brenda, Director Human Resources, HEALTHSOUTH Rehabilitation Hospital of Sarasota, Sarasota, FL, p. A139

BENNER, Melvin J., Assistant Administrator Finance, Kaiser Permanente Anaheim Medical Center, Anaheim, CA, p. A52

BENNETT, Anthony, M.D. Chief Clinical Affairs, Baptist Health Medical Center–Little Rock, Little Rock, AR, p. A46

BENNETT, Bart, Chief Financial Officer, Springbrook Behavioral Health System, Travelers Rest, SC, p. A556

BENNETT, Charlotte, Vice President Human Resources, West Virginia University Hospitals, Morgantown, WV, p. A679

BENNETT, Christin, Administrator, Oceans Behavioral Hospital of Lake Charles, Lake Charles, LA, p. A272

BENNETT, Dan, Director Operations, Waldo County General Hospital, Belfast, ME, p. A281

BENNETT, Darnell, Director Finance, Horizon Specialty Hospital, Las Vegas, NV, p. A393

BENNETT, Deborah, D.O. Chief Medical Officer, Kingman Regional Medical Center, Kingman, AZ, p. A32

BENNETT, E. Kyle, Executive Vice President, Memorial Hospital and Health Care Center, Jasper, IN, p. A207

BENNETT, Edwin, Controller, Turning Point Hospital, Moultrie, GA, p. A158

BENNETT, Elizabeth, Director of Nursing, Doctor's Hospital of Deer Creek, Leesville, LA, p. A272

BENNETT, Ellie, Chief Operating Officer, Riverside County Regional Medical Center, Moreno Valley, CA, p. A75

BENNETT, Fay, Director Human Resources, Guadalupe Regional Medical Center, Seguin, TX, p. A633

BENNETT, James B., M.D. Chief of Staff, Texas Orthopedic Hospital, Houston, TX, p. A612

BENNETT, Joan, Senior Vice President Human Resources, Cambridge Health Alliance, Cambridge, MA, p. A299

BENNETT, Karen A., Vice President Human Resources and Compliance, Children's Hospital of Richmond at VCU–Brook Road Campus, Richmond, VA, p. A660

BENNETT, Kay
Vice President Human Resources, Baptist Medical Center East, Montgomery, AL, p. A23
System Director Human Resources, Baptist Medical Center South, Montgomery, AL, p. A23

BENNETT, Kimberly, Director Patient Care, Dubuis Hospital of Alexandria, Alexandria, LA, p. A262

BENNETT, Kris, Chief Operating Officer, Lutheran Hospital, Cleveland, OH, p. A476

BENNETT, Laurie, Director Human Resources, Sarasota Memorial Hospital, Sarasota, FL, p. A139

BENNETT, Lee W., Chief Financial Officer, Sitka Community Hospital, Sitka, AK, p. A29

BENNETT, Leo, M.D. Deputy Commander Clinical Services, Bassett Army Community Hospital, Fort Wainwright, AK, p. A28

BENNETT, Lisa, Chief Financial Officer, Waverly Health Center, Waverly, IA, p. A229

BENNETT, Melissa, R.N. Chief Nursing Officer, Oak Hill Hospital, Brooksville, FL, p. A120

BENNETT, Randall, Assistant Administrator, Uintah Basin Medical Center, Roosevelt, UT, p. A646

BENNETT, Richard G., M.D., President, Johns Hopkins Bayview Medical Center, Baltimore, MD, p. A287

BENNETT, Richard I., Senior Vice President and Chief Financial Officer, Delaware County Memorial Hospital, Drexel Hill, PA, p. A524

BENNETT, Rick, Administrator, St. James Behavioral Health Hospital, Gonzales, LA, p. A267

BENNETT, Ron, Chief Financial Officer, Abilene Regional Medical Center, Abilene, TX, p. A581

BENNETT, Sharon, Manager Information Systems, Cobre Valley Regional Medical Center, Globe, AZ, p. A32

BENNETT, Sheila, R.N. Vice President & Chief Nursing Officer, Floyd Medical Center, Rome, GA, p. A159

BENNETT, Todd, Vice President, Carolinas Rehabilitation, Charlotte, NC, p. A449

BENNETT, Tony N., Chief Executive Officer, HEALTHSOUTH Emerald Coast Rehabilitation Hospital, Panama City, FL, p. A136

BENNETT, Wayne, Chief Financial Officer, Franklin Memorial Hospital, Farmington, ME, p. A283

BENNETT, William, Chief Financial Officer, RiverView Health, Crookston, MN, p. A331

BENNING, Robert J., Chief Executive Officer, Ridgeview Psychiatric Hospital and Center, Oak Ridge, TN, p. A578

BENNINGFIELD–CRELIA, Denise, Director, Nursing Operations, New Braunfels Regional Rehabilitation Hospital, New Braunfels, TX, p. A624

BENOIT, Paul, Associate Administrator, Central Louisiana State Hospital, Pineville, LA, p. A277

BENOIT, Rebecca, R.N. Chief Nursing Officer, Lafayette General Medical Center, Lafayette, LA, p. A271

BENOIT, Rebecca, Chief Operating Officer, OU Medical Center, Oklahoma City, OK, p. A504

BENSING, Gary, Vice President Human Resources, University of Louisville Hospital, Louisville, KY, p. A256

BENSON, Annie, Chief Executive Officer, Southeast Arizona Medical Center, Douglas, AZ, p. A31

BENSON, Cheryl, Chief Operating Officer, Wernersville State Hospital, Wernersville, PA, p. A543

BENSON, Dale, Vice President Human Resources, Essentia Health St. Joseph's Medical Center, Brainerd, MN, p. A329

BENSON, Eric, Vice President Human Resources, Sarah Bush Lincoln Health Center, Mattoon, IL, p. A188

BENSON, Lateka, Manager Health Information, Springbrook Behavioral Health System, Travelers Rest, SC, p. A556

BENSON, Sheena, Director Human Resources, Havasu Regional Medical Center, Lake Havasu City, AZ, p. A32

BENTLEY, Brian S., Chief Executive Officer, Gila Regional Medical Center, Silver City, NM, p. A418

BENTLEY, Polly, Chief Information Officer, Summers County ARH Hospital, Hinton, WV, p. A677

BENTLEY, Scott, Chief Financial Officer, The Woman's Hospital of Texas, Houston, TX, p. A613

BENTON, Dennis C., Administrator and Executive Director, Kaiser Permanente Panorama City Medical Center,, CA, p. A69

BENTON, Jamie, M.D. Chief of Staff, Grimes St. Joseph Health Center, Navasota, TX, p. A624

BENTON, Tony, Chief Executive Officer, Franklin Woods Community Hospital, Johnson City, TN, p. A571

BENTZ, Douglas E., Chief Executive Officer, Roane General Hospital, Spencer, WV, p. A681

BENWARE, Joel, Chief Information Officer, Alice Hyde Medical Center, Malone, NY, p. A429

BENZ, Betsy, R.N. Chief Nursing Officer, Aurora Medical Center – Manitowoc County, Two Rivers, WI, p. A698

BENZ, Blake, Director Management Information Systems, St. Joseph Hospital, Bethpage, NY, p. A421

BENZ Jr., Edward J., M.D., President and Chief Executive Officer, Dana–Farber Cancer Institute, Boston, MA, p. A296

BENZEL, Cindy, Manager Human Resources, Sanford Vermillion Medical Center, Vermillion, SD, p. A563

BEPLER, Gerold, Ph.D., President and Chief Executive Officer, Karmanos Cancer Center, Detroit, MI, p. A312

BEPPLER, Brian, Controller, Kindred Hospital–Wyoming Valley, Wilkes Barre, PA, p. A544

BERARD, Celse A., President, Riverview Hospital Association, Wisconsin Rapids, WI, p. A700

BERARDI, Paula, Manager Human Resources, Bournewood Health Systems, Brookline, MA, p. A298

BERCHER, Richard, M.D. Chief Medical Officer, Paris Regional Medical Center, Paris, TX, p. A626

BERCI, Haya, Executive Director of Nursing, Joyce Eisenberg–Keefer Medical Center, Reseda, CA, p. A82

BERDISCHEWSKY, Myron, M.D. Chief Medical Officer, Providence Saint Joseph Medical Center, Burbank, CA, p. A55

BERENS, Jeff, MS Chief Nursing Officer, Sanford Vermillion Medical Center, Vermillion, SD, p. A563

BERENZWEIG, Harold, M.D. Vice President Medical and Information Management, Texas Health Harris Methodist Hospital Fort Worth, Fort Worth, TX, p. A604

BERETTA, Dante, M.D. Chief of Staff, CentraCare Health–Melrose, Melrose, MN, p. A335

BERG, Gary L., D.O. Chief Medical Officer, St. John Macomb–Oakland Hospital, Warren, MI, p. A326

BERG, James A., Senior Vice President and Chief Quality Officer, Texas Health Presbyterian Hospital Dallas, Dallas, TX, p. A597

BERG, Jon, M.D. Chief of Staff, Sanford Northwood Deaconess Health Center, Northwood, ND, p. A468

BERGE, Ron, Executive Vice President and Chief Operating Officer, National Jewish Health, Denver, CO, p. A99

BERGEAUX, Scott, M.D. Chief Medical Staff, Abrom Kaplan Memorial Hospital, Kaplan, LA, p. A269

BERGEMANN, John, Director Human Resources, Crouse Hospital, Syracuse, NY, p. A443

BERGEN, Sharon A., Chief Operating Officer, Belmont Center for Comprehensive Treatment, Philadelphia, PA, p. A534

BERGENFELD, Joel
Chief Executive Officer, Hemet Valley Medical Center, Hemet, CA, p. A64
Chief Executive Officer, Menifee Valley Medical Center, Sun City, CA, p. A92

BERGER, George, Controller, HEALTHSOUTH Rehabilitation Hospital of Altoona, Altoona, PA, p. A519

BERGER, Jeffrey, M.D. Chief Medical Officer, Brighton Center for Recovery, Brighton, MI, p. A309

BERGERON, Pierre, Director Information Services, Wellington Regional Medical Center, West Palm Beach, FL, p. A144

BERGERSON, Melissa, R.N. Vice President Patient Care Services, Black River Memorial Hospital, Black River Falls, WI, p. A684

BERGH, Roger, Director Human Resources, Helen Newberry Joy Hospital, Newberry, MI, p. A321

BERGHERM, Bruce, Chief Executive Officer, Florida Hospital North Pinellas, Tarpon Springs, FL, p. A142

BERGHOFER, Stephen, M.D. Chief Medical Officer, St. Vincent Mercy Hospital, Elwood, IN, p. A201

BERGLIN, Sally L., Chief Executive Officer, Bronson LakeView Hospital, Paw Paw, MI, p. A321

BERGLING, Richard Q., Chief Executive Officer, Gove County Medical Center, Quinter, KS, p. A243

BERGMAN, Chris, Chief Financial Officer, Christ Hospital, Cincinnati, OH, p. A474

BERGMAN, Jim, Director Human Resources, Northeast Regional Medical Center, Kirksville, MO, p. A364

BERGMANN, Dan, M.D. Chief Medical Officer, Barnes–Jewish St. Peters Hospital, Saint Peters, MO, p. A371

BERGMANN, Peter U., President and Chief Executive Officer, Sisters of Charity Hospital of Buffalo, Buffalo, NY, p. A423

BERGSENG, John H., D.O. Vice President Medical Affairs, Glencoe Regional Health Services, Glencoe, MN, p. A332

BERKELEY, Larry L., Associate Director, Clement J. Zablocki Veterans Affairs Medical Center, Milwaukee, WI, p. A692

BERKHOUSE, Steve, Chief Financial Officer, Hocking Valley Community Hospital, Logan, OH, p. A484

BERKOWITZ, David J., Vice President and Chief Operating Officer, Palisades Medical Center, North Bergen, NJ, p. A408

BERKRAM, Treasure, Chief Financial Officer, Northern Rockies Medical Center, Cut Bank, MT, p. A375

BERLINGHOFF, Kathleen, Director Human Resources, Sharon Hospital, Sharon, CT, p. A111

BERLOT, Alvin, M.D. Medical Director, Bucktail Medical Center, Renovo, PA, p. A540

BERLOWITZ, Dan, Acting Chief of Staff, Edith Nourse Rogers Memorial Veterans Hospital, Bedford, MA, p. A295

BERLUCCHI, Scott A., FACHE, President and Chief Executive Officer, Auburn Community Hospital, Auburn, NY, p. A420

BERMAN, Manuel S., Administrator and Chief Operating Officer, Tuality Healthcare, Hillsboro, OR, p. A513

BERMUDEZ, Armand, M.D. Medical Director, Select Specialty Hospital–Zanesville, Zanesville, OH, p. A494

BERNAL, Leroy, Chief Operating Officer, Victory Medical Center – San Antonio, San Antonio, TX, p. A632

BERNARD, David, M.D. Chief Medical Officer, Beth Israel Medical Center, New York, NY, p. A430

BERNARD, Donald P., Chief Financial Officer, Kaiser Permanente Fontana Medical Center, Fontana, CA, p. A60

BERNARD, Lorrie, Manager Patient Accounts and Information Systems, Athol Memorial Hospital, Athol, MA, p. A295

BERNARD, Peter J., Chief Executive Officer, Bon Secours St. Francis Medical Center, Midlothian, VA, p. A657

BERNARD, Traci, President, Texas Health Harris Methodist Hospital Southlake, Southlake, TX, p. A634

BERNARDO, Maria, M.D. Chief of Staff, Bullock County Hospital, Union Springs, AL, p. A26

BERNATIS, Terry D., Director Human Resources, Community HealthCare System, Onaga, KS, p. A241

BERNDT, Julia L., Chief Financial Officer, Logansport Memorial Hospital, Logansport, IN, p. A209

BERNER, Tom, Vice President and Chief Financial Officer, Bristol Bay Area Health Corporation, Dillingham, AK, p. A27

BERNEY, Bernadette, Director Human Resources, Pullman Regional Hospital, Pullman, WA, p. A669

BERNICK, Michael, Vice President Finance, Clarity Child Guidance Center, San Antonio, TX, p. A631

BERNINI, A. Susan, Chief Operating Officer, Einstein Medical Center Philadelphia, Philadelphia, PA, p. A534

BERNS, Erin, Director Human Resources, Veterans Memorial Hospital, Waukon, IA, p. A229

BERNSTEIN, Lee
Regional Executive Vice President and Chief Operating Officer, SSM DePaul Health Center, Bridgeton, MO, p. A357
Interim President, SSM St. Clare Health Center, Fenton, MO, p. A360
Regional Executive Vice President and Chief Operating Officer, SSM St. Joseph Health Center, Saint Charles, MO, p. A368

BERNSTEIN, Les, Director Information Systems, Cookeville Regional Medical Center, Cookeville, TN, p. A568

BERNSTEIN, Michael, Chief Financial Officer, Tulare Regional Medical Center, Tulare, CA, p. A93

BERNSTEIN, Paul E., M.D. Area Medical Director, Kaiser Permanente San Diego Medical Center, San Diego, CA, p. A85

BERRETT, Britt, President, Texas Health Presbyterian Hospital Dallas, Dallas, TX, p. A597

BERRIGAN, Mary, Chief Operating Officer, Medical Center of Aurora, Aurora, CO, p. A97

BERRY, C. Ross, Chief Executive Officer, Shoals Hospital, Muscle Shoals, AL, p. A24

BERRY, David, Senior Vice President and Chief Operating Officer, Arkansas Children's Hospital, Little Rock, AR, p. A46

BERRY, Deborah, Director of Operations, Greene County Hospital, Leakesville, MS, p. A349

BERRY, Eilleen, Manager Information Technology, Webster County Community Hospital, Red Cloud, NE, p. A389

BERRY, Greg, Chief Financial Officer, Doctors Medical Center, Modesto, CA, p. A74

BERRY, James T., Chief Executive Officer, Purcell Municipal Hospital, Purcell, OK, p. A506

BERRY, Jonathan, Chief Support Services and Chief Financial Officer, Broughton Hospital, Morganton, NC, p. A457

BERRY, Linda, Vice President Human Resources, Memorial Hospital, Towanda, PA, p. A542

BERRY, Lisa, Director, Saint Anne's Hospital, Fall River, MA, p. A299

BERRY, Robert F., Chief Executive Officer, Lane Frost Health and Rehabilitation Center, Hugo, OK, p. A500

BERRY, Roberta, Manager Human Resources, Southeast Arizona Medical Center, Douglas, AZ, p. A31

BERRY, Tiffany, Chief Financial Officer, Twin Rivers Regional Medical Center, Kennett, MO, p. A364

BERRY, Wesley, Chief Financial Officer, Nicholas County Hospital, Carlisle, KY, p. A249

BERRYMAN, William R., M.D. Chief of Staff, Grand Junction Veterans Affairs Medical Center, Grand Junction, CO, p. A102

BERSANTE, Syd, President, St. Joseph Medical Center, Tacoma, WA, p. A673

BERSHAD, Joshua M., M.D. Senior Vice President Medical Affairs and Chief Medical Officer, Robert Wood Johnson University Hospital, New Brunswick, NJ, p. A407

BERSINGER, David, M.D. Chief of Staff, Chesterfield General Hospital, Cheraw, SC, p. A549

BERT, Alisa, Chief Financial Officer, Aventura Hospital and Medical Center, Aventura, FL, p. A118

BERTELSEN, Lori, R.N. Nursing Administrator, American Fork Hospital, American Fork, UT, p. A643

BERTKE, Bradley J., President and Chief Executive Officer, Mercy St. Anne Hospital, Toledo, OH, p. A491

BERTRAM, Jo, Vice President Finance, SSM St. Mary's Health Center, Saint Louis, MO, p. A370

BERTRAND, Joan L., Vice President Human Resources, Adcare Hospital of Worcester, Worcester, MA, p. A306

BERTRAND, Neil W., Chief Financial Officer, Longmont United Hospital, Longmont, CO, p. A104

BERTSCH, Darrold, Chief Executive Officer, Sakakawea Medical Center, Hazen, ND, p. A467

BERZAU, Ulrike, FACHE Administrator, St. Luke's Rehabilitation Institute, Spokane, WA, p. A672

BESS, Amy, Chief Financial Officer, Mizell Memorial Hospital, Opp, AL, p. A24

BESS, Timothy A., Chief Executive Officer, Wythe County Community Hospital, Wytheville, VA, p. A663

BESSEL, Marjorie, M.D. Chief Medical Officer, Banner Desert Medical Center, Mesa, AZ, p. A33

BESSER, Sherry L., R.N. Vice President Quality, Risk Management and Chief Nursing Officer, Pratt Regional Medical Center, Pratt, KS, p. A243

BESSLER, Christine, Vice President Information Services, Oconomowoc Memorial Hospital, Oconomowoc, WI, p. A693

BESSLER, September, Manager Human Resources, Brookings Health System, Brookings, SD, p. A558

BESST, Kara, President and Chief Executive Officer, Gritman Medical Center, Moscow, ID, p. A170

BESTEN, Robert, Chief Financial Officer, Mary Breckinridge ARH Hospital, Hyden, KY, p. A253

BESTGEN, Pat, Manager Human Resources, Cameron Regional Medical Center, Cameron, MO, p. A357

BESWICK, Elizabeth, Vice President Human Resources and Public Relations, Carteret General Hospital, Morehead City, NC, p. A457

BETANCOURT, Erika, Coordinator Human Resources, Cornerstone Regional Hospital, Edinburg, TX, p. A600

BETANCOURT, Salvador, Manager Information Services, Sunnyside Community Hospital, Sunnyside, WA, p. A673

BETHALA, Vasanth, M.D. Medical Director, Louisiana Heart Hospital, Lacombe, LA, p. A270

BETKE, Bryce, Chief Financial Officer, Crete Area Medical Center, Crete, NE, p. A383

BETKE–MENA, Rachel, Director Health Information Management, Colusa Regional Medical Center, Colusa, CA, p. A57

BETTEM, Kelly, Assistant Chief Operating Officer, East Ohio Regional Hospital, Martins Ferry, OH, p. A485

BETTS, Brooks
Vice President and Chief Information Officer, Miles Memorial Hospital, Damariscotta, ME, p. A283
Director Information Systems and Chief Information Officer, Pen Bay Medical Center, Rockport, ME, p. A285
Vice President and Chief Information Officer, St. Andrews Hospital and Healthcare Center, Boothbay Harbor, ME, p. A282

BETTS, Crystal
Chief Financial Officer, Incline Village Community Hospital, Incline Village, NV, p. A392
Chief Financial Officer, Tahoe Forest Hospital District, Truckee, CA, p. A93

BETTS, Nicholas, Director Information Technology, Grundy County Memorial Hospital, Grundy Center, IA, p. A222

BETZ, Paul, FACHE Chief Operating Officer and Senior Vice President, Maury Regional Hospital, Columbia, TN, p. A567

BETZ, Randal, M.D. Chief of Staff, Shriners Hospitals for Children–Philadelphia, Philadelphia, PA, p. A536

BEUS, Lance, Chief Operating Officer, Woodland Heights Medical Center, Lufkin, TX, p. A621

BEUTKE, Kenneth, Vice President Organization Development and Planning, OSF Saint James – John W. Albrecht Medical Center, Pontiac, IL, p. A192

BEVEL, John, Manager Information Systems, Shriners Hospitals for Children–Northern California, Sacramento, CA, p. A83

BEVERLY, DeAnna, Chief Operating Officer, Seven Rivers Regional Medical Center, Crystal River, FL, p. A121

BEVERLY, Douglas H., Chief Executive Officer, HEALTHSOUTH Rehabilitation Hospital of North Alabama, Huntsville, AL, p. A21

BEVERS, Donald, Chief Financial Officer, Memorial Hospital of Salem County, Salem, NJ, p. A410

BEVERS, Jonathan, M.D. Medical Director, Bloomington Meadows Hospital, Bloomington, IN, p. A199

BEWLEY, Lisa, Vice President and Chief Information Officer, Regional West Medical Center, Scottsbluff, NE, p. A389

BEWLEY, Martha, Chief Financial Officer, St. Charles Madras, Madras, OR, p. A514

BEYER, Eric J., President and Chief Executive Officer, Tufts Medical Center, Boston, MA, p. A297

BEYER, Jim, Director Human Resources, Norman Regional Health System, Norman, OK, p. A502

BEYER, Laura, Director Patient Care, Guttenberg Municipal Hospital, Guttenberg, IA, p. A222

BEYER, Laurie, Senior Vice President and Chief Financial Officer, Union Hospital, Elkton, MD, p. A291

BEYER, Teri, Chief Information Officer, Rice Memorial Hospital, Willmar, MN, p. A343

BEYER, William, M.D. Chief Medical Officer, St. Croix Regional Medical Center, St. Croix Falls, WI, p. A697

BEZUCHA, Gary, FACHE, Chief Executive Officer, North Central Health Care, Wausau, WI, p. A699

BHAMBRA, Jody, Chief Nursing Officer, Hartgrove Hospital, Chicago, IL, p. A176

BHANDARI, Raj, M.D. Physician–in–Chief, Kaiser Permanente San Jose Medical Center, San Jose, CA, p. A87

BHARGAVA, Mukesh, M.D. Vice President Medical Affairs, Henrietta D. Goodall Hospital, Sanford, ME, p. A285

BHARUCHA, Bomi, Chief Financial Officer, North Valley Hospital, Tonasket, WA, p. A673

BHATEJA, Renu, M.D. President Medical Staff, Ridgeview Psychiatric Hospital and Center, Oak Ridge, TN, p. A578

BHAYANI, Sam B., Chief Medical Officer, Barnes–Jewish West County Hospital, Saint Louis, MO, p. A369

BHOORASINGH, Merlene, Administrator, Kindred Hospital Ocala, Ocala, FL, p. A134

BHUCHAR, Subodh, M.D. Chief of Staff, Kindred Hospital Sugar Land, Sugar Land, TX, p. A635

BIALORVCKI, Tom, Chief Information Officer, Bay Medical Center Sacred Heart, Panama City, FL, p. A136

BIANCAMANO, John, Chief Financial Officer, University of Connecticut Health Center, John Dempsey Hospital, Farmington, CT, p. A108

BIANCHI, Cynthia, Chief Information Officer, Woodhull Medical and Mental Health Center,, NY, p. A437

BIAS, Richard R., Acting Vice President Information Systems and Chief Information Officer, Georgia Regents Medical Center, Augusta, GA, p. A147

BIBAL, Antoinette, Director Human Resources, Kindred Hospital–Baldwin Park, Baldwin Park, CA, p. A54

BIBB, Lisa, Director Human Resources, San Angelo Community Medical Center, San Angelo, TX, p. A630

BIBEAU, Roland R., FACHE, President, Novant Health Matthews Medical Center, Matthews, NC, p. A457

BIBER, Carl, Chief Financial Officer, Columbus Regional Healthcare System, Whiteville, NC, p. A462

BIBY, Thom, Chief Financial Officer, Tulsa Spine and Specialty Hospital, Tulsa, OK, p. A509

BICE, Rodney, R.N. Chief Nursing Officer, Pikes Peak Regional Hospital, Woodland Park, CO, p. A107

BICHIMER, Michael, Director Financial Operations, OhioHealth Dublin Methodist Hospital, Dublin, OH, p. A481

BICKEL, James, Chief Executive Officer, Columbus Regional Hospital, Columbus, IN, p. A200

BICKFORD, Carmel, Chief Financial Officer, Wyoming Behavioral Institute, Casper, WY, p. A701

BICKNELL, James, M.D. Medical Director, MidMichigan Medical Center–Midland, Midland, MI, p. A320

BIDDLE, Kenneth, Controller, Kensington Hospital, Philadelphia, PA, p. A535

BIDES, Adrienne, Assistant Chief Financial Officer and Budget Analyst, Big Spring State Hospital, Big Spring, TX, p. A588

BIDLEMAN, Angela, R.N. Chief Nursing Officer, Integris Grove General Hospital, Grove, OK, p. A499

BIE, Gary E., Chief Financial Officer, Stony Brook University Medical Center, Stony Brook, NY, p. A443

BIEBER, Courtney, Director Information Systems, Mercy Regional Medical Center, Ville Platte, LA, p. A280

BIEBER, Martin A., President and Chief Executive Officer, Kennedy Health System, Cherry Hill, NJ, p. A402

BIEDIGER, Daniel F., Vice President Human Resources, FirstHealth Moore Regional Hospital, Pinehurst, NC, p. A458

BIEDIGER, Michael J., FACHE, President and Chief Executive Officer, Lexington Medical Center, West Columbia, SC, p. A556

BIEDRON, Janet, R.N., Chief Executive Officer, Kindred Hospital–Sacramento, Folsom, CA, p. A60

BIEGANSKI, Gary, LFACHE, Interim Chief Executive Officer, Chase County Community Hospital, Imperial, NE, p. A384

BIEGERT, Dara, Vice President Human Resources, Medical Center of Lewisville, Lewisville, TX, p. A618

BIEGLER, Elizabeth A., R.N
Chief Nursing Officer, OhioHealth Dublin Methodist Hospital, Dublin, OH, p. A481
Chief Nursing Officer, OhioHealth Grady Memorial Hospital, Delaware, OH, p. A480

BIEHL, Albert, M.D. Vice President Medical Affairs, Bethesda Memorial Hospital, Boynton Beach, FL, p. A119

BIELECKI, Thomas A., Chief Financial Officer, Geisinger Wyoming Valley Medical Center, Wilkes Barre, PA, p. A544

BIEN, Jim, M.D. Vice President Quality and Patient Safety, Indiana University Health Arnett Hospital, Lafayette, IN, p. A208

BIEN, John, Vice President Finance, United Hospital, Saint Paul, MN, p. A340

BIER, Alan, M.D. Executive Vice President and Chief Medical Officer, Gwinnett Hospital System, Lawrenceville, GA, p. A156

BIERBRAUER, Cindy, Director Human Resources, Texas Health Harris Methodist Hospital Azle, Azle, TX, p. A586

BIERIG, Kirt, D.O. Chief of Staff, Share Medical Center, Alva, OK, p. A495

BIERMAN, Joan, Vice President Finance, Cherokee Regional Medical Center, Cherokee, IA, p. A218

BIERMAN, Ronald L., Chief Executive Officer, Affinity Medical Center, Massillon, OH, p. A485

BIERSCHENK, Kevin, Chief Executive Officer, Dodge County Hospital, Eastman, GA, p. A153

BIERUT, Barbara, Chief Financial Officer, HEALTHSOUTH Rehabilitation Hospital of Sarasota, Sarasota, FL, p. A139

BIFFLE, Sandra, Personnel Clerk, Quitman County Hospital, Marks, MS, p. A350

BIFULCO, William, Vice President/Chief Information Officer, Southampton Hospital, Southampton, NY, p. A443

BIGELOW, David C., PharmD, Chief Executive Officer, Samaritan Pacific Communities Hospital, Newport, OR, p. A515

BIGELOW, Debbie, Chief Financial Officer, Coulee Medical Center, Grand Coulee, WA, p. A667

BIGELOW, Timothy, Director Human Resources, Butler Hospital, Providence, RI, p. A546

BIGGINS, Lillie, R.N., President, Texas Health Harris Methodist Hospital Fort Worth, Fort Worth, TX, p. A604

BIGGS, Alan W., Vice President Financial Services, Community Howard Regional Hospital, Kokomo, IN, p. A207

BIGGS, Daniel, Director Human Resources, Valley View Hospital, Glenwood Springs, CO, p. A101

BIGHAM, Bryon, M.D. Chief of Staff, Hiawatha Community Hospital, Hiawatha, KS, p. A235

BIGHAM, Laurie S., R.N. Chief Nursing Officer, Lovelace Medical Center, Albuquerque, NM, p. A414

BIGLER, Nathan
Regional Director Human Resources, American Fork Hospital, American Fork, UT, p. A643
Regional Director Human Resources, Utah Valley Regional Medical Center, Provo, UT, p. A646

BIGLEY, John, M.D. Medical Director, Kaiser Permanente Baldwin Park Medical Center, Baldwin Park, CA, p. A54

BIGLEY, Robert F., President and Chief Executive Officer, East Georgia Regional Medical Center, Statesboro, GA, p. A160

BIGNAULT, Jon, M.D. Chief of Staff, Athens–Limestone Hospital, Athens, AL, p. A16

BIGNOTTI, Donald, M.D. Vice President Medical Affairs, St. Joseph Mercy Oakland, Pontiac, MI, p. A322

BIHUNIAK, Peter, Vice President Finance, Robert Wood Johnson University Hospital Rahway, Rahway, NJ, p. A409

BIK, Lymar, M.D. Medical Director, Coalinga Regional Medical Center, Coalinga, CA, p. A57

BILES, Don, Chief Financial Officer, Manatee Glens Hospital and Addiction Center, Bradenton, FL, p. A119

BILLECI, Theresa, Executive Director, Porterville Developmental Center, Porterville, CA, p. A80

BILLERBECK, Robert, M.D. Vice President and Chief Medical Officer, Exempla Good Samaritan Medical Center, Lafayette, CO, p. A103

BILLING, Michael D., Administrator, Mid–Valley Hospital, Omak, WA, p. A669

BILLING, Tommye, Vice President and Chief Information Officer, St. Vincent Medical Center–North, Sherwood, AR, p. A50

BILLINGS, Robert E., Chief Financial Officer, Largo Medical Center, Largo, FL, p. A129

BILLINGSLEY, Angela, Director Human Resources, Intermountain Hospital, Boise, ID, p. A167

BILLINGSLEY, Annette, Director Human Resources, Hill Hospital of Sumter County, York, AL, p. A26

BILLINGSLEY, Richard A., MSN Chief Operating Officer and Chief Nursing Officer, Mena Regional Health System, Mena, AR, p. A47

BILLINGTON, Carole, R.N. Vice President Patient Care Services, Saint Anne's Hospital, Fall River, MA, p. A299

BILLS, Jim, Chief Executive Officer, Logan Memorial Hospital, Russellville, KY, p. A260

BILLY, Frank, Chief Financial Officer, Kindred Hospital Bay Area–Tampa, Tampa, FL, p. A141

BILMER, Janice, Director, Information Services, Skiff Medical Center, Newton, IA, p. A226

BILUNKA, Dianne C., Director Human Resources, Clarion Psychiatric Center, Clarion, PA, p. A522

BINDER, Forest, Vice President Finance, St. Mary's Hospital and Medical Center, Grand Junction, CO, p. A102

BING, William W., Chief Executive Officer, Liberty Healthcare Systems, Bastrop, LA, p. A262

BINGHAM, Leslie, Senior Vice President and Chief Executive Officer, Valley Baptist Medical Center–Brownsville, Brownsville, TX, p. A590

BINGHAM, Roxane, Director Marketing, Baton Rouge Rehabilitation Hospital, Baton Rouge, LA, p. A263

BINGMAN, Ryan, Director Operations, Grundy County Memorial Hospital, Grundy Center, IA, p. A222

BINKLEY, Jr., Leonard, Interim Chief Financial Officer, Henderson County Community Hospital, Lexington, TN, p. A573

BINKLEY, Sharon, Director Human Resources, Fairfax Community Hospital, Fairfax, OK, p. A498

BIRA, Patrick G., FACHE, Chief Executive Officer, Lincoln County Medical Center, Troy, MO, p. A372

BIRCH, Misty, Director Human Resources, Castleview Hospital, Price, UT, p. A645

BIRCHLER, James, Vice President Finance, Chelsea Community Hospital, Chelsea, MI, p. A310

BIRD, Alan, Chief Executive Officer, Haskell County Community Hospital, Stigler, OK, p. A507

BIRD, Jeffrey C., M.D. Chief Medical Officer, Indiana University Health Ball Memorial Hospital, Muncie, IN, p. A210

BIRD, Julio J., M.D. Chief Medical Officer, Gundersen Lutheran Medical Center, La Crosse, WI, p. A689

BIRD, Lindsay, Director Finance, South Pointe Hospital, Warrensville Heights, OH, p. A492

BIRD, Michael, M.D. Vice President Medical Services, Akron Children's Hospital, Akron, OH, p. A470

BIRD, Michele
Chief Human Resources Officer, Hemet Valley Medical Center, Hemet, CA, p. A64
Chief Human Resources Officer, Menifee Valley Medical Center, Sun City, CA, p. A92

BIRDZELL, JoAnn, Chief Executive Officer and Administrator, St. Catherine Hospital, East Chicago, IN, p. A201

BIREN, David, Chief Financial Officer, Mayo Clinic Health System in Lake City, Lake City, MN, p. A334

BIRENBERG, Allan, Vice President Medical Affairs, MedStar Harbor Hospital, Baltimore, MD, p. A288

BIRKEL, Sue M., R.N. Director of Nursing, Butler County Health Care Center, David City, NE, p. A383

BIRKHOFER, Colleen, Chief Nursing Officer, Trenton Psychiatric Hospital, Trenton, NJ, p. A411

BIRLEW, Ron, Director Human Resources, Des Peres Hospital, Saint Louis, MO, p. A369

BIRMINGHAM, Roy, Controller, Oakwood Annapolis Hospital, Wayne, MI, p. A326

BIRNBAUM, Bernard, M.D. Senior Vice President, Vice Dean and Chief Hospital Operations, NYU Langone Medical Center, New York, NY, p. A435

BIRNER, Nancy, M.D. President Medical Staff, Red Bud Regional Hospital, Red Bud, IL, p. A193

BIRSCHBACH, Nancy, Assistant Vice President Information Services, Agnesian HealthCare, Fond Du Lac, WI, p. A686

BISCHALANEY, George, President and Chief Executive Officer, Eden Medical Center, Castro Valley, CA, p. A56

BISCONE, Mark A., Executive Director, Waldo County General Hospital, Belfast, ME, p. A281

BISGROVE, Michele, Manager Human Resources, Mad River Community Hospital, Arcata, CA, p. A53

BISH, Carol, Human Resources Coordinator, North Greenville Hospital, Travelers Rest, SC, p. A556

BISHKU, Dilek, M.D. Vice President Medical Affairs, La Rabida Children's Hospital, Chicago, IL, p. A177

BISHOP, April, Chief Executive Officer, Kindred Hospital–Central Dakotas, Mandan, ND, p. A468

BISHOP, Clint, Program Manager, Marion Veterans Affairs Medical Center, Marion, IL, p. A187

BISHOP, Jim, Chief Executive Officer, Harney District Hospital, Burns, OR, p. A511

BISHOP, John
Chief Financial Officer, Long Beach Memorial Medical Center, Long Beach, CA, p. A67
Chief Financial Officer, Madison Valley Medical Center, Ennis, MT, p. A376
Chief Financial Officer, Madison Valley Medical Center, Ennis, MT, p. A376

BISSEL, Jane, Chief Financial Officer, Wabash County Hospital, Wabash, IN, p. A214

BISSENDEN, Chris, Director Human Resources, Ogden Regional Medical Center, Ogden, UT, p. A645

BISSONETTE, Christine, R.N. Chief Nursing Officer, Kalkaska Memorial Health Center, Kalkaska, MI, p. A318

BISSONNETTE, Andre, Vice President Finance, North Country Hospital and Health Center, Newport, VT, p. A650

BISTERFELDT, Joanne, Chief Information Officer, Wheaton Franciscan Healthcare – All Saints, Racine, WI, p. A695

BISTON, Jody, Director Risk Management and Physician Clinic, Sullivan County Memorial Hospital, Milan, MO, p. A366

BITAR, Adib, M.D. Medical Director, Aurora Charter Oak Hospital, Covina, CA, p. A58

BITAR, Ali, M.D. Vice President Medical Affairs, Rehabilitation Institute of Michigan, Detroit, MI, p. A312

BITHER, Dean, Chief Financial Officer, Inland Hospital, Waterville, ME, p. A285

BITSOLI, Deborah, Chief Operating Officer, Saint Vincent Hospital, Worcester, MA, p. A306

BITTNER, Augustine, Chief Information Officer, Robley Rex Veterans Affairs Medical Center, Louisville, KY, p. A256

BITTNER, Mary J., R.N. Vice President Nursing, Barton Memorial Hospital, South Lake Tahoe, CA, p. A91

BIUNDO, Russell, M.D. Medical Director, HEALTHSOUTH MountainView Regional Rehabilitation Hospital, Morgantown, WV, p. A679

BIXLER, David, Chief Executive Officer, Daviess Community Hospital, Washington, IN, p. A214

BIXLER, Jacquelyn, Vice President Human Resources, BryLin Hospitals, Buffalo, NY, p. A422

BJELICH, Steven C., President and Chief Executive Officer, Saint Francis Medical Center, Cape Girardeau, MO, p. A358

BJELLA, Karmon T., Chief Executive Officer, Alpena Regional Medical Center, Alpena, MI, p. A308

BJERKE, Carolyn, Director Human Resources, Kingfisher Regional Hospital, Kingfisher, OK, p. A500

BJERKNES, Dan, Director Human Resources, Richard P. Stadter Psychiatric Center, Grand Forks, ND, p. A467

BJORDAHL, Kevin, M.D. Chief Medical Officer, Milbank Area Hospital Avera, Milbank, SD, p. A560

BJORGUM, Deb, Manager Data Processing, Johnson Regional Medical Center, Clarksville, AR, p. A42

BJORKLUND, Julie D., Director Human Resources, Coulee Medical Center, Grand Coulee, WA, p. A667

BJORNDAL, Judith, M.D. Medical Director, Sonoma Developmental Center, Eldridge, CA, p. A59

BJORNSTAD, Brad, M.D. Vice President and Chief Medical Officer, Florida Hospital Tampa, Tampa, FL, p. A141

BLACK, Jr., Albert P., Chief Operating Officer, Hospital of the University of Pennsylvania, Philadelphia, PA, p. A535

BLACK, Jr., Charles, Chief Financial Officer, Rockcastle Regional Hospital and Respiratory Care Center, Mount Vernon, KY, p. A258

BLACK, Doug, President, Barnes–Jewish West County Hospital, Saint Louis, MO, p. A369

BLACK, Ethel, Director Human Resources, HEALTHSOUTH Harmarville Rehabilitation Hospital, Pittsburgh, PA, p. A537

BLACK, Gary E., President and Chief Executive Officer, Lenoir Memorial Hospital, Kinston, NC, p. A456

BLACK, James M., Director Administration, Soldiers' Home in Holyoke, Holyoke, MA, p. A301

BLACK, Kim, Manager Human Resources, Dukes Memorial Hospital, Peru, IN, p. A212

BLACK, Marcey, Chief Financial Officer, Northwest Florida Community Hospital, Chipley, FL, p. A120

BLACK, Marilynn, Chief Information Officer, Verde Valley Medical Center, Cottonwood, AZ, p. A30

BLACK, Michael, Director Human Resources, East Georgia Regional Medical Center, Statesboro, GA, p. A160

BLACK, Paul S.
Controller, H. C. Watkins Memorial Hospital, Quitman, MS, p. A353
Chief Financial Officer, Jefferson Davis Community Hospital, Prentiss, MS, p. A353
Chief Financial Officer, Scott Regional Hospital, Morton, MS, p. A351

BLACK, Robert, Chief Executive Officer, Linton Hospital, Linton, ND, p. A468

BLACK, Sharon, Chief Executive Officer, Kindred Hospital Lafayette, Lafayette, LA, p. A270

BLACK, Tim, Director Human Resources, Southern Hills Hospital and Medical Center, Las Vegas, NV, p. A393

BLACKBEAR, Annabelle, Human Resources Specialist, U. S. Public Health Service Indian Hospital, Pine Ridge, SD, p. A561

BLACKBURN, Laura, Administrator, Ten Lakes Center, Dennison, OH, p. A480

BLACKBURN, Susan, Chief Operating Officer, Providence St. Mary Medical Center, Walla Walla, WA, p. A674

BLACKETT, Melrose, M.D. President Medical Staff, Baptist Memorial Hospital for Women, Memphis, TN, p. A574

BLACKMAN, Elliot, Chief Information Management and Technology, U. S. Air Force Hospital, Hampton, VA, p. A655

BLACKMAN, Jay H., Senior Vice President and Chief Operating Officer, Howard County General Hospital, Columbia, MD, p. A291

BLACKMON, Brian, Director Information Systems, Troy Regional Medical Center, Troy, AL, p. A25

BLACKMON, David, Chief Financial Officer, Comanche County Memorial Hospital, Lawton, OK, p. A500

BLACKMON, Edward, M.D. Chief of Staff, South Texas Regional Medical Center, Jourdanton, TX, p. A615

BLACKMON, Jenean
Assistant Vice President and Chief Information Officer, McLeod Medical Center Dillon, Dillon, SC, p. A551
Associate Vice President and Chief Information Officer, McLeod Regional Medical Center, Florence, SC, p. A552

BLACKMON, Tanya S., President, Novant Health Huntersville Medical Center, Huntersville, NC, p. A455

BLACKWELL, David, Vice President Human Resources, Vail Valley Medical Center, Vail, CO, p. A106

BLACKWELL, Dawn, R.N. VP of Patient Care Services, Memorial Healthcare, Owosso, MI, p. A321

BLACKWELL, Jack, Chief Financial Officer, Highlands Regional Medical Center, Prestonsburg, KY, p. A259

BLACKWELL, James
Vice President and Chief Financial Officer, Clara Barton Hospital, Hoisington, KS, p. A235
Director Information Systems, Decatur Memorial Hospital, Decatur, IL, p. A180

BLACKWELL, Kim, Chief Financial Officer, Arrowhead Behavioral Health Hospital, Maumee, OH, p. A486

BLACKWELL, Lenore, Director Human Resources, Harton Regional Medical Center, Tullahoma, TN, p. A580

BLACKWELL, Timothy, Manager Human Resources, Rolling Hills Hospital, Ada, OK, p. A495

BLACKWOOD, Jim, Chief Executive Officer, Tallahatchie General Hospital, Charleston, MS, p. A345

BLAD, Nathan, Chief Executive Officer, RC Hospital and Clinics, Olivia, MN, p. A337

BLADEN, Anthony M., Vice President Human Resources, Calvert Memorial Hospital, Prince Frederick, MD, p. A293

BLADERGROEN, Mark, M.D. Vice President Medical Affairs, Bon Secours St. Mary's Hospital, Richmond, VA, p. A660

BLADES, Stephen, Chief Executive Officer and President, Louisiana Heart Hospital, Lacombe, LA, p. A270

BLAHA, Bill, Manager Information Technology, Tri–County Hospital, Wadena, MN, p. A342

BLAHA, John E., Vice President Finance and Chief Financial Officer, Brattleboro Retreat, Brattleboro, VT, p. A649

BLAHNIK, David, Chief Operating Officer, Twin Valley Behavioral Healthcare, Columbus, OH, p. A478

BLAIN, Brenda K., MSN Chief Nursing Officer and Chief Operating Officer, Baylor Medical Center at Irving, Irving, TX, p. A614

BLAIR, Betsy, R.N. Chief Operating Officer, CJW Medical Center, Richmond, VA, p. A660

BLAIR, Brenda, Association Vice President Human Resources and Organizational Learning, Alice Peck Day Memorial Hospital, Lebanon, NH, p. A398

BLAIR, Diane, Human Resources and Admissions, Alegent Creighton Health Plainview Hospital, Plainview, NE, p. A389

BLAIR, Janet M., Director Human Resources, Clinton Memorial Hospital, Wilmington, OH, p. A493

BLAIR, Judy, Senior Vice President Clincial Services and Chief Nursing Officer, Glendale Adventist Medical Center, Glendale, CA, p. A62

BLAIR, Keith, M.D. Manager Information Systems, Lander Regional Hospital, Lander, WY, p. A702

BLAIR, Jr., Ralph W., M.D. Chief of Staff, Ennis Regional Medical Center, Ennis, TX, p. A602

BLAIR, Rebecca, Vice President Human Resources and Service Excellence, Brigham and Women's Faulkner Hospital, Boston, MA, p. A296

BLAIR, Robert D., Chief Executive Officer, The NeuroMedical Center Surgical Hospital, Baton Rouge, LA, p. A264

BLAKE, Alan, M.D. President Medical Staff, Samaritan Lebanon Community Hospital, Lebanon, OR, p. A514

BLAKE, Daphne, Chief Nursing Officer, Guadalupe Regional Medical Center, Seguin, TX, p. A633

BLAKE, Diane, Chief Executive Officer, Cascade Medical Center, Leavenworth, WA, p. A667

BLAKE, Hugo, M.D. Chief Medical Staff, Harlingen Medical Center, Harlingen, TX, p. A607

BLAKE, Kelly, Chief Executive Officer, Select Specialty Hospital–Johnstown, Johnstown, PA, p. A528

BLAKE, Robert, Chief Human Resources Officer Southwest Market, Memorial Hermann Sugar Land Hospital, Sugar Land, TX, p. A635

BLAKE, Sheryl Lewis, FACHE, Chief Executive Officer, Pennock Hospital, Hastings, MI, p. A316

BLAKE, Sue, Chief Financial Officer, Myrtue Medical Center, Harlan, IA, p. A222

BLAKELY, Amy, Assistant Executive Director Operations, Devereux Hospital and Children's Center of Florida, Melbourne, FL, p. A130

BLAKELY, Michelle, Associate Director, Jesse Brown Veterans Affairs Medical Center, Chicago, IL, p. A177

BLAKEY GORMAN, Mary, Director Human Resources, Northwest Missouri Psychiatric Rehabilitation Center, Saint Joseph, MO, p. A369

BLALOCK, Andy, M.D. Physician Executive, Our Lady of Lourdes Regional Medical Center, Lafayette, LA, p. A271

BLALOCK, Cam, Senior Vice President Corporate Services, Nash Health Care Systems, Rocky Mount, NC, p. A460

BLALOCK, L. Dwayne, Chief Executive Officer, Madison River Oaks Medical Center, Canton, MS, p. A345

BLAN, Gary J., FACHE,
  Market Chief Executive Officer, Sparks Regional Medical Center, Fort Smith, AR, p. A44
  Market Chief Executive Officer, Summit Medical Center, Van Buren, AR, p. A50

BLANCAS, Gilbert, Director Human Resources, University Medical Center of El Paso, El Paso, TX, p. A602

BLANCHARD, Timothy D., Chief Financial Officer, Kingman Regional Medical Center, Kingman, AZ, p. A32

BLANCHARD, Wayne D., Chief Executive Officer, Kindred Hospital–New Jersey Morris County, Dover, NJ, p. A403

BLANCHARD, William R., Chief Executive Officer, DeTar Healthcare System, Victoria, TX, p. A639

BLANCHET, Jacques, M.D. Director Medical Affairs, Baystate Franklin Medical Center, Greenfield, MA, p. A300

BLANCHET, Mike, President, CHI, Community Hospital North, Indianapolis, IN, p. A205

BLANCHETTE, Edward A., M.D., Director, Connecticut Department of Correction's Hospital, Somers, CT, p. A111

BLANCO, Andres, Director Management Information Systems, Westside Regional Medical Center, Plantation, FL, p. A137

BLAND, David, Chief Executive Officer, South Davis Community Hospital, Bountiful, UT, p. A643

BLAND, Douglas, Manager Information Services, Spring View Hospital, Lebanon, KY, p. A253

BLAND, James G., M.D. Chief of Staff, Jane Todd Crawford Hospital, Greensburg, KY, p. A251

BLANFORD, Donald, M.D. Chief Medical Officer, Mercy Regional Medical Center, Lorain, OH, p. A484

BLANK, Arthur J., President and Chief Executive Officer, Mount Desert Island Hospital, Bar Harbor, ME, p. A281

BLANKE, Kerry Lee, Director Financial Services, Riverside Medical Center, Waupaca, WI, p. A698

BLANKENSHIP, Diana, Director Human Resources, Welch Community Hospital, Welch, WV, p. A681

BLANKENSHIP, Jeff, CPA Vice President and Chief Financial Officer, Jackson–Madison County General Hospital, Jackson, TN, p. A570

BLANTON, Forest
  Senior VP and Chief Information Officer, Memorial Hospital Miramar, Miramar, FL, p. A133
  Chief Information Officer, Memorial Hospital Pembroke, Pembroke Pines, FL, p. A136
  Chief Information Officer, Memorial Hospital West, Pembroke Pines, FL, p. A136
  Administrator Process Engineering, Memorial Regional Hospital,, FL, p. A125

BLANTON, James
  Chief Financial Officer, East Texas Medical Center Rehabilitation Hospital, Tyler, TX, p. A638
  Chief Financial Officer, East Texas Medical Center Specialty Hospital, Tyler, TX, p. A638

BLANTON, Karen, Chief Financial Officer, Warm Springs Medical Center, Warm Springs, GA, p. A162

BLANTON, Kevin, D.O. Chief of Staff, Goodall–Witcher Healthcare, Clifton, TX, p. A592

BLANTON, Marion, Chief Financial Officer, Minneola District Hospital, Minneola, KS, p. A240

BLANTON, Ron, Chief Fiscal Services, Boise Veterans Affairs Medical Center, Boise, ID, p. A167

BLAPPERT, Bradley, M.D. Chief Medical Officer, AMG Specialty Hospital–Lafayette, Lafayette, LA, p. A270

BLASER, Karla, Director Human Resources, Trinity Muscatine, Muscatine, IA, p. A225

BLASINGAME, Billy, Chief Executive Officer, Plum Creek Specialty Hospital, Amarillo, TX, p. A582

BLASIUS, Rita, Assistant Administrator and Chief Financial Officer, Avera St. Benedict Health Center, Parkston, SD, p. A561

BLAUER, Michael, Chief Executive Officer, Providence Seaside Hospital, Seaside, OR, p. A517

BLAUFUSS, Max, Administrator and Chief Executive Officer, Lakeside Medical Center, Pine City, MN, p. A338

BLAUWET, Judy, M.P.H. Senior Vice President Operations and Chief Nursing Officer, Avera McKennan Hospital and University Health Center, Sioux Falls, SD, p. A562

BLAYLOCK, Darrell, Chief Executive Officer, Volunteer Community Hospital, Martin, TN, p. A573

BLAYLOCK, Kevin, Chief Executive Officer, Oklahoma Spine Hospital, Oklahoma City, OK, p. A504

BLAZEK, Dennis, Chief Information Officer, Clarke County Hospital, Osceola, IA, p. A226

BLAZEK, Lisa, Chief Financial Officer, Adair County Memorial Hospital, Greenfield, IA, p. A222

BLAZIER, Patty, Chief Nursing Officer, Hamilton Memorial Hospital District, McLeansboro, IL, p. A188

BLEAK, Jason, Administrator and Chief Executive Officer, Grover C. Dils Medical Center, Caliente, NV, p. A391

BLEAKNEY, David A., Chief Executive Officer and Administrator, Angleton Danbury Medical Center, Angleton, TX, p. A583

BLECHA, Timothy, M.D. Medical Director, Brodstone Memorial Hospital, Superior, NE, p. A390

BLEDSOE, Cindy, Chief Executive Officer, Forest Park Medical Center, Dallas, TX, p. A596

BLEDSOE, Richard, Director Information Systems, Novant Health Gaffney Medical Center, Gaffney, SC, p. A552

BLESI, Michael, Director Information Technology, Rainy Lake Medical Center, International Falls, MN, p. A334

BLESSING, Brian, Chief Financial Officer, Texas Health Harris Methodist Hospital Azle, Azle, TX, p. A586

BLESSITT, Harold J., Administrator, South Sunflower County Hospital, Indianola, MS, p. A348

BLEVINS, Bonnie, Chief Financial Officer, Graham Regional Medical Center, Graham, TX, p. A606

BLEVINS, Denzil, Director Information Systems, Montgomery General Hospital, Montgomery, WV, p. A678

BLEVINS, Gary, Director Human Resources, Mercy Medical Center Mount Shasta, Mount Shasta, CA, p. A75

BLEVINS, Heather, Director Human Resources, HEALTHSOUTH Rehabilitation of Gadsden, Gadsden, AL, p. A20

BLEVINS, Matthew H., Chief Executive Officer, Select Specialty Hospital–Kansas City, Kansas City, KS, p. A237

BLEVINS, Pam, R.N. Director, Clinical Informatics, Blue Ridge Regional Hospital, Spruce Pine, NC, p. A461

BLIGHTON, Gordon, Director Resource Management, Naval Hospital Camp Pendleton, Camp Pendleton, CA, p. A55

BLIK, Lior, Chief Information Officer, Hoboken University Medical Center, Hoboken, NJ, p. A405

BLISE, Cathi, Interim Chief Nursing Officer, St. Anthony's Medical Center, Saint Louis, MO, p. A370

BLISS, Ann, Manager Computer Services, Southeast Arizona Medical Center, Douglas, AZ, p. A31

BLIVEN, Donna, Vice President Patient Care Services and Chief Nursing Officer, Jones Memorial Hospital, Wellsville, NY, p. A445

BLOB, Burchkhard, Manager Human Resources, Central Virginia Training Center, Madison Heights, VA, p. A656

BLOCK, Annie, Director Human Resources, Poplar Community Hospital, Poplar, MT, p. A379

BLOCK, George, M.D. Chief Medical Officer, O'Connor Hospital, San Jose, CA, p. A88

BLOCK, Sherri, Chief Operating Officer, Aurora Vista Del Mar Hospital, Ventura, CA, p. A94

BLODGETT, Debbie, Director of Fiscal Services, Ochiltree General Hospital, Perryton, TX, p. A627

BLOEDOW, Connie, Interim Chief Financial Officer, Redwood Area Hospital, Redwood Falls, MN, p. A338

BLOEMER, Brad, Vice President Finance and Chief Financial Officer, Arkansas Methodist Medical Center, Paragould, AR, p. A49

BLOMELEY, Geoff, Interim Chief Financial Officer, Ponca City Medical Center, Ponca City, OK, p. A505

BLOOD, Barbara, Director Human Resources, Walla Walla General Hospital, Walla Walla, WA, p. A674

BLOOD, Dana, Director Human Resources, Oakdale Community Hospital, Oakdale, LA, p. A276

BLOOM, Kerry, Director Human Resources, Kalamazoo Psychiatric Hospital, Kalamazoo, MI, p. A318

BLOOM, Laura, Director Human Resources, Coffee Regional Medical Center, Douglas, GA, p. A152

BLOOM, Sarah, Director Information Systems, Belton Regional Medical Center, Belton, MO, p. A356

BLOOM, Stephanie L., FACHE, President and Chief Executive Officer, Community Medical Center, Toms River, NJ, p. A411

BLOOMFIELD, Deborah, Chief Financial Officer, Mercy Health – Anderson Hospital, Cincinnati, OH, p. A475

BLOOMQUIST, Margaret A., Assistant Administrator Human Resources, Emory University Hospital, Atlanta, GA, p. A146

BLOOMQUIST, Trudy, Director of Nursing, Warren General Hospital, Warren, PA, p. A543

BLOUGH Jr., Daniel D., Chief Executive Officer, Punxsutawney Area Hospital, Punxsutawney, PA, p. A539

BLOUGH, David, Chief Information Officer, University of South Alabama Children's and Women's Hospital, Mobile, AL, p. A23

BLUE, Gaea, Administrator and Chief Executive Officer, Avera Weskota Memorial Hospital, Wessington Springs, SD, p. A564

BLUE, Jan L., Vice President Human Resources, Hoag Memorial Hospital Presbyterian, Newport Beach, CA, p. A76

BLUE, Lawrence, Administrator and Chief Executive Officer, Cavalier County Memorial Hospital, Langdon, ND, p. A468

BLUE, Yvonne, Chief Operations Officer, Moore County Hospital District, Dumas, TX, p. A599

BLUFORD, John W.
  President and Chief Executive Officer, Truman Medical Center–Hospital Hill, Kansas City, MO, p. A364
  President and Chief Executive Officer, Truman Medical Center–Lakewood, Kansas City, MO, p. A364

BLUHM, Tom, Director Information Systems, Island Hospital, Anacortes, WA, p. A664

BLUM, Carrie, Director Information Systems, Monroe Clinic, Monroe, WI, p. A693

BLUM, Donald A., M.D. Chief of Staff, Wetzel County Hospital, New Martinsville, WV, p. A679

BLUM, Walter B., M.D. Chief of Staff, McLeod Medical Center Dillon, Dillon, SC, p. A551

BLUMENFELD, Barry, M.D. Chief Information Officer, Maine Medical Center, Portland, ME, p. A284

BLUNCK, Marilyn, Director Health Information Management, Norfolk Regional Center, Norfolk, NE, p. A386

BLUNK, Jim, D.O. Chief Medical Officer, Sumner County Hospital District One, Caldwell, KS, p. A232

BLUNT, Margaret, Director Human Resources, Cornerstone Hospital of Houston – Bellaire, Houston, TX, p. A609

BLURTON, Cheri, Director Human Resources, Great River Medical Center, Blytheville, AR, p. A41

BLUTE, III, James, M.D. Chief Medical Officer, Nazareth Hospital, Philadelphia, PA, p. A536

BLYTHE, Sheryl, Director Human Resources, St. Anthony Hospital, Lakewood, CO, p. A103

BLYTHE, Thomas W.
  Regional Vice President Human Resources, Good Samaritan Regional Health Center, Mount Vernon, IL, p. A189
  Vice President Human Resources, St. Mary's Hospital, Centralia, IL, p. A175

BOAL, Jeremy, M.D. Medical Director, Long Island Jewish Medical Center,, NY, p. A433

BOARD, Patricia, Vice President Human Resources, Community Hospital of Bremen, Bremen, IN, p. A199

BOARDMAN, Debra K., FACHE, President and Chief Executive Officer, Range Regional Health Services, Hibbing, MN, p. A334

BOAS, Erik, Vice President Finance, University of Maryland Charles Regional Medical Center, La Plata, MD, p. A292

BOATMAN, Daniel W., Chief Executive Officer, Granite County Medical Center, Philipsburg, MT, p. A378

BOATMAN, James, Chief Financial Officer, Doctors Medical Center–San Pablo Campus, San Pablo, CA, p. A88

BOATMAN, Robert, Director Information Technology, Richmond State Hospital, Richmond, IN, p. A212

BOATRIGHT, Donna, MSN, Administrator, Rolling Plains Memorial Hospital, Sweetwater, TX, p. A636

BOATWRIGHT, Damond, Chief Executive Officer, Overland Park Regional Medical Center, Overland Park, KS, p. A242

BOBBITT, Gina, Director Human Resources, Salem Memorial District Hospital, Salem, MO, p. A371

BOBBITT, James, Vice President Human Resources, Saint Agnes Hospital, Baltimore, MD, p. A289

BOBBS, Kathy J., FACHE, President Chief Executive Officer, Regional Medical Center of Acadiana, Lafayette, LA, p. A271

BOCKENEK, William, M.D. Medical Director, Carolinas Rehabilitation, Charlotte, NC, p. A449

BOCKMANN, Rick, Chief Executive Officer, Frank R. Howard Memorial Hospital, Willits, CA, p. A96

BOCKNEK, Marc, D.O. Vice President Medical Affairs, DMC Huron Valley–Sinai Hospital, Commerce Township, MI, p. A311

BODE, Patti, Chief Financial Officer, Orthopedic Hospital, Oklahoma City, OK, p. A504

BODEN, DeShawna, Director Human Resources, Harbor Oaks Hospital, New Baltimore, MI, p. A321

BODENMANN, Linda, Chief Operating Officer, Southcoast Hospitals Group, Fall River, MA, p. A300

BODENNER, Nancy, Director Human Resources, St. Joseph Health System, Tawas City, MI, p. A325

BODENSTEINER, Kim, Chief Financial Officer, Essentia Health Fosston, Fosston, MN, p. A332

BODIN, Donna L., Vice President, Woman's Hospital, Baton Rouge, LA, p. A264

BODLOVIC, Kirk, Vice President and Chief Financial Officer, St. Joseph Hospital, Polson, MT, p. A379

BODME, Maureen, Chief Clinical Officer, Kindred Hospital–San Diego, San Diego, CA, p. A85

BODNAR, Darrell, Director Information, Weeks Medical Center, Lancaster, NH, p. A398

BOECKER, Thomas J., President and Chief Executive Officer, Wilson Memorial Hospital, Sidney, OH, p. A490

BOEHLER, Richard, M.D., President and Chief Executive Officer, St. Joseph Hospital, Nashua, NH, p. A399

BOEHM, Scott D., Vice President Human Resources, Sanford Bismarck, Bismarck, ND, p. A465

BOEHNKE, Winnie, Director Human Resources, Timberlawn Mental Health System, Dallas, TX, p. A598

BOEHRER, Mark, Director Human Resources, St. Charles Hospital, Port Jefferson, NY, p. A440

BOEMER, Sally Mason
Senior Vice President Finance, Massachusetts General Hospital, Boston, MA, p. A297
Chief Financial Officer, North Shore Medical Center, Salem, MA, p. A304

BOEMMEL, Michael, Vice President and Chief Financial Officer, MedStar National Rehabilitation Hospital, Washington, DC, p. A116

BOER, Jeff, Director Information Technology, Pulaski Memorial Hospital, Winamac, IN, p. A215

BOERNER, Carol F., M.D. President Medical Staff, Valley Regional Hospital, Claremont, NH, p. A397

BOES, Jody, Vice President Patient Care Services, Ministry Door County Medical Center, Sturgeon Bay, WI, p. A697

BOGAN, James, FACHE, President and Chief Executive Officer, Portage Health, Hancock, MI, p. A316

BOGEDAIN, Carol, FACHE, Director, Veterans Affairs Roseburg Healthcare System, Roseburg, OR, p. A517

BOGEN, Mark A., Senior Vice President and Chief Financial Officer, South Nassau Communities Hospital, Oceanside, NY, p. A438

BOGGESS, Carrie
Human Resource Generalist, Carilion Giles Community Hospital, Pearisburg, VA, p. A659
Human Resources Generalist, Carilion Tazewell Community Hospital, Tazewell, VA, p. A662

BOGGESS, Jack, Chief Executive Officer, Reliant Austin, Austin, TX, p. A585

BOGGS, Danny L., President and Chief Executive Officer, Samaritan Regional Health System, Ashland, OH, p. A470

BOGGS, Lynn Ingram, Chief Executive Officer, McDowell Hospital, Marion, NC, p. A457

BOGGS, Michael S., Chief Executive Officer, Regency Hospital of Central Georgia, Macon, GA, p. A156

BOGLE, Bryan, Interim Chief Executive Officer, Winn Parish Medical Center, Winnfield, LA, p. A280

BOHALL, Karen, Director Human Resources, Woman's Christian Association Hospital, Jamestown, NY, p. A427

BOHANNON, Michelle, Director of Nursing Operations and Risk, Compliance, Quality and Safety, Wilson Medical Center, Neodesha, KS, p. A240

BOHATY, Richard, Director Information Technology, Saint Elizabeth Regional Medical Center, Lincoln, NE, p. A385

BOHLMANN, Chuck, Chief Information Officer, Community Memorial Hospital, Hicksville, OH, p. A483

BOHNENKAMP, Russ, Director Finance, Chadron Community Hospital and Health Services, Chadron, NE, p. A382

BOHNSACK, Michael, M.D. Chief of Staff, Stanly Regional Medical Center, Albemarle, NC, p. A447

BOHON, Cindy, Director Human Resources, Fayette Medical Center, Fayette, AL, p. A20

BOICE, Sheila, Director Human Resources, Barton County Memorial Hospital, Lamar, MO, p. A364

BOIKE, Darlene, Chief Financial Officer, Chippewa County–Montevideo Hospital, Montevideo, MN, p. A336

BOILEAU, Michel, M.D
Chief Clinical Officer, Pioneer Memorial Hospital, Prineville, OR, p. A517
Chief Clinical Officer, St. Charles Medical Center – Bend, Bend, OR, p. A511
Chief Clinical Officer, St. Charles Medical Center – Redmond, Redmond, OR, p. A517

BOISVERT, Gerald J., Vice President and Chief Financial Officer, Connecticut Children's Medical Center, Hartford, CT, p. A109

BOJO, Rolland, R.N. Chief Nursing Officer, Administrator Patient Care and Services, Catskill Regional Medical Center, Harris, NY, p. A427

BOK, Duard, M.D. Clinical Director, North Alabama Regional Hospital, Decatur, AL, p. A19

BOKA, Darin, Chief Information Officer, McLaren Oakland, Pontiac, MI, p. A322

BOKERN, Bob, Director Human Resources, St. Mary Medical Center, Long Beach, CA, p. A67

BOKOVITZ, Beverly, R.N
Senior Vice President and Chief Nursing Officer, Akron General Medical Center, Akron, OH, p. A470
Senior Vice President and Chief Nursing Officer, Lodi Community Hospital, Lodi, OH, p. A484

BOLAND, Susan, President and Chief Executive Officer, Wheaton Franciscan Healthcare – All Saints, Racine, WI, p. A695

BOLANDER, Patrick C., Chief Financial Officer, Georgetown Community Hospital, Georgetown, KY, p. A251

BOLCAVAGE, Ted, Vice President and Division Controller, Baylor Institute for Rehabilitation, Dallas, TX, p. A595

BOLD, Harry, Administrator, Big Sandy Medical Center, Big Sandy, MT, p. A374

BOLDA, Craig, Chief Operating Officer, St. Catherine Hospital, East Chicago, IN, p. A201

BOLDING, Kay, R.N. Vice President Patient Care Services and Chief Nursing Officer, Jackson County Memorial Hospital, Altus, OK, p. A495

BOLDUC, Tiana, Chief Information Officer, Mercy Hospital Ozark, Ozark, AR, p. A48

BOLEN, David, Vice President and Chief Financial Officer, Passavant Area Hospital, Jacksonville, IL, p. A186

BOLEN, Shannon, Director Human Resources, Baptist Memorial Hospital–Booneville, Booneville, MS, p. A345

BOLES, Glen, Vice President and Chief Financial Officer, CHRISTUS St. Michael Rehabilitation Hospital, Texarkana, TX, p. A637

BOLES, Mark D., Chief Executive Officer, Baylor Institute for Rehabilitation at Frisco, Frisco, TX, p. A605

BOLEWARE, Mike, Administrator, Franklin County Memorial Hospital, Meadville, MS, p. A350

BOLEY, Eric, Administrator and Chief Executive Officer, South Lincoln Medical Center, Kemmerer, WY, p. A702

BOLEY, Sarah, Director Human Resources, Wetzel County Hospital, New Martinsville, WV, p. A679

BOLGER, Thomas, Chief Financial Officer, Chinese Hospital, San Francisco, CA, p. A86

BOLICK, Diann, Chief Financial Officer, CarePartners Health Services, Asheville, NC, p. A447

BOLIN, Cris, Chief Executive Officer, Delta Memorial Hospital, Dumas, AR, p. A43

BOLIN, Kari, R.N. Chief Nursing Officer, Highlands Regional Medical Center, Sebring, FL, p. A140

BOLINGER, John, M.D. Vice President Medical Affairs, Union Hospital, Terre Haute, IN, p. A214

BOLLARD, Robert, Chief Financial Officer, HEALTHSOUTH Rehabilitation Hospital – Henderson, Henderson, NV, p. A392

BOLLICH, Mary, Director of Nurses, AMG Specialty Hospital–Lafayette, Lafayette, LA, p. A270

BOLOGNANI, Laurie, Human Resources Officer, Speare Memorial Hospital, Plymouth, NH, p. A400

BOLOUKI, Shawn, Chief Executive Officer, Tulare Regional Medical Center, Tulare, CA, p. A93

BOLTON, Christopher, Administrator, Providence Seward Medical Center, Seward, AK, p. A29

BOLTON, Lauri, Director Human Resources, Samaritan North Lincoln Hospital, Lincoln City, OR, p. A514

BOLTON, Neal, Chief Financial Officer, Person Memorial Hospital, Roxboro, NC, p. A460

BOMAR, Jacob, Director Information Technology, Hardin Medical Center, Savannah, TN, p. A578

BOMERSBACH, Karen, Chief Financial Officer, Dallas Medical Center, Dallas, TX, p. A595

BONAMASE, Karen, R.N. Chief Nursing Officer, Surgical Specialty Hospital of Arizona, Phoenix, AZ, p. A35

BONAMO, John F., MS, President and Chief Executive Officer, Saint Barnabas Medical Center, Livingston, NJ, p. A405

BONAR, Carrie, Chief Information Officer, Brotman Medical Center, Culver City, CA, p. A58

BONAR, Lynette, Chief Support Services, Tuba City Regional Health Care Corporation, Tuba City, AZ, p. A38

BOND, Kelly, Director Human Resources, Palo Alto County Health System, Emmetsburg, IA, p. A221

BOND, Sharon, Director Human Resources, College Station Medical Center, College Station, TX, p. A592

BOND, Troy, Chief Human Resources Officer, Atlanta Medical Center, Atlanta, GA, p. A146

BONDI, Blaise, Chief Financial Officer, Centennial Medical Center, Frisco, TX, p. A605

BONDS, Cyrillia, Administrator, United Medical Rehabilitation Hospital, Hammond, LA, p. A268

BONDURANT, Barry, Administrator and Chief Executive Officer, Baptist Memorial Hospital–Union City, Union City, TN, p. A580

BONDURANT, Charles, Chief Information Officer, Meadows Regional Medical Center, Vidalia, GA, p. A162

BONE, Janice, Director Human Resources, Parkway Regional Hospital, Fulton, KY, p. A251

BONECUTTER, Dane, Director Human Resources, Connally Medical Center, Floresville, TX, p. A602

BONFILIO, Nicholas, M.D. Chief of Staff, Great Falls Clinic Medical Center, Great Falls, MT, p. A376

BONI, Shirley M., Administrative Officer, U. S. Public Health Service Indian Hospital, San Carlos, AZ, p. A36

BONILLA, Jose A., Deputy Commander Administration, Winn Army Community Hospital, Hinesville, GA, p. A155

BONK, Daniel J., Chief Executive Officer, Aurora Medical Center Summit, Summit, WI, p. A697

BONNER, Daphne, Administrator, Greenbriar Rehabilitation Hospital, Boardman, OH, p. A472

BONNER, Gwen, Chief Operating Officer, Saint Francis Hospital–Bartlett, Bartlett, TN, p. A565

BONNER, Lauren, Director Human Resources, Cumberland Hospital, New Kent, VA, p. A657

BONNER, Lenne
Interim Chief Executive Officer, Clearwater Valley Hospital and Clinics, Orofino, ID, p. A170
Chief Financial Officer, Clearwater Valley Hospital and Clinics, Orofino, ID, p. A170
Interim Chief Executive Officer, St. Mary's Hospital, Cottonwood, ID, p. A168
Chief Financial Officer, St. Mary's Hospital, Cottonwood, ID, p. A168

BONNETTE, James C., M.D. Chief Clinical Officer, Genesys Regional Medical Center, Grand Blanc, MI, p. A314

BONNICHSEN, Daniel G., Deputy Commander for Administration, Irwin Army Community Hospital, Junction City, KS, p. A236

BONSER, Kathleen, R.N. Vice President, Nursing/CNO, SSM DePaul Health Center, Bridgeton, MO, p. A357

BONTHUIS, Michael W., Chief Financial Officer, United General Hospital, Sedro Woolley, WA, p. A672

BOOHER, Terresa O., Vice President of Patient Care Services, Highlands Regional Medical Center, Prestonsburg, KY, p. A259

BOOK, Jonathan D., M.D. Clinical Director, Springfield Hospital Center, Sykesville, MD, p. A294

BOOK, Kari, Director Human Resources, Fairfield Memorial Hospital, Fairfield, IL, p. A182

BOOKER, Angela, Director of Nursing Services, Teton Valley Health Care, Driggs, ID, p. A169

BOOKMAN, Larry, D.O. Chief Medical Officer, Yampa Valley Medical Center, Steamboat Springs, CO, p. A106

BOOMSMA, Joan, M.D. Vice President Medical Management, Advocate Condell Medical Center, Libertyville, IL, p. A187

BOONE, Bradley, M.D. Chief Medical Staff, Anderson Regional Medical Center–South Campus, Meridian, MS, p. A351

BOONE, David J., Senior Vice President, Finance, Catawba Valley Medical Center, Hickory, NC, p. A454

BOONE, Donna, R.N. Chief Nursing Officer, Weatherford Regional Medical Center, Weatherford, TX, p. A640

BOONE III, Elwood Bernard, FACHE, President, Sentara Virginia Beach General Hospital, Virginia Beach, VA, p. A662

BOONE, Keith, M.D. Medical Director, Fresno Heart and Surgical Hospital, Fresno, CA, p. A61

BOONE, Margie, Registered Health Information Technician, Cumberland River Hospital, Celina, TN, p. A566

BOONE, Richard, Chief Financial Officer, Sparks Regional Medical Center, Fort Smith, AR, p. A44

BOONE, Sherry, Chief Information Resource Management, Veterans Affairs Illiana Health Care System, Danville, IL, p. A180

BOORNAZIAN, John, M.D. Chief Medical Officer, Huggins Hospital, Wolfeboro, NH, p. A400

BOOTH, Christy, Chief Human Resources Officer, Doctors Memorial Hospital, Bonifay, FL, p. A119

BOOTH, Daniel, Vice President Operations and Chief Human Resources Officer, Inland Hospital, Waterville, ME, p. A285

BOOTH, Lorraine, Executive Director Human Resources, Orange Coast Memorial Medical Center, Fountain Valley, CA, p. A60

BOOTH, Patrick M., Chief Executive Officer, Fremont Area Medical Center, Fremont, NE, p. A383

BOOTH–MILLS, Megan
Director Planning and Marketing, Vidant Bertie Hospital, Windsor, NC, p. A463
Director Planning and Marketing, Vidant Chowan Hospital, Edenton, NC, p. A452

BOR, David, M.D. Chief of Medicine, Cambridge Health Alliance, Cambridge, MA, p. A299

BORAN, David, M.D. Chief Medical Officer, Essentia Health St. Joseph's Medical Center, Brainerd, MN, p. A329

BORCHI, Daniel, Chief Information Officer, Carilion New River Valley Medical Center, Christiansburg, VA, p. A652

BORDELON, Gloria, Human Resources Generalist, Holmes County Hospital and Clinics, Lexington, MS, p. A350

BORDEN, Eric, Chief Operating Officer and Chief Financial Officer, Jewell County Hospital, Mankato, KS, p. A239

BORDEN, Sandy, Chief Financial Officer, Brodstone Memorial Hospital, Superior, NE, p. A390

BORDENKIRCHER, Kimberly, Chief Executive Officer, Henry County Hospital, Napoleon, OH, p. A487

BORDER, Sally, Chief Financial Officer, Saint Luke¥s Cushing Medical Center, Leavenworth, KS, p. A238

BORDO, David, M.D. Vice President, Medical Affairs/Chief Medical Officer, Presence Our Lady of the Resurrection Medical Center, Chicago, IL, p. A178

BOREL, Patricia, Chief Financial Officer, Central Community Hospital, Elkader, IA, p. A221

BOREN, Shed, Administrator and Chief Executive Officer, Sister Emmanuel Hospital, Miami, FL, p. A132

BORENGASSER, Connie, Chief Executive Officer, Vista Health, Fayetteville, AR, p. A43

BORENSTEIN, Jeffrey, M.D. Medical Director, Holliswood Hospital,, NY, p. A432

BORER, Tom, Vice President Operations, ProMedica Fostoria Community Hospital, Fostoria, OH, p. A481

BORGERSON, Carol, Business Office Manager and Chief Financial Officer, Madison Hospital, Madison, MN, p. A335

BORGERT, Karen, Vice President Human Resources, Grandview Medical Center, Dayton, OH, p. A480

BORGES, Rafael, M.D. Chief of Staff, St. Anthony's Hospital, Houston, TX, p. A612

BORGSTROM, Marna P., Chief Executive Officer, Yale–New Haven Hospital, New Haven, CT, p. A110

BORING, Ronald L., Senior Vice President and Chief Operating Officer, McLeod Regional Medical Center, Florence, SC, p. A552

BORIS, Diane
Vice President and Chief Financial Officer, Schuylkill Medical Center – East Norwegian Street, Pottsville, PA, p. A539
Chief Financial Officer, Schuylkill Medical Center – South Jackson Street, Pottsville, PA, p. A539

BORIS, Jamie, M.D. President Medical Staff, Southwest Regional Medical Center, Waynesburg, PA, p. A543

BORJA, William, Chief Information Officer, Milwaukee County Behavioral Health Division, Milwaukee, WI, p. A692

BORJIAN, Fariba, Chief Information Officer, Palms West Hospital, Loxahatchee, FL, p. A129

BORLAND, Winston, FACHE, President and Chief Executive Officer, Medical Center of Arlington, Arlington, TX, p. A583

BOROSKY, Karen, Vice President and Chief Information Officer, UPMC Passavant, Pittsburgh, PA, p. A538

BOROWSKI, Thomas
Chief Information Officer, Mayo Clinic Health System in Mankato, Mankato, MN, p. A335
Chief Information Officer, Mayo Clinic Health System in Saint James, Saint James, MN, p. A339

BORTEL, Karol, Vice President Financial Services, Wood County Hospital, Bowling Green, OH, p. A472

BORTKE, Todd, Director Information Systems, St. Alexius Medical Center, Bismarck, ND, p. A465

BORTON, Jerry, Manager Information, Van Wert County Hospital, Van Wert, OH, p. A492

BORZON, Eve, R.N. Chief Operating Officer, Woodhull Medical and Mental Health Center,, NY, p. A437

BOSCH, Scott W., FACHE, President and Chief Executive Officer, Harrison Medical Center, Bremerton, WA, p. A664

BOSCIA, Michael, Chief Financial Officer, Bartow Regional Medical Center, Bartow, FL, p. A118

BOSCO, John
Vice President and Chief Information Officer, Forest Hills Hospital,, NY, p. A432
Chief Information Officer, Franklin Hospital, Valley Stream, NY, p. A445

BOSCO, Maureen, Executive Director, Central New York Psychiatric Center, Marcy, NY, p. A429

BOSER, Andrew, Chief Executive Officer, Cuba Memorial Hospital, Cuba, NY, p. A424

BOSLEY, Elizabeth, R.N. Vice President Patient Services, St. Mary's Medical Center, Huntington, WV, p. A678

BOSO, Edwin, M.D. President Medical Staff, Camden Clark Medical Center, Parkersburg, WV, p. A679

BOSS, Janice M., MS, Director, Veterans Affairs Connecticut Healthcare System, West Haven, CT, p. A113

BOSS, Virgil, Administrator, Cascade Medical Center, Cascade, ID, p. A168

BOSSE, Doyle, M.D. Chief Medical Officer, Jackson Hospital, Marianna, FL, p. A130

BOSSI, Barbara, Senior Vice President Operations and Patient Care Services, Geisinger–Community Medical Center, Scranton, PA, p. A540

BOST, Cecelia, Chief Operating Officer, Alliance HealthCare System, Holly Springs, MS, p. A348

BOST, Marcus, Director Information Services and Chief Information Officer, Adena Greenfield Medical Center, Greenfield, OH, p. A482

BOSTIC, Deborah, R.N. Chief Nursing Officer, Texas Health Presbyterian Hospital Denton, Denton, TX, p. A599

BOSTIC, William, Administrative Assistant Human Resources, Surprise Valley Healthcare District, Cedarville, CA, p. A56

BOSTON III, Ward, Chief Executive Officer, North Florida Regional Medical Center, Gainesville, FL, p. A124

BOSTROM, Gary, Chief Executive Officer and Chief Executive Financial Officer, East Adams Rural Hospital, Ritzville, WA, p. A670

BOSTROM, Stuart, M.D. Director Medical Affairs, Sutter Roseville Medical Center, Roseville, CA, p. A83

BOSTWICK, Monte J., Chief Executive Officer, Biloxi Regional Medical Center, Biloxi, MS, p. A344

BOSWELL, Debbie, Chief Operating Officer and Chief Nursing Officer, Mercy Medical Center, Roseburg, OR, p. A517

BOSWELL, Diane, Director Human Resources and Marketing, Salem Township Hospital, Salem, IL, p. A194

BOSWELL, John, Associate Chief Human Resources, University of Virginia Medical Center, Charlottesville, VA, p. A652

BOTAK, Geoff, Chief Executive Officer, Friends Hospital, Philadelphia, PA, p. A535

BOTHNER, Joan, M.D. Chief Medical Officer, Children's Hospital Colorado, Aurora, CO, p. A97

BOTHUN, Crystal, Chief Financial Officer, Johnson Memorial Health Services, Dawson, MN, p. A331

BOTTCHER, Sharon A., R.N. Vice President Patient Care Services, MedStar Union Memorial Hospital, Baltimore, MD, p. A288

BOTTGER, Barry, Chief Financial Officer, Republic County Hospital, Belleville, KS, p. A231

BOTTICELLA, Mary, R.N. Chief Nursing Officer, Fountain Valley Regional Hospital and Medical Center, Fountain Valley, CA, p. A60

BOTTOM, Paige, Director Operations, Wilmington Treatment Center, Wilmington, NC, p. A463

BOTTOMS, Amber, Director Medical Records, Chambers Memorial Hospital, Danville, AR, p. A42

BOUCHARD, Don, D.O. Chief of Staff, Borgess–Lee Memorial Hospital, Dowagiac, MI, p. A313

BOUCHARD, Lorraine, Vice President Human Resources, Southern Maine Medical Center, Biddeford, ME, p. A282

BOUCHARD, Marc, M.D. President Medical Staff, North Country Hospital and Health Center, Newport, VT, p. A650

BOUCK, Nancy, Director Human Resources, Huron Medical Center, Bad Axe, MI, p. A308

BOUGHAL, Ginni, Director Health Information and Information Technology, PeaceHealth Peace Harbor Medical Center, Florence, OR, p. A512

BOULA, Rodney C., Administrator and Chief Executive Officer, Elizabethtown Community Hospital, Elizabethtown, NY, p. A425

BOULANGER, Bernie, M.D. Chief Medical Officer, UK HealthCare Good Samaritan Hospital, Lexington, KY, p. A254

BOULENGER, Bo, Chief Executive Officer, Baptist Health South Florida, Baptist Hospital of Miami, Miami, FL, p. A131

BOUNDS, Floyd D., Chief Executive Officer, Bell Hospital, Ishpeming, MI, p. A317

BOUQUIO, George, Director Human Resources, South Beach Psychiatric Center,, NY, p. A436

BOUR, Eric, M.D., President, Hillcrest Memorial Hospital, Simpsonville, SC, p. A555

BOURDEAU, Patricia, Director Human Resources, Brook Lane Health Services, Hagerstown, MD, p. A292

BOURGASSER, Gene, M.D. Chief of Staff, Sullivan County Community Hospital, Sullivan, IN, p. A213

BOURGAULT, Catherine, Director Human Resources, Providence Hood River Memorial Hospital, Hood River, OR, p. A513

BOURGEOIS Jr., Milton D., Chief Executive Officer, Ochsner St. Anne General Hospital, Raceland, LA, p. A277

BOURLAND, Don, Vice President Human Resources, PeaceHealth Peace Harbor Medical Center, Florence, OR, p. A512

BOURLAND, Renee, Human Resources Specialist, San Antonio State Hospital, San Antonio, TX, p. A632

BOURN, Jennifer, Coordinator Health Information Systems, CenterPointe Hospital, Saint Charles, MO, p. A368

BOURNE, Kara, R.N. Chief Nursing Officer and Chief Operating Officer, Newport Specialty Hospital, Tustin, CA, p. A93

BOURQUE, Teresa, Sr. Administrator for Nursing/Chief Nurse, Hurley Medical Center, Flint, MI, p. A313

BOUTROS, Akram, FACHE, President and Chief Executive Officer, MetroHealth Medical Center, Cleveland, OH, p. A476

BOUYEA, Janine, Director Human Resources, Natividad Medical Center, Salinas, CA, p. A84

BOVEE, Michael, Vice President Finance, Riverview Hospital Association, Wisconsin Rapids, WI, p. A700

BOVIO Jr., Ernest L., Chief Executive Officer, Scott & White Hospital at Round Rock, Round Rock, TX, p. A629

BOW, Beverly
Vice President Human Resources, Salem Hospital, Salem, OR, p. A517
Vice President Human Resources, West Valley Hospital, Dallas, OR, p. A512

BOWCUTT, Marilyn A., MSN, President, University Hospital, Augusta, GA, p. A148

BOWEN, Jill Berry, President and Chief Executive Officer, Northwestern Medical Center, Saint Albans, VT, p. A650

BOWEN, John, Assistant Vice President and Administrator, Baptist Health Medical Center–Arkadelphia, Arkadelphia, AR, p. A41

BOWEN, Sandra, Chief Financial Officer, Shasta Regional Medical Center, Redding, CA, p. A81

BOWEN, Steve
Administrator, Kimble Hospital, Junction, TX, p. A615
Director Information Systems, Plateau Medical Center, Oak Hill, WV, p. A679

BOWEN, Tim, Chief Executive Officer, Mena Regional Health System, Mena, AR, p. A47

BOWER, David, M.D. Chief of Staff, Atlanta Veterans Affairs Medical Center, Decatur, GA, p. A151

BOWER, Kay, Associate Director for Patient Care Services, Battle Creek Veterans Affairs Medical Center, Battle Creek, MI, p. A309

BOWERMAN, Joeann, Director of Nursing Services, Chambers Memorial Hospital, Danville, AR, p. A42

BOWERMAN, Stephen, Chief Financial Officer, Midland Memorial Hospital, Midland, TX, p. A623

BOWERS, Dan, Chief Operating Officer, Riverside Community Hospital, Riverside, CA, p. A82

BOWERS, David, Vice President Human Resources and Support Services, Children's Hospital of The King's Daughters, Norfolk, VA, p. A658

BOWERS, David N., M.D. Medical Director, Siskin Hospital for Physical Rehabilitation, Chattanooga, TN, p. A567

BOWERS, Gary, Chief Operating Officer, CarePartners Health Services, Asheville, NC, p. A447

BOWERS, Gregory, Chief Financial Officer, Spring Harbor Hospital, Westbrook, ME, p. A286

BOWERS, Judith, D.O. Chief of Staff, Community Memorial Hospital, Oconto Falls, WI, p. A694

BOWERS, Maria, M.D. Chief of Staff, Erlanger at Hutcheson, Fort Oglethorpe, GA, p. A154

BOWERS, Sharon, R.N. Manager of Community, Public and Employee Relations, Sheridan Community Hospital, Sheridan, MI, p. A324

BOWERS, Stephen, M.D. Clinical Director, Northern Navajo Medical Center, Shiprock, NM, p. A418

BOWERS, Susan, R.N., President and Chief Nursing Officer, Mercy Allen Hospital, Oberlin, OH, p. A488

BOWERS, Tracy, Director Human Resources, Novant Health Prince William Medical Center, Manassas, VA, p. A656

BOWES, Arthur, Senior Vice President Human Resources, North Shore Medical Center, Salem, MA, p. A304

BOWES, William, Chief Financial Officer, UAMS Medical Center, Little Rock, AR, p. A47

BOWIE, Craig, Information Technology Manager, Pauls Valley General Hospital, Pauls Valley, OK, p. A505

BOWIE, Joshua, Chief Executive Officer, Yuma Rehabilitation Hospital, Yuma, AZ, p. A40

BOWLBY, Debbie, Director Information Systems, St. Luke's Hospital – Warren Campus, Phillipsburg, NJ, p. A409

BOWLEG, Teresa, R.N. Chief Nursing Officer, Murphy Medical Center, Murphy, NC, p. A458

BOWLING, Judy, Director Human Resources, Southeast Health Center of Stoddard County, Dexter, MO, p. A359

BOWLING, Karen, Chief Information Officer, St. Joseph Hospital, Bangor, ME, p. A281

BOWLING, Kay, Chief Executive Officer, Center for Restorative Care and Rehabilitation, Lynchburg, VA, p. A656

BOWLING, Kelli, Chief Culture Officer, Ministry Door County Medical Center, Sturgeon Bay, WI, p. A697

BOWMAN, Barbara, Chief Human Resource Officer, Ann & Robert H. Lurie Children's Hospital of Chicago, Chicago, IL, p. A176

BOWMAN, Dyan, Director Human Resources, Newberry County Memorial Hospital, Newberry, SC, p. A555

BOWMAN, Joseph E., Chief Financial Officer, TriStar StoneCrest Medical Center, Smyrna, TN, p. A579

BOWMAN, Julie, Chief Nursing Officer, Havasu Regional Medical Center, Lake Havasu City, AZ, p. A32

BOWMAN, Ken, Chief Executive Officer, Van Matre HEALTHSOUTH Rehabilitation Hospital, Rockford, IL, p. A194

BOWMAN, Mark, M.D. Medical Staff President, Tillamook Regional Medical Center, Tillamook, OR, p. A518

BOWMAN, Scott, Administrator, Sweetwater Hospital, Sweetwater, TN, p. A579

BOWMAN, Terry R., Chief Financial Officer, Wake Forest Baptist Health–Davie Hospital, Mocksville, NC, p. A457

BOWMAN, Wayne, Interim Chief Nursing Officer, Decatur Morgan Hospital, Decatur, AL, p. A19

BOWMAN, William, M.D. Vice President Medical Affairs, Cone Health, Greensboro, NC, p. A453

BOX, Darrel, Chief Executive Officer, Lafayette Regional Health Center, Lexington, MO, p. A365

BOX, Lynette, Director Medical Records, Arrowhead Behavioral Health Hospital, Maumee, OH, p. A486

BOX, Tom, CPA Chief Financial Officer, HEALTHSOUTH Rehabilitation Hospital–Wichita Falls, Wichita Falls, TX, p. A641

BOXELL, Shelley, R.N. Chief Nursing Officer and Quality Coordinator, Rehabilitation Hospital of Fort Wayne, Fort Wayne, IN, p. A203

BOYCE, Carol
Administrative Director Support Services, ProMedica Bixby Hospital, Adrian, MI, p. A308
Administrative Director Support Services, ProMedica Herrick Hospital, Tecumseh, MI, p. A325

BOYCE, Charlotte, Chief Nursing Officer, HEALTHSOUTH Rehabilitation Hospital Memphis–North, Memphis, TN, p. A574

BOYCE, Joe, M.D. Chief Information Officer, Heartland Regional Medical Center, Saint Joseph, MO, p. A369

BOYD, Amber, Nurse Practitioner and Director of Nursing, Devereux Georgia Treatment Network, Kennesaw, GA, p. A155

BOYD, Amy, Information Systems Manager, Vidant Beaufort Hospital, Washington, NC, p. A462

BOYD, Christopher L., Senior Vice President and Area Manager, Kaiser Permanente Santa Clara Medical Center, Santa Clara, CA, p. A89

BOYD, Dennis, Chief Financial Officer, St. Mark's Medical Center, La Grange, TX, p. A617

BOYD, Diana, Vice President Nursing, Union Hospital, Dover, OH, p. A480

BOYD, Ellen, Director Human Resources, Emanuel Medical Center, Swainsboro, GA, p. A161

BOYD, Fred, Interim Vice President Human Resources, Regional Medical Center at Memphis, Memphis, TN, p. A575

BOYD, Jason E., FACHE, Interim Chief Executive Officer, Nashville General Hospital, Nashville, TN, p. A576

BOYD, JoAnn, Administrative Assistant, Jasper General Hospital, Bay Springs, MS, p. A344

BOYD, John, Manager Information Systems, North Valley Hospital, Tonasket, WA, p. A673

BOYD, John A K, M.D. Vice President Mission and Medical Affairs and Chief Medical Officer, Mercy Regional Medical Center, Durango, CO, p. A100

BOYD, John W., PsyD, Chief Administrative Officer, Sutter Center for Psychiatry, Sacramento, CA, p. A84

BOYD Jr., Kenneth, President and Chief Executive Officer, McDonough District Hospital, Macomb, IL, p. A187

BOYD, Kim, Chief Financial Officer, Buchanan General Hospital, Grundy, VA, p. A655

BOYD, Larry, M.D. Chief of Staff, Pecos County Memorial Hospital, Fort Stockton, TX, p. A603

BOYD, Steven, R.N. Nurse Executive, Levi Hospital, Hot Springs National Park, AR, p. A45

BOYD, Travis, Manager Information Technology, Lincoln County Medical Center, Troy, MO, p. A372

BOYDEN, Jenny, Chief Financial Officer, Riverview Psychiatric Center, Augusta, ME, p. A281

BOYER, Allan, Chief Executive Officer, Ancora Psychiatric Hospital, Hammonton, NJ, p. A404

BOYER, Aurelia, Senior Vice President and Chief Information Officer, New York–Presbyterian Hospital, New York, NY, p. A435

BOYER, Charlene, Chief Nursing Officer, Kaiser Permanente Oakland Medical Center, Oakland, CA, p. A77

BOYER, Cheryl T.
Vice President Human Resources, Levindale Hebrew Geriatric Center and Hospital, Baltimore, MD, p. A288
Vice President Human Resources, Sinai Hospital of Baltimore, Baltimore, MD, p. A289

BOYER, Craig, Vice President Finance, Sanford Bemidji Medical Center, Bemidji, MN, p. A329

BOYER, Diana, Chief Information Officer, Columbus Regional Hospital, Columbus, IN, p. A200

BOYER, Gregory E., Chief Executive Officer, Renown Regional Medical Center, Reno, NV, p. A395

BOYER, Jim, Vice President Information Technology and Chief Information Officer, Rush Memorial Hospital, Rushville, IN, p. A213

BOYER, Marta, Vice President Human Resources, Children's Hospital Central California, Madera, CA, p. A73

BOYER, Roderick, M.D. Medical Director, Select Specialty Hospital–Downriver, Taylor, MI, p. A325

BOYKIN, Alfred, M.D. Chief of Staff, Wm. Jennings Bryan Dorn Veterans Affairs Medical Center, Columbia, SC, p. A551

BOYKIN, Doyle, MSN, Administrator, Presbyterian Kaseman Hospital, Albuquerque, NM, p. A415

BOYLE, Donna, Director, West Palm Hospital, West Palm Beach, FL, p. A144

BOYLE, James W., M.D. Chief Medical Officer, UPMC Passavant, Pittsburgh, PA, p. A538

BOYLE, Kathy, R.N. Chief Nursing Officer, Denver Health Medical Center, Denver, CO, p. A99

BOYLE, Patrick R.
Vice President Human Resources, Geneva General Hospital, Geneva, NY, p. A426
Vice President Human Resources, Soldiers and Sailors Memorial Hospital of Yates County, Penn Yan, NY, p. A439

BOYLE, Thomas W., Chief Financial Officer, St. Lawrence Rehabilitation Center, Lawrenceville, NJ, p. A405

BOYLES, Clay, Director Human Resources, Peachford Behavioral Health System, Atlanta, GA, p. A146

BOYLES, George, Vice President Finance and Chief Financial Officer, Mercer Health, Coldwater, OH, p. A477

BOYLES, Larry, Senior Vice President, Riverside Regional Medical Center, Newport News, VA, p. A658

BOYLES, Laura, Director Human Resources, Stanislaus Surgical Hospital, Modesto, CA, p. A74

BOYLES, Lee, President, Oakes Community Hospital, Oakes, ND, p. A468

BOYNE, Barb, Executive Director, Operations, Bethesda North Hospital, Cincinnati, OH, p. A474

BOYNTON, Kimberly, Chief Financial Officer, Crouse Hospital, Syracuse, NY, p. A443

BOYNTON, Stephanie, Administrator, Erlanger Bledsoe Hospital, Pikeville, TN, p. A578

BOYS, Edward, Chief Information Officer, Ozarks Medical Center, West Plains, MO, p. A373

BOYSEN, James, M.D. Executive Medical Director, Texas NeuroRehab Center, Austin, TX, p. A586

BOYSEN, Joan, Chief Operating Officer, District One Hospital, Faribault, MN, p. A332

BOZELL, Jerry, Administrative Director Human Resources, Jay County Hospital, Portland, IN, p. A212

BOZEMAN, Tom, Chief Information Officer, North Mississippi Medical Center – Tupelo, Tupelo, MS, p. A354

BOZZUTO, Elizabeth, R.N. Interim Chief Nursing Officer and Vice President Surgical Services, Saint Mary's Hospital, Waterbury, CT, p. A112

BRAAM, Richard, Vice President Finance, MedStar St. Mary's Hospital, Leonardtown, MD, p. A293

BRAASCH, David A., President, Alton Memorial Hospital, Alton, IL, p. A173

BRAASCH, Robert, Administrator Human Resources, Andrew McFarland Mental Health Center, Springfield, IL, p. A195

BRABAND, Jon D., FACHE, President and Chief Executive Officer, Glencoe Regional Health Services, Glencoe, MN, p. A332

BRABSON, Amanda, Director Marketing and Public Relations, LeConte Medical Center, Sevierville, TN, p. A579

BRACEY, Donny, Director Information Services, Marion General Hospital, Columbia, MS, p. A346

BRACHT, Gerald E., Chief Administrative Officer, Palomar Medical Center, Escondido, CA, p. A59

BRACKEN, Thomas H., M.D. Vice President Medical Affairs, Mille Lacs Health System, Onamia, MN, p. A337

BRACKLEY, Donna, Senior Vice President Patient Care Services, John Muir Medical Center, Concord, Concord, CA, p. A57

BRACKS, Adam, Chief Executive Officer, Southeast Health Center of Stoddard County, Dexter, MO, p. A359

BRACY, Dale, Chief Financial Officer, College Hospital Costa Mesa, Costa Mesa, CA, p. A57

BRADDOCK, Mary B., Director Human Resources, Palo Pinto General Hospital, Mineral Wells, TX, p. A623

BRADDY, Rufus, Director Management Information Systems, Roosevelt Warm Springs LTAC Hospital, Warm Springs, GA, p. A162

BRADEL, William T., President, Flagstaff Medical Center, Flagstaff, AZ, p. A31

BRADEN, III, Terence, D.O. Medical Director, HEALTHSOUTH Rehabilitation Hospital of Jonesboro, Jonesboro, AR, p. A45

BRADEY, Sarah, Vice President Finance, Mercy Hospital Hot Springs, Hot Springs National Park, AR, p. A45

BRADFORD, Anna, R.N. Chief Nursing Officer, Crosbyton Clinic Hospital, Crosbyton, TX, p. A594

BRADFORD, Beth, Director Human Resources, Floyd Medical Center, Rome, GA, p. A159

BRADFORD, David, M.D. Chief Medical Officer, Mid–Valley Hospital, Omak, WA, p. A669

BRADFORD, James, M.D. President Medical Staff, Iredell Memorial Hospital, Statesville, NC, p. A461

BRADFORD, John, Vice President Finance, Flaget Memorial Hospital, Bardstown, KY, p. A248

BRADFORD, Karin, Chief Financial Officer, LifeCare Hospitals of Dallas, Dallas, TX, p. A596

BRADFORD, Randy L., Assistant Superintendent, Eastern Shore Hospital Center, Cambridge, MD, p. A290

BRADFORD, Scot, Chief Information Officer, Baylor Medical Center at Trophy Club, Trophy Club, TX, p. A638

BRADFORD, Sue E., R.N. Chief Nursing Officer, Memorial Hospital West, Pembroke Pines, FL, p. A136

BRADLEY, Betsy, Coordinator Performance Improvement, Central State Hospital, Milledgeville, GA, p. A157

BRADLEY, Carol, MS
Senior Vice President and Chief Nursing Officer, Legacy Meridian Park Hospital, Tualatin, OR, p. A518
Senior Vice President and Chief Nursing Officer, Legacy Salmon Creek Medical Center, Vancouver, WA, p. A673

BRADLEY, Douglas, M.D. Vice President Medical Affairs, Belton Regional Medical Center, Belton, MO, p. A356

BRADLEY, Eric, Director Computer Information Services, Summit Behavioral Healthcare, Cincinnati, OH, p. A475

BRADLEY, Joel, Director Information Systems, Greenville Health System Laurens County Memorial Hospital, Clinton, SC, p. A550

BRADLEY, John, M.D. Chief of Staff, Longmont United Hospital, Longmont, CO, p. A104

BRADLEY, Linda, Chief Executive Officer, Centinela Hospital Medical Center, Inglewood, CA, p. A64

BRADLEY, Louis, Chief Operating Officer, Mesquite Specialty Hospital, Mesquite, TX, p. A622

BRADLEY, Michelle, Director Health Information Management, AMG Specialty Hospital–Wichita, Wichita, KS, p. A246

BRADLEY, Stacye, R.N. Chief Nursing Officer, Union County General Hospital, Clayton, NM, p. A415

BRADLEY, Teresa, M.D. Vice President Medical Affairs, St. Anthony's Hospital, Saint Petersburg, FL, p. A139

BRADLEY, Terri, CPA Vice President Financial Services and Chief Financial Officer, Western Missouri Medical Center, Warrensburg, MO, p. A373

BRADLEY, Virginia D., Chief Information Officer, Breckinridge Memorial Hospital, Hardinsburg, KY, p. A252

BRADLEY, William L., President and Chief Executive Officer, Washington Regional Medical Center, Fayetteville, AR, p. A43

BRADSHAW, David
Chief Information Officer, Memorial Hermann – Texas Medical Center, Houston, TX, p. A610
Chief Information, Planning and Marketing Officer, Memorial Hermann Memorial City Medical Center, Houston, TX, p. A610
Chief Information Officer, Memorial Hermann Northwest Hospital, Houston, TX, p. A611

BRADSHAW, Deborah, Director Human Resources, Holy Family Hospital and Medical Center, Methuen, MA, p. A302

BRADSHAW, Rita, Director Human Resources, Chatuge Regional Hospital and Nursing Home, Hiawassee, GA, p. A154

BRADSHAW, Thomas A., Vice President Operations, Wayne Memorial Hospital, Goldsboro, NC, p. A453

BRADSHAW, William, M.D. Chief of Staff, St. Vincent General Hospital District, Leadville, CO, p. A103

BRADY, Albert, M.D. Chief of Staff, Yakima Regional Medical and Cardiac Center, Yakima, WA, p. A674

BRADY, Jeff
Director Information Systems, Hazard ARH Regional Medical Center, Hazard, KY, p. A252
Director Information Systems, McDowell ARH Hospital, McDowell, KY, p. A257
Director Information Systems, Morgan County ARH Hospital, West Liberty, KY, p. A261
Chief Information Officer, Williamson ARH Hospital, South Williamson, KY, p. A260

BRADY, John, Vice President Physician Services and Organizational Planning, Marianjoy Rehabilitation Hospital, Wheaton, IL, p. A196

BRADY, Karen, Chief Information Officer, Silverton Hospital, Silverton, OR, p. A518

BRADY, Linda, M.D., President and Chief Executive Officer, Kingsbrook Jewish Medical Center,, NY, p. A433

BRADY, Patrick R., Chief Executive Officer, Sutter Roseville Medical Center, Roseville, CA, p. A83

BRADY, Reta, Administrative Assistant and Manager Human Resources, Houston County Community Hospital, Erin, TN, p. A568

BRADY, Tim, Director Information Systems, Mt. Washington Pediatric Hospital, Baltimore, MD, p. A288

BRAESE, Nancy, D.O. President Medical Staff, Exeter Hospital, Exeter, NH, p. A398

BRAGDON, Carol, Director Human Resources, Saint Thomas Rutherford Hospital, Murfreesboro, TN, p. A576

BRAGG, Craig, Chief Executive Officer, TrustPoint Hospital, Lubbock, TX, p. A620

BRAGG, Deborah, Director Human Resources, Webster County Memorial Hospital, Webster Springs, WV, p. A681

BRAGG, Lisa, Vice President Human Resources, Knox Community Hospital, Mount Vernon, OH, p. A487

BRAGG, Melissa, Chief Human Resources Management, Charles George Veterans Affairs Medical Center, Asheville, NC, p. A447

BRAITHWAITE, Robert, President and Chief Executive Officer, Hoag Memorial Hospital Presbyterian, Newport Beach, CA, p. A76

BRAKE, Joe, Director Information Services, Fishermen's Hospital, Marathon, FL, p. A129

BRAMBLE, Steve, Director Human Resources, LeConte Medical Center, Sevierville, TN, p. A579

BRAMLETT, Larry, Chief Information Officer, AMG Specialty Hospital–Greenwood, Greenwood, MS, p. A347

BRAMLIET, Charles, M.D. Medical Director, MMO WestEnd Hospital, Jennings, LA, p. A269

BRANCATO, Joyce A., Chief Executive Officer, Seven Rivers Regional Medical Center, Crystal River, FL, p. A121

BRANCEL, Dale, D.O. Chief of Staff, Victory Medical Center Mid–Cities, Hurst, TX, p. A614

BRANCH, Cathryn, R.N., Chief Executive Officer, Kindred Hospital–San Diego, San Diego, CA, p. A85

BRANCH, Terrance, Chief Information Management, Fort Belvoir Community Hospital, Fort Belvoir, VA, p. A654

BRANCH, Tim, Manager Information Technology, Covenant Hospital Plainview, Plainview, TX, p. A627

BRANCHICK, Jim, R.N. Chief Operating Officer, Kaiser Permanente Downey Medical Center, Downey, CA, p. A58

BRANCO, Patrick J., Chief Executive Officer, PeaceHealth Ketchikan Medical Center, Ketchikan, AK, p. A28

BRAND, James R., M.D. Chief of Staff, DeTar Healthcare System, Victoria, TX, p. A639

BRAND, Lamar, M.D. Chief of Staff, Miller County Hospital, Colquitt, GA, p. A150

BRANDENBURG, Edward M., FACHE Vice President Professional Services, Community Memorial Healthcenter, South Hill, VA, p. A661

BRANDENBURG, Valerie, Director Human Resources, Northwest Hospital, Randallstown, MD, p. A293

BRANDIS, Destin, Chief Information Officer, William Bee Ririe Hospital, Ely, NV, p. A391

BRANDNER, Nicholas R., Chief Executive Officer, Community Memorial Hospital, Redfield, SD, p. A562

BRANDON, David R., President and Chief Executive Officer, UnityPoint Health Finley, Dubuque, IA, p. A221

BRANDON, Deborah, Director Total Quality Management, Eastern Louisiana Mental Health System, Jackson, LA, p. A269

BRANDON, Paula, MSN Vice President Patient Care Services, Good Shepherd Medical Center–Marshall, Marshall, TX, p. A621

BRANDON, Wendy H., Chief Executive Officer, Central Florida Regional Hospital, Sanford, FL, p. A139

BRANDT, Cynthia, Interim Chief Financial Officer, Norton Sound Regional Hospital, Nome, AK, p. A28

BRANDT, Jason, M.D. Medical Director, Surgical Hospital of Jonesboro, Jonesboro, AR, p. A45

BRANDT, Matthew, Chief Financial Officer, St. Alexius Hospital – Broadway Campus, Saint Louis, MO, p. A370

BRANDT, Merle, Chief Financial Officer, Mason General Hospital, Shelton, WA, p. A672

BRANDT, Steve, M.D. Chief of Staff, Dale Medical Center, Ozark, AL, p. A24

BRANNAN, Debbie
Chief Financial Officer, George Regional Hospital, Lucedale, MS, p. A350
Chief Financial Officer, Greene County Hospital, Leakesville, MS, p. A349

BRANNEN, Charles C., Senior Vice President and Chief Operating Officer, Southeast Alabama Medical Center, Dothan, AL, p. A19

BRANNEN, Judy, M.D. Interim Chief of Staff, Hunter Holmes McGuire Veterans Affairs Medical Center, Richmond, VA, p. A660

BRANNIGAN, Robert C., Administrator, West Valley Hospital, Dallas, OR, p. A512

BRANNMAN, Brian G., Chief Executive Officer, University Medical Center, Las Vegas, NV, p. A394

BRANNON, Jim, Vice President Human Resources, Atlantic General Hospital, Berlin, MD, p. A289

BRANNON, Linda, Vice President Human Resources, Circles of Care, Melbourne, FL, p. A130

BRANNON, Rebecca, R.N
Chief Nursing Officer, Saint Francis Hospital, Charleston, WV, p. A676
Vice President Patient Services, Thomas Memorial Hospital, South Charleston, WV, p. A681

BRANSCOME, Eileen, Chief Operating Officer, Mason General Hospital, Shelton, WA, p. A672

BRANSFORD, Charles, M.D. Medical Director, Lakeview Hospital, Stillwater, MN, p. A341

BRANSON, Jason, Chief Executive Officer, AMG Specialty Hospital–Lafayette, Lafayette, LA, p. A270

BRANSON, Phil, M.D. President Medical Staff, Princeton Community Hospital, Princeton, WV, p. A680

BRANSTETTER, Jon, Vice President Finance, Missouri Delta Medical Center, Sikeston, MO, p. A371

BRANT, Johnny, Chief Financial Officer, Welch Community Hospital, Welch, WV, p. A681

BRANT, Mick, Chief Executive Officer, Gothenburg Memorial Hospital, Gothenburg, NE, p. A384

BRANTZ, Jerry, Chief Financial Officer, Shoshone Medical Center, Kellogg, ID, p. A169

BRASHER, Tanya, Director of Nursing, North Mississippi Medical Center–Hamilton, Hamilton, AL, p. A21

BRASSER, Brian, Chief Nursing Officer, Spectrum Health United Hospital, Greenville, MI, p. A315

BRASSER, Bruce A., R.N. VP of Inpatient and Network Operations, Mary Free Bed Rehabilitation Hospital, Grand Rapids, MI, p. A315

BRASSINGER, Cindy, Chief Operating Officer, Vibra Hospital of Southeastern Michigan, Lincoln Park, MI, p. A319

BRASWELL, Gingie, Director Human Resources, DeKalb Community Hospital, Smithville, TN, p. A579

BRATTVET, William W., Chief Executive Officer, Carrollton Springs, Carrollton, TX, p. A591

BRAUN, James R., Chief Financial Officer, Flambeau Hospital, Park Falls, WI, p. A694

BRAUN, Norma, Vice President Human Resources, Hollywood Presbyterian Medical Center, Los Angeles, CA, p. A69

BRAUN, Peggy, R.N. Vice President Patient Care Services and Chief Nurse Executive, Sentara Virginia Beach General Hospital, Virginia Beach, VA, p. A662

BRAUN, Jr., Richard G., CP
Senior Vice President and Chief Financial Officer, Bradford Regional Medical Center, Bradford, PA, p. A521
Senior Vice President and Chief Financial Officer, Olean General Hospital, Olean, NY, p. A438

BRAUN, Sahlenia, Chief Financial Officer, Wishek Community Hospital and Clinics, Wishek, ND, p. A469

BRAVO, Chebon, Director Information Systems, Green Oaks Hospital, Dallas, TX, p. A596

BRAWLEY, Carrie, Administrator, Behavioral HealthCare Center at Martin, Martin, TN, p. A573

BRAXTON, Edwin R., Director Human Resources, Lompoc Valley Medical Center, Lompoc, CA, p. A67

BRAY, Bob, Chief Information Officer, Jersey Community Hospital, Jerseyville, IL, p. A186

BRAY, Delnita, Administrator, Texas Specialty Hospital at Wichita Falls, Wichita Falls, TX, p. A641

BRAY, John, M.D. Medical Director, Select Specialty Hospital–Pensacola, Pensacola, FL, p. A137

BRAY, Karen A., R.N. Vice President Patient Care Services, Washington Hospital, Washington, PA, p. A543

BRAY, Pam, Director of Nursing and Director Inpatient Services, Kane Community Hospital, Kane, PA, p. A528

BRAYTON, Jackie, Vice President Human Resources, Portsmouth Regional Hospital, Portsmouth, NH, p. A400

BRAYTON, Ranee C., R.N. Associate Chief Executive Officer, Northeast Regional Medical Center, Kirksville, MO, p. A364

BRAZ, Marcus, Chief Executive Officer, HEALTHSOUTH Rehabilitation Hospital of Sarasota, Sarasota, FL, p. A139

BRAZASKI, Karrie, Chief Operating Officer and Chief Nursing Officer, Lovelace Westside Hospital, Albuquerque, NM, p. A414

BRAZEL, Gary, M.D. Chief Medical Officer, St. Vincent Anderson Regional Hospital, Anderson, IN, p. A198

BRAZIL, Bob, Chief Operating Officer, Memorial Health System, Abilene, KS, p. A231

BREA, Christie, Manager Human Resources, Promise Hospital of Phoenix, Mesa, AZ, p. A33

BREADY, Sharon, R.N., Chief Executive Officer, Care One at Raritan Bay Medical Center, Perth Amboy, NJ, p. A408

BREAKWELL, Michael, R.N. Nurse Executive, Twin Valley Behavioral Healthcare, Columbus, OH, p. A478

BRECKLIN, Mary Jane, Network Vice President, South Operating Group, SSM Cardinal Glennon Children's Medical Center, Saint Louis, MO, p. A370

BREEDEN, Susan M., Administrator and Chief Executive Officer, Baptist Memorial Hospital–Huntingdon, Huntingdon, TN, p. A570

BREEDING, Donnie, Chief Executive Officer, Heart of Florida Regional Medical Center, Davenport, FL, p. A121

BREEDLOVE, Jean Ann
Chief Information Officer, Children's Mercy Hospitals and Clinics, Kansas City, MO, p. A362
Chief Information Officer, Children's Mercy South, Overland Park, KS, p. A241

BREEDVELD, Stacey, R.N. Associate Director for Patient Care, Veterans Affairs Ann Arbor Healthcare System, Ann Arbor, MI, p. A308

BREEN, Charles J., M.D. Medical Director, Sanford Hillsboro Medical Center, Hillsboro, ND, p. A467

BREEN, Thomas, Vice President and Chief Financial Officer, South County Hospital, Wakefield, RI, p. A547

BREHM, Jay R., Executive Vice President and Chief Financial Officer, Franciscan St. Francis Health – Indianapolis, Indianapolis, IN, p. A205

BREHM, Robert, Division President, Kessler Institute for Rehabilitation, West Orange, NJ, p. A412

BREILAND, Keith, M.D. Medical Director, Seven Hills Behavioral Institute, Henderson, NV, p. A392

BREITBACH, Dave, Chief Financial Officer, Prairie du Chien Memorial Hospital, Prairie Du Chien, WI, p. A695

BREITENBACH, Ray, M.D. Chief of Staff, Doctors' Hospital of Michigan, Pontiac, MI, p. A322

BREITFELDER, Michelle, Chief Operating Officer, Hughston Hospital, Columbus, GA, p. A150

BREITLING, Bryan, Administrator, Avera Hand County Memorial Hospital, Miller, SD, p. A560

BRELAND, Kelly R., CPA Director Support Services, Mississippi State Hospital, Whitfield, MS, p. A355

BRELSFORD, George W., M.D. Chief Medical Staff, Effingham Hospital, Springfield, GA, p. A160

BREMER, David, D.O. Chief of Staff, MidMichigan Medical Center–Clare, Clare, MI, p. A310

BREMER Jr., Louis H., President and Chief Executive Officer, St. Francis Medical Center, Monroe, LA, p. A274

BRENAN, Kevin, Chief Financial Officer, Saint Joseph's Hospital of Atlanta, Atlanta, GA, p. A147

BRENDLE, Judi, Vice President Nursing, Lancaster General Health, Lancaster, PA, p. A528

BRENDLER, Stephen, Director Information Systems, Hilton Head Hospital, Hilton Head Island, SC, p. A553

BRENHOLT, Craig
Division Director Human Resources, Sacred Heart Hospital, Eau Claire, WI, p. A686
Director Human Resources, St. Mary's Hospital, Madison, WI, p. A690

BRENKLE, George, Chief Information Officer, UMass Memorial Medical Center, Worcester, MA, p. A307

BRENNAN, James, M.D. Chief of Staff, Carolinas Hospital System, Florence, SC, p. A551

BRENNAN, John A., M.P.H., President and Chief Executive Officer, Newark Beth Israel Medical Center, Newark, NJ, p. A407

BRENNAN, Kevin F., CPA Executive Vice President and Chief Financial Officer, Geisinger Medical Center, Danville, PA, p. A523

BRENNAN, Patrick, Director Information System Technology, Saint Louis University Hospital, Saint Louis, MO, p. A370

BRENNAN, Patrick J., M.D. Senior Vice President and Chief Medical Officer, Hospital of the University of Pennsylvania, Philadelphia, PA, p. A535

BRENNAN, Theresa, M.D. Chief Medical Officer, University of Iowa Hospitals and Clinics, Iowa City, IA, p. A223

BRENNER, Pattie, R.N. Chief Nursing Officer, HEALTHSOUTH Rehabilitation Hospital, Largo, FL, p. A128

BRENNER, William
Chief Financial Officer, Kindred Hospital Indianapolis South, Greenwood, IN, p. A204
Chief Financial Officer, Kindred Hospital–Indianapolis, Indianapolis, IN, p. A206

BRENNY, Terrence, President and Chief Executive Officer, Stoughton Hospital Association, Stoughton, WI, p. A697

BRENTANO, Gregory
Chief Financial Officer, Chino Valley Medical Center, Chino, CA, p. A56
Chief Executive Officer, Montclair Hospital Medical Center, Montclair, CA, p. A74
Chief Executive Officer, San Dimas Community Hospital, San Dimas, CA, p. A86

BRENZEL, Mark T., Chief Executive Officer, Lake Cumberland Regional Hospital, Somerset, KY, p. A260

BRES, Thomas, Vice President and Chief Information Officer, Sparrow Hospital, Lansing, MI, p. A318

BRESCIA, Michael J., M.D. Executive Medical Director, Calvary Hospital,, NY, p. A431

BRESLIN, Michael P., Interim Chief Executive Officer, Richmond University Medical Center,, NY, p. A436

BRESLIN, Tim, Chief Financial Officer, Lakeview Regional Medical Center, Covington, LA, p. A265

BRESNAHAN, Christine, Manager Human Resources, Radius Specialty Hospital Boston, Boston, MA, p. A297

BRESNAHAN, Jacky, Director Human Resources, Mahaska Health Partnership, Oskaloosa, IA, p. A226

BRESSLER, Kathy, President, St. Clare Hospital, Lakewood, WA, p. A667

BRETTNER, Eric, Vice President and Chief Financial Officer, St. Mary's Medical Center, San Francisco, CA, p. A87

BRETZ, Joseph W., Director Human Resources, St. John's Hospital, Springfield, IL, p. A195

BRETZ, Joy, Chief Financial Officer, Gove County Medical Center, Quinter, KS, p. A243

BREUDER, Andrew, M.D. Chief of Staff, Manchester Veterans Affairs Medical Center, Manchester, NH, p. A399

BREUER, Jason, President, LakeWood Health Center, Baudette, MN, p. A329

BREUER, Rick, Chief Executive Officer and Administrator, Community Memorial Hospital, Cloquet, MN, p. A330

BREUM, Linda, R.N. Chief Nursing Officer, Bert Fish Medical Center, New Smyrna Beach, FL, p. A133

BREWER, David, Director Finance, ProMedica Bay Park Hospital, Oregon, OH, p. A488

BREWER, Gary L., Chief Executive Officer, Valley View Hospital, Glenwood Springs, CO, p. A101

BREWER, Jennifer, R.N. Chief Nursing Officer and Vice President Nursing Services, Verde Valley Medical Center, Cottonwood, AZ, p. A30

BREWER, Jennifer Lynn, Chief Executive Officer, HEALTHSOUTH Plano Rehabilitation Hospital, Plano, TX, p. A627

BREWER, Jim, M.P.H. Chief Financial Officer, Healthmark Regional Medical Center, DeFuniak Springs, FL, p. A122

BREWER, Kaye, Director Human Resources, Maury Regional Hospital, Columbia, TN, p. A567

BREWER, Kelley, MSN, Chief Executive Officer, Lakeside Women's Hospital, Oklahoma City, OK, p. A503

BREWER, Patricia, Chief Nursing Officer, University Behavioral Health of Denton, Denton, TX, p. A599

BREWER, Rebecca, FACHE, Interim Chief Executive Officer, Andalusia Regional Hospital, Andalusia, AL, p. A15

BREWINGTON, Yvonne, Director Human Resources, Belton Regional Medical Center, Belton, MO, p. A356

BREWIS, Laurie, Vice President Human Resources, McLaren Greater Lansing, Lansing, MI, p. A318

BREWSTER, Joseph, M.D. Chief of Staff, Bates County Memorial Hospital, Butler, MO, p. A357

BREWSTER, Melvin, Chief Information Officer, LAC–Olive View–UCLA Medical Center,, CA, p. A70

BREWSTER, Steven, M.D., Commander, Womack Army Medical Center, Fort Bragg, NC, p. A452

BREXLER, James L., President and Chief Executive Officer, Doylestown Hospital, Doylestown, PA, p. A524

BREYFOGLE, Cynthia, Director, Charles George Veterans Affairs Medical Center, Asheville, NC, p. A447

BREZA, Lisa, R.N. Vice President and Chief Nursing Officer, Robert Wood Johnson University Hospital at Hamilton, Hamilton, NJ, p. A404

BREZNY, Angie, Director Human Resources, Prague Community Hospital, Prague, OK, p. A505

BREZOVSKY, Patricia, Director Human Resources, St. Joseph Hospital, Bangor, ME, p. A281

BRIAN, David, Director Information Services, Shriners Hospitals for Children–Lexington, Lexington, KY, p. A254

BRIAN, Francis, M.D. Senior Vice President Medical Affairs, Rapides Regional Medical Center, Alexandria, LA, p. A262

BRICHER, Joan
Senior Vice President Finance and Chief Financial Officer, Goleta Valley Cottage Hospital, Santa Barbara, CA, p. A89
Senior Vice President Finance and Chief Financial Officer, Santa Barbara Cottage Hospital, Santa Barbara, CA, p. A89
Senior Vice President Finance and Chief Financial Officer, Santa Ynez Valley Cottage Hospital, Solvang, CA, p. A91

BRICKER, Steven A., Chief Financial Officer, Sparta Community Hospital, Sparta, IL, p. A194

BRICKER, Tim
President and Chief Executive Officer, Chandler Regional Medical Center, Chandler, AZ, p. A30
President and Chief Executive Officer, Mercy Gilbert Medical Center, Gilbert, AZ, p. A31

BRICKMAN, Jeffrey, FACHE, President and Chief Executive Officer, St. Anthony Hospital, Lakewood, CO, p. A103

BRIDEN, David, Chief Information Officer, Exeter Hospital, Exeter, NH, p. A398

BRIDGE, Elaine, R.N. Interim Chief Operating Officer, Newton–Wellesley Hospital, Newton Lower Falls, MA, p. A303

BRIDGE, Lauren M., R.N. Chief Nurse Executive, Providence Milwaukie Hospital, Milwaukie, OR, p. A515

BRIDGELAND, Aaron, Director Finance, Wheaton Franciscan Healthcare – St. Francis, Milwaukee, WI, p. A692

BRIDGES, Alan J., M.D. Chief of Staff, William S. Middleton Memorial Veterans Hospital, Madison, WI, p. A690

BRIDGES, James M., Executive Vice President and Chief Operating Officer, Palmetto Health Baptist, Columbia, SC, p. A550

BRIDGES, Jane Ann, Acting Administrator, Nacogdoches Memorial Hospital, Nacogdoches, TX, p. A624

BRIDGES, Mary, Director Human Resources, Ouachita County Medical Center, Camden, AR, p. A42

BRIDGES, Stephanie, Interim Chief Executive Officer, Kindred Hospital–Charleston, Mt. Pleasant, SC, p. A554

BRIDGES, Theresa, Chief Information Officer, Crawley Memorial Hospital, Shelby, NC, p. A461

BRIDGES KEE, Lorinnsa, Director Human Resource, Cypress Fairbanks Medical Center, Houston, TX, p. A609

BRIER, Pamela S., President and Chief Executive Officer, Maimonides Medical Center,, NY, p. A434

BRIESEMEISTER, Eric, Chief Executive Officer, Jones Regional Medical Center, Anamosa, IA, p. A216

BRIETE, Mark, M.D. Vice President Medical Affairs, Mercy Hospital Jefferson, Crystal City, MO, p. A359

BRIGAITIS, Kathryn, Controller, HEALTHSOUTH Rehabilitation Hospital of Cypress, Houston, TX, p. A610

BRIGGS, Bryon, Assistant Chief Financial Officer, Select Specialty Hospital–Tulsa Midtown, Tulsa, OK, p. A509

BRIGGS, Deborah, Vice President Human Resources, Marketing, Volunteer Services and Community Relations, Ellenville Regional Hospital, Ellenville, NY, p. A425

BRIGGS, Gary, Director Human Resources, TriStar Southern Hills Medical Center, Nashville, TN, p. A577

BRIGGS, Michael, M.D. Chief Medical Officer, Essentia Health Fargo, Fargo, ND, p. A466

BRIGGS, Paul
Executive Vice President and Chief Financial Officer, Presbyterian Hospital, Albuquerque, NM, p. A414
Executive VP/Chief Operating Officer, Presbyterian Kaseman Hospital, Albuquerque, NM, p. A415

BRIGGS, Ronald O., FACHE, President and Chief Executive Officer, St. Francis Memorial Hospital, West Point, NE, p. A390

BRIGGS, Thomas, Chief Financial Officer, Integris Marshall County Medical Center, Madill, OK, p. A500

BRIGHAM, Mark, Human Resources Officer, Tri–State Memorial Hospital, Clarkston, WA, p. A665

BRIGHAM, Randy, Chief Human Resource Officer, Sterling Regional MedCenter, Sterling, CO, p. A106

BRIGHT, Cheryl, Executive Director, Lanterman Developmental Center, Pomona, CA, p. A80

BRIGHT, Shawn, Chief Executive Officer, Yadkin Valley Community Hospital, Yadkinville, NC, p. A464

BRIGHT, Tony, M.D. Administrator Medical Services, Caswell Center, Kinston, NC, p. A456

BRILEY, Jana, Director Financial Services, Murray Medical Center, Chatsworth, GA, p. A149

BRILEY, Jay, President, Vidant Duplin Hospital, Kenansville, NC, p. A455

BRILL, Beth K., Director Human Resources, Barnesville Hospital, Barnesville, OH, p. A471

BRILLANTES, Dorothy, Senior Vice President Human Resources, Howard County General Hospital, Columbia, MD, p. A291

BRILLI, Richard, M.D. Chief Medical Officer, Nationwide Children's Hospital, Columbus, OH, p. A477

BRILLIANT, Patrick D., President and Chief Executive Officer, Riverside Community Hospital, Riverside, CA, p. A82

BRILLIANT, Steven, M.D. Chief of Staff, Veterans Affairs Sierra Nevada Health Care System, Reno, NV, p. A395

BRIMHALL, Kelly, Director of Human Resources, Timpanogos Regional Hospital, Orem, UT, p. A645

BRINDLE, Charles B., M.D. Chief Medical Staff, Iowa Specialty Hospital–Belmond, Belmond, IA, p. A216

BRINDLEY, John C., FACHE, President and Chief Executive Officer, Seton Medical Center Hays, Kyle, TX, p. A617

BRINGLE, Dottie, R.N. Chief Operating Officer and Chief Nursing Officer, Mercy Hospital Joplin, Joplin, MO, p. A362

BRINK, Greg, Chief Financial Officer, Surgical Specialty Hospital of Arizona, Phoenix, AZ, p. A35

BRINKERHOFF, Cindy H., Director Human Resources, South Peninsula Hospital, Homer, AK, p. A28

BRINKHAUS, Theresa, Chief Financial Officer, St. Helena Parish Hospital, Greensburg, LA, p. A267

BRINKLEY, Terry, Vice President Finance, Paris Community Hospital, Paris, IL, p. A191

BRINKMAN, Dan, Chief Nurse Executive, Hilo Medical Center, Hilo, HI, p. A164

BRINKMAN, Janet, Director Human Resources, Colorado Plains Medical Center, Fort Morgan, CO, p. A101

BRINKMAN, Jim, Chief Financial Officer, Clay County Medical Center, Clay Center, KS, p. A232

BRINKMAN, Larry, Chief Human Resources, Miami Veterans Affairs Healthcare System, Miami, FL, p. A132

BRINSON, David, Director Information Technology, Wabash County Hospital, Wabash, IN, p. A214

BRIONES, Melba, M.D. Medical Director, Evansville State Hospital, Evansville, IN, p. A202

BRISBOE, Mark
Vice President & CFO, Sparrow Clinton Hospital, Saint Johns, MI, p. A323
Vice President and Chief Financial Officer, Sparrow Ionia Hospital, Ionia, MI, p. A316

BRISCOE, Betsy, Chief Executive Officer, Memorial Hospital, Seminole, TX, p. A633

BRISCOE, Charles G., FACHE, Chief Executive Officer, Coliseum Medical Centers, Macon, GA, p. A156

BRISCOE, Mary Beth, Chief Financial Officer, University of Alabama Hospital, Birmingham, AL, p. A17

BRISENDINE, Chad
Vice President and Chief Information Officer, St. Luke's Hospital – Miners Campus, Coaldale, PA, p. A523
Chief Information Officer, St. Luke's Hospital – Quakertown Campus, Quakertown, PA, p. A539
Chief Information Officer, St. Luke's University Hospital – Bethlehem Campus, Bethlehem, PA, p. A520

BRISTER, Kim, Director Human Resources, Gettysburg Hospital, Gettysburg, PA, p. A526

BRISTO, Cathie, Director Human Resources, Wilbarger General Hospital, Vernon, TX, p. A639

BRISTOL, Michelle, Director of Nursing, Clifton–Fine Hospital, Star Lake, NY, p. A443

BRISTOLL, Holly L., President, ProMedica Bay Park Hospital, Oregon, OH, p. A488

BRITT, Key, Associate Director, Greenwood Leflore Hospital, Greenwood, MS, p. A347

BRITT, Linda, Director Information Systems, Baptist Memorial Hospital–North Mississippi, Oxford, MS, p. A352

BRITT, Suzanne, Director Human Resources, Samaritan Memorial Hospital, Macon, MO, p. A365

BRITT, Tommy, Director Human Resources, West Georgia Health, La Grange, GA, p. A155

BRITTAIN, James G., Chief Financial Officer, Mid–Valley Hospital, Peckville, PA, p. A534

BRITTEN, Gary L., Chief Financial Officer, Stone County Medical Center, Mountain View, AR, p. A48

BRITTON, John, Director Information Services, Fisher–Titus Medical Center, Norwalk, OH, p. A487

BRITTON, Natalie J., Director Human Resources, Silverton Hospital, Silverton, OR, p. A518

BRITTON, William N., Associate Administrator Finance, Alfred I. duPont Hospital for Children, Wilmington, DE, p. A114

BRIZZEE, Celeste, Chief Nursing Officer, Connally Medical Center, Floresville, TX, p. A602

BROACH, Keith, Chief Executive Officer and President, Ferrell Hospital, Eldorado, IL, p. A181

BROADDUS, Jackie, Business Partner, Taylorville Memorial Hospital, Taylorville, IL, p. A196

BROADHEAD, Susie, Director Public Information, East Mississippi State Hospital, Meridian, MS, p. A351

BROADUS, Ronald, Assistant Administrator Human Resources, Interim LSU Public Hospital, New Orleans, LA, p. A275

BROADWATER, Gary W., Chief Financial Officer, McCready Foundation, Crisfield, MD, p. A291

BROBERG, John R., FACHE, President and Chief Executive Officer, Mercy Regional Health Center,, KS, p. A239

BROBST, Charles R., Senior Vice President and Chief Financial Officer, Saint Anthony Hospital, Chicago, IL, p. A179

BROBST, Mary, R.N. Vice President of Nursing, SSM St. Clare Health Center, Fenton, MO, p. A360

BROCCOLINO, Victor A., President and Chief Executive Officer, Howard County General Hospital, Columbia, MD, p. A291

BROCK, Berna, Vice President Human Resources, Adena Pike Medical Center, Waverly, OH, p. A492

BROCK, Doreen, Chief Operating Officer, Florala Memorial Hospital, Florala, AL, p. A20

BROCK, Jamie, Director Human Resources, Windber Medical Center, Windber, PA, p. A545

BROCK, Lisa, Vice President Human Resources, Overlake Hospital Medical Center, Bellevue, WA, p. A664

BROCK, Melinda, Director Human Resources, Woodward Regional Hospital, Woodward, OK, p. A510

BROCK, Nancy, Chief Financial Officer, CHRISTUS St. Catherine Hospital, Katy, TX, p. A615

BROCK, Robert
Vice President Finance and Business Development, Saint Joseph – London, London, KY, p. A255
Vice President Finance, Saint Joseph – Martin, Martin, KY, p. A257

BROCK, Steve, Chief Financial Officer, Medical Arts Hospital, Lamesa, TX, p. A617

BROCK, Sue, Chief Financial Officer, Indiana University Health Paoli Hospital, Paoli, IN, p. A212

BROCK, Theresa, Vice President Nursing, Good Shepherd Health Care System, Hermiston, OR, p. A513

BROCK, William, Chief Information Officer, Atlanta Veterans Affairs Medical Center, Decatur, GA, p. A151

BROCKMEYER, JoEllyn, Director Human Resources, Indiana University Health White Memorial Hospital, Monticello, IN, p. A210

BROCKUS, Harry, Chief Executive Officer, Hoopeston Regional Health Center, Hoopeston, IL, p. A185

BROCKWELL, Linda, R.N. Chief Nursing Officer, Wickenburg Community Hospital, Wickenburg, AZ, p. A39

BRODALE, Sean, D.O. Chief Medical Staff, Davis County Hospital, Bloomfield, IA, p. A217

BRODBECK, Lisa, Chief Financial Officer, Medical Center of Lewisville, Lewisville, TX, p. A618

BRODEUR, Mark S., FACHE, Chief Executive Officer, Regency Hospital of Cincinnati, Cincinnati, OH, p. A475

BRODHEAD, Richard, M.D. President Medical Staff, Ministry Eagle River Memorial Hospital, Eagle River, WI, p. A686

BRODHEAD, Richard Ross, Director Human Resources, St. Vincent Randolph Hospital, Winchester, IN, p. A215

BRODIAN, Craig R., Vice President Human Resources, Johns Hopkins Bayview Medical Center, Baltimore, MD, p. A287

BRODRICK, Theresa M., R.N. Executive Vice President and Chief Nursing Officer, Cone Health, Greensboro, NC, p. A453

BRODY, Robert J.
President and Chief Executive Officer, Franciscan St. Francis Health – Indianapolis, Indianapolis, IN, p. A205
Chief Executive Officer, Franciscan St. Francis Health–Carmel, Carmel, IN, p. A199

BRODY, Sue, R.N. Chief Nursing Officer, Silverton Hospital, Silverton, OR, p. A518

BROEKHUIS, Arlyn, Vice President and Chief Information Officer, Sanford USD Medical Center, Sioux Falls, SD, p. A562

BROEMELING, Richard, Information Systems Flight Commander, U. S. Air Force Clinic, Mountain Home AFB, ID, p. A170

BROERMANN, Robert
Senior Vice President and Chief Financial Officer, Sentara Leigh Hospital, Norfolk, VA, p. A658
Senior Vice President and Chief Financial Officer, Sentara Norfolk General Hospital, Norfolk, VA, p. A658
Senior Vice President and Chief Financial Officer, Sentara Princess Anne Hospital, Virginia Beach, VA, p. A662

BROFMAN, John, M.D. Medical Director, RML Specialty Hospital, Hinsdale, IL, p. A185

BROGGER, Portlyn, Chief Executive Officer, Kindred Hospital Victoria, Victoria, TX, p. A639

BROKKE, James, M.D. Chief of Staff, Audubon County Memorial Hospital, Audubon, IA, p. A216

BROMAN, Craig J., FACHE, President, St. Cloud Hospital, Saint Cloud, MN, p. A339

BROMLEY, Trudy, Vice President Human Resources, J. F. K. Medical Center, Atlantis, FL, p. A118

BRONER, Eloise, President and Chief Executive Officer, Good Samaritan Hospital, Dayton, OH, p. A479

BROOKE, William R., M.D. President Medical Staff, Pickens County Medical Center, Carrollton, AL, p. A18

BROOKER, Brian, Chief Executive Officer, Cypress Creek Hospital, Houston, TX, p. A609

BROOKER, Paula, Director Information Services, Pleasant Valley Hospital, Point Pleasant, WV, p. A680

BROOKES, Jeffrey, M.D
Chief Medical Officer, Parkview LaGrange Hospital, LaGrange, IN, p. A208
Medical Director, Parkview Whitley Hospital, Columbia City, IN, p. A200

BROOKHOUSER, Patrick E., M.D. Director and Chief Medical Officer, Boys Town National Research Hospital, Omaha, NE, p. A387

BROOKMAN, Mark, Director Information Technology, Hardin Memorial Hospital, Elizabethtown, KY, p. A250

BROOKS, Albert, M.D. Chief Medical Staff Services, Washington Hospital Healthcare System, Fremont, CA, p. A61

BROOKS, Ann Marie T., R.N. Vice President, Nursing, Riddle Hospital, Media, PA, p. A531

BROOKS, Christopher, Vice President Finance, Bay Medical Center Sacred Heart, Panama City, FL, p. A136

BROOKS, David, Chief Executive Officer, St. John Hospital and Medical Center, Detroit, MI, p. A312

BROOKS, Harris W., Administrator and Chief Executive Officer, Palo Pinto General Hospital, Mineral Wells, TX, p. A623

BROOKS III, J. Milton, Administrator, Pineville Community Hospital Association, Pineville, KY, p. A259

BROOKS, Janet, R.N. Vice President and Chief Nursing Officer, West Hills Hospital and Medical Center,, CA, p. A72

BROOKS, Jerome M., Chief Executive Officer, Connally Medical Center, Floresville, TX, p. A602

BROOKS, Karen, M.D. Medical Director, Cedar Crest Hospital and Residential Treatment Center, Belton, TX, p. A588

BROOKS, Kathleen, Director Human Resources, Brattleboro Retreat, Brattleboro, VT, p. A649

BROOKS, Lisa, Chief Financial Officer, Comanche County Hospital, Coldwater, KS, p. A232

BROOKS, Lori, Director Human Resources, Red Bud Regional Hospital, Red Bud, IL, p. A193

BROOKS, Patrice Gay, Chief Executive Officer, Cumberland Hospital, New Kent, VA, p. A657

BROOKS, Patti, Director Information Systems, Avera Queen of Peace Hospital, Mitchell, SD, p. A561

BROOKS, Robert, Chief Executive Officer, St. Cloud Regional Medical Center, Saint Cloud, FL, p. A138

BROOKS, Robert L., M.D. Vice President Medical Affairs, Meritus Medical Center, Hagerstown, MD, p. A292

BROOKS, Scott, Manager Information Technology, Boulder City Hospital, Boulder City, NV, p. A391

BROOKS, Steven, Vice President Human Resources, McAlester Regional Health Center, McAlester, OK, p. A501

BROOKS, Troy, Assistant Administrator Fiscal Services, Newton Medical Center, Covington, GA, p. A151

BROOKS–WILLIAMS, Denise, President and Chief Executive Officer, Henry Ford Wyandotte Hospital, Wyandotte, MI, p. A327

BROOKSHIRE, Lynn
Vice President Information Services and Chief Information Officer, CAMC Teays Valley Hospital, Hurricane, WV, p. A678
Vice President Information Services and Chief Information Officer, Charleston Area Medical Center, Charleston, WV, p. A676

BROOS, Timothy W., Vice President and Chief Information Officer, Katherine Shaw Bethea Hospital, Dixon, IL, p. A181

BROPHY, Beth, Interim VP for Human Resources, Hurley Medical Center, Flint, MI, p. A313

BROSIUS, William, Vice President and Chief Financial Officer, St. Luke's Episcopal Hospital, Houston, TX, p. A612

BROSKEY, Steven, Associate Director, Veterans Affairs Roseburg Healthcare System, Roseburg, OR, p. A517

BROSNAN, Kimberly, Director Human Resources, Norwood Hospital, Norwood, MA, p. A303

BROSS, James B., President and Chief Executive Officer, Angel Medical Center, Franklin, NC, p. A452

BROSS, Mary Ann, Vice President Human Resources, Somerset Medical Center, Somerville, NJ, p. A410

BROST, Michelle, Financial Officer, Victory Medical Center Mid–Cities, Hurst, TX, p. A614

BROSTROM, Kyle, Chief Operating Officer, Timpanogos Regional Hospital, Orem, UT, p. A645

BROTEN, Kurt, Chief Financial Officer, Palmdale Regional Medical Center, Palmdale, CA, p. A78

BROTHERS, John T., MS, Administrator, St. Joseph Memorial Hospital, Murphysboro, IL, p. A189

BROTHMAN, Daniel, Chief Executive Officer, Western Medical Center–Santa Ana, Santa Ana, CA, p. A89

BROTHMAN, Joe, Vice President Information Systems, MedStar Washington Hospital Center, Washington, DC, p. A116

BROUGH, Ken, Chief Financial Officer, Bartlett Regional Hospital, Juneau, AK, p. A28

BROUGHMAN, Robin, R.N. Chief Nursing Officer, LewisGale Hospital Alleghany, Low Moor, VA, p. A656

BROUGHMAN, Wade
Executive Vice President and Chief Financial Officer, Riverside Regional Medical Center, Newport News, VA, p. A658
Executive Vice President and Chief Financial Officer, Riverside Rehabilitation Institute, Newport News, VA, p. A658
Chief Financial Officer, Riverside Shore Memorial Hospital, Nassawadox, VA, p. A657

BROUILLETTE, Cindy
Chief Financial Officer, St. David's Medical Center, Austin, TX, p. A586
Chief Financial Officer, St. David's Rehabilitation Center, Austin, TX, p. A586

BROUSSARD, Clifford M., FACHE, Administrator, WK Bossier Health Center, Bossier City, LA, p. A264

BROUSSARD, Tammy, Chief Financial Officer, West Calcasieu Cameron Hospital, Sulphur, LA, p. A279

BROUWER, Heath, Administrator, Douglas County Memorial Hospital, Armour, SD, p. A558

BROWDER, Renate, R.N. Director of Nursing, Lake City Community Hospital, Lake City, SC, p. A554

BROWER, Fred B., President and Chief Executive Officer, Trinity Health System, Steubenville, OH, p. A490

BROWN, Alexis, Administrator, Ozarks Community Hospital, Springfield, MO, p. A372

BROWN, Allen, M.D. Vice President Medical Affairs, Ochsner Baptist Medical Center, New Orleans, LA, p. A275

BROWN, Andy, M.D. Vice President Medical Affairs, Saint Thomas Rutherford Hospital, Murfreesboro, TN, p. A576

BROWN, Ann, Director, Martinsburg Veterans Affairs Medical Center, Martinsburg, WV, p. A678

BROWN, B. Blaine, Vice President and General Counsel, Prattville Baptist Hospital, Prattville, AL, p. A25

BROWN, Barbara, D.O. Chief of Staff, Osborne County Memorial Hospital, Osborne, KS, p. A241

BROWN, Beth, Director, Louis A. Johnson Veterans Affairs Medical Center, Clarksburg, WV, p. A676

BROWN, Bill, Vice President Human Resources, North Hawaii Community Hospital, Kamuela, HI, p. A165

BROWN, Bob, Director Human Resources, The Children's Institute of Pittsburgh, Pittsburgh, PA, p. A538

BROWN, Chad, M.P.H., Chief Executive Officer, Person Memorial Hospital, Roxboro, NC, p. A460

BROWN, Cheryl, Administrator, Henderson Health Care Services, Henderson, NE, p. A384

BROWN, Christi, Director Human Resources, LSU Bogalusa Medical Center, Bogalusa, LA, p. A264

BROWN, Chuck, Administrator, Bethesda Butler Hospital, Hamilton, OH, p. A483

BROWN, Crystal, M.D. Medical Director, Peach Regional Medical Center, Fort Valley, GA, p. A154

BROWN, David A., Director Human Resources and Corporate Compliance, Pleasant Valley Hospital, Point Pleasant, WV, p. A680

BROWN, David P., Administrator, Citizens Medical Center, Victoria, TX, p. A639

BROWN, Deana, Director Administrative Services, Jasper County Hospital, Rensselaer, IN, p. A212

BROWN, Debra L., Area Financial Officer, Kaiser Permanente Manteca Medical Center, Manteca, CA, p. A73

BROWN, Denise, Vice President Human Resources, Presence Saint Joseph Hospital, Chicago, IL, p. A178

BROWN, Derek, Chief Information Officer, Jellico Community Hospital, Jellico, TN, p. A571

BROWN, Donald L., Director Human Resources, Baptist Health Paducah, Paducah, KY, p. A259

BROWN, Doris, Chief Executive Officer, Mountrail County Medical Center, Stanley, ND, p. A469

BROWN, Ed
Chief Financial Officer, Effingham Hospital, Springfield, GA, p. A160
Senior Vice President and Chief Information Officer, Gwinnett Hospital System, Lawrenceville, GA, p. A156

BROWN, Eric, Senior Business Partner, Shady Grove Adventist Hospital, Rockville, MD, p. A294

BROWN, Frank, M.D. Chief Medical Officer, Wesley Woods Geriatric Hospital of Emory University, Atlanta, GA, p. A147

BROWN, Geoffrey
Senior Vice President Information Services, Inova Alexandria Hospital, Alexandria, VA, p. A651
Chief Information Officer, Inova Fair Oaks Hospital, Fairfax, VA, p. A653
Vice President Information Systems, Inova Fairfax Hospital, Falls Church, VA, p. A653

BROWN, Gordon, Chief Information Resources Management, Edward Hines, Jr. Veterans Affairs Hospital, Hines, IL, p. A185

BROWN, Henry
   Director Plant Operations and Information Technology, Schick Shadel Hospital, Seattle, WA, p. A670
   Chief Financial Officer, Westchester General Hospital, Miami, FL, p. A132
BROWN, James, M.D. President, Tyler County Hospital, Woodville, TX, p. A642
BROWN, James H., Chief Financial Officer, Centerpoint Medical Center, Independence, MO, p. A362
BROWN, James T., M.D. President of Medical Staff, Mason District Hospital, Havana, IL, p. A184
BROWN, Janice, Chief Financial Officer, Coosa Valley Medical Center, Sylacauga, AL, p. A25
BROWN, Jay, Vice President and Chief Infomation Officer, University Hospital, Cincinnati, OH, p. A475
BROWN, Jeff, Interim Director Information Systems, Simi Valley Hospital and Health Care Services, Simi Valley, CA, p. A91
BROWN, Jeffrey L., Director Information Systems, Lawrence General Hospital, Lawrence, MA, p. A301
BROWN, Jenny, Director Human Resources and Public Relations, Vidant Pungo Hospital, Belhaven, NC, p. A448
BROWN, Jill, Chief Financial Officer, Miller County Hospital, Colquitt, GA, p. A150
BROWN, John D., Director Information Systems, Pacific Alliance Medical Center, Los Angeles, CA, p. A70
BROWN, Joni, Director Human Resources, Rehabilitation Hospital of Indiana, Indianapolis, IN, p. A206
BROWN, Joseph, M.D. Chief Medical Staff, Alta Vista Regional Hospital, Las Vegas, NM, p. A417
BROWN, Julie, Human Resources Specialist, Alegent Creighton Health Community Memorial Hospital, Missouri Valley, IA, p. A225
BROWN, Karen, Director Health Information, Community Medical Center, Falls City, NE, p. A383
BROWN, Karen C., Vice President Strategic Human Resources, OSF Saint Anthony Medical Center, Rockford, IL, p. A193
BROWN, Karla, Interim Chief Nursing Officer, Pauls Valley General Hospital, Pauls Valley, OK, p. A505
BROWN, Ken, Vice President and Chief Human Resource Officer, Pratt Regional Medical Center, Pratt, KS, p. A243
BROWN, Kenneth, M.D. Medical Director, Woman's Hospital, Baton Rouge, LA, p. A264
BROWN, Kevin F., D.O. Medical Director, Wesley Rehabilitation Hospital, Wichita, KS, p. A247
BROWN, Kris, Associate Director, Bay Pines Veterans Affairs Medical Center, Bay Pines, FL, p. A118
BROWN, Larry, Chief Financial Officer, Lucas County Health Center, Chariton, IA, p. A218
BROWN, Laurie, R.N. Chief Nursing Officer, St. Francis Hospital, Federal Way, WA, p. A666
BROWN, Linda, M.D. Chief of Staff, Island Hospital, Anacortes, WA, p. A664
BROWN, Linda, Chief Information Officer, Olympic Medical Center, Port Angeles, WA, p. A669
BROWN, Linda E., Vice President of Support Services, St. Anthony Shawnee Hospital, Shawnee, OK, p. A506
BROWN, Lisa, Director of Nursing, Pearl River County Hospital, Poplarville, MS, p. A353
BROWN, Liz, Manager Human Resources, Gunnison Valley Hospital, Gunnison, UT, p. A643
BROWN, Lori J., MSN Senior Vice President and Chief Nursing Officer, Arkansas Children's Hospital, Little Rock, AR, p. A46
BROWN, Marci, Director Information Technology, Blue Mountain Hospital, John Day, OR, p. A513
BROWN, Margaret, Director Medical Records, Vista Health, Fayetteville, AR, p. A43
BROWN, Markham, M.D. Chief Medical Staff, Mike O'Callaghan Federal Hospital, Nellis AFB, NV, p. A394
BROWN, Martin, Vice President Information Services and Chief Information Officer, Nathan Littauer Hospital and Nursing Home, Gloversville, NY, p. A426
BROWN, Mary, Chief Nursing Officer, UMass Memorial–Marlborough Hospital, Marlborough, MA, p. A302
BROWN, Mary Beth, Director Human Resources, Bertrand Chaffee Hospital, Springville, NY, p. A443
BROWN, Mary W., Senior Vice President Operations, St. Joseph's Hospital Health Center, Syracuse, NY, p. A444
BROWN, Michael, Senior Vice President Finance and Chief Financial Officer, Children's Hospital and Medical Center, Omaha, NE, p. A387
BROWN, Michael, D.O. Chief of Staff, Red River Regional Hospital, Bonham, TX, p. A589
BROWN, Michael L.
   President and Chief Executive Officer, Presence Covenant Medical Center, Urbana, IL, p. A196
   President and Chief Executive Officer, Presence United Samaritans Medical Center, Danville, IL, p. A180
BROWN, Mike, IT Manager, Highlands–Cashiers Hospital, Highlands, NC, p. A455

BROWN, Pat, R.N. Chief Nursing Officer, San Gorgonio Memorial Hospital, Banning, CA, p. A54
BROWN, Patsy, Site Coordinator Human Resources, Erlanger Bledsoe Hospital, Pikeville, TN, p. A578
BROWN, Patti, M.D. Medical Director, HEALTHSOUTH Reading Rehabilitation Hospital, Reading, PA, p. A539
BROWN, Paulette, Chief Operating Officer, Indiana University Health Goshen Hospital, Goshen, IN, p. A203
BROWN, Penny D., Human Resource Representative, Broaddus Hospital, Philippi, WV, p. A680
BROWN, Philip, D.O. Vice President Medical Affairs, Central Vermont Medical Center, Berlin, VT, p. A649
BROWN, Phyllis, Chief Executive Officer, Marshall Medical Center, Lewisburg, TN, p. A573
BROWN, Randal, M.D. Chief of Staff, Guadalupe County Hospital, Santa Rosa, NM, p. A418
BROWN, Regenia, Vice President Human Resources, Magnolia Regional Health Center, Corinth, MS, p. A346
BROWN, Rex H., Chief Executive Officer, Hillsboro Area Hospital, Hillsboro, IL, p. A185
BROWN, Rickie F., Chief Financial Officer, Monroe County Medical Center, Tompkinsville, KY, p. A260
BROWN, Rita, Director Human Resources, Richardson Medical Center, Rayville, LA, p. A277
BROWN, Robert, M.D. Chief Medical Officer, Park Plaza Hospital, Houston, TX, p. A611
BROWN, Robin
   Chief Executive, Senior Vice President, Scripps Green Hospital, La Jolla, CA, p. A65
   Chief Information Officer and Compliance Officer, St. Joseph Medical Center, Houston, TX, p. A612
BROWN, Rodger, Vice President Human Resources, North Mississippi Medical Center – Tupelo, Tupelo, MS, p. A354
BROWN, Rodney, Chief Executive Officer, Landmark Hospital, Cape Girardeau, MO, p. A357
BROWN, Samuel L., CPA Vice President Financial Services, Jennie Stuart Medical Center, Hopkinsville, KY, p. A252
BROWN, Scott, Chief Financial Officer, Valir Rehabilitation Hospital, Oklahoma City, OK, p. A504
BROWN, Shannon, Chief Executive Officer, Huntsville Memorial Hospital, Huntsville, TX, p. A614
BROWN, Sharon
   Director Human Resources, Sierra View District Hospital, Porterville, CA, p. A80
   Deputy Commande Nursing, Winn Army Community Hospital, Hinesville, GA, p. A155
BROWN, Shelia, Director Human Resources, AMG Specialty Hospital–Greenwood, Greenwood, MS, p. A347
BROWN, Sherri, Director Human Resources, Lawrence Memorial Hospital, Walnut Ridge, AR, p. A50
BROWN, Sherry
   Director Information Services, Chelsea Community Hospital, Chelsea, MI, p. A310
   Director Human Resources, Cleveland Area Hospital, Cleveland, OK, p. A497
BROWN, Stephen, M.D. Chief Medical Officer, St. Mary–Corwin Medical Center, Pueblo, CO, p. A105
BROWN, Stephen A., Chief Financial Officer, Grace Cottage Hospital, Townshend, VT, p. A650
BROWN, Steve, M.D. Chief Quality Officer, Saint Alphonsus Regional Medical Center, Boise, ID, p. A168
BROWN, Steve
   Director Information Systems, Spalding Regional Medical Center, Griffin, GA, p. A154
   Chief Information Officer, Sylvan Grove Hospital, Jackson, GA, p. A155
BROWN, Steven, Vice President Finance, OhioHealth Marion General Hospital, Marion, OH, p. A485
BROWN, Steven, M.D. Medical Director, Wyoming Behavioral Institute, Casper, WY, p. A701
BROWN, Steven E., FACHE, President and Chief Executive Officer, Mount Nittany Medical Center, State College, PA, p. A541
BROWN, Steven J., Senior Vice President and Chief Operating Officer, Faxton–St. Luke's Healthcare, Utica, NY, p. A444
BROWN, Sue, Administrator Human Resources, South Lake Hospital, Clermont, FL, p. A120
BROWN, Susan, R.N. Sr. Vice President, Chief Nursing Officer, Grace Hospital, Morganton, NC, p. A458
BROWN, Susan, Chief Human Resources Officer, North Fulton Regional Hospital, Roswell, GA, p. A159
BROWN, Susan, R.N. Sr. Vice President, Chief Nursing Officer, Valdese General Hospital, Valdese, NC, p. A462
BROWN, Theodore, Chief Operating Officer, Community Howard Regional Health, Kokomo, IN, p. A207
BROWN, Tim S., Chief Executive Officer, Claiborne County Hospital, Tazewell, TN, p. A579
BROWN, Todd A., M.D. Medical Director, Logan Regional Hospital, Logan, UT, p. A644

BROWN, Tom, Senior Vice President, Nanticoke Memorial Hospital, Seaford, DE, p. A114
BROWN, Towanda, Director Standards and Regulatory Compliance, Cumberland Hospital, New Kent, VA, p. A657
BROWN, Trisha, Director Human Resources, Community Memorial Hospital, Oconto Falls, WI, p. A694
BROWN, Wendy W., M.D. Chief of Staff, Jesse Brown Veterans Affairs Medical Center, Chicago, IL, p. A177
BROWN, Willie, Director Administration, Naval Hospital Beaufort, Beaufort, SC, p. A548
BROWN, Winfield S., President and Chief Executive Officer, Heywood Hospital, Gardner, MA, p. A300
BROWN–OLDS, Connie A., R.N. Chief Nursing Officer, Mary Free Bed Rehabilitation Hospital, Grand Rapids, MI, p. A315
BROWNE, Fred, M.D. Chief Medical Officer and Vice President Medical Affairs, New Milford Hospital, New Milford, CT, p. A111
BROWNE, J. Timothy, FACHE, Chief Executive Officer, Carolina Pines Regional Medical Center, Hartsville, SC, p. A553
BROWNE, John, Assistant Administrator Finance, Kindred Hospital–Brea, Brea, CA, p. A55
BROWNER, Warren S., M.P.H.,
   Chief Executive Officer, California Pacific Medical Center, San Francisco, CA, p. A86
   Chief Executive Officer, St. Luke's Hospital, San Francisco, CA, p. A87
BROWNING, Douglas, Chief Financial Officer, Texas Health Center for Diagnostic & Surgery, Plano, TX, p. A627
BROWNING, Michael, Interim Chief Executive Officer, Madison County Hospital, London, OH, p. A484
BROWNING, Michael P., Chief Financial Officer, Parkview Noble Hospital, Kendallville, IN, p. A207
BROWNLEE, Ernest, M.D. Medical Director, Millwood Hospital, Arlington, TX, p. A583
BROWNLOW, William R., Senior Vice President Finance, Silver Cross Hospital, New Lenox, IL, p. A190
BROWNSTEIN, Gregory, Chief Executive Officer, Westwood Lodge Hospital, Westwood, MA, p. A306
BROWNSWORTH, Ray, Chief Executive Officer, George E. Weems Memorial Hospital, Apalachicola, FL, p. A118
BROYHILL, David, Chief Information Management, San Antonio Military Medical Center, Fort Sam Houston, TX, p. A603
BROYLES, Susan, Director Human Resources and Safety, Unicoi County Memorial Hospital, Erwin, TN, p. A569
BRUCE, Bill, FACHE, Chief Executive Officer, Crawford County Memorial Hospital, Denison, IA, p. A220
BRUCE, Glenda, Director Community Relations, Rusk State Hospital, Rusk, TX, p. A630
BRUCE, Michael D., Chief Executive Officer, Lake Martin Community Hospital, Dadeville, AL, p. A18
BRUCE, Mike, Chief Financial Officer, Elmore Community Hospital, Wetumpka, AL, p. A26
BRUCE, Scott, Vice President Operations, St. Mary's Healthcare, Amsterdam, NY, p. A420
BRUCE, Sheila, Director Information System, Baptist Health Madisonville, Madisonville, KY, p. A257
BRUDNICKI, Gary F., Senior Executive Vice President, Chief Operating Officer and Chief Financial Officer, Westchester Medical Center, Valhalla, NY, p. A445
BRUEGGEMAN, Mary, Vice President Clinical Services, St. Joseph's Health Services–Gundersen Lutheran, Hillsboro, WI, p. A688
BRUEGGEMAN, Mary Jo, R.N. Vice President Patient Care, Fairview Lakes Health Services, Wyoming, MN, p. A343
BRUFF, Edward, Executive Vice President and Chief Operating Officer, Covenant Medical Center, Saginaw, MI, p. A323
BRUGGEMAN, Chris, Chief Information Officer, RiverView Health, Crookston, MN, p. A331
BRUHL, Lisa G., Chief Operating Officer, Lallie Kemp Medical Center, Independence, LA, p. A268
BRUHN, Julie, R.N. Associate Director Patient Care and Nurse Executive, Fargo Veterans Affairs Health Care System, Fargo, ND, p. A466
BRUI, Thomas M., Director Resource Management, Naval Hospital, Lemoore, CA, p. A66
BRUMBAUGH, David
   Vice President Human Resources, Children's Hospitals and Clinics of Minnesota, Minneapolis, MN, p. A336
   Vice President Human Resources, Children's Hospitals and Clinics of Minnesota, Saint Paul, MN, p. A340
BRUMFIELD, Cynthia, M.D. Chief of Staff, University of Alabama Hospital, Birmingham, AL, p. A17
BRUMMETT, Vince, Director Administrative Services, Tri–Lakes Medical Center, Batesville, MS, p. A344
BRUMMUND, Calvin J., Interim Chief Financial Officer, Neshoba County General Hospital, Philadelphia, MS, p. A352
BRUMSTED, John R., M.D., President and Chief Executive Officer, Fletcher Allen Health Care, Burlington, VT, p. A649
BRUNDISE, Cynthia, Vice President Human Resources, St. Anthony Hospital, Oklahoma City, OK, p. A504

BRUNELLE, Diane, MSN Vice President of Patient Care Services and Chief Nursing Officer, Noble Hospital, Westfield, MA, p. A306

BRUNER, Deborah, Chief Executive Officer and Administrator, Minneola District Hospital, Minneola, KS, p. A240

BRUNING, Gary, M.D. President Medical Staff, Avera Flandreau Hospital, Flandreau, SD, p. A559

BRUNKE, Renea
Vice President Human Resources, Chandler Regional Medical Center, Chandler, AZ, p. A30
Vice President Human Resources, Mercy Gilbert Medical Center, Gilbert, AZ, p. A31

BRUNNQUELL, Stephen, M.D. President Medical Staff, Englewood Hospital and Medical Center, Englewood, NJ, p. A404

BRUNNWORTH, Donald, Chief Financial Officer, Community Memorial Hospital, Staunton, IL, p. A195

BRUNO, Catherine, FACH
Chief Information Officer, Eastern Maine Medical Center, Bangor, ME, p. A281
Chief Information Officer, The Aroostook Medical Center, Presque Isle, ME, p. A285

BRUNO, Frank, Chief Executive Officer, Gracie Square Hospital, New York, NY, p. A432

BRUNO, John, Vice President Human Resources, St. Joseph's Regional Medical Center, Paterson, NJ, p. A408

BRUNO, Judy, R.N. Vice President, Clinical Operations, The Outer Banks Hospital, Nags Head, NC, p. A458

BRUNO, Yolanda, M.D. Medical Director, Coler–Goldwater Specialty Hospital and Nursing Facility, New York, NY, p. A431

BRUNSMAN, William, M.D. Chief of Staff, Mercy Medical Center, Williston, ND, p. A469

BRUNSON, Brian, Chief Executive Officer, Crossroads Regional Hospital, Alexandria, LA, p. A262

BRUNSON, Pam, Director Human Resources, South Baldwin Regional Medical Center, Foley, AL, p. A20

BRUNT, C. Hal, M.D. Medical Director, Lakeside Behavioral Health System, Memphis, TN, p. A574

BRUNTLETT, Melissa, Chief Financial Officer, Magee General Hospital, Magee, MS, p. A350

BRUNTZ, Troy, Vice President Finance and Chief Financial Officer, Community Hospital, McCook, NE, p. A386

BRUS, Sarah, Director Human Resources, Ripon Medical Center, Ripon, WI, p. A696

BRUSKI, Gayle, R.N. Chief Nursing Officer, Alpena Regional Medical Center, Alpena, MI, p. A308

BRUSS, Jonathan R., President, Advocate Trinity Hospital, Chicago, IL, p. A176

BRUSSEAU, Margie, R.N. Chief Nursing Officer, Athens Regional Medical Center, Athens, TN, p. A565

BRUTON, Jeff, Director Human Resources, Fairview Park Hospital, Dublin, GA, p. A152

BRUTSCHEA, Christine, Chief Information Technology, Nazareth Hospital, Philadelphia, PA, p. A536

BRUUN, Edward, President and Chief Executive Officer, Sparrow Clinton Hospital, Saint Johns, MI, p. A323

BRVENIK, Richard A., FACHE, President, Carteret General Hospital, Morehead City, NC, p. A457

BRYAN, Jay, President and Chief Executive Officer, Mercy Health Partners, Lakeshore Campus, Shelby, MI, p. A324

BRYAN, Kenneth E., FACHE, President and Chief Executive Officer, Hartnett Health System, Dunn, NC, p. A451

BRYAN, Linda, Vice President Human Resources, Plantation General Hospital, Plantation, FL, p. A137

BRYAN, Margaret, Administrator, Shriners Hospitals for Children–Northern California, Sacramento, CA, p. A83

BRYAN, Marilyn, Administrator, Roger Mills Memorial Hospital, Cheyenne, OK, p. A496

BRYAN, Mark, Chief Executive Officer, Delray Medical Center, Delray Beach, FL, p. A122

BRYAN, Steven, Chief Financial Officer, Kindred Hospital Sugar Land, Sugar Land, TX, p. A635

BRYAN–SMITH, Lissa, Chief Administrative Officer, Geisinger–Bloomsburg Hospital, Bloomsburg, PA, p. A521

BRYANT, Amy, Chief Financial Officer, Cornerstone Hospital of Southwest Louisiana, Sulphur, LA, p. A279

BRYANT, Dawn L.
Senior Vice President and Chief Human Resource Officer, Saint Francis Hospital and Medical Center, Hartford, CT, p. A109
Vice President Organizational Development, St. Joseph Medical Center, Kansas City, MO, p. A363

BRYANT, Gary, M.D. Chief of Staff, United Regional Medical Center, Manchester, TN, p. A573

BRYANT, Gayla, Administrator, Sage Rehabilitation Hospital, Baton Rouge, LA, p. A264

BRYANT, John F., Director Information Services, Heritage Medical Center, Shelbyville, TN, p. A579

BRYANT, Karen, Chief Support Services Officer, Prowers Medical Center, Lamar, CO, p. A103

BRYANT, Kim, Chief Executive Officer, Highlands Medical Center, Scottsboro, AL, p. A25

BRYANT, Lisa G., Director Human Resources, Cannon Memorial Hospital, Pickens, SC, p. A555

BRYANT, Mandy, Chief Information Officer, Twin Lakes Regional Medical Center, Leitchfield, KY, p. A253

BRYANT, Maureen A., FACHE, President and Chief Executive Officer, Presence Mercy Medical Center, Aurora, IL, p. A173

BRYANT, Pam
Director Human Resources, Helen Keller Hospital, Sheffield, AL, p. A25
Director Human Resources, Red Bay Hospital, Red Bay, AL, p. A25

BRYANT, Ron, President and Chief Executive Officer, Noble Hospital, Westfield, MA, p. A306

BRYANT, Rusty, Director Information Technology, Drew Memorial Hospital, Monticello, AR, p. A47

BRYANT, Stephanie, Chief Financial Officer, Twin County Regional Hospital, Galax, VA, p. A654

BRYANT, Tracy, Coordinator Information Technology, Marcum and Wallace Memorial Hospital, Irvine, KY, p. A253

BRYANT, William J., Chief Executive Officer, Kindred Hospital–Chattanooga, Chattanooga, TN, p. A566

BRYANT-MOBLEY, Phyllis, M.D. Director Medical Services, William S. Hall Psychiatric Institute, Columbia, SC, p. A550

BRYCE, Keith, Chief Financial Officer, Mt. Graham Regional Medical Center, Safford, AZ, p. A36

BRYDON, Paul, Chief Financial Officer, Tri–City Regional Medical Center, Hawaiian Gardens, CA, p. A63

BRYNER, Jennifer, Chief Nursing Officer, Petersburg Medical Center, Petersburg, AK, p. A29

BRYSON, Kellie, Director Human Resources, The Hospital at Westlake Medical Center, Austin, TX, p. A586

BUBACZ, Joe, Chief Information Officer, Soldiers and Sailors Memorial Hospital, Wellsboro, PA, p. A543

BUBRIG, Destini, Director Health Information Management, Hardtner Medical Center, Olla, LA, p. A276

BUCCI, Annette, Senior Administrator Human Resources, Burke Rehabilitation Hospital, White Plains, NY, p. A446

BUCCI, Domenick, M.D. Medical Director, Aria Health, Philadelphia, PA, p. A534

BUCCOLO, Martin A., Ph.D., Chief Executive Officer, Four Winds Hospital, Katonah, NY, p. A428

BUCH, Naishadh, Director Pharmacy and Chief Operating Officer, Lompoc Valley Medical Center, Lompoc, CA, p. A67

BUCHANAN, Dennis, Vice President Human Resources, New York Methodist Hospital,, NY, p. A435

BUCHANAN, Donna, Director Nursing, Stroud Regional Medical Center, Stroud, OK, p. A507

BUCHANAN, Herbert, Chief Executive Officer, Howard University Hospital, Washington, DC, p. A116

BUCHANAN, Kevin, Chief Information Officer, Wake Forest Baptist Health–Lexington Medical Center, Lexington, NC, p. A456

BUCHANAN, Kyle, Chief Executive Officer, Lawrence Medical Center, Moulton, AL, p. A24

BUCHANAN, Richard, Interim Chief Executive Officer, Warm Springs Medical Center, Warm Springs, GA, p. A162

BUCHANAN, Robert, Chief Information Officer, Anna Jaques Hospital, Newburyport, MA, p. A302

BUCHANAN, Ron, Director Information Services, West Central Georgia Regional Hospital, Columbus, GA, p. A150

BUCHANAN, Toni, Chief Financial Officer, Unicoi County Memorial Hospital, Erwin, TN, p. A569

BUCHANAN, Tracy, Chief Executive Officer / President, CarePartners Health Services, Asheville, NC, p. A447

BUCHART, Phyllis, Chief Operating Officer, Marina Del Rey Hospital, Marina Del Rey, CA, p. A73

BUCHELE, Paula, Chief Human Resources, Bay Pines Veterans Affairs Medical Center, Bay Pines, FL, p. A118

BUCHERT, Charles, Director Human Resources, Women and Children's Hospital, Lake Charles, LA, p. A272

BUCHHEIT, Anne, Coordinator Mental Health Local Information Systems, Buffalo Psychiatric Center, Buffalo, NY, p. A422

BUCHHEIT, Joe, Chief Information Officer, Our Lady of Bellefonte Hospital, Ashland, KY, p. A248

BUCHHOLZ, Kari, Director Health Information Management, Wishek Community Hospital and Clinics, Wishek, ND, p. A469

BUCHHOLZ, Troy, M.D. Chief Medical Staff, Community Memorial Hospital, Sumner, IA, p. A229

BUCIENSKI, Jennifer, Director Human Resources, Hayes Green Beach Memorial Hospital, Charlotte, MI, p. A310

BUCK, Catherine, Executive Vice President Operations, Froedtert Memorial Lutheran Hospital, Milwaukee, WI, p. A692

BUCK, Cheryl, Vice President Human Resources, Lake Region Healthcare, Fergus Falls, MN, p. A332

BUCK, Cindy D., Chief Executive Officer, Rutherford Regional Health System, Rutherfordton, NC, p. A460

BUCK, Gwen, R.N. Chief Nursing Officer, Greater Regional Medical Center, Creston, IA, p. A219

BUCK, Linda K., Vice President Human Resources, Proctor Hospital, Peoria, IL, p. A192

BUCK, Phylis, Controller, HEALTHSOUTH Rehabilitation Hospital of Texarkana, Texarkana, TX, p. A637

BUCK, William G., Chief Executive Officer, Northwest Mississippi Regional Medical Center, Clarksdale, MS, p. A345

BUCKHOY, Sandra, Chief Clinical Officer, Kindred Hospital Chicago–Northlake, Northlake, IL, p. A190

BUCKINGHAM, Deborah, R.N. Director Human Resources, Redington–Fairview General Hospital, Skowhegan, ME, p. A285

BUCKINGHAM, Maura, D.O. Chief of Staff, South Haven Health System, South Haven, MI, p. A324

BUCKLEY, John J., Chief Administrative Officer, Geisinger Wyoming Valley Medical Center, Wilkes Barre, PA, p. A544

BUCKLEY, Kalvin, Director Information Systems, Woodland Heights Medical Center, Lufkin, TX, p. A621

BUCKLEY, Patrick, Vice President Human Resources, St. Elizabeth Medical Center, Utica, NY, p. A444

BUCKLEY, R. Michael, M.D., Executive Director, Pennsylvania Hospital, Philadelphia, PA, p. A536

BUCKNER Jr., James E., FACHE, Administrator, Uvalde County Hospital Authority, Uvalde, TX, p. A639

BUCKNER, Terry, Chief Executive Officer, Pikes Peak Regional Hospital, Woodland Park, CO, p. A107

BUCKWORTH, Albert Bennett, Director Human Resources, Primary Children's Medical Center, Salt Lake City, UT, p. A646

BUDD, Edward, President and Chief Executive Officer, Thorek Memorial Hospital, Chicago, IL, p. A179

BUDDA, Jeff, Chief Information Officer, Floyd Medical Center, Rome, GA, p. A159

BUDIG, Aletha, R.N. Director of Nursing, Ellinwood District Hospital, Ellinwood, KS, p. A233

BUDIN, Kirsten, Director Human Resources, Northfield Hospital, Northfield, MN, p. A337

BUDINGER, David P., Interim Director, Hunter Holmes McGuire Veterans Affairs Medical Center, Richmond, VA, p. A660

BUDNICK, Michael J., FACHE Chief Operating Officer and Clinic Manager, Franklin Hospital District, Benton, IL, p. A174

BUDZINSKI, A. James, Vice President and Chief Financial Officer, WellStar Kennestone Hospital, Marietta, GA, p. A157

BUDZINSKI, William, Vice President Human Resources, Methodist Hospital of Southern California, Arcadia, CA, p. A53

BUDZINSKY, Chris, R.N. Vice President Nursing/CNO Alexian Brothers Acute Care Ministries, St. Alexius Medical Center, Hoffman Estates, IL, p. A185

BUELL, Jack, Director Information Services, Sutter Lakeside Hospital, Lakeport, CA, p. A66

BUELL, Lindsay, Chief Information Management Services, Oklahoma City Veterans Affairs Medical Center, Oklahoma City, OK, p. A504

BUELT, Madeline, Vice President Operations, Seattle Cancer Care Alliance, Seattle, WA, p. A671

BUENVENIDA, Brenda, Facility Administrator, Hiram W. Davis Medical Center, Petersburg, VA, p. A659

BUER, Shane, Director Human Resources, Presbyterian–St. Luke's Medical Center, Denver, CO, p. A100

BUFFINGTON, John, Chief Operating Officer, San Juan Regional Medical Center, Farmington, NM, p. A416

BUGG, Robert, Chief Financial Officer, Broward Health North, Deerfield Beach, FL, p. A122

BUGNA, Eric, M.D. Chief of Staff, Eastern Plumas Health Care District, Portola, CA, p. A80

BUHEIS, Nidal, M.D. Chief of Staff, The Medical Center of Southeast Texas, Port Arthur, TX, p. A628

BUHL, Michael D., Senior Vice President and Chief Financial Officer, University of Wisconsin Hospital and Clinics, Madison, WI, p. A690

BUHLKE, Brian, M.D. Medical Director, Genoa Community Hospital, Genoa, NE, p. A383

BUHOWSKI, Richard, Chief Financial Officer, Helen Hayes Hospital, West Haverstraw, NY, p. A445

BUI, Kim, Director Human Resources, East Valley Hospital Medical Center, Glendora, CA, p. A63

BUIT, Timothy, Vice President of Finance and Chief Financial Officer, Bellevue Hospital, Bellevue, OH, p. A471

BUJAK, Joseph, M.D. Vice President Medical Affairs, Kootenai Medical Center, Coeur D'Alene, ID, p. A168

BUKHARI, Kim, Manager Human Resources, Oak Valley Hospital District, Oakdale, CA, p. A77

BUKOWSKI, Cathy
Chief Financial Officer, Howard Young Medical Center, Woodruff, WI, p. A700
Regional Chief Financial Officer, Ministry Eagle River Memorial Hospital, Eagle River, WI, p. A686
Regional Chief Financial Officer, Ministry Saint Mary's Hospitals, Rhinelander, WI, p. A695

BULAU, Chris, Manager Information Technology, Sibley Medical Center, Arlington, MN, p. A328

BULEN, Susan, M.D. Medical Director, HEALTHSOUTH Rehabilitation Hospital of Southern Arizona, Tucson, AZ, p. A38

BULLARD, Brandon
Chief Financial Officer, Hillcrest Hospital Cushing, Cushing, OK, p. A497
Chief Financial Officer, Hillcrest Hospital Henryetta, Henryetta, OK, p. A499

BULLARD, Michael R., Chief Executive Officer, Doctor's Hospital – Tidwell, Houston, TX, p. A609

BULLARD, Patrick, Chief Financial Officer, Fayetteville Veterans Affairs Medical Center, Fayetteville, NC, p. A452

BULLARD, Timothy, M.D. Chief of Staff, Orlando Regional Medical Center, Orlando, FL, p. A135

BULLINGTON, Benjamin P., M.D. Chief of Staff, Pioneer Medical Center, Big Timber, MT, p. A374

BULLINGTON, Gina, Chief Nursing Officer, TriStar Horizon Medical Center, Dickson, TN, p. A568

BULLITT, Michael L., Chief Executive Officer, HEALTHSOUTH Rehabilitation Hospital–Wichita Falls, Wichita Falls, TX, p. A641

BULLOCH, Bill, Director Human Resources, Roosevelt Warm Springs Institute for Rehabilitation, Warm Springs, GA, p. A162

BULLOCK, David, Director Information Services, Northwest Medical Center, Tucson, AZ, p. A39

BULLOCK, Lance, M.D. Medical Director, St. James Behavioral Health Hospital, Gonzales, LA, p. A267

BULLOCK, Renee, Vice President Human Resources, Saint Joseph Berea, Berea, KY, p. A248

BULMAN, Laurie, Director Human Resources, Winneshiek Medical Center, Decorah, IA, p. A220

BULTEMA, Janice K., MSN Senior Vice President Human Resources, University of Wisconsin Hospital and Clinics, Madison, WI, p. A690

BULUSU, Somayaji, Chief Information Officer, Marin General Hospital, Greenbrae, CA, p. A63

BUMAN, Karen, Chief Nurse Executive, Myrtue Medical Center, Harlan, IA, p. A222

BUMATAY, Susan C., R.N. Assistant Administrator, Sutter Delta Medical Center, Antioch, CA, p. A52

BUMGARDNER, Chuck, Director Information Systems, Southeast Georgia Health System Brunswick Campus, Brunswick, GA, p. A149

BUMGARNER, William J., President, Spencer Hospital, Spencer, IA, p. A228

BUMP, Cathy, R.N. Chief Nursing Officer, Methodist Ambulatory Surgery Hospital, San Antonio, TX, p. A631

BUMPUS, Joe, Director Information Technology, St. Elizabeth Hospital, Gonzales, LA, p. A267

BUNCH, David V., Chief Executive Officer, Heritage Medical Center, Shelbyville, TN, p. A579

BUNCH, Elicia, Chief Executive Officer, Centennial Peaks Hospital, Louisville, CO, p. A104

BUNCH, Jimm, President and Chief Executive Officer, Park Ridge Health, Hendersonville, NC, p. A454

BUNCH, Kim, Director Information Technology, Marshall Medical Center North, Guntersville, AL, p. A21

BUNCH, Mark, Director Finance, Othello Community Hospital, Othello, WA, p. A669

BUNCH, Mike, Executive Vice President, Chief Operating Officer and Chief Financial Officer, KershawHealth, Camden, SC, p. A548

BUNCH, Terri, R.N. Chief Nursing Officer, Hopkins County Memorial Hospital, Sulphur Springs, TX, p. A636

BUND, Linda, Chief Information Officer and Director Education, James J. Peters Veterans Affairs Medical Center,, NY, p. A432

BUNDGARD, Susan, Vice President Human Resources, Saint Alphonsus Regional Medical Center, Boise, ID, p. A168

BUNDICK, Ida, Chief Financial Officer, Eastern Shore Hospital Center, Cambridge, MD, p. A290

BUNKER, Marla, Vice President Nursing and Chief Operating Officer, War Memorial Hospital, Sault Sainte Marie, MI, p. A324

BUNN, Barry, M.D. Chief of Staff, Vidant Edgecombe Hospital, Tarboro, NC, p. A462

BUNNER, Blake, Director Human Resources, HEALTHSOUTH Deaconess Rehabilitation Hospital, Evansville, IN, p. A202

BUNSELMEYER, Becky, Director Information Services, Memorial Hospital, Chester, IL, p. A176

BUNTING, Katherine, Chief Executive Officer, Fairfield Memorial Hospital, Fairfield, IL, p. A182

BUNTYN, Diane, MSN Vice President Patient Care Services, Southeast Alabama Medical Center, Dothan, AL, p. A19

BUNYARD, Steve, Chief Operating Officer, OhioHealth Dublin Methodist Hospital, Dublin, OH, p. A481

BUONGIORNO, Michael J.
Executive Vice President Finance and Chief Financial Officer, Bryn Mawr Hospital, Bryn Mawr, PA, p. A521
Vice President Finance and Treasurer, Bryn Mawr Rehabilitation Hospital, Malvern, PA, p. A530
Vice President Finance, Lankenau Medical Center, Wynnewood, PA, p. A545

BURASCO, Carmen, Director Human Resources, Siloam Springs Memorial Hospital, Siloam Springs, AR, p. A50

BURBANK, Jimmy, Chief Information Officer, U. S. Public Health Service Indian Hospital, Crownpoint, NM, p. A415

BURBULES, Kevin, Chief Information Officer, University of Maryland Charles Regional Medical Center, La Plata, MD, p. A292

BURCH, Eric, Chief Executive Officer, Lewis County General Hospital, Lowville, NY, p. A428

BURCH, Janel, Chief Financial Officer, Russell Regional Hospital, Russell, KS, p. A243

BURCH, Larry, M.D. Vice President Medical Affairs, Saint Anthony's Health Center, Alton, IL, p. A173

BURCH, Lee, Director Management Information Systems, Bayfront Health Brooksville, Brooksville, FL, p. A119

BURCHAM, Jim, Chief Executive Officer, Gateway Rehabilitation Hospital, Florence, KY, p. A250

BURCHELL, Pam, Director Human Resources, Lawnwood Regional Medical Center, Fort Pierce, FL, p. A124

BURCHETT, Claudia L., R.N. Vice President Patient Services, Southern Ohio Medical Center, Portsmouth, OH, p. A489

BURCHETT, Travis, Troop Commander Human Resources, Colonel Florence A. Blanchfield Army Community Hospital, Fort Campbell, KY, p. A251

BURCHFIELD, Charla, Manager Human Resources, St. James Behavioral Health Hospital, Gonzales, LA, p. A267

BURCHILL, Kevin, Chief Executive Officer, Arbour–Fuller Hospital, Attleboro, MA, p. A295

BURCZEUSKI, Jason, Controller, Conifer Park, Glenville, NY, p. A426

BURD, Vanessa, R.N. Chief Nursing Officer, Caverna Memorial Hospital, Horse Cave, KY, p. A253

BURDEN, Jennifer, Vice President Human Resources, TriStar Hendersonville Medical Center, Hendersonville, TN, p. A570

BURDETT, Gregg, Vice President Administration and Physician Services, Valley Regional Hospital, Claremont, NH, p. A397

BURDETTE, Pat, Chief Financial Officer, Sistersville General Hospital, Sistersville, WV, p. A681

BURDICK, Ginny
Senior Vice President and Chief Human Resources Officer, Clovis Community Medical Center, Clovis, CA, p. A56
Vice President Human Resources, Community Behavioral Health Center, Fresno, CA, p. A61
Vice President Human Resources, Community Regional Medical Center, Fresno, CA, p. A61

BURDICK, Hoyt J., M.D. Vice President Medical Affairs, Cabell Huntington Hospital, Huntington, WV, p. A677

BURDICK, Steven A., Chief Executive Officer, Providence St. Mary Medical Center, Walla Walla, WA, p. A674

BURGER, Janice, Administrator, Providence St. Vincent Medical Center, Portland, OR, p. A516

BURGESS, Alan J., FACHE, Chief Executive Officer, Tehachapi Valley Healthcare District, Tehachapi, CA, p. A92

BURGESS, Angela, Chief Information Officer, Randolph Hospital, Asheboro, NC, p. A447

BURGESS, Carolyn, Director Human Resources, Henrietta D. Goodall Hospital, Sanford, ME, p. A285

BURGESS, Daniel, Chief Information Officer, MaineGeneral Medical Center–Waterville Campus, Waterville, ME, p. A285

BURGESS, Debbie, Director Information Services, Bert Fish Medical Center, New Smyrna Beach, FL, p. A133

BURGESS, John, Director Information Services, Hocking Valley Community Hospital, Logan, OH, p. A484

BURGESS, Robert, President and Chief Executive Officer, St. Elizabeth Hospital, Gonzales, LA, p. A267

BURGESS, Steven, Administrator Human Resources, Henrico Doctors' Hospital, Richmond, VA, p. A660

BURGIN, Kelli, Director Information Technology, Audubon County Memorial Hospital, Audubon, IA, p. A216

BURGUILLOS, Richard, Chief Financial Officer, Care One at Raritan Bay Medical Center, Perth Amboy, NJ, p. A408

BURIANEK, Amy, Director Nurses, First Care Health Center, Park River, ND, p. A469

BURINGRUD, Duane, M.D. Chief Medical and Quality Officer, Palomar Medical Center, Escondido, CA, p. A59

BURISH, Brent
Chief Operating Officer, Heart of Florida Regional Medical Center, Davenport, FL, p. A121
Chief Executive Officer, Shands Starke Regional Medical Center, Starke, FL, p. A140

BURK, Jackie, Director Human Resources, Cedar Crest Hospital and Residential Treatment Center, Belton, TX, p. A588

BURK, Thomas J., Chief Operating Officer, Danville State Hospital, Danville, PA, p. A523

BURKE, Aron, M.D. Chief Medical Officer, Community Hospital–Fairfax, Fairfax, MO, p. A360

BURKE, Brian, M.D. President Medical Staff, Fairview Hospital, Great Barrington, MA, p. A300

BURKE, Curtis, M.D. Chief of Staff, LeConte Medical Center, Sevierville, TN, p. A579

BURKE, David, Administrator and Chief Executive Officer, Muleshoe Area Medical Center, Muleshoe, TX, p. A624

BURKE, David J., Director Finance and Chief Financial Officer, Nantucket Cottage Hospital, Nantucket, MA, p. A302

BURKE, Dennis E., President and Chief Executive Officer, Good Shepherd Health Care System, Hermiston, OR, p. A513

BURKE, Drew, Director Human Resources, Willamette Valley Medical Center, McMinnville, OR, p. A514

BURKE, Ed, Chief Financial Officer, Interim LSU Public Hospital, New Orleans, LA, p. A275

BURKE, Greg, M.D. Medical Director, Geisinger HEALTHSOUTH Rehabilitation Hospital, Danville, PA, p. A523

BURKE, James, M.D
Senior Vice President and Chief Medical Officer, Scottsdale Healthcare Shea Medical Center, Scottsdale, AZ, p. A37
Senior Vice President and Chief Medical Officer, Scottsdale Healthcare Thompson Peak Hospital, Scottsdale, AZ, p. A37
Senior Vice President and Chief Medical Officer, Scottsdale Healthcare–Osborn Medical Center, Scottsdale, AZ, p. A37

BURKE, James B., Chief Operating Officer, Hahnemann University Hospital, Philadelphia, PA, p. A535

BURKE, Jeff
Chief Information Officer, Bon Secours St. Mary's Hospital, Richmond, VA, p. A660
Chief Information Officer, Bon Secours–Richmond Community Hospital, Richmond, VA, p. A660

BURKE, Jo–Ann, R.N. Vice President Patient Care Services, Children's Hospital of The King's Daughters, Norfolk, VA, p. A658

BURKE, John, Chief Financial Officer, Nyack Hospital, Nyack, NY, p. A438

BURKE, Kaye, Administrator, Noland Hospital Dothan, Dothan, AL, p. A19

BURKE, Marsha
Senior Vice President Financial Services, WellStar Paulding Hospital, Dallas, GA, p. A151
Senior Vice President and Chief Financial Officer, WellStar Windy Hill Hospital, Marietta, GA, p. A157

BURKE, Michael, Senior Vice President and Corporate Chief Financial Officer, NYU Langone Medical Center, New York, NY, p. A435

BURKE, Paul, Administrator, Schleicher County Medical Center, Eldorado, TX, p. A602

BURKE, Thomas, M.D. Executive Vice President and Physician–in–Chief, University of Texas M.D. Anderson Cancer Center, Houston, TX, p. A613

BURKE, Timothy, M.D. Medical Director, The Brook Hospital – KMI, Louisville, KY, p. A256

BURKE, Timothy R., M.D. Chief of Staff, Veterans Affairs Butler Healthcare, Butler, PA, p. A521

BURKEL, Gregory, Chief Financial Officer, Alaska Native Medical Center, Anchorage, AK, p. A27

BURKET, Mark, Chief Executive Officer, Platte Health Center Avera, Platte, SD, p. A561

BURKETT, Eric, M.D. Vice President Medical Affairs, Monmouth Medical Center, Long Branch, NJ, p. A406

BURKETT, Evan, Chief Human Resource Officer, Sanford USD Medical Center, Sioux Falls, SD, p. A562

BURKEY, Kathleen, R.N. Vice President of Nursing, Grand View Hospital, Sellersville, PA, p. A541

BURKHARDT, Minnie, Associate Administrator, Texoma Medical Center, Denison, TX, p. A598

BURKHARDT, Raye, Chief Nursing Officer, St. John's Pleasant Valley Hospital, Camarillo, CA, p. A55

BURKHART, Brad, Assistant Administrator, Harlan ARH Hospital, Harlan, KY, p. A252

BURKHART, James R., FACHE, President and Chief Executive Officer, Tampa General Hospital, Tampa, FL, p. A142

BURKHART, Steven, M.D. Chief Medical Officer, Crittenden County Hospital, Marion, KY, p. A257

BURKHART, Tracy, Vice President Information Services, Sacred Heart Hospital, Allentown, PA, p. A519

BURKHOLDER, Adrienne, Director Human Resources, AMG Specialty Hospital–Wichita, Wichita, KS, p. A246

BURKITT, David, Director Fiscal Services, Shriners Hospitals for Children–Los Angeles, Los Angeles, CA, p. A71

BURKLOW, Bryan, Chief Executive Officer, Brandywine Hospital, Coatesville, PA, p. A523

BURKS, Felicia, Chief Financial Officer, U. S. Air Force Regional Hospital, Elmendorf AFB, AK, p. A28

BURKS, Matt, Director Information Technology, United Regional Medical Center, Manchester, TN, p. A573

BURKS, Mel, Chief Executive Officer, Hamilton Center, Terre Haute, IN, p. A213

BURKS, Tami
Chief Fiscal Services, Iraan General Hospital, Iraan, TX, p. A614
Comptroller, Rankin Hospital District, Rankin, TX, p. A628

BURLESON, Linda, Administrative Secretary, Clay County Memorial Hospital, Henrietta, TX, p. A608

BURLESON, Scott D., Executive Vice President, Chester River Health System, Chestertown, MD, p. A290

BURLESON, Stan, M.D. Chief Medical Staff, DeWitt Hospital, De Witt, AR, p. A42

BURLING, Chris, M.D. Chief of Staff, Titus Regional Medical Center, Mount Pleasant, TX, p. A623

BURMAN, Don, Chief Executive Officer, Heartland Surgical Specialty Hospital, Overland Park, KS, p. A241

BURMEISTER, Geraldine F., FACHE, Chief Executive Officer, Windom Area Hospital, Windom, MN, p. A343

BURMESTER, Mark A., Vice President Strategy and Communications, Kaiser Permanente Sunnyside Medical Center, Clackamas, OR, p. A511

BURNAM, Gregg, Chief Information Officer and Manager Business Office, Quartz Mountain Medical Center, Mangum, OK, p. A501

BURNETT, Anthony, M.D. Medical Director, Julian F. Keith Alcohol and Drug Abuse Treatment Center, Black Mountain, NC, p. A448

BURNETT, Brad, Chief Financial Officer, Heart of Texas Memorial Hospital, Brady, TX, p. A589

BURNETT, Cindi, Chief Human Resources Officer, Madison County Memorial Hospital, Madison, FL, p. A129

BURNETT, J. Michael, President and Chief Administrative Officer, Piedmont Fayette Hospital, Fayetteville, GA, p. A153

BURNETT, Karen, Regional Director Human Resources, McKay-Dee Hospital Center, Ogden, UT, p. A645

BURNETT, Mark, President and Chief Executive Officer, Scott County Hospital, Scott City, KS, p. A244

BURNETT, Michael, Chief Operating Officer, Piedmont Fayette Hospital, Fayetteville, GA, p. A153

BURNETTE, Linda, R.N. Chief Nursing Officer, Southern Virginia Regional Medical Center, Emporia, VA, p. A653

BURNETTE, Peg, Chief Financial Officer, Denver Health Medical Center, Denver, CO, p. A99

BURNETTE, Sheri, R.N., Chief Executive Officer and Administrator, Cornerstone Hospital of Bossier City, Bossier City, LA, p. A264

BURNETTE, W. Scott, President and Chief Executive Officer, Community Memorial Healthcenter, South Hill, VA, p. A661

BURNEY, Sibte, M.D. Senior Vice President Medical Affairs and Chief Medical Officer, Kingsbrook Jewish Medical Center,, NY, p. A433

BURNHAM, David, M.D. Chief of Staff, Longmont United Hospital, Longmont, CO, p. A104

BURNHAM, Sharon, Director of Nursing, Simpson General Hospital, Mendenhall, MS, p. A350

BURNHAM, Wendy, Interim Chief Nursing Officer, Homer Memorial Hospital, Homer, LA, p. A268

BURNS, Barry, Vice President, Methodist Ambulatory Surgery Hospital, San Antonio, TX, p. A631

BURNS, Becky L., Manager Health Information Management, Ellinwood District Hospital, Ellinwood, KS, p. A233

BURNS, Brantly, M.D. Medical Director, Select Specialty Hospital-Knoxville, Knoxville, TN, p. A572

BURNS, Bruce R., Chief Financial Officer, Concord Hospital, Concord, NH, p. A397

BURNS, Coreg, Human Resources Lead, West Central Georgia Regional Hospital, Columbus, GA, p. A150

BURNS, Gregory T., President and Chief Executive Officer, Cameron Memorial Community Hospital, Angola, IN, p. A198

BURNS, Helen K., Ph.D
Senior Vice President and Chief Nursing Officer, Excela Frick Hospital, Mount Pleasant, PA, p. A532
Senior Vice President and Chief Nursing Officer, Excela Health Westmoreland Hospital, Greensburg, PA, p. A526
Senior Vice President and Chief Nursing Officer, Excela Latrobe Area Hospital, Latrobe, PA, p. A529

BURNS, James P., Vice President and Chief Financial Officer, Fawcett Memorial Hospital, Port Charlotte, FL, p. A137

BURNS, Jared, Coordinator Human Resources, Regency Hospital of Hattiesburg, Hattiesburg, MS, p. A348

BURNS, Jeff, Manager of Information Technology, Mary Free Bed Rehabilitation Hospital, Grand Rapids, MI, p. A315

BURNS, Joanne, Chief Information Officer, Women's and Children's Hospital, Columbia, MO, p. A359

BURNS, Jon P.
Senior Vice President and Chief Information Officer, Maryland General Hospital, Baltimore, MD, p. A288
Chief Information Officer, University of Maryland Medical Center, Baltimore, MD, p. A289

BURNS, Katherine, Vice President Human Resources, High Point Regional Health System, High Point, NC, p. A455

BURNS, Kathryn I., R.N. Director of Nursing, Medicine Lodge Memorial Hospital, Medicine Lodge, KS, p. A240

BURNS, Kay, Chief Financial Officer, Santa Rosa Medical Center, Milton, FL, p. A133

BURNS, Jr., Larry P., Chief Operating Officer, Yavapai Regional Medical Center, Prescott, AZ, p. A36

BURNS, Lawrence, Vice President Institutional Advancement, The University of Toledo Medical Center, Toledo, OH, p. A491

BURNS, Mary Elena, Director Human Resources, Roane Medical Center, Harriman, TN, p. A569

BURNS, Melissa, Chief Nursing Officer, Southwest Healthcare System, Murrieta, CA, p. A76

BURNS, Patricia, Chief Operating Officer/Ethics and Compliance Officer, Methodist Stone Oak Hospital, San Antonio, TX, p. A631

BURNS, Patrick, Vice President Finance, ACMH Hospital, Kittanning, PA, p. A528

BURNS, Sonda, Chief Executive Officer, Select Specialty Hospital-Akron, Akron, OH, p. A470

BURNS, Steven, Director Fiscal Services, Summit Behavioral Healthcare, Cincinnati, OH, p. A475

BURNS, Terry M.
President, Greene Memorial Hospital, Xenia, OH, p. A494
President, Soin Medical Center, Beavercreek, OH, p. A471

BURNS, Tom, M.D. Chief of Staff, The Hospital at Westlake Medical Center, Austin, TX, p. A586

BURNS, Wes, Director Human Resources, Vibra Hospital of San Diego, San Diego, CA, p. A86

BURNS-TISDALE, Susan, Senior Vice President Clinical Operations, Exeter Hospital, Exeter, NH, p. A398

BURNSIDE, David, M.D. Chief Medical Officer, Alton Memorial Hospital, Alton, IL, p. A173

BURRAGE, Steve, Interim Chief Executive Officer, Pushmataha Hospital & Home Health, Antlers, OK, p. A495

BURRELL, Carol H., President and Chief Executive Officer, Northeast Georgia Medical Center, Gainesville, GA, p. A154

BURRIS, Bradley D., Chief Executive Officer, Pipestone County Medical Center Avera, Pipestone, MN, p. A338

BURRIS, Don, Chief Executive Officer, Haxtun Hospital District, Haxtun, CO, p. A102

BURRIS, J. Michael
Vice President Corporate Services and Chief Financial Officer, Martha Jefferson Hospital, Charlottesville, VA, p. A652
Chief Financial Officer, Rockingham Memorial Hospital, Harrisonburg, VA, p. A655

BURRIS, Lisa
Manager Human Resources, Frazier Rehab Institute, Louisville, KY, p. A255
Director Human Resources, Southern Indiana Rehabilitation Hospital, New Albany, IN, p. A211

BURRISS, Jessica, Chief Financial Officer, HEALTHSOUTH Rehabilitation Hospital of Columbia, Columbia, SC, p. A550

BURRISS, Steve W., Chief Operating Officer, Rex Healthcare, Raleigh, NC, p. A459

BURRITT, Joan, R.N. Chief Operating Officer, Kaiser Permanente San Diego Medical Center, San Diego, CA, p. A85

BURROUGHS, James, Chief Executive Officer, Kingwood Pines Hospital, Kingwood, TX, p. A617

BURROUGHS, Michael R., FACHE, Chief Executive Officer, Western Plains Medical Complex, Dodge City, KS, p. A233

BURROUGHS, Valentine, M.D. Chief Medical Officer, East Orange General Hospital, East Orange, NJ, p. A403

BURROWS, Randy, Director Administrative Services, McKenzie-Willamette Medical Center, Springfield, OR, p. A518

BURROWS, Susan M.
Vice President Human Resources, Children's Hospital at Mission, Mission Viejo, CA, p. A74
Vice President Human Resources, Children's Hospital of Orange County, Orange, CA, p. A77

BURRY, V. Fred, M.D. Executive Medical Director, Children's Mercy Hospitals and Clinics, Kansas City, MO, p. A362

BURT, Alan, Director Information Services, Sunrise Hospital and Medical Center, Las Vegas, NV, p. A394

BURT, Keith, Director Marketing, Woodrow Wilson Rehabilitation Center, Fishersville, VA, p. A654

BURT, Linda K.
Corporate Vice President Finance, Methodist Jennie Edmundson Hospital, Council Bluffs, IA, p. A219
Corporate Vice President Finance, Nebraska Methodist Hospital, Omaha, NE, p. A388

BURT, Noel F., Ph.D. Chief Human Resources Officer, Cone Health, Greensboro, NC, p. A453

BURTCH, Gloria, Director Human Resources, Cornerstone of Medical Arts Center Hospital, Fresh Meadows, NY, p. A426

BURTHAY, Darcy, MSN Chief Nursing Officer and Chief Operating Officer, St. Vincent Indianapolis Hospital, Indianapolis, IN, p. A206

BURTON, Charles, Chief Human Resources, Carl R. Darnall Army Medical Center, Fort Hood, TX, p. A603

BURTON, Cynthia, R.N. Chief Nursing Officer, Rockcastle Regional Hospital and Respiratory Care Center, Mount Vernon, KY, p. A258

BURTON, Faye, Director Health Information Management, Edgefield County Hospital, Edgefield, SC, p. A551

BURTON, John T., Administrator, Kindred Hospital-Pittsburgh, Oakdale, PA, p. A533

BURTON, Luanne, Director Human Resources, HEALTHSOUTH Rehabilitation Hospital of Columbia, Columbia, SC, p. A550

BURTON, Robert, Manager Finance, Utah State Hospital, Provo, UT, p. A646

BURTON, Stacey R., Director Human Resources, Okmulgee Memorial Hospital, Okmulgee, OK, p. A505

BURTRON, Sandra, MS Chief Nursing Officer, Crawford Memorial Hospital, Robinson, IL, p. A193

BURY, Peter, Vice President Finance, OhioHealth Riverside Methodist Hospital, Columbus, OH, p. A478

BURY, Randy, Chief Operating Officer, Sanford USD Medical Center, Sioux Falls, SD, p. A562

BURZYNSKI, Cheryl A., President, McLaren Bay Special Care, Bay City, MI, p. A309

BUSATTI, David A., Vice President Finance, Hutchinson Regional Medical Center, Hutchinson, KS, p. A236

BUSBEE, Cathy L., Chief Nursing Officer, Woodland Heights Medical Center, Lufkin, TX, p. A621

BUSBEE, Lara, Chief Financial Officer, Flint River Community Hospital, Montezuma, GA, p. A157

BUSBY, Billie, Assistant Director, Colorado Mental Health Institute at Fort Logan, Denver, CO, p. A99

BUSBY, Jay, M.D. President Medical Staff, Franklin Medical Center, Winnsboro, LA, p. A280

BUSBY, Kathy, Medical Record Technician, Chillicothe Hospital District, Chillicothe, TX, p. A592

BUSBY, Lisa, Manager Information Systems, Moses Ludington Hospital, Ticonderoga, NY, p. A444

BUSCH, Michael D.
Executive Vice President and Chief Operating Officer, Excela Frick Hospital, Mount Pleasant, PA, p. A532
Executive Vice President and Chief Operating Officer, Excela Health Westmoreland Hospital, Greensburg, PA, p. A526
Executive Vice President and Chief Operating Officer, Excela Latrobe Area Hospital, Latrobe, PA, p. A529
Executive Vice President and Chief Operating Officer, Excela Latrobe Area Hospital, Latrobe, PA, p. A529

BUSCH, Rebecca, Chief Financial Officer, Spooner Health System, Spooner, WI, p. A696

BUSCH, Steve, Chief Operating Officer, Midwest Medical Center, Galena, IL, p. A183

BUSH, Bruce A., M.D. Senior Vice President Medical Affairs, Indiana Regional Medical Center, Indiana, PA, p. A528

BUSH, Deborah, Director Information Services, North Florida Regional Medical Center, Gainesville, FL, p. A124

BUSH, Linda, Chief Executive Officer, Franklin County Memorial Hospital, Franklin, NE, p. A383

BUSH, Stephen, Chief Financial Officer, TMC Healthcare, Tucson, AZ, p. A39

BUSH, William
Chief Executive Officer, Riverside Hospital of Louisiana, Alexandria, LA, p. A262
Chief Executive Officer, Specialty Hospital of Winnfield, Winnfield, LA, p. A280

BUSH, William B., CP
Chief Financial Officer, University of South Alabama Children's and Women's Hospital, Mobile, AL, p. A23
Chief Financial Officer, University of South Alabama Medical Center, Mobile, AL, p. A23

BUSHAW, Darlene, Information Technology Systems Site Lead, LakeWood Health Center, Baudette, MN, p. A329

BUSHELL, Michael, Vice President Finance, Business Development and Support Services, Saint Anne's Hospital, Fall River, MA, p. A299

BUSINELLE, Denise, Account Administrator, Northlake Behavioral Hospital, Mandeville, LA, p. A273

BUSKEY, Irene, Director Human Resources, Southside Regional Medical Center, Petersburg, VA, p. A659

BUSS, Georganna, Chief Executive Officer, Harper County Community Hospital, Buffalo, OK, p. A496

BUSS, Theresa L., Vice President, Human Resources and Organizational Development, The William W. Backus Hospital, Norwich, CT, p. A111

BUSSELL, Walter, Chief Financial Officer, Memorial Hospital West, Pembroke Pines, FL, p. A136

BUSSEY, George, M.D. Chief Medical Officer, FirstHealth Richmond Memorial Hospital, Rockingham, NC, p. A459

BUSSIERE, Mark, Administrator Human Resources, New Hampshire Hospital, Concord, NH, p. A397

BUSSLER, David, Chief Information Officer, Sheridan Community Hospital, Sheridan, MI, p. A324

BUSTIN, Sherry, Chief Executive Officer, Allegiance Specialty Hospital of Kilgore, Kilgore, TX, p. A616

BUTCHER, Allen R., Vice President Finance, Camden Clark Medical Center, Parkersburg, WV, p. A679

BUTCHER, Cindi, Chief Operating Officer, East Georgia Regional Medical Center, Statesboro, GA, p. A160

BUTCHER, Gina, Chief Financial Officer, St. Mary's of Michigan, Saginaw, MI, p. A323

BUTCHER, Kay, Director Health Information Management, Stonewall Jackson Memorial Hospital, Weston, WV, p. A681

BUTCHER, Scott, Chief Executive Officer, HEALTHSOUTH Rehabilitation Institute of San Antonio, San Antonio, TX, p. A631

BUTCHER, Steven, D.O. Director Medical Affairs, Citizens Memorial Hospital, Bolivar, MO, p. A356

BUTERBAUGH, William, Director Support Services, Fulton County Medical Center, Mc Connellsburg, PA, p. A530

BUTIKOFER, Lon D., Ph.D., Chief Executive Officer, Regional Medical Center, Manchester, IA, p. A224

BUTKER, Jeff, Chief Information Officer, Memorial Hospital, Martinsville, VA, p. A657

BUTLER, Anita M., Chief Executive Officer, Spartanburg Hospital for Restorative Care, Spartanburg, SC, p. A556

BUTLER, Barbara, Chief Executive Officer, HEALTHSOUTH Deaconess Rehabilitation Hospital, Evansville, IN, p. A202

BUTLER, Brad, Network Administrator, Barton County Memorial Hospital, Lamar, MO, p. A364

BUTLER, Carol A., R.N. VP Patient Care Services & Operations, St. Anthony North Health, Westminster, CO, p. A106

BUTLER, Catherine, M.D. Chief Medical Staff, Hancock County Health System, Britt, IA, p. A217

BUTLER, Chris, Deputy CIO/System Vice President, Kimball Medical Center, Lakewood, NJ, p. A405

BUTLER, David, Chief Executive Officer, North Canyon Medical Center, Gooding, ID, p. A169

BUTLER, Debby, Director Human Resources, Wadley Regional Medical Center, Texarkana, TX, p. A637

BUTLER, Everett A.
   Chief Executive Officer, Pembina County Memorial Hospital and Wedgewood Manor, Cavalier, ND, p. A466
   Chief Executive Officer, Unity Medical Center, Grafton, ND, p. A467

BUTLER, Jeffrey, Superintendent, Richmond State Hospital, Richmond, IN, p. A212

BUTLER, John, M.D
   Director Medical Staff, Mayo Clinic Health System in Waycross, Waycross, GA, p. A162
   Vice President Medical Affairs, St. Mary's Hospital, Madison, WI, p. A690

BUTLER, Joseph, Vice President and Chief Information Officer, UPMC Hamot, Erie, PA, p. A526

BUTLER, Linda H., M.D. Chief Medical Officer, Rex Healthcare, Raleigh, NC, p. A459

BUTLER, Margaret, Vice President Human Resources, Abbott Northwestern Hospital, Minneapolis, MN, p. A335

BUTLER, Michael K., M.D. Executive Vice President and Chief Medical Officer, Jackson Health System, Miami, FL, p. A131

BUTLER, Peter W., President and Chief Operating Officer, Rush University Medical Center, Chicago, IL, p. A179

BUTLER, Randy, Chief Financial Officer, West Florida Hospital, Pensacola, FL, p. A137

BUTLER, Stuart, Director Information Technology, Sweeny Community Hospital, Sweeny, TX, p. A636

BUTT, Shiraz, M.D. Medical Director, Maryville Behavioral Health Hospital, Des Plaines, IL, p. A181

BUTTELL, Christine, Chief Operating Officer, Knoxville Hospital & Clinics, Knoxville, IA, p. A224

BUTTELL, Phil, Chief Operating Officer, Centerpoint Medical Center, Independence, MO, p. A362

BUTTERFIELD, Jon
   Chief Operating Officer, Jordan Valley Medical Center, West Jordan, UT, p. A648
   Chief Operating Officer, Pioneer Valley Hospital, West Valley City, UT, p. A648

BUTTERICK, James D., M.D. Chief Medical Officer, Cape Cod Hospital, Hyannis, MA, p. A301

BUTTERLY, John R., M.D. Medical Director, Dartmouth–Hitchcock Medical Center, Lebanon, NH, p. A398

BUTTNER, Murray, M.D. Medical Director, Cordova Community Medical Center, Cordova, AK, p. A27

BUTTON, Charlie A., President and Chief Executive Officer, Star Valley Medical Center, Afton, WY, p. A701

BUTTS, Dan, Chief Executive Officer, Select Specialty Hospital–McKeesport, McKeesport, PA, p. A531

BUTZER, John, M.D. Medical Director, Mary Free Bed Rehabilitation Hospital, Grand Rapids, MI, p. A315

BUTZLER, Hilary, Director Human Resources, Cumberland Memorial Hospital, Cumberland, WI, p. A685

BUUCK, Brian, Chief Operating Officer, Ridgeview Psychiatric Hospital and Center, Oak Ridge, TN, p. A578

BUURMAN, Rita K., Interim Chief Executive Officer, Cloud County Health Center, Concordia, KS, p. A232

BUXTON, Barton, Ed.D., President and Chief Executive Officer, McLaren Lapeer Region, Lapeer, MI, p. A318

BUYOK, Tammy K., Vice President Support Services, St. Peter's Hospital, Helena, MT, p. A377

BUZACHERO, Victor, Corporate Senior Vice President for Innovation, Human Resources and Performance Management, Scripps Green Hospital, La Jolla, CA, p. A65

BYBERG, Jeff, Manager Human Resources, Mammoth Hospital, Mammoth Lakes, CA, p. A73

BYCROFT, Victor, R.N. Chief Nursing Officer, Shenandoah Medical Center, Shenandoah, IA, p. A228

BYDA, Jeff, Vice President Information Technology, Mercy Fitzgerald Hospital, Darby, PA, p. A524

BYERS, John, M.D. Medical Director, Select Specialty Hospital–Tri Cities, Bristol, TN, p. A565

BYERS, Suzann, Director of Nursing, Southern Indiana Rehabilitation Hospital, New Albany, IN, p. A211

BYERS, Tracy, Chief Operating Officer, Harton Regional Medical Center, Tullahoma, TN, p. A580

BYERS, William, Vice President and Chief Information Officer, Western Maryland Regional Medical Center, Cumberland, MD, p. A291

BYLER, Karen, Information Technician, Warren State Hospital, Warren, PA, p. A543

BYNUM, Chigger, Chief Financial Officer, John Randolph Medical Center, Hopewell, VA, p. A655

BYNUM, Dennis T., Interim Chief Financial Officer, Watsonville Community Hospital, Watsonville, CA, p. A95

BYRD, Catherine, Vice President Patient Services, Parkview Noble Hospital, Kendallville, IN, p. A207

BYRD, David, Chief Financial Officer, Sierra Medical Center, El Paso, TX, p. A601

BYRD, O. Wayne, M.D. Chief of Staff, H. C. Watkins Memorial Hospital, Quitman, MS, p. A353

BYRD, Sue, Coordinator Human Resources, Northwest Florida Community Hospital, Chipley, FL, p. A120

BYRNE, Bobbie, M.D. Vice President Chief Information Officer, Edward Hospital, Naperville, IL, p. A189

BYRNE, Frank D., M.D., President, St. Mary's Hospital, Madison, WI, p. A690

BYRNE, Frank J., Director Finance and Treasurer, Newport Hospital, Newport, RI, p. A546

BYRNS, David, Chief Executive Officer, South Cameron Memorial Hospital, Cameron, LA, p. A265

BYROM, David, Chief Executive Officer, Coryell Memorial Hospital, Gatesville, TX, p. A606

# C

CAAMANO, Tero, Director Information Technology, Saint Clare's Health System, Denville, NJ, p. A403

CABALLERO, Mechi R., Assistant Administrator, Kaiser Permanente Panorama City Medical Center,, CA, p. A69

CABALLO, George, Chief Executive Officer, Palm Springs General Hospital, Hialeah, FL, p. A125

CABANA, David, Director Management Information Systems, Southwest Memorial Hospital, Cortez, CO, p. A98

CABANAS, Deborah, R.N. Chief Nursing Officer, HEALTHSOUTH Rehabilitation Hospital of Western Massachusetts, Ludlow, MA, p. A301

CABELL–MAINS, Susan M., Vice President Administration, Martha Jefferson Hospital, Charlottesville, VA, p. A652

CABEZZAS, Noel, Chief Operating Officer, Good Samaritan Hospital, Bakersfield, CA, p. A54

CABIGAO, Edwin, Chief Nursing Officer, Jewish Home of San Francisco, San Francisco, CA, p. A86

CABRAL, Joseph, Senior Vice President and Chief Human Resources Officer, Forest Hills Hospital,, NY, p. A432

CABUNOC, Brenda, Chief Human Resource Management Services, Memphis Veterans Affairs Medical Center, Memphis, TN, p. A575

CACCIAMANI, John D., M.D., Chief Executive Officer, Chestnut Hill Hospital, Philadelphia, PA, p. A534

CACERES, Janet L., Chief Financial Officer, Paradise Valley Hospital, National City, CA, p. A76

CADE, Paul, Administrator and Chief Executive Officer, Baptist Memorial Hospital–Golden Triangle, Columbus, MS, p. A346

CADORET, Michael, R.N. Chief Nursing Officer, Brownwood Regional Medical Center, Brownwood, TX, p. A590

CADWELL, Maureen K., Chief Executive Officer, Weston County Health Services, Newcastle, WY, p. A703

CADY, Kathy, Coordinator Human Resources, Accounts Payable and Payroll, Boise Behavioral Health Hospital, Boise, ID, p. A167

CADY, Thomas, Vice President Human Resources, Heywood Hospital, Gardner, MA, p. A300

CADY, Tina, Controller, The Women's Hospital, Newburgh, IN, p. A211

CAFASSO, Michael, Vice President Operations, St. Mary–Corwin Medical Center, Pueblo, CO, p. A105

CAFFREY, Richard, Interim Assistant Chief Financial Officer, Saint Alphonsus Medical Center – Nampa, Nampa, ID, p. A170

CAGEN, Richard M., President/Chief Executive Officer, Silverton Hospital, Silverton, OR, p. A518

CAGGIANO, Richard, M.D. Chief Medical Officer, Pullman Regional Hospital, Pullman, WA, p. A669

CAGLE, Karen, Chief Nursing Officer, Select Specialty Hospital–Nashville, Nashville, TN, p. A577

CAGLE, Mary Jo, M.D. Chief Medical Officer, Bon Secours St. Francis Health System, Greenville, SC, p. A552

CAGNA, Ralph A.
   Director Information Technology Operations, Cleveland Clinic Health System South Market, Marymount Hospital, Garfield Heights, OH, p. A482
   Director Information Technology, South Pointe Hospital, Warrensville Heights, OH, p. A492

CAHALAN, Jay P., Chief Executive Officer, Columbia Memorial Hospital, Hudson, NY, p. A427

CAHILL, Donna, Vice President Human Resources, Palisades Medical Center, North Bergen, NJ, p. A408

CAHILL, Holly, Director Human Resources, Presentation Medical Center, Rolla, ND, p. A469

CAHILL, Joseph, Executive Vice President and Chief Operating Officer, South Shore Hospital, South Weymouth, MA, p. A304

CAHILL, Kathleen, President and Chief Executive Officer, Alta Vista Regional Hospital, Las Vegas, NM, p. A417

CAHILL, Marty, Chief Executive Officer, Samaritan North Lincoln Hospital, Lincoln City, OR, p. A514

CAHILL, Peter, M.D. President Medical Staff, Vibra Hospital of Denver, Thornton, CO, p. A106

CAHN, Jack, M.D. Chief Medical Staff, Alleghany Memorial Hospital, Sparta, NC, p. A461

CAHO–MOONEY, Linda, Chief Financial Officer, Patient's Choice Medical Center of Claiborne County, Port Gibson, MS, p. A353

CAIN, Donna, Director Information Systems Department, Cypress Fairbanks Medical Center, Houston, TX, p. A609

CAIN, Julie, Administrator, Stone County Hospital, Wiggins, MS, p. A355

CAIN, Mark, Chief Executive Officer, LaFollette Medical Center, La Follette, TN, p. A572

CAIN, Roxie, Chief Financial Officer, Big Horn County Memorial Hospital, Hardin, MT, p. A376

CAINE, Claudia, Executive Vice President and Chief Operating Officer, Lutheran Medical Center,, NY, p. A433

CAINE, Kirsten, M.D. Chief Medical Staff, Wallowa Memorial Hospital, Enterprise, OR, p. A512

CAIRNS, Craig, M.D. Vice President Medical Affairs, Licking Memorial Hospital, Newark, OH, p. A487

CALABRESE, Joan L., Director Human Resources, Putnam Hospital Center, Carmel, NY, p. A423

CALABRESE, Susan, Director of Nursing, Bloomington Meadows Hospital, Bloomington, IN, p. A199

CALAIS, C. Matthew, Senior Vice President and Chief Information Officer, Legacy Good Samaritan Hospital and Medical Center, Portland, OR, p. A516

CALAMARI, Frank A., President and Chief Executive Officer, Calvary Hospital,, NY, p. A431

CALAMARI, Jacquelyn, MSN Vice President and Chief Nursing Officer, Middlesex Hospital, Middletown, CT, p. A110

CALAME, Norma, Director Human Resources, The Mount Sinai Hospital of Queens,, NY, p. A437

CALANDRELLA, Paul, Chief Operating Officer, Mt. Ascutney Hospital and Health Center, Windsor, VT, p. A650

CALANDRIELLO, John, Vice President and Chief Financial Officer, Palisades Medical Center, North Bergen, NJ, p. A408

CALAWAY, Shearmaine, Director Human Resources, East Mississippi State Hospital, Meridian, MS, p. A351

CALBONE, Angelo G., President and Chief Executive Officer, Saratoga Hospital, Saratoga Springs, NY, p. A442

CALBY, Elizabeth, Vice President Human Resources, Advocate Good Samaritan Hospital, Downers Grove, IL, p. A181

CALDARI, Patricia, Vice President, Richmond University Medical Center,, NY, p. A436

CALDERA, Ken, Director Human Resources, Kessler Institute for Rehabilitation, West Orange, NJ, p. A412

CALDERONE, John A., Ph.D., Chief Executive Officer, Olympia Medical Center, Los Angeles, CA, p. A70

CALDWELL, Carolyn W., Chief Executive Officer, Desert Regional Medical Center, Palm Springs, CA, p. A78

CALDWELL, Dari, FACHE, President, Novant Health Rowan Medical Center, Salisbury, NC, p. A460

CALDWELL, Darren, Chief Executive Officer, DeWitt Hospital, De Witt, AR, p. A42

CALDWELL, Janice, Director Human Resources, Oak Tree Hospital, Corbin, KY, p. A249

CALDWELL, Matthew T., Chief Executive Officer, University Medical Center, Lebanon, TN, p. A572

CALDWELL, Noah, Senior Vice President and Chief Information Officer, St. Barnabas Hospital,, NY, p. A436

CALDWELL, Richard E., Vice President Support Services, Jackson Hospital and Clinic, Montgomery, AL, p. A23

CALDWELL, Troy J., M.D. Chief of Staff, North Big Horn Hospital District, Lovell, WY, p. A703

CALHOUN, Cathy, Director Human Resources, River Point Behavioral Health, Jacksonville, FL, p. A126

CALHOUN, Joshua, M.D. Medical Director, Hawthorn Children Psychiatric Hospital, Saint Louis, MO, p. A369

CALHOUN, Kevin P., Chief Executive Officer, Munising Memorial Hospital, Munising, MI, p. A320

CALHOUN, Kirk A., M.D., President, University of Texas Health Science Center at Tyler, Tyler, TX, p. A639

CALHOUN, Rob, Chief Executive Officer, Parkway Regional Hospital, Fulton, KY, p. A251

CALHOUN, Royce, Business Manager, Veterans Affairs Western New York Healthcare System–Buffalo Division, Buffalo, NY, p. A423

CALHOUN, Sharon, R.N. Director Quality Management, Miller County Hospital, Colquitt, GA, p. A150

CALHOUN, Timothy, Vice President Finance and Chief Financial Officer, Lakeland Regional Medical Center–St. Joseph, Saint Joseph, MI, p. A324

CALHOUN, William, President, Mercy Medical Center, Oshkosh, WI, p. A694

CALIA, Christopher, Director Human Resources, Brazosport Regional Health System, Lake Jackson, TX, p. A617

CALIFORNIA, Randy, Chief Operating Officer, Warren General Hospital, Warren, PA, p. A543

CALIGIURI, Michael, Chief Executive Officer, James Cancer Hospital and Solove Research Institute, Columbus, OH, p. A477

CALIVA, Todd, Chief Executive Officer, West Houston Medical Center, Houston, TX, p. A613

CALKIN, Pitt, Interim Chief Financial Officer, St. Joseph Health St. Mary, Apple Valley, CA, p. A53

CALKIN, Steven, D.O. Vice President Medical Affairs, McLaren Oakland, Pontiac, MI, p. A322

CALL, Brett, D.O. Chief of Staff, Berger Health System, Circleville, OH, p. A475

CALL, Carie, Director Computer Support, Cassia Regional Medical Center, Burley, ID, p. A168

CALL, Dave, M.D. Medical Director, Select Long Term Care Hospital – Colorado Springs, Colorado Springs, CO, p. A98

CALL, Gary, M.D. Chief Medical Officer, Bingham Memorial Hospital, Blackfoot, ID, p. A167

CALLAGHAN, Barbara L., Interim Chief Executive Officer, Kindred Hospital Richmond, Richmond, VA, p. A660

CALLAGHAN III, James, M.D., President, Franciscan St. Anthony Health – Michigan City, Michigan City, IN, p. A210

CALLAHAN, Ame, Acting Manager Resource Management Service, Northern Arizona Veterans Affairs Health Care System, Prescott, AZ, p. A36

CALLAHAN, Christopher, Vice President Human Resources, Exeter Hospital, Exeter, NH, p. A398

CALLAHAN, Deanna, Director Information Systems, Titusville Area Hospital, Titusville, PA, p. A542

CALLAHAN, Jean, Manager Human Resources, Thousand Oaks Surgical Hospital, Thousand Oaks, CA, p. A92

CALLAHAN, Kelly, Public Information Officer, Elgin Mental Health Center, Elgin, IL, p. A181

CALLAHAN, Kevin J., President and Chief Executive Officer, Exeter Hospital, Exeter, NH, p. A398

CALLAHAN, Larry, Interim Vice President and Chief Human Resources Officer, University of Chicago Medical Center, Chicago, IL, p. A180

CALLAHAN, Mark, Interim President and Chief Executive Officer, Mary Lanning Healthcare, Hastings, NE, p. A384

CALLAHAN, Mary Beth, Chief Financial Officer, McLaren Lapeer Region, Lapeer, MI, p. A318

CALLAHAN, Michael E., M.D. President Medical Staff, Cole Memorial, Coudersport, PA, p. A523

CALLAHAN, Neil, Chief Executive Officer, Brooke Glen Behavioral Hospital, Fort Washington, PA, p. A526

CALLAHAN Jr., Robert W., Director, Lebanon Veterans Affairs Medical Center, Lebanon, PA, p. A529

CALLAHAN, Teresa, MSN, Chief Executive Officer, Iraan General Hospital, Iraan, TX, p. A614

CALLAIS, Elizabeth, Chief Fiscal Officer, Leonard J. Chabert Medical Center, Houma, LA, p. A268

CALLAIS, Ronnie, Chief Financial Officer, MMO WestEnd Hospital, Jennings, LA, p. A269

CALLAN, C. M., M.D. Chief of Staff, Fisher County Hospital District, Rotan, TX, p. A629

CALLAWAY, Blair, Chief Financial Officer, Texas Orthopedic Hospital, Houston, TX, p. A612

CALLECOD, David L., FACHE, President and Chief Executive Officer, Lafayette General Medical Center, Lafayette, LA, p. A271

CALLENS, Don, M.D. Chief Medical Officer, Liberty Dayton Regional Medical Center, Liberty, TX, p. A618

CALLENS, Paul A., Ph.D., Director, North Mississippi State Hospital, Tupelo, MS, p. A354

CALLISTER, T. Brian, M.D. Chief Medical Officer, Tahoe Pacific Hospitals, Reno, NV, p. A395

CALLOWAY, Jennifer, Human Resources Coordinator, Asheville Specialty Hospital, Asheville, NC, p. A447

CALLOWAY, Maria, R.N. Chief Nursing Officer, Granville Health System, Oxford, NC, p. A458

CALVARUSO, Gaspare, President, SSM St. Joseph Health Center, Saint Charles, MO, p. A368

CALVERT, Mandy, Director of Information Systems, Southern Coos Hospital and Health Center, Bandon, OR, p. A511

CALVERT, Randy, Chief Financial Officer, Gilbert Hospital, Gilbert, AZ, p. A31

CALVERT, Sarah, Chief Nursing Officer, McGehee–Desha County Hospital, McGehee, AR, p. A47

CALVIN, Jeff, Chief Financial Officer, Michiana Behavioral Health Center, Plymouth, IN, p. A212

CALVIN, Jr., Travis, M.D. Chief of Staff, Pioneers Memorial Healthcare District, Brawley, CA, p. A55

CAMARATA, Chris, M.D. Chief of Staff, Mayers Memorial Hospital District, Fall River Mills, CA, p. A60

CAMERON, Carl, Director Information Systems, Holyoke Medical Center, Holyoke, MA, p. A300

CAMERON, Don, Chief Operating Officer, Allegiance Behavioral Health Center of Plainview, Plainview, TX, p. A627

CAMERON, Kim, Manager Health Information Services, Patients' Hospital of Redding, Redding, CA, p. A81

CAMERON, Lana, Chief Nursing Officer, Central Texas Medical Center, San Marcos, TX, p. A633

CAMIRE, Patricia M., MS Chief Nursing Officer, Southern Maine Medical Center, Biddeford, ME, p. A282

CAMMACK Jr., Thomas N., Chief Administrative Officer, Mother Frances Hospital – Jacksonville, Jacksonville, TX, p. A615

CAMMENGA, Randall, M.D. Vice President Medical Affairs, Indiana University Health Goshen Hospital, Goshen, IN, p. A203

CAMP III, Claude E., Chief Executive Officer, Brownwood Regional Medical Center, Brownwood, TX, p. A590

CAMP, James, R.N.,
Chief Executive Officer, Cornerstone Hospital of Houston – Bellaire, Houston, TX, p. A609
Chief Executive Officer, Cornerstone Hospital–Medical Center of Houston, Houston, TX, p. A609

CAMP, Julie A., R.N., Chief Executive Officer, Forest Park Medical Center Frisco, Frisco, TX, p. A605

CAMP, Lea Ann, MSN Chief Nursing Officer, Greene County General Hospital, Linton, IN, p. A209

CAMPAGNA, Doncie, Administrator, Latimer County General Hospital, Wilburton, OK, p. A510

CAMPANA, Thomas, M.D. Chief of Staff, Spectrum Health Reed City Hospital, Reed City, MI, p. A322

CAMPANELLA, Alfred
Vice President and Chief Information Officer, Virtua Berlin, Berlin, NJ, p. A401
Chief Information Officer, Virtua Marlton, Marlton, NJ, p. A406
Chief Information Officer, Virtua Voorhees, Voorhees, NJ, p. A412

CAMPAS, Janice, Chief Financial Officer, Wichita County Health Center, Leoti, KS, p. A238

CAMPBELL, Ann, Chief Nursing Officer, Virtua Marlton, Marlton, NJ, p. A406

CAMPBELL, Belinda H., Director Human Resources, Legal Compliance and Risk Management, University Hospital McDuffie, Thomson, GA, p. A161

CAMPBELL, Bernard M., Administrator Human Resources, LewisGale Hospital Alleghany, Low Moor, VA, p. A656

CAMPBELL, Bob, Vice President Business Development and Chief Strategy Officer, Mercy Gilbert Medical Center, Gilbert, AZ, p. A31

CAMPBELL, C. Scott, Market Chief Executive Officer, Physicians Regional Medical Center – Pine Ridge, Naples, FL, p. A133

CAMPBELL, Chad, Chief Executive Officer, Carlsbad Medical Center, Carlsbad, NM, p. A415

CAMPBELL, Charlotte, Chief Human Resources Officer, Beatrice Community Hospital and Health Center, Beatrice, NE, p. A382

CAMPBELL, Christopher, M.D. Chief of Staff, Ashe Memorial Hospital, Jefferson, NC, p. A455

CAMPBELL, Darrell, M.D. Chief Clinical Affairs, University of Michigan Hospitals and Health Centers, Ann Arbor, MI, p. A308

CAMPBELL, David, Administrator, Perry Hospital, Perry, GA, p. A158

CAMPBELL, Dean, Vice President Information Services and Chief Information Officer, Good Samaritan Hospital, Los Angeles, CA, p. A69

CAMPBELL, Deborah, Administrator, Thomas H. Boyd Memorial Hospital, Carrollton, IL, p. A175

CAMPBELL, Debra, R.N., Administrator, Riverside Behavioral Health Center, Hampton, VA, p. A655

CAMPBELL, Don, M.D. Senior Vice President and Chief Medical Officer, WellStar Cobb Hospital, Austell, GA, p. A148

CAMPBELL, Emily, Director Human Resources, Alice Hyde Medical Center, Malone, NY, p. A429

CAMPBELL, Eric, Chief Financial Officer, Oswego Hospital, Oswego, NY, p. A439

CAMPBELL, F. J., M.D. Chief Medical Officer, Tristar Ashland City, Ashland City, TN, p. A565

CAMPBELL, Fritz, Director Information Systems, Olympia Medical Center, Los Angeles, CA, p. A70

CAMPBELL, Gina, Chief Operating Officer, Baystate Franklin Medical Center, Greenfield, MA, p. A300

CAMPBELL, John
Director Management Information Systems, Spaulding Rehabilitation Hospital, Boston, MA, p. A297
Chief Information Officer, Spaulding Rehabilitation Hospital Cape Cod, East Sandwich, MA, p. A299

CAMPBELL, Karen M., Director Finance, Bigfork Valley Hospital, Bigfork, MN, p. A329

CAMPBELL, Kevin, Administrator Compliance and Mission, Saint Thomas Hickman Hospital, Centerville, TN, p. A566

CAMPBELL, Margaret, Vice President, Associate Chief Information Officer, Health Alliance Hospitals, Leominster, MA, p. A301

CAMPBELL, Patricia
Vice President Human Resources, SSM DePaul Health Center, Bridgeton, MO, p. A357
Vice President Human Resources, SSM St. Clare Health Center, Fenton, MO, p. A360

CAMPBELL, Phil, Chief Operating Officer, King's Daughters Medical Center, Brookhaven, MS, p. A345

CAMPBELL, Richard, M.D. President Medical Staff, Comanche County Memorial Hospital, Lawton, OK, p. A500

CAMPBELL, Jr., Robert D., President, Chief Executive and Chief Operating Officer, Providence Mount Carmel Hospital, Colville, WA, p. A665

CAMPBELL Jr., Robert D., President and Chief Executive, Providence St. Joseph's Hospital, Chewelah, WA, p. A665

CAMPBELL, Rose, R.N., President, Brookville Hospital, Brookville, PA, p. A521

CAMPBELL, Sandra M., R.N. Chief Nursing Officer, Dodge County Hospital, Eastman, GA, p. A153

CAMPBELL, Stephen J., Chief Operating Officer, Pioneers Memorial Healthcare District, Brawley, CA, p. A55

CAMPBELL, Susie, Chief Executive Officer, Community Memorial Hospital, Staunton, IL, p. A195

CAMPBELL, Todd, Senior Vice President and Chief Operating Officer, St. Mary's Medical Center, Huntington, WV, p. A678

CAMPEAU, Arleen, R.N. Vice President of Patient Care Services, Chief Nursing Officer, Powell Valley Healthcare, Powell, WY, p. A703

CAMPION, John, Administrator, Essentia Health–Holy Trinity Hospital, Graceville, MN, p. A333

CAMPOS, Christina, Administrator, Guadalupe County Hospital, Santa Rosa, NM, p. A418

CAMPOS–DIAZ, Evelyn, Director Human Resources, MedStar St. Mary's Hospital, Leonardtown, MD, p. A293

CANADY, Carolyn, Chief Financial Officer, Sierra Nevada Memorial Hospital, Grass Valley, CA, p. A63

CANALE, Joseph, Business Manager, Trenton Psychiatric Hospital, Trenton, NJ, p. A411

CANALEJO, Donald, Director Human Resources, Lower Keys Medical Center, Key West, FL, p. A127

CANARD, Shannon, Chief Executive Officer, Landmark Hospital of Columbia, Columbia, MO, p. A359

CANARIOS, Mike, Vice President and Chief Financial Officer, St. Jude Children's Research Hospital, Memphis, TN, p. A575

CANAVAN, Patrick J., PsyD, Chief Executive Officer, St. Elizabeths Hospital, Washington, DC, p. A117

CANCILLA, Deborah, Chief Information Officer, Grady Memorial Hospital, Atlanta, GA, p. A146

CANDIA, Gary R., FACHE, Chief Executive Officer, Abington Health Lansdale Hospital, Lansdale, PA, p. A529

CANDILL, James W., M.D. President Medical Staff, Eye and Ear Clinic of Charleston, Charleston, WV, p. A676

CANDIO, Christine, Chief Executive Officer, Inova Alexandria Hospital, Alexandria, VA, p. A651

CANDULLO, Carl, Chief Information Officer, Munroe Regional Medical Center, Ocala, FL, p. A134

CANEDO, Jim, Chief Financial Officer, Pacific Hospital of Long Beach, Long Beach, CA, p. A67

CANFIELD, Brian, Chief Operating Officer, FirstHealth Moore Regional Hospital, Pinehurst, NC, p. A458

CANIZARO, Tom, Vice President and Chief Financial Officer, South Central Regional Medical Center, Laurel, MS, p. A349

CANN–TAYLOR, Julie, R.N. Chief Operating Officer, Senior Vice President Patient Care Services and Chief Nursing Officer, Wyoming Medical Center, Casper, WY, p. A701

CANNIDA, Ieesha, Director Human Resources, Reliant Rehabilitation Hospital Dallas, Dallas, TX, p. A597

CANNING, John, Chief Financial Officer, Blythedale Children's Hospital, Valhalla, NY, p. A445

CANNINGTON, H. D., Chief Executive Officer, Charlton Memorial Hospital, Folkston, GA, p. A153

CANNON, Brenda, R.N. Director of Nursing, Laughlin Memorial Hospital, Greeneville, TN, p. A569

CANNON, C. Ron, M.D. Medical Director, River Oaks Hospital, Flowood, MS, p. A346

CANNON, Gayle, Director Human Resources, Childress Regional Medical Center, Childress, TX, p. A591

CANNON, Linda, Chief Medical Records Services, San Diego County Psychiatric Hospital, San Diego, CA, p. A85

CANOVA, Jr., Frank, Chief Financial Officer, CHRISTUS Schumpert Medical Center, Shreveport, LA, p. A278

CANOVACA, Frank, Director Management Information Systems, Metropolitan Hospital of Miami, Miami, FL, p. A131

CANTER, Danny, Manager Information Systems, Doctors Hospital Nelsonville, Nelsonville, OH, p. A487

CANTEY, Larry D., M.D. Chief Medical Officer, Fairfield Memorial Hospital, Winnsboro, SC, p. A557

CANTLEY, J. Scott, President and Chief Executive Officer, Marietta Memorial Hospital, Marietta, OH, p. A485

CANTON, David, D.O. Vice President Medical Affairs, Emanuel Medical Center, Turlock, CA, p. A93

CANTRELL, Dedra
Chief Information Officer, Emory University Hospital, Atlanta, GA, p. A146
Chief Information Officer, Emory University Hospital Midtown, Atlanta, GA, p. A146
Chief Information Officer, Saint Joseph's Hospital of Atlanta, Atlanta, GA, p. A147
Chief Information Officer, Wesley Woods Geriatric Hospital of Emory University, Atlanta, GA, p. A147

CANTRELL, Gary, President and Chief Executive Officer, St. Lucie Medical Center, Port St. Lucie, FL, p. A138

CANTU, Ray, D.O. Chief of Staff, Rice Medical Center, Eagle Lake, TX, p. A600

CANTU–LOPEZ, Lydia, Human Resources Representative, Solara Hospital Harlingen, Harlingen, TX, p. A608

CANVER, Charles, M.D. Chief Medical Officer, Presence United Samaritans Medical Center, Danville, IL, p. A180

CAPECE Jr., Vincent G., President and Chief Executive Officer, Middlesex Hospital, Middletown, CT, p. A110

CAPITELLI, Robert, M.D. Senior Vice President and Chief Medical Officer, St. Tammany Parish Hospital, Covington, LA, p. A266

CAPIZZI, Jennifer, Director Human Resources, Magruder Memorial Hospital, Port Clinton, OH, p. A488

CAPLAN, Marcie S., Vice President, UPMC Passavant, Pittsburgh, PA, p. A538

CAPLAN, Margaret B., Director, Wilkes–Barre Veterans Affairs Medical Center, Wilkes–Barre, PA, p. A544

CAPLES, Greg, Chief Operating Officer, TriStar Summit Medical Center, Hermitage, TN, p. A570

CAPODIFERRO, Joseph, Chief Human and Learning Resources, Veterans Affairs New Jersey Health Care System, East Orange, NJ, p. A403

CAPPEL, Blaine, Director Information Systems, Memorial Health System, Abilene, KS, p. A231

CAPPELLO, Roger, M.D. Vice President Medical Affairs, Bon Secours Memorial Regional Medical Center, Mechanicsville, VA, p. A657

CAPPS, Kim, Chief Financial Officer, Hayes Green Beach Memorial Hospital, Charlotte, MI, p. A310

CAPPS, Perri Lynn, Chief Nursing Officer, Cumberland Medical Center, Crossville, TN, p. A568

CAPPS, Rick, Chief Financial Officer, Cumberland County Hospital, Burkesville, KY, p. A249

CAPUANO, Terry Ann, R.N
Chief Operating Officer, Lehigh Valley Hospital, Allentown, PA, p. A519
Chief Operating Officer, Lehigh Valley Hospital–Muhlenberg, Bethlehem, PA, p. A520

CARACCIOLO, Kevin, Chief Human Resources Officer, Palm Beach Gardens Medical Center, Palm Beach Gardens, FL, p. A135

CARALIS, George P., Interim Chief Executive Officer, SUNY Downstate Medical Center University Hospital,, NY, p. A436

CARBONE, Davide M., FACHE, Chief Executive Officer, St. Mary's Medical Center, West Palm Beach, FL, p. A143

CARBONEL MASON, Wilma, Chief Nursing Officer, Fort Duncan Regional Medical Center, Eagle Pass, TX, p. A600

CARD, Dean, Chief Financial Officer, Kindred Hospital South Florida–Fort Lauderdale, Fort Lauderdale, FL, p. A123

CARDALI, Paul, M.D. Chief of Staff, Lakeway Regional Hospital, Morristown, TN, p. A576

CARDEN, Lamar, M.D. Chief Medical Officer, Jack Hughston Memorial Hospital, Phenix City, AL, p. A24

CARDENAS, Mark, Director Plant Operations, Vibra Hospital of Northern California, Redding, CA, p. A81

CARDENAS, Michael E., M.D. Director Medical Services, Robert E. Bush Naval Hospital, Twentynine Palms, CA, p. A93

CARDENAS, Mitzi
Chief Information Officer, Truman Medical Center–Hospital Hill, Kansas City, MO, p. A364
Chief Information Officer, Truman Medical Center–Lakewood, Kansas City, MO, p. A364

CARDENAS, Noel J., FACHE, Commander, Reynolds Army Community Hospital, Fort Sill, OK, p. A499

CARDILE, Eileen K., MS, President and Chief Executive Officer, Inspira Medical Center–Woodbury, Woodbury, NJ, p. A413

CARDIN, Deborah, MS, Chief Executive Officer, Jefferson County Health Center, Fairfield, IA, p. A221

CARDINAL, Joyce, Chief Nursing Executive, Jefferson Healthcare, Port Townsend, WA, p. A669

CARDWELL, Marian, Chief Financial Officer, Potomac Valley Hospital, Keyser, WV, p. A678

CAREY, Ann, Vice President and Chief Information Officer, St. Vincent's Medical Center Riverside, Jacksonville, FL, p. A127

CAREY, Anne E., R.N. Chief Nursing Officer, Heart of Florida Regional Medical Center, Davenport, FL, p. A121

CAREY, Bruce, Chief Executive Officer, Kindred Chicago–Central Hospital, Chicago, IL, p. A177

CAREY, Calvin, VP Finance and Support Services, Holy Rosary Healthcare, Miles City, MT, p. A378

CAREY, Eric R., Vice President Information Systems and Chief Information Officer, Valley Hospital, Ridgewood, NJ, p. A410

CARGILL, Kevin, Chief Financial Officer, Southern Virginia Regional Medical Center, Emporia, VA, p. A653

CARGONARA, Douglas, Ph.D. Chief Information Officer, Pilgrim Psychiatric Center, Brentwood, NY, p. A422

CARIKER, Ann, Chief Operating Officer, Northeastern Nevada Regional Hospital, Elko, NV, p. A391

CARIKER, Kelly, Manager, Mid–Valley Hospital, Omak, WA, p. A669

CARISSIMI, Derek, Vice President Human Resources, Georgia Regents Medical Center, Augusta, GA, p. A147

CARLE, Chris, Senior Vice President and Chief Operating Officer, St. Elizabeth Florence, Florence, KY, p. A250

CARLETON, David
Chief Information Officer, Heritage Valley Beaver, Beaver, PA, p. A520
Chief Information Officer, Sewickley Valley Hospital, (A Division of Valley Medical Facilities), Sewickley, PA, p. A541

CARLINO, James, Vice President Human Resources, Deborah Heart and Lung Center, Browns Mills, NJ, p. A402

CARLISLE, Charles, Director, East Mississippi State Hospital, Meridian, MS, p. A351

CARLISLE, Harald, Acting Chief Information Officer, Birmingham Veterans Affairs Medical Center, Birmingham, AL, p. A16

CARLISLE, Mary Beth, Chief Executive Officer, Mildred Mitchell–Bateman Hospital, Huntington, WV, p. A677

CARLISLE, Sandy, Manager Human Resources, Holzer Medical Center – Jackson, Jackson, OH, p. A483

CARLOCK, Carey, Chief Executive Officer, Riveredge Hospital, Forest Park, IL, p. A182

CARLSON, Andrew, M.D. Vice President Medical Staff Services, Phoebe Sumter Medical Center, Americus, GA, p. A145

CARLSON, Bev, Chief Financial Officer, Delta County Memorial Hospital, Delta, CO, p. A99

CARLSON, Brian J., FACHE, Chief Executive Officer, Sanford Thief River Falls Medical Center, Thief River Falls, MN, p. A341

CARLSON, Carol, Director Community Relations, Memorial Health Care Systems, Seward, NE, p. A389

CARLSON, Dan, Chief Financial Officer, Bay Area Medical Center, Marinette, WI, p. A690

CARLSON, Daniel, M.D
Senior Vice President and Chief Medical Officer, Leesburg Regional Medical Center, Leesburg, FL, p. A129
Senior Vice President Medical Affairs and Chief Medical Officer, The Villages Health System, The Villages, FL, p. A142

CARLSON, David J., D.O. Chief Medical Officer, Conemaugh Memorial Medical Center, Johnstown, PA, p. A528

CARLSON, Jamie N., Chief Human Resources Officer, Nebraska Heart Hospital, Lincoln, NE, p. A385

CARLSON, Jeffrey, Administrator, Mayo Clinic Health System in Waseca, Waseca, MN, p. A342

CARLSON, Kellie, Director Human Resources, Coastal Harbor Treatment Center, Savannah, GA, p. A159

CARLSON, Kim
Director Human Resources, Essentia Health Northern Pines, Aurora, MN, p. A328
Director Human Resources, FirstLight Health System, Mora, MN, p. A337

CARLSON, Kurt, Chief Executive Officer, Otis R Bowen Center for Human Services, Warsaw, IN, p. A214

CARLSON, Lisa, Chief Financial Officer, Sanford Medical Center Fargo, Fargo, ND, p. A466

CARLSON, Nancy
Chief Financial Officer, Crawford County Memorial Hospital, Denison, IA, p. A220
Chief Executive, Providence Little Company of Mary Medical Center San Pedro,, CA, p. A71

CARLSON, Pam, Senior Vice President and Chief Nursing Officer, Phoenix Children's Hospital, Phoenix, AZ, p. A35

CARLSON, Peter, Administrator, Aurora Psychiatric Hospital, Wauwatosa, WI, p. A699

CARLSON, Richard, Chief Financial Officer, Crawford Memorial Hospital, Robinson, IL, p. A193

CARLSON, Sharon, Executive Assistant to the Director, Veterans Affairs Roseburg Healthcare System, Roseburg, OR, p. A517

CARLSON, Stephen G., President and Chief Executive Officer, Community Medical Center, Missoula, MT, p. A378

CARLSON, Wendie, Vice President, Human Resources, Jackson–Madison County General Hospital, Jackson, TN, p. A570

CARLTON, Terrie, R.N. Vice President & Chief Nursing Officer, Tuomey Healthcare System, Sumter, SC, p. A556

CARLYLE, Dave, Director Human Resources, Wayne County Hospital, Corydon, IA, p. A219

CARMACK, Timothy W., Chief Financial Officer, Lucile Salter Packard Children's Hospital at Stanford, Palo Alto, CA, p. A78

CARMAIN, Jim, Vice President Financial and Information Services, Baptist Health Paducah, Paducah, KY, p. A259

CARMAN, Thomas H., President and Chief Executive Officer, Samaritan Medical Center, Watertown, NY, p. A445

CARMEN, Lee, Associate Vice President Health Care Information Systems, University of Iowa Hospitals and Clinics, Iowa City, IA, p. A223

CARMICHAEL, Craig, Vice President, Operations, University of Maryland St. Joseph Medical Center, Towson, MD, p. A294

CARMICHAEL, Lou Ann, Director Operations, South Lincoln Medical Center, Kemmerer, WY, p. A702

CARMIN, Ron, Vice President Fiscal Affairs, Mary Rutan Hospital, Bellefontaine, OH, p. A471

CARMODY, James, Vice President Human Resources, Wilkes–Barre General Hospital, Wilkes–Barre, PA, p. A544

CARMODY, Martin T., Chief Executive Officer, Select Specialty Hospital–Downriver, Taylor, MI, p. A325

CARMODY DNP, MBA, RN, CENP, Jane, R.N
Vice President and System Chief Nursing Officer, Alegent Creighton Health Bergan Mercy Medical Center, Omaha, NE, p. A387
Vice President and System Chief Nursing Officer, Alegent Creighton Health Community Memorial Hospital, Missouri Valley, IA, p. A225
Chief Nursing Officer, Alegent Creighton Health Immanuel Medical Center, Omaha, NE, p. A387
Vice President and System Chief Nursing Officer, Alegent Creighton Health Lakeside Hospital, Omaha, NE, p. A387
Vice President and System Chief Nursing Officer, Alegent Creighton Health Mercy Hospital, Corning, IA, p. A218
Vice President and System Chief Nursing Officer, Alegent Creighton Health Mercy Hospital, Council Bluffs, IA, p. A219
Vice President and System Chief Nursing Officer, Alegent Creighton Health–Memorial Hospital, Schuyler, Schuyler, NE, p. A389
Vice President and System Chief Nursing Officer, Memorial Community Hospital and Health System, Blair, NE, p. A382

CARMONA, Helen, Acting Chief Executive Officer, Highlands Regional Rehabilitation Hospital, El Paso, TX, p. A601

CARNATHAN, Glenn, Vice President Human Resources, Baptist Hospital, Pensacola, FL, p. A136

CARNES, Ruth, Manager Human Resources, Jennings American Legion Hospital, Jennings, LA, p. A269

CARNEVALE, Raymond, Senior Vice President and Chief Operating Officer, Rome Memorial Hospital, Rome, NY, p. A441

CARNEVALE, Raymond F., Chief Executive Officer, Select Specialty Hospital–Madison, Madison, WI, p. A689

CARNEY, Kevin, Senior Information Systems Analyst, Pine Creek Medical Center, Dallas, TX, p. A597

CARNEY, Michael J., Chief Executive Officer, Brentwood Behavioral HealthCare of Mississippi, Jackson, MS, p. A348

CARNEY, Mike, Chief Executive Officer, Select Specialty Hospital–Evansville, Evansville, IN, p. A202

CARNEY, Stephen, M.D. Chief of Staff, Parkview Community Hospital Medical Center, Riverside, CA, p. A82

CARO, Vique, Chief Information Officer, Cincinnati Veterans Affairs Medical Center, Cincinnati, OH, p. A474

CAROL, Karin, Chief Operating Officer, Atlantic Shores Hospital, Fort Lauderdale, FL, p. A123

CAROLUS, Rhonda, Director of Nursing Operations, Northern Colorado Rehabilitation Hospital, Johnstown, CO, p. A102

CARON, Jacqueline, Chief Human Resources, Birmingham Veterans Affairs Medical Center, Birmingham, AL, p. A16

CARON, Phillip A.
Chief Financial Officer, East Texas Medical Center Carthage, Carthage, TX, p. A591
Chief Financial Officer, East Texas Medical Center Henderson, Henderson, TX, p. A608
Chief Financial Officer, East Texas Medical Center Jacksonville, Jacksonville, TX, p. A615

CAROSELLI, Joseph P., Chief Executive Officer, Elks Rehab Hospital, Boise, ID, p. A167

CAROZZA, Sally, Director Human Resources, Western Pennsylvania Hospital, Pittsburgh, PA, p. A539

CARPEL, Emmett, M.D. Medical Director and Chief of Staff, Phillips Eye Institute, Minneapolis, MN, p. A336

CARPENTER, Chad, Chief Financial Officer, Pocahontas Memorial Hospital, Buckeye, WV, p. A675

CARPENTER, Curt, Manager Information Technology, Coquille Valley Hospital, Coquille, OR, p. A512

CARPENTER, Dan, Chief Financial Officer, UnityPoint Health Finley, Dubuque, IA, p. A221

CARPENTER, Dennis, Director Human Resources, Boscobel Area Health Care, Boscobel, WI, p. A684

CARPENTER, Elizabeth, Director Quality Assurance and Quality Improvement and Assistant Administrator, Promise Hospital of Miss Lou, Vidalia, LA, p. A279

CARPENTER, Jackie, Office Manager, Rock County Hospital, Bassett, NE, p. A381

CARPENTER, Kayla, Health Information Management Systems Officer, Northwest Mississippi Regional Medical Center, Clarksdale, MS, p. A345

CARPENTER, Leah A., Administrator and Chief Executive Officer, Memorial Hospital Miramar, Miramar, FL, p. A133

CARPENTER, M. Troy, Chief Financial Officer, Kindred Hospital–Tucson, Tucson, AZ, p. A38

CARPENTER, Posie, R.N. Chief Administrative Officer, Santa Monica–UCLA Medical Center and Orthopaedic Hospital, Santa Monica, CA, p. A90

CARPER, Joleen, Director Quality and Risk, Tri–State Memorial Hospital, Clarkston, WA, p. A665

CARR, Charles E., Vice President, Regional Hospital, Carilion Stonewall Jackson Hospital, Lexington, VA, p. A656

CARR, David, M.D. Physician Medical Director, The Rehabilitation Institute of St. Louis, Saint Louis, MO, p. A371

CARR, Deborah, Vice President Human Resources, Orange Regional Medical Center, Middletown, NY, p. A429

CARR, Diane
Chief Information Officer, Jacobi Medical Center,, NY, p. A432
Chief Information Officer, North Central Bronx Hospital,, NY, p. A435

CARR, George, Chief Information Officer, Bryan Medical Center, Lincoln, NE, p. A385

CARR, Kevin, M.D. Chief of Staff, Southwest Health Center, Platteville, WI, p. A695

CARR, Randall, Director Human Resources, Parkwest Medical Center, Knoxville, TN, p. A572

CARR, Tim, Chief Financial Officer, Methodist Ambulatory Surgery Hospital, San Antonio, TX, p. A631

CARRANZA, Diana, Associate Director, Veterans Affairs Illiana Health Care System, Danville, IL, p. A180

CARRASCO, Anthony, Director Information Systems, Tri–City Regional Medical Center, Hawaiian Gardens, CA, p. A63

CARREN, Donald M., Information Technology Leader, Kaiser Permanente Anaheim Medical Center, Anaheim, CA, p. A52

CARRERA, Lavern H., Senior Vice President Human Resources, Northside Medical Center, Youngstown, OH, p. A494

CARRIER, Lynn, Associate Director Administration and Support, Veterans Affairs Greater Los Angeles Healthcare System, Los Angeles, CA, p. A72

CARRIER, Patrick Brian, President and Chief Executive Officer, CHRISTUS Santa Rosa Health System, San Antonio, TX, p. A630

CARRILLO, Todd, Chief Information Officer, Yoakum County Hospital, Denver City, TX, p. A599

CARRILLO, Zulema, Superintendent, El Paso Psychiatric Center, El Paso, TX, p. A601

CARRINGER, Rick, Vice President Finance and Support Services, LeConte Medical Center, Sevierville, TN, p. A579

CARRISON, Dale, M.D. Chief of Staff, University Medical Center, Las Vegas, NV, p. A394

CARRITHERS, Mary Kay, Manager Health Information, Warren Memorial Hospital, Friend, NE, p. A383

CARROCINO, Joanne, FACHE, President and Chief Executive Officer, Cape Regional Medical Center, Cape May Court House, NJ, p. A402

CARROLL, Dale, M.D. Senior Vice President Medical Affairs and Performance Improvement, Rockingham Memorial Hospital, Harrisonburg, VA, p. A655

CARROLL, David W., Chief Financial Officer, O'Connor Hospital, San Jose, CA, p. A88

CARROLL, Eric, Chief Executive Officer, Select Specialty Hospital–Tri Cities, Bristol, TN, p. A565

CARROLL, Jack, Senior Director Human Resources, Spaulding Hospital for Continuing Medical Care Cambridge, Cambridge, MA, p. A299

CARROLL, Jack A., Ph.D., President and Chief Executive Officer, Magee Rehabilitation Hospital, Philadelphia, PA, p. A535

CARROLL, Jacqueline, Director Human Resources, Los Alamos Medical Center, Los Alamos, NM, p. A417

CARROLL, Jaime, Department Head, Walter Reed National Military Medical Center, Bethesda, MD, p. A290

CARROLL, James H., Chief Information Officer, St. John Medical Center, Westlake, OH, p. A493

CARROLL, Karen, MSN Vice President and Chief Nursing Officer, Beaufort Memorial Hospital, Beaufort, SC, p. A548

CARROLL, Marsha, Director Financial Services, Screven County Hospital, Sylvania, GA, p. A161

CARROLL, Michael W., Administrator, Richland Parish Hospital, Delhi, LA, p. A266

CARROLL, Patricia, Senior Vice President and Chief Operating Officer, Saint Peter's University Hospital, New Brunswick, NJ, p. A407

CARROLL, Peggy, Chief Information Officer, Palos Community Hospital, Palos Heights, IL, p. A191

CARROLL, Richard, M.D
Chief Medical officer, Adventist Bolingbrook Hospital, Bolingbrook, IL, p. A175
Chief Medical Officer, Adventist GlenOaks Hospital, Glendale Heights, IL, p. A183

CARROLL, Sandy, Coordinator Human Resources, Norman Specialty Hospital, Norman, OK, p. A502

CARROLL, Susan, Chief Operating Officer, Inova Loudoun Hospital, Leesburg, VA, p. A656

CARROLL, Terri L., Vice President Financial Services, Hillsboro Area Hospital, Hillsboro, IL, p. A185

CARROLL, Tim, Chief Information Officer, Sunrise Canyon Hospital, Lubbock, TX, p. A620

CARROLL, Velma, Chief Information Officer, Augusta Health, Fishersville, VA, p. A654

CARRON, Patrick E., FACHE, President and Chief Executive Officer, Perry County Memorial Hospital, Perryville, MO, p. A367

CARRUTH, Gregory, Head Information Management, Naval Hospital Oak Harbor, Oak Harbor, WA, p. A668

CARRUTH, Keith, Chief Executive Officer, AMG Specialty Hospital–Feliciana, Clinton, LA, p. A265

CARRUTHERS, Robert, Chief Executive Officer, Throckmorton County Memorial Hospital, Throckmorton, TX, p. A637

CARSON, Christine, Vice President Human Resources, St. Vincent Medical Center, Los Angeles, CA, p. A72

CARSON, Debbie, Director Human Resources, Promise Hospital of Vicksburg, Vicksburg, MS, p. A354

CARSON, Gregory W., Administrator, U. S. Air Force Clinic, Mountain Home AFB, ID, p. A170

CARSON, Jim, Director Human Resources, Henry County Health Center, Mount Pleasant, IA, p. A225

CARSON, Joe, Director Human Resources, Glen Oaks Hospital, Greenville, TX, p. A607

CARSON, Kara Jo, Chief Financial Officer, Pinckneyville Community Hospital, Pinckneyville, IL, p. A192

CARSON, Mitchell C., President and Chief Executive Officer, Longmont United Hospital, Longmont, CO, p. A104

CARSTENSEN, Karla, Director Patient Care, Avera Dells Area Hospital, Dell Rapids, SD, p. A559

CARTE, Theresa, Ph.D., Administrator and Chief Executive Officer, Cordova Community Medical Center, Cordova, AK, p. A27

CARTER, Bruce C., President and Chief Executive Officer, United Hospital Center, Bridgeport, WV, p. A675

CARTER, Charla, Director Human Resources, Uvalde County Hospital Authority, Uvalde, TX, p. A639

CARTER, Cindy, Chief Nursing Officer, Northeast Regional Medical Center, Kirksville, MO, p. A364

CARTER, D. Montez, President, St. Mary's Good Samaritan Hospital, Greensboro, GA, p. A154

CARTER, Dennis, M.D. Chief of Staff, Eastern Oklahoma Medical Center, Poteau, OK, p. A505

CARTER, Donna, MSN Chief Nursing Officer, Minden Medical Center, Minden, LA, p. A274

CARTER, Doug, Chief Financial Officer, Brookwood Medical Center, Birmingham, AL, p. A16

CARTER, Frank, Chief Financial Officer, Cornerstone Hospital of Huntington, Huntington, WV, p. A677

CARTER, Gary L., M.D. Medical Director of Quality, North Kansas City Hospital, North Kansas City, MO, p. A367

CARTER, Jr., James R., Chief Operating Officer, Methodist Healthcare Memphis Hospitals, Memphis, TN, p. A575

CARTER, Jason, Chief Executive Officer, Warm Springs Specialty Hospital, Luling, TX, p. A621

CARTER, Jessica Y., Chief Financial Officer, Crisp Regional Hospital, Cordele, GA, p. A151

CARTER, Leonard M., Vice President Human Resources, FHN Memorial Hospital, Freeport, IL, p. A183

CARTER, Marcia, Director Human Resources, Bluegrass Community Hospital, Versailles, KY, p. A261

CARTER, Michael C., Executive Director, Kaiser Permanente Woodland Hills Medical Center,, CA, p. A69

CARTER, Michael J., Chief Executive Officer, Memorial Hospital and Physician Group, Frederick, OK, p. A499

CARTER, Misty, Director Human Resources, Great Plains Regional Medical Center, Elk City, OK, p. A498

CARTER, Nebo, Chief Human Resources Officer, Singing River Health System, Pascagoula, MS, p. A352

CARTER, Priscilla, Chief Financial Officer, Mesa Hills Specialty Hospital, El Paso, TX, p. A601

CARTER, Rebecca W., MSN Vice President Patient Care and Chief Operating Officer, Transylvania Regional Hospital, Brevard, NC, p. A448

CARTER, Richard, District Chief Executive Officer, Hunt Regional Medical Center, Greenville, TX, p. A607

CARTER, Richard, M.D. Chief of Staff, Tennova–Jefferson Memorial Hospital, Jefferson City, TN, p. A571

CARTER, Richard G., Chief Executive Officer, Valley View Medical Center, Fort Mohave, AZ, p. A31

CARTER, Scott, Chief Operating Officer, Center for Behavioral Medicine, Kansas City, MO, p. A362

CARTER, Steve, M.D. Chief of Staff, Childress Regional Medical Center, Childress, TX, p. A591

CARTER, Teresa, Vice President and Chief Operating Officer, Novant Health Medical Park Hospital, Winston–Salem, NC, p. A463

CARTER–ROBERTSON, Kira, President and Chief Executive Officer, Sparrow Specialty Hospital, Lansing, MI, p. A318

CARTHEW, Edward
Chief Human Resources Officer, Saint Joseph East, Lexington, KY, p. A254
Chief Human Resources Officer, Saint Joseph Hospital, Lexington, KY, p. A254

CARTWRIGHT, David, Director Management Information Systems, Danville Regional Medical Center, Danville, VA, p. A653

CARTWRIGHT, David A., Vice President Finance, Advocate Condell Medical Center, Libertyville, IL, p. A187

CARTWRIGHT, Kay B., R.N. Vice President and Chief Nursing Officer, Reid Hospital and Health Care Services, Richmond, IN, p. A212

CARTWRIGHT, Thomas, M.D. Chief of Staff, Witham Memorial Hospital, Lebanon, IN, p. A209

CARTY, Steven D., Chief Executive Officer, Mineral Community Hospital, Superior, MT, p. A380

CARUCCI, Dean, Chief Operating Officer, Overland Park Regional Medical Center, Overland Park, KS, p. A242

CARUGATI, Diane, Chief Operating Officer, Friends Hospital, Philadelphia, PA, p. A535

CARUSO, Charles, Chief Information Officer, Henrietta D. Goodall Hospital, Sanford, ME, p. A285

CARUSO, Diane M., MSN Chief Nursing Officer, HEALTHSOUTH Scottsdale Rehabilitation Hospital, Scottsdale, AZ, p. A37

CARUSO, Don, M.D. Chief Medical Officer, Cheshire Medical Center, Keene, NH, p. A398

CARUSO, Michael J.
President and Chief Executive Officer, East Ohio Regional Hospital, Martins Ferry, OH, p. A485
President and Chief Executive Officer, Ohio Valley Medical Center, Wheeling, WV, p. A682

CARVALHO, Robert M., M.D. Medical Director, Aurora Vista Del Mar Hospital, Ventura, CA, p. A94

CARVER, Leota, Chief Financial Officer, Caribou Memorial Hospital and Living Center, Soda Springs, ID, p. A172

CASABONA, Nicholas, Chief Information Officer, Winthrop–University Hospital, Mineola, NY, p. A429

CASADY, W. Stephen, M.D. Chief of Staff, Putnam County Memorial Hospital, Unionville, MO, p. A373

CASALOU, Robert F.
President and Chief Executive Officer, St. Joseph Mercy Hospital, Ypsilanti, MI, p. A327
President and Chief Executive Officer, St. Joseph Mercy Livingston Hospital, Howell, MI, p. A316

CASAREZ, Margaret, Chief Financial Officer, San Joaquin Valley Rehabilitation Hospital, Fresno, CA, p. A62

CASAS, Miguel, R.N. Chief Nursing Officer, East Texas Medical Center–Gilmer, Gilmer, TX, p. A606

CASAZZA, Jerri, Manager Human Resources, Greystone Park Psychiatric Hospital, Morris Plains, NJ, p. A406

CASCIARI, Raymond, M.D. Chief Medical Officer, St. Joseph Hospital, Orange, CA, p. A78

CASE, Beth, Vice President Human Resources, St. Mary's Healthcare, Amsterdam, NY, p. A420

CASE, Cliff, Chief Financial Officer, Mineral Community Hospital, Superior, MT, p. A380

CASE, Cora, Chief Financial Officer, Renown South Meadows Medical Center, Reno, NV, p. A395

CASE, Ed, Executive Vice President and Chief Financial Officer, Rehabilitation Institute of Chicago, Chicago, IL, p. A178

CASE, Harvey
President, Vidant Beaufort Hospital, Washington, NC, p. A462
President, Vidant Pungo Hospital, Belhaven, NC, p. A448

CASE, Matthew, Director Administration, Naval Hospital Camp Lejeune, Camp Lejeune, NC, p. A449

CASE–WIRTH, Jill, Vice President and Chief Nursing Officer, Theda Clark Medical Center, Neenah, WI, p. A693

CASERTA, Kevin, M.D. Chief Medical Officer, Providence Centralia Hospital, Centralia, WA, p. A665

CASEY, Candy J., MS, President and Chief Executive Officer, Columbia Center, Mequon, WI, p. A691

CASEY, Dina, Human Resources Officer, Lane County Hospital, Dighton, KS, p. A233

CASEY, John P., Administrator, Shodair Children's Hospital, Helena, MT, p. A377

CASEY, Joseph, Chief Financial Officer, Sturdy Memorial Hospital, Attleboro, MA, p. A295

CASEY, Richard J., Assistant Vice President Operations, NorthShore University Health System Skokie Hospital, Skokie, IL, p. A194

CASH, Jeff, Senior Vice President and Chief Information Officer, Mercy Medical Center–Cedar Rapids, Cedar Rapids, IA, p. A217

CASH, Jimmie, R.N. Executive Director and Patient Care, Saint Francis Hospital South, Tulsa, OK, p. A509

CASHMAN III, Eugene, Chief Executive Officer, Crittenden Regional Hospital, West Memphis, AR, p. A51

CASHWELL, David
Chief Operating Officer, LewisGale Hospital Montgomery, Blacksburg, VA, p. A652
Chief Operating Officer, Osceola Regional Medical Center, Kissimmee, FL, p. A127

CASIANO, Manuel, M.D. Vice President Medical Affairs, Frederick Memorial Hospital, Frederick, MD, p. A291

CASILLAS, Rosalind, Director of Nursing, Lawrence Memorial Hospital, Walnut Ridge, AR, p. A50

CASIMIR, Kenneth, M.D. Medical Director, Mendota Mental Health Institute, Madison, WI, p. A689

CASKEY, Paul, M.D. Chief of Staff, Shriners Hospitals for Children–Spokane, Spokane, WA, p. A672

CASMER, Benjamin, Assistant Chief Executive Officer, Weatherford Regional Medical Center, Weatherford, TX, p. A640

CASNER, Trina, President and Chief Executive Officer, Pana Community Hospital, Pana, IL, p. A191

CASON, Diane, Supervisor Personnel and Payroll, Lake Butler Hospital Hand Surgery Center, Lake Butler, FL, p. A128

CASON, Randall R., FACHE, President and Chief Executive Officer, Via Christi Hospital in Pittsburg, Pittsburg, KS, p. A242

CASON, Steven, Chief Information Officer, Putnam General Hospital, Eatonton, GA, p. A153

CASON, Will, Vice President Human Resources, St. Rita's Medical Center, Lima, OH, p. A484

CASPERSON, William, M.D. Vice President Medical Affairs, Memorial Hospital, Belleville, IL, p. A174

CASS, Katherine, R.N. Nurse Manager, Kindred Hospital–Dayton, Dayton, OH, p. A480

CASS, Paul, D.O. Chief Medical & Clinical Integration Officer, Wentworth–Douglass Hospital, Dover, NH, p. A397

CASSADY, Craig, Director of Nursing, Wiregrass Medical Center, Geneva, AL, p. A21

CASSADY, Richard L., Chief Financial Officer, Specialty Hospital at Kimball, Lakewood, NJ, p. A405

CASSAGNE, Nancy R., FACHE, Chief Executive Officer, West Jefferson Medical Center, Marrero, LA, p. A273

CASSARA, Pamela, Chief Financial Officer, MetroSouth Medical Center, Blue Island, IL, p. A174

CASSEDY, Ryan, Chief Executive Officer, HEALTHSOUTH Rehabilitation Hospital of Fort Smith, Fort Smith, AR, p. A44

CASSEL, Kari
Senior Vice President and Chief Information Officer, Shands at the University of Florida, Gainesville, FL, p. A124
Senior Vice President and Chief Information Officer, Shands Jacksonville Medical Center, Jacksonville, FL, p. A126

CASSELS, William H., Administrator, DCH Regional Medical Center, Tuscaloosa, AL, p. A26

CASSIDAY, Cheryl, R.N. Director of Nursing, Chadron Community Hospital and Health Services, Chadron, NE, p. A382

CASSIDY, Doris B., Associate Director, Veterans Health Care System of the Ozarks, Fayetteville, AR, p. A43

CASSIDY, Erin
Chief Executive Officer, Nexus Specialty Hospital, Shenandoah, TX, p. A633
Chief Executive Officer, Nexus Specialty Hospital The Woodlands, Spring, TX, p. A634

CASSIDY, Joseph J., Vice President, Holy Redeemer Hospital and Medical Center, Meadowbrook, PA, p. A531

CASSIDY, Lori W., FACHE Assistant Vice President, Medical Center of Central Georgia, Macon, GA, p. A156

CASTANEDA, Edmundo, President, Mercy General Hospital, Sacramento, CA, p. A83

CASTANEDA, Marissa, Chief Operating Officer and Director Marketing, Doctor's Hospital at Renaissance, Edinburg, TX, p. A600

CASTEEL, Karen, Director Human Resources, Palms of Pasadena Hospital, Saint Petersburg, FL, p. A139

CASTEEL, Lisa, Chief Financial Officer/Assistant Administrator, Henry County Medical Center, Paris, TN, p. A578

CASTEEL, Rick
Vice President Management Information Systems and Chief Information Officer, Harford Memorial Hospital, Havre De Grace, MD, p. A292
Vice President Management Information Systems and Chief Information Officer, Upper Chesapeake Medical Center, Bel Air, MD, p. A289

CASTELLO, Frank V., M.D. Medical Director, Children's Specialized Hospital–PSE&G, New Brunswick, NJ, p. A407

CASTELLO, Fred, M.D. Chief Medical Officer, Augusta Health, Fishersville, VA, p. A654

CASTELLO, Lauren, Director Human Resources, Trinity Hospital Twin City, Dennison, OH, p. A480

CASTERLINE, Carolyn, Financial Director, Roosevelt Medical Center, Culbertson, MT, p. A375

CASTILLO, Edgar, Chief Financial Officer, Larkin Community Hospital, South Miami, FL, p. A140

CASTILLO, Paul, Chief Financial Officer, University of Michigan Hospitals and Health Centers, Ann Arbor, MI, p. A308

CASTILLO, Ralph, Chief Executive Officer, Morgan Memorial Hospital, Madison, GA, p. A157

CASTILLO, Renee, Chief Nursing Officer, Plains Memorial Hospital, Dimmitt, TX, p. A599

CASTILLO, Rita S., R.N. Chief Quality Officer, South Texas Regional Medical Center, Jourdanton, TX, p. A615

CASTILLO, Robert, Director Profesional Services, Jackson County Hospital District, Edna, TX, p. A600

CASTLE, Christopher M., Commander, Dwight David Eisenhower Army Medical Center, Fort Gordon, GA, p. A154

CASTLE, Dorothy, Director Human Resources, North Mississippi Medical Center–Eupora, Eupora, MS, p. A346

CASTLE, Eric, Director Information Services, Lawnwood Regional Medical Center, Fort Pierce, FL, p. A124

CASTLE, Kenneth, Chief Information Officer, Easton Hospital, Easton, PA, p. A525

CASTLE, Samantha, Director Human Resources and Performance Improvement, Ridge Behavioral Health System, Lexington, KY, p. A254

CASTLEBERRY, David L., Chief Executive Officer, Upson Regional Medical Center, Thomaston, GA, p. A161

CASTLEBERRY, Debi
Director Information System, St. David's Medical Center, Austin, TX, p. A586
Director Information System, St. David's Rehabilitation Center, Austin, TX, p. A586

CASTLEBERRY, Ginger, Corporate Risk Manager, Quality and Patient Safety, Valir Rehabilitation Hospital, Oklahoma City, OK, p. A504

CASTOR, Susan, Chief Nursing Officer, HEALTHSOUTH Rehabilitation Hospital of Toms River, Toms River, NJ, p. A411

CASTRIOTTA, Ralph, M.D. Medical Director, Carolina Center for Behavioral Health, Greer, SC, p. A553

CASTRO, Ana, Director Information Services and Clinical Information Services, Gerald Champion Regional Medical Center, Alamogordo, NM, p. A414

CASTRO, Craig
Chief Executive Officer, Clovis Community Medical Center, Clovis, CA, p. A56
Chief Information Officer, Community Regional Medical Center, Fresno, CA, p. A61

CASTRO, Pete, D.O. Chief of Staff, Heart of Texas Memorial Hospital, Brady, TX, p. A589

CASTRO, Richard, Chief Executive Officer, Whittier Hospital Medical Center, Whittier, CA, p. A96

CASTRO, Ruben, Associate Administrator and Facility Information Security Officer, North Hills Hospital, North Richland Hills, TX, p. A625

CASTRO, Yamila, Director Human Resources, Hialeah Hospital, Hialeah, FL, p. A125

CASTROMAN, Nellie, Chief Executive Officer, Select Specialty Hospital–Orlando, Orlando, FL, p. A135

CASTRONOVA, Paul, Chief Information Officer, North Canyon Medical Center, Gooding, ID, p. A169

CASWELL, Lori, Director Information Technology, Good Samaritan Medical Center, Brockton, MA, p. A298

CATALA, Lucy, Vice President Finance, Baylor Medical Center at Irving, Irving, TX, p. A614

CATALANO, Robert A., M.D. Chief Medical Officer, St. Luke's–Roosevelt Hospital Center, New York, NY, p. A436

CATALDO, Linda, Human Resources Secretary, Prevost Memorial Hospital, Donaldsonville, LA, p. A266

CATALIOTTI, Palmira, Vice President, Chief Financial Officer and Treasurer, Winthrop–University Hospital, Mineola, NY, p. A429

CATANIA, Joseph M., Chief Executive Officer, St. Anthony's Rehabilitation Hospital, Lauderdale Lakes, FL, p. A129

CATAUDELLA, Mary
Corporate Director Human Resources, LibertyHealth–Jersey City Medical Center, Jersey City, NJ, p. A405
Corporate Director Human Resources, Meadowlands Hospital Medical Center, Secaucus, NJ, p. A410

CATE, Jina, Interim Chief Nursing Officer, Copley Hospital, Morrisville, VT, p. A649

CATE, Maurine, Chief Executive Officer, McKenzie–Willamette Medical Center, Springfield, OR, p. A518

CATENA, Cornelio R., President and Chief Executive Officer, Wilkes-Barre General Hospital, Wilkes–Barre, PA, p. A544

CATES, Erin, Director Human Resources, Hill Country Memorial Hospital, Fredericksburg, TX, p. A605

CATES, Gary, President and Chief Executive Officer, ProMedica Defiance Regional Hospital, Defiance, OH, p. A480

CATES, Jessica, Fiscal Manager, Western State Hospital, Hopkinsville, KY, p. A252

CATES, Rodney
Senior Vice President Human Resources, Covenant Children's Hospital, Lubbock, TX, p. A619
Senior Vice President Human Resources, Covenant Medical Center, Lubbock, TX, p. A620

CATHEY, Michele, Administrator and Chief Executive Officer, Hamilton General Hospital, Hamilton, TX, p. A607

CATHEY, Walt, Chief Operating Officer, Covenant Specialty Hospital, Lubbock, TX, p. A620

CATLETT, Joan, Director Human Resources, Valley General Hospital, Monroe, WA, p. A668

CATLIN, Rexford, Chief Executive Officer, Endless Mountain Health Systems, Montrose, PA, p. A532

CATON, Mark W., Interim Administrator, Hill Hospital of Sumter County, York, AL, p. A26

CATT, Robbin K., Chief Nursing Officer, Jackson Hospital, Marianna, FL, p. A130

CATT, Susan G., Director Human Resources, North Valley Hospital, Whitefish, MT, p. A380

CATTALANI, Mark, M.D. Clinical Director, Richard H. Hutchings Psychiatric Center, Syracuse, NY, p. A443

CATTELL, JoAnne, Chief Nursing Officer, St. Petersburg General Hospital, Saint Petersburg, FL, p. A139

CATUCCI, Paul
Administrative Director Human Resources, Bon Secours St. Francis Medical Center, Midlothian, VA, p. A657
Director Human Resources, Bon Secours St. Mary's Hospital, Richmond, VA, p. A660

CAUBLE, David, Chief Financial Officer, St. Vincent's Blount, Oneonta, AL, p. A24

CAUDEL, Katie, Controller, Southeast Health Center of Reynolds County, Ellington, MO, p. A360

CAUDEL–LOGSDON, Debbie, Director Information System, T. J. Samson Community Hospital, Glasgow, KY, p. A251

CAUDILL, Ralph, Director Information Systems, St. Mary's Hospital, Centralia, IL, p. A175

CAUGHELL, David, M.D. Chief of Staff, Jane Phillips Nowata Health Center, Nowata, OK, p. A502

CAUGHEY, Michelle, M.D. Physician In Chief, Kaiser Permanente South San Francisco, South San Francisco, CA, p. A91

CAULTON, Darryl, Chief Financial Officer, University of Miami Hospital, Miami, FL, p. A132

CAUSEY, Cynthia, Associate Administrator Human and Mission Services, McLeod Medical Center Dillon, Dillon, SC, p. A551

CAUSEY, Jack M., Administrator and Chief Executive Officer, Leesville Rehabilitation Hospital, Leesville, LA, p. A272

CAVA, Anthony V., Chief Operating Officer, Bayshore Community Hospital, Holmdel, NJ, p. A405

CAVANAGH, Dru, R.N. Vice President Patient Care Services and Chief Nursing Officer, Chenango Memorial Hospital, Norwich, NY, p. A438

CAVANAGH, Dru, R.N., President and Chief Executive Officer, Delaware Valley Hospital, Walton, NY, p. A445

CAVANAGH, Dru, R.N. President and Chief Executive Officer, Delaware Valley Hospital, Walton, NY, p. A445

CAVANAGH, James, Chief Information Officer, St. Joseph's Regional Medical Center, Paterson, NJ, p. A408

CAVANAUGH, James, Chief Finance Officer, Wm. Jennings Bryan Dorn Veterans Affairs Medical Center, Columbia, SC, p. A551

CAVANAUGH, Paul, Director Human Resources, Friends Hospital, Philadelphia, PA, p. A535

CAVANESS, Patricia, Chief Clinical Officer, Kindred Hospital–San Diego, San Diego, CA, p. A85

CAVE, Rogelio, M.D. Medical Director, Roseland Community Hospital, Chicago, IL, p. A178

CAVENEY, Timothy, Chief Financial Officer, South Shore Hospital, Chicago, IL, p. A179

CAVERNO, John
Chief Human Resources Officer, Excela Frick Hospital, Mount Pleasant, PA, p. A532
Chief Human Resources Officer, Excela Health Westmoreland Hospital, Greensburg, PA, p. A526
Senior Vice President and Chief Human Resource Officer, Excela Latrobe Area Hospital, Latrobe, PA, p. A529

CAVES, Donald, President, Wild Rose Community Memorial Hospital, Wild Rose, WI, p. A700

CAWLEY, Kevin J., Interim Vice President Finance, Spectrum Health Gerber Memorial, Fremont, MI, p. A314

CAWLEY, Patrick J., M.D., Vice President of Clinical Operations and Chief Executive Officer, MUSC Medical Center of Medical University of South Carolina, Charleston, SC, p. A549

CAWTHON, David, Director Financial Services, Roosevelt Warm Springs Institute for Rehabilitation, Warm Springs, GA, p. A162

CAYER, Gerald, Executive Vice President and Chief Operating Officer, Franklin Memorial Hospital, Farmington, ME, p. A283

CAZAYOUX, John, Chief Financial Officer, Pointe Coupee General Hospital, New Roads, LA, p. A276

CEBRIK, Michael M., M.D. Director Medical Staff, Veterans Home and Hospital, Rocky Hill, CT, p. A111

CECCHETTINI, Diane E., R.N., President and Chief Executive Officer, MultiCare Tacoma General Hospital, Tacoma, WA, p. A673

CECCONI, Thomas E., President and Chief Executive Officer, Mercy Medical Center, Canton, OH, p. A473

CECIL, Bruce, Chief Financial Officer, Fresno Surgical Hospital, Fresno, CA, p. A61

CECIL, Janell, R.N. Senior Vice President and Chief Nursing Officer, University of Tennessee Medical Center, Knoxville, TN, p. A572

CECIL, Jason, Chief Information Officer, Capital Region Medical Center, Jefferson City, MO, p. A362

CECIL, Jon C.
Chief Human Resource Officer, Cape Coral Hospital, Cape Coral, FL, p. A120
Chief Human Resource Officer, Gulf Coast Medical Center, Fort Myers, FL, p. A124
Chief Human Resource Officer, Lee Memorial Hospital, Fort Myers, FL, p. A124

CEDILLO–RODRIGUEZ, Laura, Chief Executive Officer, Kindred Hospital–Bay Area, Pasadena, TX, p. A626

CEDOTAL, Kiley P., Chief Executive Officer, Regency Hospital of Covington, Covington, LA, p. A266

CEHELYK, Bohdan, M.D. Chief Medical Officer, East Mountain Hospital, Belle Mead, NJ, p. A401

CEKALLA, Bernie, Manager Human Resources, Albany Area Hospital and Medical Center, Albany, MN, p. A328

CELANO, Julie, Vice President Human Resources, Brigham and Women's Hospital, Boston, MA, p. A296

CELIA, Marc, FACHE, Chief Executive Officer, Memorial Hermann Surgical Hospital Kingwood, Kingwood, TX, p. A617

CELLA, Ann S., R.N. Senior Vice President, Patient Care Services, St. Francis Hospital, Roslyn, NY, p. A442

CELLA, Robert, M.D
Vice President Medical Affairs, Berkshire Medical Center, Pittsfield, MA, p. A304
Vice President Medical Affairs, St. Peter's Hospital, Albany, NY, p. A420

CELLETTI, David, Chief Executive Officer, Northcoast Behavioral Healthcare System, Northfield, OH, p. A487

CELLUCCI, Jeff, Interim Chief Executive Officer, Kindred Hospital–Milwaukee, Greenfield, WI, p. A688

CELSOR, Reba, Chief Operating Officer, Raleigh General Hospital, Beckley, WV, p. A675

CELUCH, Paul, Vice President Human Resources and Support Services, Verdugo Hills Hospital, Glendale, CA, p. A63

CEMATE, David D., FACHE Senior Vice President and Chief Operating Officer, Mercy Medical Center, Canton, OH, p. A473

CEMENO, Michael J., Chief Information Officer, Waterbury Hospital, Waterbury, CT, p. A112

CEPERO, Jesus, Ph.D. Vice President Nursing and Chief Nursing Officer, Meritus Medical Center, Hagerstown, MD, p. A292

CERCEO, Richard, Executive Vice President and Chief Operating Officer, Mercy Hospital and Medical Center, Chicago, IL, p. A177

CERONE, Shane, President, Beaumont Hospital – Royal Oak, Royal Oak, MI, p. A323

CERRA, Jane, Market Nurse Executive and Chief Nursing Officer, Select Specialty Hospital–Milwaukee, Milwaukee, WI, p. A692

CERULLO, Timothy J., Chief Executive Officer, Wuesthoff Medical Center – Rockledge, Rockledge, FL, p. A138

CERVANTES, Mary Ann, District Director Management Information Systems, Matagorda Regional Medical Center, Bay City, TX, p. A587

CERVINO, Noel A., President and Chief Executive Officer, University of Maryland Charles Regional Medical Center, La Plata, MD, p. A292

CERVONI, Tom, M.D. Chief of Staff, Baptist Health Richmond, Richmond, KY, p. A260

CESCA, Ken, Vice President Human Resources, MidState Medical Center, Meriden, CT, p. A109

CHABALKO, John, M.D. Medical Director, Select Specialty Hospital–Wilmington, Wilmington, DE, p. A115

CHABALOWSKI, Edward, Chief Financial Officer, Geisinger–Community Medical Center, Scranton, PA, p. A540

CHABNER, David, Director Information Services, Sky Lakes Medical Center, Klamath Falls, OR, p. A514

CHABOT, Judy, R.N. Chief Nursing Officer, Placentia–Linda Hospital, Placentia, CA, p. A80

CHACKO, Benson, Chief Operating Officer, Des Peres Hospital, Saint Louis, MO, p. A369

CHADHA, Beenu, Chief Financial Officer, San Ramon Regional Medical Center, San Ramon, CA, p. A89

CHADWICK, Lionel K., Chief Executive Officer, Hi-Desert Medical Center, Joshua Tree, CA, p. A64

CHADWICK, Sharon M., Director Human Resources, Arrowhead Hospital, Glendale, AZ, p. A31

CHAFFEE, Jacob, M.D. Chief Medical Officer, Coulee Medical Center, Grand Coulee, WA, p. A667

CHAFFIN, Linda, Director Medical Review, Baptist Memorial Hospital–Booneville, Booneville, MS, p. A345

CHAFFIN, Robert A., President and Chief Executive Officer, OSF Saint Elizabeth Medical Center, Ottawa, IL, p. A191

CHAGRASULIS, Robert, M.D. Chief of Staff, Calais Regional Hospital, Calais, ME, p. A282

CHAHANOVICH, Jen, Chief Executive and Chief Operating Officer, Pali Momi Medical Center, Aiea, HI, p. A164

CHAILDIN, Roberta, Manager Human Resources, Parrish Medical Center, Titusville, FL, p. A143

CHAISSON, Greg, M.D. Chief Medical Staff, Thibodaux Regional Medical Center, Thibodaux, LA, p. A279

CHAISSON, Rebecca, Interim Chief Financial Officer, Methodist McKinney Hospital, McKinney, TX, p. A622

CHALIAN, Christopher, M.D. Medical Director, Casa Colina Hospital for Rehabilitative Medicine, Pomona, CA, p. A80

CHALK, Jackie, Director Human Resources, HEALTHSOUTH Rehabilitation Hospital, Largo, FL, p. A128

CHALMERS, Bryan, Chief Financial Officer, Memorial Hospital at Craig, Craig, CO, p. A99

CHALONER, Robert S., President and Chief Executive Officer, Southampton Hospital, Southampton, NY, p. A443

CHAMBERLAIN, Denise, Chief Financial Officer, Paradise Valley Hospital, Phoenix, AZ, p. A35

CHAMBERLAIN, Joe
Chief Operating Officer/Acting Chief Executive Officer, MedCentral – Mansfield Hospital, Mansfield, OH, p. A485
Acting Chief Executive Officer, MedCentral – Shelby Hospital, Shelby, OH, p. A489

CHAMBERLIN, Kim, Vice President Patient Services and Chief Nursing Officer, Mercy Medical Center–North Iowa, Mason City, IA, p. A225

CHAMBERLIN, William, M.D. Chief Medical Officer, University of Illinois Hospital & Health Sciences System, Chicago, IL, p. A180

CHAMBERS, Barry M., CPA Chief Financial Officer, Ochsner Medical Center–Baton Rouge, Baton Rouge, LA, p. A263

CHAMBERS, Bradley, President, MedStar Union Memorial Hospital, Baltimore, MD, p. A288

CHAMBERS, Erin, M.D. Chief Medical Officer, Houston County Community Hospital, Erin, TN, p. A568

CHAMBERS, Pamela, Chief Executive Officer, Great Bend Regional Hospital, Great Bend, KS, p. A234

CHAMBERS, Regina, Assistant Vice President Human Resource, Rome Memorial Hospital, Rome, NY, p. A441

CHAMBLEE, Jane, Manager Human Resources, North Mississippi Medical Center–Iuka, Iuka, MS, p. A348

CHAMBLESS, Kent, Chief Information Officer, Cornerstone Hospital of Houston – Bellaire, Houston, TX, p. A609

CHAMBLESS, Lesley
Vice President Human Resources, Carolinas Medical Center–Lincoln, Lincolnton, NC, p. A456
Assistant Vice President Workforce Relations, Carolinas Medical Center–NorthEast, Concord, NC, p. A450

CHAMBLESS, Marcy, Manager Business Office, Carl Vinson Veterans Affairs Medical Center, Dublin, GA, p. A152

CHAMPAGNE, Charles, Chief Financial Officer, Northeast Rehabilitation Hospital, Salem, NH, p. A400

CHAMPAVANNARATH, Vilakon, Director Information Systems, Bartow Regional Medical Center, Bartow, FL, p. A118

CHAMPION, Joshua I., Director, Florida Hospital–Flagler, Palm Coast, FL, p. A136

CHAN, Bruce, Director Business Planning and Marketing, Sonora Regional Medical Center, Sonora, CA, p. A91

CHAN, Fred, Chief Financial Officer, Intracare North Hospital, Houston, TX, p. A610

CHAN, Joyce, Chief Human Resources Officer, CentraCare Health–Melrose, Melrose, MN, p. A335

CHAN, Marsha, PharmD Chief Quality Officer, St. Francis Medical Center, Lynwood, CA, p. A72

CHANAA, Ziad, M.D. Chief of Staff, Boone Memorial Hospital, Madison, WV, p. A678

CHANCE, Matt, Chief Executive Officer, Baylor Medical Center at Uptown, Dallas, TX, p. A595

CHAND, Parveen, Chief Operating Officer, Alegent Creighton Health–Creighton University Medical Center, Omaha, NE, p. A387

CHANDLER, Laurie, Financial Officer, Prairie Community Hospital, Terry, MT, p. A380

CHANDLER, Loren, Interim, Vice President and Chief Financial Officer, Holy Cross Hospital, Chicago, IL, p. A176

CHANDLER, Ronald, Accountant II, Southwest Missouri Psychiatric Rehabilitation Center, El Dorado Springs, MO, p. A360

CHANDLER, Ryan, President and Chief Executive Officer, The Medical Center, Columbus, GA, p. A150

CHANDLER, Vincent, Director Information Services, Porterville Developmental Center, Porterville, CA, p. A80

CHANEZ, Adolfo, Vice President Finance and Chief Financial Officer, Saddleback Memorial Medical Center, Laguna Hills, CA, p. A65

CHANG, Alex
Chief Operating Officer, Englewood Community Hospital, Englewood, FL, p. A123
Vice President and Chief Operating Officer, Fawcett Memorial Hospital, Port Charlotte, FL, p. A137

CHANG, C. Joseph, President and Chief Executive Officer, East Valley Hospital Medical Center, Glendora, CA, p. A63

CHANG, Florence
Senior Vice President, Clinical Support Services and Chief Information Officer, MultiCare Good Samaritan Hospital, Puyallup, WA, p. A669
Senior Vice President, Clinical Support Services and Chief Information Officer, MultiCare Mary Bridge Children's Hospital and Health Center, Tacoma, WA, p. A673
Senior Vice President, Clinical Support Services and Chief Information Officer, MultiCare Tacoma General Hospital, Tacoma, WA, p. A673

CHANG, Sang-ick, M.D. Chief Medical Officer, Alameda County Medical Center, Oakland, CA, p. A77

CHANI, Swaranjik K., M.D. Chief of Staff, Caverna Memorial Hospital, Horse Cave, KY, p. A253

CHANNELL, Lesley
Assistant Vice President Human Resources, Dominion Hospital, Falls Church, VA, p. A653
Assistant Vice President Human Resources, Reston Hospital Center, Reston, VA, p. A659

CHANNING, Alan H.
President and Chief Executive Officer, Mount Sinai Hospital, Chicago, IL, p. A177
President and Chief Executive Officer, Schwab Rehabilitation Hospital, Chicago, IL, p. A179

CHANSKI, Jared, Administrator, Culberson Hospital, Van Horn, TX, p. A639

CHANSOLME, David, M.D. President of the Medical Staff, Integris Southwest Medical Center, Oklahoma City, OK, p. A503

CHAPARRO, Natalia, Manager Human Resources, El Paso Children's Hospital, El Paso, TX, p. A601

CHAPIN, Andy, Director Information Technology, Elbert Memorial Hospital, Elberton, GA, p. A153

CHAPIN, Norman, M.D. Medical Director, Columbia Memorial Hospital, Hudson, NY, p. A427

CHAPLIN, Steven, M.D. Medical Director, Kahi Mohala Behavioral Health, Ewa Beach, HI, p. A164

CHAPMAN, Alan, Director Information Systems, Louisiana Heart Hospital, Lacombe, LA, p. A270

CHAPMAN, Evie, Chief Nursing Officer, Tomah Memorial Hospital, Tomah, WI, p. A697

CHAPMAN, Judy, Interim Director Information Systems, Lock Haven Hospital, Lock Haven, PA, p. A530

CHAPMAN, Rick, Chief Information Officer, Kindred Hospital North Florida, Green Cove Springs, FL, p. A125

CHAPMAN, Roberta, Manager Human Resources, Appleton Medical Center, Appleton, WI, p. A683

CHAPMAN, Roland, Chief Information Officer, Northern Navajo Medical Center, Shiprock, NM, p. A418

CHAPMAN, Scott, Administrator, Manhattan Surgical Center,, KS, p. A239

CHAPMAN, Teresa, Vice President Human Resources, Marianjoy Rehabilitation Hospital, Wheaton, IL, p. A196

CHAPPELL, Brandee, Director of Nursing, LifeCare Hospitals of North Carolina, Rocky Mount, NC, p. A460

CHAPPELL, Robert, M.D. Chief Medical Officer and Chief Quality Officer, Huntsville Hospital, Huntsville, AL, p. A21

CHAPPELL, Teresa, Chief Information Officer, Johnston Health, Smithfield, NC, p. A461

CHAPPLE, Scott, Chief Operating Officer, Oroville Hospital, Oroville, CA, p. A78

CHAPRNKA, Karen, Senior Vice President and Chief Operating Officer, Allegiance Health, Jackson, MI, p. A317

CHARBONNEAU, Elissa, D.O. Medical Director, New England Rehabilitation Hospital of Portland, Portland, ME, p. A285

CHARDAVOYNE, Alan, Controller, Elizabethtown Community Hospital, Elizabethtown, NY, p. A425

CHAREST, Richard
President, Landmark Medical Center, Woonsocket, RI, p. A547
Chief Executive Officer, Rehabilitation Hospital of Rhode Island, North Smithfield, RI, p. A546

CHARETTE, Deborah, Director of Nursing, East Mountain Hospital, Belle Mead, NJ, p. A401

CHARI, Ganesh, M.D. Chief of Staff, Oak Hill Hospital, Brooksville, FL, p. A120

CHARI, Ravi, M.D. Chief Medical Officer, Tristar Centennial Medical Center, Nashville, TN, p. A577

CHARLES, Charlotte, Director Acute Patient Services, Madison Community Hospital, Madison, SD, p. A560

CHARLES, Sally, Coordinator Human Resources, Grace Medical Center, Lubbock, TX, p. A620

CHARLES, Timothy L., President and Chief Executive Officer, Mercy Medical Center–Cedar Rapids, Cedar Rapids, IA, p. A217

CHARLTON, Jr., Francis, M.D. Chief Medical Staff, St. Mary's Medical Center, San Francisco, CA, p. A87

CHARMEL, Patrick, President and Chief Executive Officer, Griffin Hospital, Derby, CT, p. A108

CHARTIER, Dianne, R.N., Interim Chief Executive Officer, Kindred Hospital–San Francisco Bay Area, San Leandro, CA, p. A88

CHARTRAND, Gregg, Chief Financial Officer, Mercy Hospital, Moose Lake, MN, p. A336

CHASE, Jean
Regional Manager Information Services, Aurora Lakeland Medical Center, Elkhorn, WI, p. A686
Regional Manager Information Services, Aurora Medical Center, Kenosha, WI, p. A688
Regional Manager Information Services, Aurora Memorial Hospital of Burlington, Burlington, WI, p. A685

CHASE, Kyle, Chief Financial Officer, Glacial Ridge Health System, Glenwood, MN, p. A333

CHASE, Layla, Chief Financial Officer, Springhill Medical Center, Springhill, LA, p. A279

CHASE, Pansy, Director Human Resources, Vidant Duplin Hospital, Kenansville, NC, p. A455

CHASE, Robert, M.D. Chief Medical Officer, West Suburban Medical Center, Oak Park, IL, p. A190

CHASE, Robert, Chief Medical Officer, Westlake Hospital, Melrose Park, IL, p. A188

CHASE, Steven, Chief Executive Officer, Craig General Hospital, Vinita, OK, p. A509

CHASE, Susan, Vice President, Carolinas Rehabilitation, Charlotte, NC, p. A449

CHASTAIN, James G., FACHE, Director, Mississippi State Hospital, Whitfield, MS, p. A355

CHASTAIN, Stephen L., M.D. Medical Director, HEALTHSOUTH Rehabilitation Hospital, Dothan, AL, p. A19

CHASTANT, Lee, M.D., Chief Executive Officer, West Feliciana Parish Hospital, Saint Francisville, LA, p. A277

CHASTELAIN, Vincent, Director Business Development, River Oaks Hospital, New Orleans, LA, p. A275

CHATMAN, Jim, Chief Financial Officer, Maria Parham Medical Center, Henderson, NC, p. A454

CHATMAN, Mark, Director Human Resources, Fremont Hospital, Fremont, CA, p. A61

CHATMAN, Rosie, R.N. Associate Director Patient and Nursing Services, Northport Veterans Affairs Medical Center, Northport, NY, p. A437

CHATTERJEE, Kanan, M.D. Chief of Staff, Lebanon Veterans Affairs Medical Center, Lebanon, PA, p. A529

CHATTO, Paulette, Finance Officer, Northern Navajo Medical Center, Shiprock, NM, p. A418

CHAUDHRY, Deepak
Vice President Information Technology, Nexus Specialty Hospital, Shenandoah, TX, p. A633
Vice President Informatin Technology, Nexus Specialty Hospital The Woodlands, Spring, TX, p. A634

CHAUHAN, Amil, M.D. Chief of Staff, Flambeau Hospital, Park Falls, WI, p. A694

CHAUSSARD, David, Chief Executive Officer, Hillcrest Hospital Claremore, Claremore, OK, p. A497

CHAVA, N. Rao, M.D. Director, Central Alabama Veterans Health Care System, Montgomery, AL, p. A23

CHAVEZ, Delilah, Human Resources Assistant, Conejos County Hospital, La Jara, CO, p. A102

CHAVEZ, Irene, Senior Vice President and Area Manager, Kaiser Permanente San Jose Medical Center, San Jose, CA, p. A87

CHAVEZ, Kevin, Chief Executive Officer, Kindred Hospital of South Bay, Gardena, CA, p. A62

CHAVEZ, Margaret, Manager Human Resources, Hammond–Henry Hospital, Geneseo, IL, p. A183

CHAVEZ, Robert, Chief Financial Officer, Horsham Clinic, Ambler, PA, p. A520

CHAVEZ, Steven, Chief Financial Officer, Greene Memorial Hospital, Xenia, OH, p. A494

CHAVEZ, Virgil, Chief Information Officer, Fort Defiance Indian Health Service Hospital, Fort Defiance, AZ, p. A31

CHAVIS, Anthony D., M.D. Vice President Medical Affairs and Patient Safety Officer, Community Hospital of the Monterey Peninsula, Monterey, CA, p. A75

CHAWLA, Nikki, M.D. Medical Director, Integris Seminole Medical Center, Seminole, OK, p. A506

CHAYER, Olivia, Lead Human Resources, York Hospital, York, ME, p. A286

CHAYKIN, Lee B., Chief Executive Officer, Westside Regional Medical Center, Plantation, FL, p. A137

CHEANEY, Theresa, Controller, Chambers County Public Hospital District 1, Anahuac, TX, p. A582

CHEATWOOD, Elizabeth, Human Resource Director and Administrative Assistant, Jackson Parish Hospital, Jonesboro, LA, p. A269

CHEEMA, Linde, Vice President Human Resources, Sequoia Hospital, Redwood City, CA, p. A82

CHEESEMAN, Karen, Director Human Resources, Mackinac Straits Health System, Saint Ignace, MI, p. A323

CHEEVER, Liz, Associate Administrator, Miracle Mile Medical Center, Los Angeles, CA, p. A70

CHEKOURAS, Christopher A., Vice President and Chief Operating Officer, Virtua Berlin, Berlin, NJ, p. A401

CHELOFF, Alec, Chief Information Officer, Massachusetts Eye and Ear Infirmary, Boston, MA, p. A297

CHEN, Linda, Chief Financial Officer, Sunbury Community Hospital and Outpatient Center, Sunbury, PA, p. A542

CHENEY, David, Chief Executive Officer, Banner Boswell Medical Center, Sun City, AZ, p. A38

CHENG, Alice, Chief Operating Officer and Senior Vice President, Beverly Hospital, Montebello, CA, p. A74

CHENG, Becky, Chief Financial Officer, Corona Regional Medical Center, Corona, CA, p. A57

CHENNAULT, Paula, Administrator, Behavioral HealthCare Center at Columbia, Columbia, TN, p. A567

CHENSVOLD, Debrah, FACHE, President and Chief Executive Officer, Palmer Lutheran Health Center, West Union, IA, p. A230

CHEPAK, Lois, R.N. Chief Clinical Officer, Eagleville Hospital, Eagleville, PA, p. A524

CHERMSIDE, Paula L., Chief Operating Officer, Aspirus Grand View Hospital, Ironwood, MI, p. A317

CHERNICH, Dale
Chief Information Officer, MedWest – Harris, Sylva, NC, p. A462
Chief Information Officer, MedWest – Swain, Bryson City, NC, p. A448

CHERONE, Nancy, Executive Director and Administrator, Nazareth Hospital, Philadelphia, PA, p. A536

CHERRY, Gay Nell, Director Human Resources, Rolling Plains Memorial Hospital, Sweetwater, TX, p. A636

CHERRY, Jean
Executive Vice President, Commonwealth Regional Specialty Hospital, Bowling Green, KY, p. A248
Executive Vice President and Chief Information Officer, Medical Center at Bowling Green, Bowling Green, KY, p. A248
Executive Vice President, Medical Center at Franklin, Franklin, KY, p. A251
Chief Information Officer, Medical Center at Scottsville, Scottsville, KY, p. A260

CHERRY, John I., M.D. Chief of Staff, Rock County Hospital, Bassett, NE, p. A381

CHERRY, Jonathan M., President and Chief Executive Officer, LifeStream Behavioral Center, Leesburg, FL, p. A129

CHERRY, Michael, Chief Financial Officer, Carolina Pines Regional Medical Center, Hartsville, SC, p. A553

CHERRY, Robert, M.D. Chief Medical Officer, Loyola University Medical Center, Maywood, IL, p. A188

CHERRY Jr., Vincent T., Chief Executive Officer, Davis Regional Medical Center, Statesville, NC, p. A461

CHESLEY, Jeanine
Controller, HEALTHSOUTH Rehabilitation Hospital, Concord, NH, p. A397
Chief Executive Officer, New England Rehabilitation Hospital of Portland, Portland, ME, p. A285

CHESNE, Robert, M.D. Chief Medical Officer, Hollywood Presbyterian Medical Center, Los Angeles, CA, p. A69

CHESNOS, Richard C., Senior Vice President Finance and Chief Financial Officer, St. Clair Memorial Hospital, Pittsburgh, PA, p. A538

CHESSARE, John B., FACHE, President and Chief Executive Officer, Greater Baltimore Medical Center, Baltimore, MD, p. A287

CHESSHIRE, Sandra, Chief Financial Officer, Shenandoah Medical Center, Shenandoah, IA, p. A228

CHESSIN, Neil A., Vice President, Jameson Hospital, New Castle, PA, p. A533

CHESSUM, George
Senior Vice President Information Systems and Chief Information Officer, Presence Holy Family Medical Center, Des Plaines, IL, p. A181
Senior Vice President and Chief Information Officer, Presence Our Lady of the Resurrection Medical Center, Chicago, IL, p. A178
Senior Vice President Information Systems and Chief Information Officer, Presence Resurrection Medical Center, Chicago, IL, p. A178
Vice President Information Systems, Presence Saint Francis Hospital, Evanston, IL, p. A182
Senior Vice President Information Systems and Chief Information Officer, Presence Saint Joseph Hospital, Chicago, IL, p. A178

CHESTEEN, Jimmy, Director Information Technology, Montfort Jones Memorial Hospital, Kosciusko, MS, p. A349

CHESTER, Julie, Director Human Resources, University Hospitals Case Medical Center, Cleveland, OH, p. A477

CHESTER, Kate, Senior Coordinator Public Relations, Providence St. Vincent Medical Center, Portland, OR, p. A516

CHESTER, Linnes L., USAF Administrator, Mike O'Callaghan Federal Hospital, Nellis AFB, NV, p. A394

CHESTER, William, Manager Human Resources, Grand Junction Veterans Affairs Medical Center, Grand Junction, CO, p. A102

CHESTNUT–RAULS, Monica, Vice President Human Resources, Peconic Bay Medical Center, Riverhead, NY, p. A440

CHEUNG, Alan, M.D. Vice President Medical Affairs, Castle Medical Center, Kailua, HI, p. A165

CHEUNG, Anna, President, St. Mary's Medical Center, San Francisco, CA, p. A87

CHEUNG, Marilou, Assistant Administrator Finance, Kaiser Permanente Woodland Hills Medical Center,, CA, p. A69

CHEVERTON, Dan, Director Information Systems, LewisGale Hospital at Pulaski, Pulaski, VA, p. A659

CHEW, Roy G., Ph.D., President, Kettering Medical Center, Kettering, OH, p. A483

CHEWNING III, Larry H., President and Chief Executive Officer, Nash Health Care Systems, Rocky Mount, NC, p. A460

CHEYNET, Sandee, Vice President Administrative Services, Bluefield Regional Medical Center, Bluefield, WV, p. A675

CHHABRA, Ankit
Director Finance, Fairview Hospital, Cleveland, OH, p. A476
Director Finance, Lakewood Hospital, Lakewood, OH, p. A483
CHIACCHIARO, Peter, Vice President Human Resources, St. Joseph Hospital, Bethpage, NY, p. A421
CHIANG, Jim, M.D. Chief of Staff, Boulder City Hospital, Boulder City, NV, p. A391
CHIANTELLA, Christopher, M.D. Chief of Staff, Inova Loudoun Hospital, Leesburg, VA, p. A656
CHIANTELLO, Charmaine, Chief Financial Officer, Aspirus Grand View Hospital, Ironwood, MI, p. A317
CHIARAMONTE, Michael J., Chief Executive Officer, MedStar Southern Maryland Hospital Center, Clinton, MD, p. A290
CHIARCHIARO, Martha, Vice President Human Resources, Clinton Hospital, Clinton, MA, p. A299
CHIAVETTA, Robert, Vice President Finance, United Memorial Medical Center, Batavia, NY, p. A421
CHICK, Melanie, Chief Executive Officer, Baylor Medical Center at Trophy Club, Trophy Club, TX, p. A638
CHICKEN, Kurt, Director Support Services, Palmer Lutheran Health Center, West Union, IA, p. A230
CHIEFFO, Ron, Chief Information Officer, Colorado River Medical Center, Needles, CA, p. A76
CHILCOTT, Stephen, Associate Director Human Resources, University of California, Davis Medical Center, Sacramento, CA, p. A84
CHILDERS, Bethany, Manager People Resources, Ogallala Community Hospital, Ogallala, NE, p. A387
CHILDERS, James R., Chief Financial Officer, Cobre Valley Regional Medical Center, Globe, AZ, p. A32
CHILDERS, Linda, Director Human Resources, Wallowa Memorial Hospital, Enterprise, OR, p. A512
CHILDRE Jr., Jimmy, Interim Chief Executive Officer, Washington County Regional Medical Center, Sandersville, GA, p. A159
CHILDS, Deborah, Chief Human Resources Officer, University of Michigan Hospitals and Health Centers, Ann Arbor, MI, p. A308
CHILDS, Joe, M.D. Vice President Medical Services, East Tennessee Children's Hospital, Knoxville, TN, p. A571
CHILDS, Michelle B., Executive Administrative Director Human Resources, Salinas Valley Memorial Healthcare System, Salinas, CA, p. A84
CHILES, John, M.D. Medical Director, Western State Hospital, Tacoma, WA, p. A673
CHILESKI, Andy, Chief Information Officer and Vice President Facilities, Berger Health System, Circleville, OH, p. A475
CHILTON, Alvin, Chief Financial Officer, Southeast Arizona Medical Center, Douglas, AZ, p. A31
CHIN, Ellyn, Vice President Finance, Gottlieb Memorial Hospital, Melrose Park, IL, p. A188
CHINBURG, Paul, M.D. Medical Director, Lane County Hospital, Dighton, KS, p. A233
CHINETTI, Peter J., Chief Financial Officer, Massachusetts Eye and Ear Infirmary, Boston, MA, p. A297
CHIODO, Deborah
Director Human Resources, Freeman Hospital West, Joplin, MO, p. A362
Director Human Resources, Freeman Neosho Hospital, Neosho, MO, p. A366
CHIOLO, Denise, Chief Human Resources Officer, Phoenixville Hospital, Phoenixville, PA, p. A537
CHIPMAN, Kim, Chief Clinical Officer, Kindred Hospital–White Rock, Dallas, TX, p. A596
CHIRICHELLA, Joseph P., President and Chief Executive Officer, Deborah Heart and Lung Center, Browns Mills, NJ, p. A402
CHIRICO, Cathy, Director Human Resources, Edward John Noble Hospital of Gouverneur, Gouverneur, NY, p. A426
CHISENSKI, Walter, Director Information Technology, Casa Grande Regional Medical Center, Casa Grande, AZ, p. A30
CHISHOLM, Ken, Director Human Resources, Martha's Vineyard Hospital, Oak Bluffs, MA, p. A303
CHISHOLM, Lisa P., Troop Commander, Tripler Army Medical Center, Honolulu, HI, p. A165
CHISHOLM, Moody L.
President & Chief Executive Officer, St. Vincent's Medical Center Riverside, Jacksonville, FL, p. A127
President and Chief Executive Officer, St. Vincent's Medical Center Southside, Jacksonville, FL, p. A127
CHISHOLM, Sharon, Director Human Resources, Texas Health Presbyterian Hospital Allen, Allen, TX, p. A581
CHISLEY, Gyasi, Site Administrator and Chief Operating Officer, Mercy Health – Anderson Hospital, Cincinnati, OH, p. A475
CHISSELL, Herbert G., M.D. Chief Medical Officer, Torrance State Hospital, Torrance, PA, p. A542
CHITAYAT, Ron, M.D. Chief Medical Staff, West Hills Hospital and Medical Center,, CA, p. A72
CHITTENDEN, Michael D., President, St. Vincent Carmel Hospital, Carmel, IN, p. A200
CHITTOM, Tommy, Vice President Information Services, East Alabama Medical Center, Opelika, AL, p. A24

CHIVERS, John, Chief Financial Officer, Lower Umpqua Hospital District, Reedsport, OR, p. A517
CHMIELEWSKI, Linda, R.N. Vice President Operations, St. Cloud Hospital, Saint Cloud, MN, p. A339
CHMURA, David, Manager Management Information Systems, Copper Queen Community Hospital, Bisbee, AZ, p. A30
CHOATE, Charlotte, Director Information Systems, Trinity Hospital of Augusta, Augusta, GA, p. A148
CHOATE, Michael, Interim Chief Financial Officer, St. Vincent General Hospital District, Leadville, CO, p. A103
CHODKOWSKI, Paul J., Chief Executive Officer, St. Anthony Summit Medical Center, Frisco, CO, p. A101
CHOINKA, Keith A., Vice President Information Systems and Chief Information Officer, St. Joseph Hospital, Nashua, NH, p. A399
CHOKSHI, Rajiv, M.D. Chief of Staff, Broward Health Medical Center, Fort Lauderdale, FL, p. A123
CHOLGER, Dave, Chief Financial Officer, Woodlawn Hospital, Rochester, IN, p. A213
CHONG, Johnnette, Chief Financial Officer, Los Angeles Community Hospital, Los Angeles, CA, p. A70
CHONGULIA, Terry, M.D. Chief of Staff, Clearview Regional Medical Center, Monroe, GA, p. A157
CHOPRA, Praveen, Chief Information and Supply Chain Officer, Children's Healthcare of Atlanta, Atlanta, GA, p. A146
CHORD, Ginger, Coordinator Human Resources, Sturgis Regional Hospital, Sturgis, SD, p. A563
CHOREY, Raymond M., President and Chief Executive Officer, Southeastern Ohio Regional Medical Center, Cambridge, OH, p. A472
CHOU, Rebecca, Director Information Systems, Palestine Regional Medical Center–East, Palestine, TX, p. A626
CHOW, Karen, Director Human Resources, Chinese Hospital, San Francisco, CA, p. A86
CHOWDHARY, Vijay K., M.D. Medical Director, Hampshire Memorial Hospital, Romney, WV, p. A680
CHOY, Ann N., Manager Human Resources and Payroll, Kuakini Medical Center, Honolulu, HI, p. A164
CHOY, Rose, Chief Financial Officer, Kahi Mohala Behavioral Health, Ewa Beach, HI, p. A164
CHOZINSKI, Joseph P., M.D. Deputy Commander Clinical Services, San Antonio Military Medical Center, Fort Sam Houston, TX, p. A603
CHRISTENSEN, Cinthia S., JD Executive Vice President and Chief Operating Officer, Children's Hospital of Wisconsin, Milwaukee, WI, p. A692
CHRISTENSEN, David, M.D. Vice President Medical Affairs and Chief Medical Officer, Children's Hospital Central California, Madera, CA, p. A73
CHRISTENSEN, Earlene, Director Human Resources, Fayette County Memorial Hospital, Washington Court House, OH, p. A492
CHRISTENSEN, Elizabeth B., Director, Human Resources, Mercy Hospital of Portland, Portland, ME, p. A284
CHRISTENSEN, G. N., M.D. Chief Medical Officer, William Bee Ririe Hospital, Ely, NV, p. A391
CHRISTENSEN, Jay, FACHE, Administrator, Mahaska Health Partnership, Oskaloosa, IA, p. A226
CHRISTENSEN, Jeffrey, Chief Executive Officer, HEALTHSOUTH Rehabilitation Institute of Tucson, Tucson, AZ, p. A38
CHRISTENSEN, Jim, Chief Executive Officer, Crittenden County Hospital, Marion, KY, p. A257
CHRISTENSEN, Marilyn, Director Information Technology, Milford Hospital, Milford, CT, p. A110
CHRISTENSEN, Mark, Assistant Administrator Finance and Chief Financial Officer, Cassia Regional Medical Center, Burley, ID, p. A168
CHRISTENSEN, Marti, Director of Psychiatric Nursing, Douglas County Community Mental Health Center, Omaha, NE, p. A388
CHRISTENSEN, Sandra
Chief Financial Officer, Dallas County Hospital, Perry, IA, p. A227
Chief Executive Officer, Sheridan Memorial Hospital, Plentywood, MT, p. A378
CHRISTENSEN, W. R., M.D. Chief of Staff, East Texas Medical Center Pittsburg, Pittsburg, TX, p. A627
CHRISTENSEN–MORES, Donna, Director Human Resources, Myrtue Medical Center, Harlan, IA, p. A222
CHRISTENSON, Cindy, Chief Clinical Officer, Barrett Hospital & HealthCare, Dillon, MT, p. A375
CHRISTENSON, Lee, Chief Executive Officer, Springwoods Behavioral Health Hospital, Fayetteville, AR, p. A43
CHRISTENSON, Paul, Chief Financial Officer, Pampa Regional Medical Center, Pampa, TX, p. A626
CHRISTENSON, Ron, Chief Financial Officer, Morris County Hospital, Council Grove, KS, p. A233
CHRISTENSON, Shannon, Director Human Resources, Aurora West Allis Medical Center, West Allis, WI, p. A699

CHRISTIAN, Alan,Naval Hospital Camp Pendleton, Camp Pendleton, CA, p. A55
CHRISTIAN, Bruce C., Chief Executive Officer, Adventist GlenOaks Hospital, Glendale Heights, IL, p. A183
CHRISTIAN, Charles, Chief Information Officer and Director Information Systems, Good Samaritan Hospital, Vincennes, IN, p. A214
CHRISTIAN, Glenn, Administrator, Mayo Clinic Health System in Cannon Falls, Cannon Falls, MN, p. A330
CHRISTIAN, Greg, Executive Director, Kaiser Permanente Fontana Medical Center, Fontana, CA, p. A60
CHRISTIAN, Karolyne, Director Human Resources, Byrd Regional Hospital, Leesville, LA, p. A272
CHRISTIAN, Patricia L., R.N., Chief Executive Officer, John Umstead Hospital, Butner, NC, p. A449
CHRISTIANSEN, Anne, Chief Financial Officer, Pioneer Memorial Hospital and Health Services, Viborg, SD, p. A563
CHRISTIANSEN, Hilary, Chief Financial Officer, George C Grape Community Hospital, Hamburg, IA, p. A222
CHRISTIANSEN, Judy A., R.N. Chief Operating Officer, OSF Saint Elizabeth Medical Center, Ottawa, IL, p. A191
CHRISTIANSEN, Kevin, Director Information Technology, University of Arizona Medical Center – South Campus, Tucson, AZ, p. A39
CHRISTIANSEN, Patrick, Ph.D., Chief Executive Officer, Inova Fairfax Hospital, Falls Church, VA, p. A653
CHRISTIANSEN, Sara, Interim Director Human Resources, Sibley Medical Center, Arlington, MN, p. A328
CHRISTIANSON, Clark P., President and Chief Executive Officer, Providence Hospital, Mobile, AL, p. A22
CHRISTIANSON, Clinton J., FACHE, President, Mercy Medical Center–Centerville, Centerville, IA, p. A218
CHRISTIANSON, Delano, Administrator, CentraCare Health–Sauk Centre, Sauk Centre, MN, p. A340
CHRISTIE, Andy, Chief Information Technology, Adair County Memorial Hospital, Greenfield, IA, p. A222
CHRISTIE, Janet L., Senior Vice President Human Resources, Shands at the University of Florida, Gainesville, FL, p. A124
CHRISTINE, Gerald, Chief Financial Officer, Lakewood Ranch Medical Center, Bradenton, FL, p. A119
CHRISTINE, Jerry, Chief Executive Officer, Putnam Community Medical Center, Palatka, FL, p. A135
CHRISTION, Lydia, Director Human Resources, HEALTHSOUTH Rehabilitation Hospital, Dothan, AL, p. A19
CHRISTISON, George, M.D. Medical Director, Patton State Hospital, Patton, CA, p. A79
CHRISTMAN, Lawrence, Chief Financial Officer and Chief Operating Officer, Riverview Hospital, Noblesville, IN, p. A211
CHRISTMAN, Lyndon J., President and Chief Executive Officer, Fayette County Memorial Hospital, Washington Court House, OH, p. A492
CHRISTMAN, Thomas C., Director Plant Operations, Kindred Hospital–St. Louis, Saint Louis, MO, p. A369
CHRISTOPHEL, Randal, President and Chief Executive Officer, Indiana University Health Goshen Hospital, Goshen, IN, p. A203
CHROBAK, Jeffrey, Vice President Finance and Chief Financial Officer, Sharon Regional Health System, Sharon, PA, p. A541
CHU, Edward, Chief Financial Officer, Leahi Hospital, Honolulu, HI, p. A164
CHUA, Jesus, M.D. Chief of Staff, Franklin Foundation Hospital, Franklin, LA, p. A267
CHUBB, John M., Chief Executive Officer, Community Regional Medical Center, Fresno, CA, p. A61
CHUGHTAI, Omar, Vice President and Chief Operating Officer, West Hills Hospital and Medical Center,, CA, p. A72
CHULACK, Peggy, Chief Administrative Officer and Chief Information Officer, Presbyterian Intercommunity Hospital, Whittier, CA, p. A96
CHUMBLEY, Bud, M.D. Chief Medical Officer, Scott & White Hospital at Round Rock, Round Rock, TX, p. A629
CHUN, Mirhee, Chief Financial Officer, Havenwyck Hospital, Auburn Hills, MI, p. A308
CHUNG, Maria, CPA Director Fiscal Services, Shriners Hospitals for Children–Boston Burns Hospital, Boston, MA, p. A297
CHUNG, Raymond, M.D. Chief of Staff, Phoenix Veterans Affairs Health Care System, Phoenix, AZ, p. A35
CHUNN, Debbie, Director Medical Records, Bastrop Rehabilitation Hospital, Bastrop, LA, p. A262
CHURCH, Kim
Manager Human Resources, G. Werber Bryan Psychiatric Hospital, Columbia, SC, p. A550
Manager Human Resources, William S. Hall Psychiatric Institute, Columbia, SC, p. A550
CHURCHILL, Julie, Director Financial Services, The Hospital at Westlake Medical Center, Austin, TX, p. A586
CHURCHILL, Larry, Director Information Services, Woodward Regional Health, Woodward, OK, p. A510
CHURCHILL, Timothy A., President, Stephens Memorial Hospital, Norway, ME, p. A284

CHURCHWELL, Kevin B., M.D., Chief Executive Officer, Alfred I. duPont Hospital for Children, Wilmington, DE, p. A114

CHUSTZ, Mark, Administrator, Greene County Hospital, Eutaw, AL, p. A19

CIAMPA, Amy, Chief Financial Officer, Park Royal Hospital, Fort Myers, FL, p. A124

CIANCIOTTO CROYLE, Allison, Vice President of Human Resources, Mercy Medical Center, Rockville Centre, NY, p. A441

CIANFRANI, Michelle, Director Information Technology, Gilbert Hospital, Gilbert, AZ, p. A31

CIAREFELLA, Donna, Director Human Resources, Kindred Hospital Park View, Springfield, MA, p. A305

CICCARELLI, John, Chief Information Officer, Parkview Community Hospital Medical Center, Riverside, CA, p. A82

CICCARELLI, Thomas, Chief Information Officer, East Orange General Hospital, East Orange, NJ, p. A403

CICERI, David P., M.D. Chief Medical Officer, Scott and White Continuing Care Hospital, Temple, TX, p. A636

CICHA, Rhonda, Director Human Resources, Creedmoor Psychiatric Center,, NY, p. A431

CICHOCKI, David, Chief Fiscal Officer, VA Central Western Massachusetts Healthcare System, Leeds, MA, p. A301

CICHOCKI, Gerald, M.D. Chief of Staff, Mt. San Rafael Hospital, Trinidad, CO, p. A106

CICIRETTI, Mary Louise, Director Human Resources, Riddle Hospital, Media, PA, p. A531

CIENCEWICKI, Michael, M.D. Vice President Medical Affairs, Raritan Bay Medical Center, Perth Amboy, NJ, p. A409

CIHA, Clayton, President and Chief Executive Officer, Alexian Brothers Behavioral Health Hospital, Hoffman Estates, IL, p. A185

CIHAK, Scott A., Chief Executive Officer, Kendall Regional Medical Center, Miami, FL, p. A131

CILLO, Laura A., Chief Operating Officer, West Boca Medical Center, Boca Raton, FL, p. A119

CIMA, Laura, R.N. Chief Nursing Officer, Hackensack University Medical Center at Pascack Valley, Westwood, NJ, p. A412

CIMINO, Anthony J., President and Chief Executive Officer, Robert Wood Johnson University Hospital at Hamilton, Hamilton, NJ, p. A404

CIMINO, Jr., Michael A., Chief Financial Officer, Banner Behavioral Health Hospital – Scottsdale, Scottsdale, AZ, p. A37

CINICOLA, John, M.D. Chief Medical Officer, Heritage Valley Beaver, Beaver, PA, p. A520

CIONE, Dean, M.D. President Medical Staff, Texas Health Presbyterian Hospital Plano, Plano, TX, p. A628

CIOTA, Mark, M.D.,
 Chief Executive Officer, Mayo Clinic Health System in Albert Lea, Albert Lea, MN, p. A328
 Chief Executive Officer, Mayo Clinic Health System in Austin, Austin, MN, p. A329

CIRALDO, Lou, Information Services Representative, University Hospitals Geauga Medical Center, Chardon, OH, p. A473

CITA, Bob, Director Information Services, SEARHC MT. Edgecumbe Hospital, Sitka, AK, p. A29

CITAK, Michael, M.D. Chief Medical Officer, Lake Cumberland Regional Hospital, Somerset, KY, p. A260

CIVAN, Dino, Chief Information Officer, Kings County Hospital Center,, NY, p. A433

CIVIC, Dave, M.D. Associate Director Clinical Services, U. S. Public Health Service Phoenix Indian Medical Center, Phoenix, AZ, p. A36

CIVITELLO, Dean, Vice President Human Resources, Public Relations and Development, St. Joseph's Medical Center, Yonkers, NY, p. A446

CLACK, Lee, R.N. Chief Nursing Officer, Lake Wales Medical Center, Lake Wales, FL, p. A128

CLADOUHOS, Joseph, Chief Executive Officer, Syringa Hospital and Clinics, Grangeville, ID, p. A169

CLAIBORNE, Ronnie, M.D. Chief Medical Officer, Good Samaritan Hospital, Bakersfield, CA, p. A54

CLAIRMONT, Thomas
 President, Franklin Regional Hospital, Franklin, NH, p. A398
 President, Lakes Region General Hospital, Laconia, NH, p. A398

CLANCY, Karen, Manager Information Systems Operations, Bath Veterans Affairs Medical Center, Bath, NY, p. A421

CLANCY, Micki, Chief Operating Officer, Miami Valley Hospital, Dayton, OH, p. A480

CLANCY, Mikki, Vice President and Chief Information Officer, Good Samaritan Hospital, Dayton, OH, p. A479

CLAPP, Ann R., Director Human Resources, HEALTHSOUTH Rehabilitation Hospital of Texarkana, Texarkana, TX, p. A637

CLAPP, Mary, Controller, Henry County Hospital, Napoleon, OH, p. A487

CLAPP, Nicole, FACHE, President and Chief Executive Officer, Grant Regional Health Center, Lancaster, WI, p. A689

CLAPSADDLE, Jason, Vice President Operations, McDowell Hospital, Marion, NC, p. A457

CLARK, Allan W., M.D. Medical Director, Southwood Psychiatric Hospital, Pittsburgh, PA, p. A538

CLARK, Amy, Vice President Human Resources, Medina Hospital, Medina, OH, p. A486

CLARK, Ben, Vice President and Chief Information Officer, Centra Lynchburg General Hospital, Lynchburg, VA, p. A656

CLARK, Chris, Chief Technology Officer, Elkview General Hospital, Hobart, OK, p. A499

CLARK, Cindy, Human Resource Consultant, Saint Joseph Mount Sterling, Mount Sterling, KY, p. A258

CLARK, Dale, Assistant Administrator and Director Human Resources, Wythe County Community Hospital, Wytheville, VA, p. A663

CLARK, David, Senior Vice President Human Resources, Monongahela Valley Hospital, Monongahela, PA, p. A532

CLARK, Ed, M.D. Chief Medical Officer, Primary Children's Medical Center, Salt Lake City, UT, p. A646

CLARK, Ed, Vice President Finance, Specialty Hospital of Washington, Washington, DC, p. A117

CLARK, Estella, Chief Nursing Officer, Pikeville Medical Center, Pikeville, KY, p. A259

CLARK, Frank, Chief Information Officer, MUSC Medical Center of Medical University of South Carolina, Charleston, SC, p. A549

CLARK, Heather, Chief Executive Officer, Caldwell Memorial Hospital, Columbia, LA, p. A265

CLARK, Holly, Chief Operating Officer, Muskogee Regional Medical Center, Muskogee, OK, p. A502

CLARK, Jeff
 Director Information Systems, Graham Regional Medical Center, Graham, TX, p. A606
 Vice President Human Resources, Kadlec Regional Medical Center, Richland, WA, p. A670

CLARK, Jeremy, Chief Executive Officer, Saint Francis Hospital–Bartlett, Bartlett, TN, p. A565

CLARK, John, Chief Financial Officer, Childrens Care Hospital and School, Sioux Falls, SD, p. A562

CLARK, Karen, MS Vice President Operations, Advocate South Suburban Hospital, Hazel Crest, IL, p. A184

CLARK, Karen, Director Administrative Services, Sonoma Developmental Center, Eldridge, CA, p. A59

CLARK, Karen S., Chief Financial Officer, St. Mary's Hospital, Streator, IL, p. A196

CLARK, Kathleen, President and Chief Executive Officer, Wilcox Memorial Hospital, Lihue, HI, p. A166

CLARK, Kaye, Assistant Director Human Resources Management, E. A. Conway Medical Center, Monroe, LA, p. A274

CLARK, Kent, M.D. Chief Medical Affairs and Quality, Waldo County General Hospital, Belfast, ME, p. A281

CLARK, Krystle, Director Medical Records, Mountrail County Medical Center, Stanley, ND, p. A469

CLARK, Lisa, Human Resources Officer, Holy Cross Hospital, Taos, NM, p. A418

CLARK, M. Victoria, Chief Executive Officer, La Paz Regional Hospital, Parker, AZ, p. A33

CLARK, Mark, Human Resources Liaison, U. S. Air Force Regional Hospital, Elmendorf AFB, AK, p. A28

CLARK, Mark A., Vice President Operations, St. Mary's Hospital, Centralia, IL, p. A175

CLARK, Michael
 Director Operations, Clay County Memorial Hospital, Henrietta, TX, p. A608
 Vice President Finance, FHN Memorial Hospital, Freeport, IL, p. A183

CLARK, Michael A., Administrator and Chief Executive Officer, Logan Regional Hospital, Logan, UT, p. A644

CLARK, N. Travis, President, Page Memorial Hospital, Luray, VA, p. A656

CLARK, Nancy, Vice President Human Resources, Regional Medical Center of San Jose, San Jose, CA, p. A88

CLARK, Patrick, Manager Information Technology, Sunnyview Rehabilitation Hospital, Schenectady, NY, p. A442

CLARK, Paul, Senior Vice President and Chief Operating Officer, Munroe Regional Medical Center, Ocala, FL, p. A134

CLARK Jr., Ralph H., FACHE, Chief Executive Officer, Medical Center Barbour, Eufaula, AL, p. A19

CLARK, Randal, Vice President Finance, Sebasticook Valley Health, Pittsfield, ME, p. A284

CLARK, Rebecca, Chief Nursing Officer, Two Rivers Behavioral Health System, Kansas City, MO, p. A364

CLARK, Renee, R.N. Vice President Nursing Services and Performance Improvement, Fort HealthCare, Fort Atkinson, WI, p. A686

CLARK, Richard, M.D. President, Medical Staff, Memorial Hospital of Sweetwater County, Rock Springs, WY, p. A703

CLARK, Richard, Chief Executive Officer, Poplar Springs Hospital, Petersburg, VA, p. A659

CLARK, Richard L., Interim Chief Executive Officer, Northridge Medical Center, Commerce, GA, p. A150

CLARK, Robert J., President and Chief Executive Officer, Bristol Bay Area Health Corporation, Dillingham, AK, p. A27

CLARK, Robin, Chief Nursing Officer, Select Specialty Hospital–Greensboro, Greensboro, NC, p. A453

CLARK, Ron, M.D. Vice President Clinical Activities and Chief Medical Officer, VCU Health System, Richmond, VA, p. A661

CLARK, Shannon, Chief Financial Officer, Drew Memorial Hospital, Monticello, AR, p. A47

CLARK, Sharon, Director Human Resources, Hillsboro Area Hospital, Hillsboro, IL, p. A185

CLARK, Shawn, Director Information Systems, The Physicians Centre Hospital, Bryan, TX, p. A590

CLARK, Steve, Chief Information Officer, Albemarle Health, Elizabeth City, NC, p. A452

CLARK, Teresa, Director of Nursing, Wichita County Health Center, Leoti, KS, p. A238

CLARK, Theo, Director Financial Services, Promise Hospital of Phoenix, Mesa, AZ, p. A33

CLARK, Thomas A., President and Chief Executive Officer, Avera Queen of Peace Hospital, Mitchell, SD, p. A561

CLARK, Tim
 Director Human Resources, Moberly Regional Medical Center, Moberly, MO, p. A366
 Chief Operating Officer, Promise Hospital of San Diego, San Diego, CA, p. A85

CLARK, Troy, Chief Operating Officer, Wellmont Holston Valley Medical Center, Kingsport, TN, p. A571

CLARK, William, M.D. Chief Clinical Affairs, Caro Center, Caro, MI, p. A310

CLARKE, James, M.D. Vice President Medical Affairs and Clinical Effectiveness, Ocean Medical Center, Brick Township, NJ, p. A402

CLARKE, Lisa, Interim Chief Financial Officer, Southwestern Medical Center, Lawton, OK, p. A500

CLARKIN, John, Director Human Resource, Abington Health Lansdale Hospital, Lansdale, PA, p. A529

CLARKSTON, Wendell, M.D. President Medical Staff, Saint Luke's South Hospital, Overland Park, KS, p. A242

CLARRY, Patrick M., Vice President Human Resources, Providence Holy Family Hospital, Spokane, WA, p. A672

CLARY, Brandon, Chief Executive Officer, Edgefield County Hospital, Edgefield, SC, p. A551

CLARY, Patrick, Vice President Human Resources, Providence Sacred Heart Medical Center & Children's Hospital, Spokane, WA, p. A672

CLATANOFF, Kris, Director Human Resources, St. Joseph Medical Center, Houston, TX, p. A612

CLAUDSON, Jackie, Administrator, South Big Horn County Hospital, Basin, WY, p. A701

CLAUDY, Frank, M.D. Vice President Medical Staff Affairs, Genesis Medical Center–Davenport, Davenport, IA, p. A219

CLAUNCH, Don, Senior Vice President, Chief Financial Officer, Wyoming Medical Center, Casper, WY, p. A701

CLAUSEN, Patricia J., R.N. Chief Nurse Executive, Kaiser Permanente Downey Medical Center, Downey, CA, p. A58

CLAUSSEN, Tammy, Human Resources Executive, Tri Valley Health System, Cambridge, NE, p. A382

CLAWSON, Tonya, Manager Human Resources, Mercy Medical Center–Centerville, Centerville, IA, p. A218

CLAXTON, Anthony, M.D. Clinical Director, Terrell State Hospital, Terrell, TX, p. A637

CLAXTON, Edmund, M.D. President, Medical Staff, Central Maine Medical Center, Lewiston, ME, p. A283

CLAY, David, Chief Operating Officer, Central Carolina Hospital, Sanford, NC, p. A460

CLAYMORE, Krystal, Chief Financial Officer, Great Plains Regional Medical Center, North Platte, NE, p. A386

CLAYTON, Edward, Chief Financial Officer, Phelps County Regional Medical Center, Rolla, MO, p. A368

CLAYTON, Kathy, Chief Financial Officer, Fairfield Memorial Hospital, Fairfield, IL, p. A182

CLAYTON, Kent G., President and Chief Executive Officer, Placentia–Linda Hospital, Placentia, CA, p. A80

CLAYTON, Philip A., President and Chief Executive Officer, Conway Medical Center, Conway, SC, p. A551

CLEARY, Margaret S., Interim Chief Executive Officer, Grace Cottage Hospital, Townshend, VT, p. A650

CLEARY, Steven R.
 Vice President Finance, St. Joseph Medical Center, Kansas City, MO, p. A363
 Vice President Finance, St. Mary's Medical Center, Blue Springs, MO, p. A356

CLEARY, Tim, Interim President and Chief Operating Officer, Northern Dutchess Hospital, Rhinebeck, NY, p. A440

CLECKLER, Jason, Chief Executive Officer, Delta County Memorial Hospital, Delta, CO, p. A99

CLELAND, Dub, Chief Financial Officer, Oklahoma Surgical Hospital, Tulsa, OK, p. A508

CLELAND, Richard C., FACHE Chief Operating Officer, Erie County Medical Center, Buffalo, NY, p. A422

CLELAND, William H., M.D. Chief Medical Officer, University Hospitals and Health System, University of Mississippi Medical Center, Jackson, MS, p. A349

CLEM, Sandra, Manager Information Management, Carl Vinson Veterans Affairs Medical Center, Dublin, GA, p. A152

CLEMEN, Linda, R.N. Vice President and Chief Nursing Officer, Katherine Shaw Bethea Hospital, Dixon, IL, p. A181

CLEMENS, Brian L.
President and Chief Executive Officer, Community Hospital, Oklahoma City, OK, p. A502
Chief Executive Officer, Northwest Surgical Hospital, Oklahoma City, OK, p. A503

CLEMENT, Bernie, Chief Information Officer, East Jefferson General Hospital, Metairie, LA, p. A273

CLEMENT, Kevin J., Chief Executive Officer, Siloam Springs Memorial Hospital, Siloam Springs, AR, p. A50

CLEMENT, Michelle, Executive Assistant/Human Resources Director, Roundup Memorial Healthcare, Roundup, MT, p. A379

CLEMENTS, John R., Vice President and Chief Financial Officer, McCullough–Hyde Memorial Hospital, Oxford, OH, p. A488

CLEMENTS, Karen, R.N. Vice President, Chief Nursing Officer, The Acadia Hospital, Bangor, ME, p. A281

CLEMENTS, Lynn
Director Human Resources, Shriners Hospitals for Children–Galveston Burns Hospital, Galveston, TX, p. A605
Director Human Resources, Shriners Hospitals for Children–Houston, Houston, TX, p. A612

CLEMMENSEN, J. Scott
Vice President Human Resources and Leadership Enhancement, Capital Health Medical Center–Hopewell, Pennington, NJ, p. A408
Vice President Human Resources and Leadership Enhancement, Capital Health Regional Medical Center, Trenton, NJ, p. A411

CLEMMER, Deb, Vice President Human Resources, Bothwell Regional Health Center, Sedalia, MO, p. A371

CLEMMONS, Mark, Director Information Systems, Community Memorial Healthcenter, South Hill, VA, p. A661

CLEMONS, Deneace, Chief Operating Officer, Twin Lakes Regional Medical Center, Leitchfield, KY, p. A253

CLEVELAND, Austin B., Chief Executive Officer, Select Specialty Hospital–Quad Cities, Davenport, IA, p. A219

CLEVELAND, Cynthia, Ph.D. Acting Associate Director, Birmingham Veterans Affairs Medical Center, Birmingham, AL, p. A16

CLEVELAND, David, M.D. Chief Medical Officer, Shelby Baptist Medical Center, Alabaster, AL, p. A15

CLEVENGER, Jerry, Vice President Human Resources, Novant Health Rowan Medical Center, Salisbury, NC, p. A460

CLEVERSY, Stephanie
Manager Health Information Services, University Hospitals Conneaut Medical Center, Conneaut, OH, p. A479
Manager Health Information Systems, University Hospitals Geneva Medical Center, Geneva, OH, p. A482

CLICK, Glenn, Chief Financial Officer, Sequoyah Memorial Hospital, Sallisaw, OK, p. A506

CLICK, Mike, Administrator, Brownfield Regional Medical Center, Brownfield, TX, p. A589

CLIFF, Barbara J., FACHE, President and Chief Executive Officer, Windber Medical Center, Windber, PA, p. A545

CLIFF, Tammy, R.N. Director Nursing Services, McKenzie Health System, Sandusky, MI, p. A324

CLIFFE, Peggy, Chief Executive Officer, Select Specialty Hospital–Wichita, Wichita, KS, p. A246

CLIFFORD, Michael J., Director Finance, Wayne Memorial Hospital, Honesdale, PA, p. A527

CLIFFORD, Ryan, M.D. Chief of Staff, Washakie Medical Center, Worland, WY, p. A704

CLIFTON, Gary, Chief Financial Officer, I–70 Community Hospital, Sweet Springs, MO, p. A372

CLIFTON–LEMAY, Sherri L., Director Human Resources, Natchez Regional Medical Center, Natchez, MS, p. A351

CLINE, Claire P., M.P.H. Senior Vice President Patient Care Services/CNO, Watauga Medical Center, Boone, NC, p. A448

CLINE, Vickie, Director Human Resources, Northwest Medical Center, Albany, MO, p. A356

CLINGENPEEL, Jeremy, Administrator, Satanta District Hospital, Satanta, KS, p. A244

CLINGER, Dallas, Administrator, Power County Hospital District, American Falls, ID, p. A167

CLINITE, Ed, D.O. Chief of Staff, Sonora Regional Medical Center, Sonora, CA, p. A91

CLINTON, David, M.D. Medical Director, Soldiers' Home in Holyoke, Holyoke, MA, p. A301

CLINTON, Lee, FACHE Vice President Operations, Perry County Memorial Hospital, Perryville, MO, p. A367

CLINTON, Lori, Chief Nursing Officer, Sparta Community Hospital, Sparta, IL, p. A194

CLIPP, Jerry, Manager Human Resources, Washakie Medical Center, Worland, WY, p. A704

CLISTER, Martha L., Director Human Resources, Canonsburg General Hospital, Canonsburg, PA, p. A522

CLONCH, Leslie, Vice President and Chief Information Officer, University Hospital, Augusta, GA, p. A148

CLONTS, Jolene, Director Human Resources, Logan Regional Hospital, Logan, UT, p. A644

CLOSE, Debra, Chief Executive Officer, Dukes Memorial Hospital, Peru, IN, p. A212

CLOSNER, Shawn, Vice President Finance, St. Mary's Community Hospital, Nebraska City, NE, p. A386

CLOUD, Avery, Vice President and Chief Information Officer, New Hanover Regional Medical Center, Wilmington, NC, p. A463

CLOUD, Sylvia, Director Human Resources, Silver Lake Medical Center, Los Angeles, CA, p. A71

CLOUGH, James L., Chief Executive Officer, Physicians' Hospital in Anadarko, Anadarko, OK, p. A495

CLOUGH, Jeanette G., President and Chief Executive Officer, Mount Auburn Hospital, Cambridge, MA, p. A299

CLOUGH, Richard, Chief Operating Officer, Robinson Memorial Hospital, Ravenna, OH, p. A489

CLOUGH, Sheila
President, Howard Young Medical Center, Woodruff, WI, p. A700
President, Ministry Eagle River Memorial Hospital, Eagle River, WI, p. A686

CLOUSE DAY, Sherry, Vice President Finance, Mercy Hospital Berryville, Berryville, AR, p. A41

CLOUTIER, Mary, Director Human Resources, Adventist Behavioral Health Rockville, Rockville, MD, p. A293

CLOUTIER, Michael, Director Information Services, Kennewick General Hospital, Kennewick, WA, p. A667

CLOVER, Robert, Superintendent and Chief Executive Officer, Logansport State Hospital, Logansport, IN, p. A209

CLUCK, Robert N., M.D. Vice President and Medical Director, Texas Health Arlington Memorial Hospital, Arlington, TX, p. A584

CLUFF, Ben, Chief Executive Officer, Ashley Regional Medical Center, Vernal, UT, p. A648

CLUNN, Amy, M.D. Medical Director, HEALTHSOUTH Rehabilitation Hospital of Ocala, Ocala, FL, p. A134

CLUTE, Gerald B., Chief Executive Officer, Providence Tarzana Medical Center,, CA, p. A71

CLYNE, Eileen, Director Human Resources, Christ Hospital, Jersey City, NJ, p. A405

CLYNE, Mary Ellen, Ph.D., President and Chief Executive Officer, Clara Maass Medical Center, Belleville, NJ, p. A401

CMIEL, Peggy, R.N. Chief Nursing Officer, Chinese Hospital, San Francisco, CA, p. A86

COAD, Christina D., Ph.D., Chief Administrative Officer, Jefferson Medical Center, Ranson, WV, p. A680

COATES, Janet E., R.N., President and Chief Executive Officer, Mother Frances Hospital – Winnsboro, Winnsboro, TX, p. A642

COATES, Jennifer, Coordinator Information Technology, Purcell Municipal Hospital, Purcell, OK, p. A506

COATS, Aaron, Information Technology Director, Mason District Hospital, Havana, IL, p. A184

COATS, Brenda, Director Human Resources, River Crest Hospital, San Angelo, TX, p. A630

COATS, John, M.D. Chief Medical Staff, Morehouse General Hospital, Bastrop, LA, p. A263

COATS, Kevin, Chief Financial Officer, Baylor Medical Center at Frisco, Frisco, TX, p. A605

COATSWORTH, Jeannine, Vice President Human Resources, Barlow Respiratory Hospital, Los Angeles, CA, p. A68

COBARRUBIAS, Ronnie O., Director Information Systems, Beverly Hospital, Montebello, CA, p. A74

COBARRUBIAS, Samuel, M.D. Chief of Staff, Clinch Memorial Hospital, Homerville, GA, p. A155

COBB, Jason E., FACHE, Chief Executive Officer, Rapides Regional Medical Center, Alexandria, LA, p. A262

COBB, Jeff, Information Technologist, Guthrie County Hospital, Guthrie Center, IA, p. A222

COBB, Maura, R.N. Chief Nursing Officer, Northridge Medical Center, Commerce, GA, p. A150

COBB, Tammy, Chief Financial Officer, Jacksonville Medical Center, Jacksonville, AL, p. A22

COBBLE, Emlyn, Vice President and Chief Support Officer, Parkwest Medical Center, Knoxville, TN, p. A572

COBBS, Wendy
Director Human Resources, Promise Hospital Baton Rouge – Main Campus, Baton Rouge, LA, p. A263
Director of Human Resources, Promise Hospital of Baton Rouge – Ochsner Campus, Baton Rouge, LA, p. A263

COBURN, Nate, Chief Financial Officer, Weiser Memorial Hospital, Weiser, ID, p. A172

COCCHI, Dean
Chief Financial Officer, Kindred Hospital North Florida, Green Cove Springs, FL, p. A125
Chief Financial Officer, Kindred Hospital Ocala, Ocala, FL, p. A134

COCHENNET, Bradley, Chief Executive Officer, Pagosa Springs Medical Center, Pagosa Springs, CO, p. A104

COCHRAN, Barry S., FACHE, Administrator, Fayette Medical Center, Fayette, AL, p. A20

COCHRAN, Dan, Chief Operating Officer, Bingham Memorial Hospital, Blackfoot, ID, p. A167

COCHRAN, Daniel, Vice President and Chief Financial Officer, Shady Grove Adventist Hospital, Rockville, MD, p. A294

COCHRAN, Janice, R.N. Director of Patient Care, Dubuis Hospital of Paris, Paris, TX, p. A626

COCHRAN, Kay P., Director Human Resources, Twin County Regional Hospital, Galax, VA, p. A654

COCHRAN, Kenneth, FACHE, President and Chief Executive Officer, East Liverpool City Hospital, East Liverpool, OH, p. A481

COCHRAN, Jr., Willie, M.D. Chief of Staff, Southern Regional Medical Center, Riverdale, GA, p. A159

COCHRANE, Andrew S.
Chief Executive Officer, Maple Grove Hospital, Maple Grove, MN, p. A335
President Hospital Operations, North Memorial Medical Center, Robbinsdale, MN, p. A338

COCHRELL, Patricia, R.N. Executive Vice President, Chief Clinical and Operating Officer, Harrison Medical Center, Bremerton, WA, p. A664

COCKER, Robert, Vice President Organizational Effectiveness, Grand Itasca Clinic and Hospital, Grand Rapids, MN, p. A333

COCKERHAM, Mary Ellen, Vice President Human Resources, Nazareth Hospital, Philadelphia, PA, p. A536

COCKING, Kathy, R.N. Vice President Operations, Barton Memorial Hospital, South Lake Tahoe, CA, p. A91

COCKRELL, Dennis, Director Human Resources, Gritman Medical Center, Moscow, ID, p. A170

COCKRELL, Jimmye Lou, Chief Executive Officer, Sundance Hospital, Arlington, TX, p. A583

COCKRELL, Tim, Chief Executive Officer, Patients Choice Medical Center of Smith County, Raleigh, MS, p. A353

COCKRELL, William, Administrator and Chief Executive Officer, Patient's Choice Medical Center of Claiborne County, Port Gibson, MS, p. A353

COCORULLO, Mark, Senior Vice President and Chief Financial Officer, Martin Health System, Stuart, FL, p. A140

CODER, Charles, Chief Financial Officer, Southside Regional Medical Center, Petersburg, VA, p. A659

CODY, Carolyn, M.D. Vice President Medical Affairs, Bryan Medical Center, Lincoln, NE, p. A385

CODY, Geraldine, Director Human Resources, Kingsboro Psychiatric Center,, NY, p. A433

CODY, James, Director, Syracuse Veterans Affairs Medical Center, Syracuse, NY, p. A444

COE, Jason, M.D. Medical Director, Greenbrier Hospital, Covington, LA, p. A265

COE, Jason C., President and Chief Executive Officer, Hackettstown Regional Medical Center, Hackettstown, NJ, p. A404

COFFELL, Randy, Manager Human Resources, Mid–Valley Hospital, Omak, WA, p. A669

COFFEY, Bryan D., Chief Executive Officer, Sac–Osage Hospital, Osceola, MO, p. A367

COFFEY, C. Edward, M.D., Chief Executive Officer and Director Behavioral Health Services, Henry Ford Kingswood Hospital, Ferndale, MI, p. A313

COFFEY, Daniel B., President and Chief Executive Officer, The Acadia Hospital, Bangor, ME, p. A281

COFFEY, Dennis J., CPA Senior Vice President and Chief Financial Officer, J. Arthur Dosher Memorial Hospital, Southport, NC, p. A461

COFFEY, Joseph, Director Facility Administration, Rochester Psychiatric Center, Rochester, NY, p. A441

COFFEY, Judy
Senior Vice President and Area Manager, Kaiser Permanente San Rafael Medical Center, San Rafael, CA, p. A89
Senior Vice President and Area Manager, Kaiser Permanente Santa Rosa Medical Center, Santa Rosa, CA, p. A90

COFFEY, Kevin, Chief Executive Officer, Winner Regional Healthcare Center, Winner, SD, p. A564

COFFEY, Timothy O., Senior Vice President Operations, Lake Charles Memorial Hospital, Lake Charles, LA, p. A272

COFFMAN, Douglas, Vice President and Chief Financial Officer, United Hospital Center, Bridgeport, WV, p. A675

COFFMAN, Joan, President and Chief Executive Officer, St. Joseph's Hospital, Chippewa Falls, WI, p. A685

COFFMAN BARNES, Julie, M.D. Chief Medical Officer, Redmond Regional Medical Center, Rome, GA, p. A159

COFIE, Daniel, M.D. Chief of Staff, Haywood Park Community Hospital, Brownsville, TN, p. A565

COFIELD, Robert, Dr.PH Chief Operating Officer and Associate Vice President, University of Virginia Medical Center, Charlottesville, VA, p. A652

COFINAS, Rebecca, Vice President and Chief Operating Executive Operations, Scripps Memorial Hospital–Encinitas, Encinitas, CA, p. A59

COFONE, Michael, Chief Financial Officer, Health Alliance Hospitals, Leominster, MA, p. A301

COGLEY, Richard, M.D. Senior Vice President Medical Affairs and Chief Medical Officer, Saint Vincent Hospital, Erie, PA, p. A525

COHEN, Aaron, Chief Financial Officer, Bellevue Hospital Center, New York, NY, p. A430

COHEN, Cindy, Director Human Resources, Stewart & Lynda Resnick Neuropsychiatric Hospital at UCLA, Los Angeles, CA, p. A72

COHEN, Gail C., Vice President Human Resources, Saint Clare's Health System, Denville, NJ, p. A403

COHEN, Ginger, Chief Nurse Executive, St. Luke's Rehabilitation Institute, Spokane, WA, p. A672

COHEN, Norman, M.D. Chief Medical Officer, Crossroads Community Hospital, Mount Vernon, IL, p. A189

COHEN, Philip A., Chief Executive Officer, Monterey Park Hospital, Monterey Park, CA, p. A75

COHEN, Robert, M.D. Chief Medical Officer, Sonoma Valley Hospital, Sonoma, CA, p. A91

COKER, Cindy, M.P.H. Vice President, Patient Care Services, Vidant Chowan Hospital, Edenton, NC, p. A452

COKER, Raymond Kirk, M.D. Chief of Staff, Baptist Health Medical Center–Stuttgart, Stuttgart, AR, p. A50

COLADONATO, Angela, MSN Chief Nursing Officer, Chester County Hospital, West Chester, PA, p. A543

COLAGUORI, Ronald J., Vice President Operations, St. Anthony's Hospital, Saint Petersburg, FL, p. A139

COLANDER, Charles, Vice President Information Systems and Chief Information Officer, Elmhurst Memorial Hospital,, IL, p. A182

COLANGELO, Nicholas, Chief Executive Officer, Clear Brook Lodge, Shickshinny, PA, p. A541

COLAS, Chuck, M.D. Medical Director, Surprise Valley Healthcare District, Cedarville, CA, p. A56

COLBERG, Gary R., FACHE, President and Chief Executive Officer, Southeast Georgia Health System Brunswick Campus, Brunswick, GA, p. A149

COLBERT, Carol, Director Human Resources, Trace Regional Hospital, Houston, MS, p. A348

COLBURN, Christopher, M.D
Chief Medical Officer, TriStar Skyline Madison Campus, Madison, TN, p. A573
Chief Medical Officer, TriStar Skyline Medical Center, Nashville, TN, p. A577

COLBURN, Douglas, Chief Information Officer, Hughston Hospital, Columbus, GA, p. A150

COLBURN, Marj A., Facility Operating Officer, Risk Manager and Performance Improvement Coordinator, Hastings Regional Center, Hastings, NE, p. A384

COLBURN, Tim, President and Chief Executive Officer, Berger Health System, Circleville, OH, p. A475

COLCHER, Marian W., President and Chief Executive Officer, Valley Forge Medical Center and Hospital, Norristown, PA, p. A533

COLE, Annette E., R.N. Vice President and Chief Nursing Officer, Sky Lakes Medical Center, Klamath Falls, OR, p. A514

COLE, Beth, Director Information Services, Lewis–Gale Medical Center, Salem, VA, p. A661

COLE, Carlene, Manager Human Resources, Kittson Memorial Healthcare Center, Hallock, MN, p. A333

COLE, F. Sessions, M.D. Chief Medical Officer, St. Louis Children's Hospital, Saint Louis, MO, p. A371

COLE, Georgeanne, Chief Executive Officer, Rehabilitation Hospital of Southwest Virginia, Bristol, VA, p. A652

COLE Jr., Harry, Administrator, Georgiana Hospital, Georgiana, AL, p. A21

COLE, James B., Chief Executive Officer, Virginia Hospital Center – Arlington, Arlington, VA, p. A651

COLE, Jason
Director Finance, Scott & White Hospital – Llano, Llano, TX, p. A619
Senior Director Finance, Scott & White Hospital at Round Rock, Round Rock, TX, p. A629

COLE, Karen S., FACHE, Chief Executive Officer, Shenandoah Medical Center, Shenandoah, IA, p. A228

COLE, Lori, Director Information Management, Wayne Memorial Hospital, Goldsboro, NC, p. A453

COLE, Lori B., R.N
Vice President Patient Care Services, Mountain View Regional Medical Center, Norton, VA, p. A658
Vice President Care Services, Wellmont Lonesome Pine Hospital, Big Stone Gap, VA, p. A651

COLE, Missy, Director Human Resources, HEALTHSOUTH Rehabilitation Hospital, Fayetteville, AR, p. A43

COLE, Robert, Chief Operating Officer, Connecticut Mental Health Center, New Haven, CT, p. A110

COLECCHI, Stephen, President and Chief Executive Officer, Robinson Memorial Hospital, Ravenna, OH, p. A489

COLEMAN, Alisa, Chief Executive Officer, Trigg County Hospital, Cadiz, KY, p. A249

COLEMAN, Andrea C., Chief Operating Officer, Penrose–St. Francis Health Services, Colorado Springs, CO, p. A98

COLEMAN, Curt, FACHE,
Administrator, Genesis Medical Center, DeWitt, De Witt, IA, p. A219
Chief Executive Officer, Jackson County Regional Health Center, Maquoketa, IA, p. A224

COLEMAN, Donna
Director Professional Services, Jackson County Hospital District, Edna, TX, p. A600
Director Human Resources, Texas Health Presbyterian Hospital Denton, Denton, TX, p. A599

COLEMAN, Doug, M.D. Chief of Staff, Jefferson Regional Medical Center, Pine Bluff, AR, p. A49

COLEMAN, James J., Ed.D., Director, Kalamazoo Psychiatric Hospital, Kalamazoo, MI, p. A318

COLEMAN, Jeff, Manager Information Systems, Navos, Seattle, WA, p. A670

COLEMAN, Jr., Jim L., Chief Operating Officer, Parkridge Medical Center, Chattanooga, TN, p. A567

COLEMAN, Judy, Chief Operating Officer and Chief Financial Officer, Indiana University Health West Hospital, Avon, IN, p. A198

COLEMAN, Keith T., Chief Financial Officer, Mount Carmel, Columbus, OH, p. A477

COLEMAN, Lenon J., Interim Chief Human Resources Officer, Vanderbilt Hospital and Clinics, Nashville, TN, p. A577

COLEMAN, Melissa, Director Human Resources, HEALTHSOUTH Rehabilitation Hospital, Sewickley, PA, p. A541

COLEMAN, Shane, Director Information Services, Delta Regional Medical Center, Greenville, MS, p. A347

COLERICK, Steven, Chief Executive Officer, Buena Vista Regional Medical Center, Storm Lake, IA, p. A229

COLETTA, Anthony V., M.D. Executive Vice President and Chief Medical Officer, Holy Redeemer Hospital and Medical Center, Meadowbrook, PA, p. A531

COLETTA, Sandra L., President and Chief Executive Officer, Kent County Memorial Hospital, Warwick, RI, p. A547

COLETTA, Tony, Vice President of Human Resources, Advocate Eureka Hospital, Eureka, IL, p. A182

COLEY, Brenda
Executive Director, Metroplex Adventist Hospital, Killeen, TX, p. A616
Executive Director, Rollins–Brook Community Hospital, Lampasas, TX, p. A618

COLGAN, Teresa, VP of Nursing, Great River Medical Center, West Burlington, IA, p. A230

COLKER, Rebecca, Chief Financial Officer, St. Mary's Hospital, Decatur, IL, p. A180

COLLAMORE, Beth, M.D. Chief of Staff, Cary Medical Center, Caribou, ME, p. A282

COLLIER, Jack, M.D. Chief of Staff, MountainView Hospital, Las Vegas, NV, p. A393

COLLIER, Lora, M.D. Chief Medical Staff, Integris Mayes County Medical Center, Pryor, OK, p. A506

COLLIER, Margaret P.
Chief Executive Officer and Managing Director, Anchor Hospital, Atlanta, GA, p. A145
Chief Executive Officer, SummitRidge Hospital, Lawrenceville, GA, p. A156

COLLIER, Russell J., FACHE, President and Chief Executive Officer, Good Shepherd Medical Center–Marshall, Marshall, TX, p. A621

COLLIER, Scarlet, Chief Information Officer, Lane Regional Medical Center, Zachary, LA, p. A280

COLLIER, Shari, Chief Financial Officer, Overland Park Regional Medical Center, Overland Park, KS, p. A242

COLLIER, Tammy, Vice President Patient Services, Huguley Memorial Medical Center, Fort Worth, TX, p. A603

COLLIER, Tom, Manager Information Systems, Missouri Rehabilitation Center, Mount Vernon, MO, p. A366

COLLINS, Ava Jo, Vice President Operations, Ochsner Baptist Medical Center, New Orleans, LA, p. A275

COLLINS, Barry, D.O. Chief of Staff, Hillsdale Community Health Center, Hillsdale, MI, p. A316

COLLINS, Bobby
Director Human Resources, Mountain View Regional Medical Center, Norton, VA, p. A658
Director Human Resources, Wellmont Lonesome Pine Hospital, Big Stone Gap, VA, p. A651

COLLINS, Chauncey, M.D. Director Operations, Austen Riggs Center, Stockbridge, MA, p. A305

COLLINS, David, Director Administration, Naval Medical Center, Portsmouth, VA, p. A659

COLLINS, Dennis, Chief Financial Officer, The Brook Hospital – KMI, Louisville, KY, p. A256

COLLINS, Edmund, Chief Information Officer, Martin Health System, Stuart, FL, p. A140

COLLINS, Harold E., JD Chief Financial Officer, Franciscan Physicians Hospital, Munster, IN, p. A211

COLLINS, James M., President and Chief Executive Officer, St. Clair Memorial Hospital, Pittsburgh, PA, p. A538

COLLINS, Jeff, M.D
Chief Medical Officer, Providence Holy Family Hospital, Spokane, WA, p. A672
Chief Medical Officer, Providence Sacred Heart Medical Center & Children's Hospital, Spokane, WA, p. A672

COLLINS, Jeffrey A., Senior Vice President and Area Manager, Kaiser Permanente Fresno Medical Center, Fresno, CA, p. A61

COLLINS, John F., President and Chief Executive Officer, Winthrop–University Hospital, Mineola, NY, p. A429

COLLINS, John R., Chief Financial Officer, Hemet Valley Medical Center, Hemet, CA, p. A64

COLLINS, Kandy, MSN, Director, Lafayette Behavioral Health, Lafayette, LA, p. A270

COLLINS, Mark, Interim Chief Finance Officer, Rogue Valley Medical Center, Medford, OR, p. A515

COLLINS, Michael F., Chief Executive Officer, Merrimack Valley Hospital, Haverhill, MA, p. A300

COLLINS, Michael L., President, Jewish Hospital–Shelbyville, Shelbyville, KY, p. A260

COLLINS, Pam, Director Human Resources, Fairway Medical Center, Covington, LA, p. A265

COLLINS, Pamela, Vice President Chief Patient Services Officer, McCullough–Hyde Memorial Hospital, Oxford, OH, p. A488

COLLINS, Richard F., M.D. Executive Vice President and Chief Medical Officer, Jefferson Regional Medical Center, Jefferson Hills, PA, p. A528

COLLINS, Ricky M., M.D. Chief of Staff, Whitesburg ARH Hospital, Whitesburg, KY, p. A261

COLLINS, Rudy
Human Resources Business Partner, Kaiser Permanente San Rafael Medical Center, San Rafael, CA, p. A89
Human Resources Business Partner, Kaiser Permanente Santa Rosa Medical Center, Santa Rosa, CA, p. A90

COLLINS, Sandra, Chief Clinical Officer, Kindred Hospital–Philadelphia, Philadelphia, PA, p. A535

COLLINS, Sharon
Director Human Resources and Executive Administrative Assistant, Russell Regional Hospital, Russell, KS, p. A243
Chief Information Officer, Salem Veterans Affairs Medical Center, Salem, VA, p. A661

COLLINS, Shaw, Director Information Technology, Methodist Hospitals, Gary, IN, p. A203

COLLINS, Terry, Chief Financial Officer, Aspen Valley Hospital District, Aspen, CO, p. A97

COLLINS, Thomas M., President, Chairman and Chief Executive Officer, Green Oaks Hospital, Dallas, TX, p. A596

COLLIPP, Dan, M.D. Chief of Staff, Wayne Memorial Hospital, Jesup, GA, p. A155

COLLISON, June, President, Community Hospital of San Bernardino, San Bernardino, CA, p. A84

COLLOTTA, Sharon
Director Human Resources, Mease Countryside Hospital, Safety Harbor, FL, p. A138
Director Human Resources, Mease Dunedin Hospital, Dunedin, FL, p. A122
Director Human Resources, Morton Plant Hospital, Clearwater, FL, p. A120
Director Team Resources, Morton Plant North Bay Hospital, New Port Richey, FL, p. A133

COLLURA, John
Executive Vice President Financial Services and Chief Financial Officer, Beth Israel Medical Center, New York, NY, p. A430
Executive Vice President and Chief Financial Officer, St. Luke's–Roosevelt Hospital Center, New York, NY, p. A436

COLMENARES, Derek, Chief Medical Officer, Agnesian HealthCare, Fond Du Lac, WI, p. A686

COLOMBO, Armando, Chief Executive Officer, Intermedical Hospital of South Carolina, Columbia, SC, p. A550

COLON, Omar, M.D. Medical Director, HEALTHSOUTH Plano Rehabilitation Hospital, Plano, TX, p. A627

COLONES, Robert L., President and Chief Executive Officer, McLeod Regional Medical Center, Florence, SC, p. A552

COLORADO, Judy, R.N. Vice President, Patient Care Services, Kimball Medical Center, Lakewood, NJ, p. A405

COLOSIMO, Marie, Human Resources Officer, Veterans Affairs Pittsburgh Healthcare System, Pittsburgh, PA, p. A538

COLPITTS, Robert, Chief Human Resources Officer, Edith Nourse Rogers Memorial Veterans Hospital, Bedford, MA, p. A295

COLPO, Susan T., Chief Executive Officer, Life Line Hospital, Steubenville, OH, p. A490

COLSON, Curt, President and Chief Executive Officer, Clara Barton Hospital, Hoisington, KS, p. A235

COLSON, Wayne, Chief Financial Officer, College Station Medical Center, College Station, TX, p. A592

COLT, Darlene, R.N. Chief Nursing Officer, Spanish Peaks Regional Health Center, Walsenburg, CO, p. A106

COLTHARP, Missy, Director, Baptist Memorial Hospital–Union County, New Albany, MS, p. A352

COLTON, Jan, M.D. Acting Clinical Director, U. S. Public Health Service Indian Hospital, Pine Ridge, SD, p. A561

COLTRAIN, Penny, Director Human Resources, Vidant Beaufort Hospital, Washington, NC, p. A462

COLUCCI, Eugene, Vice President Finance, Greenwich Hospital, Greenwich, CT, p. A109

COLUCCIO, Medrice, R.N., Chief Executive Officer, Providence St. Peter Hospital, Olympia, WA, p. A669

COLUMBUS, Rebecca, Vice President Human Resources, River Region Medical Center, Vicksburg, MS, p. A354

COLVARD, Dusty, Manager Information Technology, Tehachapi Valley Healthcare District, Tehachapi, CA, p. A92

COLVIN, Garren
Senior Vice President and Chief Financial Officer, St. Elizabeth Edgewood, Edgewood, KY, p. A250
Senior Vice President Finance and Chief Financial Officer, St. Elizabeth Florence, Florence, KY, p. A250
Senior Vice President and Chief Financial Officer, St. Elizabeth Fort Thomas, Fort Thomas, KY, p. A251

COLVIN, Robert L., Administrator, Ouachita Community Hospital, West Monroe, LA, p. A280

COLVIN, William, Human Resources Officer, Homer Memorial Hospital, Homer, LA, p. A268

COLWELL, Darla, Director Human Resources and Marketing, Clay County Hospital, Flora, IL, p. A182

COLWELL, Dean, D.O. Vice President Medical Affairs, OhioHealth Doctors Hospital, Columbus, OH, p. A478

COLYER, Valeri J.
Director Human Resources, Dickenson Community Hospital, Clintwood, VA, p. A652
Director Human Resources, Norton Community Hospital, Norton, VA, p. A658

COMAIANNI, Sheri, Vice President Human Resources, Bakersfield Memorial Hospital, Bakersfield, CA, p. A53

COMBEST, Felton, M.D. Vice President Medical Affairs, Magnolia Regional Health Center, Corinth, MS, p. A346

COMBS, Barry, Chief Financial Officer, Cedar Crest Hospital and Residential Treatment Center, Belton, TX, p. A588

COMBS, Cindy, Supervisor Human Resources, Hampshire Memorial Hospital, Romney, WV, p. A680

COMBS, Jackie, Chief Operating and Nursing Officer, Hi–Desert Medical Center, Joshua Tree, CA, p. A64

COMBS, Mike, Manager Information Technology, Holdenville General Hospital, Holdenville, OK, p. A500

COMER, Fannessa, Chief Executive Officer, Northern Navajo Medical Center, Shiprock, NM, p. A418

COMER, Jennifer, M.D. Medical Director, Valle Vista Hospital, Greenwood, IN, p. A204

COMER, Randy, Chief Operating Officer, Athens–Limestone Hospital, Athens, AL, p. A16

COMER, Scott, Director Administrative Services, Marshall Medical Center, Placerville, CA, p. A80

COMER, William J., Chief Executive Officer, Surgical Specialty Hospital of Arizona, Phoenix, AZ, p. A35

COMERFORD, Jennifer, Manager Information Services, MidState Medical Center, Meriden, CT, p. A109

COMERFORD Jr., Thomas P., Superintendent, Clarks Summit State Hospital, Clarks Summit, PA, p. A522

COMFORT, Jeff, Vice President Administration, Northcoast Behavioral Healthcare System, Northfield, OH, p. A487

COMITTO, Judy, Vice President Information Services and Chief Information Officer, Trinitas Regional Medical Center, Elizabeth, NJ, p. A403

COMO, Cheryl A., R.N. Vice President Patient Services and Chief Nursing Officer, UPMC McKeesport, McKeesport, PA, p. A531

COMO, James, Director Human Resources, Chestnut Hill Hospital, Philadelphia, PA, p. A534

COMPTON, Brenda, Manager Information Technology, Plumas District Hospital, Quincy, CA, p. A81

COMPTON, Mark, Chief Financial Officer, Laughlin Memorial Hospital, Greeneville, TN, p. A569

COMPTON, Natasha, Chief Nursing Officer, Valley View Medical Center, Fort Mohave, AZ, p. A31

COMPTON, Ty, Chief Nursing Executive, Horton Community Hospital, Horton, KS, p. A235

COMPTON–OGLE, Carri, Administrative Officer, Heartland Behavioral Health Services, Nevada, MO, p. A366

COMSTOCK, John M., Chief Executive Officer, Cherokee Regional Medical Center, Cherokee, IA, p. A218

CONALLEN, Kathryn
Chief Executive Officer, Mercy Fitzgerald Hospital, Darby, PA, p. A524
Interim Chief Executive Officer, Mercy Suburban Hospital, Norristown, PA, p. A533

CONANT, Cathy, Chief Human Resources and Personnel, Eastern Plumas Health Care District, Portola, CA, p. A80

CONANT, Sonya, Senior Director Human Resources, Alaska Native Medical Center, Anchorage, AK, p. A27

CONATY, Robert B., Executive Vice President Operations, Montefiore Medical Center,, NY, p. A434

CONAWAY, E. Edwin, M.D. Vice President Medical Affairs and Chief Medical Officer, Southeastern Ohio Regional Medical Center, Cambridge, OH, p. A472

CONCANNON, Margaret, Administrator, Veterans Home and Hospital, Rocky Hill, CT, p. A111

CONCEPCION, Walter, Chief Executive Officer, West Gables Rehabilitation Hospital, Miami, FL, p. A132

CONDIT, Edward, President and Chief Executive Officer, St. Mary's Hospital, Passaic, NJ, p. A408

CONDON, Joseph, Director Human Resources, Texas Health Harris Methodist Hospital Fort Worth, Fort Worth, TX, p. A604

CONDON, William, Deputy Administrative Officer, U. S. Public Health Service Indian Hospital, Fort Yates, ND, p. A467

CONDRY, Donna, Director Human Resources, Jones Regional Medical Center, Anamosa, IA, p. A216

CONE, Maryann, Chief Operating Officer, Sharp Grossmont Hospital, La Mesa, CA, p. A65

CONEJO, David, Chief Executive Officer, Red River Regional Hospital, Bonham, TX, p. A589

CONFALONE, Daniel, Chief Financial Officer, Good Shepherd Rehabilitation Hospital, Allentown, PA, p. A519

CONGDON, James B., M.D. Medical Director, Horsham Clinic, Ambler, PA, p. A520

CONGER, Rex D., FACHE, President and Chief Executive Officer, Perry Memorial Hospital, Princeton, IL, p. A192

CONGER, Sue, Chief Operating Officer, Eastside Psychiatric Hospital, Tallahassee, FL, p. A140

CONKLING, Victoria, Vice President Chief Nursing Officer, Delaware Valley Hospital, Walton, NY, p. A445

CONLEY, David, Chief Administrative Officer, SUNY Downstate Medical Center University Hospital,, NY, p. A436

CONLEY, Joseph M., Chief Operating Officer, Concord Hospital, Concord, NH, p. A397

CONLEY, Kirkpatrick, Chief Executive Officer, Fallbrook Hospital, Fallbrook, CA, p. A60

CONLEY, Melissa, Director Human Resources, Midwest Medical Center, Galena, IL, p. A183

CONLEY, Susan
Chief Executive Officer, DeKalb Community Hospital, Smithville, TN, p. A579
Chief Executive Officer, Stones River Hospital, Woodbury, TN, p. A580

CONLEY, Teressa
Interim President and Chief Executive Officer, St. Rose Dominican Hospitals – Rose de Lima Campus, Henderson, NV, p. A392
Chief Operating Officer, St. Rose Dominican Hospitals – San Martin Campus, Las Vegas, NV, p. A393
Chief Operating Officer, St. Rose Dominican Hospitals – Siena Campus, Henderson, NV, p. A392

CONLEY, Thomas C., Vice President Human Resources, Oconee Medical Center, Seneca, SC, p. A555

CONN, Kevin R., Chief Executive Officer, HEALTHSOUTH Sunrise Rehabilitation Hospital, Fort Lauderdale, FL, p. A123

CONNEL, Lorene, Chief Human Resources Management Service, Veterans Affairs Eastern Colorado Health Care System, Denver, CO, p. A100

CONNELL, Faith, Director of Nursing, Turning Point Hospital, Moultrie, GA, p. A158

CONNELL, Robert, PsyD, Superintendent, Larned State Hospital, Larned, KS, p. A238

CONNELLEY, Bertha Mary, Director Human Resources, Austen Riggs Center, Stockbridge, MA, p. A305

CONNELLY, Jac, Chief Financial Officer, Rose Medical Center, Denver, CO, p. A100

CONNELLY, Michael, President, Huggins Hospital, Wolfeboro, NH, p. A400

CONNELLY, Steven, M.D. Chief Medical Officer, Park Nicollet Methodist Hospital, Saint Louis Park, MN, p. A339

CONNER, Chad, Interim Administrator, Green Clinic Surgical Hospital, Ruston, LA, p. A277

CONNER, Gary F., Chief Financial Officer, City of Hope's Helford Clinical Research Hospital, Duarte, CA, p. A59

CONNER, Gloria, Director Human Resources, MMO WestEnd Hospital, Jennings, LA, p. A269

CONNER, Jeff, M.D. Chief Medical Staff, Loma Linda University Medical Center–Murrieta, Murrieta, CA, p. A75

CONNOLLY, James W., President and Chief Executive Officer, Ellis Hospital, Schenectady, NY, p. A442

CONNOLLY, Noreen B., MS Chief Nurse Executive, West Branch Regional Medical Center, West Branch, MI, p. A326

CONNOLLY, Teresa, MSN Chief Nursing Officer, Mayo Clinic Hospital, Phoenix, AZ, p. A35

CONNOR, Patrick, Chief Operating Officer, West Palm Hospital, West Palm Beach, FL, p. A144

CONNOR III, Paul J., President and Chief Executive Officer, Eastern Long Island Hospital, Greenport, NY, p. A426

CONNOR, William, Assistant Administrator and Director Human Resources, River Hospital, Alexandria Bay, NY, p. A420

CONNORS, Alfred, Senior Vice President Medical Affairs and Chief Medical Officer, MetroHealth Medical Center, Cleveland, OH, p. A476

CONNORS, Dennis, Executive Director, Lenox Hill Hospital, New York, NY, p. A433

CONNORS, Lawrence J.
Chief Operating Officer, St. Mary's Hospital Medical Center, Green Bay, WI, p. A688
Chief Operating Officer, St. Vincent Hospital, Green Bay, WI, p. A688

CONNORS, Michael
Senior Vice President and Chief Financial Officer, Cape Cod Hospital, Hyannis, MA, p. A301
Senior Vice President and Chief Financial Officer, Falmouth Hospital, Falmouth, MA, p. A300

CONNOVICH, Ron D., Vice President, Greene Memorial Hospital, Xenia, OH, p. A494

CONNY, Sophia, Deputy Administrative Officer, U. S. Public Health Service Indian Hospital, Pine Ridge, SD, p. A561

CONOCENTI, Paul, Chief Information Officer, City of Hope's Helford Clinical Research Hospital, Duarte, CA, p. A59

CONOVER, Jevne, Administrator, LifeCare Hospitals of Wisconsin, Pewaukee, WI, p. A694

CONRAD, Heidi, Vice President and Chief Financial Officer, Regions Hospital, Saint Paul, MN, p. A340

CONRAD, Terry, R.N. Interim CNO, Madison Memorial Hospital, Rexburg, ID, p. A171

CONRATH, Mark, Chief Financial Officer, Drumright Regional Hospital, Drumright, OK, p. A497

CONROW–VERVERIS, Stacy, Director Human Resources, Mineral Community Hospital, Superior, MT, p. A380

CONROY, Carol, R.N. Chief Nursing Officer, Southwestern Vermont Medical Center, Bennington, VT, p. A649

CONROY, Denis S., President, Beverly Hospital, Beverly, MA, p. A295

CONROY, Joanne M., M.D. Executive Vice President and Chief Operating Officer, Morristown Medical Center, Morristown, NJ, p. A406

CONROY, Joseph, M.D. Vice President Medical Affairs, St. Mary Medical Center, Langhorne, PA, p. A529

CONROY, Mary Ann, Chief Executive Officer, Terre Haute Regional Hospital, Terre Haute, IN, p. A214

CONROY, Michael, Chief Financial Officer, Pine Creek Medical Center, Dallas, TX, p. A597

CONROY Jr., Robert B., Chief Executive Officer, St. Petersburg General Hospital, Saint Petersburg, FL, p. A139

CONSIDINE, William H., President, Akron Children's Hospital, Akron, OH, p. A470

CONSIGLIO, Gayle
Chief Information Officer, McLaren Flint, Flint, MI, p. A313
Chief Information Officer, McLaren Lapeer Region, Lapeer, MI, p. A318

CONSIGNEY, Ginger, Vice President Human Resources, Lake Charles Memorial Hospital, Lake Charles, LA, p. A272

CONSOLVER, Roberta, Chief Clinical Officer, Kindred Hospital Sugar Land, Sugar Land, TX, p. A635

CONSTANT, Jean–Charles, Interim Chief Executive Officer, Arbour Hospital, Boston, MA, p. A295

CONSTANTINO, Chris D., Executive Director, Elmhurst Hospital Center,, NY, p. A431

CONTE, John D., Director Facility Services, Wayne Memorial Hospital, Honesdale, PA, p. A527

CONTI, John, Director Finance, Shriners Hospitals for Children–Greenville, Greenville, SC, p. A552

CONTILLO, Nancy, Director Human Resources, Day Kimball Hospital, Putnam, CT, p. A111

CONTRERA, Yleana, Executive Director Human Resources, Hoboken University Medical Center, Hoboken, NJ, p. A405

CONTRERAS, Marta, Chief Nursing Officer and Chief Operating Officer, Foundation Surgical Hospital of El Paso, El Paso, TX, p. A601

CONWAY, Gerard, Chief Executive Officer, Aurora Las Encinas Hospital, Pasadena, CA, p. A79

CONWAY, Jimmy, M.D. President Medical Staff, Northwest Surgical Hospital, Oklahoma City, OK, p. A503

CONWAY, John Paul, Executive Vice President Human Resources, Oakwood Hospital & Medical Center–Dearborn, Dearborn, MI, p. A311

CONWELL, Heather, Chief Nursing Officer, Downey Regional Medical Center, Downey, CA, p. A58

CONWILL, Michael, Director Human Resources, Corpus Christi Medical Center, Corpus Christi, TX, p. A593

CONYERS, Lois
Senior Vice President and Chief Financial Officer, Citrus Valley Medical Center, Covina, CA, p. A58
Senior Vice President and Chief Financial Officer, Foothill Presbyterian Hospital, Glendora, CA, p. A63

COOK, Aaron, Director Information Services, Women and Children's Hospital, Lake Charles, LA, p. A272

COOK, Ann Fagan, Chief Information Officer, Parkview Hospital, Wheeler, TX, p. A641

COOK, Brandy, Chief Nursing Officer, Regional Rehabilitation Hospital, Phenix City, AL, p. A24

COOK, Brian, FACHE, Chief Executive Officer, Capital Regional Medical Center, Tallahassee, FL, p. A140

COOK, David, Manager Information Systems, Advance Care Hospital, Hot Springs National Park, AR, p. A45

COOK, David, M.D. Chief Medical Officer, Novant Health Huntersville Medical Center, Huntersville, NC, p. A455

COOK, David, Vice President Human Resources, St. Louis Children's Hospital, Saint Louis, MO, p. A371

COOK, DeLynn K., Director Human Resources, Lake Chelan Community Hospital, Chelan, WA, p. A665

COOK, Diane, Chief Nursing Officer, Cornerstone Hospital of North Little Rock, Jacksonville, AR, p. A45

COOK, Elizabeth, Chief Information Officer, Mizell Memorial Hospital, Opp, AL, p. A24

COOK, Greg, Chief Financial Officer, Jackson Purchase Medical Center, Mayfield, KY, p. A257

COOK, Heidi, Chief Nursing Officer, Dr. John Warner Hospital, Clinton, IL, p. A180

COOK, Jaime, Director Human Resources, Riverside Tappahannock Hospital, Tappahannock, VA, p. A662

COOK, Jane, R.N. Chief Nursing Officer, Texas Health Presbyterian Hospital Allen, Allen, TX, p. A581

COOK, Jeffrey A., Chief Executive Officer, Appleton Area Health Services, Appleton, MN, p. A328

COOK, John
Chief Financial Officer, Mercy Harvard Hospital, Harvard, IL, p. A184
Vice President and Chief Financial Officer, Mercy Hospital and Trauma Center, Janesville, WI, p. A688

COOK, Katheryn, R.N. Nurse Executive, Cincinnati Veterans Affairs Medical Center, Cincinnati, OH, p. A474

COOK, Kathy, MSN, Interim President, St. Joseph Health Center, Warren, OH, p. A492

COOK, Kevin S., President and Chief Executive Officer, Mercy St. Vincent Medical Center, Toledo, OH, p. A491

COOK, LaMont, Administrator, F. W. Huston Medical Center, Winchester, KS, p. A247

COOK, Linda, Vice President Human Resources, St. Joseph Hospital, Eureka, CA, p. A59

COOK, Lottie, Superintendent, Evansville Psychiatric Children Center, Evansville, IN, p. A202

COOK, Marcia, Director Information Technology, Bates County Memorial Hospital, Butler, MO, p. A357

COOK, Mark, Director Human Resources, Crossgates River Oaks Hospital, Brandon, MS, p. A345

COOK, Monica, Interim Chief Executive Officer, Saint Simons by–the–Sea Hospital, Saint Simons Island, GA, p. A159

COOK, Pamela W., Chief Financial Officer, Trace Regional Hospital, Houston, MS, p. A348

COOK, Patrick, Vice President Support Services, Morgan Memorial Hospital, Madison, GA, p. A157

COOK, Phillip, Administrator, Clinch Memorial Hospital, Homerville, GA, p. A155

COOK, Roger, Director Human Resources, Golden Valley Memorial Healthcare, Clinton, MO, p. A359

COOK, Ruth, Administrator, East Texas Medical Center Fairfield, Fairfield, TX, p. A602

COOK, Scott, Chief Financial Officer, Green Oaks Hospital, Dallas, TX, p. A596

COOK, Shelia, Director Information Systems, Novant Health Charlotte Orthopaedic Hospital, Charlotte, NC, p. A450

COOK, Sheliah, Director Human Resources, Boone Memorial Hospital, Madison, WV, p. A678

COOK, Sherry P., R.N. Chief Nursing Executive, River Oaks Hospital, Flowood, MS, p. A346

COOK, Stacey, Director Human Resources, University of Maryland Charles Regional Medical Center, La Plata, MD, p. A292

COOK, Thomas J., Chief Executive Officer, UVA–HEALTHSOUTH Rehabilitation Hospital, Charlottesville, VA, p. A652

COOK, Thomas M., CPA Chief Financial Officer, St. Vincent Indianapolis Hospital, Indianapolis, IN, p. A206

COOK, Timothy W., President and Chief Executive Officer, Florida Hospital Heartland Medical Center, Sebring, FL, p. A140

COOK, Will L., President, UPMC Mercy, Pittsburgh, PA, p. A538

COOK, William, Associate Warden Business Service, California Mens Colony Hospital, San Luis Obispo, CA, p. A88

COOKE, Barbara
Director Health Information Systems, Mount Vernon Hospital, Mount Vernon, NY, p. A430
Director Health Information Systems, Sound Shore Medical Center of Westchester, New Rochelle, NY, p. A430

COOKE, David, Chief Nursing Officer, Sutter Surgical Hospital – North Valley, Yuba City, CA, p. A96

COOKE, Nancy, Chief Financial Officer, Weatherford Regional Medical Center, Weatherford, TX, p. A640

COOKE, Timothy J., Associate Medical Center Director, Martinsburg Veterans Affairs Medical Center, Martinsburg, WV, p. A678

COOKE, William, M.D. Chief of Staff, St. Joseph's Health Services–Gundersen Lutheran, Hillsboro, WI, p. A688

COOKSEY, Jill, Vice President Chief Nursing Officer, EMH Elyria Medical Center, Elyria, OH, p. A481

COOLEY, Elizabeth A., R.N., Chief Executive Officer, St. Luke's Rehabilitation Hospital, Chesterfield, MO, p. A358

COOLEY, Lamar, R.N. Director of Nursing, Washington County Hospital and Nursing Home, Chatom, AL, p. A18

COOLEY, Stephen, M.D. Chairman Executive Committee Medical Staff, Naval Hospital Oak Harbor, Oak Harbor, WA, p. A668

COOLEY, W. Carl, M.D. Chief Medical Officer, Crotched Mountain Rehabilitation Center, Greenfield, NH, p. A398

COOMBS, James, Chief Executive Officer, Grand River Hospital District, Rifle, CO, p. A105

COOMES, Larry, Chief Executive Officer, Palm Beach Gardens Medical Center, Palm Beach Gardens, FL, p. A135

COONER, Suzanne, R.N. Vice President Operations, Grinnell Regional Medical Center, Grinnell, IA, p. A222

COONEY, Darlene, Director Nursing, Sumner Regional Medical Center, Wellington, KS, p. A246

COONEY, Lauri Ann, Interim Chief Executive Officer, Wheatland Memorial Healthcare, Harlowton, MT, p. A377

COONEY, Sally, Director Human Resources, Cumberland Medical Center, Crossville, TN, p. A568

COOPER, Alisa, Manager Financial Resources, Michael E. DeBakey Veterans Affairs Medical Center, Houston, TX, p. A611

COOPER, Andrew, Manager, Information Services, McDowell Hospital, Marion, NC, p. A457

COOPER, Casey, Chief Executive Officer, Cherokee Indian Hospital, Cherokee, NC, p. A450

COOPER, Chad D., Chief Executive Officer, Riverwood Healthcare Center, Aitkin, MN, p. A328

COOPER, Cliff, Chief Financial Officer, Wills Memorial Hospital, Washington, GA, p. A162

COOPER, Curtis, Manager Information Systems, Pioneers Medical Center, Meeker, CO, p. A104

COOPER, Dena, Chief Financial Officer, Campbellton Graceville Hospital, Graceville, FL, p. A124

COOPER, Dennis, Director Human Resources, Arkansas Methodist Medical Center, Paragould, AR, p. A49

COOPER, Donald, Director Information Systems, Harton Regional Medical Center, Tullahoma, TN, p. A580

COOPER, Donald C., Director, Veterans Affairs Central Iowa Health Care System, Des Moines, IA, p. A220

COOPER, Douglas, M.D. Chief Medical Officer, Grundy County Memorial Hospital, Grundy Center, IA, p. A222

COOPER, Hunt, M.D. Chief of Staff, Siloam Springs Memorial Hospital, Siloam Springs, AR, p. A50

COOPER, Ian, Chief Executive Officer, Kindred Hospital Cleveland–Gateway, Cleveland, OH, p. A476

COOPER, Jerry, Manager Data Processing, Richland Hospital, Richland Center, WI, p. A696

COOPER, John C., Chief Executive Officer, Fremont Hospital, Fremont, CA, p. A61

COOPER, Joseph, M.D. Chief of Staff, Pender Memorial Hospital, Burgaw, NC, p. A448

COOPER, Kevin S., R.N., Chief Executive Officer and Administrator, LifeCare Hospitals of North Carolina, Rocky Mount, NC, p. A460

COOPER, MaryBeth, R.N. Chief Nursing Officer, Highland Community Hospital, Picayune, MS, p. A352

COOPER, Michael W., Chief Executive Officer, Breckinridge Memorial Hospital, Hardinsburg, KY, p. A252

COOPER, Pat, Comptroller, Conejos County Hospital, La Jara, CO, p. A102

COOPER, Scott, M.D., Chief Executive Officer, St. Barnabas Hospital,, NY, p. A436

COOPER, Sheri, Director Human Resources, Union General Hospital, Farmerville, LA, p. A267

COOPER, Tami, Acting Director of Nursing, Riverview Psychiatric Center, Augusta, ME, p. A281

COOPER, Tim, Chief Financial Officer, PMH Medical Center, Prosser, WA, p. A669

COOPER-LOHR, Willie, Chief Financial Officer, Barnesville Hospital, Barnesville, OH, p. A471

COOPERMAN, Todd, M.D. Medical Director, Rehabilitation Hospital of Tinton Falls, Tinton Falls, NJ, p. A411

COOPWOOD, Reginald W., M.D., President and Chief Executive Officer, Regional Medical Center at Memphis, Memphis, TN, p. A575

COORPENDER, William, Assistant Vice President Human Resources, North Florida Regional Medical Center, Gainesville, FL, p. A124

COOTS, Lawrence, M.D. Chief Medical Officer, Orange Park Medical Center, Orange Park, FL, p. A135

COPE, Brent A., Chief Executive Officer, Silver Lake Medical Center, Los Angeles, CA, p. A71

COPE, David, Chief Executive Officer, Carolinas Hospital System Marion, Mullins, SC, p. A554

COPE, Donald, Director Information Systems, Newman Regional Health, Emporia, KS, p. A233

COPELAND, Carolyn, Business Administrator, Madison State Hospital, Madison, IN, p. A209

COPELAND, Darlinda, Chief Operating Officer, Florida Hospital Memorial Medical Center, Daytona Beach, FL, p. A122

COPELAND, Gail, Director Management Information Systems, CrossRidge Community Hospital, Wynne, AR, p. A51

COPELAND Jr., Robert Y., FACHE,
Interim President, Mercy Hospital Independence, Independence, KS, p. A236
Chief Executive Officer, Mercy McCune–Brooks Hospital, Carthage, MO, p. A358

COPELAND, Willie Mae, Chief Financial Officer, Harmon Memorial Hospital, Hollis, OK, p. A500

COPEN, Greg, Chief Information Officer, MedWest – Haywood, Clyde, NC, p. A450

COPENHAVER, Kathy, Director Human Resources, Haven Behavioral Health of Eastern Pennsylvania, Reading, PA, p. A539

COPES, Tammy, Director Information Systems, St. Mary's of Michigan Standish Hospital, Standish, MI, p. A325

COPPLE, Brad
President, Kishwaukee Hospital, DeKalb, IL, p. A180
President, Kishwaukee Hospital, DeKalb, IL, p. A180
President, Valley West Hospital, Sandwich, IL, p. A194

COPPLE, Robert C., FACHE, Interim Administrator, Memorial Community Hospital and Health System, Blair, NE, p. A382

COPPOCK, R. Alan, FACHE, President, Oak Tree Hospital, Corbin, KY, p. A249

CORBET, Mark, Interim Chief Financial Officer, LAC/University of Southern California Medical Center, Los Angeles, CA, p. A70

CORBI, Kelly, Chief Administrative Officer and Vice President Human Resources and Development, Meritus Medical Center, Hagerstown, MD, p. A292

CORBIN, Michelle, M.D. Chief of Staff, Deer Lodge Medical Center, Deer Lodge, MT, p. A375

CORBIN, Phil, M.D. Chief Medical Officer, Parkview Noble Hospital, Kendallville, IN, p. A207

CORBIN, Scott, M.D. Chief of Staff, Northern Hospital of Surry County, Mount Airy, NC, p. A458

CORCORAN, Kevin, Chief Financial Officer, Westside Regional Medical Center, Plantation, FL, p. A137

CORCORAN, Michael, Chief Financial Officer, Chesapeake Regional Medical Center, Chesapeake, VA, p. A652

CORCORAN, Nancy R., Senior Vice President Human Resources and Quality Service, Hackensack University Medical Center, Hackensack, NJ, p. A404

CORD, Jennifer, Vice President of Operations, Presence United Samaritans Medical Center, Danville, IL, p. A180

CORDEIRO, August B., FACHE, President and Chief Executive Officer, Newport Hospital, Newport, RI, p. A546

CORDER, Earline, Chief Fiscal, Charlie Norwood Veterans Affairs Medical Center, Augusta, GA, p. A147

CORDER, Noralene, Interim Senior Vice President and Chief Operating Officer, Seton Smithville Regional Hospital, Smithville, TX, p. A634

CORDER, Scott, Controller, HEALTHSOUTH Rehabilitation Hospital at Drake, Cincinnati, OH, p. A474

CORDIA, Jennifer, Vice President and Chief Nursing Executive, Christian Hospital, Saint Louis, MO, p. A369

CORDNER, Glenn D., Chief Executive Officer, Springfield Hospital, Springfield, VT, p. A650

CORDOLA, Craig, Chief Executive Officer, Memorial Hermann – Texas Medical Center, Houston, TX, p. A610

CORDOVA, Richard D., President and Chief Executive Officer, Children's Hospital Los Angeles, Los Angeles, CA, p. A68

CORDOVA, Sheila, Director Clinical Services and Chief Operating Officer, Aurora Charter Oak Hospital, Covina, CA, p. A58

CORDTS, Paul, Commander, Colonel Florence A. Blanchfield Army Community Hospital, Fort Campbell, KY, p. A251

COREA, Rohan, Director Healthcare Information Technology, Pacific Hospital of Long Beach, Long Beach, CA, p. A67

COREY, Mark, Chief Financial Officer, Behavioral Center of Michigan, Warren, MI, p. A326

CORFITS, Joe
Senior Vice President Finance, Iowa Methodist Medical Center, Des Moines, IA, p. A220
Chief Financial Officer, UnityPoint Health – Des Moines, Des Moines, IA, p. A220

CORK, A. Scott, Chief Executive Officer, Hallmark Youthcare – Richmond, Richmond, VA, p. A660

CORK, Ronald J., President and Chief Executive Officer, Avera St. Anthony's Hospital, O'Neill, NE, p. A386

CORKERY, Thomas B., D.O. Chief Medical Officer, Canonsburg General Hospital, Canonsburg, PA, p. A522

CORLEY, Adam, M.D. Chief of Staff, Brazosport Regional Health System, Lake Jackson, TX, p. A617

CORLEY, Becky, Director Human Resources, Tyler Holmes Memorial Hospital, Winona, MS, p. A355

CORLEY, Craig, Chief Financial Officer, Thousand Oaks Surgical Hospital, Thousand Oaks, CA, p. A92

CORLEY, Janet, Accountant, Malvern Institute, Malvern, PA, p. A530

CORMIER, Laura, Director, Bellin Health Oconto Hospital, Oconto, WI, p. A694

CORN, Rick, Chief Information Officer, Huntsville Hospital, Huntsville, AL, p. A21

CORNAVA, Joanne, Director Human Resources, Marlton Rehabilitation Hospital, Marlton, NJ, p. A406

CORNEJO, C. Susan, Senior Vice President Finance and Chief Financial Officer, Providence Hospital, Mobile, AL, p. A22

CORNELIUS, Margaret E., Vice President Human Resources, Wyckoff Heights Medical Center,, NY, p. A437

CORNELIUS, Michelle
Director Human Resources, Howard Young Medical Center, Woodruff, WI, p. A700
Director Human Resources for Northern Region, Ministry Eagle River Memorial Hospital, Eagle River, WI, p. A686
Director Human Resources for the Northern Region, Ministry Saint Mary's Hospitals, Rhinelander, WI, p. A695

CORNELIUS, Senta, Director Human Resources, West Valley Medical Center, Caldwell, ID, p. A168

CORNELL, John, Vice President Finance, Meadows Regional Medical Center, Vidalia, GA, p. A162

CORNETT, Sheila, Manager Human Resources, Hazard ARH Regional Medical Center, Hazard, KY, p. A252

CORNETT, Suzanne, Director Human Resources, Southern Kentucky Rehabilitation Hospital, Bowling Green, KY, p. A249

CORNICELLI, Kari, Chief Financial Officer, Sharp Grossmont Hospital, La Mesa, CA, p. A65

CORNING, Eileen M., Director Human Resources, Largo Medical Center, Largo, FL, p. A129

CORNWALL, Thomas, M.D. Medical Director, Holly Hill Hospital, Raleigh, NC, p. A459

CORNWELL, Cheryl, Chief Financial Officer, Great Falls Clinic Medical Center, Great Falls, MT, p. A376

CORONEL, Jorge, Chief Information Officer, Regional Hospital of Scranton, Scranton, PA, p. A540

CORPORA, Don, Executive Vice President and Chief Human Resources Officer, Akron General Medical Center, Akron, OH, p. A470

CORRADINO, Richard L., Chief Financial Officer, Spanish Peaks Regional Health Center, Walsenburg, CO, p. A106

CORRADO, Theresa, Director Finance, St. Luke's Hospital – Quakertown Campus, Quakertown, PA, p. A539

CORREA, Elizabeth, Director Information Management, Big Spring State Hospital, Big Spring, TX, p. A588

CORREA, Omar, Chief Operating Officer, Texas NeuroRehab Center, Austin, TX, p. A586

CORREA, Sharon, Associate Vice President, Glendale Adventist Medical Center, Glendale, CA, p. A62

CORREIA, Antonio, Chief Financial Officer, Holyoke Medical Center, Holyoke, MA, p. A300

CORRIDON, Fran, Vice President Human Resources and Shared Services, Hackensack University Medical Center Mountainside, Montclair, NJ, p. A406

CORRIGAN, Paula, Vice President and Chief Financial Officer, OSF Saint James – John W. Albrecht Medical Center, Pontiac, IL, p. A192

CORRIGAN, Thomas L., Senior Vice President Finance, Managed Care and Chief Financial Officer, Christiana Care Health System, Newark, DE, p. A114

CORS, William K., M.D. Vice President and Chief Medical Quality Officer, Pocono Medical Center, East Stroudsburg, PA, p. A524

CORSARO, Rocco, Controller, HEALTHSOUTH Rehabilitation Hospital of Ocala, Ocala, FL, p. A134

CORSO, David, Chief Operating Officer, Beaver Dam Community Hospitals, Beaver Dam, WI, p. A684

CORTEZ, Audrey, Chief Nursing Officer, Otto Kaiser Memorial Hospital, Kenedy, TX, p. A616

CORTI, Ronald, President and Chief Executive Officer, St. John's Riverside Hospital, Yonkers, NY, p. A446

CORTRIGHT, Michael, Chief Information Officer, Ralph H. Johnson Veterans Affairs Medical Center, Charleston, SC, p. A549

CORVINO, Frank A., President and Chief Executive Officer, Greenwich Hospital, Greenwich, CT, p. A109

CORWIN, Florence, Director for Administration, Pilgrim Psychiatric Center, Brentwood, NY, p. A422

CORWIN, R. William, M.D. Vice President and Chief Medical Officer, Miriam Hospital, Providence, RI, p. A546

CORWIN, Steven J., M.D., Chief Executive Officer, New York–Presbyterian Hospital, New York, NY, p. A435

CORZINE, Judy, Administrative Director and Chief Information Officer, Stormont–Vail HealthCare, Topeka, KS, p. A245

COSBY, Bridget, Chief Executive Officer, Pauls Valley General Hospital, Pauls Valley, OK, p. A505

COSBY, Ernestine Y., Vice President Clinical Services and Chief Nursing Officer, Sheppard Pratt Health System, Baltimore, MD, p. A289

COSGROVE, Delos, M.D., President and Chief Executive Officer, Cleveland Clinic, Cleveland, OH, p. A476

COSSAIRT, Vicki, Director Human Resources, Integris Grove General Hospital, Grove, OK, p. A499

COSSIO, Eduardo M., M.D. Chief of Staff, Morgan Memorial Hospital, Madison, GA, p. A157

COSTA, Christopher P., M.D. Chief of Staff, Gordon Memorial Hospital, Gordon, NE, p. A384

COSTA, Joe
Acting Chief Fiscal Officer, Brockton Veterans Affairs Medical Center, Brockton, MA, p. A298
Chief Financial Officer, Veterans Affairs Boston Healthcare System, Boston, MA, p. A297

COSTA, Mark E., Executive Director, Kaiser Permanente Los Angeles Medical Center, Los Angeles, CA, p. A69

COSTA, Michael G.
Vice President Human Resources, Burleson St. Joseph Health Center, Caldwell, TX, p. A590
Director Human Resources, Grimes St. Joseph Health Center, Navasota, TX, p. A624
Vice President Human Resources, St. Joseph Regional Health Center, Bryan, TX, p. A590

COSTA, Vivian, Director, Barix Clinics of Pennsylvania, Langhorne, PA, p. A529

COSTANTINI, Polly, Director Human Resources, Hampton Behavioral Health Center, Westampton, NJ, p. A412

COSTANTINO, Mark J., M.D. Interim Chief Medical Officer, Athens Regional Medical Center, Athens, GA, p. A145

COSTANTINO, Vincent, Vice President Operations and Human Resources, Raritan Bay Medical Center, Perth Amboy, NJ, p. A409

COSTELLA, Jeane L., Vice President, Hudson Valley Hospital Center, Cortlandt Manor, NY, p. A424

COSTELLO, Benny, Chief Executive Officer, Promise Hospital of Miss Lou, Vidalia, LA, p. A279

COSTELLO, Jeff, Chief Financial Officer, Memorial Hospital of South Bend, South Bend, IN, p. A213

COSTELLO, Lisa, R.N., Interim Administrator, Community Behavioral Health Hospital – Rochester, Rochester, MN, p. A339

COSTER, Margaret C., R.N. Vice President Patient Services, Fairmont General Hospital, Fairmont, WV, p. A676

COSTIC, Andrew, Regional Chief Financial Officer, Abraham Lincoln Memorial Hospital, Lincoln, IL, p. A187

COSTIE, Glenn A., FACHE, Director, Dayton Veterans Affairs Medical Center, Dayton, OH, p. A479

COTA, Scott, M.D. Director Medical Services, Naval Hospital, Lemoore, CA, p. A66

COTE, Mario, M.D. Chief of Staff and President Medical Staff, Illinois Valley Community Hospital, Peru, IL, p. A192

COTHRON, Robert, MSC, Administrator, U. S. Air Force Medical Center Keesler, Keesler AFB, MS, p. A349

COTSHOTT, Angelica, Chief Executive Officer, Kindred Hospital Melbourne, Melbourne, FL, p. A130

COTT, Gary, M.D. Executive Vice President Medical and Clinical Services, National Jewish Health, Denver, CO, p. A99

COTTER, Carole
Senior Vice President and Chief Information Officer, Emma Pendleton Bradley Hospital, East Providence, RI, p. A546
Vice President and Chief Information Officer, Miriam Hospital, Providence, RI, p. A546
Senior Vice President and Chief Information Officer, Rhode Island Hospital, Providence, RI, p. A547

COTTER, Richard W., Associate Director Operations, Veterans Affairs Butler Healthcare, Butler, PA, p. A521

COTTERMAN, Rob, Assistant Superintendent Program Services, Moccasin Bend Mental Health Institute, Chattanooga, TN, p. A566

COTTI, Matthew, Chief Financial Officer, Rehabilitation Hospital of Rhode Island, North Smithfield, RI, p. A546

COTTINGHAM, Jerod, Director Information Systems, Carlinville Area Hospital, Carlinville, IL, p. A175

COTTLE, Gil, Chief Financial Officer, St. Christopher's Hospital for Children, Philadelphia, PA, p. A536

COTTON, C. Gerald, Interim Chief Executive Officer, Baptist Medical Center Leake, Carthage, MS, p. A345

COTTON, Michael, Chief Financial Officer, Gadsden Regional Medical Center, Gadsden, AL, p. A20

COTTRILL, Brian, Chief Information Officer, United Hospital Center, Bridgeport, WV, p. A675

COUCH, Beulah, Director Human Resources, Mary Breckinridge ARH Hospital, Hyden, KY, p. A253

COUCH, Bill, Chief Financial Officer, Ashley County Medical Center, Crossett, AR, p. A42

COUCH, Lorie, Assistant Superintendent, Big Spring State Hospital, Big Spring, TX, p. A588

COUCH, Robert J., Chief Executive Officer, Medical Center of Manchester, Manchester, TN, p. A573

COUGHLIN, Ann, Director Human Resources, Boundary Community Hospital, Bonners Ferry, ID, p. A168

COUGHLIN, Cynthia, MS Chief Nursing Officer, Cheshire Medical Center, Keene, NH, p. A398

COUILLARD, John, Chief Financial Officer, Kindred Hospital Boston–North Shore, Peabody, MA, p. A303

COULLIETTE, Edwina, Manager Human Resources, St. Vincent's Medical Center Southside, Jacksonville, FL, p. A127

COULTAS, David, M.D. Vice President Clinical Affairs, University of Texas Health Science Center at Tyler, Tyler, TX, p. A639

COULTER, Barbara
Director Information Systems, Franciscan St. Francis Health – Indianapolis, Indianapolis, IN, p. A205
Director Information Systems, Franciscan St. Francis Health – Mooresville, Mooresville, IN, p. A210

COULTER, David C., Senior Vice President and Administrator, WakeMed Cary Hospital, Cary, NC, p. A449

COUNTY–TEEMER, Vickie, Coordinator Human Resources, Mitchell County Hospital, Camilla, GA, p. A149

COUNTZLER, John T., Chief Executive Officer, Muhlenberg Community Hospital, Greenville, KY, p. A252

COURAGE, Kenneth F., President and Chief Executive Officer, Psychiatric Institute of Washington, Washington, DC, p. A117

COURIS, John D., President and Chief Executive Officer, Jupiter Medical Center, Jupiter, FL, p. A127

COURLISS, Richard, Chief Support Services, Cherry Hospital, Goldsboro, NC, p. A453

COURNYER, Tim, Chief Financial Officer, Morton General Hospital, Morton, WA, p. A668

COURREGE, Chad, Vice President Human Resources, Touro Infirmary, New Orleans, LA, p. A276

COURREGE, Gary, Chief Information Officer, Jennings American Legion Hospital, Jennings, LA, p. A269

COURTOIS, Harold, Chief Executive Officer, Russell Regional Hospital, Russell, KS, p. A243

COURTOIS, Robert, Vice President Finance, Otsego Memorial Hospital, Gaylord, MI, p. A314

COURTWAY, Peter, Chief Information Officer, New Milford Hospital, New Milford, CT, p. A111

COUSAR, Myra, Director Human Resources, Baptist Memorial Hospital–Tipton, Covington, TN, p. A568

COUSENS, Tim, On–Site Administrator, Sage Memorial Hospital, Ganado, AZ, p. A31

COUSINEAU, Cathy, Director Human Resources, Kaiser Permanente Woodland Hills Medical Center,, CA, p. A69

COUSINS, Kelly, Director Information Technology, Abbeville General Hospital, Abbeville, LA, p. A262

COUTURE, Elaine, R.N.,
Chief Executive, Providence Holy Family Hospital, Spokane, WA, p. A672
Chief Executive, Providence Sacred Heart Medical Center & Children's Hospital, Spokane, WA, p. A672

COVA, Charles J., President and Chief Executive Officer and Senior Vice President Operations Dignity Health Central Co, Marian Medical Center, Santa Maria, CA, p. A90

COVAULT, Julie, Vice President Finance, Wilson Memorial Hospital, Sidney, OH, p. A490

COVELL, Nancy, Director Human Resources, Cameron Memorial Community Hospital, Angola, IN, p. A198

COVERT, Charles O.
Chief Financial Officer, Saint Francis Hospital, Charleston, WV, p. A676
Vice President Finance, Thomas Memorial Hospital, South Charleston, WV, p. A681

COVEY, Staci, MS, President, Troy Community Hospital, Troy, PA, p. A542

COVIN, Charles
Chief Information Officer, Manchester Memorial Hospital, Manchester, CT, p. A109
Chief Information Officer, Rockville General Hospital, Vernon Rockville, CT, p. A112

COVINGTON, Casey, M.D. President Elect, Medical Staff, Jennie Stuart Medical Center, Hopkinsville, KY, p. A252

COVINGTON, Jerome, M.D. Chief Medical Officer, Lower Keys Medical Center, Key West, FL, p. A127

COWAN, Alan, M.D. Chief of Staff, Longview Regional Medical Center, Longview, TX, p. A619

COWAN, Dale, M.D. Vice President Medical Affairs, Parma Community General Hospital, Parma, OH, p. A488

COWAN, J. W., Administrator, Choctaw General Hospital, Butler, AL, p. A18

COWAN, Joshua, Chief Information Officer, St. Helena Hospital Clear Lake, Clearlake, CA, p. A56

COWAN, Ronald M., Vice President Information Systems, Lewistown Hospital, Lewistown, PA, p. A530

COWART, Michelle, R.N. Chief Nursing Officer, HEALTHSOUTH Chattanooga Rehabilitation Hospital, Chattanooga, TN, p. A566

COWDEN, Ella, Director Human Resources, Erlanger at Hutcheson, Fort Oglethorpe, GA, p. A154

COWGER, David, M.D. Senior Vice President Quality and Medical Affairs and Chief Medical Officer, UPMC Altoona, Altoona, PA, p. A520

COWIE, Cynthia, Chief Executive Officer, Southwest Regional Medical Center, Waynesburg, PA, p. A543

COWLES, Deborah, Vice President Human Resources, Flaget Memorial Hospital, Bardstown, KY, p. A248

COWLES, John, Chief Financial Officer, Silver Lake Medical Center, Los Angeles, CA, p. A71

COWLEY, Markie, Executive Vice President and Chief Operating Officer, Mission Hospital, Mission Viejo, CA, p. A74

COWLING, Phyllis A., CPA, President and Chief Executive Officer, United Regional Health Care System, Wichita Falls, TX, p. A642

COWPERTHWAIT, Cheri, R.N., Chief Executive Officer, Lourdes Specialty Hospital of Southern New Jersey, Willingboro, NJ, p. A412

COX, Amber, Director Human Resources, East Texas Medical Center Carthage, Carthage, TX, p. A591

COX, Brenda, Director Human Resources, Scott & White Hospital at Round Rock, Round Rock, TX, p. A629

COX, Brian, Director Information Systems, Floyd Memorial Hospital and Health Services, New Albany, IN, p. A211

COX, Charles B., M.D. Chief of Staff, Woods Memorial Hospital, Etowah, TN, p. A569

COX, Courtney, Vice President Human Resources, UPMC Northwest, Seneca, PA, p. A541

COX, Danny, Chief Executive Officer, Atrium Medical Center, Stafford, TX, p. A634

COX, David W., Chief Financial Officer, Marin General Hospital, Greenbrae, CA, p. A63

COX, Debbie D., Administrative Director Human Resources, Central Texas Medical Center, San Marcos, TX, p. A633

COX, Dina, Director Human Resources, Kansas Rehabilitation Hospital, Topeka, KS, p. A245

COX, Dorothy, Manager Information Systems, Hackettstown Regional Medical Center, Hackettstown, NJ, p. A404

COX, F. Gregory, M.D. Chief of Staff, Parkway Regional Hospital, Fulton, KY, p. A251

COX, Gray, President, St. Francis Hospital and Health Services, Maryville, MO, p. A365

COX, Jack, M.D. Senior Vice President and Chief Quality Officer, Hoag Memorial Hospital Presbyterian, Newport Beach, CA, p. A76

COX, Jay, FACHE, President and Chief Executive Officer, Tuomey Healthcare System, Sumter, SC, p. A556

COX, Keith, Administrator, LifeCare Hospitals of Shreveport, Shreveport, LA, p. A278

COX, Kenneth, M.D. Chief Medical Officer, Lucile Salter Packard Children's Hospital at Stanford, Palo Alto, CA, p. A78

COX, Kevin, Chief Financial Officer, Integris Grove General Hospital, Grove, OK, p. A499

COX, Leigh, Chief Information Officer, WellStar Windy Hill Hospital, Marietta, GA, p. A157

COX, Lynna B., Director Health Information Services, Anson General Hospital, Anson, TX, p. A583

COX, Matthew
Chief Financial Officer, Central Maine Medical Center, Lewiston, ME, p. A283
Senior Vice President and Chief Financial Officer, St. Vincent Infirmary Medical Center, Little Rock, AR, p. A47

COX, Randell, Director Data Processing, Bowie Memorial Hospital, Bowie, TX, p. A589

COX, Randy
Chief Information Officer, Lutheran Hospital of Indiana, Fort Wayne, IN, p. A202
Chief Information Officer, St. Joseph Hospital, Fort Wayne, IN, p. A203

COX, Raymond L., M.D. Chief Medical Officer, Providence Hospital, Washington, DC, p. A116

COX, Rosalie, Administrator, LifeCare Hospitals of Chester County, West Chester, PA, p. A543

COX, Sandra, Controller, Permian Regional Medical Center, Andrews, TX, p. A583

COX, Scott, Manager Information Systems, St. Vincent Salem Hospital, Salem, IN, p. A213

COX, Sheila, Director Human Resources, Cibola General Hospital, Grants, NM, p. A416

COX, Sherry, Chief Human Resources Officer, Ashe Memorial Hospital, Jefferson, NC, p. A455

COX, Steve, M.D. Chief Medical Officer, Fairfield Medical Center, Lancaster, OH, p. A483

COXE, Bob, M.D. Medical Director, Vanderbilt Stallworth Rehabilitation Hospital, Nashville, TN, p. A577

COY, Nelson, Director Human Resources, Tahoe Pacific Hospitals, Reno, NV, p. A395

COYE, Ed, Director Information Technology, Transylvania Regional Hospital, Brevard, NC, p. A448

COYLE, Joseph P., President, Southern Ocean Medical Center, Manahawkin, NJ, p. A406

COYLE, Michael F., Chief Executive Officer, West Holt Memorial Hospital, Atkinson, NE, p. A381

COYNE, Rose
Vice President and Chief Financial Officer, Cleveland Regional Medical Center, Shelby, NC, p. A460
Interim CFO, MedWest – Haywood, Clyde, NC, p. A450

COZART, Adrienne, Vice President Human Resources, University Medical Center, Lubbock, TX, p. A620

COZART, Phyllis, Director Human Resources, Haywood Park Community Hospital, Brownsville, TN, p. A565

CRABB, Ian, M.D. Medical Director, Nebraska Orthopaedic Hospital, Omaha, NE, p. A388

CRABB, Lindsay, Chief Executive Officer, Quartz Mountain Medical Center, Mangum, OK, p. A501

CRABBE, Amy
Vice President Human Resources, Charles A. Cannon Memorial Hospital, Linville, NC, p. A456
Senior Vice President Human Resources, Watauga Medical Center, Boone, NC, p. A448

CRABDREE, Nathan, Chief Financial Officer, Chesterfield General Hospital, Cheraw, SC, p. A549

CRABLE, W. Trent, Executive Vice President and Chief Operating Officer, Brooklyn Hospital Center,, NY, p. A431

CRABTREE, Douglas, Chief Executive Officer, Eastern Idaho Regional Medical Center, Idaho Falls, ID, p. A169

CRABTREE, Gordon, Chief Financial Officer, University of Utah Health Care – Hospital and Clinics, Salt Lake City, UT, p. A647

CRABTREE, Karla T., Director Personnel Systems, University of Texas Harris County Psychiatric Center, Houston, TX, p. A613

CRABTREE, Nathan, Chief Financial Officer, Springs Memorial Hospital, Lancaster, SC, p. A554

CRABTREE, Rick, Chief Operating Officer, Christus St. Vincent Regional Medical Center, Santa Fe, NM, p. A418

CRABTREE, Susan, Director Human Resources, Glendale Adventist Medical Center, Glendale, CA, p. A62

CRACOLICI, Frank J., President, St. Luke's–Roosevelt Hospital Center, New York, NY, p. A436

CRACROFT, Davis, M.D. Senior Director Medical Affairs, Scripps Mercy Hospital, San Diego, CA, p. A85

CRAFA, Regina, Vice President Human Resources, Bethesda Memorial Hospital, Boynton Beach, FL, p. A119

CRAFT, Brian, Vice President and Chief Financial Officer, Texas Health Presbyterian Hospital Plano, Plano, TX, p. A628

CRAFT, Christina, Director Information Systems, Washington County Hospital, Plymouth, NC, p. A459

CRAFT, Kirby, Chief Information Officer, Magee General Hospital, Magee, MS, p. A350

CRAIG, Celine, Director Human Resources, King's Daughters Medical Center, Brookhaven, MS, p. A345

CRAIG, Daniel, Warden, Iowa Medical and Classification Center, Oakdale, IA, p. A226

CRAIG, Donnette, Director Human Resources, CHRISTUS Coushatta Health Care Center, Coushatta, LA, p. A265

CRAIG, Emmett, Chief Human Resources Officer, Knapp Medical Center, Weslaco, TX, p. A641

CRAIG, Glenn L., Chief Operating Officer, University Medical Center, Lafayette, LA, p. A271

CRAIG, Jeff, Chief Human Resource Management, Veterans Affairs Maryland Health Care System–Baltimore Division, Baltimore, MD, p. A289

CRAIG, John D., Chief Financial Officer, St. Luke's Rehabilitation Institute, Spokane, WA, p. A672

CRAIG, Mary Anne, Chief Executive Officer, Kindred Hospital–Houston Northwest, Houston, TX, p. A610

CRAIG, Pamela, R.N. Chief Nursing Officer, Seton Medical Center Harker Heights, Harker Heights, TX, p. A607

CRAIG, Patrice, Manager Human Resources, Southern Arizona Veterans Affairs Health Care System, Tucson, AZ, p. A39

CRAIG, Paul A., R.N. Chief Human Resources and Risk Officer, UC San Diego Health System, San Diego, CA, p. A86

CRAIG, Rebecca W., Vice President and Chief Financial Officer, Wayne Memorial Hospital, Goldsboro, NC, p. A453

CRAIG, Scott, M.D. Medical Director, Van Matre HEALTHSOUTH Rehabilitation Hospital, Rockford, IL, p. A194

CRAIG, Tracy, Director Human Resources, Novant Health Huntersville Medical Center, Huntersville, NC, p. A455

CRAIG, William J., Chief Financial Officer, Howard Memorial Hospital, Nashville, AR, p. A48

CRAIGER, Lisa, Chief Nursing Officer, Jay County Hospital, Portland, IN, p. A212

CRAIGHTON, Michelle, Manager Finance, Franklin General Hospital, Hampton, IA, p. A222

CRAIGIE, Andrew, Chief Executive Officer, Garfield County Public Hospital District, Pomeroy, WA, p. A669

CRAIGIE, James N., M.D. Vice President Medical Affairs, McLeod Loris Healthcare, Loris, SC, p. A554

CRAIGIN, Jane, Chief Executive Officer, St. Vincent Williamsport Hospital, Williamsport, IN, p. A215

CRAIN, Allen, Director Human Resources, Rapides Regional Medical Center, Alexandria, LA, p. A262

CRAIN, Doris
Vice President Information Services, Broward Health Medical Center, Fort Lauderdale, FL, p. A123
Vice President and Chief Information Officer, Broward Health North, Deerfield Beach, FL, p. A122

CRAIN, Greg, FACHE, Vice President and Administrator, Baptist Health Medical Center–Little Rock, Little Rock, AR, p. A46

CRALL, Carlene B., Chief Human Resources Officer, Cheyenne Regional Medical Center, Cheyenne, WY, p. A701

CRAMBES, Terry, Manager Finance, Warren State Hospital, Warren, PA, p. A543

CRAMER, Brian J., Chief Executive Officer, Orthopaedic Hospital of Wisconsin – Glendale, Milwaukee, WI, p. A692

CRAMER, James R.
Vice President and Chief Information Officer, Scottsdale Healthcare Shea Medical Center, Scottsdale, AZ, p. A37
Chief Information Officer, Scottsdale Healthcare Thompson Peak Hospital, Scottsdale, AZ, p. A37
Vice President and Chief Information Officer, Scottsdale Healthcare–Osborn Medical Center, Scottsdale, AZ, p. A37

CRANDALL, Jeff, M.D. Chief Medical Officer, UnityPoint Health Allen, Waterloo, IA, p. A229

CRANDALL, Phillip, Director, Sempervirens Psychiatric Health Facility, Eureka, CA, p. A59

CRANDELL, Kim O., Administrator, South Lyon Medical Center, Yerington, NV, p. A396

CRANE, Aaron
Chief Financial Officer, Salem Hospital, Salem, OR, p. A517
Chief Financial Officer, West Valley Hospital, Dallas, OR, p. A512

CRANE, Margaret W., Chief Executive Officer, Barlow Respiratory Hospital, Los Angeles, CA, p. A68

CRANFORD, Melvin, Chief Fiscal Services, Cheyenne Veterans Affairs Medical Center, Cheyenne, WY, p. A701

CRANMER, John, Chief Information Officer, Mayo Clinic Hospital, Phoenix, AZ, p. A35

CRANSTON, David C., M.D. Vice President Medical Staff Affairs, Grinnell Regional Medical Center, Grinnell, IA, p. A222

CRAPSER, Douglas, Executive Vice President, Harrington Memorial Hospital, Southbridge, MA, p. A304

CRATON, Deborah W., M.D. Chief Medical Officer, St. Vincent Dunn Hospital, Bedford, IN, p. A198

CRAVEN, Darcy, Chief Executive Officer, Carolinas Hospital System, Florence, SC, p. A551

CRAWFORD, Angela, Director Human Resources, Cherry Hospital, Goldsboro, NC, p. A453

CRAWFORD, Arnita, Director Human Resources, The Woman's Hospital of Texas, Houston, TX, p. A613

CRAWFORD, Jeff, Chief Executive Officer, Reliant Northwest Houston, Houston, TX, p. A611

CRAWFORD, Jim, Chief Financial Officer, Lawrence Medical Center, Moulton, AL, p. A24

CRAWFORD, John W., Chief Financial Officer, Okmulgee Memorial Hospital, Okmulgee, OK, p. A505

CRAWFORD, Linda, R.N. Chief Nursing Officer, Cookeville Regional Medical Center, Cookeville, TN, p. A568

CRAWFORD, Lucinda, Vice President Financial Services, Vidant Duplin Hospital, Kenansville, NC, p. A455

CRAWFORD, Marian, Director of Patient Care Services, North Greenville Hospital, Travelers Rest, SC, p. A556

CRAWFORD, Mark W., Chief Executive Officer, Northwest Texas Healthcare System, Amarillo, TX, p. A582

CRAWFORD, Robin, Vice President and Chief Financial Officer, Susan B. Allen Memorial Hospital, El Dorado, KS, p. A233

CRAWFORD, Susan, Manager Human Resources, Fayette County Hospital, Vandalia, IL, p. A196

CRAWFORD, Thomas
Administrator, St. Vincent Frankfort Hospital, Frankfort, IN, p. A203
Chicago Market Chief Information Officer, UnityHealth Louis A. Weiss Memorial Hospital, Chicago, IL, p. A179

CRAWFORD, Tom
Vice President Human Resources, DeKalb Medical at Downtown Decatur, Decatur, GA, p. A152
Vice President Human Resources, DeKalb Medical at Hillandale, Lithonia, GA, p. A156

CRAYTON, Karen, Administrator, AMG Specialty Hospital–Denham Springs, Denham Springs, LA, p. A266

CREAL, Sharon, Vice President Financial Operations, Scripps Memorial Hospital–Encinitas, Encinitas, CA, p. A59

CREAMER, Ken, Chief Human Resource, Amarillo Veterans Affairs Health Care System, Amarillo, TX, p. A582

CREASON, Yonna, R.N., Interim Chief Executive Officer, Cleveland Area Hospital, Cleveland, OK, p. A497

CREECH, Ginger, Chief Executive Officer, AMG Specialty Hospital–Edmond, Edmond, OK, p. A498

CREECH, James, M.D. Chief of Staff, Avera Holy Family Hospital, Estherville, IA, p. A221

CREEL, Mary Ann, Chief Information Resource Management, Martinsburg Veterans Affairs Medical Center, Martinsburg, WV, p. A678

CREIGHTON, Brenda L., Director Human Resources, Hudson Hospital and Clinics, Hudson, WI, p. A688

CREIGHTON, Janice, Human Resources Associate, Mental Health Institute, Mount Pleasant, IA, p. A225

CREIGHTON, Peggy F., R.N. Director of Nursing Services, Methodist Hospital Union County, Morganfield, KY, p. A258

CREPEAU, Diana, Director Human Resources, HEALTHSOUTH Rehabilitation Hospital of Colorado Springs, Colorado Springs, CO, p. A98

CREPS, Barbara, Director Human Resources and Accounting, Okeene Municipal Hospital, Okeene, OK, p. A502

CRESSLEY, Pat, Vice President and Chief Financial Officer, Clearfield Hospital, Clearfield, PA, p. A522

CRESWELL, Linda, Director Human Resources, Texas Health Presbyterian Hospital–WNJ, Sherman, TX, p. A634

CREWS, Kimberly, Vice President Finance and Chief Financial Officer, High Point Regional Health System, High Point, NC, p. A455

CREWS, Michael E., Chief Financial Officer, Singing River Health System, Pascagoula, MS, p. A352

CRIBBS, Cyndie, Director of Nursing, Nor–Lea General Hospital, Lovington, NM, p. A417

CRIBBS, Susan, D.O. Chief of Staff, Tehachapi Valley Healthcare District, Tehachapi, CA, p. A92

CRIGER, Sara J., President, Mercy Hospital, Coon Rapids, MN, p. A330

CRILLY, Tom, Executive Vice President and Chief Financial Officer, Unity Hospital, Rochester, NY, p. A441

CRIM, Marcia, MSN, Chief Executive Officer, USMD Hospital at Arlington, Arlington, TX, p. A584

CRIPE, Kimberly C.
President and Chief Executive Officer, Children's Hospital at Mission, Mission Viejo, CA, p. A74
President and Chief Executive Officer, Children's Hospital of Orange County, Orange, CA, p. A77

CRIPPS, Hugh Don, M.D. Chief of Staff, DeKalb Community Hospital, Smithville, TN, p. A579

CRISANTI, John, M.D. Vice President Medical Affairs, Community Medical Center, Toms River, NJ, p. A411

CRISLER, Catherine, Executive Director Human Resources, Piedmont Fayette Hospital, Fayetteville, GA, p. A153

CRIST, Chris, Director Information Systems, Coffeyville Regional Medical Center, Coffeyville, KS, p. A232

CRISWELL, Jodie, Vice President Fiscal Services, Hammond–Henry Hospital, Geneseo, IL, p. A183

CRITTENDON, Cindy, M.D. Chief of Staff, Marlboro Park Hospital, Bennettsville, SC, p. A548

CRITTLE, Marsha, Director Human Resources, Huey P. Long Medical Center, Pineville, LA, p. A277

CRNKOVIC, A. Elaine, Chief Executive Officer, Cedar Springs Hospital, Colorado Springs, CO, p. A98

CROCKER, Daniel, M.D. Chief Medical Officer, LifeCare Hospitals of North Carolina, Rocky Mount, NC, p. A460

CROCKETT, Gary L., Administrator, Huey P. Long Medical Center, Pineville, LA, p. A277

CROCKETT, James Scott, M.D. Chief of Staff, Falls Community Hospital and Clinic, Marlin, TX, p. A621

CROCKETT, Kim, Director Management Information Systems, Shriners Hospitals for Children–Shreveport, Shreveport, LA, p. A278

CROCKETT, Mandy Lee, Director Human Resources, San Luis Valley Regional Medical Center, Alamosa, CO, p. A97

CROCKETT, Matt, Assistant Administrator and Chief Information Officer, Highline Medical Center, Burien, WA, p. A665

CROCKETT, Russ
Director Human Resources, Shriners Hospitals for Children–Salt Lake City, Salt Lake City, UT, p. A647
Director Human Resources, Shriners Hospitals for Children–Spokane, Spokane, WA, p. A672

CROFFORD, Patricia, Vice President Human Resources, Flagstaff Medical Center, Flagstaff, AZ, p. A31

CROFT, Cheryl, Chairman Information Services, Mayo Clinic Jacksonville, Jacksonville, FL, p. A126

CROFT, Shauna, Chief Financial Officer, Power County Hospital District, American Falls, ID, p. A167

CROKER, James, Director Information Systems, St. Bernardine Medical Center, San Bernardino, CA, p. A84

CROMIKA, Mike, Director Information Services, Baptist Health Paducah, Paducah, KY, p. A259

CROMWELL, Gordon N., M.D. Chief Medical Officer, Harrison Medical Center, Bremerton, WA, p. A664

CRONER, Robert, Executive Vice President and Chief Human Resources Officer, Children's Hospital of Philadelphia, Philadelphia, PA, p. A534

CRONIN, Annamarie, Director Human Resources, New England Rehabilitation Hospital, Woburn, MA, p. A306

CRONIN, David J., Regional Vice President Human Resources, Good Samaritan Medical Center, Brockton, MA, p. A298

CROOM, Jon–Paul, Chief Operating Officer, Clearview Regional Medical Center, Monroe, GA, p. A157

CROOM Jr., Kennedy L., Administrator and Chief Executive Officer, Rhea Medical Center, Dayton, TN, p. A568

CROON, Dorwyn, M.D. President Medical Staff, Valdese General Hospital, Valdese, NC, p. A462

CROPLEY, Stacey, M.D. Chief Nursing Officer, Moore County Hospital District, Dumas, TX, p. A599

CROPPER, Rosiland, M.D. Medical Director, Ascension Gonzales Rehabilitation Hospital, Gonzales, LA, p. A267

CROSBIE, John, Director Support Services, Indiana University Health Blackford Hospital, Hartford City, IN, p. A204

CROSBY, Evalie M., CPA Vice President Finance and Chief Financial Officer, Alice Peck Day Memorial Hospital, Lebanon, NH, p. A398

CROSBY, Robert, Senior Vice President and Chief Financial Officer, Heywood Hospital, Gardner, MA, p. A300

CROSHAW, Diane, Vice President Human Resources, Bacharach Institute for Rehabilitation, Pomona, NJ, p. A409

CROSS, Carol, Chief Financial Officer, Texas Health Harris Methodist Hospital Stephenville, Stephenville, TX, p. A635

CROSS, Helene M., President and Chief Executive Officer, Fairbanks, Indianapolis, IN, p. A205

CROSS, Mark A., Chief Executive Officer, Marias Medical Center, Shelby, MT, p. A379

CROSSAN, Gary, Director Information Systems, Healdsburg District Hospital, Healdsburg, CA, p. A64

CROSSER, Roxanna, Vice President, Operations, OSF St. Mary Medical Center, Galesburg, IL, p. A183

CROSSEY, Robert, D.O. Chief Medical Officer, LifeCare Hospitals of Pittsburgh – Monroeville, Monroeville, PA, p. A532

CROSSIN, Robert J., Vice President Finance, Aria Health, Philadelphia, PA, p. A534

CROSSLEY, Beth, Director Information Systems, Chestnut Hill Hospital, Philadelphia, PA, p. A534

CROSSLEY, Kent, M.D. Acting Chief of Staff, Minneapolis Veterans Affairs Health Care System, Minneapolis, MN, p. A336

CROSTON, J. Kevin, M.D. Chief Medical Officer, North Memorial Medical Center, Robbinsdale, MN, p. A338

CROTEAU, Christine, Acting Director, Edith Nourse Rogers Memorial Veterans Hospital, Bedford, MA, p. A295

CROTEAU, Gary, Assistant Vice President and Chief Information Officer, South County Hospital, Wakefield, RI, p. A547

CROTTY, Jr., Glenn, M.D. Executive Vice President and Chief Operating Officer, Charleston Area Medical Center, Charleston, WV, p. A676

CROTTY, Renee, Coordinator Marketing and Public Relations, Capital Medical Center, Olympia, WA, p. A668

CROUCH, Amy, Chief Financial Officer, DeKalb Health, Auburn, IN, p. A198

CROUCH, James, Vice President Technical Services, Northwest Medical Center, Albany, MO, p. A356

CROUCH, Matthew, Chief Executive Officer and Managing Director, Peachford Behavioral Health System, Atlanta, GA, p. A146

CROUT, Tom, MS Director Human Resources, Central Louisiana State Hospital, Pineville, LA, p. A277

CROW, Angie, Financial Director, Saint Thomas Hospital for Spinal Surgery, Nashville, TN, p. A576

CROW, Barbra, Chief Financial Officer, Little River Memorial Hospital, Ashdown, AR, p. A41

CROW, Beth, Associate Relations Representative, OhioHealth Grady Memorial Hospital, Delaware, OH, p. A480

CROW, Ralph, Director Information Technology and Systems, Sky Ridge Medical Center, Lone Tree, CO, p. A104

CROW, Ruth Ann, Administrator, Lake Whitney Medical Center, Whitney, TX, p. A641

CROWDER, Andy, Chief Information Officer, Florida Hospital, Orlando, FL, p. A135

CROWDER, Lonna, Director of Nursing, Phillips County Hospital, Malta, MT, p. A378

CROWDER, Steve, Manager Information Technology, Natchitoches Regional Medical Center, Natchitoches, LA, p. A274

CROWE, Arthur, Director Information Systems, Peconic Bay Medical Center, Riverhead, NY, p. A440

CROWE, Danny, Chief Financial Officer, Decatur Morgan Hospital, Decatur, AL, p. A19

CROWE, William R., President, Conemaugh Miners Medical Center, Hastings, PA, p. A527

CROWELL, Eric T.
President and Chief Executive Officer, Iowa Methodist Medical Center, Des Moines, IA, p. A220
President and Chief Executive Officer, UnityPoint Health – Des Moines, Des Moines, IA, p. A220

CROWELL, Lynn, Chief Executive Officer, Arkansas Valley Regional Medical Center, La Junta, CO, p. A103

CROWL, Heather N., Chief Human Resources Officer, Kingman Regional Medical Center, Kingman, AZ, p. A32

CROWLEY, Amber, Vice President Human Resources, Avera Marshall Regional Medical Center, Marshall, MN, p. A335

CROWLEY, Cathleen, Chief Information Officer, Columbia Memorial Hospital, Hudson, NY, p. A427

CROWLEY, Daryl, Director Information Services, Memorial Medical Center of West Michigan, Ludington, MI, p. A319

CROWLEY, John, M.D. Medical Director, River Crest Hospital, San Angelo, TX, p. A630

CROWLEY, Sheryl, Chief Information Officer, Falmouth Hospital, Falmouth, MA, p. A300

CROWLEY, Thomas, President and Chief Executive Officer, Saint Elizabeth's Medical Center, Wabasha, MN, p. A342

CROWSON, Carol, Administrator, Beacon Children's Hospital, Luverne, AL, p. A22

CROWTHER, Bruce K., President and Chief Executive Officer, Northwest Community Hospital, Arlington Heights, IL, p. A173

CRUM, Dennis L., Vice President and Chief Financial Officer, Tift Regional Medical Center, Tifton, GA, p. A161

CRUM, Jarett, Administrator, EastPointe Hospital, Daphne, AL, p. A18

CRUMP, Michael C., Administrator, Villa Feliciana Medical Complex, Jackson, LA, p. A269

CRUMP, Rick, Chief Financial Officer, Lakeland Behavioral Health System, Springfield, MO, p. A372

CRUMPTON, Althea H., Administrator, Magee General Hospital, Magee, MS, p. A350

CRUMPTON, Elaine, Director Human Resources, Gunnison Valley Hospital, Gunnison, CO, p. A102

CRUNK, Frances H., Vice President and Chief Financial Officer, Florida Hospital Waterman, Tavares, FL, p. A142

CRUNKLETON, Kevin, Chief Financial Officer, Summit Surgical, LLC, Hutchinson, KS, p. A236

CRUSE, Adam, Chief Financial Officer, Three Rivers Medical Center, Louisa, KY, p. A255

CRUSE, Ray, Chief Executive Officer, Lakeland Community Hospital Watervliet, Watervliet, MI, p. A326

CRUTCHFIELD, David, Vice President and Chief Information Officer, Virginia Hospital Center – Arlington, Arlington, VA, p. A651

CRUTHIRDS, Leslie, Chief Human Resource Management Service, South Texas Veterans Health Care System, San Antonio, TX, p. A632

CRUTHIRDS, Richard, Director Information Systems, Peterson Regional Medical Center, Kerrville, TX, p. A616

CRUZ, Michael, Vice President Operations, Baptist St. Anthony Health System, Amarillo, TX, p. A582

CUBELLIS, Guido J.
Chief Operating Officer, Nexus Specialty Hospital, Shenandoah, TX, p. A633
Chief Operating Officer, Nexus Specialty Hospital The Woodlands, Spring, TX, p. A634

CUBRE, Alan, M.D. Medical Director, Kindred Hospital–Sacramento, Folsom, CA, p. A60

CUDWORTH, Craig R., Interim Chief Executive Officer, Hancock Medical Center, Bay Saint Louis, MS, p. A344

CUELLAR, Eddie, Vice President Information Systems, Methodist Hospital, San Antonio, TX, p. A631

CUELLAR, Jacob, M.D., Chief Executive Officer, Laurel Ridge Treatment Center, San Antonio, TX, p. A631

CUENCA, Derrick, Chief Executive Officer, Lake Granbury Medical Center, Granbury, TX, p. A606

CUERO, Liza, Coordinator Human Resources, Central Texas Rehabilitation Hospital, Austin, TX, p. A584

CUEVAS, Jacki, Director Health Information Services, Regional Rehabilitation Hospital, Phenix City, AL, p. A24

CULBERSON, David K., Chief Executive Officer, San Joaquin General Hospital, French Camp, CA, p. A61

CULBERTSON, Laura, Director Human Resources, Southwest Healthcare System, Murrieta, CA, p. A76

CULLEN, John, M.D. Chief of Staff and Medical Director Long Term Care, Providence Valdez Medical Center, Valdez, AK, p. A29

CULLEN, John, Assistant Superintendent, Thomas B. Finan Center, Cumberland, MD, p. A291

CULLEN, Michael, Senior Vice President and Chief Financial Officer, South Shore Hospital, South Weymouth, MA, p. A304

CULLEN, Paul T., M.D. Vice President Medical Affairs, Washington Hospital, Washington, PA, p. A543

CULLITON, Gerald F., Director, Veterans Affairs Hudson Valley Health Care System–F.D. Roosevelt Hospital, Montrose, NY, p. A430

CULLIVER, Sandra, Director Human Resources, National Park Medical Center, Hot Springs, AR, p. A45

CULP, Judy, Chief Financial Officer, Hill Regional Hospital, Hillsboro, TX, p. A608

CULUMBER, Janene, Vice President and Chief Financial Officer, H. Lee Moffitt Cancer Center and Research Institute, Tampa, FL, p. A141

CULVER, Shawna, Director Information Systems, Western Plains Medical Complex, Dodge City, KS, p. A233

CUMBEE, Lib, Director Information Systems, Providence Hospital, Columbia, SC, p. A550

CUMBIE, Dan L., Chief Nursing Officer, Flowers Hospital, Dothan, AL, p. A19

CUMMINGS, Brooke, Chief Financial Officer, LSU Bogalusa Medical Center, Bogalusa, LA, p. A264

CUMMINGS, Bruce D., President and Chief Executive Officer, Lawrence + Memorial Hospital, New London, CT, p. A111

CUMMINGS, Bruce D., M.D., President and Chief Executive Officer, Westerly Hospital, Westerly, RI, p. A547

CUMMINGS, Cindy, Chief Executive Officer, Putnam County Memorial Hospital, Unionville, MO, p. A373

CUMMINGS, Elmer, Vice President and Chief Financial Officer, Hardin Memorial Hospital, Elizabethtown, KY, p. A250

CUMMINGS, Greg, Chief Financial Officer, Texas Spine & Joint Hospital, Tyler, TX, p. A638

CUMMINGS, Lisa, Director Outpatient Services, Copper Queen Community Hospital, Bisbee, AZ, p. A30

CUMMINGS, Steven, Chief Operating Officer and Chief Information Officer, Noble Hospital, Westfield, MA, p. A306

CUMMINS, Frank L.
Vice President Human Resources, John C. Lincoln Deer Valley Hospital, Phoenix, AZ, p. A34
Vice President Human Resources, John C. Lincoln North Mountain Hospital, Phoenix, AZ, p. A34

CUMMINS, Tom, M.D. Director Hospitalist Program, White River Medical Center, Batesville, AR, p. A41

CUNEO, Anthony J., Chief Operating Officer, Metropolitan St. Louis Psychiatric Center, Saint Louis, MO, p. A370

CUNLIFFE, Ronald, D.O. Chief of Staff, Highlands Medical Center, Sparta, TN, p. A579

CUNNINGHAM, Dale, M.D. Medical Director, HEALTHSOUTH Rehabilitation Hospital of Memphis, Memphis, TN, p. A574

CUNNINGHAM, Gail, Interim Chief Medical Officer, University of Maryland St. Joseph Medical Center, Towson, MD, p. A294

CUNNINGHAM, Henry, M.D. President Medical Staff, Kindred Hospital Tarrant County–Fort Worth Southwest, Fort Worth, TX, p. A604

CUNNINGHAM, James C., M.D. Chief Medical Officer, Cook Children's Medical Center, Fort Worth, TX, p. A603

CUNNINGHAM, James M., M.D. Vice President Medical Affairs, Medical Center of Central Georgia, Macon, GA, p. A156

CUNNINGHAM, Keith W., M.D. Medical Director, HEALTHSOUTH Scottsdale Rehabilitation Hospital, Scottsdale, AZ, p. A37

CUNNINGHAM, Kris, M.D. Chief of Staff, Wheatland Memorial Healthcare, Harlowton, MT, p. A377

CUNNINGHAM, Larmar, Chief Operating Officer, West Central Georgia Regional Hospital, Columbus, GA, p. A150

CUNNINGHAM, M. Edward, Chief Executive Officer, Gateway Regional Medical Center, Granite City, IL, p. A184

CUNNINGHAM, Michelle P., Chief Executive Officer, Highlands Hospital, Connellsville, PA, p. A523

CUNNINGHAM, Robert, Vice President Human Resources, Good Samaritan Hospital, Kearney, NE, p. A385

CUNNINGHAM, William, D.O. Chief Medical Officer, Metro Health Hospital, Wyoming, MI, p. A327

CUPP, Roy, Director Management Information Systems, Fayette Regional Health System, Connersville, IN, p. A200

CURCURUTO, James J., Senior Vice President Finance, St. Joseph's Medical Center, Yonkers, NY, p. A446

CURL, MaryAnn, M.D. Interim Chief of Staff, Charles George Veterans Affairs Medical Center, Asheville, NC, p. A447

CURLING, Susan, M.D. Chief Medical Officer, Memorial Hermann Northeast, Humble, TX, p. A614

CURNEL, Robin, Chief Operating Officer and Chief Nursing Officer, Crittenden County Hospital, Marion, KY, p. A257

CURNOW, Annie, Coordinator Medical Staff and Public Relations, DeSoto Memorial Hospital, Arcadia, FL, p. A118

CURNUTT, Ann
Director Information Systems, Garfield Medical Center, Monterey Park, CA, p. A75
Director Information Systems, Monterey Park Hospital, Monterey Park, CA, p. A75

CURPHY, Rona, President and Chief Executive Officer, Casa Grande Regional Medical Center, Casa Grande, AZ, p. A30

CURRAN, Maria, Vice President Human Resources, VCU Health System, Richmond, VA, p. A661

CURRAN, Robert, Director Health Information Management, SSM St. Mary's Health Center, Saint Louis, MO, p. A370

CURRANS, Sheila, Chief Executive Officer, Harrison Memorial Hospital, Cynthiana, KY, p. A250

CURREN, Rob, Director Information Technology, Center for Behavioral Medicine, Kansas City, MO, p. A362

CURRIE, Scott D., Vice President and Chief Financial Officer, MidMichigan Medical Center–Midland, Midland, MI, p. A320

CURRIER, Donald L., Vice President Human Resources, Piedmont Medical Center, Rock Hill, SC, p. A555

CURRIN, Jr., John G., President, Alamance Regional Medical Center, Burlington, NC, p. A448

CURRIN, Sue, MS, Chief Executive Officer, San Francisco General Hospital Medical Center, San Francisco, CA, p. A87

CURRY, Cheryl, Vice President Finance, Avista Adventist Hospital, Louisville, CO, p. A104

CURRY, Jeffrey T.
Executive Vice President and Chief Financial Officer, Excela Frick Hospital, Mount Pleasant, PA, p. A532
Executive Vice President and Chief Financial Officer, Excela Health Westmoreland Hospital, Greensburg, PA, p. A526
Executive Vice President and Chief Financial Officer, Excela Latrobe Area Hospital, Latrobe, PA, p. A529

CURRY, Lori, Regional Chief Human Resources Officer, Providence Holy Cross Medical Center,, CA, p. A71

CURRY, Robert H.
President and Chief Executive Officer, Citrus Valley Medical Center, Covina, CA, p. A58
President and Chief Executive Officer, Foothill Presbyterian Hospital, Glendora, CA, p. A63

CURRY, Stephen A., Director Information Services, Princeton Community Hospital, Princeton, WV, p. A680

CURRY, Thomas A., M.D. Vice President Medical Affairs for Clinical Effectiveness and Documentation, Schuylkill Medical Center – East Norwegian Street, Pottsville, PA, p. A539

CURTIN, Sean, Interim Chief Financial Officer, Massena Memorial Hospital, Massena, NY, p. A429

CURTIN, Thomas F., Vice President and Chief Financial Officer, Good Samaritan Hospital, Dayton, OH, p. A479

CURTIS, Edgar J., President and Chief Executive Officer, Memorial Medical Center, Springfield, IL, p. A195

CURTIS, George, Director Information Technology Services, Upson Regional Medical Center, Thomaston, GA, p. A161

CURTIS, Janis, Interim Director Information Technology, Duke Raleigh Hospital, Raleigh, NC, p. A459

CURTIS, Jeff, Chief Operating Officer, Greenwood Leflore Hospital, Greenwood, MS, p. A347

CURTIS, Lorna, Chief Financial Officer, Kaiser Permanente Riverside Medical Center, Riverside, CA, p. A82

CURTIS, Lynda D., Senior Vice President and Executive Director, Bellevue Hospital Center, New York, NY, p. A430

CURTIS, Marilyn K., Vice President, Professional Services, Saint Francis Medical Center, Cape Girardeau, MO, p. A358

CURTIS, Scott A., Administrator and Chief Executive Officer, Kossuth Regional Health Center, Algona, IA, p. A216

CURVIN, Thomas J., M.D. Chief of Staff, Rankin Hospital District, Rankin, TX, p. A628

CUSANO, Susan, Director Human Resources, Four Winds Hospital, Katonah, NY, p. A428

CUSATIS, Michele A., Ph.D., Administrator, Waukesha County Mental Health Center, Waukesha, WI, p. A698

CUSENZ, Bruce J., M.D. Medical Director, Eastern Niagara Health System, Lockport, NY, p. A428

CUSHING, Heidi, Director Finance, Gordon Memorial Hospital, Gordon, NE, p. A384

CUSSINS, James, Chief Financial Officer, East Morgan County Hospital, Brush, CO, p. A98

CUSTER–MITCHELL, Marilyn J., President and Chief Executive Officer, Wabash County Hospital, Wabash, IN, p. A214

CUSUMANO, Margaret M., R.N. Chief Nursing Officer and Vice President Care Services, Vassar Brothers Medical Center, Poughkeepsie, NY, p. A440

CUTLER, Nancy, R.N. Vice President Patient Services/CNO, FHN Memorial Hospital, Freeport, IL, p. A183

CUTLER, Terry, Administrator and Chief Executive Officer, East Texas Medical Center Crockett, Crockett, TX, p. A594

CUTOLO, Jr., Edward, M.D. Chief of Staff, James A. Haley Veterans' Hospital, Tampa, FL, p. A141

CUTSFORTH, Shawn, Information Systems Officer, Pioneer Memorial Hospital, Heppner, OR, p. A513

CUZZOLA, Anthony, Vice President Rehabilitation Services, JFK Johnson Rehabilitation Institute, Edison, NJ, p. A403

CWYNAR, Jan, Vice President Operations, Regency Hospital of Minneapolis, Golden Valley, MN, p. A333

CYTLAK, David
Chief Financial Officer, Blanchard Valley Hospital, Findlay, OH, p. A481
Vice President Finance, Bluffton Hospital, Bluffton, OH, p. A472

CZAHOR, John, Chief Information Officer, Botsford Hospital, Farmington Hills, MI, p. A313

CZAJKA, Paul M., Chief Operating Officer, Fountain Valley Regional Hospital and Medical Center, Fountain Valley, CA, p. A60

CZEREW, Jane, Vice President Clinical Services and Quality, Spectrum Health Zeeland Community Hospital, Zeeland, MI, p. A327

CZIPO, Kevin F., Executive Director and Chief Executive Officer, Stony Lodge Hospital, Ossining, NY, p. A439

CZUGALA, Matt, Manager Information Systems, Heartland Surgical Specialty Hospital, Overland Park, KS, p. A241

CZYZ, AnneMarie, R.N. Vice President for Clinical and Educational Services, St. Joseph's Hospital Health Center, Syracuse, NY, p. A444

# D

D'ACCURZIO, Albert, M.D. Medical Director, St. Elizabeth Medical Center, Utica, NY, p. A444

D'AGNES, Michael R., FACHE, President and Chief Executive Officer, Raritan Bay Medical Center, Perth Amboy, NJ, p. A409

D'AGOSTINO, Becky, R.N. Director of Nursing, Baraga County Memorial Hospital, L'Anse, MI, p. A318

D'ALBERTO, Richard E., FACHE, Chief Executive Officer, Greenville Health System Laurens County Memorial Hospital, Clinton, SC, p. A550

D'AMICO, Kenneth, Chief Executive Officer, Landmark Hospital of Joplin, Joplin, MO, p. A362

D'AMORE, Seanna, Director Human Resources, Elk Regional Health Center, Saint Marys, PA, p. A540

D'ANGELO, Elizabeth, M.D. Chief of Staff, Onslow Memorial Hospital, Jacksonville, NC, p. A455

D'ANGELO, Jennifer, Assistant Vice President Information Services, Christian Health Care Center, Wyckoff, NJ, p. A413

D'ANGELO, John, Chief Executive Officer, Banner Churchill Community Hospital, Fallon, NV, p. A391

D'ANGINA, Joseph, Area Finance Officer, Kaiser Permanente Vallejo Medical Center, Vallejo, CA, p. A94

D'AQUILA, Richard, President and Chief Operating Officer, Yale–New Haven Hospital, New Haven, CT, p. A110

D'ASTOUS, Jacques, M.D. Chief of Staff, Shriners Hospitals for Children–Salt Lake City, Salt Lake City, UT, p. A647

D'ENBEAU, Richard, Chief Operating Officer, Mount Carmel New Albany Surgical Hospital, New Albany, OH, p. A487

D'ESMOND, C. Thomas, FACHE, Administrator, Shriners Hospitals for Children–Boston Burns Hospital, Boston, MA, p. A297

D'ETTORRE, Joseph A., Chief Executive Officer, Wyandot Memorial Hospital, Upper Sandusky, OH, p. A491

D'SOUZA, Carol, Director Human Resources, Casa Grande Regional Medical Center, Casa Grande, AZ, p. A30

DAANE, John, Information Systems Officer, Prairie du Chien Memorial Hospital, Prairie Du Chien, WI, p. A695

DABNEY, Ann, Manager Human Resources, Spring View Hospital, Lebanon, KY, p. A253

DABNEY, Janice, Interim Chief Executive Officer, Springs Memorial Hospital, Lancaster, SC, p. A554

DACE, Linda, Vice President Finance, McDonough District Hospital, Macomb, IL, p. A187

DACEY, Michael J., M.D. Senior Vice President and Chief Medical Officer, Kent County Memorial Hospital, Warwick, RI, p. A547

DACOSTA, June, Acting Executive Director, New York City Children's Center,, NY, p. A434

DACUS, Michael E.
Vice President and Chief Financial Officer, Sheltering Arms Hospital South, Midlothian, VA, p. A657
Vice President and Chief Financial Officer, Sheltering Arms Rehabilitation Hospital, Mechanicsville, VA, p. A657
DADEY, Mary Lee, R.N. Vice President of Nursing, Windber Medical Center, Windber, PA, p. A545
DADLEZ, Christopher M.
President and Chief Executive Officer, Mount Sinai Rehabilitation Hospital, Hartford, CT, p. A109
President and Chief Executive Officer, Saint Francis Hospital and Medical Center, Hartford, CT, p. A109
DADO, Joseph, Chief Information Officer, Conemaugh Memorial Medical Center, Johnstown, PA, p. A528
DAECH, Ed, Director Human Resources, Heartland Regional Medical Center, Marion, IL, p. A187
DAEGER, Brian, Vice President Financial Services, Margaret Mary Health, Batesville, IN, p. A198
DAFOE, Joe, R.N. Chief Clinical Officer, Columbia Memorial Hospital, Astoria, OR, p. A511
DAGHER, Michel, D.O. Vice President and Chief Medical Officer, Banner Del E. Webb Medical Center, Sun City West, AZ, p. A38
DAGLIO, Michael, Chief Operating Officer, Danbury Hospital, Danbury, CT, p. A108
DAH, Cyrus E., Chief Financial Officer, Dameron Hospital, Stockton, CA, p. A91
DAHDUL, Adnan, M.D. Medical Director, HEALTHSOUTH Rehabilitation Hospital of Western Massachusetts, Ludlow, MA, p. A301
DAHL, James E., Chief Information Officer, Fort HealthCare, Fort Atkinson, WI, p. A686
DAHLBERG, Connie, Director Business and Employee, Sleepy Eye Medical Center, Sleepy Eye, MN, p. A341
DAHLEN, Gretchen M., FACHE, Chief Administrative Officer, Winneshiek Medical Center, Decorah, IA, p. A220
DAHLHAUSEN, Daniel J., M.D. President of Medical Staff/Chief Medical Officer, Cannon Memorial Hospital, Pickens, SC, p. A555
DAHLING, James D., President and Chief Executive Officer, Children's Hospital of The King's Daughters, Norfolk, VA, p. A658
DAHLMAN, Kim, Administrator, Lost Rivers Medical Center, Arco, ID, p. A167
DAHLQUIST, Clay, M.D. Chief Medical Officer, Waverly Health Center, Waverly, IA, p. A229
DAHLSTRAND, David, Associate Chief of Staff Information Technology, Hunter Holmes McGuire Veterans Affairs Medical Center, Richmond, VA, p. A660
DAHLSTROM, Josiah, Administrator, Safe Haven Hospital of Pocatello, Pocatello, ID, p. A171
DAIGLE, Charles D.
Senior Vice President and Chief Operating Officer, Willis–Knighton Medical Center, Shreveport, LA, p. A278
Chief Operating Officer, WK Bossier Health Center, Bossier City, LA, p. A264
DAIGLE, Cheryl, R.N. Director of Nursing, Northern Maine Medical Center, Fort Kent, ME, p. A283
DAIGLE, Cindy, Chief Financial Officer, Houlton Regional Hospital, Houlton, ME, p. A283
DAIGLE, J. Barry, Manager Information Systems, University Medical Center, Lafayette, LA, p. A271
DAIKEN, Michael E., Chief Financial Officer, Highlands–Cashiers Hospital, Highlands, NC, p. A455
DAIKER, David, Chief Information Resource Management, Veterans Affairs Nebraska–Western Iowa Health Care System, Lincoln, NE, p. A386
DAILEY, Linda, Acting Chief Human Resources Officer, Charlie Norwood Veterans Affairs Medical Center, Augusta, GA, p. A147
DAILY, James L., President, Porter Medical Center, Middlebury, VT, p. A649
DAISLEY, Samuel, D.O. Vice President Medical Affairs, UPMC Horizon, Greenville, PA, p. A526
DAL COL, Richard, Vice President and Chief Medical Officer, Champlain Valley Physicians Hospital Medical Center, Plattsburgh, NY, p. A439
DALBY, William, Director Fiscal Services, Shriners Hospitals for Children–Northern California, Sacramento, CA, p. A83
DALE III, David B., Chief Executive Officer, Pristine Hospital of Pasadena, Pasadena, TX, p. A626
DALE, Deborah, Chief Executive Officer, Select Specialty Hospital–Denver, Denver, CO, p. A100
DALE, Jackson, Director Management Information Services, Johnston Memorial Hospital, Abingdon, VA, p. A651
DALE, Jae, Chief Executive Officer, Oro Valley Hospital, Oro Valley, AZ, p. A33
DALEBOUT, Kenneth, Administrator and Chief Executive Officer, Arroyo Grande Community Hospital, Arroyo Grande, CA, p. A53

DALEY, Chris, M.D. Chief of Staff, Estes Park Medical Center, Estes Park, CO, p. A101
DALEY, Robert, Vice President Fiscal and Information Technology Services, Black River Memorial Hospital, Black River Falls, WI, p. A684
DALL, Jamie, Director Finance and Support Operations, New Hampshire Hospital, Concord, NH, p. A397
DALLER, Sue, R.N. Assistant Administrator of Nursing, Hermann Area District Hospital, Hermann, MO, p. A361
DALLEY, Mark F., Administrator, Gunnison Valley Hospital, Gunnison, UT, p. A643
DALPIAZ, Joseph M., Director, Philadephia Veterans Affairs Medical Center, Philadelphia, PA, p. A536
DALPOAS, Dolan, President and Chief Executive Officer, Abraham Lincoln Memorial Hospital, Lincoln, IL, p. A187
DALTON, Dayle, Vice President Human Resources, Los Robles Hospital and Medical Center, Thousand Oaks, CA, p. A92
DALTON, Eric
Chief Financial Officer, Memorial Medical Center, Modesto, CA, p. A74
Chief Financial Officer, Sutter Tracy Community Hospital, Tracy, CA, p. A93
DALTON, John, President and Chief Executive Officer, Inland Hospital, Waterville, ME, p. A285
DALTON, Ronald, M.D. Chief Medical Officer, NORTHSTAR Health System, Iron River, MI, p. A317
DALTON, Valerie, R.N., Administrator, Oceans Behavioral Hospital of Baton Rouge, Baton Rouge, LA, p. A263
DALTON, Wayne, Chief Financial Officer, Lakeview Hospital, Bountiful, UT, p. A643
DALY, Gail, Chief Operating Officer, St. Mary Medical Center, Long Beach, CA, p. A67
DALY, Sheila, President and Chief Executive Officer, Clinton Hospital, Clinton, MA, p. A299
DALY, Thomas M., Chief Financial Officer, University of Medicine and Dentistry of New Jersey–University Hospital, Newark, NJ, p. A407
DALY, Tim F., Chief Operating Officer, Kaiser Permanente Antioch Medical Center, Antioch, CA, p. A52
DALY, William, Interim Chief Executive Officer, Pennsylvania Psychiatric Institute, Harrisburg, PA, p. A527
DAMA, Sunil, M.D. Medical Director, Regency Hospital of Cincinnati, Cincinnati, OH, p. A475
DAMBOISE, Robin, Director Human Resources, Northern Maine Medical Center, Fort Kent, ME, p. A283
DAMM, Julie, Chief Financial Officer, Hancock County Health System, Britt, IA, p. A217
DAMMEYER, Matt, Ph.D. Chief Operating Officer, Central Peninsula General Hospital, Soldotna, AK, p. A29
DAMODARAN, A. N., M.D. President Medical Staff, Indiana University Health Starke Hospital, Knox, IN, p. A207
DAMON, Chad, Chief Information Officer, St. Vincent Dunn Hospital, Bedford, IN, p. A198
DANCH, Stephen M., Chief Financial Officer, UPMC Hamot, Erie, PA, p. A526
DANDRIDGE, Thomas C., FACHE, President and Chief Executive Officer, Regional Medical Center, Orangeburg, SC, p. A555
DANE, Jeff, Executive Vice President and Chief Financial Officer, University Medical Center, Lubbock, TX, p. A620
DANG, Cynthia, Vice President Human Resources, North Hills Hospital, North Richland Hills, TX, p. A625
DANG, Minh, Vice President Finance, Robert Packer Hospital, Sayre, PA, p. A540
DANGEL–PALMER, MaryClaire, Chief Operating Officer, Henry Ford West Bloomfield Hospital, West Bloomfield, MI, p. A326
DANGERFIELD, Wesley, Community Chief Executive Officer, Summers County ARH Hospital, Hinton, WV, p. A677
DANIEL, Christopher W., Chief Financial Officer, Louisiana Heart Hospital, Lacombe, LA, p. A270
DANIEL, Dena, Director Information Systems, Jackson County Memorial Hospital, Altus, OK, p. A495
DANIEL, Lisa, Interim Chief Executive Officer, Memphis Mental Health Institute, Memphis, TN, p. A575
DANIEL, Patricia, Chief Information Officer, Lake Whitney Medical Center, Whitney, TX, p. A641
DANIEL, Richard, Administrator, Wedowee Hospital, Wedowee, AL, p. A26
DANIEL, Robin, Director of Human Resources, Northridge Medical Center, Commerce, GA, p. A150
DANIEL, Ron, Manager Information Systems, Matheny Medical and Educational Center, Peapack, NJ, p. A408
DANIEL, Steven G.
Senior Vice President and Chief Operating Officer, CHRISTUS Spohn Hospital Alice, Alice, TX, p. A581
Interim Vice President and Chief Operating Officer, CHRISTUS Spohn Hospital Kleberg, Kingsville, TX, p. A616
DANIEL, Vera W., Chief Human Resources Officer, Saint Louis University Hospital, Saint Louis, MO, p. A370
DANIEL, W. D., D.O. Chief of Staff, Medical Center of Manchester, Manchester, TN, p. A573

DANIEL, William, M.D. Chief Medical Officer, Booneville Community Hospital, Booneville, AR, p. A41
DANIELS, Andy
Chief Operating Officer, Bucyrus Community Hospital, Bucyrus, OH, p. A472
Vice President Non–Clinical Operations and Information Systems, Galion Community Hospital, Galion, OH, p. A482
DANIELS, Anita, Executive Director, Rockland Children's Psychiatric Center, Orangeburg, NY, p. A439
DANIELS, Betty, M.D. Chief of Staff, St. Bernardine Medical Center, San Bernardino, CA, p. A84
DANIELS, Buddy, Chief Executive Officer, Helena Regional Medical Center, Helena, AR, p. A44
DANIELS, Craig M., Chief Financial Officer, Moab Regional Hospital, Moab, UT, p. A644
DANIELS, Jeff, Chief Financial Officer, Bingham Memorial Hospital, Blackfoot, ID, p. A167
DANIELS, John, M.D. Medical Director, LifeCare Hospitals of Wisconsin, Pewaukee, WI, p. A694
DANIELS, Judy, Vice President Human Resources, Our Lady of Bellefonte Hospital, Ashland, KY, p. A248
DANIELS, Karen, MSN Chief Nursing Officer, Halifax Regional Medical Center, Roanoke Rapids, NC, p. A459
DANIELS, Kristin, Manager Human Resources, Sutter Center for Psychiatry, Sacramento, CA, p. A84
DANIELS, Mark, M.D. Vice President Physician Enterprise, Delnor Hospital, Geneva, IL, p. A183
DANIELS, S. Janette, Director Human Resources, HEALTHSOUTH Rehabilitation Hospital of Fort Smith, Fort Smith, AR, p. A44
DANIELS, Val C., Chief Financial Officer, Adventist Rehabilitation Hospital of Maryland, Rockville, MD, p. A293
DANIELS, Yelandra, M.D. Chief of Staff, Evans Memorial Hospital, Claxton, GA, p. A150
DANIELSON, David S., Senior Vice President Operations, EvergreenHealth, Kirkland, WA, p. A667
DANITZ, Doug, Director Information Technology, West Branch Regional Medical Center, West Branch, MI, p. A326
DANKER, Doug, Administrator, Mercy Hospital El Reno, El Reno, OK, p. A498
DANKERT, Sheri
Chief Financial Officer, Mayo Clinic Health System in Albert Lea, Albert Lea, MN, p. A328
Vice President Finance, Mayo Clinic Health System in Austin, Austin, MN, p. A329
DANKO, Douglas, President and Chief Executive Officer, Jameson Hospital, New Castle, PA, p. A533
DANN, Doreen, R.N. Chief Operating Officer, Victor Valley Community Hospital, Victorville, CA, p. A95
DANTIS, Gerry, Assistant Vice President Finance, SUNY Downstate Medical Center University Hospital,, NY, p. A436
DANUSER, James, Chief Information Officer, Veterans Affairs Central Iowa Health Care System, Des Moines, IA, p. A220
DAOUD, Joudat, M.D. Chief of Staff, Community Health Center of Branch County, Coldwater, MI, p. A311
DAQUIOAG, Francis, Controller, Kahuku Medical Center, Kahuku, HI, p. A165
DARBONNE, Tina, Chief Financial Officer, Central Louisiana State Hospital, Pineville, LA, p. A277
DARBY, Doug, Director Information Systems, Pioneers Memorial Healthcare District, Brawley, CA, p. A55
DARBY, Sharon, R.N. Vice President, Clinical Operations, Children's Hospital of Richmond at VCU–Brook Road Campus, Richmond, VA, p. A660
DARCEY, Patricia, R.N. Vice President/Chief Nursing Officer, Southampton Hospital, Southampton, NY, p. A443
DARDANO, Anthony, M.D. Chief Medical Officer, Delray Medical Center, Delray Beach, FL, p. A122
DARDEAU, Sean T., Chief Operating Officer, Trinity Medical Center, Birmingham, AL, p. A17
DARDEN, David B., Chief Executive Officer, Raleigh General Hospital, Beckley, WV, p. A675
DAREY, Roland, M.D. Medical Director, Wamego City Hospital, Wamego, KS, p. A245
DARLING, Rudy, Chief Operating Officer, Baxter Regional Medical Center, Mountain Home, AR, p. A48
DARNELL, Brian, D.O. Chief of Staff, Johnson County Healthcare Center, Buffalo, WY, p. A701
DARNELL, Don, Chief Information Officer, Hamilton Memorial Hospital District, McLeansboro, IL, p. A188
DARNELL, Linda, Director Management Information Systems, King's Daughters' Health, Madison, IN, p. A209
DARNELL, Vicki A., MSN, President and Chief Executive Officer, Ephraim McDowell Regional Medical Center, Danville, KY, p. A250
DARR, Joan, R.N. Interim Chief Nursing Officer, Trumbull Memorial Hospital, Warren, OH, p. A492
DARVIN, Ken, M.D. Chief of Staff, Stroud Regional Medical Center, Stroud, OK, p. A507

DASARO, Lynda
Director Human Resources, Sutter Auburn Faith Hospital, Auburn, CA, p. A53
Director Human Resources, Sutter Roseville Medical Center, Roseville, CA, p. A83

DASCHER Jr., Norman E.
Chief Executive Officer, Samaritan Hospital, Troy, NY, p. A444
Executive Vice President, St. Mary's Hospital, Troy, NY, p. A444

DASKALAKIS, Tom G., Chief Operating Officer, West Chester Hospital, West Chester, OH, p. A493

DASS, Karla, Director Human Resources, Tri–County Hospital – Williston, Williston, FL, p. A144

DASSENKO, Dennis, Chief Information Officer, Essentia Health Duluth, Duluth, MN, p. A331

DATER, Suzanne, M.D. President Medical Staff, Bridgton Hospital, Bridgton, ME, p. A282

DAUBY, Randall W., Chief Executive Officer, Hamilton Memorial Hospital District, McLeansboro, IL, p. A188

DAUGHDRILL, Diane, Director Human Resources, Jefferson Davis Community Hospital, Prentiss, MS, p. A353

DAUGHDRILL, Richard, R.N., Chief Executive Officer, AMG Specialty Hospital–Slidell, Slidell, LA, p. A278

DAUGHERTY, Don, Director Information Systems, Fleming County Hospital, Flemingsburg, KY, p. A250

DAUGHERTY, Robert Alan, Chief Executive Officer, Mercy Regional Medical Center, Ville Platte, LA, p. A280

DAUGHERTY, Sam, Ed.D., President, Spectrum Health Reed City Hospital, Reed City, MI, p. A322

DAUGHERTY, Thomas E., Administrator, Mecosta County Medical Center, Big Rapids, MI, p. A309

DAUGHTRY, Kaci, Director Human Resources, Andalusia Regional Hospital, Andalusia, AL, p. A15

DAUTERIVE, F. Ralph, M.D. Vice President Medical Affairs, Ochsner Medical Center–Baton Rouge, Baton Rouge, LA, p. A263

DAVANT, III, Charles, M.D. Chief Medical Officer, Blowing Rock Hospital, Blowing Rock, NC, p. A448

DAVE, Bhasker J., M.D., Superintendent, Mental Health Institute, Independence, IA, p. A223

DAVENPORT, Douglas, System Chief Financial Officer, Benefis Hospitals, Great Falls, MT, p. A376

DAVENPORT, Ginger, Director Human Resources, Texas Specialty Hospital at Dallas, Dallas, TX, p. A598

DAVENPORT, Julie, Chief Executive Officer, I–70 Community Hospital, Sweet Springs, MO, p. A372

DAVENPORT, Polly J., R.N., Chief Executive Officer, Ochsner Medical Center – North Shore, Slidell, LA, p. A279

DAVENPORT, Sally, Vice President of Patient Care Services & CNO, Ephraim McDowell Regional Medical Center, Danville, KY, p. A250

DAVENPORT, Sheilah, R.N., Chief Executive Officer and Superintendent, Clifton T. Perkins Hospital Center, Jessup, MD, p. A292

DAVID, Biff, Administrator, St. Landry Extended Care Hospital, Opelousas, LA, p. A276

DAVID, Daphne, Chief Operating Officer, Garden Park Medical Center, Gulfport, MS, p. A347

DAVID, Jeffrey, D.O. Chief Medical Officer, St. Mary's Medical Center, West Palm Beach, FL, p. A143

DAVID, Lim, Vice President Finance and Chief Financial Officer, St. Joseph Medical Center, Reading, PA, p. A540

DAVID, Michelle, Interim Chief Executive Officer, Valley Hospital Phoenix, Phoenix, AZ, p. A36

DAVID, Myers M., Chief Information Officer, Iredell Memorial Hospital, Statesville, NC, p. A461

DAVID, R. Neal, Administrator and Chief of Staff, Madigan Healthcare System, Tacoma, WA, p. A673

DAVID, Robert
President and Chief Executive Officer, University Hospitals Conneaut Medical Center, Conneaut, OH, p. A479
President and Chief Executive Officer, University Hospitals Geneva Medical Center, Geneva, OH, p. A482

DAVIDOFF, Ravin, M.D. Chief Medical Officer, Boston Medical Center, Boston, MA, p. A296

DAVIDOW, Bruce B., Senior Vice President and Chief Operating Officer, Phelps Memorial Hospital Center, Sleepy Hollow, NY, p. A442

DAVIDOW, Daniel N., M.D. Medical Director, Cumberland Hospital, New Kent, VA, p. A657

DAVIDSON, Camille, Director Human Resources, Stanton County Hospital, Johnson, KS, p. A236

DAVIDSON, Charles O., M.D. Vice President Medical Affairs, Methodist Hospitals, Gary, IN, p. A203

DAVIDSON, Craig Val
Chief Executive Officer and Administrator, Beaver Valley Hospital, Beaver, UT, p. A643
Chief Executive Officer, Milford Valley Memorial Hospital, Milford, UT, p. A644

DAVIDSON, Diane, Senior Vice President Human Resources, Essentia Health Duluth, Duluth, MN, p. A331

DAVIDSON, Gary, Senior Vice President and Chief Information Officer, Lancaster General Health, Lancaster, PA, p. A528

DAVIDSON, Gary, M.D. Medical Director, Select Specialty Hospital–Johnstown, Johnstown, PA, p. A528

DAVIDSON, Gregg A., FACHE, Chief Executive Officer, Skagit Valley Hospital, Mount Vernon, WA, p. A668

DAVIDSON, James, Director of Information Services, Ferry County Memorial Hospital, Republic, WA, p. A670

DAVIDSON, John, Vice President Human Resources, Sharon Regional Health System, Sharon, PA, p. A541

DAVIDSON, Kathleen, Vice President, Patient Care Services and Chief Nursing Officer, Norwood Hospital, Norwood, MA, p. A303

DAVIDSON, Lezley, Chief Nursing Officer, Atoka County Medical Center, Atoka, OK, p. A496

DAVIDSON, Nancy, Senior Vice President and Chief Financial Officer, Jackson County Memorial Hospital, Altus, OK, p. A495

DAVIDSON, Paulette, Chief Executive Officer, Bellevue Medical Center, Bellevue, NE, p. A382

DAVIDSON, Peter, M.D. Chief Medical Officer, Blue Mountain Recovery Center, Pendleton, OR, p. A515

DAVIDSON, Randy, M.D. Chief of Staff, Medical Center of Arlington, Arlington, TX, p. A583

DAVIDSON, Rocky, Chief Financial Officer, Hollywood Pavilion,, FL, p. A125

DAVIDSON, Rowena, Manager Business Office, AMG Specialty Hospital–Edmond, Edmond, OK, p. A498

DAVIDSON, Tim, M.D. Chief Executive Physician Services, Providence St. Mary Medical Center, Walla Walla, WA, p. A674

DAVIDSON, Verno, R.N. Chief Nursing Officer, Vaughan Regional Medical Center, Selma, AL, p. A25

DAVIES, Donald, M.D. Chief of Staff, Valley View Regional Hospital, Ada, OK, p. A495

DAVIES, Janie, Chief Financial Officer, New Mexico Rehabilitation Center, Roswell, NM, p. A417

DAVILA, Susan, Chief Executive Officer and Administrator, Carson Valley Medical Center, Gardnerville, NV, p. A391

DAVIN, Joni, Director Information and Business Management Service Line, Veterans Affairs Eastern Kansas Health Care System, Topeka, KS, p. A245

DAVINI, John, Vice President, St. Rose Hospital, Hayward, CA, p. A64

DAVIS, A. Jack, Vice President Human Resources, Canton–Potsdam Hospital, Potsdam, NY, p. A440

DAVIS, Adam
Director Information Technology, Cornerstone Hospital of SouthEast Arizona, Tucson, AZ, p. A38
Chief Information Officer, Cornerstone Hospital–West Monroe, West Monroe, LA, p. A280
Chief Information Officer, Solara Hospital Harlingen, Harlingen, TX, p. A608

DAVIS, Amelia, Director of Nursing, CrossRidge Community Hospital, Wynne, AR, p. A51

DAVIS, Amy, Chief Operating Officer, Southwest Regional Rehabilitation Center, Battle Creek, MI, p. A309

DAVIS, Andrea, Assistant Administrator, Southern Hills Hospital and Medical Center, Las Vegas, NV, p. A393

DAVIS, Andrew, President, Carney Hospital, Boston, MA, p. A296

DAVIS, Andy, President, St. Vincent's Birmingham, Birmingham, AL, p. A17

DAVIS, Anne, Director Human Resources, Mason District Hospital, Havana, IL, p. A184

DAVIS, Autherine, Director Human Resources, D. W. McMillan Memorial Hospital, Brewton, AL, p. A18

DAVIS, Barry L., FACHE, President and Chief Executive Officer, Arkansas Methodist Medical Center, Paragould, AR, p. A49

DAVIS, Brandy, M.D. Chief of Staff, Forrest City Medical Center, Forrest City, AR, p. A44

DAVIS, Brenda, R.N. Vice President of Patient Services, Indiana University Health Bedford Hospital, Bedford, IN, p. A198

DAVIS, Brent
Human Resources Team Leader, Arkansas Heart Hospital, Little Rock, AR, p. A46
Chief Financial Officer, Central Valley Medical Center, Nephi, UT, p. A645

DAVIS, C. Y., M.D. Chief Medical Officer, LewisGale Hospital Montgomery, Blacksburg, VA, p. A652

DAVIS, C.J., Chief Executive Officer/ Executive Director, Four County Counseling Center, Logansport, IN, p. A209

DAVIS, Cathy J.
Director Human Resources, ProMedica Bixby Hospital, Adrian, MI, p. A308
Director Human Resources, ProMedica Herrick Hospital, Tecumseh, MI, p. A325

DAVIS, Charles A., Chief Executive Officer, Jennersville Regional Hospital, West Grove, PA, p. A544

DAVIS, Charles M., Ph.D., Director, Central State Hospital, Petersburg, VA, p. A659

DAVIS, Charlotte C., Director Human Resources, Lincoln Trail Behavioral Health System, Radcliff, KY, p. A259

DAVIS, Cory, Chief Operating Officer, West Valley Medical Center, Caldwell, ID, p. A168

DAVIS, Curtis, Director Finance, Baystate Mary Lane Hospital, Ware, MA, p. A306

DAVIS, Dan, R.N. Nurse Administrator, Park City Medical Center, Park City, UT, p. A645

DAVIS, Daniel E., Chief Financial Officer, Kingwood Medical Center, Kingwood, TX, p. A617

DAVIS, Darcy, Senior Vice President and Chief Financial Officer, Memorial Health, Savannah, GA, p. A160

DAVIS, David, Chief Operating Officer, Western Maryland Hospital Center, Hagerstown, MD, p. A292

DAVIS, Deborah W., Chief Operating Officer, VCU Health System, Richmond, VA, p. A661

DAVIS, Dell, Director Information Systems, Doctor's Hospital – Tidwell, Houston, TX, p. A609

DAVIS, Diane, Manager Business Office, HEALTHSOUTH Rehabilitation Hospital of Montgomery, Montgomery, AL, p. A23

DAVIS, Donald, Vice President Human Resources, Sparrow Hospital, Lansing, MI, p. A318

DAVIS, Donna, Chief Nursing Officer, Bourbon Community Hospital, Paris, KY, p. A259

DAVIS, Evan, Director Technology and Environmental Services, Knox County Hospital, Barbourville, KY, p. A248

DAVIS, Gannon, Director Human Resources, Medical West, Bessemer, AL, p. A16

DAVIS, Gary
Vice President Information Systems, Baptist Medical Center, San Antonio, TX, p. A630
Director Information Systems, Great River Medical Center, West Burlington, IA, p. A230

DAVIS, Gloria K., Chief Information Management, Colonel Florence A. Blanchfield Army Community Hospital, Fort Campbell, KY, p. A251

DAVIS, Gordon, Vice President Finance, USMD Hospital at Arlington, Arlington, TX, p. A584

DAVIS, Hervey E., Chief Executive Officer, Franklin Hospital District, Benton, IL, p. A174

DAVIS, James, M.D. Chief Medical Staff, Chatham Hospital, Siler City, NC, p. A461

DAVIS, Janet, R.N. Senior Vice President and Chief Nursing Officer, Tampa General Hospital, Tampa, FL, p. A142

DAVIS, Janice, Interim Director Human Resources, Gifford Medical Center, Randolph, VT, p. A650

DAVIS, Jeff
Market Information Officer, CHRISTUS Schumpert Medical Center, Shreveport, LA, p. A278
Chief Financial Officer, Harrison County Hospital, Corydon, IN, p. A200
Senior Vice President Human Resources, Massachusetts General Hospital, Boston, MA, p. A297

DAVIS, Jefferson, M.D. Medical Director, Perry Hospital, Perry, GA, p. A158

DAVIS, Jimmy, Director Human Resources, Hardin Medical Center, Savannah, TN, p. A578

DAVIS, Joe, M.D. Vice President Medical Affairs, Mary Lanning Healthcare, Hastings, NE, p. A384

DAVIS, John William, Chief Executive Officer and Chief Financial Officer, Slidell Memorial Hospital, Slidell, LA, p. A279

DAVIS, Johnette, Director of Nursing, Lake Butler Hospital Hand Surgery Center, Lake Butler, FL, p. A128

DAVIS, Johnnie, Director Human Resources, Medicine Lodge Memorial Hospital, Medicine Lodge, KS, p. A240

DAVIS, Jon, Chief Financial Officer, Cleveland Area Hospital, Cleveland, OK, p. A497

DAVIS, Jonathan S., FACHE, President, Methodist Charlton Medical Center, Dallas, TX, p. A596

DAVIS, Justin, Chief Executive Officer, Moses Taylor Hospital, Scranton, PA, p. A540

DAVIS, Kenneth, Assistant Vice President Information Systems, Kennedy Krieger Institute, Baltimore, MD, p. A287

DAVIS, LaKeitha, Director Human Resources, Medical Center of South Arkansas, El Dorado, AR, p. A43

DAVIS, Lary, President and Chief Executive Officer, Adventist La Grange Memorial Hospital, La Grange, IL, p. A186

DAVIS, Leslie C., President, Magee–Womens Hospital of UPMC, Pittsburgh, PA, p. A537

DAVIS, Lisa, Vice President Finance, Saint Thomas West Hospital, Nashville, TN, p. A577

DAVIS, Lisa A., M.D. Chief of Staff, Nix Health Care System, San Antonio, TX, p. A632

DAVIS, Lora, Chief Executive Officer, Select Specialty Hospital–Tallahassee, Tallahassee, FL, p. A141

DAVIS, Lori, Chief Financial Officer, Mayhill Hospital, Denton, TX, p. A598

DAVIS, Lorraine, Vice President Human Resources, Horn Memorial Hospital, Ida Grove, IA, p. A223

DAVIS, Lyle E., Administrator, Cozad Community Hospital, Cozad, NE, p. A382

DAVIS, Malene S., R.N., President and Chief Executive Officer, Capital Hospice, Arlington, VA, p. A651

DAVIS, Mark, Director Information Systems, Lake Taylor Transitional Care Hospital, Norfolk, VA, p. A658

DAVIS, Mary, Vice President, Avera St. Luke's Hospital, Aberdeen, SD, p. A558

DAVIS, Matt, Chief Operating Officer, North Florida Regional Medical Center, Gainesville, FL, p. A124

DAVIS, Melinda D., MSN, Interim Chief Executive Officer, Eastern Oklahoma Medical Center, Poteau, OK, p. A505

DAVIS, Melissa, Chief Operating Officer, Andalusia Regional Hospital, Andalusia, AL, p. A15

DAVIS, Pamela M., President and Chief Executive Officer, Edward Hospital, Naperville, IL, p. A189

DAVIS, Patricia, Chief Nursing Officer, South Central Kansas Medical Center, Arkansas City, KS, p. A231

DAVIS, Paula M., Chief Human Resources Officer, Sonoma Valley Hospital, Sonoma, CA, p. A91

DAVIS, Randy, Chief Information Officer, Northcrest Medical Center, Springfield, TN, p. A579

DAVIS, Ray
  Administrative Director, Providence Memorial Hospital, El Paso, TX, p. A601
  Administrative Director Information Systems, Sierra Medical Center, El Paso, TX, p. A601

DAVIS, Richard, Chief Executive Officer, Central Peninsula General Hospital, Soldotna, AK, p. A29

DAVIS, Richard, M.D. Regional Chief Medical Officer, CHRISTUS Spohn Hospital Corpus Christi Memorial, Corpus Christi, TX, p. A593

DAVIS, Richard, Chief Financial Officer, George Washington University Hospital, Washington, DC, p. A116

DAVIS, Richard B., Chief Human Resources Officer, Dartmouth–Hitchcock Medical Center, Lebanon, NH, p. A398

DAVIS, Richard O., Ph.D., President and Chief Executive Officer, Sibley Memorial Hospital, Washington, DC, p. A117

DAVIS, Rick, Chief Operating Officer and Support Services, Coshocton County Memorial Hospital, Coshocton, OH, p. A479

DAVIS, III, Robert, M.D. Chief Operating Officer, Our Lady of Lourdes Regional Medical Center, Lafayette, LA, p. A271

DAVIS, Rod A., FACHE, President and Chief Executive Officer and Senior Vice President Operations Dignity Health Nevada, St. Rose Dominican Hospitals – Siena Campus, Henderson, NV, p. A392

DAVIS, Roger K., Director Human Resources, Bourbon Community Hospital, Paris, KY, p. A259

DAVIS, Ronald, Chief Financial Officer, Specialty Hospital of Washington–Hadley, Washington, DC, p. A117

DAVIS, Ronald D., Chief Executive Officer, Titus Regional Medical Center, Mount Pleasant, TX, p. A623

DAVIS, Roy, M.D. Chief Medical Officer, Providence Alaska Medical Center, Anchorage, AK, p. A27

DAVIS, Scott
  Manager Information Technology, Arkansas Surgical Hospital, North Little Rock, AR, p. A48
  Chief Operating Officer, Ogden Regional Medical Center, Ogden, UT, p. A645

DAVIS, Sondra, Vice President Human Resources & System Development, Hartnett Health System, Dunn, NC, p. A451

DAVIS, Stephen, Chief Financial Officer, Illinois Valley Community Hospital, Peru, IL, p. A192

DAVIS, Steve, M.D
  Chief Medical Officer, Campbellton Graceville Hospital, Graceville, FL, p. A124
  Chief of Staff, Henry County Health Center, Mount Pleasant, IA, p. A225

DAVIS, Steve W., Interim Chief Information Officer, Athens Regional Medical Center, Athens, GA, p. A145

DAVIS, Susan L., FACHE, Chief Executive Officer, St. Vincent's Medical Center, Bridgeport, CT, p. A108

DAVIS, Terry, Chief Information Officer, Great Plains Regional Medical Center, Elk City, OK, p. A498

DAVIS, Teshia, Chief Clinical Officer, Carolinas Specialty Hospital, Charlotte, NC, p. A450

DAVIS, Toby, Chief Executive Officer, Red Rock Behavioral Hospital, Las Vegas, NV, p. A393

DAVIS, Todd, D.O. Chief of Staff, Comanche County Medical Center, Comanche, TX, p. A593

DAVIS, Tommy, M.D. Chief of Staff, Oakdale Community Hospital, Oakdale, LA, p. A276

DAVIS, Verlene, Director Human Resources, Blue Mountain Hospital, John Day, OR, p. A513

DAVIS, Virgil, Acting Chief Executive Officer, U. S. Public Health Service Indian Hospital, Crownpoint, NM, p. A415

DAVIS, Wayne
  Chief Human Resources, Clement J. Zablocki Veterans Affairs Medical Center, Milwaukee, WI, p. A692
  Manager Human Resources, Jesse Brown Veterans Affairs Medical Center, Chicago, IL, p. A177

DAVIS, Wilmont, Vice President Human Resources, Cooley Dickinson Hospital, Northampton, MA, p. A303

DAVIS–HAGENS, Patricia, R.N. Vice President Operations and Nursing, Chief Operating Officer and Chief Nursing Officer, Mercy Health – Fairfield Hospital, Fairfield, OH, p. A481

DAVIS–SAMPSON, Sherri, Director Human Resources, San Jacinto Methodist Hospital, Baytown, TX, p. A587

DAVISON, Angelique, Administrator Human Resources, Spring Valley Hospital Medical Center, Las Vegas, NV, p. A393

DAVISON, Regina, Director Information Systems, Murray–Calloway County Hospital, Murray, KY, p. A258

DAVY, Larry, President and Chief Executive Officer, Tillamook Regional Medical Center, Tillamook, OR, p. A518

DAWDY, David, Director Information Technology, Phelps County Regional Medical Center, Rolla, MO, p. A368

DAWES, Christopher G., President and Chief Executive Officer, Lucile Salter Packard Children's Hospital at Stanford, Palo Alto, CA, p. A78

DAWES, John M., FACHE, Chief Executive Officer, Bothwell Regional Health Center, Sedalia, MO, p. A371

DAWKINS, Jeff, Chief Operating Officer, Detroit Receiving Hospital/University Health Center, Detroit, MI, p. A311

DAWS, William, M.D. Chief of Staff, Great River Medical Center, West Burlington, IA, p. A230

DAWSON, Amy S., Chief Clinical Officer, Manning Regional Healthcare Center, Manning, IA, p. A224

DAWSON, Anthony L., FACHE, Director, Veterans Affairs Gulf Coast Veterans Health Care System, Biloxi, MS, p. A344

DAWSON, Dave, Director Information Services, Van Diest Medical Center, Webster City, IA, p. A230

DAWSON, John, Chief Executive Officer, Montfort Jones Memorial Hospital, Kosciusko, MS, p. A349

DAWSON, Nancy, M.D. Medical Director, Mayo Clinic Jacksonville, Jacksonville, FL, p. A126

DAWSON, Troy, M.D. President Medical Staff, Antelope Memorial Hospital, Neligh, NE, p. A386

DAY, Amy, Chief Nursing Officer, Memorial Medical Center, Port Lavaca, TX, p. A628

DAY, Bryan
  Interim Chief Executive Officer, Promise Hospital of Baton Rouge – Mid–City Campus, Baton Rouge, LA, p. A263
  Interim Chief Executive Officer, Promise Hospital of Baton Rouge – Ochsner Campus, Baton Rouge, LA, p. A263

DAY, Frank, Vice President Patient Services, Wood County Hospital, Bowling Green, OH, p. A472

DAY, Gordy, M.D. Medical Director, Schleicher County Medical Center, Eldorado, TX, p. A602

DAY, John M.
  Chief Operating Officer, Doctor's Hospital and Neuromuscular Center, Bremen, IN, p. A199
  Chief Executive Officer, Unity Medical & Surgical Hospital, Mishawaka, IN, p. A210

DAY, Kim, Interim President, Mercy Hospital Hot Springs, Hot Springs National Park, AR, p. A45

DAY, Mark, Chief Financial Officer, Twin Cities Hospital, Niceville, FL, p. A134

DAY, Sandra, Administrator, Chief Nursing Officer, Albany Area Hospital and Medical Center, Albany, MN, p. A328

DAY, Scott, Vice President Human Resources, Exempla Lutheran Medical Center, Wheat Ridge, CO, p. A107

DAY, Sherry Clouse, CP
  VP Finance/ Regional Chief Financial Officer, Mercy Hospital Aurora, Aurora, MO, p. A356
  Chief Financial Officer, Mercy Hospital Cassville, Cassville, MO, p. A358
  Chief Financial Officer, Mercy St. Francis Hospital, Mountain View, MO, p. A366

DAY, Therese, Chief Financial Officer, UMass Memorial Medical Center, Worcester, MA, p. A307

DAY, Timothy, Chief Administrative Officer, St. Luke's–Roosevelt Hospital Center, New York, NY, p. A436

DAY, Zed, Associate Vice President Information Technology, UK HealthCare Good Samaritan Hospital, Lexington, KY, p. A254

DAYTON, Elizabeth, M.D. Chief Medical Staff, Mountain View Hospital, Payson, UT, p. A645

DE FARIA, Ludmila, M.D. Chief Medical Officer, Eastside Psychiatric Hospital, Tallahassee, FL, p. A140

DE FUR, Kyle, FACHE, President, St. Vincent Indianapolis Hospital, Indianapolis, IN, p. A206

DE GARCIA, Carmen Bech, Director Human Resources, Lehigh Regional Medical Center, Lehigh Acres, FL, p. A129

DE HOYOS, Linda, M.D. Clinical Director, Thomas B. Finan Center, Cumberland, MD, p. A291

DE JEAN, Julie, Chief Executive Officer, Select Specialty Hospital–Springfield, Springfield, MO, p. A372

DE JESUS, Alexander, M.D. Medical Director, HEALTHSOUTH Rehabilitation Hospital of Sarasota, Sarasota, FL, p. A139

DE LA PAZ, Christine, Director Human Resources, Aurora Charter Oak Hospital, Covina, CA, p. A58

DE LA PAZ, Eva
  Regional Controller, Kindred Hospital Lafayette, Lafayette, LA, p. A270
  Chief Financial Officer, Kindred Hospital–Corpus Christi, Corpus Christi, TX, p. A594

DE LA PENA, Will, Chief Financial Officer, Saint Francis Hospital and Health Centers, Poughkeepsie, NY, p. A440

DE LOS REYES, Jay, Chief Operating Officer, HEALTHSOUTH Sunrise Rehabilitation Hospital, Fort Lauderdale, FL, p. A123

DE PASQUALE, Edward, Chief Financial Officer, Conemaugh Memorial Medical Center, Johnstown, PA, p. A528

DE PIANO, Linda, Ph.D., Chief Executive Officer, Jerome Golden Center for Behavioral Health, Inc., West Palm Beach, FL, p. A143

DE PREZ, Bernadette, Chief Operating Officer, Skyridge Medical Center, Cleveland, TN, p. A567

DE ROBERTIS, Nicholas, M.D. Medical Director, St. Joseph's Medical Center, Yonkers, NY, p. A446

DE ROSA, James, Vice President Finance, Somerset Medical Center, Somerville, NJ, p. A410

DE VACA, Alessandra, Chief Administrative Officer, Hebrew Rehabilitation Center, Boston, MA, p. A297

DE VOSS, Gerald, Acting Administrator, Duane L. Waters Hospital, Jackson, MI, p. A317

DEAK, Terry, Chief Financial Officer, Colusa Regional Medical Center, Colusa, CA, p. A57

DEAKYNE, John R., Chief Financial Officer, Saint Mary's Regional Medical Center, Reno, NV, p. A395

DEAL, Lisa, Budget Analyst, U. S. Public Health Service Indian Hospital, Eagle Butte, SD, p. A559

DEAL, Matt, Director Maintenance, Copper Basin Medical Center, Copperhill, TN, p. A568

DEAN, Donna
  Chief Financial Officer, Osawatomie State Hospital, Osawatomie, KS, p. A241
  Chief Financial Officer, Rainbow Mental Health Facility, Kansas City, KS, p. A237

DEAN, Douglas B., Chief Human Resources Officer, The Children's Hospital of Alabama, Birmingham, AL, p. A17

DEAN Jr., Douglas F., President and Chief Executive Officer, Elliot Hospital, Manchester, NH, p. A399

DEAN, Harrison M., FACHE, Senior Vice President and Administrator, Baptist Health Medical Center – North Little Rock, North Little Rock, AR, p. A48

DEAN, Joel, Director Information Services, Piedmont Medical Center, Rock Hill, SC, p. A555

DEAN, Laura, Director Human Resources, Wilson Medical Center, Neodesha, KS, p. A240

DEAN, Michele, Human Resources Specialist, Mid–Valley Hospital, Peckville, PA, p. A534

DEAN, Morre, Chief Executive Officer, Parker Adventist Hospital, Parker, CO, p. A105

DEAN, Russell, Chief Executive Officer, LifeCare Hospital of Dayton, Miamisburg, OH, p. A486

DEAN, Thomas, M.D. Chief of Staff, Avera Weskota Memorial Hospital, Wessington Springs, SD, p. A564

DEANE, Leslie, Chief Executive Officer, Select Specialty Hospital–Winston–Salem, Winston–Salem, NC, p. A463

DEANGELIS, Gene, Chief Fiscal Service, Louis Stokes Cleveland Veterans Affairs Medical Center, Cleveland, OH, p. A476

DEANOGLIS, Jean, Director Management Information Systems, CHRISTUS Spohn Hospital Alice, Alice, TX, p. A581

DEANS, Ken, Chief Information Officer, Chesapeake Regional Medical Center, Chesapeake, VA, p. A652

DEARDORFF, Chad
  Chief Financial Officer, Cornerstone Hospital of Bossier City, Bossier City, LA, p. A264
  Group Chief Financial Officer, Cornerstone Hospital of SouthEast Arizona, Tucson, AZ, p. A38

DEARDORFF, John A., Chief Executive Officer, Reston Hospital Center, Reston, VA, p. A659

DEARMENT, Carol, Director Human Resources, Nor–Lea General Hospital, Lovington, NM, p. A417

DEARTH, Ron, Chief Executive Director, Morton General Hospital, Morton, WA, p. A668

DEARY, Shirley, Director Human Resources, Glenbeigh Hospital and Outpatient Centers, Rock Creek, OH, p. A489

DEATER, Gary A., Vice President Administration, Human Resources and Risk Management, Witham Memorial Hospital, Lebanon, IN, p. A209

DEATON, David, Chief Executive Officer, Ozark Health Medical Center, Clinton, AR, p. A42

DEATON, Eric, Chief Executive Officer, Danville Regional Medical Center, Danville, VA, p. A653

DEATON, Susan Renodin, Chief Human Resources Officer, Cumberland River Hospital, Celina, TN, p. A566

DEATON, Timothy C., Administrator, Complex Care Hospital at Tenaya, Las Vegas, NV, p. A392

DEAVERS, Nancy, R.N. Vice President and Chief Operating Officer, Oswego Hospital, Oswego, NY, p. A439

DEBARBA Jr., Daniel J., President and Chief Executive Officer, Norwalk Hospital, Norwalk, CT, p. A111

DEBARROS, Paula, Director Human Resources, Southwest Connecticut Mental Health System, Bridgeport, CT, p. A108

DEBBAS, Elias, M.D. President Medical Staff, Fort Washington Medical Center, Fort Washington, MD, p. A291

DEBLASIS, John, Senior Administrator, Belmont Community Hospital, Bellaire, OH, p. A471

DEBLIEUX, Dawna, Chief Nurse Executive, Natchitoches Regional Medical Center, Natchitoches, LA, p. A274

DEBLOIS, Arthur J., Interim President and Chief Executive Officer, Memorial Hospital of Rhode Island, Pawtucket, RI, p. A546

DEBLOIS, Georgean, M.D. Chairman Medical Staff, CJW Medical Center, Richmond, VA, p. A660

DEBOER, Cynthia D., Chief Financial Officer, Cedar Springs Hospital, Colorado Springs, CO, p. A98

DEBOER, K. C., Vice President, Avera St. Luke's Hospital, Aberdeen, SD, p. A558

DEBOLT, Larry, Chief Financial Officer, Bluffton Regional Medical Center, Bluffton, IN, p. A199

DEBORD, Thomas
President, Summa Barberton Citizens Hospital, Barberton, OH, p. A471
President, Summa Wadsworth–Rittman Hospital, Wadsworth, OH, p. A492

DEBRUCE, Lucinda, MS, Chief Executive Officer, Vista Health Texarkana, Texarkana, AR, p. A50

DEBUHR, Rhonda, R.N. Chief Clinical and Nursing Officer, Waverly Health Center, Waverly, IA, p. A229

DECAMP, Kay, Chief Human Resources Officer, Jack C. Montgomery Veterans Affairs Medical Center, Muskogee, OK, p. A501

DECELL, Daniela, Chief Executive Officer, Las Colinas Medical Center, Irving, TX, p. A615

DECHABERT, Rebecca, Acting Director Personnel, New York State Psychiatric Institute, New York, NY, p. A435

DECHAIRO–MARINO, Ann, R.N. Chief Nursing Officer, Providence Holy Cross Medical Center,, CA, p. A71

DECKARD, Rick, Chief Fiscal Service, Chillicothe Veterans Affairs Medical Center, Chillicothe, OH, p. A473

DECKARD, Steven, Vice President Human Resources, Indiana University Health Bloomington Hospital, Bloomington, IN, p. A199

DECKER, Barbara, R.N. Chief Nursing Officer, Presence St. Mary's Hospital, Kankakee, IL, p. A186

DECKER, Jeanine, Manager Human Resources, Arizona State Hospital, Phoenix, AZ, p. A34

DECKER, Kevin
Interim Chief Executive Officer, Forrest City Medical Center, Forrest City, AR, p. A44
Assistant Chief Executive Officer, Medical Center of South Arkansas, El Dorado, AR, p. A43

DECKER, Lisa K., Director Public Relations and Marketing, Franciscan St. Elizabeth Health – Lafayette Central, Lafayette, IN, p. A208

DECKER, Michael, President and Chief Executive Officer, Divine Savior Healthcare, Portage, WI, p. A695

DECORTE, Raymond P., M.D. Chief Medical Officer, East Jefferson General Hospital, Metairie, LA, p. A273

DECREMER, Dean, Chief Information Officer, Dickinson County Healthcare System, Iron Mountain, MI, p. A317

DEDECKER, Troy, Chief Executive Officer, Mid–America Rehabilitation Hospital, Shawnee Mission, KS, p. A244

DEE, Thomas A., Chief Executive Officer, Southwestern Vermont Medical Center, Bennington, VT, p. A649

DEEM, Sara, Director Operations, University Pointe Surgical Hospital, West Chester, OH, p. A493

DEEMER, Miriam, Chief Executive Officer, Select Specialty Hospital–Grosse Pointe, Grosse Pointe, MI, p. A316

DEEP, Noel, M.D. Chief Medical Staff, Langlade Hospital, Antigo, WI, p. A683

DEERFIELD, Della, Vice President Finance, Marcum and Wallace Memorial Hospital, Irvine, KY, p. A253

DEFRING, Linda, R.N. Executive Vice President and Chief Operating Officer, Advocate Sherman Hospital, Elgin, IL, p. A181

DEES, Edith, Vice President Information Services and Chief Information Officer, Holy Spirit Hospital, Camp Hill, PA, p. A521

DEESE, Kim, R.N. Vice President/CNO, St. Vincent Medical Center, Los Angeles, CA, p. A72

DEETS, Daniel J., Chief Financial Officer, Hunterdon Medical Center, Flemington, NJ, p. A404

DEETS, Norm, Vice President and Chief Operating Officer, CGH Medical Center, Sterling, IL, p. A195

DEFAUW, Thomas D., FACHE, President and Chief Executive Officer, Port Huron Hospital, Port Huron, MI, p. A322

DEFAYE, Yael, Director, Information Technology, Rio Grande Hospital, Del Norte, CO, p. A99

DEFAZIO, Joseph J., Director Human Resources, Eastern Niagara Health System, Lockport, NY, p. A428

DEFER, Tamara, Director Human Resources, Baylor Regional Medical Center at Plano, Plano, TX, p. A627

DEFOORE, Richard G., FACHE, Chief Executive Officer, Stamford Memorial Hospital, Stamford, TX, p. A635

DEFORD, Drexel, Chief Information Officer, Scripps Mercy Hospital, San Diego, CA, p. A85

DEFRAIN, Douglas, Director Human Resources, Blanchard Valley Hospital, Findlay, OH, p. A481

DEFRANCESCO, Anthony, Associate Director, Veterans Affairs Long Beach Healthcare System, Long Beach, CA, p. A68

DEFURIO, Anthony C., Vice President and Chief Financial Officer, University of Colorado Hospital, Aurora, CO, p. A97

DEFURIO, Ken, President and Chief Executive Officer, Butler Health System, Butler, PA, p. A521

DEGEAR, David O., M.D. Vice President Medical Affairs, Westfields Hospital, New Richmond, WI, p. A693

DEGI, John, Director Human Resources, Henderson County Community Hospital, Lexington, TN, p. A573

DEGINA, Anthony M., President and Chief Executive Officer, Largo Medical Center, Largo, FL, p. A129

DEGRAND, Robert
Chief Information Officer, Community Memorial Hospital, Menomonee Falls, WI, p. A691
Chief Information Officer, Froedtert Memorial Lutheran Hospital, Milwaukee, WI, p. A692

DEGRAVELLE, Eric, Director Human Resources, Thibodaux Regional Medical Center, Thibodaux, LA, p. A279

DEGROFF, James, Director Technology and Network Services, St. Mary's Healthcare, Amsterdam, NY, p. A420

DEGROOT, Daniel, Chief Executive Officer, Community Memorial Hospital, Oconto Falls, WI, p. A694

DEGROOT, Randy, President and Chief Executive Officer, Community Health Center of Branch County, Coldwater, MI, p. A311

DEHAVEN, Bryce, Chief Financial Officer, Orange Park Medical Center, Orange Park, FL, p. A135

DEHNING, Cielo, M.D. Medical Director, Mid–America Rehabilitation Hospital, Shawnee Mission, KS, p. A244

DEICH, Faye L., R.N. Chief Operating Officer, Sacred Heart Hospital, Eau Claire, WI, p. A686

DEIG, Scott, FACHE, Chief Executive Officer, Vibra Hospital of Southeastern Michigan, Lincoln Park, MI, p. A319

DEIS, Terrence G., President and Chief Executive Officer, Parma Community General Hospital, Parma, OH, p. A488

DEITCH, Sally A., R.N., Chief Executive Officer, Sierra Providence East Medical Center, El Paso, TX, p. A602

DEITZEN, Denise M., Director, Veterans Affairs Northern Indiana Health Care System, Fort Wayne, IN, p. A203

DEJACO, Lynn S., Chief Financial Officer, FirstHealth Moore Regional Hospital, Pinehurst, NC, p. A458

DEJESUS, David, Vice President Human Resources, Southcoast Hospitals Group, Fall River, MA, p. A300

DEJONG, Jodi, Director Marketing, Pioneer Valley Hospital, West Valley City, UT, p. A648

DEJULIA, Jerome, M.D. Chief Medical Officer, Tyrone Hospital, Tyrone, PA, p. A542

DEKASTLE, Reuben J., Chief Nursing Officer, Weiser Memorial Hospital, Weiser, ID, p. A172

DEKEYZER, Ron, Regional Management Information Officer, CHRISTUS St. Frances Cabrini Hospital, Alexandria, LA, p. A262

DEKOK, Joni, Chief Nursing Officer, Sanford Sheldon Medical Center, Sheldon, IA, p. A227

DEKREY, Dale, MS Associate Director Operations and Resources, Fargo Veterans Affairs Health Care System, Fargo, ND, p. A466

DEKREY, Daniel, M.D. Chief of Staff, Sanford Bemidji Medical Center, Bemidji, MN, p. A329

DEL BOCCIO, Suzanne, MS Chief Nursing Officer and Vice President Patient Care Services, Indiana University Health North Hospital, Carmel, IN, p. A200

DEL CHIARO, Terri
Chief Financial Officer, Mercy Hospital Fort Scott, Fort Scott, KS, p. A234
Vice President and Chief Financial Officer, Mercy Hospital Independence, Independence, KS, p. A236

DEL LOS SANTOS, Edwin, Director Information Systems, Fountain Valley Regional Hospital and Medical Center, Fountain Valley, CA, p. A60

DEL RIO, R. Maxilimien, M.D., Facility Director, Northern Virginia Mental Health Institute, Falls Church, VA, p. A653

DELA TORRE, Victor, Command Legal Officer, Naval Hospital, Lemoore, CA, p. A66

DELAGARDELLE, Pamela K., Chief Executive Officer, UnityPoint Health Allen, Waterloo, IA, p. A229

DELAIIANTY, Michael J., D.O. Medical Director, Edwin Shaw Rehab, Cuyahoga Falls, OH, p. A479

DELANEY, Diane, Vice President Human Resources, Sharp Memorial Hospital, San Diego, CA, p. A85

DELANEY, Margaret, Chief Information Officer, Mercy Hospital and Medical Center, Chicago, IL, p. A177

DELANEY, Michael, Chief Financial Officer, Two Rivers Behavioral Health System, Kansas City, MO, p. A364

DELANO, John
Vice President Chief Information Officer, Integris Baptist Medical Center, Oklahoma City, OK, p. A503
Vice President and Chief Information Officer, Integris Southwest Medical Center, Oklahoma City, OK, p. A503

DELANO, Michael, Administrator, Spearfish Regional Surgery Center, Spearfish, SD, p. A563

DELATTE, Sandra, Director Human Resources, Villa Feliciana Medical Complex, Jackson, LA, p. A269

DELELLO, Cory
Chief Financial Officer, Aurora Charter Oak Hospital, Covina, CA, p. A58
Chief Financial Officer, Aurora Vista Del Mar Hospital, Ventura, CA, p. A94

DELEON, Joseph, President, Texas Health Harris Methodist Hospital Southwest Fort Worth, Fort Worth, TX, p. A604

DELEON, Sherilene, Controller, HEALTHSOUTH Rehabilitation Hospital–Las Vegas, Las Vegas, NV, p. A392

DELFORGE, Gary L., Administrator, Odessa Memorial Healthcare Center, Odessa, WA, p. A668

DELFS, Michael, Chief Executive Officer, Richland Hospital, Richland Center, WI, p. A696

DELGADO, Laurie, President, UH Regional Hospitals, Cleveland, OH, p. A477

DELGADO, Pete, Chief Executive Officer, Salinas Valley Memorial Healthcare System, Salinas, CA, p. A84

DELIDUKA, John, M.D. Chief Medical Officer, Cascade Medical Center, Leavenworth, WA, p. A667

DELIEN, Rudie, Director Human Resources, Devereux Georgia Treatment Network, Kennesaw, GA, p. A155

DELK, Ray, FACHE Vice President Operations, Good Shepherd Medical Center–Marshall, Marshall, TX, p. A621

DELLA LANA, David, M.D. Chief of Staff, Fairchild Medical Center, Yreka, CA, p. A96

DELLA TORRE, Linda, Senior Vice President and Chief Operating Officer, Athens Regional Medical Center, Athens, GA, p. A145

DELLEA, Eugene A., President, Fairview Hospital, Great Barrington, MA, p. A300

DELLOCONO, John, Senior Vice President and Chief Financial Officer, CentraState Healthcare System, Freehold, NJ, p. A404

DELOACH, Jerrald, Chief Operating Officer, Citrus Memorial Health System, Inverness, FL, p. A126

DELORENZO, David, Senior Director Human Resources, Sisters of Charity Hospital of Buffalo, Buffalo, NY, p. A423

DELUCA, Mike, Vice President Information Systems, Sarah Bush Lincoln Health Center, Mattoon, IL, p. A188

DELVEAUX, Joe, Manager Information Services, St. Francis Regional Medical Center, Shakopee, MN, p. A341

DEMARCO, Victor, Chief Financial Officer, Bronx–Lebanon Hospital Center Health Care System,, NY, p. A431

DEMARTINO, Pat, Chief Information Officer, Children's Specialized Hospital–PSE&G, New Brunswick, NJ, p. A407

DEMASIE, Dennis, Vice President Information Systems and Chief Information Officer, Rush–Copley Medical Center, Aurora, IL, p. A174

DEMATTEO, Kathleen, Chief Information Officer, Danbury Hospital, Danbury, CT, p. A108

DEMAY, Paul, Chief Information Officer, Northwest Medical Center, Springdale, AR, p. A50

DEMBER, Barbara, Interim President and Chief Executive Officer, Verde Valley Medical Center, Cottonwood, AZ, p. A30

DEMERICH, Lois B., Director Human Resources, Sentara Williamsburg Regional Medical Center, Williamsburg, VA, p. A663

DEMERS, Vickie, Chief Executive Officer, HEALTHSOUTH MountainView Regional Rehabilitation Hospital, Morgantown, WV, p. A679

DEMING, Mark, Controller, Oakwood Heritage Hospital, Taylor, MI, p. A325

DEMING, Peggy, Executive Vice President and Chief Financial Officer, University Health System, San Antonio, TX, p. A632

DEMING, Terra, Director Human Resources, Otsego Memorial Hospital, Gaylord, MI, p. A314

DEMONTGORENCY, Tara, Director Business Development, HEALTHSOUTH Bakersfield Rehabilitation Hospital, Bakersfield, CA, p. A54

DEMORROW, Dawn P., Chief Human Resources Service, Wilkes–Barre Veterans Affairs Medical Center, Wilkes–Barre, PA, p. A544

DEMOTTE, Laura, Vice President Human Resources, Memorial Hospital Jacksonville, Jacksonville, FL, p. A126

DEMPSEY, Charles, M.D. Medical Director, HEALTHSOUTH Rehabilitation Hospital of Spring Hill, Brooksville, FL, p. A120

DEMPSEY, Jeffrey, Vice President Operations, Mercy St. Charles Hospital, Oregon, OH, p. A488

DEMPSEY, John F., Vice President and Chief Financial Officer, Springfield Regional Medical Center, Springfield, OH, p. A490

DEMPSTER, John, President and Chief Executive Officer, Jefferson Regional Medical Center, Jefferson Hills, PA, p. A528

DEMURO, Rob, M.D. President Medical Staff, Elizabethtown Community Hospital, Elizabethtown, NY, p. A425

DENBO, John, Chief Executive Officer, Phelps County Regional Medical Center, Rolla, MO, p. A368

DENCKLAU, Larry, D.O. Chief of Staff, Lake Pointe Medical Center, Rowlett, TX, p. A630

DENEFF, Randall, Vice President Finance, Mary Free Bed Rehabilitation Hospital, Grand Rapids, MI, p. A315

DENEN, Bruce, Manager Data Processing, Fayette County Memorial Hospital, Washington Court House, OH, p. A492

DENHAM, Stephanie, Chief Financial Officer and Human Resources Officer, Phillips County Hospital, Malta, MT, p. A378

DENIO, Arthur E., Vice President and Chief Financial Officer, NorthBay Medical Center, Fairfield, CA, p. A59

DENISIENKO, Mary, Vice President Human Resources, Palos Community Hospital, Palos Heights, IL, p. A191

DENISON, Brenda, Chief Financial Officer, Hamilton General Hospital, Hamilton, TX, p. A607

DENISON, Rita, Manager Information Systems, Sturgis Hospital, Sturgis, MI, p. A325

DENKER, Jill, Executive Director Human Resources, Lexington Regional Health Center, Lexington, NE, p. A385

DENMARK, Donald, M.D. Chief Medical Officer, Carondelet St. Joseph's Hospital, Tucson, AZ, p. A38

DENNEY, David, M.D. President Medical Staff, Medical West, Bessemer, AL, p. A16

DENNING, Christine, Chief Operating Officer, Silverton Hospital, Silverton, OR, p. A518

DENNING, Earl, Interim Administrator, Memorial Medical Center – Livingston, Livingston, TX, p. A619

DENNIS, Bradley, M.D. Chief Medical Officer, Brookwood Medical Center, Birmingham, AL, p. A16

DENNIS, Michael, Director, William J. McCord Adolescent and Treatment Center, Orangeburg, SC, p. A555

DENNISON, Cindy, Senior Director Rural Division, Mercy Willard Hospital, Willard, OH, p. A493

DENNO, Charles, Chief Financial Officer, Westwood Lodge Hospital, Westwood, MA, p. A306

DENNSTEDT, Crystal
Information Officer, North Texas State Hospital, Vernon, TX, p. A639
Chief Information Officer, North Texas State Hospital, Wichita Falls Campus, Wichita Falls, TX, p. A641

DENO, Mark S., Chief Executive Officer, HEALTHSOUTH Rehabilitation Hospital of Arlington, Arlington, TX, p. A583

DENO, Mary, Vice President Human Resources, Community Medical Center, Toms River, NJ, p. A411

DENSTEDT, Ron, Acting Director, Walter P. Reuther Psychiatric Hospital, Westland, MI, p. A326

DENT, Bruce, Director Human Resources, Park City Medical Center, Park City, UT, p. A645

DENTON, Charles L., Chief Executive Officer, Grenada Lake Medical Center, Grenada, MS, p. A347

DENTON, Christopher, Chief Financial Officer, Henrico Doctors' Hospital, Richmond, VA, p. A660

DENTON, Genise, Manager Human Resources, John J. Pershing Veterans Affairs Medical Center, Poplar Bluff, MO, p. A367

DENTON, Joe, Executive Vice President and Chief Financial Officer, Mobile Infirmary Medical Center, Mobile, AL, p. A22

DENTON, Tony, JD Chief Operating Officer, University of Michigan Hospitals and Health Centers, Ann Arbor, MI, p. A308

DENUCCI, Alex, Chief Financial Officer, Franciscan Hospital for Children, Boston, MA, p. A296

DEPAULO, Theron, Manager Information Systems, Providence Mount Carmel Hospital, Colville, WA, p. A665

DEPINHO, Ronald A., M.D., President, University of Texas M.D. Anderson Cancer Center, Houston, TX, p. A613

DEPKO, Mike, Director Information Technology, Brown County Hospital, Ainsworth, NE, p. A381

DEPOYSTER, Avis, Director Human Resources, Brownfield Regional Medical Center, Brownfield, TX, p. A589

DEQUARDO, John R., M.D., Superintendent, Colorado Mental Health Institute at Pueblo, Pueblo, CO, p. A105

DERBY, Richard P., Vice President Finance, Barton Memorial Hospital, South Lake Tahoe, CA, p. A91

DERDEYN, Paul, Director Fiscal Services and Plant Operations, Connecticut Valley Hospital, Middletown, CT, p. A110

DERENZIS, Vicki, Chief Financial Officer, Highlands Regional Medical Center, Sebring, FL, p. A140

DERFLINGER, Terri, Administrator, Mercy Hospital of Franciscan Sisters, Oelwein, IA, p. A226

DERNIER, Marty, Chief Executive Officer, Kansas Rehabilitation Hospital, Topeka, KS, p. A245

DEROUEN, George Patrick, Chief Executive Officer, Savoy Medical Center, Mamou, LA, p. A273

DEROUEN, Jason, Director Management Information Systems, Grace Medical Center, Lubbock, TX, p. A620

DERRINGTON, Ken R., Chief Financial Officer, Northern Colorado Rehabilitation Hospital, Johnstown, CO, p. A102

DERSCH, Stephen, M.D. President Medical Staff, Regency Hospital of Florence, Florence, SC, p. A552

DERTZ, Donna, Director Human Resources, St. Bernard Hospital and Health Care Center, Chicago, IL, p. A179

DERUS, Charles, M.D. Vice President Medical Management, Advocate Good Samaritan Hospital, Downers Grove, IL, p. A181

DERUYTER, David N., M.D. President Medical Staff, Kindred Hospital–Atlanta, Atlanta, GA, p. A146

DESAI, Nimesh, M.D. Medical Director, Massena Memorial Hospital, Massena, NY, p. A429

DESAI, Shailesh, M.D. Chief of Staff, Baum Harmon Mercy Hospital, Primghar, IA, p. A227

DESALVO, Susan, Manager Human Resources, Bath Veterans Affairs Medical Center, Bath, NY, p. A427

DESANCTIS, Mario, FACHE, Director, Tomah Veterans Affairs Medical Center, Tomah, WI, p. A697

DESANTIS, John
Chief Financial Officer, Glenwood Regional Medical Center, West Monroe, LA, p. A280
Chief Financial Officer, Ouachita Community Hospital, West Monroe, LA, p. A280

DESANTIS, Mario V., Acting Medical Center Director, Jesse Brown Veterans Affairs Medical Center, Chicago, IL, p. A177

DESANTIS, Vincent, Vice President Finance, Phelps Memorial Hospital Center, Sleepy Hollow, NY, p. A442

DESCHAMBEAU, Wayne G., President and Chief Executive Officer, Wayne Hospital, Greenville, OH, p. A482

DESCHENE, Normand E., FACHE, President and Chief Executive Officer, Lowell General Hospital, Lowell, MA, p. A301

DESCHRYVER, Joseph, Chief Operating Officer, Sierra Vista Regional Medical Center, San Luis Obispo, CA, p. A88

DESHAIES, Roger, Chief Financial Officer, Fletcher Allen Health Care, Burlington, VT, p. A649

DESHAZO, Sheri, Chief Operating Officer, Kings Mountain Hospital, Kings Mountain, NC, p. A455

DESHIELDS, Michael S., M.D. Director Medical Affairs, Camden County Health Services Center, Blackwood, NJ, p. A401

DESIMONE, Maureen, Chief Operating Officer, Blythedale Children's Hospital, Valhalla, NY, p. A445

DESIMONE, Ralph, M.D. President Medical Staff, Culpeper Regional Hospital, Culpeper, VA, p. A653

DESIMONE, Silvana, Chief Information Officer, Coney Island Hospital,, NY, p. A431

DESJEUNES, Carol, Chief Operating Officer, Psychiatric Institute of Washington, Washington, DC, p. A117

DESKINS, Juanita, Chief Operating Officer, Pikeville Medical Center, Pikeville, KY, p. A259

DESMARAIS, John, M.D. Chief Medical Officer, Fayette County Memorial Hospital, Washington Court House, OH, p. A492

DESMARTEAU, Lisa Jo, Chief Financial Officer, Miami Jewish Home and Hospital for Aged, Miami, FL, p. A132

DESMOND, Heather, Chief Financial Officer, Bibb Medical Center, Centreville, AL, p. A18

DESMOND, P. Craig, Chief Executive Officer, Southwest General Hospital, San Antonio, TX, p. A632

DESORMEAU, Mary, Chief Nursing Officer, Grand River Hospital District, Rifle, CO, p. A105

DESOTELLE, Robert C., President and Chief Executive Officer, Asheville Specialty Hospital, Asheville, NC, p. A447

DESOTO, David, M.D. Chief of Staff, National Park Medical Center, Hot Springs, AR, p. A45

DESOTO, James, M.D
Vice President Medical Affairs, Mercy Medical Center Redding, Redding, CA, p. A81
Vice President Medical Affairs, St. Elizabeth Community Hospital, Red Bluff, CA, p. A81

DESOUZA, Jacqueline
Chief Executive Officer, Lee's Summit Medical Center, Lee's Summit, MO, p. A365
Chief Operating Officer, Research Medical Center, Kansas City, MO, p. A363

DESPRES, Paul J., Chief Executive Officer, Eleanor Slater Hospital, Cranston, RI, p. A546

DESROCHES, Jeff, Manager Information Systems, Anaheim Regional Medical Center, Anaheim, CA, p. A52

DETOR, Robert E., Chief Executive Officer, South Oaks Hospital, Amityville, NY, p. A420

DETRICK, Ann, Director, Santa Barbara County Psychiatric Health Facility, Santa Barbara, CA, p. A89

DETTERMAN, B. Lynn
Interim President and Chief Executive Officer, Mercy Tiffin Hospital, Tiffin, OH, p. A490
President and Chief Executive Officer, Mercy Willard Hospital, Willard, OH, p. A493

DETTMER, Robert E., Deputy Commander for Health Services, Irwin Army Community Hospital, Junction City, KS, p. A236

DETWILER, Courtney, R.N., Administrator, Hampton Roads Specialty Hospital, Newport News, VA, p. A657

DEUEL, Teresa L., Chief Executive Officer, Hodgeman County Health Center, Jetmore, KS, p. A236

DEURMIER, Carol, Chief Executive Officer, St. Michael's Hospital Avera, Tyndall, SD, p. A563

DEUSTERMAN, Abe, Manager Information Technology, Essentia Health Fosston, Fosston, MN, p. A332

DEUTCHMAN, Adam, M.D. Chief of Staff, Steele Memorial Medical Center, Salmon, ID, p. A171

DEVANEY, Catherine, Chief Executive Officer, HEALTHSOUTH Rehabilitation Hospital, Concord, NH, p. A397

DEVANEY, Ed, Vice President and Chief Operating Officer, Hackensack University Medical Center Mountainside, Montclair, NJ, p. A406

DEVANSKY, Gary W., Director, Coatesville Veterans Affairs Medical Center, Coatesville, PA, p. A523

DEVAUGHN, Michael D.
Senior Vice President and Chief Financial Officer, WakeMed Cary Hospital, Cary, NC, p. A449
Senior Vice President Finance and Chief Financial Officer, WakeMed Raleigh Campus, Raleigh, NC, p. A459

DEVAULT, Jennifer, Vice President Associate Services, F. F. Thompson Hospital, Canandaigua, NY, p. A423

DEVAULT, Roseann M., Chief Financial Officer, Tennova–Jefferson Memorial Hospital, Jefferson City, TN, p. A571

DEVENPORT, Genia, Administrator, New Mexico Rehabilitation Center, Roswell, NM, p. A417

DEVENUTO, Joseph, Vice President and Chief Information Officer, Norton Suburban Hospital, Louisville, KY, p. A256

DEVET, Reezie, Ph.D., President and Chief Executive Officer, McLaren Northern Michigan, Petoskey, MI, p. A321

DEVEY, Robert, Chief Financial Officer, Cambridge Health Alliance, Cambridge, MA, p. A299

DEVILLE, Linda F., Chief Executive Officer, Bunkie General Hospital, Bunkie, LA, p. A265

DEVIN, Brian V., Chief Executive Officer, Massachusetts Hospital School, Canton, MA, p. A299

DEVINE, Christina, Director Human Resources, The Rehabilitation Institute of St. Louis, Saint Louis, MO, p. A371

DEVINE, Katherine, R.N., Interim Chief Executive Officer, Keokuk Area Hospital, Keokuk, IA, p. A224

DEVINE, Sarah, M.D. Chief of Staff, Myrtue Medical Center, Harlan, IA, p. A222

DEVITO, Joseph M., Vice President Finance and Chief Operating Officer, Geisinger–Bloomsburg Hospital, Bloomsburg, PA, p. A521

DEVLIN, James, Director Information Systems, St. Cloud Regional Medical Center, Saint Cloud, FL, p. A138

DEVOCELLE, Frank H., President and Chief Executive Officer, Olathe Medical Center, Olathe, KS, p. A241

DEVOL, Marjorie, M.D. Chief of Staff, Doctors Hospital Nelsonville, Nelsonville, OH, p. A487

DEVONEY, William, Chief Financial Officer, University of Illinois Hospital & Health Sciences System, Chicago, IL, p. A180

DEVORE, Pam, Financial Manager, Hillcrest Memorial Hospital, Simpsonville, SC, p. A555

DEVORE, Paul A., M.D. Medical Director, Gladys Spellman Specialty Hospital and Nursing Center, Cheverly, MD, p. A290

DEVRIES, Russell, Chief Business Operations, Keller Army Community Hospital, West Point, NY, p. A446

DEW, Douglas, M.D. President Medical Staff, Flagler Hospital, Saint Augustine, FL, p. A138

DEWALSCHE, Diane, R.N. Chief Operating Officer, Community Hospital of Long Beach, Long Beach, CA, p. A67

DEWALT, Stephen, Warden, Federal Medical Center, Lexington, KY, p. A254

DEWAN, Vijay, M.D. Clinical Director, Lincoln Regional Center, Lincoln, NE, p. A385

DEWBERRY, Doug, Chief Executive Officer and Administrator, Lanier Health Services, Valley, AL, p. A26

DEWBERRY, Robbie, Chief Executive Officer, Mitchell County Hospital, Colorado City, TX, p. A592

DEWERFF, Mike, Chief Financial Officer, Trinity Regional Medical Center, Fort Dodge, IA, p. A221

DEWISPELARE, Cheryl M., Chief Human Resources Officer, Veterans Affairs Medical Center, Omaha, NE, p. A388

DEWITT, Pamela, Chief Financial Officer, St. Joseph's Health Services–Gundersen Lutheran, Hillsboro, WI, p. A688

DEWITT, Warren, M.D. Chief Medical Officer, Barnes–Kasson County Hospital, Susquehanna, PA, p. A542

DEXTER, Stephen P.
President and Chief Executive Officer, Saint Francis Hospital, Charleston, WV, p. A676
President and Chief Executive Officer, Thomas Memorial Hospital, South Charleston, WV, p. A681

DEXTER, Sue, Administrative Department Leader Human Resources, McDonough District Hospital, Macomb, IL, p. A187

DEYARMIN, James A., Controller, Children's Hospital of Richmond at VCU–Brook Road Campus, Richmond, VA, p. A660

DHAWAN, Kamlesh, M.D. Chief of Staff, East Los Angeles Doctors Hospital, Los Angeles, CA, p. A68

DHINGRA, Ashok, M.D. Executive Medical Director, HEALTHSOUTH Deaconess Rehabilitation Hospital, Evansville, IN, p. A202

DHULIPALA, Vasudeva, M.D. Medical Director, HEALTHSOUTH Rehabilitation Hospital of Alexandria, Alexandria, LA, p. A262

DHUPER, Arti
Regional Director Human Resources, Chino Valley Medical Center, Chino, CA, p. A56
Regional Director Human Resources, Desert Valley Hospital, Victorville, CA, p. A95
Director Human Resources, San Dimas Community Hospital, San Dimas, CA, p. A86

DI BACCO, David J., Chief Operating Officer, Eastern Niagara Health System, Lockport, NY, p. A428

DI BERNARDO, Deborah, Chief Information Officer, St. Joseph's Medical Center, Yonkers, NY, p. A446

DI LORENZO, Anthony, Vice President Operations, NorthShore University Health System Skokic Hospital, Skokie, IL, p. A194

DI MARIA, Anthony, M.D. Medical Director, Jamaica Hospital Medical Center,, NY, p. A432

DI RIENZO, Louis, Chief Information Officer, Lake Shore Health Care Center, Irving, NY, p. A427

DI STEFANO, Anthony, Director Finance, Soldiers' Home in Holyoke, Holyoke, MA, p. A301

DIAI , Jeffery
Acting Chief Executive Officer, Vidant Bertie Hospital, Windsor, NC, p. A463
Chief Operating Officer, Vidant Bertie Hospital, Windsor, NC, p. A463
Acting Chief Executive Officer, Vidant Chowan Hospital, Edonton, NC, p. A452
Chief Operating Officer, Vidant Chowan Hospital, Edenton, NC, p. A452

DIAL, Marcia R., Administrator and Chief Executive Officer, Scotland County Hospital, Memphis, MO, p. A366

DIALTO, Margaret, Vice President Human Resources, Staten Island University Hospital,, NY, p. A436

DIAMOND, Anne, JD Chief Operating Officer, University of Connecticut Health Center, John Dempsey Hospital, Farmington, CT, p. A108

DIAMOND, Lester K., President, St. Dominic–Jackson Memorial Hospital, Jackson, MS, p. A349

DIAMOND, Robert
Vice President and Chief Information Officer, Putnam Hospital Center, Carmel, NY, p. A423
Chief Information Officer, Vassar Brothers Medical Center, Poughkeepsie, NY, p. A440

DIAMOND, Timothy, Chief Information Officer, La Rabida Children's Hospital, Chicago, IL, p. A177

DIAMOND, Vickie L., MS President and Chief Executive Officer, Wyoming Medical Center, Casper, WY, p. A701

DIANGELO, John, Executive Vice President and Chief Financial Officer, Inspira Medical Center–Woodbury, Woodbury, NJ, p. A413

DIANGELO, John A.
Senior Vice President Finance and Chief Financial Officer, Inspira Medical Center–Elmer, Elmer, NJ, p. A404
Senior Vice President Finance and Chief Financial Officer, Inspira Medical Center–Vineland, Vineland, NJ, p. A412

DIANO, Robert, Director Human Resources, Broward Health Coral Springs, Coral Springs, FL, p. A121

DIAS, Walter, Vice President and Chief Operating Officer, Butler Hospital, Providence, RI, p. A546

DIAZ, Cristina, Director, Rush Oak Park Hospital, Oak Park, IL, p. A190

DIAZ, Felipe, M.D. Chief of Staff, Bath Veterans Affairs Medical Center, Bath, NY, p. A421

DIAZ, Georgina, Chief Operating Officer, Palmetto General Hospital, Hialeah, FL, p. A125

DIAZ, Jesse, Chief Information Officer, Phoebe Putney Memorial Hospital, Albany, GA, p. A145

DIAZ, Jose, Director Information Systems, Emory Johns Creek Hospital, Johns Creek, GA, p. A155

DIAZ, Joseph, M.D. Acting Chief Medical Officer, Memorial Hospital of Rhode Island, Pawtucket, RI, p. A546

DIAZ, Octavio, M.D. Chief Medical Officer, Saint Vincent Hospital, Worcester, MA, p. A306

DIAZ, Rachael, Systems Operator, Coalinga Regional Medical Center, Coalinga, CA, p. A57

DIAZ, Steve, M.D. Chief Medical Officer, MaineGeneral Medical Center–Waterville Campus, Waterville, ME, p. A285

DIAZ–LOPEZ, Emily, Director Human Resources, CHRISTUS Spohn Hospital Alice, Alice, TX, p. A581

DIBLIK, Donna, Chief Financial Officer, Presence Our Lady of the Resurrection Medical Center, Chicago, IL, p. A178

DICE, Jeffrey N., Vice President Behavioral Health, Peninsula Hospital, Louisville, TN, p. A573

DICESARE, Gayle, President and Chief Executive Officer, RiverValley Behavioral Health Hospital, Owensboro, KY, p. A258

DICESARE, Jan, Vice President Financial Operations, St. Vincent's East, Birmingham, AL, p. A17

DICK, David, Chief Executive Officer, Mitchell County Hospital Health Systems, Beloit, KS, p. A232

DICK, Lynette, Director of Support Services, Ellsworth County Medical Center, Ellsworth, KS, p. A233

DICK, Mollie, Coordinator Human Resources, Wayne County Hospital, Monticello, KY, p. A258

DICK, Myra, Manager Business Office, AMG Specialty Hospital–Wichita, Wichita, KS, p. A246

DICKERSON, Gene, M.D. Vice President Medical Affairs, Tuomey Healthcare System, Sumter, SC, p. A556

DICKERSON, Kathy, Chief Financial Officer, HEALTHSOUTH Rehabilitation Hospital of Arlington, Arlington, TX, p. A583

DICKERSON, Tammy, Director Human Resources, Carolinas Hospital System, Florence, SC, p. A551

DICKERSON, Taylor
Chief Information Officer, Lake City Medical Center, Lake City, FL, p. A128
Director Information Services, Ocala Regional Medical Center, Ocala, FL, p. A134

DICKERSON, Toby, Chief Information Resources Management Services, Durham Veterans Affairs Medical Center, Durham, NC, p. A451

DICKEY, John M., Chief Administrative Officer, Mayo Clinic Health System in Eau Claire, Eau Claire, WI, p. A686

DICKEY, Mark, Director Business Development, Valir Rehabilitation Hospital, Oklahoma City, OK, p. A504

DICKEY, Sarah J., Director Human Resources, Marshall Browning Hospital, Du Quoin, IL, p. A181

DICKINSON, Brett M., M.D
Chief of Staff, Parkland Health Center, Farmington, MO, p. A360
Chief of Staff, Parkland Health Center–Bonne Terre, Bonne Terre, MO, p. A356

DICKINSON, Galen, Chief Financial Officer, Cary Medical Center, Caribou, ME, p. A282

DICKMAN, Kathy, Director Information Technology, McCullough–Hyde Memorial Hospital, Oxford, OH, p. A488

DICKSON, Douglas, Senior Vice President Finance, Sierra View District Hospital, Porterville, CA, p. A80

DICKSON, Eric, M.D., President and Chief Executive Officer, UMass Memorial Medical Center, Worcester, MA, p. A307

DICKSON, James J., Administrator and Chief Executive Officer, Copper Queen Community Hospital, Bisbee, AZ, p. A30

DICKSON, Karen, Director, Human Resources, Maine Coast Memorial Hospital, Ellsworth, ME, p. A283

DICKSON, Lynette, Director Clinical Operations and Director of Nursing, District One Hospital, Faribault, MN, p. A332

DICKSON, Thomas C., Chief Executive Officer, Banner Thunderbird Medical Center, Glendale, AZ, p. A32

DICKSON, William, Acting Executive Director, Capital District Psychiatric Center, Albany, NY, p. A420

DICKSTEIN, Steve, Director, Newton Medical Center, Covington, GA, p. A151

DICROCE, Theresa M., M.D. Chief Medical Staff, North Valley Hospital, Tonasket, WA, p. A673

DICUS, Scott, M.D. Chief of Staff, White County Medical Center, Searcy, AR, p. A50

DIDENKO, Dima
Vice President and Chief Financial Officer, Florida Hospital Heartland Medical Center, Sebring, FL, p. A140
Vice President and Chief Financial Officer, Florida Hospital Wauchula, Wauchula, FL, p. A143

DIDIER, Debra, Vice President and Chief Financial Officer, Katherine Shaw Bethea Hospital, Dixon, IL, p. A181

DIEBLING, Tara, Chief Financial Officer, The Rehabilitation Institute of St. Louis, Saint Louis, MO, p. A371

DIECKMANN, Holli, Director Health Information, Sabetha Community Hospital, Sabetha, KS, p. A243

DIEDE, Dale, M.D. Medical Provider, Dahl Memorial Healthcare Association, Ekalaka, MT, p. A375

DIEDE, Shelby, Chief Financial Officer, Banner Lassen Medical Center, Susanville, CA, p. A92

DIEDERICH, J. Joseph
Executive Vice President and Chief Operating Officer, Oakwood Annapolis Hospital, Wayne, MI, p. A326
Executive Vice President and Chief Operating Officer, Oakwood Southshore Medical Center, Trenton, MI, p. A325

DIEDERICH, John A., Senior Vice President Operations and Chief Operating Officer, Rush–Copley Medical Center, Aurora, IL, p. A174

DIEDERICH, Thomas, Senior Vice President Human Resources, Phoenix Children's Hospital, Phoenix, AZ, p. A35

DIEHL, Kent, M.D. Chief of Staff, Jacobson Memorial Hospital Care Center, Elgin, ND, p. A466

DIER, Joy, R.N. Vice President Clinical Services and Chief Nursing Officer, Texas Institute for Surgery at Texas Health Presbyterian Dallas, Dallas, TX, p. A597

DIERKENS, Janelle, Chief Administration Officer, New York State Psychiatric Institute, New York, NY, p. A435

DIERKER, Anne, Vice President Hospital Services, Pekin Hospital, Pekin, IL, p. A191

DIERS, Suzanne, R.N. Director Patient Care Services, Shriners Hospitals for Children–Portland, Portland, OR, p. A516

DIESFELD, James, M.D. President Medical Staff, Thorek Memorial Hospital, Chicago, IL, p. A179

DIESTEL, Peter, Senior Vice President and Chief Operating Officer, Valley Hospital, Ridgewood, NJ, p. A410

DIETER, Brian, President and Chief Executive Officer, Mary Greeley Medical Center, Ames, IA, p. A216

DIETERICH, Kevin, Director Information Services, Inland Hospital, Waterville, ME, p. A285

DIETRICK, Brian, Director Information Systems, Wilson Medical Center, Wilson, NC, p. A463

DIETSCHE, Jim, Chief Financial Officer, Bellin Memorial Hospital, Green Bay, WI, p. A687

DIETZ, Brian E., FACHE, Interim President and Chief Executive officer, St. Francis Hospital, Wilmington, DE, p. A115

DIETZ, Gary, Director Information Technology Services, Walla Walla General Hospital, Walla Walla, WA, p. A674

DIETZ, Mark, Chief Medical Officer, CentraCare Health–Monticello, Monticello, MN, p. A336

DIETZ, Michael, Chief Hospital Administration, U. S. Air Force Hospital, Hampton, VA, p. A655

DIEWALD, Wayne A., President, Genesis Medical Center–Davenport, Davenport, IA, p. A219

DIFRANCO, Vincent B., Chief Executive Officer, Community Hospital, Torrington, WY, p. A704

DIGGINS, Dana, Chief Financial Officer, Landmark Medical Center, Woonsocket, RI, p. A547

DIGREGORIO, Connie L., Assistant Administrator, Cascade Valley Hospital and Clinics, Arlington, WA, p. A664

DIIESO, Nicholas T., R.N. Chief Operating Officer, Mount Auburn Hospital, Cambridge, MA, p. A299

DIIORIO, Emil, M.D., Chief Executive Officer, Surgical Specialty Center at Coordinated Health, Allentown, PA, p. A519

DILALLO, Kevin, Chief Executive Officer, Manatee Memorial Hospital, Bradenton, FL, p. A119

DILISI, Jeffrey P., Vice President and Chief Medical Officer, Virginia Hospital Center – Arlington, Arlington, VA, p. A651

DILLARD, Evan S., FACHE, President and Chief Executive Officer, Forrest General Hospital, Hattiesburg, MS, p. A347

DILLARD, Leigh, M.D. Chief of Staff, De Soto Regional Health System, Mansfield, LA, p. A273

DILLEHUNT, David B., Chief Information Officer, FirstHealth Moore Regional Hospital, Pinehurst, NC, p. A458

DILLON, Jim, Chief Financial Officer, Rangely District Hospital, Rangely, CO, p. A105

DILLON, Lorie, Chief Executive Officer, Geisinger HEALTHSOUTH Rehabilitation Hospital, Danville, PA, p. A523

DILLON, Mary E., MS Vice President Patient Care Services, Sisters of Charity Hospital of Buffalo, Buffalo, NY, p. A423

DILORENZO, Randolph, M.D. Medical Director, Syosset Hospital, Syosset, NY, p. A443

DILORETO, David, M.D. Executive Vice President and Chief Medical Officer, Presence Saint Francis Hospital, Evanston, IL, p. A182

DIMARE, John, M.D. Medical Director, Foothill Presbyterian Hospital, Glendora, CA, p. A63

DIMAURO, Cynthia, M.D. Medical Director, Hillside Rehabilitation Hospital, Warren, OH, p. A492

DIMICHELE, Maria, Administrative Assistant, Kensington Hospital, Philadelphia, PA, p. A535

DIMMIG, Thomas, M.D. Medical Director, North Carolina Specialty Hospital, Durham, NC, p. A451

DINAN, Edward M., President and Chief Executive Officer, Lawrence Hospital Center, Bronxville, NY, p. A422

DINAUER, Cathy, MSN Vice President Patient Care, Carson Tahoe Regional Healthcare, Carson City, NV, p. A391

DINGELDEIN, G. Peter, M.D. Chief Medical Officer, Wadley Regional Medical Center, Texarkana, TX, p. A637

DINGES, Brenda, Director of Nursing, Ness County Hospital, Ness City, KS, p. A240

DINGILIAN, John, M.D. Chief Medical Staff, Simi Valley Hospital and Health Care Services, Simi Valley, CA, p. A91

DINGLE, Steve, M.D. Chief Medical Officer, Arizona State Hospital, Phoenix, AZ, p. A34

DINGLER, Chance, M.D. Chief Medical Officer, Nocona General Hospital, Nocona, TX, p. A625

DINGMAN, III, Vincent, Chief Financial Officer, Columbia Memorial Hospital, Hudson, NY, p. A427

DINGO, Lynn, Director Human Resources, Crestwood Medical Center, Huntsville, AL, p. A21

DINHAM, Vilma L., R.N. Chief Nursing Officer, Encino Hospital Medical Center,, CA, p. A68

DINKHA, Duncan, M.D. Chief of Staff, Morrison Community Hospital, Morrison, IL, p. A189

DINKINS, Vicki, Director Human Resources, Louis Smith Memorial Hospital, Lakeland, GA, p. A155

DINON, Nancy, Vice President Human Resources, Orlando Regional Medical Center, Orlando, FL, p. A135

DINSLAGE, Dennis, Vice President Finance and Chief Financial Officer, St. Francis Memorial Hospital, West Point, NE, p. A390

DINSMOOR, William S., Chief Financial Officer, Nebraska Medical Center, Omaha, NE, p. A388

DIOKNO, Ananias C., M.D. Executive Vice President and Chief Medical Officer, Beaumont Hospital – Royal Oak, Royal Oak, MI, p. A323

DION, Jeff, Chief Financial Officer, UMass Memorial–Marlborough Hospital, Marlborough, MA, p. A302

DION, Jeffrey P., Vice President Finance, St. Elizabeth's Medical Center, Brighton, MA, p. A298

DION, Michael J., R.N. Vice President Patient Care Services, Windham Hospital, Willimantic, CT, p. A113

DIONNE, Michele, Chief Executive Officer, Houston Physicians Hospital, Webster, TX, p. A640

DIONNE, Philip G., Chief Executive Officer, Ottumwa Regional Health Center, Ottumwa, IA, p. A226

DIPALMA, Maureen, Director Finance, Tewksbury Hospital, Tewksbury, MA, p. A305

DIPIETRO, Joseph A., Senior Vice President and Chief Administrative Officer, Kent County Memorial Hospital, Warwick, RI, p. A547

DIPILLA, Victor, Vice President and Chief Business Development Officer, Christ Hospital, Cincinnati, OH, p. A474

DIRKS STEVENS, Amy, Chief Operating Officer, Presence Saint Joseph Medical Center, Joliet, IL, p. A186

DISANTO, Larry
  Executive Vice President and Chief Operating Officer, Capital Health Medical Center–Hopewell, Pennington, NJ, p. A408
  Executive Vice President and Chief Operating Officer, Capital Health Regional Medical Center, Trenton, NJ, p. A411

DISANZO, Frank, Vice President and Chief Information Officer, Saint Peter's University Hospital, New Brunswick, NJ, p. A407

DISCH, Catherine D., Executive Vice President and Chief Operating Officer, Truman Medical Center–Hospital Hill, Kansas City, MO, p. A364

DISESA, Verdi, Interim President, Fox Chase Cancer Center–American Oncologic Hospital, Philadelphia, PA, p. A534

DISHMAN, Leonardo, M.D. Chief Medical Officer, Alice Hyde Medical Center, Malone, NY, p. A429

DISPOTO, Martha, R.N. Chief Nursing Officer, Anaheim Regional Medical Center, Anaheim, CA, p. A52

DISSEN, James H., Interim President and Chief Executive Officer, Highland Hospital, Charleston, WV, p. A676

DISTASIO, Stephen R., Director, Veterans Affairs Black Hills Health Care System, Fort Meade, SD, p. A560

DISTEFANO, Guy, Chief Financial Officer, Hampton Behavioral Health Center, Westampton, NJ, p. A412

DITTMANN, Jerry, Vice President Human Resources, Mount Nittany Medical Center, State College, PA, p. A541

DITTO, Debbie, CPA Controller, Lincoln Trail Behavioral Health System, Radcliff, KY, p. A259

DITURO, Beth, Divisional Chief Information Officer, Lenox Hill Hospital, New York, NY, p. A433

DIVELLO, Douglas F., President and Chief Executive Officer, Alice Hyde Medical Center, Malone, NY, p. A429

DIVITO, Frank, Manager Information Systems, Jameson Hospital, New Castle, PA, p. A533

DIX, Georeg, Chief Information Officer, Olathe Medical Center, Olathe, KS, p. A241

DIX, Roger J., Senior Vice President and Chief Financial Officer, Hannibal Regional Hospital, Hannibal, MO, p. A361

DIX, Theresa, R.N. Chief Nursing Officer, Wythe County Community Hospital, Wytheville, VA, p. A663

DIXON, Christy, Chief Human Resources Officer, HEALTHSOUTH Rehabilitation Hospital, Humble, TX, p. A614

DIXON, Debbie, Director Human Resources, Pampa Regional Medical Center, Pampa, TX, p. A626

DIXON, Del, Chief Information Officer, South Shore Hospital, South Weymouth, MA, p. A304

DIXON, Florine, Vice President Clinical Services, Memorial Hospital, Carthage, IL, p. A175

DIXON, Gregg, CP
  Chief Financial Officer, Asheville Specialty Hospital, Asheville, NC, p. A447
  Chief Financial Officer, Interfaith Medical Center,, NY, p. A432

DIXON, Mary, R.N. Chief Nursing Executive, Inova Alexandria Hospital, Alexandria, VA, p. A651

DIXON, Matt, Chief Operating Officer, St. Mark's Hospital, Salt Lake City, UT, p. A647

DIXON, Michael, Director Human Resources, Self Regional Healthcare, Greenwood, SC, p. A553

DIXON, Sally J., President and Chief Executive Officer, Memorial Hospital, York, PA, p. A545

DIXON, Shannon, Manager Business Office, Weisbrod Memorial County Hospital, Eads, CO, p. A100

DIXON, Todd, R.N., Chief Executive Officer, Barrow Regional Medical Center, Winder, GA, p. A163

DIZON, Louis, M.D. Chief of Staff, Russell County Medical Center, Lebanon, VA, p. A656

DJOGAN, Djogan, Chief Financial Officer, George Nigh Rehabilitation Institute, Okmulgee, OK, p. A505

DLWGOSH, Robert, M.D. Chief of Staff, Ashtabula County Medical Center, Ashtabula, OH, p. A470

DMELLO, Artie, Director Case Management, Kindred Hospital Sugar Land, Sugar Land, TX, p. A635

DOAK, Mark, President and Chief Executive Officer, Davis Memorial Hospital, Elkins, WV, p. A676

DOAN, Angela, Chief Financial Officer, Scott Memorial Hospital, Scottsburg, IN, p. A213

DOBALIAN, Derek, M.D. Chief of Staff, Tri–City Regional Medical Center, Hawaiian Gardens, CA, p. A63

DOBBINS, Jim, Vice President Human Resources, Lenoir Memorial Hospital, Kinston, NC, p. A456

DOBIN, Jennifer, Vice President Human Resources, Bayonne Medical Center, Bayonne, NJ, p. A401

DOBIZL, Howard
  Director Information Technology Services, Howard Young Medical Center, Woodruff, WI, p. A700
  Director Information Services for the Northern Region, Ministry Saint Mary's Hospitals, Rhinelander, WI, p. A695

DOBLE, H. Peter, M.D. Director Medical Staff Affairs, St. Luke's Jerome, Jerome, ID, p. A169

DOBOSENSKI, Dave, Chief Executive Officer, St. Croix Regional Medical Center, St. Croix Falls, WI, p. A697

DOBOSH, Jr., Joseph J., Vice President and Chief Financial Officer, Children's Specialized Hospital–PSE&G, New Brunswick, NJ, p. A407

DOBRAWA, Stanley
  Area Technology Director, Kaiser Permanente San Rafael Medical Center, San Rafael, CA, p. A89
  Area Technology Director, Kaiser Permanente Santa Rosa Medical Center, Santa Rosa, CA, p. A90

DOBRINSKI, Sandra, Director of Nursing, Comanche County Hospital, Coldwater, KS, p. A232

DOBROVICH, Michael, M.D. Chief Medical Officer, St. John Medical Center, Westlake, OH, p. A493

DOBSON, Glenda, Vice President Clinical Services, Louisiana Heart Hospital, Lacombe, LA, p. A270

DOBSON, Glenn E., Chief Financial Officer, NORTHSTAR Health System, Iron River, MI, p. A317

DOBSON, Trey, M.D. Chief Medical Officer, Southwestern Vermont Medical Center, Bennington, VT, p. A649

DOCKENDORFF, Patti, Director Finance, Gundersen Tri–County Hospital and Clinics, Whitehall, WI, p. A699

DODD, Eric, Chief Information Officer, Thorek Memorial Hospital, Chicago, IL, p. A179

DODD, John, Vice President Human Resources, Central Peninsula General Hospital, Soldotna, AK, p. A29

DODDS, Cheryl, M.D. Medical Director, Three Rivers Behavioral Health, West Columbia, SC, p. A557

DODDS, Dale, Interim Chief Financial Officer, Huntsville Memorial Hospital, Huntsville, TX, p. A614

DODDS, Rick A., Vice President Human Resources, Sonora Regional Medical Center, Sonora, CA, p. A91

DODDS, Sheryl, Chief Clinical Officer, Florida Hospital, Orlando, FL, p. A135

DODERER, Marcella, President and Chief Executive Officer, Arkansas Children's Hospital, Little Rock, AR, p. A46

DODSON, Nancy, Chief Operating Officer, Gulf Coast Medical Center, Panama City, FL, p. A136

DODSON, Thomas, Executive Director, Buffalo Psychiatric Center, Buffalo, NY, p. A422

DOEHRING, Christopher, M.D. Vice President Medical Affairs, Franciscan St. Francis Health – Indianapolis, Indianapolis, IN, p. A205

DOELING, Mariann, R.N., President, Carrington Health Center, Carrington, ND, p. A465

DOGGETT, Sherri L., Vice President Patient Services, Mercy Medical Center–Centerville, Centerville, IA, p. A218

DOHERTY, Allison, Chief Financial Officer, The NeuroMedical Center Surgical Hospital, Baton Rouge, LA, p. A264

DOHERTY, Donna, R.N. Vice President of Nursing and Chief Nursing Officer, Jordan Hospital, Plymouth, MA, p. A304

DOHERTY, Randy, CPA, Chief Executive Officer, Braintree Rehabilitation Hospital, Braintree, MA, p. A298

DOHERTY, Stephen, Chief Financial Officer, Forrest City Medical Center, Forrest City, AR, p. A44

DOHM, Thomas J., Interim Chief Operating Officer, Provident Hospital of Cook County, Chicago, IL, p. A178

DOI, Kathy, Executive Director Human Resources, Anaheim Regional Medical Center, Anaheim, CA, p. A52

DOIDGE, John C., Vice President Finance, Glencoe Regional Health Services, Glencoe, MN, p. A332

DOKSUM, Kathryn, Director Finance, Samaritan North Lincoln Hospital, Lincoln City, OR, p. A514

DOLAN, John, Chief Financial Officer, Covenant Hospital–Levelland, Levelland, TX, p. A618

DOLAN, Margaret, Director People Services, St. Elizabeth's Hospital, Belleville, IL, p. A174

DOLAN, Patricia R., R.N. Vice President/ Chief Nursing Officer, Florida Hospital Waterman, Tavares, FL, p. A142

DOLAN, Paul, M.D. Chief Medical Affairs Officer, Benefis Hospitals, Great Falls, MT, p. A376

DOLBEE, Hilary, Vice President and Chief Financial Officer, Pratt Regional Medical Center, Pratt, KS, p. A243

DOLES, Patty, Chief Financial Officer, Muskogee Regional Medical Center, Muskogee, OK, p. A502

DOLL, Ana S., Manager Human Resources, Adventist Rehabilitation Hospital of Maryland, Rockville, MD, p. A293

DOLL, Katherine, R.N. Chief Nursing Officer, Sierra Medical Center, El Paso, TX, p. A601

DOLLINGER, Michael, Personnel Administrator, Deer's Head Hospital Center, Salisbury, MD, p. A294

DOLLINS, Gary, Director Management Information Systems, Poplar Bluff Regional Medical Center, Poplar Bluff, MO, p. A368

DOLLINS, Mandy, R.N. Chief Nursing Officer, Five Rivers Medical Center, Pocahontas, AR, p. A49

DOLOHANTY–JOHNSON, Bridget, R.N. Vice President Patient Care Services, Parkview Whitley Hospital, Columbia City, IN, p. A200

DOMANICO, Lee, Chief Executive Officer, Marin General Hospital, Greenbrae, CA, p. A63

DOMEIER, Sandy, Director Patient Care Services, Sibley Medical Center, Arlington, MN, p. A328

DOMINGO, Connie, M.D. Medical Director, Weisman Children's Rehabilitation Hospital, Marlton, NJ, p. A406

DOMINGO, Ramon, M.D. Chief of Staff, McCamey County Hospital District, McCamey, TX, p. A622

DOMINGUE, Buffy, Chief Executive Officer, Lafayette Surgical Specialty Hospital, Lafayette, LA, p. A271

DOMINGUE, Kevin, Director Human Resources and Medical Affairs, Our Lady of Lourdes Regional Medical Center, Lafayette, LA, p. A271

DOMINGUEZ, Brenda, Director Human Resources, Cypress Creek Hospital, Houston, TX, p. A609

DOMINGUEZ, Isabel, Director Human Resources and Payroll, Cornerstone Hospital of SouthEast Arizona, Tucson, AZ, p. A38

DOMINGUEZ, Jerry A., CPA Chief Financial Officer, East Texas Medical Center Trinity, Trinity, TX, p. A638

DOMINGUEZ, Marie, Commander, General Leonard Wood Army Community Hospital, Fort Leonard Wood, MO, p. A361

DOMINSKI, Michelle, Human Resources Officer, Veterans Affairs Butler Healthcare, Butler, PA, p. A521

DOMINSKI, Paul, Vice President Human Resources, Park Nicollet Methodist Hospital, Saint Louis Park, MN, p. A339

DOMRES, Mary Jane, Director Materials Management and Administrator Information Technology, Cavalier County Memorial Hospital, Langdon, ND, p. A468

DONAHEY, Dick, Senior Vice President Human Resources, Alamance Regional Medical Center, Burlington, NC, p. A448

DONAHEY, Kenneth C., Chief Operating Officer, TriStar Hendersonville Medical Center, Hendersonville, TN, p. A570

DONAHUE, Brian, Chief Financial Officer, Portage Health, Hancock, MI, p. A316

DONAHUE, Debra, Senior Vice President and Chief Operating Officer, Champlain Valley Physicians Hospital Medical Center, Plattsburgh, NY, p. A439

DONAHUE, Elisabeth, Associate Director Human Resources, Jeanes Hospital, Philadelphia, PA, p. A535

DONAHUE, Leslie A., President and Chief Executive Officer, Piedmont Hospital, Atlanta, GA, p. A147

DONAHUE, Michael, M.D. Medical Director, Select Specialty Hospital–Pittsburgh/UPMC, Pittsburgh, PA, p. A537

DONAHUE, Moreen, R.N. Chief Nursing Executive, Danbury Hospital, Danbury, CT, p. A108

DONAHUE, Patrick, Administrator, Methodist Hospital Union County, Morganfield, KY, p. A258

DONALD, Steve, M.D. Chief of Staff, Washington County Hospital and Nursing Home, Chatom, AL, p. A18

DONALDSON, Brooke G., Assistant Administrator Human Resources, Jackson Hospital, Marianna, FL, p. A130

DONALDSON, Les, M.D. Chief of Staff, Roosevelt General Hospital, Portales, NM, p. A417

DONALDSON, Lori, Chief Financial Officer, UC San Diego Health System, San Diego, CA, p. A86

DONALDSON, Michelle, M.D. President Medical Staff, Livingston Memorial Hospital, Livingston, MT, p. A378

DONALDSON, Sherry, Director Human Resources, Barnwell County Hospital, Barnwell, SC, p. A548

DONALDSON, Tammy, Director of Nursing, Highlands Hospital, Connellsville, PA, p. A523

DONATELLE, Lawrence, M.D. Vice President Medical Affairs, St. Elizabeth Hospital, Appleton, WI, p. A683

DONENWIRTH, Karl, Vice President Information Services, Northcoast Behavioral Healthcare System, Northfield, OH, p. A487

DONGILLI, Jr., Paul, Ph.D. Executive Vice President and Chief Operating Officer, Madonna Rehabilitation Hospital, Lincoln, NE, p. A385

DONICA, Joanna, Director Human Resource, HEALTHSOUTH Rehabilitation Hospital of Beaumont, Beaumont, TX, p. A587

DONLEY, Brian, M.D., President, Lutheran Hospital, Cleveland, OH, p. A476

DONLIN, Michael T., FACHE, Administrator, Floyd Valley Hospital, Le Mars, IA, p. A224

DONLON, Marcia, Chief Nursing Officer, Holy Family Memorial, Manitowoc, WI, p. A690

DONNELL, Dan, M.D. Chief of Staff, Midwest Regional Medical Center, Midwest City, OK, p. A501

DONNELLY, Gloria, Director Human Resources, Euclid Hospital, Euclid, OH, p. A481

DONOVAN, James W.
President and Chief Executive Officer, Miles Memorial Hospital, Damariscotta, ME, p. A283
President and Chief Executive Officer, St. Andrews Hospital and Healthcare Center, Boothbay Harbor, ME, p. A282

DONOVAN, Jenny, Director Human Resources, Wright Memorial Hospital, Trenton, MO, p. A372

DONOVAN, Kevin, Chief Executive Officer, Mt. Ascutney Hospital and Health Center, Windsor, VT, p. A650

DONOVAN, Mary, Controller, HEALTHSOUTH Rehabilitation Institute of Tucson, Tucson, AZ, p. A38

DONOVAN, Mike, Chief Financial Officer, Lemuel Shattuck Hospital, Jamaica Plain, MA, p. A301

DONOVAN, Patrick, M.D. Director Medical Staff, HEALTHSOUTH Rehabilitation Hospital of Fort Worth, Fort Worth, TX, p. A603

DONSON, Elliott, Chief Information Specialist, Lincoln Hospital, Davenport, WA, p. A666

DONZE, Richard D., D.O. Senior Vice President Medical Affairs, Chester County Hospital, West Chester, PA, p. A543

DOODY, Kris A., R.N., Chief Executive Officer, Cary Medical Center, Caribou, ME, p. A282

DOOLEY, Jerry, Interim Chief Executive Officer, Scott Memorial Hospital, Scottsburg, IN, p. A213

DOOLEY, Lisa, Health Information Officer, Middlesboro ARH Hospital, Middlesboro, KY, p. A257

DOOLEY, Mark J., Chief Executive Officer, Clinton Memorial Hospital, Wilmington, OH, p. A493

DOOLITTLE, Jon D., President and Chief Executive Officer, Northwest Medical Center, Albany, MO, p. A356

DOPSON, James, Director Human Resources, Ennis Regional Medical Center, Ennis, TX, p. A602

DORAK, John, Chief Information Officer, Nicholas H. Noyes Memorial Hospital, Dansville, NY, p. A424

DORAN, Dave, Chief Financial Officer, Pondera Medical Center, Conrad, MT, p. A375

DORAN, Judy, R.N. Vice President of Hospital Services and Chief Nurse Executive, Stanly Regional Medical Center, Albemarle, NC, p. A447

DORAN, Ken, Interim Chief Financial Officer, Westlake Regional Hospital, Columbia, KY, p. A249

DORF, Jeffrey, M.D. Medical Director, Kindred Hospital–Albuquerque, Albuquerque, NM, p. A414

DORIA, Eugene, Chief Information Officer, Coatesville Veterans Affairs Medical Center, Coatesville, PA, p. A523

DORIS, Doug, Chief Executive Officer, Central Carolina Hospital, Sanford, NC, p. A460

DORNOFF, Edward G., Associate Director, Battle Creek Veterans Affairs Medical Center, Battle Creek, MI, p. A309

DOROGY, Sharon, Director Health Information Management, The Children's Institute of Pittsburgh, Pittsburgh, PA, p. A538

DOROTHY, Jonnie, Senior Director Human Resources, Massena Memorial Hospital, Massena, NY, p. A429

DORR, Amy, Vice President Human Resources, McLaren Lapeer Region, Lapeer, MI, p. A318

DORRIS, Patricia, Executive Director, Medical Center of Southeastern Oklahoma, Durant, OK, p. A497

DORRIS, Ronald E.
Chief Executive Officer, Carrus Rehabilitation Hospital, Sherman, TX, p. A633
Chief Executive Officer, Carrus Specialty Hospital, Sherman, TX, p. A634

DORSCH, Anthony, Chief Financial Officer, Providence Alaska Medical Center, Anchorage, AK, p. A27

DORSEY, Michael A., FACHE, Chief Executive Officer, St. Joseph Medical Center, Kansas City, MO, p. A363

DORSEY, William, M.D., Board Chairman and Chief Executive Officer, Jackson Park Hospital and Medical Center, Chicago, IL, p. A177

DORST, Jake, Vice President and Chief Information Officer, Meritus Medical Center, Hagerstown, MD, p. A292

DORTON, Patty, Director of Nursing, Buchanan General Hospital, Grundy, VA, p. A655

DORUNDO, Cynthia M., President, UPMC McKeesport, McKeesport, PA, p. A531

DOSCHER, Suzanne, Vice President Operations, Waccamaw Community Hospital, Murrells Inlet, SC, p. A555

DOSS, Ann, Interim Vice President and Chief Nursing Officer, Providence Hospital, Mobile, AL, p. A22

DOSS, Justin, Chief Operating Officer, Blake Medical Center, Bradenton, FL, p. A119

DOSS, Mounir F.
Executive Vice President and Chief Financial Officer, Brookdale Hospital Medical Center,, NY, p. A431
Executive Vice President and Chief Financial Officer, Flushing Hospital Medical Center,, NY, p. A432
Executive Vice President and Chief Financial Officer, Jamaica Hospital Medical Center,, NY, p. A432

DOSSEY, Emily, Director Human Resources, Hamilton General Hospital, Hamilton, TX, p. A607

DOUBLE, Ron, Chief Information Officer, Parkview Noble Hospital, Kendallville, IN, p. A207

DOUCETTE, Elmer, Vice President and Chief Financial Officer, Eastern Maine Medical Center, Bangor, ME, p. A281

DOUCETTE, Julia, Director Human Resources, Phoenix Baptist Hospital, Phoenix, AZ, p. A35

DOUD, Tony, Controller, St. Mary's of Michigan Standish Hospital, Standish, MI, p. A325

DOUGH, Robert, M.D. Chief of Staff, Randolph Hospital, Asheboro, NC, p. A447

DOUGHERTY, Christopher J., Chief Executive Officer, Covenant Children's Hospital, Lubbock, TX, p. A619

DOUGHERTY, David, Chief Information Management Officer, Irwin Army Community Hospital, Junction City, KS, p. A236

DOUGHERTY, James, Commander, U. S. Air Force Medical Center Keesler, Keesler AFB, MS, p. A349

DOUGHERTY, Terry, Director Human Resources, Bryn Mawr Hospital, Bryn Mawr, PA, p. A521

DOUGHTY, Cathy, Vice President Human Resources, Sheppard Pratt Health System, Baltimore, MD, p. A289

DOUGHTY, Stephanie
Chief Financial Officer, Medical Center of the Rockies, Loveland, CO, p. A104
Chief Financial Officer, Poudre Valley Hospital, Fort Collins, CO, p. A101

DOUGLAS, Andy, Manager Information Technology, Burnett Medical Center, Grantsburg, WI, p. A687

DOUGLAS, Bill, Senior Vice President and Chief Financial Officer, Riverside Medical Center, Kankakee, IL, p. A186

DOUGLAS, Dora, Chief Financial Officer, Summersville Regional Medical Center, Summersville, WV, p. A681

DOUGLAS, Doug, Vice President Human Resources, AnMed Health Medical Center, Anderson, SC, p. A548

DOUGLAS, Errol, Director Human Resources, University of Miami Hospital, Miami, FL, p. A132

DOUGLAS, Jason T., Chief Executive Officer, Mercy Hospital, Moose Lake, MN, p. A336

DOUGLAS, Lesia, R.N. Vice President Patient Care Services and Chief Nurse Executive, Bon Secours Baltimore Health System, Baltimore, MD, p. A287

DOUGLAS, Paul, Vice President Human Resources, Baton Rouge General Medical Center, Baton Rouge, LA, p. A263

DOUGLASS, Claudia, Chief Operating Officer, Piedmont Medical Center, Rock Hill, SC, p. A555

DOUKAS, Michael, Chief of Staff, Tennessee Valley Healthcare System, Nashville, TN, p. A577

DOUVILLE, Arthur, M.D. Chief Medical Officer, Good Samaritan Hospital, San Jose, CA, p. A87

DOVEL, Melissa, Manager Human Resources, Atrium Medical Center of Corinth, Corinth, TX, p. A593

DOVER, James F., FACHE, President and Chief Executive Officer, O'Connor Hospital, San Jose, CA, p. A88

DOVER, Jerry, Chief Executive Officer, Sullivan County Memorial Hospital, Milan, MO, p. A366

DOVI, Sebastian, M.D. Interim Chief Medical Officer, Saint Michael's Medical Center, Newark, NJ, p. A407

DOVNARSKY, James, M.D. Director Pulmonary Medical, Kindred Hospital South Philadelphia, Philadelphia, PA, p. A535

DOWDELL, Dennis, Vice President Human Resources, Memorial Sloan–Kettering Cancer Center, New York, NY, p. A434

DOWDELL, Thomas C., FACHE Senior Vice President and Chief Operating Officer, Western Maryland Regional Medical Center, Cumberland, MD, p. A291

DOWDLE, Paula, Chief Operating Officer, Jefferson Healthcare, Port Townsend, WA, p. A669

DOWELL, James, Administrator and Chief Executive Officer, Little River Memorial Hospital, Ashdown, AR, p. A41

DOWELL, Wade, M.D. Chief of Staff, South Sunflower County Hospital, Indianola, MS, p. A348

DOWGUN, Richard, Chief Information Officer, St. Francis Medical Center, Trenton, NJ, p. A411

DOWLING, Deanna, R.N. Chief Nursing Officer, Texas Specialty Hospital at Wichita Falls, Wichita Falls, TX, p. A641

DOWLING, Lisa, Manager Finance, Mercy Hospital Tishomingo, Tishomingo, OK, p. A507

DOWN, Melanie Falls, Site Manager, Crow/Northern Cheyenne Hospital, Crow Agency, MT, p. A375

DOWN, Philip B., Chief Executive Officer, Doctors Community Hospital, Lanham, MD, p. A292

DOWNES, Patrick, Chief Operating Officer, Hialeah Hospital, Hialeah, FL, p. A125

DOWNEY, Brandon, Chief Operating Officer, Mary Black Memorial Hospital, Spartanburg, SC, p. A556

DOWNEY, Daniel, Chief Fiscal Service, Veterans Administration New York Harbor Healthcare System,, NY, p. A437

DOWNEY, Patti L., Vice President, Human Resources, Liberty Hospital, Liberty, MO, p. A365

DOWNEY, Robert, Chief Financial Officer, Marshalltown Medical & Surgical Center, Marshalltown, IA, p. A225

DOWNEY, Susan, MS, Chief Executive Officer, Kindred Hospital–Boston, Brighton, MA, p. A298

DOWNEY, William B.
Chief Operating Officer, Riverside Behavioral Health Center, Hampton, VA, p. A655
Chief Operating Officer, Riverside Regional Medical Center, Newport News, VA, p. A658
President and Chief Executive Officer, Riverside Rehabilitation Institute, Newport News, VA, p. A658

DOWNING, David, M.D. Chief Medical Officer, Fort Defiance Indian Health Service Hospital, Fort Defiance, AZ, p. A31

DOWNS, Bryan, Director Information Systems, Central Peninsula General Hospital, Soldotna, AK, p. A29

DOWNS, Connie, Chief Financial Officer, Pennock Hospital, Hastings, MI, p. A316

DOWNS, Nancy, M.D. Vice President Medical Affairs, Memorial Hospital at Gulfport, Gulfport, MS, p. A347

DOWNS, Patricia, Director Human Resources, Northern Nevada Medical Center, Sparks, NV, p. A396

DOWNS, Sue, MSN, President, Flaget Memorial Hospital, Bardstown, KY, p. A248

DOXTATOR, Rick, Chief Financial Officer, Christus St. Vincent Regional Medical Center, Santa Fe, NM, p. A418

DOYEL, Brenda K., Chief Financial Officer, Sayre Memorial Hospital, Sayre, OK, p. A506

DOYLE, Barbara J., MS, Senior Vice President and Chief Executive Officer, Inova Mount Vernon Hospital, Alexandria, VA, p. A651

DOYLE, Dennis, Commanding General, Tripler Army Medical • Center, Honolulu, HI, p. A165

DOYLE, James F., Senior Vice President Finance and Chief Financial Officer, Elmhurst Memorial Hospital,, IL, p. A182

DOYLE, Jay, Chief Financial Officer, St. James Healthcare, Butte, MT, p. A374

DOYLE, John
Vice President Finance, Paoli Hospital, Paoli, PA, p. A534
Chief Financial Officer, Wenatchee Valley Medical Center, Wenatchee, WA, p. A674

DOYLE, Kelly, Chief Executive Officer, Rothman Specialty Hospital, Bensalem, PA, p. A520

DOYLE, Mark
Chief Financial Officer, Broward Health Medical Center, Fort Lauderdale, FL, p. A123
Chief Financial Officer, St. Vincent's Medical Center Riverside, Jacksonville, FL, p. A127
Chief Financial Officer, St. Vincent's Medical Center Southside, Jacksonville, FL, p. A127

DOYLE, Michael, M.D. Deputy Commander Clinical Services, Keller Army Community Hospital, West Point, NY, p. A446

DOYLE, Patricia S., R.N. Chief Nursing Officer, Regional Medical Center, Manchester, IA, p. A224

DOZIER, Carol, President and Chief Executive Officer, King's Daughters' Health, Madison, IN, p. A209

DRABANT, Leah, Director of Finance, Complex Care Hospital at Ridgelake, Sarasota, FL, p. A139

DRAEHN, Donald, M.D. Chief of Staff, Scott & White Hospital – Brenham, Brenham, TX, p. A589

DRAGO, Susan, R.N. Chief Clinical Officer, Kindred Hospital North Florida, Green Cove Springs, FL, p. A125

DRAIME, D. Eric, Vice President and Chief Financial Officer, Galion Community Hospital, Galion, OH, p. A482

DRAKE, Dan, VP, Patient Care Services, Albemarle Health, Elizabeth City, NC, p. A452

DRAPAL, Cindy, Chief Nursing Officer, George E. Weems Memorial Hospital, Apalachicola, FL, p. A118

DRAPER, Jason, Chief Financial Officer, Volunteer Community Hospital, Martin, TN, p. A573

DRAPER, Vivian, Chief Financial Officer, U. S. Public Health Service Indian Hospital–Sells, Sells, AZ, p. A37

DRAYTON, Renee, Chief Human Resources, Prattville Baptist Hospital, Prattville, AL, p. A25

DREGNEY, Jim, Chief Financial Officer, Lakewood Health System, Staples, MN, p. A341

DREHER, Ronald, Finance Officer, Robert J. Dole Veterans Affairs Medical Center, Wichita, KS, p. A246

DRESSLER, Kaeli, R.N. Chief Nursing Officer, Peterson Regional Medical Center, Kerrville, TX, p. A616

DREUSSI, Rob, Interim Director Information Systems, Ponca City Medical Center, Ponca City, OK, p. A505

DREW, Jeff, Fiscal Officer, Aleda E. Lutz Veterans Affairs Medical Center, Saginaw, MI, p. A323

DREW, Jim, Chief Information Officer, Saint Thomas Midtown Hospital, Nashville, TN, p. A576

DREWETTE, Frederick J., Chief Financial Officer, Anaheim Regional Medical Center, Anaheim, CA, p. A52

DREXLER, Diane, R.N
　Chief Nursing Officer, Yavapai Regional  Medical Center – East, Prescott Valley, AZ, p. A36
　Chief Nursing Officer, Yavapai Regional Medical Center, Prescott, AZ, p. A36

DRIFTMIER, PHR, Tammie, Director Human Resources, Clarinda Regional Health Center, Clarinda, IA, p. A218

DRIGGERS, Steve, M.D. Chief Medical Officer, Holy Family Memorial, Manitowoc, WI, p. A690

DRINKWATER, Kenneth, Director Human Resources, Texas Health Harris Methodist Hospital Southlake, Southlake, TX, p. A634

DRINKWATER, Linda, Chief Financial Officer, Waldo County General Hospital, Belfast, ME, p. A281

DRINKWITZ, Jeremy, Chief Operating Officer, Sparks Regional Medical Center, Fort Smith, AR, p. A44

DRISCOLL, Angie, Director Human Resources, Los Alamitos Medical Center, Los Alamitos, CA, p. A68

DRISCOLL, Nancy, R.N. Chief Nursing Officer, Longmont United Hospital, Longmont, CO, p. A104

DROBIL, Frank, Director Human Resources, McCurtain Memorial Hospital, Idabel, OK, p. A500

DROBNICH, Sara, Interim Chief Executive Officer, Monroe County Hospital, Albia, IA, p. A216

DROBOT, Michael D., Chief Executive Officer, Pacific Hospital of Long Beach, Long Beach, CA, p. A67

DROEGE, Marie T., President, Robert Packer Hospital, Sayre, PA, p. A540

DRONE, Marilyn, R.N. Vice President, CNO, St. Joseph Health St. Mary, Apple Valley, CA, p. A53

DROPPERS, Larry, Chief Financial Officer, Walter Knox Memorial Hospital, Emmett, ID, p. A169

DROTTS, Jennifer, Manager Human Resources, Bigfork Valley Hospital, Bigfork, MN, p. A329

DROZD, Carol, Chief Operating Officer, St. Mark's Medical Center, La Grange, TX, p. A617

DRUCKENMILLER, Carol, R.N. Assistant Administrator and Chief Nursing Officer, University of South Alabama Children's and Women's Hospital, Mobile, AL, p. A23

DRUMMOND, Armand, Manager Human Resources, South Lincoln Medical Center, Kemmerer, WY, p. A702

DRUMMOND, Dana, Chief Nursing Officer and Administrator, Surgery Specialty Hospitals of America, Pasadena, TX, p. A626

DRUMMOND, Greg, Chief Executive Officer, West Oaks Hospital, Houston, TX, p. A614

DRUMMOND, Michael, Chief Financial Officer, Runnells Specialized Hospital of Union County, Berkeley Heights, NJ, p. A401

DRUMWRIGHT, Douglas, Chief Executive Officer, Parkview Community Hospital Medical Center, Riverside, CA, p. A82

DRUMWRIGHT, Mary, Director Human Resources, Person Memorial Hospital, Roxboro, NC, p. A460

DRVARIC, David M., M.D. Chief of Staff, Shriners Hospitals for Children–Springfield, Springfield, MA, p. A305

DRY, Laurence, Vice President, Support and Ambulatory Services, Presence Saint Joseph Hospital, Elgin, IL, p. A181

DRYBURGH, Louise, Chief Executive Officer, First Care Health Center, Park River, ND, p. A469

DRYER, Len, Chief Financial Officer, Children's Hospital Colorado, Aurora, CO, p. A97

DRYMON, Lisa, Manager, Fairfax Community Hospital, Fairfax, OK, p. A498

DRZEWIECKI–BURGER, Mary Jo, Administrative Manager, Caro Center, Caro, MI, p. A310

DU PONT, Karen, Chief Human Resource Officer, Casa Colina Hospital for Rehabilitative Medicine, Pomona, CA, p. A80

DU RALL, Marty, Executive Director Human Resources, St. Vincent Indianapolis Hospital, Indianapolis, IN, p. A206

DUANE, Paul K.
　Chief Financial Officer and Office of Health Reform, Palmetto Health Baptist, Columbia, SC, p. A550
　Chief Financial Officer and Office of Health Reform, Palmetto Health Richland, Columbia, SC, p. A550

DUBE, Cynthia, M.D. Medical Director, Mayo Clinic Health System in Austin, Austin, MN, p. A329

DUBE, Sheri, Chief Operating Officer, St. David's North Austin Medical Center, Austin, TX, p. A586

DUBEN, Julie, Chief Clinical Officer, Kindred Hospital Northland, Kansas City, MO, p. A363

DUBICKI, Robert, Executive Vice President and Chief Operating Officer, Kingsbrook Jewish Medical Center,, NY, p. A433

DUBIS, John S., FACHE,  President and Chief Executive Officer, St. Elizabeth Edgewood, Edgewood, KY, p. A250

DUBOIS, Brady, Interim Chief Executive Officer, Northern Louisiana Medical Center, Ruston, LA, p. A277

DUBOIS, Robbye N., Chief Executive Officer, Ethicus Hospital – Grapevine, Grapevine, TX, p. A607

DUBOSE, Alta, Chief Financial Officer, Carolinas Hospital System Marion, Mullins, SC, p. A554

DUBROCA, Darryl S.
　Chief Executive Officer and Managing Director, Spring Mountain Sahara, Las Vegas, NV, p. A393
　Chief Executive Officer and Managing Director, Spring Mountain Treatment Center, Las Vegas, NV, p. A393
　Interim Chief Executive Officer, West Hills Hospital, Reno, NV, p. A395

DUBROW, Melissa, Chief Operating Officer, Waynesboro Hospital, Waynesboro, PA, p. A543

DUBRUL, Bill, Director Information Technology, St. Anthony's Hospital, Houston, TX, p. A612

DUBRUYNE, Sharon, Administrative Director Support Service and Human Resources, College Hospital Costa Mesa, Costa Mesa, CA, p. A57

DUCEY, Ann, Chief Information Officer, Boys Town National Research Hospital, Omaha, NE, p. A387

DUCHARME, Adele, MSN,  Chief Executive Officer, Saint Luke¥s Cushing Medical Center, Leavenworth, KS, p. A238

DUCHARME, Maria, R.N. Interim Chief Nursing Officer, Miriam Hospital, Providence, RI, p. A546

DUCHEMIN, MaDena
　Chief Human Resources Officer, Adirondack Medical Center, Saranac Lake, NY, p. A442
　Assistant Administrator Human Resources, John Randolph Medical Center, Hopewell, VA, p. A655

DUCHENE, Pam, R.N. Vice President Patient Care Services, St. Joseph Hospital, Nashua, NH, p. A399

DUCHESNEAU, Angy, Senior Director Human Resources, Lakeview Hospital, Stillwater, MN, p. A341

DUCHMAN, Susan, R.N. Vice President and Chief Nursing Officer, Williamsport Regional Medical Center, Williamsport, PA, p. A545

DUCKOR, Steven, M.D. Chief of Staff, Chapman Medical Center, Orange, CA, p. A77

DUCKWORTH, Allison, Chief Operating Officer and Chief Nursing Officer, FirstHealth Richmond Memorial Hospital, Rockingham, NC, p. A459

DUCKWORTH, Bob, Director Information Systems, Medical West, Bessemer, AL, p. A16

DUCRO, Tom, Chief Financial Officer, University Pointe Surgical Hospital, West Chester, OH, p. A493

DUDA, David, Senior Vice President and Chief Operating Officer, Riverside Medical Center, Kankakee, IL, p. A186

DUDEK, Gerald, M.D. Chief of Staff, Mercy Hospital Cadillac, Cadillac, MI, p. A310

DUDLEY, III, Edward L., Senior Vice President and Chief Financial Officer, Catholic Medical Center, Manchester, NH, p. A399

DUES, Craig, D.O. Chief Medical Officer, Mercer Health, Coldwater, OH, p. A477

DUET, Angela, Director Information Technology, St. Charles Parish Hospital, Luling, LA, p. A272

DUETSCH, Stephen, Vice President Operations and Support, Spencer Hospital, Spencer, IA, p. A228

DUFF, Isabel, MS,
　Director, Veterans Affairs Long Beach Healthcare System, Long Beach, CA, p. A68
　Acting Director, Veterans Affairs Southern Nevada Healthcare System, North Las Vegas, NV, p. A394

DUFF, Jim, Chief Financial Officer, Colorado Mental Health Institute at Pueblo, Pueblo, CO, p. A105

DUFF, Mary Claire, CPA Chief Financial Officer, Ridgeview Psychiatric Hospital and Center, Oak Ridge, TN, p. A578

DUFFEE, Patrick, Director Medical Information Systems, Delta Medical Center, Memphis, TN, p. A574

DUFFEY, Victoria, Director of Nursing, Citizens Medical Center, Colby, KS, p. A232

DUFFIELD, Doug, Interim President and Chief Executive Officer, San Joaquin Community Hospital, Bakersfield, CA, p. A54

DUFFIN, Kelly L., Operations Officer, Intermountain Medical Center, Murray, UT, p. A644

DUFFORD, Shawn, M.D. Vice President Medical Affairs and Chief Medical Officer, Exempla Saint Joseph Hospital, Denver, CO, p. A99

DUFFY, Beth, Chief Operating Officer, Einstein Medical Center Montgomery, East Norriton, PA, p. A524

DUFFY, Daniel, D.O. Chief Medical Director, HealthSource Saginaw, Saginaw, MI, p. A323

DUFFY, Karen, R.N. Director Patient Care Services, BayCare Alliant Hospital, Dunedin, FL, p. A122

DUFFY, Kenneth, M.D. Medical Director, Seiling Community Hospital, Seiling, OK, p. A506

DUFFY, Mary Elizabeth, Senior Vice President and Chief Financial Officer, St. Luke's Cornwall Hospital, Newburgh, NY, p. A437

DUFFY, Pamela
　Vice President Patient Care Services and Chief Nursing Officer, Kishwaukee Hospital, DeKalb, IL, p. A180
　Vice President Patient Services and CNO, Valley West Hospital, Sandwich, IL, p. A194

DUFOUR, Lonnie L., Chief Operating Officer, Chief Information Officer and Director Human Resources, Bunkie General Hospital, Bunkie, LA, p. A265

DUGAL, John Charles, M.D. Medical Director, Community Specialty Hospital, Lafayette, LA, p. A270

DUGAN, Gary, M.D. Vice President Medical Affairs, DuBois Regional Medical Center, Du Bois, PA, p. A524

DUGGAN, David, M.D. Medical Director, Upstate University Hospital, Syracuse, NY, p. A444

DUGGAN, Eileen, M.D. Medical Director, Crittenton Children's Center, Kansas City, MO, p. A362

DUGGAN, James E., Director Human Resources, Western Massachusetts Hospital, Westfield, MA, p. A306

DUGGAN, Tonya, Director Human Resources, Northern Louisiana Medical Center, Ruston, LA, p. A277

DUGGER, Curtis R., Chief Financial Officer, Memorial Hospital of Converse County, Douglas, WY, p. A702

DUGGER, Sandy
　Director Human Resources, Community Hospital, Torrington, WY, p. A704
　Chief Human Resources Officer, Platte County Memorial Hospital, Wheatland, WY, p. A704

DUHAIME, Robert A., R.N. Senior Vice President Clinical Operations and Chief Nursing Officer, Catholic Medical Center, Manchester, NH, p. A399

DUHANEY, Aphreikah, R.N. Chief Nursing Officer, Logan Regional Medical Center, Logan, WV, p. A678

DUHE, Louis, Senior Director Information Technology, George Washington University Hospital, Washington, DC, p. A116

DUHON, Neal J., M.D. Chief of Staff, American Legion Hospital, Crowley, LA, p. A266

DUHON, Susan, Director Medical Records, St. James Parish Hospital, Lutcher, LA, p. A272

DUHON, Thomas, Director Human Resources, Heart Hospital of Lafayette, Lafayette, LA, p. A270

DUJON–REYNOLDS, Frances, Director Human Resources, Winnebago Mental Health Institute, Winnebago, WI, p. A700

DUKE, Deirdre J., Associate Executive Director Human Resources, North Shore University Hospital, Manhasset, NY, p. A429

DUKE, Gail R., Director Human Resources, Clarendon Memorial Hospital, Manning, SC, p. A554

DUKE, II, Lee M., M.D. Senior Vice President and Chief Physician Executive, Lancaster General Health, Lancaster, PA, p. A528

DUKOFF, Ruth, M.D. Medical Director, North Star Behavioral Health System, Anchorage, AK, p. A27

DUMONSEAU, Kent, Chief Financial Officer, Riverwood Healthcare Center, Aitkin, MN, p. A328

DUMONT, Rene, CIO/ Vice President Strategic Growth, St. Mary's Regional Medical Center, Lewiston, ME, p. A284

DUMSHA, Eileen, Manager Employee Relations, Weisman Children's Rehabilitation Hospital, Marlton, NJ, p. A406

DUNAWAY, James, Director Information Management, Mississippi State Hospital, Whitfield, MS, p. A355

DUNCAN, Charles, M.D. Medical Director, Kindred Hospital–San Antonio, San Antonio, TX, p. A631

DUNCAN, Cindy
Chief Operating Officer, Memorial Hospital and Physician Group, Frederick, OK, p. A499
Manager Human Resources, Plains Regional Medical Center, Clovis, NM, p. A415
Director Human Resources, Roosevelt General Hospital, Portales, NM, p. A417

DUNCAN, Darryl L., President and Chief Executive Officer, Monongalia General Hospital, Morgantown, WV, p. A679

DUNCAN, J. D., Director Human Resources, Pondera Medical Center, Conrad, MT, p. A375

DUNCAN, Jeremy, Director Information Systems, Lawrence Medical Center, Moulton, AL, p. A24

DUNCAN, Jimmy, Chief Human Resource Officer, North Colorado Medical Center, Greeley, CO, p. A102

DUNCAN, Lawrence, Chief Executive Officer, El Paso Children's Hospital, El Paso, TX, p. A601

DUNCAN, Lucinda, Chief Human Resources, Bayne–Jones Army Community Hospital, Fort Polk, LA, p. A267

DUNCAN, Lyman, Chief Financial Officer, San Juan Hospital, Monticello, UT, p. A644

DUNCAN, Michael J., System Chief Executive Officer, Chester County Hospital, West Chester, PA, p. A543

DUNCAN, Neal, Chief Executive Officer, Carson Tahoe Continuing Care Hospital, Carson City, NV, p. A391

DUNFORD, Ben, Chief Financial Officer, Texas Regional Medical Center at Sunnyvale, Sunnyvale, TX, p. A636

DUNFORD, Bill, Manager, Northside Hospital–Cherokee, Canton, GA, p. A149

DUNGAN, Janice L., Senior Vice President Clinical Services, Lake Regional Health System, Osage Beach, MO, p. A367

DUNHAM, David S., President, Mercy Medical Center Merced, Merced, CA, p. A74

DUNHAM, Shelly, R.N., Chief Executive Officer, Okeene Municipal Hospital, Okeene, OK, p. A502

DUNKER, Karla, Director Finance, Sedgwick County Health Center, Julesburg, CO, p. A102

DUNKIEL, Barbara, Director Human Resources, HEALTHSOUTH Sunrise Rehabilitation Hospital, Fort Lauderdale, FL, p. A123

DUNKIN, Jackie J., Director Human Resources, Platte Valley Medical Center, Brighton, CO, p. A97

DUNLAP, David L., FACHE,
President and Chief Executive Officer, Bon Secours St. Francis Xavier Hospital, Charleston, SC, p. A549
President and Chief Executive Officer, Roper Hospital, Charleston, SC, p. A549

DUNLAP, Mary Lou, Correctional Health Services Administrator, California Medical Facility, Vacaville, CA, p. A94

DUNLAY, Robert, M.D. Chief Medical Officer, Alegent Creighton Health–Creighton University Medical Center, Omaha, NE, p. A387

DUNLOP, Jr., James H., CP
Senior Vice President and Chief Financial Officer, Kenmore Mercy Hospital, Kenmore, NY, p. A428
Senior Vice President Finance and Chief Financial Officer, Mercy Hospital, Buffalo, NY, p. A422
Chief Financial Officer, Sisters of Charity Hospital of Buffalo, Buffalo, NY, p. A423

DUNMAN, Robyn, Coordinator Human Resources, Kindred Hospital–Nashville, Nashville, TN, p. A576

DUNMYER, Daniel C., Chief Executive Officer, Carolinas Specialty Hospital, Charlotte, NC, p. A450

DUNN, Adele, Director Human Resources, Larned State Hospital, Larned, KS, p. A238

DUNN, Al, Chief Nursing Officer, HEALTHSOUTH Rehabilitation Hospital, Sewickley, PA, p. A541

DUNN, Christopher, M.D. Vice President Medical Affairs, Sequoia Hospital, Redwood City, CA, p. A82

DUNN, Connie, Director Human Resources, Livingston Memorial Hospital, Livingston, MT, p. A378

DUNN, Daniel N., Vice President Operations, Wentworth–Douglass Hospital, Dover, NH, p. A397

DUNN, E. D., Vice President Human Resources, Virtua Memorial, Mount Holly, NJ, p. A406

DUNN, George, M.D. Senior Vice President Medical Affairs, Glen Cove Hospital, Glen Cove, NY, p. A426

DUNN, Jeffrey, Chief Executive Officer, North Georgia Medical Center, Ellijay, GA, p. A153

DUNN, Kim, Attorney–at–Law, Cordova Community Medical Center, Cordova, AK, p. A27

DUNN, Leonard, M.D. Chief Medical Officer, BayCare Alliant Hospital, Dunedin, FL, p. A122

DUNN, Marcy
Vice President Information Services and Chief Information Officer, Good Samaritan Hospital Medical Center, West Islip, NY, p. A446
Vice President Information Services and Chief Information Officer, Mercy Medical Center, Rockville Centre, NY, p. A441
Vice President Information Services and Chief Information Officer, St. Francis Hospital, Roslyn, NY, p. A442

DUNN, Margie, Director Human Resources, Middle Tennessee Mental Health Institute, Nashville, TN, p. A576

DUNN, Patrick A., R.N. Chief Nursing Officer, Lea Regional Medical Center, Hobbs, NM, p. A416

DUNN, Rosemary, R.N. Chief Nursing Officer, Hahnemann University Hospital, Philadelphia, PA, p. A535

DUNN, Shawn, M.D. Medical Director, The NeuroMedical Center Surgical Hospital, Baton Rouge, LA, p. A264

DUNN, Sheila, Assistant Administrator Human Resources, Dale Medical Center, Ozark, AL, p. A24

DUNN, Terry, Director Information Technology, Battle Mountain General Hospital, Battle Mountain, NV, p. A391

DUNNE, Elizabeth, Chief Executive Officer, Providence Little Company of Mary Medical Center, Torrance, CA, p. A92

DUNNE, Penny, R.N. Director Human Resources, Samaritan Pacific Communities Hospital, Newport, OR, p. A515

DUNNING, Shane, Administrator, Carnegie Tri–County Municipal Hospital, Carnegie, OK, p. A496

DUNWOODY, Robert, Chief Financial Officer, Lawnwood Regional Medical Center, Fort Pierce, FL, p. A124

DUPPER, Harold, Chief Financial Officer, Platte Valley Medical Center, Brighton, CO, p. A97

DUPPER, Larry L., Chief Financial Officer, Valley View Hospital, Glenwood Springs, CO, p. A101

DUPRE', Charlotte W., Chief Executive Officer, Central Mississippi Medical Center, Jackson, MS, p. A348

DUPREE, Erin, M.D. Chief Medical Officer, Mount Sinai Hospital, New York, NY, p. A434

DUPREE, Lucy G., Director Human Resources, District One Hospital, Faribault, MN, p. A332

DUPUIS, Pamela M., R.N. Senior Vice President Patient Care Services, Sound Shore Medical Center of Westchester, New Rochelle, NY, p. A430

DUQUE, Cynthia, R.N. Chief Operating Officer, Promise Hospital of East Los Angeles, Suburban Medical Center Campus, Paramount, CA, p. A79

DUQUETTE, Bill, Chief Executive Officer, Baptist Health South Florida, Homestead Hospital, Homestead, FL, p. A125

DUQUETTE, Connie, Director Human Resources, Sharp Memorial Hospital, San Diego, CA, p. A85

DURAKIEWICZ, Marek, M.D. Chief of Staff, Saint Thomas Hickman Hospital, Centerville, TN, p. A566

DURAND, Mark, Assistant Administrator Operations, CHRISTUS Jasper Memorial Hospital, Jasper, TX, p. A615

DURBAK, Ivan, Chief Information Officer, Bronx–Lebanon Hospital Center Health Care System,, NY, p. A431

DURDEN, Rhonda, Chief Financial Officer, Emanuel Medical Center, Swainsboro, GA, p. A161

DURHAM, Bill, M.D. Chief Medical Officer, Oak Tree Hospital, Corbin, KY, p. A249

DURHAM, Josh, D.O. Chief of Staff, Clara Barton Hospital, Hoisington, KS, p. A235

DURHAM, Leslie, Vice President Information Systems, Bethesda Memorial Hospital, Boynton Beach, FL, p. A119

DURHAM, Linda, Director Human Resources, McNairy Regional Hospital, Selmer, TN, p. A578

DURHAM, Randy, Director Personnel, Memphis Mental Health Institute, Memphis, TN, p. A575

DURHAM, Thomas, Chief Nursing Officer, Ferry County Memorial Hospital, Republic, WA, p. A670

DURNEY, Gerry, Chief Operating Officer, Good Samaritan Hospital, Suffern, NY, p. A443

DUROVICH, Christopher J., President and Chief Executive Officer, Children's Medical Center of Dallas, Dallas, TX, p. A595

DURR, Durinda, Vice President and Chief Nursing Officer, Rome Memorial Hospital, Rome, NY, p. A441

DURR, Jana, Director Human Resources, North Star Behavioral Health System, Anchorage, AK, p. A27

DURR, Michele, M.D. Medical Director, Webster County Community Hospital, Red Cloud, NE, p. A389

DURRENCE, Elizabeth, Chief Operating Officer, Kendall Regional Medical Center, Miami, FL, p. A131

DURST, Geoff, Vice President Finance, Avera St. Luke's Hospital, Aberdeen, SD, p. A558

DURST, Jennifer, Director Information Services, Washington County Hospital and Clinics, Washington, IA, p. A229

DURST, Sue, R.N. Vice President Plant Operations, McLaren Macomb, Mount Clemens, MI, p. A320

DURSTELER, Courtney, Chief Human Resources Officer, Franklin County Medical Center, Preston, ID, p. A171

DUSENBERY, Jack, President and Chief Executive Officer, Covenant Medical Center, Waterloo, IA, p. A229

DUTCHER, Phillip C., Chief Operating Officer, NCH Downtown Naples Hospital, Naples, FL, p. A133

DUTHE, Robert J., Vice President Corporate Management Information Systems, Albany Memorial Hospital, Albany, NY, p. A420

DUTLA, Nimal, M.D. Chief Medical Staff, Holzer Medical Center – Jackson, Jackson, OH, p. A483

DUTMERS, David, Manager Technology Information System, Spectrum Health United Hospital, Greenville, MI, p. A315

DUTTON, Angela, Chief Human Resources Management Service, Robley Rex Veterans Affairs Medical Center, Louisville, KY, p. A256

DUTTON, Rebecca, Director Human Resources, Larue D. Carter Memorial Hospital, Indianapolis, IN, p. A206

DUTY, Jay, Chief Operating Officer, North Hills Hospital, North Richland Hills, TX, p. A625

DUVAL, John, Chief Executive Officer, VCU Health System, Richmond, VA, p. A661

DUVAL, Rob, Chief Human Resources Officer, Emma Pendleton Bradley Hospital, East Providence, RI, p. A546

DUVALL, Gary, Chief Information Resource Management, Jack C. Montgomery Veterans Affairs Medical Center, Muskogee, OK, p. A501

DUVALL, Richard, Director Support Services and Chief Operating Officer, Carthage Area Hospital, Carthage, NY, p. A423

DUVALL, Wendy, Chief Executive Officer, Barton County Memorial Hospital, Lamar, MO, p. A364

DWIGHT, Kara, Chief of Staff, Down East Community Hospital, Machias, ME, p. A284

DWORKIN, Darren, Senior Vice President and Chief Information Officer, Cedars–Sinai Medical Center, Los Angeles, CA, p. A68

DWORKIN, Jack H., M.D. Vice President Medical Affairs and Chief Medical Officer, CentraState Healthcare System, Freehold, NJ, p. A404

DWORKIN, Paul, M.D. Physician–in–Chief, Connecticut Children's Medical Center, Hartford, CT, p. A109

DWYER, Amy L., R.N. Chief Nursing Officer, Sacred Heart Hospital, Eau Claire, WI, p. A686

DWYER, Cathy, Senior Administrator Information Systems, Burke Rehabilitation Hospital, White Plains, NY, p. A446

DWYER, James P., D.O
Chief Medical Officer, Virtua Marlton, Marlton, NJ, p. A406
Executive Vice President and Chief Medical Officer, Virtua Memorial, Mount Holly, NJ, p. A406
Executive Vice President and Chief Medical Officer, Virtua Voorhees, Voorhees, NJ, p. A412

DWYER, Karla, R.N. Chief Nursing Officer, HEALTHSOUTH Rehabilitation Hospital–Wichita Falls, Wichita Falls, TX, p. A641

DWYER, Nancy, Vice President Human Resources, Eastside Medical Center, Snellville, GA, p. A160

DWYER, William, Vice President Human Resources, Children's Specialized Hospital–PSE&G, New Brunswick, NJ, p. A407

DYBVIG, Rob, M.D. Chief Medical Officer, Osceola Medical Center, Osceola, WI, p. A694

DYCHE, Ginny, Director Community Relations, Aspen Valley Hospital District, Aspen, CO, p. A97

DYCUS, Steve, Director Marketing and Public Relations, Williamson Medical Center, Franklin, TN, p. A569

DYE, Blake A., President, St. Vincent Heart Center of Indiana, Indianapolis, IN, p. A206

DYE, Chris, Director Information Systems, Saint Joseph – Martin, Martin, KY, p. A257

DYE, Kathy, Interim Administrator, Adena Greenfield Medical Center, Greenfield, OH, p. A482

DYER, Dave, Vice President and Chief Information Officer, Somerset Medical Center, Somerville, NJ, p. A410

DYER, Edward L., Chief Executive Officer, GLOBALREHAB Hospital – San Antonio, San Antonio, TX, p. A631

DYER, Herbert A., Vice President and Project Executive, Seton Medical Center Hays, Kyle, TX, p. A617

DYER, Kathleen
Vice President and Chief Information Officer, Adventist Behavioral Health Rockville, Rockville, MD, p. A293
Vice President and Chief Information Officer, Shady Grove Adventist Hospital, Rockville, MD, p. A294

DYER, Rebecca T., Administrator, Union General Hospital, Blairsville, GA, p. A148

DYKE, Donna, Human Resources Officer, Kearney County Health Services, Minden, NE, p. A386

DYKEHOUSE, Rodney, Senior Vice President Information Services, Waukesha Memorial Hospital, Waukesha, WI, p. A698

DYKES, Bradford W., President and Chief Executive Officer, Indiana University Health Bedford Hospital, Bedford, IN, p. A198

DYKES, Jennifer, Director Human Resources, Russell County Hospital, Russell Springs, KY, p. A260

DYKES, Nichole, Chief Financial Officer and Controller, HEALTHSOUTH Rehabilitation Hospital Midland–Odessa, Midland, TX, p. A623

DYKSTERHOUSE, Trevor J., President, Forest Health Medical Center, Ypsilanti, MI, p. A327

DYKSTRA, Janet H., Chief Executive Officer, Osceola Community Hospital, Sibley, IA, p. A228

DYRKACZ, Anna, Chief Financial Officer, Kindred Hospital Park View, Springfield, MA, p. A305

DYSART, Amy, Administrator, Oceans Behavioral Hospital of Broussard, Broussard, LA, p. A264

DZIEDZICKI, Ron, R.N. Chief Support Services Officer, University Hospitals Case Medical Center, Cleveland, OH, p. A477

DZIESINSKI, Ray R., Senior Vice President and Chief Financial Officer, Children's Medical Center of Dallas, Dallas, TX, p. A595

DZURENKO, Jeanne, R.N. Chief Nursing Officer and Senior Vice President Patient Care, Good Samaritan Hospital Medical Center, West Islip, NY, p. A446

# E

EADIE, Reginald J., M.D. Vice President Medical Affairs, Harper University Hospital/Hutzel Women's Hospital, Detroit, MI, p. A312

EADIE, Reginald J., M.D., President, Sinai–Grace Hospital, Detroit, MI, p. A312

EADY, Bruce, Chief Executive Officer, Howard A. Rusk Rehabilitation Center, Columbia, MO, p. A359

EAGEN, Mary K., R.N. Executive Vice President, Chief Nursing Officer, Parkland Health & Hospital System, Dallas, TX, p. A597

EAGER, David
Senior Vice President and Chief Financial Officer, Legacy Meridian Park Hospital, Tualatin, OR, p. A518
Senior Vice President and Chief Financial Officer, Legacy Mount Hood Medical Center, Gresham, OR, p. A513
Senior Vice President and Chief Financial Officer, Legacy Salmon Creek Medical Center, Vancouver, WA, p. A673

EAGERTON, Gregory S., Ph.D. Associate Director for Patient Care Services/Nurse Executive, Birmingham Veterans Affairs Medical Center, Birmingham, AL, p. A16

EAGLEHOUSE, Louis, Site Director and Chief Information Officer, The Good Samaritan Hospital, Lebanon, PA, p. A529

EAKLE, Phyllis, Chief Financial Officer, Epic Medical Center, Eufaula, OK, p. A498

EAKS, C. Alan, Chief Executive Officer, Aurora Chicago Lakeshore Hospital, Chicago, IL, p. A176

EARDLEY, John, Chief Financial Officer, Twin Valley Behavioral Healthcare, Columbus, OH, p. A478

EARL, Anna, M.D. Chief of Staff, Liberty Medical Center, Chester, MT, p. A374

EARL, Mindy, Health Information Manager, Power County Hospital District, American Falls, ID, p. A167

EARLE, Audra, Chief Executive Officer, Watsonville Community Hospital, Watsonville, CA, p. A95

EARLE, Cletis, Vice President and Chief Information Officer, Wyckoff Heights Medical Center,, NY, p. A437

EARLEY, Robert, President and Chief Executive Officer, JPS Health Network, Fort Worth, TX, p. A604

EARLEY, Tom, Chief Financial Officer, Woodward Regional Hospital, Woodward, OK, p. A510

EARLS, Sandra, Chief Financial Officer, Coalinga Regional Medical Center, Coalinga, CA, p. A57

EARLY, Elfie, Manager Data Services, Georgia Regional Hospital at Atlanta, Decatur, GA, p. A152

EARNSHAW, Dallas, Superintendent, Utah State Hospital, Provo, UT, p. A646

EASLEY, Marsha A., Chief Operating Officer, Orange Park Medical Center, Orange Park, FL, p. A135

EASON, Laurence, M.D. Chief Medical Officer, Providence Little Company of Mary Medical Center, Torrance, CA, p. A92

EASON, William, M.D. Medical Director, HEALTHSOUTH Cane Creek Rehabilitation Hospital, Martin, TN, p. A573

EASON SMEDLEY, Jessie, Chief Executive Officer, South Texas Rehabilitation Hospital, Brownsville, TX, p. A590

EASTBURG, Mark C., Ph.D., President and Chief Executive Officer, Pine Rest Christian Mental Health Services, Grand Rapids, MI, p. A315

EASTER, Thomas, M.D. President Medical Staff, San Antonio Community Hospital, Upland, CA, p. A94

EASTERLING, Jamie, Executive Director, Operations, Good Samaritan Hospital, Cincinnati, OH, p. A474

EASTERWOOD, Diane J., Human Resources Business Partner, Kaiser Permanente San Francisco Medical Center, San Francisco, CA, p. A86

EASTMAN, Brent, M.D
Chief Medical Officer, Scripps Green Hospital, La Jolla, CA, p. A65
Chief Medical Officer, Scripps Memorial Hospital–La Jolla, La Jolla, CA, p. A65

EASTMAN, David, Site Director, Ukiah Valley Medical Center, Ukiah, CA, p. A94

EASTMAN, Joseph F., Director Human Resources, Central Carolina Hospital, Sanford, NC, p. A460

EASTON, Laura S., R.N., President and Chief Executive Officer, Caldwell Memorial Hospital, Lenoir, NC, p. A456

EATHERLY, Theresa, Chief Financial Officer, Doctor's Hospital – Tidwell, Houston, TX, p. A609

EATON, Ellen, Director Human Resources, Tift Regional Medical Center, Tifton, GA, p. A161

EATON, Jim, Chief Financial Officer, Wise Regional Health System, Decatur, TX, p. A598

EATON, Kerry, R.N. Chief Operating Officer, Sacred Heart Hospital of Pensacola, Pensacola, FL, p. A137

EATON, Philip, Chief Executive Officer and Administrator, HEALTHSOUTH Rehabilitation Hospital of Utah, Sandy, UT, p. A647

EAVENSON, J. Steven, Interim Vice President and Chief Financial Officer, Mercy Medical Center–Sioux City, Sioux City, IA, p. A228

EAVES, Clinton, Administrator, H. C. Watkins Memorial Hospital, Quitman, MS, p. A353

EBAUGH, Matthew T., Area Information Officer, Kaiser Permanente San Diego Medical Center, San Diego, CA, p. A85

EBBETT, Patricia, Chief Human Resources Officer, Catawba Hospital, Catawba, VA, p. A652

EBERLE, Michele, Assistant Administrator, Mayo Clinic Health System – Chippewa Valley in Bloomer, Bloomer, WI, p. A684

EBERSOLE, Nathan, Controller, Calhoun–Liberty Hospital, Blountstown, FL, p. A118

EBERST, Laurie, R.N.,
President and Chief Executive Officer and Senior Vice President Operations Dignity Health Southern C, St. John's Pleasant Valley Hospital, Camarillo, CA, p. A55
President and Chief Executive Officer, St. John's Regional Medical Center, Oxnard, CA, p. A78

EBERT, Cynthia, R.N. Chief Nursing Officer, Summit Healthcare Regional Medical Center, Show Low, AZ, p. A37

EBERT, Jr., Larry W., Chief Financial Officer, Northridge Medical Center, Commerce, GA, p. A150

EBERT, Michael, M.D. Chief of Staff, Veterans Affairs Connecticut Healthcare System, West Haven, CT, p. A113

EBERTH, Denise A., Director Human Resources, Allegan General Hospital, Allegan, MI, p. A308

EBINGER, William, M.D. President and Chief of Staff, Aurora Medical Center Grafton, Grafton, WI, p. A687

EBLIN, Steven E., Chief Executive Officer / President, Randolph Hospital, Asheboro, NC, p. A447

EBNER, Carl, Vice President Finance, Robinson Memorial Hospital, Ravenna, OH, p. A489

EBNER, Joseph, M.D. Chief Medical Officer, Speare Memorial Hospital, Plymouth, NH, p. A400

EBRI, Patrick D., Ph.D
Vice President, Human Resources, Southeast Georgia Health System Brunswick Campus, Brunswick, GA, p. A149
Vice President Human Resources, Southeast Georgia Health System Camden Campus, Saint Marys, GA, p. A159

EBRIGHT, Brian, Chief Financial Officer, Arizona Spine and Joint Hospital, Mesa, AZ, p. A32

EBSEN, Mona, Chief Financial Officer, Kit Carson County Memorial Hospital, Burlington, CO, p. A98

ECCHER, Robbi, Vice President Human Resources, Sauk Prairie Memorial Hospital & Clinics, Prairie Du Sac, WI, p. A695

ECCLESTON, Julie, Vice President Human Resources, Hillcrest Medical Center, Tulsa, OK, p. A508

ECHELBERGER, Scott, Vice President, Operations, Catawba Valley Medical Center, Hickory, NC, p. A454

ECHOLS, Jane, Chief Executive Officer, Wills Memorial Hospital, Washington, GA, p. A162

ECKBERG, Stephen, Vice President Human Resources, St. Joseph Health St. Mary, Apple Valley, CA, p. A53

ECKELS, Dan, Chief Financial Officer, Washington Regional Medical Center, Fayetteville, AR, p. A43

ECKENFELS, Susan, Chief Financial Officer, Ste. Genevieve County Memorial Hospital, Ste. Genevieve, MO, p. A372

ECKERD, Gayle
Chief Executive Officer, River Point Behavioral Health, Jacksonville, FL, p. A126
Chief Executive Officer, Wekiva Springs Center for Women, Jacksonville, FL, p. A127

ECKERT, Leslie, Chief Financial Officer, St. Elizabeth's Hospital, Belleville, IL, p. A174

ECKERT, Mark, Vice President Finance, Ochsner Medical Center – Kenner, Kenner, LA, p. A269

ECKERT, Mary L., President and Chief Executive Officer, Millcreek Community Hospital, Erie, PA, p. A525

ECKERT, Susan, R.N. Senior Vice President and Chief Nursing Officer, MedStar Washington Hospital Center, Washington, DC, p. A116

ECKES, Chad, Chief Information Officer, Midwestern Regional Medical Center, Zion, IL, p. A197

ECKMANN, John, Director Information Systems, Shenandoah Medical Center, Shenandoah, IA, p. A228

ECKSTEIN, Melissa, Chief Executive Officer, Salt Lake Behavioral Health, Salt Lake City, UT, p. A647

ECKSTEIN, William, Chief Financial Officer, Columbus Specialty Hospital, Columbus, GA, p. A150

EDDEY, Gary E., M.D. Medical Director, Matheny Medical and Educational Center, Peapack, NJ, p. A408

EDDINGTON, Tonya, Coordinator Human Resources, Select Specialty Hospital–Springfield, Springfield, MO, p. A372

EDDINS, Angela, Controller, HEALTHSOUTH Emerald Coast Rehabilitation Hospital, Panama City, FL, p. A136

EDDLEMAN, Patricia, Fiscal Officer, Heartland Behavioral Healthcare, Massillon, OH, p. A485

EDDY, Craig, M.D. Chief Medical Officer, The HealthCenter, Kalispell, MT, p. A377

EDELEN, Donald B., M.D. Vice President Medical Services and Quality Initiatives, Franciscan St. Elizabeth Health – Lafayette Central, Lafayette, IN, p. A208

EDELMAN, Marc D., Vice President Operations, Bristol Hospital, Bristol, CT, p. A108

EDELSTEIN, Hank, M.D. Chief of Staff, Trinity Hospital, Weaverville, CA, p. A95

EDENFIELD, Janet, Director Financial Services, Georgia Regional Hospital at Savannah, Savannah, GA, p. A160

EDGAR, Joseph H., Senior Vice President Operations, Gettysburg Hospital, Gettysburg, PA, p. A526

EDGAR, Nancy, Vice President Human Resources, Methodist Hospital, San Antonio, TX, p. A631

EDIE, Skip, Chief Information Officer, Carthage Area Hospital, Carthage, NY, p. A423

EDIN, Scott D., Chief Financial Officer, Amery Regional Medical Center, Amery, WI, p. A683

EDMINSTER, Sue, Vice President Human Resources, Agnesian HealthCare, Fond Du Lac, WI, p. A686

EDMISSON, Jete, Chief Operating Officer and Chief Financial Officer, Cullman Regional Medical Center, Cullman, AL, p. A18

EDMONDS, Kelly, Chief Financial Officer, Western Maryland Hospital Center, Hagerstown, MD, p. A292

EDMONDSON, Bobby, Controller, Regional Rehabilitation Hospital, Phenix City, AL, p. A24

EDMONDSON, James H., Chief Executive Officer, Riverview Regional Medical Center, Gadsden, AL, p. A20

EDMONDSON, Theresa, Director, Walter B. Jones Alcohol and Drug Abuse Treatment Center, Greenville, NC, p. A454

EDMONSON, Cole, R.N. Vice President and Chief Nursing Officer, Texas Health Presbyterian Hospital Dallas, Dallas, TX, p. A597

EDMUNDSON, Reed
Interim Administrator, Grimes St. Joseph Health Center, Navasota, TX, p. A624
Administrator, Madison St. Joseph Health Center, Madisonville, TX, p. A621

EDNEY, Daniel, M.D. Chief of Staff, Promise Hospital of Vicksburg, Vicksburg, MS, p. A354

EDOBOR, Mary, Chief Clinical Officer, Kindred Hospital Tarrant County–Fort Worth Southwest, Fort Worth, TX, p. A604

EDWARD, Virginia, R.N. Administrator and Chief Nursing Officer, West Anaheim Medical Center, Anaheim, CA, p. A52

EDWARDS, A. Jane, MSN Vice President, Patient Care Services, Blue Ridge Regional Hospital, Spruce Pine, NC, p. A461

EDWARDS, Annette, Chief Financial Officer, Odessa Memorial Healthcare Center, Odessa, WA, p. A668

EDWARDS, Becky, Manager Human Resources, Irwin County Hospital, Ocilla, GA, p. A158

EDWARDS Jr., Bob S., FACHE, Chief Executive Officer, Banner Lassen Medical Center, Susanville, CA, p. A92

EDWARDS, Bruce
Vice President Human Resources, Heritage Valley Beaver, Beaver, PA, p. A520
Vice President Human Resources, Sewickley Valley Hospital, (A Division of Valley Medical Facilities), Sewickley, PA, p. A541

EDWARDS, Cathy, Director Organization and Talent Effectiveness, Bronson Battle Creek, Battle Creek, MI, p. A309

EDWARDS, Chris, M.D. Chief Medical Officer, Maury Regional Hospital, Columbia, TN, p. A567

EDWARDS, Dana, Chief Financial Officer, HEALTHSOUTH Sea Pines Rehabilitation Hospital, Melbourne, FL, p. A130

EDWARDS, Danny R., Administrator, Complex Care Hospital at Ridgelake, Sarasota, FL, p. A139

EDWARDS, David, M.D. Chief Medical Officer, Banner Gateway Medical Center, Gilbert, AZ, p. A31

EDWARDS, David, Chief Financial Officer, SEARHC MT. Edgecumbe Hospital, Sitka, AK, p. A29

EDWARDS, Elizabeth, R.N. Director, Nursing Services, Sheridan Community Hospital, Sheridan, MI, p. A324

EDWARDS, Frank, M.D. Medical Director, Jones Memorial Hospital, Wellsville, NY, p. A445

EDWARDS, Gordon, Chief Financial Officer, Gundersen Lutheran Medical Center, La Crosse, WI, p. A689

EDWARDS, Gregg
  Chief People Officer, Rogue Valley Medical Center, Medford, OR, p. A515
  Chief People Officer, Three Rivers Medical Center, Grants Pass, OR, p. A513

EDWARDS, James, President, Hazleton General Hospital, Hazleton, PA, p. A527

EDWARDS, Jeff, Manager Information Services, Mendocino Coast District Hospital, Fort Bragg, CA, p. A60

EDWARDS, Jeffrey, M.D
  Chief Medical Staff, Aspirus Grand View Hospital, Ironwood, MI, p. A317
  Chief of Staff, Texas Health Harris Methodist Hospital Stephenville, Stephenville, TX, p. A635

EDWARDS, Jim, Executive Director of Information Technology, Gibson Area Hospital and Health Services, Gibson City, IL, p. A183

EDWARDS, John R., Administrator and Chief Executive Officer, Pacific Alliance Medical Center, Los Angeles, CA, p. A70

EDWARDS, Jon, Executive Director Finance, Fresno Heart and Surgical Hospital, Fresno, CA, p. A61

EDWARDS, Kathleen, Manager Information Systems Operation, HEALTHSOUTH Rehabilitation Hospital of Altoona, Altoona, PA, p. A519

EDWARDS, Kristy, M.D. Chief Medical Officer, Lillian M. Hudspeth Memorial Hospital, Sonora, TX, p. A634

EDWARDS, Mark A., Chief Executive Officer, Livingston Hospital and Healthcare Services, Salem, KY, p. A260

EDWARDS, Marti, MSN Vice President Patient Care Services, Presence Holy Family Medical Center, Des Plaines, IL, p. A181

EDWARDS, Michael R., Administrator, Scott Regional Hospital, Morton, MS, p. A351

EDWARDS, Michelle, Executive Vice President Information Technology, Palmetto Health Baptist, Columbia, SC, p. A550

EDWARDS, Rebecca, Director Human Resources, Martin General Hospital, Williamston, NC, p. A462

EDWARDS, Rick
  Vice President Finance Services, Hancock Regional Hospital, Greenfield, IN, p. A204
  Director Information Systems, Howard County General Hospital, Columbia, MD, p. A291

EDWARDS, Steven D., President and Chief Executive Officer, Lester E. Cox Medical Centers, Springfield, MO, p. A372

EDWARDS, Susan, Vice President Human Resources, Culpeper Regional Hospital, Culpeper, VA, p. A653

EDWARDS, Teresa L., Vice President and Administrator, Sentara Leigh Hospital, Norfolk, VA, p. A658

EDWARDS, Terry, Controller, Kings Mountain Hospital, Kings Mountain, NC, p. A455

EDWARDS, Todd, Director Information Management Systems, Brazosport Regional Health System, Lake Jackson, TX, p. A617

EDWARDS, William, Information Technology Generalist, Wernersville State Hospital, Wernersville, PA, p. A543

EESLEY, Michael S.
  Chief Executive Officer, Centegra Hospital – McHenry, McHenry, IL, p. A188
  Chief Executive Officer, Centegra Hospital – Woodstock, Woodstock, IL, p. A197

EFFEREN, Linda, M.D. Senior Vice President and Chief Medical Officer, South Nassau Communities Hospital, Oceanside, NY, p. A438

EGAN, Narci, Vice President and Chief Financial Officer, Beverly Hospital, Montebello, CA, p. A74

EGAN, Timothy, Chief Restructuring Officer and President, Roseland Community Hospital, Chicago, IL, p. A178

EGAN, Timothy C., Director, Human Resources, MountainView Regional Medical Center, Las Cruces, NM, p. A416

EGE, Garry, Chief Financial Officer, Coastal Harbor Treatment Center, Savannah, GA, p. A159

EGERTON, W. Eugene, M.D. Chief Medical Officer, Maryland General Hospital, Baltimore, MD, p. A288

EGGERS, Judy, Manager Human Resources, Alliance HealthCare System, Holly Springs, MS, p. A348

EHASZ, James, Chief Financial Officer, La Paz Regional Hospital, Parker, AZ, p. A33

EHINGER, Sue, Ph.D., President, Parkview Regional Medical Center, Fort Wayne, IN, p. A202

EHLER, Phyllis, Director Human Resources, Avera St. Benedict Health Center, Parkston, SD, p. A561

EHLERS, Jeffrey, Chief Financial Officer, Memorial Hospital of Union County, Marysville, OH, p. A485

EHLERS, Karan, Chief Financial Officer, West River Regional Medical Center, Hettinger, ND, p. A467

EHLINGER, Forrest, Vice President and Chief Financial Officer, Harrison Medical Center, Bremerton, WA, p. A664

EHLKE, Ranae, Administrative Secretary and Coordinator Risk Management and Human Resources, Kenmare Community Hospital, Kenmare, ND, p. A468

EHMAN, Sandra, CPA Chief Financial Officer, Powell Valley Healthcare, Powell, WY, p. A703

EHRENBERGER, David, M.D. Chief Medical Officer, Avista Adventist Hospital, Louisville, CO, p. A104

EHRET, Charlene S., FACHE, Director, James H. Quillen Veterans Affairs Medical Center, Mountain Home, TN, p. A576

EHRICH, Laurie, Chief Communications Officer, Wayne County Hospital, Corydon, IA, p. A219

EHRLICH, Frank, M.D. Chief Medical Officer, Health Alliance Hospital – Broadway Campus, Kingston, NY, p. A428

EHRLICH, Susan, M.D., Chief Executive Officer, San Mateo Medical Center, San Mateo, CA, p. A88

EICHENAUER, Donald T., Chief Executive Officer, Wyoming County Community Hospital, Warsaw, NY, p. A445

EICHENBERGER, Daniel J., M.D. Medical Director, Floyd Memorial Hospital and Health Services, New Albany, IN, p. A211

EICHER, Kim D., Chief Executive Officer, St. Francis Health Care Centre, Green Springs, OH, p. A482

EICHMAN, Cynthia, President, Ministry Our Lady of Victory Hospital, Stanley, WI, p. A697

EIDAM, JoEllen, Interim Chief Executive Officer, Adams Memorial Hospital, Decatur, IN, p. A201

EIDE, Dean, Vice President, Mayo Clinic Health System – Oakridge in Osseo, Osseo, WI, p. A694

EIDE, Tom, Chief Financial Officer, Prairie St. John's, Fargo, ND, p. A466

EIDSON, Charles, Assistant Administrator Human Resources, South Georgia Medical Center, Valdosta, GA, p. A162

EIG, Blair, M.D. Senior Vice President Medical Affairs, Holy Cross Hospital, Silver Spring, MD, p. A294

EIKE, Gail, Chief Financial Officer, Sanford Jackson Medical Center, Jackson, MN, p. A334

EILER, John M., President, St. Louis Regional Psychiatric Stabilization Center, Saint Louis, MO, p. A371

EIMERS, Katy, Human Resources Officer, Syringa Hospital and Clinics, Grangeville, ID, p. A169

EINSWEILER, Desiree, Chief Executive Officer, Palo Alto County Health System, Emmetsburg, IA, p. A221

EIPE, Joseph, M.D. Chief Medical Officer, Pacifica Hospital of the Valley,, CA, p. A71

EIQEL, Steve, Chief Financial Officer, Carroll County Memorial Hospital, Carrollton, KY, p. A249

EISCHEID, Randy, Director Information Systems, St. Anthony Regional Hospital, Carroll, IA, p. A217

EISELE, Karla, M.D. Clinical Director, State Hospital North, Orofino, ID, p. A170

EISEMANN, Bradley, Administrator, Crenshaw Community Hospital, Luverne, AL, p. A22

EISEN, Brian, Director Human Resources, Camden County Health Services Center, Blackwood, NJ, p. A401

EISENHAUER, Glenn, Vice President, Evangelical Community Hospital, Lewisburg, PA, p. A530

EISENMAN, Edward, Chief Executive Officer, Sunnyview Rehabilitation Hospital, Schenectady, NY, p. A442

EISENMANN, Claudia Ann, Chief Executive Officer, Select Specialty Hospital–Wilmington, Wilmington, DE, p. A115

EISENRING, Richard, Chief Financial Officer, Holy Cross Hospital, Taos, NM, p. A418

EISENTRAGER, Steve, Administrator, Ohio Valley Surgical Hospital, Springfield, OH, p. A490

EISENZOPH, Pete, Director Information Technology, Bay Area Medical Center, Marinette, WI, p. A690

EISMAN, Michael, M.D. Medical Director, Schuyler Hospital, Montour Falls, NY, p. A430

EISNER, Nina W., Chief Executive Officer and Managing Director, Ridge Behavioral Health System, Lexington, KY, p. A254

EITEL, Jeffrey, Chief Financial Officer, Littleton Adventist Hospital, Littleton, CO, p. A103

EITZEN, Jamie, Chief Financial Officer, Fairview Regional Medical Center, Fairview, OK, p. A499

EIXENBERGER, Timothy D., R.N. Chief Nursing Officer, St. Charles Medical Center – Bend, Bend, OR, p. A511

EKENGREN, Francie H., M.D. Chief Medical Officer, Wesley Medical Center, Wichita, KS, p. A247

EKEREN, Douglas R., Vice President Planning and Development, Avera Sacred Heart Hospital, Yankton, SD, p. A564

EKPO, Felix, Interim Manager Information Systems, Arrowhead Regional Medical Center, Colton, CA, p. A57

EKREM, Chris, Chief Executive Officer, Yoakum County Hospital, Denver City, TX, p. A599

EL MASRY, Waguih, M.D. Chief of Staff, Manatee Memorial Hospital, Bradenton, FL, p. A119

ELA, Sue, Executive Vice President and Chief Operating Officer, Aurora St. Luke's Medical Center, Milwaukee, WI, p. A691

ELAM, Moses D., M.D. Physician–in–Chief, Kaiser Permanente Manteca Medical Center, Manteca, CA, p. A73

ELANGOVAN, N., M.D. Medical Director, Essex County Hospital Center, Cedar Grove, NJ, p. A402

ELARBEE, Vernon, Director of Human Resources, Florida Hospital North Pinellas, Tarpon Springs, FL, p. A142

ELBERT, Darlene M., R.N. Assistant Administrator and Chief Nursing Officer, Kossuth Regional Health Center, Algona, IA, p. A216

ELDER, Becky, Vice President Clinical Services, Perry County Memorial Hospital, Tell City, IN, p. A213

ELDER, Penny, Manager Human Resources, University Pointe Surgical Hospital, West Chester, OH, p. A493

ELDER, Ronald J., Chief Executive Officer, Glenwood Regional Medical Center, West Monroe, LA, p. A280

ELDIB, Candace, Administrator, Batesville Specialty Hospital, Batesville, MS, p. A344

ELDIDY, Rene, M.D. Chief of Staff, CentraCare Health–Long Prairie, Long Prairie, MN, p. A334

ELDRIDGE, Janet, Director Human Resources and Personnel, Brooks County Hospital, Quitman, GA, p. A158

ELDRIDGE, Jim, Area Financial Officer, Kaiser Permanente Sacramento Medical Center, Sacramento, CA, p. A83

ELDRIDGE, Laurie, Chief Financial Officer, Marshall Medical Center, Placerville, CA, p. A80

ELDRIDGE, Lisa, Human Resources Officer, Thomas H. Boyd Memorial Hospital, Carrollton, IL, p. A175

ELEGANT, Bruce M., President and Chief Executive Officer, Rush Oak Park Hospital, Oak Park, IL, p. A190

ELENBAAS, Jerry, Administrator, Post Acute Specialty Hospital of Hammond, Hammond, LA, p. A268

ELFERT, Mike, Director Information Services, Lourdes Medical Center of Burlington County, Willingboro, NJ, p. A412

ELFORD, Dorothy J., Chief Executive Officer, Atrium Medical Center of Corinth, Corinth, TX, p. A593

ELGARICO, David, Chief Operating Officer, Rio Grande Regional Hospital, McAllen, TX, p. A622

ELGER, William, Executive Vice President and Chief Business and Finance Officer, University of Texas Medical Branch Hospitals, Galveston, TX, p. A605

ELICH, Liz, Vice President Human Resources, Frye Regional Medical Center, Hickory, NC, p. A454

ELIE, Charlene, Vice President Patient Care Services, Clinton Hospital, Clinton, MA, p. A299

ELIZALDE, David A., Director, Veterans Affairs Puget Sound Health Care System, Seattle, WA, p. A671

ELIZONDO, Diane, Director Human Resources, Harlingen Medical Center, Harlingen, TX, p. A607

ELKINGTON, Bruce
  Regional Chief Information Officer, St. Clare Hospital, Lakewood, WA, p. A667
  Regional Chief Information Officer, St. Francis Hospital, Federal Way, WA, p. A666
  Vice President Information Technology, St. Joseph Medical Center, Tacoma, WA, p. A673

ELKINGTON, Mark, M.D. Chief Medical Officer, Willow Crest Hospital, Miami, OK, p. A501

ELKINS, James N., FACHE, Superintendent, Texas Center for Infectious Disease, San Antonio, TX, p. A632

ELKINS, Wendy, Director Operations, Dundy County Hospital, Benkelman, NE, p. A382

ELLARD, Ellen, Director Human Resources, Putnam General Hospital, Eatonton, GA, p. A153

ELLEN, Jonathan M., M.D., President, All Children's Hospital, Saint Petersburg, FL, p. A138

ELLENBURG, Cynthia, Director Health Information Services, Baptist Easley Hospital, Easley, SC, p. A551

ELLER, Jeff, FACHE, President and Chief Executive Officer, Sonora Regional Medical Center, Sonora, CA, p. A91

ELLERBE, F. Dana, Chief Executive Officer, Havasu Regional Medical Center, Lake Havasu City, AZ, p. A32

ELLERT, William, M.D. Chief Medical Officer, Phoenix Baptist Hospital, Phoenix, AZ, p. A35

ELLEY, Michael, Chief Information Officer, Cox Medical Center Branson, Branson, MO, p. A357

ELLINGTON, Christopher, Executive Vice President and Chief Financial Officer, University of North Carolina Hospitals, Chapel Hill, NC, p. A449

ELLINGTON, Linda B., R.N. Interim Vice President and Chief Nursing Officer, Chatham Hospital, Siler City, NC, p. A461
ELLIOT, Anna, Head Information Technology, Dundy County Hospital, Benkelman, NE, p. A382
ELLIOTT, Barb, Chief Financial Officer, Fairbanks, Indianapolis, IN, p. A205
ELLIOTT, C. Layton, M.D. Chief of Staff, Witham Memorial Hospital, Lebanon, IN, p. A209
ELLIOTT, Charles M., M.D. Chief of Staff, Tippah County Hospital, Ripley, MS, p. A353
ELLIOTT Jr., Charles W., Chief Executive Officer, Johnston Health, Smithfield, NC, p. A461
ELLIOTT, Jim
  Director Human Resources, Bryce Hospital, Tuscaloosa, AL, p. A25
  Director Human Resources, Mary S Harper Geriatric Psychiatry Center, Tuscaloosa, AL, p. A26
ELLIOTT, Lee, Vice President Human Resources and Fund Development, Saint Francis Medical Center, Grand Island, NE, p. A384
ELLIOTT, Lee Ann, R.N. Director of Nursing, Select Rehabilitation Hospital of Denton, Denton, TX, p. A599
ELLIOTT, Marye, Chief Nursing Officer, Dyersburg Regional Medical Center, Dyersburg, TN, p. A568
ELLIOTT, Michael, Controller, Indianhead Medical Center, Shell Lake, WI, p. A696
ELLIOTT, R. James, Vice President Human Resources, The Charlotte Hungerford Hospital, Torrington, CT, p. A112
ELLIOTT, Robin, Personnel Officer, Community Memorial Hospital, Sumner, IA, p. A229
ELLIOTT, Shane, Associate Director Administration, Veterans Affairs Loma Linda Healthcare System, Loma Linda, CA, p. A67
ELLIOTT, William T., Associate Administrator Administrative and Support Services, Hawaii State Hospital, Kaneohe, HI, p. A165
ELLIOTT MSN, Randi, Chief Nursing Officer, Baylor Medical Center at Frisco, Frisco, TX, p. A605
ELLIS, Amanda, Chief Financial Officer, Knox County Hospital, Barbourville, KY, p. A248
ELLIS, Betts, Administrator Institutional Relations, MUSC Medical Center of Medical University of South Carolina, Charleston, SC, p. A549
ELLIS, Bob
  Director of Nursing, D. W. McMillan Memorial Hospital, Brewton, AL, p. A18
  Chief Financial Officer, Rutherford Regional Health System, Rutherfordton, NC, p. A460
ELLIS, Dan C., Chief Executive Officer, Coteau des Prairies Hospital, Sisseton, SD, p. A563
ELLIS, Kelly, D.O. Chief Medical Officer, Tilden Community Hospital, Tilden, NE, p. A390
ELLIS, Lynn, Chief Financial Officer, LakeWood Health Center, Baudette, MN, p. A329
ELLIS, Michael J., Chief Executive Officer, Big Bend Regional Medical Center, Alpine, TX, p. A582
ELLIS, Michelle, Director Human Resources, Whitman Hospital and Medical Center, Colfax, WA, p. A665
ELLIS, Nora, Market Chief Information Officer, UnityHealth MacNeal Hospital, Berwyn, IL, p. A174
ELLIS, Rich, Chief Operating Officer, Frye Regional Medical Center, Hickory, NC, p. A454
ELLIS, Richard, Chief Executive Officer, Medical Center Enterprise, Enterprise, AL, p. A19
ELLIS, Seth, Chief Operating Officer, Motion Picture and Television Fund Hospital and Residential Services,, CA, p. A70
ELLIS, Sharon, Senior Vice President and Chief Financial Officer, Texas Scottish Rite Hospital for Children, Dallas, TX, p. A597
ELLIS, Susan Renee', R.N. Vice President of Human Resources, Highlands Regional Medical Center, Prestonsburg, KY, p. A259
ELLIS, Thomas J., Vice President Human Resources, Mt. Washington Pediatric Hospital, Baltimore, MD, p. A288
ELLIS, Wendel, D.O. Chief Medical Staff, Greeley County Health Services, Tribune, KS, p. A245
ELLISH, Patti M., FACHE, President and Chief Executive Officer, St. Tammany Parish Hospital, Covington, LA, p. A266
ELLISON, Darcy, R.N. Senior Vice President, Chief Nursing Officer and Inpatient Flow, St. Mary's Medical Center of Evansville, Evansville, IN, p. A202
ELLISON, Mike, Information Systems Lead, Summersville Regional Medical Center, Summersville, WV, p. A681
ELLISON, Patricia, Chief Financial Officer, Perry Memorial Hospital, Princeton, IL, p. A192
ELLISON, Tracey, Vice President Human Resources, Carroll Hospital Center, Westminster, MD, p. A294
ELLZEY, Bob S., FACHE, President, Texas Health Harris Methodist Hospital Azle, Azle, TX, p. A586
ELMER, Dan, Vice President Finance, Morehead Memorial Hospital, Eden, NC, p. A451

ELMORE, Buddy, Chief Financial Officer, Sacred Heart Hospital of Pensacola, Pensacola, FL, p. A137
ELMORE, Ellen, M.D. Director Medical Services, Maniilaq Health Center, Kotzebue, AK, p. A28
ELMORE, Kevin, Chief Information Officer, Covenant Hospital–Levelland, Levelland, TX, p. A618
ELMORE, Nadine, Chief Executive Officer, Dahl Memorial Healthcare Association, Ekalaka, MT, p. A375
ELMORE, Thomas, Director Information System, National Park Medical Center, Hot Springs, AR, p. A45
ELMORE, Trent, Director Human Resources, Springs Memorial Hospital, Lancaster, SC, p. A554
ELSE, Ryan, M.D. Interim Vice President Medical Affairs, Mercy Hospital, Coon Rapids, MN, p. A330
ELSESSER, William, Director Professional Relations, Kindred Hospital North Houston, Houston, TX, p. A610
ELSIK, Kristina, Director Human Resources, DeTar Healthcare System, Victoria, TX, p. A639
ELSWICK, Shannon, President, Orlando Regional Medical Center, Orlando, FL, p. A135
ELTON, James, Chief Executive Officer, Select Long Term Care Hospital – Colorado Springs, Colorado Springs, CO, p. A98
ELWELL, Richard, Senior Vice President and Chief Financial Officer, Elliot Hospital, Manchester, NH, p. A399
ELWELL, Russell, M.D. Medical Director, Westfield Memorial Hospital, Westfield, NY, p. A446
ELY, Thomas L., D.O. Chief Medical Officer, Gateway Medical Center, Clarksville, TN, p. A567
EMANUEL, Kate, Director Human Resources, Clarke County Hospital, Osceola, IA, p. A226
EMBERS, Tom, Assistant Administrator and Chief Operating Officer, William Newton Hospital, Winfield, KS, p. A247
EMBREE, Steve, Chief Financial Officer, Carolinas Hospital System, Florence, SC, p. A551
EMBREY, Jeffrey, M.D. Vice President Medical Affairs, Baylor Medical Center at Irving, Irving, TX, p. A614
EMBRY, Debra, Associate Administrator Employee Services, Christus St. Michael Hospital–Atlanta, Atlanta, TX, p. A584
EMBURY, Stuart, M.D. Chief Medical Officer, Phelps Memorial Health Center, Holdrege, NE, p. A384
EMDUR, Larry, M.D. Chief of Staff, Promise Hospital of San Diego, San Diego, CA, p. A85
EMERICK, Ron, M.D. Chief of Staff, Doctor's Memorial Hospital, Perry, FL, p. A137
EMERSON, Cindy, Director Information Services, Mission Hospital, Mission Viejo, CA, p. A74
EMERY, Jeff, Chief Financial Officer and Chief Operating Officer, Gateways Hospital and Mental Health Center, Los Angeles, CA, p. A69
EMGE, Joann, Chief Executive Officer, Sparta Community Hospital, Sparta, IL, p. A194
EMMINGER, Dianne, Vice President Information Services, ACMH Hospital, Kittanning, PA, p. A528
EMORY, Mark L., System Director Human Resources, Transylvania Regional Hospital, Brevard, NC, p. A448
EMTER, Melanie, Director Finance, Livingston Memorial Hospital, Livingston, MT, p. A378
ENCAPERA, Kimberly, M.D. Medical Director, Rehabilitation Hospital of Southern New Mexico, Las Cruces, NM, p. A416
ENCE, Michael, Computer Specialist, Sanpete Valley Hospital, Mount Pleasant, UT, p. A644
ENCKE, Faye, Director Information Management, HEALTHSOUTH Rehabilitation Hospital of Virginia, Richmond, VA, p. A660
ENDEN, Jay, M.D. Medical Director, Southside Hospital, Bay Shore, NY, p. A421
ENDERELE, Mark A., M.D., Director, Veterans Health Care System of the Ozarks, Fayetteville, AR, p. A43
ENDERS Jr., Robert A., President, Chatham Hospital, Siler City, NC, p. A461
ENDICOTT, Sarah, M.D. Chief of Staff, North Runnels Hospital, Winters, TX, p. A642
ENDOM, Beth W., R.N. Vice President and Chief Nursing Officer, South Central Regional Medical Center, Laurel, MS, p. A349
ENDRES, Jack R., Administrator, East Texas Medical Center Jacksonville, Jacksonville, TX, p. A615
ENG, Bland, Chief Executive Officer, Brandon Regional Hospital, Brandon, FL, p. A119
ENG, Jeffrey, M.D. Medical Director, HEALTHSOUTH Rehabilitation Hospital of Montgomery, Montgomery, AL, p. A23
ENGBRECHT, Chad, Chief Financial Officer, Alvarado Parkway Institute Behavioral Health System, La Mesa, CA, p. A65
ENGEL, David, Chief Executive Officer, Phillips County Hospital, Phillipsburg, KS, p. A242
ENGEL, Terry, Manager Information Technology, Oakes Community Hospital, Oakes, ND, p. A468
ENGELKEN, Joseph T., Chief Executive Officer, Tuba City Regional Health Care Corporation, Tuba City, AZ, p. A38

ENGESSER, Edward, Chief Financial Officer and Chief Information Officer, Barlow Respiratory Hospital, Los Angeles, CA, p. A68
ENGLAND, Dave, Director Human Resources, Lakeland Behavioral Health System, Springfield, MO, p. A372
ENGLAND, Donna, Director Medical Records, HEALTHSOUTH Rehabilitation Hospital of Fort Smith, Fort Smith, AR, p. A44
ENGLE, Dan, Chief Information Officer, Thayer County Health Services, Hebron, NE, p. A384
ENGLE, Heidi, Manager Information Technology, Glacial Ridge Health System, Glenwood, MN, p. A333
ENGLE, Steve, Chief Operations Officer, Mad River Community Hospital, Arcata, CA, p. A53
ENGLEHART, Jay, M.D. Medical Director, Southeast Missouri Mental Health Center, Farmington, MO, p. A360
ENGLEKING, David, M.D. Vice President Medical Affairs, CHRISTUS St. Patrick Hospital of Lake Charles, Lake Charles, LA, p. A271
ENGLERTH, LaDonna, Administrator, East Carroll Parish Hospital, Lake Providence, LA, p. A272
ENGLISH, Anne L., Director Human Resources, Chenango Memorial Hospital, Norwich, NY, p. A438
ENGLISH, Dennis, M.D. Vice President Medical Affairs, Magee–Womens Hospital of UPMC, Pittsburgh, PA, p. A537
ENGLISH, Jeff, Vice President Human Resources, St. Mary's Health Care System, Athens, GA, p. A145
ENGLISH, Julene, Director Human Resources, Kentfield Rehabilitation and Specialty Hospital, Kentfield, CA, p. A65
ENGLISH, Kathy L., R.N. Executive Vice President and Chief Operating Officer, Children's Hospital and Medical Center, Omaha, NE, p. A387
ENGLISH, Mark E., M.D. Chief of Staff, McKenzie Health System, Sandusky, MI, p. A324
ENGLISH, Nancy M., CHief Human Resources Officer, Banner Ironwood Medical Center, San Tan Valley, AZ, p. A36
ENGSTROM, Chad P., Director Human Resources, Westfields Hospital, New Richmond, WI, p. A693
ENGSTROM, Frederick, M.D. Medical Director, Brattleboro Retreat, Brattleboro, VT, p. A649
ENICKS, Charles, Chief Information Officer, University Hospitals and Health System, University of Mississippi Medical Center, Jackson, MS, p. A349
ENJADY, Rainey, Administrative Officer, Mescalero Public Health Service Indian Hospital, Mescalero, NM, p. A417
ENNEN, Philip L.
  Vice President and Chief Executive Officer, Community Hospitals and Wellness Centers, Bryan, OH, p. A472
  President and Chief Executive Officer, Community Hospitals and Wellness Centers–Montpelier, Montpelier, OH, p. A486
ENNIS, Virgil, Chief Information Officer, Helen Hayes Hospital, West Haverstraw, NY, p. A445
ENNS, Merle, Director Information Services, Prairie View, Newton, KS, p. A240
ENOCHS, Darren, Director Human Resources, Specialty Hospital of Mid–America, Overland Park, KS, p. A242
ENOKA, Christina, Director Human Resources and Risk Management, Kahi Mohala Behavioral Health, Ewa Beach, HI, p. A164
ENRICO–SIMON, Agnes, M.D. President Medical Staff, Pleasant Valley Hospital, Point Pleasant, WV, p. A680
ENSEY, Jeremy, Chief Nursing Officer, St. Luke Hospital and Living Center, Marion, KS, p. A239
ENSLEY, Terrasina, Director Human Resources, Fannin Regional Hospital, Blue Ridge, GA, p. A148
ENSMINGER, Jennifer, Chief Operating Officer, Pacific Hospital of Long Beach, Long Beach, CA, p. A67
ENSMINGER, Randy, M.D. Chief Medical Officer, Ocean Beach Hospital, Ilwaco, WA, p. A667
ENSRUDE, Layne, Chief Financial Officer, First Care Health Center, Park River, ND, p. A469
ENTENMANN, Kim, Director People Services, St. Joseph's Hospital, Chippewa Falls, WI, p. A685
ENTLER, Paul, D.O. Medical Director, Sparrow Specialty Hospital, Lansing, MI, p. A318
ENTWISTLE, David, Chief Executive Officer, University of Utah Health Care – Hospital and Clinics, Salt Lake City, UT, p. A647
ENTZMINGER, Julie, Manager Human Resources, Oakes Community Hospital, Oakes, ND, p. A468
EOLOFF, Eric J., Chief Operating Officer, Mercy Hospital St. Louis, Saint Louis, MO, p. A370
EPPERSON, Edward L., Chief Executive Officer, Carson Tahoe Regional Healthcare, Carson City, NV, p. A391
EPPERSON, Elysia, Director Human Resources, East Texas Medical Center Jacksonville, Jacksonville, TX, p. A615
EPPERSON, Jeff, Chief Financial Officer, Millwood Hospital, Arlington, TX, p. A583
EPPLER, Todd, Chief Executive Officer, De Soto Regional Health System, Mansfield, LA, p. A273

EPPLEY, Doug, Director of Nursing, Bridgewell Hospital of Cincinnati, Cincinnati, OH, p. A474

EPPS, Donna, Vice President and Chief Human Resources Officer, Lawrence + Memorial Hospital, New London, CT, p. A111

EPPS, Michelle, MSN Chief Nursing Officer, Wellington Regional Medical Center, West Palm Beach, FL, p. A144

EPRIGHT, Janine L., Vice President and Chief Financial Officer, Gaylord Hospital, Wallingford, CT, p. A112

EPSTEIN, Michael, M.D. Senior Vice President Medical Affairs, All Children's Hospital, Saint Petersburg, FL, p. A138

ERB, Judy, Vice President Patient Care Services and Chief Nursing Officer, Aultman Orrville Hospital, Orrville, OH, p. A488

ERDMAN, Donja, Chief Financial Officer, Marcus Daly Memorial Hospital, Hamilton, MT, p. A376

ERDMANN, Dorothy, Chief Executive Officer, Shawano Medical Center, Shawano, WI, p. A696

ERDMANN, Michael, M.D. Chief of Staff, Clement J. Zablocki Veterans Affairs Medical Center, Milwaukee, WI, p. A692

ERDOS, Joseph, M.D. Chief Information Officer, Veterans Affairs Connecticut Healthcare System, West Haven, CT, p. A113

EREMAN, Melissa, R.N. Chief Nursing Officer, Coleman County Medical Center, Coleman, TX, p. A592

ERGLE, Jeanine, Chief Financial Officer, Bay Pines Veterans Affairs Medical Center, Bay Pines, FL, p. A118

ERICH, Kevin R., President and Chief Executive Officer, Feather River Hospital, Paradise, CA, p. A79

ERICKSON, Brent, Administrator, Wright Patterson Medical Center, Wright–Patterson AFB, OH, p. A493

ERICKSON, Cindy, Chief Financial Officer, Sabine County Hospital, Hemphill, TX, p. A608

ERICKSON, Doug, Chief Financial Officer, Prague Community Hospital, Prague, OK, p. A505

ERICKSON, Karyn, Director Human Resources, Delta Medical Center, Memphis, TN, p. A574

ERICKSON, Nancy, Administrator Information Systems, Kossuth Regional Health Center, Algona, IA, p. A216

ERICKSON, Robert J., Chief Executive Officer, St. Francis Health Center, Topeka, KS, p. A245

ERICKSON, Ty W., Chief Executive Officer, Regina Medical Center, Hastings, MN, p. A333

ERICKSON, William A., Vice President and Chief Operating Officer, Ministry Saint Mary's Hospitals, Rhinelander, WI, p. A695

ERICSON, Allen, President, St. Joseph's Community Hospital of West Bend, West Bend, WI, p. A699

ERICSON, Kim
  Vice President Finance, Fairview Lakes Health Services, Wyoming, MN, p. A343
  Vice President Finance, Fairview Northland Medical Center, Princeton, MN, p. A338

ERIXON, Stephen M.
  Chief Executive Officer, Lander Regional Hospital, Lander, WY, p. A702
  Interim Chief Executive Officer, Riverton Memorial Hospital, Riverton, WY, p. A703

ERKEN, Carole L., Human Resources Leader, Kaiser Permanente Panorama City Medical Center,, CA, p. A69

ERLANDSON, Lesley, Human Resources Generalist, Mercy Hospital, Valley City, ND, p. A469

ERLICH, Ian, President and Chief Executive Officer, Maniilaq Health Center, Kotzebue, AK, p. A28

ERMANN, Bill, President and Chief Executive Officer, Southwest Medical Center, Liberal, KS, p. A238

ERNDT, Robert, Site Manager, St. Mary Medical Center, Long Beach, CA, p. A67

ERNEST, Pam, R.N. CNO/ VP Patient Care Services, Franklin Memorial Hospital, Farmington, ME, p. A283

ERNST, William E., Administrator, Winkler County Memorial Hospital, Kermit, TX, p. A616

ERRICHETTI, Ann, M.D.,
  Chief Executive Officer, Albany Memorial Hospital, Albany, NY, p. A420
  Chief Executive Officer, St. Peter's Hospital, Albany, NY, p. A420

ERTLE, Alan, M.D. Chief Medical Officer, Overlake Hospital Medical Center, Bellevue, WA, p. A664

ERUKHIMOU, Jeffrey, M.D. Medical Director, Kindred Hospital–Heritage Valley, Beaver, PA, p. A520

ERVIN, Brad, Chief Executive Officer, Regency Hospital of Fort Worth, Fort Worth, TX, p. A604

ERVIN, Fulton
  Senior Vice President and Chief Financial Officer, McLeod Medical Center Dillon, Dillon, SC, p. A551
  Chief Financial Officer, McLeod Regional Medical Center, Florence, SC, p. A552

ERVIN, Richard, Chief Financial Officer, San Angelo Community Medical Center, San Angelo, TX, p. A630

ERVING–MENGEL, Tammi, Vice President, Chief Nursing Officer, High Point Regional Health System, High Point, NC, p. A455

ERWAY, Robert, Director for Administration, Bronx Psychiatric Center,, NY, p. A430

ERWIN, Connie, Manager, Samaritan Lebanon Community Hospital, Lebanon, OR, p. A514

ERWIN, Jerry A., Chief Human Resources Management Service, Dayton Veterans Affairs Medical Center, Dayton, OH, p. A479

ERWIN, Kermit, M.D. Medical Director, ProMedica Defiance Regional Hospital, Defiance, OH, p. A480

ESCARDA, Ron, Chief Executive Officer, Fairfax Hospital, Kirkland, WA, p. A667

ESCHENBRENNER, Wade, Chief Financial Officer, Lexington Regional Health Center, Lexington, NE, p. A385

ESFANDIARI, Seifolah, M.D. Chief of Staff, Western Medical Center–Santa Ana, Santa Ana, CA, p. A89

ESKANDER, Nader, Director, Franciscan St. Anthony Health – Crown Point, Crown Point, IN, p. A201

ESKENAZI, Alan, Chief Executive Officer, Holliswood Hospital,, NY, p. A432

ESKEW, Katherine, Chief Executive Officer, Kindred Hospital–San Antonio, San Antonio, TX, p. A631

ESKILDSEN, Walter, M.D. Chief of Staff, Community Hospital, McCook, NE, p. A386

ESKRA, Joanne, Supervisor Data and Information Technology, John C. Fremont Healthcare District, Mariposa, CA, p. A73

ESLINGER, Jennifer, Chief Operating Officer, Tulane Medical Center, New Orleans, LA, p. A276

ESPARZA, Caroline, Sr. VP to Patient Care Executive, Simi Valley Hospital and Health Care Services, Simi Valley, CA, p. A91

ESPELAND, Darryl, D.O. Chief Medical Staff, Fallon Medical Complex, Baker, MT, p. A374

ESPENSHIP, Carl, Director Facility Services, Wilkes Regional Medical Center, North Wilkesboro, NC, p. A458

ESPINOSA, Bruce, Manager Information Systems, Palm Drive Hospital, Sebastopol, CA, p. A90

ESPINOSA, Philip, Human Resource Director, Lovelace Medical Center, Albuquerque, NM, p. A414

ESPINOZA, Ernest, Interim Chief Operating Officer, LAC–Olive View–UCLA Medical Center,, CA, p. A70

ESPINOZA, John, Chief Human Resources Officer, University Medical Center, Las Vegas, NV, p. A394

ESPITIA, Judy, Chief Financial Officer, North Runnels Hospital, Winters, TX, p. A642

ESPOSITO, Jr., Anthony M., CPA Chief Financial Officer, Hackensack University Medical Center at Pascack Valley, Westwood, NJ, p. A412

ESPOSITO, Mary H., Assistant Executive Director, Devereux Georgia Treatment Network, Kennesaw, GA, p. A155

ESPOSITO, Pamela, Director Quality Management and Acting Director Facility Administration, Buffalo Psychiatric Center, Buffalo, NY, p. A422

ESPY, Christine, Director Human Resources, Mid–Columbia Medical Center, The Dalles, OR, p. A518

ESROCK, Brett A., President and Chief Executive Officer, Providence Health Center, Waco, TX, p. A640

ESSELMAN, Charlotte, Director Finance, Ministry Saint Clare's Hospital, Weston, WI, p. A699

ESSEX, Jeshahnton, Vice President of Administration, Riddle Hospital, Media, PA, p. A531

ESTEP, Kyle, Manager Information Technology, Marlette Regional Hospital, Marlette, MI, p. A319

ESTES, Barbara, M.D. Chief of Staff, Calvert Memorial Hospital, Prince Frederick, MD, p. A293

ESTES, Michael, Director Human Resources, University Hospitals and Health System, University of Mississippi Medical Center, Jackson, MS, p. A349

ESTES, Michelle, Chief Clinical Officer, Kindred Hospital Indianapolis South, Greenwood, IN, p. A204

ESTES, Stephen A., Chief Executive Officer, Rockcastle Regional Hospital and Respiratory Care Center, Mount Vernon, KY, p. A258

ESTEVEZ, Aurora, M.D. Chief Medical Officer, NCH Downtown Naples Hospital, Naples, FL, p. A133

ESTIS, John, Director Human Resources, HEALTHSOUTH Lakeshore Rehabilitation Hospital, Birmingham, AL, p. A16

ESTRADA, Luis, Director Multifacility Information Systems, North Shore Medical Center, Miami, FL, p. A132

ESTREM, Kristy, FACHE, President, Mercy Hospital Berryville, Berryville, AR, p. A41

ETCHASON, Barbara, HR Manager, West Gables Rehabilitation Hospital, Miami, FL, p. A132

ETHERIDGE, Darold, Vice President and Chief Financial Officer, WellStar Cobb Hospital, Austell, GA, p. A148

ETHERINGTON, Betty, Chief Financial Officer, Humboldt County Memorial Hospital, Humboldt, IA, p. A222

ETHRIDGE, Gregory, Manager Personnel, North Alabama Regional Hospital, Decatur, AL, p. A19

ETTENHEIM, Margaret, Director Human Resources, Monterey Park Hospital, Monterey Park, CA, p. A75

ETTER, Carl J., Chief Eecutive, Senior Vice President, Scripps Memorial Hospital–Encinitas, Encinitas, CA, p. A59

EUBANKS, Bill, Senior Vice President and Chief Information Officer, University Medical Center, Lubbock, TX, p. A620

EUCLIDE, Jeff, R.N. Chief Nursing Officer, Aurora Medical Center of Washington County, Hartford, WI, p. A688

EULER, Barbara, Director Human Resources, Regional Hospital of Jackson, Jackson, TN, p. A570

EULIARTE, Mary Ann, R.N. Chief Operating Officer and Chief Nursing Officer, TIRR Memorial Hermann, Houston, TX, p. A613

EUSEBIO, Barbara, R.N. Vice President, Chief Nurse Executive, St. Mary's Medical Center, San Francisco, CA, p. A87

EUSTACE, Scott, Director Health Information Technology, Trenton Psychiatric Hospital, Trenton, NJ, p. A411

EVANGELISTA, Larry, Supervisor Information Technology, Clay County Memorial Hospital, Henrietta, TX, p. A608

EVANOFF, John, M.D. Vice President Medical Affairs, ProMedica Flower Hospital, Sylvania, OH, p. A490

EVANS, Arthur D., Assistant Administrator, Bryan W. Whitfield Memorial Hospital, Demopolis, AL, p. A19

EVANS, Brian G., FACHE, Chief Executive Officer, Clarke County Hospital, Osceola, IA, p. A226

EVANS, Dan, Vice President Business and Finance, Prairie View, Newton, KS, p. A240

EVANS, Dawn, Manager Information Technology, Audrain Medical Center, Mexico, MO, p. A366

EVANS, Donald D., Chief Executive Officer, HEALTHSOUTH Rehabilitation Hospital, Largo, FL, p. A128

EVANS, Dwight, M.D. Chief of Staff, Veterans Affairs Loma Linda Healthcare System, Loma Linda, CA, p. A67

EVANS, Eric, Chief Operating Officer, The Woman's Hospital of Texas, Houston, TX, p. A613

EVANS, Frank, Director Information Services, Hillcrest Hospital – South, Tulsa, OK, p. A508

EVANS, George, Vice President and Chief Information Officer, Candler Hospital, Savannah, GA, p. A159

EVANS, Heath, Assistant Chief Executive Officer, North Okaloosa Medical Center, Crestview, FL, p. A121

EVANS, J. Eric
  Chief Executive Officer, Providence Memorial Hospital, El Paso, TX, p. A601
  Chief Executive Officer, Sierra Medical Center, El Paso, TX, p. A601

EVANS, Janice, Chief Financial Officer, John J. Madden Mental Health Center, Hines, IL, p. A185

EVANS, Jeff W., Vice President Information and Technology, Hannibal Regional Hospital, Hannibal, MO, p. A361

EVANS, John, M.D. Chief Medical Officer, Twin Lakes Regional Medical Center, Leitchfield, KY, p. A253

EVANS, Kelley, Chief Executive Officer, Beartooth Billings Clinic, Red Lodge, MT, p. A379

EVANS, Kirstie, Chief Financial Officer, Covington County Hospital, Collins, MS, p. A346

EVANS, Liz, Chief Nursing Officer, San Mateo Medical Center, San Mateo, CA, p. A88

EVANS, Lorrie, Director Human Resources, Laurel Oaks Behavioral Health Center, Dothan, AL, p. A19

EVANS, Manuel J., Senior Vice President Finance and Chief Financial Officer, Holy Spirit Hospital, Camp Hill, PA, p. A521

EVANS, Marcella, Director Human Resources, Harrison Community Hospital, Cadiz, OH, p. A472

EVANS, Melinda S.
  Vice President Finance, Saint Joseph East, Lexington, KY, p. A254
  Vice President Finance, Saint Joseph Hospital, Lexington, KY, p. A254

EVANS, Michael K., Chief Executive Officer, Park Royal Hospital, Fort Myers, FL, p. A124

EVANS, Mike, MS, President, Texas Health Presbyterian Hospital Plano, Plano, TX, p. A628

EVANS, Myra L., Chief Executive Officer, Community Hospital–Fairfax, Fairfax, MO, p. A360

EVANS, Nina, R.N. Vice President and Chief Nursing Officer, St. Mary's Health Care System, Athens, GA, p. A145

EVANS, Palmer, M.D. Chief Medical Officer, TMC Healthcare, Tucson, AZ, p. A39

EVANS, Patsy, Chief Financial Officer, Citizens Medical Center, Colby, KS, p. A232

EVANS, Rhonda, R.N. Chief Operating Officer, Community Hospital–Fairfax, Fairfax, MO, p. A360

EVANS, Richard, M.D. President Medical Staff, Mayo Regional Hospital, Dover–Foxcroft, ME, p. A283

EVANS, Robert B., Administrator and Chief Executive Officer, East Texas Medical Center Tyler, Tyler, TX, p. A638

EVANS, Sam, Chief Human Resources Management, G.V. (Sonny) Montgomery Veterans Affairs Medical Center, Jackson, MS, p. A348

EVANS, Scott, PharmD,
  Chief Executive Officer, Keck Hospital of USC, Los Angeles, CA, p. A70
  Chief Executive Officer, University of Southern California–Norris Cancer Hospital, Los Angeles, CA, p. A72
EVANS, Stephen R. T., M.D. Vice President Medical Affairs and Medical Director, MedStar Georgetown University Hospital, Washington, DC, p. A116
EVANS, Susan, Chief Nursing Officer, HEALTHSOUTH Nittany Valley Rehabilitation Hospital, Pleasant Gap, PA, p. A539
EVANS, Terry, Chief Information Officer, Thibodaux Regional Medical Center, Thibodaux, LA, p. A279
EVANS, Timothy
  Chief Financial Officer, Johnston Memorial Hospital, Abingdon, VA, p. A651
  Vice President and Chief Financial Officer, Self Regional Healthcare, Greenwood, SC, p. A553
EVANS, William E., PharmD, Director, St. Jude Children's Research Hospital, Memphis, TN, p. A575
EVE, John R., Vice President Human Resources, Wilson Memorial Hospital, Sidney, OH, p. A490
EVELYN, David M., M.D. Vice President Medical Affairs, Cayuga Medical Center at Ithaca, Ithaca, NY, p. A427
EVENS, Marsha, Acting Chief Information Resource Management, Veterans Affairs New Jersey Health Care System, East Orange, NJ, p. A403
EVENS, Richard R., Chief Executive Officer, HEALTHSOUTH Northern Kentucky Rehabilitation Hospital, Edgewood, KY, p. A250
EVENS, Tamara, Director Human Resources, Moses Ludington Hospital, Ticonderoga, NY, p. A444
EVENSON, Margie, Manager Human Resources, Osceola Medical Center, Osceola, WI, p. A694
EVERETT, John, Chief Financial Officer, Cogdell Memorial Hospital, Snyder, TX, p. A634
EVERHART, Carole, Administrative Director Human Resources, Downey Regional Medical Center, Downey, CA, p. A58
EVERHART, Martin S., Senior Vice President Human Resources, Robert Wood Johnson University Hospital, New Brunswick, NJ, p. A407
EVERLY, Nanette, Manager Human Resources and Administrative Assistant, Jefferson County Health Center, Fairfield, IA, p. A221
EVERSOLE, Matt, Regional Vice President Information Services, Mercy Health – Anderson Hospital, Cincinnati, OH, p. A475
EVERT, Barbara, M.D
  Vice President Medical Affairs, OhioHealth Dublin Methodist Hospital, Dublin, OH, p. A481
  Vice President Medical Affairs, OhioHealth Grady Memorial Hospital, Delaware, OH, p. A480
EVINS, Starling C., M.D. Chief of Staff, Williamson Medical Center, Franklin, TN, p. A569
EVOLGA, Nancy K., Executive Director Human Resources, Bert Fish Medical Center, New Smyrna Beach, FL, p. A133
EWALD, Ronald, Chief Financial Officer, Inova Fairfax Hospital, Falls Church, VA, p. A653
EWALD, Sandra
  Vice President Finance, Aurora BayCare Medical Center, Green Bay, WI, p. A687
  Vice President Finance, Aurora Medical Center – Manitowoc County, Two Rivers, WI, p. A698
  Vice President Finance, Aurora Medical Center of Oshkosh, Oshkosh, WI, p. A694
EWELL, Sandy, Chief Nursing Officer, Timpanogos Regional Hospital, Orem, UT, p. A645
EWING, Chandler, Chief Executive Officer, Select Specialty Hospital–Jackson, Jackson, MS, p. A349
EWING, Corey
  Chief Executive Officer, DeKalb Regional Medical Center, Fort Payne, AL, p. A20
  Chief Operating Officer, Gateway Medical Center, Clarksville, TN, p. A567
EWING, Thomas
  Director Information Technology, Sentara CarePlex Hospital, Hampton, VA, p. A655
  Director Information Technology, Sentara Northern Virginia Medical Center, Woodbridge, VA, p. A663
EWY, Barry, Chief Executive Officer, Select Specialty Hospital–Little Rock, Little Rock, AR, p. A46
EXLINE, Michael, Chief Financial Officer, Carrus Specialty Hospital, Sherman, TX, p. A634
EYER, Jan, Chief Executive Officer, Vibra Hospital of Denver, Thornton, CO, p. A106
EYER, Ron, Manager Information Services, Aspirus Grand View Hospital, Ironwood, MI, p. A317
EYLER, James W., FACHE, Chief Executive Officer, Coliseum Center for Behavioral Health, Macon, GA, p. A156
EZEJI, Magnus, Chief Financial Officer, Southwest Connecticut Mental Health System, Bridgeport, CT, p. A108

# F

FAAS, Michael D., President and Chief Executive Officer, Metro Health Hospital, Wyoming, MI, p. A327
FAAS, Nancy, R.N. Chief Nursing Officer, Reliant Rehabilitation Hospital Dallas, Dallas, TX, p. A597
FABER, Chris, Human Resources Analyst, ValleyCare Medical Center, Pleasanton, CA, p. A80
FABER, Tammy, Director Human Resources, Hegg Memorial Health Center Avera, Rock Valley, IA, p. A227
FABIAN, Alan J., Chief Executive Officer, LewisGale Hospital Montgomery, Blacksburg, VA, p. A652
FABIAN, Roxanne, Director of Nursing–Acute Care, LifeCare Medical Center, Roseau, MN, p. A339
FABIANO, Tom, Director Human Resources, Mount Auburn Hospital, Cambridge, MA, p. A299
FABREY, Robert, M.D. Chief Medical Officer, San Juan Regional Medical Center, Farmington, NM, p. A416
FABRICK, Peter, Vice President Clinical Operations, Mountain View Hospital, Idaho Falls, ID, p. A169
FACEY, Alice, Vice President of Patient Care Services, St. Clare Hospital, Baraboo, WI, p. A683
FACKRELL, Sherlyn, Finance Controller, Grover C. Dils Medical Center, Caliente, NV, p. A391
FACTEAU, Patrick M., Chief Financial Officer, Adirondack Medical Center, Saranac Lake, NY, p. A442
FACULAK, Roger, Chief Financial Officer, Memorial Hermann Northwest Hospital, Houston, TX, p. A611
FACURI, Mark, Director Information Systems, Tri–City Medical Center, Oceanside, CA, p. A77
FADALE, Sean, President and Chief Executive Officer, Community Memorial Hospital, Hamilton, NY, p. A426
FADLER, Jeannie, R.N. Vice President, Patient Care Services, Saint Francis Medical Center, Cape Girardeau, MO, p. A358
FADOOL, Albert, Director Information Systems, Garden City Hospital, Garden City, MI, p. A314
FAEHNLE, Steve, M.D. Vice President Medical Affairs, Hendrick Health System, Abilene, TX, p. A581
FAGAN, Erin, Manager Human Resources, George Washington University Hospital, Washington, DC, p. A116
FAGAN, Michael, Chief Financial Officer, Huntington Hospital, Huntington, NY, p. A427
FAGERBERG, Lesley, Vice President Fiscal Services, Heart of the Rockies Regional Medical Center, Salida, CO, p. A105
FAGERSTROM, Joel, Executive Vice President and Chief Operating Officer, St. Luke's Hospital – Miners Campus, Coaldale, PA, p. A523
FAGG, Cindy, Fiscal Officer, Battle Mountain General Hospital, Battle Mountain, NV, p. A391
FAGIN, Beth, Manager Information Systems, St. Vincent's Medical Center Southside, Jacksonville, FL, p. A127
FAGUNDO, Ramon, M.D. Chief of Staff, Sistersville General Hospital, Sistersville, WV, p. A681
FAHD II, Charles F., Chief Executive Officer, Massena Memorial Hospital, Massena, NY, p. A429
FAHEY, Linda L., MS Vice President and Chief Nurse Executive, Decatur Memorial Hospital, Decatur, IL, p. A180
FAHEY, Stephen P., Executive Director, Sierra Tucson, Tucson, AZ, p. A39
FAHEY, Walter, Chief Information Officer, Maimonides Medical Center,, NY, p. A434
FAHRLANDER, Jason, FACHE, Chief Executive Officer, Hillcrest Medical Center, Tulsa, OK, p. A508
FAHS, Melvin H., Chief Executive Officer, Community Memorial Hospital, Hicksville, OH, p. A483
FAILE, J. Gene, Chief Executive Officer, Wilkes Regional Medical Center, North Wilkesboro, NC, p. A458
FAILING, Richard J., Chief Executive Officer, Kittson Memorial Healthcare Center, Hallock, MN, p. A333
FAILLA, Richard, Chief Executive Officer, Research Psychiatric Center, Kansas City, MO, p. A363
FAIN, Douglas, Director Computer Services, University of Tennessee Medical Center, Knoxville, TN, p. A572
FAIRCHILD, David, M.D. Chief Medical Officer, Tufts Medical Center, Boston, MA, p. A297
FAIRCHILD, James W., FACHE, Chief Executive Officer, Harrison County Community Hospital, Bethany, MO, p. A356
FAIRCHILDS, Constance, R.N. Vice President Patient Care Services, Emanuel Medical Center, Turlock, CA, p. A93
FAIRCLOTH, Doug, Interim Chief Financial Officer, Elbert Memorial Hospital, Elberton, GA, p. A153
FAIRCLOTH, Karen, Chief Financial Officer, Memorial Hospital and Manor, Bainbridge, GA, p. A148
FAIRFAX, Tom, Director Information Systems, Bothwell Regional Health Center, Sedalia, MO, p. A371
FAKHRY, Wael, Senior Vice President and Chief Financial Officer, Indian River Medical Center, Vero Beach, FL, p. A143

FALANCE, Becky, Director Human Resources, Lovelace Rehabilitation Hospital, Albuquerque, NM, p. A414
FALASCO, Pam, Vice President, Chief Nursing Officer, Parma Community General Hospital, Parma, OH, p. A488
FALATKO, Michael J., FACHE, President and Chief Executive Officer, Hills & Dales General Hospital, Cass City, MI, p. A310
FALBO, Susan, Vice President Human Resources, Wheeling Hospital, Wheeling, WV, p. A682
FALCON, Hugo, M.D. Director Medical Services, Piedmont Geriatric Hospital, Burkeville, VA, p. A652
FALCON, Spencer P., M.D. Vice President Medical Affairs, Samaritan Medical Center, Watertown, NY, p. A445
FALCONE, Robert E., M.D. Chief of Staff, Cincinnati Veterans Affairs Medical Center, Cincinnati, OH, p. A474
FALIVENA, Richard, D.O. Vice President Medical Affairs, Cape Regional Medical Center, Cape May Court House, NJ, p. A402
FALKENBERRY, Lee, Director Information Systems, Monroe County Hospital, Monroeville, AL, p. A23
FALL, J. Mark, Chief Executive Officer, CareLink of Jackson, Jackson, MI, p. A317
FALL, Jennifer, Chief Information Officer, Gillette Children's Specialty Healthcare, Saint Paul, MN, p. A340
FALSETTI, Domonic F., M.D. Chief of Staff and Medical Director, Mount St. Mary's Hospital and Health Center, Lewiston, NY, p. A428
FALTERMAN, Jr., James B., M.D. Medical Director, University Medical Center, Lafayette, LA, p. A271
FALTZ, Lawrence L., M.D. Senior Vice President Medical Affairs and Medical Director, Phelps Memorial Hospital Center, Sleepy Hollow, NY, p. A442
FAMAKINWA, Abiodun, M.D. Acting Clinical Director, West Central Georgia Regional Hospital, Columbus, GA, p. A150
FANALE, James E., M.D. Senior Vice President System Development, Jordan Hospital, Plymouth, MA, p. A304
FANNIN, Allyson, Director Human Resources, LaSalle General Hospital, Jena, LA, p. A269
FANNIN, Pam, Coordinator Human Resources, LifeCare Hospital of Dayton, Miamisburg, OH, p. A486
FANNING, Linda T., R.N. Chief Nursing Officer, Mercy Hospital Oklahoma City, Oklahoma City, OK, p. A503
FANNING, Melinda, Chief Financial Officer and Controller, HEALTHSOUTH Southern Hills Rehabilitation Hospital, Princeton, WV, p. A680
FANNON, Susan, Chief Nursing Officer, Indian Path Medical Center, Kingsport, TN, p. A571
FANSELAU, Michael G., District Director Human Resources, Kindred Hospital–Sacramento, Folsom, CA, p. A60
FANTANO, Gene, Controller, Kindred Hospital–San Diego, San Diego, CA, p. A85
FARAH, Tony, M.D. President Medical Staff, Allegheny General Hospital, Pittsburgh, PA, p. A537
FARAHMAND, Mehrdad, M.D. Chief Medical Officer, Providence Mount Carmel Hospital, Colville, WA, p. A665
FARBER, Bobbi, M.D. Chief Medical Officer, St. Francis Hospital, Columbus, GA, p. A150
FARBER, Nancy D., Chief Executive Officer, Washington Hospital Healthcare System, Fremont, CA, p. A61
FARGASON, Crayton A., M.D. Medical Director, The Children's Hospital of Alabama, Birmingham, AL, p. A17
FARGUSON, Jack, Director Information Technology, Red River Regional Hospital, Bonham, TX, p. A589
FARHANG, Farzin, M.D. Medical Director, HEALTHSOUTH Rehabilitation Hospital–Las Vegas, Las Vegas, NV, p. A392
FARIA, Mary, FACHE, Administrator, Seton Southwest Healthcare Center, Austin, TX, p. A585
FARINA, Albert M.
  Chief Financial Officer, Mount Vernon Hospital, Mount Vernon, NY, p. A430
  Senior Vice President and Chief Financial Officer, Sound Shore Medical Center of Westchester, New Rochelle, NY, p. A430
FARINA, Jonathan, Chief Information Officer, Brattleboro Memorial Hospital, Brattleboro, VT, p. A649
FARIS, Shellie, M.D. President Medical Staff, St. Francis Hospital and Health Services, Maryville, MO, p. A365
FARISH, Audra, Vice President Human Resources, Saint Joseph's Hospital of Atlanta, Atlanta, GA, p. A147
FARKAS, Laura, Director Human Resources, Fairview Hospital, Great Barrington, MA, p. A300
FARLEY, H. Fred, FACHE,
  President and Chief Operating Officer, Arnot Ogden Medical Center, Elmira, NY, p. A425
  President and Chief Operating Officer, St. Joseph's Hospital, Elmira, NY, p. A425
FARMER, Guy, M.D. President Medical Staff, Calhoun Health Services, Calhoun City, MS, p. A345
FARMER, Kathleen, Assistant Administrator Finance and Chief Financial Officer, El Centro Regional Medical Center, El Centro, CA, p. A59

FARMER, Pat, Coordinator Human Resources and Safety Officer, Institute for Orthopaedic Surgery, Lima, OH, p. A484

FARMER, William, M.D. Chief of Staff, Evergreen Medical Center, Evergreen, AL, p. A20

FARNHAM, Diane, Acting Director Human Resources, Lallie Kemp Medical Center, Independence, LA, p. A268

FARNHAM, Krista, Chief Operating Officer, Providence Portland Medical Center, Portland, OR, p. A516

FARNSWORTH, Edward F., FACHE, President, Capital Region Medical Center, Jefferson City, MO, p. A362

FARO, Joan, M.D. Chief Medical Officer, John T. Mather Memorial Hospital, Port Jefferson, NY, p. A440

FARR, Lorraine, Manager Human Resources, Georgia Regional Hospital at Atlanta, Decatur, GA, p. A152

FARR, Ralph, Chief Information Officer, University of Texas Medical Branch Hospitals, Galveston, TX, p. A605

FARR, Ronald
Senior Vice President and Chief Financial Officer, Frazier Rehab Institute, Louisville, KY, p. A255
Chief Financial Officer, Jewish Hospital, Louisville, KY, p. A255

FARR, William L., M.D. Chief Medical Officer, University Hospital, Augusta, GA, p. A148

FARRAGE, Jim, M.D. Medical Director, Southern Kentucky Rehabilitation Hospital, Bowling Green, KY, p. A249

FARRELL, Brenda, Vice President Finance, Brookhaven Memorial Hospital Medical Center, Patchogue, NY, p. A439

FARRELL, Darin, Chief Executive Officer, Arbuckle Memorial Hospital, Sulphur, OK, p. A507

FARRELL, George, M.D. Chief of Staff, Wythe County Community Hospital, Wytheville, VA, p. A663

FARRELL, Katie, Chief Operating Officer, Abington Health Lansdale Hospital, Lansdale, PA, p. A529

FARRELL, Roy, M.D. Chief Medical Officer, Carondelet Holy Cross Hospital, Nogales, AZ, p. A33

FARRELL, Steven E., M.D. Chief Medical Officer, Forrest General Hospital, Hattiesburg, MS, p. A347

FARRELL, Terence, Administrator, Herrin Hospital, Herrin, IL, p. A184

FARRELL, Teresa, Chief Human Resources Officer, Nacogdoches Medical Center, Nacogdoches, TX, p. A624

FARRELLY, Irene, Vice President and Chief Information Officer, Brooklyn Hospital Center,, NY, p. A431

FARRIS, Bain J., President and Chief Executive Officer, Exempla Saint Joseph Hospital, Denver, CO, p. A99

FARRIS, James R., FACHE, Chief Executive Officer, Union County Hospital, Anna, IL, p. A173

FARROW, Diane, Manager Information Technology and Systems, Willamette Valley Medical Center, McMinnville, OR, p. A514

FARROW, Ed, M.D. Chief Medical Staff, Epic Medical Center, Eufaula, OK, p. A498

FARROW, Shelly, R.N. Chief Nursing Officer, South Texas Regional Medical Center, Jourdanton, TX, p. A615

FARSHAO, Nosratian, M.D. Chief Medical Staff, Memorial Hospital of Gardena, Gardena, CA, p. A62

FASANO, Philip, Chief Information Officer, Kaiser Permanente Sacramento Medical Center, Sacramento, CA, p. A83

FATCH, Casey, Chief Operating Officer, Tri–City Medical Center, Oceanside, CA, p. A77

FATTIG, Marty, Chief Executive Officer, Nemaha County Hospital, Auburn, NE, p. A381

FATULA, Suzette, Chief Financial Officer, Allen Parish Hospital, Kinder, LA, p. A270

FAUCHEAUX, Carolyn, Director Human Resources, St. Charles Parish Hospital, Luling, LA, p. A272

FAUCHEUX, Lisa, Director Human Resources, St. James Parish Hospital, Lutcher, LA, p. A272

FAUGHT, Charles J., Chief Financial Officer, Burnett Medical Center, Grantsburg, WI, p. A687

FAUL, Jennifer, Chief Operating Officer, Prairie St. John's, Fargo, ND, p. A466

FAULIS, Karen, Chief Operating Officer, Palmdale Regional Medical Center, Palmdale, CA, p. A78

FAULK, Gordon, Administrator, Elmore Community Hospital, Wetumpka, AL, p. A26

FAULKNER, Cindy, Chief Nursing Officer, Maria Parham Medical Center, Henderson, NC, p. A454

FAULKNER, David M., Chief Executive Officer, Fleming County Hospital, Flemingsburg, KY, p. A250

FAULKNER, Kristi, Director Human Resources, United Regional Health Care System, Wichita Falls, TX, p. A642

FAULKNER, Laura, Chief Human Resource Management Service, Veterans Affairs Medical Center–Lexington, Lexington, KY, p. A255

FAUST, Bill D., Administrator, Floyd County Medical Center, Charles City, IA, p. A218

FAVALE, Maria, FACHE Associate Director, Northport Veterans Affairs Medical Center, Northport, NY, p. A437

FAVATA, Valerie, R.N. Chief Nursing Officer, Oswego Hospital, Oswego, NY, p. A439

FAVRET, John M., Director, Eastern State Hospital, Williamsburg, VA, p. A663

FAWNS, Bill, Interim Manager Information Systems, Kern Medical Center, Bakersfield, CA, p. A54

FAY, Brian, Director Information Systems, Sidney Health Center, Sidney, MT, p. A380

FAYE, Darryl, Chief Financial Officer, Cameron Memorial Community Hospital, Angola, IN, p. A198

FAYEN, Edward J., Associate Administrator Operations and Support, Washington Hospital Healthcare System, Fremont, CA, p. A61

FAYRE, Gail, M.D. Medical Director, Anna Jaques Hospital, Newburyport, MA, p. A302

FEAK, Christina, Chief Information Officer, Onslow Memorial Hospital, Jacksonville, NC, p. A455

FEAR, Frank, Chief Information Officer, Memorial Healthcare, Owosso, MI, p. A321

FEASEL, Jeff, Chief Executive Officer, Halifax Health Medical Center of Daytona Beach, Daytona Beach, FL, p. A122

FEASEL, Julie, Chief Executive Officer, Kindred Hospital Bay Area–Tampa, Tampa, FL, p. A141

FEATHER, Leroy P., Vice President Finance, Community Hospitals and Wellness Centers, Bryan, OH, p. A472

FEBUS, Steven, Chief Financial Officer, Pullman Regional Hospital, Pullman, WA, p. A669

FEDELE, Jerry J., President and Chief Executive Officer, Boca Raton Regional Hospital, Boca Raton, FL, p. A118

FEDER, Diane, MSN Senior Vice President and Chief Operating Officer, Witham Memorial Hospital, Lebanon, IN, p. A209

FEDER, Eric, Executive Vice President and Chief Operating Officer, Bayfront Health St. Petersburg, Saint Petersburg, FL, p. A138

FEDERICO, Skip, Director Information Systems, Fairway Medical Center, Covington, LA, p. A265

FEDERINKO, David, Chief Information Officer, Allegan General Hospital, Allegan, MI, p. A308

FEDERSPIEL, John C., President and Chief Executive Officer, Hudson Valley Hospital Center, Cortlandt Manor, NY, p. A424

FEDORA, Deborah, Director Human Resources, Paoli Hospital, Paoli, PA, p. A534

FEE, Jeff, Chief Executive Officer, St. Patrick Hospital, Missoula, MT, p. A378

FEEMAN, Kimberly, Vice President Human Resources, The Good Samaritan Hospital, Lebanon, PA, p. A529

FEENEY, John, President and Chief Executive Officer, Berlin Memorial Hospital, Berlin, WI, p. A684

FEESS, David, President and Chief Executive Officer, Liberty Hospital, Liberty, MO, p. A365

FEGAN, Claudia, M.D. Chief Medical Officer, John H. Stroger Jr. Hospital of Cook County, Chicago, IL, p. A177

FEGAN, Theresa, Chief Clinical Officer, Tahoe Pacific Hospitals, Reno, NV, p. A395

FEGHALI, Georges, M.D
Senior Vice President Quality and Chief Medical Officer, Bethesda North Hospital, Cincinnati, OH, p. A474
Senior Vice President Quality and Chief Medical Officer, Good Samaritan Hospital, Cincinnati, OH, p. A474

FEHR, Mike, Vice President Operations and Chief Information Officer, Jupiter Medical Center, Jupiter, FL, p. A127

FEHR, Tracy, Executive Assistant and Director Human Resources, Red River Hospital, Wichita Falls, TX, p. A641

FEHRING, Marcia, Interim Chief Executive Officer, Horn Memorial Hospital, Ida Grove, IA, p. A223

FEIDT, Leslie, Chief Information Officer, Erie County Medical Center, Buffalo, NY, p. A422

FEIKE, Jeffrey, President and Chief Administrative Officer, Fort Loudoun Medical Center, Lenoir City, TN, p. A573

FEIL, Julie, Accountant, Cavalier County Memorial Hospital, Langdon, ND, p. A468

FEILER, Kenneth H., Chief Executive Officer, Rose Medical Center, Denver, CO, p. A100

FEILNER, Margaret, Director Information Services, SSM St. Joseph Health Center, Saint Charles, MO, p. A368

FEINBERG, Daniel, M.D. Chief Medical Officer, Pennsylvania Hospital, Philadelphia, PA, p. A536

FEINBERG, David, M.D., Chief Executive Officer, Ronald Reagan University of California Los Angeles Medical Center, Los Angeles, CA, p. A71

FEINBERG, Jason, M.D
Vice President Medical Affairs and Chief Medical Officer, Geneva General Hospital, Geneva, NY, p. A426
Vice President Medical Affairs and Chief Medical Officer, Soldiers and Sailors Memorial Hospital of Yates County, Penn Yan, NY, p. A439

FEINOUR, Terry, Senior Vice President Corporate Services, Bayhealth Medical Center, Dover, DE, p. A114

FEIRN, Greg, Senior Vice President and Chief Financial Officer, Children's Hospital, New Orleans, LA, p. A275

FEIST, Patricia, Manager Human Resources, Crook County Medical Services District, Sundance, WY, p. A704

FEIT, Marcy L., President and Chief Executive Officer, ValleyCare Medical Center, Pleasanton, CA, p. A80

FELBINGER, Richard, Senior Vice President and Chief Financial Officer, Borgess Medical Center, Kalamazoo, MI, p. A317

FELDMAN, David L., Executive Vice President and Treasurer, Circles of Care, Melbourne, FL, p. A130

FELDMAN, Deborah A., President and Chief Executive Officer, Children's Medical Center, Dayton, OH, p. A479

FELDMAN, Mitchell S., Chief Executive Officer, West Boca Medical Center, Boca Raton, FL, p. A119

FELDMAN, Tom, Chief Financial Officer, East Ohio Regional Hospital, Martins Ferry, OH, p. A485

FELDSTEIN, Charles S., M.D. Vice President Medical Affairs, St. Rose Hospital, Hayward, CA, p. A64

FELEGE, Lester, Controller, New England Rehabilitation Hospital, Woburn, MA, p. A306

FELGAR, Alvin D., President and Chief Executive Officer, Frisbie Memorial Hospital, Rochester, NH, p. A400

FELICETTI, Jacqueline, Director Human Resources, Chester County Hospital, West Chester, PA, p. A543

FELICI, Brian K., Chief Executive Officer, Wetzel County Hospital, New Martinsville, WV, p. A679

FELIS, Sandra L., R.N. Senior Vice President Patient Care Services and Chief Nursing Officer, Fletcher Allen Health Care, Burlington, VT, p. A649

FELIX, Larry A., FACHE, Chief Executive Officer, Ransom Memorial Hospital, Ottawa, KS, p. A241

FELIZ, Miriam, M.D. Medical Director, St. Catherine's Rehabilitation Hospital, North Miami, FL, p. A134

FELKNER, Joseph G., Senior Vice President and Chief Financial Officer, Health First Palm Bay Hospital, Melbourne, FL, p. A130

FELL, David, M.D. Chief Medical Officer, Tulsa Spine and Specialty Hospital, Tulsa, OK, p. A509

FELLER, Julie, Director Human Resources, Grays Harbor Community Hospital, Aberdeen, WA, p. A664

FELLOWES, S. Gale, M.D. Chief Medical Officer, Memorial Health Care System, Chattanooga, TN, p. A566

FELLOWS, Steven A.
Executive Vice President and Chief Operating Officer, Goleta Valley Cottage Hospital, Santa Barbara, CA, p. A89
Executive Vice President and Chief Operating Officer, Santa Barbara Cottage Hospital, Santa Barbara, CA, p. A89
Executive Vice President and Chief Operating Officer, Santa Ynez Valley Cottage Hospital, Solvang, CA, p. A91

FELMLEE, Charles, Assistant Director Fiscal Services, Central Virginia Training Center, Madison Heights, VA, p. A656

FELTMAN, Steven, CPA Interim Chief Financial Officer, Essentia Health–Virginia, Virginia, MN, p. A342

FELTON, David, Manager Information Systems, Waldo County General Hospital, Belfast, ME, p. A281

FELTON, Debby, Chief Financial Officer, Central Arkansas Veterans Healthcare System, Little Rock, AR, p. A46

FELTS, Dave, Chief Information Systems, Logan Regional Hospital, Logan, UT, p. A644

FENDT, Phil, Chief Financial Officer, Memorial Community Health, Aurora, NE, p. A381

FENELLO, Michael A., Chief Executive Officer, St. Luke's McCall, McCall, ID, p. A170

FENER, Michael
Executive Director, Plainview Hospital, Plainview, NY, p. A439
Executive Director, Syosset Hospital, Syosset, NY, p. A443

FENGEL, Anna, Personnel Assistant, Mental Health Institute, Clarinda, IA, p. A218

FENN, Mark, Director Human Resources, Pulaski Memorial Hospital, Winamac, IN, p. A215

FENNELL, Charles, Vice President Information Management, St. Joseph's Hospital Health Center, Syracuse, NY, p. A444

FENSKE, Candace, Chief Executive Officer, Madelia Community Hospital, Madelia, MN, p. A335

FENSTERER, Rob, Director Information Services, Devereux Hospital and Children's Center of Florida, Melbourne, FL, p. A130

FENWICK, Sandra, President and Chief Operating Officer, Boston Children's Hospital, Boston, MA, p. A296

FERCH, Wayne
President and Chief Executive Officer, Adventist Medical Center – Hanford, Hanford, CA, p. A63
President and Chief Executive Officer, Adventist Medical Center–Reedley, Reedley, CA, p. A82
President and Chief Executive Officer, Central Valley General Hospital, Hanford, CA, p. A63

FERETTO, Linda, Director Human Resources, Jerold Phelps Community Hospital, Garberville, CA, p. A62

FERGIE, Joy, Chief Financial Officer, Delta Medical Center, Memphis, TN, p. A574

FERGUS, Janie
Director and Chief Information Officer, Saint Joseph East, Lexington, KY, p. A254
Director and Chief Information Officer, Saint Joseph Hospital, Lexington, KY, p. A254

FERGUS, Linda, Manager Information Technology, Allegheny Valley Hospital, Natrona Heights, PA, p. A533

FERGUSON, Allison, Director Human Resources, Avoyelles Hospital, Marksville, LA, p. A273

FERGUSON, Bruce, Vice President and Chief Financial Officer, UW Medicine/Northwest Hospital & Medical Center, Seattle, WA, p. A671

FERGUSON, Cathy, R.N. VP and Chief Nursing Officer, Hamilton Medical Center, Dalton, GA, p. A151

FERGUSON, Cheryl L., Associate Administrator, Sanford Canby Medical Center, Canby, MN, p. A330

FERGUSON, Clifford, Director Information Technology and Systems, Bayshore Medical Center, Pasadena, TX, p. A626

FERGUSON, Deborah, Human Resources Consultant, Sentara Obici Hospital, Suffolk, VA, p. A662

FERGUSON, G. Thomas, Senior Vice President and Chief Human Resources Officer, New York–Presbyterian Hospital, New York, NY, p. A435

FERGUSON, Gary W., Executive Vice President and Chief Operating Officer, Christiana Care Health System, Newark, DE, p. A114

FERGUSON, Gordon B., President and Chief Executive Officer, Saint Thomas Rutherford Hospital, Murfreesboro, TN, p. A576

FERGUSON, Karen, Director Human Resources, Johnson County Healthcare Center, Buffalo, WY, p. A701

FERGUSON, Louis D., Chief Financial Officer, Palestine Regional Medical Center–East, Palestine, TX, p. A626

FERGUSON, Michael, Chief Financial Officer, Harbor Oaks Hospital, New Baltimore, MI, p. A321

FERGUSON, Nina L., Director Human Resources, Little Colorado Medical Center, Winslow, AZ, p. A40

FERGUSON, Randy, Chief Information Officer, Ridgecrest Regional Hospital, Ridgecrest, CA, p. A82

FERGUSON, Rick, Chief Executive Officer, Oklahoma Surgical Hospital, Tulsa, OK, p. A508

FERGUSON, Tonya, Interim Chief Executive Officer, HEALTHSOUTH Rehabilitation Hospital of Virginia, Richmond, VA, p. A660

FERGUSON, Zeta, Chief Human Resources, Atlanta Veterans Affairs Medical Center, Decatur, GA, p. A151

FERIGGNO, Sandie, Vice President Human Resources, Good Shepherd Medical Center, Longview, TX, p. A619

FERMANO, Joseph, Vice President Finance and Chief Financial Officer, Crotched Mountain Rehabilitation Center, Greenfield, NH, p. A398

FERNANDEZ, Alex, Chief Financial Officer, North Shore Medical Center, Miami, FL, p. A132

FERNANDEZ, Benigno J., M.D. Executive Medical Director, Laurel Ridge Treatment Center, San Antonio, TX, p. A631

FERNANDEZ, Bernardo, M.D., Chief Executive Officer, Cleveland Clinic Florida, Weston, FL, p. A144

FERNANDEZ, Emiliano, Director Information Services, Jerome Golden Center for Behavioral Health, Inc., West Palm Beach, FL, p. A143

FERNANDEZ, Genaro, M.D. Chief of Staff, Paradise Valley Hospital, National City, CA, p. A76

FERNANDEZ, Jean, Chief Information Officer, Beth Israel Deaconess Hospital–Milton, Milton, MA, p. A302

FERNANDEZ, John R., President and Chief Executive Officer, Massachusetts Eye and Ear Infirmary, Boston, MA, p. A297

FERNANDEZ, Juan, Director of Campus Operations, North Greenville Hospital, Travelers Rest, SC, p. A556

FERNANDEZ, Manuel, Vice President Nursing, Larkin Community Hospital, South Miami, FL, p. A140

FERNANDEZ, Robert, M.D. Chief Medical Staff, Southern Maine Medical Center, Biddeford, ME, p. A282

FERNANDEZ-BRAVO, Grisel, R.N. Chief Nursing Officer, Memorial Hospital West, Pembroke Pines, FL, p. A136

FERRACANE, Tony, Vice President Human Resources, St. Mary Medical Center, Hobart, IN, p. A204

FERRANS, Richard, M.D. Vice President and Medical Information Officer, Memorial Hospital at Gulfport, Gulfport, MS, p. A347

FERRANTE, Fritz, Manager Information Services, Providence Kodiak Island Medical Center, Kodiak, AK, p. A28

FERRARO, Christopher, Chief Financial Officer, Day Kimball Hospital, Putnam, CT, p. A111

FERREBEE, Mike, M.D. Vice President Medical Affairs, Monongalia General Hospital, Morgantown, WV, p. A679

FERRELL, David A.
Regional Administrator, Shriners Hospitals for Children–Galveston Burns Hospital, Galveston, TX, p. A605
Regional Administrator, Shriners Hospitals for Children–Houston, Houston, TX, p. A612
Regional Administrator, Shriners Hospitals for Children–Tampa, Tampa, FL, p. A142

FERRELL, Jennifer, Chief Nursing Officer, HEALTHSOUTH Rehabilitation Hospital of Memphis, Memphis, TN, p. A574

FERRELL, Ronald, Chief Information Officer, Veterans Affairs Medical Center, Albuquerque, NM, p. A415

FERRELLI, John J., Chief Executive Officer, Coast Plaza Hospital, Norwalk, CA, p. A76

FERREN, Alison, Vice President Information Technology and Chief Information Officer, Abington Memorial Hospital, Abington, PA, p. A519

FERRERI, Anthony C., President and Chief Executive Officer, Staten Island University Hospital,, NY, p. A436

FERRERO, Marcia L., MS Chief Nursing Officer, Heritage Valley Beaver, Beaver, PA, p. A520

FERRIELL, Kathleen, Chief Nursing Officer, Spring View Hospital, Lebanon, KY, p. A253

FERRIS, David, Chief Nursing Officer and Vice President Patient Care Services, Claxton–Hepburn Medical Center, Ogdensburg, NY, p. A438

FERRIS, Mark, M.D. Medical Director, Kindred Hospital–White Rock, Dallas, TX, p. A596

FERRONI, Karen, M.D. Medical Director, Holyoke Medical Center, Holyoke, MA, p. A300

FERRY, Jane, M.D. Vice President Medical Affairs, Grand View Hospital, Sellersville, PA, p. A541

FERRY, Thomas, Business Administrator, Oakwood Correctional Facility, Lima, OH, p. A484

FESKO, Donald P., Chief Executive Officer and Administrator, Community Hospital, Munster, IN, p. A211

FESTA, J. Keith, M.D. Vice President Medical Affairs, Saint Francis Hospital and Health Centers, Poughkeepsie, NY, p. A440

FETTERS, Valerie, Chief Financial Officer, Hillsdale Community Health Center, Hillsdale, MI, p. A316

FEUER, Tammy, Chief Executive Officer, HEALTHSOUTH Rehabilitation Hospital of Vineland, Vineland, NJ, p. A412

FEUNNING, Charles, M.D. President Medical Staff, Summa Western Reserve Hospital, Cuyahoga Falls, OH, p. A479

FEUQUAY, Judith K., Chief Executive Officer, Nevada Regional Medical Center, Nevada, MO, p. A367

FICCHI, Adrienne, Vice President Information Management, Philadephia Veterans Affairs Medical Center, Philadelphia, PA, p. A536

FICHTER, Craig R., Chief Financial Officer, Martin General Hospital, Williamston, NC, p. A462

FICKES, Catherine, R.N., President and Chief Executive Officer, St. Vincent Medical Center, Los Angeles, CA, p. A72

FICKLIN, Camille, Director Information Services, Family Health West, Fruita, CO, p. A101

FIDELI, Barbara, Chief Operating Officer, Non–clinical Services, MetroSouth Medical Center, Blue Island, IL, p. A174

FIDLER, Soniya, Senior Director Human Resources, Yampa Valley Medical Center, Steamboat Springs, CO, p. A106

FIEKER, Dan, D.O. Chief Medical Officer and Chief Operating Officer, St. Francis Health Center, Topeka, KS, p. A245

FIELD, Clifford, M.D. Medical Director, Kau Hospital, Pahala, HI, p. A166

FIELD, Kori, Director of Nursing, Brodstone Memorial Hospital, Superior, NE, p. A390

FIELD, Laurie, Director Human Resources, Eaton Rapids Medical Center, Eaton Rapids, MI, p. A313

FIELDER, Jaf, Vice President and Administrator, Willis–Knighton Medical Center, Shreveport, LA, p. A278

FIELDING, Colene, Manager Business Office, Baylor Medical Center at Uptown, Dallas, TX, p. A595

FIELDING, Laura M., Administrative Director Organizational Development, Holy Family Memorial, Manitowoc, WI, p. A690

FIELDS, Donald R., Senior Community Chief Executive Officer, Hazard ARH Regional Medical Center, Hazard, KY, p. A252

FIELDS, Duane, Interim Chief Executive Officer, Rush County Memorial Hospital, La Crosse, KS, p. A237

FIELDS, Glenn C., Vice President, Human Resources, St. Vincent Anderson Regional Hospital, Anderson, IN, p. A198

FIELDS, Lexi M., Chief Financial Officer, Wallowa Memorial Hospital, Enterprise, OR, p. A512

FIELDS, Maura G., R.N. Chief Clinical Officer, North Valley Hospital, Whitefish, MT, p. A380

FIELDS, Sarah G., R.N. Vice President Nursing, North Kansas City Hospital, North Kansas City, MO, p. A367

FIERER, Jonathan, M.D. Chief of Staff, Martinsburg Veterans Affairs Medical Center, Martinsburg, WV, p. A678

FIERRO, Barbara, Director, Human Resources, St. Francis Hospital, Roslyn, NY, p. A442

FIGLIOZZI, Charles, CPA Vice President and Chief Financial Officer, New York Eye and Ear Infirmary, New York, NY, p. A435

FIGUEIREDO, Steve, Director, Dr. J. Corrigan Mental Health Center, Fall River, MA, p. A299

FIGUEROA, Roseann, Director Human Resources, Doctors Hospital of Laredo, Laredo, TX, p. A618

FIKE, Ruthita J.
Chief Executive Officer, Loma Linda University Behavioral Medicine Center, Redlands, CA, p. A81
Chief Executive Officer, Loma Linda University Medical Center, Loma Linda, CA, p. A66
Chief Executive Officer, Loma Linda University Medical Center, Loma Linda, CA, p. A66

FILBURN, Mandi, Director Human Resources, Twin Lakes Regional Medical Center, Leitchfield, KY, p. A253

FILER, Christine, Director Human Resources, HEALTHSOUTH Rehabilitation Hospital of Altoona, Altoona, PA, p. A519

FILIAK, Thomas, Chief Operating Officer, Auburn Community Hospital, Auburn, NY, p. A420

FILIPINI, Alfred, Manager Human Resources, Ancora Psychiatric Hospital, Hammonton, NJ, p. A404

FILIPOWICZ, Thomas, M.D. Medical Director, St. Luke's Hospital – Quakertown Campus, Quakertown, PA, p. A539

FILKINS, James, Chief Information Officer, Norwegian American Hospital, Chicago, IL, p. A178

FILLER, Scott, Chief Executive Officer, HEALTHSOUTH Rehabilitation Hospital of Altoona, Altoona, PA, p. A519

FILLINGIM, Jed, Acting Chief Operating Officer and Associate Director, G.V. (Sonny) Montgomery Veterans Affairs Medical Center, Jackson, MS, p. A348

FILLIPO, Brian, M.D. Chief Medical Officer, Robert Packer Hospital, Sayre, PA, p. A540

FILOSA, Frank, Fiscal Manager, Washington DC Veterans Affairs Medical Center, Washington, DC, p. A117

FILPI, Jeanette, Chief Executive Officer, Pioneer Community Hospital of Patrick County, Stuart, VA, p. A662

FILSON, Debbie, Chief Financial Officer, Ashland Health Center, Ashland, KS, p. A231

FINAN, Timothy J., FACHE,
President and Chief Executive Officer, Bradford Regional Medical Center, Bradford, PA, p. A521
President and Chief Executive Officer, Olean General Hospital, Olean, NY, p. A438

FINCH, Joe, PsyD, Superintendent, Terrell State Hospital, Terrell, TX, p. A637

FINCH, John
Vice President Information Services, Health Alliance Hospital – Broadway Campus, Kingston, NY, p. A428
Vice President Corporate Development, Health Alliance Hospital – Mary's Avenue Campus, Kingston, NY, p. A428

FINCH, Kenneth A., President and Chief Executive Officer, Huguley Memorial Medical Center, Fort Worth, TX, p. A603

FINCH, Kim, Chief Nursing Officer, Kosciusko Community Hospital, Warsaw, IN, p. A214

FINCH, Teresa, Chief Financial Officer, Trident Medical Center, Charleston, SC, p. A549

FINDLAY, Denice C., Director Human Resources, Community Hospital of San Bernardino, San Bernardino, CA, p. A84

FINDLEY, Amber, Senior Director Nursing Services and NRC Administrator, Pleasant Valley Hospital, Point Pleasant, WV, p. A680

FINE, Allan, Senior Vice President and Chief Strategy and Operations Officer, New York Eye and Ear Infirmary, New York, NY, p. A435

FINE, James, M.D. Chief Information Officer, UW Medicine/Harborview Medical Center, Seattle, WA, p. A671

FINELLI, Peter, Chief Financial Officer, Payson Regional Medical Center, Payson, AZ, p. A34

FINESTEIN, Brian, Chief Executive Officer, Easton Hospital, Easton, PA, p. A525

FINK, Eileen, Health Information Officer, North Big Horn Hospital District, Lovell, WY, p. A703

FINK, Kelley, Coordinator Human Resources, Sitka Community Hospital, Sitka, AK, p. A29

FINK, Renee, CPA Chief Financial Officer, Chase County Community Hospital, Imperial, NE, p. A384

FINLAYSON, Susan D., R.N. Senior Vice President of Operations, Mercy Medical Center, Baltimore, MD, p. A288

FINLEY, Alan, Chief Operating Officer, Conway Regional Medical Center, Conway, AR, p. A42

FINLEY, Delvecchio, Chief Executive Officer, LAC–Harbor–University of California at Los Angeles Medical Center, Torrance, CA, p. A92

FINLEY, E. Jane, Senior Vice President and Executive Director, Kaiser Permanente Downey Medical Center, Downey, CA, p. A58

FINLEY, Edward, Administrator, Wray Community District Hospital, Wray, CO, p. A107

FINLEY, Kevan, Chief Executive Officer, Cedar Ridge Hospital, Oklahoma City, OK, p. A502

FINLEY, Mike, M.D. Chief Medical Officer, CHRISTUS St. Michael Health System, Texarkana, TX, p. A637

FINLEY, Tommy, Chief Information Officer, Rutherford Regional Health System, Rutherfordton, NC, p. A460

FORD, James, Director Human Resources, Summit Medical Center, Van Buren, AR, p. A50

FORD, LaDonna, M.D. Medical Director, E. A. Conway Medical Center, Monroe, LA, p. A274

FORD, LeeAnn, Director Human Resources and Imaging, The Physicians Centre Hospital, Bryan, TX, p. A590

FORD, Mary, Vice President and Chief Information Officer, Lakeland Regional Medical Center, Lakeland, FL, p. A128

FORD, Mike, Vice President Human Resources, Floyd Memorial Hospital and Health Services, New Albany, IN, p. A211

FORD, Raymond, Chief Executive Officer, Heritage Park Surgical Hospital, Sherman, TX, p. A634

FORD, Tammy, Executive Director Human Resources, Greene County Medical Center, Jefferson, IA, p. A223

FORD, Timothy R., Chief Executive Officer / President, Blowing Rock Hospital, Blowing Rock, NC, p. A448

FORDE, Steve, Chief Financial Officer, Nelson County Health System, Mcville, ND, p. A468

FORDHAM, Karen, Vice President Chief Operating Officer, DMC Huron Valley–Sinai Hospital, Commerce Township, MI, p. A311

FORDYCE, Carol, Director of Patient Care Services, Sullivan County Memorial Hospital, Milan, MO, p. A366

FORDYCE, Michael L., President and Chief Executive Officer, Craig Hospital, Englewood, CO, p. A100

FORE, Larry T., Controller, Great Bend Regional Hospital, Great Bend, KS, p. A234

FOREMAN, Chris, Director, Phoebe Worth Medical Center, Sylvester, GA, p. A161

FOREMAN, Lee Ann
Vice President Human Resources, Mississippi Baptist Medical Center, Jackson, MS, p. A348
Vice President Human Resources, Mississippi Hospital for Restorative Care, Jackson, MS, p. A349

FORESE, Laura, M.D. Senior Vice President and Chief Medical Officer, New York–Presbyterian Hospital, New York, NY, p. A435

FORET, Robert, Chief Financial Officer, Yoakum Community Hospital, Yoakum, TX, p. A642

FORGE, Brenda J., Vice President Human Resources, St. Joseph Regional Medical Center, Lewiston, ID, p. A169

FORGEY, Roger, President and Chief Executive Officer, Erlanger at Hutcheson, Fort Oglethorpe, GA, p. A154

FORGEY, Warren, Executive Vice President Fiscal Services and Business Development, Schneck Medical Center, Seymour, IN, p. A213

FORGUES, Dan, Chief Financial Officer, Henrietta D. Goodall Hospital, Sanford, ME, p. A285

FORKEL, Todd, President and Chief Executive Officer, Avera St. Luke's Hospital, Aberdeen, SD, p. A558

FORKNER, Christine, Executive Vice President and Chief Financial Officer, National Jewish Health, Denver, CO, p. A99

FORMAN, Stuart, M.D. Chief Professional Services, Connecticut Valley Hospital, Middletown, CT, p. A110

FORMBY, Mary Beth, Chief Financial Officer, Lakewood Regional Medical Center, Lakewood, CA, p. A66

FORMELLA, Nancy A., R.N. Chief Operating Officer, Beth Israel Deaconess Medical Center, Boston, MA, p. A296

FORNERIS, Lori, R.N. Chief Clinical Officer, Loring Hospital, Sac City, IA, p. A227

FORNIER–JOHNSON, Michelle, Group Vice President Human Resources, St. Anthony Hospital, Lakewood, CO, p. A103

FORNOFF, Gerald A., Interim Chief Executive Officer, Dauterive Hospital, New Iberia, LA, p. A275

FORREST, Brian
Director Human Resources, Arnot Ogden Medical Center, Elmira, NY, p. A425
Vice President Human Resources, St. Joseph's Hospital, Elmira, NY, p. A425

FORREST, Jr., James L., Chief Financial Officer, Southeast Colorado Hospital District, Springfield, CO, p. A105

FORREST, Mary Helen, R.N. Chief Nursing Officer, UAMS Medical Center, Little Rock, AR, p. A47

FORRESTER, John M., Director Information Services, Hamilton Medical Center, Dalton, GA, p. A151

FORRY, Bryan, Chief Financial Officer, Houston Northwest Medical Center, Houston, TX, p. A610

FORSYTH, Larry
Director Information Services, OU Medical Center, Oklahoma City, OK, p. A504
Director Information System, Wesley Medical Center, Wichita, KS, p. A247

FORT, Claudio D., President and Chief Executive Officer, North Country Hospital and Health Center, Newport, VT, p. A650

FORTENBERRY, Doris, Coordinator Human Resources, Delta Memorial Hospital, Dumas, AR, p. A43

FORTENBERRY, Rob, Chief Information Officer, Spokane Veterans Affairs Medical Center, Spokane, WA, p. A672

FORTIER, Jeanne M., R.N. Vice President Patient Care Services, Grace Cottage Hospital, Townshend, VT, p. A650

FORTIN, Amanda, Manager Finance, Decatur County Hospital and Cedar Living Center, Oberlin, KS, p. A241

FORTIN, Joanne, R.N. Director of Clinical Services, Northern Maine Medical Center, Fort Kent, ME, p. A283

FORTIN, Laura, Chief Operating Officer, St. Joseph Medical Center, Houston, TX, p. A612

FORTNER, Jessica, Director Human Resources, Indiana University Health Paoli Hospital, Paoli, IN, p. A212

FORTNEY, John, M.D. Chief Medical Officer, Adena Medical Center, Chillicothe, OH, p. A473

FORTSON, Debbie, Director Human Resources, WK Bossier Health Center, Bossier City, LA, p. A264

FORTUNATO, Philip, Interim Chief Financial Officer, San Mateo Medical Center, San Mateo, CA, p. A88

FOSDICK, Glenn A., FACHE, President and Chief Executive Officer, Nebraska Medical Center, Omaha, NE, p. A388

FOSINA, Michael, Senior Vice President and Chief Operating Officer, New York Downtown Hospital, New York, NY, p. A435

FOSNESS, Nick, Chief Executive Officer, Marshall County Healthcare Center Avera, Britton, SD, p. A558

FOSNOCHT, Kevin, M.D. Chief Medical Officer and Associate Executive Director, Penn Presbyterian Medical Center, Philadelphia, PA, p. A536

FOSS, David, Senior Director Information Systems, New London Hospital, New London, NH, p. A399

FOSS, R. Coleman, Chief Executive Officer, Skyridge Medical Center, Cleveland, TN, p. A567

FOSSUM, John, Chief Executive Officer and Administrator, Ely–Bloomenson Community Hospital, Ely, MN, p. A332

FOSTER, Becky
Manager Human Resources, Sanford Tracy Medical Center, Tracy, MN, p. A341
Manager Human Resources, Sanford Westbrook Medical Center, Westbrook, MN, p. A342

FOSTER, Beverly, Chief Executive Officer, Kindred Hospital Chicago–Northlake, Northlake, IL, p. A190

FOSTER, Bob, Assistant Administrator Information Services, South Georgia Medical Center, Valdosta, GA, p. A162

FOSTER, Brian
Vice President, Mayo Clinic Health System – Northland in Barron, Barron, WI, p. A684
Chief Information Officer, Mayo Clinic Health System in Eau Claire, Eau Claire, WI, p. A686

FOSTER, Charles
Regional Director Human Resources, CHRISTUS Hospital–St. Elizabeth, Beaumont, TX, p. A587
Region Vice President Human Resources, CHRISTUS St. John Hospital, Nassau Bay, TX, p. A624

FOSTER, Chris, Director Health Information Management, Deer Lodge Medical Center, Deer Lodge, MT, p. A375

FOSTER, Daniel J., Chief Financial Officer, South Davis Community Hospital, Bountiful, UT, p. A643

FOSTER, Gary, R.N. Assistant Administrator, Banner Estrella Medical Center, Phoenix, AZ, p. A34

FOSTER, Gary, Vice President and Chief Financial Officer, Saratoga Hospital, Saratoga Springs, NY, p. A442

FOSTER, James, Chief Financial Officer and Assistant Administrator, Ortonville Area Health Services, Ortonville, MN, p. A337

FOSTER, Joel, Director Human Resources, Massac Memorial Hospital, Metropolis, IL, p. A188

FOSTER, Mike, Manager Information Systems, Moab Regional Hospital, Moab, UT, p. A644

FOSTER, Mitzi, Director of Information Services, Hillside Hospital, Pulaski, TN, p. A578

FOSTER, Nancy, Vice President Human Resources, Wishard Health Services, Indianapolis, IN, p. A206

FOSTER, Rhonda, Interim Chief Nursing Officer, Santa Rosa Memorial Hospital, Santa Rosa, CA, p. A90

FOSTER, Richard, Chief Financial Officer, Integris Clinton Regional Hospital, Clinton, OK, p. A497

FOSTER, Robert, Director Human Resources, L. V. Stabler Memorial Hospital, Greenville, AL, p. A21

FOSTER, Stephanie, MSN Chief Nursing Officer, Longview Regional Medical Center, Longview, TX, p. A619

FOSTER, Stephanie, Director Human Resources, Memorial Hermann Northeast, Humble, TX, p. A614

FOSTER, Steven, Chief Operating Officer, Deaconess Hospital, Oklahoma City, OK, p. A503

FOSTER, Thomas, Chief Executive Officer, Bucktail Medical Center, Renovo, PA, p. A540

FOSTER, Wanda, R.N. Vice President Nursing, McDonough District Hospital, Macomb, IL, p. A187

FOTIADIS, George, M.D. Chief of Staff, Clarke County Hospital, Osceola, IA, p. A226

FOTTER, Robert L., Chief Financial Officer, Littleton Regional Hospital, Littleton, NH, p. A399

FOULKE, Elvia
Executive Vice President Healthcare Delivery and Chief Operating Officer, Citrus Valley Medical Center, Covina, CA, p. A58
Executive Vice President and Chief Operating Officer, Foothill Presbyterian Hospital, Glendora, CA, p. A63

FOUNTAIN, Wesley D., Chief Financial Officer, St. David's South Austin Medical Center, Austin, TX, p. A586

FOURNIE, Marianne, R.N. Chief Nursing Officer, Barnes–Jewish West County Hospital, Saint Louis, MO, p. A369

FOUSE, Carla, Chief Nursing Officer, St. Vincent Randolph Hospital, Winchester, IN, p. A215

FOUSE, Sarah, Associate Director of Patient Services, Captain James A. Lovell Federal Health Care Center, North Chicago, IL, p. A190

FOUST, Lisa
Senior Vice President Human Resources, Citrus Valley Medical Center, Covina, CA, p. A58
Senior Vice President Human Resources, Foothill Presbyterian Hospital, Glendora, CA, p. A63

FOUTZ, Patricia, Director Human Resources, Bath Community Hospital, Hot Springs, VA, p. A655

FOWLE, Jim, Interim Chief Financial Officer, Mayo Regional Hospital, Dover–Foxcroft, ME, p. A283

FOWLER, Andy, Senior Vice President Information Systems, Methodist Healthcare Memphis Hospitals, Memphis, TN, p. A575

FOWLER, Barry, Director Human and System Resources, Clark Fork Valley Hospital, Plains, MT, p. A378

FOWLER, Denise, R.N. Chief Clinical Officer, Whitman Hospital and Medical Center, Colfax, WA, p. A665

FOWLER, Gary, M.D. Chief of Staff Family Practice, Northwest Medical Center, Winfield, AL, p. A26

FOWLER, Kate, Chief Financial Officer, West Valley Medical Center, Caldwell, ID, p. A168

FOWLER, Kevin
Chief Financial Officer, Poplar Bluff Regional Medical Center, Poplar Bluff, MO, p. A368
Director Finance, Putnam County Hospital, Greencastle, IN, p. A204

FOWLER, Mark, Executive Director Human Resources, St. Helena Hospital Napa Valley, Saint Helena, CA, p. A84

FOWLER, Maureen, Director Human Resources, Conifer Park, Glenville, NY, p. A426

FOWLER, Perphelia, Manager Human Resources, Sage Memorial Hospital, Ganado, AZ, p. A31

FOWLER, Rose, MS, Administrator, Sartori Memorial Hospital, Cedar Falls, IA, p. A217

FOWLER, Ruth, Senior Vice President and Chief Financial Officer, Children's Healthcare of Atlanta, Atlanta, GA, p. A146

FOWLER, S. Sean, Chief Executive Officer, Barstow Community Hospital, Barstow, CA, p. A54

FOWLER, Steven, M.D. President Medical Staff, Genesis Medical Center, DeWitt, De Witt, IA, p. A219

FOWLER, W. Kevin, Chief Financial Officer, Community Heart and Vascular Hospital, Indianapolis, IN, p. A205

FOX, Alan, Chief Financial Officer, Saint Francis Memorial Hospital, San Francisco, CA, p. A87

FOX, Betsy, Director Human Resources, Shepherd Center, Atlanta, GA, p. A147

FOX, David, President, Advocate Good Samaritan Hospital, Downers Grove, IL, p. A181

FOX, David R., President, St. Vincent Medical Center–North, Sherwood, AR, p. A50

FOX, Debra, Chief Nursing Officer, McKee Medical Center, Loveland, CO, p. A104

FOX, Frank, Vice President Finance and Chief Financial Officer, St. Charles Hospital, Port Jefferson, NY, p. A440

FOX, Jay, President, Baylor Medical Center at Waxahachie, Waxahachie, TX, p. A640

FOX, John, M.D. Chief Medical Officer, Vibra Hospital of San Diego, San Diego, CA, p. A86

FOX, John E., M.D. Chief of Staff, Lincoln Community Hospital and Nursing Home, Hugo, CO, p. A102

FOX, Leana, MSN Interim Chief Nurse Executive, Bon Secours Maryview Medical Center, Portsmouth, VA, p. A659

FOX, Leticia, Chief Financial Officer, Pecos County Memorial Hospital, Fort Stockton, TX, p. A603

FOX, Patricia K., President and Chief Executive Officer, Riverview Hospital, Noblesville, IN, p. A211

FOX, Patrick, M.D. Chief of Staff, Mena Regional Health System, Mena, AR, p. A47

FOX, Steve, Chief Executive Officer, Fort Belknap U. S. Public Health Service Indian Hospital, Harlem, MT, p. A377

FOX, Wendi, Human Resources Administrative Director, St. Helena Hospital Clear Lake, Clearlake, CA, p. A56

FOX, William, Chief Executive Officer, Horizon Specialty Hospital, Las Vegas, NV, p. A393

FOXX, Randy, Chief Financial Officer, Boone Memorial Hospital, Madison, WV, p. A678

FOY, Gregory S., Human Resources System Leader, Scheurer Hospital, Pigeon, MI, p. A321

FRABLE, Arthur H., Chief Executive Officer, Bob Wilson Memorial Grant County Hospital, Ulysses, KS, p. A245

FRACK, Darla, R.N. Chief Nursing Officer, St. Luke's Hospital – Anderson Campus, Easton, PA, p. A525

FRAGGOS, Mary C., R.N. Associate Director of Nursing and Patient Care Services, Ralph H. Johnson Veterans Affairs Medical Center, Charleston, SC, p. A549

FRAIOLA, Anthony, Business Manager, Hawaii State Hospital, Kaneohe, HI, p. A165

FRAIZE, Larry, Director Management Information Systems, Milford Regional Medical Center, Milford, MA, p. A302

FRAKER, Steven, Chief Financial Officer, Banner Churchill Community Hospital, Fallon, NV, p. A391

FRALEY, Alicia, Chief Human Resources, Perkins County Health Services, Grant, NE, p. A384

FRAME, Angela, Chief Financial Officer, Jackson General Hospital, Ripley, WV, p. A680

FRANCETICH, Kane, Chief Information Officer, Gritman Medical Center, Moscow, ID, p. A170

FRANCIOLI, Carl H., Vice President Finance, Johns Hopkins Bayview Medical Center, Baltimore, MD, p. A287

FRANCIS, Beth
  Vice President Human Resources, DCH Regional Medical Center, Tuscaloosa, AL, p. A26
  Vice President Human Resources, Northport Medical Center, Northport, AL, p. A24

FRANCIS, Christy, Administrator, Hemphill County Hospital, Canadian, TX, p. A591

FRANCIS, Duane, President and Chief Executive Officer, Mid–Columbia Medical Center, The Dalles, OR, p. A518

FRANCIS, Jean, Chief Nursing Officer, HEALTHSOUTH Western Hills Rehabilitation Hospital, Parkersburg, WV, p. A679

FRANCIS, Karen, Chief Financial Officer, Casa Grande Regional Medical Center, Casa Grande, AZ, p. A30

FRANCIS, Mark J., President Chief Executive Officer and Hospital Administrator, Family Health West, Fruita, CO, p. A101

FRANCIS, Perry, Supervisory Information Technology Specialist, Chinle Comprehensive Health Care Facility, Chinle, AZ, p. A30

FRANCIS, Stephen, M.D. Vice President Medical Affairs, Robinson Memorial Hospital, Ravenna, OH, p. A489

FRANCISCO, Gerard E., M.D. Chief Medical Officer, TIRR Memorial Hermann, Houston, TX, p. A613

FRANCO, Barbara, Chief Financial Officer, Kindred Rehabilitation Hospital Clear Lake, Webster, TX, p. A640

FRANCO, Luis, M.D. Medical Director, United Medical Rehabilitation Hospital, Hammond, LA, p. A268

FRANCO, Richard, Chief Financial Officer, West Valley Hospital, Goodyear, AZ, p. A32

FRANCO, Roger, Director Human Resources, St. John's Episcopal Hospital–South Shore,, NY, p. A436

FRANDSEN, Jeff, Chief Executive Officer, Salt Lake Regional Medical Center, Salt Lake City, UT, p. A647

FRANK, Barbara, Human Resource Specialist, Caro Center, Caro, MI, p. A310

FRANK, Debra, Chief Financial Officer, Ness County Hospital, Ness City, KS, p. A240

FRANK, Jim, Chief Executive Officer, Community Memorial Hospital, Burke, SD, p. A558

FRANK, Kevin, Administrator, Louisiana Extended Care Hospital of Lafayette, Lafayette, LA, p. A271

FRANK, Kim, Chief Human Resources Officer, Virginia Gay Hospital, Vinton, IA, p. A229

FRANK, Larry, Director Information Systems, Northeast Rehabilitation Hospital, Salem, NH, p. A400

FRANK, Patricia, Chief Nursing Officer, Henry County Hospital, Napoleon, OH, p. A487

FRANK, Richard S., Vice President Operations, Edward White Hospital, Saint Petersburg, FL, p. A139

FRANK, Robert A., Chief Financial Officer, Weirton Medical Center, Weirton, WV, p. A681

FRANK, Virginia, President and Chief Executive Officer, Wellmont Holston Valley Medical Center, Kingsport, TN, p. A571

FRANKE, Paul, M.D
  Vice President Medical Affairs, Covenant Medical Center, Waterloo, IA, p. A229
  Vice President Medical Affairs, Sartori Memorial Hospital, Cedar Falls, IA, p. A217

FRANKEL, Michele, Associate Executive Director Finance, Glen Cove Hospital, Glen Cove, NY, p. A426

FRANKENSTEIN, Richard, M.D. Vice President and Chief Medical Officer, Henry Mayo Newhall Memorial Hospital, Valencia, CA, p. A94

FRANKLIN, Barry L., Executive Vice President and Chief Financial Officer, Parma Community General Hospital, Parma, OH, p. A488

FRANKLIN, Chuck, M.D. Chief Medical Staff, Weston County Health Services, Newcastle, WY, p. A703

FRANKLIN, Clay, Chief Executive Officer, Plaza Medical Center of Fort Worth, Fort Worth, TX, p. A604

FRANKLIN, James P., Administrator, Calhoun Health Services, Calhoun City, MS, p. A345

FRANKLIN, Michael A., FACHE, President and Chief Executive Officer, Atlantic General Hospital, Berlin, MD, p. A289

FRANKLIN, Vicki L., Senior Vice President and Chief Operating Officer, Lake Regional Health System, Osage Beach, MO, p. A367

FRANKO, Stephen
  Vice President Finance and Chief Financial Officer, Regional Hospital of Scranton, Scranton, PA, p. A540
  Chief Financial Officer, Special Care Hospital, Nanticoke, PA, p. A532
  Chief Financial Officer, Tyler Memorial Hospital, Tunkhannock, PA, p. A542

FRANKS, Charles, Chief Human Resources, Louis Stokes Cleveland Veterans Affairs Medical Center, Cleveland, OH, p. A476

FRANKS, Dennis, Vice President Operations, Doctors' Hospital of Michigan, Pontiac, MI, p. A322

FRANKS, Dennis, FACHE, Chief Executive Officer, Neosho Memorial Regional Medical Center, Chanute, KS, p. A232

FRANSON, John K., M.D. Chief Medical Staff, Caribou Memorial Hospital and Living Center, Soda Springs, ID, p. A172

FRANTZ, Vincent, M.D. Chief of Staff, Plumas District Hospital, Quincy, CA, p. A81

FRANZ, Jerome, M.D. Chief Medical Staff, St. Luke's Hospital, San Francisco, CA, p. A87

FRANZ, Thomas, M.D. Medical Director, HEALTHSOUTH Harmarville Rehabilitation Hospital, Pittsburgh, PA, p. A537

FRANZBLAU, David R., M.D. Chief Medical Officer, Presence Saint Joseph Medical Center, Joliet, IL, p. A186

FRANZELLA, Susan, Human Resource Business Partner, Kaiser Permanente San Jose Medical Center, San Jose, CA, p. A87

FRARDO, Virgil, M.D. Medical Director, HEALTHSOUTH Rehabilitation Hospital–Wichita Falls, Wichita Falls, TX, p. A641

FRASCA, Edith, Controller and Chief Financial Officer, The Pavilion, Champaign, IL, p. A176

FRASCELLA, Louis J., President and Chief Executive Officer, Lake Shore Health Care Center, Irving, NY, p. A427

FRASER, James, Chief Financial Officer, Ferrell Hospital, Eldorado, IL, p. A181

FRATE, Amy, Director of Nursing, Red River Hospital, Wichita Falls, TX, p. A641

FRATER, Chris, Chief Financial Officer, Lighthouse Care Center of Conway, Conway, SC, p. A551

FRATZKE, Mark, R.N. Chief Nursing Officer and Chief Operating Officer, Mayo Clinic Health System in Saint James, Saint James, MN, p. A339

FRAUENHOFER, Chris, Chief Financial Officer, Maine Coast Memorial Hospital, Ellsworth, ME, p. A283

FRAUENPREIS, Kurt, M.D. Chief Medical Staff, Bear Valley Community Hospital, Big Bear Lake, CA, p. A55

FRAY, George S., Interim Administrator, Lawrence Memorial Hospital, Walnut Ridge, AR, p. A50

FRAZIER, Amy, Supervisor Management Information Systems, Wetzel County Hospital, New Martinsville, WV, p. A679

FRAZIER, Derrick A., Chief Executive Officer, Southwest Georgia Regional Medical Center, Cuthbert, GA, p. A151

FRAZIER III, James P., Chief Executive Officer, Teche Regional Medical Center, Morgan City, LA, p. A274

FRAZIER, Joel L., M.D. Medical Director, Orthopedic Hospital, Oklahoma City, OK, p. A504

FRAZIER, Kimberly
  Chief Nursing Officer, DeKalb Community Hospital, Smithville, TN, p. A579
  Chief Nursing Officer, Stones River Hospital, Woodbury, TN, p. A580

FRAZIER, Lee, FACHE, Chief Executive Officer, Valir Rehabilitation Hospital, Oklahoma City, OK, p. A504

FREAS, Mary Ann, Vice President and Chief Financial Officer, Southwest General Health Center, Middleburg Heights, OH, p. A486

FREDERIC, Donald J., FACHE, Chief Executive Officer, Saint Mary's Regional Medical Center, Russellville, AR, p. A49

FREDERICK, Brenda, Director Human Resources, Laurel Ridge Treatment Center, San Antonio, TX, p. A631

FREDERICK, Gretchen A., R.N. Director Patient Care Services, Buffalo Hospital, Buffalo, MN, p. A330

FREDERICK, Lynn
  Administrator, Mayo Clinic – Saint Marys Hospital, Rochester, MN, p. A339
  Administrator, Rochester Methodist Hospital, Rochester, MN, p. A339

FREDERICKS, Jack, Vice President Human Resources, Little Falls Hospital, Little Falls, NY, p. A428

FREDERICKS, Raymond F., President and CEO, JFK Medical Center, Edison, NJ, p. A403

FREDERICKSON, Kathy, Information Systems Site Lead, Sutter Delta Medical Center, Antioch, CA, p. A52

FREDETTE, Beth, Chief Information Officer, Children's Medical Center, Dayton, OH, p. A479

FREDRICH, Nancy, R.N. Chief Clinical Officer, Cooper County Memorial Hospital, Boonville, MO, p. A357

FREDRICK, Rick, Director Information Technology, Cottage Hospital, Woodsville, NH, p. A400

FREDRICKSON, Dennis, Chief Financial Officer, Phillips County Hospital, Phillipsburg, KS, p. A242

FREDRICKSON, Kelley, Director Information Services, Plaza Medical Center of Fort Worth, Fort Worth, TX, p. A604

FREDRICKSON, Mark A., M.D. Medical Director, HEALTHSOUTH Rehabilitation Hospital Midland–Odessa, Midland, TX, p. A623

FREEBERG, Wayne, Chief Information Officer, Cooley Dickinson Hospital, Northampton, MA, p. A303

FREEBURG, Rick, Chief Executive Officer, Baptist Health South Florida, Mariners Hospital, Tavernier, FL, p. A142

FREEBURN, Mark, Chief Executive Officer, HEALTHSOUTH Rehabilitation Hospital of Mechanicsburg, Mechanicsburg, PA, p. A531

FREED, David H., President and Chief Executive Officer, Nyack Hospital, Nyack, NY, p. A438

FREED, Glenn, D.O. Medical Director, St. Luke's Hospital – Miners Campus, Coaldale, PA, p. A523

FREED, Nancy, Chief Financial Officer, Seiling Community Hospital, Seiling, OK, p. A506

FREED, Stuart, M.D. Medical Director, Wenatchee Valley Medical Center, Wenatchee, WA, p. A674

FREED–SIGURDSSON, Anna, M.D. Medical Director, Reliant Rehabilitation Hospital Dallas, Dallas, TX, p. A597

FREEDMAN, Barry R., President and Chief Executive Officer, Einstein Medical Center Philadelphia, Philadelphia, PA, p. A534

FREEDMAN, Kenneth, M.D. Chief Medical Officer, Lemuel Shattuck Hospital, Jamaica Plain, MA, p. A301

FREEHOF, Leonard, Chief Executive Officer and Managing Director, Spring Valley Hospital Medical Center, Las Vegas, NV, p. A393

FREEL, Christopher, Chief Information Technologist, Three Rivers Hospital, Brewster, WA, p. A665

FREELAND, R. Alan, M.D. Chief Clinical Officer, Twin Valley Behavioral Healthcare, Columbus, OH, p. A478

FREEMAN, Amy E., President and Chief Executive Officer, Providence Hospital, Washington, DC, p. A116

FREEMAN, Brian, Vice President of Operations, Stanly Regional Medical Center, Albemarle, NC, p. A447

FREEMAN, Deanna, Administrator and Chief Executive Officer, Rawlins County Health Center, Atwood, KS, p. A231

FREEMAN, Diane, R.N. Assistant Vice President and Chief Nursing Officer, St. Luke's Lakeside Hospital, The Woodlands, TX, p. A637

FREEMAN, Elizabeth Joyce, Director, Veterans Affairs Palo Alto Health Care System, Palo Alto, CA, p. A79

FREEMAN, Jerry, Chief, Human Resources Management Services, Durham Veterans Affairs Medical Center, Durham, NC, p. A447

FREEMAN, Kimberlee, R.N. Vice President Patient Care Services and Chief Nursing Officer, Wayne Hospital, Greenville, OH, p. A482

FREEMAN, Louella, Chief Nursing Officer, Salinas Valley Memorial Healthcare System, Salinas, CA, p. A84

FREEMAN, Marianne, Vice President Human Resources, Rockdale Medical Center, Conyers, GA, p. A151

FREEMAN, Michael, Director Human Resources, Huhukam Memorial Hospital, Sacaton, AZ, p. A36

FREEMAN, Mike, Director Information Technology, Sentara Williamsburg Regional Medical Center, Williamsburg, VA, p. A663

FREEMAN, Robert, Director Human Resources, Sparks Regional Medical Center, Fort Smith, AR, p. A44

FREER, Carol V., M.D. Chief Medical Officer, Penn State Milton S. Hershey Medical Center, Hershey, PA, p. A527

FREESE–DECKER, Christina, President, Spectrum Health United Hospital, Greenville, MI, p. A315

FREIER, Toby, President, New Ulm Medical Center, New Ulm, MN, p. A337

FREIMARK, Jeffrey P., Chief Executive Officer, Miami Jewish Home and Hospital for Aged, Miami, FL, p. A132

FREIMUND, Rooney, R.N. Chief Nurse Executive, Bay Area Medical Center, Marinette, WI, p. A690

FREIN, Ethel, Chief Executive Officer, Bennett County Hospital and Nursing Home, Martin, SD, p. A560

FREITAG, Donald, M.D. Chief Medical Officer, Lynn County Hospital District, Tahoka, TX, p. A636

FRELING, Eric, M.D. Director Medical Staff Affairs, Memorial Hospital West, Pembroke Pines, FL, p. A136

FRENCH, Dean O., M.D. Chief of Staff, Faith Regional Health Services, Norfolk, NE, p. A386

FRENCH III, George E., FACHE, Chief Executive Officer, Minden Medical Center, Minden, LA, p. A274

FRENCH, Holly, Chief Financial Officer, Newman Regional Health, Emporia, KS, p. A233

FRENCH, Jennifer, Director Organizational Quality, St. Vincent Clay Hospital, Brazil, IN, p. A199

FRENCH, William Chad, Chief Executive Officer, Kentucky River Medical Center, Jackson, KY, p. A253

FRENN, Debra, Chief Nursing Officer, St. Nicholas Hospital, Sheboygan, WI, p. A696

FRERICHS, Craig, Chief Information Technology Service, Grand Junction Veterans Affairs Medical Center, Grand Junction, CO, p. A102

FRESH, John, Vice President Human Resources, Conemaugh Miners Medical Center, Hastings, PA, p. A527

FRESHOUR, David, Chief Financial Officer, Gunnison Valley Hospital, Gunnison, CO, p. A102

FRESQUEZ, Juan, Chief Operating Officer, Houston Northwest Medical Center, Houston, TX, p. A610

FREUDENBERGER, Joe, Chief Executive Officer, OakBend Medical Center, Richmond, TX, p. A629

FREUND, Donna S., MSN Chief Nursing Officer, DeKalb Health, Auburn, IN, p. A198

FREY, Jack, Business Manager, Greystone Park Psychiatric Hospital, Morris Plains, NJ, p. A406

FREY, Jeff, Business Administrator, Andrew McFarland Mental Health Center, Springfield, IL, p. A195

FREY, Paul, Director Information Technology Applications, Indiana Orthopaedic Hospital, Indianapolis, IN, p. A205

FREY, Rachel, Director Human Resources, Athens–Limestone Hospital, Athens, AL, p. A16

FREYER, Mary, Chief Operating Officer, Little Company of Mary Hospital and Health Care Centers, Evergreen Park, IL, p. A182

FREYER, Sharon, Chief Nursing Unit, Westlake Hospital, Melrose Park, IL, p. A188

FREYHOFER, Cornelia Sue, M.D. Medical Director, Moses Ludington Hospital, Ticonderoga, NY, p. A444

FREYMULLER, Robert S., Chief Executive Officer, Summerlin Hospital Medical Center, Las Vegas, NV, p. A394

FREYSINGER, Edward E., Chief Executive Officer, Providence Hood River Memorial Hospital, Hood River, OR, p. A513

FREYTAG, Peter, Senior Vice President Finance and Chief Financial Officer, Bristol Hospital, Bristol, CT, p. A108

FRICK, Mark P., Vice President Human Resources, UPMC McKeesport, McKeesport, PA, p. A531

FRICK, Mary Jo, Director Finance, St. Catherine's Rehabilitation Hospital, North Miami, FL, p. A134

FRICKE, Rhett D., Chief Financial Officer, Frio Regional Hospital, Pearsall, TX, p. A626

FRICKS, Tom, Interim Senior Vice President of Information Technology, PeaceHealth Sacred Heart Medical Center at RiverBend, Springfield, OR, p. A518

FRIDOVICH, Mark, Ph.D., Administrator, Hawaii State Hospital, Kaneohe, HI, p. A165

FRIED, Guy, M.D. Chief Medical Officer, Magee Rehabilitation Hospital, Philadelphia, PA, p. A535

FRIED, Jeffrey M., FACHE, President and Chief Executive Officer, Beebe Medical Center, Lewes, DE, p. A114

FRIEDBERG, Robert, President, Delnor Hospital, Geneva, IL, p. A183

FRIEDELL, Benjamin, Vice President Medical Affairs, Aurelia Osborn Fox Memorial Hospital, Oneonta, NY, p. A438

FRIEDEN, Robert
Vice President Information Systems, Genesis Medical Center, Illini Campus, Silvis, IL, p. A194
Vice President Information Systems, Genesis Medical Center–Davenport, Davenport, IA, p. A219

FRIEDENBACH, Daryl, Director Fiscal Services, Floyd Valley Hospital, Le Mars, IA, p. A224

FRIEDMAN, Greg, Director Information Technology, Children's Hospital of Richmond at VCU–Brook Road Campus, Richmond, VA, p. A660

FRIEDMAN, Jonathan, Public Affairs Officer, Captain James A. Lovell Federal Health Care Center, North Chicago, IL, p. A190

FRIEDMAN, Lloyd, M.D. Vice President Medical Affairs and Chief Operating Officer, Milford Hospital, Milford, CT, p. A110

FRIEDMAN, Michael A., M.D., President and Chief Executive Officer, City of Hope's Helford Clinical Research Hospital, Duarte, CA, p. A59

FRIEDMAN, Steven G., M.D. Interim Chief Medical Officer and Chair, Department of Surgery, New York Downtown Hospital, New York, NY, p. A435

FRIEDMAN, Steven H., Ph.D., Executive Vice President, Methodist Hospital of Chicago, Chicago, IL, p. A177

FRIEDRICH III, Daniel J., Chief Executive Officer, Blake Medical Center, Bradenton, FL, p. A119

FRIEL, Donald F., Executive Vice President, Holy Redeemer Hospital and Medical Center, Meadowbrook, PA, p. A531

FRIEL, John P., Chief Executive Officer, Catalina Island Medical Center, Avalon, CA, p. A53

FRIELING, Jeff
Vice President Information Systems, Camden General Hospital, Camden, TN, p. A566
Vice President and Chief Information Officer, Jackson–Madison County General Hospital, Jackson, TN, p. A570
Chief Information Officer, Pathways of Tennessee, Jackson, TN, p. A570

FRIELING, Morris J., Chief Financial Officer, University of California, Irvine Healthcare, Orange, CA, p. A78

FRIEND, Lori
Director Human Resources, Integris Marshall County Medical Center, Madill, OK, p. A500
Human Resoures Director, Integris Seminole Medical Center, Seminole, OK, p. A506

FRIER, Nancy, Chief Financial Officer, Eastern Oklahoma Medical Center, Poteau, OK, p. A505

FRIES, Bob, Director Fiscal Services, Colorado Mental Health Institute at Fort Logan, Denver, CO, p. A99

FRIES, Linda, Director Personnel, Ed Fraser Memorial Hospital and Baker Community Health Center, MacClenny, FL, p. A129

FRIESEN, Carol, President and Chief Executive Officer, Crete Area Medical Center, Crete, NE, p. A383

FRIESEN, Dale L., Chief Financial Officer, CareLink of Jackson, Jackson, MI, p. A317

FRIESEN, Lynette, Manager Human Resources, Henderson Health Care Services, Henderson, NE, p. A384

FRIESEN, Nancy, Chief Financial Officer, CentraCare Health–Monticello, Monticello, MN, p. A336

FRIESEN, Quinton J., Executive Vice President and Chief Operating Officer, Greenwich Hospital, Greenwich, CT, p. A109

FRIGEN, Karen, Director Human Resources, Shriners Hospitals for Children–Twin Cities, Minneapolis, MN, p. A336

FRIGON, Shelby, Chief Financial Officer, Saint Luke's South Hospital, Overland Park, KS, p. A242

FRIGY, Alan, M.D. President Medical Staff, Pana Community Hospital, Pana, IL, p. A191

FRISBEE, Kent, Director Human Resources, Highlands Medical Center, Sparta, TN, p. A579

FRISBIE, Dawn, Chief Executive Officer, Select Specialty Hospital-Saginaw, Saginaw, MI, p. A323

FRISCHKNECHT, Michael, M.D. President Medical Staff, Sanpete Valley Hospital, Mount Pleasant, UT, p. A644

FRITSCH, Phyllis, Administrator, Upland Hills Health, Dodgeville, WI, p. A685

FRITSCH, William, M.D. Medical Director, Landmark Hospital, Cape Girardeau, MO, p. A357

FRITSCHE, Jeff, Chief Financial Officer, Silverton Hospital, Silverton, OR, p. A518

FRITTS, Doris, R.N., Executive Director, Same Day Surgery Center, Rapid City, SD, p. A562

FRITTS, Jack, Vice President Finance and Chief Financial Officer, Grinnell Regional Medical Center, Grinnell, IA, p. A222

FRITTS, Robert G.
Chief Financial Officer and Senior Vice President, Grace Hospital, Morganton, NC, p. A458
Chief Financial Officer and Senior Vice President, Valdese General Hospital, Valdese, NC, p. A462

FRITZ, John, D.O. Vice President Medical Affairs, Avera St. Luke's Hospital, Aberdeen, SD, p. A558

FRITZ, Thomas M., Chief Executive Officer, St. Luke's Rehabilitation Institute, Spokane, WA, p. A672

FRIZZELL, Neil, Chief Financial Officer, Freeman Regional Health Services, Freeman, SD, p. A560

FROCHTZWAJG, Stanley, M.D. Chief Medical Officer, Community Memorial Health System, Ventura, CA, p. A94

FROEBE, Tim, Vice President Human Resources, Mary Rutan Hospital, Bellefontaine, OH, p. A471

FROEMKE, Janet, Human Resources Officer, Lisbon Area Health Services, Lisbon, ND, p. A468

FROH, Chris, Senior Coordinator Human Resources, Select Specialty Hospital–Milwaukee, Milwaukee, WI, p. A692

FROHNHOFER, Erin J., Director Human Resources, Southwood Psychiatric Hospital, Pittsburgh, PA, p. A538

FROIMSON, Mark, President, Euclid Hospital, Euclid, OH, p. A481

FROIO, Ann M., Interim Chief Executive Officer, Arizona State Hospital, Phoenix, AZ, p. A34

FROISLAND, Jeffrey R., Chief Financial Officer, Mayo Clinic Hospital, Phoenix, AZ, p. A35

FROM, Leland, M.D. Vice President Medical Affairs, Beloit Health System, Beloit, WI, p. A684

FROMHOLD, John A., Chief Executive Officer, Hackensack University Medical Center Mountainside, Montclair, NJ, p. A406

FROMM, Robert, M.D. Senior Vice President and Chief Medical Officer, Maricopa Integrated Health System, Phoenix, AZ, p. A34

FROMMELT, William, Director Operations and Finance, River Falls Area Hospital, River Falls, WI, p. A696

FROSCH, Kevin, Chief Financial Officer, Medina Regional Hospital, Hondo, TX, p. A608

FROST, Eric, Associate Vice President Human Resources, Upstate University Hospital, Syracuse, NY, p. A444

FROST, Joan, R.N. Chief Operating Officer/Chief Nursing Officer, Mercy Hospital Washington, Washington, MO, p. A373

FROST, Sarah, Administrator, University of Arizona Medical Center – South Campus, Tucson, AZ, p. A39

FROST–KUNNEN, Jackie, Senior Vice President Operations, Mercy Medical Center–Des Moines, Des Moines, IA, p. A220

FRUGE, Jane Doucet, R.N., Chief Executive Officer, West Calcasieu Cameron Hospital, Sulphur, LA, p. A279

FRUM, Judy, R.N. Chief Nursing Officer, Memorial Hospital Pembroke, Pembroke Pines, FL, p. A136

FRUM, R. David
President, Bridgton Hospital, Bridgton, ME, p. A282
President, Rumford Hospital, Rumford, ME, p. A285

FRY, Kenneth, Chief Financial Officer, Saint Alphonsus Regional Medical Center, Boise, ID, p. A168

FRYE, Charles, Director Human Resources, Memorial Hospital of Sweetwater County, Rock Springs, WY, p. A703

FRYE, Darren, Manager, McLaren Bay Special Care, Bay City, MI, p. A309

FRYE Jr., Edward R., Chief Executive Officer, Clarendon Memorial Hospital, Manning, SC, p. A554

FRYE Jr., John W., Chief Executive Officer, Madera Community Hospital, Madera, CA, p. A73

FRYE, Kelly D., Director Human Resources, Montgomery General Hospital, Montgomery, WV, p. A678

FUCCI, Thomas, Chief Operating Officer, Saint Vincent Hospital, Erie, PA, p. A525

FUCHS, Brian P., Chief Fiscal Service, James H. Quillen Veterans Affairs Medical Center, Mountain Home, TN, p. A576

FUCHS, Jonathan, Chief Information Officer, DeWitt Hospital, De Witt, AR, p. A42

FUCILE, Joanne, R.N. Vice President Patient Care Services, Spaulding Hospital for Continuing Medical Care North Shore, Salem, MA, p. A304

FUELHRER, Susan, Director, Louis Stokes Cleveland Veterans Affairs Medical Center, Cleveland, OH, p. A476

FUENTES Jr., Miguel A., President and Chief Executive Officer, Bronx–Lebanon Hospital Center Health Care System,, NY, p. A431

FUERSTENBERG, Donna, Fiscal Chief, Sheridan Veterans Affairs Medical Center, Sheridan, WY, p. A703

FUGATTE, Cheryl, Vice President and Chief Nursing Officer, Jewish Hospital, Louisville, KY, p. A255

FUGAZY, Christopher, Chief Operating Officer, Jacobi Medical Center,, NY, p. A432

FUGITT, Kathy, Chief Information Officer, Ozark Health Medical Center, Clinton, AR, p. A42

FUHRMAN, Bradley, M.D. Physician in Chief, El Paso Children's Hospital, El Paso, TX, p. A601

FUHRMAN, Dennis, Vice President Finance, Essentia Health Fargo, Fargo, ND, p. A466

FUHS, Veronica, Chief Executive Officer, Lucas County Health Center, Chariton, IA, p. A218

FUJINAKA, Jason, Manager Information System, Wahiawa General Hospital, Wahiawa, HI, p. A166

FULBRIGHT, Jack, Acting Chief Executive Officer, Habersham Medical Center, Demorest, GA, p. A152

FULCHER, Cathe, Superintendent, Evansville State Hospital, Evansville, IN, p. A202

FULKERSON, Judy, Director Human Resources, TriStar Greenview Regional Hospital, Bowling Green, KY, p. A249

FULKERSON, Richard, Director Fiscal Services, Shriners Hospitals for Children–Springfield, Springfield, MA, p. A305

FULKS, Gerald N., President and Chief Executive Officer, West Georgia Health, La Grange, GA, p. A155

FULKS, Pam, R.N. Chief Nursing Officer, Gila Regional Medical Center, Silver City, NM, p. A418

FULLBRIGHT, Gary D., Comptroller, Citizens Memorial Hospital, Bolivar, MO, p. A356

FULLER, Cheryl, Director Information Resources, Kansas Neurological Institute, Topeka, KS, p. A244

FULLER, Dale, Vice President and Chief Information Officer, UPMC Altoona, Altoona, PA, p. A520

FULLER, David W., Chief Executive Officer, North Okaloosa Medical Center, Crestview, FL, p. A121

FULLER, Debbie, Director Health Information Systems and Chief Information Officer, Doctors Medical Center, Modesto, CA, p. A74

FULLER, Jane, Director Human Resources, Regional Medical Center of Acadiana, Lafayette, LA, p. A271

FULLER, Jill, Ph.D., President and Chief Executive Officer, Prairie Lakes Healthcare System, Watertown, SD, p. A564

FULLER, Lexie, Controller, Specialty Hospital of Meridian, Meridian, MS, p. A351

FULLER, Robert, Executive Vice President and Chief Operating Officer, Downey Regional Medical Center, Downey, CA, p. A58

FULNER, Charles, Chief Executive Officer, Cleveland Regional Medical Center, Cleveland, TX, p. A592

FULTON, Lorna, Director Human Resources, Vibra Hospital of Denver, Thornton, CO, p. A106

FULTON, Lynn, Chief Executive Officer, Kewanee Hospital, Kewanee, IL, p. A186

FUNDERBURG, Michelle, Director Human Resources, Stephens Memorial Hospital, Breckenridge, TX, p. A589

FUNDERBURK, Mark, Executive Vice President and Administrator, University Medical Center, Lubbock, TX, p. A620

FUNG, Adrian, Director Information Systems, University Medical Center, Lebanon, TN, p. A572

FUNK, Gordon, Chief Executive Officer, Summit Surgical, LLC, Hutchinson, KS, p. A236

FUNK, Luann, Administrative Assistant and Manager Human Resources, Pana Community Hospital, Pana, IL, p. A191

FUNKHOUSER, Krisy L., Manager Human Resources, Willapa Harbor Hospital, South Bend, WA, p. A672

FUNKHOUSER, Lana, Vice President Human Resources, Indiana University Health West Hospital, Avon, IN, p. A198

FUQUA, David, Director Human Resources Management, LSU Health Sciences Center, Shreveport, LA, p. A278

FUQUA, David G., Chief Executive Officer, Massac Memorial Hospital, Metropolis, IL, p. A188

FUQUA, Leon, Chief Operating Officer, Wise Regional Health System, Decatur, TX, p. A598

FUQUA, William, Administrator, Greenbrier Hospital, Covington, LA, p. A265

FURER, Darnell F., MS Vice President of Patient Care Services, Schuylkill Medical Center – East Norwegian Street, Pottsville, PA, p. A539

FUREY, Warren, M.D. Vice President Medical Affairs, Mercy Hospital and Medical Center, Chicago, IL, p. A177

FURGURSON, Carol, Acting Chief Administrative Officer, Saint Louise Regional Hospital, Gilroy, CA, p. A62

FURLAN, Matthew
   Chief Operating Officer, Appleton Medical Center, Appleton, WI, p. A683
   Chief Operating Officer, Theda Clark Medical Center, Neenah, WI, p. A693

FURLONG, Marian M., R.N., Chief Executive Officer, Hudson Hospital and Clinics, Hudson, WI, p. A688

FURLOW, Pete, Director Information Technology Services, Northeast Alabama Regional Medical Center, Anniston, AL, p. A15

FURMAN, John, Director Human Resources, Val Verde Regional Medical Center, Del Rio, TX, p. A598

FURMAN, Keith A., Chief Executive Officer, Lakeland Behavioral Health System, Springfield, MO, p. A372

FURNAS, David, Chief Information Officer, Gila Regional Medical Center, Silver City, NM, p. A418

FURNISS, Scott, Senior Vice President and Chief Financial Officer, Saint Agnes Hospital, Baltimore, MD, p. A289

FURRER, Susan, PsyD Acting Chief Operating Officer and Executive Director Behavioral Research and Training Institute, University of Medicine and Dentistry of New Jersey, University Behavioral Healthcare, Piscataway, NJ, p. A409

FUSCHILLO, Ronald, Chief Information Officer, Englewood Hospital and Medical Center, Englewood, NJ, p. A404

FUSCO, Kevin, Chief Operating Officer, Broward Health North, Deerfield Beach, FL, p. A122

FUSELIER, Gerald, Chief Operating Officer, Savoy Medical Center, Mamou, LA, p. A273

FUSELIER, Michael, FACHE Chief Financial Officer, Central Louisiana Surgical Hospital, Alexandria, LA, p. A262

FUSSELL, Eugene, M.D
   Chief Medical Officer, St. John's Pleasant Valley Hospital, Camarillo, CA, p. A55
   Chief Medical Officer, St. John's Regional Medical Center, Oxnard, CA, p. A78

FUTCH, Margaret A., Chief Executive Officer, HEALTHSOUTH Rehabilitation Hospital, Dothan, AL, p. A19

FUTRAL, Cindy, Director Human Resources, Elmore Community Hospital, Wetumpka, AL, p. A26

FUTRELL, Bradley, Chief Operating Officer, Hamilton Memorial Hospital District, McLeansboro, IL, p. A184

FYBEL, Gary G., Chief Executive, Senior Vice President, Scripps Memorial Hospital–La Jolla, La Jolla, CA, p. A65

# G

GAAL, James G., M.D. Chief of Medical Staff, Jackson General Hospital, Ripley, WV, p. A680

GAAL, John M., Deputy Commander Administration, Walter Reed National Military Medical Center, Bethesda, MD, p. A290

GAASCH, Andrew
   Chief Financial Officer, Parker Adventist Hospital, Parker, CO, p. A105
   Chief Financial Officer, Porter Adventist Hospital, Denver, CO, p. A100

GABALDON, Karen, Chief Management Information Systems, West Palm Beach Veterans Affairs Medical Center, West Palm Beach, FL, p. A144

GABAVICS, Mark, Director Human Resources, Shawano Medical Center, Shawano, WI, p. A696

GABBE, Steven, M.D., Chief Executive Officer, Ohio State University Wexner Medical Center, Columbus, OH, p. A478

GABEL, Christopher, Chief Operating Officer, Hollywood Pavilion,, FL, p. A125

GABEL, Marcia, Chief Financial Officer, Lane County Hospital, Dighton, KS, p. A233

GABEL, Phyllis, Chief Human Resource Officer, St. Luke's Rehabilitation Institute, Spokane, WA, p. A672

GABLENZ, Gordon, Vice President Finance, Ridgeview Medical Center, Waconia, MN, p. A342

GABORIAULT, Randall, Chief Information Officer, Christiana Care Health System, Newark, DE, p. A114

GABRIEL, Brenda, Director Human Resources, Harrison County Community Hospital, Bethany, MO, p. A356

GABRIEL, Scott F., Chief Operating Officer, Parkview Whitley Hospital, Columbia City, IN, p. A200

GABRIEL, Shirley, Chief Information Officer, University of Arizona Medical Center – University Campus, Tucson, AZ, p. A39

GABRIELE, Joan, Deputy Executive Director, Queens Hospital Center,, NY, p. A436

GABRIELSON, Nancy
   Administrator and Chief Executive Officer, Iowa Specialty Hospitals, Clarion, IA, p. B74
   Administrator and Chief Executive Officer, Iowa Specialty Hospital–Belmond, Belmond, IA, p. A216

GABRYEL, Timothy, M.D. Vice President Medical Affairs and Medical Director, Mercy Hospital, Buffalo, NY, p. A422

GACH, Peter, M.D. Chief of Staff, Northwest Medical Center, Margate, FL, p. A130

GADALLAH, Yousri, M.D. Chief Medical Officer, Pershing General Hospital, Lovelock, NV, p. A394

GADDIS, Cathryn, Director Human Resources, RiverValley Behavioral Health Hospital, Owensboro, KY, p. A258

GADE, Swami P., M.D. Medical Director, Tioga Medical Center, Tioga, ND, p. A469

GADEN, Paul, Vice President and Chief Operating Officer, CHRISTUS Spohn Hospital Corpus Christi Memorial, Corpus Christi, TX, p. A593

GADOMSKI, Veronica, R.N. Chief Nursing Officer, HEALTHSOUTH Rehabilitation Hospital, Albuquerque, NM, p. A414

GAEDE, John, Director Information Systems, El Centro Regional Medical Center, El Centro, CA, p. A59

GAENZLE, Jack, Senior Vice President Finance and Administration, UPMC Mercy, Pittsburgh, PA, p. A538

GAFFNEY, Laura, President and Chief Executive Officer, Interfaith Medical Center,, NY, p. A432

GAFFORD, Deborah, Chief Financial Officer, Menorah Medical Center, Overland Park, KS, p. A242

GAGE, Eileen, R.N
   Vice President Nursing, Geneva General Hospital, Geneva, NY, p. A426
   Vice President Nursing, Soldiers and Sailors Memorial Hospital of Yates County, Penn Yan, NY, p. A439

GAGE, Kevin, Chief Financial Officer, Stamford Hospital, Stamford, CT, p. A112

GAGE, Mark, D.O. Medical Director, Brookhaven Hospital, Tulsa, OK, p. A507

GAGLE, Stephen P., Manager Human Resources, Parkview Whitley Hospital, Columbia City, IN, p. A200

GAGLIO, Tony, Chief Financial Officer, Henry Ford Kingswood Hospital, Ferndale, MI, p. A313

GAGNON, Andy, Director Information Systems, Mercy Regional Health Center,, KS, p. A239

GAINDH, Ramesh, M.D. President Medical Staff, Parkview Adventist Medical Center, Brunswick, ME, p. A282

GAINER, Rolf B., Chief Executive Officer and Administrator, Brookhaven Hospital, Tulsa, OK, p. A507

GAIRE, Susan, M.D. President Medical Staff, Frisbie Memorial Hospital, Rochester, NH, p. A400

GAITAN, Alberto, M.D. Medical Director, O'Connor Hospital, Delhi, NY, p. A425

GAITER, Thomas E., M.D. Chief Medical Officer, Howard University Hospital, Washington, DC, p. A116

GAJ, Steve, Facility Chief Information Officer, Louis Stokes Cleveland Veterans Affairs Medical Center, Cleveland, OH, p. A476

GAJARE, N., M.D. Chief Clinical Affairs, Kalamazoo Psychiatric Hospital, Kalamazoo, MI, p. A318

GAJEWSKI, Christie, Director Human Resources, Pinckneyville Community Hospital, Pinckneyville, IL, p. A192

GALANDA, Chris, Chief Information Officer, Wilkes-Barre General Hospital, Wilkes-Barre, PA, p. A544

GALANG, Michael, M.D
   Chief Information Officer, Mercy Hospital, Buffalo, NY, p. A422
   Chief Information Officer, Sisters of Charity Hospital of Buffalo, Buffalo, NY, p. A423

GALARNEAU, Gerard, M.D., Chief Executive Officer and Chief Medical Officer, Catskill Regional Medical Center, Harris, NY, p. A427

GALATI, Vicki L.
   Director Finance, Texas Health Harris Methodist Hospital Cleburne, Cleburne, TX, p. A592
   Chief Financial Officer, Texas Health Specialty Hospital, Fort Worth, TX, p. A604

GALDIERI, Lou, R.N
   Chief Operating Officer and Administrator, Mease Countryside Hospital, Safety Harbor, FL, p. A138
   Chief Operating Officer and Administrator, Mease Dunedin Hospital, Dunedin, FL, p. A122

GALE, Donald I., M.D. Vice President Medical Affairs, Winter Haven Hospital, Winter Haven, FL, p. A144

GALE, Gabrielle, Chief Financial Officer, Forest View Psychiatric Hospital, Grand Rapids, MI, p. A314

GALE, Michael, Chief Financial Officer, Bournewood Health Systems, Brookline, MA, p. A298

GALEN, Julie, R.N. Chief Nursing Officer, Good Shepherd Penn Partners Specialty Hospital at Rittenhouse, Philadelphia, PA, p. A535

GALFANO, Victor J., FACHE, Chief Executive Officer, Regency Hospital of Northwest Indiana, East Chicago, IN, p. A201

GALINDO, Virgie, Chief Nurse Executive, Sutter Auburn Faith Hospital, Auburn, CA, p. A53

GALIPEAU, Michelle, Director Human Resources, St. Vincent's Birmingham, Birmingham, AL, p. A17

GALKOWSKI, James, Associate Director for Operations, Fayetteville Veterans Affairs Medical Center, Fayetteville, NC, p. A452

GALLA, Bernie
   Interim Director Management Information Systems, Howard University Hospital, Washington, DC, p. A116
   Director Information Services, Pikeville Medical Center, Pikeville, KY, p. A259

GALLAGHER, Doug, Director Human Resources, Carolinas Specialty Hospital, Charlotte, NC, p. A450

GALLAGHER, Frank, Chief Executive Officer, Virginia Beach Psychiatric Center, Virginia Beach, VA, p. A662

GALLAGHER, James P., Chief Executive Officer, Summit Oaks Hospital, Summit, NJ, p. A410

GALLAGHER, Jeannie, Human Resource Generalist, East Morgan County Hospital, Brush, CO, p. A98

GALLAGHER, John, M.D. Chief Medical Officer, St. Mary's Medical Center of Evansville, Evansville, IN, p. A202

GALLAGHER, John, Chief Executive Officer, Sunnyside Community Hospital, Sunnyside, WA, p. A673

GALLAGHER, Joseph, Chief Executive Officer, Wyoming Behavioral Institute, Casper, WY, p. A701

GALLAGHER, Karen, Vice President Human Resources and Learning, Brooks Rehabilitation Hospital, Jacksonville, FL, p. A126

GALLAGHER, Keith W., FACHE, Administrator and Chief Executive Officer, Memorial Hospital Pembroke, Pembroke Pines, FL, p. A136

GALLAGHER, Peter
   Vice President and Chief Financial Officer, Bon Secours Memorial Regional Medical Center, Mechanicsville, VA, p. A657
   Chief Financial Officer, Bon Secours St. Francis Medical Center, Midlothian, VA, p. A657
   Chief Financial Officer, Bon Secours St. Mary's Hospital, Richmond, VA, p. A660
   Senior Vice President and Chief Financial Officer, Bon Secours–Richmond Community Hospital, Richmond, VA, p. A660

GALLARDO, Ysidro, Associate Administrator Human Resources, Hazel Hawkins Memorial Hospital, Hollister, CA, p. A64

GALLATI, Todd, FACHE, President and Chief Executive Officer, Trident Medical Center, Charleston, SC, p. A549

GALLAY, Emily, Vice President and Chief Information Officer, Lakeland Regional Medical Center–St. Joseph, Saint Joseph, MI, p. A324

GALLEGOS, Colleen, Director Human Resources, Guadalupe County Hospital, Santa Rosa, NM, p. A418

GALLEGOS, Enrique, Chief Operating Officer, Sierra Medical Center, El Paso, TX, p. A601

GALLES, Dan, Chief Financial Officer, San Dimas Community Hospital, San Dimas, CA, p. A86

GALLI, Jodi, Chief Nursing Officer, Eastern Maine Medical Center, Bangor, ME, p. A281

GALLIART, Mark, Chief Executive Officer, McBride Clinic Orthopedic Hospital, Oklahoma City, OK, p. A503

GALLIN, John I., M.D., Director, National Institutes of Health Clinical Center, Bethesda, MD, p. A290

GALLO, Cathy M., Vice President and Chief Nursing Officer, Levindale Hebrew Geriatric Center and Hospital, Baltimore, MD, p. A288

GALLO, James, Chief Human Resources Officer, St. Elizabeths Hospital, Washington, DC, p. A117

GALLO, Ronald, Director Human Resources, Blythedale Children's Hospital, Valhalla, NY, p. A445

GALLO, Scott, Assistant Vice President Talent, Midwestern Regional Medical Center, Zion, IL, p. A197

GALLOWAY, Nikki, Director Personnel and Administrative Secretary, Healthmark Regional Medical Center, DeFuniak Springs, FL, p. A122

GALLOWAY, Robert
   Senior Vice President Finance and Chief Financial Officer, Health First Cape Canaveral Hospital, Cocoa Beach, FL, p. A121
   Senior Vice President Finance and Chief Financial Officer, Health First Holmes Regional Medical Center, Melbourne, FL, p. A130

GALLUCCI, Kathleen, Chief Human Resources, Highland Hospital of Rochester, Rochester, NY, p. A441

GALLUCCI, Vince
   Senior Vice President Human Resources, Mercy Medical Center, Oshkosh, WI, p. A694
   Senior Vice President Human Resources, St. Elizabeth Hospital, Appleton, WI, p. A683

GALONSKY, Ronald J., Chief Operating Officer, O'Connor Hospital, San Jose, CA, p. A88

GALT, Nick, Chief Financial Officer, Las Colinas Medical Center, Irving, TX, p. A615

GALUSHA, Fred, Chief Information Officer, St. Luke's Rehabilitation Institute, Spokane, WA, p. A672

GALVIN, Gary, M.D. Chief of Staff, Columbus Community Hospital, Columbus, WI, p. A685

GALYON, Darlene, Director Human Resources, Choctaw Memorial Hospital, Hugo, OK, p. A500

GAMACHE, Cynde, R.N. Vice President and Chief Clinical Officer, Leesburg Regional Medical Center, Leesburg, FL, p. A129

GAMACHE, Edward L., President and Chief Executive Officer, Harbor Beach Community Hospital, Harbor Beach, MI, p. A316

GAMBILL, Bill, Chief Financial Officer, Veterans Affairs Black Hills Health Care System, Fort Meade, SD, p. A560

GAMBINO, Angela, R.N. Chief Nursing Officer, Hancock Medical Center, Bay Saint Louis, MS, p. A344

GAMBLE, Allen J., Comptroller, Bullock County Hospital, Union Springs, AL, p. A26

GAMBLE, Judy, Chief Financial Officer, Williamsburg Regional Hospital, Kingstree, SC, p. A553

GAMBLE, Kathleen, Fiscal Officer, Patton State Hospital, Patton, CA, p. A79

GAMBRELL Jr., Edward C., Administrator, Stephens County Hospital, Toccoa, GA, p. A162

GAMEL, Richard B., Administrator, Alegent Creighton Health Plainview Hospital, Plainview, NE, p. A389

GAMET, Nicki, R.N
   VP/Chief Nursing Officer, Mercy Hospital Aurora, Aurora, MO, p. A356
   Chief Nursing Officer, Mercy Hospital Cassville, Cassville, MO, p. A358

GAMINO, Randall, Director Perot Site, St. Joseph's Medical Center, Stockton, CA, p. A92

GAMMIERE, Thomas A., Chief Executive, Senior Vice President, Scripps Mercy Hospital, San Diego, CA, p. A85

GAMMON, Diane, Director Information Systems, Saint Francis Medical Center, Cape Girardeau, MO, p. A358

GANCI, Alan A., Director Finance and Controller, Lodi Community Hospital, Lodi, OH, p. A484

GANCI, Deborah, Vice President Human Resources, Bellevue Hospital, Bellevue, OH, p. A471

GANDY, Patrick W., Chief Operating Officer, Lafayette General Medical Center, Lafayette, LA, p. A271

GANGEMI–SOSA, Jeannith
   Associate Executive Director, Elmhurst Hospital Center,, NY, p. A431
   Senior Associate Executive Director, Lincoln Medical and Mental Health Center,, NY, p. A433
   Senior Associate Executive Director, Queens Hospital Center,, NY, p. A436

GANGULY, Indranil, Vice President and Chief Information Officer, CentraState Healthcare System, Freehold, NJ, p. A404

GANN, Lisa, R.N. Chief Nursing Officer, TriStar Hendersonville Medical Center, Hendersonville, TN, p. A570

GANN, Michele, Vice President Patient Services, Mercy Hospital Berryville, Berryville, AR, p. A41

GANN, Sherry, Administrator, Conway Regional Rehab Hospital, Conway, AR, p. A42

GANNON, Ronnie, Director Information Services, TriStar Southern Hills Medical Center, Nashville, TN, p. A577

GANNOTTA, Richard, President, Duke Raleigh Hospital, Raleigh, NC, p. A459

GANONG, Richard, M.D. Chief of Staff, Tahoe Forest Hospital District, Truckee, CA, p. A93

GANS, Bruce M., M.D. Executive Vice President and Chief Medical Officer, Kessler Institute for Rehabilitation, West Orange, NJ, p. A412

GANSHE, Jary, Chief Financial Officer, Methodist Mansfield Medical Center, Mansfield, TX, p. A621

GANTNER, John
   Executive Vice President Finance and Partner Company Operations, Bayshore Community Hospital, Holmdel, NJ, p. A405
   Executive Vice President Finance and Partner Company Operations, Jersey Shore University Medical Center, Neptune, NJ, p. A407
   Executive Vice President Finance, Ocean Medical Center, Brick Township, NJ, p. A402
   Executive Vice President Finance, Riverview Medical Center, Red Bank, NJ, p. A410
   Executive Vice President Finance and Partner Company Operations, Southern Ocean Medical Center, Manahawkin, NJ, p. A406

GANTT, Cynthia J., Executive Officer, Robert E. Bush Naval Hospital, Twentynine Palms, CA, p. A93

GANTT, Marsha, Interim Chief Nursing Officer, Barnwell County Hospital, Barnwell, SC, p. A548

GAPSTUR, Roxanna L., Ph.D. Chief Nursing Officer, Park Nicollet Methodist Hospital, Saint Louis Park, MN, p. A339

GARAY, Kenneth, M.D
   Chief Medical Officer, LibertyHealth–Jersey City Medical Center, Jersey City, NJ, p. A405
   Chief Medical Officer, Meadowlands Hospital Medical Center, Secaucus, NJ, p. A410

GARBANZOS, Del, Director Human Resources, Delano Regional Medical Center, Delano, CA, p. A58

GARBER, Jennifer Elizabeth, Vice President Human Resources, Emory Johns Creek Hospital, Johns Creek, GA, p. A155

GARCHA, Seema, M.D. Chief of Staff, Davis Regional Medical Center, Statesville, NC, p. A461

GARCIA, Alex, Chief Executive Officer, Victory Medical Center – San Antonio, San Antonio, TX, p. A632

GARCIA, Amparo, Administrative Assistant, Frio Regional Hospital, Pearsall, TX, p. A626

GARCIA, Carlos R., Vice President Clinical Services, Larkin Community Hospital, South Miami, FL, p. A140

GARCIA, Danette, Director Human Resources, HEALTHSOUTH Valley of the Sun Rehabilitation Hospital, Glendale, AZ, p. A32

GARCIA, Donna, Vice President, Finance, Presbyterian Hospital, Albuquerque, NM, p. A414

GARCIA, Felix, Director Health Information Services, Highlands Regional Medical Center, Sebring, FL, p. A140

GARCIA, Fernando, M.D. Chief of Staff, Avoyelles Hospital, Marksville, LA, p. A273

GARCIA, Gary, M.D. Chief of Staff, Mad River Community Hospital, Arcata, CA, p. A53

GARCIA, Georgina R., Executive Director, Kaiser Permanente West Los Angeles Medical Center, Los Angeles, CA, p. A69

GARCIA, Gerard, Acting Vice President Human Resources, University of Medicine and Dentistry of New Jersey–University Hospital, Newark, NJ, p. A407

GARCIA, Irma, Job Coordinator, Rio Grande State Center/South Texas Health Care System, Harlingen, TX, p. A608

GARCIA, Joanne, Chief Operating Officer, Kindred Chicago–Central Hospital, Chicago, IL, p. A177

GARCIA, Kathleen, Controller, St. John's Episcopal Hospital–South Shore,, NY, p. A436

GARCIA, Lisa, Director Human Resources, Sunnyside Community Hospital, Sunnyside, WA, p. A673

GARCIA, Luis, Chief Executive Officer, Victory Medical Center Houston, Houston, TX, p. A613

GARCIA, Jr., Luis Mario, Director Human Resources, Methodist Sugar Land Hospital, Sugar Land, TX, p. A635

GARCIA, Margaret, Manager Human Resources, Baylor Medical Center at Frisco, Frisco, TX, p. A605

GARCIA, Michael, M.D. Medical Director, Leonard J. Chabert Medical Center, Houma, LA, p. A268

GARCIA, Michael R., Vice President Human Resources, SSM St. Joseph Health Center, Saint Charles, MO, p. A368

GARCIA, Robert W., M.D. Chief Medical Officer, Iraan General Hospital, Iraan, TX, p. A614

GARCIA, Roland
   Senior Vice President and Chief Information Officer, Baptist Medical Center Beaches, Jacksonville Beach, FL, p. A127
   Senior Vice President and Chief Information Officer, Baptist Medical Center Jacksonville, Jacksonville, FL, p. A126

GARCIA, Sharon, Human Resources Representative, Medina Regional Hospital, Hondo, TX, p. A608

GARCIA, Shawn, Manager Human Resources, Memorial Hospital Los Banos, Los Banos, CA, p. A72

GARCIA, Sylvia, Chief Accounting Officer, South Texas Spine and Surgical Hospital, San Antonio, TX, p. A632

GARCIA, Vicki, Vice President Human Resources, Roswell Park Cancer Institute, Buffalo, NY, p. A422

GARDINER, David, Operations Officer, LDS Hospital, Salt Lake City, UT, p. A646

GARDINER, Karen, Director Fiscal Services, University Medical Center, Lafayette, LA, p. A271

GARDINER, Lisa, Director Marketing and Public Relations, Physicians Regional Medical Center – Pine Ridge, Naples, FL, p. A133

GARDNER, David, Manager Human Resources, Utah State Hospital, Provo, UT, p. A646

GARDNER, Donald F., Vice President Finance/Chief Financial Officer, Caldwell Memorial Hospital, Lenoir, NC, p. A456

GARDNER, Elizabeth C., R.N. Chief Nursing Officer, Hemet Valley Medical Center, Hemet, CA, p. A64

GARDNER, Guy, M.D
   Chief Medical Affairs, Baptist Health Medical Center – North Little Rock, North Little Rock, AR, p. A48
   Chief Medical Officer, Baptist Health Medical Center–Arkadelphia, Arkadelphia, AR, p. A41

GARDNER, Jacque, Administrative Assistant, Clinic Manager, Co–Chief Financial Officer and Chief Human Resources, McCone County Health Center, Circle, MT, p. A375

GARDNER, James D., M.D. Vice President and Chief Medical Officer, Waukesha Memorial Hospital, Waukesha, WI, p. A698

GARDNER, John, Chief Executive Officer, Yuma District Hospital, Yuma, CO, p. A107

GARDNER, Jonathan H., FACHE, Director, Southern Arizona Veterans Affairs Health Care System, Tucson, AZ, p. A39

GARDNER, Norman, M.D. President Medical Staff, Presentation Medical Center, Rolla, ND, p. A469

GARDNER, Patrick, M.D. Vice President Medical Affairs, St. Joseph's Community Hospital of West Bend, West Bend, WI, p. A699

GARDNER, Paul A., CPA, Administrator, George Regional Hospital, Lucedale, MS, p. A350

GARDNER, Robb, Chief Executive Officer, Henry County Health Center, Mount Pleasant, IA, p. A225

GARDNER, Sharon, Manager Information Systems, SSM St. Joseph Hospital West, Lake Saint Louis, MO, p. A364

GARDNER, Sharon R., Vice President Human Resources, Yuma Regional Medical Center, Yuma, AZ, p. A40

GARDNER, Zoe, Manager Human Resources, Sharp Chula Vista Medical Center, Chula Vista, CA, p. A56

GARES, Donna, R.N., President and Chief Executive Officer, San Jacinto Methodist Hospital, Baytown, TX, p. A587

GARFIELD, Mark, M.D. Vice President and Chief Medical Officer, Kaweah Delta Medical Center, Visalia, CA, p. A95

GARFINKEL, Leon, Director Information Services, University of Medicine and Dentistry of New Jersey, University Behavioral Healthcare, Piscataway, NJ, p. A409

GARISON, Jerri, R.N., President, Baylor Regional Medical Center at Plano, Plano, TX, p. A627

GARKO, Michael
   Chief Financial Officer, Kaiser Permanente Moreno Valley Medical Center, Moreno Valley, CA, p. A75
   Chief Financial Officer, Menifee Valley Medical Center, Sun City, CA, p. A92
   Chief Financial Officer, St. Vincent Medical Center, Los Angeles, CA, p. A72

GARLAND, Anna, Director Human Resources, Fort Walton Beach Medical Center, Fort Walton Beach, FL, p. A124

GARLETS, Mary, Director Human Resources, Mayo Clinic Health System in Cannon Falls, Cannon Falls, MN, p. A330

GARMAN, Mary E., R.N. Chief Nursing Officer and Vice President Operations, Good Samaritan Hospital, Dayton, OH, p. A479

GARMAN, Michael, Chief Financial Officer, Avera St. Anthony's Hospital, O'Neill, NE, p. A386

GARNAS, David, Chief Executive Officer, Sedgwick County Health Center, Julesburg, CO, p. A102

GARNER, Douglas, Vice President, Thomas Hospital, Fairhope, AL, p. A20

GARNER, Ethnee, Vice President Nursing Services, Memorial Hospital, North Conway, NH, p. A399

GARNER, James H., Chief Financial Officer, Coffey County Hospital, Burlington, KS, p. A232

GARNER, Mario J., FACHE Chief Operating Officer, Regional Medical Center of Acadiana, Lafayette, LA, p. A271

GARNER, William, M.D. Chief Medical Officer, Saint Catherine Regional Hospital, Charlestown, IN, p. A200

GARNETT, Mark, M.D. Chief of Staff, Hansford Hospital, Spearman, TX, p. A634

GAROFOLA, Aaron, Chief Executive Officer, Bluffton Regional Medical Center, Bluffton, IN, p. A199

GARON, Jack, M.D. Chief Medical Officer, Mount Sinai Hospital, Chicago, IL, p. A177

GARONE, Marlene, M.D. Vice President Medical Affairs and Medical Director, Woman's Christian Association Hospital, Jamestown, NY, p. A427

GARRAMONE, Kathy
Chief Financial Officer, Jacobi Medical Center,, NY, p. A432
Chief Financial Officer, North Central Bronx Hospital,, NY, p. A435

GARRARD, Eric, Chief Executive Officer, HEALTHSOUTH Cane Creek Rehabilitation Hospital, Martin, TN, p. A573

GARRED, Sr., John, M.D. Chief Medical Officer, Burgess Health Center, Onawa, IA, p. A226

GARRETT, Alan H., Chief Executive Officer, St. Joseph Health St. Mary, Apple Valley, CA, p. A53

GARRETT, Darlene, Chief Operating Officer, Parkview Huntington Hospital, Huntington, IN, p. A205

GARRETT, David B.
Chief Information Officer, Novant Health Forsyth Medical Center, Winston-Salem, NC, p. A463
Chief Information Officer, Novant Health Matthews Medical Center, Matthews, NC, p. A457
Senior Vice President Information Technology, Novant Health Presbyterian Medical Center, Charlotte, NC, p. A450

GARRETT, Ginger, Regional Director Human Resources, Good Shepherd Medical Center–Marshall, Marshall, TX, p. A621

GARRETT, Jarren, Chief Administrative Officer, Baptist Orange Hospital, Orange, TX, p. A625

GARRETT, Kevin C., M.D. Chief Medical Officer, Christus St. Vincent Regional Medical Center, Santa Fe, NM, p. A418

GARRETT, Lisa, Director Human Resources, Arizona Spine and Joint Hospital, Mesa, AZ, p. A32

GARRETT, Mark, Chief Information Officer, Shriners Hospitals for Children–Los Angeles, Los Angeles, CA, p. A71

GARRETT, Mykl, Executive Vice President and Chief Operating Officer, Trinity Bettendorf, Bettendorf, IA, p. A216

GARRETT, Regina, Director Health Information Management, Crossroads Community Hospital, Mount Vernon, IL, p. A189

GARRETT, Robert C., FACHE, President and Chief Executive Officer, Hackensack University Medical Center, Hackensack, NJ, p. A404

GARRETT, Walter J., Chief Executive Officer, Welch Community Hospital, Welch, WV, p. A681

GARRICK, Renee, M.D. Chief Medical Officer, Westchester Medical Center, Valhalla, NY, p. A445

GARRIN, Paul, Chief Information Officer, Monmouth Medical Center, Long Branch, NJ, p. A406

GARRISON, Kenneth, M.D. Chief of Staff, Cumberland Memorial Hospital, Cumberland, WI, p. A685

GARRISON, Mark, Chief of Staff, Glenn Medical Center, Willows, CA, p. A96

GARRISON, Stephen, Interim Chief Executive Officer, Texas Regional Medical Center at Sunnyvale, Sunnyvale, TX, p. A636

GARRITY, Nerissa, Chief Financial Officer, Kula Hospital, Kula, HI, p. A166

GARROW, Dina, Chief Nursing Officer and Chief Operating Officer, Kindred Hospital–Baldwin Park, Baldwin Park, CA, p. A54

GARROW, George, M.D. Senior Vice President and Chief Medical Officer, Western Maryland Regional Medical Center, Cumberland, MD, p. A291

GARRY, William, Chief Financial Officer, Edgefield County Hospital, Edgefield, SC, p. A551

GARSA, Arebi, Chief Financial Officer, Ashland Community Hospital, Ashland, OR, p. A511

GARSKE, Tom, Director Information Systems, Wiregrass Medical Center, Geneva, AL, p. A21

GARSKI, Mary Jo, Director Human Resources, Wellington Regional Medical Center, West Palm Beach, FL, p. A144

GARVEN, Charles, M.D. Vice President Medical Operations, Lakewood Hospital, Lakewood, OH, p. A483

GARVEY, Heather, Chief Financial Officer, Raulerson Hospital, Okeechobee, FL, p. A134

GARVEY, Thomas J., Chief Financial Officer, Mercy Hospital and Medical Center, Chicago, IL, p. A177

GARVIN, Henry, Chief Executive Officer, Conejos County Hospital, La Jara, CO, p. A102

GARVIN, Jan
Vice President Human Resources, Bryan Medical Center, Lincoln, NE, p. A385
Vice President Human Resources, Franciscan St. Elizabeth Health – Lafayette Central, Lafayette, IN, p. A208

GARVIN, Sarah C., Chief Executive Officer, Cypress Pointe Hospital East, Slidell, LA, p. A278

GARWOOD, III, William D., Associate Administrator and Chief Financial Officer, Angleton Danbury Medical Center, Angleton, TX, p. A583

GARY, Al, COO, Simpson General Hospital, Mendenhall, MS, p. A350

GARY, Stacci, Director Human Resources, Parkview Community Hospital Medical Center, Riverside, CA, p. A82

GARY, Stephen M., Senior Vice President and Chief Financial officer, Akron General Medical Center, Akron, OH, p. A470

GARZA, Ismelda, Director Information Systems, Comanche County Medical Center, Comanche, TX, p. A593

GARZA, Laura, Director Human Resources, Texas Specialty Hospital at Houston, Houston, TX, p. A612

GARZA, Oscar, M.D. Chief of Medical Staff, Frio Regional Hospital, Pearsall, TX, p. A626

GARZA, Tom, Director Fiscal and Support, Rio Grande State Center/South Texas Health Care System, Harlingen, TX, p. A608

GASAWAY, Rob, Chief Financial Officer, Galesburg Cottage Hospital, Galesburg, IL, p. A183

GASBARRA, Gary, Regional Chief Financial Officer, Presence Saint Joseph Medical Center, Joliet, IL, p. A186

GASCHO, Dwight, President and Chief Executive Officer, Scheurer Hospital, Pigeon, MI, p. A321

GASH, Deborah
Vice President and Chief Information Officer, Crittenton Children's Center, Kansas City, MO, p. A362
Chief Information Officer, Saint Luke's Hospital of Kansas City, Kansas City, MO, p. A363
Chief Information Officer, Saint Luke's South Hospital, Overland Park, KS, p. A242

GASKINS, Michael W., Executive Vice President and Chief Financial Officer, Hanover Hospital, Hanover, PA, p. A526

GASPAR, Deborah L., R.N. Chief Nursing Officer, Memorial Hospital of Sweetwater County, Rock Springs, WY, p. A703

GASPARD, H. J., Chief Executive Officer, HEALTHSOUTH Rehabilitation Hospital of Beaumont, Beaumont, TX, p. A587

GASPARINI, Michael L., Vice President Clinical Services and Chief Operating Officer, Western Missouri Medical Center, Warrensburg, MO, p. A373

GASQUE, James, M.D. Chief Hospital Services, U. S. Air Force Medical Center Keesler, Keesler AFB, MS, p. A349

GAST, Edwin A., Chief Executive Officer, Marshall Browning Hospital, Du Quoin, IL, p. A181

GASTON, Jan, Administrator, Jasper Memorial Hospital, Monticello, GA, p. A157

GASTON, Tammy, Chief Information Officer, Smith County Memorial Hospital, Smith Center, KS, p. A244

GATES, John
Vice President Finance and Chief Financial Officer, California Pacific Medical Center, San Francisco, CA, p. A86
Chief Financial Officer, St. Luke's Hospital, San Francisco, CA, p. A87

GATES, Margaret, Chief Human Resources, Harris Hospital, Newport, AR, p. A48

GATES, Philip E., M.D. Chief of Staff, Shriners Hospitals for Children–Shreveport, Shreveport, LA, p. A278

GATES, Rose, Director Human Resources, Hayward Area Memorial Hospital and Nursing Home, Hayward, WI, p. A688

GATES, Tracy, Chief Financial Officer, Jones Memorial Hospital, Wellsville, NY, p. A445

GATHERS, Mary
Manager Information Systems, American Fork Hospital, American Fork, UT, p. A643
Director Information Systems, McKay–Dee Hospital Center, Ogden, UT, p. A645
Director Information Systems, Utah Valley Regional Medical Center, Provo, UT, p. A646

GATHMAN, Michael, Chief Financial Officer, Spokane Veterans Affairs Medical Center, Spokane, WA, p. A672

GATI, Ken, M.D. Chief of Staff, Medical Center of South Arkansas, El Dorado, AR, p. A43

GATIEN, Lionel J., D.O. Chief of Staff, Kindred Hospital North Florida, Green Cove Springs, FL, p. A125

GATLIFF, Peggy, Chief Financial Officer, Edward White Hospital, Saint Petersburg, FL, p. A139

GATMAITAN, Alfonso W., Chief Executive Officer, Indiana University Health Arnett Hospital, Lafayette, IN, p. A208

GATTO, Tony, Director Management Information Systems, Flushing Hospital Medical Center,, NY, p. A432

GAU, Kimberley A., FACHE, Chief Executive Officer, Guttenberg Municipal Hospital, Guttenberg, IA, p. A222

GAUBERT, Steve C., Chief Financial Officer, Thibodaux Regional Medical Center, Thibodaux, LA, p. A279

GAUDSMITH, Keith, Information Technology Officer, Weston County Health Services, Newcastle, WY, p. A703

GAUER, Natalie, Administrator, Milbank Area Hospital Avera, Milbank, SD, p. A560

GAUGHAN, Patty, Human Resource Administrative Officer, Nevada Regional Medical Center, Nevada, MO, p. A367

GAUL, Michael, Manager Information Systems, Atchison Hospital, Atchison, KS, p. A231

GAUNTT, Brandon, Director Information Systems, Hopkins County Memorial Hospital, Sulphur Springs, TX, p. A636

GAUSE, Garry L., President and Chief Executive Officer, Brookwood Medical Center, Birmingham, AL, p. A16

GAUTHIER, Bonnie B., President and Chief Executive Officer, The Hospital at Hebrew Health Care, West Hartford, CT, p. A112

GAUTHIER, Paul, Chief Information Resources Management, Veterans Affairs Montana Health Care System, Fort Harrison, MT, p. A376

GAUTNEY, Steven, Chief Executive Officer, Crisp Regional Hospital, Cordele, GA, p. A151

GAVALCHIK, Stephen M., FACHE, Community Chief Executive Officer, Morgan County ARH Hospital, West Liberty, KY, p. A261

GAVENS, Mark R., Senior Vice President Clinical Care Services and Chief Operating Officer, Cedars–Sinai Medical Center, Los Angeles, CA, p. A68

GAVIN, Donald, Chief Financial Officer, Hillside Hospital, Pulaski, TN, p. A578

GAVIN, James M., Chief Financial Officer, St. Peter's Hospital, Albany, NY, p. A420

GAVIN, Joan, R.N. Chief Nursing Officer/Vice President, Patient Services, Shore Medical Center, Somers Point, NJ, p. A410

GAVIN, Linda, Associate Executive Director Marketing and Physician Recruitment, South Central Regional Medical Center, Laurel, MS, p. A349

GAVIN, Martin J., President and Chief Executive Officer, Connecticut Children's Medical Center, Hartford, CT, p. A109

GAVIN, Patrick J., President, Crozer–Chester Medical Center, Upland, PA, p. A542

GAVIN, Tammy, Assistant Administrator and Chief Operating Officer, White River Medical Center, Batesville, AR, p. A41

GAVIOLI, R. Louis, M.D. Vice President Medical Affairs, St. Francis Medical Center, Monroe, LA, p. A274

GAVIS, Patricia, Chief Financial Officer, Ellenville Regional Hospital, Ellenville, NY, p. A425

GAVORA, George, Director Program Evaluation, Kingsboro Psychiatric Center,, NY, p. A433

GAVULIC, Melany, President & Chief Executive Officer, Hurley Medical Center, Flint, MI, p. A313

GAW, Kris
Chief Operating Officer, Renown Regional Medical Center, Reno, NV, p. A395
Chief Operating Officer, Renown Rehabilitation Hospital, Reno, NV, p. A395
Chief Operating Officer, Renown South Meadows Medical Center, Reno, NV, p. A395

GAWALUCK, David
Vice President and Chief Information Officer, Excela Frick Hospital, Mount Pleasant, PA, p. A532
Vice President and Chief Information Officer, Excela Health Westmoreland Hospital, Greensburg, PA, p. A526
Vice President and Chief Information Officer, Excela Latrobe Area Hospital, Latrobe, PA, p. A529

GAWLER, William, Chief Information Officer, Chillicothe Veterans Affairs Medical Center, Chillicothe, OH, p. A473

GAWNE, Bernard B., M.D. Vice President and Chief Medical Officer, Christ Hospital, Cincinnati, OH, p. A474

GAWORSKI, Mark, Vice President Finance, Chief Financial Officer, Spencer Hospital, Spencer, IA, p. A228

GAY, Chanda, Manager Human Resources, Jay Hospital, Jay, FL, p. A127

GAY, Christophe, M.D. Chief of Staff, Bellville St. Joseph Health Center, Bellville, TX, p. A588

GAY, Don, Director Human Resources, West Hills Hospital, Reno, NV, p. A395

GAY, Kristi
Chief Financial Officer, Memorial Medical Center – Livingston, Livingston, TX, p. A619
Chief Financial Officer, Memorial Medical Center – Lufkin, Lufkin, TX, p. A620
Chief Financial Officer, Memorial Medical Center – San Augustine, San Augustine, TX, p. A633
Chief Financial Officer, Memorial Specialty Hospital, Lufkin, TX, p. A620

GAY, Vickie, Chief Executive Officer, Montgomery General Hospital, Montgomery, WV, p. A678

GAYLER, Lisa, Director Human Resources, Select Long Term Care Hospital – Colorado Springs, Colorado Springs, CO, p. A98

GAYLOR, Rosanne, M.D., Acting Executive Director, South Beach Psychiatric Center,, NY, p. A436

GAYMAN, Rob, Director Information Systems, Riverside Shore Memorial Hospital, Nassawadox, VA, p. A657

GAYNOR, Sheila, Director Human Resources, Perry County Memorial Hospital, Tell City, IN, p. A213

GAZIT, Sharyn D., Director Human Resources, Shriners Hospitals for Children–Boston Burns Hospital, Boston, MA, p. A297

GEARHART, Danielle, Chief Executive Officer, Buchanan County Health Center, Independence, IA, p. A223

GEARY, David S., Chief Financial Officer, Cache Valley Specialty Hospital, North Logan, UT, p. A645

GEBHARD, Scott, Executive VP and Chief Operating Officer, JFK Medical Center, Edison, NJ, p. A403

GEBHART, Cheryl, Director Human Resources Providence Health Plan and Providence Medical Group, Providence Newberg Medical Center, Newberg, OR, p. A515

GEBHART Jr., Jim, FACHE, President, Mercy Hospital Oklahoma City, Oklahoma City, OK, p. A503

GEBHART, Ronald J., M.D. Chief of Staff, Veterans Affairs Salt Lake City Health Care System, Salt Lake City, UT, p. A647

GEDDINGS, Toni, Director Human Resources, Cullman Regional Medical Center, Cullman, AL, p. A18

GEE, Brian, M.D. Director Emergency Services, Lander Regional Hospital, Lander, WY, p. A702

GEE, Kyle
    Chief Financial Officer, Beartooth Billings Clinic, Red Lodge, MT, p. A379
    Chief Financial Officer, Pioneer Medical Center, Big Timber, MT, p. A374

GEE, Thomas H., Administrator, Henry County Medical Center, Paris, TN, p. A578

GEERTS, Jodi, Chief Nursing Officer, Henry County Health Center, Mount Pleasant, IA, p. A225

GEHANT, David P., President and Chief Executive Officer, Boulder Community Hospital, Boulder, CO, p. A97

GEHLAUF, Dee Ann, Senior Vice President Business and Organization Development, Marietta Memorial Hospital, Marietta, OH, p. A485

GEHLHAUSEN, Dorothy, Manager Human Resources, St. Mary's Warrick Hospital, Boonville, IN, p. A199

GEHRIG, Ryan, President, Mercy Hospital Fort Smith, Fort Smith, AR, p. A44

GEHRING, Jay, Director Information Systems, Kingman Community Hospital, Kingman, KS, p. A237

GEHRING, Sherry, R.N. Vice President Nursing, Inpatient Care and Chief Nursing Officer, Hancock Regional Hospital, Greenfield, IN, p. A204

GEHRING, Terri, Vice President Operations, McPherson Hospital, McPherson, KS, p. A239

GEIDT, Steve, Chief Executive Officer, Saddleback Memorial Medical Center, Laguna Hills, CA, p. A65

GEIER, Debra, M.D. President Medical Staff, Jamestown Regional Medical Center, Jamestown, ND, p. A467

GEIER, Peter E., Chief Operating Officer, Ohio State University Wexner Medical Center, Columbus, OH, p. A478

GEIGER, Cathy, Director Information Systems, Henry Ford Macomb Hospitals, Clinton Township, MI, p. A311

GEIGER, Charles L., D.O. Chief of Staff, Belmont Community Hospital, Bellaire, OH, p. A471

GEIGER, Judy, R.N. Chief Nursing Officer, Primary Children's Medical Center, Salt Lake City, UT, p. A646

GEIGER, Ralph, M.D. Chief of Staff, Sebastian River Medical Center, Sebastian, FL, p. A140

GEIGLE, Joseph, Director Human Resources, Fort Hamilton Hospital, Hamilton, OH, p. A483

GEIL, Kristie A., VP, Chief Nursing Officer, CGH Medical Center, Sterling, IL, p. A195

GEISSLER, Curt, President, Lakeview Hospital, Stillwater, MN, p. A341

GEISSLER, Michael E., Chief Executive Officer, Acadia Optima Hospital, Lafayette, LA, p. A270

GEIST, Jim, Chief Executive Officer, Capital Medical Center, Olympia, WA, p. A668

GEIST, Tammy, Chief Financial Officer, Novant Health Charlotte Orthopaedic Hospital, Charlotte, NC, p. A450

GEITZ, Cheri, Director Human Resources, Ellsworth Municipal Hospital, Iowa Falls, IA, p. A223

GEIVER, Betsy, Chief Human Resources Officer, Sioux Falls Veterans Affairs Health Care System, Sioux Falls, SD, p. A563

GELDHOF, Jay
    Director Information Systems, Greater El Monte Community Hospital, South El Monte, CA, p. A91
    Director Information Systems, Whittier Hospital Medical Center, Whittier, CA, p. A96

GELFAND, Andrew, M.D. Medical Director, Our Children's House at Baylor, Dallas, TX, p. A597

GELL, Michael, Director Human Resources, Boys Town National Research Hospital, Omaha, NE, p. A387

GELLENBECK, Mary Ann, Chief Operating Officer, Bethesda Butler Hospital, Hamilton, OH, p. A483

GELLER, Guy, Administrator and Chief Executive Officer, Beacham Memorial Hospital, Magnolia, MS, p. A350

GELLER, Harold S., Chief Executive Officer, St. Anthony Hospital, Pendleton, OR, p. A515

GELLER, Robert D., M.D. Vice President Medical Affairs, FHN Memorial Hospital, Freeport, IL, p. A183

GELLER, Warren, President and Chief Executive Officer, Englewood Hospital and Medical Center, Englewood, NJ, p. A404

GELMAN, Lawrence, M.D., Chief Executive Officer, Doctor's Hospital at Renaissance, Edinburg, TX, p. A600

GELORMINI, Frank, Chief Operating Officer, Community Medical Center, Toms River, NJ, p. A411

GENDER, Aloma, MSN, Administrator and Chief Nursing Officer, CHRISTUS St. Michael Rehabilitation Hospital, Texarkana, TX, p. A637

GENEVRO, Thomas A., Vice President Human Resources, Butler Health System, Butler, PA, p. A521

GENGLER, Laraine, Chief Financial Officer, Lindsborg Community Hospital, Lindsborg, KS, p. A239

GENNA, Nick, Administrator, Treasure Valley Hospital, Boise, ID, p. A168

GENNARO, John, FACHE, Director, Veterans Affairs Butler Healthcare, Butler, PA, p. A521

GENNRICH, Yvonne, Controller, Cook County North Shore Hospital, Grand Marais, MN, p. A333

GENOVESE, Vincent P., M.D. President Medical Staff, Muhlenberg Community Hospital, Greenville, KY, p. A252

GENSERT, Kurt, R.N. Vice President Operations, Platte Valley Medical Center, Brighton, CO, p. A97

GENTILE, John, M.D
    Vice President Medical Affairs, Alta Bates Summit Medical Center, Berkeley, CA, p. A54
    Vice President Medical Affairs, Alta Bates Summit Medical Center – Summit Campus, Oakland, CA, p. A77

GENTILE, Joyce, Human Resource Benefits Specialist, Marshall Medical Center, Lewisburg, TN, p. A573

GENTNER, Rocky, Chief Financial Officer, Newport Bay Hospital, Newport Beach, CA, p. A76

GENTRY, Cheryl G., Chief Executive Officer, Select Specialty Hospital–Beech Grove, Indianapolis, IN, p. A206

GENTRY, Gregg, Senior Vice President Human Resources, Erlanger Medical Center, Chattanooga, TN, p. A566

GENTRY, Jeanine, Chief Executive Officer, St. Charles Madras, Madras, OR, p. A514

GENTRY, Kelley, Chief Executive Officer, Surprise Valley Healthcare District, Cedarville, CA, p. A56

GENTRY, Lee, FACHE, Vice President and Administrator, Baptist Health Rehabilitation Institute, Little Rock, AR, p. A46

GEORGE, Alan E.
    Chief Executive Officer, Palestine Regional Medical Center, Palestine, TX, p. A625
    Chief Executive Officer, Palestine Regional Medical Center–East, Palestine, TX, p. A626

GEORGE, Amanda, Assistant Controller, St. Vincent Morrilton, Morrilton, AR, p. A47

GEORGE, Brad, Director Information Systems, Parkland Medical Center, Derry, NH, p. A397

GEORGE, Doug, Chief Financial Officer, Veterans Affairs Butler Healthcare, Butler, PA, p. A521

GEORGE, Gary
    Regional Vice President Human Resources, Mercy St. Anne Hospital, Toledo, OH, p. A491
    Regional Vice President Human Resources, Mercy St. Charles Hospital, Oregon, OH, p. A488
    Regional Vice President Human Resources, Mercy St. Vincent Medical Center, Toledo, OH, p. A491

GEORGE, Jane, Controller, Methodist Healthcare–Fayette Hospital, Somerville, TN, p. A579

GEORGE, P. A., M.D. Chief of Staff, Madison Medical Center, Fredericktown, MO, p. A361

GEORGE, Patricia, Chief Information Officer, North Shore Medical Center, Salem, MA, p. A304

GEORGE, Shayne, Chief Executive Officer, Regional Medical Center–Bayonet Point, Hudson, FL, p. A126

GEORGE, Susan, R.N. Associate Director Patient Care Services, Martinsburg Veterans Affairs Medical Center, Martinsburg, WV, p. A678

GEORGE, Tracy L., Chief Financial Officer, St. James Parish Hospital, Lutcher, LA, p. A272

GEORGE, William, M.D. Chief of Staff, Beartooth Billings Clinic, Red Lodge, MT, p. A379

GEORGES, Angelo, M.D. President Medical and Dental Staff, Wheeling Hospital, Wheeling, WV, p. A682

GERARD, Alice M., President and Chief Executive Officer, McLaren Bay Region, Bay City, MI, p. A309

GERARD, Greg D., President, Saint Joseph – London, London, KY, p. A255

GERATHS, Nathan L., Director, Edward Hines, Jr. Veterans Affairs Hospital, Hines, IL, p. A185

GERBER, Greg, M.D. Chief Medical Officer, Aurora Lakeland Medical Center, Elkhorn, WI, p. A686

GERBIG, Ralph, M.D. Chief of Staff, Johnson Memorial Health Services, Dawson, MN, p. A331

GERDTS, Elizabeth, Chief Nursing Officer, North Central Bronx Hospital,, NY, p. A435

GERETY, Meghan, M.D. Chief of Staff, Veterans Affairs Medical Center, Albuquerque, NM, p. A415

GERHART, Bobbie, President and Chief Executive Officer, Miami Valley Hospital, Dayton, OH, p. A480

GERHART, Paul, Chief Financial Officer, Sanford Canton–Inwood Medical Center, Canton, SD, p. A558

GERIG, Stacey L., Chief Executive Officer, Odessa Regional Medical Center, Odessa, TX, p. A625

GERING, Jeffrey T., Director, Veterans Affairs San Diego Healthcare System, San Diego, CA, p. A86

GERKE, Deborah, Chief Financial Officer, Complex Care Hospital at Tenaya, Las Vegas, NV, p. A392

GERLACH, George, Chief Executive Officer, Granite Falls Municipal Hospital and Manor, Granite Falls, MN, p. A333

GERLACH, Matthew S., Vice President and Chief Operating Officer, Glendale Memorial Hospital and Health Center, Glendale, CA, p. A62

GERMAN, Mike
    Chief Financial Officer, Cape Coral Hospital, Cape Coral, FL, p. A120
    Chief Financial Officer, Gulf Coast Medical Center, Fort Myers, FL, p. A124

GERMANN, William, M.D. Acting Chief of Staff, Dayton Veterans Affairs Medical Center, Dayton, OH, p. A479

GERMANY, Alan, Chief Financial Officer, Phoenix Baptist Hospital, Phoenix, AZ, p. A35

GERMUSKA, Natalie, MSN, Chief Executive Officer, Vibra Hospital of San Diego, San Diego, CA, p. A86

GERN, Sharon, R.N. Chief Nursing Officer, Ivinson Memorial Hospital, Laramie, WY, p. A702

GERNDT, Angie, Human Resources Manager, Central Community Hospital, Elkader, IA, p. A221

GERNHART, Diana, Chief Financial Officer, OHSU Hospital, Portland, OR, p. A516

GERRIOR, Marilyn, R.N. Chief Nursing Executive, Saint Louise Regional Hospital, Gilroy, CA, p. A62

GERRITS, Brad, Director Information Systems, Lakeview Medical Center, Rice Lake, WI, p. A696

GERSCH, Aaron, M.D. Chief of Staff, Albany Area Hospital and Medical Center, Albany, MN, p. A328

GERSHONE, Fern, Vice President Human Resources, Mille Lacs Health System, Onamia, MN, p. A337

GERSON, Elaine, Chief Clinical Officer and General Counsel, Aspen Valley Hospital District, Aspen, CO, p. A97

GERSTNER, Nancy, Manager Human Resources, Robert J. Dole Veterans Affairs Medical Center, Wichita, KS, p. A246

GERTEN, Michael E., Chief Executive Officer, Solara Hospital of Shawnee, Shawnee, OK, p. A506

GERTENBACH, Jennifer, Director Human Resources, Inova Fair Oaks Hospital, Fairfax, VA, p. A653

GERTH, Kevin, M.D. Chief of Staff, Spectrum Health Gerber Memorial, Fremont, MI, p. A314

GERVAIN, Edward, Chief Operating Officer, Adventist La Grange Memorial Hospital, La Grange, IL, p. A186

GERVELER, Patrick M., Vice President Finance and Chief Financial Officer, Blessing Hospital, Quincy, IL, p. A193

GESSEL, Thomas, FACHE, President and Chief Executive Officer, Mercy Regional Medical Center, Durango, CO, p. A100

GESSNER, Christopher, President, Children's Hospital of Pittsburgh of UPMC, Pittsburgh, PA, p. A537

GETMAN, Sylvia, President and Chief Executive Officer, The Aroostook Medical Center, Presque Isle, ME, p. A285

GETTINGER, Thomas, Executive Vice President and Chief Operating Officer, WakeMed Raleigh Campus, Raleigh, NC, p. A459

GETTINGS, Scott, M.D
    Vice President and Chief Medical Officer, Health First Holmes Regional Medical Center, Melbourne, FL, p. A130
    Vice President Medical Affairs, Health First Palm Bay Hospital, Melbourne, FL, p. A130

GETTO, Carl J., M.D. Senior Vice President Medical Affairs and Associate Dean Hospital Affairs, University of Wisconsin Hospital and Clinics, Madison, WI, p. A690

GETTYS, III, Roddey E., Chief Executive Officer, Baptist Easley Hospital, Easley, SC, p. A551

GETTYS, Sky, Chief Financial Officer, Fairfield Medical Center, Lancaster, OH, p. A483

GETWOOD, Charles, Assistant Chief Executive Officer, Calcasieu Oaks Geriatric Psychiatric Hospital, Lake Charles, LA, p. A271

GETZENDANER, Gail, Interim Director of Nursing, Missouri Rehabilitation Center, Mount Vernon, MO, p. A366

GEURTS, Chuck, Manager Management Information Services, Aurora BayCare Medical Center, Green Bay, WI, p. A687

GEWECKE, Tyler, Information Technology Technician, Fillmore County Hospital, Geneva, NE, p. A383

GFELLER, Michael, Director Information Systems, Medical Center of Plano, Plano, TX, p. A627

GHAFFARI, Bahram, Executive Director and Chief Financial Officer, Delano Regional Medical Center, Delano, CA, p. A58

GHALY, Christina, M.D., Interim Chief Executive Officer, LAC/University of Southern California Medical Center, Los Angeles, CA, p. A70

GHANI, Jamal, Chief Operating Officer, Metro Health Hospital, Wyoming, MI, p. A327

GHERINGHELLI, Thomas, Chief Financial Officer, New England Baptist Hospital, Boston, MA, p. A297

GHERKE, Sheila, Director Human Resources, Minnie Hamilton HealthCare Center, Grantsville, WV, p. A677

GHOSH, Tarun, Chief Information Officer, Fremont–Rideout Health Group, Marysville, CA, p. A73

GIAMALIS, John N., Senior Vice President and Chief Financial Officer, Saint Francis Hospital and Medical Center, Hartford, CT, p. A109

GIANCOLA, Louis R., President and Chief Executive Officer, South County Hospital, Wakefield, RI, p. A547

GIANELLI, Arthur A., President and Chief Executive Officer, Nassau University Medical Center, East Meadow, NY, p. A425

GIANFORTUNE, Theresa, Chief Human Resources Officer, Marin General Hospital, Greenbrae, CA, p. A63

GIANG, Daniel, M.D. Vice President for Medical Administration, Loma Linda University Medical Center, Loma Linda, CA, p. A66

GIANGARDELLA, Mike, Vice President Finance and Administration, Salem Community Hospital, Salem, OH, p. A489

GIANNUZZI, Donna, R.N. Chief Patient Care Officer, Gulf Coast Medical Center, Fort Myers, FL, p. A124

GIANSANTE, Joseph, Vice President Human Resources, Ellis Hospital, Schenectady, NY, p. A442

GIARDINA, Deborah, Director Human Resources and Medical Staff Services, Rehabilitation Hospital of Fort Wayne, Fort Wayne, IN, p. A203

GIBBARD, Laura, Vice President Human Resources, McLaren Oakland, Pontiac, MI, p. A322

GIBBENS, Lori, Controller, HEALTHSOUTH Rehabilitation Hospital of Erie, Erie, PA, p. A525

GIBBERMAN, Val, M.D. Acting Chief of Staff, Hampton Veterans Affairs Medical Center, Hampton, VA, p. A655

GIBBONS, David
   Chief Information Officer, Glendale Memorial Hospital and Health Center, Glendale, CA, p. A62
   Executive Vice President and Chief Operating Officer, UPMC Hamot, Erie, PA, p. A526

GIBBONS, H. Ray, FACHE, Chief Executive Officer, Saint Alphonsus Medical Center – Baker City, Baker City, OR, p. A511

GIBBONS, Jason, Chief Financial Officer, Minidoka Memorial Hospital, Rupert, ID, p. A171

GIBBS, Marc, Interim Chief Information Officer, Brookhaven Memorial Hospital Medical Center, Patchogue, NY, p. A439

GIBBS-MCELVY, Shelana, M.D. Medical Director, HEALTHSOUTH Rehabilitation Hospital, Sewickley, PA, p. A541

GIBSON, Amy, Chief Executive Officer, Jackson Medical Center, Jackson, AL, p. A22

GIBSON, Armetria, Human Resources Generalist, Kindred Hospital–Atlanta, Atlanta, GA, p. A146

GIBSON, Belinda D., R.N. Vice President Patient Services, Baptist St. Anthony Health System, Amarillo, TX, p. A582

GIBSON, Connie, R.N. Director Human Resources, Novant Health Gaffney Medical Center, Gaffney, SC, p. A552

GIBSON, Debra R., Chief Executive Officer, Select Specialty Hospital–Panama City, Panama City, FL, p. A136

GIBSON, Donald, M.D. Chief Medical Officer, Memorial Hermann Memorial City Medical Center, Houston, TX, p. A610

GIBSON III, Earnest, Administrator, Riverside General Hospital, Houston, TX, p. A611

GIBSON, Gerald, Director Human Resources, Walter P. Reuther Psychiatric Hospital, Westland, MI, p. A326

GIBSON, Joel, Vice President Human Resources, Henry Ford Macomb Hospitals, Clinton Township, MI, p. A311

GIBSON, Mary Helen, Director Human Resources, Floyd Valley Hospital, Le Mars, IA, p. A224

GIBSON, Megan, Nurse Manager, River Bend Hospital, West Lafayette, IN, p. A215

GIBSON, Miles, M.D. Chief of Staff, Russell County Hospital, Russell Springs, KY, p. A260

GIBSON, Richard
   Senior Vice President and Chief Information Officer, Legacy Emanuel Hospital and Health Center, Portland, OR, p. A516
   Chief Information Officer, Providence Portland Medical Center, Portland, OR, p. A516

GIBSON, Robert, Senior Director Operating Services, OSF Saint Elizabeth Medical Center, Ottawa, IL, p. A191

GIBSON, Valerie, Chief Operating Officer, Harper University Hospital/Hutzel Women's Hospital, Detroit, MI, p. A312

GIBSON, William R.
   Chief Executive Officer, Hastings Regional Center, Hastings, NE, p. A384
   Chief Executive Officer, Lincoln Regional Center, Lincoln, NE, p. A385
   Chief Executive Officer, Norfolk Regional Center, Norfolk, NE, p. A386

GICZI, Mary Beth, Director Human Resources, HEALTHSOUTH Scottsdale Rehabilitation Hospital, Scottsdale, AZ, p. A37

GIDDINGS, Claudia, R.N. Chief Nursing Officer, Our Community Hospital, Scotland Neck, NC, p. A460

GIDDINGS, Wayne, Manager Management Information Systems, East Valley Hospital Medical Center, Glendora, CA, p. A63

GIDEON, Dawn M., Interim Chief Executive Officer, Doctors Medical Center–San Pablo Campus, San Pablo, CA, p. A88

GIEGER, Julie
   Chief Financial Officer, Pioneer Community Hospital of Aberdeen, Aberdeen, MS, p. A344
   Chief Financial Officer, Pioneer Community Hospital of Newton, Newton, MS, p. A352
   Chief Financial Officer, Pioneer Community Hospital of Patrick County, Stuart, VA, p. A662
   Chief Financial Officer, S. E. Lackey Memorial Hospital, Forest, MS, p. A347

GIEKEN, Lisa, Director Human Resources, Gothenburg Memorial Hospital, Gothenburg, NE, p. A384

GIENGER, Del, Director Financial Services, Frances Mahon Deaconess Hospital, Glasgow, MT, p. A376

GIESE, Angela C., Director Human Resources, Midwest Regional Medical Center, Midwest City, OK, p. A501

GIESE, Jon, Vice President and Chief Financial Officer, Simi Valley Hospital and Health Care Services, Simi Valley, CA, p. A91

GIESECKE, Guy, Chief Operations Officer, Baptist Hospitals of Southeast Texas, Beaumont, TX, p. A587

GIESKI, Denise S., MS, Chief Executive Officer, Tyler Memorial Hospital, Tunkhannock, PA, p. A542

GIFFORD, Dean, M.D. Chief of Staff, Wabash County Hospital, Wabash, IN, p. A214

GIFFORD, Ellen, Director Human Resources, Deaconess Hospital, Oklahoma City, OK, p. A503

GIGLIOTTI, Vicki, Chief Clinical Officer, Moab Regional Hospital, Moab, UT, p. A644

GIGOT, Kelly, Assistant Administrator and Chief Financial Officer, St. Vincent Hospital, Green Bay, WI, p. A688

GIJANTO, Charles
   President, Baystate Northern Region, Baystate Franklin Medical Center, Greenfield, MA, p. A300
   President, Baystate Mary Lane Hospital, Ware, MA, p. A306

GIL, Julio, Manager Information Services, Hazel Hawkins Memorial Hospital, Hollister, CA, p. A64

GILB, Robert, Director Information Services, Shriners Hospitals for Children–Chicago, Chicago, IL, p. A179

GILBERT, Andrea F., FACHE, President, Bryn Mawr Hospital, Bryn Mawr, PA, p. A521

GILBERT, Carla, Controller, Cedar County Memorial Hospital, El Dorado Springs, MO, p. A360

GILBERT, Jack, Vice President Finance and Support Services, Advocate Illinois Masonic Medical Center, Chicago, IL, p. A176

GILBERT, Jeri, Director Human Resources, Watsonville Community Hospital, Watsonville, CA, p. A95

GILBERT, Kevin, R.N. Director Surgical and Operations, Wenatchee Valley Medical Center, Wenatchee, WA, p. A674

GILBERT, Kim, R.N. Chief Nursing Officer, Electra Memorial Hospital, Electra, TX, p. A602

GILBERT, Jr., Ronald, Chief Financial Officer, Soldiers and Sailors Memorial Hospital, Wellsboro, PA, p. A543

GILBERT, Thomas, Director Information Technology Services, Lake Cumberland Regional Hospital, Somerset, KY, p. A260

GILBERT, Thomas D., FACHE, Chief Executive Officer, Wadley Regional Medical Center, Texarkana, TX, p. A637

GILBERT, Valarie, R.N. Chief Nursing Officer, Texas Health Harris Methodist Hospital Azle, Azle, TX, p. A586

GILBERTSON, Gerry, FACHE, Administrator, CentraCare Health–Melrose, Melrose, MN, p. A335

GILBERTSON, Lesley, M.D., Executive and Medical Director, University Pointe Surgical Hospital, West Chester, OH, p. A493

GILCHRIST, Doug, Chief Operating Officer, Summit Healthcare Regional Medical Center, Show Low, AZ, p. A37

GILDEA, Christine R., Director Marketing and Community Relations, J. C. Blair Memorial Hospital, Huntingdon, PA, p. A527

GILDEA, Stephen, Chief Executive Officer, Tyrone Hospital, Tyrone, PA, p. A542

GILDON, Lisa, Chief Financial Officer, North Central Surgical Center, Dallas, TX, p. A597

GILENE, Joseph, Interim Chief Executive Officer, Morehead Memorial Hospital, Eden, NC, p. A451

GILES, Jared, Chief Operating Officer, Southwest Healthcare System, Murrieta, CA, p. A76

GILES, Steve, Chief Information Officer, Hollywood Presbyterian Medical Center, Los Angeles, CA, p. A69

GILGEN, Steve, Chief Financial Officer, Murphy Medical Center, Murphy, NC, p. A458

GILHAM, Merlin, Chief Executive Officer, U. S. Public Health Service Blackfeet Community Hospital, Saint Mary, MT, p. A379

GILKEY, Edward, M.D. Vice President Medical Affairs, St. Luke's Hospital – Warren Campus, Phillipsburg, NJ, p. A409

GILL, Brian, Chief Executive Officer, Sonora Behavioral Health Hospital, Tucson, AZ, p. A39

GILL, Margaret, Chief Executive Officer, Memorial Health, Savannah, GA, p. A160

GILL, Mark, Vice President Finance and Chief Financial Officer, Cape Regional Medical Center, Cape May Court House, NJ, p. A402

GILL, Robert D., Chief Financial Officer, Woodwinds Health Campus, Woodbury, MN, p. A343

GILLAM, Sally A., R.N. Chief Nursing Officer, St. David's South Austin Medical Center, Austin, TX, p. A586

GILLEN, Kristin, R.N. Vice President of Patient Care Services, Three Rivers Medical Center, Grants Pass, OR, p. A513

GILLEN, Mark T., Director Finance and Operations, Owatonna Hospital, Owatonna, MN, p. A337

GILLEN, Michael J., FACHE, President, Mercy Hospital Lebanon, Lebanon, MO, p. A364

GILLES, Ken
   Chief Information Officer, Essentia Health Fargo, Fargo, ND, p. A466
   Associate Chief Information Officer, Essentia Health St. Mary's Hospital – Detroit Lakes, Detroit Lakes, MN, p. A331

GILLESPIE, Anne, R.N. Associate Director Patient Care and Nursing Services, Veterans Affairs Loma Linda Healthcare System, Loma Linda, CA, p. A67

GILLESPIE, Christina, Chief Financial Officer, Harrison County Community Hospital, Bethany, MO, p. A356

GILLESPIE, Karen, Director Human Resources, Anderson County Hospital, Garnett, KS, p. A234

GILLESPIE, Lisa, M.D. Chief Medical Officer, Rockdale Medical Center, Conyers, GA, p. A151

GILLESPIE, Lynn J., Vice President Human Resources and Organizational Development, OSF Saint Francis Medical Center, Peoria, IL, p. A192

GILLESPIE, Michele, Vice President of Operations, Southwest Medical Center, Liberal, KS, p. A238

GILLESPIE, Tim, Manager Information Systems, Richland Memorial Hospital, Olney, IL, p. A191

GILLETTE, Daniel, M.D., Clinical Director, Mental Health Institute, Cherokee, IA, p. A218

GILLETTE, Kathryn, President and Chief Executive Officer, Bayfront Health St. Petersburg, Saint Petersburg, FL, p. A138

GILLETTE, Robert, Chief Information Officer, St. Elizabeth Medical Center, Utica, NY, p. A444

GILLETTE, Tom, Vice President and Chief Information Officer, Mount Sinai Medical Center, Miami Beach, FL, p. A133

GILLIAM, Eric, President, Saint Joseph East, Lexington, KY, p. A254

GILLIAM, Leslie, Director Health Information Management, Dominion Hospital, Falls Church, VA, p. A653

GILLIAN, Tom, Chief Operating Officer, River Bend Hospital, West Lafayette, IN, p. A215

GILLIANO, Patti, Chief Nursing Officer, Lake Pointe Medical Center, Rowlett, TX, p. A630

GILLIGAN, Candace L., Chief Executive Officer, Middle Tennessee Mental Health Institute, Nashville, TN, p. A576

GILLIS, Anne, Chief Financial Officer, Holy Cross Hospital, Silver Spring, MD, p. A294

GILLIS, Mike
   Controller, Select Specialty Hospital–Knoxville, Knoxville, TN, p. A572
   Controller, Select Specialty Hospital–North Knoxville, Knoxville, TN, p. A572

GILLIS, Wayne, Interim Chief Executive Officer, Phoenix Baptist Hospital, Phoenix, AZ, p. A35

GILLMAN, Jerry E., Chief Executive Officer, Tri–County Hospital – Williston, Williston, FL, p. A144

GILLMAN, Kreg, Chief Executive Officer, Montevista Hospital, Las Vegas, NV, p. A393

GILMAN, Howard, M.D. Medical Executive, Christian Health Care Center, Wyckoff, NJ, p. A413

GILMAN, Kim, Chief Administrative Officer, Phoebe Worth Medical Center, Sylvester, GA, p. A161

GILMORE, Hugh V., M.D. Vice President Medical Affairs, Seton Medical Center Williamson, Round Rock, TX, p. A629

GILMORE, Linda, Chief Nursing Officer/Chief Administrative Officer, Littleton Regional Hospital, Littleton, NH, p. A399

GILMORE, Phillip K., FACHE, Chief Executive Officer, Ashley County Medical Center, Crossett, AR, p. A42

GILMORE, Stephen, Chief Financial Officer, Saint Vincent Hospital, Worcester, MA, p. A306

GILPIN, Ann C., President and Chief Executive Officer, Oswego Hospital, Oswego, NY, p. A439

GILPIN, Michael W., Vice President Human Resources, Sampson Regional Medical Center, Clinton, NC, p. A450

GILTNER, Michelle, Interim Chief Nursing Officer, UH Regional Hospitals, Cleveland, OH, p. A477

GIN, Nancy, M.D. Area Associate Medical Director, Kaiser Permanente Anaheim Medical Center, Anaheim, CA, p. A52

GINGHER, Barbara S., R.N. Assistant Administrator for Patient Care Services, Baptist Medical Center Nassau, Fernandina Beach, FL, p. A123

GINN, Bobby, Chief Operating Officer, Crestwood Medical Center, Huntsville, AL, p. A21

GINN, Doug, Executive Vice President Operations, Peak Behavioral Health Services, Santa Teresa, NM, p. A418

GINSBERG, Ronald L., M.D. Vice President Medical Affairs, Northwest Hospital, Randallstown, MD, p. A293

GINSBURG, J. Lawrence, M.D. Vice President Medical Affairs, Evangelical Community Hospital, Lewisburg, PA, p. A530

GINTY, Neil W.
   Administrator, Louis Smith Memorial Hospital, Lakeland, GA, p. A155
   Administrator, South Georgia Medical Center Berrien Campus, Nashville, GA, p. A158

GIOIA, Anthony, Chief Financial Officer, Indiana Orthopaedic Hospital, Indianapolis, IN, p. A205

GIOIA, Gregory J., Chief Fiscal and Administrative Services, Veterans Home and Hospital, Rocky Hill, CT, p. A111

GIONFRIDDO, Paul, MS Vice President Human Resources, Moses Taylor Hospital, Scranton, PA, p. A540

GIORDANO, Paul, Vice President Human Resources, South Nassau Communities Hospital, Oceanside, NY, p. A438

GIORDANO, Roger, M.D. Medical Director, HEALTHSOUTH Rehabilitation Hospital of Virginia, Richmond, VA, p. A660

GIOVANETTI, Victor, President and Chief Executive Officer, Lewis-Gale Medical Center, Salem, VA, p. A661

GIPSON, David N., Senior Vice President and Chief Clinical Operations Officer, Union Hospital, Elkton, MD, p. A291

GIPSON, Linda Stephens, MSN Chief Nursing Officer, Whidbey General Hospital, Coupeville, WA, p. A666

GIRARD, Thomas R.
   Vice President Human Resources, Miles Memorial Hospital, Damariscotta, ME, p. A283
   Vice President Human Resources, Pen Bay Medical Center, Rockport, ME, p. A285
   Vice President Human Resources, St. Andrews Hospital and Healthcare Center, Boothbay Harbor, ME, p. A282

GIRARDIER, Cheryl, Director Information Technology, Millcreek Community Hospital, Erie, PA, p. A525

GIRTEN, David M.
   Corporate Director Financial Services, St. Vincent Seton Specialty Hospital, Indianapolis, IN, p. A206
   Corporate Director Financial Services, St. Vincent Seton Specialty Hospital, Lafayette, IN, p. A208

GIRTY, Tara, Director Human Resources, Kiowa District Hospital and Manor, Kiowa, KS, p. A237

GISH, Christine, R.N. Acute Care Director, St. Charles Madras, Madras, OR, p. A514

GISH, Kevin, Administrator and Vice President, Essentia Health Fosston, Fosston, MN, p. A332

GISH, Mary L., R.N. Vice President and Chief Nursing Officer, Sierra Nevada Memorial Hospital, Grass Valley, CA, p. A63

GISI, Richard, M.D. Chief Medical Officer, Citrus Valley Medical Center, Covina, CA, p. A58

GISLESON, Joni, Director Finance, Palmer Lutheran Health Center, West Union, IA, p. A230

GISSEL, Betty, Vice President Human Resources, University of Tennessee Medical Center, Knoxville, TN, p. A572

GITTELMAN, Michael B., Administrator, Bascom Palmer Eye Institute–Anne Bates Leach Eye Hospital, Miami, FL, p. A131

GIUDICE, William A., Vice President and Chief Financial Officer, Tallahassee Memorial HealthCare, Tallahassee, FL, p. A141

GIUGLIANO, Frank, M.D. Chief of Staff, Berwick Hospital Center, Berwick, PA, p. A520

GIULIANELLI, Victor, FACHE, President and Chief Executive Officer, St. Mary's Healthcare, Amsterdam, NY, p. A420

GIVENS, Michael K., FACHE Administrator, St. Bernards Medical Center, Jonesboro, AR, p. A45

GIVENS, Scott H., Director Human Resources, Flowers Hospital, Dothan, AL, p. A19

GIVENS, Stephen K., Assistant Vice President and Administrator, Russell County Medical Center, Lebanon, VA, p. A656

GIZINSKI, Judy, Chief Operating Officer, Health First Palm Bay Hospital, Melbourne, FL, p. A130

GIZZI, Jason, Controller, HEALTHSOUTH MountainView Regional Rehabilitation Hospital, Morgantown, WV, p. A679

GLAD, Cory, Director Human Resources, Community Memorial Hospital, Cloquet, MN, p. A330

GLADE, James, Director Human Resources, Mountain West Medical Center, Tooele, UT, p. A647

GLADFELTER, Sharon, Health Information Officer, Brook Lane Health Services, Hagerstown, MD, p. A292

GLADSTONE, Art, R.N., Chief Executive Officer, Straub Clinic & Hospital, Honolulu, HI, p. A165

GLANZER, Elgin, Chief Financial Officer, Memorial Health System, Abilene, KS, p. A231

GLASER, Ruth, President, Pender Memorial Hospital, Burgaw, NC, p. A448

GLASGO, Leah, Administrator and Chief Executive Officer, Stewart Memorial Community Hospital, Lake City, IA, p. A224

GLASNER, Greg, M.D., Interim President and Chief Executive Officer, Essentia Health Fargo, Fargo, ND, p. A466

GLASS, Deborah, R.N., Chief Executive Officer, Whitman Hospital and Medical Center, Colfax, WA, p. A665

GLASS, Gordon, Chief Financial Officer, Golden Valley Memorial Healthcare, Clinton, MO, p. A359

GLASS, Steven, Chief Financial Officer, Cleveland Clinic, Cleveland, OH, p. A476

GLASSBURN, David, Interim Chief Financial Officer, Palm Drive Hospital, Sebastopol, CA, p. A90

GLASSMAN, Randy, Chief Financial Officer, Little Colorado Medical Center, Winslow, AZ, p. A40

GLATT, Aaron, M.D., Executive Vice President and Chief Administrative Officer, Mercy Medical Center, Rockville Centre, NY, p. A441

CLAVES, Ann, Vice President Human Resources, St. Francis Regional Medical Center, Shakopee, MN, p. A341

GLAVIS, Edward S., Senior Vice President and Area Manager, Kaiser Permanente Roseville Medical Center, Roseville, CA, p. A83

GLAZIER, Alisha, Compliance Officer and Director Health Information Management, Mercy Hospital Watonga, Watonga, OK, p. A509

GLAZIER, Stephen, Chief Operating Officer, University of Texas Harris County Psychiatric Center, Houston, TX, p. A613

GLEASON, Amanda, Director Human Resources, Indiana Orthopaedic Hospital, Indianapolis, IN, p. A205

GLEASON, Jeffrey J., M.D. Chief Medical Officer, Cookeville Regional Medical Center, Cookeville, TN, p. A568

GLEASON, Mike, Vice President and Chief Financial Officer, Shands Jacksonville Medical Center, Jacksonville, FL, p. A126

GLECKLER, John, Chief Financial Officer, St. Vincent's Medical Center, Bridgeport, CT, p. A108

GLEDHILL, John E., Chief Operating Officer, Central Valley Medical Center, Nephi, UT, p. A645

GLEISNER, Roger, Interim Chief Executive Officer, Rehoboth McKinley Christian Health Care Services, Gallup, NM, p. A416

GLEN, Diane M., Assistant Administrator, Barnes–Jewish West County Hospital, Saint Louis, MO, p. A369

GLENN, Jeannette, Vice President Human Resources, Education and Training, McLeod Regional Medical Center, Florence, SC, p. A552

GLENN, Mike, Administrator and Chief Executive Officer, Jefferson Healthcare, Port Townsend, WA, p. A669

GLENN, Sue, Director Administrative Services, Kalamazoo Psychiatric Hospital, Kalamazoo, MI, p. A318

GLENN, Susan, Chief Executive Officer, HEALTHSOUTH Rehabilitation Hospital, Kingsport, TN, p. A571

GLENN, Wil A., Director Communications, Larry B. Zieverink, Sr. Alcoholism Treatment Center, Raleigh, NC, p. A459

GLENNIE, Stacy, Director Health Information Services, Pratt Regional Medical Center, Pratt, KS, p. A243

GLENNING, Robert, Executive Vice President Finance and Chief Financial Officer, Hackensack University Medical Center, Hackensack, NJ, p. A404

GLEZEN, Joseph W., M.P.H. Director Human Resources, Southeastern Health, Lumberton, NC, p. A457

GLICKMAN, Bobby, M.D. Chief of Staff, Sutter Delta Medical Center, Antioch, CA, p. A52

GLIDDEN, Nancy, Chief Financial Officer, Calais Regional Hospital, Calais, ME, p. A282

GLIDDEN, Weldon, Chief of Staff, Chillicothe Hospital District, Chillicothe, TX, p. A592

GLIDEWELL Jr., Calvin E., Chief Executive Officer, Broward Health Medical Center, Fort Lauderdale, FL, p. A123

GLIELMI, Vincent D., D.O. Senior Vice President Medical Affairs, Ephrata Community Hospital, Ephrata, PA, p. A525

GLINIECKI, Charlene, Vice President Human Resources, El Camino Hospital, Mountain View, CA, p. A75

GLOCKNER, Cheri, Director Development, Carson Tahoe Regional Healthcare, Carson City, NV, p. A391

GLODOWSKI, Brenda, Chief Financial Officer, North Central Health Care, Wausau, WI, p. A699

GLOGGNER, Peter, Vice President Human Resources, Union Hospital, Elkton, MD, p. A291

GLONER, James, Senior Vice President, North Philadelphia Health System, Philadelphia, PA, p. A536

GLOSEMEYER, Talitha, M.P.H., Administrator, Norman Specialty Hospital, Norman, OK, p. A502

GLOSS, John, FACHE, Administrator, Shriners Hospitals for Children–St. Louis, Saint Louis, MO, p. A370

GLOTZBACH, Karen, Acting Associate Director, Veterans Affairs Eastern Kansas Health Care System, Topeka, KS, p. A245

GLOTZBACK, Lee, Director Human Resources, Citrus Memorial Health System, Inverness, FL, p. A126

GLOVER, Cynthia, R.N. Chief Nursing Officer, Reston Hospital Center, Reston, VA, p. A659

GLOVER, Doug, Controller, William S. Hall Psychiatric Institute, Columbia, SC, p. A550

GLOVER, Kimberly, Director of Information Systems, Lake City Community Hospital, Lake City, SC, p. A554

GLOVER, Sharon, Director Human Resources, Somerset Hospital, Somerset, PA, p. A541

GLOWA, Meghan, Director Human Resources, Sunnyview Rehabilitation Hospital, Schenectady, NY, p. A442

GLUBKA, Theresa, Chief Executive Officer, Sutter Solano Medical Center, Vallejo, CA, p. A94

GLUCHOWSKI, Jeanne, Executive Director, Conifer Park, Glenville, NY, p. A426

GLUECKERT, John W., Administrator, Montana State Hospital, Warm Springs, MT, p. A380

GLYER, David, Vice President Finance, Community Memorial Health System, Ventura, CA, p. A94

GLYNN, Cindy, Director Human Resources, Regional Rehabilitation Hospital, Phenix City, AL, p. A24

GLYNN, John, Senior Vice President and Chief Information Officer, Unity Hospital, Rochester, NY, p. A441

GLYNN, Margaret, M.D. Chief Medical Officer, North Mississippi Medical Center–Iuka, Iuka, MS, p. A348

GLYNN, Shari, Vice President Finance and Chief Financial Officer, Eaton Rapids Medical Center, Eaton Rapids, MI, p. A313

GNAGEY, Keith, Chief Executive Officer, Teton Valley Health Care, Driggs, ID, p. A169

GNAM, Gwen, R.N. Chief Nursing Officer, Henry Ford Hospital, Detroit, MI, p. A312

GNANADEV, Dev, M.D. Medical Director, Arrowhead Regional Medical Center, Colton, CA, p. A57

GOACHER, Brad, Director Finance, Alton Memorial Hospital, Alton, IL, p. A173

GOAD, Pat, Director Human Resources, Hillcrest Hospital Claremore, Claremore, OK, p. A497

GOBEL, Bret, Chief Financial Officer, Sierra Vista Hospital, Truth or Consequences, NM, p. A418

GOBELL, James, Chief Financial Officer, UnityPoint Health St. Luke's, Sioux City, IA, p. A228

GOBLE, Jonathan R., FACHE, President and Chief Executive Officer, Indiana University Health North Hospital, Carmel, IN, p. A200

GOBLE, Mandy C., President and Chief Executive Officer, Mary Rutan Hospital, Bellefontaine, OH, p. A471

GOCHENOUR, Julia, Manager Information Systems, West River Regional Medical Center, Hettinger, ND, p. A467

GOCHIS, Paul D., M.D. Chief of Staff, St. Luke Community Healthcare, Ronan, MT, p. A379

GODDARD, Donald, M.D. Chief Medical Officer, Heatherhill Care Communities, Chardon, OH, p. A473

GODDARD, Mark, M.D. Medical Director, HEALTHSOUTH Rehabilitation Hospital at Drake, Cincinnati, OH, p. A474

GODESKY, Susan, Director Information Technology, Nanticoke Memorial Hospital, Seaford, DE, p. A114

GODFREY, Kristine, Director Human Resources, Skyridge Medical Center, Cleveland, TN, p. A567

GODFREY, Larry, Administrator, Seaside Health System, Gonzales, LA, p. A267

GODINEZ, Roxanna M., Chief Executive Officer, Cornerstone Regional Hospital, Edinburg, TX, p. A600

GODLEY, Maria, R.N., Chief Executive Officer, Northern Idaho Advanced Care Hospital, Post Falls, ID, p. A171

GODLEY, Patrick, Chief Financial Officer, Contra Costa Regional Medical Center, Martinez, CA, p. A73

GODSEY, Carol, Administrator, St. Mary's Warrick Hospital, Boonville, IN, p. A199

GODWIN, Jr., Herman A., M.D. Senior Vice President and Medical Director, Watauga Medical Center, Boone, NC, p. A448

GOEBEL, Bret, Finance Officer, Guadalupe County Hospital, Santa Rosa, NM, p. A418

GOEBEL, Donna, M.D. Chief Nursing Officer, Mitchell County Hospital, Colorado City, TX, p. A592

GOEBEL, Michael, Chief Executive Officer, Adventist Hinsdale Hospital, Hinsdale, IL, p. A185

GOEL, Amitabh, M.D. Chief Medical Officer, University Hospitals Geneva Medical Center, Geneva, OH, p. A482

GOELOE-ALSTON, Hendrina, Assistant Vice President Personnel, SUNY Downstate Medical Center University Hospital,, NY, p. A436

GOERKE, Karleen, R.N. Chief Nursing Officer, Swedish Medical Center, Englewood, CO, p. A100

GOESER, Stephen L., FACHE, President and Chief Executive Officer, Nebraska Methodist Hospital, Omaha, NE, p. A388

GOETTSCH, Barry, Chief Executive Officer, UnityPoint Health – Marengo Memorial Hospital, Marengo, IA, p. A224

GOETZINGER, Susan, Chief Financial Officer, Riverton Memorial Hospital, Riverton, WY, p. A703

GOFF, Gary E., M.D. Medical Director, Texas Specialty Hospital at Dallas, Dallas, TX, p. A598

GOFF, Mark, Owner and Administrator, Community Specialty Hospital, Lafayette, LA, p. A270

GOFORTH, Annette, Manager Administrative Services, Central Prison Hospital, Raleigh, NC, p. A459

GOGGIN, Kathy, Director Administrative Services, Devereux Georgia Treatment Network, Kennesaw, GA, p. A155

GOGIA, Harmohinder, M.D. Chief Medical Officer, Western Medical Center Anaheim, Anaheim, CA, p. A52

GOGLIETTINO, Deborah
Senior Vice President Human Resources, Manchester Memorial Hospital, Manchester, CT, p. A109
Senior Vice President Human Resources, Rockville General Hospital, Vernon Rockville, CT, p. A112

GOHNER, Cindy, Vice President Clinical Services, Jamestown Regional Medical Center, Jamestown, ND, p. A467

GOICK, Rose, MSN, Administrative Director of Operations, St. Mary's of Michigan Standish Hospital, Standish, MI, p. A325

GOINGS, Harold, Chief Human Resources, Veterans Affairs Greater Los Angeles Healthcare System, Los Angeles, CA, p. A72

GOLAS, Catherine, Administrator, Isham Health Center, Andover, MA, p. A295

GOLD, Joseph, M.D. Chief Medical Officer, McLean Hospital, Belmont, MA, p. A295

GOLDAMMER, Kyle, Chief Financial Officer, Sioux Falls Specialty Hospital, Sioux Falls, SD, p. A562

GOLDBERG, Andrew S., Associate Executive Director, Syosset Hospital, Syosset, NY, p. A443

GOLDBERG, David, M.D. Vice President Medical Affairs, Community Memorial Hospital, Menomonee Falls, WI, p. A691

GOLDBERG, David S., President, Baptist Medical Center, San Antonio, TX, p. A630

GOLDBERG, Frederick, M.D. Vice President Medical Affairs and Chief Medical Officer, Nathan Littauer Hospital and Nursing Home, Gloversville, NY, p. A426

GOLDBERG, Jonathan, Chief Information Officer, St. Peter's Hospital, Albany, NY, p. A420

GOLDBERG, Larry M., President and Chief Executive Officer, Loyola University Medical Center, Maywood, IL, p. A188

GOLDBERG, Paul R., Chief Financial Officer, LibertyHealth–Jersey City Medical Center, Jersey City, NJ, p. A405

GOLDBERG, Richard L., M.D., President, MedStar Georgetown University Hospital, Washington, DC, p. A116

GOLDBERG, Stanley, M.D. Chief of Staff, St. Mary Medical Center, Long Beach, CA, p. A67

GOLDBERG, Stephanie J., MSN Senior Vice President and Chief Nursing Officer, Hospital for Special Surgery, New York, NY, p. A432

GOLDBERGER, Joseph, M.D
Chief Medical Officer, Yavapai Regional Medical Center – East, Prescott Valley, AZ, p. A36
Chief Medical Officer, Yavapai Regional Medical Center, Prescott, AZ, p. A36

GOLDBLOOM, Alan L., M.D.,
Chief Executive Officer, Children's Hospitals and Clinics of Minnesota, Minneapolis, MN, p. A336
Chief Executive Officer, Children's Hospitals and Clinics of Minnesota, Saint Paul, MN, p. A340

GOLDEN, Joy, Chief Executive Officer, Lakeside Behavioral Health System, Memphis, TN, p. A574

GOLDENBERG, Dianne, Chief Executive Officer, Aventura Hospital and Medical Center, Aventura, FL, p. A118

GOLDFARB, Timothy M., Chief Executive Officer, Shands at the University of Florida, Gainesville, FL, p. A124

GOLDFISHER, Anne M., R.N. Chief Nursing Officer, Kaiser Permanente Santa Clara Medical Center, Santa Clara, CA, p. A89

GOLDFRACH, Andrew, Assistant Chief Executive Officer, Chestnut Hill Hospital, Philadelphia, PA, p. A534

GOLDMAN, Bruce, Chief Operating Officer, The HSC Pediatric Center, Washington, DC, p. A117

GOLDMAN, David, M.D. Vice President Medical Affairs and Education, Prince George's Hospital Center, Cheverly, MD, p. A290

GOLDMAN, Eric, Chief Executive Officer, Palms West Hospital, Loxahatchee, FL, p. A129

GOLDMAN, John S., Director, Carl Vinson Veterans Affairs Medical Center, Dublin, GA, p. A152

GOLDSCHMID, David, M.D. President Medical Staff, Seton Medical Center, Daly City, CA, p. A58

GOLDSMITH, Cheri L.
Director Financial Services, Parkland Health Center, Farmington, MO, p. A360
Director Financial Services, Parkland Health Center–Bonne Terre, Bonne Terre, MO, p. A356

GOLDSMITH, Dana L., M.D. Vice President Medical Affairs, Pen Bay Medical Center, Rockport, ME, p. A285

GOLDSMITH, Debra, Regional Administrator, Alegent Creighton Health Mercy Hospital, Corning, IA, p. A218

GOLDSTEIN, Allan, M.D. Medical Director and Chief of Staff, Select Specialty Hospital–Birmingham, Birmingham, AL, p. A17

GOLDSTEIN, Brian, M.D. Executive Vice President and Chief Operating Officer, University of North Carolina Hospitals, Chapel Hill, NC, p. A449

GOLDSTEIN, Charles, M.D. President Medical Staff, Riverside Shore Memorial Hospital, Nassawadox, VA, p. A657

GOLDSTEIN, Gary W., M.D., President and Chief Executive Officer, Kennedy Krieger Institute, Baltimore, MD, p. A287

GOLDSTEIN, Lisa, Executive Vice President and Chief Operating Officer, Hospital for Special Surgery, New York, NY, p. A432

GOLDSTEIN, Mark L., Chief Financial Officer, Anna Jaques Hospital, Newburyport, MA, p. A302

GOLDSTEIN, III, Nathan, M.D. Chief Medical Officer, Northwest Texas Healthcare System, Amarillo, TX, p. A582

GOLDSTEIN, Paul, Vice President Finance and Chief Financial Officer, Orlando Regional Medical Center, Orlando, FL, p. A135

GOLDSTEIN, Stephen, Director Information Systems, Regional Medical Center–Bayonet Point, Hudson, FL, p. A126

GOLDSTEIN, Steven I.
President and Chief Executive Officer, Highland Hospital of Rochester, Rochester, NY, p. A441
President and Chief Executive Officer, Strong Memorial Hospital of the University of Rochester, Rochester, NY, p. A441

GOLDSTEIN, Stuart, D.O. Chief of Staff, LewisGale Hospital at Pulaski, Pulaski, VA, p. A659

GOLDSTEIN, Wendy Z., President and Chief Executive Officer, Lutheran Medical Center,, NY, p. A433

GOLDSWORTHY, Patty, Interim Chief Executive Officer and Administrator, Pershing General Hospital, Lovelock, NV, p. A394

GOLDSZER, Robert, M.D. Senior Vice President and Chief Medical Officer, Mount Sinai Medical Center, Miami Beach, FL, p. A133

GOLER, Michael, M.D. Chief Medical Officer, South Lake Hospital, Clermont, FL, p. A120

GOLIGHTLY, Beverly, Director Information Technology, St. Vincent's East, Birmingham, AL, p. A17

GOLLAHER, Jeffrey, Chief Executive Officer, Hendricks Community Hospital, Hendricks, MN, p. A333

GOLOMB, Harvey, M.D. Chief Medical Officer, University of Chicago Medical Center, Chicago, IL, p. A180

GOLOVAN, Ronald, M.D. Vice President Medical Operations, Lutheran Hospital, Cleveland, OH, p. A476

GOMAN, Valerie, M.D. President Medical Staff, Baylor Medical Center at Waxahachie, Waxahachie, TX, p. A640

GOMBAR, Greg A.
Chief Financial Officer, Carolinas Medical Center, Charlotte, NC, p. A449
Chief Financial Officer, Carolinas Medical Center–Mercy, Charlotte, NC, p. A449
Chief Financial Officer, Carolinas Medical Center–University, Charlotte, NC, p. A449

GOMES, Carol, FACHE Chief Operating Officer, Stony Brook University Medical Center, Stony Brook, NY, p. A443

GOMES, Robert
Chief Executive Officer, Pioneer Memorial Hospital, Prineville, OR, p. A517
Chief Executive Officer, St. Charles Medical Center – Redmond, Redmond, OR, p. A517

GOMEZ, Carmen, Director Human Resources, North Shore Medical Center, Miami, FL, p. A132

GOMEZ, Gloria, M.D. Medical Director, East Mississippi State Hospital, Meridian, MS, p. A351

GOMEZ, Lynn M., Executive Director Human Resources, San Gorgonio Memorial Hospital, Banning, CA, p. A54

GOMEZ, Mike, Site Manager Medical Information Systems, Our Lady of Bellefonte Hospital, Ashland, KY, p. A248

GOMEZ, Omar, M.D. Chief of Staff, Cornerstone Regional Hospital, Edinburg, TX, p. A600

GOMEZ, Robin, Administrator, Alvarado Hospital, San Diego, CA, p. A84

GOMEZ, Teresa, Chief Nursing Officer, Fort Loudoun Medical Center, Lenoir City, TN, p. A573

GONDER, Christie, Chief Nursing Officer, Sierra Vista Regional Medical Center, San Luis Obispo, CA, p. A88

GONGAWARE, Robert, Senior Vice President Finance, Indiana Regional Medical Center, Indiana, PA, p. A528

GONYEA, Sonja, Director Human Resources, United Memorial Medical Center, Batavia, NY, p. A421

GONZALES, D. V., Head Information Technology Management, Naval Medical Center San Diego, San Diego, CA, p. A85

GONZALES, Ed
Vice PResident Human Resources, St. John's Pleasant Valley Hospital, Camarillo, CA, p. A55
Vice President Human Resources, St. John's Regional Medical Center, Oxnard, CA, p. A78

GONZALES, Jan, Director Human Resources, North Valley Hospital, Tonasket, WA, p. A673

GONZALES, Mary Ann, M.D. Medical Director, Central Texas Rehabilitation Hospital, Austin, TX, p. A584

GONZALES, Pamela, Chief Operating Officer, Anson General Hospital, Anson, TX, p. A583

GONZALES, Patricia, Chief Executive Officer, Eastern Louisiana Mental Health System, Jackson, LA, p. A269

GONZALES, Rachel Ann, R.N., Chief Executive Officer, Madison Memorial Hospital, Rexburg, ID, p. A171

GONZALEZ, Arthur A., FACHE, Chief Executive Officer, Denver Health Medical Center, Denver, CO, p. A99

GONZALEZ, Aurelio, Chief Financial Officer, University Hospital and Medical Center, Tamarac, FL, p. A141

GONZALEZ, Dinah, Chief Financial Officer, Doctors Hospital of Laredo, Laredo, TX, p. A618

GONZALEZ, Erin, Director Human Resources and Education, Maryvale Hospital Medical Center, Phoenix, AZ, p. A34

GONZALEZ, Hugo, M.D. Chief Medical Officer, Sister Emmanuel Hospital, Miami, FL, p. A132

GONZALEZ, Jaime, Administrator, St. Catherine's Rehabilitation Hospital, North Miami, FL, p. A134

GONZALEZ, James R., Acting President and Chief Executive Officer, University of Medicine and Dentistry of New Jersey–University Hospital, Newark, NJ, p. A407

GONZALEZ, Joni, Controller, Kindred Hospital Dallas Central, Dallas, TX, p. A596

GONZALEZ, Jorge F., M.D. Chief Medical Officer, Florida Hospital Heartland Medical Center, Sebring, FL, p. A140

GONZALEZ, Rebecca
Director Human Resources, Parkview LaGrange Hospital, LaGrange, IN, p. A208
Manager Human Resources, Parkview Noble Hospital, Kendallville, IN, p. A207

GONZALEZ, Robert, M.D., Director, Ventura County Medical Center, Ventura, CA, p. A94

GONZALEZ, Sonia I., R.N. Chief Operating Officer, Oak Hill Hospital, Brooksville, FL, p. A120

GONZALEZ–FAJARDO, Ana, Human Resources Director, Palmetto General Hospital, Hialeah, FL, p. A125

GOOCH, Chris, Information Technology Director, Hermann Area District Hospital, Hermann, MO, p. A361

GOOCH, Matthew, Chief Operating Officer, Jennersville Regional Hospital, West Grove, PA, p. A544

GOOCH, Patricia Pidge, Chief Nursing Officer, Doctors Hospital of Manteca, Manteca, CA, p. A73

GOOD, Scott, Manager Information Services, Kearny County Hospital, Lakin, KS, p. A237

GOOD, Vance A., M.D. Chief Medical Staff, Troy Community Hospital, Troy, PA, p. A542

GOODALL, David, M.D. Chief Medical Staff, Essentia Health–Deer River, Deer River, MN, p. A331

GOODBALIAN, Terry, Vice President Finance and Chief Financial Officer, Henry Ford Macomb Hospitals, Clinton Township, MI, p. A311

GOODE, Lori, Director Human Resources, Baptist Memorial Hospital–Union County, New Albany, MS, p. A352

GOODE, Richard P., Chief Financial Officer, Cook Children's Medical Center, Fort Worth, TX, p. A603

GOODE, Shayne, Administrator, Warm Springs Specialty Hospital of New Braunfels, New Braunfels, TX, p. A624

GOODE, Vicky, Director Human Resources, LifeCare Hospitals of North Carolina, Rocky Mount, NC, p. A460

GOODIN, Debbie, Vice President Human Resources, Mills–Peninsula Health Services, Burlingame, CA, p. A55

GOODISON, Sharon A., R.N. Chief Nursing Officer, Jackson Hospital and Clinic, Montgomery, AL, p. A23

GOODLETT, Lisa, Chief Financial Officer, Baptist Medical Center South, Montgomery, AL, p. A23

GOODMAN, Brenda, Chief Nursing Officer, Peach Regional Medical Center, Fort Valley, GA, p. A154

GOODMAN, David M., Ph.D. Chief Information Officer, Veterans Affairs Boston Healthcare System, Boston, MA, p. A297

GOODMAN, Douglas B., Vice President, Regional Medical Center–Bayonet Point, Hudson, FL, p. A126

GOODMAN, Louis, Vice President Human Resources, UPMC Presbyterian Shadyside, Pittsburgh, PA, p. A538

GOODMAN, Mary Jo, Chief Operating Officer, Park Plaza Hospital, Houston, TX, p. A611

GOODMAN, Steven, Chief Operating Officer, Willow Crest Hospital, Miami, OK, p. A501

GOODNO, Janell, Chief Financial Officer, Stafford County Hospital, Stafford, KS, p. A244

GOODNOW, John H., Chief Executive Officer, Benefis Hospitals, Great Falls, MT, p. A376

GOODRICH, Brenda, D.O. Chief of Staff, Tyler Memorial Hospital, Tunkhannock, PA, p. A542

GOODRICH, C. Harlan, Vice President and Chief Information Officer, MidMichigan Medical Center–Midland, Midland, MI, p. A320

GOODRICH, Zane, Vice President Finance, East Tennessee Children's Hospital, Knoxville, TN, p. A571

GOODSON, David, Chief Executive Officer, Select Specialty Hospital–Pensacola, Pensacola, FL, p. A137

GOODSTEIN, Ruth, Controller, HEALTHSOUTH Sunrise Rehabilitation Hospital, Fort Lauderdale, FL, p. A123

GOODWIN, Ervin, Manager Information Services, North Country Hospital and Health Center, Newport, VT, p. A650

GOODWIN, Jeremy, M.D. President, Medical Staff, Monroe County Hospital, Forsyth, GA, p. A153

GOODWIN, Keith D., President and Chief Executive Officer, East Tennessee Children's Hospital, Knoxville, TN, p. A571

GOODWIN, W. Jarrad, M.D. University of Miami Hospital and Clinics, Miami, FL, p. A132

GOOLSBY, Elizabeth, Director, Fayetteville Veterans Affairs Medical Center, Fayetteville, NC, p. A452

GOPALAM, Gopinath, Chief Financial Officer, St. James Behavioral Health Hospital, Gonzales, LA, p. A267

GORBACH, Debbie, Vice President and Treasurer, Edwin Shaw Rehab, Cuyahoga Falls, OH, p. A479

GORBY, David R., M.D. Vice President Quality and Patient Safety, Nash Health Care Systems, Rocky Mount, NC, p. A460

GORBY, Karen S., FACHE, Administrator and Chief Nursing Officer, Mercy Memorial Hospital, Urbana, OH, p. A491

GORCZYCA, Julie A., R.N. Chief Nursing Officer, Genesys Regional Medical Center, Grand Blanc, MI, p. A314

GORDIAN, Michael, Chief Financial Officer, Capital Regional Medical Center, Tallahassee, FL, p. A140

GORDON, Dan, Chief Financial Officer, Feather River Hospital, Paradise, CA, p. A79

GORDON, Jackie, Chief Clinical Officer, Kindred Hospital Dallas Central, Dallas, TX, p. A596

GORDON, Kevin, M.D. Chief of Staff, Medical Center of Southeastern Oklahoma, Durant, OK, p. A497

GORDON, Leilani, Director Human Resources and Payroll, Nye Regional Medical Center, Tonopah, NV, p. A396

GORDON, Mark M., Executive Vice President, Bon Secours St. Francis Medical Center, Midlothian, VA, p. A657

GORDON, Nancy Gail, R.N. CNO and VP of Nursing, Baptist Health South Florida, Homestead Hospital, Homestead, FL, p. A125

GORDON, Robert, Manager Information Systems, Halifax Regional Medical Center, Roanoke Rapids, NC, p. A459

GORDON, Steve, Director Human Resources, Lake City Medical Center, Lake City, FL, p. A128

GORDON, Steven R., President and Chief Executive Officer, Brattleboro Memorial Hospital, Brattleboro, VT, p. A649

GORDON, Wayne, Chief Financial Officer, Park Plaza Hospital, Houston, TX, p. A611

GORDY, Joseph S., President, Flagler Hospital, Saint Augustine, FL, p. A138

GORE, Tim, Chief Financial Officer, Rivendell Behavioral Health, Bowling Green, KY, p. A248

GOREAU, Judy, R.N. Director of Nursing, Eastside Psychiatric Hospital, Tallahassee, FL, p. A140

GOREE, Hal, Chief Information Officer, Franklin Foundation Hospital, Franklin, LA, p. A267

GOREY, Peter, Administrative Coordinator, Rockland Children's Psychiatric Center, Orangeburg, NY, p. A439

GORHAM, Jennie, D.O. Co–Medical Director, Missouri Rehabilitation Center, Mount Vernon, MO, p. A366

GORLEWSKI, Todd, Senior Vice President and Chief Financial Officer, St. Barnabas Hospital,, NY, p. A436

GORMAN, A. Alexander, Director Operations, Curry General Hospital, Gold Beach, OR, p. A513

GORMAN, Brandon, Interim Chief Executive Officer, Bradley County Medical Center, Warren, AR, p. A50

GORMAN, Kathleen, Chief Operating Officer and Executive Vice President Patient Care Services, Children's National Medical Center, Washington, DC, p. A116

GORMAN, Martha C., R.N. Vice President of Patient Care Services and Chief Nursing Officer, Gerald Champion Regional Medical Center, Alamogordo, NM, p. A414

GORMAN, Patricia, Chief Nurse Executive, Chinle Comprehensive Health Care Facility, Chinle, AZ, p. A30

GORMLEY, Maureen E., R.N. Chief Operating Officer, National Institutes of Health Clinical Center, Bethesda, MD, p. A290

GORMSEN, David, D.O. Chief Medical Officer, Mercy Medical Center, Canton, OH, p. A473

GORN, Angela, Vice President, Norton Sound Regional Hospital, Nome, AK, p. A28

GORRELL, Mark, Vice President Information Services, Baystate Medical Center, Springfield, MA, p. A305

GORS, Ann, Chief Executive Officer, Kentfield Rehabilitation and Specialty Hospital, Kentfield, CA, p. A65

GORSKI, William R., M.D., President and Chief Executive Officer, SwedishAmerican Hospital, Rockford, IL, p. A194

GORSUCH, Penny, Chief Nursing Officer, Wright Patterson Medical Center, Wright–Patterson AFB, OH, p. A493

GORY, James, Chief Financial Officer, Northwest Medical Center, Winfield, AL, p. A26

GOSCH, Shawn, Chief Financial Officer, Burgess Health Center, Onawa, IA, p. A226

GOSEY, J., M.D. Medical Director, Southern Surgical Hospital, Slidell, LA, p. A279

GOSHE, Nick, Chief Executive Officer, Rangely District Hospital, Rangely, CO, p. A105

GOSHIA, Rob, Chief Financial Officer, Paulding County Hospital, Paulding, OH, p. A488

GOSLINE, Peter L., Chief Executive Officer, Monadnock Community Hospital, Peterborough, NH, p. A400

GOSNELL, Dewey, Manager, Rush Oak Park Hospital, Oak Park, IL, p. A190

GOSNEY, Brett, Chief Executive Officer, Animas Surgical Hospital, Durango, CO, p. A100

GOSPODAREK, Robert E., President and Chief Executive Officer, Mercy St. Charles Hospital, Oregon, OH, p. A488

GOSS, J. Richard, M.D. Medical Director, UW Medicine/Harborview Medical Center, Seattle, WA, p. A671

GOSS, Norma, R.N. COO/CNO, Flaget Memorial Hospital, Bardstown, KY, p. A248

GOSS, Roger, Director, Information Services, North Sunflower Medical Center, Ruleville, MS, p. A353

GOSSENS, Kevin, Director Human Resources, Riverside Medical Center, Waupaca, WI, p. A698

GOTTI, Sreekant, Director Information Systems, Desert Valley Hospital, Victorville, CA, p. A95

GOTTLIEB, Harold, M.D. Medical Director, CHRISTUS St. John Hospital, Nassau Bay, TX, p. A624

GOTTLIEB, Jonathan, M.D. Senior Vice President and Chief Medical Officer, University of Maryland Medical Center, Baltimore, MD, p. A289

GOTTLIEB, Katherine, Chief Executive Officer, Alaska Native Medical Center, Anchorage, AK, p. A27

GOTTLIEB, Michael, M.D. Chief Medical Officer, MetroWest Medical Center, Framingham, MA, p. A300

GOTTSCHALK, Jack, Interim Vice President Human Resources, Children's National Medical Center, Washington, DC, p. A116

GOUGEON, Michele L., Executive Vice President and Chief Operating Officer, McLean Hospital, Belmont, MA, p. A295

GOUGH, Galal S., M.D. Chief of Staff, Coast Plaza Hospital, Norwalk, CA, p. A76

GOULD, Bill, Chief People Resource Officer, Winona Health, Winona, MN, p. A343

GOULD, Linda, Director Human Resources, Navarro Regional Hospital, Corsicana, TX, p. A594

GOULD, Lou, Vice President Human Resources, Harris Health System, Houston, TX, p. A609

GOULD, Nita, Director Information Services, Parkside Hospital, Tulsa, OK, p. A508

GOULD, Robert, Chief Executive Officer, Banner Desert Medical Center, Mesa, AZ, p. A33

GOULET, James P., Vice President Operations, Columbus Community Hospital, Columbus, NE, p. A382

GOURLEY, Paul, M.D. Chief Hospital Services, U. S. Air Force Hospital, Hampton, VA, p. A655

GOVE, Cynthia A., Chief Operating Officer, Hampstead Hospital, Hampstead, NH, p. A398

GOVINDAIAH, Rajesh G., M.D. Chief Medical Officer, Memorial Medical Center, Springfield, IL, p. A195

GOWDER, Mike, Assistant Administrator, Union General Hospital, Blairsville, GA, p. A148

GOYAL, Alok, M.D. Medical Director, Kindred Hospital–Milwaukee, Greenfield, WI, p. A688

GOZIAH, Vicky, Software Administrator, Wesley Woods Long Term Care Hospital, Atlanta, GA, p. A147

GRABER, Donald, M.D. Medical Director, Richmond State Hospital, Richmond, IN, p. A212

GRABER, Ellen, Director, Human Resources, Skiff Medical Center, Newton, IA, p. A226

GRABUS, Christina, R.N. Chief Nursing Officer, Novant Health Thomasville Medical Center, Thomasville, NC, p. A462

GRACE, Jeffery, M.D. Clinical Director, Buffalo Psychiatric Center, Buffalo, NY, p. A422

GRACE, Walter, Chief Executive Officer and Administrator, Baptist Memorial Hospital–Union County, New Albany, MS, p. A352

GRACER, Erik, M.D. Chief of Staff, San Ramon Regional Medical Center, San Ramon, CA, p. A89

GRACIA, Judy, Vice President Human Resources, St. Tammany Parish Hospital, Covington, LA, p. A266

GRACIE, Michael, Chief Information Officer, Veterans Health Care System of the Ozarks, Fayetteville, AR, p. A43

GRADDY, Steve W.
    Chief Financial Officer, Freeman Hospital West, Joplin, MO, p. A362
    Chief Financial Officer, Freeman Neosho Hospital, Neosho, MO, p. A366

GRADNEY, Angel, Chief Executive Officer, Kindred Hospital East Houston, Channelview, TX, p. A591

GRADY, John M., Associate Director, Veterans Affairs Hudson Valley Health Care System–F.D. Roosevelt Hospital, Montrose, NY, p. A430

GRADY, Phillip L., Administrator, Holmes County Hospital and Clinics, Lexington, MS, p. A350

GRAEBER, Lawrence, Chief Executive Officer, Neshoba County General Hospital, Philadelphia, MS, p. A352

GRAEBER, Tod
    Administrator, Community Memorial Hospital, Turtle Lake, ND, p. A469
    Administrator, Garrison Memorial Hospital, Garrison, ND, p. A467

GRAEBNER, David, President, Aurora Sheboygan Memorial Medical Center, Sheboygan, WI, p. A696

GRAEBNER, Nancy Kay, President and Chief Executive Officer, Chelsea Community Hospital, Chelsea, MI, p. A310

GRAF, John, Senior Vice President, Watertown Regional Medical Center, Watertown, WI, p. A698

GRAFTON, Tina, Director Information Technology, Pinckneyville Community Hospital, Pinckneyville, IL, p. A192

GRAGG, Connie, Director Human Resources, Saint Mary's Regional Medical Center, Russellville, AR, p. A49

GRAH, John A., FACHE, Chief Executive Officer, Des Peres Hospital, Saint Louis, MO, p. A369

GRAHAM, Barry A., M.D. Vice President Medical Affairs, Avera Sacred Heart Hospital, Yankton, SD, p. A564

GRAHAM, Brenda, Chief Nursing Officer, Knox County Hospital, Barbourville, KY, p. A248

GRAHAM, Brooke, Human Resources Manager, Franklin Woods Community Hospital, Johnson City, TN, p. A571

GRAHAM, Connie, Public Information Officer, Mercy Health Love County, Marietta, OK, p. A501

GRAHAM, David B., M.D. Senior Vice President and Chief Information Officer, Memorial Medical Center, Springfield, IL, p. A195

GRAHAM, Gerry J., Director Human Resources, Cottage Hospital, Woodsville, NH, p. A400

GRAHAM, J. Scott, Chief Executive Officer and Superintendent, Coulee Medical Center, Grand Coulee, WA, p. A667

GRAHAM, Jay
    Interim Chief Financial Officer, Berwick Hospital Center, Berwick, PA, p. A520
    Interim Chief Financial Officer, Brandywine Hospital, Coatesville, PA, p. A523

GRAHAM, Jeff
    Market Leader and President, Mercy Health – Anderson Hospital, Cincinnati, OH, p. A475
    Market Leader and President, Mercy Health – Clermont Hospital, Batavia, OH, p. A471

GRAHAM, Joe B., Chief Operating Officer, Nebraska Medical Center, Omaha, NE, p. A388

GRAHAM, John, Chief Financial Officer, Phoebe Worth Medical Center, Sylvester, GA, p. A161

GRAHAM, John R., President and Chief Executive Officer, St. Mary's of Michigan, Saginaw, MI, p. A323

GRAHAM, John W., Executive Vice President and Chief Operating Officer, Inspira Medical Center–Woodbury, Woodbury, NJ, p. A413

GRAHAM, Jon, Chief Financial Officer, Vidant Roanoke–Chowan Hospital, Ahoskie, NC, p. A447

GRAHAM, Kathryn, Director Communications and Community Relations, Novato Community Hospital, Novato, CA, p. A76

GRAHAM, Kimberley, R.N. Chief Nursing Officer and Chief Operating Officer, Broward Health Coral Springs, Coral Springs, FL, p. A121

GRAHAM, Larry M., FACHE, President and Chief Executive Officer, Lake Charles Memorial Hospital, Lake Charles, LA, p. A272

GRAHAM, Michael, Director Human Resources, Community Hospital, Munster, IN, p. A211

GRAHAM, Shauna, Director Human Resources, Howard County Medical Center, Saint Paul, NE, p. A389

GRAHAM, Sheri
Director Human Resources and Administrative Services, Parkland Health Center, Farmington, MO, p. A360
Director Human Resources and Administrative Services, Parkland Health Center–Bonne Terre, Bonne Terre, MO, p. A356

GRAHAM, Sonja, Chief Executive Officer, North Oak Regional Medical Center, Senatobia, MS, p. A353

GRAHAM, Yolanda, M.D. Medical Director, Devereux Georgia Treatment Network, Kennesaw, GA, p. A155

GRAHE, Raymond A., Senior Vice President Strategic Ventures and Chief Financial Officer, Meritus Medical Center, Hagerstown, MD, p. A292

GRAMBY, Tiffany, Director Health Information Management and Privacy Officer, Barnesville Hospital, Barnesville, OH, p. A471

GRAMER, Johanna, Director Human Resources, Mimbres Memorial Hospital, Deming, NM, p. A415

GRAMZA, Jeanne, Director Finance, Wheaton Franciscan Healthcare – All Saints, Racine, WI, p. A695

GRAN, Daniel, Chief Executive Officer, Freeman Regional Health Services, Freeman, SD, p. A560

GRANADO–VILLAR, Deise, M.D. Chief Medical Officer and Senior Vice President Medical Affairs, Miami Children's Hospital, Miami, FL, p. A132

GRANATO, Jerome, M.D
Senior Vice President and Chief Medical Officer, Excela Frick Hospital, Mount Pleasant, PA, p. A532
Senior Vice President and Chief Medical Officer, Excela Health Westmoreland Hospital, Greensburg, PA, p. A526
Senior Vice President and Chief Medical Officer, Excela Latrobe Area Hospital, Latrobe, PA, p. A529

GRAND, Lawrence N., Executive Vice President and Chief Operating Officer, Hunterdon Medical Center, Flemington, NJ, p. A404

GRANDIOSI, Joe, Director Information Technology, Southern Hills Hospital and Medical Center, Las Vegas, NV, p. A393

GRANGER, Chris, M.D. President Medical Staff, Beauregard Memorial Hospital, De Ridder, LA, p. A266

GRANGER, Keith, President and Chief Executive Officer, Trinity Medical Center, Birmingham, AL, p. A17

GRANGER, Laura, Director, Human Resources, New Braunfels Regional Rehabilitation Hospital, New Braunfels, TX, p. A624

GRANGER, Robert P., President and Chief Executive Officer, St. Francis Hospital, Columbus, GA, p. A150

GRANNEMAN, Joe
Regional Chief Information Officer, Adventist GlenOaks Hospital, Glendale Heights, IL, p. A183
Chief Information Officer, Adventist Hinsdale Hospital, Hinsdale, IL, p. A185

GRANT, Cathy, R.N. Associate Vice President, Patient Services, DMC Huron Valley–Sinai Hospital, Commerce Township, MI, p. A311

GRANT, Dan, Manager Business Office, Blue Mountain Recovery Center, Pendleton, OR, p. A515

GRANT, Dianna, M.D. Vice President Medical Management, Advocate Trinity Hospital, Chicago, IL, p. A176

GRANT, Howard R., M.D., President and Chief Executive Officer, Lahey Hospital & Medical Center, Burlington, Burlington, MA, p. A298

GRANT, Larry, M.D. Chief Medical Officer, Coliseum Medical Centers, Macon, GA, p. A156

GRANT, Mikki, Chief Information Officer, Fort Belknap U. S. Public Health Service Indian Hospital, Harlem, MT, p. A377

GRANT, Pauline, FACHE, Chief Executive Officer, Broward Health North, Deerfield Beach, FL, p. A122

GRANT, William, Vice President Fiscal and Support Services, Greenville Health System Laurens County Memorial Hospital, Clinton, SC, p. A550

GRANTHAM, Charlie, Manager Information Systems, Carolinas Hospital System Marion, Mullins, SC, p. A554

GRANTHAM, James, Administrator and Chief Executive Officer, Baptist Memorial Hospital–Booneville, Booneville, MS, p. A345

GRANTHAM, Keith, Director Information Technology, Covenant Medical Center, Saginaw, MI, p. A323

GRANVILLE, Brian, Director Information Technology, Buena Vista Regional Medical Center, Storm Lake, IA, p. A229

GRANVILLE, Sabrina M., Vice President Human Resources, Elliot Hospital, Manchester, NH, p. A399

GRANZOW, Steven L., Chief Executive Officer, Sheridan County Health Complex, Hoxie, KS, p. A236

GRASER, David, Chief Information Officer, Marquette General Health System, Marquette, MI, p. A319

GRASMEDER, Martin, M.D., Administrator, SEARHC MT. Edgecumbe Hospital, Sitka, AK, p. A29

GRASS, Linda J., President and Chief Executive Officer, Jeanes Hospital, Philadelphia, PA, p. A535

GRASSER, Tierney, Senior Vice President Finance, Olathe Medical Center, Olathe, KS, p. A241

GRATZ, Silvia, D.O. Chief Medical Officer, Fairmount Behavioral Health System, Philadelphia, PA, p. A534

GRATZMILLER, Annette, Director Information Services, HEALTHSOUTH Rehabilitation Hospital, Sewickley, PA, p. A541

GRAUE, Michael L., Executive Vice President and Chief Operating Officer, WellStar Kennestone Hospital, Marietta, GA, p. A157

GRAUER, David, Chief Executive Officer and Administrator, Intermountain Medical Center, Murray, UT, p. A644

GRAUPENSPERGER, Robert, Executive Vice President, Ephrata Community Hospital, Ephrata, PA, p. A525

GRAVENDER, Dave, Vice President and Chief Information Officer, Kaweah Delta Medical Center, Visalia, CA, p. A95

GRAVES, Amanda, Chief Information Systems, Washington DC Veterans Affairs Medical Center, Washington, DC, p. A117

GRAVES, Buddy, Chief Information Officer, Southern Surgical Hospital, Slidell, LA, p. A279

GRAVES, Deanna, Chief Executive Officer, Texas Specialty Hospital at Lubbock, Lubbock, TX, p. A620

GRAVES, Robert L., President, Sentara Williamsburg Regional Medical Center, Williamsburg, VA, p. A663

GRAVES, Shirley A., R.N. Chief Nursing Officer, Lake Granbury Medical Center, Granbury, TX, p. A606

GRAVES, Terri, Chief Financial Officer, Heartland Behavioral Health Services, Nevada, MO, p. A366

GRAY, Albert, Chief Executive Officer, The Children's Center, Bethany, OK, p. A496

GRAY, Anthony, Chief Financial Officer, LAC–Olive View–UCLA Medical Center,, CA, p. A70

GRAY, Clarence, Chief Financial Officer, TriStar Horizon Medical Center, Dickson, TN, p. A568

GRAY, David L., FACHE, President, Baptist Health Louisville, Louisville, KY, p. A255

GRAY, Gary, D.O. Chief Medical Officer, Natividad Medical Center, Salinas, CA, p. A84

GRAY, Herb, M.D. Chief Medical Officer, Falmouth Hospital, Falmouth, MA, p. A300

GRAY, Herman B., M.D., President, Children's Hospital of Michigan, Detroit, MI, p. A311

GRAY, James, M.D. Chief Medical Service, Amarillo Veterans Affairs Health Care System, Amarillo, TX, p. A582

GRAY, Jason, M.D. Chief Medical Officer, Mercy Medical Center, Roseburg, OR, p. A517

GRAY, John, Administrator, St. Catherine Memorial Hospital, New Orleans, LA, p. A276

GRAY, Joshua, Director Information Technology, Coon Memorial Hospital and Home, Dalhart, TX, p. A594

GRAY, Judy, Vice President Human Resources, St. Peter's Hospital, Albany, NY, p. A420

GRAY, Karen D., Director Human Resources, Vibra Hospital of Southeastern Michigan, Lincoln Park, MI, p. A319

GRAY, Larry, President, Baptist Health Corbin, Corbin, KY, p. A249

GRAY, Leigh Cher, M.D. Chief of Staff, King's Daughters Medical Center, Brookhaven, MS, p. A345

GRAY, Mark, Chief Information Officer, McLaren Northern Michigan, Petoskey, MI, p. A321

GRAY, Marty, R.N. Director of Nursing, Wyandot Memorial Hospital, Upper Sandusky, OH, p. A491

GRAY, Michelle, Nurse Executive, Atrium Medical Center of Corinth, Corinth, TX, p. A593

GRAY, Mike
Corporate Vice President Human Resources, East Texas Medical Center Rehabilitation Hospital, Tyler, TX, p. A638
Corporate Vice President Human Resources, East Texas Medical Center Specialty Hospital, Tyler, TX, p. A638
Corporate Vice President Human Resources, East Texas Medical Center Tyler, Tyler, TX, p. A638

GRAY, Patricia, Director Health Information Management, Cumberland Hall Hospital, Hopkinsville, KY, p. A252

GRAY, Stephen, Chief Executive Officer, Sutter Maternity and Surgery Center of Santa Cruz, Santa Cruz, CA, p. A90

GRAY, Tami, Chief Financial Officer, Irwin County Hospital, Ocilla, GA, p. A158

GRAY, Teresa, Chief Nursing Officer and Assistant Vice President, INTEGRIS Canadian Valley Hospital, Yukon, OK, p. A510

GRAY, Terry, Vice President Human Resources, Emanuel Medical Center, Turlock, CA, p. A93

GRAY, Thomas, M.D. Medical Director, Montana State Hospital, Warm Springs, MT, p. A380

GRAY, Val S., Chief Executive Officer, Helen Hayes Hospital, West Haverstraw, NY, p. A445

GRAY, Warren L., M.D. Chief of Staff, Indiana University Health Morgan Hospital, Martinsville, IN, p. A209

GRAYBEAL, Phillip
Chief Financial Officer, Page Memorial Hospital, Luray, VA, p. A656
Chief Financial Officer, Warren Memorial Hospital, Front Royal, VA, p. A654

GRAYBILL, Matthew P., Chief Operating Officer, Children's Medical Center, Dayton, OH, p. A479

GREASOM, Linda, Vice President Human Resources, Milford Regional Medical Center, Milford, MA, p. A302

GREBOSKY, Jamie, M.D. Vice President of Medical Affairs, Rogue Valley Medical Center, Medford, OR, p. A515

GRECO, Andrew, Chief Financial Officer, Calvary Hospital,, NY, p. A431

GRECO, Margaret, Chief Human Resources, Keller Army Community Hospital, West Point, NY, p. A446

GREELEY, Donna, Director Human Resources, Spalding Rehabilitation Hospital, Aurora, CO, p. A97

GREEN, Arnold, Senior Vice President and Chief Operating Officer, McLeod Loris Healthcare, Loris, SC, p. A554

GREEN, Barbara, Director Human Resources, O'Connor Hospital, Delhi, NY, p. A425

GREEN, Calvin, Chief Executive Officer, Oakdale Community Hospital, Oakdale, LA, p. A276

GREEN, Christine, Administrative Director Human Resources, Sutter Delta Medical Center, Antioch, CA, p. A52

GREEN, Darrin, M.D. Medical Director, De Queen Medical Center, De Queen, AR, p. A42

GREEN, David, Chief Human Resources, West Palm Beach Veterans Affairs Medical Center, West Palm Beach, FL, p. A144

GREEN, David F., M.D. Chief Medical Officer, Concord Hospital, Concord, NH, p. A397

GREEN, David R., Administrator and Chief Executive Officer, El Centro Regional Medical Center, El Centro, CA, p. A59

GREEN, Gail P., R.N
Chief Nursing Officer, Renown Rehabilitation Hospital, Reno, NV, p. A395
Chief Nursing Officer, Renown South Meadows Medical Center, Reno, NV, p. A395

GREEN, Garry Kim, FACHE, Administrator, Shriners Hospitals for Children–Shreveport, Shreveport, LA, p. A278

GREEN, Gene E., M.D., President, Suburban Hospital, Bethesda, MD, p. A290

GREEN, Haley, Chief Financial Officer, Doctors Memorial Hospital, Bonifay, FL, p. A119

GREEN, Jack W., Administrator, Antelope Memorial Hospital, Neligh, NE, p. A386

GREEN, John
Vice President Human Resources, Iredell Memorial Hospital, Statesville, NC, p. A461
Vice President Finance, St. Peter's Hospital, Helena, MT, p. A377

GREEN, Judy, Director Human Resources, Putnam County Memorial Hospital, Unionville, MO, p. A373

GREEN, Julie, Vice President Human Resources, Cheshire Medical Center, Keene, NH, p. A398

GREEN, Karen, Chief Information Officer, Brooks Rehabilitation Hospital, Jacksonville, FL, p. A126

GREEN, Kaye, FACHE, Director, W. G. (Bill) Heffner Veterans Affairs Medical Center, Salisbury, NC, p. A460

GREEN, LaDonna, Director Human Resources, Glen Rose Medical Center, Glen Rose, TX, p. A606

GREEN Jr., Larry D., Chief Executive Officer, Windhaven Psychiatric Hospital, Prescott Valley, AZ, p. A36

GREEN, Michael B., President and Chief Executive Officer, Concord Hospital, Concord, NH, p. A397

GREEN, Patrick, Chief Operating Officer, St. Anthony Hospital, Lakewood, CO, p. A103

GREEN, Peggy, Chief Operating Officer and Chief Nursing Officer, Saint Joseph – London, London, KY, p. A255

GREEN, Rhonda G., Administrator, Leonard J. Chabert Medical Center, Houma, LA, p. A268

GREEN, Ronnie, Director Information Systems, McBride Clinic Orthopedic Hospital, Oklahoma City, OK, p. A503

GREEN, Rose Marie, Director Human Resources, Humboldt General Hospital, Winnemucca, NV, p. A396

GREEN, Scott, M.D. Chief of Staff, St. Francis Memorial Hospital, West Point, NE, p. A390

GREEN, Steve, Comptroller, Jasper General Hospital, Bay Springs, MS, p. A344

GREEN, Susan, Chief Financial Officer, Lowell General Hospital, Lowell, MA, p. A301

GREENBERG, Mark, M.D
   Chief Medical Officer, Cape Coral Hospital, Cape Coral, FL, p. A120
   Medical Director, Gulf Coast Medical Center, Fort Myers, FL, p. A124

GREENE, Arthur, M.D. Vice President Medical Affairs, Sentara CarePlex Hospital, Hampton, VA, p. A655

GREENE, Barbara M., President, Franciscan Physicians Hospital, Munster, IN, p. A211

GREENE, Beth, Chief Operating Officer, Cherokee Indian Hospital, Cherokee, NC, p. A450

GREENE, Bradley, Chief Financial Officer, WellStar Douglas Hospital, Douglasville, GA, p. A152

GREENE Jr., Charles H., Administrator, Cordell Memorial Hospital, Cordell, OK, p. A497

GREENE, Michael, Chief Executive Officer, Medical Center of Newark, Newark, OH, p. A487

GREENE, Queen, Director Human Resources, Baylor University Medical Center, Dallas, TX, p. A595

GREENE, Russ, Chief Executive Officer, Physicians' Specialty Hospital, Fayetteville, AR, p. A43

GREENER, Angela, Chief Administrative Officer, West Jefferson Medical Center, Marrero, LA, p. A273

GREENFIELD, Bruce A., M.D. Chief of Staff, California Hospital Medical Center, Los Angeles, CA, p. A68

GREENFIELD, Todd, Chief Nursing Officer, Great Plains Regional Medical Center, North Platte, NE, p. A386

GREENIA, Earl, FACHE, Chief Executive Officer, HEALTHSOUTH Rehabilitation Hospital – Henderson, Henderson, NV, p. A392

GREENLEE, Kathryn M., R.N
   Vice President, Clinical Services/CNO, ProMedica Bixby Hospital, Adrian, MI, p. A308
   Vice President, Clinical Services/CNO, ProMedica Herrick Hospital, Tecumseh, MI, p. A325

GREENLY, John, Chief Financial Officer, Meadow Wood Behavioral Health System, New Castle, DE, p. A114

GREENMAN, Jennifer, Chief Information Officer, Bayfront Health St. Petersburg, Saint Petersburg, FL, p. A138

GREENMAN, Sharon, Director Human Resources, Melissa Memorial Hospital, Holyoke, CO, p. A102

GREENSPAN, Carrie, M.D. Chief of Staff, Broward Health Coral Springs, Coral Springs, FL, p. A121

GREENSTON, Matthew, M.D. Interim Chief Medical Officer, Catholic Medical Center, Manchester, NH, p. A399

GREENSWEIG, Gary, D.O
   Chief Medical Officer, Petaluma Valley Hospital, Petaluma, CA, p. A79
   Chief Medical Officer, Santa Rosa Memorial Hospital, Santa Rosa, CA, p. A90

GREENWOOD, Cathy, Manager Human Resources, LifeCare Hospitals of Dallas, Dallas, TX, p. A596

GREER, Eugene, Chief Information Officer, The HSC Pediatric Center, Washington, DC, p. A117

GREER, Nancy, R.N. Chief Nursing Officer, Saint Alphonsus Medical Center – Ontario, Ontario, OR, p. A515

GREER, Roxane, Coordinator Human Resources, Blowing Rock Hospital, Blowing Rock, NC, p. A448

GREER, Troy, Chief Executive Officer, Lovelace Medical Center, Albuquerque, NM, p. A414

GREER, William, Chief Information Officer, Birmingham Veterans Affairs Medical Center, Birmingham, AL, p. A16

GREEVER, Suzanne, Chief Executive Officer, North Central Surgical Center, Dallas, TX, p. A597

GREGERSEN, Glenn, Director Information Technology, District One Hospital, Faribault, MN, p. A332

GREGG, Hunt, Director Information Systems, Texas Scottish Rite Hospital for Children, Dallas, TX, p. A597

GREGG, Richard, M.D. Medical Director, LifeCare Hospital of Dayton, Miamisburg, OH, p. A486

GREGG, Thomas, Vice President Human Resources, St. Peter's Hospital, Helena, MT, p. A377

GREGGAIN, Don, M.D. Physician Network Director, Tri-State Memorial Hospital, Clarkston, WA, p. A665

GREGONIS, Michael, Comptroller, Naval Hospital Jacksonville, Jacksonville, FL, p. A126

GREGORIAN, Myra, Vice President Human Resources, Long Beach Memorial Medical Center, Long Beach, CA, p. A67

GREGORICH, Miki, Director Human Resources, Pioneer Medical Center, Big Timber, MT, p. A374

GREGORIO, Louis J., FACHE Vice President Human Resources, Chambersburg Hospital, Chambersburg, PA, p. A522

GREGORY, Adina, Chief Nursing Officer, Great Bend Regional Hospital, Great Bend, KS, p. A234

GREGORY, Audrey, R.N. Chief Operating Officer, Saint Francis Hospital, Memphis, TN, p. A575

GREGORY, Jan, Chief of Human Resources, Crittenden County Hospital, Marion, KY, p. A257

GREGORY, Nancy A., Acting Director, Veterans Affairs Medical Center, Omaha, NE, p. A388

GREGORY, Sean, President, Health First Holmes Regional Medical Center, Melbourne, FL, p. A130

GREGORY, Shawn, Chief Financial Officer, South Bay Hospital, Sun City Center, FL, p. A140

GREGORY, Trip
   Senior Vice President Human Resources, Palmetto Health Baptist, Columbia, SC, p. A550
   Senior Vice President Human Resources, Palmetto Health Richland, Columbia, SC, p. A550

GREGOS, Ruth, Director Finance, Shriners Hospitals for Children–Tampa, Tampa, FL, p. A142

GREIMAN, Alan W., Administrator, Royal Oaks Hospital, Windsor, MO, p. A373

GREINER, Walter, Chief Financial Officer, AtlantiCare Regional Medical Center, Atlantic City, NJ, p. A401

GREMILLION, Karen, R.N. Chief Nursing Officer, Opelousas General Health System, Opelousas, LA, p. A276

GRENALDO, Paul, Executive Vice President and Chief Operating Officer, Doctors Community Hospital, Lanham, MD, p. A292

GRENDON, M. Todd, M.D. President Medical Staff, Presence Saint Joseph Hospital, Chicago, IL, p. A178

GRENIER, Raymond, Chief Financial Officer, Northwest Texas Healthcare System, Amarillo, TX, p. A582

GRENNAN, Jr., M. Joseph, M.D
   Vice President Medical Affairs, Boca Raton Regional Hospital, Boca Raton, FL, p. A118
   Senior Vice President and Chief Medical Officer, Reading Hospital and Medical Center, West Reading, PA, p. A544

GRESKOVICH, William, Chief Information Officer, Saint Agnes Hospital, Baltimore, MD, p. A289

GRESS, Jr., Harold M., Manager Management Information Systems, Fulton County Medical Center, Mc Connellsburg, PA, p. A530

GREW, Kate, MSN Vice President/Chief Nurse Executive, Carolinas Medical Center–NorthEast, Concord, NC, p. A450

GREW, Terry, Chief Business Office, Hampton Veterans Affairs Medical Center, Hampton, VA, p. A655

GREY, Mitzi, Chief Operating Officer, Bath Community Hospital, Hot Springs, VA, p. A655

GRIBBIN, John, FACHE, President and Chief Executive Officer, CentraState Healthcare System, Freehold, NJ, p. A404

GRIBBIN, Karen, M.D. Chief of Staff, Jack C. Montgomery Veterans Affairs Medical Center, Muskogee, OK, p. A501

GRICUS, Peggy, R.N. Vice President, Patient Care Services and Chief Nursing Officer, Silver Cross Hospital, New Lenox, IL, p. A190

GRIEP, John, M.D. Chief Medical Director, St. Catherine Hospital, East Chicago, IN, p. A201

GRIESS, Dan, Chief Executive Officer, Box Butte General Hospital, Alliance, NE, p. A381

GRIEST, Mary, Vice President Finance and Chief Financial Officer, Samaritan Regional Health System, Ashland, OH, p. A470

GRIFFIN, Angela, Privacy Officer, Wayne County Hospital, Monticello, KY, p. A258

GRIFFIN, Brad, Chief Executive Officer, Colleton Medical Center, Walterboro, SC, p. A556

GRIFFIN, Brian, Director Information Services, Springhill Medical Center, Springhill, LA, p. A279

GRIFFIN, Christopher B., Chief Executive Officer, D. W. McMillan Memorial Hospital, Brewton, AL, p. A18

GRIFFIN, Cindy, Director Human Resources, Medical Center Barbour, Eufaula, AL, p. A19

GRIFFIN, Dean A., President and Chief Executive Officer, Decatur General Hospital, Decatur, AL, p. A18

GRIFFIN, Donald, CPA Chief Financial Officer, New London Hospital, New London, NH, p. A399

GRIFFIN, James, Manager Information Systems, Martin General Hospital, Williamston, NC, p. A462

GRIFFIN, Margaret Elizabeth, Vice Prsident and Chief Nursing Officer, John C. Lincoln North Mountain Hospital, Phoenix, AZ, p. A34

GRIFFIN, Matthew, M.D. Vice President Medical Affairs, Sinai–Grace Hospital, Detroit, MI, p. A312

GRIFFIN, Michael L., Chief Financial Officer, Bethesda Butler Hospital, Hamilton, OH, p. A483

GRIFFIN, Paulette
   Vice President Human Resources, Detroit Receiving Hospital/University Health Center, Detroit, MI, p. A311
   Director Human Resources, Sinai–Grace Hospital, Detroit, MI, p. A312

GRIFFIN, Shirley, Director Health Information, North Mississippi Medical Center–Eupora, Eupora, MS, p. A346

GRIFFIN, Todd, M.D. Chief Medical Officer, Stony Brook University Medical Center, Stony Brook, NY, p. A443

GRIFFIN–MAHON, Selena, Assistant Vice President Human Resources, Bronx–Lebanon Hospital Center Health Care System,, NY, p. A431

GRIFFIS, Lisa, Chief Financial Officer and Business Office Manager, Specialty Hospital of Midwest City, Midwest City, OK, p. A501

GRIFFITH, David, M.D. Medical Director, Texas Center for Infectious Disease, San Antonio, TX, p. A632

GRIFFITH, Dena, Manager Information Systems, Kern Valley Healthcare District, Lake Isabella, CA, p. A66

GRIFFITH, Duane Lee, M.D. Chief of Staff, Texas Spine & Joint Hospital, Tyler, TX, p. A638

GRIFFITH, Dusty, Director Information Systems, Bolivar Medical Center, Cleveland, MS, p. A346

GRIFFITH, James, M.D. Associate Medical Director and Professional Chief of Staff, Kaiser Permanente Medical Center, Honolulu, HI, p. A164

GRIFFITH, James, Chief Operating Officer, Salinas Valley Memorial Healthcare System, Salinas, CA, p. A84

GRIFFITH, Jeanne, Chief Nursing Officer, Coryell Memorial Hospital, Gatesville, TX, p. A606

GRIFFITH, John H., President & Chief Executive Officer, Kedren Community Mental Health Center, Los Angeles, CA, p. A70

GRIFFITH, Keitha, Chief Nursing Officer, Medical Center of South Arkansas, El Dorado, AR, p. A43

GRIFFITH, Pamela, Director Administrative Services, Devereux Hospital and Children's Center of Florida, Melbourne, FL, p. A130

GRIFFITH, Patti, R.N. Chief Nursing Officer, Methodist Hospital for Surgery, Addison, TX, p. A581

GRIFFITH, Susan M., Chief Operations Officer, Eastern State Hospital, Lexington, KY, p. A254

GRIFFITH, Wayne B., FACHE, Chief Executive Officer, Princeton Community Hospital, Princeton, WV, p. A680

GRIFFITHS, David, Vice President and Chief Financial Officer, Regional West Medical Center, Scottsbluff, NE, p. A389

GRIFFITHS, Mark
   Director Management Information Systems, Incline Village Community Hospital, Incline Village, NV, p. A392
   Chief Systems Innovation Officer, Tahoe Forest Hospital District, Truckee, CA, p. A93

GRIGG, William E., Senior Vice President and Chief Financial Officer, Methodist Hospital of Southern California, Arcadia, CA, p. A53

GRIGSBY, Stephen J., Chief Financial Officer, Jupiter Medical Center, Jupiter, FL, p. A127

GRIGSON, John A., Senior Vice President and Chief Financial Officer, Covenant Medical Center, Lubbock, TX, p. A620

GRILL, Laura D., R.N. Executive Vice President and Administrator, East Alabama Medical Center, Opelika, AL, p. A24

GRILLO, Jorge C., Chief Information Officer, Canton–Potsdam Hospital, Potsdam, NY, p. A440

GRIM, Mary Kay, Senior Vice President Human Resources, Lehigh Valley Hospital, Allentown, PA, p. A519

GRIMALDI, Richard, President Medical Staff, Highlands Hospital, Connellsville, PA, p. A523

GRIMER, Ginny, Director Human Resources, George E. Weems Memorial Hospital, Apalachicola, FL, p. A118

GRIMERT, Tom, Chief Financial Officer, Val Verde Regional Medical Center, Del Rio, TX, p. A598

GRIMES, Michael, Manager Human Resources, Kindred Hospital Bay Area–Tampa, Tampa, FL, p. A141

GRIMES, Pam, Director Human Resources, AMG Specialty Hospital–Edmond, Edmond, OK, p. A498

GRIMES, Teresa G., Chief Executive Officer, Troy Regional Medical Center, Troy, AL, p. A25

GRIMES, Walter, Director Information Technology, Good Shepherd Medical Center–Marshall, Marshall, TX, p. A621

GRIMLEY, Karen A., R.N. Chief Nursing Officer, University of California, Irvine Healthcare, Orange, CA, p. A78

GRIMSHAW, Bruce P., Chief Executive Officer, Hollywood Community Hospital, Los Angeles, CA, p. A69

GRIMSHAW, Matthew, President, Mercy Medical Center, Williston, ND, p. A469

GRINDE, Brett, Network Manager, Lucas County Health Center, Chariton, IA, p. A218

GRINNELL, Steven, President and Chief Executive Officer, Lourdes Hospital, Paducah, KY, p. A259

GRIP, Mark, Executive Director Business Development, Sierra Vista Hospital, Sacramento, CA, p. A83

GRIPPI, Michael, M.D. Chief Medical Officer, Good Shepherd Penn Partners Specialty Hospital at Rittenhouse, Philadelphia, PA, p. A606

GRISDELA, Michael, Chief Financial Officer, Karmanos Cancer Center, Detroit, MI, p. A312

GRISH, John, Chief Financial Officer, Johnson Memorial Hospital, Stafford Springs, CT, p. A112

GRISIER, Douglas, D.O. Medical Director, HEALTHSOUTH Rehabilitation Hospital of Erie, Erie, PA, p. A525

GRISNAK, Karen R.N. Chief Operating Officer and Assistant Administrator Quality Services, Kaiser Permanente Vallejo Medical Center, Vallejo, CA, p. A94

GRISSINGER, Matthew, Site Manager Information Systems, Indian Path Medical Center, Kingsport, TN, p. A571

GRISSLER, Brian G., President and Chief Executive Officer, Stamford Hospital, Stamford, CT, p. A112

GRISWOLD, Barbara, Chief Nursing Officer, Washington County Hospital and Clinics, Washington, IA, p. A229

GRITTNER, Linda
Vice President Human Resources, Providence Mount Carmel Hospital, Colville, WA, p. A665
Director Human Resources, Providence St. Joseph's Hospital, Chewelah, WA, p. A665

GROCE, David, Associate Administrator and Chief Financial Officer, Lincoln County Health System, Fayetteville, TN, p. A569

GROCHALA, Eugene
Vice President Information Systems, Capital Health Medical Center–Hopewell, Pennington, NJ, p. A408
Vice President Information Systems, Capital Health Regional Medical Center, Trenton, NJ, p. A411

GROCHOLSKI, James F., FACHE, Chief Executive Officer, Wesley Rehabilitation Hospital, Wichita, KS, p. A247

GROENEWEG, Jennifer, R.N. Director of Nursing, Spectrum Health Special Care Hospital, Grand Rapids, MI, p. A315

GROENIG, Matt, Vice President Finance, St. Luke's McCall, McCall, ID, p. A170

GROEPER, William E., Vice President Finance, Beloit Health System, Beloit, WI, p. A684

GROEPPER, Ronald, Senior Vice President and Area Manager, Kaiser Permanente Sacramento Medical Center, Sacramento, CA, p. A83

GROESBECK, John
Area Finance Officer, Kaiser Permanente San Rafael Medical Center, San Rafael, CA, p. A89
Area Finance Officer, Kaiser Permanente Santa Rosa Medical Center, Santa Rosa, CA, p. A90

GROFF, Gerald D., M.D. Vice President Medical Affairs, Bassett Medical Center, Cooperstown, NY, p. A424

GROGAN, Dennis, M.D. Chief of Staff, Shriners Hospitals for Children–Tampa, Tampa, FL, p. A142

GROGAN, Ed, Vice President Information Services and Chief Information Officer, Calvert Memorial Hospital, Prince Frederick, MD, p. A293

GROGAN, Richard, Chief Executive Officer, Memorial Hospital of Salem County, Salem, NJ, p. A410

GROH, Charles, Interim Chief Information Officer, North Adams Regional Hospital, North Adams, MA, p. A303

GRONBACH, Sue, Director Human Resources, Providence Hospital, Southfield, MI, p. A324

GRONDA, Mark E., Vice President and Chief Financial Officer, Covenant Medical Center, Saginaw, MI, p. A323

GRONEWOLD, Russell, Chief Financial Officer, Bryan Medical Center, Lincoln, NE, p. A385

GRONSETH, Timothy L., Vice President and Chief Financial Officer, Northfield Hospital, Northfield, MN, p. A337

GROOM, Scott C., Vice President Information Services and Chief Information Officer, Bassett Medical Center, Cooperstown, NY, p. A424

GROOMS, Jr., Richard W., Vice President Human Resources, Providence Hospital, Columbia, SC, p. A550

GROS, Albert, M.D. Chief Medical Officer, St. David's South Austin Medical Center, Austin, TX, p. A586

GROS, Mark, Director Human Resources, United Medical Rehabilitation Hospital, Hammond, LA, p. A268

GROSDIDIER, Jonathan L., M.D. Chief of Staff, Memorial Hospital of Converse County, Douglas, WY, p. A702

GROSE, Jana, Director Management Information Systems, Massena Memorial Hospital, Massena, NY, p. A429

GROSKREUTZ, Kevin
Chief Information Officer, Sacred Heart Hospital, Eau Claire, WI, p. A686
Chief Information Systems, St. Joseph's Hospital, Chippewa Falls, WI, p. A685

GROSS, Arthur K., FACHE Executive Vice President and Chief Information Officer, Henry Ford Wyandotte Hospital, Wyandotte, MI, p. A327

GROSS, Barry L., M.D. Executive Vice President and Chief Medical Officer, Riverside Regional Medical Center, Newport News, VA, p. A658

GROSS, Cathy, Director Health Information Management Systems, Wrangell Medical Center, Wrangell, AK, p. A29

GROSS, Cheryl, Director Human Resources, Edwards County Hospital and Healthcare Center, Kinsley, KS, p. A237

GROSS, Daniel, Senior Vice President Finance and Chief Financial Officer, Newton–Wellesley Hospital, Newton Lower Falls, MA, p. A303

GROSS, Denton, Director Information Services, Larue D. Carter Memorial Hospital, Indianapolis, IN, p. A206

GROSS, Gregory, M.D. President Medical Staff, St. Nicholas Hospital, Sheboygan, WI, p. A696

GROSS, Kristin, Director Information Technology Center, Avera McKennan Hospital and University Health Center, Sioux Falls, SD, p. A562

GROSS, Lawrence, Executive Director, Griffin Memorial Hospital, Norman, OK, p. A502

GROSS, Len, Director Human Resources, Sheridan Memorial Hospital, Sheridan, WY, p. A703

GROSS, Mark, Senior Business Director Finance, Mercy Health Partners, Lakeshore Campus, Shelby, MI, p. A324

GROSS, Melissa, Interim Administrator, Chester Mental Health Center, Chester, IL, p. A176

GROSS, Michael
Senior Vice President, Finance/Business Development, Ozarks Medical Center, West Plains, MO, p. A373
Chief Information Officer, Veterans Affairs Medical Center–Lexington, Lexington, KY, p. A255

GROSS, Paul, Human Services and Finance Officer, Larry B. Zieverink, Sr. Alcoholism Treatment Center, Raleigh, NC, p. A459

GROSS, Peter A., M.D. Senior Vice President and Chief Medical Officer, Hackensack University Medical Center, Hackensack, NJ, p. A404

GROSS, Randy, Chief Executive Officer, Plantation General Hospital, Plantation, FL, p. A137

GROSS, Tina, Director of Clinical Services, Sparrow Specialty Hospital, Lansing, MI, p. A318

GROSSET, Jessica
Director Information Technology, Mayo Clinic – Saint Marys Hospital, Rochester, MN, p. A339
Director Information Technology, Rochester Methodist Hospital, Rochester, MN, p. A339

GROSSMAN, Drew, Chief Executive Officer, Broward Health Coral Springs, Coral Springs, FL, p. A121

GROSSMAN, Ilana, Administrator, Joyce Eisenberg–Keefer Medical Center, Reseda, CA, p. A82

GROSSMAN, Joseph
Chief Financial Officer, McDowell ARH Hospital, McDowell, KY, p. A257
Vice President Fiscal Affairs, Whitesburg ARH Hospital, Whitesburg, KY, p. A261

GROSSMAN, Marty, Director Information Technology, Christ Hospital, Jersey City, NJ, p. A405

GROSSMAN, Ray G., Vice President Human Resources, Memorial Medical Center – Livingston, Livingston, TX, p. A619

GROSSMAN, Robert I., M.D., Chief Executive Officer, NYU Langone Medical Center, New York, NY, p. A435

GROSSO, Michael, M.D. Senior Vice President Medical Affairs, Huntington Hospital, Huntington, NY, p. A427

GROVER, Amy, Director, Appalachian Behavioral Healthcare, Athens, OH, p. A470

GROWNEY, Daniel, M.D. Chief of Staff, York General Hospital, York, NE, p. A390

GROWSE, Michael, M.D. Clinical Director, Federal Medical Center, Lexington, KY, p. A254

GRUBB, Lois, Vice President Human Resources, Elmhurst Memorial Hospital,, IL, p. A182

GRUBB, Michael, Chief Operating Officer and Chief Financial Officer, Kindred Hospital of South Bay, Gardena, CA, p. A62

GRUBB, Nora, Chief Financial Officer, Big Sandy Medical Center, Big Sandy, MT, p. A374

GRUBBS, Stephen, Chief Executive Officer, Paris Regional Medical Center, Paris, TX, p. A626

GRUBER, Kreg, President, Memorial Hospital of South Bend, South Bend, IN, p. A213

GRUBER, Norman F., President and Chief Executive Officer, Salem Hospital, Salem, OR, p. A517

GRUBER, Scott, M.D. Chief of Staff, John D. Dingell Veterans Affairs Medical Center, Detroit, MI, p. A312

GRUEBER, Cynthia M., Chief Operating Officer, OHSU Hospital, Portland, OR, p. A516

GRUEN, Jeremy, Director Information Systems, Pike County Memorial Hospital, Louisiana, MO, p. A365

GRUHONJIC, Osman, Chief Financial Officer, Frankfort Regional Medical Center, Frankfort, KY, p. A251

GRUN, Joseph, Chief Information Officer, New York State Psychiatric Institute, New York, NY, p. A435

GRUNDSTROM, David A., Chief Administrative Officer, Flambeau Hospital, Park Falls, WI, p. A694

GRUNWALD, Pat, MSN Chief Nursing Officer, Meriter Hospital, Madison, WI, p. A689

GRUVER, Laquita, Fiscal Officer, Grand Junction Veterans Affairs Medical Center, Grand Junction, CO, p. A102

GRUZENSKY, Denton, Director Human Resources, Feather River Hospital, Paradise, CA, p. A79

GRYWALSKI, Jr., John S., CPA Chief Financial Officer, Saint Michael's Medical Center, Newark, NJ, p. A407

GRYZBEK, Thomas J., President, Franciscan St. Margaret Health – Hammond, Hammond, IN, p. A204

GRZYBOWSKI, John, M.D. Medical Director, Mayo Clinic Health System in Albert Lea, Albert Lea, MN, p. A328

GUACCIO, Anthony, Senior Vice President & Chief Operating Officer, Swedish Covenant Hospital, Chicago, IL, p. A179

GUAJARDO, Manuel G., M.D. Medical Director, Brownsville Doctors Hospital, Brownsville, TX, p. A589

GUAJARDO, Michael, Director Finance, CHRISTUS Spohn Hospital Alice, Alice, TX, p. A581

GUANCI, Robert, Chief Operating Officer, Chesapeake Regional Medical Center, Chesapeake, VA, p. A652

GUARDIPEE, Lisa, Director, U. S. Public Health Service Indian Hospital, Fort Yates, ND, p. A467

GUARINI, Lucia A., Administrator, Essex County Hospital Center, Cedar Grove, NJ, p. A402

GUARINO, Celia, R.N. Vice President and Chief Nursing Officer, Holy Cross Hospital, Silver Spring, MD, p. A294

GUARINO, Kathleen, R.N. Vice President Patient Care Services, Mercy Hospital, Buffalo, NY, p. A422

GUARINO, Rick, M.D. Vice President Medical Affairs, Wilson Medical Center, Wilson, NC, p. A463

GUARNESCHELLI, Philip, Senior Vice President and Chief Operating Officer, Pinnacle Health System, Harrisburg, PA, p. A527

GUARRACINO, Joseph, Senior Vice President and Chief Financial Officer, Brooklyn Hospital Center,, NY, p. A431

GUARRERA, Frank, Executive Vice President and Chief Financial Officer, Motion Picture and Television Fund Hospital and Residential Services,, CA, p. A70

GUBERMAN, Wayne, Director Finance, Matheny Medical and Educational Center, Peapack, NJ, p. A408

GUELKER, Rhonda, Senior Director Finance, Rolling Plains Memorial Hospital, Sweetwater, TX, p. A636

GUERRA, Tony, Chief Financial Officer and Chief Operating Officer, Sharp Coronado Hospital and Healthcare Center, Coronado, CA, p. A57

GUERRERO, Levi, M.D. Chief of Staff, Deckerville Community Hospital, Deckerville, MI, p. A311

GUERRERO, Marisa, Director Human Resources, Laredo Specialty Hospital, Laredo, TX, p. A618

GUERRIERO, Marianne, Nurse Executive, Christian Health Care Center, Wyckoff, NJ, p. A413

GUEST, Leona, Chief Nursing Unit, Hawaii State Hospital, Kaneohe, HI, p. A165

GUEVARA, Al, FACHE, President and Chief Executive Officer, Brazosport Regional Health System, Lake Jackson, TX, p. A617

GUEVARA, Jesse, Senior Vice President and Chief Financial Officer, St. Francis Medical Center, Lynwood, CA, p. A72

GUEVIN, Scott, Chief Executive Officer, Penn State Hershey Rehabilitation Hospital, Hummelstown, PA, p. A527

GUEZ, Roberta H., Chief Operating Officer, Taunton State Hospital, Taunton, MA, p. A305

GUFFEY, Dale, Chief Financial Officer, Lower Keys Medical Center, Key West, FL, p. A127

GUFFEY, Jay, Senior Vice President and Chief Operating Officer, Mercy Hospital Springfield, Springfield, MO, p. A372

GUFFEY, Kerra, Chief Information Officer, Meriter Hospital, Madison, WI, p. A689

GUGLIELMO, Elaine, Vice President Human Resources and Organizational Development, Stamford Hospital, Stamford, CT, p. A112

GUIDERA, Kenneth, M.D. Chief of Staff, Shriners Hospitals for Children–Twin Cities, Minneapolis, MN, p. A336

GUIDRY, Carolyn, Business Manager, Community Specialty Hospital, Lafayette, LA, p. A270

GUIDRY, Floyd, M.D. Medical Director, Women and Children's Hospital, Lake Charles, LA, p. A272

GUIGNIER, Liz, Vice President Human Resources, Eisenhower Medical Center, Rancho Mirage, CA, p. A81

GUILFOIL, Thomas, Director Human Resources, Wing Memorial Hospital and Medical Centers, Palmer, MA, p. A303

GUILLOT, Karen, R.N. Chief Operating Officer, St. Charles Parish Hospital, Luling, LA, p. A272

GUIMARAES, Valerie, Director Human Resources, Livingston Regional Hospital, Livingston, TN, p. A573

GUIN Jr., Jamie W., Chief Executive Officer, Lincoln County Health System, Fayetteville, TN, p. A569

GUINANE, Gerard, Vice President Human Resources and Diversity Management, Lakeland Regional Medical Center–St. Joseph, Saint Joseph, MI, p. A324

GUINANE, Jerry, Vice President Human Resources, SwedishAmerican Hospital, Rockford, IL, p. A194

GUINLE, Mary Lou, FACHE, Chief Executive Officer, Select Specialty Hospital–Lexington, Lexington, KY, p. A254

GUINN, Judy, Chief Human Resources Officer, Graham Regional Medical Center, Graham, TX, p. A606

GUIRL, Nadine T., Senior Vice President Human Resources, Waukesha Memorial Hospital, Waukesha, WI, p. A698

GULARTE, Steven, Chief Executive Officer, Chambers County Public Hospital District 1, Anahuac, TX, p. A582

GULBENKIAN, Karen, R.N. Director Patient Care Services, John C. Fremont Healthcare District, Mariposa, CA, p. A73

GULBIS, Shannan, Director Human Resources, Methodist Richardson Medical Center, Richardson, TX, p. A628

GULDE, James E., M.D. Medical Director, Dubuis Hospital of Paris, Paris, TX, p. A626

GULIHUR, Judith, Director Human Resources and Chief Financial Officer, McCamey County Hospital District, McCamey, TX, p. A622

GULL, Joann, Chief Nursing Officer, Elmhurst Hospital Center,, NY, p. A431

GULLINGSRUD, Timothy M., Chief Executive Officer, Hayward Area Memorial Hospital and Nursing Home, Hayward, WI, p. A688

GUMBINER, Carl H., M.D. Senior Vice President Medical Affairs and Chief Medical Officer, Children's Hospital and Medical Center, Omaha, NE, p. A387

GUMBS, Milton A., M.D. Vice President and Medical Director, Bronx–Lebanon Hospital Center Health Care System,, NY, p. A431

GUMMADI, Subhaker, M.D. President Medical Staff, Promise Hospital of Baton Rouge – Mid–City Campus, Baton Rouge, LA, p. A263

GUNABALAN, Ryan, Chief Executive Officer, Behavioral Center of Michigan, Warren, MI, p. A326

GUNASEKARAN, Suresh, Assistant Vice President Information Resources, University of Texas Southwestern Medical Center, Dallas, TX, p. A598

GUNDA, Sharad, M.D. Chief of Staff, Franklin Foundation Hospital, Franklin, LA, p. A267

GUNDERSEN, Robert A., Market Chief Executive Officer, Kindred Hospital Northeast–Stoughton, Stoughton, MA, p. A305

GUNN, Deborah, Chief Information Officer, W. G. (Bill) Heffner Veterans Affairs Medical Center, Salisbury, NC, p. A460

GUNN, John R., Executive Vice President and Chief Operating Officer, Memorial Sloan–Kettering Cancer Center, New York, NY, p. A434

GUNN, Robert, Vice President Human Resources, St. Joseph Mercy Port Huron, Port Huron, MI, p. A322

GUNNELL, Nancy
 Vice President Human Resources, West Suburban Medical Center, Oak Park, IL, p. A190
 Vice President Human Resources, Westlake Hospital, Melrose Park, IL, p. A188

GUNNELS, Wheeler, M.D. Medical Director, Mizell Memorial Hospital, Opp, AL, p. A24

GUNNERSEN, Nils, Administrator, Bertrand Chaffee Hospital, Springville, NY, p. A443

GUNUKULA, Srinivas, M.D. Chief of Staff, Dallas Regional Medical Center, Mesquite, TX, p. A622

GUPTA, Apurv, M.D. Chief Medical Officer, Quincy Medical Center, Quincy, MA, p. A304

GUPTA, Arun, M.D. Vice President Medical Affairs, South Pointe Hospital, Warrensville Heights, OH, p. A492

GUPTA, Ashok K., M.D. Chief of Staff, Eaton Rapids Medical Center, Eaton Rapids, MI, p. A313

GUPTA, Vijay D., M.D. President and Chief Executive Officer, Franciscan Physicians Hospital, Munster, IN, p. A211

GURR, Lory, Chief Human Resources Division, Evans U. S. Army Community Hospital, Fort Carson, CO, p. A101

GURTO, Barbara, Manager Human Resources, University Hospitals Conneaut Medical Center, Conneaut, OH, p. A479

GURUNG, Anju, M.D. Chief Medical Officer, Mahnomen Health Center, Mahnomen, MN, p. A335

GUSHEE, Dean, M.D. Medical Director, Mason General Hospital, Shelton, WA, p. A672

GUSHO, Michael, Chief Financial Officer, St. Joseph Mercy Oakland, Pontiac, MI, p. A322

GUSSERT, Jeff, Director Operations, Dickinson County Healthcare System, Iron Mountain, MI, p. A317

GUSTAFSON, Brian, Chief Financial Officer, Veterans Affairs Montana Health Care System, Fort Harrison, MT, p. A376

GUSTAFSON, Michael, M.D., Chief Operating Officer, Brigham and Women's Faulkner Hospital, Boston, MA, p. A296

GUSTILO, Maria, M.D
 Medical Director, Osawatomie State Hospital, Osawatomie, KS, p. A241
 Medical Director, Rainbow Mental Health Facility, Kansas City, KS, p. A237

GUTH, Ron, Chief Financial Officer, Providence Hood River Memorial Hospital, Hood River, OR, p. A513

GUTHMILLER, Martin W., Chief Executive Officer, Orange City Area Health System, Orange City, IA, p. A226

GUTHRIE, Deborah S., Chief Executive Officer, HEALTHSOUTH Walton Rehabilitation Hospital, Augusta, GA, p. A148

GUTIERREZ, Albert, FACHE,
 President and Chief Executive Officer, Saint Joseph Regional Medical Center, Mishawaka, IN, p. A210
 President and Chief Executive Officer, Saint Joseph Regional Medical Center–Plymouth Campus, Plymouth, IN, p. A212

GUTIERREZ, Doris, Director Human Resources, Holy Cross Hospital, Chicago, IL, p. A176

GUTIERREZ, Lori, Chief Financial Officer, Rochelle Community Hospital, Rochelle, IL, p. A193

GUTIERREZ, Michael, Executive Director, Turquoise Lodge Hospital, Albuquerque, NM, p. A415

GUTIERREZ, Noe, Chief Financial Officer, Lake Granbury Medical Center, Granbury, TX, p. A606

GUTIERREZ, Victor A., M.D. Medical Director, Allegiance Behavioral Health Center of Plainview, Plainview, TX, p. A627

GUTJAHR, Susan, Reimbursement Specialist, Sparta Community Hospital, Sparta, IL, p. A194

GUTMAN, Luisa, Senior Vice President and Chief Operating Officer, Holy Cross Hospital, Fort Lauderdale, FL, p. A123

GUTNICK, Michael, Senior Vice President Finance, Memorial Sloan–Kettering Cancer Center, New York, NY, p. A434

GUTOW, Andrew, M.D. Medical Director, Menlo Park Surgical Hospital, Menlo Park, CA, p. A74

GUTSCH, Michael, Chief Executive Officer, Cumberland Memorial Hospital, Cumberland, WI, p. A685

GUTSCHENRITTER, John, Chief Financial Officer, Wilson Medical Center, Neodesha, KS, p. A240

GUTTENBERG, Ellen, Chief Operating Officer, Frances Mahon Deaconess Hospital, Glasgow, MT, p. A376

GUTTIN, Enrique, M.D. Chief of Staff, Veterans Affairs Medical Center, Wilmington, DE, p. A115

GUTTMACHER, Laurence, M.D. Clinical Director, Rochester Psychiatric Center, Rochester, NY, p. A441

GUTZEIT, Michael, M.D. Chief Medical Officer, Children's Hospital of Wisconsin, Milwaukee, WI, p. A692

GUYETTE, William, M.D. President Medical Staff, Livingston Hospital and Healthcare Services, Salem, KY, p. A260

GUZMAN, Elizabeth, Chief Financial Officer, Metropolitan Hospital Center, New York, NY, p. A434

GWATKIN, Betty Ann, Vice President Human Resources, Northeastern Vermont Regional Hospital, Saint Johnsbury, VT, p. A650

GWYN, Brian
 President and Chief Executive Officer, Cleveland Regional Medical Center, Shelby, NC, p. A460
 President and Chief Executive Officer, Crawley Memorial Hospital, Shelby, NC, p. A461
 President and Chief Executive Officer, Kings Mountain Hospital, Kings Mountain, NC, p. A455

GWYNN, Sherry, Administrative Director Human Resources, Care Regional Medical Center, Aransas Pass, TX, p. A583

# H

HAACK, Wanda, MSN Chief Nursing Officer, Genesis Medical Center, DeWitt, De Witt, IA, p. A219

HAACKE, David E., M.D. Chief of Staff, Collingsworth General Hospital, Wellington, TX, p. A640

HAAGENSON, Deb, R.N. Vice President of Patient Care, St. Joseph's Area Health Services, Park Rapids, MN, p. A338

HAAK, Thelma, Manager Health Information, Avera Dells Area Hospital, Dell Rapids, SD, p. A559

HAAK–MUSE, Margaret, Chief Financial Officer and Assistant Administrator, East Texas Medical Center–Mount Vernon, Mount Vernon, TX, p. A624

HAAR, Clare A., Chief Executive Officer, Eastern Niagara Health System, Lockport, NY, p. A428

HAAS, Christine, Manager Information Technology, Jersey Shore Hospital, Jersey Shore, PA, p. A528

HAAS, Marvin, Interim Chief Executive Officer, Ashland Community Hospital, Ashland, OR, p. A511

HAAS, Richard, FACHE, President, Grandview Medical Center, Dayton, OH, p. A480

HAAS, Scott A., M.D. Chief Medical Officer, Eastern State Hospital, Lexington, KY, p. A254

HAAS, Susan, Director Human Resources, Aurora Behavioral Health Care, San Diego, CA, p. A85

HAASE, Patricia, Director Information Technology and Communications, Marian Medical Center, Santa Maria, CA, p. A90

HAASE, Ron, Vice President Human Resources, St. Mary's of Michigan, Saginaw, MI, p. A323

HAASKEN, Timothy W., Chief Financial Officer, LewisGale Hospital Montgomery, Blacksburg, VA, p. A652

HAATVEDT, Cy, M.D. Chief of Staff, Huron Regional Medical Center, Huron, SD, p. A560

HABASHY, Hany Mounir, M.D. Chief Medical Director, Methodist Extended Care Hospital, Memphis, TN, p. A575

HABIB, Noel, M.D. Chief Medical Officer, Huhukam Memorial Hospital, Sacaton, AZ, p. A36

HABOWSKI, Michael J., President and Chief Executive Officer, Ashtabula County Medical Center, Ashtabula, OH, p. A470

HACHENBERG, Dennis A., FACHE, Chief Executive Officer, Anderson County Hospital, Garnett, KS, p. A234

HACKBARTH, John, CPA Senior Vice President Finance and Chief Financial Officer, Owensboro Health Regional Hospital, Owensboro, KY, p. A258

HACKER, Kenneth, M.D. Chief of Staff, Progress West HealthCare Center, Saint Charles, MO, p. A368

HACKER, Leanne, Chief Financial Officer, Eastern New Mexico Medical Center, Roswell, NM, p. A417

HACKER, Mary Dee, R.N. Vice President, Patient Care Services and Chief Nursing Officer, Children's Hospital Los Angeles, Los Angeles, CA, p. A68

HACKER, Phillip, Chief Financial Officer, Citizens Medical Center, Victoria, TX, p. A639

HACKETT, Sylvia D., Vice President Human Resources, Rex Healthcare, Raleigh, NC, p. A459

HACKMAN, James, Corporate Vice President Human Resources, Florida Hospital Tampa, Tampa, FL, p. A141

HACKMAN, Paul, Chief Executive Officer, Ridgeview Institute, Smyrna, GA, p. A160

HACKNEY, Hannah, Director Accounting and Human Resources, DeWitt Hospital, De Witt, AR, p. A42

HACKSTEDDE, Anita, M.D. Vice President Medical Affairs, Salem Community Hospital, Salem, OH, p. A489

HADDAD, Phillip A., M.D. Chief Medical Officer, Solara Hospital of Shawnee, Shawnee, OK, p. A506

HADDADIN, Maen, M.D. President Medical Staff, Alegent Creighton Health Mercy Hospital, Corning, IA, p. A218

HADDEN, Kim E., R.N. Chief Nurse Executive, Kaiser Permanente Riverside Medical Center, Riverside, CA, p. A82

HADDICAN, James, Vice President Finance, Gillette Children's Specialty Healthcare, Saint Paul, MN, p. A340

HADDIX, D. Parker, Chief Operating Officer, Davis Memorial Hospital, Elkins, WV, p. A676

HADDIX, Parker, Chief Executive Officer, William R. Sharpe, Jr. Hospital, Weston, WV, p. A682

HADDIX–HILL, Katherine, R.N. Chief Nursing Officer/Chief Operating Officer, Pender Memorial Hospital, Burgaw, NC, p. A448

HADEN, James E., President and Chief Executive Officer, Martha Jefferson Hospital, Charlottesville, VA, p. A652

HADJUK, Clare, Director Human Resources, Edward Hines, Jr. Veterans Affairs Hospital, Hines, IL, p. A185

HADLEY, Mike
 Chief Information Officer, Saint Francis Hospital, Memphis, TN, p. A575
 Director Information Systems, Saint Francis Hospital–Bartlett, Bartlett, TN, p. A565

HADLEY, Steven N., Chief Financial Officer, Kansas Medical Center, Andover, KS, p. A231

HADLEY, Susan, R.N. Director of Nursing, Dickinson County Healthcare System, Iron Mountain, MI, p. A317

HADZEGA, Angela, Chief Financial Officer, Kane Community Hospital, Kane, PA, p. A528

HADZIE, Daniel, M.D. Chief of Staff, Stonewall Memorial Hospital, Aspermont, TX, p. A584

HAEGER, Eric, M.D. President Medical Staff, Three Rivers Hospital, Brewster, WA, p. A665

HAEHN, Debra, Chief Financial Officer, Clay County Memorial Hospital, Henrietta, TX, p. A608

HAENELT, Michael, Chief Information Management, Weed Army Community Hospital, Fort Irwin, CA, p. A60

HAESEMEYER, Allan, M.D. Chief of Staff, Indianhead Medical Center, Shell Lake, WI, p. A696

HAEUSER, Jamie, Senior Vice President Operations, Woman's Hospital, Baton Rouge, LA, p. A264

HAFEMAN, Paula, R.N
 Chief Nursing Officer, St. Mary's Hospital Medical Center, Green Bay, WI, p. A688
 Chief Nursing Officer, St. Vincent Hospital, Green Bay, WI, p. A688

HAFEN, Heather, Manager Human Resources, Sanpete Valley Hospital, Mount Pleasant, UT, p. A644

HAFFNER, Randall L., Ph.D., Chief Executive Officer, Porter Adventist Hospital, Denver, CO, p. A100

HAFFORD, Juliet, Director Human Resources, Oakwood Southshore Medical Center, Trenton, MI, p. A325

HAGAN, David J., M.D. Chief Medical Officer, Gibson Area Hospital and Health Services, Gibson City, IL, p. A183

HAGAN, Donald E., Chief Financial Officer, DeTar Healthcare System, Victoria, TX, p. A639

HAGAN, Eric, R.N.,
 Vice President/Administrator, Medical Center at Franklin, Franklin, KY, p. A251
 Vice President/Administrator, Medical Center at Scottsville, Scottsville, KY, p. A260

HAGAN, Mary, Director Human Resources, Summit Park Hospital and Nursing Care Center, Pomona, NY, p. A439

HAGAN, Patrick J., President and Chief Operating Officer, Seattle Children's Hospital, Seattle, WA, p. A671

HAGELTHORN, Diane, Human Resources Generalist, Modoc Medical Center, Alturas, CA, p. A52

HAGEMANN, Margarethe, M.D. Chief of Staff, Memphis Veterans Affairs Medical Center, Memphis, TN, p. A575

HAGEN, Bruce P.
President, OhioHealth Dublin Methodist Hospital, Dublin, OH, p. A481
President, OhioHealth Grady Memorial Hospital, Delaware, OH, p. A480

HAGEN, Paulette, Director Human Resources, Paynesville Area Health Care System, Paynesville, MN, p. A338

HAGENS, Gary, Chief Operating Officer and Vice President Medical Affairs, Advocate BroMenn Medical Center, Normal, IL, p. A190

HAGENSICKER, Janice, Chief Financial Officer, Rollins–Brook Community Hospital, Lampasas, TX, p. A618

HAGER, Jeff, M.D. President Medical Staff, North Mississippi Medical Center–Hamilton, Hamilton, AL, p. A21

HAGER, Rhonda M., Director Human Resources, Stonewall Jackson Memorial Hospital, Weston, WV, p. A681

HAGGARD, Tommy, Chief Executive Officer, Bluegrass Community Hospital, Versailles, KY, p. A261

HAGGERTY, Arthur, Director Information Systems, Madera Community Hospital, Madera, CA, p. A73

HAGGERTY, Bridget, Chief Information Officer, OHSU Hospital, Portland, OR, p. A516

HAGHIGHAT, Dennis, M.D. Vice President Medical Affairs, Mission Hospital, Mission Viejo, CA, p. A74

HAGLER, Dan, M.D. Vice President and Chief Medical Officer, Carolinas Medical Center–Union, Monroe, NC, p. A457

HAGOOD, Teena, Chief Nursing Officer, Kimble Hospital, Junction, TX, p. A615

HAGUE, Samuel, M.D. Chief of Staff, Integris Blackwell Regional Hospital, Blackwell, OK, p. A496

HAGY, Kelly, Director Human Resources and Professional Affairs, Northwest Medical Center, Winfield, AL, p. A26

HAGY, Michael, Chief Financial Officer, Pikeville Medical Center, Pikeville, KY, p. A259

HAHEY, Joanne A., Senior Vice President and Chief Financial Officer, Jefferson Regional Medical Center, Jefferson Hills, PA, p. A528

HAHN, Annette, Director Human Resources, Rehabilitation Hospital of Wisconsin, Waukesha, WI, p. A698

HAHN, Bashirat, Chief Information Officer, MetroSouth Medical Center, Blue Island, IL, p. A174

HAHN, Donna S., R.N. Vice President Acute Care and Chief Nurse Executive, Rockingham Memorial Hospital, Harrisonburg, VA, p. A655

HAHN, James W., Administrator, North Mississippi Medical Center–West Point, West Point, MS, p. A355

HAHN, Joseph, M.D. Chief of Staff, Cleveland Clinic, Cleveland, OH, p. A476

HAHN, Kenneth, M.D. Chief of Staff, South Peninsula Hospital, Homer, AK, p. A28

HAHN, Victoria J., Administrator and Chief Executive Officer, Wichita County Health Center, Leoti, KS, p. A238

HAIL, Brian, Chief Executive Officer, Cherokee Nation W.W. Hastings Indian Hospital, Tahlequah, OK, p. A507

HAILE, Michael, Senior Vice President and Chief Financial Officer, Faxton–St. Luke's Healthcare, Utica, NY, p. A444

HAILSTONE, Sherlyn, FACHE, President, SSM Cardinal Glennon Children's Medical Center, Saint Louis, MO, p. A370

HAIM, Kelvin, M.D. Chief of Staff, North Georgia Medical Center, Ellijay, GA, p. A153

HAINES, Beverly J., R.N., President, Patewood Memorial Hospital, Greenville, SC, p. A552

HAIR, Laurie, Chief Financial Officer, Phoebe Sumter Medical Center, Americus, GA, p. A145

HAIR, Troy, Chief Financial Officer, Abbeville General Hospital, Abbeville, LA, p. A262

HAIRGROVE, Heath, Administrator, Tri Parish Rehabilitation Hospital, Leesville, LA, p. A272

HAIZLIP, Jr., Thomas M., M.D. Chief of Staff, Charles A. Cannon Memorial Hospital, Linville, NC, p. A456

HAJEK, Julie, Director Human Resources, St. David's North Austin Medical Center, Austin, TX, p. A586

HAKMILLER, Karl, M.D. Chief of Staff, South Baldwin Regional Medical Center, Foley, AL, p. A20

HALAKAN, Catherine, Senior Vice President, Albany Medical Center, Albany, NY, p. A420

HALAMKA, John, M.D. Chief Information Officer, Beth Israel Deaconess Medical Center, Boston, MA, p. A296

HALDEMAN, Larry, M.D. Executive Vice President and Chief Medical Officer, WellStar Windy Hill Hospital, Marietta, GA, p. A157

HALE, Becky, Director Human Resources, Hill Regional Hospital, Hillsboro, TX, p. A608

HALE, Byron, Chief Financial Officer, East Texas Medical Center Tyler, Tyler, TX, p. A638

HALE, Dana R., R.N. Vice President Nursing, Lawrence Memorial Hospital, Lawrence, KS, p. A238

HALE, Elizabeth, R.N. Vice President Patient Services and Chief Nursing Officer, Lawrence General Hospital, Lawrence, MA, p. A301

HALE, Nathan, Director Information Management, Howard Memorial Hospital, Nashville, AR, p. A48

HALE, Pat, Chief Financial Officer, Indian Path Medical Center, Kingsport, TN, p. A571

HALE, Ron, Chief Executive Officer, Alaska Psychiatric Institute, Anchorage, AK, p. A27

HALE, Tonia, Chief Nursing Officer, Newport Medical Center, Newport, TN, p. A577

HALE, Tyson, M.D. Chief of Staff, Peterson Regional Medical Center, Kerrville, TX, p. A616

HALE, Vicki, Chief Financial Officer, NCH Downtown Naples Hospital, Naples, FL, p. A133

HALEN, Catherine, Vice President Human Resources, Beebe Medical Center, Lewes, DE, p. A114

HALES, Brent, Chief Financial Officer, Uintah Basin Medical Center, Roosevelt, UT, p. A646

HALES, Joe, Director Information Systems, Primary Children's Medical Center, Salt Lake City, UT, p. A646

HALES, Tom, CPA Chief Financial Officer, Crittenden County Hospital, Marion, KY, p. A257

HALEY, Bob, Interim Chief Executive Officer, Rainy Lake Medical Center, International Falls, MN, p. A334

HALEY, James, M.D. Senior Vice President and Chief Medical Officer, Unity Hospital, Rochester, NY, p. A441

HALEY, Kevin, Chief Financial Officer, Penn State Milton S. Hershey Medical Center, Hershey, PA, p. A527

HALEY, Michael E., President and Chief Executive Officer, Indiana University Health Ball Memorial Hospital, Muncie, IN, p. A210

HALFEN, John, M.D. Medical Director, Lakewood Health System, Staples, MN, p. A341

HALFEN, John
Administrator, Chief Executive Officer and Chief Financial Officer, Northern Inyo Hospital, Bishop, CA, p. A55
Administrator, Chief Executive Officer and Chief Financial Officer, Northern Inyo Hospital, Bishop, CA, p. A55

HALFERTY, Michael, M.D. President Medical Staff, Samaritan North Lincoln Hospital, Lincoln City, OR, p. A514

HALFHILL, Patrick, Chief Financial Officer, Madison County Memorial Hospital, Madison, FL, p. A129

HALL, Alan, Chief Nursing Officer, St. Joseph's Behavioral Health Center, Stockton, CA, p. A92

HALL, Brenda, R.N. Vice President Patient Care Services, Yuma Regional Medical Center, Yuma, AZ, p. A40

HALL, Butch, Chief Financial Officer, Hardeman County Memorial Hospital, Quanah, TX, p. A628

HALL, Carla, Director of Nursing, Highland Hospital, Charleston, WV, p. A676

HALL, Catherine, Manager Human Resources, Jefferson Hospital, Louisville, GA, p. A156

HALL, Charlene, Vice President Human Resources and Guest Support Services, Indiana University Health Morgan Hospital, Martinsville, IN, p. A209

HALL, Cindy, Coordinator Human Resources, Selby General Hospital, Marietta, OH, p. A485

HALL, Clara Cordelia, Chief Human Resources Officer, Breckinridge Memorial Hospital, Hardinsburg, KY, p. A252

HALL, Dan, R.N. Director of Nursing, St. John Owasso, Owasso, OK, p. A505

HALL, Dana, Director of Nursing, Quitman County Hospital, Marks, MS, p. A350

HALL, David, Chief Information Officer, Pineville Community Hospital Association, Pineville, KY, p. A259

HALL, David, M.D. Senior Vice President and Chief Medical Officer, St. Vincent Medical Center–North, Sherwood, AR, p. A50

HALL, David, Senior Vice President and Chief Operating Officer, University of Tennessee Medical Center, Knoxville, TN, p. A572

HALL, Doug, Director Information Systems, Tri Valley Health System, Cambridge, NE, p. A382

HALL, Gary, Vice President of Information Technology, Estes Park Medical Center, Estes Park, CO, p. A101

HALL, George, M.D
Vice President Medical Affairs, St. Elizabeth Florence, Florence, KY, p. A250
Vice President Medical Affairs, St. Elizabeth Fort Thomas, Fort Thomas, KY, p. A251

HALL, Gerald, Director Resource Management, Naval Hospital Oak Harbor, Oak Harbor, WA, p. A668

HALL, Herbert L., Administrator, Reception and Medical Center, Lake Butler, FL, p. A128

HALL, Jeanne, Director Information Systems, Shriners Hospitals for Children–St. Louis, Saint Louis, MO, p. A370

HALL, Jeffrey, M.D. Chief of Staff, Great River Medical Center, Blytheville, AR, p. A41

HALL, Jeremy, Assistant Administrator and Chief Financial Officer, Middlesboro ARH Hospital, Middlesboro, KY, p. A257

HALL, Jim
Budget Officer, Caswell Center, Kinston, NC, p. A456
Acting Chief Information Officer, Central Arkansas Veterans Healthcare System, Little Rock, AR, p. A46

HALL, Les, M.D
Chief Medical Officer, University of Missouri Hospitals and Clinics, Columbia, MO, p. A359
Chief of Staff, Women's and Children's Hospital, Columbia, MO, p. A359

HALL, Leslie, R.N. Senior Vice President–Chief Nursing Officer, Nash Health Care Systems, Rocky Mount, NC, p. A460

HALL, Linda, Administrator and Chief Executive Officer, Chillicothe Hospital District, Chillicothe, TX, p. A592

HALL, Mark, Chief Financial Officer, Rehoboth McKinley Christian Health Care Services, Gallup, NM, p. A416

HALL, Mary A., Chief Medical Staff, McDowell ARH Hospital, McDowell, KY, p. A257

HALL, Melissa, Human Resources, Munising Memorial Hospital, Munising, MI, p. A320

HALL, Michael L., Chief Executive Officer, Avera Holy Family Hospital, Estherville, IA, p. A221

HALL, Mike, Risk Manager, Sistersville General Hospital, Sistersville, WV, p. A681

HALL, Robert, Chief Information Officer, Northern Hospital of Surry County, Mount Airy, NC, p. A458

HALL, Roger L.
President, Sacred Heart Hospital on the Emerald Coast, Miramar Beach, FL, p. A133
President, Sacred Heart Hospital on the Gulf, Port St. Joe, FL, p. A138

HALL, Sally, Manager Human Resources, South Texas Spine and Surgical Hospital, San Antonio, TX, p. A632

HALL, Stephanie, M.D. Chief Medical Officer, LAC/University of Southern California Medical Center, Los Angeles, CA, p. A70

HALL, Steve, Chief Financial Officer, Pekin Hospital, Pekin, IL, p. A191

HALL, Veronica, R.N. Chief Operating Officer, Henry Ford Hospital, Detroit, MI, p. A312

HALLADAY, Mark, Director Information Services, F. F. Thompson Hospital, Canandaigua, NY, p. A423

HALLAL, Joseph, M.D. Chief Medical Officer, Inova Fairfax Hospital, Falls Church, VA, p. A653

HALLAM, Gina, Administrator, Marian Center, Salt Lake City, UT, p. A646

HALLATT, Jennifer
Chief Operating Officer, Mercy Harvard Hospital, Harvard, IL, p. A184
Chief Operating Officer, Mercy Walworth Hospital and Medical Center, Lake Geneva, WI, p. A689

HALLER, III, William, M.D. Chief of Staff, Gadsden Regional Medical Center, Gadsden, AL, p. A20

HALLEY, Lisa B., Vice President Human Resources, Holzer Medical Center, Gallipolis, OH, p. A482

HALLGREN, Hugh R., Chief Executive Officer, Sitka Community Hospital, Sitka, AK, p. A29

HALLIDAY, Lisa, Director Accounting Services, Taylor Regional Hospital, Hawkinsville, GA, p. A154

HALLIGAN, Ron, Vice President Support Services, Great River Medical Center, West Burlington, IA, p. A230

HALLISEY, Thomas, Vice President Information Management, Cortland Regional Medical Center, Cortland, NY, p. A424

HALLMARK, Todd, Chief Operating Officer, Choctaw Nation Health Care Center, Talihina, OK, p. A507

HALLY, Christine, Director Human Resources, Rochester Psychiatric Center, Rochester, NY, p. A441

HALPIN, Kim, Director Human Resources, Arms Acres, Carmel, NY, p. A423

HALSAN, Carole, R.N., Chief Executive Officer, Willapa Harbor Hospital, South Bend, WA, p. A672

HALSELL, David, Senior Vice President and Chief Financial Officer, Lake Regional Health System, Osage Beach, MO, p. A367

HALSTEAD, Doug, Manager Information Systems, Bartlett Regional Hospital, Juneau, AK, p. A28

HALTER, Kevin, Chief Executive Officer, Our Lady of Bellefonte Hospital, Ashland, KY, p. A248

HALTER, Michael P., Chief Executive Officer, Hahnemann University Hospital, Philadelphia, PA, p. A535

HALTER, Susan, M.D. Chief Medical Officer, Winneshiek Medical Center, Decorah, IA, p. A220

HALTERMAN, Mary Kaye, R.N. Chief Nursing Officer, Piedmont Medical Center, Rock Hill, SC, p. A555

HALVERSON, Glen, Chief Operating Officer, Mammoth Hospital, Mammoth Lakes, CA, p. A73

HALVORSON, Linda, Director Human Resources, Mountrail County Medical Center, Stanley, ND, p. A469

HALVORSON, Marla, Director Human Resources, St. Luke's Hospital, Duluth, MN, p. A331

HAMAM, Hisham, M.D. Chief of Staff, Northern Cochise Community Hospital, Willcox, AZ, p. A39

HAMANN, Barbara, Manager People Services, St. Nicholas Hospital, Sheboygan, WI, p. A696

HAMB, Aaron, M.D. Chief Medical Officer, Provident Hospital of Cook County, Chicago, IL, p. A178

HAMBLEN, Jeffrey J., Chief Executive Officer, Little Colorado Medical Center, Winslow, AZ, p. A40

HAMBLIN, James, Chief Financial Officer, White Mountain Regional Medical Center, Springerville, AZ, p. A37

HAMEL, Cathleen, MS Vice President and Chief Nursing Officer, Baxter Regional Medical Center, Mountain Home, AR, p. A48

HAMEL, Loren, M.D.,
President and Chief Executive Officer, Lakeland Regional Medical Center–St. Joseph, Saint Joseph, MI, p. A324
President and Chief Executive Officer, Lakeland Specialty Hospital–Berrien Center, Berrien Center, MI, p. A309

HAMEL, Susan, Chief Nursing Officer, St. Luke's Hospital, Duluth, MN, p. A331

HAMILL, Dave H., President and Chief Executive Officer, Hampton Regional Medical Center, Varnville, SC, p. A556

HAMILTON, Aggie, Chief Human Resources, Veterans Affairs Montana Health Care System, Fort Harrison, MT, p. A376

HAMILTON, Bruce
Vice President Human Resources, Lutheran Hospital of Indiana, Fort Wayne, IN, p. A202
Director Human Resources, Orthopaedic Hospital of Lutheran Health Network, Fort Wayne, IN, p. A202

HAMILTON, Chanda, Chief Information Officer, Clifton T. Perkins Hospital Center, Jessup, MD, p. A292

HAMILTON, Crystal, R.N., Chief Executive Officer, Maryvale Hospital Medical Center, Phoenix, AZ, p. A34

HAMILTON, Dan, Director Inpatient Services, Nor–Lea General Hospital, Lovington, NM, p. A417

HAMILTON, James, M.D. Chief of Staff, Habersham Medical Center, Demorest, GA, p. A152

HAMILTON, John B., FACHE, Interim President and Chief Executive Officer, Central Washington Hospital, Wenatchee, WA, p. A674

HAMILTON, Joyce, Director Human Resources, McKenzie Regional Hospital, McKenzie, TN, p. A574

HAMILTON, Kay A., MS, President and Chief Executive Officer, Lewistown Hospital, Lewistown, PA, p. A530

HAMILTON, Mark C., M.D. President Medical Staff, Springfield Hospital, Springfield, VT, p. A650

HAMILTON, Neal C., Chief Human Resources, James A. Haley Veterans' Hospital, Tampa, FL, p. A141

HAMILTON, Phil, R.N., Chief Executive Officer, General John J. Pershing Memorial Hospital, Brookfield, MO, p. A357

HAMILTON, Robert U., Director, Charlie Norwood Veterans Affairs Medical Center, Augusta, GA, p. A147

HAMILTON, Scott, Vice President and Chief Financial Officer, Parkwest Medical Center, Knoxville, TN, p. A572

HAMILTON, Terry, President, St. John Macomb–Oakland Hospital, Warren, MI, p. A326

HAMILTON, Theresa, Chief Executive Officer, Fremont–Rideout Health Group, Marysville, CA, p. A73

HAMILTON, Tom, M.D. Chief of Staff, Decatur County General Hospital, Parsons, TN, p. A578

HAMILTON, William L., M.D
Urban Central Region Medical Director, Intermountain Medical Center, Murray, UT, p. A644
Chief Medical Officer, LDS Hospital, Salt Lake City, UT, p. A646

HAMILTON–BEYER, Maggie, Chief Financial Officer, Knoxville Hospital & Clinics, Knoxville, IA, p. A224

HAMILTON–CRAWFORD, Janice, Administrator, Southern Crescent Hospital for Specialty Care, Riverdale, GA, p. A158

HAMLIN, DeWayne, Director, Veterans Affairs Medical Center–Lexington, Lexington, KY, p. A255

HAMLIN, Faye, Manager Human Resources, Julian F. Keith Alcohol and Drug Abuse Treatment Center, Black Mountain, NC, p. A448

HAMLIN, Jeff, Director Finance, Oak Tree Hospital, Corbin, KY, p. A249

HAMLIN, Scott J., Chief Financial Officer, Cincinnati Children's Hospital Medical Center, Cincinnati, OH, p. A474

HAMM, David, President and Chief Executive Officer, Exempla Good Samaritan Medical Center, Lafayette, CO, p. A103

HAMMACK, Kathy, Chief Financial Officer, Western Medical Center–Santa Ana, Santa Ana, CA, p. A89

HAMMAN, Baron L., M.D., President, Texas Health Heart & Vascular Hospital Arlington, Arlington, TX, p. A584

HAMMER, Michael, Chief Executive Officer, Sanford Worthington Medical Center, Worthington, MN, p. A343

HAMMER, Patrick T., President and Chief Executive Officer, Rogers Memorial Hospital, Oconomowoc, WI, p. A693

HAMMER, Rebecca J., Chief Financial Officer, Davis Memorial Hospital, Elkins, WV, p. A676

HAMMERAN, Kevin R., Executive Vice President and Chief Operating Officer, Miami Children's Hospital, Miami, FL, p. A132

HAMMES, Paul, Senior Vice President and Chief Operating Officer, Novant Health Forsyth Medical Center, Winston–Salem, NC, p. A463

HAMMETT, George, Director Human Resources, Carolina Center for Behavioral Health, Greer, SC, p. A553

HAMMETT, Richard A., Chief Executive Officer, Medical Center of Aurora, Aurora, CO, p. A97

HAMMETT, Troy, Vice President and Chief Financial Officer, OhioHealth Doctors Hospital, Columbus, OH, p. A478

HAMMOND, Flora, M.D. Chief Medical Affairs, Rehabilitation Hospital of Indiana, Indianapolis, IN, p. A206

HAMMOND, Geoffrey, M.D. Medical Director, Larned State Hospital, Larned, KS, p. A238

HAMMOND, Kathy, Director Information Services, AnMed Health Medical Center, Anderson, SC, p. A548

HAMMOND, Michael
Chief Financial Officer, Lourdes Medical Center of Burlington County, Willingboro, NJ, p. A412
Chief Financial Officer, Our Lady of Lourdes Medical Center, Camden, NJ, p. A402

HAMMOND, Reed, Chief Operating Officer, Centennial Medical Center, Frisco, TX, p. A605

HAMMOND, Robert, Interim Chief Executive Officer, Frye Regional Medical Center, Hickory, NC, p. A454

HAMMOND, Thomas H., Chief Information Officer, St. Francis Medical Center, Monroe, LA, p. A274

HAMMONDS, Janie, Human Resources Officer, Columbus Community Hospital, Columbus, TX, p. A592

HAMMONDS, Laura, Assistant Administrator, Jasper Memorial Hospital, Monticello, GA, p. A157

HAMON, Eric, Chief Financial Officer, Driscoll Children's Hospital, Corpus Christi, TX, p. A594

HAMONS, Janet, Vice President Human Resources, Hutchinson Regional Medical Center, Hutchinson, KS, p. A236

HAMONS, Spencer, Chief Information Officer, Holy Cross Hospital, Taos, NM, p. A418

HAMP, Matthew, Chief Operating Officer, Sisters of Charity Hospital of Buffalo, Buffalo, NY, p. A423

HAMPLE, David L., Chief Executive Officer, Montrose Memorial Hospital, Montrose, CO, p. A104

HAMPTON, Angie, Director Human Resources, Porter Regional Hospital, Valparaiso, IN, p. A214

HAMPTON, David, M.D. Chief Medical Staff, Pampa Regional Medical Center, Pampa, TX, p. A626

HAMPTON, Debra C., Ph.D., Vice President, Administration and Chief Nursing Officer, Drake Center, Cincinnati, OH, p. A474

HAMPTON, Jeff, Director Information Systems, Lehigh Regional Medical Center, Lehigh Acres, FL, p. A129

HAMPTON, Laurie, Director Human Resources, Prairie du Chien Memorial Hospital, Prairie Du Chien, WI, p. A695

HAMRICK, Jan, Chief Financial Officer, Dodge County Hospital, Eastman, GA, p. A153

HAN, Ba, M.D. Clinical Director, Big Spring State Hospital, Big Spring, TX, p. A588

HAN, Kevin, Vice President and Chief Financial Officer, Stormont–Vail HealthCare, Topeka, KS, p. A245

HANAN, Rhonda Jean, Vice President of Patient Care, Mercy Hospital Ardmore, Ardmore, OK, p. A495

HANCOCK, Denise, Chief Financial Officer, Arbuckle Memorial Hospital, Sulphur, OK, p. A507

HANCOCK, J. Brian, M.D. Chief of Staff, Fargo Veterans Affairs Health Care System, Fargo, ND, p. A466

HANCOCK, Lori, Chief Business Officer, West Palm Beach Veterans Affairs Medical Center, West Palm Beach, FL, p. A144

HANCOCK, Melinda, Interim Chief Financial Officer, Good Samaritan Hospital, Suffern, NY, p. A443

HANCOCK, Sharon, Director Human Resources, Drake Center, Cincinnati, OH, p. A474

HAND, Ronald E., Administrator, Oceans Behavioral Hospital of De Ridder, Deridder, LA, p. A266

HANDELSMAN, Larry, M.D. Vice President Medical Affairs, Chelsea Community Hospital, Chelsea, MI, p. A310

HANDLER, Michael, M.D. Vice President Medical Administration, SSM St. Joseph Hospital West, Lake Saint Louis, MO, p. A364

HANDLEY, Charles R., Chief Financial Officer, Plaza Specialty Hospital, Houston, TX, p. A611

HANDLEY, Peter, M.D. Chief of Staff, Otsego Memorial Hospital, Gaylord, MI, p. A314

HANDLEY, Rhonda, Chief Financial Officer, Columbia Basin Hospital, Ephrata, WA, p. A666

HANDOL, Nelson, M.D. Medical Director, Laurel Oaks Behavioral Health Center, Dothan, AL, p. A19

HANDRICK, Carolyn, Manager Public Relations, Corning Hospital, Corning, NY, p. A424

HANDY, Steven P., CPA Senior Vice President, Chief Financial Officer and Chief Information Officer, Uniontown Hospital, Uniontown, PA, p. A542

HANEBRINK, Brad, D.O. Chief of Staff, Sheridan Memorial Hospital, Sheridan, WY, p. A703

HANEN, David G., Vice President and Chief Financial Officer, Fremont Area Medical Center, Fremont, NE, p. A383

HANEN, Marti, Director Human Resources, Providence Seaside Hospital, Seaside, OR, p. A517

HANENBURG, Thomas S., Chief Executive, Providence Medford Medical Center, Medford, OR, p. A514

HANEY, Judy, Chief Nursing Officer, Harris Hospital, Newport, AR, p. A48

HANEY, Kathryn, Chief Financial Officer, HEALTHSOUTH Valley of the Sun Rehabilitation Hospital, Glendale, AZ, p. A32

HANEY, Mark, President, WellStar Paulding Hospital, Dallas, GA, p. A151

HANGER, Kelvin, Chief Executive Officer, Evendale Medical Center, Cincinnati, OH, p. A474

HANIGAN, Hank, Chief Operating Officer, Whidbey General Hospital, Coupeville, WA, p. A666

HANISCH, Denise, M.D. Chief of Staff, Avera St. Mary's Hospital, Pierre, SD, p. A561

HANKERD, Nanci, Manager Human Resources, Trinity Hospital, Weaverville, CA, p. A95

HANKINS, Brad, Chief Operating Quality Officer, Lake Chelan Community Hospital, Chelan, WA, p. A665

HANKINSON, Scott, Chief Financial Officer, Western Plains Medical Complex, Dodge City, KS, p. A233

HANKS, Claire H., R.N. Vice President and Chief Nursing Officer, Glendale Memorial Hospital and Health Center, Glendale, CA, p. A62

HANKS, John, Director Information Systems, East Tennessee Children's Hospital, Knoxville, TN, p. A571

HANKS, Tammy, Director Human Resources, Minidoka Memorial Hospital, Rupert, ID, p. A171

HANLEY, Darlene S., R.N., President and Chief Executive Officer, St. Lawrence Rehabilitation Center, Lawrenceville, NJ, p. A405

HANLEY, Janet, Chief Nursing Officer, Sharp Grossmont Hospital, La Mesa, CA, p. A65

HANLEY, Kathleen S., Chief Financial Officer, ProMedica Flower Hospital, Sylvania, OH, p. A490

HANLEY, Patrick, D.O. Interim Vice President Medical Affairs, Palmerton Hospital, Palmerton, PA, p. A533

HANLEY, Richard, Chief Operating Officer, Spring Harbor Hospital, Westbrook, ME, p. A286

HANLY, Donna, R.N. Senior Vice President and Chief Nursing Officer, OhioHealth Grant Medical Center, Columbus, OH, p. A478

HANNA, Mitchell J., Chief Executive Officer, Sutter Auburn Faith Hospital, Auburn, CA, p. A53

HANNA, Philip S., Administrator, Battle Mountain General Hospital, Battle Mountain, NV, p. A391

HANNA, Robb, Executive Director Information Technology, Lexington Regional Health Center, Lexington, NE, p. A385

HANNAH, Jill, Director Human Resources, James Cancer Hospital and Solove Research Institute, Columbus, OH, p. A477

HANNAH, Steve, Chief Operating Officer, Gordon Hospital, Calhoun, GA, p. A149

HANNAN, Barbara E., R.N., Chief Executive Officer, Select Specialty Hospital–Northeast New Jersey, Rochelle Park, NJ, p. A410

HANNERS, Brandy, Chief Financial Officer, Memorial Hospital, Martinsville, VA, p. A657

HANNERS, Rodney, Senior Vice President and Chief Operating Officer, Children's Hospital Los Angeles, Los Angeles, CA, p. A68

HANNIFAN, Kevin R., President, St. Elizabeth's Medical Center, Brighton, MA, p. A298

HANNON, Barbara A., R.N. VP Nursing, Mount Desert Island Hospital, Bar Harbor, ME, p. A281

HANNON, Edward J., Chief Executive Officer, Mayo Regional Hospital, Dover–Foxcroft, ME, p. A283

HANNON, Jennifer, Director Human Resources, Madison County Health Care System, Winterset, IA, p. A230

HANNON, Kay, Director Information Systems, Des Peres Hospital, Saint Louis, MO, p. A369

HANNON, Trish, FACHE, President and Chief Executive Officer, New England Baptist Hospital, Boston, MA, p. A297

HANOLD, Gary, Director Management Information Systems, Angel Medical Center, Franklin, NC, p. A452

HANSCOME, Joyce, Senior Vice President and Chief Information Officer, Stafford Hospital, Stafford, VA, p. A661

HANSEL, Jimmie W., Ph.D., Chief Executive Officer, Garden County Health Services, Oshkosh, NE, p. A388

HANSEN, Becky, Chief Executive Officer, Southwest Healthcare Services, Bowman, ND, p. A465

HANSEN, Chris, Senior Vice President Ambulatory Services and Chief Information Officer, The University of Kansas Hospital, Kansas City, KS, p. A237

HANSEN, Dawn, Regional Director Information Services, Wheaton Franciscan Healthcare – St. Joseph's, Milwaukee, WI, p. A692

HANSEN, Gayle B., R.N
Chief Operating Officer, Mayo Clinic Health System in Fairmont, Fairmont, MN, p. A332
Chief Integration Officer, Mayo Clinic Health System in Saint James, Saint James, MN, p. A339

HANSEN, Jay, Director Information Services, Oconee Medical Center, Seneca, SC, p. A555

HANSEN, Kyle, Corporate Director Information Systems, Riverside Medical Center, Kankakee, IL, p. A186

HANSEN, Laurie
Associate Administrator, Emory Johns Creek Hospital, Johns Creek, GA, p. A155
Director Administrative Services, Johnson County Healthcare Center, Buffalo, WY, p. A701

HANSEN, Maggie, R.N. Chief Nursing Officer, Memorial Regional Hospital,, FL, p. A125

HANSEN, Marcia A., R.N. Vice President Patient Services and Chief Nursing Officer, Ephrata Community Hospital, Ephrata, PA, p. A525

HANSEN, Michael T., FACHE, President and Chief Executive Officer, Columbus Community Hospital, Columbus, NE, p. A382

HANSEN, Thomas N., M.D., Chief Executive Officer, Seattle Children's Hospital, Seattle, WA, p. A671

HANSMAN, Matthew, M.D. Chief of Staff, Sutter Maternity and Surgery Center of Santa Cruz, Santa Cruz, CA, p. A90

HANSON, Angie, R.N. Chief Nursing Officer, Howard Memorial Hospital, Nashville, AR, p. A48

HANSON, Bonnie, Chief Operating Officer, Dupont Hospital, Fort Wayne, IN, p. A202

HANSON, Carl, Administrator, Minidoka Memorial Hospital, Rupert, ID, p. A171

HANSON, Denise, Information Technology Specialist, St. Cloud Veterans Affairs Health Care System, Saint Cloud, MN, p. A339

HANSON, Dianne H., Director Human Resources, Moab Regional Hospital, Moab, UT, p. A644

HANSON, Gregory S., M.D., Chief Executive Officer, Clark Fork Valley Hospital, Plains, MT, p. A378

HANSON, Jane E., R.N. Chief Nursing Officer, Providence Medford Medical Center, Medford, OR, p. A514

HANSON, Jesica, Vice President and Chief Financial Officer, Bakersfield Memorial Hospital, Bakersfield, CA, p. A53

HANSON, Kristy, Chief Financial Officer, Mayo Clinic Health System – Northland in Barron, Barron, WI, p. A684

HANSON, Mark C., M.D. Chief of Staff, Newton Medical Center, Covington, GA, p. A151

HANSON, Mary Ann, Director Personnel, Mental Health Institute, Cherokee, IA, p. A218

HANSON, Paul D., President, Sanford USD Medical Center, Sioux Falls, SD, p. A562

HANSON, Rhonda, Director Human Resources, Huron Regional Medical Center, Huron, SD, p. A560

HANSON, Rita, M.D
Vice President Medical Affairs, Wheaton Franciscan Healthcare – Elmbrook Memorial, Brookfield, WI, p. A684
Vice President Medical Affairs, Wheaton Franciscan Healthcare – St. Joseph's, Milwaukee, WI, p. A692
Vice President Medical Affairs, Wheaton Franciscan Healthcare – The Wisconsin Heart Hospital, Wauwatosa, WI, p. A699

HANSSEN, Allan E.
Interim Administrator, Renown Rehabilitation Hospital, Reno, NV, p. A395
Interim Administrator, Renown South Meadows Medical Center, Reno, NV, p. A395

HANTOOT, Mark, M.D. Medical Director, Gateways Hospital and Mental Health Center, Los Angeles, CA, p. A69

HANYAK, Diana C., Chief Executive Officer, HEALTHSOUTH Tustin Rehabilitation Hospital, Tustin, CA, p. A93

HAPNEY, Sherry, Chief Financial Officer, HEALTHSOUTH Rehabilitation Hospital of Fort Worth, Fort Worth, TX, p. A603

HAPPEL, Terry J., M.D
Vice President and Chief Medical Officer, Chandler Regional Medical Center, Chandler, AZ, p. A30
Vice President and Chief Medical Officer, Mercy Gilbert Medical Center, Gilbert, AZ, p. A31

HARA, Karen, Personnel Management Specialist, Hawaii State Hospital, Kaneohe, HI, p. A165

HARALDSON, Richard, Chief Executive Officer, Sidney Health Center, Sidney, MT, p. A380

HARALSON, Gregory
Chief Executive Officer, Memorial Hermann Sugar Land Hospital, Sugar Land, TX, p. A635
Chief Operating Officer, Plaza Medical Center of Fort Worth, Fort Worth, TX, p. A604

HARARI, Jack L., M.D. Chief Medical Officer, West Boca Medical Center, Boca Raton, FL, p. A119

HARB, Gregory A., FACH
Executive Vice President and Chief Operating Officer, Baystate Mary Lane Hospital, Ware, MA, p. A306
Executive Vice President and Chief Operating Officer, Baystate Medical Center, Springfield, MA, p. A305

HARBAUGH, Charles, Director Human Resources, Mountain Lakes Medical Center, Clayton, GA, p. A150

HARBAUGH, Ken, Vice President and Chief Financial Officer, OSF Saint Francis Medical Center, Peoria, IL, p. A192

HARBERTS, Jerry, Information Technologist, Madison Hospital, Madison, MN, p. A335

HARBISON, Linda, Chief Nursing Officer, Red Bud Regional Hospital, Red Bud, IL, p. A193

HARBOR, Mike, Chief Financial Officer, Hardin Medical Center, Savannah, TN, p. A578

HARCHENKO, Vern, M.D. Chief of Staff, Garrison Memorial Hospital, Garrison, ND, p. A467

HARCLERODE, Timothy, R.N. Chief Operating Officer, Logan Regional Medical Center, Logan, WV, p. A678

HARCOURT, Jenifer, Chief Operating Officer, RiverWoods Behavioral Health System, Riverdale, GA, p. A158

HARCOURT, Roxane, Chief Executive Officer, Options Behavioral Health System, Indianapolis, IN, p. A206

HARCUP, Craig, M.D. Hospital Medical Director, Complex Care Hospital at Ridgelake, Sarasota, FL, p. A139

HARDACRE, Jerry, M.D. Chief of Staff, Wheaton Franciscan Healthcare – All Saints, Racine, WI, p. A695

HARDAN, Terry, Director Human Resources, Longview Regional Medical Center, Longview, TX, p. A619

HARDCASTLE, Kathy, Manager Human Resources, Texas Health Specialty Hospital, Fort Worth, TX, p. A604

HARDEE, Gary R., M.D. Medical Director, Plains Memorial Hospital, Dimmitt, TX, p. A599

HARDEMAN, Diane, Director Personnel, Stephens County Hospital, Toccoa, GA, p. A162

HARDEN, Jean, Vice President Human Resources, Baptist Health La Grange, La Grange, KY, p. A253

HARDESTY, Cynthia, Vice President and Chief Nursing Executive, Cole Memorial, Coudersport, PA, p. A523

HARDIN, Cecil, CPA Chief Financial Officer, Catawba Hospital, Catawba, VA, p. A652

HARDIN, Christy, Interim Administrator, Southeast Health Center of Ripley County, Doniphan, MO, p. A360

HARDIN, James, Human Resources Officer, Sheridan Veterans Affairs Medical Center, Sheridan, WY, p. A703

HARDIN, Leslie, Chief Executive Officer and Chief Financial Officer, Seymour Hospital, Seymour, TX, p. A633

HARDIN, Mark, M.D. Medical Director, Ed Fraser Memorial Hospital and Baker Community Health Center, MacClenny, FL, p. A129

HARDIN, Nicholas, Chief Executive Officer, HEALTHSOUTH Sugar Land Rehabilitation Hospital, Sugar Land, TX, p. A635

HARDING, Catherine, M.D. Medical Director, HEALTHSOUTH Rehabilitation of Gadsden, Gadsden, AL, p. A20

HARDING, Christina, Vice President Finance, Mount Desert Island Hospital, Bar Harbor, ME, p. A281

HARDING, Denise, Director Human Resources, Plumas District Hospital, Quincy, CA, p. A81

HARDING, Edward A., FACHE, President and Chief Executive Officer, Bay Area Medical Center, Marinette, WI, p. A690

HARDING, John R., Chief Executive Officer, Florida Hospital Tampa, Tampa, FL, p. A141

HARDING, Thomas, M.D. Medical Director, Milwaukee County Behavioral Health Division, Milwaukee, WI, p. A692

HARDISON, Gerald, Director Finance, Vidant Pungo Hospital, Belhaven, NC, p. A448

HARDMAN, Danny, Senior Vice President and Chief Nursing Officer, McAlester Regional Health Center, McAlester, OK, p. A501

HARDMAN, Wanda, Director Human Resources, Habersham Medical Center, Demorest, GA, p. A152

HARDOBY, Greg, Director Personnel, Runnells Specialized Hospital of Union County, Berkeley Heights, NJ, p. A401

HARDWICK, Garry, R.N. Chief Operating Officer, Newport Bay Hospital, Newport Beach, CA, p. A76

HARDY, Bob, Chief Operating Officer, Opelousas General Health System, Opelousas, LA, p. A276

HARDY, Eric S., Chief Financial Officer, Mesa View Regional Hospital, Mesquite, NV, p. A394

HARDY, Gregory, M.D. President Medical Staff, Stephens Memorial Hospital, Norway, ME, p. A284

HARDY, Janice, Chief Human Resources Management, Tuscaloosa Veterans Affairs Medical Center, Tuscaloosa, AL, p. A26

HARDY, John, Vice President Human Resources, Doctors Medical Center–San Pablo Campus, San Pablo, CA, p. A88

HARDY, Kevin, Chief Financial Officer, HEALTHSOUTH Treasure Coast Rehabilitation Hospital, Vero Beach, FL, p. A143

HARDY, Tom, D.O. Vice President Medical Affairs, Grandview Medical Center, Dayton, OH, p. A480

HARFF, Christine K., Chief Executive Officer, Bartlett Regional Hospital, Juneau, AK, p. A28

HARGETT, Stephen A., Senior Vice President and Chief Financial Officer, Marina Del Rey Hospital, Marina Del Rey, CA, p. A73

HARGIS, Chris
Chief Financial Officer, Providence Mount Carmel Hospital, Colville, WA, p. A665
Chief Financial Officer, Providence St. Joseph's Hospital, Chewelah, WA, p. A665

HARGRAVE–THOMAS, Anne, Chief Executive Officer, Oakleaf Surgical Hospital, Eau Claire, WI, p. A686

HARGREAVES, Diane
Vice President Human Resources, Presence Mercy Medical Center, Aurora, IL, p. A173
Vice President Human Resources, Presence Saint Joseph Hospital, Elgin, IL, p. A181

HARGRODER, Ty, M.D. Chief of Staff, Acadia–St. Landry Hospital, Church Point, LA, p. A265

HARGROVE, Tressa B., Director Human Resources, Jackson Purchase Medical Center, Mayfield, KY, p. A257

HARING, Don, Vice President Finance and Treasurer, SwedishAmerican Hospital, Rockford, IL, p. A194

HARKER, H. William, Chief Executive Officer, OSF Holy Family Medical Center, Monmouth, IL, p. A188

HARKEY, Shirley S., R.N. Vice President, Patient Services, Wayne Memorial Hospital, Goldsboro, NC, p. A453

HARKINS, Shelly, M.D. Chief Medical Officer, St. Elizabeth's Hospital, Belleville, IL, p. A174

HARKLEROAD, Rod, R.N., Interim Administrator, Riverview Regional Medical Center, Carthage, TN, p. A566

HARKNESS, Charles, D.O. Vice President Medical Affairs, Southeast Alabama Medical Center, Dothan, AL, p. A19

HARLAN, Kevin W., President, Joint Township District Memorial Hospital, Saint Marys, OH, p. A489

HARLAN, Thomas M., Chief Executive Officer, Palm Drive Hospital, Sebastopol, CA, p. A90

HARLAN, Thomas P., Chief Executive Officer, Harbor Hospital of Southeast Texas, Beaumont, TX, p. A587

HARLE, Connie, Chief Nursing Officer, Range Regional Health Services, Hibbing, MN, p. A334

HARLESS, Andrea, Director Information Services, Wythe County Community Hospital, Wytheville, VA, p. A663

HARLOVIC, Michael, R.N. Senior Vice President, Chief Operating Officer and Chief Nursing Officer, Allegheny Valley Hospital, Natrona Heights, PA, p. A533

HARLOW, Donald, Director of Information Services, MountainView Regional Medical Center, Las Cruces, NM, p. A416

HARLOWE, Michael, President and Chief Executive Officer, Indiana University Health Tipton Hospital, Tipton, IN, p. A214

HARMAN, David L., Chief Executive Officer, Wallowa Memorial Hospital, Enterprise, OR, p. A512

HARMAN, Kenneth, Chief Executive Officer, Pioneers Medical Center, Meeker, CO, p. A104

HARMAN, Kimberly, Regional Manager Human Resources, Western State Hospital, Staunton, VA, p. A662

HARMON, Amy, Chief Financial Officer, Kingfisher Regional Hospital, Kingfisher, OK, p. A500

HARMON, Cheryl A., Chief Financial Officer, Porter Regional Hospital, Valparaiso, IN, p. A214

HARMON, Clifford K., Chief Executive Officer, Harrison Community Hospital, Cadiz, OH, p. A472

HARMON, David, D.O. Vice President Medical Services, RiverValley Behavioral Health Hospital, Owensboro, KY, p. A258

HARMON, Martin, Director Public Relations, Roosevelt Warm Springs Institute for Rehabilitation, Warm Springs, GA, p. A162

HARMON, P. Mark, Chief Operating Officer, Carlisle Regional Medical Center, Carlisle, PA, p. A522

HARMS, Arlene, Chief Executive Officer, Rio Grande Hospital, Del Norte, CO, p. A99

HARMS, C. David, Chief Financial Officer, Kirby Medical Center, Monticello, IL, p. A189

HARMS, George, Chief Financial Officer, Good Samaritan Hospital, Kearney, NE, p. A385

HARNED, Barbara, R.N. Chief Nursing Officer, Monroe County Hospital, Monroeville, AL, p. A23

HARNESS, Lorraine L., Administrator, Pike County Memorial Hospital, Louisiana, MO, p. A365

HARTBERG, David, Administrator, Boscobel Area Health Care, Boscobel, WI, p. A684

HARTE, Brian J., M.D., President, South Pointe Hospital, Warrensville Heights, OH, p. A492

HARTER, Dan, Manager Information Systems, PMH Medical Center, Prosser, WA, p. A669

HARTERT, Jim, M.D. Senior Vice President and Medical Director, Range Regional Health Services, Hibbing, MN, p. A334

HARTGRAVES, Steve L., Chief Executive Officer, Graham Regional Medical Center, Graham, TX, p. A606

HARTLEY, Diane L., R.N. Director of Patient Care Services, Oakwood Annapolis Hospital, Wayne, MI, p. A326

HARTLEY, Joe
Director Information Systems, Hunt Regional Community Hospital, Commerce, TX, p. A593
Director Information Systems, Hunt Regional Medical Center, Greenville, TX, p. A607

HARTLEY, Melinda D., R.N. Vice President Patient Care Services, Perry Hospital, Perry, GA, p. A158

HARTLEY, Michael W., Director Human Resources, Laredo Medical Center, Laredo, TX, p. A618

HARTLEY, Norma, Director Human Resources, Power County Hospital District, American Falls, ID, p. A167

HARTLEY, Wannah, Controller, Winkler County Memorial Hospital, Kermit, TX, p. A616

HARTLING, Ross, M.D. President Medical Staff, Cascade Valley Hospital and Clinics, Arlington, WA, p. A664

HARTMAN, Daphne, Chief Financial Officer, North Big Horn Hospital District, Lovell, WY, p. A703

HARTMAN, David, M.D. Chief of Staff, Franklin Hospital District, Benton, IL, p. A174

HARTMAN, Dennis, Chief Financial Officer, Excelsior Springs Hospital, Excelsior Springs, MO, p. A360

HARTMAN, Gregory
President and Chief Executive Officer, Seton Medical Center Austin, Austin, TX, p. A585
President and Chief Executive Officer, University Medical Center at Brackenridge, Austin, TX, p. A586

HARTMAN, Robert, M.D. Vice President Medical Affairs, Valley Hospital, Spokane Valley, WA, p. A672

HARTMAN, Susan, Chief Executive Officer, HEALTHSOUTH Nittany Valley Rehabilitation Hospital, Pleasant Gap, PA, p. A539

HARTMANN, Doreen, Vice President and Chief Financial Officer, Mercy Medical Center Merced, Merced, CA, p. A74

HARTMANN, Margot, Ph.D., President and Chief Executive Officer, Nantucket Cottage Hospital, Nantucket, MA, p. A302

HARTMANN, Peter M., M.D. Vice President Medical Affairs, York Hospital, York, PA, p. A545

HARTSELL, Scott, Chief Operating Officer, Bayfront Health Brooksville, Brooksville, FL, p. A119

HARTWICK, Bryan, Vice President Human Resources, Christian Hospital, Saint Louis, MO, p. A369

HARTWIG, Michael, M.D. Chief of Staff, Perry Memorial Hospital, Perry, OK, p. A505

HARTZELL, Dee, Manager Human Resources, St. Luke's Jerome, Jerome, ID, p. A169

HARVEL, Norilina, Chief Financial Officer, Bonner General Hospital, Sandpoint, ID, p. A171

HARVEY, Anne, MSN Chief Nursing Officer, El Paso Specialty Hospital, El Paso, TX, p. A601

HARVEY, John, M.D., President and Chief Executive Officer, Oklahoma Heart Hospital, Oklahoma City, OK, p. A504

HARVEY, John, M.D. President and Chief Executive Officer, Oklahoma Heart Hospital, Oklahoma City, OK, p. A504

HARVEY, John, M.D., President and Chief Executive Officer, Oklahoma Heart Hospital South Campus, Oklahoma City, OK, p. A504

HARVEY, Kevin, Chief Financial Officer, McKenzie Regional Hospital, McKenzie, TN, p. A574

HARVEY, Laurie, Administrative Officer, Memorial Medical Center, Port Lavaca, TX, p. A628

HARVEY, Linda, Chief Financial Officer, West Feliciana Parish Hospital, Saint Francisville, LA, p. A277

HARVEY, Michael, Chief Executive Officer, Community Memorial Hospital, Syracuse, NE, p. A390

HARVEY, Stansel, FACHE, Chief Executive Officer, Delta Regional Medical Center, Greenville, MS, p. A347

HARVILL, Brian
Vice President Financial Services, Vidant Bertie Hospital, Windsor, NC, p. A463
Vice President Financial Services, Vidant Chowan Hospital, Edenton, NC, p. A452

HARYASZ, Sandy, R.N., Chief Executive Officer, Page Hospital, Page, AZ, p. A33

HASAN, Farhana, M.D. Chief of Staff, Marion Veterans Affairs Medical Center, Marion, IL, p. A187

HASART, Vicki, Nurse Manager, Avera Hand County Memorial Hospital, Miller, SD, p. A560

HASHMI, Mubashir, Chief Information Officer, Pacifica Hospital of the Valley,, CA, p. A71

HASHMI, Stephenie, Chief Clinical Officer, Kindred Hospital Kansas City, Kansas City, MO, p. A363

HASHMI, Suleman, President and Chief Executive Officer, Texas General Hospital, Grand Prairie, TX, p. A606

HASKELL, Jeffrey, M.D. Chief Medical Staff, Lost Rivers Medical Center, Arco, ID, p. A167

HASKINS, Don, Administrative Director Human Resources, Southwest Mississippi Regional Medical Center, McComb, MS, p. A350

HASKINS, Randy
Director Information Systems, Mercy Medical Center–New Hampton, New Hampton, IA, p. A226
Director Information Systems, Mercy Medical Center–North Iowa, Mason City, IA, p. A225

HASLING, Debra, Director Medical Records, Lakeview Regional Medical Center, Covington, LA, p. A265

HASNI, Kamran, M.D. Chief of Medical Staff, Knox County Hospital, Barbourville, KY, p. A248

HASSAN, Tariq, M.D. Associate Director of Patient Care, Captain James A. Lovell Federal Health Care Center, North Chicago, IL, p. A190

HASSELBARTH, William C., Chief Financial Officer, Albany Medical Center, Albany, NY, p. A420

HASSELBRACK, Jeni, Director Human Resources, Gordon Hospital, Calhoun, GA, p. A149

HASSLER, Robert, M.D. Director Medical Affairs, Novant Health Brunswick Medical Center, Bolivia, NC, p. A448

HASSON, Marie, M.D. Medical Director, Carrier Clinic, Belle Mead, NJ, p. A401

HAST, Anne S., MSN, Chief Executive Officer, Advanced Surgical Hospital, Washington, PA, p. A543

HASTIN, Kathy, Administrative Assistant Human Resources, River Valley Medical Center, Dardanelle, AR, p. A42

HASTINGS, David, Director Information Technology, Baton Rouge General Medical Center, Baton Rouge, LA, p. A263

HASTINGS, Kirk, Chief Information Technology, Veterans Affairs Butler Healthcare, Butler, PA, p. A521

HASTINGS, Sarah M., Vice President Human Resources, Ridgeview Medical Center, Waconia, MN, p. A342

HASTINGS–SMITH, Julie, Chief Financial Officer, Maryvale Hospital Medical Center, Phoenix, AZ, p. A34

HATALA, Alexander J., FACHE, President and Chief Executive Officer, Our Lady of Lourdes Medical Center, Camden, NJ, p. A402

HATCH, Mary, Chief Financial Officer, Dixie Regional Medical Center, Saint George, UT, p. A646

HATCHEL, Kimberly Kay, Chief Nursing Officer, Medical Center of McKinney, McKinney, TX, p. A622

HATCHER, Julie, Vice President Human Resources, O'Connor Hospital, San Jose, CA, p. A88

HATCHER, Melanie, Region Director Human Resources, Broward Health Imperial Point, Fort Lauderdale, FL, p. A123

HATCHER, Robert, Chief Financial Officer, Tulane Medical Center, New Orleans, LA, p. A276

HATFIELD, Chad, Chief Executive Officer, Plateau Medical Center, Oak Hill, WV, p. A679

HATFIELD, Jonathan, Supervisor Information Technology, Klickitat Valley Health, Goldendale, WA, p. A667

HATFIELD, Timothy A., Community Chief Executive Officer, Williamson ARH Hospital, South Williamson, KY, p. A260

HATHAWAY, William, M.D. Chief Medical Officer, Mission Hospital, Asheville, NC, p. A447

HATHAWAY, Woody, Chief Financial Officer, Mt. San Rafael Hospital, Trinidad, CO, p. A106

HATLESTAD, Jill, Vice President Human Resources and Organizational Support, Glencoe Regional Health Services, Glencoe, MN, p. A332

HATTEM, Marita, Interim President and Chief Operating Officer, Aspirus Wausau Hospital, Wausau, WI, p. A699

HATTON, Julia
Chief Financial Officer, Nexus Specialty Hospital, Shenandoah, TX, p. A633
Chief Financial Officer, Nexus Specialty Hospital The Woodlands, Spring, TX, p. A634

HATTON, Tad, Chief Operating Officer, St. David's Round Rock Medical Center, Round Rock, TX, p. A629

HAUG, Darin, D.O. Chief Medical Officer, Fitzgibbon Hospital, Marshall, MO, p. A365

HAUGE, Meri, R.N. Associate Director of Patient Care Services and Nurse Executive, St. Cloud Veterans Affairs Health Care System, Saint Cloud, MN, p. A339

HAUGEN, O. G., Director Resources, Naval Medical Center San Diego, San Diego, CA, p. A85

HAUGH, William, Administrator, Georgetown Community Hospital, Georgetown, KY, p. A251

HAUN, Richard, Chief Financial Officer, Wuesthoff Medical Center – Rockledge, Rockledge, FL, p. A138

HAUPERT, John M., FACHE, Chief Executive Officer, Grady Memorial Hospital, Atlanta, GA, p. A146

HAUSAUER, Patricia K., Director Finance, Baptist Medical Center Nassau, Fernandina Beach, FL, p. A123

HAUSE, Eileen, Chief Executive Officer, Kensington Hospital, Philadelphia, PA, p. A535

HAUSER, Mark J., M.D. Chief Medical Officer, Baptist Health South Florida, Baptist Hospital of Miami, Miami, FL, p. A131

HAUSER, Michael, M.D. Chief Medical Officer, The HSC Pediatric Center, Washington, DC, p. A117

HAUSHALTER, Richard L., Senior Vice President Operations and Chief Operating Officer, Rockingham Memorial Hospital, Harrisonburg, VA, p. A655

HAUSMANN, Jena, Executive Vice President and Chief Operating Officer, Children's Hospital Colorado, Aurora, CO, p. A97

HAUSMANN, Sherry, President, Via Christi Hospital on St. Francis, Wichita, KS, p. A246

HAUSWIRTH, Michael
Chief Operating Officer, Aspirus Keweenaw Hospital, Laurium, MI, p. A319
Chief Operating Officer, Aspirus Ontonagon Hospital, Ontonagon, MI, p. A321

HAUSWIRTH, Renay, Chief Financial Officer, Palo Alto County Health System, Emmetsburg, IA, p. A221

HAVARD, Greg, Administrator, Pioneer Community Hospital of Early, Blakely, GA, p. A148

HAVEL, Carol, R.N. Vice President Patient Care Services, Morris Hospital & Healthcare Centers, Morris, IL, p. A189

HAVEN, Adrian C., Site Manager, Gallup Indian Medical Center, Gallup, NM, p. A416

HAVERKAMP, Kathleen, M.D. Chief Medical Officer, Ellsworth Municipal Hospital, Iowa Falls, IA, p. A223

HAVRILLA, David A., Chief Financial Officer, MedStar Montgomery Medical Center, Olney, MD, p. A293

HAWK, James, M.D. Chief of Staff, Washington County Memorial Hospital, Potosi, MO, p. A368

HAWK, Kevin, Chief Executive Officer, Hillcrest Hospital Cushing, Cushing, OK, p. A497

HAWKINS, Bill, Director, Hiram W. Davis Medical Center, Petersburg, VA, p. A659

HAWKINS, Brian A., Director, Washington DC Veterans Affairs Medical Center, Washington, DC, p. A117

HAWKINS, Bryan, Controller, FirstHealth Montgomery Memorial Hospital, Troy, NC, p. A462

HAWKINS, Ellis, Senior Vice President and Chief Operating Officer, Phelps County Regional Medical Center, Rolla, MO, p. A368

HAWKINS, Hillary, M.D. Medical Director, Sheltering Arms Rehabilitation Hospital, Mechanicsville, VA, p. A657

HAWKINS, Janine, R.N. Chief Nursing Officer, Dameron Hospital, Stockton, CA, p. A91

HAWKINS, Jason F., President and Chief Executive Officer, Fulton County Medical Center, Mc Connellsburg, PA, p. A530

HAWKINS, Roy, Acting Associate Director, Veterans Affairs Salt Lake City Health Care System, Salt Lake City, UT, p. A647

HAWKINS, Thomas J., Administrator, Central Prison Hospital, Raleigh, NC, p. A459

HAWKINSON, Curtis R., Chief Executive Officer, Community Memorial Healthcare, Marysville, KS, p. A239

HAWLEY, Claudia, Director Human Resources, Mason General Hospital, Shelton, WA, p. A672

HAWLEY, Jason, Manager Information Services, Yuma District Hospital, Yuma, CO, p. A107

HAWLEY, William, Chief Executive Officer, Bluefield Regional Medical Center, Bluefield, WV, p. A675

HAWMAN, DeeDee, Director Human Resources, Lee's Summit Medical Center, Lee's Summit, MO, p. A365

HAWTHORNE III, Henry, President and Chief Executive Officer, Columbus Regional Healthcare System, Whiteville, NC, p. A462

HAWTHORNE, Kimberly, Administrator, Mayo Clinic Health System – Franciscan Healthcare in Sparta, Sparta, WI, p. A696

HAXTOM, Moni, Interim Chief Financial Officer, Mercy Medical Center–North Iowa, Mason City, IA, p. A225

HAXTON, Rita K., R.N. Vice President Patient Care Nursing, Rapid City Regional Hospital, Rapid City, SD, p. A562

HAY, Jody, Director Human Resources, HEALTHSOUTH Nittany Valley Rehabilitation Hospital, Pleasant Gap, PA, p. A539

HAY, Morgan, Chief Financial Officer, Gerald Champion Regional Medical Center, Alamogordo, NM, p. A414

HAYDEN, Crystal, R.N. Chief Nursing Officer, Onslow Memorial Hospital, Jacksonville, NC, p. A455

HAYDEN, Jamie, Chief Financial Officer, Eastland Memorial Hospital, Eastland, TX, p. A600

HAYDEN, John
Senior Vice President and Chief Human Resources Officer, Bronson LakeView Hospital, Paw Paw, MI, p. A321
Vice President and Chief Human Resources Officer, Bronson Methodist Hospital, Kalamazoo, MI, p. A318

HAYDEN, Karen, Director Health Information Services, Performance Improvement and Risk Management, Valle Vista Hospital, Greenwood, IN, p. A204

HAYDEN, Patrick, M.D. Chief of Staff, Logan Memorial Hospital, Russellville, KY, p. A260

HAYDEN, Sheryl, Chief Financial Officer, Sierra Surgery Hospital, Carson City, NV, p. A391

HAYES, Brian T., Commander, David Grant Medical Center, Travis AFB, CA, p. A93

HAYES, Cheryl, Chief Executive Officer, Select Specialty Hospital–Gainesville, Gainesville, FL, p. A124

HAYES, Chris, Interim Corporate Director of Finance, Saint Mary's Hospital, Waterbury, CT, p. A112

HAYES, Deborah Marie, R.N. Chief Hospital Officer and Chief Nursing Officer, Christ Hospital, Cincinnati, OH, p. A474

HAYES, Donna, Controller, Decatur County General Hospital, Parsons, TN, p. A578

HAYES, Elaine, Controller, Sts. Mary & Elizabeth Hospital, Louisville, KY, p. A256

HAYES, Elizabeth, R.N. Director of Patient Services, Blowing Rock Hospital, Blowing Rock, NC, p. A448

HAYES, Evelyn, M.D., Interim President and Chief Executive Officer, Baton Rouge General Medical Center, Baton Rouge, LA, p. A263

HAYES, George E., FACHE, President and Chief Executive Officer, Medical Center of the Rockies, Loveland, CO, p. A104

HAYES, James L., Director Human Resources, Western State Hospital, Hopkinsville, KY, p. A252

HAYES, James M., Chief Executive Officer, Trinity Muscatine, Muscatine, IA, p. A225

HAYES, Jim A., Chief Fiscal Service, Tennessee Valley Healthcare System, Nashville, TN, p. A577

HAYES, Karen, Chief Financial Officer, Phoebe North, Albany, GA, p. A145

HAYES, Kathe, Executive Director, Western New York Children's Psychiatric Center, West Seneca, NY, p. A446

HAYES, Kelly, Chief Financial Officer, North Texas Medical Center, Gainesville, TX, p. A605

HAYES, Kevin, M.D. Chief of Staff, Pioneer Community Hospital of Aberdeen, Aberdeen, MS, p. A344

HAYES, Kim, Director Human Resources, Bibb Medical Center, Centreville, AL, p. A18

HAYES, Linda S., MSN, Chief Executive Officer, Mayhill Hospital, Denton, TX, p. A598

HAYES, Marianne, Director Human Resources, Middle Park Medical Center, Kremmling, CO, p. A102

HAYES, Nolan, Director Human Resources, United Regional Medical Center, Manchester, TN, p. A573

HAYES, Oliver, D.O. Chief Medical Officer, Sewickley Valley Hospital, (A Division of Valley Medical Facilities), Sewickley, PA, p. A541

HAYES, Pamela, Director Finance, Providence Seaside Hospital, Seaside, OR, p. A517

HAYES, Paul, Executive Vice President and Chief Operating Officer, UW Medicine/Valley Medical Center, Renton, WA, p. A670

HAYES, Ruth, Director Human Resources, Patient's Choice Medical Center of Humphreys County, Belzoni, MS, p. A344

HAYES, Sharon, Chief Executive Officer, Edward White Hospital, Saint Petersburg, FL, p. A139

HAYES, Steven A., Administrator, Memorial Hospital, Chester, IL, p. A176

HAYES, Susan, Director Human Resources, Lea Regional Medical Center, Hobbs, NM, p. A416

HAYES, Thomas P., Chief Executive Officer, Eastern Plumas Health Care District, Portola, CA, p. A80

HAYES, William M., Chief Executive Officer, Northside Hospital–Cherokee, Canton, GA, p. A149

HAYGOOD, Rachel, Director Information Technology, Tyler County Hospital, Woodville, TX, p. A642

HAYNER, Jim, M.D. Medical Director, Select Specialty Hospital–Ann Arbor, Ypsilanti, MI, p. A327

HAYNES, Apryl, R.N., Vice President, Chief Operating Officer, Chief Nursing Officer and Administrator, Seton Edgar B. Davis Hospital, Luling, TX, p. A621

HAYNES, Doyle, Director Information Systems, Decatur Morgan Hospital, Decatur, AL, p. A19

HAYNES, Jamil
Regional Director Human Resources, Integris Baptist Regional Health Center, Miami, OK, p. A501
Director Human Resources, Integris Mayes County Medical Center, Pryor, OK, p. A506

HAYNES, Jill, Financial Coach, Bath Veterans Affairs Medical Center, Bath, NY, p. A421

HAYNES, Jr., John H., M.D. Chief of Medical Staff, North Caddo Medical Center, Vivian, LA, p. A280

HAYNES, Laurie, Chief Financial Officer, Gulf Coast Medical Center, Panama City, FL, p. A136

HAYNES, Mark, M.D. Chief of Staff, Homer Memorial Hospital, Homer, LA, p. A268

HAYNES, Michael, M.D. Chief Medical Officer, St. John Hospital and Medical Center, Detroit, MI, p. A312

HAYNES, Robert, FACHE, Chief Executive Officer, Guadalupe Regional Medical Center, Seguin, TX, p. A633

HAYNES, Susanne, Executive Director Finance, Baptist Health La Grange, La Grange, KY, p. A253

HAYNES, William, Director Information Technology, Central Louisiana State Hospital, Pineville, LA, p. A277

HAYNIE, Annalisa, Administrative Assistant III, Alaska Psychiatric Institute, Anchorage, AK, p. A27

HAYS, Cheryl M., FACHE, Administrator, Marshall Medical Center North, Guntersville, AL, p. A21

HAYS, Chuck, President, MaineGeneral Medical Center–Waterville Campus, Waterville, ME, p. A285

HAYS, Marilyn, Chief Financial Officer, North Valley Hospital, Whitefish, MT, p. A380

HAYS, Richard O., Chief Fiscal Service, Veterans Affairs Southern Nevada Healthcare System, North Las Vegas, NV, p. A394

HAYS, Timothy A., Vice President Human Resources, Johnston Health, Smithfield, NC, p. A461

HAYTAIAN, Mike, Head Director Information Resources Management, Naval Hospital Jacksonville, Jacksonville, FL, p. A126

HAYTON, Gregg, Vice President Finance and Chief Financial Officer, Our Lady of Lourdes Memorial Hospital, Binghamton, NY, p. A421

HAYWOOD, Nancy, Chief Financial Officer, Genesys Regional Medical Center, Grand Blanc, MI, p. A314

HAZEL, James C., FACHE, Chief Executive Officer, Murray Medical Center, Chatsworth, GA, p. A149

HAZELBAKER, Matthew, M.D. President Medical Staff, Memorial Hospital of Union County, Marysville, OH, p. A485

HAZEN, Carol, Vice President Finance, Emory–Adventist Hospital, Smyrna, GA, p. A160

HAZLETT, Kim, Chief Operating Officer/ Associate Director, Four County Counseling Center, Logansport, IN, p. A209

HAZLETT, Marybess, Director Human Resources, Ira Davenport Memorial Hospital, Bath, NY, p. A421

HEAD, David, M.D. Chief Medical Staff, Norton Sound Regional Hospital, Nome, AK, p. A28

HEADLAND, Mark
Chief Information Officer, Children's Hospital at Mission, Mission Viejo, CA, p. A74
Chief Information Officer, Children's Hospital of Orange County, Orange, CA, p. A77

HEALD, Robin R., Director Human Resources, Brattleboro Memorial Hospital, Brattleboro, VT, p. A649

HEALEY, Kevin, Vice President Human Resources, St. Mary's Regional Medical Center, Lewiston, ME, p. A284

HEALTH, Karen, M.D. Clinical Director, U. S. Public Health Service Indian Hospital, San Carlos, AZ, p. A36

HEALY, John, Manager Information Technology, Friends Hospital, Philadelphia, PA, p. A535

HEALY, Peggi, Executive Director, Mid–Hudson Forensic Psychiatric Center, New Hampton, NY, p. A430

HEANEY, Frances, R.N. Executive Vice President and Chief Operating Officer, Wyckoff Heights Medical Center,, NY, p. A437

HEANEY, Susan, M.D. Vice President Medical Affairs, SSM Cardinal Glennon Children's Medical Center, Saint Louis, MO, p. A370

HEARD, Heather, Director Human Resources, Holdenville General Hospital, Holdenville, OK, p. A500

HEARD, John E., Chief Executive Officer, McGehee–Desha County Hospital, McGehee, AR, p. A47

HEARD, M. Denise, Director Business Services, North Mississippi Medical Center–Pontotoc Hospital and Nursing Home, Pontotoc, MS, p. A352

HEARN, Gregory K., Chief Executive Officer, Ty Cobb Regional Medical Center, Lavonia, GA, p. A156

HEARNSBERGER, John, M.D. Chief of Staff, Howard Memorial Hospital, Nashville, AR, p. A48

HEARTSILL, Keith, Chief Financial Officer, Grenada Lake Medical Center, Grenada, MS, p. A347

HEATER, Floyd, President, Shenandoah Memorial Hospital, Woodstock, VA, p. A663

HEATH, Susan, Chief Executive Officer, Vanderbilt Stallworth Rehabilitation Hospital, Nashville, TN, p. A577

HEATHERLY, John
Assistant Administrator Support Services, Hunt Regional Community Hospital, Commerce, TX, p. A593
Assistant Administrator Support Services, Hunt Regional Medical Center, Greenville, TX, p. A607

HEATHERLY, Steve
Chief Executive Officer, MedWest – Harris, Sylva, NC, p. A462
Chief Executive Officer, MedWest – Swain, Bryson City, NC, p. A448

HEATHERLY–LLOYD, Sara, Chief Operating Officer, LaFollette Medical Center, La Follette, TN, p. A572

HEATLEY, Scott, Controller, Parkview Adventist Medical Center, Brunswick, ME, p. A282

HEATON, Lisa, Assistant Vice President/Administrator and Chief Nursing Officer, Johnson County Community Hospital, Mountain City, TN, p. A576

HEATON, Sheila, Chief Human Resources Officer, Lower Oconee Community Hospital, Glenwood, GA, p. A154

HEBBELER, Gregory P.
Chief Financial Officer, Methodist Hospital, Henderson, KY, p. A252
Chief Financial Officer, Methodist Hospital Union County, Morganfield, KY, p. A258

HEBEL, Barbara, Vice President Human Resources, Doylestown Hospital, Doylestown, PA, p. A524

HEBERT, Jr., Bernie
Chief Financial Officer, Doctor's Hospital and Neuromuscular Center, Bremen, IN, p. A199
Chief Financial Officer, Unity Medical & Surgical Hospital, Mishawaka, IN, p. A210

HEBERT, Bryan, Director Information Systems, The Medical Center of Southeast Texas, Port Arthur, TX, p. A628

HEBERT, Jeff, Interim Vice President Finance, Gifford Medical Center, Randolph, VT, p. A650

HEBERT, Katherine D., Chief Executive Officer, St. Martin Hospital, Breaux Bridge, LA, p. A264

HEBERT, Kim, Chief Financial Officer, Our Lady of Lourdes Regional Medical Center, Lafayette, LA, p. A271

HEBERT, Mark, M.D. President Medical Staff, Medical City Dallas Hospital, Dallas, TX, p. A596

HEBERT, Michael, Director Technology, MetroWest Medical Center, Framingham, MA, p. A300

HEBERT, Raquel, Business Manager, Sugar Land Surgical Hospital, Sugar Land, TX, p. A635

HEBERT, Timothy, Director Human Resources, Teche Regional Medical Center, Morgan City, LA, p. A274

HEBURN, William R., Chief Executive Officer, Natchez Regional Medical Center, Natchez, MS, p. A351

HECHLER, Tracy, Healthcare Director Information Services, CJW Medical Center, Richmond, VA, p. A660

HECK, III, George L., President and Chief Executive Officer, Coffee Regional Medical Center, Douglas, GA, p. A152

HECK, Terry
Vice President Finance and Chief Financial Officer, Saint Joseph Regional Medical Center, Mishawaka, IN, p. A210
Vice President Finance and Chief Financial Officer, Saint Joseph Regional Medical Center–Plymouth Campus, Plymouth, IN, p. A212

HECKATHORNE, Daniel R.
Regional Chief Financial Officer, East Los Angeles Doctors Hospital, Los Angeles, CA, p. A68
Chief Financial Officer, Memorial Hospital of Gardena, Gardena, CA, p. A62

HECKER, Cynthia, Executive Director, UW Medicine/Northwest Hospital & Medical Center, Seattle, WA, p. A671

HECKER, Lisa, Director Human Resources, Hedrick Medical Center, Chillicothe, MO, p. A358

HECKERMAN, Ray, Chief Executive Officer and Managing Director, Coastal Harbor Treatment Center, Savannah, GA, p. A159

HECKERT Jr., Robert J., Chief Executive Officer, Gerald Champion Regional Medical Center, Alamogordo, NM, p. A414

HECKEY, Robert, M.D. Chief of Staff, Sutter Medical Center of Santa Rosa, Chanate Campus, Santa Rosa, CA, p. A90

HECKLER, Edward, Administrator, Riverside Rehabilitation Institute, Newport News, VA, p. A658

HECKLER, Tura
Director Information Systems, Corona Regional Medical Center, Corona, CA, p. A57
Director Information Services, Southwest Healthcare System, Murrieta, CA, p. A76

HECKMAN, Katie, Director Community Relations, Saint Joseph Berea, Berea, KY, p. A248

HEDBERG, Beth, R.N. Director of Nursing, Lindsborg Community Hospital, Lindsborg, KS, p. A239

HEDDE, Charles C., M.D. Vice President Medical Affairs, Good Samaritan Hospital, Vincennes, IN, p. A214

HEDDERMAN, Michael, Senior Vice President Finance and Chief Financial Officer, Marianjoy Rehabilitation Hospital, Wheaton, IL, p. A196

HEDGES, David, Chief Financial Officer, Southwestern Regional Medical Center, Tulsa, OK, p. A509

HEDGES, Wesley, M.D. President Medical Staff, Mercy Tiffin Hospital, Tiffin, OH, p. A490

HEDIGER, Joseph, Chief Financial Officer, Fox Chase Cancer Center–American Oncologic Hospital, Philadelphia, PA, p. A534

HEDRIX, Michael D., Interim Chief Executive Officer, Essentia Health Sandstone, Sandstone, MN, p. A340

HEDSTROM, Marjorie, Director, John J. Pershing Veterans Affairs Medical Center, Poplar Bluff, MO, p. A367

HEEMAN, John, Director Information Systems, Huntsville Memorial Hospital, Huntsville, TX, p. A614

HEFFERNAN, Paul F., Vice President Human Resources, Women & Infants Hospital of Rhode Island, Providence, RI, p. A547

HEFFERNAN, Rebecca, Director Human Resources, MetroWest Medical Center, Framingham, MA, p. A300

HEFFERS, Margaret, Assistant Vice President Human Resources, Geisinger Wyoming Valley Medical Center, Wilkes Barre, PA, p. A544

HEFFLINGER, Larry, Director Information Systems, Fulton County Health Center, Wauseon, OH, p. A492

HEFLIN, Clyde, M.D. Chief Medical Officer, Kindred Hospital–Nashville, Nashville, TN, p. A576

HEFNER, David S., President and Chief Executive Officer, Georgia Regents Medical Center, Augusta, GA, p. A147

HEFNER, Kathy, Vice President Clinical Operations, McDowell Hospital, Marion, NC, p. A457

HEGER, Jim, Director Human Resources, Citizens Medical Center, Victoria, TX, p. A639

HEGGEM, Mark, M.D. Chief Medical Officer, Riverwood Healthcare Center, Aitkin, MN, p. A328

HEGGEN, Karra, R.N. Vice President Nursing, Elkhart General Healthcare System, Elkhart, IN, p. A201

HEGGEN, Steve, Administrative Director Human Resources, St. Joseph Hospital, Fort Wayne, IN, p. A203

HEGGER, John, Director Information Systems, Union County Hospital, Anna, IL, p. A173

HEGLAND, Larry T., M.D. Chief Medical Officer, Ministry Saint Clare's Hospital, Weston, WI, p. A699

HEGLAND, Sandra, Chief Executive Officer, HEALTHSOUTH Bakersfield Rehabilitation Hospital, Bakersfield, CA, p. A54

HEGWOOD, Wayne, Chief Financial Officer, Acuity Hospital of South Texas, San Antonio, TX, p. A630

HEHEMANN, Bryan D., President and Chief Executive Officer, McCullough–Hyde Memorial Hospital, Oxford, OH, p. A488

HEICHERT, Susan
Chief Information Officer, Mercy Hospital, Coon Rapids, MN, p. A330
Chief Information Officer, Unity Hospital, Fridley, MN, p. A332

HEIDER, John R., Vice President Finance, Augusta Health, Fishersville, VA, p. A654

HEIDT, Robert, Director Information Systems, Pembina County Memorial Hospital and Wedgewood Manor, Cavalier, ND, p. A466

HEIFNER, Robert A., Chief Executive Officer, St. Luke's Sugar Land Hospital, Sugar Land, TX, p. A635

HEIGHES, Brenna, Manager Information Technology, Mt. Ascutney Hospital and Health Center, Windsor, VT, p. A650

HEIKKINEN, Todd, Director Rehabilitation Services, Orthopaedic Hospital of Wisconsin – Glendale, Milwaukee, WI, p. A692

HEILSBERG, Jim, Chief Financial Officer and Chief Information Officer, Whitman Hospital and Medical Center, Colfax, WA, p. A665

HEIM, Richard, President, Advocate South Suburban Hospital, Hazel Crest, IL, p. A184

HEIM, Tonya, R.N. Vice President Patient Services and Chief Nursing Officer, Memorial Hospital and Health Care Center, Jasper, IN, p. A207

HEIMALL, Michael S., Commander, William Beaumont Army Medical Center, El Paso, TX, p. A602

HEIMAN, Thomas, Assistant Vice President Information Services, John T. Mather Memorial Hospital, Port Jefferson, NY, p. A440

HEINDEL, Michael, Chief Operating Officer, North Vista Hospital, North Las Vegas, NV, p. A394

HEINEMANN, Don, Administrator and Chief Executive Officer, Blount Memorial Hospital, Maryville, TN, p. A574

HEINISCH, Sheri, Compliance Officer, Lisbon Area Health Services, Lisbon, ND, p. A468

HEINRICH, Mark T., D.O. President Medical Staff, Oroville Hospital, Oroville, CA, p. A78

HEINRICH, Michael G., Executive Vice President and Chief Financial Officer, Mercy Iowa City, Iowa City, IA, p. A223

HEINRICH, Timothy, Senior Vice President and Chief Operating Officer, Memorial Medical Center of West Michigan, Ludington, MI, p. A319

HEINRICHS, Alice, CPA Chief Financial Officer, Van Diest Medical Center, Webster City, IA, p. A230

HEINS, Patrick, President, Vidant Edgecombe Hospital, Tarboro, NC, p. A462

HEINSOHN, Carmel, M.D. Medical Director, Bournewood Health Systems, Brookline, MA, p. A298

HEINZE, Kyle, Coordinator Information Technology, Riveredge Hospital, Forest Park, IL, p. A182

HEINZMAN, Jerry, Senior Vice President and Chief Financial Officer, Sampson Regional Medical Center, Clinton, NC, p. A450

HEISE, Lance, Director Human Resources, Cascade Medical Center, Leavenworth, WA, p. A667

HEISE, Rosemarie, Vice President Finance, Indiana University Health Starke Hospital, Knox, IN, p. A207

HEISE, Teresa, Coordinator Management Information Systems, Pender Community Hospital, Pender, NE, p. A389

HEISER, Eric, Chief Information Resource Management, Sioux Falls Veterans Affairs Health Care System, Sioux Falls, SD, p. A563

HEISSER, Randy, M.D. Medical Director, Kindred Hospital–Chattanooga, Chattanooga, TN, p. A566

HEIT, Ryan, Chief Financial Officer, Northern Nevada Medical Center, Sparks, NV, p. A396

HEITZENRATER, James F., FACHE, Chief Executive Officer, Wiregrass Medical Center, Geneva, AL, p. A21

HEITZMAN, Cynthia, R.N. Chief Nursing Officer, Seven Rivers Regional Medical Center, Crystal River, FL, p. A121

HELBERG, Ted, Vice President, Human Resources, The Acadia Hospital, Bangor, ME, p. A281

HELD, Karen, Site Coordinator Information Technology, St. Nicholas Hospital, Sheboygan, WI, p. A696

HELDRETH, Karen, Director Data Processing, Mercy Hospital El Reno, El Reno, OK, p. A498

HELFER, Cassandra, Chief Financial Officer, Ralph H. Johnson Veterans Affairs Medical Center, Charleston, SC, p. A549

HELFER, David, President, Texas Institute for Surgery at Texas Health Presbyterian Dallas, Dallas, TX, p. A597

HELGESON, Heidi E., M.D. Chief Medical Officer, Rio Grande Hospital, Del Norte, CO, p. A99

HELGET, Peggy, R.N. Vice President Patient SErvices and Chief Nursing Officer, Methodist Jennie Edmundson Hospital, Council Bluffs, IA, p. A219

HELLA, Timothy, Chief Information Officer, Otsego Memorial Hospital, Gaylord, MI, p. A314

HELLE, Dan, Human Resources Officer, Iowa City Veterans Affairs Health Care System, Iowa City, IA, p. A223

HELLELAND, Brian, Executive Vice President and Chief Operating Officer, St. Jude Medical Center, Fullerton, CA, p. A62

HELLER, C. Lynn, Interim Chief Executive Officer, Bowie Memorial Hospital, Bowie, TX, p. A589

HELLER, Corey
Corporate Vice President and Chief Human Resources Officer, Baptist Health South Florida, Baptist Hospital of Miami, Miami, FL, p. A131
Corporate Vice President and Chief Human Resources Officer, Baptist Health South Florida, Homestead Hospital, Homestead, FL, p. A125

HELLER, Lisa, Manager Human Resources, Mercy Medical Center–New Hampton, New Hampton, IA, p. A226

HELLER, Michael, Chief Financial Officer, Corry Memorial Hospital, Corry, PA, p. A523

HELLER, Tom, Vice President Human Resources, Camden Clark Medical Center, Parkersburg, WV, p. A679

HELM, Carrie, Chief Executive Officer, Arkansas Surgical Hospital, North Little Rock, AR, p. A48

HELM, Pamela E., Executive Director, Devereux Texas Treatment Network, League City, TX, p. A618

HELMAN, Sharon M., Director, Phoenix Veterans Affairs Health Care System, Phoenix, AZ, p. A35

HELMANDOLLAR, Billy, Director Information Services, Wallace Thomson Hospital, Union, SC, p. A556

HELMS, Candace, Director Information Services, Good Samaritan Medical Center, West Palm Beach, FL, p. A143

HELMS, Sheryl, Vice President Human Resources, Good Samaritan Regional Medical Center, Corvallis, OR, p. A512

HELPER, Mark A., Vice President, Chief Financial Officer, Munson Medical Center, Traverse City, MI, p. A325

HELSEL, David S., M.D., Chief Executive Officer, Spring Grove Hospital Center, Baltimore, MD, p. A289

HELTON, Deirdre, Director Human Resources, Lakeway Regional Hospital, Morristown, TN, p. A576

HELTON, Fay, Director Medical Records, Red River Hospital, Wichita Falls, TX, p. A641

HELTON, Michelle, Director Human Resources, Wallace Thomson Hospital, Union, SC, p. A556

HELTON, Stephanie, Chief Financial Officer, Weatherford Regional Hospital, Weatherford, OK, p. A510

HELVIE, Charlotte, M.D. Chief of Staff, Northern Inyo Hospital, Bishop, CA, p. A55

HELWIG, Kent, Chief Executive Officer, Southwest Memorial Hospital, Cortez, CO, p. A98

HEMBREE, Greg, Chief Financial Officer, South Georgia Medical Center, Valdosta, GA, p. A162

HEMEON, Frank, Interim Chief Financial Officer, Catskill Regional Medical Center, Harris, NY, p. A427

HEMETER, Donald, Administrator, Wayne General Hospital, Waynesboro, MS, p. A354

HEMINGWAY, Elizabeth, Director Health Information, Fairlawn Rehabilitation Hospital, Worcester, MA, p. A306

HEMKER, Debbie, Interim Chief Executive Officer, Kaiser Permanente Hayward Medical Center, Hayward, CA, p. A63

HEMKER, Robert
Chief Financial Officer, Palomar Medical Center, Escondido, CA, p. A59
Chief Financial Officer, Pomerado Hospital, Poway, CA, p. A80

HEMMER, Chris, Director Finance, Aurora West Allis Medical Center, West Allis, WI, p. A699

HEMMING, Stuart, Chief Operating Officer, Portsmouth Regional Hospital, Portsmouth, NH, p. A400

HEMMINGER, Linda, MSN Assistant Administrator Clinical Services, Cass County Memorial Hospital, Atlantic, IA, p. A216

HEMPEL, Stephen, M.D. President Medical Staff, Lakeland Regional Medical Center–St. Joseph, Saint Joseph, MI, p. A324

HEMPHILL, Robyn, Interim Chief Executive Officer and Chief Nursing Officer, Monroe Surgical Hospital, Monroe, LA, p. A274

HEMPHILL, Ruth, R.N. Chief Nursing Officer, Florida Hospital Zephyrhills, Zephyrhills, FL, p. A144

HEMPLER, Shannan, Director Human Resources, Norton County Hospital, Norton, KS, p. A240

HEMPLING, Randall, Chief Executive Officer, Shasta Regional Medical Center, Redding, CA, p. A81

HENDEE, Daniel, Director, Veterans Affairs Medical Center, Wilmington, DE, p. A115

HENDEL, Dawna, R.N. Chief Nursing Officer and Vice President Patient Care Services, Saint John's Health Center, Santa Monica, CA, p. A90

HENDEL, Diana, PharmD,
Chief Executive Officer, Community Hospital of Long Beach, Long Beach, CA, p. A67
Chief Executive Officer, Long Beach Memorial Medical Center, Long Beach, CA, p. A67
Chief Executive Officer, Miller Children's Hospital, Long Beach, CA, p. A67

HENDERSON, Andre, Director Information Systems, Mission Community Hospital,, CA, p. A70

HENDERSON, Anita, Director Human Resources, Pennock Hospital, Hastings, MI, p. A316

HENDERSON, Carol
Senior Vice President and Chief Talent Officer, Scottsdale Healthcare Shea Medical Center, Scottsdale, AZ, p. A37
Vice President Human Resources, Scottsdale Healthcare Thompson Peak Hospital, Scottsdale, AZ, p. A37
Vice President Human Resources, Scottsdale Healthcare–Osborn Medical Center, Scottsdale, AZ, p. A37

HENDERSON, Chad, Director Information Systems, Atoka County Medical Center, Atoka, OK, p. A496

HENDERSON, Claudia, Chief Human Resources, St. Elizabeth's Medical Center, Brighton, MA, p. A298

HENDERSON, Darilyn, Human Resources Officer, Rice Medical Center, Eagle Lake, TX, p. A600

HENDERSON, David K., M.D. Deputy Director Clinical Care, National Institutes of Health Clinical Center, Bethesda, MD, p. A290

HENDERSON, David M., Director Human Resources, Summersville Regional Medical Center, Summersville, WV, p. A681

HENDERSON, Donald G., FACHE,
President and Chief Executive Officer, Leesburg Regional Medical Center, Leesburg, FL, p. A129
President and Chief Executive Officer, The Villages Health System, The Villages, FL, p. A142

HENDERSON, Gail, Manager Human Resources, Lauderdale Community Hospital, Ripley, TN, p. A578

HENDERSON, Gary, Chief Information Resources Management Services, Huntington Veterans Affairs Medical Center, Huntington, WV, p. A677

HENDERSON, John, Chief Executive Officer, Childress Regional Medical Center, Childress, TX, p. A591

HENDERSON, Kate, Vice President and Chief Operating Officer, University Medical Center at Brackenridge, Austin, TX, p. A586

HENDERSON, Kathy, Director Human Resources, Media and Public Relations, Willow Crest Hospital, Miami, OK, p. A501

HENDERSON, Larry, M.D. Medical Director, Greene County Hospital, Leakesville, MS, p. A349

HENDERSON, Lisa, Administrative Assistant, Palacios Community Medical Center, Palacios, TX, p. A625

HENDERSON, Maryanne, D.O. Medical Director, The Children's Institute of Pittsburgh, Pittsburgh, PA, p. A538

HENDERSON, Melody, R.N. Chief Operating Officer and Chief Nursing Officer, Golden Plains Community Hospital, Borger, TX, p. A589

HENDERSON, Mike, Director Human Resources, Forest View Psychiatric Hospital, Grand Rapids, MI, p. A314

HENDERSON, Peggy, Director Health Information, Stringfellow Memorial Hospital, Anniston, AL, p. A15

HENDERSON, Sherry, Chief Financial Officer, North Fulton Regional Hospital, Roswell, GA, p. A159

HENDERSON, Teto E., Director Human Resources, Geary Community Hospital, Junction City, KS, p. A236

HENDERSON, Travis, M.D. Chief of Staff, Mobridge Regional Hospital, Mobridge, SD, p. A561

HENDERSON, Volante, Manager Human Resources, HEALTHSOUTH Walton Rehabilitation Hospital, Augusta, GA, p. A148

HENDLER, Robert S., M.D
Regional Chief Medical Officer, Centennial Medical Center, Frisco, TX, p. A605
Chief Medical Officer, Doctors Hospital at White Rock Lake, Dallas, TX, p. A595

HENDREN, Karen, Vice President of Finance, Mercy Hospital Ardmore, Ardmore, OK, p. A495

HENDRICK, William, Senior Vice President and Chief Operating Officer, The Good Samaritan Hospital, Lebanon, PA, p. A529

HENDRICKS, Barbara A., Vice President, Human Resources and Support Services, Nanticoke Memorial Hospital, Seaford, DE, p. A114

HENDRICKS, Marcia, R.N., Chief Executive Officer, Madison County Health Care System, Winterset, IA, p. A230

HENDRICKS, Nicole Smith, Vice President Operations, Belton Regional Medical Center, Belton, MO, p. A356

HENDRICKS, Vickie, Director Human Resources, Barstow Community Hospital, Barstow, CA, p. A54

HENDRICKSON, Craig L., President and Chief Executive Officer, Overlake Hospital Medical Center, Bellevue, WA, p. A664

HENDRICKSON, Roman, M.D. Medical Director, Ruby Valley Hospital, Sheridan, MT, p. A379

HENDRIX, Billie, R.N. Director of Nursing, W. J. Mangold Memorial Hospital, Lockney, TX, p. A619

HENDRIX, Jamie, Vice President,Patient Care Services, Columbus Community Hospital, Columbus, WI, p. A685

HENDRIXSON, Mark, M.D. Chief Medical Officer, Jamestown Regional Medical Center, Jamestown, TN, p. A570

HENEGAR, Edward R., D.O. Vice President, Medical Affairs, Ozarks Medical Center, West Plains, MO, p. A373

HENES, Jean M., R.N. Director of Nursing, Avera Creighton Hospital, Creighton, NE, p. A383

HENINGER, Bev, Director Nursing, Kenmare Community Hospital, Kenmare, ND, p. A468

HENKE, Mark, Chief Financial Officer, Medical Center of South Arkansas, El Dorado, AR, p. A43

HENKENIUS, Jim, Chief Financial Officer, Stewart Memorial Community Hospital, Lake City, IA, p. A224

HENLEY, Donald, Vice President Human Resources and Social Services, Grove City Medical Center, Grove City, PA, p. A526

HENNENBERG, Shayla, Director Human Resources, Essentia Health Ada, Ada, MN, p. A328

HENNESSEE, Debbie, Chief Financial Officer, Grandview Medical Center, Jasper, TN, p. A570

HENNESSEY, Ruth, Executive Vice President and Chief Administrative Officer, St. Francis Hospital, Roslyn, NY, p. A442

HENNESSY, Thomas G., President and Chief Executive Officer, Saint Francis Memorial Hospital, San Francisco, CA, p. A87

HENNIGAN, Michael, M.D. Medical Director, HEALTHSOUTH Emerald Coast Rehabilitation Hospital, Panama City, FL, p. A136

HENNIKE, Michael, Chief Executive Officer, Central Regional Hospital, Butner, NC, p. A449

HENNING, Charles, Program Director Business, Kansas City Veterans Affairs Medical Center, Kansas City, MO, p. A363

HENNING, William C., Administrator and Chief Executive Officer, Baptist Memorial Hospital–North Mississippi, Oxford, MS, p. A352

HENOCH, Malcolm S., M.D. Chief Medical Officer, Oakwood Hospital & Medical Center–Dearborn, Dearborn, MI, p. A311

HENRICH, Christy, Controller, Kindred Hospital of Northern Indiana, Mishawaka, IN, p. A210

HENRY, Anna, Chief Information Officer, Kimble Hospital, Junction, TX, p. A615

HENRY, Chris, Associate Administrator and Chief Financial Officer, Washington Hospital Healthcare System, Fremont, CA, p. A61

HENRY, Dane, Executive Vice President and Chief Operating Officer, DeKalb Medical at North Decatur, Decatur, GA, p. A152

HENRY, David
Chief Executive Officer, Henderson County Community Hospital, Lexington, TN, p. A573
President and Chief Executive Officer, Northern Montana Hospital, Havre, MT, p. A377

HENRY, Debbie, Vice President Financial Services, North Arkansas Regional Medical Center, Harrison, AR, p. A44

HENRY, Don, M.D. President Medical and Dental Staff, Community Hospital, Munster, IN, p. A211

HENRY, Donna, Director of Nursing, Four County Counseling Center, Logansport, IN, p. A209

HENRY, Ginger, Chief Executive Officer, Prattville Baptist Hospital, Prattville, AL, p. A25

HENRY, Heather, Manager Information Systems, Hammond–Henry Hospital, Geneseo, IL, p. A183

HENRY, James L., Director Human Resources, HEALTHSOUTH Sea Pines Rehabilitation Hospital, Melbourne, FL, p. A130

HENRY, Jay, Chief Executive Officer, St. Charles Medical Center – Bend, Bend, OR, p. A511

HENRY, Joy, R.N. Director Nurses, Faith Community Hospital, Jacksboro, TX, p. A615

HENRY, Joyce, Controller, HEALTHSOUTH Rehabilitation Hospital of York, York, PA, p. A545

HENRY, Patricia, Chief Financial Officer, Coastal Communities Hospital, Santa Ana, CA, p. A89

HENRY, Tim
Accountant, Chatuge Regional Hospital and Nursing Home, Hiawassee, GA, p. A154
Chief Financial Officer, Union General Hospital, Blairsville, GA, p. A148

HENRY, William
Director Human Resources, East Texas Medical Center Henderson, Henderson, TX, p. A608
Director Human Resources, East Texas Medical Center–Gilmer, Gilmer, TX, p. A606

HENSEL, David, Director Financial Operations, OhioHealth Grady Memorial Hospital, Delaware, OH, p. A480

HENSKE, Terry, Director Human Resources, Memorial Hermann Northwest Hospital, Houston, TX, p. A611

HENSLER, Paul J., Chief Executive Officer, Kern Medical Center, Bakersfield, CA, p. A54

HENSLEY, Barry, Director Information Systems, Logan Regional Medical Center, Logan, WV, p. A678

HENSLEY, Dena, Administrator, Yancey Community Medical Center, Burnsville, NC, p. A448

HENSLEY, Lori, Chief Human Resources Officer, Ness County Hospital, Ness City, KS, p. A240

HENSON, Judith, Chief Nursing Officer, Adena Medical Center, Chillicothe, OH, p. A473

HENSON, Pam, Executive Director, Pathways of Tennessee, Jackson, TN, p. A570

HENSON, Steve, Interim Chief Executive Officer, Arkansas State Hospital, Little Rock, AR, p. A46

HENTON, Thomas, Chief Executive Officer, Weisbrod Memorial County Hospital, Eads, CO, p. A100

HENTZEN PAGE, Ann, M.D. Medical Director, Summit Surgical, LLC, Hutchinson, KS, p. A236

HENZE, Michael E., Chief Executive Officer, Lake Regional Health System, Osage Beach, MO, p. A367

HEPBURN, Margaret, R.N., President and Chief Executive Officer, Sierra Vista Regional Health Center, Sierra Vista, AZ, p. A37

HEPKER, Wendy J., FACHE, Director, Chillicothe Veterans Affairs Medical Center, Chillicothe, OH, p. A473

HEPNER, Tim, M.D. Medical Director, St. John Owasso, Owasso, OK, p. A505

HERALD, Kathleen R., Vice President and Chief Information Officer, Lexington Medical Center, West Columbia, SC, p. A556

HERBECK, Marilyn, Coordinator Human Resources, Community Memorial Hospital, Staunton, IL, p. A195

HERBEK, Gary J., Chief Executive Officer, HEALTHSOUTH Rehabilitation Hospital of Northern Virginia, Aldie, VA, p. A651

HERBER, Matt, M.D. Chief of Staff, Avera Dells Area Hospital, Dell Rapids, SD, p. A559

HERBERT, Daniel, M.D. Medical Administrative Officer, Millinocket Regional Hospital, Millinocket, ME, p. A284

HERBERT, Janet, R.N. Chief Operating Officer, McKenzie Health System, Sandusky, MI, p. A324

HERBERT, Kevin, Chief Financial Officer, Oconee Medical Center, Seneca, SC, p. A555

HERBERT, Laurie, Vice President Operations, Three Rivers Health, Three Rivers, MI, p. A325

HERBERT, Peter N., M.D. Senior Vice President Medical Affairs and Chief of Staff, Yale–New Haven Hospital, New Haven, CT, p. A110

HERBERT, Suzanne, Chief Financial Officer, Mimbres Memorial Hospital, Deming, NM, p. A415

HERBST, Gary, Senior Vice President and Chief Financial Officer, Kaweah Delta Medical Center, Visalia, CA, p. A95

HERD, Jacqueline, R.N. Chief Nursing Officer, Atlanta Medical Center, Atlanta, GA, p. A146

HERDENER, Tony, Vice President Systems and Finance, Northeast Georgia Medical Center, Gainesville, GA, p. A154

HERDER, Debbie, Controller, Texas Specialty Hospital at Wichita Falls, Wichita Falls, TX, p. A641

HEREFORD, Michelle, Administrator, Transitional Care Hospital, Charlottesville, VA, p. A652

HERING, Kristine, R.N. Chief Nursing Officer, Speare Memorial Hospital, Plymouth, NH, p. A400

HERINK, Phil, Chief Executive Officer, Boise Behavioral Health Hospital, Boise, ID, p. A167

HERM, Ann, Associate Director Patient Care Services, John D. Dingell Veterans Affairs Medical Center, Detroit, MI, p. A312

HERMAN, Jeffrey, Chief Executive Officer, Meadows Psychiatric Center, Centre Hall, PA, p. A522

HERMAN, John J., Chief Operating Officer, Mercy Hospital, Buffalo, NY, p. A422

HERMAN, John W., Chief Executive Officer, Fairview Northland Medical Center, Princeton, MN, p. A338

HERMAN, Theresa, M.D. Chief Medical Officer and Chief Quality Officer, Dupont Hospital, Fort Wayne, IN, p. A202

HERMANN, Terri, R.N. Chief Nursing Officer, Franklin Hospital District, Benton, IL, p. A174

HERMANS, Louis H.
Vice President Information Systems, JFK Johnson Rehabilitation Institute, Edison, NJ, p. A403
Vice President Information Systems, JFK Medical Center, Edison, NJ, p. A403

HERMANSON, Patrick M., Administrator, Great Falls Clinic Medical Center, Great Falls, MT, p. A376

HERMOSILLO, Gilbert, Manager Information Services, Mendota Community Hospital, Mendota, IL, p. A188

HERN, Warren, President and Chief Executive Officer, Unity Hospital, Rochester, NY, p. A441

HERNANDEZ, Bernadette, R.N. Chief Operating Officer, Laredo Specialty Hospital, Laredo, TX, p. A618

HERNANDEZ Jr., George B., President and Chief Executive Officer, University Health System, San Antonio, TX, p. A632

HERNANDEZ, Hank, Chief Executive Officer, Las Palmas Medical Center, El Paso, TX, p. A601

HERNANDEZ, Hector, M.D.,
Chief Executive Officer, Community Hospital of Huntington Park, Huntington Park, CA, p. A64
Chief Executive Officer, East Los Angeles Doctors Hospital, Los Angeles, CA, p. A68

HERNANDEZ, Kim, Director Human Resources, AMG Specialty Hospital–Slidell, Slidell, LA, p. A278

HERNANDEZ, Leonard, President and Chief Executive Officer, Sumner Regional Medical Center, Wellington, KS, p. A246

HERNANDEZ, Reyna, Chief Financial Officer, HEALTHSOUTH Rehabilitation Hospital of Miami, Miami, FL, p. A131

HERNANDEZ, Sandi, Controller, Lafayette General Surgical Hospital, Lafayette, LA, p. A271

HERNANDEZ, Tony, Director Information Technology, Fort Duncan Regional Medical Center, Eagle Pass, TX, p. A600

HERNANDEZ DROZDOWICZ, Diana, M.D. Medical Director, Rogers City Rehabilitation Hospital, Rogers City, MI, p. A323

HERNANDEZ–KEEBLE, Sonia, Superintendent, Rio Grande State Center/South Texas Health Care System, Harlingen, TX, p. A608

HERNANDEZ–LICHTL, Javier, Chief Executive Officer, Baptist Health South Florida, West Kendall Baptist Hospital, Miami, FL, p. A131

HERNDON, David N., M.D. Chief of Staff, Shriners Hospitals for Children–Galveston Burns Hospital, Galveston, TX, p. A605

HERNDON, Lori, R.N., President and Chief Executive Officer, AtlantiCare Regional Medical Center, Atlantic City, NJ, p. A401

HERR, Brenda, Chief Nursing Officer, East Adams Rural Hospital, Ritzville, WA, p. A670

HERR, Michael, Chief Financial Officer, Parkview Regional Hospital, Mexia, TX, p. A623

HERRARA, Espie, Chief Financial Officer, Peak Behavioral Health Services, Santa Teresa, NM, p. A418

HERRERA, Esmeraldo, M.D. Chief of Staff, Wayne Medical Center, Waynesboro, TN, p. A580

HERRERA, Georgina, M.D. Medical Director, Mesilla Valley Hospital, Las Cruces, NM, p. A416

HERRERA, Jocelyn A., Director Human Resources, Kaiser Permanente Anaheim Medical Center, Anaheim, CA, p. A52

HERRERA, Veronica, Director Human Resources, Aurora Las Encinas Hospital, Pasadena, CA, p. A79

HERRICK, Stephen M., Ph.D., Director, Piedmont Geriatric Hospital, Burkeville, VA, p. A652

HERRIN, Curtis
Chief Financial Officer, Toppenish Community Hospital, Toppenish, WA, p. A673
Chief Financial Officer, Yakima Regional Medical and Cardiac Center, Yakima, WA, p. A674

HERRING, Jim, Senior Vice President, Children's Medical Center of Dallas, Dallas, TX, p. A595

HERRING, Randy, M.D. Chief of Staff, Coon Memorial Hospital and Home, Dalhart, TX, p. A594

HERRINGTON, Bruce, M.D. Chief Medical Officer, Louis Smith Memorial Hospital, Lakeland, GA, p. A155

HERRIOTT, Sue A., Director Human Resources, OSF St. Joseph Medical Center, Bloomington, IL, p. A174

HERRMAN, Edward, FACHE,
President, Integris Bass Baptist Health Center, Enid, OK, p. A498

President, Integris Bass Pavilion, Enid, OK, p. A498

HERRMANN, Anna L., JD Assistant Administrator, Mayo Clinic Health System in New Prague, New Prague, MN, p. A337

HERRMANN, Deborah, M.D. Chief of Staff, I-70 Community Hospital, Sweet Springs, MO, p. A372

HERRMANN, Lee, Chief Healthcare Technology Officer, Santa Clara Valley Medical Center, San Jose, CA, p. A88

HERRMANN, Marty, M.D. Medical Director, Mayo Clinic Health System in New Prague, New Prague, MN, p. A337

HERRMANN, Sarah, R.N. Chief Nursing Officer, Select Specialty Hospital–Topeka, Topeka, KS, p. A245

HERRON, Katherine, Director Human Resources, Richard H. Hutchings Psychiatric Center, Syracuse, NY, p. A443

HERRON, Mary Beth, Director of Human Resources, Illinois Valley Community Hospital, Peru, IL, p. A192

HERRON, Michael, Chief Financial Officer, Southern Hills Hospital and Medical Center, Las Vegas, NV, p. A393

HERSEY, Robert, Chief Financial Officer, Northeastern Vermont Regional Hospital, Saint Johnsbury, VT, p. A650

HERSHBERGER, Scott, Acting Chief Information Management Services, Battle Creek Veterans Affairs Medical Center, Battle Creek, MI, p. A309

HERSOM, Deborah, Director Human Resources, HEALTHSOUTH Chattanooga Rehabilitation Hospital, Chattanooga, TN, p. A566

HERT, Rebecca, Director Human Resources, Hillcrest Hospital – South, Tulsa, OK, p. A508

HERTEL, Cheryl, Coordinator Human Resources, Stamford Memorial Hospital, Stamford, TX, p. A635

HERTZ, Roger
Vice President, Methodist Jennie Edmundson Hospital, Council Bluffs, IA, p. A219

Vice President Information Technology, Nebraska Methodist Hospital, Omaha, NE, p. A388

HERTZLER, Barbara, Chief Operating Officer, St. Joseph Mercy Oakland, Pontiac, MI, p. A322

HERWALDT, Debra J., Chief Financial Officer, Los Robles Hospital and Medical Center, Thousand Oaks, CA, p. A92

HERWIG, Brian J., Chief Operating Officer, Providence Medford Medical Center, Medford, OR, p. A514

HERWIG, Karen, Vice President Human Resources, Ashland Community Hospital, Ashland, OR, p. A511

HERZBERG, Deborah L., FACHE, Chief Executive Officer, Davis County Hospital, Bloomfield, IA, p. A217

HERZBERG, Joseph W., Assistant Vice President Human Resources, WellStar Cobb Hospital, Austell, GA, p. A148

HERZOG, David, Chief Information Officer, Ventura County Medical Center, Ventura, CA, p. A94

HERZOG, Dean, Chief Financial Officer, Kona Community Hospital, Kealakekua, HI, p. A166

HERZOG, Mark P., President and Chief Executive Officer, Holy Family Memorial, Manitowoc, WI, p. A690

HERZOG, Paul F., Chief Executive Officer, Memorial Medical Center, Las Cruces, NM, p. A416

HERZOG, Vernail, Chief Executive Officer, Allegiance Specialty Hospital of Greenville, Greenville, MS, p. A347

HESCH, Dennis, Executive Vice President Finance and Chief Financial Officer, Carle Foundation Hospital, Urbana, IL, p. A196

HESS, Bob, Chief Information Officer, Bonner General Hospital, Sandpoint, ID, p. A171

HESS, Brian, Chief Executive Officer, Highlands Regional Medical Center, Sebring, FL, p. A140

HESS, David F., M.D. President Medical Staff, Reynolds Memorial Hospital, Glen Dale, WV, p. A677

HESS, Matthew, Director Human Resources, Raleigh General Hospital, Beckley, WV, p. A675

HESS, Pamela, Chief Financial Officer, St. Joseph Hospital, Fort Wayne, IN, p. A203

HESS, Phil, Chief Executive Officer, Philhaven, Mount Gretna, PA, p. A532

HESS, Rita, R.N. Chief Nursing Officer, North Shore Medical Center, Miami, FL, p. A132

HESS, Steve
Vice President & Chief Information Officer, Medical Center of the Rockies, Loveland, CO, p. A104

Vice President Information Services and Chief Information Officer, University of Colorado Hospital, Aurora, CO, p. A97

HESSE, Fred, M.D. Medical Director, Arms Acres, Carmel, NY, p. A423

HESSE, Nancy, R.N. Chief Nursing Officer, Abington Health Lansdale Hospital, Lansdale, PA, p. A529

HESSELRODE, Renee, Director Health Information Management, Landmark Hospital, Cape Girardeau, MO, p. A357

HESSHEIMER, Susan, Director Human Resources, Johnson County Hospital, Tecumseh, NE, p. A390

HESSING, Jeffrey, M.D. Medical Director, Treasure Valley Hospital, Boise, ID, p. A168

HESSMAN, Mary Pat, Chief Fiscal, Northport Veterans Affairs Medical Center, Northport, NY, p. A437

HESTER, Joyce, CPA Senior Vice President and Chief Financial Officer, Mother Frances Hospital – Tyler, Tyler, TX, p. A638

HESTER, Kathy, Chief Nursing Officer, Orange Park Medical Center, Orange Park, FL, p. A135

HESTER, Sharon
Site Manager Information Technology, St. Rose Dominican Hospitals – Rose de Lima Campus, Henderson, NV, p. A392

Site Manager Information Technology, St. Rose Dominican Hospitals – San Martin Campus, Las Vegas, NV, p. A393

Site Manager Information Technology, St. Rose Dominican Hospitals – Siena Campus, Henderson, NV, p. A392

HESTER, Steven, M.D. Vice President Medical Affairs, Norton Suburban Hospital, Louisville, KY, p. A256

HETLAGE, C. Kennon, FACHE, Administrator and Chief Executive Officer, Memorial Hospital West, Pembroke Pines, FL, p. A136

HETLETVED, Beth, Director of Nurses, Garrison Memorial Hospital, Garrison, ND, p. A467

HETRICK, Robert G., Chief Financial Officer, Northern Hospital of Surry County, Mount Airy, NC, p. A458

HETT, Sam, Manager Human Resources, Satanta District Hospital, Satanta, KS, p. A244

HETTICH, E. Paul, Chief Financial Officer, BryLin Hospitals, Buffalo, NY, p. A422

HETTINGER, JoAnn, R.N. Director of Patient Care Services, Avera Weskota Memorial Hospital, Wessington Springs, SD, p. A564

HETTINGER, MaryLou, Director Quality Management, Devereux Children's Behavioral Health Center, Malvern, PA, p. A530

HETU, Maureen, Chief Information Officer, Our Lady of Lourdes Medical Center, Camden, NJ, p. A402

HETZ, Mark
Chief Information Officer, Rogue Valley Medical Center, Medford, OR, p. A515

Chief Information Officer, Three Rivers Medical Center, Grants Pass, OR, p. A513

HEUBACH, Martha J., Chief Executive Officer, Promise Hospital of San Diego, San Diego, CA, p. A85

HEURING, Ron, Director Information Systems, Perry County Memorial Hospital, Perryville, MO, p. A367

HEUSER, Keith E., President, Mercy Hospital, Valley City, ND, p. A469

HEVER, Susan C., Director Human Resources, Brookhaven Memorial Hospital Medical Center, Patchogue, NY, p. A439

HEWIT, Craig, Executive Partner Information Technology and Chief Information Officer, Sanford Medical Center Fargo, Fargo, ND, p. A466

HEXUM, Gregory, Chief Financial Officer, Steele Memorial Medical Center, Salmon, ID, p. A171

HEYBOER Jr., Lester, President and Chief Executive Officer, HealthSource Saginaw, Saginaw, MI, p. A323

HEYDON, Larry, President and Chief Executive Officer, Johnson Memorial Hospital, Franklin, IN, p. A203

HEYE, John E., Chief Financial Officer, Maine Medical Center, Portland, ME, p. A284

HEYN, Matt, Administrator, Pawnee Valley Community Hospital, Larned, KS, p. A238

HIATT, M. K., Administrator, Allendale County Hospital, Fairfax, SC, p. A551

HIATT, Tim, Chief Information Officer, Brodstone Memorial Hospital, Superior, NE, p. A390

HIBBERT, Paul, D.O. President Medical Staff, Illini Community Hospital, Pittsfield, IL, p. A192

HIBBS, Cathryn A., FACHE, Chief Executive Officer, Deaconess Hospital, Oklahoma City, OK, p. A503

HIBEN, Daniel, Chief Executive Officer, Oswego Community Hospital, Oswego, KS, p. A241

HICCOX, Janelle, Director Human Resources, Lincoln Hospital, Davenport, WA, p. A666

HICKETHIER, Julie, R.N. Senior Vice President, Benefis Hospitals, Great Falls, MT, p. A376

HICKEY, Christopher, Chief Financial Officer, North Adams Regional Hospital, North Adams, MA, p. A303

HICKEY, Mairead, Ph.D. Executive Vice President and Chief Operating Officer, Brigham and Women's Hospital, Boston, MA, p. A296

HICKEY, Thomas P., Chief Executive Officer and Managing Director, Pembroke Hospital, Pembroke, MA, p. A303

HICKEY–BOYNTON, Meg, Director Human Resources and Marketing, Community Hospital of Anaconda, Anaconda, MT, p. A374

HICKLING, Karen, Director Human Resources, Palmdale Regional Medical Center, Palmdale, CA, p. A78

HICKMAN, George, Executive Vice President and Chief Information Officer, Albany Medical Center, Albany, NY, p. A420

HICKMAN, Louise, R.N. Vice President of Patient Care Services, Jefferson Regional Medical Center, Pine Bluff, AR, p. A49

HICKMAN, Monica, Director Fiscal Services, Shriners Hospitals for Children–Spokane, Spokane, WA, p. A672

HICKS, Angela, Controller, Our Community Hospital, Scotland Neck, NC, p. A460

HICKS, Crystal, R.N. Chief Nursing Officer, Harrison County Community Hospital, Bethany, MO, p. A356

HICKS, Joan, Chief Information Officer, University of Alabama Hospital, Birmingham, AL, p. A17

HICKS, Joe, President and Chief Executive Officer, Barnabas Health Behavioral Health Center, Toms River, NJ, p. A274

HICKS, John R., President and Chief Executive Officer, Platte Valley Medical Center, Brighton, CO, p. A97

HICKS, Kevin J., President and Chief Executive Officer, Research Medical Center, Kansas City, MO, p. A363

HICKS, Norman, M.D. Chief Medical Staff, East Texas Medical Center–Quitman, Quitman, TX, p. A628

HICKS, Shawnee, Director Human Resources, Magnolia Regional Medical Center, Magnolia, AR, p. A47

HICKS, Susan, Chief Operating Officer, Sky Ridge Medical Center, Lone Tree, CO, p. A104

HICKS, Terri, Chief Operating Officer and Chief Financial Officer, P & S Surgical Hospital, Monroe, LA, p. A274

HICKSON, Stan, FACHE, Executive Vice President and Chief Operating Officer, Palmetto Health Richland, Columbia, SC, p. A550

HIDALGO, Humberto, M.D. Chief of Staff, South Texas Health System, Edinburg, TX, p. A600

HIEB, Dorothy, Director Human Resources, Sanford Chamberlain Medical Center, Chamberlain, SD, p. A558

HIEBERT, Leslie, Chief Financial Officer, Klickitat Valley Health, Goldendale, WA, p. A667

HIERS, Mitch, Director Information Services, Colquitt Regional Medical Center, Moultrie, GA, p. A158

HIGA, Russel, JD Regional Director Human Resources, Leahi Hospital, Honolulu, HI, p. A164

HIGDON, Kevin J., Chief Financial Officer, Thorek Memorial Hospital, Chicago, IL, p. A179

HIGDON, Mark L., Commander, Moncrief Army Community Hospital, Fort Jackson, SC, p. A552

HIGGINBOTHAM, G. Douglas, President and Chief Executive Officer, South Central Regional Medical Center, Laurel, MS, p. A349

HIGGINBOTHAM, Michael, Chief Executive Officer, Texas Specialty Hospital at Houston, Houston, TX, p. A612

HIGGINS, Alana
Regional Information Management Executive, CHRISTUS St. Michael Health System, Texarkana, TX, p. A637

Regional Information Management Executive, CHRISTUS St. Michael Rehabilitation Hospital, Texarkana, TX, p. A637

HIGGINS, John, Vice President Finance, Exempla Good Samaritan Medical Center, Lafayette, CO, p. A103

HIGGINS, Kevin A., Chief Financial Officer, Olmsted Medical Center, Rochester, MN, p. A339

HIGGINS, Larry, Vice President Human Resources, King's Daughters Medical Center, Ashland, KY, p. A248

HIGGINS, Myron, Chief Operating Officer, Mercer County Hospital, Aledo, IL, p. A173

HIGGINS, Susie, Chief Financial Officer, Grafton City Hospital, Grafton, WV, p. A677

HIGGINS, William, M.D. Vice President Medical Affairs, Hudson Valley Health Center, Cortlandt Manor, NY, p. A424

HIGGINS–BOWERS, Shirley, Vice President Human Resources, JFK Medical Center, Edison, NJ, p. A403

HIGGINSON, David, Senior Vice President and Chief Information Officer, Phoenix Children's Hospital, Phoenix, AZ, p. A35

HIGH, Kim, Chief Financial Officer, Baptist Memorial Hospital–Union County, New Albany, MS, p. A352

HIGHBAUGH, Michael, M.D. Medical Director, Baylor Specialty Hospital, Dallas, TX, p. A595

HIGHSMITH, Cameron, Chief Executive Officer, Washington County Hospital, Plymouth, NC, p. A459

HIGHSMITH, Danette, Director Human Resources, Burke Medical Center, Waynesboro, GA, p. A162

HIGHTOWER, Bernita, Chief Human Resources, Martin Army Community Hospital, Fort Benning, GA, p. A153

HIGHTOWER, Skip
Chief Financial Officer, Brooks County Hospital, Quitman, GA, p. A158
Chief Financial Officer, Grady General Hospital, Cairo, GA, p. A149
Senior Vice President and Chief Financial Officer, John D. Archbold Memorial Hospital, Thomasville, GA, p. A161
Senior Vice President and Chief Financial Officer, Mitchell County Hospital, Camilla, GA, p. A149

HIGHTOWER, Thomas, R.N. Chief Operating Officer, Grays Harbor Community Hospital, Aberdeen, WA, p. A664

HILAMAN, Brad L., M.D. Chief of Staff, J. Arthur Dosher Memorial Hospital, Southport, NC, p. A461

HILBERT, Frank, Senior Vice President and Chief Information Officer, McAlester Regional Health Center, McAlester, OK, p. A501

HILBERT, Laura, Interim Chief Operating Officer, Palms West Hospital, Loxahatchee, FL, p. A129

HILBURN, Diana, Vice President Information Technology and Chief Information Officer, Via Christi Hospital on St. Francis, Wichita, KS, p. A246

HILDEBRAND, Richard D., M.D. Vice President Medical Affairs and Chief Medical Officer, UnityPoint Health St. Luke's, Sioux City, IA, p. A228

HILDEBRANDT, James, D.O. President Medical Staff, Sarah Bush Lincoln Health Center, Mattoon, IL, p. A188

HILDRETH, Beth, Vice President Human Resources, MedCentral – Mansfield Hospital, Mansfield, OH, p. A485

HILDWEIN, Robin, Chief Information Officer, Boca Raton Regional Hospital, Boca Raton, FL, p. A118

HILFIGER, Janie, President, Soldiers and Sailors Memorial Hospital, Wellsboro, PA, p. A543

HILL, Bart, M.D. Vice President Medical Affairs, St. Luke's Regional Medical Center, Boise, ID, p. A168

HILL, Bettie, Chief Financial Officer, Poplar Springs Hospital, Petersburg, VA, p. A659

HILL, Cheryl
Vice President Human Resources, Columbia St. Mary's Hospital Milwaukee, Milwaukee, WI, p. A692
Vice President Human Resources, Columbia St. Mary's Ozaukee Hospital, Mequon, WI, p. A691
Vice President Human Resources, Sacred Heart Rehabilitation Institute, Milwaukee, WI, p. A692

HILL, Chris, Chief Executive Officer, Arizona Spine and Joint Hospital, Mesa, AZ, p. A32

HILL, David, President and Chief Executive Officer, Booneville Community Hospital, Booneville, AR, p. A41

HILL, David L., Chief Executive Officer, John C. Fremont Healthcare District, Mariposa, CA, p. A73

HILL, Deborah A., FACHE, Chief Executive Officer, Summersville Regional Medical Center, Summersville, WV, p. A681

HILL, Douglas, M.D. Medical Director, Cascade Medical Center, Cascade, ID, p. A168

HILL, Duane N., Chief Executive Officer, Beaumont Bone and Joint Institute, Beaumont, TX, p. A587

HILL, Dwight, Vice President Human Resources, Northside Hospital, Atlanta, GA, p. A146

HILL, Jack, Chief Operating Officer and Administrator, The Jewish Hospital – Mercy Health, Cincinnati, OH, p. A475

HILL, Jackie, Chief Financial Officer, Brighton Center for Recovery, Brighton, MI, p. A309

HILL, James P., Senior Vice President Human Resources, MedStar Washington Hospital Center, Washington, DC, p. A116

HILL, Janice, R.N., Administrator, Baptist Memorial Restorative Care Hospital, Memphis, TN, p. A574

HILL, Jason, M.D. Chief Medical Officer, Choctaw Nation Health Care Center, Talihina, OK, p. A507

HILL, Jeff, Chief Executive Officer, Steele Memorial Medical Center, Salmon, ID, p. A171

HILL, Jill, Director Information Technology, Utah State Hospital, Provo, UT, p. A646

HILL, Jr., Joe B., Vice President Human Resources, Trident Medical Center, Charleston, SC, p. A549

HILL, John G.
Chief Executive Officer, PeaceHealth Sacred Heart Medical Center at RiverBend, Springfield, OR, p. A518
Chief Executive Officer, PeaceHealth Sacred Heart Medical Center, University District, Eugene, OR, p. A512

HILL, Karen, Director Human Resources, Baylor Institute for Rehabilitation, Dallas, TX, p. A595

HILL, Karen S., R.N. Chief Operating Officer and Chief Nursing Officer, Baptist Health Lexington, Lexington, KY, p. A253

HILL, Kent D., Director, Kansas City Veterans Affairs Medical Center, Kansas City, MO, p. A363

HILL, Mary Beth, Coordinator Human Resources, Vidant Bertie Hospital, Windsor, NC, p. A463

HILL, Michael, M.D. Chief of Staff, LaFollette Medical Center, La Follette, TN, p. A572

HILL, Ned, Chief Executive Officer, Memorial Hospital of Carbon County, Rawlins, WY, p. A703

HILL, Pamela German
Chief Financial Officer, Vista Medical Center East, Waukegan, IL, p. A196
Chief Financial Officer, Vista Medical Center West, Waukegan, IL, p. A196

HILL, Patricia, Senior Director Nurse Executive, Sentara Northern Virginia Medical Center, Woodbridge, VA, p. A663

HILL, Phillip, Interim Chief Executive Officer, Calhoun–Liberty Hospital, Blountstown, FL, p. A118

HILL, Ryan
Interim Chief Executive Officer, Essentia Health Ada, Ada, MN, p. A328
Chief Financial Officer, Essentia Health St. Mary's Hospital – Detroit Lakes, Detroit Lakes, MN, p. A331

HILL, Stephen, Vice President and Chief Nursing Officer, Valley Baptist Medical Center–Harlingen, Harlingen, TX, p. A608

HILL, Steven, Vice President Finance, University of Minnesota Medical Center, Fairview, Minneapolis, MN, p. A336

HILL, Stuart, Vice President and Treasurer, White County Medical Center, Searcy, AR, p. A50

HILL, Sue, Director Finance, Taylorville Memorial Hospital, Taylorville, IL, p. A196

HILL, Susan, Director Human Resources, East Texas Medical Center Clarksville, Clarksville, TX, p. A592

HILL, Terri L., Vice President and Administrator, Union Hospital Clinton, Clinton, IN, p. A200

HILL–DAVIS, Nancy L., Vice President Human Resources and Risk Management, Mercy Hospital and Medical Center, Chicago, IL, p. A177

HILLEBRAND, Jeffrey H., Chief Operating Officer, NorthShore University Health System Evanston Hospital, Evanston, IL, p. A182

HILLEGASS, Bonnie Essex, Chief Executive Officer, Harmon Medical and Rehabilitation Hospital, Las Vegas, NV, p. A392

HILLESTAD, Tammy, Chief Nursing Officer, Brookings Health System, Brookings, SD, p. A558

HILLIARD, David J., D.O. Chief of Staff, Barnesville Hospital, Barnesville, OH, p. A471

HILLIARD, Eva, Director Human Resources, Sutter Davis Hospital, Davis, CA, p. A58

HILLIS, David W., President and Chief Executive Officer, Adcare Hospital of Worcester, Worcester, MA, p. A306

HILLMAN, Annette, Director Human Resources, Doctor's Hospital of Deer Creek, Leesville, LA, p. A272

HILLS, Cindi, Director Human Resources, Riverwood Healthcare Center, Aitkin, MN, p. A328

HILLS, Edward, D.D.S. Interim Chief Operating Officer, MetroHealth Medical Center, Cleveland, OH, p. A476

HILT, Monica
President, Ministry Sacred Heart Hospital, Tomahawk, WI, p. A698
President and Chief Operating Officer, Ministry Saint Mary's Hospitals, Rhinelander, WI, p. A695

HILTON, Craig, Chief Executive Officer, Hampton Behavioral Health Center, Westampton, NJ, p. A412

HILTON, David, M.D. Medical Director, Hamilton Center, Terre Haute, IN, p. A213

HILTON, John, Operations Officer, Northern Cochise Community Hospital, Willcox, AZ, p. A39

HILTON, Lois, Director Human Resources, DeSoto Memorial Hospital, Arcadia, FL, p. A118

HILTON, Richard G., Administrator and Chief Executive Officer, OCH Regional Medical Center, Starkville, MS, p. A354

HILTON, Shane, Vice President and Chief Financial Officer, Johnson City Medical Center, Johnson City, TN, p. A571

HILTON–SIEBERT, Stephanie, President and Chief Executive Officer, Salem Township Hospital, Salem, IL, p. A194

HILTUNEN, Theresa, Entity Information Officer, Penn Presbyterian Medical Center, Philadelphia, PA, p. A536

HILTZ, Paul C., FACHE, Market Leader and President, Springfield Regional Medical Center, Springfield, OH, p. A490

HIME, Judy, Director Human Resources, Gibson General Hospital, Trenton, TN, p. A580

HINCHEY, Paul P.
President and Chief Executive Officer, Candler Hospital, Savannah, GA, p. A159
President and Chief Executive Officer, St. Joseph's Hospital, Savannah, GA, p. A160

HINCKLEY, Fran, Chief Information Officer, Hebrew Rehabilitation Center, Boston, MA, p. A297

HINDMAN, Robbie, Vice President Patient Care Services and Chief Nursing Officer, Walker Baptist Medical Center, Jasper, AL, p. A22

HINDS, Bob, Executive Director, Bradford Health Services at Huntsville, Madison, AL, p. A22

HINDS, Nigel, Chief Financial Officer, Florida Hospital DeLand, DeLand, FL, p. A122

HINEMAN, Elizabeth, M.D. Chief Medical Staff, Scott County Hospital, Scott City, KS, p. A244

HINER, Jill, Vice President and Chief Financial Officer, Summa Western Reserve Hospital, Cuyahoga Falls, OH, p. A479

HINER, Peggy, Executive Secretary and Manager Human Resources, Wheatland Memorial Healthcare, Harlowton, MT, p. A377

HINES, Frederick W., President and Chief Executive Officer, Clarity Child Guidance Center, San Antonio, TX, p. A631

HINES, James, Chief Financial Officer, East Texas Medical Center Clarksville, Clarksville, TX, p. A592

HINES, Linda
Vice President and Site Executive, Baltimore Washington Medical Center, Glen Burnie, MD, p. A292
Vice President Information Technology and Information Systems, Kernan Orthopaedics and Rehabilitation, Baltimore, MD, p. A287

HINES, Randall, Interim Administrator, Central State Hospital, Milledgeville, GA, p. A157

HINES, Ron, Director Information Technology, Valley View Hospital, Glenwood Springs, CO, p. A101

HINESLEY, Jay, Assistant Chief Executive Officer, DeKalb Regional Medical Center, Fort Payne, AL, p. A20

HINKLE, David, Senior Vice President and Chief Information Officer, Nash Health Care Systems, Rocky Mount, NC, p. A460

HINKLE, Stacey, Director Information Technology, Banner Desert Medical Center, Mesa, AZ, p. A33

HINNER, William J., Vice President Financial Analysis and Planning, Ministry Saint Michael's Hospital, Stevens Point, WI, p. A697

HINO, Raymond T., FACHE, Chief Executive Officer, Bear Valley Community Hospital, Big Bear Lake, CA, p. A55

HINRICHS, Becky, Vice President Human Resources, Riverside Medical Center, Kankakee, IL, p. A186

HINRICHS, Michelle, Chief Nursing Officer, St. Joseph's Hospital and Health Center, Dickinson, ND, p. A466

HINRICHS, Sandy, Director Human Resources, Burnett Medical Center, Grantsburg, WI, p. A687

HINSON, Pamela, Interim Administrator, Antelope Valley Hospital, Lancaster, CA, p. A66

HINTON, George, Administrator, Aurora Sinai Medical Center, Milwaukee, WI, p. A691

HINTON, Sharon, Chief Nursing Officer, Natchaug Hospital, Mansfield Center, CT, p. A109

HINTZE, Paul, M.D. Vice President Medical Affairs, Mercy Hospital St. Louis, Saint Louis, MO, p. A370

HIRKALER, Kim, Director Human Resources, Bon Secours Community Hospital, Port Jervis, NY, p. A440

HIROSE, Mivic, Executive Director, Laguna Honda Hospital and Rehabilitation Center, San Francisco, CA, p. A86

HIRSCH, Leslie D., FACHE, President and Chief Executive Officer, Saint Clare's Health System, Denville, NJ, p. A403

HIRSCH, Michel Y., M.D. Chief Medical Staff, Prevost Memorial Hospital, Donaldsonville, LA, p. A266

HIRSCH, Ted W., Senior Executive Director, Kalispell Regional Medical Center, Kalispell, MT, p. A377

HIRSCHMAN, Debra L., MSN, Director, Sheridan Veterans Affairs Medical Center, Sheridan, WY, p. A703

HIRSHBERG, Mark I., Chief Operating Officer, Bothwell Regional Health Center, Sedalia, MO, p. A371

HIRST, Barb, Vice President Human Resources and Chief Nursing Officer, Salem Community Hospital, Salem, OH, p. A489

HISEL, Patrick, M.D. Chief of Staff, Palo Pinto General Hospital, Mineral Wells, TX, p. A623

HISERODT, James, Senior Vice President Operations, Geneva General Hospital, Geneva, NY, p. A426

HISEY, Commie, D.O. Chief of Staff, Memorial Hospital, Gonzales, TX, p. A606

HITE–DAVIS, Anissa, Vice President Human Resources, St. Joseph's Hospital of Buckhannon, Buckhannon, WV, p. A675

HITT, Patricia A., Associate Director, Grand Junction Veterans Affairs Medical Center, Grand Junction, CO, p. A102

HIXENBAUGH, Cynthia, Director Human Resources, Pershing General Hospital, Lovelock, NV, p. A394

HIXSON, Kim, Chief Financial Officer, Providence Medical Center, Wayne, NE, p. A390

HJEMBO, Philip, Chief Financial Officer, St. Elizabeth Hospital, Enumclaw, WA, p. A666

HLAHOL, Jan, Manager Human Resources, Cleveland Clinic Children's Hospital for Rehabilitation, Cleveland, OH, p. A476

HLAVENKA, Richard, Director Management Information Systems, Jamaica Hospital Medical Center,, NY, p. A432

HLUCHY, Nicholas, Business Analyst, Support Services Manager, Baton Rouge Rehabilitation Hospital, Baton Rouge, LA, p. A263

HO, Sylvia, Director Information Services, Grady Memorial Hospital, Chickasha, OK, p. A496

HO–SHING, Viodelda, Deputy Director Administration, Creedmoor Psychiatric Center,, NY, p. A431

HOACH, Ken, Assistant Vice President and Chief Information Officer, Emanuel Medical Center, Turlock, CA, p. A93

HOAG, Jo Ann R., R.N., Chief Executive Officer, Lake View Memorial Hospital, Two Harbors, MN, p. A342

HOAG, Linda, Director Human Resources, St. Mary's Regional Medical Center, Enid, OK, p. A498

HOAGBIN, Joseph, M.D. Chief Quality Officer, Alegent Creighton Health Mercy Hospital, Council Bluffs, IA, p. A219

HOAR, Brad, Director Information and Technology, Cedar Park Regional Medical Center, Cedar Park, TX, p. A591

HOARD, Kaylee S., Chief Financial Officer, Cook Hospital and Convalescent Nursing Care Unit, Cook, MN, p. A330

HOBACK, Kim, Supervisor Information Systems, Athens–Limestone Hospital, Athens, AL, p. A16

HOBAN, Donna, M.D. Senior Vice President and Physician–in–Chief, Beaumont Hospital Grosse Pointe, Grosse Pointe, MI, p. A316

HOBAN, Douglas M., Vice President and Chief Financial Officer, Mercy Hospital Lebanon, Lebanon, MO, p. A364

HOBART, Robert, Director Management Information Systems, Heartland Behavioral Healthcare, Massillon, OH, p. A485

HOBBS, Donna, Nurse Executive, U. S. Public Health Service Indian Hospital–Sells, Sells, AZ, p. A37

HOBBS, Ed, Director Information Services, DeKalb Health, Auburn, IN, p. A198

HOBBS, Jan, M.D. Chief Medical Officer, Eastern New Mexico Medical Center, Roswell, NM, p. A417

HOBBS, Tommy, Chief Executive Officer, Illinois Valley Community Hospital, Peru, IL, p. A192

HOBECK, Susan, Chief Financial Officer, Community Memorial Hospital, Hicksville, OH, p. A483

HOBGOOD, Marcus, Director Information Services, LSU Health Sciences Center, Shreveport, LA, p. A278

HOBSON, James M., President and Chief Executive Officer, Memorial Health Care System, Chattanooga, TN, p. A566

HOCE, N. Kristopher, Chief Operating Officer, Morton Plant Hospital, Clearwater, FL, p. A120

HOCHHEISER, Lou, Chief Executive Officer, St. John's Medical Center and Living Center, Jackson, WY, p. A702

HOCK, Douglas G., Senior Vice President Operations, Children's Medical Center of Dallas, Dallas, TX, p. A595

HOCKADAY, Christina, FACHE, Administrator and Chief Operating Officer, Heart Hospital of Lafayette, Lafayette, LA, p. A270

HOCKENBERRY, Michael A., Vice President Operations, Hanover Hospital, Hanover, PA, p. A526

HOCKENBURY, Debbie, Assistant Administrator and Chief Financial Officer, William Newton Hospital, Winfield, KS, p. A247

HOCKERT, Steve, Chief Executive Officer, Solara Hospital Conroe, Conroe, TX, p. A593

HOCKING, Barbara, R.N. Chief Operating Officer, Maine Coast Memorial Hospital, Ellsworth, ME, p. A283

HOCKING, Dale E.
Chief Financial Officer, Leesburg Regional Medical Center, Leesburg, FL, p. A129
Senior Vice President and Chief Financial Officer, The Villages Health System, The Villages, FL, p. A142

HOCUM, Timothy, Chief Financial Officer, Providence Kodiak Island Medical Center, Kodiak, AK, p. A28

HODDE, Doug, M.D. Chief of Staff, Bowie Memorial Hospital, Bowie, TX, p. A589

HODGE, Pamela, R.N. Chief Nursing Officer and Coordinator Performance Improvement, Jellico Community Hospital, Jellico, TN, p. A571

HODGES, Alan, Chief Operating Officer, Ochsner Medical Center – North Shore, Slidell, LA, p. A279

HODGES, Jay, Chief Financial Officer, Red River Regional Hospital, Bonham, TX, p. A589

HODGES, Leisha, Human Resources Officer, Eastland Memorial Hospital, Eastland, TX, p. A600

HODGES, Randall H., President and Chief Executive Officer, CAMC Teays Valley Hospital, Hurricane, WV, p. A678

HODGES, Steve, Vice President Human Resources, Regional West Medical Center, Scottsbluff, NE, p. A389

HODGES, Teresa, Assistant Administrator, De Queen Medical Center, De Queen, AR, p. A42

HODGIN, Robin, R.N. Vice Administrator of Patient Care Services, Northern Hospital of Surry County, Mount Airy, NC, p. A458

HODGKINSON, Kimberly, Senior Vice President and Chief Financial Officer, St. Mary's Medical Center of Evansville, Evansville, IN, p. A202

HODGSON, Laurel, M.D. President Medical Staff, Doctors Medical Center–San Pablo Campus, San Pablo, CA, p. A88

HODSON, Don, M.D. Chief Medical Officer, St. Luke Hospital and Living Center, Marion, KS, p. A239

HOE, Adele S., Director Human Resources, Castle Medical Center, Kailua, HI, p. A165

HOEFLE, Brian
Chief Financial Officer, Yavapai Regional  Medical Center – East, Prescott Valley, AZ, p. A36
Chief Financial Officer, Yavapai Regional Medical Center, Prescott, AZ, p. A36

HOEFT, Thomas M., Executive Vice President and Chief Operating Officer, Huntington Hospital, Huntington, NY, p. A427

HOELL, James, M.D. President Medical Staff, Aurora Sheboygan Memorial Medical Center, Sheboygan, WI, p. A696

HOELL, Paul, M.D. President Medical Staff, New London Family Medical Center, New London, WI, p. A693

HOELSCHER, Steven C., Chief Operating Officer, Valley Regional Medical Center, Brownsville, TX, p. A590

HOEPPNER, David, M.D. Chief of Staff, Blue Ridge Regional Hospital, Spruce Pine, NC, p. A461

HOERTZ, Joanne, Vice President of Nursing, Brooks Rehabilitation Hospital, Jacksonville, FL, p. A126

HOFELICH, Kurt T., President, Sentara Norfolk General Hospital, Norfolk, VA, p. A658

HOFER, Renee, Senior Vice President Fiscal Services, St. Joseph's Hospital of Buckhannon, Buckhannon, WV, p. A675

HOFF, David L., Chief Executive Officer, Wayne Memorial Hospital, Honesdale, PA, p. A527

HOFF, Linda, Executive Vice President and Chief Financial Officer, Meriter Hospital, Madison, WI, p. A689

HOFF, Margaret, Account Manager, Brown County Community Treatment Center, Green Bay, WI, p. A687

HOFFELD, Thomas, M.D. Chief of Staff, Spanish Peaks Regional Health Center, Walsenburg, CO, p. A106

HOFFER, Nolan, Chief Executive Officer, Southwest Idaho Advanced Care Hospital, Boise, ID, p. A168

HOFFMAN, Barbara, M.D. Chief Medical Officer, St. Christopher's Hospital for Children, Philadelphia, PA, p. A536

HOFFMAN, Brad, Administrative Director Human Resources, Shawnee Mission Medical Center, Shawnee Mission, KS, p. A244

HOFFMAN, Brian, Director Human Resources, Lancaster Regional Medical Center, Lancaster, PA, p. A529

HOFFMAN, Brian, M.D. Chief Medical Services, Veterans Affairs Boston Healthcare System, Boston, MA, p. A297

HOFFMAN, Cara, M.D. Chief of Staff, Decatur Morgan Hospital, Decatur, AL, p. A19

HOFFMAN, Carole, Vice President, Parkridge Medical Center, Chattanooga, TN, p. A567

HOFFMAN, Charles, Vice President Financial Services and Chief Financial Officer, St. Joseph Mercy Livingston Hospital, Howell, MI, p. A316

HOFFMAN, Chris, Chief Operating Officer, Highlands Regional Medical Center, Prestonsburg, KY, p. A259

HOFFMAN, Daniel, M.D. Administrative Medical Director, Good Samaritan Regional Health Center, Mount Vernon, IL, p. A189

HOFFMAN, Debra, Manager Human Resources, Kern Valley Healthcare District, Lake Isabella, CA, p. A66

HOFFMAN, Glenn G., MS, Chief Executive Officer, Allegiance Behavioral Health Center of Plainview, Plainview, TX, p. A627

HOFFMAN, Howard, M.D. Medical Director, Psychiatric Institute of Washington, Washington, DC, p. A117

HOFFMAN, Jerry, Chief Financial Officer, Platte Health Center Avera, Platte, SD, p. A561

HOFFMAN, III, Joseph E.
Executive Vice President and Chief Financial Officer, Harford Memorial Hospital, Havre De Grace, MD, p. A292
Executive Vice President and Chief Financial Officer, Upper Chesapeake Medical Center, Bel Air, MD, p. A289

HOFFMAN, Mark, Chief Financial Officer, Oro Valley Hospital, Oro Valley, AZ, p. A33

HOFFMAN, Mary, Chief Financial Officer, Mayo Clinic Jacksonville, Jacksonville, FL, p. A126

HOFFMAN, Pamela S., Director of Human Resources, Monroe Hospital, Bloomington, IN, p. A199

HOFFMAN, Robert P., Vice President and Director Patient Care Services, Wilkes–Barre General Hospital, Wilkes–Barre, PA, p. A544

HOFFMAN, Todd, M.D. Medical Director, St. John Broken Arrow, Broken Arrow, OK, p. A496

HOFFMAN, Tom, Manager Information Systems, Wayne Memorial Hospital, Honesdale, PA, p. A527

HOFFMAN, Trudy, Executive Director, Northwest Center for Behavioral Health, Fort Supply, OK, p. A499

HOFFMAN, Val, Chief Financial Officer, Granite Falls Municipal Hospital and Manor, Granite Falls, MN, p. A333

HOFFMANN, Sally, Interim Chief Executive Officer, Kindred Hospital Springfield, Springfield, IL, p. A195

HOFFMANN, Wanda, Director Human Resources, River Oaks Hospital, New Orleans, LA, p. A275

HOFHEINS, Todd, Chief Financial Officer, Providence Regional Medical Center Everett, Everett, WA, p. A666

HOFIUS, Chuck, Chief Executive Officer, Perham Health, Perham, MN, p. A338

HOFMANN, Bill, M.D. Chief Medical Staff, Grays Harbor Community Hospital, Aberdeen, WA, p. A664

HOFSTETTER, Peter A., Chief Executive Officer, Holy Cross Hospital, Taos, NM, p. A418

HOGAN, Brian, Chief Executive Officer and Administrator, Baptist Rehabilitation–Germantown, Germantown, TN, p. A569

HOGAN, Judith, Comptroller and Director Resources and Logistics, Naval Hospital Bremerton, Bremerton, WA, p. A664

HOGAN, Michael, Chief Resource Management, General Leonard Wood Army Community Hospital, Fort Leonard Wood, MO, p. A361

HOGAN, Richard, Chief Financial Officer, Pleasant Valley Hospital, Point Pleasant, WV, p. A680

HOGAN, Richard H., CP
Chief Financial Officer, Landmark Hospital, Cape Girardeau, MO, p. A357
Chief Financial Officer, Landmark Hospital of Joplin, Joplin, MO, p. A362

HOGAN, Ronald E., Senior Vice President and Chief Financial Officer, St. Francis Medical Center, Monroe, LA, p. A274

HOGAN, Sean, President, SSM DePaul Health Center, Bridgeton, MO, p. A357

HOGAN, Timothy J., FACHE,
Regional President, Bayshore Community Hospital, Holmdel, NJ, p. A405
Regional President, Riverview Medical Center, Red Bank, NJ, p. A410

HOGG, Donna, Supervisor Medical Records, Monroe County Hospital, Forsyth, GA, p. A153

HOHENBERGER, Joseph W., Chief Financial Officer, Mecosta County Medical Center, Big Rapids, MI, p. A309

HOHMANN, Terry, Chief Financial Officer, Kindred Hospital North Houston, Houston, TX, p. A610

HOLBERT, Trisha, Vice President Human Resources, Mercy Hospital Springfield, Springfield, MO, p. A372

HOLBROOK, Chip, M.D. Chief of Staff, Simpson General Hospital, Mendenhall, MS, p. A350

HOLBROOK–PRESTON, Susan, Chief Operating Officer and Chief Nursing Officer, Community Heart and Vascular Hospital, Indianapolis, IN, p. A205

HOLCOMB, Holly, R.N. Chief Operating Officer, Childress Regional Medical Center, Childress, TX, p. A591

HOLCOMB, Mark, Administrator, Great Lakes Specialty Hospital–Muskegon, Muskegon, MI, p. A320

HOLCOMB, Ralph, Chief Information Officer, Good Shepherd Medical Center, Longview, TX, p. A619

HOLCOMBE, Sheryl, Administrative Assistant, Brownfield Regional Medical Center, Brownfield, TX, p. A589

HOLDEMAN, Royce, Chief Financial Officer, Mercy Hospital, Moundridge, KS, p. A240

HOLDEN, Carol E., Director, Center for Forensic Psychiatry, Saline, MI, p. A324

HOLDEN, Jay T., Vice President, Human Resources, Beaumont Hospital Grosse Pointe, Grosse Pointe, MI, p. A316

HOLDEN, Patricia, Chief Executive Officer, Mesa View Regional Hospital, Mesquite, NV, p. A394

HOLDEN, Peter J., President and Chief Executive Officer, Jordan Hospital, Plymouth, MA, p. A304

HOLDEN, Tami, Director Human Resources, HEALTHSOUTH Bakersfield Rehabilitation Hospital, Bakersfield, CA, p. A54

HOLDER, Hal
Director Finance, SSM DePaul Health Center, Bridgeton, MO, p. A357
Vice President Finance, SSM St. Joseph Health Center, Saint Charles, MO, p. A368
Director Finance, SSM St. Joseph Hospital West, Lake Saint Louis, MO, p. A364

HOLDER, Joanna, Director Human Resources, Novant Health Franklin Medical Center, Louisburg, NC, p. A456

HOLDER, John, Chief Financial Officer, Mission Community Hospital,, CA, p. A70

HOLDER, Whitt
Chief Financial Officer, Physicians Surgical Hospital – Panhandle Campus, Amarillo, TX, p. A582
Chief Financial Officer, Physicians Surgical Hospital – Quail Creek, Amarillo, TX, p. A582

HOLDERMAN, Clay, Chief Operating Officer–Central Delivery System, Presbyterian Hospital, Albuquerque, NM, p. A414

HOLDERMAN, Wanda, Chief Executive Officer, Fresno Heart and Surgical Hospital, Fresno, CA, p. A61

HOLEKAMP, Nicholas, M.D. Medical Director, Ranken Jordan – A Pediatric Specialty Hospital, Maryland Heights, MO, p. A365

HOLEMAN, John, M.D. Chief of Staff, Methodist Hospital Union County, Morganfield, KY, p. A258

HOLGUIN, Mindee, Manager Human Resources, Sierra Vista Hospital, Truth or Consequences, NM, p. A418

HOLINER, Joel, M.D. Executive Medical Director, Green Oaks Hospital, Dallas, TX, p. A596

HOPKINS, Laura, Director of Nursing, Mayo Clinic Health System in New Prague, New Prague, MN, p. A337

HOPKINS, Maura, R.N. Chief Nursing Officer, RML Specialty Hospital, Hinsdale, IL, p. A185

HOPKINS, Paul, Chief Financial Officer, Harry S. Truman Memorial Veterans Hospital, Columbia, MO, p. A359

HOPKINS, Wade, Administrator, Southern Virginia Mental Health Institute, Danville, VA, p. A653

HOPKINS, William, Director Finance, Carolinas Rehabilitation, Charlotte, NC, p. A449

HOPP, Eva, Chief Nurse Executive, Pinckneyville Community Hospital, Pinckneyville, IL, p. A192

HOPPS, Deborah, Chief Executive Officer, HEALTHSOUTH Rehabilitation Hospital–Cityview, Fort Worth, TX, p. A603

HOPSON, W. Briggs, M.D. Clinical Medical Director, River Region Medical Center, Vicksburg, MS, p. A354

HORAN, Chris, M.D. Chief of Staff, Saint Mary's Regional Medical Center, Russellville, AR, p. A49

HORAN, Gary S., FACHE, President and Chief Executive Officer, Trinitas Regional Medical Center, Elizabeth, NJ, p. A403

HORAN, Patrick, M.D. Chief of Staff, Town and Country Hospital, Tampa, FL, p. A142

HORAN, Sandra A., Executive Director, Margaretville Hospital, Margaretville, NY, p. A429

HORATH, Kevin, Director Human Resources, Decatur Memorial Hospital, Decatur, IL, p. A180

HORLANDER, Fred J., Vice President, Clark Memorial Hospital, Jeffersonville, IN, p. A207

HORN, Bill, Director Human Resources, Wickenburg Community Hospital, Wickenburg, AZ, p. A39

HORN, Jeff, Coordinator Information Systems, Jay County Hospital, Portland, IN, p. A212

HORN, LeeAnn, Chief Nurse Executive, Providence Kodiak Island Medical Center, Kodiak, AK, p. A28

HORN, Linda, Interim Chief Executive Officer, Sutter Coast Hospital, Crescent City, CA, p. A58

HORN, Mike, M.D. Vice President Medical Affairs, Saint Francis Medical Center, Grand Island, NE, p. A384

HORN, Syndi, Director Information Systems, Memorial Hospital, Carthage, IL, p. A175

HORNBURG, Tom, Director Information Systems, Mason General Hospital, Shelton, WA, p. A672

HORNE, Barbara, R.N. Vice President and Chief Human Resource Development Officer, Indian River Medical Center, Vero Beach, FL, p. A143

HORNE, Beth, System Administrator Information Technology, Preston Memorial Hospital, Kingwood, WV, p. A678

HORNE, Eilene, Manager Human Resources, Mountain View Hospital, Idaho Falls, ID, p. A169

HORNE, Wallace J., M.D. Vice President Medical Affairs, Hartnett Health System, Dunn, NC, p. A451

HORNER, Bryan, President and Chief Executive Officer, Shannon Medical Center, San Angelo, TX, p. A630

HORNER, Cheryl, Supervisor Data Processing, Community Memorial Hospital, Staunton, IL, p. A195

HORNER, James, Chief Information Officer, Portland Veterans Affairs Medical Center, Portland, OR, p. A516

HORNER, John, Manager Business Office, Veterans Affairs Medical Center, Omaha, NE, p. A388

HORNER, John M., President and Chief Executive Officer, Major Hospital, Shelbyville, IN, p. A213

HORNING, Phyllis, Interim Administrator, Hamilton County Hospital, Syracuse, KS, p. A244

HORNUNG, Dona, Director Information and Technology Services, Doctors Hospital, Augusta, GA, p. A147

HORNUNG, Kurt, Director, Medical Center of Trinity, Trinity, FL, p. A143

HORNUUG, Joel, M.D. Chief Medical Officer, Morris County Hospital, Council Grove, KS, p. A233

HOROWITZ, Ira, M.D. Chief Medical Officer, Emory University Hospital, Atlanta, GA, p. A146

HORRAS, Susan, Chief Financial Officer, Mahaska Health Partnership, Oskaloosa, IA, p. A226

HORROCKS, Chad, M.D. Chief of Staff, Teton Valley Health Care, Driggs, ID, p. A169

HORSLEY, Steve, Vice President and Chief Information Officer, Cone Health, Greensboro, NC, p. A453

HORSMAN, Sandra, Acting Medical Center Director, Sioux Falls Veterans Affairs Health Care System, Sioux Falls, SD, p. A563

HORSMAN, Sarah
Vice President Human Resources, MultiCare Good Samaritan Hospital, Puyallup, WA, p. A669

Senior Vice President Human Potential, MultiCare Mary Bridge Children's Hospital and Health Center, Tacoma, WA, p. A673

Senior Vice President Human Potential, MultiCare Tacoma General Hospital, Tacoma, WA, p. A673

HORST, Brad, Director Human Resources, Clear Lake Regional Medical Center, Webster, TX, p. A640

HORTON, Cynthia, M.D. Chief Medical Officer, Skyline Hospital, White Salmon, WA, p. A674

HORTON, Eileen M., Vice President, Patient Services/Chief Nursing Officer, Capital Health Regional Medical Center, Trenton, NJ, p. A411

HORTON, Greg, Director Support Services, State Hospital South, Blackfoot, ID, p. A167

HORTON, Jim, Chief Executive Officer, Pecos County Memorial Hospital, Fort Stockton, TX, p. A603

HORTON, Kenny, Director Information Systems, Walker Baptist Medical Center, Jasper, AL, p. A22

HORTON, Lynn M., Executive Director Human Resources, Fresno Heart and Surgical Hospital, Fresno, CA, p. A61

HORTON, Marie, Director Associate Relations, Bartow Regional Medical Center, Bartow, FL, p. A118

HORTON, Warren, Information Technologist, Baptist Health Medical Center–Stuttgart, Stuttgart, AR, p. A50

HORVAT, Kami, Chief Financial Officer, Doctors Hospital of West Covina, West Covina, CA, p. A95

HORVATH, Alex, Vice President Human Resources, Advocate BroMenn Medical Center, Normal, IL, p. A190

HORVATH, Dolores, Interm Chief Executive Officer, Medina Memorial Hospital, Medina, NY, p. A429

HOSKINS, Michael, Chief Operating Officer, Fairview Park Hospital, Dublin, GA, p. A152

HOSKINS, Pearly Graham, M.D. President Medical Staff, Cape Fear Valley – Bladen County Hospital, Elizabethtown, NC, p. A452

HOSKINS, Shirley, Chief Operating Officer, Meadows Regional Medical Center, Vidalia, GA, p. A162

HOSLER, Steve, Vice President Human Resources, Mercy Medical Center Redding, Redding, CA, p. A81

HOSTEENEZ, Vivie, Chief Financial Officer, U. S. Public Health Service Indian Hospital, San Carlos, AZ, p. A36

HOSTETTER, Lynne, Vice President Human Resources, The HSC Pediatric Center, Washington, DC, p. A117

HOTA, Bala, Interim Chief Information Officer, John H. Stroger Jr. Hospital of Cook County, Chicago, IL, p. A177

HOTALING, Andrew, Chief Executive Officer, Forest View Psychiatric Hospital, Grand Rapids, MI, p. A314

HOTCHKISS, Jason, Controller, Teton Valley Health Care, Driggs, ID, p. A169

HOTES, Lawrence S., M.D. Chief Medical Officer, New England Sinai Hospital and Rehabilitation Center, Stoughton, MA, p. A305

HOTT, Judith, Chief Executive Officer, Thomas B. Finan Center, Cumberland, MD, p. A291

HOTTENDORF, Catherine, MS, Executive Director, Franklin Hospital, Valley Stream, NY, p. A445

HOUCHIN, Kim, Chief Nursing Officer, Minnie Hamilton HealthCare Center, Grantsville, WV, p. A677

HOUGHTON, Roxan, Director Human Resources, Promise Hospital of Miss Lou, Vidalia, LA, p. A279

HOULE, David, Executive Vice President and Chief Financial Officer, The Hospital at Hebrew Health Care, West Hartford, CT, p. A112

HOULIHAN, David, M.D. Chief of Staff, Tomah Veterans Affairs Medical Center, Tomah, WI, p. A697

HOUMANN, Lars D., President, Florida Hospital, Orlando, FL, p. A135

HOUSE, Alan, Chief Financial Officer, Margaret R. Pardee Memorial Hospital, Hendersonville, NC, p. A454

HOUSE, David
Vice President, Baptist Health Extended Care Hospital, Little Rock, AR, p. A46

Vice President and Chief Information Officer, Baptist Health Medical Center – North Little Rock, North Little Rock, AR, p. A48

Vice President and Chief Information Officer, Baptist Health Medical Center–Arkadelphia, Arkadelphia, AR, p. A41

Vice President and Chief Information Officer, Baptist Health Medical Center–Little Rock, Little Rock, AR, p. A46

Vice President and Chief Information Officer, Baptist Health Rehabilitation Institute, Little Rock, AR, p. A46

HOUSER, Glenn, M.D. Chief Medical Officer, Garfield County Public Hospital District, Pomeroy, WA, p. A669

HOUSER, Kris, M.D. Medical Director, Peninsula Hospital, Louisville, TN, p. A573

HOUSER, Robert, FACHE, Chief Executive Officer, Blue Mountain Hospital, John Day, OR, p. A513

HOUSER–HANFELDER, Sallie, FACHE, Director, Harry S. Truman Memorial Veterans Hospital, Columbia, MO, p. A359

HOUSH, Steven C., President, Fairview Lakes Health Services, Wyoming, MN, p. A343

HOUSLEY, Kristin, Chief Management Information Systems, South Lincoln Medical Center, Kemmerer, WY, p. A702

HOUSMAN, Bradley W., M.D. Chief Medical Officer, Baptist Health Paducah, Paducah, KY, p. A259

HOUSMAN, Hunter, M.D. Chief Medical Officer, Bourbon Community Hospital, Paris, KY, p. A259

HOUSTON, Anthony, Executive Vice President, St. Marys Health Center, Jefferson City, MO, p. A362

HOUSTON, Jerry, Director Information Systems, Jennie Stuart Medical Center, Hopkinsville, KY, p. A252

HOUSTON, Sally, M.D. Senior Vice President and Chief Medical Officer, Tampa General Hospital, Tampa, FL, p. A142

HOUSTON, Sandra Davis
Vice President Human Resources, California Hospital Medical Center, Los Angeles, CA, p. A68

Vice President Human Resources and Organizational Development, Glendale Memorial Hospital and Health Center, Glendale, CA, p. A62

HOUSTON, William J., M.D. Medical Director, Indiana University Health La Porte Hospital, La Porte, IN, p. A208

HOVAN, Keith A., R.N., President and Chief Executive Officer, Southcoast Hospitals Group, Fall River, MA, p. A300

HOVENS, Michael R., M.D. Chief Medical Officer, Tri–Lakes Medical Center, Batesville, MS, p. A344

HOWALT, Lyra, Chief Financial Officer, Central Carolina Hospital, Sanford, NC, p. A460

HOWARD, Catherine, Director Human Resources, Halifax Regional Health System, South Boston, VA, p. A661

HOWARD, Charles, M.D. Chief of Staff, St. Vincent Morrilton, Morrilton, AR, p. A47

HOWARD, Cindy, Director Financial Services, Oneida County Hospital, Malad City, ID, p. A170

HOWARD, Craig, Director, Canandaigua Veterans Affairs Medical Center, Canandaigua, NY, p. A423

HOWARD, Daniel, Chief Financial Officer, Maine Veterans Affairs Medical Center, Augusta, ME, p. A281

HOWARD, Darcy, Chief Executive Officer and Chief Financial Officer, Logan County Hospital, Oakley, KS, p. A240

HOWARD, Donna, Human Resources Director, HEALTHSOUTH Rehabilitation Hospital of Ocala, Ocala, FL, p. A134

HOWARD, Eddie L.
Vice President and Chief Operating Officer, East Texas Medical Center Rehabilitation Hospital, Tyler, TX, p. A638

Vice President and Chief Operating Officer, East Texas Medical Center Specialty Hospital, Tyler, TX, p. A638

HOWARD, Gary L., Senior VP and Chief Financial Officer, Hamilton Medical Center, Dalton, GA, p. A151

HOWARD, Greg M., Director Human Resource, Health Alliance Hospital – Broadway Campus, Kingston, NY, p. A428

HOWARD, Jill, R.N. Chief Operating Officer, TriStar Skyline Madison Campus, Madison, TN, p. A573

HOWARD, Katherine, Director Human Resources, Baptist Medical Center Nassau, Fernandina Beach, FL, p. A123

HOWARD, Norma N., Chief Executive Officer, Lindsay Municipal Hospital, Lindsay, OK, p. A500

HOWARD, Pamela B., R.N., Administrator, Lake Butler Hospital Hand Surgery Center, Lake Butler, FL, p. A128

HOWARD, Randy, M.D. Chief of Staff, TriStar Hendersonville Medical Center, Hendersonville, TN, p. A570

HOWARD, Roger, M.D. Senior Vice President and Medical Director, Beaumont Hospital – Troy, Troy, MI, p. A326

HOWARD, Roger, President and Chief Executive Officer, Dearborn County Hospital, Lawrenceburg, IN, p. A208

HOWARD, Ron, Chief Financial Officer, Holly Hill Hospital, Raleigh, NC, p. A459

HOWARD, Sabra, Manager Human Resources, Harlan ARH Hospital, Harlan, KY, p. A252

HOWARD, Stacy M., R.N., Chief Executive Officer, Kindred Hospital–St. Louis, Saint Louis, MO, p. A369

HOWARD, Teresa, Manager Human Resources, Yoakum County Hospital, Denver City, TX, p. A599

HOWARD, Tim, Chief Human Resources Officer, Fountain Valley Regional Hospital and Medical Center, Fountain Valley, CA, p. A60

HOWARD, Tom, Chief Financial Officer, Texas Health Presbyterian Hospital Flower Mound, Flower Mound, TX, p. A602

HOWARD, Win, Chief Executive Officer, Three Rivers Medical Center, Grants Pass, OR, p. A513

HOWARD, SPHR, Opal R., Director Human Resources, Florida Hospital DeLand, DeLand, FL, p. A122

HOWARD–CROW, Dallis
Chief Human Resources Officer, Emory University Hospital Midtown, Atlanta, GA, p. A146

Chief Human Resources Officer, Wesley Woods Geriatric Hospital of Emory University, Atlanta, GA, p. A147

HOWART, Peg, Coordinator Human Resources and Benefits, Harlan County Health System, Alma, NE, p. A381

HOWAT, Greg, Vice President Human Resources, Eastern Maine Medical Center, Bangor, ME, p. A281

HOWDEN, Tim, Interim Chief Financial Officer, Grays Harbor Community Hospital, Aberdeen, WA, p. A664

HOWE, Debbie, Chief Executive Officer, Weatherford Regional Hospital, Weatherford, OK, p. A510

HOWE, James L., Chief Employee Relations, Pinnacle Pointe Hospital, Little Rock, AR, p. A46

HOWE, Mary Lenzini, Vice President Human Resources, Geisinger–Bloomsburg Hospital, Bloomsburg, PA, p. A521

HOWE, Scott W., Chief Executive Officer, Weeks Medical Center, Lancaster, NH, p. A398

HOWE, Vicki, Chief Information Officer, Ness County Hospital, Ness City, KS, p. A240

HOWELL, A. Todd, Chief Operating Officer, Columbus Regional Healthcare System, Whiteville, NC, p. A462

HOWELL, Amy M., Director Human Resources, St. Luke's Behavioral Health Center, Phoenix, AZ, p. A35

HOWELL, Bradley, Chief Executive Officer, Roundup Memorial Healthcare, Roundup, MT, p. A379

HOWELL, Carrie, Chief Financial Officer, Barstow Community Hospital, Barstow, CA, p. A54

HOWELL, Diana, Director Human Resources, Conroe Regional Medical Center, Conroe, TX, p. A593

HOWELL, Everette, M.D. Chief Medical Officer, Saint Thomas Hospital for Spinal Surgery, Nashville, TN, p. A576

HOWELL, Kathy A., Vice President Human Resources, Lexington Medical Center, West Columbia, SC, p. A556

HOWELL, Nathan, Chief Operating Officer, St. Elizabeth's Medical Center, Brighton, MA, p. A298

HOWELL, Pat, Chief Nursing Officer, Community Memorial Hospital, Syracuse, NE, p. A390

HOWELL, Patricia, M.D. President Medical Staff, Swedish Medical Center, Englewood, CO, p. A100

HOWELL, R. Edward, Vice President and Chief Executive Officer, University of Virginia Medical Center, Charlottesville, VA, p. A652

HOWELL, Ronene, Director Health Information Management, Bryce Hospital, Tuscaloosa, AL, p. A25

HOWELL, Sheri, Deputy Commander Nursing, San Antonio Military Medical Center, Fort Sam Houston, TX, p. A603

HOWELLS, Stephen, Chief Financial Officer, Kane County Hospital, Kanab, UT, p. A644

HOWERTER, Mark, M.D. President Medical Staff, Columbus Community Hospital, Columbus, NE, p. A382

HOWERTON, Shawn, M.D. President Medical Staff, Sampson Regional Medical Center, Clinton, NC, p. A450

HOWES, Constance A., President and Chief Executive Officer, Women & Infants Hospital of Rhode Island, Providence, RI, p. A547

HOY, Jonathan B., Chief Financial Officer, Duke Regional Hospital, Durham, NC, p. A451

HOYER, Scott, M.D. Vice President Quality and Chief Medical Officer, United Regional Health Care System, Wichita Falls, TX, p. A642

HOYLMAN, Karen, Director Information Systems, Greenbrier Valley Medical Center, Ronceverte, WV, p. A680

HOYOS, Kent, Chief Information Officer, Pomona Valley Hospital Medical Center, Pomona, CA, p. A80

HOYT, Nancy, R.N. Vice President Operations/Clinical and Chief Nursing Officer, Mercy Regional Medical Center, Durango, CO, p. A100

HRON, Janine, Chief Executive Officer, Crittenton Children's Center, Kansas City, MO, p. A362

HRUBIAK, Dan, Associate Computer Program Analyst, Western New York Children's Psychiatric Center, West Seneca, NY, p. A446

HRUBY, Deidre, Director of Patient Care, Madelia Community Hospital, Madelia, MN, p. A335

HSING, Shirley, Senior Vice President and Chief Financial Officer, North Oaks Medical Center, Hammond, LA, p. A268

HUANG, Benson, M.D. Medical Director, Laredo Specialty Hospital, Laredo, TX, p. A618

HUBBARD, Bill, Vice President, Operations, Carolinas Medical Center–NorthEast, Concord, NC, p. A450

HUBBARD, Brent, Chief Operating Officer, Mercy Hospital Fort Smith, Fort Smith, AR, p. A44

HUBBARD, Daniel, Chief Financial Officer, Sioux Falls Veterans Affairs Health Care System, Sioux Falls, SD, p. A563

HUBBARD, David, Chief Executive Officer, Daniels Memorial Healthcare Center, Scobey, MT, p. A379

HUBBARD, Kathy, Manager Human Resources, Oneida County Hospital, Malad City, ID, p. A170

HUBBARD, Mark, Vice President Risk Management, Loma Linda University Behavioral Medicine Center, Redlands, CA, p. A81

HUBBARD, Norm, Executive Vice President, Seattle Cancer Care Alliance, Seattle, WA, p. A671

HUBBELL, John, Chief Financial Officer, Livingston Hospital and Healthcare Services, Salem, KY, p. A260

HUBBS, David, M.D. Chief Medical Staff, Grove Hill Memorial Hospital, Grove Hill, AL, p. A21

HUBBS III, Olas A., FACHE, President and Chief Executive Officer, Memorial Hospital of Union County, Marysville, OH, p. A485

HUBELE, Suzanna D., M.D. Chief of Staff, Weiser Memorial Hospital, Weiser, ID, p. A172

HUBER, Joel, M.D. Chief of Staff, Avera Hand County Memorial Hospital, Miller, SD, p. A560

HUBER, Timothy, Manager Financial Support, Mercy Hospital of Franciscan Sisters, Oelwein, IA, p. A226

HUBERT, Barney, Superintendent, Kansas Neurological Institute, Topeka, KS, p. A244

HUBERT, Michael F., Vice President Human Resources, J. C. Blair Memorial Hospital, Huntingdon, PA, p. A527

HUBLEY, Grover, M.D. President Medical Staff, Madison St. Joseph Health Center, Madisonville, TX, p. A621

HUBSCHMAN, Gary
  Administrative Director Finance, Sutter Auburn Faith Hospital, Auburn, CA, p. A53
  Administrative Director Finance, Sutter Roseville Medical Center, Roseville, CA, p. A83

HUCK, Karma, Chief Operating Officer, Scott County Hospital, Scott City, KS, p. A244

HUCKABEE, Mike, Network Administrator, Coryell Memorial Hospital, Gatesville, TX, p. A606

HUCKABY, Don, Chief Information Management Service, Veterans Affairs Eastern Colorado Health Care System, Denver, CO, p. A100

HUCKSHORN, Kevin Ann, MSN, Director, Delaware Psychiatric Center, New Castle, DE, p. A114

HUDA, Edith, Director Human Resources, Daniels Memorial Healthcare Center, Scobey, MT, p. A379

HUDAK, Corey, Director Human Resources, Memorial Hospital, York, PA, p. A545

HUDDLESTON, J. Andrew, D.O. President Medical Staff, Bellevue Hospital, Bellevue, OH, p. A471

HUDDLESTON, Tina, Chief Nursing Officer, Baylor Medical Center at Trophy Club, Trophy Club, TX, p. A638

HUDGENS, Roselyn, Director Human Resources, Ballinger Memorial Hospital, Ballinger, TX, p. A587

HUDGINS, Paul
  Associate Vice President Human Resources, Bascom Palmer Eye Institute–Anne Bates Leach Eye Hospital, Miami, FL, p. A131
  Associate Vice President Human Resources, University of Miami Hospital and Clinics, Miami, FL, p. A132

HUDGINS, Thomas J., FACHE, Administrator and Chief Executive Officer, Pinckneyville Community Hospital, Pinckneyville, IL, p. A192

HUDNELL, Sharon, R.N. Chief Nursing Officer, WK Bossier Health Center, Bossier City, LA, p. A264

HUDSON, Beth, Chief Nursing Officer, Baylor Institute for Rehabilitation, Dallas, TX, p. A595

HUDSON, C. R., Senior Vice President and Chief Financial Officer, Henry Mayo Newhall Memorial Hospital, Valencia, CA, p. A94

HUDSON, Gary Mikeal, Administrator, East Texas Medical Center Carthage, Carthage, TX, p. A591

HUDSON, James, Assistant Chief Information Resource Management, Lake City Veterans Affairs Medical Center, Lake City, FL, p. A128

HUDSON, Janell, M.D. Chief Clinical Officer, Sanford Thief River Falls Medical Center, Thief River Falls, MN, p. A341

HUDSON, Kenneth J., Chief Financial Officer, Veterans Affairs Puget Sound Health Care System, Seattle, WA, p. A671

HUDSON, Kent, Chief Financial Officer, Kingman Community Hospital, Kingman, KS, p. A237

HUDSON, Kevin L., D.O. Chief of Staff, Woodland Heights Medical Center, Lufkin, TX, p. A621

HUDSON, Larry C.
  Executive Vice President and Chief Financial Officer, CAMC Teays Valley Hospital, Hurricane, WV, p. A678
  Executive Vice President and Chief Financial Officer, Charleston Area Medical Center, Charleston, WV, p. A676

HUDSON, Lowell K., Chief Financial Officer, Glen Oaks Hospital, Greenville, TX, p. A607

HUDSON, Maggie, Director Operations and Financial Services, Santiam Memorial Hospital, Stayton, OR, p. A518

HUDSON, Pamela, M.D., Chief Executive Officer, Crestwood Medical Center, Huntsville, AL, p. A21

HUDSON, Richard E., FACHE, President and Chief Executive Officer, Wilson Medical Center, Wilson, NC, p. A463

HUDSON, Robbi, Chief Financial Officer, HEALTHSOUTH Rehabilitation Hospital, Fayetteville, AR, p. A43

HUDSPETH, Todd R., President and Chief Executive Officer, Jamestown Regional Medical Center, Jamestown, ND, p. A467

HUDSPITH, Tammie, Director Human Resources, River's Edge Hospital and Clinic, Saint Peter, MN, p. A340

HUEBNER, Thomas W., President, Rutland Regional Medical Center, Rutland, VT, p. A650

HUEBNER, Timothy K., M.D. President Medical Affairs, Riverview Hospital Association, Wisconsin Rapids, WI, p. A700

HUELSKAMP, Donald P., Vice President Finance and Chief Financial Officer, Southeastern Ohio Regional Medical Center, Cambridge, OH, p. A472

HUENERGARDT, Sam, President and Chief Executive Officer, Central Texas Medical Center, San Marcos, TX, p. A633

HUERTA, Guillermo, M.D. Chief Medical Officer, Select Specialty Hospital–Omaha, Omaha, NE, p. A388

HUERTA, Jose, Chief Executive Officer, Solara Hospital McAllen, McAllen, TX, p. A622

HUERTER, Holly
  Vice President Human Resources, Methodist Jennie Edmundson Hospital, Council Bluffs, IA, p. A219
  Vice President Human Resources, Nebraska Methodist Hospital, Omaha, NE, p. A388

HUETTL, Patricia, Vice President Finance and Chief Financial Officer, Holy Family Memorial, Manitowoc, WI, p. A690

HUFF, Don, Interim Chief Information Officer, Mercy Hospital of Portland, Portland, ME, p. A284

HUFF, Jeff, Assistant Administrator Finance, Fayette Medical Center, Fayette, AL, p. A20

HUFF, Michael H., Chief Executive Officer, Hamilton Hospital, Olney, TX, p. A625

HUFFMAN, Cy, M.D. Chief Medical Officer, Erlanger Medical Center, Chattanooga, TN, p. A566

HUFFMAN, James, Chief Executive Officer and Administrator, Baptist Memorial Hospital–Desoto, Southaven, MS, p. A354

HUFFMAN, Joseph, Director Human Resources, HEALTHSOUTH MountainView Regional Rehabilitation Hospital, Morgantown, WV, p. A679

HUFFMAN, Sherry, Administrator Human Resources, Oakwood Heritage Hospital, Taylor, MI, p. A325

HUFFMAN, Steve, Chief Information Officer, Memorial Hospital of South Bend, South Bend, IN, p. A213

HUFFNER, William, M.D
  Vice President Medical Affairs, Arnot Ogden Medical Center, Elmira, NY, p. A425
  Chief Medical Officer and Senior Vice President Medical Affairs, St. Joseph's Hospital, Elmira, NY, p. A425

HUFFORD, Dustin, Chief Information Officer, Memorial Hospital, Fremont, OH, p. A481

HUFFSTUTLER, Brandon, Chief Information Officer, Electra Memorial Hospital, Electra, TX, p. A602

HUFNAGEL, Keith, Director Human Resources, Stillwater Medical Center, Stillwater, OK, p. A507

HUFNAGEL, O. E., Chief Executive Officer, Three Rivers Hospital, Brewster, WA, p. A665

HUGGINS, Lois, Chief Human Resources Officer and Senior Vice President Human Resources, Rehabilitation Institute of Chicago, Chicago, IL, p. A178

HUGGINS, Michael C., Administrator Network System, Eastern Oklahoma Medical Center, Poteau, OK, p. A505

HUGHES, April, Chief Financial Officer, Peachford Behavioral Health System, Atlanta, GA, p. A146

HUGHES, Beth, President and Chief Executive Officer, Presence Saint Joseph Medical Center, Joliet, IL, p. A186

HUGHES, Beverly, R.N. Vice President Nursing, Fayette County Memorial Hospital, Washington Court House, OH, p. A492

HUGHES, Christopher, M.D. Medical Director, Kindred Hospital Detroit, Detroit, MI, p. A312

HUGHES, Constance, Director of Nursing, West Gables Rehabilitation Hospital, Miami, FL, p. A132

HUGHES, David T., FACHE Senior Vice President Operations and Chief Operating Officer, Good Shepherd Health Care System, Hermiston, OR, p. A513

HUGHES, Edith M., R.N., President, Oakwood Southshore Medical Center, Trenton, MI, p. A325

HUGHES, James, Director Human Resources, Lake Cumberland Regional Hospital, Somerset, KY, p. A260

HUGHES, John, Administrator, Ellinwood District Hospital, Ellinwood, KS, p. A233

HUGHES, John, FACHE, President and Chief Executive Officer, Marshalltown Medical & Surgical Center, Marshalltown, IA, p. A225

HUGHES, Katherine, R.N., Interim Chief Operating Officer, Colusa Regional Medical Center, Colusa, CA, p. A57

HUGHES, Letha, Chief Executive Officer, Medical Arts Hospital, Lamesa, TX, p. A617

HUGHES, Lonnie, Comptroller, Essex County Hospital Center, Cedar Grove, NJ, p. A402

HUGHES, Lori, R.N. Chief Nursing Officer, Vice President Operations and Patient Care Services, Cottage Hospital, Woodsville, NH, p. A400

HUGHES, Michael, M.D. Medical Director, Family Health West, Fruita, CO, p. A101

HUGHES, Michelle, Director Health Information Management, Madison River Oaks Medical Center, Canton, MS, p. A345

HUGHES, Robert, Executive Director, Coler–Goldwater Specialty Hospital and Nursing Facility, New York, NY, p. A431

HUGHES, Sandra
  Chief Financial Officer, Clinch Memorial Hospital, Homerville, GA, p. A155
  Executive Director Human Resources, Scripps Memorial Hospital–La Jolla, La Jolla, CA, p. A65

HUGHES, Tena, R.N. Program Director and Director Nursing, Bastrop Rehabilitation Hospital, Bastrop, LA, p. A262

HUGHES, Terry, Manager Management Information Systems, Nantucket Cottage Hospital, Nantucket, MA, p. A302

HUGHEY, James, Chief Financial Officer, Rockdale Medical Center, Conyers, GA, p. A151

HUGHEY, Nick
Administrator, Kula Hospital, Kula, HI, p. A166
Administrator, Lanai Community Hospital, Lanai City, HI, p. A166

HUGHSON, John, Administrator, Burleson St. Joseph Health Center, Caldwell, TX, p. A590

HUGUELEY, Sandra, Assistant Administrator and Chief Nursing Officer, Methodist Extended Care Hospital, Memphis, TN, p. A575

HUHNKE, Ann, Chief Financial Officer, Lander Regional Hospital, Lander, WY, p. A702

HUIE, Robert D.
Executive Vice President and Chief Financial Officer, Willis–Knighton Medical Center, Shreveport, LA, p. A278
Chief Financial Officer, WK Bossier Health Center, Bossier City, LA, p. A264

HUISENGA, Jason, D.O. Chief Medical Staff, Buena Vista Regional Medical Center, Storm Lake, IA, p. A229

HULL, Betty, R.N. Director Patient Services, Coalinga Regional Medical Center, Coalinga, CA, p. A57

HULL, Brad, Chief Financial Officer, Dale Medical Center, Ozark, AL, p. A24

HULL, Dan, Chief Financial Officer, Healdsburg District Hospital, Healdsburg, CA, p. A64

HULL, Debbie, Chief Financial Officer, Fisher County Hospital District, Rotan, TX, p. A629

HULL, Grace, Director Human Resources, Nantucket Cottage Hospital, Nantucket, MA, p. A302

HULL, John, Chief Executive Officer, Seven Hills Behavioral Institute, Henderson, NV, p. A392

HULL, Kathy, President and Chief Executive Officer, Illini Community Hospital, Pittsfield, IL, p. A192

HULL, Ken, Director Human Resources, Inova Fairfax Hospital, Falls Church, VA, p. A653

HULLINGER, Scott, Chief Executive Officer, Two Rivers Behavioral Health System, Kansas City, MO, p. A364

HULSCHER, Ronald, Chief Financial Officer, Summit Pacific Medical Center, McCleary, WA, p. A668

HULSE, Mark, Vice President and Chief Information Officer, H. Lee Moffitt Cancer Center and Research Institute, Tampa, FL, p. A141

HUME, Craig P., Chief Executive Officer, Surgical Specialty Center of Baton Rouge, Baton Rouge, LA, p. A264

HUMES, Ronny, President and Chief Executive Officer, Magnolia Regional Health Center, Corinth, MS, p. A346

HUMMEL, E. Joseph, Chief Strategy Officer, Southern Ocean Medical Center, Manahawkin, NJ, p. A406

HUMMELKE, Arlita, Manager Human Resources, Mercy Hospital Tishomingo, Tishomingo, OK, p. A507

HUMPHREY, Dale, Interim Chief Executive Officer, Regional Hospital of Jackson, Jackson, TN, p. A570

HUMPHREY, James, Director Human and Educational Resources, Penrose–St. Francis Health Services, Colorado Springs, CO, p. A98

HUMPHREY, Randy, Chief Financial Officer, Wesley Medical Center, Hattiesburg, MS, p. A348

HUMPHREY, Richard, Vice President Finance, Texas Health Harris Methodist Hospital Fort Worth, Fort Worth, TX, p. A604

HUMPHREYS, David J., M.D. Medical Director, River Park Hospital, Huntington, WV, p. A678

HUMPHREYS, L. Ray, Chief Executive Officer, Anderson Regional Medical Center, Meridian, MS, p. A351

HUMPHREYS, Ray, Chief Executive Officer, Anderson Regional Medical Center–South Campus, Meridian, MS, p. A351

HUMPHRIES, Stefan, M.D. Medical Director, St. Luke's Rehabilitation Institute, Spokane, WA, p. A672

HUMPHRIES, Vickie, Director Human Resources, Bon Secours Maryview Medical Center, Portsmouth, VA, p. A659

HUNGER, Dennis, Chief Executive Officer, Washington County Hospital and Clinics, Washington, IA, p. A229

HUNKE, Sonja, Director Human Resources, Providence Medical Center, Wayne, NE, p. A390

HUNSBERGER, Glenn, Director Management Information Systems, Palisades Medical Center, North Bergen, NJ, p. A408

HUNSBERGER, Tom, Vice President Human Resources, Riverview Hospital Association, Wisconsin Rapids, WI, p. A700

HUNSICKER, Elizabeth, Chief Operating Officer, Rose Medical Center, Denver, CO, p. A100

HUNT, D. Deann, Director Human Resources, Gibson General Hospital, Princeton, IN, p. A212

HUNT, Deloris, Corporate Vice President Human Resources, Harper University Hospital/Hutzel Women's Hospital, Detroit, MI, p. A312

HUNT, Jacquelyn, Vice President Clinical Support and Information Services, Bellin Memorial Hospital, Green Bay, WI, p. A687

HUNT, Jeff, Chief Executive Officer, Sunbury Community Hospital and Outpatient Center, Sunbury, PA, p. A542

HUNT, Mary Miles, Chief Executive Officer, Ballard Rehabilitation Hospital, San Bernardino, CA, p. A84

HUNT, Reta, Director of Nursing, Scott & White Hospital – Llano, Llano, TX, p. A619

HUNT, Ronald, Chief Executive Officer, Extended Care of Southwest Louisiana, Lake Charles, LA, p. A272

HUNT, Sharon, Chief Financial Officer, W. J. Mangold Memorial Hospital, Lockney, TX, p. A619

HUNT, Tad M., MS, Chief Executive Officer, Litzenberg Memorial County Hospital, Central City, NE, p. A382

HUNT, William Robert, Chief Financial Officer, Reynolds Memorial Hospital, Glen Dale, WV, p. A677

HUNTER, Bart, Manager Information Technology, Effingham Hospital, Springfield, GA, p. A160

HUNTER, Becky, R.N. Chief Nursing Officer, Baptist Memorial Hospital – Memphis, Memphis, TN, p. A574

HUNTER, Byron, Vice President Human Resources, Cape Regional Medical Center, Cape May Court House, NJ, p. A402

HUNTER, David C., Chief Operating Officer, Parkview Noble Hospital, Kendallville, IN, p. A207

HUNTER, Fred, R.N., Chief Executive Officer, Marina Del Rey Hospital, Marina Del Rey, CA, p. A73

HUNTER, Jay, M.D. Chief of Staff, St. Joseph Regional Medical Center, Lewiston, ID, p. A169

HUNTER, Ken, R.N., Chief Executive Officer, Kimball Health Services, Kimball, NE, p. A385

HUNTER, Mary Ann, Director Nursing Services, Baptist Easley Hospital, Easley, SC, p. A551

HUNTER, Rick, Chief Financial Officer, Miami Veterans Affairs Healthcare System, Miami, FL, p. A132

HUNTER, Shelly, Chief Financial Officer, Mercy Hospital Joplin, Joplin, MO, p. A362

HUNTER, Tracy, Chief Human Resources Officer, East Cooper Medical Center, Mount Pleasant, SC, p. A554

HUNTLEY, Adrienne, Director, Human Resources, HEALTHSOUTH Rehabilitation Hospital Memphis–North, Memphis, TN, p. A574

HUNTLEY, Devin, Vice President Operations, Community Medical Center, Missoula, MT, p. A378

HUPF, Angela, Vice President Human Resources and Community Relations, Memorial Health Center, Medford, WI, p. A691

HURD, Jacque, Vice President Human Resources, St. Bernards Medical Center, Jonesboro, AR, p. A45

HURD, Ross, Chief Information Officer, Lake Chelan Community Hospital, Chelan, WA, p. A665

HURLBUT, Marty, M.D. Medical Director, HEALTHSOUTH Rehabilitation Hospital, Fayetteville, AR, p. A43

HURLEY, Jeff, Vice President Human Resources, Flagler Hospital, Saint Augustine, FL, p. A138

HURRAY, Joan, Regional Director Information Services, St. Joseph Mercy Hospital, Ypsilanti, MI, p. A327

HURSH, John, Vice President Human Resources, Lester E. Cox Medical Centers, Springfield, MO, p. A372

HURST, James, Chief Fiscal Service, Oklahoma City Veterans Affairs Medical Center, Oklahoma City, OK, p. A504

HURST, Marc, Chief Executive Officer, Kindred Hospital Indianapolis South, Greenwood, IN, p. A204

HURST, Steve, Information Technology Specialist, Haskell County Community Hospital, Stigler, OK, p. A507

HURT, Christie, M.D. Chief of Staff and Medical Director, Mercy Hospital Aurora, Aurora, MO, p. A356

HURT, Kelly, VP Human Resources, Great Plains Regional Medical Center, North Platte, NE, p. A386

HURTADO, Denise, Chief Financial Officer, Benson Hospital, Benson, AZ, p. A30

HURTADO, Raul, Chief Information Officer, Coleman County Medical Center, Coleman, TX, p. A592

HURWITZ, Steven, Vice President Human Resources, Seattle Children's Hospital, Seattle, WA, p. A671

HURZELER, Rosemary Johnson, President and Chief Executive Officer, The Connecticut Hospice, Branford, CT, p. A108

HUSEBY, Custer, Chief Executive Officer, Kindred Hospital Fargo, Fargo, ND, p. A466

HUSHER, Phil, Chief Financial Officer, Winner Regional Healthcare Center, Winner, SD, p. A564

HUSKEY, Jeff, Chief Executive Officer and Administrator, Clay County Memorial Hospital, Henrietta, TX, p. A608

HUSS, Cathy, Chief Financial Officer, LifeCare Medical Center, Roseau, MN, p. A339

HUSS, Eileen, Chief Nursing Officer, Methodist Stone Oak Hospital, San Antonio, TX, p. A631

HUSSAIN, Iftikhar
Chief Financial Officer, Mills–Peninsula Health Services, Burlingame, CA, p. A55
Chief Financial Officer, Sutter Maternity and Surgery Center of Santa Cruz, Santa Cruz, CA, p. A90

HUSSEY, Stephen, M.D. Chief of Staff, Lake District Hospital, Lakeview, OR, p. A514

HUSTEDT, Dale, Associate Administrator Administrative Services, Rice Memorial Hospital, Willmar, MN, p. A343

HUSTON, Gary, D.O. Chief Medical Officer, University Hospitals Conneaut Medical Center, Conneaut, OH, p. A479

HUTCHENRIDER, E. Kenneth, President, Methodist Richardson Medical Center, Richardson, TX, p. A628

HUTCHENS, Steve, Vice President General Services, Grady Memorial Hospital, Chickasha, OK, p. A496

HUTCHESON, Jane, Administrator and Director Clinical Operations, Group Health Cooperative Central Hospital, Seattle, WA, p. A670

HUTCHESON, Larry, Chief Financial Officer and Director Administrative Services, Humboldt General Hospital, Winnemucca, NV, p. A396

HUTCHESON, Lou Ellen, M.D. Chief of Staff, Bacon County Hospital and Health System, Alma, GA, p. A145

HUTCHINS, Michael T., Administrator, Jay Hospital, Jay, FL, p. A127

HUTCHINS, Roger D., Chief Financial Officer, Doctors Hospital at White Rock Lake, Dallas, TX, p. A595

HUTCHINS, Sheri, Director Health Information Management, Muenster Memorial Hospital, Muenster, TX, p. A624

HUTCHINSON, Donna, Chief Financial Officer, Beaver Dam Community Hospitals, Beaver Dam, WI, p. A684

HUTCHINSON, James, CPA Chief Financial Officer, Affinity Medical Center, Massillon, OH, p. A485

HUTCHINSON, Red, Chief Information Officer, Franklin Regional Hospital, Franklin, NH, p. A398

HUTCHISON, Barbra, Director Medical Records, Richland Parish Hospital, Delhi, LA, p. A266

HUTCHISON, Dee, Chief Executive Officer, U. S. Public Health Service Indian Hospital, Parker, AZ, p. A33

HUTCHISON, Florence N., M.D. Chief of Staff, Ralph H. Johnson Veterans Affairs Medical Center, Charleston, SC, p. A549

HUTCHISON, Harry, Vice President Fiscal Services, St. Bernards Medical Center, Jonesboro, AR, p. A45

HUTCHISON, Tammy, R.N. Director of Nursing, Gove County Medical Center, Quinter, KS, p. A243

HUTH, Richard, Chief Executive Officer, Shands Live Oak Regional Medical Center, Live Oak, FL, p. A129

HUTH, Thomas, M.D. Vice President Medical Affairs, Reid Hospital and Health Care Services, Richmond, IN, p. A212

HUTSELL, Dick, Vice President Information Technology Services, Saint Louise Regional Hospital, Gilroy, CA, p. A62

HUTSELL, Richard, Vice President and Chief Information Officer, O'Connor Hospital, San Jose, CA, p. A88

HUTSON, Mark S., Chief Information Officer, Greenwood Leflore Hospital, Greenwood, MS, p. A347

HUTSON, Marty, Chief Financial Officer, St. Mary's Health Care System, Athens, GA, p. A145

HUTSON, Wayne
Chief Financial Officer, Union Hospital, Terre Haute, IN, p. A214
Chief Financial Officer, Union Hospital Clinton, Clinton, IN, p. A200

HUTT, Si William, Chief Executive Officer, Park City Medical Center, Park City, UT, p. A645

HUVAL, Shadelle, Director Finance, St. Martin Hospital, Breaux Bridge, LA, p. A264

HUYCKE, Mark, M.D. Chief of Staff, Oklahoma City Veterans Affairs Medical Center, Oklahoma City, OK, p. A504

HYATT, Charlotte, MSN Vice President Clinical Services, Gaylord Hospital, Wallingford, CT, p. A112

HYATT, Cori, Director Human Resources, Midland Memorial Hospital, Midland, TX, p. A623

HYATT, David W., Chief Executive Officer, Jay County Hospital, Portland, IN, p. A212

HYATT, Robert, M.D. Senior Vice President Medical Affairs, Lake Regional Health System, Osage Beach, MO, p. A367

HYATT, Ronnie, Senior Vice President Finance and Chief Financial Officer, Bon Secours St. Francis Health System, Greenville, SC, p. A552

HYCHALK, Veronica T., MSN Vice President Professional Services, Northeastern Vermont Regional Hospital, Saint Johnsbury, VT, p. A650

HYDE, Cynthia, Interim Chief Information Officer, St. Mary's Medical Center of Evansville, Evansville, IN, p. A202

HYDE, Jane E., President, Gettysburg Hospital, Gettysburg, PA, p. A526

HYDE, Keith, Chief Executive Officer, Providence Milwaukie Hospital, Milwaukie, OR, p. A515

HYDE, Robert, Human Resources Business Partner, Kaiser Permanente Santa Clara Medical Center, Santa Clara, CA, p. A89

HYDE, Stephanie, Chief Executive Officer, Tyler Continuecare Hospital at Mother Frances, Tyler, TX, p. A639

HYDE, Stephen O., FACHE, Chief Executive Officer, Southwestern Medical Center, Lawton, OK, p. A500

HYDE, Van D., MS, Chief Executive Officer, Sturgis Regional Hospital, Sturgis, SD, p. A563

HYDER, Shiraz, M.D. Director Medical Affairs, St. Alexius Medical Center, Bismarck, ND, p. A465

HYDOR, LouAnn, Director Information Integrity Management, Cardinal Hill Rehabilitation Hospital, Lexington, KY, p. A254

HYLAND, Donna W., President and Chief Executive Officer, Children's Healthcare of Atlanta, Atlanta, GA, p. A146

HYLTON, Alecia, M.D. Chief of Staff, Memorial Health Center, Medford, WI, p. A691

HYLTON, Heather, Chief Financial Officer, Plateau Medical Center, Oak Hill, WV, p. A679

HYMAN, Craig, Vice President Human Resources, Conway Medical Center, Conway, SC, p. A551

HYMANS, Daniel J., President, Memorial Medical Center – Ashland, Ashland, WI, p. A683

HYMBAUGH, Mitzi, Chief Personnel, Ringgold County Hospital, Mount Ayr, IA, p. A225

HYTRY, Steven, Chief Operating Officer, Aurora Las Encinas Hospital, Pasadena, CA, p. A79

**I**

IANNONI, Joseph, Vice President Finance, Jordan Hospital, Plymouth, MA, p. A304

IBRAHIM, Tajudeen, Interim Business Administrator, Elgin Mental Health Center, Elgin, IL, p. A181

ICENHOWER, Jeremy, Administrator and Chief Executive Officer, De Queen Medical Center, De Queen, AR, p. A42

ICKOWSKI, Michael F., Vice President Finance and Chief Financial Officer, Mount St. Mary's Hospital and Health Center, Lewiston, NY, p. A428

IDBEIS, Badr, M.D., Chief Executive Officer, Kansas Medical Center, Andover, KS, p. A231

IDSTEIN, Mary, Chief Financial Officer, Porter-Starke Services, Valparaiso, IN, p. A214

IERARDI, Joseph P., Chief Executive Officer, Wayne Memorial Hospital, Jesup, GA, p. A155

IERO, Tony, Director Management Information Systems, North Philadelphia Health System, Philadelphia, PA, p. A536

IFTINIUK, Alan, Chief Executive Officer, French Hospital Medical Center, San Luis Obispo, CA, p. A88

IGLESIAS, Julio, M.D. Chief of Staff, Winn Parish Medical Center, Winnfield, LA, p. A280

IGNACIO, Manny, Controller, Riverside General Hospital, Houston, TX, p. A611

IGNACZAK, Thomas, M.D. Interim Vice President Medical Affairs, Bronson Battle Creek, Battle Creek, MI, p. A309

IGNAS, Ann, R.N. Chief Nurse Executive, Fairfield Memorial Hospital, Fairfield, IL, p. A182

IGNELZI, James, Interim Chief Executive Officer, Heartland Behavioral Healthcare, Massillon, OH, p. A485

IKNER, Don, Chief Executive Officer, Great Plains Regional Medical Center, Elk City, OK, p. A498

ILTIS, Michael T., Vice President Professional Services, Emanuel Medical Center, Turlock, CA, p. A93

IMADA, Ross, Director Information Systems, Shriners Hospitals for Children–Honolulu, Honolulu, HI, p. A165

IMBIMBO, Richard, Chief Financial Officer, University of Maryland St. Joseph Medical Center, Towson, MD, p. A294

IMLAY, Ralph, M.D. Chief of Staff, Harper Hospital District Five, Harper, KS, p. A235

IMLER, James R., Director Human Resources, Kimball Health Services, Kimball, NE, p. A385

IMSEIS, Mikhail, M.D. Chief of Staff, Ness County Hospital, Ness City, KS, p. A240

INDACOCHEA, Fernando, M.D. Chief of Staff, Grant Memorial Hospital, Petersburg, WV, p. A679

INGALLS, Dawn, Regional Manager Human Resources, Avera Dells Area Hospital, Dell Rapids, SD, p. A559

INGE, Ray, Vice President Human Resources, Pomona Valley Hospital Medical Center, Pomona, CA, p. A80

INGHAM, Raymond V., Ph.D., President and Chief Executive Officer, Witham Memorial Hospital, Lebanon, IN, p. A209

INGLE, Richard M., M.D. Chief of Staff, Humboldt General Hospital, Winnemucca, NV, p. A396

INGLES, Kimberly, Director Human Resources, Winn Parish Medical Center, Winnfield, LA, p. A280

INGRAM, David, Director Management Information Systems, Medina Hospital, Medina, OH, p. A486

INGRAM, Herman, Director, Riverside Medical Center, Franklinton, LA, p. A267

INGRAM, J. Kevin, M.D. Chief of Staff, Riverland Medical Center, Ferriday, LA, p. A267

INGRAM, Karen, Director Human Resources, Baptist Memorial Hospital for Women, Memphis, TN, p. A574

INGRAM, Kim, Chief Executive Officer, Mountain Lakes Medical Center, Clayton, GA, p. A150

INGRAM, Nathan Daniel, Chief Executive Officer and Owner, Lone Star Behavioral Health, Cypress, TX, p. A594

INGRAM, Peter
Vice President and Chief Information Officer, Mount Sinai Hospital, Chicago, IL, p. A177
Vice President and Chief Information Officer, Schwab Rehabilitation Hospital, Chicago, IL, p. A179

INGRAM, Todd, M.D. Chief of Staff, Baraga County Memorial Hospital, L'Anse, MI, p. A318

INGRODI, Travis, Flight Commander Resource Management, U. S. Air Force Hospital, Hampton, VA, p. A655

INGWERSON, Connie, Chief Financial Officer, Nemaha Valley Community Hospital, Seneca, KS, p. A244

INHOFE, Kyle, Chief Human Resources Officer, Oklahoma City Veterans Affairs Medical Center, Oklahoma City, OK, p. A504

INHULSEN, Christopher, M.D. Chief of Staff, Flint River Community Hospital, Montezuma, GA, p. A157

INKLEY, Kevin, Interim Director, Robert J. Dole Veterans Affairs Medical Center, Wichita, KS, p. A246

INMAN, Debbie
Chief Nursing Officer, Physicians Surgical Hospital – Panhandle Campus, Amarillo, TX, p. A582
Chief Nursing Officer, Physicians Surgical Hospital – Quail Creek, Amarillo, TX, p. A582

INMAN, Joanne, Vice President Operations, Sentara Virginia Beach General Hospital, Virginia Beach, VA, p. A662

INMAN, Julie, Regional Executive Officer, Southeast Missouri Mental Health Center, Farmington, MO, p. A360

INNOCENTI Sr., John, President and Chief Executive Officer, UPMC Presbyterian Shadyside, Pittsburgh, PA, p. A538

INO, Alan, Chief Financial Officer, Good Samaritan Hospital, Los Angeles, CA, p. A69

INOUYE, Valerie, Chief Financial Officer, San Francisco General Hospital Medical Center, San Francisco, CA, p. A87

INSCHO, Kimberly, Vice President Community Relations and Human Resources, Margaret Mary Health, Batesville, IN, p. A198

INZANA, Lugene A., Vice President and Chief Financial and Support Services Officer, Lawrence + Memorial Hospital, New London, CT, p. A111

IPPOLITO, Mark, Administrator, Federal Correctional Institute Hospital, Littleton, CO, p. A103

IPSAN, Charlotte, President, Norton Suburban Hospital, Louisville, KY, p. A256

IQBAL, Nayyar, M.D. Director Medical Staff, Western State Hospital, Hopkinsville, KY, p. A252

IRANI, Glenn, M.D. Chief Medical Officer, Providence Tarzana Medical Center, CA, p. A71

IRBY, John, Chief Financial Officer, Scenic Mountain Medical Center, Big Spring, TX, p. A588

IRISH, Kevin, Chief Information Officer, Lakes Region General Hospital, Laconia, NH, p. A398

IRISH–CLARDY, Katherine, M.D. Chief Medical Officer, Sparks Regional Medical Center, Fort Smith, AR, p. A44

IRIZARRI, David, Director Management Information Systems, Plantation General Hospital, Plantation, FL, p. A137

IRIZARRY, Lourdes, M.D. Chief of Staff, Albany Stratton Veterans Affairs Medical Center, Albany, NY, p. A420

IRUEGAS, Javier, FACHE, Chief Executive Officer, Mission Regional Medical Center, Mission, TX, p. A623

IRVIN, Coy, M.D. Vice President and Chief Medical Officer, Baptist Hospital, Pensacola, FL, p. A136

IRVIN, Debbie, Director Health Information Management, BHC Alhambra Hospital, Rosemead, CA, p. A83

IRVIN, Donna, Director Human Resources, Victory Medical Center Mid–Cities, Hurst, TX, p. A614

IRVIN, Miriam, CNO, HEALTHSOUTH Rehabilitation Hospital, Fayetteville, AR, p. A43

IRVIN, Sandy, Chief Nursing Officer, HEALTHSOUTH Rehabilitation Hospital of Beaumont, Beaumont, TX, p. A587

IRVIN, Thomas M., Administrator Human Resources, Ranken Jordan – A Pediatric Specialty Hospital, Maryland Heights, MO, p. A365

IRVINE, Laura, President, Methodist Dallas Medical Center, Dallas, TX, p. A596

IRVING, Edith E., R.N. Chief Nursing Officer, West Valley Medical Center, Caldwell, ID, p. A168

IRVING, Mark, Manager Management Information Systems, OSF St. Francis Hospital, Escanaba, MI, p. A313

IRWIN, Christopher, Director, Administration, Naval Medical Center San Diego, San Diego, CA, p. A85

IRWIN, Gene, Chief Financial Officer, Jefferson County Health Center, Fairfield, IA, p. A221

IRWIN, James, M.D. Chief Medical Officer, Samaritan Healthcare, Moses Lake, WA, p. A668

IRWIN, Robert G., Vice President Information Systems, Robert Wood Johnson University Hospital, New Brunswick, NJ, p. A407

IRWIN, Ruth, Associate Director Clinical Operations, Stewart & Lynda Resnick Neuropsychiatric Hospital at UCLA, Los Angeles, CA, p. A72

ISAACKS, Scott R., Associate Director, Ralph H. Johnson Veterans Affairs Medical Center, Charleston, SC, p. A549

ISAACS, Cynthia, Chief Executive Officer, Cornerstone Hospital of Huntington, Huntington, WV, p. A677

ISAACS, Diane, Director of Nursing, Ouachita County Medical Center, Camden, AR, p. A42

ISAACS, Linda, Vice President Human Resources, St. Luke's Hospital, San Francisco, CA, p. A87

ISAACS, Michael, Director Human Resources, Streamwood Behavioral Health Center, Streamwood, IL, p. A195

ISAACS, Stephen, M.D. Chief of Staff, Hugh Chatham Memorial Hospital, Elkin, NC, p. A452

ISAACSON, Alan, Vice President and Chief Operating Officer, Seton Shoal Creek Hospital, Austin, TX, p. A585

ISBELL, Gina, Administrator, Oceans Behavioral Hospital of Kentwood, Kentwood, LA, p. A270

ISEKE, Richard, M.D. Vice President Medical Affairs, Winchester Hospital, Winchester, MA, p. A306

ISEMANN, William R., President and Chief Executive Officer, KidsPeace Children's Hospital, Orefield, PA, p. A533

ISHAM, George J., M.D. Chief Health Officer and Medical Director Health Plan, Regions Hospital, Saint Paul, MN, p. A340

ISHAQUE, Saleem, Executive Medical Director, Alvarado Parkway Institute Behavioral Health System, La Mesa, CA, p. A65

ISHKANIAN, Gary, M.D. Vice President Medical Affairs, Mount Vernon Hospital, Mount Vernon, NY, p. A430

ISLER, Dorie, Director Human Resources, New Mexico Rehabilitation Center, Roswell, NM, p. A417

ISLEY, L. Lee, FACHE, Chief Executive Officer, Granville Health System, Oxford, NC, p. A458

ISMAIL, Asad, M.D. Medical Director, Wellstone Regional Hospital, Jeffersonville, IN, p. A207

ISOM, Candace, Chief Operating Officer, Indiana University Health Paoli Hospital, Paoli, IN, p. A212

ISOM, Julie, Director Human Resources, Lakeview Hospital, Bountiful, UT, p. A643

ISOM, Ruby, Associate Vice President Human Resources, Loretto Hospital, Chicago, IL, p. A177

ISON, Tamara
Chief Financial Officer, Spalding Regional Medical Center, Griffin, GA, p. A154
Chief Financial Officer, Sylvan Grove Hospital, Jackson, GA, p. A155

ISON, William G., Human Resources Manager, Select Specialty Hospital–Tri Cities, Bristol, TN, p. A565

ISOZAKI, Dan, Director Information Management, Los Robles Hospital and Medical Center, Thousand Oaks, CA, p. A92

ISRAEL, Alison, Controller, Martin County Hospital District, Stanton, TX, p. A635

ISRAEL, Michael D., President and Chief Executive Officer, Westchester Medical Center, Valhalla, NY, p. A445

ISSAI, Alice H.
Chief Operating Officer, Kaiser Permanente Los Angeles Medical Center, Los Angeles, CA, p. A69
Business Strategy and Finance Leader, Kaiser Permanente West Los Angeles Medical Center, Los Angeles, CA, p. A69
Chief Operating Officer, Los Angeles Medical Center, Los Angeles, CA, p. A69
Chief Operating Officer, University of California, Irvine Healthcare, Orange, CA, p. A78

ITO, Derek, Director Human Resources, Shriners Hospitals for Children–Honolulu, Honolulu, HI, p. A165

IVCIC, Rebecca, Chief Financial Officer, Heatherhill Care Communities, Chardon, OH, p. A473

IVERSON, Jan, R.N. Chief Nursing Officer, Skagit Valley Hospital, Mount Vernon, WA, p. A668

IVES, Matthew, Interim Chief Executive Officer and Chief Financial Officer, Keokuk County Health Center, Sigourney, IA, p. A228

IVESON, Jr., William D., Clinical Operations Officer and Director Human Resources, Barnes–Kasson County Hospital, Susquehanna, PA, p. A542

IVESTER, Roger, Manager Information Systems, Habersham Medical Center, Demorest, GA, p. A152

IVESTER, Steve, Director Human Resources, Springbrook Behavioral Health System, Travelers Rest, SC, p. A556

IVEY, Bobbie, Director Human Resources, Chicot Memorial Medical Center, Lake Village, AR, p. A46

IVEY, Mark J., M.D. Medical Director, Great Lakes Specialty Hospital–Grand Rapids Campus, Grand Rapids, MI, p. A315

IVIE, Brian K., President, Mercy San Juan Medical Center, Carmichael, CA, p. A56

IVIE, Jack, President, Glendale Memorial Hospital and Health Center, Glendale, CA, p. A62

IVORY, Brenda, Chief Executive Officer, Harlingen Medical Center, Harlingen, TX, p. A607

IVY, Jay, R.N., Chief Executive Officer, NeuroMedical Center Rehabilitation Hospital, Baton Rouge, LA, p. A263

IVY, Michael, M.D. Senior Vice President for Medical Affairs and Chief Medical Officer, Bridgeport Hospital, Bridgeport, CT, p. A108

IWEIMRIN, Salvatore, R.N., Chief Executive Officer, Advanced Specialty Hospital of Toledo, Toledo, OH, p. A490

IYER, Raju, Chief Financial Officer, Regional Medical Center of San Jose, San Jose, CA, p. A88

IZAKOVIC, Martin, M.D. Vice President Medical Staff Affairs and Chief Medical Officer, Mercy Iowa City, Iowa City, IA, p. A223

IZQUIERDO, Elizabeth L., CPA, Chief Executive Officer, HEALTHSOUTH Rehabilitation Hospital of Miami, Miami, FL, p. A131

IZZI, Denine, Site Manager Information Systems, Robert Wood Johnson University Hospital Rahway, Rahway, NJ, p. A409

IZZO, Carolyn, Interim President and Chief Executive Officer, Ellwood City Hospital, Ellwood City, PA, p. A525

# J

JABBARPOUR, Yad, M.D. Chief of Staff, Catawba Hospital, Catawba, VA, p. A652

JABLONOVER, Michael, M.D., President and Chief Executive Officer, Kernan Orthopaedics and Rehabilitation, Baltimore, MD, p. A287

JABLONOWSKI, Gerard J., President and Chief Executive Officer, St. Francis Medical Center, Trenton, NJ, p. A411

JABLONSKI, Kevin, Chief Nursing Officer, Mother Frances Hospital – Winnsboro, Winnsboro, TX, p. A642

JABLONSKI, Mark, Senior Vice President Human Resources, St. Jude Medical Center, Fullerton, CA, p. A62

JABOUR, John, Chief Information Officer, Ephrata Community Hospital, Ephrata, PA, p. A525

JACK, Claudia L., Director Associate Relations, Bayfront Health Brooksville, Brooksville, FL, p. A119

JACKES, Frederick D., Assistant Administrator and Director Human Resources, Valley Forge Medical Center and Hospital, Norristown, PA, p. A533

JACKLIN, Bonnie, R.N. Chief Nursing Officer, McKay–Dee Hospital Center, Ogden, UT, p. A645

JACKS, Anthony, Director Human Resources, Howard University Hospital, Washington, DC, p. A116

JACKSON, Bryan G., Vice President and Chief Financial Officer, Jefferson Regional Medical Center, Pine Bluff, AR, p. A49

JACKSON, Carolyn, Chief Executive Officer, St. Christopher's Hospital for Children, Philadelphia, PA, p. A536

JACKSON, Cindy, Director Human Resources, Phelps Memorial Health Center, Holdrege, NE, p. A384

JACKSON, Courtney, Director Human Resources, Logan Memorial Hospital, Russellville, KY, p. A260

JACKSON, Daniel, Chief Administrative Officer, Atlanta Medical Center – South Campus, Atlanta, GA, p. A146

JACKSON, Darryl, D.O. Chief of Staff, Prague Community Hospital, Prague, OK, p. A505

JACKSON, David, Chief Financial Officer, Baptist Medical Center Leake, Carthage, MS, p. A345

JACKSON, Fred L., FACHE, Chief Executive Officer, King's Daughters Medical Center, Ashland, KY, p. A248

JACKSON, J. D., Chief Information Officer, Highlands Regional Medical Center, Prestonsburg, KY, p. A259

JACKSON, James, M.D. Chief of Staff, Cornerstone Hospital of Bossier City, Bossier City, LA, p. A264

JACKSON, James, Chief Operating Officer, Saint Francis Memorial Hospital, San Francisco, CA, p. A87

JACKSON, James, M.D. Vice President Medical Affairs, St. Joseph's Hospital, Savannah, GA, p. A160

JACKSON Jr., James H., Executive Director, Greenwood Leflore Hospital, Greenwood, MS, p. A347

JACKSON, Janice, Director Human Resources, Shands Lake Shore Regional Medical Center, Lake City, FL, p. A128

JACKSON, Jeffrey, M.D. Medical Director, Methodist Sugar Land Hospital, Sugar Land, TX, p. A635

JACKSON, Joanne, Administrator Human Resources, Community Relations and Quality Improvement, Amery Regional Medical Center, Amery, WI, p. A683

JACKSON, John J., President, FirstHealth Richmond Memorial Hospital, Rockingham, NC, p. A459

JACKSON, Judy, Director Health Information Management and Privacy Officer, Shodair Children's Hospital, Helena, MT, p. A377

JACKSON, Kevin, On Site Administrator, Highsmith–Rainey Specialty Hospital, Fayetteville, NC, p. A452

JACKSON, Les, Manager Information Systems, Lower Keys Medical Center, Key West, FL, p. A127

JACKSON, Linda, Director Management Information Systems, Arkansas State Hospital, Little Rock, AR, p. A46

JACKSON, Linda, M.D. Chief of Staff, Lincoln County Health System, Fayetteville, TN, p. A569

JACKSON, Lori L., Director Human Resources, Verde Valley Medical Center, Cottonwood, AZ, p. A30

JACKSON, Lynn, Administrator, Northside Hospital–Forsyth, Cumming, GA, p. A151

JACKSON, Max, M.D. Chief Medical Officer, Renown South Meadows Medical Center, Reno, NV, p. A395

JACKSON, Meg, Director Biomedical and Management Information Systems, Beauregard Memorial Hospital, De Ridder, LA, p. A266

JACKSON, Melinda, Director Human Resources, Bates County Memorial Hospital, Butler, MO, p. A357

JACKSON, Michelle, Chief Financial Officer, BHC Alhambra Hospital, Rosemead, CA, p. A83

JACKSON, Mike, President and Chief Executive Officer, Ephraim McDowell Fort Logan Hospital, Stanford, KY, p. A260

JACKSON, Reese, President and Chief Executive Officer, Forbes Regional Hospital, Monroeville, PA, p. A532

JACKSON, Robert, Chief Financial Officer, Alliance Health Center, Meridian, MS, p. A350

JACKSON Jr., Robert, Chief Executive Officer, Grove City Medical Center, Grove City, PA, p. A526

JACKSON, Samatha, M.D. Chief of Staff, Elkview General Hospital, Hobart, OK, p. A499

JACKSON, Stephen, M.D. Chief of Staff, Skyridge Medical Center, Cleveland, TN, p. A567

JACKSON, Susan E., R.N. Senior Vice President, Health Central, Ocoee, FL, p. A134

JACKSON, Suzanne B., FACHE, Chief Executive Officer, John Randolph Medical Center, Hopewell, VA, p. A655

JACKSON, Tamara L., FACHE, Chief Executive Officer, Doctors Hospital of Columbus, Columbus, GA, p. A150

JACKSON, Teresa, Chief Executive Officer, Choctaw Nation Health Care Center, Talihina, OK, p. A507

JACKSON, Thomas W., Chief Executive Officer, College Station Medical Center, College Station, TX, p. A592

JACKSON, Tina
Director Human Resources, Barrow Regional Medical Center, Winder, GA, p. A163
Manager Human Resources, Williamson Memorial Hospital, Williamson, WV, p. A682

JACKSON, Tom, Chief Financial Officer, Eastside Medical Center, Snellville, GA, p. A160

JACKSON, Tommy, Chief Executive Officer, Landmark Hospital of Athens, Athens, GA, p. A145

JACKSON, Tony, Director Information Technology, Sutter Amador Hospital, Jackson, CA, p. A64

JACKSON, Vance, FACHE, Administrator and Chief Executive Officer, Hancock County Health System, Britt, IA, p. A217

JACKSON, Vaughn, M.D. Chief of Staff, Conejos County Hospital, La Jara, CO, p. A102

JACKSON, W. Anthony, Chief Executive Officer, HEALTHSOUTH Rehabilitation Hospital of Columbia, Columbia, SC, p. A550

JACO, Carol, R.N. Chief Operating Officer and Chief Nursing Officer, St. Francis Hospital, Litchfield, IL, p. A187

JACO, Mary, R.N. Director Patient Care Services and Chief Operating Officer, Shriners Hospitals for Children–Galveston Burns Hospital, Galveston, TX, p. A605

JACOB, Abraham, M.D. President Medical Staff, South Shore Hospital, Chicago, IL, p. A179

JACOB, Cheryl, Chief Operating Officer, Saddleback Memorial Medical Center, Laguna Hills, CA, p. A65

JACOBI, Robert, Chief Financial Officer, Bob Wilson Memorial Grant County Hospital, Ulysses, KS, p. A245

JACOBS, Andrea, Chief Operating Officer, South Pointe Hospital, Warrensville Heights, OH, p. A492

JACOBS, Andrew, M.D. Chief Medical Officer, Virginia Mason Medical Center, Seattle, WA, p. A671

JACOBS, Barbara Stewart, MSN Chief Nurse Officer, Suburban Hospital, Bethesda, MD, p. A290

JACOBS, Donna K., FACHE, Director, Northern Arizona Veterans Affairs Health Care System, Prescott, AZ, p. A36

JACOBS, Ian, Chief, Human Resource Management Service, Louis A. Johnson Veterans Affairs Medical Center, Clarksburg, WV, p. A676

JACOBS, Jolene, Director Human Resources, Sparrow Ionia Hospital, Ionia, MI, p. A316

JACOBS, Julie, Director Human Resources, Oklahoma Forensic Center, Vinita, OK, p. A509

JACOBS, Mark, Director Information Services, Pomerene Hospital, Millersburg, OH, p. A486

JACOBS, Michael
Vice President Human Resources, Gladys Spellman Specialty Hospital and Nursing Center, Cheverly, MD, p. A290
Vice President Human Resources, Laurel Regional Hospital, Laurel, MD, p. A293
Vice President Human Resources, Prince George's Hospital Center, Cheverly, MD, p. A290

JACOBS, Mike, Director Information Technology, Logan County Hospital, Oakley, KS, p. A240

JACOBS, Richard, Vice President Finance and Chief Financial Officer, Canton–Potsdam Hospital, Potsdam, NY, p. A440

JACOBS, Robert
Regional Director Information Management, CHRISTUS Hospital–St. Elizabeth, Beaumont, TX, p. A587
Regional Information Management Executive, CHRISTUS Jasper Memorial Hospital, Jasper, TX, p. A615

JACOBS, Steven R., Chief Financial Officer, Central Washington Hospital, Wenatchee, WA, p. A674

JACOBSEN, Barry, Chief Executive Officer, Myrtue Medical Center, Harlan, IA, p. A222

JACOBSEN, John, M.D. Chief of Staff, Fillmore County Hospital, Geneva, NE, p. A383

JACOBSEN, William D., Vice President, Regional Hospital, Carilion Franklin Memorial Hospital, Rocky Mount, VA, p. A661

JACOBSON, Andrea, Human Resource Officer, Cavalier County Memorial Hospital, Langdon, ND, p. A468

JACOBSON, Becky, Vice President Finance, St. Vincent Heart Center of Indiana, Indianapolis, IN, p. A206

JACOBSON, Carlton, Vice President Finance, Frank R. Howard Memorial Hospital, Willits, CA, p. A96

JACOBSON, Catherine A., President and Chief Executive Officer, Froedtert Memorial Lutheran Hospital, Milwaukee, WI, p. A692

JACOBSON, Gary, M.D. Chief Medical Officer, Pembroke Hospital, Pembroke, MA, p. A303

JACOBSON, Janet, Director Human Resources, Lakewood Health System, Staples, MN, p. A341

JACOBSON, Jenny, Manager Human Resources, Sanford Hillsboro Medical Center, Hillsboro, ND, p. A467

JACOBSON, John, Chief Financial Officer, Gibson Area Hospital and Health Services, Gibson City, IL, p. A183

JACOBSON, John L., Chief Executive Officer, Atchison Hospital, Atchison, KS, p. A231

JACOBSON, Mary Jo, Chief Executive Officer, San Joaquin Valley Rehabilitation Hospital, Fresno, CA, p. A62

JACOBSON, Peter, President, Essentia Health St. Mary's Hospital – Detroit Lakes, Detroit Lakes, MN, p. A331

JACOBSON, Randolph
Chief Financial Officer, Carrier Clinic, Belle Mead, NJ, p. A401
Chief Financial Officer, East Mountain Hospital, Belle Mead, NJ, p. A401

JACOBSON, Rodney D., Administrator, Bear Lake Memorial Hospital, Montpelier, ID, p. A170

JACOBSON, Shirley
Chief Financial Officer, Community Behavioral Health Hospital – Alexandria, Alexandria, MN, p. A328
Chief Financial Officer, Community Behavioral Health Hospital – St. Peter, Saint Peter, MN, p. A340

JACOBSON, Terry, Administrator and Chief Executive Officer, Essentia Health St. Mary's Hospital of Superior, Superior, WI, p. A697

JACOBY, Jamie R., Chief Financial Officer, Memorial Hospital of Texas County, Guymon, OK, p. A499

JACQUES, Teresa, Interim Chief Financial Officer, Adventist Medical Center–Reedley, Reedley, CA, p. A82

JADCZAK, Audrey, R.N
Vice President/Chief Nursing Officer, Lourdes Medical Center of Burlington County, Willingboro, NJ, p. A412
Chief Nursing Officer, Our Lady of Lourdes Medical Center, Camden, NJ, p. A402

JAEGER, Lee, FACHE, Chief Executive Officer, St. Vincent Salem Hospital, Salem, IN, p. A213

JAFFE, Darcy, R.N. Interim Chief Nursing Officer, UW Medicine/Harborview Medical Center, Seattle, WA, p. A671

JAFFE, David E., Chief Executive, Swedish/Edmonds, Edmonds, WA, p. A666

JAFFE, Gabriel, M.D. Vice President Medical Affairs, Doctors Community Hospital, Lanham, MD, p. A292

JAGER, Linda, Director Finance, Avera Weskota Memorial Hospital, Wessington Springs, SD, p. A564

JAGGI, Michael, D.O. Vice President and Chief Medical Officer, Hurley Medical Center, Flint, MI, p. A313

JAGODITZ, Chris, Chief Financial Officer, Cumberland Hall Hospital, Hopkinsville, KY, p. A252

JAHAN, Mohammad S., M.D. Clinical Director, Middle Tennessee Mental Health Institute, Nashville, TN, p. A576

JAHN, Andrew, Vice President Finance, Sonora Regional Medical Center, Sonora, CA, p. A91

JAHN, Barbara A., Chief Operating Officer, Exempla Saint Joseph Hospital, Denver, CO, p. A99

JAHN, David B., President and Chief Executive Officer, War Memorial Hospital, Sault Sainte Marie, MI, p. A324

JAHN, Gregory L., R.N., Chief Executive Officer, St. Luke's Behavioral Health Center, Phoenix, AZ, p. A35

JAHN, Kim C., Director Support Services, Manning Regional Healthcare Center, Manning, IA, p. A224

JAHNIG, Jay A., Chief Executive Officer, Faulkton Area Medical Center, Faulkton, SD, p. A559

JAHRE, Jeffrey, M.D. Vice President Medical and Academic Affairs, St. Luke's University Hospital – Bethlehem Campus, Bethlehem, PA, p. A520

JAIN, Ashok, M.D. Chief of Staff, Oakwood Annapolis Hospital, Wayne, MI, p. A326

JAIN, Rajiv, M.D. Chief of Staff, Veterans Affairs Pittsburgh Healthcare System, Pittsburgh, PA, p. A538

JAIN, Sunita, M.D. Chief Medical Officer, Baptist Rehabilitation–Germantown, Germantown, TN, p. A569

JAKACKI, Timothy
President, ProMedica Bixby Hospital, Adrian, MI, p. A308
President, ProMedica Herrick Hospital, Tecumseh, MI, p. A325

JAKOUBECK, Denise, Director Human Resources, Hancock County Health System, Britt, IA, p. A217

JAMAL, S., M.D. Medical Director, Faith Community Hospital, Jacksboro, TX, p. A615

JAMES, Bruce, Chief Executive Officer, Union Hospital, Dover, OH, p. A480

JAMES, Carmelo, Chief Nursing Officer, East Los Angeles Doctors Hospital, Los Angeles, CA, p. A68

JAMES, Craig B., FACHE, Chief Executive Officer, Highlands–Cashiers Hospital, Highlands, NC, p. A455

JAMES, Dawn, Director of Nursing, Wyoming County Community Hospital, Warsaw, NY, p. A445

JAMES, Diane R., Administrator, Florida State Hospital, Chattahoochee, FL, p. A120

JAMES, Donald, D.O. Chief Medical Officer, Phelps County Regional Medical Center, Rolla, MO, p. A368

JAMES, Douglas, Chief Nursing Officer, Caldwell Medical Center, Princeton, KY, p. A259

JAMES, Jr., Franklin, M.D. Chief Medical Staff, Sparta Community Hospital, Sparta, IL, p. A194

JAMES, Gregory L., D.O. Chief Medical Officer, St. Vincent's Birmingham, Birmingham, AL, p. A17

JAMES, Janet, Director Human Resources, Trigg County Hospital, Cadiz, KY, p. A249

JAMES, Janice, Interim Chief Executive Officer, Cortland Regional Medical Center, Cortland, NY, p. A424

JAMES, John, M.D. Chief of Staff, Russell Medical Center, Alexander City, AL, p. A15

JAMES, Kenneth, Chief Executive Officer, Twin Rivers Regional Medical Center, Kennett, MO, p. A364

JAMES, Laura, Director Human Resources, St. Francis Medical Center, Trenton, NJ, p. A411

JAMES, Mark, M.D. Chief of Staff, Riverside Medical Center, Franklinton, LA, p. A267

JAMES, Michael, Information Technology Technical Support Specialist 1, Villa Feliciana Medical Complex, Jackson, LA, p. A269

JAMES, Mike, Director Management Information Systems, Dorminy Medical Center, Fitzgerald, GA, p. A153

JAMES, Naren, M.D. Chief of Staff, Ephraim McDowell Fort Logan Hospital, Stanford, KY, p. A260

JAMES, Robert L., Director Human Resources, Oakwood Annapolis Hospital, Wayne, MI, p. A326

JAMES, Ron, Chief Financial Officer, Floyd County Medical Center, Charles City, IA, p. A218

JAMES, Sacksteder, M.D., Director Operations, Austen Riggs Center, Stockbridge, MA, p. A305

JAMES, Sherrie, R.N. Director of Nursing, The BridgeWay, North Little Rock, AR, p. A48

JAMES, Stephanie, Chief Executive Officer, Regency Hospital of Greenville, Greenville, SC, p. A552

JAMES, Stuart, Chief Information Officer, Vidant Medical Center, Greenville, NC, p. A454

JAMES, Taya, Director, Mercy Hospital Berryville, Berryville, AR, p. A41

JAMES, Teri, Chief Financial Officer, Lafayette Regional Health Center, Lexington, MO, p. A365

JAMES, Thomas L., M.D. Senior Vice President and Chief Medical Officer, Trumbull Memorial Hospital, Warren, OH, p. A492

JAMES, William B., FACHE, Chief Executive Officer, Northern Hospital of Surry County, Mount Airy, NC, p. A458

JAMESON, David, M.D. Chief of Staff, Annie Jeffrey Memorial County Health Center, Osceola, NE, p. A388

JAMESON, Traci, Manager Finance, Select Specialty Hospital–Houston Heights, Houston, TX, p. A612

JAMIESON, Anne, FACHE, Chief Executive Officer, Portsmouth Regional Hospital, Portsmouth, NH, p. A400

JAMIESON, Jess, Chief Executive Officer, Western State Hospital, Tacoma, WA, p. A673

JAMIESON, Pamela, Vice President Patient Care Services and Chief Nursing Officer, University of Maryland St. Joseph Medical Center, Towson, MD, p. A294

JAMISON, Kevin, M.D. Chief Medical Officer, Providence Willamette Falls Medical Center, Oregon City, OR, p. A515

JANATKA, Lucille A., President and Chief Executive Officer, MidState Medical Center, Meriden, CT, p. A109

JANDA, Joe, Chief Information Officer, Wenatchee Valley Medical Center, Wenatchee, WA, p. A674

JANEK, James D., Chief Executive Officer, Rice Medical Center, Eagle Lake, TX, p. A600

JANELLE, Liisa H., Vice President Human Resources, Sebasticook Valley Health, Pittsfield, ME, p. A284

JANERELLA, Wendy, Controller, Bucktail Medical Center, Renovo, PA, p. A540

JANICAK, Dan
Chief Financial Officer, Holmes County Hospital and Clinics, Lexington, MS, p. A350
Chief Financial Officer, University Hospitals and Health System, University of Mississippi Medical Center, Jackson, MS, p. A349

JANIS, Terry
Director Information Systems, Houston Northwest Medical Center, Houston, TX, p. A610
Assistant Vice President, Park Plaza Hospital, Houston, TX, p. A611

JANKE, Paul, FACHE, President and Chief Executive Officer, Bay Area Hospital, Coos Bay, OR, p. A512

JANKOWSKI, Stan, Vice President and Chief Information Officer, Hospital for Special Care, New Britain, CT, p. A110

JANLOO, Arman, M.D. Chief Medical Staff, Fairfax Community Hospital, Fairfax, OK, p. A498

JANNENE, Patricia, Vice President Patient Care Services, Porter Medical Center, Middlebury, VT, p. A649

JANNUZZI, BettyAnn, Supervisor Personnel, Essex County Hospital Center, Cedar Grove, NJ, p. A402

JANOSO, John R., President and Chief Executive Officer, Sharon Regional Health System, Sharon, PA, p. A541

JANOWSKI, Kenneth, M.D. Chief Medical Officer, Hackettstown Regional Medical Center, Hackettstown, NJ, p. A404

JANSEN, David, Vice President Human Resources, Karmanos Cancer Center, Detroit, MI, p. A312

JANSEN, Donald, M.D. Vice President Medical Affairs, Shenandoah Memorial Hospital, Woodstock, VA, p. A663

JANSEN, John, Management Information Specialist, Hawaii State Hospital, Kaneohe, HI, p. A165

JANSSEN, Darin A., Chief Executive Officer, Cimarron Memorial Hospital, Boise City, OK, p. A496

JANSSEN, Paul, President and Chief Executive Officer, Henry County Hospital, New Castle, IN, p. A211

JANSSEN, Rob, Vice President, Nursing Services, Down East Community Hospital, Machias, ME, p. A284

JANSSEN, Thomas, M.D. Chief of Staff, McBride Clinic Orthopedic Hospital, Oklahoma City, OK, p. A503

JANTZEN, Daniel, Chief Financial Officer, Dartmouth–Hitchcock Medical Center, Lebanon, NH, p. A398

JANUS, Tammy, Vice President Human Resources, Mercy Medical Center, Baltimore, MD, p. A288

JANVRIN, Susan, R.N. Chief Operating and Chief Nursing Officer, Kaiser Permanente Santa Rosa Medical Center, Santa Rosa, CA, p. A90

JANZEN, Verlin, M.D. Chief of Staff, Hutchinson Regional Medical Center, Hutchinson, KS, p. A236

JANZEN, Wes, Chief Information Officer, Wamego City Hospital, Wamego, KS, p. A245

JAPEC, Ernie, Area Information Officer, Kaiser Permanente San Jose Medical Center, San Jose, CA, p. A87

JAQUA, Terry, Director Human Resources, Shasta Regional Medical Center, Redding, CA, p. A81

JAQUEZ, Jason, Director Human Resources, Greater El Monte Community Hospital, South El Monte, CA, p. A91

JARBOE, Joe, Director Human Resources, Kosciusko Community Hospital, Warsaw, IN, p. A214

JARBOE, Lori, Chief Executive Officer, HEALTHSOUTH Lakeview Rehabilitation Hospital, Elizabethtown, KY, p. A250

JARDEN, Howard, Ph.D. Assistant Executive Director, Devereux Children's Behavioral Health Center, Malvern, PA, p. A530

JARMAN, Wayne, M.D. President Medical Staff, Lenoir Memorial Hospital, Kinston, NC, p. A456

JARNAGIN, Vince, Manager Information Technology, Northridge Medical Center, Commerce, GA, p. A150

JAROPILLO, Erwin, Director Information Systems, Lake Wales Medical Center, Lake Wales, FL, p. A128

JARRELL, Lindsey
Vice President Information Services, St. Anthony's Hospital, Saint Petersburg, FL, p. A139
Vice President Information Services, St. Joseph's Hospital, Tampa, FL, p. A142

JARRETT, Adam D., M.D. Executive Vice President and Chief Medical Officer, Holy Name Medical Center, Teaneck, NJ, p. A411

JARRETT, Brenda, Chief Financial Officer, Putnam General Hospital, Eatonton, GA, p. A153

JARRETT, Mark, M.D. Chief Medical Officer, Staten Island University Hospital, NY, p. A436

JARRY, Jacques, Administrator, Bullock County Hospital, Union Springs, AL, p. A26

JARRY, Patricia, Manager Human Resources, Crenshaw Community Hospital, Luverne, AL, p. A22

JARVIS, Diane, R.N. Director of Nursing, Phillips County Hospital, Phillipsburg, KS, p. A242

JARVIS, Keith, Director Information Systems, Longview Regional Medical Center, Longview, TX, p. A619

JARVIS, Scott, M.D. President Medical Staff, Van Wert County Hospital, Van Wert, OH, p. A492

JASPER, Harry, Administrator, Jerold Phelps Community Hospital, Garberville, CA, p. A62

JASPER, Jerry, Chief Executive Officer, HEALTHSOUTH Rehabilitation Hospital of Texarkana, Texarkana, TX, p. A637

JASPERSON, Steven W., Chief Executive Officer, Good Samaritan Regional Medical Center, Corvallis, OR, p. A512

JASTREMSKI, Michael S., M.D. Vice President Medical Affairs and Director Emergency Services, Community Memorial Hospital, Hamilton, NY, p. A426

JATCZAK, Tracy E., CPA Chief Financial Officer, Box Butte General Hospital, Alliance, NE, p. A381

JAVOIS, Laurent D.
Regional Executive Officer, Hawthorn Children Psychiatric Hospital, Saint Louis, MO, p. A369
Regional Executive Officer, Metropolitan St. Louis Psychiatric Center, Saint Louis, MO, p. A370
Regional Executive Officer, St. Louis Psychiatric Rehabilitation Center, Saint Louis, MO, p. A371

JAWOROWSKI, Brian, Director Management Information Systems, Natchaug Hospital, Mansfield Center, CT, p. A109

IAY, Chad, Chief Nursing Officer, Kimball Health Services, Kimball, NE, p. A385

JAYAKRISHNAN, Chemmele, M.D. Chief Medical Staff, St. Charles Parish Hospital, Luling, LA, p. A272

JEANE, I. Lynn, Chief Operating Officer, Kansas Heart Hospital, Wichita, KS, p. A246

JEANNETTE, Joanie, MSN, Chief Executive Officer, Lehigh Regional Medical Center, Lehigh Acres, FL, p. A129

JEANNOTTE, Alexis, Director Information Technology, Speare Memorial Hospital, Plymouth, NH, p. A400

JEANS, Joe
Vice President Finance, Providence Medical Center, Kansas City, KS, p. A237
Chief Financial Officer, Saint John Hospital, Leavenworth, KS, p. A238

JEANSONNE, James P., Chief Executive Officer, Lakeland Community Hospital, Haleyville, AL, p. A21

JEANTY, Johanne, Director Human Resources, Aurora Chicago Lakeshore Hospital, Chicago, IL, p. A176

JEFFERSON, Candace, Manager Human Resources, CHRISTUS Spohn Hospital Kleberg, Kingsville, TX, p. A616

JEFFERSON, Terrie, R.N. Chief Nursing Officer, South Bay Hospital, Sun City Center, FL, p. A140

JEFFRAS, Charles, Executive Director Human Resources, St. Vincent Carmel Hospital, Carmel, IN, p. A200

JEFFRESS, Chuck, Vice President Fiscal Services, Brazosport Regional Health System, Lake Jackson, TX, p. A617

JEFFREY, Roberta, Chief Executive Officer, Holdenville General Hospital, Holdenville, OK, p. A500

JEFFRIES, John, Chief Financial Officer, St. Joseph's Hospital, Breese, IL, p. A175

JELALIAN, Christine, M.D. Medical Director, St. Luke's Cornwall Hospital, Newburgh, NY, p. A437

JELDEN, Dennis, M.D. Chief of Staff, Melissa Memorial Hospital, Holyoke, CO, p. A102

JELESKY, Beth, Director Clinical Excellence, Linden Oaks Hospital at Edward, Naperville, IL, p. A189

JELKS, Kim, Fiscal Officer, Villa Feliciana Medical Complex, Jackson, LA, p. A269

JELLE, Laura, Executive Vice President and Chief Operating Officer, St. Clare Hospital, Baraboo, WI, p. A683

JENEY, Martie, Director Human Resources, Callaway Community Hospital, Fulton, MO, p. A361

JENKINS, Brian, Director Human Resources, Arbour–Fuller Hospital, Attleboro, MA, p. A295

JENKINS, Daisy
Vice President Human Resources, Carondelet Holy Cross Hospital, Nogales, AZ, p. A33
Vice President Human Resources, Carondelet St. Joseph's Hospital, Tucson, AZ, p. A38
Vice President Human Resources, Carondelet St. Mary's Hospital, Tucson, AZ, p. A38

JENKINS, Debbie, Chief Human Resources Management Service, Veterans Affairs Sierra Nevada Health Care System, Reno, NV, p. A395

JENKINS, Denise, Chief Clinical Officer, Kindred Hospital–Brea, Brea, CA, p. A55

JENKINS, Eric, M.D. Chief of Staff, Mercy Allen Hospital, Oberlin, OH, p. A488

JENKINS, Hopie, Director Personnel, Washington County Memorial Hospital, Potosi, MO, p. A368

JENKINS, Jill, M.D. Chief of Staff, East Adams Rural Hospital, Ritzville, WA, p. A670

JENKINS, Laura, Director Operations Finance and Business Development, Buffalo Hospital, Buffalo, MN, p. A330

JENKINS, Linda, R.N. Vice President Patient Care Services, St. Jude Medical Center, Fullerton, CA, p. A62

JENKINS, Maynard, Regional Vice President for Human Resources, Sutter Maternity and Surgery Center of Santa Cruz, Santa Cruz, CA, p. A90

JENKINS, Michelle, M.D. President Medical Staff, Herrin Hospital, Herrin, IL, p. A184

JENKINS, Rebecca, Director Human Resources Management, Harrison Memorial Hospital, Cynthiana, KY, p. A250

JENKINS, Woody, M.D. Chief of Medical Staff, Stillwater Medical Center, Stillwater, OK, p. A507

JENKS, Lyn, Chief Executive Officer, Charlevoix Area Hospital, Charlevoix, MI, p. A310

JENNER, Jody J., President and Chief Executive Officer, Broadlawns Medical Center, Des Moines, IA, p. A220

JENNETTE, Brian, Chief Financial Officer, Northside Hospital–Cherokee, Canton, GA, p. A149

JENNEY, Karol A., Director Business Operations, Southwest Regional Rehabilitation Center, Battle Creek, MI, p. A309

JENNINGS, D. Arlo, Ph.D. Chief Information Officer, Mission Hospital, Asheville, NC, p. A447

JENNINGS, Jeff, FACHE, Chief Executive Officer, Hillside Hospital, Pulaski, TN, p. A578

JENNINGS, Marilyn, Director Human Resources, Austin Surgical Hospital, Austin, TX, p. A584

JENNINGS, Mark
Director Information Systems, Northeast Georgia Medical Center, Gainesville, GA, p. A154
Chief Information Officer, Saint Anthony Hospital, Chicago, IL, p. A179

JENNINGS, William M., President and Chief Executive Officer, Bridgeport Hospital, Bridgeport, CT, p. A108

JENSEMA, Christine
Chief People Officer, St. Mary's Hospital Medical Center, Green Bay, WI, p. A688
Chief People Officer, St. Vincent Hospital, Green Bay, WI, p. A688

JENSEN, Alice J., Chief Operating Officer, Geary Community Hospital, Junction City, KS, p. A236

JENSEN, Amy, Director Human Resources, Community Health Center of Branch County, Coldwater, MI, p. A311

JENSEN, Christopher, Chief Financial Officer, Three Rivers Behavioral Health, West Columbia, SC, p. A557

JENSEN, Dave, Director Human Resources, Performance Improvement and Risk Management, Mountain View Hospital, Gadsden, AL, p. A20

JENSEN, David M A, Chief Financial Officer, Oakland Mercy Hospital, Oakland, NE, p. A387

JENSEN, Donna, Director Clinical Services, Blue Mountain Hospital, Blanding, UT, p. A643

JENSEN, Eric, Chief Executive Officer, Valley General Hospital, Monroe, WA, p. A668

JENSEN, Gail, Chief Financial Officer, Trego County–Lemke Memorial Hospital, Wakeeney, KS, p. A245

JENSEN, Jan, R.N., Chief Executive Officer and Administrator, William Bee Ririe Hospital, Ely, NV, p. A391

JENSEN, Janette, Manager Human Resources, Avera Holy Family Hospital, Estherville, IA, p. A221

JENSEN, Jeff, Finance Director, Intermountain Medical Center, Murray, UT, p. A644

JENSEN, Ken, Chief Financial Officer, ValleyCare Medical Center, Pleasanton, CA, p. A80

JENSEN, Kimberly, Vice President Human Resources, Avera Sacred Heart Hospital, Yankton, SD, p. A564

JENSEN, Leanna, Vice President Finance and Chief Financial Officer, Cobleskill Regional Hospital, Cobleskill, NY, p. A424

JENSEN, Mary, Controller, Mountain View Hospital, Gadsden, AL, p. A20

JENSEN, Michael E., Chief Executive Officer, Davis Hospital and Medical Center, Layton, UT, p. A644

JENSEN, Mons, Information Systems Team Leader, St. Helena Hospital Napa Valley, Saint Helena, CA, p. A84

JENSEN, Neal, Chief Executive Officer, Cobre Valley Regional Medical Center, Globe, AZ, p. A32

JENSEN, Pamela, FACHE, President, Memorial Hospital, Fremont, OH, p. A481

JENSEN, Paul, M.D. Chief of Staff, Regional Health Services of Howard County, Cresco, IA, p. A219

JENSEN, Renee K., Chief Executive Officer, Summit Pacific Medical Center, McCleary, WA, p. A668

JENSEN, Ronald, Manager Finance, The Orthopedic Specialty Hospital, Murray, UT, p. A644

JENSEN, Sherry, Chief Financial Officer, Halifax Regional Medical Center, Roanoke Rapids, NC, p. A459

JENSEN, Steen, M.D. Chief of Staff, Seneca Healthcare District, Chester, CA, p. A56

JENSEN, Tom, Chief Executive Officer, Grays Harbor Community Hospital, Aberdeen, WA, p. A664

JENSEN, Troy, Director Human Resources, HEALTHSOUTH Rehabilitation Hospital of Utah, Sandy, UT, p. A647

JENSEN, Twyla, Director Human Resources, Pioneers Medical Center, Meeker, CO, p. A104

JENSEN, Vicki, Senior Human Resource Business Partner, Spectrum Health United Hospital, Greenville, MI, p. A315

JENSON, Paul M., Chief Executive Officer, Midwest Regional Medical Center, Midwest City, OK, p. A501

JENTZ, Amy, M.D. Chief of Staff, Sparrow Ionia Hospital, Ionia, MI, p. A316

JEPPI, Jessi, Director Human Resources, Rockford Center, Newark, DE, p. A114

JEPSON, Brian, Chief Operating Officer, OhioHealth Riverside Methodist Hospital, Columbus, OH, p. A478

JEPSON, Gary L., Chief Executive Officer, Pekin Hospital, Pekin, IL, p. A191

JEPSON, Jeanne, Director Human Resources, Hackettstown Regional Medical Center, Hackettstown, NJ, p. A404

JEPSON, Mark, Vice President, Silver Cross Hospital, New Lenox, IL, p. A190

JERANT, Steve, Vice President Information Technology, Forest Health Medical Center, Ypsilanti, MI, p. A327

JERGER, Greg, Chief Financial Officer, Memorial Health Care Systems, Seward, NE, p. A389

JERNIGAN, Pam, Chief Financial Officer, United Regional Medical Center, Manchester, TN, p. A573

JERNIGAN Jr., Robert F., Chief Executive Officer, Select Specialty Hospital–Durham, Durham, NC, p. A451

JEROME, Marivee, Senior Human Resources Business Partner, HEALTHSOUTH Rehabilitation Hospital of Sarasota, Sarasota, FL, p. A139

JESCH, Doug, Director Human Resources, Indiana University Health Starke Hospital, Knox, IN, p. A207

JESIOLOWSKI, Craig A., FACHE, President, Saint Anne's Hospital, Fall River, MA, p. A299

JESTER, Denise, Interim Chief Financial Officer, Nanticoke Memorial Hospital, Seaford, DE, p. A114

JESTILA–PELTOLA, Gail, Chief Financial Officer, Baraga County Memorial Hospital, L'Anse, MI, p. A318

JETER, Cynthia, Director Human Resources, Sutter Surgical Hospital – North Valley, Yuba City, CA, p. A96

JETER, John, Assistant Administrator and Chief Financial Officer, Johnston Memorial Hospital, Abingdon, VA, p. A651

JETER, John H., M.D., President and Chief Executive Officer, Hays Medical Center, Hays, KS, p. A235

JETER, Larry R., Chief Executive Officer, Chestatee Regional Hospital, Dahlonega, GA, p. A151

JETT, Alisa
Director Clinical Services, Regency Hospital of Florence, Florence, SC, p. A552
Chief Executive Officer, Regency Hospital of South Atlanta, East Point, GA, p. A153

JETTERGREN, Tess, Director Clinical Informatics, Essentia Health St. Mary's Medical Center, Duluth, MN, p. A331

JETTON, Dana, Chief Information Officer, Continuous Care Centers of Tulsa, Tulsa, OK, p. A508

JEUNEHOMME, Patti, Director Human Resources, Hot Springs County Memorial Hospital, Thermopolis, WY, p. A704

JEWELL, D. Keith
Senior Vice President and Chief Operating Officer, Franciscan St. Francis Health – Indianapolis, Indianapolis, IN, p. A205
Interim Chief Executive Officer, Franciscan St. Francis Health – Mooresville, Mooresville, IN, p. A210
Senior Vice President and Chief Operating Officer, Franciscan St. Francis Health – Mooresville, Mooresville, IN, p. A210

JEWETT, Lorraine M., Vice President and Chief Operating Officer, Bristol Bay Area Health Corporation, Dillingham, AK, p. A27

JEWETT, Sherri R., Chief Executive Officer, Valle Vista Hospital, Greenwood, IN, p. A204

JEZIORSKE, John J., Director Human Resources, Abilene Regional Medical Center, Abilene, TX, p. A581

JHA, Gautam, M.D. Chief of Staff, Salem Township Hospital, Salem, IL, p. A194

JILEK, Lea, Director Finance, Bethesda Hospital, Saint Paul, MN, p. A340

JIMBOY, Twylla, Supervisor Human Resources, Lawton Indian Hospital, Lawton, OK, p. A500

JIMENEZ, Mauricio, M.D. Chief Medical Officer, Kindred Hospital El Paso, El Paso, TX, p. A601

JIMESON, Jean–Marie, Coordinator Human Resources, Kansas Spine Hospital, Wichita, KS, p. A246

JIMMERSON, Kevin, Business Manager, Mental Health Institute, Independence, IA, p. A223

JIRON, Feliciano, Chief Executive Officer, Los Alamos Medical Center, Los Alamos, NM, p. A417

JIROVEC, David, Director Finance, Ministry Good Samaritan Health Center, Merrill, WI, p. A691

JITH, Gayathri S., M.P.H. Vice President Operations, Valley Presbyterian Hospital,, CA, p. A72

JIVIDEN, Roxanne, Chief Executive Officer, Ohio Hospital for Child and Adolescent Psychiatry, Columbus, OH, p. A478

JOBBITT, Patty, Vice President Operations, Rehabilitation Institute of Michigan, Detroit, MI, p. A312

JOBE, Kathy, R.N. Chief Nursing Officer and Vice President Patient Care Services, Summa Barberton Citizens Hospital, Barberton, OH, p. A471

JOCHIM, Steven, Administrator, Cape Cod & Island Community Mental Health Center, Pocasset, MA, p. A304

JODWAY, Timothy, Chief Financial Officer, Garden City Hospital, Garden City, MI, p. A314

JOEL, Linda, Vice President Operations, Spectrum Health Special Care Hospital, Grand Rapids, MI, p. A315

JOHE, David, M.D. President Medical Staff, Elk Regional Health Center, Saint Marys, PA, p. A540

JOHLMAN, Ed, Chief Financial Officer, Sheridan Memorial Hospital, Sheridan, WY, p. A703

JOHN, Aleyamma, R.N. Director of Nursing, Kensington Hospital, Philadelphia, PA, p. A535

JOHN, Julian, Chief Financial Officer, Kings County Hospital Center,, NY, p. A433

JOHNS, Dale, Administrator, Town and Country Hospital, Tampa, FL, p. A142

JOHNS, Dawn, Director Human Resources, Colquitt Regional Medical Center, Moultrie, GA, p. A158

JOHNS, Robert, Senior Vice President Administration, Rochelle Community Hospital, Rochelle, IL, p. A193

JOHNS, Thomas Bradford, M.D. Medical Director, Ridgeview Institute, Smyrna, GA, p. A160

JOHNS, Timothy, M.D. Chief Medical Officer and Board President, Gilbert Hospital, Gilbert, AZ, p. A31

JOHNSEN, Timothy J., MS, President, Integris Baptist Medical Center, Oklahoma City, OK, p. A503

JOHNSON, Alan, Chief Information Officer, Doctors Community Hospital, Lanham, MD, p. A292

JOHNSON, Allen
Chief Financial Officer, Truman Medical Center–Hospital Hill, Kansas City, MO, p. A364
Chief Financial Officer, Truman Medical Center–Lakewood, Kansas City, MO, p. A364

JOHNSON, Alyssa, Director Human Resources, East Texas Medical Center–Quitman, Quitman, TX, p. A628

JOHNSON, Andrew, Information Technology and Purchasing Officer, Windsor–Laurelwood Center for Behavioral Medicine, Willoughby, OH, p. A493

JOHNSON, Arlan D., Chief Executive Officer, Howard County Medical Center, Saint Paul, NE, p. A389

JOHNSON, Ashley F., Chief Financial Officer, Memorial Hospital Jacksonville, Jacksonville, FL, p. A126

JOHNSON, Audrey, Director Human Resources, Parkwood Behavioral Health System, Olive Branch, MS, p. A352

JOHNSON, Barbara
Chief Financial Officer, Essentia Health Duluth, Duluth, MN, p. A331
Chief Financial Officer, Essentia Health Northern Pines, Aurora, MN, p. A328

JOHNSON, Barbara Jo, R.N. Senior Vice President Human Resources Development, Centegra Hospital – Woodstock, Woodstock, IL, p. A197

JOHNSON, Belinda, R.N. Chief Nursing Officer/Chief Clinical Officer, Russellville Hospital, Russellville, AL, p. A25

JOHNSON, Betty, Associate Administrator, LSU Health Sciences Center, Shreveport, LA, p. A278

JOHNSON, Beverly, Vice President Human Resources, North Kansas City Hospital, North Kansas City, MO, p. A367

JOHNSON, Billy, Chief Executive Officer, Coal County General Hospital, Coalgate, OK, p. A497

JOHNSON, Bonnie, R.N. Vice President of Patient Services, Perham Health, Perham, MN, p. A338

JOHNSON, Brandi, Technolgy Information Systems Site Manager, Spectrum Health Reed City Hospital, Reed City, MI, p. A322

JOHNSON, Shrea, Director Human Resources, Alliance Health Center, Meridian, MS, p. A350

JOHNSON, Steven, D.O. Chief of Staff, Fayette Regional Health System, Connersville, IN, p. A200

JOHNSON, Sy, Chief Executive Officer and Chief Mission Officer, PeaceHealth St. John Medical Center, Longview, WA, p. A667

JOHNSON, Sylvia Smith, President and Chief Executive Officer, Maryland General Hospital, Baltimore, MD, p. A288

JOHNSON, Tamatha, Director Human Resources, Stringfellow Memorial Hospital, Anniston, AL, p. A15

JOHNSON, Tami L., MSN Chief Nursing Officer, Lancaster Regional Medical Center, Lancaster, PA, p. A529

JOHNSON, Tanya, R.N. Director of Nursing, Russell Medical Center, Alexander City, AL, p. A15

JOHNSON, Thomas, Manager Management Information Systems, DuBois Regional Medical Center, Du Bois, PA, p. A524

JOHNSON, Timothy, President and Chief Executive Officer, Eaton Rapids Medical Center, Eaton Rapids, MI, p. A313

JOHNSON, Timothy J., President and Chief Executive Officer, Mayo Clinic Health System – Franciscan Healthcare in La Crosse, La Crosse, WI, p. A689

JOHNSON, Todd, Chief Financial Officer, Longview Regional Medical Center, Longview, TX, p. A619

JOHNSON, Tommy, Chief Executive Officer, Rankin Hospital District, Rankin, TX, p. A628

JOHNSON, Tricia, Coordinator Human Resources, Flint River Community Hospital, Montezuma, GA, p. A157

JOHNSON, Trudy, R.N. Chief Nursing Officer, Santa Clara Valley Medical Center, San Jose, CA, p. A88

JOHNSON, Valerie, Director Human Resources, Sullivan County Memorial Hospital, Milan, MO, p. A366

JOHNSON, Vernon, Administrator, Dale Medical Center, Ozark, AL, p. A24

JOHNSON, Victoria, R.N. Nursing Director of Surgical and Medical Services, The HealthCenter, Kalispell, MT, p. A377

JOHNSON, Vincent, Chief Operating Officer, University of California, Davis Medical Center, Sacramento, CA, p. A84

JOHNSON, Wade C., FACHE, Chief Executive Officer, Pen Bay Medical Center, Rockport, ME, p. A285

JOHNSON Jr., Walter E., President and Chief Executive Officer, Jefferson Regional Medical Center, Pine Bluff, AR, p. A49

JOHNSON, William, M.D. Chief Medical Director, Pikeville Medical Center, Pikeville, KY, p. A259

JOHNSON, Yvonne, M.D. President Medical Staff, Baptist Health South Florida, South Miami Hospital, Miami, FL, p. A131

JOHNSON–HATCHER, Dawn, Chief Financial Officer, Women and Children's Hospital, Lake Charles, LA, p. A272

JOHNSON–PHILLIPPE, Sue E., President and Chief Executive Officer, St. Joseph's Hospital of Buckhannon, Buckhannon, WV, p. A675

JOHNSRUD, Carolyn, Manager Human Resources, Missouri River Medical Center, Fort Benton, MT, p. A376

JOHNSRUD, Jill, Director of Nursing, Essentia Health–Holy Trinity Hospital, Graceville, MN, p. A333

JOHNSTON, Charles W., Chief Executive Officer, Southern Coos Hospital and Health Center, Bandon, OR, p. A511

JOHNSTON, Don, Chief Information Officer, San Joaquin General Hospital, French Camp, CA, p. A61

JOHNSTON, Jeffrey A., President, Mercy Hospital St. Louis, Saint Louis, MO, p. A370

JOHNSTON, Kevin, M.D. Chief Medical Staff, Harney District Hospital, Burns, OR, p. A511

JOHNSTON, Lauren, Deputy Executive Director, Lincoln Medical and Mental Health Center,, NY, p. A433

JOHNSTON, Lori, Chief Financial Officer and Chief Operating Officer, ProMedica St. Luke's Hospital, Maumee, OH, p. A486

JOHNSTON, Martha, M.D
Chief Medical Officer, Greene Memorial Hospital, Xenia, OH, p. A494
Chief Medical Officer, Soin Medical Center, Beavercreek, OH, p. A471

JOHNSTON, Michael V., M.D. Chief Medical Officer and Senior Vice President Medical Programs, Kennedy Krieger Institute, Baltimore, MD, p. A287

JOHNSTON, Monte, Manager Human Resources, Coquille Valley Hospital, Coquille, OR, p. A512

JOHNSTON, Phyllis, Director, Catawba Valley Medical Center, Hickory, NC, p. A454

JOHNSTON, Samantha, Chief Organizational Excellence, Memorial Hospital at Craig, Craig, CO, p. A99

JOHNSTON, Susan, Director Human Resources, East Alabama Medical Center, Opelika, AL, p. A24

JOHNSTON, Wayne, Director Information Systems, Ripon Medical Center, Ripon, WI, p. A696

JOHNSTON, William C., Interim Vice President, Information System, Brigham and Women's Hospital, Boston, MA, p. A296

JOINER, Wayne, Vice President Human Resources, The Medical Center, Columbus, GA, p. A150

JOLIVETTE, Cynthia, Chief Nursing Officer, HEALTHSOUTH Rehabilitation Hospital of Cypress, Houston, TX, p. A610

JOLLY, Gaye, FACHE, President/Chief Administrative Officer, Roane Medical Center, Harriman, TN, p. A569

JOLLY, Jay P., Chief Executive Officer, Goodland Regional Medical Center, Goodland, KS, p. A234

JONAS, Stanley W., Chief Executive Officer, Alliance Community Hospital, Alliance, OH, p. A470

JONES, Alesia, Interim Chief Human Resources Officer, University of Alabama Hospital, Birmingham, AL, p. A17

JONES, Allan, Controller, HEALTHSOUTH Rehabilitation Hospital of Jonesboro, Jonesboro, AR, p. A45

JONES, Amelia, Chief Operating Officer, Oakland Regional Hospital, Southfield, MI, p. A324

JONES, Beth, Chief Operating Officer, Reeves Memorial Medical Center, Bernice, LA, p. A264

JONES, Bill, Chief Executive Officer, Jackson County Hospital District, Edna, TX, p. A600

JONES, Bracken, Director Information Technology, Southern Virginia Mental Health Institute, Danville, VA, p. A653

JONES, Carol, Controller and Manager Business Office, Coryell Memorial Hospital, Gatesville, TX, p. A606

JONES, Catherine, Chief Nursing Officer, Ancora Psychiatric Hospital, Hammonton, NJ, p. A404

JONES, Cheryl L., Director Human Resources and Organizational Development, Baptist St. Anthony Health System, Amarillo, TX, p. A582

JONES, Chris, Chief Executive Officer, Vibra Hospital of Northern California, Redding, CA, p. A81

JONES, Christian, Chief Executive Officer, Moberly Regional Medical Center, Moberly, MO, p. A366

JONES, Dale, Administrator, Noland Hospital Tuscaloosa, Tuscaloosa, AL, p. A26

JONES, Dan, Director Human Resources, Pike County Memorial Hospital, Louisiana, MO, p. A365

JONES, Dana, R.N. Chief Nursing Officer, Springhill Medical Center, Springhill, LA, p. A279

JONES, Darrell, Chief Executive Officer, Regency Hospital of Florence, Florence, SC, p. A552

JONES, David, Chief Financial Officer, Alexian Brothers Behavioral Health Hospital, Hoffman Estates, IL, p. A185

JONES, David C., Administrator, North Caddo Medical Center, Vivian, LA, p. A280

JONES, Deborah, Controller, Houston Hospital for Specialized Surgery, Houston, TX, p. A610

JONES, Derrick, Chief Executive Officer, Lovelace Rehabilitation Hospital, Albuquerque, NM, p. A414

JONES, Derrick A., Administrator, Community Behavioral Health Hospital – Fergus Falls, Fergus Falls, MN, p. A332

JONES, Donald J., FACHE, Administrator, North Mississippi Medical Center–Hamilton, Hamilton, AL, p. A21

JONES, Douglas
Regional Chief Information Officer, Providence Holy Cross Medical Center,, CA, p. A71
Regional Chief Information Officer, Providence Little Company of Mary Medical Center, Torrance, CA, p. A92
Interim Chief Information Officer, Providence Saint Joseph Medical Center, Burbank, CA, p. A55

JONES, Douglas T., President and Chief Executive Officer, Down East Community Hospital, Machias, ME, p. A284

JONES, Elaine, M.D. Chief Medical Staff, Roger Williams Medical Center, Providence, RI, p. A547

JONES, Evan, Chief Financial Officer, Lakeland Regional Medical Center, Lakeland, FL, p. A128

JONES, Evelyn, Director Human Resources, Choctaw Nation Health Care Center, Talihina, OK, p. A507

JONES, G.R. Sonny, Vice President Finance and Chief Financial Officer, St. Claire Regional Medical Center, Morehead, KY, p. A258

JONES, Glen M., Administrator, Red Bay Hospital, Red Bay, AL, p. A25

JONES, Greg, Chief Financial Officer, Wayne Memorial Hospital, Jesup, GA, p. A155

JONES, Gregory, M.D. Chief of Staff, Vidant Pungo Hospital, Belhaven, NC, p. A448

JONES, H. Roger, Chief Financial Officer, Straith Hospital for Special Surgery, Southfield, MI, p. A324

JONES, Ian V., M.D. Vice President Clinical Performance, Advocate Sherman Hospital, Elgin, IL, p. A181

JONES, J. Stephen, M.D. Chief of Staff, Muenster Memorial Hospital, Muenster, TX, p. A624

JONES, James B., M.D. Chief of Staff, Baptist Orange Hospital, Orange, TX, p. A625

JONES, Jeffrey, Chief Financial Officer, Cone Health, Greensboro, NC, p. A453

JONES, Jennifer L., Chief Financial Officer, Edwards County Hospital and Healthcare Center, Kinsley, KS, p. A237

JONES, Jeremy A., Administrator, Mercy Hospital Healdton, Healdton, OK, p. A499

JONES, John, Interim Chief Executive Officer, Memorial Hospital of Texas County, Guymon, OK, p. A499

JONES, John, M.D. Chief Medical Staff, Sanford Chamberlain Medical Center, Chamberlain, SD, p. A558

JONES, John R., Administrator, North Mississippi Medical Center–Eupora, Eupora, MS, p. A468

JONES, Johnnie M., Acting Chief Human Resource Management and Workforce Development Service, Veterans Affairs Gulf Coast Veterans Health Care System, Biloxi, MS, p. A344

JONES, Joshua, Director of Human Resources, Evanston Regional Hospital, Evanston, WY, p. A702

JONES, Joyce, Director Human Resources, HEALTHSOUTH Rehabilitation Hospital, Kingsport, TN, p. A571

JONES, Julie L., R.N. Chief Nursing Officer, Beatrice Community Hospital and Health Center, Beatrice, NE, p. A382

JONES, Karen, M.D. Chief of Staff, Harris Hospital, Newport, AR, p. A48

JONES, Karen, Administrative Director Human Resources, Marion General Hospital, Marion, IN, p. A209

JONES, Kathy, Director Human Resources, Jackson Medical Center, Jackson, AL, p. A22

JONES, Ken M., Interim Chief Operating Officer, UCSF Medical Center, San Francisco, CA, p. A87

JONES, Kenneth, Chief Executive Officer, Orthopaedic Hospital of Lutheran Health Network, Fort Wayne, IN, p. A202

JONES, Kevin, Director Finance, Aurora Sinai Medical Center, Milwaukee, WI, p. A691

JONES, Kyle, Controller, Marshall Medical Center, Lewisburg, TN, p. A573

JONES, L. Val, M.D. Medical Director, Blue Mountain Hospital, Blanding, UT, p. A643

JONES, Lance, Chief Executive Officer, Turkey Creek Medical Center, Knoxville, TN, p. A572

JONES, Larry, M.D. Chief Medical Officer, St. Mary's Hospital, Streator, IL, p. A196

JONES, Linda, Director Medical Records, Millwood Hospital, Arlington, TX, p. A583

JONES, Louis, Director Management Information Systems, Heart of Florida Regional Medical Center, Davenport, FL, p. A121

JONES, Lynda, Financial Officer, Riverland Medical Center, Ferriday, LA, p. A267

JONES, M. Steven, President, University Hospitals Geauga Medical Center, Chardon, OH, p. A473

JONES, Mark, Chief Financial Officer, Hill Country Memorial Hospital, Fredericksburg, TX, p. A605

JONES, Mark T., President, University Medical Center of Princeton at Plainsboro, Plainsboro, NJ, p. A409

JONES, Marsha, R.N. Director Nursing, King's Daughters Hospital, Yazoo City, MS, p. A355

JONES, Marshall, Senior Vice President Human Resources, Maricopa Integrated Health System, Phoenix, AZ, p. A34

JONES, Mary Jane, R.N. Chief Nursing Officer, Providence Little Company of Mary Medical Center San Pedro, CA, p. A71

JONES, Maud, Manager Medical Records, TOPS Surgical Specialty Hospital, Houston, TX, p. A613

JONES, Melinda, R.N. Chief Nursing Officer, Morehouse General Hospital, Bastrop, LA, p. A263

JONES, Meredith, Chief Financial Officer, McNairy Regional Hospital, Selmer, TN, p. A578

JONES, Michael, M.D. Chief of Staff, Atchison Hospital, Atchison, KS, p. A231

JONES, Michael, Vice President and Chief Information Officer, Children's Hospital of Wisconsin, Milwaukee, WI, p. A692

JONES, Michael L., Ph.D. Chief Information Officer, Shepherd Center, Atlanta, GA, p. A147

JONES, Mike, Director Information Services, Marshall Medical Center, Placerville, CA, p. A80

JONES, Pat, Director Information Systems, River Oaks Hospital, Flowood, MS, p. A346

JONES, Percy E., M.D. Chief of Staff, Kindred Hospital–Greensboro, Greensboro, NC, p. A453

JONES, Philip L., Chief Financial Officer, Kindred Hospital–Nashville, Nashville, TN, p. A576

JONES, Phyllis, Chief Human Resources, Wm. Jennings Bryan Dorn Veterans Affairs Medical Center, Columbia, SC, p. A551

JONES, Ray, Vice President, Columbia Memorial Hospital, Hudson, NY, p. A427

JONES, Reginald, Business Manager, Georgia Regional Hospital at Atlanta, Decatur, GA, p. A152

JONES, Reid F., Chief Operating Officer, University of Alabama Hospital, Birmingham, AL, p. A17

JONES, Richard
Vice President and Chief Financial Officer, Boca Raton Regional Hospital, Boca Raton, FL, p. A118
Chief Financial Officer, Bon Secours Baltimore Health System, Baltimore, MD, p. A287

JONES, Richard, M.D. Medical Director, Reliant Rehabilitation Hospital North Texas, Richardson, TX, p. A628

JONES, Richard W., Chief Financial Officer, Reading Hospital and Medical Center, West Reading, PA, p. A544

JONES, Rita A., Chief Executive Officer, Dundy County Hospital, Benkelman, NE, p. A382

JONES, Rob, Chief Nursing Officer, Physicians' Medical Center, New Albany, IN, p. A211

JONES, Robert
Chief Executive Officer, McCready Foundation, Crisfield, MD, p. A291
Director Management Information Systems, St. Joseph Mercy Oakland, Pontiac, MI, p. A322

JONES, III, Robert, M.D. President Medical Staff, Jefferson Medical Center, Ranson, WV, p. A680

JONES, Rodney B., Administrator, Kindred Hospital–Heritage Valley, Beaver, PA, p. A520

JONES, Ron, Chief Financial Officer, Butler County Health Care Center, David City, NE, p. A383

JONES, Ruth, Chief Operating Officer, Regency Hospital of Northwest Arkansas, Fayetteville, AR, p. A43

JONES, Scott, Chief Executive Officer, Midwestern Regional Medical Center, Zion, IL, p. A197

JONES, Sharon, Chief Financial Officer, Evergreen Medical Center, Evergreen, AL, p. A20

JONES, Sonja, Chief Financial Officer, Peninsula Hospital, Louisville, TN, p. A573

JONES, Stephen K., President and Chief Executive Officer, Robert Wood Johnson University Hospital, New Brunswick, NJ, p. A407

JONES, Stephen K., M.D
Vice President Medical Staff Affairs, St. Rose Dominican Hospitals – Rose de Lima Campus, Henderson, NV, p. A392
Chief Medical Officer, St. Rose Dominican Hospitals – San Martin Campus, Las Vegas, NV, p. A393
Vice President Medical Staff Affairs, St. Rose Dominican Hospitals – Siena Campus, Henderson, NV, p. A392

JONES Jr., Stephen K., FACHE, Chief Executive Officer, Clear Lake Regional Medical Center, Webster, TX, p. A640

JONES, Steven K., M.D. Medical Director, Advocate Eureka Hospital, Eureka, IL, p. A182

JONES, Tamera, Director Human Resources, Whittier Hospital Medical Center, Whittier, CA, p. A96

JONES, Tara, Director Information Services, Saint Vincent Hospital, Worcester, MA, p. A306

JONES, Terry D., M.D. Interim Chief of Staff, Roundup Memorial Healthcare, Roundup, MT, p. A379

JONES, Theresa, Manager Human Resources, St. Luke Community Healthcare, Ronan, MT, p. A379

JONES, Tim, Chief Executive Officer, Heart of Texas Memorial Hospital, Brady, TX, p. A589

JONES, Timothy P., President and Chief Executive Officer, North Adams Regional Hospital, North Adams, MA, p. A303

JONES, Todd, President, Baptist Health Richmond, Richmond, KY, p. A260

JONES, Tom, Manager Information Technology, Fitzgibbon Hospital, Marshall, MO, p. A365

JONES, Tonya A., Vice President Human Resources, Maria Parham Medical Center, Henderson, NC, p. A454

JONES, Tracey, Director Human Resources, Jackson Park Hospital and Medical Center, Chicago, IL, p. A177

JONES, Trennis, Senior Vice President and Chief Administrative Officer, Seton Northwest Hospital, Austin, TX, p. A585

JONES, Valerie
Chief Financial Officer, HEALTHSOUTH Rehabilitation Hospital Memphis–North, Memphis, TN, p. A574
Chief Financial Officer, HEALTHSOUTH Rehabilitation Hospital of Memphis, Memphis, TN, p. A574

JONES, Vernita, Site Manager, PHS Santa Fe Indian Hospital, Santa Fe, NM, p. A418

JONES, W. Clark, Administrator, Cascade Valley Hospital and Clinics, Arlington, WA, p. A664

JONES, Yvette A., HIM Director, Putnam Community Medical Center, Palatka, FL, p. A135

JONES–BROWNING, Debbie, Vice President Operations and Physician Services and Chief Operating Officer, Rush Memorial Hospital, Rushville, IN, p. A213

JORDAHL, David B., FACHE Chief Operating Officer, Winneshiek Medical Center, Decorah, IA, p. A220

JORDAN, Andrew, M.D. Chief of Staff, University Medical Center, Lebanon, TN, p. A572

JORDAN, Bobby G., Administrator, Woodlands Behavioral Center, Winnfield, LA, p. A280

JORDAN, Christopher, M.D. President Medical Staff, Wilcox Memorial Hospital, Lihue, HI, p. A166

JORDAN, Gary W., FACHE, Chief Executive Officer, Wright Memorial Hospital, Trenton, MO, p. A372

JORDAN, Jill, Chief Executive Officer, Regional Rehabilitation Hospital, Phenix City, AL, p. A24

JORDAN, Linda U., Administrator, Clay County Hospital, Ashland, AL, p. A15

JORDAN, Lori, Chief Executive Officer, Oklahoma Forensic Center, Vinita, OK, p. A509

JORDAN, Michelle J., Administrator, Lewis and Clark Specialty Hospital, Yankton, SD, p. A564

JORDAN III, Patrick, Interim President, Newton–Wellesley Hospital, Newton Lower Falls, MA, p. A303

JORDAN, Peggy, Director Human Resources, Comanche County Medical Center, Comanche, TX, p. A593

JORDAN, Randall, Budget Analyst, U. S. Public Health Service Indian Hospital, Cass Lake, MN, p. A330

JORDAN, Terry, M.D. Chief of Staff, Alliance Health Center, Meridian, MS, p. A350

JORGE, Michael C., Ph.D. Associate Director, James A. Haley Veterans' Hospital, Tampa, FL, p. A141

JORGENSON, Marcey, Chief Nursing Officer, Antelope Valley Hospital, Lancaster, CA, p. A66

JOSEHART, Carl E., Chief Executive Officer, TIRR Memorial Hermann, Houston, TX, p. A613

JOSEPH, Heather, Administrator, Baypointe Behavioral Health, Mobile, AL, p. A22

JOSEPH, James, M.D. President Medical Staff, Geisinger–Bloomsburg Hospital, Bloomsburg, PA, p. A521

JOSEPH, Kevin, M.D., Chief Executive Officer, West Chester Hospital, West Chester, OH, p. A493

JOSEPH, Thomas, M.D. Chief of Staff, Gibson General Hospital, Princeton, IN, p. A212

JOSEPH, Vincent D., Executive Vice President and Chief Operating Officer, Robert Wood Johnson University Hospital, New Brunswick, NJ, p. A407

JOSEPH–TAYLOR, Terri, Chief Human Resource Manager, Ochsner Medical Center – North Shore, Slidell, LA, p. A279

JOSHI, Chandrashekhar V., M.D. Chief of Staff, Choctaw Health Center, Philadelphia, MS, p. A352

JOSLIN, Charles, M.D. Chief of Staff, Ellinwood District Hospital, Ellinwood, KS, p. A233

JOSLYN, E. Allen, M.D. Chief Medical Officer, Bedford Memorial Hospital, Bedford, VA, p. A651

JOSLYN, J. Scott, Senior Vice President and Chief Information Officer, Saddleback Memorial Medical Center, Laguna Hills, CA, p. A45

JOUD, Mohammad A., M.D. Chief of Staff, Bayfront Health Brooksville, Brooksville, FL, p. A119

JOUDEH, Jalal, M.D
Chief of Staff, DeQuincy Memorial Hospital, DeQuincy, LA, p. A266
Chief Medical Officer, Specialty Rehabilitation Hospital, Coushatta, LA, p. A265

JOURDEN, Marti, FACHE Chief Quality Officer, St. Anthony Hospital, Oklahoma City, OK, p. A504

JOY, Mike, Chief Financial Officer, Via Christi Hospital in Pittsburg, Pittsburg, KS, p. A242

JOYAL, Shirley, Director Information Systems, Regional Medical Center of San Jose, San Jose, CA, p. A88

JOYCE, Christopher, Vice President Human Resources, Methodist Hospital of Sacramento, Sacramento, CA, p. A83

JOYCE, John, M.D. Chief of Staff, West River Regional Medical Center, Hettinger, ND, p. A467

JOYCE, Maria, Chief Financial Officer, National Institutes of Health Clinical Center, Bethesda, MD, p. A290

JOYNER, Ken, Vice President of Employee Services, Bay Area Medical Center, Marinette, WI, p. A690

JOYNER, Lee Roy, M.D. Medical Director, LSU Bogalusa Medical Center, Bogalusa, LA, p. A264

JUAREZ, Rose, Chief Civilian Personnel Branch, San Antonio Military Medical Center, Fort Sam Houston, TX, p. A603

JUDD, Martin H., President and Chief Executive Officer, Presence Saints Mary & Elizabeth Medical Center, Chicago, IL, p. A178

JUDD, Russell V., President, Mercy Hospitals of Bakersfield, Bakersfield, CA, p. A54

JUDGE, Deepinder, M.D. Chief of Staff, Jackson County Hospital District, Edna, TX, p. A600

JUDGE, Leigh Ann, Manager Human Resources, Guttenberg Municipal Hospital, Guttenberg, IA, p. A222

JUDYCKI–CREPEAULT, Christine, Chief Financial Officer, Adcare Hospital of Worcester, Worcester, MA, p. A306

JUEL, De De
Director Human Resources, St. David's Medical Center, Austin, TX, p. A586
Director Human Resources, St. David's Rehabilitation Center, Austin, TX, p. A586

JUENGER, Jacqueline, R.N. Chief Nursing Officer, HEALTHSOUTH Rehabilitation Hospital of Sarasota, Sarasota, FL, p. A139

JUGE, Shannon, Human Resources Representative, The NeuroMedical Center Surgical Hospital, Baton Rouge, LA, p. A264

JULIAN, Bell, Associate Executive Director and Chief Financial Officer, James Cancer Hospital and Solove Research Institute, Columbus, OH, p. A477

JULIAN, Steve, M.D., President, Sentara Obici Hospital, Suffolk, VA, p. A662

JUMONVILLE, III, John E., Chief Operating Officer, Community Specialty Hospital, Lafayette, LA, p. A270

JUMP, Beth, Chief Information Officer, Logansport Memorial Hospital, Logansport, IN, p. A209

JUMP, David A., D.O. Chief of Staff, Mercy Willard Hospital, Willard, OH, p. A493

JUNEAU, James B., Chief Financial Officer, Opelousas General Health System, Opelousas, LA, p. A276

JUNEZ, Maria, Director Human Resources, Dameron Hospital, Stockton, CA, p. A91

JUNGBLUT, Peter R., M.D. Vice President Medical Affairs and Chief Medical Officer, Shore Medical Center, Somers Point, NJ, p. A410

JUNGWIRTH, Scott, Chief Human Resources Officer, Providence Alaska Medical Center, Anchorage, AK, p. A27

JUNIS, Jennifer, MSN Chief Nursing Officer, Kewanee Hospital, Kewanee, IL, p. A186

JUNO, Russell, M.D. Chief of Staff, St. Mark's Medical Center, La Grange, TX, p. A617

JUREK, Charlie, Business Office Manager, Specialty Hospital of Winnfield, Winnfield, LA, p. A280

JURENEC, Anne E., Chief Executive Officer, Rehabilitation Hospital of Wisconsin, Waukesha, WI, p. A698

JURGENS, Chad, Chief Financial Officer, Jefferson Community Health Center, Fairbury, NE, p. A383

JURICA, John, M.D. Vice President Medical Affairs, Riverside Medical Center, Kankakee, IL, p. A186

JURIS, Susan V., President, University Hospitals Ahuja Medical Center, Beachwood, OH, p. A471

JURKAS, Wade A., Director Computer Information Systems, Lake Region Healthcare, Fergus Falls, MN, p. A332

JURKUS, Patti
Vice President, Regional Hospital, Bedford Memorial Hospital, Bedford, VA, p. A651
Director Human Resources, Carilion New River Valley Medical Center, Christiansburg, VA, p. A652

JUSTICE, Kim, Vice President Planning and Operations, Atlantic General Hospital, Berlin, MD, p. A289

JUSTICE, Tim, Chief Information Officer, Union County General Hospital, Clayton, NM, p. A415

JUSTUS, Jason, Vice President Finance and Chief Financial Officer, Pomerene Hospital, Millersburg, OH, p. A486

# K

KA'AKIMAKA, Holly, Director Human Resources, Hilo Medical Center, Hilo, HI, p. A164

KAATZ, Gary E., President and Chief Executive Officer, Rockford Memorial Hospital, Rockford, IL, p. A193

KABERLINE, Gene, Chief Financial Officer, Mercy Hospital Watonga, Watonga, OK, p. A509

KACHIGION, Claudia, M.D. Medical Director, Alton Mental Health Center, Alton, IL, p. A173

KADDOURI, Sami, M.D. Medical Director, Cornerstone of Medical Arts Center Hospital, Fresh Meadows, NY, p. A426

KADLICK, Pamela, Vice President Nursing, Mercy St. Anne Hospital, Toledo, OH, p. A491

KAEMMERLING, Roberta B., MSN Chief Operating Officer and Chief Nursing Officer, Carondelet St. Mary's Hospital, Tucson, AZ, p. A38

KAEMS, Amanda, Manager Information Systems, Paradise Valley Hospital, National City, CA, p. A76

KAESE, James, Vice President Administration, Rush Oak Park Hospital, Oak Park, IL, p. A190

KAFKA, Rich, M.D. Chief Medical Officer, Avera Gregory Hospital, Gregory, SD, p. A560

KAFRISSEN, Steven R., M.D. Medical Director, First Hospital Wyoming Valley, Kingston, PA, p. A528

KAGAN, Richard J., M.D. Chief of Staff, Shriners Hospitals for Children–Cincinnati Burns Hospital, Cincinnati, OH, p. A475

KAHL, Tracy, M.D. Chief Medical Officer, Manning Regional Healthcare Center, Manning, IA, p. A224

KAHLE, Crystal, Director Human Resources and Marketing, Avera St. Anthony's Hospital, O'Neill, NE, p. A386

KAHLER, Ralph, M.D. Medical Director, Regency Hospital of Hattiesburg, Hattiesburg, MS, p. A348

KAHLY–MCMAHON, Heidi
Vice President Human Resources, Genesis Medical Center, Illini Campus, Silvis, IL, p. A194
Interim Vice President Human Resources, Genesis Medical Center–Davenport, Davenport, IA, p. A219

KAHN, Jalil, M.D. Chief of Staff, Atrium Medical Center of Corinth, Corinth, TX, p. A593

KAHN, Maureen A., R.N., President and Chief Executive Officer, Blessing Hospital, Quincy, IL, p. A193

KAIL, Cynthia, Chief Nursing Officer and Executive Director Public Health, Greene County Medical Center, Jefferson, IA, p. A223

KAISER, Diane, Administrator, Dubuis Hospital of Corpus Christi, Corpus Christi, TX, p. A594

KAISER, Ken, Director Information Technology, Guttenberg Municipal Hospital, Guttenberg, IA, p. A222

KAISER, Matt, Vice President of Employee Services, Wyoming Medical Center, Casper, WY, p. A701

KAJIWARA, Gary K., President and Chief Executive Officer, Kuakini Medical Center, Honolulu, HI, p. A164

KAKAVAS, Connie, Chief Human Resources Officer, Summit Healthcare Regional Medical Center, Show Low, AZ, p. A37

KAKI, Karim, M.D. Chief Medical Director, Hendry Regional Medical Center, Clewiston, FL, p. A120

KALAJAINEN, Kimberly, Vice President and Chief Information Officer, Lawrence + Memorial Hospital, New London, CT, p. A111

KALANIHUIA, Janice, President, Molokai General Hospital, Kaunakakai, HI, p. A166

KALAR, Cathy, Chief Financial Officer, Broaddus Hospital, Philippi, WV, p. A680

KALATA, John J., D.O. Chief of Staff, Millcreek Community Hospital, Erie, PA, p. A525

KALAVAR, Jagadeesh S., M.D. Chief of Staff, Michael E. DeBakey Veterans Affairs Medical Center, Houston, TX, p. A611

KALCHIK, Kevin, Chief Financial Officer, War Memorial Hospital, Sault Sainte Marie, MI, p. A324

KALE, Debra
Vice President Human Resources, Cleveland Regional Medical Center, Shelby, NC, p. A460
Vice President Human Resources, Crawley Memorial Hospital, Shelby, NC, p. A461
Director Human Resources, Kings Mountain Hospital, Kings Mountain, NC, p. A455

KALEEL, Reza, Executive Vice President and Chief Operating Officer, St. Mary's Hospital and Medical Center, Grand Junction, CO, p. A102

KALETKOWSKI, Chester B.
President and Chief Executive Officer, Inspira Medical Center–Elmer, Elmer, NJ, p. A404
President and Chief Executive Officer, Inspira Medical Center–Vineland, Vineland, NJ, p. A412

KALGAARD, Jan, Administrator, Broadwater Health Center, Townsend, MT, p. A380

KALINA, Andrea, Vice President Human Resources and Organizational Advancement, St. Clair Memorial Hospital, Pittsburgh, PA, p. A538

KALKA, Gina, R.N. Chief Nursing Officer, Pecos County Memorial Hospital, Fort Stockton, TX, p. A603

KALKOWSKI, Kelly, Chief Executive Officer, Niobrara Valley Hospital, Lynch, NE, p. A386

KALKUT, Gary, M.D. Senior Vice President and Chief Medical Officer, Montefiore Medical Center,, NY, p. A434

KALL, Greg, Chief Information Officer, Summa Health System, Akron, OH, p. A470

KALLAL, Catherine, M.D. Chief Medical Officer, Holy Cross Hospital, Chicago, IL, p. A176

KALLEN–ZURY, Karen, Chief Executive Officer, Hollywood Pavilion,, FL, p. A125

KALLENBERGER, Dianna, Chief Manpower Branch, Irwin Army Community Hospital, Junction City, KS, p. A236

KALLEVIG, Daryl, Chief Information Officer, Riverwood Healthcare Center, Aitkin, MN, p. A328

KALONICK, Roger, Business Manager, North Alabama Regional Hospital, Decatur, AL, p. A19

KALSMAN, Stephen L., Area Finance Officer, Kaiser Permanente San Jose Medical Center, San Jose, CA, p. A87

KALTHOFF, Stella, Administrative Assistant, Manager Human Resources and Coordinator Quality Improvement, Swift County–Benson Hospital, Benson, MN, p. A329

KALUA, Patricia, Chief Nurse Executive, Kona Community Hospital, Kealakekua, HI, p. A166

KAMBEROS, Peter N., Chief Operating Officer, Thorek Memorial Hospital, Chicago, IL, p. A179

KAMBIC, Phillip M., Chief Executive Officer, Riverside Medical Center, Kankakee, IL, p. A186

KAMBOJ, Pradeep, M.D. Chief Medical Staff, Tulare Regional Medical Center, Tulare, CA, p. A93

KAMERZELL, Rick, Vice President Operations, St. Thomas More Hospital, Canon City, CO, p. A98

KAMIKAWA, Cynthia, R.N. Vice President Nursing Emergency Department and Trauma and Chief Nursing Officer, Queen's Medical Center, Honolulu, HI, p. A165

KAMINSKI, Gene, Vice President Human Resources, McLaren Northern Michigan, Petoskey, MI, p. A321

KAMINSKI, Tammy, Director Human Resources, Alaska Regional Hospital, Anchorage, AK, p. A27

KAMINSKI, Toni, Director Human Resources, Medical Center Enterprise, Enterprise, AL, p. A19

KAMMERER, James M., Vice President Support Services, Great River Medical Center, West Burlington, IA, p. A230

KAMMERUD, Shawn, Manager Information Services, Osceola Medical Center, Osceola, WI, p. A694

KAMMIRE, Gordon, M.D. Chief of Staff, Wake Forest Baptist Health–Lexington Medical Center, Lexington, NC, p. A456

KAMPS, Mary Jane
Chief Information Officer, Southern Maine Medical Center, Biddeford, ME, p. A282
Chief Information Officer, Union Hospital, Elkton, MD, p. A291

KAMPWERTH, Dennis, Director Management Information Systems, Gateway Regional Medical Center, Granite City, IL, p. A184

KANANI, Bhargav, M.D. Chief of Staff, Ste. Genevieve County Memorial Hospital, Ste. Genevieve, MO, p. A372

KANE, Addy, Chief Financial Officer, Roger Williams Medical Center, Providence, RI, p. A547

KANE, Audrey, Interim Chief Financial Officer, Prowers Medical Center, Lamar, CO, p. A103

KANE, Melissa, Coordinator Human Resources, Pocahontas Memorial Hospital, Buckeye, WV, p. A675

KANE, Robert E., Administrator and Chief Executive Officer, Divine Providence Hospital, Williamsport, PA, p. A544

KANE, Terri, Chief Executive Officer, Dixie Regional Medical Center, Saint George, UT, p. A646

KANG, Balvinder, M.D. Medical Director, BryLin Hospitals, Buffalo, NY, p. A422

KANIA, Kathy, Chief Information Officer, Staten Island University Hospital,, NY, p. A436

KANKEL, LeAnne, Vice President Human Relations, Barton Memorial Hospital, South Lake Tahoe, CA, p. A91

KANNADAY, Colleen, FACHE,
President, Advocate BroMenn Medical Center, Normal, IL, p. A190
President, Advocate Eureka Hospital, Eureka, IL, p. A182

KANSGEN, Mike, Director Information Services, Community Hospital, Grand Junction, CO, p. A101

KANTHILAL, S. K., M.D. President Medical Staff, Sarah D. Culbertson Memorial Hospital, Rushville, IL, p. A194

KANTO, William, M.D. Acting Senior Vice President and Chief Medical Officer, Georgia Regents Medical Center, Augusta, GA, p. A147

KANTOS, Craig A., Chief Executive Officer, Riverside Medical Center, Waupaca, WI, p. A698

KANUCH, James A.
Vice President Finance, Allegheny Valley Hospital, Natrona Heights, PA, p. A533
Vice President Finance, Western Pennsylvania Hospital, Pittsburgh, PA, p. A539

KANWAL, Neeraj, M.D. Vice President Medical Affairs, ProMedica Toledo Hospital, Toledo, OH, p. A491

KAPASKA, David, D.O., Regional President, Avera McKennan Hospital and University Health Center, Sioux Falls, SD, p. A562

KAPHINGS, Mary, Director Human Resources, Fairview Ridges Hospital, Burnsville, MN, p. A330

KAPLAN, Gary, FACHE, Chairman and Chief Executive Officer, Virginia Mason Medical Center, Seattle, WA, p. A671

KAPLAN, Ronald, Chief Financial Officer, North Philadelphia Health System, Philadelphia, PA, p. A536

KAPLAN, Tamra, Chief Operating Officer, Long Beach Memorial Medical Center, Long Beach, CA, p. A67

KAPTAIN–DAHLEN, Mari, Chief Operating Officer, Mercy Medical Center–Sioux City, Sioux City, IA, p. A228

KARAM, Chris, President and Chief Executive Officer, CHRISTUS St. Michael Health System, Texarkana, TX, p. A637

KARANJAI, Rajohn, M.D. Chief Medical Officer, Sidney Health Center, Sidney, MT, p. A380

KARASICK, Steve, Interim Vice President Human Resources, Piedmont Hospital, Atlanta, GA, p. A147

KARBER, Steven, M.D. Medical Director, Greene County Medical Center, Jefferson, IA, p. A223

KARDOW, Vivian
Chief Human Resources Officer, Memorial Hermann – Texas Medical Center, Houston, TX, p. A610
Chief Human Resources Officer, TIRR Memorial Hermann, Houston, TX, p. A613

KAREL, Thomas, Vice President Organization and Talent Effectiveness, Saint Mary's Health Care, Grand Rapids, MI, p. A315

KARES, Timothy, Chief Financial Officer, University of Arizona Medical Center – South Campus, Tucson, AZ, p. A39

KARG, Gary, Interim Chief Financial Officer, Evanston Regional Hospital, Evanston, WY, p. A702

KARINSHAK, David, Director Information Systems, East Cooper Medical Center, Mount Pleasant, SC, p. A554

KARKENNY, James, Chief Executive Officer, Terence Cardinal Cooke Health Care Center, New York, NY, p. A436

KARL, Don, Chief Operating Officer, Las Palmas Medical Center, El Paso, TX, p. A601

KARL, Peter J.
President and Chief Executive Officer, Manchester Memorial Hospital, Manchester, CT, p. A109
President and Chief Executive Officer, Rockville General Hospital, Vernon Rockville, CT, p. A112

KARL, Thomas P., President, Parkland Health Center, Farmington, MO, p. A360

KARMACH, Izabela, R.N., Administrator, San Diego County Psychiatric Hospital, San Diego, CA, p. A85

KARN, Cielette, M.D. Chief of Staff, Riverton Memorial Hospital, Riverton, WY, p. A703

KARN, Deborah, Chief Executive Officer, Kindred Hospital Easton, Easton, PA, p. A525

KARNAP, Fred W., Vice President Finance, Iredell Memorial Hospital, Statesville, NC, p. A461

KARNER, Diana M., R.N. Chief Nursing Officer, St. Luke's Hospital, San Francisco, CA, p. A87

KARNS, Kris, FACHE, Chief Executive Officer, Acuity Hospital of South Texas, San Antonio, TX, p. A630

KARPMAN, Robert, M.D. Vice President Medical Affairs, Cortland Regional Medical Center, Cortland, NY, p. A424

KARREN, Dinah, Director Human Resources, Bingham Memorial Hospital, Blackfoot, ID, p. A167

KARSTEN, Paul H., Vice President Finance and Chief Financial Officer, Pine Rest Christian Mental Health Services, Grand Rapids, MI, p. A315

KARTHEISER, Keri, Manager Human Resources, Aspirus Grand View Hospital, Ironwood, MI, p. A317

KARUSCHAK Jr., Michael, Chief Executive Officer, Amery Regional Medical Center, Amery, WI, p. A683

KARZON, Mark, Chief Executive Officer, U.S. Public Health Service Indian Hospital, Redlake, MN, p. A338

KASABIAN, Carolyn, Chief Financial Officer, St. Mary's Regional Medical Center, Lewiston, ME, p. A284

KASAN, Nita, Chief Operating Officer and Chief Nursing Officer, Sun Coast Hospital, Largo, FL, p. A129

KASBERGER, John, Vice President and Chief Financial Officer, Mercy Medical Center, Roseburg, OR, p. A517

KASITZ, Todd, Chief Financial Officer, Newton Medical Center, Newton, KS, p. A240

KASKIE, James R., President and Chief Executive Officer, KALEIDA Health, Buffalo, NY, p. A422

KASKO, Andre, D.O. Chief Medical Staff, Hi–Desert Medical Center, Joshua Tree, CA, p. A64

KASMAN, Glenn, President, MultiCare Good Samaritan Hospital, Puyallup, WA, p. A669

KASPER, Keith, Chief Financial Officer, Hospital of the University of Pennsylvania, Philadelphia, PA, p. A535

KASPER–COPE, Shelly, M.D. Chief of Staff, Tri Valley Health System, Cambridge, NE, p. A382

KASPERBAUER, Dwight, Vice President Human Resources, The University of Kansas Hospital, Kansas City, KS, p. A237

KASS, Andrew J A, M.D. Assistant Superintendent, Albert J. Solnit Psychiatric Center – South Campus, Middletown, CT, p. A110

KASS, Bonnie, Chief Nursing Officer and Vice President Patient Care and Support Services, Huntington Memorial Hospital, Pasadena, CA, p. A79

KASSAB, Jerry, President and Chief Executive Officer, Lakeside Behavioral Healthcare–Princeton Plaza, Orlando, FL, p. A135

KASSAHN, Kristine, Chief Executive Officer, Fresno Surgical Hospital, Fresno, CA, p. A61

KASSER, Michael, Chief Financial Officer, Herrin Hospital, Herrin, IL, p. A168

KASSIS, Frederick, M.D. Chief of Staff, Rolling Plains Memorial Hospital, Sweetwater, TX, p. A636

KAST, Kevin F., President and Chief Executive Officer, St. Mary's Hospital, Decatur, IL, p. A180

KASTANIS, John N., FACHE, Chief Executive Officer, Temple University Hospital, Philadelphia, PA, p. A536

KATELEY, Trace, Manager Information Systems, San Bernardino Mountains Community Hospital District, Lake Arrowhead, CA, p. A66

KATEN–BAHENSKY, Donna, President and Chief Executive Officer, University of Wisconsin Hospital and Clinics, Madison, WI, p. A690

KATES, Josh, Information Technology Analyst, Andrew McFarland Mental Health Center, Springfield, IL, p. A195

KATES, Kenneth P., Chief Executive Officer, University of Iowa Hospitals and Clinics, Iowa City, IA, p. A223

KATHRINS, PH.D, Richard J., President and Chief Executive Officer, Bacharach Institute for Rehabilitation, Pomona, NJ, p. A409

KATNENI, Jitendra P., M.D. Medical Director, Select Specialty Hospital–Flint, Flint, MI, p. A314

KATO, Laura, Vice President Human Resources, St. Francis Medical Center, Lynwood, CA, p. A72

KATSCHKE, Jr., R. William, M.D. Medical Director, Grover C. Dils Medical Center, Caliente, NV, p. A391

KATZ, Jeffrey, M.D. Chief Medical Officer, Memorial Hermann – Texas Medical Center, Houston, TX, p. A610

KATZ, Mike, Director Information Systems, Logan Memorial Hospital, Russellville, KY, p. A260

KATZ, Richard, M.D. Vice President Medical Affairs, Mt. Washington Pediatric Hospital, Baltimore, MD, p. A288

KATZ, Robert, M.D. Vice President Clinical Affairs, University of New Mexico Hospitals, Albuquerque, NM, p. A415

KATZ, Stephen A., M.D. Chief Medical Officer and Senior Vice President Medical Affairs, Vassar Brothers Medical Center, Poughkeepsie, NY, p. A440

KATZ, Steven E., M.D. Chief Medical Officer, Jersey Shore Hospital, Jersey Shore, PA, p. A528

KATZIN, David, M.D. Chief Medical Officer, Central Carolina Hospital, Sanford, NC, p. A460

KAUFFMAN, Angie, MSN, Acting Administrator and Director of Nursing, Northwest Hills Surgical Hospital, Austin, TX, p. A585

KAUFMAN, Bob, Fiscal Officer, Hiram W. Davis Medical Center, Petersburg, VA, p. A659

KAUFMAN, Cheryl, Director Health Information Management, Bayfront Health Dade City, Dade City, FL, p. A121

KAUFMAN, Dan, Director Information Services, Paulding County Hospital, Paulding, OH, p. A488

KAUFMAN, Irvin A., M.D. Senior Vice President Health Affairs and Chief Medical Officer, Rady Children's Hospital – San Diego, San Diego, CA, p. A85

KAUFMAN, Mark, Director Human Resources, Lanterman Developmental Center, Pomona, CA, p. A80

KAUFMAN, Ronald L., M.D. Chief Medical Officer, Lakewood Regional Medical Center, Lakewood, CA, p. A66

KAUFMAN, Samuel, Chief Executive Officer and Managing Director, Desert Springs Hospital Medical Center, Las Vegas, NV, p. A392

KAUL, Stephanie, Chief Financial Officer, Platte County Memorial Hospital, Wheatland, WY, p. A704

KAUPA, Michael, Executive Vice President and Chief Operating Officer, Park Nicollet Methodist Hospital, Saint Louis Park, MN, p. A339

KAUPPILA, Glenn, D.O. Chief of Staff, Aspirus Keweenaw Hospital, Laurium, MI, p. A319

KAUTZ, Terri, Manager Human Resources, Weiser Memorial Hospital, Weiser, ID, p. A172

KAUTZER, Kenneth A., Senior Vice President Finance and Treasurer, Presence Saints Mary & Elizabeth Medical Center, Chicago, IL, p. A178

KAUZLARICH, Sidney A., M.D. Medical Director, Douglas County Community Mental Health Center, Omaha, NE, p. A388

KAVANAUGH, Paul B., President and Chief Executive Officer, Community Care Hospital, New Orleans, LA, p. A275

KAVAWAHA, Sean, Supervisor Information Technology and Information Systems, Pondera Medical Center, Conrad, MT, p. A375

KAVTARADZE, David, M.D. Chief of Staff, Crisp Regional Hospital, Cordele, GA, p. A151

KAY, Brian
Chief Financial Officer, McLaren Bay Region, Bay City, MI, p. A309
Chief Financial Officer, McLaren Bay Special Care, Bay City, MI, p. A309

KAY, Kirk, Chief Financial Officer, Veterans Affairs Medical Center, Omaha, NE, p. A388

KAY, Robert W., Senior Vice President and Chief Financial Officer, Memorial Medical Center, Springfield, IL, p. A195

KAYE, Jessie, Chief Executive Officer, Prairie View, Newton, KS, p. A240

KAZMIERCZAK, Stanley, Controller, Presence Saint Joseph Hospital, Chicago, IL, p. A178

KAZMOUZ, Safwan, M.D. Chief Medical Director, HEALTHSOUTH Rehabilitation Hospital, Concord, NH, p. A397

KEANE, Dennis M., Vice President Finance and Chief Financial Officer, St. John's Riverside Hospital, Yonkers, NY, p. A446

KEANE, Fran, Vice President Human Resources, CentraState Healthcare System, Freehold, NJ, p. A404

KEANE, Valerie E., FACHE Vice President Operations, Sentara Northern Virginia Medical Center, Woodbridge, VA, p. A663

KEARNEY, Lynn, VP Patient Services & Chief Nursing Officer, Robert Wood Johnson University Hospital Rahway, Rahway, NJ, p. A409

KEARNEY, M. Clark, Vice President Human Resources, Saint Mary's Hospital, Waterbury, CT, p. A112

KEARNS, James, Chief Information Officer, Delnor Hospital, Geneva, IL, p. A183

KEATING, Michael, President and Chief Executive Officer, Christ Hospital, Cincinnati, OH, p. A474

KEATON, Tony, Director Information Systems, Roane General Hospital, Spencer, WV, p. A681

KEATON, William A., Chief Executive Officer, Baylor Medical Center at Frisco, Frisco, TX, p. A605

KECK, Paul, M.D., President and Chief Executive Officer, Lindner Center of HOPE, Mason, OH, p. A485

KECKAN, William D., Chief Operating Officer, Marymount Hospital, Garfield Heights, OH, p. A482

KEDALIS, Bob, Director Business Development, Michiana Behavioral Health Center, Plymouth, IN, p. A212

KEDDINGTON, Richard, Chief Executive Officer, Select Specialty Hospital–Milwaukee, Milwaukee, WI, p. A692

KEE, Agnes, Financial Manager, Gallup Indian Medical Center, Gallup, NM, p. A416

KEEF, Shaun, Chief Financial Officer, Central Peninsula General Hospital, Soldotna, AK, p. A29

KEEFE, Mary Jo, R.N. Vice President Patient Care Services and Chief Nursing Officer, Chester River Health System, Chestertown, MD, p. A290

KEEFER, Russ, Chief Human Resources Officer, Kennewick General Hospital, Kennewick, WA, p. A667

KEEFOVER, Robert, M.D. Chief Medical Officer, William R. Sharpe, Jr. Hospital, Weston, WV, p. A682

KEEGAN, Julie, Vice President Finance, Craig Hospital, Englewood, CO, p. A100

KEEGAN, Justin, Director Support Services, Avera Gregory Hospital, Gregory, SD, p. A560

KEEL, Barry L., Chief Executive Officer, Bay Medical Center Sacred Heart, Panama City, FL, p. A136

KEEL, Deborah C., Chief Executive Officer, North Fulton Regional Hospital, Roswell, GA, p. A159

KEEL, Patricia
Chief Financial Officer, Good Shepherd Medical Center, Longview, TX, p. A619
Chief Financial Officer, Good Shepherd Medical Center–Marshall, Marshall, TX, p. A621

KEELAN, John E., Administrator and Chief Executive Officer, Brodstone Memorial Hospital, Superior, NE, p. A390

KEELE, Paula, Manager Information Systems, Presence United Samaritans Medical Center, Danville, IL, p. A180

KEELER, Dave, Chief Financial Officer, Pipestone County Medical Center Avera, Pipestone, MN, p. A338

KEELER, Jean, President and Chief Executive Officer, Grand View Hospital, Sellersville, PA, p. A541

KEELER, Karl, Chief Executive Officer, Saint Alphonsus Medical Center – Nampa, Nampa, ID, p. A170

KEELEY, Katherine, M.D. Chief of Staff, Sunrise Hospital and Medical Center, Las Vegas, NV, p. A394

KEELING, Kevin, Chief Financial Officer, St. Lucie Medical Center, Port St. Lucie, FL, p. A138

KEEN, Michael, Senior Vice President and Chief Financial Officer, Grand View Hospital, Sellersville, PA, p. A541

KEEN, Robert C., FACHE, President and Chief Executive Officer, Hancock Regional Hospital, Greenfield, IN, p. A204

KEENAN, Annette M., Chief Executive Officer, Webster County Memorial Hospital, Webster Springs, WV, p. A681

KEENAN, Harold, M.D. Chief Medical Officer, Garden County Health Services, Oshkosh, NE, p. A388

KEENAN, Jimmie O., Commander, Evans U. S. Army Community Hospital, Fort Carson, CO, p. A101

KEENAN, Richard, Senior Vice President Finance and Chief Financial Officer, Valley Hospital, Ridgewood, NJ, p. A410

KEENAN, Robert, M.D. Chief Quality Officer, Western Pennsylvania Hospital, Pittsburgh, PA, p. A539

KEENE, Kaaron, Vice President Patient Care Services, Memorial Health Center, Medford, WI, p. A691

KEENE, Kim, Vice President Professional Services, Thibodaux Regional Medical Center, Thibodaux, LA, p. A279

KEENE, Richard, Chief Financial Officer, Queen's Medical Center, Honolulu, HI, p. A165

KEENE, Russell G., Chief Executive Officer, Androscoggin Valley Hospital, Berlin, NH, p. A397

KEENEY, Mary Ellen, Vice President Human Resources, Thomas Jefferson University Hospital, Philadelphia, PA, p. A537

KEEVER, Jerry, Administrator, Sharkey–Issaquena Community Hospital, Rolling Fork, MS, p. A353

KEGLEY, Carl J., System Director Information Technology, Fairbanks Memorial Hospital, Fairbanks, AK, p. A28

KEGLEY, Sue, Director Human Resources, Onslow Memorial Hospital, Jacksonville, NC, p. A455

KEHRBERG, Mark, M.D. Chief Medical Officer, Calumet Medical Center, Chilton, WI, p. A685

KEHRBERG, Mark W., M.D. Senior Vice President and Chief Medical Officer, Mercy Medical Center, Oshkosh, WI, p. A694

KEHUS, Frank, Associate Director for Operations, Marion Veterans Affairs Medical Center, Marion, IL, p. A187

KEILER, Susan, Chief Operating Officer, St. Mary's Regional Medical Center, Lewiston, ME, p. A284

KEIM, Jane T., Vice President Operations, The Children's Institute of Pittsburgh, Pittsburgh, PA, p. A538

KEIM, Richard, M.D. Chief Medical Officer, Spearfish Regional Surgery Center, Spearfish, SD, p. A563

KEIM, Thomas, Chief Executive Officer, Ste. Genevieve County Memorial Hospital, Ste. Genevieve, MO, p. A372

KEISER, Trish, Comptroller, Avera Gregory Hospital, Gregory, SD, p. A560

KEISTER, Catharine L., Chief Nursing Officer, Sunbury Community Hospital and Outpatient Center, Sunbury, PA, p. A542

KEITEL, Kal, Manager Personnel Services, St. Anthony's Memorial Hospital, Effingham, IL, p. A181

KEITH, Allen, Senior Vice President and Chief Human Resources Officer, Community Memorial Hospital, Menomonee Falls, WI, p. A691

KEITH, Bridgette, Director Human Resources, HEALTHSOUTH Northern Kentucky Rehabilitation Hospital, Edgewood, KY, p. A250

KEITH, Darlene, Chief Information Systems, Alleghany Memorial Hospital, Sparta, NC, p. A461

KEITH, David N., FACHE, President and Chief Executive Officer, McAlester Regional Health Center, McAlester, OK, p. A501

KEITH, Lorraine, FACHE Chief Nursing Officer, St. Vincent's Medical Center Southside, Jacksonville, FL, p. A127

KELBAUGH, Brian, Chief Financial Officer, Grafton City Hospital, Grafton, WV, p. A677

KELBLY, Kevin, Senior Vice President Finance and Corporate Fiscal Affairs, Carroll Hospital Center, Westminster, MD, p. A294

KELLAR, Brian, Chief Executive Officer, Grundy County Memorial Hospital, Grundy Center, IA, p. A222

KELLAR, Karen, R.N. Vice President of Patient Care Services, Tillamook Regional Medical Center, Tillamook, OR, p. A518

KELLAR, Randy, Director Human Resources, Psychiatric Institute of Washington, Washington, DC, p. A117

KELLAR, Richard A., President, Aurora West Allis Medical Center, West Allis, WI, p. A699

KELLEHER, Hugh J., Chief Operating Officer, Falmouth Hospital, Falmouth, MA, p. A300

KELLEHER, John G., Manager Human Resources, Athol Memorial Hospital, Athol, MA, p. A295

KELLEHER, LaCinda, Director of Nursing, Colorado West Psychiatric Hospital, Grand Junction, CO, p. A101

KELLEHER, Mary, Vice President Human Resources, Holyoke Medical Center, Holyoke, MA, p. A300

KELLEHER, Michael, Chief Medical Officer, Ann & Robert H. Lurie Children's Hospital of Chicago, Chicago, IL, p. A176

KELLEHER, Patrick, M.D. Chief Medical Staff, Saint Joseph Berea, Berea, KY, p. A248

KELLENBARGER, Lance, Site Director Information Systems, St. Catherine Hospital, Garden City, KS, p. A234

KELLER, Alena, Chief Nursing Officer, Roundup Memorial Healthcare, Roundup, MT, p. A379

KELLER, Allen, Director Human Resources, Sumner Regional Medical Center, Wellington, KS, p. A246

KELLER, Ann, Manager Health Information Management, HEALTHSOUTH Walton Rehabilitation Hospital, Augusta, GA, p. A148

KELLER, Diane R., Chief Executive Officer, Memorial Community Health, Aurora, NE, p. A381

KELLER, J. Michael, Vice President Operations, Newton Medical Center, Newton, KS, p. A240

KELLER, Jack M., Administrator, Saint Thomas Hickman Hospital, Centerville, TN, p. A566

KELLER, James, Director Human Resources, NEA Baptist Memorial Hospital, Jonesboro, AR, p. A45

KELLER, Jane, R.N., Chief Executive Officer, Indiana Orthopaedic Hospital, Indianapolis, IN, p. A205

KELLER, Jill, R.N. Vice President for Nursing Services, Quality and Risk Management, Waynesboro Hospital, Waynesboro, PA, p. A543

KELLER, Jim
Director Information Services, Bronson Battle Creek, Battle Creek, MI, p. A309
Site Director Information Services, Saint Mary's Health Care, Grand Rapids, MI, p. A315

KELLER, Justin, Director Information Technology, Murray County Medical Center, Slayton, MN, p. A341

KELLER, Mark, M.D. President Medical Staff, Wake Forest Baptist Health–Davie Hospital, Mocksville, NC, p. A457

KELLER, Marsha, Director Human Resources, Kane Community Hospital, Kane, PA, p. A528

KELLER, Maryalice, Vice President Brand and Talent Management, Unity Hospital, Rochester, NY, p. A441

KELLER, Michael J., Vice President Financial Affairs and Chief Financial Officer, Spaulding Hospital for Continuing Medical Care Cambridge, Cambridge, MA, p. A299

KELLER, Ruey, Acting Chief Information Officer, Veterans Affairs San Diego Healthcare System, San Diego, CA, p. A86

KELLER, Thomas, Executive Vice President and Chief Operating Officer, St. Anthony Shawnee Hospital, Shawnee, OK, p. A506

KELLER, Wendy, Director Health Information Management, Atrium Medical Center of Corinth, Corinth, TX, p. A593

KELLERMAN, Scott, Chief Financial Officer, Ely–Bloomenson Community Hospital, Ely, MN, p. A332

KELLEY, Ann, Director Human Resources, Hardin Memorial Hospital, Elizabethtown, KY, p. A250

KELLEY, Brent, Director Information Technology, Nor–Lea General Hospital, Lovington, NM, p. A417

KELLEY, Jalinda, Director, Chickasaw Nation Medical Center, Ada, OK, p. A495

KELLEY, Janice, Chief Financial Officer, Marshall County Hospital, Benton, KY, p. A248

KELLEY, Jim, Vice President Finance and Support Services, Advocate Lutheran General Hospital, Park Ridge, IL, p. A191

KELLEY, Mary, Director Human Resources, The Outer Banks Hospital, Nags Head, NC, p. A458

KELLEY, R. Lewis, Administrator, Chatuge Regional Hospital and Nursing Home, Hiawassee, GA, p. A154

KELLEY, Sarah Jo, Director Human Resources, Ste. Genevieve County Memorial Hospital, Ste. Genevieve, MO, p. A372

KELLEY, Steven L., President and Chief Executive Officer, Ellenville Regional Hospital, Ellenville, NY, p. A425

KELLEY, Sue, Chief Financial Officer, Cordell Memorial Hospital, Cordell, OK, p. A497

KELLEY, Suzanne, Director Human Resources, North Suburban Medical Center, Thornton, CO, p. A106

KELLEY, Warren, Chief Information Officer, Reynolds Memorial Hospital, Glen Dale, WV, p. A677

KELLEY–ROBINSON, Kathleen, Manager Human Resources, Nebraska Orthopaedic Hospital, Omaha, NE, p. A388

KELLIHER, Brandon, IT Operations Officer, Great Plains Regional Medical Center, North Platte, NE, p. A386

KELLIHER, Michael, Vice President Human Resources, Brattleboro Memorial Hospital, Brattleboro, VT, p. A649

KELLING, Jim, M.D. Chief of Staff, Transylvania Regional Hospital, Brevard, NC, p. A448

KELLIS, Dana, M.D. Senior Vice President Medical Affairs and Chief Medical Officer, Pinnacle Health System, Harrisburg, PA, p. A527

KELLOGG, Brewster, D.O. Chief Medical Staff, Citizens Medical Center, Colby, KS, p. A232

KELLOGG, Jason, M.D. Chief of Staff, Newport Bay Hospital, Newport Beach, CA, p. A76

KELLS, Anne, Interim Chief Financial Officer, Appleton Area Health Services, Appleton, MN, p. A328

KELLUM, Craig, Director Management Information Systems, Cape Fear Valley – Bladen County Hospital, Elizabethtown, NC, p. A452

KELLY, Allen, R.N. Vice President Procedural Services & CNO, Riverside Medical Center, Kankakee, IL, p. A186

KELLY, Ashley, Manager Human Resources, Middlesboro ARH Hospital, Middlesboro, KY, p. A257

KELLY, Brian
Vice President Finance, Advocate South Suburban Hospital, Hazel Crest, IL, p. A184
Acting Chief Fiscal Service, San Franciso Veterans Affairs Medical Center, San Francisco, CA, p. A87

KELLY, Brian E., M.D. President Medical Staff, Saint Elizabeth's Medical Center, Wabasha, MN, p. A342

KELLY, Bruce, Chief Information Officer, Mercy Memorial Hospital System, Monroe, MI, p. A320

KELLY, Charles, D.O. Vice President Medical Affairs and Chief Medical Officer, Henry Ford Macomb Hospitals, Clinton Township, MI, p. A311

KELLY, Colan, Chief Financial Officer, Pineville Community Hospital Association, Pineville, KY, p. A259

KELLY, Dan, R.N. Chief Nursing Officer, Memorial Hermann Memorial City Medical Center, Houston, TX, p. A610

KELLY, Daniel J., President and Chief Executive Officer, St. Mary's Community Hospital, Nebraska City, NE, p. A386

KELLY, Daniel R., Chief Executive Officer, McKenzie County Healthcare System, Watford City, ND, p. A469

KELLY, Debbie, Chief Executive Officer, South Texas Spine and Surgical Hospital, San Antonio, TX, p. A632

KELLY, Edward, President, Milford Regional Medical Center, Milford, MA, p. A302

KELLY, John J., M.D. Chief of Staff, Abington Memorial Hospital, Abington, PA, p. A519

KELLY, Kathleen, M.D. Chief Medical Officer and Chief Quality Officer, SwedishAmerican Hospital, Rockford, IL, p. A194

KELLY, Kerry, Superintendent, Blue Mountain Recovery Center, Pendleton, OR, p. A515

KELLY, Laurence E., President and Chief Executive Officer, Nathan Littauer Hospital and Nursing Home, Gloversville, NY, p. A426

KELLY, Lynn, Vice President Human Resources, San Antonio Community Hospital, Upland, CA, p. A94

KELLY, Marcia, Manager, IT, Mercer County Hospital, Aledo, IL, p. A173

KELLY, Mark, Vice President Finance, St. Francis Medical Center, Trenton, NJ, p. A411

KELLY, Maura, Vice President Fiscal Services, Pen Bay Medical Center, Rockport, ME, p. A285

KELLY, Maureen, R.N. Chief Nursing Officer, Roswell Park Cancer Institute, Buffalo, NY, p. A422

KELLY, Melissa, Chief Operating Officer, Pender Community Hospital, Pender, NE, p. A389

KELLY, Michael
Vice President, Christian Hospital, Saint Louis, MO, p. A369
Information Systems Account Executive, Progress West HealthCare Center, Saint Charles, MO, p. A368

KELLY, Michael, M.D. President Medical Staff, Raleigh General Hospital, Beckley, WV, p. A675

KELLY, Patrick J., FACHE, Director, Minneapolis Veterans Affairs Health Care System, Minneapolis, MN, p. A336

KELLY, Peter A., President and Chief Executive Officer, Christ Hospital, Jersey City, NJ, p. A405

KELLY, Raymond, R.N. Chief Nursing Officer, Texas Health Presbyterian Hospital Plano, Plano, TX, p. A628

KELLY, Roy, Facility Director, Hawthorn Center, Northville, MI, p. A321

KELLY, Scott A., Chief Executive Officer, Rogue Valley Medical Center, Medford, OR, p. A515

KELLY, Shannon, Director Human Resources, Morton General Hospital, Morton, WA, p. A668

KELLY, Steven G., President and Chief Executive Officer, Newton Medical Center, Newton, KS, p. A240

KELLY, Sylvia K., Chief Executive Officer, HEALTHSOUTH Rehabilitation Hospital, Albuquerque, NM, p. A414

KELLY, Jr., Thomas, Chief Financial Officer, Moses Taylor Hospital, Scranton, PA, p. A540

KELLY, Thomas F., M.D. Medical Director, Deer's Head Hospital Center, Salisbury, MD, p. A294

KELLY, Thomas J., M.P.H. Vice President Medical Affairs, Union Hospital, Dover, OH, p. A480

KELLY, Timothy J., M.D. Medical Director, Fairbanks, Indianapolis, IN, p. A205

KELLY, Virginia, Chief Financial Officer, Eastside Psychiatric Hospital, Tallahassee, FL, p. A140

KELSEY, Janet, Director Business, Evansville State Hospital, Evansville, IN, p. A202

KEM, Mark
Vice President Finance and Chief Financial Officer, Chandler Regional Medical Center, Chandler, AZ, p. A30
Vice President Finance and Chief Financial Officer, Mercy Gilbert Medical Center, Gilbert, AZ, p. A31

KEMKER, S. E., M.D. President Medical Staff, St. Vincent Salem Hospital, Salem, IN, p. A213

KEMMERER, Jan, Director of Nursing, Mitchell County Hospital Health Systems, Beloit, KS, p. A232

KEMP, Jennifer, Director Marketing and Public Relations, St. Thomas More Hospital, Canon City, CO, p. A98

KEMP, Kenneth, Director Information Systems, Carlsbad Medical Center, Carlsbad, NM, p. A415

KEMP, Robin, R.N. Chief Nursing Officer, Craig General Hospital, Vinita, OK, p. A509

KEMP, Thomas, Chief Information Officer, New York Hospital Queens', NY, p. A435

KEMPF, Gary L., Administrator, CHRISTUS Coushatta Health Care Center, Coushatta, LA, p. A265

KEMPIAK, Matthew, Director Human Resources and Administrative Services, Memorial Hospital of Gardena, Gardena, CA, p. A62

KEMPINSKI, Paul D., Chief Operating Officer, Alfred I. duPont Hospital for Children, Wilmington, DE, p. A114

KEMPSON, Dave, Chief Information Officer, Maricopa Integrated Health System, Phoenix, AZ, p. A34

KEMPTON, Dana, Associate Director and Chief Financial Officer, Redington–Fairview General Hospital, Skowhegan, ME, p. A285

KENAGY, John Jay, Ph.D
Senior Vice President and Chief Information Officer, Legacy Meridian Park Hospital, Tualatin, OR, p. A518
Senior Vice President and Chief Information Officer, Legacy Mount Hood Medical Center, Gresham, OR, p. A513

KENARD, Deanna, Senior Vice President Human Resources, Methodist Charlton Medical Center, Dallas, TX, p. A596

KENDALL, Abigail, Chief Nursing Officer and Chief Operating Officer, Hillcrest Hospital Cushing, Cushing, OK, p. A497

KENDALL, Anthony
Vice President Human Resources, Baptist Health Extended Care Hospital, Little Rock, AR, p. A46
Vice President Human Resources, Baptist Health Medical Center – North Little Rock, North Little Rock, AR, p. A48
Vice President Human Resources, Baptist Health Medical Center–Arkadelphia, Arkadelphia, AR, p. A41
Vice President Human Resources, Baptist Health Medical Center–Little Rock, Little Rock, AR, p. A46
Vice President Human Resources, Baptist Health Rehabilitation Institute, Little Rock, AR, p. A46

KENDALL, Kim, Director Human Resources, Lawrence County Memorial Hospital, Lawrenceville, IL, p. A187

KENDLER, Lisa
Chief Financial Officer, Memorial Hermann Memorial City Medical Center, Houston, TX, p. A610
Chief Financial Officer, Memorial Hermann Sugar Land Hospital, Sugar Land, TX, p. A635

KENDRICK, Donovan, M.D. Chief of Staff, Baptist Medical Center South, Montgomery, AL, p. A23

KENDRICK, Gary G., Interim Chief Executive Officer, Knox County Hospital, Barbourville, KY, p. A248

KENDRICK, Jim R., Chief Executive Officer, Longview Regional Medical Center, Longview, TX, p. A619

KENDRICK, Justin, Chief Operating Officer, Texoma Medical Center, Denison, TX, p. A598

KENDRICK, Ray
Chief Human Resources Officer, Memorial Hospital Miramar, Miramar, FL, p. A133
Chief Human Resources Officer, Memorial Regional Hospital,, FL, p. A125

KENLEY, William A., Chief Executive Officer, Methodist Healthcare–Fayette Hospital, Somerville, TN, p. A579

KENNALLY, Kevin, M.D. Chief of Medical Staff, Sabetha Community Hospital, Sabetha, KS, p. A243

KENNEDY, Brad, Chief Executive Officer, HEALTHSOUTH Rehabilitation Hospital at Drake, Cincinnati, OH, p. A474

KENNEDY, Bruce, M.D. Chief Medical Officer, San Jacinto Methodist Hospital, Baytown, TX, p. A587

KENNEDY, Connie, Director Human Resources, Marlette Regional Hospital, Marlette, MI, p. A319

KENNEDY, Daniel, M.D. Chief of Staff, Sutter Davis Hospital, Davis, CA, p. A58

KENNEDY, Darla, Chief Information Officer, Newport Specialty Hospital, Tustin, CA, p. A93

KENNEDY, Diana, Director Human Resources, Meadowview Regional Medical Center, Maysville, KY, p. A257

KENNEDY, Elizabeth M., Administrator, J. Paul Jones Hospital, Camden, AL, p. A18

KENNEDY, Greg, Manager Human Resources, Windsor–Laurelwood Center for Behavioral Medicine, Willoughby, OH, p. A493

KENNEDY, Jay, Chief Operating Officer, Maria Parham Medical Center, Henderson, NC, p. A454

KENNEDY, Jerry, Administrator, Jefferson County Hospital, Fayette, MS, p. A346

KENNEDY, John, M.D. Vice President Medical Affairs, Mercy Health – Fairfield Hospital, Fairfield, OH, p. A481

KENNEDY, Kimberly, Manager Human Resources, Mendota Community Hospital, Mendota, IL, p. A188

KENNEDY, Mary, R.N. Chief Nursing Officer, Medina Hospital, Medina, OH, p. A486

KENNEDY, Pam, Vice President Regional Human Resources and Organizational Department, CHRISTUS St. Michael Health System, Texarkana, TX, p. A637

KENNEDY, R. Scott, M.D. Assistant Administrator and Chief Medical Officer, Olympic Medical Center, Port Angeles, WA, p. A669

KENNEDY, ReChelle, Chief Financial Officer, Kearny County Hospital, Lakin, KS, p. A237

KENNEDY, Ryan, Chief Operating Officer, Kingman Regional Medical Center, Kingman, AZ, p. A32

KENNEDY, Susan, Manager Human Resources, Novant Health Matthews Medical Center, Matthews, NC, p. A457

KENNEDY, Todd S., Executive Vice President and Chief Operating Officer, Providence Hospital, Mobile, AL, p. A22

KENNETH, Ron, M.D. Chief Medical Officer, West Valley Hospital, Goodyear, AZ, p. A32

KENNETT, David, Chief Financial Officer, Jersey Community Hospital, Jerseyville, IL, p. A186

KENNETT, Jerry, M.D. Chief Medical Officer, Boone Hospital Center, Columbia, MO, p. A359

KENNEY, Catherine, Chief Nursing Officer, Pampa Regional Medical Center, Pampa, TX, p. A626

KENNEY, Evan, Manager Information Technology Systems, Lee's Summit Medical Center, Lee's Summit, MO, p. A365

KENNEY, Mary Ellen, Chief Human Services, Manchester Veterans Affairs Medical Center, Manchester, NH, p. A399

KENNIFF, Peter B., CPA Chief Financial Officer, Mercy Suburban Hospital, Norristown, PA, p. A533

KENNINGTON, Lynn, Chief Financial Officer, Desert Springs Hospital Medical Center, Las Vegas, NV, p. A392

KENNINGTON, Milas H., Vice President, Human Resources, Western Medical Center–Santa Ana, Santa Ana, CA, p. A89

KENNY, Bertha, Director Human Resources, Sierra Tucson, Tucson, AZ, p. A39

KENNY, Carolyn, Executive Vice President Clinical Care, Children's Healthcare of Atlanta, Atlanta, GA, p. A146

KENNY, Richard, Vice President Human Resources, Hallmark Health System, Melrose, MA, p. A302

KENT, Alan, Chief Executive Officer, Meadows Regional Medical Center, Vidalia, GA, p. A162

KENT, Blair, Administrator, Riverton Hospital, Riverton, UT, p. A646

KENT, David, M.D. Chief Medical Officer, Boise Behavioral Health Hospital, Boise, ID, p. A167

KENT, David
Director Human Resources, Bolivar Medical Center, Cleveland, MS, p. A346
Chief Operating Officer, Southeastern Regional Medical Center, Newnan, GA, p. A158

KENT, Gerald P., Chief Executive Officer, Norristown State Hospital, Norristown, PA, p. A533

KENT, Michael, Chief Executive Officer, Muenster Memorial Hospital, Muenster, TX, p. A624

KENT, Raymer, Manager Human Resources, Lebanon Veterans Affairs Medical Center, Lebanon, PA, p. A529

KENT, Robert, D.O., President and Chief Executive Officer, Summa Western Reserve Hospital, Cuyahoga Falls, OH, p. A479

KENTERA, Amy, Chief Information Officer, Conifer Park, Glenville, NY, p. A426

KENTNER, Bob, Coordinator Information Systems, Harlan County Health System, Alma, NE, p. A381

KENTNER, Mike, Director of Nursing, Star Valley Medical Center, Afton, WY, p. A701

KENYON, Nanette, Director Human Resources, Westlake Regional Hospital, Columbia, KY, p. A249

KEOUGH, Tammy, Chief Financial Officer, William R. Sharpe, Jr. Hospital, Weston, WV, p. A682

KEOWN, Janet, Director Human Resources, Natchaug Hospital, Mansfield Center, CT, p. A109

KEPLER, Andrea, Chief Executive Officer, Wernersville State Hospital, Wernersville, PA, p. A543

KEPLINGER, Chelle, Chief Financial Officer, Massac Memorial Hospital, Metropolis, IL, p. A188

KEPLINGER, Ron, Chief Information Officer, Western Maryland Hospital Center, Hagerstown, MD, p. A292

KEPNER, Donald L., Chief Financial Officer, Ashtabula County Medical Center, Ashtabula, OH, p. A470

KEPPLE, Maryann, Chief Financial Officer, Vassar Brothers Medical Center, Poughkeepsie, NY, p. A440

KEPPLER, Edward L., M.D. Chief Medical Officer, Marion General Hospital, Marion, IN, p. A209

KEPPLER, Matthew, Chief Executive Officer, Select Specialty Hospital–Northern Kentucky, Fort Thomas, KY, p. A251

KEPPLINGER, Darcy, Manager Business Office, Landmann–Jungman Memorial Hospital Avera, Scotland, SD, p. A562

KERBS, Curtis, Vice President Information Services, Memorial Hospital, North Conway, NH, p. A399

KERCHER, Eugene, M.D. Chief Medical Officer, Kern Medical Center, Bakersfield, CA, p. A54

KERDEL, Francisco, M.D. President Medical Staff, University of Miami Hospital, Miami, FL, p. A132

KERLIN, Kerry, Vice President Information Technology, NorthShore University Health System Skokie Hospital, Skokie, IL, p. A194

KERMEN, John, D.O. Chief Medical Staff, Mendocino Coast District Hospital, Fort Bragg, CA, p. A60

KERN, Gordon, M.D. Medical Director, Oswego Community Hospital, Oswego, KS, p. A241

KERN, Howard P.
President and Chief Operating Officer, Sentara Leigh Hospital, Norfolk, VA, p. A658
Chief Operating Officer, Sentara Princess Anne Hospital, Virginia Beach, VA, p. A662

KERNELL, Shane, Chief Executive Officer, St. Mark's Medical Center, La Grange, TX, p. A617

KERNER, Donald, M.D. Vice President Medical Affairs, Franciscan St. Francis Health – Mooresville, Mooresville, IN, p. A210

KERNIZAN, Lorna, Chief Operating Officer, Aventura Hospital and Medical Center, Aventura, FL, p. A118

KERNS, Debbie S., Director Human Resources and Chief Operating Officer, Benewah Community Hospital, Saint Maries, ID, p. A171

KERR, Darrel K., M.D. Chief of Staff, Sutter Amador Hospital, Jackson, CA, p. A64

KERR, Gary, Chief Executive Officer, Memorial Hermann Northwest Hospital, Houston, TX, p. A611

KERR, Mark, Chief Executive Officer, Presentation Medical Center, Rolla, ND, p. A469

KERR, Rand, Chief Executive Officer, Lakeview Hospital, Bountiful, UT, p. A643

KERR, Sherri, Director of Nursing, Hegg Memorial Health Center Avera, Rock Valley, IA, p. A227

KERRINS, David, Vice President Informatics, Information Technology and Chief Informatics Officer, Seton Medical Center, Daly City, CA, p. A58

KERRWOOD, Patrick
Vice President Human Resources, Brandon Regional Hospital, Brandon, FL, p. A119
Vice President Human Resources, Regional Medical Center–Bayonet Point, Hudson, FL, p. A126

KERSCHEN, Susan, MS Vice President Chief Nursing Officer, Exempla Good Samaritan Medical Center, Lafayette, CO, p. A103

KERSEY, Jerry, Director Employee Relations, Eastern State Hospital, Lexington, KY, p. A254

KERSHNER, Kathy, Director of Nursing, Herington Municipal Hospital, Herington, KS, p. A235

KERSWILL, Randy, M.D. Medical Director, Winnebago Mental Health Institute, Winnebago, WI, p. A700

KERTIS, Robert, Vice President Finance, Calvert Memorial Hospital, Prince Frederick, MD, p. A293

KERWIN, George, President, Bellin Memorial Hospital, Green Bay, WI, p. A687

KESLING, Kimberly, Deputy Commander Clinical Service, Carl R. Darnall Army Medical Center, Fort Hood, TX, p. A603

KESS, Thomas, Vice President Human Resources, Pinnacle Health System, Harrisburg, PA, p. A527

KESSLER, Alexander, M.D. Chief of Staff, Northside Hospital–Cherokee, Canton, GA, p. A149

KESSLER, Annie, Human Resources Consultant, SSM St. Joseph Hospital West, Lake Saint Louis, MO, p. A364

KESSLER, D. McWilliams, President and Chief Executive Officer, New York Eye and Ear Infirmary, New York, NY, p. A435

KESSLER, David, M.D. Clinical Director, U. S. Public Health Service Indian Hospital, Zuni, NM, p. A419

KESSLER, Jeffrey R., Vice President Information Services, Dana–Farber Cancer Institute, Boston, MA, p. A296

KESSLER, Joseph, Executive Vice President and Chief Financial Officer, KALEIDA Health, Buffalo, NY, p. A422

KESSLER, Renee A., Chief Operating Officer, Saint Thomas Midtown Hospital, Nashville, TN, p. A576

KETCH, Lynn
Human Resources Recruiter Generalist, INTEGRIS Canadian Valley Hospital, Yukon, OK, p. A510
Director, Integris Southwest Medical Center, Oklahoma City, OK, p. A503

KETCHAM, Krista, Chief Financial Officer, Buena Vista Regional Medical Center, Storm Lake, IA, p. A229

KETCHAM, Michael S., President and Chief Executive Officer, Loring Hospital, Sac City, IA, p. A227

KETCHAM, Richard H., FACHE, President and Chief Executive Officer, St. Elizabeth Medical Center, Utica, NY, p. A444

KETCHER, Greg, Administrator, Lawton Indian Hospital, Lawton, OK, p. A500

KETTELLE, John, M.D. Vice President Operations and Medical Director, University of Arizona Medical Center – South Campus, Tucson, AZ, p. A39

KETTERHAGEN, James P., M.D. Senior Vice President and Chief Medical Officer, Jewish Hospital, Louisville, KY, p. A255

KETTERLING, Rhonda L., M.D. Chief Medical Officer, Sanford Medical Center Fargo, Fargo, ND, p. A466

KETTERMAN, Denise, R.N. Chief Nursing Officer, Newman Memorial Hospital, Shattuck, OK, p. A506

KETTLER, Paul, M.D. Vice President Medical Affairs, Unity Hospital, Fridley, MN, p. A332

KETZNER, Tabetha, Director Human Resources, Cheyenne County Hospital, Saint Francis, KS, p. A243

KEUSHKERIAN, Simon, M.D. Chief of Staff, Glendale Adventist Medical Center, Glendale, CA, p. A62

KEUTER, Mary Beth, Director Patient Care, Continuing Care Hospital at St. Luke's, Cedar Rapids, IA, p. A217

KEY, Lora, Chief Executive Officer, Sabetha Community Hospital, Sabetha, KS, p. A243

KEY, Sean, Director Information Technology, Mercy Medical Center, Williston, ND, p. A469

KEY, Tina, Chief Executive Officer, Vibra Specialty Hospital of Portland, Portland, OR, p. A516

KHADE, Kashmira, Coordinator Non–Clinical Services, Behavioral Center of Michigan, Warren, MI, p. A326

KHAN, Atique, M.D. Medical Director, University Behavioral Health of Denton, Denton, TX, p. A599

KHAN, Behram, M.D. Medical Director, Warm Springs Specialty Hospital of Victoria, Victoria, TX, p. A639

KHAN, Dan, M.D. Chief Medical Officer, Yoakum County Hospital, Denver City, TX, p. A599

KHAN, Humayun, M.D
Chief Medical Officer, Sacred Heart Hospital, Eau Claire, WI, p. A686
Chief Medical Officer, St. Joseph's Hospital, Chippewa Falls, WI, p. A685

KHAN, Nasir A., M.D., Chief Executive Officer, Bournewood Health Systems, Brookline, MA, p. A298

KHAN, Sarfraz, Medical Director, Meridian Health Services, Muncie, IN, p. A210

KHAN, Shahbaz, M.D. Medical Director, Two Rivers Behavioral Health System, Kansas City, MO, p. A364

KHAN, Yasin N., M.D., Chief Executive Officer, Westfield Hospital, Allentown, PA, p. A519

KHANCHANDANI, Ashok, Chief Financial Officer, Oroville Hospital, Oroville, CA, p. A78

KHANNA, Rajive, Chief Executive Officer, Grace Hospital, Cleveland, OH, p. A476

KHANNA, Vijay, M.D. Chief of Staff, Oakwood Heritage Hospital, Taylor, MI, p. A325

KHANOLKAR, Kiran, M.D. Chief of Staff, Keokuk Area Hospital, Keokuk, IA, p. A224

KHATAMI, Manoochehr, M.D. Medical Director, Hickory Trail Hospital, Desoto, TX, p. A599

KHAWANDI, Wassim, M.D. Chief of Staff, Kadlec Regional Medical Center, Richland, WA, p. A670

KHDOUR, Adel, M.D. Chief Medical Officer, Indiana University Health White Memorial Hospital, Monticello, IN, p. A210

KHOO, Alex, Interim Area Finance Officer, Kaiser Permanente San Francisco Medical Center, San Francisco, CA, p. A86

KIBAR, Nizar, M.D. Chief Medical Staff, Kiowa County Memorial Hospital, Greensburg, KS, p. A234

KIBBY, Rosalinda, Acting Chief Executive Officer, Columbia Basin Hospital, Ephrata, WA, p. A666

KIBLER, Doug, Management Information Systems Specialist, LaFollette Medical Center, La Follette, TN, p. A572

KIBLER, Laurel, Nursing Officer, Northern Cochise Community Hospital, Willcox, AZ, p. A39

KIBORT, Phillip M., M.D
Vice President Medical Affairs and Chief Medical Officer, Children's Hospitals and Clinics of Minnesota, Minneapolis, MN, p. A336
Vice President Medical Affairs and Chief Medical Officer, Children's Hospitals and Clinics of Minnesota, Saint Paul, MN, p. A340

KICHAK, J. P., Vice President Information Services, University of North Carolina Hospitals, Chapel Hill, NC, p. A449

KIDD, David, Manager Human Resources, Sentara CarePlex Hospital, Hampton, VA, p. A655

KIDD, Larry R., R.N. Vice President and Chief Nursing Officer, Henry Mayo Newhall Memorial Hospital, Valencia, CA, p. A94

KIDD, Monica, MSN, Interim Administrator, Parkview Hospital, Wheeler, TX, p. A641

KIDD, Scott, Director Human Resources, Mendocino Coast District Hospital, Fort Bragg, CA, p. A60

KIDD, Sue, Chief Financial Officer, Horton Community Hospital, Horton, KS, p. A235

KIDD, Thomas J., Assistant Administrator and Chief Financial Officer, Macon County General Hospital, Lafayette, TN, p. A572

KIDDER, Suzanne F., Director Human Resources, Opelousas General Health System, Opelousas, LA, p. A276

KIDO, Bert, Vice President Human Resources, Queen's Medical Center, Honolulu, HI, p. A165

KIEBZAK, Stanley F., R.N. Chief Nursing Officer, Reliant Northwest Houston, Houston, TX, p. A611

KIEDROWSKI, Brian, M.D. Chief Medical Director, Miami Jewish Home and Hospital for Aged, Miami, FL, p. A132

KIEF, Brian, President and Chief Executive Officer, Ministry Saint Joseph's Hospital, Marshfield, WI, p. A690

KIEFER, Patrice, Director Human Resources, Douglas County Hospital, Alexandria, MN, p. A328

KIEFER, William, Chief Nursing Officer, Red River Regional Hospital, Bonham, TX, p. A589

KIEHLE, Jessica, R.N. Chief Nursing Officer, Abilene Regional Medical Center, Abilene, TX, p. A581

KIELY, Janet, R.N. Chief Operating Officer and Chief Nursing Officer, Healdsburg District Hospital, Healdsburg, CA, p. A64

KIELY, Sharon, M.D. Senior Vice President Medical Affairs and Chief Medical Officer, Stamford Hospital, Stamford, CT, p. A112

KIENITZ, Mikaela, Assistant Administrator, UnityPoint Health – Marengo Memorial Hospital, Marengo, IA, p. A224

KIERNAN, Mike, M.D. President Medical Staff, Porter Medical Center, Middlebury, VT, p. A649

KIERNAN, Thomas, M.D. Chief of Staff, Charlie Norwood Veterans Affairs Medical Center, Augusta, GA, p. A147

KIFF, Gary V., President and Chief Executive Officer, Beverly Hospital, Montebello, CA, p. A74

KIGER, Tom, Director Information Systems, Trinity Health System, Steubenville, OH, p. A490

KIGHT, Sheila, Director Human Resources, TriStar Horizon Medical Center, Dickson, TN, p. A568

KIJEWSKI, John, Vice President and Chief Information Officer, Rutland Regional Medical Center, Rutland, VT, p. A650

KIKUKAWA, Alyne, Accountant, Molokai General Hospital, Kaunakakai, HI, p. A166

KILARSKI, David J., Chief Executive Officer, FirstHealth Moore Regional Hospital, Pinehurst, NC, p. A458

KIRK, Roger L., President and Chief Executive Officer, Bethesda Memorial Hospital, Boynton Beach, FL, p. A119

KIRK, Terry D., R.N. Chief Nursing Officer, Houston Northwest Medical Center, Houston, TX, p. A610

KIRK, Vanessa, Director of Nursing, Kiowa County Memorial Hospital, Greensburg, KS, p. A234

KIRK, Warren J., Chief Executive Officer, Doctors Medical Center, Modesto, CA, p. A74

KIRKBRIDE, Jim
Director of Support Services, Pioneer Memorial Hospital, Prineville, OR, p. A517
Director of Support Services, St. Charles Medical Center – Redmond, Redmond, OR, p. A517

KIRKER, Lynda I., Chief Financial Officer, Flagler Hospital, Saint Augustine, FL, p. A138

KIRKER NEA–BC, Donna, R.N. Vice President Patient Services and Chief Nursing Officer, Glens Falls Hospital, Glens Falls, NY, p. A426

KIRKHAM, Brett, Administrator, East Texas Medical Center Trinity, Trinity, TX, p. A638

KIRKHAM, Jeff, Chief Financial Officer, Community Hospital North, Indianapolis, IN, p. A205

KIRKHAM, Paul, Chief Executive Officer, Keystone Newport News, Newport News, VA, p. A657

KIRKS, Linda, Chief Financial Officer, Baptist Medical Center, San Antonio, TX, p. A630

KIRMAN, Lynn, R.N. Chief Nursing Officer, St. John's Medical Center and Living Center, Jackson, WY, p. A702

KIRN, Galen, Administrator, California Mens Colony Hospital, San Luis Obispo, CA, p. A88

KIRSHNER, Arthur N., Chief Information Management, Winn Army Community Hospital, Hinesville, GA, p. A155

KIRSHNER, David, Senior Vice President and Chief Financial Officer, Boston Children's Hospital, Boston, MA, p. A296

KIRSON, Joel, M.D. Medical Director, Anchor Hospital, Atlanta, GA, p. A145

KIRSTEIN, Susan N., R.N. Chief Nursing Officer, Broadlawns Medical Center, Des Moines, IA, p. A220

KISER, Greg, Chief Executive Officer, Three Rivers Medical Center, Louisa, KY, p. A255

KISER II, James R., Chief Executive Officer, St. Joseph Hospital, Polson, MT, p. A379

KISER, Pamela, R.N. Chief Nursing Executive and Vice President of Nursing, St. John Medical Center, Tulsa, OK, p. A509

KISER, Phyllis, Director Human Resources, Russell County Medical Center, Lebanon, VA, p. A656

KISER, Terry L.
Vice President and Chief Financial Officer, Georgetown Memorial Hospital, Georgetown, SC, p. A552
Chief Financial Officer, Waccamaw Community Hospital, Murrells Inlet, SC, p. A555

KISHNER, Janice, R.N. Chief Operating Officer and Nurse Executive, East Jefferson General Hospital, Metairie, LA, p. A273

KISKADDON, Robert, M.D. Chief Medical Officer, Margaret R. Pardee Memorial Hospital, Hendersonville, NC, p. A454

KISNER, Angela, Director Human Resources and Coordinator Medical Staff, Landmark Hospital, Cape Girardeau, MO, p. A357

KISTLER, Beckie, Controller, Our Lady of Peace, Louisville, KY, p. A256

KISTLER, Mike, Chief Executive Officer, Shadow Mountain Behavioral Health System, Tulsa, OK, p. A509

KITCHEN, Randy J., Chief Executive Officer, Dayton Rehabilitation Institute, Dayton, OH, p. A479

KITOWSKI, Jerome, M.D. Chief of Staff, Black River Memorial Hospital, Black River Falls, WI, p. A684

KITTELL, Elisabeth, Chief Financial Officer, Syracuse Veterans Affairs Medical Center, Syracuse, NY, p. A444

KITTNER, Bonnie, R.N. Chief Nursing Officer, Mendocino Coast District Hospital, Fort Bragg, CA, p. A60

KITTRELL, Albert, M.D. Medical Director, Arkansas State Hospital, Little Rock, AR, p. A46

KITZKE, Kris, Chief Executive Officer, Select Specialty Hospital–Memphis, Memphis, TN, p. A575

KIWALL, Walter J.
Executive Vice President and Chief Operating Officer, Mary Washington Hospital, Fredericksburg, VA, p. A654
Executive Vice President and Chief Operating Officer, Stafford Hospital, Stafford, VA, p. A661

KLARKOWSKI, Debbie, Manager Human Resources, Brown County Community Treatment Center, Green Bay, WI, p. A687

KLARNER, Lea Ann, Chief Executive Officer, Select Specialty Hospital–Fort Wayne, Fort Wayne, IN, p. A203

KLASSEN, Karen, Controller, HEALTHSOUTH Chattanooga Rehabilitation Hospital, Chattanooga, TN, p. A566

KLASSEN, Susan K., Chief Executive Officer and Administrator, Mahnomen Health Center, Mahnomen, MN, p. A335

KLAUKA, Floyd, Chief Financial Officer, Brook Lane Health Services, Hagerstown, MD, p. A292

KLAUSTERMEIER, Lisa, R.N. Chief Nursing Officer, Anderson Hospital, Maryville, IL, p. A187

KLAWITER, Thomas, Senior Vice President and Chief Operating Officer, Nix Health Care System, San Antonio, TX, p. A632

KLAWITER, Trey, Chief Operating Officer, Southwest General Hospital, San Antonio, TX, p. A632

KLAWITTER, Kyle, Vice President Human Resources, Summa Health System, Akron, OH, p. A470

KLEAM, Douglas V., Vice President and Chief Operating Officer, St. Vincent Medical Center, Los Angeles, CA, p. A72

KLEAS, Tara, Director Human Resources, HEALTHSOUTH Rehabilitation Hospital of Fort Worth, Fort Worth, TX, p. A603

KLECKNER, Megan, Vice President and Administrator, Riverside Walter Reed Hospital, Gloucester, VA, p. A655

KLEEMAN, Debbie, Manager Information Systems, Perry County Memorial Hospital, Tell City, IN, p. A213

KLEEN, Kathy, Chief Nursing Officer, Tri–County Hospital, Wadena, MN, p. A342

KLEEN, Yechiel, M.D. Medical Director, Rehabilitation Hospital of Wisconsin, Waukesha, WI, p. A698

KLEIN, Aron, Vice President of Finance, Advocate Eureka Hospital, Eureka, IL, p. A182

KLEIN, Barbara, R.N. Director of Nursing, Arms Acres, Carmel, NY, p. A423

KLEIN, Bernard, M.D., Chief Executive Officer, Providence Holy Cross Medical Center,, CA, p. A71

KLEIN, Cindy, Chief Financial Officer, Lamb Healthcare Center, Littlefield, TX, p. A618

KLEIN, Cindy C., Vice President Human Resources, PeaceHealth St. Joseph Medical Center, Bellingham, WA, p. A664

KLEIN, David G., M.D., Interim President, Baylor All Saints Medical Center at Fort Worth, Fort Worth, TX, p. A603

KLEIN, Diany, Vice President Human Resources, Community Memorial Health System, Ventura, CA, p. A94

KLEIN, Edward A., Chief Financial Officer, Johnston Health, Smithfield, NC, p. A461

KLEIN, Gerard D., Chief Executive Officer, Memorial Hospital of Sweetwater County, Rock Springs, WY, p. A703

KLEIN, Greg, Senior Director Finance, Novant Health Matthews Medical Center, Matthews, NC, p. A457

KLEIN, Jacqueline, Chief Financial Officer, Lakeview Medical Center, Rice Lake, WI, p. A696

KLEIN, Jerry, Chief Financial Officer, Lawrence County Memorial Hospital, Lawrenceville, IL, p. A187

KLEIN, Joel, Chief Executive Officer and Managing Director, Glen Oaks Hospital, Greenville, TX, p. A607

KLEIN, Julie, Chief Executive Officer, Sterling Regional MedCenter, Sterling, CO, p. A106

KLEIN, Kenneth, CPA Senior Vice President Finance and Chief Financial Officer, Menninger Clinic, Houston, TX, p. A611

KLEIN, Lynn E., Administrator, Mendota Community Hospital, Mendota, IL, p. A188

KLEIN, Ronald, M.D. Vice President and Chief Medical Officer, Brookhaven Memorial Hospital Medical Center, Patchogue, NY, p. A439

KLEIN, Steven M., Chief Executive Officer, Promise Hospital of Florida at The Villages, Oxford, FL, p. A135

KLEINE, Doug, IT Director, St. Joseph Health St. Mary, Apple Valley, CA, p. A53

KLEINHANZL, Thomas A., President and Chief Executive Officer, Frederick Memorial Hospital, Frederick, MD, p. A291

KLEINMAN, Richard, R.N. Manager Medical Informatics, Catalina Island Medical Center, Avalon, CA, p. A53

KLEINSCHMIDT, James, M.D. Vice President Medical Affairs, Shenandoah Memorial Hospital, Woodstock, VA, p. A663

KLENKE, Lisa R., R.N., Interim Chief Executive Officer, Mercer Health, Coldwater, OH, p. A477

KLEPIN, Michael R.
Administrator, Hunt Regional Community Hospital, Commerce, TX, p. A593
Administrator, Hunt Regional Medical Center, Greenville, TX, p. A607

KLEVEN, Brian, Chief Financial Officer, Alvarado Hospital, San Diego, CA, p. A84

KLEYMANN, Tiffany, Manager Human Resources, Greeley County Health Services, Tribune, KS, p. A245

KLICKSTEIN, Judith S., Chief Information Officer, Cambridge Health Alliance, Cambridge, MA, p. A299

KLIMEK, David, Chief Human Resources Officer, Olathe Medical Center, Olathe, KS, p. A241

KLIMP, Mary J., FACHE, Chief Administrative Officer, Mayo Clinic Health System in New Prague, New Prague, MN, p. A337

KLINE, Donald E.
Chief Financial Officer and Vice President Operations, Mercy Allen Hospital, Oberlin, OH, p. A488
Senior Vice President Finance, St. Elizabeth Boardman Health Center, Boardman, OH, p. A472
Senior Vice President Finance, St. Elizabeth Health Center, Youngstown, OH, p. A494
Senior Vice President Finance, St. Joseph Health Center, Warren, OH, p. A492

KLINE, Julie, Senior Vice President Patient Services, Sonora Regional Medical Center, Sonora, CA, p. A91

KLINE, Mark W., M.D. Physician in Chief, Texas Children's Hospital, Houston, TX, p. A612

KLINGA, Maria, Director Management Information Systems, Silver Hill Hospital, New Canaan, CT, p. A110

KLINGENBERG, Pat, Director Human Resources, Towner County Medical Center, Cando, ND, p. A465

KLINGLER, Michael, M.D. Chief of Staff, Clay County Hospital, Flora, IL, p. A182

KLINGSEIS, Rob, Manager Information Systems, Community Hospital of Long Beach, Long Beach, CA, p. A67

KLINIKOWSKI, Angela, Director of Nursing, Vista Health, Fayetteville, AR, p. A43

KLINKER, Suzanne M., Director, Bay Pines Veterans Affairs Medical Center, Bay Pines, FL, p. A118

KLINKNER, Donna M., Chief Financial Officer, Madelia Community Hospital, Madelia, MN, p. A335

KLITSCH, Lillian, R.N. Chief Clinical Officer, Kindred Hospital–Wyoming Valley, Wilkes Barre, PA, p. A544

KLOC, Larry, Chief Financial Officer, Hopedale Medical Complex, Hopedale, IL, p. A185

KLOCK, Kathy, R.N. Senior Vice President Clinical Operations and Human Resources, Gundersen Lutheran Medical Center, La Crosse, WI, p. A689

KLOCKMAN, Dena, Chief Financial Officer, Ogallala Community Hospital, Ogallala, NE, p. A387

KLOCKO, Daniel, Vice President Human Resources, Kootenai Medical Center, Coeur D'Alene, ID, p. A168

KLOEWER, Ron, Chief Information Officer, Montgomery County Memorial Hospital, Red Oak, IA, p. A227

KLOPFER, Rudy, Associate Director, Durham Veterans Affairs Medical Center, Durham, NC, p. A451

KLOPHER, Anthony Rudy, FACHE, Director, Veterans Affairs Eastern Kansas Health Care System, Topeka, KS, p. A245

KLOSTERMAN, Mark D., FACHE, President and Chief Executive Officer, St. Joseph's Hospital, Breese, IL, p. A175

KLOTZ, Carol, Director Human Resources, LifeCare Medical Center, Roseau, MN, p. A339

KLOTZ, Ken, M.D. Chief of Staff, Richard L. Roudebush Veterans Affairs Medical Center, Indianapolis, IN, p. A206

KLUGE, Thomas S., Chief Operating Officer, Halifax Regional Health System, South Boston, VA, p. A661

KLUGHERZ, Greg, Vice President Corporate Services and Chief Financial Officer, St. Cloud Hospital, Saint Cloud, MN, p. A339

KLUNE, Peter, Chief Executive Officer, Palo Verde Hospital, Blythe, CA, p. A55

KLUNK, Tim, Executive Director, Children's Hospital of Wisconsin–Fox Valley, Neenah, WI, p. A693

KLYCZEK, Mark F., President and Chief Executive Officer, Newark–Wayne Community Hospital, Newark, NY, p. A437

KMETZ, Thomas D., President, Kosair Children's Hospital, Louisville, KY, p. A255

KNAK, Roger, Administrator, Fairview Regional Medical Center, Fairview, OK, p. A499

KNAPHEIDE, Debbie, MSN, Site Administrator, Chief Nursing Officer and Chief Operating Officer, Carondelet Holy Cross Hospital, Nogales, AZ, p. A33

KNAPP, Anne, Chief Financial Officer, Valle Vista Hospital, Greenwood, IN, p. A204

KNAPP, Brian A., Vice President Operations, Fairview Ridges Hospital, Burnsville, MN, p. A330

KNAPP, Merlyn E., President and Chief Executive Officer, Saint Catherine Regional Hospital, Charlestown, IN, p. A200

KNAPP, Rhonda, Director Human Resources, Dahl Memorial Healthcare Association, Ekalaka, MT, p. A375

KNAUS, Ronald, Vice President Finance, Spectrum Health – Grand Rapids, Grand Rapids, MI, p. A315

KNECHT, Brian J., Chief Operating Officer, Regional Medical Center of San Jose, San Jose, CA, p. A88

KNEDLER, Marie E., R.N.,
President, Alegent Creighton Health Bergan Mercy Medical Center, Omaha, NE, p. A387
President, Alegent Creighton Health Mercy Hospital, Council Bluffs, IA, p. A219

KNELL, Daniel J., MSN, President, Quincy Medical Center, Quincy, MA, p. A304

KNIEVEL, Lon, Chief Executive Officer, Tilden Community Hospital, Tilden, NE, p. A390

KOOIMAN, Thomas, Chief Executive Officer, Prairie Ridge Hospital and Health Services, Elbow Lake, MN, p. A332

KOON, Rion, Chief Information Management Division, William Beaumont Army Medical Center, El Paso, TX, p. A602

KOONTZ, Andrea, R.N. Vice President of Nursing Services, Community Hospital of Bremen, Bremen, IN, p. A199

KOOP, Steven, M.D. Medical Director, Gillette Children's Specialty Healthcare, Saint Paul, MN, p. A340

KOOS, Shaun, Administrator, Wenatchee Valley Medical Center, Wenatchee, WA, p. A674

KOOY, Donald C., President and Chief Executive Officer, McLaren Flint, Flint, MI, p. A313

KOPEL, Samuel, M.D. Medical Director, Maimonides Medical Center,, NY, p. A434

KOPF, Chris, Chief Fiscal Officer, Summit Park Hospital and Nursing Care Center, Pomona, NY, p. A439

KOPFLE, Sue
Chief Human Resources Officer, University of Missouri Hospitals and Clinics, Columbia, MO, p. A359
Chief Human Resources Officer, Women's and Children's Hospital, Columbia, MO, p. A359

KOPINSKI, Donna, Chief Financial Officer, Crittenton Hospital Medical Center, Rochester, MI, p. A322

KOPINSKY, Kristen, Chief Operating Officer, Highlands Regional Medical Center, Sebring, FL, p. A140

KOPP, Daniel, M.D. Senior Vice President and Chief Medical Officer, Faxton–St. Luke's Healthcare, Utica, NY, p. A444

KOPP, Greg, Chief Financial Officer, Regina Medical Center, Hastings, MN, p. A333

KOPPELMAN, Benjamin, President, St. Joseph's Area Health Services, Park Rapids, MN, p. A338

KOPPENHAVER, Colleen, Chief Financial Officer, Oaklawn Hospital, Marshall, MI, p. A320

KOPPERUD, Gordon, Director Operations, Sanford Westbrook Medical Center, Westbrook, MN, p. A342

KORBEL, Tamara, Director Management Information Systems, Ridgeview Medical Center, Waconia, MN, p. A342

KORDICK, Jill, Interim Chief Executive Officer, Van Buren County Hospital, Keosauqua, IA, p. A224

KORDUCKI, Stanley R., President, Wood County Hospital, Bowling Green, OH, p. A472

KORICH, Frank, Vice President and Site Administrator, Soldiers and Sailors Memorial Hospital of Yates County, Penn Yan, NY, p. A439

KORN, Larry, Manager Finance, Southern Arizona Veterans Affairs Health Care System, Tucson, AZ, p. A39

KORN, Roy, M.D. Medical Director, Cobleskill Regional Hospital, Cobleskill, NY, p. A424

KORNBLATT, Lynne R., Vice President Human Resources, Einstein Medical Center Philadelphia, Philadelphia, PA, p. A534

KORNER, Kevin, Director Human Resources, Central Mississippi Medical Center, Jackson, MS, p. A348

KORNFIELD, Lee, M.D. Medical Director, Elks Rehab Hospital, Boise, ID, p. A167

KOROLY, Marla, M.D. Chief Medical Officer and Senior Vice President Medical Affairs, Northern Westchester Hospital, Mount Kisco, NY, p. A430

KORPELA, Donita, R.N. Director of Patient Care Services, Mercy Hospital, Moose Lake, MN, p. A336

KORTE, Fred, Chief Financial Officer, McLaren Oakland, Pontiac, MI, p. A322

KORTEMEYER, Jay, Chief Executive Officer, Brynn Marr Hospital, Jacksonville, NC, p. A455

KORTH, Mark, Chief Executive Officer and Senior Vice President Operations Dignity Health North State Service Area, Mercy Medical Center Redding, Redding, CA, p. A81

KORTH, Paul, Chief Executive Officer, Cookeville Regional Medical Center, Cookeville, TN, p. A568

KORTH–WHITE, Kirsten, Vice President Operations, Mercy Hospital Grayling, Grayling, MI, p. A315

KORTUM, Joseph M., President and Chief Mission Officer, PeaceHealth Southwest Medical Center, Vancouver, WA, p. A674

KORYNTA, Vicky, Senior Vice President and Chief Operating Officer, Range Regional Health Services, Hibbing, MN, p. A334

KOSANOVICH, John, M.D. Vice President Covenant Healthcare and Chief Executive Officer Covenant Medical Group, Covenant Medical Center, Saginaw, MI, p. A323

KOSANOVICH, John P., President, Watertown Regional Medical Center, Watertown, WI, p. A698

KOSCHKA, Ed, Network Vice President Information Technology and Chief Information Officer, Community Heart and Vascular Hospital, Indianapolis, IN, p. A205

KOSCHKA, Edward, Network Vice President Information Technology and Chief Information Officer, Community Hospital North, Indianapolis, IN, p. A205

KOSE, William H., M.D
Senior Vice President Medical Affairs, Blanchard Valley Hospital, Findlay, OH, p. A481
Vice President Quality and Medical Affairs, Bluffton Hospital, Bluffton, OH, p. A472

KOSEK, Kevin, Chief Financial Officer, Iowa City Veterans Affairs Health Care System, Iowa City, IA, p. A223

KOSINA, Thomas, M.D. Chief of Staff, Winner Regional Healthcare Center, Winner, SD, p. A564

KOSLOW, Howard B., President and Chief Executive Officer, Promise Hospital of Miss Lou, Vidalia, LA, p. A279

KOSNOSKY, David, M.D. Chief Medical Officer, University Hospitals Geauga Medical Center, Chardon, OH, p. A473

KOSSEFF, Christopher O., President and Chief Executive Officer, University of Medicine and Dentistry of New Jersey, University Behavioral Healthcare, Piscataway, NJ, p. A409

KOSTER, Tracy, Director Human Resources, Carlinville Area Hospital, Carlinville, IL, p. A175

KOSTERS, Gregory J., D.O. Chief Medical Officer, Osceola Community Hospital, Sibley, IA, p. A228

KOSTOK, Barbara, Manager Human Resources, Punxsutawney Area Hospital, Punxsutawney, PA, p. A539

KOSTROUN, Deborah, Chief Operating Officer, Manatee Glens Hospital and Addiction Center, Bradenton, FL, p. A119

KOSTURKO, MaryEllen, R.N. Senior Vice President Patient Care Operations and Chief Nursing Officer, Bridgeport Hospital, Bridgeport, CT, p. A108

KOSYLA, Gail, Chief Financial Officer and Vice President Finance, St. Mary Medical Center, Langhorne, PA, p. A529

KOSZTYO, Carol, R.N. Vice President, Patient Care Services, Carrier Clinic, Belle Mead, NJ, p. A401

KOTEWICZ, Lori, Supervisor Human Resources, Aultman Orrville Hospital, Orrville, OH, p. A488

KOTIN, Kathy, Chief Financial Officer, Banner Good Samaritan Medical Center, Phoenix, AZ, p. A34

KOTRBA, Mitchell, Chief Financial Officer, North Valley Health Center, Warren, MN, p. A342

KOTSONIS, Robert, Chief Operating Officer, Northeast Rehabilitation Hospital, Salem, NH, p. A400

KOTTENBROOK, Susan, Chief Executive Officer, Red River Behavioral Center, Bossier City, LA, p. A264

KOTZEN, Michael S., Vice President and Chief Operating Officer, Virtua Voorhees, Voorhees, NJ, p. A412

KOUKOS, Dean, M.D. Chief Medical Staff, Barnwell County Hospital, Barnwell, SC, p. A548

KOULOVATOS, James E., Chief Executive Officer, Liberty Dayton Regional Medical Center, Liberty, TX, p. A618

KOUNTZ, David, M.D. Senior Vice President Medical Affairs, Jersey Shore University Medical Center, Neptune, NJ, p. A407

KOUSKOLEKAS, Anthony, President, Village Hospital, Greer, SC, p. A553

KOUTNER–RAUSCH, Geri, Director Human Resources, St. Lawrence Psychiatric Center, Ogdensburg, NY, p. A438

KOUTOUZOS, Connie L., MSN, Chief Executive Officer and President, NORTHSTAR Health System, Iron River, MI, p. A317

KOVACH, Andrew L.
Vice President Human Resources and Chief Administrative Officer, Morristown Medical Center, Morristown, NJ, p. A406
Vice President Human Resources and Chief Administrative Officer, Newton Medical Center, Newton, NJ, p. A408
Vice President Human Resources and Chief Administrative Officer, Overlook Medical Center, Summit, NJ, p. A410

KOVACS, Amber R., Chief Human Resources Officer, Banner Gateway Medical Center, Gilbert, AZ, p. A31

KOVACS, Elizabeth, R.N. Director of Nursing, Harrison Community Hospital, Cadiz, OH, p. A472

KOVASZNAY, Beatrice, M.D. Clinical Director, Capital District Psychiatric Center, Albany, NY, p. A420

KOWALOFF, Harvey, M.D. Vice President Medical Affairs, Saint Anne's Hospital, Fall River, MA, p. A299

KOWALSKI, Richard S., FACHE, President and Chief Executive Officer, OSF St. Mary Medical Center, Galesburg, IL, p. A183

KOWITT, Jack, Senior Vice President and Chief Information Officer, Parkland Health & Hospital System, Dallas, TX, p. A597

KOWNACKI, Dawn, Director Human Resources, Brooke Glen Behavioral Hospital, Fort Washington, PA, p. A526

KOZAI, Gerald T., President, St. Francis Medical Center, Lynwood, CA, p. A72

KOZAR, Michael A., Chief Executive Officer, Carroll County Memorial Hospital, Carrollton, KY, p. A249

KOZEL, Joseph, M.D. President Medical Staff, Hoboken University Medical Center, Hoboken, NJ, p. A405

KOZEL, Kenneth D., FACHE,
President and Chief Executive Officer, Dorchester General Hospital, Cambridge, MD, p. A290
President and Chief Executive Officer, Memorial Hospital at Easton Maryland, Easton, MD, p. A291

KOZEL, Mary Ann, Chief Fiscal, Veterans Affairs Medical Center, Wilmington, DE, p. A115

KOZIK, Rhonda, Administrator, Norwood Health Center, Marshfield, WI, p. A690

KOZLOWSKI, Leon, Vice President Finance and Chief Financial Officer, Wyckoff Heights Medical Center,, NY, p. A437

KOZOROSKY, Laurie, Chief Executive Officer, Select Specialty Hospital–Laurel Highlands, Latrobe, PA, p. A529

KRABLIN, Brett, M.D. Chief of Staff, Kingfisher Regional Hospital, Kingfisher, OK, p. A500

KRAEGER, Paul, Vice President Finance and Chief Financial Officer, Samaritan Medical Center, Watertown, NY, p. A445

KRAGENBRING, Mark, Administrator, Child and Adolescent Behavioral Health Services, Willmar, MN, p. A342

KRAHNERT, John F., M.D. Chief Medical Officer, FirstHealth Moore Regional Hospital, Pinehurst, NC, p. A458

KRAJEWSKI, David, Senior Vice President and Chief Financial Officer, Sinai Hospital of Baltimore, Baltimore, MD, p. A289

KRAJEWSKI, Denise, R.N. Chief Nursing Officer, Doctors Hospital at White Rock Lake, Dallas, TX, p. A595

KRAMER, Blake, Chief Executive Officer, Franklin Medical Center, Winnsboro, LA, p. A280

KRAMER, Danette, Chief Financial Officer, Regional Medical Center, Manchester, IA, p. A224

KRAMER, Janie, Chief Operating Officer, Sharp Memorial Hospital, San Diego, CA, p. A85

KRAMER, Jared, M.D. Chief of Staff, Howard County Medical Center, Saint Paul, NE, p. A389

KRAMER, Jon, Controller and Assistant Administrator, Northport Medical Center, Northport, AL, p. A24

KRAMER, Kathryn, M.D. President Medical Staff, Pekin Hospital, Pekin, IL, p. A191

KRAMER, Richard, Interim Chief Executive Officer, Northlake Behavioral Hospital, Mandeville, LA, p. A273

KRAMER, Sheila A., Chief Executive Officer, HEALTHSOUTH Rehabilitation Hospital of Cypress, Houston, TX, p. A610

KRAMER, Susan, Director of Human Resources, Levi Hospital, Hot Springs National Park, AR, p. A45

KRAML, Louis D., FACHE,
Chief Executive Officer, Bingham Memorial Hospital, Blackfoot, ID, p. A167
Chief Executive Officer, Mountain River Birthing and Surgery Center, Blackfoot, ID, p. A167

KRAMPITS, Carrie, Director Human Resources, McKenzie Health System, Sandusky, MI, p. A324

KRANZ, Marlene, Controller, Holton Community Hospital, Holton, KS, p. A235

KRASON, Jane E., R.N., Chief Executive Officer, Appalachian Behavioral Healthcare, Athens, OH, p. A470

KRASOVEC, Rudy, Director Human Resources, St. Mary–Corwin Medical Center, Pueblo, CO, p. A105

KRASS, Todd, R.N., Chief Executive Officer, Belton Regional Medical Center, Belton, MO, p. A356

KRAUKLIS, Gene
Regional Vice President Human Resources, Aurora Lakeland Medical Center, Elkhorn, WI, p. A686
Regional Vice President Human Resources, Aurora Medical Center, Kenosha, WI, p. A688
Regional Vice President Human Resources, Aurora Memorial Hospital of Burlington, Burlington, WI, p. A685

KRAUS, John, M.D. Chief Medical Officer, Bryn Mawr Rehabilitation Hospital, Malvern, PA, p. A530

KRAUSE, Donna, Chief Information Officer, Harry S. Truman Memorial Veterans Hospital, Columbia, MO, p. A359

KRAUSE, Kim, Director Human Resources, Baylor Jack and Jane Hamilton Heart and Vascular Hospital, Dallas, TX, p. A595

KRAUSE, Mary, Vice President Finance, Valley View Regional Hospital, Ada, OK, p. A495

KRAUSE, Michele, Chief Information Management Officer, Bassett Army Community Hospital, Fort Wainwright, AK, p. A28

KRAUSE, Michelle, Manager Human Resources, VA Central Western Massachusetts Healthcare System, Leeds, MA, p. A301

KRAUSE, Steven, Manager Information Technology, Franciscan Physicians Hospital, Munster, IN, p. A211

KRAUSS, James D., President, Rockingham Memorial Hospital, Harrisonburg, VA, p. A655

KRAVETZ, Michael, M.D. Medical Director, HEALTHSOUTH Valley of the Sun Rehabilitation Hospital, Glendale, AZ, p. A32

KRAYNAK, Joseph, M.D. Chief Medical Officer, Abington Health Lansdale Hospital, Lansdale, PA, p. A529

KUENSTLER, Kristi, M.D. Chief of Staff, Texas Health Harris Methodist Hospital Azle, Azle, TX, p. A586

KUESER, Brian, M.D. Chief Medical Officer, Neosho Memorial Regional Medical Center, Chanute, KS, p. A232

KUESTERSTEFFEN, Vicki, Chief Executive Officer, J. D. McCarty Center for Children With Developmental Disabilities, Norman, OK, p. A502

KUFFLER, Julian, M.D. President Medical Staff, Mount Desert Island Hospital, Bar Harbor, ME, p. A281

KUGHN, Yvonne, Chief Executive Officer, Southeast Michigan Surgical Hospital, Warren, MI, p. A326

KUHAR, Peggy A., R.N. Chief Nursing Officer, University Hospitals Geauga Medical Center, Chardon, OH, p. A473

KUHL, Patricia, Vice President Human Resources, Chester River Health System, Chestertown, MD, p. A290

KUHLE, Terri, Director Human Resources, St. Mary's Hospital, Decatur, IL, p. A180

KUHLMANN, Chris, Chief Financial Officer, Lakeland Community Hospital Watervliet, Watervliet, MI, p. A326

KUHLMANN, George, M.D. Chief of Staff, Cuyuna Regional Medical Center, Crosby, MN, p. A331

KUHLMANN, Michelle, M.D. Director Medical Staff, Thayer County Health Services, Hebron, NE, p. A384

KUHN, Anita, Controller, Texas County Memorial Hospital, Houston, MO, p. A361

KUHN, Brenda, Ph.D. Vice President Patient Care Services, Kettering Medical Center, Kettering, OH, p. A483

KUHN, Shawn, Facility Director Human Resources, Connecticut Valley Hospital, Middletown, CT, p. A110

KUHN, Steve, Chief Financial Officer, River Park Hospital, Huntington, WV, p. A678

KUHNS, Jay, Vice President Human Resources, All Children's Hospital, Saint Petersburg, FL, p. A138

KUIDA, Elliot H., Vice President and Chief Operating Officer, Martha Jefferson Hospital, Charlottesville, VA, p. A652

KUIPER, Evert J., President & Chief Executive Officer, Saint Anthony's Health Center, Alton, IL, p. A173

KUKELHAN, Alison, Manager Human Resources, Adams Memorial Hospital, Decatur, IN, p. A201

KUKLA, Steven F., Senior Vice President and Chief Financial Officer, Mercy Medical Center–Des Moines, Des Moines, IA, p. A220

KULHANEK, Linda, Chief Financial Officer, Memorial Hermann Katy Hospital, Katy, TX, p. A616

KULIK, Alec G., Administrator, Cleveland Clinic Children's Hospital for Rehabilitation, Cleveland, OH, p. A476

KULISZ, Michael, D.O
Chief Medical Officer, Kishwaukee Hospital, DeKalb, IL, p. A180
Chief Medical Officer, Valley West Hospital, Sandwich, IL, p. A194

KULP, Paul, Director Human Resources, North Adams Regional Hospital, North Adams, MA, p. A303

KUMAR, Daryn J., Chief Executive Officer, Memorial Medical Center, Modesto, CA, p. A74

KUMAR, Nanda, M.D. Chief of Staff, Vibra Hospital of Northern California, Redding, CA, p. A81

KUMAR, Raji, Chief Executive Officer, Dallas Medical Center, Dallas, TX, p. A595

KUMM, Mandy, Vice President Fiscal Services, Boone County Health Center, Albion, NE, p. A381

KUMMER, Margaret, Vice President Human Resources, Citizens Medical Center, Colby, KS, p. A232

KUNIK, Cherie, R.N. Interim Vice President Patient Care Services & CNO, DeKalb Medical at North Decatur, Decatur, GA, p. A152

KUNNAPPILLY, Chester, M.D. Chief Medical Officer and Chief Quality Officer, San Mateo Medical Center, San Mateo, CA, p. A88

KUNSTLING, Ted, M.D. Chief Medical Officer, Duke Raleigh Hospital, Raleigh, NC, p. A459

KUNZ, Donna, Manager Human Resources, Saint Luke's South Hospital, Overland Park, KS, p. A242

KUNZE, Gloria A., R.N. Vice President Operations, St. Joseph's Regional Medical Center, Paterson, NJ, p. A408

KUPFERSTEIN, Ron, Chief Executive Officer, Monrovia Memorial Hospital, Monrovia, CA, p. A74

KUPLEN, Carol, R.N. Chief Operating Officer and Chief Nursing Officer, St. Luke's University Hospital – Bethlehem Campus, Bethlehem, PA, p. A520

KURESKA, Kirk, Chief Executive Officer, RiverWoods Behavioral Health System, Riverdale, GA, p. A158

KURIAN, Santha, M.D. Chief of Staff, James E. Van Zandt Veterans Affairs Medical Center, Altoona, PA, p. A519

KURTZ, Marvin A.
Senior Vice President Finance and Chief Financial Officer, Florida Hospital Tampa, Tampa, FL, p. A141
Chief Financial Officer, Florida Hospital–Carrollwood, Tampa, FL, p. A141

KURTZ, Jr., Thomas F., Chief Operating Officer, Georgia Regional Hospital at Savannah, Savannah, GA, p. A160

KURZ, Kenneth R., M.D. Chief of Staff, MidState Medical Center, Meriden, CT, p. A109

KURZ, Sharon H., Ph.D., Chief Executive Officer, St. Elias Specialty Hospital, Anchorage, AK, p. A27

KURZENBERGER, Richard, Chief Financial Officer, Kingwood Pines Hospital, Kingwood, TX, p. A617

KUSLER, Julie, Manager Information Services, Avera St. Luke's Hospital, Aberdeen, SD, p. A558

KUTA, Daniel, R.N. Director of Nursing, Power County Hospital District, American Falls, ID, p. A167

KUTCH, John M., President, Trinity Health, Minot, ND, p. A468

KUTCHER, Gregory, M.D., President and Chief Executive Officer, Mayo Clinic Health System in Mankato, Mankato, MN, p. A335

KUTILEK, Richard J., Chief Operating Officer, Calvary Hospital,, NY, p. A431

KUYKENDALL, Kari, Human Resources Specialist, Pauls Valley General Hospital, Pauls Valley, OK, p. A505

KUZAS, Betsy, Executive Vice President and Chief Operating Officer, Phoenix Children's Hospital, Phoenix, AZ, p. A35

KUZMA, Gregory
Vice President and Chief Financial Officer, Flagstaff Medical Center, Flagstaff, AZ, p. A31
Vice President and Chief Financial Officer, Verde Valley Medical Center, Cottonwood, AZ, p. A30

KVASNICKA, John, M.D. Medical Director, St. John's Hospital, Saint Paul, MN, p. A340

KWAK, Daniel, M.D. Chief of Staff, Ashley Regional Medical Center, Vernal, UT, p. A648

KWASS, George, M.D. Chief of Staff, Merrimack Valley Hospital, Haverhill, MA, p. A300

KWIATEK, Susan, R.N., Executive Director, Glen Cove Hospital, Glen Cove, NY, p. A426

KWIESIELEWICZ, Nancy
Human Resources Manager, Ministry Good Samaritan Health Center, Merrill, WI, p. A691
Human Resources Manager, Ministry Saint Clare's Hospital, Weston, WI, p. A699

KYGER, David, M.D. Chief Medical Officer, Solara Hospital of Muskogee, Muskogee, OK, p. A502

KYHNELL, Koreen H., Vice President Human Resources, Indiana University Health Arnett Hospital, Lafayette, IN, p. A208

KYLE, James, M.D. Vice President Medical Affairs, St. Joseph Health St. Mary, Apple Valley, CA, p. A53

KYLER, Yvonne, Director Human Resources, Texas Health Arlington Memorial Hospital, Arlington, TX, p. A584

KYLLO, Tom, Executive Vice President, Vail Valley Medical Center, Vail, CO, p. A106

KYNARD, Carmen, R.N. Chief Nursing Officer, Research Psychiatric Center, Kansas City, MO, p. A363

KYRIACOU, George M., President and Chief Executive Officer, Gaylord Hospital, Wallingford, CT, p. A112

KYWI, Alberto
Chief Information Officer, Goleta Valley Cottage Hospital, Santa Barbara, CA, p. A89
Chief Information Officer, Santa Barbara Cottage Hospital, Santa Barbara, CA, p. A89
Chief Information Officer, Santa Ynez Valley Cottage Hospital, Solvang, CA, p. A91

# L

L'HEUREUX, Dennis P., Chief Information Officer, Rockford Memorial Hospital, Rockford, IL, p. A193

L'ITALIEN, Mark, Director Information Services, Salem Community Hospital, Salem, OH, p. A489

LA CROIX, Kent, IT Supervisor, Schoolcraft Memorial Hospital, Manistique, MI, p. A319

LA FAVE, Jenny, Director, Sandhills Regional Medical Center, Hamlet, NC, p. A454

LA FRANCE, Pam, Vice President Human Resources, St. John's Riverside Hospital, Yonkers, NY, p. A446

LA PORTE, Todd
Senior Vice President and Chief Financial Officer, Scottsdale Healthcare Shea Medical Center, Scottsdale, AZ, p. A37
Chief Financial Officer, Scottsdale Healthcare Thompson Peak Hospital, Scottsdale, AZ, p. A37
Senior Vice President and Chief Financial Officer, Scottsdale Healthcare–Osborn Medical Center, Scottsdale, AZ, p. A37

LA SOTA, John, Assistant Finance Officer, Clement J. Zablocki Veterans Affairs Medical Center, Milwaukee, WI, p. A692

LABAGNARA, James, M.D. Vice President Medical Affairs, St. Joseph's Regional Medical Center, Paterson, NJ, p. A408

LABAND, Andrew, Chief Information Officer, McLean Hospital, Belmont, MA, p. A295

LABARCA, Laurie, Executive Vice President and Chief Operating Officer, Via Christi Hospital on St. Francis, Wichita, KS, p. A246

LABARGE, Robert J., Chief Executive Officer, Sturgis Hospital, Sturgis, MI, p. A325

LABELLA, Leonard, President and Chief Executive Officer, Verdugo Hills Hospital, Glendale, CA, p. A63

LABER, Susan, R.N. Chief Nursing Officer, Brandon Regional Hospital, Brandon, FL, p. A119

LABIAGA, Kimberly, Human Resources Leader, Kaiser Permanente Fontana Medical Center, Fontana, CA, p. A60

LABINE, Lance C., Administrator, Dr. Dan C. Trigg Memorial Hospital, Tucumcari, NM, p. A418

LABONTE, Robin, Leader Financial Care, York Hospital, York, ME, p. A286

LABORIE, Sheree
Director Human Resources, Lakewood Hospital, Lakewood, OH, p. A483
Director Human Resources, Lutheran Hospital, Cleveland, OH, p. A476

LABRUM, Chad, Chief Financial Officer, Ashley Regional Medical Center, Vernal, UT, p. A648

LACASSE, Paul E., D.O., President and Chief Executive Officer, Botsford Hospital, Farmington Hills, MI, p. A313

LACEFIELD, Gayla, Director Human Resources, Howard Memorial Hospital, Nashville, AR, p. A48

LACEY, Carmen, R.N., President, Charles A. Cannon Memorial Hospital, Linville, NC, p. A456

LACEY, III, John W., M.D. Senior Vice President and Chief Medical Officer, University of Tennessee Medical Center, Knoxville, TN, p. A572

LACEY, Ronald, M.D. Medical Director, Southwest Missouri Psychiatric Rehabilitation Center, El Dorado Springs, MO, p. A360

LACHANCE, Eric, Chief Executive Officer, Southern Virginia Regional Medical Center, Emporia, VA, p. A653

LACHANCE, Mary Kay, Director Information Systems, St. John Macomb–Oakland Hospital, Warren, MI, p. A326

LACHER, Paula A., MSN Chief Nursing Officer, Western Pennsylvania Hospital, Pittsburgh, PA, p. A539

LACHINA, Ignazio, M.D. Medical Director, HEALTHSOUTH Rehabilitation Hospital of Cypress, Houston, TX, p. A610

LACHINA, Michael, M.D. Chief Medical Officer, Saint Francis Hospital, Memphis, TN, p. A575

LACHOWSKY, John, M.D. Chief Medical Officer, Mercy Hospital Ozark, Ozark, AR, p. A48

LACKEY, Lori, Chief Financial Officer, Sabetha Community Hospital, Sabetha, KS, p. A243

LACKEY, Thomas O., Administrator, Hale County Hospital, Greensboro, AL, p. A21

LACKNEY, Christopher J., Director Human Resources, Grace Cottage Hospital, Townshend, VT, p. A650

LACY, Angela, Director of Nursing, Bolivar General Hospital, Bolivar, TN, p. A565

LACY, Edward L., FACHE, Vice President and Administrator, Baptist Health Medical Center–Heber Springs, Heber Springs, AR, p. A44

LACY, Tyson, Chief Financial Officer, Lincoln Hospital, Davenport, WA, p. A666

LADAROLA, Sandra, Chief Nursing Officer, Waterbury Hospital, Waterbury, CT, p. A112

LADIANA, Red, Manager Information Systems, College Hospital Costa Mesa, Costa Mesa, CA, p. A57

LADNER, Betsy, Director of Nursing, Behavioral HealthCare Center at Columbia, Columbia, TN, p. A567

LADNER, Warren, Chief Financial Officer, Natchez Community Hospital, Natchez, MS, p. A351

LAEL, Marielle, R.N. Chief Nursing Officer, Select Specialty Hospital–Fort Wayne, Fort Wayne, IN, p. A203

LAFERNEY, Jimmy, M.D. Vice President Medical Staff Affairs, Baylor Medical Center at Frisco, Frisco, TX, p. A605

LAFFERTY, Aline S., Vice President Human Resources, Henry Ford Wyandotte Hospital, Wyandotte, MI, p. A327

LAFFERTY, Douglas L., Chief Executive Officer, Plumas District Hospital, Quincy, CA, p. A81

LAFFEY, Leah, R.N., Chief Executive Officer, HEALTHSOUTH Rehabilitation Hospital, Sewickley, PA, p. A541

LAFINE, Amy, MSN, President and Chief Executive Officer, Presence St. Mary's Hospital, Kankakee, IL, p. A186

LAFLEUR, Cindy, President, Via Christi Rehabilitation Center, Wichita, KS, p. A246

LAFLEUR, Robert R., Chief Executive Officer, Cornerstone Hospital of Southwest Louisiana, Sulphur, LA, p. A279

LAFONE, Ken, Director Human Resources, Caswell Center, Kinston, NC, p. A456

LAFRANCOIS, Gregory, Chief Executive Officer, Prairie St. John's, Fargo, ND, p. A466

LAFRANCOIS, Mary, Vice President Human Resources, CHRISTUS Spohn Hospital Corpus Christi Memorial, Corpus Christi, TX, p. A593

LAGAARD, Scott, M.D. Chief of Staff, FirstLight Health System, Mora, MN, p. A337

LAGANA, Gina, Director Human Resources, Merrimack Valley Hospital, Haverhill, MA, p. A300

LAGASSE, David A., Senior Vice President Fiscal Affairs, McLean Hospital, Belmont, MA, p. A295

LAGASSE, Roger, Chief Financial Officer, Northern Maine Medical Center, Fort Kent, ME, p. A283

LAGNESE, John, M.D. Vice President Medical Affairs, UPMC St. Margaret, Pittsburgh, PA, p. A538

LAGUNZAD, Anastacia, M.D. Chief of Staff, Perry County Memorial Hospital, Tell City, IN, p. A213

LAHASKY, Doug, Chief Financial Officer, Acadia Vermilion Hospital, Lafayette, LA, p. A270

LAHATTE, Lawrence, M.D. Chief of Staff, Trinity Hospital of Augusta, Augusta, GA, p. A148

LAHAYE, Daniel, Manager, Savoy Medical Center, Mamou, LA, p. A273

LAHIDJANI, Jack, Chief Executive Officer, Miracle Mile Medical Center, Los Angeles, CA, p. A70

LAHOUT, Brenda, Chief Nurse Executive, Danville State Hospital, Danville, PA, p. A523

LAHTI, Molly, Director Human Resources, Parkland Medical Center, Derry, NH, p. A397

LAI, Iris, Chief Executive Officer, Alhambra Hospital Medical Center, Alhambra, CA, p. A52

LAIBINIS, Walter, M.D. Chief Medical Officer, Soldiers and Sailors Memorial Hospital, Wellsboro, PA, p. A543

LAIBLE, Anna, Administrator, Advocate Eureka Hospital, Eureka, IL, p. A182

LAIGN, Michael B., President and Chief Executive Officer, Holy Redeemer Hospital and Medical Center, Meadowbrook, PA, p. A531

LAIRD, Carol, R.N. Chief Nursing Officer, Crockett Hospital, Lawrenceburg, TN, p. A572

LAIRD, Jeff, Controller, Stephens County Hospital, Toccoa, GA, p. A162

LAIRD, Michael J., FACHE,
President, Aurora Medical Center Grafton, Grafton, WI, p. A687
President, Aurora Medical Center of Washington County, Hartford, WI, p. A688

LAISTER, Judy K., Director, Human Resources, Methodist Mansfield Medical Center, Mansfield, TX, p. A621

LAKE, Jane, Director Materials Management, St. Luke's Cornwall Hospital, Newburgh, NY, p. A437

LAKE, Nathan, Vice President Human Resources, Prairie Lakes Healthcare System, Watertown, SD, p. A564

LAKE, Peter M., M.D. Chief Medical Officer, Rogers Memorial Hospital, Oconomowoc, WI, p. A693

LAKINS, Tom, Director Information Systems, Physicians Regional Medical Center, Knoxville, TN, p. A572

LAKNER, Stephen, M.D. President Medical and Affiliate Staff, Shady Grove Adventist Hospital, Rockville, MD, p. A294

LAKSHMANAN, Rekha, M.D. Medical Director, Mercy Continuing Care Hospital, Chesterfield, MO, p. A358

LALIBERTE, John, Assistant Vice President, Our Lady of Lourdes Memorial Hospital, Binghamton, NY, p. A421

LALLY, James M., D.O., President and Chief Medical Officer, Chino Valley Medical Center, Chino, CA, p. A56

LALLY, Michael K., Chief Executive Officer, Calais Regional Hospital, Calais, ME, p. A282

LALLY, Jr., Robert P., Vice President Finance, MedStar Franklin Square Medical Center, Baltimore, MD, p. A288

LAMADELEINE, Joseph, Chief Financial Officer, Veterans Affairs Connecticut Healthcare System, West Haven, CT, p. A113

LAMANTIA, Joseph, Executive Vice President and Chief Operating Officer, South Nassau Communities Hospital, Oceanside, NY, p. A438

LAMARCHE, Heather, Manager Human Resources, AMG Specialty Hospital–Lafayette, Lafayette, LA, p. A270

LAMARCHE, Marie, Executive Director, Human Resources, Organizational Development, Employee Health, Harrison Medical Center, Bremerton, WA, p. A664

LAMB, Andrew, M.D. Chief of Staff, Alamance Regional Medical Center, Burlington, NC, p. A448

LAMB, Cindy, Director Human Resources, Marias Medical Center, Shelby, MT, p. A379

LAMB, Collin, Director Management Information Systems, St. Joseph Regional Medical Center, Lewiston, ID, p. A169

LAMB, Deanna, Director of Human Resources, Community Hospital–Fairfax, Fairfax, MO, p. A360

LAMB, Hope, Manager Human Resources, Kimble Hospital, Junction, TX, p. A615

LAMB, Thomas, Director Information Systems, Monongahela Valley Hospital, Monongahela, PA, p. A532

LAMB, Timothy E., Commander, Martin Army Community Hospital, Fort Benning, GA, p. A153

LAMBERT, Amand, Director Human Resources, Allen Parish Hospital, Kinder, LA, p. A270

LAMBERT, Barbara, Director Healthcare Compliance, Eastern State Hospital, Williamsburg, VA, p. A663

LAMBERT, Chelcia, Chief Operating Officer and Chief Financial Officer, Kettering Medical Center, Kettering, OH, p. A483

LAMBERT, James M., FACHE,  President and Chief Executive Officer, Conway Regional Medical Center, Conway, AR, p. A42

LAMBERT, Karen A., President, Advocate Good Shepherd Hospital, Barrington, IL, p. A174

LAMBERT, Lynn, Chief Financial Officer, Wilson Medical Center, Wilson, NC, p. A463

LAMBERT, Paul, M.D. Chief of Staff, Boise Veterans Affairs Medical Center, Boise, ID, p. A167

LAMBETH, Laura, Chief Executive Officer, Ashe Memorial Hospital, Jefferson, NC, p. A455

LAMBKE, Michael, M.D. Medical Director, Redington–Fairview General Hospital, Skowhegan, ME, p. A285

LAMBORN, Cherie, Interim Vice President Human Resources, Springfield Regional Medical Center, Springfield, OH, p. A490

LAMBORN, Cheryl, Vice President Human Resources, Allegiance Health, Jackson, MI, p. A317

LAMBRECHT, Craig, M.D.,  President, Sanford Bismarck, Bismarck, ND, p. A465

LAMBRECHT, Rebecca, Manager Finance, Alegent Creighton Health Plainview Hospital, Plainview, NE, p. A389

LAMBRECHT, Sandra, Chief Financial Officer, Haxtun Hospital District, Haxtun, CO, p. A102

LAMEN, Drake M., M.D.,  President and Chief Executive Officer, Chenango Memorial Hospital, Norwich, NY, p. A438

LAMEY, Rebecca, Vice President Human Resources, MaineGeneral Medical Center–Waterville Campus, Waterville, ME, p. A285

LAMIS, Pano, M.D. Medical Director, Atlanta Medical Center, Atlanta, GA, p. A146

LAMITIE, Timothy J., Deputy Director Administration, St. Lawrence Psychiatric Center, Ogdensburg, NY, p. A438

LAMLE, Sandra, Chief Financial Officer, Okeene Municipal Hospital, Okeene, OK, p. A502

LAMMERS, Sandra, Coordinator Human Resources and Finance, Alegent Creighton Health Mercy Hospital, Corning, IA, p. A218

LAMORELLA, Vincent M., Chief Financial Officer, Clarion Hospital, Clarion, PA, p. A522

LAMOUREUX, Bruce, Vice President and Chief Executive Officer, Providence Alaska Medical Center, Anchorage, AK, p. A27

LAMPARTER, David
Senior Vice President and Chief Financial Officer, John C. Lincoln Deer Valley Hospital, Phoenix, AZ, p. A34
Senior Vice President and Chief Financial Officer, John C. Lincoln North Mountain Hospital, Phoenix, AZ, p. A34

LAMPE, Michael, M.D. Chief of Staff, Kossuth Regional Health Center, Algona, IA, p. A216

LAMPERT, John, Chief Executive Officer, Sayre Memorial Hospital, Sayre, OK, p. A506

LAMPTON, Brett, M.D. Chief of Staff, Baptist Memorial Hospital–North Mississippi, Oxford, MS, p. A352

LAMPTON, Lucius, M.D. Medical Director, Beacham Memorial Hospital, Magnolia, MS, p. A350

LANAM, Kay, Coordinator Human Resources, Kindred Hospital Tarrant County–Fort Worth Southwest, Fort Worth, TX, p. A604

LANCASTER, Johnny, Chief Financial Officer, Vista Health, Fayetteville, AR, p. A43

LANCASTER, Tim, FACHE,  President and Chief Executive Officer, Hendrick Health System, Abilene, TX, p. A581

LANCE, Richard, Vice President Human Resources, Nix Health Care System, San Antonio, TX, p. A632

LANCIOTTI, Kevin, Chief Financial Officer, McLaren Greater Lansing, Lansing, MI, p. A318

LAND, David, D.O. Chief Medical Staff, Fort Duncan Regional Medical Center, Eagle Pass, TX, p. A600

LAND, Laura, Chief Human Resources Officer, OU Medical Center, Oklahoma City, OK, p. A504

LANDAU, Ken, Chief Financial Officer, Lake District Hospital, Lakeview, OR, p. A514

LANDERS, Alice, Administrative Director Operations, Texas Health Harris Methodist Hospital Hurst–Euless–Bedford, Bedford, TX, p. A588

LANDGARTEN, Steven, M.D. Chief Medical Officer, Hillcrest Medical Center, Tulsa, OK, p. A508

LANDIS, Bradlee, Chief Information Officer, Faith Community Hospital, Jacksboro, TX, p. A615

LANDIS, Cathy, R.N. Chief Nursing Officer, East Cooper Medical Center, Mount Pleasant, SC, p. A554

LANDMAN, Paul, Director Human Resources, Ellwood City Hospital, Ellwood City, PA, p. A525

LANDRENEAU, Derrick, Director of Nursing, Baton Rouge Rehabilitation Hospital, Baton Rouge, LA, p. A263

LANDRETH, Jonathan, Chief Executive Officer, Lafayette Physical Rehabilitation Hospital, Lafayette, LA, p. A271

LANDRETH, Sandy, Director Human Resources, Seiling Community Hospital, Seiling, OK, p. A506

LANDRETH, Shannan, Information Systems, Livingston Hospital and Healthcare Services, Salem, KY, p. A260

LANDRUM, Scott M., Interim Chief Executive Officer, Homer Memorial Hospital, Homer, LA, p. A268

LANDRY, Adam, Coordinator Computer Systems, Northern Maine Medical Center, Fort Kent, ME, p. A283

LANDRY, Candy, Chief Human Resource Officer, Eastside Psychiatric Hospital, Tallahassee, FL, p. A140

LANDRY, Ray A., Chief Executive Officer, Abbeville General Hospital, Abbeville, LA, p. A262

LANDRY, Wayne J., Chief Executive Officer, St. Bernard Parish Hospital, Chalmette, LA, p. A265

LANDSMAN, Joseph, President and Chief Executive Officer, University of Tennessee Medical Center, Knoxville, TN, p. A572

LANDSTROM, John
Vice President Human Resources and Operations, RML Specialty Hospital, Chicago, IL, p. A178
Director Human Resources, RML Specialty Hospital, Hinsdale, IL, p. A185

LANDWEHR, Katie, Acting Associate Director, Veterans Affairs Medical Center, Omaha, NE, p. A388

LANE, Kathy, Leader–ICU, Home Care, MedSurg, York Hospital, York, ME, p. A286

LANE, Kevin, D.O. Chief of Staff, Hardeman County Memorial Hospital, Quanah, TX, p. A628

LANE, Kevin, Vice President Information Systems, Silver Cross Hospital, New Lenox, IL, p. A190

LANE, Kim, Chief Fiscal Service, Overton Brooks Veterans Affairs Medical Center, Shreveport, LA, p. A278

LANE, Richard, Chief Financial Officer, Mid–America Rehabilitation Hospital, Shawnee Mission, KS, p. A244

LANE, Stacey
Executive Assistant Human Resources, Chambers Memorial Hospital, Danville, AR, p. A42
Director Human Resources, Hunt Regional Community Hospital, Commerce, TX, p. A593

LANE, Tommy, Chief Financial Officer, Lanier Health Services, Valley, AL, p. A26

LANER, Jr., Richard, Manager Information Systems, Miners' Colfax Medical Center, Raton, NM, p. A417

LANEY, Samuel Mark, M.D.,  President and Chief Executive Officer, Heartland Regional Medical Center, Saint Joseph, MO, p. A369

LANG, Anne, Vice President Human Resources and Compliance and Privacy Officer, Winchester Hospital, Winchester, MA, p. A306

LANG, Cyndi, Director Information Services, French Hospital Medical Center, San Luis Obispo, CA, p. A88

LANG, David, Vice President Human Resources, Baptist Health Madisonville, Madisonville, KY, p. A257

LANG, Everitt, Consultant Human Resources and Organizational Development, Memorial Hermann Rehabilitation Hospital – Katy, Katy, TX, p. A616

LANG, Jr., Frank, M.D. Chief of Medicine, Sierra Nevada Memorial Hospital, Grass Valley, CA, p. A63

LANG, Gordon, M.D. Chief of Staff, Trego County–Lemke Memorial Hospital, Wakeeney, KS, p. A245

LANG, Irby, Vice President Human Resources, Anderson Regional Medical Center, Meridian, MS, p. A351

LANG, Jeffrey M., Chief Executive Officer, United Hospital District, Blue Earth, MN, p. A329

LANG, John Christopher, Chief Executive Officer, Cass Regional Medical Center, Harrisonville, MO, p. A361

LANG, Nicholas P., M.D
Chief of Staff, Central Arkansas Veterans Healthcare System, Little Rock, AR, p. A46
Chief Medical Officer, UAMS Medical Center, Little Rock, AR, p. A47

LANG, Paula, Chief Executive Officer, Patient's Choice Medical Center of Humphreys County, Belzoni, MS, p. A344

LANG, Richard, Ed.D. Vice President and Chief Information Officer, Doylestown Hospital, Doylestown, PA, p. A524

LANG, Richard T., Chief Financial Officer, Edward John Noble Hospital of Gouverneur, Gouverneur, NY, p. A426

LANG, Tony, Chief Information Officer, Bullock County Hospital, Union Springs, AL, p. A26

LANGAGER, Tyrone, M.D. Chief Medical Officer, Mountrail County Medical Center, Stanley, ND, p. A469

LANGBEHN, Cody, Chief Executive Officer, St. Luke's Wood River Medical Center, Ketchum, ID, p. A169

LANGBEHN, Jennifer, Medical Director, Mayo Clinic Health System in Saint James, Saint James, MN, p. A339

LANGBERG, Michael L., M.D. Senior Vice President Medical Affairs and Chief Medical Officer, Cedars–Sinai Medical Center, Los Angeles, CA, p. A68

LANGDON, Ashlee, Controller, Yalobusha General Hospital, Water Valley, MS, p. A354

LANGENBERG, Shannon, Director Human Resources, Jackson County Regional Health Center, Maquoketa, IA, p. A224

LANGFELDER, Richard, Executive Vice President and Chief Financial Officer, Lutheran Medical Center,, NY, p. A433

LANGLITZ, Sara, Controller, Kindred Hospital–Houston, Houston, TX, p. A610

LANGLOIS, John
Vice President Finance, Citizens Baptist Medical Center, Talladega, AL, p. A25
Chief Financial Officer, Walker Baptist Medical Center, Jasper, AL, p. A22

LANGLOTZ, Karla, Director Human Resources, Central Florida Regional Hospital, Sanford, FL, p. A139

LANGMEAD, Paula A., Chief Executive Officer, Springfield Hospital Center, Sykesville, MD, p. A294

LANGSTON, Kimberly K., R.N., Chief Executive Officer, Scott and White Continuing Care Hospital, Temple, TX, p. A636

LANIG, Indria S., M.D. Medical Director, Northern Colorado Rehabilitation Hospital, Johnstown, CO, p. A102

LANKFORD, Deanna, Business Office Manager, Plano Specialty Hospital, Plano, TX, p. A627

LANNOYE, Craig, Vice President Operations, Wilson Memorial Hospital, Sidney, OH, p. A490

LANOUE, Cheryl, Chief Financial Officer, Ottawa County Health Center, Minneapolis, KS, p. A240

LANS, Sue, Comptroller, Harlan County Health System, Alma, NE, p. A381

LANSDOWNE, Lynn M., Vice President Human Resources, Pocono Medical Center, East Stroudsburg, PA, p. A524

LANSFORD, Georgene, Director Information Systems, St. Mary's Hospital, Streator, IL, p. A196

LANTOS, Phyllis R., Executive Vice President, Chief Financial Officer and Treasurer, New York–Presbyterian Hospital, New York, NY, p. A435

LANTZY, William, Vice President Finance, DMC Huron Valley–Sinai Hospital, Commerce Township, MI, p. A311

LANZA, Nicholas, Controller, St. Mary's Hospital, Passaic, NJ, p. A408

LANZA, Raymond, D.O. Medical Director, Runnells Specialized Hospital of Union County, Berkeley Heights, NJ, p. A401

LAPENSKY, Julianne, MS Vice President Patient Care Services, Unity Hospital, Fridley, MN, p. A332

LAPERLE, Linda M., Vice President Administrative Services, Androscoggin Valley Hospital, Berlin, NH, p. A397

LAPHAM, Lisa, Chief Financial Officer, HealthSource Saginaw, Saginaw, MI, p. A323

LAPUZ, Miguel H., M.D., Director, Salem Veterans Affairs Medical Center, Salem, VA, p. A661

LARA, Sergio, M.D. Chief Medical Officer, Covenant Hospital Plainview, Plainview, TX, p. A627

LARAMIE, Robert, Chief Information Officer, Beverly Hospital, Beverly, MA, p. A295

LARCAS, John, M.D. Acting Medical Director, Choate Mental Health Center, Anna, IL, p. A173

LARCEN, Stephen W., Ph.D.,
President and Chief Executive Officer, Natchaug Hospital, Mansfield Center, CT, p. A109
President and Chief Executive Officer, Windham Hospital, Willimantic, CT, p. A113

LAREAU, Daniel, Executive Director Operations and Information, St. Vincent Carmel Hospital, Carmel, IN, p. A200

LAREAU, Kim, Vice President and Chief Information Officer, Regions Hospital, Saint Paul, MN, p. A340

LARET, Mark R., Chief Executive Officer, UCSF Medical Center, San Francisco, CA, p. A87

LARIMER, Cynthia, M.D. Medical Director Emergency Room, Lake Butler Hospital Hand Surgery Center, Lake Butler, FL, p. A128

LARISCY, Robin Barton, M.D. Medical Director, Mary S Harper Geriatric Psychiatry Center, Tuscaloosa, AL, p. A26

LARISON, Sarah A., Director Health Information Management, Holton Community Hospital, Holton, KS, p. A235

LARIVIERE, Beckye, Controller, HEALTHSOUTH Rehabilitation Hospital of Charleston, Charleston, SC, p. A549

LARKIN, Ernest, M.D. Chief Medical Officer, Vidant Medical Center, Greenville, NC, p. A454

LARKIN, Kim, Chief Information Officer, Washington County Hospital, Nashville, IL, p. A190

LARKINS, Gloria, Vice President Finance, Detroit Receiving Hospital/University Health Center, Detroit, MI, p. A311

LARNER, Cheryl, Chief Financial Officer, Sentara CarePlex Hospital, Hampton, VA, p. A655

LAROCHELLE, Albert, Chief Executive Officer, Reeves County Hospital, Pecos, TX, p. A626

LAROSE, Mark, President and Chief Executive Officer, Florida Hospital DeLand, DeLand, FL, p. A122

LAROWE, Mary E., FACHE, President and Chief Executive Officer, St. James Mercy Health System, Hornell, NY, p. A427

LARRISON Jr., Robert G., President, Carolinas Rehabilitation, Charlotte, NC, p. A449

LARSEN, Anita, R.N
Interim Chief Operating Officer, University of Missouri Hospitals and Clinics, Columbia, MO, p. A359
Chief Nursing Officer, Women's and Children's Hospital, Columbia, MO, p. A359

LARSEN, Bill, Vice President Human Resources, Driscoll Children's Hospital, Corpus Christi, TX, p. A594

LARSEN, Dave M., Chief Financial Officer, LDS Hospital, Salt Lake City, UT, p. A646

LARSEN, Donald, M.D. Chief Medical Officer, Keck Hospital of USC, Los Angeles, CA, p. A70

LARSEN, L. Scott, M.D. Vice President Medical Affairs, Bayshore Community Hospital, Holmdel, NJ, p. A405

LARSEN, Michael, Director Information Systems, Baylor Medical Center at Garland, Garland, TX, p. A606

LARSEN, Rod, Chief Financial Officer, North Canyon Medical Center, Gooding, ID, p. A169

LARSEN, Ryan C., FACHE, Chief Executive Officer, Community Medical Center, Falls City, NE, p. A383

LARSON, Barbara, R.N. Chief Operating Officer, Bell Hospital, Ishpeming, MI, p. A317

LARSON, Barbara R., R.N. Vice President Patient Care Services, Avera Sacred Heart Hospital, Yankton, SD, p. A564

LARSON, Erick, Vice President and Chief Information Officer, Mid–Columbia Medical Center, The Dalles, OR, p. A518

LARSON, Gordon, Chief Executive Officer, Sanford Aberdeen Medical Center, Aberdeen, SD, p. A558

LARSON, Jon, M.D. Medical Director, HEALTHSOUTH Rehabilitation Institute of Tucson, Tucson, AZ, p. A38

LARSON, Karla, Director Human Resources, Stevens Community Medical Center, Morris, MN, p. A337

LARSON, Kirk, Chief Information Officer, Natividad Medical Center, Salinas, CA, p. A84

LARSON, Larry, Management Analyst, Dorothea Dix Psychiatric Center, Bangor, ME, p. A281

LARSON, Michael
Vice President Chief Inofmation Officer, MidMichigan Medical Center–Clare, Clare, MI, p. A310
Vice President and Chief Information Officer, MidMichigan Medical Center–Gladwin, Gladwin, MI, p. A314
Chief Information Officer, MidMichigan Medical Center–Gratiot, Alma, MI, p. A308

LARSON, Mike, Chief Financial Officer, Mayo Clinic Health System in Red Wing, Red Wing, MN, p. A338

LARSON, Nicole, Manager Human Resources, Grundy County Memorial Hospital, Grundy Center, IA, p. A222

LARSON, Pamela, Division Director Financial Services, Hutchinson Health, Hutchinson, MN, p. A334

LARSON, Peggy, R.N., Administrator, Lisbon Area Health Services, Lisbon, ND, p. A468

LARSON, Ronald, Chief Financial Officer, Veterans Affairs San Diego Healthcare System, San Diego, CA, p. A86

LARSON, Scott, M.D. Vice President Medical Affairs and Chief Medical Officer, Bronson Methodist Hospital, Kalamazoo, MI, p. A318

LARSON, Scott C., Chief Executive Officer, Sanford Canton–Inwood Medical Center, Canton, SD, p. A558

LARSON, Shelly, Chief Financial Officer, Hot Springs County Memorial Hospital, Thermopolis, WY, p. A704

LARSON, Steve, M.D. Director Information Systems, Mercy Medical Center–Sioux City, Sioux City, IA, p. A228

LARSON, Tammy, Chief Financial Officer, Towner County Medical Center, Cando, ND, p. A465

LARSON, Walt, Vice President Finance, Tillamook Regional Medical Center, Tillamook, OR, p. A518

LARSON, Wendy, Chief Clinical Officer, Promise Hospital of Phoenix, Mesa, AZ, p. A33

LASECKI, Matt, Interim Vice President Human Resources, Providence Hospital, Washington, DC, p. A116

LASH, Lashaunda, Manager Human Resources, Pioneer Community Hospital of Stokes, Danbury, NC, p. A450

LASHLEY, Leah, Chief Financial Officer, Winn Parish Medical Center, Winnfield, LA, p. A280

LASHLEY, Michael, Network Administrator, Thousand Oaks Surgical Hospital, Thousand Oaks, CA, p. A92

LASHMETT, Christinia, Director Financial Services, Missouri Baptist Sullivan Hospital, Sullivan, MO, p. A372

LASKER, Rose, Director Information Services, Bluefield Regional Medical Center, Bluefield, WV, p. A675

LASKOWSKI, Robert J., M.D., President and Chief Executive Officer, Christiana Care Health System, Newark, DE, p. A114

LASKOWSKI, Rose, R.N., Director, Caro Center, Caro, MI, p. A310

LASKY, John, Vice President Human Resources, Allegheny General Hospital, Pittsburgh, PA, p. A537

LASSITER, Melissa, Coordinator Human Resources, Columbus Specialty Hospital, Columbus, GA, p. A150

LASSITER, Rick, President and Chief Administrative Officer, Parkwest Medical Center, Knoxville, TN, p. A572

LASSITER, Susan S., FACHE, President and Chief Executive Officer, Vidant Roanoke–Chowan Hospital, Ahoskie, NC, p. A447

LASSITER III, Wright L., Chief Executive Officer, Alameda County Medical Center, Oakland, CA, p. A77

LASTER, Charles
Director Information Management, Willis–Knighton Medical Center, Shreveport, LA, p. A278
Director Information Management, WK Bossier Health Center, Bossier City, LA, p. A264

LATER, Elizabeth B., R.N. Chief Nursing Officer, Ogden Regional Medical Center, Ogden, UT, p. A645

LATHROM, Sue, Director of Nursing/Patient Care System Leader, Scheurer Hospital, Pigeon, MI, p. A321

LATHROP, Deanna, Assistant Administrator, Sabine County Hospital, Hemphill, TX, p. A608

LATTA, Tera L., Director Human Resources, Integris Bass Pavilion, Enid, OK, p. A498

LATTERNER, Renee, Director Human Resources, Lake Wales Medical Center, Lake Wales, FL, p. A128

LATTRELL, Pat, Director Human Resources, Coliseum Medical Centers, Macon, GA, p. A156

LATUCHIE, Richard, Vice President Business Development, Rapid City Regional Hospital, Rapid City, SD, p. A562

LAUBACHER, Ned, President and Chief Executive Officer, Allegheny Valley Hospital, Natrona Heights, PA, p. A533

LAUBENTHAL, Sherrie L., R.N. Chief Nursing Officer, Mercy Medical Center–New Hampton, New Hampton, IA, p. A226

LAUDERBACH, Jr., C. W., Vice President Clinical Services, St. Mary Mercy Hospital, Livonia, MI, p. A319

LAUE, Edward, M.D. Chief Medical Officer, Huguley Memorial Medical Center, Fort Worth, TX, p. A603

LAUE, Jerry, Administrator, St. Vincent Clay Hospital, Brazil, IN, p. A199

LAUENSTEIN, Deb, Director Human Resources and Marketing, St. Joseph's Community Hospital of West Bend, West Bend, WI, p. A699

LAUER, Bill, Chief Information Officer, Morris County Hospital, Council Grove, KS, p. A233

LAUF, Michael K., President and Chief Executive Officer, Cape Cod Hospital, Hyannis, MA, p. A301

LAUFFER, Daniel, FACH
Executive Vice President and Chief Operating Officer, Saint Francis Hospital, Charleston, WV, p. A676
Senior Vice President and Chief Operating Officer, Thomas Memorial Hospital, South Charleston, WV, p. A681

LAUGHLIN, Jennifer, Vice President and Chief Information Officer, Watertown Regional Medical Center, Watertown, WI, p. A698

LAUGHLIN, Warren, Vice President Human Resources, Longmont United Hospital, Longmont, CO, p. A104

LAUGHNAN Jr., Woody J., Administrator, Glenn Medical Center, Willows, CA, p. A96

LAUKAITIS, Fran, R.N. Vice President Nursing, Methodist Charlton Medical Center, Dallas, TX, p. A596

LAUMAN, Joan, Manager Clinical Systems, Abington Health Lansdale Hospital, Lansdale, PA, p. A529

LAUNIUS, Billie, Director Business Finance, Dallas County Medical Center, Fordyce, AR, p. A44

LAURENT, Merrill, M.D. Medical Director, Regency Hospital of Covington, Covington, LA, p. A266

LAURETO, Rose Ann, Chief Information Officer, University of Illinois Hospital & Health Sciences System, Chicago, IL, p. A180

LAURIN, George, Interim Chief Human Resources Officer, Rehoboth McKinley Christian Health Care Services, Gallup, NM, p. A416

LAURIN, George M., Interim Director Human Resources, Crisp Regional Hospital, Cordele, GA, p. A151

LAURO, Frank, M.D. Chief Medical Officer, Indian Path Medical Center, Kingsport, TN, p. A571

LAUTER, Keith
Vice President Finance, Franciscan St. Elizabeth Health – Crawfordsville, Crawfordsville, IN, p. A200
Chief Financial Officer, Franciscan St. Elizabeth Health – Lafayette Central, Lafayette, IN, p. A208

LAUTNER, Marty, Vice President Finance and Chief Financial Officer, Cardinal Hill Rehabilitation Hospital, Lexington, KY, p. A254

LAUVE, Lisa R., R.N. Regional Chief Nursing Executive and Chief Operating Officer, CHRISTUS St. Frances Cabrini Hospital, Alexandria, LA, p. A262

LAUVE, Timothy, Coordinator Mental Health Local Information Systems, Greater Binghamton Health Center, Binghamton, NY, p. A421

LAVALLEY, Marlinda L., Administrator, Edward John Noble Hospital of Gouverneur, Gouverneur, NY, p. A426

LAVELLE, Joseph D., Executive Vice President and Chief Operating Officer, Medical Center of Central Georgia, Macon, GA, p. A156

LAVELY, Patricia A., FACHE Chief Information Officer, Memorial Health, Savannah, GA, p. A160

LAVER, Joseph, M.D. Executive Vice President and Chief Medical Officer, St. Jude Children's Research Hospital, Memphis, TN, p. A575

LAVERDIERE, Dana, Generalist, St. Anthony Summit Medical Center, Frisco, CO, p. A101

LAVOIE, Frank, M.D. Executive Vice President and Chief Operating Officer, Southern Maine Medical Center, Biddeford, ME, p. A282

LAW, Charles, Chief Operating Officer, Catawba Hospital, Catawba, VA, p. A652

LAW, Johnny, Area Information Officer, Kaiser Permanente Oakland Medical Center, Oakland, CA, p. A77

LAW, Kate J., Director Human Resources, Maple Grove Hospital, Maple Grove, MN, p. A335

LAWATSCH, Frank, Chief Executive Officer, Swift County–Benson Hospital, Benson, MN, p. A329

LAWATY, Edward, Chief Financial Officer, Minnie Hamilton HealthCare Center, Grantsville, WV, p. A677

LAWHORN, Renee, Director Medical Records, East Texas Medical Center Carthage, Carthage, TX, p. A591

LAWHORNE, Thomas, Chief Financial Officer, Regional Medical Center–Bayonet Point, Hudson, FL, p. A126

LAWLER, Anne, Director Human Resources, North Mississippi Medical Center–Hamilton, Hamilton, AL, p. A21

LAWLER, Kay, Business Office Manager, North Mississippi Medical Center–West Point, West Point, MS, p. A355

LAWLER, Patrick, Chief Executive Officer, Youth Villages Inner Harbour Campus, Douglasville, GA, p. A152

LAWLER, Stephen, President, Vidant Medical Center, Greenville, NC, p. A454

LAWLESS, JoBeth, Director of Nursing, Nursing Services and Director Emergency Management Services, Lucas County Health Center, Chariton, IA, p. A218

LAWLESS, Rosalie, Director Human Resources, Fairlawn Rehabilitation Hospital, Worcester, MA, p. A306

LAWLOR, Kevin F., President and Chief Executive Officer, Huntington Hospital, Huntington, NY, p. A427

LAWONN, Kenneth
Senior Vice President Strategy & Technology, Alegent Creighton Health Bergan Mercy Medical Center, Omaha, NE, p. A387
Senior Vice President Strategy and Technology, Alegent Creighton Health Community Memorial Hospital, Missouri Valley, IA, p. A225
Senior Vice President Strategy and Technology, Alegent Creighton Health Immanuel Medical Center, Omaha, NE, p. A387
Senior Vice President and Chief Information Officer, Alegent Creighton Health Lakeside Hospital, Omaha, NE, p. A387
Senior Vice President and Chief Information Officer, Alegent Creighton Health Mercy Hospital, Corning, IA, p. A218
Senior Vice President and Chief Information Officer, Alegent Creighton Health Mercy Hospital, Council Bluffs, IA, p. A219
Senior Vice President and Chief Information Officer, Alegent Creighton Health Midlands Hospital, Papillion, NE, p. A389
Senior Vice President and Chief Information Officer, Alegent Creighton Health–Memorial Hospital, Schuyler, Schuyler, NE, p. A389

LAWRENCE, Dana, Chief Financial Officer, Parkway Regional Hospital, Fulton, KY, p. A251

LAWRENCE, Jeffrey T., Chief Operating Officer, Denton Regional Medical Center, Denton, TX, p. A598

LAWRENCE, Michael A., Chief Financial Officer, UnityHealth MacNeal Hospital, Berwyn, IL, p. A174

LAWRENCE, Rita, Director of Nursing, Doctors Hospital of West Covina, West Covina, CA, p. A95

LAWRENCE, Sandra A J
Executive Vice President and Chief Financial Officer, Children's Mercy Hospitals and Clinics, Kansas City, MO, p. A362
Executive Vice President and Chief Financial Officer, Children's Mercy South, Overland Park, KS, p. A241

LAWRENCE, Stephanie, Chief Financial Officer, Kentfield Rehabilitation and Specialty Hospital, Kentfield, CA, p. A65

LAWRENCE, Ursula, MSN Chief Nursing Officer, Central Carolina Hospital, Sanford, NC, p. A460

LAWRENCE, William P., President and Chief Executive Officer, McLaren Central Michigan, Mount Pleasant, MI, p. A320

LAWRENSON, Victoria
Chief Operating Officer, Bullock County Hospital, Union Springs, AL, p. A26
Chief Operating Officer, Crenshaw Community Hospital, Luverne, AL, p. A22

LAWSON, Alvin R., FACHE, Chief Executive Officer, HEALTHSOUTH Western Hills Rehabilitation Hospital, Parkersburg, WV, p. A679

LAWSON, Beth, Chief Financial Officer and Director Governmental Affairs, Sunrise Canyon Hospital, Lubbock, TX, p. A620

LAWSON, David C.
Senior Vice President Human Resources, St. Clare Hospital, Lakewood, WA, p. A667
Senior Vice President Human Resources, St. Francis Hospital, Federal Way, WA, p. A666
Senior Vice President Human Resources, St. Joseph Medical Center, Tacoma, WA, p. A673

LAWSON, Doug, Chief Operating Officer, Baylor University Medical Center, Dallas, TX, p. A595

LAWSON, Eric, Chief Financial Officer, North Florida Regional Medical Center, Gainesville, FL, p. A124

LAWSON, Judy, Director Information Services, Norton Community Hospital, Norton, VA, p. A658

LAWSON, Michael, Senior Vice President Operations, OhioHealth Grant Medical Center, Columbus, OH, p. A478

LAWSON, Michael E.
Director, Brockton Veterans Affairs Medical Center, Brockton, MA, p. A298
Director, Veterans Affairs Boston Healthcare System, Boston, MA, p. A297

LAWSON, Pam, Director Clinical Services, Select Specialty Hospital–Wilmington, Wilmington, DE, p. A115

LAWSON, Ralph E., Executive Vice President and Chief Financial Officer, Baptist Health South Florida, Baptist Hospital of Miami, Miami, FL, p. A131

LAWSON, Sandra K., Interim Director Fiscal Services, Shriners Hospitals for Children–St. Louis, Saint Louis, MO, p. A370

LAWSON, West, M.D
Chief Medical Officer, WakeMed Cary Hospital, Cary, NC, p. A449
Chief Medical Officer, WakeMed Raleigh Campus, Raleigh, NC, p. A459

LAWTON, Geoff, Vice President Operations, Littleton Adventist Hospital, Littleton, CO, p. A103

LAWYER, Kristin, Director Human Resources, Weatherford Regional Medical Center, Weatherford, TX, p. A640

LAY, Sr., A. K., M.D. Chief Medical Officer, Jasper General Hospital, Bay Springs, MS, p. A344

LAY, Barbara, Chief Executive Officer, Pocahontas Memorial Hospital, Buckeye, WV, p. A675

LAYDEN, Lisa, Chief Operating Officer, Highland Hospital, Charleston, WV, p. A676

LAYFIELD, Michael G., Chief Executive Officer, Drew Memorial Hospital, Monticello, AR, p. A47

LAYNE, Kristine, R.N. Chief Nursing Officer, Riverwood Healthcare Center, Aitkin, MN, p. A328

LAYTON, Ann, M.D. Chief of Staff, North Metro Medical Center, Jacksonville, AR, p. A45

LAYUGAN, Melvin, Director Human Resources, Horizon Specialty Hospital, Las Vegas, NV, p. A393

LAZARUS, David, M.D. Medical Director Clinical Affairs, Newton Medical Center, Newton, NJ, p. A408

LAZO, Nelson, Chief Executive Officer, Baptist Health South Florida, Doctors Hospital, Coral Gables, FL, p. A121

LAZROFF, Gary
Vice President Human Resources, St. John Medical Center, Westlake, OH, p. A493
Vice President Human Resources, St. Vincent Charity Medical Center, Cleveland, OH, p. A477

LAZURE, Lee A., Director Civil Service Commission, Douglas County Community Mental Health Center, Omaha, NE, p. A388

LAZZARO, III, Frank A., Chief Human Resources Officer, Phelps County Regional Medical Center, Rolla, MO, p. A368

LE, Emily, Director Information Technology and Services, The Woman's Hospital of Texas, Houston, TX, p. A613

LEA, Hampton P S, Chief Operating Officer, Eastern Louisiana Mental Health System, Jackson, LA, p. A269

LEA, Randy, M.D. Vice President and Chief Medical Officer, Alice Peck Day Memorial Hospital, Lebanon, NH, p. A398

LEA, Rich, Vice President Operations, Euclid Hospital, Euclid, OH, p. A481

LEACH, Craig, President and Chief Executive Officer, Torrance Memorial Medical Center, Torrance, CA, p. A93

LEACH, Leslie, Administrator, Memorial Specialty Hospital, Lufkin, TX, p. A620

LEACH, Mary Ann, Vice President and Chief Information Officer, Children's Hospital Colorado, Aurora, CO, p. A97

LEACH, Steven, M.D. Chief Medical Officer, University of Texas Southwestern Medical Center, Dallas, TX, p. A598

LEACH, Thomas J., Administrator, Lakeside Medical Center, Belle Glade, FL, p. A118

LEADER, Skip, Chief Information Officer, Choctaw Nation Health Care Center, Talihina, OK, p. A507

LEAHY, Mary P., Vice President Human Resources, St. Joseph Hospital, Orange, CA, p. A78

LEAHY, Rosanne, Vice President Nursing Services, CarolinaEast Health System, New Bern, NC, p. A458

LEAKE, Jeanne E., R.N. Chief Nursing Officer, Uvalde County Hospital Authority, Uvalde, TX, p. A639

LEAKE, Neta F., Administrative Assistant Human Resources, West Feliciana Parish Hospital, Saint Francisville, LA, p. A277

LEAKE, Sandy, MSN Associate Director, Nursing and Patient Care Services, Atlanta Veterans Affairs Medical Center, Decatur, GA, p. A151

LEAKEY, Kim, R.N. Chief Nursing Officer, Lafayette Regional Health Center, Lexington, MO, p. A365

LEAL, Carlos, Chief Information Officer, Rio Grande Regional Hospital, McAllen, TX, p. A622

LEAL, Jorge E.
Chief Executive Officer, East Texas Medical Center Pittsburg, Pittsburg, TX, p. A627
Administrator, East Texas Medical Center–Gilmer, Gilmer, TX, p. A606

LEAL, Jr., Joseph M., M.D. Medical Director, Prairie Community Hospital, Terry, MT, p. A380

LEAMING, Larry E., FACHE, Chief Executive Officer, Roosevelt General Hospital, Portales, NM, p. A417

LEAMON, Jim, Chief Financial Officer, J. F. K. Medical Center, Atlantis, FL, p. A118

LEAR, Richard, Director Information Systems, St. David's South Austin Medical Center, Austin, TX, p. A586

LEARY, Edward B., Chief Executive Officer, New Bedford Rehabilitation Hospital, New Bedford, MA, p. A302

LEARY, Matt, Chief Financial Officer, Wesley Medical Center, Wichita, KS, p. A247

LEASURE, Sandie, Senior Vice President Human Resources, O'Bleness Memorial Hospital, Athens, OH, p. A471

LEAVITT, Cynthia, R.N
Senior Vice President, Hospital Operations, Miles Memorial Hospital, Damariscotta, ME, p. A283
Senior Vice President, Hospital Operations, St. Andrews Hospital and Healthcare Center, Boothbay Harbor, ME, p. A282

LEAZER, Ronald, Chief Financial Officer, Gateway Regional Medical Center, Granite City, IL, p. A184

LEBARON, Bradley D., FACHE, President and Chief Executive Officer, Uintah Basin Medical Center, Roosevelt, UT, p. A646

LEBARRON, Tere, Vice President Planning and Integration, University of Arizona Medical Center – South Campus, Tucson, AZ, p. A39

LEBEAU, Michelle, Vice President Human Resources, Champlain Valley Physicians Hospital Medical Center, Plattsburgh, NY, p. A439

LEBLANC, Ed, M.D. Vice President Medical Affairs, Seton Northwest Hospital, Austin, TX, p. A585

LEBLANC, Garon, Chief Plant Operations, Sage Rehabilitation Hospital, Baton Rouge, LA, p. A264

LEBLANC, Karen, Director, Applications, Samaritan Hospital, Troy, NY, p. A444

LEBLANC, Stephen J., Chief Operating Officer, Dartmouth–Hitchcock Medical Center, Lebanon, NH, p. A398

LEBOWITZ, Howard, M.D. Chief Medical Officer, Specialty Hospital at Kimball, Lakewood, NJ, p. A405

LEBRUN, James, Chief Executive Officer, Perkins County Health Services, Grant, NE, p. A384

LECHMAN, Brenda, Director Human Resources, Haxtun Hospital District, Haxtun, CO, p. A102

LECHOCO, Bing, Director Human Resources, Specialty Hospital of Washington–Hadley, Washington, DC, p. A117

LECKER, Marijo, Vice President, Martha Jefferson Hospital, Charlottesville, VA, p. A652

LEDAY, Jason, Chief Executive Officer, St. Anthony's Hospital, Houston, TX, p. A612

LEDBETTER, Joy, Director Human Resources, UnityPoint Health – Methodist, Peoria, IL, p. A192

LEDDEN, Edwin L., Human Resources Director/Assistant Administrator, Henry County Medical Center, Paris, TN, p. A578

LEDER, Larry, Chief Financial Officer, Promise Hospital of Miss Lou, Vidalia, LA, p. A279

LEDERER, Jane, R.N. Vice President and Chief Nursing Officer, Kingsbrook Jewish Medical Center,, NY, p. A433

LEDERMAN, Joel, Director Information Systems, Community Health Center of Branch County, Coldwater, MI, p. A311

LEDERMAN, Mark, Chief Information Officer, Interfaith Medical Center,, NY, p. A432

LEDET, Cathi, Comptroller, University Behavioral Health of Denton, Denton, TX, p. A599

LEDFORD, Maribeth, Director Human Resources, Henry Medical Center, Stockbridge, GA, p. A161

LEDOUX, Roger C., Chief Executive Officer, Byrd Regional Hospital, Leesville, LA, p. A272

LEDYARD, Robin, M.P.H., President, Community Hospital East, Indianapolis, IN, p. A205

LEE, Brett D., Chief Executive Officer, Lake Pointe Medical Center, Rowlett, TX, p. A630

LEE, Bryan, Chief Operating Officer, Eliza Coffee Memorial Hospital, Florence, AL, p. A20

LEE, Byong, Manager Information Technology and PACS Administrator, Limestone Medical Center, Groesbeck, TX, p. A607

LEE, Cheryl D., R.N
Vice President Patient Care Services, Chief Executive Nurse and Compliance Officer, Sheltering Arms Hospital South, Midlothian, VA, p. A657
Vice President and Chief Nursing Executive Inpatient, Sheltering Arms Rehabilitation Hospital, Mechanicsville, VA, p. A657

LEE, Dana, M.D. Chief of Staff, North Hawaii Community Hospital, Kamuela, HI, p. A165

LEE, David, Interim Chief Executive Officer, Otto Kaiser Memorial Hospital, Kenedy, TX, p. A616

LEE, Deborah, Chief Nursing Officer, Community Westview Hospital, Indianapolis, IN, p. A205

LEE, Don, Chief Information Officer, Metropolitan Hospital Center, New York, NY, p. A434

LEE, Eric A., President and Chief Executive Officer, Jennie Stuart Medical Center, Hopkinsville, KY, p. A252

LEE, Gina, Chief Financial Officer, Fort Lauderdale Hospital, Fort Lauderdale, FL, p. A123

LEE, Helen, Manager Information Systems, Chinese Hospital, San Francisco, CA, p. A86

LEE, James Y., Executive Vice President and Chief Operating Officer, Lawrence Hospital Center, Bronxville, NY, p. A422

LEE, Jeannie, Director Human Resources, Marshall County Hospital, Benton, KY, p. A248

LEE, Jenny, Human Resources Generalist, Essentia Health–Holy Trinity Hospital, Graceville, MN, p. A333

LEE, John Paul, M.D. Chief of Staff, S. E. Lackey Memorial Hospital, Forest, MS, p. A347

LEE, John R., Chief Executive Officer, Mat–Su Regional Medical Center, Palmer, AK, p. A28

LEE, Joseph, M.D. President Medical Staff, Riverside Community Hospital, Riverside, CA, p. A82

LEE, Karen, MSN Chief Nursing Officer, Belton Regional Medical Center, Belton, MO, p. A356

LEE, Karen, Director Human Resources, Gallup Indian Medical Center, Gallup, NM, p. A416

LEE, Kayleen R., Chief Executive Officer, Sioux Center Community Hospital and Health Center Avera, Sioux Center, IA, p. A228

LEE, Larry, Chief Financial Officer, United Hospital District, Blue Earth, MN, p. A329

LEE, Mary Ann, Chief Nursing Officer, HEALTHSOUTH Rehabilitation Hospital of Austin, Austin, TX, p. A585

LEE, Mary C., Manager Human Resources, Jonathan M. Wainwright Memorial Veterans Affairs Medical Center, Walla Walla, WA, p. A674

LEE, Mihi, Chief Financial Officer, Coast Plaza Hospital, Norwalk, CA, p. A76

LEE, Nancy, R.N. Vice President Patient Care Services and Chief Nursing Officer, Stanford Hospital and Clinics, Palo Alto, CA, p. A79

LEE, Nathan W., Chief Executive Officer, Mary Breckinridge ARH Hospital, Hyden, KY, p. A253

LEE, Noel, Administrative Director and Chief Information Officer, Mercy Medical Center Merced, Merced, CA, p. A74

LEE, Patrick, Chief Executive Officer, Continuum Rehabilitation Hospital of North Texas, Flower Mound, TX, p. A602

LEE, Randall, Vice President and Chief Operating Officer, Baptist Health South Florida, Baptist Hospital of Miami, Miami, FL, p. A131

LEE, Robbin, Interim Chief Executive Officer, Wellington Regional Medical Center, West Palm Beach, FL, p. A144

LEE, Robert H., President, Raulerson Hospital, Okeechobee, FL, p. A134

LEE, Stephen, FACHE, President, Baptist Medical Center Nassau, Fernandina Beach, FL, p. A123

LEE, Terry, M.D. Chief of Staff, Garfield Medical Center, Monterey Park, CA, p. A75

LEE, Thomas G., Chief Financial Officer, Medicine Lodge Memorial Hospital, Medicine Lodge, KS, p. A240

LEE, Thomas J., Administrator/CEO, Providence Medical Center, Wayne, NE, p. A390

LEE, Victor N., FACHE, President and Chief Executive Officer, Boone County Health Center, Albion, NE, p. A381

LEE, Vincent H. S., FACHE, Regional Chief Executive Officer, Leahi Hospital, Honolulu, HI, p. A164

LEEDOM, Hope, Director Human Resources, Beauregard Memorial Hospital, De Ridder, LA, p. A266

LEEGSTRA, Ruurd, Chief Financial Officer, Silver Hill Hospital, New Canaan, CT, p. A110

LEEKA, Andrew B., President and Chief Executive Officer, Good Samaritan Hospital, Los Angeles, CA, p. A69

LEEMING, Rosemary, M.D. Chief Medical Officer, UH Regional Hospitals, Cleveland, OH, p. A477

LEEPER, Kevin, Chief Executive Officer, Scott & White Hospital – Llano, Llano, TX, p. A619

LEESER, Robert, M.D. Chief Medical Officer, Hayes Green Beach Memorial Hospital, Charlotte, MI, p. A310

LEET, Arabella, M.D. Chief of Staff, Shriners Hospitals for Children–Honolulu, Honolulu, HI, p. A165

LEFEVRE, Denise, Chief Information Officer, Oroville Hospital, Oroville, CA, p. A78

LEFEVRE, Steve, Chief Executive Officer and Administrator, Fisher County Hospital District, Rotan, TX, p. A629

LEFF, Marc, Vice President Human Resources, Maimonides Medical Center,, NY, p. A434

LEFFLER, Stephen, Chief Medical Officer, Fletcher Allen Health Care, Burlington, VT, p. A649

LEFKOW, Frances, Director Human Resources, La Rabida Children's Hospital, Chicago, IL, p. A177

LEFTWICH, Hal W., FACHE, Chief Executive Officer, Fishermen's Hospital, Marathon, FL, p. A129

LEGASPI, Johnson, Director Information Systems, Alhambra Hospital Medical Center, Alhambra, CA, p. A52

LEGEL, Tom, Chief Financial Officer and Chief Operating Officer, Samaritan Healthcare, Moses Lake, WA, p. A668

LEGENDZIEWICZ, Henry, Senior Vice President and Chief Financial Officer, Nathan Littauer Hospital and Nursing Home, Gloversville, NY, p. A426

LEGER, Lynn, Director Information Systems, Ridgeview Institute, Smyrna, GA, p. A160

LEGERE, Tina, President, Central Maine Medical Center, Lewiston, ME, p. A283

LEGG, Alyce, Vice President Human Resources, Samaritan Regional Health System, Ashland, OH, p. A470

LEGG, Paul, M.D. President Medical Staff, Saint Francis Hospital, Charleston, WV, p. A676

LEGG, Susan E., Interim Administrator, Noland Hospital Montgomery, Montgomery, AL, p. A23

LEGGETT III, G. Raymond, President and Chief Executive Officer, CarolinaEast Health System, New Bern, NC, p. A458

LEGRAND, Daniel, M.D. Chief Medical Officer, St. Vincent Indianapolis Hospital, Indianapolis, IN, p. A206

LEHNER, Bill, Director Management Information Systems, Amery Regional Medical Center, Amery, WI, p. A683

LEHNER, Deborah, Administrator, Greeley County Health Services, Tribune, KS, p. A245

LEIBENHAUT, Mark, M.D. Chief of Staff, Sutter Medical Center, Sacramento, Sacramento, CA, p. A84

LEIBHAM, Geri, Manager Business Office, Salina Surgical Hospital, Salina, KS, p. A243

LEIBMAN, Maurice, M.D. Chief Medical Officer, Memorial Hermann Northwest Hospital, Houston, TX, p. A611

LEICHMAN, Ann Marie, R.N. Vice President Patient Care Services and Chief Nursing Officer, Valley Hospital, Ridgewood, NJ, p. A410

LEICHNER, Raymond, Director Finance, Abington Health Lansdale Hospital, Lansdale, PA, p. A529

LEIDY, R. Grant, Vice President Finance, Deborah Heart and Lung Center, Browns Mills, NJ, p. A402

LEIF, Sue, R.N. Director Human Resources, Annie Jeffrey Memorial County Health Center, Osceola, NE, p. A388

LEIGH, Cindy, Chief Operating Officer, Fairbanks, Indianapolis, IN, p. A205

LEIMGRUBER, Jeffrey A., President, Hillcrest Hospital, Cleveland, OH, p. A476

LEINEN, Rick, Chief Financial Officer, Montgomery County Memorial Hospital, Red Oak, IA, p. A227

LEIPER, Deborah, Chief Operating Officer, Health First Viera Hospital, Melbourne, FL, p. A130

LEIS, Jr., James L., Chief Financial Officer, Doctor's Memorial Hospital, Perry, FL, p. A137

LEISE, Karen, Coordinator Human Resources, Saunders Medical Center, Wahoo, NE, p. A390

LEISHER, George, Vice President Human Resources, Northridge Hospital Medical Center–Roscoe Boulevard Campus,, CA, p. A70

LEISHER, Kenneth W., Chief Executive Officer, Heart of the Rockies Regional Medical Center, Salida, CO, p. A105

LEIST, Vincent, President and Chief Executive Officer, North Arkansas Regional Medical Center, Harrison, AR, p. A44

LEITE, Dolores
Chief Human Resource Executive, Jacobi Medical Center,, NY, p. A432
Chief Human Resource Executive, North Central Bronx Hospital,, NY, p. A435

LEITENBERGER, Donna, Director Information Services, Edward White Hospital, Saint Petersburg, FL, p. A139

LEITNER, Mark, Chief Executive Officer, East Texas Medical Center Henderson, Henderson, TX, p. A608

LEJSEK, Shari, Administrator, Patients' Hospital of Redding, Redding, CA, p. A81

LELAND, Joni, Director Human Resources, Memorial Hospital, Gonzales, TX, p. A606

LELEUX, Ross, Chief Information Officer, Iberia Medical Center, New Iberia, LA, p. A275

LEM, Alan
Vice President Finance, Fairview Ridges Hospital, Burnsville, MN, p. A330
Vice President Finance, Fairview Southdale Hospital, Edina, MN, p. A332

LEMAIRE, Joseph M., Executive Vice President and Chief Financial Officer, Holy Name Medical Center, Teaneck, NJ, p. A411

LEMAIRE, Suzanne, Manager Health Information Management Services and Corporate Compliance Officer, Scheurer Hospital, Pigeon, MI, p. A321

LEMAISTRE, Collin
Chief Operating Officer, Cypress Fairbanks Medical Center, Houston, TX, p. A609
Chief Operating Officer, Nacogdoches Medical Center, Nacogdoches, TX, p. A624

LEMANSKI, Dennis R., D.O. Senior Vice President Medical Affairs and Medical Education/CMO, Henry Ford Wyandotte Hospital, Wyandotte, MI, p. A327

LEMASTERS, Debra J., Director Human Resources, Woodlawn Hospital, Rochester, IN, p. A213

LEMIEUX, Harry, Chief Information and Innovation Officer, Morton Hospital and Medical Center, Taunton, MA, p. A305

LEMIEUX, Kandie, Administrative Assistant and Director Human Resources, Northern Rockies Medical Center, Cut Bank, MT, p. A375

LEMMER, Donn J., Vice President Finance, West Shore Medical Center, Manistee, MI, p. A319

LEMMONS, Tracy G., Director Human Resources, Mercy McCune-Brooks Hospital, Carthage, MO, p. A358

LEMON, Brian J., President, Central DuPage Hospital, Winfield, IL, p. A197

LEMON, Donna, Director Human Resources, Ward Memorial Hospital, Monahans, TX, p. A623

LEMON, Marc, Chief Executive Officer, Kindred Hospital–Tucson, Tucson, AZ, p. A38

LEMON, Rita, Director Human Resources, Avera Queen of Peace Hospital, Mitchell, SD, p. A561

LEMON, Shawn, Interim Chief Executive Officer, Highlands Behavioral Health System, Littleton, CO, p. A103

LEMON, Thomas R., Chief Executive Officer, Otsego Memorial Hospital, Gaylord, MI, p. A314

LEMONS, Elizabeth, Chief Operating Officer, Saint Thomas Rutherford Hospital, Murfreesboro, TN, p. A576

LEMONS, Tania, Assistant Chief Financial Officer, East Texas Medical Center–Quitman, Quitman, TX, p. A628

LENAHAN, Kevin
Director Corporate Accounting, Budgets, Grants and Reimbursements, Newton Medical Center, Newton, NJ, p. A408
Vice President Finance and Chief Financial Officer, Overlook Medical Center, Summit, NJ, p. A410

LENAMOND, Kevin, Information Management Service Line Executive, Michael E. DeBakey Veterans Affairs Medical Center, Houston, TX, p. A611

LENARD, Gary, Director Human Resources, Hendricks Regional Health, Danville, IN, p. A201

LENCIONI, Kathi, Chief Executive Officer, Sharp Mesa Vista Hospital, San Diego, CA, p. A86

LENGFELDER, Valerie, M.D. Chief of Staff, Powell Valley Healthcare, Powell, WY, p. A703

LENKEVICH, Ellen R., Chief Nursing Officer, Florida Hospital–Flagler, Palm Coast, FL, p. A136

LENKOWSKI, Thomas, Chief Financial Officer, Martha's Vineyard Hospital, Oak Bluffs, MA, p. A303

LENNARTZ, Randal, Vice President Finance, Highland District Hospital, Hillsboro, OH, p. A483

LENNEN, Anthony B., President, Community Hospital South, Indianapolis, IN, p. A205

LENNON, Rosylin, Chief Nursing Officer, West Suburban Medical Center, Oak Park, IL, p. A190

LENOIR, Frank, Executive Director Human Resources, Mercy Hospital Washington, Washington, MO, p. A373

LENTENBRINK, Laura, Vice-President, Human Resources, Borgess Medical Center, Kalamazoo, MI, p. A317

LENTZ, Darrell, Chief Executive Officer, Sun Coast Hospital, Largo, FL, p. A129

LENZ, Jan, Chief Nursing Officer, Athens–Limestone Hospital, Athens, AL, p. A16

LENZ, Roger W., Interim Chief Executive Officer, Pender Community Hospital, Pender, NE, p. A389

LENZO, Julie, Director Business Office, AMG Specialty Hospital–Albuquerque, Albuquerque, NM, p. A414

LEO, Elizabeth, Vice President Human Resources, Regional Hospital of Scranton, Scranton, PA, p. A540

LEON, Daniel, Chief Financial Officer, Sherman Oaks Hospital,, CA, p. A71

LEON, Luis
Chief Operating Officer, Desert Valley Hospital, Victorville, CA, p. A95
Regional Chief Executive Officer, Paradise Valley Hospital, National City, CA, p. A76

LEONARD, Anne, R.N., Interim Chief Executive Officer, TriStar Greenview Regional Hospital, Bowling Green, KY, p. A249

LEONARD, Bradley M., M.D. Vice President Medical Affairs, Baylor Regional Medical Center at Plano, Plano, TX, p. A627

LEONARD, Donavan, Chief Financial Officer, Baptist Memorial Hospital–Booneville, Booneville, MS, p. A345

LEONARD, Edward F., Executive Vice President and Chief Operating Officer, White Plains Hospital Center, White Plains, NY, p. A446

LEONARD, James C., M.D., President and Chief Executive Officer, Carle Foundation Hospital, Urbana, IL, p. A196

LEONARD, Kathy, Manager Human Resources, Community Howard Specialty Hospital, Kokomo, IN, p. A207

LEONARD, Leland, M.D., Administrator, Fort Defiance Indian Health Service Hospital, Fort Defiance, AZ, p. A31

LEONARD, Mark, Vice President Finance, Beaumont Hospital – Troy, Troy, MI, p. A326

LEONARD, Mark T.
Chief Executive Officer, Dickenson Community Hospital, Clintwood, VA, p. A652
Chief Executive Officer, Norton Community Hospital, Norton, VA, p. A658

LEONARD, Robert, Director Information Services, Sierra Vista Regional Medical Center, San Luis Obispo, CA, p. A88

LEONARD, Roger, M.D. Vice President Medical Affairs, MedStar Montgomery Medical Center, Olney, MD, p. A293

LEONARD, William H., President, Carolinas Medical Center–University, Charlotte, NC, p. A449

LEONDAR, Kimberly, Director Human Resources, Texas Health Harris Methodist Hospital Stephenville, Stephenville, TX, p. A635

LEONE, Ellen, R.N. Chief Nursing Officer, University of Connecticut Health Center, John Dempsey Hospital, Farmington, CT, p. A108

LEONELIS, Lisa, Chief Information Officer, Veterans Affairs Salt Lake City Health Care System, Salt Lake City, UT, p. A647

LEONHARDT, Darrell, Senior Vice President Information Systems, Arkansas Children's Hospital, Little Rock, AR, p. A46

LEONHARDT, Gary, M.D. Clinical Director, Walter B. Jones Alcohol and Drug Abuse Treatment Center, Greenville, NC, p. A454

LEOPARD, Jimmy, FACHE, Chief Executive Officer, Wagoner Community Hospital, Wagoner, OK, p. A509

LEPE, Patti, Chief Financial Officer, Parkview Community Hospital Medical Center, Riverside, CA, p. A82

LEPORE, Timothy J., FACS Medical Director, Nantucket Cottage Hospital, Nantucket, MA, p. A302

LEPP, Jerry, Chief Executive Officer, Ashley Medical Center, Ashley, ND, p. A465

LEPPKE, Ben, Chief Information Officer, Satanta District Hospital, Satanta, KS, p. A244

LEQUEUX, Veronica, Vice President Human Resources, Blake Medical Center, Bradenton, FL, p. A119

LEQUIRE, Mark, M.D. Chief of Staff, Vaughan Regional Medical Center, Selma, AL, p. A25

LERCH, Gail, R.N
Vice President, Kapiolani Medical Center for Women & Children, Honolulu, HI, p. A164
Vice President Human Resources, Pali Momi Medical Center, Aiea, HI, p. A164
Executive Vice President Human Resources, Straub Clinic & Hospital, Honolulu, HI, p. A165

LERCH, Shawn, Chief Executive Officer, Miners' Colfax Medical Center, Raton, NM, p. A417

LEROY, Joseph B., M.D. Clinical Director, Southwestern State Hospital, Thomasville, GA, p. A161

LEROY, Kurt, Manager Information Management, Lanier Health Services, Valley, AL, p. A26

LEROY, Michael
Senior Vice President and Chief Information Officer, Detroit Receiving Hospital/University Health Center, Detroit, MI, p. A311
Senior Vice President and Chief Information Officer, Harper University Hospital/Hutzel Women's Hospital, Detroit, MI, p. A312

LESCHKE, Gwenn, Vice President Human Resources, Advocate Condell Medical Center, Libertyville, IL, p. A187

LESINS, Ross, Chief Information Officer, Casa Colina Hospital for Rehabilitative Medicine, Pomona, CA, p. A80

LESLIE, Desdemona, Finance Officer, U. S. Public Health Service Indian Hospital–Whiteriver, Whiteriver, AZ, p. A39

LESLIE, Donald P., M.D. Medical Director, Shepherd Center, Atlanta, GA, p. A147

LESLIE, Frank, Vice President Operations, Highlands–Cashiers Hospital, Highlands, NC, p. A455

LESLIE, Kelly, Chief Financial Officer, Ferry County Memorial Hospital, Republic, WA, p. A670

LESNIAK, Jacklynn, R.N. Vice President Patient Services, Watertown Regional Medical Center, Watertown, WI, p. A698

LESTER, James, Director Fiscal Services, Shriners Hospitals for Children–Cincinnati Burns Hospital, Cincinnati, OH, p. A475

LESTER, Mark, M.D. Vice President and Chief Quality Officer, Texas Health Presbyterian Hospital Dallas, Dallas, TX, p. A597

LESTER, Ron, Chief Human Resources, Cheyenne Veterans Affairs Medical Center, Cheyenne, WY, p. A701

LESTER, Wade K., Chief Nursing and Operations Officer, Mid–Jefferson Extended Care Hospital, Nederland, TX, p. A624

LESTER, William, M.D. Vice President Medical Affairs, Cardinal Hill Rehabilitation Hospital, Lexington, KY, p. A254

LETELLIER, Jean–Pierre, M.D. Chief of Staff, Memorial Hospital, Seminole, TX, p. A633

LETSON, Robert F., FACHE, Chief Executive Officer, South Peninsula Hospital, Homer, AK, p. A28

LETT, Bryan W., Chief Executive Officer, Michiana Behavioral Health Center, Plymouth, IN, p. A212

LETT, Tammy, R.N. Chief Nursing Officer, Greenville Regional Hospital, Greenville, IL, p. A184

LETTERMAN, Rod, Chief Executive Officer, Dover Behavioral Health System, Dover, DE, p. A114

LETZ, Tom, Interim Assistant Administrator, Chief Financial Officer and Controller, Tyler County Hospital, Woodville, TX, p. A642

LEU, Christopher, President, Texas Health Harris Methodist Hospital Stephenville, Stephenville, TX, p. A635

LEUBNER, Kristel, D.O. Chief of Staff, Burleson St. Joseph Health Center, Caldwell, TX, p. A590

LEUNG, Lawrence, M.D. Chief of Staff, Veterans Affairs Palo Alto Health Care System, Palo Alto, CA, p. A79

LEVELING, Jim, Director Information Technology, Kansas City Orthopaedic Institute, Leawood, KS, p. A238

LEVENSON, Adam, Manager Information Systems, Lakeside Medical Center, Belle Glade, FL, p. A118

LEVENSON, Marc, M.D.,
Director, Manchester Veterans Affairs Medical Center, Manchester, NH, p. A399
Acting Director, White River Junction Veterans Affairs Medical Center, White River Junction, VT, p. A650

LEVER, Roger, M.D. President Medical Staff, The Outer Banks Hospital, Nags Head, NC, p. A458

LEVERETT, Carey O., Vice President Information Services, Meritus Medical Center, Hagerstown, MD, p. A292

LEVERICH, Karen, Chief Executive Officer, Specialty Hospital of Mid–America, Overland Park, KS, p. A242

LEVERING, Theresa, Director Human Resources, Doctors Hospital of Sarasota, Sarasota, FL, p. A139

LEVI, Allen, Director Information Resources, Ephraim McDowell Regional Medical Center, Danville, KY, p. A250

LEVI, John, Director of Human Resources, St. Lawrence Rehabilitation Center, Lawrenceville, NJ, p. A405

LEVINE, Alexandra, M.D
Chief Medical Officer, City of Hope's Helford Clinical Research Hospital, Duarte, CA, p. A59
Medical Director, University of Southern California–Norris Cancer Hospital, Los Angeles, CA, p. A72

LEVINE, Larry L., President and Chief Executive Officer, Blythedale Children's Hospital, Valhalla, NY, p. A445

LEVINE, Marty, Vice President Human Resources, Windham Hospital, Willimantic, CT, p. A113

LEVINE, Peter H., M.D. Executive Medical Director Behavioral Health Services, Adventist Behavioral Health Rockville, Rockville, MD, p. A293

LEVINE, Robert V., Executive Vice President and Chief Operating Officer, Flushing Hospital Medical Center,, NY, p. A432

LEVISON, Julie, Director Human Resources, Providence Medford Medical Center, Medford, OR, p. A514

LEVITAN, Kenneth, Vice President Information Systems, Einstein Medical Center Philadelphia, Philadelphia, PA, p. A534

LEVITZ, Michele, Director Finance, St. Luke's Hospital – Miners Campus, Coaldale, PA, p. A523

LEVLEIT, Spencer, Director Information Technology, Unicoi County Memorial Hospital, Erwin, TN, p. A569

LEVY, Brian, M.D. Medical Director, AMG Specialty Hospital–Edmond, Edmond, OK, p. A498

LEVY, Scott S., M.D. Vice President and Chief Medical Officer, Doylestown Hospital, Doylestown, PA, p. A524

LEVY, Susan M., M.D. Vice President Medical Affairs, Levindale Hebrew Geriatric Center and Hospital, Baltimore, MD, p. A288

LEWANDOWSKI, James, Vice President Corporate Human Resources, Alexian Brothers Behavioral Health Hospital, Hoffman Estates, IL, p. A185

LEWANDOWSKI, Terri, Director Financial Services, Ministry Our Lady of Victory Hospital, Stanley, WI, p. A697

LEWELLEN, Thomas, D.O. Chief of Staff, Delta Memorial Hospital, Dumas, AR, p. A43

LEWERKE, Jane, Manager Human Resources, Northern Arizona Veterans Affairs Health Care System, Prescott, AZ, p. A36

LEWGOOD, Tony
Interim Administrator, Shriners Hospitals for Children–Cincinnati Burns Hospital, Cincinnati, OH, p. A475
Administrator, Shriners Hospitals for Children–Lexington, Lexington, KY, p. A254

LEWIS, Angel, Senior Vice President Administration, Cookeville Regional Medical Center, Cookeville, TN, p. A568

LEWIS, Barbara, Chief Nursing Officer, Integris Seminole Medical Center, Seminole, OK, p. A506

LEWIS, Brandon, Director of Information Technology, Ivinson Memorial Hospital, Laramie, WY, p. A702

LEWIS, III, Carlisle, Senior Vice President Legal and Human Resources, Sharp Mesa Vista Hospital, San Diego, CA, p. A86

LEWIS, Chris, M.D. Vice President Medical Affairs, Mercy Hospital Independence, Independence, KS, p. A236

LEWIS, Colleen, Director Human Resources, Texas NeuroRehab Center, Austin, TX, p. A586

LEWIS, Curtis, M.D. Chief of Staff, Grady Memorial Hospital, Atlanta, GA, p. A146

LEWIS, Dana, Director Clinical Services, Southern Kentucky Rehabilitation Hospital, Bowling Green, KY, p. A249

LEWIS, Dave, Director Information Services, St. Francis Hospital and Health Services, Maryville, MO, p. A365

LEWIS, Jr., Donald C., Vice President and Chief Financial Officer, Coffee Regional Medical Center, Douglas, GA, p. A152

LEWIS, Doug, Chief Financial Officer, Elks Rehab Hospital, Boise, ID, p. A167

LEWIS, Eric, Chief Executive Officer, Olympic Medical Center, Port Angeles, WA, p. A669

LEWIS, George E., M.D., Medical Officer, Nebraska Penal and Correctional Hospital, Lincoln, NE, p. A385

LEWIS, Gerry
Chief Information Officer, Seton Edgar B. Davis Hospital, Luling, TX, p. A621
Chief Information Officer, Seton Highland Lakes, Burnet, TX, p. A590
Chief Information Officer, Seton Medical Center Austin, Austin, TX, p. A585
Chief Information Officer, Seton Medical Center Williamson, Round Rock, TX, p. A629
Chief Information Officer, Seton Northwest Hospital, Austin, TX, p. A585
Chief Information Officer, Seton Shoal Creek Hospital, Austin, TX, p. A585
Chief Information Officer, University Medical Center at Brackenridge, Austin, TX, p. A586

LEWIS, Gina, Director Human Resources, HEALTHSOUTH Rehabilitation Hospital–Las Vegas, Las Vegas, NV, p. A392

LEWIS, Gordon, Chief Executive Officer, Burnett Medical Center, Grantsburg, WI, p. A687

LEWIS, J. Steve, Director Finance, Youth Villages Inner Harbour Campus, Douglasville, GA, p. A152

LEWIS, Jackie, Director Human Resources, Bacon County Hospital and Health System, Alma, GA, p. A145

LEWIS, Jacob, Chief Financial Officer, Mark Twain St. Joseph's Hospital, San Andreas, CA, p. A84

LEWIS, Jo, Director Human Resources, Providence Tarzana Medical Center,, CA, p. A71

LEWIS, John I., President and Chief Executive Officer, ACMH Hospital, Kittanning, PA, p. A528

LEWIS, Kashion, Director Human Resources, Mayhill Hospital, Denton, TX, p. A598

LEWIS, Kathy, Chief Nursing Officer and Vice President Clinical Services, Riverview Regional Medical Center, Carthage, TN, p. A566

LEWIS, Kenneth S., JD, President and Chief Executive Officer, Union Hospital, Elkton, MD, p. A291

LEWIS, Kent, Director Information Services, Southwestern Medical Center, Lawton, OK, p. A500

LEWIS, Larry, Chief Executive Officer, Pioneers Memorial Healthcare District, Brawley, CA, p. A55

LEWIS, Libby, Chief Financial Officer, CHRISTUS Jasper Memorial Hospital, Jasper, TX, p. A615

LEWIS, Luther J., FACHE, Chief Executive Officer, Five Rivers Medical Center, Pocahontas, AR, p. A49

LEWIS, Marie, Human Resources Liaison, Veterans Affairs St. Louis Health Care System, Saint Louis, MO, p. A371

LEWIS, Michael, Chief Operating Officer, Mother Frances Hospital – Jacksonville, Jacksonville, TX, p. A615

LEWIS, Nan M., Administrator, East Central Regional Hospital, Augusta, GA, p. A147

LEWIS, Nicholas P., Chief Executive Officer, Hardin Medical Center, Savannah, TN, p. A578

LEWIS, Pam, Chief Compliance Officer, William R. Sharpe, Jr. Hospital, Weston, WV, p. A682

LEWIS, Paul, Chief Executive Officer, Holy Rosary Healthcare, Miles City, MT, p. A378

LEWIS, Rayburn, M.D., Executive, Swedish Medical Center–Cherry Hill Campus, Seattle, WA, p. A671

LEWIS, Rick, Chief Information Officer, Chester Regional Medical Center, Chester, SC, p. A549

LEWIS, Robin, Chief Financial Officer, Kiowa District Hospital and Manor, Kiowa, KS, p. A237

LEWIS, Ron, M.D. Medical Director, Dubuis Hospital of Lake Charles, Lake Charles, LA, p. A271

LEWIS, Rosalind, R.N. Chief Nursing Officer, Community HealthCare System, Onaga, KS, p. A241

LEWIS, Sharon
  Director Information Systems, Forbes Regional Hospital, Monroeville, PA, p. A532
  Chief Nursing Officer, Glenwood Regional Medical Center, West Monroe, LA, p. A280

LEWIS, Sheila, Administrator, Harmon Memorial Hospital, Hollis, OK, p. A500

LEWIS, Shirley,Chinle Comprehensive Health Care Facility, Chinle, AZ, p. A30

LEWIS, Stephen, Assistant Administrator and Chief Financial Officer, Cass County Memorial Hospital, Atlantic, IA, p. A216

LEWIS, Steven, M.D
  Senior Vice President and Chief Medical Officer, Flagstaff Medical Center, Flagstaff, AZ, p. A31
  Chief of Staff, Novant Health Gaffney Medical Center, Gaffney, SC, p. A552

LEWIS, Vicki, FACHE,
  President, Aurora Lakeland Medical Center, Elkhorn, WI, p. A686
  Vice President and Chief Administrative Officer, Aurora Memorial Hospital of Burlington, Burlington, WI, p. A685

LEWIS, Vickie, Chief Executive Officer, Central Florida Behavioral Hospital, Orlando, FL, p. A135

LEWIS, Wick, Vice President Human Resources and Clinic Management, Mt. Graham Regional Medical Center, Safford, AZ, p. A36

LEWIS, William, Vice President Human Resources, Schneck Medical Center, Seymour, IN, p. A213

LEWISTON, Jamie, R.N. Chief Nursing Officer, Aurora Psychiatric Hospital, Wauwatosa, WI, p. A699

LEWKOWSKI, William, Executive Vice President Information Services and Chief Information Officer, Metro Health Hospital, Wyoming, MI, p. A327

LEY, Gary R., President and Chief Executive Officer, Garden City Hospital, Garden City, MI, p. A314

LI, Ronald, Vice President Management Information Systems, Bergen Regional Medical Center, Paramus, NJ, p. A408

LI, Stephen, Vice President Management Information Systems, LibertyHealth–Jersey City Medical Center, Jersey City, NJ, p. A405

LIAGRE, Ruthann, Vice President Human Resources, Memorial Healthcare, Owosso, MI, p. A321

LIBBY, Kenneth, Vice President Finance, Community Memorial Healthcenter, South Hill, VA, p. A661

LIBCKE, Julia, R.N. VP Patient Care Services, Rehabilitation Institute of Michigan, Detroit, MI, p. A312

LIBENGOOD, Mary L., President, Conemaugh Meyersdale Medical Center, Meyersdale, PA, p. A532

LIBERATORE, Kristi, Chief Financial Officer, Placentia–Linda Hospital, Placentia, CA, p. A80

LICHTENWALNER, Tom, Vice President Finance, St. Luke's University Hospital – Bethlehem Campus, Bethlehem, PA, p. A520

LICINA, Leonard, Chief Executive Officer, Kahi Mohala Behavioral Health, Ewa Beach, HI, p. A164

LICKTEIQ, Teri, HR Director, Pella Regional Health Center, Pella, IA, p. A227

LIDDELL, Everett, Vice President Human Resources, Saint Francis Hospital, Memphis, TN, p. A575

LIDHOLM, Helen, Chief Executive Officer, Saint Mary's Regional Medical Center, Reno, NV, p. A395

LIEBER, Alan R., President, Overlook Medical Center, Summit, NJ, p. A410

LIEBERMAN, Jeffrey A., M.D., Executive Director, New York State Psychiatric Institute, New York, NY, p. A435

LIEBERMAN, Lawrence, M.D. Medical Director, Blake Medical Center, Bradenton, FL, p. A119

LIEBERMAN, Steven L., M.D. Chief of Staff, Veterans Affairs New Jersey Health Care System, East Orange, NJ, p. A403

LIEBERS, David, M.D. Chief Medical Officer and Vice President Medical Affairs, Ellis Hospital, Schenectady, NY, p. A442

LIEBMAN, Jeffrey H., President, Good Samaritan Medical Center, Brockton, MA, p. A298

LIEBOWITZ, Jacalyn A., Vice President Patient Care Continuum & CNO, Allegiance Health, Jackson, MI, p. A317

LIEBSACK, David, Chief Executive Officer, Baum Harmon Mercy Hospital, Primghar, IA, p. A227

LIEFER, Alan, M.D. President Medical Staff, Memorial Hospital, Chester, IL, p. A176

LIEKWEG, Richard J., President, Barnes–Jewish Hospital, Saint Louis, MO, p. A369

LIEN, Ann, R.N. Chief Nursing Officer, Meeker Memorial Hospital, Litchfield, MN, p. A334

LIEPMAN, Michael T., Chief Operating Officer, Skagit Valley Hospital, Mount Vernon, WA, p. A668

LIESMANN, George, M.D. Chief Medical Officer, Research Medical Center, Kansas City, MO, p. A363

LIGHT, Gary, Chief Information Officer, Knapp Medical Center, Weslaco, TX, p. A641

LIGHT, Rodney, M.D. Chief Medical Officer, Tomball Regional Medical Center, Tomball, TX, p. A638

LIGHTBOURNE, Olieth, Chief Nursing Officer, Streamwood Behavioral Health Center, Streamwood, IL, p. A195

LIGHTCAP, Deb, Director Human Resources, Mercy Medical Center, Roseburg, OR, p. A517

LIGHTFOOT, William M., M.D. Vice President Medical Services, Providence Hospital, Mobile, AL, p. A22

LIGHTNER, Becky, Director Information Systems, Phoebe Sumter Medical Center, Americus, GA, p. A145

LIGON, Kim
  Director Information Services, DCH Regional Medical Center, Tuscaloosa, AL, p. A26
  Director Information Services, Northport Medical Center, Northport, AL, p. A24

LIIMATTA, Connie, Director Medical Records and Business Office, Meeker Memorial Hospital, Litchfield, MN, p. A334

LILES, Richard A., M.D. Medical Director, HEALTHSOUTH Rehabilitation Hospital, Largo, FL, p. A128

LILIK, Dennis
  Chief Information Officer, Gladys Spellman Specialty Hospital and Nursing Center, Cheverly, MD, p. A290
  Chief Information Officer, Laurel Regional Hospital, Laurel, MD, p. A293
  Chief Information Officer, Prince George's Hospital Center, Cheverly, MD, p. A290

LILLEY, Jeffrey, CPA Vice President Operations, Princeton Community Hospital, Princeton, WV, p. A680

LILLI, Robert, M.D. Chief of Staff, Texas Health Harris Methodist Hospital Southwest Fort Worth, Fort Worth, TX, p. A604

LILLIE, Lynne, M.D. Medical Director, Woodwinds Health Campus, Woodbury, MN, p. A343

LILLY, Brian, Director Information Systems, Nason Hospital, Roaring Spring, PA, p. A540

LILLY, Ryan S., Acting Director, Maine Veterans Affairs Medical Center, Augusta, ME, p. A281

LILLY, Spencer
  President, Carolinas Medical Center, Charlotte, NC, p. A449
  President, Carolinas Medical Center–Mercy, Charlotte, NC, p. A449

LIMA, Robert, Director Information Systems, Massachusetts Hospital School, Canton, MA, p. A299

LIMBOCKER, Jeff, Chief Financial Officer, Our Lady of the Lake Regional Medical Center, Baton Rouge, LA, p. A263

LIN, Dean Q., FACHE, President, Ocean Medical Center, Brick Township, NJ, p. A402

LIN, Hartwell, M.D. Chief of Staff, John Muir Medical Center, Concord, Concord, CA, p. A57

LINAFELTER, Robb, Chief Executive Officer, Lincoln Surgical Hospital, Lincoln, NE, p. A385

LINARES, Manuel, Chief Executive Officer, North Shore Medical Center, Miami, FL, p. A132

LINCK, Cindy, R.N. Chief Nursing Officer, Scott and White Continuing Care Hospital, Temple, TX, p. A636

LINCKS, Brad, R.N. Chief Nursing Officer/ Vice President, Our Lady of Peace, Louisville, KY, p. A256

LIND, David, M.D. Interim Chief Medical Officer, Cheyenne Regional Medical Center, Cheyenne, WY, p. A701

LIND, Linda Knudson, Senior Vice President and Chief Operating Officer, Siskin Hospital for Physical Rehabilitation, Chattanooga, TN, p. A567

LIND, Mark, Director Information Systems, Mammoth Hospital, Mammoth Lakes, CA, p. A73

LIND, Sharon, MSN, Chief Executive Officer, Ogallala Community Hospital, Ogallala, NE, p. A387

LIND, Trent, Chief Executive Officer, Texas Orthopedic Hospital, Houston, TX, p. A612

LINDAMOOD, Laverne, Director Finance, Springfield Hospital, Springfield, VT, p. A650

LINDBERG, Randy, Director Fiscal Services, Shriners Hospitals for Children–Salt Lake City, Salt Lake City, UT, p. A647

LINDBERG, Robert, R.N. Chief Operating Officer and Chief Nursing Officer, NORTHSTAR Health System, Iron River, MI, p. A317

LINDBERG, Steven, Chief Administrative Officer, Mayo Clinic Health System – Red Cedar in Menomonie, Menomonie, WI, p. A691

LINDEMAN, Gretchen, Director Human Resources, Coastal Communities Hospital, Santa Ana, CA, p. A89

LINDEMAN, Robert, M.D., President, Community Hospital North, Indianapolis, IN, p. A205

LINDEMANN, Fran, Director Finance, Kell West Regional Hospital, Wichita Falls, TX, p. A641

LINDEN, Todd C., President and Chief Executive Officer, Grinnell Regional Medical Center, Grinnell, IA, p. A222

LINDER, Lawrence, M.D. Senior Vice President and Chief Medical Officer, Baltimore Washington Medical Center, Glen Burnie, MD, p. A292

LINDER, Lori, Chief Financial Officer, Banner Ironwood Medical Center, San Tan Valley, AZ, p. A36

LINDGREN, Allison, Chief Human Resources, Carrington Health Center, Carrington, ND, p. A465

LINDQUIST, Gina, Director Human Resources, Schoolcraft Memorial Hospital, Manistique, MI, p. A319

LINDQUIST, Lee, Administrative Director Human Services, Altru Health System, Grand Forks, ND, p. A467

LINDQUIST, Molly, Interim Chief Financial Officer, Chestatee Regional Hospital, Dahlonega, GA, p. A151

LINDSAY, Diane, Chief Financial Officer, St. Francis Hospital, Litchfield, IL, p. A187

LINDSAY, Jeffery T.
  President, Novant Health Forsyth Medical Center, Winston–Salem, NC, p. A463
  Executive Vice President and Chief Operating Officer, Novant Health Medical Park Hospital, Winston–Salem, NC, p. A463

LINDSAY–WOOD, Elizabeth, Vice President Information Systems, Tampa General Hospital, Tampa, FL, p. A142

LINDSEY, Craig, R.N. Vice President Clinical Services/Chief Nursing Officer, Park Ridge Health, Hendersonville, NC, p. A454

LINDSEY, Don, Vice President and Chief Information Officer, Tallahassee Memorial HealthCare, Tallahassee, FL, p. A141

LINDSEY, Jay, Chief Executive Officer, LifeCare Hospitals of Dallas, Dallas, TX, p. A596

LINDSEY, Jim, M.D. Senior Vice President Medical Affairs, University Medical Center at Brackenridge, Austin, TX, p. A586

LINDSEY, Kenneth, M.D. Vice President of Medical Affairs, Three Rivers Medical Center, Grants Pass, OR, p. A513

LINDSEY, Kim, Chief Human Resources Officer, Lourdes Hospital, Paducah, KY, p. A259

LINDSEY, Jr., Rob, Vice President Human Resources, Allegiance Behavioral Health Center of Plainview, Plainview, TX, p. A627

LINDSEY, Teresa L., Supervisor Human Resources, Carl Vinson Veterans Affairs Medical Center, Dublin, GA, p. A152

LINDSTROM, David, M.D. Vice President Medical Affairs, ProMedica Bay Park Hospital, Oregon, OH, p. A488

LINES, John
  Chief Financial Officer, St. Vincent Jennings Hospital, North Vernon, IN, p. A212
  Director Financial and Support Services, St. Vincent Salem Hospital, Salem, IN, p. A213

LINESCH, William
  Vice President Human Resources, Good Samaritan Hospital, Dayton, OH, p. A479
  Vice President Human Resources, Miami Valley Hospital, Dayton, OH, p. A480

LINFORD, Darin, R.N. Chief Nursing Officer, Evanston Regional Hospital, Evanston, WY, p. A702

LING, Lori, Information Technician, Windom Area Hospital, Windom, MN, p. A343

LINGAM, Venkata, M.D. Chief Clinical Affairs, Walter P. Reuther Psychiatric Hospital, Westland, MI, p. A326

LINGERFELT, Jeff, Chief Executive Officer, Heart of America Medical Center, Rugby, ND, p. A469

LINGLE, James, M.D. President Medical Staff, Sky Ridge Medical Center, Lone Tree, CO, p. A104

LINHARES, James, Administrator, Kindred Hospital of Riverside, Perris, CA, p. A79

LINK, Nate, M.D. Medical Director, Bellevue Hospital Center, New York, NY, p. A430

LINN, Steven C., M.D
  Chief Medical Officer, Inspira Medical Center–Elmer, Elmer, NJ, p. A404
  Chief Medical Officer, Inspira Medical Center–Vineland, Vineland, NJ, p. A412

LINNA, Gina, Manager Human Resources, Aspirus Ontonagon Hospital, Ontonagon, MI, p. A321

LINNES, Debra W., R.N. Chief Operating Officer, Mount Nittany Medical Center, State College, PA, p. A541

LINNEWEH Jr., Richard W., President and Chief Executive Officer, Yakima Valley Memorial Hospital, Yakima, WA, p. A674

LINSCHEID, Carol, Vice President Human Resources, Enloe Medical Center, Chico, CA, p. A56

LINSE, Margaret, Administrative Secretary and Director Human Resources, West Holt Memorial Hospital, Atkinson, NE, p. A381

LINSIN, Amy, Chief Human Resources Officer, Good Samaritan Medical Center, West Palm Beach, FL, p. A143

LINTON, Dwight, Director Human Resources, Scenic Mountain Medical Center, Big Spring, TX, p. A588

LINTON, Randall L., M.D., President and Chief Executive Officer, Mayo Clinic Health System in Eau Claire, Eau Claire, WI, p. A686

LINTOTT, Kim, Vice President, MultiCare Good Samaritan Hospital, Puyallup, WA, p. A669

LINTZ, Gordon, Chief Administrative Officer, Morristown–Hamblen Healthcare System, Morristown, TN, p. A576

LINVILLE, Kimberly, Chief Nursing Officer, Grant Memorial Hospital, Petersburg, WV, p. A679

LINZMAN, Rob, D.O. Chief of Staff, Jefferson County Hospital, Waurika, OK, p. A510

LIPARI, Cheryl, Manager Information Systems, Teche Regional Medical Center, Morgan City, LA, p. A274

LIPE, Curt, Vice President, Chief Financial Officer, OSF St. Mary Medical Center, Galesburg, IL, p. A183

LIPHAM, Eileen, Chief Nursing Officer, Highlands–Cashiers Hospital, Highlands, NC, p. A455

LIPHAM, Mary Sue
Chief Financial Officer, St. Luke's Lakeside Hospital, The Woodlands, TX, p. A637
Controller, St. Luke's The Woodlands Hospital, The Woodlands, TX, p. A637

LIPINSKI, Gary, M.D
Regional Vice President and Chief Medical Officer, Adventist Hinsdale Hospital, Hinsdale, IL, p. A185
Regional Vice President and Chief Medical Officer, Adventist La Grange Memorial Hospital, La Grange, IL, p. A186

LIPINSKI, Jim
Regional Chief Financial Officer, Franciscan St. Anthony Health – Michigan City, Michigan City, IN, p. A210
Chief Financial Officer, Franciscan St. Margaret Health – Hammond, Hammond, IN, p. A204

LIPKIND, Ethan, President and Chief Executive Officer, Deckerville Community Hospital, Deckerville, MI, p. A311

LIPMAN, Brian, M.D. Medical Director and Medical Staff Services, Oconomowoc Memorial Hospital, Oconomowoc, WI, p. A693

LIPMAN, Henry D.
Executive Vice President and Chief Financial Officer, Franklin Regional Hospital, Franklin, NH, p. A398
Senior Vice President, Financial Strategy and External Relations, Lakes Region General Hospital, Laconia, NH, p. A398

LIPNER, Zach, Vice President Human Resources, Newark Beth Israel Medical Center, Newark, NJ, p. A407

LIPPERT, Brandt, Vice President Human Resources, Adena Greenfield Medical Center, Greenfield, OH, p. A482

LIPPINCOTT, Ken, M.D. Chief of Staff, North Mississippi State Hospital, Tupelo, MS, p. A354

LIPPS, Kathy, Clinical Director, University Pointe Surgical Hospital, West Chester, OH, p. A493

LIPSCOMB, A. Brant, M.D. Chief of Medical Staff, St. Luke's Lakeside Hospital, The Woodlands, TX, p. A637

LIPSCOMB, Tracy, Vice President Financial Services and Chief Financial Officer, Garrett County Memorial Hospital, Oakland, MD, p. A293

LIPSKY, Janice G., R.N. System Vice President Human Resources and Organizational Development, St. Vincent's Medical Center Riverside, Jacksonville, FL, p. A127

LIRA, Mayra, Human Resources Specialist, Peak Behavioral Health Services, Santa Teresa, NM, p. A418

LISA, Mark P., FACHE, Chief Executive Officer, Twin Cities Community Hospital, Templeton, CA, p. A92

LISAK, Lawrence D., Superintendent, Larue D. Carter Memorial Hospital, Indianapolis, IN, p. A206

LISELL, Susan C., Vice President of Clinical Services, LifeCare Medical Center, Roseau, MN, p. A339

LISENBY, Michael, M.D. Vice President and Chief Medical Officer, East Alabama Medical Center, Opelika, AL, p. A24

LISH, David, Director Human Resources, Sierra Vista Hospital, Sacramento, CA, p. A83

LISKA, Lee Ann, President and Chief Executive Officer, University Hospital, Cincinnati, OH, p. A475

LISKE, Thomas, M.D. Chief Medical Officer, Kindred Hospital–Sycamore, Sycamore, IL, p. A196

LISONBEE, Rod
Chief Financial Officer, American Fork Hospital, American Fork, UT, p. A643
Chief Financial Officer, Orem Community Hospital, Orem, UT, p. A645
Chief Financial Officer, Utah Valley Regional Medical Center, Provo, UT, p. A646

LIST, Alan F., M.D., President and Chief Executive Officer, H. Lee Moffitt Cancer Center and Research Institute, Tampa, FL, p. A141

LISTER, Jack, Director Human Resources, Takoma Regional Hospital, Greeneville, TN, p. A569

LISTON, Denise R., R.N. Vice President Clinical and Support Services, Garrett County Memorial Hospital, Oakland, MD, p. A293

LISTON, John, Chief Financial Officer, Port Huron Hospital, Port Huron, MI, p. A322

LISZEWSKI, Richard S., Chief Executive Officer, Memorial Hospital Los Banos, Los Banos, CA, p. A72

LITAKER, Thomas, Chief Financial Officer, Skagit Valley Hospital, Mount Vernon, WA, p. A668

LITE, Myron, Director Human Resources, Fitzgibbon Hospital, Marshall, MO, p. A365

LITE, Randy, Vice President, Molokai General Hospital, Kaunakakai, HI, p. A166

LITOVITZ, Gary, M.D. Medical Director, Dominion Hospital, Falls Church, VA, p. A653

LITTLE, Christopher M., Vice President and Chief Financial Officer, Ellwood City Hospital, Ellwood City, PA, p. A525

LITTLE, Gary, M.D. Medical Director, George Washington University Hospital, Washington, DC, p. A116

LITTLE, James E., Chief Financial Officer, Siloam Springs Memorial Hospital, Siloam Springs, AR, p. A50

LITTLE, James P., M.D. Medical Director, HEALTHSOUTH Rehabilitation Hospital, Kingsport, TN, p. A571

LITTLE, Lou, President, WellStar Windy Hill Hospital, Marietta, GA, p. A157

LITTLE, Steven N., President and Chief Executive Officer, Agnesian HealthCare, Fond Du Lac, WI, p. A686

LITTLE, Suzanne, Human Resources Specialist, Columbia Basin Hospital, Ephrata, WA, p. A666

LITTLE, Vicky, Director Human Resources, Effingham Hospital, Springfield, GA, p. A160

LITTLE, William, Chief Executive Officer, Highlands Medical Center, Sparta, TN, p. A579

LITTLEFIELD, Karen, Manager Human Resources, Waldo County General Hospital, Belfast, ME, p. A281

LITTLESON, Steven G., FACHE, President, Jersey Shore University Medical Center, Neptune, NJ, p. A407

LITTLETON, Robert, Administrator, Ray County Memorial Hospital, Richmond, MO, p. A368

LITTRELL, Jeremy, Director Human Resources, Brodstone Memorial Hospital, Superior, NE, p. A390

LITTRELL, Mark, Chief Executive Officer, Lincoln Prairie Behavioral Health Center, Springfield, IL, p. A195

LITZENBERG, Karen, Public Information Officer, Sonoma Developmental Center, Eldridge, CA, p. A59

LIUZZA, Jed M., Vice President, Human Resources, Mercy Hospital Hot Springs, Hot Springs National Park, AR, p. A45

LIVELY, Carol, Chief Executive Officer, Hardeman County Memorial Hospital, Quanah, TX, p. A628

LIVELY, Corey, Chief Executive Officer, Elkview General Hospital, Hobart, OK, p. A499

LIVENGOOD, Annette, Vice President Human Resources, Garrett County Memorial Hospital, Oakland, MD, p. A293

LIVESAY, Jr., William, D.O. Medical Director, HEALTHSOUTH Rehabilitation Hospital of Charleston, Charleston, SC, p. A549

LIVIN, Lee, Chief Financial Officer, Wishard Health Services, Indianapolis, IN, p. A206

LIVINGSTON, Adrienne, Director Human Resources, Kingwood Pines Hospital, Kingwood, TX, p. A617

LIVINGSTON, Carolyn, Director Human Resources, Salt Lake Regional Medical Center, Salt Lake City, UT, p. A647

LIVINGSTON, Charles
Administrator, Dakota Plains Surgical Center, Aberdeen, SD, p. A558
Chief Executive Officer, Midwest Surgical Hospital, Omaha, NE, p. A388

LIVINGSTON, Jeffrey
Administrator, Christus Dubuis Hospital of Port Arthur, Port Arthur, TX, p. A628
Administrator, Dubuis Hospital of Beaumont, Beaumont, TX, p. A587

LIVINGSTON, Keith
Senior Vice President and Chief Information Officer, Appleton Medical Center, Appleton, WI, p. A683
Senior Vice President and Chief Information Officer, Theda Clark Medical Center, Neenah, WI, p. A693

LIVINGSTON, Sam, Information Resource Consultant, G. Werber Bryan Psychiatric Hospital, Columbia, SC, p. A550

LIVSEY, Don, Vice President and Chief Information Officer, Children's Hospital and Research Center at Oakland, Oakland, CA, p. A77

LLANO, Manuel R.
Chief Executive Officer, Atlantic Shores Hospital, Fort Lauderdale, FL, p. A123
Chief Executive Officer, Fort Lauderdale Hospital, Fort Lauderdale, FL, p. A123

LLEWELLYN, Michael R., Chief Operating Officer, Laguna Honda Hospital and Rehabilitation Center, San Francisco, CA, p. A86

LLOYD, Carey, M.D. Chief Medical Officer, Brigham City Community Hospital, Brigham City, UT, p. A643

LLOYD, Richard, D.O. Chief of Staff, Harbor Beach Community Hospital, Harbor Beach, MI, p. A316

LLOYD, Russell E., Associate Director Resources, Central Texas Veterans Healthcare System, Temple, TX, p. A636

LLOYD, Susan, Chief Health Information Management and Revenue Administration, Charlie Norwood Veterans Affairs Medical Center, Augusta, GA, p. A147

LO, Wesley, Regional Chief Executive Officer, Maui Memorial Medical Center, Wailuku, HI, p. A166

LOADER, Clifford, Chief Financial Officer, Banner Desert Medical Center, Mesa, AZ, p. A33

LOAFMAN, Mark, M.D. Vice President Medical Affairs, Norwegian American Hospital, Chicago, IL, p. A178

LOBBAN, Victoria, Vice President Finance, New England Sinai Hospital and Rehabilitation Center, Stoughton, MA, p. A305

LOBECK, Charles C., Administrator, Shriners Hospitals for Children–Twin Cities, Minneapolis, MN, p. A336

LOCHBRUNNER, Linda, Chief Financial Officer, E. A. Conway Medical Center, Monroe, LA, p. A274

LOCKARD, Dennis, Vice President Fiscal Services and Chief Financial Officer, Wayne Hospital, Greenville, OH, p. A482

LOCKCUFF, Todd, Chief Financial Officer, Inova Alexandria Hospital, Alexandria, VA, p. A651

LOCKE, Christopher, Chief Operating Officer, Spalding Regional Medical Center, Griffin, GA, p. A154

LOCKE, Marianne, R.N. Associate Director Patient Care Services, Northern Arizona Veterans Affairs Health Care System, Prescott, AZ, p. A36

LOCKE, Stuart, Interim Chief Executive Officer, Southern Kentucky Rehabilitation Hospital, Bowling Green, KY, p. A249

LOCKEE, W. Brad, M.D. Chief of Staff, Alegent Creighton Health Plainview Hospital, Plainview, NE, p. A389

LOCKER, Dan, M.D. Chief of Staff, Brownwood Regional Medical Center, Brownwood, TX, p. A590

LOCKERD, Marie Paul, M.D. Chief Medical Officer, Sanford Jackson Medical Center, Jackson, MN, p. A334

LOCKHART, Jimmy Wayne, M.D. Medical Director, HEALTHSOUTH Treasure Coast Rehabilitation Hospital, Vero Beach, FL, p. A143

LOCKLAIR, Deborah, FACHE, Administrator, McLeod Medical Center Dillon, Dillon, SC, p. A551

LOCKLEAR, Ann, Vice President, Human Resources, Scotland Health Care System, Laurinburg, NC, p. A456

LOCKWOOD, Melissa, Chief Executive Officer, Preston Memorial Hospital, Kingwood, WV, p. A678

LODGE, James S., Chief Human Resources, Veterans Affairs Ann Arbor Healthcare System, Ann Arbor, MI, p. A308

LOE, Cindy, Director of Nursing, Essentia Health Northern Pines, Aurora, MN, p. A328

LOEB, Katherine, R.N. Interim Vice President, Patient Care Services, Holy Cross Hospital, Chicago, IL, p. A176

LOEBL, John, Chief Executive Officer, Kearny County Hospital, Lakin, KS, p. A237

LOEFFELHOLZ, Tim, Account Executive Information Technology, UnityPoint Health Finley, Dubuque, IA, p. A221

LOEPP Jr., Robert A., FACHE, Chief Executive Officer, AMG Specialty Hospital–Wichita, Wichita, KS, p. A246

LOERA, Arnold, M.D. Vice President and Medical Director, Bristol Bay Area Health Corporation, Dillingham, AK, p. A27

LOERINC, Albert, M.D. Medical Director, New Bedford Rehabilitation Hospital, New Bedford, MA, p. A302

LOEWENSTEIN, Howard, Chief Information Resource Management Services, Jesse Brown Veterans Affairs Medical Center, Chicago, IL, p. A177

LOFFING, David, Chief Operating Officer, University of Illinois Hospital & Health Sciences System, Chicago, IL, p. A180

LOFGRAN, Reid, D.O. Chief of Staff, North Canyon Medical Center, Gooding, ID, p. A169

LOFTIS, Michelle, Human Resources Officer, Ferry County Memorial Hospital, Republic, WA, p. A670

LOFTUS, John, M.D. Chief of Staff, Kaiser Permanente Oakland Medical Center, Oakland, CA, p. A77

LOTHE, Eric L., Vice President and Administrator, UnityPoint Health – Des Moines, Des Moines, IA, p. A220

LOTHIAN, Nancy, Chief Operating Officer and Chief Information Officer, Central Vermont Medical Center, Berlin, VT, p. A649

LOTT, Andrea, Vice President Information Services, Northeastern Vermont Regional Hospital, Saint Johnsbury, VT, p. A650

LOTT, Jeff, Director Information Services, Touro Infirmary, New Orleans, LA, p. A276

LOTT, Rodney, Director Management Information Systems and Facility Operations, Scott & White Hospital – Llano, Llano, TX, p. A619

LOTTS, Wendy, M.D. President Medical Staff, Vista Medical Center West, Waukegan, IL, p. A196

LOTZE, Eberhard, M.D. Chief Medical Officer, The Woman's Hospital of Texas, Houston, TX, p. A613

LOUDEN CORBETT, Jeanette L., Chief Human Resources Officer, Alameda County Medical Center, Oakland, CA, p. A77

LOUDERMILK, Kerry, Senior Vice President and Chief Financial Officer, Phoebe Putney Memorial Hospital, Albany, GA, p. A145

LOUGHERY, Vicki, R.N. Chief Nursing Officer, Monadnock Community Hospital, Peterborough, NH, p. A400

LOUGHRAN, Michael, Vice President Human Resources, Kennedy Krieger Institute, Baltimore, MD, p. A287

LOUIS, Alfred, M.D. Chief Medical Staff, Texas Specialty Hospital at Houston, Houston, TX, p. A612

LOUK, Rodney, Vice President Information Systems, Washington Hospital, Washington, PA, p. A543

LOVALLO, Diane, R.N. Chief Nursing Officer, Merrimack Valley Hospital, Haverhill, MA, p. A300

LOVATO, Rhonda, R.N. Chief Clinical Officer, Kindred Hospital–Albuquerque, Albuquerque, NM, p. A414

LOVDAHL, Brian A., Chief Financial Officer, Baldwin Area Medical Center, Baldwin, WI, p. A683

LOVE, E. Clifford, Director Fiscal Services, Eastern State Hospital, Williamsburg, VA, p. A663

LOVE, Glenn Neil, M.D. Medical Director, Hilton Head Hospital, Hilton Head Island, SC, p. A553

LOVE, Jenny, M.D. Medical Director, Alaska Psychiatric Institute, Anchorage, AK, p. A27

LOVE, Tim, Director Information Services, Reid Hospital and Health Care Services, Richmond, IN, p. A212

LOVE–WATLER, Meylan, Chief Operating Officer, Lower Keys Medical Center, Key West, FL, p. A127

LOVEJOY, Leslie, R.N. Chief Nursing and Quality Officer, Sonoma Valley Hospital, Sonoma, CA, p. A91

LOVEJOY, Rob, Chief Operating Officer, Sanford Thief River Falls Medical Center, Thief River Falls, MN, p. A341

LOVELACE, Alan, Vice President and Chief Financial Officer, Stillwater Medical Center, Stillwater, OK, p. A507

LOVELACE, Donald, Chief Financial Officer, Red Bud Regional Hospital, Red Bud, IL, p. A193

LOVELESS, Craig, Interim Chief Executive Officer, Prowers Medical Center, Lamar, CO, p. A103

LOVELESS, Jane Doll, Vice President Information Services, Grand View Hospital, Sellersville, PA, p. A541

LOVELESS, Kurt, Chief Financial Officer, Summit Healthcare Regional Medical Center, Show Low, AZ, p. A37

LOVELL Jr., Charles D., FACHE, President and Chief Executive Officer, Caldwell Medical Center, Princeton, KY, p. A259

LOVELL, Mark, Vice President and Chief Financial Officer, Tuomey Healthcare System, Sumter, SC, p. A556

LOVELL, Stephanie, Vice President and General Counsel, Boston Medical Center, Boston, MA, p. A296

LOVELLETTE, Teresa A., Manager Human Resources, Herrin Hospital, Herrin, IL, p. A184

LOVERA, Carlos, Director Information Systems, Montrose Memorial Hospital, Montrose, CO, p. A104

LOVERING, Keith, Information Technician, Miller County Hospital, Colquitt, GA, p. A150

LOVERING, Richard, Corporate Vice President Human Resources and Organizational Development, AtlantiCare Regional Medical Center, Atlantic City, NJ, p. A401

LOVERSO, Felice L., Ph.D., President and Chief Executive Officer, Casa Colina Hospital for Rehabilitative Medicine, Pomona, CA, p. A80

LOVETT, Chad, Chief Executive Officer, Specialty Hospital of Midwest City, Midwest City, OK, p. A501

LOVINGOOD, Toni, Chief Operating Officer, Murphy Medical Center, Murphy, NC, p. A458

LOVRICH, John, Chief Financial Officer, Catalina Island Medical Center, Avalon, CA, p. A53

LOVSTAD, Corliss, Vice President Human Resources, Children's Hospital and Medical Center, Omaha, NE, p. A387

LOW, Lewis, M.D
Senior Vice President and Chief Medical Officer, Legacy Meridian Park Hospital, Tualatin, OR, p. A518
Senior Vice President and Chief Medical Officer, Legacy Salmon Creek Medical Center, Vancouver, WA, p. A673

LOWE, Adonna F., R.N. Chief Nursing Officer, West Jefferson Medical Center, Marrero, LA, p. A273

LOWE, Brad, Director Information Systems, Caverna Memorial Hospital, Horse Cave, KY, p. A253

LOWE, Bren, Chief Executive Officer, Livingston Memorial Hospital, Livingston, MT, p. A378

LOWE, E. Rick, FACHE Senior Vice President and Chief Administrative Officer, St. Francis Hospital, Columbus, GA, p. A150

LOWE, Elyssia, Chief Executive Officer, Three Rivers Behavioral Health, West Columbia, SC, p. A557

LOWE, Greg, Chief Executive Officer, Lake Norman Regional Medical Center, Mooresville, NC, p. A457

LOWE, Joe, Director Management Information Systems, Cumberland Medical Center, Crossville, TN, p. A568

LOWE, Lavah, Chief Operating Officer, Poplar Bluff Regional Medical Center, Poplar Bluff, MO, p. A368

LOWE, Phillip W., Chief Executive Officer, San Juan Hospital, Monticello, UT, p. A644

LOWE, Scott, Administrative Director Human Resources, Portneuf Medical Center, Pocatello, ID, p. A171

LOWE, Vickie, M.D. Medical Director, HEALTHSOUTH Lakeview Rehabilitation Hospital, Elizabethtown, KY, p. A250

LOWELL, David, M.D. Medical Director, Spaulding Rehabilitation Hospital Cape Cod, East Sandwich, MA, p. A299

LOWELL, Susan, Chief Operating Officer and Chief Nursing Officer, San Bernardino Mountains Community Hospital District, Lake Arrowhead, CA, p. A66

LOWENTHAL, David, M.D. Clinical Director, New York State Psychiatric Institute, New York, NY, p. A435

LOWENTHAL, Steve B., M.D. Senior Vice President Medical Affairs and Chief Medical Officer, Rush–Copley Medical Center, Aurora, IL, p. A174

LOWERY, Bill, Chief Financial Officer, North Texas State Hospital, Wichita Falls Campus, Wichita Falls, TX, p. A641

LOWERY, John, M.D. Deputy Commander Clinical Services, General Leonard Wood Army Community Hospital, Fort Leonard Wood, MO, p. A361

LOWERY, Josh, Director Human Resources, Highland Community Hospital, Picayune, MS, p. A352

LOWERY, Kelly, Director Health Information Management, Ed Fraser Memorial Hospital and Baker Community Health Center, MacClenny, FL, p. A129

LOWERY, William, Financial Officer, North Texas State Hospital, Vernon, TX, p. A639

LOWMAN, Christine
Vice President Finance, Hampshire Memorial Hospital, Romney, WV, p. A680
Vice President Finance, War Memorial Hospital, Berkeley Springs, WV, p. A675

LOWMAN, LeeAnn, Director Human Resources, Lake Taylor Transitional Care Hospital, Norfolk, VA, p. A658

LOWRY, Matthew, M.D. Vice President of Medical Affairs, Norwood Hospital, Norwood, MA, p. A303

LOWRY, Michael, M.D. Medical Director, University of Utah Neuropsychiatric Institute, Salt Lake City, UT, p. A647

LOYA, John R., Vice Chancellor Human Resources, University of Illinois Hospital & Health Sciences System, Chicago, IL, p. A180

LOYD, Blythe, Vice President, Mayo Clinic Health System in Eau Claire, Eau Claire, WI, p. A686

LOYO–RODRIGUEZ, Raul J., Administrative Analyst III, San Diego County Psychiatric Hospital, San Diego, CA, p. A85

LOZADA, Leonard J., M.D. Vice President Medical Affairs, OhioHealth Riverside Methodist Hospital, Columbus, OH, p. A478

LOZANO, Melanie, Chief Financial Officer, Concho County Hospital, Eden, TX, p. A600

LOZANO, Michelle, Chief Executive Officer, Lifecare Hospitals of South Texas–North McAllen, McAllen, TX, p. A622

LOZAR, Beverly, Vice President Professional and Support Services, St. Vincent Charity Medical Center, Cleveland, OH, p. A477

LOZIER, Tim, Director Human Resources, Vibra Specialty Hospital of Dallas, Desoto, TX, p. A599

LUBARSKY, Neil, Senior Vice President Finance, Thomas Jefferson University Hospital, Philadelphia, PA, p. A537

LUBAWAY, William, Chief Financial Officer, Mercy Hospital Grayling, Grayling, MI, p. A315

LUBBOS, Hanna, M.D. Chief of Staff, Byrd Regional Hospital, Leesville, LA, p. A272

LUBIN, Bertram, M.D., President and Chief Executive Officer, Children's Hospital and Research Center at Oakland, Oakland, CA, p. A77

LUBINSKY, Jeanie, Chief Financial Officer, Mayo Clinic Health System – Red Cedar in Menomonie, Menomonie, WI, p. A691

LUBITSKY, John, Deputy Chief Executive Officer Support Services, Ancora Psychiatric Hospital, Hammonton, NJ, p. A404

LUCAS, Bob, Vice President Operations, King's Daughters Medical Center, Ashland, KY, p. A248

LUCAS, Christine, M.D. Chief of Staff, Union County Hospital, Anna, IL, p. A173

LUCAS, David, R.N. Director of Nursing, Glen Oaks Hospital, Greenville, TX, p. A607

LUCAS, Glynda, M.D. Deputy Commander Clinical Services, Bayne–Jones Army Community Hospital, Fort Polk, LA, p. A267

LUCAS, Jackie
Vice President Information Systems, Baptist Health La Grange, La Grange, KY, p. A253
Vice President, Oak Tree Hospital, Corbin, KY, p. A249

LUCAS, John, M.D., Chief Executive Officer, Cheyenne Regional Medical Center, Cheyenne, WY, p. A701

LUCAS, Kelly, Chief Information Officer, Sampson Regional Medical Center, Clinton, NC, p. A450

LUCAS, Lori, Director Fiscal Services, Shriners Hospitals for Children–Shreveport, Shreveport, LA, p. A278

LUCAS, Marshall, M.D. Medical Director, Cypress Creek Hospital, Houston, TX, p. A609

LUCAS, Melissa, Chief Financial Officer, Clay County Hospital, Flora, IL, p. A182

LUCAS, Richard, Director Information Services, Weirton Medical Center, Weirton, WV, p. A681

LUCAS, Roger V., Vice President, Human Resources, Aspirus Wausau Hospital, Wausau, WI, p. A699

LUCCHESI, Michael, M.D. Interim Chief Medical Officer, SUNY Downstate Medical Center University Hospital,, NY, p. A436

LUCE, Glenda, Chief Nursing Officer, Memorial Hospital of Gardena, Gardena, CA, p. A62

LUCE, John, M.D. Chief Medical Officer, San Francisco General Hospital Medical Center, San Francisco, CA, p. A87

LUCERO, Martha, Director Special Projects, Mayers Memorial Hospital District, Fall River Mills, CA, p. A60

LUCEY, Jeffery, M.D. Clinical Director, Kingsboro Psychiatric Center,, NY, p. A433

LUCEY, Paula A., R.N., Administrator, Milwaukee County Behavioral Health Division, Milwaukee, WI, p. A692

LUCIA, John, Chief Financial Officer, St. Anthony's Hospital, Houston, TX, p. A612

LUCIA, Sandra J., Director Health Information and Corporate Compliance Officer, Hampstead Hospital, Hampstead, NH, p. A398

LUCIANO, Vicente, M.D. Chief of Staff, North Sunflower Medical Center, Ruleville, MS, p. A353

LUCIDO, John, Director Human Resources, Kindred Hospital Detroit, Detroit, MI, p. A312

LUCIER, Robbyn, Director Human Resources, Portage Health, Hancock, MI, p. A316

LUCIO, John, D.O. Vice President Medical Affairs, St. Marys Health Center, Jefferson City, MO, p. A362

LUCK, Richard, Ed.D., Facility Director, Woodrow Wilson Rehabilitation Center, Fishersville, VA, p. A654

LUCKE, Kim, Vice President Finance, Northern Montana Hospital, Havre, MT, p. A377

LUCKETT, Douglas R., Interim President and Chief Executive Officer, Gaston Memorial Hospital, Gastonia, NC, p. A453

LUDEKE, Max L., FACHE, Chief Executive Officer, North Texas Community Hospital, Bridgeport, TX, p. A589

LUDEKE, Rose, Site Administrator Management Information Systems, Mercy Hospital Fort Scott, Fort Scott, KS, p. A234

LUDFORD, Brad, Vice President Finance, Exempla Saint Joseph Hospital, Denver, CO, p. A99

LUDINGTON, Gail, Chief Financial Officer, Coquille Valley Hospital, Coquille, OR, p. A512

LUDWIG, John A., R.N. Vice President Administration, Bridgton Hospital, Bridgton, ME, p. A282

LUDWIG, Shelly, Controller, F. W. Huston Medical Center, Winchester, KS, p. A247

LUDWIG, Ted, Chief Medical Officer, War Memorial Hospital, Sault Sainte Marie, MI, p. A324

LUDWIG, Tim, Vice President Ancillary Services, CarolinaEast Health System, New Bern, NC, p. A458

LUDWIG, Walter, Chief Operating Officer, Kenmore Mercy Hospital, Kenmore, NY, p. A428

LUDWIG–BEYMER, Patti, Ph.D. Chief Nursing Officer, Edward Hospital, Naperville, IL, p. A189

LUDWIGSEN, Kevin, Interim Chief Information Officer, Southeastern Ohio Regional Medical Center, Cambridge, OH, p. A472

LUEB, Jan, Coordinator Human Resources, Nemaha Valley Community Hospital, Seneca, KS, p. A244

LUEBBERING, Tom, Chief Financial Officer, Northeast Regional Medical Center, Kirksville, MO, p. A364

LUECHT, Jackie, Chief Human Resources Officer, Mercy Medical Center–North Iowa, Mason City, IA, p. A225

LUEDERS, Kathy, R.N. Director of Nursing–Acute Care, Saint Elizabeth's Medical Center, Wabasha, MN, p. A342

LUEHRS, Bill, Chief Human Resources Officer, NorthShore University Health System Evanston Hospital, Evanston, IL, p. A182

LUEHRS, Paul R., Chief Operating Officer, Mercy San Juan Medical Center, Carmichael, CA, p. A56

LUFKIN, Kirk, M.D
VPMA, McLaren Northern Michigan, Petoskey, MI, p. A321
Chief Medical Officer, Portage Health, Hancock, MI, p. A316

LUGER, Gerald, M.D. President Medical Staff, Gottlieb Memorial Hospital, Melrose Park, IL, p. A188

LUGO, Cesar, Director Human Resources, Victor Valley Community Hospital, Victorville, CA, p. A95

LUHRS, Jason J., Vice President Fiscal Services, Westfields Hospital, New Richmond, WI, p. A693

LUJAN, Barbara, Director Human Resources, Alta Vista Regional Hospital, Las Vegas, NM, p. A417

LUKA, Norman, M.D. Medical Director Clinical Affairs, Overlook Medical Center, Summit, NJ, p. A410

LUKASZEWSKI, Mike
Chief Financial Officer, Baptist Medical Center Beaches, Jacksonville Beach, FL, p. A127
Chief Financial Officer, Baptist Medical Center Jacksonville, Jacksonville, FL, p. A126

LUKENS, Harry
Senior Vice President and Chief Information Officer, Lehigh Valley Hospital, Allentown, PA, p. A519
Senior Vice President and Chief Information Officer, Lehigh Valley Hospital–Muhlenberg, Bethlehem, PA, p. A520

LUKENS, Tammy, Director Information, Kosciusko Community Hospital, Warsaw, IN, p. A214

LUKHARD, Kenneth W., President, Advocate Christ Medical Center, Oak Lawn, IL, p. A190

LUKISH, Kris, Human Resources Officer, CJW Medical Center, Richmond, VA, p. A660

LULICH, Diane, Director Human Resources, Memorial Medical Center – Ashland, Ashland, WI, p. A683

LULOFF, Lynn, Chief Financial Officer, Winneshiek Medical Center, Decorah, IA, p. A220

LUMACO, Darell, M.D. Chief of Staff, Tuality Healthcare, Hillsboro, OR, p. A513

LUMIA, Kim, President and Chief Executive Officer, Sharon Hospital, Sharon, CT, p. A111

LUMNITZ, Janice, M.D. Chief of Staff, Bowdle Hospital, Bowdle, SD, p. A558

LUMPKINS, Deborah, MSN Chief Nursing Officer, Maury Regional Hospital, Columbia, TN, p. A567

LUMPP, Karen, Senior Vice President and Chief Financial Officer, Trinitas Regional Medical Center, Elizabeth, NJ, p. A403

LUMSDEN, Chris A., Chief Executive Officer, Halifax Regional Health System, South Boston, VA, p. A661

LUNA, Octavio C., Executive Director, Patton State Hospital, Patton, CA, p. A79

LUNA, Richard, President and Chief Executive Officer, Newport Specialty Hospital, Tustin, CA, p. A93

LUNA, Tony, M.D. Chief of Staff, Minneola District Hospital, Minneola, KS, p. A240

LUND, Alicia, Director Human Resources, Westchester General Hospital, Miami, FL, p. A132

LUND, Elizabeth, M.D. Chief of Staff, Volunteer Community Hospital, Martin, TN, p. A573

LUND, Maggie
Divisional Senior Vice President Human Resources, Mercy Health – Anderson Hospital, Cincinnati, OH, p. A475
Divisional Senior Vice President Human Resources, Mercy Health – Fairfield Hospital, Fairfield, OH, p. A481
Regional Vice President Human Resources, Mercy Health – Mt. Airy Hospital, Cincinnati, OH, p. A475

LUND, Mark, Superintendent, Mental Health Institute, Clarinda, IA, p. A218

LUNDAL, Dave, Vice President and Regional Chief Information Officer, St. Mary's Hospital, Madison, WI, p. A690

LUNDBERG, Lanetta, Vice President Culture and People, PeaceHealth Ketchikan Medical Center, Ketchikan, AK, p. A28

LUNDGREN, Charlene B., Vice President, Doctors Community Hospital, Lanham, MD, p. A292

LUNDQUIST, David W.
President and Chief Executive Officer, Health Alliance Hospital – Broadway Campus, Kingston, NY, p. A428
President and Chief Executive Officer, Health Alliance Hospital – Mary's Avenue Campus, Kingston, NY, p. A428

LUNDSTROM, Carol, Interim Director Information Systems, Lakeview Hospital, Stillwater, MN, p. A341

LUNDVALL, Mark, Controller, Van Matre HEALTHSOUTH Rehabilitation Hospital, Rockford, IL, p. A194

LUNDY–PAINE, Robert, Director Information Systems, Alameda Hospital, Alameda, CA, p. A52

LUNN, Stephen, Chief Executive Officer, Heartland Regional Medical Center, Marion, IL, p. A187

LUNN, William, M.D. Chief Operating Officer, CHRISTUS Schumpert Medical Center, Shreveport, LA, p. A278

LUNNEBORG, Brandi, Vice President Operations, Mercy Hospital, Coon Rapids, MN, p. A330

LUNNEY, Kathleen, R.N. Chief Nursing Officer, Health Alliance Hospital – Broadway Campus, Kingston, NY, p. A428

LUNSFORD, Cindy, Executive Vice President and Chief Operating Officer, Peninsula Regional Medical Center, Salisbury, MD, p. A294

LUNTZ, Adam M., Vice President Finance and Chief Financial Officer, Aultman Orrville Hospital, Orrville, OH, p. A488

LUPINACCI, Michael, M.D. Medical Director, HEALTHSOUTH Rehabilitation Hospital of Mechanicsburg, Mechanicsburg, PA, p. A531

LURIA, Milton, M.D. Chief of Medicine, Greystone Park Psychiatric Hospital, Morris Plains, NJ, p. A406

LUSKIN–HAWK, Roberta, M.D., President and Chief Executive Officer, Presence Saint Joseph Hospital, Chicago, IL, p. A178

LUSSON, Mark, Vice President Human Resources, Northwest Community Hospital, Arlington Heights, IL, p. A173

LUSTERIO, Efren, Director of Nursing, Behavioral Center of Michigan, Warren, MI, p. A326

LUTES, Michael, President, Carolinas Medical Center–Union, Monroe, NC, p. A457

LUTEY, Cheryl, Director Human Resources, Evansville State Hospital, Evansville, IN, p. A202

LUTHER, Lori, Chief Operating Officer, Indiana University Health Ball Memorial Hospital, Muncie, IN, p. A210

LUTHER, Tracie, Vice President Human Resources, Lake Shore Health Care Center, Irving, NY, p. A427

LUTTON, Lorraine, President, St. Joseph's Hospital, Tampa, FL, p. A142

LUTTRELL, Nancy, Vice President Human Resources, Anne Arundel Medical Center, Annapolis, MD, p. A287

LUTTRELL, Pat, Director Human Resources, Coliseum Northside Hospital, Macon, GA, p. A156

LUTZ, Denise, Chief Human Resources Officer, St. Joseph's Hospital and Health Center, Dickinson, ND, p. A466

LUTZ, Don, Chief Information Officer, Bayonne Medical Center, Bayonne, NJ, p. A401

LUTZ, Garman E., Chief Financial Officer, Deaconess Hospital, Spokane, WA, p. A672

LUTZ, Rich, Director Human Resources, Fairview Southdale Hospital, Edina, MN, p. A332

LUTZ, Terry, Chief Financial Officer, Scheurer Hospital, Pigeon, MI, p. A321

LUX, Teri, R.N. Vice President Patient Care Services and Chief Nursing Officer, Community Memorial Hospital, Menomonee Falls, WI, p. A691

LUZE, Brittney, Director Health Information, Avera Flandreau Hospital, Flandreau, SD, p. A559

LYDE, Shawna Martin, Director Human Resources, Fairfield Memorial Hospital, Winnsboro, SC, p. A557

LYDEN, Matthew M., Chief Executive Officer, Integris Marshall County Medical Center, Madill, OK, p. A500

LYDICK, Bryan, Chief Executive Officer, Redwood Area Hospital, Redwood Falls, MN, p. A338

LYLE, Jr., J. Kenneth, Chief Financial Officer, Fulton State Hospital, Fulton, MO, p. A361

LYLES, Virginia H., Vice President Human Resources, Piedmont Newnan Hospital, Newnan, GA, p. A158

LYMAN, Jeremy, Chief Financial Director, Blue Mountain Hospital, Blanding, UT, p. A643

LYMBEROPOULOS, Nick, Chief Financial Officer, Providence Tarzana Medical Center,, CA, p. A71

LYNAM, Gene, Interim Chief Executive Officer, Camden County Health Services Center, Blackwood, NJ, p. A401

LYNCE, Danialle
Manager Human Resources, Heatherhill Care Communities, Chardon, OH, p. A473
Manager Human Resources, University Hospitals Geauga Medical Center, Chardon, OH, p. A473

LYNCH, Becky, Manager Business Entity Management and Information Systems, OSF St. Mary Medical Center, Galesburg, IL, p. A183

LYNCH, Danile, Chief Operating Officer, Saint Luke Institute, Silver Spring, MD, p. A294

LYNCH, David
Regional Director Information Systems, Summa Barberton Citizens Hospital, Barberton, OH, p. A471
Regional Director Information Services, Summa Wadsworth–Rittman Hospital, Wadsworth, OH, p. A492

LYNCH, Dawn, R.N. Director of Patient Care Services, Clark Fork Valley Hospital, Plains, MT, p. A378

LYNCH, Elizabeth A., Vice President Human Resources, The Hospital of Central Connecticut, New Britain, CT, p. A110

LYNCH III, Ernest C., Chief Executive Officer, Medical Center of McKinney, McKinney, TX, p. A622

LYNCH, G. Michael, M.D. Chief Medical Officer, Inova Fair Oaks Hospital, Fairfax, VA, p. A653

LYNCH, Heather, M.D. Chief of Staff, Purcell Municipal Hospital, Purcell, OK, p. A506

LYNCH, Jim, Chief Financial Officer, Fairbanks Memorial Hospital, Fairbanks, AK, p. A28

LYNCH, John, M.D. Vice President and Chief Medical Officer, Barnes–Jewish Hospital, Saint Louis, MO, p. A369

LYNCH, John, Vice President Chief Information Officer, Catskill Regional Medical Center, Harris, NY, p. A427

LYNCH, Marc, D.O. Chief of Staff, Kindred Hospital–Ontario, Ontario, CA, p. A77

LYNCH, Robert, M.D., Chief Executive Officer, Tulane Medical Center, New Orleans, LA, p. A276

LYNCH, Thomas, M.D. Chief of Staff, Veterans Affairs Medical Center, Omaha, NE, p. A388

LYNCH, Tim, Interim Chief Financial Officer, Highlands Medical Center, Sparta, TN, p. A579

LYNCH, Timothy, Vice President Operations, Spaulding Hospital for Continuing Medical Care Cambridge, Cambridge, MA, p. A299

LYNCH, Torie A., Manager Human Resources, Central Montana Medical Center, Lewistown, MT, p. A377

LYNCH–KILIC, Cathy, Vice President Human Resources, St. Mary's Hospital, Passaic, NJ, p. A408

LYNN, Steve, M.D. Chief of Staff, Ashley County Medical Center, Crossett, AR, p. A42

LYNN, Teresa, D.O. Chief of Staff, Arbuckle Memorial Hospital, Sulphur, OK, p. A507

LYON, David, M.D. Chief Medical Officer, Easton Hospital, Easton, PA, p. A525

LYON, David M., Director, Southern Virginia Mental Health Institute, Danville, VA, p. A653

LYON, Robert J., Chief Executive Officer, PHS Santa Fe Indian Hospital, Santa Fe, NM, p. A418

LYON, Tami, Director Human Resources, Community Memorial Hospital, Burke, SD, p. A558

LYONS, Althea C, Vice President Human Resources and Development, Beverly Hospital, Beverly, MA, p. A295

LYONS, Bob
Senior Vice President and Chief Operating Officer, St. Vincent Infirmary Medical Center, Little Rock, AR, p. A47
Chief Operating Officer, St. Vincent Morrilton, Morrilton, AR, p. A47

LYONS, Jan, Regional Director Health Improvement Management, Ringgold County Hospital, Mount Ayr, IA, p. A225

LYONS, Joseph A., Vice President Human Resources, McLaren Bay Region, Bay City, MI, p. A309

LYSAGHT, William, Chief Financial Officer, Kindred Hospital Las Vegas–Sahara, Las Vegas, NV, p. A393

LYTOLLIS, William, M.D. Chief of Staff, Barrow Regional Medical Center, Winder, GA, p. A163

LZICAR, Leslie, Director Human Resources, East Adams Rural Hospital, Ritzville, WA, p. A670

# M

MA, Jose, M.D. Vice President Medical Affairs, Union Hospital, Elkton, MD, p. A291

MABORANG, Ellen, Chief Nursing Officer, Desert View Hospital, Pahrump, NV, p. A394

MABRY, Bradley, Chief Operating Officer, Clinton Memorial Hospital, Wilmington, OH, p. A493

MABRY, Jerry D., FACHE, Chief Executive Officer, National Park Medical Center, Hot Springs, AR, p. A45

MACAFEE, Francis M., Vice President Finance and Chief Financial Officer, Corning Hospital, Corning, NY, p. A424

MACARONAS, Thomas, Chief Financial Officer, Labette Health, Parsons, KS, p. A242

MACDONALD, Laurie, Vice President Finance, Elk Regional Health Center, Saint Marys, PA, p. A540

MACDONALD, Neil, Vice President Operations, MedStar Union Memorial Hospital, Baltimore, MD, p. A288

MACDONALD GALLAGHER, Shelley A., R.N. Senior Vice President Operations, Memorial Hospital of Rhode Island, Pawtucket, RI, p. A546

MACDOUGALL, David, Vice President Finance, Winter Haven Hospital, Winter Haven, FL, p. A144

MACE, Rick, Chief Executive Officer, Adventist Bolingbrook Hospital, Bolingbrook, IL, p. A175

MACE, Robert, M.D. Chief of Staff, Webster County Memorial Hospital, Webster Springs, WV, p. A681

MACEK, Paul E., President and Chief Executive Officer, Proctor Hospital, Peoria, IL, p. A192

MACH, Teresa, Director Information Technology, Galesburg Cottage Hospital, Galesburg, IL, p. A183

MACHADO, James, Administrator, Heart of Lancaster Regional Medical Center, Lititz, PA, p. A530

MACINTYRE, Ronald, M.D. Chief Medical Officer, Sharp Memorial Hospital, San Diego, CA, p. A85

MALEY, Shelley, Director Human Resources, St. Luke's Hospital – Quakertown Campus, Quakertown, PA, p. A539

MALIK, Amir, M.D. Cardiologist, Plaza Medical Center of Fort Worth, Fort Worth, TX, p. A604

MALIK, Azfar, M.D., Chief Executive Officer and Chief Medical Officer, CenterPointe Hospital, Saint Charles, MO, p. A368

MALIN, Seth, M.D. President Medical and Dental Staff, Delaware County Memorial Hospital, Drexel Hill, PA, p. A524

MALINA, Joanne J., M.D. Chief of Staff, Veterans Affairs Hudson Valley Health Care System–F.D. Roosevelt Hospital, Montrose, NY, p. A430

MALINDZAK, Edward, Chief Human Resources Officer, Oconomowoc Memorial Hospital, Oconomowoc, WI, p. A693

MALISH, Richard, M.D. Deputy Commander Clinical Services, Winn Army Community Hospital, Hinesville, GA, p. A155

MALLERY, Edwina, Vice President Information Systems, Lafayette General Medical Center, Lafayette, LA, p. A271

MALLETT, Belinda, R.N. Vice President Patient Care and Clinical Services, Greene Memorial Hospital, Xenia, OH, p. A494

MALLETT, Teresa, Chief Financial Officer, Madison Community Hospital, Madison, SD, p. A560

MALLON, Lisa, Chief Executive Officer, J. C. Blair Memorial Hospital, Huntingdon, PA, p. A527

MALLORY, Cheryl, M.D. Chief Medical Officer, Syringa Hospital and Clinics, Grangeville, ID, p. A169

MALLOY, Peter, Chief Information Officer, Cheshire Medical Center, Keene, NH, p. A398

MALM, Brad, Director Human Resources and Education, Lindsborg Community Hospital, Lindsborg, KS, p. A239

MALMSTROM, Ron, Information Research Specialist, Parsons State Hospital and Training Center, Parsons, KS, p. A242

MALONE, Ginger L., MSN Chief Nursing Officer, North Memorial Medical Center, Robbinsdale, MN, p. A338

MALONE, Maureen A., Chief Operating Officer, Arrowhead Regional Medical Center, Colton, CA, p. A57

MALONE, Meredith, Chief Financial Officer, Dyersburg Regional Medical Center, Dyersburg, TN, p. A568

MALONE, Michael, Vice President and Chief Human Resources Officer, Virginia Hospital Center – Arlington, Arlington, VA, p. A651

MALONE, Sherry, Director Human Resources, Twin Rivers Regional Medical Center, Kennett, MO, p. A364

MALONEY, Jay, M.D. Chief of Staff, St. John's Lutheran Hospital, Libby, MT, p. A378

MALONEY, Paul V., Chief Financial Officer, Natchaug Hospital, Mansfield Center, CT, p. A109

MALONEY, Richard J., M.P.H., Commissioner, Summit Park Hospital and Nursing Care Center, Pomona, NY, p. A439

MALONEY, Tom, Chief Financial Officer, Atrium Medical Center, Middletown, OH, p. A486

MALOTT, Deanna, Director Human Resources, Henry County Hospital, New Castle, IN, p. A211

MALOTT, Gregg, Chief Financial Officer, Pulaski Memorial Hospital, Winamac, IN, p. A215

MALOTTE, Rebecca, Executive Director and Chief Nursing Officer, The Heart Hospital at Deaconess Gateway, Newburgh, IN, p. A211

MALTE, Robert H., Chief Executive Officer, EvergreenHealth, Kirkland, WA, p. A667

MALZEWSKI, Mike, Chief Financial Officer, St. Joseph's Community Hospital of West Bend, West Bend, WI, p. A699

MAMANGAKIS, John P., Senior Vice President, Sound Shore Medical Center of Westchester, New Rochelle, NY, p. A430

MAMARY, Glenn, Chief Information Officer, Hunterdon Medical Center, Flemington, NJ, p. A404

MAMBOURG, Rolland, M.D
   Vice President Medical Affairs, Saint Mary's Health Care, Grand Rapids, MI, p. A315
   Vice President Physician Services, St. Joseph Mercy Hospital, Ypsilanti, MI, p. A327

MANALO, Francisco, Director of Information Services, Florida Hospital North Pinellas, Tarpon Springs, FL, p. A142

MANAS, Julie, President and Chief Executive Officer, Sacred Heart Hospital, Eau Claire, WI, p. A686

MANCHESTER, David, Interim President and Chief Executive Officer, Palos Community Hospital, Palos Heights, IL, p. A191

MANCHESTER, George A., M.D
   Executive Vice President and Chief Medical Officer, Muncy Valley Hospital, Muncy, PA, p. A532
   Executive Vice President Medical Affairs, Williamsport Regional Medical Center, Williamsport, PA, p. A545

MANDANAS, Renato, M.D. Vice President Medical Affairs, Oswego Hospital, Oswego, NY, p. A439

MANDEL, David, M.D. Chief of Staff, East Texas Medical Center Trinity, Trinity, TX, p. A638

MANDELL, James, M.D., Chief Executive Officer, Boston Children's Hospital, Boston, MA, p. A296

MANDERINO, Michelle, Chief Human Resources, Malcom Randall Veterans Affairs Medical Center, Gainesville, FL, p. A124

MANDHAN, Narain, M.D. President Medical Staff, Kirby Medical Center, Monticello, IL, p. A189

MANDI, Deepak, M.D. Chief of Staff, West Palm Beach Veterans Affairs Medical Center, West Palm Beach, FL, p. A144

MANDRACCHIA, Vincent, DPM Chief Medical Officer, Broadlawns Medical Center, Des Moines, IA, p. A220

MANEEN, Vincent S., Chief Financial Officer, Oneida Healthcare, Oneida, NY, p. A438

MANESS, Judith A., FACHE, President and Chief Executive Officer, Mount St. Mary's Hospital and Health Center, Lewiston, NY, p. A428

MANESTRINA, Robert, Vice President Human Resources, Inspira Medical Center–Woodbury, Woodbury, NJ, p. A413

MANFULL, Debra, Interim Chief Executive Officer, State Hospital North, Orofino, ID, p. A170

MANGANO, Richard, Administrator and Chief Executive Officer, Malvern Institute, Malvern, PA, p. A530

MANGIN, Paul, Vice President Finance, Mercy Medical Center–Clinton, Clinton, IA, p. A218

MANGIONE, Ellen, M.D. Chief of Staff, Veterans Affairs Eastern Colorado Health Care System, Denver, CO, p. A100

MANGONA, John, Chief Information Officer and Compliance Officer, Saratoga Hospital, Saratoga Springs, NY, p. A442

MANGUM, Leigh, Vice President Human Resources, Tristar Centennial Medical Center, Nashville, TN, p. A577

MANGUM, Rozanne, Administrative Assistant and Director Human Resources, Grover C. Dils Medical Center, Caliente, NV, p. A391

MANHEIMER, Dean, Senior Vice President Human Resources, Northwestern Memorial Hospital, Chicago, IL, p. A178

MANI, C. K., M.D. Chief of Staff, Memorial Medical Center – Livingston, Livingston, TX, p. A619

MANIGOLD, David O., M.D. President Medical Staff, OSF Saint Elizabeth Medical Center, Ottawa, IL, p. A191

MANKER, Marcia, Chief Executive Officer, Orange Coast Memorial Medical Center, Fountain Valley, CA, p. A60

MANKINS, Mark L., M.D. Chief of Staff, Hamilton Hospital, Olney, TX, p. A625

MANKOSKI, Susan, Vice President Human Resources, St. Marys Health Center, Jefferson City, MO, p. A362

MANLAGNIT, Maybelle, Senior Accounting Officer, Metropolitan State Hospital, Norwalk, CA, p. A76

MANLEY, John, Director Information Systems, Jackson General Hospital, Ripley, WV, p. A680

MANLEY, Warren, Administrator, Dorminy Medical Center, Fitzgerald, GA, p. A153

MANN, Brian, Chief Executive Officer, Select Specialty Hospital–Danville, Danville, PA, p. A524

MANN, Joel, Administrator Information Systems, J. D. McCarty Center for Children With Developmental Disabilities, Norman, OK, p. A502

MANN, Lindsay K., Chief Executive Officer, Kaweah Delta Medical Center, Visalia, CA, p. A95

MANN, Rhonda, Chief Nursing Officer, Franklin Woods Community Hospital, Johnson City, TN, p. A571

MANN, Thomas, M.D. Chief of Staff, Dorminy Medical Center, Fitzgerald, GA, p. A153

MANN, Todd, Senior Vice President and Chief Executive Officer, Valley Baptist Medical Center–Harlingen, Harlingen, TX, p. A608

MANNICH, Andy, Regional Administrator, Georgia Regional Hospital at Savannah, Savannah, GA, p. A160

MANNICH, H. Andrew, Chief Operating Officer, St. Louis Psychiatric Rehabilitation Center, Saint Louis, MO, p. A371

MANNING, Angela, Director Health Information Services, HEALTHSOUTH Sunrise Rehabilitation Hospital, Fort Lauderdale, FL, p. A123

MANNING, Bain, Director Human Resources, Leonard J. Chabert Medical Center, Houma, LA, p. A268

MANNING, Donald, M.D. Clinical Director, Georgia Regional Hospital at Savannah, Savannah, GA, p. A160

MANNING, James, Administrator, Pathway Rehabilitation Hospital, Bossier City, LA, p. A264

MANNING, Jay, M.D. Chief of Staff, Vidant Beaufort Hospital, Washington, NC, p. A462

MANNING, JoAnn, Chief Financial Officer, Emory Johns Creek Hospital, Johns Creek, GA, p. A155

MANNING, Kimberly, Chief Nursing Officer, Washington County Hospital, Plymouth, NC, p. A459

MANNING, Laura, Administrative Director, Corning Hospital, Corning, NY, p. A424

MANNING, Lori, Administrator Human Resources, Western State Hospital, Tacoma, WA, p. A673

MANNING, Thomas, M.D. Medical Director, St. Charles Madras, Madras, OR, p. A514

MANNION, Stephen, Assistant Vice President Information Systems Customer Service, MedStar Franklin Square Medical Center, Baltimore, MD, p. A288

MANNIX, Mary N., FACHE, President and Chief Executive Officer, Augusta Health, Fishersville, VA, p. A654

MANNS, Bill, Chief Operating Officer, Alameda County Medical Center, Oakland, CA, p. A77

MANNY, Martin, Director, I.S., Providence St. Mary Medical Center, Walla Walla, WA, p. A674

MANOCHA, Lovelesh, M.D. Chief Medical Officer, Acuity Hospital of South Texas, San Antonio, TX, p. A630

MANOHARA, Anand, Associate Administrator, Good Samaritan Hospital, Bakersfield, CA, p. A54

MANSFIELD, Al, Chief Financial Officer, Saint Vincent Hospital, Erie, PA, p. A525

MANSFIELD, David, M.D. Chief of Staff, El Paso Specialty Hospital, El Paso, TX, p. A601

MANSFIELD, Deena, Director Human Resources, Ashley Regional Medical Center, Vernal, UT, p. A648

MANSFIELD, Jean, Director Human Resources, McLean Hospital, Belmont, MA, p. A295

MANSFIELD, Jerry A., Ph.D. Chief Nursing Officer, Ohio State University Wexner Medical Center, Columbus, OH, p. A478

MANSFIELD, Kevin, Director Human Resources, Davis Hospital and Medical Center, Layton, UT, p. A644

MANSFIELD, Robert, Chief Executive Officer, Mesilla Valley Hospital, Las Cruces, NM, p. A416

MANSKE, Lou Ann, Director Human Resources, Madonna Rehabilitation Hospital, Lincoln, NE, p. A385

MANSON, David, Manager Human Resources, Santa Clara Valley Medical Center, San Jose, CA, p. A88

MANSON, III, William T., President, AnMed Health Medical Center, Anderson, SC, p. A548

MANSOOR, Ureej, M.D. Chief of Staff, Southeast Health Center of Ripley County, Doniphan, MO, p. A360

MANSUE, Amy B., President and Chief Executive Officer, Children's Specialized Hospital–PSE&G, New Brunswick, NJ, p. A407

MANSUKHANI, Martin, Chief Financial Officer, Desert Valley Hospital, Victorville, CA, p. A95

MANSURE, John F., FACHE, President, Greer Memorial Hospital, Greer, SC, p. A553

MANTE, Laurie, Administrator and Vice President, Eddy Cohoes Rehabilitation Center, Cohoes, NY, p. A424

MANTELL, Amy, Vice President Human Resources, Mercy Hospital of Folsom, Folsom, CA, p. A60

MANTERNACH, Paul, M.D. Senior Vice President Physician Integration, Mercy Medical Center–North Iowa, Mason City, IA, p. A225

MANTOOTH, Chuck, President, Watauga Medical Center, Boone, NC, p. A448

MANTZ, David, Chief Executive Officer, Chicot Memorial Medical Center, Lake Village, AR, p. A46

MANUEL, Shasta, Executive Director Finance, St. Anthony Hospital, Oklahoma City, OK, p. A504

MANUS, Kim, Chief Financial Officer, Newport Hospital and Health Services, Newport, WA, p. A668

MANZ, Louis, Director Information and Communication Services, Chatham Hospital, Siler City, NC, p. A461

MANZANERO, Bienvenido, M.D. Medical Director, Hampstead Hospital, Hampstead, NH, p. A398

MANZER, Andrew R., President and Chief Executive Officer, Schuyler Hospital, Montour Falls, NY, p. A430

MANZO, Arnold D., Vice President Human Resources, Saint Barnabas Medical Center, Livingston, NJ, p. A405

MANZOOR, Amir, M.D. Medical Director, Select Specialty Hospital–Panama City, Panama City, FL, p. A136

MAO, Chi C., M.D. Medical Director, Select Specialty Hospital–Houston Heights, Houston, TX, p. A612

MAPES, Kevin
   Regional Information Technology Director, Providence Medical Center, Kansas City, KS, p. A237
   Regional Information Technology Director, Saint John Hospital, Leavenworth, KS, p. A238
   Director Kansas Division System and Technology Service Center, St. Francis Health Center, Topeka, KS, p. A245

MAPLES, Rickie, Interim Chief Financial Officer, Southeast Health Center of Ripley County, Doniphan, MO, p. A360

MAPPIN, F Gregory, M.D. Vice President Medical Affairs, Self Regional Healthcare, Greenwood, SC, p. A553

MARANO, Angeline M., Chief Operating Officer, Memorial Regional Hospital,, FL, p. A125

MARAS, Greg, Vice President Human Resources, Meadville Medical Center, Meadville, PA, p. A531

MARBAN, Anita L., R.N. Chief Nursing Officer, HEALTHSOUTH Rehabilitation Hospital, Humble, TX, p. A614

MARCANTANO, Mark, Executive Vice President and Chief Operating Officer, Women & Infants Hospital of Rhode Island, Providence, RI, p. A547

MARCANTEL, Bill, Chief Information Systems, Allen Parish Hospital, Kinder, LA, p. A270

MARCELLAIS, Duane, Information Technology Specialist, Public Health Service Indian Hospital – Quentin N. Burdick Memorial Health Facility, Belcourt, ND, p. A465

MARCELLINO, David, Executive Vice President and Chief Operating Officer, Botsford Hospital, Farmington Hills, MI, p. A313

MARCH, Riley, Manager Information Technology, Southeast Health Center of Ripley County, Doniphan, MO, p. A360

MARCHAND, Gary G., President and Chief Executive Officer, Memorial Hospital at Gulfport, Gulfport, MS, p. A347

MARCHANT, Joseph, Administrator, Bibb Medical Center, Centreville, AL, p. A18

MARCHLEWSKI, Anthony, M.D. President Medical and Psychological Staff, Bellin Psychiatric Center, Green Bay, WI, p. A687

MARCOVICI, Mia, M.D. Chief Medical Officer, Norristown State Hospital, Norristown, PA, p. A533

MARCRUM, Jennifer, Chief Financial Officer, Sumner County Hospital District One, Caldwell, KS, p. A232

MARCUM, Derrick, Director Information Systems, Missouri Baptist Medical Center, Saint Louis, MO, p. A370

MARCUS, Donald H., M.D. Medical Director, Kaiser Permanente Los Angeles Medical Center, Los Angeles, CA, p. A69

MARCUS, Stuart, M.D. Senior Vice President and Chief Medical Officer, St. Vincent's Medical Center, Bridgeport, CT, p. A108

MARCZAK, Stanley, Chief Financial Officer, Mayo Clinic Health System in Mankato, Mankato, MN, p. A335

MARCZEWSKI, Les, M.D. Chief Medical Officer, Loring Hospital, Sac City, IA, p. A227

MARDEN–RESNIK, Hilary, Vice President Human Resources, Hennepin County Medical Center, Minneapolis, MN, p. A336

MARDINI, George, M.D. Chief of Staff, Battle Mountain General Hospital, Battle Mountain, NV, p. A391

MAREK, Kyle, Manager Information Services, Carteret General Hospital, Morehead City, NC, p. A457

MAREK, Rick, Vice President Medical Information Systems, Warm Springs Rehabilitation Hospital, San Antonio, TX, p. A632

MARGENAU, Randall, Chief Information Officer, William S. Middleton Memorial Veterans Hospital, Madison, WI, p. A690

MARGETTS, Marty, Senior Vice President Human Resources, Physicians Regional Medical Center, Knoxville, TN, p. A572

MARGO, John G., Vice President Human Resources, Oneida Healthcare, Oneida, NY, p. A438

MARGOLIS, Marilyn, Chief Nursing Officer, Emory Johns Creek Hospital, Johns Creek, GA, p. A155

MARGOLIS, Ron, Chief Information Officer, University of New Mexico Hospitals, Albuquerque, NM, p. A415

MARGOLSKEE, Howard, M.D. Chief of Staff, Sebasticook Valley Health, Pittsfield, ME, p. A284

MARGOT, Skip, Vice President Patient Care Services and Chief Nurse Executive, Shady Grove Adventist Hospital, Rockville, MD, p. A294

MARGUGLIO, Paul, M.D. Chief of Staff, Healdsburg District Hospital, Healdsburg, CA, p. A64

MARGULIS, Richard T., President and Chief Executive Officer, Brookhaven Memorial Hospital Medical Center, Patchogue, NY, p. A439

MARIANI, Ermanno, Interim Chief Executive Officer, Gulf Coast Medical Center, Wharton, TX, p. A641

MARIANI, Marilyn, R.N. Chief Nursing Officer, Lakeview Hospital, Bountiful, UT, p. A643

MARIETTA, John, M.D
Chief Medical Officer, St. David's Medical Center, Austin, TX, p. A586
Chief Medical Officer, St. David's Rehabilitation Center, Austin, TX, p. A586

MARIETTA, Megan, Chief Operating Officer, Kingwood Medical Center, Kingwood, TX, p. A617

MARIETTA, Richard, M.D. Medical Director, Clear Lake Regional Medical Center, Webster, TX, p. A640

MARINELLI, Samuel, Vice President Finance and Chief Financial Officer, Chester River Health System, Chestertown, MD, p. A290

MARINELLI, Steve, Chief Financial Officer, Northwest Mississippi Regional Medical Center, Clarksdale, MS, p. A345

MARINELLO, Anthony, Chief Executive Officer, Mountain Vista Medical Center, Mesa, AZ, p. A33

MARINI, Frank, Vice President and Chief Information Officer, TMC Healthcare, Tucson, AZ, p. A39

MARINO, A. Michael, M.D. Senior Vice President Medical Administration, Greenwich Hospital, Greenwich, CT, p. A109

MARINO, Marchita H., Vice President Human Resources, Wuesthoff Medical Center – Rockledge, Rockledge, FL, p. A138

MARINOFF, Peter, Director Operations, Paul Oliver Memorial Hospital, Frankfort, MI, p. A314

MARION, Ben, Chief Executive Officer and Managing Director, Turning Point Hospital, Moultrie, GA, p. A158

MARION, Sue, Manager Business Office, Knox County Hospital, Knox City, TX, p. A617

MARIOTTI, Denise, Chief Human Resources Officer, Pennsylvania Hospital, Philadelphia, PA, p. A536

MARK, Curtis, M.D. Chief Medical Officer, Pioneer Memorial Hospital and Health Services, Viborg, SD, p. A563

MARKANT, David, Director Information Systems, Clifton Springs Hospital and Clinic, Clifton Springs, NY, p. A424

MARKEL, Michael J., MSN Executive Director of Operations, St. Joseph Mercy Livingston Hospital, Howell, MI, p. A316

MARKER, Sheri L., Vice President Human Resources, Rush University Medical Center, Chicago, IL, p. A179

MARKETTI, Dean M., Chief Information Officer, Morris Hospital & Healthcare Centers, Morris, IL, p. A189

MARKGRAF, Janelle, Director Human Resources, Langlade Hospital, Antigo, WI, p. A683

MARKHAM, Barbara, Chief Financial Officer, Glendive Medical Center, Glendive, MT, p. A376

MARKHAM, Marlin, Chief Financial Officer, Wilkes Regional Medical Center, North Wilkesboro, NC, p. A458

MARKHAM, Patricia A., Administrator and Chief Executive Officer, Cass County Memorial Hospital, Atlantic, IA, p. A216

MARKOS, Dennis R., Chief Executive Officer, Ed Fraser Memorial Hospital and Baker Community Health Center, MacClenny, FL, p. A129

MARKOVICH, Stephen, M.D., President, OhioHealth Riverside Methodist Hospital, Columbus, OH, p. A478

MARKOWITZ, Bruce J., President and Chief Executive Officer, Palisades Medical Center, North Bergen, NJ, p. A408

MARKOWITZ, Stuart, M.D. Chief Medical Officer, Hartford Hospital, Hartford, CT, p. A109

MARKOWSKI, Stan, Chief Financial Officer, Palmetto Lowcountry Behavioral Health, Charleston, SC, p. A549

MARKS, Craig J., FACHE, President, Mark Twain St. Joseph's Hospital, San Andreas, CA, p. A84

MARKS, Jerry, Chief Financial Officer, St. Vincent Frankfort Hospital, Frankfort, IN, p. A203

MARKS, Michael, M.D. Chief of Staff, Norwalk Hospital, Norwalk, CT, p. A111

MARKS, Stanley, M.D
Chief Medical Officer, Memorial Hospital Miramar, Miramar, FL, p. A133
Chief Medical Officer, Memorial Hospital Pembroke, Pembroke Pines, FL, p. A136
Chief Medical Officer, Memorial Regional Hospital,, FL, p. A125

MARKSTROM, Susan, M.D. Chief of Staff, St. Cloud Veterans Affairs Health Care System, Saint Cloud, MN, p. A339

MARKWITH, Candace L., Chief Executive Officer, Sierra Vista Regional Medical Center, San Luis Obispo, CA, p. A88

MARLER, Ruth, Chief Operating Officer/Chief Nursing Officer, Johnston Health, Smithfield, NC, p. A461

MARLER, Steven R., Administrator, Parkland Health Center–Bonne Terre, Bonne Terre, MO, p. A356

MARLEY, Charles, D.O. Vice President Medical Affairs, Gettysburg Hospital, Gettysburg, PA, p. A526

MARLEY, Lee
VP/Information Services Chief Application Officer, Presbyterian Hospital, Albuquerque, NM, p. A414
VP/Information Services Chief Application Officer, Presbyterian Kaseman Hospital, Albuquerque, NM, p. A415

MARLEY, Mark E., FACHE, President and Chief Executive Officer, Opelousas General Health System, Opelousas, LA, p. A276

MARLEY, Michael, Chief Information Officer, VA Central Western Massachusetts Healthcare System, Leeds, MA, p. A301

MARLGE, Charles G., M.D. Chief of Staff, Marias Medical Center, Shelby, MT, p. A379

MARLOW, Gary, M.D. President Medical Staff, Texas Health Presbyterian Hospital–WNJ, Sherman, TX, p. A634

MARLOW, Gary P., Chief Financial Officer, Beverly Hospital, Beverly, MA, p. A295

MARMANDE, Susanne, Administrator, Infirmary Long Term Acute Care Hospital, Mobile, AL, p. A22

MARNELL, George, Director, Veterans Affairs Medical Center, Albuquerque, NM, p. A415

MARNEY, Terri A., R.N. Director of Nursing, Plains Regional Medical Center, Clovis, NM, p. A415

MAROC, Genice, FACHE, Administrator and Chief Executive Officer, Cox Monett, Monett, MO, p. A366

MARON, Michael, President and Chief Executive Officer, Holy Name Medical Center, Teaneck, NJ, p. A411

MAROSTICA, Tony, Director Human Resources, Spanish Peaks Regional Health Center, Walsenburg, CO, p. A106

MAROTTA, Diane, Vice President Human Resources, John T. Mather Memorial Hospital, Port Jefferson, NY, p. A440

MAROUN, Christiane, M.D. Chief of Staff, Childrens Care Hospital and School, Sioux Falls, SD, p. A562

MARPLE, Anthony, Vice President of Strategy, Mercy Hospital of Portland, Portland, ME, p. A284

MARQUARDT, Robert C., FACHE, President and Chief Executive Officer, Fairmont General Hospital, Fairmont, WV, p. A676

MARQUES, John, Vice President Human Resources, University of Arizona Medical Center – University Campus, Tucson, AZ, p. A39

MARQUES, Tony, Director Information Systems, Grace Cottage Hospital, Townshend, VT, p. A650

MARR, Debbie, Administrative Assistant and Director Human Resources, Fredonia Regional Hospital, Fredonia, KS, p. A234

MARRA, Mary Anne, R.N. Vice President/Chief Nursing Officer, East Orange General Hospital, East Orange, NJ, p. A403

MARRONI, Denise, Chief Financial Officer, Providence Centralia Hospital, Centralia, WA, p. A665

MARS, Martha, R.N. Director of Nursing, St. John Broken Arrow, Broken Arrow, OK, p. A496

MARSEE, DeWayne, Director Information Systems, Joint Township District Memorial Hospital, Saint Marys, OH, p. A489

MARSH, Amy, Chief Financial Officer, Integris Baptist Regional Health Center, Miami, OK, p. A501

MARSH, Daniel L., Director, West Texas Veterans Affairs Health Care System, Big Spring, TX, p. A588

MARSH, Leslie, Chief Executive Officer, Lexington Regional Health Center, Lexington, NE, p. A385

MARSH, Linda, Vice President Financial Services and Chief Financial Officer, Alhambra Hospital Medical Center, Alhambra, CA, p. A52

MARSH, Mark A., Chief Executive Officer, Gateway Medical Center, Clarksville, TN, p. A567

MARSH, Jr., Murray S., Chief Financial Officer, Warren General Hospital, Warren, PA, p. A543

MARSH, Paul, Director Information Systems, Parkridge Medical Center, Chattanooga, TN, p. A567

MARSH, Rob, Chief Executive Officer, Red River Hospital, Wichita Falls, TX, p. A641

MARSHALL, David R., JD Chief Nursing and Patient Care Services Officer, University of Texas Medical Branch Hospitals, Galveston, TX, p. A605

MARSHALL, Deborah K., Vice President Public Relations, Good Samaritan Hospital, Suffern, NY, p. A443

MARSHALL, Debra, Director Human Resources, Bradley County Medical Center, Warren, AR, p. A50

MARSHALL, Glen, Chief Executive Officer, Kennewick General Hospital, Kennewick, WA, p. A667

MARSHALL, James L., President, Mercy Hospital, Devils Lake, ND, p. A466

MARSHALL, Jerry, Director Information Systems, United Regional Health Care System, Wichita Falls, TX, p. A642

MARSHALL, John A., Chief Executive Officer, TriStar Horizon Medical Center, Dickson, TN, p. A568

MARSHALL, Ken, M.D. Chief Medical Officer, Indiana University Health Bloomington Hospital, Bloomington, IN, p. A199

MARSHALL, Kenneth P., Interim President, University of Louisville Hospital, Louisville, KY, p. A256

MARSHALL, Michael, Vice President Finance and Chief Financial Officer, Anderson Hospital, Maryville, IL, p. A187

MARSHALL, Michael D., Administrator and Chief Executive Officer, Bryan W. Whitfield Memorial Hospital, Demopolis, AL, p. A19

MARSHALL, Robert, Chief Executive Officer, River Parishes Hospital, La Place, LA, p. A270

MARSHALL, Sherrie, Health Information Management Services Director, The Rehabilitation Institute of St. Louis, Saint Louis, MO, p. A371

MARSILIO, Lisa
Executive Director, Good Shepherd Penn Partners Specialty Hospital at Rittenhouse, Philadelphia, PA, p. A535
Vice President and Administrator, Good Shepherd Specialty Hospital, Bethlehem, PA, p. A520

MARSO, Paul, Vice President Human Resources, Avera St. Mary's Hospital, Pierre, SD, p. A561

MARSTELLER, Brent A., President and Chief Executive Officer, Cabell Huntington Hospital, Huntington, WV, p. A677

MARTANIUK, Jean, Director Human Resources, Mt. Ascutney Hospital and Health Center, Windsor, VT, p. A650

MARTEL, Ron, Director for Administration, Naval Hospital Pensacola, Pensacola, FL, p. A136

MARTENS, Angela, Controller, Cumberland Memorial Hospital, Cumberland, WI, p. A685

MARTENS, Troy, Chief Operating Officer, Trinity Regional Medical Center, Fort Dodge, IA, p. A221

MARTIN, Amy, Director Human Resources, Mary Black Memorial Hospital, Spartanburg, SC, p. A556

MARTIN, Barbara J., R.N.,
President and Chief Executive Officer, Vista Medical Center East, Waukegan, IL, p. A196
President and Chief Executive Officer, Vista Medical Center West, Waukegan, IL, p. A196

MARTIN, Billy, Human Resource Analyst, Blue Mountain Recovery Center, Pendleton, OR, p. A515

MARTIN, Brent, Chief Executive Officer, LifeCare Specialty Hospital of North Louisiana, Ruston, LA, p. A277

MARTIN, Bruce A., Vice President Human Resources, CarolinaEast Health System, New Bern, NC, p. A458

MARTIN, C. Gregory, M.D. Chief Medical Officer, Emerson Hospital, Concord, MA, p. A299

MARTIN, Cary, Chief Executive Officer, Houston Medical Center, Warner Robins, GA, p. A162

MARTIN, Cathy, Administrator, Sterlington Rehabilitation Hospital, Sterlington, LA, p. A279

MARTIN, Cherie, FACHE, Chief Executive Officer, Banner Behavioral Health Hospital – Scottsdale, Scottsdale, AZ, p. A37

MARTIN, Cheryl
  Manager Human Resources, Columbia Memorial Hospital, Astoria, OR, p. A511
  Chief Information Officer, Tuomey Healthcare System, Sumter, SC, p. A556

MARTIN, Christine M.
  Chief Financial Officer, Crawley Memorial Hospital, Shelby, NC, p. A461
  Chief Financial Officer, St. Luke's Hospital, Columbus, NC, p. A450

MARTIN, Connie
  Vice President and Chief Support Officer, Methodist Medical Center of Oak Ridge, Oak Ridge, TN, p. A578
  Administrator, Physicians Medical Center, Houma, LA, p. A268
  Director Human Resources, Trinity Hospital of Augusta, Augusta, GA, p. A148

MARTIN, Corey, M.D. Director Medical Affairs, Buffalo Hospital, Buffalo, MN, p. A330

MARTIN, David, M.D. Vice President Medical Staff Affairs, St. David's Round Rock Medical Center, Round Rock, TX, p. A629

MARTIN, David, Assistant Administrator, Valley Hospital, Spokane Valley, WA, p. A672

MARTIN, David T., President, UPMC Passavant, Pittsburgh, PA, p. A538

MARTIN, Dean, M.D. Medical Director, Shadow Mountain Behavioral Health System, Tulsa, OK, p. A509

MARTIN, Deanna, MSN, Chief Executive Officer, HEALTHSOUTH Desert Canyon Rehabilitation Hospital, Las Vegas, NV, p. A392

MARTIN, Deborah, Assistant Administrator, Skagit Valley Hospital, Mount Vernon, WA, p. A668

MARTIN, Debra, Director of Nursing, Hamilton General Hospital, Hamilton, TX, p. A607

MARTIN, Donna, R.N. Chief Nursing Officer, Ochsner Baptist Medical Center, New Orleans, LA, p. A275

MARTIN, Elizabeth J., Vice President and Administrator, Riverside Tappahannock Hospital, Tappahannock, VA, p. A662

MARTIN, Emily Howard, Administrator, Commonwealth Regional Specialty Hospital, Bowling Green, KY, p. A248

MARTIN, Eva, M.D. Chief of Staff, Carl Vinson Veterans Affairs Medical Center, Dublin, GA, p. A152

MARTIN, Garry, Chief Fiscal, Veterans Affairs North Texas Health Care System, Dallas, TX, p. A598

MARTIN, Greg, President, Integris Grove General Hospital, Grove, OK, p. A499

MARTIN, Gregg
  Manager Management Information Systems, Arnot Ogden Medical Center, Elmira, NY, p. A425
  Chief Information Officer, St. Joseph's Hospital, Elmira, NY, p. A425
  Senior Vice President and Chief Operating Officer, Tuomey Healthcare System, Sumter, SC, p. A556

MARTIN, Harvey C., M.D. Medical Director, Red River Hospital, Wichita Falls, TX, p. A641

MARTIN, Holly, Human Resources Leader, Iowa Specialty Hospital–Clarion, Clarion, IA, p. A218

MARTIN, Jack, Director Human Resources, Texas Institute for Surgery at Texas Health Presbyterian Dallas, Dallas, TX, p. A597

MARTIN, James C., M.D. Vice President and Chief Medical Officer, CHRISTUS Santa Rosa Health System, San Antonio, TX, p. A630

MARTIN, James D.
  Chief Financial Officer, Hawthorn Children Psychiatric Hospital, Saint Louis, MO, p. A369
  Chief Financial Officer, Metropolitan St. Louis Psychiatric Center, Saint Louis, MO, p. A370
  Chief Financial Officer, St. Louis Psychiatric Rehabilitation Center, Saint Louis, MO, p. A371

MARTIN, James W., D.D.S. Chief of Staff, Baptist Memorial Hospital–Tipton, Covington, TN, p. A568

MARTIN, Jeanene R., M.P.H
  Senior Vice President Human Resources, WakeMed Cary Hospital, Cary, NC, p. A449
  Senior Vice President Human Resources, WakeMed Raleigh Campus, Raleigh, NC, p. A459

MARTIN, Jeffrey H., M.D. Chief of Staff, Murphy Medical Center, Murphy, NC, p. A458

MARTIN, Jeffrey L., President, Ministry Saint Michael's Hospital, Stevens Point, WI, p. A697

MARTIN, Jennifer, Administrative Assistant/Human Resources Coordinator, Select Specialty Hospital–North Knoxville, Knoxville, TN, p. A572

MARTIN, Joan, R.N. Chief Nursing Officer, Twin County Regional Hospital, Galax, VA, p. A654

MARTIN, Kelly, Chief Financial Officer, Fairchild Medical Center, Yreka, CA, p. A96

MARTIN, Kenneth A., M.D. Chief of Staff, Arkansas Surgical Hospital, North Little Rock, AR, p. A48

MARTIN, Kevin, M.P.H., Administrator, Shriners Hospitals for Children–Salt Lake City, Salt Lake City, UT, p. A647

MARTIN, Konnie, Chief Executive Officer, San Luis Valley Regional Medical Center, Alamosa, CO, p. A97

MARTIN, Leslie, Associate Administrator, McKee Medical Center, Loveland, CO, p. A104

MARTIN, Macky, Director Human Resources, Fairview Regional Medical Center, Fairview, OK, p. A499

MARTIN, Patrick, Director Information Systems, Calvary Hospital,, NY, p. A431

MARTIN, Patrick, M.D. Medical Director, Wilmington Treatment Center, Wilmington, NC, p. A463

MARTIN, Patsy, Manager Human Resources, Select Rehabilitation Hospital of Denton, Denton, TX, p. A599

MARTIN, Paul J., Director Human Resources, Kaiser Permanente Los Angeles Medical Center, Los Angeles, CA, p. A69

MARTIN, Ric, Information Specialist, Madison State Hospital, Madison, IN, p. A209

MARTIN, Richard A., MSN Senior Vice President and Chief Nursing Officer, Hoag Memorial Hospital Presbyterian, Newport Beach, CA, p. A76

MARTIN, Rick, Vice President of Ancillary and Support Services, St. Charles Medical Center – Bend, Bend, OR, p. A511

MARTIN, Rozanne, Assistant Administrator Human Resources, Highline Medical Center, Burien, WA, p. A665

MARTIN, Sabrina, Chief Operating Officer, Rehabilitation Hospital of Southern New Mexico, Las Cruces, NM, p. A416

MARTIN, Sharon E., M.D. President Medical Staff, Fulton County Medical Center, Mc Connellsburg, PA, p. A530

MARTIN, Stacy L., Director Human Resources, Grant Regional Health Center, Lancaster, WI, p. A689

MARTIN, Steve, Chief Information Officer, CHRISTUS Santa Rosa Health System, San Antonio, TX, p. A630

MARTIN, Susan, Vice President Finance, Middlesex Hospital, Middletown, CT, p. A110

MARTIN, Thomas J., Administrator, Lincoln Hospital, Davenport, WA, p. A666

MARTIN, Tom, Vice President and Chief Information Officer, EvergreenHealth, Kirkland, WA, p. A667

MARTIN, Val, Director Financial Management Services Center, Veterans Affairs Salt Lake City Health Care System, Salt Lake City, UT, p. A647

MARTIN, Valene J., Administrative Director Human Resources, Community Hospital of Long Beach, Long Beach, CA, p. A67

MARTIN, W. Carl, Chief Operating Officer, Providence Hospital, Columbia, SC, p. A550

MARTIN–FORMAN, Marty Ann, Chief Operating Officer, Fulton State Hospital, Fulton, MO, p. A361

MARTIN–PRATT, Diane, Director Information Systems, Niagara Falls Memorial Medical Center, Niagara Falls, NY, p. A437

MARTINEZ, Albino
  Director Budget and Finance, Miners' Colfax Medical Center, Raton, NM, p. A417
  Director Finance and Budget, New Mexico Behavioral Health Institute at Las Vegas, Las Vegas, NM, p. A417

MARTINEZ, Beverly, Director of Nursing, Rio Grande Hospital, Del Norte, CO, p. A99

MARTINEZ, Carlos J., Director Resource Management, Naval Medical Center, Portsmouth, VA, p. A659

MARTINEZ, Edward, Chief Information Officer, Miami Children's Hospital, Miami, FL, p. A132

MARTINEZ, Fernando, Vice President and Chief Information Officer, Jackson Health System, Miami, FL, p. A131

MARTINEZ, Frank, Vice President Human Resources, West Jefferson Medical Center, Marrero, LA, p. A273

MARTINEZ Jr., Fred, Chief Executive Officer, St. Charles Parish Hospital, Luling, LA, p. A272

MARTINEZ, Jose, M.D. Chief of Staff, Trinity Hospital Twin City, Dennison, OH, p. A480

MARTINEZ, Kristen, Coordinator Human Resources, Kindred Hospital–La Mirada, La Mirada, CA, p. A65

MARTINEZ, Louisa, Director of Nursing, Frio Regional Hospital, Pearsall, TX, p. A626

MARTINEZ, Michelle, Interim Chief Executive Officer, U. S. Public Health Service Indian Hospital–Whiteriver, Whiteriver, AZ, p. A39

MARTINEZ, Regina M., Director Human Resources, La Paz Regional Hospital, Parker, AZ, p. A33

MARTINEZ, Steve, Executive Director and Administrator, New Mexico Behavioral Health Institute at Las Vegas, Las Vegas, NM, p. A417

MARTINEZ, Terri, Chief Financial Officer, Plains Memorial Hospital, Dimmitt, TX, p. A599

MARTINEZ, Virginia, Manager Human Resources, Copper Queen Community Hospital, Bisbee, AZ, p. A30

MARTING, Bill, Senior Vice President and Chief Financial Officer, The University of Kansas Hospital, Kansas City, KS, p. A237

MARTINO, Anthony, Chief Executive Officer, Select Specialty Hospital–Scottsdale, Scottsdale, AZ, p. A37

MARTINO, Michael, M.D. Chief of Staff, Arkansas Valley Regional Medical Center, La Junta, CO, p. A103

MARTINSON, Erling, M.D. Medical Director, Nelson County Health System, Mcville, ND, p. A468

MARTINSON, Tiffany, Director Human Resources, Norton Sound Regional Hospital, Nome, AK, p. A28

MARTIRANO, Michael, M.D. President Medical Staff, Elmhurst Memorial Hospital,, IL, p. A182

MARTOCCIO, Debi, R.N., Chief Operating Officer, Florida Hospital at Connerton Long Term Acute Care, Land O'Lakes, FL, p. A128

MARTS, Teresa, M.D. Chief Medical Staff, Community Memorial Hospital, Burke, SD, p. A558

MARTUCCI, Kathleen, Director Human Resources, Helen Hayes Hospital, West Haverstraw, NY, p. A445

MARVER, Stacy, Director Information Technology, Ministry Saint Clare's Hospital, Weston, WI, p. A699

MARX, Edward, Vice President and Chief Information Officer, Texas Health Harris Methodist Hospital Azle, Azle, TX, p. A586

MARX, Tomasine
  Chief Financial Officer, St. John Hospital and Medical Center, Detroit, MI, p. A312
  Chief Financial Officer, St. John Macomb–Oakland Hospital, Warren, MI, p. A326
  Chief Financial Officer, St. John River District Hospital, East China, MI, p. A313

MARX, Troy, Director Human Resources, Upland Hills Health, Dodgeville, WI, p. A685

MARX, William, M.D. Chief of Staff, Syracuse Veterans Affairs Medical Center, Syracuse, NY, p. A444

MARZINZIK, John A., Vice President Finance, Frisbie Memorial Hospital, Rochester, NH, p. A400

MASCHER, Troy, Director Information Systems, Via Christi Hospital in Pittsburg, Pittsburg, KS, p. A242

MASCIARELLI, Filippo, M.D. Chief of Staff, Denton Regional Medical Center, Denton, TX, p. A598

MASHAK–EKERN, Jane, Fiscal Officer, Tomah Veterans Affairs Medical Center, Tomah, WI, p. A697

MASHINSKI, John
  Senior Vice President Human Resources, Bon Secours–DePaul Medical Center, Norfolk, VA, p. A658
  Vice President Human Resources, Mary Immaculate Hospital, Newport News, VA, p. A657

MASI, George V., Chief Operating Officer, Harris Health System, Houston, TX, p. A609

MASKELL, Denise, Chief Information Officer, Springfield Hospital Center, Sykesville, MD, p. A294

MASKUS, Jane, Vice President and Chief Information Officer, Lawrence Memorial Hospital, Lawrence, KS, p. A238

MASLYN, Jay T., Chief Financial Officer, Nicholas H. Noyes Memorial Hospital, Dansville, NY, p. A424

MASON, Bill A., Chief Executive Officer, Meadow Wood Behavioral Health System, New Castle, DE, p. A114

MASON, Cheryl S., Chief Financial Officer, Regional Medical Center, Orangeburg, SC, p. A555

MASON, Jane A., R.N. Chief Clinical Officer, Kindred Hospital of Northern Indiana, Mishawaka, IN, p. A210

MASON, Kathy, Chief Operating Officer, Atrium Medical Center of Corinth, Corinth, TX, p. A593

MASON, Keith, Chief Executive Officer, Bailey Medical Center, Owasso, OK, p. A505

MASON, Reginald, M.D. President Medical Staff, Riverside Tappahannock Hospital, Tappahannock, VA, p. A662

MASON, Rhonda, Director of Patient Care Services, Tri–State Memorial Hospital, Clarkston, WA, p. A665

MASON, Robert L., Chief Executive Officer, Van Diest Medical Center, Webster City, IA, p. A230

MASON, Sally, Director Human Resources, Golden Plains Community Hospital, Borger, TX, p. A589

MASON, Sam, Director Management Information Systems, Northwest Texas Healthcare System, Amarillo, TX, p. A582

MASON, Sandra, Director Nursing Services and Senior Nurse Executive, Robert E. Bush Naval Hospital, Twentynine Palms, CA, p. A93

MASON, Steve, Assistant Superintendent and Chief Operating Officer, Clifton T. Perkins Hospital Center, Jessup, MD, p. A292

MASON, William R., Chief Operating Officer, Brooke Glen Behavioral Hospital, Fort Washington, PA, p. A526

MASONER, Carolyn, Director Information Services, Saint Luke's North Hospital – Barry Road, Kansas City, MO, p. A363

MASOOD, Shahid, M.D. Clinical Director, Mildred Mitchell–Bateman Hospital, Huntington, WV, p. A677

MASSE, Roger A., FACHE, Chief Executive Officer, Ellsworth County Medical Center, Ellsworth, KS, p. A233

MASSENGALE, David, Chief Financial Officer, Taylor Regional Hospital, Campbellsville, KY, p. A249

MASSENGILL, Leigh, Chief Executive Officer, Medical Center of Trinity, Trinity, FL, p. A143

MASSEY, Gina, Vice President Human Resources, Clarity Child Guidance Center, San Antonio, TX, p. A631

MASSEY, Kimberly, Chief Financial Officer, Ty Cobb Regional Medical Center, Lavonia, GA, p. A156

MASSEY, Rocco K., Community Chief Executive Officer, Beckley ARH Hospital, Beckley, WV, p. A675

MASSEY, Steven, President and Chief Executive Officer, Westfields Hospital, New Richmond, WI, p. A693

MASSIE, Jamie, Chief Financial Officer, Coal County General Hospital, Coalgate, OK, p. A497

MASSIELLO, Martin, Senior Vice President and Chief Operating Officer, Eisenhower Medical Center, Rancho Mirage, CA, p. A81

MASSIET, Jill, R.N. Vice President Patient Care, Baptist Health Medical Center–Little Rock, Little Rock, AR, p. A46

MASSIMILLA, John P., FACHE Vice President Administration, Chambersburg Hospital, Chambersburg, PA, p. A522

MASSMAN, Patty, Director of Nursing, Granite Falls Municipal Hospital and Manor, Granite Falls, MN, p. A333

MASSMANN, Jerry
Chief Financial Officer, Children's Hospitals and Clinics of Minnesota, Minneapolis, MN, p. A336
Chief Financial Officer, Children's Hospitals and Clinics of Minnesota, Saint Paul, MN, p. A340

MAST, Dave
Chief Financial Officer, Providence Holy Cross Medical Center,, CA, p. A71
Chief Financial Officer, Providence Saint Joseph Medical Center, Burbank, CA, p. A55

MAST, Duane, M.D. Medical Director, Hocking Valley Community Hospital, Logan, OH, p. A484

MAST, Joelle, Ph.D. Chief Medical Officer, Blythedale Children's Hospital, Valhalla, NY, p. A445

MASTERS, Ken, Director Information Systems, Mercy McCune–Brooks Hospital, Carthage, MO, p. A358

MASTERS, Kim, M.D. Medical Director, Saint Simons by–the–Sea Hospital, Saint Simons Island, GA, p. A159

MASTERS, Regina, R.N. Director of Nursing, Continuing Care Hospital, Lexington, KY, p. A254

MASTERSON, David J., Chief Executive Officer, Sampson Regional Medical Center, Clinton, NC, p. A450

MASTERSON, Paul, Chief Financial Officer, Genesis HealthCare System, Zanesville, OH, p. A494

MASTERSON, Sammie, Chief Human Resources Officer, Harney District Hospital, Burns, OR, p. A511

MASTERTON, William, Chief Executive Officer, Piedmont Medical Center, Rock Hill, SC, p. A555

MASTRO, Mary Lou, President, Elmhurst Memorial Hospital,, IL, p. A182

MASTROIANNI, Tom, Vice President Human Resources, Lawrence Hospital Center, Bronxville, NY, p. A422

MASTROPIETRO, N. A., M.D. Medical Director, Lancaster Regional Medical Center, Lancaster, PA, p. A529

MATA, Maribel, Director Information Services, Doctors Hospital of Laredo, Laredo, TX, p. A618

MATA–GUERRERO, Rita, Nurse Director, Weslaco Rehabilitation Hospital, Weslaco, TX, p. A641

MATAI, Divya, Chief Operating Officer and Chief Financial Officer, Jack Hughston Memorial Hospital, Phenix City, AL, p. A24

MATAMOROS, Mary L., R.N., Chief Executive Officer, SeaSide Behavioral Center, New Orleans, LA, p. A276

MATEJKA, Cheryl
Chief Financial Officer, Mercy Hospital St. Louis, Saint Louis, MO, p. A370
Chief Financial Officer, Mercy Hospital Washington, Washington, MO, p. A373

MATENS, Brett, Chief Operating Officer, St. David's South Austin Medical Center, Austin, TX, p. A586

MATHAI, Matt, M.D. Medical Director, Select Specialty Hospital–Milwaukee, Milwaukee, WI, p. A692

MATHEIS, Tracey, Chief Financial Officer, Moberly Regional Medical Center, Moberly, MO, p. A366

MATHER, Kelly, Chief Executive Officer, Sonoma Valley Hospital, Sonoma, CA, p. A91

MATHER, Martha S., Chief Operating Officer and Vice President, Our Lady of Peace, Louisville, KY, p. A256

MATHERS, Larry, M.D. Chief of Staff, Newport Medical Center, Newport, TN, p. A577

MATHES, Lisa L., Director of Human Resources, Southwest Medical Center, Liberal, KS, p. A238

MATHEW, Bob, Director Finance, Griffin Memorial Hospital, Norman, OK, p. A502

MATHEW, Finny, Chief Operating Officer, Kosciusko Community Hospital, Warsaw, IN, p. A214

MATHEW, Jefy, M.D. Chief of Staff, St. Luke's The Woodlands Hospital, The Woodlands, TX, p. A637

MATHEW, Mammen, M.D. Chief Rehabilitation Medicine, Woodrow Wilson Rehabilitation Center, Fishersville, VA, p. A654

MATHEWS, Hilary G., R.N., Administrator, Mayo Clinic Jacksonville, Jacksonville, FL, p. A126

MATHEWS, Patrick J., Chief Executive Officer and Chief Financial Officer, St. Joseph Medical Center, Houston, TX, p. A612

MATHEWS, Paul G., CPA, Administrator, Hardtner Medical Center, Olla, LA, p. A276

MATHEWSON, Patricia, Chief Nursing Officer, Tulare Regional Medical Center, Tulare, CA, p. A93

MATHIAS, Debra
Chief Operating Officer, Children's Hospital at Mission, Mission Viejo, CA, p. A74
Chief Operating Officer, Children's Hospital of Orange County, Orange, CA, p. A77

MATHIEU, Jan, Director Human Resources, Heartland Surgical Specialty Hospital, Overland Park, KS, p. A241

MATHIEU, Karen, Director Human Resources, Bear Valley Community Hospital, Big Bear Lake, CA, p. A55

MATHIS, Linda, Director Human Resources, Muskogee Regional Medical Center, Muskogee, OK, p. A502

MATHIS, Rebecca, Vice President and Chief Financial Officer, Adventist Hinsdale Hospital, Hinsdale, IL, p. A185

MATHIS, Susan, Chief Operating Officer, CenterPointe Hospital, Saint Charles, MO, p. A368

MATHURIN, Jr., Emile, M.D. Medical Director, HEALTHSOUTH Rehabilitation Hospital, Humble, TX, p. A614

MATHURIN, Venra, Vice President Human Resources, Interfaith Medical Center,, NY, p. A432

MATICH, Philip, M.D. Vice President Medical Affairs, St. Joseph Mercy Port Huron, Port Huron, MI, p. A322

MATLACK, Ross A., FACHE, President and Chief Executive Officer, Fisher–Titus Medical Center, Norwalk, OH, p. A487

MATLOCK, Mike, M.D. Chief Medical Officer, Providence St. Peter Hospital, Olympia, WA, p. A669

MATNEY, James L., President and Chief Executive Officer, Colquitt Regional Medical Center, Moultrie, GA, p. A158

MATNEY, Tim, Chief Financial Officer, Logan Regional Medical Center, Logan, WV, p. A678

MATRELLA, Sandra, Manager Finance, Buffalo Hospital, Buffalo, MN, p. A330

MATSIL, Robyn, Human Resources Director, Vista Medical Center West, Waukegan, IL, p. A196

MATSINGER, John, M.D. Medical Director, Virtua Berlin, Berlin, NJ, p. A401

MATTA, Lalita, M.D. Chief Medical Officer and Vice President Medical Affairs, UMass Memorial–Marlborough Hospital, Marlborough, MA, p. A302

MATTERN, Joe, M.D. Chief Medical Officer, Jefferson Healthcare, Port Townsend, WA, p. A669

MATTES, Bryan, Associate Administrator, CrossRidge Community Hospital, Wynne, AR, p. A51

MATTES, Daniel
Chief Executive Officer, Midwest Orthopedic Specialty Hospital, Franklin, WI, p. A686
President, Wheaton Franciscan Healthcare – Franklin, Franklin, WI, p. A687
President, Wheaton Franciscan Healthcare – St. Francis, Milwaukee, WI, p. A692

MATTES, James A., President and Chief Executive Officer, Grande Ronde Hospital, La Grande, OR, p. A514

MATTES, Mark D., R.N. Assistant Administrator/Patient Care Services, Golden Valley Memorial Healthcare, Clinton, MO, p. A359

MATTEUCCI, Dolly, Interim Executive Director, Napa State Hospital, Napa, CA, p. A76

MATTHEWS, Adora, M.D. Medical Director, HEALTHSOUTH Rehabilitation Hospital, Florence, SC, p. A551

MATTHEWS, Bertt, Director Human Resources, Saint Luke¥s Cushing Medical Center, Leavenworth, KS, p. A238

MATTHEWS, Carol, Director Human Resources, Saline Memorial Hospital, Benton, AR, p. A41

MATTHEWS, Carole, Vice President Patient Care, Wood County Hospital, Bowling Green, OH, p. A472

MATTHEWS, Clinton, President and Chief Executive Officer, Reading Hospital and Medical Center, West Reading, PA, p. A544

MATTHEWS, Deborah, Administrator, Tanner Medical Center–Carrollton, Carrollton, GA, p. A149

MATTHEWS, Gwen, MSN, Chief Executive Officer, Ukiah Valley Medical Center, Ukiah, CA, p. A94

MATTHEWS, Kenneth, Manager Information Technology, Guadalupe County Hospital, Santa Rosa, NM, p. A418

MATTHEWS, Ted, Chief Executive Officer, Eastland Memorial Hospital, Eastland, TX, p. A600

MATTHEY, Michael, Facility Chief Information Officer, Louis A. Johnson Veterans Affairs Medical Center, Clarksburg, WV, p. A676

MATTHIAS, Mark, M.D. Vice President of Medical Affairs, St. Cloud Hospital, Saint Cloud, MN, p. A339

MATTHIAS, Pam, Vice President of Patient Care Services, J. C. Blair Memorial Hospital, Huntingdon, PA, p. A527

MATTICE, Thomas, Director, Richard L. Roudebush Veterans Affairs Medical Center, Indianapolis, IN, p. A206

MATTINGLY, Chris, Chief Executive Officer, Meadowbrook Rehabilitation Hospital, Gardner, KS, p. A234

MATTINGLY, Marty, Vice President Human Resources, Methodist Hospital, Henderson, KY, p. A252

MATTIS, Nancy, Chief Patient Care Services, Catalina Island Medical Center, Avalon, CA, p. A53

MATTIS, Paul, Vice President Finance, Titusville Area Hospital, Titusville, PA, p. A542

MATTISON, Kenneth R., Chief Executive Officer, Florida Hospital–Flagler, Palm Coast, FL, p. A136

MATTKE, Roger, Chief Financial Officer, Lafayette General Medical Center, Lafayette, LA, p. A271

MATTLY, Sheila, Chief Nursing Officer, Wayne County Hospital, Corydon, IA, p. A219

MATTON, Jeffrey A., President, MedStar Good Samaritan Hospital, Baltimore, MD, p. A288

MATTSON, Jodi, Director of Nursing, Cedar Springs Hospital, Colorado Springs, CO, p. A98

MATTSON, Wayne, Management Information Systems Specialist, Rogers Memorial Hospital, Oconomowoc, WI, p. A693

MATUK, Liz, Executive Director, Administrative and Clinical Services, Cleveland Clinic Florida, Weston, FL, p. A144

MATZEK, Eileen, Director Information Technology, Advocate Condell Medical Center, Libertyville, IL, p. A187

MATZENBACHER, Elaine, Chief Financial Officer, Washington County Hospital, Nashville, IL, p. A190

MATZIGKEIT, Linda, Senior Vice President Human Resources, Children's Healthcare of Atlanta, Atlanta, GA, p. A146

MAULDIN, Rick, Director Information Services, Christus St. Michael Hospital–Atlanta, Atlanta, TX, p. A584

MAURER, Gregory L., Administrator, St. Luke's Elmore, Mountain Home, ID, p. A170

MAURER, Jackie, Fiscal Officer, Julian F. Keith Alcohol and Drug Abuse Treatment Center, Black Mountain, NC, p. A448

MAURER, Linda, Vice President Patient Care Services, Wilson Memorial Hospital, Sidney, OH, p. A490

MAURER, Marjorie A., MSN Vice President Operations and Chief Nursing Executive, Advocate Good Samaritan Hospital, Downers Grove, IL, p. A181

MAURICE, Timothy, Chief Financial Officer, University of California, Davis Medical Center, Sacramento, CA, p. A84

MAURICIO, Roberto, M.D. Chief of Staff, Cumberland River Hospital, Celina, TN, p. A566

MAURIELLO, Renee, R.N. Vice President, Patient Care Services, Mercy Medical Center, Rockville Centre, NY, p. A441

MAURIN, Michael J., Chief Financial Officer, Southern Surgical Hospital, Slidell, LA, p. A279

MAUST, Richard, Chief Information Officer, Jacksonville Medical Center, Jacksonville, AL, p. A22

MAVROMATIS, Lou, Vice President Data Processing, MedStar Southern Maryland Hospital Center, Clinton, MD, p. A290

MAWYER, David, Chief Financial Officer, Western State Hospital, Staunton, VA, p. A662

MAXFIELD, Matt T., FACHE, Chief Executive Officer, Seton Medical Center Harker Heights, Harker Heights, TX, p. A607

MAXIE, Bryan K.
Chief Executive Officer, Jefferson Davis Community Hospital, Prentiss, MS, p. A353
Administrator, Marion General Hospital, Columbia, MS, p. A346
Administrator, Walthall County General Hospital, Tylertown, MS, p. A354

MAXWELL, Dale, Senior VP Chief Financial Officer, Presbyterian Kaseman Hospital, Albuquerque, NM, p. A415

MAXWELL, David, Vice President Operations, St. Vincent Anderson Regional Hospital, Anderson, IN, p. A198

MAXWELL, Jody, Manager Business Office, Smith County Memorial Hospital, Smith Center, KS, p. A244

MAXWELL, John, M.D. Chief of Staff, Glenwood Regional Medical Center, West Monroe, LA, p. A280

MAXWELL, John, Chief Operating Officer, Memorial Hospital, Martinsville, VA, p. A657

MAXWELL, Kevin, M.D. Chief of Staff, Glendive Medical Center, Glendive, MT, p. A376

MAXWELL, Mike, Administrator, Behavioral Healthcare Center at Huntsville, Huntsville, AL, p. A21

MAXWELL, Ronnie, Director Information Systems, Glenwood Regional Medical Center, West Monroe, LA, p. A280

MAY, Brandon, Chief Financial Officer, Sierra Providence East Medical Center, El Paso, TX, p. A602

MAY, Carol, Chief Financial Officer, Vice President Finance and Operations, Sauk Prairie Memorial Hospital & Clinics, Prairie Du Sac, WI, p. A695

MAY, Frank, Chief Executive Officer, Yampa Valley Medical Center, Steamboat Springs, CO, p. A106

MAY, John, Chief Executive Officer, Sistersville General Hospital, Sistersville, WV, p. A681

MAY, Kevin B.
Chief Financial Officer, Blowing Rock Hospital, Blowing Rock, NC, p. A448
System Director Finance, Charles A. Cannon Memorial Hospital, Linville, NC, p. A456
Chief Financial Officer, Watauga Medical Center, Boone, NC, p. A448

MAY, Randy, Interim Executive Director, Jim Taliaferro Community Mental Health, Lawton, OK, p. A500

MAY, Ronald B., M.D. Vice President Medical Affairs, CarolinaEast Health System, New Bern, NC, p. A458

MAY, Scott, Area Director Technology, Kaiser Permanente Santa Clara Medical Center, Santa Clara, CA, p. A89

MAY, Sonja, Director Human Resources, Morton County Health System, Elkhart, KS, p. A233

MAY, Troy, Chief Information Officer, University of Louisville Hospital, Louisville, KY, p. A256

MAY, Walter E., President and Chief Executive Officer, Pikeville Medical Center, Pikeville, KY, p. A259

MAYBEN, Casey, Chief Nursing Officer, East Texas Medical Center Pittsburg, Pittsburg, TX, p. A627

MAYER, Karen, R.N. VP Patient Care Services, Rush Oak Park Hospital, Oak Park, IL, p. A190

MAYER, Monica, M.D. Clinical Director, Public Health Service Indian Hospital – Quentin N. Burdick Memorial Health Facility, Belcourt, ND, p. A465

MAYES, James C., Manager Information Technology and Chief Security Officer, Palo Verde Hospital, Blythe, CA, p. A55

MAYES, Shelley, Director of Medical Information Services, Southwest Medical Center, Liberal, KS, p. A238

MAYEUX, Michael, Chief Financial Officer, Teche Regional Medical Center, Morgan City, LA, p. A274

MAYEWSKI, Raymond, M.D
Chief Medical Officer, Highland Hospital of Rochester, Rochester, NY, p. A441
Chief Medical Officer, Strong Memorial Hospital of the University of Rochester, Rochester, NY, p. A441

MAYFIELD, Michael Bradley, M.D. Chief of Staff, Chicot Memorial Medical Center, Lake Village, AR, p. A46

MAYHEW, Nicholas, Vice President and Chief Financial Officer, Rome Memorial Hospital, Rome, NY, p. A441

MAYHLE, Douglas, M.D. Medical Director, Nicholas H. Noyes Memorial Hospital, Dansville, NY, p. A424

MAYLE, Connie, Vice President Administrative Services, UPMC Horizon, Greenville, PA, p. A526

MAYNARD, Amy, Acting Chief Finance Service, Central Texas Veterans Healthcare System, Temple, TX, p. A636

MAYNARD, John, Director Information Systems, OSF Saint Elizabeth Medical Center, Ottawa, IL, p. A191

MAYNARD, Rhonda, Chief Financial Officer, Physicians Regional Medical Center, Knoxville, TN, p. A572

MAYO, Andrew, Chief Executive Officer and Managing Director, North Star Behavioral Health System, Anchorage, AK, p. A27

MAYO, Cindy, FACHE, Chief Executive, Providence Centralia Hospital, Centralia, WA, p. A665

MAYO, Hal, Chief Financial Officer, Liberty Dayton Regional Medical Center, Liberty, TX, p. A618

MAYO, Michael A., FACHE, President, Baptist Medical Center Jacksonville, Jacksonville, FL, p. A126

MAYO, Randy, Director Information Technology, William Newton Hospital, Winfield, KS, p. A247

MAYO, Rob, M.D
Chief Medical Officer, Newark–Wayne Community Hospital, Newark, NY, p. A437
Chief Medical Officer, Rochester General Hospital, Rochester, NY, p. A441

MAYO, Sarah, Vice President Financial and Information Services, Lenoir Memorial Hospital, Kinston, NC, p. A456

MAYORAL, Jorge, M.D. Medical Director, Rehabilitation Hospital of Rhode Island, North Smithfield, RI, p. A546

MAYS, Christine, R.N
Chief Operating Officer and Chief Nurse Executive, Saint Joseph East, Lexington, KY, p. A254
Chief Operating Officer and Chief Nurse Executive, Saint Joseph Hospital, Lexington, KY, p. A254

MAYSILLES, Nancy, R.N. Chief Nursing Officer, Medical Center of Trinity, Trinity, FL, p. A143

MAYSON, Mark J., M.D. Medical Director, Palmetto Health Baptist, Columbia, SC, p. A550

MAZO, Scott, Vice President Human Resources, Northwest Medical Center, Margate, FL, p. A130

MAZOUR, Linda, M.D. President, Franklin County Memorial Hospital, Franklin, NE, p. A383

MAZUR, Geoff, Director Information Technology, Cole Memorial, Coudersport, PA, p. A523

MAZUR, Robert, Vice President Human Resources, Capital Region Medical Center, Jefferson City, MO, p. A362

MAZZA, Mary, Director Human Resources, HEALTHSOUTH Rehabilitation Hospital of Western Massachusetts, Ludlow, MA, p. A301

MAZZO, Joseph, Chief Financial Officer, River Park Hospital, Mc Minnville, TN, p. A574

MAZZOLA, Joe, D.O
Sr. Vice President Medical Affairs/Chief Quality Officer, Grace Hospital, Morganton, NC, p. A458
Sr. Vice President Medical Affairs/Chief Quality Officer, Valdese General Hospital, Valdese, NC, p. A462

MAZZUCA, Darryl, Director Management Information Systems, Little Company of Mary Hospital and Health Care Centers, Evergreen Park, IL, p. A182

MBENGA, Saul, Manager Information Technology, Alliance HealthCare System, Holly Springs, MS, p. A348

MCADAMS, David, Chief Financial Officer, Lindner Center of HOPE, Mason, OH, p. A485

MCAFEE, Thomas J., President, Northwestern Lake Forest Hospital, Lake Forest, IL, p. A186

MCALISTER, Michael, Chief Executive Officer, Select Specialty Hospital–Nashville, Nashville, TN, p. A577

MCALLISTER, Guy, Assistant Vice President and Chief Information Officer, Tift Regional Medical Center, Tifton, GA, p. A161

MCALLISTER, Marlene, R.N. Chief Nursing Officer, Medical Center Health System, Odessa, TX, p. A625

MCALOON, Richard, Vice President Human Resources, Hartford Hospital, Hartford, CT, p. A109

MCANALLY, Eileen, Senior Vice President Human Resources, Lankenau Medical Center, Wynnewood, PA, p. A545

MCANDREW, Michael, Chief Executive Officer, Hopkins County Memorial Hospital, Sulphur Springs, TX, p. A636

MCANDREWS, Susan, R.N., Administrator, Riverside Shore Memorial Hospital, Nassawadox, VA, p. A657

MCAREAVEY, Jon, M.D. Chief Medical Staff, Prairie Lakes Healthcare System, Watertown, SD, p. A564

MCARTHUR, Ronald L., Chief Executive Officer, Summit Healthcare Regional Medical Center, Show Low, AZ, p. A37

MCARTOR, Dana, R.N. Director of Nursing, Perkins County Health Services, Grant, NE, p. A384

MCAULIFFE, Gregory, M.D. Chief Medical Officer, San Luis Valley Regional Medical Center, Alamosa, CO, p. A97

MCAULIFFE, John, M.D. Medical Director, Sauk Prairie Memorial Hospital & Clinics, Prairie Du Sac, WI, p. A695

MCBEE, Gala, Administrator, George Nigh Rehabilitation Institute, Okmulgee, OK, p. A505

MCBEE, Jeff, Administrator, Presbyterian Rust Medical Center, Rio Rancho, NM, p. A417

MCBEE, Marie, Chief Executive Officer, Warwick Manor Behavioral Health, East New Market, MD, p. A291

MCBRATNEY, Kathleen, M.D. President, Saint Luke¥s Cushing Medical Center, Leavenworth, KS, p. A238

MCBREARTY, Michael, M.D. Vice President Medical Affairs, Thomas Hospital, Fairhope, AL, p. A20

MCBRIDE, Anne, Chief Executive Officer, Regional Hospital for Respiratory and Complex Care, Seattle, WA, p. A670

MCBRIDE, Brandon, Operations Officer, Logan Regional Hospital, Logan, UT, p. A644

MCBRIDE, Dan, M.D. Chief of Staff, Spring Valley Hospital Medical Center, Las Vegas, NV, p. A393

MCBRIDE, Dina, Executive Assistant and Human Resources Director, East Adams Rural Hospital, Ritzville, WA, p. A670

MCBRIDE, Grace, Vice President Acute Care Services, St. Marys Health Center, Jefferson City, MO, p. A362

MCBRIDE, Kate, Chief Operating Officer, Poplar Springs Hospital, Petersburg, VA, p. A659

MCBRIDE, Michael J., FACHE, President and Chief Executive Officer, St. Mary's Hospital and Medical Center, Grand Junction, CO, p. A102

MCBRIDE, III, Thomas Y., Executive Vice President and Chief Financial Officer, Gwinnett Hospital System, Lawrenceville, GA, p. A156

MCBROOM, Robert, M.D. Medical Director, Texas Specialty Hospital at Wichita Falls, Wichita Falls, TX, p. A641

MCBRYDE, Richard, Senior Vice President and Chief Operating Officer, North Arkansas Regional Medical Center, Harrison, AR, p. A44

MCCABE, Jim, Chief Financial Officer, Promise Hospital of San Diego, San Diego, CA, p. A85

MCCABE, John B., M.D., Chief Executive Officer, Upstate University Hospital, Syracuse, NY, p. A444

MCCABE, Mary, Chief Financial Officer, North Colorado Medical Center, Greeley, CO, p. A102

MCCABE, Patrick, Senior Vice President Finance and Chief Financial Officer, Bridgeport Hospital, Bridgeport, CT, p. A108

MCCABE Jr., Patrick G., FACHE, President and Chief Executive Officer, Levi Hospital, Hot Springs National Park, AR, p. A45

MCCABE, Steve, Chief Executive Officer, Hill Crest Behavioral Health Services, Birmingham, AL, p. A16

MCCAFFERTY, Michael, Chief Executive Officer, Sheridan Memorial Hospital, Sheridan, WY, p. A703

MCCAHILL, Mary, Chief Nursing Officer, Thorek Memorial Hospital, Chicago, IL, p. A179

MCCAIN, Rebecca, Chief Financial Officer and Assistant Administrator, Electra Memorial Hospital, Electra, TX, p. A602

MCCAIN, Robert, M.D. Chief of Staff, TriStar Southern Hills Medical Center, Nashville, TN, p. A577

MCCALEB, Marg, Chief Human Resources Management, Veterans Affairs Black Hills Health Care System, Fort Meade, SD, p. A560

MCCALL, Brad
President and Chief Executive Officer, Physicians Surgical Hospital – Panhandle Campus, Amarillo, TX, p. A582
President and Chief Executive Officer, Physicians Surgical Hospital – Quail Creek, Amarillo, TX, p. A582

MCCALL, Cynde, R.N. Chief Nursing Officer, Select Specialty Hospital–Omaha, Omaha, NE, p. A388

MCCALL, Harlo, Chief Operating Officer, Lehigh Regional Medical Center, Lehigh Acres, FL, p. A129

MCCALL, Lee, Administrator, Winston Medical Center, Louisville, MS, p. A350

MCCALLISTER, Bob, Director Human Resources, Baptist Memorial Hospital–Golden Triangle, Columbus, MS, p. A346

MCCALLISTER, Darla, Chief Financial Officer, Lakeside Women's Hospital, Oklahoma City, OK, p. A503

MCCALLISTER, Diane, M.D. Chief Medical Officer, Porter Adventist Hospital, Denver, CO, p. A100

MCCALLISTER, Sean, Administrator, Providence Valdez Medical Center, Valdez, AK, p. A29

MCCAMPBELL, Kellie, Coordinator Human Resources, Kindred Hospital–Chattanooga, Chattanooga, TN, p. A566

MCCAMPBELL, Marcia, M.D. Chief Medical Officer, Shasta Regional Medical Center, Redding, CA, p. A81

MCCANCE, Chad, M.D. Chief of Staff, Cass County Memorial Hospital, Atlantic, IA, p. A216

MCCANDLESS, Barbara
Vice President Human Resources, Organization Development, Albany Memorial Hospital, Albany, NY, p. A420
Corporate Vice President Human Resources, Samaritan Hospital, Troy, NY, p. A444

MCCANN, Barbara, Director Human Resources, Sunrise Canyon Hospital, Lubbock, TX, p. A620

MCCANN, Joseph, Chief Information Officer, Saint Francis Hospital and Health Centers, Poughkeepsie, NY, p. A440

MCCANN, Kyle, Chief Operating Officer, Hillcrest Hospital – South, Tulsa, OK, p. A508

MCCANN, Lew, Director Management Information Systems, OSF Holy Family Medical Center, Monmouth, IL, p. A188

MCCANNA, Peter J., Executive Vice President Administration and Chief Financial Officer, Northwestern Memorial Hospital, Chicago, IL, p. A178

MCCARDELL, Tom, Administrator, Physicians Behavioral Hospital, Shreveport, LA, p. A278

MCCARTAN, Mary E., Manager Human Resources, Veterans Affairs Long Beach Healthcare System, Long Beach, CA, p. A68

MCCARTER, Scott, Chief Information Officer, Karmanos Cancer Center, Detroit, MI, p. A312

MCCARTER, Jr., Thomas G., M.D. Chief Medical Officer, Lankenau Medical Center, Wynnewood, PA, p. A545

MCCARTHY, Brian, Director Information Systems, Memorial Hospital of Salem County, Salem, NJ, p. A410

MCCARTHY, Jennifer, Chief Operating Officer, Health Central, Ocoee, FL, p. A134

MCCARTHY, Linda M., R.N. VP/ Chief Nursing Officer, Citrus Memorial Health System, Inverness, FL, p. A126

MCCARTHY, Maureen, M.D. Chief of Staff, Salem Veterans Affairs Medical Center, Salem, VA, p. A661

MCCARTHY, Robert R., Vice President Finance and Chief Financial Officer, Chenango Memorial Hospital, Norwich, NY, p. A438

MCCARTHY, Steve, Assistant Administrator Business Operations, Upland Hills Health, Dodgeville, WI, p. A685

MCCARTHY, Sue, Chief Financial Officer, Grady Memorial Hospital, Atlanta, GA, p. A146

MCCARTHY, Teresa, Interim Director Human Resources, McDowell Hospital, Marion, NC, p. A457

MCCARTY, Bernie, Director Facilities, Hoopeston Regional Health Center, Hoopeston, IL, p. A185

MCCARTY, Daniel P., Chief Operating Officer, Orange City Area Health System, Orange City, IA, p. A226

MCCARTY, Maryland, Director Information Systems, Atlanta Medical Center, Atlanta, GA, p. A146

MCCARTY, Melany, R.N. Chief Clinical Officer, Kindred Hospital–Amarillo, Amarillo, TX, p. A582

MCCARTY, Pat, Director Human Resources, Pushmataha Hospital & Home Health, Antlers, OK, p. A495

MCCARTY, Wendy, Director Human Resources, Hillsboro Community Hospital, Hillsboro, KS, p. A235

MCCARY, Steve C., Administrator, Riverside Doctors' Hospital, Williamsburg, VA, p. A663

MCCASLIN, Anna, Chief Financial Officer, Nebraska Orthopaedic Hospital, Omaha, NE, p. A388

MCCAUGHEY, James, Chief Strategy Officer, Lucile Salter Packard Children's Hospital at Stanford, Palo Alto, CA, p. A78

MCCAULEY, Bryan, Chief Executive Officer, Stringfellow Memorial Hospital, Anniston, AL, p. A15

MCCAULEY, Cynthia, Chief Financial Officer, Good Samaritan Medical Center, West Palm Beach, FL, p. A143

MCCAULEY, Dudley, Controller, Lincoln County Medical Center, Ruidoso, NM, p. A418

MCCAULEY, Sue E., Director Finance, Baum Harmon Mercy Hospital, Primghar, IA, p. A227

MCCAULEY, W. Roger, Senior Vice President Administration and Chief Financial Officer, UPMC Northwest, Seneca, PA, p. A541

MCCAWLEY, Thomas J., Director Human Resources, CGH Medical Center, Sterling, IL, p. A195

MCCLAID, Michael, M.D. President Medical Staff, Community Hospital of Bremen, Bremen, IN, p. A199

MCCLAIN, David, Executive Vice President Operations, Tahlequah City Hospital, Tahlequah, OK, p. A507

MCCLAIN, Richard, M.D. Chief Medical Officer, Chickasaw Nation Medical Center, Ada, OK, p. A495

MCCLALLEN, Gerald, President Medical Staff, St. Joseph Memorial Hospital, Murphysboro, IL, p. A189

MCCLAMMY, Lisa, Chief Nursing Officer, Glen Rose Medical Center, Glen Rose, TX, p. A606

MCCLANAHAN, Gary, Chief Information Officer, Sequoyah Memorial Hospital, Sallisaw, OK, p. A506

MCCLARIGAN, Linda, R.N. Vice President, Patient Care Services, Alice Hyde Medical Center, Malone, NY, p. A429

MCCLASKEY, Cynthia, Ph.D., Director, Southwestern Virginia Mental Health Institute, Marion, VA, p. A657

MCCLEESE, Randy, Vice President Information Services and Chief Information Officer, St. Claire Regional Medical Center, Morehead, KY, p. A258

MCCLELLAN, Ashley, Chief Executive Officer, Medical Center of Lewisville, Lewisville, TX, p. A618

MCCLENDON, Pat, MSN Chief Nursing Officer, Palmdale Regional Medical Center, Palmdale, CA, p. A78

MCCLINTICK, Cliff, Chief Information Officer, Lindner Center of HOPE, Mason, OH, p. A485

MCCLOSKEY, Louis, Chief Human Resources, Veterans Affairs Medical Center, Wilmington, DE, p. A115

MCCLUNG, James W., Chief Executive Officer, HEALTHSOUTH Rehabilitation Hospital of Alexandria, Alexandria, LA, p. A262

MCCLUNG, Lyle, M.D. Chief of Staff, Carilion Stonewall Jackson Hospital, Lexington, VA, p. A656

MCCLURE, Dan, Chief Information Officer, Hi–Desert Medical Center, Joshua Tree, CA, p. A64

MCCLURE, Gwenda, USAF Chief Nursing Officer, Mimbres Memorial Hospital, Deming, NM, p. A415

MCCLURE, Jan, Chief Executive Officer, Hill Regional Hospital, Hillsboro, TX, p. A608

MCCLURE, Joy, Chief Financial Officer, Ashe Memorial Hospital, Jefferson, NC, p. A455

MCCLURE, Thomas, M.D. Vice President Medical Affairs and Chief Medical Officer, Allegheny Valley Hospital, Natrona Heights, PA, p. A533

MCCLURG, Cathy, Director Human Resources, William Newton Hospital, Winfield, KS, p. A247

MCCLURG, Chris, Chief Financial Officer, Baptist Health Richmond, Richmond, KY, p. A260

MCCLURKAN, Mac
Chief Information Officer, Bethesda Hospital, Saint Paul, MN, p. A340
Chief Information Officer, St. John's Hospital, Saint Paul, MN, p. A340
Chief Information Officer, Woodwinds Health Campus, Woodbury, MN, p. A343

MCCLUSKEY, Tabb, M.D. Chief Medical Officer, Hendricks Community Hospital, Hendricks, MN, p. A333

MCCLUSKEY, Zachary, Chief Operating Officer, TriStar StoneCrest Medical Center, Smyrna, TN, p. A579

MCCLUSKY, Derek, M.D. Chief of Staff, Northern Louisiana Medical Center, Ruston, LA, p. A277

MCCLYMONDS, Bruce, President and Chief Executive Officer, West Virginia University Hospitals, Morgantown, WV, p. A679

MCCOBB, David
Chief Information Officer, Citrus Valley Medical Center, Covina, CA, p. A58
Chief Information Officer, Foothill Presbyterian Hospital, Glendora, CA, p. A63

MCCOIC, Kristie, Clinic Operations Officer and Director Human Resources, St. Joseph's Health Services–Gundersen Lutheran, Hillsboro, WI, p. A688

MCCOLE–WICHER, Sharon, R.N. Chief Nursing Officer, San Francisco General Hospital Medical Center, San Francisco, CA, p. A87

MCCOLLOUGH, Kristy, Assistant Administrator and Chief Financial Officer, Integris Mayes County Medical Center, Pryor, OK, p. A506

MCCOLLUM, Ken, Vice President, Human Resources, NorthBay Medical Center, Fairfield, CA, p. A59

MCCOLLUM, Rodger, Chief Executive Officer, Snoqualmie Valley Hospital, Snoqualmie, WA, p. A672

MCCOLM, Denni, Chief Information Officer, Citizens Memorial Hospital, Bolivar, MO, p. A356

MCCOMAS, James, Vice President Operations, Hutchinson Regional Medical Center, Hutchinson, KS, p. A236

MCCOMAS, Marc, Executive Director, Haven Behavioral Senior Care of North Denver, Thornton, CO, p. A106

MCCOMBS, III, William, Ph.D. Chief Information Officer, Scott and White Memorial Hospital, Temple, TX, p. A636

MCCONAUGHY, Chris, Chief Nursing Officer, Paradise Valley Hospital, Phoenix, AZ, p. A35

MCCONNELL, George, Director, Earle E. Morris Alcohol and Drug Treatment Center, Columbia, SC, p. A550

MCCONNELL, Patrick G., Chief Financial Officer, West Park Hospital, Cody, WY, p. A702

MCCONNELL, Ron, Chief Operating Officer, UPMC Altoona, Altoona, PA, p. A520

MCCORKLE Jr., Philip H., President and Chief Executive Officer, Saint Mary's Health Care, Grand Rapids, MI, p. A315

MCCORMACK, Cynthia, MS, Director, Cheyenne Veterans Affairs Medical Center, Cheyenne, WY, p. A701

MCCORMACK, J. David, President and Chief Executive Officer, Northeast Alabama Regional Medical Center, Anniston, AL, p. A15

MCCORMACK, Jane, R.N. Vice President, Chief Nursing Officer and Nursing and Patient Care Services, Unity Hospital, Rochester, NY, p. A441

MCCORMACK, Julie M., Administrator, Integris Blackwell Regional Hospital, Blackwell, OK, p. A496

MCCORMICK, Dee Dawn, Director Personnel and Human Resources, Coon Memorial Hospital and Home, Dalhart, TX, p. A594

MCCORMICK, Jason, Vice President Finance and Chief Financial Officer, Family Health West, Fruita, CO, p. A101

MCCORMICK, Jayne, M.D
Chief Medical Officer CDS, Presbyterian Hospital, Albuquerque, NM, p. A414
Chief Medical Officer CDS, Presbyterian Kaseman Hospital, Albuquerque, NM, p. A415

MCCORMICK, John, Chief Executive Officer, Oak Valley Hospital District, Oakdale, CA, p. A77

MCCORMICK, Pam, Director Human Resources, Permian Regional Medical Center, Andrews, TX, p. A583

MCCOWN, Fran, Administrator, Haskell Memorial Hospital, Haskell, TX, p. A608

MCCOY, Andrea C., M.D. Chief Medical Officer, Jeanes Hospital, Philadelphia, PA, p. A535

MCCOY, Craig, Chief Executive Officer, Emory Johns Creek Hospital, Johns Creek, GA, p. A155

MCCOY, Elizabeth, Chief Human Resources Management, Stony Brook University Medical Center, Stony Brook, NY, p. A443

MCCOY, Jessica, Director Human Resources, Cedar Springs Hospital, Colorado Springs, CO, p. A98

MCCOY, Mike, Chief Operating Officer, Saint Mary's Regional Medical Center, Russellville, AR, p. A49

MCCOY, Paul, Director Human Resources, Mayers Memorial Hospital District, Fall River Mills, CA, p. A60

MCCOY, Shawn W., Chief Administrative Officer, Deaconess Hospital, Evansville, IN, p. A202

MCCOY, Stephanie, President and Chief Executive Officer, Jackson General Hospital, Ripley, WV, p. A680

MCCRACKEN, Ann B., M.D. President Medical Staff, Solara Hospital Harlingen, Harlingen, TX, p. A608

MCCRANIE, Robbie, Director Human Resources, Plano Specialty Hospital, Plano, TX, p. A627

MCCRAW, Elizabeth, Vice President, Human Resources, Gaston Memorial Hospital, Gastonia, NC, p. A453

MCCRAW, Nicki, Assistant Vice President Human Resources, UW Medicine/Harborview Medical Center, Seattle, WA, p. A671

MCCREA, Kim, Chief Human Resources Officer, Ortonville Area Health Services, Ortonville, MN, p. A337

MCCREA, Mary Anne, Chief Nursing Officer, Desert Regional Medical Center, Palm Springs, CA, p. A78

MCCREA, Yvette, Chief Human Resources, Winn Army Community Hospital, Hinesville, GA, p. A155

MCCREARY, Michael, Chief of Services, Mercy Hospital Washington, Washington, MO, p. A373

MCCRIMMON, Scott, Manager Information Technology, Northern Arizona Veterans Affairs Health Care System, Prescott, AZ, p. A36

MCCUE, Cathy, Director Human Resources, St. Anthony's Hospital, Houston, TX, p. A612

MCCUE, Jack D., M.D. Senior Vice President and Interim Chief Medical Officer, Regional Medical Center at Memphis, Memphis, TN, p. A575

MCCUE, Robert N., Vice President Finance, Mid Coast Hospital, Brunswick, ME, p. A282

MCCUE, Steven
Chief Financial Officer, Clinton Hospital, Clinton, MA, p. A299
Chief Financial Officer, UMass Memorial–Marlborough Hospital, Marlborough, MA, p. A302

MCCULLEY, Larry W., President and Chief Executive Officer, Touchette Regional Hospitals, Centreville, IL, p. A176

MCCULLOCH, Liz, Chief Information Resource Management Systems, Cheyenne Veterans Affairs Medical Center, Cheyenne, WY, p. A701

MCCULLOUGH, Barbara A., Vice President Human Resources, Washington Hospital, Washington, PA, p. A543

MCCULLOUGH, Bobby, Chief Operating Officer, Central Florida Regional Hospital, Sanford, FL, p. A139

MCCULLOUGH, Clarence, Director Information Systems, Doctors Hospital at White Rock Lake, Dallas, TX, p. A595

MCCULLOUGH, Michael
Chief Financial Officer, Lutheran Hospital of Indiana, Fort Wayne, IN, p. A202
Chief Financial Officer, Orthopaedic Hospital of Lutheran Health Network, Fort Wayne, IN, p. A202
Chief Financial Officer, Rehabilitation Hospital of Fort Wayne, Fort Wayne, IN, p. A203

MCCULLOUGH, Paula, VP Patient Care Services, St. Vincent's Blount, Oneonta, AL, p. A24

MCCULLOUGH, Rose, R.N. Associate Administrator Patient Care and Chief Nursing Officer, Angleton Danbury Medical Center, Angleton, TX, p. A583

MCCULLOUGH, Sharon, Director Human Resources, Community Heart and Vascular Hospital, Indianapolis, IN, p. A205

MCCULLOUGH, Wadra, Chief Nursing Officer, Spalding Regional Medical Center, Griffin, GA, p. A154

MCCUMBER, Tracy, Manager Information Systems, Chenango Memorial Hospital, Norwich, NY, p. A438

MCCUNE, Becky, Director Human Resources, Community Relations and Education, Coffeyville Regional Medical Center, Coffeyville, KS, p. A232

MCCUNE, Connie, Vice President Human Resources, Via Christi Hospital in Pittsburg, Pittsburg, KS, p. A242

MCCUNE, William, President, Delaware County Memorial Hospital, Drexel Hill, PA, p. A524

MCCURDY, Brent, Director Management Information, St. Croix Regional Medical Center, St. Croix Falls, WI, p. A697

MCCURDY, Carol, Chief Information Officer, Chickasaw Nation Medical Center, Ada, OK, p. A495

MCCURRY, Mark, M.D. Chief of Staff, Haskell County Community Hospital, Stigler, OK, p. A507

MCCUTCHAN, Matt, Chief Financial Officer, Greater Regional Medical Center, Creston, IA, p. A219

MCCUTCHEON, Edna I., Chief Executive Officer, Torrance State Hospital, Torrance, PA, p. A542

MCCUTCHEON Jr., Henry, Chief Executive Officer, Lake City Community Hospital, Lake City, SC, p. A554

MCDADE, Jo Ann, Assistant Administrator Finance, Arkansas State Hospital, Little Rock, AR, p. A46

MCDANALD, Matt, M.D. Chief Medical Officer, Baptist Health La Grange, La Grange, KY, p. A253

MCDANEL, Joyce
Vice President Human Resources, Iowa Methodist Medical Center, Des Moines, IA, p. A220
Vice President Human Resources and Education, UnityPoint Health – Des Moines, Des Moines, IA, p. A220

MCDANIEL, Amy, Chief Financial Officer, Iowa Specialty Hospital–Clarion, Clarion, IA, p. A218

MCDANIEL, Burton, M.D. Medical Director, Roosevelt Warm Springs Institute for Rehabilitation, Warm Springs, GA, p. A162

MCDANIEL, Graciela, Chief Financial Officer, Philadelphia Veterans Affairs Medical Center, Philadelphia, PA, p. A536

MCDANIEL, Kim, Director Human Resources, HEALTHSOUTH Rehabilitation Hospital of Montgomery, Montgomery, AL, p. A23

MCDANIEL, LaDonna, Financial Manager, Prattville Baptist Hospital, Prattville, AL, p. A25

MCDANIEL, Lisa A., Director Human Resources, Samaritan Healthcare, Moses Lake, WA, p. A668

MCDANIEL, Ruth A., Chief Executive Officer, Spring View Hospital, Lebanon, KY, p. A253

MCDANIEL, Suzie Q., Chief Human Resource Officer, Bay Area Hospital, Coos Bay, OR, p. A512

MCDANIEL, Jr., W. Burton, M.D. Physician Executive, Roosevelt Warm Springs LTAC Hospital, Warm Springs, GA, p. A162

MCDAVID, Clarence, Vice President Human Resources, Rose Medical Center, Denver, CO, p. A100

MCDERMOTT, James, M.D. Chief of Staff, Sedan City Hospital, Sedan, KS, p. A244

MCDERMOTT, Thomas, Vice President Finance, Fayette County Memorial Hospital, Washington Court House, OH, p. A492

MCDERMOTT, Vincent, Executive Director Finance, Brigham and Women's Faulkner Hospital, Boston, MA, p. A296

MCDEVITT, Chuck, Chief Information Officer, Self Regional Healthcare, Greenwood, SC, p. A553

MCDEVITT, Mike, Chief Information Officer, The Children's Hospital of Alabama, Birmingham, AL, p. A17

MCDEVITT, Robert J., M.D. Chief of Staff, Wilson Memorial Hospital, Sidney, OH, p. A490

MCDIVITT, Robert P., FACHE, Director, Veterans Affairs Ann Arbor Healthcare System, Ann Arbor, MI, p. A308

MCDONALD, Buck, Chief Financial Officer, St. Helena Hospital Clear Lake, Clearlake, CA, p. A56

MCDONALD, Craig L., M.D. Chief Medical Officer, Angleton Danbury Medical Center, Angleton, TX, p. A583

MCDONALD, Edward A.
Senior Vice President and Chief Financial Officer, St. Helena Hospital Napa Valley, Saint Helena, CA, p. A84
Chief Financial Officer, St. Helena Hospital–Center for Behavioral Health, Vallejo, CA, p. A94

MCDONALD, Elizabeth, Director Human Resources, Wayne Memorial Hospital, Honesdale, PA, p. A527

MCDONALD, Frank, D.O. Chief of Staff, Southeast Colorado Hospital District, Springfield, CO, p. A105

MCDONALD, Gary
Assistant Administrator Human Resources, Stone County Medical Center, Mountain View, AR, p. A48
Assistant Administrator Human Resources, White River Medical Center, Batesville, AR, p. A41

MCDONALD, Gregory, Vice President Finance and Chief Financial Officer, Roswell Park Cancer Institute, Buffalo, NY, p. A422

MCDONALD, Jeff, Chief Executive Officer, Canyon Ridge Hospital, Chino, CA, p. A56

MCDONALD, John, D.O. President and Chief of Medical Staff, Good Shepherd Medical Center–Marshall, Marshall, TX, p. A621

MCDONALD, Kathy, Director Personnel, Covenant Hospital–Levelland, Levelland, TX, p. A618

MCDONALD, Larry, Director Human Resources, Miami Jewish Home and Hospital for Aged, Miami, FL, p. A132

MCDONALD, Lauren, M.D. Medical Director and Medical Staff President, Vibra Specialty Hospital of Dallas, Desoto, TX, p. A599

MCDONALD, Mark, MSN, President and Chief Executive Officer, Institute for Orthopaedic Surgery, Lima, OH, p. A484

MCDONALD, Michael, Chief Executive Officer, Holly Hill Hospital, Raleigh, NC, p. A459

MCDONALD, Rick, Chief Financial Officer, Anson General Hospital, Anson, TX, p. A583

MCDONALD, Rosalind S., MSN Vice President Nursing Services, Lenoir Memorial Hospital, Kinston, NC, p. A456

MCDONALD, Steve, Director Information Systems, Northside Hospital and Heart Institute, Saint Petersburg, FL, p. A139

MCDONALD, Stuart, M.D. President Medical Staff, Kindred Hospital–Fort Worth, Fort Worth, TX, p. A604

MCDONALD, Susan, M.D. Vice President, St. Joseph's Medical Center, Stockton, CA, p. A92

MCDONALD, William A., President and Chief Executive Officer, St. Joseph's Regional Medical Center, Paterson, NJ, p. A408

MCDONALD–UPTON, Ann, Chief Nursing Officer, St. Joseph Mercy Oakland, Pontiac, MI, p. A322

MCDONNELL, Michael J.
Vice President and Chief Operations Officer, Sheltering Arms Hospital South, Midlothian, VA, p. A657
Vice President and Chief Operating Officer, Sheltering Arms Rehabilitation Hospital, Mechanicsville, VA, p. A657

MCDONNELL, Nancy, Manager Information Systems, Illinois Valley Community Hospital, Peru, IL, p. A192

MCDONNELL, Stephen C., Senior Vice President, Chief Financial Officer and Chief Operating Officer, Sibley Memorial Hospital, Washington, DC, p. A117

MCDONOUGH, Jeffrey, Assistant Vice President Human Resources, Vassar Brothers Medical Center, Poughkeepsie, NY, p. A440

MCDONOUGH, JoAnn, Director Operations and Chief Nursing Officer, Crittenton Children's Center, Kansas City, MO, p. A362

MCDONOUGH, Sharon, Chief Executive Officer, First Street Hospital, Bellaire, TX, p. A588

MCDOUGAL, Pedro, M.D. Medical Director, Weslaco Rehabilitation Hospital, Weslaco, TX, p. A641

MCDOUGLE, Mark, Executive Vice President and Chief Operating Officer, Maimonides Medical Center, NY, p. A434

MCDOWELL, III, Arthur V., M.D. Vice President Clinical Affairs, Middlesex Hospital, Middletown, CT, p. A110

MCDOWELL, Charles, Corporate Vice President Human Resources, ProMedica Fostoria Community Hospital, Fostoria, OH, p. A481

MCDOWELL, Jane, FACHE, Administrator, Jefferson County Hospital, Waurika, OK, p. A510

MCDOWELL, Jean, Chief Financial Officer, Kindred Hospital–Dallas, Dallas, TX, p. A596

MCDOWELL, Jon, FACHE, Chief Executive Officer, The Rehabilitation Institute of St. Louis, Saint Louis, MO, p. A371

MCDOWELL, Paul L., Vice President Finance and Chief Financial Officer, King's Daughters Medical Center, Ashland, KY, p. A248

MCDOWELL, Richard, Chief Financial Officer, Ridge Behavioral Health System, Lexington, KY, p. A254

MCDRURY, Martha M., R.N. Chief Operating Officer and Chief Nursing Officer, Holy Family Hospital and Medical Center, Methuen, MA, p. A302

MCDUFF, Raoul, Director Human Resources, Palm Drive Hospital, Sebastopol, CA, p. A90

MCEACHERN, John, Controller, Sebastian River Medical Center, Sebastian, FL, p. A140

MCELDOWNEY, Erin, Manager Human Resources, Haven Senior Horizons, Phoenix, AZ, p. A34

MCELFRESH, Jim, Manager Human Resources, Norfolk Regional Center, Norfolk, NE, p. A386

MCELLIGOTT, Daniel P., FACHE, President and Chief Executive Officer, Saint Francis Medical Center, Grand Island, NE, p. A384

MCELRATH, Matthew, Chief Human Resources Officer, Keck Hospital of USC, Los Angeles, CA, p. A70

MCELROY, Maria Elena, Vice President Human Resources, HEALTHSOUTH Rehabilitation Hospital of Southern Arizona, Tucson, AZ, p. A38

MCELROY, Sherry, Director Health Information Management, Osceola Community Hospital, Sibley, IA, p. A228

MCELROY, Wayne, Administrator, Pickens County Medical Center, Carrollton, AL, p. A18

MCENROY, Karolyn, Business Office Manager, Oakland Mercy Hospital, Oakland, NE, p. A387

MCENTEE, Chris, Network Specialist, Van Buren County Hospital, Keosauqua, IA, p. A224

MCEUEN, Jacqueline, Coordinator Human Resources, Bellville St. Joseph Health Center, Bellville, TX, p. A588

MCEVILLY, Kerrie, Director Finance and Information Systems, Stevens Community Medical Center, Morris, MN, p. A337

MCEWEN, David S., Vice President Operations, Port Huron Hospital, Port Huron, MI, p. A322

MCEWEN, Mary Louise, Superintendent, Riverview Psychiatric Center, Augusta, ME, p. A281

MCEWEN, Michelle, President and Chief Executive Officer, Speare Memorial Hospital, Plymouth, NH, p. A400

MCFADDEN, Ian, President and Chief Executive Officer, Methodist Hospitals, Gary, IN, p. A203

MCFADDEN, Mary T., MSN Chief Nurse Executive, Providence Portland Medical Center, Portland, OR, p. A516

MCFALL, Cathy, Human Resources Manager, Kiowa County Memorial Hospital, Greensburg, KS, p. A234

MCFALL, Vicky, Chief Executive Officer, Monroe County Medical Center, Tompkinsville, KY, p. A260

MCFARLAND, Kenneth, President and Chief Executive Officer, Mission Hospital, Mission Viejo, CA, p. A74

MCFARLAND, Nita, Director of Nursing, Kingman Community Hospital, Kingman, KS, p. A237

MCFARLAND, Rhonda, Director Human Resources, Carolinas Medical Center–Union, Monroe, NC, p. A457

MCFARLAND, Rodney, M.D. Medical Director, Freeman Neosho Hospital, Neosho, MO, p. A366

MCFARLAND, Tracee, Chief Financial Officer, Claiborne County Hospital, Tazewell, TN, p. A579

MCFAUL, Joan, Vice President Information Technology and Chief Information Officer, Glens Falls Hospital, Glens Falls, NY, p. A426

MCFERRAN, Virginia
Chief Information Officer, Ronald Reagan University of California Los Angeles Medical Center, Los Angeles, CA, p. A71
Chief Information Officer, Santa Monica–UCLA Medical Center and Orthopaedic Hospital, Santa Monica, CA, p. A90

MCGAHEY, Nikki, Information Officer, Jefferson County Hospital, Waurika, OK, p. A510

MCGARIGLE, Kristine, R.N
Vice President Patient Care, Ministry Good Samaritan Health Center, Merrill, WI, p. A691
Vice President Patient Care, Ministry Saint Clare's Hospital, Weston, WI, p. A699

MCGARVEY, Missy, Director Computer Information Systems, Twin Valley Behavioral Healthcare, Columbus, OH, p. A478

MCGAUGH, Jamie, Controller, Atoka County Medical Center, Atoka, OK, p. A496

MCGEACHEY, Edward J., President and Chief Executive Officer, Southern Maine Medical Center, Biddeford, ME, p. A282

MCGEE, Jessica
Chief Financial Officer, AMG Specialty Hospital–Lafayette, Lafayette, LA, p. A270
Chief Financial Officer, AMG Specialty Hospital–Slidell, Slidell, LA, p. A278

MCGEE, Mark F., M.D. Chief Clinical Officer, Appalachian Behavioral Healthcare, Athens, OH, p. A470

MCGEE, Terry, Chief Operations Officer, Central State Hospital, Milledgeville, GA, p. A157

MCGHEE, Michael, M.D. Medical Director, Behavioral HealthCare Center at Clarksville, Clarksville, TN, p. A567

MCGILL, Cindy, Senior Vice President Human Resources, Presbyterian Kaseman Hospital, Albuquerque, NM, p. A415

MCGILL, Steve, Chief Financial Officer, Wabash General Hospital, Mount Carmel, IL, p. A189

MCGILL, Timothy W., Chief Executive Officer, River Park Hospital, Mc Minnville, TN, p. A574

MCGILVRAY, Greg, Chief Financial Officer, Medical Center Enterprise, Enterprise, AL, p. A19

MCGIMSEY, Erika, Controller, Jewish Hospital–Shelbyville, Shelbyville, KY, p. A260

MCGINLEY, Clement, M.D. Vice President Medical Affairs, Gnaden Huetten Memorial Hospital, Lehighton, PA, p. A530

MCGINNIS, Ronald, M.D. Medical Director, The University of Toledo Medical Center, Toledo, OH, p. A491

MCGINTY, Daniel B., Administrator, Essentia Health St. Mary's Medical Center, Duluth, MN, p. A331

MCGLADE, James, Director Human Resources, United Hospital, Saint Paul, MN, p. A340

MCGLEW, Timothy, Chief Executive Officer, Kern Valley Healthcare District, Lake Isabella, CA, p. A66

MCGLONE, Robert, Vice President Human Resources, Rapid City Regional Hospital, Rapid City, SD, p. A562

MCGLORY, Joyce, Vice President Human Resources, Methodist Hospitals, Gary, IN, p. A203

MCGLOTHLIN, Wylie, M.D. Chief Medical Officer, Henry County Hospital, New Castle, IN, p. A211

MCGOLDRICK, Margaret M., Executive Vice President and Chief Operating Officer, Abington Memorial Hospital, Abington, PA, p. A519

MCGONNELL, James, Chief Financial Officer, Memorial Medical Center, Las Cruces, NM, p. A416

MCGOVERN, Julia, Vice President Human Resources, Chilton Hospital, Pompton Plains, NJ, p. A409

MCGOVERN, Pam, Director Technology, Huggins Hospital, Wolfeboro, NH, p. A400

MCGOWAN, Donna, Administrator, Lane County Hospital, Dighton, KS, p. A233

MCGOWAN, Gloria, Chief Financial Officer, Wiregrass Medical Center, Geneva, AL, p. A21

MCGOWAN, Marion A., Executive Vice President and Chief Operating Officer, Lancaster General Health, Lancaster, PA, p. A528

MCGOWEN, Bernard A., M.D. Medical Director, Kindred Hospital Tarrant County–Arlington, Arlington, TX, p. A583

MCGOWIN, III, Norman F., M.D. Chief of Staff, L. V. Stabler Memorial Hospital, Greenville, AL, p. A21

MCGRAIL, David, Vice President Finance, Carney Hospital, Boston, MA, p. A296

MCGRAIL, Robert, Chief Financial Officer, West Branch Regional Medical Center, West Branch, MI, p. A326

MCGRATH, Denise B., Chief Executive Officer, HEALTHSOUTH Sea Pines Rehabilitation Hospital, Melbourne, FL, p. A130

MCGRATH, Lynn, M.D. Vice President Medical Affairs, Deborah Heart and Lung Center, Browns Mills, NJ, p. A402

MCGRAW, Karin L., FACHE, Director, Beckley Veterans Affairs Medical Center, Beckley, WV, p. A675

MCGRAW, Scott, M.D. Medical Director, Irving Coppell Surgical Hospital, Irving, TX, p. A615

MCGREAHAM, David S., M.D. Vice President Medical Affairs, Munson Medical Center, Traverse City, MI, p. A325

MCGREGOR, Julie
Vice President and Chief People Officer, Jewish Hospital, Louisville, KY, p. A255
Director Human Resources, Sts. Mary & Elizabeth Hospital, Louisville, KY, p. A256

MCGREGOR, Randy, M.D. Medical Director, Fairbanks Memorial Hospital, Fairbanks, AK, p. A28

MCGREW, David S., Chief Financial Officer, Santa Clara Valley Medical Center, San Jose, CA, p. A88

MCGREW, Deb, Chief Operating Officer, University of Texas Medical Branch Hospitals, Galveston, TX, p. A605

MCGUE, Lisa, Controller, HEALTHSOUTH Northern Kentucky Rehabilitation Hospital, Edgewood, KY, p. A250

MCGUFFIN, Patty, R.N. Chief Nursing Officer, Allen County Hospital, Iola, KS, p. A236

MCGUIGAN, Kevin, M.D. Medical Director, St. Lawrence Rehabilitation Center, Lawrenceville, NJ, p. A405

MCGUIGAN, Timothy, Chief Human Resources, Salem Veterans Affairs Medical Center, Salem, VA, p. A661

MCGUINNESS, Patrick, Chief Information Management, Keller Army Community Hospital, West Point, NY, p. A446

MCGUIRE, Ann M., Vice President Human Resources, Indiana University Health Ball Memorial Hospital, Muncie, IN, p. A210

MCGUIRE, Cynthia, Chief Operating Officer, Adirondack Medical Center, Saranac Lake, NY, p. A442

MCGUIRE, Glenn, Chief Financial Officer, LaFollette Medical Center, La Follette, TN, p. A572

MCGUIRE, H. Aryon, Administrator, E. A. Conway Medical Center, Monroe, LA, p. A274

MCGUIRE, Jay, Director Information Systems, Southeast Hospital, Cape Girardeau, MO, p. A358

MCGUIRE, Karen, Chief Financial Officer, Audubon County Memorial Hospital, Audubon, IA, p. A216

MCGUIRE, Kelly, Director Human Resources, HEALTHSOUTH Rehabilitation Hospital of Cypress, Houston, TX, p. A610

MCGUIRL, Mary, Director Information Systems, Oneida Healthcare, Oneida, NY, p. A438

MCGURK, Kevin, Controller, Bellin Psychiatric Center, Green Bay, WI, p. A687

MCHALE, John, Vice President Management Information Systems, Lower Bucks Hospital, Bristol, PA, p. A521

MCHUGH, Frank, Chief Financial Officer, Presence St. Mary's Hospital, Kankakee, IL, p. A186

MCHUGH, James B., Interim Chief Executive Officer, Gordon Memorial Hospital, Gordon, NE, p. A384

MCHUGH, Michael J., M.D., Medical Director, Cleveland Clinic Children's Hospital for Rehabilitation, Cleveland, OH, p. A476

MCHUGH, William, M.D. Chief Medical Officer, Trinitas Regional Medical Center, Elizabeth, NJ, p. A403

MCILROY, Gail, Director Medical Records, Texas Specialty Hospital at Wichita Falls, Wichita Falls, TX, p. A641

MCILWAIN, Lisa, Senior Director Talent Management, Maine Medical Center, Portland, ME, p. A284

MCILWAIN, T. Pinckney, M.D. Vice President Quality and Performance Improvement, St. Luke's Episcopal Hospital, Houston, TX, p. A612

MCINTIRE, Jo, Chief Nursing Officer, Adams Memorial Hospital, Decatur, IN, p. A201

MCINTOSH, Charles, Senior Director Human Resources, University of Minnesota Medical Center, Fairview, Minneapolis, MN, p. A336

MCINTOSH, Joe, Director Management Information Systems, Logansport State Hospital, Logansport, IN, p. A209

MCINTOSH, Tyler, Chief Financial Officer, Creek Nation Community Hospital, Okemah, OK, p. A502

MCINTYRE, Cindy, R.N. Administrative Director Clinical Services, Magee General Hospital, Magee, MS, p. A350

MCINTYRE, Daniel J., President and Chief Executive Officer, The Charlotte Hungerford Hospital, Torrington, CT, p. A112

MCIWAIN, John, Director Human Resources, Wayne Memorial Hospital, Jesup, GA, p. A155

MCKARRY, Victor, M.D. President Medical Staff, Presence Resurrection Medical Center, Chicago, IL, p. A178

MCKAY, Daniel E., Chief Executive Officer, Northwest Medical Center, Springdale, AR, p. A50

MCKAY, Danny H., Administrator, Noxubee General Hospital, Macon, MS, p. A350

MCKAY, Michael, Manager Information Systems, Wickenburg Community Hospital, Wickenburg, AZ, p. A39

MCKAY, Ronda, MSN Vice President Patient Care Services, Chief Nursing Officer, Community Hospital, Munster, IN, p. A211

MCKEE, Jed, M.D. Medical Director, Select Specialty Hospital–Topeka, Topeka, KS, p. A245

MCKEE, Judy, FACHE, Director, William S. Middleton Memorial Veterans Hospital, Madison, WI, p. A690

MCKEE, Robert J.
Vice President and Chief Human Resources Officer, Clearfield Hospital, Clearfield, PA, p. A522
Vice President Human Resources, DuBois Regional Medical Center, Du Bois, PA, p. A524

MCKEE, Jr., Willis P., M.D. Chief Medical Officer, Frankfort Regional Medical Center, Frankfort, KY, p. A251

MCKEEBY, Jon W., Chief Information Officer, National Institutes of Health Clinical Center, Bethesda, MD, p. A290

MCKEEN, Marcia, Director Human Resources, Twin Valley Behavioral Healthcare, Columbus, OH, p. A478

MCKELDIN, Pat, Human Resource Business Partner, Kaiser Permanente Manteca Medical Center, Manteca, CA, p. A73

MCKELVEY, Robert
Director Information System, Mergers and Integrations, Indiana University Health Ball Memorial Hospital, Muncie, IN, p. A210
Chief Information Officer, Indiana University Health Blackford Hospital, Hartford City, IN, p. A204

MCKENNA, Bertine C., Ph.D. Executive Vice President and Chief Operating Officer, Bassett Medical Center, Cooperstown, NY, p. A424

MCKENNA, Chris, Director Human Resources, Manatee Glens Hospital and Addiction Center, Bradenton, FL, p. A119

MCKENNA, Dennis, M.D. Interim Vice President Medical Affairs, Albany Medical Center, Albany, NY, p. A420

MCKENNA, Donald, President and Chief Executive Officer, St. Mary's Health Care System, Athens, GA, p. A145

MCKENNA, John F., Chief Executive Officer and Managing Director, Rockford Center, Newark, DE, p. A114

MCKENNA, Kathleen, Public Affairs Leader, Kaiser Permanente South Sacramento Medical Center, Sacramento, CA, p. A83

MCKENNA, Michael, M.D. Vice President Medical Management, Advocate Lutheran General Hospital, Park Ridge, IL, p. A191

MCKENNA, Quinn, Chief Operating Officer, University of Utah Health Care – Hospital and Clinics, Salt Lake City, UT, p. A647

MCKENZIE, Christine, Director Human Resources, Lake Norman Regional Medical Center, Mooresville, NC, p. A457

MCKENZIE, Jackie, Director Administrative Services, Beacham Memorial Hospital, Magnolia, MS, p. A350

MCKENZIE, Ryan, R.N. Director of Nursing, Aurora Phoenix Hospital, Glendale, AZ, p. A32

MCKENZIE, Sandra D., Executive Vice President and Chief Operating Officer, Hamilton Medical Center, Dalton, GA, p. A151

MCKENZIE, William G., Interim Administrator, Evergreen Medical Center, Evergreen, AL, p. A20

MCKEON, John, Vice President Human Resources, Kingsbrook Jewish Medical Center,, NY, p. A433

MCKEOWN, Colleen
Senior Vice President, Kaiser Permanente Antioch Medical Center, Antioch, CA, p. A52
Senior Vice President and Area Manager, Kaiser Permanente Walnut Creek Medical Center, Walnut Creek, CA, p. A95

MCKERNAN, Stephen W., Chief Executive Officer, University of New Mexico Hospitals, Albuquerque, NM, p. A415

MCKEVETT, Timothy M., President, Beloit Health System, Beloit, WI, p. A684

MCKIBBEN, Sean, President and Chief Operating Officer, Mount Carmel, Columbus, OH, p. A477

MCKIDDY, Paul, Director Information Technology, Monroe County Medical Center, Tompkinsville, KY, p. A260

MCKIE, Kathy, Director Human Resources, Montrose Memorial Hospital, Montrose, CO, p. A104

MCKILLIP, Ed, Director of Finance, Riddle Hospital, Media, PA, p. A531

MCKIMMY, Doyle L., FACHE,
Chief Executive Officer, Jewell County Hospital, Mankato, KS, p. A239
Chief Executive Officer, Washington County Hospital, Washington, KS, p. A246

MCKINLEY, Bryan, Chief Financial Officer, St. Mark's Hospital, Salt Lake City, UT, p. A647

MCKINLEY, Ernie, Chief Information Officer, University Medical Center, Las Vegas, NV, p. A394

MCKINLEY, Ivy, Director Human Resources, Presence Our Lady of the Resurrection Medical Center, Chicago, IL, p. A178

MCKINLEY, Katie, Assistant Administrator/Nursing, Southwest Mississippi Regional Medical Center, McComb, MS, p. A350

MCKINLEY, Mike, Information Security Officer, West Texas Veterans Affairs Health Care System, Big Spring, TX, p. A588

MCKINLEY, Ronald, Ph.D. Vice President Human Resources and Employee Services, University of Texas Medical Branch Hospitals, Galveston, TX, p. A605

MCKINLEY, Jr., Rudolph, Vice President Operations and Chief Operating Officer, East Tennessee Children's Hospital, Knoxville, TN, p. A571

MCKINNEY, Carol, Director Information Services, Western Missouri Medical Center, Warrensburg, MO, p. A373

MCKINNEY, Dan, Administrator, Hermann Area District Hospital, Hermann, MO, p. A361

MCKINNEY, Diane, R.N. Vice President Patient Care Service, Decatur County Memorial Hospital, Greensburg, IN, p. A204

MCKINNEY, Paul, Administrator, Martin County Hospital District, Stanton, TX, p. A635

MCKINNEY, Sally, Director Human Resources, Woodland Heights Medical Center, Lufkin, TX, p. A621

MCKINNEY, Tressy, Director Information Services, Research Medical Center, Kansas City, MO, p. A363

MCKINNON, Ronald A., Chief Executive Officer, Benson Hospital, Benson, AZ, p. A30

MCKINNON, Scott, President and Chief Executive Officer, Memorial Hospital, North Conway, NH, p. A399

MCKINNON, Shauna, Chief Executive Officer, Bayfront Health Dade City, Dade City, FL, p. A121

MCKINSTRY, Scott, M.D. Chief of Staff, Corpus Christi Medical Center, Corpus Christi, TX, p. A593

MCKNELLY, Lorenzo, D.O. Chief of Staff, Capital Region Medical Center, Jefferson City, MO, p. A362

MCKNIGHT, Craig L., Senior Vice President and Chief Financial Officer, Phoenix Children's Hospital, Phoenix, AZ, p. A35

MCKNIGHT, Richard B., Senior Vice President and Chief Information Officer, Novant Health Huntersville Medical Center, Huntersville, NC, p. A455

MCKOY, Lori, Business Partner, Pender Memorial Hospital, Burgaw, NC, p. A448

MCKULA, Tim, Vice President Information Systems and Chief Information Officer, Rehabilitation Institute of Chicago, Chicago, IL, p. A178

MCLAIN, Allen, M.D. Chief of Staff, Grisell Memorial Hospital District One, Ransom, KS, p. A243

MCLAIN, Cindy, Chief Executive Officer, Select Specialty Hospital–Fort Smith, Fort Smith, AR, p. A44

MCLAIN, Jerry, M.D. Chief of Staff, Chadron Community Hospital and Health Services, Chadron, NE, p. A382

MCLAIN, Kathy, Chief Financial Officer, Childress Regional Medical Center, Childress, TX, p. A591

MCLAIN, Terri L., FACHE, President, Mercy Hospital Washington, Washington, MO, p. A373

MCLANE, Kerry, Interim Chief Executive Officer, Acuity Specialty Hospital of New Jersey, Atlantic City, NJ, p. A401

MCLARTY, Walter L., Chief Human Resources Officer, Good Samaritan Hospital, Cincinnati, OH, p. A474

MCLAUGHLIN, Christine, Chief Financial Officer, Millinocket Regional Hospital, Millinocket, ME, p. A284

MCLAUGHLIN, Colleen, Director Employee Relations, Auburn Community Hospital, Auburn, NY, p. A420

MCLAUGHLIN, Gary, Vice President Finance and Chief Financial Officer, Overlake Hospital Medical Center, Bellevue, WA, p. A664

MCLAUGHLIN, Jason, Chief Financial Officer, McKenzie–Willamette Medical Center, Springfield, OR, p. A518

MCLAUGHLIN, Kathryn, Vice President and Chief Nursing Officer, Pacific Hospital of Long Beach, Long Beach, CA, p. A67

MCLAUGHLIN, Kevin, Director Information Systems, Saint Catherine Regional Hospital, Charlestown, IN, p. A200

MCLAUGHLIN, Maribeth, R.N. Vice President Patient Care Services, Magee–Womens Hospital of UPMC, Pittsburgh, PA, p. A537

MCLAUGHLIN, Neil R., R.N.,
Interim President, Hampshire Memorial Hospital, Romney, WV, p. A680
President, War Memorial Hospital, Berkeley Springs, WV, p. A675

MCLAUGHLIN, Pamela, Chief Financial Officer, HEALTHSOUTH Rehabilitation Hospital of Austin, Austin, TX, p. A585

MCLAUGHLIN, Sherry, Director Human Resources, Forrest City Medical Center, Forrest City, AR, p. A44

MCLAUGHLIN, Suzanne G., R.N. Chief Nursing Officer and Vice President Patient Care, St. Elizabeth's Medical Center, Brighton, MA, p. A298

MCLAUGHLIN, William J., Administrator, Thomas Hospital, Fairhope, AL, p. A20

MCLAURIN, Monty E., President and Chief Executive Officer, Indian Path Medical Center, Kingsport, TN, p. A571

MCLAURIN, Rod, Director Information Systems, Marlboro Park Hospital, Bennettsville, SC, p. A548

MCLEAN, Anthony, President, St. Francis Hospital, Federal Way, WA, p. A666

MCLEAN, Bill, Senior Vice President Human Resources, Avera McKennan Hospital and University Health Center, Sioux Falls, SD, p. A562

MCLEAN, Chris J., Chief Financial Officer, Methodist Healthcare Memphis Hospitals, Memphis, TN, p. A575

MCLEAN, Georgia, Director Human Resources, Mount Sinai Medical Center, Miami Beach, FL, p. A133

MCLEAN, Nicole, Chief Nursing Officer, Select Specialty Hospital–Flint, Flint, MI, p. A314

MCLELLAN, Ava, Coordinator Human Resources, HEALTHSOUTH Rehabilitation Hospital of Spring Hill, Brooksville, FL, p. A120

MCLENDON, Carla
Director Human Resources, Appling Healthcare System, Baxley, GA, p. A148
Director Information Resource Management Services, Charles George Veterans Affairs Medical Center, Asheville, NC, p. A447

MCLENDON, Connie, Director Human Resources, Piedmont Mountainside Hospital, Jasper, GA, p. A155

MCLENDON, John, Senior Vice President and Chief Information Officer, Adventist Bolingbrook Hospital, Bolingbrook, IL, p. A175

MCLENNAN, Marlene, Controller, Monroe County Hospital, Forsyth, GA, p. A153

MCLEOD, Les, Director of Nursing Services, Blue Mountain Hospital, John Day, OR, p. A513

MCLEOD, Sheldon, Chief Operating Officer, North Central Bronx Hospital,, NY, p. A435

MCLIN, Robert D., President and Chief Executive Officer, Good Samaritan Hospital, Vincennes, IN, p. A214

MCLISTER, Charles, Chief Executive Officer, Fairmount Behavioral Health System, Philadelphia, PA, p. A534

MCLOONE, Paul, M.D
   Chief Medical Officer, Trinity Bettendorf, Bettendorf, IA, p. A216
   Chief Medical Officer, Trinity Rock Island, Rock Island, IL, p. A193

MCMAHON, Chris, Chief Operating Officer, The Medical Center of Southeast Texas, Port Arthur, TX, p. A628

MCMAHON, Eugene J., M.D., President and Chief Executive Officer, Presence Saint Joseph Hospital, Elgin, IL, p. A181

MCMAHON, Nancy, Vice President Human Resources, Miriam Hospital, Providence, RI, p. A546

MCMANMON, Kristin, Chief Operating Officer, St. Mary's Hospital, Madison, WI, p. A690

MCMANUS, Kathleen A., Executive Vice President/Chief Operating Officer, Munson Medical Center, Traverse City, MI, p. A325

MCMANUS, Michael T., Chief Operating Officer, Memorial Hospital, Belleville, IL, p. A174

MCMANUS, Ronald, Senior Vice President Clinical Services and Business Entities, Peconic Bay Medical Center, Riverhead, NY, p. A440

MCMANUS, Tim, Interim Chief Executive Officer, CJW Medical Center, Richmond, VA, p. A660

MCMASTER, Sandra
   Regional Chief Information Officer, Kauai Veterans Memorial Hospital, Waimea, HI, p. A166
   Regional Chief Information Officer, Samuel Mahelona Memorial Hospital, Kapaa, HI, p. A165

MCMATH, Mark W., Chief Information Officer, Indiana University Health Bloomington Hospital, Bloomington, IN, p. A199

MCMENAMIN, Anneliese, Vice President Human Resources, Kennedy Health System, Cherry Hill, NJ, p. A402

MCMICHEN, Diane, Director Human Resources, DeKalb Regional Medical Center, Fort Payne, AL, p. A20

MCMILLAN, Deborah, Director Human Resources, Glenn Medical Center, Willows, CA, p. A96

MCMILLAN, Don, Chief Information Officer, PeaceHealth Sacred Heart Medical Center, University District, Eugene, OR, p. A512

MCMILLAN, Douglas A., Administrator and Chief Executive Officer, West Park Hospital, Cody, WY, p. A702

MCMILLAN, Irene, Chief Financial Officer, Sierra Vista Hospital, Sacramento, CA, p. A83

MCMILLAN, James, Vice President Finance, Capital Region Medical Center, Jefferson City, MO, p. A362

MCMILLAN, Linda, Human Resources Specialist, Choctaw Health Center, Philadelphia, MS, p. A352

MCMILLAN, Sheila, Chief Financial Officer, Park Nicollet Methodist Hospital, Saint Louis Park, MN, p. A339

MCMILLAN, William, M.D. Vice President Medical Affairs, Norman Regional Health System, Norman, OK, p. A502

MCMILLEN, Eric, Chief Executive Officer, Ochsner Medical Center–Baton Rouge, Baton Rouge, LA, p. A263

MCMINN, Melvin, Director Human Resources, Wernersville State Hospital, Wernersville, PA, p. A543

MCMORROUGH, Jerry L., Vice President Human Resources, Medical Center of Arlington, Arlington, TX, p. A583

MCMULLEN, Ronald B., President, Christian Hospital, Saint Louis, MO, p. A369

MCMULLEN, Thomas A., Chief Financial Officer, Kindred Hospital–Philadelphia, Philadelphia, PA, p. A535

MCMURRAY, Jean Ann, R.N. Chief Nursing Officer, Jacksonville Medical Center, Jacksonville, AL, p. A22

MCMURRAY, Sean S., FACHE, Vice President and Chief Executive Officer, Johnston Memorial Hospital, Abingdon, VA, p. A651

MCMURREN, MaryAnne, R.N., Administrator and Chief Executive Officer, PeaceHealth Cottage Grove Community Medical Center, Cottage Grove, OR, p. A512

MCMURRY, Timothy, Associate Director Operations, Iowa City Veterans Affairs Health Care System, Iowa City, IA, p. A223

MCNABB, Teresita, R.N. Vice President Nursing Services, Terrebonne General Medical Center, Houma, LA, p. A268

MCNAIR, Lisa, CP
   Senior Vice President and Chief Financial Officer, Burleson St. Joseph Health Center, Caldwell, TX, p. A590
   Senior Vice President and Chief Financial Officer, Grimes St. Joseph Health Center, Navasota, TX, p. A624
   Senior Vice President and Chief Financial Officer, St. Joseph Regional Health Center, Bryan, TX, p. A590

MCNAIR, Michael H., Chief Executive Officer, Sandhills Regional Medical Center, Hamlet, NC, p. A454

MCNALLY, John, Deputy Commander Administration, Bassett Army Community Hospital, Fort Wainwright, AK, p. A28

MCNALLY, Joseph, M.D. Medical Director, Streamwood Behavioral Health Center, Streamwood, IL, p. A195

MCNALLY, Kathy, Chief Nursing Officer, HEALTHSOUTH Rehabilitation Hospital at Drake, Cincinnati, OH, p. A474

MCNALLY, Lou–Ann, Director Human Resources, Claxton–Hepburn Medical Center, Ogdensburg, NY, p. A438

MCNAMARA, Marilyn, M.D. Vice President Medical Affairs, Southwest General Health Center, Middleburg Heights, OH, p. A486

MCNAMARA, Mike, Chief Information Officer, George L. Mee Memorial Hospital, King City, CA, p. A65

MCNAMARA, Steve, Chief Financial Officer, Orange Coast Memorial Medical Center, Fountain Valley, CA, p. A60

MCNAMARA, Thomas, D.O. Vice President Medical Management, WellStar Cobb Hospital, Austell, GA, p. A148

MCNAMARA, Timothy M.
   Senior Vice President Human Resources, Bradford Regional Medical Center, Bradford, PA, p. A521
   Senior Vice President Human Resources, Olean General Hospital, Olean, NY, p. A438

MCNAMARA, Tom, Director Information Technology, Community Hospital of the Monterey Peninsula, Monterey, CA, p. A75

MCNATT, James, Chief Financial Officer, Baylor Medical Center at Carrollton, Carrollton, TX, p. A591

MCNAUGHTON, Richard, Chief Information Management Service, Maine Veterans Affairs Medical Center, Augusta, ME, p. A281

MCNEA, Melvin, Chief Operating Officer, Great Plains Regional Medical Center, North Platte, NE, p. A386

MCNEECE, Steve, Chief Executive Officer, Community Hospital of Anaconda, Anaconda, MT, p. A374

MCNEEL, Wakelin, M.D. Medical Director, BHC Alhambra Hospital, Rosemead, CA, p. A83

MCNEICE, Keith, Vice President and Chief Information Officer, Carolinas Medical Center NorthEast, Concord, NC, p. A450

MCNEIL, Greg R., Chief Executive Officer, Lincoln County Hospital, Lincoln, KS, p. A238

MCNEIL, John, President and Chief Executive Officer, Eastern Regional Medical Center, Philadelphia, PA, p. A534

MCNEIL, Karen
   Chief Nursing Officer, University Hospitals Conneaut Medical Center, Conneaut, OH, p. A479
   Chief Nursing Officer, University Hospitals Geneva Medical Center, Geneva, OH, p. A482

MCNEILL, Michael, Chief Financial Management, Veterans Affairs Medical Center, Albuquerque, NM, p. A415

MCNETT, Dale, M.D. Medical Director, Warren General Hospital, Warren, PA, p. A543

MCNEY, Jim, Vice President Finance and Chief Financial Officer, North Kansas City Hospital, North Kansas City, MO, p. A367

MCNULTY, Stephanie, Chief Operating Officer, St. Petersburg General Hospital, Saint Petersburg, FL, p. A139

MCNUTT, Mike, Assistant Administrator, Covenant Hospital Plainview, Plainview, TX, p. A627

MCNUTT, Pamela
   Vice President Information Systems, Methodist Charlton Medical Center, Dallas, TX, p. A596
   Senior Vice President and Chief Information Officer, Methodist Dallas Medical Center, Dallas, TX, p. A596
   Senior Vice President and Chief Information Officer, Methodist Mansfield Medical Center, Mansfield, TX, p. A621

MCOLVIN, Tom, Executive Director, Sagamore Children's Psychiatric Center, Dix Hills, NY, p. A425

MCPHERSON, Lon, M.D. Senior Vice President Medical Affairs and Chief Quality Officer, Munroe Regional Medical Center, Ocala, FL, p. A134

MCPHERSON, Rhonda, Vice President Human Resources, Fayette Regional Health System, Connersville, IN, p. A200

MCPHERSON, Stephen B., President, Masonicare Health Center, Wallingford, CT, p. A112

MCPHETRES, Joyce, Vice President Human Resources, Bridgton Hospital, Bridgton, ME, p. A282

MCQUAID, Bill, Assistant Vice President and Chief Information Officer, Parkview Adventist Medical Center, Brunswick, ME, p. A282

MCQUAID, David P., FACHE, President, Thomas Jefferson University Hospital, Philadelphia, PA, p. A537

MCQUAIDE, Teresa A., Chief Executive Officer, Trenton Psychiatric Hospital, Trenton, NJ, p. A411

MCQUEEN, Elbert T., President and Chief Executive Officer, Central Georgia Rehabilitation Hospital, Macon, GA, p. A156

MCQUILLAN, Kent, Chief Information Officer, Summit Healthcare Regional Medical Center, Show Low, AZ, p. A37

MCQUILLEN, D. Paul, D.O. Chief of Staff, Mercy Medical Center–New Hampton, New Hampton, IA, p. A226

MCQUISTAN, Bob, Vice President Finance, York General Hospital, York, NE, p. A390

MCQUISTON, Mike, Director Human Resources, Wise Regional Health System, Decatur, TX, p. A598

MCRAE, Colin, Chief Executive Officer, Tennova–Jefferson Memorial Hospital, Jefferson City, TN, p. A571

MCROBERTS, Susan, R.N. Vice President and Chief Nursing Officer, Franciscan St. Francis Health – Indianapolis, Indianapolis, IN, p. A205

MCRORIE, Sherri, Director Human Resources, Anson Community Hospital, Wadesboro, NC, p. A462

MCRORY, Diana, Director Human Resources, Doctor's Memorial Hospital, Perry, FL, p. A137

MCSWAIN, Marilyn, MSN, Administrator, Lake Charles Memorial Hospital for Women, Lake Charles, LA, p. A

MCTAGGART, Jac, Chief Executive Officer, Sanford Hillsboro Medical Center, Hillsboro, ND, p. A467

MCTAGUE, Jerome, JD, Administrator and Chief Executive Officer, Physician's Choice Hospital – Fremont, Fremont, OH, p. A482

MCTIGRIT, Chris, Manager Information Technology, Delta Memorial Hospital, Dumas, AR, p. A43

MCTIGUE, Michael
   Chief Information Officer, Clara Maass Medical Center, Belleville, NJ, p. A401
   Chief Information Officer, Saint Barnabas Medical Center, Livingston, NJ, p. A405

MCVAY, Randy, Chief Executive Officer, Ocala Regional Medical Center, Ocala, FL, p. A134

MCVEIGH, Kevin
   Interim Chief Human Resources Officer, Banner Behavioral Health Hospital – Scottsdale, Scottsdale, AZ, p. A37
   Chief Human Resources Officer, Banner Desert Medical Center, Mesa, AZ, p. A33

MCVEY, Eric A., M.D. Vice President and Chief Medical Officer, Mississippi Baptist Medical Center, Jackson, MS, p. A348

MCVEY, Lynn, President and Chief Executive Officer, Meadowlands Hospital Medical Center, Secaucus, NJ, p. A410

MCVEY, Marty, Chief Executive Officer, Spring Branch Medical Center, Houston, TX, p. A612

MCVEY, Rick, Chief Nursing Officer, Select Specialty Hospital–Knoxville, Knoxville, TN, p. A572

MCVEY, Timothy J., Chief Financial Officer, Mission Regional Medical Center, Mission, TX, p. A623

MCVICKER, Sandra I., MSN, President, University Hospital McDuffie, Thomson, GA, p. A161

MCWATTERS, Pearl, Director Information Services, Highland Hospital, Charleston, WV, p. A676

MCWAY, Jacob, Senior Vice President and Chief Financial Officer, Lester E. Cox Medical Centers, Springfield, MO, p. A372

MCWHIRT, Robert, Vice President Patient Care Services and Chief Nursing Executive, Calvert Memorial Hospital, Prince Frederick, MD, p. A293

MCWHORTER III, John B., President, Baylor University Medical Center, Dallas, TX, p. A595

MCWHORTER, Sharon, Director Information Systems, Ephraim McDowell Fort Logan Hospital, Stanford, KY, p. A260

MCWILLIAMS, Terrence R., M.D. Vice President Medical Affairs, Newport Hospital, Newport, RI, p. A546

MEACHAM, Sherry, Coordinator Human Resources, Select Specialty Hospital–Winston–Salem, Winston–Salem, NC, p. A463

MEACHAM, Steve, Vice President Finance, King's Daughters' Health, Madison, IN, p. A209

MEACHAM, Verna Stroman, President and Chief Executive Officer, Fort Washington Medical Center, Fort Washington, MD, p. A291

MEACHEM, Michelle, Director Human Resources, Elizabethtown Community Hospital, Elizabethtown, NY, p. A425

MEAD, Barbara, Executive Director, Lourdes Counseling Center, Richland, WA, p. A670

MEAD, Linda, Director Human Resources, Margaretville Hospital, Margaretville, NY, p. A429

MEAD, Richard, Senior Director Human Resources, Saint Francis Memorial Hospital, San Francisco, CA, p. A87

MEAD, Rick, Human Resources Leader, Kaiser Permanente Oakland Medical Center, Oakland, CA, p. A77

MEADE, Jeff, M.D. Chief Medical Officer, Watertown Regional Medical Center, Watertown, WI, p. A698

MEADE, Kyle, M.D. Medical Director, North Greenville Hospital, Travelers Rest, SC, p. A556

MEADE, Robert C., Chief Executive Officer, Doctors Hospital of Sarasota, Sarasota, FL, p. A139

MEADOR, Debra, Assistant Administrator, Stonewall Memorial Hospital, Aspermont, TX, p. A584

MEADOWS, Barbara, Chief Financial Manager, Captain James A. Lovell Federal Health Care Center, North Chicago, IL, p. A190

MEADOWS, Danny, M.D. Medical Director, Logansport State Hospital, Logansport, IN, p. A209

MEADOWS, Hal, M.D. Chief Medical Officer, Banner Lassen Medical Center, Susanville, CA, p. A92

MEADOWS, Julia, Chief Financial Officer, Virginia Gay Hospital, Vinton, IA, p. A229

MEADOWS, Michael J., Chief Executive Officer, Livingston Regional Hospital, Livingston, TN, p. A573

MEADOWS, Nancy, Chief Financial Officer, Methodist Hospital, San Antonio, TX, p. A631

MEADOWS, Peri, Director Human Resources, Rhea Medical Center, Dayton, TN, p. A568

MEADOWS, Theresa, Chief Information Officer, Cook Children's Medical Center, Fort Worth, TX, p. A603

MEANS, Dennis, M.D. Vice President Medical Affairs, Carilion New River Valley Medical Center, Christiansburg, VA, p. A652

MEANS, Jr., William H., Administrator, Bastrop Rehabilitation Hospital, Bastrop, LA, p. A262

MEARNS, Stephanie, Vice President Patient Care Services and Chief Nurse Executive, Seton Medical Center, Daly City, CA, p. A58

MEARS, Terry, Director Information Systems, Duke Regional Hospital, Durham, NC, p. A451

MECHAM, Cindy, Health Information Director, Mountain View Hospital, Payson, UT, p. A645

MECOM, Deborah, R.N., Administrator, CHRISTUS Jasper Memorial Hospital, Jasper, TX, p. A615

MEDAGLIA, Guy A., President and Chief Executive Officer, Saint Anthony Hospital, Chicago, IL, p. A179

MEDCIROS, Ron, Director Applied Information Technology, Worcester Recovery Center and Hospital, Worcester, MA, p. A307

MEDEIROS, Barbara, R.N. Chief Nurse Executive, Memorial Hospital Los Banos, Los Banos, CA, p. A72

MEDEIROS, Katherine, President and Chief Executive Officer, Sierra Nevada Memorial Hospital, Grass Valley, CA, p. A63

MEDEROS, Ana J., Chief Executive Officer, Palmetto General Hospital, Hialeah, FL, p. A125

MEDINA, Ed, M.D. Medical Director, Phillips County Hospital, Malta, MT, p. A378

MEDINA, Eleanor, M.D. Chief Medical Officer, Behavioral Center of Michigan, Warren, MI, p. A326

MEDINA, Marco, Chief Information Officer, Stanton County Hospital, Johnson, KS, p. A236

MEDINA, Shelbie, Chief People Officer, Buchanan County Health Center, Independence, IA, p. A223

MEDIRATTA, Ravinder P., M.D. Chief of Staff, Bronson LakeView Hospital, Paw Paw, MI, p. A321

MEDLEY, Adron, M.D. Chief Medical Staff, Northern Rockies Medical Center, Cut Bank, MT, p. A375

MEDLEY, Barry, Director Information Systems, Cook Medical Center–A Campus of Tift Regional Medical Center, Adel, GA, p. A145

MEDLEY, Dennis, Administrator, Physicians' Medical Center, New Albany, IN, p. A211

MEDLEY, Wathen, M.D. Chief Medical Officer, Owensboro Health Regional Hospital, Owensboro, KY, p. A258

MEDLIN, John, Chief Nursing Officer, North Carolina Specialty Hospital, Durham, NC, p. A451

MEDLOCK, Beth, Manager Information Technology, Jackson Hospital, Marianna, FL, p. A130

MEDLOCK, Darci, Manager Human Resources, St. Vincent Dunn Hospital, Bedford, IN, p. A198

MEDOVICH, Lisa
  Senior Vice President and Chief Financial Officer, Hillside Rehabilitation Hospital, Warren, OH, p. A492
  Senior Vice President and Chief Financial Officer, Northside Medical Center, Youngstown, OH, p. A494
  Senior Vice President and Chief Financial Officer, Trumbull Memorial Hospital, Warren, OH, p. A492

MEDRANO, Ruben, M.D. President Medical Staff, OSF Holy Family Medical Center, Monmouth, IL, p. A188

MEDRANO, Samuel, M.D. Chief of Staff, Colusa Regional Medical Center, Colusa, CA, p. A57

MEDUNA, Leo L., M.D. Chief Medical Officer, Saunders Medical Center, Wahoo, NE, p. A390

MEE, Thomas, R.N. Vice President Operations, McLaren Lapeer Region, Lapeer, MI, p. A318

MEEHAN, James, Interim Chief Executive Officer, Athol Memorial Hospital, Athol, MA, p. A295

MEEHAN, Kenneth L., Interim Chief Operating Officer, Saint John's Health Center, Santa Monica, CA, p. A90

MEEHAN, Neil S., D.O. Chief Medical Officer and Chief Medical Information Officer, Lawrence General Hospital, Lawrence, MA, p. A301

MEEK, Julie, Vice President Finance, Kadlec Regional Medical Center, Richland, WA, p. A670

MEEKER, Brian, D.O. President Medical Staff, Virginia Gay Hospital, Vinton, IA, p. A229

MEEKER, Mark, D.O. Medical Staff President, OSF St. Mary Medical Center, Galesburg, IL, p. A183

MEEKINS, Lance, Administrator, Nocona General Hospital, Nocona, TX, p. A625

MEEKINS, Michelle, Manager Human Resources, Sentara Virginia Beach General Hospital, Virginia Beach, VA, p. A662

MEEKS, Janet, Chief Operating Officer, Mount Carmel St. Ann's, Westerville, OH, p. A493

MEEKS, Julia M., Chief Operating Officer, Specialty Hospital of Lorain, Amherst, OH, p. A470

MEEKS, Teresa, Chief Nursing Officer, East Texas Medical Center–Quitman, Quitman, TX, p. A628

MEENK, Susan
  Vice President Service Area, Providence Centralia Hospital, Centralia, WA, p. A665
  Vice President Service Area, Providence St. Peter Hospital, Olympia, WA, p. A669

MEERT, Tiffany, Chief Operating Officer, Northern Nevada Medical Center, Sparks, NV, p. A396

MEESE, Larry, Chief Executive Officer, Jackson Hospital, Marianna, FL, p. A130

MEESIG, Deborah, M.D. Chief of Staff, Chillicothe Veterans Affairs Medical Center, Chillicothe, OH, p. A473

MEGEHEE, Mark, Vice President and Chief Information Officer, Decatur General Hospital, Decatur, AL, p. A18

MEGGS, Christi, Director Human Resources, Marlboro Park Hospital, Bennettsville, SC, p. A548

MEGLI, Cami, Controller, Morrison Community Hospital, Morrison, IL, p. A189

MEGLIOLA, Donna M., Assistant Vice President, Johnson Memorial Hospital, Stafford Springs, CT, p. A112

MEGOW, Kimberly, M.D. Chief Medical Officer, South Georgia Medical Center, Valdosta, GA, p. A162

MEGUIAR, Ramon V., M.D. Senior Vice President and Chief Medical Officer, Memorial Health, Savannah, GA, p. A160

MEHAFFEY, M. Beth, Vice President Human Resources, Baptist Medical Center Jacksonville, Jacksonville, FL, p. A126

MEHARG, John, Director Health Information Technology, Norman Regional Health System, Norman, OK, p. A502

MEHINDRU, Vinay, M.D
  Vice President/Chief Medical Officer, Florida Hospital Waterman, Tavares, FL, p. A142
  Medical Director, Wuesthoff Medical Center – Rockledge, Rockledge, FL, p. A138

MEHLER, Philip, M.D. Chief Medical Officer, Denver Health Medical Center, Denver, CO, p. A99

MEHRINGER, Todd, Director Information Systems, Memorial Hospital and Health Care Center, Jasper, IN, p. A207

MEHTA, Kalpana, Chief Fiscal Services, Jesse Brown Veterans Affairs Medical Center, Chicago, IL, p. A177

MEHTA, Mukesh, M.D. Chief Medical Officer, Memorial Hermann Rehabilitation Hospital – Katy, Katy, TX, p. A616

MEHTA, Raj, Chief Financial Officer, Medina Memorial Hospital, Medina, NY, p. A429

MEHTA, Sonia, M.D., Chief Executive Officer and Chief Medical Officer, Loretto Hospital, Chicago, IL, p. A177

MEHUS, James, M.D. Chief of Staff, Sanford Mayville Medical Center, Mayville, ND, p. A468

MEIAR, Cindy, Human Resources and Payroll Coordinator, Trego County–Lemke Memorial Hospital, Wakeeney, KS, p. A245

MEIDINGER, Duane, Vice President Finance, Walla Walla General Hospital, Walla Walla, WA, p. A674

MEIDINGER, Sue, Manager Business Office, Linton Hospital, Linton, ND, p. A468

MEIER, Suzanne S., System Director, Compensation and Human Resources Technology, Memorial Hermann Memorial City Medical Center, Houston, TX, p. A610

MEIERGERD, Jean, Chief Information Officer, St. Francis Memorial Hospital, West Point, NE, p. A390

MEIERS, Dawn, Coordinator Medical Staff and Personnel Services, Southeast Michigan Surgical Hospital, Warren, MI, p. A326

MEIGS, Jeffrey L., Chief Financial Officer, UnityHealth Louis A. Weiss Memorial Hospital, Chicago, IL, p. A179

MEIGS, Jr., John, M.D. Chief of Staff, Bibb Medical Center, Centreville, AL, p. A18

MEINDEL, Nympha, R.N. Chief Information Officer, North Shore University Hospital, Manhasset, NY, p. A429

MEINHART, Richard, Manager Information Systems, Daviess Community Hospital, Washington, IN, p. A214

MEINKOTH, Jennifer, Chief Information Officer, Memorial Hospital, Belleville, IL, p. A174

MEIS, Fred J., Chief Executive Officer, Kearney County Health Services, Minden, NE, p. A386

MEISNER, Anne, MSN, President and Chief Executive Officer, Southeastern Regional Medical Center, Newnan, GA, p. A158

MEISSNER, Shari, Chief Financial Officer, Liberty Medical Center, Chester, MT, p. A374

MEISTER, Steven, M.D. Chief of Staff, Avera Marshall Regional Medical Center, Marshall, MN, p. A335

MEITZ, Mary, Vice President Finance, Bronson Methodist Hospital, Kalamazoo, MI, p. A318

MEKALA, Bhavani P., M.D. President Medical Staff, Christ Hospital, Jersey City, NJ, p. A405

MELAHN, Will L., M.D. Vice President Medical Affairs and Chief Medical Officer, St. Claire Regional Medical Center, Morehead, KY, p. A258

MELANCON, Derek, Director Human Resources and Marketing, Springhill Medical Center, Springhill, LA, p. A279

MELANCON, Mary, Chief Financial Officer, Abrom Kaplan Memorial Hospital, Kaplan, LA, p. A269

MELAND, Jeff, M.D. Vice President, Chief Medical Officer, Northfield Hospital, Northfield, MN, p. A337

MELARAGNO, Robert, Vice President Finance, O'Bleness Memorial Hospital, Athens, OH, p. A471

MELARAGNO, Tony, M.D., Chief Administrative Officer, Legacy Good Samaritan Hospital and Medical Center, Portland, OR, p. A516

MELBOURNE, John, M.D. Medical Director, Conifer Park, Glenville, NY, p. A426

MELBY, Gina, Chief Executive Officer, J. F. K. Medical Center, Atlantis, FL, p. A118

MELBY, Larry, Chief Executive Officer, Select Specialty Hospital–Palm Beach, Lake Worth, FL, p. A128

MELCHIODE, Joseph D., Chief Executive Officer, University Hospital and Medical Center, Tamarac, FL, p. A141

MELCHIOR, Eric L., Executive Vice President and Chief Financial Officer, Greater Baltimore Medical Center, Baltimore, MD, p. A287

MELENDEZ, Alma, Controller, Dimmit Regional Hospital, Carrizo Springs, TX, p. A591

MELENDEZ, Eddie, Director Human Resources, Brownsville Doctors Hospital, Brownsville, TX, p. A589

MELGAR, Sergio L., Vice President Health Affairs and Chief Financial Officer, UK HealthCare Good Samaritan Hospital, Lexington, KY, p. A254

MELIN, Craig N., President and Chief Executive Officer, Cooley Dickinson Hospital, Northampton, MA, p. A303

MELISSNER, Jean, District Director of Human Resources, Kindred Hospital–Wyoming Valley, Wilkes Barre, PA, p. A544

MELL, Kevin, Vice President Operations, MedStar Montgomery Medical Center, Olney, MD, p. A293

MELL, Vicki, Vice President Human Resources and Support Services, Ohio Valley General Hospital, McKees Rocks, PA, p. A531

MELLETT, David, Chief Financial Officer, Boone County Hospital, Boone, IA, p. A217

MELLO, Brett, Chief Information Officer, Rehoboth McKinley Christian Health Care Services, Gallup, NM, p. A416

MELLO, Paul, Manager Data Processing, Metropolitan State Hospital, Norwalk, CA, p. A76

MELLON, Monte, M.D. Chief of Staff, Catalina Island Medical Center, Avalon, CA, p. A53

MELODY, Brendan, Director Administration, Naval Hospital Bremerton, Bremerton, WA, p. A664

MELSON, Benjamin B., CPA Executive Vice President and Chief Financial Officer, Texas Children's Hospital, Houston, TX, p. A612

MELTON, Chad, Chief Executive Officer, Hackensack University Medical Center at Pascack Valley, Westwood, NJ, p. A412

MELTON, Georgia, Associate Vice President Human Resources, University of Texas Health Science Center at Tyler, Tyler, TX, p. A639

MELTON, Linda Dickey, Vice President Human Resources, North Arkansas Regional Medical Center, Harrison, AR, p. A44

MELTVEDT, Jr., Robert, M.D. Vice President Medical Affairs, Warren Memorial Hospital, Front Royal, VA, p. A654

MELTZER, David B., Chief Financial Officer, Texas Health Presbyterian Hospital Denton, Denton, TX, p. A599

MELVILLE, Carol, Director Human Resources, West Houston Medical Center, Houston, TX, p. A613

MELVIN, Susan, D.O. Chief Medical Officer, Long Beach Memorial Medical Center, Long Beach, CA, p. A67

MENCHINI, August F., Director Human Resources, Eastern Long Island Hospital, Greenport, NY, p. A426

MENDELOWITZ, Susan, Executive Vice President and Chief Operating Officer, Bergen Regional Medical Center, Paramus, NJ, p. A408

MENDENHALL, David, Chief Information Officer, Hutchinson Regional Medical Center, Hutchinson, KS, p. A236

MENDEZ, Alex A., Executive Vice President of Operations and Chief Financial Officer, Mount Sinai Medical Center, Miami Beach, FL, p. A133

MENDEZ, Kim K., Ed.D. Vice President and Chief Nursing Officer, Brookhaven Memorial Hospital Medical Center, Patchogue, NY, p. A439

MENDEZ, Lincoln S., Chief Executive Officer, Baptist Health South Florida, South Miami Hospital, Miami, FL, p. A131

MENDIOLA, Rosie L., Director Information Systems, South Texas Health System, Edinburg, TX, p. A600

MENDOZA, Aniceta, R.N. Chief Nursing Officer, Valley Baptist Medical Center–Brownsville, Brownsville, TX, p. A590

MENDOZA, Dana, Chief Information Officer, Maui Memorial Medical Center, Wailuku, HI, p. A166

MENDOZA, Glenda, Chief Executive Officer and Chief Nursing Executive, The Hospital at Craig Ranch, McKinney, TX, p. A622

MENDOZA, Yolanda, Director Human Resources, Rehabilitation Hospital of Southern New Mexico, Las Cruces, NM, p. A416

MENENDEZ, Deborah, Vice President Human Resources, Bayfront Health St. Petersburg, Saint Petersburg, FL, p. A138

MENGEL, Nancy, Director Information Technology, Inova Loudoun Hospital, Leesburg, VA, p. A656

MENGLE, Scott, Vice President Human Resources, St. Joseph Medical Center, Reading, PA, p. A540

MENNONNA, Guy, Senior Vice President Human Resources, Bergen Regional Medical Center, Paramus, NJ, p. A408

MENON, Rema, M.D. Clinical Director, Parsons State Hospital and Training Center, Parsons, KS, p. A242

MENOR, Peter, Vice President Operations, Chandler Regional Medical Center, Chandler, AZ, p. A30

MENSCH, Alan, M.D. Senior Vice President Medical Affairs, Plainview Hospital, Plainview, NY, p. A439

MENSEN, Amy, Chief Administrative Officer, Regional Medical Center, Manchester, IA, p. A224

MENTZER, Larry, Chief Human Resources Officer, Veterans Affairs Roseburg Healthcare System, Roseburg, OR, p. A517

MERCER, David, Coordinator Information Systems, Baptist Memorial Hospital–Union City, Union City, TN, p. A580

MERCER, Shawna, Director Human Resources, Kansas Neurological Institute, Topeka, KS, p. A244

MERCER, Sherry, Interim Vice President Finance, Texas Health Presbyterian Hospital Dallas, Dallas, TX, p. A597

MERCER, William, M.D. Director, Peterson Rehabilitation Hospital, Wheeling, WV, p. A682

MERCHANT, Ron, M.D. Medical Director, Schick Shadel Hospital, Seattle, WA, p. A670

MERCIECA, Rita, R.N., Executive Director, Forest Hills Hospital,, NY, p. A432

MERCIER, Linda, MSN, Chief Executive Officer, Houston Northwest Medical Center, Houston, TX, p. A610

MERCIER, Rita, Manager Finance, James A. Haley Veterans' Hospital, Tampa, FL, p. A141

MERCURI, Ralph, Vice President and Chief Financial Officer, Major Hospital, Shelbyville, IN, p. A213

MERCURIO, Paul, M.D. Medical Director, Summit Park Hospital and Nursing Care Center, Pomona, NY, p. A439

MEREDITH, Julie, Acting Chief Nursing Officer, Cascade Medical Center, Leavenworth, WA, p. A667

MEREDITH, Linda, MSN Chief Operating Officer, Scott & White Hospital – Llano, Llano, TX, p. A619

MEREK, Gloria, Director of Nursing, Springfield Hospital Center, Sykesville, MD, p. A294

MERGEN, Lynn M., Chief Executive Officer, Mineral Area Regional Medical Center, Farmington, MO, p. A360

MERILLO, Myra, Supervisor Health Information Management, HEALTHSOUTH Rehabilitation Hospital of Spring Hill, Brooksville, FL, p. A120

MERIWETHER, Wayne, Chief Executive Officer, Twin Lakes Regional Medical Center, Leitchfield, KY, p. A253

MERK, Richard, Executive Vice President, Allegiance Behavioral Health Center of Plainview, Plainview, TX, p. A627

MERK, Richard T., Chief Executive Officer, Bienville Medical Center, Arcadia, LA, p. A262

MERKEL, Earl, M.D. Chief of Staff, Russell Regional Hospital, Russell, KS, p. A243

MERKLE, Greg, Director Information Systems, Sheppard Pratt Health System, Baltimore, MD, p. A289

MERKLE, Richard E., Chief Human Resources Officer, Geisinger Medical Center, Danville, PA, p. A523

MERKLEY, Jason R., Chief Executive Officer, Brookings Health System, Brookings, SD, p. A558

MERLI, Geno, M.D. Chief Medical Officer, Thomas Jefferson University Hospital, Philadelphia, PA, p. A537

MERLIS, Laurence M., President and Chief Executive Officer, Abington Memorial Hospital, Abington, PA, p. A519

MERRED, Mehdi, Chief Executive Officer, Quincy Valley Medical Center, Quincy, WA, p. A670

MERRELL, Bruce, FACHE, President, St. Mary's Hospital, Centralia, IL, p. A175

MERRIGAN, Mary C., Manager Public Relations, Sanford Vermillion Medical Center, Vermillion, SD, p. A563

MERRILL, Chuck, M.D. Vice President Medical Affairs, Marian Medical Center, Santa Maria, CA, p. A90

MERRILL, Mark H., Interim Chief Executive Officer, Winchester Medical Center, Winchester, VA, p. A663

MERRILL, Michael, M.D. Interim Vice President Medical Affairs, United Memorial Medical Center, Batavia, NY, p. A421

MERRILL, Rick W., President and Chief Executive Officer, Cook Children's Medical Center, Fort Worth, TX, p. A603

MERRITT, Bradley, M.D. Medical Director, Trinity Mother Frances Rehabilitation Hospital, Tyler, TX, p. A638

MERRITT, Janet, Chief Financial Officer, St. Vincent Williamsport Hospital, Williamsport, IN, p. A215

MERRY, Duane, Chief Information Officer, Little Falls Hospital, Little Falls, NY, p. A428

MERRYMAN, Scott
 Chief Financial Officer, CHRISTUS Coushatta Health Care Center, Coushatta, LA, p. A265
 Chief Financial Officer, CHRISTUS Spohn Hospital Corpus Christi Memorial, Corpus Christi, TX, p. A593

MERRYWELL, Paul, Chief Information Officer, Sycamore Shoals Hospital, Elizabethton, TN, p. A568

MERSON, Wendy, Chief Executive Officer, Windmoor Healthcare of Clearwater, Clearwater, FL, p. A120

MERTZ, John, Chief Information Officer, South Nassau Communities Hospital, Oceanside, NY, p. A438

MERVAK, Gary, Chief Financial Officer, Northwest Medical Center, Margate, FL, p. A130

MERVES, Ed, M.D. Medical Director, Coastal Harbor Treatment Center, Savannah, GA, p. A159

MERWIN, Robert W., Chief Executive Officer, Mills–Peninsula Health Services, Burlingame, CA, p. A55

MESAROS, Dennis, Chief Operating Officer, Providence Centralia Hospital, Centralia, WA, p. A665

MESIC, John, M.D. Chief Medical Officer, Sutter Auburn Faith Hospital, Auburn, CA, p. A53

MESSELT, Mary Jo, Director Human Resources, Mercy Hospital Logan County, Guthrie, OK, p. A499

MESSER, Bristol, Chief Executive Officer, McCurtain Memorial Hospital, Idabel, OK, p. A500

MESSERSMITH, Darrell, Director Information Systems, Platte Valley Medical Center, Brighton, CO, p. A97

MESSERSMITH, Scott E., Director Human Resources, Columbus Community Hospital, Columbus, NE, p. A382

MESSINA, Arlene, R.N. Director of Nursing, Riverside Doctors' Hospital, Williamsburg, VA, p. A663

MESSINA, Daniel J., Ph.D. Senior Vice President and Chief Operating Officer, CentraState Healthcare System, Freehold, NJ, p. A404

MESSMER, Joseph
 Interim Chief Executive Officer, Avera St. Mary's Hospital, Pierre, SD, p. A561
 Interim President, St. Gabriel's Hospital, Little Falls, MN, p. A334

MESTAN, Robert E., M.D. Chief of Staff, Perry Memorial Hospital, Princeton, IL, p. A192

MESTER, Sulynn, R.N. Chief Nursing Officer, Childress Regional Medical Center, Childress, TX, p. A591

METCALF, Emma, R.N., Director, Veterans Affairs Illiana Health Care System, Danville, IL, p. A180

METCALF, Peter, M.D. President Medical Staff, Genesis Medical Center, Illini Campus, Silvis, IL, p. A194

METCALFE, Kevan, Chief Executive Officer, Corona Regional Medical Center, Corona, CA, p. A57

METHE, Joan, Chief Information Officer, Mercy Medical Center, Springfield, MA, p. A305

METHVEN, George, M.D. Chief Medical Staff, Cedar County Memorial Hospital, El Dorado Springs, MO, p. A360

METHVEN, Jeffrey M., Vice President Ambulatory Services and Chief Human Resources Officer, Saratoga Hospital, Saratoga Springs, NY, p. A442

METHVIN, Jeff, Manager Information Technology, St. Luke Hospital and Living Center, Marion, KS, p. A239

METIKO, Olushola, M.D. Medical Director, Central Prison Hospital, Raleigh, NC, p. A459

METIVIER, Roberta, Vice President Human Resources and Administrator, Western Main Nursing Home, Stephens Memorial Hospital, Norway, ME, p. A284

METOYER, Derek, M.D. Chief of Staff, Opelousas General Health System, Opelousas, LA, p. A276

METTEAUER, Ken, Chief Financial Officer, Redmond Regional Medical Center, Rome, GA, p. A159

METTS, Michael, Chief Financial Officer, Odessa Regional Medical Center, Odessa, TX, p. A625

METZ, Amy, Chief Nursing Officer, Regency Hospital of Florence, Florence, SC, p. A552

METZ, Bruce, Ph.D. Chief Information Officer, Lahey Hospital & Medical Center, Burlington, Burlington, MA, p. A298

METZ, Carl, Vice President Human Resources, Ephraim McDowell Regional Medical Center, Danville, KY, p. A250

METZ, Karen, Chief Executive Officer, Physicians Regional Medical Center, Knoxville, TN, p. A572

METZGER, John, Controller, NorthKey Community Care, Covington, KY, p. A250

MEURER, Bryan, Director Information Systems, Mat–Su Regional Medical Center, Palmer, AK, p. A28

MEUSSNER, Jean, District Director Human Resources, Kindred Hospital South Philadelphia, Philadelphia, PA, p. A535

MEWHIRTER, Michael, Chief Financial Officer, Florida Hospital North Pinellas, Tarpon Springs, FL, p. A142

MEYER, Anthony, M.D. Medical Director, Aurora Psychiatric Hospital, Wauwatosa, WI, p. A699

MEYER, Cheryl, Director Human Resources, Palmer Lutheran Health Center, West Union, IA, p. A230

MEYER, Cynthia A., Interim Chief Executive Officer, Dominion Hospital, Falls Church, VA, p. A653

MEYER, Daniel T., President, Aurora BayCare Medical Center, Green Bay, WI, p. A687

MEYER, Eugene W., President and Chief Executive Officer, Lawrence Memorial Hospital, Lawrence, KS, p. A238

MEYER, Francis, Vice President Information Systems Technology, KALEIDA Health, Buffalo, NY, p. A422

MEYER, Gary, M.D. Chief of Staff, Grand River Hospital District, Rifle, CO, p. A105

MEYER, Gary A., President and Chief Executive Officer, Schneck Medical Center, Seymour, IN, p. A213

MEYER, Gordon, Director Human Resources, Oakland Regional Hospital, Southfield, MI, p. A324

MEYER, Jeffrey K., Chief Executive Officer, Osceola Medical Center, Osceola, WI, p. A694

MEYER, Joe S., Chief Financial Officer, Scott County Hospital, Scott City, KS, p. A244

MEYER, John, M.D. Chief of Staff, Medina Regional Hospital, Hondo, TX, p. A608

MEYER, Karen, Vice President Finance and Chief Financial Officer, Rush Memorial Hospital, Rushville, IN, p. A213

MEYER, Kris, R.N. Director of Nursing, Pawnee County Memorial Hospital and Rural Health Clinic, Pawnee City, NE, p. A389

MEYER, Kurt A., Vice President Human Resources, Elkhart General Healthcare System, Elkhart, IN, p. A201

MEYER, Lori, Interim Chief Financial Officer, South Peninsula Hospital, Homer, AK, p. A28

MEYER, Nate, Director Finance, Douglas County Hospital, Alexandria, MN, p. A328

MEYER, Philip A., Director Finance, Dearborn County Hospital, Lawrenceburg, IN, p. A208

MEYER, Richard A., Chief Financial Officer, Mary Black Memorial Hospital, Spartanburg, SC, p. A556

MEYER, Robert L., President and Chief Executive Officer, Phoenix Children's Hospital, Phoenix, AZ, p. A35

MEYER, Robin, Vice President Support Services, Decatur County Memorial Hospital, Greensburg, IN, p. A204

MEYER, Roger, M.D. Chief of Staff, Warren Memorial Hospital, Friend, NE, p. A383

MEYER, Thomas, Vice President Finance, Morris Hospital & Healthcare Centers, Morris, IL, p. A189

MEYER, Timothy, M.D. Chief of Staff, Memorial Medical Center – Neillsville, Neillsville, WI, p. A693

MEYER, Wessel, M.D. Chief of Staff, Veterans Affairs Central California Health Care System, Fresno, CA, p. A62

MEYER–UYEHARA, Cathy, Administrator, Hale Ho'ola Hamakua, Honokaa, HI, p. A164

MEYERHOFER, Cheri, Vice President Human Resources, PeaceHealth Southwest Medical Center, Vancouver, WA, p. A674

MEYERS, Ann M., Chief Executive Officer, Mayo Clinic Hospital, Phoenix, AZ, p. A35

MEYERS, Audrey, FACHE, President and Chief Executive Officer, Valley Hospital, Ridgewood, NJ, p. A410

MEYERS, Betty, Chief Financial Officer, Crook County Medical Services District, Sundance, WY, p. A704

MEYERS, Larry, Chief Information Officer, Wilson Memorial Hospital, Sidney, OH, p. A490

MEYERS, Russell, President and Chief Executive Officer, Midland Memorial Hospital, Midland, TX, p. A623

MEYERS, Steve, Director Human Resources, New York Community Hospital,, NY, p. A434

MEYERS, William, Chief Information Officer, St. Luke's Hospital, Chesterfield, MO, p. A358

MEZA, Eduardo, M.D. Medical Director, Prairie St. John's, Fargo, ND, p. A466

MEZA, Lourdes, Coordinator Human Resources, Doctors Hospital of West Covina, West Covina, CA, p. A95

MEZOFF, Adam, M.D. Vice President and Chief Medical Officer, Children's Medical Center, Dayton, OH, p. A479

MEZZA, Nicholas, Chief Executive Officer, LifeCare Hospitals of Mechanicsburg, Mechanicsburg, PA, p. A531

MIANO, Christena, Human Resources Director, Medical Center of Trinity, Trinity, FL, p. A143

MIAO, Winjie Tang, President, Texas Health Harris Methodist Hospital Alliance, Fort Worth, TX, p. A604

MICCOLI, Vinny, Executive Director, Manhattan Psychiatric Center–Ward's Island, New York, NY, p. A434

MICHAEL, Amy J., Chief Operating Officer, Sullivan County Memorial Hospital, Milan, MO, p. A366

MICHAEL, Don, Chief Financial Officer, Jay County Hospital, Portland, IN, p. A212

MICHAEL, Liz, Vice President Patient Care Services and Chief Nursing Officer, Stillwater Medical Center, Stillwater, OK, p. A507

MICHAEL, Lois, Vice President Human Resources, Torrance Memorial Medical Center, Torrance, CA, p. A93

MICHAELSON, Linda, Director Human Resources, Lake District Hospital, Lakeview, OR, p. A514

MICHALEK, Debra, Chief Financial Officer, Kindred Hospital–Louisville, Louisville, KY, p. A255

MICHALSKI, Barb, Manager Human Resources, Flambeau Hospital, Park Falls, WI, p. A694

MICHALSKI, Carrie, President and Chief Executive Officer, RiverView Health, Crookston, MN, p. A331

MICHALSKI, Gene, Executive Vice President and Chief Operating Officer, Beaumont Hospital – Royal Oak, Royal Oak, MI, p. A323

MICHEL, Diane, Vice President Nursing, Children's Hospital, New Orleans, LA, p. A275

MICHEL, George J., Chief Operating Officer, Larkin Community Hospital, South Miami, FL, p. A140

MICHEL, Linda, Administrator, North Valley Hospital, Tonasket, WA, p. A673

MICHEL–OGBORN, Deborah, Chief Information Resource Management, Malcom Randall Veterans Affairs Medical Center, Gainesville, FL, p. A124

MICHELETTI, Denise D., R.N., Director, Central Virginia Training Center, Madison Heights, VA, p. A656

MICHELETTI, Susan C., Chief Operating Officer, San Ramon Regional Medical Center, San Ramon, CA, p. A89

MICHELL, Pamela W., R.N. Vice President and Chief Nursing Officer, Munroe Regional Medical Center, Ocala, FL, p. A134

MICIOTTO, Joseph M., Administrator, LSU Health Sciences Center, Shreveport, LA, p. A278

MICKENS, Walt, President and Chief Executive Officer, Queen of the Valley Medical Center, Napa, CA, p. A76

MICKIEWICZ, Nanette, M.D., President, Dominican Hospital, Santa Cruz, CA, p. A90

MIDDENDORF, Bruce, M.D. Chief Medical Officer, St. Mary's Health Care System, Athens, GA, p. A145

MIDDLETON, Jackie, Vice President Human Resources, Methodist Dallas Medical Center, Dallas, TX, p. A596

MIDGETT, Ronnie, Chief Financial Officer, Colleton Medical Center, Walterboro, SC, p. A556

MIDKIFF, Rodney, Chief Executive Officer, AMG Specialty Hospital – Muncie, Muncie, IN, p. A210

MIEDLER, Michael, M.D. Chief Medical Officer, Continuing Care Hospital, Lexington, KY, p. A254

MIER, David, Chief Financial Officer, El Paso Children's Hospital, El Paso, TX, p. A601

MIESNER, Gail, Chief Financial Officer, Memorial Hospital, Chester, IL, p. A176

MIGAUD, Christy, Controller, Ochsner Baptist Medical Center, New Orleans, LA, p. A275

MIGNOSNA, Gary, Vice President Human Resources, UPMC Passavant, Pittsburgh, PA, p. A538

MIGOYA, Carlos A., President and Chief Executive Officer, Jackson Health System, Miami, FL, p. A131

MIHALAKAKOS, Paul, M.D. Chief of Staff, Aurora Medical Center – Manitowoc County, Two Rivers, WI, p. A698

MIKELA, Mary, Vice President Mission Stewardship, Saint Anthony's Health Center, Alton, IL, p. A173

MIKELL, Jeffrey, M.D. Chief Medical Officer, Wesley Woods Long Term Care Hospital, Atlanta, GA, p. A147

MIKES, James, Administrator, Heartland Long Term Acute Care Hospital, Saint Joseph, MO, p. A368

MIKHAIL, Ashraf, M.D. Medical Director, Brynn Marr Hospital, Jacksonville, NC, p. A455

MIKI, Nobuyuki, M.D. Vice President Medical Affairs, Kuakini Medical Center, Honolulu, HI, p. A164

MIKITARIAN Jr., George, Chief Executive Officer, Parrish Medical Center, Titusville, FL, p. A143

MIKITKA, Joseph, Vice President Human Resources, Sacred Heart Hospital, Allentown, PA, p. A519

MIKKELSON, Tom, M.D. Interim Chief Operating Officer, Touchette Regional Hospitals, Centreville, IL, p. A176

MIKLAVIC, Kirk, Director, Human Resources, Central Maine Medical Center, Lewiston, ME, p. A283

MIKLOS, Maggie, Director Human Resources, Northside Hospital and Heart Institute, Saint Petersburg, FL, p. A139

MIKULIC, Jeannie, Director Human Resources, Providence Portland Medical Center, Portland, OR, p. A516

MIKUTOWSKI, Melody, Chief Human Resources Management, Portland Veterans Affairs Medical Center, Portland, OR, p. A516

MILAM, Wendy, Chief Nursing Officer, HEALTHSOUTH Rehabilitation Hospital of Ocala, Ocala, FL, p. A134

MILAND, Shelly, Vice President Finance and Chief Financial Officer, Texas Health Harris Methodist Hospital Hurst–Euless–Bedford, Bedford, TX, p. A588

MILANES, Carlos, Chief Executive Officer and Managing Director, Aiken Regional Medical Centers, Aiken, SC, p. A548

MILANO, Arthur D., Vice President Human Resources, Berkshire Medical Center, Pittsfield, MA, p. A304

MILATOVICH, Natasha, Association Vice President Human Resources, White Memorial Medical Center, Los Angeles, CA, p. A72

MILAZZO, John, Chief Financial Officer, River Region Medical Center, Vicksburg, MS, p. A354

MILBRANDT, David, M.D. Vice President Medical Affairs, Fairview Lakes Health Services, Wyoming, MN, p. A343

MILBRIDGE, Daniel, Administrator and Chief Operating Officer, Essentia Health–Virginia, Virginia, MN, p. A342

MILBURN, Sandra, Director Human Resources, HEALTHSOUTH Rehabilitation Hospital of Memphis, Memphis, TN, p. A574

MILES, David K., President and Chief Executive Officer, The Children's Institute of Pittsburgh, Pittsburgh, PA, p. A538

MILES, John, Chief Financial Officer, Piedmont Newnan Hospital, Newnan, GA, p. A158

MILES, Kerry

   Site Director, Providence Centralia Hospital, Centralia, WA, p. A665

   Chief Information Officer, Providence St. Peter Hospital, Olympia, WA, p. A669

MILES, Laverne, Chief Operating Officer, Fort Defiance Indian Health Service Hospital, Fort Defiance, AZ, p. A31

MILES, Paul V.

   Chief Operating Officer, Morgan County ARH Hospital, West Liberty, KY, p. A261

   Vice President Administration, Whitesburg ARH Hospital, Whitesburg, KY, p. A261

MILES, Senta, Director Human Resources, Medical Center of McKinney, McKinney, TX, p. A622

MILEY, Dennis C., Chief Executive Officer, Paynesville Area Health Care System, Paynesville, MN, p. A338

MILIAN, Tony, Chief Financial Officer, Palm Springs General Hospital, Hialeah, FL, p. A125

MILICEVIC, Heather, Director Human Resources, Summa Western Reserve Hospital, Cuyahoga Falls, OH, p. A479

MILIUS, Hank A., Chief Executive Officer, Meridian Health Services, Muncie, IN, p. A210

MILLARD, James M., President and Chief Executive Officer, Kenmore Mercy Hospital, Kenmore, NY, p. A428

MILLER, Alicia, Director Human Resources, Aspen Valley Hospital District, Aspen, CO, p. A97

MILLER, Amy A., Human Resources Assistant, Hawarden Regional Healthcare, Hawarden, IA, p. A222

MILLER, Annette, M.D. Medical Staff Chairman, Brown County Hospital, Ainsworth, NE, p. A381

MILLER, Barb, Director Human Resources, St. Gabriel's Hospital, Little Falls, MN, p. A334

MILLER, Barbara, Manager Business Office, Tri–County Hospital – Williston, Williston, FL, p. A144

MILLER, Barbara H., M.D. Chief Medical Officer, Newman Memorial Hospital, Shattuck, OK, p. A506

MILLER, Berry, M.D. Chief Medical Officer, Cameron Memorial Community Hospital, Angola, IN, p. A198

MILLER, Beth, Controller, HEALTHSOUTH Harmarville Rehabilitation Hospital, Pittsburgh, PA, p. A537

MILLER, Blaine K., Administrator, Republic County Hospital, Belleville, KS, p. A231

MILLER, Bryan, Chief Operating Officer, Plantation General Hospital, Plantation, FL, p. A137

MILLER, Carol R., R.N. Chief Nursing Officer, Reynolds Memorial Hospital, Glen Dale, WV, p. A677

MILLER, Chad, Chief Financial Officer, Bolivar Medical Center, Cleveland, MS, p. A346

MILLER, Charles, D.O. Chief of Staff, Unicoi County Memorial Hospital, Erwin, TN, p. A569

MILLER, Christi, Manager Human Resources, West River Regional Medical Center, Hettinger, ND, p. A467

MILLER, Christine

   Vice President Human Resources, Hanover Hospital, Hanover, PA, p. A526

   Chief Human Resources Management Services, Maine Veterans Affairs Medical Center, Augusta, ME, p. A281

MILLER, Connie, Vice President Human Resources, Overland Park Regional Medical Center, Overland Park, KS, p. A242

MILLER, Dan, Vice President Finance, Forest Health Medical Center, Ypsilanti, MI, p. A327

MILLER, Daniel

   Vice President Human Resources, EMH Elyria Medical Center, Elyria, OH, p. A481

   Chief Operating Officer, Swedish Medical Center, Englewood, CO, p. A100

MILLER, David, Chief Financial Officer, Sturgis Hospital, Sturgis, MI, p. A325

MILLER, David L., Chief Information Officer, UAMS Medical Center, Little Rock, AR, p. A47

MILLER, David R., President, River Falls Area Hospital, River Falls, WI, p. A696

MILLER, David T., Vice President and Chief Financial Officer, Children's Medical Center, Dayton, OH, p. A479

MILLER, Debra

   Administrator, Crosbyton Clinic Hospital, Crosbyton, TX, p. A594

   Senior Vice President Human Resources, Petaluma Valley Hospital, Petaluma, CA, p. A79

   Vice President Human Resources, Santa Rosa Memorial Hospital, Santa Rosa, CA, p. A90

MILLER, Derek, Senior Vice President and Chief Financial Officer, Southeast Alabama Medical Center, Dothan, AL, p. A19

MILLER, Dianne, Director Health Information Management, Van Matre HEALTHSOUTH Rehabilitation Hospital, Rockford, IL, p. A194

MILLER, Dionne, Chief Operating Officer, Sutter Roseville Medical Center, Roseville, CA, p. A83

MILLER, Donald, Vice President and Chief Financial Officer, Queen of the Valley Medical Center, Napa, CA, p. A76

MILLER, Donald, M.D. Chief of Staff, Washington County Hospital and Clinics, Washington, IA, p. A229

MILLER, Duane, Senior Vice President Finance, Carson City Hospital, Carson City, MI, p. A310

MILLER, Eileen, Director Human Resources, Northern Dutchess Hospital, Rhinebeck, NY, p. A440

MILLER, Elaine G., Director of Nursing, Oaklawn Psychiatric Center, Goshen, IN, p. A204

MILLER, Elizabeth, CPA Chief Financial Officer, Stamford Memorial Hospital, Stamford, TX, p. A635

MILLER, Gary, Chief Executive Officer, Peak View Behavioral Health, Colorado Springs, CO, p. A98

MILLER, Gary E., M.D. Medical Director, Kingwood Pines Hospital, Kingwood, TX, p. A617

MILLER, Gary L.

   Regional Director Information Systems, Saint Joseph Regional Medical Center, Mishawaka, IN, p. A210

   Regional Director Information Systems, Saint Joseph Regional Medical Center–Plymouth Campus, Plymouth, IN, p. A212

MILLER, Gary P., President and Chief Executive Officer, St. Alexius Medical Center, Bismarck, ND, p. A465

MILLER, Gene, Chief Executive Officer, Northeastern Nevada Regional Hospital, Elko, NV, p. A391

MILLER Jr., George N., Chief Executive Officer, Okmulgee Memorial Hospital, Okmulgee, OK, p. A505

MILLER, Greg, Senior Vice President Operations, Shands Jacksonville Medical Center, Jacksonville, FL, p. A126

MILLER, Harvey, Director, G. Werber Bryan Psychiatric Hospital, Columbia, SC, p. A550

MILLER, Heidi, Chief Executive Officer, Kindred Hospital Arizona–Phoenix, Phoenix, AZ, p. A34

MILLER, J. D., M.D

   Chief Medical Officer, Hazard ARH Regional Medical Center, Hazard, KY, p. A252

   Vice President Medical Affairs, Morgan County ARH Hospital, West Liberty, KY, p. A261

   Vice President Medical Affairs, Williamson ARH Hospital, South Williamson, KY, p. A260

MILLER, J. Todd, Vice President and Chief Operating Officer, Alice Peck Day Memorial Hospital, Lebanon, NH, p. A398

MILLER, Jackie, D.O. Chief of Staff, Northwest Medical Center, Albany, MO, p. A356

MILLER, James

   Interim Chief Executive Officer, Alliance Health Center, Meridian, MS, p. A350

   Director Human Resources, Lakeside Behavioral Health System, Memphis, TN, p. A574

MILLER, James, CPA Chief Financial Officer, Regional Medical Center of Acadiana, Lafayette, LA, p. A271

MILLER, James D., M.D. Chief Medical Officer, Memorial Hospital of Carbondale, Carbondale, IL, p. A175

MILLER, James J., Vice President and Chief Financial Officer, Henry Ford Wyandotte Hospital, Wyandotte, MI, p. A327

MILLER, Jason, Chief Operating Officer, The BridgeWay, North Little Rock, AR, p. A48

MILLER, Jeff, Chief Operating Officer, Citizens Memorial Hospital, Bolivar, MO, p. A356

MILLER, Jeffrey S., President and Chief Executive Officer, High Point Regional Health System, High Point, NC, p. A455

MILLER, Jennifer, Chief Executive Officer, Austin Lakes Hospital, Austin, TX, p. A584

MILLER, John, Vice President Information Services, Sanford Bismarck, Bismarck, ND, p. A465

MILLER Jr., John A., FACHE, Chief Executive Officer, AnMed Health Medical Center, Anderson, SC, p. A548

MILLER, Jon, Team Leader Accounting and Information Services, Hancock Regional Hospital, Greenfield, IN, p. A204

MILLER, Judy, Director Human Resources, Town and Country Hospital, Tampa, FL, p. A142

MILLER, Julie, Chief Operating Officer, Williamson Medical Center, Franklin, TN, p. A569

MILLER, Kelli, Vice President Human Resources, Mary Free Bed Rehabilitation Hospital, Grand Rapids, MI, p. A315

MILLER, Ken, Chief Financial Officer, Paris Regional Medical Center, Paris, TX, p. A626

MILLER, Kevin J., FACHE, President and Chief Executive Officer, Hutchinson Regional Medical Center, Hutchinson, KS, p. A236

MILLER, Kim, Chief Information Officer, Bowdle Hospital, Bowdle, SD, p. A558

MILLER, Kimberly J., FACHE, Chief Executive Officer, Beaver Dam Community Hospitals, Beaver Dam, WI, p. A684

MILLER, Kris, Senior Human Resources Business Partner, Spectrum Health Reed City Hospital, Reed City, MI, p. A322

MILLER, Leanne R., Director Human Resources, Community Hospital, McCook, NE, p. A386

MILLER, Leighton, Chief Information Officer, Meade District Hospital, Meade, KS, p. A239

MILLER, Lisa, Director Human Resources, Hendry Regional Medical Center, Clewiston, FL, p. A120

MILLER, Lisa, R.N. Director of Nursing, North Sunflower Medical Center, Ruleville, MS, p. A353

MILLER, Lynn J., Vice President Financial Services, Oaklawn Psychiatric Center, Goshen, IN, p. A204

MILLER, Mark, Chief Operating Officer, Northside Hospital and Heart Institute, Saint Petersburg, FL, p. A139

MILLER, Mark A., FACHE, Chief Executive Officer, Memorial Health System, Abilene, KS, p. A231

MILLER, Marty, Vice President and Chief Information Officer, Children's Hospital Los Angeles, Los Angeles, CA, p. A68

MILLER, Mary, Vice President Finance and Business Development, Mt. Washington Pediatric Hospital, Baltimore, MD, p. A288

MILLER, Matthew, M.D. Vice President Medical Affairs, Danbury Hospital, Danbury, CT, p. A108

MILLER, Nancy, R.N. Chief Nursing Officer, Van Matre HEALTHSOUTH Rehabilitation Hospital, Rockford, IL, p. A194

MILLER, Nate
Human Resources Manager, Intermountain Medical Center, Murray, UT, p. A644
Chief Executive Officer, Surgical Hospital of Jonesboro, Jonesboro, AR, p. A45

MILLER, Nicole, Director Human Resources, Riverside Shore Memorial Hospital, Nassawadox, VA, p. A657

MILLER, Penny, Vice President of Patient Care Services, Wellmont Bristol Regional Medical Center, Bristol, TN, p. A565

MILLER, Peter, FACHE, Chief Executive Officer, Specialty Hospital of Washington–Hadley, Washington, DC, p. A117

MILLER, Phil, Chief Financial Officer, Shelby Memorial Hospital, Shelbyville, IL, p. A194

MILLER, Redonda G., M.D. Vice President Medical Affairs, Johns Hopkins Hospital, Baltimore, MD, p. A287

MILLER, Richard
Administrator Finance, Banner Thunderbird Medical Center, Glendale, AZ, p. A32
Administrator and Chief Executive Officer, Norton County Hospital, Norton, KS, p. A240
Vice President Finance, University of Chicago Medical Center, Chicago, IL, p. A180

MILLER, Rick
Chief Financial Officer, District One Hospital, Faribault, MN, p. A332
President and Chief Operating Officer, Nationwide Children's Hospital, Columbus, OH, p. A477

MILLER, Rip, Chief Executive Officer, The Hospital at Westlake Medical Center, Austin, TX, p. A586

MILLER, Robert, Chief Executive Officer, Coshocton County Memorial Hospital, Coshocton, OH, p. A479

MILLER, Rod, Chief Information Technology, Community Hospital, Torrington, WY, p. A704

MILLER, Sam, Chief Operating Officer, North Sunflower Medical Center, Ruleville, MS, p. A353

MILLER, Scott
Director Information Services, Forrest City Medical Center, Forrest City, AR, p. A44
Chief Financial Officer, Schick Shadel Hospital, Seattle, WA, p. A670

MILLER, Sharon, Chief Information Officer, Community Howard Regional Hospital, Kokomo, IN, p. A207

MILLER, Sherry L., Director Human Resources, Springfield Hospital Center, Sykesville, MD, p. A294

MILLER, Stan, Executive Director Human Resources, St. Thomas More Hospital, Canon City, CO, p. A98

MILLER, Stephen R., Chief Executive Officer, Kosciusko Community Hospital, Warsaw, IN, p. A214

MILLER, Steve
Chief Financial Officer, East Texas Medical Center Pittsburg, Pittsburg, TX, p. A627
Chief Information Officer, Oklahoma Heart Hospital, Oklahoma City, OK, p. A504

MILLER, Steven
Chief Financial Officer, Seven Rivers Regional Medical Center, Crystal River, FL, p. A121
Chief Financial Officer, Takoma Regional Hospital, Greeneville, TN, p. A569

MILLER, Stuart P., M.D. Medical Director, HEALTHSOUTH Sea Pines Rehabilitation Hospital, Melbourne, FL, p. A130

MILLER, Susan, Financial Administrator, Faulkton Area Medical Center, Faulkton, SD, p. A559

MILLER, Tamara, R.N., Administrator, Madison Community Hospital, Madison, SD, p. A560

MILLER, Tammie, Director Marketing and Public Relations, Plateau Medical Center, Oak Hill, WV, p. A679

MILLER, Ted, Chief Financial Officer, Floyd Memorial Hospital and Health Services, New Albany, IN, p. A211

MILLER, Thomas, M.D. Medical Director, University of Utah Health Care – Hospital and Clinics, Salt Lake City, UT, p. A647

MILLER, Tim C., M.D. Vice President, Chief Medical Officer and Director Academy Affairs, OSF Saint Francis Medical Center, Peoria, IL, p. A192

MILLER, Tish, Chief Financial Officer, John C. Fremont Healthcare District, Mariposa, CA, p. A73

MILLER, Trey, Chief Executive Officer, Cambridge Hospital in Houston, Houston, TX, p. A609

MILLER, Wanda, R.N. Director of Clinical Services, Asheville Specialty Hospital, Asheville, NC, p. A447

MILLER, Wayne, D.O. Associate Chief Medical Officer, Mercy Suburban Hospital, Norristown, PA, p. A533

MILLER, Jr., Wentz J., Managing Director and Chief Financial Officer, Integris Baptist Medical Center, Oklahoma City, OK, p. A503

MILLER, William, Coordinator Management Information Systems, Livengrin Foundation, Bensalem, PA, p. A520

MILLER, DNP, Linda, R.N. Senior Vice President Operations and Chief Nursing Officer, Our Lady of Lourdes Memorial Hospital, Binghamton, NY, p. A421

MILLER–BALFOUR, Pam, Director Human Resources, Socorro General Hospital, Socorro, NM, p. A418

MILLER–CAMPBELL, Michele, Chief Financial Officer, Community Memorial Hospital, Oconto Falls, WI, p. A694

MILLER–COLLETTE, Melody M., Director Human Resources, North Okaloosa Medical Center, Crestview, FL, p. A121

MILLER–PHIPPS, Julie K., Senior Vice President and Executive Director, Kaiser Permanente Anaheim Medical Center, Anaheim, CA, p. A52

MILLHORN, Melanie, Director Human Resources, SEARHC MT. Edgecumbe Hospital, Sitka, AK, p. A29

MILLIGAN, Corbi, M.D. Chief of Staff, TriStar StoneCrest Medical Center, Smyrna, TN, p. A579

MILLIGAN, Jan, Administrator, Cook Children's Northeast Hospital, Hurst, TX, p. A614

MILLIGAN, Jeffrey, Director, Veterans Affairs North Texas Health Care System, Dallas, TX, p. A598

MILLION, Brenda, R.N. Vice President and Chief Nursing Officer, St. Bernards Medical Center, Jonesboro, AR, p. A45

MILLIRONS, Dennis C., FACHE, President, Sanford Medical Center Fargo, Fargo, ND, p. A466

MILLIS, Priscilla, Chief Executive Officer, Lakeway Regional Hospital, Morristown, TN, p. A576

MILLNER, Jane, Director Community Relations and Development, St. Lawrence Rehabilitation Center, Lawrenceville, NJ, p. A405

MILLS, Craig
Senior Financial Advisor, Park City Medical Center, Park City, UT, p. A645
Regional Vice President Culture and People, PeaceHealth Sacred Heart Medical Center at RiverBend, Springfield, OR, p. A518
Vice President Human Resources, PeaceHealth Sacred Heart Medical Center, University District, Eugene, OR, p. A512

MILLS, Dennis, Director Human Resources, San Ramon Regional Medical Center, San Ramon, CA, p. A89

MILLS, Gene, Director Information Technology, Scenic Mountain Medical Center, Big Spring, TX, p. A588

MILLS, John, President and Chief Executive Officer, United Medical Healthwest–New Orleans, Gretna, LA, p. A267

MILLS, John C., Senior Vice President Operations, Fairview Hospital, Cleveland, OH, p. A476

MILLS, Marianne, R.N. Chairperson, Stanton County Hospital, Johnson, KS, p. A236

MILLS, Nikki, Director Human Resources and Operations, Buffalo Hospital, Buffalo, MN, p. A330

MILLS, Randy, Vice President Operations and Business Development, Northcrest Medical Center, Springfield, TN, p. A579

MILLS, Scott, M.D. Vice President Medical Staff Administration and Chief Medical Officer, Mid Coast Hospital, Brunswick, ME, p. A282

MILLS, Stephanie, Vice President Information and Materials Systems, Our Lady of the Lake Regional Medical Center, Baton Rouge, LA, p. A263

MILLS, Stephen S., President and Chief Executive Officer, New York Hospital Queens,, NY, p. A435

MILLS, Vicki L., Chief Financial Officer, Anderson County Hospital, Garnett, KS, p. A234

MILLS, William, M.D
Senior Vice President Quality and Professional Affairs, Bradford Regional Medical Center, Bradford, PA, p. A521
Senior Vice President Quality and Professional Affairs, Olean General Hospital, Olean, NY, p. A438

MILLS, William H., Director, James E. Van Zandt Veterans Affairs Medical Center, Altoona, PA, p. A519

MILLS–MATHEWS, Marcy, Director Human Resources, Palms West Hospital, Loxahatchee, FL, p. A129

MILLSAPS, Janet
Chief Human Resources Officer, MedWest – Harris, Sylva, NC, p. A462
Vice President Human Resources, MedWest – Haywood, Clyde, NC, p. A450

MILLSTEAD, Bart, Administrator, Memorial Hospital of Carbondale, Carbondale, IL, p. A175

MILLWOOD, Barbara, Chief Executive Officer, Victory Medical Center Mid–Cities, Hurst, TX, p. A614

MILNE, C. Dean, D.O. Medical Director, Complex Care Hospital at Tenaya, Las Vegas, NV, p. A392

MILNES, Lynn, Chief Executive Officer, Decatur County Hospital, Leon, IA, p. A224

MILONE, Sheri, Chief Executive Officer and Administrator, Lovelace Women's Hospital, Albuquerque, NM, p. A414

MILOVICH, David, Vice President Human Resources, Saint Mary's Regional Medical Center, Reno, NV, p. A395

MILSTIEN, Kim S., President and Chief Executive Officer, Simi Valley Hospital and Health Care Services, Simi Valley, CA, p. A91

MILTENBERGER, Cynthia, Director Organizational Effectiveness, Cass Regional Medical Center, Harrisonville, MO, p. A361

MILTON, Paul A., Executive Vice President and Chief Operating Officer, Ellis Hospital, Schenectady, NY, p. A442

MILTON, Rhonda, Director Human Resources, Summit Behavioral Healthcare, Cincinnati, OH, p. A475

MILVET, Jr., Robert W., Chief Financial Officer, Preston Memorial Hospital, Kingwood, WV, p. A678

MIMOSO, Michael, FACHE, President and Chief Executive Officer, Kimball Medical Center, Lakewood, NJ, p. A405

MIMS, Staci, Chief Nursing Officer, Dorminy Medical Center, Fitzgerald, GA, p. A153

MINCIN, Kathy, Controller, HEALTHSOUTH Nittany Valley Rehabilitation Hospital, Pleasant Gap, PA, p. A539

MINCY, Lowney, Director Information Services, Southside Hospital, Bay Shore, NY, p. A421

MINDEN, Philip, Chief Executive Officer, Bartow Regional Medical Center, Bartow, FL, p. A118

MINDER, George, Chief Executive Officer, Big Horn County Memorial Hospital, Hardin, MT, p. A376

MINEAR, Michael N., Chief Information Officer, University of California, Davis Medical Center, Sacramento, CA, p. A84

MINER, Greg, Administrator, Siouxland Surgery Center, Dakota Dunes, SD, p. A559

MINER, John, Chief Financial Officer, Kindred Hospital–Central Tampa, Tampa, FL, p. A141

MINES, Kathryn, Director Human Resources, St. Joseph's Hospital, Breese, IL, p. A175

MINGLE, Regina, Senior Vice President and Chief Leadership Officer, Lancaster General Health, Lancaster, PA, p. A528

MINGS, William, M.D. Medical Director, Carl Albert Community Mental Health Center, McAlester, OK, p. A501

MINGUS, Linda, Director Human Resources, Aurora Medical Center of Oshkosh, Oshkosh, WI, p. A694

MINICK, Mark J., President and Chief Executive Officer, Van Wert County Hospital, Van Wert, OH, p. A492

MINIER, Mary, Vice President Operations, Indiana University Health White Memorial Hospital, Monticello, IN, p. A210

MINISSALE, Joseph, President, Methodist McKinney Hospital, McKinney, TX, p. A622

MINK, Linda, R.N. Vice President Clinical Service Line Development and Quality, Ivinson Memorial Hospital, Laramie, WY, p. A702

MINKEN, Stanley, M.D. Chief Medical Officer, Chester River Health System, Chestertown, MD, p. A290

MINKOWITZ, Sam, Chief Financial Officer, Woodland Heights Medical Center, Lufkin, TX, p. A621

MINNICK, Paul E., R.N. Vice President Patient Services, Beebe Medical Center, Lewes, DE, p. A114

MINNICK, Peggy, R.N., Chief Executive Officer, BHC Alhambra Hospital, Rosemead, CA, p. A83

MINNIS, Rosanne, Business Officer, Rochester Psychiatric Center, Rochester, NY, p. A441

MINON, Maria, M.D
Vice President Medical Affairs and Chief Medical Officer, Children's Hospital at Mission, Mission Viejo, CA, p. A74
Vice President Medical Affairs and Chief Medical Officer, Children's Hospital of Orange County, Orange, CA, p. A77

MINOR, Beverly, Chief Human Resources, Schleicher County Medical Center, Eldorado, TX, p. A602

MINOR, Denise, R.N. Chief Nursing Officer, Lutheran Hospital, Cleveland, OH, p. A476

MINSINGER, Linda, Vice President Hospital Division, Gifford Medical Center, Randolph, VT, p. A650

MINTONYE, Traci, Chief Financial Officer, River Hospital, Alexandria Bay, NY, p. A420

MIR, Sidney, M.D. Vice President Medical Affairs and Chief Medical Officer, Bon Secours Baltimore Health System, Baltimore, MD, p. A287

MIRABELLA, Ilene, Director Human Resources, New Bedford Rehabilitation Hospital, New Bedford, MA, p. A302

MIRANDA, A. Greg, D.O. President Medical Staff, St. Joseph's Hospital, Highland, IL, p. A184

MIRANDA, Juliet, Chief Nursing Officer, Tri–City Regional Medical Center, Hawaiian Gardens, CA, p. A63

MIRANDA, Vicki, Vice President Human Resources, Dominican Hospital, Santa Cruz, CA, p. A90

MIRDITA, Anthony, Chief Financial Officer, Putnam Hospital Center, Carmel, NY, p. A423

MIRE, Nona, Director Information Systems, Our Lady of Lourdes Regional Medical Center, Lafayette, LA, p. A271

MIRISOLA, Virginia, Fiscal Director, Spaulding Hospital for Continuing Medical Care North Shore, Salem, MA, p. A304

MIRONTI, Denise, Senior Vice President Patient Care Services, Cortland Regional Medical Center, Cortland, NY, p. A424

MIRZA, Irfan, Chief Financial Officer, Plantation General Hospital, Plantation, FL, p. A137

MISHRA, Sanjeeb, M.D. Chief of Staff, University of Maryland Charles Regional Medical Center, La Plata, MD, p. A292

MISKIMEN, Theresa, M.D. Vice President Medical Services, University of Medicine and Dentistry of New Jersey, University Behavioral Healthcare, Piscataway, NJ, p. A409

MISKO, Michael, M.D. Vice President Medical Staff Services and Chief Medical Officer, Western Missouri Medical Center, Warrensburg, MO, p. A373

MISLAN, Tim, MS Vice President Patient Care Services, Missouri Baptist Medical Center, Saint Louis, MO, p. A370

MISSI, Pamela, R.N. Vice President and Chief Nursing Officer, Columbus Regional Hospital, Columbus, IN, p. A200

MISTRETTA, Mike, Vice President Information Systems and Chief Information Officer, MedCentral – Mansfield Hospital, Mansfield, OH, p. A485

MISTROT, Cindi, Associate Administrator, South Texas Health System, Edinburg, TX, p. A600

MITCHAM, Debbie, Chief Financial Officer, Northside Hospital, Atlanta, GA, p. A146

MITCHEL, David M., Chief Executive Officer, Avoyelles Hospital, Marksville, LA, p. A273

MITCHELL, Adonna, Director Fiscal Services, North Mississippi Medical Center–Eupora, Eupora, MS, p. A346

MITCHELL, Andrew J., President and Chief Executive Officer, Peconic Bay Medical Center, Riverhead, NY, p. A440

MITCHELL, Barbara, Senior Vice President Marketing and Human Resources, UW Medicine/Valley Medical Center, Renton, WA, p. A670

MITCHELL, Bill, Administrator, Noland Hospital Anniston, Anniston, AL, p. A15

MITCHELL, Brenda, Director Human Resources, Roseland Community Hospital, Chicago, IL, p. A178

MITCHELL, Bryan, Director Information Systems, Fairfield Memorial Hospital, Fairfield, IL, p. A182

MITCHELL, Chris, Director Information Systems, Manatee Glens Hospital and Addiction Center, Bradenton, FL, p. A119

MITCHELL, Clifton, Manager Human Resources, Southwestern State Hospital, Thomasville, GA, p. A161

MITCHELL, Connie, Ph.D. Chief Information Officer, Creedmoor Psychiatric Center,, NY, p. A431

MITCHELL, Daniel, Chief Operating Officer, Radius Specialty Hospital Boston, Boston, MA, p. A297

MITCHELL, Debbie, Director Human Resources, Woodrow Wilson Rehabilitation Center, Fishersville, VA, p. A654

MITCHELL, Elizabeth C., Vice President and Administrator, Specialty Hospital of Meridian, Meridian, MS, p. A351

MITCHELL, Errol
Chief Financial Officer, INTEGRIS Canadian Valley Hospital, Yukon, OK, p. A510
Vice President, Integris Southwest Medical Center, Oklahoma City, OK, p. A503

MITCHELL, Ivan, Chief Executive Officer, Towner County Medical Center, Cando, ND, p. A465

MITCHELL, J. Stuart, Executive Vice President and Chief Operating Officer, Health First Palm Bay Hospital, Melbourne, FL, p. A130

MITCHELL, Jack C., FACHE, Chief Executive Officer, HEALTHSOUTH Rehabilitation Hospital, Fayetteville, AR, p. A43

MITCHELL, Jodie, Facility Financial Director, Sturgis Regional Hospital, Sturgis, SD, p. A563

MITCHELL, John, Assistant Vice President Operations, St. Elizabeth Grant, Williamstown, KY, p. A261

MITCHELL, Joseph J., President, Trinity Hospital Twin City, Dennison, OH, p. A480

MITCHELL, Judi, Vice President Human Resources, Navos, Seattle, WA, p. A670

MITCHELL, Kathy
Director Human Resources, Lakeview Medical Center, Rice Lake, WI, p. A696
Chief Nursing Officer, Muhlenberg Community Hospital, Greenville, KY, p. A252

MITCHELL, Kenneth W., M.D. Medical Director, St. David's North Austin Medical Center, Austin, TX, p. A586

MITCHELL, Kent, Chief Financial Officer, Hamilton Memorial Hospital District, McLeansboro, IL, p. A188

MITCHELL, Larry, M.D. Chief of Staff, Clinch Valley Medical Center, Richlands, VA, p. A660

MITCHELL, Lee, Chief Financial Officer, Red River Hospital, Wichita Falls, TX, p. A641

MITCHELL, Lori J., Chief Financial Officer, University of Washington Medical Center, Seattle, WA, p. A671

MITCHELL, Marsha, Director Human Resources, Fleming County Hospital, Flemingsburg, KY, p. A250

MITCHELL, Mary S., Chief Resource Management Services, Birmingham Veterans Affairs Medical Center, Birmingham, AL, p. A16

MITCHELL, Morris, Director Human Resources, Poplar Springs Hospital, Petersburg, VA, p. A659

MITCHELL, Naomi, Director Human Resources, Kentucky River Medical Center, Jackson, KY, p. A253

MITCHELL, Perry, M.D. Chief of Staff, Little Colorado Medical Center, Winslow, AZ, p. A40

MITCHELL, Rebekah, Chief Financial Officer, Madison County Health Care System, Winterset, IA, p. A230

MITCHELL, Richard R., Director Information Technology, Eagleville Hospital, Eagleville, PA, p. A524

MITCHELL, Sarah
Director Finance, Mary S Harper Geriatric Psychiatry Center, Tuscaloosa, AL, p. A26
Chief Financial Officer, Tilden Community Hospital, Tilden, NE, p. A390

MITCHELL, Sheena, Director Human Resources, Lafayette General Medical Center, Lafayette, LA, p. A271

MITCHELL, Steve, Chief Operating Officer, Memorial Medical Center, Modesto, CA, p. A74

MITCHELL, Susan, Vice President Patient Care Services, Vidant Roanoke–Chowan Hospital, Ahoskie, NC, p. A447

MITCHELL, Timothy, R.N. Chief Nursing Officer, Complex Care Hospital at Ridgelake, Sarasota, FL, p. A139

MITCHELL, Timothy W., Chief Executive Officer, River Oaks Hospital, Flowood, MS, p. A346

MITCHELL, Vernadine, Chief Nursing Officer, De Soto Regional Health System, Mansfield, LA, p. A273

MITCHELL III, Walton F., Director, Catawba Hospital, Catawba, VA, p. A652

MITHUN, Robert, M.D. Physician in Chief, Kaiser Permanente San Francisco Medical Center, San Francisco, CA, p. A86

MITRICK, Joseph M., FACHE, Hospital President, Baptist Medical Center Beaches, Jacksonville Beach, FL, p. A127

MITRY, Norman F.
President and Chief Executive Officer, Heritage Valley Beaver, Beaver, PA, p. A520
President and Chief Executive Officer, Sewickley Valley Hospital, (A Division of Valley Medical Facilities), Sewickley, PA, p. A541

MITTELSTAEDT, Doug, Vice President Human Resources, Children's Hospital, New Orleans, LA, p. A275

MITZNER, Jennifer C., Senior Vice President Finance and Chief Financial Officer, Hoag Memorial Hospital Presbyterian, Newport Beach, CA, p. A76

MIYAMOTO, Faye, Vice President Human Resources, Rehabilitation Hospital of the Pacific, Honolulu, HI, p. A165

MIYASAWA, Patricia, CPA Director Fiscal Service, Shriners Hospitals for Children–Honolulu, Honolulu, HI, p. A165

MIYAUCHI, Kimberly, R.N. Chief Nursing Officer, Kingman Regional Medical Center, Kingman, AZ, p. A32

MIZE, William D., Interim Chief Executive Officer, Trousdale Medical Center, Hartsville, TN, p. A570

MIZELL, Patricia A., Interim Chief Executive Officer, Riverside Medical Center, Franklinton, LA, p. A267

MIZELL, Philip L., M.D. Medical Director, The BridgeWay, North Little Rock, AR, p. A48

MIZELLE, Shelley, Chief Resource Management Division, Reynolds Army Community Hospital, Fort Sill, OK, p. A499

MIZER, Alison, Chief Financial Officer, St. Anthony North Hospital, Westminster, CO, p. A106

MIZEUR, Tracy, M.D. President Medical Staff, Abraham Lincoln Memorial Hospital, Lincoln, IL, p. A187

MIZIA, Robert, Director Information Systems and Chief Information Officer, Inspira Medical Center–Woodbury, Woodbury, NJ, p. A413

MIZONO, Gary, M.D. Physician–in–Chief, Kaiser Permanente San Rafael Medical Center, San Rafael, CA, p. A89

MIZRACH, Kenneth H., Director, Veterans Affairs New Jersey Health Care System, East Orange, NJ, p. A403

MLADY, Celine M., Chief Executive Officer, Osmond General Hospital, Osmond, NE, p. A388

MLAWSKY, Karen, Interim President and Chief Executive Officer, University of Arizona Medical Center – University Campus, Tucson, AZ, p. A39

MO, Lin H., President and Chief Executive Officer, New York Community Hospital,, NY, p. A434

MOAD, Harold, Chief Operating Officer, Elkview General Hospital, Hobart, OK, p. A499

MOAK, Jennifer, Business Office Manager, Lawrence County Hospital, Monticello, MS, p. A351

MOAK, Mike, Chief Information Officer, Southwest Mississippi Regional Medical Center, McComb, MS, p. A350

MOAKLER, Thomas J., Chief Executive Officer, Houlton Regional Hospital, Houlton, ME, p. A283

MOALLEMIAN, Patrick, Chief Executive Officer and Managing Director, Arbour H. R. I. Hospital, Brookline, MA, p. A298

MOATS, Susan, R.N. Vice President of Patient Care Services and Chief Nursing Officer, The Heart Hospital Baylor Plano, Plano, TX, p. A628

MOBERG, Kirk, M.D. Executive Vice President and Chief Medical Officer, Carle Foundation Hospital, Urbana, IL, p. A196

MOBLEY, Barbara, Chief Executive Officer, Select Specialty Hospital–Dallas, Carrollton, TX, p. A591

MOBLEY, Dana, Chief Information Officer, Our Community Hospital, Scotland Neck, NC, p. A460

MOBLEY, Paul, D.O. Clinical Director, Claremore Indian Hospital, Claremore, OK, p. A497

MOBLEY, Robert L., M.D. Executive Vice President Medical Affairs and Quality, St. Dominic–Jackson Memorial Hospital, Jackson, MS, p. A349

MOBURG, Steven T., Chief Executive Officer, Madison Hospital, Madison, MN, p. A335

MOCK, Presley, M.D. Chief of Staff, Texas Institute for Surgery at Texas Health Presbyterian Dallas, Dallas, TX, p. A597

MOCK, Sara, Director Administrative Services, Kansas Neurological Institute, Topeka, KS, p. A244

MOCKLIN, Kevin, M.D. Director Medical Staff, Lake Charles Memorial Hospital, Lake Charles, LA, p. A272

MODLIN, Stacy, Chief Operating Officer, Northwest Medical Center, Margate, FL, p. A130

MOE, Aldean J., Chief Operating Officer, Alpena Regional Medical Center, Alpena, MI, p. A308

MOEEN, Farida, M.D. Chief Operating Officer, Doctor's Hospital – Tidwell, Houston, TX, p. A609

MOELLER, Debbie A., R.N. Chief Operating Officer, Lake Pointe Medical Center, Rowlett, TX, p. A630

MOELLER, Jerry G., FACHE, President and Chief Executive Officer, Stillwater Medical Center, Stillwater, OK, p. A507

MOEN, Daniel P., President and Chief Executive Officer, Mercy Medical Center, Springfield, MA, p. A305

MOEN, Kelly, Chief Financial Officer, Memorial Medical Center – Neillsville, Neillsville, WI, p. A693

MOEN, Nellie, Coordinator Human Resources, Kindred Hospital–Bay Area, Pasadena, TX, p. A626

MOFFAT, Dodi, Supervisor Human Resources, Garden County Health Services, Oshkosh, NE, p. A388

MOFFATT, Dan, Chief Information Officer, Sanford Bemidji Medical Center, Bemidji, MN, p. A329

MOFFATT, Tracey, Chief Operating Officer, Wellmont Hancock County Hospital, Sneedville, TN, p. A579

MOFFET, Chris, Director Information Services, Bob Wilson Memorial Grant County Hospital, Ulysses, KS, p. A245

MOFFITT, Mark, Chief Information Officer, Adena Medical Center, Chillicothe, OH, p. A473

MOFFITT, Scott, Director Information Systems, Sanford Sheldon Medical Center, Sheldon, IA, p. A227

MOGHISSI, Etie, M.D. Chief Medical Staff, Centinela Hospital Medical Center, Inglewood, CA, p. A64

MOGLER, Rick A., Director Human Resources, Passavant Area Hospital, Jacksonville, IL, p. A186

MOHAMMADBHOY, Kayum, M.D. Chief of Staff, DeSoto Memorial Hospital, Arcadia, FL, p. A118

MOHAMMED, Ehtaisham, M.D. Chief Medical Officer, Sibley Medical Center, Arlington, MN, p. A328

MOHAMMED, Larry, Director Information Systems, Town and Country Hospital, Tampa, FL, p. A142

MOHAN, Amit, Executive Director, Shore Rehabilitation Institute, Brick, NJ, p. A402

MOHAN, Prabha, M.D. President Medical Staff, Texas Health Presbyterian Hospital Kaufman, Kaufman, TX, p. A616

MOHANTY, Prasanna, Assistant Administrator Finance, Kaiser Permanente Los Angeles Medical Center, Los Angeles, CA, p. A69

MOHESKY, Deb, Chief Financial Officer, Carondelet St. Mary's Hospital, Tucson, AZ, p. A38

MOHLER, Brittany, Director Human Resources, Essentia Health–Deer River, Deer River, MN, p. A331

MOHNKERN, Pearl, Vice President Human Resources, Advance Care Hospital, Hot Springs National Park, AR, p. A45

MOHR, Angela, R.N. Vice President of Nursing, St. Anthony Shawnee Hospital, Shawnee, OK, p. A506

MOHR, Steve
Senior Vice President Finance and Chief Financial Officer, Loma Linda University Behavioral Medicine Center, Redlands, CA, p. A81
Senior Vice President Finance and Chief Financial Officer, Loma Linda University Medical Center, Loma Linda, CA, p. A66

MOK, Michelle, Chief Financial Officer, Saint John's Health Center, Santa Monica, CA, p. A90

MOKFI, Shaya, M.D. Medical Director and President Medical Staff, Kindred Hospital of Northern Indiana, Mishawaka, IN, p. A210

MOKIAO, Lei, Coordinator Human Resources, Molokai General Hospital, Kaunakakai, HI, p. A166

MOLACEK, Shane, Chief Information Officer, Valley County Health System, Ord, NE, p. A388

MOLAI, Ashton, M.D. Chief Medical Officer, Wilkes Regional Medical Center, North Wilkesboro, NC, p. A458

MOLINA, Isabel, M.D. Chief Medical Officer, Lamb Healthcare Center, Littlefield, TX, p. A618

MOLINA, John, Chief Executive Officer, U. S. Public Health Service Phoenix Indian Medical Center, Phoenix, AZ, p. A36

MOLINA, Luis
Vice President Finance and Chief Financial Officer, Community Hospital, Munster, IN, p. A211
Chief Financial Officer, St. Catherine Hospital, East Chicago, IN, p. A201

MOLINARI, Michael, M.D. Chief of Staff, Corona Regional Medical Center, Corona, CA, p. A57

MOLINARO, Frank L., Chief Executive Officer, Arrowhead Hospital, Glendale, AZ, p. A31

MOLINO, C. Gene, Associate Director, Wilkes–Barre Veterans Affairs Medical Center, Wilkes–Barre, PA, p. A544

MOLITOR, Margie, R.N., Chief Executive Officer, Washakie Medical Center, Worland, WY, p. A704

MOLL, Ben, Assistant Chief Financial Officer, Nashoba Valley Medical Center, Ayer, MA, p. A295

MOLL, Gudrun, R.N. Chief Nursing Officer, St. John's Regional Medical Center, Oxnard, CA, p. A78

MOLLER, Lynn, Chief Financial Officer, Weston County Health Services, Newcastle, WY, p. A703

MOLLESTON, Julie, Executive Director Human Resources and Customer Services, University of California, Irvine Healthcare, Orange, CA, p. A78

MOLLOHAN, Joan, Vice President Human Resources, Ochsner Medical Center, New Orleans, LA, p. A275

MOLLOY, Kevin, Senior Vice President and Chief Operating Officer, Beth Israel Medical Center, New York, NY, p. A430

MOLMEN, David R., Chief Executive Officer, Altru Health System, Grand Forks, ND, p. A467

MOLTHEN, Barbara, Director Human Resources, Aurora Psychiatric Hospital, Wauwatosa, WI, p. A699

MOLYNEUX, Phyllis, Associate Administrator Human Resources and Education, Williamson Medical Center, Franklin, TN, p. A569

MOMEYER, Polly, Manager Human Resources, Millcreek Community Hospital, Erie, PA, p. A525

MON, Kathy, Vice President Operations, The Hospital at Hebrew Health Care, West Hartford, CT, p. A112

MONAGHAN, Aimee, Administrator, Compass Behavioral Center of Crowley, Crowley, LA, p. A266

MONAHAN, Jane, Director Human Resources, Monroe Clinic, Monroe, WI, p. A693

MONARCH, Beth, Executive Vice President and Chief Operating Officer, Cardinal Hill Rehabilitation Hospital, Lexington, KY, p. A254

MONASTERIO, Eugene A., M.D. Medical Director, Children's Hospital of Richmond at VCU–Brook Road Campus, Richmond, VA, p. A660

MONCHER, Daniel J., Vice President and Chief Financial Officer, Firelands Regional Health System, Sandusky, OH, p. A489

MONCRIEF, Bill, ORH IT Client Executive, Oakland Regional Hospital, Southfield, MI, p. A324

MONCZEWSKI, Patricia, Chief Operating Officer, Mercy General Hospital, Sacramento, CA, p. A83

MONDRAGON, Donald, M.D. Deputy Commander Clinical Services, Reynolds Army Community Hospital, Fort Sill, OK, p. A499

MONETTE, Steven, Chief Financial Officer, Valley Regional Hospital, Claremont, NH, p. A397

MONEY, Rory, Manager Human Resources, Methodist McKinney Hospital, McKinney, TX, p. A622

MONG, Mary, R.N. Chief Operating Officer, Coney Island Hospital,, NY, p. A431

MONGE, Catherine, Senior Vice President Operations, MedStar Washington Hospital Center, Washington, DC, p. A116

MONGE, Peter W., President, MedStar Montgomery Medical Center, Olney, MD, p. A293

MONGELL, Mitchell P., FACHE, Chief Executive Officer, Fort Walton Beach Medical Center, Fort Walton Beach, FL, p. A124

MONGER, Kenneth, Chief Financial Officer, Shawano Medical Center, Shawano, WI, p. A696

MONGER, Lloyd, Administrator, Jackson Parish Hospital, Jonesboro, LA, p. A269

MONGER, Shelton, Director Information Technology, Wayne Hospital, Greenville, OH, p. A482

MONGOVEN, Pat, Director Information Systems, Winter Haven Hospital, Winter Haven, FL, p. A144

MONIACI, Cathy, Chief Operating Officer, Shriners Hospitals for Children–Houston, Houston, TX, p. A612

MONICAL, Robert, President and Chief Executive Officer, McPherson Hospital, McPherson, KS, p. A239

MONJE, Mary Anne
Chief Financial Officer, Greater El Monte Community Hospital, South El Monte, CA, p. A91
Chief Financial Officer and Chief Operating Officer, Whittier Hospital Medical Center, Whittier, CA, p. A96

MONKRES, Paula, Administrative Assistant and Director Human Resources, Nocona General Hospital, Nocona, TX, p. A625

MONROE, Ginny, Chief Operating Officer, Newport Hospital and Health Services, Newport, WA, p. A668

MONROE, Janet J., R.N., Chief Executive Officer, Greystone Park Psychiatric Hospital, Morris Plains, NJ, p. A406

MONROE, Mary, Chief Information Officer, Tomah Veterans Affairs Medical Center, Tomah, WI, p. A697

MONSANTO, Monte, Chief Information Systems, Russell County Hospital, Russell Springs, KY, p. A260

MONSON, Kerry, Vice President Finance and Chief Financial Officer, Mercy Medical Center, Williston, ND, p. A469

MONSRUD, Michele, Director Human Resources, Clearview Regional Medical Center, Monroe, GA, p. A157

MONTAG, Kathy, Administrator Health Care, State Correctional Institution at Camp Hill, Camp Hill, PA, p. A522

MONTAGNESE, Robert A., President and Chief Executive Officer, Licking Memorial Hospital, Newark, OH, p. A487

MONTALBO, Tripp, Chief Operating Officer, Huntsville Memorial Hospital, Huntsville, TX, p. A614

MONTALVO, Cary L., Chief Executive Officer, Solara Hospital Harlingen, Harlingen, TX, p. A608

MONTALVO, Eladio, Chief Operating Officer, Doctors Hospital of Laredo, Laredo, TX, p. A618

MONTANO, Maxine, R.N. Chief Nursing Officer / Director of Patient Care, Roosevelt General Hospital, Portales, NM, p. A417

MONTANTE, Carl, Director Information Systems and Information Technology, Shriners Hospitals for Children–Portland, Portland, OR, p. A516

MONTANYE–IRELAND, Cherelle, Chief Executive Officer, Ellsworth Municipal Hospital, Iowa Falls, IA, p. A223

MONTEAGUDO, Ralph, M.D. Chief of Staff, Lincoln Hospital, Davenport, WA, p. A666

MONTECALVO, Anthony, M.D. Chief Medical Executive, Danville State Hospital, Danville, PA, p. A523

MONTELLA, Alan J., Assistant Administrator Finance, Sullivan County Community Hospital, Sullivan, IN, p. A213

MONTENEGRO, Diana, Director Human Resources, Baptist Health South Florida, South Miami Hospital, Miami, FL, p. A131

MONTENEGRO, Robert, M.D. Chief of Staff, Glacial Ridge Health System, Glenwood, MN, p. A333

MONTERA, Julie, Director Information Technology, Sutter Medical Center, Sacramento, Sacramento, CA, p. A84

MONTES, Lisa K., Chief Executive Officer, Del Amo Hospital, Torrance, CA, p. A92

MONTEYNE, Peter J., M.D. Chief Medical Staff, Promise Hospital Baton Rouge – Main Campus, Baton Rouge, LA, p. A263

MONTGOMERY, Angie, Director Human Resources, Peninsula Hospital, Louisville, TN, p. A573

MONTGOMERY, Bennie, R.N. Chief Nursing Officer and Chief Operations Officer, Kindred Hospital of Riverside, Perris, CA, p. A79

MONTGOMERY, Charles, M.D. Medical Director, Logansport Memorial Hospital, Logansport, IN, p. A209

MONTGOMERY, Dewery, Chief Operating Officer, Holmes County Hospital and Clinics, Lexington, MS, p. A350

MONTGOMERY, George H., Chief Executive Officer, Schoolcraft Memorial Hospital, Manistique, MI, p. A319

MONTGOMERY, Jackie, Director Human Resources, MetroSouth Medical Center, Blue Island, IL, p. A174

MONTGOMERY, James T., FACHE, President, Touro Infirmary, New Orleans, LA, p. A276

MONTGOMERY, Jennifer, R.N. Vice President, Nursing, Port Huron Hospital, Port Huron, MI, p. A322

MONTGOMERY, Jennifer
Chief Nursing Officer, Rochelle Community Hospital, Rochelle, IL, p. A193
Chief Financial Officer, Washakie Medical Center, Worland, WY, p. A704

MONTGOMERY, Lisa P., Administrator Finance and Support Services, MUSC Medical Center of Medical University of South Carolina, Charleston, SC, p. A549

MONTGOMERY, Mark, M.D. Vice President Quality and Medical Affairs, St. Joseph Regional Health Center, Bryan, TX, p. A590

MONTGOMERY, Mary Jim, R.N. Chief Operating Officer, Crisp Regional Hospital, Cordele, GA, p. A151

MONTGOMERY, Megan, Chief Operating Officer, Alvarado Parkway Institute Behavioral Health System, La Mesa, CA, p. A65

MONTGOMERY, Michael J., President and Chief Executive Officer, Cleo Wallace Centers Hospital, Westminster, CO, p. A106

MONTGOMERY II, Raymond W., FACHE, President and Chief Executive Officer, White County Medical Center, Searcy, AR, p. A50

MONTGOMERY, Robert, Chief Financial Officer, Shriners Hospitals for Children–Lexington, Lexington, KY, p. A254

MONTGOMERY, Tina, Chief Financial Officer, Sidney Health Center, Sidney, MT, p. A380

MONTGOMERY, Traci, Manager Human Resources, Patients' Hospital of Redding, Redding, CA, p. A81

MONTGOMERY SHAWAN, Christy, Chief Operating Officer, Black River Medical Center, Poplar Bluff, MO, p. A367

MONTOIS, John D., Chief Financial Officer, Brownwood Regional Medical Center, Brownwood, TX, p. A590

MONTOUR, Vina, Director Information Technology, U. S. Public Health Service Phoenix Indian Medical Center, Phoenix, AZ, p. A36

MONTROSS, Susan D., Vice President Human Resources, John Heinz Institute of Rehabilitation Medicine, Wilkes–Barre, PA, p. A544

MONVESKY, Kimberly, Chief Financial Officer, Pikes Peak Regional Hospital, Woodland Park, CO, p. A107

MONZINGO, Ashley, Human Resources, Accounts Payable and Payroll, TOPS Surgical Specialty Hospital, Houston, TX, p. A613

MOODY, David, Vice President Human Resources, Salina Regional Health Center, Salina, KS, p. A243

MOODY, Heather, Chief Human Resource Management, Hunter Holmes McGuire Veterans Affairs Medical Center, Richmond, VA, p. A660

MOODY, James, Chief Financial Officer, Donalsonville Hospital, Donalsonville, GA, p. A152

MOODY, Michael
Senior Vice President and Chief Financial Officer, John Muir Behavioral Health Center, Concord, CA, p. A57
Chief Financial Officer, John Muir Medical Center, Concord, Concord, CA, p. A57
Senior Vice President and Chief Financial Officer, John Muir Medical Center, Walnut Creek, Walnut Creek, CA, p. A95

MOODY, Michael L., Market Chief Executive Officer, Kindred Hospital–Louisville, Louisville, KY, p. A255

MOODY, Vicky, Director Human Resources, Houlton Regional Hospital, Houlton, ME, p. A283

MOON, Gina, Vice President Finance, New London Family Medical Center, New London, WI, p. A693

MOON, Lori, R.N. Vice President Clinical Operations/Business Development, McDonough District Hospital, Macomb, IL, p. A187

MOON, Lynn, Director Human Resources, Lock Haven Hospital, Lock Haven, PA, p. A530

MOON, Robert
Chief Financial Officer, Mercy St. Anne Hospital, Toledo, OH, p. A491
Senior Vice President Northern Region and Chief Financial Officer, Mercy St. Charles Hospital, Oregon, OH, p. A488
MOONEY, Beth, R.N. Chief Nursing Officer, HEALTHSOUTH Valley of the Sun Rehabilitation Hospital, Glendale, AZ, p. A32
MOONEY, Jamie, Vice President and Chief Information Officer, Hospital for Special Surgery, New York, NY, p. A432
MOONEY, Jimmy, Chief Executive Officer, Willingway Hospital, Statesboro, GA, p. A160
MOONEY, Katharine, R.N. Chief Nursing Officer, Upstate University Hospital, Syracuse, NY, p. A444
MOONEY, Robert W., M.D. Medical Director, Willingway Hospital, Statesboro, GA, p. A160
MOONEY, Susan E., M.D., President and Chief Executive Officer, Alice Peck Day Memorial Hospital, Lebanon, NH, p. A398
MOONEY, Thomas, M.D. President Executive Committee Medical Staff, Naval Medical Center, Portsmouth, VA, p. A659
MOORE III, Ben, President and Chief Executive Officer, River Hospital, Alexandria Bay, NY, p. A420
MOORE, Betty, Business Manager, North Mississippi Medical Center–Iuka, Iuka, MS, p. A348
MOORE, Bill, Chief Human Resources, El Centro Regional Medical Center, El Centro, CA, p. A59
MOORE, Bob, FACHE, Chief Executive Officer, Lancaster Regional Medical Center, Lancaster, PA, p. A529
MOORE, Brandon, Administrator and Chief Executive Officer, Park Place Surgical Hospital, Lafayette, LA, p. A271
MOORE, Brett, CPA Assistant Administrator Finance, Sutter Amador Hospital, Jackson, CA, p. A64
MOORE, Brian, Chief Executive Officer, St. Mary–Corwin Medical Center, Pueblo, CO, p. A105
MOORE, C. Thomas, Chief Financial Officer, Baptist Health Madisonville, Madisonville, KY, p. A257
MOORE, Carrie, Director Human Resources, Meadowbrook Rehabilitation Hospital, Gardner, KS, p. A234
MOORE, Christie, Director Human Resources, Reliant Rehabilitation Hospital Mid–Cities, Bedford, TX, p. A588
MOORE, Courtney, CPA Chief Financial Officer, Morgan Memorial Hospital, Madison, GA, p. A157
MOORE, Dana
Senior Vice President Information Services, St. Anthony Hospital, Lakewood, CO, p. A103
Senior Vice President Information Services, St. Anthony North Hospital, Westminster, CO, p. A106
MOORE, Darrell W., Chief Executive Officer, Parkridge Medical Center, Chattanooga, TN, p. A567
MOORE, Debra, Chief Executive Officer, Parkside Hospital, Tulsa, OK, p. A508
MOORE, Debra L., Senior Vice President, Memorial Health Care System, Chattanooga, TN, p. A566
MOORE, Diane C., Chief Financial Officer, Copper Queen Community Hospital, Bisbee, AZ, p. A30
MOORE, Donald F., Director, Veterans Affairs Loma Linda Healthcare System, Loma Linda, CA, p. A67
MOORE, Donna, Director Human Resources, Belmont Community Hospital, Bellaire, OH, p. A471
MOORE, Dylan, Controller, Rogers City Rehabilitation Hospital, Rogers City, MI, p. A323
MOORE, Edward H., President and Chief Executive Officer, Harrington Memorial Hospital, Southbridge, MA, p. A304
MOORE, Elizabeth, Chief Operating Officer, Silver Hill Hospital, New Canaan, CT, p. A110
MOORE, Emily, Director Human Resources and Information Technology, Haskell Memorial Hospital, Haskell, TX, p. A608
MOORE, Gary, Chief Executive Officer, Shoshone Medical Center, Kellogg, ID, p. A169
MOORE, James D., FACHE, Chief Executive Officer, Integris Southwest Medical Center, Oklahoma City, OK, p. A503
MOORE, Jane, Director, Fiscal Services, Quitman County Hospital, Marks, MS, p. A350
MOORE, Jason H., Vice President and Chief Operating Officer, Tallahassee Memorial HealthCare, Tallahassee, FL, p. A141
MOORE, Jeannie, Director Human Resources, Northern Hospital of Surry County, Mount Airy, NC, p. A458
MOORE, John, M.D. Medical Director, Granite County Medical Center, Philipsburg, MT, p. A378
MOORE, John
Administrator, Hiawatha Community Hospital, Hiawatha, KS, p. A235
Chief Executive Officer, South Lake Hospital, Clermont, FL, p. A120
MOORE, John, M.D. Vice President, Medical Affairs, SSM DePaul Health Center, Bridgeton, MO, p. A357

MOORE, John G.
Chief Financial Officer, Anson Community Hospital, Wadesboro, NC, p. A462
Vice President and Chief Financial Officer, Carolinas Medical Center–Union, Monroe, NC, p. A457
MOORE, Kadie, Director Human Resources, Vidant Edgecombe Hospital, Tarboro, NC, p. A462
MOORE, Kandi, Administrator, Specialists Hospital – Shreveport, Shreveport, LA, p. A278
MOORE, Karen, Vice President Information Technology and Chief Information Officer, Southern Regional Medical Center, Riverdale, GA, p. A159
MOORE, Kathy D., Chief Operating Officer, St. Luke's Regional Medical Center, Boise, ID, p. A168
MOORE, Kermit, R.N. Chief Operating Officer and Chief Nursing Officer, Nemaha County Hospital, Auburn, NE, p. A381
MOORE, Kerry, M.D. Chief of Staff, Carilion Tazewell Community Hospital, Tazewell, VA, p. A662
MOORE, Kim S., President and Chief Executive Officer, Saint Elizabeth Regional Medical Center, Lincoln, NE, p. A385
MOORE, Kyna, R.N. Director of Nursing, Bath Community Hospital, Hot Springs, VA, p. A655
MOORE, Larry E., Executive Vice President/Chief Operating Officer/Chief Financial Officer, Cumberland Medical Center, Crossville, TN, p. A568
MOORE, Lauralinda, Manager Finance, CHRISTUS Spohn Hospital Kleberg, Kingsville, TX, p. A616
MOORE, Leigh, Administrative Assistant Human Resources, H. C. Watkins Memorial Hospital, Quitman, MS, p. A353
MOORE, Linda, Manager Human Resources, Seymour Hospital, Seymour, TX, p. A633
MOORE, Marcia, Vice President, Tomball Regional Medical Center, Tomball, TX, p. A638
MOORE, Margaret, Manager Business Office, Sabine County Hospital, Hemphill, TX, p. A608
MOORE, Mark, Director Information Technology, Val Verde Regional Medical Center, Del Rio, TX, p. A598
MOORE, Mark E., President and Chief Executive Officer, Indiana University Health Bloomington Hospital, Bloomington, IN, p. A199
MOORE, Matthew, Senior Vice President and Chief Financial Officer, St. Francis Hospital, Columbus, GA, p. A150
MOORE, Melinda, Chief Human Resources Officer, Banner Lassen Medical Center, Susanville, CA, p. A92
MOORE, Mike, Chief Financial Officer, Jane Phillips Medical Center, Bartlesville, OK, p. A496
MOORE, Mindy S., Chief Executive Officer, Cornerstone Hospital of SouthEast Arizona, Tucson, AZ, p. A38
MOORE, Monty, Director Information Services, Summit Surgical, LLC, Hutchinson, KS, p. A236
MOORE, Nelda, Director Data Processing, Memorial Hospital and Manor, Bainbridge, GA, p. A148
MOORE, Paul, Chief Information Officer, Connecticut Mental Health Center, New Haven, CT, p. A110
MOORE, Paula, R.N. Chief Nursing Officer, Twin Cities Community Hospital, Templeton, CA, p. A92
MOORE, Phyllis, Director Information Systems and Data Center, Doctors Medical Center–San Pablo Campus, San Pablo, CA, p. A88
MOORE, Richard
Director Information Technology, Hawthorn Children Psychiatric Hospital, Saint Louis, MO, p. A369
Director Information Technology, Metropolitan St. Louis Psychiatric Center, Saint Louis, MO, p. A370
Director Information Technology, St. Louis Psychiatric Rehabilitation Center, Saint Louis, MO, p. A371
MOORE, Rick
Chief Information Officer, Bethesda North Hospital, Cincinnati, OH, p. A474
Chief Information Officer, Good Samaritan Hospital, Cincinnati, OH, p. A474
MOORE, Rita, Director Finance, Boscobel Area Health Care, Boscobel, WI, p. A684
MOORE, Robin A., Vice President Human Resources, Concord Hospital, Concord, NH, p. A397
MOORE, Rodney, M.D. Vice President Medical Affairs, Health First Cape Canaveral Hospital, Cocoa Beach, FL, p. A121
MOORE, Sandee, Chief Operating Officer, Eastern Idaho Regional Medical Center, Idaho Falls, ID, p. A169
MOORE, Sandra, Director Human Resources, Mayo Clinic Health System – Chippewa Valley in Bloomer, Bloomer, WI, p. A684
MOORE, Sandy, Interim CFO, Mercer County Hospital, Aledo, IL, p. A173
MOORE, Sheriann, Service Unit Director, U. S. Public Health Service Indian Hospital, Winnebago, NE, p. A390
MOORE, Steve, Chief Financial Officer, Southern Tennessee Medical Center, Winchester, TN, p. A580
MOORE, Susan B., Interim Chief Financial Officer, UCSF Medical Center, San Francisco, CA, p. A87

MOORE, Susan L., R.N. Director Nursing, Thayer County Health Services, Hebron, NE, p. A384
MOORE, Tim, Chief Accounting Officer and Vice President Ancillary Services, Blessing Hospital, Quincy, IL, p. A193
MOORE, Tim, R.N. Senior Vice President and Chief Information Officer, Hoag Memorial Hospital Presbyterian, Newport Beach, CA, p. A76
MOORE, Timothy H., Chief Executive Officer, North Mississippi Medical Center – Tupelo, Tupelo, MS, p. A354
MOORE, Vernon, Chief Business and Finance, University of Texas Health Science Center at Tyler, Tyler, TX, p. A639
MOORE, Warren E., Executive Vice President and Chief Operating Officer, Children's Specialized Hospital–PSE&G, New Brunswick, NJ, p. A407
MOORE, William, Chief Information Officer, Parrish Medical Center, Titusville, FL, p. A143
MOORE, William T., Chief Executive Officer, Atlanta Medical Center, Atlanta, GA, p. A146
MOORE–HARDY, Cynthia, FACHE, President and Chief Executive Officer, Lake Health, Concord Township, OH, p. A478
MOOREHOUSE, Brett, FACHE Vice President and Chief Operating Officer, Ranken Jordan – A Pediatric Specialty Hospital, Maryland Heights, MO, p. A365
MOORER, Thad, Chief Information Officer, Eastside Psychiatric Hospital, Tallahassee, FL, p. A140
MOORHEAD, David, M.D. Chief Medical Officer, Florida Hospital, Orlando, FL, p. A135
MOORMAN, Gary L., D.O. Vice President Medical Affairs, Fisher–Titus Medical Center, Norwalk, OH, p. A487
MOORMAN, Kristi, Supervisor Human Resources, Share Medical Center, Alva, OK, p. A495
MOOSS, Eric, Director Information Technology, Littleton Adventist Hospital, Littleton, CO, p. A103
MOOTS, Eric, Vice President and Chief Financial Officer, Adventist GlenOaks Hospital, Glendale Heights, IL, p. A183
MORACA, Lynn, Director Human Resources, Lodi Community Hospital, Lodi, OH, p. A484
MORAHAN, John R., FACHE, President and Chief Executive Officer, St. Joseph Medical Center, Reading, PA, p. A540
MORALES, Carlos, Manager Data Processing, Valley Baptist Medical Center–Brownsville, Brownsville, TX, p. A590
MORALES, Carmela, M.D. Chief of Staff, University Medical Center of El Paso, El Paso, TX, p. A602
MORALES, Joel, Chief Financial Officer, Fort Duncan Regional Medical Center, Eagle Pass, TX, p. A600
MORALES, John R., Chief Financial Officer, John H. Stroger Jr. Hospital of Cook County, Chicago, IL, p. A177
MORALES, Juan A., MSN, Health System Director, Tennessee Valley Healthcare System, Nashville, TN, p. A577
MORALES, Steve, Director Human Resources, Sutter Medical Center of Santa Rosa, Chanate Campus, Santa Rosa, CA, p. A90
MORALES, Trish, Director Human Resources, Lakewood Ranch Medical Center, Bradenton, FL, p. A119
MORAN, Colleen M., Director Human Resources, Spaulding Hospital for Continuing Medical Care North Shore, Salem, MA, p. A304
MORAN, Debbie, Executive Director, Carl Albert Community Mental Health Center, McAlester, OK, p. A501
MORAN, Janet, Vice President Human Resources, Lourdes Medical Center of Burlington County, Willingboro, NJ, p. A412
MORAN, Marian, Chief Information Officer, St. Mary Medical Center, Langhorne, PA, p. A529
MORAN, Tim, Interim Chief Executive Officer, Mountain West Medical Center, Tooele, UT, p. A647
MORASKO, Jerome
Chief Executive Officer, Bucyrus Community Hospital, Bucyrus, OH, p. A472
President and Chief Executive Officer, Galion Community Hospital, Galion, OH, p. A482
MORASKO, Robert A., Chief Executive Officer, Campbell County Memorial Hospital, Gillette, WY, p. A702
MORAVICK, Donna, MSN, Executive Director, Southside Hospital, Bay Shore, NY, p. A421
MORDECAI, Steve, Director Human Resources, Griffin Hospital, Derby, CT, p. A108
MOREAU, Kim, Assistant Vice President Information Systems, Carroll Hospital Center, Westminster, MD, p. A294
MOREAU, Steven C., President and Chief Executive Officer, St. Joseph Hospital, Orange, CA, p. A78
MOREFIELD, Terri, Deputy Chief Human Resources Division, Bassett Army Community Hospital, Fort Wainwright, AK, p. A28
MOREH, Swenda, Chief Executive Officer, Kindred Hospital–Baldwin Park, Baldwin Park, CA, p. A54
MOREIN, Sandy, Chief Operating Officer, Mercy Regional Medical Center, Ville Platte, LA, p. A280
MORELAND, John, M.D. Chief Medical Officer, Marcus Daly Memorial Hospital, Hamilton, MT, p. A376

MORELAND, Tresha, Vice President Human Resources, Fremont–Rideout Health Group, Marysville, CA, p. A73

MORELLI, Gerald, Director Human Resources, Philadelphia Veterans Affairs Medical Center, Philadelphia, PA, p. A536

MORELLO, Salvatore, Vice President Finance, The Mount Sinai Hospital of Queens,, NY, p. A437

MORENO, Raymond, M.D. Vice President Medical Affairs, Tift Regional Medical Center, Tifton, GA, p. A161

MORESI, Randy, Chief Executive Officer, North Hills Hospital, North Richland Hills, TX, p. A625

MORETTE, Joseph M., Executive Vice President, Methodist Rehabilitation Center, Jackson, MS, p. A348

MORETTI, Scott, M.D. Chief of Staff, Aurora Medical Center of Washington County, Hartford, WI, p. A688

MOREY, Scott, Chief Nursing Officer, Maryvale Hospital Medical Center, Phoenix, AZ, p. A34

MORGAN, Daniel R., Chief Operating Officer, Bay Medical Center Sacred Heart, Panama City, FL, p. A136

MORGAN, Derek, Director Human Resources, Avista Adventist Hospital, Louisville, CO, p. A104

MORGAN, Dwight, Vice President Human Resources, Aurora St. Luke's Medical Center, Milwaukee, WI, p. A691

MORGAN, James H., Chief Executive Officer, Louisiana Specialty Hospital, Marrero, LA, p. A273

MORGAN, Janet, Manager Human Resources, Lander Regional Hospital, Lander, WY, p. A702

MORGAN, Jeff, Director Information Systems, Northeastern Nevada Regional Hospital, Elko, NV, p. A391

MORGAN, Jennifer, Chief Executive Officer and Managing Director, Anchor Hospital, Atlanta, GA, p. A145

MORGAN, Kelly C., President and Chief Executive Officer, Mercy Medical Center, Roseburg, OR, p. A517

MORGAN, Larry, Controller, T. J. Samson Community Hospital, Glasgow, KY, p. A251

MORGAN, Lori, M.D., Chief Administrative Officer, Legacy Emanuel Hospital and Health Center, Portland, OR, p. A516

MORGAN, Mace, Director Information Systems, Minden Medical Center, Minden, LA, p. A274

MORGAN, Margaret, Director Human Resources, Centinela Hospital Medical Center, Inglewood, CA, p. A64

MORGAN, Matthew, Manager Human Resources, Lakeside Medical Center, Belle Glade, FL, p. A118

MORGAN, Michelle C., Chief Human Resource Manager, Saint Anthony Hospital, Chicago, IL, p. A179

MORGAN, Norma J., Chief Executive Officer, Effingham Hospital, Springfield, GA, p. A160

MORGAN, Nyle, Chief Information Officer, Sheridan Memorial Hospital, Sheridan, WY, p. A703

MORGAN, Rebecca
  Senior Director Human Resources, Pioneer Memorial Hospital, Prineville, OR, p. A517
  Senior Director Human Resources, St. Charles Medical Center – Bend, Bend, OR, p. A511
  Senior Director Human Resources, St. Charles Medical Center – Redmond, Redmond, OR, p. A517

MORGAN, Richard P., M.D. Chief of Staff, Sanford Luverne Medical Center, Luverne, MN, p. A334

MORGAN, Rose, R.N. Vice President Patient Care Services, Princeton Community Hospital, Princeton, WV, p. A680

MORGAN, Samuel, Senior Vice President Financial Operations, Culpeper Regional Hospital, Culpeper, VA, p. A653

MORGAN, Teresa
  Chief Financial Officer, McGehee–Desha County Hospital, McGehee, AR, p. A47
  Assistant Vice President Human Resources, Shannon Medical Center, San Angelo, TX, p. A630

MORGAN, Timothy J., Chief Financial Officer, Maryville Behavioral Health Hospital, Des Plaines, IL, p. A181

MORGAN, Vicky, Director Information Services, Centinela Hospital Medical Center, Inglewood, CA, p. A64

MORGAN, Victor, Chief Financial Officer, MidMichigan Medical Center–Gratiot, Alma, MI, p. A308

MORGAN, W. Hugh, M.D. Chief Medical Staff, Edgefield County Hospital, Edgefield, SC, p. A551

MORGENROTH, Betsy, Director Human Resources, Hoopeston Regional Health Center, Hoopeston, IL, p. A185

MORGESE, Vincent, M.D. Vice President Medical Affairs, Queen of the Valley Medical Center, Napa, CA, p. A76

MORIARTY, Bill, M.D. Chief Medical Officer, Bay Area Hospital, Coos Bay, OR, p. A512

MORILLO, Jose F., Chief Executive Officer, Bayfront Health Punta Gorda, Punta Gorda, FL, p. A138

MORIN, Linda, Director of Nursing, Copper Queen Community Hospital, Bisbee, AZ, p. A30

MORISSETTE, Daniel, Senior Vice President Finance and Administration, The University of Toledo Medical Center, Toledo, OH, p. A491

MORISSETTE, Philip, Chief Financial Officer, Bridgton Hospital, Bridgton, ME, p. A282

MORITZ, Mary, Administrator Human Resources, Humboldt County Memorial Hospital, Humboldt, IA, p. A222

MORLEY, Jr., Andrew P., M.D. Senior Vice President and Chief Medical Officer, The Medical Center, Columbus, GA, p. A150

MORLEY, Denise M., Director Human Resources, Wyoming County Community Hospital, Warsaw, NY, p. A445

MORLOCK, Paul, Vice President Human Resources, Stanly Regional Medical Center, Albemarle, NC, p. A447

MORNELLI, Ronald, Senior Vice President Operations and Chief Operating Officer, Olean General Hospital, Olean, NY, p. A438

MORNINGSTAR, Tim, Blue Star, Unity Medical & Surgical Hospital, Mishawaka, IN, p. A210

MORON, David, M.D. Clinical Director, Rio Grande State Center/South Texas Health Care System, Harlingen, TX, p. A608

MORONY, David, Chief Financial Officer, Casa Colina Hospital for Rehabilitative Medicine, Pomona, CA, p. A80

MOROSES, Mark, Vice President and Chief Information Officer, St. Luke's–Roosevelt Hospital Center, New York, NY, p. A436

MORQUECHO, Adam
  Director Information Systems, Garden Grove Hospital and Medical Center, Garden Grove, CA, p. A62
  Director Information Technology, Huntington Beach Hospital, Huntington Beach, CA, p. A64
  Director Information Technology, La Palma Intercommunity Hospital, La Palma, CA, p. A65
  Director Information Technology, West Anaheim Medical Center, Anaheim, CA, p. A52

MORREALE, Daniel, Vice President and Chief Information Officer, Kingsbrook Jewish Medical Center,, NY, p. A433

MORREALE, Gene, President and Chief Executive Officer, Oneida Healthcare, Oneida, NY, p. A438

MORRELL, Dan, Manager Information Systems, Sierra Vista Hospital, Truth or Consequences, NM, p. A418

MORRELL, Jeffrey F., Chief Executive Officer, Intermountain Hospital, Boise, ID, p. A167

MORRICAL, Michael G., Chief Executive Officer, McKenzie Regional Hospital, McKenzie, TN, p. A574

MORRIS, Alexander, Corporate Director Human Resources, Fort Washington Medical Center, Fort Washington, MD, p. A291

MORRIS, Beverly
  Vice President Human Resources, Kettering Medical Center, Kettering, OH, p. A483
  Vice President Human Resources, Sycamore Medical Center, Miamisburg, OH, p. A486

MORRIS, Christi, Director of Nursing, Chambers County Public Hospital District 1, Anahuac, TX, p. A582

MORRIS, Christopher
  Director Human Resources, Wheaton Franciscan Healthcare – Elmbrook Memorial, Brookfield, WI, p. A684
  Vice President Human Resources, Wheaton Franciscan Healthcare – St. Joseph's, Milwaukee, WI, p. A692
  Director Human Resources, Wheaton Franciscan Healthcare – The Wisconsin Heart Hospital, Wauwatosa, WI, p. A699

MORRIS, Darrel, Chief Executive Officer, Drumright Regional Hospital, Drumright, OK, p. A497

MORRIS, David, Chief Executive Officer, University Behavioral Health of El Paso, El Paso, TX, p. A602

MORRIS, Debbie M., Director Human Resources, Marcus Daly Memorial Hospital, Hamilton, MT, p. A376

MORRIS, Dennis, Area Finance Officer, Kaiser Permanente Oakland Medical Center, Oakland, CA, p. A77

MORRIS, Don, Vice President Human Resources, Wesley Medical Center, Wichita, KS, p. A247

MORRIS, Douglas
  Chief Financial Officer, St. Francis Health Care Centre, Green Springs, OH, p. A482
  Chief Financial Officer, Vibra Hospital of Southeastern Michigan, Lincoln Park, MI, p. A319

MORRIS, Dwain, Vice President and Chief Financial Officer, University of Texas M.D. Anderson Cancer Center, Houston, TX, p. A613

MORRIS, Elaine F., Chief Executive Officer, Methodist Ambulatory Surgery Hospital, San Antonio, TX, p. A631

MORRIS, George, Vice President Information Technology and Chief Information Officer, Northwest Community Hospital, Arlington Heights, IL, p. A173

MORRIS, Gerry, Administrator, Magnolia Behavioral Healthcare, Lacombe, LA, p. A270

MORRIS, Janet, Director Human Resources, HEALTHSOUTH Lakeview Rehabilitation Hospital, Elizabethtown, KY, p. A250

MORRIS, Janice, Accountant, CrossRidge Community Hospital, Wynne, AR, p. A51

MORRIS, Jarrett, Vice President Finance, Carolinas Medical Center–Lincoln, Lincolnton, NC, p. A456

MORRIS, Jeffrey, M.D
  Medical Director, Summa Barberton Citizens Hospital, Barberton, OH, p. A471
  Vice President Medical Affairs, Summa Wadsworth–Rittman Hospital, Wadsworth, OH, p. A492

MORRIS, Jim, Vice President Finance, Baptist Health Louisville, Louisville, KY, p. A255

MORRIS, Jody, President and Chief Operating Officer, Novant Health Franklin Medical Center, Louisburg, NC, p. A456

MORRIS, John, M.D. Chief of Staff, Cullman Regional Medical Center, Cullman, AL, p. A18

MORRIS, Lisa, Vice President Human Resources, Swedish Medical Center, Englewood, CO, p. A100

MORRIS, Marsha, Manager Information Services, Fairview Park Hospital, Dublin, GA, p. A152

MORRIS, Paul G., Chief Financial Officer, Alaska Regional Hospital, Anchorage, AK, p. A27

MORRIS, R. Randall, Administrator, West Carroll Memorial Hospital, Oak Grove, LA, p. A276

MORRIS, Rosanna D., R.N. CNO & Senior VP Patient Care Services, Nebraska Medical Center, Omaha, NE, p. A388

MORRIS, Shawna, Senior Vice President Operations and Chief Operating Officer, Menninger Clinic, Houston, TX, p. A611

MORRIS, Terri, Manager Information Systems, Methodist Richardson Medical Center, Richardson, TX, p. A628

MORRIS, Toni, Chief Executive Officer, Sutter Surgical Hospital – North Valley, Yuba City, CA, p. A96

MORRIS, Tony, Business Manager, Mental Health Institute, Cherokee, IA, p. A218

MORRIS, Wayne, Chief Financial Officer, Marion Veterans Affairs Medical Center, Marion, IL, p. A187

MORRIS, Will, Director Information Technology, Tri–Lakes Medical Center, Batesville, MS, p. A344

MORRISON, Chris,Naval Hospital Oak Harbor, Oak Harbor, WA, p. A668

MORRISON, Christopher, Deputy Chief Executive Officer, Trenton Psychiatric Hospital, Trenton, NJ, p. A411

MORRISON, Deane, Chief Information Officer, Concord Hospital, Concord, NH, p. A397

MORRISON, Devin, Director Administration, Naval Hospital Pensacola, Pensacola, FL, p. A136

MORRISON, Dianne, Director Human Resources, Mizell Memorial Hospital, Opp, AL, p. A24

MORRISON, Gary, Chief Operating Officer, Karmanos Cancer Center, Detroit, MI, p. A312

MORRISON, Greg, M.D. Vice President Medical Affairs, OhioHealth Grant Medical Center, Columbus, OH, p. A478

MORRISON, J. E., M.D. Chief Medical Officer, Hillcrest Baptist Medical Center, Waco, TX, p. A640

MORRISON, Kathy E., Executive Director Human Resources, St. Catherine Hospital, Garden City, KS, p. A234

MORRISON, Leon M., M.D. Vice President Medical Staff Services, Carteret General Hospital, Morehead City, NC, p. A457

MORRISON, Mark, Director Support Services, Shriners Hospitals for Children–Philadelphia, Philadelphia, PA, p. A536

MORRISON, Maureen, Vice President Financial Services, Advocate Trinity Hospital, Chicago, IL, p. A176

MORRISON, Michael, Chief Financial Officer, TriStar Hendersonville Medical Center, Hendersonville, TN, p. A570

MORRISON, Sarah, Vice President Clinical Services, Shepherd Center, Atlanta, GA, p. A147

MORRISSETT, Barbara, Vice President Human Resources, St. Mary's Medical Center, San Francisco, CA, p. A87

MORRISSETTE, Daniel, Chief Financial Officer, Stanford Hospital and Clinics, Palo Alto, CA, p. A79

MORRISSEY, Dawn, Chief Operating Officer, Northern Colorado Long Term Acute Hospital, Johnstown, CO, p. A102

MORRISSEY, Moira, Chief Operating Officer and General Counsel, Four Winds Hospital, Katonah, NY, p. A428

MORRISSEY, Una E., R.N. Senior Vice President, Chief Nursing Officer and Chief Operating Officer, New York Community Hospital,, NY, p. A434

MORROW, Jeff, Chief Executive Officer, Doctor's Hospital of Deer Creek, Leesville, LA, p. A272

MORROW, Jennifer, Director Human Resources, San Joaquin Valley Rehabilitation Hospital, Fresno, CA, p. A62

MORROW, Pat, Director Human Resources, Walker Baptist Medical Center, Jasper, AL, p. A22

MORROW, Randy, Interim Chief Executive Officer, Boone Hospital Center, Columbia, MO, p. A359

MORROW, Renee, Business Manager, Meadowbrook Rehabilitation Hospital, Gardner, KS, p. A234

MORROW, Robert, M.D. Chief of Staff, McDowell Hospital, Marion, NC, p. A457

MORROW, Shawn, Administrator, Heber Valley Medical Center, Heber City, UT, p. A644

MORROW, Susan, R.N. Chief Nursing Officer, Garfield County Public Hospital District, Pomeroy, WA, p. A669

MORROW, W. Robert, M.D. Senior Vice President and Medical Director, Arkansas Children's Hospital, Little Rock, AR, p. A46

MORSE, Brad S., Chief Executive Officer, Pampa Regional Medical Center, Pampa, TX, p. A626

MORSE, Larry, Chief Executive Officer and Administrator, Johnson Regional Medical Center, Clarksville, AR, p. A42

MORSE, Patrick, M.D. President Medical Staff, West Branch Regional Medical Center, West Branch, MI, p. A326

MORSE, Rebecca, Chief Human Resources Officer, Palo Verde Hospital, Blythe, CA, p. A55

MORSTAD, Joan, Director Information Systems, Coliseum Medical Centers, Macon, GA, p. A156

MORTENSEN, Shane, Chief Financial Officer, San Luis Valley Regional Medical Center, Alamosa, CO, p. A97

MORTENSSON, Marcie, Chief Human Resources Officer, Tahoe Forest Hospital District, Truckee, CA, p. A93

MORTH, Paul, Vice President Finance, Sanford Bismarck, Bismarck, ND, p. A465

MORTINSEN, Roy, M.D. Chief of Staff, Sanford Vermillion Medical Center, Vermillion, SD, p. A563

MORTON, David, M.D. Chief Medical Officer, St. Anthony's Medical Center, Saint Louis, MO, p. A370

MORTON, Denise, Chief Financial Officer, Alexandria Veterans Affairs Health Care System, Pineville, LA, p. A276

MORTON, Lauren, Chief Operating Officer, Sierra Providence East Medical Center, El Paso, TX, p. A602

MORTON, Robert, M.D. Medical Director, Rolling Hills Hospital, Ada, OK, p. A495

MORTON, Stan C., FACHE, President, Texas Health Presbyterian Hospital Denton, Denton, TX, p. A599

MORTON, Stephanie, Chief Information Officer, Providence Alaska Medical Center, Anchorage, AK, p. A27

MORTOZA, Angela, Administrator, Adair County Memorial Hospital, Greenfield, IA, p. A222

MORVANT, Stephanie, Chief Executive Officer, Northshore Specialty Hospital, Covington, LA, p. A266

MOSCATO, Mary K., Chief Operating Officer–Hebrew Rehabilitation Center and Hebrew Senior Life Health Care Services, Hebrew Rehabilitation Center, Boston, MA, p. A297

MOSCHITTA, Philip C., Director, Northport Veterans Affairs Medical Center, Northport, NY, p. A437

MOSCHKAU, Don, Director Human Resources, Fairview Lakes Health Services, Wyoming, MN, p. A343

MOSELY, Chisty, Director Information Management, Saint Simons by–the–Sea Hospital, Saint Simons Island, GA, p. A159

MOSER, Brenda, Vice President Finance, Regional Health Services of Howard County, Cresco, IA, p. A219

MOSER, Cindy, Director Human Resources, Allegheny Valley Hospital, Natrona Heights, PA, p. A533

MOSER, Joseph, M.D. Vice President Medical Staff Affairs, Anne Arundel Medical Center, Annapolis, MD, p. A287

MOSER, Neal, M.D. Medical Director, HEALTHSOUTH Northern Kentucky Rehabilitation Hospital, Edgewood, KY, p. A250

MOSER, Thomas B., Chief Operating Officer, Forbes Regional Hospital, Monroeville, PA, p. A532

MOSER, Tracy, Director Human Resources, Upper Valley Medical Center, Troy, OH, p. A491

MOSES, Deana, Manager Human Resources, Lincoln County Medical Center, Ruidoso, NM, p. A418

MOSESIAN, Robert, Controller, HEALTHSOUTH Bakersfield Rehabilitation Hospital, Bakersfield, CA, p. A54

MOSHIER, John, Director Human Resources, Clara Barton Hospital, Hoisington, KS, p. A235

MOSHIRPUR, Jasmin, M.D
Dean and Medical Director, Elmhurst Hospital Center,, NY, p. A431
Chief Medical Officer, Queens Hospital Center,, NY, p. A436

MOSHOFSKY, Bill, M.D. Chief of Staff, PeaceHealth Sacred Heart Medical Center, University District, Eugene, OR, p. A512

MOSIER, Dawn, Director Human Resources, HEALTHSOUTH Rehabilitation Institute of Tucson, Tucson, AZ, p. A38

MOSIER, John, D.O. Chief of Staff, Herington Municipal Hospital, Herington, KS, p. A235

MOSKOWITZ, Samuel E., President, MedStar Franklin Square Medical Center, Baltimore, MD, p. A288

MOSLEY, Brian, Coordinator Human Resources and Payroll Benefits, Kindred Hospital–San Antonio, San Antonio, TX, p. A631

MOSLEY, Christopher R., FACHE Chief Operating Officer, Grady Memorial Hospital, Atlanta, GA, p. A146

MOSLEY, Tonja, Chief Financial Officer, Heart of Florida Regional Medical Center, Davenport, FL, p. A121

MOSS, Austin, Vice President Human Resources, Jennie Stuart Medical Center, Hopkinsville, KY, p. A252

MOSS, C. Renee, M.D. Chief Medical Officer, Riverside Rehabilitation Institute, Newport News, VA, p. A658

MOSS, Misty, Director Business Administration, Logansport State Hospital, Logansport, IN, p. A209

MOSS, Stuart, Chief Financial Officer, Marlton Rehabilitation Hospital, Marlton, NJ, p. A406

MOSSOFF, Alan, Chief Financial Officer, Northern Dutchess Hospital, Rhinebeck, NY, p. A440

MOSSOP, Karen, Director Human Resources, Montgomery County Emergency Service, Norristown, PA, p. A533

MOST, Kevin, D.O. Vice President Medical Affairs, Central DuPage Hospital, Winfield, IL, p. A197

MOTAKEF, Shahin, Chief Executive Officer, Scott and White Memorial Hospital, Temple, TX, p. A636

MOTONAGA, Gregg, M.D. Chief of Staff, Central Peninsula General Hospital, Soldotna, AK, p. A29

MOTTE, Michael J., Chief Executive Officer, St. Alexius Hospital – Broadway Campus, Saint Louis, MO, p. A370

MOUGHON, Edward, Superintendent, Big Spring State Hospital, Big Spring, TX, p. A588

MOUISSET, Rena B., Director Human Resources and Contract Compliance, St. Martin Hospital, Breaux Bridge, LA, p. A264

MOUNIE, Mike, Director Finance, Sentara Obici Hospital, Suffolk, VA, p. A662

MOUNT, Mary H., Administrative Officer, Fort Belknap U. S. Public Health Service Indian Hospital, Harlem, MT, p. A377

MOUNTAIN, J. Michael, Chief Financial Officer, RiverValley Behavioral Health Hospital, Owensboro, KY, p. A258

MOUSA, Ayman, Ph.D., Chief Executive Officer, Pacifica Hospital of the Valley,, CA, p. A71

MOUSTAKAKIS, John, Senior Vice President Information Systems and Chief Information Officer, Westchester Medical Center, Valhalla, NY, p. A445

MOVER, Michael, Chief Information Officer, Riverview Hospital, Noblesville, IN, p. A211

MOWDER, Kristan, Director Administration and Patient Care Services, Eastern State Hospital, Lexington, VA, p. A254

MOYA, Linda, Director Human Resources, Mesilla Valley Hospital, Las Cruces, NM, p. A416

MOYER, Dale, Vice President Information Systems, Evangelical Community Hospital, Lewisburg, PA, p. A530

MOYER, Douglas J., Chief Executive Officer, Mary Black Memorial Hospital, Spartanburg, SC, p. A556

MOYER, Ed, Chief Operating Officer, Emory–Adventist Hospital, Smyrna, GA, p. A160

MOYER, Mark, Vice President and Chief Financial Officer, Novant Health Presbyterian Medical Center, Charlotte, NC, p. A450

MOYER, Patricia M., Chief Financial Officer, Herington Municipal Hospital, Herington, KS, p. A235

MOYER, William E., President, St. Luke's Hospital – Miners Campus, Coaldale, PA, p. A523

MOYNIER, Ryan, Chief Financial Officer, Castleview Hospital, Price, UT, p. A645

MRAMOR, Joann, Director Human Resources, Seven Rivers Regional Medical Center, Crystal River, FL, p. A121

MRUK, Donald, M.D. President Medical Staff, Athol Memorial Hospital, Athol, MA, p. A295

MUCCILLI, Pamela M., Vice President and Chief Information Officer, The William W. Backus Hospital, Norwich, CT, p. A111

MUCKENFUSS, Penny, Chief Nursing Officer, Lighthouse Care Center of Conway, Conway, SC, p. A551

MUDD, Karen, Director Marketing and Public Affairs, Sutter Tracy Community Hospital, Tracy, CA, p. A93

MUDRY, Janel, Chief Operating Officer, Southwest Regional Medical Center, Waynesburg, PA, p. A543

MUELLER, Arthur, Director Management Information Systems, Cuero Community Hospital, Cuero, TX, p. A594

MUELLER, Charles, M.D. Chief of Staff, Texas County Memorial Hospital, Houston, MO, p. A361

MUELLER, Eric, Chief Executive Officer, Reliant Rehabilitation Hospital Central Texas, Round Rock, TX, p. A629

MUELLER, Jeff T., M.D. Medical Director, Mayo Clinic Hospital, Phoenix, AZ, p. A35

MUELLER, Michael E., Chief Financial Officer, Health Central, Ocoee, FL, p. A134

MUELLER, Paul A., Chief Operating Officer, Rogers Memorial Hospital, Oconomowoc, WI, p. A693

MUELLER, Robert, M.D. Chief of Staff, Madison County Hospital, London, OH, p. A484

MUGAN, James, Senior Vice President for Clincial Services and Chief Operating Officer, Agnesian HealthCare, Fond Du Lac, WI, p. A686

MUHS, David, Chief Financial Officer, Henry County Health Center, Mount Pleasant, IA, p. A225

MULDER, Dale R., Chief Executive Officer, Kindred Rehabilitation Hospital Clear Lake, Webster, TX, p. A640

MULDER, Sherri, Director Information Technology, Clay County Hospital, Ashland, AL, p. A15

MULDER, Steven, M.D., President and Chief Executive Officer, Hutchinson Health, Hutchinson, MN, p. A334

MULDERIG, Marsha L., R.N. Chief Nursing Officer, Crisp Regional Hospital, Cordele, GA, p. A151

MULDOON, Patrick L., FACHE, President and Chief Executive Officer, Health Alliance Hospitals, Leominster, MA, p. A301

MULDOON, Sean R., M.D. Senior Vice President & Chief Medical Officer–Kindred Healthcare, Hospital Divison, Kindred Hospital Northland, Kansas City, MO, p. A363

MULKEY, Peter, Chief Executive Officer, Clinch Valley Medical Center, Richlands, VA, p. A660

MULLAHEY, Mike, Operations Manager, Albany Stratton Veterans Affairs Medical Center, Albany, NY, p. A420

MULLANEY, Ruth, Personnel Officer, Dorothea Dix Psychiatric Center, Bangor, ME, p. A281

MULLANEY, Susan, Administrator, Kaiser Permanente Sunnyside Medical Center, Clackamas, OR, p. A511

MULLEN, Ellen, M.D. Chief of Staff, Iberia Medical Center, New Iberia, LA, p. A275

MULLEN, Gary, Chief Information Officer, Madison County Health Care System, Winterset, IA, p. A230

MULLEN, Ron, Superintendent, Mental Health Institute, Mount Pleasant, IA, p. A225

MULLEN, Thomas R., President and Chief Executive Officer, Mercy Medical Center, Baltimore, MD, p. A288

MULLENAX, Paul, Business Manager, Wyoming State Hospital, Evanston, WY, p. A702

MULLENS, Allen, M.D. Chief Medical Staff, Norton Community Hospital, Norton, VA, p. A658

MULLER, A. Gary, FACHE, President and Chief Executive Officer, Marquette General Health System, Marquette, MI, p. A319

MULLER, Dorothy A., Director Human Resources, Holliswood Hospital,, NY, p. A432

MULLER, Lynn, Chief Financial Officer, North Metro Medical Center, Jacksonville, AR, p. A45

MULLER, Oz, Director Human Resources, Porter Adventist Hospital, Denver, CO, p. A100

MULLER, William, M.D. Vice President Medical Affairs, Milford Regional Medical Center, Milford, MA, p. A302

MULLIGAN, Marie, R.N. Vice President Nursing, John T. Mather Memorial Hospital, Port Jefferson, NY, p. A440

MULLIGAN, Michael, M.D. President Medical Staff, Anderson Hospital, Maryville, IL, p. A187

MULLIGAN, Regina, Vice President Nursing, Nathan Littauer Hospital and Nursing Home, Gloversville, NY, p. A426

MULLIN, Tom, Chief Executive Officer, Select Specialty Hospital–Central Pennsylvania, Camp Hill, PA, p. A522

MULLINGS, Donna, Director of Nursing, Assumption Community Hospital, Napoleonville, LA, p. A274

MULLINGS, Paul, Chief Operating Officer, Howard University Hospital, Washington, DC, p. A116

MULLINS, Cindy, Director Information Technology, Saint Mary's Regional Medical Center, Reno, NV, p. A395

MULLINS, Debbie, Director, Saint Joseph – London, London, KY, p. A255

MULLINS, Erin, D.O. Chief Medical Staff, Dickenson Community Hospital, Clintwood, VA, p. A652

MULLINS Jr., John David, Administrator, Clinton County Hospital, Albany, KY, p. A248

MULLINS, Kem, FACHE, President, WellStar Cobb Hospital, Austell, GA, p. A148

MULLINS, Larry, Chief Executive Officer, W. J. Mangold Memorial Hospital, Lockney, TX, p. A619

MULLINS, Mary Beth, Associate Administrator and Chief Nursing Officer, CAMC Teays Valley Hospital, Hurricane, WV, p. A678

MULLINS, Tommy H., Administrator, Boone Memorial Hospital, Madison, WV, p. A678

MULLNER, Darla, Director Human Resources, Rush–Copley Medical Center, Aurora, IL, p. A174

MULLOTH, Rajan, M.D. President Medical Staff, Mid–Valley Hospital, Peckville, PA, p. A534

MULROONEY, Tom, Chief Executive Officer, Story County Medical Center, Nevada, IA, p. A225

MULVEHILL, Mitch, Senior Vice President and Chief Financial Officer, Texas Health Presbyterian Hospital–WNJ, Sherman, TX, p. A634

MULVIHILL, Jody, Vice President Finance, The Children's Institute of Pittsburgh, Pittsburgh, PA, p. A538

MUMMA, Barbara, Vice President Human Resources, Ephrata Community Hospital, Ephrata, PA, p. A525

MUNCH, David, M.D. Vice President and Chief Clinical and Quality Officer, Exempla Lutheran Medical Center, Wheat Ridge, CO, p. A107

MUNDAY, Kathy, Chief Financial Officer, Veterans Affairs Sierra Nevada Health Care System, Reno, NV, p. A395

MUNDY, Mark J., President and Chief Executive Officer, New York Methodist Hospital,, NY, p. A435

MUNDY, Stephens M., President and Chief Executive Officer, Champlain Valley Physicians Hospital Medical Center, Plattsburgh, NY, p. A439

MUNFORD, Thedosia, Senior Vice President and Chief Nursing Officer, Providence Hospital, Washington, DC, p. A116

MUNGER, Richard, Administrator, Mount Grant General Hospital, Hawthorne, NV, p. A392

MUNGER, Victor, Vice President Human Resources, Quincy Medical Center, Quincy, MA, p. A304

MUNGOVAN, Sandy, Chief Information Officer, LAC–Harbor–University of California at Los Angeles Medical Center, Torrance, CA, p. A92

MUNHOLLAND, Cleta
Administrator, Louisiana Extended Care Hospital West Monroe, West Monroe, LA, p. A280
Administrator, Specialty Extended Care Hospital of Monroe, Monroe, LA, p. A274

MUNIAK, Daniel, M.D. Chief Medical Officer, Garfield County Health Center, Jordan, MT, p. A377

MUNIR, Amjad, M.D. Medical Director, HEALTHSOUTH Chattanooga Rehabilitation Hospital, Chattanooga, TN, p. A566

MUNOZ, Natalie
Director of Clinical Services, Nexus Specialty Hospital, Shenandoah, TX, p. A633
Director of Clinical Services, Nexus Specialty Hospital The Woodlands, Spring, TX, p. A634

MUNOZ, Sylvia, Director Human Resources, Promise Hospital of East Los Angeles, Suburban Medical Center Campus, Paramount, CA, p. A79

MUNOZ, Thalia H., MS, Hospital Administrator, Starr County Memorial Hospital, Rio Grande City, TX, p. A629

MUNRO, Stuart J., M.D. Clinical Director, Center for Behavioral Medicine, Kansas City, MO, p. A362

MUNSEY, Brenda, Senior Human Resources Business Partner, Saint Alphonsus Medical Center – Ontario, Ontario, OR, p. A515

MUNSON, Bill, Vice President and Chief Financial Officer, Boulder Community Hospital, Boulder, CO, p. A97

MUNSON, Jennifer, Chief Financial Officer, Three Rivers Hospital, Brewster, WA, p. A665

MUNSON, Joan, Manager Information Systems, Fairchild Medical Center, Yreka, CA, p. A96

MUNSON, John, Vice President and Chief Financial Officer, St. Anthony Regional Hospital, Carroll, IA, p. A217

MUNSON, Kris, Director Human Resources, Arbour H. R. I. Hospital, Brookline, MA, p. A298

MUNTEFERING, Denise, Vice President Patient Care Services, Avera St. Benedict Health Center, Parkston, SD, p. A561

MUNTZ, Tim, President and Chief Executive Officer, St. Margaret's Hospital, Spring Valley, IL, p. A195

MUNYAN, Lori, Director, Human Resources, HEALTHSOUTH Rehabilitation Hospital of Toms River, Toms River, NJ, p. A411

MURANSKY, Ed, Owner, Surgical Hospital at Southwoods, Youngstown, OH, p. A494

MURCHISON, Sandra, Director Medical Records, Coosa Valley Medical Center, Sylacauga, AL, p. A25

MURDOCH, William, M.D. Medical Director, Loma Linda University Behavioral Medicine Center, Redlands, CA, p. A81

MURDOCK, Guy
Vice President Human Resources, Healthbridge Children's Hospital of Houston, Houston, TX, p. A609
Vice President Human Resources, Nexus Specialty Hospital, Shenandoah, TX, p. A633
Vice President Human Resources, Nexus Specialty Hospital The Woodlands, Spring, TX, p. A634

MURDOCK–LANGAN, Patricia, Medical Director, Alegent Creighton Health Lakeside Hospital, Omaha, NE, p. A387

MURDY, James B., Chief Financial Officer, Belmont Community Hospital, Bellaire, OH, p. A471

MURFORD, Tracy, Director Human Resources, Cardinal Hill Rehabilitation Hospital, Lexington, KY, p. A254

MURPHY, Brian, M.D
Chief of Staff, Monroe Hospital, Bloomington, IN, p. A199
Chief of Staff, Valley View Hospital, Glenwood Springs, CO, p. A101

MURPHY, Bruce, M.D., President and Chief Executive Officer, Arkansas Heart Hospital, Little Rock, AR, p. A46

MURPHY, Charles J., Associate Vice President Human Resources, Strong Memorial Hospital of the University of Rochester, Rochester, NY, p. A441

MURPHY, Christy, Director Health Information Systems, Crossgates River Oaks Hospital, Brandon, MS, p. A345

MURPHY, Dennis F., Chief Operating Officer, Indiana University Health University Hospital, Indianapolis, IN, p. A205

MURPHY, Dennis M., Executive Vice President and Chief Operating Officer, Northwestern Memorial Hospital, Chicago, IL, p. A178

MURPHY, Elizabeth A., R.N. Vice President for Patient Care Services, Saint Mary's Health Care, Grand Rapids, MI, p. A315

MURPHY, Evelyn, R.N. Chief Nursing Officer, Ty Cobb Regional Medical Center, Lavonia, GA, p. A156

MURPHY, J. Patrick, Chief Financial Officer, North Baldwin Infirmary, Bay Minette, AL, p. A16

MURPHY, James, Chief Executive Officer, South Texas Surgical Hospital, Corpus Christi, TX, p. A594

MURPHY, Janice, President, Fairview Hospital, Cleveland, OH, p. A476

MURPHY, Jeffrey J., President and Chief Executive Officer, Presence Saint Francis Hospital, Evanston, IL, p. A182

MURPHY, Jim, Interim Administrator, Keefe Memorial Hospital, Cheyenne Wells, CO, p. A98

MURPHY, John B., M.D. Vice President Medical Affairs and Chief Medical Officer, Rhode Island Hospital, Providence, RI, p. A547

MURPHY, John M., M.D., President and Chief Executive Officer, Danbury Hospital, Danbury, CT, p. A108

MURPHY, Judy, Director Human Resources, Southwest General Health Center, Middleburg Heights, OH, p. A486

MURPHY, Julia, Chief Nursing Officer, Logan Memorial Hospital, Russellville, KY, p. A260

MURPHY, Julie, Chief Financial Officer, Saint Luke's North Hospital – Barry Road, Kansas City, MO, p. A363

MURPHY, Kathy, Site Manager, Mescalero Public Health Service Indian Hospital, Mescalero, NM, p. A417

MURPHY, Kelly, Director Human Resources, Family Health West, Fruita, CO, p. A101

MURPHY, Kevin G.
Senior Vice President Finance and Chief Financial Officer, Manchester Memorial Hospital, Manchester, CT, p. A109
Senior Vice President Finance and Chief Financial Officer, Rockville General Hospital, Vernon Rockville, CT, p. A112

MURPHY, Linda, Chief Financial Officer, Osborne County Memorial Hospital, Osborne, KS, p. A241

MURPHY, Lionel
Chief Executive Officer and Administrator, Bethesda Rehabilitation Hospital, Baton Rouge, LA, p. A263
Chief Executive Officer, Southeast Regional Medical Center, Kentwood, LA, p. A270

MURPHY, Lynda J., Vice President Human Resources, Logansport Memorial Hospital, Logansport, IN, p. A209

MURPHY, Margaret M., Interim Chief Executive Officer, Kindred Hospital–Philadelphia, Philadelphia, PA, p. A535

MURPHY, Martha, Vice President Human Resources, St. Joseph Mercy Oakland, Pontiac, MI, p. A322

MURPHY, Maureen, M.D. Director of Medical Affairs, St. Clare Hospital, Baraboo, WI, p. A683

MURPHY, Michael, M.D. Chief Medical Officer, Sharp Grossmont Hospital, La Mesa, CA, p. A65

MURPHY, Michael D., Chief Executive Officer, Abilene Regional Medical Center, Abilene, TX, p. A581

MURPHY, Michael J., FACHE, Director, Fargo Veterans Affairs Health Care System, Fargo, ND, p. A466

MURPHY, Mike, Chief Patient Care Officer, Beaver Dam Community Hospitals, Beaver Dam, WI, p. A684

MURPHY, Neil W., R N
Senior Vice President and Chief Nursing Officer, Centegra Hospital – McHenry, McHenry, IL, p. A188
Senior Vice President, Chief Nursing Officer, Centegra Hospital – Woodstock, Woodstock, IL, p. A197

MURPHY, Patrick, Vice President Finance, Thomas Hospital, Fairhope, AL, p. A20

MURPHY, Patrick J., M.D. Chief of Staff, Three Rivers Hospital, Waverly, TN, p. A580

MURPHY, R. Louis, M.D. Chief of Staff, Humboldt General Hospital, Humboldt, TN, p. A570

MURPHY, Richard J., President and Chief Executive Officer, South Nassau Communities Hospital, Oceanside, NY, p. A438

MURPHY, Rita, Director Human Resources, Cobre Valley Regional Medical Center, Globe, AZ, p. A32

MURPHY, Steve, Director Networks, Good Samaritan Regional Health Center, Mount Vernon, IL, p. A189

MURPHY, Steven, Executive Director, Devereux Hospital and Children's Center of Florida, Melbourne, FL, p. A130

MURPHY, Susan G., Chief Operating Officer, Kaiser Permanente Santa Clara Medical Center, Santa Clara, CA, p. A89

MURPHY, Terry
President and Chief Executive Officer, Bayhealth Medical Center, Dover, DE, p. A114
Director Information Services, Phoenixville Hospital, Phoenixville, PA, p. A537

MURPHY, Therese, Chief Nursing Officer, Florida Hospital at Connerton Long Term Acute Care, Land O'Lakes, FL, p. A128

MURPHY, Tim, Vice President, Human Resources, Mercy Hospital Fort Smith, Fort Smith, AR, p. A44

MURPHY, Tom, Chief Executive Officer, Weiser Memorial Hospital, Weiser, ID, p. A172

MURPHY–FROBISH, Erin, Vice President Human Resources, Morris Hospital & Healthcare Centers, Morris, IL, p. A189

MURRAY, Brian, M.D. Medical Director, Erie County Medical Center, Buffalo, NY, p. A422

MURRAY, Brian, Chief Financial Officer, Gunnison Valley Hospital, Gunnison, UT, p. A643

MURRAY, Cindy, R.N. Chief Nursing Officer and Chief Operating Officer, Baylor Medical Center at Waxahachie, Waxahachie, TX, p. A640

MURRAY, Diana, Director Information Systems, Grand River Hospital District, Rifle, CO, p. A105

MURRAY, Eric, Manager Public Relations, Middle Park Medical Center, Kremmling, CO, p. A102

MURRAY, Geno, President and Chief Executive Officer, Charles A. Dean Memorial Hospital, Greenville, ME, p. A283

MURRAY, Gerald, President and Chief Executive Officer, UPMC Altoona, Altoona, PA, p. A520

MURRAY, James Patrick, FACHE, Chief Executive Officer, Peterson Regional Medical Center, Kerrville, TX, p. A616

MURRAY, Jana, Manager Medical Records, Mercy St. Francis Hospital, Mountain View, MO, p. A366

MURRAY, Kent, M.D. Chief of Staff, Robert J. Dole Veterans Affairs Medical Center, Wichita, KS, p. A246

MURRAY, Kevin J., Senior Vice President, John T. Mather Memorial Hospital, Port Jefferson, NY, p. A440

MURRAY, Patricia M., Information Officer, Southern Inyo Healthcare District, Lone Pine, CA, p. A67

MURRAY, Sherri, Chief Financial Officer, Montgomery General Hospital, Montgomery, WV, p. A678

MURRAY, Susan, Director Information Services, Trident Medical Center, Charleston, SC, p. A549

MURRAY, Wesley E., Chief Executive Officer, Texas County Memorial Hospital, Houston, MO, p. A361

MURRELL, Joseph, Chief Executive Officer, Wayne County Hospital, Monticello, KY, p. A258

MURREY, Mady, R.N., Chief Operating Officer, MultiCare Mary Bridge Children's Hospital and Health Center, Tacoma, WA, p. A673

MURRILL, Mike, Vice President and Chief Financial Officer, Adventist Bolingbrook Hospital, Bolingbrook, IL, p. A175

MURROW, Carol, Vice President Business Development, Cox Medical Center Branson, Branson, MO, p. A357

MURRY, Jim, Chief Information Officer, University of California, Irvine Healthcare, Orange, CA, p. A78

MURT, Mary Lou, R.N. Senior Vice President Nursing, Monongahela Valley Hospital, Monongahela, PA, p. A532

MURTHY, Bangalore, M.D. Director Medical Staff, Jackson Park Hospital and Medical Center, Chicago, IL, p. A177

MURTOS, Kristen, FACHE, President, NorthShore University Health System Skokie Hospital, Skokie, IL, p. A194

MURZYN, Derek, Chief Executive Officer, Kindred Hospital–Greensboro, Greensboro, NC, p. A453

MUSACK, Scott, Chief Information Officer, Silver Lake Medical Center, Los Angeles, CA, p. A71

MUSSELMAN, Bud, Chief Operating Officer and Chief Financial Officer, Highline Medical Center, Burien, WA, p. A665

MUSSMAN, Rebekah, Chief Financial Officer, Kearney County Health Services, Minden, NE, p. A386

MUSSO, Lewis C., Vice President Human Resources, Trinity Health System, Steubenville, OH, p. A490

MUSTIAN, J. Perry, President and Chief Executive Officer, John D. Archbold Memorial Hospital, Thomasville, GA, p. A161

MUSUMECI, MaryAnn P., Director, James J. Peters Veterans Affairs Medical Center,, NY, p. A432

MUTARELLI, Richard, Chief Financial Officer, Munroe Regional Medical Center, Ocala, FL, p. A134

MUTCHLER, Roger, Manager Information Technology, Aultman Orrville Hospital, Orrville, OH, p. A488

MUTZIGER, John, M.D. Chief Medical Officer, Laird Hospital, Union, MS, p. A354

MWANIKI, Mary
Chief Financial Officer, Reliant Rehabilitation Hospital Dallas, Dallas, TX, p. A597
Chief Financial Officer, Reliant Rehabilitation Hospital Mid–Cities, Bedford, TX, p. A588
Chief Financial Officer, Reliant Rehabilitation Hospital North Texas, Richardson, TX, p. A628

MWEBE, David, M.D. Chief of Staff, Osmond General Hospital, Osmond, NE, p. A388

MYATT, Kevin A., Senior Vice President Human Resources, Yale–New Haven Hospital, New Haven, CT, p. A110

MYCROFT, Tina, Vice President and Chief Financial Officer, St. Joseph Hospital, Orange, CA, p. A78

MYDLER, Todd, M.D. Chief Medical Officer, Parker Adventist Hospital, Parker, CO, p. A105

MYER, Amber, Director Medical Records, Throckmorton County Memorial Hospital, Throckmorton, TX, p. A637

MYERS, Adam L., Chief Medical Officer, Methodist Mansfield Medical Center, Mansfield, TX, p. A621

MYERS, April, Administrator, Kindred Hospital–La Mirada, La Mirada, CA, p. A65

MYERS, Becky, Human Resources Specialist, Illini Community Hospital, Pittsfield, IL, p. A192

MYERS, Carl, M.D. Vice President Medical Affairs and Chief Medical Officer, Yuma Regional Medical Center, Yuma, AZ, p. A40

MYERS, Chrissy, R.N. Director of Nursing, Behavioral HealthCare Center at Clarksville, Clarksville, TN, p. A567

MYERS, Craig G., President, California Hospital Medical Center, Los Angeles, CA, p. A68

MYERS, Dan, Controller, Kossuth Regional Health Center, Algona, IA, p. A216

MYERS, Doug, Senior Vice President and Chief Financial Officer, Children's Hospital and Research Center at Oakland, Oakland, CA, p. A77

MYERS, Douglas, Executive Vice President and Chief Financial Officer, Children's National Medical Center, Washington, DC, p. A116

MYERS, Edward W., Chief Executive Officer, St. Luke's Medical Center, Phoenix, AZ, p. A35

MYERS, Frederick, M.D. Chief Medical Officer, Takoma Regional Hospital, Greeneville, TN, p. A569

MYERS, Gary, Interim Chief Executive Officer, Mammoth Hospital, Mammoth Lakes, CA, p. A73

MYERS, Grace, MSN Vice President, Nurse Executive, Sentara Princess Anne Hospital, Virginia Beach, VA, p. A662

MYERS, Jeffrey D., President and Chief Executive Officer, Hamilton Medical Center, Dalton, GA, p. A151

MYERS, Jerry, M.D., Chief Executive Officer, Kell West Regional Hospital, Wichita Falls, TX, p. A641

MYERS, Jim, Chief Financial Officer, Indiana University Health Bloomington Hospital, Bloomington, IN, p. A199

MYERS, Karen, Vice President Financial Services, Stoughton Hospital Association, Stoughton, WI, p. A697

MYERS, Karen K., MSN Vice President and Chief Nursing Officer, St. Luke's Episcopal Hospital, Houston, TX, p. A612

MYERS, Katie, Chief Financial Officer, Alleghany Memorial Hospital, Sparta, NC, p. A461

MYERS, Kevin, Director Information Systems, Lake Granbury Medical Center, Granbury, TX, p. A606

MYERS, Kimberly, Director Human Resources, Guthrie County Hospital, Guthrie Center, IA, p. A222

MYERS, Lisa, Director Human Resources, Heritage Oaks Hospital, Sacramento, CA, p. A83

MYERS, Mark, M.D. Chief Medical Officer, Continuous Care Centers of Tulsa, Tulsa, OK, p. A508

MYERS, Mary, R.N. Chief Nursing Officer, Indiana University Health West Hospital, Avon, IN, p. A198

MYERS, Michael D., Chief Executive Officer, Veterans Memorial Hospital, Waukon, IA, p. A229

MYERS, Michelle F., Director Human Resources, Florida Hospital Wauchula, Wauchula, FL, p. A143

MYERS, Paul, M.D. Neonatologist and Chief Medical Officer, Children's Hospital of Wisconsin–Fox Valley, Neenah, WI, p. A693

MYERS, Philip, M.D. Vice President Medical Affairs, Samaritan Regional Health System, Ashland, OH, p. A470

MYERS, Randy, Chief Information Officer, Information Technology, Mitchell County Hospital, Colorado City, TX, p. A592

MYERS, Robert T., Chief Operating Officer, Parkview LaGrange Hospital, LaGrange, IN, p. A208

MYERS, Russ, Senior Vice President and Chief Operating Officer, Yakima Valley Memorial Hospital, Yakima, WA, p. A674

MYERS, Shane P., Chief Operating Officer, Iberia Medical Center, New Iberia, LA, p. A275

MYERS, Sheri, Vice President Patient Care Services, McLaren Central Michigan, Mount Pleasant, MI, p. A320

MYERS, Steve, Assistant Administrator, Southeast Health Center of Reynolds County, Ellington, MO, p. A360

MYERS, Tara, Director Human Resources, AnMed Health Rehabilitation Hospital, Anderson, SC, p. A548

MYERS, William, Chief Operating Officer, Montgomery County Emergency Service, Norristown, PA, p. A533

MYHRE, Jane, MS Director Health Information, Chippewa County–Montevideo Hospital, Montevideo, MN, p. A336

MYLA, Sara, M.D. Chief of Staff, Fountain Valley Regional Hospital and Medical Center, Fountain Valley, CA, p. A60

MYLAN, Marci, Director, Veterans Affairs Nebraska–Western Iowa Health Care System, Lincoln, NE, p. A386

MYLES, Lee T., President and Chief Executive Officer, St. Mary's Regional Medical Center, Lewiston, ME, p. A284

MYSTER, Jennifer, President, Buffalo Hospital, Buffalo, MN, p. A330

# N

NABEL, Elizabeth, M.D., President, Brigham and Women's Hospital, Boston, MA, p. A296

NABER, Mary, Senior Vice President Worklife Services, St. John Hospital and Medical Center, Detroit, MI, p. A312

NACEY, Marley, Director Finance, Sentara Virginia Beach General Hospital, Virginia Beach, VA, p. A662

NACHIMUTHU, Anbu, Chief Financial Officer, Atrium Medical Center of Corinth, Corinth, TX, p. A593

NACHTIGAL, Amy, Chief Financial Officer, Saint Luke's Hospital of Kansas City, Kansas City, MO, p. A363

NACHTRIEB, Han, Vice President Human Resources, Seattle Cancer Care Alliance, Seattle, WA, p. A671

NACION, Glenn, Vice President Human Resources, Trinitas Regional Medical Center, Elizabeth, NJ, p. A403

NADEAU, Barbara, Chief Human Resources Management Service, White River Junction Veterans Affairs Medical Center, White River Junction, VT, p. A650

NADEAU, Steve, Senior Vice President Human Resources, Gwinnett Hospital System, Lawrenceville, GA, p. A156

NADER, Keoni, Director Human Resources, UnityHealth Louis A. Weiss Memorial Hospital, Chicago, IL, p. A179

NADER, Mary, Director Information Technology, Spectrum Health Special Care Hospital, Grand Rapids, MI, p. A315

NADKARNI, Manasi, M.D. Vice President Medical Affairs, Trinity Muscatine, Muscatine, IA, p. A225

NADOLNY, Stephanie, Vice President Clinical Services, Spaulding Rehabilitation Hospital Cape Cod, East Sandwich, MA, p. A299

NADONE, John, Chief Financial Officer, Southwest Memorial Hospital, Cortez, CO, p. A98

NAEVE, Clayton, Vice President and Chief Information Officer, St. Jude Children's Research Hospital, Memphis, TN, p. A575

NAFZIGER, Laurie N., President and Chief Executive Officer, Oaklawn Psychiatric Center, Goshen, IN, p. A204

NAFZIGER, Steve, M.D. Vice President Medical Affairs, Parkview Medical Center, Pueblo, CO, p. A105

NAGALA, Vani, M.D. Chief Medical Officer, Oakes Community Hospital, Oakes, ND, p. A468

NAGEL, Donna, Director Human Resources, Continuous Care Centers of Tulsa, Tulsa, OK, p. A508

NAGLE, Jolene, Director Medical Records, Peterson Rehabilitation Hospital, Wheeling, WV, p. A682

NAGLE, Mike, Director Financial Services, Jerold Phelps Community Hospital, Garberville, CA, p. A62

NAGLER, Harris M., M.D., President, Beth Israel Medical Center, New York, NY, p. A430

NAGLER, Richard, M.D. Chief of Staff, Mayo Clinic Health System – Northland in Barron, Barron, WI, p. A684

NAGLOSKY, Paul, Administrator, Indianhead Medical Center, Shell Lake, WI, p. A696

NAGOWSKI, Michael, Chief Executive Officer, Cape Fear Valley Medical Center, Fayetteville, NC, p. A452

NAGY, Jeff, Chief Financial Officer, River Bend Hospital, West Lafayette, IN, p. A215

NAGY, Kimberly, R.N. Vice President Operations and Chief Nurse Executive, Northwestern Lake Forest Hospital, Lake Forest, IL, p. A186

NAIBERK, Donald T., Administrator, Butler County Health Care Center, David City, NE, p. A383

NAILLON, Marcia, Chief Operating Officer and Administrative Registered Nurse, North Valley Hospital, Tonasket, WA, p. A673

NAIR, Chand, M.D. Medical Director, Brooke Glen Behavioral Hospital, Fort Washington, PA, p. A526

NAIR, Vijayachandran, M.D. Chief of Staff, John J. Pershing Veterans Affairs Medical Center, Poplar Bluff, MO, p. A367

NAJJAR, Maher, M.D. Medical Director, Kindred Hospital Chicago–Northlake, Northlake, IL, p. A190

NAKAGAWA, Marc

Vice President and Chief Financial Officer, Transylvania Regional Hospital, Brevard, NC, p. A448

Chief Financial Officer, Trinity Hospital of Augusta, Augusta, GA, p. A148

NAKAMOTO, Kenneth, M.D. Vice President Medical Affairs, Pomona Valley Hospital Medical Center, Pomona, CA, p. A80

NAKASUJI, Jody, Chief Financial Officer, LAC–Harbor–University of California at Los Angeles Medical Center, Torrance, CA, p. A92

NALDI, Robert, Chief Financial Officer, Maimonides Medical Center,, NY, p. A434

NALEPPA, Margaret, President and Chief Executive Officer, Peninsula Regional Medical Center, Salisbury, MD, p. A294

NALL, Brian, President and Chief Executive Officer, Greenville Regional Hospital, Greenville, IL, p. A184

NALL, Wes, Administrator, Grove Hill Memorial Hospital, Grove Hill, AL, p. A21

NALLE, Tambara, Chief Financial Officer, Eastern State Hospital, Lexington, KY, p. A254

NALLI, Jonathan, Chief Executive Officer, Porter Regional Hospital, Valparaiso, IN, p. A214

NALLS, Jacqueline, Chief Financial Officer, Phoenixville Hospital, Phoenixville, PA, p. A537

NANCE, Sally S., Chief Executive Officer, Excelsior Springs Hospital, Excelsior Springs, MO, p. A360

NANDIN, Dalia, Manager Human Resources, Kindred Rehabilitation Hospital Clear Lake, Webster, TX, p. A640

NANIA, James A., System Vice President and Chief Financial Officer, Hallmark Health System, Melrose, MA, p. A302

NANTZ, Mark S., FACHE, Chief Executive Officer, Bon Secours St. Francis Health System, Greenville, SC, p. A552

NAPIER, Lisa, Chief Financial Officer, Atlanta Medical Center, Atlanta, GA, p. A146

NAPIER, Pamela, R.N. Chief Nursing Officer, Mercy Willard Hospital, Willard, OH, p. A493

NAPIER, Randy L.

Administrator, Frazier Rehab Institute, Louisville, KY, p. A255

President, Southern Indiana Rehabilitation Hospital, New Albany, IN, p. A211

NAPIER, Troy, Chief Information Officer, Baptist Hospitals of Southeast Texas, Beaumont, TX, p. A587

NAPIERALA, Edward A., FACHE, Chief Executive Officer, West Branch Regional Medical Center, West Branch, MI, p. A326

NAPOLI, Mark, M.D. Chief of Staff, P & S Surgical Hospital, Monroe, LA, p. A274

NAPOLITANO, Mary Pat, Director Human Resources, Specialty Hospital at Kimball, Lakewood, NJ, p. A405

NAPP, Marc L., M.D. Vice President Medical Affairs, Lenox Hill Hospital, New York, NY, p. A433

NAPPS, Greg, Vice President Operations and Chief Operating Officer, Culpeper Regional Hospital, Culpeper, VA, p. A653

NAQVI, Shahid, M.D. President Medical Staff, Floyd Valley Hospital, Le Mars, IA, p. A224

NARAMORE, G. Harold, M.D. Chief Medical Officer and In house Legal Counsel, Blount Memorial Hospital, Maryville, TN, p. A574

NARANG, Steve, M.D., Chief Executive Officer, Banner Good Samaritan Medical Center, Phoenix, AZ, p. A34

NARAYAN, Satish, M.D. Medical Director, Glen Oaks Hospital, Greenville, TX, p. A607

NARBUTAS, Virgis

Chief Executive Officer, Garden Grove Hospital and Medical Center, Garden Grove, CA, p. A62

Chief Executive Officer, Huntington Beach Hospital, Huntington Beach, CA, p. A64

Chief Executive Officer, La Palma Intercommunity Hospital, La Palma, CA, p. A65

Chief Executive Officer, West Anaheim Medical Center, Anaheim, CA, p. A52

NARDO, Jeff, Director Human Resources, Brynn Marr Hospital, Jacksonville, NC, p. A455

NARROW, Ann, Director of Nursing, River Hospital, Alexandria Bay, NY, p. A420

NARY, Ed, Director Information Technology and Chief Compliance Officer, Wilbarger General Hospital, Vernon, TX, p. A639

NASET–PAYNE, Janet, R.N. Chief Operating Officer, Van Diest Medical Center, Webster City, IA, p. A230

NASH, Gayle, R.N. Chief Nursing Officer, MountainView Regional Medical Center, Las Cruces, NM, p. A416

NASH, Jan, Ph.D. Vice President Patient Services and Chief Nursing Officer, Paoli Hospital, Paoli, PA, p. A534

NASH, Jeff, Director Information Technology and Services, Mary Black Memorial Hospital, Spartanburg, SC, p. A556

NASH, John D., FACHE, President and Chief Executive Officer, Franciscan Hospital for Children, Boston, MA, p. A296

NASH, Robert, M.D. Chief of Staff, Richland Memorial Hospital, Olney, IL, p. A191

NASH, Tim, M.D. Chief of Staff, Marshall Medical Center, Lewisburg, TN, p. A573

NASIR, Iqbal, M.D. Chief of Staff, Oakwood Southshore Medical Center, Trenton, MI, p. A325

NASR, Anthony, M.D. Chief Medical Staff, Feather River Hospital, Paradise, CA, p. A79

NASRALLA, Anthony J., FACHE, President and Chief Executive Officer, Titusville Area Hospital, Titusville, PA, p. A542

NASSIEF, Raymond, Senior Vice President Operations and Clinical Transformation, John Muir Medical Center, Walnut Creek, Walnut Creek, CA, p. A95

NATALONI, Tom, Senior Director Information Technology, Hahnemann University Hospital, Philadelphia, PA, p. A535

NATCHER, Charles, Chief Financial Officer, Kindred Hospital–Los Angeles, Los Angeles, CA, p. A70

NATH, Pravene, Interim Chief Information Officer, Stanford Hospital and Clinics, Palo Alto, CA, p. A79

NATHAN, James R.

President and Chief Executive Officer, Cape Coral Hospital, Cape Coral, FL, p. A120

President and Chief Executive Officer, Gulf Coast Medical Center, Fort Myers, FL, p. A124

President and Chief Executive Officer, Lee Memorial Hospital, Fort Myers, FL, p. A124

NATHANSON, Andrea, Director Finance, Baystate Franklin Medical Center, Greenfield, MA, p. A300

NATIONS, Mary Kay, Chief Financial Officer, Kindred Hospital–New Orleans, New Orleans, LA, p. A275

NATOLI, Joseph B., Senior Vice President Business and Finance and Chief Financial Officer, University of Miami Hospital and Clinics, Miami, FL, p. A132

NATRAJAN, Sunil, M.D. Medical Director, Kindred Hospital–Tucson, Tucson, AZ, p. A38

NATZKE, Kenneth J., President and Chief Executive Officer, OSF St. Joseph Medical Center, Bloomington, IL, p. A174

NAU, James, Manager Computer and Applications Support, Delaware Psychiatric Center, New Castle, DE, p. A114

NAUGLE, Gary, Senior Vice President Human Resources, UPMC Altoona, Altoona, PA, p. A520

NAVARRO, Danielle, R.N. Chief Nursing Officer, Guthrie County Hospital, Guthrie Center, IA, p. A222

NAVARRO, Tess, Chief Financial Officer, Laguna Honda Hospital and Rehabilitation Center, San Francisco, CA, p. A86

NAWROCKI, Bernie
 Administrative Director Finance, ProMedica Bixby Hospital, Adrian, MI, p. A308
 Administrative Director Finance, ProMedica Herrick Hospital, Tecumseh, MI, p. A325

NAWROCKI, Edward, President, St. Luke's Hospital – Anderson Campus, Easton, PA, p. A525

NAYAK, Raghu, Chief Executive Officer, Hind General Hospital, Hobart, IN, p. A204

NAZ, Haroon, Chief Executive Officer, Pinnacle Hospital, Crown Point, IN, p. A201

NAZE, Jesse, Chief Financial Officer, Fall River Hospital, Hot Springs, SD, p. A560

NDOW, Emmanuel, Chief Information Officer, Marion General Hospital, Marion, IN, p. A209

NEAL, Birgitta, Data Entry and Information Technologist, Stamford Memorial Hospital, Stamford, TX, p. A635

NEAL, Bob, Director Information Technology, Sparrow Ionia Hospital, Ionia, MI, p. A316

NEAL, Brian, Chief Executive Officer, Aspire Behavioral Health of Conroe, Conroe, TX, p. A593

NEAL, Greg, Interim Chief Executive Officer, Wellmont Bristol Regional Medical Center, Bristol, TN, p. A565

NEAL, John C., Chief Executive Officer, Hood Memorial Hospital, Amite, LA, p. A262

NEAL, Roger, Vice President and Chief Information Officer, Duncan Regional Hospital, Duncan, OK, p. A497

NEALE, Debra, R.N. Chief Nursing Officer, O'Connor Hospital, Delhi, NY, p. A425

NEAPOLITAN, David, Chief Financial Officer, Emanuel Medical Center, Turlock, CA, p. A93

NEAS, Andrea, Health Information Management Director, Laughlin Memorial Hospital, Greeneville, TN, p. A569

NEAT, Gary, Director Information Management Systems, Taylor Regional Hospital, Campbellsville, KY, p. A249

NECAS, Kevin
 Chief Financial Officer, University of Missouri Hospitals and Clinics, Columbia, MO, p. A359
 Chief Financial Officer, Women's and Children's Hospital, Columbia, MO, p. A359

NECCI, Mindy, Director Human Resources, Aurora West Allis Medical Center, West Allis, WI, p. A699

NECHANICKY, Jeff
 Acting Medical Center Director, Aleda E. Lutz Veterans Affairs Medical Center, Saginaw, MI, p. A323
 Assistant Director, Richard L. Roudebush Veterans Affairs Medical Center, Indianapolis, IN, p. A206

NEEB, Verette, R.N. Chief Nursing Officer, Baylor Medical Center at Uptown, Dallas, TX, p. A595

NEECE, Patrick, Chief Information Officer, Jefferson Regional Medical Center, Pine Bluff, AR, p. A49

NEEDHAM, Kim
 Assistant Chief Executive Officer, Vista Medical Center East, Waukegan, IL, p. A196
 Assistant Chief Executive Officer, Vista Medical Center West, Waukegan, IL, p. A196

NEEDHAM, Tracy, Director of Nursing, Sutter Davis Hospital, Davis, CA, p. A58

NEEDMAN, Herbert G., President and Chief Executive Officer, Temple Community Hospital, Los Angeles, CA, p. A72

NEELAGARU, Narasimhulu, M.D. Chief of Staff, Northridge Medical Center, Commerce, GA, p. A150

NEELEY, Scott, M.D. Chief Medical Officer, St. Alexius Medical Center, Hoffman Estates, IL, p. A185

NEELY, Cindy, Administrator, Mercy Hospital Columbus, Columbus, KS, p. A232

NEELY, Dale, Chief Executive Officer, HEALTHSOUTH Rehabilitation Hospital of Tallahassee, Tallahassee, FL, p. A140

NEELY, Joseph H., FACHE, Chief Executive Officer, Hillcrest Hospital – South, Tulsa, OK, p. A508

NEELY, Randall, Chief Executive Officer, Simpson General Hospital, Mendenhall, MS, p. A350

NEELY, Rebecca, R.N. Director of Nursing, Gibson General Hospital, Trenton, TN, p. A580

NEERGHEEN, Chabilal, M.D. Medical Director, Western Massachusetts Hospital, Westfield, MA, p. A306

NEESEN, Cindy, Director of Information Technology, Butler County Health Care Center, David City, NE, p. A383

NEET, Bradley D., FACHE, Chief Executive Officer, Southwest Healthcare System, Murrieta, CA, p. A76

NEFCY, Christine, M.D. Chief Medical Officer, McKay–Dee Hospital Center, Ogden, UT, p. A645

NEFF, Mark J., FACHE, President and Chief Executive Officer, St. Claire Regional Medical Center, Morehead, KY, p. A258

NEFF, Mary L., R.N. Chief Operating Officer and Chief Nursing Officer, Mercy Hospital Cadillac, Cadillac, MI, p. A310

NEFF, Mary Beth, Director Human Resources, Sistersville General Hospital, Sistersville, WV, p. A681

NEFF, William, M.D
 Chief Medical Officer, Medical Center of the Rockies, Loveland, CO, p. A104
 Chief Medical Officer, Poudre Valley Hospital, Fort Collins, CO, p. A101

NEGOSHIAN, Carol, MSN Chief Nursing Officer, Putnam Community Medical Center, Palatka, FL, p. A135

NEGRO, Frank, Interim Chief Information Officer, New York Downtown Hospital, New York, NY, p. A435

NEIKIRK, Richard, Chief Executive Officer, Cumberland County Hospital, Burkesville, KY, p. A249

NEIL, Eric, Interim Chief Information Officer, UW Medicine/Northwest Hospital & Medical Center, Seattle, WA, p. A671

NEILSON, Richard, Director of Information Services, Timpanogos Regional Hospital, Orem, UT, p. A645

NEILSON–BEALE, Carol, Chief Financial Officer, Cypress Creek Hospital, Houston, TX, p. A609

NEIMAN, Carla, Chief Financial Officer, Clark Fork Valley Hospital, Plains, MT, p. A378

NEITZEL, Monte, Chief Executive Officer, Greater Regional Medical Center, Creston, IA, p. A219

NEKIC, John, Chief Executive Officer, Behavioral Hospital of Bellaire, Houston, TX, p. A609

NELL, Rocio, M.D., Chief Executive Officer, Montgomery County Emergency Service, Norristown, PA, p. A533

NELL, Sergio, Director Information Systems, Watsonville Community Hospital, Watsonville, CA, p. A95

NELSON, Allison
 Chief Financial Officer, Sanford Canby Medical Center, Canby, MN, p. A330
 Chief Financial Officer, Sanford Clear Lake Medical Center, Clear Lake, SD, p. A559

NELSON, Barbara J., Ph.D. Chief Nursing Executive, Sutter Roseville Medical Center, Roseville, CA, p. A83

NELSON, Betty, Director of Marketing and Development, Lindsborg Community Hospital, Lindsborg, KS, p. A239

NELSON, Bill, Chief Executive Officer, Mille Lacs Health System, Onamia, MN, p. A337

NELSON, Brian, M.D. Chief Medical Officer, Cache Valley Specialty Hospital, North Logan, UT, p. A645

NELSON, Brock D., President and Chief Executive Officer, Regions Hospital, Saint Paul, MN, p. A340

NELSON, Carol, Director Human Resources, Montevista Hospital, Las Vegas, NV, p. A393

NELSON, Charles
 Chief Executive Officer, Aspirus Grand View Hospital, Ironwood, MI, p. A317
 Chief Executive Officer, Aspirus Keweenaw Hospital, Laurium, MI, p. A319
 Chief Executive Officer, Aspirus Ontonagon Hospital, Ontonagon, MI, p. A321

NELSON, David, M.D. Medical Director, Barlow Respiratory Hospital, Los Angeles, CA, p. A68

NELSON, David A., President, St. Francis Healthcare Campus, Breckenridge, MN, p. A329

NELSON, Dawn
 Director Human Resources, Riverton Memorial Hospital, Riverton, WY, p. A703
 Director Human Resources, St. Vincent General Hospital District, Leadville, CO, p. A103

NELSON, Deana, R.N. Executive Vice President and Chief Operating Officer, Tampa General Hospital, Tampa, FL, p. A142

NELSON, Diana, R.N. Associate Director for Patient Care Services/Nurse Executive, Jonathan M. Wainwright Memorial Veterans Affairs Medical Center, Walla Walla, WA, p. A674

NELSON, Elaine, R.N. Chief Nursing Officer, Texas Health Harris Methodist Hospital Fort Worth, Fort Worth, TX, p. A604

NELSON, Evan, M.D. Medical Director, New Mexico Rehabilitation Center, Roswell, NM, p. A417

NELSON, Fritz, Administrator, Ochsner Extended Care Hospital of Kenner, Kenner, LA, p. A269

NELSON, Jack, Senior Vice President and Chief Information Officer, Mount Sinai Hospital, New York, NY, p. A434

NELSON, Jackie, Director Human Resources, Hansford Hospital, Spearman, TX, p. A634

NELSON, James, M.D. Chief Medical Staff, Lake Wales Medical Center, Lake Wales, FL, p. A128

NELSON, James J., Senior Vice President Finance and Strategic Planning, Fort HealthCare, Fort Atkinson, WI, p. A686

NELSON, Jeffrey, M.D. Chief of Staff, Nor–Lea General Hospital, Lovington, NM, p. A417

NELSON, Jennifer, Director of Nursing, Hardin Medical Center, Savannah, TN, p. A578

NELSON, Jeri, Chief Financial Officer, Eastern Plumas Health Care District, Portola, CA, p. A80

NELSON, Joseph, M.D. President Medical Staff, Lewis–Gale Medical Center, Salem, VA, p. A661

NELSON, Katey, Director Human Resources, Sevier Valley Medical Center, Richfield, UT, p. A646

NELSON, Kathleen, R.N. Chief Nursing Officer, Eastern Idaho Regional Medical Center, Idaho Falls, ID, p. A169

NELSON, Kathy
 Chief Financial Officer, Marshall Medical Center North, Guntersville, AL, p. A21
 Chief Financial Officer, Marshall Medical Center South, Boaz, AL, p. A17
 Director Marketing and Strategic Planning, Valley General Hospital, Monroe, WA, p. A668

NELSON, Kenneth W., Superintendent, Bridgewater State Hospital, Bridgewater, MA, p. A298

NELSON, Kerri, Chief Financial Officer, Memorial Medical Center of West Michigan, Ludington, MI, p. A319

NELSON, Linda M., R.N. Director of Nursing Services, Chippewa County–Montevideo Hospital, Montevideo, MN, p. A336

NELSON, Lisa M., MS, Chief Executive Officer, Reliant Rehabilitation Hospital Abilene, Abilene, TX, p. A581

NELSON, Lucy, Director Finance, Maniilaq Health Center, Kotzebue, AK, p. A28

NELSON, Lynn M., R.N. Chief Operating Officer, St. John's Riverside Hospital, Yonkers, NY, p. A446

NELSON, Marlin Pete, Vice President Fiscal Services, Divine Savior Healthcare, Portage, WI, p. A695

NELSON, Martha
 Chief Financial Officer, Antelope Memorial Hospital, Neligh, NE, p. A386
 Chief Financial Officer, Niobrara Valley Hospital, Lynch, NE, p. A386

NELSON, Meredith P., Chief Financial Officer, Willamette Valley Medical Center, McMinnville, OR, p. A514

NELSON, Michael
 Chief Financial Officer, Kindred Hospital–Greensboro, Greensboro, NC, p. A453
 Executive Vice President and Chief Financial Officer, Pomona Valley Hospital Medical Center, Pomona, CA, p. A80

NELSON, Michael E., Chief Financial Officer, Riveredge Hospital, Forest Park, IL, p. A182

NELSON, Mike, Chief Financial Officer, Saint Anthony's Health Center, Alton, IL, p. A173

NELSON, Nan
 Chief Financial Officer, Oconomowoc Memorial Hospital, Oconomowoc, WI, p. A693
 Vice President Finance, Waukesha Memorial Hospital, Waukesha, WI, p. A698

NELSON, Nick, Director Support Services, Adams Memorial Hospital, Decatur, IN, p. A201

NELSON, Nicole
 Director Human Resources, Cloud County Health Center, Concordia, KS, p. A232
 Human Resources Coordinator, Select Specialty Hospital–Omaha, Omaha, NE, p. A388

NELSON, Raymond, Acting Chief Information Resource Management, Fargo Veterans Affairs Health Care System, Fargo, ND, p. A466

NELSON, Rhonda, Chief Nursing Officer, Forrest City Medical Center, Forrest City, AR, p. A44

NELSON, Rodney M., Chief Executive Officer, Mackinac Straits Health System, Saint Ignace, MI, p. A323

NELSON, Sean, Deputy Director, Louis Stokes Cleveland Veterans Affairs Medical Center, Cleveland, OH, p. A476

NELSON, Selena, Chief Financial Officer, Fallon Medical Complex, Baker, MT, p. A374

NELSON, Shelby, Chief Executive Officer, Platte County Memorial Hospital, Wheatland, WY, p. A704

NELSON, Siri, Chief Administrative Officer, Sutter Lakeside Hospital, Lakeport, CA, p. A66

NELSON, Stewart R., Chief Financial Officer, Halifax Regional Health System, South Boston, VA, p. A661

NELSON, Tammy, Manager Human Resources, Southwest Health Center, Platteville, WI, p. A695

NELSON, Thomas, M.D. Director Emergency Room, Gibson General Hospital, Trenton, TN, p. A580

NELSON, Tom, Director Human Resources, Mitchell County Regional Health Center, Osage, IA, p. A226

NELSON, Tricia, Chief Financial Officer, RiverWoods Behavioral Health System, Riverdale, GA, p. A158

NELSON, William, M.D. Medical Director, Riverview Psychiatric Center, Augusta, ME, p. A281

NELSON–JONES, Susan, Director Human Resources, Tehachapi Valley Healthcare District, Tehachapi, CA, p. A92

NEMI, Neil, Administrator Facility Information Center, Richard H. Hutchings Psychiatric Center, Syracuse, NY, p. A443

NEONAKIS, Stephanie W., Manager Human Resources, UH Regional Hospitals, Cleveland, OH, p. A477

NESBIT, Steven, D.O. Chief Medical Officer, Via Christi Hospital on St. Francis, Wichita, KS, p. A246

NESBIT, Tom, Director Human Resources, Kendall Regional Medical Center, Miami, FL, p. A131

NESMITH, Nikki, Chief Nursing Officer, Evans Memorial Hospital, Claxton, GA, p. A150

NESPOLI, John L., Chief Executive Officer, Sacred Heart Hospital, Allentown, PA, p. A519

NESS, David L., Vice President Operations, Grinnell Regional Medical Center, Grinnell, IA, p. A222

NESS, Jon, Chief Executive Officer, Kootenai Medical Center, Coeur D'Alene, ID, p. A168

NESSEL, Mark
Executive Vice President and Chief Operating Officer, Lourdes Medical Center of Burlington County, Willingboro, NJ, p. A412
Chief Operating Officer, Our Lady of Lourdes Medical Center, Camden, NJ, p. A402

NESSELBUSH, Robert, President, Rochester General Hospital, Rochester, NY, p. A441

NESSELRODT, Derek, Director Information Systems, Grant Memorial Hospital, Petersburg, WV, p. A679

NESTER, Darlene
Market Chief Human Resources Officer, Coastal Carolina Hospital, Hardeeville, SC, p. A553
Chief Human Resources Officer, Hilton Head Hospital, Hilton Head Island, SC, p. A553

NESTER, Michael, Administrator, John C. Stennis Memorial Hospital, De Kalb, MS, p. A346

NESTER WOLFE, Cheryl R., R.N. Senior Vice President Operations and Chief Nursing Officer, Salem Hospital, Salem, OR, p. A517

NESTO, Richard W., M.D. Executive Vice President and Chief Medical Officer, Lahey Hospital & Medical Center, Burlington, Burlington, MA, p. A298

NETH, Marvin, Administrator, Callaway District Hospital, Callaway, NE, p. A382

NETTERVILLE, Chad, Administrator, Field Memorial Community Hospital, Centreville, MS, p. A345

NETTLES, Alexander, M.D. Chief of Staff, Monroe County Hospital, Monroeville, AL, p. A23

NETTLES, Angela F., Director Human Resources, KershawHealth, Camden, SC, p. A548

NETTLES, Robert, Director Human Resources, MountainView Hospital, Las Vegas, NV, p. A393

NEUBERT, Todd, Nurse Administrator, LDS Hospital, Salt Lake City, UT, p. A646

NEUENDORF, David A., FACHE, President and Chief Executive Officer, Audrain Medical Center, Mexico, MO, p. A366

NEUENDORF, Deborah, Vice President Administration, Hudson Valley Hospital Center, Cortlandt Manor, NY, p. A424

NEUENDORF, Michael, Chief Executive Officer, Wesley Medical Center, Hattiesburg, MS, p. A348

NEUMAN, Keith A.
Chief Information Officer, Dupont Hospital, Fort Wayne, IN, p. A202
Chief Information Officer, Rehabilitation Hospital of Fort Wayne, Fort Wayne, IN, p. A203

NEUMAN, Michael J., Vice President Finance, Kennedy Krieger Institute, Baltimore, MD, p. A287

NEUMAN, Richard, Assistant Administrator and Chief Human Resources Officer, Olympic Medical Center, Port Angeles, WA, p. A669

NEUMANN, Jamie, Director Human Resources, Iroquois Memorial Hospital and Resident Home, Watseka, IL, p. A196

NEUVIRTH, Stephanie, Chief Human Resource and Diversity Officer, City of Hope's Helford Clinical Research Hospital, Duarte, CA, p. A59

NEVILLE, Bette, R.N. Interim CNO and Director of Nursing, Mercy Hospital of Portland, Portland, ME, p. A284

NEVILLE, Joyce, Chief Nursing Officer, River Parishes Hospital, La Place, LA, p. A270

NEVIN, Janice E., M.D. Chief Medical Officer, Christiana Care Health System, Newark, DE, p. A114

NEVINSKI, Lois, Manager Information Services, Buffalo Hospital, Buffalo, MN, p. A330

NEW, Cathy, Vice President Clinical Services, St. Francis Hospital and Health Services, Maryville, MO, p. A365

NEWBY, Doug, Chief Information Officer, Highlands Medical Center, Scottsboro, AL, p. A25

NEWBY, Nancy M., FACHE, President and Chief Executive Officer, Washington County Hospital, Nashville, IL, p. A190

NEWCOMB, James, M.D. Vice President Medical, Ochsner Medical Center – North Shore, Slidell, LA, p. A279

NEWCOMB, Michael, D.O
Senior Vice President and Chief Operating Officer, Legacy Meridian Park Hospital, Tualatin, OR, p. A518
Senior Vice President and Chief Operating Officer, Legacy Mount Hood Medical Center, Gresham, OR, p. A513
Senior Vice President and Chief Operating Officer, Legacy Salmon Creek Medical Center, Vancouver, WA, p. A673

NEWCOMB, Nancy, Director Human Resources, Jennersville Regional Hospital, West Grove, PA, p. A544

NEWELL, Dan, Chief Financial Officer, Highlands Medical Center, Scottsboro, AL, p. A25

NEWELL, Janice
Chief Information Officer, Swedish Medical Center–Cherry Hill Campus, Seattle, WA, p. A671
Chief Information Officer, Swedish Medical Center–First Hill, Seattle, WA, p. A671

NEWELL, Rich, Chief Executive Officer, Carlisle Regional Medical Center, Carlisle, PA, p. A522

NEWELL, Ryan, M.D. Chief of Staff, Plateau Medical Center, Oak Hill, WV, p. A679

NEWEY, Mark, D.O. Chief of Staff, Mercy Hospital Healdton, Healdton, OK, p. A499

NEWHOUSE, Paul R., Chief Executive Officer, Wallace Thomson Hospital, Union, SC, p. A556

NEWLAND, Judy, R.N., Chief Nursing Officer, Incline Village Community Hospital, Incline Village, NV, p. A392

NEWLAND, Kathie R., Controller, Wheatland Memorial Healthcare, Harlowton, MT, p. A377

NEWLAND, Tammy, Coordinator Human Resources, Scotland County Hospital, Memphis, MO, p. A366

NEWMAN, Billy, Department Head, Naval Hospital, Lemoore, CA, p. A66

NEWMAN, Cynthia, Manager Human Resources, Petersburg Medical Center, Petersburg, AK, p. A29

NEWMAN, Diane, Administrator, Johnson County Hospital, Tecumseh, NE, p. A390

NEWMAN, Douglas A., Chief Executive Officer, LaSalle General Hospital, Jena, LA, p. A269

NEWMAN, Edith, Interim Administrator, John J. Madden Mental Health Center, Hines, IL, p. A185

NEWMAN, Greg, M.D. Chief of Staff, Parkview Regional Hospital, Mexia, TX, p. A623

NEWMAN, James, M.D. President Medical Staff, Kennewick General Hospital, Kennewick, WA, p. A667

NEWMAN, Julie, Vice President Finance, Tahlequah City Hospital, Tahlequah, OK, p. A507

NEWMAN, Karen, Ed.D. Vice President and Chief Nursing Officer, Baptist Health Louisville, Louisville, KY, p. A255

NEWMAN, Kari, Director Human Resources, Dayton General Hospital, Dayton, WA, p. A666

NEWMAN, Kurt, M.D., President and Chief Executive Officer, Children's National Medical Center, Washington, DC, p. A116

NEWMAN, Martin, M.D. Chief Medical Officer, Aurora Phoenix Hospital, Glendale, AZ, p. A32

NEWMAN, Sonya, R.N. Chief Nursing Officer, Blount Memorial Hospital, Maryville, TN, p. A574

NEWMAN, Thomas M., Vice President Finance, UPMC St. Margaret, Pittsburgh, PA, p. A538

NEWMILLER, Vicki, Chief Operating Officer, Great Falls Clinic Medical Center, Great Falls, MT, p. A376

NEWMYER, Joyce, President, Washington Adventist Hospital, Takoma Park, MD, p. A294

NEWMYER, Terry
President and Chief Executive Officer, St. Helena Hospital Clear Lake, Clearlake, CA, p. A56
President and Chief Executive Officer, St. Helena Hospital Napa Valley, Saint Helena, CA, p. A84
President and Chief Executive Officer, St. Helena Hospital–Center for Behavioral Health, Vallejo, CA, p. A94

NEWPOWER, Nicole, Coordinator Human Resources, Kindred Hospital–Fort Worth, Fort Worth, TX, p. A604

NEWQUIST, Dennis, Director Information Systems, Abilene Regional Medical Center, Abilene, TX, p. A581

NEWSOM, Jamie, Director Information Systems, Williamsburg Regional Hospital, Kingstree, SC, p. A553

NEWSOM, Paul, Chief Operating Officer, Kentuckiana Medical Center, Clarksville, IN, p. A200

NEWSOME, Samuel C., M.D. President Medical Staff, Pioneer Community Hospital of Stokes, Danbury, NC, p. A450

NEWTON, Gail, R.N. Vice President Patient Care Services, St. Luke's Hospital – Warren Campus, Phillipsburg, NJ, p. A409

NEWTON, John, Vice President Financial and Support Services and Chief Financial Officer, Memorial Hospital, North Conway, NH, p. A399

NEWTON, Keith, Chief Executive Officer, South Baldwin Regional Medical Center, Foley, AL, p. A20

NEWTON, Mark, President and Chief Executive Officer, Swedish Covenant Hospital, Chicago, IL, p. A179

NEWTON, Milissa, Supervisor Human Resources, Good Samaritan Hospital, Bakersfield, CA, p. A54

NEWTON, Steven R., President, Baylor Regional Medical Center at Grapevine, Grapevine, TX, p. A607

NEWTON, Susan, Chief Financial Officer, Broward Health Imperial Point, Fort Lauderdale, FL, p. A123

NEWTON, Terri, Chief Nursing Officer, Lakewood Regional Medical Center, Lakewood, CA, p. A66

NEWTON, Wilma, Executive Vice President and Chief Financial Officer, St. Vincent's Birmingham, Birmingham, AL, p. A17

NEZBETH, Jacqueline, Human Resources Officer, Select Specialty Hospital–Zanesville, Zanesville, OH, p. A494

NG, Anthony, M.D. Vice President and Chief Medical Officer, The Acadia Hospital, Bangor, ME, p. A281

NG, Thomas T., Chief Information Officer, Collingsworth General Hospital, Wellington, TX, p. A640

NG, Vincent, Director, Providence Veterans Affairs Medical Center, Providence, RI, p. A546

NGUYEN, Anh, M.D. Chief of Staff, Klickitat Valley Health, Goldendale, WA, p. A667

NGUYEN, Anhtai H., M.D. Vice President Medical Affairs and Chief Medical Officer, Fauquier Hospital, Warrenton, VA, p. A662

NGUYEN, Dat, M.D. Chief of Staff, ValleyCare Medical Center, Pleasanton, CA, p. A80

NGUYEN, Hao, M.D. Medical Director, Lanterman Developmental Center, Pomona, CA, p. A80

NGUYEN, Harry, Medical Director, The Woods at Parkside, Gahanna, OH, p. A482

NGUYEN, Vicki, Chief Financial Officer, Good Samaritan Hospital, Bakersfield, CA, p. A54

NIAZI, A., M.D. Chief of Staff, Anson Community Hospital, Wadesboro, NC, p. A462

NIAZI, Sultan, Chief Financial Officer, Arms Acres, Carmel, NY, p. A423

NIBLOCK, Christine, Chief Financial Officer, Sheridan County Health Complex, Hoxie, KS, p. A236

NICASTRO, Pam, Director Human Resources, Kenmore Mercy Hospital, Kenmore, NY, p. A428

NICELY, David E., Chief Executive Officer, Johnson City Medical Center, Johnson City, TN, p. A571

NICEWONGER, David, Chief Operating Officer, Multicare Auburn Medical Center, Auburn, WA, p. A664

NICHELSON, Kathleen, Director Human Resources, Horsham Clinic, Ambler, PA, p. A520

NICHOLAS, Connie, Interim Chief Executive Officer, L. V. Stabler Memorial Hospital, Greenville, AL, p. A21

NICHOLS, Arthur W., President and Chief Executive Officer, Cheshire Medical Center, Keene, NH, p. A398

NICHOLS, Barbara, R.N., President and Chief Executive Officer, Corry Memorial Hospital, Corry, PA, p. A523

NICHOLS, Bryan, Chief Financial Officer, The Heart Hospital Baylor Plano, Plano, TX, p. A628

NICHOLS, Dia, Chief Executive Officer, Northside Hospital and Heart Institute, Saint Petersburg, FL, p. A139

NICHOLS, Dwight J., M.D. Chief of Staff, Stephens Memorial Hospital, Breckenridge, TX, p. A589

NICHOLS, Gretchen, R.N., Chief Administrative Officer, Legacy Mount Hood Medical Center, Gresham, OR, p. A513

NICHOLS, James, Chief Information Officer, Syracuse Veterans Affairs Medical Center, Syracuse, NY, p. A444

NICHOLS, Laura L., Team Leader Human Resources, Hancock Regional Hospital, Greenfield, IN, p. A204

NICHOLS, Lorraine, Director Information Services, Alice Peck Day Memorial Hospital, Lebanon, NH, p. A398

NICHOLS, Mark, FACHE, Chief Executive Officer, LewisGale Hospital at Pulaski, Pulaski, VA, p. A659

NICHOLS, Mark, R.N. Director of Nurses, Liberty Dayton Regional Medical Center, Liberty, TX, p. A618

NICHOLS, Michael, Corporate Vice President Information Technology, Touchette Regional Hospitals, Centreville, IL, p. A176

NICHOLS, Owen, PsyD, President and Chief Executive Officer, NorthKey Community Care, Covington, KY, p. A250

NICHOLS, Robert R., M.D. Vice President Medical Affairs, Mercy Hospital Fort Scott, Fort Scott, KS, p. A234

NICHOLS, Robin
Chief Financial Officer, Coshocton County Memorial Hospital, Coshocton, OH, p. A479
Chief Financial Officer, Hartnett Health System, Dunn, NC, p. A451

NICHOLS, Sharon, D.O. Chief of Staff, Clark Fork Valley Hospital, Plains, MT, p. A378

NICHOLS, Stephen, Chief Executive Officer, Quitman County Hospital, Marks, MS, p. A350

NICHOLS, Suzanne, Director Human Resources, Muleshoe Area Medical Center, Muleshoe, TX, p. A624

NICHOLS, Terry, Chief Executive Officer, Iron County Hospital, Pilot Knob, MO, p. A367

NICHOLS, Theodore, M.D. Senior Vice President Medical Affairs, Lake Health, Concord Township, OH, p. A478

NICHOLSON, Britain, M.D. Chief Medical Officer, Massachusetts General Hospital, Boston, MA, p. A297

NICHOLSON, Cindy, Director Human Resources, Shelby Baptist Medical Center, Alabaster, AL, p. A15

NICHOLSON, Donna, Chief Nursing Officer, Gadsden Regional Medical Center, Gadsden, AL, p. A20

NICHOLSON, Kristin, Coordinator Human Resources, Genesis Medical Center, DeWitt, De Witt, IA, p. A219

NICHOLSON, Molly, R.N. Vice President of Patient Care/Chief Nurse Executive, Presence United Samaritans Medical Center, Danville, IL, p. A180

NICKEL, Craig, M.D. Chief of Staff, Lindsborg Community Hospital, Lindsborg, KS, p. A239

NICKEL, Kathleen, Director Communications, Mercy Medical Center, Roseburg, OR, p. A517

NICKELL, Jerry, Vice President Human Resource and Mission, Saint Alphonsus Medical Center – Baker City, Baker City, OR, p. A511

NICKELL, Sarah, Vice President Human Resources, Mercy Regional Medical Center, Lorain, OH, p. A484

NICKELS, John, M.D. President Medical Staff, Grace Hospital, Cleveland, OH, p. A476

NICKRAND, Tami, Director Information Technology, Harbor Beach Community Hospital, Harbor Beach, MI, p. A316

NICODEMUS, Lowell, Director Information Systems, Hendricks Regional Health, Danville, IN, p. A201

NICOLAY, Donald, M.D. Chief Medical Officer, Community Hospital, Grand Junction, CO, p. A101

NICOLETTA, Nicholas
Corporate Vice President and Chief Financial Officer, Bassett Medical Center, Cooperstown, NY, p. A424
Vice President and Chief Financial Officer, O'Connor Hospital, Delhi, NY, p. A425

NICOLL, C. Diana, Ph.D., Director, San Franciso Veterans Affairs Medical Center, San Francisco, CA, p. A87

NICOLSON, Lynne T., M.D. Medical Director, Sunnyview Rehabilitation Hospital, Schenectady, NY, p. A442

NICOSIA, Chris, Chief Financial Officer, Corpus Christi Medical Center, Corpus Christi, TX, p. A593

NIECE, Pamela S.
Chief Human Resources Officer, LDS Hospital, Salt Lake City, UT, p. A646
Director Human Resources, Orem Community Hospital, Orem, UT, p. A645

NIEDERPRUEM, Mark L., FACHE, Administrator, Shriners Hospitals for Children–Chicago, Chicago, IL, p. A179

NIELAN, Nicole, Director Information Technology, Kimball Health Services, Kimball, NE, p. A385

NIELSEN, Colleen, Director Operations, St. Joseph Hospital, Polson, MT, p. A379

NIELSEN, Gregory A., President, Great Plains Regional Medical Center, North Platte, NE, p. A386

NIELSEN, Gwen, Manager Human Resources, Indianhead Medical Center, Shell Lake, WI, p. A696

NIELSEN, Jeri, Compliance Officer, Mental Health Institute, Clarinda, IA, p. A218

NIELSEN, Kristine, Interim Chief Human Resources Officer, Alegent Creighton Health–Creighton University Medical Center, Omaha, NE, p. A387

NIELSEN, LuAnn, R.N. Chief Nursing Officer, Franklin County Medical Center, Preston, ID, p. A171

NIELSEN, Sandy J., Director, Spokane Veterans Affairs Medical Center, Spokane, WA, p. A672

NIELSEN, Wayne, Director Human Resources, Ocala Regional Medical Center, Ocala, FL, p. A134

NIELSON, Curtis, Director Finance, South Lincoln Medical Center, Kemmerer, WY, p. A702

NIELSON, Lars, M.D. Chief Medical Officer, Weeks Medical Center, Lancaster, NH, p. A398

NIELSON, P. Douglas, M.D. Chief of Staff, Kahuku Medical Center, Kahuku, HI, p. A165

NIEMANN, Lynne, Director Nurses and Patient Care, Community Memorial Hospital, Sumner, IA, p. A229

NIEMER, Peggy, Vice President Human Resources, Children's Hospital of Wisconsin, Milwaukee, WI, p. A692

NIEMEYER, Bruce, Director Human Resources, Yadkin Valley Community Hospital, Yadkinville, NC, p. A464

NIEMEYER, Romaine, President and Chief Executive Officer, Holy Spirit Hospital, Camp Hill, PA, p. A521

NIENHUESER, Roberta, Chief Financial Officer, Fitzgibbon Hospital, Marshall, MO, p. A365

NIERMAN, David M., M.D. Vice President and Chief Medical Officer, The Mount Sinai Hospital of Queens,, NY, p. A437

NIERMAN, Peter, M.D. Chief Medical Officer, Aurora Chicago Lakeshore Hospital, Chicago, IL, p. A176

NIERMAN, Stephen, Interim Chief Executive Officer, South Florida Baptist Hospital, Plant City, FL, p. A137

NIES, Lynn, Human Resources Officer, Erie Veterans Affairs Medical Center, Erie, PA, p. A525

NIESE, Mel, Chief Fiscal Service, Veterans Affairs Palo Alto Health Care System, Palo Alto, CA, p. A79

NIESSINK, Henry
Regional Director Information Technology Services, Mercy Medical Center Redding, Redding, CA, p. A81
Senior Manager Information Technology Systems, St. Elizabeth Community Hospital, Red Bluff, CA, p. A81

NIEVES, Caridad, Chief Nursing Officer and Chief Operating Officer, Coral Gables Hospital, Coral Gables, FL, p. A121

NIGHMAN, Mike, Facility Coordinator Information Systems, Shelby Baptist Medical Center, Alabaster, AL, p. A15

NIGHTENGALE, Randy, Chief Financial Officer, North Valley Hospital, Whitefish, MT, p. A380

NIGHTINGALE, Mark, Senior Administrator, Merrimack Valley Hospital, Haverhill, MA, p. A300

NIGRIN, Daniel, M.D. Vice President Information Services and Chief Information Officer, Boston Children's Hospital, Boston, MA, p. A296

NIHALANI, Sunil, M.D. Chief Medical Staff, Lake Wales Medical Center, Lake Wales, FL, p. A128

NIKOLIC, Srbo, Chief Financial Officer, Hartgrove Hospital, Chicago, IL, p. A176

NILES, Heather, Director Human Resources Operations, Mercy Harvard Hospital, Harvard, IL, p. A184

NILES, Richard, M.D. Chief of Staff, Seymour Hospital, Seymour, TX, p. A633

NILL, Michael, M.D. President Medical Staff, Marietta Memorial Hospital, Marietta, OH, p. A485

NILSSON, Keith, Chief Financial Officer, Cleveland Clinic Florida, Weston, FL, p. A144

NINNEMAN, David, Associate Director, Cincinnati Veterans Affairs Medical Center, Cincinnati, OH, p. A474

NINU, Christine, Chief Clinical Officer, Kindred Hospital–Milwaukee, Greenfield, WI, p. A688

NIPPER, Nathan, Vice President and Chief Operating Officer, Piedmont Newnan Hospital, Newnan, GA, p. A158

NISH, Paulette, MSN Vice President and Chief Nursing Officer, Pocono Medical Center, East Stroudsburg, PA, p. A524

NISSENBAUM, Mark, M.D. Chief of Staff, Tuscaloosa Veterans Affairs Medical Center, Tuscaloosa, AL, p. A26

NISTED, Karissa, Interim Chief Executive Officer, Guidance Center, Flagstaff, AZ, p. A31

NIX, Bo, Chief Information Officer, Madison Valley Medical Center, Ennis, MT, p. A376

NIXDORF, David L., Director Support Services, Frances Mahon Deaconess Hospital, Glasgow, MT, p. A376

NIXON, Margaret, Director Human Resources, St. Vincent Medical Center–North, Sherwood, AR, p. A50

NIXON, Myra, Director Human Resources, HEALTHSOUTH Rehabilitation Hospital, Concord, NH, p. A397

NOAK, Amy, Director Human Resources, St. David's Round Rock Medical Center, Round Rock, TX, p. A629

NOAKES, Timothy J., Chief Financial Officer, Memorial Hospital Los Banos, Los Banos, CA, p. A72

NOBBE, Donna, Director Information Systems, Margaret Mary Health, Batesville, IN, p. A198

NOBLE, James S., Executive Vice President, Chief Operating Officer and Chief Financial Officer, Huntington Memorial Hospital, Pasadena, CA, p. A79

NOBLE, Kerry L., Chief Financial Officer, Pemiscot Memorial Health System, Hayti, MO, p. A361

NOBLE, Mallie S., Administrator, Mary Breckinridge ARH Hospital, Hyden, KY, p. A253

NOBLE, Paula, Chief Financial Officer and Treasurer, Ann & Robert H. Lurie Children's Hospital of Chicago, Chicago, IL, p. A176

NOBLE, Stacy, Administrator, Southeast Rehabilitation Hospital, Lake Village, AR, p. A46

NOBLIN, Jeff, FACHE, Chief Executive Officer, Crockett Hospital, Lawrenceburg, TN, p. A572

NOCITA, Shawn, Chief Information Resource Management, James E. Van Zandt Veterans Affairs Medical Center, Altoona, PA, p. A519

NOCKET, Patricia, Assistant Vice President Clinical Nursing Services, Saint Francis Hospital and Health Centers, Poughkeepsie, NY, p. A440

NOE, J. Thomas, Director Human Resources, Cole Memorial, Coudersport, PA, p. A523

NOEL, Angela, Administrative Director Human Resources, Texas Health Presbyterian Hospital Plano, Plano, TX, p. A628

NOEL, III, Philip J., Assistant Administrator and Chief Operating Officer, Baptist Medical Center, San Antonio, TX, p. A630

NOEL, Vicki, Vice President Human Resources, Southern Ohio Medical Center, Portsmouth, OH, p. A489

NOFFSINGER, Sandy, Executive Assistant, Risk Manager and Director Marketing, Dundy County Hospital, Benkelman, NE, p. A382

NOGA, James W., Chief Information Officer, Massachusetts General Hospital, Boston, MA, p. A297

NOGLER, Wendy, Director Human Resources, Lincoln County Health System, Fayetteville, TN, p. A569

NOGUERAS, Juan, M.D. Chief of Staff, Cleveland Clinic Florida, Weston, FL, p. A144

NOHOS, Janet G., Executive Vice President, St. Bernard Hospital and Health Care Center, Chicago, IL, p. A179

NOKELS, Kevin J., FACHE, President, Alegent Creighton Health–Creighton University Medical Center, Omaha, NE, p. A387

NOKES, Gregory B., Vice President Human Resources, Middlesex Hospital, Middletown, CT, p. A110

NOLAN, Barbara, Manager Human Resources, Warm Springs Medical Center, Warm Springs, GA, p. A162

NOLAN, Douglas, M.D. Medical Director, Cherokee Nation W.W. Hastings Indian Hospital, Tahlequah, OK, p. A507

NOLAN, Heather, Director Information Services, Northern Louisiana Medical Center, Ruston, LA, p. A277

NOLAN, Jennifer
President, Our Lady of Peace, Louisville, KY, p. A256
President, Sts. Mary & Elizabeth Hospital, Louisville, KY, p. A256

NOLAN, Matthew, Director Facilities and Operations, Elizabethtown Community Hospital, Elizabethtown, NY, p. A425

NOLAN, Michael J.
Area Chief Operating Officer and Safety, Promise Hospital of Baton Rouge – Mid-City Campus, Baton Rouge, LA, p. A263
Area Safety Director, Promise Hospital of Baton Rouge – Ochsner Campus, Baton Rouge, LA, p. A263

NOLAN, Patrick B., President and Chief Executive Officer, Warren Memorial Hospital, Front Royal, VA, p. A654

NOLAN, Rosemary, R.N
Chief Operating Officer and Chief Nursing Officer, Heritage Valley Beaver, Beaver, PA, p. A520
Chief Operating Officer and Chief Nursing Officer, Sewickley Valley Hospital, (A Division of Valley Medical Facilities), Sewickley, PA, p. A541

NOLAND, Christopher, FACHE, Interim Chief Executive Officer, Benewah Community Hospital, Saint Maries, ID, p. A171

NOLEN, Benny
Interim Administrator, Nicholas County Hospital, Carlisle, KY, p. A249
President, Saint Joseph Mount Sterling, Mount Sterling, KY, p. A258

NOLL, Gerald A., Chief Financial Officer, Rogers Memorial Hospital, Oconomowoc, WI, p. A693

NOLL, Keith, President, York Hospital, York, PA, p. A545

NOLL, Linda
Executive Director Human Resources, Mercy Hospital Fort Scott, Fort Scott, KS, p. A234
Executive Director Human Resources, Mercy Hospital Independence, Independence, KS, p. A236

NOLLETTE, Karen, Chief Financial Officer, West Holt Memorial Hospital, Atkinson, NE, p. A381

NOLT, Lori, Director Information Technology, Philhaven, Mount Gretna, PA, p. A532

NOLTE, Darlene R., Chief Human Resource Officer, Craig General Hospital, Vinita, OK, p. A509

NOLTING, Evelyn, Chief Executive Officer and Managing Director, River Oaks Hospital, New Orleans, LA, p. A275

NOONAN, Cindy, Chief Operating Officer, ValleyCare Medical Center, Pleasanton, CA, p. A80

NOONAN, Kathryn, Director Information Management, Lemuel Shattuck Hospital, Jamaica Plain, MA, p. A301

NORBURY, Denise
Chief Executive Officer, Center for Behavioral Medicine, Kansas City, MO, p. A362
Chief Executive Officer, Northwest Missouri Psychiatric Rehabilitation Center, Saint Joseph, MO, p. A369
Regional Executive Officer, Southwest Missouri Psychiatric Rehabilitation Center, El Dorado Springs, MO, p. A360

NORBY, Kim, Chief Information Officer, Burgess Health Center, Onawa, IA, p. A226

NORBY, Michael, Interim Chief Financial Officer, Harris Health System, Houston, TX, p. A609

NORD, Gay, Chief Executive Officer, Methodist Hospital, San Antonio, TX, p. A631

NORD, Stanley K., Chief Financial Officer, West Houston Medical Center, Houston, TX, p. A613

NORDAHL, Richard E., Chief Executive Officer, Sanford Sheldon Medical Center, Sheldon, IA, p. A227

NORDING, Rodney, Vice President Organizational Support, Mayo Clinic Health System in Austin, Austin, MN, p. A329

NORDSTROM, Katie, Director Human Resources, Beartooth Billings Clinic, Red Lodge, MT, p. A379

NORDSTROM, Tawnya, Director Human Resources, Centennial Peaks Hospital, Louisville, CO, p. A104

NORDYKE, Charles, Chief Executive Officer, Vibra Hospital of Northwestern Indiana, Crown Point, IN, p. A201

NOREEN, James, M.D. Chief Medical Officer, Regina Medical Center, Hastings, MN, p. A333

NOREEN, Ron, Director Information Services, Comanche County Memorial Hospital, Lawton, OK, p. A500

NOREM, Ashley, Chief Information Systems, Indiana University Health Starke Hospital, Knox, IN, p. A207

NOREN, Mary Kay, Chief Executive Officer, Eastern Shore Hospital Center, Cambridge, MD, p. A290

NOREN, Tom, M.D. Chief Medical Officer, Marquette General Health System, Marquette, MI, p. A319

NORGAARD, Margaret B.
Chief Executive Officer, Poplar Community Hospital, Poplar, MT, p. A379
Chief Executive Officer, Trinity Hospital, Wolf Point, MT, p. A380

NORICK, Laurence, M.D. Clinical Director, U. S. Public Health Service Indian Hospital, Parker, AZ, p. A33

NORIEGA, Donna, Chief Operating Officer, Arizona State Hospital, Phoenix, AZ, p. A34

NORMAN, Debbie, Director Human Resources, Central Louisiana Surgical Hospital, Alexandria, LA, p. A262

NORMAN, Jimmy, Chief Financial Officer, Mountain Lakes Medical Center, Clayton, GA, p. A150

NORMAN, Julie, Chief Financial Officer, Yadkin Valley Community Hospital, Yadkinville, NC, p. A464

NORMAN, Lori, Chief Financial Officer, HEALTHSOUTH Rehabilitation of Gadsden, Gadsden, AL, p. A20

NORMAN, Mark, Administrator, Pioneer Community Hospital of Newton, Newton, MS, p. A352

NORMAN, Mary, R.N. Chief Nursing Officer, Bear Valley Community Hospital, Big Bear Lake, CA, p. A55

NORMAN, Michael L., Executive Vice President and Chief Operating Officer, Landmark Hospital, Cape Girardeau, MO, p. A357

NORMAN, Robin, Senior Vice President and Chief Financial Officer, Virginia Hospital Center – Arlington, Arlington, VA, p. A651

NORMAN, Rolf, Chief Financial Officer, Kaiser Permanente Sunnyside Medical Center, Clackamas, OR, p. A511

NORMAND, Lorrie, R.N. Chief Nursing Officer, Texas Health Harris Methodist Hospital Cleburne, Cleburne, TX, p. A592

NORMINGTON–SLAY, Jeremy, FACHE, Chief Executive Officer, Moundview Memorial Hospital & Clinics, Friendship, WI, p. A687

NORO, Sharon, Chief Executive Officer, Select Specialty Hospital–Youngstown, Youngstown, OH, p. A494

NORONHA, Augusto A., Vice President Finance and Chief Financial Officer, Missouri Baptist Medical Center, Saint Louis, MO, p. A370

NORQUEST, Cathy, Director Human Resources, York General Hospital, York, NE, p. A390

NORR–MCPHILLIPS, Karina, Associate Executive Director Human Resources, Franklin Hospital, Valley Stream, NY, p. A445

NORRIS, Charles, Chief Executive Officer, Memorial Hospital, Gonzales, TX, p. A606

NORRIS, Doug, Administrator and Chief Operating Officer, Western Medical Center–Santa Ana, Santa Ana, CA, p. A89

NORRIS, John, M.D. Chief Medical Officer, Johnson Memorial Hospital, Franklin, IN, p. A203

NORRIS, Marsha, Director Information Systems, Ste. Genevieve County Memorial Hospital, Ste. Genevieve, MO, p. A372

NORRIS, Phil, Chief Financial Officer, Great River Medical Center, Blytheville, AR, p. A41

NORRIS, Timothy, Chief Financial Officer, Greene County General Hospital, Linton, IN, p. A209

NORTH, Scott L., FACHE,
Senior Vice President and President of Acute Care Hospitals, St. John's Hospital, Saint Paul, MN, p. A340
Senior Vice President and President of Acute Care Hospitals, St. Joseph's Hospital, Saint Paul, MN, p. A340
Senior Vice President and President of Acute Care Hospitals, Woodwinds Health Campus, Woodbury, MN, p. A343

NORTHERN, Gail M., Director Human Resources, Blue Mountain Hospital, Blanding, UT, p. A643

NORTHROP, James, Director, Southern Nevada Adult Mental Health Services, Las Vegas, NV, p. A393

NORTHUP, Jeffrey, D.O. Chief Medical Officer, Summit Healthcare Regional Medical Center, Show Low, AZ, p. A37

NORTON, Andrew J., M.D. Senior Vice President Medical Affairs, Froedtert Memorial Lutheran Hospital, Milwaukee, WI, p. A692

NORTON, Bruce J., Senior Vice President and Chief Financial Officer, Sierra Vista Regional Health Center, Sierra Vista, AZ, p. A37

NORTON, Carole, R.N. Chief Nursing Officer, Stonewall Jackson Memorial Hospital, Weston, WV, p. A681

NORTON, Debbie, Chief Financial Officer, Medical Center Barbour, Eufaula, AL, p. A19

NORTON, Julie, Chief Financial Officer, Avera McKennan Hospital and University Health Center, Sioux Falls, SD, p. A562

NORTON, Lizette, Associate Vice President Human Resources Management, Loma Linda University Medical Center, Loma Linda, CA, p. A66

NORTON, Meg, Senior Vice President and Chief Operating Officer, Rady Children's Hospital – San Diego, San Diego, CA, p. A85

NORTON, Robert G., President and Chief Executive Officer, North Shore Medical Center, Salem, MA, p. A304

NORWOOD, Lyle, M.D. Chief of Staff, Hughston Hospital, Columbus, GA, p. A150

NOSACKA, Mark, Chief Executive Officer, Good Samaritan Medical Center, West Palm Beach, FL, p. A143

NOSBISCH, Don, Director Human Resources, Floyd County Medical Center, Charles City, IA, p. A218

NOSEWORTHY, Ed, President and Chief Executive Officer, Florida Hospital Fish Memorial, Orange City, FL, p. A134

NOTARANTONIO, Rosemary, MSN, Chief Executive Officer, Brentwood Meadows, Newburgh, IN, p. A211

NOTEMAN, Laurali, Director Human Resources, Kane County Hospital, Kanab, UT, p. A644

NOTTEBART, Cathy, Acting Superintendent, Austin State Hospital, Austin, TX, p. A584

NOTTIDGE, Andrew, Director Human Resources, Physicians Regional Medical Center – Pine Ridge, Naples, FL, p. A133

NOTTINGHAM, Cheryl, Chief Financial Officer, Atlantic General Hospital, Berlin, MD, p. A289

NOUNA, Nabil, M.D. Chief of Staff, Allegan General Hospital, Allegan, MI, p. A308

NOVAK, Christopher, Chief Operating Officer, Alexian Brothers Behavioral Health Hospital, Hoffman Estates, IL, p. A185

NOVAK, Georgene, Director Human Resources, Littleton Regional Hospital, Littleton, NH, p. A399

NOVAK, James, Vice President, Human Resources, St. Francis Medical Center, Monroe, LA, p. A274

NOVAK, Joseph, PsyD, Chief Executive Officer, Maryville Behavioral Health Hospital, Des Plaines, IL, p. A181

NOVAK, Kristen, Manager Human Resources, River Falls Area Hospital, River Falls, WI, p. A696

NOVAK, Michael, Vice President Operations, Saint Mary's Hospital, Waterbury, CT, p. A112

NOVAK, Sharon, CPA Vice President Finance, Adena Pike Medical Center, Waverly, OH, p. A492

NOWACHEK, Debra S., Director Human Resources, Grinnell Regional Medical Center, Grinnell, IA, p. A222

NOWELL, Laura
Chief Financial Officer, Cornerstone Hospital–West Monroe, West Monroe, LA, p. A280
Vice President Accounting and Finance, Solara Hospital Harlingen, Harlingen, TX, p. A608

NOWICKI, Becky, Director Human Resources, Michiana Behavioral Health Center, Plymouth, IN, p. A212

NOWICKI, Zigmund, Director Human Resources, Catskill Regional Medical Center, Harris, NY, p. A427

NOWLAND, Bob, M.D. Chief of Staff, Texas Health Harris Methodist Hospital Hurst–Euless–Bedford, Bedford, TX, p. A588

NOWLIN, Angela, Senior Vice President, Operations, Magnolia Regional Health Center, Corinth, MS, p. A346

NOWLIN, Jeffrey D., Vice President, Chief Operating Officer, St. John Medical Center, Tulsa, OK, p. A509

NOWLIN, Patricia, Director of Accounting, Cooper County Memorial Hospital, Boonville, MO, p. A357

NOWLING, Tara, Director Human Resources, Monroe County Hospital, Monroeville, AL, p. A23

NOYES, Debra, Chief Financial Officer, Putnam Community Medical Center, Palatka, FL, p. A135

NUCKLES, Craig, Chief Executive Officer and Regional Vice President, Timberlawn Mental Health System, Dallas, TX, p. A598

NUDD, Brandon M., Director, Organizational Development, Park Ridge Health, Hendersonville, NC, p. A454

NUDENCE, Robert, M.D. Chief of Staff, Highlands Regional Medical Center, Sebring, FL, p. A140

NUESSLEIN, Cindy, Chief Executive Officer, Interim LSU Public Hospital, New Orleans, LA, p. A275

NUNELLEY, Preston, M.D. Chief Medical Officer, Baptist Health Lexington, Lexington, KY, p. A253

NUNES, Vonnie, Interim Chief Executive Officer, Corcoran District Hospital, Corcoran, CA, p. A57

NUNEZ, Milton, Executive Director, Lincoln Medical and Mental Health Center,, NY, p. A433

NUNLEY, Julie, R.N.,
Chief Executive Officer, Banner Goldfield Medical Center, Apache Junction, AZ, p. A30
Chief Executive Officer, Banner Ironwood Medical Center, San Tan Valley, AZ, p. A36

NUNLEY, Penny, Vice President Human Resources, Hannibal Regional Hospital, Hannibal, MO, p. A361

NUNN, Chalmers, M.D. Chief Medical Officer and Senior Vice President, Centra Lynchburg General Hospital, Lynchburg, VA, p. A656

NUNNELLEY, Greg, Director Human Resources, Pineville Community Hospital Association, Pineville, KY, p. A259

NUNNERY, Reece, Chief Financial Officer, Southwest Mississippi Regional Medical Center, McComb, MS, p. A350

NUNNES, Maria, Director Information Systems, Gnaden Huetten Memorial Hospital, Lehighton, PA, p. A530

NURICK, Paul E., Chief Executive Officer, Kittitas Valley Community Hospital, Ellensburg, WA, p. A666

NUSBAUM, Neil, M.D. Chief of Staff, VA Central Western Massachusetts Healthcare System, Leeds, MA, p. A301

NUSS, Michelle, M.D. Chief Medical Officer, West Virginia University Hospitals, Morgantown, WV, p. A679

NUTTER, Robert, COO, Vice President of Human Resources and Support Services, Mercy Hospital of Portland, Portland, ME, p. A284

NWANGBURUKA, Okechukwu, M.D. Medical Director, Sierra Vista Hospital, Sacramento, CA, p. A83

NYBERG, Becky T., Chief Financial Officer, Bloomington Meadows Hospital, Bloomington, IN, p. A199

NYHUS, Corey, M.D. President Medical Staff, Perham Health, Perham, MN, p. A338

NYIKES, Debra, Director Finance and Chief Financial Officer, Cleveland Clinic Children's Hospital for Rehabilitation, Cleveland, OH, p. A476

NYKAMP, Robert, Vice President and Chief Operating Officer, Pine Rest Christian Mental Health Services, Grand Rapids, MI, p. A315

NYLUND, Barbara, M.D. Chief of Staff, Novato Community Hospital, Novato, CA, p. A76

## O

NYP, Randall G., FACHE,
President and Chief Executive Officer, Providence Medical Center, Kansas City, KS, p. A237
President and Chief Executive Officer, Saint John Hospital, Leavenworth, KS, p. A238

O'BAR, Dorothy, R.N., Regional Administrator, Mercy Hospital Waldron, Waldron, AR, p. A50

O'BRIEN Jr., Charles M., President and Chief Executive Officer, Weirton Medical Center, Weirton, WV, p. A681

O'BRIEN, Dan, D.O. Medical Director, Indiana University Health Paoli Hospital, Paoli, IN, p. A212

O'BRIEN, Darcey, Chief Executive Officer, Integris Clinton Regional Hospital, Clinton, OK, p. A497

O'BRIEN, David, M.D., Interim President and Chief Executive Officer, Redwood Memorial Hospital, Fortuna, CA, p. A60

O'BRIEN, David, M.D. Senior Vice President, COO, St. Joseph Health St. Mary, Apple Valley, CA, p. A53

O'BRIEN, David, M.D., Interim President and Chief Executive Officer, St. Joseph Hospital, Eureka, CA, p. A59

O'BRIEN, Elizabeth, Chief Financial Officer, Northern Nevada Adult Mental Health Services, Sparks, NV, p. A395

O'BRIEN, Gracie, Chief Information Officer, Sequoia Hospital, Redwood City, CA, p. A82

O'BRIEN, Jane E., M.D. Medical Director, Franciscan Hospital for Children, Boston, MA, p. A296

O'BRIEN, John, Chief Executive Officer, Manning Regional Healthcare Center, Manning, IA, p. A224

O'BRIEN, John, M.D. Chief of Staff, Natchez Regional Medical Center, Natchez, MS, p. A351

O'BRIEN, John A., FACHE Chief Operating Officer, Laurel Regional Hospital, Laurel, MD, p. A293

O'BRIEN, John A., FACHE, President, Prince George's Hospital Center, Cheverly, MD, p. A290

O'BRIEN, Karen, Director Human Resources, Gerald Champion Regional Medical Center, Alamogordo, NM, p. A414

O'BRIEN, Kelly, Vice President Operations, Riverview Medical Center, Red Bank, NJ, p. A410

O'BRIEN, Kevin, Interim Chief Executive Officer, Newman Memorial Hospital, Shattuck, OK, p. A506

O'BRIEN, Laureen, Chief Information Officer, Providence Newberg Medical Center, Newberg, OR, p. A515

O'BRIEN, Maureen, Chief Operating Officer, Kaiser Permanente Redwood City Medical Center, Redwood City, CA, p. A82

O'BRIEN, Pat, Interim Chief Executive Officer, Mt. Graham Regional Medical Center, Safford, AZ, p. A36

O'BRIEN, Renee, Director Human Resources, Greater Binghamton Health Center, Binghamton, NY, p. A421

O'BRIEN, Yvonne M., MS Chief of Nursing, Pella Regional Health Center, Pella, IA, p. A227

O'BRYANT, G. Mark, President and Chief Executive Officer, Tallahassee Memorial HealthCare, Tallahassee, FL, p. A141

O'CONNER, Marcia, Chief Executive Officer, Choctaw Memorial Hospital, Hugo, OK, p. A500

O'CONNOR, Annalise, Director Human Resources, Sierra Nevada Memorial Hospital, Grass Valley, CA, p. A63

O'CONNOR, Carol Lee, Interim Chief Executive Officer, Kindred Hospital Las Vegas–Sahara, Las Vegas, NV, p. A393

O'CONNOR, Daniel
Vice President Human Resources, Munroe Regional Medical Center, Ocala, FL, p. A134
Chief Information Officer, United Memorial Medical Center, Batavia, NY, p. A421

O'CONNOR, David, Executive Vice President and Chief Financial Officer, Gaston Memorial Hospital, Gastonia, NC, p. A453

O'CONNOR, Delia, FACHE, President and Chief Executive Officer, Anna Jaques Hospital, Newburyport, MA, p. A302

O'CONNOR, Dennis, M.D. Medical Director, Ira Davenport Memorial Hospital, Bath, NY, p. A421

O'CONNOR, Ellen, Chief Nursing Officer, Jacobi Medical Center,, NY, p. A432

O'CONNOR, J. T., M.D. Medical Director, Mercy Health Love County, Marietta, OK, p. A501

O'CONNOR, James, Executive Vice President and Chief Administrative Officer, St. Charles Hospital, Port Jefferson, NY, p. A440

O'CONNOR, Kathy, Vice President, Finance and Chief Financial Officer, St. Joseph Mercy Hospital, Ypsilanti, MI, p. A327

O'CONNOR, Kevin, D.O. President Medical Staff, Spectrum Health United Hospital, Greenville, MI, p. A315

O'CONNOR, Michael, M.D. Chief Medical Officer, Banner Ironwood Medical Center, San Tan Valley, AZ, p. A36

O'CONNOR, Michael F., Senior Vice President Finance, York Hospital, York, PA, p. A545

O'CONNOR, Nicholas, Vice President and Chief Information Officer, Plainview Hospital, Plainview, NY, p. A439

O'CONNOR, Patrick, Chief Operating Officer, Morris Hospital & Healthcare Centers, Morris, IL, p. A189

O'CONNOR, Steve, Manager Human Resources, Kern Medical Center, Bakersfield, CA, p. A54

O'CONNOR, Thomas, President, United Hospital, Saint Paul, MN, p. A340

O'CONNOR, Timothy P., Executive Vice President and Chief Financial Officer, Lahey Hospital & Medical Center, Burlington, Burlington, MA, p. A298

O'DAY, Ken, Supervisor Information Systems, Corry Memorial Hospital, Corry, PA, p. A523

O'DEA, Edward, Chief Financial Officer, Lehigh Valley Hospital–Muhlenberg, Bethlehem, PA, p. A520

O'DELL, Darrell, Director Information Services, Good Samaritan Hospital, San Jose, CA, p. A87

O'DELL, Janet, Administrative Director, Eastern Louisiana Mental Health System, Jackson, LA, p. A269

O'DONNELL, Chris, Director for Administration, Naval Hospital Pensacola, Pensacola, FL, p. A136

O'DONNELL, Michael, Chief Financial Officer, Peconic Bay Medical Center, Riverhead, NY, p. A440

O'DONNELL, Patrick W., CPA, President and Chief Executive Officer, Chambersburg Hospital, Chambersburg, PA, p. A522

O'DONNELL, Patrick W., CPA Vice President Finance, Waynesboro Hospital, Waynesboro, PA, p. A543

O'DONNELL, Randall L., Ph.D.,
President and Chief Executive Officer, Children's Mercy Hospitals and Clinics, Kansas City, MO, p. A362
President and Chief Executive Officer, Children's Mercy South, Overland Park, KS, p. A241

O'DONOGHUE, Brian, M.D. Chief Medical Officer, Breckinridge Memorial Hospital, Hardinsburg, KY, p. A252

O'FLANAGAN, Jayne, Director Human Resources, Incline Village Community Hospital, Incline Village, NV, p. A392

O'GORMAN, Jr., Thomas, Chief Financial Officer, East Texas Medical Center–Gilmer, Gilmer, TX, p. A606

O'HALLA, Mark S., President and Chief Executive Officer, McLaren Macomb, Mount Clemens, MI, p. A320

O'HARA, Denise, Vice President Human Resources, Wilson Medical Center, Wilson, NC, p. A463

O'HARA, Kathleen, Vice President Human Resources, Erie County Medical Center, Buffalo, NY, p. A422

O'HARA, Michael
Senior Executive Director Human Resources, Houston Medical Center, Warner Robins, GA, p. A162
Senior Executive Director, Perry Hospital, Perry, GA, p. A158

O'HARE, Rose Ann, R.N. Vice President Patient Services, Lawrence Hospital Center, Bronxville, NY, p. A422

O'KEEFE, Charles, Director Health Information Services, HEALTHSOUTH Rehabilitation Hospital of Tallahassee, Tallahassee, FL, p. A140

O'KEEFE, James, Chief Financial Officer, Westerly Hospital, Westerly, RI, p. A547

O'KEEFE, James M., President and Chief Executive Officer, Mile Bluff Medical Center, Mauston, WI, p. A690

O'KEEFE, John, Chief Executive Officer, Select Specialty Hospital–Gulf Coast, Gulfport, MS, p. A347

O'KEEFE, Kathy, Executive Director, Pilgrim Psychiatric Center, Brentwood, NY, p. A422

O'KEEFE, Michael N., President and Chief Executive Officer, Evangelical Community Hospital, Lewisburg, PA, p. A530

O'KEEFFE, Maureen, Vice President Human Resources, St. Luke's Regional Medical Center, Boise, ID, p. A168

O'LASKEY, Bonnie, Vice President Human Resources, Edward White Hospital, Saint Petersburg, FL, p. A139

O'LEARY, Daniel H., M.D. Chief Medical Officer, Health Alliance Hospitals, Leominster, MA, p. A301

O'LEARY, Kevin J., Senior Vice President and Chief Financial Officer, Exeter Hospital, Exeter, NH, p. A398

O'LEARY, Megan A., Vice President Human Resources and Rehabilitation Services, McKenzie–Willamette Medical Center, Springfield, OR, p. A518

O'LEARY, Rand, Senior Vice President and Chief Operating Officer, Henry Ford Wyandotte Hospital, Wyandotte, MI, p. A327

O'LOUGHLIN, James F., President and Chief Executive Officer, Memorial Hospital Jacksonville, Jacksonville, FL, p. A126

O'MALLEY, Constance, Chief Nursing Officer, St. John Macomb–Oakland Hospital, Warren, MI, p. A326

O'MALLEY, Erin, M.D. Chief Clinical Officer, Kindred Hospital North Houston, Houston, TX, p. A610

O'MALLEY, John F., FACHE, Chief Executive Officer, Select Specialty Hospital–Ann Arbor, Ypsilanti, MI, p. A327

O'MALLEY, Jon P., Chief Executive Officer, Select Specialty Hospital–Macomb County, Mount Clemens, MI, p. A320

O'MALLEY, Mary Jo, R.N. Vice President Diagnostics and Support Services, Oconomowoc Memorial Hospital, Oconomowoc, WI, p. A693

O'MALLEY, Terry, Vice President Human Resources, Frederick Memorial Hospital, Frederick, MD, p. A291

O'MALLEY, Trevor, Site Manager, Presence Saint Joseph Hospital, Elgin, IL, p. A181

O'NEAL, Michael, Administrator and Chief Executive Officer, George C Grape Community Hospital, Hamburg, IA, p. A222

O'NEAL, Nancy L., Director Operations, Lakeside Medical Center, Belle Glade, FL, p. A118

O'NEAL, Stephen, R.N. Chief Nursing Officer, Henry County Medical Center, Paris, TN, p. A578

O'NEIL, Jeremy, Manager Finance, Providence Valdez Medical Center, Valdez, AK, p. A29

O'NEIL, Linda B., R.N., Chief Executive Officer, Hospital for Extended Recovery, Norfolk, VA, p. A658

O'NEIL Jr., Mark T., President and Chief Executive Officer, Hilton Head Hospital, Hilton Head Island, SC, p. A553"

O'NEILL, Bonnie, Vice President Employee Services, Northern Montana Hospital, Havre, MT, p. A377

O'NEILL, Joseph J., M.D. Vice President Medical Affairs, South County Hospital, Wakefield, RI, p. A547

O'NEILL, Lynn, R.N. Chief Nursing Officer, Medical Center of Lewisville, Lewisville, TX, p. A618

O'NEILL, Michael, M.D. Chief Medical Officer, Eastside Medical Center, Snellville, GA, p. A160

O'NEILL, Michelle, M.D. President Medical Staff, Fairfield Memorial Hospital, Fairfield, IL, p. A182

O'NEILL, Stephan, Vice President Information Services, Hartford Hospital, Hartford, CT, p. A109

O'NEILL, Stephen, Clinical Director, Norfolk Regional Center, Norfolk, NE, p. A386

O'REAR, Caleb F., Chief Executive Officer, Denton Regional Medical Center, Denton, TX, p. A598

O'REAR, Christie, Human Resources Officer, Collingsworth General Hospital, Wellington, TX, p. A640

O'SHAUGHNESSY, Bryan, Chief Information Officer, Ellwood City Hospital, Ellwood City, PA, p. A525

O'SHEA, James E.
Administrator, Springbrook Hospital, Brooksville, FL, p. A120
Administrator, Willough Healthcare System, Naples, FL, p. A133

O'SHEA, Kristen, R.N. Vice President Patient Care Services, Gettysburg Hospital, Gettysburg, PA, p. A526

O'SHIELDS, Hugh, M.D. President Medical Staff, Trinity Medical Center, Birmingham, AL, p. A17

O'SULLIVAN, Barbara, M.D. Medical Director, Rockefeller University Hospital, New York, NY, p. A436

O'SULLIVAN, Colin
Administrator, Complex Care Hospital of Idaho, Meridian, ID, p. A170
Administrator, Tahoe Pacific Hospitals, Reno, NV, p. A395

O'SULLIVAN, Peggy, Director Patient Services, Spearfish Regional Surgery Center, Spearfish, SD, p. A563

OAKES, Julie P., R.N. Manager Risk and Quality, Ocean Beach Hospital, Ilwaco, WA, p. A667

OAKES, Patti
Director Human Resources, Medical Center of the Rockies, Loveland, CO, p. A104
Interim Vice President Human Resources, Poudre Valley Hospital, Fort Collins, CO, p. A101

OAKLEY, Lisa, Chief Financial Officer, Harper County Community Hospital, Buffalo, OK, p. A496

OAKS, Dana, Chief Executive Officer, West Palm Hospital, West Palm Beach, FL, p. A144

OATES, John
Director Information Systems, Geneva General Hospital, Geneva, NY, p. A426
Director Information Systems, Soldiers and Sailors Memorial Hospital of Yates County, Penn Yan, NY, p. A439

OATES, Susie, Assistant Superintendent for Administration, Southwestern State Hospital, Thomasville, GA, p. A161

OBER, Kathleen, M.D. Chief Medical Officer, Blue Hill Memorial Hospital, Blue Hill, ME, p. A282

OBER, Tammy L., Chief Executive Officer, Lancaster Rehabilitation Hospital, Lancaster, PA, p. A529

OBERHEU, Todd, Chief Executive Officer, Spanish Peaks Regional Health Center, Walsenburg, CO, p. A106

OBERMAN, Shannon, Coordinator Human Resources, Select Specialty Hospital–Wilmington, Wilmington, DE, p. A115

OBERMIER, Jenny, VP, Director of Nursing, York General Hospital, York, NE, p. A390

OBERRIEDER, Marsha, Vice President Operations, Northwestern Lake Forest Hospital, Lake Forest, IL, p. A186

OBERST, Larry, Vice President Finance, Spectrum Health Special Care Hospital, Grand Rapids, MI, p. A315

OBRYCKI, Travis, Director Information Systems, Memorial Medical Center – Neillsville, Neillsville, WI, p. A693

OCASIO, J. Manuel, Vice President Human Resources, Holy Cross Hospital, Silver Spring, MD, p. A294

OCCHIOGROSSO, Kathleen, Vice President Human Resources, St. Mary's Hospital, Troy, NY, p. A444

OCHOA, Nikki
 Interim Chief Financial Officer, St. Joseph's Behavioral Health Center, Stockton, CA, p. A92
 Interim Chief Financial Officer, St. Joseph's Medical Center, Stockton, CA, p. A92

OCHOA, Yolanda, Director Human Resources, Acuity Hospital of South Texas, San Antonio, TX, p. A630

OCHS, David T., President and Chief Executive Officer, OSF Saint James – John W. Albrecht Medical Center, Pontiac, IL, p. A192

OCHS, Kristine, R.N., Administrator, Grisell Memorial Hospital District One, Ransom, KS, p. A243

OCHSENDORF, Derrick, Manager Information Technology and Systems, Johnson Memorial Health Services, Dawson, MN, p. A331

OCON, Paul, R.N. Chief Nursing Officer, El Paso Children's Hospital, El Paso, TX, p. A601

OCTAVIANI, Raul, M.D. Chief Medical Officer, Radius Specialty Hospital Boston, Boston, MA, p. A297

ODATO, David, Chief Administrative and Chief Human Resources Officer, UCSF Medical Center, San Francisco, CA, p. A87

ODDIS, Joseph M., Chief Executive Officer, Bon Secours Maryview Medical Center, Portsmouth, VA, p. A659

ODEGAARD, Daniel, Chief Executive Officer, Bigfork Valley Hospital, Bigfork, MN, p. A329

ODELL, Cheryl, Chief Nursing Officer, Sharp Mesa Vista Hospital, San Diego, CA, p. A86

ODOM, Keli, Chief Operating Officer, North Central Surgical Center, Dallas, TX, p. A597

ODOM, Mary, Accountant, Larned State Hospital, Larned, KS, p. A238

ODOM, Robbin, R.N. Chief Nursing Officer, Women and Children's Hospital, Lake Charles, LA, p. A272

OEHLERS, Randi, Site Director Management Information Systems, Mercy Hospital Cadillac, Cadillac, MI, p. A310

OEHLKE, Tammy, Director Human Resources, St. Mark's Medical Center, La Grange, TX, p. A617

OEHM, Janice, Manager Business Office, Johnson County Hospital, Tecumseh, NE, p. A390

OELMAN, Mary B., R.N. Chief Operating Officer and Chief Clinical Officer, Barlow Respiratory Hospital, Los Angeles, CA, p. A68

OESTREICH, Alyssa, Chief Operating Officer, Odessa Memorial Healthcare Center, Odessa, WA, p. A668

OESTREICH, Pearl, Director Human Resources, Scott & White Hospital – Llano, Llano, TX, p. A619

OETTING, Phyllis, Director Human Resources, Mitchell County Hospital Health Systems, Beloit, KS, p. A232

OETZEL, Gerald P., Chief Financial Officer, Jeanes Hospital, Philadelphia, PA, p. A535

OFFUTT, Dan, Manager Finance, Knox County Hospital, Knox City, TX, p. A617

OFNER, Lori, Vice President Human Resources, Easton Hospital, Easton, PA, p. A525

OGAWA, Quin, Vice President and Chief Financial Officer, Kuakini Medical Center, Honolulu, HI, p. A164

OGBURN, Wayne
 Chief Executive Officer, Liberty Medical Center, Chester, MT, p. A374
 Chief Executive Officer, Pondera Medical Center, Conrad, MT, p. A375

OGDEN, Judy, Director Information Technology, Franklin Medical Center, Winnsboro, LA, p. A280

OGDEN, Michael L., President and Chief Executive Officer, Little Falls Hospital, Little Falls, NY, p. A428

OGEDA, Fidel, M.D. Chief of Staff, Medical Arts Hospital, Lamesa, TX, p. A617

OGG, Tom, Vice President Information Services and Chief Information Officer, Akron Children's Hospital, Akron, OH, p. A470

OGILVIE, Patrick, M.D. Chief Medical Officer, Summit Pacific Medical Center, McCleary, WA, p. A668

OGILVIE, Richard, Chief Information Officer, Southwestern Vermont Medical Center, Bennington, VT, p. A649

OGLESBY, Darrell M., Administrator, Putnam General Hospital, Eatonton, GA, p. A153

OGLESBY, Michele, Manager Human Resources, Eastern Oklahoma Medical Center, Poteau, OK, p. A505

OGORZALEK, Ed, Chief Financial Officer, Rutland Regional Medical Center, Rutland, VT, p. A650

OHASHI, Curtis, Chief Executive Officer, Select Specialty Hospital–Cincinnati, Cincinnati, OH, p. A475

OHE, Darin, Chief Financial Officer, Richard P. Stadter Psychiatric Center, Grand Forks, ND, p. A467

OHE, Gregory P., President and Chief Executive Officer, Health Central, Ocoee, FL, p. A134

OHL, Connie, Acting Chief Human Resources, Veterans Affairs Illiana Health Care System, Danville, IL, p. A180

OHLE, Rick L., Chief Operating Officer, St. Mary's of Michigan, Saginaw, MI, p. A323

OHM, Barbara, Administrator, The Orthopedic Specialty Hospital, Murray, UT, p. A644

OHMART, Dean, Assistant Administrator and Chief Financial Officer, Ransom Memorial Hospital, Ottawa, KS, p. A241

OHNOUTKA, Debra, Chief Nursing Officer, St. Joseph Medical Center, Kansas City, MO, p. A363

OHRT, James M., M.D. Director Medical Staff, Henderson Health Care Services, Henderson, NE, p. A384

OISHI, Gregg, Senior Vice President and Chief Operating Officer, Kuakini Medical Center, Honolulu, HI, p. A164

OJEDA, Filiberto J., Director Quality Improvement, Risk Management and Information System, Greenwood County Hospital, Eureka, KS, p. A233

OKABE, David
 Senior Vice President, Chief Financial Officer and Treasurer, Kapiolani Medical Center for Women & Children, Honolulu, HI, p. A164
 Executive Vice President, Chief Financial Officer and Treasurer, Pali Momi Medical Center, Aiea, HI, p. A164
 Executive Vice President, Chief Financial Officer and Treasurer, Straub Clinic & Hospital, Honolulu, HI, p. A165
 Executive Vice President, Chief Financial Officer and Treasurer, Wilcox Memorial Hospital, Lihue, HI, p. A166

OKASHIMA, Mark, Area Finance Officer, Kaiser Permanente South San Francisco, South San Francisco, CA, p. A91

OKECHUKWU, Vitalis C., M.D. President Medical Staff, Kindred Hospital Lafayette, Lafayette, LA, p. A270

OKERSON, Alan, Director Information Technology, Kenmare Community Hospital, Kenmare, ND, p. A468

OKESON, Keith, President and Chief Executive Officer, LifeCare Medical Center, Roseau, MN, p. A339

OKSENDAHL, Elaine, Administrator, Schick Shadel Hospital, Seattle, WA, p. A670

OKUHARA, Mary, Director Human Resources, Lakewood Regional Medical Center, Lakewood, CA, p. A66

OLAND, Charisse S., FACHE, Chief Executive Officer, Rusk County Memorial Hospital and Nursing Home, Ladysmith, WI, p. A689

OLANDER, Scott, Vice President and Chief Financial Officer, Yakima Valley Memorial Hospital, Yakima, WA, p. A674

OLAZAGASTI, Rafael, M.D. Vice President Medical Affairs and Network Development, Health Alliance Hospital – Mary's Avenue Campus, Kingston, NY, p. A428

OLD ELK, Clayton, Service Unit Director, Crow/Northern Cheyenne Hospital, Crow Agency, MT, p. A375

OLDEN, R. Don, Chief Executive Officer, Wahiawa General Hospital, Wahiawa, HI, p. A166

OLDER, Michael, M.D. President Medical Staff, Nashoba Valley Medical Center, Ayer, MA, p. A295

OLDHAM, Benjamin, M.D. Chief of Staff, East Georgia Regional Medical Center, Statesboro, GA, p. A160

OLDHAM, Jennie, Director Human Resources, Goodall–Witcher Healthcare, Clifton, TX, p. A592

OLDHAM, John M., M.D. Senior Vice President and Chief of Staff, Menninger Clinic, Houston, TX, p. A611

OLDHAM, Lawrence, Chief Financial Officer, Austin Surgical Hospital, Austin, TX, p. A584

OLDHAM, Marriner, M.D. Chief Medical Officer, U. S. Air Force Regional Hospital, Elmendorf AFB, AK, p. A28

OLDS, Susan, Chief Financial Officer, St. Anthony's Hospital, Saint Petersburg, FL, p. A139

OLEJNIK, Marilyn A., Vice President Finance, Porter Medical Center, Middlebury, VT, p. A649

OLENGINSKI, Jon, D.O. Medical Director of Hospital Services, Kindred Hospital–Wyoming Valley, Wilkes Barre, PA, p. A544

OLESON, Chuck, Chief Information Officer, Butler Health System, Butler, PA, p. A521

OLESON, Vail, Chief Executive Officer, Morrill County Community Hospital, Bridgeport, NE, p. A382

OLEY, Edwin M., President and Chief Executive Officer, Mercy Regional Medical Center, Lorain, OH, p. A484

OLINDE, Chad E., Administrator and Chief Executive Officer, Pointe Coupee General Hospital, New Roads, LA, p. A276

OLINGER, Richard P., Chief Financial Officer, Millcreek Community Hospital, Erie, PA, p. A525

OLINGER, Terry, System Chief Human Resources Officer, Benefis Hospitals, Great Falls, MT, p. A376

OLIPHANT, Gerald P., Executive Vice President and Chief Operating Officer, Good Samaritan Hospital, Cincinnati, OH, p. A474

OLIPHANT, Phillip, Chief Information Officer, U. S. Air Force Regional Hospital, Elmendorf AFB, AK, p. A28

OLIVA, Anthony F., D.O. Sr. Vice President & Chief Medical Officer, Borgess Medical Center, Kalamazoo, MI, p. A317

OLIVA, Damaso, M.D. Chief Medical Officer, Southwest General Hospital, San Antonio, TX, p. A632

OLIVA, George, Associate Information Systems Analyst, Lanterman Developmental Center, Pomona, CA, p. A80

OLIVARES, Rafael, Controller, Starr County Memorial Hospital, Rio Grande City, TX, p. A629

OLIVAS, Ray, Chief Fiscal Service, West Texas Veterans Affairs Health Care System, Big Spring, TX, p. A588

OLIVE, Alan C.
 Chief Executive Officer, Northern Nevada Medical Center, Sparks, NV, p. A396
 Chief Executive Officer, Sierra Surgery Hospital, Carson City, NV, p. A391

OLIVEIRA, Edgar, M.D
 Chief Medical Staff, Linton Hospital, Linton, ND, p. A468
 Chief of Staff, Wishek Community Hospital and Clinics, Wishek, ND, p. A469

OLIVER, Athan, Administrator and Chief Executive Officer, Iberia Rehabilitation Hospital, New Iberia, LA, p. A275

OLIVER, David, Director Information Systems, King's Daughters Medical Center, Ashland, KY, p. A248

OLIVER, Diane, R.N. Chief Nursing Officer, Parkwest Medical Center, Knoxville, TN, p. A572

OLIVER, Doug, Chief Financial Officer, Windhaven Psychiatric Hospital, Prescott Valley, AZ, p. A36

OLIVER, Julie, Chief Human Resources Officer, Mayo Clinic Health System in Mankato, Mankato, MN, p. A335

OLIVER, Karen, Vice President Human Resources, West Florida Hospital, Pensacola, FL, p. A137

OLIVER, Vincent, Administrator, Island Hospital, Anacortes, WA, p. A664

OLIVERA, Sue, Vice President, Aultman Hospital, Canton, OH, p. A473

OLIVIER, Edward, Chief Financial Officer, Charles A. Dean Memorial Hospital, Greenville, ME, p. A283

OLIVIERI, Michael, Chief Financial Officer, Lower Bucks Hospital, Bristol, PA, p. A521

OLLER, Darrell, Director Information Systems, Abraham Lincoln Memorial Hospital, Lincoln, IL, p. A187

OLLI, Cindy, R.N. Chief Nursing Officer, Schoolcraft Memorial Hospital, Manistique, MI, p. A319

OLLIE, Edwin J., Executive Vice President and Chief Financial Officer, New Hanover Regional Medical Center, Wilmington, NC, p. A463

OLLIS, Linda Neu, FACHE Chief Operating Officer, Monongalia General Hospital, Morgantown, WV, p. A679

OLLSON, Joanne, Vice President Human Resources, Noble Hospital, Westfield, MA, p. A306

OLM, Brad, Director Human Resources, Edgerton Hospital and Health Services, Edgerton, WI, p. A686

OLMSTEAD, David, Associate Administrator and Director Human Resources, Lake Pointe Medical Center, Rowlett, TX, p. A630

OLMSTEAD, Linda, Director, Human Resources, UW Medicine/Northwest Hospital & Medical Center, Seattle, WA, p. A671

OLS, Timothy A., FACHE, President and Chief Executive Officer, Sarah Bush Lincoln Health Center, Mattoon, IL, p. A188

OLSCAMP, Karen E., President and Chief Executive Officer, Baltimore Washington Medical Center, Glen Burnie, MD, p. A292

OLSEN, Ryan, Vice President of Operations, St. Jude Medical Center, Fullerton, CA, p. A62

OLSEN, Sabrina, Chief Financial Officer, Duke University Hospital, Durham, NC, p. A451

OLSON, Cheryl, Chief Human Resources Officer, Othello Community Hospital, Othello, WA, p. A669

OLSON, Christine K., FACHE, President, Aurora Medical Center, Kenosha, WI, p. A688

OLSON, Diana
 Chief Human Resources Officer, Mercy Tiffin Hospital, Tiffin, OH, p. A490
 Chief Human Resources Officer, Mercy Willard Hospital, Willard, OH, p. A493

OLSON, Eric, Chief Financial Officer, Providence Portland Medical Center, Portland, OR, p. A516

OLSON, Forrest, M.D. Chief Medical Officer, Enloe Medical Center, Chico, CA, p. A56

OLSON, Gary R., President and Chief Executive Officer, St. Luke's Hospital, Chesterfield, MO, p. A358

OLSON, Gregory A., President and Chief Executive Officer, Memorial Health Center, Medford, WI, p. A691

OLSON, John L., M.D. Medical Director, Lakeview Medical Center, Rice Lake, WI, p. A696

OLSON, John N., Chief Executive Officer, Walter Knox Memorial Hospital, Emmett, ID, p. A169

OLSON, Kent, Administrator and Chief Executive Officer, Philip Health Services, Philip, SD, p. A561

OLSON, Kevin, Director Information Systems, St. Anthony Hospital, Oklahoma City, OK, p. A504

OLSON, Lynn R., Director Human Resources, Hendricks Community Hospital, Hendricks, MN, p. A333

OLSON, Marcia, Business Office Manager, Webster County Community Hospital, Red Cloud, NE, p. A389

OLSON, MariBeth, R.N. Vice President Patient Care Services, Mercy Hospital, Coon Rapids, MN, p. A330

OLSON, Michael R., Administrator, American Fork Hospital, American Fork, UT, p. A643

OLSON, Nate, Chief Executive Officer, St. Peter's Hospital, Helena, MT, p. A377

OLSON, Randall M., Chief Executive Officer, Lane Regional Medical Center, Zachary, LA, p. A280

OLSON, Rick, M.D. Chief of Staff, Kaiser Permanente Sunnyside Medical Center, Clackamas, OR, p. A511

OLSON, Tim
Senior Vice President Finance, Appleton Medical Center, Appleton, WI, p. A683
Senior Vice President Finance, Theda Clark Medical Center, Neenah, WI, p. A693

OLSON, William, Director Finance, Providence St. Vincent Medical Center, Portland, OR, p. A516

OLSSON, Clifford Lee, Chief Financial Officer, Tuba City Regional Health Care Corporation, Tuba City, AZ, p. A38

OLSSON, Dave, Director of Marketing, Aspirus Keweenaw Hospital, Laurium, MI, p. A319

OLSZEWSKI, Joseph, Director Information Services, Aria Health, Philadelphia, PA, p. A534

OMAN, Michelle, D.O. Chief Medical Officer, Essentia Health Northern Pines, Aurora, MN, p. A328

OMAR, Sharif, Chief Executive Officer, Pottstown Memorial Medical Center, Pottstown, PA, p. A539

OMEL, John, Interim Vice President Human Resources, Good Samaritan Hospital, San Jose, CA, p. A87

OMER, Robert W., FACHE, Chief Executive Officer and Administrator, Southeast Colorado Hospital District, Springfield, CO, p. A105

OMOLARA, Khar, M.D. Chief Medical Staff, Jefferson County Hospital, Fayette, MS, p. A346

OMOTUNDE, Olukayode S., M.D. Chief Medical Staff, First Care Health Center, Park River, ND, p. A469

OMRAN, Yasser, M.D. President Medical Staff, Pomerene Hospital, Millersburg, OH, p. A486

OMTA, Stephen R., Chief Operating Officer, PeaceHealth St. Joseph Medical Center, Bellingham, WA, p. A664

ONG, Jesus M., President, South Shore Hospital, Chicago, IL, p. A179

ONG, Richard B., Chief Information Officer, Saint Vincent Hospital, Erie, PA, p. A525

ONIFATHER, Jeff, Chief Financial Officer, Cornerstone of Medical Arts Center Hospital, Fresh Meadows, NY, p. A426

ONOFRE, Bonnie J., MS Vice President and Chief Nursing Officer, Robert Packer Hospital, Sayre, PA, p. A540

OPDAHL, Jim, Administrator, Jacobson Memorial Hospital Care Center, Elgin, ND, p. A466

OPHEIKENS, Robyn, Assistant Administrator Human Resources, St. Mark's Hospital, Salt Lake City, UT, p. A647

OPIE, Timothy, M.D. President Professional Staff, Providence Seaside Hospital, Seaside, OR, p. A517

OPPITO, Glenn, Vice President Human Resources, Monmouth Medical Center, Long Branch, NJ, p. A406

OPRISKO, Judy P., Chief Human Resources Officer, Allied Services Rehabilitation Hospital, Scranton, PA, p. A540

ORCUTT, David, Chief Executive Officer, Weatherford Regional Medical Center, Weatherford, TX, p. A640

ORDYNA, Daniel, Chief Executive Officer, Willamette Valley Medical Center, McMinnville, OR, p. A514

ORE, Ruta, Director Human Resources, Pottstown Memorial Medical Center, Pottstown, PA, p. A539

OREAR, Kathy, Director Human Resources, Newman Regional Health, Emporia, KS, p. A233

OREGEL, Omar, Controller, Kindred Hospital–Ontario, Ontario, CA, p. A77

OREY, Lon, Vice President Human Resources, Presbyterian Intercommunity Hospital, Whittier, CA, p. A96

ORIOL, Albert, Vice President Information Management and Chief Information Officer, Rady Children's Hospital – San Diego, San Diego, CA, p. A85

ORLANDI, Mary, Manager Human Resources, Carney Hospital, Boston, MA, p. A296

ORLANDO, Anthony T., Senior Vice President Finance, Englewood Hospital and Medical Center, Englewood, NJ, p. A404

ORLANDO, Charles, Interim Chief Executive Officer, MetroWest Medical Center, Framingham, MA, p. A300

ORLANDO, Joseph S., President, Bergen Regional Medical Center, Paramus, NJ, p. A408

ORLANDO, Lorraine, Vice President Human Resources, New York Hospital Queens,, NY, p. A435

ORLOWSKI, Janis M., M.D. Senior Vice President Medical Affairs and Chief Medical Officer, MedStar Washington Hospital Center, Washington, DC, p. A116

ORMAN Jr., Bernard A., Administrator, Samaritan Memorial Hospital, Macon, MO, p. A365

ORMOND, Evalyn, Chief Executive Officer, Union General Hospital, Farmerville, LA, p. A267

ORMOND, Jack, Chief Financial Officer, Cuba Memorial Hospital, Cuba, NY, p. A424

ORMS, J. Michael, M.D. Chief of Staff, East Texas Medical Center Fairfield, Fairfield, TX, p. A602

ORMSBY, Joan
Interim Chief Executive Officer, West Suburban Medical Center, Oak Park, IL, p. A190
Chief Operating Officer, West Suburban Medical Center, Oak Park, IL, p. A190
Interim Chief Executive Officer, Westlake Hospital, Melrose Park, IL, p. A188
Chief Operating Officer, Westlake Hospital, Melrose Park, IL, p. A188

ORNELAS, Henry, Chief Operating Officer, LAC/University of Southern California Medical Center, Los Angeles, CA, p. A70

ORONA, Rene, M.D. Chief of Staff, Marshall Medical Center, Placerville, CA, p. A80

OROZCO, Jorge, Chief Executive Officer, Rancho Los Amigos National Rehabilitation Center, Downey, CA, p. A58

ORR, Shirley, R.N. Chief Nursing Officer, Holdenville General Hospital, Holdenville, OK, p. A500

ORR, Stephanie, R.N. Chief Nursing Officer, Steele Memorial Medical Center, Salmon, ID, p. A171

ORRELL, Carolyn, Chief Information Officer, Saint Mary's Hospital, Waterbury, CT, p. A112

ORRELL, Linda, Interim Chief Nursing Officer, Drew Memorial Hospital, Monticello, AR, p. A47

ORRICK, Charles H., Administrator, Donalsonville Hospital, Donalsonville, GA, p. A152

ORRISON, Pat, Director Information Services, Marianjoy Rehabilitation Hospital, Wheaton, IL, p. A196

ORSAG, Melanie, Director Health Information Services, Cedar Crest Hospital and Residential Treatment Center, Belton, TX, p. A588

ORSINI, Bob, Chief Operating Officer, HEALTHSOUTH Walton Rehabilitation Hospital, Augusta, GA, p. A148

ORSINI, Thomas J., President and Chief Executive Officer, Lake Taylor Transitional Care Hospital, Norfolk, VA, p. A658

ORSKEY, David, Administrator, Physicians Care Surgical Hospital, Royersford, PA, p. A540

ORT, Linda, Chief Financial Officer, Piggott Community Hospital, Piggott, AR, p. A49

ORTEGA, Cesar, M.D. Chief of Staff, Doctor's Hospital – Tidwell, Houston, TX, p. A609

ORTEGA, Debbie, Chief Human Resource Officer and Vice President Administrative Services, Huntington Memorial Hospital, Pasadena, CA, p. A79

ORTEGA, Jose, Chief Executive Officer, Greater El Monte Community Hospital, South El Monte, CA, p. A91

ORTHAUS, Denis, Director Human Resources, Philhaven, Mount Gretna, PA, p. A532

ORTIZ, Jr., Blas, Assistant Superintendent and Public Information Officer, Rio Grande State Center/South Texas Health Care System, Harlingen, TX, p. A608

ORTIZ, Carlos, M.D. Senior Vice President Medical Services, F. F. Thompson Hospital, Canandaigua, NY, p. A423

ORTIZ-BITNER, Olivia, Acting Chief Financial Officer, Veterans Affairs Greater Los Angeles Healthcare System, Los Angeles, CA, p. A72

ORTOLANI, Philip A., Vice President Operations, Mid Coast Hospital, Brunswick, ME, p. A282

ORTON, Sharon, Director Information Services and Technology, Corpus Christi Medical Center, Corpus Christi, TX, p. A593

ORTON, Wendy, Chief Executive Officer, Alleghany Memorial Hospital, Sparta, NC, p. A461

OSANTOSKI, Tina, Director Human Resources, Harbor Beach Community Hospital, Harbor Beach, MI, p. A316

OSBAHR, Leah, Administrator, Washington County Memorial Hospital, Potosi, MO, p. A368

OSBERG, Art, M.D. Vice President and Chief Medical Officer, Ocala Regional Medical Center, Ocala, FL, p. A134

OSBORN, Matt, M.D. Chief of Staff, Integris Baptist Regional Health Center, Miami, OK, p. A501

OSBORN, Tom, D.O. Chief Medical Staff, Holdenville General Hospital, Holdenville, OK, p. A500

OSBORNE, Anna, Chief Human Resources Management Service, West Texas Veterans Affairs Health Care System, Big Spring, TX, p. A588

OSBORNE, Jay, M.D. Senior Vice President Medical Affairs, Northside Medical Center, Youngstown, OH, p. A494

OSBORNE, Kimberly, Vice President and Chief Financial Officer, Eisenhower Medical Center, Rancho Mirage, CA, p. A81

OSBORNE, Matt, Flight Chief Medical Information Systems, Wright Patterson Medical Center, Wright–Patterson AFB, OH, p. A493

OSBORNE, Phil, Director Information Technology, Bourbon Community Hospital, Paris, KY, p. A259

OSBORNE, Terry W., CPA, Chief Executive Officer, American Legion Hospital, Crowley, LA, p. A266

OSCADAL, Martin
Vice President Human Resources, St. Elizabeth Edgewood, Edgewood, KY, p. A250
Senior Vice President Human Resources, St. Elizabeth Florence, Florence, KY, p. A250
Senior Vice President Human Resources, St. Elizabeth Fort Thomas, Fort Thomas, KY, p. A251

OSEGARD, Jeff, Chief Information Officer, Lakewood Health System, Staples, MN, p. A341

OSER, William F., M.D. Senior Vice President and Chief Medical Officer, JFK Medical Center, Edison, NJ, p. A403

OSINSKI, Kathleen, Chief Human Resources Service, John D. Dingell Veterans Affairs Medical Center, Detroit, MI, p. A312

OSKIN, Jeffrey, Vice President Ancillary and Support Services, Florida Hospital Tampa, Tampa, FL, p. A141

OSLIN, Dave, M.D. Chief of Staff, Philadephia Veterans Affairs Medical Center, Philadelphia, PA, p. A536

OSMUS, Richard D., Chief Executive Officer, Abbeville Area Medical Center, Abbeville, SC, p. A548

OSSELLO, Susan, Chief Financial Officer, Granite County Medical Center, Philipsburg, MT, p. A378

OSTASZEWSKI, Patricia, MS, Chief Executive Officer, HEALTHSOUTH Rehabilitation Hospital of Toms River, Toms River, NJ, p. A411

OSTBERG, Melissa, Chief Financial Officer, Marias Medical Center, Shelby, MT, p. A379

OSTBLOOM, Jan, Human Resources Consultant, Our Lady of Peace, Louisville, KY, p. A256

OSTEEN, Tom J., Director Area Technology, Kaiser Permanente Manteca Medical Center, Manteca, CA, p. A73

OSTER, Rebecca, Director Human Resources, HealthSource Saginaw, Saginaw, MI, p. A323

OSTERBERG, Valerie, Chief Financial Officer, Sanford Vermillion Medical Center, Vermillion, SD, p. A563

OSTERHOUT, David, Assistant Superintendent and Chief Financial Officer, El Paso Psychiatric Center, El Paso, TX, p. A601

OSTERLY, Eric, Chief Financial Officer, Florida Hospital Fish Memorial, Orange City, FL, p. A134

OSTRANDER, Maria DC, R.N. Chief Nurse Executive, San Antonio State Hospital, San Antonio, TX, p. A632

OSTRANDER, Mark, Vice President Financial Services, Community Medical Center, Toms River, NJ, p. A411

OSTROWSKI, Lawrence, M.D. Chief Clinical Officer, Summit Behavioral Healthcare, Cincinnati, OH, p. A475

OSWALD, Kathy, Senior Vice President and Chief Human Resources Officer, Henry Ford Hospital, Detroit, MI, p. A312

OSWALD, Michelle, Director of Information Systems, Community Hospital–Fairfax, Fairfax, MO, p. A360

OSWALD, Traci L., Vice President Human Resources, Galion Community Hospital, Galion, OH, p. A482

OSWALT, Charles, Vice President and Chief Financial Officer, Levi Hospital, Hot Springs National Park, AR, p. A45

OTERO, Victoria, Director Human Resources, HEALTHSOUTH Rehabilitation Hospital, Albuquerque, NM, p. A414

OTHMAN, Sami, Regional Site Director Information Process Services, Mercy Allen Hospital, Oberlin, OH, p. A488

OTHOLE, Jean, Chief Executive Officer, U. S. Public Health Service Indian Hospital, Zuni, NM, p. A419

OTT, Christopher, M.D. Interim Chief Medical Officer, St. Anthony Hospital, Lakewood, CO, p. A103

OTT, Darin, D.O. Chief of Staff, Kane County Hospital, Kanab, UT, p. A644

OTT, Kathryn Lynne, MSN Vice President Patient Care Services/Chief Nursing Officer, Fitzgibbon Hospital, Marshall, MO, p. A365

OTT, Pamela, Financial Site Manager, St. Nicholas Hospital, Sheboygan, WI, p. A696

OTT, Ronald A., Chief Executive Officer, Fitzgibbon Hospital, Marshall, MO, p. A365

OTT, Ronald H.
President, Excela Frick Hospital, Mount Pleasant, PA, p. A532
President, Excela Health Westmoreland Hospital, Greensburg, PA, p. A526

OTT, Wes, Chief Operating Officer, Health First Cape Canaveral Hospital, Cocoa Beach, FL, p. A121

OTTATI, David, Chief Executive Officer, Florida Hospital Waterman, Tavares, FL, p. A142

OTTE, Elaine, Chief Operating Officer, Clarinda Regional Health Center, Clarinda, IA, p. A218

OTTMAR, Kellie, Manager Information Services, East Adams Rural Hospital, Ritzville, WA, p. A670

OTTO, Sara, Director Human Resources, North Canyon Medical Center, Gooding, ID, p. A169

OTTO, Steve
Chief Executive Officer, TriStar Skyline Madison Campus, Madison, TN, p. A573
Chief Executive Officer, TriStar Skyline Medical Center, Nashville, TN, p. A577

OTTONE, Robert, Administrator, Maniilaq Health Center, Kotzebue, AK, p. A28

OUBRE, Chris, Director Information Systems, Singing River Health System, Pascagoula, MS, p. A352

OUBRE Jr., Nathaniel L., Senior Vice President and Area Manager, Kaiser Permanente Oakland Medical Center, Oakland, CA, p. A77

OUELETTE, Lisa, Director Human Resources, Beaumont Hospital – Troy, Troy, MI, p. A326

OUELLETTE, Demetra, Chief Operating Officer, Rehabilitation Hospital of Rhode Island, North Smithfield, RI, p. A546

OUIMET, Mary Elizabeth, MSN Senior Vice President and Chief Nursing Officer, Wheaton Franciscan Healthcare – All Saints, Racine, WI, p. A695

OURS, Matt, Chief Executive Officer, Kempsville Center for Behavioral Health, Norfolk, VA, p. A658

OUSEY, Tracy, Director Human Resources, Washington County Hospital and Clinics, Washington, IA, p. A229

OUTLAW, Debbie, R.N. Director Patient Care Services, Riverside Rehabilitation Institute, Newport News, VA, p. A658

OVANDO, Benjamin, Chief Operations Officer, Rancho Los Amigos National Rehabilitation Center, Downey, CA, p. A58

OVERBEY, Bill
Chief Financial Officer and Chief Information Officer, Hays Medical Center, Hays, KS, p. A235
Chief Financial Officer, Pawnee Valley Community Hospital, Larned, KS, p. A238

OVERBY, Roger, Executive Director Information Systems, Greene County Medical Center, Jefferson, IA, p. A223

OVEREEM, Mark, Chief Financial Officer, Centinela Hospital Medical Center, Inglewood, CA, p. A64

OVERMAN, David S.
Chief Operating Officer, Children's Hospitals and Clinics of Minnesota, Minneapolis, MN, p. A336
Chief Operating Officer, Children's Hospitals and Clinics of Minnesota, Saint Paul, MN, p. A340

OVERSTREET, Alyson, Chief Financial Officer, Washington County Hospital and Nursing Home, Chatom, AL, p. A18

OVERSTREET, Amy, Director Human Resources, Trousdale Medical Center, Hartsville, TN, p. A570

OVERTON, Deana, Director Human Resources, Mitchell County Hospital, Colorado City, TX, p. A592

OWCZARZAK, Margaret, Facility Chief Information Officer, Veterans Affairs Western New York Healthcare System–Buffalo Division, Buffalo, NY, p. A423

OWEN, Laura, Senior Vice President and Chief Executive Officer, Mother Frances Hospital – Tyler, Tyler, TX, p. A638

OWEN, Ronald S., FACHE, Chief Executive Officer, Southeast Alabama Medical Center, Dothan, AL, p. A19

OWEN, Sabrina, Human Resources Officer, Veterans Affairs Central Iowa Health Care System, Des Moines, IA, p. A220

OWEN, Sandra, Director Fiscal and Accounting, Harper Hospital District Five, Harper, KS, p. A235

OWEN–PLIETZ, Carrie, Chief Executive Officer, Sutter Medical Center, Sacramento, Sacramento, CA, p. A84

OWENS, Betina, Chief Information Officer, LSU Bogalusa Medical Center, Bogalusa, LA, p. A264

OWENS, Beverly, Controller, Central Georgia Rehabilitation Hospital, Macon, GA, p. A156

OWENS, Brian, Chief Operating Officer, Lindner Center of HOPE, Mason, OH, p. A485

OWENS, Craig A., President, WellStar Douglas Hospital, Douglasville, GA, p. A152

OWENS, Diane, Administrator, St. David's Rehabilitation Center, Austin, TX, p. A586

OWENS, Johnathan, Chief Executive Officer, Decatur County Hospital and Cedar Living Center, Oberlin, KS, p. A241

OWENS, Leon, Director, Caswell Center, Kinston, NC, p. A456

OWENS, Loma, Data Manager, Southwestern State Hospital, Thomasville, GA, p. A161

OWENS, Mark, M.D. Vice President Medical Affairs, Mercy San Juan Medical Center, Carmichael, CA, p. A56

OWENS, Pamela, Director Health Information Management, Hanover Hospital, Hanover, PA, p. A526

OWENS, Richard, Chief Financial Officer, D. W. McMillan Memorial Hospital, Brewton, AL, p. A18

OWENS, Shawn, Chief Operating Officer, Laurel Ridge Treatment Center, San Antonio, TX, p. A631

OWENS, Stephanie, Manager Human Resources, McDowell ARH Hospital, McDowell, KY, p. A257

OWENS, Thomas, M.D. Chief Medical Officer, Duke University Hospital, Durham, NC, p. A451

OWENSBY, Karen, R.N. Chief Operating Officer and Chief Nursing Officer, Florida Hospital North Pinellas, Tarpon Springs, FL, p. A142

OWINGS, David C., Director Information Management Service Line, Wm. Jennings Bryan Dorn Veterans Affairs Medical Center, Columbia, SC, p. A551

OWINGS, Raymond, Vice President Finance, Albemarle Health, Elizabeth City, NC, p. A452

OWREY, Donald R., President, UPMC Horizon, Greenville, PA, p. A526

OXENDALE, Roger A., Chief Executive Officer, Nemours Children's Hospital, Orlando, FL, p. A135

OXENDALE, Sharon, Chief Operating Officer, Northwest Texas Healthcare System, Amarillo, TX, p. A582

OXFORD, Tammy, Director Human Resources, Bob Wilson Memorial Grant County Hospital, Ulysses, KS, p. A245

OXLEY, Dawn, R.N. Associate Director Patient Care Services and Nurse Executive, Iowa City Veterans Affairs Health Care System, Iowa City, IA, p. A223

OXLEY, James, D.O. Vice President Medical Affairs, Orange Regional Medical Center, Middletown, NY, p. A429

OXLEY, Scott, Interim Chief Financial Officer, Blue Hill Memorial Hospital, Blue Hill, ME, p. A282

OXTON, Alice, Director Information Technology, Sentara Obici Hospital, Suffolk, VA, p. A662

OZBORN, Charles, M.D. Chief of Staff, North Mississippi Medical Center–Eupora, Eupora, MS, p. A346

OZBURN, Thomas H., Chief Executive Officer, TriStar Southern Hills Medical Center, Nashville, TN, p. A577

OZEL, A. Deniz, M.D. Medical Director, New England Rehabilitation Hospital, Woburn, MA, p. A306

OZKAN, Babur, Chief Financial Officer, Olympia Medical Center, Los Angeles, CA, p. A70

# P

PAASCH, Michael, Regional Vice President and Chief Information Officer, SSM Cardinal Glennon Children's Medical Center, Saint Louis, MO, p. A370

PABLO, Victoria, Human Resource Specialist, U. S. Public Health Service Indian Hospital, Crownpoint, NM, p. A415

PABON–RAMIREZ, Felix, Chief Information Officer, St. Charles Hospital, Port Jefferson, NY, p. A440

PACCAPANICCIA, Dominic, Chief Operating Officer, Indiana Regional Medical Center, Indiana, PA, p. A528

PACE, Debbie, Chief Operating Officer, Vaughan Regional Medical Center, Selma, AL, p. A25

PACE, Kathleen, MSN Chief Nursing Officer, Englewood Community Hospital, Englewood, FL, p. A123

PACEK, Thomas
Vice President Information Systems and Chief Information Officer, Inspira Medical Center–Elmer, Elmer, NJ, p. A404
Vice President Information Systems and Chief Information Officer, Inspira Medical Center–Vineland, Vineland, NJ, p. A412

PACEY, Amy, Vice President Human Resources, Exempla Good Samaritan Medical Center, Lafayette, CO, p. A103

PACHECO, Mike, Human Resources Manager, Hillsdale Community Health Center, Hillsdale, MI, p. A316

PACK, Kathy, Manager Human Resources, Copper Basin Medical Center, Copperhill, TN, p. A568

PACK, William
Chief Financial Officer, Memorial Hermann – Texas Medical Center, Houston, TX, p. A610
Chief Financial Officer, TIRR Memorial Hermann, Houston, TX, p. A613

PACK–HOOKFIN, Sherre, Administrator, Lallie Kemp Medical Center, Independence, LA, p. A268

PACKER, Eric, Administrator, Bear River Valley Hospital, Tremonton, UT, p. A647

PACKER, Steven J., M.D., President and Chief Executive Officer, Community Hospital of the Monterey Peninsula, Monterey, CA, p. A75

PACKETT, Lee, Administrator, South Florida State Hospital,, FL, p. A125

PACURA, Lori, MSN, Senior Vice President, Holy Cross Hospital, Chicago, IL, p. A176

PACZKOWSKI, Rick, Chief Executive Officer, Millwood Hospital, Arlington, TX, p. A583

PACZKOWSKI, Ronald R., Executive Vice President, Mayo Clinic Health System – Franciscan Healthcare in La Crosse, La Crosse, WI, p. A689

PADALINO, Robert, Interim Chief Executive Officer, Select Specialty Hospital–Battle Creek, Battle Creek, MI, p. A309

PADDEN, Ernest C., Chief Financial Officer, Bon Secours Maryview Medical Center, Portsmouth, VA, p. A659

PADEN, Tawnya, Director Human Resources, Weatherford Regional Hospital, Weatherford, OK, p. A510

PADGETT, Martin, President and Chief Executive Officer, Clark Memorial Hospital, Jeffersonville, IN, p. A207

PADGETT, Randal, Manager Information Systems, Barnwell County Hospital, Barnwell, SC, p. A548

PADGETT, Shirley, Director Human Resources, Cook Medical Center–A Campus of Tift Regional Medical Center, Adel, GA, p. A145

PADILLA, Ami, Director Human Resources, Arroyo Grande Community Hospital, Arroyo Grande, CA, p. A53

PADRO, Silvia, Director Information Services, Largo Medical Center, Largo, FL, p. A129

PAGANELLI, Deborah, President, Texas Health Harris Methodist Hospital Hurst–Euless–Bedford, Bedford, TX, p. A588

PAGE, Alison, Chief Executive Officer, Baldwin Area Medical Center, Baldwin, WI, p. A683

PAGE, Billy, Chief Financial Officer, Natchitoches Regional Medical Center, Natchitoches, LA, p. A274

PAGE, Bob, Chief Executive Officer, The University of Kansas Hospital, Kansas City, KS, p. A237

PAGE, Deborah, Chief Human Resources Officer, Duke University Hospital, Durham, NC, p. A451

PAGE, Keith Allen, President and Chief Executive Officer, Anderson Hospital, Maryville, IL, p. A187

PAGE, Michael J., M.D. Chief Medical Officer, Carrington Health Center, Carrington, ND, p. A465

PAGE, Pattie, Director Marketing and Public Relations, Eastside Medical Center, Snellville, GA, p. A160

PAGE, Sue, Director Human Resources, Monroe County Medical Center, Tompkinsville, KY, p. A260

PAGE, Susan M., President and Chief Executive Officer, Pratt Regional Medical Center, Pratt, KS, p. A243

PAGE, Timothy, Chief Executive Officer, Kindred Hospital the Palm Beaches, Riviera Beach, FL, p. A138

PAGELER, Robert, Director Information Services, Swedish/Edmonds, Edmonds, WA, p. A666

PAGELS, George A., M.D
Senior Vice President and Chief Medical Officer, Anderson County Hospital, Garnett, KS, p. A234
President and Chief Executive Officer, Hedrick Medical Center, Chillicothe, MO, p. A358

PAGET, Cindy E., Human Resources Manager, St. Luke's McCall, McCall, ID, p. A170

PAGLIUZZA, Greg
Chief Financial Officer, Trinity Bettendorf, Bettendorf, IA, p. A216
Chief Financial Officer, Trinity Muscatine, Muscatine, IA, p. A225
Chief Financial Officer, Trinity Rock Island, Rock Island, IL, p. A193

PAIGE, Kevin, Chief Operations Officer, Mayo Clinic Hospital, Phoenix, AZ, p. A35

PAINE, Lincoln, M.D. Medical Director, River Oaks Hospital, New Orleans, LA, p. A275

PAINE, Russ, Human Resources Officer, Murphy Medical Center, Murphy, NC, p. A458

PAKKALA, Mark, Director Human Resources, Spectrum Health Special Care Hospital, Grand Rapids, MI, p. A315

PALAGI, Richard L., Chief Executive Officer, Saint Alphonsus Medical Center – Ontario, Ontario, OR, p. A515

PALANGE, Kathleen, R.N., Chief Executive Officer, Menlo Park Surgical Hospital, Menlo Park, CA, p. A74

PALAZZOLO, Christopher, Senior Vice President and Chief Operating Officer, Genesys Regional Medical Center, Grand Blanc, MI, p. A314

PALECEK, Steve
Controller, Sacred Heart Hospital, Eau Claire, WI, p. A686
Divisional Director of Financial Services, St. Joseph's Hospital, Chippewa Falls, WI, p. A685

PALETTA, Lisa A., R.N. Chief Nursing Officer, Utah Valley Regional Medical Center, Provo, UT, p. A646

PALIGO, Terry, Chief Financial Officer, Union County Hospital, Anna, IL, p. A173

PALIS, Adar, Executive Vice President and Chief Administrative & Operating Officer, Harrison Medical Center, Bremerton, WA, p. A664

PALITZ, Harvey, M.D. Chief of Staff, Stanislaus Surgical Hospital, Modesto, CA, p. A74

PALKOWSKI, Chris, M.D. Physician in Chief, Kaiser Permanente Sacramento Medical Center, Sacramento, CA, p. A83

PALLAS, Drew, Executive Vice President and Chief Administrative Officer, St. Joseph Hospital, Bethpage, NY, p. A421

PALLY, Madhava, M.D. Chief of Staff, Lehigh Regional Medical Center, Lehigh Acres, FL, p. A129

PALMA, Susan, R.N., Administrator, Runnells Specialized Hospital of Union County, Berkeley Heights, NJ, p. A401

PALMBERG, Kent, M.D. Senior Vice President and Chief Medical Officer, Stormont–Vail HealthCare, Topeka, KS, p. A245

PALMER, Barbara, Corporate Vice President Human Resources, Botsford Hospital, Farmington Hills, MI, p. A313

PALMER, Dennis, D.O. Chief of Staff, Mercer County Hospital, Aledo, IL, p. A173

PALMER, Isaac
Chief Operating Officer, Florida Hospital Heartland Medical Center, Sebring, FL, p. A140
Chief Operating Officer, Florida Hospital Wauchula, Wauchula, FL, p. A143

PALMER, Janel M., Director Human Resources, Greenwood County Hospital, Eureka, KS, p. A233

PALMER, Keith, Assistant Administrator, Winkler County Memorial Hospital, Kermit, TX, p. A616

PALMER, Kelly, M.D. Medical Director, State Hospital South, Blackfoot, ID, p. A167

PALMER, Linda, Coordinator Medical Records, San Gorgonio Memorial Hospital, Banning, CA, p. A54

PALMER, Trisha, Director, St. James Healthcare, Butte, MT, p. A374

PALMIER, Michael L., Chief Human Resources Management, Overton Brooks Veterans Affairs Medical Center, Shreveport, LA, p. A278

PALO, Alan, Chief Financial Officer, Sarah D. Culbertson Memorial Hospital, Rushville, IL, p. A194

PALSROK, Jerri, Manager Business Office, Osceola Community Hospital, Sibley, IA, p. A228

PALUMBO, Denise S., MSN Executive Vice President and Chief Operating Officer, Lawrence General Hospital, Lawrence, MA, p. A301

PALUMBO, Michael, M.D. Executive Vice President and Medical Director, White Plains Hospital Center, White Plains, NY, p. A446

PAMPERIEN, Linda, Chief Financial Officer, Texas County Memorial Hospital, Houston, MO, p. A361

PANDIT, Rajiv, M.D. Medical Director, Methodist Hospital for Surgery, Addison, TX, p. A581

PANDL, Therese B.
President and Chief Executive Officer, St. Mary's Hospital Medical Center, Green Bay, WI, p. A688
President and Chief Executive Officer, St. Vincent Hospital, Green Bay, WI, p. A688

PANDOLFINI, Paul, Chief Financial Officer, Coney Island Hospital,, NY, p. A431

PANDOLPH, Philip, Chief Executive Officer, Meadville Medical Center, Meadville, PA, p. A531

PANDYA, Sherrie, Administrator, Kane County Hospital, Kanab, UT, p. A644

PANGLE, Brian, Chief Executive Officer, Great Lakes Specialty Hospital–Grand Rapids Campus, Grand Rapids, MI, p. A315

PANGLE, Jenny, Chief Officer Information and Technology, Memphis Veterans Affairs Medical Center, Memphis, TN, p. A575

PANICHI, Robert, Chief Information Officer, Ohio Valley Medical Center, Wheeling, WV, p. A682

PANICO, Paul, Chief Operating Officer, Cheyenne Regional Medical Center, Cheyenne, WY, p. A701

PANICUCCI, Michele
Senior Vice President and Chief Financial Officer, Covenant Medical Center, Waterloo, IA, p. A229
Chief Financial Officer, Sartori Memorial Hospital, Cedar Falls, IA, p. A217

PANIK, Anne, MS Senior Vice President Care Services and Chief Nursing Officer, Lehigh Valley Hospital–Muhlenberg, Bethlehem, PA, p. A520

PANKEY, Susan, Vice President Clinical Services, Keokuk Area Hospital, Keokuk, IA, p. A224

PANKOW, Thomas, Chief Information Officer, Jackson Park Hospital and Medical Center, Chicago, IL, p. A177

PANKOWSKI, Charles, Manager Human Resources, Select Specialty Hospital–Columbus, Columbus, OH, p. A478

PANKS, Tim
Chief Financial Officer, Mercy Medical Center Mount Shasta, Mount Shasta, CA, p. A75
Regional Vice President Finance and Chief Financial Officer, Mercy Medical Center Redding, Redding, CA, p. A81
Chief Financial Officer, St. Elizabeth Community Hospital, Red Bluff, CA, p. A81

PANNCE, Sukhbir, M.D. Chief Medical Officer, Banner Churchill Community Hospital, Fallon, NV, p. A391

PANSA, Leonard F., Senior Vice President Human Resources, Mercy Medical Center, Springfield, MA, p. A305

PANZA Jr., Louis J., President and Chief Executive Officer, Monongahela Valley Hospital, Monongahela, PA, p. A532

PANZETTA, Frank, Director Human Resources, St. Joseph's Hospital Health Center, Syracuse, NY, p. A444

PAOLUCCI, Benjamin, D.O. Chief of Staff, Southeast Michigan Surgical Hospital, Warren, MI, p. A326

PAPA, Alan, President, Akron General Medical Center, Akron, OH, p. A470

PAPACOSTAS, Arthur C., M.D
Vice President and Chief Information Officer, Jeanes Hospital, Philadelphia, PA, p. A535
Vice President and Chief Information Officer, Temple University Hospital, Philadelphia, PA, p. A536

PAPADAKOS, James, Chief Financial Officer, Signature Healthcare Brockton Hospital, Brockton, MA, p. A298

PAPALIA, Fern, Vice President, Patient Care Services, Community Medical Center, Toms River, NJ, p. A411

PAPALIA, John P., FACHE, Chief Executive Officer, Warren General Hospital, Warren, PA, p. A543

PAPE, Becky A., R.N., Chief Executive Officer, Samaritan Lebanon Community Hospital, Lebanon, OR, p. A514

PAPE, Carolyn, Director Human Resources, Whidbey General Hospital, Coupeville, WA, p. A666

PAPPAN, Clayton, Director Human Resources and Marketing, South Central Kansas Medical Center, Arkansas City, KS, p. A231

PAPPAS, Charles, M.D. Chief Operating Officer, Bascom Palmer Eye Institute–Anne Bates Leach Eye Hospital, Miami, FL, p. A131

PAPPAS, Kirk, M.D. Physician–in–Chief, Kaiser Permanente Santa Rosa Medical Center, Santa Rosa, CA, p. A90

PAPPAS, Nick, Chief Information Officer, Downey Regional Medical Center, Downey, CA, p. A58

PAPPAS, Sharon H., R.N. Chief Nursing Officer, Porter Adventist Hospital, Denver, CO, p. A100

PAPPAS, Sheryl L., Chief Financial Officer, Sanford Webster Medical Center, Webster, SD, p. A564

PAPPAS, Theron, Director Management Information Systems, Holy Family Memorial, Manitowoc, WI, p. A690

PARADIS, Brian, Chief Operating Officer, Florida Hospital, Orlando, FL, p. A135

PARADIS, James, President, Paoli Hospital, Paoli, PA, p. A534

PARADIS, Jeanne, Director Information Services, The Acadia Hospital, Bangor, ME, p. A281

PARASIDA, Tammy, Manager Business Office, Peterson Rehabilitation Hospital, Wheeling, WV, p. A682

PARAUDA, Martina A., Director, Veterans Administration New York Harbor Healthcare System,, NY, p. A437

PARCEL, Jim, Director Information Technology, Maury Regional Hospital, Columbia, TN, p. A567

PARCELLS, Patrick, Senior Vice President and Administrator, Riverside Regional Medical Center, Newport News, VA, p. A658

PARCHMENT, Deborah, Executive Director, Kingsboro Psychiatric Center,, NY, p. A433

PARDUE, Cherie, Interim Chief Information Officer, Children's National Medical Center, Washington, DC, p. A116

PARDUE, Michelle, M.D. Chief Medical Staff, Springhill Medical Center, Springhill, LA, p. A279

PAREEK, Yogesh, M.D. Clinical Director, Brown County Community Treatment Center, Green Bay, WI, p. A687

PARENT, Paula A., R.N. Director Human Resources and Nursing Administration, Cary Medical Center, Caribou, ME, p. A282

PARENTEAU, Michael, Chief Financial Officer, Providence St. Mary Medical Center, Walla Walla, WA, p. A674

PARET, Jason, Chief Executive Officer, Bath Community Hospital, Hot Springs, VA, p. A655

PARIS, Cindy, R.N., President, Texas Health Presbyterian Hospital of Rockwall, Rockwall, TX, p. A629

PARIS, David, Chief Executive Officer, Perry County General Hospital, Richton, MS, p. A353

PARIS, John, M.D. Chief Medical Officer, Riverview Hospital, Noblesville, IN, p. A211

PARIS, Richard, M.D. Chief Medical Officer, Somerset Medical Center, Somerville, NJ, p. A410

PARIS, Trevor, M.D. Medical Director, Brooks Rehabilitation Hospital, Jacksonville, FL, p. A126

PARISH, Karen, Director Information Systems, Orange Park Medical Center, Orange Park, FL, p. A135

PARISH, Thomas, Chief Financial Officer, Howard County Medical Center, Saint Paul, NE, p. A389

PARISI, Ernest R., Interim Chief Executive Officer and Administrator, Stephens Memorial Hospital, Breckenridge, TX, p. A589

PARK, Bockhi
Chief Executive Officer, Encino Hospital Medical Center,, CA, p. A68
Chief Executive Officer, Sherman Oaks Hospital,, CA, p. A71

PARK, Denten, Chief Executive Officer, MountainView Regional Medical Center, Las Cruces, NM, p. A416

PARK, Eddie, Acting Director Human Resources, Metropolitan State Hospital, Norwalk, CA, p. A76

PARK, Gary L., President, University of North Carolina Hospitals, Chapel Hill, NC, p. A449

PARK, Ronald, Chief Executive Officer, Somerset Hospital, Somerset, PA, p. A541

PARK, Theron, Chief Executive Officer, Providence Portland Medical Center, Portland, OR, p. A516

PARKER, Audrey, Budget Analyst, U. S. Public Health Service Indian Hospital, Winnebago, NE, p. A390

PARKER, Christopher J., R.N. Chief Nursing Officer, Memorial Hospital at Easton Maryland, Easton, MD, p. A291

PARKER, Cythia, Fiscal Director, Washington County Regional Medical Center, Sandersville, GA, p. A159

PARKER, David, Vice President Information Technology, Magnolia Regional Health Center, Corinth, MS, p. A346

PARKER, Donald J., President and Chief Executive Officer, Carrier Clinic, Belle Mead, NJ, p. A401

PARKER, Grace E., R.N. Interim Chief Nursing Officer, University of Washington Medical Center, Seattle, WA, p. A671

PARKER, Janie, Chief Financial Officer, Hardin County General Hospital, Rosiclare, IL, p. A194

PARKER, Jim, M.D. President Medical Staff, Southeastern Health, Lumberton, NC, p. A457

PARKER, Jon–Michael, R.N. Chief Nursing Officer, Lillian M. Hudspeth Memorial Hospital, Sonora, TX, p. A634

PARKER, Judy Goforth, Ph.D., Administrator, Chickasaw Nation Medical Center, Ada, OK, p. A495

PARKER, Karen, Administrator, Audubon Behavioral Healthcare of Lufkin, Lufkin, TX, p. A620

PARKER, Marty, Chief Information Officer, Carolinas Hospital System, Florence, SC, p. A551

PARKER, Michael, M.D. Chief of Staff, Sharon Hospital, Sharon, CT, p. A111

PARKER, Paula, Chief Financial Officer, Wyoming County Community Hospital, Warsaw, NY, p. A445

PARKER, Robert, Chief Executive Officer, Meadowview Regional Medical Center, Maysville, KY, p. A257

PARKER, Rodney, Senior Associate Executive Director, Coney Island Hospital,, NY, p. A431

PARKER, Stephanie, Chief Financial Officer, Methodist Stone Oak Hospital, San Antonio, TX, p. A631

PARKER, Teresa, Vice President and Chief Nursing Officer, Baptist Medical Center South, Montgomery, AL, p. A23

PARKER, Thomas, Chief Executive Officer, Upper Valley Medical Center, Troy, OH, p. A491

PARKER, Tina, Director Human Resources, HEALTHSOUTH Rehabilitation Hospital Midland–Odessa, Midland, TX, p. A623

PARKER, Valerie, M.D. Clinical Director, U. S. Public Health Service Indian Hospital, Rosebud, SD, p. A562

PARKES, Brian, M.D. Chief Medical Officer, Scotland Health Care System, Laurinburg, NC, p. A456

PARKEY, Kasey, Coordinator Payroll and Benefits, Kindred Hospital–Corpus Christi, Corpus Christi, TX, p. A594

PARKHILL, Cherie, Chief Financial Officer, Crosbyton Clinic Hospital, Crosbyton, TX, p. A594

PARKHURST, James E., President and Chief Executive Officer, Newport Bay Hospital, Newport Beach, CA, p. A76

PARKINSON, Michelle A., Director Human Resources, Prairie St. John's, Fargo, ND, p. A466

PARKS, Audrey, Senior Administrative Director Information Technology, Salinas Valley Memorial Healthcare System, Salinas, CA, p. A84

PARKS, Cary, Chief Information Resource Management, Hampton Veterans Affairs Medical Center, Hampton, VA, p. A655

PARKS, Dave, Chief Information Officer, Three Rivers Health, Three Rivers, MI, p. A325

PARKS, Ginger, Director Human Resources, Cape Fear Valley – Bladen County Hospital, Elizabethtown, NC, p. A452

PARKS, Jim, Chief Operating Officer, Box Butte General Hospital, Alliance, NE, p. A381

PARKS, Jody, Administrator, Ottawa County Health Center, Minneapolis, KS, p. A240

PARKS, Michelle, Administrator, RiverValley Behavioral Health Hospital, Owensboro, KY, p. A258

PARKS, Richard H., FACHE, President and Chief Executive Officer, Covenant Medical Center, Lubbock, TX, p. A620

PARKS, Sherry, R.N. Chief Nursing Officer, Saint Alphonsus Regional Medical Center, Boise, ID, p. A168

PARKS, Vicki, Vice President, Murray–Calloway County Hospital, Murray, KY, p. A258

PARMER, David N., Chief Executive Officer, Baptist Hospitals of Southeast Texas, Beaumont, TX, p. A587

PARMER, Dennis, M.D. Chief Medical Staff, Community Hospital of Long Beach, Long Beach, CA, p. A67

PARNEL, George, Chief Financial Officer, Clifton T. Perkins Hospital Center, Jessup, MD, p. A292

PARNELL, Dennis, Senior Vice President Human Resources, Suburban Hospital, Bethesda, MD, p. A290

PAROBY, Carmen, Chief Executive Officer, West Florida Community Care Center, Milton, FL, p. A133

PAROD, Daniel A., Senior Vice President Hospital and Administrative Affairs, Rockford Memorial Hospital, Rockford, IL, p. A193

PAROSKI, Margaret, M.D. Executive Vice President and Chief Medical Officer, KALEIDA Health, Buffalo, NY, p. A422

PARR, Lynnette, Chief Financial Officer, Down East Community Hospital, Machias, ME, p. A284

PARRA, Michelle, Director Human Resources, Kindred Hospital of South Bay, Gardena, CA, p. A62

PARRINELLO, Kathleen M., Ph.D. Chief Operating Officer, Strong Memorial Hospital of the University of Rochester, Rochester, NY, p. A441

PARRIS, Jill, Network Vice President Human Resources, Community Hospital North, Indianapolis, IN, p. A205

PARRIS, Pat, Chief Financial Officer, University Hospital McDuffie, Thomson, GA, p. A161

PARRISH, Becky, Director Human Resources, Southern Virginia Regional Medical Center, Emporia, VA, p. A653

PARRISH, E. Al, Director Human Resources, Southampton Memorial Hospital, Franklin, VA, p. A654

PARRISH, James G., FACHE, Chief Executive Officer, Humboldt General Hospital, Winnemucca, NV, p. A396

PARRISH, Jerry A., Vice President, AnMed Health Medical Center, Anderson, SC, p. A548

PARRISH, Pamela, Director Information Systems, Novant Health Brunswick Medical Center, Bolivia, NC, p. A448

PARRISH, Priscilla, Chief Financial Officer, Blake Medical Center, Bradenton, FL, p. A119

PARRISH, Suann, Chief Financial Officer, Yoakum County Hospital, Denver City, TX, p. A599

PARRY, Timothy, R.N. Vice President Nursing, Highland District Hospital, Hillsboro, OH, p. A483

PARSEGHIAN, Donald, Chief Financial Officer, Meadowlands Hospital Medical Center, Secaucus, NJ, p. A410

PARSON, Taft, M.D. Medical Director, Henry Ford Kingswood Hospital, Ferndale, MI, p. A313

PARSONS, Beth, R.N., Administrator, Dubuis Hospital of Alexandria, Alexandria, LA, p. A262

PARSONS, Brad, Administrator and Chief Executive Officer, NEA Baptist Memorial Hospital, Jonesboro, AR, p. A45

PARSONS, Jamie, Vice President Human Resources, Johnson City Medical Center, Johnson City, TN, p. A571

PARSONS, Lauren, M.D. Clinical Director, North Texas State Hospital, Wichita Falls Campus, Wichita Falls, TX, p. A641

PARSONS, Lisa, M.D. Chief Medical Officer, Windhaven Psychiatric Hospital, Prescott Valley, AZ, p. A36

PARSONS, Roger, Senior Vice President Finance, San Antonio Community Hospital, Upland, CA, p. A94

PARSONS, Suzanne, Vice President Human Resources, UMass Memorial–Marlborough Hospital, Marlborough, MA, p. A302

PARSONS, Terri L., Administrator, Advanced Care Hospital of White County, Searcy, AR, p. A49

PARSONS, Vicki L.
Regional Vice President Human Resources, Covenant Medical Center, Waterloo, IA, p. A229
Regional Vice President Human Resources, Mercy Hospital of Franciscan Sisters, Oelwein, IA, p. A226
Regional Vice President Human Resources, Sartori Memorial Hospital, Cedar Falls, IA, p. A217

PARTAMIAN, Gregory A., Chief Operating Officer, Crittenton Hospital Medical Center, Rochester, MI, p. A322

PARTEE, Paris I., Associate Administrator and Director Human Resources, John H. Stroger Jr. Hospital of Cook County, Chicago, IL, p. A177

PARTENZA, John, Vice President and Treasurer, Northern Westchester Hospital, Mount Kisco, NY, p. A430

PARTHEMORE, Warrenette, Director Human Resources, Memorial Hospital, Fremont, OH, p. A481

PARTIN, Gary, M.D. President Medical Staff, Westlake Regional Hospital, Columbia, KY, p. A249

PARUCH, Randy J., Director, Information Systems, Holland Hospital, Holland, MI, p. A316

PARUNGAO, AMy, Director of Nursing, Rehabilitation Hospital of the Pacific, Honolulu, HI, p. A165

PARVEZ, Syed, M.D., Administrator, Community General Hospital, Dilley, TX, p. A599

PASANEN, Wayne, M.D. Vice President Medical Affairs, Lowell General Hospital, Lowell, MA, p. A301

PASCASIO, Robert A., FACHE, Chief Executive Officer, Lillian M. Hudspeth Memorial Hospital, Sonora, TX, p. A634

PASCOE, John, M.D. Executive Medical Director, Timberlawn Mental Health System, Dallas, TX, p. A598

PASCUZZI, Robert, Chief Financial Officer, Mercy San Juan Medical Center, Carmichael, CA, p. A56

PASQUALE, Mark
Vice President Information Services and Chief Information Officer, Piedmont Fayette Hospital, Fayetteville, GA, p. A153
Vice President Information Systems, Piedmont Hospital, Atlanta, GA, p. A147

PASQUALONI, Sara, M.D. Chief of Staff, Los Alamos Medical Center, Los Alamos, NM, p. A417

PASSANNANTE, Jr., Anthony, M.D. Vice President, Chief Medical Officer and Co–Chief Quality Officer, Saint Peter's University Hospital, New Brunswick, NJ, p. A407

PASSMORE, Gary, Chief Information Officer, Endless Mountain Health Systems, Montrose, PA, p. A532

PASTERNAK, L. Reuven, M.P.H., Vice President for Health System and Chief Executive Officer, Stony Brook University Medical Center, Stony Brook, NY, p. A443

PASTORE, Raymond, M.D. Chief Medical Officer, St. John's Episcopal Hospital–South Shore,, NY, p. A436

PASZTOR, Barbara J., R.N. Vice President Nursing and Patient Care Services, Bluffton Hospital, Bluffton, OH, p. A472

PATAK, David, President and Chief Executive Officer, Our Lady of Lourdes Memorial Hospital, Binghamton, NY, p. A421

PATASHNICK, Melvyn, President and Chief Executive Officer, Copley Hospital, Morrisville, VT, p. A649

PATCHELL, Lee, Lead Human Resources Business Partner, Presbyterian Hospital, Albuquerque, NM, p. A414

PATCHIN, J. Craig
Administrator, Shriners Hospitals for Children–Portland, Portland, OR, p. A516
Interim Administrator, Shriners Hospitals for Children–Spokane, Spokane, WA, p. A672

PATE, Danny, M.D. Medical Staff, Vidant Duplin Hospital, Kenansville, NC, p. A455

PATE, Jim S., President and Chief Executive Officer, Unicoi County Memorial Hospital, Erwin, TN, p. A569

PATE, John, M.D. Chief Medical Officer, Tri–County Hospital, Wadena, MN, p. A342

PATE, Linda, Director Human Resources, Wake Forest Baptist Health–Davie Hospital, Mocksville, NC, p. A457

PATEL, Deepak, M.D. Medical Director, Cumberland Hall Hospital, Hopkinsville, KY, p. A252

PATEL, Fatma, M.D. Vice President Medical Affairs, Niagara Falls Memorial Medical Center, Niagara Falls, NY, p. A437

PATEL, Hema, Director Medical Records, RiverWoods Behavioral Health System, Riverdale, GA, p. A158

PATEL, Ketul J., Executive Vice President and Chief Operations and Strategy Officer, Hackensack University Medical Center, Hackensack, NJ, p. A404

PATEL, Keyar, M.D. President Medical Staff, Sturgis Hospital, Sturgis, MI, p. A325

PATEL, Malini, M.D. Medical Director, Elgin Mental Health Center, Elgin, IL, p. A181

PATEL, Mitesh, M.D. Vice President Medical Affairs, NorthBay Medical Center, Fairfield, CA, p. A59

PATEL, Nalin, M.D. Medical Director, Meadows Psychiatric Center, Centre Hall, PA, p. A522

PATEL, Natu M., M.D. Chief of Staff, Phoebe Worth Medical Center, Sylvester, GA, p. A161

PATEL, Nayan, Director Information Systems, The Heart Hospital Baylor Plano, Plano, TX, p. A628

PATEL, Prakash Chandra, M.D. Chief of Staff, Kindred Hospital–La Mirada, La Mirada, CA, p. A65

PATEL, Pravinchandra, M.D. Chief Medical Officer, North Oak Regional Medical Center, Senatobia, MS, p. A353

PATEL, Rajesh, M.D. Chief of Staff, Lock Haven Hospital, Lock Haven, PA, p. A530

PATEL, Rakesh, D.O. Medical Director, HEALTHSOUTH Rehabilitation Hospital of Altoona, Altoona, PA, p. A519

PATEL, Sharad, M.D. Medical Director, Florida Hospital at Connerton Long Term Acute Care, Land O'Lakes, FL, p. A128

PATEL, Suresh, M.D. Chief Medical Officer, Cavalier County Memorial Hospital, Langdon, ND, p. A468

PATEL, Viraj, M.D. Chief Medical Officer, Unity Medical & Surgical Hospital, Mishawaka, IN, p. A210

PATER, Tom
Vice President Finance and Chief Financial Officer, RML Specialty Hospital, Chicago, IL, p. A178
Chief Financial Officer, RML Specialty Hospital, Hinsdale, IL, p. A185

PATHI, Janna, M.D. Chief Medical Officer, Ohio County Hospital, Hartford, KY, p. A252

PATIL, Steve, Chief Financial Officer, W. G. (Bill) Heffner Veterans Affairs Medical Center, Salisbury, NC, p. A460

PATILLO, Laura, Manager Human Resources, Fresno Surgical Hospital, Fresno, CA, p. A61

PATLA, Rich, Director Information Technology, California Hospital Medical Center, Los Angeles, CA, p. A68

PATRIAS, Tom, Chief Operating Officer, St. Cloud Regional Medical Center, Saint Cloud, FL, p. A138

PATRICK, Barbara, Director Human Resources, Chestatee Regional Hospital, Dahlonega, GA, p. A151

PATRICK, Christian C., M.D. Chief Medical Officer, Baptist Memorial Hospital – Memphis, Memphis, TN, p. A574

PATRICK, Deborah A., Vice President Human Resources, Lehigh Valley Hospital–Muhlenberg, Bethlehem, PA, p. A520

PATRICK, John E., Director, Portland Veterans Affairs Medical Center, Portland, OR, p. A516

PATRICK, Lisa, Chief Operating Officer, Caldwell Memorial Hospital, Columbia, LA, p. A265

PATRICK, Ronald, Chief Financial Officer, Northwest Medical Center, Tucson, AZ, p. A39

PATRICK, Sandra, Chief Financial Officer, Three Rivers Hospital, Waverly, TN, p. A580

PATRICK, Sean, Director Information Systems, Gifford Medical Center, Randolph, VT, p. A650

PATRICK, Wade, Senior Vice President Information Services, Indiana Regional Medical Center, Indiana, PA, p. A528

PATRNCHAK, Joseph, Chief Human Resources Officer, Cleveland Clinic, Cleveland, OH, p. A476

PATTEN, Bill D., Chief Executive Officer, Powell Valley Healthcare, Powell, WY, p. A703

PATTEN, Douglas, M.D. Chief Medical Officer, Phoebe Putney Memorial Hospital, Albany, GA, p. A145

PATTEN, Gregg, M.D. Chief Medical Officer, CareLink of Jackson, Jackson, MI, p. A317

PATTERSON, Alan, Director Human Resources, Wenatchee Valley Medical Center, Wenatchee, WA, p. A674

PATTERSON, Amy, Chief Operating Officer and Chief Nursing Officer, Florida Hospital North Pinellas, Tarpon Springs, FL, p. A142

PATTERSON, Anthony, Interim Chief Executive Officer, University of Alabama Hospital, Birmingham, AL, p. A17

PATTERSON, Barbara, Chief Financial Officer, Provident Hospital of Cook County, Chicago, IL, p. A178

PATTERSON, Benjamin, Chief Executive Officer, Fairway Medical Center, Covington, LA, p. A265

PATTERSON, Camie, Senior Vice President and Chief Operating Officer, Self Regional Healthcare, Greenwood, SC, p. A553

PATTERSON, Christina, Chief Financial Officer, River Park Hospital, Mc Minnville, TN, p. A574

PATTERSON, Dave, Information Systems Manager, Memorial Hospital of Converse County, Douglas, WY, p. A702

PATTERSON, David, Director Human Resources, Parkside Hospital, Tulsa, OK, p. A508

PATTERSON, Debbie, Director Health Information Management, Wesley Rehabilitation Hospital, Wichita, KS, p. A247

PATTERSON, Donna, Director of Nursing, Samuel Simmonds Memorial Hospital, Barrow, AK, p. A27

PATTERSON, Lisa, Director Human Resources, Pointe Coupee General Hospital, New Roads, LA, p. A276

PATTERSON, Marcia, Chief Financial Officer, Valley Regional Medical Center, Brownsville, TX, p. A590

PATTERSON, Maria, Manager Health Information Management, Canyon Ridge Hospital, Chino, CA, p. A56

PATTERSON, Michael C., Chief Executive Officer, Southwest Regional Medical Center, Georgetown, OH, p. A482

PATTERSON, Michael J., Vice President Operations, Trinity Rock Island, Rock Island, IL, p. A193

PATTERSON, Michael N., Chief Executive Officer, Colorado Plains Medical Center, Fort Morgan, CO, p. A101

PATTERSON, Mike, Director of Operations, Northside Hospital–Cherokee, Canton, GA, p. A149

PATTERSON, Philip A., Chief Executive Officer, Good Samaritan Hospital, Suffern, NY, p. A443

PATTERSON, Renee A., Vice President Employment and Training Services, Rogers Memorial Hospital, Oconomowoc, WI, p. A693

PATTERSON, Richard, Chief Financial Officer, TriStar Greenview Regional Hospital, Bowling Green, KY, p. A249

PATTERSON, Robert, Vice President Human Resources and Rehabilitation Services, Central Vermont Medical Center, Berlin, VT, p. A649

PATTERSON, Sam, Chief Financial Officer, Bay Area Hospital, Coos Bay, OR, p. A512

PATTERSON, Sarah, Executive Vice President and Chief Operating Officer, Virginia Mason Medical Center, Seattle, WA, p. A671

PATTERSON, Stuart, M.D. Chief of Staff, Bartow Regional Medical Center, Bartow, FL, p. A118

PATTERSON, Tony, Chief Financial Officer, James B. Haggin Memorial Hospital, Harrodsburg, KY, p. A252

PATTERSON, William
Chief Executive Officer, Delta Medical Center, Memphis, TN, p. A574
Chief Financial Officer, Parkview Medical Center, Pueblo, CO, p. A105

PATTI, Rosa, Chief Financial Officer, Cameron Regional Medical Center, Cameron, MO, p. A357

PATTON, Ben, Chief Executive Officer, Integrity Transitional Hospital, Denton, TX, p. A598

PATTON, Christina, Chief Financial Officer, Colorado Plains Medical Center, Fort Morgan, CO, p. A101

PATTON, Daniel, Director Information Systems, Henrico Doctors' Hospital, Richmond, VA, p. A660

PATTON, David J., Vice President Operations, UPMC Northwest, Seneca, PA, p. A541

PATTON, Donald, Medical Staff President, Memorial Medical Center – Ashland, Ashland, WI, p. A683

PATTON, Elaine, Vice President Nursing, Olathe Medical Center, Olathe, KS, p. A241

PATTON, Joy, Chief Information Services, Pampa Regional Medical Center, Pampa, TX, p. A626

PATTON, Kevin, Chief Executive Officer, Old Vineyard Behavioral Health Services, Winston–Salem, NC, p. A463

PATTON, Meghan, Vice President Human Resources, Abington Memorial Hospital, Abington, PA, p. A519

PAUGH, J. William, FACHE, President and Chief Executive Officer, Wayne Memorial Hospital, Goldsboro, NC, p. A453

PAUL, Adam, Chief Financial Officer, Prairie Lakes Healthcare System, Watertown, SD, p. A564

PAUL, Darrick, Vice President and Chief People Officer, St. Vincent Infirmary Medical Center, Little Rock, AR, p. A47

PAUL, Donn
Vice President Human Resources, Pioneer Community Hospital of Patrick County, Stuart, VA, p. A662
Chief Human Resources, S. E. Lackey Memorial Hospital, Forest, MS, p. A347

PAUL, Joseph M., Chief Financial Officer, Palms West Hospital, Loxahatchee, FL, p. A129

PAUL, Louisa, M.D. Chief Medical Officer, Sanford Tracy Medical Center, Tracy, MN, p. A341

PAUL, Mary
Chief Information Officer, Columbia St. Mary's Hospital Milwaukee, Milwaukee, WI, p. A692
Chief Information Officer, Columbia St. Mary's Ozaukee Hospital, Mequon, WI, p. A691
Vice President and Chief Information Officer, Sacred Heart Rehabilitation Institute, Milwaukee, WI, p. A692

PAULE, Gerald, Chief Financial Officer, Kennewick General Hospital, Kennewick, WA, p. A667

PAULEY, Clarence, Vice President Human Resources, University Hospital, Cincinnati, OH, p. A475

PAULK, Nikki, Chief Executive Officer, Bleckley Memorial Hospital, Cochran, GA, p. A150

PAULK, Pamela, Senior Vice President Human Resources, Johns Hopkins Hospital, Baltimore, MD, p. A287

PAULOSKY, David, Chief Financial Officer, Bayonne Medical Center, Bayonne, NJ, p. A401

PAULSEN, Mark, M.D. Medical Director, Middle Park Medical Center, Kremmling, CO, p. A102

PAULSON, Adam, Director Finance, CentraCare Health–Melrose, Melrose, MN, p. A335

PAULSON, Gordon, Manager Personnel, Glacial Ridge Health System, Glenwood, MN, p. A333

PAULSON, Mark E., Chief Executive Officer, Chippewa County–Montevideo Hospital, Montevideo, MN, p. A336

PAULSON, Sybil K., R.N. Administrator, North Oaks Rehabilitation Hospital, Hammond, LA, p. A268

PAULUS, Ronald A., M.D. President and Chief Executive Officer, Mission Hospital, Asheville, NC, p. A447

PAULY, Audrey, M.D. Chief of Staff, Mammoth Hospital, Mammoth Lakes, CA, p. A73

PAUTLER, Stephen, FACHE Chief Operating Officer, Peterson Regional Medical Center, Kerrville, TX, p. A616

PAVEY, Joyal, Executive Director, Rogers City Rehabilitation Hospital, Rogers City, MI, p. A323

PAVIK, Sarah, Director Human Resources and Guest Services, Inova Loudoun Hospital, Leesburg, VA, p. A656

PAVILANIS, Charlotte J., R.N. Director of Patient Care Services, Sturgis Hospital, Sturgis, MI, p. A325

PAVON, Ricardo, Chief Financial Officer, Kendall Regional Medical Center, Miami, FL, p. A131

PAVOURIS, Nicolas, M.D. Chief of Medical Staff, Florida Hospital North Pinellas, Tarpon Springs, FL, p. A142

PAWLAK, Paul, President and Chief Executive Officer, Silver Cross Hospital, New Lenox, IL, p. A190

PAWLIKOWSKI, Mary, Vice President and Chief Operating Officer, Carrier Clinic, Belle Mead, NJ, p. A401

PAWLOWICZ, James E., Director Human Resources, Shriners Hospitals for Children–Chicago, Chicago, IL, p. A179

PAWLOWSKI, Phil, Chief Financial Officer, Glenbeigh Hospital and Outpatient Centers, Rock Creek, OH, p. A489

PAWOLA, Ken
Chief Operating Officer, RML Specialty Hospital, Chicago, IL, p. A178
Chief Operating Officer, RML Specialty Hospital, Hinsdale, IL, p. A185

PAXSON, Gary, Chief Information Officer, White River Medical Center, Batesville, AR, p. A41

PAYLOR, Tarry, Director Human Resources, Children's Hospital of Michigan, Detroit, MI, p. A311

PAYNE, Gary, Chief Executive Officer, Cardinal Hill Rehabilitation Hospital, Lexington, KY, p. A254

PAYNE, James, Director Information Systems, Southern Tennessee Medical Center, Winchester, TN, p. A580

PAYNE, Janet S.
Vice President Human Resources, Presence Covenant Medical Center, Urbana, IL, p. A196
Vice President Human Resources, Presence United Samaritans Medical Center, Danville, IL, p. A180

PAYNE, Jeffery L., Vice President Human Resources, Lakeland Regional Medical Center, Lakeland, FL, p. A128

PAYNE, Judy, R.N. Chief Operating Officer, Turning Point Hospital, Moultrie, GA, p. A158

PAYNE, Kenneth G., Chief Financial Officer, Holzer Medical Center, Gallipolis, OH, p. A482

PAYNE, Michael, M.D. Chief of Staff, Dallas County Medical Center, Fordyce, AR, p. A44

PAYNE, Michael E., Administrator, Girard Medical Center, Girard, KS, p. A234

PAYNE, Rick, Director Information Systems, Santa Rosa Medical Center, Milton, FL, p. A133

PAYNE, Steven, Chief Financial Officer, Salt Lake Regional Medical Center, Salt Lake City, UT, p. A647

PAYTON, Becky J., Vice President Human Resources, Mercy Hospital Oklahoma City, Oklahoma City, OK, p. A503

PAYTON, J. Ronald, Director Human Resources, Gateway Regional Medical Center, Granite City, IL, p. A184

PAZ, Harold L., M.D. Chief Executive Officer, Penn State Milton S. Hershey Medical Center, Hershey, PA, p. A527

PAZDERNIK, Mary, Chief Financial Officer, Mahnomen Health Center, Mahnomen, MN, p. A335

PEA, Gary, Chief Financial Officer, Glenn Medical Center, Willows, CA, p. A96

PEA, Richard, Director Human Resources, Memorial Hospital and Health Care Center, Jasper, IN, p. A207

PEABODY, Joyce L., M.D. Vice President and Chief Medical Officer, Saratoga Hospital, Saratoga Springs, NY, p. A442

PEABODY, Kim, Chief Operating Officer, The Brook Hospital – KMI, Louisville, KY, p. A256

PEABODY, Paul, Chief Information Officer, Palomar Medical Center, Escondido, CA, p. A59

PEACE, James, M.D. Chief of Staff, Olympia Medical Center, Los Angeles, CA, p. A70

PEACE III, Lother E., President and Chief Executive Officer, Russell Medical Center, Alexander City, AL, p. A15

PEACH, Larry, Assistant Administrator and Chief Financial Officer, Mendota Community Hospital, Mendota, IL, p. A188

PEACH, Susan M., R.N. Chief Executive Officer, Sumner Regional Medical Center, Gallatin, TN, p. A569

PEACOCK, Gary G., Senior Vice President and Chief Financial Officer, Decatur Memorial Hospital, Decatur, IL, p. A180

PEACOCK, Steve, Assistant Vice President, Plaza Specialty Hospital, Houston, TX, p. A611

PEAK, Daniel, M.D. Chief Medical Staff, Southampton Memorial Hospital, Franklin, VA, p. A654

PEAL, Chip, Chief Executive Officer, Frankfort Regional Medical Center, Frankfort, KY, p. A251

PEARCE, Charles T.
Chief Financial and Information Officer, Kalispell Regional Medical Center, Kalispell, MT, p. A377
CFIO, The HealthCenter, Kalispell, MT, p. A377

PEARCE, Edward, M.D. Chief of Staff, Caldwell Memorial Hospital, Lenoir, NC, p. A456

PEARCE, Kelly, Vice President of Operations, SSM St. Clare Health Center, Fenton, MO, p. A360

PEARCE, Margaret, R.N. Chief Nursing Officer, University of Utah Health Care – Hospital and Clinics, Salt Lake City, UT, p. A647

PEARCH, William, Chief Information Officer, Yukon–Kuskokwim Delta Regional Hospital, Bethel, AK, p. A27

PEARCY, Joetta J., Director, Human Resources, Glendive Medical Center, Glendive, MT, p. A376

PEARLMAN, Helen, Nurse Executive, Minneapolis Veterans Affairs Health Care System, Minneapolis, MN, p. A336

PEARSALL, Craig K., Director Human Resources, Lourdes Counseling Center, Richland, WA, p. A670

PEARSALL, Cynthia, Chief Nursing Officer, Fairfield Medical Center, Lancaster, OH, p. A483

PEARSALL, Tracy, Director Human Resources, Arkansas State Hospital, Little Rock, AR, p. A46

PEARSON, Bruce, FACHE, Chief Executive Officer, John C. Lincoln North Mountain Hospital, Phoenix, AZ, p. A34

PEARSON, David, Chief Information Officer, St. Luke's Hospital, Columbus, NC, p. A450

PEARSON, Dawn, Director Human Resources, HEALTHSOUTH Rehabilitation Hospital of Vineland, Vineland, NJ, p. A412

PEARSON, Debra, Chief Financial Officer, Jonathan M. Wainwright Memorial Veterans Affairs Medical Center, Walla Walla, WA, p. A674

PEARSON, Fenorris
Chief Human Resources Officer, Seton Medical Center Austin, Austin, TX, p. A585
Chief Human Resources Officer, University Medical Center at Brackenridge, Austin, TX, p. A586

PEARSON, George, Chief Human Resources Management Office, Martinsburg Veterans Affairs Medical Center, Martinsburg, WV, p. A678

PEARSON, Jeff, Vice President and Chief Information Officer, Mother Frances Hospital – Tyler, Tyler, TX, p. A638

PEARSON, Kellie, Director Human Resources, Lower Bucks Hospital, Bristol, PA, p. A521

PEARSON, Linnie, Coordinator Human Resources and Benefits, Montfort Jones Memorial Hospital, Kosciusko, MS, p. A349

PEARSON, Madelyn, R.N. Sr. Vice President Patient Care Services, Englewood Hospital and Medical Center, Englewood, NJ, p. A404

PEARSON, Marshall, Director Management Information Systems, St. David's North Austin Medical Center, Austin, TX, p. A586

PEARSON, Matthew Paul, Chief Executive Officer, Select Specialty Hospital–Western Missouri, Kansas City, MO, p. A363

PEARSON, Sandra, Manager Human Resources, St. Vincent Rehabilitation Hospital, Sherwood, AR, p. A50

PEART, Carol, Chief Financial Officer, Aurora Chicago Lakeshore Hospital, Chicago, IL, p. A176

PEASNALL, Arlene F., Senior Vice President Human Resources, Kaiser Permanente Medical Center, Honolulu, HI, p. A164

PEBURN, Eric, Chief Financial Officer, Halifax Health Medical Center of Daytona Beach, Daytona Beach, FL, p. A122

PECHACEK, Judith, R.N. Vice President Patient Care, Fairview Southdale Hospital, Edina, MN, p. A332

PECHOUS, Bryan, M.D. Vice President Medical Affairs, UnityPoint Health Finley, Dubuque, IA, p. A221

PECK, Bob, Chief Financial Officer, Wesley Rehabilitation Hospital, Wichita, KS, p. A247

PECK, Charles A., M.D.,
Interim President, Frazier Rehab Institute, Louisville, KY, p. A255
Interim President, Jewish Hospital, Louisville, KY, p. A255

PECK, Darin, M.D. Chief of Staff, Charles A. Dean Memorial Hospital, Greenville, ME, p. A283

PECK, Kathey, Manager Health Information, Caribou Memorial Hospital and Living Center, Soda Springs, ID, p. A172

PECK, Kay E., Ph.D., Chief Executive Officer, Kindred Hospital–Amarillo, Amarillo, TX, p. A582

PECK, Kay E., Ph.D. Chief Executive Officer, Kindred Hospital–Amarillo, Amarillo, TX, p. A582

PECK, Kay E., Ph.D., Chief Executive Officer, Kindred Rehabilitation Hospital Amarillo, Amarillo, TX, p. A582

PECK, Lori, Vice President Finance, Memorial Health Center, Medford, WI, p. A691

PECK, Michael D., Assistant Administrator, Caribou Memorial Hospital and Living Center, Soda Springs, ID, p. A172

PECK, Thomas R., Chief Executive Officer, Franciscan St. Elizabeth Health – Crawfordsville, Crawfordsville, IN, p. A200

PEDERSEN, Alan, Vice President Human Resources, Cayuga Medical Center at Ithaca, Ithaca, NY, p. A427

PEDERSEN, Darren, Coordinator Information Technology, Weisman Children's Rehabilitation Hospital, Marlton, NJ, p. A406

PEDERSEN, Paul E., M.D. Vice President and Chief Medical Officer, OSF St. Joseph Medical Center, Bloomington, IL, p. A174

PEDERSON, Karn, Manager Health Information Management, McKenzie County Healthcare System, Watford City, ND, p. A469

PEDERSON, Randall K., Chief Executive Officer, Tioga Medical Center, Tioga, ND, p. A469

PEDLEY, Joe, CPA Vice President and Chief Financial Officer, Lawrence Memorial Hospital, Lawrence, KS, p. A238

PEDLOW, Bernadette R., Senior Vice President Business and Chief Operating Officer, Albany Medical Center, Albany, NY, p. A420

PEDROZA, Fernando
Director Information Systems, Medical Center of the Rockies, Loveland, CO, p. A104
Chief Information Officer, Poudre Valley Hospital, Fort Collins, CO, p. A101

PEEBLES, Robert J., President and Chief Executive Officer, Mercy Medical Center–Sioux City, Sioux City, IA, p. A228

PEED, Nancy, Administrator and Chief Executive Officer, Peach Regional Medical Center, Fort Valley, GA, p. A154

PEEK, Michael Scott, Chief Executive Officer, Chambers Memorial Hospital, Danville, AR, p. A42

PEEK, Scott, FACHE, President, Baylor Medical Center at McKinney, McKinney, TX, p. A622

PEELGREN, Jim, Chief Information Officer, Tulare Regional Medical Center, Tulare, CA, p. A93

PEER, Julie, Vice President Finance, Brookville Hospital, Brookville, PA, p. A521

PEERY, Lori, Chief Human Resource Management Services, Veterans Affairs Palo Alto Health Care System, Palo Alto, CA, p. A79

PEET, Carole, MSN, President and Chief Executive Officer, St. Anthony North Hospital, Westminster, CO, p. A106

PEETERS, Marie, Director Human Resources, Mercy Iowa City, Iowa City, IA, p. A223

PEGE, Diane, M.D. Vice President Medical Affairs, Sutter Lakeside Hospital, Lakeport, CA, p. A66

PEHRSON, Felicia, M.D., Commanding Officer, Keller Army Community Hospital, West Point, NY, p. A446

PEHRSON, Timothy T., Chief Executive Officer, McKay–Dee Hospital Center, Ogden, UT, p. A645

PEIFFER, Paul V., Chief Executive Officer, Covington County Hospital, Collins, MS, p. A346

---

PEKOFSKE, Robert, Vice President Finance, Advocate Christ Medical Center, Oak Lawn, IL, p. A190

PELACCIA, Joseph, President and Chief Executive Officer, Milford Hospital, Milford, CT, p. A110

PELLE, Fred L., FACHE,
Interim President and Chief Executive Officer, Lee Regional Medical Center, Pennington Gap, VA, p. A659
Interim President and Chief Executive Officer, Mountain View Regional Medical Center, Norton, VA, p. A658
Interim Chief Executive Officer, Wellmont Hancock County Hospital, Sneedville, TN, p. A579
Interim Chief Executive Officer, Wellmont Hawkins County Memorial Hospital, Rogersville, TN, p. A578
Interim President and Chief Executive Officer, Wellmont Lonesome Pine Hospital, Big Stone Gap, VA, p. A651

PELLECCHIA, Joseph, M.D. Chief of Staff, Veterans Affairs Medical Center-Lexington, Lexington, KY, p. A255

PELLEGRINO, Cynthia Miller, Chief Executive Officer, Western Maryland Hospital Center, Hagerstown, MD, p. A292

PELLETIER, Stephen, Leader Guest Services, York Hospital, York, ME, p. A286

PELLICONE, John T., M.D. Medical Director, Helen Hayes Hospital, West Haverstraw, NY, p. A445

PELSMAN, Mara, Chief Executive Officer, Gateways Hospital and Mental Health Center, Los Angeles, CA, p. A69

PELTIER, Glenn, Chief Financial Officer, Mother Frances Hospital – Winnsboro, Winnsboro, TX, p. A642

PELTIER, Robert, M.D. Senior Vice President and Chief Medical Officer, North Oaks Medical Center, Hammond, LA, p. A268

PELTOLA, Gene, President and Chief Executive Officer, Yukon–Kuskokwim Delta Regional Hospital, Bethel, AK, p. A27

PELTON, Deborah, R.N. Chief Nursing Officer, Texas Spine & Joint Hospital, Tyler, TX, p. A638

PELZ, Thomas, M.D. Chief of Staff, Boscobel Area Health Care, Boscobel, WI, p. A684

PEMBERTON, John S., Director Human Resources, Tuba City Regional Health Care Corporation, Tuba City, AZ, p. A38

PENA, Julie, Director Finance, Community Howard Specialty Hospital, Kokomo, IN, p. A207

PENCE, Julie, Associate Director Human Resources, Highland District Hospital, Hillsboro, OH, p. A483

PENDER, John, M.D. Medical Director, Texas Health Specialty Hospital, Fort Worth, TX, p. A604

PENDER, Laura, Human Resources Site Manager, Turkey Creek Medical Center, Knoxville, TN, p. A572

PENDERGAST, Debra, Senior Vice President Patient Care Services and Chief Nursing Officer, John Muir Medical Center, Walnut Creek, Walnut Creek, CA, p. A95

PENDERGAST, Jim, Administrator Human Resources, University of New Mexico Hospitals, Albuquerque, NM, p. A415

PENDERGRAFT, Tina, Chief Nursing Officer, Satanta District Hospital, Satanta, KS, p. A244

PENDLETON, Debbie, Human Resources Specialist, Weslaco Rehabilitation Hospital, Weslaco, TX, p. A641

PENDLETON, Gretchen, Chief Human Resources Officer, Mercy Suburban Hospital, Norristown, PA, p. A533

PENDLETON, Kevin, Chief Information Technology, Lakeside Behavioral Health System, Memphis, TN, p. A574

PENDLETON, Timothy, M.D. President Medical Staff, Brookville Hospital, Brookville, PA, p. A521

PENICK, Lisa, R.N. Chief Nursing Officer, Carroll County Memorial Hospital, Carrollton, KY, p. A249

PENLAND, Jennifer
Controller, Kindred Hospital Tarrant County-Arlington, Arlington, TX, p. A583
Controller, Kindred Hospital–White Rock, Dallas, TX, p. A596
Controller, Kindred Rehabilitation Hospital Arlington, Arlington, TX, p. A583

PENNER, Jerome, Chief Executive Officer, Murray–Calloway County Hospital, Murray, KY, p. A258

PENNEY, Cindy L., R.N. Vice President Nursing, Mercy Iowa City, Iowa City, IA, p. A223

PENNINGTON, Jack, Chief Executive Officer, Pemiscot Memorial Health System, Hayti, MO, p. A361

PENNINGTON, James, Chief Information Officer, JPS Health Network, Fort Worth, TX, p. A604

PENNINGTON, Keith, President and Chief Executive Officer, Medical West, Bessemer, AL, p. A16

PENNINGTON, Stephen G., Chief Executive Officer, Gadsden Regional Medical Center, Gadsden, AL, p. A20

PENNINO, Jackie, Director Human Resources, Old Vineyard Behavioral Health Services, Winston–Salem, NC, p. A463

PENNISSON, Jay M., Chief Financial Officer, Piedmont Medical Center, Rock Hill, SC, p. A555

PENNOCK, Kathy, Director Human Resources, Morrison Community Hospital, Morrison, IL, p. A189

PENNY, Randy, Chief Executive Officer, Reliant Rehabilitation Hospital Dallas, Dallas, TX, p. A597

PENOVICH, Carrie L., Director Clinical and Support Services, Aurora Medical Center – Manitowoc County, Two Rivers, WI, p. A698

PENQUE, Sue, R.N. Senior Vice President and Chief Nursing Officer, South Nassau Communities Hospital, Oceanside, NY, p. A438

PENROD, Kirt, Chief Financial Officer, Shadow Mountain Behavioral Health System, Tulsa, OK, p. A509

PENROD, Pat, Controller, HEALTHSOUTH Rehabilitation Hospital of Colorado Springs, Colorado Springs, CO, p. A98

PENROSE, Lee, President and Chief Executive Officer, St. Jude Medical Center, Fullerton, CA, p. A62

PENTON, Lance, Director Information Technology and Systems, Fort Walton Beach Medical Center, Fort Walton Beach, FL, p. A124

PENTZ, Thomas R., President and Chief Executive Officer, Orange Park Medical Center, Orange Park, FL, p. A135

PENUEL, Jennifer, Director Human Resources, Madison Medical Center, Fredericktown, MO, p. A361

PEOPLES, Kathleen K., R.N. Vice President and Nursing, St. Joseph Hospital and Health Center, Kokomo, IN, p. A207

PEOPLES, Phyllis, R.N., President and Chief Executive Officer, Terrebonne General Medical Center, Houma, LA, p. A268

PEPE, Joseph, M.D., President and Chief Executive Officer, Catholic Medical Center, Manchester, NH, p. A399

PEPE, Michael, Ph.D
Chief Human Resources Officer, Virtua Berlin, Berlin, NJ, p. A401
Chief Human Resources, Virtua Marlton, Marlton, NJ, p. A406

PEPPEL, David, Director Operations, Richard H. Hutchings Psychiatric Center, Syracuse, NY, p. A443

PEPPER, Paula, Lan Administrator, Holmes County Hospital and Clinics, Lexington, MS, p. A350

PEPPLER, Lisa, Financial Operations Analyst, Parkview Whitley Hospital, Columbia City, IN, p. A200

PERAL, Sherry, Manager Information Systems, Oak Valley Hospital District, Oakdale, CA, p. A77

PERALTA, Nora, Chief Nursing Officer, St. Anthony's Hospital, Houston, TX, p. A612

PERALTA, Pennie, R.N. VP, Nursing & Chief Nursing Officer, Bon Secours St. Francis Xavier Hospital, Charleston, SC, p. A549

PERCELLO, Thomas, Chief Financial Officer, Kimball Medical Center, Lakewood, NJ, p. A405

PERCIVAL, Steve, Director Human Resources, Washington Regional Medical Center, Fayetteville, AR, p. A43

PERDUE, Eric, Chief Human Resource Officer, Adena Medical Center, Chillicothe, OH, p. A473

PERDUE, Randy, Assistant Vice President, Mother Frances Hospital – Tyler, Tyler, TX, p. A638

PEREACE, Vicki, Manager Human Resources, William Bee Ririe Hospital, Ely, NV, p. A391

PERECKO, Gary L., President, Riddle Hospital, Media, PA, p. A531

PEREL, Michael
Regional Chief Financial Officer, Kauai Veterans Memorial Hospital, Waimea, HI, p. A166
Regional Chief Financial Officer, Samuel Mahelona Memorial Hospital, Kapaa, HI, p. A165

PEREZ, Brenda, R.N. Chief Clinical Officer, Kindred Hospital–White Rock, Dallas, TX, p. A596

PEREZ, David, Chief Information Officer, Eisenhower Medical Center, Rancho Mirage, CA, p. A81

PEREZ, James, M.D. Chief Medical Officer, Kit Carson County Memorial Health Center, Burlington, CO, p. A98

PEREZ, Leo Dan, Controller, Weslaco Rehabilitation Hospital, Weslaco, TX, p. A641

PEREZ, Miguel, Director Information Systems, Driscoll Children's Hospital, Corpus Christi, TX, p. A594

PEREZ, Nina, R.N. Chief Nursing Officer, North Okaloosa Medical Center, Crestview, FL, p. A121

PEREZ, Tony, M.D. President Medical Staff, Jewish Hospital–Shelbyville, Shelbyville, KY, p. A260

PEREZ–FOUTAN, Julio, M.D. Executive Vice President Medical Affairs, Children's Medical Center of Dallas, Dallas, TX, p. A595

PERILLI, Ernest N., Administrator, Shriners Hospitals for Children–Philadelphia, Philadelphia, PA, p. A536

PERILLI, John, M.D., Health Services Director, Ossining Correctional Facilities Hospital, Ossining, NY, p. A439

PERIMENIS, Vasilia, Vice President Human Resources, Novant Health Medical Park Hospital, Winston–Salem, NC, p. A463

PERKERSON, Robyn, Chief Clinical Officer, LifeCare Hospitals of North Carolina, Rocky Mount, NC, p. A460

PERKES, Neil C., Operations Officer, Logan Regional Hospital, Logan, UT, p. A644

PERKET, William, Vice President Human Resources, North Country Hospital and Health Center, Newport, VT, p. A650

PERKINS, A. William, Interim Administrator, Atmore Community Hospital, Atmore, AL, p. A16

PERKINS, Brett, M.D. Chief Medical Staff, Madison County Memorial Hospital, Madison, FL, p. A129

PERKINS, Chris
Chief Executive Officer, Acadia Abilene Hospital, Abilene, TX, p. A581
Director Information Services, Clinch Valley Medical Center, Richlands, VA, p. A660

PERKINS, Dan, Corporate Director Human Resources, Cornerstone Hospital–West Monroe, West Monroe, LA, p. A280

PERKINS, Evelyn, Director Human Resources, Eastern Louisiana Mental Health System, Jackson, LA, p. A269

PERKINS, Gary A., FACHE, President and Chief Executive Officer, Children's Hospital and Medical Center, Omaha, NE, p. A387

PERKINS, Jeanne, Vice President Nursing and Interim Manager Human Resources, Bucyrus Community Hospital, Bucyrus, OH, p. A472

PERKINS, Jeffery, Chief Operating Officer, Boundary Community Hospital, Bonners Ferry, ID, p. A168

PERKINS, Kathryn, M.D. Chief Medical Officer, Banner Thunderbird Medical Center, Glendale, AZ, p. A32

PERKINS, Kelly, Director Human Resources, New Horizons Health Systems, Owenton, KY, p. A258

PERKINS, Mike, Vice President and Administrator, Baptist Health Extended Care Hospital, Little Rock, AR, p. A46

PERKINS, Richard, Chief Financial Officer, Hillcrest Baptist Medical Center, Waco, TX, p. A640

PERKINS, Sherry, Ph.D. Chief Operating Officer and Chief Nursing Officer, Anne Arundel Medical Center, Annapolis, MD, p. A287

PERKINS, Steven J., Chief Executive Officer, South Central Kansas Medical Center, Arkansas City, KS, p. A231

PERKINS, Tom, Chief Information Officer, Shannon Medical Center, San Angelo, TX, p. A630

PERKINS–PEPPERS, Andrea, Manager Information Services, Forks Community Hospital, Forks, WA, p. A666

PERKO, Tina, Vice President Operations, Adena Pike Medical Center, Waverly, OH, p. A492

PERLICH, Gwynn, Vice President of Patient Services and Chief Nursing Officer, St. Vincent Carmel Hospital, Carmel, IN, p. A200

PERLIN, Mitch, Chief Information Officer, Interim LSU Public Hospital, New Orleans, LA, p. A275

PERLMAN, Joel A., Executive Vice President Finance, Montefiore Medical Center, NY, p. A434

PERMENTER, Ethan, Chief Executive Officer, Parkwood Behavioral Health System, Olive Branch, MS, p. A352

PERMETTI, Thomas, Regional Chief Operating Officer and Administrator, CHRISTUS St. John Hospital, Nassau Bay, TX, p. A624

PERNAU, James O., Chief Executive Officer, Edgerton Hospital and Health Services, Edgerton, WI, p. A686

PERNICE, Paul, Vice President Finance, Beebe Medical Center, Lewes, DE, p. A114

PERONA, Lorene, Chief Executive Officer, Kindred Hospital Sugar Land, Sugar Land, TX, p. A635

PERRA, Scott H., President and Chief Executive Officer, Faxton–St. Luke's Healthcare, Utica, NY, p. A444

PERRIGOT, Keri, Assistant Administrator Human Resources, Cassia Regional Medical Center, Burley, ID, p. A168

PERRINE, Vicki, Chief Operating Officer and Vice President Clinical Services, Claxton–Hepburn Medical Center, Ogdensburg, NY, p. A438

PERRITT, Daniel, Chief Financial Officer, Sunrise Hospital and Medical Center, Las Vegas, NV, p. A394

PERRONG, Elizabeth, Vice President Human Resources, Hazleton General Hospital, Hazleton, PA, p. A527

PERROTTE, Kenneth, Director Operations, Rockland Children's Psychiatric Center, Orangeburg, NY, p. A439

PERROTTI, Paul R., CPA Chief Financial Officer, West Georgia Health, La Grange, GA, p. A155

PERRY, Amy, President, Sinai Hospital of Baltimore, Baltimore, MD, p. A289

PERRY, Ann, Chief Financial Officer, Pike County Memorial Hospital, Louisiana, MO, p. A365

PERRY, Bill, Director Information Systems, Mercy Hospital Hot Springs, Hot Springs National Park, AR, p. A45

PERRY, Carol, R.N. Vice President and Chief Nursing Officer, Stormont–Vail HealthCare, Topeka, KS, p. A245

PERRY, Cheryl
Chief Financial Officer, New Bedford Rehabilitation Hospital, New Bedford, MA, p. A302
Director Human Resources, Paris Regional Medical Center, Paris, TX, p. A626

PERRY, Christopher, Director Human Resources, Memorial Hospital West, Pembroke Pines, FL, p. A136

PERRY, Doug, M.D. Chief of Staff, Baptist Medical Center Leake, Carthage, MS, p. A345

PERRY, George H., Ph.D., Chief Executive Officer, Belmont Pines Hospital, Youngstown, OH, p. A494

PERRY, James, Chief Executive Officer, Mental Health Services for Clark and Madison Counties, Springfield, OH, p. A490

PERRY, Jan, R.N. Vice President Patient Care Services, Community Medical Center, Missoula, MT, p. A378

PERRY, Jeff
Director Information Technology, St. John's Pleasant Valley Hospital, Camarillo, CA, p. A55
Director Information Technology, St. John's Regional Medical Center, Oxnard, CA, p. A78

PERRY, John, M.D. Chief of Staff, Wagoner Community Hospital, Wagoner, OK, p. A509

PERRY, Karen, Chief Information Resource Management Services, James H. Quillen Veterans Affairs Medical Center, Mountain Home, TN, p. A576

PERRY, Kathleen, Vice President and Chief Information Officer, Mercy Medical Center, Baltimore, MD, p. A288

PERRY, Keith, Associate Vice President and Deputy Chief Information Officer, University of Texas M.D. Anderson Cancer Center, Houston, TX, p. A613

PERRY, Marcia F., Chief Operating Officer, Hawthorn Children Psychiatric Hospital, Saint Louis, MO, p. A369

PERRY, Matthew, Director Information Systems, Andalusia Regional Hospital, Andalusia, AL, p. A15

PERRY, Matthew J., President and Chief Executive Officer, Genesis HealthCare System, Zanesville, OH, p. A494

PERRY, Megan R., Corporate Vice President and President, Sentara Northern Virginia Medical Center, Woodbridge, VA, p. A663

PERRY, Michael R., M.D., President and Chief Executive Officer, FHN Memorial Hospital, Freeport, IL, p. A183

PERRY, Peggy, Assistant Director, Texas Center for Infectious Disease, San Antonio, TX, p. A632

PERRY, Phil, M.D
Chief Medical Officer, St. Vincent's Medical Center Riverside, Jacksonville, FL, p. A127
Chief Medical Officer, St. Vincent's Medical Center Southside, Jacksonville, FL, p. A127

PERRY, Rhonda, Chief Financial Officer, Medical Center of Central Georgia, Macon, GA, p. A156

PERRY, Shaun, Chief Information Officer, McGehee–Desha County Hospital, McGehee, AR, p. A47

PERRY, Solette, Regional Director Human Resources, Kauai Veterans Memorial Hospital, Waimea, HI, p. A166

PERRY, V. Mark, Chief Financial Officer, Adventist Medical Center–Portland, Portland, OR, p. A515

PERRYMAN, Daniel L., President and Chief Executive Officer, St. Francis Hospital, Litchfield, IL, p. A187

PERRYMAN, Margaret E., President and Chief Executive Officer, Gillette Children's Specialty Healthcare, Saint Paul, MN, p. A340

PERRYMAN, Mike, Chief Financial Officer, Baptist Memorial Hospital–Union City, Union City, TN, p. A580

PERSE, David, M.D., President, St. Vincent Charity Medical Center, Cleveland, OH, p. A477

PERSINGER, Keith D., Senior Vice President Finance and Chief Financial Officer, University of Maryland Medical Center, Baltimore, MD, p. A289

PERSONS, Linda, Executive Director, Atascadero State Hospital, Atascadero, CA, p. A53

PERT, Robert M., Vice President Finance and Chief Financial Officer, United Regional Health Care System, Wichita Falls, TX, p. A642

PERUSHEK, John R., Chief Executive Officer, Reagan Memorial Hospital, Big Lake, TX, p. A588

PERUSSE, Margo, Administrator and Chief Nursing Officer, La Palma Intercommunity Hospital, La Palma, CA, p. A65

PESKIN, Ted, M.D. Acute Care Medical Director, Hilo Medical Center, Hilo, HI, p. A164

PESSAGNO, Paul, Chief Financial Officer, Richard L. Roudebush Veterans Affairs Medical Center, Indianapolis, IN, p. A206

PETER, David, M.D
Senior Vice President Medical Affairs and Chief Medical Director, Akron General Medical Center, Akron, OH, p. A470
Senior Vice President Medical Affairs and Chief Medical Officer, Lodi Community Hospital, Lodi, OH, p. A484

PETER, Douglas G., M.D. Chief Medical Officer, Gallup Indian Medical Center, Gallup, NM, p. A416

PETER, Edith S., Chief Financial Officer and Vice President Finance, Cooley Dickinson Hospital, Northampton, MA, p. A303

PETER, Jan D., Vice President Fiscal Services and Chief Financial Officer, Good Shepherd Health Care System, Hermiston, OR, p. A513

PETERMAN, Tammy, R.N. Executive Vice President, Chief Operating Officer and Chief Nursing Officer, The University of Kansas Hospital, Kansas City, KS, p. A237

PETERMEIER, Jill, Senior Executive Human Resources, Marshalltown Medical & Surgical Center, Marshalltown, IA, p. A225

PETERS, Brian, Chief Information Officer, St. Vincent Indianapolis Hospital, Indianapolis, IN, p. A206

PETERS, Bruce, Vice President and Chief Operating Officer, Bakersfield Memorial Hospital, Bakersfield, CA, p. A53

PETERS, Cindy, Chief Information Officer, Oak Hill Hospital, Brooksville, FL, p. A120

PETERS, Connie, R.N., Regional Administrator, Alegent Creighton Health–Memorial Hospital, Schuyler, Schuyler, NE, p. A389

PETERS, Dave, Chief Human Resources Officer, Veterans Affairs Nebraska–Western Iowa Health Care System, Lincoln, NE, p. A386

PETERS, Gerald, Vice President Information Technologies and Chief Information Officer, Lake Health, Concord Township, OH, p. A478

PETERS, Jan, Vice President Human Resources, Saint Vincent Hospital, Worcester, MA, p. A306

PETERS, John, Chief Financial Officer, St. Joseph's Hospital and Medical Center, Phoenix, AZ, p. A35

PETERS, Ken
Director Human Resources Management, Bellin Memorial Hospital, Green Bay, WI, p. A687
Director Human Resources, Bellin Psychiatric Center, Green Bay, WI, p. A687

PETERS, Mark J., M.D., President and Chief Executive Officer, East Jefferson General Hospital, Metairie, LA, p. A273

PETERS, Patrick, Chief Executive Officer, Guthrie County Hospital, Guthrie Center, IA, p. A222

PETERS, Regina, Chief Executive Officer, Stroud Regional Medical Center, Stroud, OK, p. A507

PETERS, Sue, Vice President Human Resources, Munson Medical Center, Traverse City, MI, p. A325

PETERS, Violeta, R.N., Chief Executive Officer, Specialty Hospital at Kimball, Lakewood, NJ, p. A405

PETERS–LEWIS, Angelleen, R.N. Chief Nurse and Senior Vice President Patient Care, Women & Infants Hospital of Rhode Island, Providence, RI, p. A547

PETERSEN, Brenda, Director Human Resources, Sanford Wheaton Medical Center, Wheaton, MN, p. A342

PETERSEN, Debbie, R.N. Chief Operating Officer and Chief Nursing Officer, Spalding Rehabilitation Hospital, Aurora, CO, p. A97

PETERSEN, Gary, Chief Operating Officer, Kaiser Permanente Sunnyside Medical Center, Clackamas, OR, p. A511

PETERSEN, Julie, Chief Executive Officer, PMH Medical Center, Prosser, WA, p. A669

PETERSEN, Keith J., Chief Executive Officer, Phoebe Sumter Medical Center, Americus, GA, p. A145

PETERSEN, Richard W., President and Chief Executive Officer, Maine Medical Center, Portland, ME, p. A284

PETERSON, Anita, Chief Executive Officer, TrustPoint Hospital, Murfreesboro, TN, p. A576

PETERSON, Anne, Vice President Human Resources and Support Services, Licking Memorial Hospital, Newark, OH, p. A487

PETERSON, Bill
Director Human Resources, John F. Kennedy Memorial Hospital, Indio, CA, p. A64
Chief Human Resources Director, Sierra Vista Regional Medical Center, San Luis Obispo, CA, p. A88

PETERSON, Bonnie, Chief Operating Officer and Vice President Clinical Services, Richard P. Stadter Psychiatric Center, Grand Forks, ND, p. A467

PETERSON, Brent A., Administrator, Cherry County Hospital, Valentine, NE, p. A390

PETERSON, Bruce, Chief Information Officer, Rome Memorial Hospital, Rome, NY, p. A441

PETERSON, Chad, Chief Information Officer, Sanford Northwood Deaconess Health Center, Northwood, ND, p. A468

PETERSON, Cheryl, Business Office Manager, Surgical Institute of Reading, Wyomissing, PA, p. A545

PETERSON, Cindy, Vice President and Chief Information Officer, Henry Mayo Newhall Memorial Hospital, Valencia, CA, p. A94

PETERSON, Dane C., Chief Operating Officer, Emory University Hospital Midtown, Atlanta, GA, p. A146

PETERSON, Daniel, Chief Human Resource Management Service, Central Arkansas Veterans Healthcare System, Little Rock, AR, p. A46

PETERSON, David
Regional Chief Information Officer, Memorial Health Care System, Chattanooga, TN, p. A566
Regional Chief Information Officer, St. Vincent Infirmary Medical Center, Little Rock, AR, p. A47

PETERSON, Dennis, Chief Information Officer, George E. Weems Memorial Hospital, Apalachicola, FL, p. A118

PETERSON, Douglas R., President and Chief Executive Officer, Chippewa Valley Hospital and Oakview Care Center, Durand, WI, p. A685

PETERSON, Eric
Director Information Technology, Lakeview Hospital, Bountiful, UT, p. A643
Director, Ogden Regional Medical Center, Ogden, UT, p. A645

PETERSON, Erica, Chief Executive Officer, Sanford Chamberlain Medical Center, Chamberlain, SD, p. A558

PETERSON, Gary, M.D. Vice President Medical Affairs and Medical Director, St. Luke's Hospital, Duluth, MN, p. A331

PETERSON, James, Senior Vice President Finance, Habersham Medical Center, Demorest, GA, p. A152

PETERSON, Jeff, M.D. Chief of Staff, Essentia Health Ada, Ada, MN, p. A328

PETERSON, Jeffrey, M.D. Medical Director, Cooperstown Medical Center, Cooperstown, ND, p. A466

PETERSON, John, Vice President Information Systems, Longmont United Hospital, Longmont, CO, p. A104

PETERSON, Josilyn, Chief Financial Officer, Ballinger Memorial Hospital, Ballinger, TX, p. A587

PETERSON, Judy, R.N. Chief Nursing Officer, East Texas Medical Center Carthage, Carthage, TX, p. A591

PETERSON, Julie, Chief Financial Officer, Sutter Delta Medical Center, Antioch, CA, p. A52

PETERSON, Kathy, Director Information Services, OSF Saint Anthony Medical Center, Rockford, IL, p. A193

PETERSON, Katie, R.N. Director of Nursing, Pender Community Hospital, Pender, NE, p. A389

PETERSON, Larry, Chief Financial Officer, Allen County Hospital, Iola, KS, p. A236

PETERSON, Margaret R., R.N., Chief Executive Officer, Desert Valley Hospital, Victorville, CA, p. A95

PETERSON, Mercy, Interim Chief Executive Officer, Nye Regional Medical Center, Tonopah, NV, p. A396

PETERSON, Michael, Vice President Ancillary and Support Services and Chief Information Officer, Sebasticook Valley Health, Pittsfield, ME, p. A284

PETERSON, Philip, Executive Vice President and Chief Financial Officer, Mercy Medical Center–Cedar Rapids, Cedar Rapids, IA, p. A217

PETERSON, Randall, President and Chief Executive Officer, Stormont–Vail HealthCare, Topeka, KS, p. A245

PETERSON, Robert
Chief Financial Officer, Hackettstown Regional Medical Center, Hackettstown, NJ, p. A404
Chief Operating Officer, West Florida Hospital, Pensacola, FL, p. A137

PETERSON, Ron, FACHE, President and Chief Executive Officer, Baxter Regional Medical Center, Mountain Home, AR, p. A48

PETERSON, Ron, Chief Information Officer, Pottstown Memorial Medical Center, Pottstown, PA, p. A539

PETERSON, Ronald R., President, Johns Hopkins Hospital, Baltimore, MD, p. A287

PETERSON, Scott, Vice President of People and Organizational Development, Peninsula Regional Medical Center, Salisbury, MD, p. A294

PETERSON, Seth, Director Information Services, Coshocton County Memorial Hospital, Coshocton, OH, p. A479

PETERSON, Shelley, Vice President Patient Services and Chief Nursing Officer, St. Mary's Hospital and Medical Center, Grand Junction, CO, p. A102

PETERSON, Stephen, Director Information Systems, Garrett County Memorial Hospital, Oakland, MD, p. A293

PETERSON, Thomas, M.D., Chief Executive Officer, Richard P. Stadter Psychiatric Center, Grand Forks, ND, p. A467

PETERSON, Tim, M.D. Chief of Staff, Meeker Memorial Hospital, Litchfield, MN, p. A334

PETERSON, Tracie, R.N. Chief Nursing Officer, Great Lakes Specialty Hospital–Grand Rapids Campus, Grand Rapids, MI, p. A315

PETIK, Jason, Chief Executive Officer, Sidney Regional Medical Center, Sidney, NE, p. A389

PETITT, Michael
Director of Finance, Wheaton Franciscan Healthcare – Elmbrook Memorial, Brookfield, WI, p. A684
Director of Finance, Wheaton Franciscan Healthcare – St. Joseph's, Milwaukee, WI, p. A692
Director of Finance, Wheaton Franciscan Healthcare – The Wisconsin Heart Hospital, Wauwatosa, WI, p. A699

PETRE, Patrick A., Administrator, Arrowhead Regional Medical Center, Colton, CA, p. A57

PETRECCIA, David, M.D. Physician Advisor, Placentia–Linda Hospital, Placentia, CA, p. A80

PETRICK, Teresa D., President, UPMC St. Margaret, Pittsburgh, PA, p. A538

PETRIE, Lori, Chief Financial Officer, Mercy Regional Medical Center, Ville Platte, LA, p. A280

PETRILLO, Mary Ann, Acting Associate Director, Nursing, Edith Nourse Rogers Memorial Veterans Hospital, Bedford, MA, p. A295

PETRILLO, Nancy, Director Human Resources, Matheny Medical and Educational Center, Peapack, NJ, p. A408

PETRINA, Robert
Chief Financial Officer, Alta Bates Summit Medical Center, Berkeley, CA, p. A54
Chief Financial Officer, Alta Bates Summit Medical Center – Summit Campus, Oakland, CA, p. A77

PETRINO, Robert, M.D. Chief of Staff, Northwest Medical Center, Springdale, AR, p. A50

PETRITZ, Jennifer J., Director Human Resources, University of Washington Medical Center, Seattle, WA, p. A671

PETRO, Lisa, Director Human Resources, Southwest Regional Medical Center, Waynesburg, PA, p. A543

PETROFF, Thomas, D.O. Vice President Medical Affairs, McLaren Greater Lansing, Lansing, MI, p. A318

PETROVICH, Lawrence, M.D. Chief Medical Officer, York Hospital, York, ME, p. A286

PETRUCCI, Peter E., M.D. Vice President Patient Safety, Quality and Medical Affairs, Sibley Memorial Hospital, Washington, DC, p. A117

PETTEY, Robbie, Chief Financial Officer, National Park Medical Center, Hot Springs, AR, p. A45

PETTIJOHN, Trent, M.D. Chief Medical Officer, The Heart Hospital Baylor Plano, Plano, TX, p. A628

PETTINATO, Paul J., M.D. Chief Information Officer, Signature Healthcare Brockton Hospital, Brockton, MA, p. A298

PETTIT, Donny, Chief Financial Officer, Coon Memorial Hospital and Home, Dalhart, TX, p. A594

PETTIT, Harlan, M.D. Chief of Staff, Fishermen's Hospital, Marathon, FL, p. A129

PETTITE, Shirley F., Chief, Human Resources, Tennessee Valley Healthcare System, Nashville, TN, p. A577

PETTREY, Lisa J., R.N., Chief Executive Officer, Regency Hospital of Columbus, Columbus, OH, p. A478

PETTUS, Lisa, Manager Information Systems, Cherry Hospital, Goldsboro, NC, p. A453

PETTY, Jane, Director Human Resources, Hillside Hospital, Pulaski, TN, p. A578

PETTY, Kent
System Chief Information Officer, Wellmont Bristol Regional Medical Center, Bristol, TN, p. A565
Chief Information Officer, Wellmont Hancock County Hospital, Sneedville, TN, p. A579
Chief Information Officer, Wellmont Holston Valley Medical Center, Kingsport, TN, p. A571

PETTY, Russ, M.D. Chief of Staff, Towner County Medical Center, Cando, ND, p. A465

PETTY, Vicki, Manager Human Resources, Wayne Medical Center, Waynesboro, TN, p. A580

PETULA, Ron, Vice President Finance, Good Shepherd Penn Partners Specialty Hospital at Rittenhouse, Philadelphia, PA, p. A535

PEZZIA, Marlene, Director, Tomball Regional Medical Center, Tomball, TX, p. A638

PFAFF, Joni, Chief Nursing Officer, Grisell Memorial Hospital District One, Ransom, KS, p. A243

PFAFF, Karen, Director Human Resources, Carroll County Memorial Hospital, Carrollton, MO, p. A358

PFAFF, Tony, Interim Chief Executive Officer, Deer Lodge Medical Center, Deer Lodge, MT, p. A375

PFAFF, Wanda, Vice President Human Resources, St. Alexius Medical Center, Bismarck, ND, p. A465

PFAU, Ben, Chief Facility and Operations Officer, Bay Area Hospital, Coos Bay, OR, p. A512

PFAU, Beth, M.D. Chief Medical Officer, Larue D. Carter Memorial Hospital, Indianapolis, IN, p. A206

PFEFFER, Wayne L., FACHE, Director, Robley Rex Veterans Affairs Medical Center, Louisville, KY, p. A256

PFEIFER, Mark P., M.D. Senior Vice President and Chief Medical Officer, University of Louisville Hospital, Louisville, KY, p. A256

PFEIFFER, James A., FACHE, President and Chief Executive Officer, Self Regional Healthcare, Greenwood, SC, p. A553

PFEIFFER, Margaret, R.N. Vice President Patient Care Services, Good Samaritan Hospital, Los Angeles, CA, p. A69

PFISTER, Joann M.
Director Human Resources, Providence Milwaukie Hospital, Milwaukie, OR, p. A515
Director Human Resources, Providence Willamette Falls Medical Center, Oregon City, OR, p. A515

PFISTER, Pam, Interim Chief Executive Officer, Morrison Community Hospital, Morrison, IL, p. A189

PFISTER, Scott, Chief Financial Officer, Gateway Medical Center, Clarksville, TN, p. A567

PFRANK, Kym
Senior Vice President and Chief Information Officer, Union Hospital, Terre Haute, IN, p. A214
Vice President Information Systems, Union Hospital Clinton, Clinton, IN, p. A200

PHAIRE, Jean C., Executive Vice President Patient Care Services and Chief Nursing Executive, United Medical Center, Washington, DC, p. A117

PHAM, K., M.D. Chief of Staff, Winkler County Memorial Hospital, Kermit, TX, p. A616

PHARR, Ryan, M.D. Chief Medical Staff, Salem Memorial District Hospital, Salem, MO, p. A371

PHELAN, Cynthia, Vice President Human Resources, Lawrence General Hospital, Lawrence, MA, p. A301

PHELPS, Craig, M.D. Chief of Staff, Great Plains Regional Medical Center, Elk City, OK, p. A498

PHELPS, David E., President and Chief Executive Officer, Berkshire Medical Center, Pittsfield, MA, p. A304

PHELPS, Joel, Chief Operating Officer, Salina Regional Health Center, Salina, KS, p. A243

PHELPS, Kathleen, Director Human Resources, Treasure Valley Hospital, Boise, ID, p. A168

PHELPS, Mark H., M.D. Chief of Staff and Medical Director, Jerold Phelps Community Hospital, Garberville, CA, p. A62

PHILIPS III, Grady W., Chief Executive Officer, Memorial Hospital, Martinsville, VA, p. A657

PHILIPS, J. Michael, Chief Strategy Officer, San Juan Regional Medical Center, Farmington, NM, p. A416

PHILLIPE, James R., President, Holzer Medical Center, Gallipolis, OH, p. A482

PHILLIPPE II, James R., President, Holzer Medical Center – Jackson, Jackson, OH, p. A483

PHILLIPS, Alan M., Controller, HEALTHSOUTH Rehabilitation Hospital of Virginia, Richmond, VA, p. A660

PHILLIPS, Annette S., President and Chief Executive Officer, Mercy Memorial Hospital System, Monroe, MI, p. A320

PHILLIPS, Barry
Executive Director Human Resources, Camden General Hospital, Camden, TN, p. A566
Director Human Resources, Pathways of Tennessee, Jackson, TN, p. A570

PHILLIPS, Bill, Vice President Information Services, University Health System, San Antonio, TX, p. A632

PHILLIPS, Chance, Chief Financial Officer, Oak Hill Hospital, Brooksville, FL, p. A120

PHILLIPS, Courtney, Chief Financial Officer, Delta Regional Medical Center, Greenville, MS, p. A347

PHILLIPS, David D., Chief Executive Officer and Administrator, Barnesville Hospital, Barnesville, OH, p. A471

PHILLIPS, David L.
Chief Executive Officer, St. John Broken Arrow, Broken Arrow, OK, p. A496
President and Chief Executive Officer, St. John Owasso, Owasso, OK, p. A505

PHILLIPS, Donna, President, Bryn Mawr Rehabilitation Hospital, Malvern, PA, p. A530

PHILLIPS, Donna Z., M.D., Chief Executive Officer, HEALTHSOUTH Rehabilitation Hospital of Fredericksburg, Fredericksburg, VA, p. A654

PHILLIPS, Glenn, Director Information Systems, Gadsden Regional Medical Center, Gadsden, AL, p. A20

PHILLIPS, Heath, Administrator and Chief Executive Officer, HEALTHSOUTH Lakeshore Rehabilitation Hospital, Birmingham, AL, p. A16

PHILLIPS, J. Randall, FACHE, Chief Executive Officer, North Alabama Regional Hospital, Decatur, AL, p. A19

PHILLIPS, John, Vice President Information Services, St. Joseph Regional Health Center, Bryan, TX, p. A590

PHILLIPS, John E., FACHE, President, Methodist Mansfield Medical Center, Mansfield, TX, p. A621

PHILLIPS, Joseph, Director Information Systems, Aurelia Osborn Fox Memorial Hospital, Oneonta, NY, p. A438

PHILLIPS, Kimberly A., Chief Financial Officer, The Children's Home of Pittsburgh, Pittsburgh, PA, p. A538

PHILLIPS, Lionel J., Vice President Financial Services, Fauquier Hospital, Warrenton, VA, p. A662

PHILLIPS, Lori, Vice President and Chief Nursing Officer, Gibson General Hospital, Princeton, IN, p. A212

PHILLIPS, Lucas, Director Information Technology, South Baldwin Regional Medical Center, Foley, AL, p. A20

PHILLIPS, Margaret, Director Human Resources, Memorial Hospital, North Conway, NH, p. A399

PHILLIPS, Mark, Chief Nursing Officer, Dominion Hospital, Falls Church, VA, p. A653

PHILLIPS, Michael, Chief Executive Officer, Elkhorn Valley Rehabilitation Hospital, Casper, WY, p. A701

PHILLIPS, Pam, Chief Human Resource Officer, Wiregrass Medical Center, Geneva, AL, p. A21

PHILLIPS, Richard, Chief Financial Officer, Desert Regional Medical Center, Palm Springs, CA, p. A78

PHILLIPS, Robert, Administrator, Walker Baptist Medical Center, Jasper, AL, p. A22

PHILLIPS, Steve, Information Officer, Greene County General Hospital, Linton, IN, p. A209

PHILLIPS, Tanya, R.N. Director Patient Care, Memorial Hermann Rehabilitation Hospital – Katy, Katy, TX, p. A616

PHILLIPS, Todd, M.D. Interim Vice President, Medical Affairs, Kimball Medical Center, Lakewood, NJ, p. A405

PHINNEY, Cody, Administrator, Northern Nevada Adult Mental Health Services, Sparks, NV, p. A395

PHIPPS, Bonnie, President and Chief Executive Officer, Saint Agnes Hospital, Baltimore, MD, p. A289

PHIPPS, Jackie G., Director Human Resources, Johnston Memorial Hospital, Abingdon, VA, p. A651

PHIPPS–ADAMS, Holly, Vice President Human Resources, MedStar Union Memorial Hospital, Baltimore, MD, p. A288

PIARULLI, Sue, Administrative Director Operations, Paradise Valley Hospital, Phoenix, AZ, p. A35

PIATKOWSKI, John S., M.D.,
Vice President, Regional Hospital, Carilion New River Valley Medical Center, Christiansburg, VA, p. A652
Vice President, Regional Hospital, Carilion Tazewell Community Hospital, Tazewell, VA, p. A662

PIATKOWSKI, Shannon
Director Information Technology, Blake Medical Center, Bradenton, FL, p. A119
Chief Information Officer, Brandon Regional Hospital, Brandon, FL, p. A119

PIAZZA, Tony, Director Human Resources, Titus Regional Medical Center, Mount Pleasant, TX, p. A623

PICCIONE, Jennifer, Chief Nursing and Clinical Services Officer, Madison County Hospital, London, OH, p. A484

PICCONE, Robert, President, Clear Brook Manor, Wilkes–Barre, PA, p. A544

PICKEL, Joseph, Director Resource Management, Walter Reed National Military Medical Center, Bethesda, MD, p. A290

PICKENS, Troy, Chief Financial Officer, Barnwell County Hospital, Barnwell, SC, p. A548

PICKETT, Beverly, R.N. Chief Nursing Officer, Oklahoma Surgical Hospital, Tulsa, OK, p. A508

PICKETT, Lisa C., M.D. Chief Medical Officer, Duke Regional Hospital, Durham, NC, p. A451

PICKOFF, Robert M., M.D. Vice President Medical Affairs, Glens Falls Hospital, Glens Falls, NY, p. A426

PICOU, Timothy, Manager Information Technology, Lower Umpqua Hospital District, Reedsport, OR, p. A517

PIEKARCZYK, Wally, Chief Financial Officer, Iberia Medical Center, New Iberia, LA, p. A275

PIEMONT, Joseph G., Executive Vice President and Chief Operating Officer, Carolinas Medical Center–Mercy, Charlotte, NC, p. A449

PIEPER, Blaine, Chief Executive Officer, Ohio County Hospital, Hartford, KY, p. A252

PIEPRZYCA, Shaneece, Director Information Technology, Otto Kaiser Memorial Hospital, Kenedy, TX, p. A616

PIERCE, Eddie, M.D. Chief Medical Staff, Kearney County Health Services, Minden, NE, p. A386

PIERCE, Eva, Chief Information Officer, Corcoran District Hospital, Corcoran, CA, p. A57

PIERCE, Jennifer, Administrative Director of Finance, St. Anthony Shawnee Hospital, Shawnee, OK, p. A506

PIERCE, Kenneth, Chief Financial Officer, Brookhaven Hospital, Tulsa, OK, p. A507

PIERCE, Laura, Chief Administrative Officer Human Resources, Memorial Medical Center, Las Cruces, NM, p. A416

PIERCE, Margaret H., Executive Director, Kaiser Permanente Baldwin Park Medical Center, Baldwin Park, CA, p. A54

PIERCE, Michael L., Chief Executive Officer, HEALTHSOUTH Rehabilitation Hospital of Memphis, Memphis, TN, p. A574

PIERCE, Pamela, Chief Human Resource, Windhaven Psychiatric Hospital, Prescott Valley, AZ, p. A36

PIERCE, Pat, Director Information Systems, Lakewood Regional Medical Center, Lakewood, CA, p. A66

PIERCE, Trent, R.N., Chief Executive Officer, HEALTHSOUTH Rehabilitation Hospital of Fort Worth, Fort Worth, TX, p. A603

PIERDON, Steven, M.D. Executive Vice President and Chief Medical Officer, Geisinger Wyoming Valley Medical Center, Wilkes Barre, PA, p. A544

PIERRE, Letonia, Coordinator Human Resources, Assumption Community Hospital, Napoleonville, LA, p. A274

PIERSON, John, Chief Executive Officer, Vibra Hospital of Fort Wayne, Fort Wayne, IN, p. A203

PIERSON, Kari, Manager, Howard County Medical Center, Saint Paul, NE, p. A389

PIERSON, Kim, R.N. Chief Nursing Officer, Matagorda Regional Medical Center, Bay City, TX, p. A587

PIERSON, Lois K., Chief Financial Officer, University of Texas Harris County Psychiatric Center, Houston, TX, p. A613

PIERSON, Marc, M.D. Vice President Clinical Information and Quality, PeaceHealth St. Joseph Medical Center, Bellingham, WA, p. A664

PIETRANGELO, Steve, Director Information Services, War Memorial Hospital, Sault Sainte Marie, MI, p. A324

PIETRO, Daniel, M.D. Medical Director, Sturdy Memorial Hospital, Attleboro, MA, p. A295

PIETSCH, Al, CPA Senior Vice President and Chief Financial Officer, Baltimore Washington Medical Center, Glen Burnie, MD, p. A292

PIFER, Eric, M.D. Chief Medical Officer, El Camino Hospital, Mountain View, CA, p. A75

PIFKO, Duane, Interim Director Financial Services, Drake Center, Cincinnati, OH, p. A474

PIGG, Charles, Chief Information Officer, St. Bernards Medical Center, Jonesboro, AR, p. A45

PIGG, Russell, Chief Executive Officer, Eliza Coffee Memorial Hospital, Florence, AL, p. A20

PIGOTT, John, M.D. Chief Medical Officer, Tulane Medical Center, New Orleans, LA, p. A276

PIGOTT, Randall, Chief Financial Officer, Marion General Hospital, Columbia, MS, p. A346

PIKE, David, Interim Chief Financial Officer, Memorial Hospital of Carbon County, Rawlins, WY, p. A703

PIKE, David R., Chief Financial Officer, Lower Oconee Community Hospital, Glenwood, GA, p. A154

PIKE, Irving, M.D. Chief Medical Officer, John Muir Medical Center, Walnut Creek, Walnut Creek, CA, p. A95

PIKE, Pauline, Chief Operating Officer, Beverly Hospital, Beverly, MA, p. A295

PIKE, Randi, Director of Nursing, Pioneer Medical Center, Big Timber, MT, p. A374

PIKE, Ronald F., M.D. Medical Director, Adcare Hospital of Worcester, Worcester, MA, p. A306

PIKE, Tim, M.D. Chief Medical Officer, Portsmouth Regional Hospital, Portsmouth, NH, p. A400

PIKER, John F., M.D. Medical Director, Villa Feliciana Medical Complex, Jackson, LA, p. A269

PIL, Pieter, M.D. Chief Medical Staff, Martha's Vineyard Hospital, Oak Bluffs, MA, p. A303

PILARCZYK, Penny, Vice President Human Resources, Advocate Lutheran General Hospital, Park Ridge, IL, p. A191

PILE, Larry, Director Human Resources, Deaconess Hospital, Evansville, IN, p. A202

PILKINGTON III, Albert, Chief Executive Officer, Toppenish Community Hospital, Toppenish, WA, p. A673

PILLION, Scott, Chief Executive Officer, Helen Newberry Joy Hospital, Newberry, MI, p. A321

PILONG, Alfred E., President, Munson Medical Center, Traverse City, MI, p. A325

PINA, Ignacio, Director Administrative Services, Lanterman Developmental Center, Pomona, CA, p. A80

PINAC, Gil, Chief Executive Officer, Crowley Rehabilitation Hospital, Crowley, LA, p. A266

PINCUS, Emil R., M.D. Medical Director, Stony Lodge Hospital, Ossining, NY, p. A439

PINE, Richard M., President and Chief Executive Officer, Livengrin Foundation, Bensalem, PA, p. A520

PINEDA, Omar, R.N. Chief Nursing Officer, Medical Center of Arlington, Arlington, TX, p. A583

PING, Patricia, Director Information Services, Gibson General Hospital, Princeton, IN, p. A212

PINKELMAN, Janet, Director Human Resources, Faith Regional Health Services, Norfolk, NE, p. A386

PINKERTON, Patricia, Vice President and Chief Financial Officer, Sheppard Pratt Health System, Baltimore, MD, p. A289

PINKOSKY, Frank
 Senior Vice President, Robert Packer Hospital, Sayre, PA, p. A540
 Senior Vice President, Troy Community Hospital, Troy, PA, p. A542

PINO, Elena, Chief Operating Officer and Chief Nursing Officer, Mesa Hills Specialty Hospital, El Paso, TX, p. A601

PINO, Joseph, M.D. Chief Medical Officer, Regional Medical Center–Bayonet Point, Hudson, FL, p. A126

PINO, Loretta Ortiz y, M.D. Chief Medical Officer, Holy Cross Hospital, Taos, NM, p. A418

PINSKY, Karen, M.D. Chief Medical Information Officer, Chester County Hospital, West Chester, PA, p. A543

PINTO, Frank, Chief Information Officer, The Hospital of Central Connecticut, New Britain, CT, p. A110

PINTO, Karen, Coordinator Human Resources, Forest Health Medical Center, Ypsilanti, MI, p. A327

PIPER, Daniel, M.D. President Medical Staff, Galesburg Cottage Hospital, Galesburg, IL, p. A183

PIPER, Ed, President and Chief Executive Officer, Onslow Memorial Hospital, Jacksonville, NC, p. A455

PIPER, Kevin, Director Information Systems, Florida Hospital DeLand, DeLand, FL, p. A122

PIPER, Vicky, Vice President Human Resources, Loyola University Medical Center, Maywood, IL, p. A188

PIPKIN, Barry, Chief Executive Officer, The BridgeWay, North Little Rock, AR, p. A48

PIPKINS, David, Controller, HEALTHSOUTH Rehabilitation Hospital of Beaumont, Beaumont, TX, p. A587

PIPPIN, Kim, Chief Nursing Officer, Select Specialty Hospital–Augusta, Augusta, GA, p. A148

PIRKL, Rollie, Chief Financial Officer, Sierra Vista Regional Medical Center, San Luis Obispo, CA, p. A88

PIRO, Michael J., Chief Information Officer, St. John's Episcopal Hospital–South Shore,, NY, p. A436

PIROG, Steve, Vice President Finance, Saint Mary's Health Care, Grand Rapids, MI, p. A315

PIRTLE, Kathleen, Director Human Resources, HEALTHSOUTH Rehabilitation Hospital–Wichita Falls, Wichita Falls, TX, p. A641

PIRTLE, Randy B., Chief Financial Officer, King's Daughters Medical Center, Brookhaven, MS, p. A345

PISARICH, Teresa, Acting Chief Financial Officer, Veterans Affairs Gulf Coast Veterans Health Care System, Biloxi, MS, p. A344

PISCIOTTA, Michael J., Chief Executive Officer, Southern Surgical Hospital, Slidell, LA, p. A279

PISPISA, D. Patricia, Vice President Patient Care Services, Eastern Long Island Hospital, Greenport, NY, p. A426

PISTONE, Maureen, Senior Vice President Human Resources, Theda Clark Medical Center, Neenah, WI, p. A693

PITCHER, Ellen, MSN Chief Operating Officer and Chief Nursing Officer, Baylor Regional Medical Center at Plano, Plano, TX, p. A627

PITCHER, Karen, Vice President and Chief Executive Officer, Promise Hospital of San Antonio, San Antonio, TX, p. A632

PITCHFORD, Edward C., President and Chief Executive Officer, Cole Memorial, Coudersport, PA, p. A523

PITCOCK, Nancy, Vice President of Nursing and Chief Nursing Officer, St. Vincent Anderson Regional Hospital, Anderson, IN, p. A198

PITMAN, David R., Vice President Finance, MedStar Harbor Hospital, Baltimore, MD, p. A288

PITOSCIA, Susan, MSN Chief Operating Officer, Touro Infirmary, New Orleans, LA, p. A276

PITTMAN, Cyndi, Chief Financial Officer, Baptist Memorial Hospital – Memphis, Memphis, TN, p. A574

PITTMAN, Gregory R., M.D. Chief of Staff, Hillcrest Hospital – South, Tulsa, OK, p. A508

PITTMAN, Jennifer, Chief Financial Officer, Shelby Baptist Medical Center, Alabaster, AL, p. A15

PITTMAN, Michael
 Chief Nursing Officer, Memorial Hospital, Martinsville, VA, p. A657
 Chief Executive Officer, Scott & White Hospital – Brenham, Brenham, TX, p. A589

PITTMAN, Nancy, MS Chief Operating Officer and Chief Nursing Executive, CHRISTUS St. John Hospital, Nassau Bay, TX, p. A624

PITTS, Celeste, Chief Financial Officer, Weeks Medical Center, Lancaster, NH, p. A398

PITTS, Clara, Director Human Resources, Lanier Health Services, Valley, AL, p. A26

PITTS, Lynn, Director Human Resources, Calhoun–Liberty Hospital, Blountstown, FL, p. A118

PITTS, Mark, M.D. Chief of Staff, Pali Momi Medical Center, Aiea, HI, p. A164

PITTS, Robert, Executive Director, Wilmington Treatment Center, Wilmington, NC, p. A463

PITTS, Ron, Chief Financial Officer, Veterans Affairs Loma Linda Healthcare System, Loma Linda, CA, p. A67

PITTS, Sherry J., Chief Executive Officer, Woman's Hospital, Flowood, MS, p. A346

PITTS, Stephen R., Chief Executive Officer, Morehouse General Hospital, Bastrop, LA, p. A263

PITZER, Kevin M., President and Chief Executive Officer, Bozeman Deaconess Hospital, Bozeman, MT, p. A374

PIVONKA, Mary, Director Quality Management, Rockland Children's Psychiatric Center, Orangeburg, NY, p. A439

PIZZI, Chris, Assistant Administrator Fiscal Services, Providence Medford Medical Center, Medford, OR, p. A514

PLACE, Michael, M.D. Deputy Commander Clinical Services, Colonel Florence A. Blanchfield Army Community Hospital, Fort Campbell, KY, p. A251

PLACE, Ronald, M.D., Commander, Winn Army Community Hospital, Hinesville, GA, p. A155

PLAISANCE, Stephen, Chief Financial Officer, Meeker Memorial Hospital, Litchfield, MN, p. A334

PLAMONDON, Richard, Vice President Finance and Chief Financial Officer, St. Joseph Hospital, Nashua, NH, p. A399

PLANO, Crystal, Controller, St. Vincent Dunn Hospital, Bedford, IN, p. A198

PLANT, Steven L., Chief Financial Officer, Cottage Hospital, Woodsville, NH, p. A400

PLASS, Robert, M.D. Chief Medical Officer, Fremont–Rideout Health Group, Marysville, CA, p. A73

PLATER, Queenie C., Vice President and Chief Human Resources Officer, Sibley Memorial Hospital, Washington, DC, p. A117

PLATOU, Kenneth E. S., President, Mercy Medical Center Mount Shasta, Mount Shasta, CA, p. A75

PLATT, Anne, Chief Executive Officer, Sutter Amador Hospital, Jackson, CA, p. A64

PLATT, C. James, Chief Executive Officer, Fort Madison Community Hospital, Fort Madison, IA, p. A221

PLATZ, Dena, Director Human Resources, St. Elizabeth Community Hospital, Red Bluff, CA, p. A81

PLATZ, Scott, Director Finance, UH Regional Hospitals, Cleveland, OH, p. A477

PLATZKE, Samantha M.
 Senior Vice President Finance and Chief Financial Officer, Mercy Hospital of Defiance, Defiance, OH, p. A480
 Senior Vice President Finance and Chief Financial Officer, Mercy St. Vincent Medical Center, Toledo, OH, p. A491

PLAVIN, Joshua, M.D. Medical Director Medicine Division, Gifford Medical Center, Randolph, VT, p. A650

PLEDGER, Michelle, Coordinator Human Resources, Grady General Hospital, Cairo, GA, p. A149

PLEDGER, Tim, Director Information Technology, Lynn County Hospital District, Tahoka, TX, p. A636

PLEMMONS, Debbie, MSN Chief Nursing Officer, St. Luke's Elmore, Mountain Home, ID, p. A170

PLESKOW, Eric D., President and Chief Executive Officer, BryLin Hospitals, Buffalo, NY, p. A422

PLETZ, Richard
 Administrator, LifeCare Hospitals of Pittsburgh, Pittsburgh, PA, p. A537
 Administrator, LifeCare Hospitals of Pittsburgh – Monroeville, Monroeville, PA, p. A532

PLOPPER, Michael, M.D. Chief Medical Officer, Sharp Mesa Vista Hospital, San Diego, CA, p. A86

PLOUSHA–MOORE, Debra, Senior Vice President Human Resources, Carolinas Medical Center, Charlotte, NC, p. A449

PLUARD, Dennis, Vice President Operations, Sarah Bush Lincoln Health Center, Mattoon, IL, p. A188

PLUMERI, Thomas R., Chief of Staff, Sheridan County Health Complex, Hoxie, KS, p. A236

PLUMLEE, Steve
 Chief Operating Officer, Select Specialty Hospital–Knoxville, Knoxville, TN, p. A572
 Chief Executive Officer, Select Specialty Hospital–North Knoxville, Knoxville, TN, p. A572
 Chief Operating Officer, Select Specialty Hospital–North Knoxville, Knoxville, TN, p. A572

PLUMMER, Carey W., President and Chief Executive Officer, Jersey Shore Hospital, Jersey Shore, PA, p. A528

PLUMMER, Debra, Chief Executive Officer, Kindred Hospital–Central Tampa, Tampa, FL, p. A141

PLUMMER, James S., Chief Executive Officer, Aurora Behavioral Health Care, San Diego, CA, p. A85

PLUNKETT, Alicia, Director of Nursing, Parkwood Behavioral Health System, Olive Branch, MS, p. A352

PLUTA, Dave, Chief Information Officer, Vail Valley Medical Center, Vail, CO, p. A106

PLYMELL, Shane, Chief Financial Officer, Shannon Medical Center, San Angelo, TX, p. A630

POBLETE, Ronald, M.D. President Medical and Dental Staff, St. Mary's Hospital, Passaic, NJ, p. A408

POCKRANDT, Barry R., Commander, Irwin Army Community Hospital, Junction City, KS, p. A236

POCOCK, Donald, M.D
 Chief Medical Officer, Mease Countryside Hospital, Safety Harbor, FL, p. A138
 Chief Medical Officer, Mease Dunedin Hospital, Dunedin, FL, p. A122
 Chief Medical Officer, Morton Plant Hospital, Clearwater, FL, p. A120
 Chief Medical Officer, Morton Plant North Bay Hospital, New Port Richey, FL, p. A133

PODESTA, Charles H., Vice President Information Services, Fletcher Allen Health Care, Burlington, VT, p. A649

PODGES, Christopher J., Vice President and Chief Information Officer, Munson Medical Center, Traverse City, MI, p. A325

PODLEY, Sandra C., Administrator, Presbyterian Hospital, Albuquerque, NM, p. A414

PODZIMEK, Marcia, Chief Human Resources Officer, Wagner Community Memorial Hospital Avera, Wagner, SD, p. A563

POE, Bernard T., Administrator, New Horizons Health Systems, Owenton, KY, p. A258

POE, Dale
Chief Financial Officer, Wellmont Hancock County Hospital, Sneedville, TN, p. A579
Chief Financial Officer, Wellmont Hawkins County Memorial Hospital, Rogersville, TN, p. A578

POE, Stephen, Chief Financial Officer, Pushmataha Hospital & Home Health, Antlers, OK, p. A495

POEL, Mary L., M.D. Chief Medical Officer, Rehoboth McKinley Christian Health Care Services, Gallup, NM, p. A416

POEST, Scott, Chief Information Officer, Lake Regional Health System, Osage Beach, MO, p. A367

POFAHL, Barnetta, Director Human Resources, Wagoner Community Hospital, Wagoner, OK, p. A509

POFF, Heather, Director Human Resources, Princeton Community Hospital, Princeton, WV, p. A680

POGAS, George, CPA Senior Vice President and Chief Financial Officer, Witham Memorial Hospital, Lebanon, IN, p. A209

POHAR, Twyla, Manager Computer Systems, James Cancer Hospital and Solove Research Institute, Columbus, OH, p. A477

POHJALA, Eric, Vice President and Chief Financial Officer, Lima Memorial Health System, Lima, OH, p. A484

POHL, David, M.D. Chief of Staff, Cornerstone Hospital of Austin, Austin, TX, p. A585

POHREN, Allen E., Administrator, Montgomery County Memorial Hospital, Red Oak, IA, p. A227

POISKER, Karen C., MSN Vice President Patient Care Services and Chief Nursing Officer, Peninsula Regional Medical Center, Salisbury, MD, p. A294

POISSON, Keith R., Executive Vice President and Chief Operating Officer, Greater Baltimore Medical Center, Baltimore, MD, p. A287

POITRA, Peggy, Financial Management Specialist, Public Health Service Indian Hospital – Quentin N. Burdick Memorial Health Facility, Belcourt, ND, p. A465

POLAND, David, Vice President Finance, Grove City Medical Center, Grove City, PA, p. A526

POLING, Rodney, M.D. Medical Director, Behavioral HealthCare Center at Columbia, Columbia, TN, p. A567

POLING, Susan, Director Human Resources, King's Daughters' Health, Madison, IN, p. A209

POLIZZI, Arturo
Chief Human Resources Officer, ProMedica Flower Hospital, Sylvania, OH, p. A490
Chief Operating Officer, ProMedica Toledo Hospital, Toledo, OH, p. A491

POLK, Brent, M.D. Chair Department of Pediatrics and Vice President Academic Affairs, Children's Hospital Los Angeles, Los Angeles, CA, p. A68

POLLA, Dale E., Chief Executive Officer, Dayton General Hospital, Dayton, WA, p. A666

POLLACK, Murray, M.D. Vice President and Chief Medical Officer, Phoenix Children's Hospital, Phoenix, AZ, p. A35

POLLACK, Richard, Vice President Information Services, VCU Health System, Richmond, VA, p. A661

POLLARD, Amy, R.N., President and Chief Executive Officer, Nicholas H. Noyes Memorial Hospital, Dansville, NY, p. A424

POLLARD, Dennis, President, Community Memorial Hospital, Menomonee Falls, WI, p. A691

POLLESCH, Bobbie, Chief Financial Officer, Ripon Medical Center, Ripon, WI, p. A696

POLLOCK, Jeffrey, Chief Information Officer, Wentworth–Douglass Hospital, Dover, NH, p. A397

POLLOCK, Jill, Administrator, Loma Linda University Behavioral Medicine Center, Redlands, CA, p. A81

POLLOCK, Maureen King, Chief Executive Officer, Eagleville Hospital, Eagleville, PA, p. A524

POLLOCK, Tina, R.N. Chief Nursing Officer, Dallas Regional Medical Center, Mesquite, TX, p. A622

POLO, Fabian, Chief Operating Officer, Baylor Institute for Rehabilitation, Dallas, TX, p. A595

POLONSKY, Dana, Vice President of Clinical Services, Craig Hospital, Englewood, CO, p. A100

POLONSKY, Kenneth, M.D., Chief Executive Officer, University of Chicago Medical Center, Chicago, IL, p. A180

POLOVICH, Joyce, Manager Information Systems, Western Pennsylvania Hospital, Pittsburgh, PA, p. A539

POLSELLI, Donna, Chief Operating Officer, Franciscan Hospital for Children, Boston, MA, p. A296

POLSTER, Peggy, Manager Personnel and Administrative Assistant, Falls Community Hospital and Clinic, Marlin, TX, p. A621

POLTRACK, Andrew, M.D. Chief of Staff, Margaret Mary Health, Batesville, IN, p. A198

POLZIN, Greg, Chief Financial Officer, Iowa Specialty Hospital–Belmond, Belmond, IA, p. A216

POMA, Frank W., President, St. John River District Hospital, East China, MI, p. A313

PONCE, Joseph A., Chief Information Management, Dwight David Eisenhower Army Medical Center, Fort Gordon, GA, p. A154

PONCE, Martha, Director Information Technologies and Telecommunications, Saint John's Health Center, Santa Monica, CA, p. A90

POND, Dwight, TIS Boise, Saint Alphonsus Regional Medical Center, Boise, ID, p. A168

POND–BELL, Michele, R.N. Administrator Nursing, Cassia Regional Medical Center, Burley, ID, p. A168

PONDER, David, Information Technology Officer, Claremore Indian Hospital, Claremore, OK, p. A497

PONETA, Jan, Director Information Services, Mercy Hospital Jefferson, Crystal City, MO, p. A359

PONT, Allan, M.D. Vice President Medical Affairs, California Pacific Medical Center, San Francisco, CA, p. A86

PONTI, Mary–Anne D., R.N. Chief Operating Officer and Chief Nurse Executive, McLaren Northern Michigan, Petoskey, MI, p. A321

PONTIOUS, Becky, Human Resources/Accounting, Loring Hospital, Sac City, IA, p. A227

PONTREMOLI, Del, Director Human Resources, Spaulding Rehabilitation Hospital Cape Cod, East Sandwich, MA, p. A299

POOCH, Fred, Supervisor Information Technology, Johnson County Hospital, Tecumseh, NE, p. A390

POOK, Lots, Chief Information Officer, National Jewish Health, Denver, CO, p. A99

POOLAW, Bryce, M.D. Clinical Director, Lawton Indian Hospital, Lawton, OK, p. A500

POOLE, Karen, Chief Operating Officer, Boca Raton Regional Hospital, Boca Raton, FL, p. A118

POOLE, Ken, Coordinator Information Systems, Stone County Medical Center, Mountain View, AR, p. A48

POOLE, Rob, Director, Jane Phillips Medical Center, Bartlesville, OK, p. A496

POOLE–ADAMS, Veronica, R.N
Vice President, Chief Operating Officer and Chief Nursing Executive, Cleveland Regional Medical Center, Shelby, NC, p. A460
Vice President and Chief Nursing Officer, Crawley Memorial Hospital, Shelby, NC, p. A461

POORE, Justin, D.O. Chief Medical Staff, Cloud County Health Center, Concordia, KS, p. A232

POORE, Timothy T., Chief Executive Officer, HEALTHSOUTH Scottsdale Rehabilitation Hospital, Scottsdale, AZ, p. A37

POPARAD, Paul C., R.N. Chief Nursing Officer, Clinton Memorial Hospital, Wilmington, OH, p. A493

POPE, Alan R., M.D
Vice President, Medical Affairs, Lourdes Medical Center of Burlington County, Willingboro, NJ, p. A412
Vice President Medical Affairs, Our Lady of Lourdes Medical Center, Camden, NJ, p. A402

POPE, Brad W., Vice President Human Resources, Memorial Health Care System, Chattanooga, TN, p. A566

POPE, Eddie
Director Information Systems, Pioneer Community Hospital of Patrick County, Stuart, VA, p. A662
Chief Information Officer, S. E. Lackey Memorial Hospital, Forest, MS, p. A347

POPE, J. Larry, Vice President Finance, Baptist Easley Hospital, Easley, SC, p. A551

POPE, Jayne E., Chief Executive Officer, Hill Country Memorial Hospital, Fredericksburg, TX, p. A605

POPE, Lona
Director Financial Services, Shriners Hospitals for Children–Galveston Burns Hospital, Galveston, TX, p. A605
Director Fiscal Services, Shriners Hospitals for Children–Houston, Houston, TX, p. A612

POPE, Richard, Vice President Human Resources, Jackson County Memorial Hospital, Altus, OK, p. A495

POPE, Robert, Information Technology Director and Ministry Liaison, St. Vincent Anderson Regional Hospital, Anderson, IN, p. A198

POPKIN, Barbara, R.N. Associate Executive Director Patient Care Services, Franklin Hospital, Valley Stream, NY, p. A445

POPKIN, Steve
Chief Executive Officer, Promise Hospital of East Los Angeles, Los Angeles, CA, p. A71
Chief Executive Officer, Promise Hospital of East Los Angeles, Suburban Medical Center Campus, Paramount, CA, p. A79

POPKO, George A., Senior Vice President and Chief Financial Officer, Christ Hospital, Jersey City, NJ, p. A405

POPLAWSKI, Steven, M.D. Medical Director, Forest Health Medical Center, Ypsilanti, MI, p. A327

POPLI, Anand, Medical Director, Porter–Starke Services, Valparaiso, IN, p. A214

POPOVICH, Cal, Vice President Information Technology, All Children's Hospital, Saint Petersburg, FL, p. A138

POPOVICH, John, M.D., President and Chief Executive Officer, Henry Ford Hospital, Detroit, MI, p. A312

POPP, Adam, Director Information Systems, Avera St. Benedict Health Center, Parkston, SD, p. A561

POPP, Jason, Chief of Medical Staff, Rochelle Community Hospital, Rochelle, IL, p. A193

POPP, Susan, Controller, Kindred Hospital–Fort Worth, Fort Worth, TX, p. A604

POQUETTE, Gary R., FACHE, Chief Executive Officer, Niobrara Health and Life Center, Lusk, WY, p. A703

PORADA, John, Chief Financial Officer, TriStar Southern Hills Medical Center, Nashville, TN, p. A577

PORTCHY, Mindy, Manager Human Resources, Summit Pacific Medical Center, McCleary, WA, p. A668

PORTEN, Hank J., FACHE, President and Chief Executive Officer, Holyoke Medical Center, Holyoke, MA, p. A300

PORTER, Cedric, M.D. President Medical Staff, Emanuel Medical Center, Swainsboro, GA, p. A161

PORTER, Dan, Vice President and Chief Financial Officer, Ottumwa Regional Health Center, Ottumwa, IA, p. A226

PORTER, Dorothy L., Director of Compliance/Risk/Quality, Asheville Specialty Hospital, Asheville, NC, p. A447

PORTER, Glen, Vice President Human Resources, Essentia Health St. Mary's Medical Center, Duluth, MN, p. A331

PORTER, Greg, Chief Financial Officer, Rio Grande Hospital, Del Norte, CO, p. A99

PORTER, James, M.D. Vice President Medical Affairs, Deaconess Hospital, Evansville, IN, p. A202

PORTER, Jody, R.N. Senior Vice President Patient Care Services and Chief Nursing Officer, Greater Baltimore Medical Center, Baltimore, MD, p. A287

PORTER Jr., John M., President and Chief Executive Officer, Ephrata Community Hospital, Ephrata, PA, p. A525

PORTER, Joyce, Chief Human Resources Officer, Adams County Regional Medical Center, Seaman, OH, p. A489

PORTER, Lance, Assistant Chief Executive Officer, Galesburg Cottage Hospital, Galesburg, IL, p. A183

PORTER, Lisa, Director Human Resources, Leadership and Education, Veterans Affairs Salt Lake City Health Care System, Salt Lake City, UT, p. A647

PORTER, Patricia, Chief Financial Officer, South Oaks Hospital, Amityville, NY, p. A420

PORTER, Sharon, Chief Financial Officer, Massachusetts Hospital School, Canton, MA, p. A299

PORTER, Stephen D., President, Sentara Princess Anne Hospital, Virginia Beach, VA, p. A662

PORTER, T. J., Director Human Resources, Bennett County Hospital and Nursing Home, Martin, SD, p. A560

PORTNER, Barry, M.D. Chief of Staff, Prowers Medical Center, Lamar, CO, p. A103

PORTNER, Michael, M.D. Chief Medical Staff, Bolivar Medical Center, Cleveland, MS, p. A346

PORTWOOD, David A., Chief Operating Officer, Coliseum Medical Centers, Macon, GA, p. A156

PORTWOOD, Lee, Chief Information Officer, Mother Frances Hospital – Jacksonville, Jacksonville, TX, p. A615

PORWOLL, Amy, Vice President of Information Systems, St. Cloud Hospital, Saint Cloud, MN, p. A339

POSAR, Steven, M.D. Chief of Medicine, Doctor's Hospital and Neuromuscular Center, Bremen, IN, p. A199

POSCH, David R., Chief Executive Officer, Vanderbilt Hospital and Clinics, Nashville, TN, p. A577

POSCH, Tim B., Business Manager and Director Personnel, Parsons State Hospital and Training Center, Parsons, KS, p. A242

POSECAI, Scott J., Executive Vice President and Chief Financial Officer, Ochsner Medical Center, New Orleans, LA, p. A275

POSEY, Dawn, Chief Operating Officer, Promise Hospital of Vicksburg, Vicksburg, MS, p. A354

POSEY, M. Kenneth, FACHE, Administrator, Jasper General Hospital, Bay Springs, MS, p. A344

POSEY, Richard B., Director Human Resources, Baptist Easley Hospital, Easley, SC, p. A551

POSMOGA, Paul, Chief Financial Officer, Twin Cities Community Hospital, Templeton, CA, p. A92

POST, Kevin, D.O. Chief Medical Officer, Hegg Memorial Health Center Avera, Rock Valley, IA, p. A227

POST, Kimberly, R.N., Vice President and Administrator, Scottsdale Healthcare Thompson Peak Hospital, Scottsdale, AZ, p. A37

POSTERNACK, Charles, M.D. Chief Medical Officer, J. F. K. Medical Center, Atlantis, FL, p. A118

POSTLETHWAIT, Betsy, President, Princeton Baptist Medical Center, Birmingham, AL, p. A17

POSTON, Ann, Director Financial Services, Roosevelt Warm Springs LTAC Hospital, Warm Springs, GA, p. A162

POSTON, Anne, Director of Human Resources/Compliance, Lake City Community Hospital, Lake City, SC, p. A554

POSTON, Sharon, Chief Executive Officer, Williamsburg Regional Hospital, Kingstree, SC, p. A553

POSTULKA, Carol, Administrative Coordinator, Avera Gregory Hospital, Gregory, SD, p. A560

POTEETE, Robin
Manager Human Resources, Wellmont Hancock County Hospital, Sneedville, TN, p. A579
Manager Human Resources, Wellmont Hawkins County Memorial Hospital, Rogersville, TN, p. A578

POTHAST, Joyce, Vice President Human and Environmental Services, Van Wert County Hospital, Van Wert, OH, p. A492

POTTENGER, Jay, Administrator, Missouri River Medical Center, Fort Benton, MT, p. A376

POTTER, Carolyn, Vice President Human Resources, McLaren Central Michigan, Mount Pleasant, MI, p. A320

POTTER, Joe, M.D. Chief of Staff, Integris Marshall County Medical Center, Madill, OK, p. A500

POTTER, Kevin, Chief Financial Officer, Jewish Home of San Francisco, San Francisco, CA, p. A86

POTTER, Rhonda, Director Human Resources, De Soto Regional Health System, Mansfield, LA, p. A273

POTTER, Steve, Manager Business and Information Systems, Clifton-Fine Hospital, Star Lake, NY, p. A443

POTTER, Val, Director Human Resources, St. Vincent Salem Hospital, Salem, IN, p. A213

POTTI, Esther, M.D. Chief Medical Staff, Sanford Bagley Medical Center, Bagley, MN, p. A329

POTTS, Dennis B., President, Aurora St. Luke's Medical Center, Milwaukee, WI, p. A691

POTTS, Mary Ann, Director Personnel, Community Hospitals and Wellness Centers, Bryan, OH, p. A472

POUGNAUD, Teresa, Vice President Human Resources, McLeod Loris Healthcare, Loris, SC, p. A554

POULTON, Connie, Vice President Colleague Relations, Alliance Community Hospital, Alliance, OH, p. A470

POUND, Steven, Vice President Human Resources, Hamilton Medical Center, Dalton, GA, p. A151

POUND, Terry, Chief Financial Officer, Rice County District Hospital, Lyons, KS, p. A239

POURIER, William, Service Unit Director, U. S. Public Health Service Indian Hospital, Pine Ridge, SD, p. A561

POVICH, Mark, D.O. Medical Director, OSF St. Francis Hospital, Escanaba, MI, p. A313

POWE, Lee, Director Management Information Systems, Hugh Chatham Memorial Hospital, Elkin, NC, p. A452

POWEL, Linda J., M.D. Medical Director, Odessa Memorial Healthcare Center, Odessa, WA, p. A668

POWELL, Candy, Administrator, Collingsworth General Hospital, Wellington, TX, p. A640

POWELL, Charles, Chief Financial Officer, Arkansas Surgical Hospital, North Little Rock, AR, p. A48

POWELL, Charles R., Director, Marion-Citrus Mental Health Centers, Ocala, FL, p. A134

POWELL, Claudia, R.N. Director of Nursing, Melissa Memorial Hospital, Holyoke, CO, p. A102

POWELL, D. Jerome, M.D
Chief Information Officer, Highland Hospital of Rochester, Rochester, NY, p. A441
Chief Information Officer, Strong Memorial Hospital of the University of Rochester, Rochester, NY, p. A441

POWELL, Darla, Administrative Assistant, Mayhill Hospital, Denton, TX, p. A598

POWELL, Frank R., Chief Financial Officer, Houston Medical Center, Warner Robins, GA, p. A162

POWELL, Holly
Interim Administrator, Dubuis Hospital of Shreveport, Shreveport, LA, p. A278
Administrator, Dubuis Hospital of Texarkana, Texarkana, TX, p. A637

POWELL, Jackie, Director Human Resources, Pemiscot Memorial Health System, Hayti, MO, p. A361

POWELL, Jimmy, Manager Human Resources, Harry S. Truman Memorial Veterans Hospital, Columbia, MO, p. A359

POWELL, Kay, Director Human Resources, CHRISTUS Jasper Memorial Hospital, Jasper, TX, p. A615

POWELL, Lorie, Interim Chief Executive Officer, Regency Hospital of Jackson, Jackson, MS, p. A349

POWELL, Mary Lou, MSN Chief Nursing Officer, Rex Healthcare, Raleigh, NC, p. A459

POWELL, Michelle, Chief Executive Officer, Select Rehabilitation Hospital of Denton, Denton, TX, p. A599

POWELL, Mike, Executive Director, Missouri Rehabilitation Center, Mount Vernon, MO, p. A366

POWELL, Parker
Interim Chief Executive Officer, Glendive Medical Center, Glendive, MT, p. A376
Administrator, Prairie Community Hospital, Terry, MT, p. A380

POWELL, Robyn L., Chief Financial Officer, Marion General Hospital, Marion, IN, p. A209

POWELL, Steven, M.D. Chief Medical Officer, New London Hospital, New London, NH, p. A399

POWELL, Traci, Director Human Resources, HEALTHSOUTH Emerald Coast Rehabilitation Hospital, Panama City, FL, p. A136

POWELL, Troy, Chief Executive Officer, HEALTHSOUTH Rehabilitation Hospital of Charleston, Charleston, SC, p. A549

POWELL, Virginia, Director Finance, Wilmington Treatment Center, Wilmington, NC, p. A463

POWELL-STAFFORD, Valerie L., Chief Operating Officer, Doctors Hospital of Sarasota, Sarasota, FL, p. A139

POWELSON, Jeffrey A., Chief Executive Officer, Broaddus Hospital, Philippi, WV, p. A680

POWER, Bob
Vice President Information Services, Good Samaritan Regional Medical Center, Corvallis, OR, p. A512
Vice President Information Services, Samaritan Lebanon Community Hospital, Lebanon, OR, p. A514

POWER, Robert, Associate Executive Director Finance, Southside Hospital, Bay Shore, NY, p. A421

POWERS, Anthony, Vice President Patient Care Services, Baptist Health Corbin, Corbin, KY, p. A249

POWERS, Brent, M.D. Vice President/Chief Medical Officer, Lexington Medical Center, West Columbia, SC, p. A556

POWERS, Charles, M.D. Administrative Medical Director, WK Bossier Health Center, Bossier City, LA, p. A264

POWERS, Jack, Director Human Resources, Central Washington Hospital, Wenatchee, WA, p. A674

POWERS, Jamekia, Assistant Director Human Resources, Georgia Regional Hospital at Savannah, Savannah, GA, p. A160

POWERS, Kelli, Chief Executive Officer, Athens-Limestone Hospital, Athens, AL, p. A16

POWERS, Marcia, Vice President Human Resources, Norwegian American Hospital, Chicago, IL, p. A178

POWERS, Melinda, D.O. Chief of Staff, Jackson County Memorial Hospital, Altus, OK, p. A495

POWERS, Michael K., FACHE, Chief Executive Officer, Fairbanks Memorial Hospital, Fairbanks, AK, p. A28

POWERS, Richard, M.D. Chief of Staff, Palm Drive Hospital, Sebastopol, CA, p. A90

POWERS, Ryan J., Vice President Finance, Spectrum Health Zeeland Community Hospital, Zeeland, MI, p. A327

POWERS, Taylor, Administrator, Tanner Medical Center-Villa Rica, Villa Rica, GA, p. A162

POWRIE, Raymond, M.D. Senior Vice President Quality and Clinical Effectiveness, Women & Infants Hospital of Rhode Island, Providence, RI, p. A547

POYNTER, Carmen, Director Human Resources, Rockcastle Regional Hospital and Respiratory Care Center, Mount Vernon, KY, p. A258

POZNIAK, Richard A., Director Marketing and Communications, Hallmark Health System, Melrose, MA, p. A302

PRABHU, Asha, M.D. Chief Medical Officer, Warren State Hospital, Warren, PA, p. A543

PRACHEIL, Michael, Chief Financial Officer, Thayer County Health Services, Hebron, NE, p. A384

PRACHT, Matthew, Vice President Finance, Scotland Health Care System, Laurinburg, NC, p. A456

PRADA, Janina
Director Information Technology, El Paso Children's Hospital, El Paso, TX, p. A601
Director Information Services, University Medical Center of El Paso, El Paso, TX, p. A602

PRAGER, Jay E., Chief Executive Officer, Reynolds Memorial Hospital, Glen Dale, WV, p. A677

PRAKASH, Amitabh, M.D. Chief Medical Officer, Anaheim Regional Medical Center, Anaheim, CA, p. A52

PRATER, Jeffrey, Chief Executive Officer, Samuel Simmonds Memorial Hospital, Barrow, AK, p. A27

PRATER, Marsha A., Ph.D. Senior Vice President and Chief Nursing Officer, Memorial Medical Center, Springfield, IL, p. A195

PRATER, Robin, Director Human Resources, Howard A. Rusk Rehabilitation Center, Columbia, MO, p. A359

PRATHER, Bobbie L., Chief Financial Officer, Baptist Health Lexington, Lexington, KY, p. A253

PRATI, Richard, Chief Executive Officer, Fort Duncan Regional Medical Center, Eagle Pass, TX, p. A600

PRATT, Bonnie, R.N. Chief Nursing Officer, Lakeview Regional Medical Center, Covington, LA, p. A265

PRATT, Debbie, Chief Financial Officer, Washington County Memorial Hospital, Potosi, MO, p. A368

PRATT, Elizabeth, Director Health Information Management, University Behavioral Health of Denton, Denton, TX, p. A599

PRATT, Lisa, Vice President Human Resources, Memorial Hospital of Rhode Island, Pawtucket, RI, p. A546

PRATT, Mary Ellen, FACHE, Chief Executive Officer, St. James Parish Hospital, Lutcher, LA, p. A272

PRATT, Timothy J., M.D. Vice President of Medical Affairs/Chief Medical Officer, SSM St. Clare Health Center, Fenton, MO, p. A360

PRAY, Jan, Coordinator Payroll and Benefits, Kindred Hospital Boston-North Shore, Peabody, MA, p. A303

PRAYTOR, Trent, MSN Chief Nursing Officer, AnMed Health Rehabilitation Hospital, Anderson, SC, p. A548

PRAYWELL, Hunter, Vice President Information Technology and Chief Information Officer, Queen's Medical Center, Honolulu, HI, p. A165

PREAU, William, M.D. Medical Director, Fairway Medical Center, Covington, LA, p. A265

PRECHT, James, Chief Financial Officer, Goodland Regional Medical Center, Goodland, KS, p. A234

PREIB, Barbara, Director of Nursing, Maryville Behavioral Health Hospital, Des Plaines, IL, p. A181

PRENGLER, Irving, M.D. Vice President Medical Staff Affairs, Baylor University Medical Center, Dallas, TX, p. A595

PREPIERI, Tim, Director Human Resources, Mercy Hospital Watonga, Watonga, OK, p. A509

PRESCOTT, Tina, Vice President, Hospital Services, Jackson-Madison County General Hospital, Jackson, TN, p. A570

PRESS, Christopher E., FACHE President, Blanchard Valley Regional Health Center, Blanchard Valley Hospital, Findlay, OH, p. A481

PRESS, Robert, M.D. Chief Medical Officer, NYU Langone Medical Center, New York, NY, p. A435

PRESSER, Jonathan, Vice President Finance and Operations, Norton Audubon Hospital, Louisville, KY, p. A256

PRESSMAN, Eric, D.O. Chair Department of Medicine, Englewood Community Hospital, Englewood, FL, p. A123

PREST, Craig, Director Operation Services, Humboldt General Hospital, Winnemucca, NV, p. A396

PRESTON, Troy, Director Human Resources, Schuyler Hospital, Montour Falls, NY, p. A430

PRETE, Mark, M.D. Vice President Medical Affairs, The Charlotte Hungerford Hospital, Torrington, CT, p. A112

PRETTYMAN, Edgar E., PsyD,
Chief Executive Officer, Texas NeuroRehab Center, Austin, TX, p. A586
Chief Executive Officer, Texas Star Recovery, Austin, TX, p. A586

PREUSS, Heather, M.D. Medical Director, Fall River Hospital, Hot Springs, SD, p. A560

PREWITT, Connie F., Chief Financial Officer, Billings Clinic, Billings, MT, p. A374

PRIBYL, Stephen J., FACHE, Chief Executive Officer, District One Hospital, Faribault, MN, p. A332

PRICE, Alysia, Director Human Resources, Colleton Medical Center, Walterboro, SC, p. A556

PRICE, Brad H.
Chief Operating Officer, Wellmont Bristol Regional Medical Center, Bristol, TN, p. A565
Vice President Finance and Operations, Wellmont Holston Valley Medical Center, Kingsport, TN, p. A571

PRICE, Cecil, M.D., Director, Wake Forest University Health Service, Winston-Salem, NC, p. A464

PRICE, Ed, R.N. Chief Clinical Officer, Nacogdoches Medical Center, Nacogdoches, TX, p. A624

PRICE, Eric, Financial Specialist, Senior, State Hospital South, Blackfoot, ID, p. A167

PRICE, Fred, R.N., President and Chief Executive Officer, DeKalb Health, Auburn, IN, p. A198

PRICE, Jeffrey, Director Information Technology, Nevada Regional Medical Center, Nevada, MO, p. A367

PRICE, John D., Chief Financial Officer, FirstHealth Richmond Memorial Hospital, Rockingham, NC, p. A459

PRICE, Julie
Chief Financial Officer, Rooks County Health Center, Plainville, KS, p. A242
Chief Financial Officer, Union County General Hospital, Clayton, NM, p. A415

PRICE, Kevin A., Vice President and Chief Operating Officer, Sparrow Clinton Hospital, Saint Johns, MI, p. A323

PRICE, Kim
Chief Executive Officer, Franklin General Hospital, Hampton, IA, p. A222
Chief Executive Officer, Mercy Medical Center-New Hampton, New Hampton, IA, p. A226

PRICE, Larry, Chief Executive Officer, Limestone Medical Center, Groesbeck, TX, p. A607

PRICE, Lori, President, Gottlieb Memorial Hospital, Melrose Park, IL, p. A188

PRICE, Lorraine B., Associate Director, Hampton Veterans Affairs Medical Center, Hampton, VA, p. A655

PRICE, Manuel, Director Information Systems, Brookwood Medical Center, Birmingham, AL, p. A16

PRICE, Norma Jean, Manager Personnel, Riverland Medical Center, Ferriday, LA, p. A267

PRICE, Norman M., FACHE, Chief Executive Officer, Southwest Mississippi Regional Medical Center, McComb, MS, p. A350

PRICE, Peggy Cain, Vice President and Chief Operating Officer, Exempla Lutheran Medical Center, Wheat Ridge, CO, p. A107

PRICE, Sam, Executive Vice President Finance/Chief Financial Officer, East Alabama Medical Center, Opelika, AL, p. A24

PRICE, Shari, Director Information Services, Baptist Health Louisville, Louisville, KY, p. A255

PRICE, Sheila C., R.N. Chief Nursing Officer/Vice President of Nursing, Angel Medical Center, Franklin, NC, p. A452

PRICE, Toni, Director Human Resources, Lincoln County Medical Center, Troy, MO, p. A372

PRICE, Wendy, Manager Human Resources, Nicholas County Hospital, Carlisle, KY, p. A249

PRICHARD, Barbara, Assistant Administrator, South Sunflower County Hospital, Indianola, MS, p. A348

PRIDDY, III, Ernest C., Chief Financial Officer, Old Vineyard Behavioral Health Services, Winston–Salem, NC, p. A463

PRIDDY, Steven L., M.D. Vice President Physician Affairs and Chief Medical Officer, St. Vincent Carmel Hospital, Carmel, IN, p. A200

PRIDEAUX, Heather, Director Finance, Rawlins County Health Center, Atwood, KS, p. A231

PRIEBE, Cedric T., M.D
  Vice President and Chief Information Officer, Butler Hospital, Providence, RI, p. A546
  Senior Vice President and Chief Information Officer, Kent County Memorial Hospital, Warwick, RI, p. A547
  Senior Vice President and Chief Information Officer, Women & Infants Hospital of Rhode Island, Providence, RI, p. A547

PRIEST, Claude, Chief Financial Officer, Prairie Ridge Hospital and Health Services, Elbow Lake, MN, p. A332

PRIEST, David, Director Information Systems, Charlevoix Area Hospital, Charlevoix, MI, p. A310

PRIEST, Geoff, M.D. Chief Medical Officer, Meriter Hospital, Madison, WI, p. A689

PRIEST, James H., D.D.S. Chief Medical Officer, Halifax Regional Health System, South Boston, VA, p. A661

PRIEST, Mike, M.D. Chief of Staff, Pawhuska Hospital, Pawhuska, OK, p. A505

PRIESTLEY, Betty, Manager Business Office, Texas Specialty Hospital at Houston, Houston, TX, p. A612

PRIESTLEY, Carlos W., Chief Operating Officer, Providence Little Company of Mary Medical Center San Pedro,, CA, p. A71

PRIMEAUX, Pam, Chief Financial Officer, Jennings American Legion Hospital, Jennings, LA, p. A269

PRINCE, Clay C., Chief Medical Officer, Madison Memorial Hospital, Rexburg, ID, p. A171

PRINCE, Gayle, Director Human Resources, Washington County Regional Medical Center, Sandersville, GA, p. A159

PRINCE, Sue, Director Information Systems, Northern Westchester Hospital, Mount Kisco, NY, p. A430

PRINCE, Thomas A., Vice President Operations and Human Resources, Northeast Rehabilitation Hospital, Salem, NH, p. A400

PRINGLE–MILLER, Letitia, Administrative Director, Tuomey Healthcare System, Sumter, SC, p. A556

PRINTY, Wayne
  Chief Financial Officer and Senior Vice President Finance, Miles Memorial Hospital, Damariscotta, ME, p. A283
  Chief Financial Officer and Senior Vice President Finance, St. Andrews Hospital and Healthcare Center, Boothbay Harbor, ME, p. A282

PRINTZ, David, Vice President and Chief Information Officer, Central DuPage Hospital, Winfield, IL, p. A197

PRIOLA, Pat, Chief Financial Officer, Jerome Golden Center for Behavioral Health, Inc., West Palm Beach, FL, p. A143

PRIORE, Jacqueline, Chief Nursing Officer, Samaritan Hospital, Troy, NY, p. A444

PRISELAC, Thomas M., President and Chief Executive Officer, Cedars–Sinai Medical Center, Los Angeles, CA, p. A68

PRISTER, James R.
  President and Chief Executive Officer, RML Specialty Hospital, Chicago, IL, p. A178
  President and Chief Executive Officer, RML Specialty Hospital, Hinsdale, IL, p. A185

PRITCHARD, Joann, Chief Financial Officer, Erie Veterans Affairs Medical Center, Erie, PA, p. A525

PRITCHARD, Teresa, Vice President, Yakima Valley Memorial Hospital, Yakima, WA, p. A674

PRITCHETT, Greg, Controller, Cuero Community Hospital, Cuero, TX, p. A594

PRITHVIRAJ, Panju, M.D. President Medical Staff, Magruder Memorial Hospital, Port Clinton, OH, p. A488

PRIVETT, David, Deputy Director, Western New York Children's Psychiatric Center, West Seneca, NY, p. A446

PROBASCO, Brent, Chief Financial Officer, Cass Regional Medical Center, Harrisonville, MO, p. A361

PROCHILO, John F., Chief Executive Officer and Administrator, Northeast Rehabilitation Hospital, Salem, NH, p. A400

PROCHNOW, Bryan, Chief Financial Officer, Matagorda Regional Medical Center, Bay City, TX, p. A587

PROCTOR, III, Folsom, M.D. Vice President and Chief Medical Officer, Piedmont Mountainside Hospital, Jasper, GA, p. A155

PROCTOR, George M., Senior Vice President and Executive Director, Woodhull Medical and Mental Health Center,, NY, p. A437

PROCTOR, Kenneth S., MS Director Human Resources, Mayo Regional Hospital, Dover–Foxcroft, ME, p. A283

PROCTOR, Sandra, R.N. Chief Nurse Executive, Memorial Medical Center, Modesto, CA, p. A74

PROCTOR, Stephen, Director of Human Resources/Risk, Russellville Hospital, Russellville, AL, p. A25

PROCTOR, Steven M., President, Matheny Medical and Educational Center, Peapack, NJ, p. A408

PROEHL, Sheila R., Chief Financial Officer, Hudson Hospital and Clinics, Hudson, WI, p. A688

PROKOSCH, Brian, M.D. Vice President Medical Affairs, St. Francis Regional Medical Center, Shakopee, MN, p. A341

PRONI, John, CPA Manager Finance, BayCare Alliant Hospital, Dunedin, FL, p. A122

PROSKE, Donna, MS Executive Vice President, Chief Operating Officer and Chief Nursing Executive, Staten Island University Hospital,, NY, p. A436

PROSPER, Charles
  Chief Executive Officer, Alta Bates Summit Medical Center, Berkeley, CA, p. A54
  Chief Executive Officer, Alta Bates Summit Medical Center – Summit Campus, Oakland, CA, p. A77

PROTHERO, Marie, MSN, Chief Executive Officer, Utah Valley Specialty Hospital, Provo, UT, p. A646

PROTO, Robert, Director Information Systems, Torrance Memorial Medical Center, Torrance, CA, p. A93

PROTOS, George, Director Human Resources, Healdsburg District Hospital, Healdsburg, CA, p. A64

PROUD, James, Vice President Human Resources and Marketing, Uniontown Hospital, Uniontown, PA, p. A542

PROULX, David R., Assistant Vice President Operations, Valley West Hospital, Sandwich, IL, p. A194

PRUIETT, Bobby, Chief Financial Officer, Texoma Medical Center, Denison, TX, p. A598

PRUIETT, Linda, Vice President Human Resources, Sky Ridge Medical Center, Lone Tree, CO, p. A104

PRUITT, Angela L., Director Health Information Management and Quality Improvement, Timberlawn Mental Health System, Dallas, TX, p. A598

PRUITT, Michael W., Administrator and Chief Executive Officer, Coleman County Medical Center, Coleman, TX, p. A592

PRUNCHUNAS, Edward M., Senior Vice President and Chief Financial Officer, Cedars–Sinai Medical Center, Los Angeles, CA, p. A68

PRUNOSKE, Mark, Chief Financial Officer and Senior Vice President Finance, F. F. Thompson Hospital, Canandaigua, NY, p. A423

PRUSATIS, Michael, Vice President Finance, Sinai–Grace Hospital, Detroit, MI, p. A312

PRYBYLO, Mary, President and Chief Executive Officer, St. Joseph Hospital, Bangor, ME, p. A281

PRYOR, David, Chief Executive Officer, Williamson Memorial Hospital, Williamson, WV, p. A682

PRYOR, Dennis P., Administrator, Salem Memorial District Hospital, Salem, MO, p. A371

PRYOR, Jon, Chief Executive Officer, Hennepin County Medical Center, Minneapolis, MN, p. A336

PRYOR, Shanna, R.N. Chief Nursing Officer, Helena Regional Medical Center, Helena, AR, p. A44

PRYOR, Vincent, Senior Vice President Finance and Chief Financial Officer, Edward Hospital, Naperville, IL, p. A189

PRYOR, William B., Senior Vice President, Human Resources, Cape Fear Valley Medical Center, Fayetteville, NC, p. A452

PRZYBYLSKI, David, Interim Controller, Sparrow Specialty Hospital, Lansing, MI, p. A318

PSAILA, Justin P., M.D. Vice President Medical Affairs, St. Luke's Hospital – Anderson Campus, Easton, PA, p. A525

PSHEA, Pam, R.N. Chief Nursing Officer, San Ramon Regional Medical Center, San Ramon, CA, p. A89

PUCKETT, Clay, Assistant Administrator and Chief Information Officer, Blount Memorial Hospital, Maryville, TN, p. A574

PUCKETT, Doug, President and Chief Executive Officer, Indiana University Health Morgan Hospital, Martinsville, IN, p. A209

PUCKETT, Frank, M.D. Chief Medical Officer, Pocahontas Memorial Hospital, Buckeye, WV, p. A675

PUCKETT, Kimberly, Manager Human Resources, Carroll County Memorial Hospital, Carrollton, KY, p. A249

PUCKETT, Kristi, Director Human Resources, Grande Ronde Hospital, La Grande, OR, p. A514

PUENTES, Francisco, Human Resource Officer, San Diego County Psychiatric Hospital, San Diego, CA, p. A85

PUFFENBERGER, James, Vice President and Chief Financial Officer, Reid Hospital and Health Care Services, Richmond, IN, p. A212

PUGH, Janelle, Vice President Finance and Operations, Saint Joseph Mount Sterling, Mount Sterling, KY, p. A258

PUGH, William H., Senior Vice President Corporate Finance and Chief Financial Officer, Pinnacle Health System, Harrisburg, PA, p. A527

PUGSLEY, Tim, Manager Information Technology, Nebraska Orthopaedic Hospital, Omaha, NE, p. A388

PUHY, Dorothy E., Chief Operating Officer, Dana–Farber Cancer Institute, Boston, MA, p. A296

PUKALA, Shirley, R.N. Assistant Administrator of Operations, St. Lawrence Rehabilitation Center, Lawrenceville, NJ, p. A405

PULASKI, Jason, Controller, HEALTHSOUTH Reading Rehabilitation Hospital, Reading, PA, p. A539

PULCO, Dominic J., Executive Vice President Finance and Chief Financial Officer, VCU Health System, Richmond, VA, p. A661

PULEO, Mark, Vice President and Chief Human Resources Officer, Henry Mayo Newhall Memorial Hospital, Valencia, CA, p. A94

PULIDO, Michael, Process Leader Human Resources, Heartland Regional Medical Center, Saint Joseph, MO, p. A369

PULLARKAT, Sajit, Chief Executive Officer and Managing Director, Centennial Hills Hospital Medical Center, Las Vegas, NV, p. A392

PULLEY, Bob, Interim Chief Financial Officer, Lehigh Regional Medical Center, Lehigh Acres, FL, p. A129

PULLIN, Dennis W., Chief Executive Officer, MedStar Harbor Hospital, Baltimore, MD, p. A288

PULLIN, Tadd M., Interim Vice President, Human Resources, Nebraska Medical Center, Omaha, NE, p. A388

PULLMAN, Debbie, Director Finance, Avera Hand County Memorial Hospital, Miller, SD, p. A560

PULLMAN, Jayson, Chief Executive Officer, Hawarden Regional Healthcare, Hawarden, IA, p. A222

PULSIPHER, Gary W., President and Chief Executive Officer, Mercy Hospital Joplin, Joplin, MO, p. A362

PUNG, Margaret, R.N. Chief Nursing Officer, University of Texas Harris County Psychiatric Center, Houston, TX, p. A613

PUNJABI, Rishab, Chief Financial Officer, Kindred Hospital–New Jersey Morris County, Dover, NJ, p. A403

PUNZIRUDU, Debbie, Controller, HEALTHSOUTH Rehabilitation Hospital of Spring Hill, Brooksville, FL, p. A120

PURANIK, Prakash, M.D. Chief of Staff, Beckley ARH Hospital, Beckley, WV, p. A675

PURCELL, Sandra, Administrative Director Business and Financial Services, Illini Community Hospital, Pittsfield, IL, p. A192

PURCELL, Terry
  Vice President Support Services and Ambulatory Care, Gnaden Huetten Memorial Hospital, Lehighton, PA, p. A530
  Director Information Services, Lea Regional Medical Center, Hobbs, NM, p. A416
  Vice President Ambulatory Care and Support Services, Palmerton Hospital, Palmerton, PA, p. A533

PURDY, Bruce, M.D. Chief of Staff, Muleshoe Area Medical Center, Muleshoe, TX, p. A624

PURGETT, Thomas, M.D. Chief Medical Staff, Baylor Regional Medical Center at Grapevine, Grapevine, TX, p. A607

PURINGTON, Denise, Vice President and Chief Information Officer, Elliot Hospital, Manchester, NH, p. A399

PURINTON, Sandy, Chief Nursing Officer, Trego County–Lemke Memorial Hospital, Wakeeney, KS, p. A245

PUROHIT, Amish, Chief Executive Officer, Huhukam Memorial Hospital, Sacaton, AZ, p. A36

PUROHIT, Kumar, Chief Financial Officer, Rockford Center, Newark, DE, p. A114

PURRINGTON, Janice, Coordinator Medical Records, Avera Hand County Memorial Hospital, Miller, SD, p. A560

PURSLEY, Roger, Chief Executive Officer, Western Mental Health Institute, Bolivar, TN, p. A565

PURTELL, Greg, Vice President Human Resources, McLaren Bay Special Care, Bay City, MI, p. A309

PURTLE, Mark, M.D
  Vice President Medical Affairs, Iowa Methodist Medical Center, Des Moines, IA, p. A220
  Vice President Medical Affairs, UnityPoint Health – Des Moines, Des Moines, IA, p. A220

PURUSHOTHAM, Sanjay, Executive Director Information Systems, Bon Secours Baltimore Health System, Baltimore, MD, p. A287

PURVANCE, Clint, M.D. Chief Medical Officer, Barton Memorial Hospital, South Lake Tahoe, CA, p. A91

PURVES, Stephen A., FACHE, President and Chief Executive Officer, Munroe Regional Medical Center, Ocala, FL, p. A134

PURVIS, Jay, Administrator, Wabash General Hospital, Mount Carmel, IL, p. A189

PURVIS, Michael L., Chief Executive Officer, Cook Medical Center–A Campus of Tift Regional Medical Center, Adel, GA, p. A145

PURVIS, Mike, Chief Administrative Officer, Sutter Medical Center of Santa Rosa, Chanate Campus, Santa Rosa, CA, p. A90

PUSTINA, Karl, Assistant Administrator Finance, Upland Hills Health, Dodgeville, WI, p. A685

PUSZKARSKA, Lucyna M., M.D. Medical Director, Riveredge Hospital, Forest Park, IL, p. A182

PUTNAM, Mark, M.D. Medical Director, Haven Behavioral Health of Eastern Pennsylvania, Reading, PA, p. A539

PUTNAM, Stewart C., Executive Vice President and Chief Operating Officer, Unity Hospital, Rochester, NY, p. A441

PUTNAM, Timothy L., FACHE, President and Chief Executive Officer, Margaret Mary Health, Batesville, IN, p. A198

PUU, Linda, Chief Nursing Officer, Kaiser Permanente Medical Center, Honolulu, HI, p. A164

PUVOGEL, LuAnn, R.N., Administrator, Salina Surgical Hospital, Salina, KS, p. A243

PUZO, Thomas C., President and Chief Operating Officer, Cornerstone of Medical Arts Center Hospital, Fresh Meadows, NY, p. A426

PUZZUTO, David, M.D. Vice President Medical Affairs and Chief Medical Officer, Waterbury Hospital, Waterbury, CT, p. A112

PYE, Irma L.
 Chief Human Resource Officer, Valley Baptist Medical Center–Brownsville, Brownsville, TX, p. A590
 Senior Vice President and Chief Human Resource Officer, Valley Baptist Medical Center–Harlingen, Harlingen, TX, p. A608

PYLE, David, M.D. Vice President Medical Affairs, St. Bernards Medical Center, Jonesboro, AR, p. A45

PYLE, Diana, Director Human Resources, Cedar County Memorial Hospital, El Dorado Springs, MO, p. A360

PYLE, Julia, R.N. Chief Nursing Officer, Newman Regional Health, Emporia, KS, p. A233

PYLE, Rick, Director Information Systems, Harrisburg Medical Center, Harrisburg, IL, p. A184

PYPER, Thomas, Chief Executive Officer, Trinity Hospital, Weaverville, CA, p. A95

PYRAH, Scott, Director Information Systems, Elks Rehab Hospital, Boise, ID, p. A167

PYTLEWSKI, David, M.D. Clinical Director, Eastern Shore Hospital Center, Cambridge, MD, p. A290

PYTLINSKI, Doug, Vice President Administration, Alton Memorial Hospital, Alton, IL, p. A173

# Q

QUACH, Steve, M.D. Chief Medical Officer, University of Texas Medical Branch Hospitals, Galveston, TX, p. A605

QUACKENBUSH, Kirk, M.D. Chief of Staff, Platte Valley Medical Center, Brighton, CO, p. A97

QUALLS, Brenda, Chief Financial Officer, Oconee Regional Medical Center, Milledgeville, GA, p. A157

QUALLS Jr., Paul E., Interim Chief Executive Officer, Cornerstone Hospital of North Little Rock, Jacksonville, AR, p. A45

QUAM, David, M.D. Area Medical Director, Kaiser Permanente Fontana Medical Center, Fontana, CA, p. A60

QUANSTROM, Julie, Director Information Systems and Reimbursement Specialist, Wilson Medical Center, Neodesha, KS, p. A240

QUARANTE, Dino, Chief Financial Officer, Aurora Phoenix Hospital, Glendale, AZ, p. A32

QUARLES, Christopher, M.D. Director Medical Services, Naval Hospital Jacksonville, Jacksonville, FL, p. A126

QUARTIER, Michael J., Vice President Administration and Human Resources, Huntington Hospital, Huntington, NY, p. A427

QUATTROCCHI, Robert, President and Chief Executive Officer, Northside Hospital, Atlanta, GA, p. A146

QUENAN, James, M.D. Chief Medical Officer, Amery Regional Medical Center, Amery, WI, p. A683

QUIGLEY, Michelle Ann, MS Vice President and Chief Nursing Officer, Valley Presbyterian Hospital, , CA, p. A72

QUIGLEY, Scott, Director Information Services, Grays Harbor Community Hospital, Aberdeen, WA, p. A664

QUIGLEY, Stephen J., Chief Executive Officer, Southwood Psychiatric Hospital, Pittsburgh, PA, p. A538

QUILLEN, Suzanne, R.N., Chief Executive Officer, Advanced Care Hospital of Southern New Mexico, Las Cruces, NM, p. A416

QUILLIN, Gayla, Administrator, Parmer Medical Center, Friona, TX, p. A605

QUINLAN, Christine, MS Chief Nursing Officer, Alexian Brothers Behavioral Health Hospital, Hoffman Estates, IL, p. A185

QUINLAN, Michael, M.D. Chief of Staff, Audrain Medical Center, Mexico, MO, p. A366

QUINLAN, Patrick J., M.D. Chief Executive Officer, Ochsner Medical Center, New Orleans, LA, p. A275

QUINLIVAN, John, Chief Executive Officer, Redmond Regional Medical Center, Rome, GA, p. A159

QUINLIVAN, Kathy, Director Management Information Systems, Avera Sacred Heart Hospital, Yankton, SD, p. A564

QUINN, Clifton, Chief Executive Officer, Regency Hospital of Meridian, Meridian, MS, p. A351

QUINN, Donna, Vice President Operations and Quality, Driscoll Children's Hospital, Corpus Christi, TX, p. A594

QUINN, Edward M., Interim Chief Financial Officer, J. C. Blair Memorial Hospital, Huntingdon, PA, p. A527

QUINN, Jennifer, Quality and Safety Coordinator, Shawano Medical Center, Shawano, WI, p. A696

QUINN, John A.
 Chief Executive Officer, Spalding Regional Medical Center, Griffin, GA, p. A154
 Chief Executive Officer, Sylvan Grove Hospital, Jackson, GA, p. A155

QUINN, Mary Anna, Vice President, St. Jude Children's Research Hospital, Memphis, TN, p. A575

QUINN, Matthew, Executive Director, Ten Broeck Tennessee Treatment Facility, Cookeville, TN, p. A568

QUINT–BOUZID, Marjorie, Chief Nursing Officer and Vice President Patient Care Services, Fort Washington Medical Center, Fort Washington, MD, p. A291

QUINTANA, Jay, Vice President Operations, Cornerstone Hospital–West Monroe, West Monroe, LA, p. A280

QUINTANA, Sonya, R.N. Chief Nursing Officer, Osceola Regional Medical Center, Kissimmee, FL, p. A127

QUINTANAR, Humberto, Chief Information Officer, Antelope Valley Hospital, Lancaster, CA, p. A66

QUINTO, Mike
 Chief Information Officer, Blowing Rock Hospital, Blowing Rock, NC, p. A448
 Chief Information Officer, Charles A. Cannon Memorial Hospital, Linville, NC, p. A456
 Chief Information Officer, Watauga Medical Center, Boone, NC, p. A448

QUINTON, Byron, Chief Executive Officer, Clarion Hospital, Clarion, PA, p. A522

QUINTON, J. Ben, Administrator, William Newton Hospital, Winfield, KS, p. A247

QUINTYNE, Stephen, Chief Executive Officer, The Vines, Ocala, FL, p. A134

QUIRIN, Julie L., FACHE, Chief Executive Officer, Saint Luke's Hospital of Kansas City, Kansas City, MO, p. A363

QUIRING, Robert, Vice President Human Resources, Integris Baptist Medical Center, Oklahoma City, OK, p. A503

QUIRK, Pamela, Director of Nursing, Soldiers' Home in Holyoke, Holyoke, MA, p. A301

QUIRKE, David, Vice President Information Services, Frederick Memorial Hospital, Frederick, MD, p. A291

QUIROGA, Pam, Vice President Human Resources, South Oaks Hospital, Amityville, NY, p. A420

QUIST, Robert, Chief Executive Officer, Mt. San Rafael Hospital, Trinidad, CO, p. A106

QUIST, Ryan, Administrative Assistant, Biggs–Gridley Memorial Hospital, Gridley, CA, p. A63

QUITO, Arturo L., M.D. Chief of Staff, Erlanger Bledsoe Hospital, Pikeville, TN, p. A578

# R

RAAB, Daniel J., President and Chief Executive Officer, Taylorville Memorial Hospital, Taylorville, IL, p. A196

RAB, Shafiq, Chief Information Officer, Orange Regional Medical Center, Middletown, NY, p. A429

RABAGO, Janie, Chief Accountant, San Antonio State Hospital, San Antonio, TX, p. A632

RABALAIS, David, M.D. Chief Medical Staff, Lane Regional Medical Center, Zachary, LA, p. A280

RABBIT, Kera, Assistant Administrator, Finance, UW Medicine/Harborview Medical Center, Seattle, WA, p. A671

RABER, Conrad, Chief Information Resources Management Service, Durham Veterans Affairs Medical Center, Durham, NC, p. A451

RABIDEAU, Ray, M.D. Medical Director, Memorial Hospital, North Conway, NH, p. A399

RABIN, Barry, M.D. Medical Director, Linden Oaks Hospital at Edward, Naperville, IL, p. A189

RABINE, Traci, Vice President Clinic Operations, Prairie Lakes Healthcare System, Watertown, SD, p. A564

RABINOWITZ, Abraham, Assistant Finance Officer, William S. Middleton Memorial Veterans Hospital, Madison, WI, p. A690

RABORN, Janelle, Chief Operating Officer, Lovelace Women's Hospital, Albuquerque, NM, p. A414

RACHAL, I. M., Chief Fiscal Service, South Texas Veterans Health Care System, San Antonio, TX, p. A632

RACHESKY, Ingrid, M.D. President Medical Staff, Bay Medical Center Sacred Heart, Panama City, FL, p. A136

RACHUIG, Sue, Director Information Services, Tulane Medical Center, New Orleans, LA, p. A276

RACKLIFFE, David, Assistant Vice President Information Services, Bristol Hospital, Bristol, CT, p. A108

RACKOVAN, Patricia G., Senior Vice President & Chief Nurse Executive, JFK Medical Center, Edison, NJ, p. A403

RACZEK, James, M.D. Sr. Vice President of Operations and Chief Medical Officer, Eastern Maine Medical Center, Bangor, ME, p. A281

RADANDT, Jeremiah, Chief Financial Officer, Primary Children's Medical Center, Salt Lake City, UT, p. A646

RADCLIFF, Joey, Chief Financial Officer, Five Rivers Medical Center, Pocahontas, AR, p. A49

RADCLIFFE, Eric, M.D. Medical Director, United Hospital Center, Bridgeport, WV, p. A675

RADCLIFFE, Kerry, JD Chief Nursing Officer, Central Texas Rehabilitation Hospital, Austin, TX, p. A584

RADEMACHER, Frank, Director, Information Systems, St. Joseph Mercy Livingston Hospital, Howell, MI, p. A316

RADEMAKER, John, M.D. Medical Director, Physicians' Medical Center, New Albany, IN, p. A211

RADENHEIMER, Tony, Network Administrator, River Park Hospital, Huntington, WV, p. A678

RADER, Herbert, M.D. Vice President and Medical Director, New York Community Hospital, NY, p. A434

RADER, Mark, FACHE, Chief Executive Officer, Northwest Medical Center, Margate, FL, p. A130

RADER, Michael E., M.D. Vice President and Medical Director, Nyack Hospital, Nyack, NY, p. A438

RADFORD, Jeffrey, Chief Nursing Officer, Select Specialty Hospital–Tri Cities, Bristol, TN, p. A565

RADFORD, Joanna, Chief Human Resources Officer, Shoshone Medical Center, Kellogg, ID, p. A169

RADFORD, Juanita, Coordinator Team Resource, South Florida Baptist Hospital, Plant City, FL, p. A137

RADKE, Sam, Vice President of Finance, Estes Park Medical Center, Estes Park, CO, p. A101

RADLEY, Karen M., M.D. Chief of Staff, Castleview Hospital, Price, UT, p. A645

RADOTICH, Maureen, Director Human Resources, Providence Valdez Medical Center, Valdez, AK, p. A29

RADUNSKY, Daniel, M.D. Medical Staff President, Union County General Hospital, Clayton, NM, p. A415

RADZEVICH, Jason, Vice President Finance, Beth Israel Deaconess Hospital–Milton, Milton, MA, p. A302

RADZIESKI, Shauna, Chief Executive Officer, Roxbury Treatment Center, Shippensburg, PA, p. A541

RAETHEL, Kathryn A., M.P.H., President and Chief Executive Officer, Castle Medical Center, Kailua, HI, p. A165

RAFALA, Paula, Director, Human Resources, Memorial Medical Center, Modesto, CA, p. A74

RAFALSKI, Mark, CPA Chief Financial Officer, Indiana University Health La Porte Hospital, La Porte, IN, p. A208

RAFFERTY, Diane
 Chief Operating Officer, Brotman Medical Center, Culver City, CA, p. A58
 Chief Executive Officer, Oklahoma State University Medical Center, Tulsa, OK, p. A508

RAFFERTY, Joseph, Chief Executive Officer, Healthbridge Children's Hospital of Houston, Houston, TX, p. A609

RAFFERTY, Joyce, Vice President Finance, Champlain Valley Physicians Hospital Medical Center, Plattsburgh, NY, p. A439

RAFFERTY, Patrick W.
 Executive Vice President and Chief Operating Officer, Community Behavioral Health Center, Fresno, CA, p. A61
 Executive Vice President and Chief Operating Officer, Community Regional Medical Center, Fresno, CA, p. A61

RAFFETY, Leannette, Administrative Generalist, Stroud Regional Medical Center, Stroud, OK, p. A507

RAFFOUL, John, Senior Vice President Finance, White Memorial Medical Center, Los Angeles, CA, p. A72

RAFUS, Matthew, Chief Information Officer, White River Junction Veterans Affairs Medical Center, White River Junction, VT, p. A650

RAGEL, Larry, Chief Financial Officer, St. John's Hospital, Springfield, IL, p. A195

RAGGIO, James J., Chief Executive Officer, Lompoc Valley Medical Center, Lompoc, CA, p. A67

RAGGIO, Sharon, President and Chief Executive Officer, Colorado West Psychiatric Hospital, Grand Junction, CO, p. A101

RAGLE, Bertha, Director Personnel, CrossRidge Community Hospital, Wynne, AR, p. A51

RAGON, Rebecca, Coordinator Public Relations and Marketing, Pomerene Hospital, Millersburg, OH, p. A486

RAGONA, Robert A., Vice President Finance, Eastern Long Island Hospital, Greenport, NY, p. A426

RAGOTHAMAN, Krishna, M.D. Chief of Staff, Mercy St. Charles Hospital, Oregon, OH, p. A488

RAGSDALE, Mary, Director Human Resources, Broughton Hospital, Morganton, NC, p. A457

RAGSDALE, Sara, D.O. Chief Medical Staff, Newport Hospital and Health Services, Newport, WA, p. A668

RAGSDALE, Sarah, R.N. Chief Nursing Officer, Smith County Memorial Hospital, Smith Center, KS, p. A244

RAHAMAN, Suara, M.D. Chief Medical Staff, Bolivar General Hospital, Bolivar, TN, p. A565

RAHDERT, Richard, M.D. Medical Director, River Bend Hospital, West Lafayette, IN, p. A215

RAHMAN, Randy
Chief Information Officer, Yavapai Regional Medical Center – East, Prescott Valley, AZ, p. A36
Chief Information Officer, Yavapai Regional Medical Center, Prescott, AZ, p. A36

RAHMAN, Syed, M.D. Chief of Staff, Horizon Specialty Hospital, Las Vegas, NV, p. A393

RAHN, Douglas L., Senior Vice President and Chief Operating Officer, Memorial Medical Center, Springfield, IL, p. A195

RAI, Amrita, Administrator, Riverside Center for Behavioral Medicine, Riverside, CA, p. A82

RAICA, Dagmar Ann, R.N. Chief Nursing Officer, Marquette General Health System, Marquette, MI, p. A319

RAINA, Suresh, M.D. Vice President Medical Staff and Chief Medical Officer, Palisades Medical Center, North Bergen, NJ, p. A408

RAINBOLT, Mike, Chief Financial Officer, Rivendell Behavioral Health Services of Arkansas, Benton, AR, p. A41

RAINDL, Donna, Manager Business Office, Lynn County Hospital District, Tahoka, TX, p. A636

RAINER, George P., Senior Vice President Human Resources, Winthrop–University Hospital, Mineola, NY, p. A429

RAINES, Chris, Chief Fiscal Services, Beckley Veterans Affairs Medical Center, Beckley, WV, p. A675

RAINEY, Jackie, Assistant Administrator and Controller, Christus St. Michael Hospital–Atlanta, Atlanta, TX, p. A584

RAINS, Celeste, D.O. Chief of Staff, Logan County Hospital, Oakley, KS, p. A240

RAINS, Debbie, Coordinator Health Information Management, Erlanger Bledsoe Hospital, Pikeville, TN, p. A578

RAINS, Gail, R.N. Director Patient Care Services, Shriners Hospitals for Children–Shreveport, Shreveport, LA, p. A278

RAINS, Jeff, Administrator and Chief Executive Officer, Baptist Medical Center East, Montgomery, AL, p. A23

RAINS, Paul, MSN, President, St. Joseph's Behavioral Health Center, Stockton, CA, p. A92

RAINS, Steve, Director Information Services, McKee Medical Center, Loveland, CO, p. A104

RAINSTEIN, Miguel, M.D. Acting Chief of Staff, Veterans Affairs Western New York Healthcare System–Buffalo Division, Buffalo, NY, p. A423

RAISNER, Gary, Chief Operating Officer, Norristown State Hospital, Norristown, PA, p. A533

RAJASEKARAN, Smita, M.D. Chief Medical Officer, Gundersen Tri–County Hospital and Clinics, Whitehall, WI, p. A699

RAJATATNAM, Richard, M.D. Area Medical Director, Kaiser Permanente Riverside Medical Center, Riverside, CA, p. A82

RAJPARA, Suresh, M.D. Chief Medical Officer, Jerome Golden Center for Behavioral Health, Inc., West Palm Beach, FL, p. A143

RAK, Roger, Director Human Resources, South Shore Hospital, Chicago, IL, p. A179

RAK, Ronald C., JD, Chief Executive Officer, Saint Peter's University Hospital, New Brunswick, NJ, p. A407

RAKES–STEPHENS, Kim, M.D. Chief Medical Staff, Colleton Medical Center, Walterboro, SC, p. A556

RAKOV, Robert, M.D. Chief Medical Officer, Cogdell Memorial Hospital, Snyder, TX, p. A634

RALPH, Chandler M., President and Chief Executive Officer, Adirondack Medical Center, Saranac Lake, NY, p. A442

RALPH, Stephen A., President and Chief Executive Officer, Huntington Memorial Hospital, Pasadena, CA, p. A79

RALSTIN, Char, Director of Nursing, Haven Senior Horizons, Phoenix, AZ, p. A34

RALSTON, Mary Beth, Manager Human Resources, North Georgia Medical Center, Ellijay, GA, p. A153

RAMAEKERS, Gina, Director Human Resources, St. Anthony Regional Hospital, Carroll, IA, p. A217

RAMAGE, Gary, M.D. Chief Medical Officer, McKenzie County Healthcare System, Watford City, ND, p. A469

RAMAN, Jayashree, Vice President and Chief Information Officer, Reading Hospital and Medical Center, West Reading, PA, p. A544

RAMAZANI, Regina, Chief Financial Officer, Garden Park Medical Center, Gulfport, MS, p. A347

RAMBHATLA, Kamalakar, M.D. Chief of Staff, Greater El Monte Community Hospital, South El Monte, CA, p. A91

RAMER, Gary, Manager Information Management, Jonathan M. Wainwright Memorial Veterans Affairs Medical Center, Walla Walla, WA, p. A674

RAMEY, Jan, MSN Chief Nursing Officer, Person Memorial Hospital, Roxboro, NC, p. A460

RAMEY, Michael, Director Human Resources, The Heart Hospital Baylor Plano, Plano, TX, p. A628

RAMEY, Rita, Director Information Systems, Buchanan General Hospital, Grundy, VA, p. A655

RAMEY, Robert L., President, Russell County Hospital, Russell Springs, KY, p. A260

RAMEY, Steve, Chief Financial Officer, Southampton Memorial Hospital, Franklin, VA, p. A654

RAMIREZ, Conrad, Director Information Services, St. Mary's Regional Medical Center, Enid, OK, p. A498

RAMIREZ, Corazon, M.D., Chief Executive Officer, Pine Creek Medical Center, Dallas, TX, p. A597

RAMIREZ, Eddy, Assistant Vice President Business Development, Ochsner Medical Center – Kenner, Kenner, LA, p. A269

RAMIREZ, Jaime, Chief Executive Officer, McCamey County Hospital District, McCamey, TX, p. A622

RAMIREZ, Marcos, Manager Human Resources, Baylor Medical Center at Waxahachie, Waxahachie, TX, p. A640

RAMIREZ, Omar, Chief Executive Officer, Los Angeles Community Hospital, Los Angeles, CA, p. A70

RAMIREZ, Willie, Manager Labor Relations, Laguna Honda Hospital and Rehabilitation Center, San Francisco, CA, p. A86

RAMLO, Ricki, Vice President Human Resources, Jamestown Regional Medical Center, Jamestown, ND, p. A467

RAMMLER, Linda, R.N. Chief Nursing Officer, Bonner General Hospital, Sandpoint, ID, p. A171

RAMOS, Cecilia, M.D. Chief of Staff, Lompoc Valley Medical Center, Lompoc, CA, p. A67

RAMOS, Eric, M.D. Chief Medical Officer, Doctors Medical Center, Modesto, CA, p. A74

RAMOS, Holly, R.N. Chief Clinical Officer, Kindred Hospital–Ontario, Ontario, CA, p. A77

RAMOS, Jet, Head Staff Administration, Naval Hospital Camp Pendleton, Camp Pendleton, CA, p. A55

RAMOS, Raymond, Vice President and Chief Executive Officer, CHRISTUS Spohn Hospital Beeville, Beeville, TX, p. A588

RAMPP, Randal D., M.D. Chief Medical Officer, River Park Hospital, Mc Minnville, TN, p. A574

RAMSAY, Kathy, R.N. Director Communications and Development, Rooks County Health Center, Plainville, KS, p. A242

RAMSEY, Beryl O., FACHE, Chief Executive Officer, Methodist Willowbrook Hospital, Houston, TX, p. A611

RAMSEY, Bill, Director Human Resources, Ochsner Baptist Medical Center, New Orleans, LA, p. A275

RAMSEY, David L., President and Chief Executive Officer, Charleston Area Medical Center, Charleston, WV, p. A676

RAMSEY, Gina B., Vice President Financial Services and Chief Financial Officer, Wake Forest Baptist Medical Center, Winston–Salem, NC, p. A464

RAMSEY, James, Vice President Finance, Carolinas Medical Center–NorthEast, Concord, NC, p. A450

RAMSEY, Lisa, Chief Financial Officer, Greenwood County Hospital, Eureka, KS, p. A233

RAMSEY, Roy M., Executive Director, Bradford Health Services at Warrior Lodge, Warrior, AL, p. A26

RAMSEY, Tara, M.D. President Medical Staff, Passavant Area Hospital, Jacksonville, IL, p. A186

RAMSEY, Thomas, Chief Financial Officer, River Parishes Hospital, La Place, LA, p. A270

RAMTHUN, Jane, Chief Financial Officer, Story County Medical Center, Nevada, IA, p. A225

RANA, Irfan, M.D. Chief of Staff, Cozby–Germany Hospital, Grand Saline, TX, p. A606

RAND, David, M.D. Chief of Staff, Torrance Memorial Medical Center, Torrance, CA, p. A93

RAND, Kevin, M.D. Clinical Director, Chinle Comprehensive Health Care Facility, Chinle, AZ, p. A30

RAND, Richard, Director Human Resources, Ely–Bloomenson Community Hospital, Ely, MN, p. A332

RANDALL, Bryan J.
Vice President Finance and Chief Financial Officer, Heritage Valley Beaver, Beaver, PA, p. A520
Vice President Finance and Chief Financial Officer, Sewickley Valley Hospital, (A Division of Valley Medical Facilities), Sewickley, PA, p. A541

RANDALL, Cherry, Business Officer, Greater Binghamton Health Center, Binghamton, NY, p. A421

RANDALL, JoEllen, Administrative Director Human Resources, Ottumwa Regional Health Center, Ottumwa, IA, p. A226

RANDALL, Kenneth W., Chief Executive Officer, Artesia General Hospital, Artesia, NM, p. A415

RANDALL, Ralph X., FACHE, Chief Executive Officer, Jefferson Hospital, Louisville, GA, p. A156

RANDLE, Emily, Vice President Operations, Orange Coast Memorial Medical Center, Fountain Valley, CA, p. A60

RANDLE, James M., M.D. Chief of Staff, Nacogdoches Medical Center, Nacogdoches, TX, p. A624

RANDLE, Michael, Chief Financial Officer, Homer Memorial Hospital, Homer, LA, p. A268

RANDOLPH, Arianne, Director Human Resources, Pikes Peak Regional Hospital, Woodland Park, CO, p. A107

RANDOLPH, Bonnie, M.D. Chief of Staff, Community Hospital, Torrington, WY, p. A704

RANDOLPH, Bruce, Chief Information Technology, Arizona State Hospital, Phoenix, AZ, p. A34

RANDOLPH, Geoffrey, M.D. Chief Medical Officer, Lutheran Hospital of Indiana, Fort Wayne, IN, p. A202

RANDOLPH, Karsten, Vice President Finance/Chief Financial Officer, Park Ridge Health, Hendersonville, NC, p. A454

RANDOLPH, Jr., Leonard M., M.D
Senior Vice President and Chief Medical Officer, Mercy Health – Anderson Hospital, Cincinnati, OH, p. A475
Senior Vice President and Divisional Chief Medical Officer, Mercy Health – Mt. Airy Hospital, Cincinnati, OH, p. A475

RANDOLPH, Linda, Director Personnel Services, Washington County Hospital and Nursing Home, Chatom, AL, p. A18

RANERI, Samuel, Senior Vice President Operations and Business Development, Excela Latrobe Area Hospital, Latrobe, PA, p. A529

RANGAVIZ, Rassoul, Chief Financial Officer, Copley Hospital, Morrisville, VT, p. A649

RANGHELLI, Gloria, Deputy Chief Financial Officer, Coler–Goldwater Specialty Hospital and Nursing Facility, New York, NY, p. A431

RANKIN, Beverley A., R.N. Vice President & Chief Nursing Officer, Alice Peck Day Memorial Hospital, Lebanon, NH, p. A398

RANKIN III, Fred M.
President and Chief Executive Officer, Mary Washington Hospital, Fredericksburg, VA, p. A654
President and Chief Executive Officer, Stafford Hospital, Stafford, VA, p. A661

RANNEY, Timothy, M.D. Vice President Medical Affairs and Chief Medical Officer, Missouri Baptist Medical Center, Saint Louis, MO, p. A370

RANSOM, Jim, Chief Executive Officer, Reliant Rehabilitation Hospital North Texas, Richardson, TX, p. A628

RANSOM, Natalie, Chief Nursing Officer, Southern Hills Hospital and Medical Center, Las Vegas, NV, p. A393

RAO, Gutti, M.D. Medical Director, AMG Specialty Hospital–Greenwood, Greenwood, MS, p. A347

RAO, Kalapala, M.D. Medical Director, HEALTHSOUTH Western Hills Rehabilitation Hospital, Parkersburg, WV, p. A679

RAO, Noel, M.D. Medical Director, Marianjoy Rehabilitation Hospital, Wheaton, IL, p. A196

RAO, Raghu, M.D. Chief of Staff, Helen Newberry Joy Hospital, Newberry, MI, p. A321

RAPAPORT, Gary D., Chief Executive Officer, Sutter Delta Medical Center, Antioch, CA, p. A52

RAPENSKE, Jennifer, Manager Financial Services, Mercy Medical Center–New Hampton, New Hampton, IA, p. A226

RAPP, Catherine, R.N. Vice President Nursing, Oconomowoc Memorial Hospital, Oconomowoc, WI, p. A693

RAPP, David, Chief Information Officer, Wheeling Hospital, Wheeling, WV, p. A682

RAPP, Larry, M.D. Chief Medical Officer, Prairie Ridge Hospital and Health Services, Elbow Lake, MN, p. A332

RAPP, Peter F., Vice President and Executive Director, OHSU Hospital, Portland, OR, p. A516

RAPP, Robin, R.N., Chief Executive Officer, Kindred Hospital–Ontario, Ontario, CA, p. A77

RAPP, Ron, Controller, Cole Memorial, Coudersport, PA, p. A523

RARICK, Karen
Director Information Technology, Schuylkill Medical Center – East Norwegian Street, Pottsville, PA, p. A539
Director Information Systems, Schuylkill Medical Center – South Jackson Street, Pottsville, PA, p. A539

RASCHKE, Judy, Director Human Resources, Pipestone County Medical Center Avera, Pipestone, MN, p. A338

RASH, Doug, Director Information Technology, Ferrell Hospital, Eldorado, IL, p. A181

RASINA, Stacia, Director Human Resources, Promise Hospital of San Diego, San Diego, CA, p. A85

RASK, Brenda, Vice President Operations, Carrington Health Center, Carrington, ND, p. A465

RASKE, Jamie, Information Technology Lead, Avera St. Mary's Hospital, Pierre, SD, p. A561

RASMUSSEN, David D., Chief Executive Officer, Westlake Regional Hospital, Columbia, KY, p. A249

RASMUSSEN, Diane, Director Human Resources, Cambridge Medical Center, Cambridge, MN, p. A330

RASMUSSEN, Jeanell, R.N. Vice President/Chief Nursing Officer, Providence Centralia Hospital, Centralia, WA, p. A665

RASMUSSEN, Kyle R., Chief Executive Officer, Meeker Memorial Hospital, Litchfield, MN, p. A334

RASMUSSEN, Renee, Senior Vice President and Chief Financial Officer, UnityPoint Health Allen, Waterloo, IA, p. A229

RASMUSSEN, Roger, Chief Administrative Officer, Newport Hospital and Health Services, Newport, WA, p. A668

RASMUSSEN, Scott, Director Human Resources, Lincoln Regional Center, Lincoln, NE, p. A385

RASMUSSEN, Steven, M.D. Medical Director, Butler Hospital, Providence, RI, p. A546

RASMUSSON, Duane, Vice President Human Resources, St. Cloud Hospital, Saint Cloud, MN, p. A339

RASOOL, Chaudri, D.O. Chief of Staff, Palmer Lutheran Health Center, West Union, IA, p. A230

RASOR, Linda, R.N., Chief Executive Officer, Plains Memorial Hospital, Dimmitt, TX, p. A599

RASPER, Deborah Y., FACHE, Administrator, St. Vincent Mercy Hospital, Elwood, IN, p. A201

RASTER, Robert, M.D. Medical Director, Michiana Behavioral Health Center, Plymouth, IN, p. A212

RATCLIFF, David, M.D. Chief Medical Affairs, Washington Regional Medical Center, Fayetteville, AR, p. A43

RATCLIFF, Paul, Director Information Services, Baylor Medical Center at Carrollton, Carrollton, TX, p. A591

RATCLIFFE, Alma, M.D. Executive Vice President Medical Staff and Business Development, Saint Clare's Health System, Denville, NJ, p. A403

RATCLIFFE, Denise, Executive Vice President and Chief Operating Officer, Christian Health Care Center, Wyckoff, NJ, p. A413

RATH, Marilyn, Co–Director Management Information Systems and Chief Information Officer, Day Kimball Hospital, Putnam, CT, p. A111

RATHBUN, Lori, Vice President Operations, Mercy Medical Center–Centerville, Centerville, IA, p. A218

RATLIFF, Ada, Chief Information Officer, Patient's Choice Medical Center of Claiborne County, Port Gibson, MS, p. A353

RATLIFF, Kim, Director Health Information Management, Southwestern Virginia Mental Health Institute, Marion, VA, p. A657

RATLIFF, Maggie, Chief Information Officer, St. Joseph Medical Center, Kansas City, MO, p. A363

RATLIFF, Steve, Director Information, Guadalupe Regional Medical Center, Seguin, TX, p. A633

RATLIFF, Thomas W., M.D. President Medical Staff, Saint Francis Hospital–Bartlett, Bartlett, TN, p. A565

RATLIFFE, Kathy, Director Human Resources, Tuality Healthcare, Hillsboro, OR, p. A513

RATNAKAR, Nitesh, M.D. Chief Medical Officer, Davis Memorial Hospital, Elkins, WV, p. A676

RATNER, Jeffrey, M.D. Senior Vice President Medical Affairs, Mount Nittany Medical Center, State College, PA, p. A541

RATTRAY, Cindy Stewart, Director Human Resources, Jewish Hospital–Shelbyville, Shelbyville, KY, p. A260

RAU, John, President and Chief Executive Officer, Stevens Community Medical Center, Morris, MN, p. A337

RAU, Robin, Chief Executive Officer, Miller County Hospital, Colquitt, GA, p. A150

RAUCH, Deena R., R.N. Chief Nursing Officer, Gritman Medical Center, Moscow, ID, p. A170

RAUCH, Scott C., Vice President Human Resources, Reid Hospital and Health Care Services, Richmond, IN, p. A212

RAUCH, Scott L., M.D., President, McLean Hospital, Belmont, MA, p. A295

RAUCHER, Beth, M.D. Senior Vice President and Chief Medical Officer, Lutheran Medical Center,, NY, p. A433

RAUH, Cindy, R.N. Vice President and Chief Nursing Officer, Duncan Regional Hospital, Duncan, OK, p. A497

RAUPERS, Debra, MSN Chief Nursing Officer, Corning Hospital, Corning, NY, p. A424

RAUSCH, Steve, Manager Information Technology, Hillsdale Community Health Center, Hillsdale, MI, p. A316

RAUSCHER, Andrew, M.D. Medical Director, Little Falls Hospital, Little Falls, NY, p. A428

RAVELING, Lynn, Chief Financial Officer, Pocahontas Community Hospital, Pocahontas, IA, p. A227

RAVI, Nathan, M.D. Chief of Staff, Veterans Affairs St. Louis Health Care System, Saint Louis, MO, p. A371

RAVLIN, Suzanne M., Director Human Resources, Katherine Shaw Bethea Hospital, Dixon, IL, p. A181

RAWLINGS, Linda, Director Human Resources and Personnel, Three Rivers Hospital, Waverly, TN, p. A580

RAWSON, Richard L., Chief Executive Officer, Loma Linda University Medical Center–Murrieta, Murrieta, CA, p. A75

RAY, Beverly, Director Human Resources, Dyersburg Regional Medical Center, Dyersburg, TN, p. A568

RAY, Denise, President and Chief Administrative Officer, Piedmont Mountainside Hospital, Jasper, GA, p. A155

RAY, Donald, Vice President of Operations, Maryland General Hospital, Baltimore, MD, p. A288

RAY, Dwayne, Chief Financial Officer, Medical Center of McKinney, McKinney, TX, p. A622

RAY, Elaine, Administrator, Choate Mental Health Center, Anna, IL, p. A173

RAY, Evan
President, St. Vincent's Blount, Oneonta, AL, p. A24
President, St. Vincent's St. Clair, Pell City, AL, p. A24

RAY, Holly, Director Human Resources, Mid–America Rehabilitation Hospital, Shawnee Mission, KS, p. A244

RAY, Jerilyn, Manager Human Resources, St. Elizabeth Hospital, Enumclaw, WA, p. A666

RAY, Kirk M., Chief Executive Officer, Northside Medical Center, Youngstown, OH, p. A494

RAY, Lisa, R.N. Vice President, Patient Care Services, Murray–Calloway County Hospital, Murray, KY, p. A258

RAY, Rachel, Chief Financial Officer, Unity Medical Center, Grafton, ND, p. A467

RAY, Roger A., M.D. Executive Vice President and Chief Medical Officer, Carolinas Medical Center, Charlotte, NC, p. A449

RAY, Todd A., Director Human Resources, Greenville Regional Hospital, Greenville, IL, p. A184

RAYL, Cheryl, Chief Executive Officer, Behavioral Health Center of the Permian Basin, Midland, TX, p. A623

RAYMER, Chris, R.N
Chief Operating Officer and Chief Nursing Officer, Great River Medical Center, Blytheville, AR, p. A41
Interim Chief Operating Officer, South Mississippi County Regional Medical Center, Osceola, AR, p. A48

RAYMOND, Jane, Vice President and Chief Operating Officer, Reston Hospital Center, Reston, VA, p. A659

RAYMOND, Michael, M.D. Chief Medical Officer, NorthShore University Health System Skokie Hospital, Skokie, IL, p. A194

RAYMOND, Mindy, Vice President Human Resources, Boca Raton Regional Hospital, Boca Raton, FL, p. A118

RAYMOND, Scott, Director Information Systems, Orange Coast Memorial Medical Center, Fountain Valley, CA, p. A60

RAYNAUD, Gene, Administrator, Shriners Hospitals for Children–Honolulu, Honolulu, HI, p. A165

RAYNER, Susan, M.D. Executive Vice President, Schwab Rehabilitation Hospital, Chicago, IL, p. A179

RAYNES, Anthony, M.D. Psychiatrist in Chief, Arbour H. R. I. Hospital, Brookline, MA, p. A298

RAYNES, Scott, President and Chief Executive Officer, Northcrest Medical Center, Springfield, TN, p. A579

RAYNOR, Robert, Human Resources Director, Park Royal Hospital, Fort Myers, FL, p. A124

RAYUDU, Subbu, M.D. Chief of Staff, Alliance HealthCare System, Holly Springs, MS, p. A348

RAZAGHI, Ahmad, Chief Executive Officer, Sage Memorial Hospital, Ganado, AZ, p. A31

RAZAK, Mohamed, M.D. Chief of Staff, Heart of Florida Regional Medical Center, Davenport, FL, p. A121

RAZMIC, Tammy, Associate Administrator Finance and Chief Financial Officer, Inova Mount Vernon Hospital, Alexandria, VA, p. A651

RAZO, Virginia, Chief Operating Officer, Incline Village Community Hospital, Incline Village, NV, p. A392

RAZVI, Mohammed, M.D. Chief of Staff, Iroquois Memorial Hospital and Resident Home, Watseka, IL, p. A196

REA, Jerry A., Ph.D., Superintendent, Parsons State Hospital and Training Center, Parsons, KS, p. A242

READ, Richard
Chief Financial Officer, Haywood Park Community Hospital, Brownsville, TN, p. A565
Chief Financial Officer, Regional Hospital of Jackson, Jackson, TN, p. A570

READ, Susan, Director Information Technology Support, Great Bend Regional Hospital, Great Bend, KS, p. A234

READING, Matt, Director Human Resources, Indiana Regional Medical Center, Indiana, PA, p. A528

READY, Janet L., President and Chief Operating Officer, Vassar Brothers Medical Center, Poughkeepsie, NY, p. A440

REAGAN, David, M.D. Chief of Staff, James H. Quillen Veterans Affairs Medical Center, Mountain Home, TN, p. A576

REAGAN Jr., James H., Ph.D., Chief Executive Officer, Morris County Hospital, Council Grove, KS, p. A233

REAL, Lawrence A., M.D. Medical Director, Belmont Center for Comprehensive Treatment, Philadelphia, PA, p. A534

REALE, Kelli, Vice President Human Resources, Magee–Womens Hospital of UPMC, Pittsburgh, PA, p. A537

REAM, Tom, Regional Chief Information Officer, Sutter Auburn Faith Hospital, Auburn, CA, p. A53

REAMER, Roger J., Chief Executive Officer, Memorial Health Care Systems, Seward, NE, p. A389

REANDEAU, Michael
Chief Information Officer, Mills–Peninsula Health Services, Burlingame, CA, p. A55
Regional Chief Information Officer, Sutter Maternity and Surgery Center of Santa Cruz, Santa Cruz, CA, p. A90

REANO, Paul, Chief Executive Officer, Atoka County Medical Center, Atoka, OK, p. A496

REARDON, Jerry, Director Information Systems, Catawba Valley Medical Center, Hickory, NC, p. A454

REAVIS, Mack, M.D., President and Chief Medical Officer, Lakeland Regional Medical Center, Lakeland, FL, p. A128

REBLOCK, Kimberly, M.D. Chief Operating Officer, The Children's Home of Pittsburgh, Pittsburgh, PA, p. A538

RECA, Sr., Thomas, Senior Vice President Finance and Chief Financial Officer, Staten Island University Hospital,, NY, p. A436

RECHSTEINER, Hans, M.D. Chief of Staff, Burnett Medical Center, Grantsburg, WI, p. A687

RECKDENWALD, Jeanine, Vice President Human Resources and Support Services, Bristol Hospital, Bristol, CT, p. A108

RECKERT, Sandy, Director Communications and Public Affairs, Johns Hopkins Bayview Medical Center, Baltimore, MD, p. A287

RECKEWEY, Kent, M.D., Chief Executive Officer, Nebraska Heart Hospital, Lincoln, NE, p. A385

RECTOR, III, Fax, Director Information Technology, Sunbury Community Hospital and Outpatient Center, Sunbury, PA, p. A542

RECUPERO, David, Chief Financial Officer, San Gorgonio Memorial Hospital, Banning, CA, p. A54

RECUPERO, Patricia R., JD, President and Chief Executive Officer, Butler Hospital, Providence, RI, p. A546

RED THUNDER, Charlene, Chief Executive Officer, U. S. Public Health Service Indian Hospital, Eagle Butte, SD, p. A559

REDD, Dakota, R.N
Chief Clinical Officer, Kindred Hospital–St. Louis, Saint Louis, MO, p. A369
Chief Nursing Officer, The Rehabilitation Institute of St. Louis, Saint Louis, MO, p. A371

REDD, James, M.D. Chief Medical Officer, San Juan Hospital, Monticello, UT, p. A644

REDDEN, Robert, Site Director Information Technology, Community Hospital of San Bernardino, San Bernardino, CA, p. A84

REDDICK, Lisa, Director Organizational Resources, Tri–County Hospital, Wadena, MN, p. A342

REDDICK, Michelle, Director Human Resources, Turning Point Hospital, Moultrie, GA, p. A158

REDDICK, Shawn, Director Information Management, Flint River Community Hospital, Montezuma, GA, p. A157

REDDING, Lisa, Manager Human Resources, Morgan County ARH Hospital, West Liberty, KY, p. A261

REDDY, Dipak, Director Information Technology, Miracle Mile Medical Center, Los Angeles, CA, p. A70

REDDY, Krishna K., M.D. President Medical Staff, Lanier Health Services, Valley, AL, p. A26

REDDY, Lex, Chief Executive Officer, St. Rose Hospital, Hayward, CA, p. A64

REDDY, Sunil, Chief Executive Officer, Care Regional Medical Center, Aransas Pass, TX, p. A583

REDHORSE–CHARLEY, Gloria, Director Human Resources, Northern Navajo Medical Center, Shiprock, NM, p. A418

REDING, Janeen K., Director Human Resources, St. Anthony Hospital, Pendleton, OR, p. A515

REDINGTON, James, M.D. Chief of Staff, Bath Community Hospital, Hot Springs, VA, p. A655

REDMON, Gary, Chief Financial Officer, South Texas Regional Medical Center, Jourdanton, TX, p. A615

REDMOND, Michael, Senior Vice President and Chief Operating Officer, Crotched Mountain Rehabilitation Center, Greenfield, NH, p. A398

REDMOND, Paula, Controller, HEALTHSOUTH Tustin Rehabilitation Hospital, Tustin, CA, p. A93

REDUTO, Lawrence A., M.D. President and Chief Medical Officer, St. Joseph Hospital, Bethpage, NY, p. A421

REECE, Jeff
Chief Executive Officer, Chesterfield General Hospital, Cheraw, SC, p. A549
Chief Executive Officer, Marlboro Park Hospital, Bennettsville, SC, p. A548

REECE, Morris A.
EVP/COO, Laird Hospital, Union, MS, p. A354
Executive Vice President and Chief Operating Officer, Rush Foundation Hospital, Meridian, MS, p. A351

REECER, Jeff
President, Texas Health Presbyterian Hospital Allen, Allen, TX, p. A581
Chief Operating Officer, Texas Health Presbyterian Hospital Denton, Denton, TX, p. A599

REED, Cindy, Director Community Relations, Austin State Hospital, Austin, TX, p. A584

REED, Dianne, Director Information Systems, Higgins General Hospital, Bremen, GA, p. A148

REED, Gregory C., FACHE, Chief Executive Officer, United General Hospital, Sedro Woolley, WA, p. A672

REED, Hollis, M.D. Chief of Staff, Alexandria Veterans Affairs Health Care System, Pineville, LA, p. A276

REED, Jan A., CPA, Administrator and Chief Executive Officer, Electra Memorial Hospital, Electra, TX, p. A602

REED, John E., M.D. Medical Director, Baptist Memorial Hospital–Golden Triangle, Columbus, MS, p. A346

REED, Karen
  Chief Nursing Officer, Pioneer Memorial Hospital, Prineville, OR, p. A517
  Interim Chief Nursing Officer, St. Charles Medical Center – Redmond, Redmond, OR, p. A517

REED, Kathleen, Manager Human Resources, Missouri Baptist Sullivan Hospital, Sullivan, MO, p. A372

REED, Kirby, Director Information Systems, Jasper County Hospital, Rensselaer, IN, p. A212

REED, Leslie, Chief Financial Officer, Wright Memorial Hospital, Trenton, MO, p. A372

REED, Lester, M.D
  Vice President Medical Affairs and Acute Care, MultiCare Mary Bridge Children's Hospital and Health Center, Tacoma, WA, p. A673
  Vice President Medical Affairs and Acute Care, MultiCare Tacoma General Hospital, Tacoma, WA, p. A673

REED, Linda
  Vice President and Chief Information Officer, Morristown Medical Center, Morristown, NJ, p. A406
  Vice President Information Systems and Chief Information Officer, Newton Medical Center, Newton, NJ, p. A408
  Vice President and Chief Information Officer, Overlook Medical Center, Summit, NJ, p. A410

REED, Marie, Director Human Resources, Antelope Valley Hospital, Lancaster, CA, p. A66

REED, Ronald R., President and Chief Executive Officer, Mercy Iowa City, Iowa City, IA, p. A223

REED, Victoria L., FACHE, Chief Executive Officer, James B. Haggin Memorial Hospital, Harrodsburg, KY, p. A252

REEDER, Carol, R.N. Chief Nursing Officer, St. Joseph Hospital, Eureka, CA, p. A59

REEDER, Wendy, R.N. Chief Nursing Officer, Harrison Memorial Hospital, Cynthiana, KY, p. A250

REEFER, John C., M.D. Director, Butler Health System, Butler, PA, p. A521

REEG, Kari, Manager Human Resources, Genoa Community Hospital, Genoa, NE, p. A383

REEL, Stephanie L., Senior Vice President Information Services, Johns Hopkins Hospital, Baltimore, MD, p. A287

REES, Adam, President, Essentia Health St. Joseph's Medical Center, Brainerd, MN, p. A329

REES, Elizabeth, Chief Executive Officer, AMG Specialty Hospital–Albuquerque, Albuquerque, NM, p. A414

REES, Jeff, Director Information Systems, Bacharach Institute for Rehabilitation, Pomona, NJ, p. A409

REES, Matthew, Chief Executive Officer, Mayers Memorial Hospital District, Fall River Mills, CA, p. A60

REESE, Bert
  Chief Information Officer, Sentara Leigh Hospital, Norfolk, VA, p. A658
  Chief Information Officer, Sentara Norfolk General Hospital, Norfolk, VA, p. A658
  Chief Information Officer, Sentara Princess Anne Hospital, Virginia Beach, VA, p. A662

REESE, Kathie, Administrator, Dubuis Hospital of Paris, Paris, TX, p. A626

REESE, Linda, Administrator, Telecare Heritage Psychiatric Health Center, Oakland, CA, p. A77

REESE, Maryann, FACHE, President and Chief Executive Officer, St. Elizabeth's Hospital, Belleville, IL, p. A174

REESE, Pamela A., FACHE Chief Clinical Officer, Citizens Memorial Hospital, Bolivar, MO, p. A356

REESE, Sandra, Administrator, Lower Umpqua Hospital District, Reedsport, OR, p. A517

REESE, Willis L., Administrator, Falls Community Hospital and Clinic, Marlin, TX, p. A621

REETZ, Brenda, R.N., Chief Executive Officer, Greene County General Hospital, Linton, IN, p. A209

REETZ, Renee, Director Human Resources, St. Mary's of Michigan Standish Hospital, Standish, MI, p. A325

REEVE, Jay A., President and Chief Executive Officer, Eastside Psychiatric Hospital, Tallahassee, FL, p. A140

REEVES, Amy D., Director Human Resources, Cedar Park Regional Medical Center, Cedar Park, TX, p. A591

REEVES, Carol, Interim Area Finance Officer, Kaiser Permanente Santa Clara Medical Center, Santa Clara, CA, p. A89

REEVES, Cory, Chief Financial Officer, Gordon Hospital, Calhoun, GA, p. A149

REEVES, Jeanne, Chief Nursing Officer, Methodist Mansfield Medical Center, Mansfield, TX, p. A621

REEVES, Jennifer, Chief Nursing Officer, Texas Specialty Hospital at Lubbock, Lubbock, TX, p. A620

REEVES, Katy, Vice President Human Resources, Fauquier Hospital, Warrenton, VA, p. A662

REEVES, Kaylene, Director, Tahoe Pacific Hospitals, Reno, NV, p. A395

REEVES, Mary, Controller, Rehabilitation Hospital of Wisconsin, Waukesha, WI, p. A698

REEVES, Mike
  Vice President, St. John Medical Center, Tulsa, OK, p. A509
  Chief Information Officer, St. John Owasso, Owasso, OK, p. A505

REEVES, Pamela J., M.D., Director, John D. Dingell Veterans Affairs Medical Center, Detroit, MI, p. A312

REEVES, Rachel, Manager Human Resources, Kindred Hospital Victoria, Victoria, TX, p. A639

REEVES, William C., D.O. Chief of Staff, Mercy Hospital of Defiance, Defiance, OH, p. A480

REGAN, Christine, Vice President Human Resources, Massachusetts Eye and Ear Infirmary, Boston, MA, p. A297

REGEHR, Stan, President and Chief Executive Officer, Nemaha Valley Community Hospital, Seneca, KS, p. A244

REGIER, Donald, M.D. Chief Medical Officer, Sedgwick County Health Center, Julesburg, CO, p. A102

REGIER, Marion, Chief Executive Officer, Hillsboro Community Hospital, Hillsboro, KS, p. A235

REGLING, Anne, Interim Chief Executive Officer, Bronson Battle Creek, Battle Creek, MI, p. A309

REGULA, John
  Chief Information Officer, Allied Services Rehabilitation Hospital, Scranton, PA, p. A540
  Chief Information Officer, John Heinz Institute of Rehabilitation Medicine, Wilkes–Barre, PA, p. A544

REHM, Janice, Manager Human Resources, University of South Alabama Children's and Women's Hospital, Mobile, AL, p. A23

REICH, David L., M.D., Interim President, Mount Sinai Hospital, New York, NY, p. A434

REICH, Joel R., M.D
  Senior Vice President Medical Affairs, Manchester Memorial Hospital, Manchester, CT, p. A109
  Senior Vice President Medical Affairs, Rockville General Hospital, Vernon Rockville, CT, p. A112

REICHARD, Steve, Manager Information Systems, Brigham City Community Hospital, Brigham City, UT, p. A643

REICHFIELD, Michael L., President, OhioHealth Doctors Hospital, Columbus, OH, p. A478

REICHLE, Paula, Executive Vice President and Chief Operating Officer, Sparrow Hospital, Lansing, MI, p. A318

REICHMAN, Joseph, M.D. Vice President Medical Affairs and Clinical Effectiveness, Riverview Medical Center, Red Bank, NJ, p. A410

REID, Barbara S., Chief Financial Officer, Willingway Hospital, Statesboro, GA, p. A160

REID, Bev, Chief Financial Officer, St. Luke Hospital and Living Center, Marion, KS, p. A239

REID, Deressa, Interim Chief Executive Officer, Hoag Orthopedic Institute, Irvine, CA, p. A64

REID, Jim
  Vice President and Chief Information Officer, Covenant Children's Hospital, Lubbock, TX, p. A619
  Vice President and Chief Information Officer, Covenant Medical Center, Lubbock, TX, p. A620

REID, Karl, Chief Information Officer, Minneapolis Veterans Affairs Health Care System, Minneapolis, MN, p. A336

REID, Kenneth G., President and Chief Executive Officer, Carlinville Area Hospital, Carlinville, IL, p. A175

REID, Parlane, M.D. Chief Medical Officer, Sarasota Memorial Hospital, Sarasota, FL, p. A139

REID, Richard, Chief Financial Officer, Sonoma Valley Hospital, Sonoma, CA, p. A91

REID, Stephanie, R.N. Vice President of Quality and Chief Nursing Officer, Carroll Hospital Center, Westminster, MD, p. A294

REID, Timothy, M.D. Chief Medical Staff, Carroll County Memorial Hospital, Carrollton, MO, p. A358

REIDER, Rodney D., President, Saint Alphonsus Regional Medical Center, Boise, ID, p. A168

REIDY, Margaret, M.D. Vice President Medical Affairs, UPMC Presbyterian Shadyside, Pittsburgh, PA, p. A538

REIFF, Troy T.
  Corporate Director Operations, St. Vincent Seton Specialty Hospital, Indianapolis, IN, p. A206
  Corporate Director Operations, St. Vincent Seton Specialty Hospital, Lafayette, IN, p. A208

REIFSNYDER, Daniel, M.D. President Medical and Dental Staff, Lewistown Hospital, Lewistown, PA, p. A530

REILEY, Peggy J., R.N., Senior Vice President and Chief Clinical Officer, Scottsdale Healthcare Shea Medical Center, Scottsdale, AZ, p. A37

REILLY, Brian M., Chief Financial Officer, Robert Wood Johnson University Hospital, New Brunswick, NJ, p. A407

REILLY, Dennis A., President and Chief Executive Officer, Little Company of Mary Hospital and Health Care Centers, Evergreen Park, IL, p. A182

REILLY, Jeff
  Senior Vice President Operations, Bon Secours Community Hospital, Port Jervis, NY, p. A440
  Senior Vice President Operations, St. Anthony Community Hospital, Warwick, NY, p. A445

REILLY, John, M.D. Vice President Medical Affairs and Chief Medical Officer, Mercy Medical Center, Rockville Centre, NY, p. A441

REILLY, Richard, Deputy Executive Director, Syosset Hospital, Syosset, NY, p. A443

REILLY, Robert, Vice President and Chief Financial Officer, Anne Arundel Medical Center, Annapolis, MD, p. A287

REILLY, Theresa, R.N. Interim Chief Nursing Officer, Abington Memorial Hospital, Abington, PA, p. A519

REILLY, Tiffany, Director Human Resources, Childrens Care Hospital and School, Sioux Falls, SD, p. A562

REIMER, Arlo, M.D. Chief of Staff, Kearny County Hospital, Lakin, KS, p. A237

REIMER, Charm, Chief Financial Officer, Western State Hospital, Tacoma, WA, p. A673

REIMER, Randy, Chief Financial Officer, Adventist Behavioral Health Hospital, Rockville, MD, p. A293

REIMER, Ronda, R.N. Chief Nursing Officer, Davis County Hospital, Bloomfield, IA, p. A217

REIN, Mitchell S., M.D. Chief Medical Officer, North Shore Medical Center, Salem, MA, p. A304

REINART, Greg, Chief Financial Officer, Hereford Regional Medical Center, Hereford, TX, p. A608

REINEKE, Marilyn, Director Human Resources, Mercy Hospital of Defiance, Defiance, OH, p. A480

REINER, Rosemary, MSN Vice President and Chief Clinical Officer, The Villages Health System, The Villages, FL, p. A142

REINERT, Brenda, Director Human Resources, Tomah Memorial Hospital, Tomah, WI, p. A697

REINERT, Chad, Director Information Technology, Hamilton General Hospital, Hamilton, TX, p. A607

REINHARD, Diane, R.N. Vice President of Patient Care Services, Craig Hospital, Englewood, CO, p. A100

REINHARD, Russ, Chief Executive, Providence Willamette Falls Medical Center, Oregon City, OR, p. A515

REINHARDT, Nicole, Chief Executive Officer, Kindred Hospital–Aurora, Aurora, CO, p. A97

REINHART, Jeffery, M.D. Chief of Staff, Drew Memorial Hospital, Monticello, AR, p. A47

REINKE, Bradley, M.D. Chief of Staff, Dameron Hospital, Stockton, CA, p. A91

REINKE, N. Sue, Vice President Human Resources, Lewistown Hospital, Lewistown, PA, p. A530

REINKE, Ryan
  Chief Financial Officer, Alegent Creighton Health Lakeside Hospital, Omaha, NE, p. A387
  Chief Financial Officer, Alegent Creighton Health Midlands Hospital, Papillion, NE, p. A389

REISELT, Doug
  Vice President and Chief Information Officer, Baptist Memorial Hospital – Memphis, Memphis, TN, p. A574
  Vice President and Chief Information Officer, Baptist Memorial Hospital–Collierville, Collierville, TN, p. A567

REISLER, Harold, Controller, Methodist Hospital of Chicago, Chicago, IL, p. A177

REISMAN, Ernestine O., Vice President Human Resources, Down East Community Hospital, Machias, ME, p. A284

REISMAN, Ronald, M.D
  Chief Medical Director, St. Vincent Seton Specialty Hospital, Indianapolis, IN, p. A206
  rireisma@stvincent.org, St. Vincent Seton Specialty Hospital, Lafayette, IN, p. A208

REISNER, Monica, Director Human Resources Operations, Wilcox Memorial Hospital, Lihue, HI, p. A166

REISZ, Carol, Chief Financial Officer, North Caddo Medical Center, Vivian, LA, p. A280

REITER, Scott, D.O. Chief of Staff, Scheurer Hospital, Pigeon, MI, p. A321

REITES, Tammy, Vice President Patient Financial Services, Children's Hospital, New Orleans, LA, p. A275

REITZ, Brent, Vice President and Administrator, Adventist Rehabilitation Hospital of Maryland, Rockville, MD, p. A293

REITZ, Judy A., Sc.D. Executive Vice President and Chief Operating Officer, Johns Hopkins Hospital, Baltimore, MD, p. A287

REITZ, Robert, Ph.D., Regional Executive Officer, Fulton State Hospital, Fulton, MO, p. A361

RELPH, Daren, Chief Executive Officer, Wayne County Hospital, Corydon, IA, p. A219

REMALEY, Anne, Vice President Human Resources, ACMH Hospital, Kittanning, PA, p. A528

REMARK, Christopher, Chief Operating Officer, Aultman Hospital, Canton, OH, p. A473

REMBECKI, Roger, M.D. Chief of Staff, Missouri Baptist Sullivan Hospital, Sullivan, MO, p. A372

REMBIS, Michael A., FACHE, Chief Executive Officer, Providence Saint Joseph Medical Center, Burbank, CA, p. A55

REMIGIO, Odalys, Assistant Vice President, Finance, Baptist Health South Florida, West Kendall Baptist Hospital, Miami, FL, p. A131

REMILLARD, Jean D., M.D. Chief Medical Officer/Chief Quality Officer, Lovelace Medical Center, Albuquerque, NM, p. A414

REMILLARD, John R., President, Aurelia Osborn Fox Memorial Hospital, Oneonta, NY, p. A438

REMINGTON, Amanda
Director Human Resources, Spalding Regional Medical Center, Griffin, GA, p. A154
Director Human Resources, Sylvan Grove Hospital, Jackson, GA, p. A155

REMSPECHER, Mark, Director Human Resources, Southeast Missouri Mental Health Center, Farmington, MO, p. A360

REMSTEIN, Robert, D.O
Vice President Medical Affairs, Capital Health Medical Center–Hopewell, Pennington, NJ, p. A408
Vice President Medical Affairs, Capital Health Regional Medical Center, Trenton, NJ, p. A411

RENDON, Eloise, Director Human Resources, Twin Cities Community Hospital, Templeton, CA, p. A92

RENEDO, David, M.D. Chief of Staff, St. Joseph Hospital, Bangor, ME, p. A281

RENEY, Michael, Chief Financial Officer, Brigham and Women's Hospital, Boston, MA, p. A296

RENFREE, Mark, Chief Financial Officer, La Rabida Children's Hospital, Chicago, IL, p. A177

RENIER, Hugh, M.D
Vice President Medical Affairs, Essentia Health Duluth, Duluth, MN, p. A331
Vice President Medical Affairs, Essentia Health St. Mary's Medical Center, Duluth, MN, p. A331

RENNEKER, James M., MSN Chief Operating Officer and Chief Nursing Officer, UnityHealth Louis A. Weiss Memorial Hospital, Chicago, IL, p. A179

RENNER, Dianne, Director Human Resources, Logansport State Hospital, Logansport, IN, p. A209

RENO, III, William, M.D. President Medical Staff, Wesley Medical Center, Hattiesburg, MS, p. A348

RENSHAW, Dee, Chief Executive Officer, Hillcrest Hospital Henryetta, Henryetta, OK, p. A499

RENSHAW, Preston, M.D. Chief Medical Officer, Avera St. Anthony's Hospital, O'Neill, NE, p. A386

RENTSCH, Richard E., President, Stroud Regional Medical Center, Stroud, OK, p. A507

RENTZ, Norman G., President and Chief Executive Officer, Cannon Memorial Hospital, Pickens, SC, p. A555

REOHR, Sara, Regional Controller, West Gables Rehabilitation Hospital, Miami, FL, p. A132

REPAC, Kimberly S., Senior Vice President and Chief Financial Officer, Western Maryland Regional Medical Center, Cumberland, MD, p. A291

REPASS, Lois, Quality Assurance Specialist and Coordinator Performance Improvement, Northern Nevada Adult Mental Health Services, Sparks, NV, p. A395

REPINO, Thomas, Executive Director Ancillary Services, Connally Medical Center, Floresville, TX, p. A602

REPLOGLE, Raymond L., President and Chief Executive Officer, Continuous Care Centers of Tulsa, Tulsa, OK, p. A508

REQUIERME, Glenn P., Director Information Technology, Kindred Hospital–Baldwin Park, Baldwin Park, CA, p. A54

RESCH–SILVESTRI, Jennifer, Director Public Affairs, Kaiser Permanente Fontana Medical Center, Fontana, CA, p. A60

RESENDEZ, James R., Chief Executive Officer, South Texas Regional Medical Center, Jourdanton, TX, p. A615

RESETAR, Gayle L., Vice President and Chief Operating Officer, Georgetown Memorial Hospital, Georgetown, SC, p. A552

RESNEDER, Norma, Senior Vice President Human Resources and Organizational Development, Valley Presbyterian Hospital,, CA, p. A72

RESSLER, Dennis, Chief Financial Officer, St. Joseph Hospital and Health Center, Kokomo, IN, p. A207

RESTREPO, Macarena, Manager Business Office, Sister Emmanuel Hospital, Miami, FL, p. A132

RESTREPO, Nicolas, M.D. Vice President Medical Affairs, Winchester Medical Center, Winchester, VA, p. A663

RESTUCCIA, Michael, Chief Information Officer, Hospital of the University of Pennsylvania, Philadelphia, PA, p. A535

RESTUM, William H., Ph.D., President, Rehabilitation Institute of Michigan, Detroit, MI, p. A312

RETALIC, Tammy B., R.N. Vice President Nursing and Patient and Family Centered Care, Hebrew Rehabilitation Center, Boston, MA, p. A297

RETTGER, Linda, M.D. President Medical Staff, Kane Community Hospital, Kane, PA, p. A528

RETTIG, Linda, Director Financial Services, Washington County Hospital, Washington, KS, p. A246

RETZLAFF, Nancy, Director Human Resources, OakBend Medical Center, Richmond, TX, p. A629

REULAND, Charlie, Sc.D. Executive Vice President and Chief Operating Officer, Johns Hopkins Bayview Medical Center, Baltimore, MD, p. A287

REVELS, Beverly, Director Human Resources, Sutter Amador Hospital, Jackson, CA, p. A64

REVERMAN, Larry, Director Information Systems, Clark Memorial Hospital, Jeffersonville, IN, p. A207

REVIEL, Jackie, R.N. Vice President Patient Care Services, Beauregard Memorial Hospital, De Ridder, LA, p. A266

REWERTS, Karen
Vice President Finance, SSM Cardinal Glennon Children's Medical Center, Saint Louis, MO, p. A370
Vice President Finance and Chief Financial Officer, SSM St. Clare Health Center, Fenton, MO, p. A360

REXFORD, Linda, Director Human Resources, Weeks Medical Center, Lancaster, NH, p. A398

REXROAD, Ann, Director Information Technology, Grafton City Hospital, Grafton, WV, p. A677

REXWINKLE, Lori, Chief Nursing Officer, Coffeyville Regional Medical Center, Coffeyville, KS, p. A232

REYES, Arnold, Administrator, U. S. Penitentiary Infirmary, Lewisburg, PA, p. A530

REYES, Roxanne, Director of Nursing, Cornerstone Regional Hospital, Edinburg, TX, p. A600

REYMAN, Reed, President, St. Joseph's Hospital and Health Center, Dickinson, ND, p. A466

REYNOLDS, Angela D., Chief Financial Officer, Lewis–Gale Medical Center, Salem, VA, p. A661

REYNOLDS, Benjamin, Director Information Systems, Brookville Hospital, Brookville, PA, p. A521

REYNOLDS, Denise, Chief Nursing Officer, Memorial Hospital Miramar, Miramar, FL, p. A133

REYNOLDS, George, M.D. Vice President, Chief Information Officer and Chief Medical Information Officer, Children's Hospital and Medical Center, Omaha, NE, p. A387

REYNOLDS, Hope, Executive Director Human Resources and Support Services, Margaret R. Pardee Memorial Hospital, Hendersonville, NC, p. A454

REYNOLDS, James B., M.D. Medical Director, Northwest Missouri Psychiatric Rehabilitation Center, Saint Joseph, MO, p. A369

REYNOLDS, Jay, M.D. Chief Operating Officer and Chief Medical Officer, The Aroostook Medical Center, Presque Isle, ME, p. A285

REYNOLDS, Mark, Controller, Central State Hospital, Louisville, KY, p. A255

REYNOLDS, Mike, Chief Financial Officer, Newberry County Memorial Hospital, Newberry, SC, p. A555

REYNOLDS, Paul, M.D. Medical Director, Coleman County Medical Center, Coleman, TX, p. A592

REYNOLDS, Phyllis, R.N. VP, Nursing, Beaumont Hospital Grosse Pointe, Grosse Pointe, MI, p. A316

REYNOLDS, Randee, President, Parkview Adventist Medical Center, Brunswick, ME, p. A282

REYNOLDS, Ray, Chief Executive Officer, Glen Rose Medical Center, Glen Rose, TX, p. A606

REYNOLDS, Robert, Director Information Systems, Mary Rutan Hospital, Bellefontaine, OH, p. A471

REYNOLDS, Ronald J., President, Muncy Valley Hospital, Muncy, PA, p. A532

REYNOLDS, Teresa, Chief Operating Officer, MedWest – Haywood, Clyde, NC, p. A450

REYNOLDS, Terry, M.D. Chief of Staff, Southeast Georgia Health System Brunswick Campus, Brunswick, GA, p. A149

REYNOLDS, Todd, Chief Information Officer, Memorial Medical Center – Ashland, Ashland, WI, p. A683

REYNOLDS, Vance V., CPA, Chief Executive Officer, Texas Health Presbyterian Hospital–WNJ, Sherman, TX, p. A634

REZAC, Pamela J., Regional President, Avera Sacred Heart Hospital, Yankton, SD, p. A564

RHEE, Carolyn F., Chief Executive Officer, LAC–Olive View–UCLA Medical Center,, CA, p. A70

RHEINHEIMER, Rick, Chief Clinical Officer, Kindred Hospital–Chattanooga, Chattanooga, TN, p. A566

RHINE, Kathleen, Vice President Administrative Services and Chief Operating Officer, St. Joseph Mercy Hospital, Ypsilanti, MI, p. A327

RHINEHART, Jennie R., Administrator and Chief Executive Officer, Community Hospital, Tallassee, AL, p. A25

RHOADES, Charles E., M.D., Chief Executive Officer, Kansas City Orthopaedic Institute, Leawood, KS, p. A238

RHOADES, Mark, Vice President and Chief Human Resources Officer, Duncan Regional Hospital, Duncan, OK, p. A497

RHOADES, Shelly, Chief Financial Officer, Clarion Psychiatric Center, Clarion, PA, p. A522

RHOADS, Pam, Chief Financial Officer, Fairfax Hospital, Kirkland, WA, p. A667

RHODEN, Patty, Chief Financial Officer, Banner Estrella Medical Center, Phoenix, AZ, p. A34

RHODES, Becky, Interim Chief Executive Officer, Allen Parish Hospital, Kinder, LA, p. A270

RHODES, Eric, Assistant Vice President of Operations, Presence Covenant Medical Center, Urbana, IL, p. A196

RHODES, Gary, Interim Chief Executive Officer, Brooks Memorial Hospital, Dunkirk, NY, p. A425

RHODES, Helen, R.N. Associate Director Operations, Veterans Affairs Northern Indiana Health Care System, Fort Wayne, IN, p. A203

RHODES, J. Gary, FACHE, Chief Executive Officer, Kane Community Hospital, Kane, PA, p. A528

RHODES, Kay, R.N. Chief Nursing Officer, Redmond Regional Medical Center, Rome, GA, p. A159

RHODES, Lee, Chief Executive Officer, Central Montana Medical Center, Lewistown, MT, p. A377

RHODES, Liz, Director Information Services, Specialty Hospital Jacksonville, Jacksonville, FL, p. A127

RHODES, Robert
Chief Information Officer, Houston Medical Center, Warner Robins, GA, p. A162
Director Information Systems, Perry Hospital, Perry, GA, p. A158

RHODES, Roger, Chief Executive Officer, Baylor Surgical Hospital at Fort Worth, Fort Worth, TX, p. A603

RHODES, Sally, M.D. Administrative Director, Institute for Orthopaedic Surgery, Lima, OH, p. A484

RHUDY, Kenneth D., Chief Executive Officer, Brooks County Hospital, Quitman, GA, p. A158

RHYNE, Catherine A., R.N. Interim Vice President Clinical Services, Wilson Medical Center, Wilson, NC, p. A463

RIAL, Joanne, Chief Financial Officer, Cumberland Hospital, New Kent, VA, p. A657

RIALS, Joe, Director Fiscal Services, North Mississippi State Hospital, Tupelo, MS, p. A354

RIALS, Loren, Chief Financial Officer, Heartland Regional Medical Center, Marion, IL, p. A187

RIANO, Omaira D., Chief Nursing Officer, HEALTHSOUTH Sunrise Rehabilitation Hospital, Fort Lauderdale, FL, p. A123

RIAZ, Mohammad, M.D. Chief of Staff, Raulerson Hospital, Okeechobee, FL, p. A134

RICARD, Joan M., FACHE, Director, Edward Hines, Jr. Veterans Affairs Hospital, Hines, IL, p. A185

RICARTTI, Rebecca R., Interim Director Human Resources, Garfield Medical Center, Monterey Park, CA, p. A75

RICCI, David A., President and Chief Executive Officer, Saint Michael's Medical Center, Newark, NJ, p. A407

RICCIO, John A., M.D. Chief Medical Officer, Auburn Community Hospital, Auburn, NY, p. A420

RICCIONI, Mich
Chief Financial Officer, Petaluma Valley Hospital, Petaluma, CA, p. A79
Chief Financial Officer, Santa Rosa Memorial Hospital, Santa Rosa, CA, p. A90

RICCITELLI, Anthony, Chief Operating Officer, Worcester Recovery Center and Hospital, Worcester, MA, p. A307

RICCITELLI, Vincent, Vice President and Chief Financial Officer, Hoboken University Medical Center, Hoboken, NJ, p. A405

RICE, Amy, Chief Financial Officer, Helena Regional Medical Center, Helena, AR, p. A44

RICE, Ann Madden, Chief Executive Officer, University of California, Davis Medical Center, Sacramento, CA, p. A84

RICE, Craig, Director Information, Schneck Medical Center, Seymour, IN, p. A213

RICE, David, M.D. Vice President Medical Affairs, Northport Medical Center, Northport, AL, p. A24

RICE, James W., Director, Oscar G. Johnson Veterans Affairs Medical Center, Iron Mountain, MI, p. A317

RICE, Mark, CPA Controller, Jersey Shore Hospital, Jersey Shore, PA, p. A528

RICE, Mark, Administrator, Mid–Jefferson Extended Care Hospital, Nederland, TX, p. A624

RICE, Peter, M.D. Medical Director, PeaceHealth Ketchikan Medical Center, Ketchikan, AK, p. A28

RICE, R. Timothy, Chief Executive Officer, Cone Health, Greensboro, NC, p. A453

RICE, Thomas J., FACHE, President and Chief Executive Officer, Fawcett Memorial Hospital, Port Charlotte, FL, p. A137

RICE, Tim, President and Chief Executive Officer, Lakewood Health System, Staples, MN, p. A341

RICH, Dan, Director Finance, Texas Health Presbyterian Hospital Allen, Allen, TX, p. A581

RILEY, Randy
  Chief Financial Officer, Center for Behavioral Medicine, Kansas City, MO, p. A362
  Fiscal and Administrative Manager, Northwest Missouri Psychiatric Rehabilitation Center, Saint Joseph, MO, p. A369
RILEY, Robert, Chief Financial Officer, Novant Health Prince William Medical Center, Manassas, VA, p. A656
RILEY, Susan, Director Human Resources, HEALTHSOUTH Rehabilitation Hospital of Miami, Miami, FL, p. A131
RILEY, Tim, Vice President, Hendrick Center for Extended Care, Abilene, TX, p. A581
RILEY, Jr., William, M.D. Chief of Staff, Memorial Hermann Sugar Land Hospital, Sugar Land, TX, p. A635
RIMA, Pat, Health Care Manager, State Penitentiary Hospital, Walla Walla, WA, p. A674
RIMAR, Stephen, M.D. Senior Vice President Medical Affairs, New York Hospital Queens,, NY, p. A435
RIMEL, Jeff, Chief Financial Officer, Cibola General Hospital, Grants, NM, p. A416
RINALDI, Anthony, Executive Vice President, Fairview Hospital, Great Barrington, MA, p. A300
RINALDI, Daniel, Chief Financial Officer, Ellis Hospital, Schenectady, NY, p. A442
RINAUDO, Helen, Vice President Human Resources, Saint Francis Hospital and Health Centers, Poughkeepsie, NY, p. A440
RINDFLEISCH, Jody, Manager Human Resources, Redwood Area Hospital, Redwood Falls, MN, p. A338
RINDLER, Kyle, Director Information Systems, Mercer Health, Coldwater, OH, p. A477
RINDLER, Michael, Chief Executive Officer, St. Anthony's Medical Center, Saint Louis, MO, p. A370
RINDLISBACHER, Diane, Manager Information Systems, Orem Community Hospital, Orem, UT, p. A645
RINEHARDT, Mark, Chief Executive Officer, Wishek Community Hospital and Clinics, Wishek, ND, p. A469
RINEHART, Rick, Chief Information Officer, Carle Foundation Hospital, Urbana, IL, p. A196
RINEY, Jeremy, Chief Operating Officer, Abilene Regional Medical Center, Abilene, TX, p. A581
RINEY, Steven, Vice President Information Technology and Chief Information Officer, UnityPoint Health – Methodist, Peoria, IL, p. A192
RING, Brian K., Chief Operating Officer, Henry County Hospital, New Castle, IN, p. A211
RING, Cynthia, Vice President Human Resources, Health Alliance Hospitals, Leominster, MA, p. A301
RING, Melissa, Ph.D. Chief Operating Officer, Southeast Missouri Mental Health Center, Farmington, MO, p. A360
RINGE, Kathy, Director Human Resources, Sage Rehabilitation Hospital, Baton Rouge, LA, p. A264
RINGER, Dave, M.D. Chief of Staff, St. Mary's Good Samaritan Hospital, Greensboro, GA, p. A154
RINGLER, Judith A., Chief Information Resources Management, San Franciso Veterans Affairs Medical Center, San Francisco, CA, p. A87
RINTOUL, Alexander M., Chief Executive Officer, The Medical Center at Elizabeth Place, Dayton, OH, p. A480
RION, Trey, Chief Information Officer, West Calcasieu Cameron Hospital, Sulphur, LA, p. A279
RIOS, Cindy, Chief Financial Officer, Medical Center of Southeastern Oklahoma, Durant, OK, p. A497
RIPPE, Diana, Chief Financial Officer, Tri Valley Health System, Cambridge, NE, p. A382
RIPPERGER, Ted, Administrative Director Human Resources, Atrium Medical Center, Middletown, OH, p. A486
RIPPEY, Wesley E., M.D. Chief Medical Officer, Adventist Medical Center–Portland, Portland, OR, p. A515
RISBY, Emile, M.D. Clinical Director, Georgia Regional Hospital at Atlanta, Decatur, GA, p. A152
RISER, Donna, Administrator, S. E. Lackey Memorial Hospital, Forest, MS, p. A347
RISH, Matthew, Vice President Finance, St. Vincent Charity Medical Center, Cleveland, OH, p. A477
RISHA, Holly, Administrative Director Human Resources, College Hospital, Cerritos, CA, p. A56
RISINGER, Jennifer, M.D. Chief of Staff, Palmetto Health Richland, Columbia, SC, p. A550
RISK II, Carl W., Administrator, St. Vincent Jennings Hospital, North Vernon, IN, p. A212
RISKA, Marilouise, Chief Executive Officer, Select Specialty Hospital–Northwest Detroit, Detroit, MI, p. A312
RISLOW, Deb, Chief Information Officer, Gundersen Lutheran Medical Center, La Crosse, WI, p. A689
RISPOLI, Anthony C.
  Vice President Finance, Anderson Regional Medical Center, Meridian, MS, p. A351
  Vice President Finance, Anderson Regional Medical Center–South Campus, Meridian, MS, p. A351

RISSE, Thomas
  Chief Financial Officer and Vice President Business Services, Kaiser Permanente Medical Center, Honolulu, HI, p. A164
  Chief Financial Officer, Providence St. Peter Hospital, Olympia, WA, p. A669
RISSI, Daniel, M.D. Vice President, Chief Medical and Clinical Operations Officer, Lawrence + Memorial Hospital, New London, CT, p. A111
RITCHIE, Ann, Director Human Resources, Ochsner St. Anne General Hospital, Raceland, LA, p. A277
RITCHIE, Bruce, Vice President of Finance and Chief Financial Officer, Peninsula Regional Medical Center, Salisbury, MD, p. A294
RITCHIE, Jim, Director Management Information Systems, South Shore Hospital, Chicago, IL, p. A179
RITCHIE, Shannan, Chief Operating Officer, Lakewood Hospital, Lakewood, OH, p. A483
RITON, John, Director Information Services, Memorial Hospital of Tampa, Tampa, FL, p. A141
RITTENOUR, Melanie, Director Human Resources, Paulding County Hospital, Paulding, OH, p. A488
RITTER, J. Trees, D.O. Chief of Staff, French Hospital Medical Center, San Luis Obispo, CA, p. A88
RITTER, Jane, R.N. Chief Nursing Officer, Lovelace Women's Hospital, Albuquerque, NM, p. A414
RITTER, Randall, Associate Director, Veterans Affairs Ann Arbor Healthcare System, Ann Arbor, MI, p. A308
RITTER, Robert G., Associate Director, Harry S. Truman Memorial Veterans Hospital, Columbia, MO, p. A359
RITTMAN, Todd, Director of Nursing, Larue D. Carter Memorial Hospital, Indianapolis, IN, p. A206
RITZ, Robert P.
  President, Mercy Medical Center – West Lakes, West Des Moines, IA, p. A230
  President, Mercy Medical Center–Des Moines, Des Moines, IA, p. A220
  President and Chief Executive Officer, St. John's Hospital, Springfield, IL, p. A195
RIVARD, Betty, Vice President Human Resources, Gillette Children's Specialty Healthcare, Saint Paul, MN, p. A340
RIVAS, Jessica, R.N. Vice President and Chief Nursing Officer, John C. Lincoln Deer Valley Hospital, Phoenix, AZ, p. A34
RIVAS, Ray, Chief Financial Officer, Chapman Medical Center, Orange, CA, p. A77
RIVERA, Anthony, Director Human Resources, Hartgrove Hospital, Chicago, IL, p. A176
RIVERA, Catherine, Nurse Manager, Kindred Hospital–San Diego, San Diego, CA, p. A85
RIVERA, Christina, Director Human Resources, Southwest General Hospital, San Antonio, TX, p. A632
RIVERA, Cristina, Chief Executive Officer, Rio Grande Regional Hospital, McAllen, TX, p. A622
RIVERA, Joe, Chief Information Technology Officer, Laredo Medical Center, Laredo, TX, p. A618
RIVERA, Maria, Director Human Resources, Westside Regional Medical Center, Plantation, FL, p. A137
RIVERA, Philip, Chief Operating Officer, Memorial Medical Center, Las Cruces, NM, p. A416
RIVERS, Guy, Chief Financial Officer, Columbia Memorial Hospital, Astoria, OR, p. A511
RIVERS, Kenneth I., President and Chief Executive Officer, Hollywood Presbyterian Medical Center, Los Angeles, CA, p. A69
RIVERS, Rose, R.N. Chief Nursing Officer, St. Vincent's Medical Center Riverside, Jacksonville, FL, p. A127
RIVES, Patricia, R.N. Chief Nursing Officer, Western Medical Center–Santa Ana, Santa Ana, CA, p. A89
RIVEST, Jeffrey A., FACHE, President and Chief Executive Officer, University of Maryland Medical Center, Baltimore, MD, p. A289
RIZK, Magdy, M.D. Chief of Staff, West Houston Medical Center, Houston, TX, p. A613
RIZK, Norman, M.D. Interim Chief Medical Officer, Stanford Hospital and Clinics, Palo Alto, CA, p. A79
RIZK, Rob, Information Technology Director, Good Shepherd Health Care System, Hermiston, OR, p. A513
ROACH, David, Vice President Information Systems, Kadlec Regional Medical Center, Richland, WA, p. A670
ROACH, Dee A., M.D. Chief of Staff, Mitchell County Hospital, Colorado City, TX, p. A592
ROACH, Donna, Chief Information Officer, Borgess Medical Center, Kalamazoo, MI, p. A317
ROACH, Geoff, Director Human Resources, Forks Community Hospital, Forks, WA, p. A666
ROACH, Maureen
  Chief Financial Officer, Kindred Hospital Kansas City, Kansas City, MO, p. A363
  Senior Chief Financial Officer, Kindred Hospital–St. Louis, Saint Louis, MO, p. A369

ROACH, Steven P., Chief Executive Officer, Nashoba Valley Medical Center, Ayer, MA, p. A295
ROADCAP, Carla, MSN, Chief Executive Officer, Good Shepherd Medical Center–Linden, Linden, TX, p. A618
ROADER, Charles, Vice President Finance, Edgerton Hospital and Health Services, Edgerton, WI, p. A686
ROARK, Chris, Chief Information Officer, Stillwater Medical Center, Stillwater, OK, p. A507
ROARK, Robert, Director Human Resources, Laughlin Memorial Hospital, Greeneville, TN, p. A569
ROARTY, Maureen, Vice President Human Resources, Nassau University Medical Center, East Meadow, NY, p. A425
ROAT, David, D.O. Acting Medical Director, Ancora Psychiatric Hospital, Hammonton, NJ, p. A404
ROATH, Lee, System Chief Information Officer, Benefis Hospitals, Great Falls, MT, p. A376
ROATH, Shawna, Director Human Resources, Crittenton Children's Center, Kansas City, MO, p. A362
ROB, Lee, Director Human Resources, Pioneer Community Hospital of Aberdeen, Aberdeen, MS, p. A344
ROBB, Joy, Vice President Human Resources, Prairie View, Newton, KS, p. A240
ROBB, Lee, Director Human Resources, Covington County Hospital, Collins, MS, p. A346
ROBBINS, Dan, Information Technology and Account Executive, St. Vincent Medical Center, Los Angeles, CA, p. A72
ROBBINS, Danielle A., Vice President Human Resources, St. Catherine of Siena Medical Center, Smithtown, NY, p. A442
ROBBINS, Howard M., M.D. Senior Vice President and Chief Medical Officer, Martin Health System, Stuart, FL, p. A140
ROBBINS, Joe, M.D. Vice President Medical Affairs, Sentara Williamsburg Regional Medical Center, Williamsburg, VA, p. A663
ROBBINS, Juanita D., Chief Operating and Development Officer, Kernan Orthopaedics and Rehabilitation, Baltimore, MD, p. A287
ROBBINS, Kenneth, M.D. Chief Medical Officer, Straub Clinic & Hospital, Honolulu, HI, p. A165
ROBBIO, Joan M., Senior Vice President and Chief Human Resources Officer, Lahey Hospital & Medical Center, Burlington, Burlington, MA, p. A298
ROBEANO, Karen, MS Chief Nursing Officer and Vice President Patient Care Services, FirstHealth Moore Regional Hospital, Pinehurst, NC, p. A458
ROBERGE, Jeremy
  Director Reimbursement, Androscoggin Valley Hospital, Berlin, NH, p. A397
  Chief Financial Officer, Huggins Hospital, Wolfeboro, NH, p. A400
ROBERSON, Imelda, Director Finance, St. Vincent's St. Clair, Pell City, AL, p. A24
ROBERSON, Lynda, Senior Program Director, Rusk State Hospital, Rusk, TX, p. A630
ROBERSON, Madeleine, Chief Executive Officer, Presbyterian–St. Luke's Medical Center, Denver, CO, p. A100
ROBERTS, Alden, M.D. Chief Medical Officer, PeaceHealth Southwest Medical Center, Vancouver, WA, p. A674
ROBERTS, Allyson, CPA Chief Financial Officer, Nor–Lea General Hospital, Lovington, NM, p. A417
ROBERTS, Barbara, Chief Financial Officer, Robley Rex Veterans Affairs Medical Center, Louisville, KY, p. A256
ROBERTS, Brad, Network Administrator, Swisher Memorial Hospital District, Tulia, TX, p. A638
ROBERTS, Cathy, Director Human Resources, Mercy Regional Medical Center, Durango, CO, p. A100
ROBERTS, Charles, M.D. Medical Director, Children's Mercy South, Overland Park, KS, p. A241
ROBERTS, Cheryl, Chief Nursing Officer, McCamey County Hospital District, McCamey, TX, p. A622
ROBERTS, Curtis L., Chief Executive Officer, Select Specialty Hospital–Augusta, Augusta, GA, p. A148
ROBERTS, Cyndi, Director Human Resources, Plaza Medical Center of Fort Worth, Fort Worth, TX, p. A604
ROBERTS, Debra, Director of Human Resources, St. Luke's Lakeside Hospital, The Woodlands, TX, p. A637
ROBERTS, Floyd, M.D. Chief Medical Officer, Baton Rouge General Medical Center, Baton Rouge, LA, p. A263
ROBERTS, Glen, Chief Financial Officer, Delta Medical Center, Memphis, TN, p. A574
ROBERTS, Greg, Superintendent, Oregon State Hospital, Salem, OR, p. A517
ROBERTS, Jack, Director Information Systems, Twin County Regional Hospital, Galax, VA, p. A654
ROBERTS, John, Director Information Systems, Mena Regional Health System, Mena, AR, p. A47
ROBERTS, Jonelle A., Chief Financial Officer, Cleo Wallace Centers Hospital, Westminster, CO, p. A106
ROBERTS, Kenneth D., President, John T. Mather Memorial Hospital, Port Jefferson, NY, p. A440

ROBERTS, Kevin A., FACHE, President and Chief Executive Officer, Glendale Adventist Medical Center, Glendale, CA, p. A62

ROBERTS, Laurel, R.N., Interim Chief Executive Officer, Rolling Hills Hospital, Franklin, TN, p. A569

ROBERTS, Lisa, Chief Operating Officer, Purcell Municipal Hospital, Purcell, OK, p. A506

ROBERTS, Matthew S., Chief Executive Officer, The Medical Center of Southeast Texas, Port Arthur, TX, p. A628

ROBERTS, Michele, Hospital Recruiter, Kindred Hospital–Greensboro, Greensboro, NC, p. A453

ROBERTS, Mickey, Director Information Systems, Huey P. Long Medical Center, Pineville, LA, p. A277

ROBERTS, Pamela W., Chief Executive Officer, McNairy Regional Hospital, Selmer, TN, p. A578

ROBERTS, Phillip, Vice President Finance and Chief Financial Officer, Columbus Community Hospital, Columbus, WI, p. A685

ROBERTS, Robert C.
Vice President, Baptist Health Extended Care Hospital, Little Rock, AR, p. A46
Senior Vice President Financial Services, Baptist Health Medical Center – North Little Rock, North Little Rock, AR, p. A48
Vice President and Chief Financial Officer, Baptist Health Medical Center–Arkadelphia, Arkadelphia, AR, p. A41
Senior Vice President Financial Services, Baptist Health Medical Center–Little Rock, Little Rock, AR, p. A46
Senior Vice President, Baptist Health Rehabilitation Institute, Little Rock, AR, p. A46

ROBERTS, Roslyn, Manager, Northside Hospital–Cherokee, Canton, GA, p. A149

ROBERTS, Shane H., Chief Executive Officer, St. Luke Community Healthcare, Ronan, MT, p. A379

ROBERTS, Stacie
Coordinator Human Resources, Baylor Specialty Hospital, Dallas, TX, p. A595
Coordinator Human Resources, Our Children's House at Baylor, Dallas, TX, p. A597

ROBERTS, Stephen, Chief Information Officer, Edith Nourse Rogers Memorial Veterans Hospital, Bedford, MA, p. A295

ROBERTS, Teresa, Chief Financial Officer, Ringgold County Hospital, Mount Ayr, IA, p. A225

ROBERTSON, Bradley, Chief Financial Officer, Saint Francis Hospital, Memphis, TN, p. A575

ROBERTSON, Casey, Chief Executive Officer, Woodland Heights Medical Center, Lufkin, TX, p. A621

ROBERTSON, Darcy, Financial Officer, Northern Cochise Community Hospital, Willcox, AZ, p. A39

ROBERTSON, Gary W., Chief Executive Officer, Ferry County Memorial Hospital, Republic, WA, p. A670

ROBERTSON, James, Chief Executive Officer, White Mountain Regional Medical Center, Springerville, AZ, p. A37

ROBERTSON, Jean, M.D. Chief Information Officer, Fairfield Medical Center, Lancaster, OH, p. A483

ROBERTSON, Jimmy, Chief Financial Officer, Baptist Memorial Hospital–Golden Triangle, Columbus, MS, p. A346

ROBERTSON, Jr., Jimmy, Director Information Systems, Bothwell Regional Health Center, Sedalia, MO, p. A371

ROBERTSON, John L., Administrator, West Central Georgia Regional Hospital, Columbus, GA, p. A150

ROBERTSON, Larry, President, Texas Health Center for Diagnostic & Surgery, Plano, TX, p. A627

ROBERTSON, Laura, R.N.,
Chief Executive Officer, Banner Baywood Medical Center, Mesa, AZ, p. A32
Chief Executive Officer, Banner Heart Hospital, Mesa, AZ, p. A33

ROBERTSON, Michelle, R.N.,
President and Chief Executive Officer, Seton Highland Lakes, Burnet, TX, p. A590
President and Chief Executive Officer, Seton Medical Center Williamson, Round Rock, TX, p. A629
President and Chief Executive Officer, Seton Northwest Hospital, Austin, TX, p. A585

ROBERTSON, Patricia L., Executive Vice President, Mary Immaculate Hospital, Newport News, VA, p. A657

ROBERTSON, Steve
Vice President, Kapiolani Medical Center for Women & Children, Honolulu, HI, p. A164
Senior Vice President, Pali Momi Medical Center, Aiea, HI, p. A164
Executive Vice President and Chief Information Officer, Straub Clinic & Hospital, Honolulu, HI, p. A165
Executive Vice President Revenue Cycle Management and Chief Information Officer, Wilcox Memorial Hospital, Lihue, HI, p. A166

ROBERTSON, Tana, Chief Operating Officer, McCamey County Hospital District, McCamey, TX, p. A622

ROBERTSON–KECK, Karen, Vice President Human Resources, MedStar Franklin Square Medical Center, Baltimore, MD, p. A288

ROBERTSTAD, John R., FACHE,
President, Oconomowoc Memorial Hospital, Oconomowoc, WI, p. A693
President, Waukesha Memorial Hospital, Waukesha, WI, p. A698

ROBESON, Gail, Vice President Patient Services, Huron Regional Medical Center, Huron, SD, p. A560

ROBESON, Ricky, Chief Executive Officer, AMG Specialty Hospital–Houma, Houma, LA, p. A268

ROBICHEAUX, Warren, Administrator, East Texas Medical Center–Quitman, Quitman, TX, p. A628

ROBINS, Scott, M.D
Chief Medical Officer, Covenant Children's Hospital, Lubbock, TX, p. A619
Chief Medical Officer, Covenant Medical Center, Lubbock, TX, p. A620

ROBINSON, Alan, Chief Financial Officer, Logan Regional Hospital, Logan, UT, p. A644

ROBINSON, Bradley, Chief Financial Officer, Evans U. S. Army Community Hospital, Fort Carson, CO, p. A101

ROBINSON, Chris, M.D. Chief of Staff, Lincoln County Medical Center, Ruidoso, NM, p. A418

ROBINSON, Dan, Vice President Operations, Poudre Valley Hospital, Fort Collins, CO, p. A101

ROBINSON, David, D.O. Medical Director, St. Joseph's Behavioral Health Center, Stockton, CA, p. A92

ROBINSON, Eric, Chief Executive Officer, Natchez Community Hospital, Natchez, MS, p. A351

ROBINSON, Girard, M.D. Chief Medical Officer, Spring Harbor Hospital, Westbrook, ME, p. A286

ROBINSON, Glenn A., Chief Executive Officer, Hillcrest Baptist Medical Center, Waco, TX, p. A640

ROBINSON, Helen, Chief Clinical Officer, Ellenville Regional Hospital, Ellenville, NY, p. A425

ROBINSON, Jack, Chief Financial Officer, St. Joseph's Regional Medical Center, Paterson, NJ, p. A408

ROBINSON, James, Chief Financial Officer, George E. Weems Memorial Hospital, Apalachicola, FL, p. A118

ROBINSON, Jennifer, Administrator, Behavioral HealthCare Center at Clarksville, Clarksville, TN, p. A567

ROBINSON, John, M.D. Clinical Director, U.S. Public Health Service Indian Hospital, Redlake, MN, p. A338

ROBINSON, Lance, Associate Director, Amarillo Veterans Affairs Health Care System, Amarillo, TX, p. A582

ROBINSON, Mark, Associate Administrator and Chief Financial Officer, Hazel Hawkins Memorial Hospital, Hollister, CA, p. A64

ROBINSON, Mark, FACHE, Chief Executive Officer, Lake City Medical Center, Lake City, FL, p. A128

ROBINSON, Michael
Chief Executive Officer, Bon Secours Memorial Regional Medical Center, Mechanicsville, VA, p. A657
Executive Vice President and Administrator, Bon Secours–Richmond Community Hospital, Richmond, VA, p. A660

ROBINSON, Nellie C., R.N. Executive Vice President, Patient Services & Chief Nursing Officer, Children's National Medical Center, Washington, DC, p. A116

ROBINSON, Pat, Manager Accounting, St. Vincent Rehabilitation Hospital, Sherwood, AR, p. A50

ROBINSON, Paul H., M.D. Medical Director, American Fork Hospital, American Fork, UT, p. A643

ROBINSON, Phillip D., President, Lankenau Medical Center, Wynnewood, PA, p. A545

ROBINSON, Richard H., Chief Executive Officer, Yakima Regional Medical and Cardiac Center, Yakima, WA, p. A674

ROBINSON, Stephen, Chief Operating Officer, Lakeview Regional Medical Center, Covington, LA, p. A265

ROBINSON, Susan Beth, Vice President Human Resources, St. Mary's Medical Center, Huntington, WV, p. A678

ROBINSON, Thaddeus, Chief Information Officer, Welch Community Hospital, Welch, WV, p. A681

ROBINSON, Tim, Executive Vice President, Chief Financial and Administrative Officer and Treasurer, Nationwide Children's Hospital, Columbus, OH, p. A477

ROBINSON, Vance, Chief Information Officer, Homer Memorial Hospital, Homer, LA, p. A268

ROBINSON, William, Director Human Resources, HEALTHSOUTH Rehabilitation Hospital of Erie, Erie, PA, p. A525

ROBINSON, William J., Senior Vice President and Treasurer, Shands at the University of Florida, Gainesville, FL, p. A124

ROBISCH, Christine, Senior Vice President and Area Manager, Kaiser Permanente San Francisco Medical Center, San Francisco, CA, p. A86

ROBISON, Bruce, Vice President and Chief Information Officer, Lester E. Cox Medical Centers, Springfield, MO, p. A372

ROBISON, Deborah, R.N., Chief Executive Officer and Administrator, Christus St. Michael Hospital–Atlanta, Atlanta, TX, p. A584

ROBISON, Keith, Chief Information Officer, Woman's Christian Association Hospital, Jamestown, NY, p. A427

ROBISON, Neely, Director Human Resources, The BridgeWay, North Little Rock, AR, p. A48

ROBISON, Ryan, Nursing Administrator, Sanpete Valley Hospital, Mount Pleasant, UT, p. A644

ROBISON, Wendell, M.D. Chief of Staff, Sheridan Veterans Affairs Medical Center, Sheridan, WY, p. A703

ROBITAILLE, Mark E., President and Chief Executive Officer, Martin Health System, Stuart, FL, p. A140

ROBSON, Alan M., M.D. Senior Vice President and Medical Director, Children's Hospital, New Orleans, LA, p. A275

ROBSON, Marcia, R.N. Chief Nursing Officer, Ozarks Medical Center, West Plains, MO, p. A373

ROBSON, Melissa, President, Novant Health Prince William Medical Center, Manassas, VA, p. A656

ROCA, Robert, M.D. Vice President Medical Affairs, Sheppard Pratt Health System, Baltimore, MD, p. A289

ROCHE, Alana, Director Human Resources, Louisiana Heart Hospital, Lacombe, LA, p. A270

ROCHE, Joseph E.
Chief Executive Officer, Monroe Hospital, Bloomington, IN, p. A199
Chief Executive Officer, St. Vincent Dunn Hospital, Bedford, IN, p. A198

ROCHE, Kathleen M., R.N. Executive Vice President and Chief Operating Officer, Saint Francis Hospital and Medical Center, Hartford, CT, p. A109

ROCHE, Lori, Chief Operating Officer, Wyoming County Community Hospital, Warsaw, NY, p. A445

ROCHE, Richard J., Vice President Human Resources and Support Services, Memorial Health, Savannah, GA, p. A160

ROCK, Betty Ann, Vice President Nursing and Chief Nursing Officer, Uniontown Hospital, Uniontown, PA, p. A542

ROCK, Brian, Director Information Systems, Culpeper Regional Hospital, Culpeper, VA, p. A653

ROCK, Michael, M.D
Chief Medical Officer, Mayo Clinic – Saint Marys Hospital, Rochester, MN, p. A339
Chief Medical Officer, Rochester Methodist Hospital, Rochester, MN, p. A339

ROCKSMITH, Eugenio, M.D. Medical Director, HEALTHSOUTH Rehabilitation Hospital of Vineland, Vineland, NJ, p. A412

ROCKWELL, Jane, Director Support Services, North Metro Medical Center, Jacksonville, AR, p. A45

ROCKWOOD, John D., President, MedStar National Rehabilitation Hospital, Washington, DC, p. A116

ROCKWOOD, Judith Ann, Administrator, Cheyenne County Hospital, Saint Francis, KS, p. A243

RODDEN, Celeste, Chief Information Officer, Hillcrest Hospital Claremore, Claremore, OK, p. A497

RODDY, Thomas, Assistant Administrator, Sandhills Regional Medical Center, Hamlet, NC, p. A454

RODDY, Tim, M.D. Vice President Medical Affairs, Swedish/Edmonds, Edmonds, WA, p. A666

RODDY, Walt, Director Information Management Systems, Natchez Regional Medical Center, Natchez, MS, p. A351

RODEN, George
Vice President Human Resources, Mercy Hospital Aurora, Aurora, MO, p. A356
Vice President Human Resources, Mercy Hospital Cassville, Cassville, MO, p. A358

RODENBAUGH, Cathy, Director Human Resources, Holy Rosary Healthcare, Miles City, MT, p. A378

RODERICK, Travis W., Chief Executive Officer, North Texas Hospital, Denton, TX, p. A599

RODGE, Mark, Director Information Systems, Eaton Rapids Medical Center, Eaton Rapids, MI, p. A313

RODGERS, April, Vice President, Human Resources, Holy Name Medical Center, Teaneck, NJ, p. A411

RODGERS, Jamie, Chief Executive Officer and Administrator, Baptist Memorial Hospital–Tipton, Covington, TN, p. A568

RODGERS, Larry, Chief Executive Officer, Scenic Mountain Medical Center, Big Spring, TX, p. A588

RODGERS, Susan K., MSN Chief Operating Officer, Lovelace Medical Center, Albuquerque, NM, p. A414

RODGES, Teresa, Executive Director Marketing and Public Relations, McLaren Oakland, Pontiac, MI, p. A322

RODIER, James Barton, M.D. Chief Quality Officer, Health Central, Ocoee, FL, p. A134

RODOWICZ, Darlene, Chief Financial Officer, Berkshire Medical Center, Pittsfield, MA, p. A304

RODRIGUES, Pablo, M.D. Medical Director, Kindred Hospital–Amarillo, Amarillo, TX, p. A582

RODRIGUEZ, Alex
  Vice President and Chief Information Officer, St. Elizabeth Edgewood, Edgewood, KY, p. A250
  Vice President and Chief Information Officer, St. Elizabeth Florence, Florence, KY, p. A250
  Vice President and Chief Information Officer, St. Elizabeth Fort Thomas, Fort Thomas, KY, p. A251
RODRIGUEZ, Ben A., Chief Executive Officer, Hialeah Hospital, Hialeah, FL, p. A125
RODRIGUEZ, Catherine, Chief Financial Officer, Ventura County Medical Center, Ventura, CA, p. A94
RODRIGUEZ, Enrique, M.D. Medical Director, Ilano Specialty Hospital of Lubbock, Lubbock, TX, p. A620
RODRIGUEZ, Joe, Chief Executive Officer, South Texas Health System, Edinburg, TX, p. A600
RODRIGUEZ, Joseph, Chief Executive Officer, Acadia Vermilion Hospital, Lafayette, LA, p. A270
RODRIGUEZ, Leticia, Controller, Ward Memorial Hospital, Monahans, TX, p. A623
RODRIGUEZ, Luis, M.D. Chief of Staff, Vidant Roanoke–Chowan Hospital, Ahoskie, NC, p. A447
RODRIGUEZ, Marco, Chief Financial Officer, Navarro Regional Hospital, Corsicana, TX, p. A594
RODRIGUEZ, Mario, Chief Executive Officer, Laredo Specialty Hospital, Laredo, TX, p. A618
RODRIGUEZ, Martha, Chief Financial Officer, Sunnyside Community Hospital, Sunnyside, WA, p. A673
RODRIGUEZ, Patricia, Senior Vice President and Area Manager, Kaiser Permanente South Sacramento Medical Center, Sacramento, CA, p. A83
RODRIGUEZ, Ramon J., President and Chief Executive Officer, Wyckoff Heights Medical Center,, NY, p. A437
RODRIGUEZ, Rufus, M.D. Medical Director, Mayo Clinic Health System in Fairmont, Fairmont, MN, p. A332
RODRIGUEZ, Tony, Director Human Resources, South Texas Rehabilitation Hospital, Brownsville, TX, p. A590
RODRIGUEZ, Wilfredo, M.D. Chief of Staff, Battle Creek Veterans Affairs Medical Center, Battle Creek, MI, p. A309
RODRIQUEZ, Daisy, Director Human Resources, Fort Duncan Regional Medical Center, Eagle Pass, TX, p. A600
ROE, Barbara, Vice President and Director Human Resources, Christus St. Vincent Regional Medical Center, Santa Fe, NM, p. A418
ROE, Timothy, Chief Information Officer, Hillside Rehabilitation Hospital, Warren, OH, p. A492
ROE, Timothy J., President and Chief Executive Officer, Rehabilitation Hospital of the Pacific, Honolulu, HI, p. A165
ROEBACK, Jason, President, UPMC Northwest, Seneca, PA, p. A541
ROEBKEN, Curtis, M.D. Chief Medical Staff, Kentfield Rehabilitation and Specialty Hospital, Kentfield, CA, p. A65
ROEDER, Donna, Chief Financial Officer, Jackson County Regional Health Center, Maquoketa, IA, p. A224
ROEDER, Werner, M.D. Vice President Medical Affairs, Lawrence Hospital Center, Bronxville, NY, p. A422
ROEDERER, Chris, Vice President Human Resources, Tampa General Hospital, Tampa, FL, p. A142
ROEHRICH, Jeff, Chief Financial Officer, Spearfish Regional Surgery Center, Spearfish, SD, p. A563
ROEHRLE, Andreas, Director Finance, Sentara Williamsburg Regional Medical Center, Williamsburg, VA, p. A663
ROEMER, Dennis, Executive Vice President and Chief Financial Officer, Lancaster General Health, Lancaster, PA, p. A528
ROESER, William, President and Chief Executive Officer, Sparrow Ionia Hospital, Ionia, MI, p. A316
ROETMAN, James D., President and Chief Executive Officer, Pocahontas Community Hospital, Pocahontas, IA, p. A227
ROEVER, Judy, MSN Chief Nursing Officer, Scenic Mountain Medical Center, Big Spring, TX, p. A588
ROFF, Lynette A., Director, Veterans Affairs Eastern Colorado Health Care System, Denver, CO, p. A100
ROGALSKI, Ted, Chief Executive Officer, Mercer County Hospital, Aledo, IL, p. A173
ROGAN, Edie, Manager Human Resources, Eastern State Hospital, Williamsburg, VA, p. A663
ROGENESS, Graham, M.D. Medical Director, Clarity Child Guidance Center, San Antonio, TX, p. A631
ROGERS, Aaron, Chief Executive Officer, Mountainview Medical Center, White Sulphur Springs, MT, p. A380
ROGERS, Bard, M.D. Chief of Staff, Golden Plains Community Hospital, Borger, TX, p. A589
ROGERS, David, Chief Executive Officer, Sanford Webster Medical Center, Webster, SD, p. A564
ROGERS, Doris, Vice President Human Resources, Saint Luke's Hospital of Kansas City, Kansas City, MO, p. A363
ROGERS, Emily, Manager Human Resources, Community Westview Hospital, Indianapolis, IN, p. A205
ROGERS, Gregory H., President, MidMichigan Medical Center–Midland, Midland, MI, p. A320

ROGERS, James E., Executive Director, Sonoma Developmental Center, Eldridge, CA, p. A59
ROGERS, James H., FACHE, Chief Executive Officer, Select Specialty Hospital–Savannah, Savannah, GA, p. A160
ROGERS, Jared, M.D. Chief Medical Officer, Presence Covenant Medical Center, Urbana, IL, p. A196
ROGERS, Joan, R.N. Chief Nursing Officer, St. Helena Hospital Clear Lake, Clearlake, CA, p. A56
ROGERS, Joel, Chief Operating Officer, Minidoka Memorial Hospital, Rupert, ID, p. A171
ROGERS, Joseph J., Vice President and Chief Operating Officer, Redwood Memorial Hospital, Fortuna, CA, p. A60
ROGERS, Judith, Ph.D., President and Chief Executive Officer, Holy Cross Hospital, Silver Spring, MD, p. A294
ROGERS, Kathy, Vice President Marketing, Conejos County Hospital, La Jara, CO, p. A102
ROGERS, Keith
  Administrator, Advance Care Hospital, Hot Springs National Park, AR, p. A45
  Interim Administrator, Advance Care Hospital of Fort Smith, Fort Smith, AR, p. A44
ROGERS, LaDonna, Director Human Resources, T. J. Samson Community Hospital, Glasgow, KY, p. A251
ROGERS, Lucy, Chief Information Resource Management Systems, Veterans Affairs North Texas Health Care System, Dallas, TX, p. A598
ROGERS, Mark E., Interim Chief Executive Officer, Kindred Hospital– Oklahoma City, Oklahoma City, OK, p. A503
ROGERS, Mark G.
  Interim Vice President Finance and Chief Financial Officer, Genesis Medical Center, Illini Campus, Silvis, IL, p. A194
  Interim Vice President Finance and Chief Financial Officer, Genesis Medical Center–Davenport, Davenport, IA, p. A219
ROGERS, Matt, Chief Financial Officer, Philhaven, Mount Gretna, PA, p. A532
ROGERS, Michael, Vice President Fiscal Services, Brattleboro Memorial Hospital, Brattleboro, VT, p. A649
ROGERS, Paul
  Chief Financial Officer, Crittenden Regional Hospital, West Memphis, AR, p. A51
  Chief Financial Officer, Mena Regional Health System, Mena, AR, p. A47
  Chief Financial Officer, Mineral Area Regional Medical Center, Farmington, MO, p. A360
ROGERS, Ralph, M.D. Vice President Medical Affairs and Chief Medical Officer, Spectrum Health – Grand Rapids, Grand Rapids, MI, p. A315
ROGERS, Randy, Chief Financial Officer, Vaughan Regional Medical Center, Selma, AL, p. A25
ROGERS, Rhonda
  Chief Financial Officer, Des Peres Hospital, Saint Louis, MO, p. A369
  Chief Financial Officer, Nacogdoches Medical Center, Nacogdoches, TX, p. A624
ROGERS, Rich
  Senior Vice President Support Services and Chief Information Officer, Health First Cape Canaveral Hospital, Cocoa Beach, FL, p. A121
  Senior Vice President Support Services and Chief Information Officer, Health First Holmes Regional Medical Center, Melbourne, FL, p. A130
ROGERS, Richard K., FACHE Vice President Human Resources, Wayne Memorial Hospital, Goldsboro, NC, p. A453
ROGERS, II, Robert T., M.D. Medical Director, Canton–Potsdam Hospital, Potsdam, NY, p. A440
ROGERS, Scott, Chief Operating Officer, Bear Valley Community Hospital, Big Bear Lake, CA, p. A55
ROGERS, Sherry L., MS Chief Nursing Officer, Redington–Fairview General Hospital, Skowhegan, ME, p. A285
ROGERS, Valerie J., Director of Nursing, Cherokee Nation W.W. Hastings Indian Hospital, Tahlequah, OK, p. A507
ROGERS, W. Kent, Chief Executive Officer, Valley View Regional Hospital, Ada, OK, p. A495
ROGERS, William, Chief Medical Officer, Gilmore Memorial Regional Medical Center, Amory, MS, p. A344
ROGNESS, Robin, Vice President and Chief Financial Officer, Mercy Hospital of Folsom, Folsom, CA, p. A60
ROGOLS, Kevin L., FACHE, Chief Executive Officer, UNM Sandoval Regional Medical Center, Rio Rancho, NM, p. A417
ROGOZ, Brian, Vice President Finance and Treasurer, The Hospital of Central Connecticut, New Britain, CT, p. A110
ROHAN, Colleen, Director Human Resources, Little Company of Mary Hospital and Health Care Centers, Evergreen Park, IL, p. A182
ROHAN, Heather J., Chief Executive Officer, Tristar Centennial Medical Center, Nashville, TN, p. A577
ROHM, Stephen G., M.D. VP and Chief Medical Officer, Hamilton Medical Center, Dalton, GA, p. A151

ROHMAN, Cindy, R.N. Vice President/Chief Nursing Officer, Lexington Medical Center, West Columbia, SC, p. A556
ROHRBACH, Dan D., President and Chief Executive Officer, Southwest Health Center, Platteville, WI, p. A695
ROHRBACH, William K., Vice President Fiscal Affairs, Memorial Hospital, Towanda, PA, p. A542
ROHRER, Harry
  Chief Financial Officer, Bascom Palmer Eye Institute–Anne Bates Leach Eye Hospital, Miami, FL, p. A131
  Chief Financial Officer, University of Miami Hospital, Miami, FL, p. A132
  Chief Financial Officer, University of Miami Hospital and Clinics, Miami, FL, p. A132
ROHRER, Mark, M.D. Chief Medical Officer, Kindred Hospital–Boston, Brighton, MA, p. A298
ROIG, Emilio, M.D. Network Medical Director, Devereux Hospital and Children's Center of Florida, Melbourne, FL, p. A130
ROIZ, PHR, JoAnn, Director Human Resources, HEALTHSOUTH Tustin Rehabilitation Hospital, Tustin, CA, p. A93
ROJAS, Anna, Chief Executive Officer, Kindred Hospital Tarrant County–Fort Worth Southwest, Fort Worth, TX, p. A604
ROJAS, CiCi
  Vice President Community Engagement, Truman Medical Center–Hospital Hill, Kansas City, MO, p. A364
  Vice President Community Engagement, Truman Medical Center–Lakewood, Kansas City, MO, p. A364
ROKAVEC, Kathleen, M.D. Medical Director, Kona Community Hospital, Kealakekua, HI, p. A166
ROKOSZ, Gregory, D.O. Senior Vice President Medical and Academic Affairs, Saint Barnabas Medical Center, Livingston, NJ, p. A405
ROLAND, Brian, Chief Executive Officer, Hamlin Memorial Hospital, Hamlin, TX, p. A607
ROLFE, David, Chief Information Officer, Madonna Rehabilitation Hospital, Lincoln, NE, p. A385
ROLFE, Randall H., President, Bakersfield Heart Hospital, Bakersfield, CA, p. A53
ROLFF, Christi, Director Business Development, San Joaquin Valley Rehabilitation Hospital, Fresno, CA, p. A62
ROLING, Robin, President and Chief Executive Officer, Hot Springs County Memorial Hospital, Thermopolis, WY, p. A704
ROLL, Susan, Chief Human Resources, National Jewish Health, Denver, CO, p. A99
ROLLINS, David, Chief Resource Management, Carl R. Darnall Army Medical Center, Fort Hood, TX, p. A603
ROLLINS, J. Michael, M.D. Chief of Staff, St. Joseph's Hospital of Buckhannon, Buckhannon, WV, p. A675
ROLLINS, James
  Chief Financial Officer, Arbour H. R. I. Hospital, Brookline, MA, p. A298
  Chief Financial Officer, Arbour–Fuller Hospital, Attleboro, MA, p. A295
ROLLINS, James, M.D. President Medical Staff, Saint Joseph Mount Sterling, Mount Sterling, KY, p. A258
ROLLINS, Larry, Supervisor Information Technology, McCamey County Hospital District, McCamey, TX, p. A622
ROLLMAN, Ann, Vice President Human Resources, Southeastern Ohio Regional Medical Center, Cambridge, OH, p. A472
ROLOFF, Maria, Vice President Human Resources, Mission Hospital, Asheville, NC, p. A447
ROMAN, Edward
  Chief Information Officer and Chief Privacy Officer, Mid–Valley Hospital, Peckville, PA, p. A534
  Chief Information Officer and Chief Privacy Officer, Moses Taylor Hospital, Scranton, PA, p. A540
ROMAN, Eloy, M.D. Chief of Staff, Palmetto General Hospital, Hialeah, FL, p. A125
ROMAN, Linda K., Administrator, Coast Plaza Hospital, Norwalk, CA, p. A76
ROMAN, Tracy, Chief Financial Officer, Doctors Hospital of Manteca, Manteca, CA, p. A73
ROMANIELLO, Guy, Director Fiscal Services, Belmont Center for Comprehensive Treatment, Philadelphia, PA, p. A534
ROMANO, C. James, M.D. President Medical Staff, St. Francis Medical Center, Trenton, NJ, p. A411
ROMANO, Jana, Manager Human Resources, Good Shepherd Penn Partners Specialty Hospital at Rittenhouse, Philadelphia, PA, p. A535
ROMANO, Michael A., M.D. Vice President Medical Affairs, Methodist Jennie Edmundson Hospital, Council Bluffs, IA, p. A219
ROMANO, Sara, R.N. Vice President, Mountain View Hospital, Gadsden, AL, p. A20
ROMANOW, Sandra, Director Management Information Systems, Piedmont Newnan Hospital, Newnan, GA, p. A158
ROMANS, Alan, Director Information Technology, Ashland Health Center, Ashland, KS, p. A231
ROMARY, Paul, Chief Executive Officer, Lemuel Shattuck Hospital, Jamaica Plain, MA, p. A301

ROMBERGER, Randall R., Administrator, Shriners Hospitals for Children–Greenville, Greenville, SC, p. A552

ROMEO, Betty, Chief Information Officer, Rancho Los Amigos National Rehabilitation Center, Downey, CA, p. A58

ROMERO, Brenda, Administrator, Espanola Hospital, Espanola, NM, p. A416

ROMERO, Cynthia, M.D. Chief Medical Officer, Chesapeake Regional Medical Center, Chesapeake, VA, p. A652

ROMERO, Ed, Chief Financial Officer, Laredo Medical Center, Laredo, TX, p. A618

ROMERO, Jose, Director Human Resources, Corcoran District Hospital, Corcoran, CA, p. A57

ROMERO, Matt, Vice President Finance and Chief Financial Officer, Hillcrest Hospital – South, Tulsa, OK, p. A508

ROMIG, Glenn, Chief Financial Officer, Osceola Regional Medical Center, Kissimmee, FL, p. A127

ROMINE, Andy, Chief Nursing Officer, Trinity Medical Center, Birmingham, AL, p. A17

ROMINE, Donnie
    Chief Operating Officer, St. Vincent's Medical Center Riverside, Jacksonville, FL, p. A127
    Chief Operating Officer, St. Vincent's Medical Center Southside, Jacksonville, FL, p. A127

ROMINE, Mickey, Manager, Creek Nation Community Hospital, Okemah, OK, p. A502

ROMITO, Ed, Director Information Systems, Genesis HealthCare System, Zanesville, OH, p. A494

ROMITO, John A., M.D. Chief Medical Officer, Overland Park Regional Medical Center, Overland Park, KS, p. A242

ROMO, Jose, M.D. Chief of Staff, Copper Queen Community Hospital, Bisbee, AZ, p. A30

ROMO, Jose, Vice President of Operations, Rogue Valley Medical Center, Medford, OR, p. A515

RONAN, Barry P., President and Chief Executive Officer, Western Maryland Regional Medical Center, Cumberland, MD, p. A291

RONCA, Cyndi, Director Human Resources, Twin Cities Hospital, Niceville, FL, p. A134

RONKE, Lisa, Director Finance, St. Michael's Hospital Avera, Tyndall, SD, p. A563

RONSMAN, Randy, Director Information Services, Bellin Psychiatric Center, Green Bay, WI, p. A687

ROODMAN, Richard D., Chief Executive Officer, UW Medicine/Valley Medical Center, Renton, WA, p. A670

ROOKER, Mark, Director Information Systems, Susan B. Allen Memorial Hospital, El Dorado, KS, p. A233

ROONEY, Al, Director Information Systems, St. Vincent Healthcare, Billings, MT, p. A374

ROONEY, Jeffrey, Chief Financial Officer, MetroHealth Medical Center, Cleveland, OH, p. A476

ROONEY, Thomas, Chief Information Resource Management, Veterans Affairs Hudson Valley Health Care System–F.D. Roosevelt Hospital, Montrose, NY, p. A430

ROOSA, Carol, Chief Information Officer, Monadnock Community Hospital, Peterborough, NH, p. A400

ROOT, Jim, Vice President Human Resources, Saint Elizabeth's Medical Center, Wabasha, MN, p. A342

ROOT, Rodney Mark, D.O. Vice President Medical Affairs, Bakersfield Memorial Hospital, Bakersfield, CA, p. A53

ROPER, Doni, Director Human Resources, Madison St. Joseph Health Center, Madisonville, TX, p. A621

ROPER, Embra, Chief Medical Officer, Regional Hospital for Respiratory and Complex Care, Seattle, WA, p. A670

ROPER, Sandra, Chief Human Resources, General Leonard Wood Army Community Hospital, Fort Leonard Wood, MO, p. A361

ROQUE–VELASCO, Ismael, M.D., Chief Executive Officer, Metropolitan Hospital of Miami, Miami, FL, p. A131

RORAFF, Gregory E., President and Chief Executive Officer, Blue Hill Memorial Hospital, Blue Hill, ME, p. A282

ROSAAEN, Nancy, Chief Executive Officer, McCone County Health Center, Circle, MT, p. A375

ROSALES, Teresa, M.D. Clinical Director, Mental Health Institute, Clarinda, IA, p. A218

ROSARIO, Peter, M.D. Chief Medical Officer, St. Mary's Warrick Hospital, Boonville, IN, p. A199

ROSAS, John, Compliance Officer, Essex County Hospital Center, Cedar Grove, NJ, p. A402

ROSATO, Ricardo, M.D. President Medical Staff, Shands Lake Shore Regional Medical Center, Lake City, FL, p. A128

ROSBOROUGH, Heidi, Manager Human Resources, Health Alliance Hospital – Mary's Avenue Campus, Kingston, NY, p. A428

ROSBURG, Deb, Chief Financial Officer, Sanford Sheldon Medical Center, Sheldon, IA, p. A227

ROSCHEWSKI, Dwana, Director Fiscal Services, Dundy County Hospital, Benkelman, NE, p. A382

ROSCOE, Joan
    Chief Information Officer, Shenandoah Memorial Hospital, Woodstock, VA, p. A663
    Chief Information Officer, Winchester Medical Center, Winchester, VA, p. A663

ROSE, Cheryl, Human Resources Director, Fulton County Medical Center, Mc Connellsburg, PA, p. A530

ROSE, Hugh, Vice President Fiscal Management, Palos Community Hospital, Palos Heights, IL, p. A191

ROSE, J. Anthony, President and Chief Executive Officer, Catawba Valley Medical Center, Hickory, NC, p. A454

ROSE, Laurie, Director Human Resources, Sutter Medical Center, Sacramento, Sacramento, CA, p. A84

ROSE, Mary R., R.N. Chief Clinical Officer, Community Health Center of Branch County, Coldwater, MI, p. A311

ROSE, Mary Beth, Vice President Human Resources, Saint Michael's Medical Center, Newark, NJ, p. A407

ROSE, May, Director Human Resources, Memorial Hospital, Chester, IL, p. A176

ROSE, Michael S., Senior Vice President Finance and Chief Financial Officer, Southern New Hampshire Medical Center, Nashua, NH, p. A399

ROSE, Richard T., Associate Director, Manchester Veterans Affairs Medical Center, Manchester, NH, p. A399

ROSE, Robert, R.N. Senior Vice President/System Chief Nursing Offcer, Mother Frances Hospital – Tyler, Tyler, TX, p. A638

ROSE, Robin, R.N. Chief Nursing Officer, Gibson Area Hospital and Health Services, Gibson City, IL, p. A183

ROSE, Steven P., Chief Financial Officer, Conway Regional Medical Center, Conway, AR, p. A42

ROSE, Steven A., R.N., Chief Executive Officer, Nanticoke Memorial Hospital, Seaford, DE, p. A114

ROSECRANS, Brenda, Director Human Resources and Education, Albemarle Health, Elizabeth City, NC, p. A452

ROSEN, Barry, M.D. Vice President Medical Management, Advocate Good Shepherd Hospital, Barrington, IL, p. A174

ROSEN, Michael, M.D. Chief Medical Officer, Havasu Regional Medical Center, Lake Havasu City, AZ, p. A32

ROSEN, Raymond, FACHE Vice President Operations, York Hospital, York, PA, p. A545

ROSENA, Robens, Director Information Systems, Delray Medical Center, Delray Beach, FL, p. A122

ROSENBECK, James, D.O. Chief of Staff, Central Valley Medical Center, Nephi, UT, p. A645

ROSENBERG, Patricia, R.N. Vice President Patient Care Services and Chief Nursing Officer, McLaren Macomb, Mount Clemens, MI, p. A320

ROSENBERG, Steven
    Chief Financial Officer, Danbury Hospital, Danbury, CT, p. A108
    Senior Vice President, Chief Financial Officer and Treasurer, New Milford Hospital, New Milford, CT, p. A111

ROSENBERG, Stuart E., Chief Executive Officer, Johnson Memorial Hospital, Stafford Springs, CT, p. A112

ROSENBERGER, Robert
    Executive Vice President and Chief Financial Officer, Centegra Hospital – McHenry, McHenry, IL, p. A188
    Executive Vice President, Chief Financial Officer, Centegra Hospital – Woodstock, Woodstock, IL, p. A197

ROSENBLATT, Michael, M.D. Medical Director, Kindred Rehabilitation Hospital Clear Lake, Webster, TX, p. A640

ROSENBURG, Deborah L., Director Human Resources, West Valley Hospital, Goodyear, AZ, p. A32

ROSENBUSH, Rachel, Account Manager, Sanford Bagley Medical Center, Bagley, MN, p. A329

ROSENCRANCE, Daris, Chief Financial Officer, Monongalia General Hospital, Morgantown, WV, p. A679

ROSENCRANCE, Michael, Vice President Information Services, Spectrum Health – Grand Rapids, Grand Rapids, MI, p. A315

ROSENDAHL, Lisa, Director Human Resources, St. Cloud Veterans Affairs Health Care System, Saint Cloud, MN, p. A339

ROSENDORFF, Clive, M.D. Chief Medical Program, James J. Peters Veterans Affairs Medical Center,, NY, p. A432

ROSENFELD, Merryll, Vice President Human Resources, Southern New Hampshire Medical Center, Nashua, NH, p. A399

ROSENSTEIN, Gaynor, Vice President Operations, Bon Secours Community Hospital, Port Jervis, NY, p. A440

ROSENTHAL, J. Robert, M.D. Senior Vice President Medical Affairs, New York Eye and Ear Infirmary, New York, NY, p. A435

ROSENTHAL, J. Thomas, M.D. Chief Medical Officer, Ronald Reagan University of California Los Angeles Medical Center, Los Angeles, CA, p. A71

ROSETTA, Kathy, Chief Nursing Officer, Laurel Ridge Treatment Center, San Antonio, TX, p. A631

ROSILES, Nancy, Coordinator Human Resources, HEALTHSOUTH Rehabilitation Hospital of Arlington, Arlington, TX, p. A583

ROSKOVSKI, Stephanie, Chief Operating Officer, Butler Health System, Butler, PA, p. A521

ROSLER, Andrea P., Vice President Human Resources, Huntsville Hospital, Huntsville, AL, p. A21

ROSMAN, Joseph, M.D. Chief Medical Director, RML Specialty Hospital, Chicago, IL, p. A178

ROSNER, Neil, Area Director Human Resources, Kindred Hospital–New Jersey Morris County, Dover, NJ, p. A403

ROSNO, Shawn, Deputy Director Operations, Elmira Psychiatric Center, Elmira, NY, p. A425

ROSS, Aletha, Vice President Human Resources, Ingalls Memorial Hospital, Harvey, IL, p. A184

ROSS, Candace, Coordinator Human Resources, HEALTHSOUTH Western Hills Rehabilitation Hospital, Parkersburg, WV, p. A679

ROSS, Carmella, Manager Human Resources, The Hospital at Hebrew Health Care, West Hartford, CT, p. A112

ROSS, Charles, M.D. Vice President Medical Affairs, Chilton Hospital, Pompton Plains, NJ, p. A409

ROSS, Craig A., M.D. Chief of Staff, College Hospital Costa Mesa, Costa Mesa, CA, p. A57

ROSS, Harvey, Chief Executive Officer, Kindred Hospital–Denver, Denver, CO, p. A99

ROSS, Hoyt, Chief Executive Officer, Kindred Hospital North Florida, Green Cove Springs, FL, p. A125

ROSS, Jacqueline, Chief Human Resources Officer, Spokane Veterans Affairs Medical Center, Spokane, WA, p. A672

ROSS, James E., Chief Operating Officer, Camden General Hospital, Camden, TN, p. A566

ROSS, James E., FACHE, President and Chief Executive Officer, Chester River Health System, Chestertown, MD, p. A290

ROSS, James E., Vice President and Chief Operating Officer, Jackson–Madison County General Hospital, Jackson, TN, p. A570

ROSS, Jay, Chief Financial Officer, St. Joseph's Area Health Services, Park Rapids, MN, p. A338

ROSS, Jeffrey, M.D. Medical Director, AMG Specialty Hospital–Albuquerque, Albuquerque, NM, p. A414

ROSS, John, Vice President, Franciscan St. Francis Health – Mooresville, Mooresville, IN, p. A203

ROSS, John M., Vice President Finance and Chief Financial Officer, Rochelle Community Hospital, Rochelle, IL, p. A193

ROSS, Joseph, Chief Financial Officer, Livingston Regional Hospital, Livingston, TN, p. A573

ROSS, Joseph P., President and Chief Executive Officer, Meritus Medical Center, Hagerstown, MD, p. A292

ROSS, Julie, R.N. Chief Nursing Officer, Select Specialty Hospital–Zanesville, Zanesville, OH, p. A494

ROSS, Kathy
    Chief Information Officer, Providence Hospital, Mobile, AL, p. A22
    Chief Information Officer, Sacred Heart Hospital of Pensacola, Pensacola, FL, p. A137

ROSS, Kelly, M.D. Chief of Staff, Mitchell County Regional Health Center, Osage, IA, p. A226

ROSS, Lisa, Human Resources Officer, Greater Regional Medical Center, Creston, IA, p. A219

ROSS, Phil, Chief Executive Officer, Surgical Hospital of Oklahoma, Oklahoma City, OK, p. A504

ROSS, Robert, M.D. Chief of Staff, Ortonville Area Health Services, Ortonville, MN, p. A337

ROSS, Robert, Executive Vice President and Chief Operating Officer, St. Luke's Cornwall Hospital, Newburgh, NY, p. A437

ROSS, Samuel Lee, MS, Chief Executive Officer, Bon Secours Baltimore Health System, Baltimore, MD, p. A287

ROSS Jr., Semmes, Administrator, Lawrence County Hospital, Monticello, MS, p. A351

ROSS, Zeff, FACHE, Senior Vice President and Chief Executive Officer, Memorial Regional Hospital,, FL, p. A125

ROSS–COLE, Melissa, Director Human Resources, Regency Hospital of Northwest Arkansas, Fayetteville, AR, p. A43

ROSS–SPANG, Carol, Senior Vice President, Methodist Healthcare Memphis Hospitals, Memphis, TN, p. A575

ROSSDALE, Robert, Deputy Executive Director, Queens Hospital Center,, NY, p. A436

ROSSETTI, Stephen J., Ph.D., President and Chief Executive Officer, Saint Luke Institute, Silver Spring, MD, p. A294

ROSSFELD, John, Interim Chief Executive Officer, Newman Regional Health, Emporia, KS, p. A233

ROSSI, Alfred N., M.D., Chief Executive Officer, Hopedale Medical Complex, Hopedale, IL, p. A185

ROSSI, Coleen, Director Quality Services, HEALTHSOUTH Rehabilitation Hospital of Toms River, Toms River, NJ, p. A411

ROSSI, Frank J., Senior Vice President Human Resources, Cook Children's Medical Center, Fort Worth, TX, p. A603

ROSSI, Lawrence, M.D. Clinical Director, Trenton Psychiatric Hospital, Trenton, NJ, p. A411

ROSSI, Mark F., Chief Operating Officer and General Counsel, Hopedale Medical Complex, Hopedale, IL, p. A185

ROSSITTO, Erica, R.N. Chief Nursing Officer, North Suburban Medical Center, Thornton, CO, p. A106

ROSSMAN, Greg, Chief Human Resource Officer, Denver Health Medical Center, Denver, CO, p. A99

ROSSMANN, Barbara, R.N., President and Chief Executive Officer, Henry Ford Macomb Hospitals, Clinton Township, MI, p. A311

ROSSMANN, Samuel H., Chief Executive Officer, TOPS Surgical Specialty Hospital, Houston, TX, p. A613

ROSSYION, Stephanie, Chief Clinical Officer, Kindred Hospital Lafayette, Lafayette, LA, p. A270

ROSVOLD, Robert, Director Finance, Virtua Voorhees, Voorhees, NJ, p. A412

ROTELLA, William, Vice President Human Resources, University of North Carolina Hospitals, Chapel Hill, NC, p. A449

ROTENBERRY-BAGGETT, Katie, Administrative Assistant and Human Resources, Yalobusha General Hospital, Water Valley, MS, p. A354

ROTERT, Jeffrey J., Chief Operating Officer, Sanford Worthington Medical Center, Worthington, MN, p. A343

ROTH, Anna M., Chief Executive Officer, Contra Costa Regional Medical Center, Martinez, CA, p. A73

ROTH, Chris, Chief Executive Officer, St. Luke's Regional Medical Center, Boise, ID, p. A168

ROTH III, Edward J., President and Chief Executive Officer, Aultman Hospital, Canton, OH, p. A473

ROTH, Eugene, Vice President Information Services, Mercy Hospital St. Louis, Saint Louis, MO, p. A370

ROTH, Norman G., Executive Vice President and Chief Operating Officer, Bridgeport Hospital, Bridgeport, CT, p. A108

ROTH, Steven, Vice President Informatics and Chief Information Officer, Pinnacle Health System, Harrisburg, PA, p. A527

ROTHE, Brian, Site Director Information Systems, Castle Medical Center, Kailua, HI, p. A165

ROTHMAN, Marc, M.D. Medical Director, Friends Hospital, Philadelphia, PA, p. A535

ROTHSCHILD, Marylee, M.D. Chief of Staff, Robley Rex Veterans Affairs Medical Center, Louisville, KY, p. A256

ROTHSTEIN, Fred C., M.D., President, University Hospitals Case Medical Center, Cleveland, OH, p. A477

ROTHSTEIN, Robert, M.D. Vice President Medical Affairs, Suburban Hospital, Bethesda, MD, p. A290

ROTY, Chris, President, Baptist Health La Grange, La Grange, KY, p. A253

ROUND, Valerie, Chief Executive Officer, St. John Sapulpa, Sapulpa, OK, p. A506

ROUNDS, George, M.D. Chief of Staff, Bigfork Valley Hospital, Bigfork, MN, p. A329

ROUNDS, Jason, Chief Operating Officer, CHRISTUS St. Michael Rehabilitation Hospital, Texarkana, TX, p. A637

ROUNDY, Ann, Vice President Employee Services, Columbus Community Hospital, Columbus, WI, p. A685

ROUNSLEY, Karen, Controller, HEALTHSOUTH Chesapeake Rehabilitation Hospital, Salisbury, MD, p. A294

ROUSH, Barbara, Chief Operating Officer, Sierra Vista Hospital, Sacramento, CA, p. A83

ROUSH, Sharon L., Chief Executive Officer, South Bay Hospital, Sun City Center, FL, p. A140

ROUSSEAU, Mickie, Director Human Resources, Terrebonne General Medical Center, Houma, LA, p. A268

ROUSSEL, Steve
Chief Financial Officer, Baylor Medical Center at McKinney, McKinney, TX, p. A622
Vice President Finance, Baylor Medical Center at Waxahachie, Waxahachie, TX, p. A640

ROUTH, Lori, R.N
Nurse Administrator, Mayo Clinic Health System in Albert Lea, Albert Lea, MN, p. A328
Nurse Administrator, Mayo Clinic Health System in Austin, Austin, MN, p. A329

ROUX, Roger, Senior Vice President Financial Affairs and Chief Financial Officer, Rady Children's Hospital – San Diego, San Diego, CA, p. A85

ROUZER, Cindy, Director Human Resources, Spooner Health System, Spooner, WI, p. A696

ROVITO, Kevin, Chief Financial Officer, Jackson Hospital, Marianna, FL, p. A130

ROWAN, Dan, M.D. President Medical Staff, Little Company of Mary Hospital and Health Care Centers, Evergreen Park, IL, p. A182

ROWAN, R. C., Director Human Resources, Neosho Memorial Regional Medical Center, Chanute, KS, p. A232

ROWAND, Sean, Chief Information Officer, Erie Veterans Affairs Medical Center, Erie, PA, p. A525

ROWE, Chad D., Director Human Resources, Aspirus Keweenaw Hospital, Laurium, MI, p. A319

ROWE, Jeanne M., M.D. Chief Medical Officer, Shore Medical Center, Somers Point, NJ, p. A410

ROWE, Linda, R.N. Chief Nursing Officer, Carson Valley Medical Center, Gardnerville, NV, p. A391

ROWE, Paul W., Director Information Technology, St. Francis Hospital, Wilmington, DE, p. A115

ROWE, Scott, Chief Executive Officer, HEALTHSOUTH Chattanooga Rehabilitation Hospital, Chattanooga, TN, p. A566

ROWELL, Jim H., Vice President Human Resources, Rutherford Regional Health System, Rutherfordton, NC, p. A460

ROWEN, Jennifer, Director Human Resources, Cornerstone Hospital of North Little Rock, Jacksonville, AR, p. A45

ROWLAND, Claire, Director Human Resources, Acadia Vermilion Hospital, Lafayette, LA, p. A270

ROWLAND, Martha Tolbert, Vice President Finance, Saint Thomas Rutherford Hospital, Murfreesboro, TN, p. A576

ROWLAND, Michael, M.D. Vice President Medical Affairs, Franklin Memorial Hospital, Farmington, ME, p. A283

ROWLAND, Robert, M.D. Medical Director, HEALTHSOUTH Rehabilitation Hospital of Tallahassee, Tallahassee, FL, p. A140

ROWLANDS, Dewey R., Vice President Finance and Chief Financial Officer, Oneida Healthcare, Oneida, NY, p. A438

ROWLEY, Mike, Chief Executive Officer, Springbrook Behavioral Health System, Travelers Rest, SC, p. A556

ROWLEY, Tim, Chief Operating Officer, Perkins County Health Services, Grant, NE, p. A384

ROWSHAN, Omid, M.D. President Medical Staff, Lower Bucks Hospital, Bristol, PA, p. A521

ROY, Joel, Manager Information Systems, The Brook Hospital – KMI, Louisville, KY, p. A256

ROY, Merri, Director Information Services, Weatherford Regional Medical Center, Weatherford, TX, p. A640

ROY, Rock, Professional Services Director, Power County Hospital District, American Falls, ID, p. A167

ROY, Schindelheim, M.D. Chief of Staff, George L. Mee Memorial Hospital, King City, CA, p. A65

ROYAL, Jennifer A., Administrator, Burke Medical Center, Waynesboro, GA, p. A162

ROYAL, Keli, Director Human Resources, Shenandoah Medical Center, Shenandoah, IA, p. A228

ROYAL, Ty, Executive Director of Support Services and Human Resources, Gibson Area Hospital and Health Services, Gibson City, IL, p. A183

ROYER, Jerry, M.D. Chief Medical Officer, San Joaquin General Hospital, French Camp, CA, p. A61

ROYSTER, Randy, Vice President Human Resources, Lovelace Medical Center, Albuquerque, NM, p. A414

ROZARIO, Nirmala, M.D. Chief of Staff, Spokane Veterans Affairs Medical Center, Spokane, WA, p. A672

ROZELL, Becky, Chief Human Resources Officer, Madison County Hospital, London, OH, p. A484

ROZMUS, Mike, Director Information Systems, Rockingham Memorial Hospital, Harrisonburg, VA, p. A655

ROZNOVSKY, Karen, Director Human Resources, Yoakum Community Hospital, Yoakum, TX, p. A642

RUBAR, Jackie, Administrative Assistant and Director Human Resources, Leesville Rehabilitation Hospital, Leesville, LA, p. A272

RUBE, David M., M.D. Clinical Director, New York City Children's Center,, NY, p. A434

RUBENS, Deborah, Director Human Resources, Shriners Hospitals for Children–Northern California, Sacramento, CA, p. A83

RUBERDALL, Stephen, M.D. Chief Medical Officer, Grady General Hospital, Cairo, GA, p. A149

RUBERTI, Charlene, Director Information Technology Development, Ancora Psychiatric Hospital, Hammonton, NJ, p. A404

RUBIN, Amir Dan, President and Chief Executive Officer, Stanford Hospital and Clinics, Palo Alto, CA, p. A79

RUBIN, Richard, M.D. Chief Medical Officer, St. Mary's Hospital, Troy, NY, p. A444

RUBIN, Vincent, Chief Financial Officer, Brotman Medical Center, Culver City, CA, p. A58

RUBINATE, Donna, R.N. Chief Operating Officer, Good Samaritan Medical Center, Brockton, MA, p. A298

RUBINSTEIN, Mitchell, M.D. Vice President Medical Affairs, Valley Hospital, Ridgewood, NJ, p. A410

RUBIO, Felipe, M.D. Medical Director, Kindred Hospital–Dayton, Dayton, OH, p. A480

RUBLE, Charalene, Chief Nursing Officer, Ilano Specialty Hospital of Lubbock, Lubbock, TX, p. A620

RUCHTI, Kevin, Coordinator Information Systems, Grant Regional Health Center, Lancaster, WI, p. A689

RUCHTI, Robert D., Chief Executive Officer, Buchanan General Hospital, Grundy, VA, p. A655

RUCKEL, Michael R., Vice President Finance, Decatur County Memorial Hospital, Greensburg, IN, p. A204

RUCKER, Alisa, Vice President Finance and Chief Financial Officer, Washington Hospital, Washington, PA, p. A543

RUCKER, Billy, Administrator, Riverland Medical Center, Ferriday, LA, p. A267

RUCKER, Craig
Senior Vice President and Chief Financial Officer, Bethesda North Hospital, Cincinnati, OH, p. A474
Senior Vice President and Chief Financial Officer, Good Samaritan Hospital, Cincinnati, OH, p. A474

RUCKER, Sheryl, Chief Information Officer, Edgerton Hospital and Health Services, Edgerton, WI, p. A686

RUDD, Barry, Chief Information Officer, Mayo Clinic Health System in Waycross, Waycross, GA, p. A162

RUDD, John, Chief Financial Officer, Cayuga Medical Center at Ithaca, Ithaca, NY, p. A427

RUDDEN, Elizabeth, Vice President Human Resources, Connecticut Children's Medical Center, Hartford, CT, p. A109

RUDEK, Charles M., Chief Information Officer, UPMC St. Margaret, Pittsburgh, PA, p. A538

RUDIN, Joel, Chief Executive Officer, New England Rehabilitation Hospital, Woburn, MA, p. A306

RUDIS, Lorrie, Director Human Resources, Crotched Mountain Rehabilitation Center, Greenfield, NH, p. A398

RUDITZ, Bettiann S., Chief Nursing Officer, Broward Health North, Deerfield Beach, FL, p. A122

RUDOLF, Steven, Vice President Human Resources, Baptist Health Louisville, Louisville, KY, p. A255

RUDOLPH, Dawn, Chief Executive Officer, Saint Thomas West Hospital, Nashville, TN, p. A577

RUDZIK, Donna, Director Human Resources, Hopkins County Memorial Hospital, Sulphur Springs, TX, p. A636

RUE, Robert, Controller, Ellenville Regional Hospital, Ellenville, NY, p. A425

RUECKERT, Sebastian, M.D. Chief Medical Officer, Christian Hospital, Saint Louis, MO, p. A369

RUEDISUELI, Amy, Chief Financial Officer, McKenzie Health System, Sandusky, MI, p. A324

RUELLO, Rocky, Vice President Human Resources, Mercy Hospital St. Louis, Saint Louis, MO, p. A370

RUFAT, Berta, Controller, Baptist Health South Florida, South Miami Hospital, Miami, FL, p. A131

RUFF, Victoria, M.D. Medical Director, Select Specialty Hospital–Columbus, Columbus, OH, p. A178

RUFFING, Jr., John J., M.D. Chief of Staff, Box Butte General Hospital, Alliance, NE, p. A381

RUFFOLO, Joseph A., President and Chief Executive Officer, Niagara Falls Memorial Medical Center, Niagara Falls, NY, p. A437

RUGE, Randy, Chief Operating Officer, Paulding County Hospital, Paulding, OH, p. A488

RUGGERO, Robert, Senior Vice President Operations, Lourdes Medical Center of Burlington County, Willingboro, NJ, p. A412

RUHLEN, Michael, M.D. Chief Medical Officer, Carolinas Medical Center–Mercy, Charlotte, NC, p. A449

RUIZ, Javier, M.D. Medical Director, Intracare North Hospital, Houston, TX, p. A610

RUIZ, Jesus, Chief Executive Officer, Mesa Hills Specialty Hospital, El Paso, TX, p. A601

RUIZ, Mary, Chief Executive Officer, Manatee Glens Hospital and Addiction Center, Bradenton, FL, p. A119

RUIZ, Ralph, Director Information Technology and Services, Kendall Regional Medical Center, Miami, FL, p. A131

RUIZ, Tony, Chief Operating Officer, Medical Center Health System, Odessa, TX, p. A625

RUKAVINA, Mark, M.D. Chief Medical Staff, Marcum and Wallace Memorial Hospital, Irvine, KY, p. A253

RUKSTAD, Julie, Chief Financial Officer, Olympic Medical Center, Port Angeles, WA, p. A669

RUMANS, Mark C., M.D. Physician in Chief, Billings Clinic, Billings, MT, p. A374

RUMBAUT, Michelle, Chief Operating Officer, Guadalupe Regional Medical Center, Seguin, TX, p. A633

RUMFORD, Darren K., Chief Financial Officer, Geary Community Hospital, Junction City, KS, p. A236

RUMMEL, Jennifer
Director Human Resources, East Texas Medical Center Athens, Athens, TX, p. A584
Director Human Resources, East Texas Medical Center Fairfield, Fairfield, TX, p. A602

RUNGE, Andrew, Chief Operating Officer, Mercy Hospital Hot Springs, Hot Springs National Park, AR, p. A45

RUNKE, David, Chief Financial Officer, Riverside County Regional Medical Center, Moreno Valley, CA, p. A75

RUNOLFSON, Kevin, Chief Executive Officer, Mitchell County Regional Health Center, Osage, IA, p. A226

RUNT, David, Chief Information Officer, Banner Del E. Webb Medical Center, Sun City West, AZ, p. A38

RUNYAN, Duane, Chief Executive Officer and Managing Director, Rivendell Behavioral Health Services of Arkansas, Benton, AR, p. A41

RUNYAN, Mark, Director Information Services, Salt Lake Regional Medical Center, Salt Lake City, UT, p. A647

RUOTOLO, Frank, Chief Information Officer, Gateway Medical Center, Clarksville, TN, p. A567

RUPERT, Duke, President and Chief Executive Officer, Western Pennsylvania Hospital, Pittsburgh, PA, p. A539

RUPERT, James M., Chief Fiscal Services, Battle Creek Veterans Affairs Medical Center, Battle Creek, MI, p. A309

RUPERT, Michael J., Chief Financial Officer, Veterans Affairs Long Beach Healthcare System, Long Beach, CA, p. A68

RUPP, Robert, Chief Executive Officer, Harris Hospital, Newport, AR, p. A48

RUPPEL, Rick, Chief Financial Officer, Memorial Hospital, Fremont, OH, p. A481

RUPPERT SCHILLER, Kerri
Senior Vice President and Chief Financial Officer, Children's Hospital at Mission, Mission Viejo, CA, p. A74
Senior Vice President and Chief Financial Officer, Children's Hospital of Orange County, Orange, CA, p. A77

RUSCITTO, Kathryn H., President, St. Joseph's Hospital Health Center, Syracuse, NY, p. A444

RUSH, Ann Marie, Chief Financial Officer, Penobscot Valley Hospital, Lincoln, ME, p. A284

RUSH, Christopher, Vice President and Administrator, Rush Foundation Hospital, Meridian, MS, p. A351

RUSH, Cindy, Director Human Resources, Clay County Medical Center, Clay Center, KS, p. A232

RUSH, Domenica, Chief Executive Officer, Sierra Vista Hospital, Truth or Consequences, NM, p. A418

RUSH, Donald J., Chief Executive Officer, Providence Kodiak Island Medical Center, Kodiak, AK, p. A28

RUSH, Ed, President and Chief Executive Officer, Iredell Memorial Hospital, Statesville, NC, p. A461

RUSH, Jeff W.
Interim Vice President Finance, Angel Medical Center, Franklin, NC, p. A452
Chief Financial Officer, Wallace Thomson Hospital, Union, SC, p. A556

RUSH, Matthew, President and Chief Executive Officer, Hayes Green Beach Memorial Hospital, Charlotte, MI, p. A310

RUSHIN, Denise, Director Human Resources, Poplar Bluff Regional Medical Center, Poplar Bluff, MO, p. A368

RUSHING, R. Lynn, Chief Executive Officer, Brook Lane Health Services, Hagerstown, MD, p. A292

RUSHING, Robyn, Administrator, Lakeview Specialty Hospital and Rehabilitation Center, Waterford, WI, p. A698

RUSHING, Tracy, Executive Assistant Human Resources and Payroll, Pioneer Community Hospital of Newton, Newton, MS, p. A352

RUSHNELL, Christi C., Vice President Information Technology, Health First Palm Bay Hospital, Melbourne, FL, p. A130

RUSIGNUOLO, Brian, Senior Vice President Information Services, Baylor Institute for Rehabilitation, Dallas, TX, p. A595

RUSK, Scott, M.D. Vice President Medical Administration, Mercy Hospital of Portland, Portland, ME, p. A284

RUSKOWSKI, David, President, Franciscan St. Anthony Health – Crown Point, Crown Point, IN, p. A201

RUSSAKOFF, David, M.D. Chief Medical Officer, Princeton Baptist Medical Center, Birmingham, AL, p. A17

RUSSELL, Dardanella, Chief Human Resources Management Service, Veterans Affairs Hudson Valley Health Care System–F.D. Roosevelt Hospital, Montrose, NY, p. A430

RUSSELL, Dee B., M.D. Vice President & Chief of Medical Affairs, Floyd Medical Center, Rome, GA, p. A159

RUSSELL, Donald
Vice President, Adventist GlenOaks Hospital, Glendale Heights, IL, p. A183
Regional Vice President Human Resources, Adventist Hinsdale Hospital, Hinsdale, IL, p. A185

RUSSELL, Erin, Controller, Kindred Hospital–San Antonio, San Antonio, TX, p. A631

RUSSELL, Eunice, Manager Human Resources, Arrowhead Behavioral Health Hospital, Maumee, OH, p. A486

RUSSELL, Freda, Interim Chief Executive Officer, Three Rivers Hospital, Waverly, TN, p. A580

RUSSELL, Georgette, Vice President of Talent & Organizational Effectiveness, Carson City Hospital, Carson City, MI, p. A310

RUSSELL, James G., Chief Operating Officer, Medical Center of Lewisville, Lewisville, TX, p. A618

RUSSELL, John D., President and Chief Executive Officer, Columbus Community Hospital, Columbus, WI, p. A685

RUSSELL, Jon
Chief Information Officer, Greene Memorial Hospital, Xenia, OH, p. A494
Vice President Information Systems, Kettering Medical Center, Kettering, OH, p. A483
Chief Information Officer, Sycamore Medical Center, Miamisburg, OH, p. A486

RUSSELL, Judy, Director of Nurses, Ochiltree General Hospital, Perryton, TX, p. A627

RUSSELL, Karen, Director Human Resources, Perry Memorial Hospital, Princeton, IL, p. A192

RUSSELL, Kathy, R.N. Chief Nursing Officer, Bluegrass Community Hospital, Versailles, KY, p. A261

RUSSELL, Kim, M.D. Chief of Staff, Scott & White Hospital – Llano, Llano, TX, p. A619

RUSSELL, Linda, Director Human Resources, Kindred Hospital–Indianapolis, Indianapolis, IN, p. A206

RUSSELL, Linda B., Chief Executive Officer, The Woman's Hospital of Texas, Houston, TX, p. A613

RUSSELL, Marvin
Corporate Senior Vice President Human Resources, Beth Israel Medical Center, New York, NY, p. A430
Senior Vice President Human Resources, St. Luke's–Roosevelt Hospital Center, New York, NY, p. A436

RUSSELL, Michelle L., Administrator, Community Howard Specialty Hospital, Kokomo, IN, p. A207

RUSSELL, Nancy, Chief Financial Officer, Clifton–Fine Hospital, Star Lake, NY, p. A443

RUSSELL, Robert, Chief Operating Officer, Atlanta Medical Center, Atlanta, GA, p. A146

RUSSELL, Robert J., Associate Executive Director Operations, Penn Presbyterian Medical Center, Philadelphia, PA, p. A536

RUSSELL, Shelia, Director Human Resources, Jamestown Regional Medical Center, Jamestown, TN, p. A570

RUSSELL, Sherrie
Vice President and Chief Information Officer, Alexian Brothers Behavioral Health Hospital, Hoffman Estates, IL, p. A185
Chief Information Officer, St. Alexius Medical Center, Hoffman Estates, IL, p. A185

RUSSELL, Thomas, President and Chief Executive Officer, Adventist Medical Center–Portland, Portland, OR, p. A515

RUSSELL, Tim, Administrator, Stillwater Community Hospital, Columbus, MT, p. A375

RUSSELL, William B., Chief Executive Officer, Three Rivers Health, Three Rivers, MI, p. A325

RUSSELL–COOK, Donna, President, St. Elizabeth Hospital, Enumclaw, WA, p. A666

RUSSO, Arthur, M.D. Director Medical Affairs, Harrington Memorial Hospital, Southbridge, MA, p. A304

RUSSO, Kimberly, Chief Operating Officer, George Washington University Hospital, Washington, DC, p. A116

RUSSO, Michael, Chief Administrative Officer, Saint Anthony's Health Center, Alton, IL, p. A173

RUSSO, Mike, Vice President Information Systems, Grimes St. Joseph Health Center, Navasota, TX, p. A624

RUSSO, Paul M., FACHE, Director, Miami Veterans Affairs Healthcare System, Miami, Fl., p. A132

RUTH, Daniel R., President and Chief Executive Officer, Jewish Home of San Francisco, San Francisco, CA, p. A86

RUTH, Joseph, Executive Vice President and Chief Operating Officer, Sparrow Hospital, Lansing, MI, p. A318

RUTHER, Randy, Vice President Finance and Chief Financial Officer, Little Company of Mary Hospital and Health Care Centers, Evergreen Park, IL, p. A182

RUTHERFORD, Cynthia, Manager Business Office, Hood Memorial Hospital, Amite, LA, p. A262

RUTHERFORD, Dennis E., Chief Financial Officer, Palo Verde Hospital, Blythe, CA, p. A55

RUTHERFORD, George W., Vice President and Chief Operating Officer, Sparrow Ionia Hospital, Ionia, MI, p. A316

RUTHERFORD, Michael, Chief Financial Officer, Ohio State University Wexner Medical Center, Columbus, OH, p. A478

RUTHERFORD, Theresa, FACHE, President and Chief Executive Officer, St. Anthony's Memorial Hospital, Effingham, IL, p. A181

RUTHERFORD, Theresa, R.N. Chief Operating Officer, St. Mary's Hospital, Decatur, IL, p. A180

RUTKOWSKI, James C., Chief Financial Officer, Southwest Regional Medical Center, Waynesburg, PA, p. A543

RUTKOWSKI, Jennifer, R.N. Vice President Professional Services, Grant Regional Health Center, Lancaster, WI, p. A689

RUTLEDGE, Geri, Director Business, East Mississippi State Hospital, Meridian, MS, p. A351

RUTLEDGE, Virginia, Assistant Administrator, Barton County Memorial Hospital, Lamar, MO, p. A364

RUTTER, James, M.D. Chief of Staff, Integris Grove General Hospital, Grove, OK, p. A499

RUWOLDT, Steven T., Chief Executive Officer, Salem Community Hospital, Salem, OH, p. A489

RUYTER, Mary J., Chief Executive Officer, Sanford Jackson Medical Center, Jackson, MN, p. A334

RYALS, Billie, Human Resources Director, Sullivan County Memorial Hospital, Milan, MO, p. A366

RYAN, Chris, Chief Information Officer, Auburn Community Hospital, Auburn, NY, p. A420

RYAN, Christina M., R.N., Chief Executive Officer, The Women's Hospital, Newburgh, IN, p. A211

RYAN, Colleen
Director Management Information Systems, Landmark Medical Center, Woonsocket, RI, p. A547
Chief Information Officer and Vice President Professional Services, Rehabilitation Hospital of Rhode Island, North Smithfield, RI, p. A546

RYAN, Cory, M.D. Chief of Staff, Wayne County Hospital, Monticello, KY, p. A258

RYAN, David, Vice President Human Resources, Falmouth Hospital, Falmouth, MA, p. A300

RYAN, Debora, R.N. Vice President Patient Care, St. Francis Regional Medical Center, Shakopee, MN, p. A341

RYAN, Dennis, Senior Vice President and Chief Financial Officer, Children's Hospital of The King's Daughters, Norfolk, VA, p. A658

RYAN, Frank, Chief Financial Officer, Manchester Veterans Affairs Medical Center, Manchester, NH, p. A399

RYAN, J. Thomas, M.D
Executive Vice President and Chief Medical Officer, Mary Washington Hospital, Fredericksburg, VA, p. A654
Executive Vice President and Chief Medical Officer, Stafford Hospital, Stafford, VA, p. A661

RYAN, Jacqueline, Director Human Resources, Mayo Clinic Health System in Lake City, Lake City, MN, p. A334

RYAN, Kimberly, Chief Executive Officer, Eastside Medical Center, Snellville, GA, p. A160

RYAN, Lisa M., Coordinator Human Resources, Hampstead Hospital, Hampstead, NH, p. A398

RYAN, Maria, Ph.D., Chief Executive Officer, Cottage Hospital, Woodsville, NH, p. A400

RYAN, Michael, Senior Vice President Finance, Memorial Hospital of Rhode Island, Pawtucket, RI, p. A546

RYAN, Michael J., Chief Executive Officer, Herington Municipal Hospital, Herington, KS, p. A235

RYAN, Mike, Director of Information Services, Gunnison Valley Hospital, Gunnison, UT, p. A643

RYAN, Patrice
Vice President Human Resources, Goleta Valley Cottage Hospital, Santa Barbara, CA, p. A89
Vice President Human Resources, Santa Barbara Cottage Hospital, Santa Barbara, CA, p. A89
Vice President Human Resources, Santa Ynez Valley Cottage Hospital, Solvang, CA, p. A91

RYAN, Patrick, M.D. Chief of Staff, Greenbrier Valley Medical Center, Ronceverte, WV, p. A680

RYAN, Raymond, M.D. Chief of Staff, Fayette County Hospital, Vandalia, IL, p. A196

RYAN, Rebecca, Interim Director Human Resources and Employee Health, Ukiah Valley Medical Center, Ukiah, CA, p. A94

RYAN, Stacy, Corporate Director Human Resources, Warren General Hospital, Warren, PA, p. A543

RYAN, Tim, Director Finance, Centennial Peaks Hospital, Louisville, CO, p. A104

RYAN, Jr., Timothy J., Director Human Resources, Lewis County General Hospital, Lowville, NY, p. A428

RYBA, Janice L., JD, Chief Executive Officer, St. Mary Medical Center, Hobart, IN, p. A204

RYBA, Thomas L., Chief Executive Officer, Lighthouse Care Center of Conway, Conway, SC, p. A551

RYBA, Tomi S., President and Chief Executive Officer, El Camino Hospital, Mountain View, CA, p. A75

RYBICKI, Cathy, Chief Operating Officer, Spectrum Health Reed City Hospital, Reed City, MI, p. A322

RYBOLT, Andrew
Vice President and Chief Financial Officer, Redwood Memorial Hospital, Fortuna, CA, p. A60
Chief Financial Officer, St. Joseph Hospital, Eureka, CA, p. A59

RYCHENER, Michelle, Chief Operating Officer, Henry County Hospital, Napoleon, OH, p. A487

RYDER, Doug, Vice President Clinical Operations and Service Lines, Advocate Good Shepherd Hospital, Barrington, IL, p. A174

RYDER, Jeff, Director Information Systems, Saint Joseph Mount Sterling, Mount Sterling, KY, p. A258

RYDER, Jennifer, Director of Nursing, Mercy Continuing Care Hospital, Chesterfield, MO, p. A358

RYDER, John
Interim Administrator and Chief Operating Officer, Borgess–Lee Memorial Hospital, Dowagiac, MI, p. A313
Chief Operating Officer, Borgess–Lee Memorial Hospital, Dowagiac, MI, p. A313
Administrator and Chief Executive Officer, Borgess–Pipp Hospital, Plainwell, MI, p. A322

RYDER, Rebecca L., R.N., President and Chief Executive Officer, Franklin Memorial Hospital, Farmington, ME, p. A283

RYDER, Ronald, D.O. President of the Medical Staff, Robert Wood Johnson University Hospital at Hamilton, Hamilton, NJ, p. A404

RYERSON, Michelle, Chief Nursing Officer, University Medical Center at Brackenridge, Austin, TX, p. A586

RYERSON, Nancy, Director Information Systems, Central Florida Regional Hospital, Sanford, FL, p. A139

RYKERT, Lauren P., Senior Vice President, The Methodist Hospital, Houston, TX, p. A613

RYLAND, Jennifer M., R.N. Chief Administrative Officer, Jackson Medical Center, Jackson, AL, p. A22

RYLE, Barry, Chief Information Officer, Oswego Hospital, Oswego, NY, p. A439

RYLE, Deborah L., Administrator and Chief Executive Officer, St. David's Round Rock Medical Center, Round Rock, TX, p. A629

# S

SAAL, A. Kim, M.D. President Medical Staff, Mount Auburn Hospital, Cambridge, MA, p. A299

SAALFELD, Thomas, Senior Vice President and Chief Operating Officer, St. Elizabeth Fort Thomas, Fort Thomas, KY, p. A251

SAAVEDRA, JayLynn, Chief Information Officer, U. S. Public Health Service Indian Hospital, Parker, AZ, p. A33

SAAVEDRA, John, Service Area Director Human Resources, Providence Saint Joseph Medical Center, Burbank, CA, p. A55

SABA, Fadi, M.D. Chief of Staff, Edward White Hospital, Saint Petersburg, FL, p. A139

SABA, Francis M., Chief Executive Officer, Milford Regional Medical Center, Milford, MA, p. A302

SABAHI, Hugh, M.D. President Professional Staff, Columbia Memorial Hospital, Astoria, OR, p. A511

SABAHI, Mojtaba, M.D. Chief of Staff, Promise Hospital of East Los Angeles, Suburban Medical Center Campus, Paramount, CA, p. A79

SABANDIT, Elizabeth, Director Human Resources, Alhambra Hospital Medical Center, Alhambra, CA, p. A52

SABHARRWAL, Parajeet, Administrator, Minimally Invasive Surgery Center, Lenexa, KS, p. A238

SABIA, John, M.D. Medical Director, Northern Dutchess Hospital, Rhinebeck, NY, p. A440

SABIN, Bridget, Director Human Resources, Madison Hospital, Madison, MN, p. A335

SABIN, Margaret D., President and Chief Executive Officer, Penrose–St. Francis Health Services, Colorado Springs, CO, p. A98

SABITTI, Jesse, M.D. Chief Medical Officer, Kenmare Community Hospital, Kenmare, ND, p. A468

SABOTTA, John, Director Information Systems, St. Margaret's Hospital, Spring Valley, IL, p. A195

SABUS, Matthew, Director Information Systems, Boone County Hospital, Boone, IA, p. A217

SACHDEV, Aruna, M.D. Medical Director, Massachusetts Hospital School, Canton, MA, p. A299

SACHS, III, Henry T., M.D. Medical Director, Emma Pendleton Bradley Hospital, East Providence, RI, p. A546

SACHTLEBEN, Michael, Chief Operating Officer, MedStar Georgetown University Hospital, Washington, DC, p. A116

SACK, Michael V., FACHE, President and Chief Executive Officer, Hallmark Health System, Melrose, MA, p. A302

SACKETT, John, Chief Executive Officer, Shady Grove Adventist Hospital, Rockville, MD, p. A294

SACKETT, Walter, President, Sycamore Medical Center, Miamisburg, OH, p. A486

SACKSTEDER, James, M.D. Medical Director and Chief Executive Officer, Austen Riggs Center, Stockbridge, MA, p. A305

SADA, Judy, Chief Financial Officer, Memorial Hospital Miramar, Miramar, FL, p. A133

SADLER, Joy, Director Human Resources, Bear River Valley Hospital, Tremonton, UT, p. A647

SADR, Farrokh, M.D. Chief Medical Officer, Sacred Heart Hospital, Allentown, PA, p. A519

SAFDIE, Ezra R., Associate Director, San Francisco Veterans Affairs Medical Center, San Francisco, CA, p. A87

SAFF, Eric, Senior Vice President and Chief Information Officer, John Muir Behavioral Health Center, Concord, CA, p. A57

SAFIAN, Keith F., President and Chief Executive Officer, Phelps Memorial Hospital Center, Sleepy Hollow, NY, p. A442

SAFLEY, Thomas, Chief Financial Officer, St. Joseph Regional Medical Center, Lewiston, ID, p. A169

SAFYER, Steven M., M.D., President and Chief Executive Officer, Montefiore Medical Center,, NY, p. A434

SAGAR, Karen S., Vice President Human Resources, Franciscan St. Francis Health – Indianapolis, Indianapolis, IN, p. A205

SAGEMAN, Scott, M.D. Vice President and Chief Medical Officer, St. Joseph Hospital, Eureka, CA, p. A59

SAGMIT, Rodney, Chief Information Management, Veterans Affairs Long Beach Healthcare System, Long Beach, CA, p. A68

SAHA, Sanjay K., Executive Vice President, Operations, Wake Forest Baptist Medical Center, Winston-Salem, NC, p. A464

SAHLSTROM, Christopher, M.D. Chief of Staff, Mat-Su Regional Medical Center, Palmer, AK, p. A28

SAHMAUNT, Sarabeth, Supervisory Accountant, Lawton Indian Hospital, Lawton, OK, p. A500

SAIA, Carrie L., R.N.,  Chief Executive Officer, Holton Community Hospital, Holton, KS, p. A235

SAINTZ, Jeffrey, Vice President Human Resources, Titusville Area Hospital, Titusville, PA, p. A542

SAIYED, Ashfaq, M.D. Medical Director, Irwin County Hospital, Ocilla, GA, p. A158

SAJID, Muhammad W., M.D. Medical Director, Lincoln Trail Behavioral Health System, Radcliff, KY, p. A259

SALAMA, Mustafa, M.D. Chief of Staff, Val Verde Regional Medical Center, Del Rio, TX, p. A598

SALANGER, Matthew J., President and Chief Executive Officer, United Health Services Hospitals–Binghamton, Binghamton, NY, p. A422

SALAS, Victor, M.D. President Medical Staff, Jones Regional Medical Center, Anamosa, IA, p. A216

SALAZAR, Kathy, Manager Human Resources, Michael E. DeBakey Veterans Affairs Medical Center, Houston, TX, p. A611

SALAZAR, Linda C., Information Technology Leader, Kaiser Permanente Baldwin Park Medical Center, Baldwin Park, CA, p. A54

SALAZAR, Margie, Director Human Resources, Valley Regional Medical Center, Brownsville, TX, p. A590

SALAZAR, Pamela, M.D. Chief of Staff, HEALTHSOUTH Walton Rehabilitation Hospital, Augusta, GA, p. A148

SALDIVAR, Duke, FACHE,  Chief Executive Officer, HEALTHSOUTH Rehabilitation Hospital of Austin, Austin, TX, p. A585

SALEM, Gary, M.D. Vice President Medical Affairs, McLaren Lapeer Region, Lapeer, MI, p. A318

SALEM, Michael, M.D.,  President and Chief Executive Officer, National Jewish Health, Denver, CO, p. A99

SALERNO, Thomas A., President and Chief Executive Officer, St. Mary Medical Center, Long Beach, CA, p. A67

SALGADO, Joe, M.D. Chief of Staff, Artesia General Hospital, Artesia, NM, p. A415

SALGADO, Laura, Administrator, Baptist Emergency Hospital, San Antonio, TX, p. A630

SALINAS, Daniel, M.D. Senior Vice President and Chief Medical Officer, Children's Healthcare of Atlanta, Atlanta, GA, p. A146

SALISBURY, Dennis, M.D. Vice President for Medical Affairs, St. James Healthcare, Butte, MT, p. A374

SALISBURY, Margaret A., Director Marketing, Runnells Specialized Hospital of Union County, Berkeley Heights, NJ, p. A401

SALISBURY, Renee A., Director Human Resources, Kewanee Hospital, Kewanee, IL, p. A186

SALISBURY, Tracy
Director Human Resources, Central State Hospital, Petersburg, VA, p. A659
Director Human Resources, Hiram W. Davis Medical Center, Petersburg, VA, p. A659

SALLEE, Lynda L., R.N. Chief Nursing Officer, Roane Medical Center, Harriman, TN, p. A569

SALLER, William
Chief Financial Officer, North Hills Hospital, North Richland Hills, TX, p. A625
Chief Financial Officer, Rio Grande Regional Hospital, McAllen, TX, p. A622

SALLEY, Wanda, Administrative Director Human Resources, Gulf Coast Medical Center, Panama City, FL, p. A136

SALLIS, Tom, Director Information Systems, Sparks Regional Medical Center, Fort Smith, AR, p. A44

SALLOUM, Fadi, M.D. Medical Director, Select Specialty Hospital–Pontiac, Pontiac, MI, p. A322

SALMAN, Wael, M.D. Vice President Medical Affairs, Memorial Healthcare, Owosso, MI, p. A321

SALMON, Chuck, Chief Executive, Swedish/Issaquah, Issaquah, WA, p. A667

SALMON, Gretchen, M.D. Medical Director, Hale Ho'ola Hamakua, Honokaa, HI, p. A164

SALNAS, Todd
President and Chief Executive Officer, Petaluma Valley Hospital, Petaluma, CA, p. A79
President and Chief Executive Officer, Santa Rosa Memorial Hospital, Santa Rosa, CA, p. A90

SALO, Saliba, President, Northridge Hospital Medical Center–Roscoe Boulevard Campus,, CA, p. A70

SALOME, Jenny, Chief Financial Officer and Assistant Administrator, Northwest Hills Surgical Hospital, Austin, TX, p. A585

SALOMON, Kathryn, Director Human Resources, Kona Community Hospital, Kealakekua, HI, p. A166

SALOUM, Herbert A., M.D. Medical Director, St. Michael's Hospital Avera, Tyndall, SD, p. A563

SALSBERRY, David, Chief Financial Officer, JPS Health Network, Fort Worth, TX, p. A604

SALTAFORMAGGIO, Cheri, Chief Executive Officer, St. Charles Surgical Hospital, New Orleans, LA, p. A276

SALTZMAN, Ronald, M.D. Chief of Staff, Saddleback Memorial Medical Center, Laguna Hills, CA, p. A65

SALVADOR, Ed, Chief Financial Officer, St. Jude Medical Center, Fullerton, CA, p. A62

SALVATI, Mario, Director Fiscal Services, Shriners Hospitals for Children–Philadelphia, Philadelphia, PA, p. A536

SALVINO, Sonia, Vice President Finance, University Hospitals Case Medical Center, Cleveland, OH, p. A477

SALVITTI, Alfred, Chief Financial Officer, Eagleville Hospital, Eagleville, PA, p. A524

SALVITTI, Alfred P., Chief Financial Officer, Friends Hospital, Philadelphia, PA, p. A535

SALVO, Stephen, Vice President Human Resources, Anna Jaques Hospital, Newburyport, MA, p. A302

SALVO, Thomas, Associate Executive Director Human Resources, Glen Cove Hospital, Glen Cove, NY, p. A426

SALYER, Steven, Chief Executive Officer, Sebastian River Medical Center, Sebastian, FL, p. A140

SALZBERG, Ron, Executive Director Human Resources, Saddleback Memorial Medical Center, Laguna Hills, CA, p. A65

SAM, Charlene, Manager Health Information, Choctaw Health Center, Philadelphia, MS, p. A352

SAMILO, Nick, Vice President Fiscal Services and Chief Financial Officer, Stanly Regional Medical Center, Albemarle, NC, p. A447

SAMMARCO, Michael, M.D. Chief Financial Officer, Erie County Medical Center, Buffalo, NY, p. A422

SAMMONS, Craig, Chief Financial Officer, Sky Ridge Medical Center, Lone Tree, CO, p. A104

SAMPLES, Patience M., R.N. Chief Nursing Officer, East Morgan County Hospital, Brush, CO, p. A98

SAMPSON, Bob
Vice President Human Resources, Providence Regional Medical Center Everett, Everett, WA, p. A666
Vice President Human Resources, Redwood Memorial Hospital, Fortuna, CA, p. A60

SAMPSON, Cherie L., Director Human Resources, Kaiser Permanente San Diego Medical Center, San Diego, CA, p. A85

SAMPSON, Jill, Director Human Resources, Lemuel Shattuck Hospital, Jamaica Plain, MA, p. A301

SAMS, Tricia, M.D. Medical Director, Memorial Health Care Systems, Seward, NE, p. A389

SAMSON, Ley, Director Management Information Systems, Clear Lake Regional Medical  Center, Webster, TX, p. A640

SAMUDRALA, Siresha, M.D. Medical Director, Mercy Rehabilitation Hospital, Chesterfield, MO, p. A358

SAMUEL, Guy, Director Human Resources, St. Petersburg General Hospital, Saint Petersburg, FL, p. A139

SAMUELS, Steven, M.D. Medical Director, Kindred Hospital Indianapolis South, Greenwood, IN, p. A204

SAMUELS, Tammy, Director Human Resources, Union County Hospital, Anna, IL, p. A173

SAMUELSON, Melissa A., R.N. Chief Nurse Executive, Poplar Bluff Regional Medical Center, Poplar Bluff, MO, p. A368

SAMYN, Mike, Vice President, Finance and Chief Financial Officer, St. Mary Mercy Hospital, Livonia, MI, p. A319

SAMZ, Jeff, Chief Operating Officer, Huntsville Hospital, Huntsville, AL, p. A21

SAN FILIPPO, Bruce, M.D. Chief Medical Officer, Memorial Medical Center, Las Cruces, NM, p. A416

SANBORN, Michael, FACHE,  President, Baylor Medical Center at Carrollton, Carrollton, TX, p. A591

SANBORN, Randall, Director Information Technology, HealthSource Saginaw, Saginaw, MI, p. A323

SANCHEZ, Emalie, Director Human Resources, Baylor Medical Center at Uptown, Dallas, TX, p. A595

SANCHEZ, Freddie T., Director Information Systems, Placentia–Linda Hospital, Placentia, CA, p. A80

SANCHEZ, John, Vice President Human Resources, White Plains Hospital Center, White Plains, NY, p. A446

SANCHEZ, Jon, M.D. Chief of Staff, Bluegrass Community Hospital, Versailles, KY, p. A261

SANCHEZ, Jose R., President and Chief Executive Officer, Norwegian American Hospital, Chicago, IL, p. A178

SANCHEZ, Nancy, Senior Vice President and Vice Dean Human Resources, NYU Langone Medical Center, New York, NY, p. A435

SANCHEZ, Patty, Site Manager Human Resources, Adventist La Grange Memorial Hospital, La Grange, IL, p. A186

SANCHEZ, Rachel, Director Information Systems, Providence Little Company of Mary Medical Center San Pedro,, CA, p. A71

SANCHEZ, Rebecca, R.N. Director of Nursing, Texas Center for Infectious Disease, San Antonio, TX, p. A632

SANCHEZ–BICKLEY, Michelle
Vice President Human Resources, Renown Regional Medical Center, Reno, NV, p. A395
Vice President Human Resources, Renown Rehabilitation Hospital, Reno, NV, p. A395
Vice President Human Resources, Renown South Meadows Medical Center, Reno, NV, p. A395

SANCHEZ–JIMENEZ, Aida, M.D. Chief Medical Officer, Osceola Regional Medical Center, Kissimmee, FL, p. A127

SANDBERG, Todd, Chief Executive Officer and Administrator, Sibley Medical Center, Arlington, MN, p. A328

SANDENE, Jeff, Chief Finance, Sanford USD Medical Center, Sioux Falls, SD, p. A562

SANDER, Cindy, Coordinator Human Resources, Kindred Hospital–St. Louis, Saint Louis, MO, p. A369

SANDER, Wendy, Director Human Resources, Kaiser Permanente Riverside Medical Center, Riverside, CA, p. A82

SANDERS, Amy, Chief Human Resources, Captain James A. Lovell Federal Health Care Center, North Chicago, IL, p. A190

SANDERS, David, Chief Financial Officer, Jackson Parish Hospital, Jonesboro, LA, p. A269

SANDERS, David S., Chief Executive Officer, Fannin Regional Hospital, Blue Ridge, GA, p. A148

SANDERS, Gale H., Director, Gadsden Regional Medical Center, Gadsden, AL, p. A20

SANDERS, Harv, Chief Financial Officer, Rhea Medical Center, Dayton, TN, p. A568

SANDERS, Janet, R.N., Interim Administrator, Shriners Hospitals for Children–Los Angeles, Los Angeles, CA, p. A71

SANDERS, Jeff, Chief Operating Officer, Maine Medical Center, Portland, ME, p. A284

SANDERS, Jeffrey, M.D. Chief of Staff, Carson Tahoe Regional Healthcare, Carson City, NV, p. A391

SANDERS, John W., President, OhioHealth Marion General Hospital, Marion, OH, p. A485

SANDERS, Kelly, Vice President Human Resources, Good Shepherd Health Care System, Hermiston, OR, p. A513

SANDERS, Kris, Chief Financial Officer, Methodist Extended Care Hospital, Memphis, TN, p. A575

SANDERS, Lee Anne, Director Human Resources, Cozby–Germany Hospital, Grand Saline, TX, p. A606

SANDERS, Michael B., President and Chief Executive Officer, Monroe Clinic, Monroe, WI, p. A693

SANDERS, Robert, M.D. Chief Medical Officer, Texoma Medical Center, Denison, TX, p. A598

SANDERS, Ryan, Director Information Services, Doctors Hospital of Columbus, Columbus, GA, p. A150

SANDERS, Steve, Chief Financial Officer, Washington County Hospital and Clinics, Washington, IA, p. A229

SANDERS, Susie Sherrod, Budget Officer, Cherry Hospital, Goldsboro, NC, p. A453

SANDERS, Todd, Manager Finance, Alta View Hospital, Sandy, UT, p. A647

SANDERSON, Kevin, Director Information Systems, Goodland Regional Medical Center, Goodland, KS, p. A234

SANDIFER, Ron, Chief Information Officer, Community Memorial Health System, Ventura, CA, p. A94

SANDIFER, Tawny, R.N. Vice President Patient Care, Capital Region Medical Center, Jefferson City, MO, p. A362

SANDIN, James H., M.D. Assistant Administrator Medical Affairs, Hunt Regional Medical Center, Greenville, TX, p. A607

SANDLER, Vivian, Director Human Resources, Memorial Regional Hospital South,, FL, p. A125

SANDLIN, Keith, Chief Executive Officer, Cartersville Medical Center, Cartersville, GA, p. A149

SANDLIN, Michael, M.D. Chief of Staff, Okmulgee Memorial Hospital, Okmulgee, OK, p. A505

SANDOVAL, Yvonne, Director of Nursing Operations, Rehabilitation Hospital of Southern New Mexico, Las Cruces, NM, p. A416

SANDS, Sherry, R.N. Chief Nursing Officer, Hillside Hospital, Pulaski, TN, p. A578

SANDS, Tiffany, Manager Health Information, Arbuckle Memorial Hospital, Sulphur, OK, p. A507

SANDSTROM, C. Bruce, Vice President and Chief Financial Officer, The Aroostook Medical Center, Presque Isle, ME, p. A285

SANFORD, Lisa, VP Patient Care/CNO, Holy Rosary Healthcare, Miles City, MT, p. A378

SANFORD, Sharon K., Director Human Resources, Jersey Community Hospital, Jerseyville, IL, p. A186

SANGER, David, M.D. Chief Medical Officer, Pawnee Valley Community Hospital, Larned, KS, p. A238

SANGER, Marla I., R.N., Interim Chief Executive Officer, Wrangell Medical Center, Wrangell, AK, p. A29

SANGHI, Harishankar, M.D. Clinical Director, St. Lawrence Psychiatric Center, Ogdensburg, NY, p. A438

SANKARAN, Jaya, M.D. Chief of Staff, St. Mary's of Michigan Standish Hospital, Standish, MI, p. A325

SANKOORIKAL, Joseph, M.D. Chief Medical Staff, Kansas Rehabilitation Hospital, Topeka, KS, p. A245

SANKOVICH, Mary Lou, MSN, Chief Executive Officer and Chief Nursing Officer, Vibra Hospital of Mahoning Valley, Boardman, OH, p. A472

SANNUTO, John, Chief Executive Officer, Port St. Lucie Hospital, Port St. Lucie, FL, p. A138

SANS, Heather, Human Resource Generalist, Edwin Shaw Rehab, Cuyahoga Falls, OH, p. A479

SANTAMARIA, Mark A., President, MidMichigan Medical Center–Gratiot, Alma, MI, p. A308

SANTANGELO, Charles J., CP
Executive Vice President and Chief Financial Officer, Muncy Valley Hospital, Muncy, PA, p. A532
Executive Vice President and Chief Financial Officer, Williamsport Regional Medical Center, Williamsport, PA, p. A545

SANTANGELO, John, Director Information Technology, Cleveland Clinic Florida, Weston, FL, p. A144

SANTANGELO, Linda, Ph.D., Director, Desert Willow Treatment Center, Las Vegas, NV, p. A392

SANTARELLI, James, M.D. President Medical Staff, Aurora Medical Center, Kenosha, WI, p. A688

SANTILLI, Robert J., Chief Executive Officer, Gunnison Valley Hospital, Gunnison, CO, p. A102

SANTISTEVAN, Vivian, Chief Human Resources, Fort Defiance Indian Health Service Hospital, Fort Defiance, AZ, p. A31

SANTMAN, Kim D., Vice President Finance, St. Margaret's Hospital, Spring Valley, IL, p. A195

SANTORE, Richard, M.D. Chief Medical Officer, Sharp Memorial Hospital, San Diego, CA, p. A85

SANTOS, Alfred, Administrator, Lincoln County Medical Center, Ruidoso, NM, p. A418

SANTOS, David, Chief Operating Officer (VP Operations), St. Helena Hospital Clear Lake, Clearlake, CA, p. A56

SANTOS, George, M.D. Executive Medical Director, West Oaks Hospital, Houston, TX, p. A614

SANTOS, Hugo, Vice President Human Resources, Children's Hospital Los Angeles, Los Angeles, CA, p. A68

SANTOS, Ismael, Director Human Resources, Valle Vista Hospital, Greenwood, IN, p. A204

SANTOS, Lori, Vice President Finance, Albany Memorial Hospital, Albany, NY, p. A420

SANTOS, Thomas, R.N. Chief Nursing Officer and Director Quality Services, Parkview Community Hospital Medical Center, Riverside, CA, p. A82

SANTULLI, Patricia, Director Human Resources, Elmira Psychiatric Center, Elmira, NY, p. A425

SANZ, Lawrence A., Senior Vice President Finance and Chief Financial Officer, Midland Memorial Hospital, Midland, TX, p. A623

SANZ, Sean M., Chief Operating Officer, Novant Health Rowan Medical Center, Salisbury, NC, p. A460

SAPOLIS, Richard, Director Clinical Operations, First Hospital Wyoming Valley, Kingston, PA, p. A528

SAPPINGTON–CRITTENDEN, Shana, Chief Operating Officer, Westside Regional Medical Center, Plantation, FL, p. A137

SAQUATON, Antonio, M.D. Chief Medical Officer, Select Specialty Hospital–Omaha, Omaha, NE, p. A388

SARBACHER, James, Chief Information Officer, State Hospital North, Orofino, ID, p. A170

SARDANA, Sadhana, M.D. Clinical Director, Rockland Children's Psychiatric Center, Orangeburg, NY, p. A439

SARDONE, Frank J., President and Chief Executive Officer, Bronson Methodist Hospital, Kalamazoo, MI, p. A318

SARGEANT, Marty
Chief Operating Officer, City of Hope's Helford Clinical Research Hospital, Duarte, CA, p. A59
Chief Operating Officer, Cleveland Clinic Florida, Weston, FL, p. A144

SARGENT, J. Dale, M.D
Chief Medical Officer, Wellmont Hancock County Hospital, Sneedville, TN, p. A579
Chief Medical Officer, Wellmont Holston Valley Medical Center, Kingsport, TN, p. A571

SARGENT, Kimberly, Vice President Patient Services, St. Luke's Hospital – Miners Campus, Coaldale, PA, p. A523

SARGENT, Patrick D., Commander, Carl R. Darnall Army Medical Center, Fort Hood, TX, p. A603

SARGENT, Reed
Assistant Administrator Finance, Garfield Memorial Hospital and Clinics, Panguitch, UT, p. A645
Assistant Administrator Finance, Valley View Medical Center, Cedar City, UT, p. A643

SARIDAKIS, Michael, M.D. Physician Adviser, Regional Hospital of Jackson, Jackson, TN, p. A570

SARMENTO, Joann, Manager Human Resources, Fairchild Medical Center, Yreka, CA, p. A96

SARNECKI, Robert (Bob), Chief Information Officer, Kingman Regional Medical Center, Kingman, AZ, p. A32

SAROFIN, Michelle, Superintendent, Albert J. Solnit Psychiatric Center – South Campus, Middletown, CT, p. A110

SARPA, John, Interim Chief Executive Officer, Aspen Valley Hospital District, Aspen, CO, p. A97

SARRICO, Christine, Chief Financial Officer, Saint Agnes Medical Center, Fresno, CA, p. A61

SARVER, Troy, Chief Nursing Officer, Texas Orthopedic Hospital, Houston, TX, p. A612

SASS, Judy A., Chief Human Resources Officer, McGehee–Desha County Hospital, McGehee, AR, p. A47

SASS, Kevin, FACHE Chief Operating Officer, St. Francis Hospital, Columbus, GA, p. A150

SASSER, Kelley, Director Information Systems, Florida Hospital Zephyrhills, Zephyrhills, FL, p. A144

SASSMAN, Gregory, Interim Chief Executive Officer, Restora Hospital of Sun City, Sun City, AZ, p. A38

SATCHER, Richard H., Market Chief Executive Officer, Bayfront Health Port Charlotte, Port Charlotte, FL, p. A137

SATKOSKI, Linda L., R.N. Chief Operating Officer, Indiana University Health La Porte Hospital, La Porte, IN, p. A208

SATTAR, Parhez, Senior Director Information Technology, Grande Ronde Hospital, La Grande, OR, p. A514

SATTLER, Alan, President, ProMedica Flower Hospital, Sylvania, OH, p. A490

SAUCEDO, Jesse, Chief Financial Officer, Heartland Surgical Specialty Hospital, Overland Park, KS, p. A241

SAUER, Bernie, Director Information Technology, San Gabriel Valley Medical Center, San Gabriel, CA, p. A87

SAUER, Mary R., R.N. Chief Nursing Officer, Lakewood Hospital, Lakewood, OH, p. A483

SAUERS, Preston, Chief Financial Officer, Ellsworth County Medical Center, Ellsworth, KS, p. A233

SAUK, Michael, Chief Information Officer, University of Wisconsin Hospital and Clinics, Madison, WI, p. A690

SAULLO, Nancy, Director Human Resources, Warren State Hospital, Warren, PA, p. A543

SAULNIER, Robert, MSN, Chief Executive Officer, Columbus Specialty Hospital, Columbus, GA, p. A150

SAULS, Randy, Chief Executive Officer and Administrator, South Georgia Medical Center, Valdosta, GA, p. A162

SAUM, Anita, Director Human Resources, Rehabilitation Hospital of Tinton Falls, Tinton Falls, NJ, p. A411

SAUNAITIS, Tamara L., Chief Human Resources Officer, Meriter Hospital, Madison, WI, p. A689

SAUNDERS, Brooke, Administrator, Kindred Hospital–Westminster, Westminster, CA, p. A95

SAUNDERS, John R., M.D. Senior Vice President Medical Affairs and Chief Medical Officer, Greater Baltimore Medical Center, Baltimore, MD, p. A287

SAUNDERS, Jonathan, Chief Financial Officer, Baylor Medical Center at Trophy Club, Trophy Club, TX, p. A638

SAUNDERS, Kristi K., Director and Compliance Officer, Calais Regional Hospital, Calais, ME, p. A282

SAUNDERS, M. Patricia, R.N. Vice President Nursing, Hanover Hospital, Hanover, PA, p. A526

SAUNDERS, Ninfa, Chief Executive Officer, Medical Center of Central Georgia, Macon, GA, p. A156

SAUNDERS, Rosanne C., Senior Vice President and Chief Human Resources Officer, Jefferson Regional Medical Center, Jefferson Hills, PA, p. A528

SAUNDERS, Theodore, Assistant Controller, Wesley Woods Long Term Care Hospital, Atlanta, GA, p. A147

SAUVE, Seth A., FACHE, Chief Executive Officer, Kindred Rehabilitation Hospital Arlington, Arlington, TX, p. A583

SAVAGE, Josh, Chief Financial Officer, Brownfield Regional Medical Center, Brownfield, TX, p. A589

SAVAGE, Kim, Interim Controller, Charlton Memorial Hospital, Folkston, GA, p. A153

SAVAGE, Steve, Chief Executive Officer and Chief Operating Officer, Stonecrest Center, Detroit, MI, p. A312

SAVAGE–TRACY, Elizabeth, Vice President and Human Resources Officer, Winchester Medical Center, Winchester, VA, p. A663

SAVERESE, Joseph, Director Information Systems, New York Methodist Hospital,, NY, p. A435

SAVINO, Linda A., MS, Chief Executive Officer, Rehabilitation Hospital of Tinton Falls, Tinton Falls, NJ, p. A411

SAVITCH, Lane A., President, Kadlec Regional Medical Center, Richland, WA, p. A670

SAVOY III, F. Peter, Chief Executive Officer, Acadia–St. Landry Hospital, Church Point, LA, p. A265

SAVOY, Greg, M.D. Chief Medical Officer, Savoy Medical Center, Mamou, LA, p. A273

SAVOY, Remi, Administrator, Oceans Behavioral Hospital of Opelousas, Opelousas, LA, p. A276

SAVSTROM, Curt, Chief Financial Officer and Chief Information Officer, River's Edge Hospital and Clinic, Saint Peter, MN, p. A340

SAWA, Kendall, R.N., Chief Executive Officer, Ocean Beach Hospital, Ilwaco, WA, p. A667

SAWDEY, Don, M.D. Medical Director, Daniels Memorial Healthcare Center, Scobey, MT, p. A379

SAWYER, Anne, Chief Financial Officer, Wayne County Hospital, Monticello, KY, p. A258

SAWYER, Colleen A., MSN,
Executive Director, Mohawk Valley Psychiatric Center, Utica, NY, p. A444
Executive Director, Richard H. Hutchings Psychiatric Center, Syracuse, NY, p. A443

SAWYER, Gregory D., M.D. Vice President Physician Practices, Yakima Valley Memorial Hospital, Yakima, WA, p. A674

SAWYER, Robert, Senior Project Specialist, Spaulding Hospital for Continuing Medical Care North Shore, Salem, MA, p. A304

SAWYER, Scott, Chief Financial Officer, Community Medical Center, Falls City, NE, p. A383

SAWYER, Stephen
Chief Financial Officer, Dickenson Community Hospital, Clintwood, VA, p. A652
Chief Financial Officer, Norton Community Hospital, Norton, VA, p. A658

SAXTON, Beth, R.N. Vice President Patient Care Services, Yuma District Hospital, Yuma, CO, p. A107

SAYDACK, Roger, Interim Chief Operating Officer, PeaceHealth Sacred Heart Medical Center at RiverBend, Springfield, OR, p. A518

SAYLER, Beth, Director Human Resources, Regency Hospital of Covington, Covington, LA, p. A266

SAYLER, Elizabeth, M.D. Chief of Staff, Lead–Deadwood Regional Hospital, Deadwood, SD, p. A559

SAYLER, Mark, Chief Financial Officer, Curry General Hospital, Gold Beach, OR, p. A513

SAYLER, Roger, Finance Officer, Fargo Veterans Affairs Health Care System, Fargo, ND, p. A466

SAYLER, Timothy, President and Chief Executive Officer, St. Joseph Regional Medical Center, Lewiston, ID, p. A169

SAYLES, Debbie, R.N. Vice President and Chief Nursing Officer, Texas Scottish Rite Hospital for Children, Dallas, TX, p. A597

SAYLOR, Craig M., Vice President and Chief Operating Officer, Somerset Hospital, Somerset, PA, p. A541

SAYLOR, Richard F., M.D. Chief Medical Officer, Pottstown Memorial Medical Center, Pottstown, PA, p. A539

SAYLORS, Julie, Controller, AnMed Health Rehabilitation Hospital, Anderson, SC, p. A548

SAYRE, Amy, Director Human Resources, General John J. Pershing Memorial Hospital, Brookfield, MO, p. A357

SAYRE, Michelle, R.N. Chief Nursing Officer, Arrowhead Regional Medical Center, Colton, CA, p. A57

SCAFIDI, Frank
Vice President and Chief Information Officer, Georgetown Memorial Hospital, Georgetown, SC, p. A552
Chief Information Officer, Waccamaw Community Hospital, Murrells Inlet, SC, p. A555

SCALISE, Paul, M.D. Chief Pulmonary Medicine and Internal Medicine, Hospital for Special Care, New Britain, CT, p. A110

SCALLEN, Jr., Joseph, Chief Financial Officer, Children's Hospital of Michigan, Detroit, MI, p. A311

SCALLION, Jessica, Administrator, Beacon Behavioral Hospital – New Orleans, New Orleans, LA, p. A275

SCALLON, Jean, Chief Executive Officer, Bloomington Meadows Hospital, Bloomington, IN, p. A199

SCANLAN, Dennis P., Vice President Finance, Doctors Community Hospital, Lanham, MD, p. A292

SCANLON, Donald, Chief Financial Officer, Mount Sinai Hospital, New York, NY, p. A434

SCANLON, Jill, Director Human Resources, Northern Colorado Rehabilitation Hospital, Johnstown, CO, p. A102

SCANLON, John, DPM Chief Medical Officer, Chestnut Hill Hospital, Philadelphia, PA, p. A534

SCANLON, Shaun J., Senior Vice President Finance and Chief Financial Officer, Vail Valley Medical Center, Vail, CO, p. A106

SCANNELL, Stephen J., Chief Financial Officer, McLaren Northern Michigan, Petoskey, MI, p. A321

SCARBORO, Parrish, Chief Operating Officer, John F. Kennedy Memorial Hospital, Indio, CA, p. A64

SCARPINO, David
Senior Vice President Finance and Chief Financial Officer, Health Alliance Hospital – Broadway Campus, Kingston, NY, p. A428
Senior Vice President and Chief Financial Officer, Health Alliance Hospital – Mary's Avenue Campus, Kingston, NY, p. A428
Chief Financial Officer, Margaretville Hospital, Margaretville, NY, p. A429

SCENNA, Maria, Chief Operating Officer, St. Christopher's Hospital for Children, Philadelphia, PA, p. A536

SCEPANSKI, Theresa, Vice President People and Organizational Development, University Health System, San Antonio, TX, p. A632

SCERCY, Charles, Chief Executive Officer, Snowden at Fredericksburg, Fredericksburg, VA, p. A654

SCHAAB, Ben, VP Fiscal Services/ Chief Financial Officer, CGH Medical Center, Sterling, IL, p. A195

SCHAACK, Gregory J., CP
Vice President and Chief Financial Officer, Candler Hospital, Savannah, GA, p. A159
Vice President and Chief Financial Officer, St. Joseph's Hospital, Savannah, GA, p. A160

SCHAAF, Jerry, M.D. Chief Medical Officer, Shenandoah Medical Center, Shenandoah, IA, p. A228

SCHAAF, Kay, Chief Nursing Officer, Prairie Community Hospital, Terry, MT, p. A380

SCHABERG, Dennis, M.D. Chief Medicine, Veterans Affairs Greater Los Angeles Healthcare System, Los Angeles, CA, p. A72

SCHACHTNER, Janet, R.N. Senior Vice President, Patient Care Services, Mount Nittany Medical Center, State College, PA, p. A541

SCHADE, Sue, Chief Information Officer, University of Michigan Hospitals and Health Centers, Ann Arbor, MI, p. A308

SCHAEFBAUER, Brian, Director Information Technology, Mobridge Regional Hospital, Mobridge, SD, p. A561

SCHAEFER, Becky, Chief Financial Officer, University of Utah Neuropsychiatric Institute, Salt Lake City, UT, p. A647

SCHAEFER, Carol, Human Resources, Hermann Area District Hospital, Hermann, MO, p. A361

SCHAEFER, Daniel, Vice President Information Services, Mayo Clinic Health System – Franciscan Healthcare in La Crosse, La Crosse, WI, p. A689

SCHAEFER, Jamie, Vice President Finance, Avera Sacred Heart Hospital, Yankton, SD, p. A564

SCHAEFER, Michael J., Executive Vice President and Chief Financial Officer, Methodist Charlton Medical Center, Dallas, TX, p. A596

SCHAEFER, Michelle, Chief Financial Officer, Lillian M. Hudspeth Memorial Hospital, Sonora, TX, p. A634

SCHAEFER, Stephen, Chief Executive Officer, HEALTHSOUTH Rehabilitation Hospital of Colorado Springs, Colorado Springs, CO, p. A98

SCHAEFFER, Andre, M.D. Chief of Staff, Union General Hospital, Blairsville, GA, p. A148

SCHAEFFER, Bryon, M.D. Chief of Medical Staff, Knoxville Hospital & Clinics, Knoxville, IA, p. A224

SCHAEFFER, Richard, Vice President Information Systems and Chief Information Officer, St. Clair Memorial Hospital, Pittsburgh, PA, p. A538

SCHAETTI, Susan, Administrator, Kindred Hospital–Mansfield, Mansfield, TX, p. A621

SCHAFER, Michael, Chief Executive Officer and Administrator, Spooner Health System, Spooner, WI, p. A696

SCHAFER, Mona
Regional Manager Human Resources, Avera Flandreau Hospital, Flandreau, SD, p. A559
Regional Manager Human Resources, Milbank Area Hospital Avera, Milbank, SD, p. A560

SCHAFF, Vicki, Chief Operating Officer, Epic Medical Center, Eufaula, OK, p. A498

SCHAFFER, Megan, Administrative Assistant, Surgical Institute of Reading, Wyomissing, PA, p. A545

SCHAFFNER, Leroy, Chief Executive Officer, Coon Memorial Hospital and Home, Dalhart, TX, p. A594

SCHAFFNER, Linda, Chief Information Officer, Keokuk Area Hospital, Keokuk, IA, p. A224

SCHAFFNER, Richard, Senior Vice President and Chief Operating Officer, Holy Spirit Hospital, Camp Hill, PA, p. A521

SCHALES, Marion, Chief Financial Officer, Alameda County Medical Center, Oakland, CA, p. A77

SCHALLER, Bobby L., Chief Engineer, Southeast Colorado Hospital District, Springfield, CO, p. A105

SCHALSKI, Paula, Director Human Resources, Atoka County Medical Center, Atoka, OK, p. A496

SCHAMP, Cindy K., President, Baylor Medical Center at Irving, Irving, TX, p. A614

SCHANDLER, Jon B., Chief Executive Officer, White Plains Hospital Center, White Plains, NY, p. A446

SCHANTZ, Cathy Ann, MSN Vice President Patient Care Services and Chief Nursing Officer, Canton–Potsdam Hospital, Potsdam, NY, p. A440

SCHANWALD, Pamela R., Chief Executive Officer, The Children's Home of Pittsburgh, Pittsburgh, PA, p. A538

SCHAPP, Susan, Vice President Finance and Treasurer, The Charlotte Hungerford Hospital, Torrington, CT, p. A112

SCHAPPER, Robert A., Chief Executive Officer, Tahoe Forest Hospital District, Truckee, CA, p. A93

SCHARBER, Laurel
Administrative Assistant and Coordinator Human Resources, Kindred Hospital–Ontario, Ontario, CA, p. A77
Coordinator Human Resources, Kindred Hospital–San Francisco Bay Area, San Leandro, CA, p. A88

SCHARDIN, Janice, MS, Administrator and Chief Executive Officer, Avera De Smet Memorial Hospital, De Smet, SD, p. A559

SCHARENBROCK, Chris, M.D. Chief Medical Staff, David Grant Medical Center, Travis AFB, CA, p. A93

SCHARFF, Tom, Director Information Services, University Hospital and Medical Center, Tamarac, FL, p. A141

SCHARLES, Susan L., Director Human Resources, Valley View Medical Center, Fort Mohave, AZ, p. A31

SCHARNHORST, Alicia, Human Resources and Business Office Manager, Garfield County Public Hospital District, Pomeroy, WA, p. A669

SCHAUBERGER, Charles W., M.D. Vice President and Chief Medical Officer, UnityPoint Health St. Luke's, Cedar Rapids, IA, p. A217

SCHAUF, Victoria, M.D. Chief of Staff, Ridgecrest Regional Hospital, Ridgecrest, CA, p. A82

SCHAY, Maria, Chief Information Officer, Veterans Administration New York Harbor Healthcare System,, NY, p. A437

SCHEAFFEL, Margaret, R.N. Vice President and Chief Nursing Officer, Holy Cross Hospital, Fort Lauderdale, FL, p. A123

SCHECTER, Lawrence, M.D. Chief Medical Officer, Providence Regional Medical Center Everett, Everett, WA, p. A666

SCHEER, Michael, M.D. President Medical Staff, Vista Medical Center East, Waukegan, IL, p. A196

SCHEETS, Frank, Senior Vice President, Lutheran Medical Center,, NY, p. A433

SCHEETZ, Allison, M.D. Medical Director, Central Georgia Rehabilitation Hospital, Macon, GA, p. A156

SCHEFANO, Frank, M.D. Chief of Staff, Arkansas Methodist Medical Center, Paragould, AR, p. A49

SCHEFFLER, Robert, Chief Executive Officer, Clarion Psychiatric Center, Clarion, PA, p. A522

SCHEFFLER, Tom, Chief Fiscal Officer, Veterans Affairs Maryland Health Care System–Baltimore Division, Baltimore, MD, p. A289

SCHEIB, Garry L., Executive Director, Hospital of the University of Pennsylvania, Philadelphia, PA, p. A535

SCHEINBERG, Paul, M.D. Chief of Staff, Saint Joseph's Hospital of Atlanta, Atlanta, GA, p. A147

SCHEINBLUM, Richard, Chief Financial Officer, Monadnock Community Hospital, Peterborough, NH, p. A400

SCHELL, James, M.D. Vice President Medical Affairs, Saint Francis Medical Center, Cape Girardeau, MO, p. A358

SCHELLER, Sharon, Chief Executive Officer, Northern Colorado Rehabilitation Hospital, Johnstown, CO, p. A102

SCHELLPFEFFER, Donald A., M.D., Chief Executive Officer, Sioux Falls Specialty Hospital, Sioux Falls, SD, p. A562

SCHEMPP, Jennifer, Manager Information Systems, St. Alexius Hospital – Broadway Campus, Saint Louis, MO, p. A370

SCHENCK, Debbie, Administrator, Omega Hospital, Metairie, LA, p. A273

SCHENK, Jill, M.D. Chief of Staff, Mercy Medical Center Mount Shasta, Mount Shasta, CA, p. A75

SCHEPMANN, Jane, Vice President and Chief Nursing Officer, Clara Barton Hospital, Hoisington, KS, p. A235

SCHERAMIC, Mychail, M.D., Chief Executive Officer, Northwest Ohio Psychiatric Hospital, Toledo, OH, p. A491

SCHERER, Tom, Interim Vice President Finance, Berger Health System, Circleville, OH, p. A475

SCHERLER, Jay, Director Information Systems and Vice President Business Services, Providence Health Center, Waco, TX, p. A640

SCHERNECK, Michael D.
Executive Vice President and Chief Financial Officer, Southeast Georgia Health System Brunswick Campus, Brunswick, GA, p. A149
Executive Vice President, Southeast Georgia Health System Camden Campus, Saint Marys, GA, p. A159

SCHERTZ, David A., President and Chief Executive Officer, OSF Saint Anthony Medical Center, Rockford, IL, p. A193

SCHIEFELBEIN, Shelia, Director Human Resources, HEALTHSOUTH Rehabilitation Hospital of Tallahassee, Tallahassee, FL, p. A140

SCHIELDS, Dale, Director Human Resources, Goodland Regional Medical Center, Goodland, KS, p. A234

SCHIELE, Jeremey, Chief Information Officer, Jamestown Regional Medical Center, Jamestown, ND, p. A467

SCHIERECK, Stacie, Manager Business Office, Mendota Mental Health Institute, Madison, WI, p. A689

SCHIFFLER, Tillie, Director Human Resources, Lima Memorial Health System, Lima, OH, p. A484

SCHILLER, Ann Mattia, Vice President Human Resources, Pacific Hospital of Long Beach, Long Beach, CA, p. A67

SCHILLING, Thomas, Chief Financial Officer and Senior Vice President Finance, Mercy Memorial Hospital System, Monroe, MI, p. A320

SCHIMEROWSKI, Deborah
Vice President Finance and Chief Financial Officer, Presence Covenant Medical Center, Urbana, IL, p. A196
Chief Financial Officer, Presence United Samaritans Medical Center, Danville, IL, p. A180

SCHIMMOELLER, Randy, Vice President Human Resources, ProMedica Toledo Hospital, Toledo, OH, p. A491

SCHINDEL, Lester P., President and Chief Executive Officer, Holy Family Hospital and Medical Center, Methuen, MA, p. A302

SCHIRALLI, Rocco, President/Chief Executive Officer, Porter–Starke Services, Valparaiso, IN, p. A214

SCHIRMER, Sharon, R.N. Chief Clinical Officer, Promise Hospital of San Antonio, San Antonio, TX, p. A632

SCHIROS, Judith, Chief Executive Officer, Restora Hospital of Mesa, Mesa, AZ, p. A33

SCHITTONE, Angelo, Chief Information Officer, Saint Michael's Medical Center, Newark, NJ, p. A407

SCHLATTER, Christina, Chief Financial Officer, Oswego Community Hospital, Oswego, KS, p. A241

SCHLECHTER, Sandy, Chief Executive Officer, Bowdle Hospital, Bowdle, SD, p. A558

SCHLEGEL, Patricia, Executive Director Finance, Minnesota Valley Health Center, Le Sueur, MN, p. A334

SCHLEGELMILCH, Kurt W., FACHE, Director, Veterans Affairs Sierra Nevada Health Care System, Reno, NV, p. A395

SCHLEICHER, Larry, Manager Information Services, Dr. John Warner Hospital, Clinton, IL, p. A180

SCHLEIF, John V., Senior Vice President and Chief Operating Officer, Henry Mayo Newhall Memorial Hospital, Valencia, CA, p. A94

SCHLEMMER, Tom, Chief Financial Officer, St. Mary's Medical Center, West Palm Beach, FL, p. A143

SCHLENKER, Jim, Vice President and Chief Financial Officer, St. Anthony Hospital, Pendleton, OR, p. A515

SCHLENKER, Patrick A., FACHE, President and Chief Executive Officer, Northwest Florida Community Hospital, Chipley, FL, p. A120

SCHLESENBERG, Avery, Chief Financial Officer, Sutter Medical Center of Santa Rosa, Chanate Campus, Santa Rosa, CA, p. A90

SCHLESINGER, James, Interim Chief Information Officer, MetroHealth Medical Center, Cleveland, OH, p. A476

SCHLESSMAN, Alissa, Administrator, Beaver County Memorial Hospital, Beaver, OK, p. A496

SCHLEY, Kurt, President, St. Anthony Hospital, Gig Harbor, WA, p. A666

SCHLOBOHM, Phillip, M.D. Executive Medical Director, Riverside Behavioral Health Center, Hampton, VA, p. A655

SCHLOSS, William, Senior Vice President, Laureate Psychiatric Clinic and Hospital, Tulsa, OK, p. A508

SCHLUTER, Robin M., Chief Executive Officer, Regional Health Services of Howard County, Cresco, IA, p. A219

SCHMALTZ, Vern J., Vice President Finance, Indiana University Health Tipton Hospital, Tipton, IN, p. A214

SCHMEIDLER, David, M.D. Chief Medical Staff, South Central Kansas Medical Center, Arkansas City, KS, p. A231

SCHMELZEL, Mark, M.D. Vice President and Medical Director, CGH Medical Center, Sterling, IL, p. A195

SCHMID, Nancy, Chief Executive Officer, Healdsburg District Hospital, Healdsburg, CA, p. A64

SCHMIDLY, Scott, Chief Executive Officer, Saint Joseph's Hospital of Atlanta, Atlanta, GA, p. A147

SCHMIDT, Allen J., M.D. President, Medical Staff, Decatur General Hospital, Decatur, AL, p. A18

SCHMIDT, Brad
Chief Financial Officer, Mayo Clinic – Saint Marys Hospital, Rochester, MN, p. A339
Chief Financial Officer, Rochester Methodist Hospital, Rochester, MN, p. A339

SCHMIDT, Brent, Chief Financial Officer, St. Joseph's Area Health Services, Park Rapids, MN, p. A338

SCHMIDT, Holly, Chief Information Officer, Hill Country Memorial Hospital, Fredericksburg, TX, p. A605

SCHMIDT, James A., Chief Financial Officer, Northcrest Medical Center, Springfield, TN, p. A579

SCHMIDT, Joan E., Director Human Resources, St. Francis Health Care Centre, Green Springs, OH, p. A482

SCHMIDT, Jodi A., President and Chief Executive Officer, Labette Health, Parsons, KS, p. A242

SCHMIDT, Mark, President and Chief Executive Officer, Avera Gettysburg Hospital, Gettysburg, SD, p. A560

SCHMIDT Jr., Richard O.
President and Chief Executive Officer, United Health System–Kenosha Campus, Kenosha, WI, p. A689
President and Chief Executive Officer, United Hospital System, St. Catherine's Medical Center Campus, Pleasant Prairie, WI, p. A695

SCHMIDT, Robert, Director Human Resources, Hocking Valley Community Hospital, Logan, OH, p. A484

SCHMIDT, Steve, Director Information Systems, Evans Memorial Hospital, Claxton, GA, p. A150

SCHMIDT, Timothy E., Chief Executive Officer, Laredo Medical Center, Laredo, TX, p. A618

SCHMIDT, Veronica, Chief Executive Officer, Custer Regional Hospital, Custer, SD, p. A559

SCHMIDT, William, President and Chief Executive Officer, New London Family Medical Center, New London, WI, p. A693

SCHMIDTBERGER, Sheryl, Chief Financial Officer, Integris Blackwell Regional Hospital, Blackwell, OK, p. A496

SCHMIEDT, Jason, Chief Financial Officer, Logan Memorial Hospital, Russellville, KY, p. A260

SCHMIEG, Greg
Executive Director, Roosevelt Warm Springs Institute for Rehabilitation, Warm Springs, GA, p. A162
Executive Director, Roosevelt Warm Springs LTAC Hospital, Warm Springs, GA, p. A162

SCHMIEGE, Ardis, Chief Financial Officer, Cascade Valley Hospital and Clinics, Arlington, WA, p. A664

SCHMIER, Joe, Director Human Resources, Payroll & Employee Health, Community Medical Center, Missoula, MT, p. A378

SCHMIT–CLINE, Annette, M.D. Medical Director, Mayo Clinic Health System in Springfield, Springfield, MN, p. A341

SCHMITGEN, Jamie, Chair Human Resources, Mayo Clinic Hospital, Phoenix, AZ, p. A35

SCHMITT, John, Senior Vice President and Chief Financial Officer, Kingsbrook Jewish Medical Center,, NY, p. A433

SCHMITT, Joseph, Chief Information Officer, St. Elizabeth's Medical Center, Brighton, MA, p. A298

SCHMITT, III, Joseph, Senior Vice President Finance and Chief Financial Officer, Henry Ford Hospital, Detroit, MI, p. A312

SCHMITT, Karl, M.D. Chief of Staff, St. Elizabeth Edgewood, Edgewood, KY, p. A250

SCHMITT, Michael, M.D., Chief Executive Officer, Kindred Hospital–Atlanta, Atlanta, GA, p. A146

SCHMITT, Jr., Milton G., M.D. Chief Medical Officer, Rockford Memorial Hospital, Rockford, IL, p. A193

SCHMITT, Peggy, President and Chief Executive Officer, North Kansas City Hospital, North Kansas City, MO, p. A367

SCHMITT II, Robert C., Chief Executive Officer, Gibson Area Hospital and Health Services, Gibson City, IL, p. A183

SCHMITT, Thomas M., Chief Executive Officer, Kansas Spine Hospital, Wichita, KS, p. A246

SCHMITTER, Angela, Director Health Information Management, Scotland County Hospital, Memphis, MO, p. A366

SCHMITZ, Bonnie
Vice President and Chief Financial Officer, Agnesian HealthCare, Fond Du Lac, WI, p. A686
Chief Financial Officer, Waupun Memorial Hospital, Waupun, WI, p. A698

SCHMITZ, Brenda, Manager Finance, Central Alabama Veterans Health Care System, Montgomery, AL, p. A23

SCHMITZ, Christopher, Director Human Resources, Stoughton Hospital Association, Stoughton, WI, p. A697

SCHMITZ, Joseph, Chief Financial Officer, St. Cloud Veterans Affairs Health Care System, Saint Cloud, MN, p. A339

SCHMITZ, Vince
Senior Vice President and Chief Financial Officer, MultiCare Mary Bridge Children's Hospital and Health Center, Tacoma, WA, p. A673
Senior Vice President and Chief Financial Officer, MultiCare Tacoma General Hospital, Tacoma, WA, p. A673

SCHNACK, Tim H.
Chief Financial Officer, Alegent Creighton Health Immanuel Medical Center, Omaha, NE, p. A387
Chief Financial Officer, Alegent Creighton Health–Creighton University Medical Center, Omaha, NE, p. A387
Chief Financial Officer, Alegent Creighton Health–Memorial Hospital, Schuyler, Schuyler, NE, p. A389

SCHNEE, Lee, M.D. Chief Medical Staff, Holton Community Hospital, Holton, KS, p. A235

SCHNEEBERGER, Marie, Director of Health, Madelia Community Hospital, Madelia, MN, p. A335

SCHNEIDER, Barbara, R.N., Chief Executive Officer, Brotman Medical Center, Culver City, CA, p. A58

SCHNEIDER, Brenda, Chief Financial Officer, Skyline Hospital, White Salmon, WA, p. A674

SCHNEIDER, Brian, Chief Financial Officer, Dupont Hospital, Fort Wayne, IN, p. A202

SCHNEIDER, Carol L., President and Chief Executive Officer, Mercy Hospital and Medical Center, Chicago, IL, p. A177

SCHNEIDER, Catherine, M.D. Chief Medical Officer, Mt. Ascutney Hospital and Health Center, Windsor, VT, p. A650

SCHNEIDER, David R., Executive Director, Langlade Hospital, Antigo, WI, p. A683

SCHNEIDER, Doug, Director Information Systems, Raulerson Hospital, Okeechobee, FL, p. A134

SCHNEIDER, Greg, Director Information Technology, Winnebago Mental Health Institute, Winnebago, WI, p. A700

SCHNEIDER, H. Frank, Chief Executive Officer, Kindred Hospital Northland, Kansas City, MO, p. A363

SCHNEIDER, Jessie, Director Human Resources, Community Memorial Healthcare, Marysville, KS, p. A239

SCHNEIDER, John, Human Resources Director, Putnam Community Medical Center, Palatka, FL, p. A135

SCHNEIDER, Ken
Chair Human Resources, Mayo Clinic – Saint Marys Hospital, Rochester, MN, p. A339
Chair Human Resources, Rochester Methodist Hospital, Rochester, MN, p. A339

SCHNEIDER, Maureen, MSN Senior Vice President Clinical Program Development and Chief Operating Officer, Somerset Medical Center, Somerville, NJ, p. A410

SCHNEIDER, Shanon, Chief Information Officer, Greeley County Health Services, Tribune, KS, p. A245

SCHNEIDER, Stacie A., Director Human Resources, Aurora Medical Center – Manitowoc County, Two Rivers, WI, p. A698

SCHNEIDER, Stephen, Manager Information Services, Alaska Psychiatric Institute, Anchorage, AK, p. A27

SCHNEIDER, Valerie, Director Human Resources, Gove County Medical Center, Quinter, KS, p. A243

SCHNEIDER, William, Chief Financial Officer, St. Joseph's Hospital and Health Center, Dickinson, ND, p. A466

SCHNEIDERMAN, Henry, M.D. Vice President Medical Services and Physician in Chief, The Hospital at Hebrew Health Care, West Hartford, CT, p. A112

SCHNELL, Dawn, Chief Nursing Officer, Sanford Jackson Medical Center, Jackson, MN, p. A334

SCHNELL, Mary, R.N. Chief Nursing Officer, Howard A. Rusk Rehabilitation Center, Columbia, MO, p. A359

SCHNICHELS, Marlene, R.N., Interim Administrator, Community Behavioral Health Hospital – St. Peter, Saint Peter, MN, p. A340

SCHNIEDERS, Michael H., FACHE, President and Chief Executive Officer, Good Samaritan Hospital, Kearney, NE, p. A385

SCHNIER, Martin, D.O. Chief of Staff, West Texas Veterans Affairs Health Care System, Big Spring, TX, p. A588

SCHNOOR, Jeff, Director Information Technology and Systems, North Suburban Medical Center, Thornton, CO, p. A106

SCHOCK, Marilyn, Chief Executive Officer, McKee Medical Center, Loveland, CO, p. A104

SCHODDE, Joseph, Vice President Financial Services, Charlevoix Area Hospital, Charlevoix, MI, p. A310

SCHOELL, Mark C., Chief Executive Officer, United Memorial Medical Center, Batavia, NY, p. A421

SCHOELLER, Betsy V., Director Human Resources and Education, Mary Greeley Medical Center, Ames, IA, p. A216

SCHOEN, Greg, M.D. Regional Medical Director, Fairview Northland Medical Center, Princeton, MN, p. A338

SCHOEN, Lynn, Chief Executive Officer, Kindred Hospital–Dayton, Dayton, OH, p. A480

SCHOENDIENST, Gerald A., Chief Executive Officer, Jeff Davis Hospital, Hazlehurst, GA, p. A154

SCHOENECKER, Perry L., M.D. Chief of Staff, Shriners Hospitals for Children–St. Louis, Saint Louis, MO, p. A370

SCHOENIG, Tom
System Director Information Services, Desert Springs Hospital Medical Center, Las Vegas, NV, p. A392
Regional Director Information Services, Valley Hospital Medical Center, Las Vegas, NV, p. A394
Chief Information Officer, Wyoming Medical Center, Casper, WY, p. A701

SCHOETTLE, Steve, M.D. Chief Medical Staff, Ozark Health Medical Center, Clinton, AR, p. A42

SCHOFIELD, John, Chief Information Officer, Flagstaff Medical Center, Flagstaff, AZ, p. A31

SCHOFIELD, Sherry, Director Human Resources, Memorial Hospital, Martinsville, VA, p. A657

SCHOLEFIELD, Robert, Chief Operating Officer, St. Elizabeth Medical Center, Utica, NY, p. A444

SCHOLER, Duane, Chief Executive Officer, Arizona Orthopedic Surgical Hospital, Chandler, AZ, p. A30

SCHOLTEN, Ted, Chief Operating Officer, Rehabilitation Hospital of Fort Wayne, Fort Wayne, IN, p. A203

SCHOLZ, Suzanne, Director Medical Records, Horsham Clinic, Ambler, PA, p. A520

SCHON, John, Administrator and Chief Executive Officer, Dickinson County Healthcare System, Iron Mountain, MI, p. A317

SCHONEBERY, Jeremy, Director Information Technology, Heart of America Medical Center, Rugby, ND, p. A469
SCHONLAU, Dan, Chief Financial Officer, Nebraska Heart Hospital, Lincoln, NE, p. A385
SCHOOLER, Nevelyn, Health Information Manager, Garfield County Public Hospital District, Pomeroy, WA, p. A669
SCHOOLER, Richard D., M.D. Chief Medical Officer, Freeman Hospital West, Joplin, MO, p. A362
SCHOOLER, Rick, Vice President and Chief Information Officer, Orlando Regional Medical Center, Orlando, FL, p. A135
SCHOPER, Marian, Manager Human Resources, Mayo Clinic Health System in Springfield, Springfield, MN, p. A341
SCHOR, Mark, Chief Executive Officer, First Hospital Wyoming Valley, Kingston, PA, p. A528
SCHORI, Melissa, M.D. Medical Director, Lincoln Medical and Mental Health Center,, NY, p. A433
SCHOTT, Connie, Administrative Assistant, Florida Hospital Memorial Medical Center, Daytona Beach, FL, p. A122
SCHOU, Howard, Chief Financial Officer, Franklin Hospital District, Benton, IL, p. A174
SCHOULTIES, Daniel L., M.D. Vice President Medical Affairs, Good Samaritan Hospital, Dayton, OH, p. A479
SCHOWENGERDT, Daniel, M.D. Chief of Staff, Comanche County Hospital, Coldwater, KS, p. A232
SCHRADER, Guillermo, M.D. Acting Medical Director, Eastern State Hospital, Williamsburg, VA, p. A663
SCHRAEDER, David, Director Information Systems, Russell Regional Hospital, Russell, KS, p. A243
SCHRAGE, Larry E., Administrator, Genoa Community Hospital, Genoa, NE, p. A383
SCHRAMM, Michael, Chief Executive Officer, Rice Memorial Hospital, Willmar, MN, p. A343
SCHRAMM, Steven R., Chief Financial Officer, Mountain View Hospital, Payson, UT, p. A645
SCHRECK, Rhonda, Director Human Resources, Keokuk Area Hospital, Keokuk, IA, p. A224
SCHREEG, Timothy M., President and Chief Executive Officer, Jasper County Hospital, Rensselaer, IN, p. A212
SCHREIBER, Anne, Manager Human Resources, Fairfax Hospital, Kirkland, WA, p. A667
SCHREIBER, Elizabeth, R.N. Director Patient Care Services, Flambeau Hospital, Park Falls, WI, p. A694
SCHREIBER, Mary Jo, R.N. Vice President Patient Services, Winter Haven Hospital, Winter Haven, FL, p. A144
SCHREIBER, Matthew, M.D. Chief Medical Officer, Piedmont Hospital, Atlanta, GA, p. A147
SCHREIBER, Rob, M.D. Chief Medical Officer, Hebrew Rehabilitation Center, Boston, MA, p. A297
SCHREIER, Susan, R.N. Chief Nursing Executive, Rockford Memorial Hospital, Rockford, IL, p. A193
SCHREINER, David L., FACHE, President and Chief Executive Officer, Katherine Shaw Bethea Hospital, Dixon, IL, p. A181
SCHREITMUELLER, Julie, Chief Operating Officer, Story County Medical Center, Nevada, IA, p. A225
SCHREIVOGEL, Herman, Chief Executive Officer, Lincoln Community Hospital and Nursing Home, Hugo, CO, p. A102
SCHRODER, Loren D., Chief Financial Officer, Phelps Memorial Health Center, Holdrege, NE, p. A384
SCHROEDER, Brian D., M.D. Senior Vice President Medical Affairs, Sparrow Hospital, Lansing, MI, p. A318
SCHROEDER, Christine, R.N. Chief Nursing Officer, Carrington Health Center, Carrington, ND, p. A465
SCHROEDER, Cygnet, D.O. Medical Director, HEALTHSOUTH Rehabilitation Hospital of Fort Smith, Fort Smith, AR, p. A44
SCHROEDER, Gary, Chief Financial Officer, Dayton General Hospital, Dayton, WA, p. A666
SCHROEDER, Heather, R.N. Chief Nurse Executive and Vice President of Nursing, Aurora BayCare Medical Center, Green Bay, WI, p. A687
SCHROEDER, Larry, Chief Executive Officer, Sauk Prairie Memorial Hospital & Clinics, Prairie Du Sac, WI, p. A695
SCHROEDER, Rick, Chief Executive Officer, North Big Horn Hospital District, Lovell, WY, p. A703
SCHROEDL, Greg, M.D. Vice President, Medical and Chief Medical Officer, UW Medicine/Northwest Hospital & Medical Center, Seattle, WA, p. A671
SCHROFFEL, Bruce, President and Chief Executive Officer, University of Colorado Hospital, Aurora, CO, p. A97
SCHROYER, Mike, Chief Operating Officer, St. Vincent Heart Center of Indiana, Indianapolis, IN, p. A206
SCHROYER, Renee, Chief Financial Officer, Sutter Surgical Hospital – North Valley, Yuba City, CA, p. A96
SCHRUM, Andrew, Director Information Systems, Washington County Memorial Hospital, Potosi, MO, p. A368
SCHRUMPF, Jason, President, Missouri Delta Medical Center, Sikeston, MO, p. A371
SCHUBERT, Bob, Director Human Resources, Scott & White Hospital – Brenham, Brenham, TX, p. A589
SCHUCKMAN, Tim, Chief Financial Officer, Jennie M. Melham Memorial Medical Center, Broken Bow, NE, p. A382

SCHUE, Janine
Senior Vice President People Resources, Newark–Wayne Community Hospital, Newark, NY, p. A437
Senior Vice President Human Resources, Rochester General Hospital, Rochester, NY, p. A441
SCHUELER, Joe, Chief Financial Officer, Morrow County Hospital, Mount Gilead, OH, p. A486
SCHUESSLER, Donald, M.D. Medical Director, Edward John Noble Hospital of Gouverneur, Gouverneur, NY, p. A426
SCHUESSLER, Dwight, Chief Information Officer, Iowa City Veterans Affairs Health Care System, Iowa City, IA, p. A223
SCHUESSLER, Joel, Interim Vice President Human Resources, DeKalb Medical at North Decatur, Decatur, GA, p. A152
SCHUETT, Susan M., Chief Information Officer, Olmsted Medical Center, Rochester, MN, p. A339
SCHUETZ, Charles D., Chief Executive Officer, University General Hospital, Houston, TX, p. A613
SCHUETZ, Jill, Director Human Resources, LifeCare Hospitals of Wisconsin, Pewaukee, WI, p. A694
SCHUH, Jason, M.D. Chief of Staff, Wise Regional Health System, Decatur, TX, p. A598
SCHUITEMAN, Jackson, Chief Financial Officer, Sioux Center Community Hospital and Health Center Avera, Sioux Center, IA, p. A228
SCHUKNECHT, Amy, Manager Human Resources, Lynn County Hospital District, Tahoka, TX, p. A636
SCHULER, Allison, R.N. Chief Nursing Officer, Montfort Jones Memorial Hospital, Kosciusko, MS, p. A349
SCHULER, Kathy, R.N. Vice President of Patient Care Services, Winchester Hospital, Winchester, MA, p. A306
SCHULER, William, M.D. President Medical Staff, Mendota Community Hospital, Mendota, IL, p. A188
SCHULHOF, Alicia, Chief Operating Officer, Brandon Regional Hospital, Brandon, FL, p. A119
SCHULTE, Mark, Chief Executive Officer, Avera Creighton Hospital, Creighton, NE, p. A383
SCHULTEIS, Chris, Vice President/Chief Financial Officer, Southampton Hospital, Southampton, NY, p. A443
SCHULTHEIS, David, Chief Financial Officer, Devereux Children's Behavioral Health Center, Malvern, PA, p. A530
SCHULTHEIS, Hal, Director Information Systems, TriStar Hendersonville Medical Center, Hendersonville, TN, p. A570
SCHULTZ, Bradley
Chief Financial Officer, TriStar Skyline Madison Campus, Madison, TN, p. A573
Chief Financial Officer, TriStar Skyline Medical Center, Nashville, TN, p. A577
SCHULTZ, David W., FACHE Executive Vice President and Chief Operating Officer, Overlake Hospital Medical Center, Bellevue, WA, p. A664
SCHULTZ, Diana, Chief Executive Officer, Kindred Hospital–Corpus Christi, Corpus Christi, TX, p. A594
SCHULTZ, Jacky, R.N. Executive Vice President and Chief Operating Officer, Suburban Hospital, Bethesda, MD, p. A290
SCHULTZ, Karl W., M.D. Chief of Staff, Elkhart General Healthcare System, Elkhart, IN, p. A201
SCHULTZ, Kim, Manager Information, Connally Medical Center, Floresville, TX, p. A602
SCHULTZ, Mary Kay, Director Human Resources, Sturgis Hospital, Sturgis, MI, p. A325
SCHULTZ, Rachelle H., President and Chief Executive Officer, Winona Health, Winona, MN, p. A343
SCHULTZ, Teresa L., R.N. Vice President of Patient Care, Rogers Memorial Hospital, Oconomowoc, WI, p. A693
SCHULZ, Charles K., Chief Executive Officer, York General Hospital, York, NE, p. A390
SCHULZ, Larry A., Chief Executive Officer, Lake Region Healthcare, Fergus Falls, MN, p. A332
SCHULZ, Marcie, Director Patient Care, Sakakawea Medical Center, Hazen, ND, p. A467
SCHUMACHER, Ann, MSN, President, Alegent Creighton Health Immanuel Medical Center, Omaha, NE, p. A387
SCHUMACHER, Debbie, Manager Human Resource, St. Mary's Hospital, Cottonwood, ID, p. A168
SCHUMACHER, Kevin, Director of Information Services, LifeCare Medical Center, Roseau, MN, p. A339
SCHUMACHER, Linda, Chief Operating Officer, Chinese Hospital, San Francisco, CA, p. A86
SCHUMACHER, Rodney, Interim Chief Executive Officer, Deaconess Hospital, Spokane, WA, p. A672
SCHUMM, Herbert, M.D. Vice President Medical Affairs, St. Rita's Medical Center, Lima, OH, p. A484
SCHUPP, Frank, Chief Executive Officer, Flint River Community Hospital, Montezuma, GA, p. A157
SCHURKAMP, Christine, Senior Human Resources Business Partner, Spectrum Health Gerber Memorial, Fremont, MI, p. A314
SCHUSTER, Catherine, Chief Information Officer, Northern Dutchess Hospital, Rhinebeck, NY, p. A440

SCHUSTER, Christine C., R.N., President and Chief Executive Officer, Emerson Hospital, Concord, MA, p. A299
SCHUSTER, Emmett C., President and Chief Executive Officer, Gibson General Hospital, Princeton, IN, p. A212
SCHUSTER, Jolene, Director Information Technology, Trego County–Lemke Memorial Hospital, Wakeeney, KS, p. A245
SCHUSTER, Lexie, Vice President Human Resources, Good Samaritan Hospital, Los Angeles, CA, p. A69
SCHWAB, Bob, M.D
Chief Medical Officer, Texas Health Presbyterian Hospital Allen, Allen, TX, p. A581
Chief Quality Officer, Texas Health Presbyterian Hospital Denton, Denton, TX, p. A599
SCHWAB, Caryn A., Executive Director, The Mount Sinai Hospital of Queens,, NY, p. A437
SCHWABENBAUER, Mary Ann, Director Information Technology, Elk Regional Health Center, Saint Marys, PA, p. A540
SCHWAGER, Mary A., Director Human Resources, Antelope Memorial Hospital, Neligh, NE, p. A386
SCHWALL, Garry, Chief Operating Officer, Winthrop–University Hospital, Mineola, NY, p. A429
SCHWAN, Joni, Director Human Resources, Excelsior Springs Hospital, Excelsior Springs, MO, p. A360
SCHWANER, III, Charles, Chief Financial Officer, Doctors Hospital of Sarasota, Sarasota, FL, p. A139
SCHWANKE, Daniel, President, ProMedica Fostoria Community Hospital, Fostoria, OH, p. A481
SCHWARM, Tony, President, Missouri Baptist Sullivan Hospital, Sullivan, MO, p. A372
SCHWARTZ, Ave, Chief Information Officer, Austen Riggs Center, Stockbridge, MA, p. A305
SCHWARTZ, David M., D.O. Vice President, Medical Affairs, Sentara Northern Virginia Medical Center, Woodbridge, VA, p. A663
SCHWARTZ, Jonathon, M.D. Medical Director and Chief Medical Officer, Spaulding Hospital for Continuing Medical Care Cambridge, Cambridge, MA, p. A299
SCHWARTZ, Judy, M.D. Chief Medical Officer, Knox Community Hospital, Mount Vernon, OH, p. A487
SCHWARTZ, Kenneth V., M.D. Medical Director, Griffin Hospital, Derby, CT, p. A108
SCHWARTZ, Kim K., Assistant Administrator of Human Resources and Physician Services, Boone County Hospital, Boone, IA, p. A217
SCHWARTZ, Peggy, Vice President Human Resources, Wayne Hospital, Greenville, OH, p. A482
SCHWARTZ, Peter
Manager Information Services, Carrier Clinic, Belle Mead, NJ, p. A401
Director Information Systems, East Mountain Hospital, Belle Mead, NJ, p. A401
SCHWARTZ, Roberta, Executive Vice President, The Methodist Hospital, Houston, TX, p. A613
SCHWARTZ, Ronald, M.D. Medical Director, Masonicare Health Center, Wallingford, CT, p. A112
SCHWARTZ, Sharon, Director Medical Records, Scott & White Hospital – Brenham, Brenham, TX, p. A589
SCHWARZBACH, Jerry, M.D. Medical Director, East Texas Medical Center Rehabilitation Hospital, Tyler, TX, p. A638
SCHWARZKOPF, Ruth, R.N. Chief Nursing Officer, West Boca Medical Center, Boca Raton, FL, p. A119
SCHWEAGEL, Glen
Vice President Finance, Barnes–Jewish St. Peters Hospital, Saint Peters, MO, p. A371
Chief Financial Officer, Progress West HealthCare Center, Saint Charles, MO, p. A368
SCHWEERS, Michele, Vice President Human Resources, Kimball Medical Center, Lakewood, NJ, p. A405
SCHWEICKHARDT, Mary Jo, Vice President Human Resources, MedStar Georgetown University Hospital, Washington, DC, p. A116
SCHWEIGERT, Matthew B., Administrator, Mercy Continuing Care Hospital, Chesterfield, MO, p. A358
SCHWEIGERT, Nicole, Director Human Resources, Texas Health Presbyterian Hospital Flower Mound, Flower Mound, TX, p. A602
SCHWEIGHARDT, Chris, MSN, Interim President, Saint Joseph Berea, Berea, KY, p. A248
SCHWEIGHART, Karen, MS, Administrator, Andrew McFarland Mental Health Center, Springfield, IL, p. A195
SCHWEIKART, Jay
Chief Financial Officer, Kindred Hospital Chicago Northlake, Northlake, IL, p. A190
Chief Financial Officer, Kindred Hospital–Sycamore, Sycamore, IL, p. A196
SCHWEISS, Sue, Director of Nursing, Sleepy Eye Medical Center, Sleepy Eye, MN, p. A341
SCHWEITZER, Alex, Superintendent and Chief Executive Officer, North Dakota State Hospital, Jamestown, ND, p. A468

SCHWEITZER, Michael, M.D. Chief Medical Officer, St. Vincent Healthcare, Billings, MT, p. A374

SCHWEITZER, Tammy, Chief Financial Officer, Grisell Memorial Hospital District One, Ransom, KS, p. A243

SCHWEIZER, Brenda, Coordinator Human Resources, Kindred Hospital of Northern Indiana, Mishawaka, IN, p. A210

SCHWENZFEIER, Jeni, Chief Financial Officer, Kittson Memorial Healthcare Center, Hallock, MN, p. A333

SCHWIND, David, Chief Financial Officer, Capital Hospice, Arlington, VA, p. A651

SCHWIND, Mary, R.N. Chief Clinical Officer, Kindred Hospital–San Francisco Bay Area, San Leandro, CA, p. A88

SCHWINGLER, Joyce, Chief Financial Officer, Eureka Community Health Services Avera, Eureka, SD, p. A559

SCHWOEBLE, Walter, Vice President Human Resources, Akron Children's Hospital, Akron, OH, p. A469

SCIALDONE, Michael A., Interim Chief Executive Officer, Memorial Health System, Colorado Springs, CO, p. A98

SCIARRO, Jason
President and Chief Operating Officer, Centegra Hospital – McHenry, McHenry, IL, p. A188
Chief Operating Officer, Centegra Hospital – Woodstock, Woodstock, IL, p. A197

SCIBELLI, Tony, Vice President Human Resources and Operations, Faxton–St. Luke's Healthcare, Utica, NY, p. A444

SCIESZINSKI, Robert C., Vice President Finance, Ministry Door County Medical Center, Sturgeon Bay, WI, p. A697

SCIONTI, Jeff, Chief Operating Officer, Parkland Medical Center, Derry, NH, p. A397

SCIORTINO, John E., Senior Vice President and Chief Operating Officer, New York Hospital Queens,, NY, p. A435

SCIOSCIA, Angela, M.D. Chief Medical Officer, UC San Diego Health System, San Diego, CA, p. A86

SCIULLO, Armando, D.O. Chief of Staff, Grove City Medical Center, Grove City, PA, p. A526

SCIURBA, John, Vice President and Chief Financial Officer, White Plains Hospital Center, White Plains, NY, p. A446

SCLAIR, Max
Vice President Human Resources, Brookdale Hospital Medical Center,, NY, p. A431
Vice President Human Resources, Flushing Hospital Medical Center,, NY, p. A432
Vice President Human Resources, Jamaica Hospital Medical Center,, NY, p. A432

SCLAMA, Tony, M.D. Vice President Medical Affairs, MedStar Franklin Square Medical Center, Baltimore, MD, p. A288

SCOBIE, Robbin, Vice President Nursing, Aurelia Osborn Fox Memorial Hospital, Oneonta, NY, p. A438

SCOCCIA, Vincent, D.O. Chief Medical Staff, Nye Regional Medical Center, Tonopah, NV, p. A396

SCOGGIN, Terry, Chief Financial Officer, Titus Regional Medical Center, Mount Pleasant, TX, p. A623

SCOGGINS, Kim, Administrator, Polk Medical Center, Cedartown, GA, p. A149

SCOPAC, Paul A., Vice President of Operations and Chief Operating Officer, Oneida Healthcare, Oneida, NY, p. A438

SCORZELLI, Gerard, Chief Financial Officer, Albany Stratton Veterans Affairs Medical Center, Albany, NY, p. A420

SCOTT, Arthur B., Vice President Operations, North Adams Regional Hospital, North Adams, MA, p. A303

SCOTT, Camille, Chief Executive Officer, Forks Community Hospital, Forks, WA, p. A666

SCOTT, Charles F., President and Chief Executive Officer, Henry Medical Center, Stockbridge, GA, p. A161

SCOTT, Colleen M., Vice President Finance, Waterbury Hospital, Waterbury, CT, p. A112

SCOTT, Craig, Interim Director Management Information Systems, University of Miami Hospital, Miami, FL, p. A132

SCOTT, David W., President and Chief Executive Officer, Ohio Valley General Hospital, McKees Rocks, PA, p. A531

SCOTT, Debbie, Chief Operating Officer, Davis County Hospital, Bloomfield, IA, p. A217

SCOTT, Doug, Director Human Resources, Jacksonville Medical Center, Jacksonville, AL, p. A22

SCOTT, Ernie, Director Human Resources, Natchitoches Regional Medical Center, Natchitoches, LA, p. A274

SCOTT, Ginger, Vice President Human Resources, Columbus Regional Healthcare System, Whiteville, NC, p. A462

SCOTT, Heath, M.D. Chief of Staff, King's Daughters Hospital, Yazoo City, MS, p. A355

SCOTT, James, M.D. Vice President Medical Affairs, Candler Hospital, Savannah, GA, p. A159

SCOTT, Jeffrey, Chief Information Officer, St. Joseph Hospital and Health Center, Kokomo, IN, p. A207

SCOTT, Jerry, Chief Operating Officer, Navos, Seattle, WA, p. A670

SCOTT, Jon W., Chief Executive Officer, Select Specialty Hospital–Topeka, Topeka, KS, p. A245

SCOTT, Joseph F., FACHE, President and Chief Executive Officer, LibertyHealth–Jersey City Medical Center, Jersey City, NJ, p. A405

SCOTT, Julie, Chief Nursing Officer, HEALTHSOUTH Rehabilitation Hospital of York, York, PA, p. A545

SCOTT, Kimberley, Director Health Care Services, Kansas Neurological Institute, Topeka, KS, p. A244

SCOTT, Kurt M., FACHE, Administrator, LSU Bogalusa Medical Center, Bogalusa, LA, p. A264

SCOTT, M Daryl, Assistant Vice President, Jefferson Regional Medical Center, Pine Bluff, AR, p. A49

SCOTT, Michael E., M.D. Director Medical Services, Sierra Tucson, Tucson, AZ, p. A39

SCOTT, Robert F., Vice President Human Resources, Advocate Good Shepherd Hospital, Barrington, IL, p. A174

SCOTT, Ron, Vice President Human Resources, Queen of the Valley Medical Center, Napa, CA, p. A76

SCOTT, Seth, M.D. Chief of Staff, George Regional Hospital, Lucedale, MS, p. A350

SCOTT, Stacy, Director of Nursing, Sabetha Community Hospital, Sabetha, KS, p. A243

SCOTT, Steve, Chief Operating Officer, Sheridan Community Hospital, Sheridan, MI, p. A324

SCOTT, Susan, Director Medical Records, Beartooth Billings Clinic, Red Lodge, MT, p. A379

SCOTT, Thomas, Chief Operating Officer, Chilton Hospital, Pompton Plains, NJ, p. A409

SCOTT, Vanda, Chief Executive Officer, Select Specialty Hospital–Knoxville, Knoxville, TN, p. A572

SCOTT, William, M.D. Vice President Medical Affairs, Regional Medical Center of San Jose, San Jose, CA, p. A88

SCOTT, William, Chief Financial Officer, Specialty Hospital of Mid–America, Overland Park, KS, p. A242

SCOTT, William P., M.D. Chief of Staff, River Valley Medical Center, Dardanelle, AR, p. A42

SCOTTEN, Dianne, Chief Clinical Officer, Central Montana Medical Center, Lewistown, MT, p. A377

SCOTTO, Dan, Director Data Processing, Eastern Long Island Hospital, Greenport, NY, p. A426

SCOWN, Kent, Director Operations and Information Services, Jerold Phelps Community Hospital, Garberville, CA, p. A62

SCRASE, David R., M.D. Executive Senior Vice President and Chief Operating Officer, Presbyterian Kaseman Hospital, Albuquerque, NM, p. A415

SCREMIN, Karen, Vice President Finance, Exempla Lutheran Medical Center, Wheat Ridge, CO, p. A107

SCRIBER, Rachel, Director of Marketing & Public Relations, Medical Center of South Arkansas, El Dorado, AR, p. A43

SCRIVEN, Richard, M.D. Chief of Staff, North Hills Hospital, North Richland Hills, TX, p. A625

SCRIVO, Jr., Joseph A., Director Human Resources, Mercy Hospital, Buffalo, NY, p. A422

SCRUGGS, Kisha, Chief Financial Officer, Brentwood Hospital, Shreveport, LA, p. A277

SCRUGGS, Sherry
Administrator, Gibson General Hospital, Trenton, TN, p. A580
Administrator, Humboldt General Hospital, Humboldt, TN, p. A570
Administrator, Milan General Hospital, Milan, TN, p. A575

SCULCO, Thomas P., M.D. Surgeon–in–Chief and Medical Director, Hospital for Special Surgery, New York, NY, p. A432

SCULLY, Charles
Chief Information Officer, Renown Regional Medical Center, Reno, NV, p. A395
Chief Information Officer, Renown Rehabilitation Hospital, Reno, NV, p. A395
Chief Information Officer, Renown South Meadows Medical Center, Reno, NV, p. A395

SCULLY, Trish
Manager Employment Services, Massachusetts Hospital School, Canton, MA, p. A299
Director Human Resources, Taunton State Hospital, Taunton, MA, p. A305

SCURLOCK, Scott, Chief Information Officer, Doctors Memorial Hospital, Bonifay, FL, p. A119

SCZYGELSKI, Sidney C., Senior Vice President Finance and Chief Financial Officer, Aspirus Wausau Hospital, Wausau, WI, p. A699

SEAFORD, Jeff, Director Human Resources, Hugh Chatham Memorial Hospital, Elkin, NC, p. A452

SEAGO, Terri, Chief Financial Officer, Baptist Memorial Hospital–Collierville, Collierville, TN, p. A567

SEAGROVES, Matthew, Chief Financial Officer, Bayfront Health Brooksville, Brooksville, FL, p. A119

SEAHORN, Martha, R.N. Chief Nurse Office, Shelby Baptist Medical Center, Alabaster, AL, p. A15

SEAL, John, Director Human Resources, Riverside Medical Center, Franklinton, LA, p. A267

SEAL, Ronald T., Chief Executive Officer, Texoma Medical Center, Denison, TX, p. A598

SEALE, Corey A., Administrator, Kaiser Permanente Moreno Valley Medical Center, Moreno Valley, CA, p. A75

SEALE, Edward, Chief Information Officer, New Horizons Health Systems, Owenton, KY, p. A258

SEALE, Paul E., FACHE Chief Operating Officer, Upstate University Hospital, Syracuse, NY, p. A444

SEALS, Carol, Chief Financial Officer, Indiana University Health Ball Memorial Hospital, Muncie, IN, p. A210

SEALS, Frank, Chief Financial Officer, Reeves County Hospital, Pecos, TX, p. A626

SEALS, Molly
Senior Vice President Human Resources and Learning, St. Elizabeth Boardman Health Center, Boardman, OH, p. A472
Senior Vice President Human Resources and Learning, St. Elizabeth Health Center, Youngstown, OH, p. A494
Senior Vice President Human Resources and Learning, St. Joseph Health Center, Warren, OH, p. A492

SEALS, Robert, D.O. Medical Director, Carson City Hospital, Carson City, MI, p. A310

SEAMON, Robert L., Chief Executive Officer, Clifton–Fine Hospital, Star Lake, NY, p. A443

SEARBY, Tonya L., Chief Human Resources, Marion Veterans Affairs Medical Center, Marion, IL, p. A187

SEARLE, Anne, Chief Information Officer, University Medical Center of Princeton at Plainsboro, Plainsboro, NJ, p. A409

SEARLE, Reynolds, Director Information Systems, Fairfield Memorial Hospital, Winnsboro, SC, p. A557

SEARS, Frank, Vice President Information Services, Memorial Hospital of Carbondale, Carbondale, IL, p. A175

SEARS, Marilyn, President and Chief Executive Officer, Shelby Memorial Hospital, Shelbyville, IL, p. A194

SEARS, Michael A., Chief Financial Officer, Wayne Medical Center, Waynesboro, TN, p. A580

SEARS, Michelle, Director Information Systems, Helen Newberry Joy Hospital, Newberry, MI, p. A321

SEASE, Peggy, Vice President Human Resources, Southeast Alabama Medical Center, Dothan, AL, p. A19

SEAVER, Roger E., President and Chief Executive Officer, Henry Mayo Newhall Memorial Hospital, Valencia, CA, p. A94

SEAY, Lisa, Director Human Resources, Baylor Medical Center at Irving, Irving, TX, p. A614

SEBASTIAN, Peggy A., R.N., President and Chief Executive Officer, St. Joseph's Hospital, Highland, IL, p. A184

SEBEK, Brenda Jean, R.N. Chief Nursing Officer, St. Mary's Community Hospital, Nebraska City, NE, p. A386

SECHI, Patricia, Chief Operating Officer, North Shore Medical Center, Miami, FL, p. A132

SECKINGER, Jenn, Chief Financial Officer, Community Memorial Hospital, Syracuse, NE, p. A390

SECKINGER, Mark R., Administrator and Chief Executive Officer, Hardin Memorial Hospital, Kenton, OH, p. A483

SECOR, Diane K., Director Human Resources, Lawrence Medical Center, Moulton, AL, p. A24

SECOR, Jr., Richard, M.D. Chief of Staff, Mineral Area Regional Medical Center, Farmington, MO, p. A360

SEDGWICK, Sally, Manager Public Relations and Marketing, Bigfork Valley Hospital, Bigfork, MN, p. A329

SEDMINIK, Vince, Chief Executive Officer, Springhill Medical Center, Springhill, LA, p. A279

SEEDER, Rachael, Controller, Santiam Memorial Hospital, Stayton, OR, p. A518

SEEHAFER, Kevin
Chief Financial Officer, Kenmare Community Hospital, Kenmare, ND, p. A468
Chief Financial Officer, Trinity Health, Minot, ND, p. A468

SEEKINS, DeAnne, Director, Durham Veterans Affairs Medical Center, Durham, NC, p. A451

SEELEY, Kevin, Chief Information Officer, Mike O'Callaghan Federal Hospital, Nellis AFB, NV, p. A394

SEELMAN, Michael, Chief Operating Officer, Northside Medical Center, Youngstown, OH, p. A494

SEELY, Paula, Manager Human Resources, Kossuth Regional Health Center, Algona, IA, p. A216

SEEMS, Steven, Director of Information Technology, Phillips County Hospital, Phillipsburg, KS, p. A242

SEESE, Rebecca, Chief Operating Officer, U. S. Air Force Regional Hospital, Elmendorf AFB, AK, p. A28

SEEVER, Jennifer, Regional Chief Financial Officer, Sedan City Hospital, Sedan, KS, p. A244

SEGAL, Jonathan, Chief Financial Officer, New York State Psychiatric Institute, New York, NY, p. A435

SEGELEON, Kurt, Director Health Information Management, Kindred Hospital–Pittsburgh, Oakdale, PA, p. A533

SEGIN, Robert
Chief Financial Officer, Virtua Berlin, Berlin, NJ, p. A401
Executive Vice President & Chief Financial Officer, Virtua Marlton, Marlton, NJ, p. A406
Chief Financial Officer, Virtua Memorial, Mount Holly, NJ, p. A406

SEGLER, Randall K., FACHE, Chief Executive Officer, Comanche County Memorial Hospital, Lawton, OK, p. A500

SEGRAVES, Steven, M.D. Medical Director, Research Psychiatric Center, Kansas City, MO, p. A363

SEHRT, Lori, Chief Financial Officer, McKee Medical Center, Loveland, CO, p. A104

SEIBERT, Nancy, Director Human Resources, Franklin Hospital District, Benton, IL, p. A174

SEID, Lynette, Area Chief Financial Officer, Kaiser Permanente San Diego Medical Center, San Diego, CA, p. A85

SEIDE, Rob, Manager Marketing and Communications, St. Luke's Hospital, San Francisco, CA, p. A87

SEIDL, Doris A., Vice President Human Resources, Port Huron Hospital, Port Huron, MI, p. A322

SEIDLER, Richard A., FACHE,
President and Chief Executive Officer, Trinity Bettendorf, Bettendorf, IA, p. A216
President and Chief Executive Officer, Trinity Rock Island, Rock Island, IL, p. A193

SEIFER, Jill, Vice President Human Resources, Oaklawn Psychiatric Center, Goshen, IN, p. A204

SEIGLER, Leslie G., Executive Assistant and Coordinator Human Resources, Edgefield County Hospital, Edgefield, SC, p. A551

SEILER, Edward H., Director, Huntington Veterans Affairs Medical Center, Huntington, WV, p. A677

SEITZ, Stewart R., Chief Executive Officer, Gladys Spellman Specialty Hospital and Nursing Center, Cheverly, MD, p. A290

SELBOVITZ, Leslie, M.D. Senior Vice President Medical Affairs, Newton–Wellesley Hospital, Newton Lower Falls, MA, p. A303

SELBY, Eric, R.N. Chief Nursing Officer, Chicot Memorial Medical Center, Lake Village, AR, p. A46

SELDEN, Thomas A., FACHE, President and Chief Executive Officer, Southwest General Health Center, Middleburg Heights, OH, p. A486

SELENKE, Darcy, M.D. Chief of Staff, Mercy Hospital Columbus, Columbus, KS, p. A232

SELEY, Jim, Chief Information Officer, Clay County Medical Center, Clay Center, KS, p. A232

SELF, Debbie, Chief Financial Officer, North Georgia Medical Center, Ellijay, GA, p. A153

SELF, Douglas, Chief Operating Officer, Carson Tahoe Regional Healthcare, Carson City, NV, p. A391

SELF, Joshua, Chief Operating Officer, Barrow Regional Medical Center, Winder, GA, p. A163

SELFRIDGE, Tara, Manager Human Resources, Purcell Municipal Hospital, Purcell, OK, p. A506

SELHORST, Sonya, Administrator, Mercy Hospital of Defiance, Defiance, OH, p. A480

SELIGMAN, Joel, President and Chief Executive Officer, Northern Westchester Hospital, Mount Kisco, NY, p. A430

SELIGMAN, Morris H., M.D. Chief Medical Officer and Chief Medical Information Officer, Sycamore Shoals Hospital, Elizabethton, TN, p. A568

SELL, Paula, Director Human Resources, Allen County Hospital, Iola, KS, p. A236

SELLARDS, Michael G., President and Chief Executive Officer, St. Mary's Medical Center, Huntington, WV, p. A678

SELLERS, Larry W., M.D. Chief Medical Officer, Mercy Medical Center–Sioux City, Sioux City, IA, p. A228

SELLERS, Laura, Director Information Systems, Youth Villages Inner Harbour Campus, Douglasville, GA, p. A152

SELLERS, Liz, R.N. Chief Nursing Officer, Southwest Memorial Hospital, Cortez, CO, p. A98

SELLERS, Regena, Chief Nursing Officer, Three Rivers Behavioral Health, West Columbia, SC, p. A557

SELLERS, Robert R., President, Clay County Hospital, Flora, IL, p. A182

SELLHEIM, Kevin, Chief Executive Officer, Sleepy Eye Medical Center, Sleepy Eye, MN, p. A341

SELLICK, Kathleen Ann, President and Chief Executive Officer, Rady Children's Hospital – San Diego, San Diego, CA, p. A85

SELLMANN, Laura, Director Finance, Aurora Sheboygan Memorial Medical Center, Sheboygan, WI, p. A696

SELLS, Angie Phelps, Manager Human Resources, Harrison County Hospital, Corydon, IN, p. A200

SELLS, Matt, CPA Chief Financial Officer, Brown County Hospital, Ainsworth, NE, p. A381

SELMAN, David G.
Corporate Vice President Information Resources, ProMedica Bay Park Hospital, Oregon, OH, p. A488
Corporate Vice President Information Resources, ProMedica Fostoria Community Hospital, Fostoria, OH, p. A481
Chief Information Officer, ProMedica Toledo Hospital, Toledo, OH, p. A491

SELMON, Patricia, Director Public Relations and Chief Human Resources, Jefferson County Hospital, Fayette, MS, p. A346

SELPH, Wendy, Director Human Resources, Dodge County Hospital, Eastman, GA, p. A153

SELSOR, Doug, Director Finance, Select Rehabilitation Hospital of Denton, Denton, TX, p. A599

SELTMAN, Pam, Director Human Resources, Rush County Memorial Hospital, La Crosse, KS, p. A237

SELTZER, Paul, M.D. Chief of Staff, West Palm Hospital, West Palm Beach, FL, p. A144

SELVAGGI, Richard, M.D. Chief of Staff, Hunt Regional Community Hospital, Commerce, TX, p. A593

SELVAM, A. Panneer, M.D. Chief of Staff, Northern Arizona Veterans Affairs Health Care System, Prescott, AZ, p. A36

SELVIDGE, Sandra, Chief Fiscal Service, Cincinnati Veterans Affairs Medical Center, Cincinnati, OH, p. A474

SELZ, Timothy P., Vice President, Orange Regional Medical Center, Middletown, NY, p. A429

SEMAR, Dale, Controller, Medina Regional Hospital, Hondo, TX, p. A608

SEMELSBERGER, Kimberly, Vice President Financial Operations, Conemaugh Miners Medical Center, Hastings, PA, p. A527

SEMERDJIAN, Gregory, M.D. Senior Vice President Medical Affairs, St. Joseph Medical Center, Tacoma, WA, p. A673

SEMINGSON, John H., Chief Executive Officer, Ruby Valley Hospital, Sheridan, MT, p. A379

SEMRAD, Marianne, Associate Director Administrative Services, Captain James A. Lovell Federal Health Care Center, North Chicago, IL, p. A190

SENDAYDIEGO, Fe, Director Information Systems, Sonoma Valley Hospital, Sonoma, CA, p. A91

SENELICK, Richard, M.D. Medical Director, HEALTHSOUTH Rehabilitation Institute of San Antonio, San Antonio, TX, p. A631

SENESAC, Marc, Vice President Human Resources, Advocate Illinois Masonic Medical Center, Chicago, IL, p. A176

SENGER, Richard, Chief Financial Officer, Portsmouth Regional Hospital, Portsmouth, NH, p. A400

SENGER, Tricia, Chief Financial Officer, St. Luke's Elmore, Mountain Home, ID, p. A170

SENKER, Thomas J., FACHE, President and Chief Executive Officer, Newton Medical Center, Newton, NJ, p. A408

SENNEFF, Robert G., FACHE, President and Chief Executive Officer, Graham Hospital, Canton, IL, p. A175

SENNETT, Nancy, R.N. Vice President Nursing Services, Franciscan St. Elizabeth Health – Crawfordsville, Crawfordsville, IN, p. A200

SENNISH, James, Vice President Human Resources, Firelands Regional Health System, Sandusky, OH, p. A489

SEO, Harlan, Accountant, Hale Ho'ola Hamakua, Honokaa, HI, p. A164

SEPCOSKI, John, Director Information Technology, Barnes–Kasson County Hospital, Susquehanna, PA, p. A542

SEPP Jr., Howard W., FACHE, Vice President and Administrator, Southeast Georgia Health System Camden Campus, Saint Marys, GA, p. A159

SEPPANEN, Carol, Director Human Resources, Baraga County Memorial Hospital, L'Anse, MI, p. A318

SERAFIN, Deborah J., Vice President Human Resources, Mount St. Mary's Hospital and Health Center, Lewiston, NY, p. A428

SERENO, Joe, Interim Chief Financial Officer, Southwest General Hospital, San Antonio, TX, p. A632

SERENO, Joseph, Chief Financial Officer, Lovelace Women's Hospital, Albuquerque, NM, p. A414

SERFLING, G. Aubrey, President and Chief Executive Officer, Eisenhower Medical Center, Rancho Mirage, CA, p. A81

SERKETICH, Steve, Manager Information Services, Aurora Sheboygan Memorial Medical Center, Sheboygan, WI, p. A696

SERLE, John, FACHE, President and Chief Executive Officer, Lourdes Medical Center, Pasco, WA, p. A669

SERNULKA, John M., Chief Executive Officer, Carroll Hospital Center, Westminster, MD, p. A294

SERNYAK, Michael, M.D., Director, Connecticut Mental Health Center, New Haven, CT, p. A110

SERRATT, Jim, Chief Executive Officer, Willow Springs Center, Reno, NV, p. A395

SESSA, Bonnie, Vice President and Chief Information Officer, Beth Israel Medical Center, New York, NY, p. A430

SESSIONS, Tracey, Administrator, State Hospital South, Blackfoot, ID, p. A167

SESSLER, Connie, Director Human Resources, ProMedica St. Luke's Hospital, Maumee, OH, p. A486

SETCHEL, David P., Vice President Operations, Bon Secours–DePaul Medical Center, Norfolk, VA, p. A658

SETILI, Rick, Manager Information Systems, Warren General Hospital, Warren, PA, p. A543

SETTELMEYER, Camille, Assistant Administrator Clinical Services, Mercy Hospital, Valley City, ND, p. A469

SETTLE, Andrea, Director Human Resources, Taylor Regional Hospital, Campbellsville, KY, p. A249

SETTLES, April, Chief Financial Officer, Greene County General Hospital, Linton, IN, p. A209

SETTLES, Laura, Director Human Resources, Baylor Medical Center at Garland, Garland, TX, p. A606

SETZKORN–MEYER, Marsha, Director Public Relations and Marketing, Hillsboro Community Hospital, Hillsboro, KS, p. A235

SEUFERER, Stanley, D.O. Chief of Staff, Memorial Medical Center of West Michigan, Ludington, MI, p. A319

SEVCO, Mark, President, UPMC East, Monroeville, PA, p. A532

SEVENICH, Mark, Director Human Resources, Owatonna Hospital, Owatonna, MN, p. A337

SEVILLIAN, Clarence, President and Chief Executive Officer, McLaren Oakland, Pontiac, MI, p. A322

SEWELL, Lance, Chief Financial Officer, South Lake Hospital, Clermont, FL, p. A120

SEWELL, Sue, Chief Nursing Officer, Wise Regional Health System, Decatur, TX, p. A598

SEXTON, Cheryl, Director Nursing Operations, South Texas Rehabilitation Hospital, Brownsville, TX, p. A590

SEXTON, Cindy
Chief Financial Officer, St. David's North Austin Medical Center, Austin, TX, p. A586
Chief Financial Officer, St. David's Round Rock Medical Center, Round Rock, TX, p. A629

SEXTON, Kevin, Director Information Systems, Raleigh General Hospital, Beckley, WV, p. A675

SEXTON, William J., Administrator, Wyoming State Hospital, Evanston, WY, p. A702

SEXTON, William P., Chief Executive Officer, Prairie du Chien Memorial Hospital, Prairie Du Chien, WI, p. A695

SEY, Mark, Vice President and Chief Administrative Officer, Lodi Memorial Hospital, Lodi, CA, p. A66

SEYBOLD, Henry, Senior Vice President and Chief Financial Officer, Rockford Memorial Hospital, Rockford, IL, p. A193

SEYMOUR, Anthea, Chief Operating Officer, St. Elizabeths Hospital, Washington, DC, p. A117

SEYMOUR, Galen, M.D. Chief of Staff, Horton Community Hospital, Horton, KS, p. A235

SEYMOUR, Jose, Chief Information Resource Management, James A. Haley Veterans' Hospital, Tampa, FL, p. A141

SEYMOUR, Kathy, Acting Chief Human Resources Management Service, Aleda E. Lutz Veterans Affairs Medical Center, Saginaw, MI, p. A323

SHACKELFORD, Gerald, Staff Support Specialist, Texas Center for Infectious Disease, San Antonio, TX, p. A632

SHADLE, Jacque, Chief Executive Officer, Baton Rouge Rehabilitation Hospital, Baton Rouge, LA, p. A263

SHADOWEN, Michael, M.D. Chief of Staff, T. J. Samson Community Hospital, Glasgow, KY, p. A251

SHADWICK, Shirley A., Administrator Human Resources, Desert Springs Hospital Medical Center, Las Vegas, NV, p. A392

SHAFER, Natalie, Chief Executive Officer, Brownsville Doctors Hospital, Brownsville, TX, p. A589

SHAFER, Robert
Vice President Finance, Mercy Medical Center–Dubuque, Dubuque, IA, p. A220
Vice President Finance, Mercy Medical Center–Dyersville, Dyersville, IA, p. A221

SHAFER, Timothy, M.D. Medical Director, Grace Cottage Hospital, Townshend, VT, p. A650

SHAFFER, Linda, Director Human Resources, ProMedica Defiance Regional Hospital, Defiance, OH, p. A480

SHAFFER, Michael, Vice President Fiscal Services, St. Joseph's Hospital Health Center, Syracuse, NY, p. A444

SHAFFER, Sarah Dale, Director Human Resources, Northwest Mississippi Regional Medical Center, Clarksdale, MS, p. A345

SHAFICI, Khaled, M.D. President Medical Staff, Cornerstone Hospital–West Monroe, West Monroe, LA, p. A280

SHAH, Aman Ali, M.D. Chief Medical Staff, Lake Whitney Medical Center, Whitney, TX, p. A641

SHAH, Avani D., M.D. Chief of Medical Staff, MedStar St. Mary's Hospital, Leonardtown, MD, p. A293

SHAH, Chetan, M.D. Chief of Staff, Rhea Medical Center, Dayton, TN, p. A568

SHAH, Girishkumar, M.D. Clinical Director, Northlake Behavioral Hospital, Mandeville, LA, p. A273

SHAH, Gita, M.D. Vice President Medical Affairs, Laurel Regional Hospital, Laurel, MD, p. A293

SHAH, Jayendra H., M.D. Chief Medical Officer, Southern Arizona Veterans Affairs Health Care System, Tucson, AZ, p. A39

SHAH, Paresh, Director Information Systems, Reston Hospital Center, Reston, VA, p. A659

SHAH, Rizwan, M.D. Medical Director, HEALTHSOUTH Rehabilitation Hospital of Arlington, Arlington, TX, p. A583

SHAH, Shalin
    Chief Financial Officer, Northside Hospital and Heart Institute, Saint Petersburg, FL, p. A139
    Chief Operating Officer, Regional Medical Center–Bayonet Point, Hudson, FL, p. A126
SHAH, Vital, M.D., Director, Central State Hospital, Louisville, KY, p. A255
SHAHAN, Mary Jo, Vice President and Chief Financial Officer, West Virginia University Hospitals, Morgantown, WV, p. A679
SHAHAN, Matthew, Director Information Systems, Glendive Medical Center, Glendive, MT, p. A376
SHAHEEN, Jim, President, Peak Behavioral Health Services, Santa Teresa, NM, p. A418
SHAHRYAR, Syed, M.D. Medical Director, Promise Hospital of Phoenix, Mesa, AZ, p. A33
SHAHSAVARI, Mehan, R.N. Director Nursing, Norman Specialty Hospital, Norman, OK, p. A502
SHAHZADA, Kamran, M.D. Chief Medical Staff, South Central Kansas Medical Center, Arkansas City, KS, p. A231
SHALLASH, Anthony J., M.D. Interim Medical Director, Franklin Hospital, Valley Stream, NY, p. A445
SHALLOCK, James R., Chief Financial Officer, OakBend Medical Center, Richmond, TX, p. A629
SHAMBLES, Terry W., Chief Financial Officer, Perry Memorial Hospital, Perry, OK, p. A505
SHAMIYEH, Souhail, M.D. Chief of Staff, Mountain View Regional Medical Center, Norton, VA, p. A658
SHANAHAN, Thomas, Chief Financial Officer and Senior Vice President, Raritan Bay Medical Center, Perth Amboy, NJ, p. A409
SHANKLES, Ellen, Chief Executive Officer, Kindred Hospital–Dallas, Dallas, TX, p. A596
SHANLEY, Diane, Deputy Service Unit Director, U. S. Public Health Service Indian Hospital–Sells, Sells, AZ, p. A37
SHANLEY, Kevin, Vice President Finance and Chief Financial Officer, Morristown Medical Center, Morristown, NJ, p. A406
SHANLEY, Linda, Vice President and Chief Information Officer, Saint Francis Hospital and Medical Center, Hartford, CT, p. A109
SHANNON, David A., Chief Executive Officer, Penobscot Valley Hospital, Lincoln, ME, p. A284
SHANNON, Greg, Director Human Resources, Ozarks Medical Center, West Plains, MO, p. A373
SHANNON, John Jay, M.D., Interim Chief Operating Officer, John H. Stroger Jr. Hospital of Cook County, Chicago, IL, p. A177
SHANNON, Lisa, Chief Operating Officer, Spectrum Health – Grand Rapids, Grand Rapids, MI, p. A315
SHANNON, Richard, M.D. Chief of Staff, Montrose Memorial Hospital, Montrose, CO, p. A104
SHANNON, Ruth, Director Human Resources, Sharp Grossmont Hospital, La Mesa, CA, p. A65
SHAPIRO, David, M.D
    Vice President Medical Affairs and Chief Medical Officer, Columbia St. Mary's Hospital Milwaukee, Milwaukee, WI, p. A692
    Vice President Medical Affairs and Chief Medical Officer, Columbia St. Mary's Ozaukee Hospital, Mequon, WI, p. A691
    Vice President Medical Affairs and Chief Medical Officer, Sacred Heart Rehabilitation Institute, Milwaukee, WI, p. A692
SHAPIRO, Ira, M.D. Chief Medical Officer, St. Mary's Regional Medical Center, Lewiston, ME, p. A284
SHAPIRO, Louis A., President and Chief Executive Officer, Hospital for Special Surgery, New York, NY, p. A432
SHAPIRO, Marc, M.D. Chief Medical Officer, St. Helena Hospital Clear Lake, Clearlake, CA, p. A56
SHAPIRO, Robert S., Senior Vice President and Chief Financial Officer, Forest Hills Hospital,, NY, p. A432
SHAPIRO, Steven D., M.D
    Chief Medical Officer, Bon Secours St. Francis Xavier Hospital, Charleston, SC, p. A549
    Chief Medical Officer, Mount Pleasant Hospital, Mount Pleasant, SC, p. A554
    Vice President Medical Affairs, Roper Hospital, Charleston, SC, p. A549
SHARANGPANI, Rojesh, M.D. Chief of Staff, Capital Medical Center, Olympia, WA, p. A668
SHARFSTEIN, Steven S., M.D., President and Chief Executive Officer, Sheppard Pratt Health System, Baltimore, MD, p. A289
SHARKEY, Linda, R.N. Vice President Patient Care Services and Chief Nurse Executive, Fauquier Hospital, Warrenton, VA, p. A662
SHARMA, Aika, M.D. President Medical Staff, Alameda Hospital, Alameda, CA, p. A52
SHARMA, Chandra, M.D. Chief of Staff, Welch Community Hospital, Welch, WV, p. A681

SHARP, Barry D., Director, Iowa City Veterans Affairs Health Care System, Iowa City, IA, p. A223
SHARP, Cindy, M.D. Chief Medical Officer, Madison Valley Medical Center, Ennis, MT, p. A376
SHARP, Gina, FACHE, President, Linden Oaks Hospital at Edward, Naperville, IL, p. A189
SHARP, John K., Chief Financial Officer, Seton Medical Center Harker Heights, Harker Heights, TX, p. A607
SHARP, Julie
    Supervisor Human Resources, Chase County Community Hospital, Imperial, NE, p. A384
    Chief Operations Officer, Falls Community Hospital and Clinic, Marlin, TX, p. A621
SHARP, Richard, M.D. Medical Director, CHRISTUS St. Michael Rehabilitation Hospital, Texarkana, TX, p. A637
SHARPNACK, Linton, R.N. Director Nursing, Heatherhill Care Communities, Chardon, OH, p. A473
SHARRER, Steven, Vice President Human Resources, Saint John's Health Center, Santa Monica, CA, p. A90
SHARTLE, William, Senior Vice President Human Resources, Holy Spirit Hospital, Camp Hill, PA, p. A521
SHARUM, Gary, Administrator, Mercy Hospital Tishomingo, Tishomingo, OK, p. A507
SHARUM, Melinda
    Director of Human Resources, Mercy Hospital Ardmore, Ardmore, OK, p. A495
    Director Human Resources, Mercy Hospital Healdton, Healdton, OK, p. A499
SHARY, Dave, Administrator Human Resources, Ridgecrest Regional Hospital, Ridgecrest, CA, p. A82
SHATAVA, Angie, Director Human Resources, Adair County Memorial Hospital, Greenfield, IA, p. A222
SHATRAW, Thomas, Director Human Resources, Samaritan Medical Center, Watertown, NY, p. A445
SHAUB, Diane, Director Human Resources, OhioHealth Dublin Methodist Hospital, Dublin, OH, p. A481
SHAUGHNESSY, Mary
    Vice President Finance, Spaulding Rehabilitation Hospital, Boston, MA, p. A297
    Vice President Finance, Spaulding Rehabilitation Hospital Cape Cod, East Sandwich, MA, p. A299
SHAULL, Ty, Chief Operating Officer, Wyandot Memorial Hospital, Upper Sandusky, OH, p. A491
SHAVER, John, Chief Financial Officer, Noble Hospital, Westfield, MA, p. A306
SHAVER, Robert D., M.D. Vice President Medical Affairs, The Good Samaritan Hospital, Lebanon, PA, p. A529
SHAW, Brigitte W., Chief Operating Officer, Pepin Heart Hospital, Florida Hospital Tampa, Tampa, FL, p. A141
SHAW, David
    Vice President and Chief Operating Officer, Susan B. Allen Memorial Hospital, El Dorado, KS, p. A233
    Vice President Information Systems, Wishard Health Services, Indianapolis, IN, p. A206
SHAW, David B., Chief Executive Officer and Administrator, Nor–Lea General Hospital, Lovington, NM, p. A417
SHAW, Douglas A., Chief Executive Officer, Mad River Community Hospital, Arcata, CA, p. A53
SHAW, Gary, President, Cambridge Medical Center, Cambridge, MN, p. A330
SHAW, Gene, Chief Information Officer, Yuma Regional Medical Center, Yuma, AZ, p. A40
SHAW, Greg, Vice President and Chief Financial Officer, Audrain Medical Center, Mexico, MO, p. A366
SHAW, Jan, Director Personnel, River Bend Hospital, West Lafayette, IN, p. A215
SHAW, John C., M.D. Medical Director, Southern Indiana Rehabilitation Hospital, New Albany, IN, p. A211
SHAW, Karen, Chief Nursing Officer and Director of Clinical Services, St. Vincent Jennings Hospital, North Vernon, IN, p. A212
SHAW, Kathy, Chief Executive Officer, Haven Senior Horizons, Phoenix, AZ, p. A34
SHAW, Kendra, Manager Information Services, Mayo Clinic Health System in Red Wing, Red Wing, MN, p. A338
SHAW, Mandy, M.D. Chief of Staff, Sidney Regional Medical Center, Sidney, NE, p. A389
SHAW, Michael R., Chief Executive Officer, Kindred Hospital–Albuquerque, Albuquerque, NM, p. A414
SHAW, Patrick, Chief Executive Officer, Grafton City Hospital, Grafton, WV, p. A677
SHAW, Robert C., President and Chief Executive Officer, Thousand Oaks Surgical Hospital, Thousand Oaks, CA, p. A92
SHAW, Ted, Interim Chief Financial Officer, East Jefferson General Hospital, Metairie, LA, p. A273
SHAW, Violet, R.N. Director of Nursing, Grafton City Hospital, Grafton, WV, p. A677
SHAWGO, Darla, Director Human Resources, Sparta Community Hospital, Sparta, IL, p. A194

SHEA, Drew, Chief Financial Officer, Coastal Carolina Hospital, Hardeeville, SC, p. A553
SHEA, Peter H., M.D. Senior Vice President and Chief Medical Officer, The William W. Backus Hospital, Norwich, CT, p. A111
SHEAGREN, Craig, Vice President Finance, Sarah Bush Lincoln Health Center, Mattoon, IL, p. A188
SHEALY, Keith, M.D. Chief of Staff, Springs Memorial Hospital, Lancaster, SC, p. A554
SHEAR, Larry, Administrative Assistant, Norwood Health Center, Marshfield, WI, p. A690
SHEARER, Christopher, M.D. Chief Medical Officer, John C. Lincoln North Mountain Hospital, Phoenix, AZ, p. A34
SHEARER, Ron, M.D. Regional Medical Director, PeaceHealth Peace Harbor Medical Center, Florence, OR, p. A512
SHEEHAN, John, Chief Executive Officer, Douglas County Community Mental Health Center, Omaha, NE, p. A388
SHEEHAN, Karen, Director Information Systems, Swedish Covenant Hospital, Chicago, IL, p. A179
SHEEHAN, Terrence P., M.D. Medical Director, Adventist Rehabilitation Hospital of Maryland, Rockville, MD, p. A293
SHEEHY, Earl N., Chief Executive Officer, Dr. John Warner Hospital, Clinton, IL, p. A180
SHEEHY, Joseph, Chief Executive Officer and Managing Director, The Pavilion, Champaign, IL, p. A176
SHEEKS, Margaret, R.N. Vice President, Patient Services, Sauk Prairie Memorial Hospital & Clinics, Prairie Du Sac, WI, p. A695
SHEERIN, Cathy, R.N. Director Patient Care Services, Glen Cove Hospital, Glen Cove, NY, p. A426
SHEERIN, Rick, Vice President Fiscal Services, Floyd Medical Center, Rome, GA, p. A159
SHEETS, Cindy, Chief Information Officer, Mount Carmel, Columbus, OH, p. A477
SHEETS, Jim, Chief Executive Officer and Administrator, LDS Hospital, Salt Lake City, UT, p. A646
SHEFFIELD, J D, D.O. President Medical Staff, Coryell Memorial Hospital, Gatesville, TX, p. A606
SHEFFIELD, William, M.D. President, Ogden Regional Medical Center, Ogden, UT, p. A645
SHEFFO, Gregory, M.D. Chief Medical Officer, Clearfield Hospital, Clearfield, PA, p. A522
SHEHAN, Mary, R.N. Senior Vice President and Chief Nursing Officer, Swedish Covenant Hospital, Chicago, IL, p. A179
SHEHATA, Adel R., M.D. Medical Director, Desert Springs Hospital Medical Center, Las Vegas, NV, p. A392
SHEHATA, Nady, M.D. Vice President Medical Affairs, Sisters of Charity Hospital of Buffalo, Buffalo, NY, p. A423
SHEHI, G. Michael, M.D., Interim Chief Executive Officer, Mountain View Hospital, Gadsden, AL, p. A20
SHELBURNE, John D., M.D. Chief of Staff, Durham Veterans Affairs Medical Center, Durham, NC, p. A451
SHELBY, Dennis R., Chief Executive Officer, Wilson Medical Center, Neodesha, KS, p. A240
SHELBY, Joyce, Manager Human Resources, Hardin County General Hospital, Rosiclare, IL, p. A194
SHELDON, Diana, CNO, Stone County Medical Center, Mountain View, AR, p. A48
SHELDON, Donald S., M.D., President and Chief Executive Officer, EMH Elyria Medical Center, Elyria, OH, p. A481
SHELDON, Lyle Ernest, FACHE,
    President and Chief Executive Officer, Harford Memorial Hospital, Havre De Grace, MD, p. A292
    President and Chief Executive Officer, Upper Chesapeake Medical Center, Bel Air, MD, p. A289
SHELDON, Mo S., Chief Operating Officer, Glen Rose Medical Center, Glen Rose, TX, p. A606
SHELDON, Richard, M.D. Vice President Medical Affairs, San Gorgonio Memorial Hospital, Banning, CA, p. A54
SHELFORD, Dave, Assistant Superintendent, Richmond State Hospital, Richmond, IN, p. A212
SHELT, Elizabeth, Civilian Personnel Officer, Dwight David Eisenhower Army Medical Center, Fort Gordon, GA, p. A154
SHELTON, Carol, Director Human Resources, Lovelace Women's Hospital, Albuquerque, NM, p. A414
SHELTON, Darlene, Coordinator Team Resources, BayCare Alliant Hospital, Dunedin, FL, p. A122
SHELTON, John
    President and Chief Executive Officer, DeKalb Medical at Downtown Decatur, Decatur, GA, p. A152
    Executive Vice President and Chief Operating Officer, DeKalb Medical at Downtown Decatur, Decatur, GA, p. A152
    President and Chief Executive Officer, DeKalb Medical at Hillandale, Lithonia, GA, p. A156
    Chief Operating Officer, DeKalb Medical at Hillandale, Lithonia, GA, p. A156
    President and Chief Executive Officer, DeKalb Medical at North Decatur, Decatur, GA, p. A152

SHELTON, Kathy
   Director Human Resources, East Texas Medical Center
      Pittsburg, Pittsburg, TX, p. A627
   Director Human Resources, East Texas Medical
      Center–Mount Vernon, Mount Vernon, TX, p. A624
SHELTON, Scott, Executive Vice President and Chief Financial
   Officer, Miami Valley Hospital, Dayton, OH, p. A480
SHELVOCK, Kathy, R.N. Assistant Administrator Patient Care
   Services, Fairchild Medical Center, Yreka, CA, p. A96
SHEN, Mark W., M.D., Chief Executive Officer, Dell Children's
   Medical Center of Central Texas, Austin, TX, p. A585
SHENKER, Charles, M.D. Chief of Staff, Aventura Hospital and
   Medical Center, Aventura, FL, p. A118
SHEPARD, Charles, M.D. Medical Director, Winona Health,
   Winona, MN, p. A343
SHEPARD, Karen
   Senior Vice President and Chief Financial Officer, Pioneer
      Memorial Hospital, Prineville, OR, p. A517
   Senior Vice President Finance and Chief Financial Officer, St.
      Charles Medical Center – Bend, Bend, OR, p. A511
   Senior Vice President Finance and Chief Financial Officer, St.
      Charles Medical Center – Redmond, Redmond, OR,
      p. A517
SHEPARD, Sheila, Accounting Manager, HEALTHSOUTH
   Rehabilitation Hospital, Humble, TX, p. A614
SHEPHARD, Russ, Senior Systems Analyst, Dyersburg Regional
   Medical Center, Dyersburg, TN, p. A568
SHEPHERD, Stephen C., Chief Executive Officer, Candler County
   Hospital, Metter, GA, p. A157
SHEPHERD, Thomas, Executive Vice President and Chief
   Financial Officer, Gwinnett Hospital System, Lawrenceville,
   GA, p. A156
SHEPLER, Mary, R.N. Vice President and Chief Nursing Officer,
   Exempla Saint Joseph Hospital, Denver, CO, p. A99
SHEPPARD, Sharon, Manager Human Resources, Sycamore
   Shoals Hospital, Elizabethton, TN, p. A568
SHEPPARD, Varinya, R.N. Chief Nursing Officer, St. Elizabeth
   Medical Center, Utica, NY, p. A444
SHERBELL, Stanley, M.D. Executive Vice President Medical
   Affairs, New York Methodist Hospital,, NY, p. A435
SHERBONDY, Lori, Director Human Resources, Battle Mountain
   General Hospital, Battle Mountain, NV, p. A391
SHERBUN, Michael, Ph.D., Chief Executive Officer, Cedar Hills
   Hospital, Portland, OR, p. A516
SHERER, Susan, Chief Information Resource Management,
   Dayton Veterans Affairs Medical Center, Dayton, OH, p. A479
SHERIDAN, Bridget, Chief Human Resources Officer, Beaver
   Dam Community Hospitals, Beaver Dam, WI, p. A684
SHERIDAN, Cheryl, R.N
   Senior Vice President and Chief Nursing Officer,
      Newark–Wayne Community Hospital, Newark, NY, p. A437
   Senior Vice President Patient Care Services, Rochester
      General Hospital, Rochester, NY, p. A441
SHERIDAN, Elizabeth, Chief Operating Officer, Inspira Medical
   Center–Vineland, Vineland, NJ, p. A412
SHERIDAN Jr., John P., President and Chief Executive Officer,
   Cooper Health System, Camden, NJ, p. A402
SHERLIN, Anthony, Director Information Systems, DeKalb
   Regional Medical Center, Fort Payne, AL, p. A20
SHERMAN, Frederick C., M.D. Chief Medical Officer, The
   Children's Home of Pittsburgh, Pittsburgh, PA, p. A538
SHERMAN, James, Executive Director Hospital Operations,
   Tri–City Regional Medical Center, Hawaiian Gardens, CA,
   p. A63
SHERMAN, Shelly, Director Human Resources, Mercy Health –
   Clermont Hospital, Batavia, OH, p. A471
SHERMAN, Stephanie, Chief Human Resources Officer, West
   Boca Medical Center, Boca Raton, FL, p. A119
SHERON, William E., Chief Executive Officer, Wooster
   Community Hospital, Wooster, OH, p. A493
SHERRARD, Mark, D.O. Chief Medical Officer and Senior Vice
   President Medical Affairs, Mercy Memorial Hospital System,
   Monroe, MI, p. A320
SHERRETT, John, Chief Financial Officer and Chief Operating
   Officer, Forks Community Hospital, Forks, WA, p. A666
SHERRILL, Angela
   Chief Information Officer, Laird Hospital, Union, MS, p. A354
   Corporate Director Information System, Rush Foundation
      Hospital, Meridian, MS, p. A351
   Corporate Director Information System, Specialty Hospital of
      Meridian, Meridian, MS, p. A351
SHERROD, Mike, Chief Executive Officer, Coliseum Northside
   Hospital, Macon, GA, p. A156
SHERROD, Rhonda Kay, MSN, Administrator, Shands Lake
   Shore Regional Medical Center, Lake City, FL, p. A128
SHERRY, Bernard, President and Chief Executive Officer, Saint
   Thomas Midtown Hospital, Nashville, TN, p. A576
SHERWOOD, Charlotte, Chief Financial Officer, North Sunflower
   Medical Center, Ruleville, MS, p. A353

SHERWOOD, Rose, Information Technology Specialist, Kingfisher
   Regional Hospital, Kingfisher, OK, p. A500
SHETH, Shishir, M.D. President Medical Staff, Ministry Saint
   Mary's Hospitals, Rhinelander, WI, p. A695
SHETLER, Charles L., CPA Chief Financial Officer, Indiana
   University Health Bedford Hospital, Bedford, IN, p. A198
SHETTLESWORTH, Amanda, Director Human Resources,
   Bloomington Meadows Hospital, Bloomington, IN, p. A199
SHEW, Angel
   Director Area Technology, Kaiser Permanente Redwood City
      Medical Center, Redwood City, CA, p. A82
   Director Area Technology, Kaiser Permanente South San
      Francisco, South San Francisco, CA, p. A91
SHEWBRIDGE, Rick, M.D. Vice President Medical Operations,
   Medina Hospital, Medina, OH, p. A486
SHICKOLOVICH, William, Chief Information Officer, Tufts Medical
   Center, Boston, MA, p. A297
SHIELDS, Anna, Executive Director Information Systems, Santa
   Rosa Memorial Hospital, Santa Rosa, CA, p. A90
SHIELDS, Charlie, Chief Operating Officer, Truman Medical
   Center–Lakewood, Kansas City, MO, p. A364
SHIELDS, Diane, Chief Human Resources Officer, Alpena
   Regional Medical Center, Alpena, MI, p. A308
SHIELDS, Leanne, Chief Financial Officer, Spring Valley Hospital
   Medical Center, Las Vegas, NV, p. A393
SHIEPE, Clifford, President and Chief Executive Officer, Tri–City
   Regional Medical Center, Hawaiian Gardens, CA, p. A63
SHIFF, Mary Treacy, Chief Financial Officer, Kindred
   Chicago–Central Hospital, Chicago, IL, p. A177
SHIFFERMILLER, William, M.D. Vice President Medical Affairs,
   Nebraska Methodist Hospital, Omaha, NE, p. A388
SHIHADY, Sharon, Director Human Resources, HEALTHSOUTH
   Cane Creek Rehabilitation Hospital, Martin, TN, p. A573
SHILKAITIS, Mary, Vice President Patient Care and Chief Nursing
   Officer, Rush–Copley Medical Center, Aurora, IL, p. A174
SHINAMAN, Keith C McLean, Senior Vice President Finance,
   Baystate Medical Center, Springfield, MA, p. A305
SHINGLETON, Kathy J., Ed.D. Vice President, Human
   Resources, Virginia Mason Medical Center, Seattle, WA,
   p. A671
SHINICK, Mary K., Vice President Human Resources, Nyack
   Hospital, Nyack, NY, p. A438
SHININGER, Kimberly R., Director Human Resources, Wabash
   County Hospital, Wabash, IN, p. A214
SHIPIERSKI, Sally, Controller, Geisinger HEALTHSOUTH
   Rehabilitation Hospital, Danville, PA, p. A523
SHIPLEY, Kurt
   Chief Financial Officer, Jordan Valley Medical Center, West
      Jordan, UT, p. A648
   Chief Financial Officer, Pioneer Valley Hospital, West Valley
      City, UT, p. A648
SHIPP, Geraldine H., Director of Risk Management, Sampson
   Regional Medical Center, Clinton, NC, p. A450
SHIPP, Rhonda, Chief Financial Officer, Ozark Health Medical
   Center, Clinton, AR, p. A42
SHIRAH, Anita, Director Human Resources, University of South
   Alabama Medical Center, Mobile, AL, p. A23
SHIRLEN, David
   Vice President Human Resources, Grace Hospital, Morganton,
      NC, p. A458
   Vice President Human Resources, Valdese General Hospital,
      Valdese, NC, p. A462
SHIRLEY, Christian, Director Human Resources, Geisinger
   HEALTHSOUTH Rehabilitation Hospital, Danville, PA, p. A523
SHIRLEY, Douglas E., Senior Executive Vice President and Chief
   Financial Officer, Cooper Health System, Camden, NJ,
   p. A402
SHIRLEY, Phil, Director Information Resource Management,
   Broughton Hospital, Morganton, NC, p. A457
SHIRLEY, Steve, Chief Information Officer, Parkview Medical
   Center, Pueblo, CO, p. A105
SHISLER, Pearl, Director Human Resources, HEALTHSOUTH
   Treasure Coast Rehabilitation Hospital, Vero Beach, FL,
   p. A143
SHIVERY, Toni M.
   Vice President Human Resources, Harford Memorial Hospital,
      Havre De Grace, MD, p. A292
   Vice President Human Resources, Upper Chesapeake Medical
      Center, Bel Air, MD, p. A289
SHMERLING, James E., President and Chief Executive Officer,
   Children's Hospital Colorado, Aurora, CO, p. A97
SHOBE, Franklin, Administrator and Chief Executive Officer,
   Black Hills Surgery Center, Rapid City, SD, p. A561
SHOBE, Susan, Director Administration and Support Services,
   Alton Mental Health Center, Alton, IL, p. A173
SHOCKEY, Kathryn L., Director Human Resources,
   Lead–Deadwood Regional Hospital, Deadwood, SD, p. A559
SHOCKLEY, Mary, Director Human Resources, Russell Medical
   Center, Alexander City, AL, p. A15

SHOCKNEY, Brian T., FACHE Chief Operating Officer, Indiana
   University Health Arnett Hospital, Lafayette, IN, p. A208
SHOEMAKER, Larry D., M.D. Chief Medical Officer, Singing River
   Health System, Pascagoula, MS, p. A352
SHOEMAKER, Robert, M.D. Chief of Staff Community Heart and
   Vascular, Community Heart and Vascular Hospital,
   Indianapolis, IN, p. A205
SHOEN, Jay, Controller, LifeCare Hospitals of Mechanicsburg,
   Mechanicsburg, PA, p. A531
SHOEN, Timothy, M.D. Vice President Medical Staff Services,
   St. Mary's Healthcare, Amsterdam, NY, p. A420
SHOENER, Carl, Chief Information Officer, Hazleton General
   Hospital, Hazleton, PA, p. A527
SHOLLER, Peter, M.D. Medical Director, Spectrum Health
   Special Care Hospital, Grand Rapids, MI, p. A315
SHOMAKER, Susan, Director Information Management Systems,
   J. Arthur Dosher Memorial Hospital, Southport, NC, p. A461
SHONNARD, John, M.D. Medical Director, UPMC Northwest,
   Seneca, PA, p. A541
SHONTZ, Maggie, VP, Human Resources, UnityHealth MacNeal
   Hospital, Berwyn, IL, p. A174
SHOOK, Don, Chief Executive Officer, Select Specialty
   Hospital–Flint, Flint, MI, p. A314
SHOOK, Rod, Chief Financial Officer, Wagoner Community
   Hospital, Wagoner, OK, p. A509
SHOOKS, Charles, M.D. Chief of Staff, Windham Hospital,
   Willimantic, CT, p. A113
SHOPE, Amy, Chief Executive Officer, Twin Creeks Rehabilitation
   Hospital, Allen, TX, p. A581
SHOR, Joel, M.D. Chief of Staff, Bluefield Regional Medical
   Center, Bluefield, WV, p. A675
SHORES, David G., D.O. President Medical Staff, Fairview Park
   Hospital, Dublin, GA, p. A152
SHORES, Larry, M.D. Executive Medical Director, Cedar Springs
   Hospital, Colorado Springs, CO, p. A98
SHORK, Michael, M.D. Director Information Systems Services,
   Mercy St. Charles Hospital, Oregon, OH, p. A488
SHORT, Kathy, D.O. Family Practice, Carroll County Memorial
   Hospital, Carrollton, KY, p. A249
SHORT, M. Andrew, Vice President Information Services,
   Samaritan Medical Center, Watertown, NY, p. A445
SHORT, Margaret W., Coordinator Information Technology,
   Webster County Memorial Hospital, Webster Springs, WV,
   p. A681
SHORT, Peter H., M.D. Senior Vice President Medical Affairs,
   Beverly Hospital, Beverly, MA, p. A295
SHORT, Steve, Executive Vice President Finance and
   Administration, Tampa General Hospital, Tampa, FL, p. A142
SHORT, Ted, Chief Financial Officer, Fairview Park Hospital,
   Dublin, GA, p. A152
SHORT, W. L., M.D. Chief Medical Officer, Memorial Health
   System, Abilene, KS, p. A231
SHOUKAIR, Sami, M.D. Chief Medical Officer, La Palma
   Intercommunity Hospital, La Palma, CA, p. A65
SHOUP, Chris, President, Methodist Hospital for Surgery,
   Addison, TX, p. A581
SHOUSE, Shellie, Chief Financial Officer, Bluegrass Community
   Hospital, Versailles, KY, p. A261
SHOWERS, Russell H., Vice President Human Resources, Valley
   Hospital, Ridgewood, NJ, p. A410
SHOWS, Carla
   Payroll Clerk, George Regional Hospital, Lucedale, MS,
      p. A350
   Payroll Clerk, Greene County Hospital, Leakesville, MS,
      p. A349
SHRADER, David, M.D. Chief of Staff, Star Valley Medical
   Center, Afton, WY, p. A701
SHREEVE, Susan
   Chief Financial Officer, Belton Regional Medical Center,
      Belton, MO, p. A356
   Chief Financial Officer, Research Medical Center, Kansas City,
      MO, p. A363
   Chief Financial Officer, Research Psychiatric Center, Kansas
      City, MO, p. A363
SHREVE, Susan, Executive Director Information Technology,
   Boone Memorial Hospital, Madison, WV, p. A678
SHREVES, Anna, Vice President Patient Care Services, St.
   Joseph's Hospital of Buckhannon, Buckhannon, WV, p. A675
SHREVES, Melissa, Director Human Resources, Monongalia
   General Hospital, Morgantown, WV, p. A679
SHREWSBURY, Kim, Vice President and Chief Financial Officer,
   Decatur General Hospital, Decatur, AL, p. A18
SHRIVER, Debra, R.N. Chief Nurse Executive, Trinity Regional
   Medical Center, Fort Dodge, IA, p. A221
SHROADES, David W., Vice President Technology Services,
   Alliance Community Hospital, Alliance, OH, p. A470

SHRODER, Robert W.
President and Chief Executive Officer, St. Elizabeth Health Center, Youngstown, OH, p. A494
President and Chief Executive Officer, St. Joseph Health Center, Warren, OH, p. A492
SHROFF, Rajendra, M.D. Administrative Medical Director, St. Mary's Hospital, Centralia, IL, p. A175
SHROYER, Linda K., Administrator, Potomac Valley Hospital, Keyser, WV, p. A678
SHUBIN, Allan, Chief Financial Officer, Pacific Alliance Medical Center, Los Angeles, CA, p. A70
SHUEY, Keith, M.D. Chief Medical Staff, Johnson County Hospital, Tecumseh, NE, p. A390
SHUFFIELD, Sean, Regional Chief Information Officer, University of Maryland St. Joseph Medical Center, Towson, MD, p. A294
SHUFFIELD, Shawn, Executive Director Information Services, Saline Memorial Hospital, Benton, AR, p. A41
SHUFFLEBARGER, Tom, Chief Operating Officer, The Children's Hospital of Alabama, Birmingham, AL, p. A17
SHUFORD, Little, Manager Medical Information, Kindred Hospital–Greensboro, Greensboro, NC, p. A453
SHUGARMAN, Mark D., President and Chief Executive Officer, Floyd Memorial Hospital and Health Services, New Albany, IN, p. A211
SHUGHART, Deborah A., Vice President and Chief Financial Officer, Fulton County Medical Center, Mc Connellsburg, PA, p. A530
SHUGRUE, Dianne, R.N., President and Chief Executive Officer, Glens Falls Hospital, Glens Falls, NY, p. A426
SHULER, Conrad K., M.D. Chief Medical Officer, Oconee Medical Center, Seneca, SC, p. A555
SHULER, Trish, Chief Clinical Officer, Landmark Hospital of Joplin, Joplin, MO, p. A362
SHULIK, David, Vice President and Chief Financial Officer, UPMC Horizon, Greenville, PA, p. A526
SHULKIN, David J., M.D., President and Chief Executive Officer, Morristown Medical Center, Morristown, NJ, p. A406
SHULL, Jennifer, R.N. Chief Nursing Officer, Florida Hospital Fish Memorial, Orange City, FL, p. A134
SHULL, Kenneth A., FACHE, Chief Executive Officer, St. Luke's Hospital, Columbus, NC, p. A450
SHULMAN, Lawrence N., M.D. Senior Vice President Medical Affairs and Chief Medical Officer, Dana–Farber Cancer Institute, Boston, MA, p. A296
SHULTS, Randi L., Chief Executive Officer, North Carolina Specialty Hospital, Durham, NC, p. A451
SHULTZ, P. Stephen, M.D. Vice President Medical Affairs, Mayo Clinic Health System – Franciscan Healthcare in La Crosse, La Crosse, WI, p. A689
SHUMAN, Betty, Director Human Resources, Wesley Rehabilitation Hospital, Wichita, KS, p. A247
SHUMAN, Daniel, D.O. Chief Medical Officer, Ashland Health Center, Ashland, KS, p. A231
SHUMATE, Karen J., R.N. Chief Operating Officer, Lawrence Memorial Hospital, Lawrence, KS, p. A238
SHUMWAY, Barbara, Director Human Resources, North Big Horn Hospital District, Lovell, WY, p. A703
SHUMWAY, Donald L., Chief Executive Officer, Crotched Mountain Rehabilitation Center, Greenfield, NH, p. A398
SHUPP, Susie, Director Human Resources, Nemaha County Hospital, Auburn, NE, p. A381
SHUR, Kenneth L., FACHE Vice President and Chief Operating Officer, Waynesboro Hospital, Waynesboro, PA, p. A543
SHUSTER, Jamie, Director Associate Relations, Anderson Regional Medical Center–South Campus, Meridian, MS, p. A351
SHUTE, Keith M., M.D. Senior Vice President Medical Affairs and Clinical Services, Androscoggin Valley Hospital, Berlin, NH, p. A397
SHUTE, Leonard J.
Chief Financial Officer, Highland Hospital of Rochester, Rochester, NY, p. A441
Chief Financial Officer, Strong Memorial Hospital of the University of Rochester, Rochester, NY, p. A441
SHUTER, Mark H., President and Chief Executive Officer, Adena Medical Center, Chillicothe, OH, p. A473
SHUTTA, Rudy, Chief Financial Officer, Bear Valley Community Hospital, Big Bear Lake, CA, p. A55
SHYAVITZ, Linda, President and Chief Executive Officer, Sturdy Memorial Hospital, Attleboro, MA, p. A295
SIAL, Jay, Chief Financial Officer, University of Kentucky Albert B. Chandler Hospital, Lexington, KY, p. A254
SIBLEY, Cherie, R.N., Chief Executive Officer, Clark Regional Medical Center, Winchester, KY, p. A261
SIBLEY, Jeri, Director Revenue Cycle, Riverside Tappahannock Hospital, Tappahannock, VA, p. A662
SICA, Vincent A., President and Chief Executive Officer, DeSoto Memorial Hospital, Arcadia, FL, p. A118
SICILIA, Bruce, M.D. Medical Director, HEALTHSOUTH Rehabilitation Hospital of York, York, PA, p. A545

SIDDIQI, Ather, M.D
Medical Director, Nexus Specialty Hospital, Shenandoah, TX, p. A633
Medical Director, Nexus Specialty Hospital The Woodlands, Spring, TX, p. A634
SIDDIQUI, Hugh, Senior Applications Analyst, Linden Oaks Hospital at Edward, Naperville, IL, p. A189
SIDES, Tim
Chief Financial Officer, Aurora Behavioral Health Care, San Diego, CA, p. A85
Chief Financial Officer, Aurora Las Encinas Hospital, Pasadena, CA, p. A79
SIEBE, Sonya, Manager Human Resources, San Mateo Medical Center, San Mateo, CA, p. A88
SIEBENALER, Christopher, Chief Executive Officer, Methodist Sugar Land Hospital, Sugar Land, TX, p. A635
SIEBERT, Kristy, Manager Finance, John J. Pershing Veterans Affairs Medical Center, Poplar Bluff, MO, p. A367
SIEBERT, Matt, Assistant Administrator of Ancillary Services, Hermann Area District Hospital, Hermann, MO, p. A361
SIEBRECHT, Kaylee, Director Human Resources, Story County Medical Center, Nevada, IA, p. A225
SIEFKIN, Allan, M.D. Chief Medical Officer, University of California, Davis Medical Center, Sacramento, CA, p. A84
SIEGEL, Fredric, M.D. Chief of Staff, Desert View Hospital, Pahrump, NV, p. A394
SIEGEL, Lesley, M.D. Medical Director, Albert J. Solnit Psychiatric Center – South Campus, Middletown, CT, p. A110
SIEGELMAN, Gary M., M.D. Senior Vice President and Chief Medical Officer, Bayhealth Medical Center, Dover, DE, p. A114
SIEGFRIED, Bryan, M.D. President Medical Staff, Community Memorial Hospital, Staunton, IL, p. A195
SIEGLEN, Linda, M.D. Vice President Medical Affairs, University Medical Center of Princeton at Plainsboro, Plainsboro, NJ, p. A409
SIEK, Terry, MSN Chief Nursing Officer, Hays Medical Center, Hays, KS, p. A235
SIELEMAN, Sharron, R.N. VP, Nursing, Central Maine Medical Center, Lewiston, ME, p. A283
SIEMER, Brenda, Director of Information Technology, Harrison County Community Hospital, Bethany, MO, p. A356
SIEMERS, Thomas R., Chief Executive Officer, J. Arthur Dosher Memorial Hospital, Southport, NC, p. A461
SIEWERT, Charles
Director Human Resources, Buffalo Psychiatric Center, Buffalo, NY, p. A422
Director Human Resources, Western New York Children's Psychiatric Center, West Seneca, NY, p. A446
SIFERS, Carl, Director Information Technology and System Services, Centerpoint Medical Center, Independence, MO, p. A362
SIFFRING, Connie K., Chief Executive Officer, Select Specialty Hospital–Midland, Midland, TX, p. A623
SIGEL, Jay, M.D. Chief Medical Staff, Crane Memorial Hospital, Crane, TX, p. A594
SIGLER, Wes, Chief Executive Officer, Tri–Lakes Medical Center, Batesville, MS, p. A344
SIGNOR, Kristin, Director Finance, Sunnyview Rehabilitation Hospital, Schenectady, NY, p. A442
SIGSBURY, John R., President and Chief Executive Officer, Emanuel Medical Center, Turlock, CA, p. A93
SILARD, Kathleen A., R.N. Executive Vice President Operations and Chief Operating Officer, Stamford Hospital, Stamford, CT, p. A112
SILKWORTH, Jim, Chief Human Resources Officer, Our Lady of Lourdes Memorial Hospital, Binghamton, NY, p. A421
SILL–LEAHY, Janet, Manager Human Resources, Schick Shadel Hospital, Seattle, WA, p. A670
SILLIMAN, Walter, Chief Information Officer, Ouachita County Medical Center, Camden, AR, p. A42
SILLIS, Scott, Interim Chief Financial Officer, Mountrail County Medical Center, Stanley, ND, p. A469
SILLS, Doug, Chief Executive Officer, River Region Medical Center, Vicksburg, MS, p. A354
SILLS, John M., Chief Information Officer, Health Central, Ocoee, FL, p. A134
SILSBEE, Dave, Chief Information Officer, Cary Medical Center, Caribou, ME, p. A282
SILSBY, Harry, M.D. Medical Director, Intermountain Hospital, Boise, ID, p. A167
SILVA, Carmen, R.N. Chief Operating Officer, Doctors Hospital of Manteca, Manteca, CA, p. A73
SILVA, Lori, Director Human Resources, Mt. San Rafael Hospital, Trinidad, CO, p. A106
SILVA, Margaret, Executive Assistant and Coordinator Human Resources, Promise Hospital of San Antonio, San Antonio, TX, p. A632
SILVA, Shawn, Chief Executive Officer, Heritage Oaks Hospital, Sacramento, CA, p. A83

SILVER, Michael R., M.D. Vice President Medical Affairs, Rush Oak Park Hospital, Oak Park, IL, p. A190
SILVER, Timothy, M.D. Medical Director, Sheltering Arms Hospital South, Midlothian, VA, p. A657
SILVERHATBAND, Darlene J., Supervisory Human Resource Specialist, Chinle Comprehensive Health Care Facility, Chinle, AZ, p. A30
SILVERMAN, Daniel C., M.D
Senior Vice President Medical Affairs, Albany Memorial Hospital, Albany, NY, p. A420
Chief Medical Officer, Acute Care Troy, Samaritan Hospital, Troy, NY, p. A444
Vice President and Chief Medical Officer, Sinai Hospital of Baltimore, Baltimore, MD, p. A289
SILVERMAN, Glen M., Chief Executive Officer, Crossgates River Oaks Hospital, Brandon, MS, p. A345
SILVERSTEIN, Douglas M., President, NorthShore University Health System Evanston Hospital, Evanston, IL, p. A182
SILVERSTEIN, Joel, M.D. Chief Medical Officer, Copley Hospital, Morrisville, VT, p. A649
SILVERTHORNE, Samuel, Chief Information Officer, U. S. Air Force Medical Center Keesler, Keesler AFB, MS, p. A349
SILVEUS, Patrick, M.D. Medical Director, Kosciusko Community Hospital, Warsaw, IN, p. A214
SILVIA, Charles B., M.D. Chief Medical Officer and Vice President Medical Affairs, Peninsula Regional Medical Center, Salisbury, MD, p. A294
SILVIA, Clarence J., President and Chief Executive Officer, The Hospital of Central Connecticut, New Britain, CT, p. A110
SIM, Carol, Chief Executive Officer, HEALTHSOUTH Treasure Coast Rehabilitation Hospital, Vero Beach, FL, p. A143
SIMCHUK, Cathy J., Chief Operating Officer, Providence Holy Family Hospital, Spokane, WA, p. A672
SIMIA, Greg, Chief Financial Officer, St. Mary's Hospital Medical Center, Green Bay, WI, p. A688
SIMKINS, Palma, Chief Human Resources Management Services, Battle Creek Veterans Affairs Medical Center, Battle Creek, MI, p. A309
SIMMONS, Angela L., Chief Executive Officer, HEALTHSOUTH Rehabilitation Hospital, Humble, TX, p. A614
SIMMONS, Brad, Chief Operating Officer, Saint Luke's Hospital of Kansas City, Kansas City, MO, p. A363
SIMMONS, Daniel F., Senior Vice President and Treasurer, Monongahela Valley Hospital, Monongahela, PA, p. A532
SIMMONS, David, M.D. Chief of Staff, Grenada Lake Medical Center, Grenada, MS, p. A347
SIMMONS, Donald, M.D. Chief Medical Staff, Good Shepherd Medical Center–Linden, Linden, TX, p. A618
SIMMONS, Dorlynn, Chief Executive Officer, Mescalero Public Health Service Indian Hospital, Mescalero, NM, p. A417
SIMMONS, Eileen, Chief Financial Officer, Magee–Womens Hospital of UPMC, Pittsburgh, PA, p. A537
SIMMONS, Kermit, Administrator, Louisiana Extended Care Hospital of Natchitoches, Natchitoches, LA, p. A274
SIMMONS, Linda V., President and Chief Executive Officer, Decatur County Memorial Hospital, Greensburg, IN, p. A204
SIMMONS, Nancy B., Executive Vice President and Chief Administrative Officer, Good Samaritan Hospital Medical Center, West Islip, NY, p. A446
SIMMONS, Preston M., Chief Executive Officer, Providence Regional Medical Center Everett, Everett, WA, p. A666
SIMMONS, Randy, President and Chief Executive Officer, Paris Community Hospital, Paris, IL, p. A191
SIMMONS, Roger
Chief Financial Officer, Coliseum Medical Centers, Macon, GA, p. A156
Chief Financial Officer, Coliseum Northside Hospital, Macon, GA, p. A156
SIMMONS, Sherry, Vice President Patient Care Services and Chief Nursing Officer, Camden Clark Medical Center, Parkersburg, WV, p. A679
SIMMONS, Steven, Chief Human Resources Officer, Hahnemann University Hospital, Philadelphia, PA, p. A535
SIMMONS, Terry E., Chief Nursing Officer, Madison County Health Care System, Winterset, IA, p. A230
SIMMONS, Tim C., Chief Executive Officer, Westbury Community Hospital, Houston, TX, p. A614
SIMMONS, William, Chief Executive Officer, St. Luke's Patients Medical Center, Pasadena, TX, p. A626
SIMMS, Jennifer, Director Human Resources, University Medical Center, Lafayette, LA, p. A271
SIMMS, Sr., Michael S., Vice President Human Resources, Northeast Alabama Regional Medical Center, Anniston, AL, p. A15
SIMODEJKA, John E.
President and Chief Executive Officer, Schuylkill Medical Center – East Norwegian Street, Pottsville, PA, p. A539
President and Chief Executive Officer, Schuylkill Medical Center – South Jackson Street, Pottsville, PA, p. A539

SIMON, Anha, Director Human Resources, Winnie Community Hospital, Winnie, TX, p. A642

SIMON, Ashley, Chief Financial Officer, Kansas Surgery and Recovery Center, Wichita, KS, p. A246

SIMON, Deborah R., R.N., President and Chief Executive Officer, UnityPoint Health – Methodist, Peoria, IL, p. A192

SIMON, Keri, Executive Director, Women's and Children's Hospital, Columbia, MO, p. A359

SIMON, Lloyd, M.D. Medical Director, Eastern Long Island Hospital, Greenport, NY, p. A426

SIMON, Patricia, Manager Information Systems, Canandaigua Veterans Affairs Medical Center, Canandaigua, NY, p. A423

SIMON, Paul, M.D. Medical Director, Cornerstone Hospital of SouthEast Arizona, Tucson, AZ, p. A38

SIMON, Richard, M.D. Chief of Staff, University of Connecticut Health Center, John Dempsey Hospital, Farmington, CT, p. A108

SIMON, Stuart, M.D. Medical Director, North Central Surgical Center, Dallas, TX, p. A597

SIMON, Teresa, Director Information Systems, Nacogdoches Medical Center, Nacogdoches, TX, p. A624

SIMON, Thresa, M.D. Medical Director, Poplar Springs Hospital, Petersburg, VA, p. A659

SIMONDS, Brock, Interim Chief Financial Officer, Chatham Hospital, Siler City, NC, p. A461

SIMONE, James M., Vice President and Chief Financial Officer, EMH Elyria Medical Center, Elyria, OH, p. A481

SIMONIN, Steven J.
 Chief Executive Officer, Iowa Specialty Hospital–Clarion, Clarion, IA, p. B74
 Chief Executive Officer, Iowa Specialty Hospitals, Clarion, IA, p. B74
 Chief Executive Officer, Iowa Specialty Hospital–Clarion, Clarion, IA, p. A218, B74

SIMONS, Chris, Director Health Information Management and Utilization Review, Spring Harbor Hospital, Westbrook, ME, p. A286

SIMONS, Janice, FACHE, Chief Executive Officer, Medina Regional Hospital, Hondo, TX, p. A608

SIMONSON, John F., M.D. President Medical Staff, Memorial Community Hospital and Health System, Blair, NE, p. A382

SIMONSON, Paul, Vice President, Trinity Health, Minot, ND, p. A468

SIMPATICO, Thomas, M.D., Facility Director and Network System Manager, Chicago–Read Mental Health Center, Chicago, IL, p. A176

SIMPSON, Bob, Vice President Finance, Methodist Richardson Medical Center, Richardson, TX, p. A628

SIMPSON, Chris, Chief Executive Officer, Cornerstone Hospital–West Monroe, West Monroe, LA, p. A280

SIMPSON, Dana, Manager Human Resources, Riverview Regional Medical Center, Gadsden, AL, p. A20

SIMPSON, Katrina, Director Human Resources, Valley View Regional Hospital, Ada, OK, p. A495

SIMPSON, Keith J., Chief Operating Officer, Jennings American Legion Hospital, Jennings, LA, p. A269

SIMPSON, Jr., Lee A., Chief Executive Officer, Kindred Hospital Tulsa, Tulsa, OK, p. A508

SIMPSON, Linda, Vice President Human Resources, OhioHealth Grant Medical Center, Columbus, OH, p. A478

SIMPSON, Pamela, Director Human Resources, Select Specialty Hospital–Houston Heights, Houston, TX, p. A612

SIMPSON Jr., Robert E., M.P.H., President and Chief Executive Officer, Brattleboro Retreat, Brattleboro, VT, p. A649

SIMPSON–TUGGLE, Delois, Vice President Human Resources and Organizational Development and Chief Human Resources Officer, Greater Baltimore Medical Center, Baltimore, MD, p. A287

SIMS, Abraham, Chief Executive Officer, Reliant Rehabilitation Hospital North Houston, Shenandoah, TX, p. A633

SIMS, B. Wayne, President and Chief Executive Officer, KVC Psychiatric Hospital, Kansas City, KS, p. A237

SIMS, Blake, Director, Operations, St. Luke's Lakeside Hospital, The Woodlands, TX, p. A637

SIMS, Brian, Director Administrative Services, Knoxville Hospital & Clinics, Knoxville, IA, p. A224

SIMS, Jason, M.D. Chief Medical Officer, Cleveland Area Hospital, Cleveland, OK, p. A497

SIMS, Kathleen
 Vice President Operations, Manchester Memorial Hospital, Manchester, CT, p. A109
 Vice President Operations, Rockville General Hospital, Vernon Rockville, CT, p. A112

SIMS, Laura, Chief Executive Officer, Cornerstone Hospital of Austin, Austin, TX, p. A585

SIMS, Mark E., Chief Executive Officer, TriStar StoneCrest Medical Center, Smyrna, TN, p. A579

SIMS, Tina, Director Human Resources, Methodist Extended Care Hospital, Memphis, TN, p. A575

SIMS, W. Larry, Chief Financial Officer and Vice President Financial Services, Colquitt Regional Medical Center, Moultrie, GA, p. A158

SIMS, Wanda
 Chief Information Officer, Baptist Medical Center East, Montgomery, AL, p. A23
 Chief Information Officer, Baptist Medical Center South, Montgomery, AL, p. A23

SINACORE–JABERG, Janie, FACHE, Chief Executive Officer, MedWest – Haywood, Clyde, NC, p. A450

SINCICH, Robert, Vice President Human Resources, Ashtabula County Medical Center, Ashtabula, OH, p. A470

SINCLAIR, Brad
 Chief Financial Officer, Crossgates River Oaks Hospital, Brandon, MS, p. A345
 Chief Financial Officer, River Oaks Hospital, Flowood, MS, p. A346

SINCLAIR, Deb Arend, Vice President Human Resources, DeKalb Health, Auburn, IN, p. A198

SINCLAIR, Jan, Director Personnel, Oaklawn Hospital, Marshall, MI, p. A320

SINCLAIR, Jennifer, Vice President Finance, St. Dominic–Jackson Memorial Hospital, Jackson, MS, p. A349

SINCLAIR, Kathy, Vice President Human Resources, Spartanburg Regional Medical Center, Spartanburg, SC, p. A556

SINCLAIR, Laura, Director Human Resources, Kansas City Orthopaedic Institute, Leawood, KS, p. A238

SINCLAIR, Michael, Chief Executive Officer, Rooks County Health Center, Plainville, KS, p. A242

SINCOCK, Gregory M., Information Technology Leader, Kaiser Permanente West Los Angeles Medical Center, Los Angeles, CA, p. A69

SINDLINGER, Julie A., Director of Human Resources, Weston County Health Services, Newcastle, WY, p. A703

SINGAL, Manisha, M.D. Medical Director, Specialty Hospital of Washington, Washington, DC, p. A117

SINGER, Donna, Chief Executive Officer, Blue Mountain Hospital, Blanding, UT, p. A643

SINGER, Susan, Director Human Resources, New York Eye and Ear Infirmary, New York, NY, p. A435

SINGH, Inderjit, M.D. Clinical Director, Pilgrim Psychiatric Center, Brentwood, NY, p. A422

SINGH, Prableen, Chief Information Officer, Newton Medical Center, Newton, KS, p. A240

SINGH–SANDHU, Mohinder S., M.D. President Medical Staff, Henry Ford Wyandotte Hospital, Wyandotte, MI, p. A327

SINGLE, John L., Chief Executive Officer, Huron Regional Medical Center, Huron, SD, p. A560

SINGLES, James L., Chief Financial Officer, Marlette Regional Hospital, Marlette, MI, p. A319

SINGLETARY, Robert G., President and Chief Executive Officer, Maria Parham Medical Center, Henderson, NC, p. A454

SINGLETON, Al, M.D. Chief Psychiatry and Chief Medical Staff, Colorado Mental Health Institute at Pueblo, Pueblo, CO, p. A105

SINGLETON, Larry, Chief Financial Officer, Lakeside Medical Center, Belle Glade, FL, p. A118

SINGLETON, Roy, Director Computer Information Systems, Palmdale Regional Medical Center, Palmdale, CA, p. A78

SINICROPE, Jr., Frank J., Vice President Financial Services, Princeton Community Hospital, Princeton, WV, p. A680

SINISI, Albert, Director Information Systems, Doctors' Hospital of Michigan, Pontiac, MI, p. A322

SINISI, Linda, Intity Information Officer, Pennsylvania Hospital, Philadelphia, PA, p. A536

SINKEVICH, Doris, MS, Interim Chief Executive Officer, Beth Israel Deaconess Hospital–Milton, Milton, MA, p. A302

SINNER, Laurie K., Director Human Resources, Community Hospital, Grand Junction, CO, p. A101

SINNOTT, James, M.D. Chief Medical Staff, Coquille Valley Hospital, Coquille, OR, p. A512

SINOTTE, Brian, Chief Operating Officer, Porter Regional Hospital, Valparaiso, IN, p. A214

SIOSON, Stephanie
 Director Human Resources, Garden Grove Hospital and Medical Center, Garden Grove, CA, p. A62
 Director Human Resources, Huntington Beach Hospital, Huntington Beach, CA, p. A64
 Director Human Resources, La Palma Intercommunity Hospital, La Palma, CA, p. A65
 Director Human Resources, West Anaheim Medical Center, Anaheim, CA, p. A52

SIPEK, John, Supervisor Client Services, Aurora Medical Center of Washington County, Hartford, WI, p. A688

SIREK, David, Chief Information Officer, Myrtue Medical Center, Harlan, IA, p. A222

SIRK, David R., Chief Executive Officer, Vaughan Regional Medical Center, Selma, AL, p. A25

SIRK, Donald, Director Information Systems, MedStar St. Mary's Hospital, Leonardtown, MD, p. A293

SIROIS, Peter, Interim Chief Executive Officer, Northern Maine Medical Center, Fort Kent, ME, p. A283

SIROTTA, Ted D., Chief Financial Officer, Northwestern Medical Center, Saint Albans, VT, p. A650

SISARCICK, Barbara, Administrator, Peterson Rehabilitation Hospital, Wheeling, WV, p. A682

SISK, Glenn C., President, Coosa Valley Medical Center, Sylacauga, AL, p. A25

SISK, Jack, Chief Financial Officer, Punxsutawney Area Hospital, Punxsutawney, PA, p. A539

SISK, Katie, Director Human Resources, Hiawatha Community Hospital, Hiawatha, KS, p. A235

SISK, Lori, R.N.,
 Chief Executive Officer, Sanford Canby Medical Center, Canby, MN, p. A330
 Chief Executive Officer, Sanford Clear Lake Medical Center, Clear Lake, SD, p. A559

SISK, Rodney, Chief Financial Officer, Fannin Regional Hospital, Blue Ridge, GA, p. A148

SISLER, Debbie, Director Human Resources, Vidant Roanoke–Chowan Hospital, Ahoskie, NC, p. A447

SISLER, Rebecca, Director Human Resources, Box Butte General Hospital, Alliance, NE, p. A381

SISON, Joseph, M.D. Medical Director, Heritage Oaks Hospital, Sacramento, CA, p. A83

SISSON, Travis, Chief Operating Officer, Wesley Medical Center, Hattiesburg, MS, p. A348

SISSON, William G., President, Baptist Health Lexington, Lexington, KY, p. A253

SISTO, Steven A., Senior Vice President and Chief Operating Officer, Methodist Hospital of Southern California, Arcadia, CA, p. A53

SITTIG, Kevin, M.D. Senior Associate Dean and Chief Medical Officer, LSU Health Sciences Center, Shreveport, LA, p. A278

SITTLOW, Jo, Senior Director of Patient Care and Chief Nursing Officer, Lakeview Hospital, Stillwater, MN, p. A341

SIVESS, Chuck, Vice President Human Resources, Providence Health Center, Waco, TX, p. A640

SIVLEY, Susanna S., Chief Personnel Officer, Highlands Medical Center, Scottsboro, AL, p. A25

SIX, Deborah, Coordinator Data Processing, Wayne Memorial Hospital, Jesup, GA, p. A155

SIZEMORE, Darin, Controller, Bell Hospital, Ishpeming, MI, p. A317

SKAARE, Dolores, R.N. Chief Nursing Officer, Plantation General Hospital, Plantation, FL, p. A137

SKABELUND, Hoyt, Administrator, Plains Regional Medical Center, Clovis, NM, p. A415

SKADEN, John, Chief Financial Officer, Ministry Saint Joseph's Hospital, Marshfield, WI, p. A690

SKAGGS, Lynda, Chief Nursing Officer, Fleming County Hospital, Flemingsburg, KY, p. A250

SKALA, Pat
 Chief Information Officer, Laguna Honda Hospital and Rehabilitation Center, San Francisco, CA, p. A86
 Chief Information Officer, San Francisco General Hospital Medical Center, San Francisco, CA, p. A87

SKARULIS, Patricia, Vice President Information Systems, Memorial Sloan-Kettering Cancer Center, New York, NY, p. A434

SKARZYNSKI, Joseph, M.D
 Medical Director, Jacobi Medical Center,, NY, p. A432
 Medical Director, North Central Bronx Hospital,, NY, p. A435

SKEANS, John, Chief Financial Officer, St. Anthony's Medical Center, Saint Louis, MO, p. A370

SKELDON, Timothy K., Senior Vice President and Chief Financial Officer, Parrish Medical Center, Titusville, FL, p. A143

SKELTON, Amy, Chief Financial Officer, Kindred Hospital Tarrant County–Fort Worth Southwest, Fort Worth, TX, p. A604

SKELTON, Jeff, Chief Financial Officer, Carolina Center for Behavioral Health, Greer, SC, p. A553

SKELTON, John, Director Finance, Temple Community Hospital, Los Angeles, CA, p. A72

SKIDMORE, Jocelyn, Director Finance, St. Francis Hospital and Health Services, Maryville, MO, p. A365

SKIEM, Paul
 Senior Vice President Human Resources, Presence Holy Family Medical Center, Des Plaines, IL, p. A181
 Senior Vice President Human Resources, Presence Resurrection Medical Center, Chicago, IL, p. A178
 Senior Vice President Human Resources, Presence Saint Francis Hospital, Evanston, IL, p. A182

SKILLINGS, Charles E., President and Chief Executive Officer, St. Anthony Shawnee Hospital, Shawnee, OK, p. A506

SKILLINGS, Lois N., MSN, President and Chief Executive Officer, Mid Coast Hospital, Brunswick, ME, p. A282

SKILLINGS, Michelle, Chief Nursing Officer, Sanford Clear Lake Medical Center, Clear Lake, SD, p. A559

SKILLMAN, Sally, Director Human Resources, Shriners Hospitals for Children–Cincinnati Burns Hospital, Cincinnati, OH, p. A475

SKINNER, Eileen F., FACHE, President and Chief Executive Officer, Mercy Hospital of Portland, Portland, ME, p. A284

SKINNER, Gwendolyn, Executive Director, Devereux Georgia Treatment Network, Kennesaw, GA, p. A155

SKINNER, Jeannette, FACHE, Chief Executive Officer, Wuesthoff Medical Center – Melbourne, Melbourne, FL, p. A130

SKINNER, Jon C., President, Baylor Institute for Rehabilitation, Dallas, TX, p. A595

SKINNER, Marjorie, Director Finance, Pershing General Hospital, Lovelock, NV, p. A394

SKINNER, Ross, Director Information Systems, Payson Regional Medical Center, Payson, AZ, p. A34

SKLAMBERG, Todd, President, Sunrise Hospital and Medical Center, Las Vegas, NV, p. A394

SKLAR, Joel, M.D. Chief Medical Officer, Marin General Hospital, Greenbrae, CA, p. A63

SKORICH, Brenda, Manager Business and Medical Records, Essentia Health–Virginia, Virginia, MN, p. A342

SKORNIAK, Stan, MS Associate Medical Center Director, John J. Pershing Veterans Affairs Medical Center, Poplar Bluff, MO, p. A367

SKOV, Randy, Vice President, Mid–Columbia Medical Center, The Dalles, OR, p. A518

SKRINDE, Tracie, Director Human Resources, United General Hospital, Sedro Woolley, WA, p. A672

SKRIPPS, Michele M., R.N., Chief Executive Officer, AnMed Health Rehabilitation Hospital, Anderson, SC, p. A548

SKULA, Erika, President and Chief Executive Officer, Manchester Memorial Hospital, Manchester, KY, p. A257

SKUPIEN, Mary Beth, Director, Battle Creek Veterans Affairs Medical Center, Battle Creek, MI, p. A309

SKVARENINA, Michael, Assistant Vice President Information Systems, Holy Name Medical Center, Teaneck, NJ, p. A411

SKYLES, Jill, R.N. Vice President Patient Care Services, Barnes–Jewish St. Peters Hospital, Saint Peters, MO, p. A371

SLABA, Bryan, Chief Executive Officer, Wagner Community Memorial Hospital Avera, Wagner, SD, p. A563

SLADKY, Todd J., Chief Financial Officer, Great River Medical Center, West Burlington, IA, p. A230

SLAGLE, Amy, M.D. President Medical Staff, Menominee Tribal Clinic, Shawano Medical Center, Shawano, WI, p. A696

SLANE, Eric, M.D. Chief of Staff, Grant Regional Health Center, Lancaster, WI, p. A689

SLATE, Clyde, Assistant Superintendent Administrative Services, Memphis Mental Health Institute, Memphis, TN, p. A575

SLATE, Sonny, Chief Operating Officer, Georgia Regional Hospital at Atlanta, Decatur, GA, p. A152

SLATER, Craig M., M.D. Chief Medical Officer, Columbus Regional Healthcare System, Whiteville, NC, p. A462

SLATER, Mark, Director Information Systems, Lake Pointe Medical Center, Rowlett, TX, p. A630

SLATON, Brenda, Administrator, Rusk State Hospital, Rusk, TX, p. A630

SLATON, Charlie, Interim Chief Executive Officer, Golden Plains Community Hospital, Borger, TX, p. A589

SLATTERY, Greg, Vice President Information, Community Hospitals and Wellness Centers, Bryan, OH, p. A472

SLATTERY, Sue, Director Human Resources, UnityPoint Health St. Luke's, Cedar Rapids, IA, p. A217

SLATTMAN, Robin, Chief Nursing Officer, Memorial Hospital of Union County, Marysville, OH, p. A485

SLAVIN, Kevin J., FACHE, President and Chief Executive Officer, East Orange General Hospital, East Orange, NJ, p. A403

SLAVIN, Peter L., M.D., President, Massachusetts General Hospital, Boston, MA, p. A297

SLAWITSKY, Bruce, Vice President Human Resources, Hospital for Special Surgery, New York, NY, p. A432

SLAWKOWSKI, Ken, Interim Director Information Systems, Holy Cross Hospital, Chicago, IL, p. A176

SLAYDON, Cindy, Chief Nursing Executive, Sparks Regional Medical Center, Fort Smith, AR, p. A44

SLAYTON, Lisa C., Senior Vice President Human Resources, Bon Secours St. Francis Health System, Greenville, SC, p. A552

SLAYTON, Val, M.D. Vice President Medical Affairs, Sts. Mary & Elizabeth Hospital, Louisville, KY, p. A256

SLEDGE, Cynthia Moore, M.D. Medical Director, Bryce Hospital, Tuscaloosa, AL, p. A25

SLEPIN, Robert, Vice President and Chief Information Officer, John C. Lincoln North Mountain Hospital, Phoenix, AZ, p. A34

SLETTE, Katie, Director Human Resources and Marketing, Windom Area Hospital, Windom, MN, p. A343

SLICK, Lois, Director Human Resources, LakeWood Health Center, Baudette, MN, p. A329

SLIDER, Carol, Chief Nursing Officer, Titus Regional Medical Center, Mount Pleasant, TX, p. A623

SLIETER Jr., Richard G.
Administrator, Community Behavioral Health Hospital – Baxter, Baxter, MN, p. A329
Administrator, Community Behavioral Health Hospital – Bemidji, Bemidji, MN, p. A329

SLIGER, Susan, Director Human Resources, War Memorial Hospital, Sault Sainte Marie, MI, p. A324

SLINGERLAND, Micki J.
Chief Operating Officer, Tristar Ashland City, Ashland City, TN, p. A565
Chief Operating Officer, Tristar Centennial Medical Center, Nashville, TN, p. A577

SLITER, Elizabeth, M.D. Chairman Medical Staff, Decatur County Hospital and Cedar Living Center, Oberlin, KS, p. A241

SLIWA, James, M.D. Chief Medical Officer, Rehabilitation Institute of Chicago, Chicago, IL, p. A178

SLIWINSKI, Jeff, Chief Financial Officer, Clear Lake Regional Medical Center, Webster, TX, p. A640

SLIWINSKI, Ron, Chief Operations Officer, University of Wisconsin Hospital and Clinics, Madison, WI, p. A690

SLOAN, Gary, Chief Executive Officer, San Ramon Regional Medical Center, San Ramon, CA, p. A89

SLOAN, Mona, Chief Nursing Officer, Comanche County Medical Center, Comanche, TX, p. A593

SLOAN, Prudence, Coordinator Human Resources, Select Specialty Hospital–Pittsburgh/UPMC, Pittsburgh, PA, p. A537

SLOAN, Ronald A., FACHE, President, The Outer Banks Hospital, Nags Head, NC, p. A458

SLOAN, Steve, Chief Financial Officer, Lake Cumberland Regional Hospital, Somerset, KY, p. A260

SLOCUM, Brandon H., Senior Vice President and Chief Financial Officer, Medical West, Bessemer, AL, p. A16

SLOCUM, Gregg Y., Chief Financial Officer, Valley Forge Medical Center and Hospital, Norristown, PA, p. A533

SLONIM, Sheryl A., Executive Vice President and Chief Nursing Officer, Holy Name Medical Center, Teaneck, NJ, p. A411

SLONINA, Marrianne, Director Human Resources, Georgetown Community Hospital, Georgetown, KY, p. A251

SLUSHER, Michael, Community Chief Executive Officer, Middlesboro ARH Hospital, Middlesboro, KY, p. A257

SLY–SMITH, Michelle, Chief Executive Officer, Sullivan County Community Hospital, Sullivan, IN, p. A213

SMALE, Cindy, Director Human Resources, Indiana University Health Bedford Hospital, Bedford, IN, p. A198

SMALL, Annette, R.N., Chief Executive Officer, St. Mary's Medical Center, Blue Springs, MO, p. A356

SMALL, David R., Interim Chief Executive Officer, United Medical Center, Washington, DC, p. A117

SMALL, Deborah C., R.N. Chief Nursing Officer and Vice President Patient Care Services, Fairview Hospital, Cleveland, OH, p. A476

SMALL, Jonathan, Chief Operations Information and Technology, John D. Dingell Veterans Affairs Medical Center, Detroit, MI, p. A312

SMALL, Terry L., Assistant Chief Executive Officer, William R. Sharpe, Jr. Hospital, Weston, WV, p. A682

SMALTZ, Herb, Chief Information Officer, Ohio State University Wexner Medical Center, Columbus, OH, p. A478

SMANIK, Robert E., FACHE, President and Chief Executive Officer, Day Kimball Hospital, Putnam, CT, p. A111

SMARR, Susan, M.D. Physician–in–Chief, Kaiser Permanente Santa Clara Medical Center, Santa Clara, CA, p. A89

SMART, Dan, Chief Information Management Officer, Permian Regional Medical Center, Andrews, TX, p. A583

SMART, George J., VP Finance & IT, Alpena Regional Medical Center, Alpena, MI, p. A308

SMART, Paul, CPA Chief Financial Officer, Franklin County Medical Center, Preston, ID, p. A171

SMART, Robert M., Chief Executive Officer, Reliant Rehabilitation Hospital Mid–Cities, Bedford, TX, p. A588

SMEEKS, Frank C., M.D. Chief Medical Officer, Frye Regional Medical Center, Hickory, NC, p. A454

SMELTZER, Sharon, Chief Executive Officer, Mercy Rehabilitation Hospital Oklahoma City, Oklahoma City, OK, p. A503

SMESNY, Michael, Chief Financial Officer, Kindred Hospital El Paso, El Paso, TX, p. A601

SMESTAD, Craig, M.D. Chief Medical Officer, Brandon Regional Hospital, Brandon, FL, p. A119

SMIGA, Lance, Chief Financial Officer, Jackson County Hospital District, Edna, TX, p. A600

SMILEY, Christy, Director Human Resources, Audrain Medical Center, Mexico, MO, p. A366

SMITH, Alan H.
Chief Financial Officer, Garden Grove Hospital and Medical Center, Garden Grove, CA, p. A62
Chief Financial Officer, Huntington Beach Hospital, Huntington Beach, CA, p. A64
Chief Financial Officer, La Palma Intercommunity Hospital, La Palma, CA, p. A65
Chief Financial Officer, West Anaheim Medical Center, Anaheim, CA, p. A52

SMITH, Andrew, M.D. Chief Medical Staff, Guttenberg Municipal Hospital, Guttenberg, IA, p. A222

SMITH, Andrew
Chief Information Management, Madigan Healthcare System, Tacoma, WA, p. A673
CFO, St. Petersburg General Hospital, Saint Petersburg, FL, p. A139

SMITH, Anna M.
Chief Administrative Officer, UK HealthCare Good Samaritan Hospital, Lexington, KY, p. A254
Chief Administrative Officer, University of Kentucky Albert B. Chandler Hospital, Lexington, KY, p. A254

SMITH, Barbara H., Senior Vice President & Chief Operating Officer, Robert Wood Johnson University Hospital at Hamilton, Hamilton, NJ, p. A404

SMITH, Becky, Manager Human Resources, McKenzie County Healthcare System, Watford City, ND, p. A469

SMITH, Bennie, Director Human Resources and Risk Management, Lady of the Sea General Hospital, Cut Off, LA, p. A266

SMITH, Bernie, Chief Financial Officer, Troy Community Hospital, Troy, PA, p. A542

SMITH, Beth, Controller, Mercy Hospital, Valley City, ND, p. A469

SMITH, Bethany, Controller, HEALTHSOUTH Cane Creek Rehabilitation Hospital, Martin, TN, p. A573

SMITH, Bobby, Vice President Physician Services and Quality, Illinois Valley Community Hospital, Peru, IL, p. A192

SMITH, Bradley, President and Chief Executive Officer, Rush Memorial Hospital, Rushville, IN, p. A213

SMITH, Brenda, Director Financial Services, Alliance Health Center, Meridian, MS, p. A350

SMITH, Brent, M.D. Chief Medical Officer and Vice President Clinical Integration, Edward Hospital, Naperville, IL, p. A189

SMITH, Brent, Chief Financial Officer, Jennersville Regional Hospital, West Grove, PA, p. A544

SMITH, Brian
Executive Vice President and Chief Operating Officer, St. Rita's Medical Center, Lima, OH, p. A484
Director Risk Management, Quality and Safety, Wamego City Hospital, Wamego, KS, p. A245

SMITH, Carl, Director Information Systems, King's Daughters Medical Center, Brookhaven, MS, p. A345

SMITH, Chris, Vice President Information Technology, North Oaks Medical Center, Hammond, LA, p. A268

SMITH, Cindy, Chief Executive Officer, Kindred Hospital–Sycamore, Sycamore, IL, p. A196

SMITH, Coke R., M.D. Medical Director, Sunnyside Community Hospital, Sunnyside, WA, p. A673

SMITH, Connie
Chief Executive Officer, Medical Center at Bowling Green, Bowling Green, KY, p. A248
Chief Executive Officer and Chief Operating Officer, Medical Center at Scottsville, Scottsville, KY, p. A260

SMITH, Dale, Director Human Resources, Texas Health Harris Methodist Hospital Hurst–Euless–Bedford, Bedford, TX, p. A588

SMITH, Dan, Director Human Resources, Memorial Hospital, Carthage, IL, p. A175

SMITH, Daniel
Interim Chief Executive Officer, Sugar Land Surgical Hospital, Sugar Land, TX, p. A635
Chief Financial Officer, TOPS Surgical Specialty Hospital, Houston, TX, p. A613

SMITH, Daniel B.
Vice President Finance, Good Samaritan Regional Medical Center, Corvallis, OR, p. A512
Vice President Finance, Samaritan Albany General Hospital, Albany, OR, p. A511
Vice President Finance, Samaritan Lebanon Community Hospital, Lebanon, OR, p. A514

SMITH, Daniel W., Chief Financial Officer, Pioneers Memorial Healthcare District, Brawley, CA, p. A55

SMITH, Danny, Director Human Resources, Bryan W. Whitfield Memorial Hospital, Demopolis, AL, p. A19

SMITH, Darline, R.N. Vice President Patient Care Services and Chief Nursing Officer, St. Francis Medical Center, Monroe, LA, p. A274

SMITH, Darrin, Vice President Human Resources, Parkview Medical Center, Pueblo, CO, p. A105

SMITH, Darwin K., Vice President Human Resources, Union Hospital, Dover, OH, p. A480

SMITH, David
Chief Executive Officer, GLOBALREHAB Hospital – Dallas, Dallas, TX, p. A596
Manager Data Center, Huguley Memorial Medical Center, Fort Worth, TX, p. A603
Senior Director Human Resources, Marquette General Health System, Marquette, MI, p. A319
Chief Financial Officer, Memorial Regional Hospital,, FL, p. A125

SMITH, David A., Vice President and Chief Operating Officer, Avista Adventist Hospital, Louisville, CO, p. A104

SMITH, David B., Assistant Vice President Information Services, MedStar Harbor Hospital, Baltimore, MD, p. A288

SMITH, David N., M.D. Vice President Medical Affairs, Novant Health Rowan Medical Center, Salisbury, NC, p. A460

SMITH, Debra, Chief Executive Officer, St. Joseph's Health Services–Gundersen Lutheran, Hillsboro, WI, p. A688

SMITH, Denise
Director Financial Services, Florida State Hospital, Chattahoochee, FL, p. A120
Director Health Information, HEALTHSOUTH Chattanooga Rehabilitation Hospital, Chattanooga, TN, p. A566

SMITH, Dennis H., Director, Veterans Affairs Maryland Health Care System–Baltimore Division, Baltimore, MD, p. A289

SMITH, Dennis J., Chief Operating Officer, James Cancer Hospital and Solove Research Institute, Columbus, OH, p. A477

SMITH, Denny R., Administrator, Camden General Hospital, Camden, TN, p. A566

SMITH, Diana B., Chief Financial Officer, Texas Specialty Hospital at Dallas, Dallas, TX, p. A598

SMITH, Diane, Chief Nursing Officer, Baptist Health Extended Care Hospital, Little Rock, AR, p. A46

SMITH, Dick, Director Human Resources, West Park Hospital, Cody, WY, p. A702

SMITH, Donna P., R.N. Vice President Patient Care Services and Chief Nursing Officer, Clifton Springs Hospital and Clinic, Clifton Springs, NY, p. A424

SMITH, Donnie
Chief Human Resources Officer, Laird Hospital, Union, MS, p. A354
Director Human Resources, Rush Foundation Hospital, Meridian, MS, p. A351

SMITH, Doug, Chief Financial Officer, McKay–Dee Hospital Center, Ogden, UT, p. A645

SMITH, Douglas, Chief Financial Officer, Mesilla Valley Hospital, Las Cruces, NM, p. A416

SMITH Jr., Edward H., President and Chief Executive Officer, St. Anthony Regional Hospital, Carroll, IA, p. A217

SMITH, Eric, Chief Financial Officer, East Georgia Regional Medical Center, Statesboro, GA, p. A160

SMITH, Ericka, Chief Operating Officer, Monterey Park Hospital, Monterey Park, CA, p. A75

SMITH, Eugene, Chief Information Officer, Maniilaq Health Center, Kotzebue, AK, p. A28

SMITH, G. Todd, President, St. Elizabeth Community Hospital, Red Bluff, CA, p. A81

SMITH, Gary, Manager Information Technology, Paynesville Area Health Care System, Paynesville, MN, p. A338

SMITH, Gene
Senior Vice President Operations, AMG Specialty Hospital–Slidell, Slidell, LA, p. A278
Interim Chief Financial Officer, West Suburban Medical Center, Oak Park, IL, p. A190

SMITH, Gene, M.D. Interim Chief Financial Officer, Westlake Hospital, Melrose Park, IL, p. A188

SMITH, Ginger S., Chief Nursing Officer, Homer Memorial Hospital, Homer, LA, p. A268

SMITH, Gregory
Chief Information Officer, Covenant Medical Center, Waterloo, IA, p. A229
Senior Vice President and Chief Information Officer, Wheaton Franciscan Healthcare – St. Francis, Milwaukee, WI, p. A692
Senior Vice President and Chief Information Officer, Wheaton Franciscan Healthcare – The Wisconsin Heart Hospital, Wauwatosa, WI, p. A699

SMITH, Gretchen, Vice President Nursing and Compliance and Risk, Rush Memorial Hospital, Rushville, IN, p. A213

SMITH, Harley, Chief Executive Officer, Wayne Medical Center, Waynesboro, TN, p. A580

SMITH Jr., Harry L., President, Novant Health Presbyterian Medical Center, Charlotte, NC, p. A450

SMITH, Heather
Director Finance, Conemaugh Meyersdale Medical Center, Meyersdale, PA, p. A532
Director Information Services, Holy Cross Hospital, Silver Spring, MD, p. A294

SMITH, Jack, Acting Chief Information Resources Management Service, Veterans Affairs Sierra Nevada Health Care System, Reno, NV, p. A395

SMITH, James E.
Superintendent, North Texas State Hospital, Vernon, TX, p. A639
Superintendent, North Texas State Hospital, Wichita Falls Campus, Wichita Falls, TX, p. A641

SMITH, James L., Chief Financial Officer, Greeley County Health Services, Tribune, KS, p. A245

SMITH, James M., M.D. Medical Director, Bastrop Rehabilitation Hospital, Bastrop, LA, p. A262

SMITH, Janet, Chief Financial Officer, Troy Regional Medical Center, Troy, AL, p. A25

SMITH, Jay, Director Information Systems, Brownwood Regional Medical Center, Brownwood, TX, p. A590

SMITH, Jeanna, Administrative Assistant and Human Resources Officer, Polk Medical Center, Cedartown, GA, p. A149

SMITH, Jeff, Chief Information Officer, Holy Cross Hospital, Fort Lauderdale, FL, p. A123

SMITH, Jeffrey, Chief Executive Officer, Kindred Rehabilitation Hospital Northeast Houston, Humble, TX, p. A614

SMITH, Jill, Administrative Coordinator, J. Paul Jones Hospital, Camden, AL, p. A18

SMITH, Jim, Director Information Systems, Mineral Area Regional Medical Center, Farmington, MO, p. A360

SMITH, Jo Beth
Director Support Services and Human Resources, Decatur County Hospital, Leon, IA, p. A224
Director Human Resources, Medical Arts Hospital, Lamesa, TX, p. A617

SMITH, Joanne C., M.D., President and Chief Executive Officer, Rehabilitation Institute of Chicago, Chicago, IL, p. A178

SMITH, Jodi, Administrative Assistant Human Resources, Eureka Springs Hospital, Eureka Springs, AR, p. A43

SMITH, John, Chief Executive Officer, Coffeyville Regional Medical Center, Coffeyville, KS, p. A232

SMITH, Jonathan, Chief Financial Officer, Assistant Administrator, Blount Memorial Hospital, Maryville, TN, p. A574

SMITH, Joseph B., Vice President Finance, MedStar Union Memorial Hospital, Baltimore, MD, p. A288

SMITH, Joseph S., Chief Executive Officer, Boone County Hospital, Boone, IA, p. A217

SMITH, Josh, Vice President Human Resources, Palmetto Lowcountry Behavioral Health, Charleston, SC, p. A549

SMITH, Judy, M.D. Medical Director, Roswell Park Cancer Institute, Buffalo, NY, p. A422

SMITH, Julia
Chief Financial Officer, Kindred Hospital–Charleston, Mt. Pleasant, SC, p. A554
Chief Financial Officer, Kindred Hospital–Chattanooga, Chattanooga, TN, p. A566

SMITH, Julie, R.N. Director of Nursing, Jersey Community Hospital, Jerseyville, IL, p. A186

SMITH, Justin, Chief Executive Officer, Kindred Hospital Dallas Central, Dallas, TX, p. A596

SMITH, Karen, Interim Chief Executive Officer, Coffey County Hospital, Burlington, KS, p. A232

SMITH, Karen S., Director Information Services, Chilton Hospital, Pompton Plains, NJ, p. A409

SMITH, Karyl, Director Human Resources, LAC–Harbor–University of California at Los Angeles Medical Center, Torrance, CA, p. A92

SMITH, Kathleen, Interim Vice President Human Resources, Glens Falls Hospital, Glens Falls, NY, p. A426

SMITH, Kelli, M.D. Chief of Staff, Magee General Hospital, Magee, MS, p. A350

SMITH, Kelly C., Division President, Oakwood Heritage Hospital, Taylor, MI, p. A325

SMITH, Ken, Chief Financial Officer, Cooperstown Medical Center, Cooperstown, ND, p. A466

SMITH, Kenneth, M.D. Chief of Staff, John C. Fremont Healthcare District, Mariposa, CA, p. A73

SMITH, Kevin, Vice President Finance and Support Services, Rehabilitation Institute of Michigan, Detroit, MI, p. A312

SMITH, Kevin E., Acting Administrator and Chief Operating Officer, Scott & White Hospital – Taylor, Taylor, TX, p. A636

SMITH, Kevin F., President and Chief Executive Officer, Winchester Hospital, Winchester, MA, p. A264

SMITH, Kevin M., Director Human Resources, Indian Path Medical Center, Kingsport, TN, p. A571

SMITH, Lana, Director Human Resources, Davis Regional Medical Center, Statesville, NC, p. A461

SMITH, Larry, Senior Vice President and Chief Financial Officer, UW Medicine/Valley Medical Center, Renton, WA, p. A670

SMITH, LaVonne, Director Health Information Technology, Tomah Memorial Hospital, Tomah, WI, p. A697

SMITH, Lawrence, M.D. Senior Vice President and Chief Medical Officer, Forest Hills Hospital,, NY, p. A432

SMITH, Leighton B., M.D. Vice President Medical Affairs, Northwest Community Hospital, Arlington Heights, IL, p. A173

SMITH, Leora, Information System and Health Information Management Team Leader, Phelps Memorial Health Center, Holdrege, NE, p. A384

SMITH, Lex, Chief Executive Officer, George L. Mee Memorial Hospital, King City, CA, p. A65

SMITH, Linda, FACHE, Chief Executive Officer, Santa Clara Valley Medical Center, San Jose, CA, p. A88

SMITH, Linda C., M.D. Medical Director, HEALTHSOUTH Rehabilitation Hospital of Beaumont, Beaumont, TX, p. A587

SMITH, Linda D., FACHE, Director, Cincinnati Veterans Affairs Medical Center, Cincinnati, OH, p. A474

SMITH, Linda T., Director Human Resources, Clay County Hospital, Ashland, AL, p. A15

SMITH, Linda V., Director Human Resources, Englewood Community Hospital, Englewood, FL, p. A123

SMITH, Lori, Chief Financial Officer, Meade District Hospital, Meade, KS, p. A239

SMITH, Lorie, Director Human Resources, Nason Hospital, Roaring Spring, PA, p. A540

SMITH, Jr., Louis G., Chief Executive Officer, Memorial Hermann Northeast, Humble, TX, p. A614

SMITH, Marisa, Director Information Services, East Georgia Regional Medical Center, Statesboro, GA, p. A160

SMITH, Mark H., M.D. Chief of Staff, Iowa City Veterans Affairs Health Care System, Iowa City, IA, p. A223

SMITH, Mark T., CPA, President, Fort Hamilton Hospital, Hamilton, OH, p. A483

SMITH, Martha, Chief Executive Officer, Kapiolani Medical Center for Women & Children, Honolulu, HI, p. A164

SMITH, Martha M., R.N. Chief Nursing Officer, Park Plaza Hospital, Houston, TX, p. A611

SMITH, Mary Clare, M.D. Medical Director, Western State Hospital, Staunton, VA, p. A662

SMITH, Marybeth
Director Human Resources, Saint Francis Hospital, Charleston, WV, p. A676
Director Human Resources, Thomas Memorial Hospital, South Charleston, WV, p. A681

SMITH, Matthew, Operations Director Finance and Support Services, Alegent Creighton Health Community Memorial Hospital, Missouri Valley, IA, p. A225

SMITH, Melinda, Chief Information Systems, H. C. Watkins Memorial Hospital, Quitman, MS, p. A353

SMITH, Melissa
Controller, Select Specialty Hospital–Jackson, Jackson, MS, p. A349
Vice President and Controller, Select Specialty Hospital–Wilmington, Wilmington, DE, p. A115

SMITH, Michael, Director Support Services and Information Technology, Medina Regional Hospital, Hondo, TX, p. A608

SMITH, Michael K., D.O. Vice President Medical Affairs, McLaren Macomb, Mount Clemens, MI, p. A320

SMITH, Michael K., R.N., Regional Administrator, Mercy Hospital Ozark, Ozark, AR, p. A48

SMITH, Michelle, Coordinator Human Resources, Baton Rouge Rehabilitation Hospital, Baton Rouge, LA, p. A263

SMITH, Michelle T., R.N. Chief Nursing Officer, Greenville Memorial Hospital, Greenville, SC, p. A552

SMITH, Mickey, Chief Executive Officer, Oak Hill Hospital, Brooksville, FL, p. A120

SMITH, Mike
Chief Information Officer, Cape Coral Hospital, Cape Coral, FL, p. A120
Chief Information Officer, Gulf Coast Medical Center, Fort Myers, FL, p. A124
Chief Information Officer, Lee Memorial Hospital, Fort Myers, FL, p. A124

SMITH, Nadine, Director Human Resources, Reeves County Hospital, Pecos, TX, p. A626

SMITH, Neil, M.D. Chief Medical Officer, Fairview Hospital, Cleveland, OH, p. A476

SMITH, Nekisha, Director Medical Records, Riverland Medical Center, Ferriday, LA, p. A267

SMITH, Norine, Chief Executive Officer, U. S. Public Health Service Indian Hospital, Cass Lake, MN, p. A330

SMITH, Ollie, Vice President Human Resources, Paris Community Hospital, Paris, IL, p. A191

SMITH, Pam, Director Human Resources, East Liverpool City Hospital, East Liverpool, OH, p. A481

SMITH, Pat J., Vice President Nursing, Oconee Medical Center, Seneca, SC, p. A555

SMITH, Patrick, M.D. Chief Medical Officer, Arrowhead Hospital, Glendale, AZ, p. A31

SMITH, Paul, Chief Financial Officer, Kindred Hospital of Riverside, Perris, CA, p. A79

SMITH, Paula
  Senior Vice President Chief Information Officer, Oakwood Annapolis Hospital, Wayne, MI, p. A326
  Chief Information Officer, Oakwood Heritage Hospital, Taylor, MI, p. A325
  Leader Information Services and Chief Information Officer, Oakwood Hospital & Medical Center–Dearborn, Dearborn, MI, p. A311
  Vice President Information Services and Chief Information Officer, Oakwood Southshore Medical Center, Trenton, MI, p. A325
SMITH, Peg, Vice President and Chief Nursing Officer, Chandler Regional Medical Center, Chandler, AZ, p. A30
SMITH, Peyton A., Chief Executive Officer, Lower Oconee Community Hospital, Glenwood, GA, p. A154
SMITH, Phyllis
  Acting Director, Birmingham Veterans Affairs Medical Center, Birmingham, AL, p. A16
  Vice President Human Resources, Tahlequah City Hospital, Tahlequah, OK, p. A507
SMITH, Randall, Executive Vice President, Jackson Park Hospital and Medical Center, Chicago, IL, p. A177
SMITH, Rebecca, Vice President and Chief Operating Officer, Caldwell Memorial Hospital, Lenoir, NC, p. A456
SMITH, Rebekah, R.N., President and Chief Executive Officer, St. Joseph Mercy Port Huron, Port Huron, MI, p. A322
SMITH, Rhonda, Director Human Resources, Shriners Hospitals for Children–Portland, Portland, OR, p. A516
SMITH, Rhonda E., R.N
  Vice President Patient Care Services and Chief Nursing Officer, Union Hospital, Terre Haute, IN, p. A214
  Chief Nursing Officer, Union Hospital Clinton, Clinton, IN, p. A200
SMITH, Rich, Vice President Human Resources, Kaiser Permanente Sunnyside Medical Center, Clackamas, OR, p. A511
SMITH, Richard C., Senior Vice President and Chief Financial Officer, JFK Medical Center, Edison, NJ, p. A403
SMITH, Rick, Director Information Systems, Jamestown Regional Medical Center, Jamestown, TN, p. A570
SMITH, Robert, Chief Information Officer, Fulton State Hospital, Fulton, MO, p. A361
SMITH, Robert, M.D. Chief of Staff, Grant Regional Health Center, Lancaster, WI, p. A689
SMITH, Robert L., Interim Chief Executive Officer, Parkland Health & Hospital System, Dallas, TX, p. A597
SMITH, Robert M., M.D. Chief of Staff, Veterans Affairs San Diego Healthcare System, San Diego, CA, p. A86
SMITH, Robin S., Chief Nursing Officer, Indiana University Health White Memorial Hospital, Monticello, IN, p. A210
SMITH, Rodney, Chief Executive Officer, Harrisburg Medical Center, Harrisburg, IL, p. A184
SMITH, Rodney R., Chief Executive Officer, Lawnwood Regional Medical Center, Fort Pierce, FL, p. A124
SMITH, Ron, Chief Financial Officer, Wickenburg Community Hospital, Wickenburg, AZ, p. A39
SMITH, Roy, Chief Financial Officer, Onslow Memorial Hospital, Jacksonville, NC, p. A455
SMITH, Ryan J., Administrator, Mayo Clinic Health System in Saint James, Saint James, MN, p. A339
SMITH, Ryan K., Chief Executive Officer, Memorial Hospital of Converse County, Douglas, WY, p. A702
SMITH, Sandra K., Chief Executive Officer, Deer's Head Hospital Center, Salisbury, MD, p. A294
SMITH, Scott, M.D. Chief of Staff, Adams Memorial Hospital, Decatur, IN, p. A201
SMITH, Scott D., Chief Financial Officer, Adams County Regional Medical Center, Seaman, OH, p. A489
SMITH, Scott M.
  Chief Executive Officer, Bolivar Medical Center, Cleveland, MS, p. A346
  Chief Executive Officer, Lake Wales Medical Center, Lake Wales, FL, p. A128
SMITH, Seneca, Chief Operating Officer, Creek Nation Community Hospital, Okemah, OK, p. A502
SMITH, Shane, M.D. Physician, Sanford Sheldon Medical Center, Sheldon, IA, p. A227
SMITH, Sherry, Manager Human Resources, Dallas County Hospital, Perry, IA, p. A227
SMITH, Sherry Bea, R.N., Chief Executive Officer, Lead–Deadwood Regional Hospital, Deadwood, SD, p. A559
SMITH, Shirley M., Chief Financial Officer, Andalusia Regional Hospital, Andalusia, AL, p. A15
SMITH, Sid, Director Information Resources, Larned State Hospital, Larned, KS, p. A238
SMITH, Stephen, Administrator, Selby General Hospital, Marietta, OH, p. A485
SMITH, Stephen B., M.D. Chief Medical Officer, Nebraska Medical Center, Omaha, NE, p. A388

SMITH, Steve
  Chief Financial Officer, Albany Area Hospital and Medical Center, Albany, MN, p. A328
  Chief Financial Officer, Kansas Heart Hospital, Wichita, KS, p. A246
SMITH, Steven
  Chief Financial Officer, Kindred Hospital Detroit, Detroit, MI, p. A312
  Chief Financial Officer, Lea Regional Medical Center, Hobbs, NM, p. A416
  Chief Information Officer, Presence Saints Mary & Elizabeth Medical Center, Chicago, IL, p. A178
SMITH, Steven L., Chief Executive Officer, Matagorda Regional Medical Center, Bay City, TX, p. A587
SMITH, Tammy, Director Human Resources, St. Vincent Morrilton, Morrilton, AR, p. A47
SMITH, Teresa, Chief Financial Officer, Memorial Hospital, Carthage, IL, p. A175
SMITH, Terrance, M.D. Chairman Medical Staff, Sanford Clear Lake Medical Center, Clear Lake, SD, p. A559
SMITH, Thomas, Chief Information Officer, NorthShore University Health System Evanston Hospital, Evanston, IL, p. A182
SMITH III, Thomas C., FACHE, Director, Central Texas Veterans Healthcare System, Temple, TX, p. A636
SMITH, Thomas G., Administrator and Chief Executive Officer, Audubon County Memorial Hospital, Audubon, IA, p. A216
SMITH, Tiffany, Director Human Resources, Wellstone Regional Hospital, Jeffersonville, IN, p. A207
SMITH, Tim
  Director Information Systems, Iroquois Memorial Hospital and Resident Home, Watseka, IL, p. A196
  Chief Executive Officer, Sharp Memorial Hospital, San Diego, CA, p. A85
SMITH, Todd A., Chief Executive Officer, Aurora Charter Oak Hospital, Covina, CA, p. A58
SMITH, Tracy, Director Human Resources, Mercy St. Francis Hospital, Mountain View, MO, p. A366
SMITH, Trevor, Chief Management Information Services, Gunnison Valley Hospital, Gunnison, CO, p. A102
SMITH, Trueman, M.D. Chief Medical Officer, Livingston Regional Hospital, Livingston, TN, p. A573
SMITH, Tyson, M.D. Chief Medical Officer, MedWest – Haywood, Clyde, NC, p. A450
SMITH, Vincent
  Chief Information Officer, Elmhurst Hospital Center,, NY, p. A431
  Chief Information Officer, Queens Hospital Center,, NY, p. A436
SMITH, Wayne, President and Chief Executive Officer, Southeast Hospital, Cape Girardeau, MO, p. A358
SMITH, Wendell, Chief Operating Officer, St. James Behavioral Health Hospital, Gonzales, LA, p. A267
SMITH, Windell, Chief Operating Officer, Mayo Clinic Health System in Waycross, Waycross, GA, p. A162
SMITH–HILL, Janet
  Senior Vice President Human Resources, Novant Health Forsyth Medical Center, Winston–Salem, NC, p. A463
  Senior Vice President Human Resources, Novant Health Presbyterian Medical Center, Charlotte, NC, p. A450
SMITHERS, John, Network Specialist, River Hospital, Alexandria Bay, NY, p. A420
SMITHHART, Paula, Director Human Resources, Coryell Memorial Hospital, Gatesville, TX, p. A606
SMITHHISLER, John E., President, Saint Joseph Hospital, Lexington, KY, p. A254
SMITHMIER, Kenneth L., President and Chief Executive Officer, Decatur Memorial Hospital, Decatur, IL, p. A180
SMOCK, Tait, Manager Information Systems, Pella Regional Health Center, Pella, IA, p. A227
SMOCYNSKI, Nancy, Director Payroll, Personnel and Human Resources, Kindred Hospital–Pittsburgh, Oakdale, PA, p. A533
SMOKER, Bret, M.D. Clinical Director, PHS Santa Fe Indian Hospital, Santa Fe, NM, p. A418
SMOLIK, Anton, M.D. Chief of Medical Staff, Harlan County Health System, Alma, NE, p. A381
SMOLIK, James Christian, Chief Executive Officer, Memorial Hospital at Craig, Craig, CO, p. A99
SMOOT, Brannon, M.D. Medical Director, Austin Surgical Hospital, Austin, TX, p. A584
SMOOT, Steve, Administrator, Utah Valley Regional Medical Center, Provo, UT, p. A646
SMOOT, Todd, Chief Information Officer, Jefferson Medical Center, Ranson, WV, p. A680
SMOTHERS, Carol, M.D. Chief of Staff, Pointe Coupee General Hospital, New Roads, LA, p. A276
SMOTHERS, Kevin, M.D. Senior Vice President Medical Affairs and Chief Medical and Quality Officer, Carroll Hospital Center, Westminster, MD, p. A294

SMOTHERS, Margaret Shawn, Administrator, Kenmare Community Hospital, Kenmare, ND, p. A468
SMOTHERS, Mark, M.D. Chief Medical Staff, Holmes County Hospital and Clinics, Lexington, MS, p. A350
SNAPP, III, William R.
  Vice President and Chief Financial Officer, Ephraim McDowell Fort Logan Hospital, Stanford, KY, p. A260
  Vice President Finance and Chief Financial Officer, Ephraim McDowell Regional Medical Center, Danville, KY, p. A250
SNAVELY, Gretchen, Director Human Resources, Holton Community Hospital, Holton, KS, p. A235
SNEDEGAR, Michael, Chief Financial Officer, Bourbon Community Hospital, Paris, KY, p. A259
SNEED, Farron, FACHE, Chief Executive Officer, Lovelace Westside Hospital, Albuquerque, NM, p. A414
SNEED, Jim, Chief Financial Officer, Lauderdale Community Hospital, Ripley, TN, p. A578
SNELGROVE, Steven C.
  Administrator, Wake Forest Baptist Health–Davie Hospital, Mocksville, NC, p. A457
  Chief Executive Officer, Wake Forest Baptist Health–Lexington Medical Center, Lexington, NC, p. A456
SNELL, Donald F., Executive Vice President and Chief Operating Officer, Lahey Hospital & Medical Center, Burlington, Burlington, MA, p. A298
SNELL, Peggy, Chief Finance Officer, Cherry County Hospital, Valentine, NE, p. A390
SNELL, Steve, M.D. Chief of Staff, Southwestern Medical Center, Lawton, OK, p. A500
SNENK, Don, Chief Financial Officer, Mercy Fitzgerald Hospital, Darby, PA, p. A524
SNIDER, Charles, Vice President Human Resources, Oak Hill Hospital, Brooksville, FL, p. A120
SNIDER, Glenn R., M.D. Chief of Staff, Louis A. Johnson Veterans Affairs Medical Center, Clarksburg, WV, p. A676
SNIDER, Tim, Senior Vice President and Chief Financial Officer, Upper Valley Medical Center, Troy, OH, p. A491
SNIDER, Timothy, Manager Information Systems, Fannin Regional Hospital, Blue Ridge, GA, p. A148
SNIDERMAN, Howard, Chief Operating Officer, Fairfield Medical Center, Lancaster, OH, p. A483
SNODGRASS, Liz, Chief Financial Officer, Trigg County Hospital, Cadiz, KY, p. A249
SNOOK, Joel, Chief Financial Officer, Arrowhead Hospital, Glendale, AZ, p. A31
SNOW, Brian, Manager Information Systems, Appling Healthcare System, Baxley, GA, p. A148
SNOW, Charlyn, Director Human Resources, Northwest Texas Healthcare System, Amarillo, TX, p. A582
SNOW, David, Area Information Officer, Kaiser Permanente Woodland Hills Medical Center,, CA, p. A69
SNOW, Dorothy, M.D. Chief of Staff, Veterans Affairs Maryland Health Care System–Baltimore Division, Baltimore, MD, p. A289
SNOW, Meldon L., Chief Executive Officer, Murray County Medical Center, Slayton, MN, p. A341
SNOWDEN, Raymond W., President and Chief Executive Officer, Memorial Hospital and Health Care Center, Jasper, IN, p. A207
SNYDER, Alice, Vice President, Chief Nursing Officer, OSF St. Mary Medical Center, Galesburg, IL, p. A183
SNYDER, Dallas, Chief Financial Officer, Springfield Hospital Center, Sykesville, MD, p. A294
SNYDER, Daniel J., Chief Executive Officer, University of Miami Hospital, Miami, FL, p. A132
SNYDER, David, M.D. Chief of Staff, DeKalb Medical at Downtown Decatur, Decatur, GA, p. A152
SNYDER, David, Chief Information Officer and Vice President Information Technology, Ellis Hospital, Schenectady, NY, p. A442
SNYDER, Jeffrey, Chief Operating Officer, Pocono Medical Center, East Stroudsburg, PA, p. A524
SNYDER, John, Executive Vice President and Chief Operating Officer, Carle Foundation Hospital, Urbana, IL, p. A196
SNYDER, Kristy, Director Human Resources, Fulton County Health Center, Wauseon, OH, p. A492
SNYDER, Marilyn, Chief Information Officer, Liberty Medical Center, Chester, MT, p. A374
SNYDER, Marjorie, M.D. Clinical Director, Dorothea Dix Psychiatric Center, Bangor, ME, p. A281
SNYDER, Mary E., Chief Operations Officer, Montrose Memorial Hospital, Montrose, CO, p. A104
SNYDER, Norman, M.D. Medical Director, Vista Health, Fayetteville, AR, p. A43
SNYDER, R. Brad, Chief Operating Officer, Torrance State Hospital, Torrance, PA, p. A542
SNYDER, Renae, Chief Financial Officer, Sakakawea Medical Center, Hazen, ND, p. A467
SNYDER, Ron, Chief Financial Officer, Hardin Memorial Hospital, Kenton, OH, p. A483

SNYDER, Steven, Vice President Human Resources, Franciscan Hospital for Children, Boston, MA, p. A296

SNYDER, Tony, Administrator and Chief Executive Officer, Pomerene Hospital, Millersburg, OH, p. A486

SNYDER, Vicky, Chief Operating Officer and Chief Financial Officer, Medina Hospital, Medina, OH, p. A486

SNYDER, Wendy
Director Finance, University Hospitals Conneaut Medical Center, Conneaut, OH, p. A479
Director Finance, University Hospitals Geneva Medical Center, Geneva, OH, p. A482

SOARES, Denise C., R.N., Executive Director, Harlem Hospital Center, New York, NY, p. A432

SOARES, Jair C., M.D., Executive Director, University of Texas Harris County Psychiatric Center, Houston, TX, p. A613

SOBECK, Brenda, Director of Human Resources, Jones Memorial Hospital, Wellsville, NY, p. A445

SOBIECK, Bridget, Director of Nursing, Cook County North Shore Hospital, Grand Marais, MN, p. A333

SOCHA, Jake, Chief Executive Officer, Kindred Hospital Park View, Springfield, MA, p. A305

SODERHOLM, Jon, President, Avera Heart Hospital of South Dakota, Sioux Falls, SD, p. A562

SODERLING, Marcia, R.N. Hospital Nurse Executive, Legacy Mount Hood Medical Center, Gresham, OR, p. A513

SOEKORO, Julie, Chief Financial Officer, Trinity Medical Center, Birmingham, AL, p. A17

SOHN, Steven, M.D. President Medical Staff, Dallas County Hospital, Perry, IA, p. A227

SOILEAU, D. Kirk, Chief Executive Officer, Natchitoches Regional Medical Center, Natchitoches, LA, p. A274

SOK, James E., FACHE,
President and Chief Executive Officer, Sheltering Arms Hospital South, Midlothian, VA, p. A657
President and Chief Executive Officer, Sheltering Arms Rehabilitation Hospital, Mechanicsville, VA, p. A657

SOKOLA, Thomas P., Chief Administrative Officer, Geisinger Medical Center, Danville, PA, p. A523

SOKOLOW, Norman J., Chairman and Chief Executive Officer, Cornerstone of Medical Arts Center Hospital, Fresh Meadows, NY, p. A426

SOKOLOWSKI, Magdalena, R.N. Director of Nursing, St. Lawrence Rehabilitation Center, Lawrenceville, NJ, p. A405

SOLAIMAN, Shereen, Vice President Human Resources, OhioHealth Riverside Methodist Hospital, Columbus, OH, p. A478

SOLARE, Frank A., Chief Executive Officer, Kindred Hospital Northwest Indiana, Hammond, IN, p. A204

SOLAZZO, Mark J.
Senior Vice President and Chief Operating Officer, Forest Hills Hospital, NY, p. A432
Executive Vice President and Chief Operating Officer, Franklin Hospital, Valley Stream, NY, p. A445
Regional Chief Operating Officer, Syosset Hospital, Syosset, NY, p. A443

SOLBERG, Bradley, FACHE, Chief Executive Officer, Hammond–Henry Hospital, Geneseo, IL, p. A183

SOLDATIS, Jeffrey J., M.D. Chairman Medical Executive Committee, Indiana Orthopaedic Hospital, Indianapolis, IN, p. A205

SOLDO, Stephen, M.D. Chief Medical Officer, Saint Agnes Medical Center, Fresno, CA, p. A61

SOLEM, Terry S., System Vice President Human Resources, Presence Saint Joseph Medical Center, Joliet, IL, p. A186

SOLER, Eddie, Chief Financial Officer, Florida Hospital, Orlando, FL, p. A135

SOLHEIM, John H., Chief Executive Officer, Cuyuna Regional Medical Center, Crosby, MN, p. A331

SOLIE, Carol M., M.D. Chief Medical Officer, Wyoming Medical Center, Casper, WY, p. A701

SOLIMAN, Russell
System Manager Client Services and Management Information Services, Presence Saint Joseph Medical Center, Joliet, IL, p. A186
Director Information Services, Presence St. Mary's Hospital, Kankakee, IL, p. A186

SOLIMON, Russ, Chief Information Officer, Adventist La Grange Memorial Hospital, La Grange, IL, p. A186

SOLIN, Andrea, Chief Financial Officer, Lovelace Rehabilitation Hospital, Albuquerque, NM, p. A414

SOLINSKI, Ruth, Vice President Organizational Development, Bell Hospital, Ishpeming, MI, p. A317

SOLIS, Gloria, R.N. Chief Operating Officer and Chief Nursing Officer, Saint Luke's East Hospital, Lee's Summit, MO, p. A365

SOLLE, Craig E., Administrator, Adena Pike Medical Center, Waverly, OH, p. A492

SOLLENBERGER, Donna K., Executive Vice President and Chief Executive Officer, University of Texas Medical Branch Hospitals, Galveston, TX, p. A605

SOLOMON, Elizabeth, R.N. Regional Quality/Risk Director and Interim Chief Nursing Officer, HEALTHSOUTH Rehabilitation Hospital–Las Vegas, Las Vegas, NV, p. A392

SOLOMON, John, M.D., Director, South Carolina Department of Corrections Hospital, Columbia, SC, p. A550

SOLOMON, Steven, Vice President Human Resources, Garden City Hospital, Garden City, MI, p. A314

SOLORZANO, Rosa, Interim Director Human Resources, Toppenish Community Hospital, Toppenish, WA, p. A673

SOLOW, Jodie, Director Human Resources, Chatham Hospital, Siler City, NC, p. A461

SOLVERSON, Paul, Interim Chief Information Officer, Centegra Hospital – Woodstock, Woodstock, IL, p. A197

SOMBAR, Jr., Michael J., Chief Financial Officer, Jefferson Hospital, Louisville, GA, p. A156

SOMERVILLE, Jacqueline G., R.N. Senior Vice President for Patient Care Services and Chief Nursing Officer, Brigham and Women's Hospital, Boston, MA, p. A296

SOMERVILLE, Susan, R.N., Executive Director, North Shore University Hospital, Manhasset, NY, p. A429

SOMISETTY, Sreedhar, M.D. Chief Medical Officer, Mahaska Health Partnership, Oskaloosa, IA, p. A226

SOMMERS, Belinda, Chief Information Officer, Lake Charles Memorial Hospital, Lake Charles, LA, p. A272

SOMMERS, Thomas W., FACHE, President and Chief Executive Officer, Beatrice Community Hospital and Health Center, Beatrice, NE, p. A382

SONDERMAN, Betty, Manager Human Resources, Ridgeview Institute, Smyrna, GA, p. A160

SONDERMAN, Thomas, M.D. Vice President and Chief Medical Officer, Columbus Regional Hospital, Columbus, IN, p. A200

SONENREICH, Steven D., President and Chief Executive Officer, Mount Sinai Medical Center, Miami Beach, FL, p. A133

SONG, Daniel, Chief Financial Officer, Monterey Park Hospital, Monterey Park, CA, p. A75

SONGER, Lucille, Acting Chief Operating Officer, Athol Memorial Hospital, Athol, MA, p. A295

SONNENBERG, Martha, M.D. Chief of Staff, Brotman Medical Center, Culver City, CA, p. A58

SONNENBERG, Stephanie, Director Information Management Systems, ProMedica Defiance Regional Hospital, Defiance, OH, p. A480

SONNENBERG, William, M.D. President Medical Staff, Titusville Area Hospital, Titusville, PA, p. A542

SONNENSCHEIN, Silvia, M.D. Chief of Staff, Kohala Hospital, Kohala, HI, p. A166

SONNINO, Victor, M.D. Vice President Medical Affairs, Sentara Princess Anne Hospital, Virginia Beach, VA, p. A662

SONS, Regina K., Administrative Director Human Ressources and Volunteer Services Associate Ethics and Compliance Officer, Mineral Area Regional Medical Center, Farmington, MO, p. A360

SONTHEIMER, Dan, M.D. Vice President Medical Affairs, Lester E. Cox Medical Centers, Springfield, MO, p. A372

SOOHOO, Richard
Chief Financial Officer, Sutter Davis Hospital, Davis, CA, p. A58
Chief Financial Officer, Sutter Medical Center, Sacramento, Sacramento, CA, p. A84

SOPER, Brent, Chief Financial Officer, San Joaquin Community Hospital, Bakersfield, CA, p. A54

SOPER, Thomas, D.O. Medical Director, Sterling Regional MedCenter, Sterling, CO, p. A106

SOPKO, Jeffrey
West Region Director of HR, Kindred Hospital Northland, Kansas City, MO, p. A363
District Director Human Resources, Kindred Hospital–San Diego, San Diego, CA, p. A85

SOPT, Michael, M.D. Chief of Staff, Brooks County Hospital, Quitman, GA, p. A158

SORBELLO, Bud, Director Management Information Systems, Hudson Valley Hospital Center, Cortlandt Manor, NY, p. A424

SORENSEN, Shannon, Chief Executive Officer, Brown County Hospital, Ainsworth, NE, p. A381

SORENSEN, Todd, M.D., Chief Executive Officer, Regional West Medical Center, Scottsbluff, NE, p. A389

SORENSON, Dennis, Supervisor Information Technology, South Haven Health System, South Haven, MI, p. A324

SORENSON, Ed, Vice President Finance and Chief Financial Officer, Community Hospital of San Bernardino, San Bernardino, CA, p. A84

SORENSON, Eric C., Chief Fiscal Office, Martinsburg Veterans Affairs Medical Center, Martinsburg, WV, p. A678

SORENSON, Euretta, R.N. Chief Nursing Officer, CentraCare Health–Monticello, Monticello, MN, p. A336

SOREY, Sharon, R.N., Regional Administrator, Mercy Hospital Paris, Paris, AR, p. A49

SORIANO, Miriam, M.D. Chief Medical Staff, Ashland Community Hospital, Ashland, OR, p. A511

SORRELL, Sr., Ralph W., Chief Financial Officer, Adena Greenfield Medical Center, Greenfield, OH, p. A482

SOSA–GUERRERO, Sandra, Chief Executive Officer, Larkin Community Hospital, South Miami, FL, p. A140

SOSENKO, Alexander, M.D. Chief of Staff, Silver Cross Hospital, New Lenox, IL, p. A190

SOSTMAN, Dirk, M.D. Executive Vice President, Chief Medical Officer and Chief Academic Officer, The Methodist Hospital, Houston, TX, p. A613

SOSTROM, Cynthia, Chief Information Officer, Sheridan Veterans Affairs Medical Center, Sheridan, WY, p. A703

SOTERAKIS, Jack, M.D. Executive Vice President Medical Affairs, St. Francis Hospital, Roslyn, NY, p. A442

SOTOS, Steven, M.D. President Medical Staff, LifeCare Hospitals of Pittsburgh, Pittsburgh, PA, p. A537

SOTTILE, Frank, M.D., Interim Chief Executive Officer, Crittenton Hospital Medical Center, Rochester, MI, p. A322

SOUDERS, Stuart, Coordinator Human Resources, William S. Middleton Memorial Veterans Hospital, Madison, WI, p. A690

SOUKUP, Paul, Chief Financial Officer, St. Luke Community Healthcare, Ronan, MT, p. A379

SOUSA, Francine, Director Management Information Service, New England Sinai Hospital and Rehabilitation Center, Stoughton, MA, p. A305

SOUSLEY, Dennis, Vice President of Clinical Services, Fitzgibbon Hospital, Marshall, MO, p. A365

SOUTHARD, Suzanne, Director Finance, Community Hospital–Fairfax, Fairfax, MO, p. A360

SOUTHERLAND, David, Chief Operating Officer, Twin County Regional Hospital, Galax, VA, p. A654

SOUTHERN, Joel, MSN, Interim Chief Executive Officer, Haywood Park Community Hospital, Brownsville, TN, p. A565

SOUTHERS, Nancy J., Vice President and Chief Financial Officer, The HSC Pediatric Center, Washington, DC, p. A117

SOUTHWICK, Bill, R.N. Chief Nursing Officer, Mountain Vista Medical Center, Mesa, AZ, p. A33

SOUTHWORTH, Barbara, R.N. Associate Director for Patient Care Services, Marion Veterans Affairs Medical Center, Marion, IL, p. A187

SOUTHWORTH, Scott, M.D. Medical Director, South Davis Community Hospital, Bountiful, UT, p. A643

SOUZA, Darlene, Vice President, St. Joseph Health Services of Rhode Island, North Providence, RI, p. A546

SOUZA, Greg, Vice President Human Resources, Lucile Salter Packard Children's Hospital at Stanford, Palo Alto, CA, p. A78

SOVETSKHY, Ed, Director Information Services, Portsmouth Regional Hospital, Portsmouth, NH, p. A400

SOWA, Phillip E., Chief Executive Officer, Saint Louis University Hospital, Saint Louis, MO, p. A370

SOWDER, Sam, Director Information Systems, Southwest General Hospital, San Antonio, TX, p. A632

SOWDERS, Dale, President and Chief Executive Officer, Holland Hospital, Holland, MI, p. A316

SOWELL, Ronald G.
Executive Vice President, Commonwealth Regional Specialty Hospital, Bowling Green, KY, p. A248
Executive Vice President, Medical Center at Bowling Green, Bowling Green, KY, p. A248
Executive Vice President, Medical Center at Franklin, Franklin, KY, p. A251
Chief Financial Officer, Medical Center at Scottsville, Scottsville, KY, p. A260

SOWERS, Kevin W., MSN, President, Duke University Hospital, Durham, NC, p. A451

SPACKMAN, Jared, Chief Financial Officer, Davis Hospital and Medical Center, Layton, UT, p. A644

SPACONE, Alan, M.D. Chief Medical Officer, Tuba City Regional Health Care Corporation, Tuba City, AZ, p. A38

SPACONE, Celia, M.D. Director Operations, Buffalo Psychiatric Center, Buffalo, NY, p. A422

SPADE, Ann, Chief Nursing Executive, Carlisle Regional Medical Center, Carlisle, PA, p. A522

SPALDING, Marsha, M.D. Medical Director, Sunrise Canyon Hospital, Lubbock, TX, p. A620

SPANGLER, Elizabeth L., M.D
Vice President Medical Affairs and Chief Medical Officer, CAMC Teays Valley Hospital, Hurricane, WV, p. A678
Vice President Medical Affairs, Charleston Area Medical Center, Charleston, WV, p. A676

SPANGLER, Wendell J., M.D. Chief of Staff, Paulding County Hospital, Paulding, OH, p. A488

SPANN, Debbie, Director Human Resources, Morehouse General Hospital, Bastrop, LA, p. A263

SPANN, Lori, Director Human Resources, Iberia Medical Center, New Iberia, LA, p. A275

SPANO, Dennis, M.D. Medical Director, Mayo Clinic Health System in Lake City, Lake City, MN, p. A334

SPANO, Jason, Manager Information Technology, Prowers Medical Center, Lamar, CO, p. A103

SPARACINO, Michael, M.D. Chief Medical Staff, River's Edge Hospital and Clinic, Saint Peter, MN, p. A340

SPARE, John, Accountant, Parsons State Hospital and Training Center, Parsons, KS, p. A242

SPARKMAN, Dena C., FACHE, Community Chief Executive Officer, Whitesburg ARH Hospital, Whitesburg, KY, p. A261

SPARKMAN, Jill, Director Human Resources, Odessa Regional Medical Center, Odessa, TX, p. A625

SPARKS, Gary R., Administrator, CrossRidge Community Hospital, Wynne, AR, p. A51

SPARKS, Jason, Director, Human Resources, HEALTHSOUTH Rehabilitation Hospital at Drake, Cincinnati, OH, p. A474

SPARKS, Jennifer, Human Resources Generalist, Complex Care Hospital at Ridgelake, Sarasota, FL, p. A139

SPARLING, Nicki, Manager Human Resources, Major Hospital, Shelbyville, IN, p. A213

SPARPANA, Eileen, Director Finance, Dickinson County Healthcare System, Iron Mountain, MI, p. A317

SPARROW, Francis D., M.D. Medical Director, Philhaven, Mount Gretna, PA, p. A532

SPARZO, John, M.D. Vice President Medical Affairs, Hendricks Regional Health, Danville, IN, p. A201

SPATH, Deborah, R.N. Associate Director Patient and Nurses Services, Albany Stratton Veterans Affairs Medical Center, Albany, NY, p. A420

SPAUDE, Paul A., FACHE, President and Chief Executive Officer, Borgess Medical Center, Kalamazoo, MI, p. A317

SPEAR, James, Executive Vice President and Chief Financial Officer, Central DuPage Hospital, Winfield, IL, p. A197

SPEARE, Mark
  Senior Associate Director Human Resources, Ronald Reagan University of California Los Angeles Medical Center, Los Angeles, CA, p. A71
  Senior Associate Director Patient Relations and Human Resources, Santa Monica–UCLA Medical Center and Orthopaedic Hospital, Santa Monica, CA, p. A90

SPEARMAN, John, President and Chief Operating Officer, Laurel Regional Hospital, Laurel, MD, p. A293

SPEARS, David, D.O. Chief of Staff, Selby General Hospital, Marietta, OH, p. A485

SPEARS, James, Chief Financial Officer, Harrison Memorial Hospital, Cynthiana, KY, p. A250

SPEARS, LaLana, Supervisor Accounting, Claremore Indian Hospital, Claremore, OK, p. A497

SPEARS, Michael, Vice President of Human Resources, St. Anthony Shawnee Hospital, Shawnee, OK, p. A506

SPEARS, Tim, D.O. Chief of Staff, Allen County Hospital, Iola, KS, p. A236

SPEASE, Dorothy, Manager Business Office, Douglas County Memorial Hospital, Armour, SD, p. A558

SPECK, Michelle A., Vice President Human Resources, UPMC Bedford Memorial, Everett, PA, p. A526

SPEECH, Thomas, M.D., Director, Winnebago Mental Health Institute, Winnebago, WI, p. A700

SPEEDLING, Ed, Chief Executive Officer and Managing Director, Arrowhead Behavioral Health Hospital, Maumee, OH, p. A486

SPEER, Kevin, Chief Executive Officer, Hendricks Regional Health, Danville, IN, p. A201

SPEES, Jonathan, Chief Financial Officer, Keck Hospital of USC, Los Angeles, CA, p. A70

SPEIGHT, Becky
  Chief Financial Officer, Bailey Medical Center, Owasso, OK, p. A505
  Chief Financial Officer, Lake Pointe Medical Center, Rowlett, TX, p. A630

SPEIGHT, Marianne, Vice President Information System and Chief Information Officer, Cincinnati Children's Hospital Medical Center, Cincinnati, OH, p. A474

SPEIGHTS, Rosetta, R.N. Chief Nursing Officer, Vista Medical Center West, Waukegan, IL, p. A196

SPEKTOR, Mark, M.D., President and Chief Executive Officer, Bayonne Medical Center, Bayonne, NJ, p. A401

SPELL, Dale, Chief Executive Officer, Appling Healthcare System, Baxley, GA, p. A148

SPELL, Kenneth R., Vice President Operations, Baptist Health South Florida, Homestead Hospital, Homestead, FL, p. A125

SPELLACY, Tara, Director Human Resources, Braintree Rehabilitation Hospital, Braintree, MA, p. A298

SPELLMAN, Kean, Interim Chief Executive Officer, Grady Memorial Hospital, Chickasha, OK, p. A496

SPENCE, Monte, Chief Operating Officer, Rehabilitation Hospital of Indiana, Indianapolis, IN, p. A206

SPENCE, Terri
  Chief Information Officer, Bon Secours Maryview Medical Center, Portsmouth, VA, p. A659
  Vice President Information Services, Mary Immaculate Hospital, Newport News, VA, p. A657

SPENCE, William, Director, Roseland Community Hospital, Chicago, IL, p. A178

SPENCER, James, Chief Financial Officer, Mildred Mitchell–Bateman Hospital, Huntington, WV, p. A677

SPENCER, John, Director Human Resources, Alleghany Memorial Hospital, Sparta, NC, p. A461

SPENCER, Marianne, R.N. Vice President Operations and Chief Operating Officer, Edward Hospital, Naperville, IL, p. A189

SPENCER, Marie, Chief Nursing Officer and Senior Administrator, Burke Rehabilitation Hospital, White Plains, NY, p. A446

SPENCER, Mike, Chief Information Officer, Henry County Hospital, New Castle, IN, p. A211

SPENCER, Misti, Director Inpatient Services, Selby General Hospital, Marietta, OH, p. A485

SPENCER, Richard, M.D. Clinical Director, Utah State Hospital, Provo, UT, p. A646

SPENCER, Susan, Chief Financial Officer, Samaritan Memorial Hospital, Macon, MO, p. A365

SPENCER, Todd, M.D. Chief Medical Staff, Adventist Medical Center–Reedley, Reedley, CA, p. A82

SPENST, Brett, Chief Executive Officer, Littleton Adventist Hospital, Littleton, CO, p. A103

SPERLING, Louis, Vice President Human Resources, Rhode Island Hospital, Providence, RI, p. A547

SPERRING, Kim, Chief Operating Officer, Canonsburg General Hospital, Canonsburg, PA, p. A522

SPICER, Charles, President and Chief Executive Officer, OU Medical Center, Oklahoma City, OK, p. A504

SPICER, John R.
  President and Chief Executive Officer, Mount Vernon Hospital, Mount Vernon, NY, p. A430
  President and Chief Executive Officer, Sound Shore Medical Center of Westchester, New Rochelle, NY, p. A430

SPICER, Michael J., President and Chief Executive Officer, St. Joseph's Medical Center, Yonkers, NY, p. A446

SPICER, Sam, M.D. Vice President Medical Affairs, New Hanover Regional Medical Center, Wilmington, NC, p. A463

SPIDLE, Tara, Controller, Decatur County Hospital, Leon, IA, p. A224

SPIEGEL, Kevin M., FACHE, Chief Executive Officer, Erlanger Medical Center, Chattanooga, TN, p. A566

SPIER, Deborah, Administrator, Oceans Behavioral Hospital of Greater New Orleans, Kenner, LA, p. A269

SPIER, Scott A., M.D. Senior Vice President Medical Affairs, Mercy Medical Center, Baltimore, MD, p. A288

SPIGEL, Michael, Executive Vice President & Chief Operating Officer, Brooks Rehabilitation Hospital, Jacksonville, FL, p. A126

SPIKE, Colleen A., Chief Executive Officer, River's Edge Hospital and Clinic, Saint Peter, MN, p. A340

SPILLERS, David S., Chief Executive Officer, Huntsville Hospital, Huntsville, AL, p. A21

SPINA, Lori, Vice President Human Resources, Good Samaritan Hospital Medical Center, West Islip, NY, p. A446

SPINHARNEY, Sarah, Senior Vice President, Baptist Medical Center, San Antonio, TX, p. A630

SPINOLO, Jorge, M.D. Chief of Staff, Henry Medical Center, Stockbridge, GA, p. A161

SPITULNIK, Aric, President and Chief Operating Officer, Levindale Hebrew Geriatric Center and Hospital, Baltimore, MD, p. A288

SPIVAK, Natalie, Director Information Services, Oaklawn Hospital, Marshall, MI, p. A320

SPIVEY, David A., President and Chief Executive Officer, St. Mary Mercy Hospital, Livonia, MI, p. A319

SPIVEY, Sue, Administrator, Irwin County Hospital, Ocilla, GA, p. A158

SPLAINE, Kevin, President, Spectrum Health – Grand Rapids, Grand Rapids, MI, p. A315

SPOELMAN, Roger
  President and Chief Executive Officer, Mercy Health Partners, Hackley Campus, Muskegon, MI, p. A320
  President and Chief Executive Officer, Mercy Health Partners, Mercy Campus, Muskegon, MI, p. A321

SPONG, Bernadette, Chief Financial Officer, Rex Healthcare, Raleigh, NC, p. A459

SPONSLER, Betsy A., Chief Financial Officer, Valley Hospital Medical Center, Las Vegas, NV, p. A394

SPOON, Barry, M.D. Chief of Staff, Mercy St. Francis Hospital, Mountain View, MO, p. A366

SPOONER, Allan M., President, Sacred Heart Rehabilitation Institute, Milwaukee, WI, p. A692

SPOONER, Christopher, M.D. Chief of Staff, Southeast Arizona Medical Center, Douglas, AZ, p. A31

SPOONER, Jennifer, Controller, HEALTHSOUTH Rehabilitation Hospital of Tallahassee, Tallahassee, FL, p. A140

SPOONER, William T.
  Senior Vice President and Chief Information Officer, Sharp Grossmont Hospital, La Mesa, CA, p. A65
  Senior Vice President and Chief Information Officer, Sharp Memorial Hospital, San Diego, CA, p. A85
  Senior Vice President Information Systems, Sharp Mesa Vista Hospital, San Diego, CA, p. A86

SPRADLIN, John, Information Systems Director, Franklin Foundation Hospital, Franklin, LA, p. A267

SPRAGG, Cherie, R.N. Senior Vice President Nursing Services, Fisher–Titus Medical Center, Norwalk, OH, p. A487

SPRAGGINS, Tommy, Director Information Services, Russell Medical Center, Alexander City, AL, p. A15

SPRAGUE, F. Remington, M.D
  Chief Medical Officer, Mercy Health Partners, Hackley Campus, Muskegon, MI, p. A320
  Chief Medical Officer, Mercy Health Partners, Mercy Campus, Muskegon, MI, p. A321

SPRAGUE, Sharon, Director Therapeutic Services, Dorothea Dix Psychiatric Center, Bangor, ME, p. A281

SPRATLING, Larry, M.D. Chief Medical Officer, Banner Baywood Medical Center, Mesa, AZ, p. A32

SPRAY, William R., Chief Executive Officer, Harton Regional Medical Center, Tullahoma, TN, p. A580

SPRIGGS, Larry, Controller, HEALTHSOUTH Rehabilitation Institute of San Antonio, San Antonio, TX, p. A631

SPRING, Jason A., FACHE, Chief Executive Officer, North Valley Hospital, Whitefish, MT, p. A380

SPRINGATE, Brian, Chief Nursing Officer, Bourbon Community Hospital, Paris, KY, p. A259

SPRINGER, David, M.D. President Medical Staff, Sanford Rock Rapids Medical Center, Rock Rapids, IA, p. A227

SPRINGER, Madge, Director Human Resources, Florida Hospital Waterman, Tavares, FL, p. A142

SPRINGER, Theresa, Chief Financial Officer, OSF Holy Family Medical Center, Monmouth, IL, p. A188

SPRINGMANN, Tressa, Chief Information Officer, Greater Baltimore Medical Center, Baltimore, MD, p. A287

SPRINKLE, Joseph, Chief Information Officer, Doctor's Memorial Hospital, Perry, FL, p. A137

SPROUT, Merry, R.N. Chief Nursing Officer, Antelope Memorial Hospital, Neligh, NE, p. A386

SPROWL, Chris, M.D. Vice President, PeaceHealth St. Joseph Medical Center, Bellingham, WA, p. A664

SPRUIT, Jr., Jacob, Chief Financial Officer, Atlanta Medical Center – South Campus, Atlanta, GA, p. A146

SPRUYT, James, Chief Executive Officer, Cumberland Hall Hospital, Hopkinsville, KY, p. A252

SPUHLER, Richard, Chief Executive Officer, Brigham City Community Hospital, Brigham City, UT, p. A643

SPURGEON, Sharon A., Chief Executive Officer, Coalinga Regional Medical Center, Coalinga, CA, p. A57

SPURGIN, Gregory, M.D. Chief of Staff, Indiana University Health West Hospital, Avon, IN, p. A198

SPURLOCK, Shirley, Director Human Resources, Millwood Hospital, Arlington, TX, p. A583

SPYROW, Florence, President, Genesis Medical Center, Illini Campus, Silvis, IL, p. A194

SQUIRES, Danny, Vice President and Chief Financial Officer, Wake Forest Baptist Health–Lexington Medical Center, Lexington, NC, p. A456

SQUIRES, Paula C., Senior Vice President Human Resources, Baystate Medical Center, Springfield, MA, p. A305

SQUIRES, Teresa, R.N. Chief Nursing Officer, Lake District Hospital, Lakeview, OR, p. A514

SREBINSKI, Ron, Chief Financial Officer, Caro Community Hospital, Caro, MI, p. A310

SREERAMA, Ravi K., M.D. Chief of Staff, East Texas Medical Center Clarksville, Clarksville, TX, p. A592

SRIBNICK, Wayne, M.D. Senior Vice President and Chief Medical Officer, Providence Hospital, Columbia, SC, p. A550

SRINIVASAN, Rajachandran, M.D. Medical Director, Porterville Developmental Center, Porterville, CA, p. A80

SRIPADA, Subra
  Senior Vice President and Chief Information Officer, Beaumont Hospital – Royal Oak, Royal Oak, MI, p. A323
  Senior Vice President and Chief Information Officer, Beaumont Hospital – Troy, Troy, MI, p. A326
  Senior Vice President and Chief Information Officer, Beaumont Hospital Grosse Pointe, Grosse Pointe, MI, p. A316

SRIVASTAVA, Mohit, M.D. Chief of Staff, Bunkie General Hospital, Bunkie, LA, p. A265

SROCK, Timothy G., Vice President Human Resources, McLaren Flint, Flint, MI, p. A313

ST CLAIR, Jeffery M., President and Chief Executive Officer, Springhill Memorial Hospital, Mobile, AL, p. A22

ST GEORGE, Scott, Senior Vice President and Chief Financial Officer, St. Mary's Hospital, Troy, NY, p. A444

ST MARTIN, Lee Anne, Director Operations, Soldiers' Home in Holyoke, Holyoke, MA, p. A301

ST. AMANT, Tracy, Director Human Resources, Phoebe North, Albany, GA, p. A145

ST. CLAIR, Jeffery M., President and Chief Executive Officer, Springhill Memorial Hospital, Mobile, AL, p. A22

ST. JOHN, Ryan, Assistant Administrator, Summers County ARH Hospital, Hinton, WV, p. A677

ST. JULIEN, Linda M., R.N. Chief Nursing Officer and Chief Operating Officer of Clinical Services, MetroSouth Medical Center, Blue Island, IL, p. A174

ST. LEGER, John, Chief Executive Officer, Select Specialty Hospital–Pittsburgh/UPMC, Pittsburgh, PA, p. A537

ST. MARTIN, Andrew, M.D. Chief of Staff, River Parishes Hospital, La Place, LA, p. A270

ST. ONGE, Donald, Chief Operating Officer, Day Kimball Hospital, Putnam, CT, p. A111

STAAB, Mary, Director Finance, Cordova Community Medical Center, Cordova, AK, p. A27

STABILE, Barry, Chief Operating Officer, Springfield Hospital Center, Sykesville, MD, p. A294

STACEY, Brian
Chief Financial Officer, Elmhurst Hospital Center,, NY, p. A431
Chief Financial Officer, Queens Hospital Center,, NY, p. A436

STACIE, Beverly, Director Human Resources, Clifton T. Perkins Hospital Center, Jessup, MD, p. A292

STACKHOUSE, Jenni, Chief Financial Officer, River Point Behavioral Health, Jacksonville, FL, p. A126

STACKHOUSE, Rebecca J., Associate Director, Wm. Jennings Bryan Dorn Veterans Affairs Medical Center, Columbia, SC, p. A551

STACKHOUSE, Sharon, Assistant Administrator and Director Risk Management, Peachford Behavioral Health System, Atlanta, GA, p. A146

STACY, James, Director Human Resources, Southwest Missouri Psychiatric Rehabilitation Center, El Dorado Springs, MO, p. A360

STADLER, Thomas, M.D. Vice President Medical Affairs and Chief Medical Officer, Madonna Rehabilitation Hospital, Lincoln, NE, p. A385

STADNYK, Sheldon, M.D. Chief Medical Officer, North Colorado Medical Center, Greeley, CO, p. A102

STAFFORD, Cindy, Chief Executive Officer, North Metro Medical Center, Jacksonville, AR, p. A45

STAFFORD, Walt, Director Information Technology, Chatuge Regional Hospital and Nursing Home, Hiawassee, GA, p. A154

STAGG, Kevin, Executive Vice President Finance and Chief Financial Officer, Christian Health Care Center, Wyckoff, NJ, p. A413

STAHL, Anthony, Director Human Resources, Florida Hospital Heartland Medical Center, Sebring, FL, p. A140

STAHL, Daniel, M.D. Medical Director, Mayo Clinic Health System in Waseca, Waseca, MN, p. A342

STAHL, Daniel, D.O. Chief of Staff, Rush Memorial Hospital, Rushville, IN, p. A213

STAHL, Marlin G., M.D. Chief Medical Officer, Bellevue Medical Center, Bellevue, NE, p. A382

STAHL, Ronald, M.D. Chief Medical Officer, Crouse Hospital, Syracuse, NY, p. A443

STAHL, Sherri, R.N. Summit Health Vice President for Patient Services, Chambersburg Hospital, Chambersburg, PA, p. A522

STAHL, William D., Chief Operating Officer, Rooks County Health Center, Plainville, KS, p. A242

STAHLKUPPE, Robert F., M.D. Chief of Staff, Chatuge Regional Hospital and Nursing Home, Hiawassee, GA, p. A154

STAIGER, Tom, M.D. Medical Director, University of Washington Medical Center, Seattle, WA, p. A671

STALBAUM, Angela, R.N. Chief Nursing Officer, Seton Medical Center Austin, Austin, TX, p. A585

STALCUP, Connie, Manager Information Systems, Murphy Medical Center, Murphy, NC, p. A458

STALCUP, Linda, Chief Executive Officer, Stevens County Hospital, Hugoton, KS, p. A236

STALEY, John H., Ph.D. Senior Associate Director and Interim Chief Operating Officer, University of Iowa Hospitals and Clinics, Iowa City, IA, p. A223

STALKER, Neil, M.D. Chief of Staff, Dukes Memorial Hospital, Peru, IN, p. A212

STALL, Kristi, Chief Human Resources Officer, Mahnomen Health Center, Mahnomen, MN, p. A335

STALLINGS, Elizabeth, Chief Operating Officer, John Muir Behavioral Health Center, Concord, CA, p. A57

STALLWORTH, Monica, M.D. Chief of Staff, Western Maryland Hospital Center, Hagerstown, MD, p. A292

STALLWORTH, Terresa, M.D. Clinical Director, San Antonio State Hospital, San Antonio, TX, p. A632

STALNAKER, Avah, Chief Executive Officer, Stonewall Jackson Memorial Hospital, Weston, WV, p. A681

STAMAS, Peter, M.D. Vice President Medical Affairs, Ministry Saint Joseph's Hospital, Marshfield, WI, p. A690

STAMATERIS, Connie, M.D. Director Medical Services, Naval Hospital Pensacola, Pensacola, FL, p. A136

STAMBAUGH, Lynn E., R.N.,  Chief Executive Officer, Sarah D. Culbertson Memorial Hospital, Rushville, IL, p. A194

STAMPOHAR, Jeffry, Chief Executive Officer, Essentia Health–Deer River, Deer River, MN, p. A331

STANCILL, Linda, Vice President and Chief Financial Officer, St. Joseph Health System, Tawas City, MI, p. A325

STANDEFFER, Luke, Administrator, Northport Medical Center, Northport, AL, p. A24

STANDER, Paul, M.D. Chief Medical Officer, Banner Good Samaritan Medical Center, Phoenix, AZ, p. A34

STANDISH, James F., Chief Financial Officer, Masonicare Health Center, Wallingford, CT, p. A112

STANDRIDGE, Debra K.
President, Wheaton Franciscan Healthcare – Elmbrook Memorial, Brookfield, WI, p. A684
President, Wheaton Franciscan Healthcare – St. Joseph's, Milwaukee, WI, p. A692
President, Wheaton Franciscan Healthcare – The Wisconsin Heart Hospital, Wauwatosa, WI, p. A699

STANEK, Janet, Executive Vice President, Stormont–Vail HealthCare, Topeka, KS, p. A245

STANFIELD, Alma, Director Human Resources, WellStar Cobb Hospital, Austell, GA, p. A148

STANFILL, Timothy, Chief Financial Officer, TriStar Summit Medical Center, Hermitage, TN, p. A570

STANFORD, Brian, Director Human Resources, Biloxi Regional Medical Center, Biloxi, MS, p. A344

STANGE KOLO, Tracey, Vice President Human Resources, UPMC St. Margaret, Pittsburgh, PA, p. A538

STANGL, Abbey, Chief Financial Officer, Manning Regional Healthcare Center, Manning, IA, p. A224

STANIC, Steve M.
Vice President and Chief Information Officer, Mississippi Baptist Medical Center, Jackson, MS, p. A348
Vice President and Chief Information Officer, Mississippi Hospital for Restorative Care, Jackson, MS, p. A349

STANLEY, Cassandra, Director Personnel, Eastern Shore Hospital Center, Cambridge, MD, p. A290

STANLEY, Ed
Director Information Systems, Barrow Regional Medical Center, Winder, GA, p. A163
Director Information Systems, Clearview Regional Medical Center, Monroe, GA, p. A157

STANLEY, Jennifer, M.D. President Medical Staff, St. Vincent Jennings Hospital, North Vernon, IN, p. A212

STANLEY, John T.
Vice President Planning and Information Systems, Riverside Regional Medical Center, Newport News, VA, p. A658
Vice President Planning and Information Systems, Riverside Rehabilitation Institute, Newport News, VA, p. A658

STANLEY, Kimi, Director of Information Services, Cannon Memorial Hospital, Pickens, SC, p. A555

STANLEY, Lynda, Senior Vice President and Chief Operating Officer, J. Arthur Dosher Memorial Hospital, Southport, NC, p. A461

STANLEY, Mark, Director Fiscal Services, Middle Tennessee Mental Health Institute, Nashville, TN, p. A576

STANLEY, Robert
Chief Financial Officer, Ilano Specialty Hospital of Lubbock, Lubbock, TX, p. A620
Chief Financial Officer, Texas Specialty Hospital at Lubbock, Lubbock, TX, p. A620

STANNARD, Mark, M.D. Chief of Staff, Hudson Hospital and Clinics, Hudson, WI, p. A688

STANSEL, Robert, Vice President of Human Resources, Estes Park Medical Center, Estes Park, CO, p. A101

STANSKI, Vickie, Financial Analyst, Parkview LaGrange Hospital, LaGrange, IN, p. A208

STANTON, Lowell, Chief Financial Officer, Methodist Sugar Land Hospital, Sugar Land, TX, p. A635

STANTON, Melanie, R.N. Chief Nursing Officer, Sycamore Shoals Hospital, Elizabethton, TN, p. A568

STANTON, Mike, D.O. Medical Director, Baylor Medical Center at Trophy Club, Trophy Club, TX, p. A638

STANUSH, Chris, Director Information Management, San Antonio State Hospital, San Antonio, TX, p. A632

STAPLES, Deborah L., Chief Operating Officer, Pennsylvania Hospital, Philadelphia, PA, p. A536

STAPLES, Janet, Vice President Human Resources, South Central Regional Medical Center, Laurel, MS, p. A349

STAPLETON, Carla J., Director Human Resources, Paul B. Hall Regional Medical Center, Paintsville, KY, p. A259

STAPLETON, Michael, MS, President and Chief Executive Officer, F. F. Thompson Hospital, Canandaigua, NY, p. A423

STAPLETON, Robert, Director Administration, Richard H. Hutchings Psychiatric Center, Syracuse, NY, p. A443

STAPP, Clint, Vice President, Baylor Specialty Hospital, Dallas, TX, p. A595

STARA, Jeanne, R.N. Chief Nursing Officer, Ponca City Medical Center, Ponca City, OK, p. A505

STARBIRD, William, M.D. Chief of Staff, Marlette Regional Hospital, Marlette, MI, p. A319

STAREN, Edgar, M.D. Senior Vice President Medical Affairs, Midwestern Regional Medical Center, Zion, IL, p. A197

STARESINIC, Barbara, Director Human Resources, Hi–Desert Medical Center, Joshua Tree, CA, p. A64

STARK, David, Chief Financial Officer, Lancaster Rehabilitation Hospital, Lancaster, PA, p. A529

STARK, Donna, Director Human Resources, Baylor Regional Medical Center at Grapevine, Grapevine, TX, p. A607

STARK, Jared, Chief Executive Officer, University Medical Center, Lafayette, LA, p. A271

STARK, Patricia Ann, R.N. CNO, Florida Hospital DeLand, DeLand, FL, p. A122

STARK, Steve, Chief Information Officer, Cass County Memorial Hospital, Atlantic, IA, p. A216

STARKEBAUM, Gordon, M.D. Chief of Staff, Veterans Affairs Puget Sound Health Care System, Seattle, WA, p. A671

STARKES, Henry, M.D. Medical Director, Biggs–Gridley Memorial Hospital, Gridley, CA, p. A63

STARKEY, Shelly, Personnel Coordinator, Cook County North Shore Hospital, Grand Marais, MN, p. A333

STARLING, James F., M.D. Chief Medical Officer, Danville Regional Medical Center, Danville, VA, p. A653

STARLING, Mark, M.D. Chief Medical Officer, Banner Heart Hospital, Mesa, AZ, p. A33

STARLING, Susan, President and Chief Executive Officer, Marcum and Wallace Memorial Hospital, Irvine, KY, p. A253

STARNES, Gregory D., Chief Executive Officer, Fayette County Hospital, Vandalia, IL, p. A196

STARNS, Mark, Administrator, Pinnacle Specialty Hospital, Tulsa, OK, p. A508

STARON, Willard, Chief Financial Officer, Crittenton Children's Center, Kansas City, MO, p. A362

STARR, Kay, Manager Human Resources, Vernon Memorial Healthcare, Viroqua, WI, p. A698

STARR, Linda, Director of Nursing, Horsham Clinic, Ambler, PA, p. A520

STASIK, Randall, President and Chief Executive Officer, Spectrum Health Gerber Memorial, Fremont, MI, p. A314

STASIKELIS, Peter J., M.D. Chief of Staff, Shriners Hospitals for Children–Greenville, Greenville, SC, p. A552

STASKIN, David
Director Human Resources, HEALTHSOUTH Rehabilitation Hospital of Mechanicsburg, Mechanicsburg, PA, p. A531
Director Human Resources, LifeCare Hospitals of Mechanicsburg, Mechanicsburg, PA, p. A531

STASTNY, Eric, Vice President Human Resources, Emerson Hospital, Concord, MA, p. A299

STASTNY, Mark
Vice President Information Technology, Laureate Psychiatric Clinic and Hospital, Tulsa, OK, p. A508
Vice President Information Technology, Saint Francis Hospital, Tulsa, OK, p. A508
Vice President Information Technology, Saint Francis Hospital South, Tulsa, OK, p. A509

STATA, Stephen C., Interim Chief Technology Officer, Northwestern Medical Center, Saint Albans, VT, p. A650

STATEN, Gary L., Chief Executive Officer, Trace Regional Hospital, Houston, MS, p. A348

STATEN, James, Senior Vice President Finance, Yale–New Haven Hospital, New Haven, CT, p. A110

STATES, Chuck, Director Information Systems, Punxsutawney Area Hospital, Punxsutawney, PA, p. A539

STATON, Donna, Chief Information Officer, Fauquier Hospital, Warrenton, VA, p. A662

STATON, Paul
Chief Financial Officer, Ronald Reagan University of California Los Angeles Medical Center, Los Angeles, CA, p. A71
Chief Financial Officer, Santa Monica–UCLA Medical Center and Orthopaedic Hospital, Santa Monica, CA, p. A90

STATZ, Lila, M.D. Chief of Staff, Haxtun Hospital District, Haxtun, CO, p. A102

STAUFFER, Keith, Regional Chief Information Officer, Carrington Health Center, Carrington, ND, p. A465

STAUFFER, Sharon, Chief Civilian Personnel, Wright Patterson Medical Center, Wright–Patterson AFB, OH, p. A493

STAUSS, Laura, Director of Human Resources, Huggins Hospital, Wolfeboro, NH, p. A400

STAZINSKI, Larry, Vice President Finance, Franciscan St. Anthony Health – Crown Point, Crown Point, IN, p. A201

STEAD, William, Associate Vice Chancellor for Health Affairs, Director Informatics Center and Chief Strategy and Information Officer, Vanderbilt Hospital and Clinics, Nashville, TN, p. A577

STEADHAM, Emily, Administrative Assistant Human Resources and Public Relations, Grove Hill Memorial Hospital, Grove Hill, AL, p. A21

STEADHAM, Mark B., President and Chief Executive Officer, Morris Hospital & Healthcare Centers, Morris, IL, p. A189

STEBBINS, Deborah E., FACHE, Chief Executive Officer, Alameda Hospital, Alameda, CA, p. A52

STEBBINS, Michael, Director Organization and Talent Effectiveness, Mercy Hospital Cadillac, Cadillac, MI, p. A310

STEBBINS, Trish, Director Management Information Systems, Florida Hospital Fish Memorial, Orange City, FL, p. A134

STECKEL, Cindy, Vice President Chief Nurse and Operations Executive, Scripps Memorial Hospital–La Jolla, La Jolla, CA, p. A65

STECKER, Tim, Chief Financial Officer, Kindred Hospital–Denver, Denver, CO, p. A99

STECKLER, Michael J., President and Chief Executive Officer, Jennie M. Melham Memorial Medical Center, Broken Bow, NE, p. A382

STEED, Robert A., Director Information Systems, Capital Regional Medical Center, Tallahassee, FL, p. A140

STEELE, Chrys, Director Information Systems, Springs Memorial Hospital, Lancaster, SC, p. A554

STEELE, Erik N., D.O. Senior Vice President and Chief Medical Officer, Summa Health System, Akron, OH, p. A470

STEELE, Mark, M.D
  Chief Medical Officer, Truman Medical Center–Hospital Hill, Kansas City, MO, p. A364
  Chief Medical Officer, Truman Medical Center–Lakewood, Kansas City, MO, p. A364

STEELE, Michael, M.D. Chief of Staff, Perry County Memorial Hospital, Perryville, MO, p. A367

STEELE, Robert, M.D., President, Mercy Hospital Springfield, Springfield, MO, p. A372

STEELE, Terry L., Vice President Finance and Chief Financial Officer, Holland Hospital, Holland, MI, p. A316

STEELE, Tina, Chief Executive Officer and Chief Financial Officer, Fairfax Community Hospital, Fairfax, OK, p. A498

STEELE, Wes, M.D. Chief of Staff, Fairmont General Hospital, Fairmont, WV, p. A676

STEELMAN, Jeffrey, Director Information Systems, LewisGale Hospital Alleghany, Low Moor, VA, p. A656

STEENPORT, John, Director Information Technology, Portage Health, Hancock, MI, p. A316

STEEVENS, Alan, Director Information Management, St. Clare Hospital, Baraboo, WI, p. A683

STEFANEK, Allen, Chief Financial Officer, Hollywood Presbyterian Medical Center, Los Angeles, CA, p. A69

STEFANOWICZ, Alex
  Vice President Human Resources, USMD Hospital at Arlington, Arlington, TX, p. A584
  Vice President Human Resources, USMD Hospital at Fort Worth, Fort Worth, TX, p. A604

STEFFEN, Elly, Chief Executive Officer and Administrator, Continuing Care Hospital at St. Luke's, Cedar Rapids, IA, p. A217

STEFFEN, Keith E., President and Chief Executive Officer, OSF Saint Francis Medical Center, Peoria, IL, p. A192

STEFFENS, Aaron, Chief Operating Officer, Mercy Hospital Oklahoma City, Oklahoma City, OK, p. A503

STEFKA, Darryl, Administrator, Cuero Community Hospital, Cuero, TX, p. A594

STEFL, William, Director Information Systems, Mercy Health Partners, Hackley Campus, Muskegon, MI, p. A320

STEFO, Andrew, Senior Vice President Finance and Chief Financial Officer, Ingalls Memorial Hospital, Harvey, IL, p. A184

STEGALL, Christopher A.
  Regional Chief Financial Officer and Chief Operating Officer, Promise Hospital Baton Rouge – Main Campus, Baton Rouge, LA, p. A263
  Regional Chief Financial Officer and Chief Operating Officer, Promise Hospital of Vicksburg, Vicksburg, MS, p. A354

STEGALL, Paula, R.N. Chief Nurse Executive, Anson Community Hospital, Wadesboro, NC, p. A462

STEGGE, Sherri, Director Human Resources, Kaiser Permanente Vallejo Medical Center, Vallejo, CA, p. A94

STEICHEN, Barry L.
  Executive Vice President, Chief Administrative Officer and Chief Financial Officer, Laureate Psychiatric Clinic and Hospital, Tulsa, OK, p. A508
  Executive Vice President and Chief Financial Officer, Saint Francis Hospital, Tulsa, OK, p. A508
  Executive Vice President, Saint Francis Hospital South, Tulsa, OK, p. A509

STEICHEN, Elizabeth, Human Resources, Lewis and Clark Specialty Hospital, Yankton, SD, p. A564

STEIDLE, Ernie, Chief Operating Officer, Woodrow Wilson Rehabilitation Center, Fishersville, VA, p. A654

STEIG, Nancy, Director Fiscal Services, Mayo Clinic Health System – Oakridge in Osseo, Osseo, WI, p. A694

STEIGER, Nancy, R.N., Chief Executive Officer and Chief Mission Officer, PeaceHealth St. Joseph Medical Center, Bellingham, WA, p. A664

STEIGMAN, Don S., Chief Operating Officer, Jackson Health System, Miami, FL, p. A131

STEIGMEYER, Robert P., President and Chief Executive Officer, Geisinger–Community Medical Center, Scranton, PA, p. A540

STEIMEL, Ronald, Vice President Administration and Chief Operating Officer, Mercy Medical Center, Rockville Centre, NY, p. A441

STEIN, Eric H., FACHE, President and Chief Executive Officer, Cobleskill Regional Hospital, Cobleskill, NY, p. A424

STEIN, Keith L., M.D
  Chief Medical Officer, Baptist Medical Center Beaches, Jacksonville Beach, FL, p. A127
  Senior Vice President Medical Affairs and Chief Medical Officer, Baptist Medical Center Jacksonville, Jacksonville, FL, p. A126

STEIN, Patrick, M.D. Clinical Director, Western New York Children's Psychiatric Center, West Seneca, NY, p. A446

STEIN, Richard, M.D. Chief Medical Officer, Bay Area Medical Center, Marinette, WI, p. A690

STEIN, Robert, M.D. Vice President Medical Management, Advocate Christ Medical Center, Oak Lawn, IL, p. A190

STEIN, Robert
  Chief Executive Officer, Kindred Hospital Midtown, Houston, TX, p. A610
  Chief Executive Officer, Kindred Hospital–Houston, Houston, TX, p. A610

STEIN, Sandra, Chief Human Resources Management, Veterans Affairs Central California Health Care System, Fresno, CA, p. A62

STEIN, Sheldon J., President and Chief Executive Officer, Mt. Washington Pediatric Hospital, Baltimore, MD, p. A288

STEINBERG, Dina, Chief People Resources Officer, Banner Estrella Medical Center, Phoenix, AZ, p. A34

STEINBERG, James P., M.D. Chief Medical Officer, Emory University Hospital Midtown, Atlanta, GA, p. A146

STEINBERG, Marc E., Vice President Community Relations and Physician Recruitment, Passavant Area Hospital, Jacksonville, IL, p. A186

STEINBLOCK, Matthew, Systems Administrator, Community Memorial Hospital, Syracuse, NE, p. A390

STEINER, Dana, R.N. Executive Director of Nursing Services, Lexington Regional Health Center, Lexington, NE, p. A385

STEINER, J. Scott, Interim Chief Executive Officer, UnityHealth MacNeal Hospital, Berwyn, IL, p. A174

STEINER, Jeffrey T., Vice President Finance, Memorial Hospital at Gulfport, Gulfport, MS, p. A347

STEINER, Julie, Manager Marketing and Public Relations, Vernon Memorial Healthcare, Viroqua, WI, p. A698

STEINER, Thomas, Chief Operating Officer, Beebe Medical Center, Lewes, DE, p. A114

STEINES, Jeanne, D.O. Medical Director, Connecticut Mental Health Center, New Haven, CT, p. A110

STEINGALL, Patricia, R.N. Vice President, Patient Care Services, Hunterdon Medical Center, Flemington, NJ, p. A404

STEINHART, Curt, M.D. Chief Medical Officer, OU Medical Center, Oklahoma City, OK, p. A504

STEINKE, Paul, D.O., President and Chief Executive Officer, CGH Medical Center, Sterling, IL, p. A195

STEINKRUGER, Roger W., Chief Executive Officer, Tri Valley Health System, Cambridge, NE, p. A382

STEINKUHLER, Diane, Administrative Assistant Human Resources, I–70 Community Hospital, Sweet Springs, MO, p. A372

STEINLE, Carrie, Chief Human Resources, South Texas Regional Medical Center, Jourdanton, TX, p. A615

STEINMANN, David
  VP/COO, Mercy Hospital Aurora, Aurora, MO, p. A356
  Chief Operating Officer, Mercy Hospital Cassville, Cassville, MO, p. A358

STEINMANN, Robin, Administrative Director Human Resources, Anderson Hospital, Maryville, IL, p. A187

STEITZ, David P., Interim Chief Executive Officer, Jacksonville Medical Center, Jacksonville, AL, p. A22

STELIGA, Kymm, Human Resources Specialist, Belmont Center for Comprehensive Treatment, Philadelphia, PA, p. A534

STELL, G. Max, M.D. Medical Director, Minden Medical Center, Minden, LA, p. A274

STELLING, Jonathan, M.D. Chief Medical Officer, St. Mary's Community Hospital, Nebraska City, NE, p. A386

STELLY, Donna, Human Resources Coordinator, Kindred Hospital Lafayette, Lafayette, LA, p. A270

STELTENPOHL, Robert, Controller, Southern Indiana Rehabilitation Hospital, New Albany, IN, p. A211

STELTER, Carolyn, M.D. Chief of Staff, Minnesota Valley Health Center, Le Sueur, MN, p. A334

STELZER, Jason, Director Human Resources, St. Clare Hospital, Baraboo, WI, p. A683

STEMMERMAN, Jill, R.N. Vice President Nursing, Saint Anthony Hospital, Chicago, IL, p. A179

STENDEL–FREELS, Robin, Coordinator Human Resources, AMG Specialty Hospital–Albuquerque, Albuquerque, NM, p. A414

STENERSON, David, Vice President Fiscal Services and Chief Financial Officer, OSF Saint Anthony Medical Center, Rockford, IL, p. A193

STENGER, Michael J., Interim President and Chief Executive Officer, Iroquois Memorial Hospital and Resident Home, Watseka, IL, p. A196

STENGER, Sandra, Acting Chief Human Resources, Cincinnati Veterans Affairs Medical Center, Cincinnati, OH, p. A474

STENNETT, Kevin T., M.D. Chief of Staff, W. J. Mangold Memorial Hospital, Lockney, TX, p. A619

STENSON, Richard, President and Chief Executive Officer, Tuality Healthcare, Hillsboro, OR, p. A513

STENSRUD, Kirk A., Chief Executive Officer, Glacial Ridge Health System, Glenwood, MN, p. A333

STEPANSKY, David, M.D. Chief Medical Officer, Phoenixville Hospital, Phoenixville, PA, p. A537

STEPHANY, Mark
  Executive Director, Elmira Psychiatric Center, Elmira, NY, p. A425
  Executive Director, Greater Binghamton Health Center, Binghamton, NY, p. A421

STEPHENS, Carrie, Coordinator Information Systems, Saunders Medical Center, Wahoo, NE, p. A390

STEPHENS, Dana, Director Information Technology, St. Elizabeth's Hospital, Belleville, IL, p. A174

STEPHENS, Donita, Director Financial Services, Choctaw Health Center, Philadelphia, MS, p. A352

STEPHENS, Eddy, Vice President Information Technology, Mobile Infirmary Medical Center, Mobile, AL, p. A22

STEPHENS, Ellen, Vice President Information Services, Mercy Hospital Oklahoma City, Oklahoma City, OK, p. A503

STEPHENS, Larry
  Chief Financial Officer, Collingsworth General Hospital, Wellington, TX, p. A640
  Chief Financial Officer, Kimble Hospital, Junction, TX, p. A615
  Chief Financial Officer, Schleicher County Medical Center, Eldorado, TX, p. A602

STEPHENS, Michael R.
  Market Leader and President, Mercy Health – Mt. Airy Hospital, Cincinnati, OH, p. A475
  Market Leader and President, Mercy Health – Western Hills Hospital, Cincinnati, OH, p. A475

STEPHENS, Mike, Chief Financial Officer, Turkey Creek Medical Center, Knoxville, TN, p. A572

STEPHENS, Norman F., Chief Executive Officer, St. Luke's Hospital at the Vintage, Houston, TX, p. A612

STEPHENS, Peggy, M.D. Superintendent and Medical Director, Madison State Hospital, Madison, IN, p. A209

STEPHENS, Terry A., Chief Executive Officer, River Park Hospital, Huntington, WV, p. A678

STEPHENS, PHR, Maria, Director Human Resources, Education and Occupational Health and Wellness, Community Memorial Healthcenter, South Hill, VA, p. A661

STEPHENSON, Ben, M.D. Chief of Staff, Phillips County Hospital, Phillipsburg, KS, p. A242

STEPHENSON, Darlene, Vice President Operations, Mary Immaculate Hospital, Newport News, VA, p. A657

STEPHENSON, John, M.D. Chief of Staff, Mackinac Straits Health System, Saint Ignace, MI, p. A323

STEPHENSON, Melinda, Chief Executive Officer, Kingwood Medical Center, Kingwood, TX, p. A617

STEPHENSON, Penny, Chief Financial Officer, Ellinwood District Hospital, Ellinwood, KS, p. A233

STEPHENSON, Ronald, Chief Operating Officer, Brookhaven Memorial Hospital Medical Center, Patchogue, NY, p. A439

STEPHENSON, Steve R., M.D. Executive Vice President and Chief Operating Officer, Iowa Methodist Medical Center, Des Moines, IA, p. A220

STEPP, Dana, Human Resources Officer, Marcum and Wallace Memorial Hospital, Irvine, KY, p. A253

STERBACH, Maureen, Vice President Human Resources, St. Joseph's Hospital and Medical Center, Phoenix, AZ, p. A35

STERLING, Jacci, R.N. Chief Nursing Executive, Sutter Maternity and Surgery Center of Santa Cruz, Santa Cruz, CA, p. A90

STERLING, Julie, Manager Information System, South Sunflower County Hospital, Indianola, MS, p. A348

STERLING, Michelle, R.N. Acting Chief Nursing Officer, Rancho Los Amigos National Rehabilitation Center, Downey, CA, p. A58

STERLING, Terrie, R.N. Chief Operating Officer, Our Lady of the Lake Regional Medical Center, Baton Rouge, LA, p. A263

STERMER, Susan, Director Finance, LifeCare Hospitals of Wisconsin, Pewaukee, WI, p. A694

STERNBERG, Janet, President and Chief Executive Officer, Huron Medical Center, Bad Axe, MI, p. A308

STERNBERG, Paul, M.D. Professor and Chairman, Vanderbilt Hospital and Clinics, Nashville, TN, p. A577

STESNEY-RIDENOUR, Chris, Vice President Operations, Beaumont Hospital Grosse Pointe, Grosse Pointe, MI, p. A316

STETTHEIMER, Timothy
  Vice President and Chief Information Officer, St. Vincent's Birmingham, Birmingham, AL, p. A17
  Regional Chief Information Officer, St. Vincent's Blount, Oneonta, AL, p. A24

STEUSSY, William, Chief Financial Officer, Greene County Medical Center, Jefferson, IA, p. A223

STEUTER, Krista, Director Human Resources, Catalina Island Medical Center, Avalon, CA, p. A53

STEVEN, Eva, Chief Financial Officer, Roosevelt General Hospital, Portales, NM, p. A417

STEVENS, Ann Marie, Chief Executive Officer, Mid-Valley Hospital, Peckville, PA, p. A534

STEVENS, Bryan N., Chief Financial Officer, Highland Community Hospital, Picayune, MS, p. A352

STEVENS, Chris E., Chief Information Officer, Billings Clinic, Billings, MT, p. A374

STEVENS, Diane L., MS Director Human Resources and Compliance Officer, Huntsville Memorial Hospital, Huntsville, TX, p. A614

STEVENS, Dori, Chief Nursing Officer, Sutter Delta Medical Center, Antioch, CA, p. A52

STEVENS, Emily, Chief Nursing Officer, Mat-Su Regional Medical Center, Palmer, AK, p. A28

STEVENS, George, Chief Financial Officer, University Medical Center, Las Vegas, NV, p. A394

STEVENS, Janis, Director Human Resources, Raulerson Hospital, Okeechobee, FL, p. A134

STEVENS, Kelly, Manager Human Resources, St. Joseph Memorial Hospital, Murphysboro, IL, p. A189

STEVENS, Lianne, Vice President Information Technology, Nebraska Medical Center, Omaha, NE, p. A388

STEVENS, Lisa, Chief Clinical Officer and Chief Operating Officer, Vibra Hospital of Northern California, Redding, CA, p. A81

STEVENS, Rick, Chief Administrative Officer, St. Luke's Hospital, San Francisco, CA, p. A87

STEVENS, Robert, President and Chief Executive Officer, Ridgeview Medical Center, Waconia, MN, p. A342

STEVENS, Saundra J., Chief Executive Officer, Adams County Regional Medical Center, Seaman, OH, p. A489

STEVENS, Shelbourn, President, Novant Health Brunswick Medical Center, Bolivia, NC, p. A448

STEVENS, Susan, Director Human Resources, The HealthCenter, Kalispell, MT, p. A377

STEVENS, Tammy, Chief Operating Officer, Madison County Memorial Hospital, Madison, FL, p. A129

STEVENS, Tom, Director Personnel, Morehead Memorial Hospital, Eden, NC, p. A451

STEVENS, Velinda, President, Kalispell Regional Medical Center, Kalispell, MT, p. A377

STEVENSON, Angelia, Manager Finance, Tuscaloosa Veterans Affairs Medical Center, Tuscaloosa, AL, p. A26

STEVENSON, John, M.D. Senior Vice President and Chief Medical Officer, South Shore Hospital, South Weymouth, MA, p. A304

STEVENSON, Michael, Chief Executive Officer, Murphy Medical Center, Murphy, NC, p. A458

STEVERSON, Denise, Director Human Resources, Dorminy Medical Center, Fitzgerald, GA, p. A153

STEVES, Sonja
  Senior Vice President Human Resources and Marketing, Legacy Emanuel Hospital and Health Center, Portland, OR, p. A516
  Vice President Marketing, Legacy Good Samaritan Hospital and Medical Center, Portland, OR, p. A516
  Vice President Human Resources and Marketing, Legacy Meridian Park Hospital, Tualatin, OR, p. A518
  Senior Vice President Human Resources, Legacy Mount Hood Medical Center, Gresham, OR, p. A513
  Senior Vice President Human Resources, Legacy Salmon Creek Medical Center, Vancouver, WA, p. A673

STEWARD, Rachel, Manager Human Resources, Bailey Medical Center, Owasso, OK, p. A505

STEWARD, Todd E., Chief Executive Officer, St. David's South Austin Medical Center, Austin, TX, p. A586

STEWART, Charles L., Chief Executive Officer, Poplar Bluff Regional Medical Center, Poplar Bluff, MO, p. A368

STEWART, Charles R., Vice President Business, Finance and Corporate Compliance, MedStar Southern Maryland Hospital Center, Clinton, MD, p. A290

STEWART, Christine R., FACHE, Chief Executive Officer, Russellville Hospital, Russellville, AL, p. A25

STEWART, Clint, Vice President Finance/Business Operations, McDowell Hospital, Marion, NC, p. A457

STEWART, Craig, Chief Financial Officer, Gila Regional Medical Center, Silver City, NM, p. A418

STEWART, Daphne, Director Human Resources, Northlake Behavioral Hospital, Mandeville, LA, p. A273

STEWART, David K., Chief Financial Officer, Mercy Medical Center, Canton, OH, p. A473

STEWART, Debbie, Human Resources Officer, Herington Municipal Hospital, Herington, KS, p. A235

STEWART, Dianne, Controller, Burke Medical Center, Waynesboro, GA, p. A162

STEWART, Evelyn G., Chief Executive Officer, El Paso LTAC Hospital, El Paso, TX, p. A601

STEWART, Greg, Chief Executive Officer, Wellstone Regional Hospital, Jeffersonville, IN, p. A207

STEWART, Hedda, Director Human Resources, Neshoba County General Hospital, Philadelphia, MS, p. A352

STEWART, Inez, Vice President, Boston Children's Hospital, Boston, MA, p. A296

STEWART, Jane, Director Information Services, J. F. K. Medical Center, Atlantis, FL, p. A118

STEWART, John, Director Finance, Burke Rehabilitation Hospital, White Plains, NY, p. A446

STEWART, Joseph A., President and Chief Executive Officer, Sierra View District Hospital, Porterville, CA, p. A80

STEWART, Kendall, M.D. Medical Director, Southern Ohio Medical Center, Portsmouth, OH, p. A489

STEWART, Marc, M.D. Vice President and Medical Director, Seattle Cancer Care Alliance, Seattle, WA, p. A671

STEWART, Marian, M.D. Chief of Staff, Jay Hospital, Jay, FL, p. A127

STEWART, Nova
  Chief Information Officer, Chapman Medical Center, Orange, CA, p. A77
  Chief Information Officer, Western Medical Center Anaheim, Anaheim, CA, p. A52
  Chief Information Officer, Western Medical Center-Santa Ana, Santa Ana, CA, p. A89

STEWART, Patty, Chief Financial Officer, Memorial Hospital, Gonzales, TX, p. A606

STEWART, Paul, M.D. Medical Director, Kindred Hospital Las Vegas-Sahara, Las Vegas, NV, p. A393

STEWART, Paul R., President and Chief Executive Officer, Sky Lakes Medical Center, Klamath Falls, OR, p. A514

STEWART, Paula, M.D. Medical Director, HEALTHSOUTH Lakeshore Rehabilitation Hospital, Birmingham, AL, p. A16

STEWART, Russell L., M.D. Chief Medical Officer, Braxton County Memorial Hospital, Gassaway, WV, p. A676

STEWART, Scott, M.D. Vice President Medical Management, Good Samaritan Medical Center, Brockton, MA, p. A298

STEWART, Scott, Manager Information Services, Rochelle Community Hospital, Rochelle, IL, p. A193

STEWART, Steve, Director Information Technology, Henry County Health Center, Mount Pleasant, IA, p. A225

STEWART, Terry, Director Information Systems, Dauterive Hospital, New Iberia, LA, p. A275

STEWART, Tim, Chief Information Officer, Abbeville Area Medical Center, Abbeville, SC, p. A548

STEWART, SPHR, Ronnelle, Chief Human Resources Officer, Brookwood Medical Center, Birmingham, AL, p. A16

STICKLER, Debra, Chief Information Officer, Lebanon Veterans Affairs Medical Center, Lebanon, PA, p. A529

STIEB, Pamela, Chief Financial Officer, Sterling Regional MedCenter, Sterling, CO, p. A106

STIEGMANN, Greg, M.D. Vice President Clinical Affairs, University of Colorado Hospital, Aurora, CO, p. A97

STIEKES, Robert, Chief Financial Officer, Bayfront Health Port Charlotte, Port Charlotte, FL, p. A137

STIENE, Susan M., MS, Interim Chief Administrative Officer, Mayo Clinic Health System in Lake City, Lake City, MN, p. A334

STIFF, Patrick, Coordinator Information Technology, Madison County Memorial Hospital, Madison, FL, p. A129

STIGLIANESE, Amber, Manager Human Resources, Coalinga Regional Medical Center, Coalinga, CA, p. A57

STIKELEATHER, Janie, Director Marketing and Community Relations, Davis Regional Medical Center, Statesville, NC, p. A461

STILES, Susan M., President and Chief Executive Officer, Western Missouri Medical Center, Warrensburg, MO, p. A373

STILES, Suzanne, Chief Human Resources Officer & Sr. Vice President/Administrative and Support Services, Lakes Region General Hospital, Laconia, NH, p. A398

STILLER, Brian G.
  Director Medical Center, Veterans Affairs Western New York Healthcare System-Batavia Division, Batavia, NY, p. A421
  Director Medical Center, Veterans Affairs Western New York Healthcare System-Buffalo Division, Buffalo, NY, p. A423

STILLMAN, Elizabeth M., Acting Director, Colorado Mental Health Institute at Fort Logan, Denver, CO, p. A99

STILLMAN, Michelle, Director of Care Management, Asheville Specialty Hospital, Asheville, NC, p. A447

STILLO, Joseph, M.D. Medical Director, HEALTHSOUTH Rehabilitation Hospital of Toms River, Toms River, NJ, p. A411

STILLWORD, Joseph, Chief of Staff, Putnam Community Medical Center, Palatka, FL, p. A135

STILTNER, Wanda, Director Human Resources, Buchanan General Hospital, Grundy, VA, p. A655

STIMSON-RUSIN, Judi, Chief Financial Officer, Palm Beach Gardens Medical Center, Palm Beach Gardens, FL, p. A135

STINSON, Katy, Director Information Services, Medical Center of Southeastern Oklahoma, Durant, OK, p. A497

STINSON, Martha, Director, West Palm Hospital, West Palm Beach, FL, p. A144

STIPE, Christopher R., FACHE, Chief Executive Officer, Clarinda Regional Health Center, Clarinda, IA, p. A218

STIRE, David R., President and Chief Executive Officer, Jane Phillips Medical Center, Bartlesville, OK, p. A496

STIRLE, Roger, Business Manager, Mental Health Institute, Clarinda, IA, p. A218

STITT, Bobby, R.N.,
  Interim Chief Executive Officer, Kingfisher Regional Hospital, Kingfisher, OK, p. A500
  Administrator, Mercy Hospital Watonga, Watonga, OK, p. A509

STITZER, Philip, D.O. Chief Medical Officer, Moberly Regional Medical Center, Moberly, MO, p. A366

STOB, David, Chief Financial Officer, Kindred Hospital Seattle-Northgate, Seattle, WA, p. A670

STOCK, Constance, M.D. Chief of Staff, Sturgis Regional Hospital, Sturgis, SD, p. A563

STOCK, Greg K., Chief Executive Officer, Thibodaux Regional Medical Center, Thibodaux, LA, p. A279

STOCK, Neil, Director Technology and Facilities, Mercy Regional Medical Center, Durango, CO, p. A100

STOCKARD, Herbert, M.D. Chief Medical Officer, Mercy St. Anne Hospital, Toledo, OH, p. A491

STOCKHAUSEN, Christopher, Chief Financial Officer, UPMC McKeesport, McKeesport, PA, p. A531

STOCKLEY, Selena, Chief Executive Officer, Rolling Hills Hospital, Ada, OK, p. A495

STOCKMAN, Troy P., Chief Executive Officer, Nebraska Spine Hospital, Omaha, NE, p. A388

STOCKSTILL, Mark, R.N., Administrator, Highland Community Hospital, Picayune, MS, p. A352

STOCKTON, Brad, Chief Operating Officer, Turkey Creek Medical Center, Knoxville, TN, p. A572

STOCKTON, Kevin, Chief Executive Officer, Northwest Medical Center, Tucson, AZ, p. A39

STOCKTON, Linda, Chief Financial Officer, Bayfront Health Dade City, Dade City, FL, p. A121

STOCKTON, Rick, Chief Executive Officer, Promise Hospital of Louisiana – Shreveport Campus, Shreveport, LA, p. A278

STODDARD, Benita K., FACHE, Acting Director, Hampton Veterans Affairs Medical Center, Hampton, VA, p. A655

STODDARD, Mark R., President, Central Valley Medical Center, Nephi, UT, p. A645

STOECKELER, Joel, M.D. Chief of Staff, Baldwin Area Medical Center, Baldwin, WI, p. A683

STOECKMAN, Bill, Chief Information Officer, Spearfish Regional Surgery Center, Spearfish, SD, p. A563

STOEKE, Jason, Director Management Information Systems, Community Memorial Hospital, Cloquet, MN, p. A330

STOFFERSON, Laura, Director of Nursing, Ellsworth County Medical Center, Ellsworth, KS, p. A233

STOJAKOVICH, Edward R.
  Chief Financial Officer, Dominion Hospital, Falls Church, VA, p. A653
  Chief Financial Officer, Reston Hospital Center, Reston, VA, p. A659

STOKER, Rick, Director Management Information Systems, TriStar Horizon Medical Center, Dickson, TN, p. A568

STOKES, Elia, Chief Financial Officer, Plaza Medical Center of Fort Worth, Fort Worth, TX, p. A604

STOKES, Gary L., Chief Executive Officer, Nacogdoches Medical Center, Nacogdoches, TX, p. A624

STOKES, Lisa, R.N. Vice President Patient Care Services, Shenandoah Memorial Hospital, Woodstock, VA, p. A663

STOKES, Priscilla, MS Vice President Patient Care and Chief Nursing Officer, UnityPoint Health St. Luke's, Sioux City, IA, p. A228

STOKES, Randell G., Chief Executive Officer, LifeCare Hospitals of San Antonio, San Antonio, TX, p. A631

STOKES, Richard, CPA Chief Financial Officer, Clarendon Memorial Hospital, Manning, SC, p. A554

STOKES, Tina, Manager Human Resources, Regency Hospital of Florence, Florence, SC, p. A552

STOLBA, Robert J., Chief Financial Officer, Mason District Hospital, Havana, IL, p. A184

STOLDT, Garrick J., Vice President and Chief Financial Officer, Saint Peter's University Hospital, New Brunswick, NJ, p. A407

STOLLER, Theo, Director Human Resources, Jacobson Memorial Hospital Care Center, Elgin, ND, p. A466

STOLTZ, Kyla, Vice President Human Resources, Centerpoint Medical Center, Independence, MO, p. A362

STOLTZ, Lori, Chief Financial Officer, Benewah Community Hospital, Saint Maries, ID, p. A171

STOLTZFUS, William F., Interim Chief Financial Officer, Hendry Regional Medical Center, Clewiston, FL, p. A120

STOLYAR, Edward B., D.O. Director Management Information Systems, New York Community Hospital,, NY, p. A434

STOLZE, Jeffery
Vice President Human Resources, Trinity Bettendorf, Bettendorf, IA, p. A216
Vice President Human Resources, Trinity Rock Island, Rock Island, IL, p. A193

STOMBERG, LeAnn, Chief Financial Officer, Minneapolis Veterans Affairs Health Care System, Minneapolis, MN, p. A336

STOMP, Gregory, Chief Executive Officer, Cooperstown Medical Center, Cooperstown, ND, p. A466

STONE, Bud, Director Information Systems, Eastern State Hospital, Lexington, KY, p. A254

STONE, Dan, Community Chief Executive Officer, Harlan ARH Hospital, Harlan, KY, p. A252

STONE, Duncan, D.D.S. Chief Medical Staff, Mississippi State Hospital, Whitfield, MS, p. A355

STONE, Eric, Commander, U. S. Air Force Hospital, Hampton, VA, p. A655

STONE, Janice, Vice President Clinical Integration, Spectrum Health Gerber Memorial, Fremont, MI, p. A314

STONE, Jeanette, Vice President Operations, Baptist Health South Florida, South Miami Hospital, Miami, FL, p. A131

STONE, Jeff, Director Human Resources, Marshall Medical Center North, Guntersville, AL, p. A21

STONE, Joanna, Chief Nursing Officer, Livingston Hospital and Healthcare Services, Salem, KY, p. A260

STONE, Matthew M., Chief Operating Officer, Valley Baptist Medical Center–Brownsville, Brownsville, TX, p. A590

STONE, Michelle, D.O. Chief Medical Staff, Community Memorial Healthcare, Marysville, KS, p. A239

STONE, Richard, M.D. Medical Director, Metropolitan Hospital Center, New York, NY, p. A434

STONE, Ronald W., Regional Chief Human Resource Officer, Long Island Jewish Medical Center,, NY, p. A433

STONE, Susan, Director Human Resources, Claiborne County Hospital, Tazewell, TN, p. A579

STONE, Susan, Ph.D., Senior Vice President and Chief Executive Officer, Sharp Coronado Hospital and Healthcare Center, Coronado, CA, p. A57

STONE, Terry, Chief Financial Officer and Chief Information Officer, Willapa Harbor Hospital, South Bend, WA, p. A672

STONE, Thomas J., FACHE, Chief Executive Officer, Monroe County Hospital, Monroeville, AL, p. A23

STONE, Timothy D., Executive Vice President and Chief Operating Officer, Decatur Memorial Hospital, Decatur, IL, p. A180

STONEBURG, John, Chief Information Officer, Tuality Healthcare, Hillsboro, OR, p. A513

STONEHOCKER, Lori, D.O. Chief Medical Staff, Dundy County Hospital, Benkelman, NE, p. A382

STONER, Courtney E., Director Marketing Operations, HEALTHSOUTH Rehabilitation Hospital of York, York, PA, p. A545

STONER, Donald, M.D. Chief Medical Officer, Halifax Health Medical Center of Daytona Beach, Daytona Beach, FL, p. A122

STONER, James, Chief Financial Officer, Lake Norman Regional Medical Center, Mooresville, NC, p. A457

STONER, Steve, Chief Information Officer, Richard L. Roudebush Veterans Affairs Medical Center, Indianapolis, IN, p. A206

STOOPS, Stephens, M.D
Chief Medical Officer, St. Joseph Medical Center, Kansas City, MO, p. A363
Chief Medical Officer, St. Mary's Medical Center, Blue Springs, MO, p. A356

STOPPER, Jim, Interim Chief Financial Officer, Evangelical Community Hospital, Lewisburg, PA, p. A530

STORCK, William H., Chief Financial Officer, Community Memorial Healthcare, Marysville, KS, p. A239

STORER, William, M.D. Medical Director, St. Vincent Heart Center of Indiana, Indianapolis, IN, p. A206

STOREY, Kam, Director Human Resources, Sebastian River Medical Center, Sebastian, FL, p. A140

STOREY, Kevin, Chief Executive Officer, Comanche County Medical Center, Comanche, TX, p. A593

STOREY, Paul
Chief Executive Officer, Greenbrier Valley Medical Center, Ronceverte, WV, p. A680
Chief Information Officer, Helen Keller Hospital, Sheffield, AL, p. A25

STORM, Dave, Director Business Support, St. Anthony's Memorial Hospital, Effingham, IL, p. A181

STORMANNS, Thomas, Chief Executive Officer, Pinnacle Pointe Hospital, Little Rock, AR, p. A46

STORMS, Bruce, M.D. Chief of Staff, Grady Memorial Hospital, Chickasha, OK, p. A496

STORR, Katie, Director Personnel, Mississippi State Hospital, Whitfield, MS, p. A355

STORTO, David E., President, Spaulding Rehabilitation Hospital, Boston, MA, p. A297

STORTZUM, Christopher, M.D. President Medical Staff, McDonough District Hospital, Macomb, IL, p. A187

STORY, Cathy N., Interim Chief Executive Officer, North Vista Hospital, North Las Vegas, NV, p. A394

STOTTLEMYRE, Georgan L., Director Human Resources, Northern Inyo Hospital, Bishop, CA, p. A55

STOUGH, Robin
Chief Financial Officer, Belmont Pines Hospital, Youngstown, OH, p. A494
Chief Financial Officer, Windsor–Laurelwood Center for Behavioral Medicine, Willoughby, OH, p. A493

STOUT, Bess, Director Human Resources, LaFollette Medical Center, La Follette, TN, p. A572

STOUT, Deana, Vice President Financial Services, MedStar Good Samaritan Hospital, Baltimore, MD, p. A288

STOUT, Don, Administrator, Fond Du Lac County Mental Health Center, Fond Du Lac, WI, p. A686

STOUT, Patsy, Director Personnel, Richland Parish Hospital, Delhi, LA, p. A266

STOUT, Sandy, Director Human Resources, Vista Health, Fayetteville, AR, p. A43

STOUT–TORRES, Sherri, Chief Nursing Officer, Watsonville Community Hospital, Watsonville, CA, p. A95

STOVALL, Henry, President, Sacred Heart Hospital of Pensacola, Pensacola, FL, p. A137

STOVALL, Richard G., Senior Vice President Fiscal Services and Chief Financial Officer, Southern Regional Medical Center, Riverdale, GA, p. A159

STOVALL, Susan M., Chief Executive Officer, Kindred Hospital Rome, Rome, GA, p. A159

STOVER, Angie, Administrative Assistant, Surgical Hospital of Jonesboro, Jonesboro, AR, p. A45

STOVER, Benny, Vice President Finance, Mercy Hospital Rogers, Rogers, AR, p. A49

STOVER, George M., Chief Executive Officer, Rice County District Hospital, Lyons, KS, p. A239

STOVER, Patricia A., Administrator Nursing, Doylestown Hospital, Doylestown, PA, p. A524

STOVER, Raymond
President and Chief Executive Officer, MidMichigan Medical Center–Clare, Clare, MI, p. A310
President and Chief Executive Officer, MidMichigan Medical Center–Gladwin, Gladwin, MI, p. A314

STOVER, Ryan, Chief Financial Officer, Norton County Hospital, Norton, KS, p. A240

STOVERINK, Mike, Chief Financial Officer, Richland Memorial Hospital, Olney, IL, p. A191

STOWELL, Dana A., Chief Information Officer, McCurtain Memorial Hospital, Idabel, OK, p. A500

STOWMAN, Amber, Controller, Lisbon Area Health Services, Lisbon, ND, p. A468

STOY, Gale, Manager Information Systems, Mid Coast Hospital, Brunswick, ME, p. A282

STOY, Thomas, M.D. Chief of Staff, St. Gabriel's Hospital, Little Falls, MN, p. A334

STOYANOFF, Pamela
Executive Vice President and Chief Operating Officer, Methodist Charlton Medical Center, Dallas, TX, p. A596
Executive Vice President and Chief Operating Officer, Methodist Dallas Medical Center, Dallas, TX, p. A596

STRABEL, Elizabeth, M.D. Chief Medical Staff, Divine Savior Healthcare, Portage, WI, p. A695

STRACHAN, Eileen, Coordinator Human Resources, Kindred Hospital–Sycamore, Sycamore, IL, p. A196

STRACHAN, Ronald
Chief Information Officer, WellStar Douglas Hospital, Douglasville, GA, p. A152
Senior Vice President and Chief Information Officer, WellStar Kennestone Hospital, Marietta, GA, p. A157

STRACK, Diane, R.N. Chief Nursing Officer, Aurora West Allis Medical Center, West Allis, WI, p. A699

STRACK, Kirk, Vice President and Chief Financial Officer, Clark Memorial Hospital, Jeffersonville, IN, p. A207

STRADER, Lynn, Chief Financial Officer, CJW Medical Center, Richmond, VA, p. A660

STRADER, Yvonne M., Chief Nursing Officer, Providence St. Mary Medical Center, Walla Walla, WA, p. A674

STRAHAN, Greg, Chief Operating Officer, Owensboro Health Regional Hospital, Owensboro, KY, p. A258

STRAIN, Donna, Director Human Resources, Ray County Memorial Hospital, Richmond, MO, p. A368

STRANGE, John, President and Chief Executive Officer, St. Luke's Hospital, Duluth, MN, p. A331

STRANGE, Roger, Chief Information Officer, St. Vincent Heart Center of Indiana, Indianapolis, IN, p. A206

STRASSNER III, Lawrence F., R.N. Vice President, Patient Care Services and Chief Nursing Officer, MedStar Franklin Square Medical Center, Baltimore, MD, p. A288

STRATTON, Doug, Chief Resource Management Division, Bassett Army Community Hospital, Fort Wainwright, AK, p. A28

STRATTON, Jim, Vice President Finance, Graham Hospital, Canton, IL, p. A175

STRATTON, Joseph, FACHE, Chief Executive Officer, Geary Community Hospital, Junction City, KS, p. A236

STRATTON, Mary, Director Human Resources, River Park Hospital, Huntington, WV, p. A678

STRAUGHAN, John, Director Information Technology, Wallowa Memorial Hospital, Enterprise, OR, p. A512

STRAUMANIS, John P., M.D. Vice President Medical Affairs and Chief Medical Officer, Kernan Orthopaedics and Rehabilitation, Baltimore, MD, p. A287

STRAUSBAUGH, Andy, Vice President Finance and Operations, Norton Brownsboro Hospital, Louisville, KY, p. A256

STRAUSS, Alan
Chief Financial Officer, Carondelet Holy Cross Hospital, Nogales, AZ, p. A33
Chief Financial Officer, Carondelet St. Joseph's Hospital, Tucson, AZ, p. A38

STRAUSS, Andrejs, M.D. Interim Vice President Medical Affairs, Beebe Medical Center, Lewes, DE, p. A114

STRAUSS, Thomas J., President and Chief Executive Officer, Summa Health System, Akron, OH, p. A470

STRAWN, Jill, Chief Executive Officer, HEALTHSOUTH Rehabilitation Hospital, Florence, SC, p. A551

STRAWN, Keith A., Vice President Human Resources, New Hanover Regional Medical Center, Wilmington, NC, p. A463

STRAWSER, Debbie A., Director Human Resources, Lindner Center of HOPE, Mason, OH, p. A485

STRAYER, Lorna, Senior Vice President Administration and Business Development, Fisher–Titus Medical Center, Norwalk, OH, p. A487

STRAYHAM, Joan, R.N. Chief Operating Officer, River Oaks Hospital, Flowood, MS, p. A346

STREATER, Vivian, Chief Nursing Officer and Co–Acting Chief Executive Officer, Broughton Hospital, Morganton, NC, p. A457

STRECK, William F., M.D., President and Chief Executive Officer, Bassett Medical Center, Cooperstown, NY, p. A424

STRECKER, Dede, Chief Nursing Officer, White River Medical Center, Batesville, AR, p. A41

STRECKER, Kevin, President, Via Christi Hospital on St. Teresa, Wichita, KS, p. A246

STREET, Rex, Senior Vice President and Chief Financial Officer, Alamance Regional Medical Center, Burlington, NC, p. A448

STREET, Scott, President and Chief Executive Officer, Mercy Hospital Rogers, Rogers, AR, p. A49

STREET MERRIWEATHER, Nancy, Chief Financial Officer, Four County Counseling Center, Logansport, IN, p. A209

STREETER, Alan W., Chief Financial Officer, Beatrice Community Hospital and Health Center, Beatrice, NE, p. A382

STREETER, Matthew, Chief Financial Officer, Southwest Health Center, Platteville, WI, p. A695

STREETER, Robert, M.D. Vice President Medical Affairs, Mercy Medical Center Merced, Merced, CA, p. A74

STREETT, David, M.D. Medical Director, Pinnacle Pointe Hospital, Little Rock, AR, p. A46

STREICH, Rebecca, Manager Human Resources and Education Manager, Hutchinson Health, Hutchinson, MN, p. A334

STRENGTH, Perry, Director Information Services, San Antonio Community Hospital, Upland, CA, p. A94

STREVY, Sonia R., Chief Nursing Officer, Wabash County Hospital, Wabash, IN, p. A214

STREYLE, Edward, MS Senior Vice President and Chief Nursing Officer, Maryland General Hospital, Baltimore, MD, p. A288

STRICKER, Sean, Chief Executive Officer, Select Specialty Hospital–San Antonio, San Antonio, TX, p. A632

STRICKER, Steven, M.D. Physician in Chief, Kaiser Permanente Vallejo Medical Center, Vallejo, CA, p. A94

STRICKLAND, Connie, Chief Executive Officer, Select Specialty Hospital–Oklahoma City, Oklahoma City, OK, p. A504

STRICKLAND, Gina, Administrative Assistant and Director Human Resources, Little River Memorial Hospital, Ashdown, AR, p. A41

STRICKLAND, Lee, Regional Director Information Technology, Park Ridge Health, Hendersonville, NC, p. A454

STRICKLAND, Morris S., Chief Financial Officer, Helen Keller Hospital, Sheffield, AL, p. A25

STRICKLAND, Samuel A., Chief Financial Officer, Red Bay Hospital, Red Bay, AL, p. A25

STRICKLING, Keith, Chief Accountant, Jay Hospital, Jay, FL, p. A127

STRIEBY, John F., Chief Executive Officer, Nix Health Care System, San Antonio, TX, p. A632

STRING, Sherrie, Vice President Human Resources, Via Christi Hospital on St. Francis, Wichita, KS, p. A246

STRITTMATTER, Brenda M., Patient Services Officer, Berger Health System, Circleville, OH, p. A475

STRITTMATTER, Julie, Director Human Resources, Baylor All Saints Medical Center at Fort Worth, Fort Worth, TX, p. A603

STROBEL, Jane, Interim Chief Financial Officer, Mercy Regional Medical Center, Durango, CO, p. A100

STROBEL, Rand, Vice President Information Technology, UW Medicine/Valley Medical Center, Renton, WA, p. A670

STROBURG, Cynthia S., Chief Nursing Officer, TriStar StoneCrest Medical Center, Smyrna, TN, p. A579

STRODE, Marc, Chief Executive Officer, Val Verde Regional Medical Center, Del Rio, TX, p. A598

STROEMEL, Douglas M.
President, Mercy Hospital Aurora, Aurora, MO, p. A356
President, Mercy Hospital Cassville, Cassville, MO, p. A358

STROHMYER, Jeffrey, M.D. Chief Medical Officer, Alegent Creighton Health Midlands Hospital, Papillion, NE, p. A389

STROMBERG, Audrey, Administrator, Roosevelt Medical Center, Culbertson, MT, p. A375

STROMSTAD, Darlene, FACHE, President and Chief Executive Officer, Waterbury Hospital, Waterbury, CT, p. A112

STRONG, David
Chief Financial Officer/Vice President Finance, Cox Medical Center Branson, Branson, MO, p. A357
Vice President and Chief Financial Officer, Southeast Hospital, Cape Girardeau, MO, p. A358

STRONG, David W., President, Rex Healthcare, Raleigh, NC, p. A459

STRONG, Douglas, Chief Executive Officer, University of Michigan Hospitals and Health Centers, Ann Arbor, MI, p. A308

STRONG, Tricia, Chief Financial Officer, Cumberland River Hospital, Celina, TN, p. A566

STROP, Judith, Director Finance, Rusk County Memorial Hospital and Nursing Home, Ladysmith, WI, p. A689

STROPLE, Kenneth, President and Chief Executive Officer, Downey Regional Medical Center, Downey, CA, p. A58

STROSNIDER, Preston, M.D. Vice President Medical Affairs, Conway Medical Center, Conway, SC, p. A551

STROSS, Daniel, Chief Information Officer, Genesys Regional Medical Center, Grand Blanc, MI, p. A314

STROUCKEN, Christian, Chief Operating Officer, Carney Hospital, Boston, MA, p. A296

STROUD, Teresa, Chief Financial Officer, Salem Township Hospital, Salem, IL, p. A194

STROUD, William, M.D. Physician Advisor, East Cooper Medical Center, Mount Pleasant, SC, p. A554

STROUGH, Joe, Administrator, Mobile Infirmary Medical Center, Mobile, AL, p. A22

STROUSE, Thomas, M.D., Medical Director, Stewart & Lynda Resnick Neuropsychiatric Hospital at UCLA, Los Angeles, CA, p. A72

STRUCK, Tony, Chief Financial Officer, Yuma Regional Medical Center, Yuma, AZ, p. A40

STRUGATZ, Joshua, Associate Executive Director Operations, Glen Cove Hospital, Glen Cove, NY, p. A426

STRUMWASSER, Todd, M.D., Chief Executive, Swedish Medical Center–First Hill, Seattle, WA, p. A671

STRUYK, Douglas A., CPA, President and Chief Executive Officer, Christian Health Care Center, Wyckoff, NJ, p. A413

STRZEMPKO, Stanley, M.D. Vice President Medical Affairs and Chief Medical Officer, Noble Hospital, Westfield, MA, p. A306

STUART, Donald W., Associate Director, Albany Stratton Veterans Affairs Medical Center, Albany, NY, p. A420

STUART, Jimmy D., Chief Executive Officer, Integris Seminole Medical Center, Seminole, OK, p. A506

STUART, Philip J., Administrator and Chief Executive Officer, Tomah Memorial Hospital, Tomah, WI, p. A697

STUART, Robin, Chief Operating Officer, Morrill County Community Hospital, Bridgeport, NE, p. A382

STUBBLEFIELD, Greg, Vice President and Administrator, Baptist Health Medical Center–Arkadelphia, Arkadelphia, AR, p. A41

STUBBS, Don
Vice President Human Resources, Candler Hospital, Savannah, GA, p. A159
Vice President Human Resources, St. Joseph's Hospital, Savannah, GA, p. A160

STUBBS, Karen, Chief Nursing Officer, Northwest Medical Center, Tucson, AZ, p. A39

STUBBS, Richard, M.D. Vice President Medical Affairs, Casa Grande Regional Medical Center, Casa Grande, AZ, p. A30

STUBER, Joseph A., President and Chief Executive Officer, Perry County Memorial Hospital, Tell City, IN, p. A213

STUCK, Julie, R.N., Interim Chief Executive Officer, Hocking Valley Community Hospital, Logan, OH, p. A484

STUCKY, Nancy, Director Human Resources and Public Relations, Kingman Community Hospital, Kingman, KS, p. A237

STUCZYNSKI, Joseph, Assistant Administrator Finance and Support, Memorial Hospital Pembroke, Pembroke Pines, FL, p. A136

STUDEBAKER, Shelly, Director Management Information Systems, Clinch Memorial Hospital, Homerville, GA, p. A155

STUDLEY, Brett, M.D. Chief of Staff, Beatrice Community Hospital and Health Center, Beatrice, NE, p. A382

STUDLEY, Jason, Chief Executive Officer, Trinity Hospital of Augusta, Augusta, GA, p. A148

STUENKEL, Kurt, FACHE, President and Chief Executive Officer, Floyd Medical Center, Rome, GA, p. A159

STUERSEL, Marie, Director Human Resources, Seneca Healthcare District, Chester, CA, p. A56

STUEVE, Jo W., Co–Chief Operating Officer, Children's Mercy Hospitals and Clinics, Kansas City, MO, p. A362

STULL, Regenia, R.N. Chief Nurse Executive, Phelps County Regional Medical Center, Rolla, MO, p. A368

STULTS, Kim, Director Education, Bellevue Hospital, Bellevue, OH, p. A471

STULTZ, James R.
Senior Vice President Human Resources, East Ohio Regional Hospital, Martins Ferry, OH, p. A485
Senior Vice President Human Resources, Ohio Valley Medical Center, Wheeling, WV, p. A682

STUMBAUGH, Terri, R.N. Director Patient Care Services, Johnson Regional Medical Center, Clarksville, AR, p. A42

STUMBO, Kathy, President, Saint Joseph – Martin, Martin, KY, p. A257

STUMP, Jerry, Chief Financial Officer, Good Samaritan Hospital, Vincennes, IN, p. A214

STUMPF, Robert, M.D. President Medical Staff, Columbia Center, Mequon, WI, p. A691

STUMPO, Barbara J., R.N. Vice President Patient Care Services, Griffin Hospital, Derby, CT, p. A108

STURANS, Joanne, Vice President Human Resources, Phelps Memorial Health Center, Sleepy Hollow, NY, p. A442

STURGEON, Jim, Area Director Human Resources, Kindred Hospital Las Vegas–Sahara, Las Vegas, NV, p. A393

STURGEON, Wade, Chief Executive Officer and Chief Financial Officer, Biggs–Gridley Memorial Hospital, Gridley, CA, p. A63

STURGIS, Daniel, Ph.D. Director Psychology, Norfolk Regional Center, Norfolk, NE, p. A386

STURGIS, Gayle, Vice President Nursing, Glencoe Regional Health Services, Glencoe, MN, p. A332

STURGIS, James D., Associate Administrator, Texas Scottish Rite Hospital for Children, Dallas, TX, p. A597

STURGIS, Jonathan, Chief Financial Officer, San Jacinto Methodist Hospital, Baytown, TX, p. A587

STURGIS, Paul, Vice President Human Resources, Rehabilitation Institute of Michigan, Detroit, MI, p. A312

STURM, Brenda L., MSN Vice President, Patient Care Services, Northern Montana Hospital, Havre, MT, p. A377

STURSA, Robin, Chief Information Officer, St. Vincent Charity Medical Center, Cleveland, OH, p. A477

STYER, Brent, Director Information Technology, Whitesburg ARH Hospital, Whitesburg, KY, p. A261

STYER, George, Director Information Systems, Valley Presbyterian Hospital,, CA, p. A72

STYLES, Kelly R., Vice President and Chief Information Officer, Connecticut Children's Medical Center, Hartford, CT, p. A109

SUAREZ, Jose David, M.D. Chief of Staff, Larkin Community Hospital, South Miami, FL, p. A140

SUAREZ, Lauren, Chief Executive Officer, Kindred Hospital Seattle–Northgate, Seattle, WA, p. A670

SUAREZ, Orlando, Manager Information Technology, Larkin Community Hospital, South Miami, FL, p. A140

SUAREZ, Pam, Director Marketing and Business Development, Rehabilitation Hospital of Southern New Mexico, Las Cruces, NM, p. A416

SUBER, Mandy, Controller, Calhoun Health Services, Calhoun City, MS, p. A345

SUBLETTE, Elizabeth
Chief Financial Officer, Providence Milwaukie Hospital, Milwaukie, OR, p. A515
Chief Finance Officer, Providence Willamette Falls Medical Center, Oregon City, OR, p. A515

SUCADO, Daniel J., M.D. Chief of Staff, Texas Scottish Rite Hospital for Children, Dallas, TX, p. A597

SUCH, William
Chief Executive Officer, Wesley Woods Geriatric Hospital of Emory University, Atlanta, GA, p. A147
Chief Executive Officer, Wesley Woods Long Term Care Hospital, Atlanta, GA, p. A147

SUCHER, Randy, Executive Vice President, Springhill Memorial Hospital, Mobile, AL, p. A22

SUCHER, Therese O., Senior Vice President Operations, Southern Regional Medical Center, Riverdale, GA, p. A159

SUDA, Shirley, M.D. Area Medical Director, Kaiser Permanente Woodland Hills Medical Center,, CA, p. A69

SUDDARTH, Jonathan, D.O. Chief of Staff, Madison County Health Care System, Winterset, IA, p. A230

SUDDUTH, Anthony G., CPA Chief Financial Officer, T. J. Samson Community Hospital, Glasgow, KY, p. A251

SUDICKY, Mary, Chief Financial Officer, St. Mary Medical Center, Hobart, IN, p. A204

SUDOLCAN, Joseph, M.D. Medical Director, Reagan Memorial Hospital, Big Lake, TX, p. A588

SUEHS, JoAnne, Manager Human Resources, Chapman Medical Center, Orange, CA, p. A77

SUGAR, Bev, Associate Administrator and Director Human Resources, Inova Mount Vernon Hospital, Alexandria, VA, p. A651

SUGG, Amy, Director Human Resources, Scott Regional Hospital, Morton, MS, p. A351

SUGG, William T., President and Chief Executive Officer, Valley County Health System, Ord, NE, p. A388

SUGHRUE, Timothy H., Chief Executive Officer, Rapid City Regional Hospital, Rapid City, SD, p. A562

SUGIYAMA, Deborah, President, NorthBay Medical Center, Fairfield, CA, p. A59

SUHR, Nancy, Manager Human Resources, Pender Community Hospital, Pender, NE, p. A389

SUHRE, Elizabeth, Executive Director, Rochester Psychiatric Center, Rochester, NY, p. A441

SUIRE, Bridget, Acting Administrator, MMO Rehabilitation and Wellness Center, Plaquemine, LA, p. A277

SUITTER, Marie, Chief Financial Officer, The Acadia Hospital, Bangor, ME, p. A281

SUKENIK, Richard, CPA Vice President Finance and Chief Financial Officer, Windber Medical Center, Windber, PA, p. A545

SUKIN, Debra F.
Chief Executive Officer, St. Luke's Lakeside Hospital, The Woodlands, TX, p. A637
Chief Executive Officer, St. Luke's The Woodlands Hospital, The Woodlands, TX, p. A637

SULIK, Sandra, M.D. Vice President Medical Affairs, St. Joseph's Hospital Health Center, Syracuse, NY, p. A444

SULIT, Maria Teresa, Director Human Resources, Holly Hill Hospital, Raleigh, NC, p. A459

SULLIVAN, Christopher, M.D. Chief Medical Officer, Centerpoint Medical Center, Independence, MO, p. A362

SULLIVAN, Craig, Chief Financial Officer, Saint Thomas Hickman Hospital, Centerville, TN, p. A566

SULLIVAN, Danita S., R.N. Chief Nursing Officer, Tulane Medical Center, New Orleans, LA, p. A276

SULLIVAN, David, Director Human Resources, OhioHealth Doctors Hospital, Columbus, OH, p. A478

SULLIVAN, Donald, M.D. Medical Director, HEALTHSOUTH Rehabilitation Hospital Memphis–North, Memphis, TN, p. A574

SULLIVAN, George, Director Management Information Systems, Mary Lanning Healthcare, Hastings, NE, p. A384

SULLIVAN, Jennie, Director Finance, Wray Community District Hospital, Wray, CO, p. A107

SULLIVAN, Jennifer, Senior Vice President Finance and Chief Financial Officer, St. James Mercy Health System, Hornell, NY, p. A427

SULLIVAN, John
Vice President Human Resources, Health Central, Ocoee, FL, p. A134
President, MedStar Washington Hospital Center, Washington, DC, p. A116
Chief Executive Officer, Mount Pleasant Hospital, Mount Pleasant, SC, p. A554
Chief Executive Officer, Mount Pleasant Hospital, Mount Pleasant, SC, p. A554

SULLIVAN, Jude, Chief Clinical Officer, Kindred Hospital–La Mirada, La Mirada, CA, p. A65

SULLIVAN, Keith, Associate Director, Chillicothe Veterans Affairs Medical Center, Chillicothe, OH, p. A473

SULLIVAN, Marie, R.N. Chief Nursing Officer and Administrator, Northeast Rehabilitation Hospital, Salem, NH, p. A400

SULLIVAN, Mark J., Vice President Human Resources, Western Maryland Regional Medical Center, Cumberland, MD, p. A291

SULLIVAN, Martha, Chief Information Officer, Harrison Memorial Hospital, Cynthiana, KY, p. A250

SULLIVAN, Mary Patricia, R.N. Chief Nursing Officer, Overlook Medical Center, Summit, NJ, p. A410

SULLIVAN, Maurita, Administrator, Mayo Clinic Health System – Northland in Barron, Barron, WI, p. A684

SULLIVAN, Michael, M.D. Chief Medical Officer, Northern Maine Medical Center, Fort Kent, ME, p. A283

SULLIVAN, Michael Dean, M.D. Chief of Staff, Mercy Hospital El Reno, El Reno, OK, p. A498

SULLIVAN, Patrick L., FACHE, Director, Captain James A. Lovell Federal Health Care Center, North Chicago, IL, p. A190

SULLIVAN, Patrick L., Chief Operating Officer, St. John's Episcopal Hospital–South Shore, NY, p. A436

SULLIVAN, Theresa, Chief Operating Officer, Cuyuna Regional Medical Center, Crosby, MN, p. A331

SULLIVAN, Thomas
Vice President Fiscal Services, Harrington Memorial Hospital, Southbridge, MA, p. A304
Chief Transition Officer, Phoebe North, Albany, GA, p. A145

SULLIVAN, Wardell, Director Human Resources, Touchette Regional Hospitals, Centreville, IL, p. A176

SULLIVAN, William, Chief Financial Officer, Mount Auburn Hospital, Cambridge, MA, p. A299

SULOG, Amy, Comptroller, Robert E. Bush Naval Hospital, Twentynine Palms, CA, p. A93

SULSER, Jamey, Director Human Resources, South Davis Community Hospital, Bountiful, UT, p. A643

SULU, Dorothy, Chief Financial Officer, Hopi Health Care Center, Kearns Canyon, AZ, p. A32

SUMMERER, Mike H., M.D., Chief Executive Officer, University of Connecticut Health Center, John Dempsey Hospital, Farmington, CT, p. A108

SUMMERS, Andrew, Vice President Business Operations, Texas Institute for Surgery at Texas Health Presbyterian Dallas, Dallas, TX, p. A597

SUMMERS, Barbara L., Ph.D. Vice President Nursing Practice and Chief Nursing Officer, University of Texas M.D. Anderson Cancer Center, Houston, TX, p. A613

SUMMERS, Curtis, Chief Executive Officer, Summit Medical Center, Edmond, OK, p. A498

SUMMERS, David A.
Chief Financial Officer, Tristar Ashland City, Ashland City, TN, p. A565
Chief Financial Officer, Tristar Centennial Medical Center, Nashville, TN, p. A577

SUMMERS, Heather, Director, Chickasaw Nation Medical Center, Ada, OK, p. A495

SUMMERS, Jeff, M.D. Medical Director, Select Specialty Hospital–North Knoxville, Knoxville, TN, p. A572

SUMMERS, Paul, Chief Financial Officer, Delaware Valley Hospital, Walton, NY, p. A445

SUMMERS, Sharon K., R.N. Executive Vice President and Chief Operating Officer, FHN Memorial Hospital, Freeport, IL, p. A183

SUMMERS, Stephen M., FACHE, Chief Executive Officer, Wise Regional Health System, Decatur, TX, p. A598

SUMMERVILLE, Wendell, Chief Financial Officer, Bryce Hospital, Tuscaloosa, AL, p. A25

SUMNER, J. Andrew, M.D. Vice President Medical Affairs, MedStar Southern Maryland Hospital Center, Clinton, MD, p. A290

SUMNER, Jack R., Assistant Administrator Finance, Providence Newberg Medical Center, Newberg, OR, p. A515

SUMRA, K. S., M.D. Chief of Staff, Pembina County Memorial Hospital and Wedgewood Manor, Cavalier, ND, p. A466

SUMRALL, Mary Ellen, Chief Nursing Officer, Baptist Memorial Hospital–Golden Triangle, Columbus, MS, p. A346

SUMTER, Rob, Executive Vice President and Chief Operating Officer, Regional Medical Center at Memphis, Memphis, TN, p. A575

SUND, Lynn A., R.N. Senior Vice President, Administrator and Chief Nursing Executive, Laureate Psychiatric Clinic and Hospital, Tulsa, OK, p. A508

SUND, Lynn A., MS, Senior Vice President, Administrator and Chief Nursing Executive, Saint Francis Hospital, Tulsa, OK, p. A508

SUND, Lynn A., R.N. Senior Vice President, Administrator and Chief Nursing Executive, Saint Francis Hospital, Tulsa, OK, p. A508

SUNDBERG, Nita, Director Human Resources, Three Rivers Behavioral Health, West Columbia, SC, p. A557

SUNDBLOM, Karin, Chief Nursing Officer, Saint Luke¥s Cushing Medical Center, Leavenworth, KS, p. A238

SUNDIN, Jon, M.D. Medical Director, The Orthopedic Specialty Hospital, Murray, UT, p. A644

SUNDQUIST, Philip, M.D. Chief Medical Staff, Lucas County Health Center, Chariton, IA, p. A218

SUNDRUD, Diane
Director Human Resources, Essentia Health Fosston, Fosston, MN, p. A332
Human Resource Service Partner, Essentia Health St. Mary's Hospital – Detroit Lakes, Detroit Lakes, MN, p. A331

SUNGA, Marcos N., M.D. Chief of Staff, Hardin County General Hospital, Rosiclare, IL, p. A194

SUNKAVALLE, Krishna, M.D. Chief Medical Officer, Hamlin Memorial Hospital, Hamlin, TX, p. A607

SUNTHA, Mohan, M.D., President and Chief Executive Officer, University of Maryland St. Joseph Medical Center, Towson, MD, p. A294

SUNTRAPAK, Todd, President and Chief Executive Officer, Children's Hospital Central California, Madera, CA, p. A73

SUPPAN, Marchelle, DPM, President and Chief Executive Officer, Aultman Orrville Hospital, Orrville, OH, p. A488

SUPPLEE, Linda, Chief Executive Officer, Select Specialty Hospital–Zanesville, Zanesville, OH, p. A494

SURANI, Salim, M.D. Medical Director, Kindred Hospital–Corpus Christi, Corpus Christi, TX, p. A594

SURBER, Randy, Chief Operating Officer, Florida Hospital DeLand, DeLand, FL, p. A122

SURESH, Srinivasan, M.D. Chief Medical Information Officer, Children's Hospital of Michigan, Detroit, MI, p. A311

SURKALA, Karen, Vice President, Westfield Memorial Hospital, Westfield, NY, p. A446

SURL, Deepak, Chief Information Officer, Eastern New Mexico Medical Center, Roswell, NM, p. A417

SURRATT, Shawn, M.D. Chief of Staff, Memorial Hospital and Manor, Bainbridge, GA, p. A148

SURROCK, Lester, Chief Financial Officer, Nix Health Care System, San Antonio, TX, p. A632

SUSI, Jeffrey L., President and Chief Executive Officer, Indian River Medical Center, Vero Beach, FL, p. A143

SUSICK, Nancy, MSN, President, Beaumont Hospital – Troy, Troy, MI, p. A326

SUSSMAN, Andrew, M.D. Chief Operating Officer, UMass Memorial Medical Center, Worcester, MA, p. A307

SUSTERICH, Tim, Chief Financial Officer, Metro Health Hospital, Wyoming, MI, p. A327

SUTER, Brian, Chief Financial Officer, Mayo Clinic Health System in Fairmont, Fairmont, MN, p. A332

SUTER, Janice, R.N. Vice President Services and Chief Nursing Officer, Culpeper Regional Hospital, Culpeper, VA, p. A653

SUTER, Mia, Chief Administration Officer, Owensboro Health Regional Hospital, Owensboro, KY, p. A258

SUTHERLAND, Genevieve, Health Information Management Director, Memorial Medical Center, Port Lavaca, TX, p. A628

SUTHERLAND, Jenna, Manager Human Resources, Denton Regional Medical Center, Denton, TX, p. A598

SUTHERLAND, Shea, Chief Financial Officer, Midwest Regional Medical Center, Midwest City, OK, p. A501

SUTHERLIN, Shara, R.N. Director Patient Care Services, South Peninsula Hospital, Homer, AK, p. A28

SUTIKA, John, President, DuBois Regional Medical Center, Du Bois, PA, p. A524

SUTTLES, Robert W.
Vice President Human Resources, Health First Cape Canaveral Hospital, Cocoa Beach, FL, p. A121
Vice President Human Resources, Health First Holmes Regional Medical Center, Melbourne, FL, p. A130
Vice President Human Resources, Health First Palm Bay Hospital, Melbourne, FL, p. A130

SUTTON, Elaine, Chief Information Officer, General John J. Pershing Memorial Hospital, Brookfield, MO, p. A357

SUTTON, Fred, M.D. Chief Medical Officer, Harris Health System, Houston, TX, p. A609

SUTTON, Janet, M.D. Medical Director, McLaren Bay Special Care, Bay City, MI, p. A309

SUTTON, Jesse, Chief Financial Officer, Central Texas Medical Center, San Marcos, TX, p. A633

SUTTON, Julie, Director Performance Improvement, State Hospital South, Blackfoot, ID, p. A167

SUTTON, Michele K., FACHE, Administrator, North Oaks Medical Center, Hammond, LA, p. A268

SUTTON, Pat, Director Human Resources, Dearborn County Hospital, Lawrenceburg, IN, p. A208

SUTTON, Rhonda, Director Human Resources, Richland Hospital, Richland Center, WI, p. A696

SUTTON, Richard O., Chief Executive Officer, North Colorado Medical Center, Greeley, CO, p. A102

SUTTON, Thomas, Associate Director, Malcom Randall Veterans Affairs Medical Center, Gainesville, FL, p. A124

SUVER, James A., FACHE, Chief Executive Officer, Ridgecrest Regional Hospital, Ridgecrest, CA, p. A82

SUZUKI, Daniel, M.D. Medical Director, Aurora Las Encinas Hospital, Pasadena, CA, p. A79

SVENDSEN, Mark Deyo, M.D. Medical Director, Mayo Clinic Health System – Red Cedar in Menomonie, Menomonie, WI, p. A691

SVENSSON, Travis, M.D. Medical Director, Fremont Hospital, Fremont, CA, p. A61

SVETLIK, Joe, Vice President Finance, Reedsburg Area Medical Center, Reedsburg, WI, p. A695

SVIHOVEC, Angelia K., Chief Executive Officer, Mobridge Regional Hospital, Mobridge, SD, p. A561

SWAB, Joseph, Chief Financial Officer, Muhlenberg Community Hospital, Greenville, KY, p. A252

SWAB, Joseph A., Chief Financial Officer, Iroquois Memorial Hospital and Resident Home, Watseka, IL, p. A196

SWAGERTY, Jill, Director Human Resources, Union County General Hospital, Clayton, NM, p. A415

SWAIN, Art, Vice President Support Services, Joint Township District Memorial Hospital, Saint Marys, OH, p. A489

SWAINE, Richard P., President, Beaumont Hospital Grosse Pointe, Grosse Pointe, MI, p. A316

SWALLER, Pat, R.N. Chief Operating Officer, Placentia–Linda Hospital, Placentia, CA, p. A80

SWAN, Dennis A., FACHE, President and Chief Executive Officer, Sparrow Hospital, Lansing, MI, p. A318

SWANGER, Cae, Chief Information Officer, Riverside Community Hospital, Riverside, CA, p. A82

SWANGER, Carol, Chief Nursing Officer, Kansas Rehabilitation Hospital, Topeka, KS, p. A245

SWANK, Georgia, Chief Nursing Officer, Ridge Behavioral Health System, Lexington, KY, p. A254

SWANSON, Darlene, Business Manager, Sanford Hillsboro Medical Center, Hillsboro, ND, p. A467

SWANSON, Kerry, President, St. Mary's Janesville Hospital, Janesville, WI, p. A688

SWANSON, Peter, Assistant Administrator Fiscal Services, Island Hospital, Anacortes, WA, p. A664

SWARTOUT, Judi, Chief Financial Officer, Sutter Coast Hospital, Crescent City, CA, p. A58

SWARTOUT, Paula, HR Manager, Dickinson County Healthcare System, Iron Mountain, MI, p. A317

SWARTS, Lori, Controller and Interim Vice President, Mercy Hospital Cadillac, Cadillac, MI, p. A310

SWARTWOOD, Philip, Director Information Systems, Grove City Medical Center, Grove City, PA, p. A526

SWARTZ, Edward, Chief Financial Officer, Spring Grove Hospital Center, Baltimore, MD, p. A289

SWARTZ, Michael J., FACHE, Medical Center Director, Bath Veterans Affairs Medical Center, Bath, NY, p. A421

SWASAND, Berri, M.D. Chief of Staff, Shoshone Medical Center, Kellogg, ID, p. A169

SWAUNCY, Felicia, Chief Financial Officer, Lakeside Behavioral Health System, Memphis, TN, p. A574

SWEARINGEN, Angela, Vice President Finance, St. Mary's Medical Center, Huntington, WV, p. A678

SWEDIEN, Scott, Director Information Services, Baldwin Area Medical Center, Baldwin, WI, p. A683

SWEENEY, Mary, Vice President Colleague Services and Development, St. Mary Medical Center, Langhorne, PA, p. A529

SWEENEY, Michael, Chief Information Officer, Fox Chase Cancer Center–American Oncologic Hospital, Philadelphia, PA, p. A534

SWEENEY, Rick, Director Information Services, Alegent Creighton Health–Creighton University Medical Center, Omaha, NE, p. A387

SWEENEY, Tracey, Director Business and Support Services, Montana State Hospital, Warm Springs, MT, p. A380

SWEET, Constance, M.D. President Medical Staff, Memorial Hospital, Towanda, PA, p. A542

SWEET, Mary, Administrator, Kiowa County Memorial Hospital, Greensburg, KS, p. A234

SWEET, Renae, Chief Financial Officer, Surprise Valley Healthcare District, Cedarville, CA, p. A56

SWEETNICH, Ed, Vice President Human Resources, Mercer Health, Coldwater, OH, p. A477

SWEETON, Pat, Chief Nursing Officer, Heritage Medical Center, Shelbyville, TN, p. A579

SWEGER, Pamela K., Director Human Resources, Atchison Hospital, Atchison, KS, p. A231

SWENSON, Cathy, Chief Executive Officer, Nelson County Health System, Mcville, ND, p. A468

SWENSON, Daniel J., FACHE, Administrator and Chief Executive Officer, CentraCare Health–Long Prairie, Long Prairie, MN, p. A334

SWENSON, Diane, Director of Staff Services and Chief Nursing Officer, Carrus Specialty Hospital, Sherman, TX, p. A634

SWENSON, Jeff, M.D. Chief of Staff, Minidoka Memorial Hospital, Rupert, ID, p. A171

SWENSON, Kirstin D., Director Human Resources, Regina Medical Center, Hastings, MN, p. A333

SWENSON, Nena, Financial Manager, Tahoe Pacific Hospitals, Reno, NV, p. A395

SWENSON, Nina, Director Business Services, Newport Bay Hospital, Newport Beach, CA, p. A76

SWENSON, Paula C., R.N. Vice President and Chief Nursing Officer, St. Catherine Hospital, East Chicago, IN, p. A201

SWENSON, Roberta Suzanne, M.P.H., Interim Chief Executive Officer, Estes Park Medical Center, Estes Park, CO, p. A101

SWENSON, Wade, M.D. Chief of Staff, Lake Region Healthcare, Fergus Falls, MN, p. A332

SWENSON, Warren, Chief Financial Officer, United Medical Rehabilitation Hospital, Hammond, LA, p. A268

SWICEGOOD, Debbie, Director Human Resources, Vidant Chowan Hospital, Edenton, NC, p. A452

SWICK, Michael D., President and Chief Executive Officer, Lima Memorial Health System, Lima, OH, p. A484

SWIDERSKI, Tom, Chief Financial Officer, Orthopaedic Hospital of Wisconsin – Glendale, Milwaukee, WI, p. A692

SWIFT, Brian M., Senior Administrator Plant Operations, Burke Rehabilitation Hospital, White Plains, NY, p. A446

SWIFT, David
Vice President Human Resources, Volunteer and Community Services, Kernan Orthopaedics and Rehabilitation, Baltimore, MD, p. A287
Vice President Human Resources, Maryland General Hospital, Baltimore, MD, p. A288

SWIFT, Kyle, Chief Executive Officer, Medical Center of South Arkansas, El Dorado, AR, p. A43

SWIFT, Mark, D.O. President Medical Staff, East Liverpool City Hospital, East Liverpool, OH, p. A481

SWIFT, Nick, Chief Financial Officer, Maury Regional Hospital, Columbia, TN, p. A567

SWIGER, Jared, Director Information Systems, Ashtabula County Medical Center, Ashtabula, OH, p. A470

SWINDELL, Terry
Controller, Bolivar General Hospital, Bolivar, TN, p. A565
Chief Financial Officer, Camden General Hospital, Camden, TN, p. A566
Controller, Gibson General Hospital, Trenton, TN, p. A580
Chief Financial Officer, Humboldt General Hospital, Humboldt, TN, p. A570

SWINFARD, Ronald W., M.D.,
President and Chief Executive Officer, Lehigh Valley Hospital, Allentown, PA, p. A519
President and Chief Executive Officer, Lehigh Valley Hospital–Muhlenberg, Bethlehem, PA, p. A520

SWINGLE, Dale
Vice President Information Services, Robert Packer Hospital, Sayre, PA, p. A540
Vice President Information Services, Troy Community Hospital, Troy, PA, p. A542

SWINT, Ken, Vice President Finance and Chief Financial Officer, ProMedica Fostoria Community Hospital, Fostoria, OH, p. A481

SWINT, Patricia, Director Information Technology, ProMedica St. Luke's Hospital, Maumee, OH, p. A486

SWISHER, Gena, Vice President Nursing, Hampshire Memorial Hospital, Romney, WV, p. A680

SWISHER, Kay, Vice President and Chief Operating Officer, Greenville Health System Laurens County Memorial Hospital, Clinton, SC, p. A550

SWISHER, Reagan, Director Human Resources, Iowa Specialty Hospital–Belmond, Belmond, IA, p. A216

SWISSHELM, Patricia, Acting Chief Fiscal Service, Veterans Affairs Medical Center Lexington, Lexington, KY, p. A255

SWITZEN, Seth, M.D. Chief of Staff, St. Mary's Regional Medical Center, Enid, OK, p. A498

SWOBODA, Mary, R.N. Chief Nursing Officer, Skiff Medical Center, Newton, IA, p. A226

SWOFFORD, Lisa, Director Administrative Services, Ozark Health Medical Center, Clinton, AR, p. A42

SYED, Imran, Manager Technology Information Services, Spectrum Health Zeeland Community Hospital, Zeeland, MI, p. A327

SYED, Mamoon, Vice President Human Resources, Rady Children's Hospital – San Diego, San Diego, CA, p. A85

SYKES, Angel, Director Human Resources, Memorial Hospital and Manor, Bainbridge, GA, p. A148

SYKES, Christina, Director Human Resources, Labette Health, Parsons, KS, p. A242

SYKES, Lisa
IS/Communications Director, Anson Community Hospital, Wadesboro, NC, p. A462
Director Information Services, Carolinas Medical Center–Union, Monroe, NC, p. A457

SYKES, Rebecca S., Chief Information Officer, Mercy St. Anne Hospital, Toledo, OH, p. A491

SYLVESTER, Sandy, Chief Operating Officer, Three Rivers Hospital, Brewster, WA, p. A665

SYLVIA, John B., President, St. Luke's Hospital – Quakertown Campus, Quakertown, PA, p. A539

SYLVIA–HUTCHINSON, Doreen M., Vice President Operations and Chief Nurse Executive, Fairview Hospital, Great Barrington, MA, p. A300

SYNDER, Judy, Director Human Resources, Olympia Medical Center, Los Angeles, CA, p. A70

SYPIEN, Troy, Director Information Technology and Systems, Medical City Dallas Hospital, Dallas, TX, p. A596

SZABO, Cathy, Director Human Resources, Caverna Memorial Hospital, Horse Cave, KY, p. A253

SZABO, Charleen R., FACHE, Director, West Palm Beach Veterans Affairs Medical Center, West Palm Beach, FL, p. A144

SZABO, Sandor, M.D. Chief of Staff, Veterans Affairs Long Beach Healthcare System, Long Beach, CA, p. A68

SZCZEPANSKI, Bernadette S.
Vice President, Human Resources Development, Centegra Hospital – McHenry, McHenry, IL, p. A188
Vice President Human Resources Development, Centegra Hospital – Woodstock, Woodstock, IL, p. A197

SZCZUROWSKI, Richard, Director Human Resources, Norristown State Hospital, Norristown, PA, p. A533

SZEKELY, Lauraine, R.N. Senior Vice President, Patient Care, Northern Westchester Hospital, Mount Kisco, NY, p. A430

SZENCZY, Catherine
Senior Vice President and Chief Information Officer, MedStar Georgetown University Hospital, Washington, DC, p. A116
Senior Vice President and Chief Information Officer, MedStar Union Memorial Hospital, Baltimore, MD, p. A288

SZEWCZYK, Edwin, Chief Financial Officer, Wetzel County Hospital, New Martinsville, WV, p. A679

SZYMANSKI, Candra, R.N., Interim President and Chief Executive Officer, UMass Memorial–Marlborough Hospital, Marlborough, MA, p. A302

# T

TAAFFE, Janette, Administrator Human Resources, St. Luke's Hospital, Chesterfield, MO, p. A358

TABB, Kevin, M.D., President and Chief Executive Officer, Beth Israel Deaconess Medical Center, Boston, MA, p. A296

TABBAH, Isam, M.D. Chief of Staff, Harrison Community Hospital, Cadiz, OH, p. A472

TABIBI, Wasae S., M.D. President Medical Staff, Plaza Specialty Hospital, Houston, TX, p. A611

TAROADO, Ketty, Chief Financial Officer, Gladys Spellman Specialty Hospital and Nursing Center, Cheverly, MD, p. A290

TABOR, Barbara, Chief Financial Officer, Grant Regional Health Center, Lancaster, WI, p. A689

TABOR, J. Britton, Senior VP and Chief Financial Officer, Erlanger Medical Center, Chattanooga, TN, p. A566

TABOR, Jeffrey, Director Human Resources, Jackson General Hospital, Ripley, WV, p. A680

TABOR, Randy, Chief Financial Officer, Lady of the Sea General Hospital, Cut Off, LA, p. A266

TABUENCA, Arnold, M.D. Medical Director, Riverside County Regional Medical Center, Moreno Valley, CA, p. A75

TACHIBANA, Charleen, R.N. Senior Vice President and Hospital Administrator, Virginia Mason Medical Center, Seattle, WA, p. A671

TADROS, Magdy, M.D. Medical Director, Meadowbrook Rehabilitation Hospital, Gardner, KS, p. A234

TADURAN, Virgilio, M.D. Chief Medical Officer, Satanta District Hospital, Satanta, KS, p. A244

TADYCH, Michael C., Associate Director, Veterans Affairs Sierra Nevada Health Care System, Reno, NV, p. A395

TAFFE, Patrick, Vice President Information Services, North Memorial Medical Center, Robbinsdale, MN, p. A338

TAFOYA, Debbie, Vice President and Chief Information Officer, Huntington Memorial Hospital, Pasadena, CA, p. A79

TAFOYA, Debra, Director Human Resources, Complex Care Hospital at Tenaya, Las Vegas, NV, p. A392

TAFT, Kenneth L., Executive Vice President and Chief Operating Officer, Bronson Methodist Hospital, Kalamazoo, MI, p. A318

TAFUR, Mario, M.D. Chief of Staff, St. Luke's Behavioral Health Center, Phoenix, AZ, p. A35

TAGAI, Lee, Director Human Resources, Lafayette Regional Health Center, Lexington, MO, p. A365

TAGGART, Travis, Director Information Technology, RiverValley Behavioral Health Hospital, Owensboro, KY, p. A258

TAHBO, Robin, Financial Management Officer, U. S. Public Health Service Indian Hospital, Parker, AZ, p. A33

TAIT, Darlene, Director Human Resources, Charlton Memorial Hospital, Folkston, GA, p. A153

TAKACS, Susan, Chief Operating Officer, Quincy Medical Center, Quincy, MA, p. A304

TAKES, Kay, R.N. Vice President Patient Care Services and Chief Nursing Officer, Mercy Medical Center–Dubuque, Dubuque, IA, p. A220

TALBERT, Bradley S., FACHE, Chief Executive Officer, Coastal Carolina Hospital, Hardeeville, SC, p. A553

TALBOT, Angela, Manager Human Resources, Hamilton County Hospital, Syracuse, KS, p. A244

TALBOT, Lisa, Director Human Resources, St. David's South Austin Medical Center, Austin, TX, p. A586

TALBOT, Tom, Chief Executive Officer, Community Mental Health Center, Lawrenceburg, IN, p. A208

TALBOTT, Drew, Vice President Operations, Via Christi Hospital in Pittsburg, Pittsburg, KS, p. A242

TALBOTT, Sarah, Chief Nursing Officer, Sanford Chamberlain Medical Center, Chamberlain, SD, p. A558

TALENTO, Rick, Senior Vice President and Chief Financial Officer, Providence Hospital, Washington, DC, p. A116

TALLANT–BALL, Mary Jo, Director Health Information Systems, Dallas Medical Center, Dallas, TX, p. A595

TALLARICO, Dominica, President, Advocate Condell Medical Center, Libertyville, IL, p. A187

TALLERY, Jeremy, D.O. Chief of Staff, Hermann Area District Hospital, Hermann, MO, p. A361

TALLEY, Amanda, Human Resources Director, Highlands–Cashiers Hospital, Highlands, NC, p. A455

TALLEY, Cyndi, Director Information Systems, TriStar Greenview Regional Hospital, Bowling Green, KY, p. A249

TALLEY, Stephanie S.
Director Human Resources, Centennial Medical Center, Frisco, TX, p. A605
Associate Administrator and Director Human Resources, Dallas Medical Center, Dallas, TX, p. A595

TALLMAN, Derrick, Chief Executive Officer, Western Massachusetts Hospital, Westfield, MA, p. A306

TALLON, Joe, Vice President Finance, Salina Regional Health Center, Salina, KS, p. A243

TALLON, Richard, Chief Financial Officer, Jefferson County Hospital, Waurika, OK, p. A510

TALLURI, Jay, M.D. Chief Medical Officer, East Morgan County Hospital, Brush, CO, p. A98

TALTON, James R., FACHE, Director, Central Alabama Veterans Health Care System, Montgomery, AL, p. A23

TAM, David A., FACHE, Chief Administrative Officer, Pomerado Hospital, Poway, CA, p. A80

TAMAR, Earl J., Chief Executive Officer, Galesburg Cottage Hospital, Galesburg, IL, p. A183

TAMBURELLO, Leonardo, Divisional Chief Financial Officer, New York Community Hospital,, NY, p. A434

TAMMINEN, John, M.D. President Medical Staff, Carilion Giles Community Hospital, Pearisburg, VA, p. A659

TANAKA, Steven, Chief Information Officer, Pomerado Hospital, Poway, CA, p. A80

TANDY, Gary R., Chief Financial Officer, General John J. Pershing Memorial Hospital, Brookfield, MO, p. A357

TANG, Shirley, R.N. Chief Nursing Officer, Garfield Medical Center, Monterey Park, CA, p. A75

TANGEMAN, Todd, Director Human Resources, Newton Medical Center, Newton, KS, p. A240

TANGUAY, Denis, Chief Information Officer, Central Maine Medical Center, Lewiston, ME, p. A283

TANIS, Earl P., Senior Vice President Financial Operations, Bayhealth Medical Center, Dover, DE, p. A114

TANKEL, Nancy, R.N. Chief Nurse Executive, Kaiser Permanente Woodland Hills Medical Center,, CA, p. A69

TANNA, Manish, M.D. President Medical Staff, Presence Holy Family Medical Center, Des Plaines, IL, p. A181

TANNENBAUM, Scott, M.D. Medical Director, HEALTHSOUTH Sunrise Rehabilitation Hospital, Fort Lauderdale, FL, p. A123

TANNER, Arlan, Chief Information Officer, Kit Carson County Memorial Hospital, Burlington, CO, p. A98

TANNER, Douglas, Chief Executive Officer, Washington County Hospital and Nursing Home, Chatom, AL, p. A18

TANNER, James, M.D. Vice President and Chief Medical Officer, St. Vincent Infirmary Medical Center, Little Rock, AR, p. A47

TANNER, Kaylee, Human Resources Business Partner, Abraham Lincoln Memorial Hospital, Lincoln, IL, p. A187

TANNER, Laureen K., FACHE, President and Chief Executive Officer, Ranken Jordan – A Pediatric Specialty Hospital, Maryland Heights, MO, p. A365

TANTHOREY, Geoff, Director Information Systems, Granville Health System, Oxford, NC, p. A458

TAPIA, Francis, M.D. President Medical Staff, Terre Haute Regional Hospital, Terre Haute, IN, p. A214

TAPIA, Leonard, Chief Financial Officer, Alta Vista Regional Hospital, Las Vegas, NM, p. A417

TAPLETT, Dean, Controller, Quincy Valley Medical Center, Quincy, WA, p. A670

TAPPAN, Hugh C., President and Chief Executive Officer, Wesley Medical Center, Wichita, KS, p. A247

TAPPER, Shane, Director Management Information Systems, Fort Madison Community Hospital, Fort Madison, IA, p. A221

TARANTINO, Kathryn, Vice President Administration, Robert Wood Johnson University Hospital Rahway, Rahway, NJ, p. A409

TARAR, Ahmad, M.D. Medical Director, Heartland Behavioral Health Services, Nevada, MO, p. A366

TARASOVICH, James
Chief Financial Officer, Mayo Clinic Health System in Saint James, Saint James, MN, p. A339
Chief Financial Officer, Mayo Clinic Health System in Springfield, Springfield, MN, p. A341

TARBELL, Tim, Assistant Administrator Support Services, Scott & White Hospital – Taylor, Taylor, TX, p. A636

TARBET, Joyce, M.D. Chief Medical Officer, Murray County Medical Center, Slayton, MN, p. A341

TARBET, Michele T., R.N., Chief Executive Officer, Sharp Grossmont Hospital, La Mesa, CA, p. A65

TARLOW, Eli, Chief Information Officer, Bellevue Hospital Center, New York, NY, p. A430

TARNOWSKI, Tim, Chief Information Officer, University of Kentucky Albert B. Chandler Hospital, Lexington, KY, p. A254

TARR, John S., M.D. Chief Medical Officer, Gunnison Valley Hospital, Gunnison, CO, p. A102

TARRANT, Maureen, Chief Executive Officer, Sky Ridge Medical Center, Lone Tree, CO, p. A104

TARTAGLIA, Judith C., President and Chief Executive Officer, Central Vermont Medical Center, Berlin, VT, p. A649

TARULLI, Pamela, Senior Vice President Human Resources, Good Samaritan Hospital, Suffern, NY, p. A443

TASSEY, Karen, MS Chief Operating Officer, Albany Memorial Hospital, Albany, NY, p. A420

TASSIN, Bruce J., President and Chief Executive Officer, Christus St. Vincent Regional Medical Center, Santa Fe, NM, p. A418

TASSO, Tina, Manager Human Resources, The Orthopedic Specialty Hospital, Murray, UT, p. A644

TATE, Charlene, M.D. Chief Medical Staff and Clinical Services, Eleanor Slater Hospital, Cranston, RI, p. A546

TATE, Charles, Director Information Technology, Lallie Kemp Medical Center, Independence, LA, p. A268

TATE, James, M.D. Chief of Staff, Patients' Hospital of Redding, Redding, CA, p. A81

TATE, Jean, Manager Human Resources, RiverView Health, Crookston, MN, p. A331

TATE, Jodie, Director Human Resources, Westerly Hospital, Westerly, RI, p. A547

TATE, Kimberly J., Director Human Resources, Meadows Psychiatric Center, Centre Hall, PA, p. A522

TATELBAUM, Ronald, M.D. Interim Vice President Medical Affairs, Putnam Hospital Center, Carmel, NY, p. A423

TATNALL, Andrew, Administrator, Noland Hospital Shelby, Alabaster, AL, p. A15

TATRO, Chad, Supervisor Information Systems, Northeast Regional Medical Center, Kirksville, MO, p. A364

TATUM, Martha F., Chief Executive Officer, Evans Memorial Hospital, Claxton, GA, p. A150

TATUM, Robert, M.D. Chief of Staff, Madison River Oaks Medical Center, Canton, MS, p. A345

TATUM, Stanley D., FACHE, Chief Executive Officer, St. Mary's Regional Medical Center, Enid, OK, p. A498

TAUNER, Gary, Chief Operating Officer, St. John's Medical Center and Living Center, Jackson, WY, p. A702

TAUNTON, David, M.D. Chief of Staff, Texas Health Harris Methodist Hospital Southlake, Southlake, TX, p. A634

TAVAKOLI, Kenda, Vice President Information Technology and Chief Information Officer, Sibley Memorial Hospital, Washington, DC, p. A117

TAVARY, James, Chief Executive Officer, Wickenburg Community Hospital, Wickenburg, AZ, p. A39

TAVASOLI, Reza, Information Officer, Orthopedic Hospital, Oklahoma City, OK, p. A504

TAVELLA, Christopher, Executive Director, Rockland Psychiatric Center, Orangeburg, NY, p. A439

TAVENNER, Matt, Assistant Administrator, Jackson Purchase Medical Center, Mayfield, KY, p. A257

TAWNEY, Michael W., D.O. Vice President Medical Affairs, Port Huron Hospital, Port Huron, MI, p. A322

TAYLOR, Adam, Manager Information Technology, Northern Inyo Hospital, Bishop, CA, p. A55

TAYLOR, Alfred P., President, Stanly Regional Medical Center, Albemarle, NC, p. A447

TAYLOR, Alice, MSN, Chief Executive Officer, Broward Health Imperial Point, Fort Lauderdale, FL, p. A123

TAYLOR, Alvin, Chief Human Resources, Five Rivers Medical Center, Pocahontas, AR, p. A49

TAYLOR, Anthony, Manager Information Technology, Cherokee Indian Hospital, Cherokee, NC, p. A450

TAYLOR, Beth, Director Human Resources, Newton–Wellesley Hospital, Newton Lower Falls, MA, p. A303

TAYLOR, Cecilia, Chief Financial Officer, Midwestern Regional Medical Center, Zion, IL, p. A197

TAYLOR, Cherie, Chief Executive Officer, Northern Rockies Medical Center, Cut Bank, MT, p. A375

TAYLOR, Cheryl, R.N. Director of Nursing, Henry Ford Kingswood Hospital, Ferndale, MI, p. A313

TAYLOR, Christina, Director Human Resources, The Brook Hospital – KMI, Louisville, KY, p. A256

TAYLOR, Clay, Chief Financial Officer, Covenant Hospital Plainview, Plainview, TX, p. A627

TAYLOR, Dana Shantel, Director of Organizational Development, Fairfield Memorial Hospital, Fairfield, IL, p. A182

TAYLOR, David, Vice President Information Systems and Chief Information Officer, Stamford Hospital, Stamford, CT, p. A112

TAYLOR, Diana, Administrator, Sabine County Hospital, Hemphill, TX, p. A608

TAYLOR, Dwayne, Chief Executive Officer, Sycamore Shoals Hospital, Elizabethton, TN, p. A568

TAYLOR, Ernest Lee, M.D. Vice President Medical Affairs, St. Mary's Medical Center, Huntington, WV, p. A678

TAYLOR, Gary, Manager Information Services, Paris Community Hospital, Paris, IL, p. A191

TAYLOR, Gene, Chief Financial Officer, Princeton Baptist Medical Center, Birmingham, AL, p. A17

TAYLOR, Gregory, Chief Financial Officer, Cornerstone Hospital of Austin, Austin, TX, p. A585

TAYLOR, Gregory W., M.D. Vice President and Chief Operating Officer, High Point Regional Health System, High Point, NC, p. A455

TAYLOR, Iris, R.N., President, Detroit Receiving Hospital/University Health Center, Detroit, MI, p. A311

TAYLOR, Janet, CPA Chief Financial Officer, Ozarks Community Hospital, Springfield, MO, p. A372

TAYLOR, Janey, Chief Information and Technology, Overton Brooks Veterans Affairs Medical Center, Shreveport, LA, p. A278

TAYLOR, Jeff
Senior Vice President Finance, Magnolia Regional Health Center, Corinth, MS, p. A346
Vice President Finance, St. Luke's Regional Medical Center, Boise, ID, p. A168

TAYLOR, Jeremy, Director Information Services, Saint Francis Hospital, Charleston, WV, p. A676

TAYLOR, Jim, Chief Business Office, Malcom Randall Veterans Affairs Medical Center, Gainesville, FL, p. A124

TAYLOR, Joel, Administrator, Citizens Baptist Medical Center, Talladega, AL, p. A25

TAYLOR, Judd, Chief Financial Officer, Ogden Regional Medical Center, Ogden, UT, p. A645

TAYLOR, Julia, Area Director Human Resources, Kindred Hospital–Charleston, Mt. Pleasant, SC, p. A554

TAYLOR, Julie, Chief Executive Officer, West Valley Medical Center, Caldwell, ID, p. A168

TAYLOR, Kendra, Director Inpatient Nursing, Salem Township Hospital, Salem, IL, p. A194

TAYLOR, Kent, Director Human Resources, Riverside Walter Reed Hospital, Gloucester, VA, p. A655

TAYLOR, Kevin C.
Chief Operating Officer, John D. Archbold Memorial Hospital, Thomasville, GA, p. A161
Chief Operating Officer, Mitchell County Hospital, Camilla, GA, p. A149

TAYLOR, Konnie, Chief Financial Officer, Carl Albert Community Mental Health Center, McAlester, OK, p. A501

TAYLOR, Kristie, Chief Financial Officer, Crockett Hospital, Lawrenceburg, TN, p. A572

TAYLOR, Lee, M.D. Vice President and Chief Medical Officer, Southeast Hospital, Cape Girardeau, MO, p. A358

TAYLOR, Lisa, Director of Nursing, Mountain View Hospital, Payson, UT, p. A645

TAYLOR, Loren L., Chief Executive Officer, North Memorial Medical Center, Robbinsdale, MN, p. A338

TAYLOR, Marcia, Chief Executive Officer, HEALTHSOUTH Rehabilitation Hospital Memphis–North, Memphis, TN, p. A574

TAYLOR, Mark R., FACHE,
President and Chief Executive Officer, Columbia St. Mary's Hospital Milwaukee, Milwaukee, WI, p. A692
President and Chief Executive Officer, Columbia St. Mary's Ozaukee Hospital, Mequon, WI, p. A691

TAYLOR, Meredith, Comptroller, South Sunflower County Hospital, Indianola, MS, p. A348

TAYLOR, Merle, Vice President Operations, UPMC McKeesport, McKeesport, PA, p. A531

TAYLOR, Michael
Chief Information Officer, Bon Secours St. Francis Xavier Hospital, Charleston, SC, p. A549
Chief Information Officer, Mount Pleasant Hospital, Mount Pleasant, SC, p. A554
Chief Information Officer, Roper Hospital, Charleston, SC, p. A549
Vice President Financial Services and Chief Financial Officer, St. Rose Hospital, Hayward, CA, p. A64

TAYLOR, Michael V.
Senior Vice President Human Resources, Sentara Leigh Hospital, Norfolk, VA, p. A658
Vice President Human Resources, Sentara Princess Anne Hospital, Virginia Beach, VA, p. A662

TAYLOR, Mimi
Corporate Vice President Information Technology, Baptist Health South Florida, Baptist Hospital of Miami, Miami, FL, p. A131
Corporate Vice President Information Technology, Baptist Health South Florida, Homestead Hospital, Homestead, FL, p. A125
Vice President Information Technology, Baptist Health South Florida, Mariners Hospital, Tavernier, FL, p. A142
Vice President Information Technology, Baptist Health South Florida, South Miami Hospital, Miami, FL, p. A131

TAYLOR, Mitzie, Interim Director of Nursing, Humboldt General Hospital, Humboldt, TN, p. A570

TAYLOR, Patricia, Director, Patient Care Services, Vidant Bertie Hospital, Windsor, NC, p. A463

TAYLOR, Patrick, M.D., President and Chief Executive Officer, Holy Cross Hospital, Fort Lauderdale, FL, p. A123

TAYLOR, Paul, Administrator, Ozarks Community Hospital, Gravette, AR, p. A44

TAYLOR, Renie, Administrator, Stone County Medical Center, Mountain View, AR, p. A48

TAYLOR, Richard, Chief Financial Officer, Western Mental Health Institute, Bolivar, TN, p. A565

TAYLOR, Richard S., M.D. Chief Medical Officer, Cape Fear Valley Medical Center, Fayetteville, NC, p. A452

TAYLOR, Rob, Corporate Director Human Resources, East Los Angeles Doctors Hospital, Los Angeles, CA, p. A68

TAYLOR, Robbie, Director Human Resources, North Sunflower Medical Center, Ruleville, MS, p. A353

TAYLOR, Robert, Director Information Services, St. Christopher's Hospital for Children, Philadelphia, PA, p. A536

TAYLOR, III, Robert, M.D. Vice President Medical Affairs, Our Lady of Lourdes Memorial Hospital, Binghamton, NY, p. A421

TAYLOR, Ross, M.D. Clinical Director, Austin State Hospital, Austin, TX, p. A584

TAYLOR, Scott J., President and Chief Executive Officer, St. Catherine Hospital, Garden City, KS, p. A234

TAYLOR, Shawnia, Chief Financial Officer, Richardson Medical Center, Rayville, LA, p. A277

TAYLOR, Shelia, Director, Taylor Hardin Secure Medical Facility, Tuscaloosa, AL, p. A26

TAYLOR, Stacy, Chief Financial Officer, Nemaha County Hospital, Auburn, NE, p. A381

TAYLOR, Steven L., Chief Executive Officer, Harrison County Hospital, Corydon, IN, p. A200

TAYLOR, Susan L., Chief Executive Officer, College Hospital Costa Mesa, Costa Mesa, CA, p. A57

TAYLOR, Terry, Associate Director, Dayton Veterans Affairs Medical Center, Dayton, OH, p. A479

TAYLOR, Tim, Chief Operating Officer, Warren State Hospital, Warren, PA, p. A543

TAYLOR, Todd, Chief Executive Officer, Stafford County Hospital, Stafford, KS, p. A244

TAYLOR, Tony, Vice President Operations, Colleton Medical Center, Walterboro, SC, p. A556

TAYLOR, Tyrone, Chief Financial Officer, Veterans Affairs New Jersey Health Care System, East Orange, NJ, p. A403

TAYLOR, Venus, Director Human Resources, BHC Alhambra Hospital, Rosemead, CA, p. A83

TAYLOR–WHITEHEAD, Cheryl, Commander, Weed Army Community Hospital, Fort Irwin, CA, p. A60

TCHELEBI, Mounzer, M.D. Medical Director, Wyckoff Heights Medical Center,, NY, p. A437

TEAFORD, Carrie, Vice President Finance, Saint Thomas Midtown Hospital, Nashville, TN, p. A576

TEAGUE, Anna B., M.D. Chief of Staff, Fayetteville Veterans Affairs Medical Center, Fayetteville, NC, p. A452

TEAGUE, Dean, Chief Operating Officer, Calvert Memorial Hospital, Prince Frederick, MD, p. A293

TEAL, Dianne P., MSN Vice President Clinical Operations, CHRISTUS St. Patrick Hospital of Lake Charles, Lake Charles, LA, p. A271

TEAS, Gregory, M.D. Chief Medical Officer, Alexian Brothers Behavioral Health Hospital, Hoffman Estates, IL, p. A185

TEASDALE, Peggy, Director Human Resources, Southeast Health Center of Ripley County, Doniphan, MO, p. A360

TEBA, Luis, M.D. Vice President and Chief Medical Officer, Gaylord Hospital, Wallingford, CT, p. A112

TEBBE, James, M.D. Vice President Medical Affairs, Ochsner Medical Center – Kenner, Kenner, LA, p. A269

TEDDER, Cookie, Human Resources Manager, Texas Health Center for Diagnostic & Surgery, Plano, TX, p. A627

TEDESCHI, Anthony, M.P.H., Chief Executive Officer and Chief Medical Officer, UnityHealth Louis A. Weiss Memorial Hospital, Chicago, IL, p. A179

TEETER, Richard, Chief Financial Officer, Muenster Memorial Hospital, Muenster, TX, p. A624

TEEUWEN, Pat, Director Team Resources, St. Joseph's Hospital, Tampa, FL, p. A142

TEFERA, Tad, Vice President Finance, Ohio Valley General Hospital, McKees Rocks, PA, p. A531

TEFFETELLER, Scott L.
President and Chief Executive Officer, Union Hospital, Terre Haute, IN, p. A214
President and Chief Executive Officer, Union Hospital Clinton, Clinton, IN, p. A200

TEGETHOFF, Jennifer, M.D. President Medical Staff, Avera Queen of Peace Hospital, Mitchell, SD, p. A561

TEIGEN, Bobbe L., FACHE, Chief Executive Officer, Memorial Medical Center – Neillsville, Neillsville, WI, p. A693

TEITELBAUM, Karen
Executive Vice President and Chief Operating Officer, Mount Sinai Hospital, Chicago, IL, p. A177
Executive Vice President and Chief Operating Officer, Schwab Rehabilitation Hospital, Chicago, IL, p. A179

TEJADA, Vanessa, Manager Human Resources, HEALTHSOUTH Rehabilitation Institute of San Antonio, San Antonio, TX, p. A631

TEJEDA, Nicholas R., FACHE, Chief Executive Officer, Doctors Hospital of Manteca, Manteca, CA, p. A73

TELITZ, Rita, Director Human Resources, Rusk County Memorial Hospital and Nursing Home, Ladysmith, WI, p. A689

TELL, Marjorie, Vice President Information Technology, Riverview Hospital Association, Wisconsin Rapids, WI, p. A700

TELLER, Michele, Director Human Resources, Fishermen's Hospital, Marathon, FL, p. A129

TELLO, Anthoney M., M.D. Medical Director, Sanford Bismarck, Bismarck, ND, p. A465

TELLOR, Tammy, Acting Director Human Resources, Choate Mental Health Center, Anna, IL, p. A173

TELTHORSTER, Marcia M., Vice President Human Resources, University Medical Center of Princeton at Plainsboro, Plainsboro, NJ, p. A409

TEMECK, Barbara, M.D. Chief of Staff, Edward Hines, Jr. Veterans Affairs Hospital, Hines, IL, p. A185

TEMPELMEYER, Zak, M.D. Chief Medical Staff, Community Memorial Hospital, Syracuse, NE, p. A390

TEMPEST, Wendy, Director Human Resources, Vibra Hospital of Northern California, Redding, CA, p. A81

TEMPLE, John, Director Information Systems, York General Hospital, York, NE, p. A390

TEMPLET, Carrie E., FACHE, Chief Executive Officer, Lafayette General Surgical Hospital, Lafayette, LA, p. A271

TEMPLETON, Gary, M.D. Medical Director, Regency Hospital of Northwest Arkansas, Fayetteville, AR, p. A43

TEMPLETON, Parker, FACHE, Chief Executive Officer, Franklin Foundation Hospital, Franklin, LA, p. A267

TEMPLETON, Sheryl, Chief Financial Officer, Scotland County Hospital, Memphis, MO, p. A366

TEMPLETON, III, William, M.D. Medical Director, Clark Memorial Hospital, Jeffersonville, IN, p. A207

TEMPLIN, Nancy, Vice President Finance and Chief Financial Officer, All Children's Hospital, Saint Petersburg, FL, p. A138

TENHOUSE, Steven, FACHE, Chief Executive Officer, Kirby Medical Center, Monticello, IL, p. A189

TENNANT, Gail, Director, H. Douglas Singer Mental Health and Developmental Center, Rockford, IL, p. A193

TENNISON, Gary, D.O. Chief of Staff, Crawford Memorial Hospital, Robinson, IL, p. A193

TENNYSON, Guy, Director Information Systems and Telecommunications, San Ramon Regional Medical Center, San Ramon, CA, p. A89

TENNYSON, Ruby, Director Administration, Naval Hospital Jacksonville, Jacksonville, FL, p. A126

TENREIRO, Edgardo, Chief Operating Officer, Baton Rouge General Medical Center, Baton Rouge, LA, p. A263

TEODO, Paul M., Chief Operating Officer, Holy Cross Hospital, Chicago, IL, p. A176

TEPEDINO, Michael, M.D. Chief of Staff, Harton Regional Medical Center, Tullahoma, TN, p. A580

TEPEDINO, Miguel, M.D. Chief Medicine, Lake City Medical Center, Lake City, FL, p. A128

TEPPER, Gil, M.D. Chief of Staff, Miracle Mile Medical Center, Los Angeles, CA, p. A70

TERAN, Maria, Personnel Officer, Ventura County Medical Center, Ventura, CA, p. A94

TERBUSH, Jennifer, Director of Nursing, Hills & Dales General Hospital, Cass City, MI, p. A310

TERNES, Howard, Chief Executive Officer, San Gabriel Valley Medical Center, San Gabriel, CA, p. A87

TERPSTRA, Dale, D.O. Vice President Physician Services, Spectrum Health Zeeland Community Hospital, Zeeland, MI, p. A327

TERPSTRA, Kelli, R.N
Chief Nursing Officer, Baylor Specialty Hospital, Dallas, TX, p. A595
Chief Nursing Officer, Our Children's House at Baylor, Dallas, TX, p. A597

TERRELL, Freddie, M.D. Chief of Staff, Clark Regional Medical Center, Winchester, KY, p. A261

TERRELL, Greg, Senior Vice President and Chief Operating Officer, Norman Regional Health System, Norman, OK, p. A502

TERRELL, Jay, Manager Management Information Systems, Riverview Regional Medical Center, Gadsden, AL, p. A20

TERRELL, Michael T., Chief Financial Officer, Brandon Regional Hospital, Brandon, FL, p. A119

TERRINONI, Gary G., Chief Financial Officer and Senior Vice President, Kennedy Health System, Cherry Hill, NJ, p. A402

TERRIO, James, M.D. Chief Medical Officer, Evans U. S. Army Community Hospital, Fort Carson, CO, p. A101

TERRY, Sr., Darrell K., Senior Vice President Operations, Newark Beth Israel Medical Center, Newark, NJ, p. A407

TERRY, Micheal, President and Chief Executive Officer, Salina Regional Health Center, Salina, KS, p. A243

TERRY, Richard, Vice President & Chief Information Officer, Carson City Hospital, Carson City, MI, p. A310

TERRYBERRY, Daniel S., M.D. Chief Medical Officer, Albemarle Health, Elizabeth City, NC, p. A452

TERTEL, Jenifer K., Director Human Resources, Medical City Dallas Hospital, Dallas, TX, p. A596

TERWILLIGER, James G., President, Indiana University Health University Hospital, Indianapolis, IN, p. A205

TESKE, Mark, Chief Financial Officer, Hill Crest Behavioral Health Services, Birmingham, AL, p. A16

TESSARZIK, Connie, Business Manager, Albert J. Solnit Psychiatric Center – South Campus, Middletown, CT, p. A110

TETER, Heather, Chief Financial Officer, Los Alamos Medical Center, Los Alamos, NM, p. A417

TETZ, Warren, Senior Vice President and Chief Operating Officer, Glendale Adventist Medical Center, Glendale, CA, p. A62

TETZLAFF, Sue, Vice President of Nursing, War Memorial Hospital, Sault Sainte Marie, MI, p. A324

TEUBNER, Sandra, Chief Financial Officer, St. Aloisius Medical Center, Harvey, ND, p. A467

TEUFEL, George, Vice President Finance, Advocate Good Shepherd Hospital, Barrington, IL, p. A174

TEUMER, Chris, Vice President and Chief Information Officer, Newark–Wayne Community Hospital, Newark, NY, p. A437

TEW, Brian, Vice President and Chief Information Officer, Catholic Medical Center, Manchester, NH, p. A399

TEWKSBURY, Randy E., Vice President Finance, Lewistown Hospital, Lewistown, PA, p. A530

THACKER, Bruce, Controller, Madison St. Joseph Health Center, Madisonville, TX, p. A621

THACKER, Roland, Chief Financial Officer, Hughston Hospital, Columbus, GA, p. A150

THALL, Barry, M.D. Medical Director, Los Robles Hospital and Medical Center, Thousand Oaks, CA, p. A92

THAMES, Thomas B., M.D. Vice President Medical Affairs, Sentara Virginia Beach General Hospital, Virginia Beach, VA, p. A662

THARASRI, Luke, Chief Executive Officer, Coastal Communities Hospital, Santa Ana, CA, p. A89

THARP, Beth S., R.N., President and Chief Executive Officer, Community Hospital of Anderson and Madison County, Anderson, IN, p. A198

THARP, Stephen, M.D. Medical Director, St. Vincent Frankfort Hospital, Frankfort, IN, p. A203

THATE, Mark
Vice President Human Resources, Kishwaukee Hospital, DeKalb, IL, p. A180
Vice President Human Resources, Valley West Hospital, Sandwich, IL, p. A194

THAW, James G., President and Chief Executive Officer, Athens Regional Medical Center, Athens, GA, p. A145

THAYER, Gilbert M., M.D. Chief Medical Staff, Hardin Medical Center, Savannah, TN, p. A578

THEBARGE, Steven, Chief Operating Officer and Chief Financial Officer, Dorothea Dix Psychiatric Center, Bangor, ME, p. A281

THEILER, Brian, President and Chief Executive Officer, Gundersen Tri–County Hospital and Clinics, Whitehall, WI, p. A699

THEIRING, James, Interim Chief Executive Officer, Mission Community Hospital,, CA, p. A70

THEISEN, Janet
Chief Information Officer, Sanford Tracy Medical Center, Tracy, MN, p. A341
Chief Information Officer, Sanford Westbrook Medical Center, Westbrook, MN, p. A342

THELEN, Brent A., Ph.D. Associate Director, John D. Dingell Veterans Affairs Medical Center, Detroit, MI, p. A312

THELEN, Brent A., Ph.D., Interim Director, Marion Veterans Affairs Medical Center, Marion, IL, p. A187

THEMELIS, Carol, Vice President Human Resources, Frisbie Memorial Hospital, Rochester, NH, p. A400

THERIOT, Lyle, Director Human Resources, Lakeview Regional Medical Center, Covington, LA, p. A265

THERIOT, Paul, Chief Operating Officer, Gadsden Regional Medical Center, Gadsden, AL, p. A20

THEROULT, Thomas N., Chief Executive Officer, Select Specialty Hospital–Omaha, Omaha, NE, p. A388

THERRIEN, Charles D., Chief Executive Officer, Maine Coast Memorial Hospital, Ellsworth, ME, p. A283

THETFORD, Carol, Chief Nursing Officer, Baptist Memorial Hospital for Women, Memphis, TN, p. A574

THEUS, Thomas L., M.D. Chief of Medicine, Doctors Hospital of Columbus, Columbus, GA, p. A150

THEUS, Will, M.D. Chief of Staff, Gordon Hospital, Calhoun, GA, p. A149

THIBODEAU, Jan, Director Human Resources, HEALTHSOUTH Southern Hills Rehabilitation Hospital, Princeton, WV, p. A680

THIBODEAUX, Annette, Director Human Resources, Savoy Medical Center, Mamou, LA, p. A273

THIBODEAUX, Douglas, M.D. Chief Medical Officer, OakBend Medical Center, Richmond, TX, p. A629

THIEL, Scott, M.D. Chief of Staff, Boone County Hospital, Boone, IA, p. A217

THIELE, Rosemary, Chief Executive Officer, Progressive Hospital, Las Vegas, NV, p. A393

THIELEN, Kurt, Manager Business Office, Minneapolis Veterans Affairs Health Care System, Minneapolis, MN, p. A336

THIELKE, Jayne, Chief Financial Officer, Swift County–Benson Hospital, Benson, MN, p. A329

THIELST, Christina B., Chief Operating Officer, Ventura County Medical Center, Ventura, CA, p. A94

THIEMAN, Richard, Chief Financial Officer, Wilbarger General Hospital, Vernon, TX, p. A639

THIESFELD, Rebecca A., Executive Director Human Resources, Cuyuna Regional Medical Center, Crosby, MN, p. A331

THIESSEN, David, Associate Director Support Services, Missouri Rehabilitation Center, Mount Vernon, MO, p. A366

THIGPEN, Kevin, Vice President Human Resources, Athens Regional Medical Center, Athens, GA, p. A145

THILGES, Michael, Chief Financial Officer, Clarke County Hospital, Osceola, IA, p. A226

THIMIS, Nicholas, Chief Information Officer, West Jefferson Medical Center, Marrero, LA, p. A273

THOENDEL, Victor, M.D. Chief Medical Officer, Butler County Health Care Center, David City, NE, p. A383

THOMAS, Adeeb, M.D. Vice President Medical Affairs, St. Vincent's East, Birmingham, AL, p. A17

THOMAS, Amy, Vice President Finance, Memorial Hospital, Belleville, IL, p. A174

THOMAS, Brian E., Administrator, Alton Mental Health Center, Alton, IL, p. A173

THOMAS, Brian N., Senior Vice President and Chief Operating Officer, Jefferson Regional Medical Center, Pine Bluff, AR, p. A49

THOMAS, Brook, Chief Financial Officer, West Boca Medical Center, Boca Raton, FL, p. A119

THOMAS, IV, Calvin, Chief Operating Officer, St. Lucie Medical Center, Port St. Lucie, FL, p. A138

THOMAS, Chris, FACHE, President and Chief Executive Officer, Community Hospital, Grand Junction, CO, p. A101

THOMAS, Cristina, Vice President and Chief Information Officer, Mercy Medical Center–Des Moines, Des Moines, IA, p. A220

THOMAS, Curt, Administrator, Ness County Hospital, Ness City, KS, p. A240

THOMAS, Debbie, Chief Operating Officer, Dorminy Medical Center, Fitzgerald, GA, p. A153

THOMAS, Debora, Chief Financial Officer, Florida Hospital Memorial Medical Center, Daytona Beach, FL, p. A122

THOMAS, Denise, Chief Financial Officer, Spring View Hospital, Lebanon, KY, p. A253

THOMAS, Drake, Chief Information Officer, CarePartners Health Services, Asheville, NC, p. A447

THOMAS, Geogy, M.D. Chief of Staff, Jellico Community Hospital, Jellico, TN, p. A571

THOMAS, James, Chief Financial Officer, Montfort Jones Memorial Hospital, Kosciusko, MS, p. A349

THOMAS, Jayne, Chief Nursing Officer, Deaconess Hospital, Oklahoma City, OK, p. A503

THOMAS, Jennifer, Director Public Relations, Lake Butler Hospital Hand Surgery Center, Lake Butler, FL, p. A128

THOMAS, Joan, Chief Financial Officer, Novant Health Brunswick Medical Center, Bolivia, NC, p. A448

THOMAS, Jody, Director Human Resources, Texas Health Harris Methodist Hospital Southwest Fort Worth, Fort Worth, TX, p. A604

THOMAS, John, Chief Operating Officer, San Mateo Medical Center, San Mateo, CA, p. A88

THOMAS, John A., M.D. Chief Medical Staff, Culberson Hospital, Van Horn, TX, p. A639

THOMAS, John H., M.D. Chief of Staff, Healthmark Regional Medical Center, DeFuniak Springs, FL, p. A122

THOMAS, Karen A.
Vice President and Chief Information Officer, Bryn Mawr Hospital, Bryn Mawr, PA, p. A521
Chief Information Officer, Bryn Mawr Rehabilitation Hospital, Malvern, PA, p. A530
Acting Vice President and Chief Information Officer, Lankenau Medical Center, Wynnewood, PA, p. A545
Vice President and Chief Information Officer, Paoli Hospital, Paoli, PA, p. A534

THOMAS, Keith, M.D. Chief of Staff, Blue Mountain Hospital, John Day, OR, p. A513

THOMAS, Kirk E., Vice President Operations, Lewistown Hospital, Lewistown, PA, p. A530

THOMAS, Lizbeth, M.D. Vice President Medical Affairs, Fairview Ridges Hospital, Burnsville, MN, p. A330

THOMAS, Maggie, Vice President Human Resources and Practice Management, South County Hospital, Wakefield, RI, p. A547

THOMAS, Michael, Associate Administrator, Wayne County Hospital, Corydon, IA, p. A219

THOMAS, Michael P., Administrator, Meade District Hospital, Meade, KS, p. A239

THOMAS, Michael S., President and Chief Administrative Officer, John Muir Medical Center, Concord, Concord, CA, p. A57

THOMAS, Mitchell T., Chief Financial Officer, Presbyterian Intercommunity Hospital, Whittier, CA, p. A96

THOMAS, Nathan, M.D. President Medical Staff, Conemaugh Meyersdale Medical Center, Meyersdale, PA, p. A532

THOMAS, Nicky, Director Human Resources, Baptist Memorial Hospital–Union City, Union City, TN, p. A580

THOMAS, Patricia F., Chief Nursing Officer, Halifax Regional Health System, South Boston, VA, p. A661

THOMAS, Paula, R.N. Vice President Patient Services, UPMC Bedford Memorial, Everett, PA, p. A526

THOMAS, Robert, Chief Executive Officer and Administrator, Columbus Community Hospital, Columbus, TX, p. A592

THOMAS, Ronald J., Coordinator Information Systems, North Alabama Regional Hospital, Decatur, AL, p. A19

THOMAS, Ruth, Chief Operating Officer, Mercy Fitzgerald Hospital, Darby, PA, p. A524

THOMAS, Scott C., Administrative Director Human Resources/Communication, Granville Health System, Oxford, NC, p. A458

THOMAS, Shawn M., Director Human Resources, Payson Regional Medical Center, Payson, AZ, p. A34

THOMAS, Spencer, Chief Executive Officer, Newport Medical Center, Newport, TN, p. A577

THOMAS, Stephanie, Chief Operating Officer, Denver Health Medical Center, Denver, CO, p. A99

THOMAS, Sue
Manager Human Resources, Beckley ARH Hospital, Beckley, WV, p. A675
Director Human Resources, Mercy Regional Medical Center, Ville Platte, LA, p. A280

THOMAS, Tracy, Director Human Resources, Cumberland Hall Hospital, Hopkinsville, KY, p. A252

THOMAS, Wanda W., Director Health Information, Neosho Memorial Regional Medical Center, Chanute, KS, p. A232

THOMAS, Jr., William, M.D. Medical Director Clinical and Internal Affairs, Molokai General Hospital, Kaunakakai, HI, p. A166

THOMAS–FOLDS, Lana, System Director Human Resources, Jack Hughston Memorial Hospital, Phenix City, AL, p. A24

THOMASON, Joe D., Chief Executive Officer, Centennial Medical Center, Frisco, TX, p. A605

THOMASON, Rose, Interim Vice President Human Resources, JPS Health Network, Fort Worth, TX, p. A604

THOMASSON, Mark, Vice President Human Resources, Providence Memorial Hospital, El Paso, TX, p. A601

THOMPSON, Alan, M.D. President Medical Staff, Warm Springs Medical Center, Warm Springs, GA, p. A162

THOMPSON, Albert, M.D. Chief of Staff, Charlton Memorial Hospital, Folkston, GA, p. A153

THOMPSON, Angela S., Vice President Human Resources and Support Services, Indiana University Health North Hospital, Carmel, IN, p. A200

THOMPSON, Becki, Controller, Oakes Community Hospital, Oakes, ND, p. A468

THOMPSON, Belinda, Coordinator Human Resources, HEALTHSOUTH Chesapeake Rehabilitation Hospital, Salisbury, MD, p. A294

THOMPSON, Betsy, Director Human Resources, Northern Virginia Mental Health Institute, Falls Church, VA, p. A653

THOMPSON, Bobby, Director Information Technology, Stephens Memorial Hospital, Breckenridge, TX, p. A589

THOMPSON, Bonnie, Chief Operating Officer and Chief Nursing Executive, Providence Seaside Hospital, Seaside, OR, p. A517

THOMPSON, C. Lynn, M.D. Vice President Medical Affairs, Lima Memorial Health System, Lima, OH, p. A484

THOMPSON, Chad, Chief Financial Officer, Lallie Kemp Medical Center, Independence, LA, p. A268

THOMPSON, Charlotte, Chief Financial Officer, Reeves Memorial Medical Center, Bernice, LA, p. A264

THOMPSON, Cheryl, Chief Nursing Officer, Garden Park Medical Center, Gulfport, MS, p. A347

THOMPSON, Chris
Chief Financial Officer, Delta Community Medical Center, Delta, UT, p. A643
Chief Financial Officer, Fillmore Community Medical Center, Fillmore, UT, p. A643
Chief Financial Officer, Sanpete Valley Hospital, Mount Pleasant, UT, p. A644
Chief Financial Officer, Sevier Valley Medical Center, Richfield, UT, p. A646

THOMPSON, Cindy, Chief Financial Officer, Northwest Surgical Hospital, Oklahoma City, OK, p. A503

THOMPSON, Craig B., M.D., President and Chief Executive Officer, Memorial Sloan–Kettering Cancer Center, New York, NY, p. A434

THOMPSON, Dale, Chief Operating Officer, Western State Hospital, Tacoma, WA, p. A673

THOMPSON, David, M.D. Chief of Staff, Richardson Medical Center, Rayville, LA, p. A277

THOMPSON, David
Chief Financial Officer, St. Anthony Hospital, Lakewood, CO, p. A103
Chief Financial Officer, St. Anthony Summit Medical Center, Frisco, CO, p. A101

THOMPSON, David M., Chief Executive Officer, Sutter Tracy Community Hospital, Tracy, CA, p. A93

THOMPSON, Donna K., Chief Executive Officer, Allegiance Health Center of Ruston, Ruston, LA, p. A277

THOMPSON, Douglas, Director Information Systems, Brookdale Hospital Medical Center,, NY, p. A431

THOMPSON, Dwight, Chief Financial Officer, Altru Health System, Grand Forks, ND, p. A467

THOMPSON, Frederick G., Ph.D., President, Anson Community Hospital, Wadesboro, NC, p. A462

THOMPSON, Helen, Interim Director, Indian Health Service Hospital, Rapid City, SD, p. A561

THOMPSON, James H., FACHE, Owner and Chief Executive Officer, Healthmark Regional Medical Center, DeFuniak Springs, FL, p. A122

THOMPSON, Jane, Administrator and Chief Operating Officer, York General Hospital, York, NE, p. A390

THOMPSON, Janis, Chief Executive Officer, Life Center Specialty Hospital, Sherman, TX, p. A634

THOMPSON, Jeff, M.D. Chief of Staff, DeKalb Regional Medical Center, Fort Payne, AL, p. A20

THOMPSON, Jeffrey E., M.D., Chief Executive Officer, Gundersen Lutheran Medical Center, La Crosse, WI, p. A689

THOMPSON, Jerry
Chief Financial Officer, Sanford Tracy Medical Center, Tracy, MN, p. A341
Chief Financial Officer, Sanford Westbrook Medical Center, Westbrook, MN, p. A342

THOMPSON, John W., M.D. Chief of Staff, Eastern Louisiana Mental Health System, Jackson, LA, p. A269

THOMPSON, Kevin
Chief Financial Officer, Sharp Memorial Hospital, San Diego, CA, p. A85
Chief Financial Officer, Sharp Mesa Vista Hospital, San Diego, CA, p. A86

THOMPSON, Linda
Chief Operating Officer, Fairfax Community Hospital, Fairfax, OK, p. A498
Vice President Human Resources, New England Baptist Hospital, Boston, MA, p. A297

THOMPSON, Lisa, MSN Director of Nursing, Hiawatha Community Hospital, Hiawatha, KS, p. A235

THOMPSON, Loree, CPA Chief Financial Officer, Sierra Tucson, Tucson, AZ, p. A39

THOMPSON, Marion A., FACHE, Administrator and Chief Executive Officer, Fulton County Hospital, Salem, AR, p. A49

THOMPSON, Mark, Vice President Finance and Chief Financial Officer, Lourdes Hospital, Paducah, KY, p. A259

THOMPSON, Mark, M.D. Chief Medical Officer, Monroe Clinic, Monroe, WI, p. A693

THOMPSON, Mark, Vice President Financial Services, Rapid City Regional Hospital, Rapid City, SD, p. A562

THOMPSON, Matthew J., Chief Executive Officer, Carson City Hospital, Carson City, MI, p. A310

THOMPSON, Melanie, M.D. Acting Chief of Staff, White River Junction Veterans Affairs Medical Center, White River Junction, VT, p. A650

THOMPSON, Melissa, M.D. Chief Medical Officer, Adair County Memorial Hospital, Greenfield, IA, p. A222

THOMPSON, Michael S., Chief Executive Officer, Frio Regional Hospital, Pearsall, TX, p. A626

THOMPSON, Michael W., Chief Executive Officer, HEALTHSOUTH Rehabilitation of Gadsden, Gadsden, AL, p. A20

THOMPSON, Michele T., Deputy Chief Operating Officer, Provident Hospital of Cook County, Chicago, IL, p. A178

THOMPSON, Ormand P., Administrator, North Baldwin Infirmary, Bay Minette, AL, p. A16

THOMPSON, Pamela, Chief Operations Officer, Huhukam Memorial Hospital, Sacaton, AZ, p. A36

THOMPSON, Patricia
Treasurer and Chief Financial Officer, Geneva General Hospital, Geneva, NY, p. A426
Treasurer and Chief Financial Officer, Soldiers and Sailors Memorial Hospital of Yates County, Penn Yan, NY, p. A439

THOMPSON, Ranae M., MSN Director Patient Care Services, Shriners Hospitals for Children–Greenville, Greenville, SC, p. A552

THOMPSON, Robert, M.D. Chief of Staff, Mission Community Hospital,, CA, p. A70

THOMPSON, Sarah, Vice President Operations, Tift Regional Medical Center, Tifton, GA, p. A161

THOMPSON, Sherene, Director Human Resources, Methodist Willowbrook Hospital, Houston, TX, p. A611

THOMPSON, Sheri, Director Information Technology, Crete Area Medical Center, Crete, NE, p. A383

THOMPSON, Stuart, Director Human Resources, Cleveland Clinic Florida, Weston, FL, p. A144

THOMPSON, Susan K., President and Chief Executive Officer, Trinity Regional Medical Center, Fort Dodge, IA, p. A221

THOMPSON, Susie, Executive Director Fiscal Services, Hamilton Center, Terre Haute, IN, p. A213

THOMPSON, Terry, Director Information Services, North Star Behavioral Health System, Anchorage, AK, p. A27

THOMPSON, Thomas R., Chief Executive Officer, Samaritan Healthcare, Moses Lake, WA, p. A668

THOMPSON, Sr., Timothy L., Senior Vice President and Chief Information Officer, The Methodist Hospital, Houston, TX, p. A613

THOMPSON, Tina H., Coordinator Human Resources, FirstHealth Montgomery Memorial Hospital, Troy, NC, p. A462

THOMPSON, Tom, Vice President and Chief Financial Officer, Raleigh General Hospital, Beckley, WV, p. A675

THOMPSON, Trinise, Director Human Resources, St. Luke's Medical Center, Phoenix, AZ, p. A35

THOMPSON, William, M.D. Chief Medical Officer, Saint Thomas Midtown Hospital, Nashville, TN, p. A576

THOMSEN, Jan, Director Human Resources, Tyler County Hospital, Woodville, TX, p. A642

THOMSEN, Sue, Chief Financial Officer, South Texas Rehabilitation Hospital, Brownsville, TX, p. A590

THOMSEN, Vicki, Director Human Resources, Aurora Phoenix Hospital, Glendale, AZ, p. A32

THOMSON, Doug, M.D. Chief Medical Officer, Commonwealth Regional Specialty Hospital, Bowling Green, KY, p. A248

THOMSON, Ken, M.D. Medical Director, Sugar Land Surgical Hospital, Sugar Land, TX, p. A635

THOMSON, Nicole, Chief Financial Officer, Saint Louise Regional Hospital, Gilroy, CA, p. A62

THOMSON, Sean, CPA Chief Financial Officer, Spotsylvania Regional Medical Center, Fredericksburg, VA, p. A654

THOMSON, Steven, M.D. Medical Director, Heartland Behavioral Healthcare, Massillon, OH, p. A485

THORDARSON, G. Thor, President and Chief Executive Officer, Indiana University Health La Porte Hospital, La Porte, IN, p. A208

THORE, Joe, Chief Operating Officer, Ashe Memorial Hospital, Jefferson, NC, p. A455

THOREEN, Peter W., FACHE, President and Chief Executive Officer, UnityPoint Health St. Luke's, Sioux City, IA, p. A228

THORESON, Scott D., FACHE, Administrator, Mayo Clinic Health System in Springfield, Springfield, MN, p. A341

THORFINNSON, Barry, Chief Financial Officer, Southwest Healthcare System, Murrieta, CA, p. A76

THORGUSON, Kimberly, M.D. Chief of Staff, Teche Regional Medical Center, Morgan City, LA, p. A274

THORN, III, Eugene A., Vice President Finance and Chief Financial Officer, Union Hospital, Dover, OH, p. A480

THORNBRUGH, Mitchell, Administrative Officer, Cherokee Nation W.W. Hastings Indian Hospital, Tahlequah, OK, p. A507

THORNE, Dana, Administrator Human Resources, Valley Hospital Medical Center, Las Vegas, NV, p. A394

THORNE, Paul, M.D. Chief Medical Director, St. Cloud Regional Medical Center, Saint Cloud, FL, p. A138

THORNE, Rob, Director of Human Resources, Heritage Medical Center, Shelbyville, TN, p. A579

THORNE Jr., William, Chief Executive Officer, Acoma–Canoncito–Laguna Hospital, Acoma, NM, p. A414

THORNELL, Timothy, FACHE, Chief Executive Officer, Lea Regional Medical Center, Hobbs, NM, p. A416

THORNQUIST, Betsy, Chief Information Officer, St. Vincent's Medical Center, Bridgeport, CT, p. A108

THORNSBERRY, Michael, M.D. Chief of Staff, Birmingham Veterans Affairs Medical Center, Birmingham, AL, p. A16

THORNTON, Bob, Executive Vice President and Chief Financial Officer, Bayfront Health St. Petersburg, Saint Petersburg, FL, p. A138

THORNTON, Cayetano, Chief Information Officer, Walter Reed National Military Medical Center, Bethesda, MD, p. A290

THORNTON, Daryl W., Chief Operating Officer, Kansas Medical Center, Andover, KS, p. A231

THORNTON, Jillisa, Director of Nursing, Coastal Harbor Treatment Center, Savannah, GA, p. A159

THORNTON, Ryan, Chief Clinical Officer, Ashley Regional Medical Center, Vernal, UT, p. A648

THORNTON, Timothy J., Chief Financial Officer, Russell Medical Center, Alexander City, AL, p. A15

THORPE, Linda, Chief Executive Officer, East Morgan County Hospital, Brush, CO, p. A98

THORPE, Wendy, Area Director Information Systems, St. Joseph Hospital, Eureka, CA, p. A59

THORSEN, Erik, Chief Executive Officer, Columbia Memorial Hospital, Astoria, OR, p. A511

THORWALD, Robert, Chief Information Officer, Washington Hospital Healthcare System, Fremont, CA, p. A61

THOTAKURA, Raj, M.D. Medical Director, Old Vineyard Behavioral Health Services, Winston–Salem, NC, p. A463

THRASHER, Barton, M.D. Chief of Staff, Methodist Healthcare–Fayette Hospital, Somerville, TN, p. A579

THRASHER, Charlotte, Vice President and Chief Operating Officer, Seton Medical Center Austin, Austin, TX, p. A585

THREEWITS, Sheree, Director Human Resources, Manatee Memorial Hospital, Bradenton, FL, p. A119

THRUSH, Warren, Coordinator Human Resources, Brookville Hospital, Brookville, PA, p. A521

THULI, Karen, Coordinator Information Systems, Upland Hills Health, Dodgeville, WI, p. A685

THUN, Todd, Director Human Resources, Montana State Hospital, Warm Springs, MT, p. A380

THUNELL, Adam, Chief Operating Officer and Vice President Operations, Community Memorial Health System, Ventura, CA, p. A94

THURMER, DeAnn, Chief Operating Officer, Waupun Memorial Hospital, Waupun, WI, p. A698

THURMOND, David, Chief Information Resource Management Service, Alexandria Veterans Affairs Health Care System, Pineville, LA, p. A276

THURMOND, Jeff, Vice President Information Systems, Baptist Health Corbin, Corbin, KY, p. A249

THURSTON, Leigh, Vice President Information Systems, Community Medical Center, Missoula, MT, p. A378

THURSTON, Richard, M.D. Chief of Staff, Benewah Community Hospital, Saint Maries, ID, p. A171

THURSTON, Thomas, M.D. Medical Director, J. D. McCarty Center for Children With Developmental Disabilities, Norman, OK, p. A502

THYGESON, Cindy, M.D. Director Medical Affairs, Sutter Center for Psychiatry, Sacramento, CA, p. A84

TIBBETT, Cheryl, Chief Financial Officer, Bayfront Health Punta Gorda, Punta Gorda, FL, p. A138

TIBBITS, Richard M., Vice President and Chief Operating Officer, Loma Linda University Medical Center–Murrieta, Murrieta, CA, p. A75

TIBBS, E. W., President and Chief Executive Officer, Centra Lynchburg General Hospital, Lynchburg, VA, p. A656

TICE, Darlette, Chief Nursing Officer, Manatee Memorial Hospital, Bradenton, FL, p. A119

TICE, Heidi, Chief Financial Officer, Cheyenne County Hospital, Saint Francis, KS, p. A243

TICE, Kirk C., President and Chief Executive Officer, Robert Wood Johnson University Hospital Rahway, Rahway, NJ, p. A409

TICE, Linda, Director Information Systems, Riverton Memorial Hospital, Riverton, WY, p. A703

TICHENOR, John, Chief Financial Officer, Ohio County Hospital, Hartford, KY, p. A252

TIDWELL, Joseph, Administrator, Phoenix Behavioral Hospital, Rayne, LA, p. A277

TIEDT, Jerry, Director Information Systems, Waverly Health Center, Waverly, IA, p. A229

TIEFENTHALER, Brenda Marie, R.N. Vice President Patient Care and Informatics, Spencer Hospital, Spencer, IA, p. A228

TIEMENS, Linda, Chief Executive Officer, Select Specialty Hospital–Tulsa Midtown, Tulsa, OK, p. A509

TIEMEYER, Nancy, Director Health Information Management, George C Grape Community Hospital, Hamburg, IA, p. A222

TIERNAN, Kelley, Chief Financial Officer, Claxton–Hepburn Medical Center, Ogdensburg, NY, p. A438

TIERNEY, Mark A., Chief Financial Officer, Manatee Memorial Hospital, Bradenton, FL, p. A119

TIETJEN, George, M.D. Chief of Staff, Wayne Memorial Hospital, Honesdale, PA, p. A527

TIGGELAAR, Tom, Vice President Finance, Mayo Clinic Health System – Franciscan Healthcare in La Crosse, La Crosse, WI, p. A689

TILLER, Gary L., Chief Executive Officer, Kingman Community Hospital, Kingman, KS, p. A237

TILLETT, Grant, Chief Information Officer, Prairie Lakes Healthcare System, Watertown, SD, p. A564

TILLIRSON, Mike, D.O. Executive Vice President and Chief Medical Officer, AnMed Health Medical Center, Anderson, SC, p. A548

TILLMAN, Barry, M.D. Chief Medical Staff, Promise Hospital of Miss Lou, Vidalia, LA, p. A279

TILLMAN, Jill, Assistant Chief Executive Officer, Brandywine Hospital, Coatesville, PA, p. A523

TILLMAN, Kanner, Chief Financial Officer, Encino Hospital Medical Center,, CA, p. A68

TILLMAN, Michael, Vice President Patient Services and Chief Operating Officer, United Hospital Center, Bridgeport, WV, p. A675

TILSON, Natalie, Controller, HEALTHSOUTH Rehabilitation Hospital, Kingsport, TN, p. A571

TILUS, Sheryl, R.N. Vice President Clinical Services/Chief Nursing Officer, Cox Medical Center Branson, Branson, MO, p. A357

TIMANUS, Anthony, Chief Executive Officer, Avera Gregory Hospital, Gregory, SD, p. A560

TIMBERS, Christopher T., Vice President and Chief Information Officer, Suburban Hospital, Bethesda, MD, p. A290

TIMLIN, Marie, R.N. Chief Nursing Officer, Yampa Valley Medical Center, Steamboat Springs, CO, p. A106

TIMM, Mark
Director Human Resouces, Yavapai Regional Medical Center – East, Prescott Valley, AZ, p. A36
Director Human Resources, Yavapai Regional Medical Center, Prescott, AZ, p. A36

TIMM, Matt, M.D. Medical Director, Pender Community Hospital, Pender, NE, p. A389

TIMMER, Kari, Chief Financial Officer, Hegg Memorial Health Center Avera, Rock Valley, IA, p. A227

TIMMERMAN, Candace, Director Human Resources, Avera Creighton Hospital, Creighton, NE, p. A383

TIMMERMAN, Jo, Manager Accounting, Norwood Health Center, Marshfield, WI, p. A690

TIMMONS, Bret, D.O. Chief Medical Staff, Power County Hospital District, American Falls, ID, p. A167

TIMMONS, William, Chief Executive Officer, Los Ninos Hospital, Phoenix, AZ, p. A34

TIMPE, David A., Interim President and Chief Executive Officer, Childrens Care Hospital and School, Sioux Falls, SD, p. A562

TIMPE, Ronald, Associate Administrator, Buchanan County Health Center, Independence, IA, p. A223

TINCH, Paula, Interim Chief Financial Officer, Newark–Wayne Community Hospital, Newark, NY, p. A437

TINCHER, Pat, Director Finance, Langlade Hospital, Antigo, WI, p. A683

TINDLE, Jeff A., Chief Executive Officer, Carroll County Memorial Hospital, Carrollton, MO, p. A358

TINDLE, Tim, Chief Information Officer, Harris Health System, Houston, TX, p. A609

TINGLE, Billy, Director Information Systems and Respiratory Therapy, Avoyelles Hospital, Marksville, LA, p. A273

TINGSTAD, Jonathan, Vice President and Chief Financial Officer, Seattle Cancer Care Alliance, Seattle, WA, p. A671

TINKER, Peter, Chief Human Resources Officer, James J. Peters Veterans Affairs Medical Center,, NY, p. A432

TINNEY, Sean, FACHE, President and Chief Operating Officer, St. Vincent's East, Birmingham, AL, p. A17

TINSA, Udom, M.D. Medical Director, Ashley Medical Center, Ashley, ND, p. A465

TINSLEY, Austin, M.D. Chief Medical Officer, Poplar Bluff Regional Medical Center, Poplar Bluff, MO, p. A368

TINSLEY, Cassie, Director, Human Resources, Powell Valley Healthcare, Powell, WY, p. A703

TINSLEY III, Edward D., Chief Executive Officer, McLeod Loris Healthcare, Loris, SC, p. A554

TINSLEY, Kay
Vice President Fiscal Services, Good Samaritan Regional Health Center, Mount Vernon, IL, p. A189
Vice President Finance, St. Mary's Hospital, Centralia, IL, p. A175

TINTLE, Keith D., Chief Executive Officer, Timpanogos Regional Hospital, Orem, UT, p. A645

TIPPIN, Philip, M.D. Chief of Staff, Chambers Memorial Hospital, Danville, AR, p. A42

TIPPIN, Russell, Chief Executive Officer and Administrator, Permian Regional Medical Center, Andrews, TX, p. A583

TIPPS, Linda, Director Human Resources, Southern Tennessee Medical Center, Winchester, TN, p. A580

TIPTON, Peggy, Chief Operating Officer and Chief Nursing Officer, Oklahoma Heart Hospital, Oklahoma City, OK, p. A504

TIPTON, Silvia A., Chief Financial Officer and Director Human Resources, Throckmorton County Memorial Hospital, Throckmorton, TX, p. A637

TIRA, Cheryl, Director Information Systems, Columbus Community Hospital, Columbus, NE, p. A382

TIRMAN, Kerry R., FACHE, President, Mississippi Baptist Medical Center, Jackson, MS, p. A348

TISCHLER, James F., M.D. Chief of Staff, Coatesville Veterans Affairs Medical Center, Coatesville, PA, p. A523

TISDALE, Willis E., Director Human Resources, Shriners Hospitals for Children–Greenville, Greenville, SC, p. A552

TISDALL, Renae, Chief Financial Officer, Mobridge Regional Hospital, Mobridge, SD, p. A561

TISSIER, Becky, Chief Fiscal Service, Veterans Affairs Illiana Health Care System, Danville, IL, p. A180

TITSWORTH, Sue, Director Human Resources, Coleman County Medical Center, Coleman, TX, p. A592

TITTLE, JoDee, Director Community and Human Resources, St. Charles Madras, Madras, OR, p. A514

TITUS, Marilyn, Vice President and Chief Operating Officer, Hillside Rehabilitation Hospital, Warren, OH, p. A492

TOADVINE, Stephen, M.D. Chief Medical Officer, Hardin Memorial Hospital, Elizabethtown, KY, p. A250

TOBER, James Chadwick, M.D. Chief of Staff, Beaufort Memorial Hospital, Beaufort, SC, p. A548

TOBEY, Shelley R., R.N. Chief Operating Officer and Chief Nursing Officer, Texas Health Presbyterian Hospital Flower Mound, Flower Mound, TX, p. A602

TOBIN, Hugh, Chief Financial Officer, DeKalb Regional Medical Center, Fort Payne, AL, p. A20

TOBIN, Karen A., R.N. Chief Operating Officer, Sanford Medical Center Fargo, Fargo, ND, p. A466

TOBIN, Timothy C., FACHE, President and Chief Executive Officer, Spotsylvania Regional Medical Center, Fredericksburg, VA, p. A654

TOBLER, Randy, M.D. Chief Medical Officer, Scotland County Hospital, Memphis, MO, p. A366

TOBON–STEVENS, Paula, Associate Administrator, Angleton Danbury Medical Center, Angleton, TX, p. A583

TODD, Bob, Director Information Systems, Mount Auburn Hospital, Cambridge, MA, p. A299

TODD, David, M.D. President Medical Staff, Memorial Specialty Hospital, Lufkin, TX, p. A620

TODD, Dianna, Director Human Resources, Boulder City Hospital, Boulder City, NV, p. A391

TODD, Fred O., Senior Vice President Finance, McLeod Loris Healthcare, Loris, SC, p. A554

TODD, James, Chief Financial Officer, River Oaks Hospital, New Orleans, LA, p. A275

TODD, Robbie, Director Information Technology, Horn Memorial Hospital, Ida Grove, IA, p. A223

TODD, Steve J., Chief Operating Officer, St. Luke Community Healthcare, Ronan, MT, p. A379

TODOROW, Thomas, Chief Financial Officer, Children's Hospital of Philadelphia, Philadelphia, PA, p. A534

TOEBBE, Nelson, Chief Executive Officer, St. John's Episcopal Hospital–South Shore,, NY, p. A436

TOEDT, Michael E., M.D. Director Clinical Services, Cherokee Indian Hospital, Cherokee, NC, p. A450

TOERING, Marla, Chief Operating Officer, Sioux Center Community Hospital and Health Center Avera, Sioux Center, IA, p. A228

TOFANI, Gerald, Chief Financial Officer, Monmouth Medical Center, Long Branch, NJ, p. A406

TOL, Daryl, Chief Executive Officer, Florida Hospital Memorial Medical Center, Daytona Beach, FL, p. A122

TOLEFREE, Paulette, Chief Nursing Officer, Bradley County Medical Center, Warren, AR, p. A50

TOLLEFSON, Sue, Coordinator Payroll Personnel, Granite Falls Municipal Hospital and Manor, Granite Falls, MN, p. A333

TOLOSKY, Mark R., FACHE, President and Chief Executive Officer, Baystate Medical Center, Springfield, MA, p. A305

TOLSON, Rick, Chief Administrative Officer and Chief Human Resources Officer, Christ Hospital, Cincinnati, OH, p. A474

TOM, Adrian, Supervisor Management Information Systems, Hopi Health Care Center, Kearns Canyon, AZ, p. A32

TOMAS, George, Director Information Services, Griffin Hospital, Derby, CT, p. A108

TOMASINO, Tom, Administrator and Chief Executive Officer, Whidbey General Hospital, Coupeville, WA, p. A666

TOMASSETTI, Dennis, Chief Financial Officer, UPMC Passavant, Pittsburgh, PA, p. A538

TOMBERLIN, Terri, Manager Human Resources, Curry General Hospital, Gold Beach, OR, p. A513

TOMIMOTO, Ty, Acting Vice President Financial Affairs, Rehabilitation Hospital of the Pacific, Honolulu, HI, p. A165

TOMLIN, Kerry W., Associate Administrator, Clay County Hospital, Ashland, AL, p. A15

TOMLINSON, Charles M., M.D. Vice President and Chief Medical Officer, Crawley Memorial Hospital, Shelby, NC, p. A461

TOMLINSON, Daniel, Chair Human Resources, Mayo Clinic Jacksonville, Jacksonville, FL, p. A126

TOMLINSON, David
   Senior Vice President, Chief Information Officer, Centegra Hospital – McHenry, McHenry, IL, p. A188
   Senior Vice President, Chief Information Officer, Centegra Hospital – Woodstock, Woodstock, IL, p. A197

TOMLINSON, Norma J., FACHE, Associate Vice President and Interim Executive Director, The University of Toledo Medical Center, Toledo, OH, p. A491

TOMLINSON, Sallie, Manager Human Resources, Arbuckle Memorial Hospital, Sulphur, OK, p. A507

TOMO, Ronald A., Vice President and Chief Information Officer, Nassau University Medical Center, East Meadow, NY, p. A425

TOMORY, Gerald, M.D
   Regional Medical Director, Kauai Veterans Memorial Hospital, Waimea, HI, p. A166
   Regional Medical Director, Samuel Mahelona Memorial Hospital, Kapaa, HI, p. A165

TOMPKINS, Charles, M.D. Chief of Staff, Crenshaw Community Hospital, Luverne, AL, p. A22

TOMPKINS, John, Administrator, Pioneer Community Hospital of Stokes, Danbury, NC, p. A450

TOMPKINS, Kim, Director Information Services, DeTar Healthcare System, Victoria, TX, p. A639

TOMPKINS, Ronald G., M.D. Chief of Staff and Director Research, Shriners Hospitals for Children–Boston Burns Hospital, Boston, MA, p. A297

TONER, Tina, Director of Nursing, North Big Horn Hospital District, Lovell, WY, p. A703

TONEY, Mark, President and Chief Executive Officer, Brookdale Hospital Medical Center,, NY, p. A431

TONEY, Scott, R.N. Chief Nursing Officer, HEALTHSOUTH Northern Kentucky Rehabilitation Hospital, Edgewood, KY, p. A250

TONG, Cheryl, Chief Financial Officer, Antelope Valley Hospital, Lancaster, CA, p. A66

TONGATE, Scott, Chief Executive Officer, Lauderdale Community Hospital, Ripley, TN, p. A578

TONJES, Ken, Chief Financial Officer, PeaceHealth Ketchikan Medical Center, Ketchikan, AK, p. A28

TONNU, Lannie, Senior Vice President and Chief Financial Officer, Children's Hospital Los Angeles, Los Angeles, CA, p. A68

TOOKE, Landon, Chief Executive Officer, Reeves Memorial Medical Center, Bernice, LA, p. A264

TOOKE, Michael, M.D
   Vice President Medical Affairs, Dorchester General Hospital, Cambridge, MD, p. A290
   Chief Medical Officer, Memorial Hospital at Easton Maryland, Easton, MD, p. A291

TOOKE, Ryan, Interim Chief Executive Officer, Rosebud Health Care Center, Forsyth, MT, p. A376

TOOKER, Deby, Director Human Resources, Surgical Specialty Hospital of Arizona, Phoenix, AZ, p. A35

TOOLE, LaDon, Chief Operating Officer and Administrator, Grady General Hospital, Cairo, GA, p. A149

TOOLE, Patricia, Vice President Human Resources, East Mountain Hospital, Belle Mead, NJ, p. A401

TOOLE, Trish, Vice President Administrative Services, Carrier Clinic, Belle Mead, NJ, p. A401

TOOMEY, Richard Kirk, FACHE, President and Chief Executive Officer, Beaufort Memorial Hospital, Beaufort, SC, p. A548

TOON, William
   Director, Baptist Orange Hospital, Orange, TX, p. A625
   Director Information Technology, Wesley Medical Center, Hattiesburg, MS, p. A348

TOPALSKY, George V., M.D. Vice President Medical Operations, Marymount Hospital, Garfield Heights, OH, p. A482

TOPJIAN, Diana, MSN Vice President and Chief Nursing Executive, Mount Pleasant Hospital, Mount Pleasant, SC, p. A554

TOPMILLER, Darrell, Director Finance, Fulton County Health Center, Wauseon, OH, p. A492

TOPOLEWSKI, Ted, Administrator, Community Medical Center of Izard County, Calico Rock, AR, p. A41

TOPPER, John E., Senior Vice President and Chief Financial Officer, Mercy Medical Center, Baltimore, MD, p. A288

TORCHIA, Joseph, M.D. Senior Vice President Medical Affairs and Chief Medical Officer, Holy Spirit Hospital, Camp Hill, PA, p. A521

TORCHIA, Jude, Chief Executive Officer, OrthoColorado Hospital, Lakewood, CO, p. A103

TORDESILLAS, Victor, Director Human Resources, Arrowhead Regional Medical Center, Colton, CA, p. A57

TORMANEN, John, Director Mission and Human Resources, St. Joseph's Area Health Services, Park Rapids, MN, p. A338

TORN, Michael, Chief Executive Officer, Edgewood Surgical Hospital, Transfer, PA, p. A542

TOROSSIAN, Lynn M., President, DMC Huron Valley–Sinai Hospital, Commerce Township, MI, p. A311

TORPEY, Carol, Chief Nursing Officer, Valley Hospital, Spokane Valley, WA, p. A672

TORRES, Harvey
   Vice President Finance and Chief Financial Officer, Harlingen Medical Center, Harlingen, TX, p. A607
   Chief Financial Officer, Valley Baptist Medical Center–Brownsville, Brownsville, TX, p. A590

TORTELLA, Anthony, Chief Financial Officer, Fairmount Behavioral Health System, Philadelphia, PA, p. A534

TOSI, Stephen, M.D. Chief Medical Officer, UMass Memorial Medical Center, Worcester, MA, p. A307

TOSTENSON, Brad, Chief Information Officer, Essentia Health–Holy Trinity Hospital, Graceville, MN, p. A333

TOSTI, Debra, Chief Executive Officer, Tewksbury Hospital, Tewksbury, MA, p. A305

TOTH, Jackie, Administrator, Acute Care Specialty Hospital of Aultman, Canton, OH, p. A473

TOUPS, Sharon A., Senior Vice President and Chief Operating Officer, St. Tammany Parish Hospital, Covington, LA, p. A266

TOURIGNY, Barry, Vice President Human Resources and Organizational Development, Cabell Huntington Hospital, Huntington, WV, p. A677

TOUROS, Krista, Assistant Administrator Finance, Sutter Lakeside Hospital, Lakeport, CA, p. A66

TOUSIGNANT, Grace, R.N. Chief Nursing Officer, Aspirus Keweenaw Hospital, Laurium, MI, p. A319

TOUVELLE, Cynthia, R.N. Senior Director Care Management and Chief Nursing Officer, Barnesville Hospital, Barnesville, OH, p. A471

TOVAR, Richard, M.D. Chief of Staff, Beaver Dam Community Hospitals, Beaver Dam, WI, p. A684

TOWERS, Darleen, Director Human Resources, Lake Whitney Medical Center, Whitney, TX, p. A641

TOWLE, Michael, Vice President Finance, Alice Hyde Medical Center, Malone, NY, p. A429

TOWLE, Sonya, Director Human Resources, Mercy Hospital, Moose Lake, MN, p. A336

TOWN, Alex, Chief Financial Officer, Tri–State Memorial Hospital, Clarkston, WA, p. A665

TOWNER, Chad, Chief Executive Officer, Dupont Hospital, Fort Wayne, IN, p. A202

TOWNES, Tim, Director Information Systems, Trinity Medical Center, Birmingham, AL, p. A17

TOWNLEY, Nancy, R.N. Senior Vice President Operations, United Regional Health Care System, Wichita Falls, TX, p. A642

TOWNSEND, Cathy, Chief Nursing Officer, Banner Ironwood Medical Center, San Tan Valley, AZ, p. A36

TOWNSEND, Dona E., Chief Nursing Officer, Northeastern Nevada Regional Hospital, Elko, NV, p. A391

TOWNSEND, Gary, Chief Information Officer, Hurley Medical Center, Flint, MI, p. A313

TOWNSEND, Roxane A., M.D., Chief Executive Officer, UAMS Medical Center, Little Rock, AR, p. A47

TOWNSEND, Tanya
   Chief Information Officer, St. Mary's Hospital Medical Center, Green Bay, WI, p. A688
   Chief Information Officer, St. Vincent Hospital, Green Bay, WI, p. A688

TOWNSEND, Theodore E., FACHE, President and Chief Executive Officer, UnityPoint Health St. Luke's, Cedar Rapids, IA, p. A217

TOWNSLEY, Malcolm, M.D. Chief of Staff, St. Anthony Hospital, Pendleton, OR, p. A515

TOY, Linda, Director Information Systems, Havasu Regional Medical Center, Lake Havasu City, AZ, p. A32

TOYE, Lawrence J., Chief Financial Officer, Kindred Hospital–Boston, Brighton, MA, p. A298

TOZER, Chuck, Administrator, Spectrum Health Special Care Hospital, Grand Rapids, MI, p. A315

TOZIER, Kenneth, M.D. Chief of Surgery, Milan General Hospital, Milan, TN, p. A575

TRACEY, Karen, Chief Human Resources, Select Specialty Hospital–Greensboro, Greensboro, NC, p. A453

TRACHTA, Michael D., FACHE Executive Vice President and Chief Operating Officer, Mercy Medical Center–Cedar Rapids, Cedar Rapids, IA, p. A217

TRACKWELL, Anita M., R.N. Chief Nursing Officer, Johnson Memorial Hospital, Franklin, IN, p. A203

TRACY, Allen R., Senior Vice President and Chief Financial Officer, St. John Medical Center, Westlake, OH, p. A493

TRACY, Larry, FACHE,
   President, Barnes–Jewish St. Peters Hospital, Saint Peters, MO, p. A371
   President, Progress West HealthCare Center, Saint Charles, MO, p. A368

TRACY, Timothy J., Chief Executive Officer, Sanford Vermillion Medical Center, Vermillion, SD, p. A563

TRAHAN, Lyman, Chief Executive Officer, Abrom Kaplan Memorial Hospital, Kaplan, LA, p. A269

TRAHERN, Sheri
   Chief Financial Officer, St. Mary–Corwin Medical Center, Pueblo, CO, p. A105
   Chief Administrative Officer and Chief Financial Officer, St. Thomas More Hospital, Canon City, CO, p. A98

TRAHERN CPA, MBA,, Sheri, Chief Administrative and Chief Financial Officer, St. Thomas More Hospital, Canon City, CO, p. A98

TRAIL, Alan, Director Information Systems, Muhlenberg Community Hospital, Greenville, KY, p. A252

TRAINER, Michael, Chief Financial Officer, Akron Children's Hospital, Akron, OH, p. A470

TRAINOR, Karyn, Director Human Resources, St. Patrick Hospital, Missoula, MT, p. A378

TRAINOR, Sara, Chief Financial Officer, Community Memorial Hospital, Sumner, IA, p. A229

TRAISTER, Lynne, Controller, Rehabilitation Hospital of Tinton Falls, Tinton Falls, NJ, p. A411

TRAMMEL, Patrick, Chief Operating Officer, Redmond Regional Medical Center, Rome, GA, p. A159

TRAMMELL, Angela, Controller, Trinity Hospital Twin City, Dennison, OH, p. A480

TRAMMELL, Patrick, Chief Executive Officer, Cherokee Medical Center, Centre, AL, p. A18

TRAMP, Francis G., President, Burgess Health Center, Onawa, IA, p. A226

TRAN, Khiem, M.D. Acting Chief of Staff, Veterans Affairs Illiana Health Care System, Danville, IL, p. A180

TRAN, Lac, Senior Vice President Information Services, Rush University Medical Center, Chicago, IL, p. A179

TRANQUILLO, Stephen, Chief Information Officer, Thomas Jefferson University Hospital, Philadelphia, PA, p. A537

TRANTALIS, Cary, R.N. Vice President Operations, Windham Hospital, Willimantic, CT, p. A113

TRANTHAM, Susan, Director Human Resources, HEALTHSOUTH Rehabilitation Hospital, Florence, SC, p. A551

TRAPNELL, Kerry A., Chief Executive Officer, Greenwood Regional Rehabilitation Hospital, Greenwood, SC, p. A553

TRAUB, Bruce, Chief Financial Officer, University Medical Center of Princeton at Plainsboro, Plainsboro, NJ, p. A409

TRAUTMAN, Bob, Chief Executive Officer, Saline Memorial Hospital, Benton, AR, p. A41

TRAVIS, Calee, R.N. Chief Nursing Officer, Centennial Medical Center, Frisco, TX, p. A605

TRAVIS, David A.
   Chief Financial Officer, East Texas Medical Center Athens, Athens, TX, p. A584
   Chief Financial Officer, East Texas Medical Center Fairfield, Fairfield, TX, p. A602

TRAVIS, Dee Dee, Director Community Relations, Calais Regional Hospital, Calais, ME, p. A282

TRAVIS, Stephen, M.D. Chief of Staff, Mercy Hospital Logan County, Guthrie, OK, p. A499

TRAWEEK, Brenda H., R.N. Chief Operating Officer, Brookwood Medical Center, Birmingham, AL, p. A16

TRAXLER, Martin J., Director, Alexandria Veterans Affairs Health Care System, Pineville, LA, p. A276

TRAYLOR, Jerri Sue, Manager Human Resources, The Women's Hospital, Newburgh, IN, p. A211

TRAYNOR, Karen, Chief Financial Officer, Richland Hospital, Richland Center, WI, p. A696

TRCZINSKI, Judi, Vice President and Chief Human Resources Officer, Hospital for Special Care, New Britain, CT, p. A110

TREACY, Nancy, Director Finance, Cambridge Medical Center, Cambridge, MN, p. A330

TREACY–SHIFF, Mary, Vice President Finance, Advocate Good Samaritan Hospital, Downers Grove, IL, p. A181

TREADWAY, Michael G., Controller, Trinity Mother Frances Rehabilitation Hospital, Tyler, TX, p. A638

TREADWELL, Karen, Director Human Resources, Lake Martin Community Hospital, Dadeville, AL, p. A18

TREASE, Kevin, Chief Information Officer, Antelope Memorial Hospital, Neligh, NE, p. A386

TREASURE, Jeffrey S., Senior Vice President Finance and Chief Financial Officer, Glens Falls Hospital, Glens Falls, NY, p. A426

TREASURE, Martin
Director Human Resources, Schuylkill Medical Center – East Norwegian Street, Pottsville, PA, p. A539
Director Human Resources, Schuylkill Medical Center – South Jackson Street, Pottsville, PA, p. A539

TREFNEY, Frank, M.D. Chief Medical Staff, Williamsburg Regional Hospital, Kingstree, SC, p. A553

TREGLOWN, Brad, Director Information Systems, Redmond Regional Medical Center, Rome, GA, p. A159

TREHAN, Rajeev, M.D. Chief of Staff, Veterans Affairs Eastern Kansas Health Care System, Topeka, KS, p. A245

TREMAINE, Richard, Associate Director, VA Central Western Massachusetts Healthcare System, Leeds, MA, p. A301

TREMBLAY, Marilyn, Chief Information Officer and Vice President, Regional Medical Center, Orangeburg, SC, p. A555

TREMBLE, John, Chief Financial Officer, St. Croix Regional Medical Center, St. Croix Falls, WI, p. A697

TREMBULAK, Frank J., Executive Vice President and Chief Operating Officer, Geisinger Medical Center, Danville, PA, p. A523

TREMONTI, Carl
Chief Financial Officer, Mease Countryside Hospital, Safety Harbor, FL, p. A138
Chief Financial Officer, Mease Dunedin Hospital, Dunedin, FL, p. A122
Chief Financial Officer, Morton Plant Hospital, Clearwater, FL, p. A120
Chief Financial Officer, Morton Plant North Bay Hospital, New Port Richey, FL, p. A133

TREMONTI, Yvette, Vice President Human Resources, H. Lee Moffitt Cancer Center and Research Institute, Tampa, FL, p. A141

TRENARY, Thomas J., President, Baylor Medical Center at Garland, Garland, TX, p. A606

TRENDE, Gary D., FACH
Chief Operating Officer, Tennessee Valley Healthcare System, Nashville, TN, p. A577
Associate Director, Tuscaloosa Veterans Affairs Medical Center, Tuscaloosa, AL, p. A26

TRENKLE, Kevan, Chief Executive Officer, Citizens Medical Center, Colby, KS, p. A232

TRENT, Cindy, Manager Personnel, Fall River Hospital, Hot Springs, SD, p. A560

TREPAGNIER, Katherine, Director Human Resources, River Parishes Hospital, La Place, LA, p. A270

TRESSA, John, MSN, Chief Executive Officer, Park Plaza Hospital, Houston, TX, p. A611

TRETINA, Mike, Vice President and Chief Financial Officer, Mary Greeley Medical Center, Ames, IA, p. A216

TRETTER, Stan, M.D. President Medical Staff, Memorial Hospital and Health Care Center, Jasper, IN, p. A207

TREUTLEIN, Scott, M.D. Medical Director, Wyoming County Community Hospital, Warsaw, NY, p. A445

TREVATHAN, Dave, Director Information Systems, Rose Medical Center, Denver, CO, p. A100

TREVINO, Carlos, Chief Operating Officer, Mission Regional Medical Center, Mission, TX, p. A623

TREVINO, Guillermo, M.D. President Medical Staff, Wayne Hospital, Greenville, OH, p. A482

TREVINO, Malissa, Director Human Resources, Pecos County Memorial Hospital, Fort Stockton, TX, p. A603

TREVINO, Paul, Administrator, CHRISTUS Hospital–St. Elizabeth, Beaumont, TX, p. A587

TREVISANI, Michael F., M.D
Vice President Medical Affairs and Chief Medical Officer, Chenango Memorial Hospital, Norwich, NY, p. A438
Executive Vice President and Chief Medical Officer, Delaware Valley Hospital, Walton, NY, p. A445

TREXLER, Don, Chief Executive Officer, Cypress Pointe Surgical Hospital, Hammond, LA, p. A268

TRIBBLE, Terry, Chief Financial Officer, East Central Regional Hospital, Augusta, GA, p. A147

TRICE, Richard
Director Operations, University Hospitals Conneaut Medical Center, Conneaut, OH, p. A479
Director Operations, University Hospitals Geneva Medical Center, Geneva, OH, p. A482

TRIEBES, David G., Chief Executive Officer, Samaritan Albany General Hospital, Albany, OR, p. A511

TRIGG, Pat, Coordinator Personnel and Credentialing, El Campo Memorial Hospital, El Campo, TX, p. A600

TRIGG, Terry, Director Human Resources, Wesley Medical Center, Hattiesburg, MS, p. A348

TRIGIANI, Charles, D.O. Medical Director, Hampton Behavioral Health Center, Westampton, NJ, p. A412

TRILIVAS, Judy, Vice President and Chief Operating Officer, The Mount Sinai Hospital of Queens,, NY, p. A437

TRIMBLE, Charley O., Chief Executive Officer, Grace Medical Center, Lubbock, TX, p. A620

TRIMBLE, Deborah, R.N., Chief Executive Officer, Paul B. Hall Regional Medical Center, Paintsville, KY, p. A259

TRIMBLE, Donald, CPA Chief Financial Officer, Vibra Specialty Hospital of Dallas, Desoto, TX, p. A599

TRIMBLE, Kevin T., FACHE, President and Chief Executive Officer, Saint Luke's North Hospital – Barry Road, Kansas City, MO, p. A363

TRIMM, Robert M., Chief Administrative Officer, Mayo Clinic Health System in Waycross, Waycross, GA, p. A162

TRIMMER, Mary R., Interim Chief Operating Officer, Mount Carmel, Columbus, OH, p. A477

TRIMMER, Matt, Director Information Services, Mercy Medical Center–Dubuque, Dubuque, IA, p. A220

TRINIDAD, Terry, Director Management Information Systems, Clearfield Hospital, Clearfield, PA, p. A522

TRIPLETT, John, D.O. President Medical Staff, Saint Joseph – Martin, Martin, KY, p. A257

TRIPLETT, Robin, Chief Financial Officer, Southern Coos Hospital and Health Center, Bandon, OR, p. A511

TRIPP, Gina, Director Information Systems, TIRR Memorial Hermann, Houston, TX, p. A613

TRISCHLER, Roni Sue, Director Nursing Services, Ohio Valley General Hospital, McKees Rocks, PA, p. A531

TRITTIN, Kim, Manager Human Resources, Mayo Clinic Health System in Red Wing, Red Wing, MN, p. A338

TROCINO, Mark
Chief Information Officer, DeKalb Medical at Hillandale, Lithonia, GA, p. A156
Chief Information Officer, DeKalb Medical at North Decatur, Decatur, GA, p. A152

TROGMAN, Richard, FACHE Chief Operating Officer, Kaiser Permanente Woodland Hills Medical Center,, CA, p. A69

TROLLOPE, Grant, Chief Financial Officer, Northeastern Nevada Regional Hospital, Elko, NV, p. A391

TROMBLEY, Barb, Director Financial Services, Munising Memorial Hospital, Munising, MI, p. A320

TROMPETER, Dawn, Vice President Finance, OSF Saint Elizabeth Medical Center, Ottawa, IL, p. A191

TRONCONE, Michael T., Chief Human Resources Officer, Calvary Hospital,, NY, p. A431

TROSCLAIR, Andree, Vice President Human Resources, Arkansas Children's Hospital, Little Rock, AR, p. A46

TROSIN, Jill A., R.N. Chief Nursing Officer, Memorial Hospital, Fremont, OH, p. A481

TROTTER, Wally, Director Human Resources, Mountain View Hospital, Payson, UT, p. A645

TROUP, Matthew, Chief Operating Officer, Hillcrest Medical Center, Tulsa, OK, p. A508

TROUSDALE, Cindy, Chief Financial Officer, Verdugo Hills Hospital, Glendale, CA, p. A63

TROUT, Gene, Chief Financial Officer, Canonsburg General Hospital, Canonsburg, PA, p. A522

TROUTMAN, Gary, CP
Chief Financial Officer, Baptist Hospitals of Southeast Texas, Beaumont, TX, p. A587
Chief Financial Officer, Baptist Orange Hospital, Orange, TX, p. A625

TROWER, Brad
Administrator, Jenkins County Hospital, Millen, GA, p. A157
Administrator, Optim Medical Center – Tattnall, Reidsville, GA, p. A158
Chief Executive Officer, Screven County Hospital, Sylvania, GA, p. A161

TROWHILL, Jan, Director Health Information Management Systems, HEALTHSOUTH Cane Creek Rehabilitation Hospital, Martin, TN, p. A573

TROXELL, Larry, Chief Executive Officer, Seiling Community Hospital, Seiling, OK, p. A506

TROY, Peggy N.
President and Chief Executive Officer, Children's Hospital of Wisconsin, Milwaukee, WI, p. A692
President and Chief Executive Officer, Children's Hospital of Wisconsin–Fox Valley, Neenah, WI, p. A693

TROYER, David, Chief Information Officer, Veterans Affairs Northern Indiana Health Care System, Fort Wayne, IN, p. A203

TROYER, Devin, M.D. Medical Director, HEALTHSOUTH Rehabilitation Hospital of Columbia, Columbia, SC, p. A550

TROYO, Glynda, Chief Executive Officer, St. Theresa Specialty Hospital, Metairie, LA, p. A273

TRUAX, Bradley, M.D. Senior Vice President Medical Affairs and Chief Medical Officer, St. James Mercy Health System, Hornell, NY, p. A427

TRUAX, Christopher, Chief Executive Officer, Morrow County Hospital, Mount Gilead, OH, p. A486

TRUE, Janet E., M.D. Clinical Director, Kerrville State Hospital, Kerrville, TX, p. A616

TRUEBLOOD, Susan, Chief Executive Officer, Georgia Regional Hospital at Atlanta, Decatur, GA, p. A152

TRUESDALE, Jr., Fred A., Administrator, North Mississippi Medical Center–Iuka, Iuka, MS, p. A348

TRUITT, Louise, Vice President Human Resources, Capital Regional Medical Center, Tallahassee, FL, p. A140

TRUITT, Ron, Director Information Services, Palms of Pasadena Hospital, Saint Petersburg, FL, p. A139

TRUJILLO, Jesse, Chief Information Officer, St. Mark's Hospital, Salt Lake City, UT, p. A647

TRUKENMILLER, Denise, Director Human Resources, Burgess Health Center, Onawa, IA, p. A226

TRUMAN, Mark, Vice President of Operations, Floyd Memorial Hospital and Health Services, New Albany, IN, p. A211

TRUMBULL, Kathryn E., R.N. Chief Nursing Officer and Vice President Patient Care Services, Samaritan Healthcare, Moses Lake, WA, p. A668

TRUMP, Donald L., M.D., President and Chief Executive Officer, Roswell Park Cancer Institute, Buffalo, NY, p. A422

TRUSSELL, Robert, Chief Executive Officer, Foundation Surgical Hospital of San Antonio, San Antonio, TX, p. A631

TRUWIT, Jonathon D., M.D. Chief Medical Officer, University of Virginia Medical Center, Charlottesville, VA, p. A652

TRYON, Ellen, R.N. Chief Nursing Officer, Adventist Medical Center–Portland, Portland, OR, p. A515

TRZNADEL, Marc, Chief Nursing Officer, Loretto Hospital, Chicago, IL, p. A177

TSALATE, Cynthia, Human Resource Specialist, U. S. Public Health Service Indian Hospital, Zuni, NM, p. A419

TSAMBIRAS, Petros, M.D. Chief of Staff, Bayfront Health Dade City, Dade City, FL, p. A121

TSCHABRUN, Dawn M., R.N., Chief Executive Officer, Lovelace Regional Hospital, Roswell, NM, p. A417

TSENG, Allen, Administrative Director, Texas Health Harris Methodist Hospital Southwest Fort Worth, Fort Worth, TX, p. A604

TSO, Ronald, Chief Executive Officer, Chinle Comprehensive Health Care Facility, Chinle, AZ, p. A30

TSUI–WU, Jane, Interim Chief Information Officer, Stony Brook University Medical Center, Stony Brook, NY, p. A443

TUBBS, John, M.D. Chief of Staff, West Holt Memorial Hospital, Atkinson, NE, p. A381

TUBERVILLE, Abby, Human Resource Generalist, Fillmore County Hospital, Geneva, NE, p. A383

TUCK, April E., Vice President Human Resources and Compliance, Copley Hospital, Morrisville, VT, p. A649

TUCKER, Carol, Worklife Services Consultant, Brighton Center for Recovery, Brighton, MI, p. A309

TUCKER, Carolyn J., Director Human Resources, Island Hospital, Anacortes, WA, p. A664

TUCKER, Cathy, Director Human Resources, Iraan General Hospital, Iraan, TX, p. A614

TUCKER, Jr., G. Edward, Vice President Corporate Services, Forrest General Hospital, Hattiesburg, MS, p. A347

TUCKER, Gary, Senior Vice President Operations and Chief Operating Officer, Mount St. Mary's Hospital and Health Center, Lewiston, NY, p. A428

TUCKER, H. Jaquita, Executive Director Human Resources, Providence Hospital, Mobile, AL, p. A22

TUCKER, John A., Chief Executive Officer, Iberia Medical Center, New Iberia, LA, p. A275

TUCKER, John R., FACHE, Administrator and Chief Executive Officer, Dallas County Medical Center, Fordyce, AR, p. A44

TUCKER, Joseph B., Senior Vice President and Chief Financial Officer, Fort Washington Medical Center, Fort Washington, MD, p. A291

TUCKER, Joshua, Administrator, Mercy Hospital Logan County, Guthrie, OK, p. A499

TUCKER, Lisa, Chief Information Officer, University Hospital McDuffie, Thomson, GA, p. A161

TUCKER, Mona, Director Human Resources, Seton Medical Center Harker Heights, Harker Heights, TX, p. A607

TUCKER, Rebecca
Chief Financial Officer, Integris Bass Baptist Health Center, Enid, OK, p. A498
Chief Financial Officer, Integris Bass Pavilion, Enid, OK, p. A498

TUCKER, Robert, M.D. Chief Medical Officer, Murray–Calloway County Hospital, Murray, KY, p. A258

TUCKER, Ron, Business Office Manager, Kiowa County Memorial Hospital, Greensburg, KS, p. A234

TUCKER, Sidney, Chief Executive Officer, North Runnels Hospital, Winters, TX, p. A642

TUCKER, Steven E., President, Conemaugh Memorial Medical Center, Johnstown, PA, p. A528

TUDOR, Nathan, Chief Executive Officer and Administrator, Beauregard Memorial Hospital, De Ridder, LA, p. A266

TUELL, William J., MSN, Facility Director, Commonwealth Center for Children and Adolescents, Staunton, VA, p. A662

TUFTS, Patrick, M.D. Medical Director, Mineral Community Hospital, Superior, MT, p. A380

TULISIAK, Thomas, M.D., President, Medina Hospital, Medina, OH, p. A486

TULLMAN, Stephen M., Chief Executive Officer, Phoenixville Hospital, Phoenixville, PA, p. A537

TUMA, Bonnie, Human Resources Team Lead, National Institutes of Health Clinical Center, Bethesda, MD, p. A290

TUMLIN, Richard, Chief Operating Officer, TriStar Southern Hills Medical Center, Nashville, TN, p. A577

TUMMURU, Ramireddy K., M.D. Chief Medical Officer, Porter Regional Hospital, Valparaiso, IN, p. A214

TUNGATE, Rex A.
Administrator, Casey County Hospital, Liberty, KY, p. A255
Administrator, Jane Todd Crawford Hospital, Greensburg, KY, p. A251

TUNNELL, Richard, Director Information Systems Technology and Health Management Information Systems, University of Medicine and Dentistry of New Jersey–University Hospital, Newark, NJ, p. A407

TUNNEY, Niona, Director Human Resources, Cochran Memorial Hospital, Morton, TX, p. A623

TUNSON, Lynn, Manager Medical Records, Complex Care Hospital at Tenaya, Las Vegas, NV, p. A392

TUPPER, Kevin, Director Information Technology, Windham Hospital, Willimantic, CT, p. A113

TUPPONCE, David, M.D., Interim Chief Executive Officer, Paradise Valley Hospital, Phoenix, AZ, p. A35

TURBAK, Shelly, R.N. Chief Nursing Officer, Prairie Lakes Healthcare System, Watertown, SD, p. A564

TURCO, Joseph, Director Human Resources, Columbus Regional Hospital, Columbus, IN, p. A200

TUREK, Beth, Site Manager Information Systems, Advocate South Suburban Hospital, Hazel Crest, IL, p. A184

TURGEON, Jim, Vice President Finance, Allegiance Behavioral Health Center of Plainview, Plainview, TX, p. A627

TURK, Edward, Vice President Finance, Scripps Mercy Hospital, San Diego, CA, p. A85

TURK, Jan, Chief Executive Officer, Kindred Hospital Detroit, Detroit, MI, p. A312

TURKAL–BARRETT, Kari, Flight Commander Resource Management Officer, Mike O'Callaghan Federal Hospital, Nellis AFB, NV, p. A394

TURKEL, Brooks, Chief Executive Officer, Regional Hospital of Scranton, Scranton, PA, p. A540

TURLEY, Mary Ann, D.O. Medical Director, John C. Lincoln Deer Valley Hospital, Phoenix, AZ, p. A34

TURLEY, Susan S., Chief Financial Officer, Doctor's Hospital at Renaissance, Edinburg, TX, p. A600

TURMAN, Anna, Chief Information Officer, Chadron Community Hospital and Health Services, Chadron, NE, p. A382

TURNA, Tarlochan, M.D. Medical Director, Mayo Clinic Health System in Cannon Falls, Cannon Falls, MN, p. A330

TURNBULL, James, Chief Information Officer, University of Utah Health Care – Hospital and Clinics, Salt Lake City, UT, p. A647

TURNER, Amy, Director Human Resources, Bethesda Butler Hospital, Hamilton, OH, p. A483

TURNER, Bill, Vice President Human Resources, Valir Rehabilitation Hospital, Oklahoma City, OK, p. A504

TURNER, Brenda C.
Chief Human Resources Officer, Palomar Medical Center, Escondido, CA, p. A59
Chief Human Resources Officer, Pomerado Hospital, Poway, CA, p. A80

TURNER, Carol, President and Chief Executive Officer, Atrium Medical Center, Middletown, OH, p. A486

TURNER, Cindy R., Chief Executive Officer, Bacon County Hospital and Health System, Alma, GA, p. A145

TURNER, Dale, Vice President Human Resources, Reedsburg Area Medical Center, Reedsburg, WI, p. A695

TURNER, Dane J., Director Human Resources, West Branch Regional Medical Center, West Branch, MI, p. A326

TURNER, Deborah, Vice President Human Resources, St. Luke's Cornwall Hospital, Newburgh, NY, p. A437

TURNER, Farell, Chief Financial Officer, Appling Healthcare System, Baxley, GA, p. A148

TURNER, Glenda, Director Personnel, Oakwood Correctional Facility, Lima, OH, p. A484

TURNER, Howard D., Chief Executive Officer, Perry Memorial Hospital, Perry, OK, p. A505

TURNER, Jeff, FACHE, Chief Executive Officer, Moore County Hospital District, Dumas, TX, p. A599

TURNER, Kathy, Director Human Resources, East Texas Medical Center Trinity, Trinity, TX, p. A638

TURNER, Kelly, Senior Vice President Finance and Chief Financial Officer, Glendale Adventist Medical Center, Glendale, CA, p. A62

TURNER, Laurie
Chief Nursing Officer, TriStar Skyline Madison Campus, Madison, TN, p. A573
Chief Nursing Officer, TriStar Skyline Medical Center, Nashville, TN, p. A577

TURNER, Linda, Manager Health Information Management, Brown County Community Treatment Center, Green Bay, WI, p. A687

TURNER, Marc, Chief Operating Officer, Palmetto Lowcountry Behavioral Health, Charleston, SC, p. A549

TURNER, Mark J., President and Chief Executive Officer, Memorial Hospital, Belleville, IL, p. A174

TURNER, Mark S., Chief Executive Officer, San Gorgonio Memorial Hospital, Banning, CA, p. A54

TURNER, Melissa, Senior Vice President Human Resources, Bridgeport Hospital, Bridgeport, CT, p. A108

TURNER, Michael, M.D. Chief of Staff, Abbeville Area Medical Center, Abbeville, SC, p. A548

TURNER, Nancy, Director Communications, Sutter Roseville Medical Center, Roseville, CA, p. A83

TURNER, Pamela, Executive Director, Bronx Psychiatric Center,, NY, p. A430

TURNER, Patricia, R.N. Director of Nursing, Sac–Osage Hospital, Osceola, MO, p. A367

TURNER, Randy, Chief Human Resource Management Services, Boise Veterans Affairs Medical Center, Boise, ID, p. A167

TURNER, Saundra G., Director Human Resources, Mercy Hospital Jefferson, Crystal City, MO, p. A359

TURNER, Shelly, Chief Clinical Services Officer, Medical Center of Manchester, Manchester, TN, p. A573

TURNER, Sherrilyn, Director Human Resources, Southeast Colorado Hospital District, Springfield, CO, p. A105

TURNER, Spencer, Chief Executive Officer, Texas Health Presbyterian Hospital Flower Mound, Flower Mound, TX, p. A602

TURNER, Steve, Director Information Technology, Salem Township Hospital, Salem, IL, p. A194

TURNER, Wade, M.D. Chief of Staff, William Newton Hospital, Winfield, KS, p. A247

TURNEY, Brian, Chief Executive Officer, Kingman Regional Medical Center, Kingman, AZ, p. A32

TURNEY, Larry, Administrator, Cochran Memorial Hospital, Morton, TX, p. A623

TURNEY, Vern
Director Information Services, Lourdes Counseling Center, Richland, WA, p. A670
Director Information Technology, Lourdes Medical Center, Pasco, WA, p. A669

TURNQUIST, Carrie, Director Human Resources, Buena Vista Regional Medical Center, Storm Lake, IA, p. A229

TURSKY, Martin, President and Chief Executive Officer, Firelands Regional Health System, Sandusky, OH, p. A489

TURSO, Janet, Controller, HEALTHSOUTH Rehabilitation Hospital of Toms River, Toms River, NJ, p. A411

TUSA, Edward A., Chief Financial Officer, Mayo Clinic Health System in Cannon Falls, Cannon Falls, MN, p. A330

TUSCANY, Joanne E., Director Worklife Services, St. John Macomb–Oakland Hospital, Warren, MI, p. A326

TUSTEN, Jay, Chief Executive Officer, Stanton County Hospital, Johnson, KS, p. A236

TUTTLE, Jamie, Coordinator Human Resources, Warren Memorial Hospital, Friend, NE, p. A383

TUTTLE, Kathryn, Clinical Director of Nursing, Memorial Medical Center – Ashland, Ashland, WI, p. A683

TVEIT, Charles B., Chief Executive Officer, Lake District Hospital, Lakeview, OR, p. A514

TWARDY, Cindi, Manager Human Resources, Meeker Memorial Hospital, Litchfield, MN, p. A334

TWIDALE, Margaret, Manager Information Systems, Kane Community Hospital, Kane, PA, p. A528

TWIDWELL, Lisa, Administrator, Madison Medical Center, Fredericktown, MO, p. A361

TWILLIGEAR, Cindy, Manager Human Resources, Alexandria Veterans Affairs Health Care System, Pineville, LA, p. A276

TWO BEARS, Eric, Chief Information Officer, Pioneer Community Hospital of Newton, Newton, MS, p. A352

TWO HAWK, Sophie M., Chief Executive Officer, U. S. Public Health Service Indian Hospital, Rosebud, SD, p. A562

TYE, Angie, Director Human Resources, Waverly Health Center, Waverly, IA, p. A229

TYK, Robert C., Chief Financial Officer, Hi–Desert Medical Center, Joshua Tree, CA, p. A64

TYLER, Holley, R.N. Chief Nursing Officer, Valley Regional Medical Center, Brownsville, TX, p. A590

TYLER, James E., Vice President, Regional Hospital, Carilion Giles Community Hospital, Pearisburg, VA, p. A659

TYLER, Philene, Chief Finance Officer, Chinle Comprehensive Health Care Facility, Chinle, AZ, p. A30

TYLER, Richard, Corporate Director Human Resources, Conway Regional Medical Center, Conway, AR, p. A42

TYLER, Rick, M.D. Vice President Medical Affairs, CHRISTUS Hospital–St. Elizabeth, Beaumont, TX, p. A587

TYLER, Rosamond M., Administrator, Tyler Holmes Memorial Hospital, Winona, MS, p. A355

TYLER, Tanya
Vice President Human Resources, Memorial Medical Center – Lufkin, Lufkin, TX, p. A620
Vice President Human Resources, Memorial Specialty Hospital, Lufkin, TX, p. A620

TYLKOWSKI, Chester, M.D. Chief of Staff, Shriners Hospitals for Children–Lexington, Lexington, KY, p. A254

TYNES, Jr., L. Lee, M.D. Medical Director, Central Louisiana State Hospital, Pineville, LA, p. A277

TYRA, Diana, Director Health Information, Kentucky River Medical Center, Jackson, KY, p. A253

TYRRELL, Lawrence, Chief Financial Officer, Pacifica Hospital of the Valley,, CA, p. A71

TYRRELL, Shawn O., R.N. VP/Chief Nursing Officer, Adventist Hinsdale Hospital, Hinsdale, IL, p. A185

TYSON, Bill, Chief Information Officer, Miami Veterans Affairs Healthcare System, Miami, FL, p. A132

TYSON, Charlotte C., Chief Operating Officer, Lewis–Gale Medical Center, Salem, VA, p. A661

TYSON, Peggy, Director Human Resources, Research Psychiatric Center, Kansas City, MO, p. A363

# U

UBBING, Mina H., President and Chief Executive Officer, Fairfield Medical Center, Lancaster, OH, p. A483

UBER, Charlotte M., Chief Executive Officer, Warren State Hospital, Warren, PA, p. A543

UDALL, Ben, M.D. Chief of Staff, Kimble Hospital, Junction, TX, p. A615

UDALL, Jared, Chief Financial Officer, Rehabilitation Hospital of Southern New Mexico, Las Cruces, NM, p. A416

UFFER, Mark H., Chief Executive Officer, Colorado River Medical Center, Needles, CA, p. A76

UGHOUWA, Ejiro, M.D. Chief of Staff, Allen Parish Hospital, Kinder, LA, p. A270

UHLIK, Allen, M.D. Chief of Staff, Copper Basin Medical Center, Copperhill, TN, p. A568

UHLIR, Tricia, Chief Executive Officer, Fall River Hospital, Hot Springs, SD, p. A560

ULBRICHT, John E., Chief Operating Officer, Laredo Medical Center, Laredo, TX, p. A618

ULBRICHT, William G., President, St. Anthony's Hospital, Saint Petersburg, FL, p. A139

ULDRICH, Patricia, R.N. Chief Nursing Officer, St. James Mercy Health System, Hornell, NY, p. A427

ULI, James, Chief Financial Officer, Loma Linda University Medical Center–Murrieta, Murrieta, CA, p. A75

ULICNY, Gary R., Ph.D., President and Chief Executive Officer, Shepherd Center, Atlanta, GA, p. A147

ULLRICH, Nathan, M.D. Chief Medical Officer, Whitman Hospital and Medical Center, Colfax, WA, p. A665

ULMER, Carlton, Chief Executive Officer, Gulf Coast Medical Center, Panama City, FL, p. A136

ULMER, Carol, Chief Executive Officer, Select Specialty Hospital–Sioux Falls, Sioux Falls, SD, p. A562

ULREICH, Shawn, R.N. Vice President Clinical Operations and Chief Nursing Executive, Spectrum Health – Grand Rapids, Grand Rapids, MI, p. A315

ULREY, Chris, Director Management Information Systems, St. Luke's Behavioral Health Center, Phoenix, AZ, p. A35

ULRICH Jr., James P., President and Chief Executive Officer, Community Hospital, McCook, NE, p. A386

ULRICH, Tanya, Director Human Resources, Forbes Regional Hospital, Monroeville, PA, p. A532

ULSETH, Randy, Chief Executive Officer, FirstLight Health System, Mora, MN, p. A337

UMPHREY, Thomas, Senior Vice President Human Resources, The Aroostook Medical Center, Presque Isle, ME, p. A285

UNDERDAHL, Steve, Chief Executive Officer, Northfield Hospital, Northfield, MN, p. A337

UNDERWOOD, Debbie, Manager Human Resources, Plains Memorial Hospital, Dimmitt, TX, p. A599

UNDERWOOD, Ken, Chief Executive Officer, Hazel Hawkins Memorial Hospital, Hollister, CA, p. A64

UNDERWOOD, Mal, Interim Sr. VP and Chief Financial Officer, DeKalb Medical at North Decatur, Decatur, GA, p. A152

UNDERWOOD, Martha, Chief Human Resources Officer, Saint Thomas Midtown Hospital, Nashville, TN, p. A576

UNDERWOOD, Patricia A., Chief Financial Officer, Magee Rehabilitation Hospital, Philadelphia, PA, p. A535

UNDERWOOD, Vickie, Director Human Resources, Wyandot Memorial Hospital, Upper Sandusky, OH, p. A491

UNELL, Deonna, Chief Executive Officer, Irving Coppell Surgical Hospital, Irving, TX, p. A615

UNG, Oon Soo, Chief Financial Officer, West Palm Hospital, West Palm Beach, FL, p. A144

UNGER, Kevin L., FACHE, President and Chief Executive Officer, Poudre Valley Hospital, Fort Collins, CO, p. A101

UNROE, Larry, Interim Chief Executive Officer, Pleasant Valley Hospital, Point Pleasant, WV, p. A680

UNRUH, Greg, Chief Executive Officer, Community HealthCare System, Onaga, KS, p. A241

UNTCH, Matt, Controller, Research Psychiatric Center, Kansas City, MO, p. A363

UNZEN, John, Chief Financial Officer, Mille Lacs Health System, Onamia, MN, p. A337

UPADHYAY, Yogendra, M.D. Senior Vice President Medical Affairs, South Oaks Hospital, Amityville, NY, p. A420

UPCHURCH, Jim, M.D. Chief Medical Officer, Crow/Northern Cheyenne Hospital, Crow Agency, MT, p. A375

UPDIKE, Wanda, M.D. Chief of Staff, Salt Lake Regional Medical Center, Salt Lake City, UT, p. A647

UPFIELD, Jaclyn, Chief Operating Officer, G. Werber Bryan Psychiatric Hospital, Columbia, SC, p. A550

UPHAM, Kevin, Chief Human Resources Officer, Minneapolis Veterans Affairs Health Care System, Minneapolis, MN, p. A336

UPTON, Daniel, Vice President and Chief Financial Officer, Doylestown Hospital, Doylestown, PA, p. A524

UPTON, Scott, Administrator, Jane Phillips Nowata Health Center, Nowata, OK, p. A502

URADNIK, Michael, Chief Operating Officer, Fairfax Hospital, Kirkland, WA, p. A667

URAIZEE, Rizwan A., Chief Financial Officer, Kedren Community Mental Health Center, Los Angeles, CA, p. A70

URBACH, Marlene R., Chief Human Resources Officer, Doctors Hospital at White Rock Lake, Dallas, TX, p. A595

URBAN, Dan, Vice President of Finance, Monroe Hospital, Bloomington, IN, p. A199

URBAN, Frank
Chief Financial Officer, River Crest Hospital, San Angelo, TX, p. A630
Chief Financial Officer, Southwood Psychiatric Hospital, Pittsburgh, PA, p. A538

URBAN, Louise, R.N. Executive Vice President and Chief Operating Officer, Jefferson Regional Medical Center, Jefferson Hills, PA, p. A528

URRAN, Thomas S., Market Leader and President, Mercy Health – Fairfield Hospital, Fairfield, OH, p. A481

URBAN, Tom, Director Human Resources, Wills Memorial Hospital, Washington, GA, p. A162

URBANCSIK, Don
Director Finance, Euclid Hospital, Euclid, OH, p. A481
Director Finance, Lutheran Hospital, Cleveland, OH, p. A476

URBANSKI, Joanne, President and Chief Executive Officer, South Haven Health System, South Haven, MI, p. A324

URBANSKI, Pamela A., R.N. Chief Nursing Officer, Senior Vice President, Patient Care Services, Mercy Memorial Hospital System, Monroe, MI, p. A320

URBISTONDO, Lisa, Chief Financial Officer, Peach Regional Medical Center, Fort Valley, GA, p. A154

URDANETA, Alfonso, M.D. President Medical Staff, Washington County Hospital, Nashville, IL, p. A190

URLAUB, Charles J., President and Chief Executive Officer, Mercy Hospital, Buffalo, NY, p. A422

UROFSKY, Michele L., Executive Vice President and Chief Administrative Officer, Holy Redeemer Hospital and Medical Center, Meadowbrook, PA, p. A531

URQUHART, Mary, Vice President Patient Care, Brattleboro Memorial Hospital, Brattleboro, VT, p. A649

URVAND, Leslie O., Administrator, St. Luke's Hospital, Crosby, ND, p. A466

URZAK, Staci, Director Patient Care Services, Regional Health Services of Howard County, Cresco, IA, p. A219

USELMAN, Krista, Chief Executive Officer, HEALTHSOUTH Rehabilitation Hospital of North Houston, Conroe, TX, p. A593

USHAK, Don, Director Information Systems, New York Eye and Ear Infirmary, New York, NY, p. A435

USHER, David, Chief Financial Officer, Kimball Health Services, Kimball, NE, p. A385

USHER, Paul L., President and Chief Executive Officer, Marion General Hospital, Marion, IN, p. A209

USHIJIMA, Arthur A., President, Queen's Medical Center, Honolulu, HI, p. A165

UTECHT, Dawan, Chief Executive Officer, Community Behavioral Health Center, Fresno, CA, p. A61

UTECHT, Tom, M.D. Chief Quality Officer, Community Regional Medical Center, Fresno, CA, p. A61

UTEMARK, Paul, Chief Executive Officer, Fillmore County Hospital, Geneva, NE, p. A383

UTLEY, Donna, Vice President Human Resources, Mercy San Juan Medical Center, Carmichael, CA, p. A56

UTLEY, Kelly, Chief Financial Officer, Sidney Regional Medical Center, Sidney, NE, p. A389

UTTENDORFSKY, Rob, Director Information Management, Lewis County General Hospital, Lowville, NY, p. A428

UTTERBACK, Julie, Vice President and Chief Financial Officer, Methodist Medical Center of Oak Ridge, Oak Ridge, TN, p. A578

UY, Rogelio, M.D. Chief of Staff, Middlesboro ARH Hospital, Middlesboro, KY, p. A257

UYEMURA, Monte, M.D. Chief of Staff, Wray Community District Hospital, Wray, CO, p. A107

UZZELL, Justina M.
Chief Human Resources Officer, Banner Baywood Medical Center, Mesa, AZ, p. A32
Chief People Resources Officer, Banner Heart Hospital, Mesa, AZ, p. A33

# V

VAAGENES, Carl P., Chief Executive Officer, Douglas County Hospital, Alexandria, MN, p. A328

VAALER, Mark, M.D
Chief Medical Officer, South Florida Baptist Hospital, Plant City, FL, p. A137
Vice President Medical Staff Affairs, St. Joseph's Hospital, Tampa, FL, p. A142

VACCO, Michael, M.D. Chief Medical Officer, Wellmont Lonesome Pine Hospital, Big Stone Gap, VA, p. A651

VACHEK, Paul, Vice President of Finance/Operations, Saint Alphonsus Medical Center – Ontario, Ontario, OR, p. A515

VACHON, Scott, Director Information Technology, Littleton Regional Hospital, Littleton, NH, p. A399

VADEN, Jim, Director Information Systems, Lauderdale Community Hospital, Ripley, TN, p. A578

VAGUE, Jeff, Regional Manager Information Systems, Mercy Hospitals of Bakersfield, Bakersfield, CA, p. A54

VAHLBERG, Susan, Director Employee and Community Relations, Walter Knox Memorial Hospital, Emmett, ID, p. A169

VAIL, B. J., Director Information Systems, Morehouse General Hospital, Bastrop, LA, p. A263

VAIL, Bryan, Chief Information Officer, Clement J. Zablocki Veterans Affairs Medical Center, Milwaukee, WI, p. A692

VAIL, Lisa M., R.N. Chief Nursing Officer and Vice President of Patient Care Services, Bryan Medical Center, Lincoln, NE, p. A385

VAIL, Lucy M.
Director Human Resources & Partner Relations, Sparrow Clinton Hospital, Saint Johns, MI, p. A323
Director HR Partner Relationships, Sparrow Specialty Hospital, Lansing, MI, p. A318

VAIL, Ronald, M.D. Chief of Staff, Lower Umpqua Hospital District, Reedsport, OR, p. A517

VAIL, Terrence, Acting Chief Human Resources Management Services, San Francisco Veterans Affairs Medical Center, San Francisco, CA, p. A87

VAILLANCOURT, Alex, Chief Information Officer, Christ Hospital, Cincinnati, OH, p. A474

VAILLANCOURT, Stacy, Vice President Marketing, Communications, Advocacy and Human Resources, Saint Agnes Medical Center, Fresno, CA, p. A61

VAIOLETI, Stephany, Administrator, Kahuku Medical Center, Kahuku, HI, p. A165

VAKHARIA, Mahaveer, M.D. Medical Director, RiverWoods Behavioral Health System, Riverdale, GA, p. A158

VALBUENA, Richard, M.D. Medical Director, Latimer County General Hospital, Wilburton, OK, p. A510

VALDERA, Trummell, Senior Vice President and Chief Human Resources Officer, Jackson Health System, Miami, FL, p. A131

VALDERAZ, Leonard, Administrator, Sunrise Canyon Hospital, Lubbock, TX, p. A620

VALDESPINO, Gustavo A., President and Chief Executive Officer, Valley Presbyterian Hospital,, CA, p. A72

VALDEZ, Mary, Chief Operating Officer, South Texas Rehabilitation Hospital, Brownsville, TX, p. A590

VALENCERINA, Madeline, Chief Operating Officer, Kedren Community Mental Health Center, Los Angeles, CA, p. A70

VALENTE, Anthony, M.D. Vice President Medical Affairs, Hazleton General Hospital, Hazleton, PA, p. A527

VALENTI, James N., FACHE, President and Chief Executive Officer, University Medical Center of El Paso, El Paso, TX, p. A602

VALENTINE, Lisa R., Interim Chief Executive Officer, Henrico Doctors' Hospital, Richmond, VA, p. A660

VALENTINE, Mark, President, The Heart Hospital Baylor Plano, Plano, TX, p. A628

VALENTINE, Robert A., Regional Administrator, Alegent Creighton Health Community Memorial Hospital, Missouri Valley, IA, p. A225

VALENTO, Jessica, Director Information Systems, Range Regional Health Services, Hibbing, MN, p. A334

VALK, Keith, Vice President Human Resources, Aurelia Osborn Fox Memorial Hospital, Oneonta, NY, p. A438

VALLADOLID, Sara, M.D. Medical Director, Sage Memorial Hospital, Ganado, AZ, p. A31

VALLES, John, Senior Vice President and Chief Financial Officer, Loretto Hospital, Chicago, IL, p. A177

VALLEY, Curt, Customer Site Manager, McLaren Bay Region, Bay City, MI, p. A309

VALLIANT, Mary T., MS, Chief Executive Officer, Barnwell County Hospital, Barnwell, SC, p. A548

VALLIDO, Gabe, Chief Information Officer, Naval Hospital Camp Pendleton, Camp Pendleton, CA, p. A55

VALLIERE, George, Chief Executive Officer, Claremore Indian Hospital, Claremore, OK, p. A497

VALLIERE, Mark, M.D. Senior Vice President Medical Affairs and Chief Medical Officer, Mercy Medical Center–Cedar Rapids, Cedar Rapids, IA, p. A217

VALLIERRE, Walter, Chief Administrative Officer, St. Elizabeths Hospital, Washington, DC, p. A117

VAMPRINE, Laurene, Senior Vice President Information Systems, Erlanger Medical Center, Chattanooga, TN, p. A566

VAN ARSDAL, Al, Director Human Resources, Covenant Medical Center, Saginaw, MI, p. A323

VAN BOENING, Jon, President and Chief Executive Officer and Senior Vice President Operations Dignity Health Central Va, Bakersfield Memorial Hospital, Bakersfield, CA, p. A53

VAN BREE, Margaret M., Dr.PH, Chief Executive Officer, St. Luke's Episcopal Hospital, Houston, TX, p. A612

VAN BUREN, Shelly, Director Human Resources, Frances Mahon Deaconess Hospital, Glasgow, MT, p. A376

VAN BUSKIRK, George F., M.D. Chief of Staff, Bay Pines Veterans Affairs Medical Center, Bay Pines, FL, p. A118

VAN CAMP, Keith, Vice President Information Services, St. Dominic–Jackson Memorial Hospital, Jackson, MS, p. A349

VAN CLEAVE, Bruce L., M.D
Senior Vice President and Chief Medical Officer, Aurora Medical Center of Oshkosh, Oshkosh, WI, p. A694
Senior Vice President and Chief Medical Officer, Aurora St. Luke's Medical Center, Milwaukee, WI, p. A691

VAN CLEAVE, Vanetta, Chief Financial Officer, Yukon–Kuskokwim Delta Regional Hospital, Bethel, AK, p. A27

VAN DE KREEKE, Jeffrey, Senior Vice President Finance, Froedtert Memorial Lutheran Hospital, Milwaukee, WI, p. A692

VAN DECAR, Tama, M.D. Chief Medical Officer, Fort Walton Beach Medical Center, Fort Walton Beach, FL, p. A124

VAN DEE, Keith, Director Human Resources, Drew Memorial Hospital, Monticello, AR, p. A47

VAN DER HORST, Hendrik, Chief Information Officer, Ira Davenport Memorial Hospital, Bath, NY, p. A421

VAN DONSELAAR, Lois J., R.N. Vice President & Chief Nursing Officer, Borgess Medical Center, Kalamazoo, MI, p. A317

VAN DRIEL, Allen, FACHE, Administrator, Smith County Memorial Hospital, Smith Center, KS, p. A244

VAN GHELUWE, Betty, Chief Operating Officer, St. Luke's Elmore, Mountain Home, ID, p. A170

VAN GUNDY, Milt, M.D. President Medical Staff, Marshalltown Medical & Surgical Center, Marshalltown, IA, p. A225

VAN HEUSEN, Melanie, Director Human Resources, Gateways Hospital and Mental Health Center, Los Angeles, CA, p. A69

VAN HOFF, Cynthia, Chief Financial Officer, Sutter Solano Medical Center, Vallejo, CA, p. A94

VAN HORN, Jeff, Chief Executive Officer, Mountain View Regional Hospital, Casper, WY, p. A701

VAN HORN, William, M.D. Medical Director, Lighthouse Care Center of Conway, Conway, SC, p. A551

VAN HYNING, Jill, Director Human Resources, Richland Memorial Hospital, Olney, IL, p. A191

VAN KAMPEN, Cindy, Chief Nursing Officer, North Ottawa Community Hospital, Grand Haven, MI, p. A314

VAN LOON, Glen, M.D. Chief of Staff, Marshall County Hospital, Benton, KY, p. A248

VAN LOOY, James, M.D. Chief Medical Executive, Altru Health System, Grand Forks, ND, p. A467

VAN LUVEN, Audrey C., Senior Vice President and Chief Human Resources Officer, Christiana Care Health System, Newark, DE, p. A114

VAN MATRE, Jennifer, Director Finance and Information Technology, Trinity Hospital, Weaverville, CA, p. A95

VAN MEETEREN, Robert, President and Chief Executive Officer, Reedsburg Area Medical Center, Reedsburg, WI, p. A695

VAN METER, Rex, President, INTEGRIS Canadian Valley Hospital, Yukon, OK, p. A510

VAN NORMAN, Steven, M.D. Medical Director, Dixie Regional Medical Center, Saint George, UT, p. A646

VAN NOY, William J., Chief Financial Officer, Tehachapi Valley Healthcare District, Tehachapi, CA, p. A92

VAN RYBROEK, Greg, Chief Executive Officer, Mendota Mental Health Institute, Madison, WI, p. A689

VAN SCOYK, Mitch, Manager Information Systems, Delta County Memorial Hospital, Delta, CO, p. A99

VAN STRATEN, Elizabeth, President and Chief Executive Officer, St. Bernard Hospital and Health Care Center, Chicago, IL, p. A179

VAN STRATTON, Kate, Manager Human Resources, University Hospitals Geneva Medical Center, Geneva, OH, p. A482

VAN VICKLE, Robin, Chief Financial Officer, Bristow Medical Center, Bristow, OK, p. A496

VAN VRANKEN, Arthur, M.D. Chief Medical Officer, Essentia Health–Holy Trinity Hospital, Graceville, MN, p. A333

VAN VRANKEN, Ross, Executive Director, University of Utah Neuropsychiatric Institute, Salt Lake City, UT, p. A647

VAN WHY, Susan, Director Human Resources, St. Luke's Hospital – Miners Campus, Coaldale, PA, p. A523

VAN WINKLE, Melanie, Chief Financial Officer, Mammoth Hospital, Mammoth Lakes, CA, p. A73

VAN ZANTEN, Lorinda, MSN, Chief Executive Officer, Providence Newberg Medical Center, Newberg, OR, p. A515

VAN ZANTEN, Niko, M.D. Chief of Staff, Sac–Osage Hospital, Osceola, MO, p. A367

VANASKIE, William F., Executive Vice President and Chief Operating Officer, Maricopa Integrated Health System, Phoenix, AZ, p. A34

VANBEEK, Jan, Chief Executive Officer, Crook County Medical Services District, Sundance, WY, p. A704

VANBOEKEL, Tony, Director Information Systems, Shasta Regional Medical Center, Redding, CA, p. A81

VANCE, Amy
  Executive Vice President and Chief Operating Officer, Novant Health Matthews Medical Center, Matthews, NC, p. A457
  Executive Vice President and Chief Operating Officer, Novant Health Presbyterian Medical Center, Charlotte, NC, p. A450

VANCE, Ellen B.
  Vice President Human Resources, Sheltering Arms Hospital South, Midlothian, VA, p. A657
  Chief Human Resource Officer, Sheltering Arms Rehabilitation Hospital, Mechanicsville, VA, p. A657

VANCE, Mark, M.D. Chief Medical Officer, Quincy Valley Medical Center, Quincy, WA, p. A670

VANCE, Stacie, Vice President Clinical Services, Indiana Orthopaedic Hospital, Indianapolis, IN, p. A205

VANCONIA, R. Brent, President, St. Marys Health Center, Jefferson City, MO, p. A362

VANCOURT, Bernie, Chief Operating Officer, Bay Area Medical Center, Marinette, WI, p. A690

VANDENBARK, Heather, Human Resources Specialist, State Hospital North, Orofino, ID, p. A170

VANDENBERG, Andra, Director Human Resources, Butler County Health Care Center, David City, NE, p. A383

VANDENBOSCH, Darryl, Vice President and Chief Financial Officer, St. Bernardine Medical Center, San Bernardino, CA, p. A84

VANDER DOES, Victor, Interim Administrator and Chief Executive Officer, Pioneer Memorial Hospital, Heppner, OR, p. A513

VANDERBEEK, Sam, Chief Information Officer, W. J. Mangold Memorial Hospital, Lockney, TX, p. A619

VANDERHOOFT, J. Eric, M.D. President Medical Staff, St. Mark's Hospital, Salt Lake City, UT, p. A647

VANDERMARK, Jay H., Chief Financial Officer, Veterans Affairs Northern Indiana Health Care System, Fort Wayne, IN, p. A203

VANDERPOOL, Lee, Vice President, Dominican Hospital, Santa Cruz, CA, p. A90

VANDERSLICE, Doug, Vice President and Chief Financial Officer, St. Louis Children's Hospital, Saint Louis, MO, p. A371

VANDERSTEK, Eliott R., Chief Fiscal Service, Veterans Affairs Eastern Colorado Health Care System, Denver, CO, p. A100

VANDERSTOUW, Karl, Director Management Information Systems, Lenoir Memorial Hospital, Kinston, NC, p. A456

VANDERVLIET, William, M.D. Vice President Medical Affairs, Holland Hospital, Holland, MI, p. A316

VANDERWEGE, Larry, Administrator and Chief Executive Officer, Lindsborg Community Hospital, Lindsborg, KS, p. A239

VANDERWERF, Quinten, M.D. Chief Medical Officer, Eisenhower Medical Center, Rancho Mirage, CA, p. A81

VANDETTE, Joan, Vice President Human Resources, Brooks Memorial Hospital, Dunkirk, NY, p. A425

VANDEVEER Jr., Alden M., FACHE, Chief Executive Officer, Kiowa District Hospital and Manor, Kiowa, KS, p. A237

VANDEWEGE, Dana, Director Human Resources, Capital Medical Center, Olympia, WA, p. A668

VANDORT, Patti J., MSN Vice President Nursing/Chief Nursing Officer, Holland Hospital, Holland, MI, p. A316

VANDRUFF, John, M.D. Chief of Staff, Payson Regional Medical Center, Payson, AZ, p. A34

VANEK, James, Chief Executive Officer, Lavaca Medical Center, Hallettsville, TX, p. A607

VANES, Wendell, Chief Financial Officer, Saint Mary's Regional Medical Center, Russellville, AR, p. A49

VANGARI, Veena, R.N. Director of Nursing, Trinity Hospital, Weaverville, CA, p. A95

VANGENDEREN, Nathan, Chief Financial Officer, Sentara Northern Virginia Medical Center, Woodbridge, VA, p. A663

VANHAREN, James, M.D. Medical Director, Forest View Psychiatric Hospital, Grand Rapids, MI, p. A314

VANHOUWELING, Mason, Chief Operating Officer, Spring Valley Hospital Medical Center, Las Vegas, NV, p. A393

VANMARCKE, Thibaut, Chief Operating Officer, Medical Center of Trinity, Trinity, FL, p. A143

VANMEETREN, Victoria J., President, St. Rose Dominican Hospitals – San Martin Campus, Las Vegas, NV, p. A393

VANNETT, Vince, Director Human Resources, Jellico Community Hospital, Jellico, TN, p. A571

VANNOY, Patricia, Controller, Oakwood Southshore Medical Center, Trenton, MI, p. A325

VANOSDOL, Thomas J., President, St. Vincent Anderson Regional Hospital, Anderson, IN, p. A198

VANRAVENSWAAY, Mark, Coordinator Information Systems, Wagner Community Memorial Hospital Avera, Wagner, SD, p. A563

VANSANT, Scott, M.D. Chief Medical Officer, Central State Hospital, Milledgeville, GA, p. A157

VANVEEN, Thomas, M.D. Chief Medical Officer, Santiam Memorial Hospital, Stayton, OR, p. A518

VANWICHEN, Ward C., Chief Executive Officer, Phillips County Hospital, Malta, MT, p. A378

VANWYHE, Brenda, Senior Vice President Finance and Chief Financial Officer, Rush–Copley Medical Center, Aurora, IL, p. A174

VARA, John, M.D. Chief of Staff, Miami Veterans Affairs Healthcare System, Miami, FL, p. A132

VARELA, Nancy, Director Human Resources, Patton State Hospital, Patton, CA, p. A79

VARGA, Patrick, Chief Operating Officer, Mercy Medical Center Redding, Redding, CA, p. A81

VARGAS, Jose L., M.D. Medical Director, West Gables Rehabilitation Hospital, Miami, FL, p. A132

VARGAS, Margie, Director Human Resources, Memorial Hospital Pembroke, Pembroke Pines, FL, p. A136

VARGAS, Nancy
  Director Human Resources, Mark Twain St. Joseph's Hospital, San Andreas, CA, p. A84
  Chief Human Resources, St. Joseph's Behavioral Health Center, Stockton, CA, p. A92
  Vice President Human Resources, St. Joseph's Medical Center, Stockton, CA, p. A92

VARGHESE, Roy, M.D. Chief of Staff, Mary Breckinridge ARH Hospital, Hyden, KY, p. A253

VARGHESE, Shibu, Vice President Human Resources, University of Texas M.D. Anderson Cancer Center, Houston, TX, p. A613

VARIAN, Grant, M.D. Medical Director, Mary Rutan Hospital, Bellefontaine, OH, p. A471

VARK, Lawrence, M.D. Chief Medical Officer, Creek Nation Community Hospital, Okemah, OK, p. A502

VARLAND, Drew, Chief Nursing Officer and Chief Operating Officer, Pioneers Medical Center, Meeker, CO, p. A104

VARLEY, Kevin
  Chief Financial Officer, Kindred Hospital South Philadelphia, Philadelphia, PA, p. A535
  Chief Financial Officer, Kindred Hospital–Heritage Valley, Beaver, PA, p. A520
  Chief Financial Officer, Kindred Hospital–Pittsburgh, Oakdale, PA, p. A533

VARNADO, Anjanette, M.D. Chief Medical Officer, St. Helena Parish Hospital, Greensburg, LA, p. A267

VARNADO, Darryl, Vice President Human Resources, University of Colorado Hospital, Aurora, CO, p. A97

VARNADO, Krystyna, Director Human Resources, Garden Park Medical Center, Gulfport, MS, p. A347

VARNADOE, Milo, Director Information Systems, Warm Springs Medical Center, Warm Springs, GA, p. A162

VARNER, Terry, Administrator, Yalobusha General Hospital, Water Valley, MS, p. A354

VARNUM, Daniel, President and Chief Executive Officer, Mercy Medical Center–North Iowa, Mason City, IA, p. A225

VARTELAS, Helene M., Chief Executive Officer, Connecticut Valley Hospital, Middletown, CT, p. A110

VASHISHTA, Ashok, M.D
  Vice President Medical Affairs, McLaren Bay Region, Bay City, MI, p. A309
  Vice President Medical Affairs, McLaren Central Michigan, Mount Pleasant, MI, p. A320

VASKELIS, Glenna L., CPA, President and Administrator and Senior Vice President Operations Dignity Health Bay Area Service Are, Sequoia Hospital, Redwood City, CA, p. A82

VASQUEZ, Alberto, Administrator, Garfield Memorial Hospital and Clinics, Panguitch, UT, p. A645

VASQUEZ, Chris, Executive Vice President and Chief Operating Officer, University Health System, San Antonio, TX, p. A632

VASQUEZ, George
  Chief Technology Officer, Clovis Community Medical Center, Clovis, CA, p. A56
  Vice President Information Services, Community Behavioral Health Center, Fresno, CA, p. A61

VASQUEZ, Miguel, Chief Financial Officer, Sister Emmanuel Hospital, Miami, FL, p. A132

VASQUEZ, Nelson, Vice President Finance, Jackson Park Hospital and Medical Center, Chicago, IL, p. A177

VASS, Kathy, Head Human Resources, Naval Hospital Oak Harbor, Oak Harbor, WA, p. A668

VASSALL, John, M.D
  Chief Medical Officer, Swedish Medical Center–Cherry Hill Campus, Seattle, WA, p. A671
  Chief Medical Officer, Swedish Medical Center–First Hill, Seattle, WA, p. A671

VASSAR, Debra, Chief Nursing Officer, Arkansas Methodist Medical Center, Paragould, AR, p. A49

VASUNAGA, Amy, Chief Nurse Executive, Leahi Hospital, Honolulu, HI, p. A164

VATH, Richard, M.D. Vice President Medical Affairs, Our Lady of the Lake Regional Medical Center, Baton Rouge, LA, p. A263

VATSAVAI, Sundararama R., M.D. Medical Director, Baton Rouge Rehabilitation Hospital, Baton Rouge, LA, p. A263

VAUGHAN, Aaron, Coordinator Information Systems, Pocahontas Memorial Hospital, Buckeye, WV, p. A675

VAUGHAN, Amanda, Chief Financial Officer, St. Catherine Hospital, Garden City, KS, p. A234

VAUGHAN, Brandon, Chief Financial Officer, Jacobson Memorial Hospital Care Center, Elgin, ND, p. A466

VAUGHAN, Brian, Chief Financial Officer, Lovelace Medical Center, Albuquerque, NM, p. A414

VAUGHAN, Page H., Chief Executive Officer, Chester Regional Medical Center, Chester, SC, p. A549

VAUGHAN, Peggy, M.D
  Senior Vice President Medical Affairs, Harford Memorial Hospital, Havre De Grace, MD, p. A292
  Senior Vice President Medical Affairs, Upper Chesapeake Medical Center, Bel Air, MD, p. A289

VAUGHAN, Rob, Chief Financial Officer, Carilion New River Valley Medical Center, Christiansburg, VA, p. A652

VAUGHAN, Steve, Chief Executive Officer, Pearl River County Hospital, Poplarville, MS, p. A353

VAUGHN, Anita, Administrator and Chief Executive Officer, Baptist Memorial Hospital for Women, Memphis, TN, p. A574

VAUGHN, Barbara, Chief Nursing Officer, Baylor Medical Center at Carrollton, Carrollton, TX, p. A591

VAUGHN, Dennise
  Vice President Corporate Resources, Edward Hospital, Naperville, IL, p. A189
  Vice President Corporate Resources, Linden Oaks Hospital at Edward, Naperville, IL, p. A189

VAUGHN, Kerry, Chief Information Officer, St. Mary's Health Care System, Athens, GA, p. A145

VAUGHN, Kevin P., Chief Financial Officer, Kansas Spine Hospital, Wichita, KS, p. A246

VAUGHN, Michael, Chief Financial Officer, Monroe County Hospital, Monroeville, AL, p. A23

VAUGHN, Sandy, Director Information Services, Baylor All Saints Medical Center at Fort Worth, Fort Worth, TX, p. A603

VAUGHN, Ted W., Director Human Resources, Trinity Regional Medical Center, Fort Dodge, IA, p. A221

VAZIRI, H. Kevin, President, Woodland Healthcare, Woodland, CA, p. A96

VAZQUEZ, Emilio, M.D. Chief Medical Officer, DeKalb Health, Auburn, IN, p. A198

VAZQUEZ, Francisco, Associate Director, Michael E. DeBakey Veterans Affairs Medical Center, Houston, TX, p. A611

VEENSTRA, Henry A., President, Spectrum Health Zeeland Community Hospital, Zeeland, MI, p. A327

VEGA, James, Director Information Systems, Palm Beach Gardens Medical Center, Palm Beach Gardens, FL, p. A135

VEILLETTE, David, President and Chief Executive Officer, Western Regional Medical Center, Goodyear, AZ, p. A32

VEILLEUX, Jeffrey
  Senior Vice President and Chief Financial Officer, Swedish Medical Center–Cherry Hill Campus, Seattle, WA, p. A671
  Executive Vice President and Chief Financial Officer, Swedish Medical Center–First Hill, Seattle, WA, p. A671

VOELKEL, Jonathon, Chief Executive Officer, Wilbarger General Hospital, Vernon, TX, p. A639

VOELKER, Dolph, Director Information Services, Indiana University Health Goshen Hospital, Goshen, IN, p. A203

VOELKER, Justin, Chief Financial Officer, Valley Hospital, Spokane Valley, WA, p. A672

VOGEL, Jennifer, Director Human Resources, Aurora Sheboygan Memorial Medical Center, Sheboygan, WI, p. A696

VOGELSANG, Mark, Director Information Services, Providence Holy Family Hospital, Spokane, WA, p. A672

VOGENTIZ, William, M.D. Medical Director, AnMed Health Rehabilitation Hospital, Anderson, SC, p. A548

VOGT, Allen J., Chief Executive Officer, Cook Hospital and Convalescent Nursing Care Unit, Cook, MN, p. A330

VOGT, Dennis, Director Information Technology, Madison County Hospital, London, OH, p. A484

VOHS, Lester, Chief Information Management, Osawatomie State Hospital, Osawatomie, KS, p. A241

VOISARD, Victor, Director Human Resources, San Gabriel Valley Medical Center, San Gabriel, CA, p. A87

VOISELLE, Dana, Director Human Resources, Baptist Medical Center Beaches, Jacksonville Beach, FL, p. A127

VOLANTO, John, Vice President and Chief Information Officer, Nyack Hospital, Nyack, NY, p. A438

VOLENTINE, Robert, Director Information Services, Cibola General Hospital, Grants, NM, p. A416

VOLGER, Helen, Director of Information Services, Memorial Health Center, Medford, WI, p. A691

VOLINSKI, Douglas R., Vice President and Chief Financial Officer, Duncan Regional Hospital, Duncan, OK, p. A497

VOLK, Marita, M.D. Director Medical Services and Chief of Staff, Euclid Hospital, Euclid, OH, p. A481

VOLKERDING, Elizabeth, Director Workforce Excellence, San Juan Regional Medical Center, Farmington, NM, p. A416

VOLLMER, Cyndy, Director of Human Resources, Southern Coos Hospital and Health Center, Bandon, OR, p. A511

VOLOCH, Bill, Chief Operating Officer, Wesley Medical Center, Wichita, KS, p. A247

VOLPE, Buddy, Director Human Resources, Peterson Regional Medical Center, Kerrville, TX, p. A616

VOLPE, Michele M., Executive Director and Chief Executive Officer, Penn Presbyterian Medical Center, Philadelphia, PA, p. A536

VOLTAIRE, Adler, Chief Administrative Officer, Interim LSU Public Hospital, New Orleans, LA, p. A275

VON BEHREN, Rachel, Director Financial Services, Jones Regional Medical Center, Anamosa, IA, p. A216

VONDERAU, Mary, Vice President Strategy and Operations, Presence Mercy Medical Center, Aurora, IL, p. A173

VONK, Gail, Director Human Resources and Marketing, Sioux Center Community Hospital and Health Center Avera, Sioux Center, IA, p. A228

VOORDE, Christine T., Chief Executive Officer, Kindred Hospital of Northern Indiana, Mishawaka, IN, p. A210

VOORHEES, Michael, MS, Executive Director, East Mountain Hospital, Belle Mead, NJ, p. A401

VOSBURGH, Margaret, Chief Operating Officer, Stanford Hospital and Clinics, Palo Alto, CA, p. A79

VOSBURGH, Mary M., R.N
Vice President Nursing and Chief Nursing Officer, Arnot Ogden Medical Center, Elmira, NY, p. A425
Vice President Nursing and Chief Nursing Officer, St. Joseph's Hospital, Elmira, NY, p. A425

VOSHELL, Shane, Director Human Resources, Adventist Medical Center–Portland, Portland, OR, p. A515

VOSKAMP, Lynne, Chief Nursing Officer, Citizens Medical Center, Victoria, TX, p. A639

VOSS, Daryle, FACHE, President, Mercy Hospital Ardmore, Ardmore, OK, p. A495

VOSS, Kathy, Director Human Resources, CentraCare Health–Monticello, Monticello, MN, p. A336

VOSS, Robert
Chief Financial Officer, Laredo Specialty Hospital, Laredo, TX, p. A618
Chief Financial Officer, New Braunfels Regional Rehabilitation Hospital, New Braunfels, TX, p. A624

VOSS, Wayne M., Chief Executive Officer, Methodist West Houston Hospital, Houston, TX, p. A611

VOSSBERG, Brad, M.D. Chief Rehabilitation, Community Howard Specialty Hospital, Kokomo, IN, p. A207

VOSSLER, Jeffrey W., Vice President Financial Services, Joint Township District Memorial Hospital, Saint Marys, OH, p. A489

VOTAW, Anthony, Chief Information Officer, Cayuga Medical Center at Ithaca, Ithaca, NY, p. A427

VOTTO, John J., D.O., President and Chief Executive Officer, Hospital for Special Care, New Britain, CT, p. A110

VOZOS, Frank J., FACS, President and Chief Executive Officer, Monmouth Medical Center, Long Branch, NJ, p. A406

VRANA, Daniel A., Area Controller, HEALTHSOUTH Rehabilitation Hospital, Sewickley, PA, p. A541

VRAZEL, Desiree, Director of Nurses, El Campo Memorial Hospital, El Campo, TX, p. A600

VRBA, Frank, Chief Information Officer, Annie Jeffrey Memorial County Health Center, Osceola, NE, p. A388

VROTSOS, Darlene, R.N. Vice President and Chief Nursing Officer, Virginia Hospital Center – Arlington, Arlington, VA, p. A651

VUCHAK, Jerry
Vice President Information Systems, Barnes–Jewish Hospital, Saint Louis, MO, p. A369
Vice President Information Systems, Barnes–Jewish West County Hospital, Saint Louis, MO, p. A369

VUGRINEC, Barbara P., Vice President Information Systems, Beebe Medical Center, Lewes, DE, p. A114

VUKICH, David, M.D. Senior Vice President, Chief Medical Officer and Chief Quality Officer, Shands Jacksonville Medical Center, Jacksonville, FL, p. A126

VUKOVICH, Pamela S.
Senior Vice President, Chief Financial Officer and Treasurer, Legacy Emanuel Hospital and Health Center, Portland, OR, p. A516
Senior Vice President, Chief Financial Officer and Treasurer, Legacy Good Samaritan Hospital and Medical Center, Portland, OR, p. A516

VUKSTA, Jeanne, Chief Financial Officer, Bacharach Institute for Rehabilitation, Pomona, NJ, p. A409

VUOCOLO, Philip, M.D. Chief Medical Officer, Monadnock Community Hospital, Peterborough, NH, p. A400

# W

WAARALA, Kirsten, D.O. Vice President Medical Services, Garden City Hospital, Garden City, MI, p. A314

WABLE, Chad W., President and Chief Executive Officer, Saint Mary's Hospital, Waterbury, CT, p. A112

WACHTEL, R. Andrew, FACHE, Chief Executive Officer, Ponca City Medical Center, Ponca City, OK, p. A505

WACK, Mark, Chief Financial Officer, Biloxi Regional Medical Center, Biloxi, MS, p. A344

WADDELL, Lesa, Director Human Resources, UnityPoint Health – Marengo Memorial Hospital, Marengo, IA, p. A224

WADE, Donald, Interim Chief Executive Officer, Kit Carson County Memorial Hospital, Burlington, CO, p. A98

WADE, Donna, Senior Director Human Resources, Comanche County Memorial Hospital, Lawton, OK, p. A500

WADE, Glenn, Director Information Systems, Highlands Medical Center, Sparta, TN, p. A579

WADE, Hong, Chief Financial Officer, Sweeny Community Hospital, Sweeny, TX, p. A636

WADE, Jonathan O., President and Chief Executive Officer, Mercy St. Francis Hospital, Mountain View, MO, p. A366

WADE, Karen, Chief Information Officer, U. S. Public Health Service Indian Hospital–Sells, Sells, AZ, p. A37

WADE, Linda, Chief Executive Officer, HEALTHSOUTH Rehabilitation Hospital of Montgomery, Montgomery, AL, p. A23

WADE, Nancy, M.D. Chief of Staff, Hills & Dales General Hospital, Cass City, MI, p. A310

WADEWITZ, Martin, Chief Operations Officer/ Vice President, Operations, Angel Medical Center, Franklin, NC, p. A452

WADMAN, Timothy, Chief Executive Officer, SSM Rehabilitation Hospital, Bridgeton, MO, p. A357

WAFFORD, Marty, Chief Financial Officer, Chickasaw Nation Medical Center, Ada, OK, p. A495

WAGERS, Rick, Senior Executive Vice President and Chief Financial Officer, Regional Medical Center at Memphis, Memphis, TN, p. A575

WAGGENER, Yvonne, Chief Financial Officer, San Bernardino Mountains Community Hospital District, Lake Arrowhead, CA, p. A66

WAGGONER, Craig, Chief Operating Officer, Clovis Community Medical Center, Clovis, CA, p. A56

WAGGONER, Jeff, M.D. Chief of Staff, Weisbrod Memorial County Hospital, Eads, CO, p. A100

WAGGONER, Michelle, Vice President Human Resources and Physician Services, Community Memorial Hospital, Hicksville, OH, p. A483

WAGNER, Alan, Chief Operating Officer, Coulee Medical Center, Grand Coulee, WA, p. A667

WAGNER, Arthur, Senior Vice President and Executive Director, Coney Island Hospital,, NY, p. A431

WAGNER, Dale, Chief Financial Officer, Kindred Hospital–Westminster, Westminster, CA, p. A95

WAGNER, David D., Chief Information Management Service, Veterans Affairs Gulf Coast Veterans Health Care System, Biloxi, MS, p. A344

WAGNER, Jack W., Executive Vice President and Chief Financial Officer, Shawnee Mission Medical Center, Shawnee Mission, KS, p. A244

WAGNER, Janet, R.N., Chief Executive Officer, Sutter Davis Hospital, Davis, CA, p. A58

WAGNER, Linda, Chief Financial Officer, Sanford Worthington Medical Center, Worthington, MN, p. A343

WAGNER, Linda S., MSN, Chief Executive Officer, Seneca Healthcare District, Chester, CA, p. A56

WAGNER, Randall J., Chief Operating Officer, Saint Mary's Health Care, Grand Rapids, MI, p. A315

WAGNER, Richard, M.D. Chief of Staff, Jackson–Madison County General Hospital, Jackson, TN, p. A570

WAGNER, Russell R., Senior Vice President and Chief Financial Officer, Holy Redeemer Hospital and Medical Center, Meadowbrook, PA, p. A531

WAGNER, Sherry, Director Human Resources, Oklahoma Center for Orthopedic and Multi–Specialty Surgery, Oklahoma City, OK, p. A503

WAGNER, Suzie, Director Human Resources, HEALTHSOUTH Rehabilitation Hospital of Alexandria, Alexandria, LA, p. A262

WAGNER, Terry, R.N. Chief Operating Officer, Pocahontas Memorial Hospital, Buckeye, WV, p. A675

WAGNER, Terry, Chief Information Officer, Upstate University Hospital, Syracuse, NY, p. A444

WAGNER, Timothy, M.D. Chief Medical Staff, Yoakum Community Hospital, Yoakum, TX, p. A642

WAGNER, Tom, Interim Vice President Finance, Avera St. Mary's Hospital, Pierre, SD, p. A561

WAGNER, Vanessa, Chief Financial Officer, Lawrence Memorial Hospital, Walnut Ridge, AR, p. A50

WAGNON, LaNell, Director Medical Records, Comanche County Hospital, Coldwater, KS, p. A232

WAGNON, William, Chief Executive Officer, MountainView Hospital, Las Vegas, NV, p. A393

WAGONER, Dean, Director Human Resources, Good Samaritan Hospital, Vincennes, IN, p. A214

WAHL, Gene O., Chief Financial Officer, North Dakota State Hospital, Jamestown, ND, p. A468

WAHL, Josephine Sclafani, R.N. VP, Patient Care Services & CNO, Henry Ford Wyandotte Hospital, Wyandotte, MI, p. A327

WAHL, Tony, Chief Executive Officer, Texas Spine & Joint Hospital, Tyler, TX, p. A638

WAHLUND, Keith, Vice President Human Resources, Essentia Health Fargo, Fargo, ND, p. A466

WAIBEL, David, M.D. Medical Director, Clarks Summit State Hospital, Clarks Summit, PA, p. A522

WAIND, Mark, Administrative Director Information Services, Altru Health System, Grand Forks, ND, p. A467

WAITE, Douglas, M.D. Vice President Medical Affairs, Day Kimball Hospital, Putnam, CT, p. A111

WAITE, Douglas D.
Chief Financial Officer, Seton Edgar B. Davis Hospital, Luling, TX, p. A621
Senior Vice President and Chief Financial Officer, Seton Highland Lakes, Burnet, TX, p. A590
Chief Financial Officer, Seton Medical Center Austin, Austin, TX, p. A585
Senior Vice President and Chief Financial Officer, Seton Medical Center Williamson, Round Rock, TX, p. A629
Chief Financial Officer, Seton Northwest Hospital, Austin, TX, p. A585
Chief Financial Officer, Seton Shoal Creek Hospital, Austin, TX, p. A585
Chief Financial Officer, University Medical Center at Brackenridge, Austin, TX, p. A586

WAITES, Cherri, Chief Financial Officer, Palacios Community Medical Center, Palacios, TX, p. A625

WAJDA, David, Chief Financial Officer, Nazareth Hospital, Philadelphia, PA, p. A536

WAKEFIELD, Brett
Vice President Human Resources, Gottlieb Memorial Hospital, Melrose Park, IL, p. A188
Director Human Resources, Thorek Memorial Hospital, Chicago, IL, p. A179

WAKEFIELD, Mamie
Vice President Finance and Chief Financial Officer, Emma Pendleton Bradley Hospital, East Providence, RI, p. A546
Chief Financial Officer, Miriam Hospital, Providence, RI, p. A546
Senior Vice President and Chief Financial Officer, Rhode Island Hospital, Providence, RI, p. A547

WAKEMAN, Daniel L., President, ProMedica St. Luke's Hospital, Maumee, OH, p. A486

WAKIM, Tina, Vice President Information, Northside Hospital, Atlanta, GA, p. A146

WAKSMONSKI, Teresa, Chief Fiscal Service, James E. Van Zandt Veterans Affairs Medical Center, Altoona, PA, p. A519

WAKULCHIK, Grace, R.N. Chief Operating Officer, Akron Children's Hospital, Akron, OH, p. A470

WALAS, Steven, Chief Executive Officer, HEALTHSOUTH Chesapeake Rehabilitation Hospital, Salisbury, MD, p. A294

WALCEK, Peter, Vice President Finance, Wentworth–Douglass Hospital, Dover, NH, p. A397

WALCZAK, Charles, FACHE, Regional Administrator, Shriners Hospitals for Children–Springfield, Springfield, MA, p. A305

WALDBART, Andy, Department Manager, Heart of the Rockies Regional Medical Center, Salida, CO, p. A105

WALDBILLIG, Karla, Director Human Resources, UnityPoint Health Finley, Dubuque, IA, p. A221

WALDEN, Anita, Vice President and Chief Nursing Officer, Decatur General Hospital, Decatur, AL, p. A18

WALDEN, Kristy, R.N., Interim Administrator, Kindred Hospital–Indianapolis, Indianapolis, IN, p. A206

WALDERA, John, Director Information Technology, Gundersen Tri–County Hospital and Clinics, Whitehall, WI, p. A699

WALDO, Allen J., CPA, Chief Executive Officer, Cooper County Memorial Hospital, Boonville, MO, p. A357

WALDO, Bruce
Chief Executive Officer, Aurora Phoenix Hospital, Glendale, AZ, p. A32
Chief Executive Officer, Aurora Tempe Hospital, Tempe, AZ, p. A38

WALDO, Gail, Director Information Technology, Rockdale Medical Center, Conyers, GA, p. A151

WALDOW, Dee, Chief Financial Officer, Palo Pinto General Hospital, Mineral Wells, TX, p. A623

WALDRON, Michele, Vice President and Chief Financial Officer, Children's Hospital Central California, Madera, CA, p. A73

WALDRON, Ray, Director Information Technology, Gordon Memorial Hospital, Gordon, NE, p. A384

WALDROP, Cathy, Director, Hospital Nursing Services, North Mississippi Medical Center–Pontotoc Hospital and Nursing Home, Pontotoc, MS, p. A352

WALDROUP, Gerald E., Senior Vice President, Good Samaritan Hospital, Vincennes, IN, p. A214

WALDY, Byron, Director Human Resources, St. Francis Health Center, Topeka, KS, p. A245

WALENTA, Jason, M.D. Medical Director, Willow Springs Center, Reno, NV, p. A395

WALERSTEIN, Steven, M.D. Executive Vice President and Medical Director, Nassau University Medical Center, East Meadow, NY, p. A425

WALI, Jyotika, M.D. Chief of Staff, Kindred Hospital–Brea, Brea, CA, p. A55

WALIGURA, R. Curtis, D.O. Vice President Medical Affairs, Chief Medical Officer, UPMC McKeesport, McKeesport, PA, p. A531

WALKER, Alene, Director Human Resources, Quincy Valley Medical Center, Quincy, WA, p. A670

WALKER, Andrew, Chief Financial Officer, Johnson Memorial Hospital, Franklin, IN, p. A203

WALKER, Angela, M.D. Medical Director, HEALTHSOUTH Rehabilitation Hospital, Albuquerque, NM, p. A414

WALKER, Austin, Accounting Manager, Kindred Hospital Northland, Kansas City, MO, p. A363

WALKER, Beth, R.N., President, FirstHealth Montgomery Memorial Hospital, Troy, NC, p. A462

WALKER, Bruce, R.N., Chief Executive Officer, Ascension Gonzales Rehabilitation Hospital, Gonzales, LA, p. A267

WALKER, C. O., M.D. Chief of Staff, Donalsonville Hospital, Donalsonville, GA, p. A152

WALKER, Carol, Chief Financial Officer, Oklahoma Heart Hospital, Oklahoma City, OK, p. A504

WALKER, Chad A., Director Human Resources, Caldwell Medical Center, Princeton, KY, p. A259

WALKER, Cheri, R.N. Chief Nursing Officer, King's Daughters Medical Center, Brookhaven, MS, p. A345

WALKER, Codie, Chief Financial Officer, Salem Veterans Affairs Medical Center, Salem, VA, p. A661

WALKER, Daniel T., Vice President Finance and Chief Financial Officer, Manchester Memorial Hospital, Manchester, KY, p. A257

WALKER, Donna, Chief Nurse Executive, Weeks Medical Center, Lancaster, NH, p. A398

WALKER, Gale N., President and Chief Executive Officer, Avera St. Benedict Health Center, Parkston, SD, p. A561

WALKER, Gregory J., Chief Executive Officer, Wentworth–Douglass Hospital, Dover, NH, p. A397

WALKER, Jan
Director Human Resources, Centra Lynchburg General Hospital, Lynchburg, VA, p. A656
Director Human Resources, Glenwood Regional Medical Center, West Monroe, LA, p. A280

WALKER, Janice L., R.N. Chief Nursing Officer and Chief Operating Officer, Baylor Medical Center at Garland, Garland, TX, p. A606

WALKER, Jerry
Interim Regional Chief Executive Officer, Kauai Veterans Memorial Hospital, Waimea, HI, p. A166
Interim Regional Chief Executive Officer, Samuel Mahelona Memorial Hospital, Kapaa, HI, p. A165

WALKER, John E., FACHE, Chief Executive Officer, Logan Regional Medical Center, Logan, WV, p. A678

WALKER, Kevin, Vice President Operations, Research Psychiatric Center, Kansas City, MO, p. A363

WALKER, Kristie, Director Human Resources, LewisGale Hospital Montgomery, Blacksburg, VA, p. A652

WALKER, Larry D., Chief Operating Officer, Glenwood Regional Medical Center, West Monroe, LA, p. A280

WALKER, Larry Joe, Administrator and Chief Executive Officer, Hardy Wilson Memorial Hospital, Hazlehurst, MS, p. A348

WALKER, Lawrence, M.D. Chief of Staff, San Bernardino Mountains Community Hospital District, Lake Arrowhead, CA, p. A66

WALKER, LeRoy
Vice President Human Resources, St. Rose Dominican Hospitals – San Martin Campus, Las Vegas, NV, p. A393
Vice President Human Resources, St. Rose Dominican Hospitals – Siena Campus, Henderson, NV, p. A392

WALKER, Lynette, R.N. Vice President Human Resources, Baptist Health Lexington, Lexington, KY, p. A253

WALKER, Mary, Manager Information Technology, HEALTHSOUTH Rehabilitation Hospital–Wichita Falls, Wichita Falls, TX, p. A641

WALKER, Melissa, Senior Vice President and Chief Financial Officer, McAlester Regional Health Center, McAlester, OK, p. A501

WALKER, Michael, D.O. Chief of Staff, East Texas Medical Center–Mount Vernon, Mount Vernon, TX, p. A624

WALKER, Paul A., FACHE, President and Chief Executive Officer, Hoboken University Medical Center, Hoboken, NJ, p. A405

WALKER, Pia, Director Human Resources, Carolinas Medical Center–Mercy, Charlotte, NC, p. A449

WALKER, Randy
Vice President, Methodist Dallas Medical Center, Dallas, TX, p. A596
Director Nursing Services, State Hospital South, Blackfoot, ID, p. A167

WALKER, Renee, Director Human Resources, Bastrop Rehabilitation Hospital, Bastrop, LA, p. A262

WALKER, Robert, M.D. Medical Director, HEALTHSOUTH Southern Hills Rehabilitation Hospital, Princeton, WV, p. A680

WALKER, Robert L., President and Chief Executive Officer, Texas Scottish Rite Hospital for Children, Dallas, TX, p. A597

WALKER, Ronald P., Interim Chief Financial Officer, United Medical Center, Washington, DC, p. A117

WALKER, Scott, Chief Financial Officer, Southeastern Regional Medical Center, Newnan, GA, p. A158

WALKER, Scott, M.D. Chief Medical Staff, Weatherford Regional Medical Center, Weatherford, TX, p. A640

WALKER, Steven, Chief Executive Officer, South Hampton Community Hospital, Dallas, TX, p. A597

WALKER, Suzi, Manager Business Office, Cozby–Germany Hospital, Grand Saline, TX, p. A606

WALKER, Tim, Manager Information Services, PeaceHealth Ketchikan Medical Center, Ketchikan, AK, p. A28

WALKER, Troy, Director Finance, St. Clare Hospital, Baraboo, WI, p. A683

WALKER, Tyree, Chief Human Resources Officer, Vidant Medical Center, Greenville, NC, p. A454

WALKER Jr., William J., Chief Executive Officer, Memorial Hospital and Manor, Bainbridge, GA, p. A148

WALKLEY, Peter, M.D
Chief of Staff, Franklin Regional Hospital, Franklin, NH, p. A398
Chief Medical Officer, Lakes Region General Hospital, Laconia, NH, p. A398

WALKUP, Jessica, Controller, HEALTHSOUTH Western Hills Rehabilitation Hospital, Parkersburg, WV, p. A679

WALL, Daniel J., President and Chief Executive Officer, Emma Pendleton Bradley Hospital, East Providence, RI, p. A546

WALL, J. C., M.D. Chief of Staff, Stones River Hospital, Woodbury, TN, p. A580

WALL, Kathryn S.
Executive Vice President Human Resources and Organizational Development, Mary Washington Hospital, Fredericksburg, VA, p. A654
Executive Vice President Human Resources and Organizational Development, Stafford Hospital, Stafford, VA, p. A661

WALL, Michael L., FACHE, Interim President and Chief Executive Officer, Saint John's Health Center, Santa Monica, CA, p. A90

WALLACE, Arthur, Chief Financial Officer, Broward Health Coral Springs, Coral Springs, FL, p. A121

WALLACE, Bernadine L., MSN Chief Nursing Officer and Chief Operating Officer, Marion General Hospital, Marion, IN, p. A209

WALLACE, Brenda, R.N. Chief Nursing Officer, Ouachita Community Hospital, West Monroe, LA, p. A280

WALLACE, Carolyn, Director Human Resources, Connecticut Mental Health Center, New Haven, CT, p. A110

WALLACE, David, Chief Executive Officer, Woodward Regional Hospital, Woodward, OK, p. A510

WALLACE, Debbye, Chief Operating Officer, Hill Country Memorial Hospital, Fredericksburg, TX, p. A605

WALLACE, Dianne, County Information Manager, Douglas County Community Mental Health Center, Omaha, NE, p. A388

WALLACE, Donna Geiken, Chief Operating Officer and Chief Financial Officer, Hopkins County Memorial Hospital, Sulphur Springs, TX, p. A636

WALLACE, Glenn, Chief Operating Officer, Medical Center of Plano, Plano, TX, p. A627

WALLACE, Jennifer, Chief Executive Officer, AMG Specialty Hospital–Greenwood, Greenwood, MS, p. A347

WALLACE, Jo Lynn, Vice President of Nursing, Rogue Valley Medical Center, Medford, OR, p. A515

WALLACE, Kelly, Senior Vice President and Chief Financial Officer, Seattle Children's Hospital, Seattle, WA, p. A671

WALLACE, Linda, Director Human Resources, Sierra Medical Center, El Paso, TX, p. A601

WALLACE, Mark A., President and Chief Executive Officer, Texas Children's Hospital, Houston, TX, p. A612

WALLACE, Mark T., Director Human Resources, Lodi Memorial Hospital, Lodi, CA, p. A66

WALLACE, Melanie, Manager Human Resources, Sutter Tracy Community Hospital, Tracy, CA, p. A93

WALLACE, Michael S., President and Chief Executive Officer, Fort HealthCare, Fort Atkinson, WI, p. A686

WALLACE, Nancy
Vice President Human Resources, Alegent Creighton Health Bergan Mercy Medical Center, Omaha, NE, p. A387
Vice President Human Resources, Alegent Creighton Health Immanuel Medical Center, Omaha, NE, p. A387
Vice President Human Resources, Alegent Creighton Health Lakeside Hospital, Omaha, NE, p. A387
Senior Vice President Human Resources, Alegent Creighton Health Mercy Hospital, Council Bluffs, IA, p. A219
Interim Senior Vice President Human Resources, Alegent Creighton Health Midlands Hospital, Papillion, NE, p. A389
Vice President Human Resources, Alegent Creighton Health–Memorial Hospital, Schuyler, Schuyler, NE, p. A389

WALLACE, Patrick L., Administrator, East Texas Medical Center Athens, Athens, TX, p. A584

WALLACE, Penny, Chief Financial Officer, Guadalupe Regional Medical Center, Seguin, TX, p. A633

WALLACE, Rick D., FACHE, President and Chief Executive Officer, San Juan Regional Medical Center, Farmington, NM, p. A416

WALLACE, Sandra, Chief Financial Officer, Parkwood Behavioral Health System, Olive Branch, MS, p. A352

WALLACE, Tabatha, Director Human Resources, Bayfront Health Dade City, Dade City, FL, p. A121

WALLACE, Teresa L., Chief Nurse Executive, Sutter Lakeside Hospital, Lakeport, CA, p. A66

WALLACE, Terri, Controller, Bowie Memorial Hospital, Bowie, TX, p. A589

WALLACE–MOORE, Patrice, Chief Executive Officer and Executive Director, Arms Acres, Carmel, NY, p. A423

WALLEN, Carla, Manager Human Resources, Cass Regional Medical Center, Harrisonville, MO, p. A361

WALLENHAUPT, Stephen, M.D. Executive Vice President Medical Affairs, Novant Health Presbyterian Medical Center, Charlotte, NC, p. A450

WALLER, Kenneth, Fiscal Administrator, Deer's Head Hospital Center, Salisbury, MD, p. A294

WALLER, Patricia A., R.N. Assistant Administrator Patient Care Services, Newton Medical Center, Covington, GA, p. A151

WALLER, Raymond, Director, Brighton Center for Recovery, Brighton, MI, p. A309

WALLING, John R., President, River Bend Hospital, West Lafayette, IN, p. A215

WALLIS, Carla, Director Human Resources, North Ottawa Community Hospital, Grand Haven, MI, p. A314

WALLIS, Eric, R.N. Vice President Patient Care and Chief Nursing Officer, OhioHealth Marion General Hospital, Marion, OH, p. A485

WALLIS, Pam, Vice President, Nursing Services, Magnolia Regional Health Center, Corinth, MS, p. A346

WALLMAN, Gerald H., Administrator, Doctors Hospital of West Covina, West Covina, CA, p. A95

WALLS, Randy, Manager Information Services, Fairbanks, Indianapolis, IN, p. A205

WALLSCHLAEGER, Erich, Chief Financial Officer, Cedar Park Regional Medical Center, Cedar Park, TX, p. A591

WALMSLEY III, George J., CPA,
President and Chief Executive Officer, Girard Medical Center, Philadelphia, PA, p. A535
President and Chief Executive Officer, North Philadelphia Health System, Philadelphia, PA, p. A536

WALMUS, Adam C.
Director, Michael E. DeBakey Veterans Affairs Medical Center, Houston, TX, p. A611
Interim Director, Oklahoma City Veterans Affairs Medical Center, Oklahoma City, OK, p. A504

WALSER, Bill, Coordinator Technology, Cameron Regional Medical Center, Cameron, MO, p. A357

WALSH, Barbara, Chief Executive Officer, Specialty Hospital Jacksonville, Jacksonville, FL, p. A127

WALSH, Bob, R.N. Chief Operating Officer, OhioHealth Grady Memorial Hospital, Delaware, OH, p. A480

WALSH, Debbie, MSN, Chief Executive Officer, Fountain Valley Regional Hospital and Medical Center, Fountain Valley, CA, p. A60

WALSH, Gerard M.
Senior Vice President and Chief Operating Officer, Dorchester General Hospital, Cambridge, MD, p. A290
Senior Vice President and Chief Operating Officer, Memorial Hospital at Easton Maryland, Easton, MD, p. A291

WALSH, John, M.D. Chief Medical Officer, Florida Hospital–Flagler, Palm Coast, FL, p. A136

WALSH, John
Interim Chief Executive Officer, Trumbull Memorial Hospital, Warren, OH, p. A492
Chief Fiscal Services, Veterans Affairs Hudson Valley Health Care System–F.D. Roosevelt Hospital, Montrose, NY, p. A430

WALSH, Kate, President and Chief Executive Officer, Boston Medical Center, Boston, MA, p. A296

WALSH, Ken, Chief Financial Officer, St. Luke's Medical Center, Phoenix, AZ, p. A35

WALSH, Kim, Chief Nursing Officer, Signature Healthcare Brockton Hospital, Brockton, MA, p. A298

WALSH, Len, Executive Vice President and Chief Operating Officer, St. Barnabas Hospital,, NY, p. A436

WALSH, Leon, Chief Financial Officer, Petersburg Medical Center, Petersburg, AK, p. A29

WALSH, Marcia S., M.P.H. Chief Operating Officer, Community HealthCare System, Onaga, KS, p. A241

WALSH, Marilyn J., Vice President Human Resources, Kent County Memorial Hospital, Warwick, RI, p. A547

WALSH, Mary Beth, M.D., Chief Executive Officer, Burke Rehabilitation Hospital, White Plains, NY, p. A446

WALSH, Michael, Senior Vice President Finance and Chief Financial Officer, Abington Memorial Hospital, Abington, PA, p. A519

WALSH, Richard, Executive Vice President and Chief Operating Officer, SwedishAmerican Hospital, Rockford, IL, p. A194

WALSH, Richard J., Ph.D. Chief Human Resources Officer, Duke Regional Hospital, Durham, NC, p. A451

WALSH, Shawn, Chief Operating Officer, Rockford Center, Newark, DE, p. A114

WALSH, Timothy J., Chief Executive Officer, Martha's Vineyard Hospital, Oak Bluffs, MA, p. A303

WALSH, William P.
Senior Vice President and Executive Director, Jacobi Medical Center,, NY, p. A432
Executive Director, North Central Bronx Hospital,, NY, p. A435

WALSTON, John, Chief Information Officer, Southern Arizona Veterans Affairs Health Care System, Tucson, AZ, p. A39

WALTER, Gayle, Director of Nursing, Thomas B. Finan Center, Cumberland, MD, p. A291

WALTER, Melissa, Chief Financial Officer, Clarinda Regional Health Center, Clarinda, IA, p. A218

WALTER, Stephen
Senior Vice President and Chief Financial Officer, Community Behavioral Health Center, Fresno, CA, p. A61
Senior Vice President and Chief Financial Officer, Community Regional Medical Center, Fresno, CA, p. A61

WALTERS, David, D.O. Vice President and Chief Medical Officer, Botsford Hospital, Farmington Hills, MI, p. A313

WALTERS, Joan, MSN, Administrator, Prague Community Hospital, Prague, OK, p. A505

WALTERS, Julie, Chief Nursing Officer, Hillsdale Community Health Center, Hillsdale, MI, p. A316

WALTERS, Kevin
Chief Financial Officer, St. Rose Dominican Hospitals – Rose de Lima Campus, Henderson, NV, p. A392
Chief Financial Officer, St. Rose Dominican Hospitals – San Martin Campus, Las Vegas, NV, p. A393
Chief Financial Officer, St. Rose Dominican Hospitals – Siena Campus, Henderson, NV, p. A392

WALTERS, Mary, Chief Nursing Officer, Central Community Hospital, Elkader, IA, p. A221

WALTERS, Patrick, Interim Chief Executive Officer, Inova Loudoun Hospital, Leesburg, VA, p. A656

WALTERS, Wayne, Administrator, North Sunflower Medical Center, Ruleville, MS, p. A353

WALTHALL, Wayne, Interim Chief Financial Officer, Oklahoma State University Medical Center, Tulsa, OK, p. A508

WALTMAN, DeeDee, Information Officer, Garden County Health Services, Oshkosh, NE, p. A388

WALTON, Brian, Vice President and Chief Financial Officer, Baptist St. Anthony Health System, Amarillo, TX, p. A582

WALTON, Carlyle L. E.
Chief Executive Officer, Metroplex Adventist Hospital, Killeen, TX, p. A616
President and Chief Executive Officer, Rollins–Brook Community Hospital, Lampasas, TX, p. A618

WALTON, Charles E., Corporate Director Human Resources, Shenandoah Memorial Hospital, Woodstock, VA, p. A663

WALTON, Dawn, Chief Financial Officer, The Children's Hospital of Alabama, Birmingham, AL, p. A17

WALTON, Gary, M.D. Chief Medical Officer, Hill Hospital of Sumter County, York, AL, p. A26

WALTON, Georgian, Director Human Resources, Elbert Memorial Hospital, Elberton, GA, p. A153

WALTON, Greg, Chief Information Officer, El Camino Hospital, Mountain View, CA, p. A75

WALTON, Harold, M.D. Chief of Staff, Bayshore Medical Center, Pasadena, TX, p. A626

WALTZ, Brenda M., FACHE, Chief Executive Officer, Garden Park Medical Center, Gulfport, MS, p. A347

WALZ, Pat, President and Chief Executive Officer, Yuma Regional Medical Center, Yuma, AZ, p. A40

WAMPLER, Robert B., CPA, Interim Chief Executive Officer, Muskogee Regional Medical Center, Muskogee, OK, p. A502

WAMSLEY, Marie, Chief Financial Officer, Memorial Hospital of Lafayette County, Darlington, WI, p. A685

WANG, Alan, M.D. Chief Medical Officer, Emory Johns Creek Hospital, Johns Creek, GA, p. A155

WANGER, David S.
Chief Executive Officer, Florence Hospital at Anthem, Florence, AZ, p. A31
Chief Executive Officer, Gilbert Hospital, Gilbert, AZ, p. A31

WANGSMO, Gary L., Chief Financial Officer, George L. Mee Memorial Hospital, King City, CA, p. A65

WANGSNESS, Erik, Chief Executive Officer, Jellico Community Hospital, Jellico, TN, p. A571

WANNER, David, Chief Information Officer, St. Mary's of Michigan, Saginaw, MI, p. A323

WANTLAND, Margaret, Chief Financial Officer, Kindred Hospital–Albuquerque, Albuquerque, NM, p. A414

WAPPELHORST, Andrea, Chief Nursing Officer, TOPS Surgical Specialty Hospital, Houston, TX, p. A613

WARD, Brook, Executive Vice President, Washington Hospital, Washington, PA, p. A543

WARD, Cary, M.D. Chief Medical Officer, Saint Elizabeth Regional Medical Center, Lincoln, NE, p. A385

WARD, David M., Senior Vice President and Chief Financial Officer, Cabell Huntington Hospital, Huntington, WV, p. A677

WARD, Gayle, R.N. Vice President and Chief Nursing Officer, UW Medicine/Northwest Hospital & Medical Center, Seattle, WA, p. A671

WARD, Greg, Vice President Operations, Copley Hospital, Morrisville, VT, p. A649

WARD, Henry J., Vice President and Chief Financial Officer, Westfield Memorial Hospital, Westfield, NY, p. A446

WARD, James, M.D
Chief Medical Officer, Sacred Heart Hospital of Pensacola, Pensacola, FL, p. A137
President Medical Staff, USMD Hospital at Arlington, Arlington, TX, p. A584

WARD, Jeanne L., R.N., President and Chief Executive Officer, Oconee Medical Center, Seneca, SC, p. A555

WARD, Kenneth
Regional Director Information Services, Shriners Hospitals for Children–Boston Burns Hospital, Boston, MA, p. A297
Director Information Services, Shriners Hospitals for Children–Springfield, Springfield, MA, p. A305

WARD, Kevin J., Vice President and Chief Financial Officer, New York Hospital Queens,, NY, p. A435

WARD, Lesli, Vice President Human Resources, Shands Jacksonville Medical Center, Jacksonville, FL, p. A126

WARD, Lisa, Director Management Information Systems, Columbus Regional Healthcare System, Whiteville, NC, p. A462

WARD, Louise, Vice President Financial and Support Services, Roane General Hospital, Spencer, WV, p. A681

WARD, Michael
Director Information Services, Anderson Hospital, Maryville, IL, p. A187
Chief Executive Officer, HEALTHSOUTH Rehabilitation Hospital–Las Vegas, Las Vegas, NV, p. A392

WARD, Mike
Senior Vice President, Chief Information Officer, Covenant, Methodist Medical Center of Oak Ridge, Oak Ridge, TN, p. A578
Senior Vice President Chief Information Officer, Roane Medical Center, Harriman, TN, p. A569

WARD, Sandy, Administrator, Johnson County Healthcare Center, Buffalo, WY, p. A701

WARD, Silva, Director Human Resources, Center for Behavioral Medicine, Kansas City, MO, p. A362

WARD, Stormy, Chief Nurse Executive, Big Spring State Hospital, Big Spring, TX, p. A588

WARD, Vaughn, Chief Executive Officer, Northwest Specialty Hospital, Post Falls, ID, p. A171

WARD, Virginia, Human Resources Officer, Robert E. Bush Naval Hospital, Twentynine Palms, CA, p. A93

WARD, Wendy, Director Human Resources, Mercy Hospital El Reno, El Reno, OK, p. A498

WARD–PRESSON, Kathryn M., R.N. Associate Director for Patient Care Services, Durham Veterans Affairs Medical Center, Durham, NC, p. A451

WARDA, Paul, Chief Financial Officer, MedStar Georgetown University Hospital, Washington, DC, p. A116

WARDELL, Kevin S., President, Norton Hospital, Louisville, KY, p. A256

WARDELL, Patrick R., Chief Executive Officer, Cambridge Health Alliance, Cambridge, MA, p. A299

WARDEN, Michael S.
Senior Vice President Information Technology, Banner Good Samaritan Medical Center, Phoenix, AZ, p. A34
Senior Vice President and Chief Information Officer, Banner Heart Hospital, Mesa, AZ, p. A33
Senior Vice President and Chief Information Officer, East Morgan County Hospital, Brush, CO, p. A98

WARDWELL, Robert D.
Chief Financial Officer, St. John's Pleasant Valley Hospital, Camarillo, CA, p. A55
Chief Financial Officer, St. John's Regional Medical Center, Oxnard, CA, p. A78

WARE, Bobbie K., R.N. Vice President/Patient Care/Chief Nursing Officer, Mississippi Baptist Medical Center, Jackson, MS, p. A348

WARE, Bobbie K., FACHE, Chief Executive Officer and Chief Nursing Officer, Mississippi Hospital for Restorative Care, Jackson, MS, p. A349

WARE, Judy, Director Human Resources, Johnson Memorial Hospital, Franklin, IN, p. A203

WARE, Karen, Director Human Resources, Integris Blackwell Regional Hospital, Blackwell, OK, p. A496

WARE, Scott T., Chief Operating Officer, Baptist Health Paducah, Paducah, KY, p. A259

WARE, Shannon, President and Chief Executive Officer, Eastern State Hospital, Lexington, KY, p. A254

WAREING, Colleen, Vice President Patient Care Services, Atlantic General Hospital, Berlin, MD, p. A289

WARFIELD, William, Chief Human Resources Management, Veterans Affairs Boston Healthcare System, Boston, MA, p. A297

WARLITNER, Todd, Vice President Business Operations, The Outer Banks Hospital, Nags Head, NC, p. A458

WARM, Ira, Senior Vice President Human Resources, Brooklyn Hospital Center,, NY, p. A431

WARMAN, Debbie, Vice President Human Resources, MetroHealth Medical Center, Cleveland, OH, p. A476

WARMAN Jr., Harold C., FACHE, President and Chief Executive Officer, Highlands Regional Medical Center, Prestonsburg, KY, p. A259

WARMBOLD, Steve, Director Information Management Service Line, Veterans Affairs St. Louis Health Care System, Saint Louis, MO, p. A371

WARMERDAM, David, Chief Financial Officer, Brynn Marr Hospital, Jacksonville, NC, p. A455

WARNER, John, M.D., Chief Executive Officer, University of Texas Southwestern Medical Center, Dallas, TX, p. A598

WARNER, Norma, Area Director Health Information Management, Kindred Hospital–Fort Worth, Fort Worth, TX, p. A604

WARNER–PACHECO, Paula, Chief Human Resources, Rio Grande Hospital, Del Norte, CO, p. A99

WARNOCK, Dawn, Director Medical Records, Taylor Regional Hospital, Hawkinsville, GA, p. A154

WARREN, Beka, R.N. Interim Chief Clinical Officer, Memorial Hospital at Craig, Craig, CO, p. A99

WARREN, Bradley J., Senior Vice President and Chief People Officer, Memorial Medical Center, Springfield, IL, p. A195

WARREN, Charlene, R.N. Chief Nursing Officer, Greenbrier Valley Medical Center, Ronceverte, WV, p. A680

WARREN, Danny, Chief Financial Officer, Lake Wales Medical Center, Lake Wales, FL, p. A128

WARREN, Gorman, Chief Financial Officer, Texas Health Harris Methodist Hospital Southlake, Southlake, TX, p. A634

WARREN, Jennifer, Chief Financial Officer, Purcell Municipal Hospital, Purcell, OK, p. A506

WARREN, Karen
Chief Nursing Officer, Klickitat Valley Health, Goldendale, WA, p. A667
Fiscal Officer, Porterville Developmental Center, Porterville, CA, p. A80

WARREN, Linda, Director Human Resources, Cogdell Memorial Hospital, Snyder, TX, p. A634

WARREN, Merritt, M.D. Medical Director and Chief of Staff, Brookings Health System, Brookings, SD, p. A558

WARREN, Michael D., President, Good Samaritan Regional Health Center, Mount Vernon, IL, p. A189

WARREN, Richard
Vice President Health Information Systems, Allegiance Health, Jackson, MI, p. A317
Chief Information Officer, Hillcrest Baptist Medical Center, Waco, TX, p. A640

WARREN, Roger D., M.D., Administrator, Hanover Hospital, Hanover, KS, p. A234

WARREN, Ron, Director Information Systems, Loretto Hospital, Chicago, IL, p. A177

WARREN, Sarah, Coordinator Human Resources, Hickory Trail Hospital, Desoto, TX, p. A599

WARREN, Seth C. R., President, Franciscan St. James Hospital and Health Centers, Olympia Fields, IL, p. A191

WARREN, Shanna, Director Human Resources, Medical Center of Plano, Plano, TX, p. A627

WARREN Jr., Wm. Michael, Chief Executive Officer, The Children's Hospital of Alabama, Birmingham, AL, p. A17

WARRINER, Ken, Chief Financial Officer, Madison River Oaks Medical Center, Canton, MS, p. A345

WARRINGTON, Sr., James E., M.D. Chief of Staff, Quitman County Hospital, Marks, MS, p. A350

WARSING, Tracy, M.D. Site Leader Chief of Staff, Mayo Clinic Health System – Franciscan Healthcare in Sparta, Sparta, WI, p. A696

WARTCHOW, Leann, Assistant Chief Executive Officer and Certified Risk Manager, Lost Rivers Medical Center, Arco, ID, p. A167

WARTENBERG, Daniel, PsyD, Acting Chief Executive Officer, Southwest Connecticut Mental Health System, Bridgeport, CT, p. A108

WAS, Gregory J., CPA Chief Financial Officer, Melissa Memorial Hospital, Holyoke, CO, p. A102

WASDEN, Mitchell L., Ed.D., Chief Executive Officer and Chief Operating Officer, University of Missouri Hospitals and Clinics, Columbia, MO, p. A359

WASDEN, Ricky, Manager Information Technology, Jefferson Hospital, Louisville, GA, p. A156

WASEMILLER–SMITH, Lisa, M.D. Chief Medical Officer, Lakeside Women's Hospital, Oklahoma City, OK, p. A503

WASHAM, Mark, Chief Information Officer, Shriners Hospitals for Children–Cincinnati Burns Hospital, Cincinnati, OH, p. A475

WASHBURN, Sheryl M., MSN Vice President Patient Care Services, North Country Hospital and Health Center, Newport, VT, p. A650

WASHBURN, Tonya, M.D. Medical Director, Valir Rehabilitation Hospital, Oklahoma City, OK, p. A504

WASHECKA, James, Chief Financial Officer, Easton Hospital, Easton, PA, p. A525

WASHINGTON, Carolyn, Director of Human Resources, Doctor's Hospital – Tidwell, Houston, TX, p. A609

WASHINGTON, Glen A., Senior Vice President and Chief Operating Officer, Cabell Huntington Hospital, Huntington, WV, p. A677

WASHINGTON, Lorraine, Vice President Human Resources, St. Dominic–Jackson Memorial Hospital, Jackson, MS, p. A349

WASHINGTON, Lydia, Controller, Acuity Hospital of South Texas, San Antonio, TX, p. A630

WASHINGTON, Reginald, M.D. Chief Medical Officer, Presbyterian–St. Luke's Medical Center, Denver, CO, p. A100

WASHINGTON, Stephanie, Director Community Relations and Human Resources, King's Daughters Hospital, Yazoo City, MS, p. A355

WASIUK, Pauline, Director Human Resources, Southern Virginia Mental Health Institute, Danville, VA, p. A653

WASSALL, Dianne, Director Human Resources, University of Maryland St. Joseph Medical Center, Towson, MD, p. A294

WASSILAK, Leighton, Manager, Information Systems/ Telecommunications, SSM St. Clare Health Center, Fenton, MO, p. A360

WASSON, Phil, Chief Information Officer, SwedishAmerican Hospital, Rockford, IL, p. A194

WATERBURY, Brad, Director Human Resources, Bonner General Hospital, Sandpoint, ID, p. A171

WATERCUTTER, William, Director Management Information System, Upper Valley Medical Center, Troy, OH, p. A491

WATERS, Danny, Director Information Technology and Systems, South Bay Hospital, Sun City Center, FL, p. A140

WATERS, Eric, Vice President Operations, Pen Bay Medical Center, Rockport, ME, p. A285

WATERS, Gina, Director Human Resources, Evans Memorial Hospital, Claxton, GA, p. A150

WATERS, Glenn D., FACHE
President, Mease Countryside Hospital, Safety Harbor, FL, p. A138
President and Chief Executive Officer, Mease Dunedin Hospital, Dunedin, FL, p. A122
President, Morton Plant Hospital, Clearwater, FL, p. A120
President, Morton Plant North Bay Hospital, New Port Richey, FL, p. A133

WATERS, Karen, Chief Nursing Officer, St. Mary's Warrick Hospital, Boonville, IN, p. A199

WATERS, Mickey, Director Information Technology, Conway Medical Center, Conway, SC, p. A551

WATERS, Nancy, Interim Chief Information Officer, High Point Regional Health System, High Point, NC, p. A455

WATERS, Patrick, Director Information Technology, Marshall County Hospital, Benton, KY, p. A248

WATERS, Stephen F., M.D. Medical Director, Atlantic General Hospital, Berlin, MD, p. A289

WATERS, Victor, M.D. Chief of Staff, Sioux Falls Veterans Affairs Health Care System, Sioux Falls, SD, p. A563

WATERSTON, Judith C., MS, President and Chief Executive Officer, New England Sinai Hospital and Rehabilitation Center, Stoughton, MA, p. A305

WATHEN, Cheryl A., Interim Chief Financial Officer, Deaconess Hospital, Evansville, IN, p. A202

WATKINS, Chris, Director of Information Technology, Craig Hospital, Englewood, CO, p. A100

WATKINS, Pamela, Chief Financial Officer, Atlanta Veterans Affairs Medical Center, Decatur, GA, p. A151

WATKINS, Paul, Chief Administrative Officer, Santa Monica–UCLA Medical Center and Orthopaedic Hospital, Santa Monica, CA, p. A90

WATKINS, Scott, Director Human Resources, Catholic Medical Center, Manchester, NH, p. A399

WATKINS, Terri, R.N. Chief Nursing Officer, Castleview Hospital, Price, UT, p. A645

WATKINS, William D., Chief Administrative Officer, Bluffton Hospital, Bluffton, OH, p. A472

WATLAND, Judy A., R.N. Chief Nursing Officer, O'Connor Hospital, San Jose, CA, p. A88

WATRY, Margaret, Director of Patient Care Services and Nurse Executive, Phillips Eye Institute, Minneapolis, MN, p. A336

WATSON, Betty A., Chief Financial Officer, Syringa Hospital and Clinics, Grangeville, ID, p. A169

WATSON, Brent, M.D. Chief Medical Staff, Roane General Hospital, Spencer, WV, p. A681

WATSON, Christopher, M.D. Chief Medical Officer, Bellin Memorial Hospital, Green Bay, WI, p. A687

WATSON, Dean, M.D. Chief Medical Officer, Tallahassee Memorial HealthCare, Tallahassee, FL, p. A141

WATSON, Deborah
Senior Vice President and Chief Operating Officer, Bayhealth Medical Center, Dover, DE, p. A114
Vice President, Patient Care Services, Providence Mount Carmel Hospital, Colville, WA, p. A665

WATSON, Dolores, Director Health Information Management, Arms Acres, Carmel, NY, p. A423

WATSON, H. Alan, FACHE, Chief Executive Officer, Maury Regional Hospital, Columbia, TN, p. A567

WATSON, Heath
Controller, HEALTHSOUTH Rehabilitation Hospital, Dothan, AL, p. A19
Controller, HEALTHSOUTH Rehabilitation Hospital of Montgomery, Montgomery, AL, p. A23

WATSON, James B., Chief Operating Officer, Ira Davenport Memorial Hospital, Bath, NY, p. A421

WATSON, Jim, Chief Financial Officer, OU Medical Center, Oklahoma City, OK, p. A504

WATSON, Kathy, R.N., Administrator and Chief Nursing Officer, Saint Thomas Hospital for Spinal Surgery, Nashville, TN, p. A576

WATSON, Kerry, President, Duke Regional Hospital, Durham, NC, p. A451

WATSON, Lisa, Chief Executive Officer, St. Vincent Rehabilitation Hospital, Sherwood, AR, p. A50

WATSON, Luke, M.D. Chief of Staff, Pacific Hospital of Long Beach, Long Beach, CA, p. A67

WATSON, Mary Lou, MS Vice President Nursing, MedStar St. Mary's Hospital, Leonardtown, MD, p. A293

WATSON, Michelle, Chief Operating Officer and Chief Nursing Officer, Livingston Regional Hospital, Livingston, TN, p. A573

WATSON, Nancy, Director Human Resources, Mercy Hospital, Coon Rapids, MN, p. A330

WATSON, Scott, JD Vice President Human Resources and Support Services, Mercy Hospital Joplin, Joplin, MO, p. A362

WATSON, Shane, Chief Executive Officer, Red Bud Regional Hospital, Red Bud, IL, p. A193

WATSON, Teresa C., Vice President Administration, Carolinas Medical Center–Lincoln, Lincolnton, NC, p. A456

WATSON, Trey, Network Administrator, Sumner County Hospital District One, Caldwell, KS, p. A232

WATSON, Vicki, Manager Human Resources, Select Specialty Hospital–Jackson, Jackson, MS, p. A349

WATSON, Virgil, Administrator, Sumner County Hospital District One, Caldwell, KS, p. A232

WATT, Andrew, M.D. Vice President, Chief Information Officer and Chief Medical Information Officer, Southern New Hampshire Medical Center, Nashua, NH, p. A399

WATT, Ella, Chief Financial Officer, University of New Mexico Hospitals, Albuquerque, NM, p. A415

WATT, Tracy, Director Information Systems, Jackson Purchase Medical Center, Mayfield, KY, p. A257

WATTENBARGER, Mike, Chief Information Officer, LifeCare Hospitals of San Antonio, San Antonio, TX, p. A631

WATTERS, Greg, Chief Financial Officer, El Paso Specialty Hospital, El Paso, TX, p. A601

WATTOO, Dost, M.D. Chief of Staff, Valley Hospital Medical Center, Las Vegas, NV, p. A394

WATTS, Gary, M.D. Chief Medical Officer, Mayhill Hospital, Denton, TX, p. A598

WATTS, Hugh, M.D. Chief of Staff, Shriners Hospitals for Children–Los Angeles, Los Angeles, CA, p. A71

WATTS, Larry, Chief Medical Officer, Hays Medical Center, Hays, KS, p. A235

WATTS–JOHNSON, Christine M., Assistant Vice President, Madera Community Hospital, Madera, CA, p. A73

WAUN, Cynthia, Chief Operating Officer and Risk Manager, Brynn Marr Hospital, Jacksonville, NC, p. A455

WAUTERS, Ron, Chief Financial Officer, Pella Regional Health Center, Pella, IA, p. A227

WAY, Harold, Chief Financial Officer and Chief Operating Officer, San Gabriel Valley Medical Center, San Gabriel, CA, p. A87

WAYNE, Jim, Chief Financial Officer, OSF St. Francis Hospital, Escanaba, MI, p. A313

WAYNE, Kenneth, M.D. Chief Medical Officer, Ottumwa Regional Health Center, Ottumwa, IA, p. A226

WAYRAUCH, Karen, Interim Director Information Systems, East Ohio Regional Hospital, Martins Ferry, OH, p. A485

WEADICK, James F., Administrator and Chief Executive Officer, Newton Medical Center, Covington, GA, p. A151

WEAKS, Lyndell H., Chief Executive Officer, Methodist Rehabilitation Hospital, Dallas, TX, p. A596

WEAR, Sondra, Director Financial Services, Eureka Springs Hospital, Eureka Springs, AR, p. A43

WEATHERFORD, Dennis, Chief Executive Officer, Putnam County Hospital, Greencastle, IN, p. A204

WEATHERFORD, Ted, Chief Financial Officer, Howard A. Rusk Rehabilitation Center, Columbia, MO, p. A359

WEATHERLY, Dan, On Site Administrator, Cape Fear Valley – Bladen County Hospital, Elizabethtown, NC, p. A152

WEATHERWAX, Marlene, Vice President and Chief Financial Officer, Columbus Regional Hospital, Columbus, IN, p. A200

WEAVER, Angie L., Director Human Resources, Gilmore Memorial Regional Medical Center, Amory, MS, p. A344

WEAVER, Daryl W., Chief Executive Officer, King's Daughters Hospital, Yazoo City, MS, p. A355

WEAVER, Douglas K., FACHE, President, Integris Mayes County Medical Center, Pryor, OK, p. A506

WEAVER, Jason
Director Information Systems, Crockett Hospital, Lawrenceburg, TN, p. A572
Finance Manager, Maple Grove Hospital, Maple Grove, MN, p. A335

WEAVER, Jeff, Chief Financial Officer, Morton County Health System, Elkhart, KS, p. A233

WEAVER, Joe, Chief Operating Officer and Vice President Operations, Northeast Alabama Regional Medical Center, Anniston, AL, p. A15

WEAVER, Judy K., MS, Chief Executive Officer, Acuity Specialty Hospitals Ohio Valley, Steubenville, OH, p. A490

WEAVER, Kim, CPA Chief Financial Officer, Sumner Regional Medical Center, Wellington, KS, p. A246

WEAVER, Kimberli, Chief Nursing Officer, L. V. Stabler Memorial Hospital, Greenville, AL, p. A21

WEAVER, Nancy, Vice President of Nursing, Chief Nursing Officer, Carson City Hospital, Carson City, MI, p. A310

WEAVER, Rudolph D., Vice President Human Resources, Southwestern Vermont Medical Center, Bennington, VT, p. A649

WEAVER, William, Chief Executive Officer, Brentwood Hospital, Shreveport, LA, p. A277

WEBB Jr., Charles L., Chief Executive Officer, Lincoln Trail Behavioral Health System, Radcliff, KY, p. A259

WEBB, Craig R., M.D. Deputy Commander for Clinical Services, Irwin Army Community Hospital, Junction City, KS, p. A236

WEBB, David, Chief Financial Officer, NEA Baptist Memorial Hospital, Jonesboro, AR, p. A45

WEBB, Dee, Vice President Human Resources, St. Bernardine Medical Center, San Bernardino, CA, p. A84

WEBB, Donald, Chief Executive Officer, Williamson Medical Center, Franklin, TN, p. A569

WEBB, Gary, Director Human Resources, Corry Memorial Hospital, Corry, PA, p. A523

WEBB, Herbert, M.D. Chief Medical Officer, Providence Little Company of Mary Medical Center San Pedro, CA, p. A71

WEBB, Jeffrey D., CPA Chief Financial Officer, Jasper County Hospital, Rensselaer, IN, p. A212

WEBB, Joseph, Chief Operating Officer, Northwest Mississippi Regional Medical Center, Clarksdale, MS, p. A345

WEBB, Karen, M.D
  Chief Medical Officer, Des Peres Hospital, Saint Louis, MO, p. A369
  Chief Medical Officer, Saint Louis University Hospital, Saint Louis, MO, p. A370

WEBB, Kevin C., Ph.D., President, ProMedica Toledo Hospital, Toledo, OH, p. A491

WEBB, Kimberly, Chief Financial Officer, Cheyenne Regional Medical Center, Cheyenne, WY, p. A701

WEBB, Linda, R.N. Chief Nursing Executive, Pulaski Memorial Hospital, Winamac, IN, p. A215

WEBB, Lisa, Vice President Finance and Chief Financial Officer, Saint Francis Medical Center, Grand Island, NE, p. A384

WEBB, Melanie R.
  Director Human Resources, Houston Northwest Medical Center, Houston, TX, p. A610
  Chief Human Resources Officer, Park Plaza Hospital, Houston, TX, p. A611

WEBB, Paula, Chief Financial Officer, Lake Butler Hospital Hand Surgery Center, Lake Butler, FL, p. A128

WEBB, Paula J., R.N. Chief Nursing Officer, Cook Children's Medical Center, Fort Worth, TX, p. A603

WEBB, Renick, M.D. Chief Medical Director, Central Louisiana Surgical Hospital, Alexandria, LA, p. A262

WEBB, Robin, Director Human Resources, Perry Memorial Hospital, Perry, OK, p. A505

WEBB, W. Larry, Senior Vice President and Chief Financial Officer, Athens Regional Medical Center, Athens, GA, p. A145

WEBBER, Cathy, Chief Information Officer, Franklin County Memorial Hospital, Franklin, NE, p. A383

WEBBER, Chelsea, Director Human Resources, LifeCare Hospitals of Pittsburgh – Monroeville, Monroeville, PA, p. A532

WEBBER, Deborah G., Chief Operating Officer, Anaheim Regional Medical Center, Anaheim, CA, p. A52

WEBBER, Joyce, Chief Financial Officer, Spalding Rehabilitation Hospital, Aurora, CO, p. A97

WEBDALE, Ralph, Vice President Finance, Brooks Memorial Hospital, Dunkirk, NY, p. A425

WEBER, Ayanna, Director Human Resources, DMC Huron Valley–Sinai Hospital, Commerce Township, MI, p. A311

WEBER, Barbara, Chief Operating Officer, Advocate Lutheran General Hospital, Park Ridge, IL, p. A191

WEBER, Carmen, Interim Administrator, Eureka Community Health Services Avera, Eureka, SD, p. A559

WEBER, Jr., Ernest P., Interim Chief Information Officer, SUNY Downstate Medical Center University Hospital,, NY, p. A436

WEBER, Frank, Chief Executive Officer, Select Specialty Hospital–Charleston, Charleston, WV, p. A676

WEBER, Gordon, Chief Operating Officer, Clarks Summit State Hospital, Clarks Summit, PA, p. A522

WEBER, James, D.O. Chief of Staff, Washington County Memorial Hospital, Potosi, MO, p. A368

WEBER, Lauren, Administrator, Audubon Behavioral Healthcare of Longview, Longview, TX, p. A619

WEBER, Marcy, R.N. Chief Nursing Officer, Hillcrest Baptist Medical Center, Waco, TX, p. A640

WEBER, Pete M., President and Chief Executive Officer, Gordon Hospital, Calhoun, GA, p. A149

WEBER, Rebecca
  Senior Vice President and Chief Information Officer, Bayshore Community Hospital, Holmdel, NJ, p. A405
  Senior Vice President and Chief Information Officer, Jersey Shore University Medical Center, Neptune, NJ, p. A407
  Senior Vice President and Chief Information Officer, Ocean Medical Center, Brick Township, NJ, p. A402
  Senior Vice President Information Technology, Riverview Medical Center, Red Bank, NJ, p. A410
  Senior Vice President and Chief Information Officer, Southern Ocean Medical Center, Manahawkin, NJ, p. A406

WEBER, Robert, M.D. Chief Medical Staff, Watsonville Community Hospital, Watsonville, CA, p. A95

WEBER, Tiffany, Chief Financial Officer, Perkins County Health Services, Grant, NE, p. A384

WEBSTER, Cindy, Vice President Financial Services, Licking Memorial Hospital, Newark, OH, p. A487

WEBSTER, Janice, Director Human Resources, West Oaks Hospital, Houston, TX, p. A614

WEBSTER, Joanne, Director Human Resources, Community Hospital of the Monterey Peninsula, Monterey, CA, p. A75

WEBSTER, Kathleen, R.N. Vice President Patient Services, Hudson Valley Hospital Center, Cortlandt Manor, NY, p. A424

WEBSTER, Kim, Manager Information Systems, Novant Health Franklin Medical Center, Louisburg, NC, p. A456

WEBSTER, Mark
  President and Chief Executive Officer, Claxton–Hepburn Medical Center, Ogdensburg, NY, p. A438
  Vice President Finance, Hudson Valley Hospital Center, Cortlandt Manor, NY, p. A424

WEBSTER, William W., FACHE, Chief Executive Officer, Medical Center Health System, Odessa, TX, p. A625

WEBSTER–SMITH, Nancy, Administrator, Anoka–Metropolitan Regional Treatment Center, Anoka, MN, p. A328

WECKENBORG, Janet, FACHE VP Operations, Capital Region Medical Center, Jefferson City, MO, p. A362

WEDEL, Sandy, Director Human Resources, Ellsworth County Medical Center, Ellsworth, KS, p. A233

WEDGEWORTH, Joyce, Financial Clerk, Hill Hospital of Sumter County, York, AL, p. A26

WEE, Donald, Chief Executive Officer, Tri–State Memorial Hospital, Clarkston, WA, p. A665

WEED, III, John, M.D. Medical Director, Little River Healthcare, Rockdale, TX, p. A629

WEED, Warren
  Director Human Resources, River Oaks Hospital, Flowood, MS, p. A346
  Director Associate Relations, Woman's Hospital, Flowood, MS, p. A346

WEEKLEY, Steve, Director Information Technology, Cooper County Memorial Hospital, Boonville, MO, p. A357

WEEKS, Donnie J., FACHE, President and Chief Executive Officer, KershawHealth, Camden, SC, p. A548

WEEKS, James, Chief Information Officer, Greenwich Hospital, Greenwich, CT, p. A109

WEEKS, Margaret, Manager Personnel, Tippah County Hospital, Ripley, MS, p. A353

WEELDREYER, Jim, Manager Information Technology, Pershing General Hospital, Lovelock, NV, p. A394

WEEMS, Reva, Director Human Resources, Crossroads Community Hospital, Mount Vernon, IL, p. A189

WEERTS, Michael, Director Human Resources, Grand River Hospital District, Rifle, CO, p. A105

WEG, Jennifer, R.N. Chief Nursing Officer, Sanford Worthington Medical Center, Worthington, MN, p. A343

WEGG, Daniel, M.D. Medical Director, St. Vincent Randolph Hospital, Winchester, IN, p. A215

WEGHORST, George, M.D. Chief Medical Officer, Providence Newberg Medical Center, Newberg, OR, p. A515

WEGLARZ, Ron, Chief Executive Officer and Managing Director, Streamwood Behavioral Health Center, Streamwood, IL, p. A195

WEGNER, Mike, Chief Financial Officer, Via Christi Hospital on St. Francis, Wichita, KS, p. A246

WEHLING, Robert D., Interim Chief Financial Officer, Saint Alphonsus Medical Center – Baker City, Baker City, OR, p. A511

WEHNER, Jill, Vice President Financial Services, Harbor Beach Community Hospital, Harbor Beach, MI, p. A316

WEHR, Julie, Director Human Resources, Odessa Memorial Healthcare Center, Odessa, WA, p. A668

WEHRMEISTER, Erica, Chief Operating Officer, Lutheran Hospital of Indiana, Fort Wayne, IN, p. A202

WEIDEMANN, Donald, Administrator, Union County General Hospital, Clayton, NM, p. A415

WEIDER, Will
  Chief Information Officer, Calumet Medical Center, Chilton, WI, p. A685
  Chief Information Officer, Mercy Medical Center, Oshkosh, WI, p. A694
  Chief Information Officer, Ministry Eagle River Memorial Hospital, Eagle River, WI, p. A686
  Chief Information Officer, Ministry Saint Joseph's Hospital, Marshfield, WI, p. A690
  Chief Information Officer, Ministry Saint Michael's Hospital, Stevens Point, WI, p. A697
  Chief Information Officer, St. Elizabeth Hospital, Appleton, WI, p. A683

WEIDNER, Deborah, M.D. Chief Medical Officer, Natchaug Hospital, Mansfield Center, CT, p. A109

WEIDNER, James, President, Cullman Regional Medical Center, Cullman, AL, p. A18

WEIDNER, Peter, Director Management Information Systems, St. John's Riverside Hospital, Yonkers, NY, p. A446

WEIGEL, Cherry, Director Health Information Management, RC Hospital and Clinics, Olivia, MN, p. A337

WEIGEL, Christine H., R.N. Clinical Operating Officer, McBride Clinic Orthopedic Hospital, Oklahoma City, OK, p. A503

WEIL, David S., Senior Vice President and Administrator, Saint Francis Hospital South, Tulsa, OK, p. A509

WEIL, Robert, M.D., President, Lakewood Hospital, Lakewood, OH, p. A483

WEILAND, David, M.D. Vice President Medical Affairs, Bayfront Health St. Petersburg, Saint Petersburg, FL, p. A138

WEILENMAN, Shelly L., R.N. Administrator and Chief Nursing Executive, Summit Medical Center, Van Buren, AR, p. A50

WEINBAUM, Frederic, M.D. Executive Vice President Operations and Chief Medical Officer, Southampton Hospital, Southampton, NY, p. A443

WEINBERG, Assa, M.D. Chief of Staff, Temple Community Hospital, Los Angeles, CA, p. A72

WEINBERG, Meryl, Executive Director, Metropolitan Hospital Center, New York, NY, p. A434

WEINBERG, Mitch, M.D. Chief of Staff, EvergreenHealth, Kirkland, WA, p. A667

WEINER, Gary
  Vice President Information Technology, Chief Information Officer, Community Hospital, Munster, IN, p. A211
  Chief Information Officer, St. Catherine Hospital, East Chicago, IN, p. A201
  Vice President Information Technology and Chief Information Officer, St. Mary Medical Center, Hobart, IN, p. A204

WEINER, Jack, President and Chief Executive Officer, St. Joseph Mercy Oakland, Pontiac, MI, p. A322

WEINER, Jerome, M.D. Senior Vice President Medical Affairs, Good Samaritan Hospital Medical Center, West Islip, NY, p. A446

WEINER, Martin E., M.D. Chief of Staff, Seton Edgar B. Davis Hospital, Luling, TX, p. A621

WEINER, Ronald, Chief Financial Officer, Magruder Memorial Hospital, Port Clinton, OH, p. A488

WEINGARTNER, Ronald, Chief Operating Officer, St. Charles Hospital, Port Jefferson, NY, p. A440

WEINHOLD, Chantal, Executive Director, Long Island Jewish Medical Center,, NY, p. A433

WEINHOLD, Robert, Chief Executive Officer, Foundations Behavioral Health, Doylestown, PA, p. A524

WEINKRANTZ, Alan, Chief Financial Officer, University of Medicine and Dentistry of New Jersey, University Behavioral Healthcare, Piscataway, NJ, p. A409

WEINMANN, Shannon, Director Human Resources, Community Medical Center, Falls City, NE, p. A383

WEINMEISTER, Kurt, Executive Vice President and Chief Operating Officer, Pomona Valley Hospital Medical Center, Pomona, CA, p. A80

WEINMEISTER III, Oscar K., FACHE, President and Chief Executive Officer, Blue Ridge Regional Hospital, Spruce Pine, NC, p. A461

WEINREIS, Brian, Vice President Operations and Finance, Abbott Northwestern Hospital, Minneapolis, MN, p. A335

WEINSTEIN, Barry S., Chief Financial Officer, Four Winds Hospital, Katonah, NY, p. A428

WEINSTEIN, Brian, M.D. Chief of Staff, Westside Regional Medical Center, Plantation, FL, p. A137

WEINSTEIN, Freddie, M.D. Chief Medical Officer, Dominican Hospital, Santa Cruz, CA, p. A90

WEINSTEIN, Gary B., President and Chief Executive Officer, Washington Hospital, Washington, PA, p. A543

WEINSTEIN, James, M.D., President and Chief Executive Officer, Dartmouth–Hitchcock Medical Center, Lebanon, NH, p. A398

WEINSTEIN, Roslyn, Chief Operating Officer, Kings County Hospital Center,, NY, p. A433

WEINTZ, Charles, D.O. Chief of Staff, Stanton County Hospital, Johnson, KS, p. A236

WEIS, Charis, Director Human Resources, Klickitat Valley Health, Goldendale, WA, p. A667

WEIS, Charles
  Chief Financial Officer, Mount Sinai Hospital, Chicago, IL, p. A177
  Chief Financial Officer, Schwab Rehabilitation Hospital, Chicago, IL, p. A179

WEIS, Harry, Chief Executive Officer, Natividad Medical Center, Salinas, CA, p. A84

WEIS, Maurine
  Vice President Patient Care Service and Chief Nursing Officer, ProMedica Bay Park Hospital, Oregon, OH, p. A488
  Vice President Nursing and Chief Nursing Officer, ProMedica Flower Hospital, Sylvania, OH, p. A490

WEIS, Shirley
  Chief Administrative Officer, Mayo Clinic – Saint Marys Hospital, Rochester, MN, p. A339
  Chief Administrative Officer, Rochester Methodist Hospital, Rochester, MN, p. A339

WEIS, Wade, Senior Director Finance, Grande Ronde Hospital, La Grande, OR, p. A514

WEISE, Charles, M.D. Medical Director, Highland Hospital, Charleston, WV, p. A676

WEISENBERGER, Scott, Administrator, Kirkbride Center, Philadelphia, PA, p. A535

WEISENFREUND, Jochanan, M.D. Senior Vice President Academic and Medical Affairs, Interfaith Medical Center,, NY, p. A432

WEISFIELD, Phyllis, Chief Executive Officer and Managing Director, Horsham Clinic, Ambler, PA, p. A520

WEISHAPL, Natasha, Manager Business Office and Human Resources, Decatur County Hospital and Cedar Living Center, Oberlin, KS, p. A241

WEISNER, Brad, Executive Vice President and Chief Operating Officer, Nash Health Care Systems, Rocky Mount, NC, p. A460

WEISS, Allen S., M.D., President and Chief Executive Officer, NCH Downtown Naples Hospital, Naples, FL, p. A133

WEISS, Clay, Administrator, Northwest Texas Surgery Center, Amarillo, TX, p. A582

WEISS, David, Vice President Information System, Alton Memorial Hospital, Alton, IL, p. A173

WEISS, Gary, Chief Financial Officer, NorthShore University Health System Evanston Hospital, Evanston, IL, p. A182

WEISS, Linda W., FACHE, Director, Albany Stratton Veterans Affairs Medical Center, Albany, NY, p. A420

WEISS, Phyllis, Director Human Resources, Alameda Hospital, Alameda, CA, p. A52

WEISS, Terri, Chief Financial Officer, Reliant Rehabilitation Hospital North Houston, Shenandoah, TX, p. A633

WEISSENBERGER, Ralf, Director Information Systems, White Memorial Medical Center, Los Angeles, CA, p. A72

WEISSER, Lisa, Supervisor Finance, Wagner Community Memorial Hospital Avera, Wagner, SD, p. A563

WEISTREICH, Tracy, Ph.D. Associate Director Patient Care Services/Nurse Executive, Veterans Affairs Roseburg Healthcare System, Roseburg, OR, p. A517

WEISUL, Jonathan, M.D
  Vice President Medical Affairs and Chief Medical Officer, CHRISTUS Coushatta Health Care Center, Coushatta, LA, p. A265

  Chief Medical Officer and Vice President Innovation, Community Medical Center, Missoula, MT, p. A378

WELCH, Abbey, Director Human Resources, Harmon Memorial Hospital, Hollis, OK, p. A500

WELCH, Andrew, Director, Amarillo Veterans Affairs Health Care System, Amarillo, TX, p. A582

WELCH, Bonnie, Chief Information Officer, St. James Mercy Health System, Hornell, NY, p. A427

WELCH, Bryant, Chief Human Resources, Washington Hospital Healthcare System, Fremont, CA, p. A61

WELCH, Charolotte, Chief Nursing Officer, Haskell Memorial Hospital, Haskell, TX, p. A608

WELCH, David, M.D. Medical Director, Clifton–Fine Hospital, Star Lake, NY, p. A443

WELCH, David, Director Information Technology, Simpson General Hospital, Mendenhall, MS, p. A350

WELCH, Donald E., Chief Operating Officer, Florida Hospital Zephyrhills, Zephyrhills, FL, p. A144

WELCH, Douglas, Chief Executive Officer, Doctors Hospital, Augusta, GA, p. A147

WELCH, Jeffrey M., Chief Executive Officer, Coral Gables Hospital, Coral Gables, FL, p. A121

WELCH, Kenneth, M.D. Chief Medical Officer, Banner Estrella Medical Center, Phoenix, AZ, p. A34

WELCH, Melissa, Director Health Information Management, Oakdale Community Hospital, Oakdale, LA, p. A276

WELCH, Rosemary C., R.N. Vice President and Chief Nursing Officer, MedStar National Rehabilitation Hospital, Washington, DC, p. A116

WELCH, Shelly, R.N. Senior Vice President and Chief Nursing Officer, North Oaks Medical Center, Hammond, LA, p. A268

WELCH, Tony
  VP Human Resources, Englewood Community Hospital, Englewood, FL, p. A123

  Vice President Human Resources, Fawcett Memorial Hospital, Port Charlotte, FL, p. A137

WELCH, William L., FACHE, Chief Executive Officer, Jefferson Community Health Center, Fairbury, NE, p. A383

WELDAY, Douglas D., Division President, Oakwood Hospital & Medical Center–Dearborn, Dearborn, MI, p. A311

WELDER, Linda R., M.D. Chief of Staff, Highland District Hospital, Hillsboro, OH, p. A483

WELDING, Theodore L., Administrator, Kindred Hospital South Florida–Fort Lauderdale, Fort Lauderdale, FL, p. A123

WELDON, Jim, Chief Information Officer, St. Anthony's Medical Center, Saint Louis, MO, p. A370

WELDON, Marie L., FACHE, Director, South Texas Veterans Health Care System, San Antonio, TX, p. A632

WELDON, William W., Ph.D., Interim Chief Executive Officer, Cogdell Memorial Hospital, Snyder, TX, p. A634

WELDY, Alan, Vice President Human Resources, Compliance and Legal Services, Indiana University Health Goshen Hospital, Goshen, IN, p. A203

WELKER, Suzanne, Chief Human Resources Officer and Vice President Marketing Strategy, Berger Health System, Circleville, OH, p. A475

WELKIE, Katy, R.N., Chief Executive Officer, Primary Children's Medical Center, Salt Lake City, UT, p. A646

WELLENDORF, Sharon A., Chief Nursing Officer, Horn Memorial Hospital, Ida Grove, IA, p. A223

WELLENDORF, Tracey, M.D. Chief of Staff, St. Anthony Regional Hospital, Carroll, IA, p. A217

WELLING, Richard, M.D. Chief of Staff, Bartlett Regional Hospital, Juneau, AK, p. A28

WELLMANN, Jane, Chief Financial Officer, Scott & White Hospital – Brenham, Brenham, TX, p. A589

WELLS, A. Shane, Chief Financial Officer, Cornerstone Hospital of Houston – Bellaire, Houston, TX, p. A609

WELLS, Alphe, Vice President Human Resources and Support Services, Delta Regional Medical Center, Greenville, MS, p. A347

WELLS, Carol, R.N. Chief Nursing Officer, Central Louisiana Surgical Hospital, Alexandria, LA, p. A262

WELLS, Dale, Senior Vice President Finance and Operations, Alliance Community Hospital, Alliance, OH, p. A470

WELLS, Jason, Chief Human Resources Management Service, Fargo Veterans Affairs Health Care System, Fargo, ND, p. A466

WELLS, Jonathan, Supervisor Information Technology, Kansas Surgery and Recovery Center, Wichita, KS, p. A246

WELLS, Mary S., R.N., Chief Executive Officer, Community Memorial Hospital, Sumner, IA, p. A229

WELLS, Mary Ellen, Administrator, CentraCare Health–Monticello, Monticello, MN, p. A336

WELLS, Molly, Chief Nursing Officer, Martin General Hospital, Williamston, NC, p. A462

WELLS, Robert, M.D. Chief Medical Officer, Providence Portland Medical Center, Portland, OR, p. A516

WELLS, Scott E., MSN Chief Nursing Officer, St. Francis Health Center, Topeka, KS, p. A245

WELLS, Valerie, Manager Human Resources, HEALTHSOUTH Rehabilitation Hospital of North Houston, Conroe, TX, p. A593

WELSH, Cari, Interim Chief Financial Officer, Fountain Valley Regional Hospital and Medical Center, Fountain Valley, CA, p. A60

WELSH Jr., J. Luckey, Chief Executive Officer, Cherry Hospital, Goldsboro, NC, p. A453

WENGER, Cheryl, Manager Health Information and Quality Assurance, Hiawatha Community Hospital, Hiawatha, KS, p. A235

WENGER, Jill, Vice President Human Resources, McPherson Hospital, McPherson, KS, p. A239

WENGER–KELLER, David, M.D. Chief of Staff, Fort Madison Community Hospital, Fort Madison, IA, p. A221

WENGERD, Gary, Vice President Finance and Chief Financial Officer, Mercy Regional Medical Center, Lorain, OH, p. A484

WENTZ, Robert J., President and Chief Executive Officer, Oroville Hospital, Oroville, CA, p. A78

WENTZEL, Chris, M.D. Interim Medical Director, Corning Hospital, Corning, NY, p. A424

WENZEL, Matthew J., Chief Executive Officer, Hedrick Medical Center, Chillicothe, MO, p. A358

WERFT, Ronald C.
  President and Chief Executive Officer, Goleta Valley Cottage Hospital, Santa Barbara, CA, p. A89

  President and Chief Executive Officer, Santa Barbara Cottage Hospital, Santa Barbara, CA, p. A89

  President and Chief Executive Officer, Santa Ynez Valley Cottage Hospital, Solvang, CA, p. A91

WERKOWSKI, Richard F., Chief Financial Officer, Speare Memorial Hospital, Plymouth, NH, p. A400

WERNECKE, Jennie, Human Resources Manager, Dr. John Warner Hospital, Clinton, IL, p. A180

WERNER, Don, Chief Executive Officer, Lady of the Sea General Hospital, Cut Off, LA, p. A266

WERNER, Edward, Director Human Resources, HEALTHSOUTH Reading Rehabilitation Hospital, Reading, PA, p. A539

WERNER, John W., Chief Executive Officer, Oakland Mercy Hospital, Oakland, NE, p. A387

WERNER, Julie, Chief Operating Officer, Community Memorial Hospital, Syracuse, NE, p. A390

WERNER, Kurt, M.D. Chief of Staff, Veterans Affairs Montana Health Care System, Fort Harrison, MT, p. A376

WERNER, Mark D., M.D. Executive Vice President and Chief Medical Officer, Carilion Medical Center, Roanoke, VA, p. A661

WERNER, Sandy, Director Human Resources, Simi Valley Hospital and Health Care Services, Simi Valley, CA, p. A91

WERNER, Todd S., Chief Executive Officer, Banner Gateway Medical Center, Gilbert, AZ, p. A31

WERNICK, Joel, President and Chief Executive Officer, Phoebe Putney Memorial Hospital, Albany, GA, p. A145

WERNKE, Chris, Chief Operating Officer, Dominican Hospital, Santa Cruz, CA, p. A90

WERRBACH, John P., Chief Executive Officer, Alexian Brothers Medical Center, Elk Grove Village, IL, p. A182

WERTH–SWEENEY, Stacey, Facility Operating Officer, Lincoln Regional Center, Lincoln, NE, p. A385

WERTHMAN, Ronald J., Senior Vice President Finance, Chief Financial Officer and Treasurer, Johns Hopkins Hospital, Baltimore, MD, p. A287

WERTZ, Barbara
  Vice President Patient Care Services, Providence Medical Center, Kansas City, KS, p. A237

  Vice President Patient Care Services, Saint John Hospital, Leavenworth, KS, p. A238

WERTZ, Jackie, Director Human Resources, George C Grape Community Hospital, Hamburg, IA, p. A222

WERTZ, Randy S., Chief Executive Officer, Golden Valley Memorial Healthcare, Clinton, MO, p. A359

WESCOTT, Lisle, President, SSM St. Joseph Hospital West, Lake Saint Louis, MO, p. A364

WESENER DIECK, Jill, Director Human Resources, Gundersen Tri–County Hospital and Clinics, Whitehall, WI, p. A699

WESLEY, Deb, MSN Chief Nursing Officer, The Children's Hospital of Alabama, Birmingham, AL, p. A17

WESLEY, Jim
  Interim Senior Vice President and Chief Information Officer, John Muir Medical Center, Concord, Concord, CA, p. A57

  Interim Chief Information Officer, John Muir Medical Center, Walnut Creek, Walnut Creek, CA, p. A95

WESLEY, Lois Sprengeler, Director Quality Management, U. S. Public Health Service Indian Hospital, San Carlos, AZ, p. A36

WESSBERG, Barb, Administrator, Essentia Health Duluth, Duluth, MN, p. A331

WESSELS, Jana, Associate Vice President Human Resources, University of Iowa Hospitals and Clinics, Iowa City, IA, p. A223

WEST, Arthur, Chief Financial Officer, Hialeah Hospital, Hialeah, FL, p. A125

WEST, Dan, Director Information Technology Systems, Saint Thomas Rutherford Hospital, Murfreesboro, TN, p. A576

WEST, David, Chief Operating Officer, Deckerville Community Hospital, Deckerville, MI, p. A311

WEST, Heather, Director Human Resources, Lakeland Community Hospital Watervliet, Watervliet, MI, p. A326

WEST, James R., President and Chief Executive Officer, Presbyterian Intercommunity Hospital, Whittier, CA, p. A96

WEST, Joanell, Human Resources Generalist, Methodist Healthcare–Fayette Hospital, Somerville, TN, p. A579

WEST, Judy, Vice President Human Resources, Maine Medical Center, Portland, ME, p. A284

WEST, Karen M., Administrator Support Services, Wild Rose Community Memorial Hospital, Wild Rose, WI, p. A700

WEST, Margaret M., MS, Chief Executive Officer, Magnolia Regional Medical Center, Magnolia, AR, p. A47

WEST, Michael C., M.D. Chief of Staff, McCurtain Memorial Hospital, Idabel, OK, p. A500

WEST, Michele, Director Human Resources, Doctors Medical Center, Modesto, CA, p. A74

WEST, Scott H., M.D. Chief Medical Officer, Lakeview Hospital, Bountiful, UT, p. A643

WEST, Steve, M.D. Chief Medical Officer, Capital Regional Medical Center, Tallahassee, FL, p. A140

WEST, Steven J., Chief Executive Officer, Indiana University Health Blackford Hospital, Hartford City, IN, p. A204

WEST, Tamara, R.N. Vice President Patient Care, Nicholas H. Noyes Memorial Hospital, Dansville, NY, p. A424

WEST, Warren K., FACHE, Chief Executive Officer, Littleton Regional Hospital, Littleton, NH, p. A399

WEST, William, M.D. Chief of Staff, Edgerton Hospital and Health Services, Edgerton, WI, p. A686

WESTENFELDER, Grant, M.D. Chief Medical Officer, Midwest Medical Center, Galena, IL, p. A183

WESTENHOFER, Steve, Chief Executive Officer, Mimbres Memorial Hospital, Deming, NM, p. A415

WESTER, K. Scott, FACHE, President and Chief Executive Officer, Our Lady of the Lake Regional Medical Center, Baton Rouge, LA, p. A263

WESTERHEIDE, Karen, Chief Financial Officer, Veterans Affairs St. Louis Health Care System, Saint Louis, MO, p. A371

WESTFALL, Gay, Senior Vice President Human Resources, Kaiser Permanente Sacramento Medical Center, Sacramento, CA, p. A83

WESTFIELD, Brian W., MSN, Director, Jonathan M. Wainwright Memorial Veterans Affairs Medical Center, Walla Walla, WA, p. A674

WESTGARD, David E., M.D. Chief Medical Officer, Olmsted Medical Center, Rochester, MN, p. A339

WESTMAN, Ken, Chief Executive Officer, Barrett Hospital & HealthCare, Dillon, MT, p. A375

WESTMORELAND, Penny
Chief Financial Officer, Lakeland Community Hospital, Haleyville, AL, p. A21
Chief Financial Officer, Russellville Hospital, Russellville, AL, p. A25

WESTON, Betty, Chief Human Resources Officer, U. S. Public Health Service Phoenix Indian Medical Center, Phoenix, AZ, p. A36

WESTON, Nancy R., R.N. Vice President Nursing Services, Memorial Hospital, Belleville, IL, p. A174

WESTON, Terry, M.D. Vice President Physician Services, MedCentral – Mansfield Hospital, Mansfield, OH, p. A485

WESTON–HALL, Patricia, Chief Executive Officer, Glenbeigh Hospital and Outpatient Centers, Rock Creek, OH, p. A489

WESTOVER, Gerald, M.D. Medical Director, Upper Connecticut Valley Hospital, Colebrook, NH, p. A397

WESTPHAL, James, M.D. Medical Director, Hawaii State Hospital, Kaneohe, HI, p. A165

WETHERS, Darren E., M.D. President Medical Staff, SSM St. Mary's Health Center, Saint Louis, MO, p. A370

WETHINGTON, Bud, Chief Executive Officer, Tomball Regional Medical Center, Tomball, TX, p. A638

WETHINGTON, Patti, R.N. Chief Nursing Officer, Spectrum Health Gerber Memorial, Fremont, MI, p. A314

WEVER, Kurt, M.D. Chief of Staff, Pikes Peak Regional Hospital, Woodland Park, CO, p. A107

WEXLER, Erik G., President and Chief Executive Officer, Saint Vincent Hospital, Worcester, MA, p. A306

WEYMOUTH, Deborah K., Executive Director and Senior Vice President, New Milford Hospital, New Milford, CT, p. A111

WEYMOUTH, Linda, Chief Financial Officer, Manatee Palms Youth Services, Bradenton, FL, p. A119

WHALEN, David, Chief Executive Officer, Twin Cities Hospital, Niceville, FL, p. A134

WHALEN, Eileen, R.N., Executive Director, UW Medicine/Harborview Medical Center, Seattle, WA, p. A671

WHALEN, Patti, Manager Human Resources, Wichita County Health Center, Leoti, KS, p. A238

WHALEN, Scott, FACHE,
President and Chief Executive Officer, Saint Vincent Hospital, Erie, PA, p. A525
President and Chief Executive Officer, Westfield Memorial Hospital, Westfield, NY, p. A446

WHALEN, Thomas
Chief Financial Officer, Braintree Rehabilitation Hospital, Braintree, MA, p. A298
Vice President Finance, Good Samaritan Medical Center, Brockton, MA, p. A298

WHALEN, Thomas, M.D. Chief Medical Officer, Lehigh Valley Hospital–Muhlenberg, Bethlehem, PA, p. A520

WHALEY, Joseph, Chief, Human Resources Management Service, Fayetteville Veterans Affairs Medical Center, Fayetteville, NC, p. A452

WHALEY, Mary, Director of Acute Care, Johnson County Healthcare Center, Buffalo, WY, p. A701

WHARTON, Joe H., M.D. Chief of Staff, Bradley County Medical Center, Warren, AR, p. A50

WHEAT, Ken, Chief Operating Officer, Desert Regional Medical Center, Palm Springs, CA, p. A78

WHEATLEY, Jane, Chief Executive Officer, Taylor Regional Hospital, Campbellsville, KY, p. A249

WHEATLEY, Jason
Manager Information Systems, Presence Covenant Medical Center, Urbana, IL, p. A196
Manager Information Systems, Presence United Samaritans Medical Center, Danville, IL, p. A180

WHEATLEY, Richard, Chief Information Officer, Cape Regional Medical Center, Cape May Court House, NJ, p. A402

WHEATON, David, Director Human Resources, Blue Hill Memorial Hospital, Blue Hill, ME, p. A282

WHEELAN, Kevin, M.D. Medical Director, Baylor Jack and Jane Hamilton Heart and Vascular Hospital, Dallas, TX, p. A595

WHEELER, Barb, Business Manager, Mental Health Institute, Mount Pleasant, IA, p. A225

WHEELER, Brent, Vice President Ancillary and Support Services, McLaren Flint, Flint, MI, p. A313

WHEELER, Butch, FACHE, Chief Executive Officer, Hughston Hospital, Columbus, GA, p. A150

WHEELER, Dana
Director Human Resources, South Bay Hospital, Sun City Center, FL, p. A140
Director Human Resources, Venice Regional Medical Center, Venice, FL, p. A143

WHEELER, Dane, Chief Financial Officer, Adams Memorial Hospital, Decatur, IN, p. A201

WHEELER, Dawne, Chief Executive Officer, Select Specialty Hospital–Canton, Canton, OH, p. A473

WHEELER, Deborah, Director Human Resources, North Carolina Specialty Hospital, Durham, NC, p. A451

WHEELER, Denise, Chief Information Officer, Star Valley Medical Center, Afton, WY, p. A701

WHEELER, James A., Vice President Human Relations and Community Development, Androscoggin Valley Hospital, Berlin, NH, p. A397

WHEELER, Jim, Executive Vice President and Chief Financial Officer, South Haven Health System, South Haven, MI, p. A324

WHEELER, Katrina, Chief Financial Officer, Mayo Clinic Health System in Waycross, Waycross, GA, p. A162

WHEELER, Kevin, Information Technology Leader, Kaiser Permanente Walnut Creek Medical Center, Walnut Creek, CA, p. A95

WHEELER, Lois, Manager Human Resources, F. W. Huston Medical Center, Winchester, KS, p. A247

WHEELER, Lynette, MSN Chief Nursing Officer, Truman Medical Center–Lakewood, Kansas City, MO, p. A364

WHEELER, Pamela R., Manager Human Resources, Scott County Hospital, Scott City, KS, p. A244

WHEELER, Rebecca, Director Finance, Kaiser Permanente Baldwin Park Medical Center, Baldwin Park, CA, p. A54

WHEELER, Robert
Controller, HEALTHSOUTH Rehabilitation Hospital, Florence, SC, p. A551
Vice President Human Resources, South Shore Hospital, South Weymouth, MA, p. A304

WHEELER, Terry J., Chief Executive Officer, Cypress Fairbanks Medical Center, Houston, TX, p. A609

WHEELER, Zach, Senior Vice President Human Resources, John D. Archbold Memorial Hospital, Thomasville, GA, p. A161

WHEELESS, Jane, Director Human Resources, Crosbyton Clinic Hospital, Crosbyton, TX, p. A594

WHEELOCK, Linda, Director of Nursing, Milan General Hospital, Milan, TN, p. A575

WHELAN, Doris, Chief Information Officer, Moberly Regional Medical Center, Moberly, MO, p. A366

WHELAN, Laurie A., Senior Vice President Finance and Chief Financial Officer, Hospital for Special Care, New Britain, CT, p. A110

WHELAN, Melissa, Director Health Information, Brighton Center for Recovery, Brighton, MI, p. A309

WHELAN, Thomas
President, Edwin Shaw Rehab, Cuyahoga Falls, OH, p. A479
President, Lodi Community Hospital, Lodi, OH, p. A484

WHELAN, Wendy, Director Talent, Southwestern Regional Medical Center, Tulsa, OK, p. A509

WHERRY, Richard, M.D. Chief of Staff, Chestatee Regional Hospital, Dahlonega, GA, p. A151

WHERRY, Robin, Risk Manager and Director Quality Assurance and Health Information Management, HEALTHSOUTH MountainView Regional Rehabilitation Hospital, Morgantown, WV, p. A679

WHETSTINE, Tyler, Director of Information Systems, Citrus Memorial Health System, Inverness, FL, p. A126

WHETTON, Matthew, Chief Business Administration, Veterans Affairs Central California Health Care System, Fresno, CA, p. A62

WHICHARD, Forrest, Chief Financial Officer, Ochsner Medical Center – North Shore, Slidell, LA, p. A279

WHIDDON, William, Chief Financial Officer, The Medical Center of Southeast Texas, Port Arthur, TX, p. A628

WHILDEN, Sean
Chief Financil Officer, Houston Medical Center, Warner Robins, GA, p. A162
Chief Financial Officer, Perry Hospital, Perry, GA, p. A158

WHILES, David, Director Health Information Systems, Midland Memorial Hospital, Midland, TX, p. A623

WHILLOCK, Mary C., R.N. Associate Nursing Officer and Chief Operating Officer, Florida Hospital–Carrollwood, Tampa, FL, p. A141

WHIPKEY, Jared, Chief Financial Officer, Barrow Regional Medical Center, Winder, GA, p. A163

WHIPPLE, C. Cynthia, Administrative Director and Director of Nursing, Muncy Valley Hospital, Muncy, PA, p. A532

WHIPPLE, Glenn, Chief Information Officer, Dameron Hospital, Stockton, CA, p. A91

WHIPPLE, James, Administrator and Chief Executive Officer, Marshall Medical Center, Placerville, CA, p. A80

WHITAKER, Charles, Director Information Technology, Madison Parish Hospital, Tallulah, LA, p. A279

WHITAKER, David D., FACHE, President and Chief Executive Officer, Norman Regional Health System, Norman, OK, p. A502

WHITAKER, Doris, Vice President Human Resources, Booneville Community Hospital, Booneville, AR, p. A41

WHITAKER, E. Berton, FACHE, President, Baptist Health Madisonville, Madisonville, KY, p. A257

WHITAKER, James B., President, Circles of Care, Melbourne, FL, p. A130

WHITAKER, Jimmy, Director Information Systems, Central Carolina Hospital, Sanford, NC, p. A460

WHITAKER, Neil, M.D. Chief Medical Director, Orem Community Hospital, Orem, UT, p. A645

WHITE, A. Randle, M.D. Chief Medical Staff, Greenwood Leflore Hospital, Greenwood, MS, p. A347

WHITE, Al, CPA Senior Vice President Business Services, Broadlawns Medical Center, Des Moines, IA, p. A220

WHITE, Alexander, Vice President Medical Affairs, Carney Hospital, Boston, MA, p. A296

WHITE, Alison, R.N. Vice President Nursing and Quality, Central Vermont Medical Center, Berlin, VT, p. A649

WHITE, Andrea, Chief Executive Officer, Select Specialty Hospital–Birmingham, Birmingham, AL, p. A17

WHITE, Becky, M.D. Chief of Staff, Newberry County Memorial Hospital, Newberry, SC, p. A555

WHITE, Beverly, MS, Facility Director, Mary S Harper Geriatric Psychiatry Center, Tuscaloosa, AL, p. A26

WHITE, Brian M., President, Northwest Hospital, Randallstown, MD, p. A293

WHITE, Bruce D., Chief Executive Officer, Knox Community Hospital, Mount Vernon, OH, p. A487

WHITE, Charles, Chief Administrative Officer, Upper Connecticut Valley Hospital, Colebrook, NH, p. A397

WHITE, Chris L., Administrator, Grover M. Herman Hospital, Callicoon, NY, p. A423

WHITE, Cindy, CPA Vice President of Operations, INTEGRIS Canadian Valley Hospital, Yukon, OK, p. A510

WHITE, Clifford, M.D. Chief of Staff, Uvalde County Hospital Authority, Uvalde, TX, p. A639

WHITE, Cole, Chief Executive Officer, Middle Park Medical Center, Kremmling, CO, p. A102

WHITE, Darrell, R.N., Administrator/Chief Nursing Officer, Tristar Ashland City, Ashland City, TN, p. A565

WHITE, Debbie
Chief Financial Officer, CHRISTUS St. Frances Cabrini Hospital, Alexandria, LA, p. A262
Chief Financial Officer, CHRISTUS St. Patrick Hospital of Lake Charles, Lake Charles, LA, p. A271

WHITE, Deborah, Director Human Resources, Maniilaq Health Center, Kotzebue, AK, p. A28

WHITE, Debra, Chief Nursing Officer, Saint Luke's Hospital of Kansas City, Kansas City, MO, p. A363

WHITE, Diane B., Director Human Resources, Jerome Golden Center for Behavioral Health, Inc., West Palm Beach, FL, p. A143

WHITE, Diane K., MSN Chief Clinical Officer, Kindred Hospital South Philadelphia, Philadelphia, PA, p. A535

WHITE, Donna, Director Human Resources, HEALTHSOUTH Rehabilitation Hospital of Charleston, Charleston, SC, p. A549

WHITE, Doug, Chief Executive Officer, Grand Strand Regional Medical Center, Myrtle Beach, SC, p. A555

WHITE, Dudley R., Administrator and Chief Executive Officer, Concho County Hospital, Eden, TX, p. A600

WHITE, Gary B., M.D. Chief Medical Staff, Uintah Basin Medical Center, Roosevelt, UT, p. A646

WHITE, Harold, Vice Chancellor, LSU Health Sciences Center, Shreveport, LA, p. A278

WHITE, J. B., Director Information Systems, River Region Medical Center, Vicksburg, MS, p. A354

WHITE, James P., M.D. Chief Medical Officer, Integris Baptist Medical Center, Oklahoma City, OK, p. A503

WHITE, Jean, Vice President Finance, Avera Heart Hospital of South Dakota, Sioux Falls, SD, p. A562

WHITE, Jeffrey L., Senior Vice President and Chief Financial Officer, Beaufort Memorial Hospital, Beaufort, SC, p. A548

WHITE, Jim
Chief Information Officer, Lompoc Valley Medical Center, Lompoc, CA, p. A67
Chief Financial Officer, Parkside Hospital, Tulsa, OK, p. A508

WHITE, Joanne, Chief Information Officer, Wood County Hospital, Bowling Green, OH, p. A472

WHITE, Joe
Chief Financial Officer, Central Texas Hospital, Cameron, TX, p. A591
Chief Financial Officer, Lake Whitney Medical Center, Whitney, TX, p. A641

WHITE, John, M.D. Medical Director, Parkside Hospital, Tulsa, OK, p. A508

WHITE, John D., Chief Financial Officer, Wythe County Community Hospital, Wytheville, VA, p. A663

WHITE, John R., Chief Executive Officer and Superintendent, Klickitat Valley Health, Goldendale, WA, p. A667

WHITE, Joseph, Executive Vice President and Chief Operating Officer, Lowell General Hospital, Lowell, MA, p. A301

WHITE, Kathy, R.N. Interim Chief Operating Officer, Doctors Medical Center–San Pablo Campus, San Pablo, CA, p. A88

WHITE, Kay, Director Human Resources and Diversity, Carolinas Hospital System Marion, Mullins, SC, p. A554

WHITE, Kelli, Manager Human Resources, CenterPointe Hospital, Saint Charles, MO, p. A368

WHITE, Kevin A., Administrator, Medicine Lodge Memorial Hospital, Medicine Lodge, KS, p. A240

WHITE, Linda, Director Fiscal Services, Memphis Mental Health Institute, Memphis, TN, p. A575

WHITE, Lindy P., President and Chief Executive Officer, Smyth County Community Hospital, Marion, VA, p. A656

WHITE, Louise, R.N
  Vice President Patient Care Services and Chief Nursing Officer, Children's Hospital at Mission, Mission Viejo, CA, p. A74
  Vice President Patient Care Services and Chief Nursing Officer, Children's Hospital of Orange County, Orange, CA, p. A77

WHITE, Mark, Director Information Services, Mount Desert Island Hospital, Bar Harbor, ME, p. A281

WHITE, Mary M., Chief Executive Officer, Swedish Medical Center, Englewood, CO, p. A100

WHITE, Mary–Louise, M.D., Chief Executive Officer, Dr. Solomon Carter Fuller Mental Health Center, Boston, MA, p. A296

WHITE, Nathan, Director Information Systems, Caldwell Memorial Hospital, Lenoir, NC, p. A456

WHITE, Olinda, Chief Financial Officer, Wrangell Medical Center, Wrangell, AK, p. A29

WHITE, Padraic, Administrator, Chief Executive Officer and Chief Financial Officer, Ward Memorial Hospital, Monahans, TX, p. A623

WHITE, Patricia, Vice President Human Resources, Seton Medical Center, Daly City, CA, p. A58

WHITE, Patty, MS, President, St. Joseph's Hospital and Medical Center, Phoenix, AZ, p. A35

WHITE, Randall, Chief Executive Officer, Fayette Regional Health System, Connersville, IN, p. A200

WHITE, Randy, Chief Nursing Officer, Baptist Memorial Hospital–Union County, New Albany, MS, p. A352

WHITE, Robert, Director Information Technology, Helena Regional Medical Center, Helena, AR, p. A44

WHITE, Robin, Assistant Vice President Human Resources, Parkview Adventist Medical Center, Brunswick, ME, p. A282

WHITE, Sabrina, Coordinator Human Resources, Select Specialty Hospital–Charleston, Charleston, WV, p. A676

WHITE, Shelia, Director Human Resources, Bon Secours–Richmond Community Hospital, Richmond, VA, p. A660

WHITE, Shirley, Director Human Resources, Ashley County Medical Center, Crossett, AR, p. A42

WHITE, Steve, M.D. Chief Medical Officer, Guadalupe Regional Medical Center, Seguin, TX, p. A633

WHITE, Thomas, Director Human Resources, Blue Ridge Regional Hospital, Spruce Pine, NC, p. A461

WHITE, Wayne, Director Computer Services, Sage Memorial Hospital, Ganado, AZ, p. A31

WHITE, Wendy
  Vice President Human Resources, CHRISTUS Schumpert Medical Center, Shreveport, LA, p. A278
  Regional Vice President Human Resources, CHRISTUS St. Frances Cabrini Hospital, Alexandria, LA, p. A262
  Assistant Administrator Human Resources, CHRISTUS St. Patrick Hospital of Lake Charles, Lake Charles, LA, p. A271

WHITE, Wesley D., Chief Financial Officer, Community Hospital, Grand Junction, CO, p. A101

WHITE, Willie, M.D. Director Medical Staff, J. Paul Jones Hospital, Camden, AL, p. A18

WHITE, Woody, Chief Financial Officer, Wellington Regional Medical Center, West Palm Beach, FL, p. A144

WHITE HOUSE, Judy, Vice President Human Resources, St. Mary's Hospital and Medical Center, Grand Junction, CO, p. A102

WHITE–JACOBS, Mary Beth, R.N., President and Chief Executive Officer, Black River Memorial Hospital, Black River Falls, WI, p. A684

WHITEAKER, Les, Vice President and Chief Financial Officer, Memorial Medical Center – Ashland, Ashland, WI, p. A683

WHITED, Brian, M.D. Medical Director, Mayo Clinic Health System in Mankato, Mankato, MN, p. A335

WHITED, Steve, Chief Executive Officer, Minnie Hamilton HealthCare Center, Grantsville, WV, p. A677

WHITEHEAD, Alva W., M.D. Vice President Medical Services, McLeod Regional Medical Center, Florence, SC, p. A552

WHITEHEAD, David, President and Chief Executive Officer, The William W. Backus Hospital, Norwich, CT, p. A111

WHITEHORN, Jeffrey T., Chief Executive Officer, TriStar Summit Medical Center, Hermitage, TN, p. A570

WHITEHURST, Carolyn, Director Human Resources, Texas Health Presbyterian Hospital Kaufman, Kaufman, TX, p. A616

WHITEHURST, Rob, Chief, Office of Information and Technology, Veterans Affairs Ann Arbor Healthcare System, Ann Arbor, MI, p. A308

WHITENACK, Barbara, Manager Human Resources, St. Vincent Mercy Hospital, Elwood, IN, p. A201

WHITENACK, John, Chief Operating Officer, Greystone Park Psychiatric Hospital, Morris Plains, NJ, p. A406

WHITESIDE, Patrick, Manager Technology Information Systems, Spectrum Health Gerber Memorial, Fremont, MI, p. A314

WHITESIDE, Timothy, M.D. Chief of Staff, Wahiawa General Hospital, Wahiawa, HI, p. A166

WHITETHORNE, Priscilla, Chief Executive Officer, U. S. Public Health Service Indian Hospital–Sells, Sells, AZ, p. A37

WHITFIELD, Bruce, CPA, Chief Executive Officer and Chief Financial Officer, St. John's Lutheran Hospital, Libby, MT, p. A378

WHITFIELD Jr., Charles H., President and Chief Executive Officer, Laughlin Memorial Hospital, Greeneville, TN, p. A569

WHITFIELD, Jay, Chief Financial Officer, Baylor University Medical Center, Dallas, TX, p. A595

WHITFIELD, Teresa L., MS Director Quality and Outcomes, Eastern Plumas Health Care District, Portola, CA, p. A80

WHITING, Barbara, Director Health Information Management, Promise Hospital of Vicksburg, Vicksburg, MS, p. A354

WHITLEY, Kathleen, R.N. Director Clinical and Professional Service, Worcester Recovery Center and Hospital, Worcester, MA, p. A307

WHITLEY, Pam, R.N. Chief Operating Officer and Chief Nursing Officer, Green Oaks Hospital, Dallas, TX, p. A596

WHITLOCK, Jr., James A., M.D. Medical Director, Northeast Rehabilitation Hospital, Salem, NH, p. A400

WHITLOCK, Nancy, Manager Human Resources, Summers County ARH Hospital, Hinton, WV, p. A677

WHITMAN, Bill, Chief Operating Officer, JPS Health Network, Fort Worth, TX, p. A604

WHITMORE, Ray B., Chief Financial Officer, McCurtain Memorial Hospital, Idabel, OK, p. A500

WHITMORE, W. Patrick, Chief Financial Officer, Medical Center of Plano, Plano, TX, p. A627

WHITNEY, Donald, Director Human Resources, Kindred Hospital–Albuquerque, Albuquerque, NM, p. A414

WHITNEY, Nancy, Chief Financial Officer, St. Francis Healthcare Campus, Breckenridge, MN, p. A329

WHITNUM, Rhonda, Director Health Improvement Management, Prague Community Hospital, Prague, OK, p. A505

WHITSON, Charles P., CPA Senior Vice President Finance, Lake Charles Memorial Hospital, Lake Charles, LA, p. A272

WHITT, Charles Christopher, Chief Nursing Officer, River Park Hospital, Huntington, WV, p. A678

WHITTAKER, Shawn, Chief Nursing Officer, Miller County Hospital, Colquitt, GA, p. A150

WHITTAKER, Sheena, M.D. President Medical Staff, Maine Coast Memorial Hospital, Ellsworth, ME, p. A283

WHITTEMORE, Marjorie, Director Human Resources, Rio Grande Regional Hospital, McAllen, TX, p. A622

WHITTIER, John J., Vice President Finance, Hampstead Hospital, Hampstead, NH, p. A398

WHITTINGTON, Bruce
  Vice President Human Resources, Hays Medical Center, Hays, KS, p. A235
  Vice President Human Resources, Pawnee Valley Community Hospital, Larned, KS, p. A238

WHITTINGTON, Carol, Chief Human Resources Officer, Sacred Heart Hospital of Pensacola, Pensacola, FL, p. A137

WHITTINGTON, Hilary, Chief Financial Officer, Jefferson Healthcare, Port Townsend, WA, p. A669

WHITTINGTON, Laurie A., Chief Operating Officer, Memorial Hospital of Union County, Marysville, OH, p. A485

WHITTINGTON, Shane, Chief Financial Officer, Caldwell Medical Center, Princeton, KY, p. A259

WHITTLE, Ingrid, Chief Executive Officer, Cedar Crest Hospital and Residential Treatment Center, Belton, TX, p. A588

WHITTLE, Timothy E., M.D. Chief Medical Staff, North Mississippi Medical Center–West Point, West Point, MS, p. A355

WHOLLEY, Diane, Director Fiscal Services, Bridgewater State Hospital, Bridgewater, MA, p. A298

WHYTE, Alec, M.D. Clinical Director, Elmira Psychiatric Center, Elmira, NY, p. A425

WIBBENMEYER, Christopher, Director Human Resources, Perry County Memorial Hospital, Perryville, MO, p. A367

WIBBENS, Cheryl, M.D. Vice President Medical Staff Affairs, Memorial Hospital of South Bend, South Bend, IN, p. A213

WIBORG, Shelley, MS Chief Nursing Officer, Mercer County Hospital, Aledo, IL, p. A173

WICKE, III, Julius, Vice President Finance and Hospital Financial Officer, Baylor Jack and Jane Hamilton Heart and Vascular Hospital, Dallas, TX, p. A595

WICKE, Regina, Chief Financial Officer, Columbus Community Hospital, Columbus, TX, p. A592

WICKENS, Jeanne, Chief Financial Officer, Allegiance Health, Jackson, MI, p. A317

WICKER, Kenneth R., Chief Executive Officer, Bayfront Health Brooksville, Brooksville, FL, p. A119

WICKERSHAM, Jason, M.D. Chief of Staff, Avera St. Benedict Health Center, Parkston, SD, p. A561

WICKIZER, Jr., Boyd, M.D. Chief Medical Officer, Southside Regional Medical Center, Petersburg, VA, p. A659

WICKLINE, Melissa, Director Marketing, Greenbrier Valley Medical Center, Ronceverte, WV, p. A680

WICKLUND, Grant, President and Chief Executive Officer, Exempla Lutheran Medical Center, Wheat Ridge, CO, p. A107

WIDEMAN, Jeff, Director Information Systems, Gilmore Memorial Regional Medical Center, Amory, MS, p. A344

WIDENER, William, Administrator and Chief Executive Officer, Harper Hospital District Five, Harper, KS, p. A235

WIDHELM, Timothy, M.D. Chief of Staff, Memorial Community Health, Aurora, NE, p. A381

WIDNER, Eric W., Division President, Oakwood Annapolis Hospital, Wayne, MI, p. A326

WIDRA, Linda S., R.N., Interim Chief Executive Officer, Lakewood Ranch Medical Center, Bradenton, FL, p. A119

WIEBE, Robert, M.D. Chief Medical Officer, Mercy General Hospital, Sacramento, CA, p. A83

WIECK, Jennifer, Business Manager, Genoa Community Hospital, Genoa, NE, p. A383

WIECZOREK, Pawel, Director Information Technology, BryLin Hospitals, Buffalo, NY, p. A422

WIEGENSTEIN, Robert, Chief Financial Officer, Lake Chelan Community Hospital, Chelan, WA, p. A665

WIEMANN, Michael, M.D., President, Providence Hospital, Southfield, MI, p. A324

WIENAND, Michael, Manager Human Resources, Clarion Hospital, Clarion, PA, p. A522

WIENS, Ron, Chief Financial Officer, Shodair Children's Hospital, Helena, MT, p. A377

WIENTJES, Keri, Director Human Resources, Mobridge Regional Hospital, Mobridge, SD, p. A561

WIEPKING, Deb, MSN Chief Clinical Officer, Valley View Hospital, Glenwood Springs, CO, p. A101

WIERZBICKI, Barb, Manager Human Resources, Select Specialty Hospital–Downriver, Taylor, MI, p. A325

WIESNER, Gerald, Administrator, Miami County Medical Center, Paola, KS, p. A242

WIEWIORA, Nancy, Chief Operating Officer, Vibra Hospital of San Diego, San Diego, CA, p. A86

WIEWORA, Ron, M.D. Chief Medical Officer, Lakeside Medical Center, Belle Glade, FL, p. A118

WIGGINS, Carla, Director Human Resources, Livingston Hospital and Healthcare Services, Salem, KY, p. A260

WIGGINS, Jennifer, Interim Chief Executive Officer, Windsor–Laurelwood Center for Behavioral Medicine, Willoughby, OH, p. A493

WIGGINS, John, Chief Financial Officer, Evans Memorial Hospital, Claxton, GA, p. A150

WIGGINS, Josh
  Vice President Controller, MidMichigan Medical Center–Clare, Clare, MI, p. A310
  Vice President and Controller, MidMichigan Medical Center–Gladwin, Gladwin, MI, p. A314

WIGGINS, Laura, Chief Executive Officer, Cozby–Germany Hospital, Grand Saline, TX, p. A606

WIGGINS, Leslie, Director, Atlanta Veterans Affairs Medical Center, Decatur, GA, p. A151

WIGGINS, Mike, M.D. Chief of Staff, Greenville Health System Laurens County Memorial Hospital, Clinton, SC, p. A550

WIGGINS, Stephen P., Director, Western State Hospital, Hopkinsville, KY, p. A252

WIGGINTON, Gwynn, Controller, El Campo Memorial Hospital, El Campo, TX, p. A600

WIGHTMAN, Lori, FACHE, President, Unity Hospital, Fridley, MN, p. A332

WIGINGTON, James, M.D. Chief of Staff, Heart of the Rockies Regional Medical Center, Salida, CO, p. A105

WIGNALL, Terry A.
  Director Human Resources, St. Vincent Seton Specialty Hospital, Indianapolis, IN, p. A206
  Director Human Resources, St. Vincent Seton Specialty Hospital, Lafayette, IN, p. A208

WIIK, Jennifer, Chief Nursing Officer, Ortonville Area Health Services, Ortonville, MN, p. A337

WIJEWARDANE, Chamath, Director Information Technology, OCH Regional Medical Center, Starkville, MS, p. A354

WILBANKS, John F., FACH
  Chief Operating Officer, Baptist Medical Center Beaches, Jacksonville Beach, FL, p. A127
  Chief Operating Officer, Baptist Medical Center Jacksonville, Jacksonville, FL, p. A126

WILBERDING, Deborah, Controller, Rush Oak Park Hospital, Oak Park, IL, p. A190

WILBUR, Thomas W., Chief Executive Officer and Superintendent, Newport Hospital and Health Services, Newport, WA, p. A668

WILBURN, Sharon, Chief Operating Officer, Bridgewell Hospital of Cincinnati, Cincinnati, OH, p. A474

WILBURN, Sue, Vice President Human Resources and Organizational Development, East Tennessee Children's Hospital, Knoxville, TN, p. A571

WILCHER, Greta
Senior Vice President and Chief Financial Officer, Mercy Hospital Fort Smith, Fort Smith, AR, p. A44
Senior Vice President and Chief Financial Officer, Mercy Hospital Waldron, Waldron, AR, p. A50

WILCOX, Billy, Chief Financial Officer, Specialty Hospital Jacksonville, Jacksonville, FL, p. A127

WILCOX, Jack, Chief Financial Officer, Ennis Regional Medical Center, Ennis, TX, p. A602

WILCOX, James, Chief Executive Officer, El Paso Specialty Hospital, El Paso, TX, p. A601

WILCZEK, Joseph, Chief Executive Officer, St. Elizabeth Hospital, Enumclaw, WA, p. A666

WILD, James, M.D. Medical Director, Lake Shore Health Care Center, Irving, NY, p. A427

WILD, Jane, Director Information Technology, St. Mary's Hospital and Medical Center, Grand Junction, CO, p. A102

WILD, Mary Lou, Vice President Patient Care Services, Sarah Bush Lincoln Health Center, Mattoon, IL, p. A188

WILD, William, Chief Executive Officer, Morton County Health System, Elkhart, KS, p. A233

WILDE, Gary, President and Chief Executive Officer, Community Memorial Health System, Ventura, CA, p. A94

WILDEBRANDT, David, Administrator, Baptist Hospital, Pensacola, FL, p. A136

WILDER, Janet, Director Human Resources, Knox County Hospital, Barbourville, KY, p. A248

WILDER, Jeanine, Director Human Resources, Nicholas H. Noyes Memorial Hospital, Dansville, NY, p. A424

WILDER, John, Director Information Systems, Spaulding Hospital for Continuing Medical Care Cambridge, Cambridge, MA, p. A299

WILDER, Kathy, R.N. Chief Clinical Officer, Medical Center Barbour, Eufaula, AL, p. A19

WILDER, Norman, M.D. Vice President Medical Affairs, Alaska Regional Hospital, Anchorage, AK, p. A27

WILDER, Norman, Director Information Systems, Alta Vista Regional Hospital, Las Vegas, NM, p. A417

WILEY, Chuck, Manager Information Systems, Harrison County Hospital, Corydon, IN, p. A200

WILEY, Donald J., President and Chief Executive Officer, St. Joseph's Medical Center, Stockton, CA, p. A92

WILEY, Mark, Manager Information Systems Development, UPMC Bedford Memorial, Everett, PA, p. A526

WILEY, Rebecca J., R.N., Director, Wm. Jennings Bryan Dorn Veterans Affairs Medical Center, Columbia, SC, p. A551

WILFONG, Mario, Vice President Finance and Administration, UPMC Bedford Memorial, Everett, PA, p. A526

WILFORD, Linda, CPA Senior Vice President and Chief Financial Officer, Holy Cross Hospital, Fort Lauderdale, FL, p. A123

WILHARDT, Lindsey, Resource Manager Flight Commander, Wright Patterson Medical Center, Wright–Patterson AFB, OH, p. A493

WILHELM, Bruce W., Vice President Human Resources, Bassett Medical Center, Cooperstown, NY, p. A424

WILHELM, Christine, Vice President Operations, Charlevoix Area Hospital, Charlevoix, MI, p. A310

WILHELM, Connie, Chief Financial Officer, Swisher Memorial Hospital District, Tulia, TX, p. A638

WILHELM, Jr., John O., Senior Vice President and Chief Financial Officer, Emerson Hospital, Concord, MA, p. A299

WILHELM, Paul, M.D. Chief of Staff, Kiowa District Hospital and Manor, Kiowa, KS, p. A237

WILHELMSEN Jr., Thomas E., President and Chief Executive Officer, Southern New Hampshire Medical Center, Nashua, NH, p. A399

WILHITE, Jade, Manager Human Resource, Memorial Hospital at Craig, Craig, CO, p. A99

WILHITE, James, Director Systems Information, North Mississippi State Hospital, Tupelo, MS, p. A354

WILHITE, Jerald, Administrator Human Resources, Heartland Behavioral Healthcare, Massillon, OH, p. A485

WILHITE, Mark C., Commander, Bayne–Jones Army Community Hospital, Fort Polk, LA, p. A267

WILHOIT, Ellen, President and Chief Administrative Officer, LeConte Medical Center, Sevierville, TN, p. A579

WILHOITE, David, CP
Senior Vice President Finance and Chief Financial Officer, Sumner Regional Medical Center, Gallatin, TN, p. A569
Senior Vice President Finance and Chief Financial Officer, Trousdale Medical Center, Hartsville, TN, p. A570

WILK, Leonard, President and Chief Executive Officer, St. Alexius Medical Center, Hoffman Estates, IL, p. A185

WILK, Michael, Senior President Financial Services and Chief Financial Officer, Pocono Medical Center, East Stroudsburg, PA, p. A524

WILK, Terry, Chief Information Officer, Henry Medical Center, Stockbridge, GA, p. A161

WILKE, Julie, Vice President and Chief Financial Officer, Monroe Clinic, Monroe, WI, p. A693

WILKE, Kris, Manager Health Information, Granite Falls Municipal Hospital and Manor, Granite Falls, MN, p. A333

WILKEN, Thomas
Senior Vice President and Chief Human Resources Officer, Mother Frances Hospital – Tyler, Tyler, TX, p. A638
Vice President Human Resources, Seton Medical Center Williamson, Round Rock, TX, p. A629
Vice President Human Resources, Seton Shoal Creek Hospital, Austin, TX, p. A585

WILKENS, Carie, Director of Human Resources, Carson Tahoe Regional Healthcare, Carson City, NV, p. A391

WILKER, Johnathan, Vice President Finance and Chief Financial Officer, Faith Regional Health Services, Norfolk, NE, p. A386

WILKERSON, Donald H., Chief Executive Officer, St. David's Medical Center, Austin, TX, p. A586

WILKERSON, Jacquelyn, R.N. Chief Nursing Officer, Conway Regional Medical Center, Conway, AR, p. A42

WILKERSON, Michelle, Director Human Resources, Paradise Valley Hospital, Phoenix, AZ, p. A35

WILKERSON–UDDYBACK, Patricia, M.D., Interim President, Harper University Hospital/Hutzel Women's Hospital, Detroit, MI, p. A312

WILKES, Chris, MS Director Human Resources, Blount Memorial Hospital, Maryville, TN, p. A574

WILKES, Wendell, Chief Financial Officer, Byrd Regional Hospital, Leesville, LA, p. A272

WILKIE, Paula, Chief Financial Officer, Presentation Medical Center, Rolla, ND, p. A469

WILKINS, Michael, Chief Operating Officer, Advocate Christ Medical Center, Oak Lawn, IL, p. A190

WILKINSON, David, M.D. Chief of Staff, Columbus Community Hospital, Columbus, TX, p. A592

WILKINSON, Paul G., Chief Operating Officer, Providence St. Peter Hospital, Olympia, WA, p. A669

WILKINSON, Robyn, Senior Vice President Human Resources, Mercy Medical Center–Des Moines, Des Moines, IA, p. A220

WILKINSON, Steven D., President and Chief Executive Officer, Menorah Medical Center, Overland Park, KS, p. A242

WILL, DeDe, Director Finance, Douglas County Community Mental Health Center, Omaha, NE, p. A388

WILL–MOWERY, Nicki L., Ph.D., Chief Executive Officer, Lower Keys Medical Center, Key West, FL, p. A127

WILLAMS, Brandon, Chief Financial Officer, East Cooper Medical Center, Mount Pleasant, SC, p. A554

WILLAMS, Kyle, Chief Information Officer, Kirby Medical Center, Monticello, IL, p. A189

WILLAMS, Mike, Chief Information Officer, FHN Memorial Hospital, Freeport, IL, p. A183

WILLARD, Craig, Director Information Technology and Systems, Frankfort Regional Medical Center, Frankfort, KY, p. A251

WILLARS, Susan, Vice President Human Resources, Mission Regional Medical Center, Mission, TX, p. A623

WILLE, Lesley A., Administrator and Executive Director, Kaiser Permanente South Bay Medical Center,, CA, p. A69

WILLE, Matt, Chief Executive Officer, Dallas County Hospital, Perry, IA, p. A227

WILLEKE, Louis R., Administrator, Refugio County Memorial Hospital, Refugio, TX, p. A628

WILLEMSEN, Jane, Chief Administrative Officer, John Muir Medical Center, Walnut Creek, Walnut Creek, CA, p. A95

WILLET, Terry, Controller, Allen Parish Hospital, Kinder, LA, p. A270

WILLETT, Richard, Chief Executive Officer, Redington–Fairview General Hospital, Skowhegan, ME, p. A285

WILLETT, Simon, Director Administrative Operations, South Texas Veterans Health Care System, San Antonio, TX, p. A632

WILLETT, Terry, Chief Financial Officer, Bunkie General Hospital, Bunkie, LA, p. A265

WILLETT, Vita M., Administrator and Executive Director, Kaiser Permanente Riverside Medical Center, Riverside, CA, p. A82

WILLEY, Randy
Business Manager, Lincoln Regional Center, Lincoln, NE, p. A385
Business Manager, Norfolk Regional Center, Norfolk, NE, p. A386

WILLHITE, Jean, Director Human Resources, Sutter Solano Medical Center, Vallejo, CA, p. A94

WILLIAMS, Adrian, Chief Executive Officer and Administrator, Serenity Springs Specialty Hospital, Farmerville, LA, p. A266

WILLIAMS, Alec, Chief Information Officer, Samaritan Regional Health System, Ashland, OH, p. A470

WILLIAMS, Althea, Senior Vice President Human Resources, Grady Memorial Hospital, Atlanta, GA, p. A146

WILLIAMS, Antoinette, Chief Nursing Officer, John H. Stroger Jr. Hospital of Cook County, Chicago, IL, p. A177

WILLIAMS, Arthur, M.D. Medical Director, Braintree Rehabilitation Hospital, Braintree, MA, p. A298

WILLIAMS, Ashley, Manager Human Resources, Southern Inyo Healthcare District, Lone Pine, CA, p. A67

WILLIAMS, Avilla, MS, President, INTEGRIS Health Edmond, Edmond, OK, p. A498

WILLIAMS, Beverly, R.N. Chief Nursing Officer, Washington County Memorial Hospital, Potosi, MO, p. A368

WILLIAMS, Bob, President and Chief Executive Officer, Baptist St. Anthony Health System, Amarillo, TX, p. A582

WILLIAMS, Brian, Director Information Systems, St. Joseph's Hospital of Buckhannon, Buckhannon, WV, p. A675

WILLIAMS, Brit, M.D. President Medical Staff, Dr. John Warner Hospital, Clinton, IL, p. A180

WILLIAMS, Cara, Director Human Resources, Scripps Memorial Hospital–Encinitas, Encinitas, CA, p. A59

WILLIAMS, Carrie, R.N. Chief Nursing Officer, Henry County Hospital, New Castle, IN, p. A211

WILLIAMS, Catherine, M.D. Medical Director, Lewis County General Hospital, Lowville, NY, p. A428

WILLIAMS, Cecille, Assistant Administrator, Shamrock General Hospital, Shamrock, TX, p. A633

WILLIAMS, Charles, Chief Operating Officer, Doctors Hospital at White Rock Lake, Dallas, TX, p. A595

WILLIAMS, Cheryl, Director Human Resources, Seton Edgar B. Davis Hospital, Luling, TX, p. A621

WILLIAMS, Christopher, M.D. Chief of Staff, Keefe Memorial Hospital, Cheyenne Wells, CO, p. A98

WILLIAMS, Claudia, R.N. CNO, Washington Regional Medical Center, Fayetteville, AR, p. A43

WILLIAMS, Cynthia T., R.N. Interim Chief Nursing Officer, St. Vincent's East, Birmingham, AL, p. A17

WILLIAMS, Dana, Assistant Administrator and Chief Financial Officer, Baptist Memorial Hospital–North Mississippi, Oxford, MS, p. A352

WILLIAMS, Dana D., Chief Executive Officer, Jennings American Legion Hospital, Jennings, LA, p. A269

WILLIAMS, Daniel J., Senior Director Finance, Truman Medical Center–Lakewood, Kansas City, MO, p. A364

WILLIAMS, Darek, Director Human Resources, Elgin Mental Health Center, Elgin, IL, p. A181

WILLIAMS, Darlene, R.N., Administrator, Memorial Medical Center – San Augustine, San Augustine, TX, p. A633

WILLIAMS, David, Director Information Technology, Franklin Hospital District, Benton, IL, p. A174

WILLIAMS, David C., D.O., Interim President and Chief Executive Officer, Community Westview Hospital, Indianapolis, IN, p. A205

WILLIAMS, David L., M.D. Chief Medical Officer, St. Joseph Hospital and Health Center, Kokomo, IN, p. A207

WILLIAMS, David R., Chief Executive Officer, Centerpoint Medical Center, Independence, MO, p. A362

WILLIAMS, Deanna, R.N. Director of Nursing, Bacon County Hospital and Health System, Alma, GA, p. A145

WILLIAMS, Dionne, Director Human Resources, Vaughan Regional Medical Center, Selma, AL, p. A25

WILLIAMS, Frank L., Executive Vice President/ Medical Director, Kedren Community Mental Health Center, Los Angeles, CA, p. A70

WILLIAMS, Gary
Chief Financial Officer, Gulf Coast Medical Center, Wharton, TX, p. A641
Administrator, Houston Hospital for Specialized Surgery, Houston, TX, p. A610

WILLIAMS, Ginger, M.D., President and Chief Executive Officer, Oaklawn Hospital, Marshall, MI, p. A320

WILLIAMS, Homer, Chief Civilian Personnel Branch, Reynolds Army Community Hospital, Fort Sill, OK, p. A499

WILLIAMS, Jackie, Director Human Resources, Madison River Oaks Medical Center, Canton, MS, p. A345

WILLIAMS, James, M.D
Chief Medical Staff, Granville Health System, Oxford, NC, p. A458
Chief of Staff, Riverside Medical Center, Waupaca, WI, p. A698

WILLIAMS, James M., D.O. Vice President Medical Affairs, Community Westview Hospital, Indianapolis, IN, p. A205

WILLIAMS, Jay, Director Information Services, Presbyterian–St. Luke's Medical Center, Denver, CO, p. A100

WILLIAMS, Jeremy, Chief Financial Officer, Banner Boswell Medical Center, Sun City, AZ, p. A38

WILLIAMS, Jim, Chief Financial Officer, Minden Medical Center, Minden, LA, p. A274

WILLIAMS, Joan, Administrative Assistant/Human Resources, Lamb Healthcare Center, Littlefield, TX, p. A618

WILLIAMS, John
Chief Information Officer, Bay Pines Veterans Affairs Medical Center, Bay Pines, FL, p. A118
Chief Financial Officer, Upson Regional Medical Center, Thomaston, GA, p. A161

WILLIAMS, John G., President and Chief Executive Officer, Barton Memorial Hospital, South Lake Tahoe, CA, p. A91

WILLIAMS, Judith L., Director Human Resources, Davis Memorial Hospital, Elkins, WV, p. A676

WILLIAMS, Julie, Chief Financial Officer, Smith County Memorial Hospital, Smith Center, KS, p. A244

WILLIAMS, Karen
Director Human Resources, CHRISTUS St. Michael Rehabilitation Hospital, Texarkana, TX, p. A637
Chief Financial Officer, Streamwood Behavioral Health Center, Streamwood, IL, p. A195

WILLIAMS, Kathy, M.D. Chief Medical Staff, Moab Regional Hospital, Moab, UT, p. A644

WILLIAMS, Kenneth, Chief Information Officer, Fayetteville Veterans Affairs Medical Center, Fayetteville, NC, p. A452

WILLIAMS, L. Dale, M.D. Vice President and Chief Medical Director, High Point Regional Health System, High Point, NC, p. A455

WILLIAMS, Lauren, R.N. Vice President of Professional Services and Chief Nursing Officer, Lawrence + Memorial Hospital, New London, CT, p. A111

WILLIAMS, Linda, Director of Nursing, Villa Feliciana Medical Complex, Jackson, LA, p. A269

WILLIAMS, Lucia, M.D. Chief of Staff, East Texas Medical Center Jacksonville, Jacksonville, TX, p. A615

WILLIAMS, Lynn
Vice President, Commonwealth Regional Specialty Hospital, Bowling Green, KY, p. A248
Vice President Human Resources, Medical Center at Bowling Green, Bowling Green, KY, p. A248
Vice President Human Resources, Medical Center at Scottsville, Scottsville, KY, p. A260

WILLIAMS, Margaret, Chief Financial Officer, Baptist Memorial Hospital for Women, Memphis, TN, p. A574

WILLIAMS, Margo L., R.N. Chief Nursing Officer, Anderson County Hospital, Garnett, KS, p. A234

WILLIAMS, Mark, M.D. Chief Medical Officer, Atrium Medical Center, Middletown, OH, p. A486

WILLIAMS, Mark, Chief Financial Officer, Citrus Memorial Health System, Inverness, FL, p. A126

WILLIAMS, Mary, Director Human Resources, Medina Memorial Hospital, Medina, NY, p. A429

WILLIAMS, Michael, FACHE, Administrator, Fairfield Memorial Hospital, Winnsboro, SC, p. A557

WILLIAMS, Michael L., FACHE Vice President Human Resources, Community Howard Regional Hospital, Kokomo, IN, p. A207

WILLIAMS, Michelle, Administrator, Sedan City Hospital, Sedan, KS, p. A244

WILLIAMS, Mickey, Manager Information Technology, Moccasin Bend Mental Health Institute, Chattanooga, TN, p. A566

WILLIAMS, Mike, Accountant, Limestone Medical Center, Groesbeck, TX, p. A607

WILLIAMS, Nancy M., R.N. Director of Nursing, Brooks County Hospital, Quitman, GA, p. A158

WILLIAMS, Pam, Chief Executive Officer, Minnesota Valley Health Center, Le Sueur, MN, p. A334

WILLIAMS, Pamela G., Director Human Resources, White County Medical Center, Searcy, AR, p. A50

WILLIAMS, Pamela S., Vice President Human Resources, MedStar Harbor Hospital, Baltimore, MD, p. A288

WILLIAMS, Paul, Director Human Resources, Mission Community Hospital, CA, p. A70

WILLIAMS Sr., Perry E., Administrator and Chief Executive Officer, Alliance HealthCare System, Holly Springs, MS, p. A348

WILLIAMS, R. Martin, Director Financial Services, Cox Monett, Monett, MO, p. A366

WILLIAMS, R. D., Chief Executive Officer, Hendry Regional Medical Center, Clewiston, FL, p. A120

WILLIAMS, Randy, Director Management Information Systems, Maria Parham Medical Center, Henderson, NC, p. A454

WILLIAMS, Rich, Director Human Resources, Upson Regional Medical Center, Thomaston, GA, p. A161

WILLIAMS, Richard, Chief Operating Officer, Southwest Mississippi Regional Medical Center, McComb, MS, p. A350

WILLIAMS, Robert, Chief Executive Officer, HEALTHSOUTH Southern Hills Rehabilitation Hospital, Princeton, WV, p. A680

WILLIAMS, Robert D., Chief Executive Officer, Special Care Hospital, Nanticoke, PA, p. A532

WILLIAMS, Roby D., Administrator, Hardin County General Hospital, Rosiclare, IL, p. A194

WILLIAMS, Rod, Manager Information Systems, Citizens Medical Center, Colby, KS, p. A232

WILLIAMS, Rodney W., M.D. Vice President Medical Affairs, Good Samaritan Hospital, Suffern, NY, p. A443

WILLIAMS, Roger, Chief Financial Officer, New Horizons Health Systems, Owenton, KY, p. A258

WILLIAMS, Ronald, M.D. Medical Director, Landmark Hospital of Joplin, Joplin, MO, p. A362

WILLIAMS, Sandi, Manager Business Officer, Garfield County Health Center, Jordan, MT, p. A377

WILLIAMS, Sandra
Chief Financial Officer, Cape Fear Valley – Bladen County Hospital, Elizabethtown, NC, p. A452
Chief Financial Officer, Cape Fear Valley Medical Center, Fayetteville, NC, p. A452

WILLIAMS, Scott
Chief Executive Officer, Northwest Medical Center, Winfield, AL, p. A26
Chief Executive Officer, Regency Hospital Cleveland East, Warrensville Heights, OH, p. A492

WILLIAMS, Sean J., President and Chief Executive Officer, Mercy Medical Center–Clinton, Clinton, IA, p. A218

WILLIAMS, Shane, Director Information Systems, Davis Hospital and Medical Center, Layton, UT, p. A644

WILLIAMS, Sharon, Vice President Finance and Information Technology, Avera Marshall Regional Medical Center, Marshall, MN, p. A335

WILLIAMS, Sheila, Chief Executive Officer, H.S.C. Medical Center, Malvern, AR, p. A47

WILLIAMS, Stephanie, R.N. Chief Nursing Officer, Washington Hospital Healthcare System, Fremont, CA, p. A61

WILLIAMS, Thomas, D.O. Chief of Staff, Sullivan County Memorial Hospital, Milan, MO, p. A366

WILLIAMS, Tina, Chief Financial Officer, Alaska Psychiatric Institute, Anchorage, AK, p. A27

WILLIAMS, Todd, M.D. President Medical Staff, Eastern Idaho Regional Medical Center, Idaho Falls, ID, p. A169

WILLIAMS, Tom, Director Human Resources, Lake Regional Health System, Osage Beach, MO, p. A367

WILLIAMS, Tonja, R.N., President, Continuing Care Hospital, Lexington, KY, p. A254

WILLIAMS, Warren, CPA Director Fiscal Services, Mississippi State Hospital, Whitfield, MS, p. A355

WILLIAMS, Jr., Wendell H., M.D. Medical Director, Specialty Hospital Jacksonville, Jacksonville, FL, p. A127

WILLIAMS, Winifred
Vice President Human Resources, Providence Medical Center, Kansas City, KS, p. A237
Vice President Human Resources, Saint John Hospital, Leavenworth, KS, p. A238

WILLIAMSON, John, Human Resources Site Manager, Baptist Health South Florida, Mariners Hospital, Tavernier, FL, p. A142

WILLIAMSON, Johnny, M.D. Chief Medical Officer, Hartgrove Hospital, Chicago, IL, p. A176

WILLIAMSON, Marilyn
Director Human Resources, Osawatomie State Hospital, Osawatomie, KS, p. A241
Chief Human Resources Officer, Rainbow Mental Health Facility, Kansas City, KS, p. A237

WILLIAMSON, Sharon, Chief Information Technology, Robert J. Dole Veterans Affairs Medical Center, Wichita, KS, p. A246

WILLIAMSON, William P., M.D. Medical Director, Frazier Rehab Institute, Louisville, KY, p. A255

WILLINGHAM, Alex, M.D. Medical Director, Warm Springs Rehabilitation Hospital, San Antonio, TX, p. A632

WILLINGHAM, Debbie, Administrative Assistant, Field Memorial Community Hospital, Centreville, MS, p. A345

WILLINGHAM, John, Chief Executive Officer and Managing Director, Carolina Center for Behavioral Health, Greer, SC, p. A553

WILLIS, Bill, Director Information Technology, River Point Behavioral Health, Jacksonville, FL, p. A126

WILLIS, Joy, Acting Chief Fiscal Service, G.V. (Sonny) Montgomery Veterans Affairs Medical Center, Jackson, MS, p. A348

WILLIS, Kathleen, R.N. Chief Nursing Officer, Hillcrest Medical Center, Tulsa, OK, p. A508

WILLIS, Kathy, M.D. Medical Director, Lallie Kemp Medical Center, Independence, LA, p. A268

WILLIS, Mona M.
Director Human Resources, Landmark Medical Center, Woonsocket, RI, p. A547
Director Human Resources, Rehabilitation Hospital of Rhode Island, North Smithfield, RI, p. A546

WILLIS, Rebecca, Chief Nursing Officer, Sampson Regional Medical Center, Clinton, NC, p. A450

WILLIS, Sandra, Manager Human Resources, Citizens Baptist Medical Center, Talladega, AL, p. A25

WILLIS, Sherita, M.D. Chief of Staff, South Mississippi County Regional Medical Center, Osceola, AR, p. A48

WILLIS, Toni, M.D. Medical Director, Reliant Rehabilitation Hospital Mid–Cities, Bedford, TX, p. A588

WILLIS, Walt, M.D. Medical Director, Neshoba County General Hospital, Philadelphia, MS, p. A352

WILLIS, Wendy L., Assistant Vice President Human Resources, Ochsner Medical Center – Kenner, Kenner, LA, p. A269

WILLIS, William L., Administrator, Dubuis Hospital of Lake Charles, Lake Charles, LA, p. A271

WILLMANN, Adam, President and Chief Executive Officer, Goodall–Witcher Healthcare, Clifton, TX, p. A592

WILLMON, Brian, M.D. Medical Director, Plains Regional Medical Center, Clovis, NM, p. A415

WILLMORE, Lois, Supervisor Health Information Management, Cedar County Memorial Hospital, El Dorado Springs, MO, p. A360

WILLMS, Frederick, M.D. Vice President Medical Affairs, Piedmont Fayette Hospital, Fayetteville, GA, p. A153

WILLS, Kim, Chief Operating Officer, Cook Medical Center–A Campus of Tift Regional Medical Center, Adel, GA, p. A145

WILLS, Laura S., Administrator, Noland Hospital Birmingham, Birmingham, AL, p. A16

WILLS, Lawrence E., Vice President Operations, OSF St. Joseph Medical Center, Bloomington, IL, p. A174

WILLS, Michele, Registered Health Information Administrator, Caro Center, Caro, MI, p. A310

WILLS, Shannon, Director Human Resources, Delray Medical Center, Delray Beach, FL, p. A122

WILLSIE, Brett, Vice President Human Resources, Sentara Northern Virginia Medical Center, Woodbridge, VA, p. A663

WILLWERTH, Deborah J., R.N. Chief Operating Officer, Lancaster Regional Medical Center, Lancaster, PA, p. A529

WILMOT, Joan, Chief Finance Officer, White River Junction Veterans Affairs Medical Center, White River Junction, VT, p. A650

WILMOTH, Donna, Vice President Patient Care Services and Chief Nursing Officer, Sentara Williamsburg Regional Medical Center, Williamsburg, VA, p. A663

WILSON, Alice, FACHE Vice President Administration, St. Luke's Hospital – Warren Campus, Phillipsburg, NJ, p. A409

WILSON, Amy, M.D. Medical Director, Baylor Institute for Rehabilitation, Dallas, TX, p. A595

WILSON, Amy, Interim Chief Nursing Officer, Sacred Heart Hospital of Pensacola, Pensacola, FL, p. A137

WILSON, Andrew, M.D. Interim Chief Medical Officer, Salinas Valley Memorial Healthcare System, Salinas, CA, p. A84

WILSON, Ann, Acting Director Human Resources, Hopedale Medical Complex, Hopedale, IL, p. A185

WILSON, Becky, Manager Human Resources, Allegiance Specialty Hospital of Kilgore, Kilgore, TX, p. A616

WILSON, Bill, Chief Financial Officer, North Carolina Specialty Hospital, Durham, NC, p. A451

WILSON, Bobbie, Director Human Resources, Crete Area Medical Center, Crete, NE, p. A383

WILSON, Brian, D.O. Medical Staff President, Spencer Hospital, Spencer, IA, p. A228

WILSON, Carolyn, President, University of Minnesota Medical Center, Fairview, Minneapolis, MN, p. A336

WILSON, Charlene J., Vice President Human Resources, St. Francis Hospital, Wilmington, DE, p. A115

WILSON, Charles, Chief Human Resources Officer, Penn State Milton S. Hershey Medical Center, Hershey, PA, p. A527

WILSON, Cheryl A., Chief Operating Officer, Rapides Regional Medical Center, Alexandria, LA, p. A262

WILSON, Christopher, M.D. Inpatient Medical Director, South Texas Rehabilitation Hospital, Brownsville, TX, p. A590

WILSON, Cynthia, M.D. Chief of Staff, Mercy Hospital Rogers, Rogers, AR, p. A49

WILSON, David C., President and Chief Executive Officer, Shelby Baptist Medical Center, Alabaster, AL, p. A15

WILSON, David R., M.D. Chief of Staff, St. Vincent's Blount, Oneonta, AL, p. A24

WILSON, Deanna, VP Patient Care Services/Site Manager, Aspirus Ontonagon Hospital, Ontonagon, MI, p. A321

WILSON, Deb, Director Human Resources, Kalispell Regional Medical Center, Kalispell, MT, p. A377

WILSON, Deborah J., Senior Vice President and Chief Financial Officer, Lawrence General Hospital, Lawrence, MA, p. A301

WILSON, Dottie, Director Human Resources, Pickens County Medical Center, Carrollton, AL, p. A18

WILSON, Eleanor, R.N. Vice President and Chief Operating Officer, Doylestown Hospital, Doylestown, PA, p. A524

WILSON, Elizabeth M., Coordinator Human Resources, Regency Hospital of Cincinnati, Cincinnati, OH, p. A475

WILSON, Jr., Floyd, Executive Vice President Human Resources, Metro Health Hospital, Wyoming, MI, p. A327

WILSON, Greg, Chief Operating Officer and Chief Financial Officer, Paynesville Area Health Care System, Paynesville, MN, p. A338

WILSON, Hamlin J.
Senior Vice President Human Resources, Wellmont Bristol Regional Medical Center, Bristol, TN, p. A565
Senior Vice President Human Resources, Wellmont Holston Valley Medical Center, Kingsport, TN, p. A571

WILSON, Harold E., Chief Executive Officer, Eastern State Hospital, Medical Lake, WA, p. A668

WILSON, Jason, Administrator, Valley View Medical Center, Cedar City, UT, p. A643

WILSON, Jim
Vice President Information Technology, Promise Hospital of East Los Angeles, Suburban Medical Center Campus, Paramount, CA, p. A79
Vice President Information Technology, Promise Hospital of San Diego, San Diego, CA, p. A85

WILSON, Jodi, Site Administrator, Diley Ridge Medical Center, Canal Winchester, OH, p. A472

WILSON, John P., Chief Financial Officer, Heartland Regional Medical Center, Saint Joseph, MO, p. A369

WILSON, John R., Vice President, Human Resources, Murray–Calloway County Hospital, Murray, KY, p. A258

WILSON, John W., Chief Executive Officer, Warren Memorial Hospital, Friend, NE, p. A383

WILSON, Kim, Director of Nursing, Benewah Community Hospital, Saint Maries, ID, p. A171

WILSON, Kim A., R.N
Chief Operating Officer, St. John's Pleasant Valley Hospital, Camarillo, CA, p. A55
Chief Operating Officer, St. John's Regional Medical Center, Oxnard, CA, p. A78

WILSON, Kimberly P.
Associate Vice President, UK HealthCare Good Samaritan Hospital, Lexington, KY, p. A254
Director Human Resources, University of Kentucky Albert B. Chandler Hospital, Lexington, KY, p. A254

WILSON, Lerae, R.N. Vice President Patient Services and Chief Nursing Officer, St. Claire Regional Medical Center, Morehead, KY, p. A258

WILSON, Lois, Controller, Roger Mills Memorial Hospital, Cheyenne, OK, p. A496

WILSON, Mark, Manager Information Systems, Pender Memorial Hospital, Burgaw, NC, p. A448

WILSON, Mary L., M.D. Area Medical Director, Kaiser Permanente Panorama City Medical Center,, CA, p. A69

WILSON, Nancy, Chief Nurse Executive, Wilcox Memorial Hospital, Lihue, HI, p. A166

WILSON, Nancy V., Chief Financial Officer, Kindred Hospital–La Mirada, La Mirada, CA, p. A65

WILSON, Patricia, Vice President Human Resources, Englewood Hospital and Medical Center, Englewood, NJ, p. A404

WILSON, Preshie
Vice President Finance, Baylor All Saints Medical Center at Fort Worth, Fort Worth, TX, p. A603
Vice President Finance Services, Baylor Regional Medical Center at Grapevine, Grapevine, TX, p. A607

WILSON, Rhonda, Director Human Resources, Mayo Clinic Health System – Oakridge in Osseo, Osseo, WI, p. A694

WILSON, Robert, D.O. Director Medical Services, Eagleville Hospital, Eagleville, PA, p. A524

WILSON, Robert, M.D. Chief of Staff, Southeast Georgia Health System Camden Campus, Saint Marys, GA, p. A159

WILSON, Robert E.
Vice President and Chief Information Officer, Crozer-Chester Medical Center, Upland, PA, p. A542
Vice President and Chief Information Officer, Delaware County Memorial Hospital, Drexel Hill, PA, p. A524

WILSON, Roger D., M.D. Medical Director, St. John Sapulpa, Sapulpa, OK, p. A506

WILSON, Roy, M.D. Medical Director, St. Louis Psychiatric Rehabilitation Center, Saint Louis, MO, p. A371

WILSON, Sherry, R.N. Chief Nursing Officer Long Term Care, Mayers Memorial Hospital District, Fall River Mills, CA, p. A60

WILSON, Sondra, R.N. Chief Nursing Officer, Tyler County Hospital, Woodville, TX, p. A642

WILSON, Stephan A., Chief Financial Officer, Montrose Memorial Hospital, Montrose, CO, p. A104

WILSON, Terrance E.
President and Chief Executive Officer, Franciscan St. Elizabeth Health – Lafayette Central, Lafayette, IN, p. A208
President and Chief Executive Officer, Franciscan St. Elizabeth Health – Lafayette East, Lafayette, IN, p. A208

WILSON, Terry, Director Human Resources and Compliance, Doctors Hospital Nelsonville, Nelsonville, OH, p. A487

WILSON, Timothy, Vice President Finance and Chief Financial Officer, Cardinal Hill Rehabilitation Hospital, Lexington, KY, p. A254

WILSON, William, Interim Chief Financial Officer, Valley Presbyterian Hospital,, CA, p. A72

WILSON, William G., President and Chief Executive Officer, Jackson County Memorial Hospital, Altus, OK, p. A495

WILSON, Yolande, Chief Executive Officer, Kindred Hospital Boston–North Shore, Peabody, MA, p. A303

WILSON–NEIL, Carla, Chief Operating Officer, Pennock Hospital, Hastings, MI, p. A316

WILTERMOOD, Michael C., President and Chief Executive Officer, Enloe Medical Center, Chico, CA, p. A56

WILTROUT, Kristy, R.N. Chief Operating Officer, Vernon Memorial Healthcare, Viroqua, WI, p. A698

WILTROUT, Terry, Chief Executive Officer, Canonsburg General Hospital, Canonsburg, PA, p. A522

WIMMER, Donna, Director Human Resources, Franciscan St. Anthony Health – Crown Point, Crown Point, IN, p. A201

WIMMER, Keri, R.N. Patient Care Director, CentraCare Health–Melrose, Melrose, MN, p. A335

WIMSATT, Michael, Director Human Resources, Piedmont Geriatric Hospital, Burkeville, VA, p. A652

WIN, Aye Mya, M.D. Chief Medical Staff, Western Plains Medical Complex, Dodge City, KS, p. A233

WINBERY, Ben, Chief Financial Officer, Montevista Hospital, Las Vegas, NV, p. A393

WINCH, James, Vice President Finance, Essentia Health St. Joseph's Medical Center, Brainerd, MN, p. A329

WINCHESTER, David, Interim Vice President and Chief Financial Officer, Memorial Health Care System, Chattanooga, TN, p. A566

WINDER, Todd V., Administrator and Chief Executive Officer, Oneida County Hospital, Malad City, ID, p. A170

WINDHAM, Joel R., Director Human Resources, Trinity Medical Center, Birmingham, AL, p. A17

WINDHAM, Michael, Chief Nursing Officer, Doctor's Memorial Hospital, Perry, FL, p. A137

WINDHAM, Vann, Chief Financial Officer, L. V. Stabler Memorial Hospital, Greenville, AL, p. A21

WINDLAND, J. Michael, M.D. Chief of Staff, Hillside Hospital, Pulaski, TN, p. A578

WINDLE, Jane, R.N. Director of Nurses, North Mississippi Medical Center–West Point, West Point, MS, p. A355

WINEGARNER, Rodney, Chief Financial Officer, Mercy Hospitals of Bakersfield, Bakersfield, CA, p. A54

WINEGEART, Steve, Chief Financial Officer, Hillcrest Medical Center, Tulsa, OK, p. A508

WINEINGER, Stephanie, Director of Nursing, Greeley County Health Services, Tribune, KS, p. A245

WINFIELD, Gary, M.D. Medical Director, Memorial Hospital Jacksonville, Jacksonville, FL, p. A126

WINFREE, Kersey, M.D. Chief Medical Officer, St. Anthony Hospital, Oklahoma City, OK, p. A504

WINFREY, John W., Vice President Finance and Chief Financial Officer, DCH Regional Medical Center, Tuscaloosa, AL, p. A26

WING, Mitch, Network Administrator, Cloud County Health Center, Concordia, KS, p. A232

WING, Yakesun, Business Strategy and Finance Leader, Kaiser Permanente Walnut Creek Medical Center, Walnut Creek, CA, p. A95

WINGATE, Phyllis A., FACHE, Division President, Carolinas Medical Center–NorthEast, Concord, NC, p. A450

WINGET, Mary, Director Human Resources, Minden Medical Center, Minden, LA, p. A274

WINGFIELD, Gena, Senior Vice President and Chief Financial Officer, Arkansas Children's Hospital, Little Rock, AR, p. A46

WINKLE, Derek, Director Human Resources, Morristown–Hamblen Healthcare System, Morristown, TN, p. A576

WINKLER, Gordon W., Administrator and Chief Executive Officer, Ringgold County Hospital, Mount Ayr, IA, p. A225

WINN, Eleyce, Assistant Administrator, Clarendon Memorial Hospital, Manning, SC, p. A554

WINN, George, Chief Executive Officer, Evanston Regional Hospital, Evanston, WY, p. A702

WINN, Holly, Vice President Human Resources and Ancillary Services, Black River Memorial Hospital, Black River Falls, WI, p. A684

WINN, Michael R., Director, Central Arkansas Veterans Healthcare System, Little Rock, AR, p. A46

WINN, Roger P., President, UPMC Bedford Memorial, Everett, PA, p. A526

WINNENBERG, William
Chief Information Officer, Pioneer Memorial Hospital, Prineville, OR, p. A517
Chief Information Officer, St. Charles Medical Center – Bend, Bend, OR, p. A511
Chief Information Officer, St. Charles Medical Center – Redmond, Redmond, OR, p. A517

WINNER, Douglas, Chief Financial Officer, Providence Hospital, Southfield, MI, p. A324

WINRIGHT, Donna, Director Human Resources and Senior Services, Kearny County Hospital, Lakin, KS, p. A237

WINSELL, Susan, Vice President Human Resources, Marian Medical Center, Santa Maria, CA, p. A90

WINSETT, Gracia, Chief Financial Officer, Wellstone Regional Hospital, Jeffersonville, IN, p. A207

WINSLOW, Grover C., M.D. Chief of Staff, Sabine County Hospital, Hemphill, TX, p. A608

WINSTON, Bob, M.D. Medical Director, Acadia Vermilion Hospital, Lafayette, LA, p. A270

WINTER, Jan, Chief Executive Officer, Bristow Medical Center, Bristow, OK, p. A496

WINTER, Jon R., D.O. Chief of Staff, Camden General Hospital, Camden, TN, p. A566

WINTER, Melissa, R.N. Chief Operating Officer and Chief Nursing Officer, Baylor Medical Center at McKinney, McKinney, TX, p. A622

WINTERS, Gene, Chief Financial Officer, Dallas Regional Medical Center, Mesquite, TX, p. A622

WINTERS, Janice, Controller, Pickens County Medical Center, Carrollton, AL, p. A18

WINTERS, Mary Ellen, Director Human Resources, Mena Regional Health System, Mena, AR, p. A47

WINTHROP, Michael, President, Bellevue Hospital, Bellevue, OH, p. A471

WIRKKULA, James, M.D. Chief Medical Officer, Ellett Memorial Hospital, Appleton City, MO, p. A356

WIRTHGEN, Doug
Facility Chief Information Officer, Veterans Affairs Loma Linda Healthcare System, Loma Linda, CA, p. A67
Chief Information Officer, Veterans Affairs Palo Alto Health Care System, Palo Alto, CA, p. A79

WIRTZ, Carman, Vice President Human Resources, Memorial Hospital of Union County, Marysville, OH, p. A485

WISCHKAEMPER, Jo Nell, Administrator and Chief Executive Officer, Lamb Healthcare Center, Littlefield, TX, p. A618

WISE, Gregory, M.D
Vice President Medical Affairs, Kettering Medical Center, Kettering, OH, p. A483
Vice President Medical Affairs, Sycamore Medical Center, Miamisburg, OH, p. A486

WISE, Jennifer, Chief Nursing Officer, Franklin Foundation Hospital, Franklin, LA, p. A267

WISE, Jerry, Controller, Mercy Rehabilitation Hospital, Chesterfield, MO, p. A358

WISE, Robert P., FACHE, President and Chief Executive Officer, Hunterdon Medical Center, Flemington, NJ, p. A404

WISEMAN, Roger D., Chief Financial Officer, MetroWest Medical Center, Framingham, MA, p. A300

WISNER, Donna, Chief Financial Officer, Dr. John Warner Hospital, Clinton, IL, p. A180

WISNIESKI, Thomas, FACHE,
Director, Lake City Veterans Affairs Medical Center, Lake City, FL, p. A128
Director, Malcom Randall Veterans Affairs Medical Center, Gainesville, FL, p. A124

WISNIEWSKI, Cass, Interim Chief Financial Officer, Hurley Medical Center, Flint, MI, p. A313

WISNIEWSKI, Richard, Senior Vice President Finance and Chief Financial Officer, Mount Nittany Medical Center, State College, PA, p. A541

WISNOSKI, Joseph, Vice President Finance and Chief Financial Officer, John T. Mather Memorial Hospital, Port Jefferson, NY, p. A440

WISS, Albert, Chief Financial Officer, Share Medical Center, Alva, OK, p. A495

WISSEL, Andrew
Director Human Resources, Mount Sinai Hospital, Chicago, IL, p. A177
Director Human Resources, Schwab Rehabilitation Hospital, Chicago, IL, p. A179

WISSLER, James, President and Chief Executive Officer, Hanover Hospital, Hanover, PA, p. A526

WISWELL, Ashleigh, Director Human Resources, Moore County Hospital District, Dumas, TX, p. A599

WITENSKE, James, Chief Information Officer, Jefferson Regional Medical Center, Jefferson Hills, PA, p. A528

WITHERSPOON, Lynn, Vice President and Chief Information Officer, Ochsner Medical Center, New Orleans, LA, p. A275

WITHIAM, Cathy, Director Human Resources, McBride Clinic Orthopedic Hospital, Oklahoma City, OK, p. A503

WITKOWICZ, Victor J., Senior Vice President and Chief Financial Officer, Madonna Rehabilitation Hospital, Lincoln, NE, p. A385

WITKOWSKI, Richard J., Director Management Information Systems, Mount St. Mary's Hospital and Health Center, Lewiston, NY, p. A428

WITMER, Bruce, M.D. Medical Director, Fresno Surgical Hospital, Fresno, CA, p. A61

WITMER, Craig, Chief Information Officer, Providence Tarzana Medical Center,, CA, p. A71

WOODS, Josh, Director Information Systems, Camden Clark Medical Center, Parkersburg, WV, p. A679

WOODS, Julia, R.N. Vice President and Chief Nursing Officer, Saint Luke's South Hospital, Overland Park, KS, p. A242

WOODS, Matthew, Executive Vice President Finance and Chief Financial Officer, Winchester Hospital, Winchester, MA, p. A306

WOODS, Rashawn, Director Human Resources, Shriners Hospitals for Children–Los Angeles, Los Angeles, CA, p. A71

WOODS, Suzanne, President and Chief Executive Officer, Flowers Hospital, Dothan, AL, p. A19

WOODS, Suzanne, R.N. Vice President Nursing and Chief Nursing Officer, Health First Palm Bay Hospital, Melbourne, FL, p. A130

WOODS–NYCE, Karen, Chief Executive Officer, Twin Valley Behavioral Healthcare, Columbus, OH, p. A478

WOODWAR, David E., Executive Director, Devereux Children's Behavioral Health Center, Malvern, PA, p. A530

WOODWARD, Andy, Chief Financial Officer, Forrest General Hospital, Hattiesburg, MS, p. A347

WOODWARD, Ashley, Director Financial Services, Valley County Health System, Ord, NE, p. A388

WOODWARD, James L., President and Chief Executive Officer, Meriter Hospital, Madison, WI, p. A689

WOODWARD, Kevin, Chief Financial Officer, Biggs–Gridley Memorial Hospital, Gridley, CA, p. A63

WOODWARD, Martin D., Director Acute Care Services, Larry B. Zieverink, Sr. Alcoholism Treatment Center, Raleigh, NC, p. A459

WOODWARD, Russell, M.D. Chief Medical Officer, Methodist Hospital, San Antonio, TX, p. A631

WOODWARD, Teresa, Director Human Resources, Landmark Hospital of Joplin, Joplin, MO, p. A362

WOODWARD, Will, Director Finance, Mercy Health – Clermont Hospital, Batavia, OH, p. A471

WOODYARD, Elizabeth, MSN, Chief Executive Officer, Petersburg Medical Center, Petersburg, AK, p. A29

WOODYARD, Nancy, Chief Financial Officer, Neosho Memorial Regional Medical Center, Chanute, KS, p. A232

WOOL, Julius, Executive Director, Queens Hospital Center,, NY, p. A436

WOOLF, Louis J., President, Hebrew Rehabilitation Center, Boston, MA, p. A297

WOOLLEN, Susan, R.N. Director of Nursing, Lafayette General Surgical Hospital, Lafayette, LA, p. A271

WOOLLEY, Diane, Vice President Human Resources, Waterbury Hospital, Waterbury, CT, p. A112

WOOLLEY, Jacqueline, Vice President Human Resources, St. Joseph Hospital, Nashua, NH, p. A399

WOOLLEY, Sheila, R.N. Vice President, Patient Care Services, Wentworth–Douglass Hospital, Dover, NH, p. A397

WOOLSTENHULME, Daren, Chief Financial Officer, HEALTHSOUTH Rehabilitation Hospital of Utah, Sandy, UT, p. A647

WOOTEN, Mark D., M.D. Chief of Staff, Veterans Affairs Northern Indiana Health Care System, Fort Wayne, IN, p. A203

WORD, Jenni, Chief Nursing Officer, Wallowa Memorial Hospital, Enterprise, OR, p. A512

WORDEN, Jerry L., Chief Financial Officer, Marquette General Health System, Marquette, MI, p. A319

WORDEN, Kieth Anne, Director Human Resources, Mildred Mitchell–Bateman Hospital, Huntington, WV, p. A677

WORKMAN, Jennifer, Director Human Resources, Jane Phillips Medical Center, Bartlesville, OK, p. A496

WORKMAN, John R.
Chief Executive Officer, Athens Regional Medical Center, Athens, TN, p. A565
Chief Executive Officer, Woods Memorial Hospital, Etowah, TN, p. A569

WORKMAN, Mark, M.D. Chief Medical Officer, West Jefferson Medical Center, Marrero, LA, p. A273

WORLEY III, John C., Chief Executive Officer, Cache Valley Specialty Hospital, North Logan, UT, p. A645

WORLEY, Kathy, Director Human Resources, Brigham City Community Hospital, Brigham City, UT, p. A643

WORLEY, Steve, President and Chief Executive Officer, Children's Hospital, New Orleans, LA, p. A275

WORRELL, James W., Chief Financial Officer, Pioneers Medical Center, Meeker, CO, p. A104

WORRICK, Gerald M., President and Chief Executive Officer, Ministry Door County Medical Center, Sturgeon Bay, WI, p. A697

WORSOWICZ, Gregory, M.D. Medical Director, Howard A. Rusk Rehabilitation Center, Columbia, MO, p. A359

WORTHAM, Christopher, Chief Executive Officer, HEALTHSOUTH Rehabilitation Hospital Midland–Odessa, Midland, TX, p. A623

WORTHAM, Stephanie, Director Financial Services, Norman Specialty Hospital, Norman, OK, p. A502

WORTHAM, Turner, Chief Financial Officer, Grand Strand Regional Medical Center, Myrtle Beach, SC, p. A555

WORTHINGTON, Diane, Director Human Resources, Placentia–Linda Hospital, Placentia, CA, p. A80

WORTMAN, Rand J., Chief Executive Officer, Kadlec Regional Medical Center, Richland, WA, p. A670

WOZNIAK, Gregory T., President and Chief Executive Officer, St. Mary Medical Center, Langhorne, PA, p. A529

WOZNIAK, Ilona, Vice President and Chief Operating Officer, WellStar Cobb Hospital, Austell, GA, p. A148

WOZNIAK, Peter, R.N., Chief Executive Officer, Venice Regional Medical Center, Venice, FL, p. A143

WOZNIAK, Susan C., R.N. Senior Vice President and Chief Operating Officer, OSF Saint Francis Medical Center, Peoria, IL, p. A192

WRAALSTAD, Kimber L., FACHE, Administrator, Cook County North Shore Hospital, Grand Marais, MN, p. A333

WRAGGE, Jean, Director of Nurses, Limestone Medical Center, Groesbeck, TX, p. A607

WRATTEN, Carol, M.D. Vice President Medical Affairs, Seton Medical Center Austin, Austin, TX, p. A585

WRAY, Char, Vice President Chief Clinical Operations and Chief Information Oficer, EMH Elyria Medical Center, Elyria, OH, p. A481

WRAY, Christine R., President, MedStar St. Mary's Hospital, Leonardtown, MD, p. A293

WRAY, Dean, Vice President Finance, Southern Ohio Medical Center, Portsmouth, OH, p. A489

WRAY, Robert, D.O. Chief Medical Staff, Edwards County Hospital and Healthcare Center, Kinsley, KS, p. A237

WRAY, Thomas, Director Information, Geisinger–Bloomsburg Hospital, Bloomsburg, PA, p. A521

WREN, Mark A., M.D. Medical Director, HEALTHSOUTH Rehabilitation Hospital of Texarkana, Texarkana, TX, p. A637

WREN, Patricia J., Chief Human Resources Officer, Hospital of the University of Pennsylvania, Philadelphia, PA, p. A535

WREN, Timothy, Chief Financial Officer, Abbeville Area Medical Center, Abbeville, SC, p. A548

WRIGHT, Ann L., R.N. Assistant Central Delivery System CNO, Presbyterian Hospital, Albuquerque, NM, p. A414

WRIGHT, Betsy T., President and Chief Executive Officer, Woman's Christian Association Hospital, Jamestown, NY, p. A427

WRIGHT, Brady, Information Technology Network Administrator, Washington County Hospital and Nursing Home, Chatom, AL, p. A18

WRIGHT, Carlene, Chief Financial Officer, Kindred Hospital–Amarillo, Amarillo, TX, p. A582

WRIGHT, Charles T., President and Chief Executive Officer, St. James Healthcare, Butte, MT, p. A374

WRIGHT, Claudia, Director Health Information Management, Weatherford Regional Hospital, Weatherford, OK, p. A510

WRIGHT, Connie, Director Human Resources, Texas Health Presbyterian Hospital Dallas, Dallas, TX, p. A597

WRIGHT, Dan
Vice President Human Resources, Children's Mercy Hospitals and Clinics, Kansas City, MO, p. A362
Vice President Human Resources, Children's Mercy South, Overland Park, KS, p. A241

WRIGHT, Daniel, Director Information Technology, Saint Alphonsus Medical Center – Nampa, Nampa, ID, p. A170

WRIGHT, Dawn, Director Human Resources, Artesia General Hospital, Artesia, NM, p. A415

WRIGHT, Debra J., R.N., Chief Executive Officer, Howard Memorial Hospital, Nashville, AR, p. A48

WRIGHT, Gene B., Interim Chief Executive Officer, CHRISTUS St. Catherine Hospital, Katy, TX, p. A615

WRIGHT, Ivan, M.D. Vice President Medical Affairs, Trinity Health System, Steubenville, OH, p. A490

WRIGHT, James, M.D. Chief Financial Officer, Cypress Fairbanks Medical Center, Houston, TX, p. A609

WRIGHT, Janet, R.N. Vice President Patient Care Executive, Lourdes Medical Center, Pasco, WA, p. A669

WRIGHT, Jean, M.D. Chief Medical Officer, Carolinas Medical Center–NorthEast, Concord, NC, p. A450

WRIGHT, Joe, Chief Financial Officer, Mitchell County Hospital, Colorado City, TX, p. A592

WRIGHT, John B., M.D. Chief of Staff, Memorial Medical Center, Port Lavaca, TX, p. A628

WRIGHT, Julie M., Director Human Resources, Ridgeview Psychiatric Hospital and Center, Oak Ridge, TN, p. A578

WRIGHT, Krista, Director Human Resources, St. Vincent Frankfort Hospital, Frankfort, IN, p. A203

WRIGHT, Linda
Chief Finanical Officer, HEALTHSOUTH Rehabilitation Hospital of Alexandria, Alexandria, LA, p. A262
Director Information, Ottawa County Health Center, Minneapolis, KS, p. A240

WRIGHT, Mark, Vice President, Aultman Hospital, Canton, OH, p. A473

WRIGHT, Mark J., Vice President Finance, Aurelia Osborn Fox Memorial Hospital, Oneonta, NY, p. A438

WRIGHT, Mary Lynne, R.N., President, Madison Hospital, Madison, AL, p. A22

WRIGHT, Patricia, Personal Analyst, San Joaquin General Hospital, French Camp, CA, p. A61

WRIGHT, Peter J., Chief Executive Officer, Valley Regional Hospital, Claremont, NH, p. A397

WRIGHT II, Phil A., Chief Executive Officer, Southampton Memorial Hospital, Franklin, VA, p. A654

WRIGHT, Phillip L., FACHE, Chief Executive Officer, Santa Rosa Medical Center, Milton, FL, p. A133

WRIGHT, Randall P., Executive Vice President and Chief Operating Officer, Texas Children's Hospital, Houston, TX, p. A612

WRIGHT, Rick, President and Chief Executive Officer, McLaren Greater Lansing, Lansing, MI, p. A318

WRIGHT, Robert, M.D. Chief of Staff, Washington County Regional Medical Center, Sandersville, GA, p. A159

WRIGHT, Robert N., Chief Executive Officer, Kindred Hospital Peoria, Peoria, IL, p. A192

WRIGHT, Roger, Director Human Resources, Porterville Developmental Center, Porterville, CA, p. A80

WRIGHT, Rory, M.D. President Medical Staff, Orthopaedic Hospital of Wisconsin – Glendale, Milwaukee, WI, p. A692

WRIGHT, Ruth, Director Information Services, Erlanger at Hutcheson, Fort Oglethorpe, GA, p. A154

WRIGHT, Sandra, Acting Chief Information Technology Services, Central Texas Veterans Healthcare System, Temple, TX, p. A636

WRIGHT, Sandra Gayle, Ed.D., Chief Executive Officer, Tyler County Hospital, Woodville, TX, p. A642

WRIGHT, Stephanie, Director Human Resources Management, Veterans Affairs San Diego Healthcare System, San Diego, CA, p. A86

WRIGHT, Stephen C., M.D. Chief Medical Officer, Brigham and Women's Faulkner Hospital, Boston, MA, p. A296

WRIGHT, Stephen F.
President and Chief Executive Officer, CHRISTUS Schumpert Medical Center, Shreveport, LA, p. A278
President and Chief Executive Officer, CHRISTUS St. Frances Cabrini Hospital, Alexandria, LA, p. A262
President and Chief Executive Officer, CHRISTUS St. Patrick Hospital of Lake Charles, Lake Charles, LA, p. A271

WRIGHT, Stuart M., CPA Chief Financial Officer, Upstate University Hospital, Syracuse, NY, p. A444

WRIGHT, Tony, Chief Financial Officer, Mercy McCune–Brooks Hospital, Carthage, MO, p. A358

WRIGHT, Wes, Senior Vice President and Chief Information Officer, Seattle Children's Hospital, Seattle, WA, p. A671

WRINN, Denise, Vice President Financial Services and Chief Financial Officer, Cortland Regional Medical Center, Cortland, NY, p. A424

WROBLEWSKI, Edmund, M.D
Vice President Medical Affairs and Chief Medical Officer, Goleta Valley Cottage Hospital, Santa Barbara, CA, p. A89
Vice President Medical Affairs and Chief Medical Officer, Santa Barbara Cottage Hospital, Santa Barbara, CA, p. A89
Vice President Medical Affairs and Chief Medical Officer, Santa Ynez Valley Cottage Hospital, Solvang, CA, p. A91

WROGG, Frank, Director Information Technology, Mayo Clinic Health System – Red Cedar in Menomonie, Menomonie, WI, p. A691

WU, Kenneth, M.D. Medical Director, Marlton Rehabilitation Hospital, Marlton, NJ, p. A406

WUEBBELS, Carman, R.N. Chief Nursing Officer and Assistant Administrator, Mason District Hospital, Havana, IL, p. A184

WUESTE, David, Director Information Services, University of Southern California–Norris Cancer Hospital, Los Angeles, CA, p. A72

WUKITSCH, Michael, Chief Human Resources Officer, Children's Hospital Colorado, Aurora, CO, p. A97

WUNDERWALD, Wendie, Vice President Patient Care Services, Samaritan Lebanon Community Hospital, Lebanon, OR, p. A514

WURGLER, Brad D., Chief Financial Officer, Perham Health, Perham, MN, p. A338

WURTH, Jackie, Director of Nursing, Cumberland Hall Hospital, Hopkinsville, KY, p. A252

WURTH, Marie, Vice President Human Resources and Public Relations Officer, Sierra Vista Regional Health Center, Sierra Vista, AZ, p. A37

WURTZEL, Leann, Director Human Resources, Mayo Clinic Health System – Red Cedar in Menomonie, Menomonie, WI, p. A691

WYANT, Sandy, Director Human Resources, St. Mary's Medical Center, West Palm Beach, FL, p. A143

WYATT, Basil, Chief Financial Officer, Continuous Care Centers of Tulsa, Tulsa, OK, p. A508

# X

# Y

YOUNG, Eric L.
Vice President Finance and Chief Financial Officer, Marietta Memorial Hospital, Marietta, OH, p. A485
Chief Financial Officer, Selby General Hospital, Marietta, OH, p. A485
YOUNG, J. Phillip, FACHE, Chief Executive Officer, Southern Tennessee Medical Center, Winchester, TN, p. A580
YOUNG, James, Senior Vice President Finance and Chief Financial Officer, Howard County General Hospital, Columbia, MD, p. A291
YOUNG, James, M.D. Chief of Staff, McGehee–Desha County Hospital, McGehee, AR, p. A47
YOUNG, Jeffrey D.
Chief Information Officer, Children's Hospitals and Clinics of Minnesota, Minneapolis, MN, p. A336
Chief Information Officer, Children's Hospitals and Clinics of Minnesota, Saint Paul, MN, p. A340
YOUNG, Jeremie, M.D. Chief of Staff, Tri–County Hospital – Williston, Williston, FL, p. A144
YOUNG, Jimmy, Chief Financial Officer, Gilmore Memorial Regional Medical Center, Amory, MS, p. A344
YOUNG, Joyce, R.N. VP, Patient Services & Chief Nursing Officer, St. Joseph Mercy Livingston Hospital, Howell, MI, p. A316
YOUNG, Judy, Chief Financial Officer, Acadia–St. Landry Hospital, Church Point, LA, p. A265
YOUNG, Kathlene A., FACHE, President and Chief Executive Officer, St. Joseph Hospital and Health Center, Kokomo, IN, p. A207
YOUNG, Kevin, FACHE, President, Adventist Behavioral Health Rockville, Rockville, MD, p. A293
YOUNG, Kimberly, Chief Financial Officer, Baptist Memorial Hospital–Desoto, Southaven, MS, p. A354
YOUNG, Lori, Manager Health Information Management, Sumner Regional Medical Center, Wellington, KS, p. A246
YOUNG, Martha, Director Human Resources, Cumberland County Hospital, Burkesville, KY, p. A249
YOUNG, Mary, Director Human Resources, Colorado Mental Health Institute at Pueblo, Pueblo, CO, p. A105
YOUNG, Mathew, Manager Information Systems, Boscobel Area Health Care, Boscobel, WI, p. A684
YOUNG, Michael, Chief Financial Officer, Mad River Community Hospital, Arcata, CA, p. A53
YOUNG, Michael A., FACHE, President and Chief Executive Officer, Pinnacle Health System, Harrisburg, PA, p. A527
YOUNG, Pam, Human Resources Leader, Davis County Hospital, Bloomfield, IA, p. A217
YOUNG, Patty, R.N. Hospital Director of Nursing, Ashland Health Center, Ashland, KS, p. A231
YOUNG, Russ, Network Administrator, Wheatland Memorial Healthcare, Harlowton, MT, p. A377
YOUNG, Russell T., Chief Financial Officer, Riverside Community Hospital, Riverside, CA, p. A82
YOUNG, Rusty, Chief Financial Officer, Brownsville Doctors Hospital, Brownsville, TX, p. A589
YOUNG, Sandra G., Vice President Human Resources, Missouri Baptist Medical Center, Saint Louis, MO, p. A370
YOUNG, Sheila, Vice President Human Resources, Mobile Infirmary Medical Center, Mobile, AL, p. A22
YOUNG, Stephanie, Chief Information Technology, Aleda E. Lutz Veterans Affairs Medical Center, Saginaw, MI, p. A323
YOUNG, Steve, Director Information Systems, Baylor Medical Center at Frisco, Frisco, TX, p. A605
YOUNG, Steven W.
Acting Director, Veterans Affairs Montana Health Care System, Fort Harrison, MT, p. A376
Director, Veterans Affairs Salt Lake City Health Care System, Salt Lake City, UT, p. A647
YOUNG, Susan M., Chief Executive Officer, University Behavioral Health of Denton, Denton, TX, p. A599
YOUNG, Tammy, Controller, HEALTHSOUTH Lakeshore Rehabilitation Hospital, Birmingham, AL, p. A16
YOUNG, Terry, Chief Information Officer, Plains Memorial Hospital, Dimmitt, TX, p. A599
YOUNG, Tyce, Patient Services Officer, Clay County Medical Center, Clay Center, KS, p. A232
YOUNG Jr., William A., President and Chief Executive Officer, St. John Medical Center, Westlake, OH, p. A493
YOUNG–HISE, Teri R., Director of Nursing, Waldo County General Hospital, Belfast, ME, p. A281
YOUNGBLOOD, Elizabeth
President, Baylor Specialty Hospital, Dallas, TX, p. A595
President, Our Children's House at Baylor, Dallas, TX, p. A597
YOUNGBLOOD, Erin R., Chief Human Resources Officer, Behavioral Center of Michigan, Warren, MI, p. A326
YOUNGER, Lonnie D., Chief Financial Officer, Huntsville Hospital, Huntsville, AL, p. A21
YOUNGS, Patsy, President, Texas Health Presbyterian Hospital Kaufman, Kaufman, TX, p. A616

YOUNKIN, Ken, Comptroller, J. D. McCarty Center for Children With Developmental Disabilities, Norman, OK, p. A502
YOUREE, Ben, Chief Executive Officer, Dyersburg Regional Medical Center, Dyersburg, TN, p. A568
YOURZEK, Tari, Chief Nursing Officer, Boundary Community Hospital, Bonners Ferry, ID, p. A168
YOUSAITIS, Zoe, Director Human Resources, Eagleville Hospital, Eagleville, PA, p. A524
YOUSO, Michael, Chief Executive Officer, Grand Itasca Clinic and Hospital, Grand Rapids, MN, p. A333
YOX, John, Senior Vice President and Chief Operating Officer, St. Catherine Hospital, Garden City, KS, p. A234
YU, Alex, Chief Financial Officer, Tri–City Medical Center, Oceanside, CA, p. A77
YU, Derrick, Interim Chief Executive Officer, Dallas Regional Medical Center, Mesquite, TX, p. A622
YUEN, Kit, R.N. Interim Chief Nursing Officer, New York Downtown Hospital, New York, NY, p. A435
YUHAS, John, D.O. Medical Director, St. Francis Health Care Centre, Green Springs, OH, p. A482
YULICH, Michael, Director Information Services, Mercy Suburban Hospital, Norristown, PA, p. A533
YUNGMANN, Michael, Chief Executive Officer, Southside Regional Medical Center, Petersburg, VA, p. A659
YUNIS, Norm, M.D. Medical Director, Regency Hospital of Minneapolis, Golden Valley, MN, p. A333
YUNUSOV, Ed, Coordinator Facility Information Center, New York City Children's Center,, NY, p. A434
YURKIEWICZ, Sharon, Chief Executive Officer, Kindred Hospital–Wyoming Valley, Wilkes Barre, PA, p. A544
YUSKA, Connie, R.N. Chief Nursing Officer, Aurora Medical Center, Kenosha, WI, p. A688
YUST, Randall C., Chief Operating Officer and Chief Financial Officer, Indiana University Health North Hospital, Carmel, IN, p. A200

# Z

ZABAWSKI, Denise, Vice President Information Services and Chief Information Officer, Nationwide Children's Hospital, Columbus, OH, p. A477
ZABIELSKI, Gerald C., M.D. Chief Medical Staff, Wright Memorial Hospital, Trenton, MO, p. A372
ZABINSKY, Hadley, Chief Information Officer, Harrington Memorial Hospital, Southbridge, MA, p. A304
ZACHARIASEN, Keith, Chief Financial Officer, Wamego City Hospital, Wamego, KS, p. A245
ZACHARY, Beth D., President and Chief Executive Officer, White Memorial Medical Center, Los Angeles, CA, p. A72
ZACHARY, Kevin
Chief Executive Officer, Ennis Regional Medical Center, Ennis, TX, p. A602
Chief Executive Officer, Parkview Regional Hospital, Mexia, TX, p. A623
ZACHRICH, Jane, Chief Nursing Officer, Community Memorial Hospital, Hicksville, OH, p. A483
ZADYLAK, Robert, M.D. Vice President Medical Management, Advocate Illinois Masonic Medical Center, Chicago, IL, p. A176
ZAFONTE, Ross, D.O. Chief, Physical Medicine and Rehabilitation and Vice President Medical Affairs, Research and Education, Spaulding Rehabilitation Hospital, Boston, MA, p. A297
ZAGERMAN, Robert, Chief Financial Officer, Brooke Glen Behavioral Hospital, Fort Washington, PA, p. A526
ZAGLAMA, Chris, Director Information Services, Southwest Regional Medical Center, Waynesburg, PA, p. A543
ZAGLUL, Jose, M.D. Chief Medical Officer, Manatee Glens Hospital and Addiction Center, Bradenton, FL, p. A119
ZAHN, Chip, Chief Operating Officer, Las Colinas Medical Center, Irving, TX, p. A615
ZAIDBERG, Edward A., Senior Vice President Finance, New York Methodist Hospital,, NY, p. A435
ZAIDI, Syed A., M.D. Chief of Staff, Lauderdale Community Hospital, Ripley, TN, p. A578
ZAJAC, Walter
Senior Vice President and Chief Financial Officer, Dorchester General Hospital, Cambridge, MD, p. A290
Senior Vice President and Chief Financial Officer, Memorial Hospital at Easton Maryland, Easton, MD, p. A291
ZAJEC, Doris A.
Human Resources Business Partner, Marymount Hospital, Garfield Heights, OH, p. A482
Director Human Resources, South Pointe Hospital, Warrensville Heights, OH, p. A492
ZAJIC, Holly, Vice President Human Resources and Physician Services, Ivinson Memorial Hospital, Laramie, WY, p. A702

ZAJICEK, Tammy, Director of Nursing, Jackson County Hospital District, Edna, TX, p. A600
ZAKAI, Aminadav, M.D. Medical Director, Arbour–Fuller Hospital, Attleboro, MA, p. A295
ZALDIVAR, Rogelio, M.D. Medical Director, Westchester General Hospital, Miami, FL, p. A132
ZALMAN, Tisha, Chief Executive Officer, El Campo Memorial Hospital, El Campo, TX, p. A600
ZALOUDEK, Lisa, Chief Human Resources Officer, Ponca City Medical Center, Ponca City, OK, p. A505
ZALUD, Nicolette, Customer Site Manager, McLaren Central Michigan, Mount Pleasant, MI, p. A320
ZALUSKI, Heather, M.D. President Medical Staff, Shodair Children's Hospital, Helena, MT, p. A377
ZAMBITO, Paolo, Chief Executive Officer, Ochsner Medical Center – Kenner, Kenner, LA, p. A269
ZAMBRANA, David, R.N. Chief Operating Officer and Chief Nursing Officer, University of Miami Hospital, Miami, FL, p. A132
ZAMBRINI, Christine, Chief Operating Officer and Chief Nursing Officer, Henry Ford West Bloomfield Hospital, West Bloomfield, MI, p. A326
ZAMORA, Don, Director Human Resources, Decatur Morgan Hospital, Decatur, AL, p. A19
ZAMORA DE AGUERO, Hilde, Human Resources Site Director, Baptist Health South Florida, West Kendall Baptist Hospital, Miami, FL, p. A131
ZANE, Kristi, Chief Human Resources Officer, Crawford Memorial Hospital, Robinson, IL, p. A193
ZANI, Carl, Director Information Systems, Memorial Hospital of Union County, Marysville, OH, p. A485
ZANKMAN, Lisa, Senior Vice President Human Resources, Beth Israel Deaconess Medical Center, Boston, MA, p. A296
ZAPPALA, Phyllis, Vice President Human Resources, Danbury Hospital, Danbury, CT, p. A108
ZAPPALA, Phyllis F., Senior Vice President Human Resources, New Milford Hospital, New Milford, CT, p. A111
ZARA, George A., President and Chief Executive Officer, Providence Hospital, Columbia, SC, p. A550
ZARAK, Tamie, Director Human Resources, Memorial Medical Center – Neillsville, Neillsville, WI, p. A693
ZAREN, Douglas, FACHE, Administrator, Memorial Regional Hospital South,, FL, p. A125
ZARITSKY, Arno, M.D. Senior Vice President Clinical Services, Children's Hospital of The King's Daughters, Norfolk, VA, p. A658
ZARRILLA, Peter, Vice President and Chief Human Resources Officer, Lowell General Hospital, Lowell, MA, p. A301
ZASTOCKI, Deborah, FACHE, President and Chief Executive Officer, Chilton Hospital, Pompton Plains, NJ, p. A409
ZASTOUPIL, Rockford, President and Chief Executive Officer, St. Aloisius Medical Center, Harvey, ND, p. A467
ZAUNER, Mike, Chief Executive Officer, Sierra Vista Hospital, Sacramento, CA, p. A83
ZAVATCHEN, Nancy, Director Information Technology, Cullman Regional Medical Center, Cullman, AL, p. A18
ZAVODNICK, Jacquelyn, M.D. Medical Director, Devereux Children's Behavioral Health Center, Malvern, PA, p. A530
ZAWACKI, Brenda, Manager Human Resources, Providence Kodiak Island Medical Center, Kodiak, AK, p. A28
ZAWISZA, Walter, Chief Financial Officer, Veterans Affairs Ann Arbor Healthcare System, Ann Arbor, MI, p. A308
ZBIERAJEWSKI, Judy, Chief Nursing Officer and Vice President Patient Care, Mercy St. Charles Hospital, Oregon, OH, p. A488
ZDEBLICK, Mike, Chief Operating Officer, El Camino Hospital, Mountain View, CA, p. A75
ZECHMAN, David M., FACHE, President and Chief Executive Officer, Ozarks Medical Center, West Plains, MO, p. A373
ZEDRECK, Judith F., R.N., Interim Chief Executive Officer, Allegheny General Hospital, Pittsburgh, PA, p. A537
ZEH, Gianna, Commander, U. S. Air Force Regional Hospital, Eglin AFB, FL, p. A122
ZEHM, Laura, Vice President and Chief Financial Officer, Community Hospital of the Monterey Peninsula, Monterey, CA, p. A75
ZEHNER, Douglas A., Senior Vice President and Chief Financial Officer, MedStar Washington Hospital Center, Washington, DC, p. A116
ZEICHNER, Veronica, Chief Financial Officer, Newark Beth Israel Medical Center, Newark, NJ, p. A407
ZEIGLER, Michele
Vice President and Chief Information Officer, Chambersburg Hospital, Chambersburg, PA, p. A522
Vice President Information Services, Waynesboro Hospital, Waynesboro, PA, p. A543
ZEITLER, Irvin, D.O. Vice President Medical Affairs, Shannon Medical Center, San Angelo, TX, p. A630
ZEITLER, Jenny, Network Administrator, North Okaloosa Medical Center, Crestview, FL, p. A121

ZELENKA, Anthony, Chief Administrative Officer, Berkeley Medical Center, Martinsburg, WV, p. A678

ZELINSKI, Barbara C., Chief Operating Officer, Kaiser Permanente Panorama City Medical Center,, CA, p. A69

ZELL, John R., Chief Financial Officer, OSF St. Joseph Medical Center, Bloomington, IL, p. A174

ZELLER, Brad, Vice President Operations, Hayward Area Memorial Hospital and Nursing Home, Hayward, WI, p. A688

ZELLER, Clifford, M.D. Chief Medical Officer, Banner Behavioral Health Hospital – Scottsdale, Scottsdale, AZ, p. A37

ZELLER, Paul, Vice President Human Resources, MedStar Southern Maryland Hospital Center, Clinton, MD, p. A290

ZEMANEK, William, Assistant Chief Financial Officer, Artesia General Hospital, Artesia, NM, p. A415

ZENDER, Dale, Regional Vice President Finance and Chief Financial Officer, PeaceHealth St. Joseph Medical Center, Bellingham, WA, p. A664

ZENGOTITA, Jamie, M.D. Chief Medical Staff, Mercy Hospital Cassville, Cassville, MO, p. A358

ZENN, Michael B., Executive Vice President, Chief Operating Officer and Chief Financial Officer, Northwest Community Hospital, Arlington Heights, IL, p. A173

ZENONE, Michael, Chief Financial Officer, Tyrone Hospital, Tyrone, PA, p. A542

ZEOLI, Diane, Chief Executive Officer, Kindred Hospital–Brea, Brea, CA, p. A55

ZEPHIER, Michelle, Human Resource Specialist, U. S. Public Health Service Indian Hospital, Rosebud, SD, p. A562

ZEPS, Joseph, Vice President Finance, Tomah Memorial Hospital, Tomah, WI, p. A697

ZEROSKE, Joanne, President and Chief Executive Officer, Marymount Hospital, Garfield Heights, OH, p. A482

ZERRER, Lana, M.D. Chief of Staff, Harry S. Truman Memorial Veterans Hospital, Columbia, MO, p. A359

ZETTER, David, M.D. Chief of Staff, Jackson Purchase Medical Center, Mayfield, KY, p. A257

ZEVENBERGEN, Glenn, Chief Executive Officer, Hegg Memorial Health Center Avera, Rock Valley, IA, p. A227

ZEWE, Jeff S., R.N. Vice President Patient Care Services and Chief Nursing Officer, Olean General Hospital, Olean, NY, p. A438

ZIA, Michael, M.D. Vice President Quality Systems and Medical Affairs, Decatur Memorial Hospital, Decatur, IL, p. A180

ZICHAL, Frances J., Chief Executive Officer, Central Community Hospital, Elkader, IA, p. A221

ZIDANSEK, John A., Chief Executive Officer, Lock Haven Hospital, Lock Haven, PA, p. A530

ZIDEK, Nancy, M.D. Chief of Staff, Community HealthCare System, Onaga, KS, p. A241

ZIECHECK, Hal, Chief Operating Officer, Morton Plant North Bay Hospital, New Port Richey, FL, p. A133

ZIEGELE, Paul, Chief Financial Officer, Florida Hospital Zephyrhills, Zephyrhills, FL, p. A144

ZIEGLER, Bernie, Manager Information Systems, Methodist Hospital of Chicago, Chicago, IL, p. A177

ZIEGLER, Derick, Administrator and Chief Executive Officer, Baptist Memorial Hospital – Memphis, Memphis, TN, p. A574

ZIEGLER, John C., FACHE Vice Presidnet Human Resources, Memorial Hospital, Belleville, IL, p. A174

ZIEGLER, Peter, M.D. Acting Chief Medical Officer, U. S. Public Health Service Indian Hospital–Sells, Sells, AZ, p. A37

ZIELASKIEWICZ, Michael E., R.N. Vice President Patient Care Services and Chief Nursing Officer, Portneuf Medical Center, Pocatello, ID, p. A171

ZIELAZINSKI, Mark, Chief Information Officer, Alameda County Medical Center, Oakland, CA, p. A77

ZIELINSKI, Dennis G., Chief Executive Officer and Administrator, Coquille Valley Hospital, Coquille, OR, p. A512

ZIELINSKI, Sharon
Manager Health Information, HEALTHSOUTH Rehabilitation Hospital of Erie, Erie, PA, p. A525
Chief Information Resource Officer, Veterans Affairs Maryland Health Care System–Baltimore Division, Baltimore, MD, p. A289

ZIEMBA, Mike, Information Technology Project Lead, Northlake Behavioral Hospital, Mandeville, LA, p. A273

ZIEMER, John, M.D. Chief of Staff, Rusk County Memorial Hospital and Nursing Home, Ladysmith, WI, p. A689

ZIEMER, Patrick C., Chief Executive Officer, Alvarado Parkway Institute Behavioral Health System, La Mesa, CA, p. A65

ZIENIEWICZ, Stephen P., FACHE, Executive Director, University of Washington Medical Center, Seattle, WA, p. A671

ZIEROLD, Bob, Senior Vice President Human Resources, Christian Health Care Center, Wyckoff, NJ, p. A413

ZIESMER, Bill, Chief Financial Officer, Skyridge Medical Center, Cleveland, TN, p. A567

ZIESMER, Valerie, Chief Financial Officer, Florida Hospital–Flagler, Palm Coast, FL, p. A136

ZIGLOR, Danyale, Assistant Director Human Resources, WellStar Douglas Hospital, Douglasville, GA, p. A152

ZILKOW, Jon, Chief Financial Officer, Fountain Valley Regional Hospital and Medical Center, Fountain Valley, CA, p. A60

ZILM, Michael E., Interim Chief Executive Officer and Administrator, Bellville St. Joseph Health Center, Bellville, TX, p. A588

ZIMA, Cheryl F., Vice President Human Resources, Ministry Saint Michael's Hospital, Stevens Point, WI, p. A697

ZIMMEL, Robert, Senior Vice President Human Resources, St. Luke's University Hospital – Bethlehem Campus, Bethlehem, PA, p. A520

ZIMMER, Jan, R.N. Chief Nursing Officer, Regional Hospital of Jackson, Jackson, TN, p. A570

ZIMMER, Paul, M.D. Chief of Staff, Providence Kodiak Island Medical Center, Kodiak, AK, p. A28

ZIMMERLY, Kara, Manager Human Resources, ProMedica Bay Park Hospital, Oregon, OH, p. A488

ZIMMERMAN, Coleen, Interim Chief Executive Officer, Select Specialty Hospital–Erie, Erie, PA, p. A525

ZIMMERMAN, David, M.D. Chief of Staff, MedWest – Swain, Bryson City, NC, p. A448

ZIMMERMAN, Don, Director Human Resources, Morris County Hospital, Council Grove, KS, p. A233

ZIMMERMAN, Maria, R.N. Chief Nursing Officer, Sheridan County Health Complex, Hoxie, KS, p. A236

ZIMMERMAN, Mark, Vice President Human Resources Development and Support Services, Rockingham Memorial Hospital, Harrisonburg, VA, p. A655

ZIMMERMAN, Michael
Vice President Human Resources, Dorchester General Hospital, Cambridge, MD, p. A290
Vice President Human Resources, Memorial Hospital at Easton Maryland, Easton, MD, p. A291

ZIMMERMAN, Nancy, R.N., Administrator, Comanche County Hospital, Coldwater, KS, p. A232

ZIMMERMANN, Wayne, Chief Operating Officer, Elmhurst Hospital Center,, NY, p. A431

ZIMMERMANN, William
Chief Information Officer, Grady General Hospital, Cairo, GA, p. A149
Senior Vice President Information Services, John D. Archbold Memorial Hospital, Thomasville, GA, p. A161
Chief Information Officer, Mitchell County Hospital, Camilla, GA, p. A149

ZIMPFER, Mary, Vice President Quality Management, Grace Hospital, Cleveland, OH, p. A476

ZINKULA, Lisa, Chief Financial Officer, Grundy County Memorial Hospital, Grundy Center, IA, p. A222

ZINN, David, M.D. Vice President Medical Affairs, Northeast Alabama Regional Medical Center, Anniston, AL, p. A15

ZINNER, Barbara, Interim Chief Nursing Officer, Marymount Hospital, Garfield Heights, OH, p. A482

ZIOLKOWSKI, David
Chief Operating Officer, Petaluma Valley Hospital, Petaluma, CA, p. A79
Chief Operating Officer, Santa Rosa Memorial Hospital, Santa Rosa, CA, p. A90

ZIPPARO, Maureen, President and Chief Operating Officer, Putnam Hospital Center, Carmel, NY, p. A423

ZIRBSER, Glenn, Chief Financial Officer, Inova Loudoun Hospital, Leesburg, VA, p. A656

ZIRKELBACH, Mark, Chief Information Officer, Loma Linda University Medical Center, Loma Linda, CA, p. A66

ZIRKELBACK, Mark, Chief Information Officer, Loma Linda University Behavioral Medicine Center, Redlands, CA, p. A81

ZIRKLE, William, Manager Information Systems, Halifax Regional Health System, South Boston, VA, p. A661

ZISKIN, Robert, Chief Information Officer, Northport Veterans Affairs Medical Center, Northport, NY, p. A437

ZLOTOWICZ, Jan, Vice President Human Resources, Motion Picture and Television Fund Hospital and Residential Services,, CA, p. A70

ZMRHAL, Gary, Interim Vice President Finance, St. Francis Health Center, Topeka, KS, p. A245

ZOCH, Jeremy, Chief Operating Officer, Mercy Hospitals of Bakersfield, Bakersfield, CA, p. A54

ZOGELMAN, Sharon, Director Human Resources, St. Luke Hospital and Living Center, Marion, KS, p. A239

ZOLKIWSKY, Walter R., M.D. Vice President Medical Affairs, Reston Hospital Center, Reston, VA, p. A659

ZONA, Michael, M.D. Medical Director, Centennial Peaks Hospital, Louisville, CO, p. A104

ZOPH, Timothy R.
Senior Vice President and Chief Information Officer, Northwestern Lake Forest Hospital, Lake Forest, IL, p. A186
Senior Vice President and Chief Information Officer, Northwestern Memorial Hospital, Chicago, IL, p. A178

ZORZA, Elizabeth, Assistant Administrator, OSF St. Francis Hospital, Escanaba, MI, p. A313

ZOUCHA, Larry, Chief Information Officer, Boone County Health Center, Albion, NE, p. A381

ZUANICH, Elizabeth
Chief Financial Officer, Providence Little Company of Mary Medical Center, Torrance, CA, p. A92
Chief Financial Officer, Providence Little Company of Mary Medical Center San Pedro,, CA, p. A71

ZUBIENA, John, Chief Human Resources Officer, Northwest Medical Center, Tucson, AZ, p. A39

ZUBKO, Elizabeth, Associate Executive Director Finance, Franklin Hospital, Valley Stream, NY, p. A445

ZUEL, Sally
Vice President Human Resources and Education, Union Hospital, Terre Haute, IN, p. A214
Vice President Human Resources, Union Hospital Clinton, Clinton, IN, p. A200

ZUHD, Dajani, M.D. President Medical Staff, Punxsutawney Area Hospital, Punxsutawney, PA, p. A539

ZUIDEMA, Paul, Chief Financial Officer, South Mississippi County Regional Medical Center, Osceola, AR, p. A48

ZUINO, Matthew, Vice President, Virtua Memorial, Mount Holly, NJ, p. A406

ZULIANI, Michael E., Chief Executive Officer, HEALTHSOUTH Huntington Rehabilitation Hospital, Huntington, WV, p. A677

ZULICK, Lewis, M.D., Chief Executive Officer, Clifton Springs Hospital and Clinic, Clifton Springs, NY, p. A424

ZULK, Susan, Vice President Marketing and Fund Development, Spencer Hospital, Spencer, IA, p. A228

ZULTANKY, Lynne, Director Corporate Communications and Media Relations, Bon Secours–DePaul Medical Center, Norfolk, VA, p. A658

ZUMPANO, Anthony, Chief Financial Officer, Penn Presbyterian Medical Center, Philadelphia, PA, p. A536

ZUNNO, Gerard, R.N. Vice President Patient Care Services, Peconic Bay Medical Center, Riverhead, NY, p. A440

ZVANUT, Michelle, Vice President Human Resources, Boone Hospital Center, Columbia, MO, p. A359

ZWALLY, Paula, Director Quality Improvement Services and Compliance, Southwest Connecticut Mental Health System, Bridgeport, CT, p. A108

ZWANZIGER, Marcia, Vice President Finance, Huron Regional Medical Center, Huron, SD, p. A560

ZWARTVERWER, Rick, M.D. Vice President Medical Affairs, Sky Lakes Medical Center, Klamath Falls, OR, p. A514

ZWENG, Thomas, M.D. Senior Vice President Medical Affairs, Novant Health Matthews Medical Center, Matthews, NC, p. A457

ZWICKEY, Tim E., Chief Executive Officer, Baraga County Memorial Hospital, L'Anse, MI, p. A318

ZWINGER, Glenn, Manager Information Systems Services, Veterans Affairs Puget Sound Health Care System, Seattle, WA, p. A671

ZWINGMAN–BAGLEY, Cheryl, R.N. Chief Nursing Officer, Calais Regional Hospital, Calais, ME, p. A282

ZYBERT, Edmund, Chief Operating Officer, Helen Hayes Hospital, West Haverstraw, NY, p. A445

# AHA Membership Categories

*The American Hospital Association is primarily an organization of hospitals and related institutions. Its object, according to its bylaws, is "to promote high-quality health care and health services for all the people through leadership in the development of public policy, leadership in the representation and advocacy of hospital and health care organization interests, and leadership in the provision of services to assist hospitals and health care organizations in meeting the health care needs of their communities."*

## Institutional Members

**Hospitals or health services organizations or systems which provide a continuum of integrated, community health resources and which include at least one licensed hospital that is owned, leased, managed or religiously sponsored.**

Institutional members include hospitals, health care systems, integrated delivery systems, and physician hospital organizations (PHOs) and health maintenance organizations (HMOs) wholly or partially owned by or owning a member hospital or system. An Institutional member hospital, health care system or integrated delivery system may, at its discretion and upon approval of a membership application by the Association chief executive officer, extend membership to the health care provider organizations, other than a hospital that it owns, leases, or fully controls.

### Freestanding Health Care Provider Organizations

These are health provider organizations, other than registered hospitals, that provide patient care services, including, but not limited to, ambulatory, preventive, rehabilitative, specialty, post-acute and continuing care, as well as physician groups, health insurance services, and staff and group model health maintenance organizations without a hospital component. Freestanding Health Care Provider Organizations members are not owned or controlled by an Institutional member hospital, health care system or integrated delivery system member. They may, however, be part of an organization eligible for, but not holding, Institutional membership.

### Other Organizations

This category includes organizations interested in the objectives of the American Hospital Association, but not eligible for Institutional or Freestanding Health Care Provider Organization Membership. Organizations eligible for Other membership shall include, but not be limited to, associations, societies, foundations, corporations, educational and academic institutions, companies, government agencies, international health providers, and organizations having an interest in and a desire to support the objectives of the Association.

### Provisional Members

Hospitals that are in the planning or construction stage and that, on completion, will be eligible for institutional membership. Provisional membership may also be granted to applicant institutions that cannot, at present, meet the requirements of Institutional or Freestanding Health Care Provider Organization membership.

### Government Institution Group Members

Groups of government hospitals operated by the same unit of government may obtain institutional membership under a group plan. Membership dues are based on a special schedule set forth in the bylaws of the AHA.

## Other Institutional Members

### Hospitals

*U.S. hospitals and hospitals in areas associated with the U.S. that are Institutional members of the American Hospital Association are included in the list of hospitals in section A. Canadian Institutional members of the American Hospital Association are listed below.*

## Canada

### ALBERTA

**Lamont:** LAMONT HEALTH CARE CENTRE, P.O. Bag 10, Zip T0B 2R0; tel. 780/895–2211; Harold James, Executive Director

### MANITOBA

**Winnipeg:** RIVERVIEW HEALTH CENTRE, 1 Morley Avenue East, Zip R3L 2P4; tel. 204/452–3411; Norman R. Kasian, President and Chief Executive Officer

### ONTARIO

**Renfrew:** RENFREW VICTORIA HOSPITAL, 499 Raglan Street North, Zip K7V 1P6; tel. 613/432–4851; Randy V. Penney, Executive Director
**Thornhill:** SHOULDICE HOSPITAL, 7750 Bayview Avenue, Zip L3T 4A3; tel. 905/889–1125; John Hughes, Chief Administrative Officer

### QUEBEC

**Montreal:** MOUNT SINAI HOSPITAL CENTER, 5690 Cavendish Cote St–Luc', Zip H4W 1S7; tel. 514/369–2222; Michel Amar, Executive Director

# Associated University Programs in Health Administration

## CALIFORNIA

**San Diego:** CALIFORNIA COLLEGE SAN DIEGO, 2820 Camino Del Rio South, Suite 300, Zip 92108–3821; tel. 619/295–5784; Barbara Thomas, Chief Operations Officer

**San Francisco:** GOLDEN GATE UNIVERSITY, 536 Mission Street, Univ Library, Zip 94105–2968; tel. 415/442–7242; Steven Dunlap, Head Technical Services

## IOWA

**Iowa City:** DEPARTMENT OF HEALTH MANAGEMENT AND POLICY, UNIVERSITY OF IOWA, 105 River Street, N232A CPHB, Zip 52246; tel. 319/384–3830; Keith Mueller, Ph.D., Professor and Head

## MARYLAND

**Bethesda:** NAVAL SCHOOL OF HEALTH SCIENCES, Naval Medical Command, National Region, Zip 20889–5611; tel. 301/295–1251; Commander DuWayne Griepentrog, Director Administration

## MISSOURI

**Columbia:** UNIVERSITY OF MISSOURI, HEALTH MANAGEMENT AND INFORMATICS, CE707 Clinical Support and Education Building, DC 00600, One Hospital Drive, Zip 65212; tel. 573/882–6179; Lanis Hicks, Ph.D., Professor and Associate Chair

## PENNSYLVANIA

**University Park:** PENNSYLVANIA STATE UNIVERSITY, 604 Ford Building, Zip 16802; tel. 814/863–2859; Dennis Shea, Department Head

## TEXAS

**Brooks AFB:** U. S. AIR FORCE SCHOOL OF AEROSPACE MEDICINE, USAFSAM–CCE, Zip 78235–5301; tel. 210/536–4251; Colonel Richard E. Bachmann, Jr., Commander

**San Antonio:** ARMY–BAYLOR UNIVERSITY PROGRAM IN HEALTH CARE ADMINISTRATION, 3151 Scott Road, Building 2841, Zip 78234–6135; tel. 210/221–6443; Lieutenant Colonel M. Nicholas Coppola, Program Director

TRINITY UNIVERSITY, One Trinity Place, #58, Zip 78212–7200; tel. 210/736–8107; Mary E. Stefl, Ph.D., Chairman

**Sheppard AFB:** U. S. AIR FORCE SCHOOL OF HEALTH CARE SCIENCES, Building 1900, MST/114, Academic Library, Zip 76311; tel. 817/851–2511

## PUERTO RICO

**San Juan:** SCHOOL OF PUBLIC HEALTH, P.O. Box 5067, Zip 00936; tel. 809/767–9626; Orlando Nieves, Dean

# Hospital Schools
# of Nursing

**NEW YORK**

**Elmira:** ARNOT–OGDEN MEMORIAL HOSPITAL School of Nursing

**PENNSYLVANIA**

**New Castle:** JAMESON HOSPITAL School of Nursing

# Nonhospital Preacute and Postacute Care Facilities

## ALABAMA

**Fort Rucker:** LYSTER ARMY HEALTH CLINIC, Andrews Lane, Building 301, Zip 36362–5000; tel. 334/255–7359; Colonel Patrick N. Denman, Commander
**Maxwell Afb:** MAXWELL CLINIC, 300 Twining Street, Zip 36112–6027; tel. 334/953–7801; Colonel Bart O. Iddins, Commander

## ALASKA

**Anchorage:** ALASKA VETERANS AFFAIRS HEALTHCARE SYSTEM, 1201 North Muldoon Road, Zip 99504–6104; tel. 907/257–6930; Alex Spector, Director

## ARIZONA

**Davis–Monthan AFB:** U. S. AIR FORCE CLINIC, 4175 South Alamo Avenue, Zip 85707–4405; tel. 520/228–2930
**Fort Huachuca:** RAYMOND W. BLISS ARMY HEALTH CENTER, 45001 Winrow Avenue, Zip 85613–7040; tel. 520/533–2350; Colonel Thomas W. Smith, M.D., MSC, Commander
**Glendale:** U. S. AIR FORCE HOSPITAL LUKE, Luke AFB, 7219 North Litchfield Road, Zip 85309–1525; tel. 623/856–7502; Colonel Schuyler K. Geller, Commander

## ARKANSAS

**Jacksonville:** U. S. AIR FORCE CLINIC LITTLE ROCK, Little Rock AFB, Zip 72099–5057; tel. 501/987–7411; Colonel Rebecca A. Russell, USAF, Commander

## CALIFORNIA

**Beale AFB:** U. S. AIR FORCE HOSPITAL, 15301 Warren Shingle Road, Zip 95903–1907; tel. 530/634–4838; Lieutenant Colonel Robert G. Quinn, MSC, USAF, FACHE, Administrator
**Edwards AFB:** U. S. AIR FORCE CLINIC, 10 Hospital Road, Building 5500, Zip 93524–1730; tel. 661/277–2010; Colonel Sally Petty, Commander
**Los Angeles:** DEPARTMENT OF VETERANS AFFAIRS, OUTPATIENT CLINIC, 351 East Temple Street, Zip 90012; tel. 213/253–5000; Jules Morevac, Ph.D., Director
**Martinez:** VETERANS AFFAIRS NORTHERN CALIFORNIA HEALTH SYSTEM, 150 Muir Road, Zip 94553; tel. 925/372–2000; Brian J. O'Neill, M.D., Director
**Moss Beach:** SETON MEDICAL CENTER COASTSIDE, 600 Marine Boulevard, Zip 94038–9641; tel. 650/563–7100; James P. Schuessler, Interim President and Chief Executive Officer
**Port Hueneme:** NAVAL AMBULATORY CARE CENTER, Zip 93043; tel. 805/982–6301; Major Frederick White, Officer–in–Charge
**San Francisco:** VETERANS AFFAIRS OUTPATIENT CLINIC, 4150 Clement Street, Zip 94121; tel. 415/221–4810; Lawrence C. Stewart, Director
**Sepulveda:** VETERANS AFFAIRS MEDICAL CENTER, 16111 Plummer Street, Zip 91343; tel. 818/891–7711; Charles M. Doorman, Acting Director
**Vandenberg AFB:** U. S. AIR FORCE HOSPITAL, 338 South Dakota Street, Zip 93437–6307; tel. 805/606–1110; Commander Janice Wallace, Commander
**Winterhaven:** U. S. PUBLIC HEALTH SERVICE INDIAN HOSPITAL, P.O. Box 1368, Zip 85366–1368; tel. 760/572–0217; Kent Smalley, M.D., Acting Chief Executive Officer and Clinical Director

## COLORADO

**Las Animas:** SOUTHERN COLORADO HEALTHCARE SYSTEM, P.O. Box 390, Zip 81054–0390; tel. 719/456–1260; Stuart C. Collyer, Director
**USAF Academy:** U. S. AIR FORCE ACADEMY CLINIC, 4102 Pinion Drive, Zip 80840–4000; tel. 719/333–5102; Colonel Alan B. Berg, Commander

## CONNECTICUT

**Groton:** NAVAL HOSPITAL, 1 Wahoo Drive, Box 600, Zip 06349–5600; tel. 860/694–3261
**Newington:** VETERANS AFFAIRS MEDICAL CENTER–NEWINGTON CAMPUS, 555 Willard Avenue, Zip 06111–2600; tel. 860/666–6951; Roger L. Johnson, Director

## DELAWARE

**Dover:** U. S. AIR FORCE HOSPITAL DOVER, 300 Tuskegee Boulevard, Zip 19902–7307; tel. 302/677–2525; Colonel Genanne Hansen–Bayless, Administrator
**New Castle:** CHRISTIANA CARE VISITING NURSE ASSOCIATION, One Reads Way, Zip 19720; tel. 302/327–8200; Lynn C. Jones, President
PHYSICAL THERAPY PLUS, 1 Reads Way, Suite 300, Zip 19720; tel. 302/326–8755; Stephen Rombach, Director
**Newark:** CHRISTIANA CARE IMAGING CENTER, 4751 Ogletown–Stanton Road, Zip 19713; tel. 302/731–9800; Stephanie Cooper, Director
CHRISTIANA SURGICENTER, 4755 Ogletown–Stanton Road, Zip 19718; tel. 302/733–6900; Margaret Wojcik, Coordinator
HEALTH CARE CENTER AT CHRISTIANA, 200 Hygeia Drive, Zip 19714
**Wilmington:** EUGENE DUPONT PREVENTIVE MEDICINE AND REHABILITATION INSTITUTE, 3506 Kennett Pike, Zip 19807; tel. 302/655–4041; Katherine A. Kolb, Director

## FLORIDA

**Jacksonville:** BAPTIST HOME HEALTH CARE, 3563 Philips Highway, Suite 202, Zip 32207; tel. 904/202–4300; Diane Jones, Director
BAPTIST OCCUPATIONAL HEALTH, 1325 San Marco Boulevard, Suite 301, Zip 32207; tel. 904/202–2395; Donna Snider, Director
BAPTIST PRIMARY CARE, 3563 Philips Highway, Suite 101, Zip 32207; tel. 904/376–3744; Berl O'Malley, Administrator
NEMOURS CHILDREN'S CLINIC, 807 Children's Way, Zip 32207; tel. 904/390–3600; William A. Cover, Administrator
PAVILION INFUSION THERAPY, 3563 Philips Highway, Suite 202, Zip 32207; tel. 904/202–5730; Diane Jones, Director
PSYCHIATRIC AND PSYCHOLOGICAL CARE, 4160 University Boulevard South, Zip 32216; tel. 904/376–3800; Mark A. Masters, Ph.D., Director
**Key West:** NAVAL REGIONAL MEDICAL CLINIC, 1500 Douglas Circle, Zip 33040; tel. 305/293–4613; Lieutenant Commander Michael Grande, Officer–in–Charge
**MacDill AFB:** U. S. AIR FORCE HOSPITAL, 8415 Bayshore Boulevard, Zip 33621–1607; tel. 813/827–9521
**Patrick AFB:** U. S. AIR FORCE CLINIC, 1381 South Patrick Drive, Zip 32925–3606; tel. 407/494–8102; Colonel William Swindling, Commanding Officer
**Tyndall AFB:** U. S. AIR FORCE CLINIC, 340 Magnolia Avenue, Zip 32403–5612; tel. 850/283–7515; Colonel Michael J. Murphy, Commander

## GEORGIA

**Calhoun:** ALLIANT HEALTH PLANS, INC., 401 South Wall Street, Suite 201, Zip 30701; tel. 706/629–8848; Judy Pair, Chief Executive Officer
GEORGIA HEALTH PLUS, 401 South Wall Street, Suite 201, Zip 30701; tel. 706/629–1833
**Columbus:** AZALEA TRACE, 910 Talbotton Road, Zip 31901; tel. 706/323–9513; Todd West, Administrator
HAMILTON HOUSE NURSING CENTER/ADULT LIVING CENTER, 1911 Hamilton Road, Zip 31901; tel. 706/571–1850; John Sims, Administrator
**Comer:** COBB HEALTH CARE CENTER, PO Box 566, Zip 30629; tel. 706/783–5116; Michael Gay, Administrator
**Hartwell:** HARTWELL HEALTH CARE CENTER, 94 Cade Street, Zip 30643–1814; tel. 706/856–6992; Marsha Beck, Administrator
**Moody AFB:** U. S. AIR FORCE HOSPITAL MOODY, 3278 Mitchell Boulevard, Zip 31699–1500; tel. 229/257–3772
**Robins AFB:** U. S. AIR FORCE CLINIC, 655 Seventh Street, Zip 31098–2227; tel. 912/327–7996; Colonel John A. Lee, USAF, MSC, Commander
**Rome:** CENTREX, 420 East Second Avenue, Zip 30161; tel. 706/235–1006; Dee B. Russell, M.D., Chief Executive Officer
COMMUNITY HOSPICECARE, P.O. Box 233, Zip 30162–0233; tel. 706/232–0807; Kurt Stuenkel, FACHE, President and Chief Executive Officer
FLOYD HOME HEALTH AGENCY, P.O. Box 6248, Zip 30162–6248; tel. 706/802–4600; Kurt Stuenkel, FACHE, President and Chief Executive Officer
FLOYD MEDICAL OUTPATIENT SURGERY, P.O. Box 233, Zip 30162–0233; tel. 706/802–2070; Kurt Stuenkel, FACHE, President and Chief Executive Officer
FLOYD REHABILITATION CENTER, P.O. Box 233, Zip 30162–0233; tel. 706/802–2091; Kurt Stuenkel, FACHE, President and Chief Executive Officer
**Royston:** BROWN MEMORIAL CONVALESCENT CENTER, P.O. Box 589, Zip 30662–0589; tel. 706/245–1900; Deborah Payne, Administrator

## HAWAII

**Honolulu:** KAISER MOANALUA, 3288 Moanalua Road, Zip 96819–1469; tel. 808/432–0000; Melodee J. Deutsch, MS, M.P.H., Director Quality
MALUHIA HOSPITAL, 1027 Hala Drive, Zip 96817; tel. 808/832–5874; Sally T. Ishikawa, Administrator
VETERANS AFFAIRS PACIFIC ISLANDS HEALTHCARE SYSTEM, 459 Patterson Road, Zip 96819; tel. 808/433–0600; James E. Hastings, M.D., Director
**Pearl Harbor:** NAVAL HEALTH CLINIC HAWAII, Box 121, Building 1750, Zip 96860–5080; tel. 808/471–3025; Lieutenant Commander David Lang, Director Administration

## ILLINOIS

**North Chicago:** CAPTAIN JAMES A. LOVELL FEDERAL HEALTH CENTER, 3001 Green Bay Road, Zip 60064–3048; tel. 847/688–1900; Commander Christian Wallis, Assistant Director Facility Support
**Oak Forest:** OAK FOREST HEALTH CENTER OF COOK COUNTY, 15900 South Cicero Avenue, Zip 60452–4006; tel. 708/687–7200
**Peoria Heights:** SAINT CLARE HOME, 5533 North Galena Road, Zip 61614–4499; tel. 309/682–5428; Candy Conover, Administrator
**Scott AFB:** SCOTT MEDICAL CENTER, 310 West Losey Street, Zip 62225–5252; tel. 618/256–7456; Colonel Bret D. Burton, Commander

## KANSAS

**Fort Leavenworth:** MUNSON ARMY HEALTH CENTER, 550 Pope Avenue, Zip 66027–2332; tel. 913/684–6420; Colonel David Bitterman, Commander

**Great Bend:** ST. ROSE FAMILY MEDICINE AND URGENT CARE, 3515 Broadway Street, Zip 67530–3633; tel. 620/792–2511; Leanne M. Irsik, R.N., Senior Vice President and Administrator

**Wichita:** U. S. AIR FORCE HOSPITAL, 59570 Leavenworth Street, Suite 6E4, Zip 67221–5300; tel. 316/759–5421

## LOUISIANA

**Barksdale AFB:** U. S. AIR FORCE CLINIC, 243 Curtiss Road, Suite 100, Zip 71110–5300; tel. 318/456–6004; Colonel James M. Benge, Commander

**New Orleans:** NAVAL MEDICAL CLINIC, 1 Sanctuary Drive, Zip 70142–5300; tel. 504/678–2400; Lieutenant Commander Edward Brinston, Officer–in–Charge

SOUTHEAST LOUISIANA VETERANS HEALTH CARE SYSTEM, 1601 Perdido Street, Zip 70112–1262; tel. 504/412–3700; Julie A. Catellier, Director

## MAINE

**Damariscotta:** COVE'S EDGE, 26 Schooner Street, Zip 04543; tel. 207/563–4645; Judy McGuire, Administrator

MILES MEDICAL GROUP, INC., 35 Miles Street, Zip 04543; tel. 207/563–1234; Stacey Miller–Friant, Director

**Kennebunk:** SOUTHERN MAINE HEALTH AND HOME SERVICES, P.O. Box 739, Zip 04043; tel. 207/985–4767; Elaine Brady, R.N., Executive Director

## MARYLAND

**Andrews AFB:** MALCOLM GROW MEDICAL CLINIC, 1050 West Perimeter, Suite B5–10, Zip 20762–6600; tel. 240/857–3001; Colonel Rudolph Cachuela, Commanding Officer

**Annapolis:** NAVAL HEALTH CLINIC ANNAPOLIS, 250 Wood Road, Zip 21402–1257; tel. 410/293–1330; Lieutenant Commander Matthew Holcomb, Director Administration

**Baltimore:** ST. AGNES HEALTH SERVICES, 900 Caton Avenue, Zip 21229; tel. 410/368–2945; Peter Clay, Senior Vice President Managed Care

ST. AGNES HOME CARE AND HOSPICE, 3421 Benson Avenue, Suite G100, Zip 21227; tel. 410/368–2825; Robin Dowell, Director

**Ellicott City:** ST. AGNES NURSING AND REHABILITATION CENTER, 3000 North Ridge Road, Zip 21043; tel. 410/461–7577; Barbara A. Gustke, R.N., Administrator Extended Care Facility

**Fort George G Meade:** KIMBROUGH ARMY HEALTH CENTER, 2480 Llewellyn Avenue, Zip 20755; tel. 301/677–4171; Colonel Billie J. Mielcarek, Commanding Officer

**Fort Howard:** VETERANS AFFAIRS MARYLAND HEALTH CARE SYSTEM–FORT HOWARD DIVISION, 9600 North Point Road, Zip 21052–9989; tel. 410/477–1800; Patricia Vicari, Director

**Patuxent River:** NAVAL HEALTH CLINIC PATUXENT RIVER, 47149 Buse Road, Zip 20670–5370; tel. 301/342–1418; Commander Romeo Tizon, Director Administration

## MASSACHUSETTS

**Boston:** JOSLIN DIABETES CENTER, One Joslin Place, Zip 02215; tel. 617/732–2400; John L. Brooks, III., President and Chief Executive Officer

**Springfield:** BAY STATE VISITING NURSE ASSOCIATION AND HOSPICE, 50 Maple Street, Zip 01105; tel. 413/781–5070; Ruth Odgren, President

**Turners Falls:** FARREN CARE CENTER, 340 Montague City Road, Zip 01376–9983; tel. 413/774–3111; James Clifford, Administrator

## MICHIGAN

**Big Rapids:** MECOSTA HEALTH SERVICES, 650 Linden Street, Zip 49307; tel. 231/796–3200; Gail Bullard, Director

**Detroit:** ADVANTAGE FAMILY HEALTH CENTER, 4777 East Outer Drive, Zip 48234–0401; tel. 313/369–9100; Sandra Freeman, Vice President

RIVERVIEW URGENT CARE CENTER, 7733 East Jefferson Avenue, Zip 48214–2598; tel. 313/499–4000; Joseph M. Tasse, FACHE, President and Chief Executive Officer

**Port Huron:** MARWOOD MANOR NURSING HOME, 1300 Beard Street, Zip 48060; tel. 818/982–2594; Brian Oberly, Administrator

TRI–HOSPITAL E.M.S., 309 Grand River Street, Zip 48060; tel. 313/985–7115; Ken Cummings, Chief Executive Officer

WILLOW ENTERPRISES, INC., 1221 Pine Grove Avenue, Zip 48060; tel. 313/989–3737; John Liston, President

**Saline:** ST. JOSEPH MERCY SALINE, 400 West Russell Street, Zip 48176–1183; tel. 734/429–1500; Barbara Fielder, Operations Director

**Sault Sainte Marie:** SAULT SAINTE MARIE TRIBAL HEALTH AND HUMAN SERVICES CENTER, 2864 Ashmun Street, Zip 49783; tel. 906/495–5651; Russell Vizina, Division Director Health

**Warren:** HENRY FORD MACOMB HOSPITAL–WARREN CAMPUS, 13355 East Ten Mile Road, Zip 48089–2048; tel. 586/759–7300; Barbara Rossmann, R.N., President and Chief Executive Officer

## MINNESOTA

**Saint Paul:** HEALTHEAST CARE, INC., 1690 University Avenue W, Suite 370, Zip 55104–3729; tel. 651/232–5070

HEALTHEAST HOME CARE, INC., 1700 University Avenue, Zip 55104; tel. 651/232–2800; Catherine Barr, Vice President Home Health

HEALTHEAST MEDICAL RESEARCH INSTITUTE, 559 Capitol Boulevard, Zip 55103; tel. 651/232–2300

## MISSISSIPPI

**Columbus:** U. S. AIR FORCE CLINIC, 201 Independence, Suite 101, Zip 39701–5300; tel. 662/434–2297; Colonel Dave Armstrong, Commander

## MISSOURI

**Independence:** SURGI–CARE CENTER OF INDEPENDENCE, 2311 Redwood Avenue, Zip 64057; tel. 816/373–7995

**Whiteman AFB:** U. S. AIR FORCE CLINIC WHITEMAN, 331 Sijan Avenue, Zip 65305–5001; tel. 660/687–1194; Lieutenant Colonel David Wilmot, USAF, MSC, Administrator

## MONTANA

**Malmstrom AFB:** U. S. AIR FORCE CLINIC, Zip 59402–5300; tel. 406/731–3863; Colonel David L. Doty, Administrator

**Miles City:** VETERANS AFFAIRS MEDICAL CENTER, 210 South Winchester Avenue, Zip 59301–4742; tel. 406/232–3060

## NEBRASKA

**Grand Island:** GRAND ISLAND DIVISION, 2211 North Broadwell Avenue, Zip 68803–2196; tel. 308/382–3660; Gary N. Nugent, Chief Executive Officer

**North Platte:** GREAT PLAINS PHO, INC., P.O. Box 1167, Zip 69103; tel. 308/535–7496; Todd Hlavaty, M.D., Chairman

**Offutt AFB:** EHRLING BERGQUIST HOSPITAL, 2501 Capehart Road, Zip 68113–2160; tel. 402/294–7312; Colonel Howard Googins, Deputy Commander

## NEW HAMPSHIRE

**Portsmouth:** NAVAL MEDICAL CLINIC, Building H–1, Zip 03801; tel. 207/439–1000; Commander Kendra Nowak, Officer–in–Charge

## NEW JERSEY

**Egg Harbor Township:** ATLANTICARE BEHAVIORAL HEALTH, 2511 Fire Road, Suite B10, Zip 08234; tel. 609/272–6392; Julia Drew, Executive Director

ATLANTICARE SURGERY CENTER, 2500 English Creek Avenue, Building 700, Suite 702, Zip 08234–5549; tel. 609/407–2200; James P. Nolan, Jr., Senior Vice President Finance

**Fort Monmouth:** PATTERSON ARMY HEALTH CLINIC, Stephenson Avenue, Building 1075, Zip 07703–5504; tel. 908/532–1266; Colonel Don Speers, Commander

**Jersey City:** ST. FRANCIS HOSPITAL, 25 McWilliams Place, Zip 07302–1698; tel. 201/418–1000

**Millburn:** ATLANTIC HOME CARE AND HOSPICE, 33 Bleeker Street, Zip 07041; tel. 973/379–8400; Susan Quinn, Administrator

**Morristown:** ALLIANCE IMAGING CENTER, 65 Maple Street, Zip 07960; tel. 973/267–5700; Barbara Picorale, Administrator

**Succasunna:** DIALYSIS CENTER OF NORTHWEST NEW JERSEY, 170 Righter Road, Zip 07876; tel. 973/584–1117; Carol Cahill, Administrator

## NEW MEXICO

**Albuquerque:** ALBUQUERQUE IHS HEALTH CENTER, 801 Vassar Drive N.E., Zip 87106–2799; tel. 505/248–4000; Maria Rickert, Chief Executive Officer

**Cannon AFB:** U. S. AIR FORCE CLINIC, 208 West Casablanca Avenue, Zip 88103–5300; tel. 505/784–6318; Lieutenant Colonel Michelle Pufall, Administrator

**Holloman AFB:** U. S. AIR FORCE CLINIC, 280 First Street, Zip 88330–8273; tel. 505/572–5587

**Kirtland AFB:** U. S. AIR FORCE CLINIC–KIRTLAND, 2050 A Second Street S.E., Zip 87117–5559; tel. 505/846–3547; Colonel Regina Aune, Commander

## NEW YORK

**Bronx:** MORRISANIA DIAGNOSTIC AND TREATMENT CENTER, 1225 Gerard Avenue, Zip 10452; tel. 718/960–2777; Victor Hernandez, Administrator

SEGUNDO RUIZ BELVIS DIAGNOSTIC AND TREATMENT CENTER, 545 East 142nd Street, Zip 10454; tel. 718/579–4000; Victor Hernandez, Administrator

**Brooklyn:** CUMBERLAND DIAGNOSTIC AND TREATMENT CENTER, 100 North Portland Avenue, Zip 11205; tel. 718/260–7500; Candis Best, Administrator

DR. SUSAN SMITH NURSING REHABILITATION CENTER, 594 Albany Avenue, Zip 11203; tel. 718/245–7000; Peola Small, Chief Operating Officer

EAST NEW YORK DIAGNOSTIC AND TREATMENT CENTER, 2094 Pitkin Avenue, Zip 11207; tel. 718/240–0400; Yvette Isaac, Administrator

**Buffalo:** MERCY NURSING FACILITY, 565 Abbott Road, Zip 14220; tel. 716/828–2301; Christine Kluckhohn, President, Continuing Care

NAZARETH HOME, 291 West North Street, Zip 14201; tel. 716/881–2323; Christine Kluckhohn, President, Continuing Care

ST. CATHERINE LABOURE, 2157 Main Street, Zip 14214; tel. 716/862–1451; Christine Kluckhohn, President, Continuing Care

ST. FRANCIS OF BUFFALO, 34 Benwood Avenue, Zip 14214; tel. 716/862–2500; Christine Kluckhohn, President, Continuing Care

**Cheektowaga:** MCAULEY SETON HOME CARE, 2875 Union Road, Suite 14, Zip 14227; tel. 716/685–4870; Mark A. Sullivan, President and Senior Administrative Officer

MERCY HOME CARE, 2875 Union Road, Suite 14, Zip 14227; tel. 716/685–4870; Mark A. Sullivan, President and Senior Administrative Officer

**Dunkirk:** ST. VINCENT'S HOME, 319 Washington Avenue, Zip 14048; tel. 716/366–2066; J. Thomas Briody, Senior Vice President Long Term Care and Ambulatory Services

**Fort Drum:** U. S. ARMY MEDICAL DEPARTMENT ACTIVITY, 11050 Mount Belvedere Boulevard, Zip 13602–5004; tel. 315/772–4024; Colonel Mark W. Thompson, MC, Commander

**Kenmore:** MCAULEY RESIDENCE, 1503 Military Road, Zip 14217; tel. 716/447–6600; Christine Kluckhohn, President, Continuing Care

**Lancaster:** ST. ELIZABETH'S HOME, 5539 Broadway, Zip 14086; tel. 716/683–5150; Christine Kluckhohn, President, Continuing Care

**New York:** GOUVERNEUR HOSPITAL, 227 Madison Street, Zip 10002; tel. 212/238–7000; Gregory M. Kaladjian, Executive Director
RENAISSANCE DIAGNOSTIC AND TREATMENT CENTER, 215 West 125 Street, Zip 10027; tel. 212/932–6500; Rose Garcia, Administrator
**Olean:** ST. JOSEPH MANOR, 2211 West State Street, Zip 14760; tel. 716/372–7810; Christine Kluckhohn, President, Continuing Care
**Orchard Park:** FATHER BAKER MANOR, 6400 Powers Road, Zip 14127; tel. 716/667–0001; Christine Kluckhohn, President, Continuing Care
**Staten Island:** SEA VIEW HOSPITAL REHABILITATION CENTER AND HOME, 460 Brielle Avenue, Zip 10314; tel. 212/390–8181; Jane M. Lyons, Executive Director
**Tuckahoe:** HOME NURSING ASSOCIATION OF WESTCHESTER, 69 Main Street, Zip 10707; tel. 919/961–2818; Mary Wehrberger, Director
**Williamsville:** ST. FRANCIS OF WILLIAMSVILLE, 147 Reist Street, Zip 14221; tel. 716/633–5400; Christine Kluckhohn, President, Continuing Care

### NORTH CAROLINA

**Cherry Point:** NAVAL HEALTH CLINIC CHERRY POINT, PSC Box 8023, Zip 28533–0023; tel. 252/466–0266; Lieutenant Commander Tim Barnes, Director Administration
**Jefferson:** AMH SEGRAVES CARE CENTER, 200 Hospital Avenue, Zip 28640; tel. 336/246–7101
**Seymour Johnson AFB:** U. S. AIR FORCE HOSPITAL SEYMOUR JOHNSON, 1050 Curtis Avenue, Zip 27531–5300; tel. 919/722–1812; Colonel Donna M. Lake, Commanding Officer
**Southern Pines:** ST. JOSEPH OF THE PINES HOSPITAL, 590 Central Drive, Zip 28387; tel. 910/246–1000; Ken Cormier, President and Chief Executive Officer
**Wilson:** WILMED NURSING CARE CENTER, 1705 Tarboro Street S.W., Zip 27893–3428; tel. 252/399–8998; Gene Fulcher, Administrator

### NORTH DAKOTA

**Grand Forks AFB:** U. S. AIR FORCE HOSPITAL, 220 G Street, Zip 58205–6332; tel. 701/747–5391
**Minot:** U. S. AIR FORCE REGIONAL HOSPITAL, 10 Missile Avenue, Zip 58705–5024; tel. 701/723–5103; Colonel Lawrence Riddles, Commander

### OHIO

**Cleveland:** KAISER PERMANENTE, 1001 Lakeside, Zip 44114; tel. 216/362–2000; Patricia Kennedy–Scott, President
METROHEALTH CENTER FOR SKILLED NURSING CARE, 4229 Pearl Road, Zip 44109; tel. 216/957–3675; Yvette Bozman, Administrator
**Columbus:** CHALMERS WYLIE VETERANS AFFAIRS AMBULATORY CARE CENTER, 420 North James Road, Zip 43219–1834; tel. 614/257–5200; Lillian T. Thone, Chief Executive Officer
OHIOHEALTH GROUP, 445 Hutchinson Avenue, Suite 300, Zip 43235–5677; tel. 614/566–0123; John Burns, Chief Executive Officer
**Worthington:** HOMEREACH, 404 East Wilson Bridge Road, Suite H., Zip 43085; tel. 614/566–0888; Fran Baby, Vice President Home and Hospice Services

### OKLAHOMA

**Altus:** U. S. AIR FORCE CLINIC ALTUS, 301 North First Street, Zip 73523–5005; tel. 580/481–5204; Colonel Charles W. Cotta, USAF, Commander

**Clinton:** U. S. PUBLIC HEALTH SERVICE INDIAN HOSPITAL, Route 1, Box 3060, Zip 73601–9303; tel. 580/323–2884
**Enid:** U. S. AIR FORCE CLINIC, Vance AFB, Building 810, Zip 73705–5000; tel. 405/249–7494; Lieutenant Colonel Andrew F. Love, MSC, USAF, Commander Medical Group
**Eufaula:** EUFALA INDIAN HEALTH CENTER, 800 Forest Avenue, Zip 74432; tel. 918/689–2547; Shelly Crow, Health System Administrator
**Okmulgee:** OKMULGEE INDIAN HEALTH SYSTEM, 1313 East 20th, Zip 74447; tel. 918/758–1926; Steve Landsberry, Administrator
**Sapulpa:** SAPULPA INDIAN HEALTH CENTER, 1125 East Clevelend, Zip 74066; tel. 918/224–9310
**Tinker AFB:** U. S. AIR FORCE HOSPITAL TINKER, 5700 Arnold Street, Zip 73145; tel. 405/736–2084; Colonel Lloyd A. Reinke, Commander
**Tulsa:** WARREN CLINIC, 6600 South Yale Avenue, Zip 74136; tel. 918/502–7300; James Kaltenbachner, Senior Vice President

### OREGON

**White City:** VETERANS AFFAIRS DOMICILIARY, Zip 97503; tel. 503/826–2111; Frank A. Drake, Director

### PENNSYLVANIA

**Chester:** COMMUNITY HOSPITAL, DIVISION OF THE CROZER–CHESTER MEDICAL CENTER, Ninth and Wilson Streets, Zip 19013–2098; tel. 610/494–0700; Kevin Caputo, M.D., Vice President Operations
**Dallastown:** WELLSPAN MEDICAL GROUP, 757 South Pleasant Avenue, Zip 17313; tel. 717/851–6515
**Warminster:** ABINGTON MEMORIAL HEALTH CENTER – WARMINSTER CAMPUS, 225 Newtown Road, Zip 18974–5221; tel. 215/441–6600; Katie Farrell, Chief Executive Officer
**York:** SOUTH CENTRAL PREFERRED, 45 Monument Road, Suite 200, Zip 17403; tel. 717/741–9511; Charles H. Chodroff, M.D., Executive Director
WELLSPAN HEALTH CARE SERVICES, 1001 South George Street, Zip 17405; tel. 717/851–2121; Bruce M. Bartels, President

### RHODE ISLAND

**Newport:** NAVAL HEALTH CLINIC NEW ENGLAND, 43 Smith Road, Zip 02841–1006; tel. 401/841–3771; Lieutenant Commander Jason Lewis

### SOUTH CAROLINA

**North Charleston:** NAVAL HEALTH CLINIC – CHARLESTON, 3600 Rivers Avenue, Zip 29405; tel. 843/794–6621; Commander Amy Smith, Director Administration
**Shaw AFB:** U. S. AIR FORCE HOSPITAL SHAW, 431 Meadowlark Street, Zip 29152–5019; tel. 803/895–6324; Colonel Troy Molnar, Commander

### SOUTH DAKOTA

**Ellsworth AFB:** U. S. AIR FORCE CLINIC, 2900 Doolittle Drive, Zip 57706–4821; tel. 605/385–3201; Colonel Chris Gray, Commanding Officer

### TEXAS

**Abilene:** U. S. AIR FORCE CLINIC, 697 Hospital Road, Zip 79607–1367; tel. 915/696–5429; Major John G. Wiseman, Administrator

**Corpus Christi:** CORPUS CHRISTI MEDICAL CENTER – NORTHWEST, 13725 Northwest Boulevard, Zip 78410–5199; tel. 361/767–4400; Jay Woodall, Chief Executive Officer
NAVAL HEALTH CLINIC CORPUS CHRISTI, 10651 E Street, Zip 78419–5131; tel. 361/961–2688; Lieutenant Commander Dennis Tolentino
**Dallas:** NAVAL HOSPITAL BRANCH MEDICAL CLINIC, Naval Air Station, Zip 75211–9516; tel. 214/266–6281; Lieutenant Commander Jayson Huber
SURGICARE OF TRAVIS CENTER, INC., 13355 Noel Road, Suite 650, Zip 75240–6694; tel. 713/520–1782
**El Paso:** EL PASO VETERANS AFFAIRS HEALTH CARE SYSTEM, 5001 North Piedras Street, Zip 79930–4211; tel. 915/564–6100; John A. Mendoza, Director
**Houston:** GRAMERCY OUTPATIENT SURGERY CENTER. LTD., 2727 Gramercy, Zip 77025; tel. 713/660–6900; Hamel Patel, Administrator
WEST HOUSTON SURGICARE, 970 Campbell Road, Zip 77024; tel. 713/461–3547
**Laughlin AFB:** U. S. AIR FORCE HOSPITAL, 590 Mitchell Boulevard, Zip 78843–5200; tel. 210/298–6311
**San Antonio:** U. S. AIR FORCE CLINIC BROOKS, Building 615, Zip 78235–5300; tel. 210/536–2087; Lieutenant Colonel Donald Sampson, Commanding Officer
WILFORD HALL AMBULATORY SURGICAL CENTER, 2200 Bergquist Drive, Suite 1, Zip 78236–9908; tel. 210/292–7412; Brigadier General Thomas Travis, Commanding Officer
**Sheppard AFB:** U. S. AIR FORCE REGIONAL HOSPITAL–SHEPPARD, 149 Hart Street, Suite 1, Zip 76311–3478; tel. 940/676–5874; Lieutenant Colonel Lance Rogers, Administrator
**Universal City:** U. S. AIR FORCE CLINIC RANDOLPH, 221 3rd Street West, Zip 78150–4801; tel. 210/652–5701; Lieutenant Colonel Dennis E. Franks, Administrator
**Webster:** BAY AREA SURGICARE CENTER, 502 Medical Center Boulevard, Zip 77598; tel. 281/332–2433; Carol Simons, Administrator

### VIRGINIA

**Fort Eustis:** MCDONALD ARMY HEALTH CENTER, Jefferson Avenue, Zip 23604–5548; tel. 757/314–7501; Colonel Cass Scott, Administrator
**Fort Lee:** KENNER ARMY HEALTH CENTER, 700 24th Street, Zip 23801–1716; tel. 804/734–9256; Colonel Vivian T. Hutson, Commander
**Quantico:** NAVAL HEALTH CLINIC, QUANTICO, 3259 Catlin Avenue, Zip 22134; tel. 703/784–1699; Lieutenant Commander Dawn Freeman, Director Administration

### WASHINGTON

**Fairchild AFB:** U. S. AIR FORCE CLINIC, 701 Hospital Loop, Suite 102, Zip 99011–8701; tel. 509/247–5217; Colonel Barbara Jefts, R.N., MS, Commanding Officer

### WISCONSIN

**Green Bay:** UNITY HOSPICE, P.O. Box 28345, Zip 54324–8345; tel. 920/494–0225; Donald Seibel, Executive Director

### WYOMING

**Cheyenne:** U. S. AIR FORCE HOSPITAL, 6900 Alden Drive, Zip 82005–3913; tel. 307/773–2045; Major Brenda Bullard, Administrator

# Provisional Hospitals

*This listing includes organizations that, as of July 8, 2013, were in the planning or construction stage and that, on completion, will be eligible for Institutional membership. Some hospitals are granted provisional membership for reasons related to other Association requirements. Hospitals classified as provisional members for reasons other than being under construction are indicated by a bullet ( ● ).*

## CALIFORNIA

**Ontario:** ONTARIO MEDICAL CENTER, 2295 South Vineyard Avenue, Zip 91761–7925; tel. 909/724–5000; Greg Christian, Executive Director

## FLORIDA

**Kissimmee:** POINCIANA MEDICAL CENTER, 325 Cypress Parkway, Zip 34758; tel. 800/447–8206; Joanna J. Conley, FACHE, Chief Executive Officer

## INDIANA

**Fishers:** ST. VINCENT FISHERS HOSPITAL, 13861 Olio Road, Zip 46037; tel. 317/415–9048; Gary Fammartino, Administrator

## TEXAS

**College Station:** SCOTT & WHITE HOSPITAL – COLLEGE STATION, 700 Scott & White Drive, Zip 77845; tel. 800/299–1212; Jason Jennings, Chief Executive Officer

**Marble Falls:** WAYNE & EILEEN HURD REGIONAL MEDICAL CENTER – SCOTT & WHITE, U.S. 281 and Highway 71, Zip 78654; tel. 830/598–1204; Kevin Leeper, Chief Executive Officer

## Ambulatory Centers and Home Care Agencies

### United States

#### NEW HAMPSHIRE

DARTMOUTH COLLEGE HEALTH SERVICE, 7 Rope Ferry Road, Hanover, Zip 03755–1421; tel. 603/650–1400; John H. Turco, M.D., Director

#### PENNSYLVANIA

WILLS EYE HOSPITAL, 840 Walnut Street, Philadelphia, Zip 19107–5109; tel. 215/928–3000; Joseph P. Bilson, Executive Director

## Blue Cross Plans

### United States

#### ARIZONA

BLUE CROSS AND BLUE SHIELD OF ARIZONA, Box 13466, Phoenix, Zip 85002–3466; tel. 602/864–4541; Vishu Jhaveri, M.D., Senior Vice President and Chief Medical Officer

#### PENNSYLVANIA

HIGHMARK BLUE CROSS BLUE SHIELD, 120 Fifth Avenue Place, Suite 3014, Pittsburgh, Zip 15222; tel. 412/544–7646; Sandra R. Tomlinson, Senior Vice President, Provider Services

# Other Members

## UNITED STATES

### Architecture:

DEVENNEY GROUP ARCHITECTS, 201 West Indian School Road, Phoenix, Arizona Zip 85013–3203; tel. 602/943–8950; Julie Barkenbush, Chief Executive Officer; www.devenneygroup.com

EARL SWENSSON ASSOCIATES, INC., 2100 West End Avenue, Suite 1200, Nashville, Tennessee Zip 37203; tel. 615/329–9445; Richard L. Miller, President; www.esarch.com

HDR ARCHITECTURE, INC., 8404 Indian Hills Drive, Omaha, Nebraska Zip 68114; tel. 402/399–1000; Doug Wignall, Executive Vice President; www.hdrinc.com

MATTHEI AND COLIN ASSOCIATES, 332 South Michigan Avenue, Suite 614, Chicago, Illinois Zip 60604; tel. 312/939–4002; Ronald G. Kobold, Managing Partner

MESSER CONSTRUCTION COMPANY, 5158 Fishwick Drive, Cincinnati, Ohio Zip 45216; tel. 513/242–1541; Tiffany Witham, Director Marketing; www.messer.com

MMC CONTRACTORS, 4717 F. Street, Omaha, Nebraska Zip 68117–1404; tel. 402/861–0681; Patrick Ryan, Senior Project Manager; www.mmcontractors.com

PERKINS & WILL, INC., 617 West Seventh Street, Suite 1200, Los Angeles, California Zip 90017–3830; tel. 312/755–0770; Timothy Pettigrew, Associate, Healthcare Knowledge Coordinator; www.perkinswill.com

RLF, 4750 New Broad Street, Orlando, Florida Zip 32814–6422; tel. 407/647–1039; Vincent Della Donna, Senior Healthcare Architect; www.rlfae.com

SMITHGROUP, INC., 301 Battery Street, San Francisco, California Zip 94104–4250; tel. 415/227–0100; James T. Hannon, Senior Vice President; www.sf.smithgroup.com

STANTEC, 400 Morgan Center, 101 East Diamond Street, Butler, Pennsylvania Zip 16001–5977; tel. 724/285–4761; Bruce Knepper, Vice President; www.burthill.com

### Bank:

**BANK OF AMERICA, 101 South Tryon Street, Charlotte, North Carolina Zip 28255–0001; tel. 704/388–2255; Gayle Higaki, Senior Vice President; www.bankofamerica.com**

WELLS FARGO SECURITIES, 230 West Monroe Street, Chicago, Illinois Zip 60606–4703; tel. 312/845–9779; Philip J. Kaplan, Vice President; www.wellsfargo.com

### Communication Systems Org:

**AT & T, 1010 Wilshire Boulevard, Room 1240, Los Angeles, California Zip 90017; tel. 805/648–2463; Deborah Sunday, Director Product Marketing Management**

AVAILITY, LLC, 740 East Campbell Road, Suite 1000, Richardson, Texas Zip 75081–1886; tel. 904/470–4984; Andrea Overman, Director, Marketing; www.availity.com

BECKER'S HOSPITAL REVIEW, 315 Vernon Avenue, Glencoe, Illinois Zip 60022–2136; tel. 800/417–2035; Scott Becker, Publisher; www.beckersasc.com

**COOPER SIGNAGE & GRAPHICS, INC., 2405 Lance Court, Loganville, Georgia Zip 30052–4613; tel. 800/297–2324; Randy R. Cooper, President; www.sinsystems.org**

### Construction Firm:

KBR BUILDING GROUP, 10 Cadillac Drive, Suite 460, Brentwood, Tennessee Zip 37027–5096; tel. 615/742–6610; Michael Pierle, Executive Vice President

### Consulting Firm:

**ACUSTAF SOFTWARE, 7601 France Avenue, Suite 575, Edina, Minnesota Zip 55435–5968; tel. 952/831–4122; Terry Suby, President; www.acustafsoftware.com**

ARAMARK, 1101 Market Street, Philadelphia, Pennsylvania Zip 19107–2988; tel. 215/238–4054; Anthony C. Stanowski, Vice President Industrial Relations; www.aramark.com

ATHENA HEALTH, 1500 Urban Center Drive, Suite 500, Birmingham, Alabama Zip 35242–2566; tel. 205/970–3330; Jerry C. Smith, Vice President Finance; www.athenahealth.com

BEST DOCTORS, INC., 100 Federal Street, 21st Floor, Boston, Massachusetts Zip 02110–1802; tel. 617/426–3666; Ryan Schoenecker, Vice President Business Development; www.bestdoctors.com

**BMGI, 1200 17th Street, Suite 180, Denver, Colorado Zip 80202–5815; tel. 303/827–0010; Scott McAllister, Senior Performance Excellence Consultant; www.bmgi.com/default.aspx**

**BOXWOOD TECHNOLOGY, INC, 11350 McCormick Road, Suite 101, Hunt Valley, Maryland Zip 21031; tel. 888/491–8833; John Bell, Chairman; www.boxwoodtech.com**

**BURWOOD GROUP, INC., 125 South Wacker Drive, Suite 2950, Chicago, Illinois Zip 60602; tel. 312/327–4600; Mark Theoharous, President; www.burwood.com**

**CARE TECH SOLUTIONS, 901 Wilshire Drive, Suite 100, Troy, Michigan Zip 48084; tel. 248/823–9000; Colleen Hanley, Vice President, Marketing, Communications and Government Affairs; www.caretech.com**

CAREMEDIC, 800 Carillon Parkway, Suite 250, Saint Petersburg, Florida Zip 33716; tel. 727/329–7838; Richard Nelli, Vice President Product and Solution Management; www.caremedic.com

CODING P.I., 161 Thunder Drive #212, Vista, California Zip 92083–6016; tel. 780/941–7309; Deniene Vivas, Chief Coding Officer; www.codingpi.com

CONIFER HEALTH SOLUTIONS, 2401 Internet Boulevard, Suite 201, Frisco, Texas Zip 75034–5977; tel. 972/335–6120; Vanessa Harris, Senior Market Research Specialist; www.coniferhealth.com

**COPYRIGHT CLEARANCE CENTER, 222 Rosewood Drive, Danvers, Massachusetts Zip 01923–4520; tel. 978/646–2633; Stephanie Fox, Alliances Director; www.copyright.com**

**DEVELOPMENT DIMENSIONS INTERNATIONAL, 1225 Washington Pike, Bridgeville, Pennsylvania Zip 15017–2838; tel. 412/257–3623; Colby Fazio, Marketing Consultant; www.ddiworld.com**

**DIXON HUGHES GOODMAN, 102 First Street, Suite 201, Hudson, Ohio Zip 44236–5386; tel. 330/650–1752; Jim Yanci, Principal; www.dhgllp.com**

**DRAEGER, 3135 Quarry Road, Telford, Pennsylvania Zip 18969–1042; tel. 215/660–2310; Susan Thornton, Senior Marketing Manager, Information Technology Solutions; www.draeger.com**

**ECLIPSYS, 76 Batterson Park Road, Farmington, Connecticut Zip 06032; tel. 860/246–3000; Marvin S. Goldwasser, Vice President Product Marketing, Patient Flow and Performance Management; www.eclipsys.com**

ELSEVIER, INC., 245 Peachtree Center Avenue, N.E., Atlanta, Georgia Zip 30303–1222; tel. 314/447–8000; Azelia Cutts, Marketing Operations Coordinator; www.clinicaldecisionsupport.com

ERDMAN, P.O. Box 44975, Madison, Wisconsin Zip 53744–4975; tel. 608/410–8000; Molly Hamm, Research Librarian; www.erdman.com

ERNST & YOUNG, 41 South High Street, Columbus, Ohio Zip 43215–6101; tel. 949/437–0220; Jonathan G. Weaver, Partner

ERNST & YOUNG, 5 Times Square, 14th Floor, New York, New York Zip 10036–6530; tel. 212/773–3000; Frank Bresz, Senior Manager; www.ey.com/global/content.nsf/us/home

**EXECUTIVE HEALTH RESOURCES, INC., 15 Campus Boulevard, Suite 200, Newtown Square, Pennsylvania Zip 19073; tel. 610/446–6100; Thomas Mercer, President and Chief Executive Officer; www.ehrdocs.com**

FIDELITY INVESTMENTS, 100 Magellan Way, Mail Zone KW23, Covington, Kentucky Zip 41015–1987; tel. 859/386–3117; John Campbell, Manager; www.fmr.com

**GETWELLNETWORK, INC., 7920 Norfolk Avenue, 11th Floor, Bethesda, Maryland Zip 20814–2500; tel. 240/482–3200; Michael B. O'Neil, Jr., President and Chief Executive Officer; www.getwellnetwork.com**

**GLOBAL HEALTHCARE EXCHANGE, LLC, 1315 West Century Drive, Louisville, Colorado Zip 80027–9560; tel. 720/887–7000; www.ghx.com**

GOLDMAN, SACHS AND COMPANY, 200 West Street, New York, New York Zip 10282–2198; Calla Frett, Director

GREAT AMERICAN INSURANCE GROUP, 301 East 4th Street, 21st Floor North, Cincinnati, Ohio Zip 45202–4201; tel. 513/763–6165; Merita Sohn, Marketing Manager; www.greatamericaninsurance.com

**H. R. S. INTERNATIONAL, 25 East Washington, 6th Floor, Chicago, Illinois Zip 60602; tel. 312/236–7770; Carrie Parks, Marketing Specialist; www.hrsolutions.com**

HEALTH IT PLUS, 131 Elden Street, Suite 200, Herndon, Virginia Zip 20170–4876; tel. 301/977–7884; Richard Blickenstaff, Senior Sales Associate; www.healthitplus.com

HEALTHPORT, 925 North Point Parkway, Alpharetta, Georgia Zip 30005–5210; tel. 770/360–1700; Catherine Valyi, Vice President Marketing; www.healthport.com

INTEGRATED HEALTHCARE STRATEGIES, tel. 612/339–0919; Julie McCauley, Senior Vice President, Corporate; www.ihstrategies.com

**INTERWOVEN, 160 East Tasman Drive, San Jose, California Zip 95134; tel. 408/774–2000; Joe Cowan, Chief Executive Officer and Director; www.interwoven.com**

IPROTEAN, LLC, 12255 El Camino Real, Suite 300, San Diego, California Zip 92130–4087; tel. 800/771–9490; Gordon R. Clark, President and Chief Executive Officer; www.iprotean.com

**KAUFMAN HALL, 5202 Old Orchard Road, Suite N700, Skokie, Illinois Zip 60077; tel. 847/441–8780; Jason H. Sussman, Partner; www.kaufmanhall.com**

**KROLL ONTRACK, INC., 18350 Mount Langley Street, Suite 110, Fountain Valley, California Zip 92708; tel. 800/872–2599; Stacey May, Manager; www.krollontrack.com**

KURT SALMON ASSOCIATES, 1355 Peachtree Street N.E., Suite 900, Atlanta, Georgia Zip 30309–0900; tel. 404/892–0321; Wendi B. Farris, Administrative Assistant; www.kurtsalmon.com

LATHAM AND WATKINS, LLP, 633 West 5th Street, Suite 4000, Los Angeles, California Zip 90071; tel. 213/485–1234; Daniel K. Settelmayer, Partner; www.lw.com

**LEXISNEXIS, 1000 Alderman Drive, Alpharetta, Georgia Zip 30005; tel. 404/577–1779; Sarah J. Stansberry, Senior Director, Marketing; www.lexisnexis.com**

**LIVEPROCESS, 271 Grove Avenue, Building D., Verona, New Jersey Zip 07044; tel. 973/571–2500; Nathaniel Weiss, Chief Executive Officer; www.liveprocess.com**

**MARITZ, INC., 1375 North Highway Drive, Fenton, Missouri Zip 63099; tel. 636/827–4000; Amy Kramer, Healthcare Section Strategist; www.maritz.com**

MCDONALD HOPKINS, LLC, 600 Superior Avenue East, Suite 2100, Cleveland, Ohio Zip 44114–2690; tel. 216/348–5400; Richard S. Cooper, Member; www.mcdonaldhopkins.com

MCKESSON PROVIDER TECHNOLOGIES, 5995 Windward Parkway, Alpharetta, Georgia Zip 30005; tel. 404/338–3519; Jocelyn B. Green, Legal Assistant

**MEDASSETS, 100 North Pointe Center East, Suite 200, Alpharetta, Georgia Zip 30022–1506; tel. 678/323–2790; John Bardis, Chairman and Chief Executive Officer; www.medassets.com**

**MEDICAL SIMULATION CORPORATION, 4643 South Ulster Street, Suite 650, Denver, Colorado Zip 80237–2964; tel. 888/889–5882; Amy Wedeking Shannon, Vice President Business and Strategic Market Development; www.medsimulation.com**

**MOSS ADAMS LLP, 999 3rd Avenue, Suite 3300, Seattle, Washington Zip 98104–4002; tel. 206/302–6800; Meg Tronquet, Marketing Coordinator; www.mossadams.com**

**NAVEX GLOBAL, 6000 Meadows Road, Suite 200, Lake Oswego, Oregon Zip 97035–3172; tel. 503/924–1640; Stephen J. Molen, Vice President Strategic Solutions; www.navexglobal.com**

NES ASSOCIATES, LLC, 6363 Walker Lane, Suite 130, Alexandria, Virginia Zip 22310–3261; tel. 703/224–2607; Mark Rose, Director Healthcare Programs; www.nesassociates.com

NORTH AMERICAN PARTNERS IN ANESTHESIA, 68 South Service Road, Suite 350, Melville, New York Zip 11747–2358; tel. 516/945–3000; Jill Aaronson, Marketing Coordinator; www.napaanesthesia.com

**NVOQ, 1715 38th Street, Boulder, Colorado Zip 80301–2603; tel. 720/562–4500; Charles Corfield, Chief Executive Officer; www.mvoq.com**

O.C. TANNER COMPANY, 1930 South State Street, Salt Lake City, Utah Zip 84115–2311; tel. 801/493–3310; Cordell Clinger, Manager Exhibits; www.octanner.com

OPPENHEIMER MULTIFAMILY HOUSING AND HEALTHCARE FINANCE, 1180 Welsh Road, Suite 210, North Wales, Pennsylvania Zip 19454–2057; tel. 215/631–9151; Thomas P. Cassidy, Associate Vice President; www.opcomortgagefinance.com

**PACKETMOTION, INC., 260 Santa Ana Court, Sunnyvale, California Zip 94085–4512; tel. 408/449–4300; Ravi Khatod, Senior Vice President, Sales and Business Development; www.packetmotion.com**

**PEER CONSULTING, 2856 80Th Avenue S.E., Suite 200, Mercer Island, Washington Zip 98040–2984; tel. 206/236–1300; Rick Nunn, Senior Managing Partner; www.peerconsulting.net**

PHYSICIAN WELLNESS SERVICES, 5000 West 36th Street, Suite 230, Minneapolis, Minnesota Zip 55416–2771; tel. 877/731–3949; Lori Brostrom, Vice President Marketing; www.physicianwellnessservices.com

**PREMIERE GLOBAL SERVICES, 3280 Peachtree Road N.W., Suite 1000, Atlanta, Georgia Zip 30305–2422; tel. 404/543–9449; Mark H. Horne, Vice President Marketing, Notifications and Reminders; www.premiereglobal.com**

**PRESS GANEY ASSOCIATES, INC., 404 Columbia Place, South Bend, Indiana Zip 46601–2315; tel. 800/232–8032; Kathryn Ryan, Marketing Director; www.pressganey.com**

PROFESSIONAL RESEARCH CONSULTANTS, INC., 11326 P. Street, Omaha, Nebraska Zip 68137–2316; tel. 800/428–7455; Janna Binder, Director Marketing and Public Relations; www.prconline.com

PUBLIC FINANCIAL MANAGEMENT, INC., 99 Summer Street, Suite 1020, Boston, Massachusetts Zip 02110–1200; tel. 617/330–6914; Christine Doyle, Managing Director; www.pfm.com

QUAMMEN HEALTH CARE CONSULTANTS, 522B Brandies Circle, Suite 4, Murfreesboro, Tennessee Zip 37128–4873; tel. 407/539–2015; Robecca Quammen, President; www.quammengroup.com

RYCAN, P.O. Box 306, Marshall, Minnesota Zip 56258–0306; tel. 800/201–3324; Marg Louwagie, Administrative Assistant; www.rycan.com

**SAMUELI INSTITUTE, 1737 King Street, Suite 600, Alexandria, Virginia Zip 22314–2764; tel. 703/299–4800; Bonnie R. Sakallaris, Vice President Optimal Healing Environments; www.siib.org**

SHERIDAN HEALTHCARE, INC., 1613 North Harrison Parkway, Suite 200, Sunrise, Florida Zip 33323–2853; tel. 954/838–2749; Terri Burgess, Director Operations, Business Development; www.sheridanhealthcare.com

**SIEMENS HEALTHCARE, 51 Valley Stream Parkway, Malvern, Pennsylvania Zip 19355; tel. 610/448–4500; Barbara Sivek, Senior Director Industry Relations; www.medical.siemens.com**

SODEXO HEALTH CARE, 86 Hopmeadow Street, Simsbury, Connecticut Zip 06089; tel. 860/325–1220; Shirley Palmieri, Director Creative Services; www.sodexo.com

SOYRING CONSULTING, 880 21st Avenue North, Saint Petersburg, Florida Zip 33704; tel. 727/822–8774; Adam Higman, Consultant; www.soyringconsulting.com

SPECIALTYCARE, 3100 West End Avenue, Suite 800, Nashville, Tennessee Zip 37203; tel. 615/345–5400; Nancy R. Becker, Director Corporate Services and Product Development; www.specialtycare.net

**STOCKAMP AND ASSOCIATES, INC., 6000 S.W. Meadows Road, Suite 300, Lake Oswego, Oregon Zip 97035; tel. 503/303–1200; Karen Andrews, Senior Marketing Manager; www.stockamp.com**

STRATFORD FIDELITY, 901 Marquette Avenue, Suite 2200, Minneapolis, Minnesota Zip 55402–3721; tel. 877/815–6366; Gary D. Aden, Senior Vice President; www.stratfordfidelity.com

STROUDWATER ASSOCIATES, 50 Sewall Street, Suite 102, Portland, Maine Zip 04102–2646; tel. 207/221–8255; Marc Voyvodich, Chief Executive Officer

SULLIVAN, COTTER AND ASSOCIATES, INC., 1100 Peachtree Street, Suite 620, Atlanta, Georgia Zip 30309; tel. 678/551–7190; Maureen Cotter, Director Research and Information; www.sullivancotter.com

SURGICAL CARE AFFILIATES, 3000 Galleria Boulevard, Suite 500, Birmingham, Alabama Zip 35244; tel. 205/545–2759; Julie Dunn, Vice President; www.scasurgery.com

**SURGICAL INFORMATION SYSTEMS, 11605 Haynes Bridge Road, Alpharetta, Georgia Zip 30004; tel. 678/507–1706; Kelly R. Pinkerton, Manager Marketing; www.sisfirst.com**

**SYSCOM SERVICES, INC, 1010 Wayne Avenue, Suite 320, Silver Spring, Maryland Zip 20910; tel. 301/768–0118; Lee Weinstein, President; www.syscomservices.com**

**TESTSOURCE, 4344 Plainfield Avenue N.E., Grand Rapids, Michigan Zip 49525; tel. 800/691–3737; Mark Wiersma, President; www.testsource.com**

THE CHARTIS GROUP, 220 West Kinzie Street, Chicago, Illinois Zip 60654; tel. 312/260–2000; Randall Thorne, Director Firm Development; www.chartis.com

THE HSM GROUP, LTD, 8777 East Via de Ventura #188, Scottsdale, Arizona Zip 85258; tel. 480/947–8078; Sheryl Bronkesh, President; www.hsmgroup.com

THE JACKSON GROUP, INC., 219 1st Avenue S.W., Hickory, North Carolina Zip 28602–2922; tel. 828/328–8968; Alan Jackson, President; www.thejacksongroup.com

**THE STUDER GROUP, 8222 Douglas Avenue, Suite 780, Dallas, Texas Zip 75225–5923; tel. 972/860–0551; B. G. Porter, Chief Executive Officer and President; www.studergroup.com**

TIAA CREF, 8500 Andrew Carnegie Boulevard, B208, Charlotte, North Carolina Zip 28262–8500; tel. 704/988–8064; Kevin S. Nazworth, Vice President Healthcare Market; www.tiaa-cref.org

**VECNA TECHNOLOGIES, INC., 36 Cambridgepark Drive, Cambridge, Massachusetts Zip 02140; tel. 617/864–0636; Amanda Baldi, Director, Marketing and Communications; www.vecna.com**

VENDOR CREDENTIALING SERVICE, INC., 616 Cypress Creek Parkway, Suite 800, Houston, Texas Zip 77090–3029; tel. 281/863–9500; Troy Kyle, President and Chief Executive Officer; www.vcsdatabase.com

**VERITY, INC, 5758 West Las Positas Boulevard, Suite 100, Pleasanton, California Zip 94588; tel. 925/598–3003; Michael Pliner, President; www.verity.com**

**WASTE MANAGEMENT, 1001 Fannin St. Suite 4000, Houston, Texas Zip 77002–6711; tel. 713/265–1352; Bill Turpin, Director Strategic Development**

WESTERN HEALTHCARE ALLIANCE, tel. 970/683–5223; Carolyn S. Bruce, Chief Executive Officer; www.wha1.org

XANITOS, INC., 3809 West Chester Pike, Suite 210, Newtown Square, Pennsylvania Zip 19073–2304; tel. 484/654–2300; Graeme A. Crothall, Chairman and Chief Executive Officer; www.xanitos.com

### Educational Services:

NATIONAL RURAL HEALTH RESOURCE CENTER, 600 East Superior Street, Suite 404, Duluth, Minnesota Zip 55802; tel. 218/727–9390; Terry J. Hill, Executive Director; www.ruralcenter.org

**RAYTHEON PROFESSIONAL SERVICES, 870 Winter Street, Waltham, Massachusetts Zip 02451–1449; tel. 781/522–3000; Dave Letts, Vice President and General Manager; www.raytheon.com**

### Information Systems:

**3M HEALTH INFORMATION SYSTEMS, 575 West Murray Boulevard, Murray, Utah Zip 84123–4611; tel. 801/265–4390; Ann Chenoweth, Senior Director, Industry Relations; www.mmm.com**

**ALLSCRIPTS, 3 Ravinia Drive, Suite 1100, Atlanta, Georgia Zip 30346–2134; tel. 800/654–0889; Shari A. Cox, Director, Strategic Programs**

CERNER CORPORATION, 2800 Rockcreek Parkway, Kansas City, Missouri Zip 64117; tel. 816/221–1024; Brandon Most, Manager; www.cerner.com

**DESIGN CLINICALS, 5200 Southcenter Boulevard, Suite 250, Seattle, Washington Zip 98188–7911; tel. 888/633–7320; Dewey Howell, Chief Executive Officer; www.designclinicals.com**

**HEALTHLAND, 1600 Utica Avenue South, Suite 300, Minneapolis, Minnesota Zip 55416–1468; tel. 612/787–3120; Tracey Schroeder, Vice President Marketing**

**IMPRIVATA, INC., 10 Maguire Road Building 4, Lexington, Massachusetts Zip 02421–3110; tel. 781/674–2700; Ed Gaudel, Chief Marketing Officer; www.imprivata.com**

**KPMG LLP, AON Center, 200 East Randolph Street, Suite 5500, Chicago, Illinois Zip 60601–6607; tel. 312/665–2073; Edward J. Giniat, National Line of Business Leader, Healthcare and Pharmaceuticals Practice**

**SCC SOFT COMPUTER, 5400 Tech Data Drive, Clearwater, Florida Zip 33760–3116; tel. 727/789–0100; Gilbert Hakim, Chief Executive Officer; www.softcomputer.com**

**SHIFTWISE, 1800 S.W. 1st Avenue, Suite 510, Portland, Oregon Zip 97201; tel. 503/548–2030; Nick Haselwander, Marketing Manager; www.shiftwise.com**

**VALENCE HEALTH, 600 West Jackson Boulevard, Chicago, Illinois Zip 60661–5636; tel. 312/273–6623; Kevin Weinstein, Chief Marketing Officer; www.valencehealth.com**

### Insurance Broker:

**AMERICAN FIDELITY ASSURANCE COMPANY, 2000 North Classen Boulevard, Oklahoma City, Oklahoma Zip 73106; tel. 877/967–5748; Brian Mauck, National Sales Director; www.af-group.com**

**BOSTON MUTUAL LIFE INSURANCE COMPANY, 120 Royall Street, Canton, Massachusetts Zip 02021; tel. 781/828–7000; Peter Tillson, Vice President; www.bostonmutual.com**

CHUBB INSURANCE, P.O. Box 2002, Simsbury, Connecticut Zip 06070; tel. 860/408–2017; Kimberly Holmes, Assistant Vice President Healthcare; www.chubb.com

DYE & ESKIN, 1324 Vincent Place, Mc Lean, Virginia Zip 22101; tel. 703/556–0744; Rick Eskin, President

G. E. FINANCIAL, GE Appliance Park Building, Suite 100, Louisville, Kentucky Zip 40225; tel. 502/254–1756; Greg Miller, Director Business Development; www.ge.com

ING EMPLOYEE BENEFITS, 20 Washington Avenue South, Minneapolis, Minnesota Zip 55401; tel. 612/372–1122; Steve Pitzer, Vice President

ISR CONSULTING GROUP, 695 Trade Center Boulevard, Suite 110, Chesterfield, Missouri Zip 63005–1276; tel. 636/530–4606; Jeffrey A. Combs, Executive Vice President; www.isricg.com

**LOYAL INSURANCE, 423 Westport Road, Suite 201, Kansas City, Missouri Zip 64111; tel. 816/841–3597; Michael Reidy, Vice President**

*The members listed in* **bold** *are Associate Advantage members.*

MEDICAL PROTECTIVE, 5814 Reed Road, Fort Wayne, Indiana Zip 46835; tel. 260/486–0814; Bruce Whitmore, Hospital and Facilities Sales Leader; www.medpro.com

MESIROW FINANCIAL, 353 North Clark Street, Chicago, Illinois Zip 60654–4704; tel. 312/595–7183; Sheila Kelly, Senior Managing Director; www.mesirowfinancial.com

NEBCO, 1264 Knollwood Drive West, West Chester, Pennsylvania Zip 19380; tel. 877/739–3330; James M. Mattison, Vice President; www.nebenefit.com

THE ALLEN J. FLOOD COMPANIES, INC., 2 Madison Avenue, Larchmont, New York Zip 10538; tel. 914/834–9326; Allen J. Flood, President; www.ajfusa.com

UNITED CONCORDIA COMPANY, INC., 4401 Deer Path Road, Harrisburg, Pennsylvania Zip 17110; tel. 717/260–6800; Brett Altland, Product Development Analyst; www.ucci.com

VALIC, 2929 Allen Parkway (L6–40), Houston, Texas Zip 77019–2111; tel. 713/831–6128; Nicole Mott, Associate Director Marketing; www.valic.com

ZURICH INSURANCE GROUP, tel. 312/496–9418; Daniel R. Nash, National Healthcare Practice Leader; www.zurichna.com/healthcare

## Managed Care/Utilization:

CENTENE CORPORATION, 111 East Capitol Street, Suite 500, Jackson, Mississippi Zip 39201; tel. 601/863–0835; K. Michael Bailey, Vice President; www.centene.com

## Manufacturer/Supplier:

AMERISOURCE BERGEN, 1300 Morris Drive, Chesterbrook, Pennsylvania Zip 19087–5559; tel. 610/727–2441; Claire Biermaas, Manager Market Development; www.amerisourcebergen.com

BAXTER HEALTHCARE CORPORATION, Route 120 and Wilson Road, Round Lake, Illinois Zip 60073; tel. 847/270–5440; Tom Progar, Vice President Marketing Strategy and Operations; www.baxter.com

DIOMEDIX, 178 East Ninth Street, Saint Paul, Minnesota Zip 55101; tel. 651/762–4010; Lyndsay Toensing, Director of Marketing Communications and Events; www.biomedix.com

BOSTON SCIENTIFIC, 100 Boston Scientific Way, Marlborough, Massachusetts Zip 01752–1234; tel. 508/683–4000; David Wilson, Senior Manager Health Economics and Reimbursement; www.bostonscientific.com

CARDINAL HEALTH, 2215 Citygate Drive, Columbus, Ohio Zip 43219–3589; tel. 614/757–5000; Seham Yennes, Vice President, Marketing Acute; www.cardinal.com

CARDINAL HEALTH MEDICAL DEVICE DIVISION, 7000 Cardinal Place, Dublin, Ohio Zip 43017–1091; tel. 614/553–4526; Lisa Ashby, President, Medical Devices and Diagnostics; www.cardinalhealth.com

CAREFUSION CORPORATION, 3750 Torrey View Court, San Diego, California Zip 92130–2622; tel. 858/617–2000; Jocelyn Ochinang, Senior Associate, Market Research; www.carefusion.com

EXTENSION, INC, 6435 West Jefferson Boulevard, Suite 201, Fort Wayne, Indiana Zip 46804–6203; tel. 877/207–3753; Whitney St. Pierre, Director Marketing; www.opentheredbox.com

GE HEALTHCARE, 3000 North Grandview Boulevard, Waukesha, Wisconsin Zip 53188; tel. 262/312–7915; Patrick Connolly, Information Management and Strategy Manager; www.gehealthcare.com

HILL–ROM, 1069 State Route 46 East, Batesville, Indiana Zip 47006–9167; tel. 812/934–7958; Thomas J. Jeffers, Director Government Relations; www.hill-rom.com

JOHNSON & JOHNSON, 829 Williamsburg Boulevard, Downingtown, Pennsylvania Zip 19335–4124; tel. 610/518–7295; Larry Westfall, Director Healthcare Quality Alliances

LILLY USA, LLC, Lilly Corporate Center–DC 5021, Indianapolis, Indiana Zip 46285–4113; tel. 317/277–8173; John H. Poulin, Advisor Professional Relations; www.lilly.com

MEDICAL INTERACTIVE COMMUNITY, One Galleria Boulevard, Suite 700, Metairie, Louisiana Zip 70001–2082; tel. 855/464–7475; Dawer A. Azizi, Vice President Operations; www.medicalinteractive.com

MEDTRONIC, INC., 8200 Coral Sea Street N.E. MV522, Mounds View, Minnesota Zip 55112–4391; tel. 763/526–2947; Stephanie Waite, Administrative Assistant; www.medtronic.com

OTSUKA AMERICA PHARMACEUTICAL, INC., 2440 Research Boulevard, Rockville, Maryland Zip 20850; tel. 301/990–0030; Jennifer Greaney, Director; www.otsuka.com

RICOH AMERICAS CORPORATION, 70 Valley Stream Parkway, Malvern, Pennsylvania Zip 19355–1407; tel. 610/722–1429; Michael Campana, Senior Manager Healthcare Marketing; www.ricoh–usa.com

SWISSLOG HEALTHCARE SOLUTIONS, 10825 East 47th Avenue, Denver, Colorado Zip 80239–2913; tel. 800/764–0300; Marion M. Robinson, Vice President Marketing; www.swisslog.com

UMF CORPORATION, 4709 Golf Road, Suite 300A, Skokie, Illinois Zip 60076–1231; tel. 847/920–0370; Red Degala, Director Finance; www.perfectclean.com

WAKO DIAGNOSTICS, 1025 Terra Bella Avenue, Suite A., Mountain View, California Zip 94043–1829; tel. 650/210–9153; Audrey Long, Director, Marketing

## Metro Hospital Assn:

HOSPITAL ASSOCIATION OF SOUTHERN CALIFORNIA, 515 South Figueroa Street, Suite 1300, Los Angeles, California Zip 90071–3300; tel. 213/538–0700; James D. Barber, President; www.hasc.org

## National Health Care Prof Assn:

NATIONAL ASSOCIATION FOR HEALTHCARE QUALITY, 4700 West Lake Avenue, Glenview, Illinois Zip 60025–1468; tel. 847/375–4867; Stacy Sochacki, Executive Director

## Other:

3N, 505 North Brand Boulevard, Suite 700, Glendale, California Zip 91203; tel. 818/230–9728; Steve Kirchmeier, Vice President Healthcare; www.3nonline.com

ACCRETIVE HEALTH, 401 North Michigan Avenue, Suite 2700, Chicago, Illinois Zip 60611–4255, tel. 312/324–5477; Joseph Evans, Manager; www.accretivehealth.com

AEROSCOUT, 1300 Island Drive, Suite 202, Redwood City, California Zip 94065; tel. 650/596–2994; Gabi Daniely, Vice President Marketing and Product Strategy; www.aeroscout.com

AG MEDICAL SYSTEMS, INC., 13 Prosper Court, Lake In The Hills, Illinois Zip 60156–9603; tel. 800/262–2344; Denise Hammer, Manager, Marketing Business Development

AGILITY RECOVERY SOLUTIONS, 11030 Circle Point Road, Suite 450, Westminster, Colorado Zip 80020–2791; tel. 877/495–9615; Jenny Boyd, Director Marketing Account; www.agilityrecovery.com

AIR METHODS CORPORATION, 7301 South Peoria Street, Englewood, Colorado Zip 80112–4133; tel. 303/792–7565; Ryan Frazier, Senior Advisor to the Chief Executive Officer Strategic Relations; www.airmethods.com

AMERICA'S BLOOD CENTERS, 725 15th Street N.W., Suite 700, Washington, District of Columbia Zip 20005; tel. 202/393–5725; William M. Coenen, Interim Chief Executive Officer

AMERICAN ACADEMY OF PHYSICIAN ASSISTANTS, 2318 Mill Road, Suite 1300, Alexandria, Virginia Zip 22314–6833; tel. 703/836–2272; Jennifer L. Dorn, Chief Executive Officer; www.aapa.org

AMERICAN ASSOCIATION FOR WOUND CARE MANAGEMENT, 4109 Glenrose Street, Kensington, Maryland Zip 20895–3718; tel. 301/933–2200; Jule Crider, Executive Director; www.aawcm.org

AMERICAN ASSOCIATION OF NURSE ANESTHETISTS, 222 South Prospect Avenue, Park Ridge, Illinois Zip 60068–4001; tel. 847/655–1100; Wanda O. Wilson, Executive Director and Chief Executive Officer; www.aana.org

AMERICAN BOARD OF MEDICAL SPECIALTIES, 222 North La Salle Street, Suite 1500, Chicago, Illinois Zip 60601–1003; tel. 847/491–9091; Kevin B. Weiss, President and Chief Executive Officer; www.abms.org

AMERICAN COLLEGE OF HEALTHCARE EXECUTIVES, One North Franklin, Suite 1700, Chicago, Illinois Zip 60606–4425; tel. 312/424–2800; Deborah Bowen, President and Chief Executive Officer; www.ache.org

AMERICAN DENTAL EDUCATION ASSOCIATION, 1400 K Street N.W., Suite 1100, Washington, District of Columbia Zip 20005; tel. 202/289–7201; Richard Valachovic, Executive Director; www.adea.org

AMERICAN HEALTH INFORMATION MANAGEMENT ASSOCIATION, 233 North Michigan Avenue, Suite 2150, Chicago, Illinois Zip 60601–5806; tel. 312/233–1100; David A. Sweet, Director Library Services

AMERINET, 500 Commonwealth Drive, Warrendale, Pennsylvania Zip 15086–7516; tel. 877/711–5700; Laurie McGrath, Vice President Marketing; www.amerinet–gpo.com

AMN HEALTHCARE, INC., 12400 High Bluff Drive, Suite 100, San Diego, California Zip 92130–3581; tel. 866/871–8519; Steve Wehn, Senior Vice President of Corporate Development

ANTHELIO HEALTHCARE SOLUTIONS INC, tel. 214/257–7000; Mary Gael Senko, Brand Manager; www.antheliohealth.com

APOGEE PHYSICIANS, 2525 East Camelback Road, Suite 1100, Phoenix, Arizona Zip 85016–4282; tel. 602/778–3600; Michael Gregory, Chairman; www.apogeephysicians.com

ARC GROUP ASSOCIATES, 330 South Warminster Road, Suite 345, Hatboro, Pennsylvania Zip 19040; tel. 215/881–9500; Eric Malakoff, Vice President Sales and Marketing; www.arcgroup.net

ARMED FORCES INSTITUTE OF PATHOLOGY, 6825 16th Street N.W., Building 54, Washington, District of Columbia Zip 20306–6000; tel. 202/782–2100; Colonel Renata Greenspan, Director; www.afip.osd.mil

ASSOCIATION OF PERIOPERATIVE REGISTERED NURSES, 2170 South Parker Road, Suite 400, Denver, Colorado Zip 80231; tel. 303/755–6304; Linda Kay Groah, Executive Director and Chief Executive Officer; www.aorn.org

AVATAR HR SOLUTIONS, 25 East Washington Street, Suite 600, Chicago, Illinois Zip 60602; tel. 312/236–7170; Kevin Sheridan, Senior Vice President – HR Optimization; www.hrsolutionsinc.com

BERNARD HODES GROUP, 220 East 42nd Street, 14th Floor, New York, New York Zip 10017; tel. 888/438–9911; Karen Hart, Senior Vice President Healthcare Division; www.hodes.com

BEST UPON REQUEST, 8170 Corporate Park Drive, Suite 300, Cincinnati, Ohio Zip 45242; tel. 513/605–7800; Kirsten Lecky, Vice President Business Development; www.bestuponrequest.com

BKD, LLP, P.O. Box 1190, Springfield, Missouri Zip 65801–1900; tel. 417/831–7283; Shelbey Stockton, Marketing and Business Development; www.bkd.com

BLUE CROSS AND BLUE SHIELD ASSOCIATION, 225 North Michigan Avenue, Chicago, Illinois Zip 60601–7680; tel. 312/297–6000; Scott P. Serota, President and Chief Executive Officer; www.bcbs.com

BUREAU OF MEDICINE AND SURGERY, DEPARTMENT OF THE NAVY, 2300 East Street N.W., Washington, District of Columbia Zip 20372–5300; tel. 202/762–3701; Vice Admiral Matthew L. Nathan, Surgeon General

CANON BUSINESS SOLUTIONS, 300 Commerce Square Boulevard, Burlington, New Jersey Zip 08016–1270; tel. 847/706–3411; Paul T. Murphy, Director Strategic Contract Support; www.solutions.canon.com

CAP SITE INC., 85 South Prospect Street, Burlington, Vermont Zip 05401–3444; tel. 802/383–0675; Gino Johnson, Senior Vice President; www.capsite.com

CARETECH SOLUTIONS, INC., tel. 248/823–0800; Paula Gwyn, Senior Manager Business Development; www.caretechsolutions.com

CCM ADVISORS, LLC, 190 South La Salle Street, Suite 2800, Chicago, Illinois Zip 60603; tel. 312/444–6200; Michael Randall, Director Sales and Marketing; www.ahafunds.org

CERTIPHI SCREENING, INC., 1105 Industrial Highway, Southampton, Pennsylvania Zip 18966; tel. 888/260–1370; Tony D'Orazio, President; www.certiphi.com

CHAN HEALTHCARE AUDITORS, 231 South Bemiston Avenue, Suite 300, Saint Louis, Missouri Zip 63105; tel. 314/802–2008; Dan Clayton, Director, Knowledge Management; www.chanllc.com

CISCO SYSTEMS, 165 Needletree Lane, Glastonbury, Connecticut Zip 06033; tel. 860/657–8127; Michael Haymaker, Director Healthcare Industry Marketing; www.cisco.com

CLAREDI CORPORATION, 2525 Lake Park Boulevard, Salt Lake City, Utah Zip 84120; tel. 801/982–3001; Kepa Zubeldia, Senior Vice President; www.claredi.com

COMPUTER ASSOCIATES, One Computer Associates Plaza, Islandia, New York Zip 11749; tel. 800/225–5224; Michael McDermand, Vice President Healthcare; www.ca.com

CONCUITY, INCORPORATED, 200 North Fairway Drive Suite 182, Vernon Hills, Illinois Zip 60061–1861; tel. 847/465–6003; James Farrar, Vice President Sales; www.concuity.com

COVENANT HOSPICE, 5041 North 12th Avenue, Pensacola, Florida Zip 32504; tel. 850/433–2155; Dale O. Knee, President and Chief Executive Officer; www.covenanthospice.org

CRANEWARE, INC., 3340 Peachtree Road N.E. Suite 850, Atlanta, Georgia Zip 30326–1072; tel. 404/364–2037; Ann Marie Brown, Executive Vice President Marketing; www.craneware.com

CUSHMAN & WAKEFIELD, 107 Elm Street, 4 Stamford Plaza, 8th Floor, Stamford, Connecticut Zip 06902–3834; tel. 203/326–5829; Alina Schoepfer, Market Analysis Specialist; www.cushwake.com

CYRACOM, 5780 North Swan Road, Tucson, Arizona Zip 85718–4527; tel. 800/713–4950; Jeremy Woan, President and Chief Executive Officer; www.cyracom.com

DELPHI TECHNOLOGY, INC., tel. 617/259–1200; Bonnie Clark, Vice President Marketing; www.delphi-tech.com

DEPARTMENT OF AIR FORCE MEDICAL SERVICE, HQ USAF/SG, Bolling AFB, District of Columbia Zip 20332–6188; tel. 202/545–6700

DEPARTMENT OF THE ARMY, OFFICE OF THE SURGEON GENERAL, 5109 Leesburg Pike, Falls Church, Virginia Zip 22041–3258; tel. 202/690–6467

DHHS, PUBLIC HEALTH SERVICE, INDIAN HEALTH SERVICE, DIVISION OF BUSINESS OFFICE ENHANCEMENT, 12300 Twinbrook Parkway, Suite 360–57, Rockville, Maryland Zip 20852; tel. 301/443–0227; Frank Martin, Management Analyst; www.ihs.gov

DILIGENT, A DIVISION OF ARJO, 2349 West Lake Street, Suite 250, Addison, Illinois Zip 60101–6183; tel. 800/323–1245; Andrew Hepburn, Vice President; www.arjohuntleigh.com

DNV HEALTHCARE, INC., 400 Techne Center Drive, Suite 350, Milford, Ohio Zip 45150–2792; tel. 513/388–4863; Beverly J. Eller, Manager Business Operations; www.dnvhealthcareinc.com

EKTRON, INC., 542 Amherst Street, Nashua, New Hampshire Zip 03063–1016; tel. 603/594–0249; Richard Brown, Director Channel, Alliances and Healthcare; www.ektron.com

EMERGENCY CONSULTANTS, INC., 4075 Copper Ridge Drive, Traverse City, Michigan Zip 49684–4796; tel. 800/253–1795; James Johnson, President; www.eci-med.com

FIRST AMERICAN EQUIPMENT FINANCE, 255 Woodcliff Drive, Fairport, New York Zip 14450–4219; tel. 585/643–3266; Mike Wiedemer, Senior Vice President, Sales; www.faef.com

FTI HEALTHCARE, 5310 Maryland Way, Suite 250, Brentwood, Tennessee Zip 37027–5370; tel. 615/324–8500; Iain Briggs, Senior Managing Director; www.ftihealthcare.com

FUOCO GROUP, 200 Parkway Drive South, Suite 302, Hauppauge, New York Zip 11788–2024; tel. 631/360–1700; Lou J. Fuoco, Managing Director; www.fuoco.com

HEALTH PARK HOSPITALITY, 181 South Northwest Highway, Barrington, Illinois Zip 60010–4607; tel. 847/842–8366; Dominic Chiovari, President and Chief Executive Officer

HEALTHCARE BUSINESS ASSOCIATES, P.O. Box 1188, Rancho Mirage, California Zip 92270–1188; tel. 888/292–6929; Jack C. Nixon, President

HIPAA ACADEMY, 14225 University Avenue, Suite 240, Waukee, Iowa Zip 50263; tel. 515/453–8247; Lorna L. Waggoner, Director Business Development

HMS, 355 Quartermaster Court, Jeffersonville, Indiana Zip 47130–3670; tel. 812/704–5747; Rich Flaherty, Vice President Sales and Marketing; www.hms.com

HOOPER, LUNDY & BOOKMAN, INC., 1875 Century Park East, Suite 1600, Los Angeles, California Zip 90067; tel. 310/551–8111; Lloyd Bookman, Partner; www.health-law.com

HQ ACC/SGMS, 162 Dodd, Suite 100, Langley AFB, Virginia Zip 23665–1995

HQ AETC/SGAL, 63 Main Circle, Suite 3, Randolph AFB, Texas Zip 78150–4549

HQ AFMC/SGAR, 4225 Logistics Avenue, N–209, Dayton, Ohio Zip 45433–5761; tel. 937/656–3655; Alice Rohrbach

HQ AFSPC/SGAL, 150 Vandenberg Street, Suite 1105, Petterson AFB, Colorado Zip 80914–4550

HQ AMC/SGSL, 203 West Losey Street, Room 1180, Scott AFB, Illinois Zip 62225–5219

HQ PACAF/SGAL, 25 East Street, Suite D1, Hickam AFB, Hawaii Zip 96853–5418

HQ USAFA/SGAL, Pinion Drive, Building 4102, Suite 3, USAF Academy, Colorado Zip 80840

HYLAND SOFTWARE, INC., 28500 Clemens Road, Westlake, Ohio Zip 44145; tel. 440/788–5814; Michael Kortan, Director Health Care Solutions; www.onbase.com

I.D. EXPERTS, 10300 S.W. Greenburg Road, Suite 570, Portland, Oregon Zip 97223–5410; tel. 866/726–4271; Sally Gray, Manager Sales Support; www.idexpertcorp.com

IDENTITY FORCE, 1257 Worcester Road, Suite 308, Framingham, Massachusetts Zip 01701; tel. 508/788–6660; Mike Lawson, Vice President; www.identityforce.com

INNOVATIVE CAPITAL LLC, 1489 Baltimore Pike Building 400, Springfield, Pennsylvania Zip 19064–3958; tel. 610/543–2490; Alan P. Richman, President and Chief Executive Officer; www.innovativecapital.com

INTERACTIVE HEALTH SOLUTIONS, 3800 North Wilke Road, Suite 155, Arlington Heights, Illinois Zip 60004–1278; tel. 847/754–2698; Joseph O'Brien, President; www.interactivesolutions.com

INTERNATIONAL ASSOCIATION FOR HEALTHCARE SECURITY AND SAFETY, P.O. Box 5038, Glendale Heights, Illinois Zip 60139; tel. 630/529–3913; Nancy Felesena, Executive Assistant; www.iahss.org

IPC THE HOSPITALIST COMPANY, INC., 4605 Lankershim Boulevard, Suite 617, North Hollywood, California Zip 91602–1818; tel. 818/766–3502; Todd J. Kislak, Vice President Marketing and Development; www.hospitalist.com

IRONPORT, 950 Elm Avenue, San Bruno, California Zip 94066; tel. 650/989–6500; Jeff Williams, Vice President Sales; www.ironport.com

JANI-KING, 16885 Dallas Parkway, Addison, Texas Zip 75001; tel. 972/991–0900; Bob Carabajal, Director Healthcare Services; www.janiking.com

JEWISH GUILD HEALTHCARE, 15 West 65th Street, New York, New York Zip 10023; tel. 212/769–6200; Alan R. Morse, President and Chief Executive Officer; www.jgb.org

LIFE LINE SCREENING, 6150 Oak Tree Boulevard, Suite 200, Independence, Ohio Zip 44131–2569; tel. 800/897–9177; Kellie D. Privette, Senior Vice President; www.lifelinescreening.com

LITTLER MENDELSON, P.C., 1100 Superior Avenue, 20th Floor, Cleveland, Ohio Zip 44114–2530; tel. 216/623–6104; Angela Lupardus, Manager, Regional Business Development and Marketing; www.littler.com

LODGENET INTERACTIVE CORPORATION, 3900 West Innovation Street, Sioux Falls, South Dakota Zip 57107; tel. 605/988–1418; Stacy Forsch, Administrative Assistant II; www.lodgenet.com

MAGELLAN HEALTH SERVICES, 6950 Columbia Gateway Drive, Columbia, Maryland Zip 21046; tel. 314/387–4000; Rick Lee, President Employer Solutions; www.magellanhealth.com

MEDIMPACT HEALTHCARE SYSTEMS, INC, 10680 Treena Street, San Diego, California Zip 92128; tel. 858/566–2727; Dana Felthouse, Vice President Marketing; www.medimpact.com

MEDQUIST TRANSCRIPTIONS LTD, 9009 Carothers Parkway, Suite C–2, Franklin, Tennessee Zip 37067–1704; tel. 615/798–6000; Michael Zinn, Manager Sales and Marketing Support Center; www.medquist.com

METLIFE RESOURCES, 300 Davidson Avenue, Somerset, New Jersey Zip 08873–4162; tel. 732/652–1268; Anthony Agentowicz, Divisional Marketing Director; www.metlife.com

MODERN HEALTHCARE, 360 North Michigan Avenue, Chicago, Illinois Zip 60601–3806; tel. 312/649–5491; Fawn Lopez, Publisher; www.modernhealthcare.com

MRI INTERNATIONAL, INC./CLAIMS SERVICING OF AMERICA, 5330 South Durango Drive, Las Vegas, Nevada Zip 89113–1835; tel. 702/396–8822; Linda Martinez

NATIONAL GIFT CARD CORPORATION, 600 Church Road, Elgin, Illinois Zip 60123–9340; tel. 847/792–2276; Lizz Wheeler, Business Development Director; www.ngc–group.com

NAVAL REGIONAL MEDICAL CENTER, PSC 1005, Box 36, FPO, Armed Forces Africa, Canada, E Zip 09593–0136

NOBLIS, 3150 Fairview Park South, Falls Church, Virginia Zip 22042; tel. 703/610–2255; Alan Dowling, Executive Director; www.mitretek.org

PERKINELMER GENETICS, INC., P.O. Box 219, Bridgeville, Pennsylvania Zip 15017; tel. 412/220–2300; Joseph M. Quashnock, Laboratory Director; www.perkinelmergenetics.com

PILAT, 460 U.S. Highway 22 West Suite 408, Whitehouse Station, New Jersey Zip 08889–3447; tel. 908/823–9417; Travis Lupo, Director Business Development; www.pilat-nai.com

PINSTRIPE, 200 South Executive Drive, Suite 400, Brookfield, Wisconsin Zip 53005–4216; tel. 262/754–5061; Jill Schwieters, Executive Vice President; www.pinstripetalent.com

PRICEWATERHOUSE COOPERS, 300 Madison Avenue, New York, New York Zip 10017–6232; tel. 813/348–7457; Betty Croft, Senior Manager Business Information Services; www.pwc.com

QUADRAMED CORPORATION, 12110 Sunset Hills Road, Suite 600, Reston, Virginia Zip 20190; tel. 800/393–0278; Laura Adams, Director Manager; www.quadramed.com

RF TECHNOLOGIES, 3125 North 126th Street, Brookfield, Wisconsin Zip 53005; tel. 800/669–9946; Glenn Jonas, President and Chief Executive Officer; www.rft.com

ROSARIO INCORPORATED, 501 Burwood Drive, Winston Salem, North Carolina Zip 27127; tel. 866/279–8485; Sandra R. Rosario, Director/Owner; www.rosarioinc.com

SHIPMAN & GOODWIN LLP, One Constitution Plaza, Hartford, Connecticut Zip 06103–1919; tel. 860/251–5056; Joan W. Feldman, Partner

SIMPLEX GRINNELL, 50 Technology Drive, Westminster, Massachusetts Zip 01441; tel. 978/731–8486; Suzanne Rahall, Marketing Manager, Healthcare Communications; www.simplexgrinnell.com

ST. LOUIS EYE SURGERY, 12990 Manchester Road, Suite 103, Saint Louis, Missouri Zip 63131–1860; tel. 314/686–4220; Melanie Kofron, Administrator

SUBWAY, 325 Bic Drive, Milford, Connecticut Zip 06461; tel. 800/888–4848; Joanne Kilgore, Global Account Manager; www.subway.com

TANDBERG, 29 Norfolk Avenue, Peabody, Massachusetts Zip 01960; tel. 978/531–1516; Luke Leininger, Senior Product Manager, Healthcare TelePresence; www.tandberg.com

THE ADVISORY BOARD COMPANY, 2445 M Street N.W., Washington, District of Columbia Zip 20037–2403; tel. 202/266–5600; Britton Perry, Associate Director, Information Resource Center; www.advisory.com

THE AMERICAN COLLEGE OF OBSTETRICIANS AND GYNECOLOGISTS, 409 12th Street, S.W., Washington, District of Columbia Zip 20024–2188; tel. 202/638–5577; Hal Lawrence, Executive Vice President; www.acog.org

THE WALKER COMPANY, 4848 Hastings Drive, Lake Oswego, Oregon Zip 97035; tel. 503/534–9461; Larry W. Walker, Principal; www.walkercompany.com

THEREX, INC., 341 Cool Springs Boulevard, Franklin, Tennessee Zip 37067; tel. 615/236–2550; Michael G. Skiera, President and Chief Executive Officer; www.therex.us

THERMO USCS, 120 Bishop's Way, Brookfield, Wisconsin Zip 53008; tel. 262/784–5600; Christine Miller, Executive Vice President Healthcare Group; www.thermo.com

TRANSAMERICA RETIREMENT SOLUTIONS, 4 Manhattanville Road, Purchase, New York Zip 10577; tel. 914/697–8952; Peter Kunkel, President and Chief Executive Officer; www.https://www.trsretire.com

TRANSUNION, LLC, 445 Hutchinson Avenue, Suite 800, Columbus, Ohio Zip 43235; tel. 614/785–6411; Martin Callahan, Vice President Business Development; www.transunion.com

TRAVELERS INSURANCE COMPANY, One Tower Square, Hartford, Connecticut Zip 06183–1134; tel. 860/277–9830; Wayne Tryon, Director Business Development; www.travelers.com

*The members listed in **bold** are Associate Advantage members.* © 2013 AHA Guide

U. S. ARMY MEDICAL COMMAND, 2050 Worth Road, Suite 10, San Antonio, Texas Zip 78234–6010; tel. 210/221–2212; Ann Russell Potter

UNIFORM DATA SYSTEM FOR MEDICAL REHABILITATION, 270 Northpointe Parkway, Suite 300, Amherst, New York Zip 14228; tel. 716/817–7800; Beth Demakos, Associate Product Manager; www.udsmr.org

**VERGE SOLUTIONS, LLC, 710 Johnnie Dodds Boulevard, Suite 202, Mount Pleasant, South Carolina Zip 29464–3045; tel. 843/628–4168; Katie Layman, Marketing Manager; www.verge–solutions.com**

**VERISYS CORPORATION, 1001 North Fairfax Avenue, Suite 640, Alexandria, Virginia Zip 22314–1798; tel. 703/535–1471; John Benson, Chief Operating Officer; www.verisys.com/**

**VERSUS TECHNOLOGY, INC., 2600 Miller Creek Road, Traverse City, Michigan Zip 49684; tel. 231/946–5868; Stephanie Bertschy, Director Marketing; www.versustech.com**

**VERTICAL CLAIMS MANAGEMENT, L.L.C., Three Gateway Center, 15 North, Pittsburgh, Pennsylvania Zip 15222; tel. 800/501–6248; Clare Bello, President; www.vcm–llc.com**

**VOCERA COMMUNICATIONS, 525 Race Street, Suite 150, San Jose, California Zip 95126–3495; tel. 408/882–5100; Diana Cropley, Marketing Program Specialist; www.vocera.com**

**WALGREENS HEALTH SERVICES, 1411 Lake Cook Road, MS L414, Deerfield, Illinois Zip 60015; tel. 847/374–2640; Marlin Hutchens, Marketing Vice President; www.walgreens.com**

**WESTERN LITIGATION, INC, 9821 Katy Freeway, Suite 600, Houston, Texas Zip 77024–1206; tel. 800/588–0619; Robert B. Blasio, President and Chief Executive Officer; www.westernlitigation.com**

WIGGIN AND DANA, LLP, P.O. Box 1832, New Haven, Connecticut Zip 06508–1832; tel. 203/498–4400; Maureen Weaver, Partner

XEROX BUSINESS SERVICES, LLC, 2828 North Haskell Avenue, Dallas, Texas Zip 75204–2909; tel. 214/584–5408; Andrea Cohen, Manager, Marketing and Communications, Healthcare Provider Solutions; www.acs–hcs.com

### Recruitment Services:

**B. E. SMITH, 8801 Renner Avenue, Lenexa, Kansas Zip 66219–9746; tel. 913/752–4533; Allison Murphy, Marketing Manager; www.besmith.com**

DOCCAFE.COM, tel. 715/302–8881; Laura Fitzsimmons, Managing Member; www.doccafe.com

**FURST GROUP, 2902 McFarland Road, Rockford, Illinois Zip 61107–6801; tel. 800/642–9940; Patrick Kampert, Director of Communications; www.furstgroup.com**

UNITED ANESTHESIA, P.O. Box 1847, Kernersville, North Carolina Zip 27285–1847; tel. 800/334–8320; Tracy Strother–Mayer, Chief Operating Officer; www.unitedanesthesia.com

### Regional Health Care Assn:

TEXAS ORGANIZATION OF RURAL & COMMUNITY HOSPITALS, P.O. Box 14547, Austin, Texas Zip 78761; tel. 512/873–0045; David Pearson, President and Chief Executive Officer; www.torchnet.org

## CANADA

### Consulting Firm:

IMPARK, 601 West Cordova Street, Suite 300, Vancouver, British Columbia Zip V6B 1G1; tel. 604/331–7216; Jeffrey Powell, Coordinator Marketing; www.impark.com

**RL SOLUTIONS, INC., 1 Yonge Street, Suite 2300, Toronto, Ontario Zip M5E 1E5; tel. 416/410–8456; Sanjay Malaviya, President and CEO; www.rl–solutions.com**

### Other:

**HALOGEN SOFTWARE CORPORATION, 495 March Road, Suite 500, Ottawa, Ontario Zip K2K 3G1; tel. 613/270–1011; Lorna Daly, Channel Manager Healthcare; www.halogensoftware.com**

INTERNATIONAL MEDICAL INTERPRETERS ASSOCIATION, 80 Corporatate Drive, Suite 305, Toronto, Zip M1H 3G5; tel. 416/296–0842; Izabel Arocha, Executive Director; www.imiaweb.org

### Provincial Hospital Assn:

ONTARIO HOSPITAL ASSOCIATION, 200 Front Street West, Suite 2800, Toronto, Ontario Zip M5V 3L1; tel. 416/205–1300; Warren Di Clemente, Vice President Educational Services and Operations; www.oha.com

## FOREIGN

## ALBANIA

### Other:

AMERICAN HOSPITAL, Rruga Lord Bayron – Laprake, Tirane, Zip 10026; tel. 003/235–7535; Klodian Allaybeu, Chief Executive Officer; www.spitaliamerikan.com/index2.php

## BAHAMAS

### Other:

PRINCESS MARGARET HOSPITAL, P.O. Box N–8200, Nassau, tel. 242/322–2861; Coralie Adderley, Chief Hospital Administrator; www.phabahamas.org

## BAHRAIN

### Other:

INTERNATIONAL HOSPITAL OF BAHRAIN, P.O. Box 1084, Manama, F. S. Zeerah, President

## BANGLADESH

### Consulting Firm:

U. S. BANGLADESH FOUNDATION, House 32, Road 10, Block D., Banani, Dhaka, Zip 1213; tel. 880/881–3070; Mohammad Zahurul Haque, Chief Executive Officer; www.banglasoy.com/usbdf.htm

## BERMUDA

### Other:

KING EDWARD VII MEMORIAL HOSPITAL, P.O. Box HM1023, Hamilton, L. Keitha Bassett, Health Sciences Librarian

## BRAZIL

### Other:

HOSPITAL SAMARITANO, Rua Conselheiro Brotero, 1486, Sao Paulo, Zip 01232–010; Jose Antonio de Lima, General Superintendent; www.samaritano.com.br

## COLOMBIA

### Other:

ASOCIACION COLOMBIANA DE HOSPITALES Y CLINICAS, Carrera 4, No 73–15, Bogota, Juan Carlos Giraldo Valencia, Director General; www.achc.org.co

## ECUADOR

### Other:

JUNTA DE BENEFICENCIA DE GUAYAQUIL, P.O. Box 09–01–789, Guayaquil, Lautaro Aspiazu Wright, Director; www.jbg.org.ec

## GEORGIA

### Other:

ARCHANGEL ST. MICHAEL MULTIPROFILE CLINICAL HOSPITAL, 21 Lubliana Street, Tbilisi, Zip 0159; tel. 995/295–1100; Anna Rekhviashvili, Professor and Cardiologist

MEDI CLUB GEORGIA, 22A, Tashkenti Street, Tbilisi, Zip 0160; tel. 995/225–1991; Dimitri Makhatadze, General Director; www.mediclubgeorgia.ge

## GERMANY

### Other:

HQ USAFE/SGPXL, Unit 3050, Box 130, Ramstein AB, Armed Forces Africa, Canada, E Zip 09094–5001

## GREECE

### Other:

DIAGNOSTIC AND THERAPEUTIC CENTRE OF ATHENS HYGEIA, S A, 4 Erythrou Stavrou & Kifissiap, Athens, Andreas Kartapanis, General Manager

## ISRAEL

### Other:

HADASSAH MEDICAL ORGANIZATION, Box 12000, Jerusalem, Zip 91120; Ehud Kokia, Director General; www.hadassah.org.il

## JAPAN

### Other:

KAMEDA MEDICAL CENTER AND CLINICS, 929 Higashi–Cho, Kamogawa City, Zip 296–8602; John C. Wocher, Executive Vice President; www.kameda.com

ST. LUKE'S INTERNATIONAL HOSPITAL, 10–1 Akashi–Cho, Chuo–Ku, Tokyo 104, Shigeaki Hinohara, Honorary President

U.S. NAVAL HOSPITAL OKINAWA, U.S. Naval Base, FPO,
Armed Forces Pacific Zip 96362; tel. 011/743–7555;
Commander Martin Kerr;
www.med.navy.mil/sites/nhoki/Pages/default.aspx

## JORDAN

**Other:**

SPECIALTY HOSPITAL, P.O. Box 930186, Amman,
Zip 11193; Fawzi Al–Hammouri, General Manager;
www.specialty–hospital.com

## LEBANON

**Other:**

AMERICAN UNIVERSITY OF BEIRUT MEDICAL CENTER, 3 Dag
Hammarskjold Plaza, 8th Floor, New York, New York
Zip 10017–2303; Munthir Kuzayli, Medical Center
Director

SAINT GEORGE HOSPITAL UNIVERSITY MEDICAL CENTER,
P.O. Box 166378, Beirut, Zip 1100–2807; Ziad Kamel,
Administrative Director; www.stgeorgehospital.org

## MEXICO

**Other:**

SHRINERS HOSPITAL FOR CHILDREN, Av Del Iman 257, Col
Pedregal de Santa Ursula, Delegacion Coyoacan,
Mexico City, Zip 04600; Araceli Nagore, Administrator

## MYANMAR

**Other:**

ASIA ROYAL GENERAL HOSPITAL, 14 Baho Street,
Sanchaung Township, Yangon, Zip 11162;
tel. 951/153–8055; Myat Thu, Managing Director;
www.asiaroyalmedical.com

## NETHERLANDS ANTILLES

**Other:**

SINT MAARTEN MEDICAL CENTER FOUNDATION, Welgelegen
Road 30 Ut 1 Cay Hill, Sint Maarten,
tel. 599/543–1111; George Scot, General Director

## PANAMA

**Other:**

CLINICA HOSPITAL SAN FERNANDO, S. A., Dept PTY 1663,
P.O. Box 25207, Miami, Florida Zip 33102–5207;
tel. 507/305–6399; Edgardo Fernandez, Medical
Director; www.hospitalsanfernando.com

## PERU

**Hospital:**

SANNA HEALTHCARE NETWORK, Av. Aurelio Miro Quesada
1030, San Isidro, Zip Lima; tel. 950/922–2555;
Santiago Rivera, Chief Executive Officer; www.sanna.pe

**Other:**

BRITISH AMERICAN HOSPITAL, Avenue Alfredo Salazar 3 Era,
Lima 27, tel. 511/712–3000; Gonzalo Garrido–Lecca,
Director; www.angloamericana.com.pe

## PHILIPPINES

**Ambulatory Care Center:**

DEPARTMENT OF VETERANS AFFAIRS, OUTPATIENT CLINIC,
Pasay City, APO, Zip 96440; tel. 632/833–4566;
Artemio Arugay, Commander; www.va.gov

**Other:**

ST. LUKE'S MEDICAL CENTER, 279 East Rodriguez Sr
Boulevard, Quezon City, Jose F. G. Ledesma, Chief
Executive Officer

## SAUDI ARABIA

**Other:**

ABDUL RAHMAN AL MISHARI GENERAL HOSPITAL, Olaya,
Riyadh 11564, Abdul Rahman Al Mishari, President

AL HAMMADI HOSPITAL, P.O. Box 55004, Riyadh,
Zip 11534; Mohammed Al Hammadi, Executive Director

MUHAMMAD SALEH BASHARAHIL HOSPITAL, P.O. Box
10505, Madinah Road, Omora Gadida, Makkah,
tel. 009/520–4444; Turki M. Basharahil, General
Manager

## SIERRA LEONE

**Other:**

HANDS OF CHARITY RURAL HOME BASE HOSPITAL, 52th
Freetown Road, Babdorie Lumley, Freetown,
tel. 002/912–3424; Kingibomeh Nyandoeboh, Director
and Founder

## TURKEY

**Other:**

ANADOLU MEDICAL CENTER, Cumhuriyet Mahallesi 2255
Sokak Gebze, Kocaeli, Zip 41400; Robert Gerard Kiely,
President and Chief Executive Officer;
www.anadolusaglik.org

ISTANBUL MEMORIAL HOSPITAL, Piyale Pasa Bulvari,
Okmeydani, Istanbul, Zip 80270; Sevin Suekinci,
Assistant Medical Director and Coordinator Quality

MEDICANA INTERNATIONAL ANKARA HOSPITAL, Sogutozu
Caddesi 2165 Sokak No. 6, Ankara, Zip 06520;
tel. 905/749–0384; Oguz Engiz, Chief Executive
Officer; www.medicana.com

## UNITED ARAB EMIRATES

**Other:**

AMERICAN HOSPITAL–DUBAI, P.O. Box 59, Dubai, Saeed M.
Almulla, Chairman

　*The members listed in **bold** are Associate Advantage members.*　© 2013 AHA Guide

# Notes

# Notes

# Notes

# Notes

# Notes

# Notes

# Notes

# Notes

# Notes

# Notes

# Health Care Systems

# B

## Health Care Systems, Networks and Alliances

Section B

This section includes listings for networks, health care systems and alliances.

## Health Care Systems

To reflect the diversity that exists among health care organizations, this publication uses the term health care system to identify both multihospital and diversified single hospital systems.

### Multihospital Systems

A multihospital health care system is two or more hospitals owned, leased, sponsored, or contract managed by a central organization.

### Single Hospital Systems

Single, freestanding member hospitals may be categorized as health care systems by bringing into membership three or more, and at least 25 percent, of their owned or leased non–hospital preacute and postacute health care organizations. (For purposes of definition, health care delivery is the availability of professional healthcare staff during all hours of the organization's operations). Organizations provide, or provide and finance, diagnostic, therapeutic, and/or consultative patient or client services that normally precede or follow acute, inpatient, hospitalization; or that serve to prevent or substitute for such hospitalization. These services are provided in either a freestanding facility not eligible for licensure as a hospital under state statue or through one that is a subsidiary of a hospital.

The first part of this section is an alphabetical list of health care systems which are listed under the system by state. Data for this section were compiled from the 2012 *Annual Survey* and the membership information base as published in section A of the *AHA Guide*.

One of the following codes appears after the name of each system listed to indicate the type of organizational control reported by that system:

| | |
|---|---|
| **CC** | Catholic (Roman) church–related system, not–for–profit |
| **CO** | Other church–related system, not–for–profit |
| **NP** | Other not–for–profit system, including nonfederal, governmental systems |
| **IO** | Investor–owned, for profit system |
| **FG** | Federal Government |

One of the following codes appears after the name of each hospital to indicate how that hospital is related to the system:

| | |
|---|---|
| **O** | Owned |
| **L** | Leased |
| **S** | Sponsored |
| **CM** | Contract–managed |

## Health System Classification System

An identification system for Health Systems was developed jointly by the American Hospital Association's Health Research and Education Trust and Health Forum, and the University of California-Berkeley.[1] A health system is assigned to one of five categories based on how much they differentiate and centralized their hospital services, physician arrangements, and provider-based insurance products. Differentiation refers to the number of different products or services that the organization offers. Centralization refers to whether decision-making and service delivery emanate from the system level more so than individual hospitals.

## Categories:

*Centralized Health System:* A delivery system in which the system centrally organizes individual hospital service delivery, physician arrangements, and insurance product development. The number of different products/services that are offered across the system is moderate.

*Centralized Physician/Insurance Health System:* A delivery system with highly centralized physician arrangements and insurance product development. Within this group, hospital services are relatively decentralized with individual hospitals having discretion over the array of services they offer. The number of different products/services that are offered across the system is moderate.

*Moderately Centralized Health System:* A delivery system that is distinguished by the presence of both centralized and decentralized activity for hospital services, physician arrangements, and insurance product development. For example, a system within this group may have centralized care of expensive, high technology services, such as open heart surgery, but allows individual hospitals to provide an array of other health services based on local needs. The number of different products/services that are offered across the system is moderate.

*Decentralized Health System:* A delivery system with a high degree of decentralized of hospital services, physician arrangements, and insurance product development. Within this group, systems may lack an overarching structure for coordination. Service and product differentiation is high, which may explain why centralization is hard to achieve. In this group, the system may simply service a role in sharing information and providing administrative support to highly developed local delivery systems centered around hospitals.

*Independent Hospital System:* A delivery system with limited differentiation in hospital services, physician arrangements, and insurance product development. These systems are largely horizontal affiliations of autonomous hospitals.

*No Assignment:* For some systems sufficient data from the Annual Survey were not available to determine a cluster assignment.

The second part of this section lists health care systems indexed geographically by state and city. Every effort has been made to be as inclusive and accurate as possible. However, as in all efforts of this type, there may be omissions. For further information, write to the Section for Health Care Systems, American Hospital Association, 155 N. Wacker Drive, Chicago, IL 60606.

## Networks

The *AHA Guide* shows listings of networks. A network is defined as a group of hospitals, physicians, other providers, insurers and/or community agencies that work together to coordinate and deliver a broad spectrum of services to their community. Organizations listed represent the lead or hub of the network activity. Networks are listed by state, then alphabetically by name including participating partners.

The network identification process has purposely been designed to capture networks of varying organization type. Sources include but are not limited to the following: *AHA Annual Survey*, national, state and metropolitan associations, national news and periodical searches, and the networks and their health care providers themselves. Therefore, networks are included regardless of whether a hospital or healthcare system is the network lead. When an individual hospital does appear in the listing, it is indicative of the role the hospital plays as the network lead. In addition, the network listing is **not** mutually exclusive of the hospital, health care system or alliance listings within this publication.

Networks are very fluid in their composition as goals evolve and partners change. Therefore, some of the networks included in this listing may have dissolved, reformed, or simply been renamed as this section was being produced for publication.

The network identification process is an ongoing and responsive initiative. As more information is collected and validated, it will be made available in other venues, in addition to the *AHA Guide*. For more information concerning the network identification process, please contact The American Hospital Association Resource Center at 312/422–2050.

## Alliances

An alliance is a formal organization, usually owned by shareholders/members, that works on behalf of its individual members in the provision of services and products and in the promotion of activities and ventures. The organization functions under a set of bylaws or other written rules to which each member agrees to abide.

Alliances are listed alphabetically by name. Its members are listed alphabetically by state, city, and then by member name.

[1] Bazzoli, CJ; Shortell, SM; Dubbs, N; Chan, C; and Kralovec, P; "A Taxonomy of Health networks and Systems: Bringing Order Out of Chaos" *Health Services Research*, February; 1999

# Statistics for Health Care Systems and their Hospitals

The following tables describing health care systems refers to information in section B of the 2014 *AHA Guide*.

Table 1 shows the number of health care systems by type of control. Table 2 provides a breakdown of the number of systems that own, lease, sponsor or contract manage hospitals within each control category. Table 3 gives the number of hospitals and beds in each control category as well as total hospitals and beds. Finally, shows the percentage of hospitals and beds in each control category.

For more information on health care systems, please write to the Section for Health Care Systems, 155 N. Wacker Drive, Chicago, Illinois 60606 or call 312/422–3000.

### Table 1. Health Care Systems, by Type of Organizaton Control

| Type of Control | Code | Number of Systems |
|---|---|---|
| Catholic (Roman) church–related | CC | 36 |
| Other church–related | CO | 10 |
| Subtotal, church–related | | 46 |
| Other not–for–profit | NP | 305 |
| Subtotal, not–for–profit | | 351 |
| Investor Owned | IO | 82 |
| Federal Government | FG | 5 |
| Total | | 438 |

### Table 2. Health Care Systems, by Type of Ownership and Control

| Type of Ownership | Catholic Church–Related (CC) | Other Church–Related (CO) | Total Church–Related (CC + CO) | Other Not–for–Profit (NP) | Total Not–for–Profit (CC, CO, + NP) | Investor–Owned (IO) | Federal Government (FG) | All Systems |
|---|---|---|---|---|---|---|---|---|
| Systems that only own, lease or sponsor | 28 | 6 | 34 | 270 | 304 | 74 | 5 | 383 |
| Systems that only contract–manage | 0 | 0 | 0 | 1 | 1 | 2 | 0 | 3 |
| Systems that manage, own, lease, or sponsor | 8 | 3 | 11 | 27 | 38 | 6 | 0 | 44 |
| Total | 36 | 9 | 45 | 298 | 343 | 82 | 5 | 430 |

### Table 3. Hospitals and Beds in Health Care Systems, by Type of Ownership and Control

| Type of Ownership | Catholic Church–Related (CC) H | B | Other Church–Related (CO) H | B | Total Church–Related (CC + CO) H | B | Other Not–for–Profit (NP) H | B | Total Not–for–Profit (CC, CO, + NP) H | B | Investor–Owned (IO) H | B | Federal Government (FG) H | B | All Systems H | B |
|---|---|---|---|---|---|---|---|---|---|---|---|---|---|---|---|---|
| Owned, leased or sponsored | 558 | 104,621 | 87 | 18,958 | 645 | 123,579 | 1,427 | 310,671 | 2,072 | 434,250 | 1,303 | 152,872 | 209 | 38,972 | 3,584 | 626,094 |
| Contract–managed | 41 | 1,709 | 6 | 662 | 47 | 2,371 | 80 | 6,043 | 127 | 8,414 | 113 | 6,959 | 0 | 0 | 240 | 15,373 |
| Total | 599 | 106,330 | 93 | 19,620 | 692 | 125,950 | 1,507 | 316,714 | 2,199 | 442,664 | 1,416 | 159,831 | 209 | 38,972 | 3,824 | 641,467 |

**H** = hospitals; **B** = beds.

### Table 4. Hospitals and Beds in Health Care Systems, by Type of Ownership and Control as a Percentage of All Systems

| Type of Ownership | Catholic Church–Related (CC) H | B | Other Church–Related (CO) H | B | Total Church–Related (CC + CO) H | B | Other Not–for–Profit (NP) H | B | Total Not–for–Profit (CC, CO, + NP) H | B | Investor–Owned (IO) H | B | Federal Government (FG) H | B | All Systems H | B |
|---|---|---|---|---|---|---|---|---|---|---|---|---|---|---|---|---|
| Owned, leased or sponsored | 15.6 | 16.7 | 2.4 | 3.0 | 18.0 | 19.7 | 39.8 | 49.6 | 57.8 | 69.4 | 36.4 | 24.4 | 5.8 | 6.2 | 100.0 | 100.0 |
| Contract–managed | 17.1 | 11.1 | 2.5 | 4.3 | 19.6 | 15.4 | 33.3 | 39.3 | 52.9 | 54.7 | 47.1 | 45.3 | 0.0 | 0.0 | 100.0 | 100.0 |
| Total | 15.7 | 16.6 | 2.4 | 3.1 | 18.1 | 19.6 | 39.4 | 49.4 | 57.5 | 69.0 | 37.0 | 24.9 | 5.5 | 6.1 | 100.0 | 100.0 |

**H** = hospitals; **B** = beds.
*Please note that figures may not always equal the provided subtotal or total percentages due to rounding.

**2375: ABINGTON HEALTH** (NP)
1200 Old York Road, Abington, PA Zip 19001; tel. 215/576–2000; Laurence M. Merlis, President and Chief Executive Officer

**PENNSYLVANIA:** ABINGTON HEALTH LANSDALE HOSPITAL (O, 135 beds) 100 Medical Campus Drive, Lansdale, PA Zip 19446–1200; tel. 215/368–2100; Gary R. Candia, Ph.D., FACHE, Chief Executive Officer
**Web address:** www.amh.org/lansdale/index.aspx

ABINGTON MEMORIAL HOSPITAL (O, 621 beds) 1200 Old York Road, Abington, PA Zip 19001–3720; tel. 215/481–2000; Laurence M. Merlis, President and Chief Executive Officer
**Web address:** www.amh.org

| | | |
|---|---|---|
| Owned, leased, sponsored: | 2 hospitals | 756 beds |
| Contract–managed: | 0 hospitals | 0 beds |
| Totals: | 2 hospitals | 756 beds |

**0091: ACADIA HEALTHCARE COMPANY, INC.** (IO)
830 Crescent Centre Drive, Suite 610, Franklin, TN Zip 37067–7323; tel. 615/861–6000; Joey Jacobs, Chairman and Chief Executive Officer
**(Independent Hospital System)**

**ARIZONA:** SONORA BEHAVIORAL HEALTH HOSPITAL (O, 70 beds) 6050 North Corona Road, Tucson, AZ Zip 85704–1096; tel. 520/469–8700; Brian Gill, Chief Executive Officer

**DELAWARE:** MEADOW WOOD BEHAVIORAL HEALTH SYSTEM (O, 53 beds) 575 South Dupont Highway, New Castle, DE Zip 19720–4606; tel. 302/328–3330; Bill A. Mason, Chief Executive Officer
**Web address:** www.meadowwoodhospital.com

**FLORIDA:** PARK ROYAL HOSPITAL (O, 76 beds) 9241 Park Royal Drive, Fort Myers, FL Zip 33908–9204; tel. 239/985–2700; Michael K. Evans, Chief Executive Officer
**Web address:** www.ParkRoyalHospital.com

**GEORGIA:** RIVERWOODS BEHAVIORAL HEALTH SYSTEM (O, 75 beds) 233 Medical Center Drive, Riverdale, GA Zip 30274–2640; tel. 770/991–8500; Kirk Kureska, Chief Executive Officer
**Web address:** www.riverwoodsbehavioral.com

**INDIANA:** OPTIONS BEHAVIORAL HEALTH SYSTEM (O, 42 beds) 5602 Caito Drive, Indianapolis, IN Zip 46226–1346; tel. 317/544–4340; Roxane Harcourt, Chief Executive Officer

**LOUISIANA:** ACADIA OPTIMA HOSPITAL (O, 24 beds) 1131 Rue De Belier, Lafayette, LA Zip 70506–6532; tel. 337/991–0571; Michael E. Geissler, Chief Executive Officer
**Web address:** www.optimaspecialtyhospital.com/

ACADIA VERMILION HOSPITAL (O, 54 beds) 2520 North University Avenue, Lafayette, LA Zip 70507–5306; tel. 337/234–5614; Joseph Rodriguez, Chief Executive Officer
**Web address:** www.acadiavermilion.com

**MICHIGAN:** HARBOR OAKS HOSPITAL (O, 45 beds) 35031 23 Mile Road, New Baltimore, MI Zip 48047–3649; tel. 586/725–5777; Sari Abromovich, Chief Executive Officer
**Web address:** www.harboroaks.com

STONECREST CENTER (O, 81 beds) 15000 Gratiot Avenue, Detroit, MI Zip 48205–1973; tel. 313/245–0600; Steve Savage, Chief Executive Officer and Chief Operating Officer
**Web address:** www.bcastonecrestcenter.com

**MISSOURI:** LAKELAND BEHAVIORAL HEALTH SYSTEM (O, 86 beds) 440 South Market Street, Springfield, MO Zip 65806–2026; tel. 417/865–5581; Keith A. Furman, Chief Executive Officer
**Web address:** www.lakeland–hospital.com

**NEVADA:** SEVEN HILLS BEHAVIORAL INSTITUTE (O, 58 beds) 3021 West Horizon Ridge Parkway, Henderson, NV Zip 89052–3990; tel. 702/646–5000; John Hull, Chief Executive Officer
**Web address:** www.sevenhillsbi.com

**OHIO:** OHIO HOSPITAL FOR CHILD AND ADOLESCENT PSYCHIATRY (O, 78 beds) 880 Greenlawn Avenue, Columbus, OH Zip 43223–2616; tel. 614/449–9664; Roxanne Jividen, Chief Executive Officer
**Web address:** www.bca–corp.com

TEN LAKES CENTER (O, 16 beds) 819 North First Street, 3rd Floor, Dennison, OH Zip 44621–1003; tel. 740/922–7499; Laura Blackburn, Administrator
**Web address:** www.tenlakescenter.com/

**OKLAHOMA:** ROLLING HILLS HOSPITAL (O, 44 beds) 1000 Rolling Hills Lane, Ada, OK Zip 74820–9415; tel. 580/436–3600; Selena Stockley, Chief Executive Officer
**Web address:** www.rollinghillshospital.com

**PENNSYLVANIA:** SOUTHWOOD PSYCHIATRIC HOSPITAL (O, 112 beds) 2575 Boyce Plaza Road, Pittsburgh, PA Zip 15241–3925; tel. 412/257–2290; Stephen J. Quigley, Chief Executive Officer
**Web address:** www.southwoodhospital.com

**TENNESSEE:** DELTA MEDICAL CENTER (O, 170 beds) 3000 Getwell Road, Memphis, TN Zip 38118–2299; tel. 901/369–8100; William Patterson, Chief Executive Officer
**Web address:** www.deltamedcenter.com

**TEXAS:** ACADIA ABILENE HOSPITAL (O, 92 beds) 4225 Woods Place, Abilene, TX Zip 79602–7991, Mailing Address: P.O. Box 5559, Zip 79608–5559; tel. 325/698–6600; Chris Perkins, Chief Executive Officer
**Web address:** www.acadiaabilene.com

CEDAR CREST HOSPITAL AND RESIDENTIAL TREATMENT CENTER (O, 70 beds) 3500 I–35 South, Belton, TX Zip 76513; tel. 254/939–2100; Ingrid Whittle, Chief Executive Officer
**Web address:** www.cedarcresthospital.com

RED RIVER HOSPITAL (O, 74 beds) 1505 Eighth Street, Wichita Falls, TX Zip 76301–3106; tel. 940/322–3171; Rob Marsh, Chief Executive Officer
**Web address:** www.redriverhospital.com

| | | |
|---|---|---|
| Owned, leased, sponsored: | 19 hospitals | 1320 beds |
| Contract–managed: | 0 hospitals | 0 beds |
| Totals: | 19 hospitals | 1320 beds |

**★0640: ACUITYHEALTHCARE, LP** (IO)
10200 Mallard Creek Road, Suite 300, Charlotte, NC Zip 28262–9705; tel. 704/887–7280; Edwin H. Cooper, Jr., MS, President and Chief Executive Officer
**(Independent Hospital System)**

**NEW JERSEY:** ACUITY SPECIALTY HOSPITAL OF NEW JERSEY (O, 30 beds) 1925 Pacific Avenue, 7th Floor, Atlantic City, NJ Zip 08401–6713; tel. 609/441–2122; Kerry McLane, Interim Chief Executive Officer
**Web address:** www.acuityhealthcare.net

LOURDES SPECIALTY HOSPITAL OF SOUTHERN NEW JERSEY (O, 69 beds) 218 Sunset Road, Willingboro, NJ Zip 08046–1110; tel. 609/835–3650; Cheri Cowperthwait, R.N., Chief Executive Officer
**Web address:** www.acuityhealthcarenj.com

**NORTH CAROLINA:** CAROLINAS SPECIALTY HOSPITAL (C, 38 beds) 2001 Vail Avenue, 7th Floor, Charlotte, NC Zip 28207–1248; tel. 704/304–6450; Daniel C. Dunmyer, Chief Executive Officer
**Web address:** www.cshnc.com

**OHIO:** ACUITY SPECIALTY HOSPITALS OHIO VALLEY (O, 40 beds) 380 Summit Avenue, 3rd Floor, Steubenville, OH Zip 43952–2667; tel. 740/283–7600; Judy K. Weaver, MS, Chief Executive Officer
**Web address:** www.acuityhealthcare.net

For explanation of codes following names, see page B2.
★ Indicates Type III membership in the American Hospital Association.

**TEXAS:** ACUITY HOSPITAL OF SOUTH TEXAS (O, 30 beds) 718 Lexington Avenue, San Antonio, TX Zip 78212–4768; tel. 210/572–4600; Kris Karns, Ph.D., FACHE, Chief Executive Officer
**Web address:** www.acuityhealthcare.net

ICON HOSPITAL (C, 42 beds) 19211 McKay Boulevard, Humble, TX Zip 77338–5502; tel. 281/883–5500; Hilda Long, Chief Executive Officer
**Web address:** www.acuityhealthcare.net

| | | |
|---|---|---|
| Owned, leased, sponsored: | 4 hospitals | 169 beds |
| Contract–managed: | 2 hospitals | 80 beds |
| Totals: | 6 hospitals | 249 beds |

## 0895: ADENA HEALTH SYSTEM (NP)

272 Hospital Road, Chillicothe, OH Zip 45601–9031; tel. 740/779–7500; Mark H. Shuter, President and Chief Executive Officer

**OHIO:** ADENA GREENFIELD MEDICAL CENTER (O, 25 beds) 550 Mirabeau Street, Greenfield, OH Zip 45123–1617; tel. 937/981–9400; Kathy Dye, Interim Administrator
**Web address:** www.adena.org

ADENA MEDICAL CENTER (O, 279 beds) 272 Hospital Road, Chillicothe, OH Zip 45601–9031; tel. 740/779–7500; Mark H. Shuter, President and Chief Executive Officer
**Web address:** www.adena.org

ADENA PIKE MEDICAL CENTER (O, 25 beds) 100 Dawn Lane, Waverly, OH Zip 45690–9138; tel. 740/947–2186; Craig E. Solle, Administrator
**Web address:** www.pikecommunityhospital.org

| | | |
|---|---|---|
| Owned, leased, sponsored: | 3 hospitals | 329 beds |
| Contract–managed: | 0 hospitals | 0 beds |
| Totals: | 3 hospitals | 329 beds |

## ★0235: ADVENTIST HEALTH (CO)

2100 Douglas Boulevard, Roseville, CA Zip 95661–3898, Mailing Address: P.O. Box 619002, Zip 95661–9002; tel. 916/781–2000; Robert G. Carmen, President
**(Moderately Centralized Health System)**

**CALIFORNIA:** ADVENTIST MEDICAL CENTER – HANFORD (O, 94 beds) 115 Mall Drive, Hanford, CA Zip 93230–3513; tel. 559/582–9000; Wayne Ferch, President and Chief Executive Officer
**Web address:** www.adventisthealthcv.com/hospital_newhanfordhospital.aspx

ADVENTIST MEDICAL CENTER–REEDLEY (L, 44 beds) 372 West Cypress Avenue, Reedley, CA Zip 93654–2199; tel. 559/638–8155; Wayne Ferch, President and Chief Executive Officer
**Web address:** www.skdh.org

CENTRAL VALLEY GENERAL HOSPITAL (O, 30 beds) 1025 North Douty Street, Hanford, CA Zip 93230–3722, Mailing Address: P.O. Box 480, Zip 93232–0480; tel. 559/583–2100; Wayne Ferch, President and Chief Executive Officer
**Web address:** www.hanfordhealth.com

FEATHER RIVER HOSPITAL (O, 86 beds) 5974 Pentz Road, Paradise, CA Zip 95969–5509; tel. 530/877–9361; Kevin R. Erich, President and Chief Executive Officer
**Web address:** www.frhosp.org

FRANK R. HOWARD MEMORIAL HOSPITAL (L, 25 beds) One Madrone Street, Willits, CA Zip 95490–4225; tel. 707/459–6801; Rick Bockmann, Chief Executive Officer
**Web address:** www.howardhospital.com

GLENDALE ADVENTIST MEDICAL CENTER (O, 462 beds) 1509 Wilson Terrace, Glendale, CA Zip 91206–4007; tel. 818/409–8000; Kevin A. Roberts, FACHE, President and Chief Executive Officer
**Web address:** www.glendaleadventist.com

SAN JOAQUIN COMMUNITY HOSPITAL (O, 255 beds) 2615 Chester Avenue, Bakersfield, CA Zip 93301–2014, Mailing Address: P.O. Box 2615, Zip 93303–2615; tel. 661/395–3000; Hal Chilton, Interim President and Chief Executive Officer
**Web address:** www.sanjoaquinhospital.org

SIMI VALLEY HOSPITAL AND HEALTH CARE SERVICES (O, 82 beds) 2975 North Sycamore Drive, Simi Valley, CA Zip 93065–1201; tel. 805/955–6000; Kim S. Milstien, President and Chief Executive Officer
**Web address:** www.simivalleyhospital.com

SONORA REGIONAL MEDICAL CENTER (O, 152 beds) 1000 Greenley Road, Sonora, CA Zip 95370–5200; tel. 209/536–5000; Jeff Eller, FACHE, President and Chief Executive Officer
**Web address:** www.sonoramedicalcenter.org/

ST. HELENA HOSPITAL CLEAR LAKE (O, 25 beds) 15630 18th Avenue, Clearlake, CA Zip 95422–9336, Mailing Address: P.O. Box 6710, Zip 95422; tel. 707/994–6486; Terry Newmyer, President and Chief Executive Officer
**Web address:** www.adventisthealth.org

ST. HELENA HOSPITAL NAPA VALLEY (O, 116 beds) 10 Woodland Road, Saint Helena, CA Zip 94574–9554; tel. 707/963–3611; Terry Newmyer, President and Chief Executive Officer
**Web address:** www.sthelenahospital.org

ST. HELENA HOSPITAL–CENTER FOR BEHAVIORAL HEALTH (O, 61 beds) 525 Oregon Street, Vallejo, CA Zip 94590–3201; tel. 707/648–2200; Terry Newmyer, President and Chief Executive Officer
**Web address:** www.sthelenahospital.org/Behavioral/

UKIAH VALLEY MEDICAL CENTER (O, 48 beds) 275 Hospital Drive, Ukiah, CA Zip 95482–4531; tel. 707/462–3111; Gwen Matthews, R.N., MSN, Chief Executive Officer
**Web address:** www.adventisthealth.org

WHITE MEMORIAL MEDICAL CENTER (O, 280 beds) 1720 Cesar Chavez Avenue, Los Angeles, CA Zip 90033–2414; tel. 323/268–5000; Beth D. Zachary, President and Chief Executive Officer
**Web address:** www.whitememorial.com

**HAWAII:** CASTLE MEDICAL CENTER (O, 160 beds) 640 Ulukahiki Street, Kailua, HI Zip 96734–4454; tel. 808/263–5500; Kathryn A. Raethel, R.N., M.P.H., President and Chief Executive Officer
**Web address:** www.castlemed.org

**OREGON:** ADVENTIST MEDICAL CENTER–PORTLAND (O, 248 beds) 10123 S.E. Market Street, Portland, OR Zip 97216–2599; tel. 503/257–2500; Thomas Russell, President and Chief Executive Officer
**Web address:** www.adventisthealthnw.com

TILLAMOOK REGIONAL MEDICAL CENTER (L, 25 beds) 1000 Third Street, Tillamook, OR Zip 97141–3430; tel. 503/842–4444; Larry Davy, President and Chief Executive Officer
**Web address:** www.tcgh.com

**WASHINGTON:** WALLA WALLA GENERAL HOSPITAL (O, 37 beds) 1025 South Second Avenue, Walla Walla, WA Zip 99362–4116, Mailing Address: P.O. Box 1398, Zip 99362–0309; tel. 509/525–0480; Monty E. Knittel, President and Chief Executive Officer
**Web address:** www.wwgh.com

| | | |
|---|---|---|
| Owned, leased, sponsored: | 18 hospitals | 2230 beds |
| Contract–managed: | 0 hospitals | 0 beds |
| Totals: | 18 hospitals | 2230 beds |

## ★4165: ADVENTIST HEALTH SYSTEM SUNBELT HEALTH CARE CORPORATION (CO)

900 Hope Way, Altamonte Springs, FL Zip 32714–1502; tel. 407/357–1000; Donald L. Jernigan, Ph.D., President and Chief Executive Officer
**(Decentralized Health System)**

**COLORADO:** AVISTA ADVENTIST HOSPITAL (O, 114 beds) 100 Health Park Drive, Louisville, CO Zip 80027–9583; tel. 303/673–1000; Jim Boyle, Interim Chief Executive Officer
**Web address:** www.avistahospital.org

LITTLETON ADVENTIST HOSPITAL (O, 202 beds) 7700 South Broadway Street, Littleton, CO Zip 80122–2628; tel. 303/730–8900; Brett Spenst, Chief Executive Officer
**Web address:** www.centura.org

PARKER ADVENTIST HOSPITAL (O, 143 beds) 9395 Crown Crest Boulevard, Parker, CO Zip 80138–8573; tel. 303/269–4000; Morre Dean, Chief Executive Officer
**Web address:** www.parkerhospital.org

For explanation of codes following names, see page B2.
★ Indicates Type III membership in the American Hospital Association.

PORTER ADVENTIST HOSPITAL (O, 250 beds) 2525 South Downing Street, Denver, CO Zip 80210–5876; tel. 303/778–1955; Randall L. Haffner, Ph.D., Chief Executive Officer
**Web address:** www.centura.org

**FLORIDA:** FLORIDA HOSPITAL (O, 2338 beds) 601 East Rollins Street, Orlando, FL Zip 32803–1248; tel. 407/303–6611; Lars D. Houmann, President
**Web address:** www.flhosp.org

FLORIDA HOSPITAL AT CONNERTON LONG TERM ACUTE CARE (O, 50 beds) 9441 Health Center Drive, Land O'Lakes, FL Zip 34637–5837; tel. 813/903–3701; Debi Martoccio, R.N., Chief Operating Officer
**Web address:** www.elevatinghealthcare.org

FLORIDA HOSPITAL DELAND (O, 156 beds) 701 West Plymouth Avenue, DeLand, FL Zip 32720–3236; tel. 386/943–4522; Mark LaRose, President and Chief Executive Officer
**Web address:** www.fhdeland.org

FLORIDA HOSPITAL FISH MEMORIAL (O, 175 beds) 1055 Saxon Boulevard, Orange City, FL Zip 32763–8468; tel. 386/917–5000; Ed Noseworthy, President and Chief Executive Officer
**Web address:** www.fhfishmemorial.org

FLORIDA HOSPITAL HEARTLAND MEDICAL CENTER (O, 214 beds) 4200 Sun'n Lake Boulevard, Sebring, FL Zip 33872–1986, Mailing Address: P.O. Box 9400, Zip 33871–9400; tel. 863/314–4466; Timothy W. Cook, President and Chief Executive Officer
**Web address:** www.fhheartland.org/

FLORIDA HOSPITAL MEMORIAL MEDICAL CENTER (O, 211 beds) 301 Memorial Medical Parkway, Daytona Beach, FL Zip 32117–5167; tel. 386/676–6000; Daryl Tol, Chief Executive Officer
**Web address:** www.floridahospitalmemorial.org

FLORIDA HOSPITAL NORTH PINELLAS (O, 168 beds) 1395 South Pinellas Avenue, Tarpon Springs, FL Zip 34689–3790; tel. 727/942–5000; Bruce Bergherm, Chief Executive Officer
**Web address:** www.fhnorthpinellas.com/

FLORIDA HOSPITAL TAMPA (O, 365 beds) 3100 East Fletcher Avenue, Tampa, FL Zip 33613–4688; tel. 813/971–6000; John R. Harding, Chief Executive Officer
**Web address:** www.uch.org

FLORIDA HOSPITAL WATERMAN (O, 269 beds) 1000 Waterman Way, Tavares, FL Zip 32778–5266; tel. 352/253–3333; David Ottati, Chief Executive Officer
**Web address:** www.fhwat.org

FLORIDA HOSPITAL WAUCHULA (O, 25 beds) 533 West Carlton Street, Wauchula, FL Zip 33873–3407; tel. 863/773–3101; Linda Adler, Administrator
**Web address:** www.fh.floridahospital.com/heartland/home.aspx

FLORIDA HOSPITAL WESLEY CHAPEL (O, 83 beds) 2600 Bruce B. Downs Bouelvard, Wesley Chapel, FL Zip 33544–9207; tel. 813/929–5000; Brian Adams, Chief Executive Officer

FLORIDA HOSPITAL ZEPHYRHILLS (O, 139 beds) 7050 Gall Boulevard, Zephyrhills, FL Zip 33541–1399; tel. 813/788–0411; Douglas Duffield, President and Chief Executive Officer
**Web address:** www.fhzeph.org

FLORIDA HOSPITAL–CARROLLWOOD (O, 90 beds) 7171 North Dale Mabry Highway, Tampa, FL Zip 33614–2665; tel. 813/932–2222; Joel Johnson, Chief Executive Officer
**Web address:** www.uch.org

FLORIDA HOSPITAL–FLAGLER (O, 99 beds) 60 Memorial Medical Parkway, Palm Coast, FL Zip 32164–5980; tel. 386/586–2000; Kenneth R. Mattison, Chief Executive Officer
**Web address:** www.floridahospitalflagler.com/

**GEORGIA:** EMORY–ADVENTIST HOSPITAL (O, 52 beds) 3949 South Cobb Drive S.E., Smyrna, GA Zip 30080–6300; tel. 770/434–0710; Dennis Kiley, President
**Web address:** www.emoryadventist.org

GORDON HOSPITAL (O, 85 beds) 1035 Red Bud Road, Calhoun, GA Zip 30701–2082, Mailing Address: P.O. Box 12938, Zip 30703–7013; tel. 706/629–2895; Pete M. Weber, President and Chief Executive Officer
**Web address:** www.gordonhospital.com

**ILLINOIS:** ADVENTIST BOLINGBROOK HOSPITAL (O, 148 beds) 500 Remington Boulevard, Bolingbrook, IL Zip 60440–4906; tel. 630/312–5000; Rick Mace, Chief Executive Officer
**Web address:** www.keepingyouwell.com/abh/

ADVENTIST GLENOAKS HOSPITAL (O, 141 beds) 701 Winthrop Avenue, Glendale Heights, IL Zip 60139–1403; tel. 630/545–8000; Bruce C. Christian, Chief Executive Officer
**Web address:** www.keepingyouwell.com

ADVENTIST HINSDALE HOSPITAL (O, 277 beds) 120 North Oak Street, Hinsdale, IL Zip 60521–3890; tel. 630/856–9000; Michael Goebel, Chief Executive Officer
**Web address:** www.keepingyouwell.com

ADVENTIST LA GRANGE MEMORIAL HOSPITAL (O, 187 beds) 5101 South Willow Spring Road, La Grange, IL Zip 60525–2600; tel. 708/245–9000; Lary Davis, President and Chief Executive Officer
**Web address:** www.keepingyouwell.com

**KANSAS:** SHAWNEE MISSION MEDICAL CENTER (O, 376 beds) 9100 West 74th Street, Shawnee Mission, KS Zip 66204–4004, Mailing Address: Box 2923, Zip 66201–1323; tel. 913/676–2000; Ken J. Bacon, President and Chief Executive Officer
**Web address:** www.shawneemission.org

**KENTUCKY:** MANCHESTER MEMORIAL HOSPITAL (O, 63 beds) 210 Marie Langdon Drive, Manchester, KY Zip 40962–6388; tel. 606/598–5104; Erika Skula, President and Chief Executive Officer
**Web address:** www.manchestermemorial.org

**NORTH CAROLINA:** PARK RIDGE HEALTH (O, 98 beds) 100 Hospital Drive, Hendersonville, NC Zip 28792–5272; tel. 828/684–8501; Jimm Bunch, President and Chief Executive Officer
**Web address:** www.parkridgehealth.org

**TENNESSEE:** JELLICO COMMUNITY HOSPITAL (L, 31 beds) 188 Hospital Lane, Jellico, TN Zip 37762–4400; tel. 423/784–7252; Erik Wangsness, Chief Executive Officer
**Web address:** www.jellicohospital.com

TAKOMA REGIONAL HOSPITAL (C, 100 beds) 401 Takoma Avenue, Greeneville, TN Zip 37743–4647; tel. 423/639–3151; Daniel Wolcott, President
**Web address:** www.takoma.org

**TEXAS:** CENTRAL TEXAS MEDICAL CENTER (O, 140 beds) 1301 Wonder World Drive, San Marcos, TX Zip 78666–7544; tel. 512/353–8979; Sam Huenergardt, President and Chief Executive Officer
**Web address:** www.ctmc.org

HUGULEY MEMORIAL MEDICAL CENTER (C, 192 beds) 11801 South Freeway, Fort Worth, TX Zip 76028–7021, Mailing Address: P.O. Box 6337, Zip 76115–0337; tel. 817/293–9110; Kenneth A. Finch, President and Chief Executive Officer
**Web address:** www.huguley.org

METROPLEX ADVENTIST HOSPITAL (O, 177 beds) 2201 South Clear Creek Road, Killeen, TX Zip 76549–4110; tel. 254/526–7523; Carlyle L. E. Walton, Chief Executive Officer
**Web address:** www.mplex.org

ROLLINS–BROOK COMMUNITY HOSPITAL (O, 35 beds) 608 North Key Avenue, Lampasas, TX Zip 76550–1106, Mailing Address: P.O. Box 589, Zip 76550–0032; tel. 512/556–3682; Carlyle L. E. Walton, President and Chief Executive Officer
**Web address:** www.mplex.org

**WISCONSIN:** CHIPPEWA VALLEY HOSPITAL AND OAKVIEW CARE CENTER (O, 75 beds) 1220 Third Avenue West, Durand, WI Zip 54736–1600, Mailing Address: P.O. Box 224, Zip 54736–0224; tel. 715/672–4211; Douglas R. Peterson, President and Chief Executive Officer
**Web address:** www.chippewavalleyhospital.com/

| | | |
|---|---|---|
| Owned, leased, sponsored: | 32 hospitals | 6976 beds |
| Contract–managed: | 2 hospitals | 292 beds |
| **Totals:** | 34 hospitals | 7268 beds |

**★0214: ADVENTIST HEALTHCARE** (NP)
820 West Diamond Avenue, Suite 600, Gaithersburg, MD Zip 20878–1419; tel. 301/315–3030; William G. Robertson, President and Chief Executive Officer
**(Independent Hospital System)**

**MARYLAND:** ADVENTIST BEHAVIORAL HEALTH ROCKVILLE (O, 283 beds) 14901 Broschart Road, Rockville, MD Zip 20850–3318; tel. 301/251–4500; Kevin Young, FACHE, President
**Web address:** www.adventistbehavioralhealth.com

For explanation of codes following names, see page B2.
★ Indicates Type III membership in the American Hospital Association.

ADVENTIST REHABILITATION HOSPITAL OF MARYLAND (O, 77 beds) 9909 Medical Center Drive, Rockville, MD Zip 20850–6361; tel. 240/864–6000; Brent Reitz, Vice President and Administrator
**Web address:** www.adventistrehab.com

SHADY GROVE ADVENTIST HOSPITAL (O, 327 beds) 9901 Medical Center Drive, Rockville, MD Zip 20850–3395; tel. 240/826–6000; John Sackett, Chief Executive Officer
**Web address:** www.adventisthealthcare.com

WASHINGTON ADVENTIST HOSPITAL (O, 204 beds) 7600 Carroll Avenue, Takoma Park, MD Zip 20912–6392; tel. 301/891–7600; Joyce Newmyer, President
**Web address:** www.adventisthealthcare.com

**NEW JERSEY:** HACKETTSTOWN REGIONAL MEDICAL CENTER (O, 111 beds) 651 Willow Grove Street, Hackettstown, NJ Zip 07840–1799; tel. 908/852–5100; Jason C. Coe, President and Chief Executive Officer
**Web address:** www.hrmcnj.org

| | | |
|---|---|---|
| Owned, leased, sponsored: | 5 hospitals | 1002 beds |
| Contract–managed: | 0 hospitals | 0 beds |
| Totals: | 5 hospitals | 1002 beds |

---

**★0064:    ADVOCATE HEALTH CARE** (NP)
3075 Highland Parkway, Suite 600, Downers Grove, IL Zip 60515–1206; tel. 630/929–8700; Jim H. Skogsbergh, President and Chief Executive Officer
**(Moderately Centralized Health System)**

**ILLINOIS:** ADVOCATE BROMENN MEDICAL CENTER (O, 204 beds) 1304 Franklin Avenue, Normal, IL Zip 61761–3558, Mailing Address: P.O. Box 2850, Bloomington, Zip 61702–2850; tel. 309/454–1400; Colleen Kannaday, FACHE, President
**Web address:** www.bromenn.org

ADVOCATE CHRIST MEDICAL CENTER (O, 684 beds) 4440 West 95th Street, Oak Lawn, IL Zip 60453–2699; tel. 708/684–8000; Kenneth W. Lukhard, President
**Web address:** www.advocatehealth.com/christ

ADVOCATE CONDELL MEDICAL CENTER (O, 279 beds) 801 South Milwaukee Avenue, Libertyville, IL Zip 60048–3199; tel. 847/362–2900; Dominica Tallarico, President
**Web address:** www.advocatehealth.com/condell/

ADVOCATE EUREKA HOSPITAL (O, 18 beds) 101 South Major Street, Eureka, IL Zip 61530–1246; tel. 309/467–2371; Colleen Kannaday, FACHE, President
**Web address:** www.advocatehealth.com/eureka/

ADVOCATE GOOD SAMARITAN HOSPITAL (O, 326 beds) 3815 Highland Avenue, Downers Grove, IL Zip 60515–1590; tel. 630/275–5900; David Fox, President
**Web address:** www.advocatehealth.com/gsam

ADVOCATE GOOD SHEPHERD HOSPITAL (O, 169 beds) 450 West Highway 22, Barrington, IL Zip 60010–1919; tel. 847/381–0123; Karen A. Lambert, President
**Web address:** www.advocatehealth.com/gshp/

ADVOCATE ILLINOIS MASONIC MEDICAL CENTER (O, 330 beds) 836 West Wellington Avenue, Chicago, IL Zip 60657–5147; tel. 773/975–1600; Susan Nordstrom Lopez, President
**Web address:** www.advocatehealth.com/masonic

ADVOCATE LUTHERAN GENERAL HOSPITAL (O, 624 beds) 1775 Dempster Street, Park Ridge, IL Zip 60068–1174; tel. 847/723–2210; Anthony A. Armada, President
**Web address:** www.advocatehealth.com/luth/

ADVOCATE SHERMAN HOSPITAL (O, 255 beds) 1425 North Randall Road, Elgin, IL Zip 60123–2300; tel. 847/742–9800; Richard B. Floyd, President and Chief Executive Officer
**Web address:** www.shermanhealthsystems.com

ADVOCATE SOUTH SUBURBAN HOSPITAL (O, 240 beds) 17800 South Kedzie Avenue, Hazel Crest, IL Zip 60429–0989; tel. 708/799–8000; Richard Heim, President
**Web address:** www.advocatehealth.com/ssub/

ADVOCATE TRINITY HOSPITAL (O, 188 beds) 2320 East 93rd Street, Chicago, IL Zip 60617–3983; tel. 773/967–2000; Jonathan R. Bruss, President
**Web address:** www.advocatehealth.com/trinity

| | | |
|---|---|---|
| Owned, leased, sponsored: | 11 hospitals | 3317 beds |
| Contract–managed: | 0 hospitals | 0 beds |
| Totals: | 11 hospitals | 3317 beds |

---

**0312:    AHMC & HEALTHCARE, INC.** (IO)
55 South Raymond Avenue, Suite 105, Alhambra, CA Zip 91801–7101; tel. 626/457–9600; Jonathan Wu, M.D., President and Chairman
**(Independent Hospital System)**

**CALIFORNIA:** ALHAMBRA HOSPITAL MEDICAL CENTER (O, 144 beds) 100 South Raymond Avenue, Alhambra, CA Zip 91801–3199, Mailing Address: P.O. Box 510, Zip 91802–2510; tel. 626/570–1606; Iris Lai, Chief Executive Officer
**Web address:** www.alhambrahospital.com

ANAHEIM REGIONAL MEDICAL CENTER (O, 223 beds) 1111 West La Palma Avenue, Anaheim, CA Zip 92801–2881; tel. 714/774–1450; Donald A. Lorack, Jr., Chief Executive Officer
**Web address:** www.anaheimregionalmc.com

GARFIELD MEDICAL CENTER (O, 210 beds) 525 North Garfield Avenue, Monterey Park, CA Zip 91754–1205; tel. 626/573–2222; David J. Batista, Chief Executive Officer
**Web address:** www.garfieldmedicalcenter.com

GREATER EL MONTE COMMUNITY HOSPITAL (O, 46 beds) 1701 Santa Anita Avenue, South El Monte, CA Zip 91733–3411; tel. 626/579–7777; Jose Ortega, Chief Executive Officer
**Web address:** www.greaterelmonte.com

MONTEREY PARK HOSPITAL (O, 101 beds) 900 South Atlantic Boulevard, Monterey Park, CA Zip 91754–4780; tel. 626/570–9000; Philip A. Cohen, Chief Executive Officer
**Web address:** www.montereyparkhosp.com

SAN GABRIEL VALLEY MEDICAL CENTER (O, 269 beds) 438 West Las Tunas Drive, San Gabriel, CA Zip 91776–1216, Mailing Address: P.O. Box 1507, Zip 91778–1507; tel. 626/289–5454; Howard Ternes, Chief Executive Officer
**Web address:** www.sgvmc.org

WHITTIER HOSPITAL MEDICAL CENTER (O, 100 beds) 9080 Colima Road, Whittier, CA Zip 90605–1600; tel. 562/945–3561; Richard Castro, Chief Executive Officer
**Web address:** www.whittierhospital.com

| | | |
|---|---|---|
| Owned, leased, sponsored: | 7 hospitals | 1093 beds |
| Contract–managed: | 0 hospitals | 0 beds |
| Totals: | 7 hospitals | 1093 beds |

---

**★0247:    AKRON GENERAL HEALTH SYSTEM** (NP)
400 Wabash Avenue, Akron, OH Zip 44307–2433; tel. 330/344–6000; Thomas L. Stover, M.D., President and Chief Executive Officer
**(Moderately Centralized Health System)**

**OHIO:** AKRON GENERAL MEDICAL CENTER (O, 498 beds) 400 Wabash Avenue, Akron, OH Zip 44307–2433; tel. 330/344–6000; Alan Papa, President
**Web address:** www.akrongeneral.org

EDWIN SHAW REHAB (O, 38 beds) 330 Broadway Street East, Cuyahoga Falls, OH Zip 44221–3312; tel. 330/436–0910; Thomas Whelan, President
**Web address:** www.edwinshaw.com

LODI COMMUNITY HOSPITAL (O, 25 beds) 225 Elyria Street, Lodi, OH Zip 44254–1096; tel. 330/948–1222; Thomas Whelan, President
**Web address:** www.lodihospital.org

| | | |
|---|---|---|
| Owned, leased, sponsored: | 3 hospitals | 561 beds |
| Contract–managed: | 0 hospitals | 0 beds |
| Totals: | 3 hospitals | 561 beds |

---

**1685:    ALBERT EINSTEIN HEALTHCARE NETWORK** (NP)
5501 Old York Road, Philadelphia, PA Zip 19141–3098; tel. 215/456–7890; Barry R. Freedman, President and Chief Executive Officer
**(Independent Hospital System)**

For explanation of codes following names, see page B2.
★ Indicates Type III membership in the American Hospital Association.

Section B

**PENNSYLVANIA:** BELMONT CENTER FOR COMPREHENSIVE TREATMENT (O, 147 beds) 4200 Monument Road, Philadelphia, PA Zip 19131–1625; tel. 215/877–2000; Sharon A. Bergen, Chief Operating Officer
**Web address:** www.einstein.edu/locations/belmont–behavioral–health/

EINSTEIN MEDICAL CENTER MONTGOMERY (O, 146 beds) 559 West Germantown Pike, East Norriton, PA Zip 19403–4250; tel. 484/622–1000; Beth Duffy, Chief Operating Officer

EINSTEIN MEDICAL CENTER PHILADELPHIA (O, 637 beds) 5501 Old York Road, Philadelphia, PA Zip 19141–3098; tel. 215/456–7890; Barry R. Freedman, President and Chief Executive Officer
**Web address:** www.einstein.edu/locations/einstein–medical–center–philadelphia/

| | | |
|---|---|---|
| Owned, leased, sponsored: | 3 hospitals | 930 beds |
| Contract–managed: | 0 hospitals | 0 beds |
| Totals: | 3 hospitals | 930 beds |

---

**0413: ALLEGIANCE HEALTH MANAGEMENT** (IO)
504 Texas Street, Suite 200, Shreveport, LA Zip 71101–3526; tel. 318/226–8202; Rock Bordelon, President and Chief Executive Officer
**(Independent Hospital System)**

**ARKANSAS:** EUREKA SPRINGS HOSPITAL (O, 15 beds) 24 Norris Street, Eureka Springs, AR Zip 72632–3541; tel. 479/253–7400; Christopher L. Bariola, Chief Executive Officer
**Web address:** www.eurekaspringshospital.com

BIENVILLE MEDICAL CENTER (O, 21 beds) 1175 Pine Street, Suite 200, Arcadia, LA Zip 71001–3122; tel. 318/263–4700; Kirk Lemoine, Chief Executive Office

NORTH METRO MEDICAL CENTER (O, 76 beds) 1400 West Braden Street, Jacksonville, AR Zip 72076–3788; tel. 501/985–7000; Cindy Stafford, Chief Executive Officer
**Web address:** www.northmetromed.com

RIVER VALLEY MEDICAL CENTER (O, 35 beds) 200 North Third Street, Dardanelle, AR Zip 72834–3802, Mailing Address: P.O. Box 578, Zip 72834–0578; tel. 479/229–4677; Christopher L. Bariola, Chief Executive Officer

**LOUISIANA:** ALLEGIANCE HEALTH CENTER OF RUSTON (O, 14 beds) 1401 Ezelle Street, Ruston, LA Zip 71270–7218; tel. 318/255–8085; Donna K. Thompson, Chief Executive Officer
**Web address:** www.ahmgt.com

BIENVILLE MEDICAL CENTER (O, 21 beds) 1175 Pine Street, Suite 200, Arcadia, LA Zip 71001–3122; tel. 318/263–4700; Kirk Lemoine, Chief Exeuctive Officer

SABINE MEDICAL CENTER (O, 44 beds) 240 Highland Drive, Many, LA Zip 71449–3718; tel. 318/256–5691; Chris Beddoe, Chief Executive Officer
**Web address:** www.sabinemedicalcenter.net

**MISSISSIPPI:** ALLEGIANCE SPECIALTY HOSPITAL OF GREENVILLE (O, 39 beds) 300 South Washington Avenue, 3rd Floor, Greenville, MS Zip 38701–4719; tel. 662/332–7344; Vernail Herzog, Chief Executive Officer
**Web address:** www.ahmgt.com

**TEXAS:** ALLEGIANCE BEHAVIORAL HEALTH CENTER OF PLAINVIEW (O, 20 beds) 2601 Dimmit Road, 4th Floor, Plainview, TX Zip 79072–1833; tel. 806/296–9191; Glenn G. Hoffman, MS, Chief Executive Officer
**Web address:** www.ahmgt.com

ALLEGIANCE SPECIALTY HOSPITAL OF KILGORE (O, 60 beds) 1612 South Henderson Boulevard, Kilgore, TX Zip 75662–3594; tel. 903/984–3505; Sherry Bustin, Chief Executive Officer
**Web address:** www.ahmgt.com

BEHAVIORAL HEALTH CENTER OF THE PERMIAN BASIN (O, 48 beds) 3300 South FM 1788, Midland, TX Zip 79706–2601; tel. 432/561–5915; Cheryl Rayl, Chief Executive Officer
**Web address:** www.ahmgt.com

| | | |
|---|---|---|
| Owned, leased, sponsored: | 10 hospitals | 372 beds |
| Contract–managed: | 0 hospitals | 0 beds |
| Totals: | 10 hospitals | 372 beds |

---

**0317: ALLIANT MANAGEMENT SERVICES** (IO)
2650 Eastpoint Parkway, Suite 300, Louisville, KY Zip 40223–5164; tel. 502/992–3525; Timothy L. Jarm, President and Chief Executive Officer
**(Decentralized Health System)**

**FLORIDA:** NORTHWEST FLORIDA COMMUNITY HOSPITAL (C, 59 beds) 1360 Brickyard Road, Chipley, FL Zip 32428–6303, Mailing Address: P.O. Box 889, Zip 32428–0889; tel. 850/638–1610; Patrick A. Schlenker, FACHE, President and Chief Executive Officer
**Web address:** www.nfch.org

**ILLINOIS:** FAIRFIELD MEMORIAL HOSPITAL (C, 55 beds) 303 N.W. 11th Street, Fairfield, IL Zip 62837–1203; tel. 618/842–2611; Katherine Bunting, Chief Executive Officer
**Web address:** www.fairfieldmemorial.org

FAYETTE COUNTY HOSPITAL (O, 110 beds) 650 West Taylor Street, Vandalia, IL Zip 62471–1296; tel. 618/283–1231; Gregory D. Starnes, Chief Executive Officer
**Web address:** www.fayettecountyhospital.org

FRANKLIN HOSPITAL DISTRICT (C, 25 beds) 201 Bailey Lane, Benton, IL Zip 62812–1969; tel. 618/439–3161; Hervey E. Davis, Chief Executive Officer
**Web address:** www.franklinhospital.net

PARIS COMMUNITY HOSPITAL (C, 25 beds) 721 East Court Street, Paris, IL Zip 61944–2460; tel. 217/465–4141; Randy Simmons, President and Chief Executive Officer
**Web address:** www.pariscommunityhospital.com

WABASH GENERAL HOSPITAL (C, 25 beds) 1418 College Drive, Mount Carmel, IL Zip 62863–2638; tel. 618/262–8621; Jay Purvis, Administrator
**Web address:** www.wabashgeneral.com

**INDIANA:** GIBSON GENERAL HOSPITAL (C, 70 beds) 1808 Sherman Drive, Princeton, IN Zip 47670–1043; tel. 812/385–3401; Emmett C. Schuster, President and Chief Executive Officer
**Web address:** www.gibsongeneral.com

PERRY COUNTY MEMORIAL HOSPITAL (C, 25 beds) 1 Hospital Road, Tell City, IN Zip 47586–2750; tel. 812/547–7011; Joseph A. Stuber, President and Chief Executive Officer
**Web address:** www.pchospital.org

WABASH COUNTY HOSPITAL (C, 50 beds) 710 North East Street, Wabash, IN Zip 46992–1924, Mailing Address: P.O. Box 548, Zip 46992–0548; tel. 260/563–3131; Marilyn J. Custer–Mitchell, President and Chief Executive Officer
**Web address:** www.wchospital.com

**KENTUCKY:** BRECKINRIDGE MEMORIAL HOSPITAL (C, 43 beds) 1011 Old Highway 60, Hardinsburg, KY Zip 40143–2597; tel. 270/756–7000; Michael W. Cooper, Chief Executive Officer
**Web address:** www.breckhealth.org

CARROLL COUNTY MEMORIAL HOSPITAL (C, 25 beds) 309 11th Street, Carrollton, KY Zip 41008–1400; tel. 502/732–4321; Michael A. Kozar, Chief Executive Officer
**Web address:** www.ccmhosp.com

CAVERNA MEMORIAL HOSPITAL (C, 25 beds) 1501 South Dixie Street, Horse Cave, KY Zip 42749–1477; tel. 270/786–2191; Alan B. Alexander, Chief Executive Officer
**Web address:** www.cavernahospital.com

JAMES B. HAGGIN MEMORIAL HOSPITAL (C, 25 beds) 464 Linden Avenue, Harrodsburg, KY Zip 40330–1862; tel. 859/734–5441; Victoria L. Reed, R.N., FACHE, Chief Executive Officer
**Web address:** www.hagginhosp.org

LIVINGSTON HOSPITAL AND HEALTHCARE SERVICES (C, 25 beds) 131 Hospital Drive, Salem, KY Zip 42078–8043; tel. 270/988–2299; Mark A. Edwards, Chief Executive Officer
**Web address:** www.lhhs.org

MUHLENBERG COMMUNITY HOSPITAL (C, 105 beds) 440 Hopkinsville Street, Greenville, KY Zip 42345–1172, Mailing Address: P.O. Box 387, Zip 42345–0387; tel. 270/338–8000; John T. Countzler, Chief Executive Officer
**Web address:** www.mchky.org

TWIN LAKES REGIONAL MEDICAL CENTER (C, 75 beds) 910 Wallace Avenue, Leitchfield, KY Zip 42754–2414; tel. 270/259–9400; Wayne Meriwether, Chief Executive Officer
**Web address:** www.tlrmc.com

---

For explanation of codes following names, see page B2.
★ Indicates Type III membership in the American Hospital Association.

**NORTH CAROLINA:** ALLEGHANY MEMORIAL HOSPITAL (C, 25 beds) 233 Doctors Street, Sparta, NC Zip 28675–9247, Mailing Address: P.O. Box 9, Zip 28675–0009; tel. 336/372–5511; Wendy Orton, Chief Executive Officer
**Web address:** www.amhsparta.org

HUGH CHATHAM MEMORIAL HOSPITAL (C, 208 beds) 180 Parkwood Drive, Elkin, NC Zip 28621–2430, Mailing Address: P.O. Box 560, Zip 28621–0560; tel. 336/527–7000; Michael J. Arno, Interim Chief Executive Officer
**Web address:** www.hughchatham.org

| Owned, leased, sponsored: | 1 hospital | 110 beds |
|---|---|---|
| Contract–managed: | 17 hospitals | 890 beds |
| Totals: | 18 hospitals | 1000 beds |

---

**★0041: ALLINA HEALTH** (NP)
2925 Chicago Avenue, Minneapolis, MN Zip 55407–1321, Mailing Address: P.O. Box 43, Zip 55440–0043; tel. 612/262–5000; Ken Paulus, President and Chief Executive Officer
**(Moderately Centralized Health System)**

**MINNESOTA:** ABBOTT NORTHWESTERN HOSPITAL (O, 631 beds) 800 East 28th Street, Minneapolis, MN Zip 55407–3799; tel. 612/863–4000; Ben Bache–Wiig, M.D., President
**Web address:** www.abbottnorthwestern.com

BUFFALO HOSPITAL (O, 44 beds) 303 Catlin Street, Buffalo, MN Zip 55313–1947; tel. 763/682–1212; Jennifer Myster, President
**Web address:** www.buffalohospital.org

CAMBRIDGE MEDICAL CENTER (O, 78 beds) 701 South Dellwood Street, Cambridge, MN Zip 55008–1920; tel. 763/689–7700; Gary Shaw, President
**Web address:** www.allina.com/ahs/cambridge.nsf

HUTCHINSON HEALTH (C, 57 beds) 1095 Highway 15 South, Hutchinson, MN Zip 55350–3182; tel. 320/234–5000; Steven Mulder, M.D., President and Chief Executive Officer
**Web address:** www.hutchhealth.com

MERCY HOSPITAL (O, 254 beds) 4050 Coon Rapids Boulevard, Coon Rapids, MN Zip 55433–2586; tel. 763/236–6000; Sara J. Criger, President
**Web address:** www.allinamercy.org

NEW ULM MEDICAL CENTER (O, 45 beds) 1324 Fifth Street North, New Ulm, MN Zip 56073–1553; tel. 507/217–5000; Toby Freier, President
**Web address:** www.newulmmedicalcenter.com

OWATONNA HOSPITAL (O, 43 beds) 2250 N.W. 26th Street, Owatonna, MN Zip 55060–5503; tel. 507/451–3850; David L. Albrecht, President
**Web address:** www.owatonnahospital.com

PHILLIPS EYE INSTITUTE (O, 8 beds) 2215 Park Avenue, Minneapolis, MN Zip 55404–3756; tel. 612/775–8800; Joan M. Arbach, Interim President
**Web address:** www.allinahealth.org/ahs/pei.nsf/

ST. FRANCIS REGIONAL MEDICAL CENTER (O, 86 beds) 1455 St. Francis Avenue, Shakopee, MN Zip 55379–3380; tel. 952/428–3000; Michael A. Baumgartner, President
**Web address:** www.stfrancis-shakopee.com

UNITED HOSPITAL (O, 398 beds) 333 North Smith Avenue, Saint Paul, MN Zip 55102–2389; tel. 651/241–8000; Thomas O'Connor, President
**Web address:** www.allina.com

UNITY HOSPITAL (O, 220 beds) 550 Osborne Road N.E., Fridley, MN Zip 55432–2799; tel. 763/236–5000; Lori Wightman, R.N., MSN, FACHE, President
**Web address:** www.allina.com

**WISCONSIN:** RIVER FALLS AREA HOSPITAL (O, 16 beds) 1629 East Division Street, River Falls, WI Zip 54022–1571; tel. 715/425–6155; David R. Miller, President
**Web address:** www.allina.com

| Owned, leased, sponsored: | 11 hospitals | 1823 beds |
|---|---|---|
| Contract–managed: | 1 hospital | 57 beds |
| Totals: | 12 hospitals | 1880 beds |

---

**0187: ALTA HEALTHCARE SYSTEM** (IO)
10780 Santa Monica Boulevard, Suite 400, Los Angeles, CA Zip 90025–7616; tel. 310/943–4500; David Topper, Chief Executive Officer

**CALIFORNIA:** HOLLYWOOD COMMUNITY HOSPITAL (O, 45 beds) 6245 De Longpre Avenue, Los Angeles, CA Zip 90028–9001; tel. 323/462–2271; Bruce P. Grimshaw, Chief Executive Officer
**Web address:** www.hollywoodcommunityhospital.org/

LOS ANGELES COMMUNITY HOSPITAL (O, 180 beds) 4081 East Olympic Boulevard, Los Angeles, CA Zip 90023–3330; tel. 323/267–0477; Omar Ramirez, Chief Executive Officer

| Owned, leased, sponsored: | 2 hospitals | 225 beds |
|---|---|---|
| Contract–managed: | 0 hospitals | 0 beds |
| Totals: | 2 hospitals | 225 beds |

---

**0877: ALTAPOINTE HEALTH SYSTEMS** (IO)
5750–A Southland Drive, Mobile, AL Zip 36693–3316; tel. 251/473–4423; J. Tuerk Schlesinger, Chief Executive Officer

**ALABAMA:** BAYPOINTE BEHAVIORAL HEALTH (O, 60 beds) 5800 Southland Drive, Mobile, AL Zip 36693–3313; tel. 251/661–0153; Heather Joseph, Hospital Administrator
**Web address:** www.altapointe.org

EASTPOINTE HOSPITAL (O, 18 beds) 7400 Roper Lane, Daphne, AL Zip 36526–5274; tel. 251/378–6500; Jarett Crum, Administrator
**Web address:** www.altapointe.org/eastpointe.php

| Owned, leased, sponsored: | 2 hospitals | 78 beds |
|---|---|---|
| Contract–managed: | 0 hospitals | 0 beds |
| Totals: | 2 hospitals | 78 beds |

---

**2295: AMERICAN PROVINCE OF LITTLE COMPANY OF MARY SISTERS** (CC)
9350 South California Avenue, Evergreen Park, IL Zip 60805–2595; tel. 708/229 5491; Sister Kathleen McIntyre, Province Leader
**(Moderately Centralized Health System)**

**ILLINOIS:** LITTLE COMPANY OF MARY HOSPITAL AND HEALTH CARE CENTERS (O, 288 beds) 2800 West 95th Street, Evergreen Park, IL Zip 60805–2795; tel. 708/422–6200; Dennis A. Reilly, President and Chief Executive Officer
**Web address:** www.lcmh.org

**INDIANA:** MEMORIAL HOSPITAL AND HEALTH CARE CENTER (O, 133 beds) 800 West Ninth Street, Jasper, IN Zip 47546–2516; tel. 812/996–2345; Raymond W. Snowden, President and Chief Executive Officer
**Web address:** www.mhhcc.org

| Owned, leased, sponsored: | 2 hospitals | 421 beds |
|---|---|---|
| Contract–managed: | 0 hospitals | 0 beds |
| Totals: | 2 hospitals | 421 beds |

---

**0644: AMG INTEGRATED HEALTHCARE MANAGEMENT** (IO)
101 La Rue France, Suite 500, Lafayette, LA Zip 70508–3144; tel. 337/269–9828; August J. Rantz, III, Founder and Chief Executive Officer
**(Independent Hospital System)**

**KANSAS:** AMG SPECIALTY HOSPITAL–WICHITA (O, 26 beds) 8080 East Pawnee Street, Wichita, KS Zip 67207–5475; tel. 316/682–0004; Robert A. Loepp, Jr., FACHE, Chief Executive Officer
**Web address:** www.amgwichita.com/

**LOUISIANA:** AMG SPECIALTY HOSPITAL–DENHAM SPRINGS (O, 117 beds) 8375 Florida Boulevard, Denham Springs, LA Zip 70726–7806; tel. 225/665–2664; Karen Crayton, Administrator
**Web address:** www.amgdenham.com/

AMG SPECIALTY HOSPITAL–FELICIANA (O, 16 beds) 9725 Grace Lane, Clinton, LA Zip 70722–4925; tel. 225/683–1600; Keith Carruth, Chief Executive Officer
**Web address:** www.amgfeliciana.com/

AMG SPECIALTY HOSPITAL–HOUMA (O, 40 beds) 629 Dunn Street, Houma, LA Zip 70360–4707; tel. 985/274–0001; Ricky Robeson, Chief Executive Officer

For explanation of codes following names, see page B2.
★ Indicates Type III membership in the American Hospital Association.

AMG SPECIALTY HOSPITAL–LAFAYETTE (O, 58 beds) 310 Youngsville Highway, Lafayette, LA Zip 70508–4524; tel. 337/839–9880; Jason Branson, Chief Executive Officer
**Web address:** www.amglafayette.com

AMG SPECIALTY HOSPITAL–SLIDELL (O, 40 beds) 1400 Lindberg Drive, Slidell, LA Zip 70458–8056; tel. 985/326–0440; Richard Daughdrill, R.N., Chief Executive Officer
**Web address:** www.amgslidell.com/

LAFAYETTE PHYSICAL REHABILITATION HOSPITAL (O, 32 beds) 307 Polly Lane, Lafayette, LA Zip 70508–4960; tel. 337/314–1111; Jonathan Landreth, Chief Executive Officer

NEUROMEDICAL CENTER REHABILITATION HOSPITAL (O, 23 beds) 10101 Park Rowe Avenue, Suite 500, Baton Rouge, LA Zip 70810–1685; tel. 225/906–2999; Jay Ivy, R.N., Chief Executive Officer
**Web address:** www.theneuromedicalcenter.com

**MISSISSIPPI:** AMG SPECIALTY HOSPITAL–GREENWOOD (O, 40 beds) 1401 River Road Floor 2, Greenwood, MS Zip 38930–4030; tel. 662/459–2681; Jennifer Wallace, Chief Executive Officer
**Web address:** www.amggreenwood.com/

**NEW MEXICO:** AMG SPECIALTY HOSPITAL–ALBUQUERQUE (O, 24 beds) 235 Elm Street N.E., Albuquerque, NM Zip 87102–3672; tel. 505/842–5550; Elizabeth Rees, Chief Executive Officer
**Web address:** www.amgalbuquerque.com/

**OKLAHOMA:** AMG SPECIALTY HOSPITAL–EDMOND (O, 37 beds) 1100 East Ninth Street, Edmond, OK Zip 73034–5755; tel. 405/341–8150; Ginger Creech, Chief Executive Officer
**Web address:** www.amgedmond.com/

| | | |
|---|---|---|
| Owned, leased, sponsored: | 11 hospitals | 453 beds |
| Contract–managed: | 0 hospitals | 0 beds |
| Totals: | 11 hospitals | 453 beds |

● **0389: ANMED HEALTH** (NP)
800 North Fant Street, Anderson, SC Zip 29621–5793; tel. 864/512–1000; John A. Miller, Jr., FACHE, Chief Executive Officer
**(Moderately Centralized Health System)**

**SOUTH CAROLINA:** ANMED HEALTH MEDICAL CENTER (O, 322 beds) 800 North Fant Street, Anderson, SC Zip 29621–5793; tel. 864/512–1000; John A. Miller, Jr., FACHE, Chief Executive Officer
**Web address:** www.anmedhealth.org

| | | |
|---|---|---|
| Owned, leased, sponsored: | 1 hospital | 322 beds |
| Contract–managed: | 0 hospitals | 0 beds |
| Totals: | 1 hospital | 322 beds |

★ **0866: APPALACHIAN REGIONAL HEALTHCARE SYSTEM** (NP)
336 Deerfield Road, Boone, NC Zip 28607–5008, Mailing Address: P.O. Box 2600, Zip 28607–2600; tel. 828/262–4100; Richard G. Sparks, President and Chief Executive Officer
**(Independent Hospital System)**

**NORTH CAROLINA:** BLOWING ROCK HOSPITAL (C, 97 beds) 418 Chestnut Street, Blowing Rock, NC Zip 28605–0148, Mailing Address: P.O. Box 148, Zip 28605–0148; tel. 828/295–3136; Timothy R. Ford, Chief Executive Officer / President
**Web address:** www.https://apprhs.org/locations/blowing–rock–hospital

CHARLES A. CANNON MEMORIAL HOSPITAL (C, 35 beds) 434 Hospital Drive, Linville, NC Zip 28646, Mailing Address: P.O. Box 767, Zip 28646–0767; tel. 828/737–7000; Carmen Lacey, MSN, R.N., President
**Web address:** www.https://apprhs.org/locations/cannon–memorial–hospital

WATAUGA MEDICAL CENTER (C, 99 beds) 336 Deerfield Road, Boone, NC Zip 28607–5008, Mailing Address: P.O. Box 2600, Zip 28607–2600; tel. 828/262–4100; Chuck Mantooth, President
**Web address:** www.https://apprhs.org/locations/watauga–medical–center

| | | |
|---|---|---|
| Owned, leased, sponsored: | 0 hospitals | 0 beds |
| Contract–managed: | 3 hospitals | 231 beds |
| Totals: | 3 hospitals | 231 beds |

**0145: APPALACHIAN REGIONAL HEALTHCARE, INC.** (NP)
2285 Executive Drive, Suite 400, Lexington, KY Zip 40505–4810, Mailing Address: P.O. Box 8086, Zip 40533–8086; tel. 859/226–2440; Jerry Haynes, President and Chief Executive Officer
**(Decentralized Health System)**

**KENTUCKY:** HARLAN ARH HOSPITAL (O, 137 beds) 81 Ball Park Road, Harlan, KY Zip 40831–1792; tel. 606/573–8100; Dan Stone, Community Chief Executive Officer
**Web address:** www.arh.org

HAZARD ARH REGIONAL MEDICAL CENTER (O, 308 beds) 100 Medical Center Drive, Hazard, KY Zip 41701–9421; tel. 606/439–6600; Donald R. Fields, Senior Community Chief Executive Officer
**Web address:** www.arh.org

MARY BRECKINRIDGE ARH HOSPITAL (O, 25 beds) 130 Kate Ireland Drive, Hyden, KY Zip 41749–9071, Mailing Address: P.O. Box 447–A, Zip 41749–0717; tel. 606/672–2901; Mallie S. Noble, Administrator
**Web address:** www.frontiernursing.org

MCDOWELL ARH HOSPITAL (O, 25 beds) Route 122, McDowell, KY Zip 41647, Mailing Address: P.O. Box 247, Zip 41647–0247; tel. 606/377–3400; Russell Barker, Community Chief Executive Officer
**Web address:** www.arh.org

MIDDLESBORO ARH HOSPITAL (O, 96 beds) 3600 West Cumberland Avenue, Middlesboro, KY Zip 40965–2614, Mailing Address: P.O. Box 340, Zip 40965–0340; tel. 606/242–1100; Michael Slusher, Community Chief Executive Officer
**Web address:** www.arh.org/middlesboro

MORGAN COUNTY ARH HOSPITAL (L, 25 beds) 476 Liberty Road, West Liberty, KY Zip 41472–2049, Mailing Address: P.O. Box 579, Zip 41472–0579; tel. 606/743–3186; Stephen M. Gavalchik, FACHE, Community Chief Executive Officer
**Web address:** www.arh.org

WHITESBURG ARH HOSPITAL (O, 85 beds) 240 Hospital Road, Whitesburg, KY Zip 41858–7627; tel. 606/633–3600; Dena C. Sparkman, FACHE, Community Chief Executive Officer
**Web address:** www.arh.org/whitesburg

WILLIAMSON ARH HOSPITAL (O, 126 beds) 260 Hospital Drive, South Williamson, KY Zip 41503–4072; tel. 606/237–1710; Timothy A. Hatfield, Community Chief Executive Officer
**Web address:** www.arh.org

**WEST VIRGINIA:** BECKLEY ARH HOSPITAL (O, 169 beds) 306 Stanaford Road, Beckley, WV Zip 25801–3142; tel. 304/255–3000; Rocco K. Massey, Community Chief Executive Officer
**Web address:** www.arh.org

SUMMERS COUNTY ARH HOSPITAL (L, 25 beds) Terrace Street, Hinton, WV Zip 25951–2407, Mailing Address: Drawer 940, Zip 25951–0940; tel. 304/466–1000; Wesley Dangerfield, Community Chief Executive Officer
**Web address:** www.arh.org

| | | |
|---|---|---|
| Owned, leased, sponsored: | 10 hospitals | 1021 beds |
| Contract–managed: | 0 hospitals | 0 beds |
| Totals: | 10 hospitals | 1021 beds |

★ **0104: ARCHBOLD MEDICAL CENTER** (NP)
910 South Broad Street, Thomasville, GA Zip 31792–6113; tel. 229/228–2739; J. Perry Mustian, President
**(Moderately Centralized Health System)**

**GEORGIA:** BROOKS COUNTY HOSPITAL (L, 25 beds) 903 North Court Street, Quitman, GA Zip 31643–1315, Mailing Address: P.O. Box 5000, Zip 31643–5000; tel. 229/263–4171; Kenneth D. Rhudy, Chief Executive Officer
**Web address:** www.archbold.org

For explanation of codes following names, see page B2.
★ Indicates Type III membership in the American Hospital Association.
● Single hospital health care system

GRADY GENERAL HOSPITAL (L, 48 beds) 1155 Fifth Street S.E., Cairo, GA Zip 39828–3142, Mailing Address: P.O. Box 360, Zip 39828–0360; tel. 229/377–1150; LaDon Toole, Chief Operating Officer and Administrator
**Web address:** www.archbold.org

JOHN D. ARCHBOLD MEMORIAL HOSPITAL (O, 293 beds) 915 Gordon Avenue, Thomasville, GA Zip 31792–6614, Mailing Address: P.O. Box 1018, Zip 31799–1018; tel. 229/228–2000; J. Perry Mustian, President and Chief Executive Officer
**Web address:** www.archbold.org

MITCHELL COUNTY HOSPITAL (L, 181 beds) 90 East Stephens Street, Camilla, GA Zip 31730–1836, Mailing Address: P.O. Box 639, Zip 31730–0639; tel. 229/336–5284; Mark E. Kimball, Administrator
**Web address:** www.archbold.org

| | | |
|---|---|---|
| Owned, leased, sponsored: | 4 hospitals | 547 beds |
| Contract–managed: | 0 hospitals | 0 beds |
| Totals: | 4 hospitals | 547 beds |

---

★**0069:   ARDENT HEALTH SERVICES** (IO)
1 Burton Hills Boulevard, Suite 250, Nashville, TN Zip 37215–6195; tel. 615/296–3000; David T. Vandewater, President and Chief Executive Officer
**(Moderately Centralized Health System)**

**NEW MEXICO:** LOVELACE MEDICAL CENTER (O, 263 beds) 601 Martin Luther King Avenue N.E., Albuquerque, NM Zip 87102–3619; tel. 505/727–8000; Troy Greer, Chief Executive Officer
**Web address:** www.lovelace.com/albuquerque–hospital/lovelace–medical–center#.UDZ1laDhf48

LOVELACE REGIONAL HOSPITAL (O, 26 beds) 117 East 19th Street, Roswell, NM Zip 88201–5151; tel. 575/627–7000; Dawn M. Tschabrun, R.N., Chief Executive Officer
**Web address:** www.roswellregional.com

LOVELACE REHABILITATION HOSPITAL (O, 62 beds) 505 Elm Street N.E., Albuquerque, NM Zip 87102–2500; tel. 505/727–4700; Derrick Jones, Chief Executive Officer
**Web address:** www.lovelace.com

LOVELACE WESTSIDE HOSPITAL (O, 80 beds) 10501 Golf Course Road N.W., Albuquerque, NM Zip 87114–5000, Mailing Address: P.O. Box 25555, Zip 87125–0555; tel. 505/727–2000; Farron Sneed, FACHE, Chief Executive Officer
**Web address:** www.lovelace.com/albuquerque–hospital/lovelace–westside–hospital#.UDZ1t6Dhf48

LOVELACE WOMEN'S HOSPITAL (O, 78 beds) 4701 Montgomery Boulevard N.E., Albuquerque, NM Zip 87109–1251, Mailing Address: P.O. Box 25555, Zip 87125–0555; tel. 505/727–7800; Sheri Milone, Chief Executive Officer and Administrator
**Web address:** www.lovelace.com/albuquerque–hospital/lovelace–womens–hospital#.UDZ17KDhf48

**OKLAHOMA:** BAILEY MEDICAL CENTER (O, 37 beds) 10502 North 110th East Avenue, Owasso, OK Zip 74055–6655; tel. 918/376–8000; Keith Mason, Chief Executive Officer
**Web address:** www.baileymedicalcenter.com

HILLCREST HOSPITAL – SOUTH (O, 160 beds) 8801 South 101st East Avenue, Tulsa, OK Zip 74133–5716; tel. 918/294–4000; Joseph H. Neely, FACHE, Chief Executive Officer
**Web address:** www.southcresthospital.com

HILLCREST HOSPITAL CLAREMORE (O, 55 beds) 1202 North Muskogee Place, Claremore, OK Zip 74017–3036; tel. 918/341–2556; David Chaussard, Chief Executive Officer
**Web address:** www.hillcrestclaremore.com

HILLCREST HOSPITAL CUSHING (O, 95 beds) 1027 East Cherry Street, Cushing, OK Zip 74023–4101, Mailing Address: P.O. Box 1409, Zip 74023–1409; tel. 918/225–2915; Kevin Hawk, Chief Executive Officer
**Web address:** www.hillcrestcushing.com/

HILLCREST HOSPITAL HENRYETTA (O, 41 beds) Dewey Bartlett & Main Streets, Henryetta, OK Zip 74437–6820, Mailing Address: P.O. Box 1269, Zip 74437–1269; tel. 918/650–1100; Dee Renshaw, Chief Executive Officer
**Web address:** www.hillcresthenryetta.com/

HILLCREST MEDICAL CENTER (O, 532 beds) 1120 South Utica, Tulsa, OK Zip 74104–4090; tel. 918/579–1000; Jason Fahrlander, FACHE, Chief Executive Officer
**Web address:** www.hillcrest.com

| | | |
|---|---|---|
| Owned, leased, sponsored: | 11 hospitals | 1429 beds |
| Contract–managed: | 0 hospitals | 0 beds |
| Totals: | 11 hospitals | 1429 beds |

---

★**0809:   ARNOT HEALTH** (NP)
600 Roe Avenue, Elmira, NY Zip 14905–1629; tel. 607/737–4100; Anthony J. Cooper, FACHE, President and Chief Executive Officer
**(Centralized Physician/Insurance Health System)**

**NEW YORK:** ARNOT OGDEN MEDICAL CENTER (O, 244 beds) 600 Roe Avenue, Elmira, NY Zip 14905–1629; tel. 607/737–4100; H. Fred Farley, R.N., Ph.D., FACHE, President and Chief Operating Officer
**Web address:** www.aomc.org

IRA DAVENPORT MEMORIAL HOSPITAL (O, 156 beds) 7571 State Route 54, Bath, NY Zip 14810–9590; tel. 607/776–8500; James B. Watson, Chief Operating Officer
**Web address:** www.davenportandtaylor.org

ST. JOSEPH'S HOSPITAL (O, 212 beds) 555 St. Joseph's Boulevard, Elmira, NY Zip 14901–3223; tel. 607/733–6541; H. Fred Farley, R.N., Ph.D., FACHE, President and Chief Operating Officer
**Web address:** www.stjosephs.org

| | | |
|---|---|---|
| Owned, leased, sponsored: | 3 hospitals | 612 beds |
| Contract–managed: | 0 hospitals | 0 beds |
| Totals: | 3 hospitals | 612 beds |

---

★**0094:   ASANTE HEALTH SYSTEM** (NP)
2650 Siskiyou Boulevard, Suite 200, Medford, OR Zip 97504–8170; tel. 541/789–4100; Roy G. Vinyard, FACHE, President and Chief Executive Officer
**(Moderately Centralized Health System)**

**OREGON:** ASHLAND COMMUNITY HOSPITAL (O, 36 beds) 280 Maple Street, Ashland, OR Zip 97520–1593; tel. 541/201–4000; Marvin Haas, Interim Chief Executive Officer
**Web address:** www.ashlandhospital.org

ROGUE VALLEY MEDICAL CENTER (O, 307 beds) 2825 East Barnett Road, Medford, OR Zip 97504–8332; tel. 541/789–7000; Scott A. Kelly, Chief Executive Officer
**Web address:** www.asante.org/rrmc/

THREE RIVERS MEDICAL CENTER (O, 107 beds) 500 S.W. Ramsey Avenue, Grants Pass, OR Zip 97527–5554; tel. 541/472–7000; Win Howard, Chief Executive Officer
**Web address:** www.asante.org/trmc/

| | | |
|---|---|---|
| Owned, leased, sponsored: | 3 hospitals | 450 beds |
| Contract–managed: | 0 hospitals | 0 beds |
| Totals: | 3 hospitals | 450 beds |

---

★**0198:   ASCENSION HEALTH** (CC)
4600 Edmundson Road, Saint Louis, MO Zip 63134–3806; tel. 314/733–8000; Robert J. Henkel, FACHE, President and Chief Executive Officer
**(Decentralized Health System)**

**ALABAMA:** PROVIDENCE HOSPITAL (S, 349 beds) 6801 Airport Boulevard, Mobile, AL Zip 36608–3785, Mailing Address: P.O. Box 850429, Zip 36685–0429; tel. 251/633–1000; Clark P. Christianson, President and Chief Executive Officer
**Web address:** www.providencehospital.org

ST. VINCENT'S BIRMINGHAM (S, 409 beds) 810 St. Vincent's Drive, Birmingham, AL Zip 35205–1695, Mailing Address: P.O. Box 12407, Zip 35202–2407; tel. 205/939–7000; Andy Davis, President
**Web address:** www.stvhs.com

For explanation of codes following names, see page B2.
★ Indicates Type III membership in the American Hospital Association.

Section B

ST. VINCENT'S BLOUNT (S, 40 beds) 150 Gilbreath, Oneonta, AL
Zip 35121–2827, Mailing Address: P.O. Box 1000, Zip 35121–0013;
tel. 205/274–3000; Evan Ray, President
**Web address:** www.stvhs.com

ST. VINCENT'S EAST (S, 336 beds) 50 Medical Park East Drive, Birmingham,
AL Zip 35235–9987; tel. 205/838–3000; Sean Tinney, FACHE, President
and Chief Operating Officer
**Web address:** www.stvhs.com

ST. VINCENT'S ST. CLAIR (S, 46 beds) 7063 Veterans Parkway, Pell City, AL
Zip 35125–1499; tel. 205/338–3301; Evan Ray, President
**Web address:** www.stvhs.com

**ARIZONA:** CARONDELET HOLY CROSS HOSPITAL (S, 56 beds) 1171 West
Target Range Road, Nogales, AZ Zip 85621–2415; tel. 520/285–3000;
Debbie Knapheide, MSN, Site Administrator, Chief Nursing Officer and
Chief Operating Officer
**Web address:** www.carondelet.org

CARONDELET ST. JOSEPH'S HOSPITAL (S, 449 beds) 350 North Wilmot
Road, Tucson, AZ Zip 85711–2678; tel. 520/296–3211; Tony Fonze,
President and Chief Executive Officer
**Web address:** www.carondelet.org

CARONDELET ST. MARY'S HOSPITAL (S, 429 beds) 1601 West St. Mary's
Road, Tucson, AZ Zip 85745–2682; tel. 520/872–3000; Amy Beiter, M.D.,
President and Chief Executive Officer
**Web address:** www.carondelet.org

**CONNECTICUT:** ST. VINCENT'S MEDICAL CENTER (S, 414 beds) 2800 Main
Street, Bridgeport, CT Zip 06606–4292; tel. 203/576–5454; Susan L.
Davis, R.N., Ed.D., FACHE, Chief Executive Officer
**Web address:** www.stvincents.org

**DISTRICT OF COLUMBIA:** PROVIDENCE HOSPITAL (S, 541 beds) 1150
Varnum Street N.E., Washington, DC Zip 20017–2104;
tel. 202/269–7000; Amy E. Freeman, President and Chief Executive
Officer
**Web address:** www.provhosp.org

**FLORIDA:** SACRED HEART HOSPITAL OF PENSACOLA (S, 466 beds) 5151
North Ninth Avenue, Pensacola, FL Zip 32504–8795, Mailing Address:
P.O. Box 2700, Zip 32513–2700; tel. 850/416–7000; Henry Stovall,
President
**Web address:** www.sacred–heart.org

SACRED HEART HOSPITAL ON THE EMERALD COAST (S, 58 beds) 7800
Highway 98 West, Miramar Beach, FL Zip 32550; tel. 850/278–3000; Roger
L. Hall, President
**Web address:** www.sacredheartemerald.org

SACRED HEART HOSPITAL ON THE GULF (S, 19 beds) 3801 East Highway
98, Port St. Joe, FL Zip 32456–5318; tel. 850/229–5600; Roger L. Hall,
President
**Web address:** www.sacred–heart.org/gulf/

ST. VINCENT'S MEDICAL CENTER RIVERSIDE (S, 501 beds) 1 Shircliff Way,
Jacksonville, FL Zip 32204–4748, Mailing Address: P.O. Box 2982,
Zip 32203–2982; tel. 904/308–7300; Moody L. Chisholm, President & Chief
Executive Officer
**Web address:** www.jaxhealth.com

ST. VINCENT'S MEDICAL CENTER SOUTHSIDE (S, 269 beds) 4201 Belfort
Road, Jacksonville, FL Zip 32216–1431; tel. 904/296–3700; Moody L.
Chisholm, President and Chief Executive Officer
**Web address:** www.jaxhealth.com

**IDAHO:** ST. JOSEPH REGIONAL MEDICAL CENTER (S, 119 beds) 415 Sixth
Street, Lewiston, ID Zip 83501–2431; tel. 208/743–2511; Timothy
Sayler, President and Chief Executive Officer
**Web address:** www.sjrmc.org

**ILLINOIS:** ALEXIAN BROTHERS BEHAVIORAL HEALTH HOSPITAL (O, 141 beds)
1650 Moon Lake Boulevard, Hoffman Estates, IL Zip 60169–1010;
tel. 847/882–1600; Clayton Ciha, President and Chief Executive Officer
**Web address:** www.abbhh.org

ALEXIAN BROTHERS MEDICAL CENTER (O, 370 beds) 800 Biesterfield Road,
Elk Grove Village, IL Zip 60007–3397; tel. 847/437–5500; John P.
Werrbach, Chief Executive Officer
**Web address:** www.alexian.org

ST. ALEXIUS MEDICAL CENTER (O, 305 beds) 1555 Barrington Road,
Hoffman Estates, IL Zip 60169–1019; tel. 847/843–2000; Leonard Wilk,
President and Chief Executive Officer
**Web address:** www.stalexius.org

**INDIANA:** ST. JOSEPH HOSPITAL AND HEALTH CENTER (S, 137 beds) 1907
West Sycamore Street, Kokomo, IN Zip 46901–4197, Mailing Address:
P.O. Box 9010, Zip 46904–9010; tel. 765/452–5611; Kathlene A.
Young, MS, FACHE, President and Chief Executive Officer
**Web address:** www.stjoseph.stvincent.org

ST. MARY'S WARRICK HOSPITAL (S, 35 beds) 1116 Millis Avenue, Boonville,
IN Zip 47601–2204; tel. 812/897–4800; Carol Godsey, Administrator
**Web address:** www.stmarys.org/warrick

ST. MARY'S MEDICAL CENTER OF EVANSVILLE (S, 433 beds) 3700
Washington Avenue, Evansville, IN Zip 47714–0541; tel. 812/485–4000;
Timothy A. Flesch, President and Chief Executive Officer
**Web address:** www.stmarys.org

ST. VINCENT ANDERSON REGIONAL HOSPITAL (S, 185 beds) 2015 Jackson
Street, Anderson, IN Zip 46016–4339; tel. 765/649–2511; Thomas J.
VanOsdol, President
**Web address:** www.stvincent.org/Saint–Johns/Default.aspx

ST. VINCENT CARMEL HOSPITAL (S, 107 beds) 13500 North Meridian Street,
Carmel, IN Zip 46032–1456; tel. 317/582–7000; Michael D. Chittenden,
President
**Web address:** www.stvincent.org

ST. VINCENT CLAY HOSPITAL (S, 25 beds) 1206 East National Avenue,
Brazil, IN Zip 47834–2797, Mailing Address: P.O. Box 489,
Zip 47834–0489; tel. 812/442–2500; Jerry Laue, Administrator
**Web address:** www.stvincent.org

ST. VINCENT DUNN HOSPITAL (S, 25 beds) 1600 23rd Street, Bedford, IN
Zip 47421–4704; tel. 812/275–3331; Joseph E. Roche, Chief Executive
Officer
**Web address:** www.stvincent.org/St–Vincent–Dunn/Default.aspx

ST. VINCENT FRANKFORT HOSPITAL (S, 25 beds) 1300 South Jackson
Street, Frankfort, IN Zip 46041–3394, Mailing Address: P.O. Box 669,
Zip 46041–0669; tel. 765/656–3000; Thomas Crawford, Administrator
**Web address:** www.stvincent.org

ST. VINCENT HEART CENTER OF INDIANA (S, 107 beds) 10580 North
Meridian Street, Indianapolis, IN Zip 46290–1028; tel. 317/583–5000; Blake
A. Dye, President
**Web address:** www.bestheartcare.com/

ST. VINCENT INDIANAPOLIS HOSPITAL (S, 903 beds) 2001 West 86th Street,
Indianapolis, IN Zip 46260–1991, Mailing Address: P.O. Box 40970,
Zip 46240–0970; tel. 317/338–2345; Kyle De Fur, FACHE, President
**Web address:** www.stvincent.org

ST. VINCENT JENNINGS HOSPITAL (S, 25 beds) 301 Henry Street, North
Vernon, IN Zip 47265–1097; tel. 812/352–4200; Carl W. Risk, II,
Administrator
**Web address:** www.stvincent.org

ST. VINCENT MERCY HOSPITAL (S, 25 beds) 1331 South A Street, Elwood,
IN Zip 46036–1942; tel. 765/552–4600; Deborah Y. Rasper, FACHE,
Administrator
**Web address:** www.stvincent.org

ST. VINCENT RANDOLPH HOSPITAL (S, 16 beds) 473 Greenville Avenue,
Winchester, IN Zip 47394–9436, Mailing Address: P.O. Box 407,
Zip 47394–0407; tel. 765/584–0004; Francis G. Albarano, Administrator
**Web address:** www.stvincent.org

ST. VINCENT SALEM HOSPITAL (S, 25 beds) 911 North Shelby Street, Salem,
IN Zip 47167–1694; tel. 812/883–5881; Lee Jaeger, FACHE, Chief
Executive Officer
**Web address:** www.stvincent.org/St–Vincent–Salem/Default.aspx

ST. VINCENT SETON SPECIALTY HOSPITAL (S, 30 beds) 1501 Hartford
Street, Lafayette, IN Zip 47904–2134; tel. 765/236–8900; Peter H.
Alexander, Administrator
**Web address:** www.stvincent.org

ST. VINCENT SETON SPECIALTY HOSPITAL (S, 74 beds) 8050 Township Line
Road, Indianapolis, IN Zip 46260–2478; tel. 317/415–8353; Peter H.
Alexander, Administrator
**Web address:** www.stvincent.org/

ST. VINCENT WILLIAMSPORT HOSPITAL (S, 16 beds) 412 North Monroe
Street, Williamsport, IN Zip 47993–1049; tel. 765/762–4000; Jane Craigin,
Chief Executive Officer
**Web address:** www.stvincent.org

**KANSAS:** MERCY REGIONAL HEALTH CENTER (O, 96 beds) 1823 College
Avenue, Manhattan, KS Zip 66502–3346; tel. 785/776–3322; John R.
Broberg, FACHE, President and Chief Executive Officer
**Web address:** www.mercyregional.org

For explanation of codes following names, see page B2.
★ Indicates Type III membership in the American Hospital Association.

SEDAN CITY HOSPITAL (C, 25 beds) 300 North Street, Sedan, KS Zip 67361–1051, Mailing Address: P.O. Box C, Zip 67361–0427; tel. 620/725–3115; Michelle Williams, Administrator

VIA CHRISTI HOSPITAL IN PITTSBURG (O, 111 beds) 1 Mt. Carmel Way, Pittsburg, KS Zip 66762–7587; tel. 620/232–0109; Randall R. Cason, FACHE, President and Chief Executive Officer
**Web address:** www.viachristi.org

VIA CHRISTI HOSPITAL ON ST. FRANCIS (O, 751 beds) 929 North St. Francis Street, Wichita, KS Zip 67214–3882; tel. 316/268–5000; Sherry Hausmann, President
**Web address:** www.via–christi.org

VIA CHRISTI HOSPITAL ON ST. TERESA (O, 70 beds) 14800 West St. Teresa, Wichita, KS Zip 67235–9602; tel. 316/796–7000; Kevin Strecker, President
**Web address:** www.via–christi.org/st-teresa

VIA CHRISTI REHABILITATION CENTER (O, 58 beds) 1151 North Rock Road, Wichita, KS Zip 67206–1262; tel. 316/634–3400; Cindy LaFleur, President
**Web address:** www.via–christi.org

**MARYLAND:** SAINT AGNES HOSPITAL (S, 344 beds) 900 Caton Avenue, Baltimore, MD Zip 21229–5201; tel. 410/368–6000; Bonnie Phipps, President and Chief Executive Officer
**Web address:** www.stagnes.org

**MICHIGAN:** BORGESS MEDICAL CENTER (S, 387 beds) 1521 Gull Road, Kalamazoo, MI Zip 49048–1640; tel. 269/226–7000; Paul A. Spaude, FACHE, President and Chief Executive Officer
**Web address:** www.borgess.com

BORGESS–LEE MEMORIAL HOSPITAL (S, 25 beds) 420 West High Street, Dowagiac, MI Zip 49047–1943; tel. 269/782–8681; John Ryder, Interim Administrator and Chief Operating Officer
**Web address:** www.borgess.com

BORGESS–PIPP HOSPITAL (S, 43 beds) 411 Naomi Street, Plainwell, MI Zip 49080–1222; tel. 269/685–6811; John Ryder, Administrator and Chief Executive Officer
**Web address:** www.borgess.com

BRIGHTON CENTER FOR RECOVERY (S, 99 beds) 12851 Grand River Road, Brighton, MI Zip 48116–8506; tel. 810/227–1211; Raymond Waller, Director
**Web address:** www.brightonhospital.org

GENESYS REGIONAL MEDICAL CENTER (S, 410 beds) One Genesys Parkway, Grand Blanc, MI Zip 48439–8066; tel. 810/606–5000; Elizabeth Aderholdt, President
**Web address:** www.genesys.org

PROVIDENCE HOSPITAL (S, 565 beds) 16001 West Nine Mile Road, Southfield, MI Zip 48075–4818, Mailing Address: P.O. Box 2043, Zip 48037–2043; tel. 248/424–3000; Michael Wiemann, M.D., President
**Web address:** www.providence–stjohnhealth.org

ST. JOHN HOSPITAL AND MEDICAL CENTER (S, 673 beds) 22101 Moross Road, Detroit, MI Zip 48236–2148; tel. 313/343–4000; David Brooks, Chief Executive Officer
**Web address:** www.stjohn.org

ST. JOHN MACOMB–OAKLAND HOSPITAL (S, 495 beds) 11800 East 12 Mile Road, Warren, MI Zip 48093–3472; tel. 586/573–5000; Terry Hamilton, President
**Web address:** www.stjohnprovidence.org/macomb

ST. JOHN RIVER DISTRICT HOSPITAL (S, 68 beds) 4100 River Road, East China, MI Zip 48054–2909; tel. 810/329–7111; Frank W. Poma, President
**Web address:** www.stjohn.org

ST. JOSEPH HEALTH SYSTEM (S, 20 beds) 200 Hemlock Street, Tawas City, MI Zip 48763–9237, Mailing Address: P.O. Box 659, Zip 48764–0659; tel. 989/362–3411; Ann M. Balfour, R.N., President
**Web address:** www.sjhsys.org

ST. MARY'S OF MICHIGAN (S, 236 beds) 800 South Washington Avenue, Saginaw, MI Zip 48601–2594; tel. 989/907–8000; John R. Graham, President and Chief Executive Officer
**Web address:** www.stmarysofmichigan.org

ST. MARY'S OF MICHIGAN STANDISH HOSPITAL (S, 64 beds) 805 West Cedar Street, Standish, MI Zip 48658–9526; tel. 989/846–4521; Rose Goick, MSN, Administrative Director of Operations
**Web address:** www.stmarysofmichigan.org/standish

**MINNESOTA:** SAINT ELIZABETH'S MEDICAL CENTER (O, 166 beds) 1200 Grant Boulevard West, Wabasha, MN Zip 55981–1042; tel. 651/565–4531; Thomas Crowley, President and Chief Executive Officer
**Web address:** www.stelizabethswabasha.org

**MISSOURI:** ST. JOSEPH MEDICAL CENTER (S, 191 beds) 1000 Carondelet Drive, Kansas City, MO Zip 64114–4673; tel. 816/942–4400; Michael A. Dorsey, FACHE, Chief Executive Officer
**Web address:** www.carondelethealth.org

ST. MARY'S MEDICAL CENTER (S, 131 beds) 201 West R. D. Mize Road, Blue Springs, MO Zip 64014–2518; tel. 816/228–5900; Annette Small, R.N., Chief Executive Officer
**Web address:** www.carondelethealth.org

**NEW YORK:** MOUNT ST. MARY'S HOSPITAL AND HEALTH CENTER (S, 405 beds) 5300 Military Road, Lewiston, NY Zip 14092–1903; tel. 716/297–4800; Judith A. Maness, FACHE, President and Chief Executive Officer
**Web address:** www.msmh.org

OUR LADY OF LOURDES MEMORIAL HOSPITAL (S, 154 beds) 169 Riverside Drive, Binghamton, NY Zip 13905–4246; tel. 607/798–5111; David Patak, President and Chief Executive Officer
**Web address:** www.lourdes.com

ST. MARY'S HEALTHCARE (S, 290 beds) 427 Guy Park Avenue, Amsterdam, NY Zip 12010–1054; tel. 518/842–1900; Victor Giulianelli, FACHE, President and Chief Executive Officer
**Web address:** www.smha.org

**OKLAHOMA:** JANE PHILLIPS MEDICAL CENTER (O, 140 beds) 3500 East Frank Phillips Boulevard, Bartlesville, OK Zip 74006–2411; tel. 918/333–7200; David R. Stire, President and Chief Executive Officer
**Web address:** www.jpmc.org

JANE PHILLIPS NOWATA HEALTH CENTER (O, 13 beds) 237 South Locust Street, Nowata, OK Zip 74048–3660, Mailing Address: P.O. Box 426, Zip 74048–0426; tel. 918/273–3102; Scott Upton, Administrator
**Web address:** www.jpmc.org

PAWHUSKA HOSPITAL (C, 27 beds) 1101 East 15th Street, Pawhuska, OK Zip 74056–1920; tel. 918/287–3232; Karen Arrowsmith, Administrator

ST. JOHN BROKEN ARROW (O, 44 beds) 1000 West Boise Circle, Broken Arrow, OK Zip 74012–4900; tel. 918/994–8100; David L. Phillips, Chief Executive Officer
**Web address:** www.stjohnbrokenarrow.com

ST. JOHN MEDICAL CENTER (O, 547 beds) 1923 South Utica Avenue, Tulsa, OK Zip 74104–6502; tel. 918/744–2345; Jeffrey D. Nowlin, Vice President, Chief Operating Officer
**Web address:** www.sjmc.org

ST. JOHN OWASSO (O, 36 beds) 12451 East 100th Street North, Owasso, OK Zip 74055–4600; tel. 918/274–5000; David L. Phillips, President and Chief Executive Officer
**Web address:** www.stjohnowasso.com

ST. JOHN SAPULPA (O, 25 beds) 519 South Division Street, Sapulpa, OK Zip 74066–4501, Mailing Address: P.O. Box 1368, Zip 74067–1368; tel. 918/224–4280; Valerie Round, Chief Executive Officer
**Web address:** www.sjmc.org

**TENNESSEE:** SAINT THOMAS MIDTOWN HOSPITAL (S, 425 beds) 2000 Church Street, Nashville, TN Zip 37236–0002; tel. 615/284–5555; Bernard Sherry, President and Chief Executive Officer
**Web address:** www.baptisthospital.com

SAINT THOMAS HOSPITAL FOR SPINAL SURGERY (S, 23 beds) 2011 Murphy Avenue, Suite 400, Nashville, TN Zip 37203–2065; tel. 615/341–7500; Kathy Watson, R.N., Administrator and Chief Nursing Officer
**Web address:** www.centerforspinalsurgery.com

SAINT THOMAS HICKMAN HOSPITAL (S, 65 beds) 135 East Swan Street, Centerville, TN Zip 37033–1417; tel. 931/729–4271; Jack M. Keller, Administrator
**Web address:** www.hickmanhospital.com

SAINT THOMAS RUTHERFORD HOSPITAL (S, 286 beds) 1700 Medical Center Parkway, Murfreesboro, TN Zip 37129–2245; tel. 615/396–4100; Gordon B. Ferguson, President and Chief Executive Officer
**Web address:** www.mtmc.org

For explanation of codes following names, see page B2.
★ Indicates Type III membership in the American Hospital Association.

Section B

SAINT THOMAS WEST HOSPITAL (S, 395 beds) 4220 Harding Road, Nashville, TN Zip 37205–2095, Mailing Address: P.O. Box 380, Zip 37202–0380; tel. 615/222–2111; Dawn Rudolph, Chief Executive Officer
**Web address:** www.stthomas.org

**TEXAS:** DELL CHILDREN'S MEDICAL CENTER OF CENTRAL TEXAS (S, 176 beds) 4900 Mueller Boulevard, Austin, TX Zip 78723–3079; tel. 512/324–0000; Mark W. Shen, M.D., Chief Executive Officer
**Web address:** www.dellchildrens.net

PROVIDENCE HEALTH CENTER (S, 647 beds) 6901 Medical Parkway, Waco, TX Zip 76712–7998, Mailing Address: P.O. Box 2589, Zip 76702–2589; tel. 254/751–4764; Brett A. Esrock, President and Chief Executive Officer
**Web address:** www.providence.net

SETON EDGAR B. DAVIS HOSPITAL (S, 25 beds) 130 Hays Street, Luling, TX Zip 78648–3207; tel. 830/875–7000; Apryl Haynes, R.N., Vice President, Chief Operating Officer, Chief Nursing Officer and Administrator
**Web address:** www.seton.net/locations/edgar_davis/

SETON HIGHLAND LAKES (S, 25 beds) 3201 South Water Street, Burnet, TX Zip 78611–4510, Mailing Address: P.O. Box 1219, Zip 78611–7219; tel. 512/715–3000; Michelle Robertson, R.N., President and Chief Executive Officer
**Web address:** www.seton.net

SETON MEDICAL CENTER AUSTIN (S, 425 beds) 1201 West 38th Street, Austin, TX Zip 78705–1006; tel. 512/324–1000; Gregory Hartman, President and Chief Executive Officer
**Web address:** www.seton.net

SETON MEDICAL CENTER HAYS (O, 83 beds) 6001 Kyle Parkway, Kyle, TX Zip 78640–6112, Mailing Address: 6001 Kyle Prkway, Zip 78640–6112; tel. 512/504–5000; John C. Brindley, FACHE, President and Chief Executive Officer
**Web address:** www.seton.net/locations/seton_medical_center_hays/

SETON MEDICAL CENTER WILLIAMSON (S, 143 beds) 201 Seton Parkway, Round Rock, TX Zip 78665–8000; tel. 512/324–4000; Michelle Robertson, R.N., President and Chief Executive Officer
**Web address:** www.seton.net/williamson

SETON NORTHWEST HOSPITAL (S, 121 beds) 11113 Research Boulevard, Austin, TX Zip 78759–5236; tel. 512/324–6000; Michelle Robertson, R.N., President and Chief Executive Officer
**Web address:** www.seton.net

SETON SHOAL CREEK HOSPITAL (S, 92 beds) 3501 Mills Avenue, Austin, TX Zip 78731–6391; tel. 512/324–2000; Alan Isaacson, Vice President and Chief Operating Officer
**Web address:** www.seton.net

SETON SMITHVILLE REGIONAL HOSPITAL (O, 10 beds) 800 East Highway 71, Smithville, TX Zip 78957–1730; tel. 512/237–3214; Noralene Corder, Interim Senior Vice President and Chief Operating Officer
**Web address:** www.srhnet.org

SETON SOUTHWEST HEALTHCARE CENTER (S, 17 beds) 7900 F. M. 1826, Austin, TX Zip 78737–1407; tel. 512/324–9000; Mary Faria, FACHE, Administrator
**Web address:** www.seton.net

UNIVERSITY MEDICAL CENTER AT BRACKENRIDGE (S, 244 beds) 601 East 15th Street, Austin, TX Zip 78701–1996; tel. 512/324–7000; Gregory Hartman, President and Chief Executive Officer
**Web address:** www.seton.net

**WASHINGTON:** LOURDES COUNSELING CENTER (S, 20 beds) 1175 Carondelet Drive, Richland, WA Zip 99354–3300; tel. 509/943–9104; Barbara Mead, Executive Director
**Web address:** www.lourdeshealth.net

LOURDES MEDICAL CENTER (S, 35 beds) 520 North Fourth Avenue, Pasco, WA Zip 99301–5257, Mailing Address: P.O. Box 2568, Zip 99302–2568; tel. 509/547–7704; John Serle, FACHE, President and Chief Executive Officer
**Web address:** www.lourdeshealth.net

**WISCONSIN:** CALUMET MEDICAL CENTER (O, 15 beds) 614 Memorial Drive, Chilton, WI Zip 53014–1597; tel. 920/849–2386; Timothy Richman, President
**Web address:** www.affinityhealth.org

COLUMBIA ST. MARY'S HOSPITAL MILWAUKEE (S, 324 beds) 2301 North Lake Drive, Milwaukee, WI Zip 53211–4508; tel. 414/291–1000; Mark R. Taylor, FACHE, President and Chief Executive Officer
**Web address:** www.columbia–stmarys.org

COLUMBIA ST. MARY'S OZAUKEE HOSPITAL (S, 102 beds) 13111 North Port Washington Road, Mequon, WI Zip 53097–2416; tel. 262/243–7300; Mark R. Taylor, FACHE, President and Chief Executive Officer
**Web address:** www.columbia–stmarys.org

FLAMBEAU HOSPITAL (O, 25 beds) 98 Sherry Avenue, Park Falls, WI Zip 54552–1467, Mailing Address: P.O. Box 310, Zip 54552–0310; tel. 715/762–2484; David A. Grundstrom, Chief Administrative Officer
**Web address:** www.flambeauhospital.org

HOWARD YOUNG MEDICAL CENTER (O, 35 beds) 240 Maple Street, Woodruff, WI Zip 54568–9190, Mailing Address: P.O. Box 470, Zip 54568–0470; tel. 715/356–8000; Sheila Clough, President
**Web address:** www.ministryhealth.org

MERCY MEDICAL CENTER (O, 137 beds) 500 South Oakwood Road, Oshkosh, WI Zip 54904–7944, Mailing Address: P.O. Box 3370, Zip 54903–3370; tel. 920/223–2000; William Calhoun, President
**Web address:** www.affinityhealth.org

MINISTRY DOOR COUNTY MEDICAL CENTER (O, 55 beds) 323 South 18th Avenue, Sturgeon Bay, WI Zip 54235–1495; tel. 920/743–5566; Gerald M. Worrick, President and Chief Executive Officer
**Web address:** www.ministryhealth.org

MINISTRY EAGLE RIVER MEMORIAL HOSPITAL (O, 12 beds) 201 Hospital Road, Eagle River, WI Zip 54521–8835; tel. 715/479–7411; Sheila Clough, President
**Web address:** www.ministryhealth.org

MINISTRY GOOD SAMARITAN HEALTH CENTER (O, 16 beds) 601 South Center Avenue, Merrill, WI Zip 54452–3404; tel. 715/536–5511; Mary T. Krueger, President
**Web address:** www.ministryhealth.org

MINISTRY OUR LADY OF VICTORY HOSPITAL (O, 4 beds) 1120 Pine Street, Stanley, WI Zip 54768–1297; tel. 715/644–5571; Cynthia Eichman, President
**Web address:** www.ministryhealth.org

MINISTRY SACRED HEART HOSPITAL (O, 6 beds) 401 West Mohawk Drive, Tomahawk, WI Zip 54487–2274; tel. 715/453–7700; Monica Hilt, President
**Web address:** www.ministryhealth.org

MINISTRY SAINT CLARE'S HOSPITAL (O, 69 beds) 3400 Ministry Parkway, Weston, WI Zip 54476–5220; tel. 715/393–3000; Mary T. Krueger, President
**Web address:** www.ministryhealth.org

MINISTRY SAINT JOSEPH'S HOSPITAL (O, 319 beds) 611 St. Joseph Avenue, Marshfield, WI Zip 54449–1898; tel. 715/387–1713; Brian Kief, President and Chief Executive Officer
**Web address:** www.stjosephs–marshfield.org

MINISTRY SAINT MARY'S HOSPITALS (O, 67 beds) 2251 North Shore Drive, Rhinelander, WI Zip 54501–6710; tel. 715/361–2000; Monica Hilt, President and Chief Operating Officer
**Web address:** www.ministryhealth.org

MINISTRY SAINT MICHAEL'S HOSPITAL (O, 51 beds) 900 Illinois Avenue, Stevens Point, WI Zip 54481–3196; tel. 715/346–5000; Jeffrey L. Martin, President
**Web address:** www.ministryhealth.org/SMH/home.nws

SACRED HEART REHABILITATION INSTITUTE (S, 20 beds) 2025 East Newport Avenue, Milwaukee, WI Zip 53211–2906; tel. 414/298–6700; Allan M. Spooner, President
**Web address:** www.columbia–stmarys.com

| Owned, leased, sponsored: | 101 hospitals | 18681 beds |
|---|---|---|
| Contract–managed: | 2 hospitals | 52 beds |
| Totals: | 103 hospitals | 18733 beds |

★**0519: ASPIRUS, INC.** (NP)
425 Pine Ridge Boulevard, Wausau, WI Zip 54401–4123; tel. 715/847–2118; Matthew Heywood, Chief Executive Officer
**(Moderately Centralized Health System)**

**MICHIGAN:** ASPIRUS GRAND VIEW HOSPITAL (O, 25 beds) N10561 Grand View Lane, Ironwood, MI Zip 49938–9622; tel. 906/932–2525; Charles Nelson, Chief Executive Officer
**Web address:** www.gvh.org

For explanation of codes following names, see page B2.
★ Indicates Type III membership in the American Hospital Association.

ASPIRUS KEWEENAW HOSPITAL (O, 25 beds) 205 Osceola Street, Laurium, MI Zip 49913–2134; tel. 906/337–6500; Charles Nelson, Chief Executive Officer
**Web address:** www.aspiruskeweenaw.org

ASPIRUS ONTONAGON HOSPITAL (O, 18 beds) 601 South Seventh Street, Ontonagon, MI Zip 49953–1459; tel. 906/884–8000; Charles Nelson, Chief Executive Officer
**Web address:** www.aspirus–ontonagon.org

**WISCONSIN:** ASPIRUS WAUSAU HOSPITAL (O, 257 beds) 333 Pine Ridge Boulevard, Wausau, WI Zip 54401–4187; tel. 715/847–2121; Marita Hattem, Interim President and Chief Operating Officer
**Web address:** www.aspirus.org

MEMORIAL HEALTH CENTER (O, 124 beds) 135 South Gibson Street, Medford, WI Zip 54451–1696; tel. 715/748–8100; Gregory A. Olson, President and Chief Executive Officer
**Web address:** www.memhc.com

| | | |
|---|---|---|
| **Owned, leased, sponsored:** | 5 hospitals | 449 beds |
| **Contract–managed:** | 0 hospitals | 0 beds |
| **Totals:** | 5 hospitals | 449 beds |

**★0865: ATLANTIC HEALTH** (NP)
475 South Street, Morristown, NJ Zip 07962, Mailing Address: P.O. Box 1905, Zip 07962–1905; tel. 973/660–3270; Joseph A. Trunfio, Ph.D., President and Chief Executive Officer
**(Moderately Centralized Health System)**

**NEW JERSEY:** MORRISTOWN MEDICAL CENTER (O, 656 beds) 100 Madison Avenue, Morristown, NJ Zip 07960–6136; tel. 973/971–5000; David J. Shulkin, M.D., President and Chief Executive Officer
**Web address:** www.atlantichealth.org/Morristown/

NEWTON MEDICAL CENTER (O, 148 beds) 175 High Street, Newton, NJ Zip 07860–1004; tel. 973/383–2121; Thomas J. Senker, FACHE, President and Chief Executive Officer
**Web address:** www.atlantichealth.org/newton/

OVERLOOK MEDICAL CENTER (O, 428 beds) 99 Beauvoir Avenue, Summit, NJ Zip 07901–3533; tel. 908/522–2000; Alan R. Lieber, President
**Web address:** www.atlantichealth.org/Overlook

| | | |
|---|---|---|
| **Owned, leased, sponsored:** | 3 hospitals | 1232 beds |
| **Contract–managed:** | 0 hospitals | 0 beds |
| **Totals:** | 3 hospitals | 1232 beds |

**● ★0293: ATLANTICARE** (NP)
2500 English Creek Avenue, Building 500, Suite 501, Egg Harbor Township, NJ Zip 08234; tel. 609/407–2309; David P. Tilton, President and Chief Executive Officer
**(Centralized Health System)**

ATLANTICARE REGIONAL MEDICAL CENTER (O, 534 beds) 1925 Pacific Avenue, Atlantic City, NJ Zip 08401–6713; tel. 609/441–8994; Lori Herndon, R.N., President and Chief Executive Officer
**Web address:** www.atlanticare.org

| | | |
|---|---|---|
| **Owned, leased, sponsored:** | 1 hospital | 534 beds |
| **Contract–managed:** | 0 hospitals | 0 beds |
| **Totals:** | 1 hospital | 534 beds |

**0894: AUDUBON BEHAVIORAL HEALTHCARE** (IO)
100 West Hawkins, Suite D., Longview, TX Zip 75605; tel. 903/212–2930; William V. Brown, Chief Executive Officer

**TEXAS:** AUDUBON BEHAVIORAL HEALTHCARE OF LONGVIEW (O, 24 beds) 615 Clinic Drive, Longview, TX Zip 75605–5172; tel. 903/212–3105; Lauren Weber, Administrator
**Web address:** www.audubonbehavioral.com

AUDUBON BEHAVIORAL HEALTHCARE OF LUFKIN (O, 24 beds) 302 Gobblers Knob, Lufkin, TX Zip 75904–5419; tel. 936/632–2276; Karen Parker, Administrator
**Web address:** www.audubonbehavioral.com

| | | |
|---|---|---|
| **Owned, leased, sponsored:** | 2 hospitals | 48 beds |
| **Contract–managed:** | 0 hospitals | 0 beds |
| **Totals:** | 2 hospitals | 48 beds |

**0859: AULTMAN HEALTH FOUNDATION** (NP)
2600 Sixth Street S.W., Canton, OH Zip 44710–1702; tel. 330/452–9911; Edward J. Roth, III, President and Chief Executive Officer
**(Moderately Centralized Health System)**

**OHIO:** AULTMAN HOSPITAL (O, 547 beds) 2600 Sixth Street S.W., Canton, OH Zip 44710–1702; tel. 330/452–9911; Edward J. Roth, III, President and Chief Executive Officer
**Web address:** www.aultman.com

AULTMAN ORRVILLE HOSPITAL (O, 25 beds) 832 South Main Street, Orrville, OH Zip 44667–2208; tel. 330/682–3010; Marchelle Suppan, DPM, President and Chief Executive Officer
**Web address:** www.aultmanorrville.org

| | | |
|---|---|---|
| **Owned, leased, sponsored:** | 2 hospitals | 572 beds |
| **Contract–managed:** | 0 hospitals | 0 beds |
| **Totals:** | 2 hospitals | 572 beds |

**0360: AURORA BEHAVIORAL HEALTH CARE** (IO)
4238 Green River Road, Corona, CA Zip 92880–1669; tel. 951/549–8032; Soon K. Kim, M.D., President and Chief Executive Officer
**(Independent Hospital System)**

**ARIZONA:** AURORA PHOENIX HOSPITAL (O, 80 beds) 6015 West Peoria Avenue, Glendale, AZ Zip 85302–1213; tel. 623/344–4400; Bruce Waldo, Chief Executive Officer
**Web address:** www.aurorabehavioral.com

AURORA TEMPE HOSPITAL (O, 70 beds) 6350 Maple Street, Tempe, AZ Zip 85283–2857; tel. 480/345–5400; Bruce Waldo, Chief Executive Officer

**CALIFORNIA:** AURORA BEHAVIORAL HEALTH CARE (O, 80 beds) 11878 Avenue of Industry, San Diego, CA Zip 92128–3423; tel. 858/487–3200; James S. Plummer, Chief Executive Officer
**Web address:** www.sandiego.aurorabehavioral.com/

AURORA CHARTER OAK HOSPITAL (O, 95 beds) 1161 East Covina Boulevard, Covina, CA Zip 91724–1599; tel. 626/966–1632; Todd A. Smith, Chief Executive Officer
**Web address:** www.aurorabehavioral.com

AURORA LAS ENCINAS HOSPITAL (O, 138 beds) 2900 East Del Mar Boulevard, Pasadena, CA Zip 91107–4399; tel. 626/795–9901; Gerard Conway, Chief Executive Officer
**Web address:** www.lasencinashospital.com

AURORA VISTA DEL MAR HOSPITAL (O, 87 beds) 801 Seneca Street, Ventura, CA Zip 93001–1411; tel. 805/653–6434; Mayla Krebsbach, Chief Executive Officer
**Web address:** www.vistadelmarhospital.com

**ILLINOIS:** AURORA CHICAGO LAKESHORE HOSPITAL (O, 115 beds) 4840 North Marine Drive, Chicago, IL Zip 60640–4296; tel. 773/878–9700; C. Alan Eaks, Chief Executive Officer
**Web address:** www.chicagolakeshorehospital.com

| | | |
|---|---|---|
| **Owned, leased, sponsored:** | 7 hospitals | 665 beds |
| **Contract–managed:** | 0 hospitals | 0 beds |
| **Totals:** | 7 hospitals | 665 beds |

**★2215: AURORA HEALTH CARE** (NP)
3000 West Montana, Milwaukee, WI Zip 53215–3628, Mailing Address: P.O. Box 341880, Zip 53234–1880; tel. 414/647–3000; Nick Turkal, M.D., President and Chief Executive Officer
**(Decentralized Health System)**

**WISCONSIN:** AURORA BAYCARE MEDICAL CENTER (O, 167 beds) 2845 Greenbrier Road, Green Bay, WI Zip 54311–6519, Mailing Address: P.O. Box 8900, Zip 54308–8900; tel. 920/288–8000; Daniel T. Meyer, President
**Web address:** www.aurorabaycare.com

For explanation of codes following names, see page B2.
★ Indicates Type III membership in the American Hospital Association.
● Single hospital health care system

**Section B**

AURORA LAKELAND MEDICAL CENTER (O, 75 beds) W3985 County Road NN, Elkhorn, WI Zip 53121–4389; tel. 262/741–2000; Vicki Lewis, R.N., MS, FACHE, President
**Web address:** www.aurorahealthcare.org

AURORA MEDICAL CENTER (O, 73 beds) 10400 South 75th Street, Kenosha, WI Zip 53142–7884; tel. 262/948–5600; Christine K. Olson, R.N., MSN, FACHE, President
**Web address:** www.aurorahealthcare.org

AURORA MEDICAL CENTER – MANITOWOC COUNTY (O, 65 beds) 5000 Memorial Drive, Two Rivers, WI Zip 54241–3900; tel. 920/794–5000; Cathie A. Kocourek, President
**Web address:** www.aurorahealthcare.org

AURORA MEDICAL CENTER GRAFTON (O, 96 beds) 975 Port Washington Road, Grafton, WI Zip 53024–9201; tel. 262/329–1000; Michael J. Laird, FACHE, President
**Web address:** www.aurorahealthcare.org

AURORA MEDICAL CENTER OF OSHKOSH (O, 61 beds) 855 North Westhaven Drive, Oshkosh, WI Zip 54904–7668; tel. 920/456–6000; Jeffrey Bard, President
**Web address:** www.aurorahealthcare.com

AURORA MEDICAL CENTER OF WASHINGTON COUNTY (O, 39 beds) 1032 East Sumner Street, Hartford, WI Zip 53027–1698; tel. 262/673–2300; Michael J. Laird, FACHE, President
**Web address:** www.aurorahealthcare.org

AURORA MEDICAL CENTER SUMMIT (O, 75 beds) 36500 Aurora Drive, Summit, WI Zip 53066–4899; tel. 262/434–1000; Daniel J. Bonk, Chief Executive Officer
**Web address:** www.aurorahealthcare.org

AURORA MEMORIAL HOSPITAL OF BURLINGTON (O, 65 beds) 252 McHenry Street, Burlington, WI Zip 53105–1828; tel. 262/767–6000; Vicki Lewis, R.N., MS, FACHE, Vice President and Chief Administrative Officer
**Web address:** www.aurorahealthcare.org

AURORA PSYCHIATRIC HOSPITAL (O, 78 beds) 1220 Dewey Avenue, Wauwatosa, WI Zip 53213–2598; tel. 414/454–6600; Peter Carlson, Administrator
**Web address:** www.aurorahealthcare.org

AURORA SHEBOYGAN MEMORIAL MEDICAL CENTER (O, 134 beds) 2629 North Seventh Street, Sheboygan, WI Zip 53083–4998; tel. 920/451–5000; David Graebner, President
**Web address:** www.aurorahealthcare.org

AURORA SINAI MEDICAL CENTER (O, 177 beds) 945 North 12th Street, Milwaukee, WI Zip 53233–1337, Mailing Address: P.O. Box 342, Zip 53201–0342; tel. 414/219–2000; George Hinton, Administrator
**Web address:** www.aurorahealthcare.org

AURORA ST. LUKE'S MEDICAL CENTER (O, 680 beds) 2900 West Oklahoma Avenue, Milwaukee, WI Zip 53215–4330, Mailing Address: P.O. Box 2901, Zip 53201–2901; tel. 414/649–6000; Dennis B. Potts, President
**Web address:** www.aurorahealthcare.org

AURORA WEST ALLIS MEDICAL CENTER (O, 220 beds) 8901 West Lincoln Avenue, West Allis, WI Zip 53227–2409, Mailing Address: P.O. Box 27901, Zip 53227–0901; tel. 414/328–6000; Richard A. Kellar, President
**Web address:** www.aurorahealthcare.org

| | | |
|---|---|---|
| Owned, leased, sponsored: | 14 hospitals | 2005 beds |
| Contract–managed: | 0 hospitals | 0 beds |
| Totals: | 14 hospitals | 2005 beds |

**0869: AVANTI HOSPITALS** (IO)
222 North Sepulveda Boulevard, Suite 950, El Segundo, CA Zip 90245–5614; tel. 310/356–0550; Edward Mirzabegian, Corporate Chief Executive Officer
**(Independent Hospital System)**

**CALIFORNIA:** COAST PLAZA HOSPITAL (O, 123 beds) 13100 Studebaker Road, Norwalk, CA Zip 90650–2531; tel. 562/868–3751; John J. Ferrelli, Chief Executive Officer
**Web address:** www.coastplaza.com

COMMUNITY HOSPITAL OF HUNTINGTON PARK (O, 81 beds) 2623 East Slauson Avenue, Huntington Park, CA Zip 90255–2926; tel. 323/583–1931; Hector Hernandez, M.D., Chief Executive Officer
**Web address:** www.chhplax.com

EAST LOS ANGELES DOCTORS HOSPITAL (O, 127 beds) 4060 East Whittier Boulevard, Los Angeles, CA Zip 90023–2526; tel. 323/268–5514; Hector Hernandez, M.D., Chief Executive Officer
**Web address:** www.elalax.com

MEMORIAL HOSPITAL OF GARDENA (O, 172 beds) 1145 West Redondo Beach Boulevard, Gardena, CA Zip 90247–3528; tel. 310/532–4200; Araceli Lonergan, Chief Executive Officer
**Web address:** www.mhglax.com/

| | | |
|---|---|---|
| Owned, leased, sponsored: | 4 hospitals | 503 beds |
| Contract–managed: | 0 hospitals | 0 beds |
| Totals: | 4 hospitals | 503 beds |

**★5255: AVERA HEALTH** (CC)
3900 West Avera Drive, Suite 301, Sioux Falls, SD Zip 57108–5721; tel. 605/322–4700; John T. Porter, President and Chief Executive Officer
**(Decentralized Health System)**

**IOWA:** AVERA HOLY FAMILY HOSPITAL (O, 25 beds) 826 North Eighth Street, Estherville, IA Zip 51334–1598; tel. 712/362–2631; Michael L. Hall, Chief Executive Officer
**Web address:** www.avera–holyfamily.org

FLOYD VALLEY HOSPITAL (C, 25 beds) 714 Lincoln Street N.E., Le Mars, IA Zip 51031–3314; tel. 712/546–7871; Michael T. Donlin, FACHE, Administrator
**Web address:** www.floydvalleyhospital.org

HEGG MEMORIAL HEALTH CENTER AVERA (C, 85 beds) 1202 21st Avenue, Rock Valley, IA Zip 51247–1497; tel. 712/476–8000; Glenn Zevenbergen, Chief Executive Officer
**Web address:** www.hegghc.org

OSCEOLA COMMUNITY HOSPITAL (C, 25 beds) 600 Ninth Avenue North, Sibley, IA Zip 51249–1012, Mailing Address: P.O. Box 258, Zip 51249–0258; tel. 712/754–2574; Janet H. Dykstra, Chief Executive Officer
**Web address:** www.osceolacommunityhospital.org

SIOUX CENTER COMMUNITY HOSPITAL AND HEALTH CENTER AVERA (C, 90 beds) 605 South Main Avenue, Sioux Center, IA Zip 51250–1398; tel. 712/722–1271; Kayleen R. Lee, Chief Executive Officer
**Web address:** www.schospital.org

**MINNESOTA:** AVERA MARSHALL REGIONAL MEDICAL CENTER (O, 111 beds) 300 South Bruce Street, Marshall, MN Zip 56258–3900; tel. 507/532–9661; Mary B. Maertens, FACHE, President and Chief Executive Officer
**Web address:** www.averamarshall.org

PIPESTONE COUNTY MEDICAL CENTER AVERA (C, 25 beds) 916 4th Avenue S.W., Pipestone, MN Zip 56164–1890; tel. 507/825–5811; Bradley D. Burris, Chief Executive Officer
**Web address:** www.pcmchealth.org

TYLER HEALTHCARE CENTER AVERA (C, 56 beds) 240 Willow Street, Tyler, MN Zip 56178–1166; tel. 507/247–5521; Dale K. Kruger, Chief Executive Officer and Chief Financial Officer
**Web address:** www.www1.avera.org/amck/regionalfacilities/tyler/index.aspx

**NEBRASKA:** AVERA CREIGHTON HOSPITAL (O, 54 beds) 1503 Main Street, Creighton, NE Zip 68729–3007, Mailing Address: P.O. Box 186, Zip 68729–0186; tel. 402/358–5700; Mark Schulte, Chief Executive Officer
**Web address:** www.avera.org/creighton/

AVERA ST. ANTHONY'S HOSPITAL (O, 25 beds) 302 North Second Street, O'Neill, NE Zip 68763–1514, Mailing Address: P.O. Box 270, Oneill, Zip 68763–0270; tel. 402/336–2611; Ronald J. Cork, President and Chief Executive Officer
**Web address:** www.avera.org/st-anthonys

**SOUTH DAKOTA:** AVERA DE SMET MEMORIAL HOSPITAL (L, 14 beds) 306 Prairie Avenue S.W., De Smet, SD Zip 57231–2285, Mailing Address: P.O. Box 160, Zip 57231–0160; tel. 605/854–3329; Janice Schardin, R.N., MS, Administrator and Chief Executive Officer
**Web address:** www.desmetmemorial.org

For explanation of codes following names, see page B2.
★ Indicates Type III membership in the American Hospital Association.

**B16** Health Care Systems, Networks and Alliances

© 2013 AHA Guide

AVERA DELLS AREA HOSPITAL (L, 23 beds) 909 North Iowa Avenue, Dell Rapids, SD Zip 57022–1231; tel. 605/428–5431; Lindsay Leischner, R.N., Administrator and Chief Executive Officer
**Web address:** www.www1.avera. org/amck/regionalfacilities/dellsareahealth/index.aspx

AVERA FLANDREAU HOSPITAL (L, 18 beds) 214 North Prairie Street, Flandreau, SD Zip 57028–1243; tel. 605/997–2433; Lindsay Leischner, R.N., Administrator and Chief Executive Officer
**Web address:** www.flandreaumedical.org

AVERA GETTYSBURG HOSPITAL (O, 60 beds) 606 East Garfield Avenue, Gettysburg, SD Zip 57442–1398; tel. 605/765–2480; Mark Schmidt, President and Chief Executive Officer
**Web address:** www.st–marys.com

AVERA GREGORY HOSPITAL (O, 67 beds) 400 Park Avenue, Gregory, SD Zip 57533–1302, Mailing Address: P.O. Box 408, Zip 57533–0408; tel. 605/835–8394; Anthony Timanus, Chief Executive Officer
**Web address:** www.gregoryhealthcare.org

AVERA HAND COUNTY MEMORIAL HOSPITAL (L, 16 beds) 300 West Fifth Street, Miller, SD Zip 57362–1238; tel. 605/853–2421; Bryan Breitling, Administrator
**Web address:** www.avera.org

AVERA HEART HOSPITAL OF SOUTH DAKOTA (O, 53 beds) 4500 West 69th Street, Sioux Falls, SD Zip 57108–8148; tel. 605/977–7000; Jon Soderholm, President
**Web address:** www.southdakotaheart.com

AVERA MCKENNAN HOSPITAL AND UNIVERSITY HEALTH CENTER (O, 403 beds) 800 East 21st Street, Sioux Falls, SD Zip 57105–1096, Mailing Address: P.O. Box 5045, Zip 57117–5045; tel. 605/322–8000; David Kapaska, D.O., Regional President
**Web address:** www.averamckennan.org

AVERA QUEEN OF PEACE HOSPITAL (O, 196 beds) 525 North Foster, Mitchell, SD Zip 57301–2999; tel. 605/995–2000; Thomas A. Clark, President and Chief Executive Officer
**Web address:** www.averaqueenofpeace.org

AVERA SACRED HEART HOSPITAL (O, 293 beds) 501 Summit Avenue, Yankton, SD Zip 57078–3855; tel. 605/668–8000; Pamela J. Rezac, Regional President
**Web address:** www.averasacredheart.com

AVERA ST. BENEDICT HEALTH CENTER (O, 100 beds) 401 West Glynn Drive, Parkston, SD Zip 57366–9605; tel. 605/928–3311; Gale N. Walker, President and Chief Executive Officer
**Web address:** www.averastbenedict.org

AVERA ST. LUKE'S HOSPITAL (O, 270 beds) 305 South State Street, Aberdeen, SD Zip 57401–4527; tel. 605/622–5000; Todd Forkel, President and Chief Executive Officer
**Web address:** www.avera.org/st–lukes–hospital/

AVERA ST. MARY'S HOSPITAL (O, 164 beds) 801 East Sioux Avenue, Pierre, SD Zip 57501–3323; tel. 605/224–3100; Joseph Messmer, Interim Chief Executive Officer
**Web address:** www.avera.org/st–marys–pierre/

AVERA WESKOTA MEMORIAL HOSPITAL (L, 23 beds) 604 First Street N.E., Wessington Springs, SD Zip 57382–2166; tel. 605/539–1201; Gaea Blue, Administrator and Chief Executive Officer
**Web address:** www.averaweskota.org

EUREKA COMMUNITY HEALTH SERVICES AVERA (C, 6 beds) 410 Ninth Street, Eureka, SD Zip 57437–2182, Mailing Address: P.O. Box 517, Zip 57437–0517; tel. 605/284–2661; Carmen Weber, Interim Administrator
**Web address:** www.avera.org

LANDMANN–JUNGMAN MEMORIAL HOSPITAL AVERA (C, 19 beds) 600 Billars Street, Scotland, SD Zip 57059–2026; tel. 605/583–2226; Lee Baldwin, Administrator and Chief Executive Officer
**Web address:** www.ljmh.org

MARSHALL COUNTY HEALTHCARE CENTER AVERA (C, 18 beds) 413 Ninth Street, Britton, SD Zip 57430–2274; tel. 605/448–2253; Nick Fosness, Chief Executive Officer
**Web address:** www.avera.org

MILBANK AREA HOSPITAL AVERA (L, 25 beds) 901 East Virgil Avenue, Milbank, SD Zip 57252–2124; tel. 605/432–4538; Natalie Gauer, Administrator
**Web address:** www.averamilbank.org

PLATTE HEALTH CENTER AVERA (C, 65 beds) 601 East Seventh, Platte, SD Zip 57369–2123, Mailing Address: P.O. Box 200, Zip 57369–0200; tel. 605/337–3364; Mark Burket, Chief Executive Officer
**Web address:** www.phcavera.org

ST. MICHAEL'S HOSPITAL AVERA (C, 25 beds) 410 West 16th Avenue, Tyndall, SD Zip 57066–2318; tel. 605/589–3341; Carol Deurmier, Chief Executive Officer
**Web address:** www.stmichaels–bhfp.org

WAGNER COMMUNITY MEMORIAL HOSPITAL AVERA (C, 20 beds) 513 Third Street S.W., Wagner, SD Zip 57380–9675, Mailing Address: P.O. Box 280, Zip 57380–0280; tel. 605/384–3611; Bryan Slaba, Chief Executive Officer
**Web address:** www.avera.org/wagnerhospital

| | | |
|---|---|---|
| Owned, leased, sponsored: | 19 hospitals | 1940 beds |
| Contract–managed: | 12 hospitals | 459 beds |
| **Totals:** | 31 hospitals | 2399 beds |

---

★**0633: AVITA HEALTH SYSTEM** (NP)
269 Portland Way South, Galion, OH Zip 44833–2399; tel. 419/468–4841; Jerome Morasko, President and Chief Executive Officer
**(Independent Hospital System)**

**OHIO:** BUCYRUS COMMUNITY HOSPITAL (O, 25 beds) 629 North Sandusky Avenue, Bucyrus, OH Zip 44820–1821; tel. 419/562–4677; Jerome Morasko, Chief Executive Officer
**Web address:** www.bchonline.org

GALION COMMUNITY HOSPITAL (O, 35 beds) 269 Portland Way South, Galion, OH Zip 44833–2399; tel. 419/468–4841; Jerome Morasko, President and Chief Executive Officer
**Web address:** www.galionhospital.org

| | | |
|---|---|---|
| Owned, leased, sponsored: | 2 hospitals | 60 beds |
| Contract–managed: | 0 hospitals | 0 beds |
| **Totals:** | 2 hospitals | 60 beds |

---

★**0194: BANNER HEALTH** (NP)
1441 North 12th Street, Phoenix, AZ Zip 85006–2837, Mailing Address: P.O. Box 25489, Zip 85002–5489; tel. 602/747–4000; Peter S. Fine, FACHE, President and Chief Executive Officer
**(Decentralized Health System)**

**ALASKA:** FAIRBANKS MEMORIAL HOSPITAL (L, 217 beds) 1650 Cowles Street, Fairbanks, AK Zip 99701–5998; tel. 907/452–8181; Michael K. Powers, FACHE, Chief Executive Officer
**Web address:** www.bannerhealth.com/locations/alaska/fairbanks+memorial+Hospital

**ARIZONA:** BANNER BAYWOOD MEDICAL CENTER (O, 340 beds) 6644 East Baywood Avenue, Mesa, AZ Zip 85206–1797; tel. 480/321–2000; Laura Robertson, R.N., Chief Executive Officer
**Web address:** www.bannerhealth.com/locations/Arizona/banner+baywood+medical+center

BANNER BEHAVIORAL HEALTH HOSPITAL – SCOTTSDALE (O, 94 beds) 7575 East Earll Drive, Scottsdale, AZ Zip 85251–6915; tel. 480/941–7500; Cherie Martin, R.N., MSN, FACHE, Chief Executive Officer
**Web address:** www.bannerhealth.com/Locations/Arizona/Banner+Behavioral+Health

BANNER BOSWELL MEDICAL CENTER (O, 454 beds) 10401 West Thunderbird Boulevard, Sun City, AZ Zip 85351–3004, Mailing Address: P.O. Box 1690, Zip 85372–1690; tel. 623/832–4000; David Cheney, Chief Executive Officer
**Web address:** www.bannerhealth.com/Locations/Arizona/Banner+Boswell+Medical+Center

BANNER DEL E. WEBB MEDICAL CENTER (O, 373 beds) 14502 West Meeker Boulevard, Sun City West, AZ Zip 85375–5299, Mailing Address: P.O. Box 5169, Zip 85376–5169; tel. 623/214–4000; Debbie Flores, Chief Executive Officer
**Web address:** www.bannerhealth.com/Locations/Arizona/Banner+Del+Webb+Medical+Center/

Section B

For explanation of codes following names, see page B2.
★ Indicates Type III membership in the American Hospital Association.

BANNER DESERT MEDICAL CENTER (O, 549 beds) 1400 South Dobson Road, Mesa, AZ Zip 85202–4707; tel. 480/412–3000; Robert Gould, Chief Executive Officer
**Web address:** www.bannerhealth.com/Locations/Arizona/Banner+Desert+Medical+Center

BANNER ESTRELLA MEDICAL CENTER (O, 214 beds) 9201 West Thomas Road, Phoenix, AZ Zip 85037–3332; tel. 623/327–4000; Debra J. Krmpotic, R.N., Chief Executive Officer
**Web address:** www.bannerhealth.com/Locations/Arizona/Banner+Estrella+Medical+Center/

BANNER GATEWAY MEDICAL CENTER (O, 177 beds) 1900 North Higley Road, Gilbert, AZ Zip 85234–1604; tel. 480/543–2000; Todd S. Werner, Chief Executive Officer
**Web address:** www.bannerhealth.com/Locations/Arizona/Banner+Gateway+Medical+Center/

BANNER GOLDFIELD MEDICAL CENTER (O, 30 beds) 2050 West Southern Avenue, Apache Junction, AZ Zip 85120–7305; tel. 480/733–3300; Julie Nunley, R.N., Chief Executive Officer
**Web address:** www.bannerhealth.com/Locations/Arizona/Banner+Goldfield+Medical+Center/_Welcome+to+Banner+Goldfield.htm

BANNER GOOD SAMARITAN MEDICAL CENTER (O, 653 beds) 1111 East McDowell Road, Phoenix, AZ Zip 85006–2666, Mailing Address: P.O. Box 2989, Zip 85062–2989; tel. 602/239–2000; Steve Narang, M.D., Chief Executive Officer
**Web address:** www.bannerhealth.com/Locations/Arizona/Banner+Good+Samaritan+Medical+Center

BANNER HEART HOSPITAL (O, 111 beds) 6750 East Baywood Avenue, Mesa, AZ Zip 85206–1749; tel. 480/854–5000; Laura Robertson, R.N., Chief Executive Officer
**Web address:** www.bannerhealth.com/Locations/Arizona/Banner+Heart+Hospital/

BANNER IRONWOOD MEDICAL CENTER (O, 53 beds) 37000 North Gantzel Road, San Tan Valley, AZ Zip 85140–7303; tel. 480/394–4000; Julie Nunley, R.N., Chief Executive Officer
**Web address:** www.bannerhealth.com/Locations/Arizona/Banner+Ironwood/

BANNER THUNDERBIRD MEDICAL CENTER (O, 504 beds) 5555 West Thunderbird Road, Glendale, AZ Zip 85306–4696; tel. 602/865–5555; Thomas C. Dickson, Chief Executive Officer
**Web address:** www.bannerhealth.com/Locations/Arizona/Banner+Thunderbird+Medical+Center/

PAGE HOSPITAL (C, 25 beds) 501 North Navajo Drive, Page, AZ Zip 86040, Mailing Address: P.O. Box 1447, Zip 86040–1447; tel. 928/645–2424; Sandy Haryasz, R.N., Chief Executive Officer
**Web address:** www.bannerhealth.com/Locations/Arizona/Page+Hospital

**CALIFORNIA:** BANNER LASSEN MEDICAL CENTER (O, 25 beds) 1800 Spring Ridge Drive, Susanville, CA Zip 96130–6100; tel. 530/252–2000; Bob S. Edwards, Jr., FACHE, Chief Executive Officer
**Web address:** www.bannerhealth.com/Locations/California/Banner+Lassen+Medical+Center

**COLORADO:** EAST MORGAN COUNTY HOSPITAL (L, 19 beds) 2400 West Edison Street, Brush, CO Zip 80723–1640; tel. 970/842–6200; Linda Thorpe, Chief Executive Officer
**Web address:** www.emchbrush.com

MCKEE MEDICAL CENTER (O, 105 beds) 2000 Boise Avenue, Loveland, CO Zip 80538–4281; tel. 970/669–4640; Marilyn Schock, Chief Executive Officer
**Web address:** www.mckeeloveland.com

NORTH COLORADO MEDICAL CENTER (L, 258 beds) 1801 16th Street, Greeley, CO Zip 80631–5154; tel. 970/352–4121; Richard O. Sutton, Chief Executive Officer
**Web address:** www.ncmcgreeley.com

STERLING REGIONAL MEDCENTER (O, 25 beds) 615 Fairhurst Street, Sterling, CO Zip 80751–4523; tel. 970/522–0122; Julie Klein, Chief Executive Officer
**Web address:** www.bannerhealth.com/Locations/Colorado/Sterling+Regional+MedCenter

**NEBRASKA:** OGALLALA COMMUNITY HOSPITAL (L, 18 beds) 2601 North Spruce Street, Ogallala, NE Zip 69153–2465; tel. 308/284–4011; Sharon Lind, MSN, Chief Executive Officer
**Web address:** www.bannerhealth.com/Locations/Nebraska/Ogallala+Community+Hospital

**NEVADA:** BANNER CHURCHILL COMMUNITY HOSPITAL (O, 40 beds) 801 East Williams Avenue, Fallon, NV Zip 89406–3052; tel. 775/867–7000; John D'Angelo, Chief Executive Officer
**Web address:** www.bannerhealth.com/Locations/Nevada/Banner+Churchill+Community+Hospital

**WYOMING:** COMMUNITY HOSPITAL (O, 25 beds) 2000 Campbell Drive, Torrington, WY Zip 82240–1597; tel. 307/532–4181; Vincent B. DiFranco, Chief Executive Officer
**Web address:** www.bannerhealth.com/Locations/Wyoming/Community+Hospital/

PLATTE COUNTY MEMORIAL HOSPITAL (L, 25 beds) 201 14th Street, Wheatland, WY Zip 82201–3201, Mailing Address: P.O. Box 848, Zip 82201–0848; tel. 307/322–3636; Shelby Nelson, Chief Executive Officer
**Web address:** www.bannerhealth.com/Locations/Wyoming/Platte+County+Memorial+Hospital

WASHAKIE MEDICAL CENTER (L, 25 beds) 400 South 15th Street, Worland, WY Zip 82401–3531, Mailing Address: P.O. Box 700, Zip 82401–0700; tel. 307/347–3221; Margie Molitor, R.N., Chief Executive Officer
**Web address:** www.washakiemedicalcenter.com

| | | |
|---|---|---|
| Owned, leased, sponsored: | 23 hospitals | 4334 beds |
| Contract–managed: | 1 hospital | 25 beds |
| Totals: | 24 hospitals | 4359 beds |

★**0005:  BAPTIST HEALTH** (NP)
841 Prudential Drive, Suite 1601, Jacksonville, FL Zip 32207–8202; tel. 904/202–4011; Hugh Greene, President and Chief Executive Officer
**(Moderately Centralized Health System)**

**FLORIDA:** BAPTIST MEDICAL CENTER BEACHES (O, 136 beds) 1350 13th Avenue South, Jacksonville Beach, FL Zip 32250–3205; tel. 904/627–2900; Joseph M. Mitrick, FACHE, President
**Web address:** www.community.e–baptisthealth.com/bmc/beaches/index.html

BAPTIST MEDICAL CENTER JACKSONVILLE (O, 844 beds) 800 Prudential Drive, Jacksonville, FL Zip 32207–8202; tel. 904/202–2000; Michael A. Mayo, FACHE, President
**Web address:** www.e–baptisthealth.com

BAPTIST MEDICAL CENTER NASSAU (O, 52 beds) 1250 South 18th Street, Fernandina Beach, FL Zip 32034–3098; tel. 904/321–3500; Stephen Lee, FACHE, President
**Web address:** www.community.e–baptisthealth.com/bmc/nassau/index.html

| | | |
|---|---|---|
| Owned, leased, sponsored: | 3 hospitals | 1032 beds |
| Contract–managed: | 0 hospitals | 0 beds |
| Totals: | 3 hospitals | 1032 beds |

★**0150:  BAPTIST HEALTH** (NP)
301 Brown Springs Road, Montgomery, AL Zip 36117–7005; tel. 334/273–4400; W. Russell Tyner, President and Chief Executive Officer
**(Independent Hospital System)**

**ALABAMA:** BAPTIST MEDICAL CENTER EAST (O, 182 beds) 400 Taylor Road, Montgomery, AL Zip 36117–3512, Mailing Address: P.O. Box 241267, Zip 36124–1267; tel. 334/277–8330; J. Peter Selman, Administrator and Chief Executive Officer
**Web address:** www.baptistfirst.org

BAPTIST MEDICAL CENTER SOUTH (O, 386 beds) 2105 East South Boulevard, Montgomery, AL Zip 36116–2409, Mailing Address: Box 11010, Zip 36111–0010; tel. 334/288–2100; Robin Barca, Chief Executive Officer
**Web address:** www.baptistfirst.org

PRATTVILLE BAPTIST HOSPITAL (O, 56 beds) 124 South Memorial Drive, Prattville, AL Zip 36067–3619, Mailing Address: P.O. Box 681630, Zip 36068–1638; tel. 334/365–0651; Ginger Henry, Chief Executive Officer
**Web address:** www.baptistfirst.org/facilities/prattville–baptist–hospital/default.aspx

For explanation of codes following names, see page B2.
★ Indicates Type III membership in the American Hospital Association.

Section B

| | | |
|---|---|---|
| Owned, leased, sponsored: | 3 hospitals | 624 beds |
| Contract–managed: | 0 hospitals | 0 beds |
| Totals: | 3 hospitals | 624 beds |

**★0315: BAPTIST HEALTH** (CO)
2701 Eastpoint Parkway, Louisville, KY Zip 40223;
tel. 502/896–5000; Stephen C. Hanson, President and Chief
Executive Officer
**(Centralized Physician/Insurance Health System)**

**KENTUCKY:** BAPTIST HEALTH CORBIN (O, 273 beds) 1 Trillium Way, Corbin,
KY Zip 40701–8420; tel. 606/528–1212; Larry Gray, President
**Web address:** www.baptistregional.com

BAPTIST HEALTH LA GRANGE (O, 108 beds) 1025 New Moody Lane, La
Grange, KY Zip 40031–9154; tel. 502/222–5388; Chris Roty, President
**Web address:** www.baptistnortheast.com

BAPTIST HEALTH LEXINGTON (O, 344 beds) 1740 Nicholasville Road,
Lexington, KY Zip 40503–1499; tel. 859/260–6100; William G. Sisson,
President
**Web address:** www.centralbap.com

BAPTIST HEALTH LOUISVILLE (O, 519 beds) 4000 Kresge Way, Louisville, KY
Zip 40207–4676; tel. 502/897–8100; David L. Gray, FACHE, President
**Web address:** www.baptisteast.com

BAPTIST HEALTH MADISONVILLE (O, 198 beds) 900 Hospital Drive,
Madisonville, KY Zip 42431–1694; tel. 270/825–5100; E. Berton Whitaker,
FACHE, President
**Web address:** www.troverfoundation.org

BAPTIST HEALTH PADUCAH (O, 320 beds) 2501 Kentucky Avenue, Paducah,
KY Zip 42003–3200; tel. 270/575–2100; Larry O. Barton, FACHE, President
**Web address:** www.westernbaptist.com

BAPTIST HEALTH RICHMOND (O, 66 beds) 801 Eastern Bypass, Richmond,
KY Zip 40475–2405, Mailing Address: P.O. Box 1600, Zip 40476–2603;
tel. 859/623–3131; Todd Jones, President
**Web address:** www.baptisthealthrichmond.com

HARDIN MEMORIAL HOSPITAL (C, 268 beds) 913 North Dixie Avenue,
Elizabethtown, KY Zip 42701–2503; tel. 270/737–1212; Dennis B. Johnson,
President
**Web address:** www.hmh.net

OAK TREE HOSPITAL (O, 32 beds) 1 Trillium Way, Lower Level, Corbin, KY
Zip 40701–8727; tel. 606/523–5150; R. Alan Coppock, FACHE, President
**Web address:** www.oaktreecorbin.com

RUSSELL COUNTY HOSPITAL (C, 25 beds) 153 Dowell Road, Russell Springs,
KY Zip 42642–4579, Mailing Address: P.O. Box 1610, Zip 42642–1610;
tel. 270/866–4141; Robert L. Ramey, President
**Web address:** www.russellcohospital.org

| | | |
|---|---|---|
| Owned, leased, sponsored: | 8 hospitals | 1860 beds |
| Contract–managed: | 2 hospitals | 293 beds |
| Totals: | 10 hospitals | 2153 beds |

**★0355: BAPTIST HEALTH** (NP)
9601 Interstate 630, Exit 7, Little Rock, AR Zip 72205–7299;
tel. 501/202–2000; Russell D. Harrington, Jr., FACHE, President and
Chief Executive Officer
**(Centralized Health System)**

**ARKANSAS:** BAPTIST HEALTH EXTENDED CARE HOSPITAL (O, 37 beds)
9601 Interstate 630, Exit 7, 10th Floor, Little Rock, AR Zip 72205–7202;
tel. 501/202–1070; Mike Perkins, Vice President and Administrator
**Web address:** www.baptist–health.com/maps–directions/bh_extended_
care/default.aspx

BAPTIST HEALTH MEDICAL CENTER – NORTH LITTLE ROCK (O, 220 beds)
3333 Springhill Drive, North Little Rock, AR Zip 72117–2922;
tel. 501/202–3000; Harrison M. Dean, FACHE, Senior Vice President and
Administrator
**Web address:** www.baptist–health.com/locations/accesspoint.
aspx?accessPointID=190

BAPTIST HEALTH MEDICAL CENTER–ARKADELPHIA (L, 25 beds) 3050 Twin
Rivers Drive, Arkadelphia, AR Zip 71923–4299; tel. 870/245–2622; John
Bowen, Assistant Vice President and Administrator
**Web address:** www.baptist–health.com/locations/accesspoint.
aspx?accessPointID=187

BAPTIST HEALTH MEDICAL CENTER–HEBER SPRINGS (O, 25 beds) 1800
Bypass Road, Heber Springs, AR Zip 72543–9135; tel. 501/887–3000;
Edward L. Lacy, FACHE, Vice President and Administrator
**Web address:** www.baptist–health.
com/maps–directions/bhmc–heber–springs

BAPTIST HEALTH MEDICAL CENTER–LITTLE ROCK (O, 687 beds) 9601
Interstate 630, Exit 7, Little Rock, AR Zip 72205–7299; tel. 501/202–2000;
Greg Crain, FACHE, Vice President and Administrator
**Web address:** www.baptist–health.org/maps–directions/bhmc–lr

BAPTIST HEALTH MEDICAL CENTER–STUTTGART (L, 49 beds) North Buerkle
Road, Stuttgart, AR Zip 72160–3420, Mailing Address: P.O. Box 1905,
Zip 72160–1905; tel. 870/673–3511; Terry L. Amstutz, FACHE, Vice
President and Administrator
**Web address:** www.baptist–health.
org/maps–directions/bhmc–stuttgart/default.aspx

BAPTIST HEALTH REHABILITATION INSTITUTE (O, 100 beds) 9601 Interstate
630, Exit 7, Little Rock, AR Zip 72205–7202; tel. 501/202–7000; Lee
Gentry, FACHE, Vice President and Administrator
**Web address:** www.baptist–health.com/locations/accesspoint.
aspx?accessPointID=202

| | | |
|---|---|---|
| Owned, leased, sponsored: | 7 hospitals | 1143 beds |
| Contract–managed: | 0 hospitals | 0 beds |
| Totals: | 7 hospitals | 1143 beds |

**★0185: BAPTIST HEALTH CARE CORPORATION** (NP)
1717 North E Street Suite 320, Pensacola, FL Zip 32501–6377,
Mailing Address: P.O. Box 17500, Zip 32522–7500;
tel. 850/434–4011; Mark T. Faulkner, President
**(Centralized Health System)**

**ALABAMA:** ATMORE COMMUNITY HOSPITAL (L, 49 beds) 401 Medical Park
Drive, Atmore, AL Zip 36502–3091; tel. 251/368–2500; A. William
Perkins, Interim Administrator
**Web address:** www.ebaptisthealthcare.org/AtmoreCommunityHospital/

**FLORIDA:** BAPTIST HOSPITAL (O, 339 beds) 1000 West Moreno, Pensacola,
FL Zip 32501–2316, Mailing Address: P.O. Box 17500, Zip 32522–7500;
tel. 850/434–4011; David Wildebrandt, Administrator
**Web address:** www.ebaptisthealthcare.org

GULF BREEZE HOSPITAL (O, 77 beds) 1110 Gulf Breeze Parkway, Gulf
Breeze, FL Zip 32561–4884; tel. 850/934–2000; Robert Harriman, M.D.,
Administrator
**Web address:** www.ebaptisthealthcare.org/GulfBreezeHospital/

JAY HOSPITAL (L, 49 beds) 14114 South Alabama Street, Jay, FL
Zip 32565–1219; tel. 850/675–8000; Michael T. Hutchins, Administrator
**Web address:** www.bhcpns.org/jayhospital/

| | | |
|---|---|---|
| Owned, leased, sponsored: | 4 hospitals | 514 beds |
| Contract–managed: | 0 hospitals | 0 beds |
| Totals: | 4 hospitals | 514 beds |

**★0122: BAPTIST HEALTH SOUTH FLORIDA** (NP)
6855 Red Road, Suite 600, Coral Gables, FL Zip 33143–3632;
tel. 786/662–7111; Brian E. Keeley, President and Chief Executive
Officer
**(Centralized Health System)**

BAPTIST HEALTH SOUTH FLORIDA, BAPTIST HOSPITAL OF MIAMI (O, 672
beds) 8900 North Kendall Drive, Miami, FL Zip 33176–2197;
tel. 786/596–1960; Bo Boulenger, Chief Executive Officer
**Web address:** www.baptisthealth.net

BAPTIST HEALTH SOUTH FLORIDA, DOCTORS HOSPITAL (O, 146 beds) 5000
University Drive, Coral Gables, FL Zip 33146–2094; tel. 786/308–3000;
Nelson Lazo, Chief Executive Officer
**Web address:** www.baptisthealth.net

Section B

For explanation of codes following names, see page B2.
★ Indicates Type III membership in the American Hospital Association.

BAPTIST HEALTH SOUTH FLORIDA, HOMESTEAD HOSPITAL (O, 142 beds) 975 Baptist Way, Homestead, FL Zip 33033–7600; tel. 786/243–8000; Bill Duquette, Chief Executive Officer
**Web address:** www.baptisthealth.net

BAPTIST HEALTH SOUTH FLORIDA, MARINERS HOSPITAL (O, 25 beds) 91500 Overseas Highway, Tavernier, FL Zip 33070–2547; tel. 305/434–3000; Rick Freeburg, Chief Executive Officer
**Web address:** www.baptisthealth.net/en/facilities/mariners–hospital/Pages/default.aspx

BAPTIST HEALTH SOUTH FLORIDA, SOUTH MIAMI HOSPITAL (O, 374 beds) 6200 S.W. 73rd Street, Miami, FL Zip 33143–4679; tel. 786/662–4000; Lincoln S. Mendez, Chief Executive Officer
**Web address:** www.baptisthealth.net

BAPTIST HEALTH SOUTH FLORIDA, WEST KENDALL BAPTIST HOSPITAL (O, 133 beds) 9555 S.W. 162nd Avenue, Miami, FL Zip 33196–6408; tel. 786/467–2000; Javier Hernandez–Lichtl, Chief Executive Officer
**Web address:** www.baptisthealth.net/en/facilities/West–Kendall–Baptist–Hospital/Pages/default.aspx

| | | |
|---|---|---|
| Owned, leased, sponsored: | 6 hospitals | 1492 beds |
| Contract–managed: | 0 hospitals | 0 beds |
| Totals: | 6 hospitals | 1492 beds |

**0345: BAPTIST HEALTH SYSTEM** (CO)
3201 Fourth Avenue South, Birmingham, AL Zip 35222–1723, Mailing Address: P.O. Box 830605, Zip 35283–0605; tel. 205/715–5319; M. Shane Spees, President and Chief Executive Officer

**(Centralized Physician/Insurance Health System)**

**ALABAMA:** CITIZENS BAPTIST MEDICAL CENTER (O, 116 beds) 604 Stone Avenue, Talladega, AL Zip 35160–2217, Mailing Address: P.O. Box 978, Zip 35161–0978; tel. 256/362–8111; Joel Taylor, Administrator
**Web address:** www.bhsala.com/home_citizens.cfm?id=38

PRINCETON BAPTIST MEDICAL CENTER (O, 295 beds) 701 Princeton Avenue S.W., Birmingham, AL Zip 35211–1303; tel. 205/783–3000; Betsy Postlethwait, President
**Web address:** www.bhsala.com

SHELBY BAPTIST MEDICAL CENTER (O, 206 beds) 1000 First Street North, Alabaster, AL Zip 35007–8703; tel. 205/620–8100; David C. Wilson, President and Chief Executive Officer
**Web address:** www.bhsala.com/shelby/Home.aspx

WALKER BAPTIST MEDICAL CENTER (O, 236 beds) 3400 Highway 78 East, Jasper, AL Zip 35501–8907, Mailing Address: P.O. Box 3547, Zip 35502–3547; tel. 205/387–4000; Robert Phillips, Administrator
**Web address:** www.bhsala.com/home_walker.cfm?id=41

| | | |
|---|---|---|
| Owned, leased, sponsored: | 4 hospitals | 853 beds |
| Contract–managed: | 0 hospitals | 0 beds |
| Totals: | 4 hospitals | 853 beds |

**★1625: BAPTIST MEMORIAL HEALTH CARE CORPORATION** (NP)
350 North Humphreys Boulevard, Memphis, TN Zip 38120–2177; tel. 901/227–5117; Stephen Curtis Reynolds, President and Chief Executive Officer

**(Decentralized Health System)**

**ARKANSAS:** NEA BAPTIST MEMORIAL HOSPITAL (O, 100 beds) 3024 Stadium Boulevard, Jonesboro, AR Zip 72401–7415; tel. 870/972–7000; Brad Parsons, Administrator and Chief Executive Officer
**Web address:** www.neabaptist.com

**MISSISSIPPI:** BAPTIST MEMORIAL HOSPITAL–BOONEVILLE (L, 66 beds) 100 Hospital Street, Booneville, MS Zip 38829–3359; tel. 662/720–5000; James Grantham, Administrator and Chief Executive Officer
**Web address:** www.bmhcc.org/booneville

BAPTIST MEMORIAL HOSPITAL–DESOTO (O, 263 beds) 7601 Southcrest Parkway, Southaven, MS Zip 38671–4742; tel. 662/772–4000; James Huffman, Chief Executive Officer and Administrator
**Web address:** www.baptistonline.org/desoto/

BAPTIST MEMORIAL HOSPITAL–GOLDEN TRIANGLE (O, 249 beds) 2520 Fifth Street North, Columbus, MS Zip 39705–2095, Mailing Address: P.O. Box 1307, Zip 39703–1307; tel. 662/244–1000; Paul Cade, Administrator and Chief Executive Officer
**Web address:** www.baptistonline.org/golden–triangle/

BAPTIST MEMORIAL HOSPITAL–NORTH MISSISSIPPI (O, 217 beds) 2301 South Lamar Boulevard, Oxford, MS Zip 38655–5373, Mailing Address: P.O. Box 946, Zip 38655–6002; tel. 662/232–8100; William C. Henning, Administrator and Chief Executive Officer
**Web address:** www.baptistonline.org/north–mississippi/

BAPTIST MEMORIAL HOSPITAL–UNION COUNTY (L, 153 beds) 200 Highway 30 West, New Albany, MS Zip 38652–3112; tel. 662/538–7631; Walter Grace, Chief Executive Officer and Administrator
**Web address:** www.baptistonline.org/union–county/

**TENNESSEE:** BAPTIST MEMORIAL HOSPITAL – MEMPHIS (O, 605 beds) 6019 Walnut Grove Road, Memphis, TN Zip 38120–2173; tel. 901/226–5000; Derick Ziegler, Administrator and Chief Executive Officer
**Web address:** www.baptistonline.org/memphis/

BAPTIST MEMORIAL HOSPITAL FOR WOMEN (O, 140 beds) 6225 Humphreys Boulevard, Memphis, TN Zip 38120–2373; tel. 901/227–9000; Anita Vaughn, Administrator and Chief Executive Officer
**Web address:** www.baptistonline.org/womens/

BAPTIST MEMORIAL HOSPITAL–COLLIERVILLE (O, 61 beds) 1500 West Poplar Avenue, Collierville, TN Zip 38017–0601; tel. 901/861–9400; Kyle E. Armstrong, Administrator and Chief Executive Officer
**Web address:** www.baptistonline.org/collierville/

BAPTIST MEMORIAL HOSPITAL–HUNTINGDON (O, 33 beds) 631 R.B. Wilson Drive, Huntingdon, TN Zip 38344–1727; tel. 731/986–4461; Susan M. Breeden, Administrator and Chief Executive Officer
**Web address:** www.baptistonline.org/huntingdon/

BAPTIST MEMORIAL HOSPITAL–TIPTON (O, 44 beds) 1995 Highway 51 South, Covington, TN Zip 38019–3635; tel. 901/476–2621; Jamie Rodgers, Chief Executive Officer and Administrator
**Web address:** www.baptistonline.org/tipton/

BAPTIST MEMORIAL HOSPITAL–UNION CITY (O, 85 beds) 1201 Bishop Street, Union City, TN Zip 38261–5403, Mailing Address: P.O. Box 310, Zip 38281–0310; tel. 731/885–2410; Barry Bondurant, Administrator and Chief Executive Officer
**Web address:** www.baptistonline.org/union–city/

BAPTIST MEMORIAL RESTORATIVE CARE HOSPITAL (O, 30 beds) 6019 Walnut Grove Road, Memphis, TN Zip 38120–2113; tel. 901/226–1400; Janice Hill, R.N., Administrator
**Web address:** www.baptistonline.org/restorative–care/

BAPTIST REHABILITATION–GERMANTOWN (O, 68 beds) 2100 Exeter Road, Germantown, TN Zip 38138–3978; tel. 901/757–1350; Brian Hogan, Chief Executive Officer and Administrator
**Web address:** www.baptistonline.org/germantown/

| | | |
|---|---|---|
| Owned, leased, sponsored: | 14 hospitals | 2114 beds |
| Contract–managed: | 0 hospitals | 0 beds |
| Totals: | 14 hospitals | 2114 beds |

**★0118: BARNABAS HEALTH** (NP)
95 Old Short Hills Road, West Orange, NJ Zip 07052–1008; tel. 973/322–4000; Barry Ostrowsky, President and Chief Executive Officer

**(Moderately Centralized Health System)**

**NEW JERSEY:** BARNABAS HEALTH BEHAVIORAL HEALTH CENTER (O, 40 beds) 1691 Highway 9, Toms River, NJ Zip 08755–1245; tel. 732/914–1688; Joe Hicks, President and Chief Executive Officer
**Web address:** www.barnabashealth.org/hospitals/psychiatric/index.html

CLARA MAASS MEDICAL CENTER (O, 429 beds) One Clara Maass Drive, Belleville, NJ Zip 07109–3557; tel. 973/450–2000; Mary Ellen Clyne, Ph.D., President and Chief Executive Officer
**Web address:** www.barnabashealth.org/hospitals/clara_maass/index.html

COMMUNITY MEDICAL CENTER (O, 533 beds) 99 Route 37 West, Toms River, NJ Zip 08755–6423; tel. 732/557–8051; Stephanie L. Bloom, FACHE, President and Chief Executive Officer
**Web address:** www.barnabashealth.org/hospitals/community_medical/index.html

For explanation of codes following names, see page B2.
★ Indicates Type III membership in the American Hospital Association.

KIMBALL MEDICAL CENTER (O, 240 beds) 600 River Avenue, Lakewood, NJ Zip 08701–5237; tel. 732/363–1900; Michael Mimoso, FACHE, President and Chief Executive Officer
**Web address:** www.barnabashealth.org/hospitals/kimbal_medical/index.html

MONMOUTH MEDICAL CENTER (O, 329 beds) 300 Second Avenue, Long Branch, NJ Zip 07740–6303; tel. 732/222–5200; Frank J. Vozos, M.D., FACS, President and Chief Executive Officer
**Web address:** www.barnabashealth.org/hospitals/monmouth_medical/index.html

NEWARK BETH ISRAEL MEDICAL CENTER (O, 408 beds) 201 Lyons Avenue, Newark, NJ Zip 07112–2027; tel. 973/926–7000; John A. Brennan, M.D., M.P.H., President and Chief Executive Officer
**Web address:** www.barnabashealth.org/hospitals/newark_beth_israel/index.html

SAINT BARNABAS MEDICAL CENTER (O, 577 beds) 94 Old Short Hills Road, Livingston, NJ Zip 07039–5672; tel. 973/322–5000; John F. Bonamo, M.D., MS, President and Chief Executive Officer
**Web address:** www.barnabashealth.org/hospitals/saint_barnabas/index.html

| | | |
|---|---|---|
| Owned, leased, sponsored: | 7 hospitals | 2556 beds |
| Contract–managed: | 0 hospitals | 0 beds |
| Totals: | 7 hospitals | 2556 beds |

---

★**0528: BASSETT HEALTHCARE NETWORK** (NP)
1 Atwell Road, Cooperstown, NY Zip 13326–1301; tel. 607/547–3456; William F. Streck, M.D., President and Chief Executive Officer
**(Independent Hospital System)**

**NEW YORK:** AURELIA OSBORN FOX MEMORIAL HOSPITAL (O, 220 beds) 1 Norton Avenue, Oneonta, NY Zip 13820–2629; tel. 607/432–2000; John R. Remillard, President
**Web address:** www.aofoxhospital.com

BASSETT MEDICAL CENTER (O, 164 beds) One Atwell Road, Cooperstown, NY Zip 13326–1394; tel. 607/547–3100; William F. Streck, M.D., President and Chief Executive Officer
**Web address:** www.bassett.org

COBLESKILL REGIONAL HOSPITAL (O, 40 beds) 178 Grandview Drive, Cobleskill, NY Zip 12043–5144; tel. 518/254–3456; Eric H. Stein, FACHE, President and Chief Executive Officer
**Web address:** www.cobleskillhospital.org

LITTLE FALLS HOSPITAL (O, 59 beds) 140 Burwell Street, Little Falls, NY Zip 13365–1725; tel. 315/823–1000; Michael L. Ogden, President and Chief Executive Officer
**Web address:** www.lfhny.org

O'CONNOR HOSPITAL (O, 16 beds) 460 Andes Road, State Route 28, Delhi, NY Zip 13753–7407; tel. 607/746–0300; Daniel M. Ayres, Chief Executive Officer
**Web address:** www.oconnorhosp.org

| | | |
|---|---|---|
| Owned, leased, sponsored: | 5 hospitals | 499 beds |
| Contract–managed: | 0 hospitals | 0 beds |
| Totals: | 5 hospitals | 499 beds |

---

★**0095: BAYLOR HEALTH CARE SYSTEM** (CO)
3500 Gaston Avenue, Dallas, TX Zip 75246–2017; tel. 214/820–0111; Joel T. Allison, President and Chief Executive Officer
**(Centralized Health System)**

**TEXAS:** BAYLOR ALL SAINTS MEDICAL CENTER AT FORT WORTH (O, 395 beds) 1400 Eighth Avenue, Fort Worth, TX Zip 76104–4192; tel. 817/926–2544; David G. Klein, M.D., Interim President
**Web address:** www.baylorhealth.com/PhysiciansLocations/AllSaints/Pages/Default.aspx

BAYLOR INSTITUTE FOR REHABILITATION (O, 78 beds) 909 North Washington Avenue, Dallas, TX Zip 75246–1520; tel. 214/820–9300; Jon C. Skinner, President
**Web address:** www.baylorhealth.com/PhysiciansLocations/BIR/Pages/Default.aspx

BAYLOR MEDICAL CENTER AT GARLAND (O, 240 beds) 2300 Marie Curie Drive, Garland, TX Zip 75042–5706; tel. 972/487–5000; Thomas J. Trenary, President
**Web address:** www.baylorhealth.com/PhysiciansLocations/Garland/Pages/Default.aspx

BAYLOR MEDICAL CENTER AT IRVING (L, 231 beds) 1901 North MacArthur Boulevard, Irving, TX Zip 75061–2220; tel. 972/579–8100; Cindy K. Schamp, President
**Web address:** www.baylorhealth.com/PhysiciansLocations/Irving/Pages/Default.aspx

BAYLOR MEDICAL CENTER AT MCKINNEY (O, 95 beds) 5252 West University Drive, McKinney, TX Zip 75071–7822; tel. 469/764–1000; Scott Peek, FACHE, President
**Web address:** www.baylorhealth.com/PhysiciansLocations/McKinney/Pages/Default.aspx

BAYLOR MEDICAL CENTER AT WAXAHACHIE (O, 54 beds) 1405 West Jefferson Street, Waxahachie, TX Zip 75165–2275; tel. 972/923–7000; Jay Fox, President
**Web address:** www.baylorhealth.com/PhysiciansLocations/Waxahachie/Pages/Default.aspx

BAYLOR REGIONAL MEDICAL CENTER AT GRAPEVINE (O, 269 beds) 1650 West College Street, Grapevine, TX Zip 76051–3565; tel. 817/481–1588; Steven R. Newton, President
**Web address:** www.https://www.baylorhealth.com/PhysiciansLocations/Grapevine/Pages/Default.aspx

BAYLOR REGIONAL MEDICAL CENTER AT PLANO (O, 160 beds) 4700 Alliance Boulevard, Plano, TX Zip 75093–5323; tel. 469/814–2000; Jerri Garison, R.N., President
**Web address:** www.baylorhealth.com/PhysiciansLocations/Plano/Pages/Default.aspx

BAYLOR SPECIALTY HOSPITAL (O, 61 beds) 3504 Swiss Avenue, Dallas, TX Zip 75204–6224; tel. 214/820–9700; Elizabeth Youngblood, President
**Web address:** www.baylorhealth.com/PhysiciansLocations/BSH/Pages/Default.aspx

BAYLOR UNIVERSITY MEDICAL CENTER (O, 876 beds) 3500 Gaston Avenue, Dallas, TX Zip 75246–2088; tel. 214/820–0111; John B. McWhorter, III, President
**Web address:** www.baylorhealth.com/PhysiciansLocations/Dallas/Pages/Default.aspx

OUR CHILDREN'S HOUSE AT BAYLOR (O, 54 beds) 1208 North Hall Street, Dallas, TX Zip 75204; tel. 214/820–9838; Elizabeth Youngblood, President
**Web address:** www.baylorhealth.com/PhysiciansLocations/OCH/Pages/Default.aspx

| | | |
|---|---|---|
| Owned, leased, sponsored: | 11 hospitals | 2513 beds |
| Contract–managed: | 0 hospitals | 0 beds |
| Totals: | 11 hospitals | 2513 beds |

---

★**1095: BAYSTATE HEALTH, INC.** (NP)
759 Chestnut Street, Springfield, MA Zip 01199–0001; tel. 413/794–0000; Mark R. Tolosky, JD, FACHE, President and Chief Executive Officer
**(Centralized Physician/Insurance Health System)**

**MASSACHUSETTS:** BAYSTATE FRANKLIN MEDICAL CENTER (O, 90 beds) 164 High Street, Greenfield, MA Zip 01301–2613; tel. 413/773–0211; Charles Gijanto, President, Baystate Northern Region
**Web address:** www.baystatehealth.com/fmc

BAYSTATE MARY LANE HOSPITAL (O, 25 beds) 85 South Street, Ware, MA Zip 01082–1697; tel. 413/967–6211; Charles Gijanto, President
**Web address:** www.baystatehealth.com

BAYSTATE MEDICAL CENTER (O, 716 beds) 759 Chestnut Street, Springfield, MA Zip 01199–0001; tel. 413/794–0000; Mark R. Tolosky, JD, FACHE, President and Chief Executive Officer
**Web address:** www.baystatehealth.org/bmc

| | | |
|---|---|---|
| Owned, leased, sponsored: | 3 hospitals | 831 beds |
| Contract–managed: | 0 hospitals | 0 beds |
| Totals: | 3 hospitals | 831 beds |

---

For explanation of codes following names, see page B2.
★ Indicates Type III membership in the American Hospital Association.

Section B

★**9575: BEAUMONT HEALTH SYSTEM** (NP)
3711 West 13 Mile Road, Royal Oak, MI Zip 48073–6767;
tel. 248/898–5000; Gene Michalski, President and Chief Executive
Officer
**(Centralized Health System)**

**MICHIGAN:** BEAUMONT HOSPITAL – ROYAL OAK (O, 1070 beds) 3601 West
Thirteen Mile Road, Royal Oak, MI Zip 48073–6712; tel. 248/898–5000;
Shane Cerone, President
**Web address:** www.beaumont.edu/royal–oak–hospital–campus

BEAUMONT HOSPITAL – TROY (O, 418 beds) 44201 Dequindre Road, Troy,
MI Zip 48085–1117; tel. 248/964–5000; Nancy Susick, MSN, President
**Web address:** www.beaumont.edu/troy–hospital–campus

BEAUMONT HOSPITAL GROSSE POINTE (O, 250 beds) 468 Cadieux Road,
Grosse Pointe, MI Zip 48230–1507; tel. 313/473–1000; Richard P. Swaine,
President
**Web address:** www.beaumont.edu/grosse–pointe–hospital–campus

| | | |
|---|---|---|
| Owned, leased, sponsored: | 3 hospitals | 1738 beds |
| Contract–managed: | 0 hospitals | 0 beds |
| Totals: | 3 hospitals | 1738 beds |

**0545: BENEDICTINE SISTERS OF THE ANNUNCIATION** (CC)
7520 University Drive, Bismarck, ND Zip 58504–9653;
tel. 701/255–1520; Sister Susan Berger, Prioress
**(Moderately Centralized Health System)**

**NORTH DAKOTA:** GARRISON MEMORIAL HOSPITAL (S, 22 beds) 407 Third
Avenue S.E., Garrison, ND Zip 58540–7235; tel. 701/463–2275; Tod
Graeber, Administrator
**Web address:** www.garrisonmh.com

ST. ALEXIUS MEDICAL CENTER (S, 283 beds) 900 East Broadway, Bismarck,
ND Zip 58501–4586, Mailing Address: P.O. Box 5510, Zip 58506–5510;
tel. 701/530–7000; Gary P. Miller, President and Chief Executive Officer
**Web address:** www.st.alexius.org

| | | |
|---|---|---|
| Owned, leased, sponsored: | 2 hospitals | 305 beds |
| Contract–managed: | 0 hospitals | 0 beds |
| Totals: | 2 hospitals | 305 beds |

**0538: BENEFIS HEALTH SYSTEM** (NP)
1101 26th Street South, Great Falls, MT Zip 59405–5161;
tel. 406/455–5000; John H. Goodnow, Chief Executive Officer
**(Moderately Centralized Health System)**

**MONTANA:** BENEFIS HOSPITALS (O, 463 beds) 1101 26th Street South,
Great Falls, MT Zip 59405–5104; tel. 406/455–5000; John H. Goodnow,
Chief Executive Officer
**Web address:** www.benefis.org

MISSOURI RIVER MEDICAL CENTER (C, 52 beds) 1501 St. Charles Street,
Fort Benton, MT Zip 59442–0249, Mailing Address: P.O. Box 249,
Zip 59442–0249; tel. 406/622–3331; Jay Pottenger, Administrator
**Web address:** www.mrmcfb.org

| | | |
|---|---|---|
| Owned, leased, sponsored: | 1 hospital | 463 beds |
| Contract–managed: | 1 hospital | 52 beds |
| Totals: | 2 hospitals | 515 beds |

★**2435: BERKSHIRE HEALTH SYSTEMS, INC.** (NP)
725 North Street, Pittsfield, MA Zip 01201–4124;
tel. 413/447–2743; David E. Phelps, President and Chief Executive
Officer
**(Independent Hospital System)**

**MASSACHUSETTS:** BERKSHIRE MEDICAL CENTER (O, 253 beds) 725 North
Street, Pittsfield, MA Zip 01201–4124; tel. 413/447–2000; David E.
Phelps, President and Chief Executive Officer
**Web address:** www.bhs1.org/body_bmc.cfm?id=43

FAIRVIEW HOSPITAL (O, 24 beds) 29 Lewis Avenue, Great Barrington, MA
Zip 01230–1713; tel. 413/528–0790; Eugene A. Dellea, President
**Web address:** www.bhs1.org/body_fh.cfm?id=39

| | | |
|---|---|---|
| Owned, leased, sponsored: | 2 hospitals | 277 beds |
| Contract–managed: | 0 hospitals | 0 beds |
| Totals: | 2 hospitals | 277 beds |

★**0051: BJC HEALTHCARE** (NP)
4901 Forest Park Avenue, Suite 1200, Saint Louis, MO
Zip 63108–1402; tel. 314/747–9322; Steven H. Lipstein, President
and Chief Executive Officer
**(Centralized Health System)**

**ILLINOIS:** ALTON MEMORIAL HOSPITAL (O, 253 beds) One Memorial Drive,
Alton, IL Zip 62002–6722; tel. 618/463–7311; David A. Braasch,
President
**Web address:** www.altonmemorialhospital.org

CLAY COUNTY HOSPITAL (C, 18 beds) 911 Stacy Burk Drive, Flora, IL
Zip 62839–3241, Mailing Address: P.O. Box 280, Zip 62839–0280;
tel. 618/662–2131; Robert R. Sellers, President
**Web address:** www.claycountyhospital.org

**MISSOURI:** BARNES–JEWISH HOSPITAL (O, 1310 beds) 1 Barnes–Jewish
Hospital Plaza, Saint Louis, MO Zip 63110–1003; tel. 314/747–3000;
Richard J. Liekweg, President
**Web address:** www.barnesjewish.org

BARNES–JEWISH ST. PETERS HOSPITAL (O, 113 beds) 10 Hospital Drive,
Saint Peters, MO Zip 63376–1659; tel. 636/916–9000; Larry Tracy, FACHE,
President
**Web address:** www.bjsph.org/

BARNES–JEWISH WEST COUNTY HOSPITAL (O, 77 beds) 12634 Olive
Boulevard, Saint Louis, MO Zip 63141–6337; tel. 314/996–8000; Doug
Black, President
**Web address:** www.barnesjewishwestcounty.org

BOONE HOSPITAL CENTER (L, 360 beds) 1600 East Broadway, Columbia,
MO Zip 65201–5844; tel. 573/815–8000; Randy Morrow, Interim Chief
Executive Officer
**Web address:** www.boone.org

CHRISTIAN HOSPITAL (O, 258 beds) 11133 Dunn Road, Saint Louis, MO
Zip 63136–6119; tel. 314/653–5000; Ronald B. McMullen, President
**Web address:** www.christianhospital.org

MISSOURI BAPTIST MEDICAL CENTER (O, 445 beds) 3015 North Ballas Road,
Saint Louis, MO Zip 63131–2329; tel. 314/996–5000; John Antes, President
**Web address:** www.missouribaptistmedicalcenter.org

MISSOURI BAPTIST SULLIVAN HOSPITAL (O, 35 beds) 751 Sappington Bridge
Road, Sullivan, MO Zip 63080–2354; tel. 573/468–4186; Tony Schwarm,
President
**Web address:** www.missouribaptistsullivan.org

PARKLAND HEALTH CENTER (O, 98 beds) 1101 West Liberty Street,
Farmington, MO Zip 63640–1921; tel. 573/756–6451; Thomas P. Karl,
President
**Web address:** www.parklandhealthcenter.org

PARKLAND HEALTH CENTER–BONNE TERRE (O, 3 beds) 7245 Raider Road,
Bonne Terre, MO Zip 63628–3767; tel. 573/358–1400; Steven R. Marler,
Administrator
**Web address:** www.parklandhealthcenter.org

PROGRESS WEST HEALTHCARE CENTER (O, 42 beds) Two Progress Point,
Saint Charles, MO Zip 63368–2208; tel. 636/344–2273; Larry Tracy,
FACHE, President
**Web address:** www.progresswesthealthcare.org

ST. LOUIS CHILDREN'S HOSPITAL (O, 258 beds) One Children's Place, Saint
Louis, MO Zip 63110–1002; tel. 314/454–6000; Joan Magruder, President
**Web address:** www.stlouischildrens.org

| | | |
|---|---|---|
| Owned, leased, sponsored: | 12 hospitals | 3252 beds |
| Contract–managed: | 1 hospital | 18 beds |
| Totals: | 13 hospitals | 3270 beds |

★**0852: BLANCHARD VALLEY HEALTH SYSTEM** (NP)
1900 South Main Street, Findlay, OH Zip 45840–1214;
tel. 419/423–4500; Scott C. Malaney, President and Chief Executive
Officer
**(Independent Hospital System)**

For explanation of codes following names, see page B2.
★ Indicates Type III membership in the American Hospital Association.

**OHIO:** BLANCHARD VALLEY HOSPITAL (O, 181 beds) 1900 South Main Street, Findlay, OH Zip 45840–1214; tel. 419/423–4500; Scott C. Malaney, President and Chief Executive Officer
**Web address:** www.bvhealthsystem.org/?id=204&sid=1

BLUFFTON HOSPITAL (O, 25 beds) 139 Garau Street, Bluffton, OH Zip 45817–1027; tel. 419/358–9010; William D. Watkins, Chief Administrative Officer
**Web address:** www.bvhealthsystem.org/?id=203&sid=1

| Owned, leased, sponsored: | 2 hospitals | 206 beds |
|---|---|---|
| Contract–managed: | 0 hospitals | 0 beds |
| Totals: | 2 hospitals | 206 beds |

### 0300: BLUE MOUNTAIN HEALTH SYSTEM (NP)
211 North 12th Street, Lehighton, PA Zip 18235–1138; tel. 610/377–1300; Andrew E. Harris, President and Chief Executive Officer
**(Independent Hospital System)**

**PENNSYLVANIA:** GNADEN HUETTEN MEMORIAL HOSPITAL (O, 181 beds) 211 North 12th Street, Lehighton, PA Zip 18235–1138; tel. 610/377–1300; Andrew E. Harris, Chief Executive Officer
**Web address:** www.ghmh.org/content/GnadenHuettenMemorialHospital.htm

PALMERTON HOSPITAL (O, 60 beds) 135 Lafayette Avenue, Palmerton, PA Zip 18071–1596; tel. 610/826–3141; Andrew E. Harris, Chief Executive Officer
**Web address:** www.ghmh.org/content/palmertoncampus.htm

| Owned, leased, sponsored: | 2 hospitals | 241 beds |
|---|---|---|
| Contract–managed: | 0 hospitals | 0 beds |
| Totals: | 2 hospitals | 241 beds |

### 0308: BLUE RIDGE HEALTHCARE (NP)
2201 South Sterling Street, Morganton, NC Zip 28655; tel. 828/580–5000; Kathy C. Bailey, Ph.D., FACHE, President and Chief Executive Officer

**NORTH CAROLINA:** GRACE HOSPITAL (O, 132 beds) 2201 South Sterling Street, Morganton, NC Zip 28655–4058; tel. 828/580–5000; Kathy C. Bailey, Ph.D., FACHE, President and Chief Executive Officer
**Web address:** www.blueridgehealth.org/grace–hospital.html

VALDESE GENERAL HOSPITAL (O, 155 beds) 720 Malcolm Boulevard, Valdese, NC Zip 28690–2872, Mailing Address: P.O. Box 700, Zip 28690–0700; tel. 828/874–2251; Kathy C. Bailey, Ph.D., FACHE, President and Chief Executive Officer
**Web address:** www.blueridgehealth.org

| Owned, leased, sponsored: | 2 hospitals | 287 beds |
|---|---|---|
| Contract–managed: | 0 hospitals | 0 beds |
| Totals: | 2 hospitals | 287 beds |

### ●★0053: BLUE WATER HEALTH SERVICES CORPORATION (NP)
1221 Pine Grove Avenue, Port Huron, MI Zip 48060–3511; tel. 810/989–3717; Thomas D. DeFauw, FACHE, President and Chief Executive Officer
**(Independent Hospital System)**

**MICHIGAN:** PORT HURON HOSPITAL (O, 186 beds) 1221 Pine Grove Avenue, Port Huron, MI Zip 48060–3511; tel. 810/987–5000; Thomas D. DeFauw, FACHE, President and Chief Executive Officer
**Web address:** www.porthuronhospital.org

| Owned, leased, sponsored: | 1 hospital | 186 beds |
|---|---|---|
| Contract–managed: | 0 hospitals | 0 beds |
| Totals: | 1 hospital | 186 beds |

### ★5085: BON SECOURS HEALTH SYSTEM, INC. (CC)
1505 Marriottsville Road, Marriottsville, MD Zip 21104–1399; tel. 410/442–5511; Richard Statuto, President and Chief Executive Officer
**(Moderately Centralized Health System)**

**KENTUCKY:** OUR LADY OF BELLEFONTE HOSPITAL (O, 151 beds) St. Christopher Drive, Ashland, KY Zip 41101, Mailing Address: P.O. Box 789, Zip 41105–0789; tel. 606/833–3333; Kevin Halter, Chief Executive Officer
**Web address:** www.olbh.com

**MARYLAND:** BON SECOURS BALTIMORE HEALTH SYSTEM (O, 93 beds) 2000 West Baltimore Street, Baltimore, MD Zip 21223–1558; tel. 410/362–3000; Samuel Lee Ross, M.D., MS, Chief Executive Officer
**Web address:** www.bonsecoursbaltimore.com

**NEW YORK:** BON SECOURS COMMUNITY HOSPITAL (O, 187 beds) 160 East Main Street, Port Jervis, NY Zip 12771–2245, Mailing Address: P.O. Box 1014, Zip 12771–0268; tel. 845/858–7000; Jeff Reilly, Senior Vice President Operations
**Web address:** www.bonsecourscommunityhosp.org

GOOD SAMARITAN HOSPITAL (O, 308 beds) 255 Lafayette Avenue, Suffern, NY Zip 10901–4869; tel. 845/368–5000; Philip A. Patterson, Chief Executive Officer
**Web address:** www.goodsamhosp.org

ST. ANTHONY COMMUNITY HOSPITAL (O, 73 beds) 15 Maple Avenue, Warwick, NY Zip 10990–1028; tel. 845/986–2276; Jeff Reilly, Senior Vice President Operations
**Web address:** www.stanthonycommunityhosp.org

**SOUTH CAROLINA:** BON SECOURS ST. FRANCIS HEALTH SYSTEM (O, 331 beds) One St. Francis Drive, Greenville, SC Zip 29601–3207; tel. 864/255–1000; Mark S. Nantz, FACHE, Chief Executive Officer
**Web address:** www.stfrancishealth.org

**VIRGINIA:** BON SECOURS MARYVIEW MEDICAL CENTER (O, 466 beds) 3636 High Street, Portsmouth, VA Zip 23707–3270; tel. 757/398–2200; Joseph M. Oddis, Chief Executive Officer
**Web address:** www.bonsecourshamptonroads.com

BON SECOURS MEMORIAL REGIONAL MEDICAL CENTER (O, 225 beds) 8260 Atlee Road, Mechanicsville, VA Zip 23116–1844; tel. 804/764–6000; Michael Robinson, Chief Executive Officer
**Web address:** www.bonsecours.com

BON SECOURS ST. FRANCIS MEDICAL CENTER (O, 130 beds) 13710 St. Francis Boulevard, Midlothian, VA Zip 23114–3267; tel. 804/594–7300; Mark M. Gordon, Executive Vice President
**Web address:** www.bonsecours.com/sfmc/default.asp

BON SECOURS ST. MARY'S HOSPITAL (O, 391 beds) 5801 Bremo Road, Richmond, VA Zip 23226–1907; tel. 804/285–2011; Toni R. Ardabell, R.N., Chief Executive Officer
**Web address:** www.bonsecours.com

BON SECOURS–DEPAUL MEDICAL CENTER (O, 204 beds) 150 Kingsley Lane, Norfolk, VA Zip 23505–4650; tel. 757/889–5000; John E. Barrett, III, Chief Executive Officer
**Web address:** www.bonsecourshamptonroads.com

BON SECOURS–RICHMOND COMMUNITY HOSPITAL (O, 101 beds) 1500 North 28th Street, Richmond, VA Zip 23223–5396, Mailing Address: P.O. Box 27184, Zip 23261–7184; tel. 804/225–1700; Michael Robinson, Executive Vice President and Administrator
**Web address:** www.bonsecours.com

MARY IMMACULATE HOSPITAL (O, 232 beds) 2 Bernardine Drive, Newport News, VA Zip 23602–4499; tel. 757/886–6000; Patricia L. Robertson, Executive Vice President
**Web address:** www.bonsecourshamptonroads.com

| Owned, leased, sponsored: | 13 hospitals | 2892 beds |
|---|---|---|
| Contract–managed: | 0 hospitals | 0 beds |
| Totals: | 13 hospitals | 2892 beds |

For explanation of codes following names, see page B2.
★ Indicates Type III membership in the American Hospital Association.
● Single hospital health care system

Section B

**2455: BRADFORD HEALTH SERVICES** (IO)
2101 Magnolia Avenue South, Suite 518, Birmingham, AL
Zip 35205–2853; tel. 205/251–7753; Jerry W. Crowder, President
and Chief Executive Officer

**ALABAMA:** BRADFORD HEALTH SERVICES AT HUNTSVILLE (O, 84 beds)
1600 Browns Ferry Road, Madison, AL Zip 35758–9601, Mailing Address:
P.O. Box 1488, Zip 35758–0176; tel. 256/461–7272; Bob Hinds,
Executive Director
**Web address:** www.bradfordhealth.com

BRADFORD HEALTH SERVICES AT WARRIOR LODGE (O, 100 beds) 1189
Allbritt Road, Warrior, AL Zip 35180, Mailing Address: P.O. Box 129,
Zip 35180–0129; tel. 205/647–1945; Roy M. Ramsey, Executive Director
**Web address:** www.bradfordhealth.com

| | | |
|---|---|---|
| Owned, leased, sponsored: | 2 hospitals | 184 beds |
| Contract–managed: | 0 hospitals | 0 beds |
| Totals: | 2 hospitals | 184 beds |

**★0595: BRONSON HEALTHCARE GROUP, INC.** (NP)
301 John Street, Kalamazoo, MI Zip 49007–5295;
tel. 269/341–6000; Frank J. Sardone, President and Chief Executive
Officer
**(Independent Hospital System)**

**MICHIGAN:** BRONSON BATTLE CREEK (O, 218 beds) 300 North Avenue,
Battle Creek, MI Zip 49017–3307; tel. 269/966–8000; Anne Regling,
Interim Chief Executive Officer
**Web address:** www.bchealth.com

BRONSON LAKEVIEW HOSPITAL (O, 35 beds) 408 Hazen Street, Paw Paw, MI
Zip 49079–1019, Mailing Address: P.O. Box 209, Zip 49079–0209;
tel. 269/657–3141; Sally L. Berglin, Chief Executive Officer
**Web address:** www.bronsonhealth.com/lakeview

BRONSON METHODIST HOSPITAL (O, 415 beds) 601 John Street,
Kalamazoo, MI Zip 49007–5346; tel. 269/341–6000; Frank J. Sardone,
President and Chief Executive Officer
**Web address:** www.bronsonhealth.com

| | | |
|---|---|---|
| Owned, leased, sponsored: | 3 hospitals | 668 beds |
| Contract–managed: | 0 hospitals | 0 beds |
| Totals: | 3 hospitals | 668 beds |

**★3115: BROWARD HEALTH** (NP)
303 S.E. 17th Street, Fort Lauderdale, FL Zip 33316–2523;
tel. 954/355–5100; Frank P. Nask, President and Chief Executive
Officer

**FLORIDA:** BROWARD HEALTH CORAL SPRINGS (O, 182 beds) 3000 Coral
Hills Drive, Coral Springs, FL Zip 33065–4108; tel. 954/344–3000; Drew
Grossman, Chief Executive Officer
**Web address:** www.browardhealth.org

BROWARD HEALTH IMPERIAL POINT (O, 180 beds) 6401 North Federal
Highway, Fort Lauderdale, FL Zip 33308–1495; tel. 954/776–8500; Alice
Taylor, R.N., MSN, Chief Executive Officer
**Web address:** www.browardhealth.org

BROWARD HEALTH MEDICAL CENTER (O, 656 beds) 1600 South Andrews
Avenue, Fort Lauderdale, FL Zip 33316–2510; tel. 954/355–4400; Calvin E.
Glidewell, Jr., Chief Executive Officer
**Web address:** www.browardhealth.org

BROWARD HEALTH NORTH (O, 342 beds) 201 East Sample Road, Deerfield
Beach, FL Zip 33064–3502; tel. 954/941–8300; Pauline Grant, FACHE, Chief
Executive Officer
**Web address:** www.browardhealth.org

| | | |
|---|---|---|
| Owned, leased, sponsored: | 4 hospitals | 1360 beds |
| Contract–managed: | 0 hospitals | 0 beds |
| Totals: | 4 hospitals | 1360 beds |

**★0400: BRYAN HEALTH** (NP)
1600 South 48th Street, Lincoln, NE Zip 68506–1283;
tel. 402/481–1111; Kimberly A. Russel, FACHE, President and Chief
Executive Officer
**(Centralized Physician/Insurance Health System)**

**NEBRASKA:** BRYAN MEDICAL CENTER (O, 351 beds) 1600 South 48th
Street, Lincoln, NE Zip 68506–1299; tel. 402/489–0200; John T.
Woodrich, President and Chief Operating Officer
**Web address:** www.bryanhealth.com

CRETE AREA MEDICAL CENTER (O, 24 beds) 2910 Betten Drive, Crete, NE
Zip 68333–3084, Mailing Address: P.O. Box 220, Zip 68333–0220;
tel. 402/826–2102; Carol Friesen, President and Chief Executive Officer
**Web address:** www.creteareamedicalcenter.com

| | | |
|---|---|---|
| Owned, leased, sponsored: | 2 hospitals | 375 beds |
| Contract–managed: | 0 hospitals | 0 beds |
| Totals: | 2 hospitals | 375 beds |

**9655: BUREAU OF MEDICINE AND SURGERY, DEPARTMENT
OF THE NAVY** (FG)
2300 East Street N.W., Washington, DC Zip 20372–5300;
tel. 202/762–3701; Vice Admiral Matthew L. Nathan, Surgeon
General
**(Independent Hospital System)**

**CALIFORNIA:** NAVAL HOSPITAL (O, 16 beds) 937 Franklin Avenue, Lemoore,
CA Zip 93246–5004; tel. 559/998–4481; ,
**Web address:** www.med.navy.mil/sites/nhlem/Pages/index.aspx

NAVAL HOSPITAL CAMP PENDLETON (O, 72 beds) Santa Margarita Road,
Building H100, Camp Pendleton, CA Zip 92055–5191, Mailing Address: P.O.
Box 555191, Zip 92055–5191; tel. 760/725–1304; Commander Alan
Christian,
**Web address:** www.cpen.med.navy.mil/

NAVAL MEDICAL CENTER SAN DIEGO (O, 285 beds) 34800 Bob Wilson Drive,
San Diego, CA Zip 92134–5000; tel. 619/532–6400; Captain Christopher
Irwin, Director, Administration
**Web address:** www.med.navy.mil/sites/nmcsd/Pages/default.aspx

ROBERT E. BUSH NAVAL HOSPITAL (O, 39 beds) Twentynine Palms, CA
Zip 92278; tel. 760/830–2190; Lieutenant Commander Brennan Autry,
Director Administration
**Web address:** www.med.navy.mil/sites/nhtp/Pages/default.aspx

**FLORIDA:** NAVAL HOSPITAL JACKSONVILLE (O, 64 beds) 2080 Child Street,
Jacksonville, FL Zip 32214–5000; tel. 904/542–7300; Captain Ruby
Tennyson, Director Administration
**Web address:** www.med.navy.
mil/SITES/NAVALHOSPITALJAX/Pages/default.aspx

NAVAL HOSPITAL PENSACOLA (O, 28 beds) 6000 West Highway 98,
Pensacola, FL Zip 32512–0003; tel. 850/505–6413; Commander Devin
Morrison, Director Administration
**Web address:** www.med.navy.mil/sites/pcola/Pages/default.aspx

**GUAM:** U. S. NAVAL HOSPITAL GUAM (O, 55 beds) Agana, GU Zip 96910;
FPO, APtel. 671/344–9340; Lieutenant Commander Rona Green,
**Web address:** www.med.navy.mil/sites/usnhguam/Pages/default.aspx

**MARYLAND:** WALTER REED NATIONAL MILITARY MEDICAL CENTER (O, 240
beds) 8901 Wisconsin Avenue, Bethesda, MD Zip 20889–5600;
tel. 301/295–4611; Colonel John M. Gaal, Deputy Commander
Administration
**Web address:** www.wrnmmc.capmed.mil/SitePages/home.aspx

**NORTH CAROLINA:** NAVAL HOSPITAL CAMP LEJEUNE (O, 117 beds) 100
Brewster Boulevard, Camp Lejeune, NC Zip 28547–2538, Mailing
Address: P.O. Box 10100, Zip 28547–0100; tel. 910/450–4300;
Commander Matthew Case, Director Administration
**Web address:** www.med.navy.mil/sites/nhcl/Pages/default.aspx

**SOUTH CAROLINA:** NAVAL HOSPITAL BEAUFORT (O, 20 beds) 1 Pinckney
Boulevard, Beaufort, SC Zip 29902–6122; tel. 843/228–5301; Lieutenant
Commander Willie Brown, Director Administration
**Web address:** www.med.navy.mil/sites/nhbeaufort/Pages/Welcome_
Page.aspx

For explanation of codes following names, see page B2.
★ Indicates Type III membership in the American Hospital Association.

**VIRGINIA:** NAVAL MEDICAL CENTER (O, 274 beds) 620 John Paul Jones Circle, Portsmouth, VA Zip 23708–2197; tel. 757/953–0700; Captain David Collins, Director Administration
**Web address:** www.nmcphc.med.navy.mil/

**WASHINGTON:** NAVAL HOSPITAL BREMERTON (O, 40 beds) One Boone Road, Bremerton, WA Zip 98312–1898; tel. 360/475–4000; Commander Brendan Melody, Director Administration
**Web address:** www.med.navy.mil/sites/nhbrem/Pages/default.aspx

NAVAL HOSPITAL OAK HARBOR (O, 29 beds) 3475 North Saratoga Street, Oak Harbor, WA Zip 98278–8800; tel. 360/257–9500; Lieutenant Commander Chris Morrison,
**Web address:** www.med.navy.mil/sites/nhoh/Pages/default.aspx

| Owned, leased, sponsored: | 13 hospitals | 1279 beds |
|---|---|---|
| Contract–managed: | 0 hospitals | 0 beds |
| Totals: | 13 hospitals | 1279 beds |

---

**★0813: CADENCE HEALTH** (NP)
25 North Winfield Road, Winfield, IL Zip 60190; tel. 630/933–1600; Michael Vivoda, Chief Executive Officer
**(Centralized Health System)**

**ILLINOIS:** CENTRAL DUPAGE HOSPITAL (O, 344 beds) 25 North Winfield Road, Winfield, IL Zip 60190; tel. 630/933–1600; Brian J. Lemon, President
**Web address:** www.cdh.org

DELNOR HOSPITAL (O, 159 beds) 300 Randall Road, Geneva, IL Zip 60134–4200; tel. 630/208–3000; Robert Friedberg, President
**Web address:** www.delnor.com

| Owned, leased, sponsored: | 2 hospitals | 503 beds |
|---|---|---|
| Contract–managed: | 0 hospitals | 0 beds |
| Totals: | 2 hospitals | 503 beds |

---

**0113: CANCER TREATMENT CENTERS OF AMERICA** (IO)
1336 Basswood Road, Schaumburg, IL Zip 60173–4544; tel. 847/342–7400; Stephen B. Bonner, President and Chief Executive Officer

**ARIZONA:** WESTERN REGIONAL MEDICAL CENTER (O, 24 beds) 14200 West Fillmore Street, Goodyear, AZ Zip 85338–3005; tel. 623/207–3000; David Veillette, President and Chief Executive Officer
**Web address:** www.cancercenter.com/western–hospital.cfm

**GEORGIA:** SOUTHEASTERN REGIONAL MEDICAL CENTER (O, 25 beds) 600 Parkway N., Newnan, GA Zip 30265–8000; tel. 770/400–6000; Anne Meisner, MSN, President and Chief Executive Officer
**Web address:** www.cancercenter.com/southeastern–hospital.cfm

**ILLINOIS:** MIDWESTERN REGIONAL MEDICAL CENTER (O, 73 beds) 2520 Elisha Avenue, Zion, IL Zip 60099–2587; tel. 847/872–4561; Scott Jones, Chief Executive Officer
**Web address:** www.cancercenter.com

**OKLAHOMA:** SOUTHWESTERN REGIONAL MEDICAL CENTER (O, 43 beds) 10109 East 79th Street, Tulsa, OK Zip 74133–4564; tel. 918/286–5000; Steve Mackin, President and Chief Executive Officer
**Web address:** www.cancercenter.com

**PENNSYLVANIA:** EASTERN REGIONAL MEDICAL CENTER (O, 22 beds) 1331 East Wyoming Avenue, Philadelphia, PA Zip 19124–3808; tel. 800/294–8333; John McNeil, President and Chief Executive Officer
**Web address:** www.cancercenter.com

| Owned, leased, sponsored: | 5 hospitals | 187 beds |
|---|---|---|
| Contract–managed: | 0 hospitals | 0 beds |
| Totals: | 5 hospitals | 187 beds |

---

**★0124: CAPE COD HEALTHCARE, INC.** (NP)
27 Park Street, Hyannis, MA Zip 02601–5230; tel. 508/862–5121; Michael K. Lauf, President and Chief Executive Officer
**(Centralized Health System)**

**MASSACHUSETTS:** CAPE COD HOSPITAL (O, 259 beds) 27 Park Street, Hyannis, MA Zip 02601–5230; tel. 508/771–1800; Michael K. Lauf, President and Chief Executive Officer
**Web address:** www.capecodhealth.org

FALMOUTH HOSPITAL (O, 95 beds) 100 Ter Heun Drive, Falmouth, MA Zip 02540–2599; tel. 508/548–5300; Hugh J. Kelleher, Chief Operating Officer
**Web address:** www.capecodhealth.org

| Owned, leased, sponsored: | 2 hospitals | 354 beds |
|---|---|---|
| Contract–managed: | 0 hospitals | 0 beds |
| Totals: | 2 hospitals | 354 beds |

---

**0835: CAPE FEAR VALLEY HEALTH SYSTEM** (NP)
1638 Owen Drive, Fayetteville, NC Zip 28304–3424, Mailing Address: P.O. Box 2000, Zip 28302–2000; tel. 910/615–4000; Michael Nagowski, President and Chief Executive Officer
**(Moderately Centralized Health System)**

**NORTH CAROLINA:** CAPE FEAR VALLEY – BLADEN COUNTY HOSPITAL (O, 26 beds) 501 South Poplar Street, Elizabethtown, NC Zip 28337–9375, Mailing Address: P.O. Box 398, Zip 28337–0398; tel. 910/862–5100; Dan Weatherly, On Site Administrator
**Web address:** www.bchn.org

CAPE FEAR VALLEY MEDICAL CENTER (O, 666 beds) 1638 Owen Drive, Fayetteville, NC Zip 28304–3431, Mailing Address: P.O. Box 2000, Zip 28302–2000; tel. 910/615–4000; Michael Nagowski, Chief Executive Officer
**Web address:** www.capefearvalley.com

HIGHSMITH–RAINEY SPECIALTY HOSPITAL (O, 133 beds) 150 Robeson Street, Fayetteville, NC Zip 28301–5570; tel. 910/615–1000; Kevin Jackson, On Site Administrator
**Web address:** www.capefearvalley.com

| Owned, leased, sponsored: | 3 hospitals | 825 beds |
|---|---|---|
| Contract–managed: | 0 hospitals | 0 beds |
| Totals: | 3 hospitals | 825 beds |

---

**0337: CAPELLA HEALTHCARE** (IO)
501 Corporate Centre Drive, Suite 200, Franklin, TN Zip 37067–2662; tel. 615/764–3000; Daniel S. Slipkovich, Chief Executive Officer
**(Moderately Centralized Health System)**

**ARKANSAS:** NATIONAL PARK MEDICAL CENTER (O, 191 beds) 1910 Malvern Avenue, Hot Springs, AR Zip 71901–7799; tel. 501/321–1000; Jerry D. Mabry, FACHE, Chief Executive Officer
**Web address:** www.nationalparkmedical.com

SAINT MARY'S REGIONAL MEDICAL CENTER (O, 151 beds) 1808 West Main Street, Russellville, AR Zip 72801–2724; tel. 479/968–2841; Donald J. Frederic, FACHE, Chief Executive Officer
**Web address:** www.saintmarysregional.com

**MISSOURI:** MINERAL AREA REGIONAL MEDICAL CENTER (O, 98 beds) 1212 Weber Road, Farmington, MO Zip 63640–3325; tel. 573/756–4581; Lynn M. Mergen, Chief Executive Officer
**Web address:** www.marmc.net

**OKLAHOMA:** MUSKOGEE REGIONAL MEDICAL CENTER (L, 181 beds) 300 Rockefeller Drive, Muskogee, OK Zip 74401–5081; tel. 918/682–5501; Robert B. Wampler, CPA, Interim Chief Executive Officer
**Web address:** www.muskogeehealth.com

SOUTHWESTERN MEDICAL CENTER (O, 178 beds) 5602 S.W. Lee Boulevard, Lawton, OK Zip 73505–9635; tel. 580/531–4700; Stephen O. Hyde, FACHE, Chief Executive Officer
**Web address:** www.swmconline.com

**OREGON:** WILLAMETTE VALLEY MEDICAL CENTER (O, 88 beds) 2700 S.E. Stratus Avenue, McMinnville, OR Zip 97128–6255; tel. 503/472–6131; Daniel Ordyna, Chief Executive Officer
**Web address:** www.wvmcweb.com

---

For explanation of codes following names, see page B2.
★ Indicates Type III membership in the American Hospital Association.

---

**TENNESSEE:** DEKALB COMMUNITY HOSPITAL (O, 56 beds) 520 West Main Street, Smithville, TN Zip 37166–1138, Mailing Address: P.O. Box 640, Zip 37166–0640; tel. 615/215–5000; Susan Conley, Chief Executive Officer
**Web address:** www.dekalbcommunityhospital.com

GRANDVIEW MEDICAL CENTER (O, 68 beds) 1000 Highway 28, Jasper, TN Zip 37347–3638; tel. 423/837–9500; Bruce A. Baldwin, Chief Executive Officer
**Web address:** www.grandviewhospital.com

HIGHLANDS MEDICAL CENTER (O, 44 beds) 401 Sewell Road, Sparta, TN Zip 38583–1299; tel. 931/738–9211; William Little, Chief Executive Officer
**Web address:** www.whitecountyhospital.com

RIVER PARK HOSPITAL (O, 85 beds) 1559 Sparta Street, Mc Minnville, TN Zip 37110–1316; tel. 931/815–4000; Timothy W. McGill, Chief Executive Officer
**Web address:** www.riverparkhospital.com

STONES RIVER HOSPITAL (O, 60 beds) 324 Doolittle Road, Woodbury, TN Zip 37190–1139; tel. 615/563–4001; Susan Conley, Chief Executive Officer
**Web address:** www.stonesriverhospital.com

**WASHINGTON:** CAPITAL MEDICAL CENTER (O, 110 beds) 3900 Capital Mall Drive S.W., Olympia, WA Zip 98502–5026, Mailing Address: P.O. Box 19002, Zip 98507–0013; tel. 360/754–5858; Jim Geist, Chief Executive Officer
**Web address:** www.capitalmedical.com

| Owned, leased, sponsored: | 12 hospitals | 1310 beds |
|---|---|---|
| Contract–managed: | 0 hospitals | 0 beds |
| Totals: | 12 hospitals | 1310 beds |

---

**★0297: CAPITAL HEALTH** (NP)
750 Brunswick Avenue, Trenton, NJ Zip 08638–4143; tel. 609/394–6000; Al Maghazehe, Ph.D., FACHE, Chief Executive Officer
**(Independent Hospital System)**

**NEW JERSEY:** CAPITAL HEALTH MEDICAL CENTER–HOPEWELL (O, 223 beds) 1 Capital Way, Pennington, NJ Zip 08534–2520; tel. 609/303–4000; Al Maghazehe, Ph.D., FACHE, Chief Executive Officer
**Web address:** www.capitalhealth.org

CAPITAL HEALTH REGIONAL MEDICAL CENTER (O, 271 beds) 750 Brunswick Avenue, Trenton, NJ Zip 08638–4143; tel. 609/394–6000; Al Maghazehe, Ph.D., FACHE, Chief Executive Officer
**Web address:** www.capitalhealth.org

| Owned, leased, sponsored: | 2 hospitals | 494 beds |
|---|---|---|
| Contract–managed: | 0 hospitals | 0 beds |
| Totals: | 2 hospitals | 494 beds |

---

**★0099: CARE NEW ENGLAND HEALTH SYSTEM** (NP)
45 Willard Avenue, Providence, RI Zip 02905–3218; tel. 401/453–7900; Dennis D. Keefe, President and Chief Executive Officer
**(Centralized Health System)**

**RHODE ISLAND:** BUTLER HOSPITAL (O, 117 beds) 345 Blackstone Boulevard, Providence, RI Zip 02906–4829; tel. 401/455–6200; Patricia R. Recupero, M.D., JD, President and Chief Executive Officer
**Web address:** www.butler.org

KENT COUNTY MEMORIAL HOSPITAL (O, 306 beds) 455 Tollgate Road, Warwick, RI Zip 02886–2770; tel. 401/737–7000; Sandra L. Coletta, President and Chief Executive Officer
**Web address:** www.kentri.org

WOMEN & INFANTS HOSPITAL OF RHODE ISLAND (O, 247 beds) 101 Dudley Street, Providence, RI Zip 02905–2499; tel. 401/274–1100; Constance A. Howes, President and Chief Executive Officer
**Web address:** www.womenandinfants.org

| Owned, leased, sponsored: | 3 hospitals | 670 beds |
|---|---|---|
| Contract–managed: | 0 hospitals | 0 beds |
| Totals: | 3 hospitals | 670 beds |

---

**★0070: CARILION CLINIC** (NP)
1906 Belleview Avenue S.E., Roanoke, VA Zip 24014–1838, Mailing Address: P.O. Box 13367, Zip 24033–3367; tel. 540/981–7000; Nancy Howell Agee, President and Chief Executive Officer
**(Moderately Centralized Health System)**

**VIRGINIA:** BEDFORD MEMORIAL HOSPITAL (O, 124 beds) 1613 Oakwood Street, Bedford, VA Zip 24523–1213, Mailing Address: P.O. Box 688, Zip 24523–0688; tel. 540/586–2441; Patti Jurkus, Vice President, Regional Hospital
**Web address:** www.bmhva.com

CARILION FRANKLIN MEMORIAL HOSPITAL (O, 32 beds) 180 Floyd Avenue, Rocky Mount, VA Zip 24151–1389; tel. 540/483–5277; William D. Jacobsen, Vice President, Regional Hospital
**Web address:** www.carilionclinic.org/Carilion/Franklin+Memorial+Hospital

CARILION GILES COMMUNITY HOSPITAL (O, 25 beds) 159 Hartley Way, Pearisburg, VA Zip 24134–2471; tel. 540/921–6000; James E. Tyler, Vice President, Regional Hospital
**Web address:** www.carilionclinic.org/Carilion/cgch

CARILION MEDICAL CENTER (O, 624 beds) Belleview at Jefferson Street, Roanoke, VA Zip 24014, Mailing Address: P.O. Box 13367, Zip 24033–3367; tel. 540/981–7000; Nancy Howell Agee, President and Chief Executive Officer
**Web address:** www.carilionclinic.org

CARILION NEW RIVER VALLEY MEDICAL CENTER (O, 146 beds) 2900 Lamb Circle, Christiansburg, VA Zip 24073–6344, Mailing Address: P.O. Box 5, Radford, Zip 24143–0005; tel. 540/731–2000; John S. Piatkowski, M.D., Vice President, Regional Hospital
**Web address:** www.carilionclinic.org/Carilion/cnrv

CARILION STONEWALL JACKSON HOSPITAL (O, 17 beds) 1 Health Circle, Lexington, VA Zip 24450–2492; tel. 540/458–3300; Charles E. Carr, Vice President, Regional Hospital
**Web address:** www.carilionclinic.org/Carilion/csjh

CARILION TAZEWELL COMMUNITY HOSPITAL (O, 12 beds) 141 Ben Bolt Avenue, Tazewell, VA Zip 24651–9700; tel. 276/988–8700; John S. Piatkowski, M.D., Vice President, Regional Hospital
**Web address:** www.carilionclinic.org/Carilion/Carilion+Tazewell+Community+Hospital

| Owned, leased, sponsored: | 7 hospitals | 980 beds |
|---|---|---|
| Contract–managed: | 0 hospitals | 0 beds |
| Totals: | 7 hospitals | 980 beds |

---

**★0705: CAROLINAS HEALTHCARE SYSTEM** (NP)
1000 Blythe Boulevard, Charlotte, NC Zip 28203–5871, Mailing Address: P.O. Box 32861, Zip 28232–2861; tel. 704/355–2000; Michael C. Tarwater, Chief Executive Officer
**(Moderately Centralized Health System)**

**NORTH CAROLINA:** ANSON COMMUNITY HOSPITAL (O, 125 beds) 500 Morven Road, Wadesboro, NC Zip 28170–2745; tel. 704/694–5131; Frederick G. Thompson, Ph.D., President
**Web address:** www.carolinashealthcare.org/anson–community–hospital

CAROLINAS MEDICAL CENTER (O, 874 beds) 1000 Blythe Boulevard, Charlotte, NC Zip 28203–5871, Mailing Address: P.O. Box 32861, Zip 28232–2861; tel. 704/355–2000; Spencer Lilly, President
**Web address:** www.carolinasmedicalcenter.org

CAROLINAS MEDICAL CENTER–LINCOLN (O, 101 beds) 433 McAlister Road, Lincolnton, NC Zip 28092–4147; tel. 980/212–2000; Peter W. Acker, President and Chief Executive Officer
**Web address:** www.carolinashealthcare.org/body.cfm?id=7626

CAROLINAS MEDICAL CENTER–MERCY (O, 348 beds) 2001 Vail Avenue, Charlotte, NC Zip 28207–1289; tel. 704/304–5000; Spencer Lilly, President
**Web address:** www.carolinashealthcare.org/cmc–mercy

CAROLINAS MEDICAL CENTER–NORTHEAST (O, 450 beds) 920 Church Street North, Concord, NC Zip 28025–2983; tel. 704/403–3000; Phyllis A. Wingate, FACHE, Division President
**Web address:** www.carolinashealthcare.org

CAROLINAS MEDICAL CENTER–UNION (L, 239 beds) 600 Hospital Drive, Monroe, NC Zip 28112–6000, Mailing Address: P.O. Box 5003, Zip 28111–5003; tel. 704/283–3100; Michael Lutes, President
**Web address:** www.carolinashealthcare.org/cmc–uniong

For explanation of codes following names, see page B2.
★ Indicates Type III membership in the American Hospital Association.

**B26** Health Care Systems, Networks and Alliances

© 2013 AHA Guide

Section B

CAROLINAS MEDICAL CENTER–UNIVERSITY (O, 94 beds) 8800 North Tryon Street, Charlotte, NC Zip 28262–3300, Mailing Address: P.O. Box 560727, Zip 28256–0727; tel. 704/863–6000; William H. Leonard, President
**Web address:** www.carolinashealthcare.org/cmc–university

CAROLINAS REHABILITATION (O, 169 beds) 1100 Blythe Boulevard, Charlotte, NC Zip 28203–5864; tel. 704/355–4300; Robert G. Larrison, Jr., President
**Web address:** www.carolinashealthcare.org/carolinas–rehab

CLEVELAND REGIONAL MEDICAL CENTER (L, 364 beds) 201 East Grover Street, Shelby, NC Zip 28150–3917; tel. 704/487–3000; Brian Gwyn, President and Chief Executive Officer
**Web address:** www.clevelandregional.org

COLUMBUS REGIONAL HEALTHCARE SYSTEM (C, 103 beds) 500 Jefferson Street, Whiteville, NC Zip 28472–3634; tel. 910/642–8011; Henry Hawthorne, III, President and Chief Executive Officer
**Web address:** www.crhealthcare.org

CONE HEALTH (C, 1018 beds) 1200 North Elm Street, Greensboro, NC Zip 27401–1020; tel. 336/832–7000; R. Timothy Rice, Chief Executive Officer
**Web address:** www.conehealth.com

CRAWLEY MEMORIAL HOSPITAL (L, 41 beds) 315 West College Avenue, Shelby, NC Zip 28152, Mailing Address: P.O. Box 996, Boiling Springs, Zip 28017–0996; tel. 704/434–9466; Brian Gwyn, President and Chief Executive Officer
**Web address:** www.clevelandcountyhealthcaresystem. com/crawley–memorial.html

KINGS MOUNTAIN HOSPITAL (O, 59 beds) 706 West King Street, Kings Mountain, NC Zip 28086–2708; tel. 980/487–5000; Brian Gwyn, President and Chief Executive Officer
**Web address:** www.clevelandregional.org/kings–mountain–hospital.html

MURPHY MEDICAL CENTER (C, 191 beds) 3990 U.S. Highway 64 East Alt, Murphy, NC Zip 28906–7917; tel. 828/837–8161; Michael Stevenson, Chief Executive Officer
**Web address:** www.murphymedical.org

SCOTLAND HEALTH CARE SYSTEM (C, 152 beds) 500 Lauchwood Drive, Laurinburg, NC Zip 28352–5599; tel. 910/291–7000; Gregory C. Wood, President and Chief Executive Officer
**Web address:** www.scotlandhealth.org

ST. LUKE'S HOSPITAL (C, 35 beds) 101 Hospital Drive, Columbus, NC Zip 28722–6418; tel. 828/894–3311; Kenneth A. Shull, FACHE, Chief Executive Officer
**Web address:** www.saintlukeshospital.com

STANLY REGIONAL MEDICAL CENTER (C, 104 beds) 301 Yadkin Street, Albemarle, NC Zip 28001–3441, Mailing Address: P.O. Box 1489, Zip 28002–1489; tel. 704/984–4000; Alfred P. Taylor, President
**Web address:** www.stanly.org

WILKES REGIONAL MEDICAL CENTER (C, 98 beds) 1370 West D Street, North Wilkesboro, NC Zip 28659–3506, Mailing Address: P.O. Box 609, Zip 28659–0609; tel. 336/651–8100; J. Gene Faile, Chief Executive Officer
**Web address:** www.wilkesregional.org

**SOUTH CAROLINA:** BON SECOURS ST. FRANCIS XAVIER HOSPITAL (C, 179 beds) 2095 Henry Tecklenburg Drive, Charleston, SC Zip 29414–5733; tel. 843/402–1000; David L. Dunlap, FACHE, President and Chief Executive Officer
**Web address:** www.ropersaintfrancis.com

CANNON MEMORIAL HOSPITAL (C, 38 beds) 123 West G. Acker Drive, Pickens, SC Zip 29671–2739, Mailing Address: P.O. Box 188, Zip 29671–0188; tel. 864/878–4791; Norman G. Rentz, President and Chief Executive Officer
**Web address:** www.cannonhospital.org

MOUNT PLEASANT HOSPITAL (C, 50 beds) 3500 Highway 17 North, Mount Pleasant, SC Zip 29466–9123, Mailing Address: 3500 North Highway 17, Zip 29466–9123; tel. 843/606–7000; John Sullivan, Chief Executive Officer
**Web address:** www.mymountpleasanthospital.com

ROPER HOSPITAL (C, 328 beds) 316 Calhoun Street, Charleston, SC Zip 29401–1125; tel. 843/724–2000; David L. Dunlap, FACHE, President and Chief Executive Officer
**Web address:** www.ropersaintfrancis.com

| | | |
|---|---|---|
| Owned, leased, sponsored: | 11 hospitals | 2864 beds |
| Contract–managed: | 11 hospitals | 2296 beds |
| Totals: | 22 hospitals | 5160 beds |

**0656: CARRUS HOSPITALS** (IO)
1810 West U.S. Highway 82, Sherman, TX Zip 75092–7069; tel. 903/870–2600; Ronald E. Dorris, Chief Executive Officer
**(Independent Hospital System)**

**TEXAS:** CARRUS REHABILITATION HOSPITAL (O, 24 beds) 1810 West U.S. Highway 82, Suite 100, Sherman, TX Zip 75092–7069; tel. 903/870–2600; Ronald E. Dorris, Chief Executive Officer
**Web address:** www.carrushospital.com

CARRUS SPECIALTY HOSPITAL (O, 16 beds) 1810 West U.S. Highway 82, Sherman, TX Zip 75092–7069; tel. 903/870–2600; Ronald E. Dorris, Chief Executive Officer
**Web address:** www.carrushospital.com

| | | |
|---|---|---|
| Owned, leased, sponsored: | 2 hospitals | 40 beds |
| Contract–managed: | 0 hospitals | 0 beds |
| Totals: | 2 hospitals | 40 beds |

**★0136: CATHOLIC HEALTH EAST** (CC)
3805 West Chester Pike, Suite 100, Newtown Square, PA Zip 19073–2329; tel. 610/355–2000; Judith M. Persichilli, Chief Executive Officer
**(Decentralized Health System)**

**DELAWARE:** ST. FRANCIS HOSPITAL (O, 214 beds) Seventh and Clayton Streets, Wilmington, DE Zip 19805–0500, Mailing Address: P.O. Box 2500, Zip 19805–0500; tel. 302/421–4100; Brian E. Dietz, FACHE, Interim President and Chief Executive officer
**Web address:** www.stfrancishealthcare.org

**FLORIDA:** HOLY CROSS HOSPITAL (O, 571 beds) 4725 North Federal Highway, Fort Lauderdale, FL Zip 33308–4668, Mailing Address: P.O. Box 23460, Zip 33307–3460; tel. 954/771–8000; Patrick Taylor, M.D., President and Chief Executive Officer
**Web address:** www.holy–cross.com

SOUTH FLORIDA BAPTIST HOSPITAL (S, 147 beds) 301 North Alexander Street, Plant City, FL Zip 33563–4303, Mailing Address: Drawer H, Zip 33564–9058; tel. 813/757–1200; Stephen Nierman, Interim Chief Executive Officer
**Web address:** www.sjbhealth.org

ST. ANTHONY'S HOSPITAL (S, 344 beds) 1200 Seventh Avenue North, Saint Petersburg, FL Zip 33705–1388, Mailing Address: P.O. Box 12588, Zip 33733–2588; tel. 727/825–1100; William G. Ulbricht, President
**Web address:** www.stanthonys.com/

ST. JOSEPH'S HOSPITAL (S, 964 beds) 3001 West Martin Luther King Jr. Boulevard, Tampa, FL Zip 33607–6387, Mailing Address: P.O. Box 4227, Zip 33677–4227; tel. 813/870–4000; Lorraine Lutton, Interim Chief Executive Officer
**Web address:** www.sjbhealth.org

**GEORGIA:** ST. MARY'S GOOD SAMARITAN HOSPITAL (O, 25 beds) 1201 Siloam Highway, Greensboro, GA Zip 30642–2811; tel. 706/453–7331; D. Montez Carter, President
**Web address:** www.stmarysgoodsam.org

ST. MARY'S HEALTH CARE SYSTEM (O, 165 beds) 1230 Baxter Street, Athens, GA Zip 30606–3791; tel. 706/389–3000; Donald McKenna, President and Chief Executive Officer
**Web address:** www.stmarysathens.com

**MAINE:** MERCY HOSPITAL OF PORTLAND (O, 148 beds) 144 State Street, Portland, ME Zip 04101–3795; tel. 207/879–3000; Eileen F. Skinner, FACHE, President and Chief Executive Officer
**Web address:** www.mercyhospitalstories.org/cms/

**MASSACHUSETTS:** MERCY MEDICAL CENTER (O, 301 beds) 271 Carew Street, Springfield, MA Zip 01104–2398, Mailing Address: P.O. Box 9012, Zip 01102–9012; tel. 413/748–9000; Daniel P. Moen, President and Chief Executive Officer
**Web address:** www.mercycares.com

**NEW JERSEY:** LOURDES MEDICAL CENTER OF BURLINGTON COUNTY (O, 154 beds) 218–A Sunset Road, Willingboro, NJ Zip 08046–1162; tel. 609/835–2900; Mark Nessel, Executive Vice President and Chief Operating Officer
**Web address:** www.lourdesnet.org

For explanation of codes following names, see page B2.
★ Indicates Type III membership in the American Hospital Association.

Section B

OUR LADY OF LOURDES MEDICAL CENTER (O, 350 beds) 1600 Haddon Avenue, Camden, NJ Zip 08103–3117; tel. 856/757–3500; Alexander J. Hatala, FACHE, President and Chief Executive Officer
**Web address:** www.lourdesnet.org

SAINT MICHAEL'S MEDICAL CENTER (O, 170 beds) 111 Central Avenue, Newark, NJ Zip 07102–1909; tel. 973/877–5549; David A. Ricci, President and Chief Executive Officer
**Web address:** www.smmcnj.org

ST. FRANCIS MEDICAL CENTER (O, 163 beds) 601 Hamilton Avenue, Trenton, NJ Zip 08629–1986; tel. 609/599–5000; Gerard J. Jablonowski, President and Chief Executive Officer
**Web address:** www.stfrancismedical.com

**NEW YORK:** ALBANY MEMORIAL HOSPITAL (O, 165 beds) 600 Northern Boulevard, Albany, NY Zip 12204–1083; tel. 518/471–3221; Ann Errichetti, M.D., Chief Executive Officer
**Web address:** www.nehealth.com

SAMARITAN HOSPITAL (O, 134 beds) 2215 Burdett Avenue, Troy, NY Zip 12180–2475; tel. 518/271–3300; Norman E. Dascher, Jr., Chief Executive Officer
**Web address:** www.nehealth.com

ST. JAMES MERCY HEALTH SYSTEM (O, 222 beds) 411 Canisteo Street, Hornell, NY Zip 14843–2197; tel. 607/324–8000; Mary E. LaRowe, FACHE, President and Chief Executive Officer
**Web address:** www.stjamesmercy.org

ST. MARY'S HOSPITAL (O, 173 beds) 1300 Massachusetts Avenue, Troy, NY Zip 12180–1695; tel. 518/268–5000; Norman E. Dascher, Jr., Executive Vice President
**Web address:** www.setonhealth.org

ST. PETER'S HOSPITAL (O, 487 beds) 315 South Manning Boulevard, Albany, NY Zip 12208–1789; tel. 518/525–1550; Ann Errichetti, M.D., Chief Executive Officer
**Web address:** www.sphcs.org

SUNNYVIEW REHABILITATION HOSPITAL (O, 115 beds) 1270 Belmont Avenue, Schenectady, NY Zip 12308–2104; tel. 518/382–4500; Edward Eisenman, Chief Executive Officer
**Web address:** www.sunnyview.org

**PENNSYLVANIA:** MERCY FITZGERALD HOSPITAL (O, 391 beds) 1500 South Lansdowe Avenue, Darby, PA Zip 19023–1200; tel. 610/237–4000; Kathryn Conallen, Chief Executive Officer
**Web address:** www.mercyhealth.org

MERCY SUBURBAN HOSPITAL (O, 126 beds) 2701 DeKalb Pike, Norristown, PA Zip 19401–1820; tel. 610/278–2000; Kathryn Conallen, Interim Chief Executive Officer
**Web address:** www.mercyhealth.org

NAZARETH HOSPITAL (O, 231 beds) 2601 Holme Avenue, Philadelphia, PA Zip 19152–2096; tel. 215/335–6000; Nancy Cherone, Executive Director and Administrator
**Web address:** www.nazarethhospital.org

ST. MARY MEDICAL CENTER (O, 320 beds) 1201 Langhorne–Newtown Road, Langhorne, PA Zip 19047–1201; tel. 215/710–2000; Gregory T. Wozniak, President and Chief Executive Officer
**Web address:** www.stmaryhealthcare.org

| | | |
|---|---|---|
| **Owned, leased, sponsored:** | 23 hospitals | 6080 beds |
| **Contract–managed:** | 0 hospitals | 0 beds |
| **Totals:** | 23 hospitals | 6080 beds |

---

**★0092: CATHOLIC HEALTH INITIATIVES** (CC)
198 Inverness Drive West, Suite 800, Englewood, CO Zip 80112–5202; tel. 303/298–9100; Kevin E. Lofton, FACHE, President and Chief Executive Officer
**(Decentralized Health System)**

**ARKANSAS:** ST. VINCENT INFIRMARY MEDICAL CENTER (S, 447 beds) Two St. Vincent Circle, Little Rock, AR Zip 72205–5499; tel. 501/552–3000; Peter D. Banko, FACHE, President and Chief Executive Officer
**Web address:** www.stvincenthealth.org

ST. VINCENT MEDICAL CENTER–NORTH (S, 58 beds) 2215 Wildwood Avenue, Sherwood, AR Zip 72120–5089; tel. 501/552–7100; David R. Fox, President
**Web address:** www.stvincenthealth.com

ST. VINCENT MORRILTON (S, 25 beds) 4 Hospital Drive, Morrilton, AR Zip 72110–4510; tel. 501/977–2300; Leslie Arnold, Chief Executive Officer
**Web address:** www.stanthonysmorrilton.com/

**COLORADO:** MERCY REGIONAL MEDICAL CENTER (S, 82 beds) 1010 Three Springs Boulevard, Durango, CO Zip 81301–8296; tel. 970/247–4311; Thomas Gessel, FACHE, President and Chief Executive Officer
**Web address:** www.mercydurango.org

PENROSE–ST. FRANCIS HEALTH SERVICES (S, 405 beds) 2222 North Nevada Avenue, Colorado Springs, CO Zip 80907–6799, Mailing Address: P.O. Box 7021, Zip 80933–7021; tel. 719/776–5000; Margaret D. Sabin, President and Chief Executive Officer
**Web address:** www.penrosestfrancis.org

ST. ANTHONY HOSPITAL (S, 222 beds) 11600 West Second Place, Lakewood, CO Zip 80228–1527; tel. 720/321–0000; Jeffrey Brickman, FACHE, President and Chief Executive Officer
**Web address:** www.stanthonyhosp.org

ST. ANTHONY NORTH HOSPITAL (S, 138 beds) 2551 West 84th Avenue, Westminster, CO Zip 80031–3807; tel. 303/426–2151; Carole Peet, R.N., MSN, President and Chief Executive Officer
**Web address:** www.stanthonynorth.org

ST. ANTHONY SUMMIT MEDICAL CENTER (S, 34 beds) 340 Peak One Drive, Frisco, CO Zip 80443, Mailing Address: P.O. Box 738, Zip 80443–0738; tel. 970/668–3300; Paul J. Chodkowski, Chief Executive Officer
**Web address:** www.summitmedicalcenter.org

ST. MARY–CORWIN MEDICAL CENTER (S, 202 beds) 1008 Minnequa Avenue, Pueblo, CO Zip 81004–3798; tel. 719/557–4000; Brian Moore, President and Chief Executive Officer
**Web address:** www.centura.org

ST. THOMAS MORE HOSPITAL (S, 55 beds) 1338 Phay Avenue, Canon City, CO Zip 81212–2302; tel. 719/285–2000; Robert Ryder, Chief Executive Officer
**Web address:** www.stmhospital.org

**INDIANA:** SOUTHERN INDIANA REHABILITATION HOSPITAL (O, 60 beds) 3104 Blackiston Boulevard, New Albany, IN Zip 47150–9579; tel. 812/941–8300; Randy L. Napier, President
**Web address:** www.sirh.org

**IOWA:** ALEGENT CREIGHTON HEALTH COMMUNITY MEMORIAL HOSPITAL (S, 16 beds) 631 North Eighth Street, Missouri Valley, IA Zip 51555–1102; tel. 712/642–2784; Robert A. Valentine, Regional Administrator
**Web address:** www.alegentcreighton.com/community–memorial

ALEGENT CREIGHTON HEALTH MERCY HOSPITAL (S, 22 beds) 603 Rosary Drive, Corning, IA Zip 50841–1683; tel. 641/322–3121; Debra Goldsmith, Regional Administrator
**Web address:** www.alegent.com

ALEGENT CREIGHTON HEALTH MERCY HOSPITAL (S, 163 beds) 800 Mercy Drive, Council Bluffs, IA Zip 51503–3128, Mailing Address: P.O. Box 1C, Zip 51502–3001; tel. 712/328–5000; Marie E. Knedler, R.N., President
**Web address:** www.alegent.com/mercy

MERCY MEDICAL CENTER – WEST LAKES (O, 82 beds) 1755 59th Place, West Des Moines, IA Zip 50266–7737; tel. 515/358–8000; Robert P. Ritz, FACHE, President
**Web address:** www.mercywestlakes.org/

MERCY MEDICAL CENTER–CENTERVILLE (S, 45 beds) 1 St. Joseph's Drive, Centerville, IA Zip 52544–8055; tel. 641/437–4111; Clinton J. Christianson, FACHE, President
**Web address:** www.mercycenterville.org

MERCY MEDICAL CENTER–DES MOINES (S, 567 beds) 1111 6th Avenue, Des Moines, IA Zip 50314–2611; tel. 515/247–3121; Robert P. Ritz, FACHE, President
**Web address:** www.mercydesmoines.org

**KANSAS:** ST. CATHERINE HOSPITAL (S, 110 beds) 401 East Spuce Street, Garden City, KS Zip 67846–5679; tel. 620/272–2561; Scott J. Taylor, President and Chief Executive Officer
**Web address:** www.stcath–hosp.org

**KENTUCKY:** CONTINUING CARE HOSPITAL (S, 45 beds) 150 North Eagle Creek Drive, 5th Floor, Lexington, KY Zip 40509–1805; tel. 859/967–5744; Tonja Williams, MSN, R.N., President

FLAGET MEMORIAL HOSPITAL (S, 40 beds) 4305 New Shepherdsville Road, Bardstown, KY Zip 40004–9019; tel. 502/350–5000; Sue Downs, R.N., MSN, President
**Web address:** www.flaget.com

For explanation of codes following names, see page B2.
★ Indicates Type III membership in the American Hospital Association.

FRAZIER REHAB INSTITUTE (O, 79 beds) 220 Abraham Flexner Way, Louisville, KY Zip 40202–1887; tel. 502/582–7400; Charles A. Peck, M.D., Interim President
**Web address:** www.frazierrehab.org

JEWISH HOSPITAL (O, 387 beds) 200 Abraham Flexner Way, Louisville, KY Zip 40202–1886; tel. 502/587–4011; Charles A. Peck, M.D., Interim President
**Web address:** www.jewishhospital.org

JEWISH HOSPITAL–SHELBYVILLE (O, 41 beds) 727 Hospital Drive, Shelbyville, KY Zip 40065–1699; tel. 502/647–4000; Michael L. Collins, President
**Web address:** www.jhsmh.org

OUR LADY OF PEACE (O, 261 beds) 2020 Newburg Road, Louisville, KY Zip 40205–1879; tel. 502/479–4500; Jennifer Nolan, President
**Web address:** www.hopehasaplace.org

SAINT JOSEPH – LONDON (S, 110 beds) 310 East Ninth Street, London, KY Zip 40741–1299; tel. 606/330–6000; Greg D. Gerard, President
**Web address:** www.saintjosephhealthsystem.org

SAINT JOSEPH – MARTIN (S, 25 beds) 11203 Main Street, Martin, KY Zip 41649; tel. 606/285–6400; Kathy Stumbo, President
**Web address:** www.saintjosephmartin.org

SAINT JOSEPH BEREA (S, 25 beds) 305 Estill Street, Berea, KY Zip 40403–1909; tel. 859/986–3151; Chris Schweighardt, R.N., MSN, Interim President
**Web address:** www.saintjosephberea.org

SAINT JOSEPH EAST (S, 183 beds) 150 North Eagle Creek Drive, Lexington, KY Zip 40509–1805; tel. 859/967–5000; Eric Gilliam, President
**Web address:** www.sjhlex.org

SAINT JOSEPH HOSPITAL (S, 298 beds) One St. Joseph Drive, Lexington, KY Zip 40504–3754; tel. 859/278–3436; John E. Smithhisler, President
**Web address:** www.sjhlex.org

SAINT JOSEPH MOUNT STERLING (S, 42 beds) 50 Sterling Avenue, Mount Sterling, KY Zip 40353–1158, Mailing Address: P.O. Box 7, Zip 40353–0007; tel. 859/497–5000; Benny Nolen, President
**Web address:** www.sjhlex.org

STS. MARY & ELIZABETH HOSPITAL (O, 163 beds) 1850 Bluegrass Avenue, Louisville, KY Zip 40215–1199; tel. 502/361–6000; Jennifer Nolan, President
**Web address:** www.jhsmh.org

TAYLOR REGIONAL HOSPITAL (C, 90 beds) 1700 Old Lebanon Road, Campbellsville, KY Zip 42718–9600; tel. 270/465–3561; Jane Wheatley, Chief Executive Officer
**Web address:** www.trhosp.org

**MINNESOTA:** ALBANY AREA HOSPITAL AND MEDICAL CENTER (S, 17 beds) 300 Third Avenue, Albany, MN Zip 56307–9363; tel. 320/845–2121; Sandra Day, Administrator, Chief Nursing Officer
**Web address:** www.albanyareahospital.com

LAKEWOOD HEALTH CENTER (S, 55 beds) 600 Main Avenue South, Baudette, MN Zip 56623–2855; tel. 218/634–2120; Jason Breuer, President
**Web address:** www.lakewoodhealthcenter.org

ST. FRANCIS HEALTHCARE CAMPUS (S, 145 beds) 2400 St. Francis Drive, Breckenridge, MN Zip 56520–1025; tel. 218/643–3000; David A. Nelson, President
**Web address:** www.sfcare.org

ST. GABRIEL'S HOSPITAL (S, 25 beds) 815 Second Street S.E., Little Falls, MN Zip 56345–3596; tel. 320/632–5441; Joseph Messmer, Interim President
**Web address:** www.stgabriels.com

ST. JOSEPH'S AREA HEALTH SERVICES (S, 25 beds) 600 Pleasant Avenue, Park Rapids, MN Zip 56470–1431; tel. 218/732–3311; Benjamin Koppelman, President
**Web address:** www.sjahs.org

**NEBRASKA:** ALEGENT CREIGHTON HEALTH BERGAN MERCY MEDICAL CENTER (S, 341 beds) 7500 Mercy Road, Omaha, NE Zip 68124–2319; tel. 402/398–6060; Marie E. Knedler, R.N., President
**Web address:** www.alegent.com/bergan

ALEGENT CREIGHTON HEALTH IMMANUEL MEDICAL CENTER (S, 285 beds) 6901 North 72nd Street, Omaha, NE Zip 68122–1799; tel. 402/572–2121; Ann Schumacher, R.N., MSN, President
**Web address:** www.alegent.com/immanuel

ALEGENT CREIGHTON HEALTH LAKESIDE HOSPITAL (S, 137 beds) 16901 Lakeside Hills Court, Omaha, NE Zip 68130–2318; tel. 402/717–8000; Cindy Alloway, President
**Web address:** www.alegent.org

ALEGENT CREIGHTON HEALTH MIDLANDS HOSPITAL (S, 61 beds) 11111 South 84th Street, Papillion, NE Zip 68046–4122; tel. 402/593–3000; Cindy Alloway, President
**Web address:** www.alegent.org/midlands

ALEGENT CREIGHTON HEALTH PLAINVIEW HOSPITAL (S, 16 beds) 704 North Third Street, Plainview, NE Zip 68769–2047, Mailing Address: P.O. Box 489, Zip 68769–0489; tel. 402/582–4245; Richard B. Gamel, Administrator
**Web address:** www.alegentcreighton.com/plainview–hospital

ALEGENT CREIGHTON HEALTH–CREIGHTON UNIVERSITY MEDICAL CENTER (S, 223 beds) 601 North 30th Street, Omaha, NE Zip 68131–2197; tel. 402/449–4000; Kevin J. Nokels, FACHE, President
**Web address:** www.alegentcreighton.com

ALEGENT CREIGHTON HEALTH–MEMORIAL HOSPITAL, SCHUYLER (S, 25 beds) 104 West 17th Street, Schuyler, NE Zip 68661–1304; tel. 402/352–2441; Connie Peters, R.N., Regional Administrator
**Web address:** www.alegent.org

GOOD SAMARITAN HOSPITAL (S, 229 beds) 10 East 31st Street, Kearney, NE Zip 68847–2926, Mailing Address: P.O. Box 1990, Zip 68848–1990; tel. 308/865–7100; Michael H. Schnieders, FACHE, President and Chief Executive Officer
**Web address:** www.gshs.org

NEBRASKA HEART HOSPITAL (S, 52 beds) 7500 South 91st Street, Lincoln, NE Zip 68526–9437; tel. 402/327–2700; Kent Reckewey, M.D., Chief Executive Officer
**Web address:** www.neheart.com

NEBRASKA SPINE HOSPITAL (O, 34 beds) 6901 North 72nd Street, Suite 20300, Omaha, NE Zip 68122–1755, Mailing Address: 6901 North 72nd Street, Zip 68122–1709; tel. 402/572–3000; Troy P. Stockman, Chief Executive Officer
**Web address:** www.nebraskaspinehospital.com

SAINT ELIZABETH REGIONAL MEDICAL CENTER (S, 260 beds) 555 South 70th Street, Lincoln, NE Zip 68510–2494; tel. 402/219–8000; Kim S. Moore, President and Chief Executive Officer
**Web address:** www.saintelizabethonline.com

SAINT FRANCIS MEDICAL CENTER (S, 190 beds) 2620 West Faidley Avenue, Grand Island, NE Zip 68803–4297, Mailing Address: P.O. Box 9804, Zip 68802–9804; tel. 308/384–4600; Daniel P. McElligott, FACHE, President and Chief Executive Officer
**Web address:** www.saintfrancisgi.org

ST. MARY'S COMMUNITY HOSPITAL (S, 18 beds) 1314 Third Avenue, Nebraska City, NE Zip 68410–1930; tel. 402/873–3321; Daniel J. Kelly, President and Chief Executive Officer
**Web address:** www.stmaryshospitalnecity.org

**NEW JERSEY:** SAINT CLARE'S HEALTH SYSTEM (S, 433 beds) 25 Pocono Road, Denville, NJ Zip 07834–2954; tel. 973/625–6000; Leslie D. Hirsch, FACHE, President and Chief Executive Officer
**Web address:** www.saintclares.org

**NORTH DAKOTA:** CARRINGTON HEALTH CENTER (S, 49 beds) 800 North Fourth Street, Carrington, ND Zip 58421–1217, Mailing Address: P.O. Box 461, Zip 58421–0461; tel. 701/652–3141; Mariann Doeling, R.N., President
**Web address:** www.carringtonhealthcenter.org

LISBON AREA HEALTH SERVICES (S, 25 beds) 905 Main Street, Lisbon, ND Zip 58054–4334, Mailing Address: P.O. Box 353, Zip 58054–0353; tel. 701/683–5241; Peggy Larson, R.N., Administrator
**Web address:** www.lisbonhospital.com

MERCY HOSPITAL (S, 25 beds) 1031 Seventh Street N.E., Devils Lake, ND Zip 58301–2798; tel. 701/662–2131; James L. Marshall, President
**Web address:** www.mercyhospitaldl.com

MERCY HOSPITAL (S, 19 beds) 570 Chautauqua Boulevard, Valley City, ND Zip 58072–3199; tel. 701/845–6400; Keith E. Heuser, President
**Web address:** www.mercyhospitalvalleycity.org

MERCY MEDICAL CENTER (S, 25 beds) 1301 15th Avenue West, Williston, ND Zip 58801–3896; tel. 701/774–7400; Matthew Grimshaw, President
**Web address:** www.mercy–williston.org

OAKES COMMUNITY HOSPITAL (S, 12 beds) 1200 North Seventh Street, Oakes, ND Zip 58474–2502; tel. 701/742–3291; Lee Boyles, President
**Web address:** www.oakeshospital.com

For explanation of codes following names, see page B2.
★ Indicates Type III membership in the American Hospital Association.

ST. JOSEPH'S HOSPITAL AND HEALTH CENTER (S, 25 beds) 30 Seventh Street West, Dickinson, ND Zip 58601–4399; tel. 701/456–4000; Reed Reyman, President
**Web address:** www.stjoeshospital.org

**OHIO:** GOOD SAMARITAN HOSPITAL (S, 504 beds) 375 Dixmyth Avenue, Cincinnati, OH Zip 45220–2489; tel. 513/862–1400; Jamie Easterling, Executive Director, Operations
**Web address:** www.trihealth.com

GOOD SAMARITAN HOSPITAL (S, 341 beds) 2222 Philadelphia Drive, Dayton, OH Zip 45406–1813; tel. 937/734–2612; Eloise Broner, President and Chief Executive Officer
**Web address:** www.goodsamdayton.com

**OREGON:** MERCY MEDICAL CENTER (S, 141 beds) 2700 Stewart Parkway, Roseburg, OR Zip 97471–1281; tel. 541/673–0611; Kelly C. Morgan, President and Chief Executive Officer
**Web address:** www.mercyrose.org

ST. ANTHONY HOSPITAL (S, 25 beds) 1601 S.E. Court Avenue, Pendleton, OR Zip 97801–3217; tel. 541/276–5121; Harold S. Geller, Chief Executive Officer
**Web address:** www.sahpendleton.org

**PENNSYLVANIA:** ST. JOSEPH MEDICAL CENTER (S, 180 beds) 2500 Bernville Road, Reading, PA Zip 19605–9453, Mailing Address: P.O. Box 316, Zip 19603–0316; tel. 610/378–2000; John R. Morahan, FACHE, President and Chief Executive Officer
**Web address:** www.thefutureofhealthcare.org

**TENNESSEE:** MEMORIAL HEALTH CARE SYSTEM (S, 336 beds) 2525 De Sales Avenue, Chattanooga, TN Zip 37404–1161; tel. 423/495–2525; James M. Hobson, President and Chief Executive Officer
**Web address:** www.memorial.org

**TEXAS:** ST. LUKE'S EPISCOPAL HOSPITAL (O, 690 beds) 6720 Bertner Avenue, Houston, TX Zip 77030–2697, Mailing Address: P.O. Box 20269, Zip 77225–0269; tel. 832/355–1000; Margaret M. Van Bree, Dr.PH, Chief Executive Officer
**Web address:** www.stlukestexas.com

ST. LUKE'S HOSPITAL AT THE VINTAGE (O, 78 beds) 20171 Chasewood Park Drive, Houston, TX Zip 77070–1437; tel. 832/534–5000; Norman F. Stephens, Chief Executive Officer
**Web address:** www.stlukesvintage.com/

ST. LUKE'S LAKESIDE HOSPITAL (O, 30 beds) 17400 St. Luke's Way, The Woodlands, TX Zip 77384–8036; tel. 936/266–9000; Debra F. Sukin, Chief Executive Officer
**Web address:** www.stlukeslakeside.com/

ST. LUKE'S PATIENTS MEDICAL CENTER (O, 61 beds) 4600 East Sam Houston Parkway South, Pasadena, TX Zip 77505–3948; tel. 713/948–7000; William Simmons, Chief Executive Officer
**Web address:** www.stlukestexas.com

ST. LUKE'S SUGAR LAND HOSPITAL (O, 58 beds) 1317 Lake Pointe Parkway, Sugar Land, TX Zip 77478–3997; tel. 281/637–7000; Robert A. Heifner, Chief Executive Officer
**Web address:** www.stlukessugarland.com

ST. LUKE'S THE WOODLANDS HOSPITAL (O, 154 beds) 17200 St. Luke's Way, The Woodlands, TX Zip 77384–8007; tel. 936/266–2000; Debra F. Sukin, Chief Executive Officer
**Web address:** www.stlukeswoodlands.com

**WASHINGTON:** ST. ANTHONY HOSPITAL (O, 80 beds) 11567 Canterwood Boulevard N.W., Gig Harbor, WA Zip 98332–5812; tel. 253/530–2000; Kurt Schley, President
**Web address:** www.fhshealth.org/

ST. CLARE HOSPITAL (S, 104 beds) 11315 Bridgeport Way S.W., Lakewood, WA Zip 98499–3004; tel. 253/588–1711; Kathy Bressler, President
**Web address:** www.fhshealth.org

ST. ELIZABETH HOSPITAL (S, 25 beds) 1455 Battersby Avenue, Enumclaw, WA Zip 98022–3634, Mailing Address: P.O. Box 218, Zip 98022–0218; tel. 360/284–4171; Donna Russell–Cook, President
**Web address:** www.fhshealth.org

ST. FRANCIS HOSPITAL (S, 120 beds) 34515 Ninth Avenue South, Federal Way, WA Zip 98003–6799; tel. 253/944–8100; Anthony McLean, President
**Web address:** www.fhshealth.org

ST. JOSEPH MEDICAL CENTER (S, 363 beds) 1717 South J Street, Tacoma, WA Zip 98405–3004, Mailing Address: P.O. Box 2197, Zip 98401–2197; tel. 253/426–4101; Syd Bersante, President
**Web address:** www.fhshealth.org

| | | |
|---|---|---|
| Owned, leased, sponsored: | 74 hospitals | 10473 beds |
| Contract–managed: | 1 hospital | 90 beds |
| Totals: | 75 hospitals | 10563 beds |

★**5155: CATHOLIC HEALTH PARTNERS** (CC)
615 Elsinore Place, Cincinnati, OH Zip 45202–1459; tel. 513/639–2800; Michael D. Connelly, President and Chief Executive Officer
**(Moderately Centralized Health System)**

**KENTUCKY:** LOURDES HOSPITAL (O, 280 beds) 1530 Lone Oak Road, Paducah, KY Zip 42003–7900, Mailing Address: P.O. Box 7100, Zip 42002–7100; tel. 270/444–2444; Steven Grinnell, President and Chief Executive Officer
**Web address:** www.lourdes–pad.org

MARCUM AND WALLACE MEMORIAL HOSPITAL (O, 25 beds) 60 Mercy Court, Irvine, KY Zip 40336–1331; tel. 606/723–2115; Susan Starling, President and Chief Executive Officer
**Web address:** www.marcumandwallace.org

**OHIO:** INSTITUTE FOR ORTHOPAEDIC SURGERY (O, 3 beds) 801 Medical Drive, Suite B., Lima, OH Zip 45804–4030; tel. 419/224–7586; Mark McDonald, MD, President and Chief Executive Officer
**Web address:** www.ioshospital.com

MERCY ALLEN HOSPITAL (O, 25 beds) 200 West Lorain Street, Oberlin, OH Zip 44074–1077; tel. 440/775–1211; Susan Bowers, R.N., President and Chief Nursing Officer
**Web address:** www.mercyonline.org/mercy_allen_hospital.aspx

MERCY HEALTH – ANDERSON HOSPITAL (O, 188 beds) 7500 State Road, Cincinnati, OH Zip 45255–2492; tel. 513/624–4500; Jeff Graham, Market Leader and President
**Web address:** www.e–mercy.com

MERCY HEALTH – CLERMONT HOSPITAL (O, 119 beds) 3000 Hospital Drive, Batavia, OH Zip 45103–1921; tel. 513/732–8200; Jeff Graham, Market Leader and President
**Web address:** www.e–mercy.com

MERCY HEALTH – FAIRFIELD HOSPITAL (O, 229 beds) 3000 Mack Road, Fairfield, OH Zip 45014–5335; tel. 513/870–7000; Thomas S. Urban, Market Leader and President
**Web address:** www.e–mercy.com

MERCY HEALTH – MT. AIRY HOSPITAL (O, 170 beds) 2446 Kipling Avenue, Cincinnati, OH Zip 45239–6650; tel. 513/853–5000; Michael R. Stephens, Market Leader and President
**Web address:** www.e–mercy.com

MERCY HEALTH – WESTERN HILLS HOSPITAL (O, 156 beds) 3131 Queen City Avenue, Cincinnati, OH Zip 45238–2396; tel. 513/389–5000; Michael R. Stephens, Market Leader and President
**Web address:** www.e–mercy.com

MERCY HOSPITAL OF DEFIANCE (O, 23 beds) 1404 East Second Street, Defiance, OH Zip 43512–2440; tel. 419/782–8444; Sonya Selhorst, Administrator
**Web address:** www.ehealthconnection.com/regions/toledo/

MERCY MEMORIAL HOSPITAL (O, 8 beds) 904 Scioto Street, Urbana, OH Zip 43078–2200; tel. 937/653–5231; Karen S. Gorby, R.N., MSN, FACHE, Administrator and Chief Nursing Officer
**Web address:** www.health–partners.org

MERCY REGIONAL MEDICAL CENTER (O, 253 beds) 3700 Kolbe Road, Lorain, OH Zip 44053–1697; tel. 440/960–4000; Edwin M. Oley, President and Chief Executive Officer
**Web address:** www.community–health–partners.com

MERCY ST. ANNE HOSPITAL (O, 96 beds) 3404 West Sylvania Avenue, Toledo, OH Zip 43623–4467; tel. 419/407–2663; Bradley J. Bertke, President and Chief Executive Officer
**Web address:** www.mercyweb.org

MERCY ST. CHARLES HOSPITAL (O, 264 beds) 2600 Navarre Avenue, Oregon, OH Zip 43616–3297; tel. 419/696–7200; Robert E. Gospodarek, President and Chief Executive Officer
**Web address:** www.mercyweb.org

For explanation of codes following names, see page B2.
★ Indicates Type III membership in the American Hospital Association.

MERCY ST. VINCENT MEDICAL CENTER (O, 431 beds) 2213 Cherry Street, Toledo, OH Zip 43608–2691; tel. 419/251–3232; Kevin S. Cook, President and Chief Executive Officer
**Web address:** www.mercyweb.org

MERCY TIFFIN HOSPITAL (O, 51 beds) 45 St. Lawrence Drive, Tiffin, OH Zip 44883–8310; tel. 419/455–7000; B. Lynn Detterman, Interim President and Chief Executive Officer
**Web address:** www.mercyweb.org

MERCY WILLARD HOSPITAL (O, 20 beds) 1100 Neal Zick Road, Willard, OH Zip 44890–9287; tel. 419/964–5000; B. Lynn Detterman, President and Chief Executive Officer
**Web address:** www.mercyweb.org

SPRINGFIELD REGIONAL MEDICAL CENTER (O, 254 beds) 100 Medical Center Drive, Springfield, OH Zip 45504–2687; tel. 937/523–1000; Paul C. Hiltz, FACHE, Market Leader and President
**Web address:** www.communityhospital.com

ST. ELIZABETH BOARDMAN HEALTH CENTER (O, 128 beds) 8401 Market Street, Boardman, OH Zip 44512–6777; tel. 330/729–2929; Eugenia Aubel, President
**Web address:** www.ehealthconnection. com/regions/youngstown/content/show_facility.asp?facility_id=190

ST. ELIZABETH HEALTH CENTER (O, 429 beds) 1044 Belmont Avenue, Youngstown, OH Zip 44504–1096, Mailing Address: P.O. Box 1790, Zip 44501–1790; tel. 330/746–7211; Robert W. Shroder, President and Chief Executive Officer
**Web address:** www.hmpartners.org

ST. JOSEPH HEALTH CENTER (O, 141 beds) 667 Eastland Avenue S.E., Warren, OH Zip 44484–4531; tel. 330/841–4000; Kathy Cook, R.N., MSN, Interim President
**Web address:** www.hmpartners.org

ST. RITA'S MEDICAL CENTER (O, 415 beds) 730 West Market Street, Lima, OH Zip 45801–4602; tel. 419/227–3361; Robert O. Baxter, President and Chief Executive Officer
**Web address:** www.stritas.org

THE JEWISH HOSPITAL – MERCY HEALTH (O, 209 beds) 4777 East Galbraith Road, Cincinnati, OH Zip 45236–2725; tel. 513/686–3000; Steve Holman, Market Leader and President
**Web address:** www.jewishhospitalcincinnati.com/

| Owned, leased, sponsored: | 23 hospitals | 3917 beds |
|---|---|---|
| Contract–managed: | 0 hospitals | 0 beds |
| Totals: | 23 hospitals | 3917 beds |

## 0903: CATHOLIC HEALTH SERVICES (CC)
4790 North State Road 7, Lauderdale Lakes, FL Zip 33319–5860; tel. 954/484–1515; Joseph M. Catania, President and Chief Executive Officer

**FLORIDA:** ST. ANTHONY'S REHABILITATION HOSPITAL (S, 26 beds) 3485 N.W. 30th Street, Lauderdale Lakes, FL Zip 33311–1890; tel. 954/739–6233; Joseph M. Catania, Chief Executive Officer
**Web address:** www.catholichealthservices.org

ST. CATHERINE'S REHABILITATION HOSPITAL (S, 60 beds) 1050 N.E. 125th Street, North Miami, FL Zip 33161–5881; tel. 305/357–1735; Jaime Gonzalez, Administrator
**Web address:** www.catholichealthservices.org

| Owned, leased, sponsored: | 2 hospitals | 86 beds |
|---|---|---|
| Contract–managed: | 0 hospitals | 0 beds |
| Totals: | 2 hospitals | 86 beds |

## 0233: CATHOLIC HEALTH SERVICES OF LONG ISLAND (CC)
992 North Village Avenue, 1st Floor, Rockville Centre, NY Zip 11570–1002; tel. 516/705–3700; Alan D. Guerci, M.D., President and Chief Executive Officer
**(Centralized Physician/Insurance Health System)**

**NEW YORK:** GOOD SAMARITAN HOSPITAL MEDICAL CENTER (O, 447 beds) 1000 Montauk Highway, West Islip, NY Zip 11795–4927; tel. 631/376–3000; Nancy B. Simmons, Executive Vice President and Chief Administrative Officer
**Web address:** www.good–samaritan–hospital.org

MERCY MEDICAL CENTER (O, 234 beds) 1000 North Village Avenue, Rockville Centre, NY Zip 11570–1000; tel. 516/705–2525; Aaron Glatt, M.D., Executive Vice President and Chief Administrative Officer
**Web address:** www.mercymedicalcenter.chsli.org

ST. CATHERINE OF SIENA MEDICAL CENTER (O, 535 beds) 50 Route 25–A, Smithtown, NY Zip 11787–1348; tel. 631/862–3000; Dennis Verzi, Executive Vice President and Chief Administrative Officer
**Web address:** www.stcatherinemedicalcenter.org

ST. CHARLES HOSPITAL (O, 231 beds) 200 Belle Terre Road, Port Jefferson, NY Zip 11777–1928; tel. 631/474–6000; James O'Connor, Executive Vice President and Chief Administrative Officer
**Web address:** www.stcharleshospital.chsli.org

ST. FRANCIS HOSPITAL (O, 306 beds) 100 Port Washington Boulevard, Roslyn, NY Zip 11576–1353; tel. 516/562–6000; Ruth Hennessey, Executive Vice President and Chief Administrative Officer
**Web address:** www.stfrancisheartcenter.com/index.html

ST. JOSEPH HOSPITAL (S, 140 beds) 4295 Hempstead Turnpike, Bethpage, NY Zip 11714–5769; tel. 516/579–6000; Drew Pallas, Executive Vice President and Chief Administrative Officer
**Web address:** www.newislandhospital.org

| Owned, leased, sponsored: | 6 hospitals | 1893 beds |
|---|---|---|
| Contract–managed: | 0 hospitals | 0 beds |
| Totals: | 6 hospitals | 1893 beds |

## ★0234: CATHOLIC HEALTH SYSTEM (CC)
2121 Main Street, Suite 300, Buffalo, NY Zip 14214–2673; tel. 716/862–2410; Joseph D. McDonald, President and Chief Executive Officer
**(Independent Hospital System)**

KENMORE MERCY HOSPITAL (O, 315 beds) 2950 Elmwood Avenue, Kenmore, NY Zip 14217–1390; tel. 716/447–6100; James M. Millard, President and Chief Executive Officer
**Web address:** www.chsbuffalo.org

MERCY HOSPITAL (O, 438 beds) 565 Abbott Road, Buffalo, NY Zip 14220–2095; tel. 716/826–7000; Charles J. Urlaub, President and Chief Executive Officer
**Web address:** www.chsbuffalo.org

SISTERS OF CHARITY HOSPITAL OF BUFFALO (O, 467 beds) 2157 Main Street, Buffalo, NY Zip 14214–2692; tel. 716/862–1000; Peter U. Bergmann, President and Chief Executive Officer
**Web address:** www.chsbuffalo.org

| Owned, leased, sponsored: | 3 hospitals | 1220 beds |
|---|---|---|
| Contract–managed: | 0 hospitals | 0 beds |
| Totals: | 3 hospitals | 1220 beds |

## ★0298: CENTEGRA HEALTH SYSTEM (NP)
385 Millennium Drive, Crystal Lake, IL Zip 60012–3761; tel. 815/788–5800; Michael S. Eesley, Chief Executive Officer
**(Independent Hospital System)**

**ILLINOIS:** CENTEGRA HOSPITAL – MCHENRY (O, 173 beds) 4201 Medical Center Drive, McHenry, IL Zip 60050–8409; tel. 815/344–5000; Michael S. Eesley, Chief Executive Officer
**Web address:** www.centegra.org

CENTEGRA HOSPITAL – WOODSTOCK (O, 135 beds) 3701 Doty Road, Woodstock, IL Zip 60098–7509, Mailing Address: P.O. Box 1990, Zip 60098–1990; tel. 815/338–2500; Michael S. Eesley, Chief Executive Officer
**Web address:** www.centegra.org

| Owned, leased, sponsored: | 2 hospitals | 308 beds |
|---|---|---|
| Contract–managed: | 0 hospitals | 0 beds |
| Totals: | 2 hospitals | 308 beds |

## 0634: CENTERRE HEALTHCARE (IO)
5250 Virginia Way, Suite 240, Brentwood, TN Zip 37027–7576; tel. 615/846–9508; Patrick A. Foster, President and Chief Executive Officer

For explanation of codes following names, see page B2.
★ Indicates Type III membership in the American Hospital Association.

**Section B**

**OKLAHOMA:** MERCY REHABILITATION HOSPITAL OKLAHOMA CITY (O, 50 beds) 5401 West Memorial Road, Oklahoma City, OK Zip 73142–2026; tel. 405/752–3935; Sharon Smeltzer, Chief Executive Officer

**PENNSYLVANIA:** LANCASTER REHABILITATION HOSPITAL (O, 10 beds) 675 Good Drive, Lancaster, PA Zip 17601–2426; tel. 717/406–3000; Tammy L. Ober, Chief Executive Officer
**Web address:** www.lancastergeneral.org

**TEXAS:** TEXAS REHABILITATION HOSPITAL OF FORT WORTH (O, 50 beds) 425 Alabama Avenue, Fort Worth, TX Zip 76104–1022; tel. 817/820–3400; Russell Bailey, Chief Executive Officer
**Web address:** www.texasrehabhospital.com/

**WISCONSIN:** REHABILITATION HOSPITAL OF WISCONSIN (O, 40 beds) 1625 Coldwater Creek Drive, Waukesha, WI Zip 53188–8028; tel. 262/521–8800; Anne E. Jurenec, Chief Executive Officer
**Web address:** www.rehabhospitalwi.com

| Owned, leased, sponsored: | 4 hospitals | 150 beds |
| Contract–managed: | 0 hospitals | 0 beds |
| **Totals:** | 4 hospitals | 150 beds |

---

**2265: CENTRA HEALTH, INC.** (NP)
1920 Atherholt Road, Lynchburg, VA Zip 24501–1104; tel. 434/200–3000; E. W. Tibbs, President and Chief Executive Officer
**(Centralized Physician/Insurance Health System)**

**VIRGINIA:** CENTRA LYNCHBURG GENERAL HOSPITAL (O, 1081 beds) 1920 Atherholt Road, Lynchburg, VA Zip 24501–1104; tel. 434/200–4700; E. W. Tibbs, President and Chief Executive Officer
**Web address:** www.centrahealth.com

CENTRA SOUTHSIDE COMMUNITY HOSPITAL (O, 86 beds) 800 Oak Street, Farmville, VA Zip 23901–1199; tel. 434/392–8811; William L. Bass, Jr., Vice President and Chief Executive Officer
**Web address:** www.sch.centrahealth.com/

| Owned, leased, sponsored: | 2 hospitals | 1167 beds |
| Contract–managed: | 0 hospitals | 0 beds |
| **Totals:** | 2 hospitals | 1167 beds |

---

★**0184: CENTRACARE HEALTH** (NP)
1406 Sixth Avenue North, Saint Cloud, MN Zip 56303–1900; tel. 320/251–2700; Terence Pladson, M.D., President and Chief Executive Officer
**(Moderately Centralized Health System)**

**MINNESOTA:** CENTRACARE HEALTH–LONG PRAIRIE (O, 20 beds) 20 Ninth Street S.E., Long Prairie, MN Zip 56347–1404; tel. 320/732–2141; Daniel J. Swenson, FACHE, Administrator and Chief Executive Officer
**Web address:** www.centracare.com

CENTRACARE HEALTH–MELROSE (O, 93 beds) 525 Main Street West, Melrose, MN Zip 56352–1043; tel. 320/256–4231; Gerry Gilbertson, FACHE, Administrator
**Web address:** www.centracare.com

CENTRACARE HEALTH–MONTICELLO (O, 25 beds) 1013 Hart Boulevard, Monticello, MN Zip 55362–8230; tel. 763/295–2945; Mary Ellen Wells, FACHE, Administrator
**Web address:** www.newrivermedical.com

CENTRACARE HEALTH–SAUK CENTRE (O, 85 beds) 425 North Elm Street, Sauk Centre, MN Zip 56378–1010; tel. 320/352–2221; Delano Christianson, Administrator
**Web address:** www.centracare.com/hospitals/sauk_centre/index.html

ST. CLOUD HOSPITAL (O, 485 beds) 1406 Sixth Avenue North, Saint Cloud, MN Zip 56303–1901; tel. 320/251–2700; Craig J. Broman, FACHE, President
**Web address:** www.centracare.com

| Owned, leased, sponsored: | 5 hospitals | 708 beds |
| Contract–managed: | 0 hospitals | 0 beds |
| **Totals:** | 5 hospitals | 708 beds |

---

**0856: CENTRAL FLORIDA HEALTH ALLIANCE** (NP)
600 East Dixie Avenue, Leesburg, FL Zip 34748–5925; tel. 352/323–5762; Donald G. Henderson, FACHE, Chief Executive Officer

**FLORIDA:** LEESBURG REGIONAL MEDICAL CENTER (O, 331 beds) 600 East Dixie Avenue, Leesburg, FL Zip 34748–5999; tel. 352/323–5762; Donald G. Henderson, FACHE, President and Chief Executive Officer
**Web address:** www.cfhalliance.org

THE VILLAGES HEALTH SYSTEM (O, 223 beds) 1451 El Camino Real, The Villages, FL Zip 32159–0041; tel. 352/751–8000; Donald G. Henderson, FACHE, President and Chief Executive Officer
**Web address:** www.cfhalliance.org

| Owned, leased, sponsored: | 2 hospitals | 554 beds |
| Contract–managed: | 0 hospitals | 0 beds |
| **Totals:** | 2 hospitals | 554 beds |

---

★**0955: CHARLESTON AREA MEDICAL CENTER HEALTH SYSTEM, INC.** (NP)
501 Morris Street, Charleston, WV Zip 25301–1300, Mailing Address: P.O. Box 1547, Zip 25326–1547; tel. 304/388–5432; David L. Ramsey, President and Chief Executive Officer
**(Independent Hospital System)**

**WEST VIRGINIA:** CAMC TEAYS VALLEY HOSPITAL (O, 70 beds) 1400 Hospital Drive, Hurricane, WV Zip 25526–9202; tel. 304/757–1700; Randall H. Hodges, President and Chief Executive Officer
**Web address:** www.camc.org

CHARLESTON AREA MEDICAL CENTER (O, 795 beds) 501 Morris Street, Charleston, WV Zip 25301–1300, Mailing Address: P.O. Box 1547, Zip 25326–1547; tel. 304/388–5432; David L. Ramsey, President and Chief Executive Officer
**Web address:** www.camc.org

| Owned, leased, sponsored: | 2 hospitals | 865 beds |
| Contract–managed: | 0 hospitals | 0 beds |
| **Totals:** | 2 hospitals | 865 beds |

---

**0407: CHILDREN'S HOSPITAL AND HEALTH SYSTEM** (NP)
9000 West Wisconsin Avenue, Milwaukee, WI Zip 53226–4810, Mailing Address: P.O. Box 1997, Zip 53201–1997; tel. 414/226–2000; Peggy N. Troy, President and Chief Executive Officer
**(Independent Hospital System)**

**WISCONSIN:** CHILDREN'S HOSPITAL OF WISCONSIN (O, 296 beds) 9000 West Wisconsin Avenue, Milwaukee, WI Zip 53226–4810, Mailing Address: P.O. Box 1997, Zip 53201–1997; tel. 414/266–2000; Peggy N. Troy, President and Chief Executive Officer
**Web address:** www.chw.org

CHILDREN'S HOSPITAL OF WISCONSIN–FOX VALLEY (O, 42 beds) 130 Second Avenue, 3rd Floor South, Neenah, WI Zip 54956–2883; tel. 920/969–7900; Peggy N. Troy, President and Chief Executive Officer
**Web address:** www.chw.org

| Owned, leased, sponsored: | 2 hospitals | 338 beds |
| Contract–managed: | 0 hospitals | 0 beds |
| **Totals:** | 2 hospitals | 338 beds |

---

**0331: CHILDREN'S HOSPITALS AND CLINICS OF MINNESOTA** (NP)
2525 Chicago Avenue South, Minneapolis, MN Zip 55404–4518; tel. 612/813–6100; Alan L. Goldbloom, M.D., President and Chief Executive Officer
**(Moderately Centralized Health System)**

**MINNESOTA:** CHILDREN'S HOSPITALS AND CLINICS OF MINNESOTA (O, 381 beds) 2525 Chicago Avenue South, Minneapolis, MN Zip 55404–4518; tel. 612/813–6100; Alan L. Goldbloom, M.D., Chief Executive Officer
**Web address:** www.childrensmn.org

---

For explanation of codes following names, see page B2.
★ Indicates Type III membership in the American Hospital Association.

CHILDREN'S HOSPITALS AND CLINICS OF MINNESOTA (O, 133 beds) 345 North Smith Avenue, Saint Paul, MN Zip 55102–2346; tel. 651/220–6000; Alan L. Goldbloom, M.D., Chief Executive Officer
Web address: www.childrensmn.org

| | | |
|---|---|---|
| Owned, leased, sponsored: | 2 hospitals | 514 beds |
| Contract–managed: | 0 hospitals | 0 beds |
| Totals: | 2 hospitals | 514 beds |

● ★0131:  CHRISTIANA CARE HEALTH SYSTEM (NP)
501 West 14th Street, Wilmington, DE Zip 19801–1013, Mailing Address: P.O. Box 1668, Zip 19899–1668; tel. 302/733–1000; Robert J. Laskowski, M.D., President and Chief Executive Officer
(Moderately Centralized Health System)

DELAWARE: CHRISTIANA CARE HEALTH SYSTEM (O, 985 beds) 4755 Ogletown–Stanton Road, Newark, DE Zip 19718–0002, Mailing Address: P.O. Box 6001, Zip 19714–6001; tel. 302/733–1000; Robert J. Laskowski, M.D., President and Chief Executive Officer
Web address: www.christianacare.org

| | | |
|---|---|---|
| Owned, leased, sponsored: | 1 hospital | 985 beds |
| Contract–managed: | 0 hospitals | 0 beds |
| Totals: | 1 hospital | 985 beds |

★0192:  CHRISTUS HEALTH (CC)
919 Hidden Ridge Drive, Irving, TX Zip 75038; tel. 469/282–2000; Ernie W. Sadau, President and Chief Executive Officer
(Moderately Centralized Health System)

ARKANSAS: MAGNOLIA REGIONAL MEDICAL CENTER (C, 49 beds) 101 Hospital Drive, Magnolia, AR Zip 71753–2415, Mailing Address: P.O. Box 629, Zip 71754 0629; tel. 870/235–3000; Margaret M. West, MS, Chief Executive Officer
Web address: www.magnoliahospital.org

LOUISIANA: CHRISTUS COUSHATTA HEALTH CARE CENTER (O, 25 beds) 1635 Marvel Street, Coushatta, LA Zip 71019–9022, Mailing Address: P.O. Box 589, Zip 71019–0589; tel. 318/932–2000; Gary L. Kempf, Administrator
Web address: www.christuscoushatta.org

CHRISTUS SCHUMPERT MEDICAL CENTER (O, 302 beds) One St. Mary Place, Shreveport, LA Zip 71101–4399; tel. 318/681–4500; Stephen F. Wright, President and Chief Executive Officer
Web address: www.christusschumpert.org

CHRISTUS ST. FRANCES CABRINI HOSPITAL (O, 281 beds) 3330 Masonic Drive, Alexandria, LA Zip 71301–3899; tel. 318/487–1122; Stephen F. Wright, President and Chief Executive Officer
Web address: www.cabrini.org/

CHRISTUS ST. PATRICK HOSPITAL OF LAKE CHARLES (O, 160 beds) 524 Dr. Michael Debakey Drive, Lake Charles, LA Zip 70601–5799, Mailing Address: P.O. Box 3401, Zip 70602–3401; tel. 337/436–2511; Stephen F. Wright, President and Chief Executive Officer
Web address: www.stpatrickhospital.org

NATCHITOCHES REGIONAL MEDICAL CENTER (C, 208 beds) 501 Keyser Avenue, Natchitoches, LA Zip 71457–6036, Mailing Address: P.O. Box 2009, Zip 71457–2009; tel. 318/214–4200; D. Kirk Soileau, Chief Executive Officer
Web address: www.natchitocheshospital.org

NEW MEXICO: CHRISTUS ST. VINCENT REGIONAL MEDICAL CENTER (O, 195 beds) 455 St. Michael's Drive, Santa Fe, NM Zip 87505–7663, Mailing Address: P.O. Box 2107, Zip 87504–2107; tel. 505/983–3361; Bruce J. Tassin, President and Chief Executive Officer
Web address: www.stvin.org

TEXAS: CHRISTUS HOSPITAL–ST. ELIZABETH (O, 448 beds) 2830 Calder Avenue, Beaumont, TX Zip 77702–1809, Mailing Address: P.O. Box 5405, Zip 77726–5405; tel. 409/892–7171; Paul Trevino, Administrator
Web address: www.christushospital.org

CHRISTUS JASPER MEMORIAL HOSPITAL (L, 50 beds) 1275 Marvin Hancock Drive, Jasper, TX Zip 75951–4995; tel. 409/384–5461; Deborah Mecom, R.N., Administrator
Web address: www.christusjasper.org

CHRISTUS SANTA ROSA HEALTH SYSTEM (O, 766 beds) 333 North Santa Rosa Street, San Antonio, TX Zip 78207–3108; tel. 210/704–4184; Patrick Brian Carrier, President and Chief Executive Officer
Web address: www.christussantarosa.org

CHRISTUS SPOHN HOSPITAL ALICE (O, 115 beds) 2500 East Main Street, Alice, TX Zip 78332–4169; tel. 361/661–8000; Steven G. Daniel, Senior Vice President and Chief Operating Officer
Web address: www.christusspohn.org/locations_alice.htm

CHRISTUS SPOHN HOSPITAL BEEVILLE (L, 49 beds) 1500 East Houston Street, Beeville, TX Zip 78102–5312; tel. 361/354–2000; Raymond Ramos, Vice President and Chief Executive Officer
Web address: www.christusspohn.org

CHRISTUS SPOHN HOSPITAL CORPUS CHRISTI MEMORIAL (O, 783 beds) 2606 Hospital Boulevard, Corpus Christi, TX Zip 78405–1804, Mailing Address: P.O. Box 5280, Zip 78465–5280; tel. 361/902–4000; Paul Gaden, Vice President and Chief Operating Officer
Web address: www.christusspohn.org

CHRISTUS SPOHN HOSPITAL KLEBERG (O, 79 beds) 1311 General Cavazos Boulevard, Kingsville, TX Zip 78363–7130; tel. 361/595–1661; Steven G. Daniel, Interim Vice President and Chief Operating Officer
Web address: www.christusspohn.org

CHRISTUS ST. CATHERINE HOSPITAL (O, 102 beds) 701 Fry Road, Katy, TX Zip 77450–2255; tel. 281/599–5700; Gene B. Wright, Interim Chief Executive Officer
Web address: www.christusstcatherine.org

CHRISTUS ST. JOHN HOSPITAL (O, 121 beds) 18300 St. John Drive, Nassau Bay, TX Zip 77058–6302; tel. 281/333–5503; Thomas Permetti, Regional Chief Operating Officer and Administrator
Web address: www.christusstjohn.org

CHRISTUS ST. MICHAEL HEALTH SYSTEM (O, 312 beds) 2600 St. Michael Drive, Texarkana, TX Zip 75503–5220; tel. 903/614–1000; Chris Karam, President and Chief Executive Officer
Web address: www.christusstmichael.org

CHRISTUS ST. MICHAEL REHABILITATION HOSPITAL (O, 50 beds) 2400 St. Michael Drive, Texarkana, TX Zip 75503–2374; tel. 903/614–4000; Aloma Gender, R.N., MSN, Administrator and Chief Nursing Officer
Web address: www.christusstmichael.org/rehab

| | | |
|---|---|---|
| Owned, leased, sponsored: | 16 hospitals | 3838 beds |
| Contract–managed: | 2 hospitals | 257 beds |
| Totals: | 18 hospitals | 4095 beds |

0350:  CIRRUS HEALTH (IO)
9301 North Central Expressway, Suite 360, Dallas, TX Zip 75231–0826; tel. 214/217–0100; Timothy Parris, President and Chief Executive Officer
(Independent Hospital System)

BAYLOR MEDICAL CENTER AT TROPHY CLUB (O, 20 beds) 2850 East State Highway 114, Trophy Club, TX Zip 76262–5302; tel. 817/837–4600; Melanie Chick, Chief Executive Officer
Web address: www.tc–mc.com

NORTH TEXAS HOSPITAL (O, 16 beds) 2801 South Mayhill Road, Denton, TX Zip 76208–5910; tel. 940/220–0600; Travis W. Roderick, Chief Executive Officer
Web address: www.northtexashospital.com

| | | |
|---|---|---|
| Owned, leased, sponsored: | 2 hospitals | 36 beds |
| Contract–managed: | 0 hospitals | 0 beds |
| Totals: | 2 hospitals | 36 beds |

0101:  CITRUS VALLEY HEALTH PARTNERS (NP)
210 West San Bernardino Road, Covina, CA Zip 91723–1515; tel. 626/331–7331; Robert H. Curry, President and Chief Executive Officer

CALIFORNIA: CITRUS VALLEY MEDICAL CENTER (O, 343 beds) 210 West San Bernadino Road, Covina, CA Zip 91723–1515, Mailing Address: P.O. Box 6108, Zip 91722–5108; tel. 626/331–7331; Robert H. Curry, President and Chief Executive Officer
Web address: www.cvhp.org

For explanation of codes following names, see page B2.
★ Indicates Type III membership in the American Hospital Association.
● Single hospital health care system

FOOTHILL PRESBYTERIAN HOSPITAL (O, 75 beds) 250 South Grand Avenue, Glendora, CA Zip 91741–4218; tel. 626/963–8411; Robert H. Curry, President and Chief Executive Officer
**Web address:** www.cvhp.org/Our_Facilities/Foothill_Presbyterian.aspx

| | | |
|---|---|---|
| Owned, leased, sponsored: | 2 hospitals | 418 beds |
| Contract–managed: | 0 hospitals | 0 beds |
| Totals: | 2 hospitals | 418 beds |

### ★0212:   CLEVELAND CLINIC HEALTH SYSTEM (NP)
9500 Euclid, Cleveland, OH Zip 44195–5108; tel. 216/444–2200; Delos Cosgrove, M.D., President and Chief Executive Officer
**(Centralized Health System)**

**FLORIDA:** CLEVELAND CLINIC FLORIDA (O, 155 beds) 3100 Weston Road, Weston, FL Zip 33331–3602; tel. 954/659–6001; Bernardo Fernandez, M.D., Chief Executive Officer
**Web address:** www.clevelandclinic.org/florida

**OHIO:** CLEVELAND CLINIC (O, 1268 beds) 9500 Euclid Avenue, Cleveland, OH Zip 44195–5108; tel. 216/444–2200; Delos Cosgrove, M.D., President and Chief Executive Officer
**Web address:** www.clevelandclinic.org

CLEVELAND CLINIC CHILDREN'S HOSPITAL FOR REHABILITATION (O, 25 beds) 2801 Martin Luther King Jr. Drive, Cleveland, OH Zip 44104–3865; tel. 216/448–6400; Michael J. McHugh, M.D., Medical Director
**Web address:** www.my.clevelandclinic.org/childrens–hospital/default.aspx

EUCLID HOSPITAL (O, 231 beds) 18901 Lake Shore Boulevard, Euclid, OH Zip 44119–1090; tel. 216/531–9000; Mark Froimson, President
**Web address:** www.euclidhospital.org

FAIRVIEW HOSPITAL (O, 410 beds) 18101 Lorain Avenue, Cleveland, OH Zip 44111–5656; tel. 216/476–7000; Janice Murphy, President
**Web address:** www.fairviewhospital.org

HILLCREST HOSPITAL (O, 412 beds) 6780 Mayfield Road, Cleveland, OH Zip 44124–2203; tel. 440/312–4500; Jeffrey A. Leimgruber, President
**Web address:** www.hillcresthospital.org

LAKEWOOD HOSPITAL (O, 250 beds) 14519 Detroit Avenue, Lakewood, OH Zip 44107–4383; tel. 216/521–4200; Robert Weil, M.D., President
**Web address:** www.lakewoodhospital.org

LUTHERAN HOSPITAL (O, 198 beds) 1730 West 25th Street, Cleveland, OH Zip 44113–3170; tel. 216/696–4300; Brian Donley, M.D., President
**Web address:** www.lutheranhospital.org

MARYMOUNT HOSPITAL (O, 315 beds) 12300 McCracken Road, Garfield Heights, OH Zip 44125–2975; tel. 216/581–0500; Joanne Zeroske, President and Chief Executive Officer
**Web address:** www.marymount.org

MEDINA HOSPITAL (O, 127 beds) 1000 East Washington Street, Medina, OH Zip 44256–2170; tel. 330/725–1000; Thomas Tulisiak, M.D., President
**Web address:** www.medinahospital.org

SOUTH POINTE HOSPITAL (O, 173 beds) 20000 Harvard Road, Warrensville Heights, OH Zip 44122–6805; tel. 216/491–6000; Brian J. Harte, M.D., President
**Web address:** www.southpointehospital.org

| | | |
|---|---|---|
| Owned, leased, sponsored: | 11 hospitals | 3564 beds |
| Contract–managed: | 0 hospitals | 0 beds |
| Totals: | 11 hospitals | 3564 beds |

### 0076:   COLLEGE HEALTH ENTERPRISES (IO)
11627 Telegraph Road, Suite 200, Santa Fe Springs, CA Zip 90670–6814; tel. 562/923–9449; Barry J. Weiss, Chairman of the Board

**CALIFORNIA:** COLLEGE HOSPITAL (O, 157 beds) 10802 College Place, Cerritos, CA Zip 90703–1579; tel. 562/924–9581; Stephen Witt, President and Chief Executive Officer
**Web address:** www.collegehospitals.com

COLLEGE HOSPITAL COSTA MESA (O, 122 beds) 301 Victoria Street, Costa Mesa, CA Zip 92627–7131; tel. 949/642–2734; Susan L. Taylor, Chief Executive Officer
**Web address:** www.collegehospitals.com/cosHome

| | | |
|---|---|---|
| Owned, leased, sponsored: | 2 hospitals | 279 beds |
| Contract–managed: | 0 hospitals | 0 beds |
| Totals: | 2 hospitals | 279 beds |

### ★0161:   COLUMBUS REGIONAL HEALTHCARE SYSTEM (NP)
707 Center Street, Suite 400, Columbus, GA Zip 31901–1575; tel. 706/660–6100; Charles A. Stark, FACHE, President and Chief Executive Officer
**(Centralized Health System)**

**GEORGIA:** DOCTORS HOSPITAL OF COLUMBUS (O, 171 beds) 616 19th Street, Columbus, GA Zip 31901–1528, Mailing Address: P.O. Box 2188, Zip 31902–2188; tel. 706/494–4262; Tamara L. Jackson, R.N., MSN, FACHE, Chief Executive Officer
**Web address:** www.doctorshospital.net

HUGHSTON HOSPITAL (O, 100 beds) 100 Frist Court, Columbus, GA Zip 31909–3578, Mailing Address: P.O. Box 7188, Zip 31908–7188; tel. 706/494–2100
**Web address:** www.hughstonhospital.com

THE MEDICAL CENTER (O, 497 beds) 710 Center Street, Columbus, GA Zip 31901–1527, Mailing Address: P.O. Box 951, Zip 31902–0951; tel. 706/571–1000; Ryan Chandler, President and Chief Executive Officer
**Web address:** www.columbusregional.com

| | | |
|---|---|---|
| Owned, leased, sponsored: | 3 hospitals | 758 beds |
| Contract–managed: | 0 hospitals | 0 beds |
| Totals: | 3 hospitals | 758 beds |

### 0520:   COMMONWEALTH HEALTH CORPORATION (NP)
800 Park Street, Bowling Green, KY Zip 42101–2356; tel. 270/745–1500; Connie Smith, President and Chief Executive Officer
**(Moderately Centralized Health System)**

**KENTUCKY:** COMMONWEALTH REGIONAL SPECIALTY HOSPITAL (O, 24 beds) 250 Park Drive, 6th Floor, Bowling Green, KY Zip 42101–1760, Mailing Address: P.O. Box 90010, Zip 42102–9010; tel. 270/796–6200; Emily Howard Martin, Administrator
**Web address:** www.commonwealthregionalspecialtyhospital.org

MEDICAL CENTER AT BOWLING GREEN (O, 337 beds) 250 Park Street, Bowling Green, KY Zip 42101–1795, Mailing Address: P.O. Box 90010, Zip 42102–9010; tel. 270/745–1000; Connie Smith, Chief Executive Officer
**Web address:** www.themedicalcenter.org

MEDICAL CENTER AT FRANKLIN (O, 25 beds) 1100 Brookhaven Road, Franklin, KY Zip 42134–2746; tel. 270/598–4800; Eric Hagan, R.N., Vice President/Administrator
**Web address:** www.themedicalcenterfranklin.org

MEDICAL CENTER AT SCOTTSVILLE (O, 135 beds) 456 Burnley Road, Scottsville, KY Zip 42164–6355; tel. 270/622–2800; Eric Hagan, R.N., Vice President/Administrator
**Web address:** www.themedicalcenterscottsville.org/

| | | |
|---|---|---|
| Owned, leased, sponsored: | 4 hospitals | 521 beds |
| Contract–managed: | 0 hospitals | 0 beds |
| Totals: | 4 hospitals | 521 beds |

### 0401:   COMMUNITY HEALTH NETWORK (NP)
7330 Shadeland Station, Indianapolis, IN Zip 46256–3957; tel. 317/355–1411; Bryan A. Mills, President and Chief Executive Officer
**(Independent Hospital System)**

**INDIANA:** COMMUNITY HEART AND VASCULAR HOSPITAL (O, 56 beds) 8075 North Shadeland Avenue, Indianapolis, IN Zip 46250–2693; tel. 317/621–8000; Thomas A. Malasto, Chief Executive Officer
**Web address:** www.hearthospital.org

COMMUNITY HOSPITAL EAST (O, 233 beds) 1500 North Ritter Avenue, Indianapolis, IN Zip 46219–3095; tel. 317/355–1411; Robin Ledyard, M.D., M.P.H., President
**Web address:** www.ecommunity.com/east/

For explanation of codes following names, see page B2.
★ Indicates Type III membership in the American Hospital Association.

COMMUNITY HOSPITAL NORTH (O, 389 beds) 7150 Clearvista Drive, Indianapolis, IN Zip 46256–1695; tel. 317/621–6262; Robert Lindeman, M.D., President
**Web address:** www.ecommunity.com

COMMUNITY HOSPITAL OF ANDERSON AND MADISON COUNTY (O, 318 beds) 1515 North Madison Avenue, Anderson, IN Zip 46011–3453; tel. 765/298–4242; Beth S. Tharp, R.N., President and Chief Executive Officer
**Web address:** www.communityanderson.com

COMMUNITY HOSPITAL SOUTH (O, 108 beds) 1402 East County Line Road South, Indianapolis, IN Zip 46227–0963; tel. 317/887–7000; Anthony B. Lennen, President
**Web address:** www.ecommunity.com

COMMUNITY HOWARD REGIONAL HOSPITAL (O, 168 beds) 3500 South Lafountain Street, Kokomo, IN Zip 46902–3803, Mailing Address: P.O. Box 9011, Zip 46904–9011; tel. 765/453–0702; James P. Alender, President and Chief Executive Officer
**Web address:** www.howardregional.org

COMMUNITY HOWARD SPECIALTY HOSPITAL (O, 30 beds) 829 North Dixon Road, Kokomo, IN Zip 46901–7709; tel. 765/452–6700; Michelle L. Russell, Administrator
**Web address:** www.howardregional.org

COMMUNITY WESTVIEW HOSPITAL (O, 68 beds) 3630 Guion Road, Indianapolis, IN Zip 46222–1699; tel. 317/924–6661; David C. Williams, D.O., Interim President and Chief Executive Officer
**Web address:** www.westviewhospital.org

| | | |
|---|---|---|
| Owned, leased, sponsored: | 8 hospitals | 1370 beds |
| Contract–managed: | 0 hospitals | 0 beds |
| Totals: | 8 hospitals | 1370 beds |

---

★**0080: COMMUNITY HEALTH SYSTEMS, INC.** (IO)
4000 Meridian Boulevard, Franklin, TN Zip 37067–6325, Mailing Address: P.O. Box 689020, Zip 37068–9020; tel. 615/465–7000; Wayne T. Smith, Chairman, President and Chief Executive Officer
**(Decentralized Health System)**

**ALABAMA:** CHEROKEE MEDICAL CENTER (O, 45 beds) 400 Northwood Drive, Centre, AL Zip 35960–1023; tel. 256/927–5531; Jay Hinesley, Interim Chief Executive Officer
**Web address:** www.cherokeemedicalcenter.com

CRESTWOOD MEDICAL CENTER (O, 150 beds) One Hospital Drive, Huntsville, AL Zip 35801–3403; tel. 256/429–4000; Pamela Hudson, M.D., Chief Executive Officer
**Web address:** www.crestwoodmedcenter.com

DEKALB REGIONAL MEDICAL CENTER (O, 121 beds) 200 Medical Center Drive, Fort Payne, AL Zip 35968–3458, Mailing Address: P.O. Box 680778, Zip 35968–1608; tel. 256/845–3150; Jeff G. Rains, Chief Executive Officer
**Web address:** www.dekalbregional.com

FLOWERS HOSPITAL (O, 235 beds) 4370 West Main Street, Dothan, AL Zip 36305–4000, Mailing Address: P.O. Box 6907, Zip 36302–6907; tel. 334/793–5000; Suzanne Woods, President and Chief Executive Officer
**Web address:** www.flowershospital.com

GADSDEN REGIONAL MEDICAL CENTER (O, 299 beds) 1007 Goodyear Avenue, Gadsden, AL Zip 35903–1195; tel. 256/494–4000; Stephen G. Pennington, Chief Executive Officer
**Web address:** www.gadsdenregional.com

L. V. STABLER MEMORIAL HOSPITAL (O, 61 beds) 29 L. V. Stabler Drive, Greenville, AL Zip 36037–3800; tel. 334/382–2671; Connie Nicholas, Interim Chief Executive Officer
**Web address:** www.lvstabler.com

MEDICAL CENTER ENTERPRISE (O, 117 beds) 400 North Edwards Street, Enterprise, AL Zip 36330–2510; tel. 334/347–0584; Richard Ellis, Chief Executive Officer
**Web address:** www.mcehospital.com

SOUTH BALDWIN REGIONAL MEDICAL CENTER (L, 112 beds) 1613 North McKenzie Street, Foley, AL Zip 36535–2299; tel. 251/949–3400; Keith Newton, Chief Executive Officer
**Web address:** www.southbaldwinrmc.com

TRINITY MEDICAL CENTER (O, 379 beds) 800 Montclair Road, Birmingham, AL Zip 35213–1984; tel. 205/592–1000; Keith Granger, President and Chief Executive Officer
**Web address:** www.bhsala.com

**ALASKA:** MAT–SU REGIONAL MEDICAL CENTER (O, 74 beds) 2500 South Woodworth Loop, Palmer, AK Zip 99645–8984, Mailing Address: P.O. Box 1687, Zip 99645–1687; tel. 907/861–6000; John R. Lee, Chief Executive Officer
**Web address:** www.matsuregional.com

**ARIZONA:** NORTHWEST MEDICAL CENTER (O, 270 beds) 6200 North La Cholla Boulevard, Tucson, AZ Zip 85741–3599; tel. 520/742–9000; Kevin Stockton, Chief Executive Officer
**Web address:** www.northwestmedicalcenter.com

ORO VALLEY HOSPITAL (O, 144 beds) 1551 East Tangerine Road, Oro Valley, AZ Zip 85755–6213; tel. 520/901–3500; Jae Dale, Chief Executive Officer
**Web address:** www.nmcorovalley.com

PAYSON REGIONAL MEDICAL CENTER (L, 44 beds) 807 South Ponderosa Street, Payson, AZ Zip 85541–5599; tel. 928/474–3222; R. Chris Wolf, Chief Executive Officer
**Web address:** www.paysonhospital.com

WESTERN ARIZONA REGIONAL MEDICAL CENTER (O, 139 beds) 2735 Silver Creek Road, Bullhead City, AZ Zip 86442–8303; tel. 928/763–2273; Alex Villa, Chief Executive Officer
**Web address:** www.warmc.com

**ARKANSAS:** FORREST CITY MEDICAL CENTER (L, 70 beds) 1601 Newcastle Road, Forrest City, AR Zip 72335–2218; tel. 870/261–0000; Kevin Decker, Interim Chief Executive Officer
**Web address:** www.forrestcitymedicalcenter.com

HARRIS HOSPITAL (O, 104 beds) 1205 McLain Street, Newport, AR Zip 72112–3533; tel. 870/523–8911; Robert Rupp, Chief Executive Officer
**Web address:** www.harrishospital.com

HELENA REGIONAL MEDICAL CENTER (L, 100 beds) 1801 Martin Luther King Drive, Helena, AR Zip 72342, Mailing Address: P.O. Box 788, Zip 72342–0788; tel. 870/338–5800; Buddy Daniels, Chief Executive Officer
**Web address:** www.helenarmc.com

MEDICAL CENTER OF SOUTH ARKANSAS (L, 116 beds) 700 West Grove Street, El Dorado, AR Zip 71730–4416, Mailing Address: P.O. Box 1998, Zip 71731–1998; tel. 870/863–2000; Kyle Swift, Chief Executive Officer
**Web address:** www.themedcenter.net

NORTHWEST MEDICAL CENTER (O, 358 beds) 609 West Maple Avenue, Springdale, AR Zip 72764–5394, Mailing Address: P.O. Box 47, Zip 72765–0047; tel. 501/751–5711; Daniel E. McKay, Chief Executive Officer
**Web address:** www.northwesthealth.com

SILOAM SPRINGS MEMORIAL HOSPITAL (O, 43 beds) 205 East Jefferson Street, Siloam Springs, AR Zip 72761–3697; tel. 479/524–4141; Kevin J. Clement, Chief Executive Officer
**Web address:** www.ssrh.net/Pages/home.aspx

**CALIFORNIA:** BARSTOW COMMUNITY HOSPITAL (L, 30 beds) 555 South Seventh Avenue, Barstow, CA Zip 92311–3043; tel. 760/256–1761; S. Sean Fowler, Chief Executive Officer
**Web address:** www.barstowhospital.com

FALLBROOK HOSPITAL (L, 86 beds) 624 East Elder Street, Fallbrook, CA Zip 92028–3099; tel. 760/728–1191; Kirkpatrick Conley, Chief Executive Officer
**Web address:** www.fallbrookhospital.com

WATSONVILLE COMMUNITY HOSPITAL (O, 106 beds) 75 Nielson Street, Watsonville, CA Zip 95076–2468; tel. 831/724–4741; Audra Earle, Chief Executive Officer
**Web address:** www.watsonvillehospital.com

**FLORIDA:** LAKE WALES MEDICAL CENTER (O, 131 beds) 410 South 11th Street, Lake Wales, FL Zip 33853–4256; tel. 863/676–1433; Scott M. Smith, Chief Executive Officer
**Web address:** www.lakewalesmedicalcenter.com

NORTH OKALOOSA MEDICAL CENTER (O, 110 beds) 151 Redstone Avenue S.E., Crestview, FL Zip 32539–6026; tel. 850/689–8100; David W. Fuller, Chief Executive Officer
**Web address:** www.northokaloosa.com

---

For explanation of codes following names, see page B2.
★ Indicates Type III membership in the American Hospital Association.

Section B

**GEORGIA:** FANNIN REGIONAL HOSPITAL (O, 50 beds) 2855 Old Highway 5, Blue Ridge, GA Zip 30513–6248; tel. 706/632–3711; David S. Sanders, Chief Executive Officer
**Web address:** www.fanninregionalhospital.com

TRINITY HOSPITAL OF AUGUSTA (O, 105 beds) 2260 Wrightsboro Road, Augusta, GA Zip 30904–4726; tel. 706/481–7000; Jason Studley, Chief Executive Officer
**Web address:** www.trinityofaugusta.com

**ILLINOIS:** CROSSROADS COMMUNITY HOSPITAL (O, 41 beds) 8 Doctors Park Road, Mount Vernon, IL Zip 62864–6224; tel. 618/244–5500; Finny Mathew, Chief Executive Officer
**Web address:** www.crossroadscommunityhospital.com

GALESBURG COTTAGE HOSPITAL (O, 119 beds) 695 North Kellogg Street, Galesburg, IL Zip 61401–2885; tel. 309/343–8131; Earl J. Tamar, Chief Executive Officer
**Web address:** www.cottagehospital.com

GATEWAY REGIONAL MEDICAL CENTER (O, 337 beds) 2100 Madison Avenue, Granite City, IL Zip 62040–4799; tel. 618/798–3000; M. Edward Cunningham, Chief Executive Officer
**Web address:** www.gatewayregional.net

HEARTLAND REGIONAL MEDICAL CENTER (O, 92 beds) 3333 West DeYoung, Marion, IL Zip 62959–5884; tel. 618/998–7000; Stephen Lunn, Chief Executive Officer
**Web address:** www.heartlandregional.com

METROSOUTH MEDICAL CENTER (O, 180 beds) 12935 South Gregory Street, Blue Island, IL Zip 60406–2470; tel. 708/597–2000; Enrique Beckmann, M.D., Ph.D., President and Chief Executive Officer
**Web address:** www.metrosouthmedicalcenter.com

RED BUD REGIONAL HOSPITAL (O, 140 beds) 325 Spring Street, Red Bud, IL Zip 62278–1105; tel. 618/282–3831; Shane Watson, Chief Executive Officer
**Web address:** www.redbudhospital.com

UNION COUNTY HOSPITAL (L, 47 beds) 517 North Main Street, Anna, IL Zip 62906–1696; tel. 618/833–4511; James R. Farris, FACHE, Chief Executive Officer
**Web address:** www.unioncountyhospital.com

VISTA MEDICAL CENTER EAST (O, 192 beds) 1324 North Sheridan Road, Waukegan, IL Zip 60085–2161; tel. 847/360–3000; Barbara J. Martin, R.N., President and Chief Executive Officer
**Web address:** www.vistahealth.com

VISTA MEDICAL CENTER WEST (O, 67 beds) 2615 Washington Street, Waukegan, IL Zip 60085–4988; tel. 847/249–3900; Barbara J. Martin, R.N., President and Chief Executive Officer
**Web address:** www.vistahealth.com

**INDIANA:** BLUFFTON REGIONAL MEDICAL CENTER (O, 79 beds) 303 South Main Street, Bluffton, IN Zip 46714–2503; tel. 260/824–3210; Aaron Garofola, Chief Executive Officer
**Web address:** www.blufftonregional.com

DUKES MEMORIAL HOSPITAL (O, 25 beds) 275 West 12th Street, Peru, IN Zip 46970–1638; tel. 765/472–8000; Debra Close, Chief Executive Officer
**Web address:** www.dukesmemorialhosp.com

DUPONT HOSPITAL (O, 131 beds) 2520 East Dupont Road, Fort Wayne, IN Zip 46825–1675; tel. 260/416–3000; Chad Towner, Chief Executive Officer
**Web address:** www.thedupontdifference.com

KOSCIUSKO COMMUNITY HOSPITAL (O, 72 beds) 2101 East Dubois Drive, Warsaw, IN Zip 46580–3288; tel. 574/267–3200; Stephen R. Miller, Chief Executive Officer
**Web address:** www.kch.com

LUTHERAN HOSPITAL OF INDIANA (O, 396 beds) 7950 West Jefferson Boulevard, Fort Wayne, IN Zip 46804–4140; tel. 260/435–7001; Joe Dorko, Chief Executive Officer
**Web address:** www.lutheranhospital.com

ORTHOPAEDIC HOSPITAL OF LUTHERAN HEALTH NETWORK (O, 44 beds) 7952 West Jefferson Boulevard, Fort Wayne, IN Zip 46804–4140; tel. 260/435–2999; Kenneth Jones, Chief Executive Officer
**Web address:** www.theorthohospital.com

PORTER REGIONAL HOSPITAL (O, 276 beds) 814 La Porte Avenue, Valparaiso, IN Zip 46383–5898; tel. 219/263–4600; Jonathan Nalli, Chief Executive Officer
**Web address:** www.porterhealth.org

REHABILITATION HOSPITAL OF FORT WAYNE (O, 36 beds) 7970 West Jefferson Boulevard, Fort Wayne, IN Zip 46804–4140; tel. 260/435–6100; Brian Bauer, Chief Operating Officer
**Web address:** www.rehabhospital.com

ST. JOSEPH HOSPITAL (O, 182 beds) 700 Broadway, Fort Wayne, IN Zip 46802–1493; tel. 260/425–3000; Eric N. Looper, Chief Executive Officer
**Web address:** www.stjoehospital.com

**KENTUCKY:** KENTUCKY RIVER MEDICAL CENTER (L, 54 beds) 540 Jett Drive, Jackson, KY Zip 41339–9622; tel. 606/666–6000; William Chad French, Chief Executive Officer
**Web address:** www.kentuckyrivermc.com

PARKWAY REGIONAL HOSPITAL (O, 70 beds) 2000 Holiday Lane, Fulton, KY Zip 42041–8468; tel. 270/472–2522; Rob Calhoun, Chief Executive Officer
**Web address:** www.parkwayregionalhospital.com

THREE RIVERS MEDICAL CENTER (O, 80 beds) Highway 644, Louisa, KY Zip 41230–9632, Mailing Address: P.O. Box 769, Zip 41230–0769; tel. 606/638–9451; Greg Kiser, Chief Executive Officer
**Web address:** www.threeriversmedicalcenter.com

**LOUISIANA:** BYRD REGIONAL HOSPITAL (O, 60 beds) 1020 West Fertitta Boulevard, Leesville, LA Zip 71446–4645; tel. 337/239–9041; Roger C. LeDoux, Chief Executive Officer
**Web address:** www.byrdregional.com

NORTHERN LOUISIANA MEDICAL CENTER (O, 91 beds) 401 East Vaughn Avenue, Ruston, LA Zip 71270–5950; tel. 318/254–2100; Brady Dubois, Interim Chief Executive Officer
**Web address:** www.northernlouisianamedicalcenter.com

WOMEN AND CHILDREN'S HOSPITAL (O, 88 beds) 4200 Nelson Road, Lake Charles, LA Zip 70605–4118; tel. 337/474–6370; Bryan S. Bateman, Chief Executive Officer
**Web address:** www.women–childrens.com

**MISSISSIPPI:** RIVER REGION MEDICAL CENTER (O, 297 beds) 2100 Highway 61 North, Vicksburg, MS Zip 39183–8211, Mailing Address: P.O. Box 590, Zip 39181–0590; tel. 601/883–5000; Doug Sills, Chief Executive Officer
**Web address:** www.riverregion.com

WESLEY MEDICAL CENTER (O, 211 beds) 5001 Hardy Street, Hattiesburg, MS Zip 39402–1308, Mailing Address: P.O. Box 16509, Zip 39404–6509; tel. 601/268–8000; Michael Neuendorf, Chief Executive Officer
**Web address:** www.wesley.com

**MISSOURI:** MOBERLY REGIONAL MEDICAL CENTER (O, 94 beds) 1515 Union Avenue, Moberly, MO Zip 65270–9449; tel. 660/263–8400; Christian Jones, Chief Executive Officer
**Web address:** www.moberlyhospital.com

NORTHEAST REGIONAL MEDICAL CENTER (L, 115 beds) 315 South Osteopathy, Kirksville, MO Zip 63501–6401, Mailing Address: P.O. Box C8502, Zip 63501–8599; tel. 660/785–1000; Eric A. Barber, Chief Executive Officer
**Web address:** www.nermc.com

**NEVADA:** MESA VIEW REGIONAL HOSPITAL (O, 25 beds) 1299 Bertha Howe Avenue, Mesquite, NV Zip 89027–7500; tel. 702/346–8040; Patricia Holden, Chief Executive Officer
**Web address:** www.mesaviewhospital.com

**NEW JERSEY:** MEMORIAL HOSPITAL OF SALEM COUNTY (O, 110 beds) 310 Woodstown Road, Salem, NJ Zip 08079–2080; tel. 856/935–1000; Richard Grogan, Chief Executive Officer
**Web address:** www.salemhospitalnj.org

**NEW MEXICO:** ALTA VISTA REGIONAL HOSPITAL (O, 54 beds) 104 Legion Drive, Las Vegas, NM Zip 87701–4804; tel. 505/426–3500; Kathleen Cahill, President and Chief Executive Officer
**Web address:** www.altavistaregionalhospital.com

CARLSBAD MEDICAL CENTER (O, 127 beds) 2430 West Pierce Street, Carlsbad, NM Zip 88220–3597; tel. 575/887–4100; Chad Campbell, Chief Executive Officer
**Web address:** www.carlsbadmedicalcenter.com

EASTERN NEW MEXICO MEDICAL CENTER (O, 149 beds) 405 West Country Club Road, Roswell, NM Zip 88201–5209; tel. 575/622–8170; Maridel Acosta, Chief Executive Officer
**Web address:** www.enmmc.com

For explanation of codes following names, see page B2.
★ Indicates Type III membership in the American Hospital Association.

LEA REGIONAL MEDICAL CENTER (O, 214 beds) 5419 North Lovington Highway, Hobbs, NM Zip 88240–9125, Mailing Address: P.O. Box 3000, Zip 88241–9501; tel. 575/492–5000; Timothy Thornell, FACHE, Chief Executive Officer
**Web address:** www.learegionalmedical.com

MIMBRES MEMORIAL HOSPITAL (O, 75 beds) 900 West Ash Street, Deming, NM Zip 88030–4098, Mailing Address: P.O. Box 710, Zip 88031–0710; tel. 575/546–2761; Steve Westenhofer, Chief Executive Officer
**Web address:** www.mimbresmemorial.com

MOUNTAINVIEW REGIONAL MEDICAL CENTER (O, 142 beds) 4311 East Lohman Avenue, Las Cruces, NM Zip 88011–8255; tel. 575/556–7600; Denten Park, Chief Executive Officer
**Web address:** www.mountainviewregional.com

**NORTH CAROLINA:** MARTIN GENERAL HOSPITAL (L, 49 beds) 310 South McCaskey Road, Williamston, NC Zip 27892–2150, Mailing Address: P.O. Box 1128, Zip 27892–1128; tel. 252/809–6179; Jodi Beauregard, Chief Executive Officer
**Web address:** www.martingeneral.com

**OHIO:** AFFINITY MEDICAL CENTER (O, 112 beds) 875 Eighth Street N.E., Massillon, OH Zip 44646–8503, Mailing Address: P.O. Box 805, Zip 44648–0805; tel. 330/832–8761; Ronald L. Bierman, Chief Executive Officer
**Web address:** www.affinitymedicalcenter.com

HILLSIDE REHABILITATION HOSPITAL (O, 65 beds) 8747 Squires Lane N.E., Warren, OH Zip 44484–1649; tel. 330/841–3700; Marilyn Titus, Vice President and Chief Operating Officer
**Web address:** www.valleycarehealth.net

NORTHSIDE MEDICAL CENTER (O, 373 beds) 500 Gypsy Lane, Youngstown, OH Zip 44504–1315; tel. 330/884–1000; Kirk M. Ray, Chief Executive Officer
**Web address:** www.northsidemedicalcenter.net

TRUMBULL MEMORIAL HOSPITAL (O, 292 beds) 1350 East Market Street, Warren, OH Zip 44483–6628; tel. 330/841–9011; John Walsh, Chief Executive Officer
**Web address:** www.valleycarehealth.net

**OKLAHOMA:** DEACONESS HOSPITAL (O, 273 beds) 5501 North Portland Avenue, Oklahoma City, OK Zip 73112–2099; tel. 405/604–6000; Cathryn A. Hibbs, FACHE, Chief Executive Officer
**Web address:** www.deaconessokc.com

PONCA CITY MEDICAL CENTER (O, 72 beds) 1900 North 14th Street, Ponca City, OK Zip 74601–2099; tel. 580/765–3321; R. Andrew Wachtel, FACHE, Chief Executive Officer
**Web address:** www.poncamedcenter.com

WOODWARD REGIONAL HOSPITAL (L, 40 beds) 900 17th Street, Woodward, OK Zip 73801–2448; tel. 580/256–5511; David Wallace, Chief Executive Officer
**Web address:** www.woodwardhospital.com

**OREGON:** MCKENZIE–WILLAMETTE MEDICAL CENTER (O, 113 beds) 1460 G Street, Springfield, OR Zip 97477–4197; tel. 541/726–4400; Maurine Cate, Chief Executive Officer
**Web address:** www.mckweb.com

**PENNSYLVANIA:** BERWICK HOSPITAL CENTER (O, 341 beds) 701 East 16th Street, Berwick, PA Zip 18603–2397; tel. 570/759–5000; Ronald R. Beer, Chief Executive Officer
**Web address:** www.berwick–hospital.com

BRANDYWINE HOSPITAL (O, 164 beds) 201 Reeceville Road, Coatesville, PA Zip 19320–1536; tel. 610/383–8000; Bryan Burklow, Chief Executive Officer
**Web address:** www.brandywinehospital.com

CHESTNUT HILL HOSPITAL (O, 135 beds) 8835 Germantown Avenue, Philadelphia, PA Zip 19118–2718; tel. 215/248–8200; John D. Cacciamani, M.D., Chief Executive Officer
**Web address:** www.chhealthsystem.com

EASTON HOSPITAL (O, 224 beds) 250 South 21st Street, Easton, PA Zip 18042–3892; tel. 610/250–4000; Brian Finestein, Chief Executive Officer
**Web address:** www.easton–hospital.com

FIRST HOSPITAL WYOMING VALLEY (O, 107 beds) 562 Wyoming Avenue, Kingston, PA Zip 18704–3721; tel. 570/552–3900; Mark Schor, Chief Executive Officer
**Web address:** www.firsthospital.net/Pages/home.aspx

JENNERSVILLE REGIONAL HOSPITAL (O, 59 beds) 1015 West Baltimore Pike, West Grove, PA Zip 19390–9459; tel. 610/869–1000; Charles A. Davis, Chief Executive Officer
**Web address:** www.jennersville.com

LOCK HAVEN HOSPITAL (O, 59 beds) 24 Cree Drive, Lock Haven, PA Zip 17745–2699; tel. 570/893–5000; John A. Zidansek, Chief Executive Officer
**Web address:** www.lockhavenhospital.com

MEMORIAL HOSPITAL (O, 100 beds) 325 South Belmont Street, York, PA Zip 17403–2609, Mailing Address: P.O. Box 15118, Zip 17405–7118; tel. 717/843–8623; Sally J. Dixon, President and Chief Executive Officer
**Web address:** www.mhyork.org

MID–VALLEY HOSPITAL (O, 25 beds) 1400 Main Street, Peckville, PA Zip 18452–2009; tel. 570/383–5500; Ann Marie Poslock, Chief Executive Officer
**Web address:** www.mth.org

MOSES TAYLOR HOSPITAL (O, 217 beds) 700 Quincy Avenue, Scranton, PA Zip 18510–1724; tel. 570/340–2100; Justin Davis, Chief Executive Officer
**Web address:** www.mth.org

PHOENIXVILLE HOSPITAL (O, 118 beds) 140 Nutt Road, Phoenixville, PA Zip 19460–3900, Mailing Address: P.O. Box 3001, Zip 19460–0916; tel. 610/983–1000; Stephen M. Tullman, Chief Executive Officer
**Web address:** www.phoenixvillehospital.com

POTTSTOWN MEMORIAL MEDICAL CENTER (O, 232 beds) 1600 East High Street, Pottstown, PA Zip 19464–5093; tel. 610/327–7000; Sharif Omar, Chief Executive Officer
**Web address:** www.pottstownmemorial.com

REGIONAL HOSPITAL OF SCRANTON (O, 224 beds) 746 Jefferson Avenue, Scranton, PA Zip 18510–1624; tel. 570/348–7100; Brooks Turkel, Chief Executive Officer
**Web address:** www.regionalhospitalofscranton.net

SPECIAL CARE HOSPITAL (O, 64 beds) 128 West Washington Street, Nanticoke, PA Zip 18634–3113; tel. 570/735–5000; Robert D. Williams, Chief Executive Officer
**Web address:** www.specialcarehospital.net

SUNBURY COMMUNITY HOSPITAL AND OUTPATIENT CENTER (O, 76 beds) 350 North Eleventh Street, Sunbury, PA Zip 17801–1611; tel. 570/286–3333; Jeff Hunt, Chief Executive Officer
**Web address:** www.sunburyhospital.com

TYLER MEMORIAL HOSPITAL (O, 58 beds) 880 State Road 6 West, Tunkhannock, PA Zip 18657–6149; tel. 570/836–2161; Denise S. Gieski, MS, Chief Executive Officer
**Web address:** www.tylermemorialhospital.net

WILKES–BARRE GENERAL HOSPITAL (O, 374 beds) 575 North River Street, Wilkes–Barre, PA Zip 18764–0001; tel. 570/829–8111; Cornelio R. Catena, President and Chief Executive Officer
**Web address:** www.wvhc.org

**SOUTH CAROLINA:** CAROLINAS HOSPITAL SYSTEM (O, 429 beds) 805 Pamplico Highway, Florence, SC Zip 29505–6050, Mailing Address: P.O. Box 100550, Zip 29502–0550; tel. 843/674–5000; Darcy Craven, Chief Executive Officer
**Web address:** www.carolinashospital.com

CAROLINAS HOSPITAL SYSTEM MARION (O, 216 beds) 2829 East Highway 76, Mullins, SC Zip 29574–6035, Mailing Address: P.O. Drawer 1150, Marion, Zip 29571–1150; tel. 843/431–2000; Darcy Craven, Chief Executive Officer
**Web address:** www.carolinashospitalmarion.com/Pages/Home.aspx

CHESTERFIELD GENERAL HOSPITAL (L, 59 beds) 711 Chesterfield Highway, Cheraw, SC Zip 29520–7002; tel. 843/537–7881; Jeff Reece, Chief Executive Officer
**Web address:** www.chesterfieldgeneral.com

MARLBORO PARK HOSPITAL (L, 102 beds) 1138 Cheraw Highway, Bennettsville, SC Zip 29512–2466; tel. 843/479–2881; Jeff Reece, Chief Executive Officer
**Web address:** www.marlboroparkhospital.com

MARY BLACK MEMORIAL HOSPITAL (O, 181 beds) 1700 Skylyn Drive, Spartanburg, SC Zip 29307–1061, Mailing Address: P.O. Box 3217, Zip 29304–3217; tel. 864/573–3000; Douglas J. Moyer, Chief Executive Officer
**Web address:** www.maryblackhealthsystem.com

For explanation of codes following names, see page B2.
★ Indicates Type III membership in the American Hospital Association.

© 2013 AHA Guide    Health Care Systems, Networks and Alliances    **B37**

Section B

SPRINGS MEMORIAL HOSPITAL (O, 186 beds) 800 West Meeting Street, Lancaster, SC Zip 29720–2298; tel. 803/286–1214; Janice Dabney, Interim Chief Executive Officer
**Web address:** www.springsmemorial.com

**TENNESSEE:** DYERSBURG REGIONAL MEDICAL CENTER (O, 120 beds) 400 East Tickle Street, Dyersburg, TN Zip 38024–3120; tel. 731/285–2410; Ben Youree, Chief Executive Officer
**Web address:** www.dyersburgregionalmc.com

GATEWAY MEDICAL CENTER (O, 247 beds) 651 Dunlop Lane, Clarksville, TN Zip 37040–5015, Mailing Address: P.O. Box 31629, Zip 37040–0028; tel. 931/502–1000; Mark A. Marsh, Chief Executive Officer
**Web address:** www.ghsystem.com

HAYWOOD PARK COMMUNITY HOSPITAL (O, 36 beds) 2545 North Washington Avenue, Brownsville, TN Zip 38012–1610; tel. 731/772–4110; Joel Southern, R.N., MSN, Interim Chief Executive Officer
**Web address:** www.haywoodparkcommunity.com

HENDERSON COUNTY COMMUNITY HOSPITAL (O, 36 beds) 200 West Church Street, Lexington, TN Zip 38351–2038; tel. 731/968–3646; David Henry, Chief Executive Officer
**Web address:** www.hendersoncchospital.com

HERITAGE MEDICAL CENTER (O, 70 beds) 2835 Highway 231 North, Shelbyville, TN Zip 37160–7327; tel. 931/685–5433; David V. Bunch, Chief Executive Officer
**Web address:** www.heritagemedicalcenter.com

LAKEWAY REGIONAL HOSPITAL (O, 135 beds) 726 McFarland Street, Morristown, TN Zip 37814–3990; tel. 423/586–2302; Clyde Wood, Chief Executive Officer
**Web address:** www.lakewayregionalhospital.com

MCKENZIE REGIONAL HOSPITAL (O, 35 beds) 161 Hospital Drive, McKenzie, TN Zip 38201–1636; tel. 731/352–5344; Michael G. Morrical, Chief Executive Officer
**Web address:** www.mckenzieregionalhospital.com

MCNAIRY REGIONAL HOSPITAL (O, 45 beds) 705 East Poplar Avenue, Selmer, TN Zip 38375–1828; tel. 731/645–3221; Pamela W. Roberts, Chief Executive Officer
**Web address:** www.mcnairyregionalhospital.com

REGIONAL HOSPITAL OF JACKSON (O, 129 beds) 367 Hospital Boulevard, Jackson, TN Zip 38305–2080; tel. 731/661–2000; Dale Humphrey, Chief Executive Officer
**Web address:** www.regionalhospitaljackson.com/Pages/Home.aspx

SKYRIDGE MEDICAL CENTER (O, 208 beds) 2305 Chambliss Avenue N.W., Cleveland, TN Zip 37311–3847, Mailing Address: P.O. Box 3060, Zip 37320–3060; tel. 423/559–6000; R. Coleman Foss, Chief Executive Officer
**Web address:** www.skyridgemedicalcenter.net

VOLUNTEER COMMUNITY HOSPITAL (O, 65 beds) 161 Mount Pelia Road, Martin, TN Zip 38237–3811; tel. 731/587–4261; Darrell Blaylock, Chief Executive Officer
**Web address:** www.volunteercommunityhospital.com

**TEXAS:** ABILENE REGIONAL MEDICAL CENTER (O, 205 beds) 6250 U.S. Highway 83, Abilene, TX Zip 79606–5299; tel. 325/428–1000; Michael D. Murphy, Chief Executive Officer
**Web address:** www.abileneregional.com

BIG BEND REGIONAL MEDICAL CENTER (O, 25 beds) 2600 Highway 118 North, Alpine, TX Zip 79830–2002; tel. 432/837–3447; Michael J. Ellis, Chief Executive Officer
**Web address:** www.bigbendhealthcare.com

BROWNWOOD REGIONAL MEDICAL CENTER (O, 168 beds) 1501 Burnet Drive, Brownwood, TX Zip 76801–8520, Mailing Address: P.O. Box 760, Zip 76804–0760; tel. 325/646–8541; Claude E. Camp, III, Chief Executive Officer
**Web address:** www.brmc–cares.com

CEDAR PARK REGIONAL MEDICAL CENTER (O, 85 beds) 1401 Medical Parkway, Cedar Park, TX Zip 78613–7763; tel. 512/528–7000; Brad D. Holland, Chief Executive Officer
**Web address:** www.cedarparkregional.com

COLLEGE STATION MEDICAL CENTER (O, 167 beds) 1604 Rock Prairie Road, College Station, TX Zip 77845–8345, Mailing Address: P.O. Box 10000, Zip 77842–3500; tel. 979/764–5100; Thomas W. Jackson, Chief Executive Officer
**Web address:** www.csmedcenter.com

DETAR HEALTHCARE SYSTEM (O, 222 beds) 506 East San Antonio Street, Victoria, TX Zip 77901–6060, Mailing Address: P.O. Box 2089, Zip 77902–2089; tel. 361/575–7441; William R. Blanchard, Chief Executive Officer
**Web address:** www.detar.com

HILL REGIONAL HOSPITAL (O, 66 beds) 101 Circle Drive, Hillsboro, TX Zip 76645–2670; tel. 254/580–8500; Jan McClure, Chief Executive Officer
**Web address:** www.chs.net

LAKE GRANBURY MEDICAL CENTER (L, 83 beds) 1310 Paluxy Road, Granbury, TX Zip 76048–5655; tel. 817/573–2273; Derrick Cuenca, Chief Executive Officer
**Web address:** www.lakegranburymedicalcenter.com

LAREDO MEDICAL CENTER (O, 326 beds) 1700 East Saunders Avenue, Laredo, TX Zip 78041–5474, Mailing Address: P.O. Box 2068, Zip 78044–2068; tel. 956/796–5000; Timothy E. Schmidt, Chief Executive Officer
**Web address:** www.laredomedical.com

LONGVIEW REGIONAL MEDICAL CENTER (O, 127 beds) 2901 North Fourth Street, Longview, TX Zip 75605–5191, Mailing Address: P.O. Box 14000, Zip 75607–4000; tel. 903/758–1818; Jim R. Kendrick, Chief Executive Officer
**Web address:** www.longviewregional.com

NAVARRO REGIONAL HOSPITAL (O, 148 beds) 3201 West State Highway 22, Corsicana, TX Zip 75110–2469; tel. 903/654–6800; Xavier Villarreal, Chief Executive Officer
**Web address:** www.navarrohospital.com

SAN ANGELO COMMUNITY MEDICAL CENTER (O, 131 beds) 3501 Knickerbocker Road, San Angelo, TX Zip 76904–7698; tel. 325/949–9511; Eric Becker, Chief Executive Officer
**Web address:** www.sacmc.com

SCENIC MOUNTAIN MEDICAL CENTER (O, 75 beds) 1601 West 11th Place, Big Spring, TX Zip 79720–4198; tel. 432/263–1211; Larry Rodgers, Chief Executive Officer
**Web address:** www.smmccares.com

SOUTH TEXAS REGIONAL MEDICAL CENTER (O, 67 beds) 1905 Highway 97 East, Jourdanton, TX Zip 78026–1504; tel. 830/769–3515; James R. Resendez, Chief Executive Officer
**Web address:** www.strmc.com

TOMBALL REGIONAL MEDICAL CENTER (O, 289 beds) 605 Holderrieth Street, Tomball, TX Zip 77375–6445, Mailing Address: P.O. Box 889, Zip 77377–0889; tel. 281/401–7500; Bud Wethington, Chief Executive Officer
**Web address:** www.tomballregionalmedicalcenter.com

WEATHERFORD REGIONAL MEDICAL CENTER (O, 86 beds) 713 East Anderson Street, Weatherford, TX Zip 76086–5705; tel. 817/596–8751; David Orcutt, Chief Executive Officer
**Web address:** www.weatherfordregional.com

WOODLAND HEIGHTS MEDICAL CENTER (O, 115 beds) 505 South John Redditt Drive, Lufkin, TX Zip 75904–3157, Mailing Address: P.O. Box 150610, Zip 75904; tel. 936/634–8311; Casey Robertson, Chief Executive Officer
**Web address:** www.woodlandheights.net

**UTAH:** MOUNTAIN WEST MEDICAL CENTER (O, 31 beds) 2055 North Main Street, Tooele, UT Zip 84074–9819; tel. 435/843–3600; Philip Eaton, Interim Chief Executive Officer
**Web address:** www.mountainwestmc.com

**VIRGINIA:** SOUTHAMPTON MEMORIAL HOSPITAL (O, 72 beds) 100 Fairview Drive, Franklin, VA Zip 23851–1238, Mailing Address: P.O. Box 817, Zip 23851–0817; tel. 757/569–6100; Phil A. Wright, II, Chief Executive Officer
**Web address:** www.smhfranklin.com

SOUTHERN VIRGINIA REGIONAL MEDICAL CENTER (O, 80 beds) 727 North Main Street, Emporia, VA Zip 23847–1274; tel. 434/348–4400; Eric LaChance, Chief Executive Officer
**Web address:** www.svrmc.com

For explanation of codes following names, see page B2.
★ Indicates Type III membership in the American Hospital Association.

SOUTHSIDE REGIONAL MEDICAL CENTER (O, 300 beds) 200 Medical Park Boulevard, Petersburg, VA Zip 23805–9274; tel. 804/765–5000; Michael Yungmann, Chief Executive Officer
**Web address:** www.srmconline.com

**WASHINGTON:** DEACONESS HOSPITAL (O, 388 beds) 800 West Fifth Avenue, Spokane, WA Zip 99204–2803, Mailing Address: P.O. Box 248, Zip 99210–0248; tel. 509/458–5800; Rodney Schumacher, Chief Executive Officer
**Web address:** www.deaconess–spokane.org

VALLEY HOSPITAL (O, 123 beds) 12606 East Mission Avenue, Spokane Valley, WA Zip 99216–1090; tel. 509/924–6650; Dennis Barts, Chief Executive Officer
**Web address:** www.valleyhospital.org

**WEST VIRGINIA:** BLUEFIELD REGIONAL MEDICAL CENTER (O, 240 beds) 500 Cherry Street, Bluefield, WV Zip 24701–3390; tel. 304/327–1100; William Hawley, Chief Executive Officer
**Web address:** www.bluefield.org

GREENBRIER VALLEY MEDICAL CENTER (O, 113 beds) 202 Maplewood Avenue, Ronceverte, WV Zip 24970–1334, Mailing Address: P.O. Box 497, Zip 24970–0497; tel. 304/647–4411; Paul Storey, Chief Executive Officer
**Web address:** www.gvmc.com

PLATEAU MEDICAL CENTER (O, 25 beds) 430 Main Street, Oak Hill, WV Zip 25901–3455; tel. 304/469–8600; Chad Hatfield, Chief Executive Officer
**Web address:** www.plateaumedicalcenter.com

**WYOMING:** EVANSTON REGIONAL HOSPITAL (O, 42 beds) 190 Arrowhead Drive, Evanston, WY Zip 82930–9266; tel. 307/789–3636; George Winn, Chief Executive Officer
**Web address:** www.evanstonregionalhospital.com

| | | |
|---|---|---|
| Owned, leased, sponsored: | 133 hospitals | 18175 beds |
| Contract–managed: | 0 hospitals | 0 beds |
| Totals: | 133 hospitals | 18175 beds |

---

**0249:    COMMUNITY HEALTHCARE SYSTEM** (NP)
901 MacArthur Boulevard, Hammond, IN Zip 46321–2959; tel. 219/836–1600; Donald Powers, Chairman, President and Chief Executive Officer
**(Moderately Centralized Health System)**

**INDIANA:** COMMUNITY HOSPITAL (O, 447 beds) 901 MacArthur Boulevard, Munster, IN Zip 46321–2959; tel. 219/836–1600; Donald P. Fesko, Chief Executive Officer and Administrator
**Web address:** www.comhs.org

ST. CATHERINE HOSPITAL (O, 189 beds) 4321 Fir Street, East Chicago, IN Zip 46312–3097; tel. 219/392–1700; JoAnn Birdzell, Chief Executive Officer and Administrator
**Web address:** www.stcatherinehospital.org

ST. MARY MEDICAL CENTER (O, 195 beds) 1500 South Lake Park Avenue, Hobart, IN Zip 46342–6699; tel. 219/942–0551; Janice L. Ryba, JD, Chief Executive Officer
**Web address:** www.comhs.org

| | | |
|---|---|---|
| Owned, leased, sponsored: | 3 hospitals | 831 beds |
| Contract–managed: | 0 hospitals | 0 beds |
| Totals: | 3 hospitals | 831 beds |

---

**★0384:    COMMUNITY HOSPITAL CORPORATION** (NP)
5801 Tennyson Parkway, Suite 550, Plano, TX Zip 75024–6116; tel. 972/943–6400; Michael D. Williams, President and Chief Executive Officer
**(Independent Hospital System)**

**NEW MEXICO:** ARTESIA GENERAL HOSPITAL (L, 43 beds) 702 North 13th Street, Artesia, NM Zip 88210–1199; tel. 575/748–3333; Kenneth W. Randall, Chief Executive Officer
**Web address:** www.artesiageneral.com

**TEXAS:** BAPTIST HOSPITALS OF SOUTHEAST TEXAS (O, 376 beds) 3080 College Street, Beaumont, TX Zip 77701–4689, Mailing Address: P.O. Box 1591, Zip 77704–1591; tel. 409/212–5000; David N. Parmer, Chief Executive Officer
**Web address:** www.bhset.net

BAPTIST ORANGE HOSPITAL (O, 40 beds) 608 Strickland Drive, Orange, TX Zip 77630–4717; tel. 409/883–9361; Jarren Garrett, Chief Administrative Officer
**Web address:** www.bhset.net

ST. MARK'S MEDICAL CENTER (O, 44 beds) One St. Mark's Place, La Grange, TX Zip 78945; tel. 979/242–2200; Shane Kernell, Chief Executive Officer
**Web address:** www.smmctx.org

YOAKUM COMMUNITY HOSPITAL (L, 25 beds) 1200 Carl Ramert Drive, Yoakum, TX Zip 77995–4868, Mailing Address: P.O. Box 753, Zip 77995–0753; tel. 361/293–2321; Karen Barber, Chief Executive Officer
**Web address:** www.yoakumhospital.org

| | | |
|---|---|---|
| Owned, leased, sponsored: | 5 hospitals | 528 beds |
| Contract–managed: | 0 hospitals | 0 beds |
| Totals: | 5 hospitals | 528 beds |

---

**1085:    COMMUNITY MEDICAL CENTERS** (NP)
Fresno and Maddy Drive, Fresno, CA Zip 93721, Mailing Address: P.O. Box 1232, Zip 93715–1232; tel. 559/459–6000; Tim A. Joslin, President and Chief Executive Officer
**(Moderately Centralized Health System)**

**CALIFORNIA:** CLOVIS COMMUNITY MEDICAL CENTER (O, 109 beds) 2755 Herndon Avenue, Clovis, CA Zip 93611–6800; tel. 559/324–4000; Craig Castro, Chief Executive Officer
**Web address:** www.communitymedical.org

COMMUNITY BEHAVIORAL HEALTH CENTER (O, 60 beds) 7171 North Cedar Avenue, Fresno, CA Zip 93720–3311; tel. 559/449–8000; Dawan Utecht, Chief Executive Officer
**Web address:** www.communitymedical.org

COMMUNITY REGIONAL MEDICAL CENTER (O, 793 beds) 2823 Fresno Street, Fresno, CA Zip 93721–1324; tel. 559/459–6000; John M. Chubb, Chief Executive Officer
**Web address:** www.communitymedical.org

| | | |
|---|---|---|
| Owned, leased, sponsored: | 3 hospitals | 962 beds |
| Contract–managed: | 0 hospitals | 0 beds |
| Totals: | 3 hospitals | 962 beds |

---

**0909:    COMPASS HEALTH** (NP)
1526 North Avenue I., Crowley, LA Zip 70526–2434; tel. 337/788–3330

**LOUISIANA:** COMPASS BEHAVIORAL CENTER OF CROWLEY (O, 34 beds) 1526 North Avenue I., Crowley, LA Zip 70526–2434; tel. 337/788–3380; Aimee Monaghan, Administrator
**Web address:** www.compasshealthcare.com

COMPASS BEHAVIORAL CENTER OF HOUMA, INC. (O, 20 beds) 4701 West Park Avenue, Houma, LA Zip 70364–4426; tel. 985/876–1715; ,
**Web address:** www.compasshealthcare.com/site83.php

| | | |
|---|---|---|
| Owned, leased, sponsored: | 2 hospitals | 54 beds |
| Contract–managed: | 0 hospitals | 0 beds |
| Totals: | 2 hospitals | 54 beds |

---

**★0339:    CONEMAUGH HEALTH SYSTEM** (NP)
1086 Franklin Street, Johnstown, PA Zip 15905–4398; tel. 814/534–9000; Scott A. Becker, Chief Executive Officer
**(Centralized Physician/Insurance Health System)**

**PENNSYLVANIA:** CONEMAUGH MEMORIAL MEDICAL CENTER (O, 555 beds) 1086 Franklin Street, Johnstown, PA Zip 15905–4398; tel. 814/534–9000; Steven E. Tucker, President
**Web address:** www.conemaugh.org

CONEMAUGH MEYERSDALE MEDICAL CENTER (O, 20 beds) 200 Hospital Drive, Meyersdale, PA Zip 15552–1249; tel. 814/634–5911; Mary L. Libengood, President
**Web address:** www.conemaugh.org

For explanation of codes following names, see page B2.
★ Indicates Type III membership in the American Hospital Association.

CONEMAUGH MINERS MEDICAL CENTER (O, 30 beds) 290 Haida Avenue, Hastings, PA Zip 16646–5610, Mailing Address: P.O. Box 689, Zip 16646–0689; tel. 814/247–3100; William R. Crowe, President
**Web address:** www.minersmedicalcenter.org

| | | |
|---|---|---|
| Owned, leased, sponsored: | 3 hospitals | 605 beds |
| Contract–managed: | 0 hospitals | 0 beds |
| Totals: | 3 hospitals | 605 beds |

### 0014: CONNECTICUT DEPARTMENT OF MENTAL HEALTH AND ADDICTION SERVICES (NP)

410 Capitol Avenue, Hartford, CT Zip 06106–1367, Mailing Address: P.O. Box 341431, Zip 06134–1431; tel. 860/418–7000; Patricia Rehmer, Commissioner
**(Independent Hospital System)**

**CONNECTICUT:** CONNECTICUT MENTAL HEALTH CENTER (O, 39 beds) 34 Park Street, New Haven, CT Zip 06519–1109, Mailing Address: P.O. Box 1842, Zip 06508–1842; tel. 203/974–7144; Michael Sernyak, M.D., Director
**Web address:** www.ct.gov/dmhas/cwp/view.asp?a=2906&q=334596

CONNECTICUT VALLEY HOSPITAL (O, 604 beds) Eastern Drive, Middletown, CT Zip 06457–3947, Mailing Address: PO BOX 351, Zip 06457–7023; tel. 860/262–5000; Helene M. Vartelas, Chief Executive Officer
**Web address:** www.ct.gov/dmhas/cwp/view.asp?a=3519&q=416778

SOUTHWEST CONNECTICUT MENTAL HEALTH SYSTEM (O, 62 beds) 97 Middle Street, Bridgeport, CT Zip 06604–4410; tel. 203/551–7400; Daniel Wartenberg, PsyD, Acting Chief Executive Officer
**Web address:** www.ct.gov/dmhas/cwp/view.asp?a=2946&q=378936

| | | |
|---|---|---|
| Owned, leased, sponsored: | 3 hospitals | 705 beds |
| Contract–managed: | 0 hospitals | 0 beds |
| Totals: | 3 hospitals | 705 beds |

### ★0127: CONTINUUM HEALTH PARTNERS (NP)

555 West 57th Street, New York, NY Zip 10019–2925; tel. 212/523–8130; Stanley Brezenoff, President and Chief Executive Officer
**(Moderately Centralized Health System)**

**NEW YORK:** BETH ISRAEL MEDICAL CENTER (O, 856 beds) First Avenue and 16th Street, New York, NY Zip 10003–3803; tel. 212/420–2000; Harris M. Nagler, M.D., President
**Web address:** www.bethisraelny.org

NEW YORK EYE AND EAR INFIRMARY (O, 32 beds) 310 East 14th Street, New York, NY Zip 10003–4201; tel. 212/979–4000; D. McWilliams Kessler, President and Chief Executive Officer
**Web address:** www.nyee.edu

ST. LUKE'S–ROOSEVELT HOSPITAL CENTER (O, 690 beds) 1111 Amsterdam Avenue, New York, NY Zip 10025–1716; tel. 212/523–4000; Frank J. Cracolici, President
**Web address:** www.stlukeshospitalnyc.org

| | | |
|---|---|---|
| Owned, leased, sponsored: | 3 hospitals | 1578 beds |
| Contract–managed: | 0 hospitals | 0 beds |
| Totals: | 3 hospitals | 1578 beds |

### 0016: COOK COUNTY HEALTH AND HOSPITALS SYSTEM (NP)

1900 West Polk Street, Suite 220, Chicago, IL Zip 60612–3723; tel. 312/864–6820; Ramanathan Raju, M.D., Chief Executive Officer
**(Moderately Centralized Health System)**

**ILLINOIS:** JOHN H. STROGER JR. HOSPITAL OF COOK COUNTY (O, 460 beds) 1901 West Harrison Street, Chicago, IL Zip 60612–3714; tel. 312/864–6000; John Jay Shannon, M.D., Interim Chief Operating Officer
**Web address:** www.cookcountyhealth.net

PROVIDENT HOSPITAL OF COOK COUNTY (O, 25 beds) 500 East 51st Street, Chicago, IL Zip 60615–2494; tel. 312/572–2000; Thomas J. Dohm, Interim Chief Operating Officer
**Web address:** www.ccbhs.org/pages/ProvidentHospitalofCookCounty.htm

| | | |
|---|---|---|
| Owned, leased, sponsored: | 2 hospitals | 485 beds |
| Contract–managed: | 0 hospitals | 0 beds |
| Totals: | 2 hospitals | 485 beds |

### 0905: CORNERSTONE HEALTHCARE GROUP (IO)

2200 Ross Avenue, Suite 3060, Dallas, TX Zip 75201–7984; tel. 469/621–6700; David Smith, President and Chief Operating Officer
**(Independent Hospital System)**

**ARIZONA:** CORNERSTONE HOSPITAL OF SOUTHEAST ARIZONA (O, 54 beds) 7220 East Rosewood Drive, Tucson, AZ Zip 85710–1350; tel. 520/546–4595; Mindy S. Moore, Chief Executive Officer
**Web address:** www.chghospitals.com

**ARKANSAS:** CORNERSTONE HOSPITAL OF NORTH LITTLE ROCK (O, 40 beds) 1400 Braden Street, Jacksonville, AR Zip 72076–3721; tel. 501/985–7026; Paul E. Qualls, Jr., Interim Chief Executive Officer
**Web address:** www.chghospitals.com/littlerock/

**LOUISIANA:** CORNERSTONE HOSPITAL OF BOSSIER CITY (O, 54 beds) 4900 Medical Drive, Bossier City, LA Zip 71112–4521; tel. 318/747–9500; Sheri Burnette, R.N., Chief Executive Officer and Administrator
**Web address:** www.chghospitals.com/

CORNERSTONE HOSPITAL OF SOUTHWEST LOUISIANA (O, 30 beds) 703 Cypress Street, Sulphur, LA Zip 70663–5053; tel. 337/527–1102; Robert R. Lafleur, Chief Executive Officer
**Web address:** www.chghospitals.com/chswl.html

CORNERSTONE HOSPITAL–WEST MONROE (O, 40 beds) 6198 Cypress Street, West Monroe, LA Zip 71291–9010; tel. 318/396–5600; Chris Simpson, Chief Executive Officer
**Web address:** www.chghospitals.com/chwm.html

**OKLAHOMA:** SOLARA HOSPITAL OF MUSKOGEE (O, 41 beds) 351 South 40th Street, Muskogee, OK Zip 74401–4916; tel. 918/682–6161; Craig Koele, Chief Executive Officer
**Web address:** www.chghospitals.com/muskogee/

SOLARA HOSPITAL OF SHAWNEE (O, 34 beds) 1900 Gordon Cooper Drive, 2nd Floor, Shawnee, OK Zip 74801–8603; tel. 405/395–5800; Michael E. Gerten, Chief Executive Officer
**Web address:** www.chghospitals.com/shawnee/

**TEXAS:** CORNERSTONE HOSPITAL OF AUSTIN (O, 64 beds) 4207 Burnet Road, Austin, TX Zip 78756–3396; tel. 512/706–1900; Laura Sims, Chief Executive Officer
**Web address:** www.chghospitals.com/austin/

CORNERSTONE HOSPITAL OF HOUSTON – BELLAIRE (O, 134 beds) 5314 Dashwood, Houston, TX Zip 77081–4603; tel. 713/295–5300; James Camp, R.N., Chief Executive Officer
**Web address:** www.chghospitals.com

CORNERSTONE HOSPITAL–MEDICAL CENTER OF HOUSTON (O, 30 beds) 2001 Hermann Park Drive, Houston, TX Zip 77004; tel. 713/756–8660; James Camp, R.N., Chief Executive Officer
**Web address:** www.chghospitals.com

SOLARA HOSPITAL CONROE (O, 41 beds) 1500 Grand Lake Drive, Conroe, TX Zip 77304–2891; tel. 936/523–1800; Steve Hockert, Chief Executive Officer
**Web address:** www.chghospitals.com/conroe/

SOLARA HOSPITAL HARLINGEN (O, 82 beds) 508 Victoria Lane, Harlingen, TX Zip 78550–3225; tel. 956/425–9600; Cary L. Montalvo, Chief Executive Officer
**Web address:** www.chghospitals.com/harlingen/

SOLARA HOSPITAL MCALLEN (O, 78 beds) 301 West Expressway 83, McAllen, TX Zip 78503–3045; tel. 956/632–4880; Jose Huerta, Chief Executive Officer
**Web address:** www.chghospitals.com/mcallen/

**WEST VIRGINIA:** CORNERSTONE HOSPITAL OF HUNTINGTON (O, 28 beds) 2900 First Avenue, Two East, Huntington, WV Zip 25702–1241; tel. 304/399–2600; Cynthia Isaacs, Chief Executive Officer
**Web address:** www.chghospitals.com

---

For explanation of codes following names, see page B2.
★ Indicates Type III membership in the American Hospital Association.

| Owned, leased, sponsored: | 14 hospitals | 750 beds |
|---|---|---|
| Contract–managed: | 0 hospitals | 0 beds |
| **Totals:** | 14 hospitals | 750 beds |

★**0103: COTTAGE HEALTH SYSTEM** (NP)
400 West Pueblo Street, Santa Barbara, CA Zip 93105–4353,
Mailing Address: P.O. Box 689, Zip 93102–0689;
tel. 805/569–7290; Ronald C. Werft, President and Chief Executive
Officer
**(Independent Hospital System)**

**CALIFORNIA:** GOLETA VALLEY COTTAGE HOSPITAL (O, 72 beds) 351 South
Patterson Avenue, Santa Barbara, CA Zip 93111–2496, Mailing Address:
Box 6306, Zip 93160–6306; tel. 805/967–3411; Ronald C. Werft,
President and Chief Executive Officer
**Web address:** www.sbch.org

SANTA BARBARA COTTAGE HOSPITAL (O, 351 beds) 400 West Pueblo
Street, Santa Barbara, CA Zip 93105–4390, Mailing Address: P.O. Box 689,
Zip 93102–0689; tel. 805/682–7111; Ronald C. Werft, President and Chief
Executive Officer
**Web address:** www.cottagehealthsystem.org

SANTA YNEZ VALLEY COTTAGE HOSPITAL (O, 10 beds) 2050 Viborg Road,
Solvang, CA Zip 93463–2295; tel. 805/688–6431; Ronald C. Werft,
President and Chief Executive Officer
**Web address:** www.cottagehealthsystem.org

| Owned, leased, sponsored: | 3 hospitals | 433 beds |
|---|---|---|
| Contract–managed: | 0 hospitals | 0 beds |
| **Totals:** | 3 hospitals | 433 beds |

★**0123: COVENANT HEALTH** (NP)
100 Fort Sanders West Boulevard, Knoxville, TN Zip 37922–3353;
tel. 865/531–5555; Anthony Spezia, President and Chief Executive
Officer
**(Centralized Health System)**

**TENNESSEE:** FORT LOUDOUN MEDICAL CENTER (L, 30 beds) 550 Fort
Loudoun Medical Center Drive, Lenoir City, TN Zip 37772–5673;
tel. 865/271–6000; Jeffrey Feike, President and Chief Administrative
Officer
**Web address:** www.covenanthealth.com

FORT SANDERS REGIONAL MEDICAL CENTER (O, 402 beds) 1901 West
Clinch Avenue, Knoxville, TN Zip 37916–2307; tel. 865/541–1111; Keith
Altshuler, President and Chief Administrative Officer
**Web address:** www.covenanthealth.com

LECONTE MEDICAL CENTER (O, 123 beds) 742 Middle Creek Road,
Sevierville, TN Zip 37862–5019, Mailing Address: P.O. Box 8005,
Zip 37864–8005; tel. 865/446–7000; Ellen Wilhoit, President and Chief
Administrative Officer
**Web address:** www.lecontemedicalcenter.com

METHODIST MEDICAL CENTER OF OAK RIDGE (O, 255 beds) 990 Oak Ridge
Turnpike, Oak Ridge, TN Zip 37830–6976, Mailing Address: P.O. Box 2529,
Zip 37831–2529; tel. 865/835–1000; Michael Belbeck, President and Chief
Administrative Officer
**Web address:** www.mmcoakridge.com

MORRISTOWN–HAMBLEN HEALTHCARE SYSTEM (O, 147 beds) 908 West
Fourth North Street, Morristown, TN Zip 37814–3894, Mailing Address: P.O.
Box 1178, Zip 37816–1178; tel. 423/586–4231; Gordon Lintz, Chief
Administrative Officer
**Web address:** www.mhhs1.org

PARKWEST MEDICAL CENTER (O, 297 beds) 9352 Park West Boulevard,
Knoxville, TN Zip 37923–4325, Mailing Address: P.O. Box 22993,
Zip 37933–0993; tel. 865/373–1000; Rick Lassiter, President and Chief
Administrative Officer
**Web address:** www.yesparkwest.com

ROANE MEDICAL CENTER (O, 36 beds) 412 Devonia Street, Harriman, TN
Zip 37748–2009, Mailing Address: P.O. Box 489, Zip 37748–0489;
tel. 865/882–1323; Gaye Jolly, FACHE, President/Chief Administrative Officer
**Web address:** www.roanemedical.com

| Owned, leased, sponsored: | 7 hospitals | 1290 beds |
|---|---|---|
| Contract–managed: | 0 hospitals | 0 beds |
| **Totals:** | 7 hospitals | 1290 beds |

★**0036: COVENANT HEALTH SYSTEM** (NP)
3615 19th Street, Lubbock, TX Zip 79410–1203;
tel. 806/725–0447; Richard H. Parks, FACHE, President and Chief
Executive Officer
**(Centralized Physician/Insurance Health System)**

**TEXAS:** COVENANT CHILDREN'S HOSPITAL (O, 73 beds) 4015 22nd Place,
Lubbock, TX Zip 79410; tel. 806/725–1011; Christopher J. Dougherty,
Chief Executive Officer
**Web address:** www.covenanthealth.
org/About–Us/Facilities/Childrens–Hospital.aspx

COVENANT HOSPITAL PLAINVIEW (L, 68 beds) 2601 Dimmitt Road, Plainview,
TX Zip 79072–1833; tel. 806/296–5531; Alan N. King, FACHE, Chief
Executive Officer
**Web address:** www.covenantplainview.org

COVENANT HOSPITAL–LEVELLAND (L, 22 beds) 1900 South College Avenue,
Levelland, TX Zip 79336–6508; tel. 806/894–4963; Alan N. King, FACHE,
Interim Chief Executive Officer
**Web address:** www.covenanthospitallevelland.com/

COVENANT MEDICAL CENTER (O, 646 beds) 3615 19th Street, Lubbock, TX
Zip 79410–1203, Mailing Address: P.O. Box 1201, Zip 79408–1201;
tel. 806/725–0000; Richard H. Parks, FACHE, President and Chief Executive
Officer
**Web address:** www.covenanthealth.org

COVENANT SPECIALTY HOSPITAL (O, 56 beds) 3815 20th Street, Lubbock,
TX Zip 79410–1235; tel. 806/725–9200; Walt Cathey, Chief Operating
Officer
**Web address:** www.covenanthealth.org/view/Facilities/Specialty_Hospital

| Owned, leased, sponsored: | 5 hospitals | 865 beds |
|---|---|---|
| Contract–managed: | 0 hospitals | 0 beds |
| **Totals:** | 5 hospitals | 865 beds |

★**5885: COVENANT HEALTH SYSTEMS, INC.** (CC)
100 Ames Pond Drive, Suite 102, Tewksbury, MA Zip 01876–1240;
tel. 978/654–6363; David R. Lincoln, FACHE, President and Chief
Executive Officer
**(Moderately Centralized Health System)**

**MAINE:** ST. JOSEPH HOSPITAL (O, 84 beds) 360 Broadway, Bangor, ME
Zip 04401–3979, Mailing Address: P.O. Box 403, Zip 04402–0403;
tel. 207/262–1000; Mary Prybylo, President and Chief Executive Officer
**Web address:** www.sjhhealth.com

ST. MARY'S REGIONAL MEDICAL CENTER (O, 171 beds) 330 Sabattus Street,
Lewiston, ME Zip 04240–5553, Mailing Address: P.O. Box 291,
Zip 04243–0291; tel. 207/777–8100; Lee T. Myles, President and Chief
Executive Officer
**Web address:** www.stmarysmaine.com

**NEW HAMPSHIRE:** ST. JOSEPH HOSPITAL (O, 144 beds) 172 Kinsley Street,
Nashua, NH Zip 03060–3648; tel. 603/882–3000; Richard Boehler, M.D.,
President and Chief Executive Officer
**Web address:** www.stjosephhospital.com

| Owned, leased, sponsored: | 3 hospitals | 399 beds |
|---|---|---|
| Contract–managed: | 0 hospitals | 0 beds |
| **Totals:** | 3 hospitals | 399 beds |

★**0008: CROZER–KEYSTONE HEALTH SYSTEM** (NP)
100 West Sproul Road, Springfield, PA Zip 19064–2033;
tel. 610/338–8205; Joan K. Richards, President and Chief Executive
Officer
**(Moderately Centralized Health System)**

**PENNSYLVANIA:** CROZER–CHESTER MEDICAL CENTER (O, 472 beds) One
Medical Center Boulevard, Upland, PA Zip 19013–3995;
tel. 610/447–2000; Patrick J. Gavin, President
**Web address:** www.crozer.org

For explanation of codes following names, see page B2.
★ Indicates Type III membership in the American Hospital Association.

Section B

DELAWARE COUNTY MEMORIAL HOSPITAL (O, 209 beds) 501 North Lansdowne Avenue, Drexel Hill, PA Zip 19026–1114; tel. 610/284–8100; William McCune, President

| | | |
|---|---|---|
| Owned, leased, sponsored: | 2 hospitals | 681 beds |
| Contract–managed: | 0 hospitals | 0 beds |
| Totals: | 2 hospitals | 681 beds |

★1075: **DAUGHTERS OF CHARITY HEALTH SYSTEM** (CC)
26000 Altamont Road, Los Altos Hills, CA Zip 94022–4317; tel. 650/917–4500; Robert Issai, President and Chief Executive Officer
**(Moderately Centralized Health System)**

**CALIFORNIA:** O'CONNOR HOSPITAL (O, 202 beds) 2105 Forest Avenue, San Jose, CA Zip 95128–1471; tel. 408/947–2500; James F. Dover, FACHE, President and Chief Executive Officer
**Web address:** www.oconnorhospital.org

SAINT LOUISE REGIONAL HOSPITAL (O, 93 beds) 9400 No Name Uno, Gilroy, CA Zip 95020–3528; tel. 408/848–2000; Carol Furgurson, Acting Chief Administrative Officer
**Web address:** www.dochs.org

SETON MEDICAL CENTER (O, 429 beds) 1900 Sullivan Avenue, Daly City, CA Zip 94015–2229; tel. 650/992–4000; Joanne E. Allen, President and Chief Executive Officer
**Web address:** www.setonmedicalcenter.org

ST. FRANCIS MEDICAL CENTER (O, 323 beds) 3630 East Imperial Highway, Lynwood, CA Zip 90262–2636; tel. 310/900–8900; Gerald T. Kozai, President
**Web address:** www.dochs.org

ST. VINCENT MEDICAL CENTER (O, 271 beds) 2131 West Third Street, Los Angeles, CA Zip 90057–1901, Mailing Address: P.O. Box 57992, Zip 90057–0992; tel. 213/484–7111; Catherine Fickes, R.N., President and Chief Executive Officer
**Web address:** www.stvincentmedicalcenter.com

| | | |
|---|---|---|
| Owned, leased, sponsored: | 5 hospitals | 1318 beds |
| Contract–managed: | 0 hospitals | 0 beds |
| Totals: | 5 hospitals | 1318 beds |

★0864: **DAVIS HEALTH SYSTEM** (NP)
Reed Street and Gorman Avenue, Elkins, WV Zip 26241, Mailing Address: P.O. Box 1697, Zip 26241–1697; tel. 304/636–3300; Mark Doak, President and Chief Executive Officer
**(Independent Hospital System)**

**WEST VIRGINIA:** BROADDUS HOSPITAL (O, 72 beds) 1 Healthcare Drive, Philippi, WV Zip 26416–9405, Mailing Address: P.O. Box 930, Zip 26416–0930; tel. 304/457–1760; Jeffrey A. Powelson, Chief Executive Officer
**Web address:** www.davishealthsystem.org/

DAVIS MEMORIAL HOSPITAL (O, 90 beds) Gorman Avenue and Reed Street, Elkins, WV Zip 26241, Mailing Address: P.O. Box 1484, Zip 26241–1484; tel. 304/636–3300; Mark Doak, President and Chief Executive Officer
**Web address:** www.davishealthsystem.com

| | | |
|---|---|---|
| Owned, leased, sponsored: | 2 hospitals | 162 beds |
| Contract–managed: | 0 hospitals | 0 beds |
| Totals: | 2 hospitals | 162 beds |

1825: **DCH HEALTH SYSTEM** (NP)
809 University Boulevard East, Tuscaloosa, AL Zip 35401–2029; tel. 205/759–7111; Bryan N. Kindred, FACHE, President and Chief Executive Officer
**(Moderately Centralized Health System)**

**ALABAMA:** DCH REGIONAL MEDICAL CENTER (O, 622 beds) 809 University Boulevard East, Tuscaloosa, AL Zip 35401–2029; tel. 205/759–7111; William H. Cassels, Administrator
**Web address:** www.dchsystem.com

FAYETTE MEDICAL CENTER (L, 167 beds) 1653 Temple Avenue North, Fayette, AL Zip 35555–1314, Mailing Address: P.O. Drawer 710, Zip 35555–0710; tel. 205/932–5966; Barry S. Cochran, FACHE, Administrator
**Web address:** www.dchsystem.com

NORTHPORT MEDICAL CENTER (O, 196 beds) 2700 Hospital Drive, Northport, AL Zip 35476–3360; tel. 205/333–4500; Luke Standeffer, Administrator
**Web address:** www.dchsystem.com

| | | |
|---|---|---|
| Owned, leased, sponsored: | 3 hospitals | 985 beds |
| Contract–managed: | 0 hospitals | 0 beds |
| Totals: | 3 hospitals | 985 beds |

★0313: **DEACONESS HEALTH SYSTEM** (NP)
600 Mary Street, Evansville, IN tel. 812/450–5000; Linda E. White, President and Chief Executive Officer
**(Centralized Health System)**

**INDIANA:** DEACONESS HOSPITAL (O, 523 beds) 600 Mary Street, Evansville, IN Zip 47710–1658; tel. 812/450–5000; Shawn W. McCoy, Chief Administrative Officer
**Web address:** www.deaconess.com

THE WOMEN'S HOSPITAL (O, 74 beds) 4199 Gateway Boulevard, Newburgh, IN Zip 47630–8940; tel. 812/842–4200; Christina M. Ryan, R.N., Chief Executive Officer
**Web address:** www.deaconess.com

| | | |
|---|---|---|
| Owned, leased, sponsored: | 2 hospitals | 597 beds |
| Contract–managed: | 0 hospitals | 0 beds |
| Totals: | 2 hospitals | 597 beds |

0330: **DEKALB REGIONAL HEALTH SYSTEM** (NP)
2701 North Decatur Road, Decatur, GA Zip 30033–5918; tel. 404/501–1000; John Shelton, President and Chief Executive Officer
**(Independent Hospital System)**

**GEORGIA:** DEKALB MEDICAL AT DOWNTOWN DECATUR (O, 44 beds) 450 North Candler Street, Decatur, GA Zip 30030–2671; tel. 404/501–6700; John Shelton, President and Chief Executive Officer
**Web address:** www.dekalbmedicalcenter.org

DEKALB MEDICAL AT HILLANDALE (O, 100 beds) 2801 DeKalb Medical Parkway, Lithonia, GA Zip 30058–4996; tel. 404/501–8700; John Shelton, President and Chief Executive Officer
**Web address:** www.dekalbmedical.org

DEKALB MEDICAL AT NORTH DECATUR (O, 418 beds) 2701 North Decatur Road, Decatur, GA Zip 30033–5995; tel. 404/501–1000; John Shelton, President and Chief Executive Officer
**Web address:** www.dekalbmedical.org

| | | |
|---|---|---|
| Owned, leased, sponsored: | 3 hospitals | 562 beds |
| Contract–managed: | 0 hospitals | 0 beds |
| Totals: | 3 hospitals | 562 beds |

9495: **DEPARTMENT OF THE AIR FORCE** (FG)
1420 Pentagon, Room 4E1084, Washington, DC Zip 20330–1420; tel. 202/767–4765; Lieutenant General Charles B. Green, M.D., Surgeon General
**(Independent Hospital System)**

**ALASKA:** U. S. AIR FORCE REGIONAL HOSPITAL (O, 64 beds) 5955 Zeamer Avenue, Elmendorf AFB, AK Zip 99506–3702; tel. 907/580–3006; Colonel Thomas Harrell, Commander
**Web address:** www.elmendorf.af.mil/

**CALIFORNIA:** DAVID GRANT MEDICAL CENTER (O, 116 beds) 101 Bodin Circle, Travis AFB, CA Zip 94535–1809; tel. 707/423–7300; Colonel Brian T. Hayes, Commander
**Web address:** www.travis.af.mil/units/dgmc/index.asp

For explanation of codes following names, see page B2.
★ Indicates Type III membership in the American Hospital Association.

**FLORIDA:** U. S. AIR FORCE REGIONAL HOSPITAL (O, 57 beds) 307 Boatner Road, Suite 114, Eglin AFB, FL Zip 32542–1282; tel. 850/883–8221; Colonel Gary Walker, Commander
**Web address:** www.eglin.af.mil

**IDAHO:** U. S. AIR FORCE CLINIC (O, 10 beds) 90 Hope Drive, Building 600, Mountain Home AFB, ID Zip 83648–1057; tel. 208/828–7610; Lieutenant Colonel Gregory W. Carson, Administrator

**MISSISSIPPI:** U. S. AIR FORCE MEDICAL CENTER KEESLER (O, 56 beds) 301 Fisher Street, Room 1A132, Keesler AFB, MS Zip 39534–2519; tel. 228/376–2550; Colonel Robert Cothron, USAF, MSC, Administrator
**Web address:** www.keesler.af.mil

**NEVADA:** MIKE O'CALLAGHAN FEDERAL HOSPITAL (O, 46 beds) 4700 Las Vegas Boulevard North, Suite 2419, Nellis AFB, NV Zip 89191–6600; tel. 702/653–2000; Colonel Christian Benjamin, USAF, MC, Commander
**Web address:** www.lasvegas.va.gov/

**OHIO:** WRIGHT PATTERSON MEDICAL CENTER (O, 52 beds) 4881 Sugar Maple Drive, Wright–Patterson AFB, OH Zip 45433–5529; tel. 937/257–9144; Brent Erickson, Administrator
**Web address:** www.wpafb.af.mil/units/wpmc/

**VIRGINIA:** U. S. AIR FORCE HOSPITAL (O, 65 beds) 77 Nealy Avenue, Hampton, VA Zip 23665–2040; tel. 757/764–6969; Colonel Eric Stone, Commander
**Web address:** www.jble.af.mil

| | | |
|---|---|---|
| **Owned, leased, sponsored:** | 8 hospitals | 474 beds |
| **Contract–managed:** | 0 hospitals | 0 beds |
| **Totals:** | 8 hospitals | 474 beds |

## 9395: DEPARTMENT OF THE ARMY, OFFICE OF THE SURGEON GENERAL (FG)

5109 Leesburg Pike, Falls Church, VA Zip 22041–3215; tel. 703/681–3000; Lieutenant General Eric B. Schoomaker, Surgeon General
**(Moderately Centralized Health System)**

**ALASKA:** BASSETT ARMY COMMUNITY HOSPITAL (O, 24 beds) 1060 Gaffney Road, Box 7400, Fort Wainwright, AK Zip 99703–5001, Mailing Address: 1060 Gaffney Road, Box 7440, Zip 99703–5001; tel. 907/361–5172; John McNally, Deputy Commander Administration
**Web address:** www.alaska.amedd.army.mil

**CALIFORNIA:** WEED ARMY COMMUNITY HOSPITAL (O, 27 beds) Inner Loop Road and 4th Street, Building 166, Fort Irwin, CA Zip 92310–5065, Mailing Address: P.O. Box 105109, Zip 92310–5109; tel. 760/380–3108; Colonel Cheryl Taylor–Whitehead, Commander
**Web address:** www.irwin.amedd.army.mil

**COLORADO:** EVANS U. S. ARMY COMMUNITY HOSPITAL (O, 57 beds) 1650 Cochrane Circle, Building 7500, Fort Carson, CO Zip 80913–4613; tel. 719/526–7200; Colonel Jimmie O. Keenan, Commander
**Web address:** www.evans.amedd.army.mil

**GEORGIA:** DWIGHT DAVID EISENHOWER ARMY MEDICAL CENTER (O, 107 beds) 300 West Hospital Road, Fort Gordon, GA Zip 30905–5741; tel. 706/787–5811; Commander Christopher M. Castle, Commander
**Web address:** www.ddeamc.amedd.army.mil

MARTIN ARMY COMMUNITY HOSPITAL (O, 57 beds) 7950 Martin Loop, Fort Benning, GA Zip 31905–5648, Mailing Address: 7950 Martin Loop, B9200, Room 010, Zip 31905–5648; tel. 706/544–2516; Colonel Timothy E. Lamb, Commander
**Web address:** www.martin.amedd.army.mil

WINN ARMY COMMUNITY HOSPITAL (O, 79 beds) 1061 Harmon Avenue, Hinesville, GA Zip 31314–5641, Mailing Address: 1061 Harmon Avenue, Suite 2311B, Zip 31314–5641; tel. 912/435–6965; Colonel Ronald Place, M.D., Commander
**Web address:** www.winn.amedd.army.mil/

**HAWAII:** TRIPLER ARMY MEDICAL CENTER (O, 198 beds) 1 Jarrct White Road, Honolulu, HI Zip 96859–5001; tel. 808/433–6661; Brigadier General Dennis Doyle, Commanding General
**Web address:** www.tamc.amedd.army.mil

**KANSAS:** IRWIN ARMY COMMUNITY HOSPITAL (O, 44 beds) 600 Caisson Hill Road, Junction City, KS Zip 66442–7037; tel. 785/239–7000; Colonel Barry R. Pockrandt, Commander
**Web address:** www.iach.amedd.army.mil

**KENTUCKY:** COLONEL FLORENCE A. BLANCHFIELD ARMY COMMUNITY HOSPITAL (O, 66 beds) 650 Joel Drive, Fort Campbell, KY Zip 42223–5318; tel. 270/798–8040; Colonel Paul Cordts, Commander
**Web address:** www.campbell.amedd.army.mil/

IRELAND ARMY COMMUNITY HOSPITAL (O, 33 beds) 289 Ireland Avenue, Fort Knox, KY Zip 40121–5111; tel. 502/624–9333; Colonel Cornelius C. Maher, Commander
**Web address:** www.iach.knox.amedd.army.mil/

**LOUISIANA:** BAYNE–JONES ARMY COMMUNITY HOSPITAL (O, 22 beds) 1585 3rd Street, Fort Polk, LA Zip 71459–5102; tel. 337/531–3928; Colonel Mark C. Wilhite, Commander
**Web address:** www.polk.amedd.army.mil

**MARSHALL ISLANDS:** KWAJALEIN HOSPITAL (O, 14 beds) U.S. Army Kwajalein Atoll, Kwajalein Island, MH Zip 96960, Mailing Address: Box 1702, APO, APZip 96555–5000; tel. 805/355–2225; Elaine McMahon, Administrator

**MISSOURI:** GENERAL LEONARD WOOD ARMY COMMUNITY HOSPITAL (O, 54 beds) 126 Missouri Avenue, Fort Leonard Wood, MO Zip 65473–8952; tel. 573/596–0414; Colonel Marie Dominguez, Commander
**Web address:** www.glwach.amedd.army.mil/

**NEW YORK:** KELLER ARMY COMMUNITY HOSPITAL (O, 31 beds) 900 Washington Road, West Point, NY Zip 10996–1197, Mailing Address: U.S. Military Academy, Building 900, Zip 10996–1197; tel. 845/938–5169; Colonel Felicia Pehrson, M.D., Commanding Officer
**Web address:** www.kach.amedd.army.mil/

**NORTH CAROLINA:** WOMACK ARMY MEDICAL CENTER (O, 156 beds) Normandy Drive, Fort Bragg, NC Zip 28307–5000; tel. 910/907–6000; Colonel Steven Brewster, M.D., Commander
**Web address:** www.wamc.amedd.army.mil/

**OKLAHOMA:** REYNOLDS ARMY COMMUNITY HOSPITAL (O, 24 beds) 4301 Wilson Street, Fort Sill, OK Zip 73503–4472; tel. 580/558–3000; Colonel Nocl J. Cardenas, FACHE, Commander
**Web address:** www.rach.sill.amedd.army.mil

**SOUTH CAROLINA:** MONCRIEF ARMY COMMUNITY HOSPITAL (O, 60 beds) 4500 Stuart Street, Fort Jackson, SC Zip 29207–5700; tel. 803/751–2160; Colonel Mark L. Higdon, Commander
**Web address:** www.moncrief.amedd.army.mil

**TEXAS:** CARL R. DARNALL ARMY MEDICAL CENTER (O, 109 beds) 36000 Darnall Loop, Fort Hood, TX Zip 76544–5095; tel. 254/288–8000; Colonel Patrick D. Sargent, Commander
**Web address:** www.crdamc.amedd.army.mil

SAN ANTONIO MILITARY MEDICAL CENTER (O, 226 beds) 3851 Roger Brookes Drive, Fort Sam Houston, TX Zip 78234–4501; tel. 210/916–4141; Major General M. Ted Wong, Commanding General
**Web address:** www.bamc.amedd.army.mil

WILLIAM BEAUMONT ARMY MEDICAL CENTER (O, 209 beds) 5005 North Piedras Street, El Paso, TX Zip 79920–5001; tel. 915/742–2121; Colonel Michael S. Heimall, Commander
**Web address:** www.wbamc.amedd.army.mil

**VIRGINIA:** FORT BELVOIR COMMUNITY HOSPITAL (O, 46 beds) 9300 Dewitt Loop, Fort Belvoir, VA Zip 22060–5285; tel. 703/805–0510; Colonel Susan Annicelli, Commander
**Web address:** www.fbch.capmed.mil/SitePages/Home.aspx

**WASHINGTON:** MADIGAN HEALTHCARE SYSTEM (O, 227 beds) Fitzsimmons Drive, Building 9040, Tacoma, WA Zip 98431–1100; tel. 253/968–1110; Colonel Dallas Homas, Commander
**Web address:** www.mamc.amedd.army.mil

| | | |
|---|---|---|
| **Owned, leased, sponsored:** | 22 hospitals | 1870 beds |
| **Contract–managed:** | 0 hospitals | 0 beds |
| **Totals:** | 22 hospitals | 1870 beds |

For explanation of codes following names, see page B2.
★ Indicates Type III membership in the American Hospital Association.

## 9295: DEPARTMENT OF VETERANS AFFAIRS (FG)
810 Vermont Avenue N.W., Washington, DC Zip 20420–0001; tel. 202/273–5781; Robert A. Petzel, M.D., Under Secretary for Health

**(Decentralized Health System)**

**ALABAMA:** BIRMINGHAM VETERANS AFFAIRS MEDICAL CENTER (O, 151 beds) 700 South 19th Street, Birmingham, AL Zip 35233–1927; tel. 205/933–8101; Phyllis Smith, Acting Director
**Web address:** www.birmingham.va.gov/

CENTRAL ALABAMA VETERANS HEALTH CARE SYSTEM (O, 261 beds) 215 Perry Hill Road, Montgomery, AL Zip 36109–3798; tel. 334/272–4670; James R. Talton, MS, FACHE, Director
**Web address:** www.centralalabama.va.gov/

TUSCALOOSA VETERANS AFFAIRS MEDICAL CENTER (O, 366 beds) 3701 Loop Road East, Tuscaloosa, AL Zip 35404–5015; tel. 205/554–2000; Maria Andrews, MS, Director
**Web address:** www.tuscaloosa.va.gov

**ARIZONA:** NORTHERN ARIZONA VETERANS AFFAIRS HEALTH CARE SYSTEM (O, 137 beds) 500 Highway 89 North, Prescott, AZ Zip 86313–5000; tel. 928/445–4860; Donna K. Jacobs, FACHE, Director
**Web address:** www.prescott.va.gov/

PHOENIX VETERANS AFFAIRS HEALTH CARE SYSTEM (O, 197 beds) 650 East Indian School Road, Phoenix, AZ Zip 85012–1892; tel. 602/277–5551; Sharon M. Helman, Director
**Web address:** www.phoenix.va.gov/

SOUTHERN ARIZONA VETERANS AFFAIRS HEALTH CARE SYSTEM (O, 285 beds) 3601 South 6th Avenue, Tucson, AZ Zip 85723–0002; tel. 520/792–1450; Jonathan H. Gardner, FACHE, Director
**Web address:** www.tucson.va.gov

**ARKANSAS:** CENTRAL ARKANSAS VETERANS HEALTHCARE SYSTEM (O, 551 beds) 4300 West Seventh Street, Little Rock, AR Zip 72205–5484; tel. 501/257–1000; Michael R. Winn, Director
**Web address:** www.littlerock.va.gov/

VETERANS HEALTH CARE SYSTEM OF THE OZARKS (O, 72 beds) 1100 North College Avenue, Fayetteville, AR Zip 72703–1944; tel. 479/443–4301; Mark A. Enderele, M.D., Director
**Web address:** www.fayettevillear.va.gov

**CALIFORNIA:** SAN FRANCISO VETERANS AFFAIRS MEDICAL CENTER (O, 244 beds) 4150 Clement Street, San Francisco, CA Zip 94121–1598; tel. 415/221–4810; C. Diana Nicoll, M.D., Ph.D., Director
**Web address:** www.sanfrancisco.va.gov/

VETERANS AFFAIRS CENTRAL CALIFORNIA HEALTH CARE SYSTEM (O, 117 beds) 2615 East Clinton Avenue, Fresno, CA Zip 93703–2223; tel. 559/225–6100; Joanne Krumberger, R.N., FACHE, Director
**Web address:** www.fresno.va.gov/

VETERANS AFFAIRS GREATER LOS ANGELES HEALTHCARE SYSTEM (O, 1087 beds) 11301 Wilshire Boulevard, Los Angeles, CA Zip 90073–1003; tel. 310/478–3711; Donna M. Beiter, R.N., MSN, Director
**Web address:** www.losangeles.va.gov/

VETERANS AFFAIRS LOMA LINDA HEALTHCARE SYSTEM (O, 270 beds) 11201 Benton Street, Loma Linda, CA Zip 92357–1000; tel. 909/825–7084; Donald F. Moore, Director
**Web address:** www.lomalinda.va.gov

VETERANS AFFAIRS LONG BEACH HEALTHCARE SYSTEM (O, 356 beds) 5901 East 7th Street, Long Beach, CA Zip 90822–5201; tel. 562/826–8000; Isabel Duff, MS, Director
**Web address:** www.longbeach.va.gov/

VETERANS AFFAIRS PALO ALTO HEALTH CARE SYSTEM (O, 808 beds) 3801 Miranda Avenue, Palo Alto, CA Zip 94304–1207; tel. 650/493–5000; Elizabeth Joyce Freeman, Director
**Web address:** www.paloalto.va.gov/

VETERANS AFFAIRS SAN DIEGO HEALTHCARE SYSTEM (O, 232 beds) 3350 LaJolla Village Drive, San Diego, CA Zip 92161–0002; tel. 858/552–8585; Jeffrey T. Gering, Director
**Web address:** www.sandiego.va.gov

**COLORADO:** GRAND JUNCTION VETERANS AFFAIRS MEDICAL CENTER (O, 23 beds) 2121 North Avenue, Grand Junction, CO Zip 81501–6428; tel. 970/242–0731; Terry S. Atienza, Director
**Web address:** www.grandjunction.va.gov/

VETERANS AFFAIRS EASTERN COLORADO HEALTH CARE SYSTEM (O, 229 beds) 1055 Clermont Street, Denver, CO Zip 80220–3877; tel. 303/399–8020; Lynette A. Roff, Director
**Web address:** www.denver.va.gov/

**CONNECTICUT:** VETERANS AFFAIRS CONNECTICUT HEALTHCARE SYSTEM (O, 197 beds) 950 Campbell Avenue, West Haven, CT Zip 06516–2770; tel. 203/932–5711; Janice M. Boss, MS, Director
**Web address:** www.va.gov/sta/guide/home.asp

**DELAWARE:** VETERANS AFFAIRS MEDICAL CENTER (O, 120 beds) 1601 Kirkwood Highway, Wilmington, DE Zip 19805–4989; tel. 302/994–2511; Daniel Hendee, Director
**Web address:** www.va.gov/wilmington

**DISTRICT OF COLUMBIA:** WASHINGTON DC VETERANS AFFAIRS MEDICAL CENTER (O, 291 beds) 50 Irving Street N.W., Washington, DC Zip 20422–0002; tel. 202/745–8000; Brian A. Hawkins, Director
**Web address:** www.washingtondc.va.gov/

**FLORIDA:** BAY PINES VETERANS AFFAIRS MEDICAL CENTER (O, 394 beds) 10000 Bay Pines Boulevard, Bay Pines, FL Zip 33744–8200, Mailing Address: P.O. Box 5005, Zip 33744–5005; tel. 727/398–6661; Suzanne M. Klinker, Director
**Web address:** www.baypines.va.gov/

JAMES A. HALEY VETERANS' HOSPITAL (O, 566 beds) 13000 Bruce B. Downs Boulevard, Tampa, FL Zip 33612–4745; tel. 813/972–2000; Kathleen R. Fogarty, Director
**Web address:** www.tampa.va.gov/

LAKE CITY VETERANS AFFAIRS MEDICAL CENTER (O, 277 beds) 619 South Marion Avenue, Lake City, FL Zip 32025–5898; tel. 386/755–3016; Thomas Wisnieski, FACHE, Director
**Web address:** www.northflorida.va.gov/

MALCOM RANDALL VETERANS AFFAIRS MEDICAL CENTER (O, 277 beds) 1601 S.W. Archer Road, Gainesville, FL Zip 32608–1197; tel. 352/376–1611; Thomas Wisnieski, FACHE, Director
**Web address:** www.northflorida.va.gov/

MIAMI VETERANS AFFAIRS HEALTHCARE SYSTEM (O, 401 beds) 1201 N.W. 16th Street, Miami, FL Zip 33125–1624; tel. 305/575–7000; Paul M. Russo, FACHE, Director
**Web address:** www.miami.va.gov/

WEST PALM BEACH VETERANS AFFAIRS MEDICAL CENTER (O, 133 beds) 7305 North Military Trail, West Palm Beach, FL Zip 33410–6400; tel. 561/422–8262; Charleen R. Szabo, FACHE, Director
**Web address:** www.westpalmbeach.va.gov/

**GEORGIA:** ATLANTA VETERANS AFFAIRS MEDICAL CENTER (O, 239 beds) 1670 Clairmont Road, Decatur, GA Zip 30033–4004; tel. 404/321–6111; Leslie Wiggins, Director
**Web address:** www.atlanta.va.gov/

CARL VINSON VETERANS AFFAIRS MEDICAL CENTER (O, 178 beds) 1826 Veterans Boulevard, Dublin, GA Zip 31021–3620; tel. 478/272–1210; John S. Goldman, Director
**Web address:** www.dublin.va.gov/

CHARLIE NORWOOD VETERANS AFFAIRS MEDICAL CENTER (O, 338 beds) 1 Freedom Way, Augusta, GA Zip 30904–6285; tel. 706/733–0188; Robert U. Hamilton, Director
**Web address:** www.augusta.va.gov/

**IDAHO:** BOISE VETERANS AFFAIRS MEDICAL CENTER (O, 85 beds) 500 West Fort Street, Boise, ID Zip 83702–4598; tel. 208/422–1000; David P. Wood, FACHE, Director
**Web address:** www.boise.va.gov/

**ILLINOIS:** CAPTAIN JAMES A. LOVELL FEDERAL HEALTH CARE CENTER (O, 103 beds) 3001 Green Bay Road, North Chicago, IL Zip 60064–3049; tel. 847/688–1900; Patrick L. Sullivan, FACHE, Director
**Web address:** www.lovell.fhcc.va.gov/

EDWARD HINES, JR. VETERANS AFFAIRS HOSPITAL (O, 450 beds) 5000 South Fifth Avenue, Hines, IL Zip 60141–3030, Mailing Address: P.O. Box 5000, Zip 60141–5000; tel. 708/202–8387; Joan M. Ricard, R.N., FACHE, Director
**Web address:** www.hines.va.gov/

JESSE BROWN VETERANS AFFAIRS MEDICAL CENTER (O, 240 beds) 820 South Damen, Chicago, IL Zip 60612–3776; tel. 312/569–8387; Mario V. DeSantis, Acting Medical Center Director
**Web address:** www.chicago.va.gov/

For explanation of codes following names, see page B2.
★ Indicates Type III membership in the American Hospital Association.

MARION VETERANS AFFAIRS MEDICAL CENTER (O, 225 beds) 2401 West Main Street, Marion, IL Zip 62959–1188; tel. 618/997–5311; Brent A. Thelen, Ph.D., Interim Director
**Web address:** www.marion.va.gov

VETERANS AFFAIRS ILLIANA HEALTH CARE SYSTEM (O, 221 beds) 1900 East Main Street, Danville, IL Zip 61832–5198; tel. 217/554–3000; Emma Metcalf, MSN, R.N., Director
**Web address:** www.danville.va.gov/

**INDIANA:** RICHARD L. ROUDEBUSH VETERANS AFFAIRS MEDICAL CENTER (O, 209 beds) 1481 West Tenth Street, Indianapolis, IN Zip 46202–2884; tel. 317/554–0000; Thomas Mattice, Director
**Web address:** www.indianapolis.va.gov

VETERANS AFFAIRS NORTHERN INDIANA HEALTH CARE SYSTEM (O, 26 beds) 2121 Lake Avenue, Fort Wayne, IN Zip 46805–5100; tel. 260/426–5431; Denise M. Deitzen, Director
**Web address:** www.northernindiana.va.gov/

**IOWA:** IOWA CITY VETERANS AFFAIRS HEALTH CARE SYSTEM (O, 65 beds) 601 Highway 6 West, Iowa City, IA Zip 52246–2208; tel. 319/338–0581; Barry D. Sharp, Director
**Web address:** www.iowacity.va.gov/

VETERANS AFFAIRS CENTRAL IOWA HEALTH CARE SYSTEM (O, 255 beds) 3600 30th Street, Des Moines, IA Zip 50310–5753; tel. 515/699–5999; Donald C. Cooper, Director
**Web address:** www.centraliowa.va.gov/

**KANSAS:** ROBERT J. DOLE VETERANS AFFAIRS MEDICAL CENTER (O, 41 beds) 5500 East Kellogg, Wichita, KS Zip 67218–1607; tel. 316/685–2221; Kevin Inkley, Interim Director
**Web address:** www.wichita.va.gov

VETERANS AFFAIRS EASTERN KANSAS HEALTH CARE SYSTEM (O, 213 beds) 2200 Gage Boulevard, Topeka, KS Zip 66622–0002; tel. 785/350–3111; Anthony Rudy Klopher, FACHE, Director
**Web address:** www.topeka.va.gov/

**KENTUCKY:** ROBLEY REX VETERANS AFFAIRS MEDICAL CENTER (O, 116 beds) 800 Zorn Avenue, Louisville, KY Zip 40206–1499; tel. 502/287–4000; Wayne L. Pfeffer, FACHE, Director
**Web address:** www.louisville.va.gov

VETERANS AFFAIRS MEDICAL CENTER–LEXINGTON (O, 199 beds) 1101 Veterans Drive, Lexington, KY Zip 40502–2235; tel. 859/233–4511; DeWayne Hamlin, Director
**Web address:** www.lexington.va.gov/

**LOUISIANA:** ALEXANDRIA VETERANS AFFAIRS HEALTH CARE SYSTEM (O, 143 beds) 2495 Shreveport Highway, 71 N., Pineville, LA Zip 71360–4044, Mailing Address: P.O. Box 69004, Alexandria, Zip 71306–9004; tel. 318/473–0010; Martin J. Traxler, Director
**Web address:** www.alexandria.va.gov/

OVERTON BROOKS VETERANS AFFAIRS MEDICAL CENTER (O, 100 beds) 510 East Stoner Avenue, Shreveport, LA Zip 71101–4295; tel. 318/221–8411; Shirley Bealer, Medical Center Director
**Web address:** www.shreveport.va.gov/

**MAINE:** MAINE VETERANS AFFAIRS MEDICAL CENTER (O, 181 beds) 1 VA Center, Augusta, ME Zip 04330–6719; tel. 207/623–8411; Ryan S. Lilly, Acting Director
**Web address:** www.maine.va.gov/

**MARYLAND:** VETERANS AFFAIRS MARYLAND HEALTH CARE SYSTEM–BALTIMORE DIVISION (O, 727 beds) 10 North Greene Street, Baltimore, MD Zip 21201–1524; tel. 410/605–7001; Dennis H. Smith, Director
**Web address:** www.maryland.va.gov/

**MASSACHUSETTS:** BROCKTON VETERANS AFFAIRS MEDICAL CENTER (O, 375 beds) 940 Belmont Street, Brockton, MA Zip 02301–5596; tel. 508/583–4500; Michael E. Lawson, Director
**Web address:** www.boston.va.gov/

EDITH NOURSE ROGERS MEMORIAL VETERANS HOSPITAL (O, 147 beds) 200 Springs Road, Bedford, MA Zip 01730–1198; tel. 781/687–2000; Christine Croteau, Acting Director
**Web address:** www.va.gov/sta/guide/home.asp

VA CENTRAL WESTERN MASSACHUSETTS HEALTHCARE SYSTEM (O, 167 beds) 421 North Main Street, Leeds, MA Zip 01053–9764; tel. 413/582–3000; Roger L. Johnson, Director
**Web address:** www.centralwesternmass.va.gov/

VETERANS AFFAIRS BOSTON HEALTHCARE SYSTEM (O, 361 beds) 1400 VFW Parkway, Boston, MA Zip 02132–4927; tel. 857/203–6000; Michael E. Lawson, Director
**Web address:** www.boston.va.gov/

**MICHIGAN:** ALEDA E. LUTZ VETERANS AFFAIRS MEDICAL CENTER (O, 100 beds) 1500 Weiss Street, Saginaw, MI Zip 48602–5298; tel. 989/497–2500; Major Jeff Nechanicky, Acting Medical Center Director
**Web address:** www.saginaw.va.gov/

BATTLE CREEK VETERANS AFFAIRS MEDICAL CENTER (O, 204 beds) 5500 Armstrong Road, Battle Creek, MI Zip 49037–7314; tel. 269/966–5600; Mary Beth Skupien, Director
**Web address:** www.battlecreek.va.gov/

JOHN D. DINGELL VETERANS AFFAIRS MEDICAL CENTER (O, 188 beds) 4646 John R Street, Detroit, MI Zip 48201–1932; tel. 313/576–1000; Pamela J. Reeves, M.D., Director
**Web address:** www.detroit.va.gov/

OSCAR G. JOHNSON VETERANS AFFAIRS MEDICAL CENTER (O, 17 beds) 325 East H Street, Iron Mountain, MI Zip 49801–4792; tel. 906/774–3300; James W. Rice, Director
**Web address:** www.ironmountain.va.gov/

VETERANS AFFAIRS ANN ARBOR HEALTHCARE SYSTEM (O, 145 beds) 2215 Fuller Road, Ann Arbor, MI Zip 48105–2399; tel. 734/769–7100; Robert P. McDivitt, FACHE, Director
**Web address:** www.annarbor.va.gov

**MINNESOTA:** MINNEAPOLIS VETERANS AFFAIRS HEALTH CARE SYSTEM (O, 305 beds) One Veterans Drive, Minneapolis, MN Zip 55417–2399; tel. 612/725–2000; Patrick J. Kelly, FACHE, Director
**Web address:** www.minneapolis.va.gov

ST. CLOUD VETERANS AFFAIRS HEALTH CARE SYSTEM (O, 388 beds) 4801 Veterans Drive, Saint Cloud, MN Zip 56303–2099; tel. 320/252–1670; Barry I. Bahl, Director
**Web address:** www.stcloud.va.gov

**MISSISSIPPI:** G.V. (SONNY) MONTGOMERY VETERANS AFFAIRS MEDICAL CENTER (O, 323 beds) 1500 East Woodrow Wilson Drive, Jackson, MS Zip 39216–5199; tel. 601/362–4471; Joe Battle, Interim Director
**Web address:** www.jackson.va.gov/

VETERANS AFFAIRS GULF COAST VETERANS HEALTH CARE SYSTEM (O, 392 beds) 400 Veterans Avenue, Biloxi, MS Zip 39531–2410; tel. 228/523–5000; Anthony L. Dawson, FACHE, Director
**Web address:** www.biloxi.va.gov/

**MISSOURI:** HARRY S. TRUMAN MEMORIAL VETERANS HOSPITAL (O, 126 beds) 800 Hospital Drive, Columbia, MO Zip 65201–5275; tel. 573/814–6000; Sallie Houser–Hanfelder, FACHE, Director
**Web address:** www.columbiamo.va.gov

JOHN J. PERSHING VETERANS AFFAIRS MEDICAL CENTER (O, 58 beds) 1500 North Westwood Boulevard, Poplar Bluff, MO Zip 63901–3318; tel. 573/686–4151; Marjorie Hedstrom, Director
**Web address:** www.poplarbluff.va.gov

KANSAS CITY VETERANS AFFAIRS MEDICAL CENTER (O, 157 beds) 4801 East Linwood Boulevard, Kansas City, MO Zip 64128–2226; tel. 816/861–4700; Kent D. Hill, Director
**Web address:** www.kansascity.va.gov/

VETERANS AFFAIRS ST. LOUIS HEALTH CARE SYSTEM (O, 356 beds) 915 North Grand, Saint Louis, MO Zip 63106–1621; tel. 314/652–4100; Marc Magill, Acting Director
**Web address:** www.stlouis.va.gov/

**MONTANA:** VETERANS AFFAIRS MONTANA HEALTH CARE SYSTEM (O, 65 beds) 3687 Veterans Drive, Fort Harrison, MT Zip 59636–9703, Mailing Address: P.O. Box 1500, Zip 59636–1500; tel. 406/442–6410; Steven W. Young, Acting Director
**Web address:** www.montana.va.gov/

**NEBRASKA:** VETERANS AFFAIRS MEDICAL CENTER (O, 100 beds) 4101 Woolworth Avenue, Omaha, NE Zip 68105–1873; tel. 402/346–8800; Nancy A. Gregory, Acting Director
**Web address:** www.nebraska.va.gov/

VETERANS AFFAIRS NEBRASKA–WESTERN IOWA HEALTH CARE SYSTEM (O, 186 beds) 600 South 70th Street, Lincoln, NE Zip 68510–2493; tel. 402/489–3802; Marci Mylan, Director
**Web address:** www.nebraska.va.gov/

Section B

For explanation of codes following names, see page B2.
★ Indicates Type III membership in the American Hospital Association.

**NEVADA:** VETERANS AFFAIRS SIERRA NEVADA HEALTH CARE SYSTEM (O, 124 beds) 975 Kirman Avenue, Reno, NV Zip 89502–0993; tel. 775/786–7200; Kurt W. Schlegelmilch, M.D., FACHE, Director
**Web address:** www.reno.va.gov/

VETERANS AFFAIRS SOUTHERN NEVADA HEALTHCARE SYSTEM (O, 58 beds) 6900 North Pecos Road, North Las Vegas, NV Mailing Address: P.O. Box 360001, Zip 89036–8108; tel. 702/791–9000; Isabel Duff, MS, Acting Director
**Web address:** www.lasvegas.va.gov/

**NEW HAMPSHIRE:** MANCHESTER VETERANS AFFAIRS MEDICAL CENTER (O, 90 beds) 718 Smyth Road, Manchester, NH Zip 03104–4098; tel. 603/624–4366; Marc Levenson, M.D., Director
**Web address:** www.manchester.va.gov/

**NEW JERSEY:** VETERANS AFFAIRS NEW JERSEY HEALTH CARE SYSTEM (O, 439 beds) 385 Tremont Avenue, East Orange, NJ Zip 07018–1095; tel. 973/676–1000; Kenneth H. Mizrach, Director
**Web address:** www.newjersey.va.gov/

**NEW MEXICO:** VETERANS AFFAIRS MEDICAL CENTER (O, 281 beds) 1501 San Pedro S.E., Albuquerque, NM Zip 87108–5153; tel. 505/265–1711; George Marnell, Director
**Web address:** www.southwest.va.gov/albuquerque/

**NEW YORK:** ALBANY STRATTON VETERANS AFFAIRS MEDICAL CENTER (O, 150 beds) 113 Holland Avenue, Albany, NY Zip 12208–3473; tel. 518/626–5000; Linda W. Weiss, MS, FACHE, Director
**Web address:** www.albany.va.gov/

BATH VETERANS AFFAIRS MEDICAL CENTER (O, 371 beds) 76 Veterans Avenue, Bath, NY Zip 14810–0842; tel. 607/664–4000; Michael J. Swartz, FACHE, Medical Center Director
**Web address:** www.bath.va.gov

CANANDAIGUA VETERANS AFFAIRS MEDICAL CENTER (O, 196 beds) 400 Fort Hill Avenue, Canandaigua, NY Zip 14424–1159; tel. 585/394–2000; Craig Howard, Director
**Web address:** www.canandaigua.va.gov/

JAMES J. PETERS VETERANS AFFAIRS MEDICAL CENTER (O, 325 beds) 130 West Kingsbridge Road, Bronx, NY Zip 10468–3904; tel. 718/584–9000; MaryAnn P. Musumeci, Director
**Web address:** www.bronx.va.gov/

NORTHPORT VETERANS AFFAIRS MEDICAL CENTER (O, 502 beds) 79 Middleville Road, Northport, NY Zip 11768–2200; tel. 631/261–4400; Philip C. Moschitta, Director
**Web address:** www.northport.va.gov/index.asp

SYRACUSE VETERANS AFFAIRS MEDICAL CENTER (O, 235 beds) 800 Irving Avenue, Syracuse, NY Zip 13210–2716; tel. 315/425–4400; James Cody, Director
**Web address:** www.syracuse.va.gov/

VETERANS ADMINISTRATION NEW YORK HARBOR HEALTHCARE SYSTEM (O, 517 beds) 800 Poly Place, Brooklyn, NY Zip 11209–7104; tel. 718/630–3500; Martina A. Parauda, Director
**Web address:** www.nyharbor.va.gov

VETERANS AFFAIRS HUDSON VALLEY HEALTH CARE SYSTEM–F.D. ROOSEVELT HOSPITAL (O, 383 beds) 2094 Albany Post Road, Montrose, NY Zip 10548–1454, Mailing Address: P.O. Box 100, Zip 10548–0100; tel. 914/737–4400; Gerald F. Culliton, Director
**Web address:** www.hudsonvalley.va.gov/

VETERANS AFFAIRS WESTERN NEW YORK HEALTHCARE SYSTEM–BATAVIA DIVISION (O, 128 beds) 222 Richmond Avenue, Batavia, NY Zip 14020–1288; tel. 585/297–1000; Brian G. Stiller, Director Medical Center
**Web address:** www.buffalo.va.gov/batavia.asp

VETERANS AFFAIRS WESTERN NEW YORK HEALTHCARE SYSTEM–BUFFALO DIVISION (O, 113 beds) 3495 Bailey Avenue, Buffalo, NY Zip 14215–1129; tel. 716/834–9200; Brian G. Stiller, Director Medical Center
**Web address:** www.buffalo.va.gov/index.asp

**NORTH CAROLINA:** CHARLES GEORGE VETERANS AFFAIRS MEDICAL CENTER (O, 257 beds) 1100 Tunnel Road, Asheville, NC Zip 28805–2087; tel. 828/298–7911; Cynthia Breyfogle, Director
**Web address:** www.asheville.va.gov/

DURHAM VETERANS AFFAIRS MEDICAL CENTER (O, 265 beds) 508 Fulton Street, Durham, NC Zip 27705–3897; tel. 919/286–0411; DeAnne Seekins, Director
**Web address:** www.durham.va.gov/

FAYETTEVILLE VETERANS AFFAIRS MEDICAL CENTER (O, 58 beds) 2300 Ramsey Street, Fayetteville, NC Zip 28301–3899; tel. 910/488–2120; Elizabeth Goolsby, Director
**Web address:** www.fayettevillenc.va.gov

W. G. (BILL) HEFFNER VETERANS AFFAIRS MEDICAL CENTER (O, 171 beds) 1601 Brenner Avenue, Salisbury, NC Zip 28144–2559; tel. 704/638–9000; Kaye Green, FACHE, Director
**Web address:** www.salisbury.va.gov

**NORTH DAKOTA:** FARGO VETERANS AFFAIRS HEALTH CARE SYSTEM (O, 77 beds) 2101 Elm Street North, Fargo, ND Zip 58102–2498; tel. 701/232–3241; Michael J. Murphy, FACHE, Director
**Web address:** www.fargo.va.gov/

**OHIO:** CHILLICOTHE VETERANS AFFAIRS MEDICAL CENTER (O, 297 beds) 17273 State Route 104, Chillicothe, OH Zip 45601–9718; tel. 740/773–1141; Wendy J. Hepker, FACHE, Director
**Web address:** www.chillicothe.va.gov/

CINCINNATI VETERANS AFFAIRS MEDICAL CENTER (O, 268 beds) 3200 Vine Street, Cincinnati, OH Zip 45220–2288; tel. 513/475–6300; Linda D. Smith, FACHE, Director
**Web address:** www.cincinnati.va.gov/

DAYTON VETERANS AFFAIRS MEDICAL CENTER (O, 500 beds) 4100 West Third Street, Dayton, OH Zip 45428–9000; tel. 937/268–6511; Glenn A. Costie, FACHE, Director
**Web address:** www.dayton.va.gov/

LOUIS STOKES CLEVELAND VETERANS AFFAIRS MEDICAL CENTER (O, 585 beds) 10701 East Boulevard, Cleveland, OH Zip 44106–1702; tel. 216/791–3800; Susan Fuehrer, Director
**Web address:** www.cleveland.va.gov/

**OKLAHOMA:** JACK C. MONTGOMERY VETERANS AFFAIRS MEDICAL CENTER (O, 83 beds) 1011 Honor Heights Drive, Muskogee, OK Zip 74401–1318; tel. 918/577–3000; James R. Floyd, Director
**Web address:** www.muskogee.va.gov

OKLAHOMA CITY VETERANS AFFAIRS MEDICAL CENTER (O, 192 beds) 921 N.E. 13th Street, Oklahoma City, OK Zip 73104–5028; tel. 405/456–1000; Adam C. Walmus, Interim Director
**Web address:** www.oklahoma.va.gov

**OREGON:** PORTLAND VETERANS AFFAIRS MEDICAL CENTER (O, 303 beds) 3710 S.W. U.S. Veterans Hospital Road, Portland, OR Zip 97239–2964, Mailing Address: P.O. Box 1034, Zip 97207–1034; tel. 503/220–8262; John E. Patrick, Director
**Web address:** www.portland.va.gov/

VETERANS AFFAIRS ROSEBURG HEALTHCARE SYSTEM (O, 88 beds) 913 N.W. Garden Valley Boulevard, Roseburg, OR Zip 97471–6513; tel. 541/440–1000; Carol Bogedain, FACHE, Director
**Web address:** www.roseburg.va.gov/

**PENNSYLVANIA:** COATESVILLE VETERANS AFFAIRS MEDICAL CENTER (O, 306 beds) 1400 Black Horse Hill Road, Coatesville, PA Zip 19320–2040; tel. 610/384–7711; Gary W. Devansky, Director
**Web address:** www.coatesville.va.gov/

ERIE VETERANS AFFAIRS MEDICAL CENTER (O, 26 beds) 135 East 38th Street, Erie, PA Zip 16504–1559; tel. 814/860–2576; Michael Adelman, M.D., Director
**Web address:** www.erie.va.gov/

JAMES E. VAN ZANDT VETERANS AFFAIRS MEDICAL CENTER (O, 68 beds) 2907 Pleasant Valley Boulevard, Altoona, PA Zip 16602–4305; tel. 877/626–2500; William H. Mills, Director
**Web address:** www.altoona.va.gov/

LEBANON VETERANS AFFAIRS MEDICAL CENTER (O, 213 beds) 1700 South Lincoln Avenue, Lebanon, PA Zip 17042–7529; tel. 717/272–6621; Robert W. Callahan, Jr., Director
**Web address:** www.lebanon.va.gov

PHILADELPHIA VETERANS AFFAIRS MEDICAL CENTER (O, 280 beds) 3900 Woodland Avenue, Philadelphia, PA Zip 19104–4594; tel. 215/823–5800; Joseph M. Dalpiaz, Director
**Web address:** www.philadelphia.va.gov/

For explanation of codes following names, see page B2.
★ Indicates Type III membership in the American Hospital Association.

VETERANS AFFAIRS BUTLER HEALTHCARE (O, 126 beds) 325 New Castle Road, Butler, PA Zip 16001–2480; tel. 724/287–4781; John Gennaro, FACHE, Director
**Web address:** www.butler.va.gov

VETERANS AFFAIRS PITTSBURGH HEALTHCARE SYSTEM (O, 447 beds) University Drive, Pittsburgh, PA Zip 15240–1001; tel. 412/688–6000; Terry Gerigk Wolf, FACHE, Director and Chief Executive Officer
**Web address:** www.pittsburgh.va.gov/

WILKES–BARRE VETERANS AFFAIRS MEDICAL CENTER (O, 161 beds) 1111 East End Boulevard, Wilkes–Barre, PA Zip 18711–0030; tel. 570/824–3521; Margaret B. Caplan, Director
**Web address:** www.va.gov/vamcwb

**PUERTO RICO:** VETERANS AFFAIRS CARIBBEAN HEALTHCARE SYSTEM (O, 330 beds) 10 Casia Street, San Juan, PR Zip 00921–3201; tel. 787/641–7582; Wanda Mims, Director
**Web address:** www.caribbean.va.gov/

**RHODE ISLAND:** PROVIDENCE VETERANS AFFAIRS MEDICAL CENTER (O, 73 beds) 830 Chalkstone Avenue, Providence, RI Zip 02908–4799; tel. 401/273–7100; Vincent Ng, Director
**Web address:** www.providence.va.gov/

**SOUTH CAROLINA:** RALPH H. JOHNSON VETERANS AFFAIRS MEDICAL CENTER (O, 98 beds) 109 Bee Street, Charleston, SC Zip 29401–5799; tel. 843/577–5011; Carolyn L. Adams, Director
**Web address:** www.charleston.va.gov/

WM. JENNINGS BRYAN DORN VETERANS AFFAIRS MEDICAL CENTER (O, 216 beds) 6439 Garners Ferry Road, Columbia, SC Zip 29209–1639; tel. 803/776–4000; Rebecca J. Wiley, R.N., Director
**Web address:** www.columbiasc.va.gov/

**SOUTH DAKOTA:** SIOUX FALLS VETERANS AFFAIRS HEALTH CARE SYSTEM (O, 98 beds) 2501 West 22nd Street, Sioux Falls, SD Zip 57105–1305, Mailing Address: P.O. Box 5046, Zip 57117–5046; tel. 605/336–3230; Sandra Horsman, Acting Medical Center Director
**Web address:** www.siouxfalls.va.gov

VETERANS AFFAIRS BLACK HILLS HEALTH CARE SYSTEM (O, 308 beds) 113 Comanche Road, Fort Meade, SD Zip 57741–1099; tel. 605/347–2511; Stephen R. DiStasio, Director
**Web address:** www.blackhills.va.gov/

**TENNESSEE:** JAMES H. QUILLEN VETERANS AFFAIRS MEDICAL CENTER (O, 98 beds) Corner of Lamont & Veterans Way, Mountain Home, TN Zip 37684, Mailing Address: P.O. Box 4000, Zip 37684–4000; tel. 423/926–1171; Charlene S. Ehret, FACHE, Director
**Web address:** www.mountainhome.va.gov/

MEMPHIS VETERANS AFFAIRS MEDICAL CENTER (O, 262 beds) 1030 Jefferson Avenue, Memphis, TN Zip 38104–2193; tel. 901/523–8990; C. Diane Knight, M.D., Interim Director and Chief Executive Officer
**Web address:** www.memphis.va.gov/

TENNESSEE VALLEY HEALTHCARE SYSTEM (O, 520 beds) 1310 24th Avenue South, Nashville, TN Zip 37212–2637; tel. 615/327–4751; Juan A. Morales, R.N., MSN, Health System Director
**Web address:** www.tennesseevalley.va.gov

**TEXAS:** AMARILLO VETERANS AFFAIRS HEALTH CARE SYSTEM (O, 55 beds) 6010 West Amarillo Boulevard, Amarillo, TX Zip 79106–1992; tel. 806/355–9703; Andrew Welch, Director
**Web address:** www.amarillo.va.gov/

CENTRAL TEXAS VETERANS HEALTHCARE SYSTEM (O, 1532 beds) 1901 Veterans Memorial Drive, Temple, TX Zip 76504–7493; tel. 254/778–4811; Thomas C. Smith, III, FACHE, Director
**Web address:** www.centraltexas.va.gov/

MICHAEL E. DEBAKEY VETERANS AFFAIRS MEDICAL CENTER (O, 479 beds) 2002 Holcombe Boulevard, Houston, TX Zip 77030–4298; tel. 713/791–1414; Adam C. Walmus, Director
**Web address:** www.houston.va.gov

SOUTH TEXAS VETERANS HEALTH CARE SYSTEM (O, 838 beds) 7400 Merton Minter Boulevard, San Antonio, TX Zip 78229–4404; tel. 210/617–5300; Marie L. Weldon, FACHE, Director
**Web address:** www.southtexas.va.gov/

VETERANS AFFAIRS NORTH TEXAS HEALTH CARE SYSTEM (O, 875 beds) 4500 South Lancaster Road, Dallas, TX Zip 75216–7167; tel. 214/742–8387; Jeffrey Milligan, Director
**Web address:** www.northtexas.va.gov/

WEST TEXAS VETERANS AFFAIRS HEALTH CARE SYSTEM (O, 149 beds) 300 Veterans Boulevard, Big Spring, TX Zip 79720–5500; Big Springs, tel. 432/263–7361; Daniel L. Marsh, Director
**Web address:** www.bigspring.va.gov/about/

**UTAH:** VETERANS AFFAIRS SALT LAKE CITY HEALTH CARE SYSTEM (O, 121 beds) 500 Foothill Drive, Salt Lake City, UT Zip 84148–0002; tel. 801/582–1565; Steven W. Young, Director
**Web address:** www.saltlakecity.va.gov/

**VERMONT:** WHITE RIVER JUNCTION VETERANS AFFAIRS MEDICAL CENTER (O, 60 beds) 215 North Main Street, White River Junction, VT Zip 05009–0001; tel. 802/295–9363; Marc Levenson, M.D., Acting Director
**Web address:** www.whiteriver.va.gov/

**VIRGINIA:** HAMPTON VETERANS AFFAIRS MEDICAL CENTER (O, 395 beds) 100 Emancipation Drive, Hampton, VA Zip 23667–0001; tel. 757/722–9961; Benita K. Stoddard, FACHE, Acting Director
**Web address:** www.hampton.va.gov/

HUNTER HOLMES MCGUIRE VETERANS AFFAIRS MEDICAL CENTER (O, 427 beds) 1201 Broad Rock Boulevard, Richmond, VA Zip 23249–0002; tel. 804/675–5000; David P. Budinger, Interim Director
**Web address:** www.richmond.va.gov/

SALEM VETERANS AFFAIRS MEDICAL CENTER (O, 200 beds) 1970 Roanoke Boulevard, Salem, VA Zip 24153–6478; tel. 540/982–2463; Miguel H. LaPuz, M.D., Director
**Web address:** www.salem.va.gov

**WASHINGTON:** JONATHAN M. WAINWRIGHT MEMORIAL VETERANS AFFAIRS MEDICAL CENTER (O, 14 beds) 77 Wainwright Drive, Walla Walla, WA Zip 99362–3994; tel. 509/525–5200; Brian W. Westfield, MSN, Director
**Web address:** www.wallawalla.va.gov

SPOKANE VETERANS AFFAIRS MEDICAL CENTER (O, 70 beds) 4815 North Assembly Street, Spokane, WA Zip 99205–6197; tel. 509/434–7000; Sandy J. Nielsen, Director
**Web address:** www.spokane.va.gov/

VETERANS AFFAIRS PUGET SOUND HEALTH CARE SYSTEM (O, 358 beds) 1660 South Columbian Way, Seattle, WA Zip 98108–1597; tel. 206/762–1010; David A. Elizalde, Director
**Web address:** www.pugetsound.va.gov/

**WEST VIRGINIA:** BECKLEY VETERANS AFFAIRS MEDICAL CENTER (O, 40 beds) 200 Veterans Avenue, Beckley, WV Zip 25801–6499; tel. 304/255–2121; Karin L. McGraw, MSN, FACHE, Director
**Web address:** www.beckley.va.gov/

HUNTINGTON VETERANS AFFAIRS MEDICAL CENTER (O, 80 beds) 1540 Spring Valley Drive, Huntington, WV Zip 25704–9300; tel. 304/429–6741; Edward H. Seiler, Director
**Web address:** www.huntington.va.gov/

LOUIS A. JOHNSON VETERANS AFFAIRS MEDICAL CENTER (O, 71 beds) 1 Medical Center Drive, Clarksburg, WV Zip 26301–4199; tel. 304/623–3461; Beth Brown, Director
**Web address:** www.clarksburg.va.gov

MARTINSBURG VETERANS AFFAIRS MEDICAL CENTER (O, 246 beds) 510 Butler Avenue, Martinsburg, WV Zip 25405–9990; tel. 304/263–0811; Ann Brown, Director
**Web address:** www.martinsburg.va.gov/

**WISCONSIN:** CLEMENT J. ZABLOCKI VETERANS AFFAIRS MEDICAL CENTER (O, 637 beds) 5000 West National Avenue, Milwaukee, WI Zip 53295–0001; tel. 414/384–2000; Robert H. Beller, FACHE, Director
**Web address:** www.milwaukee.va.gov/

TOMAH VETERANS AFFAIRS MEDICAL CENTER (O, 71 beds) 500 East Veterans Street, Tomah, WI Zip 54660–3105; tel. 608/372–3971; Mario DeSanctis, FACHE, Director
**Web address:** www.tomah.va.gov

WILLIAM S. MIDDLETON MEMORIAL VETERANS HOSPITAL (O, 87 beds) 2500 Overlook Terrace, Madison, WI Zip 53705–2286; tel. 608/256–1901; Judy McKee, FACHE, Director
**Web address:** www.madison.va.gov

**WYOMING:** CHEYENNE VETERANS AFFAIRS MEDICAL CENTER (O, 21 beds) 2360 East Pershing Boulevard, Cheyenne, WY Zip 82001–5392; tel. 307/778–7550; Cynthia McCormack, MS, Director
**Web address:** www.cheyenne.va.gov/

For explanation of codes following names, see page B2.
★ Indicates Type III membership in the American Hospital Association.

Section B

SHERIDAN VETERANS AFFAIRS MEDICAL CENTER (O, 185 beds) 1898 Fort Road, Sheridan, WY Zip 82801–8320; tel. 307/672–3473; Debra L. Hirschman, R.N., MSN, Director
**Web address:** www.sheridan.va.gov/

| | | |
|---|---|---|
| Owned, leased, sponsored: | 135 hospitals | 34253 beds |
| Contract–managed: | 0 hospitals | 0 beds |
| Totals: | 135 hospitals | 34253 beds |

**0845: DEVEREUX** (NP)
444 Devereux Drive, Villanova, PA Zip 19085–1932, Mailing Address: P.O. Box 638, Zip 19085–0638; tel. 610/520–3000; Robert Q. Kreider, President and Chief Executive Officer
**(Independent Hospital System)**

**FLORIDA:** DEVEREUX HOSPITAL AND CHILDREN'S CENTER OF FLORIDA (O, 100 beds) 8000 Devereux Drive, Melbourne, FL Zip 32940–7907; tel. 321/242–9100; Steven Murphy, Executive Director
**Web address:** www.devereux.org

**GEORGIA:** DEVEREUX GEORGIA TREATMENT NETWORK (O, 100 beds) 1291 Stanley Road N.W., Kennesaw, GA Zip 30152–4359; tel. 770/427–0147; Gwendolyn Skinner, Executive Director
**Web address:** www.devereuxga.org

**PENNSYLVANIA:** DEVEREUX CHILDREN'S BEHAVIORAL HEALTH CENTER (O, 33 beds) 655 Sugartown Road, Malvern, PA Zip 19355–3303, Mailing Address: P.O. Box 275, Zip 19355–0275; tel. 800/345–1292; David E. Woodwar, Executive Director
**Web address:** www.devereux.org

**TEXAS:** DEVEREUX TEXAS TREATMENT NETWORK (O, 60 beds) 1150 Devereux Drive, League City, TX Zip 77573–2043; tel. 281/335–1000; Pamela E. Helm, Executive Director
**Web address:** www.devereux.org

| | | |
|---|---|---|
| Owned, leased, sponsored: | 4 hospitals | 293 beds |
| Contract–managed: | 0 hospitals | 0 beds |
| Totals: | 4 hospitals | 293 beds |

**★5205: DIGNITY HEALTH** (CC)
185 Berry Street, Suite 300, San Francisco, CA Zip 94107–1773; tel. 415/438–5500; Lloyd H. Dean, President and Chief Executive Officer
**(Decentralized Health System)**

**ARIZONA:** CHANDLER REGIONAL MEDICAL CENTER (O, 243 beds) 1955 West Frye Road, Chandler, AZ Zip 85224–6282; tel. 480/728–3000; Tim Bricker, President and Chief Executive Officer
**Web address:** www.chandlerregional.com

MERCY GILBERT MEDICAL CENTER (S, 212 beds) 3555 South Val Vista Road, Gilbert, AZ Zip 85297–7323; tel. 480/728–8000; Tim Bricker, President and Chief Executive Officer
**Web address:** www.mercygilbert.org

ST. JOSEPH'S HOSPITAL AND MEDICAL CENTER (S, 592 beds) 350 West Thomas Road, Phoenix, AZ Zip 85013–4496, Mailing Address: P.O. Box 2071, Zip 85001–2071; tel. 602/406–3000; Patty White, R.N., MS, President
**Web address:** www.stjosephs–phx.org

**CALIFORNIA:** ARROYO GRANDE COMMUNITY HOSPITAL (O, 67 beds) 345 South Halcyon Road, Arroyo Grande, CA Zip 93420–3899; tel. 805/489–4261; Kenneth Dalebout, Administrator and Chief Executive Officer
**Web address:** www.arroyograndehospital.org

BAKERSFIELD MEMORIAL HOSPITAL (O, 406 beds) 420 34th Street, Bakersfield, CA Zip 93301–2237; tel. 661/327–1792; Jon Van Boening, President and Chief Executive Officer and Senior Vice President Operations Dignity Health Central Valley Service Area
**Web address:** www.bakersfieldmemorial.org

CALIFORNIA HOSPITAL MEDICAL CENTER (O, 318 beds) 1401 South Grand Avenue, Los Angeles, CA Zip 90015–3010; tel. 213/748–2411; Craig G. Myers, President
**Web address:** www.chmcla.org

COMMUNITY HOSPITAL OF SAN BERNARDINO (O, 321 beds) 1805 Medical Center Drive, San Bernardino, CA Zip 92411–1214; tel. 909/887–6333; June Collison, President
**Web address:** www.chsb.org

DOMINICAN HOSPITAL (S, 276 beds) 1555 Soquel Drive, Santa Cruz, CA Zip 95065–1794; tel. 831/462–7700; Nanette Mickiewicz, M.D., President
**Web address:** www.dominicanhospital.org

FRENCH HOSPITAL MEDICAL CENTER (O, 112 beds) 1911 Johnson Avenue, San Luis Obispo, CA Zip 93401–4131; tel. 805/543–5353; Alan Iftiniuk, Chief Executive Officer
**Web address:** www.frenchmedicalcenter.org

GLENDALE MEMORIAL HOSPITAL AND HEALTH CENTER (O, 334 beds) 1420 South Central Avenue, Glendale, CA Zip 91204–2508; tel. 818/502–1900; Jack Ivie, President
**Web address:** www.glendalememorial.com

MARIAN MEDICAL CENTER (S, 286 beds) 1400 East Church Street, Santa Maria, CA Zip 93454–5906; tel. 805/739–3000; Charles J. Cova, President and Chief Executive Officer and Senior Vice President Operations Dignity Health Central Coast Service Area
**Web address:** www.marianmedicalcenter.org

MARK TWAIN ST. JOSEPH'S HOSPITAL (O, 25 beds) 768 Mountain Ranch Road, San Andreas, CA Zip 95249–9707; tel. 209/754–3521; Craig J. Marks, FACHE, President
**Web address:** www.marktwainhospital.com

MERCY GENERAL HOSPITAL (S, 286 beds) 4001 J Street, Sacramento, CA Zip 95819–3600; tel. 916/453–4545; Edmundo Castaneda, President
**Web address:** www.mercygeneral.org

MERCY HOSPITAL OF FOLSOM (S, 106 beds) 1650 Creekside Drive, Folsom, CA Zip 95630–3405; tel. 916/983–7400; Michael R. Ricks, President
**Web address:** www.mercyfolsom.org

MERCY HOSPITALS OF BAKERSFIELD (S, 222 beds) 2215 Truxtun Avenue, Bakersfield, CA Zip 93301–3698, Mailing Address: P.O. Box 119, Zip 93302–0119; tel. 661/632–5000; Russell V. Judd, President
**Web address:** www.mercybakersfield.org

MERCY MEDICAL CENTER MERCED (S, 186 beds) 333 Mercy Avenue, Merced, CA Zip 95340–8319; tel. 209/564–5000; David S. Dunham, President
**Web address:** www.mercymercedcares.org

MERCY MEDICAL CENTER MOUNT SHASTA (S, 33 beds) 914 Pine Street, Mount Shasta, CA Zip 96067–2143; tel. 530/926–6111; Kenneth E. S. Platou, President
**Web address:** www.mercymtshasta.org

MERCY MEDICAL CENTER REDDING (S, 260 beds) 2175 Rosaline Avenue, Redding, CA Zip 96001–2549, Mailing Address: P.O. Box 496009, Zip 96049–6009; tel. 530/225–6000; Mark Korth, Chief Executive Officer and Senior Vice President Operations Dignity Health North State Service Area
**Web address:** www.mercy.org

MERCY SAN JUAN MEDICAL CENTER (S, 359 beds) 6501 Coyle Avenue, Carmichael, CA Zip 95608–0306, Mailing Address: P.O. Box 479, Zip 95609–0479; tel. 916/537–5000; Brian K. Ivie, President
**Web address:** www.mercysanjuan.org

METHODIST HOSPITAL OF SACRAMENTO (O, 325 beds) 7500 Hospital Drive, Sacramento, CA Zip 95823–5477; tel. 916/423–3000; Eugene Bassett, President and Chief Executive Officer
**Web address:** www.methodistsacramento.org

NORTHRIDGE HOSPITAL MEDICAL CENTER–ROSCOE BOULEVARD CAMPUS (O, 371 beds) 18300 Roscoe Boulevard, Northridge, CA Zip 91325–4167; tel. 818/885–8500; Saliba Salo, President
**Web address:** www.northridgehospital.org

OAK VALLEY HOSPITAL DISTRICT (O, 150 beds) 350 South Oak Street, Oakdale, CA Zip 95361–3519; tel. 209/847–3011; John McCormick, Chief Executive Officer
**Web address:** www.oakvalleycares.org

SAINT FRANCIS MEMORIAL HOSPITAL (O, 239 beds) 900 Hyde Street, San Francisco, CA Zip 94109–4899, Mailing Address: P.O. Box 7726, Zip 94120–7726; tel. 415/353–6000; Thomas G. Hennessy, President and Chief Executive Officer
**Web address:** www.saintfrancismemorial.org

For explanation of codes following names, see page B2.
★ Indicates Type III membership in the American Hospital Association.

SEQUOIA HOSPITAL (O, 128 beds) 170 Alameda De Las Pulgas, Redwood City, CA Zip 94062–2799; tel. 650/369–5811; Glenna L. Vaskelis, CPA, President and Administrator and Senior Vice President Operations Dignity Health Bay Area Service Area
**Web address:** www.sequoiahospital.org

SIERRA NEVADA MEMORIAL HOSPITAL (O, 121 beds) 155 Glasson Way, Grass Valley, CA Zip 95945–5723, Mailing Address: P.O. Box 1029, Zip 95945–1029; tel. 530/274–6000; Katherine Medeiros, President and Chief Executive Officer
**Web address:** www.snmh.org

ST. BERNARDINE MEDICAL CENTER (S, 250 beds) 2101 North Waterman Avenue, San Bernardino, CA Zip 92404–4836; tel. 909/883–8711; Steven R. Barron, President and Senior Vice President Operations Dignity Health Southern California East Service Area
**Web address:** www.stbernardinemedicalcenter.com

ST. ELIZABETH COMMUNITY HOSPITAL (S, 65 beds) 2550 Sister Mary Columba Drive, Red Bluff, CA Zip 96080–4397; tel. 530/529–8000; G. Todd Smith, President
**Web address:** www.mercy.org

ST. JOHN'S PLEASANT VALLEY HOSPITAL (S, 127 beds) 2309 Antonio Avenue, Camarillo, CA Zip 93010–1414; tel. 805/389–5800; Laurie Eberst, R.N., President and Chief Executive Officer and Senior Vice President Operations Dignity Health Southern California West Service Area
**Web address:** www.stjohnshealth.org

ST. JOHN'S REGIONAL MEDICAL CENTER (S, 161 beds) 1600 North Rose Avenue, Oxnard, CA Zip 93030–3723; tel. 805/988–2500; Laurie Eberst, R.N., President and Chief Executive Officer
**Web address:** www.stjohnshealth.org

ST. JOSEPH'S BEHAVIORAL HEALTH CENTER (S, 35 beds) 2510 North California Street, Stockton, CA Zip 95204–5502; tel. 209/461–2000; Paul Rains, R.N., MSN, President
**Web address:** www.stjosephscanhelp.org

ST. JOSEPH'S MEDICAL CENTER (S, 273 beds) 1800 North California Street, Stockton, CA Zip 95204–6019, Mailing Address: P.O. Box 213008, Zip 95213–9008; tel. 209/943–2000; Donald J. Wiley, President and Chief Executive Officer
**Web address:** www.stjosephsCARES.org

ST. MARY MEDICAL CENTER (S, 165 beds) 1050 Linden Avenue, Long Beach, CA Zip 90813–3321, Mailing Address: P.O. Box 887, Zip 90801–0887; tel. 562/491–9000; Thomas A. Salerno, President and Chief Executive Officer
**Web address:** www.stmarymedicalcenter.org

ST. MARY'S MEDICAL CENTER (S, 232 beds) 450 Stanyan Street, San Francisco, CA Zip 94117–1019; tel. 415/668–1000; Anna Cheung, President
**Web address:** www.stmarysmedicalcenter.com

WOODLAND HEALTHCARE (O, 111 beds) 1325 Cottonwood Street, Woodland, CA Zip 95695–5199; tel. 530/662–3961; H. Kevin Vaziri, President
**Web address:** www.woodlandhealthcare.org

**NEVADA:** ST. ROSE DOMINICAN HOSPITALS – ROSE DE LIMA CAMPUS (S, 119 beds) 102 East Lake Mead Parkway, Henderson, NV Zip 89015–5524; tel. 702/616–5000; Teressa Conley, Interim President and Chief Executive Officer
**Web address:** www.strosehospitals.org

ST. ROSE DOMINICAN HOSPITALS – SAN MARTIN CAMPUS (O, 147 beds) 8280 West Warm Springs Road, Las Vegas, NV Zip 89113–3612; tel. 702/492–8000; Victoria J. VanMeetren, President
**Web address:** www.strosehospitals.org

ST. ROSE DOMINICAN HOSPITALS – SIENA CAMPUS (S, 219 beds) 3001 St. Rose Parkway, Henderson, NV Zip 89052; tel. 702/616–5000; Rod A. Davis, FACHE, President and Chief Executive Officer and Senior Vice President Operations Dignity Health Nevada
**Web address:** www.strosehospitals.com

| | | |
|---|---|---|
| Owned, leased, sponsored: | 37 hospitals | 7882 beds |
| Contract–managed: | 0 hospitals | 0 beds |
| Totals: | 37 hospitals | 7882 beds |

**0029: DIMENSIONS HEALTHCARE SYSTEM** (NP)
3001 Hospital Drive, 3rd Floor, Cheverly, MD Zip 20785–1189; tel. 301/583–4000; Neil J. Moore, President and Chief Executive Officer
**(Moderately Centralized Health System)**

**MARYLAND:** LAUREL REGIONAL HOSPITAL (O, 166 beds) 7300 Van Dusen Road, Laurel, MD Zip 20707–9463; tel. 301/725–4300; John Spearman, President and Chief Operating Officer
**Web address:** www.laurelregionalhospital.org

PRINCE GEORGE'S HOSPITAL CENTER (O, 302 beds) 3001 Hospital Drive, Cheverly, MD Zip 20785–1189; tel. 301/618–2000; John A. O'Brien, FACHE, President
**Web address:** www.princegeorgeshospital.org

| | | |
|---|---|---|
| Owned, leased, sponsored: | 2 hospitals | 468 beds |
| Contract–managed: | 0 hospitals | 0 beds |
| Totals: | 2 hospitals | 468 beds |

**0010: DIVISION OF MENTAL HEALTH AND ADDICTION SERVICES, DEPARTMENT OF HUMAN SERVICES, STATE OF NEW JERSEY** (NP)
222 South Warren Street, Trenton, NJ Zip 08608–2306, Mailing Address: P.O. Box 700, Zip 08625–0700; tel. 609/777–0702; Lynn Kovich, Assistant Commissioner
**(Independent Hospital System)**

**NEW JERSEY:** ANCORA PSYCHIATRIC HOSPITAL (O, 500 beds) 301 Spring Garden Road, Hammonton, NJ Zip 08037–9699; tel. 609/561–1700; Allan Boyer, Chief Executive Officer
**Web address:** www.state.nj.us/humanservices/dmhs/oshm/aph/

GREYSTONE PARK PSYCHIATRIC HOSPITAL (O, 506 beds) 59 Koch Avenue, Morris Plains, NJ Zip 07950–4400; tel. 973/538–1800; Janet J. Monroe, R.N., Chief Executive Officer
**Web address:** www.state.nj.us/humanservices/dmhs/oshm/gpph/

TRENTON PSYCHIATRIC HOSPITAL (O, 392 beds) Route 29 and Sullivan Way, Trenton, NJ Zip 08628–3425, Mailing Address: P.O. Box 7500, West Trenton, Zip 08628–0500; tel. 609/633–1500; Teresa A. McQuaide, Chief Executive Officer
**Web address:** www.state.nj.us/humanservices/dmhs/oshm/tph/

| | | |
|---|---|---|
| Owned, leased, sponsored: | 3 hospitals | 1398 beds |
| Contract–managed: | 0 hospitals | 0 beds |
| Totals: | 3 hospitals | 1398 beds |

**0536: DIVISION OF MENTAL HEALTH, DEPARTMENT OF HUMAN SERVICES** (NP)
319 East Madison Street, S–3B, Springfield, IL Zip 62701–1035; tel. 217/785–6023; Lorrie Rickman Jones, Ph.D., Director
**(Independent Hospital System)**

**ILLINOIS:** ALTON MENTAL HEALTH CENTER (O, 165 beds) 4500 College Avenue, Alton, IL Zip 62002–5099; tel. 618/474–3800; Brian E. Thomas, Administrator

CHESTER MENTAL HEALTH CENTER (O, 245 beds) Chester Road, Chester, IL Zip 62233–0031, Mailing Address: Box 31, Zip 62233–0031; tel. 618/826–4571; Melissa Gross, Interim Administrator

CHICAGO–READ MENTAL HEALTH CENTER (O, 200 beds) 4200 North Oak Park Avenue, Chicago, IL Zip 60634–1457; tel. 773/794–4000; Thomas Simpatico, M.D., Facility Director and Network System Manager

CHOATE MENTAL HEALTH CENTER (O, 79 beds) 1000 North Main Street, Anna, IL Zip 62906–1699; tel. 618/833–5161; Elaine Ray, Administrator

ELGIN MENTAL HEALTH CENTER (O, 500 beds) 750 South State Street, Elgin, IL Zip 60123–7692; tel. 847/742–1040; Amparo Lopez, Region Executive Director
**Web address:** www.dhs.state.il.us

H. DOUGLAS SINGER MENTAL HEALTH AND DEVELOPMENTAL CENTER (O, 162 beds) 4402 North Main Street, Rockford, IL Zip 61103–1278; tel. 815/987–7096; Gail Tennant, Director

---

For explanation of codes following names, see page B2.
★ Indicates Type III membership in the American Hospital Association.

JOHN J. MADDEN MENTAL HEALTH CENTER (O, 150 beds) 1200 South First Avenue, Hines, IL Zip 60141–0800; tel. 708/338–7202; Edith Newman, Interim Administrator

| | | |
|---|---|---|
| **Owned, leased, sponsored:** | 7 hospitals | 1501 beds |
| **Contract–managed:** | 0 hospitals | 0 beds |
| **Totals:** | 7 hospitals | 1501 beds |

---

**★0226: DUBUIS HEALTH SYSTEM (CC)**
1700 West Loop South, Suite 1100A, Houston, TX Zip 77027–3007; tel. 713/277–2300; Stephen Mills, Chief Executive Officer
**(Independent Hospital System)**

**ARKANSAS:** ADVANCE CARE HOSPITAL (C, 26 beds) 300 Werner Street, 3rd Floor East, Hot Springs National Park, AR Zip 71913–6406; tel. 501/609–4300; Keith Rogers, Administrator
**Web address:** www.dubuis.org/AdvanceCareHospitalofHotSprings

ADVANCE CARE HOSPITAL OF FORT SMITH (C, 25 beds) 7301 Rogers Avenue, 4th Floor, Fort Smith, AR Zip 72903–4100; tel. 479/314–4900; Keith Rogers, Interim Administrator
**Web address:** www.dubuis.org/AdvanceCareHospitalofFortSmith

**GEORGIA:** SOUTHERN CRESCENT HOSPITAL FOR SPECIALTY CARE (C, 30 beds) 11 Upper Riverdale Road S.W., 6th Floor, Riverdale, GA Zip 30274–2615; tel. 770/897–7603; Janice Hamilton–Crawford, Administrator
**Web address:** www.dubuis.org/SouthernCrescentHospitalforSpecialtyCare

**IOWA:** CONTINUING CARE HOSPITAL AT ST. LUKE'S (C, 16 beds) 1026 A Avenue N.E., 6th Floor, Cedar Rapids, IA Zip 52402–5036; tel. 319/369–8142; Elly Steffen, Chief Executive Officer and Administrator
**Web address:** www.dubuis.org/ContinuingCareHospitalatStLukes

**LOUISIANA:** DUBUIS HOSPITAL OF ALEXANDRIA (O, 25 beds) 3330 Masonic Drive, 4th Floor, Alexandria, LA Zip 71301–3841; tel. 318/448–4938; Beth Parsons, R.N., Administrator
**Web address:** www.christusdubuis.org/CHRISTUSDubuisHospitalofAlexandriaLA

DUBUIS HOSPITAL OF LAKE CHARLES (O, 24 beds) 524 Dr. Michael DeBakey Drive, 5th Floor, Lake Charles, LA Zip 70601–5725; tel. 337/491–7752; William L. Willis, Administrator
**Web address:** www.dubuis.org/DubuisHospitalofLakeCharles

DUBUIS HOSPITAL OF SHREVEPORT (O, 36 beds) One St. Mary Place, 6th Floor, Shreveport, LA Zip 71101; tel. 318/221–3802; Holly Powell, Interim Administrator
**Web address:** www.dubuis.org/shreveport

**MISSOURI:** MERCY CONTINUING CARE HOSPITAL (O, 54 beds) 13190 South Outer Forty Road, Chesterfield, MO Zip 63017–5917; tel. 314/392–6380; Matthew B. Schweigert, Administrator
**Web address:** www.dubuis.org/mercycontinuingcarehospital

**TEXAS:** CHRISTUS DUBUIS HOSPITAL OF BRYAN (O, 30 beds) 1600 Joseph Drive, 2nd Floor, Bryan, TX Zip 77802–1502; tel. 979/821–5000; Judy Wolfe, Chief Executive Officer
**Web address:** www.dubuis.org/CHRISTUSDubuisHospitalofBryan

CHRISTUS DUBUIS HOSPITAL OF PORT ARTHUR (O, 15 beds) 3600 Gates Boulevard, Port Arthur, TX Zip 77642–3858; tel. 409/989–5300; Jeffrey Livingston, Administrator
**Web address:** www.dubuis.org/CHRISTUSDubuisHospitalofPortArthur

DUBUIS HOSPITAL OF BEAUMONT (O, 51 beds) 2830 Calder Avenue, 4th Floor, Beaumont, TX Zip 77702–1809; tel. 409/899–8154; Jeffrey Livingston, Administrator
**Web address:** www.dubuis.org/BeaumontandPortArthurSystem–CHRISTUSDubuisHospitalofBeaumont

DUBUIS HOSPITAL OF CORPUS CHRISTI (O, 22 beds) 600 Elizabeth Street, 3rd Floor, Corpus Christi, TX Zip 78404–2235; tel. 361/881–3223; Diane Kaiser, Administrator
**Web address:** www.dubuis.org/DubuisHospitalofCorpusChristi

DUBUIS HOSPITAL OF PARIS (O, 25 beds) 865 Deshong Drive, 5th Floor, Paris, TX Zip 75460–9313; tel. 903/782–2961; Kathie Reese, Administrator
**Web address:** www.dubuis.org/CHRISTUSDubuisHospitalofParis

DUBUIS HOSPITAL OF TEXARKANA (O, 49 beds) 2400 St. Michael Drive, 2nd Floor, Texarkana, TX Zip 75503–2372; tel. 903/614–7600; Holly Powell, Administrator
**Web address:** www.dubuis.org/DubuisHospitalofTexarkanaSystem

| | | |
|---|---|---|
| **Owned, leased, sponsored:** | 10 hospitals | 331 beds |
| **Contract–managed:** | 4 hospitals | 97 beds |
| **Totals:** | 14 hospitals | 428 beds |

---

**0861: DUKE LIFEPOINT HEALTHCARE (IO)**
103 Powell Court, Brentwood, TN Zip 37027–5079; tel. 615/372–8540; Jeffrey G. Seraphine, FACHE, Division President
**(Moderately Centralized Health System)**

**NORTH CAROLINA:** MARIA PARHAM MEDICAL CENTER (O, 102 beds) 566 Ruin Creek Road, Henderson, NC Zip 27536–2927; tel. 252/438–4143; Robert G. Singletary, President and Chief Executive Officer
**Web address:** www.mariaparham.com

PERSON MEMORIAL HOSPITAL (O, 106 beds) 615 Ridge Road, Roxboro, NC Zip 27573–4629; tel. 336/599–2121; Chad Brown, M.P.H., Chief Executive Officer
**Web address:** www.personhospital.com

**VIRGINIA:** TWIN COUNTY REGIONAL HOSPITAL (O, 86 beds) 200 Hospital Drive, Galax, VA Zip 24333–2227; tel. 276/236–8181; Jon D. Applebaum, Chief Executive Officer
**Web address:** www.tcrh.org

| | | |
|---|---|---|
| **Owned, leased, sponsored:** | 3 hospitals | 294 beds |
| **Contract–managed:** | 0 hospitals | 0 beds |
| **Totals:** | 3 hospitals | 294 beds |

---

**★0190: DUKE UNIVERSITY HEALTH SYSTEM (NP)**
201 Trent Drive, Durham, NC Zip 27710–3037, Mailing Address: P.O. Box 3701, Zip 27710–3701; tel. 919/684–2255; Victor J. Dzau, M.D., President and Chief Executive Officer
**(Centralized Health System)**

**NORTH CAROLINA:** DUKE RALEIGH HOSPITAL (O, 148 beds) 3400 Wake Forest Road, Raleigh, NC Zip 27609–7373, Mailing Address: P.O. Box 28280, Zip 27611–8280; tel. 919/954–3000; Richard Gannotta, President
**Web address:** www.dukehealthraleigh.org

DUKE UNIVERSITY HOSPITAL (O, 819 beds) 2301 Erwin Road, Durham, NC Zip 27705–4699, Mailing Address: P.O. Box 3708, Zip 27710–3708; tel. 919/684–8111; Kevin W. Sowers, R.N., MSN, President
**Web address:** www.dukehealth.org

DUKE REGIONAL HOSPITAL (L, 194 beds) 3643 North Roxboro Road, Durham, NC Zip 27704–2763; tel. 919/470–4000; Kerry Watson, President
**Web address:** www.durhamregional.org

| | | |
|---|---|---|
| **Owned, leased, sponsored:** | 3 hospitals | 1161 beds |
| **Contract–managed:** | 0 hospitals | 0 beds |
| **Totals:** | 3 hospitals | 1161 beds |

---

**★1895: EAST TEXAS MEDICAL CENTER REGIONAL HEALTHCARE SYSTEM (NP)**
1000 South Beckham Street, Tyler, TX Zip 75701–1908, Mailing Address: P.O. Box 6400, Zip 75711–6400; tel. 903/535–6211; Elmer G. Ellis, FACHE, President and Chief Executive Officer
**(Centralized Physician/Insurance Health System)**

**TEXAS:** EAST TEXAS MEDICAL CENTER ATHENS (L, 127 beds) 2000 South Palestine Street, Athens, TX Zip 75751–5610; tel. 903/676–1000; Patrick L. Wallace, Administrator
**Web address:** www.etmc.org

EAST TEXAS MEDICAL CENTER CARTHAGE (L, 23 beds) 409 Cottage Road, Carthage, TX Zip 75633–1466, Mailing Address: P.O. Box 549, Zip 75633–0549; tel. 903/693–3841; Gary Mikeal Hudson, Administrator
**Web address:** www.etmc.org

EAST TEXAS MEDICAL CENTER CLARKSVILLE (L, 36 beds) 3000 West Main Street, Clarksville, TX Zip 75426–3371, Mailing Address: P.O. Box 1270, Zip 75426–1270; tel. 903/427–6400; Matthew Wylie, Administrator
**Web address:** www.etmc.org

---

For explanation of codes following names, see page B2.
★ Indicates Type III membership in the American Hospital Association.

EAST TEXAS MEDICAL CENTER CROCKETT (L, 49 beds) 1100 Loop 304 East, Crockett, TX Zip 75835–1810; tel. 936/546–3862; Terry Cutler, Administrator and Chief Executive Officer
**Web address:** www.etmc.org

EAST TEXAS MEDICAL CENTER FAIRFIELD (L, 20 beds) 125 Newman Street, Fairfield, TX Zip 75840–1499; tel. 903/389–2121; Ruth Cook, Administrator
**Web address:** www.etmc.org

EAST TEXAS MEDICAL CENTER HENDERSON (O, 47 beds) 300 Wilson Street, Henderson, TX Zip 75652–5956; tel. 903/657–7541; Mark Leitner, Chief Executive Officer
**Web address:** www.etmc.org/etmchenderson/

EAST TEXAS MEDICAL CENTER JACKSONVILLE (O, 38 beds) 501 South Ragsdale Street, Jacksonville, TX Zip 75766–2413; tel. 903/541–5000; Jack R. Endres, Administrator
**Web address:** www.etmc.org

EAST TEXAS MEDICAL CENTER PITTSBURG (L, 25 beds) 2701 Highway 271 North, Pittsburg, TX Zip 75686–1032; tel. 903/946–5000; Jorge E. Leal, Chief Executive Officer
**Web address:** www.etmc.org/newpittsburg.htm

EAST TEXAS MEDICAL CENTER REHABILITATION HOSPITAL (O, 49 beds) 701 Olympic Plaza Circle, Tyler, TX Zip 75701–1950, Mailing Address: P.O. Box 7530, Zip 75711–7530; tel. 903/596–3000; Eddie L. Howard, Vice President and Chief Operating Officer
**Web address:** www.etmc.org

EAST TEXAS MEDICAL CENTER SPECIALTY HOSPITAL (O, 36 beds) 1000 South Beckham, 5th Floor, Tyler, TX Zip 75701–1908, Mailing Address: P.O. Box 7018, Zip 75711–7018; tel. 903/596–3600; Eddie L. Howard, Vice President and Chief Operating Officer
**Web address:** www.etmc.org

EAST TEXAS MEDICAL CENTER TRINITY (L, 22 beds) 317 Prospect Drive, Trinity, TX Zip 75862–6202, Mailing Address: P.O. Box 3169, Zip 75862–3169; tel. 936/744–1100; Brett Kirkham, Administrator
**Web address:** www.etmc.org

EAST TEXAS MEDICAL CENTER TYLER (O, 450 beds) 1000 South Beckham Street, Tyler, TX Zip 75701–1908, Mailing Address: Box 6400, Zip 75711–6400; tel. 903/597–0351; Robert B. Evans, Administrator and Chief Executive Officer
**Web address:** www.etmc.org

EAST TEXAS MEDICAL CENTER–GILMER (O, 35 beds) 712 North Wood Street, Gilmer, TX Zip 75644–1751; tel. 903/841–7100; Jorge E. Leal, Administrator
**Web address:** www.etmc.org

EAST TEXAS MEDICAL CENTER–MOUNT VERNON (L, 30 beds) 500 Highway 37 South, Mount Vernon, TX Zip 75457–6550, Mailing Address: P.O. Box 477, Zip 75457–0477; tel. 903/537–8000; Jamie–Crystal Wylie, Chief Executive Officer
**Web address:** www.etmc.org/etmcmountvernon/

EAST TEXAS MEDICAL CENTER–QUITMAN (L, 25 beds) 117 Winnsboro Street, Quitman, TX Zip 75783–2144, Mailing Address: P.O. Box 1000, Zip 75783–1000; tel. 903/763–6300; Warren Robicheaux, Administrator
**Web address:** www.etmc.org/etmcquitman/

| Owned, leased, sponsored: | 15 hospitals | 1012 beds |
|---|---|---|
| Contract–managed: | 0 hospitals | 0 beds |
| Totals: | 15 hospitals | 1012 beds |

---

**★0270:  EASTERN CONNECTICUT HEALTH NETWORK** (NP)
71 Haynes Street, Manchester, CT Zip 06040–4131; tel. 860/533–3400; Peter J. Karl, President and Chief Executive Officer
**(Centralized Physician/Insurance Health System)**

**CONNECTICUT:** MANCHESTER MEMORIAL HOSPITAL (O, 156 beds) 71 Haynes Street, Manchester, CT Zip 06040–4188; tel. 860/646–1222; Peter J. Karl, President and Chief Executive Officer
**Web address:** www.echn.org

ROCKVILLE GENERAL HOSPITAL (O, 47 beds) 31 Union Street, Vernon Rockville, CT Zip 06066–3160; tel. 860/872–0501; Peter J. Karl, President and Chief Executive Officer
**Web address:** www.echn.org

| Owned, leased, sponsored: | 2 hospitals | 203 beds |
|---|---|---|
| Contract–managed: | 0 hospitals | 0 beds |
| Totals: | 2 hospitals | 203 beds |

---

**★0555:   EASTERN MAINE HEALTHCARE SYSTEMS** (NP)
43 Whiting Hill Road, Brewer, ME Zip 04412–1005; tel. 207/973–7045; M. Michelle Hood, President and Chief Executive Officer
**(Centralized Health System)**

**MAINE:** BLUE HILL MEMORIAL HOSPITAL (O, 25 beds) 57 Water Street, Blue Hill, ME Zip 04614–5231, Mailing Address: P.O. Box 1029, Zip 04614–1029; tel. 207/374–3400; Gregory E. Roraff, President and Chief Executive Officer
**Web address:** www.bhmh.org

CHARLES A. DEAN MEMORIAL HOSPITAL (O, 36 beds) 364 Pritham Avenue, Greenville, ME Zip 04441–1395, Mailing Address: P.O. Box 1129, Zip 04441–1129; tel. 207/695–5200; Geno Murray, President and Chief Executive Officer
**Web address:** www.cadean.org

EASTERN MAINE MEDICAL CENTER (O, 357 beds) 489 State Street, Bangor, ME Zip 04401–6674, Mailing Address: P.O. Box 404, Zip 04402–0404; tel. 207/973–7000; Deborah Carey Johnson, R.N., President and Chief Executive Officer
**Web address:** www.emh.org

INLAND HOSPITAL (O, 46 beds) 200 Kennedy Memorial Drive, Waterville, ME Zip 04901–4595; tel. 207/861–3000; John Dalton, President and Chief Executive Officer
**Web address:** www.inlandhospital.org

SEBASTICOOK VALLEY HEALTH (O, 25 beds) 447 North Main Street, Pittsfield, ME Zip 04967–3707; tel. 207/487–4000; Terri Vieira, Interim Chief Executive Officer
**Web address:** www.sebasticookvalleyhealth.org

THE ACADIA HOSPITAL (O, 68 beds) 268 Stillwater Avenue, Bangor, ME Zip 04401–3945, Mailing Address: P.O. Box 422, Zip 04402–0422; tel. 207/973–6100; Daniel B. Coffey, President and Chief Executive Officer
**Web address:** www.acadiahospital.org

THE AROOSTOOK MEDICAL CENTER (O, 122 beds) 140 Academy Street, Presque Isle, ME Zip 04769–3171, Mailing Address: P.O. Box 151, Zip 04769–0151; tel. 207/768–4000; Sylvia Getman, President and Chief Executive Officer
**Web address:** www.tamc.org

| Owned, leased, sponsored: | 7 hospitals | 679 beds |
|---|---|---|
| Contract–managed: | 0 hospitals | 0 beds |
| Totals: | 7 hospitals | 679 beds |

---

**0879:   EMERUS** (IO)
10077 Grogan's Mill, Suite 100, The Woodlands, TX Zip 77380–1022; tel. 281/292–2450; Toby Hamilton, Chief Executive Officer

**TEXAS:** BAYLOR EMERGENCY MEDICAL CENTER AT AUBREY (O, 8 beds) 26791 Highway 380, Aubrey, TX Zip 76227; tel. 972/347–2525; John Wood, Chief Executive Officer
**Web address:** www.emerus.com

EMERUS (O, 7 beds) 16000 Southwest Freeway, Suite 100, Sugar Land, TX Zip 77479–2674; tel. 281/277–0911; Mike Kohler, Chief Executive Officer
**Web address:** www.emerus.com

| Owned, leased, sponsored: | 2 hospitals | 15 beds |
|---|---|---|
| Contract–managed: | 0 hospitals | 0 beds |
| Totals: | 2 hospitals | 15 beds |

---

For explanation of codes following names, see page B2.
★ Indicates Type III membership in the American Hospital Association.

Section B

**★0256: EMORY HEALTHCARE** (NP)
1440 Clifton Road N.E., Suite 145, Atlanta, GA Zip 30322–1102;
tel. 404/778–5000; John T. Fox, Chief Executive Officer
**(Centralized Health System)**

**GEORGIA:** EMORY JOHNS CREEK HOSPITAL (O, 84 beds) 6325 Hospital
Parkway, Johns Creek, GA Zip 30097–5775; tel. 678/474–7000; Craig
McCoy, Chief Executive Officer
**Web address:** www.emoryjohnscreek.com

EMORY UNIVERSITY HOSPITAL (O, 579 beds) 1364 Clifton Road N.E., Atlanta,
GA Zip 30322–1102; tel. 404/712–2000; Robert J. Bachman, Chief
Operating Officer
**Web address:** www.emoryhealthcare.org

EMORY UNIVERSITY HOSPITAL MIDTOWN (O, 435 beds) 550 Peachtree
Street N.E., Atlanta, GA Zip 30308–2247; tel. 404/686–4411; Dane C.
Peterson, Chief Operating Officer
**Web address:** www.emoryhealthcare.org

SAINT JOSEPH'S HOSPITAL OF ATLANTA (O, 253 beds) 5665 Peachtree
Dunwoody Road N.E., Atlanta, GA Zip 30342–1701; tel. 678/843–7001;
Scott Schmidly, Chief Executive Officer
**Web address:** www.stjosephsatlanta.org

WESLEY WOODS GERIATRIC HOSPITAL OF EMORY UNIVERSITY (O, 276 beds)
1821 Clifton Road N.E., Atlanta, GA Zip 30329–4021; tel. 404/728–6200;
William Such, Chief Executive Officer
**Web address:** www.emoryhealthcare.org

WESLEY WOODS LONG TERM CARE HOSPITAL (O, 18 beds) 1821 Clifton
Road N.E., 2nd Floor, Atlanta, GA Zip 30329–4021; tel. 404/728–6200;
William Such, Chief Executive Officer
**Web address:** www.emoryhealthcare.org

| Owned, leased, sponsored: | 6 hospitals | 1645 beds |
|---|---|---|
| Contract–managed: | 0 hospitals | 0 beds |
| Totals: | 6 hospitals | 1645 beds |

**0647: ENCORE HEALTHCARE** (IO)
7150 Columbia Gateway Drive, Suite J., Columbia, MD
Zip 21046–2974; tel. 443/539–2350; Tim Nicholson, Chief
Executive Officer
**(Independent Hospital System)**

**OKLAHOMA:** SPECIALTY HOSPITAL OF MIDWEST CITY (O, 31 beds) 8210
National Avenue, Midwest City, OK Zip 73110–8518; tel. 405/739–0800;
Chad Lovett, Chief Executive Officer
**Web address:** www.encore–healthcare.com/specialty_midwest/index.
aspx

**TEXAS:** MESA HILLS SPECIALTY HOSPITAL (O, 32 beds) 2311 North Oregon
Street, El Paso, TX Zip 79902–3216; tel. 915/545–1823; Jesus Ruiz,
Chief Executive Officer
**Web address:** www.encore–healthcare.com/mesa_hills/index.aspx

PLANO SPECIALTY HOSPITAL (O, 43 beds) 1621 Coit Road, Plano, TX
Zip 75075–6141; tel. 972/758–5200; Jerry Amato, Chief Executive Officer
**Web address:** www.encore–healthcare.com/plano/index.aspx

PLUM CREEK SPECIALTY HOSPITAL (O, 47 beds) 5601 Plum Creek Drive,
Amarillo, TX Zip 79124–1801; tel. 806/351–1000; Billy Blasingame, Chief
Executive Officer
**Web address:** www.specialtyhospital–plumcreek.net

| Owned, leased, sponsored: | 4 hospitals | 153 beds |
|---|---|---|
| Contract–managed: | 0 hospitals | 0 beds |
| Totals: | 4 hospitals | 153 beds |

**0525: ERLANGER HEALTH SYSTEM** (NP)
975 East Third Street, Chattanooga, TN Zip 37403–2147;
tel. 423/778–7000; Kevin M. Spiegel, FACHE, President and Chief
Executive Officer
**(Independent Hospital System)**

**GEORGIA:** ERLANGER AT HUTCHESON (C, 185 beds) 100 Gross Crescent
Circle, Fort Oglethorpe, GA Zip 30742–3669; tel. 706/858–2000; Roger
Forgey, President and Chief Executive Officer
**Web address:** www.hutcheson.org

**TENNESSEE:** ERLANGER BLEDSOE HOSPITAL (C, 25 beds) 71 Wheeler
Avenue, Pikeville, TN Zip 37367, Mailing Address: P.O. Box 699,
Zip 37367–0699; tel. 423/447–2112; Stephanie Boynton, Administrator
**Web address:** www.erlanger.org

ERLANGER MEDICAL CENTER (O, 540 beds) 632 Morrison Springs Road,
Chattanooga, TN Zip 37415–3402; tel. 423/778–7000; Kevin M. Spiegel,
FACHE, Chief Executive Officer
**Web address:** www.erlanger.org

| Owned, leased, sponsored: | 1 hospital | 540 beds |
|---|---|---|
| Contract–managed: | 2 hospitals | 210 beds |
| Totals: | 3 hospitals | 750 beds |

**0382: ERNEST HEALTH, INC.** (IO)
7770 Jefferson Street N.E., Suite 320, Albuquerque, NM
Zip 87109–4386; tel. 505/856–5300; Darby Brockette, Chief
Executive Officer
**(Independent Hospital System)**

**ARIZONA:** MOUNTAIN VALLEY REGIONAL REHABILITATION HOSPITAL (O, 16
beds) 3700 North Windsong Drive, Prescott Valley, AZ Zip 86314–1253;
tel. 928/759–8800; Judy Baum, Chief Executive Officer
**Web address:** www.mvrrh.ernesthealth.com

**COLORADO:** NORTHERN COLORADO LONG TERM ACUTE HOSPITAL (O, 20
beds) 4401A Union Street, Johnstown, CO Zip 80534;
tel. 970/619–3663; Dawn Morrissey, Chief Operating Officer
**Web address:** www.ncltah.ernesthealth.com/

NORTHERN COLORADO REHABILITATION HOSPITAL (O, 40 beds) 4401 Union
Street, Johnstown, CO Zip 80534–2800; tel. 970/619–3400; Sharon
Scheller, Chief Executive Officer
**Web address:** www.ncrh.ernesthealth.com

**IDAHO:** NORTHERN IDAHO ADVANCED CARE HOSPITAL (O, 40 beds) 600
North Cecil Road, Post Falls, ID Zip 83854–6200; tel. 208/262–2800;
Maria Godley, R.N., Chief Executive Officer
**Web address:** www.niach.ernesthealth.com

SOUTHWEST IDAHO ADVANCED CARE HOSPITAL (O, 40 beds) 6651 West
Franklin Road, Boise, ID Zip 83709–0914; tel. 208/376–5700; Nolan Hoffer,
Chief Executive Officer
**Web address:** www.siach.ernesthealth.com/

**MONTANA:** ADVANCED CARE HOSPITAL OF MONTANA (O, 40 beds) 3528
Gabel Road, Billings, MT Zip 59102–7307; tel. 406/373–8000; Kerry
Ashment, Chief Executive Officer
**Web address:** www.achm.ernesthealth.com

**NEW MEXICO:** ADVANCED CARE HOSPITAL OF SOUTHERN NEW MEXICO (O,
40 beds) 4451 East Lohman Avenue, Las Cruces, NM Zip 88011–8267;
tel. 575/521–6600; Suzanne Quillen, R.N., Chief Executive Officer
**Web address:** www.achsnm.ernesthealth.com

REHABILITATION HOSPITAL OF SOUTHERN NEW MEXICO (O, 40 beds) 4441
East Lohman Avenue, Las Cruces, NM Zip 88011–8267; tel. 575/521–6400;
Sabrina Martin, Chief Operating Officer
**Web address:** www.rhsnm.ernesthealth.com

**SOUTH CAROLINA:** GREENWOOD REGIONAL REHABILITATION HOSPITAL (O,
56 beds) 1530 Parkway, Greenwood, SC Zip 29646–4027;
tel. 864/330–9070; Kerry A. Trapnell, Chief Executive Officer
**Web address:** www.grrh.ernesthealth.com

**TEXAS:** LAREDO SPECIALTY HOSPITAL (O, 60 beds) 2005 Bustamente
Street, Laredo, TX Zip 78041–5470; tel. 956/753–5353; Mario
Rodriguez, Chief Executive Officer
**Web address:** www.lsh.ernesthealth.com

MESQUITE REHABILITATION INSTITUTE (O, 20 beds) 1023 North Belt Line
Road, Mesquite, TX Zip 75149–1788; tel. 972/216–2400; Brian Abraham,
Chief Operating Officer
**Web address:** www.mesquiterehab.ernesthealth.com/

MESQUITE SPECIALTY HOSPITAL (O, 40 beds) 1024 North Galloway Avenue,
Mesquite, TX Zip 75149–2434; tel. 972/216–2300; Louis Bradley, Chief
Operating Officer
**Web address:** www.msh.ernesthealth.com

For explanation of codes following names, see page B2.
★ Indicates Type III membership in the American Hospital Association.

Section B

NEW BRAUNFELS REGIONAL REHABILITATION HOSPITAL (O, 40 beds) 2041 Sundance Parkway, New Braunfels, TX Zip 78130–2779; tel. 830/625–6700; Jennifer Malatek, Chief Executive Officer
**Web address:** www.nbrrh.ernesthealth.com

SOUTH TEXAS REHABILITATION HOSPITAL (O, 40 beds) 425 East Alton Gloor Boulevard, Brownsville, TX Zip 78526–3361; tel. 956/554–6000; Jessie Eason Smedley, Chief Executive Officer
**Web address:** www.strh.ernesthealth.com

**UTAH:** UTAH VALLEY SPECIALTY HOSPITAL (O, 40 beds) 306 River Bend Lane, Provo, UT Zip 84604–5625; tel. 801/226–8880; Marie Prothero, R.N., MSN, Chief Executive Officer
**Web address:** www.uvsh.ernesthealth.com

**WYOMING:** ELKHORN VALLEY REHABILITATION HOSPITAL (O, 40 beds) 5715 East 2nd Street, Casper, WY Zip 82609–4322; tel. 307/265–0005; Michael Phillips, Chief Executive Officer
**Web address:** www.evrh.ernesthealth.com/

| Owned, leased, sponsored: | 16 hospitals | 612 beds |
| --- | --- | --- |
| Contract–managed: | 0 hospitals | 0 beds |
| Totals: | 16 hospitals | 612 beds |

---

## 0396: ESSENTIA HEALTH (NP)
502 East Second Street, Duluth, MN Zip 55805–1913; tel. 218/786–8376; Peter E. Person, M.D., Chief Executive Officer
**(Moderately Centralized Health System)**

**IDAHO:** CLEARWATER VALLEY HOSPITAL AND CLINICS (O, 23 beds) 301 Cedar, Orofino, ID Zip 83544–9029; tel. 208/476–4555; Lenne Bonner, Interim Chief Executive Officer
**Web address:** www.smh–cvhc.org

ST. MARY'S HOSPITAL (O, 28 beds) Lewiston and North Streets, Cottonwood, ID Zip 83522–9750, Mailing Address: P.O. Box 137, Zip 83522–0137; tel. 208/962–3251; Lenne Bonner, Interim Chief Executive Officer
**Web address:** www.smh–cvhc.org/getpage.php?name=index

**MINNESOTA:** ESSENTIA HEALTH ADA (O, 14 beds) 201 9th Street West, Ada, MN Zip 56510–1279; tel. 218/784–5000; Ryan Hill, Interim Chief Executive Officer
**Web address:** www.essentiahealth.org

ESSENTIA HEALTH DULUTH (O, 154 beds) 502 East Second Street, Duluth, MN Zip 55805–1982; tel. 218/727–8762; Barb Wessberg, Administrator
**Web address:** www.smdcmedicalcenter.org

ESSENTIA HEALTH FOSSTON (O, 75 beds) 900 Hilligoss Boulevard S.E., Fosston, MN Zip 56542–1599; tel. 218/435–1133; Kevin Gish, Administrator and Vice President
**Web address:** www.firstcare.org

ESSENTIA HEALTH NORTHERN PINES (O, 58 beds) 5211 Highway 110, Aurora, MN Zip 55705–1599; tel. 218/229–2211; Laura Ackman, Chief Operating Officer and Administrator
**Web address:** www.essentiahealth.org/NorthernPines/FindaClinic/Essentia–HealthNorthern–Pines–36.aspx

ESSENTIA HEALTH SANDSTONE (O, 85 beds) 109 Court Avenue South, Sandstone, MN Zip 55072–5120; tel. 320/245–2212; Michael D. Hedrix, Interim Chief Executive Officer
**Web address:** www.pinemedicalcenter.org

ESSENTIA HEALTH ST. JOSEPH'S MEDICAL CENTER (O, 162 beds) 523 North Third Street, Brainerd, MN Zip 56401–3098; tel. 218/829–2861; Adam Rees, President
**Web address:** www.sjmcmn.org

ESSENTIA HEALTH ST. MARY'S HOSPITAL – DETROIT LAKES (O, 131 beds) 1027 Washington Avenue, Detroit Lakes, MN Zip 56501–3409; tel. 218/847–5611; Peter Jacobson, President
**Web address:** www.trustedcareforlife.org

ESSENTIA HEALTH ST. MARY'S MEDICAL CENTER (O, 341 beds) 407 East Third Street, Duluth, MN Zip 55805–1984; tel. 218/786–4000; Daniel B. McGinty, Administrator
**Web address:** www.essentiahealth.org/StMarysMedicalCenter/FindaClinic/Essentia–HealthSt–Marys–Medical–Center–46.aspx

ESSENTIA HEALTH–HOLY TRINITY HOSPITAL (O, 65 beds) 115 West Second Street, Graceville, MN Zip 56240–4845, Mailing Address: P.O. Box 157, Zip 56240–0157; tel. 320/748–7223; John Campion, Administrator
**Web address:** www.essentiahealth.org/HolyTrinityHospital/FindaClinic/Essentia–HealthHoly–Trinity–Hospital–96.aspx

MINNESOTA VALLEY HEALTH CENTER (O, 110 beds) 621 South Fourth Street, Le Sueur, MN Zip 56058–2298; tel. 507/665–3375; Pam Williams, Chief Executive Officer
**Web address:** www.mvhc.org

**NORTH DAKOTA:** ESSENTIA HEALTH FARGO (O, 117 beds) 3000 32nd Avenue South, Fargo, ND Zip 58103–6132; tel. 701/364–8000; Greg Glasner, M.D., Interim President and Chief Executive Officer
**Web address:** www.essentiahealth.com

**WISCONSIN:** ESSENTIA HEALTH ST. MARY'S HOSPITAL OF SUPERIOR (O, 25 beds) 3500 Tower Avenue, Superior, WI Zip 54880–5395; tel. 715/817–7000; Terry Jacobson, Administrator and Chief Executive Officer
**Web address:** www.essentiahealth.org/StMarysHospitalSuperior/FindaClinic/Essentia–Health–St–Marys–HospitalSu.aspx

| Owned, leased, sponsored: | 14 hospitals | 1388 beds |
| --- | --- | --- |
| Contract–managed: | 0 hospitals | 0 beds |
| Totals: | 14 hospitals | 1388 beds |

---

## 2395: EXCELA HEALTH (NP)
134 Industrial Park Road, Greensburg, PA Zip 15601–7328; tel. 724/832–5050; Robert Rogalski, Chief Executive Officer
**(Centralized Health System)**

**PENNSYLVANIA:** EXCELA FRICK HOSPITAL (O, 65 beds) 508 South Church Street, Mount Pleasant, PA Zip 15666–1790; tel. 724/547–1500; Ronald H. Ott, President
**Web address:** www.excelahealth.org/PatientsandVisitors/HospitalsFacilities/Hospitals/Frick.aspx

EXCELA HEALTH WESTMORELAND HOSPITAL (O, 359 beds) 532 West Pittsburgh Street, Greensburg, PA Zip 15601–2282; tel. 724/832–4000; Ronald H. Ott, President
**Web address:** www.excelahealth.org

EXCELA LATROBE AREA HOSPITAL (O, 121 beds) One Mellon Way, Latrobe, PA Zip 15650–1096; tel. 724/537–1000; Michael D. Busch, Executive Vice President and Chief Operating Officer
**Web address:** www.excelahealth.org

| Owned, leased, sponsored: | 3 hospitals | 545 beds |
| --- | --- | --- |
| Contract–managed: | 0 hospitals | 0 beds |
| Totals: | 3 hospitals | 545 beds |

---

## ★1325: FAIRVIEW HEALTH SERVICES (NP)
2450 Riverside Avenue, Minneapolis, MN Zip 55454–1400; tel. 612/672–6141; Charles Mooty, Interim Chief Executive Officer
**(Centralized Physician/Insurance Health System)**

**MINNESOTA:** FAIRVIEW LAKES HEALTH SERVICES (O, 47 beds) 5200 Fairview Boulevard, Wyoming, MN Zip 55092–8013; tel. 651/982–7000; Steven C. Housh, President
**Web address:** www.fairview.org/

FAIRVIEW NORTHLAND MEDICAL CENTER (O, 31 beds) 911 Northland Drive, Princeton, MN Zip 55371–2173; tel. 763/389–1313; John W. Herman, Chief Executive Officer
**Web address:** www.northland.fairview.org

FAIRVIEW RIDGES HOSPITAL (O, 165 beds) 201 East Nicollet Boulevard, Burnsville, MN Zip 55337–5799; tel. 952/892–2000; Beth Krehbiel, President and Chief Executive Officer
**Web address:** www.fairview.org

FAIRVIEW SOUTHDALE HOSPITAL (O, 326 beds) 6401 France Avenue South, Edina, MN Zip 55435–2199; tel. 952/924–5000; Bradley Beard, President
**Web address:** www.fairview.org

Section B

---

For explanation of codes following names, see page B2.
★ Indicates Type III membership in the American Hospital Association.

RANGE REGIONAL HEALTH SERVICES (O, 85 beds) 750 East 34th Street, Hibbing, MN Zip 55746–4600; tel. 218/262–4881; Debra K. Boardman, FACHE, President and Chief Executive Officer
**Web address:** www.range.fairview.org

UNIVERSITY OF MINNESOTA MEDICAL CENTER, FAIRVIEW (O, 825 beds) 2450 Riverside Avenue, Minneapolis, MN Zip 55454–1400; tel. 612/672–6000; Carolyn Wilson, President
**Web address:** www.fairview.org

| Owned, leased, sponsored: | 6 hospitals | 1479 beds |
|---|---|---|
| Contract–managed: | 0 hospitals | 0 beds |
| **Totals:** | 6 hospitals | 1479 beds |

## 0814:  FAITH REGIONAL HEALTH SERVICES (NP)
2700 West Norfolk Avenue, Norfolk, NE Zip 68701–4438, Mailing Address: P.O. Box 869, Zip 68702–0869; tel. 402/644–7201; Tim Auwarter, Interim President and Chief Executive Officer
**(Moderately Centralized Health System)**

**NEBRASKA:** FAITH REGIONAL HEALTH SERVICES (O, 146 beds) 2700 West Norfolk Avenue, Norfolk, NE Zip 68701–4438, Mailing Address: P.O. Box 869, Zip 68702–0869; tel. 402/644–7201; Tim Auwarter, Interim President and Chief Executive Officer
**Web address:** www.frhs.org

NIOBRARA VALLEY HOSPITAL (C, 20 beds) 401 South Fifth Street, Lynch, NE Zip 68746–0118, Mailing Address: P.O. Box 118, Zip 68746–0118; tel. 402/569–2451; Kelly Kalkowski, Chief Executive Officer
**Web address:** www.ci.lynch.ne.us/health.htm

TILDEN COMMUNITY HOSPITAL (C, 12 beds) 308 West Second Street, Tilden, NE Zip 68781–4760, Mailing Address: P.O. Box 340, Zip 68781–0340; tel. 402/368–5343; Lon Knievel, Chief Executive Officer
**Web address:** www.tildenhospital.org

WEST HOLT MEMORIAL HOSPITAL (C, 18 beds) 406 West Neely Street, Atkinson, NE Zip 68713–4801; tel. 402/925–2811; Michael F. Coyle, Chief Executive Officer
**Web address:** www.westholtmed.org

| Owned, leased, sponsored: | 1 hospital | 146 beds |
|---|---|---|
| Contract–managed: | 3 hospitals | 50 beds |
| **Totals:** | 4 hospitals | 196 beds |

## 0397:  FINGER LAKES HEALTH (NP)
196 North Street, Geneva, NY Zip 14456–1651; tel. 315/787–4000; Jose Acevedo, M.D., President and Chief Executive Officer
**(Independent Hospital System)**

**NEW YORK:** GENEVA GENERAL HOSPITAL (O, 132 beds) 196 North Street, Geneva, NY Zip 14456–1694; tel. 315/787–4000; Jose Acevedo, M.D., President and Chief Executive Officer
**Web address:** www.flhealth.org

SOLDIERS AND SAILORS MEMORIAL HOSPITAL OF YATES COUNTY (O, 186 beds) 418 North Main Street, Penn Yan, NY Zip 14527–1085; tel. 315/531–2000; Jose Acevedo, M.D., President and Chief Executive Officer
**Web address:** www.flhealth.org

| Owned, leased, sponsored: | 2 hospitals | 318 beds |
|---|---|---|
| Contract–managed: | 0 hospitals | 0 beds |
| **Totals:** | 2 hospitals | 318 beds |

## ★0243:  FIRSTHEALTH OF THE CAROLINAS (NP)
155 Memorial Drive, Pinehurst, NC Zip 28374–8710, Mailing Address: P.O. Box 3000, Zip 28374–3000; tel. 910/715–1000; David J. Kilarski, Chief Executive Officer
**(Centralized Physician/Insurance Health System)**

**NORTH CAROLINA:** FIRSTHEALTH MONTGOMERY MEMORIAL HOSPITAL (O, 25 beds) 520 Allen Street, Troy, NC Zip 27371–2802, Mailing Address: P.O. Box 486, Zip 27371–0486; tel. 910/572–1301; Beth Walker, R.N., President
**Web address:** www.firsthealth.org

FIRSTHEALTH MOORE REGIONAL HOSPITAL (O, 379 beds) 155 Memorial Drive, Pinehurst, NC Zip 28374–8710, Mailing Address: P.O. Box 3000, Zip 28374–3000; tel. 910/715–1000; David J. Kilarski, Chief Executive Officer
**Web address:** www.firsthealth.org

FIRSTHEALTH RICHMOND MEMORIAL HOSPITAL (O, 91 beds) 925 Long Drive, Rockingham, NC Zip 28379–4835; tel. 910/417–3000; John J. Jackson, President
**Web address:** www.firsthealth.org

| Owned, leased, sponsored: | 3 hospitals | 495 beds |
|---|---|---|
| Contract–managed: | 0 hospitals | 0 beds |
| **Totals:** | 3 hospitals | 495 beds |

## 0378:  FIVE STAR QUALITY CARE (IO)
400 Centre Street, Newton, MA Zip 02458–2094; tel. 617/796–8387; Bruce J. Mackey, Jr., President and Chief Executive Officer
**(Independent Hospital System)**

**MASSACHUSETTS:** BRAINTREE REHABILITATION HOSPITAL (O, 187 beds) 250 Pond Street, Braintree, MA Zip 02184–5351; tel. 781/348–2500; Randy Doherty, CPA, Chief Executive Officer
**Web address:** www.braintreerehabhospital.com

NEW ENGLAND REHABILITATION HOSPITAL (O, 210 beds) Two Rehabilitation Way, Woburn, MA Zip 01801–6098; tel. 781/935–5050; Joel Rudin, Chief Executive Officer
**Web address:** www.newenglandrehab.com

| Owned, leased, sponsored: | 2 hospitals | 397 beds |
|---|---|---|
| Contract–managed: | 0 hospitals | 0 beds |
| **Totals:** | 2 hospitals | 397 beds |

## 0900:  FOUNDATION SURGICAL HOSPITAL AFFILIATES (IO)
14000 North Portland Avenue, Suite 204, Oklahoma City, OK Zip 73134–4002; tel. 405/608–1700; Thomas A. Michaud, Chief Executive Officer

**TEXAS:** FOUNDATION SURGICAL HOSPITAL OF EL PASO (O, 20 beds) 1416 George Dieter Drive, El Paso, TX Zip 79936–7601; tel. 915/598–4240; Marta Contreras, Chief Nursing Officer and Chief Operating Officer
**Web address:** www.physiciansmedcenter.com

FOUNDATION SURGICAL HOSPITAL OF SAN ANTONIO (O, 20 beds) 9522 Huebner Road, San Antonio, TX Zip 78240–1548; tel. 210/478–5400; Robert Trussell, Chief Executive Officer
**Web address:** www.fshsanantonio.com/bariatric–foundation–surgical.html

HERITAGE PARK SURGICAL HOSPITAL (O, 12 beds) 3601 North Calais Street, Sherman, TX Zip 75090–1785; tel. 903/870–0999; Raymond Ford, Chief Executive Officer
**Web address:** www.heritageparksurgicalhospital.com

HOUSTON ORTHOPEDIC AND SPINE HOSPITAL (O, 64 beds) 5410 West Loop South, Bellaire, TX Zip 77401–2103; tel. 713/314–4500; Andrew Knizley, Chief Executive Officer
**Web address:** www.foundationsurgicalhospital.com

| Owned, leased, sponsored: | 4 hospitals | 116 beds |
|---|---|---|
| Contract–managed: | 0 hospitals | 0 beds |
| **Totals:** | 4 hospitals | 116 beds |

## 5345:  FRANCISCAN ALLIANCE (CC)
1515 Dragoon Trail, Mishawaka, IN Zip 46544–4710, Mailing Address: P.O. Box 1290, Zip 46546–1290; tel. 574/256–3935; Kevin D. Leahy, President and Chief Executive Officer
**(Moderately Centralized Health System)**

**ILLINOIS:** FRANCISCAN ST. JAMES HOSPITAL AND HEALTH CENTERS (O, 398 beds) 20201 South Crawford Avenue, Olympia Fields, IL Zip 60461–1010; tel. 708/747–4000; Seth C. R. Warren, President
**Web address:** www.stjameshhc.org

For explanation of codes following names, see page B2.
★ Indicates Type III membership in the American Hospital Association.

**INDIANA:** FRANCISCAN PHYSICIANS HOSPITAL (O, 32 beds) 701 Superior Avenue, Munster, IN Zip 46321–4037; tel. 219/924–1300; Barbara M. Greene, President
**Web address:** www.franciscanphysicianshospital.org

FRANCISCAN ST. ANTHONY HEALTH – CROWN POINT (O, 254 beds) 1201 South Main Street, Crown Point, IN Zip 46307–8483; tel. 219/738–2100; David Ruskowski, President
**Web address:** www.stanthonymedicalcenter.com

FRANCISCAN ST. ANTHONY HEALTH – MICHIGAN CITY (O, 171 beds) 301 West Homer Street, Michigan City, IN Zip 46360–4358; tel. 219/879–8511; James Callaghan, III, M.D., President
**Web address:** www.saintanthonymemorial.org

FRANCISCAN ST. ELIZABETH HEALTH – CRAWFORDSVILLE (O, 76 beds) 1710 Lafayette Road, Crawfordsville, IN Zip 47933–1099; tel. 765/362–2800; Thomas R. Peck, Chief Executive Officer
**Web address:** www.stclaremedical.org

FRANCISCAN ST. ELIZABETH HEALTH – LAFAYETTE CENTRAL (O, 302 beds) 1501 Hartford Street, Lafayette, IN Zip 47904–2134; tel. 765/423–6011; Terrance E. Wilson, President and Chief Executive Officer
**Web address:** www.ste.org

FRANCISCAN ST. ELIZABETH HEALTH – LAFAYETTE EAST (O, 140 beds) 1701 South Creasy Lane, Lafayette, IN Zip 47905–4972; tel. 765/502–4000; Terrance E. Wilson, President and Chief Executive Officer
**Web address:** www.ste.org

FRANCISCAN ST. FRANCIS HEALTH – INDIANAPOLIS (O, 486 beds) 8111 South Emerson Avenue, Indianapolis, IN Zip 46237–8601; tel. 317/528–5000; Robert J. Brody, President and Chief Executive Officer
**Web address:** www.stfrancishospitals.org

FRANCISCAN ST. FRANCIS HEALTH – MOORESVILLE (O, 116 beds) 1201 Hadley Road, Mooresville, IN Zip 46158–1789; tel. 317/831–1160; D. Keith Jewell, Interim Chief Executive Officer
**Web address:** www.franciscanalliance.org/hospitals/mooresville/Pages/default.aspx

FRANCISCAN ST. FRANCIS HEALTH–CARMEL (O, 6 beds) 12188B North Meridian Street, Carmel, IN Zip 46032–4840; tel. 317/705–4500; Robert J. Brody, Chief Executive Officer
**Web address:** www.franciscanalliance.org/hospitals/carmel/Pages/default.aspx

FRANCISCAN ST. MARGARET HEALTH – HAMMOND (O, 500 beds) 5454 Hohman Avenue, Hammond, IN Zip 46320–1999; tel. 219/933–2074; Thomas J. Gryzbek, President
**Web address:** www.smmhc.com

| | | |
|---|---|---|
| Owned, leased, sponsored: | 11 hospitals | 2481 beds |
| Contract–managed: | 0 hospitals | 0 beds |
| Totals: | 11 hospitals | 2481 beds |

---

★**1475: FRANCISCAN MISSIONARIES OF OUR LADY HEALTH SYSTEM, INC.** (CC)
4200 Essen Lane, Baton Rouge, LA Zip 70809–2158; tel. 225/923–2701; John J. Finan, Jr., FACHE, President and Chief Executive Officer
**(Moderately Centralized Health System)**

**LOUISIANA:** ASSUMPTION COMMUNITY HOSPITAL (O, 6 beds) 135 Highway 402, Napoleonville, LA Zip 70390–2217; tel. 985/369–3600; Wayne M. Arboneaux, Chief Executive Officer
**Web address:** www.ololrmc.com

OUR LADY OF LOURDES REGIONAL MEDICAL CENTER (O, 186 beds) 4801 Ambassador Caffery Parkway, Lafayette, LA Zip 70508–6917; tel. 337/470–2000; William F. Barrow, II, President and Chief Executive Officer
**Web address:** www.lourdesrmc.com

OUR LADY OF THE LAKE REGIONAL MEDICAL CENTER (O, 1042 beds) 5000 Hennessy Boulevard, Baton Rouge, LA Zip 70808–4375; tel. 225/765–6565; K. Scott Wester, FACHE, President and Chief Executive Officer
**Web address:** www.ololrmc.com

ST. ELIZABETH HOSPITAL (O, 48 beds) 1125 West Highway 30, Gonzales, LA Zip 70737–5004; tel. 225/647–5000; Robert Burgess, President and Chief Executive Officer
**Web address:** www.steh.com

ST. FRANCIS MEDICAL CENTER (O, 343 beds) 309 Jackson Street, Monroe, LA Zip 71201–7407, Mailing Address: P.O. Box 1901, Zip 71210–1901; tel. 318/966–4000; Louis H. Bremer, Jr., President and Chief Executive Officer
**Web address:** www.stfran.com

| | | |
|---|---|---|
| Owned, leased, sponsored: | 5 hospitals | 1625 beds |
| Contract–managed: | 0 hospitals | 0 beds |
| Totals: | 5 hospitals | 1625 beds |

---

★**1455: FRANCISCAN SISTERS OF CHRISTIAN CHARITY SPONSORED MINISTRIES, INC.** (CC)
1415 South Rapids Road, Manitowoc, WI Zip 54220–9302; tel. 920/684–7071; Sister Laura J. Wolf, President
**(Moderately Centralized Health System)**

**NEBRASKA:** ST. FRANCIS MEMORIAL HOSPITAL (O, 92 beds) 430 North Monitor Street, West Point, NE Zip 68788–1555; tel. 402/372–2404; Ronald O. Briggs, FACHE, President and Chief Executive Officer
**Web address:** www.fcswp.org

**OHIO:** GENESIS HEALTHCARE SYSTEM (O, 353 beds) 2951 Maple Avenue, Zanesville, OH Zip 43701–1406; tel. 740/454–5000; Matthew J. Perry, President and Chief Executive Officer
**Web address:** www.genesishcs.org

**WISCONSIN:** HOLY FAMILY MEMORIAL (O, 62 beds) 2300 Western Avenue, Manitowoc, WI Zip 54220–3712, Mailing Address: P.O. Box 1450, Zip 54221–1450; tel. 920/320–2011; Mark P. Herzog, President and Chief Executive Officer
**Web address:** www.hfmhealth.org

| | | |
|---|---|---|
| Owned, leased, sponsored: | 3 hospitals | 507 beds |
| Contract–managed: | 0 hospitals | 0 beds |
| Totals: | 3 hospitals | 507 beds |

---

★**0271: FREEMAN HEALTH SYSTEM** (NP)
1102 West 32nd Street, Joplin, MO Zip 64804–3503; tel. 417/347–1111; Paula F. Baker, President and Chief Executive Officer
**(Centralized Health System)**

**MISSOURI:** FREEMAN HOSPITAL WEST (O, 413 beds) 1102 West 32nd Street, Joplin, MO Zip 64804–3503; tel. 417/347–1111; Paula F. Baker, President and Chief Executive Officer
**Web address:** www.freemanhealth.com

FREEMAN NEOSHO HOSPITAL (O, 25 beds) 113 West Hickory Street, Neosho, MO Zip 64850–1705; tel. 417/455–4352; Paula F. Baker, President and Chief Executive Officer
**Web address:** www.freemanhealth.com

| | | |
|---|---|---|
| Owned, leased, sponsored: | 2 hospitals | 438 beds |
| Contract–managed: | 0 hospitals | 0 beds |
| Totals: | 2 hospitals | 438 beds |

---

**0182: FUNDAMENTAL LONG TERM CARE HOLDINGS, LLC** (IO)
930 Ridgebrook Road, Sparks Glencoe, MD Zip 21152–9390; tel. 410/773–1000; W. Bradley Bennett, President and Chief Executive Officer
**(Independent Hospital System)**

**KANSAS:** SPECIALTY HOSPITAL OF MID–AMERICA (O, 104 beds) 6509 West 103rd Street, Overland Park, KS Zip 66212–1728; tel. 913/649–3701; Karen Leverich, Chief Executive Officer
**Web address:** www.thicare.com/SpecHospOfMidAmerica/

**NEVADA:** HARMON MEDICAL AND REHABILITATION HOSPITAL (O, 118 beds) 2170 East Harmon Avenue, Las Vegas, NV Zip 89119–7840; tel. 702/794–0100; Bonnie Essex Hillegass, Chief Executive Officer

HORIZON SPECIALTY HOSPITAL (O, 49 beds) 640 Desert Lane, Las Vegas, NV Zip 89106–4207; tel. 702/382–3155; Dave Tupper, Chief Executive Officer and Administrator

For explanation of codes following names, see page B2.
★ Indicates Type III membership in the American Hospital Association.

Section B

**TEXAS:** LLANO SPECIALTY HOSPITAL OF LUBBOCK (O, 30 beds) 1409 9th Street, Lubbock, TX Zip 79401–2601; tel. 806/767–9133; Dennis Fleenor, R.N., Chief Executive Officer
**Web address:** www.fundltc.com/Healthcare%20Facility%20Locator/facility_page.aspx?locationID=190

TEXAS SPECIALTY HOSPITAL AT DALLAS (O, 62 beds) 7955 Harry Hines Boulevard, Dallas, TX Zip 75235–3305; tel. 214/637–0000; Scott Athans, Chief Executive Officer
**Web address:** www.texasspecialtydallas.com/index.html

TEXAS SPECIALTY HOSPITAL AT HOUSTON (O, 25 beds) 6160 South Loop East, Houston, TX Zip 77087–1010; tel. 713/640–2400; Michael Higginbotham, Chief Executive Officer
**Web address:** www.thicare.com

TEXAS SPECIALTY HOSPITAL AT LUBBOCK (O, 37 beds) 4302 Princeton Street, Lubbock, TX Zip 79415–1304; tel. 806/723–8700; Deanna Graves, Chief Executive Officer

TEXAS SPECIALTY HOSPITAL AT WICHITA FALLS (O, 31 beds) 1103 Grace Street, Wichita Falls, TX Zip 76301–4414; tel. 940/720–6633; Delnita Bray, Administrator

| | | |
|---|---|---|
| Owned, leased, sponsored: | 8 hospitals | 456 beds |
| Contract–managed: | 0 hospitals | 0 beds |
| Totals: | 8 hospitals | 456 beds |

**★5570: GEISINGER HEALTH SYSTEM** (NP)
100 North Academy Avenue, Danville, PA Zip 17822–9800; tel. 570/271–6211; Glenn Steele, Jr., M.D., Ph.D., President and Chief Executive Officer
**(Centralized Physician/Insurance Health System)**

**PENNSYLVANIA:** GEISINGER MEDICAL CENTER (O, 545 beds) 100 North Academy Avenue, Danville, PA Zip 17822–2201; tel. 570/271–6211; Thomas P. Sokola, Chief Administrative Officer
**Web address:** www.geisinger.org

GEISINGER WYOMING VALLEY MEDICAL CENTER (O, 238 beds) 1000 East Mountain Boulevard, Wilkes Barre, PA Zip 18711–0027; tel. 570/808–7300; John J. Buckley, Chief Administrative Officer
**Web address:** www.geisinger.org

GEISINGER–BLOOMSBURG HOSPITAL (O, 72 beds) 549 Fair Street, Bloomsburg, PA Zip 17815–1419; tel. 570/387–2100; Lissa Bryan–Smith, Chief Administrative Officer
**Web address:** www.bloomhealth.net

GEISINGER–COMMUNITY MEDICAL CENTER (O, 248 beds) 1800 Mulberry Street, Scranton, PA Zip 18510–2369; tel. 570/969–8000; Robert P. Steigmeyer, President and Chief Executive Officer
**Web address:** www.cmccare.org/

| | | |
|---|---|---|
| Owned, leased, sponsored: | 4 hospitals | 1103 beds |
| Contract–managed: | 0 hospitals | 0 beds |
| Totals: | 4 hospitals | 1103 beds |

**★0311: GENESIS HEALTH SYSTEM** (NP)
1227 East Rusholme Street, Davenport, IA Zip 52803–2498; tel. 563/421–1000; Douglas P. Cropper, President and Chief Executive Officer
**(Centralized Physician/Insurance Health System)**

**ILLINOIS:** GENESIS MEDICAL CENTER, ILLINI CAMPUS (O, 101 beds) 801 Illini Drive, Silvis, IL Zip 61282–1893; tel. 309/281–4000; Florence Spyrow, President
**Web address:** www.genesishealth.com

MERCER COUNTY HOSPITAL (O, 22 beds) 409 N.W. Ninth Avenue, Aledo, IL Zip 61231–1296; tel. 309/582–5301; Ted Rogalski, Administrator
**Web address:** www.mercerhospital.org

**IOWA:** GENESIS MEDICAL CENTER, DEWITT (O, 86 beds) 1118 11th Street, De Witt, IA Zip 52742–1296; tel. 563/659–4200; Curt Coleman, FACHE, Administrator
**Web address:** www.genesishealth.com

GENESIS MEDICAL CENTER–DAVENPORT (O, 347 beds) 1227 East Rusholme Street, Davenport, IA Zip 52803–2498; tel. 563/421–1000; Wayne A. Diewald, President
**Web address:** www.genesishealth.com

JACKSON COUNTY REGIONAL HEALTH CENTER (C, 25 beds) 700 West Grove Street, Maquoketa, IA Zip 52060–2163; tel. 563/652–2474; Curt Coleman, FACHE, Administrator
**Web address:** www.jcrhc.org

| | | |
|---|---|---|
| Owned, leased, sponsored: | 4 hospitals | 556 beds |
| Contract–managed: | 1 hospitals | 25 beds |
| Totals: | 5 hospitals | 581 beds |

**★0812: GEORGETOWN HOSPITAL SYSTEM** (NP)
606 Black River Road, Georgetown, SC Zip 29440–3304, Mailing Address: P.O. Box 421718, Zip 29442–4203; tel. 843/527–7000; Bruce P. Bailey, President and Chief Executive Officer
**(Independent Hospital System)**

**SOUTH CAROLINA:** GEORGETOWN MEMORIAL HOSPITAL (O, 131 beds) 606 Black River Road, Georgetown, SC Zip 29440–3368, Mailing Address: Drawer 421718, Zip 29442–4203; tel. 843/527–7000; Bruce P. Bailey, Chief Executive Officer
**Web address:** www.georgetownhospitalsystem.org

WACCAMAW COMMUNITY HOSPITAL (O, 169 beds) 4070 Highway 17 Bypass, Murrells Inlet, SC Zip 29576–5033, Mailing Address: P.O. Drawer 3350, Zip 29576–2673; tel. 843/652–1000; Suzanne Doscher, Vice President Operations
**Web address:** www.gmhsc.com

| | | |
|---|---|---|
| Owned, leased, sponsored: | 2 hospitals | 300 beds |
| Contract–managed: | 0 hospitals | 0 beds |
| Totals: | 2 hospitals | 300 beds |

**0283: GILLIARD HEALTH SERVICES** (IO)
3091 Carter Hill Road, Montgomery, AL Zip 36111–1801; tel. 334/265–5009; William G. McKenzie, President, Chief Executive Officer and Chairman

**ALABAMA:** EVERGREEN MEDICAL CENTER (O, 42 beds) 101 Crestview Avenue, Evergreen, AL Zip 36401–3333, Mailing Address: P.O. Box 706, Zip 36401–0706; tel. 251/578–2480; William G. McKenzie, Interim Administrator
**Web address:** www.evergreenmedical.org

JACKSON MEDICAL CENTER (O, 26 beds) 220 Hospital Drive, Jackson, AL Zip 36545–2459, Mailing Address: P.O. Box 428, Zip 36545–0428; tel. 251/246–9021; Amy Gibson, Chief Executive Officer
**Web address:** www.jacksonmedicalcenter.org

| | | |
|---|---|---|
| Owned, leased, sponsored: | 2 hospitals | 68 beds |
| Contract–managed: | 0 hospitals | 0 beds |
| Totals: | 2 hospitals | 68 beds |

**0654: GLOBALREHAB** (IO)
1420 West Mockingbird Lane, Suite 100, Dallas, TX Zip 75247–4932, Mailing Address: 1340 Empire Central Drive, Zip 75247–4022; tel. 214/879–7500; Hooman Sedighi, M.D., President and Chief Executive Officer
**(Independent Hospital System)**

**TEXAS:** GLOBALREHAB HOSPITAL – DALLAS (O, 42 beds) 1340 Empire Central Drive, Dallas, TX Zip 75247–4022; tel. 214/879–7300; David Smith, Chief Executive Officer
**Web address:** www.globalrehabhospitals.com

GLOBALREHAB HOSPITAL – FORT WORTH (O, 42 beds) 6601 Harris Parkway, Fort Worth, TX Zip 76132–6108; tel. 817/433–9600; ,
**Web address:** www.globalrehabhospitals.com

GLOBALREHAB HOSPITAL – SAN ANTONIO (O, 42 beds) 19126 Stonehue Road, San Antonio, TX Zip 78258–3490; tel. 210/482–3400; Edward L. Dyer, Chief Executive Officer
**Web address:** www.globalrehabhospitals.com

| | | |
|---|---|---|
| Owned, leased, sponsored: | 3 hospitals | 126 beds |
| Contract–managed: | 0 hospitals | 0 beds |
| Totals: | 3 hospitals | 126 beds |

For explanation of codes following names, see page B2.
★ Indicates Type III membership in the American Hospital Association.

**0522: GOOD SHEPHERD HEALTH SYSTEM** (NP)
700 East Marshall Avenue, Longview, TX Zip 75601–5580;
tel. 903/315–2000; Steve Altmiller, Chief Executive Officer
**(Independent Hospital System)**

GOOD SHEPHERD MEDICAL CENTER (O, 399 beds) 700 East Marshall
Avenue, Longview, TX Zip 75601–5580; tel. 903/315–2000; Kenneth C.
Cunningham, Interim Chief Executive Officer
**Web address:** www.gsmc.org

GOOD SHEPHERD MEDICAL CENTER–LINDEN (O, 25 beds) 404 North
Kaufman Street, Linden, TX Zip 75563–5234; tel. 903/756–5561; Carla
Roadcap, R.N., MSN, Chief Executive Officer
**Web address:** www.gsmclinden.org

GOOD SHEPHERD MEDICAL CENTER–MARSHALL (O, 142 beds) 811 South
Washington Avenue, Marshall, TX Zip 75670–5336, Mailing Address: P.O. Box
1599, Zip 75671–1599; tel. 903/927–6000; Russell J. Collier, FACHE,
President and Chief Executive Officer
**Web address:** www.gsmcmarshall.org

| | | |
|---|---|---|
| Owned, leased, sponsored: | 3 hospitals | 566 beds |
| Contract–managed: | 0 hospitals | 0 beds |
| Totals: | 3 hospitals | 566 beds |

**0648: GOOD SHEPHERD REHABILITATION NETWORK** (IO)
850 South Fifth Street, Allentown, PA Zip 18103–3308;
tel. 610/776–3100; John Kristel, President and Chief Executive
Officer
**(Independent Hospital System)**

**PENNSYLVANIA:** GOOD SHEPHERD REHABILITATION HOSPITAL (O, 102
beds) 850 South 5th Street, Allentown, PA Zip 18103–3308;
tel. 610/776–3299; John Kristel, President and Chief Executive Officer
**Web address:** www.goodshepherdrehab.org

GOOD SHEPHERD SPECIALTY HOSPITAL (O, 32 beds) 2545 Schoenersville
Road, 3rd Floor, Bethlehem, PA Zip 18017–7300; tel. 484/884–5051; Greg
Wuchter, Administrator
**Web address:** www.goodshepherdrehab.org

| | | |
|---|---|---|
| Owned, leased, sponsored: | 2 hospitals | 134 beds |
| Contract–managed: | 0 hospitals | 0 beds |
| Totals: | 2 hospitals | 134 beds |

**★1535: GREAT PLAINS HEALTH ALLIANCE, INC.** (NP)
250 North Rock Road, Suite 160, Wichita, KS Zip 67206–2241;
tel. 316/685–1223; Dave Dellasega, President and Chief Executive
Officer
**(Decentralized Health System)**

**KANSAS:** ASHLAND HEALTH CENTER (C, 45 beds) 709 Oak Street, Ashland,
KS Zip 67831–0188, Mailing Address: P.O. Box 188, Zip 67831–0188;
tel. 620/635–2241; Roger Barnhart, Chief Executive Officer
**Web address:** www.ashlandhc.org

CHEYENNE COUNTY HOSPITAL (L, 16 beds) 210 West First Street, Saint
Francis, KS Zip 67756–3540; Mailing Address: P.O. Box 547,
Zip 67756–0547; tel. 785/332–2104; Judith Ann Rockwood, Administrator
**Web address:** www.cheyennecountyhospital.com

COMANCHE COUNTY HOSPITAL (C, 12 beds) 202 South Frisco Street,
Coldwater, KS Zip 67029–9101, Mailing Address: HC 65, Box 8A,
Zip 67029–9500; tel. 620/582–2144; Nancy Zimmerman, R.N.,
Administrator
**Web address:** www.gpha.com

ELLINWOOD DISTRICT HOSPITAL (L, 25 beds) 605 North Main Street,
Ellinwood, KS Zip 67526–1440; tel. 620/564–2548; John Hughes,
Administrator
**Web address:** www.ellinwood.org

FREDONIA REGIONAL HOSPITAL (C, 34 beds) 1527 Madison Street, Fredonia,
KS Zip 66736–1751, Mailing Address: P.O. Box 579, Zip 66736–0579;
tel. 620/378–2121; Alan Fisher, Chief Executive Officer
**Web address:** www.fredoniaregionalhospital.org

GRISELL MEMORIAL HOSPITAL DISTRICT ONE (C, 46 beds) 210 South
Vermont Avenue, Ransom, KS Zip 67572–9525; tel. 785/731–2231; Kristine
Ochs, R.N., Administrator
**Web address:** www.grisellmemorialhospital.org

KIOWA COUNTY MEMORIAL HOSPITAL (L, 15 beds) 721 West Kansas Avenue,
Greensburg, KS Zip 67054–1633; tel. 620/723–3341; Mary Sweet,
Administrator
**Web address:** www.kcmh.net

LANE COUNTY HOSPITAL (C, 31 beds) 235 West Vine, Dighton, KS
Zip 67839–0969, Mailing Address: P.O. Box 969, Zip 67839–0969;
tel. 620/397–5321; Donna McGowan, Administrator
**Web address:** www.lchospital.com

MEDICINE LODGE MEMORIAL HOSPITAL (C, 25 beds) 710 North Walnut
Street, Medicine Lodge, KS Zip 67104–1019; tel. 620/886–3771; Kevin A.
White, Administrator
**Web address:** www.mlmh.net/

MINNEOLA DISTRICT HOSPITAL (C, 54 beds) 212 Main Street, Minneola, KS
Zip 67865–8511, Mailing Address: P.O. Box 127, Zip 67865–0127;
tel. 620/885–4264; Deborah Bruner, Chief Executive Officer and
Administrator
**Web address:** www.minneolahealthcare.com

OSBORNE COUNTY MEMORIAL HOSPITAL (C, 25 beds) 424 West New
Hampshire Street, Osborne, KS Zip 67473–2314, Mailing Address: P.O. Box
70, Zip 67473–0070; tel. 785/346–2121; Kiley Floyd, Administrator
**Web address:** www.ocmh.org

OTTAWA COUNTY HEALTH CENTER (L, 42 beds) 215 East Eighth,
Minneapolis, KS Zip 67467–1902, Mailing Address: P.O. Box 290,
Zip 67467–0290; tel. 785/392–2122; Jody Parks, Administrator
**Web address:** www.ottawacountyhealthcenter.com

PHILLIPS COUNTY HOSPITAL (L, 25 beds) 1150 State Street, Phillipsburg, KS
Zip 67661–1743, Mailing Address: P.O. Box 607, Zip 67661–0607;
tel. 785/543–5226; David Engel, Chief Executive Officer
**Web address:** www.phillipshospital.org

RAWLINS COUNTY HEALTH CENTER (C, 24 beds) 707 Grant Street, Atwood,
KS Zip 67730–1526, Mailing Address: P.O. Box 47, Zip 67730–0047;
tel. 785/626–3211; Deanna Freeman, Administrator and Chief Executive
Officer
**Web address:** www.rchc.us

REPUBLIC COUNTY HOSPITAL (L, 63 beds) 2420 G Street, Belleville, KS
Zip 66935–2400; tel. 785/527–2254; Blaine K. Miller, Administrator
**Web address:** www.rphospital.org

SABETHA COMMUNITY HOSPITAL (L, 25 beds) 14th and Oregon Streets,
Sabetha, KS Zip 66534–0229, Mailing Address: P.O. Box 229,
Zip 66534–0229; tel. 785/284–2121; Lora Key, Chief Executive Officer
**Web address:** www.sabethahospital.com

SATANTA DISTRICT HOSPITAL (C, 57 beds) 401 South Cheyenne Street,
Satanta, KS Zip 67870–0159, Mailing Address: P.O. Box 159,
Zip 67870–0159; tel. 620/649–2761; Jeremy Clingenpeel, Administrator
**Web address:** www.satantahospital.org

SMITH COUNTY MEMORIAL HOSPITAL (L, 53 beds) 614 South Main Street,
Smith Center, KS Zip 66967–3001; tel. 785/282–6845; Allen Van Driel,
FACHE, Administrator
**Web address:** www.gpha.com

TREGO COUNTY–LEMKE MEMORIAL HOSPITAL (C, 62 beds) 320 North 13th
Street, Wakeeney, KS Zip 67672–2099; tel. 785/743–2182; Harold
Courtois, Administrator and Chief Executive Officer
**Web address:** www.tclmh.org

**NEBRASKA:** HARLAN COUNTY HEALTH SYSTEM (C, 19 beds) 717 North
Brown Street, Alma, NE Zip 68920–2132, Mailing Address: P.O. Box 836,
Zip 68920–0836; tel. 308/928–2151; Manuela Wolf, Interim Chief
Executive Officer
**Web address:** www.harlancountyhealth.com

| | | |
|---|---|---|
| Owned, leased, sponsored: | 8 hospitals | 264 beds |
| Contract–managed: | 12 hospitals | 434 beds |
| Totals: | 20 hospitals | 698 beds |

For explanation of codes following names, see page B2.
★ Indicates Type III membership in the American Hospital Association.

Section B

**0144: GREATER HUDSON VALLEY HEALTH SYSTEM** (NP)
60 Prospect Avenue, Middletown, NY Zip 10940–4133;
tel. 845/568–6050; Scott Batulis, President and Chief Executive
Officer

**NEW YORK:** CATSKILL REGIONAL MEDICAL CENTER (O, 196 beds) 68 Harris
Bushville Road, Harris, NY Zip 12742–5030, Mailing Address: P.O. Box
800, Zip 12742–0800; tel. 845/794–3300; Gerard Galarneau, M.D.,
Chief Executive Officer and Chief Medical Officer
**Web address:** www.crmcny.org

GROVER M. HERMAN HOSPITAL (O, 25 beds) 8881 Route 97, Callicoon, NY
Zip 12723; tel. 845/887–5530; Chris L. White, Administrator
**Web address:** www.crmcny.org

ORANGE REGIONAL MEDICAL CENTER (O, 301 beds) 707 East Main Street,
Middletown, NY Zip 10940–2650; tel. 845/333–1000; Scott Batulis,
President and Chief Executive Officer
**Web address:** www.ormc.org

| Owned, leased, sponsored: | 3 hospitals | 522 beds |
|---|---|---|
| Contract–managed: | 0 hospitals | 0 beds |
| Totals: | 3 hospitals | 522 beds |

**★1555: GREENVILLE HEALTH SYSTEM** (NP)
701 Grove Road, Greenville, SC Zip 29605–5611;
tel. 864/455–7000; Michael C. Riordan, President and Chief
Executive Officer
**(Centralized Health System)**

**SOUTH CAROLINA:** GREENVILLE MEMORIAL HOSPITAL (O, 820 beds) 701
Grove Road, Greenville, SC Zip 29605–4295; tel. 864/455–7000; Paul F.
Johnson, President
**Web address:** www.ghs.org

GREENVILLE HEALTH SYSTEM LAURENS COUNTY MEMORIAL HOSPITAL (L,
87 beds) Highway 76 East, Clinton, SC Zip 29325–2331, Mailing Address:
P.O. Box 976, Zip 29325–0976; tel. 864/833–9100; Richard E. D'Alberto,
FACHE, Chief Executive Officer
**Web address:** www.lchcs.org

GREER MEMORIAL HOSPITAL (O, 70 beds) 830 South Bumcombe Road,
Greer, SC Zip 29650–2400; tel. 864/797–8000; John F. Mansure, FACHE,
President
**Web address:** www.ghs.org

HILLCREST MEMORIAL HOSPITAL (O, 36 beds) 729 S.E. Main Street,
Simpsonville, SC Zip 29681–3280; tel. 864/454–6100; Eric Bour, M.D.,
President
**Web address:** www.ghs.org

PATEWOOD MEMORIAL HOSPITAL (O, 36 beds) 175 Patewood Drive,
Greenville, SC Zip 29615–3570; tel. 864/797–1000; Beverly J. Haines, R.N.,
President
**Web address:** www.ghs.org/patewood

| Owned, leased, sponsored: | 5 hospitals | 1049 beds |
|---|---|---|
| Contract–managed: | 0 hospitals | 0 beds |
| Totals: | 5 hospitals | 1049 beds |

**★0675: GUTHRIE HEALTHCARE SYSTEM** (NP)
Guthrie Square, Sayre, PA Zip 18840; tel. 570/887–4312; Joseph A.
Scopelliti, M.D., President and Chief Executive Officer
**(Moderately Centralized Health System)**

**NEW YORK:** CORNING HOSPITAL (O, 82 beds) 176 Denison Parkway East,
Corning, NY Zip 14830–2899; tel. 607/937–7200; Shirley P. Magana,
R.N., MSN, President and Chief Operating Officer
**Web address:** www.corninghospital.com

**PENNSYLVANIA:** ROBERT PACKER HOSPITAL (O, 238 beds) 1 Guthrie
Square, Sayre, PA Zip 18840–1698; tel. 570/888–6666; Marie T.
Droege, President
**Web address:** www.guthrie.org

TROY COMMUNITY HOSPITAL (O, 25 beds) 101 Elmira Street, Troy, PA
Zip 16947–1271; tel. 570/297–2121; Staci Covey, R.N., MS, President
**Web address:** www.guthrie.org

| Owned, leased, sponsored: | 3 hospitals | 345 beds |
|---|---|---|
| Contract–managed: | 0 hospitals | 0 beds |
| Totals: | 3 hospitals | 345 beds |

**0541: HARTFORD HEALTHCARE** (NP)
One State Street, 19th Floor, Hartford, CT Zip 06103;
tel. 860/263–4120; Elliot T. Joseph, President and Chief Executive
Officer
**(Moderately Centralized Health System)**

**CONNECTICUT:** HARTFORD HOSPITAL (O, 798 beds) 80 Seymour Street,
Hartford, CT Zip 06102–8000, Mailing Address: P.O. Box 5037,
Zip 06102–5037; tel. 860/545–5000; Jeffrey A. Flaks, President and
Chief Executive Officer
**Web address:** www.harthosp.org

MIDSTATE MEDICAL CENTER (O, 134 beds) 435 Lewis Avenue, Meriden, CT
Zip 06451–2101; tel. 203/694–8200; Lucille A. Janatka, President and Chief
Executive Officer
**Web address:** www.midstatemedical.org

NATCHAUG HOSPITAL (O, 57 beds) 189 Storrs Road, Mansfield Center, CT
Zip 06250–1683; tel. 860/456–1311; Stephen W. Larcen, Ph.D., President
and Chief Executive Officer
**Web address:** www.natchaug.org

THE HOSPITAL OF CENTRAL CONNECTICUT (O, 229 beds) 100 Grand Street,
New Britain, CT Zip 06052–2017, Mailing Address: P.O. Box 100,
Zip 06050–0100; tel. 860/224–5011; Clarence J. Silvia, President and Chief
Executive Officer
**Web address:** www.thocc.org

WINDHAM HOSPITAL (O, 79 beds) 112 Mansfield Avenue, Willimantic, CT
Zip 06226–2040; tel. 860/456–9116; Stephen W. Larcen, Ph.D., President
and Chief Executive Officer
**Web address:** www.windhamhospital.org

| Owned, leased, sponsored: | 5 hospitals | 1297 beds |
|---|---|---|
| Contract–managed: | 0 hospitals | 0 beds |
| Totals: | 5 hospitals | 1297 beds |

**0637: HAVEN BEHAVIORAL HEALTHCARE** (IO)
652 West Iris Drive, Nashville, TN Zip 37204–3191;
tel. 615/250–9500; Vern Westrich, President and Chief Executive
Officer

**ARIZONA:** HAVEN SENIOR HORIZONS (O, 30 beds) 1201 South 7th Avenue,
Suite 200, Phoenix, AZ Zip 85007–4076; tel. 623/236–2000; Kathy
Shaw, Chief Executive Officer
**Web address:** www.havenbehavioral.com

**COLORADO:** HAVEN BEHAVIORAL SENIOR CARE OF NORTH DENVER (O, 40
beds) 8451 Pearl Street, Suite 100, Thornton, CO Zip 80229–4804;
tel. 303/288–7807; Marc McComas, Executive Director
**Web address:** www.havenbehavioral.com/seniorcare/denver

HAVEN BEHAVIORAL WAR HEROES HOSPITAL (O, 20 beds) 1008 Minnequa
Avenue, Suite 6100, Pueblo, CO Zip 81004–3733; tel. 719/546–6000;
Carrin Harper, M.D., Chief Executive Officer

**PENNSYLVANIA:** HAVEN BEHAVIORAL HEALTH OF EASTERN PENNSYLVANIA
(O, 48 beds) 145 North 6th Street, 3rd Floor, Reading, PA
Zip 19601–3096; tel. 610/406–4340; John Baker, Interim Chief
Executive Officer
**Web address:** www.havenbehavioralhospital.com

| Owned, leased, sponsored: | 4 hospitals | 138 beds |
|---|---|---|
| Contract–managed: | 0 hospitals | 0 beds |
| Totals: | 4 hospitals | 138 beds |

**★3555: HAWAII HEALTH SYSTEMS CORPORATION** (NP)
3675 Kilauea Avenue, Honolulu, HI Zip 96816–2333;
tel. 808/733–4151; Bruce S. Anderson, Ph.D., President and Chief
Executive Officer
**(Independent Hospital System)**

For explanation of codes following names, see page B2.
★ Indicates Type III membership in the American Hospital Association.

Section B

**HAWAII:** HALE HO'OLA HAMAKUA (O, 52 beds) 45–547 Plumeria Street, Honokaa, HI Zip 96727–6902; tel. 808/775–7211; Cathy Meyer–Uyehara, Administrator
**Web address:** www.hhsc.org

HILO MEDICAL CENTER (O, 276 beds) 1190 Waianuenue Avenue, Hilo, HI Zip 96720–2089; tel. 808/932–3000; Howard N. Ainsley, Regional Chief Executive Officer
**Web address:** www.hmc.hhsc.org

KAU HOSPITAL (O, 21 beds) 1 Kamani Street, Pahala, HI Zip 96777, Mailing Address: P.O. Box 40, Zip 96777–0040; tel. 808/928–2050; Merilyn Harris, Administrator
**Web address:** www.hhsc.org

KAUAI VETERANS MEMORIAL HOSPITAL (O, 45 beds) Waimea Canyon Road, Waimea, HI Zip 96796, Mailing Address: P.O. Box 337, Zip 96796–0337; tel. 808/338–9431; Jerry Walker, Interim Regional Chief Executive Officer
**Web address:** www.kvmh.hhsc.org

KOHALA HOSPITAL (O, 28 beds) 54–383 Hospital Road, Kohala, HI Zip 96755, Mailing Address: P.O. Box 10, Kapaau, Zip 96755–0010; tel. 808/889–6211; Eugene Amar, Jr., Administrator
**Web address:** www.koh.hhsc.org

KONA COMMUNITY HOSPITAL (O, 94 beds) 79–1019 Haukapila Street, Kealakekua, HI Zip 96750–7920; tel. 808/322–9311; Jay E. Kreuzer, FACHE, Chief Executive Officer
**Web address:** www.kch.hhsc.org

KULA HOSPITAL (O, 6 beds) 100 Keokea Place, Kula, HI Zip 96790–7450; tel. 808/878–1221; Nick Hughey, Administrator
**Web address:** www.hhsc.org

LANAI COMMUNITY HOSPITAL (O, 24 beds) 628 Seventh Street, Lanai City, HI Zip 96763–0650, Mailing Address: P.O. Box 630650, Zip 96763–0650; tel. 808/565–8450; Nick Hughey, Administrator
**Web address:** www.lch.hhsc.org

LEAHI HOSPITAL (O, 188 beds) 3675 Kilauea Avenue, Honolulu, HI Zip 96816–2398; tel. 808/733–8000; Vincent H. S. Lee, FACHE, Regional Chief Executive Officer
**Web address:** www.hhsc.org

MAUI MEMORIAL MEDICAL CENTER (O, 213 beds) 221 Mahalani Street, Wailuku, HI Zip 96793–2581; tel. 808/244–9056; Wesley Lo, Regional Chief Executive Officer
**Web address:** www.mmmc.hhsc.org

SAMUEL MAHELONA MEMORIAL HOSPITAL (O, 80 beds) 4800 Kawaihau Road, Kapaa, HI Zip 96746–1971; tel. 808/822–4961; Jerry Walker, Interim Regional Chief Executive Officer
**Web address:** www.smmh.hhsc.org

| | | |
|---|---|---|
| Owned, leased, sponsored: | 11 hospitals | 1027 beds |
| Contract–managed: | 0 hospitals | 0 beds |
| Totals: | 11 hospitals | 1027 beds |

**0266: HAWAII PACIFIC HEALTH** (NP)
55 Merchant Street, Honolulu, HI Zip 96813–4306; tel. 808/949–9355; Raymond P. Vara, Jr., President and Chief Executive Officer
**(Independent Hospital System)**

KAPIOLANI MEDICAL CENTER FOR WOMEN & CHILDREN (O, 225 beds) 1319 Punahou Street, Honolulu, HI Zip 96826–1001; tel. 808/983–6000; Martha Smith, Chief Executive Officer
**Web address:** www.kapiolani.org

PALI MOMI MEDICAL CENTER (O, 126 beds) 98–1079 Moanalua Road, Aiea, HI Zip 96701–4713; tel. 808/486–6000; Jen Chahanovich, Chief Executive Officer
**Web address:** www.kapiolani.org

STRAUB CLINIC & HOSPITAL (O, 111 beds) 888 South King Street, Honolulu, HI Zip 96813–3097; tel. 808/522–4000; Art Gladstone, R.N., Chief Executive Officer
**Web address:** www.straubhealth.org

WILCOX MEMORIAL HOSPITAL (O, 64 beds) 3–3420 Kuhio Highway, Lihue, HI Zip 96766–1099; tel. 808/245–1100; Kathleen Clark, President and Chief Executive Officer
**Web address:** www.wilcoxhealth.org

| | | |
|---|---|---|
| Owned, leased, sponsored: | 4 hospitals | 526 beds |
| Contract–managed: | 0 hospitals | 0 beds |
| Totals: | 4 hospitals | 526 beds |

**★0048: HCA** (IO)
One Park Plaza, Nashville, TN Zip 37203–1548; tel. 615/344–9551; Richard M. Bracken, Chairman and Chief Executive Officer
**(Decentralized Health System)**

**ALASKA:** ALASKA REGIONAL HOSPITAL (O, 132 beds) 2801 Debarr Road, Anchorage, AK Zip 99508–2997, Mailing Address: P.O. Box 143889, Zip 99514–3889; tel. 907/264–1754; Annie Holt, FACHE, Chief Executive Officer
**Web address:** www.alaskaregional.com

**CALIFORNIA:** GOOD SAMARITAN HOSPITAL (O, 373 beds) 2425 Samaritan Drive, San Jose, CA Zip 95124–3997, Mailing Address: P.O. Box 240002, Zip 95154–2402; tel. 408/559–2011; Paul Beaupre, M.D., Chief Executive Officer
**Web address:** www.goodsamsanjose.com

LOS ROBLES HOSPITAL AND MEDICAL CENTER (O, 273 beds) 215 West Janss Road, Thousand Oaks, CA Zip 91360–1847; tel. 805/497–2727; Gregory R. Angle, President and Chief Executive Officer
**Web address:** www.losrobleshospital.com

REGIONAL MEDICAL CENTER OF SAN JOSE (O, 216 beds) 225 North Jackson Avenue, San Jose, CA Zip 95116–1603; tel. 408/259–5000; Michael T. Johnson, Chief Executive Officer
**Web address:** www.regionalmedicalsanjose.com

RIVERSIDE COMMUNITY HOSPITAL (O, 373 beds) 4445 Magnolia Avenue, Riverside, CA Zip 92501–4199, Mailing Address: P.O. Box 1669, Zip 92502–1669; tel. 951/788–3000; Patrick D. Brilliant, President and Chief Executive Officer
**Web address:** www.riversidecommunityhospital.com

WEST HILLS HOSPITAL AND MEDICAL CENTER (O, 293 beds) 7300 Medical Center Drive, West Hills, CA Zip 91307–1902; tel. 818/676–4000; Douglas Long, President and Chief Executive Officer
**Web address:** www.westhillshospital.com

**COLORADO:** MEDICAL CENTER OF AURORA (O, 303 beds) 1501 South Potomac Street, Aurora, CO Zip 80012–5411; tel. 303/695–2600; Richard A. Hammett, Chief Executive Officer
**Web address:** www.auroramed.com

NORTH SUBURBAN MEDICAL CENTER (O, 115 beds) 9191 Grant Street, Thornton, CO Zip 80229–4341; tel. 303/451–7800; Jennifer Alderfer, Chief Executive Officer
**Web address:** www.northsuburban.com

PRESBYTERIAN–ST. LUKE'S MEDICAL CENTER (O, 389 beds) 1719 East 19th Avenue, Denver, CO Zip 80218–1281; tel. 303/839–6000; Madeleine Roberson, Chief Executive Officer
**Web address:** www.pslmc.com

ROSE MEDICAL CENTER (O, 262 beds) 4567 East Ninth Avenue, Denver, CO Zip 80220–3941; tel. 303/320–2121; Kenneth H. Feiler, Chief Executive Officer
**Web address:** www.rosebabies.com

SKY RIDGE MEDICAL CENTER (O, 184 beds) 10101 Ridge Gate Parkway, Lone Tree, CO Zip 80124–5522; tel. 720/225–1000; Maureen Tarrant, Chief Executive Officer
**Web address:** www.skyridgemedcenter.com

SPALDING REHABILITATION HOSPITAL (O, 40 beds) 900 Potomac Steet, Aurora, CO Zip 80011–6716; tel. 303/367–1166; Cynthia Kreutz, Chief Executive Officer
**Web address:** www.spaldingrehab.com

SWEDISH MEDICAL CENTER (O, 343 beds) 501 East Hampden Avenue, Englewood, CO Zip 80113–2702; tel. 303/788–5000; Mary M. White, Chief Executive Officer
**Web address:** www.swedishhospital.com

**FLORIDA:** AVENTURA HOSPITAL AND MEDICAL CENTER (O, 359 beds) 20900 Biscayne Boulevard, Aventura, FL Zip 33180–1407; tel. 305/682–7000; Dianne Goldenberg, Chief Executive Officer
**Web address:** www.aventurahospital.com

For explanation of codes following names, see page B2.
★ Indicates Type III membership in the American Hospital Association.

Section B

BLAKE MEDICAL CENTER (O, 294 beds) 2020 59th Street West, Bradenton, FL Zip 34209–4669; tel. 941/792–6611; Daniel J. Friedrich, III, Chief Executive Officer
**Web address:** www.blakemedicalcenter.com

BRANDON REGIONAL HOSPITAL (O, 359 beds) 119 Oakfield Drive, Brandon, FL Zip 33511–5779; tel. 813/681–5551; Bland Eng, Chief Executive Officer
**Web address:** www.brandonhospital.com

CAPITAL REGIONAL MEDICAL CENTER (O, 198 beds) 2626 Capital Medical Boulevard, Tallahassee, FL Zip 32308–4499; tel. 850/325–5000; Brian Cook, FACHE, Chief Executive Officer
**Web address:** www.capitalregionalmedicalcenter.com

CENTRAL FLORIDA REGIONAL HOSPITAL (O, 226 beds) 1401 West Seminole Boulevard, Sanford, FL Zip 32771–6764; tel. 407/321–4500; Wendy H. Brandon, Chief Executive Officer
**Web address:** www.centralfloridaregional.com

DOCTORS HOSPITAL OF SARASOTA (O, 168 beds) 5731 Bee Ridge Road, Sarasota, FL Zip 34233–5056; tel. 941/342–1100; Robert C. Meade, Chief Executive Officer
**Web address:** www.doctorsofsarasota.com

EDWARD WHITE HOSPITAL (O, 110 beds) 2323 Ninth Avenue North, Saint Petersburg, FL Zip 33713–6898, Mailing Address: P.O. Box 12018, Zip 33733–2018; tel. 727/323–1111; Sharon Hayes, Chief Executive Officer
**Web address:** www.edwardwhitehospital.com

ENGLEWOOD COMMUNITY HOSPITAL (O, 100 beds) 700 Medical Boulevard, Englewood, FL Zip 34223–3978; tel. 941/475–6571; Dale Alward, Chief Executive Officer
**Web address:** www.englewoodcommunityhospital.com

FAWCETT MEMORIAL HOSPITAL (O, 238 beds) 21298 Olean Boulevard, Port Charlotte, FL Zip 33952–6765, Mailing Address: P.O. Box 494960, Punta Gorda, Zip 33949–4960; tel. 941/629–1181; Thomas J. Rice, FACHE, President and Chief Executive Officer
**Web address:** www.fawcetthospital.com

FORT WALTON BEACH MEDICAL CENTER (O, 257 beds) 1000 Mar–Walt Drive, Fort Walton Beach, FL Zip 32547–6795; tel. 850/862–1111; Mitchell P. Mongell, FACHE, Chief Executive Officer
**Web address:** www.fwbmc.com

GULF COAST MEDICAL CENTER (O, 176 beds) 449 West 23rd Street, Panama City, FL Zip 32405–4593, Mailing Address: P.O. Box 15309, Zip 32406–5309; tel. 850/769–8341; Carlton Ulmer, Chief Executive Officer
**Web address:** www.egulfcoastmedical.com

J. F. K. MEDICAL CENTER (O, 424 beds) 5301 South Congress Avenue, Atlantis, FL Zip 33462–1197; tel. 561/965–7300; Gina Melby, Chief Executive Officer
**Web address:** www.jfkmc.com

KENDALL REGIONAL MEDICAL CENTER (O, 300 beds) 11750 Bird Road, Miami, FL Zip 33175–3530; tel. 305/223–3000; Scott A. Cihak, Chief Executive Officer
**Web address:** www.kendallmed.com

LAKE CITY MEDICAL CENTER (O, 67 beds) 340 N.W. Commerce Drive, Lake City, FL Zip 32055–4709; tel. 386/719–9000; Mark Robinson, FACHE, Chief Executive Officer
**Web address:** www.lakecitymedical.com

LARGO MEDICAL CENTER (O, 243 beds) 201 14th Street S.W., Largo, FL Zip 33770–3133, Mailing Address: P.O. Box 2905, Zip 33779–2905; tel. 727/588–5200; Anthony M. Degina, President and Chief Executive Officer
**Web address:** www.largomedical.com

LAWNWOOD REGIONAL MEDICAL CENTER (O, 331 beds) 1700 South 23rd Street, Fort Pierce, FL Zip 34950–4803; tel. 772/461–4000; Rodney R. Smith, Chief Executive Officer
**Web address:** www.lawnwoodmed.com

MEDICAL CENTER OF TRINITY (O, 282 beds) 9330 State Road 54, Trinity, FL Zip 34655–1808, Mailing Address: P.O. Box 996, New Port Richey, Zip 34656–0996; tel. 727/834–4900; Leigh Massengill, Chief Executive Officer
**Web address:** www.medicalcentertrinity.com

MEMORIAL HOSPITAL JACKSONVILLE (O, 425 beds) 3625 University Boulevard South, Jacksonville, FL Zip 32216–4207, Mailing Address: P.O. Box 16325, Zip 32245–6325; tel. 904/399–6111; James F. O'Loughlin, President and Chief Executive Officer
**Web address:** www.memorialhospitaljax.com

NORTH FLORIDA REGIONAL MEDICAL CENTER (O, 349 beds) 6500 Newberry Road, Gainesville, FL Zip 32605–4392, Mailing Address: P.O. Box 147006, Zip 32614–7006; tel. 352/333–4000; Ward Boston, III, Chief Executive Officer
**Web address:** www.nfrmc.com

NORTHSIDE HOSPITAL AND HEART INSTITUTE (O, 225 beds) 6000 49th Street North, Saint Petersburg, FL Zip 33709–2145; tel. 727/521–4411; Dia Nichols, Chief Executive Officer
**Web address:** www.northsidehospital.com

NORTHWEST MEDICAL CENTER (O, 223 beds) 2801 North State Road 7, Margate, FL Zip 33063–5727; tel. 954/974–0400; Mark Rader, FACHE, Chief Executive Officer
**Web address:** www.northwestmed.com

OAK HILL HOSPITAL (O, 234 beds) 11375 Cortez Boulevard, Brooksville, FL Zip 34613–5409; tel. 352/596–6632; Mickey Smith, Chief Executive Officer
**Web address:** www.oakhillhospital.com

OCALA REGIONAL MEDICAL CENTER (O, 270 beds) 1431 S.W. First Avenue, Ocala, FL Zip 34471–6500, Mailing Address: P.O. Box 2200, Zip 34478–2200; tel. 352/401–1000; Randy McVay, Chief Executive Officer
**Web address:** www.ocalaregional.com

ORANGE PARK MEDICAL CENTER (O, 230 beds) 2001 Kingsley Avenue, Orange Park, FL Zip 32073–5156; tel. 904/276–8500; Thomas R. Pentz, President and Chief Executive Officer
**Web address:** www.opmedical.com

OSCEOLA REGIONAL MEDICAL CENTER (O, 235 beds) 700 West Oak Street, Kissimmee, FL Zip 34741–4996; tel. 407/846–2266; Robert M. Krieger, Interim Chief Executive Officer
**Web address:** www.osceolaregional.com

PALMS WEST HOSPITAL (O, 166 beds) 13001 Southern Boulevard, Loxahatchee, FL Zip 33470–9203; tel. 561/798–3300; Eric Goldman, Chief Executive Officer
**Web address:** www.palmswesthospital.com

PLANTATION GENERAL HOSPITAL (O, 264 beds) 401 N.W. 42nd Avenue, Plantation, FL Zip 33317–2882; tel. 954/587–5010; Randy Gross, Chief Executive Officer
**Web address:** www.plantationgeneral.com

RAULERSON HOSPITAL (O, 100 beds) 1796 Highway 441 North, Okeechobee, FL Zip 34972–1918, Mailing Address: P.O. Box 1307, Zip 34973–1307; tel. 863/763–2151; Robert H. Lee, President
**Web address:** www.raulersonhospital.com

REGIONAL MEDICAL CENTER–BAYONET POINT (O, 290 beds) 14000 Fivay Road, Hudson, FL Zip 34667–7199; tel. 727/869–5400; Shayne George, Chief Executive Officer
**Web address:** www.rmchealth.com

SOUTH BAY HOSPITAL (O, 112 beds) 4016 Sun City Center Boulevard, Sun City Center, FL Zip 33573–5298; tel. 813/634–3301; Sharon L. Roush, Chief Executive Officer
**Web address:** www.southbayhospital.com

SPECIALTY HOSPITAL JACKSONVILLE (O, 62 beds) 4901 Richard Street, Jacksonville, FL Zip 32207–7328; tel. 904/737–3120; Barbara Walsh, Chief Executive Officer
**Web address:** www.specialtyhospitaljax.com

ST. LUCIE MEDICAL CENTER (O, 194 beds) 1800 S.E. Tiffany Avenue, Port St. Lucie, FL Zip 34952–7521; tel. 772/335–4000; Gary Cantrell, President and Chief Executive Officer
**Web address:** www.stluciemed.com

ST. PETERSBURG GENERAL HOSPITAL (O, 219 beds) 6500 38th Avenue North, Saint Petersburg, FL Zip 33710–1629; tel. 727/384–1414; Robert B. Conroy, Jr., Chief Executive Officer
**Web address:** www.stpetegeneral.com

TWIN CITIES HOSPITAL (O, 57 beds) 2190 Highway 85 North, Niceville, FL Zip 32578–1045; tel. 850/678–4131; David Whalen, Chief Executive Officer
**Web address:** www.tchealthcare.com

UNIVERSITY HOSPITAL AND MEDICAL CENTER (O, 317 beds) 7201 North University Drive, Tamarac, FL Zip 33321–2996; tel. 954/721–2200; Joseph D. Melchiode, Chief Executive Officer
**Web address:** www.uhmchealth.com

WEST FLORIDA HOSPITAL (O, 339 beds) 8383 North Davis Highway, Pensacola, FL Zip 32514–6088; tel. 850/494–4000; Brian Baumgardner, Chief Executive Officer
**Web address:** www.westfloridahospital.com

For explanation of codes following names, see page B2.
★ Indicates Type III membership in the American Hospital Association.

WEST PALM HOSPITAL (O, 245 beds) 2201 45th Street, West Palm Beach, FL Zip 33407–2047; tel. 561/842–6141; Dana Oaks, Chief Executive Officer
**Web address:** www.westpalmhospital.com

WESTSIDE REGIONAL MEDICAL CENTER (O, 215 beds) 8201 West Broward Boulevard, Plantation, FL Zip 33324–2701; tel. 954/473–6600; Lee B. Chaykin, Chief Executive Officer
**Web address:** www.westsideregional.com

**GEORGIA:** CARTERSVILLE MEDICAL CENTER (O, 80 beds) 960 Joe Frank Harris Parkway, Cartersville, GA Zip 30120–2129; tel. 770/382–1530; Keith Sandlin, Chief Executive Officer
**Web address:** www.cartersvillemedical.com

COLISEUM CENTER FOR BEHAVIORAL HEALTH (O, 44 beds) 340 Hospital Drive, Macon, GA Zip 31217–3838; tel. 478/741–1355; James W. Eyler, FACHE, Chief Executive Officer
**Web address:** www.coliseumhealthsystem.com

COLISEUM MEDICAL CENTERS (O, 227 beds) 350 Hospital Drive, Macon, GA Zip 31217–3871; tel. 478/765–7000; Charles G. Briscoe, FACHE, Chief Executive Officer
**Web address:** www.coliseumhealthsystem.com

COLISEUM NORTHSIDE HOSPITAL (O, 103 beds) 400 Charter Boulevard, Macon, GA Zip 31210–4853, Mailing Address: P.O. Box 4627, Zip 31208–4627; tel. 478/757–8200; Mike Sherrod, Chief Executive Officer
**Web address:** www.coliseumhealthsystem.com

DOCTORS HOSPITAL (O, 307 beds) 3651 Wheeler Road, Augusta, GA Zip 30909–6426; tel. 706/651–3232; Douglas Welch, Chief Executive Officer
**Web address:** www.doctors–hospital.net

EASTSIDE MEDICAL CENTER (O, 247 beds) 1700 Medical Way, Snellville, GA Zip 30078–2195; tel. 770/979–0200; Kimberly Ryan, Chief Executive Officer
**Web address:** www.eastsidemedical.com

FAIRVIEW PARK HOSPITAL (O, 168 beds) 200 Industrial Boulevard, Dublin, GA Zip 31021–2997, Mailing Address: P.O. Box 1408, Zip 31040–1408; tel. 478/275–2000; Donald R. Avery, FACHE, President and Chief Executive Officer
**Web address:** www.fairviewparkhospital.com

REDMOND REGIONAL MEDICAL CENTER (O, 230 beds) 501 Redmond Road, Rome, GA Zip 30165–1415, Mailing Address: P.O. Box 107001, Zip 30162–7001; tel. 706/291–0291; John Quinlivan, Chief Executive Officer
**Web address:** www.redmondregional.com

**IDAHO:** EASTERN IDAHO REGIONAL MEDICAL CENTER (O, 309 beds) 3100 Channing Way, Idaho Falls, ID Zip 83404–7533, Mailing Address: P.O. Box 2077, Zip 83403–2077; tel. 208/529–6111; Douglas Crabtree, Chief Executive Officer
**Web address:** www.eirmc.com

WEST VALLEY MEDICAL CENTER (O, 118 beds) 1717 Arlington, Caldwell, ID Zip 83605–4802; tel. 208/459–4641; Julie Taylor, Chief Executive Officer
**Web address:** www.westvalleymedctr.com

**INDIANA:** TERRE HAUTE REGIONAL HOSPITAL (O, 208 beds) 3901 South Seventh Street, Terre Haute, IN Zip 47802–5709; tel. 812/232–0021; Mary Ann Conroy, Chief Executive Officer
**Web address:** www.regionalhospital.com

**KANSAS:** ALLEN COUNTY HOSPITAL (O, 25 beds) 101 South First Street, Iola, KS Zip 66749–3505, Mailing Address: P.O. Box 540, Zip 66749–0540; tel. 620/365–1000; Ron Baker, Chief Executive Officer
**Web address:** www.allencountyhospital.com

MENORAH MEDICAL CENTER (O, 158 beds) 5721 West 119th Street, Overland Park, KS Zip 66209–3722; tel. 913/498–6000; Steven D. Wilkinson, President and Chief Executive Officer
**Web address:** www.menorahmedicalcenter.com

OVERLAND PARK REGIONAL MEDICAL CENTER (O, 276 beds) 10500 Quivira Road, Overland Park, KS Zip 66215–2306, Mailing Address: P.O. Box 15959, Zip 66215–5959; tel. 913/541–5000; Damond Boatwright, Chief Executive Officer
**Web address:** www.oprmc.com

WESLEY MEDICAL CENTER (O, 595 beds) 550 North Hillside, Wichita, KS Zip 67214–4976; tel. 316/962–2000; Hugh C. Tappan, President and Chief Executive Officer
**Web address:** www.wesleymc.com

**KENTUCKY:** FRANKFORT REGIONAL MEDICAL CENTER (O, 134 beds) 299 King's Daughters Drive, Frankfort, KY Zip 40601–4186; tel. 502/875–5240; Chip Peal, Chief Executive Officer
**Web address:** www.frankfortregional.com

TRISTAR GREENVIEW REGIONAL HOSPITAL (O, 167 beds) 1801 Ashley Circle, Bowling Green, KY Zip 42104–3362; tel. 270/793–1000; Anne Leonard, R.N., Interim Chief Executive Officer
**Web address:** www.greenviewhospital.com

**LOUISIANA:** DAUTERIVE HOSPITAL (O, 103 beds) 600 North Lewis Street, New Iberia, LA Zip 70563–2043; tel. 337/365–7311; Gerald A. Fornoff, Interim Chief Executive Officer
**Web address:** www.dauterivehospital.com

LAKEVIEW REGIONAL MEDICAL CENTER (O, 172 beds) 95 Judge Tanner Boulevard, Covington, LA Zip 70433–7507; tel. 985/867–3800; Bret Kolman, Chief Executive Officer
**Web address:** www.lakeviewregional.com

RAPIDES REGIONAL MEDICAL CENTER (O, 349 beds) 211 Fourth Street, Alexandria, LA Zip 71301–8421; tel. 318/473–3000; Jason E. Cobb, FACHE, Chief Executive Officer
**Web address:** www.rapidesregional.com

REGIONAL MEDICAL CENTER OF ACADIANA (O, 142 beds) 2810 Ambassador Caffery Parkway, Lafayette, LA Zip 70506–5906; tel. 337/981–2949; Kathy J. Bobbs, FACHE, President Chief Executive Officer
**Web address:** www.medicalcenterofacadiana.com

TULANE MEDICAL CENTER (O, 327 beds) 1415 Tulane Avenue, New Orleans, LA Zip 70112–2600; tel. 504/988–5263; Robert Lynch, M.D., Chief Executive Officer
**Web address:** www.tuhc.com

**MISSISSIPPI:** GARDEN PARK MEDICAL CENTER (O, 130 beds) 15200 Community Road, Gulfport, MS Zip 39503–3085, Mailing Address: P.O. Box 1240, Zip 39502–1240; tel. 228/575–7000; Brenda M. Waltz, FACHE, Chief Executive Officer
**Web address:** www.gpmedical.com

**MISSOURI:** BELTON REGIONAL MEDICAL CENTER (O, 38 beds) 17065 South 71 Highway, Belton, MO Zip 64012–4631; tel. 816/348–1200; Todd Krass, R.N., Chief Executive Officer
**Web address:** www.beltonregionalmedicalcenter.com

CENTERPOINT MEDICAL CENTER (O, 221 beds) 19600 East 39th Street, Independence, MO Zip 64057–2301; tel. 816/698–7000; David R. Williams, Chief Executive Officer
**Web address:** www.centerpointmedical.com

LAFAYETTE REGIONAL HEALTH CENTER (O, 25 beds) 1500 State Street, Lexington, MO Zip 64067–1107; tel. 660/259–2203; Darrel Box, Chief Executive Officer
**Web address:** www.lafayetteregionalhealthcenter.com

LEE'S SUMMIT MEDICAL CENTER (O, 64 beds) 2100 S.E. Blue Parkway, Lee's Summit, MO Zip 64063–1007; tel. 816/282–5000; Jacqueline DeSouza, Chief Executive Officer
**Web address:** www.leessummitmedicalcenter.com

RESEARCH MEDICAL CENTER (O, 366 beds) 2316 East Meyer Boulevard, Kansas City, MO Zip 64132–1136; tel. 816/276–4000; Kevin J. Hicks, President and Chief Executive Officer
**Web address:** www.researchmedicalcenter.com

RESEARCH PSYCHIATRIC CENTER (O, 100 beds) 2323 East 63rd Street, Kansas City, MO Zip 64130–3462; tel. 816/444–8161; Richard Failla, Chief Executive Officer
**Web address:** www.researchpsychiatriccenter.com

**NEVADA:** MOUNTAINVIEW HOSPITAL (O, 235 beds) 3100 North Tenaya Way, Las Vegas, NV Zip 89128–0436; tel. 702/255–5000; William Wagnon, Chief Executive Officer
**Web address:** www.mountainview–hospital.com

SOUTHERN HILLS HOSPITAL AND MEDICAL CENTER (O, 134 beds) 9300 West Sunset Road, Las Vegas, NV Zip 89148–4844; tel. 702/880–2100; Kimball Anderson, FACHE, Chief Executive Officer
**Web address:** www.southernhillshospital.com

SUNRISE HOSPITAL AND MEDICAL CENTER (O, 641 beds) 3186 Maryland Parkway, Las Vegas, NV Zip 89109–2306, Mailing Address: P.O. Box 98530, Zip 89193; tel. 702/731–8000; Todd Sklamberg, President
**Web address:** www.sunrisehospital.com

For explanation of codes following names, see page B2.
★ Indicates Type III membership in the American Hospital Association.

**NEW HAMPSHIRE:** PARKLAND MEDICAL CENTER (O, 82 beds) One Parkland Drive, Derry, NH Zip 03038–2750; tel. 603/432–1500; Chris Accashian, Chief Executive Officer
**Web address:** www.parklandmedicalcenter.com

PORTSMOUTH REGIONAL HOSPITAL (O, 165 beds) 333 Borthwick Avenue, Portsmouth, NH Zip 03801–7128; tel. 603/436–5110; Anne Jamieson, FACHE, Chief Executive Officer
**Web address:** www.portsmouthhospital.com

**OKLAHOMA:** OU MEDICAL CENTER (O, 680 beds) 1200 Everett Drive, Oklahoma City, OK Zip 73104–5047, Mailing Address: P.O. Box 26307, Zip 73126–0307; tel. 405/271–3636; Charles Spicer, President and Chief Executive Officer
**Web address:** www.oumedicine.com/oumedicalcenter

**SOUTH CAROLINA:** COLLETON MEDICAL CENTER (O, 131 beds) 501 Robertson Boulevard, Walterboro, SC Zip 29488–5714; tel. 843/782–2000; Brad Griffin, Chief Executive Officer
**Web address:** www.colletonmedical.com

GRAND STRAND REGIONAL MEDICAL CENTER (O, 271 beds) 809 82nd Parkway, Myrtle Beach, SC Zip 29572–4607; tel. 843/692–1000; Doug White, Chief Executive Officer
**Web address:** www.grandstrandmed.com

TRIDENT MEDICAL CENTER (O, 403 beds) 9330 Medical Plaza Drive, Charleston, SC Zip 29406–9195; tel. 843/797–7000; Todd Gallati, FACHE, President and Chief Executive Officer
**Web address:** www.tridenthealthsystem.com

**TENNESSEE:** PARKRIDGE MEDICAL CENTER (O, 433 beds) 2333 McCallie Avenue, Chattanooga, TN Zip 37404–3258; tel. 423/698–6061; Darrell W. Moore, Chief Executive Officer
**Web address:** www.parkridgemedicalcenter.com

TRISTAR ASHLAND CITY (O, 12 beds) 313 North Main Street, Ashland City, TN Zip 37015–1347; tel. 615/792–3030; Darrell White, R.N., Administrator/Chief Nursing Officer
**Web address:** www.tristarcentennial.com

TRISTAR CENTENNIAL MEDICAL CENTER (O, 641 beds) 2300 Patterson Street, Nashville, TN Zip 37203–1528; tel. 615/342–1000; Heather J. Rohan, Chief Executive Officer
**Web address:** www.tristarcentennial.com

TRISTAR HENDERSONVILLE MEDICAL CENTER (O, 81 beds) 355 New Shackle Island Road, Hendersonville, TN Zip 37075–2479; tel. 615/338–1000; Regina Bartlett, Chief Executive Officer
**Web address:** www.hendersonvillemedicalcenter.com

TRISTAR HORIZON MEDICAL CENTER (O, 130 beds) 111 Highway 70 East, Dickson, TN Zip 37055–2080; tel. 615/446–0446; John A. Marshall, Chief Executive Officer
**Web address:** www.horizonmedicalcenter.com

TRISTAR SKYLINE MADISON CAMPUS (O, 284 beds) 500 Hospital Drive, Madison, TN Zip 37115–5032; tel. 615/769–5000; Steve Otto, Chief Executive Officer
**Web address:** www.skylinemadison.com

TRISTAR SKYLINE MEDICAL CENTER (O, 295 beds) 3441 Dickerson Pike, Nashville, TN Zip 37207–2539; tel. 615/769–2000; Steve Otto, Chief Executive Officer
**Web address:** www.skylinemedicalcenter.com

TRISTAR SOUTHERN HILLS MEDICAL CENTER (O, 101 beds) 391 Wallace Road, Nashville, TN Zip 37211–4859; tel. 615/781–4000; Thomas H. Ozburn, Chief Executive Officer
**Web address:** www.southernhills.com

TRISTAR STONECREST MEDICAL CENTER (O, 101 beds) 200 StoneCrest Boulevard, Smyrna, TN Zip 37167–6810; tel. 615/768–2000; Mark E. Sims, Chief Executive Officer
**Web address:** www.stonecrestmedical.com

TRISTAR SUMMIT MEDICAL CENTER (O, 188 beds) 5655 Frist Boulevard, Hermitage, TN Zip 37076–2053; tel. 615/316–3000; Jeffrey T. Whitehorn, Chief Executive Officer
**Web address:** www.summitmedctr.com

**TEXAS:** BAYSHORE MEDICAL CENTER (O, 476 beds) 4000 Spencer Highway, Pasadena, TX Zip 77504–1202; tel. 713/359–2000; Jeanna Barnard, Chief Executive Officer
**Web address:** www.bayshoremedical.com

CLEAR LAKE REGIONAL MEDICAL CENTER (O, 655 beds) 500 Medical Center Boulevard, Webster, TX Zip 77598–4220; tel. 281/332–2511; Stephen K. Jones, Jr., FACHE, Chief Executive Officer
**Web address:** www.clearlakermc.com

CONROE REGIONAL MEDICAL CENTER (O, 292 beds) 504 Medical Boulevard, Conroe, TX Zip 77304, Mailing Address: P.O. Box 1538, Zip 77305–1538; tel. 936/539–1111; Thomas A. Holt, Interim Chief Executive Officer
**Web address:** www.conroeregional.com/

CORPUS CHRISTI MEDICAL CENTER (O, 421 beds) 3315 South Alameda Street, Corpus Christi, TX Zip 78411–1883, Mailing Address: P.O. Box 8991, Zip 78468–8991; tel. 361/761–1400; Jay Woodall, Chief Executive Officer
**Web address:** www.ccmedicalcenter.com

DENTON REGIONAL MEDICAL CENTER (O, 208 beds) 3535 South 1–35 East, Denton, TX Zip 76210; tel. 940/384–3535; Caleb F. O'Rear, Chief Executive Officer
**Web address:** www.dentonregional.com

GREEN OAKS HOSPITAL (O, 106 beds) 7808 Clodus Fields Drive, Dallas, TX Zip 75251–2206; tel. 972/991–9504; Thomas M. Collins, President, Chairman and Chief Executive Officer
**Web address:** www.greenoakspsych.com

KINGWOOD MEDICAL CENTER (O, 262 beds) 22999 U.S. Highway 59 North, Kingwood, TX Zip 77339; tel. 281/348–8000; Melinda Stephenson, Chief Executive Officer
**Web address:** www.kingwoodmedical.com

LAS COLINAS MEDICAL CENTER (O, 90 beds) 6800 North MacArthur Boulevard, Irving, TX Zip 75039–2422; tel. 972/969–2000; Daniela Decell, Chief Executive Officer
**Web address:** www.lascolinasmedical.com

LAS PALMAS MEDICAL CENTER (O, 570 beds) 1801 North Oregon Street, El Paso, TX Zip 79902–3591; tel. 915/521–1200; Hank Hernandez, Chief Executive Officer
**Web address:** www.laspalmashealth.com

MEDICAL CENTER OF ARLINGTON (O, 284 beds) 3301 Matlock Road, Arlington, TX Zip 76015–2998; tel. 817/465–3241; Winston Borland, FACHE, President and Chief Executive Officer
**Web address:** www.medicalcenterarlington.com

MEDICAL CENTER OF LEWISVILLE (O, 166 beds) 500 West Main, Lewisville, TX Zip 75057–3699; tel. 972/420–1000; Ashley McClellan, Chief Executive Officer
**Web address:** www.lewisvillemedical.com

MEDICAL CENTER OF MCKINNEY (O, 217 beds) 4500 Medical Center Drive, McKinney, TX Zip 75069–1650; tel. 972/547–8000; Ernest C. Lynch, III, Chief Executive Officer
**Web address:** www.medicalcenterofmckinney.com

MEDICAL CENTER OF PLANO (O, 309 beds) 3901 West 15th Street, Plano, TX Zip 75075–7738; tel. 972/596–6800; Troy Villarreal, Chief Executive Officer
**Web address:** www.medicalcenterplano.com

MEDICAL CITY DALLAS HOSPITAL (O, 540 beds) 7777 Forest Lane, Dallas, TX Zip 75230–2598; tel. 972/566–7000; Erol R. Akdamar, President and Chief Executive Officer
**Web address:** www.medicalcityhospital.com

METHODIST AMBULATORY SURGERY HOSPITAL (O, 23 beds) 9150 Huebner Road, Suite 100, San Antonio, TX Zip 78240–1545; tel. 210/575–5000; Elaine F. Morris, Chief Executive Officer
**Web address:** www.sahealth.com

METHODIST HOSPITAL (O, 1604 beds) 7700 Floyd Curl Drive, San Antonio, TX Zip 78229–3993; tel. 210/575–4000; Gay Nord, Chief Executive Officer
**Web address:** www.sahealth.com

METHODIST STONE OAK HOSPITAL (O, 140 beds) 1139 East Sonterra Boulevard, San Antonio, TX Zip 78258–4347; tel. 210/638–2100; Dean M. Alexander, Chief Executive Officer
**Web address:** www.stoneoakhealth.com

NORTH HILLS HOSPITAL (O, 176 beds) 4401 Booth Calloway Road, North Richland Hills, TX Zip 76180–7399; tel. 817/255–1000; Randy Moresi, Chief Executive Officer
**Web address:** www.northhillshospital.com

PLAZA MEDICAL CENTER OF FORT WORTH (O, 217 beds) 900 Eighth Avenue, Fort Worth, TX Zip 76104–3902; tel. 817/336–2100; Clay Franklin, Chief Executive Officer
**Web address:** www.plazamedicalcenter.com

For explanation of codes following names, see page B2.
★ Indicates Type III membership in the American Hospital Association.

RIO GRANDE REGIONAL HOSPITAL (O, 320 beds) 101 East Ridge Road, McAllen, TX Zip 78503–1299; tel. 956/632–6000; Cristina Rivera, Chief Executive Officer
**Web address:** www.riohealth.com

ST. DAVID'S MEDICAL CENTER (O, 484 beds) 919 East 32nd Street, Austin, TX Zip 78705–2709, Mailing Address: P.O. Box 4039, Zip 78765–4039; tel. 512/476–7111; Donald H. Wilkerson, Chief Executive Officer
**Web address:** www.stdavids.com

ST. DAVID'S NORTH AUSTIN MEDICAL CENTER (O, 332 beds) 12221 North MoPac Expressway, Austin, TX Zip 78758–2496; tel. 512/901–1000; Allen Harrison, Chief Executive Officer
**Web address:** www.northaustin.com

ST. DAVID'S REHABILITATION CENTER (O, 64 beds) 1005 East 32nd Street, Austin, TX Zip 78705–2713, Mailing Address: P.O. Box 4270, Zip 78765–4270; tel. 512/544–5100; Diane Owens, Administrator
**Web address:** www.stdavidsrehab.com/home.aspx

ST. DAVID'S ROUND ROCK MEDICAL CENTER (O, 156 beds) 2400 Round Rock Avenue, Round Rock, TX Zip 78681–4097; tel. 512/341–1000; Deborah L. Ryle, Administrator and Chief Executive Officer
**Web address:** www.stdavids.com

ST. DAVID'S SOUTH AUSTIN MEDICAL CENTER (O, 233 beds) 901 West Ben White Boulevard, Austin, TX Zip 78704–6903; tel. 512/447–2211; Todd E. Steward, Chief Executive Officer
**Web address:** www.southaustinmc.com

TEXAS ORTHOPEDIC HOSPITAL (O, 49 beds) 7401 South Main Street, Houston, TX Zip 77030–4509; tel. 713/799–8600; Trent Lind, Chief Executive Officer
**Web address:** www.texasorthopedic.com

THE WOMAN'S HOSPITAL OF TEXAS (O, 367 beds) 7600 Fannin Street, Houston, TX Zip 77054–1906; tel. 713/790–1234; Linda B. Russell, Chief Executive Officer
**Web address:** www.womanshospital.com

VALLEY REGIONAL MEDICAL CENTER (O, 214 beds) 100A Alton Gloor Boulevard, Brownsville, TX Zip 78526–3354, Mailing Address: P.O. Box 3710, Zip 78523–3710; tel. 956/350–7101; Susan Andrews, Chief Executive Officer
**Web address:** www.valleyregionalmedicalcenter.com

WEST HOUSTON MEDICAL CENTER (O, 238 beds) 12141 Richmond Avenue, Houston, TX Zip 77082–2499; tel. 281/558–3444; Todd Caliva, Chief Executive Officer
**Web address:** www.westhoustonmedical.com

**UTAH:** BRIGHAM CITY COMMUNITY HOSPITAL (O, 39 beds) 950 South Medical Drive, Brigham City, UT Zip 84302–4724; tel. 435/734–9471; Richard Spuhler, Chief Executive Officer
**Web address:** www.brighamcityhospital.com

LAKEVIEW HOSPITAL (O, 116 beds) 630 East Medical Drive, Bountiful, UT Zip 84010–4908; tel. 801/299–2200; Rand Kerr, Chief Executive Officer
**Web address:** www.lakeviewhospital.com

MOUNTAIN VIEW HOSPITAL (O, 114 beds) 1000 East 100 North, Payson, UT Zip 84651–1600; tel. 801/465–7000; Kevin Johnson, Chief Executive Officer
**Web address:** www.mvhpayson.com

OGDEN REGIONAL MEDICAL CENTER (O, 167 beds) 5475 South 500 East, Ogden, UT Zip 84405–6905; tel. 801/479–2111; Mark B. Adams, Chief Executive Officer
**Web address:** www.ogdenregional.com

ST. MARK'S HOSPITAL (O, 317 beds) 1200 East 3900 South, Salt Lake City, UT Zip 84124–1390; tel. 801/268–7111; Steven B. Bateman, Chief Executive Officer
**Web address:** www.stmarkshospital.com

TIMPANOGOS REGIONAL HOSPITAL (O, 117 beds) 750 West 800 North, Orem, UT Zip 84057–3660; tel. 801/714–6000; Keith D. Tintle, Chief Executive Officer
**Web address:** www.timpanogosregionalhospital.com

**VIRGINIA:** CJW MEDICAL CENTER (O, 627 beds) 7101 Jahnke Road, Richmond, VA Zip 23225–4044; tel. 804/320–3911; Tim McManus, Interim Chief Executive Officer
**Web address:** www.cjwmedical.com

DOMINION HOSPITAL (O, 94 beds) 2960 Sleepy Hollow Road, Falls Church, VA Zip 22044–2030; tel. 703/536–2000; Cynthia A. Meyer, Interim Chief Executive Officer
**Web address:** www.dominionhospital.com

HENRICO DOCTORS' HOSPITAL (O, 488 beds) 1602 Skipwith Road, Richmond, VA Zip 23229–5205; tel. 804/289–4500; Lisa R. Valentine, Interim Chief Executive Officer
**Web address:** www.henricodoctorshospital.com

JOHN RANDOLPH MEDICAL CENTER (O, 118 beds) 411 West Randolph Road, Hopewell, VA Zip 23860–2938; tel. 804/541–1600; Suzanne B. Jackson, FACHE, Chief Executive Officer
**Web address:** www.johnrandolphmed.com

LEWIS–GALE MEDICAL CENTER (O, 521 beds) 1900 Electric Road, Salem, VA Zip 24153–7494; tel. 540/776–4000; Victor Giovanetti, President and Chief Executive Officer
**Web address:** www.lewis–gale.com

LEWISGALE HOSPITAL ALLEGHANY (O, 146 beds) One ARH Lane, Low Moor, VA Zip 24457, Mailing Address: P.O. Box 7, Zip 24457–0007; tel. 540/862–6011; Greg T. Madsen, Chief Executive Officer
**Web address:** www.alleghanyregional.com

LEWISGALE HOSPITAL AT PULASKI (O, 54 beds) 2400 Lee Highway, Pulaski, VA Zip 24301–2326, Mailing Address: P.O. Box 759, Zip 24301–0759; tel. 540/994–8100; Mark Nichols, FACHE, Chief Executive Officer
**Web address:** www.pch–va.com/

LEWISGALE HOSPITAL MONTGOMERY (O, 103 beds) 3700 South Main Street, Blacksburg, VA Zip 24060–7081, Mailing Address: P.O. Box 90004, Zip 24062–9004; tel. 540/951–1111; Alan J. Fabian, Chief Executive Officer
**Web address:** www.mrhospital.com

RESTON HOSPITAL CENTER (O, 187 beds) 1850 Town Center Parkway, Reston, VA Zip 20190–3219; tel. 703/689–9000; John A. Deardorff, Chief Executive Officer
**Web address:** www.restonhospital.com

SPOTSYLVANIA REGIONAL MEDICAL CENTER (O, 100 beds) 4600 Spotsylvania Parkway, Fredericksburg, VA Zip 22408–7762; tel. 540/834–1500; Timothy C. Tobin, FACHE, President and Chief Executive Officer
**Web address:** www.spotsrmc.com

| | | |
|---|---|---|
| Owned, leased, sponsored: | 144 hospitals | 35161 beds |
| Contract–managed: | 0 hospitals | 0 beds |
| Totals: | 144 hospitals | 35161 beds |

---

**0328: HEALTH FIRST, INC.** (NP)
6450 U.S. Highway 1, Rockledge, FL Zip 32955–5747; tel. 321/434–7000; Steven P. Johnson, Ph.D., President and Chief Executive Officer
**(Centralized Physician/Insurance Health System)**

**FLORIDA:** HEALTH FIRST CAPE CANAVERAL HOSPITAL (O, 145 beds) 701 West Cocoa Beach Causeway, Cocoa Beach, FL Zip 32931–5595, Mailing Address: P.O. Box 320069, Zip 32932–0069; tel. 321/799–7111; Wes Ott, Chief Operating Officer
**Web address:** www.health–first.org

HEALTH FIRST HOLMES REGIONAL MEDICAL CENTER (O, 514 beds) 1350 South Hickory Street, Melbourne, FL Zip 32901–3224; tel. 321/434–7000; Sean Gregory, President
**Web address:** www.health–first.org

HEALTH FIRST PALM BAY HOSPITAL (O, 119 beds) 1425 Malabar Road N.E., Melbourne, FL Zip 32907–2506; tel. 321/434–8000; Judy Gizinski, Chief Operating Officer
**Web address:** www.health–first.org

HEALTH FIRST VIERA HOSPITAL (O, 84 beds) 8745 North Wickham Road, Melbourne, FL Zip 32940–5997; tel. 321/434–9164; Deborah Leiper, Chief Operating Officer
**Web address:** www.vierahospital.org

| | | |
|---|---|---|
| Owned, leased, sponsored: | 4 hospitals | 862 beds |
| Contract–managed: | 0 hospitals | 0 beds |
| Totals: | 4 hospitals | 862 beds |

---

For explanation of codes following names, see page B2.
★ Indicates Type III membership in the American Hospital Association.

**1775: HEALTH MANAGEMENT ASSOCIATES** (IO)
5811 Pelican Bay Boulevard, Suite 500, Naples, FL
Zip 34108–2711; tel. 239/598–3131; Gary D. Newsome, President
and Chief Executive Officer
**(Decentralized Health System)**

**ALABAMA:** RIVERVIEW REGIONAL MEDICAL CENTER (O, 250 beds) 600 South
Third Street, Gadsden, AL Zip 35901–5399; tel. 256/543–5200; James
H. Edmondson, Chief Executive Officer
**Web address:** www.riverviewregional.com

STRINGFELLOW MEMORIAL HOSPITAL (C, 75 beds) 301 East 18th Street,
Anniston, AL Zip 36207–3952; tel. 256/235–8900; Bryan McCauley, Chief
Executive Officer
**Web address:** www.stringfellowhealth.com

**ARKANSAS:** SPARKS REGIONAL MEDICAL CENTER (O, 303 beds) 100
Towson Avenue, Fort Smith, AR Zip 72901–2632, Mailing Address: P.O.
Box 17006, Zip 72917–7006; tel. 479/441–4000; Gary J. Blan, FACHE,
Market Chief Executive Officer
**Web address:** www.sparks.org

SUMMIT MEDICAL CENTER (L, 103 beds) East Main and South 20th Streets,
Van Buren, AR Zip 72956–5715, Mailing Address: P.O. Box 409,
Zip 72957–0409; tel. 479/474–3401; Gary J. Blan, FACHE, Market Chief
Executive Officer
**Web address:** www.summitmedicalcenter.net

**FLORIDA:** BARTOW REGIONAL MEDICAL CENTER (O, 72 beds) 2200 Osprey
Boulevard, Bartow, FL Zip 33830–3308, Mailing Address: P.O. Box 1050,
Zip 33831–1050; tel. 863/533–8111; Philip Minden, Chief Executive
Officer
**Web address:** www.bartowregional.com

BAYFRONT HEALTH SAINT PETERSBURG (O, 395 beds) 701 Sixth Street
South, Saint Petersburg, FL Zip 33701–4891; tel. 727/823–1234; Kathryn
Gillette, President and Chief Executive Officer
**Web address:** www.bayfront.org

BAYFRONT HEALTH BROOKSVILLE (L, 120 beds) 17240 Cortez Boulevard,
Brooksville, FL Zip 34601–8921, Mailing Address: P.O. Box 37,
Zip 34605–0037; tel. 352/796–5111; Kenneth R. Wicker, Chief Executive
Officer
**Web address:** www.brooksvilleregionalhospital.org

BAYFRONT HEALTH PUNTA GORDA (O, 208 beds) 809 East Marion Avenue,
Punta Gorda, FL Zip 33950–3819, Mailing Address: P.O. Box 51–1328,
Zip 33951–1328; tel. 941/639–3131; Jose F. Morillo, Chief Executive Officer
**Web address:** www.charlotteregional.com

HEART OF FLORIDA REGIONAL MEDICAL CENTER (O, 194 beds) 40100
Highway 27, Davenport, FL Zip 33837–5906; tel. 863/422–4971; Donnie
Breeding, Chief Executive Officer
**Web address:** www.heartofflorida.com

HIGHLANDS REGIONAL MEDICAL CENTER (L, 126 beds) 3600 South
Highlands Avenue, Sebring, FL Zip 33870–5495, Mailing Address: Drawer
2066, Zip 33871–2066; tel. 863/471–5800; Brian Hess, Chief Executive
Officer
**Web address:** www.highlandsregional.com

LEHIGH REGIONAL MEDICAL CENTER (O, 88 beds) 1500 Lee Boulevard,
Lehigh Acres, FL Zip 33936–4835; tel. 239/369–2101; Joanie Jeannette,
MSN, Chief Executive Officer
**Web address:** www.lehighregional.com

LOWER KEYS MEDICAL CENTER (L, 90 beds) 5900 College Road, Key West,
FL Zip 33040–4396, Mailing Address: P.O. Box 9107, Zip 33041–9107;
tel. 305/294–5531; Nicki L. Will–Mowery, Ph.D., Chief Executive Officer
**Web address:** www.lkmc.com

PASCO REGIONAL MEDICAL CENTER (O, 120 beds) 13100 Fort King Road,
Dade City, FL Zip 33525–5294; tel. 352/521–1100; Shauna McKinnon, Chief
Executive Officer
**Web address:** www.pascoregionalmc.com

BAYFRONT HEALTH PORT CHARLOTTE (O, 190 beds) 2500 Harbor
Boulevard, Port Charlotte, FL Zip 33952–5000; tel. 941/766–4122; Richard
H. Satcher, Market Chief Executive Officer
**Web address:** www.peaceriverregional.com

PHYSICIANS REGIONAL MEDICAL CENTER – PINE RIDGE (O, 70 beds) 6101
Pine Ridge Road, Naples, FL Zip 34119–3900; tel. 239/348–4000; C. Scott
Campbell, Market Chief Executive Officer
**Web address:** www.physiciansregional.com

SANTA ROSA MEDICAL CENTER (L, 105 beds) 1450 Berryhill Road, Milton, FL
Zip 32570–5062, Mailing Address: P.O. Box 648, Zip 32572–0648;
tel. 850/626–7762; Phillip L. Wright, FACHE, Chief Executive Officer
**Web address:** www.santarosamedicalcenter.org

SEBASTIAN RIVER MEDICAL CENTER (O, 115 beds) 13695 North U.S.
Highway 1, Sebastian, FL Zip 32958–3230, Mailing Address: Box 780838,
Zip 32978–0838; tel. 772/589–3186; Steven Salyer, Chief Executive Officer
**Web address:** www.sebastianrivermedical.com

SEVEN RIVERS REGIONAL MEDICAL CENTER (O, 128 beds) 6201 North
Suncoast Boulevard, Crystal River, FL Zip 34428–6712; tel. 352/795–6560;
Joyce A. Brancato, Chief Executive Officer
**Web address:** www.srrmc.com

SHANDS LAKE SHORE REGIONAL MEDICAL CENTER (O, 90 beds) 368 N.E.
Franklin Street, Lake City, FL Zip 32055–3047; tel. 386/292–8000; Rhonda
Kay Sherrod, R.N., MSN, Administrator
**Web address:** www.shandslakeshore.com

SHANDS LIVE OAK REGIONAL MEDICAL CENTER (O, 25 beds) 1100 S.W.
11th Street, Live Oak, FL Zip 32064–3608; tel. 386/362–0800; Richard
Huth, Chief Executive Officer
**Web address:** www.shands.org

SHANDS STARKE REGIONAL MEDICAL CENTER (O, 25 beds) 922 East Call
Street, Starke, FL Zip 32091–3699; tel. 904/368–2300; Brent Burish, Chief
Executive Officer
**Web address:** www.shands.org

ST. CLOUD REGIONAL MEDICAL CENTER (O, 84 beds) 2906 17th Street,
Saint Cloud, FL Zip 34769–6099; tel. 407/892–2135; Robert Brooks, Chief
Executive Officer
**Web address:** www.stcloudregional.com

VENICE REGIONAL MEDICAL CENTER (O, 220 beds) 540 The Rialto, Venice,
FL Zip 34285–2900; tel. 941/485–7711; Peter Wozniak, MS, R.N., Chief
Executive Officer
**Web address:** www.veniceregional.com

WUESTHOFF MEDICAL CENTER – MELBOURNE (O, 119 beds) 250 North
Wickham Road, Melbourne, FL Zip 32935–8625; tel. 321/752–1200;
Jeannette Skinner, R.N., FACHE, Chief Executive Officer
**Web address:** www.wuesthoff.org

WUESTHOFF MEDICAL CENTER – ROCKLEDGE (O, 298 beds) 110 Longwood
Avenue, Rockledge, FL Zip 32955–2887, Mailing Address: P.O. Box 565002,
Mail Stop 1, Zip 32956–5002; tel. 321/636–2211; Timothy J. Cerullo, Chief
Executive Officer
**Web address:** www.wuesthoff.org

**GEORGIA:** BARROW REGIONAL MEDICAL CENTER (O, 56 beds) 316 North
Broad Street, Winder, GA Zip 30680–2150, Mailing Address: P.O. Box
688, Zip 30680–0688; tel. 770/867–3400; Todd Dixon, R.N., Chief
Executive Officer
**Web address:** www.barrowregional.com

CLEARVIEW REGIONAL MEDICAL CENTER (O, 115 beds) 2151 West Spring
Street, Monroe, GA Zip 30655–3115; tel. 770/267–8461; J. T. Barnhart,
Chief Executive Officer
**Web address:** www.waltonregional.com

EAST GEORGIA REGIONAL MEDICAL CENTER (O, 150 beds) 1499 Fair Road,
Statesboro, GA Zip 30458–1683, Mailing Address: P.O. Box 1048,
Zip 30459–1048; tel. 912/486–1000; Robert F. Bigley, President and Chief
Executive Officer
**Web address:** www.eastgeorgiaregional.com

**KENTUCKY:** PAUL B. HALL REGIONAL MEDICAL CENTER (O, 72 beds) 625
James S. Trimble Boulevard, Paintsville, KY Zip 41240–0000;
tel. 606/789–3511; Deborah Trimble, R.N., Chief Executive Officer
**Web address:** www.pbhrmc.com

**MISSISSIPPI:** BILOXI REGIONAL MEDICAL CENTER (L, 198 beds) 150 Reynoir
Street, Biloxi, MS Zip 39530–4199, Mailing Address: P.O. Box 128,
Zip 39533–0128; tel. 228/432–1571; Monte J. Bostwick, Chief Executive
Officer
**Web address:** www.biloxiregional.net

CENTRAL MISSISSIPPI MEDICAL CENTER (L, 367 beds) 1850 Chadwick Drive,
Jackson, MS Zip 39204–3479, Mailing Address: P.O. Box 59001,
Zip 39284–9001; tel. 601/376–1000; Charlotte W. Dupre', Chief Executive
Officer
**Web address:** www.centralmississippimedicalcenter.com

For explanation of codes following names, see page B2.
★ Indicates Type III membership in the American Hospital Association.

CROSSGATES RIVER OAKS HOSPITAL (L, 149 beds) 350 Crossgates Boulevard, Brandon, MS Zip 39042–2698; tel. 601/825–2811; J. Allen Tyra, Chief Executive Officer
**Web address:** www.crossgatesriveroaks.com

GILMORE MEMORIAL REGIONAL MEDICAL CENTER (O, 95 beds) 1105 Earl Frye Boulevard, Amory, MS Zip 38821–5500, Mailing Address: P.O. Box 459, Zip 38821–0459; tel. 662/256–7111; L. Dwayne Blaylock, Chief Executive Officer
**Web address:** www.gilmorehealth.com

MADISON RIVER OAKS MEDICAL CENTER (L, 67 beds) Highway 16 East, Canton, MS Zip 39046–8823, Mailing Address: P.O. Box 1607, Zip 39046–1607; tel. 601/859–1331; Glen Silverman, Chief Executive Officer
**Web address:** www.madisonriveroaks.com

NATCHEZ COMMUNITY HOSPITAL (O, 101 beds) 129 Jefferson Davis Boulevard, Natchez, MS Zip 39120–5100, Mailing Address: P.O. Box 1203, Zip 39121–1203; tel. 601/445–6200; Eric Robinson, Chief Executive Officer
**Web address:** www.natchezcommunityhospital.com/default.aspx

NORTHWEST MISSISSIPPI REGIONAL MEDICAL CENTER (L, 195 beds) 1970 Hospital Drive, Clarksdale, MS Zip 38614–7202, Mailing Address: P.O. Box 1218, Zip 38614–1218; tel. 662/627–3211; William G. Buck, Chief Executive Officer
**Web address:** www.northwestregional.org

RIVER OAKS HOSPITAL (O, 158 beds) 1030 River Oaks Drive, Flowood, MS Zip 39232–9553, Mailing Address: P.O. Box 5100, Jackson, Zip 39296–5100; tel. 601/932–1030; Timothy W. Mitchell, Chief Executive Officer
**Web address:** www.riveroakshosp.com

TRI–LAKES MEDICAL CENTER (O, 112 beds) 303 Medical Center Drive, Batesville, MS Zip 38606–8608; tel. 662/563–5611; Wes Sigler, Chief Executive Officer
**Web address:** www.trilakesmc.com

WOMAN'S HOSPITAL (O, 60 beds) 1026 North Flowood Drive, Flowood, MS Zip 39232–9532, Mailing Address: P.O. Box 4546, Jackson, Zip 39296–4546; tel. 601/932–1000; Sherry J. Pitts, Chief Executive Officer
**Web address:** www.womanshospitalms.com

**MISSOURI:** POPLAR BLUFF REGIONAL MEDICAL CENTER (O, 287 beds) 3100 Oak Grove Road, Poplar Bluff, MO Zip 63901, Mailing Address: P.O. Box 88, Zip 63902–0088; tel. 573/776–2000; Charles L. Stewart, Chief Executive Officer
**Web address:** www.poplarbluffregional.com

TWIN RIVERS REGIONAL MEDICAL CENTER (O, 116 beds) 1301 First Street, Kennett, MO Zip 63857–2508, Mailing Address: P.O. Box 728, Zip 63857–0728; tel. 573/888–4522; Kenneth James, Chief Executive Officer
**Web address:** www.twinriversmedctr.com

**NORTH CAROLINA:** DAVIS REGIONAL MEDICAL CENTER (O, 131 beds) 218 Old Mocksville Road, Statesville, NC Zip 28625–1930, Mailing Address: P.O. Box 1823, Zip 28687–1823; tel. 704/873–0281; Vincent T. Cherry, Jr., Chief Executive Officer
**Web address:** www.davisregional.com

LAKE NORMAN REGIONAL MEDICAL CENTER (O, 100 beds) 171 Fairview Road, Mooresville, NC Zip 28117–9500, Mailing Address: P.O. Box 3250, Zip 28117–3250; tel. 704/660–4000; Greg Lowe, Chief Executive Officer
**Web address:** www.lnrmc.com

SANDHILLS REGIONAL MEDICAL CENTER (O, 64 beds) 1000 West Hamlet Avenue, Hamlet, NC Zip 28345–4522, Mailing Address: P.O. Box 1109, Zip 28345–1109; tel. 910/205–8000; Michael H. McNair, Chief Executive Officer
**Web address:** www.sandhillsregional.com

**OKLAHOMA:** INTEGRIS BLACKWELL REGIONAL HOSPITAL (O, 39 beds) 710 South 13th Street, Blackwell, OK Zip 74631–3700; tel. 580/363–2311; Julie M. McCormack, Administrator
**Web address:** www.integris–health.com

INTEGRIS CLINTON REGIONAL HOSPITAL (O, 49 beds) 100 North 30th Street, Clinton, OK Zip 73601–3117, Mailing Address: P.O. Box 1569, Zip 73601–1569; tel. 580/323–2363; Darcey O'Brien, Chief Executive Officer
**Web address:** www.integris–health.com

INTEGRIS MARSHALL COUNTY MEDICAL CENTER (O, 21 beds) 1 Hospital Drive, Madill, OK Zip 73446, Mailing Address: P.O. Box 827, Zip 73446–0827; tel. 580/795–3384; Matthew M. Lyden, Chief Executive Officer
**Web address:** www.integrismarshallcounty.com

INTEGRIS MAYES COUNTY MEDICAL CENTER (O, 24 beds) 111 North Bailey Street, Pryor, OK Zip 74361–4201, Mailing Address: P.O. Box 278, Zip 74362–0278; tel. 918/825–1600; Douglas K. Weaver, FACHE, President
**Web address:** www.integrismayescounty.com

INTEGRIS SEMINOLE MEDICAL CENTER (O, 32 beds) 2401 Wrangler Boulevard, Seminole, OK Zip 74868–1917; tel. 405/303–4000; Jimmy D. Stuart, Chief Executive Officer
**Web address:** www.hma.com

MEDICAL CENTER OF SOUTHEASTERN OKLAHOMA (O, 148 beds) 1800 University Boulevard, Durant, OK Zip 74701–3006, Mailing Address: P.O. Box 1207, Zip 74702–1207; tel. 580/924–3080; Patricia Dorris, Executive Director
**Web address:** www.mymcso.com

MIDWEST REGIONAL MEDICAL CENTER (L, 255 beds) 2825 Parklawn Drive, Midwest City, OK Zip 73110–4258; tel. 405/610–4411; Paul M. Jenson, Chief Executive Officer
**Web address:** www.midwestregional.com

**PENNSYLVANIA:** CARLISLE REGIONAL MEDICAL CENTER (O, 165 beds) 361 Alexander Spring Road, Carlisle, PA Zip 17015–6940; tel. 717/249–1212; Rich Newell, Chief Executive Officer
**Web address:** www.carlislermc.com/default.aspx

HEART OF LANCASTER REGIONAL MEDICAL CENTER (O, 148 beds) 1500 Highlands Drive, Lititz, PA Zip 17543–7694; tel. 717/625–5000; James Machado, Administrator
**Web address:** www.heartoflancaster.com

LANCASTER REGIONAL MEDICAL CENTER (O, 150 beds) 250 College Avenue, Lancaster, PA Zip 17603–3363, Mailing Address: P.O. Box 3434, Zip 17604–3434; tel. 717/291–8211; Bob Moore, FACHE, Chief Executive Officer
**Web address:** www.lancasterregional.com

**SOUTH CAROLINA:** CAROLINA PINES REGIONAL MEDICAL CENTER (O, 116 beds) 1304 West Bobo Newsom Highway, Hartsville, SC Zip 29550–4710; tel. 843/339–2100; J. Timothy Browne, FACHE, Chief Executive Officer
**Web address:** www.cprmc.com

CHESTER REGIONAL MEDICAL CENTER (L, 136 beds) 1 Medical Park Drive, Chester, SC Zip 29706–9769; tel. 803/581–3151; Page H. Vaughan, Chief Executive Officer
**Web address:** www.chospital.org

**TENNESSEE:** HARTON REGIONAL MEDICAL CENTER (O, 104 beds) 1801 North Jackson Street, Tullahoma, TN Zip 37388–8259; tel. 931/393–3000; William R. Spray, Chief Executive Officer
**Web address:** www.hartonmedicalcenter.com

JAMESTOWN REGIONAL MEDICAL CENTER (O, 85 beds) 436 Central Avenue West, Jamestown, TN Zip 38556–3031, Mailing Address: P.O. Box 1500, Zip 38556–1500; tel. 931/879–8171; Kimberly L. Anthony, Chief Executive Officer
**Web address:** www.jamestownregional.org

LAFOLLETTE MEDICAL CENTER (L, 164 beds) 923 East Central Avenue, La Follette, TN Zip 37766–2768, Mailing Address: P.O. Box 1301, Zip 37766–1301; tel. 423/907–1200; Mark Cain, Chief Executive Officer
**Web address:** www.hma.com

NEWPORT MEDICAL CENTER (O, 47 beds) 435 Second Street, Newport, TN Zip 37821–3799; tel. 423/625–2200; Spencer Thomas, Chief Executive Officer
**Web address:** www.tennova.com

PHYSICIANS REGIONAL MEDICAL CENTER (O, 233 beds) 900 East Oak Hill Avenue, Knoxville, TN Zip 37917–4556; tel. 865/545–8000; Karen Metz, Chief Executive Officer
**Web address:** www.hma.com/content/physicians–regional–medical–center

TENNOVA–JEFFERSON MEMORIAL HOSPITAL (L, 54 beds) 110 Hospital Drive, Jefferson City, TN Zip 37760–5281; tel. 865/471–2500; Colin McRae, Chief Executive Officer
**Web address:** www.tennova.com/

For explanation of codes following names, see page B2.
★ Indicates Type III membership in the American Hospital Association.

**Section B**

TURKEY CREEK MEDICAL CENTER (O, 101 beds) 10820 Parkside Drive, Knoxville, TN Zip 37934–1956; tel. 865/218–7094; Lance Jones, Chief Executive Officer
**Web address:** www.hma.com/content/turkey–creek–medical–center

UNIVERSITY MEDICAL CENTER (O, 245 beds) 1411 Baddour Parkway, Lebanon, TN Zip 37087–2513; tel. 615/444–8262; Matthew T. Caldwell, Chief Executive Officer
**Web address:** www.universitymedicalcenter.com

**TEXAS:** DALLAS REGIONAL MEDICAL CENTER (O, 85 beds) 1011 North Galloway Avenue, Mesquite, TX Zip 75149–2433; tel. 214/320–7000; Derrick Yu, Interim Chief Executive Officer
**Web address:** www.dallasregionalmedicalcenter.com

**WASHINGTON:** TOPPENISH COMMUNITY HOSPITAL (O, 63 beds) 502 West Fourth Avenue, Toppenish, WA Zip 98948–1616, Mailing Address: P.O. Box 672, Zip 98948–0672; tel. 509/865–3105; Albert Pilkington, III, Chief Executive Officer
**Web address:** www.toppenishhospital.com

YAKIMA REGIONAL MEDICAL AND CARDIAC CENTER (O, 214 beds) 110 South Ninth Avenue, Yakima, WA Zip 98902–3315; tel. 509/575–5000; Richard H. Robinson, Chief Executive Officer
**Web address:** www.yakimaregional.net

**WEST VIRGINIA:** WILLIAMSON MEMORIAL HOSPITAL (O, 76 beds) 859 Alderson Street, Williamson, WV Zip 25661–3215, Mailing Address: P.O. Box 1980, Zip 25661–1980; tel. 304/235–2500; David Pryor, Chief Executive Officer
**Web address:** www.williamsonmemorial.net

| Owned, leased, sponsored: | 67 hospitals | 8885 beds |
|---|---|---|
| Contract–managed: | 1 hospital | 75 beds |
| Totals: | 68 hospitals | 8960 beds |

---

**★0307:   HEALTH QUEST SYSTEMS, INC.** (NP)
1351 Route 55, LaGrangeville, NY Zip 12540–5108; tel. 845/475–9500; Donna McGregor and Denise George, Interim Co–Chief Executive Officers
**(Moderately Centralized Health System)**

**NEW YORK:** NORTHERN DUTCHESS HOSPITAL (O, 68 beds) 6511 Springbrook Avenue, Rhinebeck, NY Zip 12572–3709, Mailing Address: P.O. Box 5002, Zip 12572–5002; tel. 845/876–3001; Tim Cleary, Interim President and Chief Operating Officer
**Web address:** www.health–quest.org/home_nd.cfm?id=9

PUTNAM HOSPITAL CENTER (O, 164 beds) 670 Stoneleigh Avenue, Carmel, NY Zip 10512–3997; tel. 845/279–5711; Maureen Zipparo, President and Chief Operating Officer
**Web address:** www.putnamhospital.org

VASSAR BROTHERS MEDICAL CENTER (O, 365 beds) 45 Reade Place, Poughkeepsie, NY Zip 12601–3947; tel. 845/454–8500; Janet L. Ready, President and Chief Operating Officer
**Web address:** www.health–quest.org

| Owned, leased, sponsored: | 3 hospitals | 597 beds |
|---|---|---|
| Contract–managed: | 0 hospitals | 0 beds |
| Totals: | 3 hospitals | 597 beds |

---

**0534:   HEALTHALLIANCE OF THE HUDSON VALLEY** (NP)
396 Broadway, Kingston, NY Zip 12401–4626; tel. 845/331–3131; David W. Lundquist, President and Chief Executive Officer
**(Independent Hospital System)**

HEALTH ALLIANCE HOSPITAL – BROADWAY CAMPUS (O, 150 beds) 396 Broadway, Kingston, NY Zip 12401–4692; tel. 845/331–3131; David W. Lundquist, President and Chief Executive Officer
**Web address:** www.kingstonregionalhealth.org

HEALTH ALLIANCE HOSPITAL – MARY'S AVENUE CAMPUS (O, 120 beds) 105 Marys Avenue, Kingston, NY Zip 12401–5894; tel. 845/338–2500; David W. Lundquist, President and Chief Executive Officer
**Web address:** www.benedictine.org

MARGARETVILLE HOSPITAL (O, 15 beds) 42084 State Highway 28, Margaretville, NY Zip 12455–2820; tel. 845/586–2631; Sandra A. Horan, Executive Director
**Web address:** www.margaretvillehospital.org

| Owned, leased, sponsored: | 3 hospitals | 285 beds |
|---|---|---|
| Contract–managed: | 0 hospitals | 0 beds |
| Totals: | 3 hospitals | 285 beds |

---

**★2185:   HEALTHEAST CARE SYSTEM** (NP)
559 Capitol Boulevard, 6–South, Saint Paul, MN Zip 55103–0000; tel. 651/232–2300; Kathryn G. Correia, President and Chief Executive Officer
**(Centralized Physician/Insurance Health System)**

**MINNESOTA:** BETHESDA HOSPITAL (O, 126 beds) 559 Capitol Boulevard, Saint Paul, MN Zip 55103–2101; tel. 651/232–2000; Catherine Barr, Senior Vice President and President, Bethesda Hospital
**Web address:** www.healtheast.org

ST. JOHN'S HOSPITAL (O, 192 beds) 1575 Beam Avenue, Saint Paul, MN Zip 55109–1126; tel. 651/232–7000; Scott L. North, FACHE, Senior Vice President and President of Acute Care Hospitals
**Web address:** www.stjohnshospital–mn.org

ST. JOSEPH'S HOSPITAL (O, 232 beds) 45 West 10th Street, Saint Paul, MN Zip 55102–1053; tel. 651/232–3000; Scott L. North, FACHE, Senior Vice President and President of Acute Care Hospitals
**Web address:** www.healtheast.org

WOODWINDS HEALTH CAMPUS (O, 86 beds) 1925 Woodwinds Drive, Woodbury, MN Zip 55125–4445; tel. 651/232–0228; Scott L. North, FACHE, Senior Vice President and President of Acute Care Hospitals
**Web address:** www.woodwinds.org

| Owned, leased, sponsored: | 4 hospitals | 636 beds |
|---|---|---|
| Contract–managed: | 0 hospitals | 0 beds |
| Totals: | 4 hospitals | 636 beds |

---

**0342:   HEALTHPARTNERS** (NP)
8170 33rd Avenue South, Bloomington, MN Zip 55425–4516; tel. 952/883–7600; Mary K. Brainerd, President and Chief Executive Officer
**(Moderately Centralized Health System)**

GLENCOE REGIONAL HEALTH SERVICES (C, 135 beds) 1805 Hennepin Avenue North, Glencoe, MN Zip 55336–1416; tel. 320/864–3121; Jon D. Braband, FACHE, President and Chief Executive Officer
**Web address:** www.grhsonline.org

LAKEVIEW HOSPITAL (O, 66 beds) 927 Churchill Street West, Stillwater, MN Zip 55082–6605; tel. 651/439–5330; Curt Geissler, President
**Web address:** www.lakeview.org

PARK NICOLLET METHODIST HOSPITAL (O, 426 beds) 6500 Excelsior Boulevard, Saint Louis Park, MN Zip 55426–4702; Minneapolis, tel. 952/993–5000; David Abelson, M.D., President and Chief Executive Officer
**Web address:** www.parknicollet.com

REGIONS HOSPITAL (O, 454 beds) 640 Jackson Street, Saint Paul, MN Zip 55101–2595; tel. 651/254–3456; Brock D. Nelson, President and Chief Executive Officer
**Web address:** www.regionshospital.com

**WISCONSIN:** WESTFIELDS HOSPITAL (O, 25 beds) 535 Hospital Road, New Richmond, WI Zip 54017–1449; tel. 715/243–2600; Steven Massey, President and Chief Executive Officer
**Web address:** www.westfieldshospital.com

| Owned, leased, sponsored: | 4 hospitals | 971 beds |
|---|---|---|
| Contract–managed: | 1 hospital | 135 beds |
| Totals: | 5 hospitals | 1106 beds |

---

**★0023:   HEALTHSOUTH CORPORATION** (IO)
3660 Grandview Parkway, Suite 200, Birmingham, AL Zip 35243–3332; tel. 205/967–7116; Jay F. Grinney, President and Chief Executive Officer
**(Independent Hospital System)**

---

For explanation of codes following names, see page B2.
★ Indicates Type III membership in the American Hospital Association.

**ALABAMA:** HEALTHSOUTH LAKESHORE REHABILITATION HOSPITAL (O, 100 beds) 3800 Ridgeway Drive, Birmingham, AL Zip 35209–5599; tel. 205/868–2000; Heath Phillips, Administrator and Chief Executive Officer
**Web address:** www.healthsouthlakeshorerehab.com

HEALTHSOUTH REHABILITATION HOSPITAL (O, 39 beds) 1736 East Main Street, Dothan, AL Zip 36301–3040, Mailing Address: P.O. Box 6708, Zip 36302–6708; tel. 334/712–6333; Margaret A. Futch, Chief Executive Officer
**Web address:** www.healthsouthdothan.com

HEALTHSOUTH REHABILITATION HOSPITAL OF MONTGOMERY (O, 70 beds) 4465 Narrow Lane Road, Montgomery, AL Zip 36116–2900; tel. 334/284–7700; Linda Wade, Chief Executive Officer
**Web address:** www.healthsouthmontgomery.com

HEALTHSOUTH REHABILITATION HOSPITAL OF NORTH ALABAMA (O, 70 beds) 107 Governors Drive S.W., Huntsville, AL Zip 35801–4326; tel. 256/535–2300; Douglas H. Beverly, Chief Executive Officer
**Web address:** www.healthsouthhuntsville.com

HEALTHSOUTH REHABILITATION OF GADSDEN (O, 44 beds) 801 Goodyear Avenue, Gadsden, AL Zip 35903–1133; tel. 256/439–5000; Michael W. Thompson, Chief Executive Officer
**Web address:** www.healthsouth.com

REGIONAL REHABILITATION HOSPITAL (O, 48 beds) 3715 Highway 280/431 North, Phenix City, AL Zip 36867; tel. 334/732–2200; Jill Jordan, Chief Executive Officer
**Web address:** www.regionalrehabhospital.com

**ARIZONA:** HEALTHSOUTH EAST VALLEY REHABILITATION HOSPITAL (O, 40 beds) 5652 East Baseline Road, Mesa, AZ Zip 85206–4713; tel. 480/567–0350; ,
**Web address:** www.healthsoutheastvalley.com

HEALTHSOUTH REHABILITATION HOSPITAL OF SOUTHERN ARIZONA (O, 60 beds) 1921 West Hospital Drive, Tucson, AZ Zip 85704–7806; tel. 520/742–2800; Robert C. Honeycutt, FACHE, Chief Executive Officer
**Web address:** www.healthsouthsouthernarizona.com

HEALTHSOUTH REHABILITATION INSTITUTE OF TUCSON (O, 80 beds) 2650 North Wyatt Drive, Tucson, AZ Zip 85712–6108; tel. 520/325–1300; Jeffrey Christensen, Chief Executive Officer
**Web address:** www.rehabinstituteoftucson.com

HEALTHSOUTH SCOTTSDALE REHABILITATION HOSPITAL (O, 60 beds) 9630 East Shea Boulevard, Scottsdale, AZ Zip 85260–6267; tel. 480/551–5400; Timothy T. Poore, Chief Executive Officer
**Web address:** www.healthsouthscottsdale.com

HEALTHSOUTH VALLEY OF THE SUN REHABILITATION HOSPITAL (O, 75 beds) 13460 North 67th Avenue, Glendale, AZ Zip 85304–1042; tel. 623/878–8800; Beth Bacher, Chief Executive Officer
**Web address:** www.healthsouthvalleyofthesun.com

YUMA REHABILITATION HOSPITAL (O, 41 beds) 901 West 24th Street, Yuma, AZ Zip 85364–6384; tel. 928/726–5000; Joshua Bowie, Chief Executive Officer
**Web address:** www.yumarehabhospital.com

**ARKANSAS:** HEALTHSOUTH REHABILITATION HOSPITAL (O, 60 beds) 153 East Monte Painter Drive, Fayetteville, AR Zip 72703–4002; tel. 479/444–2200; Jack C. Mitchell, FACHE, Chief Executive Officer
**Web address:** www.healthsouthfayetteville.com

HEALTHSOUTH REHABILITATION HOSPITAL OF FORT SMITH (O, 60 beds) 1401 South J Street, Fort Smith, AR Zip 72901–5155; tel. 479/785–3300; Ryan Cassedy, Chief Executive Officer
**Web address:** www.healthsouthfortsmith.com

HEALTHSOUTH REHABILITATION HOSPITAL OF JONESBORO (O, 67 beds) 1201 Fleming Avenue, Jonesboro, AR Zip 72401–4311, Mailing Address: P.O. Box 1680, Zip 72403–1680; tel. 870/932–0440; Donna Harris, Chief Executive Officer
**Web address:** www.healthsouthjonesboro.com

ST. VINCENT REHABILITATION HOSPITAL (O, 71 beds) 2201 Wildwood Avenue, Sherwood, AR Zip 72120–5074, Mailing Address: P.O. Box 6930, Zip 72124–6930; tel. 501/834–1800; Lisa Watson, Chief Executive Officer
**Web address:** www.stvincenthealth.com/svrehabhospital/index.html

**CALIFORNIA:** HEALTHSOUTH BAKERSFIELD REHABILITATION HOSPITAL (O, 66 beds) 5001 Commerce Drive, Bakersfield, CA Zip 93309–0689; tel. 661/323–5500; Sandra Hegland, Chief Executive Officer
**Web address:** www.healthsouthbakersfield.com

HEALTHSOUTH TUSTIN REHABILITATION HOSPITAL (O, 48 beds) 14851 Yorba Street, Tustin, CA Zip 92780–2925; tel. 714/832–9200; Diana C. Hanyak, Chief Executive Officer
**Web address:** www.tustinrehab.com

**COLORADO:** HEALTHSOUTH REHABILITATION HOSPITAL OF COLORADO SPRINGS (O, 64 beds) 325 Parkside Drive, Colorado Springs, CO Zip 80910–3134; tel. 719/630–8000; Stephen Schaefer, Chief Executive Officer
**Web address:** www.healthsouthcoloradosprings.com

**FLORIDA:** HEALTHSOUTH EMERALD COAST REHABILITATION HOSPITAL (O, 75 beds) 1847 Florida Avenue, Panama City, FL Zip 32405–4640; tel. 850/914–8600; Tony N. Bennett, Chief Executive Officer
**Web address:** www.healthsouthpanamacity.com

HEALTHSOUTH REHABILITATION HOSPITAL (O, 70 beds) 901 North Clearwater–Largo Road, Largo, FL Zip 33770–4126; tel. 727/586–2999; Donald D. Evans, Chief Executive Officer
**Web address:** www.healthsouthlargo.com

HEALTHSOUTH REHABILITATION HOSPITAL OF MIAMI (O, 60 beds) 20601 Old Cutler Road, Miami, FL Zip 33189–2400; tel. 305/251–3800; Elizabeth L. Izquierdo, CPA, Chief Executive Officer
**Web address:** www.healthsouthmiami.com

HEALTHSOUTH REHABILITATION HOSPITAL OF OCALA (O, 40 beds) 2275 S.W. 22nd Lane, Ocala, FL Zip 34471–7710; tel. 352/282–4000; Ellen Witterstaeter, FACHE, Chief Executive Officer
**Web address:** www.healthsouthocala.com

HEALTHSOUTH REHABILITATION HOSPITAL OF SARASOTA (O, 96 beds) 6400 Edgelake Drive, Sarasota, FL Zip 34240–8813; tel. 941/921–8600; Marcus Braz, Chief Executive Officer
**Web address:** www.healthsouthsarasota.com

HEALTHSOUTH REHABILITATION HOSPITAL OF SPRING HILL (O, 80 beds) 12440 Cortez Boulevard, Brooksville, FL Zip 34613–2628; tel. 352/592–4250; Lori Bedard, Chief Executive Officer
**Web address:** www.healthsouthspringhill.com

HEALTHSOUTH REHABILITATION HOSPITAL OF TALLAHASSEE (O, 76 beds) 1675 Riggins Road, Tallahassee, FL Zip 32308–5315; tel. 850/656–4800; Dale Neely, Chief Executive Officer
**Web address:** www.healthsouthtallahassee.com

HEALTHSOUTH SEA PINES REHABILITATION HOSPITAL (O, 90 beds) 101 East Florida Avenue, Melbourne, FL Zip 32901–8301; tel. 321/984–4600; Denise B. McGrath, Chief Executive Officer
**Web address:** www.healthsouthseapines.com

HEALTHSOUTH SUNRISE REHABILITATION HOSPITAL (O, 126 beds) 4399 Nob Hill Road, Fort Lauderdale, FL Zip 33351–5899; tel. 954/749–0300; Kevin R. Conn, Chief Executive Officer
**Web address:** www.healthsouthsunrise.com

HEALTHSOUTH TREASURE COAST REHABILITATION HOSPITAL (O, 90 beds) 1600 37th Street, Vero Beach, FL Zip 32960–4863; tel. 772/778–2100; Carol Sim, Chief Executive Officer
**Web address:** www.healthsouthtreasurecoast.com

**GEORGIA:** HEALTHSOUTH WALTON REHABILITATION HOSPITAL (O, 58 beds) 1355 Independence Drive, Augusta, GA Zip 30901–1037; tel. 706/724–7746; Deborah S. Guthrie, Chief Executive Officer
**Web address:** www.healthsouthwalton.com/

**ILLINOIS:** VAN MATRE HEALTHSOUTH REHABILITATION HOSPITAL (O, 50 beds) 950 South Mulford Road, Rockford, IL Zip 61108–4274; tel. 815/381–8500; Ken Bowman, Chief Executive Officer
**Web address:** www.healthsouth.com

**INDIANA:** HEALTHSOUTH DEACONESS REHABILITATION HOSPITAL (O, 80 beds) 4100 Covert Avenue, Evansville, IN Zip 47714–5567, Mailing Address: P.O. Box 5349, Zip 47716–5349; tel. 812/476–9983; Barbara Butler, Chief Executive Officer
**Web address:** www.healthsouthdeaconess.com

**KANSAS:** KANSAS REHABILITATION HOSPITAL (O, 59 beds) 1504 S.W. Eighth Avenue, Topeka, KS Zip 66606–1632; tel. 785/235–6600; Marty Dernier, Chief Executive Officer
**Web address:** www.kansasrehabhospital.com

MID–AMERICA REHABILITATION HOSPITAL (O, 98 beds) 5701 West 110th Street, Shawnee Mission, KS Zip 66211–2503; tel. 913/491–2400; Troy DeDecker, Chief Executive Officer
**Web address:** www.midamericarehabhospital.com

For explanation of codes following names, see page B2.
★ Indicates Type III membership in the American Hospital Association.

Section B

WESLEY REHABILITATION HOSPITAL (O, 65 beds) 8338 West 13th Street North, Wichita, KS Zip 67212–2984; tel. 316/729–9999; James F. Grocholski, FACHE, Chief Executive Officer
**Web address:** www.wesleyrehabhospital.com

**KENTUCKY:** HEALTHSOUTH LAKEVIEW REHABILITATION HOSPITAL (O, 40 beds) 134 Heartland Drive, Elizabethtown, KY Zip 42701–2778; tel. 270/769–3100; Lori Jarboe, Chief Executive Officer
**Web address:** www.healthsouthlakeview.com

HEALTHSOUTH NORTHERN KENTUCKY REHABILITATION HOSPITAL (O, 40 beds) 201 Medical Village Drive, Edgewood, KY Zip 41017–3407; tel. 859/341–2044; Richard R. Evens, Chief Executive Officer
**Web address:** www.healthsouthkentucky.com

**LOUISIANA:** HEALTHSOUTH REHABILITATION HOSPITAL OF ALEXANDRIA (O, 47 beds) 104 North Third Street, Alexandria, LA Zip 71301–8581; tel. 318/449–1370; James W. McClung, Chief Executive Officer
**Web address:** www.healthsouthalexandria.com

**MAINE:** NEW ENGLAND REHABILITATION HOSPITAL OF PORTLAND (O, 90 beds) 335 Brighton Avenue, Portland, ME Zip 04102–2363; tel. 207/775–4000; Jeanine Chesley, Chief Executive Officer
**Web address:** www.nerhp.org

**MARYLAND:** HEALTHSOUTH CHESAPEAKE REHABILITATION HOSPITAL (O, 54 beds) 220 Tilghman Road, Salisbury, MD Zip 21804–1921; tel. 410/546–4600; Steven Walas, Chief Executive Officer
**Web address:** www.healthsouthchesapeake.com

**MASSACHUSETTS:** FAIRLAWN REHABILITATION HOSPITAL (O, 110 beds) 189 May Street, Worcester, MA Zip 01602–4339; tel. 508/791–6351; R. David Richer, Chief Executive Officer
**Web address:** www.fairlawnrehab.org

HEALTHSOUTH REHABILITATION HOSPITAL OF WESTERN MASSACHUSETTS (O, 53 beds) 14 Chestnut Place, Ludlow, MA Zip 01056–3476; tel. 413/589–7581; Scott R. Keen, Chief Executive Officer
**Web address:** www.healthsouthrehab.org

**MISSOURI:** HOWARD A. RUSK REHABILITATION CENTER (O, 60 beds) 315 Business Loop 70 West, Columbia, MO Zip 65203–3248; tel. 573/817–2703; Bruce Eady, Chief Executive Officer
**Web address:** www.ruskrehab.com

THE REHABILITATION INSTITUTE OF ST. LOUIS (O, 96 beds) 4455 Duncan Avenue, Saint Louis, MO Zip 63110–1111; tel. 314/658–3800; Jon McDowell, FACHE, Chief Executive Officer
**Web address:** www.rehabinstitutestl.com

**NEVADA:** HEALTHSOUTH DESERT CANYON REHABILITATION HOSPITAL (O, 50 beds) 9175 West Oquendo Road, Las Vegas, NV Zip 89148–1234; tel. 702/252–7342; Deanna Martin, MSN, Chief Executive Officer
**Web address:** www.healthsouthdesertcanyon.com

HEALTHSOUTH REHABILITATION HOSPITAL – HENDERSON (O, 90 beds) 10301 Jeffreys Street, Henderson, NV Zip 89052–3922; tel. 702/939–9400; Earl Greenia, FACHE, Chief Executive Officer
**Web address:** www.hendersonrehabhospital.com

HEALTHSOUTH REHABILITATION HOSPITAL–LAS VEGAS (O, 79 beds) 1250 South Valley View Boulevard, Las Vegas, NV Zip 89102–1861; tel. 702/877–8898; Michael Ward, Chief Executive Officer
**Web address:** www.healthsouthlasvegas.com

**NEW HAMPSHIRE:** HEALTHSOUTH REHABILITATION HOSPITAL (O, 50 beds) 254 Pleasant Street, Concord, NH Zip 03301–2508; tel. 603/226–9800; Catherine Devaney, Chief Executive Officer
**Web address:** www.healthsouthrehabconcordnh.com

**NEW JERSEY:** HEALTHSOUTH REHABILITATION HOSPITAL OF TOMS RIVER (O, 92 beds) 14 Hospital Drive, Toms River, NJ Zip 08755–6470; tel. 732/244–3100; Patricia Ostaszewski, MS, Chief Executive Officer
**Web address:** www.rehabnj.com/tomsriver

HEALTHSOUTH REHABILITATION HOSPITAL OF VINELAND (O, 41 beds) 1237 West Sherman Avenue, Vineland, NJ Zip 08360–6920; tel. 856/696–7100; Tammy Feuer, Chief Executive Officer
**Web address:** www.healthsouthvineland.com

REHABILITATION HOSPITAL OF TINTON FALLS (O, 60 beds) 2 Centre Plaza, Tinton Falls, NJ Zip 07724–9744; tel. 732/460–5320; Linda A. Savino, MS, Chief Executive Officer
**Web address:** www.rehabnj.com

**NEW MEXICO:** HEALTHSOUTH REHABILITATION HOSPITAL (O, 87 beds) 7000 Jefferson Street N.E., Albuquerque, NM Zip 87109–4313; tel. 505/344–9478; Sylvia K. Kelly, Chief Executive Officer
**Web address:** www.healthsouthnewmexico.com

**OHIO:** HEALTHSOUTH REHABILITATION HOSPITAL AT DRAKE (O, 40 beds) 151 West Galbraith Road, Cincinnati, OH Zip 45216–1015; tel. 513/418–5600; Brad Kennedy, Chief Executive Officer
**Web address:** www.healthsouthatdrake.com

**PENNSYLVANIA:** GEISINGER HEALTHSOUTH REHABILITATION HOSPITAL (O, 42 beds) 2 Rehab Lane, Danville, PA Zip 17821–8498; tel. 570/271–6733; Lorie Dillon, Chief Executive Officer
**Web address:** www.geisingerhealthsouth.com

HEALTHSOUTH HARMARVILLE REHABILITATION HOSPITAL (O, 202 beds) Guys Run Road, Pittsburgh, PA Zip 15238–0460, Mailing Address: P.O. Box 11460, Zip 15238–0460; tel. 412/828–1300; Kenneth J. Anthony, Chief Executive Officer
**Web address:** www.healthsouthharmarville.com

HEALTHSOUTH NITTANY VALLEY REHABILITATION HOSPITAL (O, 73 beds) 550 West College Avenue, Pleasant Gap, PA Zip 16823–7401; tel. 814/359–3421; Susan Hartman, Chief Executive Officer
**Web address:** www.nittanyvalleyrehab.com

HEALTHSOUTH READING REHABILITATION HOSPITAL (O, 60 beds) 1623 Morgantown Road, Reading, PA Zip 19607–9455; tel. 610/796–6000; Richard Kruczek, Chief Executive Officer
**Web address:** www.healthsouthreading.com

HEALTHSOUTH REHABILITATION HOSPITAL (O, 44 beds) 303 Camp Meeting Road, Sewickley, PA Zip 15143–8322; tel. 412/741–9500; Leah Laffey, MSN, R.N., Chief Executive Officer
**Web address:** www.healthsouthsewickley.com

HEALTHSOUTH REHABILITATION HOSPITAL OF ALTOONA (O, 80 beds) 2005 Valley View Boulevard, Altoona, PA Zip 16602–4598; tel. 814/944–3535; Scott Filler, Chief Executive Officer
**Web address:** www.healthsouthaltoona.com

HEALTHSOUTH REHABILITATION HOSPITAL OF ERIE (O, 100 beds) 143 East Second Street, Erie, PA Zip 16507–1501; tel. 814/878–1200; Lucretia Atti, Chief Executive Officer
**Web address:** www.healthsoutherie.com

HEALTHSOUTH REHABILITATION HOSPITAL OF MECHANICSBURG (O, 75 beds) 175 Lancaster Boulevard, Mechanicsburg, PA Zip 17055–3562, Mailing Address: P.O. Box 2016, Zip 17055–0736; tel. 717/691–3700; Mark Freeburn, Chief Executive Officer
**Web address:** www.healthsouthpa.com

HEALTHSOUTH REHABILITATION HOSPITAL OF YORK (O, 90 beds) 1850 Normandie Drive, York, PA Zip 17408–1534; tel. 717/767–6941; Steven Alwine, Chief Executive Officer
**Web address:** www.healthsouthyork.com

**PUERTO RICO:** HEALTHSOUTH HOSPITAL OF MANATI (O, 40 beds) Carretera 2, Kilometro 47 7, Manati, PR Zip 00674; tel. 787/621–3800; Enrique A. Vicens–Rivera, Jr., JD, Chief Executive Officer
**Web address:** www.healthsouth.com

HEALTHSOUTH REHABILITATION HOSPITAL OF SAN JUAN (O, 32 beds) University Hospital, 3rd Floor, San Juan, PR Zip 00923, Mailing Address: P.O. Box 70344, Zip 00923; tel. 787/274–5100; Daniel Del Castillo, Chief Executive Officer
**Web address:** www.healthsouth.com

**SOUTH CAROLINA:** ANMED HEALTH REHABILITATION HOSPITAL (O, 45 beds) 1 Spring Back Way, Anderson, SC Zip 29621–2676; tel. 864/716–2600; Michele M. Skripps, R.N., Chief Executive Officer
**Web address:** www.anmedrehab.com

HEALTHSOUTH REHABILITATION HOSPITAL (O, 88 beds) 900 East Cheves Street, Florence, SC Zip 29506–2704; tel. 843/679–9000; Jill Strawn, Chief Executive Officer
**Web address:** www.healthsouthflorence.com

HEALTHSOUTH REHABILITATION HOSPITAL (O, 50 beds) 1795 Dr. Frank Gaston Boulevard, Rock Hill, SC Zip 29732–1190; tel. 803/326–3500; ,
**Web address:** www.healthsouthrockhill.com

HEALTHSOUTH REHABILITATION HOSPITAL OF CHARLESTON (O, 49 beds) 9181 Medcom Street, Charleston, SC Zip 29406–9168; tel. 843/820–7777; Troy Powell, Chief Executive Officer
**Web address:** www.healthsouthcharleston.com

For explanation of codes following names, see page B2.
★ Indicates Type III membership in the American Hospital Association.

HEALTHSOUTH REHABILITATION HOSPITAL OF COLUMBIA (O, 96 beds) 2935 Colonial Drive, Columbia, SC Zip 29203–6811; tel. 803/254–7777; W. Anthony Jackson, Chief Executive Officer
**Web address:** www.healthsouthcolumbia.com

**TENNESSEE:** HEALTHSOUTH CANE CREEK REHABILITATION HOSPITAL (O, 40 beds) 180 Mt Pelia Road, Martin, TN Zip 38237–3812; tel. 731/587–4231; Eric Garrard, Chief Executive Officer
**Web address:** www.healthsouthcanecreek.com

HEALTHSOUTH CHATTANOOGA REHABILITATION HOSPITAL (O, 46 beds) 2412 McCallie Avenue, Chattanooga, TN Zip 37404–3398; tel. 423/698–0221; Scott Rowe, Chief Executive Officer
**Web address:** www.healthsouthchattanooga.com

HEALTHSOUTH REHABILITATION HOSPITAL (O, 50 beds) 113 Cassel Drive, Kingsport, TN Zip 37660–3775; tel. 423/246–7240; Susan Glenn, Chief Executive Officer
**Web address:** www.healthsouthkingsport.com

HEALTHSOUTH REHABILITATION HOSPITAL MEMPHIS–NORTH (O, 40 beds) 4100 Austin Peay Highway, Memphis, TN Zip 38128–2502; tel. 901/213–5400; Marcia Taylor, Chief Executive Officer
**Web address:** www.healthsouthnorthmemphis.com

HEALTHSOUTH REHABILITATION HOSPITAL OF MEMPHIS (O, 72 beds) 1282 Union Avenue, Memphis, TN Zip 38104–3414; tel. 901/722–2000; Michael L. Pierce, Chief Executive Officer
**Web address:** www.healthsouthmemphis.com

VANDERBILT STALLWORTH REHABILITATION HOSPITAL (O, 80 beds) 2201 Childrens Way, Nashville, TN Zip 37212–3165; tel. 615/320–7600; Susan Heath, Chief Executive Officer
**Web address:** www.vanderbiltstallworthrehab.com

**TEXAS:** HEALTHSOUTH PLANO REHABILITATION HOSPITAL (O, 83 beds) 2800 West 15th Street, Plano, TX Zip 75075–7526; tel. 972/612–9000; Jennifer Lynn Brewer, Chief Executive Officer
**Web address:** www.healthsouthplano.com

HEALTHSOUTH REHABILITATION HOSPITAL (O, 60 beds) 19002 McKay Drive, Humble, TX Zip 77338–5701; tel. 281/446–6148; Angela L. Simmons, Chief Executive Officer
**Web address:** www.healthsouthhumble.com

HEALTHSOUTH REHABILITATION HOSPITAL MIDLAND ODESSA (O, 60 beds) 1800 Heritage Boulevard, Midland, TX Zip 79707–9750; tel. 432/520–1600; Christopher Wortham, Chief Executive Officer
**Web address:** www.healthsouthmidland.com

HEALTHSOUTH REHABILITATION HOSPITAL OF ARLINGTON (O, 85 beds) 3200 Matlock Road, Arlington, TX Zip 76015–2911; tel. 817/468–4000; Mark S. Deno, Chief Executive Officer
**Web address:** www.healthsoutharlington.com

HEALTHSOUTH REHABILITATION HOSPITAL OF AUSTIN (O, 40 beds) 1215 Red River Street, Austin, TX Zip 78701–1921; tel. 512/474–5700; Duke Saldivar, FACHE, Chief Executive Officer
**Web address:** www.healthsouthaustin.com

HEALTHSOUTH REHABILITATION HOSPITAL OF BEAUMONT (O, 61 beds) 3340 Plaza 10 Boulevard, Beaumont, TX Zip 77707–2551; tel. 409/835–0835; H. J. Gaspard, Chief Executive Officer
**Web address:** www.healthsouthbeaumont.com

HEALTHSOUTH REHABILITATION HOSPITAL OF CYPRESS (O, 40 beds) 13031 Wortham Center Drive, Houston, TX Zip 77065–5662; tel. 832/280–2500; Sheila A. Kramer, Chief Executive Officer
**Web address:** www.healthsouthcypress.com

HEALTHSOUTH REHABILITATION HOSPITAL OF FORT WORTH (O, 60 beds) 1212 West Lancaster Avenue, Fort Worth, TX Zip 76102–4510; tel. 817/870–2336; Trent Pierce, R.N., Chief Executive Officer
**Web address:** www.healthsouthfortworth.com

HEALTHSOUTH REHABILITATION HOSPITAL OF NORTH HOUSTON (O, 84 beds) 18550 'IH' 45 South, Conroe, TX Zip 77384; tel. 281/364–2000; Krista Uselman, Chief Executive Officer
**Web address:** www.healthsouth.com

HEALTHSOUTH REHABILITATION HOSPITAL OF TEXARKANA (O, 60 beds) 515 West 12th Street, Texarkana, TX Zip 75501–4416; tel. 903/793–0088; Jerry Jasper, Chief Executive Officer
**Web address:** www.healthsouthtexarkana.com

HEALTHSOUTH REHABILITATION HOSPITAL–CITYVIEW (O, 62 beds) 6701 Oakmont Boulevard, Fort Worth, TX Zip 76132–2957; tel. 817/370–4700; Deborah Hopps, Chief Executive Officer
**Web address:** www.healthsouthcityview.com

HEALTHSOUTH REHABILITATION HOSPITAL–WICHITA FALLS (O, 63 beds) 3901 Armory Road, Wichita Falls, TX Zip 76302–2204; tel. 940/720–5700; Michael L. Bullitt, Chief Executive Officer
**Web address:** www.healthsouthwichitafalls.com

HEALTHSOUTH REHABILITATION INSTITUTE OF SAN ANTONIO (O, 96 beds) 9119 Cinnamon Hill, San Antonio, TX Zip 78240–5401; tel. 210/691–0737; Scott Butcher, Chief Executive Officer
**Web address:** www.hsriosa.com

HEALTHSOUTH SUGAR LAND REHABILITATION HOSPITAL (O, 50 beds) 1325 Highway 6, Sugar Land, TX Zip 77478–4906; tel. 281/276–7574; Nicholas Hardin, Chief Executive Officer
**Web address:** www.healthsouthsugarland.com

TRINITY MOTHER FRANCES REHABILITATION HOSPITAL (O, 74 beds) 3131 Troup Highway, Tyler, TX Zip 75701–8352; tel. 903/510–7000; Sharla Anderson, Chief Executive Officer
**Web address:** www.tmfrehabhospital.com

**UTAH:** HEALTHSOUTH REHABILITATION HOSPITAL OF UTAH (O, 105 beds) 8074 South 1300 East, Sandy, UT Zip 84094–0743; tel. 801/561–3400; Philip Eaton, Chief Executive Officer and Administrator
**Web address:** www.healthsouthutah.com

**VIRGINIA:** HEALTHSOUTH REHABILITATION HOSPITAL OF FREDERICKSBURG (O, 40 beds) 300 Park Hill Drive, Fredericksburg, VA Zip 22401–3387; tel. 540/368–7300; Donna Z. Phillips, M.D., Chief Executive Officer
**Web address:** www.fredericksburgrehabhospital.com

HEALTHSOUTH REHABILITATION HOSPITAL OF NORTHERN VIRGINIA (O, 40 beds) 24430 Millstream Drive, Aldie, VA Zip 20105–3098; tel. 703/957–2000; Gary J. Herbek, Chief Executive Officer
**Web address:** www.healthsouthnorthernvirginia.com

HEALTHSOUTH REHABILITATION HOSPITAL OF PETERSBURG (O, 53 beds) 95 Pinehill Boulevard, Petersburg, VA Zip 23805–9233; tel. 804/504–8100; ,
**Web address:** www.healthsouthpetersburg.com

HEALTHSOUTH REHABILITATION HOSPITAL OF VIRGINIA (O, 40 beds) 5700 Fitzhugh Avenue, Richmond, VA Zip 23226–1800; tel. 804/288–5700; Tonya Ferguson, Interim Chief Executive Officer
**Web address:** www.healthsouthrichmond.com

REHABILITATION HOSPITAL OF SOUTHWEST VIRGINIA (O, 25 beds) 103 North Street, Bristol, VA Zip 24201–3201; tel. 276/642–7900; Georgeanne Cole, Chief Executive Officer
**Web address:** www.rehabilitationhospitalswvirginia.com

UVA–HEALTHSOUTH REHABILITATION HOSPITAL (O, 50 beds) 515 Ray C. Hunt Drive, Charlottesville, VA Zip 22903–2981; tel. 434/244–2000; Thomas J. Cook, Chief Executive Officer
**Web address:** www.uvahealthsouth.com

**WEST VIRGINIA:** HEALTHSOUTH HUNTINGTON REHABILITATION HOSPITAL (O, 52 beds) 6900 West Country Club Drive, Huntington, WV Zip 25705–2000; tel. 304/733–1060; Michael E. Zuliani, Chief Executive Officer
**Web address:** www.healthsouthhuntington.com

HEALTHSOUTH MOUNTAINVIEW REGIONAL REHABILITATION HOSPITAL (O, 80 beds) 1160 Van Voorhis Road, Morgantown, WV Zip 26505–3437; tel. 304/598–1100; Vickie Demers, Chief Executive Officer
**Web address:** www.healthsouthmountainview.com

HEALTHSOUTH SOUTHERN HILLS REHABILITATION HOSPITAL (O, 42 beds) 120 Twelfth Street, Princeton, WV Zip 24740–2352; tel. 304/487–8000; Robert Williams, Chief Executive Officer
**Web address:** www.healthsouthsouthernhills.com

HEALTHSOUTH WESTERN HILLS REHABILITATION HOSPITAL (O, 50 beds) 3 Western Hills Drive, Parkersburg, WV Zip 26105–8122; tel. 304/420–1300; Alvin R. Lawson, JD, FACHE, Chief Executive Officer
**Web address:** www.healthsouthwesternhills.com

| | | |
|---|---|---|
| **Owned, leased, sponsored:** | 101 hospitals | 6604 beds |
| **Contract–managed:** | 0 hospitals | 0 beds |
| **Totals:** | 101 hospitals | 6604 beds |

For explanation of codes following names, see page B2.
★ Indicates Type III membership in the American Hospital Association.

★**0585:  HEALTHTECH MANAGEMENT SERVICES** (IO)
405 Duke Drive, Suite 210, Franklin, TN Zip 37067–2709;
tel. 615/309–6053; Derek Morkel, Chief Executive Officer
**(Decentralized Health System)**

**ARIZONA:** COBRE VALLEY REGIONAL MEDICAL CENTER (C, 25 beds) 5880
South Hospital Drive, Globe, AZ Zip 85501–9454; tel. 928/425–3261;
Neal Jensen, Chief Executive Officer
**Web address:** www.cvrmc.org

**GEORGIA:** UPSON REGIONAL MEDICAL CENTER (C, 75 beds) 801 West
Gordon Street, Thomaston, GA Zip 30286–3426, Mailing Address: P.O.
Box 1059, Zip 30286–0027; tel. 706/647–8111; David L. Castleberry,
Chief Executive Officer
**Web address:** www.urmc.org

**ILLINOIS:** CARLINVILLE AREA HOSPITAL (C, 25 beds) 20733 North Broad
Street, Carlinville, IL Zip 62626–1499; tel. 217/854–3141; Kenneth G.
Reid, President and Chief Executive Officer
**Web address:** www.cahcare.com

HAMMOND–HENRY HOSPITAL (C, 61 beds) 600 North College Avenue,
Geneseo, IL Zip 61254–1099; tel. 309/944–4625; Bradley Solberg, FACHE,
Chief Executive Officer
**Web address:** www.hammondhenry.com

HILLSBORO AREA HOSPITAL (C, 25 beds) 1200 East Tremont Street,
Hillsboro, IL Zip 62049–1900; tel. 217/532–6111; Rex H. Brown, Chief
Executive Officer
**Web address:** www.hillsborohealth.org

**LOUISIANA:** IBERIA MEDICAL CENTER (C, 84 beds) 2315 East Main Street,
New Iberia, LA Zip 70560–4031, Mailing Address: P.O. Box 13338,
Zip 70562–3338; tel. 337/364–0441; John A. Tucker, Chief Executive
Officer
**Web address:** www.iberiamedicalcenter.com

**MONTANA:** BARRETT HOSPITAL & HEALTHCARE (C, 25 beds) 600 Highway
91 South, Dillon, MT Zip 59725–7379; tel. 406/683–3000; Ken
Westman, Chief Executive Officer
**Web address:** www.barretthospital.org

**NEBRASKA:** TRI VALLEY HEALTH SYSTEM (C, 51 beds) 1305 West Highway
6 and 34, Cambridge, NE Zip 69022–0488, Mailing Address: P.O. Box
488, Zip 69022–0488; tel. 308/697–3329; Roger W. Steinkruger,
Executive Officer
**Web address:** www.trivalleyhealth.com

**NEW MEXICO:** UNION COUNTY GENERAL HOSPITAL (C, 21 beds) 300 Wilson
Street, Clayton, NM Zip 88415–3304, Mailing Address: P.O. Box 489,
Zip 88415–0489; tel. 575/374–2585; Donald Weidemann, Administrator
**Web address:** www.unioncountygeneral.com

**NEW YORK:** ADIRONDACK MEDICAL CENTER (C, 271 beds) 2233 State
Route 86, Saranac Lake, NY Zip 12983–5644, Mailing Address: P.O. Box
471, Zip 12983–0471; tel. 518/891–4141; Chandler M. Ralph, President
and Chief Executive Officer
**Web address:** www.amccares.org

**OREGON:** BLUE MOUNTAIN HOSPITAL (C, 64 beds) 170 Ford Road, John
Day, OR Zip 97845–2009; tel. 541/575–1311; Robert Houser, FACHE,
Chief Executive Officer
**Web address:** www.bluemountainhospital.org

**WASHINGTON:** SUNNYSIDE COMMUNITY HOSPITAL (C, 25 beds) 1016
Tacoma Avenue, Sunnyside, WA Zip 98944–2263, Mailing Address: P.O.
Box 719, Zip 98944–0719; tel. 509/837–1500; John Gallagher, Chief
Executive Officer
**Web address:** www.sunnysidehospital.com

**WISCONSIN:** GRANT REGIONAL HEALTH CENTER (C, 8 beds) 507 South
Monroe Street, Lancaster, WI Zip 53813–2054; tel. 608/723–2143;
Nicole Clapp, R.N., MSN, FACHE, President and Chief Executive Officer
**Web address:** www.grantregional.com

SPOONER HEALTH SYSTEM (C, 25 beds) 819 Ash Street, Spooner, WI
Zip 54801–1299; tel. 715/635–2111; Michael Schafer, Chief Executive
Officer and Administrator
**Web address:** www.spoonerhealthsystem.com

TOMAH MEMORIAL HOSPITAL (C, 25 beds) 321 Butts Avenue, Tomah, WI
Zip 54660–1412; tel. 608/372–2181; Philip J. Stuart, Administrator and
Chief Executive Officer
**Web address:** www.tomahhospital.org

**WYOMING:** HOT SPRINGS COUNTY MEMORIAL HOSPITAL (C, 25 beds) 150
East Arapahoe Street, Thermopolis, WY Zip 82443–2498;
tel. 307/864–3121; Robin Roling, President and Chief Executive Officer
**Web address:** www.hscmh.org

POWELL VALLEY HEALTHCARE (C, 125 beds) 777 Avenue H, Powell, WY
Zip 82435–2296; tel. 307/754–2267; Bill D. Patten, Chief Executive Officer
**Web address:** www.pvhc.org

| | | |
|---|---|---|
| **Owned, leased, sponsored:** | 0 hospitals | 0 beds |
| **Contract–managed:** | 17 hospitals | 960 beds |
| **Totals:** | 17 hospitals | 960 beds |

★**9505:  HENRY FORD HEALTH SYSTEM** (NP)
One Ford Place, Detroit, MI Zip 48202–3450; tel. 313/876–8708;
Nancy M. Schlichting, Chief Executive Officer
**(Centralized Health System)**

**MICHIGAN:** HENRY FORD HOSPITAL (O, 751 beds) 2799 West Grand
Boulevard, Detroit, MI Zip 48202–2608; tel. 313/916–2600; John
Popovich, M.D., President and Chief Executive Officer
**Web address:** www.henryfordhealth.org

HENRY FORD KINGSWOOD HOSPITAL (O, 100 beds) 10300 West Eight Mile
Road, Ferndale, MI Zip 48220–2100; tel. 248/398–3200; C. Edward Coffey,
M.D., Chief Executive Officer and Director Behavioral Health Services
**Web address:** www.henryford.com

HENRY FORD MACOMB HOSPITALS (O, 433 beds) 15855 19 Mile Road,
Clinton Township, MI Zip 48038–6324; tel. 586/263–2300; Barbara
Rossmann, R.N., President and Chief Executive Officer
**Web address:** www.henryfordmacomb.com

HENRY FORD WEST BLOOMFIELD HOSPITAL (O, 191 beds) 6777 West Maple
Road, West Bloomfield, MI Zip 48322–3013; tel. 248/661–4100; MaryClaire
Dangel–Palmer, Chief Operating Officer
**Web address:** www.henryford.com

HENRY FORD WYANDOTTE HOSPITAL (O, 348 beds) 2333 Biddle Avenue,
Wyandotte, MI Zip 48192–4668; tel. 734/246–6000; Denise
Brooks–Williams, President and Chief Executive Officer
**Web address:** www.henryfordhealth.org

| | | |
|---|---|---|
| **Owned, leased, sponsored:** | 5 hospitals | 1823 beds |
| **Contract–managed:** | 0 hospitals | 0 beds |
| **Totals:** | 5 hospitals | 1823 beds |

**0309:  HERITAGE VALLEY HEALTH SYSTEM** (NP)
1000 Dutch Ridge Road, Beaver, PA Zip 15009–9727;
tel. 724/773–2024; Norman F. Mitry, President and Chief Executive
Officer
**(Independent Hospital System)**

**PENNSYLVANIA:** HERITAGE VALLEY BEAVER (O, 312 beds) 1000 Dutch
Ridge Road, Beaver, PA Zip 15009–9727; tel. 724/728–7000; Norman F.
Mitry, President and Chief Executive Officer
**Web address:** www.heritagevalley.org

SEWICKLEY VALLEY HOSPITAL, (A DIVISION OF VALLEY MEDICAL FACILITIES)
(O, 171 beds) 720 Blackburn Road, Sewickley, PA Zip 15143–1459;
tel. 412/741–6600; Norman F. Mitry, President and Chief Executive Officer
**Web address:** www.heritagevalley.org

| | | |
|---|---|---|
| **Owned, leased, sponsored:** | 2 hospitals | 483 beds |
| **Contract–managed:** | 0 hospitals | 0 beds |
| **Totals:** | 2 hospitals | 483 beds |

★**5355:  HOSPITAL SISTERS HEALTH SYSTEM** (CC)
4936 LaVerna Road, Springfield, IL Zip 62707–9797, Mailing
Address: P.O. Box 19456, Zip 62794–9456; tel. 217/523–4747;
Mary Starmann–Harrison, FACHE, President and Chief Executive
Officer
**(Decentralized Health System)**

**ILLINOIS:** ST. ANTHONY'S MEMORIAL HOSPITAL (O, 146 beds) 503 North
Maple Street, Effingham, IL Zip 62401–2099; tel. 217/342–2121; Mark
W. Reifsteck, Interim President and Chief Executive Officer
**Web address:** www.stanthonyshospital.org

For explanation of codes following names, see page B2.
★ Indicates Type III membership in the American Hospital Association.

Section B

ST. ELIZABETH'S HOSPITAL (O, 260 beds) 211 South Third Street, Belleville, IL Zip 62220–1998; tel. 618/234–2120; Maryann Reese, R.N., FACHE, President and Chief Executive Officer
**Web address:** www.steliz.org

ST. FRANCIS HOSPITAL (O, 25 beds) 1215 Franciscan Drive, Litchfield, IL Zip 62056–1799, Mailing Address: P.O. Box 1215, Zip 62056–0999; tel. 217/324–2191; Daniel L. Perryman, President and Chief Executive Officer
**Web address:** www.stfrancis–litchfield.org

ST. JOHN'S HOSPITAL (O, 430 beds) 800 East Carpenter Street, Springfield, IL Zip 62769–0002; tel. 217/544–6464; Robert P. Ritz, President and Chief Executive Officer
**Web address:** www.st–johns.org

ST. JOSEPH'S HOSPITAL (O, 47 beds) 9515 Holy Cross Lane, Breese, IL Zip 62230–3618; tel. 618/526–4511; Mark D. Klosterman, FACHE, President and Chief Executive Officer
**Web address:** www.stjoebreese.com

ST. JOSEPH'S HOSPITAL (O, 25 beds) 1515 Main Street, Highland, IL Zip 62249–1656; tel. 618/654–7421; Peggy A. Sebastian, MSN, R.N., President and Chief Executive Officer
**Web address:** www.stjosephshighland.com

ST. MARY'S HOSPITAL (O, 232 beds) 1800 East Lake Shore Drive, Decatur, IL Zip 62521–3883; tel. 217/464–2966; Kevin F. Kast, President and Chief Executive Officer
**Web address:** www.stmarysdecatur.com

ST. MARY'S HOSPITAL (O, 98 beds) 111 Spring Street, Streator, IL Zip 61364–3399; tel. 815/673–2311; John T. Flanders, MS, R.N., President and Chief Executive Officer
**Web address:** www.stmaryshospital.org

**WISCONSIN:** SACRED HEART HOSPITAL (O, 212 beds) 900 West Clairemont Avenue, Eau Claire, WI Zip 54701–6122; tel. 715/717–4121; Julie Manas, President and Chief Executive Officer
**Web address:** www.sacredhearteauclaire.org

ST. JOSEPH'S HOSPITAL (O, 102 beds) 2661 County Highway I, Chippewa Falls, WI Zip 54729–1498; tel. 715/723–1811; Joan Coffman, President and Chief Executive Officer
**Web address:** www.stjoeschipfalls.com

ST. MARY'S HOSPITAL MEDICAL CENTER (O, 83 beds) 1726 Shawano Avenue, Green Bay, WI Zip 54303–3282; tel. 920/498–4200; Therese B. Pandl, President and Chief Executive Officer
**Web address:** www.stmgb.org

ST. NICHOLAS HOSPITAL (O, 55 beds) 3100 Superior Avenue, Sheboygan, WI Zip 53081–1948; tel. 920/459–8300; Andrew Bagnall, President and Chief Executive Officer
**Web address:** www.stnicholashospital.org

ST. VINCENT HOSPITAL (O, 255 beds) 835 South Van Buren Street, Green Bay, WI Zip 54301–3526, Mailing Address: P.O. Box 13508, Zip 54307–3508; tel. 920/433–0111; Therese B. Pandl, President and Chief Executive Officer
**Web address:** www.stvincenthospital.org

| | | |
|---|---|---|
| Owned, leased, sponsored: | 13 hospitals | 1970 beds |
| Contract–managed: | 0 hospitals | 0 beds |
| Totals: | 13 hospitals | 1970 beds |

---

**★0642: HOUSTON HEALTHCARE SYSTEM** (NP)
1601 Watson Boulevard, Warner Robins, GA Zip 31093–3431, Mailing Address: P.O. Box 2886, Zip 31099–2886; tel. 478/922–4281; Cary Martin, Chief Executive Officer
**(Independent Hospital System)**

**GEORGIA:** HOUSTON MEDICAL CENTER (O, 237 beds) 1601 Watson Boulevard, Warner Robins, GA Zip 31093–3431, Mailing Address: P.O. Box 2886, Zip 31099–2886; tel. 478/922–4281; Cary Martin, Chief Executive Officer
**Web address:** www.hhc.org

PERRY HOSPITAL (O, 39 beds) 1120 Morningside Drive, Perry, GA Zip 31069–2906; tel. 478/987–3600; David Campbell, Administrator
**Web address:** www.hhc.org

| | | |
|---|---|---|
| Owned, leased, sponsored: | 2 hospitals | 276 beds |
| Contract–managed: | 0 hospitals | 0 beds |
| Totals: | 2 hospitals | 276 beds |

---

**0907: HUNT REGIONAL HEALTHCARE** (NP)
4215 Joe Ramsey Boulevard, Greenville, TX Zip 75401–7852, Mailing Address: P.O. Box 1059, Zip 75403–1059; tel. 903/408–5000; Richard Carter, Chief Executive Officer

**TEXAS:** HUNT REGIONAL COMMUNITY HOSPITAL (O, 15 beds) 2900 Sterling Hart Drive, Commerce, TX Zip 75428–3912; tel. 903/886–3161; Michael R. Klepin, Administrator
**Web address:** www.huntregional.org

HUNT REGIONAL MEDICAL CENTER (O, 206 beds) 4215 Joe Ramsey Boulevard, Greenville, TX Zip 75401–7899, Mailing Address: P.O. Box 1059, Zip 75403–1059; tel. 903/408–5000; Richard Carter, District Chief Executive Officer
**Web address:** www.huntregional.org

| | | |
|---|---|---|
| Owned, leased, sponsored: | 2 hospitals | 221 beds |
| Contract–managed: | 0 hospitals | 0 beds |
| Totals: | 2 hospitals | 221 beds |

---

**0117: HUNTSVILLE HOSPITAL HEALTH SYSTEM** (NP)
101 Sivley Road S.W., Huntsville, AL Zip 35801–4421; tel. 265/256–1000; David S. Spillers, Chief Executive Officer
**(Centralized Physician/Insurance Health System)**

**ALABAMA:** DECATUR MORGAN HOSPITAL (O, 120 beds) 1874 Beltline Road S.W., Decatur, AL Zip 35601–5509, Mailing Address: P.O. Box 2239, Zip 35609–2239; tel. 256/350–2211; Nathaniel Richardson, Jr., President
**Web address:** www.parkwaymedicalcenter.com

HUNTSVILLE HOSPITAL (O, 835 beds) 101 Sivley Road S.W., Huntsville, AL Zip 35801–4470; tel. 256/265–1000; David S. Spillers, Chief Executive Officer
**Web address:** www.huntsvillehospital.org

MADISON HOSPITAL (O, 43 beds) 8375 Highway 72 West, Madison, AL Zip 35758–9573; tel. 256/265–2012; Mary Lynne Wright, R.N., President
**Web address:** www.madisonalhospital.org/

| | | |
|---|---|---|
| Owned, leased, sponsored: | 3 hospitals | 998 beds |
| Contract–managed: | 0 hospitals | 0 beds |
| Totals: | 3 hospitals | 998 beds |

---

**0201: IASIS HEALTHCARE** (IO)
117 Seaboard Lane, Building E., Franklin, TN Zip 37067–2855; tel. 615/844–2747; Carl Whitmer, President and Chief Executive Officer
**(Moderately Centralized Health System)**

**ARIZONA:** MOUNTAIN VISTA MEDICAL CENTER (O, 172 beds) 1301 South Crismon Road, Mesa, AZ Zip 85209–3767; tel. 480/358–6100; Anthony Marinello, Chief Executive Officer
**Web address:** www.mvmedicalcenter.com

ST. LUKE'S BEHAVIORAL HEALTH CENTER (O, 85 beds) 1800 East Van Buren, Phoenix, AZ Zip 85006–3742; tel. 602/251–8546; Gregory L. Jahn, R.N., Chief Executive Officer
**Web address:** www.iasishealthcare.com

ST. LUKE'S MEDICAL CENTER (O, 225 beds) 1800 East Van Buren Street, Phoenix, AZ Zip 85006–3742; tel. 602/251–8100; Edward W. Myers, Chief Executive Officer
**Web address:** www.stlukesmedcenter.com

**ARKANSAS:** WADLEY REGIONAL MEDICAL CENTER AT HOPE (O, 79 beds) 2001 South Main Street, Hope, AR Zip 71801–8194; tel. 870/777–2323; Thomas D. Gilbert, FACHE, Chief Executive Officer
**Web address:** www.wadleyhealthathope.com

**COLORADO:** PIKES PEAK REGIONAL HOSPITAL (O, 15 beds) 16420 West Highway 24, Woodland Park, CO Zip 80863; tel. 719/687–9999; Terry Buckner, Chief Executive Officer
**Web address:** www.pprmc.org

For explanation of codes following names, see page B2.
★ Indicates Type III membership in the American Hospital Association.

Section B

**FLORIDA:** MEMORIAL HOSPITAL OF TAMPA (O, 139 beds) 2901 Swann Avenue, Tampa, FL Zip 33609–4057; tel. 813/873–6400; John J. Mainieri, Chief Executive Officer
**Web address:** www.memorialhospitaltampa.com

PALMS OF PASADENA HOSPITAL (O, 307 beds) 1501 Pasadena Avenue South, Saint Petersburg, FL Zip 33707–3798; tel. 727/381–1000; Brian T. Flynn, Chief Executive Officer
**Web address:** www.palmspasadena.com

TOWN AND COUNTRY HOSPITAL (O, 200 beds) 6001 Webb Road, Tampa, FL Zip 33615–3291; tel. 813/888–7060; Dale Johns, Administrator
**Web address:** www.townandcountryhospital.com

**LOUISIANA:** GLENWOOD REGIONAL MEDICAL CENTER (O, 247 beds) 503 McMillan Road, West Monroe, LA Zip 71291–5327; tel. 318/329–4200; Ronald J. Elder, Chief Executive Officer
**Web address:** www.grmc.com

**NEVADA:** NORTH VISTA HOSPITAL (O, 198 beds) 1409 East Lake Mead Boulevard, North Las Vegas, NV Zip 89030–7197; tel. 702/649–7711; Cathy N. Story, Interim Chief Executive Officer
**Web address:** www.northvistahospital.com

**TEXAS:** ODESSA REGIONAL MEDICAL CENTER (O, 230 beds) 520 East Sixth Street, Odessa, TX Zip 79761–4565, Mailing Address: P.O. Box 4859, Zip 79760–4859; tel. 432/582–8000; Stacey L. Gerig, Chief Executive Officer
**Web address:** www.odessaregionalmedicalcenter.com

SOUTHWEST GENERAL HOSPITAL (O, 265 beds) 7400 Barlite Boulevard, San Antonio, TX Zip 78224–1399; tel. 210/921–2000; P. Craig Desmond, Chief Executive Officer
**Web address:** www.swgeneralhospital.com

ST. JOSEPH MEDICAL CENTER (O, 384 beds) 1401 St. Joseph Parkway, Houston, TX Zip 77002–8301; tel. 713/757–1000; Patrick J. Mathews, Chief Executive Officer and Chief Financial Officer
**Web address:** www.sjmctx.com

THE MEDICAL CENTER OF SOUTHEAST TEXAS (O, 185 beds) 2555 Jimmy Johnson Boulevard, Port Arthur, TX Zip 77640–2007; tel. 409/724–7389; Matthew S. Roberts, Chief Executive Officer
**Web address:** www.medicalcentersetexas.com

WADLEY REGIONAL MEDICAL CENTER (O, 177 beds) 1000 Pine Street, Texarkana, TX Zip 75501–5170; tel. 903/798–8000; Thomas D. Gilbert, FACHE, Chief Executive Officer
**Web address:** www.wadleyhealth.com

**UTAH:** DAVIS HOSPITAL AND MEDICAL CENTER (O, 200 beds) 1600 West Antelope Drive, Layton, UT Zip 84041–1142; tel. 801/807–1000; Michael E. Jensen, Chief Executive Officer
**Web address:** www.davishospital.com

JORDAN VALLEY MEDICAL CENTER (O, 183 beds) 3580 West 9000 South, West Jordan, UT Zip 84088–8812; tel. 801/561–8888; Steven Anderson, Chief Executive Officer
**Web address:** www.jordanvalleymc.com

PIONEER VALLEY HOSPITAL (O, 101 beds) 3460 South Pioneer Parkway, West Valley City, UT Zip 84120–2049; tel. 801/964–3100; Steven Anderson, Chief Executive Officer
**Web address:** www.pioneervalleyhospital.com

SALT LAKE REGIONAL MEDICAL CENTER (O, 132 beds) 1050 East South Temple, Salt Lake City, UT Zip 84102–1507; tel. 801/350–4111; Jeff Frandsen, Chief Executive Officer
**Web address:** www.saltlakeregional.com

| | | |
|---|---|---|
| Owned, leased, sponsored: | 19 hospitals | 3524 beds |
| Contract–managed: | 0 hospitals | 0 beds |
| Totals: | 19 hospitals | 3524 beds |

**★0231: INDIANA UNIVERSITY HEALTH** (NP)
340 West 10th Street, Suite 6100, Indianapolis, IN Zip 46202–3082, Mailing Address: P.O. Box 1367, Zip 46206–1367; tel. 317/962–5900; Daniel F. Evans, Jr., JD, President and Chief Executive Officer
**(Centralized Physician/Insurance Health System)**

**INDIANA:** INDIANA UNIVERSITY HEALTH ARNETT HOSPITAL (O, 180 beds) 5165 McCarty Lane, Lafayette, IN Zip 47905–8764, Mailing Address: P.O. Box 5545, Zip 47903–5545; tel. 765/448–8000; Alfonso W. Gatmaitan, Chief Executive Officer
**Web address:** www.iuhealth.org

INDIANA UNIVERSITY HEALTH BALL MEMORIAL HOSPITAL (O, 346 beds) 2401 University Avenue, Muncie, IN Zip 47303–3499; tel. 765/747–3111; Michael E. Haley, President and Chief Executive Officer
**Web address:** www.iuhealth.org

INDIANA UNIVERSITY HEALTH BEDFORD HOSPITAL (O, 25 beds) 2900 West 16th Street, Bedford, IN Zip 47421–3583; tel. 812/275–1200; Bradford W. Dykes, President and Chief Executive Officer
**Web address:** www.iuhealth.org

INDIANA UNIVERSITY HEALTH BLACKFORD HOSPITAL (O, 15 beds) 410 Pilgrim Boulevard, Hartford City, IN Zip 47348–1897; tel. 765/348–0300; Steven J. West, Chief Executive Officer
**Web address:** www.iuhealth.org

INDIANA UNIVERSITY HEALTH BLOOMINGTON HOSPITAL (O, 293 beds) 601 West Second Street, Bloomington, IN Zip 47403–2317, Mailing Address: P.O. Box 1149, Zip 47402–1149; tel. 812/336–6821; Mark E. Moore, President and Chief Executive Officer
**Web address:** www.iuhealth.org

INDIANA UNIVERSITY HEALTH GOSHEN HOSPITAL (O, 122 beds) 200 High Park Avenue, Goshen, IN Zip 46526–4899, Mailing Address: P.O. Box 139, Zip 46527–0139; tel. 574/533–2141; Randal Christophel, President and Chief Executive Officer
**Web address:** www.iuhealth.org

INDIANA UNIVERSITY HEALTH LA PORTE HOSPITAL (O, 204 beds) 1007 Lincolnway, La Porte, IN Zip 46350–3201, Mailing Address: P.O. Box 250, Zip 46352–0250; tel. 219/326–1234; G. Thor Thordarson, President and Chief Executive Officer
**Web address:** www.iuhealth.org

INDIANA UNIVERSITY HEALTH MORGAN HOSPITAL (O, 92 beds) 2209 John R. Wooden Drive, Martinsville, IN Zip 46151–1840, Mailing Address: P.O. Box 1717, Zip 46151–0717; tel. 765/342–8441; Doug Puckett, President and Chief Executive Officer
**Web address:** www.iuhealth.org/morgan/

INDIANA UNIVERSITY HEALTH NORTH HOSPITAL (O, 161 beds) 11700 North Meridian Avenue, Carmel, IN Zip 46032–4656; tel. 317/688–2000; Jonathan R. Goble, FACHE, President and Chief Executive Officer
**Web address:** www.iuhealth.org

INDIANA UNIVERSITY HEALTH PAOLI HOSPITAL (O, 24 beds) 642 West Hospital Road, Paoli, IN Zip 47454–9672, Mailing Address: P.O. Box 499, Zip 47454–0499; tel. 812/723–2811; Larry Bailey, Chief Executive Officer
**Web address:** www.iuhealth.org/paoli

INDIANA UNIVERSITY HEALTH STARKE HOSPITAL (O, 20 beds) 102 East Culver Road, Knox, IN Zip 46534–2216, Mailing Address: P.O. Box 339, Zip 46534–0339; tel. 574/772–6231; Jared Beasley, Interim President
**Web address:** www.iuhealth.org/starke/

INDIANA UNIVERSITY HEALTH TIPTON HOSPITAL (O, 25 beds) 1000 South Main Street, Tipton, IN Zip 46072–9799; tel. 765/675–8500; Michael Harlowe, President and Chief Executive Officer
**Web address:** www.iuhealth.org

INDIANA UNIVERSITY HEALTH UNIVERSITY HOSPITAL (O, 1371 beds) 550 University Boulevard, Indianapolis, IN Zip 46202–5149, Mailing Address: P.O. Box 1367, Zip 46206–1367; tel. 317/944–5000; James G. Terwilliger, President
**Web address:** www.iuhealth.org

INDIANA UNIVERSITY HEALTH WEST HOSPITAL (O, 127 beds) 1111 North Ronald Reagan Parkway, Avon, IN Zip 46123–7085; tel. 317/217–3000; Matthew D. Bailey, FACHE, President and Chief Executive Officer
**Web address:** www.iuhealth.org

INDIANA UNIVERSITY HEALTH WHITE MEMORIAL HOSPITAL (O, 25 beds) 720 South Sixth Street, Monticello, IN Zip 47960–8182; tel. 574/583–7111; Stephanie Long, Chief Executive Officer
**Web address:** www.iuhealth.org/white–memorial

JAY COUNTY HOSPITAL (C, 35 beds) 500 West Votaw Street, Portland, IN Zip 47371–1322; tel. 260/726–7131; David W. Hyatt, Chief Executive Officer
**Web address:** www.jaycountyhospital.com

For explanation of codes following names, see page B2.
★ Indicates Type III membership in the American Hospital Association.

© 2013 AHA Guide

| Owned, leased, sponsored: | 15 hospitals | 3030 beds |
|---|---|---|
| Contract–managed: | 1 hospital | 35 beds |
| Totals: | 16 hospitals | 3065 beds |

## 2025:  INFIRMARY HEALTH SYSTEM (NP)

5 Mobile Infirmary Circle, Mobile, AL Zip 36607–3513; tel. 251/435–5500; D. Mark Nix, President and Chief Executive Officer

**ALABAMA:** INFIRMARY LONG TERM ACUTE CARE HOSPITAL (L, 191 beds) 5644 Girby Road, Mobile, AL Zip 36693–3320; tel. 251/660–5239; Susanne Marmande, Administrator
**Web address:** www.theinfirmary.com/

MOBILE INFIRMARY MEDICAL CENTER (O, 526 beds) 5 Mobile Infirmary Drive North, Mobile, AL Zip 36607–3513, Mailing Address: P.O. Box 2144, Zip 36652–2144; tel. 251/435–2400; Joe Strough, Administrator
**Web address:** www.mobileinfirmary.org

NORTH BALDWIN INFIRMARY (L, 35 beds) 1815 Hand Avenue, Bay Minette, AL Zip 36507–4110, Mailing Address: P.O. Box 1409, Zip 36507–1409; tel. 251/937–5521; Ormand P. Thompson, Administrator
**Web address:** www.mobileinfirmary.org

THOMAS HOSPITAL (L, 136 beds) 750 Morphy Avenue, Fairhope, AL Zip 36532–1812, Mailing Address: P.O. Drawer 929, Zip 36533–0929; tel. 251/928–2375; William J. McLaughlin, Administrator
**Web address:** www.thomashospital.com

| Owned, leased, sponsored: | 4 hospitals | 888 beds |
|---|---|---|
| Contract–managed: | 0 hospitals | 0 beds |
| Totals: | 4 hospitals | 888 beds |

## ★1305:  INOVA HEALTH SYSTEM (NP)

8110 Gatehouse Road, Suite 200 East, Falls Church, VA Zip 22042–1252; tel. 703/289–2069; J. Knox Singleton, President and Chief Executive Officer
**(Centralized Health System)**

**VIRGINIA:** INOVA ALEXANDRIA HOSPITAL (O, 334 beds) 4320 Seminary Road, Alexandria, VA Zip 22304–1535; tel. 703/504–3167; Christine Candio, Chief Executive Officer
**Web address:** www.inova.org

INOVA FAIR OAKS HOSPITAL (O, 196 beds) 3600 Joseph Siewick Drive, Fairfax, VA Zip 22033–1798; tel. 703/391–3600; John L. Fitzgerald, Chief Executive Officer
**Web address:** www.inova.org

INOVA FAIRFAX HOSPITAL (O, 926 beds) 3300 Gallows Road, Falls Church, VA Zip 22042–3300; tel. 703/776–4001; Patrick Christiansen, Ph.D., Chief Executive Officer
**Web address:** www.inova.org

INOVA LOUDOUN HOSPITAL (O, 290 beds) 44045 Riverside Parkway, Leesburg, VA Zip 20176–5101, Mailing Address: P.O. Box 6000, Zip 20177–0600; tel. 703/858–6000; Patrick Walters, Interim Chief Executive Officer
**Web address:** www.inova.org

INOVA MOUNT VERNON HOSPITAL (O, 237 beds) 2501 Parker's Lane, Alexandria, VA Zip 22306–3209; tel. 703/664–7000; Barbara J. Doyle, R.N., MS, Senior Vice President and Chief Executive Officer
**Web address:** www.inova.org

| Owned, leased, sponsored: | 5 hospitals | 1983 beds |
|---|---|---|
| Contract–managed: | 0 hospitals | 0 beds |
| Totals: | 5 hospitals | 1983 beds |

## ★0151:  INSPIRA HEALTH NETWORK (NP)

2950 College Drive, Suite 1E, Vineland, NJ Zip 08360; tel. 856/641–8000; Chester B. Kaletkowski, President and Chief Executive Officer
**(Centralized Health System)**

**NEW JERSEY:** INSPIRA MEDICAL CENTER–ELMER (O, 88 beds) 501 West Front Street, Elmer, NJ Zip 08318–2101; tel. 856/363–1000; Chester B. Kaletkowski, President and Chief Executive Officer
**Web address:** www.sjhealthcare.net

INSPIRA MEDICAL CENTER–VINELAND (O, 331 beds) 1505 West Sherman Avenue, Vineland, NJ Zip 08360–6912; tel. 856/641–8000; Chester B. Kaletkowski, President and Chief Executive Officer
**Web address:** www.sjhealthcare.net

INSPIRA MEDICAL CENTER–WOODBURY (O, 240 beds) 509 North Broad Street, Woodbury, NJ Zip 08096–1697; tel. 856/845–0100; Eileen K. Cardile, R.N., MS, President and Chief Executive Officer
**Web address:** www.umhospital.org

| Owned, leased, sponsored: | 3 hospitals | 659 beds |
|---|---|---|
| Contract–managed: | 0 hospitals | 0 beds |
| Totals: | 3 hospitals | 659 beds |

## 0333:  INTEGRATED HEALTHCARE (IO)

1301 North Tustin Avenue, Santa Ana, CA Zip 92705–8619; tel. 714/953–3652; Kenneth K. Westbrook, President and Chief Executive Officer
**(Independent Hospital System)**

**CALIFORNIA:** CHAPMAN MEDICAL CENTER (O, 100 beds) 2601 East Chapman Avenue, Orange, CA Zip 92869–3206; tel. 714/633–0011; Don Kreitz, Chief Executive Officer
**Web address:** www.chapmanmedicalcenter.com

COASTAL COMMUNITIES HOSPITAL (O, 178 beds) 2701 South Bristol Street, Santa Ana, CA Zip 92704–6201; tel. 714/754–5454; Luke Tharasri, Chief Executive Officer
**Web address:** www.coastalcommhospital.com

WESTERN MEDICAL CENTER ANAHEIM (O, 181 beds) 1025 South Anaheim Boulevard, Anaheim, CA Zip 92805–5806; tel. 714/533–6220; Dennis M. Knox, Chief Executive Officer
**Web address:** www.westernmedanaheim.com

WESTERN MEDICAL CENTER–SANTA ANA (O, 282 beds) 1001 North Tustin Avenue, Santa Ana, CA Zip 92705–3577; tel. 714/835–3555; Daniel Brothman, Chief Executive Officer
**Web address:** www.westernmedicalcenter.com

| Owned, leased, sponsored: | 4 hospitals | 741 beds |
|---|---|---|
| Contract–managed: | 0 hospitals | 0 beds |
| Totals: | 4 hospitals | 741 beds |

## ★0305:  INTEGRIS HEALTH (NP)

3366 N.W. Expressway, Suite 800, Oklahoma City, OK Zip 73112–9756; tel. 405/949–6066; Bruce Lawrence, President and Chief Executive Officer
**(Moderately Centralized Health System)**

**OKLAHOMA:** INTEGRIS BAPTIST MEDICAL CENTER (O, 569 beds) 3300 N.W. Expressway, Oklahoma City, OK Zip 73112–4418; tel. 405/949–3011; Timothy J. Johnsen, MS, President
**Web address:** www.integrisok.com

INTEGRIS BAPTIST REGIONAL HEALTH CENTER (O, 84 beds) 200 Second Street S.W., Miami, OK Zip 74354–6830, Mailing Address: P.O. Box 1207, Zip 74355–1207; tel. 918/542–6611; Joel A. Hart, FACHE, President
**Web address:** www.integris–health.com

INTEGRIS BASS BAPTIST HEALTH CENTER (O, 167 beds) 600 South Monroe Street, Enid, OK Zip 73701–7211, Mailing Address: P.O. Box 3168, Zip 73702–3168; tel. 580/233–2300; Edward Herrman, R.N., FACHE, President
**Web address:** www.integris–health.com

INTEGRIS CANADIAN VALLEY HOSPITAL (O, 75 beds) 1201 Health Center Parkway, Yukon, OK Zip 73099–6381; tel. 405/717–6800; Rex Van Meter, President
**Web address:** www.integris–health.com

INTEGRIS GROVE GENERAL HOSPITAL (O, 58 beds) 1001 East 18th Street, Grove, OK Zip 74344–2907; tel. 918/786–2243; Greg Martin, President
**Web address:** www.integris–health.com

For explanation of codes following names, see page B2.
★ Indicates Type III membership in the American Hospital Association.

INTEGRIS HEALTH EDMOND (O, 40 beds) 4801 Integris Parkway, Edmond, OK Zip 73034–8864; tel. 405/657–3000; Avilla Williams, MS, President
**Web address:** www.integrisok.com/edmond

INTEGRIS SOUTHWEST MEDICAL CENTER (O, 305 beds) 4401 South Western, Oklahoma City, OK Zip 73109–3413; tel. 405/636–7000; James D. Moore, FACHE, Chief Executive Officer
**Web address:** www.integris–health.com

| | | |
|---|---|---|
| **Owned, leased, sponsored:** | 7 hospitals | 1298 beds |
| **Contract–managed:** | 0 hospitals | 0 beds |
| **Totals:** | 7 hospitals | 1298 beds |

---

**★1815:  INTERMOUNTAIN HEALTHCARE, INC.** (NP)
36 South State Street, 22nd Floor, Salt Lake City, UT Zip 84111–1453; tel. 801/442–2000; Charles W. Sorenson, Jr., M.D., Chief Executive Officer
**(Decentralized Health System)**

**IDAHO:** CASSIA REGIONAL MEDICAL CENTER (O, 25 beds) 1501 Hiland Avenue, Burley, ID Zip 83318–2688; tel. 208/678–4444; Rod Barton, Administrator
**Web address:** www.cassiaregional.org

**UTAH:** ALTA VIEW HOSPITAL (O, 71 beds) 9660 South 1300 East, Sandy, UT Zip 84094–3793; tel. 801/501–2600; Bryan L. Johnson, Administrator
**Web address:** www.intermountainhealthcare.org

AMERICAN FORK HOSPITAL (O, 88 beds) 170 North 1100 East, American Fork, UT Zip 84003–2096; tel. 801/855–3300; Michael R. Olson, Administrator
**Web address:** www.intermountainhealthcare.org

BEAR RIVER VALLEY HOSPITAL (O, 14 beds) 905 North 1000 West, Tremonton, UT Zip 84337–2497; tel. 435/207–4500; Eric Packer, Administrator
**Web address:** www.intermountainhealthcare.org/hospitals/bearriver

DELTA COMMUNITY MEDICAL CENTER (O, 18 beds) 126 South White Sage Avenue, Delta, UT Zip 84624–8937; tel. 435/864–5591; James E. Beckstrand, Administrator
**Web address:** www.ihc.com

DIXIE REGIONAL MEDICAL CENTER (O, 261 beds) 1380 East Medical Center Drive, Saint George, UT Zip 84790–2123; tel. 435/251–1000; Terri Kane, Chief Executive Officer
**Web address:** www.intermountainhealthcare.org

FILLMORE COMMUNITY MEDICAL CENTER (O, 19 beds) 674 South Highway 99, Fillmore, UT Zip 84631–5013; tel. 435/743–5591; James E. Beckstrand, Administrator
**Web address:** www.ihc.com

GARFIELD MEMORIAL HOSPITAL AND CLINICS (C, 41 beds) 200 North 400 East, Panguitch, UT Zip 84759, Mailing Address: P.O. Box 389, Zip 84759–0389; tel. 435/676–8811; Alberto Vasquez, Administrator
**Web address:** www.ihc.com/hospitals/garfield

HEBER VALLEY MEDICAL CENTER (O, 19 beds) 1485 South Highway 40, Heber City, UT Zip 84032–3522; tel. 435/654–2500; Shawn Morrow, Administrator
**Web address:** www.ihc.com

INTERMOUNTAIN MEDICAL CENTER (O, 452 beds) 5121 South Cottonwood Street, Murray, UT Zip 84107–5701; tel. 801/507–7000; David Grauer, Chief Executive Officer and Administrator
**Web address:** www.intermountainhealthcare.org

LDS HOSPITAL (O, 241 beds) Eighth Avenue and C Street, Salt Lake City, UT Zip 84143–0001; tel. 801/408–1100; Jim Sheets, Chief Executive Officer and Administrator
**Web address:** www.intermountainhealthcare.org

LOGAN REGIONAL HOSPITAL (O, 135 beds) 1400 North 500 East, Logan, UT Zip 84341–2455; tel. 435/716–1000; Michael A. Clark, Administrator and Chief Executive Officer
**Web address:** www.loganregionalhospital.org

MCKAY–DEE HOSPITAL CENTER (O, 310 beds) 4401 Harrison Boulevard, Ogden, UT Zip 84403–3195; tel. 801/387–2800; Timothy T. Pehrson, Chief Executive Officer
**Web address:** www.mckay–dee.org

OREM COMMUNITY HOSPITAL (O, 18 beds) 331 North 400 West, Orem, UT Zip 84057–1999; tel. 801/224–4080; Steven Badger, R.N., FACHE, Administrator
**Web address:** www.intermountainhealthcare.org

PARK CITY MEDICAL CENTER (O, 26 beds) 900 Round Valley Drive, Park City, UT Zip 84060–7552; tel. 435/658–7000; Si William Hutt, Chief Executive Officer
**Web address:** www.intermountainhealthcare.org

PRIMARY CHILDREN'S MEDICAL CENTER (O, 289 beds) 100 North Mario Capecchi Drive, Salt Lake City, UT Zip 84113–1100; tel. 801/662–1000; Katy Welkie, R.N., Chief Executive Officer
**Web address:** www.intermountainhealthcare.org

RIVERTON HOSPITAL (O, 92 beds) 3741 West 12600 South, Riverton, UT Zip 84065–7215; tel. 801/285–4000; Blair Kent, Administrator
**Web address:** www.intermountainhealthcare.org/

SANPETE VALLEY HOSPITAL (O, 19 beds) 1100 South Medical Drive, Mount Pleasant, UT Zip 84647–2222; tel. 435/462–2441; Mark L. Allen, FACHE, Administrator
**Web address:** www.intermountainhealthcare.com

SEVIER VALLEY MEDICAL CENTER (O, 27 beds) 1000 North Main Street, Richfield, UT Zip 84701–1857; tel. 435/896–8271; Gary E. Beck, Administrator
**Web address:** www.intermountain.com

THE ORTHOPEDIC SPECIALTY HOSPITAL (O, 36 beds) 5848 South 300 East, Murray, UT Zip 84107–6121; tel. 801/314–4100; Barbara Ohm, Administrator
**Web address:** www.intermountainhealthcare.org

UTAH VALLEY REGIONAL MEDICAL CENTER (O, 367 beds) 1034 North 500 West, Provo, UT Zip 84604–3337; tel. 801/357–7850; Steve Smoot, Administrator
**Web address:** www.utahvalleyregional.org

VALLEY VIEW MEDICAL CENTER (O, 48 beds) 1303 North Main Street, Cedar City, UT Zip 84721–9746; tel. 435/868–5000; Jason Wilson, Administrator
**Web address:** www.ihc.com

| | | |
|---|---|---|
| **Owned, leased, sponsored:** | 21 hospitals | 2575 beds |
| **Contract–managed:** | 1 hospital | 41 beds |
| **Totals:** | 22 hospitals | 2616 beds |

---

**★0902:  IOWA SPECIALTY HOSPITALS** (NP)
1316 South Main Street, Clarion, IA Zip 50525–2019; tel. 515/532–2811; Steven J. Simonin, Chief Executive Officer

**IOWA:** IOWA SPECIALTY HOSPITAL–BELMOND (C, 22 beds) 403 First Street SE, Belmond, IA Zip 50421–1201; tel. 641/444–3223; Nancy Gabrielson, Administrator and Chief Executive Officer
**Web address:** www.iowaspecialtyhospital.com

IOWA SPECIALTY HOSPITAL–CLARION (C, 25 beds) 1316 South Main Street, Clarion, IA Zip 50525–2019; tel. 515/532–2811; Steven J. Simonin, Chief Executive Officer
**Web address:** www.iowaspecialtyhospital.com

| | | |
|---|---|---|
| **Owned, leased, sponsored:** | 0 hospitals | 0 beds |
| **Contract–managed:** | 2 hospitals | 47 beds |
| **Totals:** | 2 hospitals | 47 beds |

---

**★7775:  JEFFERSON HEALTH SYSTEM** (NP)
259 Radnor–Chester Road, Suite 290, Radnor, PA Zip 19087–5288; tel. 610/225–6200; Joseph T. Sebastianelli, President and Chief Executive Officer
**(Moderately Centralized Health System)**

**PENNSYLVANIA:** BRYN MAWR HOSPITAL (O, 319 beds) 130 South Bryn Mawr Avenue, Bryn Mawr, PA Zip 19010–3160; tel. 484/337–3000; Andrea F. Gilbert, FACHE, President
**Web address:** www.brynmawrhospital.org

BRYN MAWR REHABILITATION HOSPITAL (O, 148 beds) 414 Paoli Pike, Malvern, PA Zip 19355–3300, Mailing Address: P.O. Box 3007, Zip 19355–0707; tel. 484/596–5400; Donna Phillips, President
**Web address:** www.brynmawrrehab.org

---

For explanation of codes following names, see page B2.
★ Indicates Type III membership in the American Hospital Association.

LANKENAU MEDICAL CENTER (O, 339 beds) 100 Lancaster Avenue West, Wynnewood, PA Zip 19096–3411; tel. 484/476–2000; Phillip D. Robinson, President
**Web address:** www.mainlinehealth.org

MAGEE REHABILITATION HOSPITAL (O, 96 beds) 1513 Race Street, Philadelphia, PA Zip 19102–1177; tel. 215/587–3000; Jack A. Carroll, Ph.D., President and Chief Executive Officer
**Web address:** www.mageerehab.org

PAOLI HOSPITAL (O, 226 beds) 255 West Lancaster Avenue, Paoli, PA Zip 19301–1763; tel. 484/565–1000; James Paradis, President
**Web address:** www.mainlinehealth.org

RIDDLE HOSPITAL (O, 204 beds) 1068 West Baltimore Pike, Media, PA Zip 19063–5177; tel. 484/227–9400; Gary L. Perecko, President
**Web address:** www.riddlehospital.org

| | | |
|---|---|---|
| **Owned, leased, sponsored:** | 6 hospitals | 1332 beds |
| **Contract–managed:** | 0 hospitals | 0 beds |
| **Totals:** | 6 hospitals | 1332 beds |

---

### ★8855: JFK HEALTH SYSTEM (NP)
80 James Street, 2nd Floor, Edison, NJ Zip 08820–3938; tel. 732/632–1503; Raymond F. Fredericks, President and Chief Executive Officer

**NEW JERSEY:** JFK JOHNSON REHABILITATION INSTITUTE (O, 92 beds) 65 James Street, Edison, NJ Zip 08820–3947; tel. 732/321–7050; Anthony Cuzzola, Vice President Rehabilitation Services
**Web address:** www.njrehab.org

JFK MEDICAL CENTER (O, 441 beds) 65 James Street, Edison, NJ Zip 08820–3947; tel. 732/321–7000; Raymond F. Fredericks, President and CEO
**Web address:** www.jfkmc.org

| | | |
|---|---|---|
| **Owned, leased, sponsored:** | 2 hospitals | 533 beds |
| **Contract–managed:** | 0 hospitals | 0 beds |
| **Totals:** | 2 hospitals | 533 beds |

---

### ★0218: JOHN C. LINCOLN HEALTH NETWORK (NP)
2500 West Utopia Road, Suite 100, Phoenix, AZ Zip 85027–4172; tel. 623/434–6230; Rhonda Forsyth, President and Chief Executive Officer
**(Independent Hospital System)**

**ARIZONA:** JOHN C. LINCOLN DEER VALLEY HOSPITAL (O, 204 beds) 19829 North 27th Avenue, Phoenix, AZ Zip 85027–4002; tel. 623/879–6100; John L. Harrington, Jr., FACHE, Chief Executive Officer
**Web address:** www.jcl.com

JOHN C. LINCOLN NORTH MOUNTAIN HOSPITAL (O, 262 beds) 250 East Dunlap Avenue, Phoenix, AZ Zip 85020–2825; tel. 602/943–2381; Bruce Pearson, FACHE, Chief Executive Officer
**Web address:** www.jcl.com

| | | |
|---|---|---|
| **Owned, leased, sponsored:** | 2 hospitals | 466 beds |
| **Contract–managed:** | 0 hospitals | 0 beds |
| **Totals:** | 2 hospitals | 466 beds |

---

### ★0324: JOHN MUIR HEALTH (NP)
1400 Treat Boulevard, Walnut Creek, CA Zip 94597–2142; tel. 925/941–2100; Calvin K. Knight, President and Chief Executive Officer
**(Centralized Health System)**

**CALIFORNIA:** JOHN MUIR BEHAVIORAL HEALTH CENTER (O, 70 beds) 2740 Grant Street, Concord, CA Zip 94520–2265; tel. 925/674–4100; Elizabeth Stallings, Chief Operating Officer
**Web address:** www.johnmuirhealth.com

JOHN MUIR MEDICAL CENTER, CONCORD (O, 182 beds) 2540 East Street, Concord, CA Zip 94520–1906; tel. 925/682–8200; Michael S. Thomas, President and Chief Administrative Officer
**Web address:** www.johnmuirhealth.com

JOHN MUIR MEDICAL CENTER, WALNUT CREEK (O, 367 beds) 1601 Ygnacio Valley Road, Walnut Creek, CA Zip 94598–3194; tel. 925/939–3000; Jane Willemsen, Chief Administrative Officer
**Web address:** www.jmmdhs.com/index.php/jmmdhs_jmmc.html

| | | |
|---|---|---|
| **Owned, leased, sponsored:** | 3 hospitals | 619 beds |
| **Contract–managed:** | 0 hospitals | 0 beds |
| **Totals:** | 3 hospitals | 619 beds |

---

### ★1015: JOHNS HOPKINS HEALTH SYSTEM (NP)
733 North Broadway, BRB 104, Baltimore, MD Zip 21205–1832; tel. 410/955–5000; Ronald R. Peterson, President
**(Centralized Health System)**

**DISTRICT OF COLUMBIA:** SIBLEY MEMORIAL HOSPITAL (O, 246 beds) 5255 Loughboro Road N.W., Washington, DC Zip 20016–2633; tel. 202/537–4000; Richard O. Davis, Ph.D., President and Chief Executive Officer
**Web address:** www.sibley.org

**FLORIDA:** ALL CHILDREN'S HOSPITAL (O, 259 beds) 501 6th Avenue South, Saint Petersburg, FL Zip 33701–4634; tel. 727/898–7451; Jonathan M. Ellen, M.D., President
**Web address:** www.allkids.org

**MARYLAND:** HOWARD COUNTY GENERAL HOSPITAL (O, 256 beds) 5755 Cedar Lane, Columbia, MD Zip 21044–2999; tel. 410/740–7890; Victor A. Broccolino, President and Chief Executive Officer
**Web address:** www.hcgh.org

JOHNS HOPKINS BAYVIEW MEDICAL CENTER (O, 477 beds) 4940 Eastern Avenue, Baltimore, MD Zip 21224–2780; tel. 410/550–0100; Richard G. Bennett, M.D., President
**Web address:** www.hopkinsbayview.org

JOHNS HOPKINS HOSPITAL (O, 951 beds) 600 North Wolfe Street, Baltimore, MD Zip 21287–2182; tel. 410/955–5000; Ronald R. Peterson, President
**Web address:** www.hopkinsmedicine.org

SUBURBAN HOSPITAL (O, 233 beds) 8600 Old Georgetown Road, Bethesda, MD Zip 20814–1497; tel. 301/896–3100; Gene E. Green, M.D., President
**Web address:** www.suburbanhospital.org

| | | |
|---|---|---|
| **Owned, leased, sponsored:** | 6 hospitals | 2422 beds |
| **Contract–managed:** | 0 hospitals | 0 beds |
| **Totals:** | 6 hospitals | 2422 beds |

---

### ★2105: KAISER FOUNDATION HOSPITALS (NP)
One Kaiser Plaza, Oakland, CA Zip 94612–3600; tel. 510/271–5910; George C. Halvorson, Chairman and Chief Executive Officer
**(Decentralized Health System)**

**CALIFORNIA:** KAISER PERMANENTE ANAHEIM MEDICAL CENTER (O, 436 beds) 3430 East La Palma Avenue, Anaheim, CA Zip 92806–2020; tel. 714/644–2000; Julie K. Miller–Phipps, Senior Vice President and Executive Director
**Web address:** www.kp.org

KAISER PERMANENTE ANTIOCH MEDICAL CENTER (O, 150 beds) 4501 Sand Creek Road, Antioch, CA Zip 94531–8687; tel. 925/813–6500; Colleen McKeown, Senior Vice President
**Web address:** www.https://health.kaiserpermanente.org/wps/portal/facility/100382

KAISER PERMANENTE BALDWIN PARK MEDICAL CENTER (O, 254 beds) 1011 Baldwin Park Boulevard, Baldwin Park, CA Zip 91706–5806; tel. 626/851–1011; Margaret H. Pierce, Executive Director
**Web address:** www.kp.org

KAISER PERMANENTE FONTANA MEDICAL CENTER (O, 390 beds) 9961 Sierra Avenue, Fontana, CA Zip 92335–6720; tel. 909/427–5000; Greg Christian, Executive Director
**Web address:** www.kaiserpermanente.org

KAISER PERMANENTE FRESNO MEDICAL CENTER (O, 169 beds) 7300 North Fresno Street, Fresno, CA Zip 93720–2941; tel. 559/448–4500; Jeffrey A. Collins, Senior Vice President and Area Manager
**Web address:** www.kaiserpermanente.org

For explanation of codes following names, see page B2.
★ Indicates Type III membership in the American Hospital Association.

KAISER PERMANENTE HAYWARD MEDICAL CENTER (O, 208 beds) 27400 Hesperian Boulevard, Hayward, CA Zip 94545–4235; tel. 510/784–4000; Debbie Hemker, Interim Chief Executive Officer
**Web address:** www.kaiserpermanente.org

KAISER PERMANENTE DOWNEY MEDICAL CENTER (O, 342 beds) 9333 Imperial Highway, Downey, CA Zip 90242–2812; tel. 562/657–9000; E. Jane Finley, Senior Vice President and Executive Director
**Web address:** www.kaiserpermanente.org

KAISER PERMANENTE LOS ANGELES MEDICAL CENTER (O, 464 beds) 4867 Sunset Boulevard, Los Angeles, CA Zip 90027–5969; tel. 323/783–4011; Mark E. Costa, Executive Director
**Web address:** www.kaiserpermanente.org

KAISER PERMANENTE MANTECA MEDICAL CENTER (O, 184 beds) 1777 West Yosemite Avenue, Manteca, CA Zip 95337–5187; tel. 209/825–3500; Corwin N. Harper, Senior Vice President and Area Manager
**Web address:** www.kaiserpermanente.org

KAISER PERMANENTE MORENO VALLEY MEDICAL CENTER (O, 71 beds) 27300 Iris Avenue, Moreno Valley, CA Zip 92555–4800; tel. 951/243–0811; Corey A. Seale, Administrator

KAISER PERMANENTE OAKLAND MEDICAL CENTER (O, 267 beds) 280 West MacArthur Boulevard, Oakland, CA Zip 94611–5693; tel. 510/752–1000; Nathaniel L. Oubre, Jr., Senior Vice President and Area Manager
**Web address:** www.kaiserpermanente.org

KAISER PERMANENTE PANORAMA CITY MEDICAL CENTER (O, 154 beds) 13652 Cantara Street, Panorama City, CA Zip 91402–5497; tel. 818/375–2000; Dennis C. Benton, Administrator and Executive Director
**Web address:** www.kaiserpermanente.org

KAISER PERMANENTE REDWOOD CITY MEDICAL CENTER (O, 213 beds) 1150 Veterans Boulevard, Redwood City, CA Zip 94063–2037; tel. 650/299–2000; Frank T. Beirne, Senior Vice President and Area Manager
**Web address:** www.kaiserpermanente.org

KAISER PERMANENTE RIVERSIDE MEDICAL CENTER (O, 226 beds) 10800 Magnolia Avenue, Riverside, CA Zip 92505–3000; tel. 951/353–2000; Vita M. Willett, Administrator and Executive Director
**Web address:** www.kaiserpermanente.org

KAISER PERMANENTE ROSEVILLE MEDICAL CENTER (O, 340 beds) 1600 Eureka Road, Roseville, CA Zip 95661–3027; tel. 916/784–4000; Edward S. Glavis, Senior Vice President and Area Manager
**Web address:** www.kp.org

KAISER PERMANENTE SACRAMENTO MEDICAL CENTER (O, 287 beds) 2025 Morse Avenue, Sacramento, CA Zip 95825–2115; tel. 916/973–5000; Ronald Groepper, Senior Vice President and Area Manager
**Web address:** www.kp.org

KAISER PERMANENTE SAN DIEGO MEDICAL CENTER (O, 414 beds) 4647 Zion Avenue, San Diego, CA Zip 92120–2507; tel. 619/528–5000; Mary Ann Barnes, Senior Vice President and Executive Director
**Web address:** www.kaiserpermanente.org

KAISER PERMANENTE SAN FRANCISCO MEDICAL CENTER (O, 215 beds) 2425 Geary Boulevard, San Francisco, CA Zip 94115–3358; tel. 415/833–2000; Christine Robisch, Senior Vice President and Area Manager
**Web address:** www.kaiserpermanente.org

KAISER PERMANENTE SAN JOSE MEDICAL CENTER (O, 217 beds) 250 Hospital Parkway, San Jose, CA Zip 95119–1199; tel. 408/972–7000; Irene Chavez, Senior Vice President and Area Manager
**Web address:** www.kaiserpermanente.org

KAISER PERMANENTE SAN RAFAEL MEDICAL CENTER (O, 116 beds) 99 Montecillo Road, San Rafael, CA Zip 94903–3308; tel. 415/444–2000; Judy Coffey, Senior Vice President and Area Manager
**Web address:** www.kaiserpermanente.org

KAISER PERMANENTE SANTA CLARA MEDICAL CENTER (O, 327 beds) 700 Lawrence Expressway, Santa Clara, CA Zip 95051–5173; tel. 408/851–1000; Christopher L. Boyd, Senior Vice President and Area Manager
**Web address:** www.kaiserpermanente.org

KAISER PERMANENTE SANTA ROSA MEDICAL CENTER (O, 117 beds) 401 Bicentennial Way, Santa Rosa, CA Zip 95403–2192; tel. 707/571–4000; Judy Coffey, Senior Vice President and Area Manager
**Web address:** www.kaiserpermanente.org

KAISER PERMANENTE SOUTH BAY MEDICAL CENTER (O, 231 beds) 25825 South Vermont Avenue, Harbor City, CA Zip 90710–3599; tel. 310/325–5111; Lesley A. Wille, Administrator and Executive Director
**Web address:** www.kaiserpermanente.org

KAISER PERMANENTE SOUTH SACRAMENTO MEDICAL CENTER (O, 181 beds) 6600 Bruceville Road, Sacramento, CA Zip 95823–4671; tel. 916/688–2430; Patricia Rodriguez, Senior Vice President and Area Manager
**Web address:** www.kp.org

KAISER PERMANENTE SOUTH SAN FRANCISCO (O, 120 beds) 1200 El Camino Real, South San Francisco, CA Zip 94080–3299; tel. 650/742–2000; Frank T. Beirne, Senior Vice President and Area Manager
**Web address:** www.kaiserpermanente.org

KAISER PERMANENTE VACAVILLE MEDICAL CENTER (O, 64 beds) 1 Quality Drive, Vacaville, CA Zip 95688–9494; tel. 707/624–4000; Max Villalobos, Senior Vice President
**Web address:** www.kp.org

KAISER PERMANENTE VALLEJO MEDICAL CENTER (O, 248 beds) 975 Sereno Drive, Vallejo, CA Zip 94589–2441; tel. 707/651–1000; Max Villalobos, Senior Vice President and Area Manager
**Web address:** www.kaiserpermanente.org

KAISER PERMANENTE WALNUT CREEK MEDICAL CENTER (O, 233 beds) 1425 South Main Street, Walnut Creek, CA Zip 94596–5300; tel. 925/295–4000; Colleen McKeown, Senior Vice President and Area Manager
**Web address:** www.kaiserpermanente.org

KAISER PERMANENTE WEST LOS ANGELES MEDICAL CENTER (O, 172 beds) 6041 Cadillac Avenue, Los Angeles, CA Zip 90034–1702; tel. 323/857–2201; Georgina R. Garcia, Executive Director
**Web address:** www.kaiserpermanente.org

KAISER PERMANENTE WOODLAND HILLS MEDICAL CENTER (O, 175 beds) 5601 DeSoto Avenue, Woodland Hills, CA Zip 91367–6701; tel. 818/719–2000; Michael C. Carter, Executive Director
**Web address:** www.kaiserpermanente.org

**HAWAII:** KAISER PERMANENTE MEDICAL CENTER (O, 235 beds) 3288 Moanalua Road, Honolulu, HI Zip 96819–1469; tel. 808/432–0000; Peter E. Makowski, Administrator
**Web address:** www.kaiserpermanente.org

**OREGON:** KAISER PERMANENTE SUNNYSIDE MEDICAL CENTER (O, 283 beds) 10180 S.E. Sunnyside Road, Clackamas, OR Zip 97015–8970; tel. 503/652–2880; Susan Mullaney, Administrator
**Web address:** www.kaiserpermanente.org

| | | |
|---|---|---|
| Owned, leased, sponsored: | 32 hospitals | 7503 beds |
| Contract–managed: | 0 hospitals | 0 beds |
| **Totals:** | 32 hospitals | 7503 beds |

---

**★0258:  KETTERING HEALTH NETWORK** (NP) 3965 Southern Boulevard, Dayton, OH Zip 45429–1229; tel. 937/395–8150; Fred M. Manchur, Chief Executive Officer **(Moderately Centralized Health System)**

**OHIO:** FORT HAMILTON HOSPITAL (O, 194 beds) 630 Eaton Avenue, Hamilton, OH Zip 45013–2770; tel. 513/867–2000; Mark T. Smith, JD, CPA, President
**Web address:** www.khnetwork.org/fort_hamilton

GRANDVIEW MEDICAL CENTER (O, 284 beds) 405 Grand Avenue, Dayton, OH Zip 45405–4796; tel. 937/226–3200; Richard Haas, FACHE, President
**Web address:** www.khnetwork.org

GREENE MEMORIAL HOSPITAL (O, 58 beds) 1141 North Monroe Drive, Xenia, OH Zip 45385–1600; tel. 937/352–2000; Terry M. Burns, President
**Web address:** www.greenehealth.org

KETTERING MEDICAL CENTER (O, 386 beds) 3535 Southern Boulevard, Kettering, OH Zip 45429–1221; tel. 937/298–4331; Roy G. Chew, Ph.D., President
**Web address:** www.kmcnetwork.org

SOIN MEDICAL CENTER (O, 71 beds) 3535 Pentagon Boulevard, Beavercreek, OH Zip 45431–1705; tel. 937/702–4000; Terry M. Burns, President
**Web address:** www.khnetwork.org/soin

For explanation of codes following names, see page B2.
★ Indicates Type III membership in the American Hospital Association.

SYCAMORE MEDICAL CENTER (O, 170 beds) 4000 Miamisburg–Centerville Road, Miamisburg, OH Zip 45342–7615; tel. 937/866–0551; Walter Sackett, President
**Web address:** www.khnetwork.org

| | | |
|---|---|---|
| Owned, leased, sponsored: | 6 hospitals | 1163 beds |
| Contract–managed: | 0 hospitals | 0 beds |
| Totals: | 6 hospitals | 1163 beds |

---

### ★0026: KINDRED HEALTHCARE (IO)

680 South Fourth Street, Louisville, KY Zip 40202–2412; tel. 502/596–7300; Paul J. Diaz, President and Chief Executive Officer
**(Independent Hospital System)**

**ARIZONA:** KINDRED HOSPITAL ARIZONA–PHOENIX (O, 58 beds) 40 East Indianola Avenue, Phoenix, AZ Zip 85012–2059; tel. 602/280–7000; Heidi Miller, Chief Executive Officer
**Web address:** www.khphoenix.com/

KINDRED HOSPITAL–TUCSON (O, 51 beds) 355 North Wilmot Road, Tucson, AZ Zip 85711–2601; tel. 520/584–4500; Marc Lemon, Chief Executive Officer
**Web address:** www.khtucson.com

**CALIFORNIA:** KINDRED HOSPITAL OF RIVERSIDE (O, 40 beds) 2224 Medical Center Drive, Perris, CA Zip 92571–2638; tel. 951/436–3535; James Linhares, Administrator
**Web address:** www.khriverside.com

KINDRED HOSPITAL OF SOUTH BAY (O, 84 beds) 1246 West 155th Street, Gardena, CA Zip 90247–4011; tel. 310/323–5330; Kevin Chavez, Chief Executive Officer
**Web address:** www.khsouthbay.com/

KINDRED HOSPITAL RANCHO (O, 55 beds) 10841 White Oak Avenue, Rancho Cucamonga, CA Zip 91730–3811; tel. 909/581–6400; Jody Knox, Administrator
**Web address:** www.khrancho.com

KINDRED HOSPITAL–BALDWIN PARK (C, 72 beds) 14148 East Francisquito Avenue, Baldwin Park, CA Zip 91706–6120; tel. 626/388–2700; Swenda Moreh, Chief Executive Officer
**Web address:** www.khbaldwinpark.com

KINDRED HOSPITAL–BREA (O, 48 beds) 875 North Brea Boulevard, Brea, CA Zip 92821–2699; tel. 714/529–6842; Diane Zeoli, Chief Executive Officer
**Web address:** www.kindredhospitalbrea.com/

KINDRED HOSPITAL–LA MIRADA (O, 216 beds) 14900 East Imperial Highway, La Mirada, CA Zip 90638–2172; tel. 562/944–1900; April Myers, Administrator
**Web address:** www.kindredlamirada.com/

KINDRED HOSPITAL–LOS ANGELES (O, 81 beds) 5525 West Slauson Avenue, Los Angeles, CA Zip 90056–1067; tel. 310/642–0325; Phillip R. Wolfe, Administrator
**Web address:** www.kindredhospitalla.com/

KINDRED HOSPITAL–ONTARIO (O, 91 beds) 550 North Monterey Avenue, Ontario, CA Zip 91764–3399; tel. 909/391–0333; Robin Rapp, MS, R.N., Chief Executive Officer
**Web address:** www.khontario.com/

KINDRED HOSPITAL–SACRAMENTO (O, 34 beds) 330 Montrose Drive, Folsom, CA Zip 95630–2720; tel. 916/351–9151; Janet Biedron, R.N., Chief Executive Officer
**Web address:** www.kindredsacramento.com/

KINDRED HOSPITAL–SAN DIEGO (O, 70 beds) 1940 El Cajon Boulevard, San Diego, CA Zip 92104–1096; tel. 619/543–4500; Cathryn Branch, R.N., Chief Executive Officer
**Web address:** www.kindredsandiego.com

KINDRED HOSPITAL–SAN FRANCISCO BAY AREA (O, 78 beds) 2800 Benedict Drive, San Leandro, CA Zip 94577–6840; tel. 510/357–8300; Dianne Chartier, R.N., Interim Chief Executive Officer
**Web address:** www.kindredhospitalsfba.com

KINDRED HOSPITAL–WESTMINSTER (O, 99 beds) 200 Hospital Circle, Westminster, CA Zip 92683–3910; tel. 714/893–4541; Brooke Saunders, Administrator
**Web address:** www.khwestminster.com/

**COLORADO:** KINDRED HOSPITAL–AURORA (O, 37 beds) 700 Potomac Street 2nd Floor, Aurora, CO Zip 80011–6844; tel. 720/857–8333; Nicole Reinhardt, Chief Executive Officer
**Web address:** www.khaurora.com/

KINDRED HOSPITAL–DENVER (O, 68 beds) 1920 High Street, Denver, CO Zip 80218–1213; tel. 303/320–5871; Harvey Ross, Chief Executive Officer
**Web address:** www.kh-denver.com

**FLORIDA:** KINDRED HOSPITAL BAY AREA–TAMPA (O, 155 beds) 4555 South Manhattan Avenue, Tampa, FL Zip 33611–2397; tel. 813/839–6341; Julie Feasel, Chief Executive Officer
**Web address:** www.khtampa.com/

KINDRED HOSPITAL MELBOURNE (O, 42 beds) 765 West Nasa Boulevard, Melbourne, FL Zip 32901–1815; tel. 321/733–5725; Angelica Cotshott, Chief Executive Officer
**Web address:** www.khmelbourne.com

KINDRED HOSPITAL NORTH FLORIDA (O, 80 beds) 801 Oak Street, Green Cove Springs, FL Zip 32043–4317; tel. 904/284–9230; Hoyt Ross, Chief Executive Officer
**Web address:** www.khnorthflorida.com

KINDRED HOSPITAL OCALA (O, 31 beds) 1500 S.W. 1st Avenue, Ocala, FL Zip 34471–6504; tel. 352/369–0513; Merlene Bhoorasingh, Administrator
**Web address:** www.kindredocala.com/

KINDRED HOSPITAL SOUTH FLORIDA–FORT LAUDERDALE (O, 70 beds) 1516 East Las Olas Boulevard, Fort Lauderdale, FL Zip 33301–2399; tel. 954/764–8900; Theodore L. Welding, Administrator
**Web address:** www.khfortlauderdale.com/

KINDRED HOSPITAL THE PALM BEACHES (O, 70 beds) 5555 West Blue Heron Boulevard, Riviera Beach, FL Zip 33418–7813; tel. 561/840–0754; Timothy Page, Chief Executive Officer
**Web address:** www.khthepalmbeaches.com/

KINDRED HOSPITAL–CENTRAL TAMPA (O, 96 beds) 4801 North Howard Avenue, Tampa, FL Zip 33603–1411; tel. 813/874–7575; Debra Plummer, Chief Executive Officer
**Web address:** www.kindredcentraltampa.com/

**GEORGIA:** KINDRED HOSPITAL ROME (O, 45 beds) 304 Turner McCall Boulevard, Rome, GA Zip 30165–5621; tel. 706/378–6800; Susan M. Stovall, Chief Executive Officer
**Web address:** www.kindredrome.com

KINDRED HOSPITAL–ATLANTA (O, 70 beds) 705 Juniper Street N.E., Atlanta, GA Zip 30308–1307; tel. 404/873–2871; Michael Schmitt, M.D., Chief Executive Officer
**Web address:** www.kindredatlanta.com/

**ILLINOIS:** KINDRED CHICAGO–CENTRAL HOSPITAL (O, 54 beds) 4058 West Melrose Street, Chicago, IL Zip 60641–4797; tel. 773/736–7000; Bruce Carey, Chief Executive Officer
**Web address:** www.khchicagocentral.com

KINDRED HOSPITAL CHICAGO–NORTHLAKE (O, 94 beds) 365 East North Avenue, Northlake, IL Zip 60164–2628; tel. 708/345–8100; Beverly Foster, Chief Executive Officer
**Web address:** www.kindrednorthlake.com/

KINDRED HOSPITAL PEORIA (O, 50 beds) 500 West Romeo B. Garrett Avenue, Peoria, IL Zip 61605–2301; tel. 309/680–1500; Robert N. Wright, Chief Executive Officer
**Web address:** www.khpeoria.com/

KINDRED HOSPITAL SPRINGFIELD (O, 50 beds) 701 North Walnut Street, Springfield, IL Zip 62702–4931; tel. 217/528–1217; Sally Hoffmann, Interim Chief Executive Officer
**Web address:** www.kindredspringfield.com/

KINDRED HOSPITAL–SYCAMORE (O, 69 beds) 225 Edward Street, Sycamore, IL Zip 60178–2137; tel. 815/895–2144; Cindy Smith, Chief Executive Officer
**Web address:** www.kindredhospitalsyc.com/

**INDIANA:** KINDRED HOSPITAL INDIANAPOLIS SOUTH (O, 52 beds) 607 Greenwood Springs Drive, Greenwood, IN Zip 46143–6377; tel. 317/888–8155; Marc Hurst, Chief Executive Officer
**Web address:** www.khindysouth.com/

KINDRED HOSPITAL NORTHWEST INDIANA (O, 70 beds) 5454 Hohman Avenue, 5th Floor, Hammond, IN Zip 46320–1931; tel. 219/937–9900; Frank A. Solare, Chief Executive Officer
**Web address:** www.khnwindiana.com

For explanation of codes following names, see page B2.
★ Indicates Type III membership in the American Hospital Association.

KINDRED HOSPITAL OF NORTHERN INDIANA (O, 32 beds) 215 West Fourth Street, Suite 200, Mishawaka, IN ZIP 46544–1917; tel. 574/252–2000; Christine T. Voorde, Chief Executive Officer
**Web address:** www.khnorthernindiana.com

KINDRED HOSPITAL–INDIANAPOLIS (O, 59 beds) 1700 West 10th Street, Indianapolis, IN ZIP 46222–3802; tel. 317/636–4400; Kristy Walden, R.N., Interim Administrator
**Web address:** www.kindredhospitalindy.com/

**KENTUCKY:** KINDRED HOSPITAL–LOUISVILLE (O, 164 beds) 1313 Saint Anthony Place, Louisville, KY ZIP 40204–1740; tel. 502/587–7001; Michael L. Moody, Market Chief Executive Officer
**Web address:** www.kindredlouisville.com/

**LOUISIANA:** KINDRED HOSPITAL LAFAYETTE (O, 50 beds) 204 Energy Parkway, Lafayette, LA ZIP 70508–3816; tel. 337/232–1905; Sharon Black, Chief Executive Officer
**Web address:** www.khlafayette.com

KINDRED HOSPITAL–NEW ORLEANS (O, 75 beds) 3601 Coliseum Street, New Orleans, LA ZIP 70115–3606; tel. 504/899–1555; Thomas Alexander, Chief Executive Officer
**Web address:** www.kindredhospitalnola.com

**MASSACHUSETTS:** KINDRED HOSPITAL BOSTON–NORTH SHORE (O, 50 beds) 15 King Street, Peabody, MA ZIP 01960–4379; tel. 978/531–2900; Yolande Wilson, Chief Executive Officer
**Web address:** www.kindredbns.com

KINDRED HOSPITAL NORTHEAST–STOUGHTON (O, 170 beds) 909 Sumner Street, 1st Floor, Stoughton, MA ZIP 02072–3396; tel. 781/297–8200; Robert A. Gundersen, Market Chief Executive Officer
**Web address:** www.khstoughton.com

KINDRED HOSPITAL PARK VIEW (O, 202 beds) 1400 State Street, Springfield, MA ZIP 01109–2550; tel. 413/726–6700; Jake Socha, Chief Executive Officer
**Web address:** www.khparkview.com/

KINDRED HOSPITAL–BOSTON (O, 59 beds) 1515 Commonwealth Avenue, Brighton, MA ZIP 02135–3617; tel. 617/254–1100; Susan Downey, R.N., MS, Chief Executive Officer
**Web address:** www.kindredbos.com/

**MICHIGAN:** KINDRED HOSPITAL DETROIT (O, 77 beds) 4777 East Outer Drive, Detroit, MI ZIP 48234–3241; tel. 313/369–5800; Jan Turk, Chief Executive Officer
**Web address:** www.kindreddetroit.com/

**MISSOURI:** KINDRED HOSPITAL KANSAS CITY (O, 130 beds) 8701 Troost Avenue, Kansas City, MO ZIP 64131–2767; tel. 816/995–2000; Aaron Anothayanontha, Chief Executive Officer
**Web address:** www.kindredhospitalkc.com

KINDRED HOSPITAL NORTHLAND (O, 35 beds) 500 Northwest 68th Street, Kansas City, MO ZIP 64118–2455; tel. 816/420–6300; H. Frank Schneider, Chief Executive Officer
**Web address:** www.khnorthland.com

KINDRED HOSPITAL–ST. LOUIS (O, 98 beds) 4930 Lindell Boulevard, Saint Louis, MO ZIP 63108–1510; tel. 314/361–8700; Stacy M. Howard, R.N., Chief Executive Officer
**Web address:** www.kindredstlouis.com/

ST. LUKE'S REHABILITATION HOSPITAL (O, 35 beds) 14709 Olive Boulevard, Chesterfield, MO ZIP 63017–2221; tel. 314/317–5700; Elizabeth A. Cooley, R.N., Chief Executive Officer
**Web address:** www.khrehabstluke.com

**NEVADA:** KINDRED HOSPITAL LAS VEGAS–SAHARA (O, 238 beds) 5110 West Sahara Avenue, Las Vegas, NV ZIP 89146–3406; tel. 702/871–1418; Carol Lee O'Connor, Interim Chief Executive Officer
**Web address:** www.kindredhospitallvs.com/

**NEW JERSEY:** KINDRED HOSPITAL–NEW JERSEY MORRIS COUNTY (O, 117 beds) 400 West Blackwell Street, Dover, NJ ZIP 07801–2525; tel. 973/537–3818; Wayne D. Blanchard, Chief Executive Officer
**Web address:** www.khmorriscounty.com/

**NEW MEXICO:** KINDRED HOSPITAL–ALBUQUERQUE (O, 61 beds) 700 High Street N.E., Albuquerque, NM ZIP 87102–2565; tel. 505/242–4444; Michael R. Shaw, Chief Executive Officer
**Web address:** www.kindredalbuquerque.com/

**NORTH CAROLINA:** KINDRED HOSPITAL–GREENSBORO (O, 101 beds) 2401 Southside Boulevard, Greensboro, NC ZIP 27406–3311; tel. 336/271–2800; Derek Murzyn, Chief Executive Officer
**Web address:** www.khgreensboro.com

**NORTH DAKOTA:** KINDRED HOSPITAL FARGO (O, 31 beds) 1720 University Drive South, Fargo, ND ZIP 58103–4940; tel. 701/241–9099; Custer Huseby, Chief Executive Officer
**Web address:** www.khfargo.com

KINDRED HOSPITAL–CENTRAL DAKOTAS (O, 41 beds) 1000 18th Street N.W., Mandan, ND ZIP 58554–1612; tel. 701/667–2000; April Bishop, Chief Executive Officer
**Web address:** www.khcentraldakotas.com

**OHIO:** KINDRED HOSPITAL CLEVELAND–GATEWAY (O, 153 beds) 2351 East 22nd Street, 7th Floor, Cleveland, OH ZIP 44115–3111; tel. 216/363–2671; Ian Cooper, Chief Executive Officer
**Web address:** www.kindredgateway.com

KINDRED HOSPITAL LIMA (O, 26 beds) 730 West Market Street, 6th Floor, Lima, OH ZIP 45801–4602; tel. 419/224–1888; Susan Krinke, Chief Executive Officer
**Web address:** www.khlima.com

KINDRED HOSPITAL OF CENTRAL OHIO (O, 33 beds) 335 Glessner Avenue, 5th Floor, Mansfield, OH ZIP 44903–2269; tel. 419/526–0777; Vanessa Acevedo, Chief Executive Officer
**Web address:** www.khcentralohio.com/

KINDRED HOSPITAL–DAYTON (O, 67 beds) One Elizabeth Place, 5th Floor, Dayton, OH ZIP 45417–3445; tel. 937/222–5963; Lynn Schoen, Chief Executive Officer
**Web address:** www.khdayton.com

**OKLAHOMA:** KINDRED HOSPITAL TULSA (O, 60 beds) 3219 South 79th East Avenue, Tulsa, OK ZIP 74145–1343; tel. 918/663–8183; Lee A. Simpson, Jr., Chief Executive Officer
**Web address:** www.khtulsa.com

KINDRED HOSPITAL– OKLAHOMA CITY (O, 93 beds) 1407 North Robinson Avenue, Oklahoma City, OK ZIP 73103–4823; tel. 405/232–8000; Mark E. Rogers, Interim Chief Executive Officer
**Web address:** www.kindredoklahoma.com

**PENNSYLVANIA:** KINDRED HOSPITAL EASTON (O, 31 beds) 250 South 21st Street, 3rd Floor, Easton, PA ZIP 18042–3851; tel. 610/250–4724; Deborah Karn, Chief Executive Officer
**Web address:** www.kheaston.com/

KINDRED HOSPITAL PITTSBURGH–NORTH SHORE (O, 111 beds) 1004 Arch Street, Pittsburgh, PA ZIP 15212–5235; tel. 412/323–5800; David Johnson, Chief Executive Officer
**Web address:** www.kindrednorthshore.com/

KINDRED HOSPITAL SOUTH PHILADELPHIA (O, 58 beds) 1930 South Broad Street, Philadelphia, PA ZIP 19145–2328; tel. 267/570–5200; Garrett Arneson, Chief Executive Officer
**Web address:** www.khsouthphilly.com

KINDRED HOSPITAL–HERITAGE VALLEY (O, 35 beds) 1000 Dutch Ridge Road, Beaver, PA ZIP 15009–9727; tel. 724/773–8480; Rodney B. Jones, Administrator
**Web address:** www.kindredhospitalhv.com/

KINDRED HOSPITAL–PHILADELPHIA (O, 52 beds) 6129 Palmetto Street, Philadelphia, PA ZIP 19111–5729; tel. 215/722–8555; Margaret M. Murphy, Interim Chief Executive Officer
**Web address:** www.kindredphila.com/

KINDRED HOSPITAL–PITTSBURGH (O, 63 beds) 7777 Steubenville Pike, Oakdale, PA ZIP 15071–3409; tel. 412/494–5500; John T. Burton, Administrator
**Web address:** www.kindredhospitalpittsburgh.com/

KINDRED HOSPITAL–WYOMING VALLEY (O, 36 beds) 575 North River Street, 7th Floor, Wilkes Barre, PA ZIP 18764–0999; tel. 570/552–7620; Sharon Yurkiewicz, Chief Executive Officer
**Web address:** www.kindredhospitalwv.com/

**SOUTH CAROLINA:** KINDRED HOSPITAL–CHARLESTON (O, 55 beds) 1200 Hospital Drive, Mt. Pleasant, SC ZIP 29464; tel. 843/876–8670; Stephanie Bridges, Interim Chief Executive Officer
**Web address:** www.khcharleston.com

For explanation of codes following names, see page B2.
★ Indicates Type III membership in the American Hospital Association.

**TENNESSEE:** KINDRED HOSPITAL–CHATTANOOGA (O, 44 beds) 709 Walnut Street, Chattanooga, TN Zip 37402–1916; tel. 423/266–7721; William J. Bryant, Chief Executive Officer
**Web address:** www.kindredchattanooga.com/

KINDRED HOSPITAL–NASHVILLE (O, 58 beds) 1412 County Hospital Road, Nashville, TN Zip 37218–3007; tel. 615/687–2600; William P. Macri, Chief Executive Officer
**Web address:** www.khnashville.com/

**TEXAS:** CENTRAL TEXAS REHABILITATION HOSPITAL (O, 50 beds) 700 West 45th Street, Austin, TX Zip 78751–2800; tel. 512/407–2111; Peggy Barrett, R.N., Chief Executive Officer
**Web address:** www.khrehabcentraltexas.com/

KINDRED HOSPITAL DALLAS CENTRAL (O, 60 beds) 8050 Meadows Road, Dallas, TX Zip 75231–3406; tel. 469/232–6500; Justin Smith, Chief Executive Officer
**Web address:** www.khdallascentral.com/

KINDRED HOSPITAL EAST HOUSTON (O, 230 beds) 15101 East Freeway, Channelview, TX Zip 77530–4104; tel. 832/200–5500; Angel Gradney, Chief Executive Officer
**Web address:** www.kheasthouston.com

KINDRED HOSPITAL EL PASO (O, 62 beds) 1740 Curie Drive, El Paso, TX Zip 79902–2901; tel. 915/351–9044; Aleen D. Arabit, Chief Executive Officer
**Web address:** www.khelpaso.com/

KINDRED HOSPITAL MIDTOWN (O, 40 beds) 105 Drew Avenue, Houston, TX Zip 77006–1527; tel. 713/529–8922; Robert Stein, Chief Executive Officer
**Web address:** www.khmidtown.com

KINDRED HOSPITAL NORTH HOUSTON (O, 288 beds) 7407 North Freeway, Houston, TX Zip 77076–1314; tel. 832/200–6000; Larkin Virden, Interim Chief Executive Officer
**Web address:** www.khnorthhouston.com

KINDRED HOSPITAL SUGAR LAND (O, 171 beds) 1550 First Colony Boulevard, Sugar Land, TX Zip 77479–4000; tel. 281/275–6000; Lorene Perona, Chief Executive Officer
**Web address:** www.khsugarland.com

KINDRED HOSPITAL TARRANT COUNTY–ARLINGTON (O, 78 beds) 1000 North Cooper Street, Arlington, TX Zip 76011–5540; tel. 817/548 3400; Christina Richard, Administrator
**Web address:** www.kindredhospitalarl.com/

KINDRED HOSPITAL TARRANT COUNTY–FORT WORTH SOUTHWEST (O, 78 beds) 7800 Oakmont Boulevard, Fort Worth, TX Zip 76132–4299; tel. 817/346–0094; Anna Rojas, Chief Executive Officer
**Web address:** www.kindredhospitalfwsw.com/

KINDRED HOSPITAL VICTORIA (O, 23 beds) 506 East San Antonio Street, 3rd Floor, Victoria, TX Zip 77901–6060; tel. 361/575–1445; Portlyn Brogger, Chief Executive Officer
**Web address:** www.khvictoria.com

KINDRED HOSPITAL–AMARILLO (O, 72 beds) 7501 Wallace Boulevard, Amarillo, TX Zip 79124–2150; tel. 806/467–7000; Kay E. Peck, Ph.D., Chief Executive Officer
**Web address:** www.khamarillo.com/

KINDRED HOSPITAL–BAY AREA (O, 74 beds) 4801 East Sam Houston Parkway South, Pasadena, TX Zip 77505–3955; tel. 281/991–5463; Laura Cedillo-Rodriguez, Chief Executive Officer
**Web address:** www.khbayareahouston.com/

KINDRED HOSPITAL–CORPUS CHRISTI (O, 68 beds) 6226 Saratoga Boulevard, Corpus Christi, TX Zip 78414–3421; tel. 361/986–1600; Diana Schultz, Chief Executive Officer
**Web address:** www.khcorpuschristi.com/

KINDRED HOSPITAL–DALLAS (O, 50 beds) 9525 Greenville Avenue, Dallas, TX Zip 75243–4116; tel. 214/355–2600; Ellen Shankles, Chief Executive Officer
**Web address:** www.khdallas.com

KINDRED HOSPITAL–FORT WORTH (O, 54 beds) 815 Eighth Avenue, Fort Worth, TX Zip 76104–2609; tel. 817/332–4812; Angela Harris, Chief Executive Officer
**Web address:** www.kindredfortworth.com/

KINDRED HOSPITAL–HOUSTON (O, 105 beds) 6441 Main Street, Houston, TX Zip 77030–1596; tel. 713/790–0500; Robert Stein, Chief Executive Officer
**Web address:** www.khhouston.com/

KINDRED HOSPITAL–HOUSTON NORTHWEST (O, 84 beds) 11297 Fallbrook Drive, Houston, TX Zip 77065–4292; tel. 281/897–8114; Mary Anne Craig, Chief Executive Officer
**Web address:** www.khhoustonnw.com/

KINDRED HOSPITAL–MANSFIELD (O, 55 beds) 1802 Highway 157 North, Mansfield, TX Zip 76063–3923; tel. 817/473–6101; Susan Schaetti, Administrator
**Web address:** www.kindredmansfield.com

KINDRED HOSPITAL–SAN ANTONIO (O, 59 beds) 3636 Medical Drive, San Antonio, TX Zip 78229–2183; tel. 210/616–0616; Katherine Eskew, Chief Executive Officer
**Web address:** www.khsanantonio.com/

KINDRED HOSPITAL–WHITE ROCK (O, 25 beds) 9440 Poppy Drive, 5th Floor, Dallas, TX Zip 75218–3652; tel. 214/324–6562; Brenda Perez, R.N., MSN, Interim Administrator
**Web address:** www.khwhiterock.com

KINDRED REHABILITATION HOSPITAL AMARILLO (O, 44 beds) 7200 West 9th Avenue, Amarillo, TX Zip 79106–1703; tel. 806/468–2900; Kay E. Peck, Ph.D., Chief Executive Officer
**Web address:** www.khrehabamarillo.com/

KINDRED REHABILITATION HOSPITAL ARLINGTON (O, 24 beds) 2601 West Randol Mill Road, Arlington, TX Zip 76012–4289; tel. 817/804–4400; Seth A. Sauve, FACHE, Chief Executive Officer
**Web address:** www.khrehabarlington.com/

KINDRED REHABILITATION HOSPITAL CLEAR LAKE (O, 60 beds) 655 East Medical Center Boulevard, Webster, TX Zip 77598–4328; tel. 281/286–1500; Dale R. Mulder, Chief Executive Officer
**Web address:** www.khrehabclearlake.com/

KINDRED REHABILITATION HOSPITAL NORTHEAST HOUSTON (O, 46 beds) 18839 McKay Road, Humble, TX Zip 77338–5721; tel. 281/964–6600; Jeffrey Smith, Chief Executive Officer
**Web address:** www.khrehabnortheasthouston.com

**VIRGINIA:** KINDRED HOSPITAL RICHMOND (O, 60 beds) 2220 Edward Holland Drive, Richmond, VA Zip 23230–2519; tel. 804/678–7000; Barbara L. Callaghan, Interim Chief Executive Officer
**Web address:** www.kindredrichmond.com/

**WASHINGTON:** KINDRED HOSPITAL SEATTLE–NORTHGATE (O, 42 beds) 10631 8th Avenue N.E., Seattle, WA Zip 98125–7213; tel. 206/364–2050; Lauren Suarez, Chief Executive Officer
**Web address:** www.kindredhospitalseattle.com/

**WISCONSIN:** KINDRED HOSPITAL–MILWAUKEE (O, 56 beds) 5017 South 110Th Street, Greenfield, WI Zip 53228–3131; tel. 414/427–8282; Jeff Cellucci, Interim Chief Executive Officer
**Web address:** www.khmilwaukee.com/

| | | |
|---|---|---|
| **Owned, leased, sponsored:** | 94 hospitals | 7066 beds |
| **Contract–managed:** | 1 hospital | 72 beds |
| **Totals:** | 95 hospitals | 7138 beds |

★**0149: KISH HEALTH SYSTEM** (NP)
1 Kish Hospital Drive, DeKalb, IL Zip 60115–9602, Mailing Address: P.O. Box 707, Zip 60115–0707; tel. 815/756–1521; Kevin P. Poorten, President and Chief Executive Officer
**(Independent Hospital System)**

**ILLINOIS:** KISHWAUKEE HOSPITAL (O, 98 beds) 1 Kish Hospital Drive, DeKalb, IL Zip 60115–9602, Mailing Address: P.O. Box 707, Zip 60115–0707; tel. 815/756–1521; Brad Copple, President
**Web address:** www.kishhospital.org

VALLEY WEST HOSPITAL (O, 24 beds) 11 East Pleasant Avenue, Sandwich, IL Zip 60548–0901; tel. 815/786–8484; Brad Copple, President
**Web address:** www.vwch.org

| | | |
|---|---|---|
| **Owned, leased, sponsored:** | 2 hospitals | 122 beds |
| **Contract–managed:** | 0 hospitals | 0 beds |
| **Totals:** | 2 hospitals | 122 beds |

For explanation of codes following names, see page B2.
★ Indicates Type III membership in the American Hospital Association.

**0891:  LAHEY HEALTH** (NP)
41 Mall Road, Burlington, MA Zip 01805–0001; tel. 781/744–7100; Howard R. Grant, JD, M.D., President and Chief Executive Officer

**MASSACHUSETTS:** BEVERLY HOSPITAL (O, 320 beds) 85 Herrick Street, Beverly, MA Zip 01915–1777; tel. 978/922–3000; Denis S. Conroy, President
**Web address:** www.beverlyhospital.org

LAHEY HOSPITAL & MEDICAL CENTER, BURLINGTON (O, 327 beds) 41 Mall Road, Burlington, MA Zip 01805–0001; tel. 781/744–5100; Howard R. Grant, JD, M.D., President and Chief Executive Officer
**Web address:** www.lahey.org

| | | |
|---|---|---|
| Owned, leased, sponsored: | 2 hospitals | 647 beds |
| Contract–managed: | 0 hospitals | 0 beds |
| Totals: | 2 hospitals | 647 beds |

**0056:  LAKELAND HEALTHCARE** (NP)
1234 Napier Avenue, Saint Joseph, MI Zip 49085–2158; tel. 269/983–8300; Loren Hamel, M.D., President and Chief Executive Officer
**(Independent Hospital System)**

**MICHIGAN:** LAKELAND COMMUNITY HOSPITAL WATERVLIET (O, 38 beds) 400 Medical Park Drive, Watervliet, MI Zip 49098–9225; tel. 269/463–3111; Ray Cruse, Chief Executive Officer

LAKELAND REGIONAL MEDICAL CENTER–ST. JOSEPH (O, 250 beds) 1234 Napier Avenue, Saint Joseph, MI Zip 49085–2158; tel. 269/983–8300; Loren Hamel, M.D., President and Chief Executive Officer
**Web address:** www.lakelandhealth.org

LAKELAND SPECIALTY HOSPITAL–BERRIEN CENTER (O, 183 beds) 6418 Deans Hill Road, Berrien Center, MI Zip 49102–9750; tel. 269/473–3003; Loren Hamel, M.D., President and Chief Executive Officer
**Web address:** www.lakelandhealth.org

| | | |
|---|---|---|
| Owned, leased, sponsored: | 3 hospitals | 471 beds |
| Contract–managed: | 0 hospitals | 0 beds |
| Totals: | 3 hospitals | 471 beds |

**0393:  LANDMARK HOSPITALS** (IO)
3255 Independence Street, Cape Girardeau, MO Zip 63701–4914; tel. 573/335–1091; William K. Kapp, III, M.D., President and Chief Executive Officer
**(Independent Hospital System)**

**GEORGIA:** LANDMARK HOSPITAL OF ATHENS (O, 42 beds) 775 Sunset Drive, Athens, GA Zip 30606–2211; tel. 706/425–1500; Tommy Jackson, Chief Executive Officer
**Web address:** www.landmarkhospitals.com

**MISSOURI:** LANDMARK HOSPITAL (O, 30 beds) 3255 Independence Street, Cape Girardeau, MO Zip 63701–4914; tel. 573/335–1091; Rodney Brown, Chief Executive Officer
**Web address:** www.landmarkhospitals.com

LANDMARK HOSPITAL OF COLUMBIA (O, 42 beds) 604 Old 63 North, Columbia, MO Zip 65201–6308; tel. 573/499–6600; Shannon Canard, Chief Executive Officer
**Web address:** www.landmarkhospitals.com

LANDMARK HOSPITAL OF JOPLIN (O, 30 beds) 2040 West 32nd Street, Joplin, MO Zip 64804–3512; tel. 417/627–1300; Kenneth D'Amico, Chief Executive Officer
**Web address:** www.landmarkhospitals.com

| | | |
|---|---|---|
| Owned, leased, sponsored: | 4 hospitals | 144 beds |
| Contract–managed: | 0 hospitals | 0 beds |
| Totals: | 4 hospitals | 144 beds |

**0904:  LAWRENCE+MEMORIAL HEALTH SYSTEM** (NP)
365 Montauk Avenue, New London, CT Zip 06320–4700; tel. 860/442–0711; Bruce D. Cummings, President and Chief Executive Officer

**CONNECTICUT:** LAWRENCE + MEMORIAL HOSPITAL (O, 256 beds) 365 Montauk Avenue, New London, CT Zip 06320–4769; tel. 860/442–0711; Bruce D. Cummings, President and Chief Executive Officer
**Web address:** www.lmhospital.org

**RHODE ISLAND:** WESTERLY HOSPITAL (O, 100 beds) 25 Wells Street, Westerly, RI Zip 02891–2934; tel. 401/596–6000; Christopher Lehrach, M.D., Chief Transformation Officer for Interim Operations
**Web address:** www.westerlyhospital.org

| | | |
|---|---|---|
| Owned, leased, sponsored: | 2 hospitals | 356 beds |
| Contract–managed: | 0 hospitals | 0 beds |
| Totals: | 2 hospitals | 356 beds |

**0369:  LEE MEMORIAL HEALTH SYSTEM** (NP)
2776 Cleveland Avenue, Fort Myers, FL Zip 33901–5856, Mailing Address: P.O. Box 2218, Zip 33902–2218; tel. 239/343–2000; James R. Nathan, President and Chief Executive Officer
**(Centralized Health System)**

**FLORIDA:** CAPE CORAL HOSPITAL (O, 291 beds) 636 Del Prado Boulevard, Cape Coral, FL Zip 33990–2695; tel. 239/424–2000; James R. Nathan, President and Chief Executive Officer
**Web address:** www.leememorial.org

GULF COAST MEDICAL CENTER (O, 349 beds) 13681 Doctor's Way, Fort Myers, FL Zip 33912–4300; tel. 239/343–1000; James R. Nathan, President and Chief Executive Officer
**Web address:** www.leememorial.org

LEE MEMORIAL HOSPITAL (O, 835 beds) 2776 Cleveland Avenue, Fort Myers, FL Zip 33901–5855, Mailing Address: P.O. Box 2218, Zip 33902–2218; tel. 239/332–1111; James R. Nathan, President and Chief Executive Officer
**Web address:** www.leememorial.org

| | | |
|---|---|---|
| Owned, leased, sponsored: | 3 hospitals | 1475 beds |
| Contract–managed: | 0 hospitals | 0 beds |
| Totals: | 3 hospitals | 1475 beds |

**★2755:  LEGACY HEALTH** (NP)
1919 N.W. Lovejoy Street, Portland, OR Zip 97209–1503; tel. 503/415–5600; George J. Brown, M.D., President and Chief Executive Officer
**(Centralized Health System)**

**OREGON:** LEGACY EMANUEL HOSPITAL AND HEALTH CENTER (O, 419 beds) 2801 North Gantenbein Avenue, Portland, OR Zip 97227–1674; tel. 503/413–2200; Lori Morgan, M.D., Chief Administrative Officer
**Web address:** www.legacyhealth.org

LEGACY GOOD SAMARITAN HOSPITAL AND MEDICAL CENTER (O, 248 beds) 1015 N.W. 22nd Avenue, Portland, OR Zip 97210–3099; tel. 503/413–7711; Tony Melaragno, M.D., Chief Administrative Officer
**Web address:** www.legacyhealth.org

LEGACY MERIDIAN PARK HOSPITAL (O, 130 beds) 19300 S.W. 65th Avenue, Tualatin, OR Zip 97062–9741; tel. 503/692–1212; Allyson Anderson, Chief Administrative Officer
**Web address:** www.legacyhealth.org

LEGACY MOUNT HOOD MEDICAL CENTER (O, 91 beds) 24800 S.E. Stark, Gresham, OR Zip 97030–3378; tel. 503/667–1122; Gretchen Nichols, R.N., Chief Administrative Officer
**Web address:** www.legacyhealth.org

**WASHINGTON:** LEGACY SALMON CREEK MEDICAL CENTER (O, 194 beds) 2211 N.E. 139th Street, Vancouver, WA Zip 98686–2742; tel. 360/487–1000; Jonathan Avery, Chief Administrative Officer
**Web address:** www.legacyhealth.org

| | | |
|---|---|---|
| Owned, leased, sponsored: | 5 hospitals | 1082 beds |
| Contract–managed: | 0 hospitals | 0 beds |
| Totals: | 5 hospitals | 1082 beds |

For explanation of codes following names, see page B2.
★ Indicates Type III membership in the American Hospital Association.

Section B

★**0370: LEHIGH VALLEY HEALTH NETWORK** (NP)
1200 South Cedar Crest Boulevard, Allentown, PA Zip 18103–6202, Mailing Address: P.O. Box 689, Zip 18105–1556; tel. 610/402–8000; Ronald W. Swinfard, M.D., President and Chief Executive Officer
**(Centralized Health System)**

**PENNSYLVANIA:** LEHIGH VALLEY HOSPITAL (O, 793 beds) 1200 South Cedar Crest Boulevard, Allentown, PA Zip 18103–6248, Mailing Address: P.O. Box 689, Zip 18105–1556; tel. 610/402–8000; Ronald W. Swinfard, M.D., President and Chief Executive Officer
**Web address:** www.lvhhn.org

LEHIGH VALLEY HOSPITAL–MUHLENBERG (O, 186 beds) 2545 Schoenersville Road, Bethlehem, PA Zip 18017–7300; tel. 484/884–2201; Ronald W. Swinfard, M.D., President and Chief Executive Officer
**Web address:** www.lvhhn.org

| | | |
|---|---|---|
| Owned, leased, sponsored: | 2 hospitals | 979 beds |
| Contract–managed: | 0 hospitals | 0 beds |
| Totals: | 2 hospitals | 979 beds |

**0179: LESTER E. COX MEDICAL CENTERS** (NP)
1423 North Jefferson Avenue, Springfield, MO Zip 65802–1988; tel. 417/269–3108; Steven D. Edwards, President and Chief Executive Officer
**(Centralized Physician/Insurance Health System)**

**MISSOURI:** COX MEDICAL CENTER BRANSON (O, 126 beds) 251 Skaggs Road, Branson, MO Zip 65616–2031, Mailing Address: P.O. Box 650, Zip 65615–0650; tel. 417/335–7000; William K. Mahoney, President and Chief Executive Officer
**Web address:** www.skaggs.net

COX MONETT (O, 25 beds) 801 North Lincoln Avenue, Monett, MO Zip 65708–1641; tel. 417/235–3144; Genice Maroc, FACHE, Administrator and Chief Executive Officer
**Web address:** www.coxhealth.com

LESTER E. COX MEDICAL CENTERS (O, 647 beds) 1423 North Jefferson Street, Springfield, MO Zip 65802–1988; tel. 417/269–3000; Steven D. Edwards, President and Chief Executive Officer
**Web address:** www.coxhealth.com

| | | |
|---|---|---|
| Owned, leased, sponsored: | 3 hospitals | 798 beds |
| Contract–managed: | 0 hospitals | 0 beds |
| Totals: | 3 hospitals | 798 beds |

**0632: LHC GROUP** (IO)
420 West Pinhook Road, Lafayette, LA Zip 70503–2131; tel. 337/223–1307; Keith G. Myers, Chairman and Chief Executive Officer

**LOUISIANA:** LOUISIANA EXTENDED CARE HOSPITAL OF LAFAYETTE (O, 42 beds) 1214 Coolidge Boulevard, 8th Floor, Lafayette, LA Zip 70503–2621; tel. 337/289–8180; Kevin Frank, Administrator
**Web address:** www.lhcgroup.com

LOUISIANA EXTENDED CARE HOSPITAL OF NATCHITOCHES (O, 21 beds) 501 Keyser Avenue, Natchitoches, LA Zip 71457–6018; tel. 318/354–2044; Kermit Simmons, Administrator
**Web address:** www.lhcgroup.com

LOUISIANA EXTENDED CARE HOSPITAL WEST MONROE (O, 18 beds) 503 McMillan Road, 3rd Floor, West Monroe, LA Zip 71291–5327; tel. 318/329–4300; Cleta Munholland, Administrator

OCHSNER EXTENDED CARE HOSPITAL OF KENNER (O, 34 beds) 180 West Esplanade Avenue, 5th Floor, Kenner, LA Zip 70065–2467; tel. 504/464–8590; Fritz Nelson, Administrator
**Web address:** www.lhcgroup.com/

| | | |
|---|---|---|
| Owned, leased, sponsored: | 4 hospitals | 115 beds |
| Contract–managed: | 0 hospitals | 0 beds |
| Totals: | 4 hospitals | 115 beds |

★**0394: LHP HOSPITAL GROUP** (IO)
2400 North Dallas Parkway, Suite 450, Plano, TX Zip 75093–5994; tel. 866/465–9222; Daniel J. Moen, Chief Executive Officer
**(Independent Hospital System)**

**FLORIDA:** BAY MEDICAL CENTER SACRED HEART (L, 273 beds) 615 North Bonita Avenue, Panama City, FL Zip 32401–3600, Mailing Address: P.O. Box 59515, Zip 32412–0515; tel. 850/769–1511; Barry L. Keel, Chief Executive Officer
**Web address:** www.baymedical.org

**IDAHO:** PORTNEUF MEDICAL CENTER (O, 175 beds) 777 Hospital Way, Pocatello, ID Zip 83201–5175; tel. 208/239–1000; John Abreu, Interim Chief executive Officer
**Web address:** www.portmed.org

**NEW JERSEY:** HACKENSACK UNIVERSITY MEDICAL CENTER AT PASCACK VALLEY (O, 128 beds) 250 Old Hook Road, Westwood, NJ Zip 07675–3123; tel. 201/880–2700; Chad Melton, Chief Executive Officer
**Web address:** www.hackensackumcpv.com/

HACKENSACK UNIVERSITY MEDICAL CENTER MOUNTAINSIDE (O, 228 beds) 1 Bay Avenue, Montclair, NJ Zip 07042–4898; tel. 973/429–6000; John A. Fromhold, Chief Executive Officer
**Web address:** www.mountainsidenow.com

**TEXAS:** SETON MEDICAL CENTER HARKER HEIGHTS (O, 83 beds) 850 West Central Texas Expressway, Harker Heights, TX Zip 76548–1890; tel. 254/690–0900; Matt T. Maxfield, FACHE, Chief Executive Officer
**Web address:** www.setonharkerheights.net

TEXAS HEALTH PRESBYTERIAN HOSPITAL–WNJ (O, 235 beds) 500 North Highland Avenue, Sherman, TX Zip 75092–7354; tel. 903/870–4611; Vance V. Reynolds, FACHE, CPA, Chief Executive Officer
**Web address:** www.wnj.org

| | | |
|---|---|---|
| Owned, leased, sponsored: | 6 hospitals | 1122 beds |
| Contract–managed: | 0 hospitals | 0 beds |
| Totals: | 6 hospitals | 1122 beds |

★**0158: LIFEBRIDGE HEALTH** (NP)
2401 West Belvedere Avenue, Baltimore, MD Zip 21215–5216; tel. 410/601–5134; Neil M. Meltzer, President and Chief Executive Officer
**(Centralized Health System)**

**MARYLAND:** LEVINDALE HEBREW GERIATRIC CENTER AND HOSPITAL (O, 481 beds) 2434 West Belvedere Avenue, Baltimore, MD Zip 21215–5267; tel. 410/466–8700; Aric Spitulnik, President and Chief Operating Officer
**Web address:** www.sinai-balt.com

NORTHWEST HOSPITAL (O, 244 beds) 5401 Old Court Road, Randallstown, MD Zip 21133–5185; tel. 410/521–2200; Brian M. White, President
**Web address:** www.lifebridgehealth.org

SINAI HOSPITAL OF BALTIMORE (O, 460 beds) 2401 West Belvedere Avenue, Baltimore, MD Zip 21215–5271; tel. 410/601–9000; Amy Perry, President
**Web address:** www.lifebridgehealth.org

| | | |
|---|---|---|
| Owned, leased, sponsored: | 3 hospitals | 1185 beds |
| Contract–managed: | 0 hospitals | 0 beds |
| Totals: | 3 hospitals | 1185 beds |

★**0191: LIFECARE MANAGEMENT SERVICES** (IO)
5340 Legacy Drive, Suite 150, Plano, TX Zip 75024–3131; tel. 469/241–2100; Phillip B. Douglas, Chairman and Chief Executive Officer
**(Independent Hospital System)**

**COLORADO:** COLORADO ACUTE LONG TERM HOSPITAL (O, 63 beds) 1690 North Meade Street, Denver, CO Zip 80204–1552; tel. 303/264–6900; Craig Bailey, MS, Chief Executive Officer and Administrator
**Web address:** www.lifecare–hospitals.com/hospital/colorado

**FLORIDA:** COMPLEX CARE HOSPITAL AT RIDGELAKE (O, 40 beds) 6150 Edgelake Drive, Sarasota, FL Zip 34240–8803; tel. 941/342–3000; Danny R. Edwards, Administrator
**Web address:** www.lifecare–hospitals.com/hospital.php?id=23

For explanation of codes following names, see page B2.
★ Indicates Type III membership in the American Hospital Association.

Section B

**IDAHO:** COMPLEX CARE HOSPITAL OF IDAHO (O, 35 beds) 2131 South Bonito Way, Meridian, ID Zip 83642–1659; tel. 877/801–2244; Colin O'Sullivan, Administrator
**Web address:** www.lifecare–hospitals.com

**LOUISIANA:** LIFECARE HOSPITALS OF SHREVEPORT (O, 119 beds) 9320 Linwood Avenue, Shreveport, LA Zip 71106–7003; tel. 318/688–8504; Keith Cox, Administrator
**Web address:** www.lifecare–hospitals.com

LIFECARE SPECIALTY HOSPITAL OF NORTH LOUISIANA (O, 70 beds) 1401 Ezell Street, Ruston, LA Zip 71270–7218; tel. 318/251–3126; Brent Martin, Chief Executive Officer
**Web address:** www.lifecare–hospitals.com/hospital.php?id=19

**NEVADA:** COMPLEX CARE HOSPITAL AT TENAYA (O, 70 beds) 2500 North Tenaya, Las Vegas, NV Zip 89128–0482; tel. 702/562–2021; Timothy C. Deaton, Administrator
**Web address:** www.lifecare–hospitals.com

TAHOE PACIFIC HOSPITALS (O, 60 beds) 201 West Liberty Street, Suite 310, Reno, NV Zip 89501–2017; tel. 775/355–5970; Colin O'Sullivan, Administrator
**Web address:** www.lifecare–hospitals.com

**NORTH CAROLINA:** LIFECARE HOSPITALS OF NORTH CAROLINA (O, 40 beds) 1051 Noell Lane, Rocky Mount, NC Zip 27804–1761; tel. 252/451–2300; Kevin S. Cooper, R.N., Chief Executive Officer and Administrator
**Web address:** www.lifecare–hospitals.com

**OHIO:** LIFECARE HOSPITAL OF DAYTON (O, 44 beds) 4000 Miamisburg–Centerville Road, Miamisburg, OH Zip 45342–7615; tel. 937/384–8300; Russell Dean, Chief Executive Officer
**Web address:** www.lifecare–hospitals.com

**PENNSYLVANIA:** LIFECARE HOSPITALS OF CHESTER COUNTY (O, 39 beds) 400 East Marshall Street, West Chester, PA Zip 19380–5412; tel. 484/826–0400; Rosalie Cox, Administrator
**Web address:** www.lifecare–hospitals.com

LIFECARE HOSPITALS OF MECHANICSBURG (O, 68 beds) 4950 Wilson Lane, Mechanicsburg, PA Zip 17055–4442; tel. 717/697–7706; Nicholas Mezza, Chief Executive Officer
**Web address:** www.lifecare–hospitals.com/hospital.php?id=20

LIFECARE HOSPITALS OF PITTSBURGH (O, 236 beds) 225 Penn Avenue, Pittsburgh, PA Zip 15221–2148; tel. 412/247–2424; Richard Pletz, Administrator
**Web address:** www.lifecare–hospitals.com

LIFECARE HOSPITALS OF PITTSBURGH – MONROEVILLE (O, 87 beds) 2380 McGinley Road, Monroeville, PA Zip 15146–4400; tel. 412/856–2400; Richard Pletz, Administrator
**Web address:** www.lifecare–hospitals.com/hospital.php?id=8

**TEXAS:** LIFECARE HOSPITALS OF DALLAS (O, 60 beds) 1950 Record Crossing Road, Dallas, TX Zip 75235–6223; tel. 214/640–9600; Jay Lindsey, Chief Executive Officer
**Web address:** www.lifecare–hospitals.com/hospital/dallas

LIFECARE HOSPITALS OF SAN ANTONIO (O, 62 beds) 8902 Floyd Curl Drive, San Antonio, TX Zip 78240–1681; tel. 210/690–7000; Randell G. Stokes, Chief Executive Officer
**Web address:** www.lifecare–hospitals.com

LIFECARE HOSPITALS OF SOUTH TEXAS–NORTH MCALLEN (O, 84 beds) 5101 North Jackson, McAllen, TX Zip 78504–6343; tel. 956/926–7000; Michelle Lozano, Chief Executive Officer
**Web address:** www.lifecare–hospitals.com/hospital/southtexas

**WISCONSIN:** LIFECARE HOSPITALS OF WISCONSIN (O, 34 beds) 2400 Golf Road, Pewaukee, WI Zip 53072–5590; tel. 262/524–2600; Jevne Conover, Administrator
**Web address:** www.lifecare–hospitals.com

| | | |
|---|---|---|
| Owned, leased, sponsored: | 17 hospitals | 1211 beds |
| Contract–managed: | 0 hospitals | 0 beds |
| Totals: | 17 hospitals | 1211 beds |

**★0180: LIFEPOINT HOSPITALS, INC.** (IO)
103 Powell Court, Suite 200, Brentwood, TN Zip 37027–5079; tel. 615/372–8500; William F. Carpenter, III, Chairman and Chief Executive Officer
**(Moderately Centralized Health System)**

**ALABAMA:** ANDALUSIA REGIONAL HOSPITAL (O, 88 beds) 849 South Three Notch Street, Andalusia, AL Zip 36420–5325, Mailing Address: P.O. Box 760, Zip 36420–1214; tel. 334/222–8466; Rebecca Brewer, FACHE, Interim Chief Executive Officer
**Web address:** www.andalusiaregionalhospital.com

LAKELAND COMMUNITY HOSPITAL (O, 56 beds) Highway 195 East, Haleyville, AL Zip 35565–9536, Mailing Address: P.O. Box 780, Zip 35565–0780; tel. 205/486–5213; Cindy Nichols, MSN, RN, Chief Executive Officer
**Web address:** www.lifepointhospitals. com/serving–communities/community/lakeland–community–hospital/

NORTHWEST MEDICAL CENTER (O, 76 beds) 1530 U.S. Highway 43, Winfield, AL Zip 35594–5056; tel. 205/487–7000; Scott Williams, Chief Executive Officer
**Web address:** www.northwestmedcenter.com

RUSSELLVILLE HOSPITAL (O, 92 beds) 15155 Highway 43, Russellville, AL Zip 35653–1975, Mailing Address: P.O. Box 1089, Zip 35653–1089; tel. 256/332–1611; Christine R. Stewart, FACHE, Chief Executive Officer
**Web address:** www.russellvillehospital.com

VAUGHAN REGIONAL MEDICAL CENTER (O, 149 beds) 1015 Medical Center Parkway, Selma, AL Zip 36701–6352; tel. 334/418–4100; David R. Sirk, Chief Executive Officer
**Web address:** www.vaughanregional.com

**ARIZONA:** HAVASU REGIONAL MEDICAL CENTER (O, 138 beds) 101 Civic Center Lane, Lake Havasu City, AZ Zip 86403–5683; tel. 928/855–8185; F. Dana Ellerbe, Chief Executive Officer
**Web address:** www.havasuregional.com

VALLEY VIEW MEDICAL CENTER (O, 66 beds) 5330 South Highway 95, Fort Mohave, AZ Zip 86426–9225; tel. 928/788–2273; Richard G. Carter, Chief Executive Officer
**Web address:** www.valleyviewmedicalcenter.net

**COLORADO:** COLORADO PLAINS MEDICAL CENTER (L, 50 beds) 1000 Lincoln Street, Fort Morgan, CO Zip 80701–3298; tel. 970/867–3391; Michael N. Patterson, Chief Executive Officer
**Web address:** www.coloradoplainsmedicalcenter.com

**FLORIDA:** PUTNAM COMMUNITY MEDICAL CENTER (O, 99 beds) Highway 20 West, Palatka, FL Zip 32177–8118, Mailing Address: P.O. Box 778, Zip 32178–0778; tel. 386/328–5711; Jerry Christine, Chief Executive Officer
**Web address:** www.pcmcfl.com

**GEORGIA:** ROCKDALE MEDICAL CENTER (O, 146 beds) 1412 Milstead Avenue N.E., Conyers, GA Zip 30012–3877; tel. 770/918–3000; Deborah Armstrong, Chief Executive Officer
**Web address:** www.rockdalemedicalcenter.org

**INDIANA:** SCOTT MEMORIAL HOSPITAL (O, 25 beds) 1415 North Gardner Street, Scottsburg, IN Zip 47170, Mailing Address: Box 430, Zip 47170–0430; tel. 812/752–3456; Jerry Dooley, Interim Chief Executive Officer
**Web address:** www.scottmemorial.com

**KANSAS:** WESTERN PLAINS MEDICAL COMPLEX (O, 89 beds) 3001 Avenue A, Dodge City, KS Zip 67801–6508, Mailing Address: P.O. Box 1478, Zip 67801–1478; tel. 620/225–8400; Michael R. Burroughs, FACHE, Chief Executive Officer
**Web address:** www.westernplainsmc.com

**KENTUCKY:** BLUEGRASS COMMUNITY HOSPITAL (O, 25 beds) 360 Amsden Avenue, Versailles, KY Zip 40383–1286; tel. 859/873–3111; Tommy Haggard, Chief Executive Officer
**Web address:** www.bluegrasscommunityhospital.com

BOURBON COMMUNITY HOSPITAL (O, 58 beds) 9 Linville Drive, Paris, KY Zip 40361–2196; tel. 859/987–3600; Joseph G. Koch, Chief Executive Officer
**Web address:** www.bourbonhospital.com

CLARK REGIONAL MEDICAL CENTER (O, 100 beds) 175 Hospital Drive, Winchester, KY Zip 40391–9591; tel. 859/745–3500; Cherie Sibley, R.N., Chief Executive Officer
**Web address:** www.clarkregional.org

---

For explanation of codes following names, see page B2.
★ Indicates Type III membership in the American Hospital Association.

GEORGETOWN COMMUNITY HOSPITAL (O, 58 beds) 1140 Lexington Road, Georgetown, KY Zip 40324–9362; tel. 502/868–1100; William Haugh, Administrator
**Web address:** www.georgetowncommunityhospital.com

JACKSON PURCHASE MEDICAL CENTER (O, 106 beds) 1099 Medical Center Circle, Mayfield, KY Zip 42066–1159; tel. 270/251–4100; David Anderson, Chief Executive Officer
**Web address:** www.jacksonpurchase.com

LAKE CUMBERLAND REGIONAL HOSPITAL (O, 295 beds) 305 Langdon Street, Somerset, KY Zip 42503–2750, Mailing Address: P.O. Box 620, Zip 42502–0620; tel. 606/679–7441; Mark T. Brenzel, Chief Executive Officer
**Web address:** www.lakecumberlandhospital.com

LOGAN MEMORIAL HOSPITAL (O, 53 beds) 1625 South Nashville Road, Russellville, KY Zip 42276–8834, Mailing Address: P.O. Box 10, Zip 42276–0010; tel. 270/726–4011; Jim Bills, Chief Executive Officer
**Web address:** www.loganmemorial.com

MEADOWVIEW REGIONAL MEDICAL CENTER (O, 101 beds) 989 Medical Park Drive, Maysville, KY Zip 41056–8750; tel. 606/759–5311; Robert Parker, Chief Executive Officer
**Web address:** www.meadowviewregional.com

SPRING VIEW HOSPITAL (O, 60 beds) 320 Loretto Road, Lebanon, KY Zip 40033–1300; tel. 270/692–3161; Ruth A. McDaniel, Chief Executive Officer
**Web address:** www.springviewhospital.com

**LOUISIANA:** MERCY REGIONAL MEDICAL CENTER (O, 70 beds) 800 East Main Street, Ville Platte, LA Zip 70586–4618, Mailing Address: P.O. Box 349, Zip 70586–0349; tel. 337/363–5684; Robert Alan Daugherty, Chief Executive Officer
**Web address:** www.mercyregionalmedicalcenter.com

MINDEN MEDICAL CENTER (O, 161 beds) 1 Medical Plaza, Minden, LA Zip 71055–3330, Mailing Address: P.O. Box 5003, Zip 71058–5003; tel. 318/377–2321; George E. French, III, FACHE, Chief Executive Officer
**Web address:** www.mindenmedicalcenter.com

RIVER PARISHES HOSPITAL (O, 106 beds) 500 Rue De Sante, La Place, LA Zip 70068–5418; tel. 985/652–7000; Robert Marshall, Chief Executive Officer
**Web address:** www.riverparisheshospital.com

TECHE REGIONAL MEDICAL CENTER (L, 165 beds) 1125 Marguerite Street, Morgan City, LA Zip 70380–1855, Mailing Address: P.O. Box 2308, Zip 70381–2308; tel. 985/384–2200; James P. Frazier, III, Chief Executive Officer
**Web address:** www.techeregional.com

**MISSISSIPPI:** BOLIVAR MEDICAL CENTER (L, 127 beds) 901 East Sunflower Road, Cleveland, MS Zip 38732–2833, Mailing Address: P.O. Box 1380, Zip 38732–1380; tel. 662/846–0061; Scott M. Smith, Chief Executive Officer
**Web address:** www.bolivarmedical.com

**NEVADA:** NORTHEASTERN NEVADA REGIONAL HOSPITAL (O, 50 beds) 2001 Errecart Boulevard, Elko, NV Zip 89801–8333; tel. 775/738–5151; Gene Miller, Chief Executive Officer
**Web address:** www.nnrhospital.com

**NEW MEXICO:** LOS ALAMOS MEDICAL CENTER (O, 38 beds) 3917 West Road, Los Alamos, NM Zip 87544–2293; tel. 505/661–9500; Feliciano Jiron, Chief Executive Officer
**Web address:** www.losalamosmedicalcenter.com

MEMORIAL MEDICAL CENTER (L, 224 beds) 2450 South Telshor Boulevard, Las Cruces, NM Zip 88011–5076; tel. 575/522–8641; Paul F. Herzog, Chief Executive Officer
**Web address:** www.mmclc.org

**TENNESSEE:** ATHENS REGIONAL MEDICAL CENTER (O, 63 beds) 1114 West Madison Avenue, Athens, TN Zip 37303–4150, Mailing Address: P.O. Box 250, Zip 37371–0250; tel. 423/745–1411; John R. Workman, Chief Executive Officer
**Web address:** www.athensrmc.com

CROCKETT HOSPITAL (O, 90 beds) 1607 South Locust Avenue, Lawrenceburg, TN Zip 38464–4011, Mailing Address: P.O. Box 847, Zip 38464–0847; tel. 931/762–6571; Jeff Noblin, FACHE, Chief Executive Officer
**Web address:** www.crocketthospital.com

HILLSIDE HOSPITAL (O, 50 beds) 1265 East College Street, Pulaski, TN Zip 38478–4541; tel. 931/363–7531; Jeff Jennings, FACHE, Chief Executive Officer
**Web address:** www.hillsidehospital.com

LIVINGSTON REGIONAL HOSPITAL (O, 82 beds) 315 Oak Street, Livingston, TN Zip 38570–1728, Mailing Address: P.O. Box 550, Zip 38570–0550; tel. 931/823–5611; Michael J. Meadows, Chief Executive Officer
**Web address:** www.livingstonregionalhospital.com

RIVERVIEW REGIONAL MEDICAL CENTER (O, 63 beds) 158 Hospital Drive, Carthage, TN Zip 37030–1096; tel. 615/735–1560; Rod Harkleroad, R.N., Administrator
**Web address:** www.myriverviewmedical.com/

SOUTHERN TENNESSEE MEDICAL CENTER (O, 188 beds) 185 Hospital Road, Winchester, TN Zip 37398–2404; tel. 931/967–8200; J. Phillip Young, FACHE, Chief Executive Officer
**Web address:** www.southerntennessee.com

SUMNER REGIONAL MEDICAL CENTER (O, 145 beds) 555 Hartsville Pike, Gallatin, TN Zip 37066–2400, Mailing Address: P.O. Box 1558, Zip 37066–1558; tel. 615/452–4210; Susan M. Peach, R.N., R.N., Chief Executive Officer
**Web address:** www.mysumnermedical.com

TROUSDALE MEDICAL CENTER (O, 25 beds) 500 Church Street, Hartsville, TN Zip 37074–1744; tel. 615/374–2221; William D. Mize, Interim Chief Executive Officer
**Web address:** www.mytrousdalemedical.com

WOODS MEMORIAL HOSPITAL (O, 140 beds) 886 Highway 411 North, Etowah, TN Zip 37331–1912; tel. 423/263–3600; John R. Workman, Chief Executive Officer
**Web address:** www.woodshospital.org

**TEXAS:** ENNIS REGIONAL MEDICAL CENTER (L, 58 beds) 2201 West Lampasas Street, Ennis, TX Zip 75119–5644; tel. 972/875–0900; Kevin Zachary, Chief Executive Officer
**Web address:** www.ennisregional.com

PALESTINE REGIONAL MEDICAL CENTER (O, 12 beds) 4000 South Loop 256, Palestine, TX Zip 75801–8467, Mailing Address: P.O. Box 4070, Zip 75802–4070; tel. 903/731–5100; Alan E. George, Chief Executive Officer
**Web address:** www.palestineregional.com

PALESTINE REGIONAL MEDICAL CENTER–EAST (O, 113 beds) 2900 South Loop 256, Palestine, TX Zip 75801–6958; tel. 903/731–1000; Alan E. George, Chief Executive Officer
**Web address:** www.palestineregional.com

PARKVIEW REGIONAL HOSPITAL (L, 58 beds) 600 South Bonham, Mexia, TX Zip 76667–3603; tel. 254/562–0408; Kevin Zachary, Chief Executive Officer
**Web address:** www.parkviewregional.com

**UTAH:** ASHLEY REGIONAL MEDICAL CENTER (O, 39 beds) 150 West 100 North, Vernal, UT Zip 84078–2036; tel. 435/789–3342; Stephen R. Selzer, Interim Chief Executive Officer
**Web address:** www.ashleyregional.com

CASTLEVIEW HOSPITAL (O, 49 beds) 300 North Hospital Drive, Price, UT Zip 84501–4200; tel. 435/637–4800; Mark Holyoak, Chief Executive Officer
**Web address:** www.castleviewhospital.net

**VIRGINIA:** CLINCH VALLEY MEDICAL CENTER (O, 111 beds) 6801 Governor G. C. Peery Highway, Richlands, VA Zip 24641–2194; tel. 276/596–6000; Peter Mulkey, Interim Chief Executive Officer
**Web address:** www.clinchvalleymedicalcenter.com

DANVILLE REGIONAL MEDICAL CENTER (O, 151 beds) 142 South Main Street, Danville, VA Zip 24541–2922; tel. 434/799–2100; Eric Deaton, Chief Executive Officer
**Web address:** www.danvilleregional.org

MEMORIAL HOSPITAL (O, 220 beds) 320 Hospital Drive, Martinsville, VA Zip 24112–1981, Mailing Address: P.O. Box 4788, Zip 24115–4788; tel. 276/666–7200; Grady W. Philips, III, Chief Executive Officer
**Web address:** www.martinsvillehospital.com

WYTHE COUNTY COMMUNITY HOSPITAL (L, 90 beds) 600 West Ridge Road, Wytheville, VA Zip 24382–1099; tel. 276/228–0200; Timothy A. Bess, Chief Executive Officer
**Web address:** www.wcch.org

Section B

For explanation of codes following names, see page B2.
★ Indicates Type III membership in the American Hospital Association.

**WEST VIRGINIA:** LOGAN REGIONAL MEDICAL CENTER (O, 129 beds) 20 Hospital Drive, Logan, WV Zip 25601–3452; tel. 304/831–1101; John E. Walker, FACHE, Chief Executive Officer
**Web address:** www.loganregionalmedicalcenter.com

RALEIGH GENERAL HOSPITAL (O, 229 beds) 1710 Harper Road, Beckley, WV Zip 25801–3397; tel. 304/256–4100; David B. Darden, Chief Executive Officer
**Web address:** www.raleighgeneral.com

**WYOMING:** LANDER REGIONAL HOSPITAL (O, 89 beds) 1320 Bishop Randall Drive, Lander, WY Zip 82520–3996; tel. 307/332–4420; Stephen M. Erixon, Chief Executive Officer
**Web address:** www.landerhospital.com

RIVERTON MEMORIAL HOSPITAL (O, 37 beds) 2100 West Sunset Drive, Riverton, WY Zip 82501–2274; tel. 307/856–4161; Stephen M. Erixon, Chief Executive Officer
**Web address:** www.riverton–hospital.com

| | | |
|---|---|---|
| Owned, leased, sponsored: | 52 hospitals | 5102 beds |
| Contract–managed: | 0 hospitals | 0 beds |
| **Totals:** | 52 hospitals | 5102 beds |

---

**0060:  LIFESPAN CORPORATION** (NP)
167 Point Street, Providence, RI Zip 02903–4771; tel. 401/444–3500; Timothy J. Babineau, M.D., President and Chief Executive Officer
**(Moderately Centralized Health System)**

**RHODE ISLAND:** EMMA PENDLETON BRADLEY HOSPITAL (O, 51 beds) 1011 Veterans Memorial Parkway, East Providence, RI Zip 02915–5099; tel. 401/432–1000; Daniel J. Wall, President and Chief Executive Officer
**Web address:** www.lifespan.org

MIRIAM HOSPITAL (O, 247 beds) 164 Summit Avenue, Providence, RI Zip 02906–2853; tel. 401/793–2500; Timothy J. Babineau, M.D., President and Chief Executive Officer
**Web address:** www.lifespan.org

NEWPORT HOSPITAL (O, 124 beds) 11 Friendship Street, Newport, RI Zip 02840–2299; tel. 401/846–6400; August B. Cordeiro, FACHE, President and Chief Executive Officer
**Web address:** www.newporthospital.org

RHODE ISLAND HOSPITAL (O, 645 beds) 593 Eddy Street, Providence, RI Zip 02903–4900; tel. 401/444–4000; Timothy J. Babineau, M.D., President and Chief Executive Officer
**Web address:** www.rhodeislandhospital.org/

| | | |
|---|---|---|
| Owned, leased, sponsored: | 4 hospitals | 1067 beds |
| Contract–managed: | 0 hospitals | 0 beds |
| **Totals:** | 4 hospitals | 1067 beds |

---

**2175:  LOMA LINDA UNIVERSITY ADVENTIST HEALTH SCIENCES CENTER** (NP)
11175 Campus Street, Loma Linda, CA Zip 92350–1700; tel. 909/558–7572; Richard H. Hart, M.D., President and Chief Executive Officer
**(Moderately Centralized Health System)**

**CALIFORNIA:** LOMA LINDA UNIVERSITY BEHAVIORAL MEDICINE CENTER (O, 89 beds) 1710 Barton Road, Redlands, CA Zip 92373–5304; tel. 909/558–9200; Jill Pollock, Administrator
**Web address:** www.llu.edu

LOMA LINDA UNIVERSITY MEDICAL CENTER (O, 825 beds) 11234 Anderson Street, Loma Linda, CA Zip 92354–2804, Mailing Address: P.O. Box 2000, Zip 92354–0200; tel. 909/558–4000; Ruthita J. Fike, Chief Executive Officer
**Web address:** www.llumc.edu

LOMA LINDA UNIVERSITY MEDICAL CENTER–MURRIETA (O, 106 beds) 28062 Baxter Road, Murrieta, CA Zip 92563–1401; tel. 951/290–4000; Richard L. Rawson, Chief Executive Officer
**Web address:** www.llumcmurrieta.org

| | | |
|---|---|---|
| Owned, leased, sponsored: | 3 hospitals | 1020 beds |
| Contract–managed: | 0 hospitals | 0 beds |
| **Totals:** | 3 hospitals | 1020 beds |

---

**5755:  LOS ANGELES COUNTY–DEPARTMENT OF HEALTH SERVICES** (NP)
313 North Figueroa Street, Room 912, Los Angeles, CA Zip 90012–2691; tel. 213/240–8101; Mitchell H. Katz, M.D., Director
**(Independent Hospital System)**

LAC–HARBOR–UNIVERSITY OF CALIFORNIA AT LOS ANGELES MEDICAL CENTER (O, 350 beds) 1000 West Carson Street, Torrance, CA Zip 90502–2004; tel. 310/222–2345; Delvecchio Finley, Chief Executive Officer
**Web address:** www.humc.edu

LAC–OLIVE VIEW–UCLA MEDICAL CENTER (O, 275 beds) 14445 Olive View Drive, Sylmar, CA Zip 91342–1437; tel. 818/364–1555; Carolyn F. Rhee, Chief Executive Officer
**Web address:** www.ladhs.org

LAC/UNIVERSITY OF SOUTHERN CALIFORNIA MEDICAL CENTER (O, 633 beds) 1200 North State Street, Los Angeles, CA Zip 90033–1029; tel. 323/226–2622; Christina Ghaly, M.D., Interim Chief Executive Officer
**Web address:** www.lacusc.org

RANCHO LOS AMIGOS NATIONAL REHABILITATION CENTER (O, 207 beds) 7601 East Imperial Highway, Downey, CA Zip 90242–3496; tel. 562/401–7022; Jorge Orozco, Chief Executive Officer
**Web address:** www.rancho.org

| | | |
|---|---|---|
| Owned, leased, sponsored: | 4 hospitals | 1465 beds |
| Contract–managed: | 0 hospitals | 0 beds |
| **Totals:** | 4 hospitals | 1465 beds |

---

**0047:  LOUISIANA STATE HOSPITALS** (NP)
628 North 4th Street, Baton Rouge, LA Zip 70802–5342, Mailing Address: P.O. Box 629, Zip 70821–0628; tel. 225/342–9500; Shelby Price, Chief Executive Officer
**(Independent Hospital System)**

**LOUISIANA:** CENTRAL LOUISIANA STATE HOSPITAL (O, 128 beds) 242 West Shamrock Avenue, Pineville, LA Zip 71360–6439, Mailing Address: P.O. Box 5031, Zip 71361–5031; tel. 318/484–6200; ,
**Web address:** www.dhh.la.gov/omh/inpatient–serv/clsh.htm

EASTERN LOUISIANA MENTAL HEALTH SYSTEM (O, 473 beds) 4502 Highway 951, Jackson, LA Zip 70748–5842, Mailing Address: P.O. Box 498, Zip 70748–0498; tel. 225/634–0100; Patricia Gonzales, Chief Executive Officer
**Web address:** www.wwwprd.doa.louisiana. gov/laservices/publicpages/ServiceDetail.cfm?service_id=2445

| | | |
|---|---|---|
| Owned, leased, sponsored: | 2 hospitals | 601 beds |
| Contract–managed: | 0 hospitals | 0 beds |
| **Totals:** | 2 hospitals | 601 beds |

---

**★0320:  LRGHEALTHCARE** (NP)
80 Highland Street, Laconia, NH Zip 03246–3298; tel. 603/524–3211; Thomas Clairmont, President
**(Independent Hospital System)**

**NEW HAMPSHIRE:** FRANKLIN REGIONAL HOSPITAL (O, 25 beds) 15 Aiken Avenue, Franklin, NH Zip 03235–1299; tel. 603/934–2060; Thomas Clairmont, President
**Web address:** www.lrgh.org

LAKES REGION GENERAL HOSPITAL (O, 88 beds) 80 Highland Street, Laconia, NH Zip 03246–3298; tel. 603/524–3211; Thomas Clairmont, President
**Web address:** www.lrgh.org

| | | |
|---|---|---|
| Owned, leased, sponsored: | 2 hospitals | 113 beds |
| Contract–managed: | 0 hospitals | 0 beds |
| **Totals:** | 2 hospitals | 113 beds |

---

**0715:  LSU HEALTH CARE SERVICES DIVISION** (NP)
5429 Airline Highway, Baton Rouge, LA Zip 70805, Mailing Address: P.O. Box 91308, Zip 70821–4400; tel. 225/354–7000; Michael Kaiser, M.D., Interim Chief Executive Officer
**(Moderately Centralized Health System)**

For explanation of codes following names, see page B2.
★ Indicates Type III membership in the American Hospital Association.

**LOUISIANA:** LALLIE KEMP MEDICAL CENTER (O, 25 beds) 52579 Highway 51 South, Independence, LA Zip 70443–2231; tel. 985/878–9421; Sherre Pack–Hookfin, Administrator
**Web address:** www.lsuhospitals.org

LEONARD J. CHABERT MEDICAL CENTER (O, 74 beds) 1978 Industrial Boulevard, Houma, LA Zip 70363–7094; tel. 985/873–2200; Rhonda G. Green, Administrator
**Web address:** www.lsuhospitals.org/hospitals/ljc/default.htm

LSU BOGALUSA MEDICAL CENTER (O, 74 beds) 433 Plaza Street, Bogalusa, LA Zip 70427–3793; tel. 985/730–6700; Kurt M. Scott, FACHE, Administrator
**Web address:** www.lsuhospitals.org

UNIVERSITY MEDICAL CENTER (O, 100 beds) 2390 West Congress Street, Lafayette, LA Zip 70506–4298, Mailing Address: P.O. Box 69300, Zip 70596–9300; tel. 337/261–6001; Jared Stark, Chief Executive Officer
**Web address:** www.lsuhospitals.org

| Owned, leased, sponsored: | 4 hospitals | 273 beds |
|---|---|---|
| Contract–managed: | 0 hospitals | 0 beds |
| Totals: | 4 hospitals | 273 beds |

**0614:  MAINEHEALTH** (NP)
110 Free Street, Portland, ME Zip 04101–3537; William L. Caron, Jr., President
**(Moderately Centralized Health System)**

**MAINE:** MAINE MEDICAL CENTER (O, 637 beds) 22 Bramhall Street, Portland, ME Zip 04102–3175; tel. 207/662–0111; Richard W. Petersen, President and Chief Executive Officer
**Web address:** www.mmc.org

MILES MEMORIAL HOSPITAL (O, 38 beds) 35 Miles Street, Damariscotta, ME Zip 04543–4047; tel. 207/563–1234; James W. Donovan, President and Chief Executive Officer
**Web address:** www.lchcare.org

PEN BAY MEDICAL CENTER (O, 165 beds) 6 Glen Cove Drive, Rockport, ME Zip 04856–4240; tel. 207/596–8000; Wade C. Johnson, MS, FACHE, Chief Executive Officer
**Web address:** www.pcnbayhealthcare.org

SOUTHERN MAINE MEDICAL CENTER (O, 110 beds) One Medical Center Drive, Biddeford, ME Zip 04005–9496, Mailing Address: P.O. Box 626, Zip 04005–0626; tel. 207/283–7000; Edward J. McGeachey, President and Chief Executive Officer
**Web address:** www.smmc.org

SPRING HARBOR HOSPITAL (O, 88 beds) 123 Andover Road, Westbrook, ME Zip 04092–3850; tel. 207/761–2200; Dennis P. King, Chief Executive Officer
**Web address:** www.springharbor.org

ST. ANDREWS HOSPITAL AND HEALTHCARE CENTER (O, 73 beds) 6 St. Andrews Lane, Boothbay Harbor, ME Zip 04538–1732, Mailing Address: P.O. Box 417, Zip 04538–0417; tel. 207/633–2121; James W. Donovan, President and Chief Executive Officer
**Web address:** www.lincolncountyhealthcare.org

STEPHENS MEMORIAL HOSPITAL (O, 25 beds) 181 Main Street, Norway, ME Zip 04268–5664; tel. 207/743–5933; Timothy A. Churchill, President
**Web address:** www.wmhcc.com

WALDO COUNTY GENERAL HOSPITAL (O, 25 beds) 118 Northport Avenue, Belfast, ME Zip 04915–6072, Mailing Address: P.O. Box 287, Zip 04915–0287; tel. 207/338–2500; Mark A. Biscone, Executive Director
**Web address:** www.wchi.com

| Owned, leased, sponsored: | 8 hospitals | 1161 beds |
|---|---|---|
| Contract–managed: | 0 hospitals | 0 beds |
| Totals: | 8 hospitals | 1161 beds |

**★1975:  MARSHALL HEALTH SYSTEM** (NP)
227 Britany Road, Guntersville, AL Zip 35976–5766; tel. 256/894–6615; Gary R. Gore, Chief Executive Officer
**(Independent Hospital System)**

**ALABAMA:** MARSHALL MEDICAL CENTER NORTH (O, 90 beds) 8000 Alabama Highway 69, Guntersville, AL Zip 35976; tel. 256/753–8000; Cheryl M. Hays, FACHE, Administrator
**Web address:** www.mmcenters.com

MARSHALL MEDICAL CENTER SOUTH (O, 114 beds) U.S. Highway 431 North, Boaz, AL Zip 35957–0999, Mailing Address: P.O. Box 758, Zip 35957–0758; tel. 256/593–8310; John D. Anderson, FACHE, Administrator
**Web address:** www.mmcenters.com//index.php/facilities/marshall_south

| Owned, leased, sponsored: | 2 hospitals | 204 beds |
|---|---|---|
| Contract–managed: | 0 hospitals | 0 beds |
| Totals: | 2 hospitals | 204 beds |

**★0523:  MARY WASHINGTON HEALTHCARE** (NP)
2300 Fall Hill Avenue, Suite 308, Fredericksburg, VA Zip 22401–3343; tel. 540/741–3100; Fred M. Rankin, III, President and Chief Executive Officer
**(Centralized Health System)**

**VIRGINIA:** MARY WASHINGTON HOSPITAL (O, 437 beds) 1001 Sam Perry Boulevard, Fredericksburg, VA Zip 22401–3354; tel. 540/741–1100; Fred M. Rankin, III, President and Chief Executive Officer
**Web address:** www.marywashingtonhealthcare. com/locations/mary–washington–hospital

STAFFORD HOSPITAL (O, 100 beds) 101 Hospital Center Boulevard, Stafford, VA Zip 22554–6200; tel. 540/741–9000; Fred M. Rankin, III, President and Chief Executive Officer
**Web address:** www.mwhc.com

| Owned, leased, sponsored: | 2 hospitals | 537 beds |
|---|---|---|
| Contract–managed: | 0 hospitals | 0 beds |
| Totals: | 2 hospitals | 537 beds |

**0013:  MASSACHUSETTS DEPARTMENT OF MENTAL HEALTH** (NP)
25 Staniford Street, Boston, MA Zip 02114–2575; tel. 617/626–8123; Marcia Fowler, Commissioner

**MASSACHUSETTS:** DR. J. CORRIGAN MENTAL HEALTH CENTER (O, 16 beds) 49 Hillside Street, Fall River, MA Zip 02720–5266; tel. 508/235–7200; Steve Figueiredo, Director

TAUNTON STATE HOSPITAL (O, 185 beds) 60 Hodges Avenue Extension, Taunton, MA Zip 02780–3034, Mailing Address: PO Box 4007, Zip 02780–0997; tel. 508/977–3000; Roberta H. Guez, Chief Operating Officer

WORCESTER RECOVERY CENTER AND HOSPITAL (O, 126 beds) 305 Belmont Street, Worcester, MA Zip 01604–1695; tel. 508/368–3300; Anthony Riccitelli, Chief Operating Officer

| Owned, leased, sponsored: | 3 hospitals | 327 beds |
|---|---|---|
| Contract–managed: | 0 hospitals | 0 beds |
| Totals: | 3 hospitals | 327 beds |

**0280:  MASSACHUSETTS DEPARTMENT OF PUBLIC HEALTH** (NP)
250 Washington Street, Boston, MA Zip 02108–4619; tel. 617/624–6000; Sandra Akers, Bureau Director, Public Health Hospitals
**(Independent Hospital System)**

LEMUEL SHATTUCK HOSPITAL (O, 260 beds) 170 Morton Street, Jamaica Plain, MA Zip 02130–3735; tel. 617/522–8110; Paul Romary, Chief Executive Officer
**Web address:** www.mass.gov/shattuckhospital

MASSACHUSETTS HOSPITAL SCHOOL (O, 93 beds) 3 Randolph Street, Canton, MA Zip 02021–2351; tel. 781/828–2440; Brian V. Devin, Chief Executive Officer
**Web address:** www.mhsf.us/

TEWKSBURY HOSPITAL (O, 381 beds) 365 East Street, Tewksbury, MA Zip 01876–1998; tel. 978/851–7321; Debra Tosti, Chief Executive Officer
**Web address:** www.mass.gov

Section B

WESTERN MASSACHUSETTS HOSPITAL (O, 70 beds) 91 East Mountain Road, Westfield, MA Zip 01085–1801; tel. 413/562–4131; Derrick Tallman, Chief Executive Officer
**Web address:** www.mass.
gov/eohhs/gov/departments/dph/programs/western–massachusetts–hospital.
html

| | | |
|---|---|---|
| Owned, leased, sponsored: | 4 hospitals | 804 beds |
| Contract–managed: | 0 hospitals | 0 beds |
| Totals: | 4 hospitals | 804 beds |

★**0882: MAURY REGIONAL HEALTH SYSTEM** (NP)
1224 Trotwood Avenue, Columbia, TN Zip 38401–4802;
tel. 931/381–1111; H. Alan Watson, FACHE, Chief Executive Officer

**TENNESSEE:** MARSHALL MEDICAL CENTER (O, 12 beds) 1080 North Ellington Parkway, Lewisburg, TN Zip 37091–2227, Mailing Address: P.O. Box 1609, Zip 37091–1609; tel. 931/359–6241; Phyllis Brown, Chief Executive Officer
**Web address:** www.mauryregional.com

MAURY REGIONAL HOSPITAL (O, 232 beds) 1224 Trotwood Avenue, Columbia, TN Zip 38401–4802; tel. 931/381–1111; H. Alan Watson, FACHE, Chief Executive Officer
**Web address:** www.mauryregional.com

WAYNE MEDICAL CENTER (L, 78 beds) 103 J. V. Mangubat Drive, Waynesboro, TN Zip 38485–2440, Mailing Address: P.O. Box 580, Zip 38485–0580; tel. 931/722–5411; Harley Smith, Chief Executive Officer
**Web address:** www.mauryregional.com

| | | |
|---|---|---|
| Owned, leased, sponsored: | 3 hospitals | 322 beds |
| Contract–managed: | 0 hospitals | 0 beds |
| Totals: | 3 hospitals | 322 beds |

★**1875: MAYO CLINIC HEALTH SYSTEM** (NP)
200 S.W. First Street, Rochester, MN Zip 55905–0002;
tel. 507/284–2511; John Noseworthy, M.D., President and Chief Executive Officer
**(Decentralized Health System)**

**ARIZONA:** MAYO CLINIC HOSPITAL (O, 268 beds) 5777 East Mayo Boulevard, Phoenix, AZ Zip 85054–4502; tel. 480/515–6296; Ann M. Meyers, Chief Executive Officer
**Web address:** www.mayoclinic.org/arizona/

**FLORIDA:** MAYO CLINIC JACKSONVILLE (O, 214 beds) 4500 San Pablo Road South, Jacksonville, FL Zip 32224–1865; tel. 904/953–2000; Hilary G. Mathews, MS, R.N., Administrator
**Web address:** www.mayoclinic.org

**GEORGIA:** MAYO CLINIC HEALTH SYSTEM IN WAYCROSS (O, 199 beds) 410 Darling Avenue, Waycross, GA Zip 31501–6357, Mailing Address: P.O. Box 139, Zip 31502–0139; tel. 912/283–3030; Robert M. Trimm, Chief Administrative Officer
**Web address:** www.satilla.org

**IOWA:** FLOYD COUNTY MEDICAL CENTER (C, 25 beds) 800 Eleventh Street, Charles City, IA Zip 50616–3499; tel. 641/228–6830; Bill D. Faust, Administrator
**Web address:** www.fcmc.us.com/

WINNESHIEK MEDICAL CENTER (C, 25 beds) 901 Montgomery Street, Decorah, IA Zip 52101–2325; tel. 563/382–2911; Gretchen M. Dahlen, FACHE, Chief Administrative Officer
**Web address:** www.winmedical.org

**MINNESOTA:** MAYO CLINIC – SAINT MARYS HOSPITAL (O, 797 beds) 1216 Second Street S.W., Rochester, MN Zip 55902–1970;
tel. 507/255–5123; Lynn Frederick, Administrator
**Web address:** www.mayoclinic.org

MAYO CLINIC HEALTH SYSTEM IN ALBERT LEA (O, 129 beds) 404 West Fountain Street, Albert Lea, MN Zip 56007–2473; tel. 507/373–2384; Mark Ciota, M.D., Chief Executive Officer
**Web address:** www.almedcenter.org

MAYO CLINIC HEALTH SYSTEM IN AUSTIN (O, 82 beds) 1000 First Drive N.W., Austin, MN Zip 55912–2904; tel. 507/433–7351; Mark Ciota, M.D., Chief Executive Officer
**Web address:** www.austinmedicalcenter.org

MAYO CLINIC HEALTH SYSTEM IN CANNON FALLS (O, 21 beds) 1116 West Mill Street, Cannon Falls, MN Zip 55009–1898; tel. 507/263–4221; Thomas J. Witt, M.D., President and Chief Executive Officer
**Web address:** www.mayoclinichealthsystem.org/locations/cannon–falls

MAYO CLINIC HEALTH SYSTEM IN FAIRMONT (O, 96 beds) 800 Medical Center Drive, Fairmont, MN Zip 56031–4575; tel. 507/238–8100; Robert Bartingale, Administrator
**Web address:** www.fairmontmedicalcenter.org

MAYO CLINIC HEALTH SYSTEM IN LAKE CITY (O, 108 beds) 500 West Grant Street, Lake City, MN Zip 55041–1143; tel. 651/345–3321; Susan M. Stiene, R.N., MS, Interim Chief Administrative Officer
**Web address:** www.lakecitymedicalcenter.org

MAYO CLINIC HEALTH SYSTEM IN MANKATO (O, 166 beds) 1025 Marsh Street, Mankato, MN Zip 56001–4752, Mailing Address: P.O. Box 8673, Zip 56002–8673; tel. 507/625–4031; Gregory Kutcher, M.D., President and Chief Executive Officer
**Web address:** www.isj–mhs.org

MAYO CLINIC HEALTH SYSTEM IN NEW PRAGUE (O, 25 beds) 301 Second Street N.E., New Prague, MN Zip 56071–1799; tel. 952/758–4431; Mary J. Klimp, FACHE, Chief Administrative Officer
**Web address:** www.mayoclinichealthsystem.org/locations/new–prague

MAYO CLINIC HEALTH SYSTEM IN RED WING (O, 134 beds) 701 Hewitt Boulevard, Red Wing, MN Zip 55066–2848, Mailing Address: P.O. Box 95, Zip 55066–0095; tel. 651/267–5000; Thomas J. Witt, M.D., President and Chief Executive Officer
**Web address:** www.mayoclinichealthsystem.org/locations/red–wing

MAYO CLINIC HEALTH SYSTEM IN SAINT JAMES (O, 13 beds) 1101 Moulton and Parsons Drive, Saint James, MN Zip 56081–5550; tel. 507/375–3261; Ryan J. Smith, Administrator
**Web address:** www.mayoclinichealthsystem.org/locations/st–james

MAYO CLINIC HEALTH SYSTEM IN SPRINGFIELD (O, 24 beds) 625 North Jackson Avenue, Springfield, MN Zip 56087–1714, Mailing Address: P.O. Box 146, Zip 56087–0146; tel. 507/723–6201; Scott D. Thoreson, FACHE, Administrator
**Web address:** www.smc–mhs.org

MAYO CLINIC HEALTH SYSTEM IN WASECA (O, 25 beds) 501 North State Street, Waseca, MN Zip 56093–2811; tel. 507/835–1210; Jeffrey Carlson, Administrator
**Web address:** www.mayoclinichealthsystem.org

ROCHESTER METHODIST HOSPITAL (O, 335 beds) 201 West Center Street, Rochester, MN Zip 55902–3084; tel. 507/266–7890; Lynn Frederick, Administrator
**Web address:** www.mayoclinic.org

**WISCONSIN:** MAYO CLINIC HEALTH SYSTEM – CHIPPEWA VALLEY IN BLOOMER (O, 55 beds) 1501 Thompson Street, Bloomer, WI Zip 54724–1299; tel. 715/568–2000; Edward A. Wittrock, Vice President Regional System
**Web address:** www.bloomermedicalcenter.org

MAYO CLINIC HEALTH SYSTEM – FRANCISCAN HEALTHCARE IN LA CROSSE (O, 155 beds) 700 West Avenue South, La Crosse, WI Zip 54601–4783; tel. 608/785–0940; Timothy J. Johnson, President and Chief Executive Officer
**Web address:** www.franciscanskemp.org

MAYO CLINIC HEALTH SYSTEM – FRANCISCAN HEALTHCARE IN SPARTA (O, 13 beds) 310 West Main Street, Sparta, WI Zip 54656–2171;
tel. 608/269–2132; Kimberly Hawthorne, Administrator
**Web address:** www.mayohealthsystem.com

MAYO CLINIC HEALTH SYSTEM – NORTHLAND IN BARRON (O, 38 beds) 1222 Woodland Avenue, Barron, WI Zip 54812–1798; tel. 715/537–3186; Maurita Sullivan, Administrator
**Web address:** www.luthermidelfortnorthland.org

MAYO CLINIC HEALTH SYSTEM – OAKRIDGE IN OSSEO (O, 39 beds) 13025 Eighth Street, Osseo, WI Zip 54758–7634, Mailing Address: P.O. Box 70, Zip 54758–0070; tel. 715/597–3121; Dean Eide, Vice President
**Web address:** www.mayoclinichealthsystem.org/locations/osseo

MAYO CLINIC HEALTH SYSTEM – RED CEDAR IN MENOMONIE (O, 25 beds) 2321 Stout Road, Menomonie, WI Zip 54751–2397; tel. 715/235–5531; Steven Lindberg, Chief Administrative Officer
**Web address:** www.rcmc–mhs.org

For explanation of codes following names, see page B2.
★ Indicates Type III membership in the American Hospital Association.

MAYO CLINIC HEALTH SYSTEM IN EAU CLAIRE (O, 204 beds) 1221 Whipple Street, Eau Claire, WI Zip 54703–5270, Mailing Address: P.O. Box 5, Zip 54702–0005; tel. 715/838–3311; Randall L. Linton, M.D., President and Chief Executive Officer
**Web address:** www.mhs.mayo.edu

| | | |
|---|---|---|
| **Owned, leased, sponsored:** | 23 hospitals | 3165 beds |
| **Contract–managed:** | 2 hospitals | 50 beds |
| **Totals:** | 25 hospitals | 3215 beds |

---

★**0252:  MCLAREN HEALTH CARE CORPORATION** (NP)
G3235 Beecher Road, Suite B., Flint, MI Zip 48532–3650; tel. 810/342–1100; Philip A. Incarnati, President and Chief Executive Officer
**(Moderately Centralized Health System)**

**MICHIGAN:** MCLAREN BAY REGION (O, 338 beds) 1900 Columbus Avenue, Bay City, MI Zip 48708–6831; tel. 989/894–3000; Alice M. Gerard, President and Chief Executive Officer
**Web address:** www.bayregional.org

MCLAREN BAY SPECIAL CARE (O, 26 beds) 3250 East Midland Road, Suite 1, Bay City, MI Zip 48706–2835; tel. 989/667–6802; Cheryl A. Burzynski, President
**Web address:** www.bayspecialcare.org

MCLAREN CENTRAL MICHIGAN (O, 78 beds) 1221 South Drive, Mount Pleasant, MI Zip 48858–3257; tel. 989/772–6700; William P. Lawrence, President and Chief Executive Officer
**Web address:** www.cmch.org

MCLAREN FLINT (O, 350 beds) 401 South Ballenger Highway, Flint, MI Zip 48532–3685; tel. 810/342–2000; Donald C. Kooy, President and Chief Executive Officer
**Web address:** www.mclarenregional.org

MCLAREN GREATER LANSING (O, 322 beds) 401 West Greenlawn Avenue, Lansing, MI Zip 48910–2819; tel. 517/975–6000; Rick Wright, President and Chief Executive Officer
**Web address:** www.irmc.org

MCLAREN LAPEER REGION (O, 157 beds) 1375 North Main Street, Lapeer, MI Zip 48446–1350; tel. 810/667–5500; Barton Buxton, Ed.D., President and Chief Executive Officer
**Web address:** www.lapeerregional.org

MCLAREN MACOMB (O, 288 beds) 1000 Harrington Boulevard, Mount Clemens, MI Zip 48043–2992; tel. 586/493–8000; Mark S. O'Halla, President and Chief Executive Officer
**Web address:** www.mcrmc.org

MCLAREN NORTHERN MICHIGAN (O, 178 beds) 416 Connable Avenue, Petoskey, MI Zip 49770–2297; tel. 231/487–4000; Reezie DeVet, R.N., Ph.D., President and Chief Executive Officer
**Web address:** www.northernhealth.org

MCLAREN OAKLAND (O, 285 beds) 50 North Perry Street, Pontiac, MI Zip 48342–2253; tel. 248/338–5000; Clarence Sevillian, President and Chief Executive Officer
**Web address:** www.pohmedical.org

| | | |
|---|---|---|
| **Owned, leased, sponsored:** | 9 hospitals | 2022 beds |
| **Contract–managed:** | 0 hospitals | 0 beds |
| **Totals:** | 9 hospitals | 2022 beds |

---

**0874:  MCLEOD HEALTH** (NP)
555 East Cheves Street, Florence, SC Zip 29506–2617, Mailing Address: P.O. Box 100551, Zip 29502–0551; tel. 843/777–2000; Robert L. Colones, President and Chief Executive Officer

**SOUTH CAROLINA:** MCLEOD LORIS HEALTHCARE (O, 243 beds) 3655 Mitchell Street, Loris, SC Zip 29569–2827; tel. 843/716–7000; Edward D. Tinsley, III, Chief Executive Officer
**Web address:** www.mcleodhealth.org

MCLEOD MEDICAL CENTER DILLON (O, 63 beds) 301 East Jackson Street, Dillon, SC Zip 29536–2509, Mailing Address: P.O. Box 1327, Zip 29536–1327; tel. 843/774–4111; Deborah Locklair, FACHE, Administrator
**Web address:** www.mcleodhealth.org

MCLEOD REGIONAL MEDICAL CENTER (O, 538 beds) 555 East Cheves Street, Florence, SC Zip 29506–2617, Mailing Address: P.O. Box 100551, Zip 29502–0551; tel. 843/777–2000; Robert L. Colones, President and Chief Executive Officer
**Web address:** www.mcleodhealth.org

| | | |
|---|---|---|
| **Owned, leased, sponsored:** | 3 hospitals | 844 beds |
| **Contract–managed:** | 0 hospitals | 0 beds |
| **Totals:** | 3 hospitals | 844 beds |

---

**0391:  MEDCENTRAL HEALTH SYSTEM** (NP)
335 Glessner Avenue, Mansfield, OH Zip 44903–2269; tel. 419/526–8000; Joe Chamberlain, Acting Chief Executive Officer
**(Moderately Centralized Health System)**

**OHIO:** MEDCENTRAL – MANSFIELD HOSPITAL (O, 238 beds) 335 Glessner Avenue, Mansfield, OH Zip 44903–2265; tel. 419/526–8000; Joe Chamberlain, Acting Chief Executive Officer
**Web address:** www.medcentral.org

MEDCENTRAL – SHELBY HOSPITAL (O, 25 beds) 199 West Main Street, Shelby, OH Zip 44875–1490; tel. 419/342–5015; Joe Chamberlain, Acting Chief Executive Officer
**Web address:** www.medcentral.org/body.cfm?id=153

| | | |
|---|---|---|
| **Owned, leased, sponsored:** | 2 hospitals | 263 beds |
| **Contract–managed:** | 0 hospitals | 0 beds |
| **Totals:** | 2 hospitals | 263 beds |

---

★**0154:  MEDSTAR HEALTH** (NP)
5565 Sterrett Place, 5th Floor, Columbia, MD Zip 21044–2665; tel. 410/772–6500; Kenneth A. Samet, President and Chief Executive Officer
**(Decentralized Health System)**

**DISTRICT OF COLUMBIA:** MEDSTAR GEORGETOWN UNIVERSITY HOSPITAL (O, 396 beds) 3800 Reservoir Road N.W., Washington, DC Zip 20007–2197; tel. 202/444–2000; Richard L. Goldberg, M.D., President
**Web address:** www.georgetownuniversityhospital.org

MEDSTAR NATIONAL REHABILITATION HOSPITAL (O, 137 beds) 102 Irving Street N.W., Washington, DC Zip 20010–2949; tel. 202/877–1000; John D. Rockwood, President
**Web address:** www.medstarnrh.org

MEDSTAR WASHINGTON HOSPITAL CENTER (O, 777 beds) 110 Irving Street N.W., Washington, DC Zip 20010–3017; tel. 202/877–7000; John Sullivan, President
**Web address:** www.whcenter.org

**MARYLAND:** MEDSTAR FRANKLIN SQUARE MEDICAL CENTER (O, 377 beds) 9000 Franklin Square Drive, Baltimore, MD Zip 21237–3901; tel. 443/777–7000; Samuel E. Moskowitz, President
**Web address:** www.medstarfranklin.org

MEDSTAR GOOD SAMARITAN HOSPITAL (O, 308 beds) 5601 Loch Raven Boulevard, Baltimore, MD Zip 21239–2995; tel. 443/444–8000; Jeffrey A. Matton, President
**Web address:** www.goodsam-md.org

MEDSTAR HARBOR HOSPITAL (O, 192 beds) 3001 South Hanover Street, Baltimore, MD Zip 21225–1290; tel. 410/350–3200; Dennis W. Pullin, Chief Executive Officer
**Web address:** www.harborhospital.org

MEDSTAR MONTGOMERY MEDICAL CENTER (O, 158 beds) 18101 Prince Philip Drive, Olney, MD Zip 20832–1512; tel. 301/774–8882; Peter W. Monge, President
**Web address:** www.montgomerygeneral.com

MEDSTAR SOUTHERN MARYLAND HOSPITAL CENTER (O, 262 beds) 7503 Surratts Road, Clinton, MD Zip 20735–3358; tel. 301/868–8000; Michael J. Chiaramonte, Chief Executive Officer
**Web address:** www.smhchealth.org

MEDSTAR ST. MARY'S HOSPITAL (O, 90 beds) 25500 Point Lookout Road, Leonardtown, MD Zip 20650–2015, Mailing Address: P.O. Box 527, Zip 20650–0527; tel. 301/475–6001; Christine R. Wray, President
**Web address:** www.medstarstmarys.org

---

For explanation of codes following names, see page B2.
★ Indicates Type III membership in the American Hospital Association.

Section B

MEDSTAR UNION MEMORIAL HOSPITAL (O, 238 beds) 201 East University Parkway, Baltimore, MD Zip 21218–2895; tel. 410/554–2000; Bradley Chambers, President
**Web address:** www.unionmemorial.org

| | | |
|---|---|---|
| Owned, leased, sponsored: | 10 hospitals | 2935 beds |
| Contract–managed: | 0 hospitals | 0 beds |
| Totals: | 10 hospitals | 2935 beds |

★**0323:** **MEDWEST HEALTH SYSTEM** (NP)
68 Hospital Road, Sylva, NC Zip 28779–2722; tel. 828/586–7000; Steve Heatherly, President
**(Independent Hospital System)**

**NORTH CAROLINA:** MEDWEST – HARRIS (O, 86 beds) 68 Hospital Road, Sylva, NC Zip 28779–2722; tel. 828/586–7000; Steve Heatherly, Chief Executive Officer
**Web address:** www.westcare.org

MEDWEST – HAYWOOD (O, 146 beds) 262 Leroy George Drive, Clyde, NC Zip 28721–7430; tel. 828/456–7311; Janie Sinacore–Jaberg, R.N., MS, FACHE, Chief Executive Officer
**Web address:** www.haymed.org

MEDWEST – SWAIN (O, 25 beds) 45 Plateau Street, Bryson City, NC Zip 28713–4200; tel. 828/488–2155; Steve Heatherly, Chief Executive Officer
**Web address:** www.westcare.org

| | | |
|---|---|---|
| Owned, leased, sponsored: | 3 hospitals | 257 beds |
| Contract–managed: | 0 hospitals | 0 beds |
| Totals: | 3 hospitals | 257 beds |

★**0086:** **MEMORIAL HEALTH SYSTEM** (NP)
701 North First Street, Springfield, IL Zip 62781–0001; tel. 217/788–3000; Edgar J. Curtis, President and Chief Executive Officer
**(Moderately Centralized Health System)**

**ILLINOIS:** ABRAHAM LINCOLN MEMORIAL HOSPITAL (O, 25 beds) 200 Stahlhut Drive, Lincoln, IL Zip 62656–5066; tel. 217/732–2161; Dolan Dalpoas, President and Chief Executive Officer
**Web address:** www.almh.org

MEMORIAL MEDICAL CENTER (O, 473 beds) 701 North First Street, Springfield, IL Zip 62781–0001; tel. 217/788–3000; Edgar J. Curtis, President and Chief Executive Officer
**Web address:** www.memorialmedical.com

TAYLORVILLE MEMORIAL HOSPITAL (O, 45 beds) 201 East Pleasant Street, Taylorville, IL Zip 62568–1597; tel. 217/824–3331; Daniel J. Raab, President and Chief Executive Officer
**Web address:** www.taylorvillememorial.org

| | | |
|---|---|---|
| Owned, leased, sponsored: | 3 hospitals | 543 beds |
| Contract–managed: | 0 hospitals | 0 beds |
| Totals: | 3 hospitals | 543 beds |

**0176:** **MEMORIAL HEALTH SYSTEM OF EAST TEXAS** (NP)
1201 Frank Avenue, Lufkin, TX Zip 75904–3357; tel. 936/634–8111; Gary N. Looper, President and Chief Executive Officer
**(Moderately Centralized Health System)**

**TEXAS:** MEMORIAL MEDICAL CENTER – LIVINGSTON (O, 66 beds) 1717 Highway 59 Bypass, Livingston, TX Zip 77351–1257, Mailing Address: P.O. Box 1257, Zip 77351–0022; tel. 936/329–8700; Earl Denning, Interim Administrator
**Web address:** www.memorialhealth.org

MEMORIAL MEDICAL CENTER – LUFKIN (O, 217 beds) 1201 West Frank Avenue, Lufkin, TX Zip 75904–3357, Mailing Address: P.O. Box 1447, Zip 75902–1447; tel. 936/634–8111; Gary N. Looper, Chief Executive Officer
**Web address:** www.memorialhealth.us/centers/lufkin

MEMORIAL MEDICAL CENTER – SAN AUGUSTINE (O, 18 beds) 511 East Hospital Street, San Augustine, TX Zip 75972–2121, Mailing Address: P.O. Box 658, Zip 75972–0658; tel. 936/275–3446; Darlene Williams, R.N., Administrator
**Web address:** www.memorialhealth.org

MEMORIAL SPECIALTY HOSPITAL (O, 26 beds) 1201 West Frank Avenue, Lufkin, TX Zip 75904–3357; tel. 936/639–7975; Leslie Leach, Administrator
**Web address:** www.memorialhealth.org

| | | |
|---|---|---|
| Owned, leased, sponsored: | 4 hospitals | 327 beds |
| Contract–managed: | 0 hospitals | 0 beds |
| Totals: | 4 hospitals | 327 beds |

★**0083:** **MEMORIAL HEALTHCARE SYSTEM** (NP)
3501 Johnson Street, Hollywood, FL Zip 33021–5421; tel. 954/265–5805; Frank V. Sacco, FACHE, President and Chief Executive Officer
**(Centralized Health System)**

**FLORIDA:** MEMORIAL HOSPITAL MIRAMAR (O, 178 beds) 1901 S.W. 172nd Avenue, Miramar, FL Zip 33029–5592; tel. 954/538–5000; Leah A. Carpenter, Administrator and Chief Executive Officer
**Web address:** www.mhs.net

MEMORIAL HOSPITAL PEMBROKE (L, 149 beds) 7800 Sheridan Street, Pembroke Pines, FL Zip 33024–2536; tel. 954/883–8482; Keith W. Gallagher, FACHE, Administrator and Chief Executive Officer
**Web address:** www.memorialpembroke.com/

MEMORIAL HOSPITAL WEST (O, 384 beds) 703 North Flamingo Road, Pembroke Pines, FL Zip 33028–1014; tel. 954/436–5000; C. Kennon Hetlage, FACHE, Administrator and Chief Executive Officer
**Web address:** www.mhs.net

MEMORIAL REGIONAL HOSPITAL (O, 757 beds) 3501 Johnson Street, Hollywood, FL Zip 33021–5421; tel. 954/987–2000; Zeff Ross, FACHE, Senior Vice President and Chief Executive Officer
**Web address:** www.mhs.net

MEMORIAL REGIONAL HOSPITAL SOUTH (O, 280 beds) 3600 Washington Street, Hollywood, FL Zip 33021–8216; tel. 954/966–4500; Douglas Zaren, FACHE, Administrator
**Web address:** www.memorialregionalsouth.com

| | | |
|---|---|---|
| Owned, leased, sponsored: | 5 hospitals | 1748 beds |
| Contract–managed: | 0 hospitals | 0 beds |
| Totals: | 5 hospitals | 1748 beds |

★**2645:** **MEMORIAL HERMANN HEALTHCARE SYSTEM** (NP)
929 Gessner, Suite 2700, Houston, TX Zip 77024–2593; tel. 713/242–2700; Daniel J. Wolterman, President and Chief Executive Officer
**(Centralized Health System)**

**TEXAS:** MEMORIAL HERMANN – TEXAS MEDICAL CENTER (O, 897 beds) 6411 Fannin Street, Houston, TX Zip 77030–1501; tel. 713/704–4000; Craig Cordola, Chief Executive Officer
**Web address:** www.mhhs.org

MEMORIAL HERMANN KATY HOSPITAL (O, 142 beds) 23900 Katy Freeway, Katy, TX Zip 77494–1323; tel. 281/644–7000; Brian S. Barbe, Chief Executive Officer
**Web address:** www.memorialhermann.org/locations/katy/

MEMORIAL HERMANN MEMORIAL CITY MEDICAL CENTER (L, 383 beds) 921 Gessner Road, Houston, TX Zip 77024–2501; tel. 713/242–3000; Keith N. Alexander, Chief Executive Officer
**Web address:** www.memorialhermann.org

MEMORIAL HERMANN NORTHEAST (L, 227 beds) 18951 North Memorial Drive, Humble, TX Zip 77338–4297; tel. 281/540–7700; Louis G. Smith, Jr., Chief Executive Officer
**Web address:** www.memorialhermann.org

MEMORIAL HERMANN NORTHWEST HOSPITAL (O, 1180 beds) 1635 North Loop West, Houston, TX Zip 77008–1532; tel. 713/867–3380; Gary Kerr, Chief Executive Officer
**Web address:** www.mhbh.org

For explanation of codes following names, see page B2.
★ Indicates Type III membership in the American Hospital Association.

MEMORIAL HERMANN REHABILITATION HOSPITAL – KATY (O, 35 beds) 21720 Kingsland Boulevard, Katy, TX Zip 77450–2550; tel. 281/579–5555; Noelle Lopez, Executive Director
**Web address:** www.memorialhermann.com

MEMORIAL HERMANN SUGAR LAND HOSPITAL (O, 77 beds) 17500 West Grand Parkway South, Sugar Land, TX Zip 77479–2562; tel. 281/725–5000; Gregory Haralson, Chief Executive Officer
**Web address:** www.memorialhermann.org

TIRR MEMORIAL HERMANN (O, 119 beds) 1333 Moursund Street, Houston, TX Zip 77030–3405; tel. 713/799–5000; Carl E. Josehart, Chief Executive Officer
**Web address:** www.memorialhermann.org/locations/tirr.html

| | | |
|---|---|---|
| Owned, leased, sponsored: | 8 hospitals | 3060 beds |
| Contract–managed: | 0 hospitals | 0 beds |
| Totals: | 8 hospitals | 3060 beds |

---

**0084:  MEMORIALCARE** (NP)
17360 Brookhurst Street, Fountain Valley, CA Zip 92708–3720, Mailing Address: P.O. Box 1428, Long Beach, Zip 90801–1428; tel. 714/377–2900; Barry S. Arbuckle, Ph.D., President and Chief Executive Officer
**(Centralized Health System)**

**CALIFORNIA:** COMMUNITY HOSPITAL OF LONG BEACH (O, 148 beds) 1720 Termino Avenue, Long Beach, CA Zip 90804–2180; tel. 562/498–1000; Diana Hendel, PharmD, Chief Executive Officer
**Web address:** www.chlb.org

LONG BEACH MEMORIAL MEDICAL CENTER (O, 420 beds) 2801 Atlantic Avenue, Long Beach, CA Zip 90806–1701, Mailing Address: P.O. Box 1428, Zip 90801–1428; tel. 562/933–2000; Diana Hendel, PharmD, Chief Executive Officer
**Web address:** www.memorialcare.org/LongBeach

MILLER CHILDREN'S HOSPITAL (O, 383 beds) 2801 Atlantic Avenue, Long Beach, CA Zip 90806–1701; tel. 562/933–5437; Diana Hendel, PharmD, Chief Executive Officer
**Web address:** www.memorialcare.org

ORANGE COAST MEMORIAL MEDICAL CENTER (O, 218 beds) 9920 Talbert Avenue, Fountain Valley, CA Zip 92708–5153; tel. 714/378–7000; Marcia Manker, Chief Executive Officer
**Web address:** www.memorialcare.org

SADDLEBACK MEMORIAL MEDICAL CENTER (O, 313 beds) 24451 Health Center Drive, Laguna Hills, CA Zip 92653–3689; tel. 949/837–4500; Steve Geidt, Chief Executive Officer
**Web address:** www.memorialcare.org

| | | |
|---|---|---|
| Owned, leased, sponsored: | 5 hospitals | 1482 beds |
| Contract–managed: | 0 hospitals | 0 beds |
| Totals: | 5 hospitals | 1482 beds |

---

**★5185:  MERCY HEALTH** (CC)
14528 South Outer 40, Suite 100, Chesterfield, MO Zip 63017–5743; tel. 314/579–6100; Lynn Britton, President and Chief Executive Officer
**(Decentralized Health System)**

**ARKANSAS:** MERCY HOSPITAL BERRYVILLE (O, 25 beds) 214 Carter Street, Berryville, AR Zip 72616–4303; tel. 870/423–3355; Kristy Estrem, FACHE, President
**Web address:** www.mercy.net/berryvillear

MERCY HOSPITAL FORT SMITH (O, 383 beds) 7301 Rogers Avenue, Fort Smith, AR Zip 72903–4189, Mailing Address: P.O. Box 17000, Zip 72917–7000; tel. 479/314–6000; Ryan Gehrig, President
**Web address:** www.stedwardmercy.com

MERCY HOSPITAL HOT SPRINGS (O, 282 beds) 300 Werner Street, Hot Springs National Park, AR Zip 71913–6406, Mailing Address: P.O. Box 29001, Zip 71903–9001; tel. 501/622–1000; Kim Day, Interim President
**Web address:** www.saintjosephs.com

MERCY HOSPITAL OZARK (O, 25 beds) 801 West River Street, Ozark, AR Zip 72949–3000; tel. 479/667–4138; Michael K. Smith, R.N., Regional Administrator
**Web address:** www.mercy.net/northwestarar/practice/mercy–hospital–ozark

MERCY HOSPITAL PARIS (O, 16 beds) 500 East Academy, Paris, AR Zip 72855–4099; tel. 479/963–6101; Sharon Sorey, R.N., Regional Administrator
**Web address:** www.stedwardmercy.com

MERCY HOSPITAL ROGERS (O, 141 beds) 2710 Rife Medical Lane, Rogers, AR Zip 72758–1452; tel. 479/338–8000; Scott Street, President and Chief Executive Officer
**Web address:** www.mercyhealthnwa.smhs.com

MERCY HOSPITAL WALDRON (O, 24 beds) 1341 West 6th Street, Waldron, AR Zip 72958–7642; tel. 479/637–4135; Dorothy O'Bar, R.N., Regional Administrator
**Web address:** www.stedwardmercy.com

**KANSAS:** MERCY HOSPITAL COLUMBUS (O, 18 beds) 220 North Pennsylvania Avenue, Columbus, KS Zip 66725–1110; tel. 620/429–2545; Cindy Neely, Administrator
**Web address:** www.mercy.net/northwestarar/practice/mercy–maude–norton–hospital–columbus

MERCY HOSPITAL FORT SCOTT (O, 61 beds) 401 Woodland Hills Boulevard, Fort Scott, KS Zip 66701–8797; tel. 620/223–2200; Reta K. Baker, President
**Web address:** www.mercykansas.com

MERCY HOSPITAL INDEPENDENCE (O, 40 beds) 800 West Myrtle Street, Independence, KS Zip 67301–3240, Mailing Address: P.O. Box 388, Zip 67301–0388; tel. 620/331–2200; Robert Y. Copeland, Jr., FACHE, Interim President
**Web address:** www.mercykansas.com

**MISSOURI:** MERCY HOSPITAL AURORA (O, 25 beds) 500 Porter Street, Aurora, MO Zip 65605–2365; tel. 417/678–2122; Douglas M. Stroemel, President
**Web address:** www.stjohns.com/aboutus/aurora.aspx

MERCY HOSPITAL CASSVILLE (O, 18 beds) 94 Main Street, Cassville, MO Zip 65625–1610; tel. 417/847–6000; Douglas M. Stroemel, President
**Web address:** www.mercy.net/northwestarar/practice/mercy–hospital–cassville

MERCY HOSPITAL JEFFERSON (O, 215 beds) Highway 61 South, Crystal City, MO Zip 63019, Mailing Address: P.O. Box 350, Zip 63019–0350; tel. 636/933–1000; Eric Ammons, President
**Web address:** www.jhsmo.org

MERCY HOSPITAL JOPLIN (O, 180 beds) 2817 South St. John's Boulevard, Joplin, MO Zip 64804–1626; tel. 417/781–2727; Gary W. Pulsipher, President and Chief Executive Officer
**Web address:** www.stj.com

MERCY HOSPITAL LEBANON (O, 62 beds) 100 Hospital Drive, Lebanon, MO Zip 65536–9210; tel. 417/533–6100; Michael J. Gillen, FACHE, President
**Web address:** www.stjohnslebanon.com

MERCY HOSPITAL SPRINGFIELD (O, 678 beds) 1235 East Cherokee Street, Springfield, MO Zip 65804–2263; tel. 417/820–2000; Robert Steele, M.D., President
**Web address:** www.stjohns.com

MERCY HOSPITAL ST. LOUIS (O, 979 beds) 615 South New Ballas Road, Saint Louis, MO Zip 63141–8277; tel. 314/569–6000; Jeffrey A. Johnston, President
**Web address:** www.mercy.net/stlouismo

MERCY HOSPITAL WASHINGTON (O, 187 beds) 901 East Fifth Street, Washington, MO Zip 63090–3127; tel. 636/239–8000; Terri L. McLain, FACHE, President
**Web address:** www.mercy.net

MERCY MCCUNE–BROOKS HOSPITAL (L, 25 beds) 3125 Drive Russell Smith Way, Carthage, MO Zip 64836–7402; tel. 417/358–8121; Robert Y. Copeland, Jr., FACHE, Chief Executive Officer
**Web address:** www.mccune–brooks.org

MERCY REHABILITATION HOSPITAL (O, 90 beds) 14561 North Outer Forty Road, Chesterfield, MO Zip 63017; tel. 314/881–4000; Donna M. Flannery, Chief Executive Officer
**Web address:** www.stjohnsmercyrehab.com

MERCY ST. FRANCIS HOSPITAL (O, 20 beds) 100 West Highway 60, Mountain View, MO Zip 65548–7125; tel. 417/934–7000; Jonathan O. Wade, President and Chief Executive Officer
**Web address:** www.stjohns.com/aboutus/stfrancis.aspx

---

For explanation of codes following names, see page B2.
★ Indicates Type III membership in the American Hospital Association.

Section B

**OKLAHOMA:** ARBUCKLE MEMORIAL HOSPITAL (C, 13 beds) 2011 West Broadway Street, Sulphur, OK Zip 73086–4221; tel. 580/622–2161; Darin Farrell, Chief Executive Officer
**Web address:** www.arbucklehospital.com/

KINGFISHER REGIONAL HOSPITAL (C, 25 beds) 1000 Kingfisher Regional Hospital Drive, Kingfisher, OK Zip 73750–3528, Mailing Address: P.O. Box 59, Zip 73750–0059; tel. 405/375–3141; Bobby Stitt, R.N., Interim Chief Executive Officer
**Web address:** www.kingfisherhospital.com

MERCY HEALTH LOVE COUNTY (C, 25 beds) 300 Wanda Street, Marietta, OK Zip 73448–1200; tel. 580/276–3347; Richard Barker, Administrator
**Web address:** www.mercyhealthlovecounty.com

MERCY HOSPITAL ARDMORE (O, 190 beds) 1011 14th Avenue N.W., Ardmore, OK Zip 73401–1828; tel. 580/223–5400; Daryle Voss, FACHE, President
**Web address:** www.mercyok.net

MERCY HOSPITAL EL RENO (L, 48 beds) 2115 Parkview Drive, El Reno, OK Zip 73036–2199, Mailing Address: P.O. Box 129, Zip 73036–0129; tel. 405/262–2640; Doug Danker, Administrator
**Web address:** www.mercyok.net

MERCY HOSPITAL HEALDTON (L, 22 beds) 918 South 8th Street, Healdton, OK Zip 73438–0928, Mailing Address: P.O. Box 928, Zip 73438–0928; tel. 580/229–0701; Jeremy A. Jones, Administrator
**Web address:** www.mercyok.com

MERCY HOSPITAL LOGAN COUNTY (O, 25 beds) 200 South Academy Road, Guthrie, OK Zip 73044–8727, Mailing Address: P.O. Box 1017, Zip 73044–1017; tel. 405/282–6700; Joshua Tucker, Administrator
**Web address:** www.loganmedicalcenter.com

MERCY HOSPITAL OKLAHOMA CITY (O, 369 beds) 4300 West Memorial Road, Oklahoma City, OK Zip 73120–8362; tel. 405/755–1515; Jim Gebhart, Jr., FACHE, President
**Web address:** www.mercyok.net

MERCY HOSPITAL TISHOMINGO (L, 25 beds) 1000 South Byrd Street, Tishomingo, OK Zip 73460–3299; tel. 580/371–2327; Gary Sharum, Administrator
**Web address:** www.mercy.net/

MERCY HOSPITAL WATONGA (L, 17 beds) 500 North Clarence Nash Boulevard, Watonga, OK Zip 73772–2845, Mailing Address: P.O. Box 370, Zip 73772–0370; tel. 580/623–7211; Bobby Stitt, R.N., Administrator
**Web address:** www.mercy.net/watongaok/practice/mercy–hospital–watonga

SAYRE MEMORIAL HOSPITAL (C, 25 beds) 911 Hospital Drive, Sayre, OK Zip 73662–1206; tel. 580/928–5541; John Lampert, Chief Executive Officer
**Web address:** www.sayrehospital.org

VALLEY VIEW REGIONAL HOSPITAL (C, 131 beds) 430 North Monta Vista, Ada, OK Zip 74820–4610; tel. 580/332–2323; W. Kent Rogers, Chief Executive Officer
**Web address:** www.valleyviewregional.com

| | | |
|---|---|---|
| Owned, leased, sponsored: | 28 hospitals | 4190 beds |
| Contract–managed: | 5 hospitals | 219 beds |
| Totals: | 33 hospitals | 4409 beds |

**0649: MERCY HEALTH SYSTEM** (NP)
1000 Mineral Point Avenue, Janesville, WI Zip 53548–2940, Mailing Address: P.O. Box 5003, Zip 53547–5003; tel. 608/756–6000; Javon R. Bea, President and Chief Executive Officer
**(Centralized Physician/Insurance Health System)**

**ILLINOIS:** MERCY HARVARD HOSPITAL (O, 35 beds) 901 Grant Street, Harvard, IL Zip 60033–1898, Mailing Address: P.O. Box 850, Zip 60033–0850; tel. 815/943–5431; Jennifer Hallatt, Chief Operating Officer
**Web address:** www.mercyhealthsystem.org

**WISCONSIN:** MERCY HOSPITAL AND TRAUMA CENTER (O, 148 beds) 1000 Mineral Point Avenue, Janesville, WI Zip 53548–2982, Mailing Address: P.O. Box 5003, Zip 53547–5003; tel. 608/756–6000; Javon R. Bea, President and Chief Executive Officer
**Web address:** www.mercyhealthsystem.org

MERCY WALWORTH HOSPITAL AND MEDICAL CENTER (O, 15 beds) N2950 State Road 67, Lake Geneva, WI Zip 53147–2655; tel. 262/245–0535; Jennifer Hallatt, Chief Operating Officer
**Web address:** www.mercyhealthsystem.org

| | | |
|---|---|---|
| Owned, leased, sponsored: | 3 hospitals | 198 beds |
| Contract–managed: | 0 hospitals | 0 beds |
| Totals: | 3 hospitals | 198 beds |

**★0257: MERIDIAN HEALTH** (NP)
1350 Campus Parkway, Wall Township, NJ Zip 07753–6821; tel. 732/751–7510; John K. Lloyd, President and Chief Executive Officer
**(Centralized Health System)**

**NEW JERSEY:** BAYSHORE COMMUNITY HOSPITAL (O, 147 beds) 727 North Beers Street, Holmdel, NJ Zip 07733–1598; tel. 732/739–5900; Timothy J. Hogan, FACHE, Regional President
**Web address:** www.bchs.com

JERSEY SHORE UNIVERSITY MEDICAL CENTER (O, 546 beds) 1945 Route 33, Neptune, NJ Zip 07754–0397; tel. 732/775–5500; Steven G. Littleson, FACHE, President
**Web address:** www.meridianhealth.com

OCEAN MEDICAL CENTER (O, 265 beds) 425 Jack Martin Boulevard, Brick Township, NJ Zip 08724–7732; tel. 732/840–2200; Dean Q. Lin, FACHE, President
**Web address:** www.meridianhealth.com

RIVERVIEW MEDICAL CENTER (O, 270 beds) 1 Riverview Plaza, Red Bank, NJ Zip 07701–1864; tel. 732/741–2700; Timothy J. Hogan, FACHE, Regional President
**Web address:** www.riverviewmedicalcenter.com

SOUTHERN OCEAN MEDICAL CENTER (O, 132 beds) 1140 Route 72 West, Manahawkin, NJ Zip 08050–2499; tel. 609/978–8900; Joseph P. Coyle, President
**Web address:** www.soch.com

| | | |
|---|---|---|
| Owned, leased, sponsored: | 5 hospitals | 1360 beds |
| Contract–managed: | 0 hospitals | 0 beds |
| Totals: | 5 hospitals | 1360 beds |

**★2735: METHODIST HEALTH SYSTEM** (NP)
1441 North Beckley Avenue, Dallas, TX Zip 75203–1201, Mailing Address: P.O. Box 655999, Zip 75265–5999; tel. 214/947–8181; Stephen L. Mansfield, Ph.D., FACHE, President and Chief Executive Officer
**(Independent Hospital System)**

**TEXAS:** METHODIST CHARLTON MEDICAL CENTER (O, 265 beds) 3500 West Wheatland Road, Dallas, TX Zip 75237–3460, Mailing Address: P.O. Box 225357, Zip 75222–5357; tel. 214/947–7777; Jonathan S. Davis, FACHE, President
**Web address:** www.methodisthealthsystem.org/charlton

METHODIST DALLAS MEDICAL CENTER (O, 409 beds) 1441 North Beckley Avenue, Dallas, TX Zip 75203–1201, Mailing Address: P.O. Box 655999, Zip 75265–5999; tel. 214/947–8181; Laura Irvine, President
**Web address:** www.methodisthealthsystem.org/Dallas

METHODIST HOSPITAL FOR SURGERY (O, 32 beds) 17101 North Dallas Parkway, Addison, TX Zip 75001–7103; tel. 469/248–3900; Chris Shoup, President
**Web address:** www.methodisthospitalforsurgery.com/

METHODIST MANSFIELD MEDICAL CENTER (O, 161 beds) 2700 East Broad Street, Mansfield, TX Zip 76063–5899; tel. 682/622–2000; John E. Phillips, FACHE, President
**Web address:** www.methodisthealthsystem.org/mansfield

METHODIST MCKINNEY HOSPITAL (O, 23 beds) 8000 West Eldorado Parkway, McKinney, TX Zip 75070–5940; tel. 972/569–2700; Joseph Minissale, President
**Web address:** www.methodistmckinneyhospital.com

METHODIST REHABILITATION HOSPITAL (O, 40 beds) 3020 West Wheatland Road, Dallas, TX Zip 75237–3537; tel. 972/708–8604; Lyndell H. Weaks, Chief Executive Officer
**Web address:** www.methodist–rehab.com

METHODIST RICHARDSON MEDICAL CENTER (O, 160 beds) 401 West Campbell Road, Richardson, TX Zip 75080–3416; tel. 972/498–4000; E. Kenneth Hutchenrider, President
**Web address:** www.richardsonregional.com

For explanation of codes following names, see page B2.
★ Indicates Type III membership in the American Hospital Association.

Section B

| Owned, leased, sponsored: | 7 hospitals | 1090 beds |
|---|---|---|
| Contract–managed: | 0 hospitals | 0 beds |
| Totals: | 7 hospitals | 1090 beds |

**9345: METHODIST LE BONHEUR HEALTHCARE** (CO)
1211 Union Avenue, Suite 700, Memphis, TN Zip 38104–6600;
tel. 901/516–0543; Gary S. Shorb, President and Chief Executive
Officer
**(Centralized Health System)**

**TENNESSEE:** METHODIST EXTENDED CARE HOSPITAL (O, 36 beds) 225
South Claybrook Street, Memphis, TN Zip 38104–3537;
tel. 901/516–2152; Sandra Bailey–DeLeeuw, Chief Executive Officer
**Web address:** www.methodisthealth.org

METHODIST HEALTHCARE MEMPHIS HOSPITALS (O, 1324 beds) 1265 Union
Avenue, Memphis, TN Zip 38104–3415; tel. 901/516–7000; James R.
Carter, Jr., Interim Chief Executive Officer
**Web address:** www.methodisthealth.org

METHODIST HEALTHCARE–FAYETTE HOSPITAL (O, 10 beds) 214 Lakeview
Drive, Somerville, TN Zip 38068–9737; tel. 901/516–4000; William A.
Kenley, Chief Executive Officer
**Web address:** www.methodisthealth.org

| Owned, leased, sponsored: | 3 hospitals | 1370 beds |
|---|---|---|
| Contract–managed: | 0 hospitals | 0 beds |
| Totals: | 3 hospitals | 1370 beds |

**0208: MID ATLANTIC HEALTH MANAGEMENT, INC.** (IO)
1220 Butterworth Court, Stevensville, MD Zip 21666–2504;
tel. 410/643–3393; Harold A. McBee, Jr., President
**(Independent Hospital System)**

**WEST VIRGINIA:** POTOMAC VALLEY HOSPITAL (O, 25 beds) 100 Pin Oak
Lane, Keyser, WV Zip 26726–5908; tel. 304/597–3500; Linda K.
Shroyer, Administrator
**Web address:** www.potomacvalleyhospital.com

**WISCONSIN:** INDIANHEAD MEDICAL CENTER (O, 25 beds) 113 Fourth
Avenue, Shell Lake, WI Zip 54871–4457, Mailing Address: P.O. Box 300,
Zip 54871–0300; tel. 715/468–7833; Paul Naglosky, Administrator
**Web address:** www.indianheadmedicalcenter.com

| Owned, leased, sponsored: | 2 hospitals | 50 beds |
|---|---|---|
| Contract–managed: | 0 hospitals | 0 beds |
| Totals: | 2 hospitals | 50 beds |

**★0001: MIDMICHIGAN HEALTH** (NP)
4000 Wellness Drive, Midland, MI Zip 48670–0001;
tel. 989/839–3000; Diane Postler–Slattery, Ph.D., President and
Chief Executive Officer
**(Centralized Health System)**

**MICHIGAN:** MIDMICHIGAN MEDICAL CENTER–CLARE (O, 49 beds) 703 North
McEwan Street, Clare, MI Zip 48617–1440; tel. 989/802–5000;
Raymond Stover, President and Chief Executive Officer
**Web address:** www.midmichigan.org

MIDMICHIGAN MEDICAL CENTER–GLADWIN (O, 25 beds) 515 Quarter Street,
Gladwin, MI Zip 48624–1959; tel. 989/426–9286; Raymond Stover,
President and Chief Executive Officer
**Web address:** www.midmichigan.org

MIDMICHIGAN MEDICAL CENTER–GRATIOT (O, 100 beds) 300 East Warwick
Drive, Alma, MI Zip 48801–1014; tel. 989/463–1101; Mark A. Santamaria,
President
**Web address:** www.midmichigan.org/gratiot

MIDMICHIGAN MEDICAL CENTER–MIDLAND (O, 265 beds) 4000 Wellness
Drive, Midland, MI Zip 48670–2000; tel. 989/839–3000; Gregory H. Rogers,
President
**Web address:** www.midmichigan.org

| Owned, leased, sponsored: | 4 hospitals | 439 beds |
|---|---|---|
| Contract–managed: | 0 hospitals | 0 beds |
| Totals: | 4 hospitals | 439 beds |

**0368: MINNESOTA DEPARTMENT OF HUMAN SERVICES** (NP)
540 Cedar Street, Saint Paul, MN Zip 55101–2208, Mailing Address:
P.O. Box 64998, Zip 55164–0998; tel. 651/431–3212; Anne Barry,
Deputy Commissioner
**(Independent Hospital System)**

**MINNESOTA:** ANOKA–METROPOLITAN REGIONAL TREATMENT CENTER (O,
112 beds) 3301 Seventh Avenue, Anoka, MN Zip 55303–4516;
tel. 763/712–4000; Nancy Webster–Smith, Administrator
**Web address:** www.health.state.mn.us

COMMUNITY BEHAVIORAL HEALTH HOSPITAL – ALEXANDRIA (O, 16 beds)
1610 8th Avenue East, Alexandria, MN Zip 56308–2472;
tel. 320/335–6201; Pamela R. Bajari, R.N., Interim Administrator
**Web address:** www.health.state.mn.us

COMMUNITY BEHAVIORAL HEALTH HOSPITAL – ANNANDALE (O, 16 beds)
400 Annandale Boulevard, Annandale, MN Zip 55302–3141;
tel. 651/259–3850; Denise Barger, R.N., Interim Administrator
**Web address:** www.health.state.mn.us

COMMUNITY BEHAVIORAL HEALTH HOSPITAL – BAXTER (O, 16 beds) 14241
Grand Oaks Drive, Baxter, MN Zip 56425–8749; tel. 218/316–3101; Richard
G. Slieter, Jr., Administrator

COMMUNITY BEHAVIORAL HEALTH HOSPITAL – BEMIDJI (O, 16 beds) 800
Bemidji Avenue North, Bemidji, MN Zip 56601–3054; tel. 218/308–2400;
Richard G. Slieter, Jr., Administrator

COMMUNITY BEHAVIORAL HEALTH HOSPITAL – FERGUS FALLS (O, 16 beds)
1801 West Alcott Avenue, Fergus Falls, MN Zip 56537–2661, Mailing
Address: P.O. Box 478, Zip 56538–0478; tel. 218/332–5001; Derrick A.
Jones, Administrator

COMMUNITY BEHAVIORAL HEALTH HOSPITAL – ROCHESTER (O, 16 beds)
251 Wood Lake Drive S.E., Rochester, MN Zip 55904–5530;
tel. 507/206–2561; Lisa Costello, R.N., Interim Administrator
**Web address:** www.health.state.mn.us

COMMUNITY BEHAVIORAL HEALTH HOSPITAL – ST. PETER (O, 16 beds)
2000 Klein Street, Saint Peter, MN Zip 56082–5800; tel. 507/933–5001;
Marlene Schnichels, R.N., Interim Administrator
**Web address:** www.health.state.mn.us

| Owned, leased, sponsored: | 8 hospitals | 224 beds |
|---|---|---|
| Contract–managed: | 0 hospitals | 0 beds |
| Totals: | 8 hospitals | 224 beds |

**★0143: MISSION HEALTH SYSTEM** (CO)
509 Biltmore Avenue, Asheville, NC Zip 28801–4601;
tel. 828/213–1111; Ronald A. Paulus, M.D., President and Chief
Executive Officer
**(Independent Hospital System)**

**NORTH CAROLINA:** ANGEL MEDICAL CENTER (C, 25 beds) 120 Riverview
Street, Franklin, NC Zip 28734–2612, Mailing Address: P.O. Box 1209,
Zip 28744–0569; tel. 828/524–8411; James B. Bross, President and
Chief Executive Officer
**Web address:** www.angelmed.org

ASHEVILLE SPECIALTY HOSPITAL (O, 31 beds) 428 Biltmore Avenue, 4th
Floor, Asheville, NC Zip 28801–4502; tel. 828/213–5400; Robert C.
Desotelle, President and Chief Executive Officer
**Web address:** www.missionhospitals.org/acute–care

BLUE RIDGE REGIONAL HOSPITAL (O, 42 beds) 125 Hospital Drive, Spruce
Pine, NC Zip 28777–3035, Mailing Address: P.O. Drawer 9,
Zip 28777–0009; tel. 828/765–4201; Oscar K. Weinmeister, III, FACHE,
President and Chief Executive Officer
**Web address:** www.spchospital.org

MCDOWELL HOSPITAL (O, 49 beds) 430 Rankin Drive, Marion, NC
Zip 28752–6568, Mailing Address: P.O. Box 730, Zip 28752–0730;
tel. 828/659–5000; Lynn Ingram Boggs, Chief Executive Officer
**Web address:** www.mcdhospital.org

For explanation of codes following names, see page B2.
★ Indicates Type III membership in the American Hospital Association.

Section B

MISSION HOSPITAL (O, 744 beds) 509 Biltmore Avenue, Asheville, NC Zip 28801–4690; tel. 828/213–1111; Ronald A. Paulus, M.D., President and Chief Executive Officer
**Web address:** www.missionhospitals.org

TRANSYLVANIA REGIONAL HOSPITAL (C, 52 beds) 260 Hospital Drive, Brevard, NC Zip 28712–3378; tel. 828/884–9111; Robert J. Bednarek, President and Chief Executive Officer
**Web address:** www.trhospital.org

| | | |
|---|---|---|
| Owned, leased, sponsored: | 4 hospitals | 866 beds |
| Contract–managed: | 2 hospitals | 77 beds |
| Totals: | 6 hospitals | 943 beds |

★**0336: MISSISSIPPI BAPTIST HEALTH SYSTEM** (NP)
1225 North State Street, Jackson, MS Zip 39202–2064; tel. 601/968–1000; Mark F. Slyter, FACHE, President and Chief Executive Officer
**(Moderately Centralized Health System)**

**MISSISSIPPI:** BAPTIST MEDICAL CENTER LEAKE (O, 69 beds) 310 Ellis Street, Carthage, MS Zip 39051–3809, Mailing Address: P.O. Box 909, Zip 39051–0909; tel. 601/267–1100; C. Gerald Cotton, Interim Chief Executive Officer
**Web address:** www.mbhs.com/locations/baptist–medical–center–leake/

MISSISSIPPI BAPTIST MEDICAL CENTER (O, 638 beds) 1225 North State Street, Jackson, MS Zip 39202–2064; tel. 601/968–1000; Kerry R. Tirman, JD, FACHE, President
**Web address:** www.mbhs.org

MISSISSIPPI HOSPITAL FOR RESTORATIVE CARE (O, 25 beds) 1225 North State Street, Jackson, MS Zip 39202–2097, Mailing Address: P.O. Box 23695, Zip 39225–3695; tel. 601/968–1000; Bobbie K. Ware, R.N., FACHE, Chief Executive Officer and Chief Nursing Officer
**Web address:** www.mbhs.org

| | | |
|---|---|---|
| Owned, leased, sponsored: | 3 hospitals | 732 beds |
| Contract–managed: | 0 hospitals | 0 beds |
| Totals: | 3 hospitals | 732 beds |

**2475: MISSISSIPPI COUNTY HOSPITAL SYSTEM** (NP)
1520 North Division Street, Blytheville, AR Zip 72315–1448, Mailing Address: P.O. Box 108, Zip 72316–0108; tel. 870/838–7300; Ralph E. Beaty, Chief Executive Officer
**(Independent Hospital System)**

**ARKANSAS:** GREAT RIVER MEDICAL CENTER (O, 73 beds) 1520 North Division Street, Blytheville, AR Zip 72315–1448, Mailing Address: P.O. Box 108, Zip 72316–0108; tel. 870/838–7300; Ralph E. Beaty, Chief Executive Officer

SOUTH MISSISSIPPI COUNTY REGIONAL MEDICAL CENTER (O, 25 beds) 611 West Lee Avenue, Osceola, AR Zip 72370–3001, Mailing Address: P.O. Box 607, Zip 72370–0607; tel. 870/563–7000; Ralph E. Beaty, Chief Executive Officer
**Web address:** www.mchealthsystem.com

| | | |
|---|---|---|
| Owned, leased, sponsored: | 2 hospitals | 98 beds |
| Contract–managed: | 0 hospitals | 0 beds |
| Totals: | 2 hospitals | 98 beds |

**0017: MISSISSIPPI STATE DEPARTMENT OF MENTAL HEALTH** (NP)
1101 Robert East Lee Building, 239 North Lamar Street, Jackson, MS Zip 39201–1101; tel. 601/359–1288; Edwin C. LeGrand, III, Executive Director
**(Independent Hospital System)**

**MISSISSIPPI:** EAST MISSISSIPPI STATE HOSPITAL (O, 251 beds) 4555 Highland Park Drive, Meridian, MS Zip 39307–5498, Mailing Address: Box 4128, West Station, Zip 39304–4128; tel. 601/482–6186; Charles Carlisle, Director
**Web address:** www.emsh.state.ms.us

MISSISSIPPI STATE HOSPITAL (O, 794 beds) 3550 Highway 468 West, Whitfield, MS Zip 39193–5529, Mailing Address: P.O. Box 157–A, Zip 39193–0157; tel. 601/351–8000; James G. Chastain, FACHE, Director
**Web address:** www.msh.state.ms.us

NORTH MISSISSIPPI STATE HOSPITAL (O, 50 beds) 1937 Briar Ridge Road, Tupelo, MS Zip 38804–5963; tel. 662/690–4200; Paul A. Callens, Ph.D., Director
**Web address:** www.nmsh.state.ms.us

SOUTH MISSISSIPPI STATE HOSPITAL (O, 50 beds) 823 Highway 589, Purvis, MS Zip 39475–4194; tel. 601/794–0100; Clint Ashley, Director
**Web address:** www.smsh.state.ms.us

| | | |
|---|---|---|
| Owned, leased, sponsored: | 4 hospitals | 1145 beds |
| Contract–managed: | 0 hospitals | 0 beds |
| Totals: | 4 hospitals | 1145 beds |

**1335: MORTON PLANT MEASE HEALTH CARE** (NP)
300 Pinellas Street, Clearwater, FL Zip 33756–3804, Mailing Address: P.O. Box 210, Zip 33757–0210; tel. 727/462–7000; Glenn D. Waters, FACHE, President

**FLORIDA:** MEASE COUNTRYSIDE HOSPITAL (O, 300 beds) 3231 McMullen–Booth Road, Safety Harbor, FL Zip 34695–6607, Mailing Address: P.O. Box 1098, Zip 34695–1098; tel. 727/725–6222; Glenn D. Waters, FACHE, President
**Web address:** www.mpmhealth.com

MEASE DUNEDIN HOSPITAL (O, 124 beds) 601 Main Street, Dunedin, FL Zip 34698–5891, Mailing Address: P.O. Box 760, Zip 34697–0760; tel. 727/733–1111; Glenn D. Waters, FACHE, President and Chief Executive Officer
**Web address:** www.mpmhealth.com

MORTON PLANT HOSPITAL (O, 666 beds) 300 Pinellas Street, Clearwater, FL Zip 33756–3804, Mailing Address: P.O. Box 210, Zip 33757–0210; tel. 727/462–7000; Glenn D. Waters, FACHE, President
**Web address:** www.mortonplant.com

MORTON PLANT NORTH BAY HOSPITAL (O, 226 beds) 6600 Madison Street, New Port Richey, FL Zip 34652–1900; tel. 727/842–8468; Glenn D. Waters, FACHE, President
**Web address:** www.mpmhealth.com

| | | |
|---|---|---|
| Owned, leased, sponsored: | 4 hospitals | 1316 beds |
| Contract–managed: | 0 hospitals | 0 beds |
| Totals: | 4 hospitals | 1316 beds |

**0167: MOUNTAIN STATES HEALTH ALLIANCE** (NP)
400 North State of Franklin Road, Johnson City, TN Zip 37604–6035; tel. 423/431–1040; Dennis Vonderfecht, President and Chief Executive Officer
**(Centralized Health System)**

**TENNESSEE:** FRANKLIN WOODS COMMUNITY HOSPITAL (O, 80 beds) 300 MedTech Parkway, Johnson City, TN Zip 37604–2277; tel. 423/302–1000; Tony Benton, Chief Executive Officer
**Web address:** www.msha.com

INDIAN PATH MEDICAL CENTER (O, 189 beds) 2000 Brookside Drive, Kingsport, TN Zip 37660–4627; tel. 423/857–7000; Monty E. McLaurin, President and Chief Executive Officer
**Web address:** www.msha.com

JOHNSON CITY MEDICAL CENTER (O, 514 beds) 400 North State of Franklin Road, Johnson City, TN Zip 37604–6094; tel. 423/431–6111; David E. Nicely, Chief Executive Officer
**Web address:** www.msha.com

JOHNSON COUNTY COMMUNITY HOSPITAL (O, 2 beds) 1901 South Shady Street, Mountain City, TN Zip 37683–2271; tel. 423/727–1100; Lisa Heaton, Assistant Vice President/Administrator and Chief Nursing Officer
**Web address:** www.msha.com

SYCAMORE SHOALS HOSPITAL (O, 79 beds) 1501 West Elk Avenue, Elizabethton, TN Zip 37643–2874; tel. 423/542–1300; Dwayne Taylor, Chief Executive Officer
**Web address:** www.msha.com

For explanation of codes following names, see page B2.
★ Indicates Type III membership in the American Hospital Association.

**VIRGINIA:** DICKENSON COMMUNITY HOSPITAL (O, 2 beds) 312 Hospital Drive, Clintwood, VA Zip 24228, Mailing Address: P.O. Box 1440, Zip 24228–1440; tel. 276/926–0300; Mark T. Leonard, Chief Executive Officer
**Web address:** www.msha.com/dch

JOHNSTON MEMORIAL HOSPITAL (O, 116 beds) 16000 Johnston Memorial Drive, Abingdon, VA Zip 24211–7659; tel. 276/676–7000; Sean S. McMurray, FACHE, Vice President and Chief Executive Officer
**Web address:** www.jmh.org

NORTON COMMUNITY HOSPITAL (O, 50 beds) 100 15th Street N.W., Norton, VA Zip 24273–1616; tel. 276/679–9600; Mark T. Leonard, Chief Executive Officer
**Web address:** www.msha.com/nch

RUSSELL COUNTY MEDICAL CENTER (O, 78 beds) 58 Carroll Street, Lebanon, VA Zip 24266, Mailing Address: P.O. Box 3600, Zip 24266–0200; tel. 276/883–8000; Stephen K. Givens, Assistant Vice President and Administrator
**Web address:** www.msha.com/rcmc

SMYTH COUNTY COMMUNITY HOSPITAL (O, 153 beds) 245 Medical Park Drive, Marion, VA Zip 24354, Mailing Address: P.O. Box 880, Zip 24354–0880; tel. 276/378–1000; Lindy P. White, President and Chief Executive Officer
**Web address:** www.msha.com/scch

| | | |
|---|---|---|
| Owned, leased, sponsored: | 10 hospitals | 1263 beds |
| Contract–managed: | 0 hospitals | 0 beds |
| Totals: | 10 hospitals | 1263 beds |

**6555: MULTICARE HEALTH SYSTEM** (NP)
315 Martin Luther King Jr. Way, Tacoma, WA Zip 98405–4234, Mailing Address: P.O. Box 5299, Zip 98415–0299; tel. 253/403–1000; Diane E. Cecchettini, R.N., President and Chief Executive Officer
**(Moderately Centralized Health System)**

**WASHINGTON:** MULTICARE AUBURN MEDICAL CENTER (O, 120 beds) 202 North Division, Plaza One, Auburn, WA Zip 98001–4908; tel. 253/833–7711; David Nicewonger, Chief Operating Officer
**Web address:** www.auburnregional.com

MULTICARE GOOD SAMARITAN HOSPITAL (O, 265 beds) 407 14th Avenue S.E., Puyallup, WA Zip 98372–3770, Mailing Address: P.O. Box 1247, Zip 98371–0192; tel. 253/697–4000; Glenn Kasman, President
**Web address:** www.goodsamhealth.org

MULTICARE MARY BRIDGE CHILDREN'S HOSPITAL AND HEALTH CENTER (O, 72 beds) 317 Martin Luther King Jr. Way, Tacoma, WA Zip 98405–4234, Mailing Address: P.O. Box 5299, Zip 98415–0299; tel. 253/403–1400; Mady Murrey, R.N., Chief Operating Officer
**Web address:** www.multicare.org/marybridge

MULTICARE TACOMA GENERAL HOSPITAL (O, 402 beds) 315 Martin Luther King Jr. Way, Tacoma, WA Zip 98405–4234, Mailing Address: P.O. Box 5299, Zip 98415–0299; tel. 253/403–1000; Diane E. Cecchettini, R.N., President and Chief Executive Officer
**Web address:** www.multicare.org

| | | |
|---|---|---|
| Owned, leased, sponsored: | 4 hospitals | 859 beds |
| Contract–managed: | 0 hospitals | 0 beds |
| Totals: | 4 hospitals | 859 beds |

**★1465: MUNSON HEALTHCARE** (NP)
1105 Sixth Street, Traverse City, MI Zip 49684–2386; tel. 231/935–6703; Edwin Ness, President and Chief Executive Officer
**(Centralized Physician/Insurance Health System)**

**MICHIGAN:** KALKASKA MEMORIAL HEALTH CENTER (O, 96 beds) 419 South Coral Street, Kalkaska, MI Zip 49646–2503; tel. 231/258–7500; James D. Austin, FACHE, Administrator
**Web address:** www.munsonhealthcare.org

MUNSON MEDICAL CENTER (O, 391 beds) 1105 Sixth Street, Traverse City, MI Zip 49684–2386; tel. 231/935–5000; Alfred E. Pilong, President
**Web address:** www.munsonhealthcare.org

PAUL OLIVER MEMORIAL HOSPITAL (O, 47 beds) 224 Park Avenue, Frankfort, MI Zip 49635–9658; tel. 231/352–2200; James D. Austin, FACHE, Administrator
**Web address:** www.munsonhealthcare.org

| | | |
|---|---|---|
| Owned, leased, sponsored: | 3 hospitals | 534 beds |
| Contract–managed: | 0 hospitals | 0 beds |
| Totals: | 3 hospitals | 534 beds |

**0261: NATIONAL SURGICAL HOSPITALS** (IO)
250 South Wacker Drive, Suite 500, Chicago, IL Zip 60606–5897; tel. 312/627–8400; David Crane, Chief Executive Officer
**(Independent Hospital System)**

**ARIZONA:** ARIZONA SPINE AND JOINT HOSPITAL (O, 23 beds) 4620 East Baseline Road, Mesa, AZ Zip 85206–4624; tel. 480/832–4770; Chris Hill, Chief Executive Officer
**Web address:** www.azspineandjoint.com

**IDAHO:** NORTHWEST SPECIALTY HOSPITAL (O, 22 beds) 1593 East Polston Avenue, Post Falls, ID Zip 83854–5326; tel. 208/262–2300; Vaughn Ward, Chief Executive Officer
**Web address:** www.northwestspecialtyhospital.com

**LOUISIANA:** LAFAYETTE SURGICAL SPECIALTY HOSPITAL (O, 20 beds) 1101 Kaliste Saloom Road, Lafayette, LA Zip 70508–5705; tel. 337/769–4100; Buffy Domingue, Chief Executive Officer
**Web address:** www.lafayettesurgical.com

**MICHIGAN:** SOUTHEAST MICHIGAN SURGICAL HOSPITAL (O, 13 beds) 21230 Dequindre, Warren, MI Zip 48091–2287; tel. 586/427–1000; Yvonne Kughn, Chief Executive Officer
**Web address:** www.nshinc.com

**NORTH CAROLINA:** NORTH CAROLINA SPECIALTY HOSPITAL (O, 18 beds) 3916 Ben Franklin Boulevard, Durham, NC Zip 27704–2383; tel. 919/956–9300; Randi L. Shults, Chief Executive Officer
**Web address:** www.ncspecialty.com

**TEXAS:** EL PASO SPECIALTY HOSPITAL (O, 27 beds) 1755 Curie Drive, El Paso, TX Zip 79902–2919; tel. 915/544–3636; James Wilcox, Chief Executive Officer
**Web address:** www.elpasospecialtyhospital.com

SOUTH TEXAS SPINE AND SURGICAL HOSPITAL (O, 30 beds) 18600 Hardy Oak Boulevard, San Antonio, TX Zip 78258–4206; tel. 210/507–4090; Debbie Kelly, Chief Executive Officer
**Web address:** www.southtexassurgical.com

SOUTH TEXAS SURGICAL HOSPITAL (O, 20 beds) 6130 Parkway Drive, Corpus Christi, TX Zip 78414–2455; tel. 361/993–2000; James Murphy, Chief Executive Officer
**Web address:** www.nshinc.com

**UTAH:** CACHE VALLEY SPECIALTY HOSPITAL (O, 15 beds) 2380 North 400 East, North Logan, UT Zip 84341–6000; tel. 435/713–9700; John C. Worley, III, Chief Executive Officer
**Web address:** www.cvsh.com

**WISCONSIN:** OAKLEAF SURGICAL HOSPITAL (O, 13 beds) 3802 West Oakwood Mall Drive, Eau Claire, WI Zip 54701–3016; tel. 715/831–8130; Anne Hargrave–Thomas, Chief Executive Officer
**Web address:** www.oakleafmedical.com

**WYOMING:** MOUNTAIN VIEW REGIONAL HOSPITAL (O, 23 beds) 6550 East Second Street, Casper, WY Zip 82609–4321, Mailing Address: P.O. Box 51888, Zip 82605–1888; tel. 307/995–8100; Jeff Van Horn, Chief Executive Officer
**Web address:** www.mountainviewregionalhospital.com

| | | |
|---|---|---|
| Owned, leased, sponsored: | 11 hospitals | 224 beds |
| Contract–managed: | 0 hospitals | 0 beds |
| Totals: | 11 hospitals | 224 beds |

**★9265: NEBRASKA METHODIST HEALTH SYSTEM, INC.** (CO)
8511 West Dodge Road, Omaha, NE Zip 68114–3403; tel. 402/354–5411; John M. Fraser, President and Chief Executive Officer
**(Moderately Centralized Health System)**

For explanation of codes following names, see page B2.
★ Indicates Type III membership in the American Hospital Association.

Section B

**IOWA:** METHODIST JENNIE EDMUNDSON HOSPITAL (O, 114 beds) 933 East Pierce Street, Council Bluffs, IA Zip 51503–4652, Mailing Address: P.O. Box 2C, Zip 51502–3002; tel. 712/396–6000; Steven P. Baumert, President and Chief Executive Officer
**Web address:** www.bestcare.org

**NEBRASKA:** NEBRASKA METHODIST HOSPITAL (O, 460 beds) 8303 Dodge Street, Omaha, NE Zip 68114–4199; tel. 402/354–4000; Stephen L. Goeser, FACHE, President and Chief Executive Officer
**Web address:** www.bestcare.org

| | | |
|---|---|---|
| Owned, leased, sponsored: | 2 hospitals | 574 beds |
| Contract–managed: | 0 hospitals | 0 beds |
| Totals: | 2 hospitals | 574 beds |

**0892: NEMOURS** (NP)
10140 Centurion Parkway North, Jacksonville, FL Zip 32256–0532; tel. 904/697–4100; David J. Bailey, M.D., President and Chief Executive Officer

**DELAWARE:** ALFRED I. DUPONT HOSPITAL FOR CHILDREN (O, 195 beds) 1600 Rockland Road, Wilmington, DE Zip 19803–3616, Mailing Address: Box 269, Zip 19899–0269; tel. 302/651–4000; Kevin B. Churchwell, M.D., Chief Executive Officer
**Web address:** www.nemours.org

**FLORIDA:** NEMOURS CHILDREN'S HOSPITAL (O, 95 beds) 13535 Nemours Parkway, Orlando, FL Zip 32827–7402; tel. 407/567–4000; Roger A. Oxendale, Chief Executive Officer
**Web address:** www.nemours.org

| | | |
|---|---|---|
| Owned, leased, sponsored: | 2 hospitals | 290 beds |
| Contract–managed: | 0 hospitals | 0 beds |
| Totals: | 2 hospitals | 290 beds |

**★0213: NEW HANOVER REGIONAL MEDICAL CENTER** (NP)
2131 South 17th Street, Wilmington, NC Zip 28401–7407; tel. 910/343–7040; John K. Barto, Jr., President and Chief Executive Officer
**(Moderately Centralized Health System)**

**NORTH CAROLINA:** NEW HANOVER REGIONAL MEDICAL CENTER (O, 678 beds) 2131 South 17th Street, Wilmington, NC Zip 28401–7483, Mailing Address: P.O. Box 9000, Zip 28402–9000; tel. 910/343–7000; John K. Barto, Jr., President and Chief Executive Officer
**Web address:** www.nhhn.org

PENDER MEMORIAL HOSPITAL (C, 68 beds) 507 East Freemont Street, Burgaw, NC Zip 28425–5131; tel. 910/259–5451; Ruth Glaser, President
**Web address:** www.pendermemorial.org

| | | |
|---|---|---|
| Owned, leased, sponsored: | 1 hospital | 678 beds |
| Contract–managed: | 1 hospital | 68 beds |
| Totals: | 2 hospitals | 746 beds |

**★3075: NEW YORK CITY HEALTH AND HOSPITALS CORPORATION** (NP)
125 Worth Street, Room 514, New York, NY Zip 10013–4006; tel. 212/788–3321; Alan D. Aviles, President
**(Decentralized Health System)**

**NEW YORK:** BELLEVUE HOSPITAL CENTER (O, 807 beds) 462 First Avenue, New York, NY Zip 10016–9198; tel. 212/562–4141; Lynda D. Curtis, Senior Vice President and Executive Director
**Web address:** www.nyc.gov/bellevue

COLER–GOLDWATER SPECIALTY HOSPITAL AND NURSING FACILITY (O, 2016 beds) One Main Street, New York, NY Zip 10044–0052; tel. 212/318–8000; Robert Hughes, Executive Director
**Web address:** www.coler–goldwater.org

CONEY ISLAND HOSPITAL (O, 371 beds) 2601 Ocean Parkway, Brooklyn, NY Zip 11235–7795; tel. 718/616–3000; Arthur Wagner, Senior Vice President and Executive Director
**Web address:** www.nyc.gov/html/hhc/html/facilities/coneyisland.shtml

ELMHURST HOSPITAL CENTER (O, 551 beds) 79–01 Broadway, Elmhurst, NY Zip 11373–1329; tel. 718/334–4000; Chris D. Constantino, Executive Director
**Web address:** www.nyc.gov/html/hhc/ehc/html/home/home.shtml

HARLEM HOSPITAL CENTER (O, 272 beds) 506 Lenox Avenue, New York, NY Zip 10037–1802; tel. 212/939–1000; Denise C. Soares, R.N., Executive Director
**Web address:** www.nyc.gov/html/hhc/harlem

JACOBI MEDICAL CENTER (O, 457 beds) 1400 Pelham Parkway South, Bronx, NY Zip 10461–1197; tel. 718/918–5000; William P. Walsh, Senior Vice President and Executive Director
**Web address:** www.nyc.gov/html/hhc/jacobi/home.html

KINGS COUNTY HOSPITAL CENTER (O, 601 beds) 451 Clarkson Avenue, Brooklyn, NY Zip 11203–2097; tel. 718/245–3131; Ernest Baptiste, Executive Director
**Web address:** www.nyc.gov/html/hhc/kchc/html/home/home.shtml

LINCOLN MEDICAL AND MENTAL HEALTH CENTER (O, 335 beds) 234 East 149th Street, Bronx, NY Zip 10451–5504; tel. 718/579–5700; Milton Nunez, Executive Director
**Web address:** www.nyc.gov/html/hhc/lincoln/

METROPOLITAN HOSPITAL CENTER (O, 324 beds) 1901 First Avenue, New York, NY Zip 10029–7404; tel. 212/423–6262; Meryl Weinberg, Executive Director
**Web address:** www.nyc.gov/html/hhc/mhc/html/home/home.shtml

NORTH CENTRAL BRONX HOSPITAL (O, 207 beds) 3424 Kossuth Avenue, Bronx, NY Zip 10467–2489; tel. 718/519–3500; William P. Walsh, Executive Director
**Web address:** www.nyc.gov/html/hhc/ncbh/html/home/home.shtml

QUEENS HOSPITAL CENTER (O, 271 beds) 82–68 164th Street, Jamaica, NY Zip 11432–1104; tel. 718/883–3000; Julius Wool, Executive Director
**Web address:** www.nyc.gov/html/hhc/qhc/html/home/home.shtml

WOODHULL MEDICAL AND MENTAL HEALTH CENTER (O, 332 beds) 760 Broadway, Brooklyn, NY Zip 11206–5383; tel. 718/963–8000; George M. Proctor, Senior Vice President and Executive Director
**Web address:** www.nyc.gov/html/hhc

| | | |
|---|---|---|
| Owned, leased, sponsored: | 12 hospitals | 6544 beds |
| Contract–managed: | 0 hospitals | 0 beds |
| Totals: | 12 hospitals | 6544 beds |

**0142: NEW YORK PRESBYTERIAN HEALTHCARE SYSTEM** (NP)
25 East 68th Street, Box 182, New York, NY Zip 10065; tel. 212/746–7905; Steven J. Corwin, M.D., Chief Executive Officer
**(Moderately Centralized Health System)**

BROOKLYN HOSPITAL CENTER (S, 312 beds) 121 DeKalb Avenue, Brooklyn, NY Zip 11201–5425; tel. 718/250–8000; Richard B. Becker, M.D., President, Chief Executive Officer and Interim Chief Medical Officer
**Web address:** www.tbh.org

GRACIE SQUARE HOSPITAL (S, 157 beds) 420 East 76th Street, New York, NY Zip 10021–3396; tel. 212/988–4400; Frank Bruno, Chief Executive Officer
**Web address:** www.nygsh.org

HOSPITAL FOR SPECIAL SURGERY (S, 203 beds) 535 East 70th Street, New York, NY Zip 10021–4898; tel. 212/606–1000; Louis A. Shapiro, President and Chief Executive Officer
**Web address:** www.hss.edu

NEW YORK COMMUNITY HOSPITAL (S, 125 beds) 2525 Kings Highway, Brooklyn, NY Zip 11229–1705; tel. 718/692–5300; Lin H. Mo, President and Chief Executive Officer
**Web address:** www.nych.com

NEW YORK DOWNTOWN HOSPITAL (O, 128 beds) 170 William Street, New York, NY Zip 10038–2649; tel. 212/312–5000; Michael Fosina, Senior Vice President and Chief Operating Officer
**Web address:** www.downtownhospital.org

NEW YORK HOSPITAL QUEENS (S, 519 beds) 56–45 Main Street, Flushing, NY Zip 11355–5045; tel. 718/670–1231; Stephen S. Mills, President and Chief Executive Officer
**Web address:** www.nyhq.org

For explanation of codes following names, see page B2.
★ Indicates Type III membership in the American Hospital Association.

NEW YORK METHODIST HOSPITAL (S, 591 beds) 506 Sixth Street, Brooklyn, NY Zip 11215–3609; tel. 718/780–3000; Mark J. Mundy, President and Chief Executive Officer
**Web address:** www.nym.org

NEW YORK–PRESBYTERIAN HOSPITAL (O, 2262 beds) 525 East 68th Street, New York, NY Zip 10065–4870; tel. 212/746–5454; Steven J. Corwin, M.D., Chief Executive Officer
**Web address:** www.nyp.org

NYACK HOSPITAL (S, 375 beds) 160 North Midland Avenue, Nyack, NY Zip 10960–1998; tel. 845/348–2000; David H. Freed, President and Chief Executive Officer
**Web address:** www.nyackhospital.org

| | | |
|---|---|---|
| Owned, leased, sponsored: | 9 hospitals | 4672 beds |
| Contract–managed: | 0 hospitals | 0 beds |
| Totals: | 9 hospitals | 4672 beds |

## 0009: NEW YORK STATE OFFICE OF MENTAL HEALTH (NP)
44 Holland Avenue, Albany, NY Zip 12208–3411; tel. 518/474–7056; Kristin M. Woodlock, R.N., Acting Commissioner
**(Independent Hospital System)**

BRONX PSYCHIATRIC CENTER (O, 450 beds) 1500 Waters Place, Bronx, NY Zip 10461–2796; tel. 718/931–0600; Pamela Turner, Executive Director
**Web address:** www.omh.ny.gov

BUFFALO PSYCHIATRIC CENTER (O, 240 beds) 400 Forest Avenue, Buffalo, NY Zip 14213–1298; tel. 716/885–2261; Thomas Dodson, Executive Director
**Web address:** www.omh.ny.gov

CAPITAL DISTRICT PSYCHIATRIC CENTER (O, 200 beds) 75 New Scotland Avenue, Albany, NY Zip 12208–3474; tel. 518/447–9611; William Dickson, Acting Executive Director
**Web address:** www.omh.ny.gov/omhweb/facilities/cdpc/facility.htm

CENTRAL NEW YORK PSYCHIATRIC CENTER (O, 226 beds) Marcy, NY Zip 13403; tel. 315/765–3600; Maureen Bosco, Executive Director
**Web address:** www.omh.ny.gov

CREEDMOOR PSYCHIATRIC CENTER (O, 380 beds) 79–25 Winchester Boulevard, Jamaica, NY Zip 11427–2128; tel. 718/264–3600, Ann Marie Barbarotta, Executive Director
**Web address:** www.omh.ny.gov

ELMIRA PSYCHIATRIC CENTER (O, 100 beds) 100 Washington Street, Elmira, NY Zip 14901–2898; tel. 607/737–4739; Mark Stephany, Executive Director
**Web address:** www.omh.ny.gov/omhweb/facilities/elpc/facility.htm

GREATER BINGHAMTON HEALTH CENTER (O, 115 beds) 425 Robinson Street, Binghamton, NY Zip 13904–1735; tel. 607/724–1391; Mark Stephany, Executive Director
**Web address:** www.omh.ny.gov/omhweb/facilities/bipc/facility.htm

KINGSBORO PSYCHIATRIC CENTER (O, 290 beds) 681 Clarkson Avenue, Brooklyn, NY Zip 11203–2125; tel. 718/221–7395; Deborah Parchment, Executive Director
**Web address:** www.omh.ny.gov/omhweb/facilities/kbpc/facility/htm

MANHATTAN PSYCHIATRIC CENTER–WARD'S ISLAND (O, 745 beds) 600 East 125th Street, New York, NY Zip 10035–6000; tel. 646/672–6767; Vinny Miccoli, Executive Director
**Web address:** www.omh.ny.gov

MID–HUDSON FORENSIC PSYCHIATRIC CENTER (O, 268 beds) Route 17M, New Hampton, NY Zip 10958, Mailing Address: P.O. Box 158, Zip 10958–0158; tel. 845/374–8700; Peggi Healy, Executive Director
**Web address:** www.omh.ny.gov

MOHAWK VALLEY PSYCHIATRIC CENTER (O, 614 beds) 1400 Noyes Street, Utica, NY Zip 13502–3854; tel. 315/738–3800; Colleen A. Sawyer, R.N., MSN, Executive Director
**Web address:** www.omh.ny.gov/omhweb/facilities/mvpc/facility.htm

NEW YORK CITY CHILDREN'S CENTER (O, 84 beds) 74–03 Commonwealth Boulevard, Jamaica, NY Zip 11426–1890; tel. 718/264–4506; June DaCosta, Acting Executive Director
**Web address:** www.omh.ny.gov

NEW YORK STATE PSYCHIATRIC INSTITUTE (O, 58 beds) 1051 Riverside Drive, New York, NY Zip 10032–1007; tel. 212/543–5000; Jeffrey A. Lieberman, M.D., Executive Director
**Web address:** www.nyspi.org

PILGRIM PSYCHIATRIC CENTER (O, 569 beds) 998 Crooked Hill Road, Brentwood, NY Zip 11717–1019; tel. 631/761–3500; Kathy O'Keefe, Executive Director
**Web address:** www.omh.ny.gov/omhweb/facilities/pgpc/facility.htm

RICHARD H. HUTCHINGS PSYCHIATRIC CENTER (O, 131 beds) 620 Madison Street, Syracuse, NY Zip 13210–2319; tel. 315/426–3632; Colleen A. Sawyer, R.N., MSN, Executive Director
**Web address:** www.omh.ny.gov

ROCHESTER PSYCHIATRIC CENTER (O, 180 beds) 1111 Elmwood Avenue, Rochester, NY Zip 14620–3005; tel. 585/241–1200; Elizabeth Suhre, Executive Director
**Web address:** www.omh.ny.gov/omhweb/facilities/ropc/facility.htm

ROCKLAND CHILDREN'S PSYCHIATRIC CENTER (O, 54 beds) 599 Convent Road, Orangeburg, NY Zip 10962–1162; tel. 845/359–7400; Anita Daniels, Executive Director
**Web address:** www.omh.ny.gov/

ROCKLAND PSYCHIATRIC CENTER (O, 525 beds) 140 Old Orangeburg Road, Orangeburg, NY Zip 10962–1157; tel. 845/359–1000; Christopher Tavella, Executive Director
**Web address:** www.omh.ny.gov/

SAGAMORE CHILDREN'S PSYCHIATRIC CENTER (O, 69 beds) 197 Half Hollow Road, Dix Hills, NY Zip 11746–5861; tel. 631/370–1700; Tom McOlvin, Executive Director
**Web address:** www.omh.ny.gov

SOUTH BEACH PSYCHIATRIC CENTER (O, 340 beds) 777 Seaview Avenue, Staten Island, NY Zip 10305–3409; tel. 718/667–2300; Rosanne Gaylor, M.D., Acting Executive Director
**Web address:** www.omh.ny.gov/omhweb/facilities/sbpc/facility.htm

ST. LAWRENCE PSYCHIATRIC CENTER (O, 146 beds) 1 Chimney Point Drive, Ogdensburg, NY Zip 13669–2291; tel. 315/541–2001; Samua A. Bastien, IV, Ph.D., Executive Director
**Web address:** www.omh.ny.gov/omhweb/facilities/slpc/facility.htm

WESTERN NEW YORK CHILDREN'S PSYCHIATRIC CENTER (O, 46 beds) 1010 East and West Road, West Seneca, NY Zip 14224–3602; tel. 716/677–7000; Kathe Hayes, Executive Director
**Web address:** www.omh.ny.gov

| | | |
|---|---|---|
| Owned, leased, sponsored: | 22 hospitals | 5830 beds |
| Contract–managed: | 0 hospitals | 0 beds |
| Totals: | 22 hospitals | 5830 beds |

## 0353: NEXUS HEALTH SYSTEMS (IO)
One Riverway, Suite 600, Houston, TX Zip 77056–1993; tel. 713/355–6111; John W. Cassidy, M.D., President, Chief Executive Officer and Chief Medical Officer
**(Independent Hospital System)**

**CALIFORNIA:** HEALTHBRIDGE CHILDRENS REHABILITATION HOSPITAL (O, 27 beds) 393 South Tustin Street, Orange, CA Zip 92866–2501; tel. 714/289–2400; Allan G. Komarek, Ph.D., Chief Executive Officer and Administrator
**Web address:** www.HealthBridgeOrange.com

**TEXAS:** HEALTHBRIDGE CHILDREN'S HOSPITAL OF HOUSTON (O, 40 beds) 2929 Woodland Park Drive, Houston, TX Zip 77082–2687; tel. 281/293–7774; Joseph Rafferty, Chief Executive Officer
**Web address:** www.healthbridgehouston.com/

NEXUS SPECIALTY HOSPITAL (O, 75 beds) 123 Vision Park Boulevard, Shenandoah, TX Zip 77384–3001; tel. 281/364–0317; Erin Cassidy, Chief Executive Officer
**Web address:** www.nexusspecialty.com

| | | |
|---|---|---|
| Owned, leased, sponsored: | 3 hospitals | 142 beds |
| Contract–managed: | 0 hospitals | 0 beds |
| Totals: | 3 hospitals | 142 beds |

Section B

**0349: NOLAND HEALTH SERVICES, INC.** (NP)
600 Corporate Parkway, Suite 100, Birmingham, AL
Zip 35242–5451; tel. 205/783–8484; Gary M. Glasscock, President
and Chief Executive Officer

**ALABAMA:** NOLAND HOSPITAL ANNISTON (O, 38 beds) 400 East 10th
Street, 4th Floor, Anniston, AL Zip 36207–4716; tel. 256/741–6141; Bill
Mitchell, Administrator
**Web address:** www.nolandhealth.com

NOLAND HOSPITAL BIRMINGHAM (O, 45 beds) 50 Medical Park East Drive,
8th Floor, Birmingham, AL Zip 35235; tel. 205/808–5100; Laura S. Wills,
Administrator
**Web address:** www.nolandhealth.com

NOLAND HOSPITAL DOTHAN (O, 35 beds) 1108 Ross Clark Circle, 4th Floor,
Dothan, AL Zip 36301–3022; tel. 334/699–4300; Kaye Burke, Administrator
**Web address:** www.nolandhealth.com

NOLAND HOSPITAL MONTGOMERY (O, 65 beds) 1725 Pine Street, 5 North,
Montgomery, AL Zip 36106–1109; tel. 334/240–0532; Susan E. Legg,
Interim Administrator
**Web address:** www.nolandhealth.com

NOLAND HOSPITAL SHELBY (O, 52 beds) 1000 First Street North, 3rd Floor,
Alabaster, AL Zip 35007–8703; tel. 205/620–8641; Andrew Tatnall,
Administrator
**Web address:** www.nolandhospitals.com/nhs.html

NOLAND HOSPITAL TUSCALOOSA (O, 32 beds) 809 University Boulevard E,
4th Floor, Tuscaloosa, AL Zip 35401–2029; tel. 205/759–7241; Dale Jones,
Administrator
**Web address:** www.nolandhealth.com

| | | |
|---|---|---|
| Owned, leased, sponsored: | 6 hospitals | 267 beds |
| Contract–managed: | 0 hospitals | 0 beds |
| Totals: | 6 hospitals | 267 beds |

★**0887: NORTH MEMORIAL HEALTH CARE** (NP)
3300 Oakdale Avenue North, Robbinsdale, MN Zip 55422–2926;
tel. 763/520–5200; Loren L. Taylor, Chief Executive Officer

**MINNESOTA:** MAPLE GROVE HOSPITAL (C, 90 beds) 9875 Hospital Drive,
Maple Grove, MN Zip 55369–4648; tel. 763/581–1000; Andrew S.
Cochrane, Chief Executive Officer
**Web address:** www.maplegrovehospital.org

NORTH MEMORIAL MEDICAL CENTER (O, 355 beds) 3300 Oakdale Avenue
North, Robbinsdale, MN Zip 55422–2926; tel. 763/520–5200; Loren L.
Taylor, Chief Executive Officer
**Web address:** www.northmemorial.com

| | | |
|---|---|---|
| Owned, leased, sponsored: | 1 hospital | 355 beds |
| Contract–managed: | 1 hospital | 90 beds |
| Totals: | 2 hospitals | 445 beds |

★**0032: NORTH MISSISSIPPI HEALTH SERVICES, INC.** (NP)
830 South Gloster Street, Tupelo, MS Zip 38801–4996;
tel. 662/377–3136; John R. Heer, President and Chief Executive
Officer
**(Centralized Physician/Insurance Health System)**

**ALABAMA:** NORTH MISSISSIPPI MEDICAL CENTER–HAMILTON (O, 36 beds)
1256 Military Street South, Hamilton, AL Zip 35570–5003;
tel. 205/921–6200; Donald J. Jones, FACHE, Administrator
**Web address:** www.nmhs.net

**MISSISSIPPI:** CALHOUN HEALTH SERVICES (C, 150 beds) 140
Burke–Calhoun City Road, Calhoun City, MS Zip 38916–9690;
tel. 662/628–6611; James P. Franklin, Administrator
**Web address:** www.nmhs.net/calhoun_city

NORTH MISSISSIPPI MEDICAL CENTER–TUPELO (O, 757 beds) 830 South
Gloster Street, Tupelo, MS Zip 38801–4934; tel. 662/377–3000; Steve
Altmiller, President and Chief Executive Officer
**Web address:** www.nmhs.net

NORTH MISSISSIPPI MEDICAL CENTER–EUPORA (O, 73 beds) 70 Medical
Plaza, Eupora, MS Zip 39744–4018; tel. 662/258–6221; John R. Jones,
Administrator
**Web address:** www.nmhs.net/eupora

NORTH MISSISSIPPI MEDICAL CENTER–IUKA (O, 48 beds) 1777 Curtis Drive,
Iuka, MS Zip 38852–1001, Mailing Address: P.O. Box 860, Zip 38852–0860;
tel. 662/423–6051; Fred A. Truesdale, Jr., Administrator
**Web address:** www.nmhs.net

NORTH MISSISSIPPI MEDICAL CENTER–PONTOTOC HOSPITAL AND NURSING
HOME (L, 69 beds) 176 South Main Street, Pontotoc, MS Zip 38863–3311,
Mailing Address: P.O. Box 790, Zip 38863–0790; tel. 662/488–7640; Fred
B. Hood, FACHE, Administrator
**Web address:** www.nmhs.net

NORTH MISSISSIPPI MEDICAL CENTER–WEST POINT (O, 60 beds) 835
Medical Center Drive, West Point, MS Zip 39773–9320; tel. 662/495–2300;
James W. Hahn, Administrator
**Web address:** www.nmhs.net/westpoint

| | | |
|---|---|---|
| Owned, leased, sponsored: | 6 hospitals | 1043 beds |
| Contract–managed: | 1 hospital | 150 beds |
| Totals: | 7 hospitals | 1193 beds |

**0867: NORTH OAKS HEALTH SYSTEM** (NP)
15790 Paul Vega MD Drive, Hammond, LA Zip 70403–1436, Mailing
Address: P.O. Box 2668, Zip 70404–2668; tel. 985/345–2700;
James E. Cathey, Jr., Chief Executive Officer
**(Independent Hospital System)**

**LOUISIANA:** NORTH OAKS MEDICAL CENTER (O, 251 beds) 15790 Paul
Vega, M. D. Drive, Hammond, LA Zip 70403–1436, Mailing Address: PO
Box 2668, Zip 70404–2668; tel. 985/345–2700; Michele K. Sutton,
FACHE, Administrator
**Web address:** www.northoaks.org

NORTH OAKS REHABILITATION HOSPITAL (O, 27 beds) 1900 South Morrison
Boulevard, Hammond, LA Zip 70403–5742; tel. 504/230–5700; Sybil K.
Paulson, R.N., Administrator
**Web address:** www.northoaks.org

| | | |
|---|---|---|
| Owned, leased, sponsored: | 2 hospitals | 278 beds |
| Contract–managed: | 0 hospitals | 0 beds |
| Totals: | 2 hospitals | 278 beds |

★**0062: NORTH SHORE–LONG ISLAND JEWISH HEALTH
SYSTEM** (NP)
145 Community Drive, Great Neck, NY Zip 11021–5502;
tel. 516/465–8100; Michael J. Dowling, President and Chief
Executive Officer
**(Centralized Health System)**

**NEW YORK:** FOREST HILLS HOSPITAL (O, 235 beds) 102–01 66th Road,
Forest Hills, NY Zip 11375–2029; tel. 718/830–4000; Rita Mercieca,
R.N., Executive Director
**Web address:** www.northshorelij.com

FRANKLIN HOSPITAL (O, 330 beds) 900 Franklin Avenue, Valley Stream, NY
Zip 11580–2190; tel. 516/256–6000; Catherine Hottendorf, R.N., MS,
Executive Director
**Web address:** www.northshorelij.com

GLEN COVE HOSPITAL (O, 235 beds) 101 St. Andrews Lane, Glen Cove, NY
Zip 11542–2254; tel. 516/674–7300; Susan Kwiatek, R.N., Executive
Director
**Web address:** www.northshorelij.com

HUNTINGTON HOSPITAL (O, 288 beds) 270 Park Avenue, Huntington, NY
Zip 11743–2799; tel. 631/351–2200; Kevin F. Lawlor, President and Chief
Executive Officer
**Web address:** www.hunthosp.org

LENOX HILL HOSPITAL (O, 508 beds) 100 East 77th Street, New York, NY
Zip 10075–1850; tel. 212/434–2000; Dennis Connors, Executive Director
**Web address:** www.lenoxhillhospital.org

LONG ISLAND JEWISH MEDICAL CENTER (O, 868 beds) 270–05 76th
Avenue, New Hyde Park, NY Zip 11040–1496; tel. 718/470–7000; Chantal
Weinhold, Executive Director
**Web address:** www.lij.edu

NORTH SHORE UNIVERSITY HOSPITAL (O, 804 beds) 300 Community Drive,
Manhasset, NY Zip 11030–3816; tel. 516/562–0100; Susan Somerville,
R.N., Executive Director
**Web address:** www.northshorelij.com

For explanation of codes following names, see page B2.
★ Indicates Type III membership in the American Hospital Association.

PLAINVIEW HOSPITAL (O, 204 beds) 888 Old Country Road, Plainview, NY Zip 11803–4978; tel. 516/719–3000; Michael Fener, Executive Director
**Web address:** www.northshorelij.com

SOUTH OAKS HOSPITAL (O, 260 beds) 400 Sunrise Highway, Amityville, NY Zip 11701–2508; tel. 631/264–4000; Robert E. Detor, Chief Executive Officer
**Web address:** www.longislandhome.org

SOUTHSIDE HOSPITAL (O, 300 beds) 301 East Main Street, Bay Shore, NY Zip 11706–8458; tel. 631/968–3000; Donna Moravick, R.N., MSN, Executive Director
**Web address:** www.southsidehospital.org

STATEN ISLAND UNIVERSITY HOSPITAL (O, 663 beds) 475 Seaview Avenue, Staten Island, NY Zip 10305–3436; tel. 718/226–9000; Anthony C. Ferreri, President and Chief Executive Officer
**Web address:** www.siuh.edu

SYOSSET HOSPITAL (O, 72 beds) 221 Jericho Turnpike, Syosset, NY Zip 11791–4515; tel. 516/496–6400; Michael Fener, Executive Director
**Web address:** www.northshorelij.com

| | | |
|---|---|---|
| **Owned, leased, sponsored:** | 12 hospitals | 4767 beds |
| **Contract–managed:** | 0 hospitals | 0 beds |
| **Totals:** | 12 hospitals | 4767 beds |

★**0281:  NORTHERN ARIZONA HEALTHCARE** (NP)
1200 North Beaver Street, Flagstaff, AZ Zip 86001–3118; tel. 928/779–3366; William T. Bradel, President and Chief Executive Officer
**(Moderately Centralized Health System)**

**ARIZONA:** FLAGSTAFF MEDICAL CENTER (O, 267 beds) 1200 North Beaver Street, Flagstaff, AZ Zip 86001–3118; tel. 928/779–3366; William T. Bradel, President
**Web address:** www.flagstaffmedicalcenter.com

VERDE VALLEY MEDICAL CENTER (O, 110 beds) 269 South Candy Lane, Cottonwood, AZ Zip 86326–4170; tel. 928/639–6000; Barbara Dember, Interim President and Chief Executive Officer
**Web address:** www.nahealth.com

| | | |
|---|---|---|
| **Owned, leased, sponsored:** | 2 hospitals | 377 beds |
| **Contract–managed:** | 0 hospitals | 0 beds |
| **Totals:** | 2 hospitals | 377 beds |

★**0470:  NORTHSHORE UNIVERSITY HEALTHSYSTEM** (NP)
1301 Central Street, Evanston, IL Zip 60201–1613; tel. 847/570–2000; Mark R. Neaman, President and Chief Executive Officer
**(Moderately Centralized Health System)**

**ILLINOIS:** NORTHSHORE UNIVERSITY HEALTH SYSTEM EVANSTON HOSPITAL (O, 690 beds) 1301 Central Street, Evanston, IL Zip 60201–1613; tel. 847/570–2000; Douglas M. Silverstein, President
**Web address:** www.northshore.org

NORTHSHORE UNIVERSITY HEALTH SYSTEM SKOKIE HOSPITAL (O, 234 beds) 9600 Gross Point Road, Skokie, IL Zip 60076–1257; tel. 847/677–9600; Kristen Murtos, FACHE, President
**Web address:** www.northshore.org

| | | |
|---|---|---|
| **Owned, leased, sponsored:** | 2 hospitals | 924 beds |
| **Contract–managed:** | 0 hospitals | 0 beds |
| **Totals:** | 2 hospitals | 924 beds |

★**0410:  NORTHSIDE HEALTHCARE SYSTEM** (NP)
1000 Johnson Ferry Road N.E., Atlanta, GA Zip 30342–1611; tel. 404/851–8000; Robert Quattrocchi, President and Chief Executive Officer

**GEORGIA:** NORTHSIDE HOSPITAL (O, 551 beds) 1000 Johnson Ferry Road N.E., Atlanta, GA Zip 30342–1611; tel. 404/851–8000; Robert Quattrocchi, President and Chief Executive Officer
**Web address:** www.northside.com

NORTHSIDE HOSPITAL–CHEROKEE (O, 88 beds) 201 Hospital Road, Canton, GA Zip 30114–2408, Mailing Address: P.O. Box 906, Zip 30169–0906; tel. 770/720–5100; William M. Hayes, Chief Executive Officer
**Web address:** www.northside.com

NORTHSIDE HOSPITAL–FORSYTH (O, 213 beds) 1200 Northside Forsyth Drive, Cumming, GA Zip 30041–7659; tel. 770/844–3200; Lynn Jackson, Administrator
**Web address:** www.northside.com

| | | |
|---|---|---|
| **Owned, leased, sponsored:** | 3 hospitals | 852 beds |
| **Contract–managed:** | 0 hospitals | 0 beds |
| **Totals:** | 3 hospitals | 852 beds |

★**0024:  NORTHWESTERN MEMORIAL HEALTHCARE** (NP)
251 East Huron Street, Chicago, IL Zip 60611–2908; tel. 312/926–2000; Dean M. Harrison, President and Chief Executive Officer
**(Moderately Centralized Health System)**

**ILLINOIS:** NORTHWESTERN LAKE FOREST HOSPITAL (O, 188 beds) 660 North Westmoreland Road, Lake Forest, IL Zip 60045–1696; tel. 847/234–5600; Thomas J. McAfee, President
**Web address:** www.lfh.org

NORTHWESTERN MEMORIAL HOSPITAL (O, 885 beds) 251 East Huron Street, Chicago, IL Zip 60611–2908; tel. 312/926–2000; Dean M. Harrison, President and Chief Executive Officer
**Web address:** www.nmh.org

| | | |
|---|---|---|
| **Owned, leased, sponsored:** | 2 hospitals | 1073 beds |
| **Contract–managed:** | 0 hospitals | 0 beds |
| **Totals:** | 2 hospitals | 1073 beds |

★**2285:  NORTON HEALTHCARE** (NP)
4967 U.S. Highway 42, Suite 100, Louisville, KY Zip 40222–6363, Mailing Address: P.O. Box 35070, Zip 40232–5070; tel. 502/629–8000; Stephen Williams, President
**(Centralized Physician/Insurance Health System)**

**KENTUCKY:** KOSAIR CHILDREN'S HOSPITAL (O, 271 beds) 231 East Chestnut Street, Louisville, KY Zip 40202–1821; tel. 502/629–6000; Thomas D. Kmetz, President
**Web address:** www.kosairchildrens.com/

NORTON AUDUBON HOSPITAL (O, 278 beds) One Audubon Plaza Drive, Louisville, KY Zip 40217–1300, Mailing Address: P.O. Box 17550, Zip 40217–0550; tel. 502/636–7111; Steven MacLauchlan, President
**Web address:** www.nortonhealthcare.com/NortonAudubonHospital

NORTON BROWNSBORO HOSPITAL (O, 103 beds) 4960 Norton Healthcare Boulevard, Louisville, KY Zip 40241–2831; tel. 502/446–8000; John D. Harryman, President
**Web address:** www.nortonhealthcare.com/nortonbrownsborohospital

NORTON HOSPITAL (O, 370 beds) 200 East Chestnut Street, Louisville, KY Zip 40202–1800, Mailing Address: P.O. Box 35070, Zip 40232–5070; tel. 502/629–8000; Kevin S. Wardell, President
**Web address:** www.nortonhealthcare.com/nortonhospital

NORTON SUBURBAN HOSPITAL (O, 359 beds) 4001 Dutchmans Lane, Louisville, KY Zip 40207–4799; tel. 502/893–1000; Charlotte Ipsan, President
**Web address:** www.nortonhealthcare.com/nortonsuburbanhospital

| | | |
|---|---|---|
| **Owned, leased, sponsored:** | 5 hospitals | 1381 beds |
| **Contract–managed:** | 0 hospitals | 0 beds |
| **Totals:** | 5 hospitals | 1381 beds |

Section B

**★0139: NOVANT HEALTH** (NP)
2085 Frontis Plaza Boulevard, Winston Salem, NC Zip 27103–5614; tel. 336/718–5600; Carl S. Armato, President and Chief Executive Officer
**(Moderately Centralized Health System)**

**NORTH CAROLINA:** NOVANT HEALTH BRUNSWICK MEDICAL CENTER (O, 60 beds) 240 Hospital Drive N.E., Bolivia, NC Zip 28422–8346; tel. 910/721–1000; Shelbourn Stevens, President
**Web address:** www.brunswicknovant.org

NOVANT HEALTH FORSYTH MEDICAL CENTER (O, 672 beds) 3333 Silas Creek Parkway, Winston–Salem, NC Zip 27103–3090; tel. 336/718–5000; Jeffery T. Lindsay, President
**Web address:** www.forsythmedicalcenter.org

NOVANT HEALTH FRANKLIN MEDICAL CENTER (O, 43 beds) 100 Hospital Drive, Louisburg, NC Zip 27549–2256, Mailing Address: P.O. Box 609, Zip 27549–0609; tel. 919/497–8401; Jody Morris, President and Chief Operating Officer
**Web address:** www.franklinregional.org

NOVANT HEALTH MEDICAL PARK HOSPITAL (O, 22 beds) 1950 South Hawthorne Road, Winston–Salem, NC Zip 27103–3993; tel. 336/718–0600; Teresa Carter, Vice President and Chief Operating Officer
**Web address:** www.novanthealth.org

NOVANT HEALTH PRESBYTERIAN MEDICAL CENTER (O, 595 beds) 200 Hawthorne Lane, Charlotte, NC Zip 28204–2528, Mailing Address: P.O. Box 33549, Zip 28233–3549; tel. 704/384–4000; Harry L. Smith, Jr., President
**Web address:** www.presbyterian.org

NOVANT HEALTH PRESBYTERIAN HUNTERSVILLE MEDICAL CENTER (O, 72 beds) 10030 Gilead Road, Huntersville, NC Zip 28078–7545, Mailing Address: P.O. Box 3508, Zip 28070–3508; tel. 704/316–4000; Tanya S. Blackmon, President
**Web address:** www.novanthealth.org

NOVANT HEALTH MATTHEWS MEDICAL CENTER (O, 117 beds) 1500 Matthews Township Parkway, Matthews, NC Zip 28105–4656, Mailing Address: P.O. Box 3310, Zip 28106–3310; tel. 704/384–6500; Roland R. Bibeau, FACHE, President
**Web address:** www.presbyterian.org

NOVANT HEALTH CHAROLOTTE ORTHOPAEDIC HOSPITAL (O, 80 beds) 1901 Randolph Road, Charlotte, NC Zip 28207–1195; tel. 704/316–2000; Mike Riley, Senior Vice President and Chief Operating Officer
**Web address:** www.novanthealth.org

NOVANT HEALTH ROWAN MEDICAL CENTER (O, 200 beds) 612 Mocksville Avenue, Salisbury, NC Zip 28144–2799; tel. 704/210–5000; Dari Caldwell, R.N., Ph.D., FACHE, President
**Web address:** www.rowan.org

NOVANT HEALTH THOMASVILLE MEDICAL CENTER (O, 101 beds) 207 Old Lexington Road, Thomasville, NC Zip 27360–3428, Mailing Address: P.O. Box 789, Zip 27361–0789; tel. 336/472–2000; Kathie A. Johnson, R.N., MS, Ph.D., Chief Executive Officer
**Web address:** www.thomasvillemedicalcenter.org

**SOUTH CAROLINA:** NOVANT HEALTH GAFFNEY MEDICAL CENTER (O, 125 beds) 1530 North Limestone Street, Gaffney, SC Zip 29340–4738; tel. 864/487–4271; Brian Yates, Administrator
**Web address:** www.upstatecarolina.org

**VIRGINIA:** NOVANT HEALTH PRINCE WILLIAM MEDICAL CENTER (O, 168 beds) 8700 Sudley Road, Manassas, VA Zip 20110–4418, Mailing Address: P.O. Box 2610, Zip 20108–0867; tel. 703/369–8000; Melissa Robson, President
**Web address:** www.pwhs.org

| | | |
|---|---|---|
| **Owned, leased, sponsored:** | 12 hospitals | 2255 beds |
| **Contract–managed:** | 0 hospitals | 0 beds |
| **Totals:** | 12 hospitals | 2255 beds |

**★1165: OAKWOOD HEALTHCARE, INC.** (NP)
One Parklane Boulevard, Suite 1000E, Dearborn, MI Zip 48126–2400; tel. 313/253–6050; Brian M. Connolly, President and Chief Executive Officer
**(Centralized Health System)**

**MICHIGAN:** OAKWOOD ANNAPOLIS HOSPITAL (O, 204 beds) 33155 Annapolis Street, Wayne, MI Zip 48184–2405; tel. 734/467–4000; Eric W. Widner, Division President
**Web address:** www.oakwood.org

OAKWOOD HERITAGE HOSPITAL (O, 145 beds) 10000 Telegraph Road, Taylor, MI Zip 48180–3330; tel. 313/295–5000; Kelly C. Smith, Division President
**Web address:** www.oakwood.org

OAKWOOD HOSPITAL & MEDICAL CENTER–DEARBORN (O, 555 beds) 18101 Oakwood Boulevard, Dearborn, MI Zip 48124–4089, Mailing Address: P.O. Box 2500, Zip 48123–2500; tel. 313/593–7000; Douglas D. Welday, Division President
**Web address:** www.oakwood.org

OAKWOOD SOUTHSHORE MEDICAL CENTER (O, 144 beds) 5450 Fort Street, Trenton, MI Zip 48183–4625; tel. 734/671–3800; Edith M. Hughes, R.N., President
**Web address:** www.oakwood.org

| | | |
|---|---|---|
| **Owned, leased, sponsored:** | 4 hospitals | 1048 beds |
| **Contract–managed:** | 0 hospitals | 0 beds |
| **Totals:** | 4 hospitals | 1048 beds |

**0616: OCEANS HEALTHCARE** (IO)
2720 Rue de Jardin, Suite 100, Lake Charles, LA Zip 70605–4050; tel. 337/721–1900; Jason Reed, President and Chief Executive Officer

**LOUISIANA:** OCEANS BEHAVIORAL HOSPITAL OF ALEXANDRIA (O, 24 beds) 2621 North Bolton Avenue, Alexandria, LA Zip 71303–4506; tel. 318/448–8473; Gene Amons, Administrator
**Web address:** www.obha.info/

OCEANS BEHAVIORAL HOSPITAL OF BATON ROUGE (O, 20 beds) 11135 Florida Boulevard, Baton Rouge, LA Zip 70815–2013; tel. 225/356–7030; Valerie Dalton, R.N., Administrator
**Web address:** www.obhbr.info/

OCEANS BEHAVIORAL HOSPITAL OF BROUSSARD (O, 38 beds) 418 Albertson Parkway, Broussard, LA Zip 70518–4971; tel. 337/237–6444; Amy Dysart, Administrator
**Web address:** www.obhb.info/

OCEANS BEHAVIORAL HOSPITAL OF DE RIDDER (O, 20 beds) 1420 Blankenship Drive, Deridder, LA Zip 70634–4604; tel. 337/460–9472; Ronald E. Hand, Administrator
**Web address:** www.obhd.info/

OCEANS BEHAVIORAL HOSPITAL OF GREATER NEW ORLEANS (O, 30 beds) 716 Village Road, Kenner, LA Zip 70065–2751; tel. 504/464–8895; Deborah Spier, Administrator
**Web address:** www.obhgno.info/

OCEANS BEHAVIORAL HOSPITAL OF KENTWOOD (O, 18 beds) 921 Avenue G., Kentwood, LA Zip 70444–2636; tel. 985/229–0717; Gina Isbell, Administrator
**Web address:** www.obhk.info/

OCEANS BEHAVIORAL HOSPITAL OF LAKE CHARLES (O, 20 beds) 302 West Mcneese Street, Lake Charles, LA Zip 70605–5604; tel. 337/474–7581; Christin Bennett, Administrator
**Web address:** www.obhlc.info/

OCEANS BEHAVIORAL HOSPITAL OF OPELOUSAS (O, 20 beds) 1310 Heather Drive, Opelousas, LA Zip 70570–7714; tel. 337/948–8820; Remi Savoy, Administrator
**Web address:** www.obho.info/

| | | |
|---|---|---|
| **Owned, leased, sponsored:** | 8 hospitals | 190 beds |
| **Contract–managed:** | 0 hospitals | 0 beds |
| **Totals:** | 8 hospitals | 190 beds |

**★0359: OCHSNER HEALTH SYSTEM** (NP)
1514 Jefferson Highway, New Orleans, LA Zip 70121–2429; tel. 800/874–8984; Warner L. Thomas, FACHE, President and Chief Executive Officer
**(Moderately Centralized Health System)**

For explanation of codes following names, see page B2.
★ Indicates Type III membership in the American Hospital Association.

Section B

OCHSNER BAPTIST MEDICAL CENTER (O, 55 beds) 2700 Napoleon Avenue, New Orleans, LA Zip 70115–6914; tel. 504/899–9311; Dawn Anuszkiewicz, Chief Executive Officer
**Web address:** www.ochsner.org

OCHSNER MEDICAL CENTER (O, 771 beds) 1514 Jefferson Highway, New Orleans, LA Zip 70121–2429; tel. 504/842–3000; Robert Wolterman, Chief Executive Officer
**Web address:** www.ochsner.org

OCHSNER MEDICAL CENTER – KENNER (O, 119 beds) 180 West Esplanade Avenue, Kenner, LA Zip 70065–6001; tel. 504/468–8600; Paolo Zambito, Chief Executive Officer
**Web address:** www.ochsner.org/locations/ochsner_health_center_kenner_w_esplanade_ave/

OCHSNER MEDICAL CENTER – NORTH SHORE (L, 110 beds) 100 Medical Center Drive, Slidell, LA Zip 70461–5520; tel. 985/646–5000; Polly J. Davenport, R.N., Chief Executive Officer
**Web address:** www.ochsner.org/locations/northshore

OCHSNER MEDICAL CENTER–BATON ROUGE (O, 115 beds) 17000 Medical Center Drive, Baton Rouge, LA Zip 70816–3224; tel. 225/752–2470; Eric McMillen, Chief Executive Officer
**Web address:** www.ochsner.org/page.cfm?id=103

OCHSNER ST. ANNE GENERAL HOSPITAL (O, 38 beds) 4608 Highway 1, Raceland, LA Zip 70394–2623; tel. 985/537–6841; Milton D. Bourgeois, Jr., Chief Executive Officer
**Web address:** www.ochsnerstanne.org

| Owned, leased, sponsored: | 6 hospitals | 1208 beds |
|---|---|---|
| Contract–managed: | 0 hospitals | 0 beds |
| **Totals:** | 6 hospitals | 1208 beds |

---

**0388:  OCONEE REGIONAL HEALTH SYSTEMS** (NP) 821 North Cobb Street, Milledgeville, GA Zip 31061–2343; tel. 478/454–3505; Jean Aycock, President and Chief Executive Officer
**(Independent Hospital System)**

**GEORGIA:** JASPER MEMORIAL HOSPITAL (O, 67 beds) 898 College Street, Monticello, GA Zip 31064–1258; tel. 706/468–6411; Jan Gaston, Administrator
**Web address:** www.jaspermemorialhospital.org

OCONEE REGIONAL MEDICAL CENTER (O, 90 beds) 821 North Cobb Street, Milledgeville, GA Zip 31061–2351, Mailing Address: P.O. Box 690, Zip 31059–0690; tel. 478/454–3500; Jean Aycock, President and Chief Executive Officer
**Web address:** www.oconeeregional.com

| Owned, leased, sponsored: | 2 hospitals | 157 beds |
|---|---|---|
| Contract–managed: | 0 hospitals | 0 beds |
| **Totals:** | 2 hospitals | 157 beds |

---

**0537:  OHIO DEPARTMENT OF MENTAL HEALTH** (NP) 30 East Broad Street, 8th Floor, Columbus, OH Zip 43215–3430; tel. 614/466–2297; Tracy Plouck, Director
**(Independent Hospital System)**

**OHIO:** APPALACHIAN BEHAVIORAL HEALTHCARE (O, 224 beds) 100 Hospital Drive, Athens, OH Zip 45701–2301; tel. 740/594–5000; Jane E. Krason, R.N., Chief Executive Officer
**Web address:** www.mh.state.oh.us

HEARTLAND BEHAVIORAL HEALTHCARE (O, 130 beds) 3000 Erie Street, Massillon, OH Zip 44646–7993, Mailing Address: P.O. Box 540, Zip 44648–0540; tel. 330/833–3135; James Ignelzi, Interim Chief Executive Officer
**Web address:** www.mh.state.oh.us/ibhs/bhos/hoh.html

NORTHCOAST BEHAVIORAL HEALTHCARE SYSTEM (O, 260 beds) 1756 Sagamore Road, Northfield, OH Zip 44067–1086; tel. 330/467–7131; David Celletti, Chief Executive Officer
**Web address:** www.mh.state.oh.us

NORTHWEST OHIO PSYCHIATRIC HOSPITAL (O, 114 beds) 930 Detroit Avenue, Toledo, OH Zip 43614–2701; tel. 419/381–1881; Mychail Scheramic, M.D., Chief Executive Officer
**Web address:** www.mh.state.oh.us/

SUMMIT BEHAVIORAL HEALTHCARE (O, 291 beds) 1101 Summit Road, Cincinnati, OH Zip 45237–2652; tel. 513/948–3600; Elizabeth Banks, Chief Executive Officer
**Web address:** www.mh.state.oh.us/

TWIN VALLEY BEHAVIORAL HEALTHCARE (O, 248 beds) 2200 West Broad Street, Columbus, OH Zip 43223–1297; tel. 614/752–0333; Karen Woods–Nyce, Chief Executive Officer
**Web address:** www.mh.state.oh.us/ibhs/bhos/tvbh.html

| Owned, leased, sponsored: | 6 hospitals | 1267 beds |
|---|---|---|
| Contract–managed: | 0 hospitals | 0 beds |
| **Totals:** | 6 hospitals | 1267 beds |

---

**★0251:   OHIO STATE UNIVERSITY HEALTH SYSTEM** (NP) 370 West Ninth Avenue, Columbus, OH Zip 43210–1238; tel. 614/247–5555; Peter E. Geier, Chief Executive Officer
**(Centralized Health System)**

JAMES CANCER HOSPITAL AND SOLOVE RESEARCH INSTITUTE (O, 209 beds) 300 West Tenth Avenue, Columbus, OH Zip 43210–1280; tel. 614/293–3300; Michael Caligiuri, Chief Executive Officer
**Web address:** www.jamesline.com

OHIO STATE UNIVERSITY WEXNER MEDICAL CENTER (O, 971 beds) 370 West 9th Avenue, Columbus, OH Zip 43210–1238; tel. 614/293–8000; Steven Gabbe, M.D., Chief Executive Officer
**Web address:** www.medicalcenter.osu.edu

| Owned, leased, sponsored: | 2 hospitals | 1180 beds |
|---|---|---|
| Contract–managed: | 0 hospitals | 0 beds |
| **Totals:** | 2 hospitals | 1180 beds |

---

**3315:  OHIO VALLEY HEALTH SERVICES AND EDUCATION CORPORATION** (NP) 2000 Eoff Street, Wheeling, WV Zip 26003–3823; tel. 304/234–8383; Michael J. Caruso, President and Chief Executive Officer
**(Moderately Centralized Health System)**

EAST OHIO REGIONAL HOSPITAL (O, 161 beds) 90 North Fourth Street, Martins Ferry, OH Zip 43935–1648; tel. 740/633–1100; Michael J. Caruso, President and Chief Executive Officer
**Web address:** www.ovmc–eorh.com

**WEST VIRGINIA:** OHIO VALLEY MEDICAL CENTER (O, 185 beds) 2000 Eoff Street, Wheeling, WV Zip 26003–3870; tel. 304/234–0123; Michael J. Caruso, President and Chief Executive Officer
**Web address:** www.ovmc–eorh.com

| Owned, leased, sponsored: | 2 hospitals | 346 beds |
|---|---|---|
| Contract–managed: | 0 hospitals | 0 beds |
| **Totals:** | 2 hospitals | 346 beds |

---

**★0162:   OHIOHEALTH** (NP) 180 East Broad Street, Columbus, OH Zip 43215–3707; tel. 614/544–4455; David P. Blom, President and Chief Executive Officer
**(Centralized Physician/Insurance Health System)**

**OHIO:** DOCTORS HOSPITAL NELSONVILLE (O, 25 beds) 1950 Mount Saint Mary Drive, Nelsonville, OH Zip 45764–1280; tel. 740/753–1931; LaMar L. Wyse, Chief Operating Officer
**Web address:** www.ohiohealth.com

HARDIN MEMORIAL HOSPITAL (O, 25 beds) 921 East Franklin Street, Kenton, OH Zip 43326–2099; tel. 419/673–0761; Mark R. Seckinger, Administrator and Chief Executive Officer
**Web address:** www.hardinmemorial.org

MORROW COUNTY HOSPITAL (C, 53 beds) 651 West Marion Road, Mount Gilead, OH Zip 43338–1027; tel. 419/946–5015; Christopher Truax, Chief Executive Officer
**Web address:** www.morrowcountyhospital.com

O'BLENESS MEMORIAL HOSPITAL (C, 132 beds) 55 Hospital Drive, Athens, OH Zip 45701–2302; tel. 740/593–5551; Greg Long, Chief Executive Officer
**Web address:** www.obleness.org

For explanation of codes following names, see page B2.
★ Indicates Type III membership in the American Hospital Association.

OHIOHEALTH DOCTORS HOSPITAL (O, 262 beds) 5100 West Broad Street, Columbus, OH Zip 43228–1607; tel. 614/544–1000; Michael L. Reichfield, President
**Web address:** www.ohiohealth.com

OHIOHEALTH DUBLIN METHODIST HOSPITAL (O, 92 beds) 7500 Hospital Drive, Dublin, OH Zip 43016–8518; tel. 614/544–8000; Bruce P. Hagen, President
**Web address:** www.ohiohealth.com

OHIOHEALTH GRADY MEMORIAL HOSPITAL (O, 61 beds) 561 West Central Avenue, Delaware, OH Zip 43015–1410; tel. 740/615–1000; Bruce P. Hagen, President
**Web address:** www.ohiohealth.com

OHIOHEALTH GRANT MEDICAL CENTER (O, 427 beds) 111 South Grant Avenue, Columbus, OH Zip 43215–1898; tel. 614/566–9000; Vinson Yates, President
**Web address:** www.ohiohealth.com

OHIOHEALTH MARION GENERAL HOSPITAL (O, 170 beds) 1000 McKinley Park Drive, Marion, OH Zip 43302–6397; tel. 740/383–8400; John W. Sanders, President
**Web address:** www.ohiohealth.com/mariongeneral

OHIOHEALTH RIVERSIDE METHODIST HOSPITAL (O, 765 beds) 3535 Olentangy River Road, Columbus, OH Zip 43214–3998; tel. 614/566–5000; Stephen Markovich, M.D., President
**Web address:** www.ohiohealth.com

| | | |
|---|---|---|
| **Owned, leased, sponsored:** | 8 hospitals | 1827 beds |
| **Contract–managed:** | 2 hospitals | 185 beds |
| **Totals:** | 10 hospitals | 2012 beds |

**0018:  OKLAHOMA DEPARTMENT OF MENTAL HEALTH AND SUBSTANCE ABUSE SERVICES** (NP)
1200 N.E. 13th Street, Oklahoma City, OK Zip 73117–1022, Mailing Address: P.O. Box 53277, Zip 73152–3277; tel. 405/522–3908; Terri White, Commissioner
**(Independent Hospital System)**

**OKLAHOMA:** GRIFFIN MEMORIAL HOSPITAL (O, 120 beds) 900 East Main Street, Norman, OK Zip 73071–5305, Mailing Address: P.O. Box 151, Zip 73070–0151; tel. 405/321–4880; Lawrence Gross, Executive Director
**Web address:** www.odmhsas.org

NORTHWEST CENTER FOR BEHAVIORAL HEALTH (O, 28 beds) 1 Mi East Highway 270, Fort Supply, OK Zip 73841; tel. 580/766–2311; Trudy Hoffman, Executive Director
**Web address:** www.ncbhok.org/

OKLAHOMA FORENSIC CENTER (O, 200 beds) 24800 South 4420 Road, Vinita, OK Zip 74301–5544, Mailing Address: P.O. Box 69, Zip 74301–0069; tel. 918/256–7841; Lori Jordan, Chief Executive Officer

| | | |
|---|---|---|
| **Owned, leased, sponsored:** | 3 hospitals | 348 beds |
| **Contract–managed:** | 0 hospitals | 0 beds |
| **Totals:** | 3 hospitals | 348 beds |

**3355:  ORLANDO HEALTH** (NP)
1414 Kuhl Avenue, Orlando, FL Zip 32806–2093; tel. 407/841–5111; Sherrie Sitarik, President and Chief Executive Officer
**(Moderately Centralized Health System)**

**FLORIDA:** HEALTH CENTRAL (O, 399 beds) 10000 West Colonial Drive, Ocoee, FL Zip 34761–3499; tel. 407/296–1000; Gregory P. Ohe, President and Chief Executive Officer
**Web address:** www.healthcentral.org

ORLANDO REGIONAL MEDICAL CENTER (O, 1468 beds) 1414 Kuhl Avenue, Orlando, FL Zip 32806–2093; tel. 407/841–5111; Shannon Elswick, President
**Web address:** www.orhs.org

SOUTH LAKE HOSPITAL (O, 122 beds) 1900 Don Wickham Drive, Clermont, FL Zip 34711–1979; tel. 352/394–4071; John Moore, Chief Executive Officer
**Web address:** www.southlakehospital.com

| | | |
|---|---|---|
| **Owned, leased, sponsored:** | 3 hospitals | 1989 beds |
| **Contract–managed:** | 0 hospitals | 0 beds |
| **Totals:** | 3 hospitals | 1989 beds |

**★5335:  OSF HEALTHCARE SYSTEM** (CC)
800 N.E. Glen Oak Avenue, Peoria, IL Zip 61603–3200; tel. 309/655–2850; Kevin D. Schoeplein, Chief Executive Officer
**(Centralized Physician/Insurance Health System)**

**ILLINOIS:** OSF HOLY FAMILY MEDICAL CENTER (O, 23 beds) 1000 West Harlem Avenue, Monmouth, IL Zip 61462–1007; tel. 309/734–3141; Patricia A. Luker, Chief Executive Officer
**Web address:** www.osfholyfamily.org

OSF SAINT ANTHONY MEDICAL CENTER (O, 235 beds) 5666 East State Street, Rockford, IL Zip 61108–2425; tel. 815/226–2000; David A. Schertz, President and Chief Executive Officer
**Web address:** www.osfhealth.com

OSF SAINT ELIZABETH MEDICAL CENTER (O, 90 beds) 1100 East Norris Drive, Ottawa, IL Zip 61350–1687; tel. 815/433–3100; Robert A. Chaffin, President and Chief Executive Officer
**Web address:** www.ottawaregional.org

OSF SAINT FRANCIS MEDICAL CENTER (O, 631 beds) 530 N.E. Glen Oak Avenue, Peoria, IL Zip 61637–0001; tel. 309/655–2000; Keith E. Steffen, President and Chief Executive Officer
**Web address:** www.osfsaintfrancis.org

OSF SAINT JAMES – JOHN W. ALBRECHT MEDICAL CENTER (O, 42 beds) 2500 West Reynolds, Pontiac, IL Zip 61764–9774; tel. 815/842–2828; David T. Ochs, President and Chief Executive Officer
**Web address:** www.osfsaintjames.org

OSF ST. JOSEPH MEDICAL CENTER (O, 149 beds) 2200 East Washington Street, Bloomington, IL Zip 61701–4323; tel. 309/662–3311; Kenneth J. Natzke, President and Chief Executive Officer
**Web address:** www.osfstjoseph.org

OSF ST. MARY MEDICAL CENTER (O, 90 beds) 3333 North Seminary Street, Galesburg, IL Zip 61401–1299; tel. 309/344–3161; Richard S. Kowalski, FACHE, President and Chief Executive Officer
**Web address:** www.osfstmary.org

**MICHIGAN:** OSF ST. FRANCIS HOSPITAL (O, 48 beds) 3401 Ludington Street, Escanaba, MI Zip 49829–1377; tel. 906/786–3311; David Lord, President and Chief Executive Officer
**Web address:** www.osfstfrancis.org

| | | |
|---|---|---|
| **Owned, leased, sponsored:** | 8 hospitals | 1308 beds |
| **Contract–managed:** | 0 hospitals | 0 beds |
| **Totals:** | 8 hospitals | 1308 beds |

**0367:  PACER HEALTH CORPORATION** (IO)
14100 Palmetto Frontage Road, Suite 110, Miami Lakes, FL Zip 33016; tel. 305/828–7660; Rainier Gonzalez, Chairman and Chief Executive Officer

**KENTUCKY:** KNOX COUNTY HOSPITAL (O, 25 beds) 80 Hospital Drive, Barbourville, KY Zip 40906–7363, Mailing Address: P.O. Box 10, Zip 40906–0010; tel. 606/546–4175; Gary G. Kendrick, Interim Chief Executive Officer
**Web address:** www.knoxcohospital.com

**LOUISIANA:** CALCASIEU OAKS GERIATRIC PSYCHIATRIC HOSPITAL (O, 24 beds) 2837 Ernest Street, Lake Charles, LA Zip 70601–8785; tel. 337/439–8111; Charles Getwood, Assistant Chief Executive Officer

| | | |
|---|---|---|
| **Owned, leased, sponsored:** | 2 hospitals | 49 beds |
| **Contract–managed:** | 0 hospitals | 0 beds |
| **Totals:** | 2 hospitals | 49 beds |

**★5235:  PALLOTTINE HEALTH SERVICES** (CC)
2900 First Avenue, Huntington, WV Zip 25702–1241; tel. 304/526–1234; Michael G. Sellards, Chief Executive Officer
**(Independent Hospital System)**

For explanation of codes following names, see page B2.
★ Indicates Type III membership in the American Hospital Association.

**WEST VIRGINIA:** ST. JOSEPH'S HOSPITAL OF BUCKHANNON (O, 69 beds) 1 Amalia Drive, Buckhannon, WV Zip 26201–2276; tel. 304/473–2000; Sue E. Johnson–Phillippe, President and Chief Executive Officer
**Web address:** www.stj.net

ST. MARY'S MEDICAL CENTER (O, 375 beds) 2900 First Avenue, Huntington, WV Zip 25702–1272; tel. 304/526–1234; Michael G. Sellards, President and Chief Executive Officer
**Web address:** www.st–marys.org

| | | |
|---|---|---|
| Owned, leased, sponsored: | 2 hospitals | 444 beds |
| Contract–managed: | 0 hospitals | 0 beds |
| Totals: | 2 hospitals | 444 beds |

---

★**4155: PALMETTO HEALTH** (NP)
1301 Taylor Street, Suite 9–A, Columbia, SC Zip 29201–2942, Mailing Address: P.O. Box 2266, Zip 29202–2266; tel. 803/296–2100; Charles D. Beaman, Jr., Chief Executive Officer
**(Moderately Centralized Health System)**

**SOUTH CAROLINA:** BAPTIST EASLEY HOSPITAL (O, 89 beds) 200 Fleetwood Drive, Easley, SC Zip 29640–2022, Mailing Address: P.O. Box 2129, Zip 29641–2129; tel. 864/442–7200; Roddey E. Gettys, III, Chief Executive Officer
**Web address:** www.baptisteasley.org

PALMETTO HEALTH BAPTIST (O, 412 beds) Taylor at Marion Street, Columbia, SC Zip 29220–0001; tel. 803/296–5010; James M. Bridges, Executive Vice President and Chief Operating Officer
**Web address:** www.palmettohealth.org

PALMETTO HEALTH RICHLAND (O, 674 beds) Five Richland Medical Park Drive, Columbia, SC Zip 29203–6897; tel. 803/434–7000; Stan Hickson, FACHE, Executive Vice President and Chief Operating Officer
**Web address:** www.palmettohealth.org

| | | |
|---|---|---|
| Owned, leased, sponsored: | 3 hospitals | 1175 beds |
| Contract–managed: | 0 hospitals | 0 beds |
| Totals: | 3 hospitals | 1175 beds |

---

★**7555: PALOMAR HEALTH** (NP)
456 East Grand Avenue, Escondido, CA Zip 92025–3319; tel. 760/740–6393; Michael H. Covert, FACHE, Chief Executive Officer
**(Moderately Centralized Health System)**

**CALIFORNIA:** PALOMAR MEDICAL CENTER (O, 368 beds) 2185 West Citracado Parkway, Escondido, CA Zip 92029–4159; tel. 760/739–3000; Gerald E. Bracht, Chief Administrative Officer
**Web address:** www.pph.org

POMERADO HOSPITAL (O, 236 beds) 15615 Pomerado Road, Poway, CA Zip 92064–2460; tel. 858/613–4000; David A. Tam, M.D., FACHE, Chief Administrative Officer
**Web address:** www.pph.org

| | | |
|---|---|---|
| Owned, leased, sponsored: | 2 hospitals | 604 beds |
| Contract–managed: | 0 hospitals | 0 beds |
| Totals: | 2 hospitals | 604 beds |

---

★**0159: PARKVIEW HEALTH** (NP)
10501 Corporate Drive, Fort Wayne, IN Zip 46845–1700, Mailing Address: P.O. Box 5600, Zip 46895–5600; tel. 260/373–7001; Michael J. Packnett, President and Chief Executive Officer
**(Centralized Physician/Insurance Health System)**

**INDIANA:** PARKVIEW HUNTINGTON HOSPITAL (O, 36 beds) 2001 Stults Road, Huntington, IN Zip 46750–1291; tel. 260/355–3000; Darlene Garrett, Chief Operating Officer
**Web address:** www.parkview.com

PARKVIEW LAGRANGE HOSPITAL (O, 25 beds) 207 North Townline Road, LaGrange, IN Zip 46761–1325; tel. 260/463–2143; Robert T. Myers, Chief Operating Officer
**Web address:** www.parkview.com

PARKVIEW NOBLE HOSPITAL (O, 31 beds) 401 Sawyer Road, Kendallville, IN Zip 46755–2568; tel. 260/347–8700; David C. Hunter, Chief Operating Officer
**Web address:** www.parkview.com

PARKVIEW REGIONAL MEDICAL CENTER (O, 636 beds) 11109 Parkview Plaza Drive, Fort Wayne, IN Zip 46845–1701; tel. 260/373–4000; Sue Ehinger, Ph.D., President
**Web address:** www.parkview.com

PARKVIEW WHITLEY HOSPITAL (O, 97 beds) 1260 East State Road 205, Columbia City, IN Zip 46725–9492; tel. 260/248–9000; Scott F. Gabriel, Chief Operating Officer
**Web address:** www.parkview.com

| | | |
|---|---|---|
| Owned, leased, sponsored: | 5 hospitals | 825 beds |
| Contract–managed: | 0 hospitals | 0 beds |
| Totals: | 5 hospitals | 825 beds |

---

★**1785: PARTNERS HEALTHCARE SYSTEM, INC.** (NP)
800 Boylston Street, Suite 1150, Boston, MA Zip 02199–8123; tel. 617/278–1004; Gary L. Gottlieb, M.D., President and Chief Executive Officer
**(Centralized Health System)**

**MASSACHUSETTS:** BRIGHAM AND WOMEN'S FAULKNER HOSPITAL (O, 86 beds) 1153 Centre Street, Boston, MA Zip 02130–3446; tel. 617/983–7000; Michael Gustafson, M.D., Chief Operating Officer
**Web address:** www.brighamandwomensfaulkner.org/index.asp

BRIGHAM AND WOMEN'S HOSPITAL (O, 779 beds) 75 Francis Street, Boston, MA Zip 02115–6110; tel. 617/732–5500; Elizabeth Nabel, M.D., President
**Web address:** www.brighamandwomens.org

MARTHA'S VINEYARD HOSPITAL (O, 25 beds) One Hospital Road, Oak Bluffs, MA Zip 02557, Mailing Address: P.O. Box 1477, Zip 02557–1477; tel. 508/693–0410; Timothy J. Walsh, Chief Executive Officer
**Web address:** www.marthasvineyardhospital.org

MASSACHUSETTS GENERAL HOSPITAL (O, 947 beds) 55 Fruit Street, Boston, MA Zip 02114–2696; tel. 617/726–2000; Peter L. Slavin, M.D., President
**Web address:** www.massgeneral.org

MCLEAN HOSPITAL (O, 177 beds) 115 Mill Street, Belmont, MA Zip 02478–1064; tel. 617/855–2000; Scott L. Rauch, M.D., President
**Web address:** www.mclean.harvard.edu

NANTUCKET COTTAGE HOSPITAL (O, 19 beds) 57 Prospect Street, Nantucket, MA Zip 02554–2799; tel. 508/825–8100; Margot Hartmann, M.D., Ph.D., President and Chief Executive Officer
**Web address:** www.nantuckethospital.org

NEWTON–WELLESLEY HOSPITAL (O, 216 beds) 2014 Washington Street, Newton Lower Falls, MA Zip 02462–1699; tel. 617/243–6000; Patrick Jordan, III, Interim President
**Web address:** www.nwh.org

NORTH SHORE MEDICAL CENTER (O, 411 beds) 81 Highland Avenue, Salem, MA Zip 01970–2714; tel. 978/741–1200; Robert G. Norton, President and Chief Executive Officer
**Web address:** www.nsmc.partners.org

SPAULDING HOSPITAL FOR CONTINUING MEDICAL CARE NORTH SHORE (O, 160 beds) 1 Dove Avenue, Salem, MA Zip 01970–2999; tel. 978/825–8900; Maureen Banks, R.N., MS, President
**Web address:** www.shaughnessy–kaplan.org

SPAULDING HOSPITAL FOR CONTINUING MEDICAL CARE CAMBRIDGE (O, 180 beds) 1575 Cambridge Street, Cambridge, MA Zip 02138–4308; tel. 617/876–4344; Maureen Banks, R.N., MS, President
**Web address:** www.spauldingnetwork.org

SPAULDING REHABILITATION HOSPITAL (O, 196 beds) 125 Nashua Street, Boston, MA Zip 02114–1198; tel. 617/573–7000; David E. Storto, President
**Web address:** www.spauldingrehab.org

---

For explanation of codes following names, see page B2.
★ Indicates Type III membership in the American Hospital Association.

SPAULDING REHABILITATION HOSPITAL CAPE COD (O, 60 beds) 311 Service Road, East Sandwich, MA Zip 02537–1370; tel. 508/833–4000; Maureen Banks, R.N., MS, President and Chief Executive Officer
**Web address:** www.rhci.org

| Owned, leased, sponsored: | 12 hospitals | 3256 beds |
|---|---|---|
| Contract–managed: | 0 hospitals | 0 beds |
| Totals: | 12 hospitals | 3256 beds |

---

★**5415: PEACEHEALTH** (CC)
1115 S.E. 164th Avenue, Vancouver, WA Zip 98683; tel. 425/747–1711; Alan R. Yordy, President and Chief Mission Officer
**(Moderately Centralized Health System)**

**ALASKA:** PEACEHEALTH KETCHIKAN MEDICAL CENTER (L, 54 beds) 3100 Tongass Avenue, Ketchikan, AK Zip 99901–5746; tel. 907/225–5171; Patrick J. Branco, Chief Executive Officer
**Web address:** www.peacehealth.org

**OREGON:** PEACEHEALTH COTTAGE GROVE COMMUNITY MEDICAL CENTER (O, 14 beds) 1515 Village Drive, Cottage Grove, OR Zip 97424–9700; tel. 541/942–0511; MaryAnne McMurren, R.N., Administrator and Chief Executive Officer
**Web address:** www.peacehealth.org

PEACEHEALTH PEACE HARBOR MEDICAL CENTER (O, 21 beds) 400 Ninth Street, Florence, OR Zip 97439–7398; tel. 541/997–8412; Rick Yecny, Chief Executive Officer
**Web address:** www.peacehealth.org

PEACEHEALTH SACRED HEART MEDICAL CENTER AT RIVERBEND (O, 379 beds) 3333 Riverbend Drive, Springfield, OR Zip 97477–8800; tel. 541/222–7300; John G. Hill, Chief Executive Officer
**Web address:** www.peacehealth.org

PEACEHEALTH SACRED HEART MEDICAL CENTER, UNIVERSITY DISTRICT (O, 104 beds) 1255 Hilyard Street, Eugene, OR Zip 97401–3700, Mailing Address: P.O. Box 10905, Zip 97440–2905; tel. 541/686–7300; John G. Hill, Chief Executive Officer
**Web address:** www.peacehealth.org

**WASHINGTON:** PEACEHEALTH PEACE ISLAND MEDICAL CENTER (O, 10 beds) 1117 Spring Street, Friday Harbor, WA Zip 98250–9782; tel. 360/378–2141; James R. Barnhart, Chief Administrator Officer
**Web address:** www.peacehealth.org

PEACEHEALTH SOUTHWEST MEDICAL CENTER (O, 450 beds) 400 N.E. Mother Joseph Place, Vancouver, WA Zip 98664–3200, Mailing Address: P.O. Box 1600, Zip 98668–1600; tel. 360/256–2000; Joseph M. Kortum, President and Chief Mission Officer
**Web address:** www.swmedicalcenter.org

PEACEHEALTH ST. JOHN MEDICAL CENTER (O, 202 beds) 1615 Delaware Street, Longview, WA Zip 98632–2367, Mailing Address: P.O. Box 3002, Zip 98632–0302; tel. 360/414–2000; Sy Johnson, Chief Executive Officer and Chief Mission Officer
**Web address:** www.peacehealth.org

PEACEHEALTH ST. JOSEPH MEDICAL CENTER (O, 253 beds) 2901 Squalicum Parkway, Bellingham, WA Zip 98225–1851; tel. 360/734–5400; Nancy Steiger, R.N., Chief Executive Officer and Chief Mission Officer
**Web address:** www.peacehealth.org

| Owned, leased, sponsored: | 9 hospitals | 1487 beds |
|---|---|---|
| Contract–managed: | 0 hospitals | 0 beds |
| Totals: | 9 hospitals | 1487 beds |

---

★**0314: PHOEBE PUTNEY HEALTH SYSTEM** (NP)
417 Third Avenue, Albany, GA Zip 31701–1943; tel. 229/312–1000; Joel Wernick, President and Chief Executive Officer
**(Moderately Centralized Health System)**

**GEORGIA:** PHOEBE NORTH (O, 102 beds) 2000 Palmyra Road, Albany, GA Zip 31701–1528, Mailing Address: P.O. Box 1908, Zip 31702–1908; tel. 229/434–2000; Thomas Sullivan, Chief Transition Officer
**Web address:** www.palmyramedicalcenters.com

PHOEBE PUTNEY MEMORIAL HOSPITAL (O, 440 beds) 417 Third Avenue, Albany, GA Zip 31701–1943, Mailing Address: P.O. Box 1828, Zip 31702–1828; tel. 229/883–1800; Joel Wernick, President and Chief Executive Officer
**Web address:** www.phoebeputney.com

PHOEBE SUMTER MEDICAL CENTER (O, 45 beds) 126 Highway 280 West, Americus, GA Zip 31719; tel. 229/924–6011; Keith J. Petersen, Chief Executive Officer
**Web address:** www.phoebesumter.org

PHOEBE WORTH MEDICAL CENTER (O, 25 beds) 807 South Isabella Street, Sylvester, GA Zip 31791–7554, Mailing Address: P.O. Box 545, Zip 31791–0545; tel. 229/776–6961; Kim Gilman, Chief Administrative Officer
**Web address:** www.phoebeputney.com

| Owned, leased, sponsored: | 4 hospitals | 612 beds |
|---|---|---|
| Contract–managed: | 0 hospitals | 0 beds |
| Totals: | 4 hospitals | 612 beds |

---

**0043: PHYSICIANS FOR HEALTHY HOSPITALS** (IO)
1117 East Devonshire Avenue, Hemet, CA Zip 92543–3083; tel. 951/652–2811; Joel Bergenfeld, Chief Executive Officer

**CALIFORNIA:** HEMET VALLEY MEDICAL CENTER (O, 159 beds) 1117 East Devonshire Avenue, Hemet, CA Zip 92543–3083; tel. 951/652–2811; Joel Bergenfeld, Chief Executive Officer
**Web address:** www.valleyhealthsystem.com

MENIFEE VALLEY MEDICAL CENTER (O, 82 beds) 28400 McCall Boulevard, Sun City, CA Zip 92585–9537; tel. 951/679–8888; Joel Bergenfeld, Chief Executive Officer
**Web address:** www.valleyhealthsystem.com

| Owned, leased, sponsored: | 2 hospitals | 241 beds |
|---|---|---|
| Contract–managed: | 0 hospitals | 0 beds |
| Totals: | 2 hospitals | 241 beds |

---

**0620: PHYSICIANS HOSPITAL SYSTEM** (IO)
1625 East Jefferson Boulevard, Mishawaka, IN Zip 46545–7103; tel. 574/255–1400; Cameron R. Gilbert, Ph.D., President and Chief Executive Officer
**(Independent Hospital System)**

**INDIANA:** DOCTOR'S HOSPITAL AND NEUROMUSCULAR CENTER (O, 20 beds) 411 South Whitlock Street, Bremen, IN Zip 46506–1626, Mailing Address: P.O. Box 36, Zip 46506–0036; tel. 574/546–3830; DeWayne Long, Chief Executive Officer
**Web address:** www.physicianshospitalsystem.net

RIVERCREST SPECIALTY HOSPITAL (O, 30 beds) 1625 East Jefferson Boulevard, Mishawaka, IN Zip 46545–7103; tel. 574/255–1400; Ronni Banks, Administrator
**Web address:** www.physicianshospitalsystem.net/

UNITY MEDICAL & SURGICAL HOSPITAL (O, 15 beds) 4455 Edison Lakes Parkway, Mishawaka, IN Zip 46545–1442; tel. 574/968–0867; John M. Day, Chief Executive Officer
**Web address:** www.physicianshospitalsystem.net

| Owned, leased, sponsored: | 3 hospitals | 65 beds |
|---|---|---|
| Contract–managed: | 0 hospitals | 0 beds |
| Totals: | 3 hospitals | 65 beds |

---

★**0310: PIEDMONT HEALTHCARE** (NP)
1800 Howell Mill Road N.W., Suite 850, Atlanta, GA Zip 30318–0923; tel. 404/425–1314; Kevin Brown, President and Chief Executive Officer
**(Moderately Centralized Health System)**

**GEORGIA:** HENRY MEDICAL CENTER (L, 289 beds) 1133 Eagle's Landing Parkway, Stockbridge, GA Zip 30281–5099; tel. 678/604–1000; Charles F. Scott, President and Chief Executive Officer
**Web address:** www.henrymedical.com

---

For explanation of codes following names, see page B2.
★ Indicates Type III membership in the American Hospital Association.

PIEDMONT FAYETTE HOSPITAL (O, 148 beds) 1255 Highway 54 West, Fayetteville, GA Zip 30214–4526; tel. 770/719–7000; J. Michael Burnett, President and Chief Administrative Officer
**Web address:** www.fayettehospital.org

PIEDMONT HOSPITAL (O, 484 beds) 1968 Peachtree Road N.W., Atlanta, GA Zip 30309–1281; tel. 404/605–5000; Leslie A. Donahue, President and Chief Executive Officer
**Web address:** www.piedmonthospital.org

PIEDMONT MOUNTAINSIDE HOSPITAL (O, 48 beds) 1266 Highway 515 South, Jasper, GA Zip 30143–4872; tel. 706/692–2441; Denise Ray, President and Chief Administrative Officer
**Web address:** www.piedmontmountainsidehospital.org

PIEDMONT NEWNAN HOSPITAL (O, 143 beds) 745 Poplar Road, Newnan, GA Zip 30265–1618; tel. 770/253–1912; G. Michael Bass, President and Chief Executive Officer
**Web address:** www.piedmontnewnan.org

| | | |
|---|---|---|
| **Owned, leased, sponsored:** | 5 hospitals | 1112 beds |
| **Contract–managed:** | 0 hospitals | 0 beds |
| **Totals:** | 5 hospitals | 1112 beds |

---

**★0326: PIONEER HEALTH SERVICES** (IO)
110 Pioneer Way, Magee, MS Zip 39111–5501, Mailing Address: P.O. Box 1100, Zip 39111–1100; tel. 601/849–6440; Joseph S. McNulty, III, President and Chief Executive Officer
**(Independent Hospital System)**

GEORGIA: PIONEER COMMUNITY HOSPITAL OF EARLY (L, 152 beds) 11740 Columbia Street, Blakely, GA Zip 39823–2574; tel. 229/723–4241; Greg Havard, Administrator
**Web address:** www.pchearly.com

**MISSISSIPPI:** PIONEER COMMUNITY HOSPITAL OF ABERDEEN (L, 35 beds) 400 South Chestnut Street, Aberdeen, MS Zip 39730–3335, Mailing Address: P.O. Box 548, Zip 39730–0548; tel. 662/369–2455; Sean Johnson, Administrator
**Web address:** www.pchaberdeen.com

PIONEER COMMUNITY HOSPITAL OF CHOCTAW (L, 72 beds) 311 West Cherry Street, Ackerman, MS Zip 39735–8708; tel. 662/285–6235; Sean Johnson, Chief Executive Officer
**Web address:** www.pchchoctaw.com

PIONEER COMMUNITY HOSPITAL OF NEWTON (O, 30 beds) 9421 Eastside Drive, Newton, MS Zip 39345–8063; tel. 601/683–2031; Mark Norman, Administrator
**Web address:** www.pchnewton.com

S. E. LACKEY MEMORIAL HOSPITAL (C, 55 beds) 330 Broad Street, Forest, MS Zip 39074–3508, Mailing Address: P.O. Box 428, Zip 39074–0428; tel. 601/469–4151; Donna Riser, Administrator
**Web address:** www.lackeymemorialhospital.com

**NORTH CAROLINA:** PIONEER COMMUNITY HOSPITAL OF STOKES (L, 25 beds) 1570 Highway 8 and 89 North, Danbury, NC Zip 27016, Mailing Address: P.O. Box 10, Zip 27016–0010; tel. 336/593–2831; John Tompkins, Administrator
**Web address:** www.pchstokes.com

**VIRGINIA:** PIONEER COMMUNITY HOSPITAL OF PATRICK COUNTY (O, 25 beds) 18688 Jeb Stuart Highway, Stuart, VA Zip 24171–1559; tel. 276/694–3151; Jeanette Filpi, Chief Executive Officer
**Web address:** www.phscorporate.com

| | | |
|---|---|---|
| **Owned, leased, sponsored:** | 6 hospitals | 339 beds |
| **Contract–managed:** | 1 hospital | 55 beds |
| **Totals:** | 7 hospitals | 394 beds |

---

**0899: POLARIS HOSPITAL COMPANY** (IO)
10 Cadillac Drive, Suite 470, Brentwood, TN Zip 37027–1045; tel. 615/577–1111; Kevin D. Lee, Director and Chief Executive Officer

**TENNESSEE:** TRUSTPOINT HOSPITAL (O, 60 beds) 1009 North Thompson Lane, Murfreesboro, TN Zip 37129–4351; tel. 615/867–1111; Anita Peterson, Chief Executive Officer
**Web address:** www.trustpointhospital.com

**TEXAS:** TRUSTPOINT HOSPITAL (O, 64 beds) 4302 Princeton Street, Lubbock, TX Zip 79415–1304; tel. 806/749–2222; Craig Bragg, Chief Executive Officer
**Web address:** www.trustpointhospital.com/

| | | |
|---|---|---|
| **Owned, leased, sponsored:** | 2 hospitals | 124 beds |
| **Contract–managed:** | 0 hospitals | 0 beds |
| **Totals:** | 2 hospitals | 124 beds |

---

**0617: POST ACUTE MEDICAL, LLC** (IO)
3500 Market Street, Suite 202, Camp Hill, PA Zip 17011–4354; tel. 717/731–9660; Anthony F. Misitano, President and Chief Executive Officer
**(Independent Hospital System)**

**LOUISIANA:** NORTHSHORE SPECIALTY HOSPITAL (O, 58 beds) 20050 Crestwood Boulevard, Covington, LA Zip 70433–5207; tel. 985/875–7525; Stephanie Morvant, Chief Executive Officer
**Web address:** www.northshoreltach.com

**TEXAS:** WARM SPRINGS REHABILITATION HOSPITAL (O, 138 beds) 5101 Medical Drive, San Antonio, TX Zip 78229–4801; tel. 210/616–0100; Steve Flaherty, Chief Executive Officer
**Web address:** www.warmsprings.org

WARM SPRINGS SPECIALTY HOSPITAL (O, 34 beds) 200 Memorial Drive, Luling, TX Zip 78648–3213; tel. 830/875–8400; Jason Carter, Chief Executive Officer
**Web address:** www.warmsprings.org

WARM SPRINGS SPECIALTY HOSPITAL OF VICTORIA (O, 26 beds) 102 Medical Drive, Victoria, TX Zip 77904–3101; tel. 361/576–6200; Brian Holt, Chief Executive Officer
**Web address:** www.warmsprings.org

| | | |
|---|---|---|
| **Owned, leased, sponsored:** | 4 hospitals | 256 beds |
| **Contract–managed:** | 0 hospitals | 0 beds |
| **Totals:** | 4 hospitals | 256 beds |

---

**0240: PREFERRED MANAGEMENT CORPORATION** (IO)
120 West MacArthur, Suite 121, Shawnee, OK Zip 74804–2005; tel. 405/878–0202; Donald Freeman, President and Chief Executive Officer
**(Independent Hospital System)**

**TEXAS:** COLEMAN COUNTY MEDICAL CENTER (L, 25 beds) 310 South Pecos Street, Coleman, TX Zip 76834–4159; tel. 325/625–2135; Mr. Michael W. Pruitt, Administrator and Chief Executive Officer
**Web Address:** www.colemantexas.org/hospital.htm

COLLINGSWORTH GENERAL HOSPITAL (L, 13 beds) 1013 15th Street, Wellington, TX Zip 79095–3703, Mailing Address: P.O. Box 1112, Zip 79095–1112; tel. 806/447–2521; Candy Powell, Administrator
**Web address:** www.collingsworthgeneral.net

CULBERSON HOSPITAL (L, 14 beds) Eisenhower–Farm Market Road 2185, Van Horn, TX Zip 79855, Mailing Address: P.O. Box 609, Zip 79855–0609; tel. 432/283–2760; Jared Chanski, Administrator
**Web address:** www.culbersonhospital.org

KIMBLE HOSPITAL (O, 15 beds) 349 Reid Road, Junction, TX Zip 76849–3049; tel. 325/446–3321; Steve Bowen, Administrator
**Web address:** www.kimblehospital.org/

PARMER MEDICAL CENTER (C, 15 beds) 1307 Cleveland Avenue, Friona, TX Zip 79035–1121; tel. 806/250–2754; Gayla Quillin, Administrator
**Web address:** www.parmermedicalcenter.com

SABINE COUNTY HOSPITAL (L, 25 beds) Highway 83 West, Hemphill, TX Zip 75948, Mailing Address: P.O. Box 750, Zip 75948–0750; tel. 409/787–3300; Diana Taylor, Administrator
**Web address:** www.sabinecountyhospital.com/

Section B

For explanation of codes following names, see page B2.
★ Indicates Type III membership in the American Hospital Association.

SCHLEICHER COUNTY MEDICAL CENTER (L, 14 beds) 400 West Murchison, Eldorado, TX Zip 76936, Mailing Address: P.O. Box V., Zip 76936–1246; tel. 325/853–2507; Paul Burke, Administrator
**Web address:** www.scmc.us

| | | |
|---|---|---|
| **Owned, leased, sponsored:** | 6 hospitals | 106 beds |
| **Contract–managed:** | 1 hospital | 15 beds |
| **Totals:** | 7 hospitals | 121 beds |

---

**★3505: PRESBYTERIAN HEALTHCARE SERVICES** (NP)
2501 Buena Vista Drive, S.E., Albuquerque, NM Zip 87106–4260, Mailing Address: P.O. Box 26666, Zip 87125–6666; tel. 505/841–1234; James H. Hinton, President and Chief Executive Officer
**(Centralized Physician/Insurance Health System)**

**NEW MEXICO:** DR. DAN C. TRIGG MEMORIAL HOSPITAL (L, 14 beds) 301 East Miel De Luna Avenue, Tucumcari, NM Zip 88401–3810, Mailing Address: P.O. Box 608, Zip 88401–0608; tel. 575/461–7000; Lance C. Labine, Administrator
**Web address:** www.phs.org

ESPANOLA HOSPITAL (O, 70 beds) 1010 Spruce Street, Espanola, NM Zip 87532–2746; tel. 505/753–7111; Brenda Romero, Administrator
**Web address:** www.phs.org

LINCOLN COUNTY MEDICAL CENTER (L, 25 beds) 211 Sudderth Drive, Ruidoso, NM Zip 88345–6043, Mailing Address: P.O. Box 8000, Zip 88355–8000; tel. 575/257–8200; Alfred Santos, Administrator
**Web address:** www.phs.org

PLAINS REGIONAL MEDICAL CENTER (O, 106 beds) 2100 Martin Luther King Boulevard, Clovis, NM Zip 88101–9412, Mailing Address: P.O. Box 1688, Zip 88102–1688; tel. 575/769–2141; Hoyt Skabelund, Administrator
**Web address:** www.phs.org

PRESBYTERIAN HOSPITAL (O, 488 beds) 1100 Central Avenue S.E., Albuquerque, NM Zip 87106–4934, Mailing Address: P.O. Box 26666, Zip 87125–6666; tel. 505/841–1234; Sandra C. Podley, Administrator
**Web address:** www.phs.org

PRESBYTERIAN KASEMAN HOSPITAL (O, 111 beds) 8300 Constitution Avenue N.E., Albuquerque, NM Zip 87110–7624, Mailing Address: P.O. Box 26666, Zip 87125–6666; tel. 505/291–2000; Doyle Boykin, R.N., MSN, Administrator
**Web address:** www.phs.org

PRESBYTERIAN RUST MEDICAL CENTER (O, 95 beds) 2400 Unser Boulevard S.E., Rio Rancho, NM Zip 87124–4740; tel. 505/253–7878; Jeff McBee, Administrator
**Web address:** www.phs.org/phs/riorancho/index.htm

SOCORRO GENERAL HOSPITAL (O, 24 beds) 1202 Highway 60 West, Socorro, NM Zip 87801–3914, Mailing Address: P.O. Box 1009, Zip 87801–1009; tel. 505/835–1140; Bo Beames, Administrator
**Web address:** www.phs.org

| | | |
|---|---|---|
| **Owned, leased, sponsored:** | 8 hospitals | 933 beds |
| **Contract–managed:** | 0 hospitals | 0 beds |
| **Totals:** | 8 hospitals | 933 beds |

---

**★0851: PRESENCE HEALTH** (CC)
7435 West Talcott Avenue, Chicago, IL Zip 60631–3707; tel. 773/792–5150; Sandra B. Bruce, FACHE, President and Chief Executive Officer
**(Moderately Centralized Health System)**

**ILLINOIS:** PRESENCE COVENANT MEDICAL CENTER (O, 181 beds) 1400 West Park Street, Urbana, IL Zip 61801–2396; tel. 217/337–2000; Michael L. Brown, President and Chief Executive Officer
**Web address:** www.provena.org/covenant

PRESENCE HOLY FAMILY MEDICAL CENTER (O, 118 beds) 100 North River Road, Des Plaines, IL Zip 60016–1255; tel. 847/297–1800; Pamela Bell, R.N., President and Chief Executive Officer
**Web address:** www.presencehealth.org

PRESENCE MERCY MEDICAL CENTER (O, 123 beds) 1325 North Highland Avenue, Aurora, IL Zip 60506–1449; tel. 630/859–2222; Maureen A. Bryant, FACHE, President and Chief Executive Officer
**Web address:** www.provena.org/mercy/

PRESENCE OUR LADY OF THE RESURRECTION MEDICAL CENTER (O, 279 beds) 5645 West Addison Street, Chicago, IL Zip 60634–4403; tel. 773/282–7000; John D. Baird, President and Chief Executive Officer
**Web address:** www.presencehealth.org

PRESENCE RESURRECTION MEDICAL CENTER (O, 402 beds) 7435 West Talcott Avenue, Chicago, IL Zip 60631–3746; tel. 773/774–8000; John D. Baird, Chief Executive Officer
**Web address:** www.reshealthcare.org

PRESENCE SAINT FRANCIS HOSPITAL (O, 244 beds) 355 Ridge Avenue, Evanston, IL Zip 60202–3399; tel. 847/316–4000; Jeffrey J. Murphy, President and Chief Executive Officer
**Web address:** www.reshealth.org

PRESENCE SAINT JOSEPH HOSPITAL (O, 327 beds) 2900 North Lake Shore Drive, Chicago, IL Zip 60657–6274; tel. 773/665–3000; Roberta Luskin–Hawk, M.D., President and Chief Executive Officer
**Web address:** www.reshealth.org

PRESENCE SAINT JOSEPH HOSPITAL (O, 125 beds) 77 North Airlite Street, Elgin, IL Zip 60123–4912; tel. 847/695–3200; Eugene J. McMahon, M.D., President and Chief Executive Officer
**Web address:** www.provena.org

PRESENCE SAINT JOSEPH MEDICAL CENTER (O, 457 beds) 333 North Madison Street, Joliet, IL Zip 60435–8200; tel. 815/725–7133; Beth Hughes, President and Chief Executive Officer
**Web address:** www.provena.org/stjoes

PRESENCE SAINTS MARY & ELIZABETH MEDICAL CENTER (O, 493 beds) 2233 West Division Street, Chicago, IL Zip 60622–3086; tel. 312/770–2000; Martin H. Judd, President and Chief Executive Officer
**Web address:** www.smemc.reshealth.org

PRESENCE ST. MARY'S HOSPITAL (O, 143 beds) 500 West Court Street, Kankakee, IL Zip 60901–3661; tel. 815/937–2400; Amy LaFine, R.N., MSN, President and Chief Executive Officer
**Web address:** www.provena.org/stmarys/

PRESENCE UNITED SAMARITANS MEDICAL CENTER (O, 127 beds) 812 North Logan, Danville, IL Zip 61832–3788; tel. 217/443–5000; Michael L. Brown, President and Chief Executive Officer
**Web address:** www.provena.org/usmc

| | | |
|---|---|---|
| **Owned, leased, sponsored:** | 12 hospitals | 3019 beds |
| **Contract–managed:** | 0 hospitals | 0 beds |
| **Totals:** | 12 hospitals | 3019 beds |

---

**0357: PRIME HEALTHCARE SERVICES** (IO)
3300 East Guasti Road, Ontario, CA Zip 91761–8655; tel. 909/235–4400; Prem Reddy, M.D., Interim President and Chief Executive Officer
**(Independent Hospital System)**

**CALIFORNIA:** ALVARADO HOSPITAL (O, 83 beds) 6655 Alvarado Road, San Diego, CA Zip 92120–5208; tel. 619/287–3270; Robin Gomez, Administrator
**Web address:** www.alvaradohospital.com

CENTINELA HOSPITAL MEDICAL CENTER (O, 369 beds) 555 East Hardy Street, Inglewood, CA Zip 90301–4011, Mailing Address: P.O. Box 720, Zip 90312–6720; tel. 310/673–4660; Linda Bradley, Chief Executive Officer
**Web address:** www.centinelamed.com

CHINO VALLEY MEDICAL CENTER (O, 112 beds) 5451 Walnut Avenue, Chino, CA Zip 91710–2672; tel. 909/464–8600; James M. Lally, D.O., President and Chief Medical Officer
**Web address:** www.cvmc.com

DESERT VALLEY HOSPITAL (O, 75 beds) 16850 Bear Valley Road, Victorville, CA Zip 92395–5794; tel. 760/241–8000; Margaret R. Peterson, Ph.D., R.N., Chief Executive Officer
**Web address:** www.dvmc.com

ENCINO HOSPITAL MEDICAL CENTER (O, 66 beds) 16237 Ventura Boulevard, Encino, CA Zip 91436–2201; tel. 818/995–5000; Bockhi Park, Chief Executive Officer
**Web address:** www.encinomed.com

GARDEN GROVE HOSPITAL AND MEDICAL CENTER (O, 74 beds) 12601 Garden Grove Boulevard, Garden Grove, CA Zip 92843–1908; tel. 714/537–5160; Virgis Narbutas, Chief Executive Officer
**Web address:** www.gardengrovehospital.com

For explanation of codes following names, see page B2.
★ Indicates Type III membership in the American Hospital Association.

HUNTINGTON BEACH HOSPITAL (O, 130 beds) 17772 Beach Boulevard, Huntington Beach, CA Zip 92647–6819; tel. 714/843–5000; Virgis Narbutas, Chief Executive Officer
**Web address:** www.hbhospital.com

LA PALMA INTERCOMMUNITY HOSPITAL (O, 141 beds) 7901 Walker Street, La Palma, CA Zip 90623–1722; tel. 714/670–7400; Virgis Narbutas, Chief Executive Officer
**Web address:** www.lapalmaintercommunityhospital.com

MONTCLAIR HOSPITAL MEDICAL CENTER (O, 102 beds) 5000 San Bernardino Street, Montclair, CA Zip 91763–2326; tel. 909/625–5411; Gregory Brentano, Chief Executive Officer
**Web address:** www.montclair–hospital.com

PARADISE VALLEY HOSPITAL (O, 205 beds) 2400 East Fourth Street, National City, CA Zip 91950–2099; tel. 619/470–4321; Luis Leon, Regional Chief Executive Officer
**Web address:** www.paradisevalleyhospital.org

SAN DIMAS COMMUNITY HOSPITAL (O, 101 beds) 1350 West Covina Boulevard, San Dimas, CA Zip 91773–3219; tel. 909/599–6811; Gregory Brentano, Chief Executive Officer
**Web address:** www.sandimashospital.com

SHASTA REGIONAL MEDICAL CENTER (O, 120 beds) 1100 Butte Street, Redding, CA Zip 96001–0853, Mailing Address: P.O. Box 496072, Zip 96049–6072; tel. 530/244–5400; Randall Hempling, Chief Executive Officer
**Web address:** www.shastaregional.com

SHERMAN OAKS HOSPITAL (O, 77 beds) 4929 Van Nuys Boulevard, Sherman Oaks, CA Zip 91403–1702; tel. 818/981–7111; Bockhi Park, Chief Executive Officer
**Web address:** www.shermanoakshospital.com

VICTOR VALLEY COMMUNITY HOSPITAL (O, 115 beds) 15248 Eleventh Street, Victorville, CA Zip 92395–3704; tel. 760/245–8691; Suzanne Richards, R.N., M.P.H., Interim Chief Executive Officer
**Web address:** www.vvch.org

WEST ANAHEIM MEDICAL CENTER (O, 219 beds) 3033 West Orange Avenue, Anaheim, CA Zip 92804–3156; tel. 714/827–3000; Virgis Narbutas, Chief Executive Officer
**Web address:** www.westanaheimmedctr.com

**NEVADA:** SAINT MARY'S REGIONAL MEDICAL CENTER (O, 272 beds) 235 West Sixth Street, Reno, NV Zip 89503–4548; tel. 775/770–3000; Helen Lidholm, Chief Executive Officer
**Web address:** www.saintmarysreno.org

**PENNSYLVANIA:** ROXBOROUGH MEMORIAL HOSPITAL (O, 137 beds) 5800 Ridge Avenue, Philadelphia, PA Zip 19128–1737; tel. 215/483–9900; Peter J. Adamo, Chief Executive Officer
**Web address:** www.roxboroughmemorial.com

**TEXAS:** DALLAS MEDICAL CENTER (O, 78 beds) Seven Medical Parkway, Dallas, TX Zip 75234–7823, Mailing Address: P.O. Box 819094, Zip 75381–9094; tel. 972/247–1000; Raji Kumar, Chief Executive Officer
**Web address:** www.dallasmedcenter.com

HARLINGEN MEDICAL CENTER (O, 88 beds) 5501 South Expressway 77, Harlingen, TX Zip 78550–3213; tel. 956/365–1000; Brenda Ivory, Chief Executive Officer
**Web address:** www.harlingenmedicalcenter.com

PAMPA REGIONAL MEDICAL CENTER (O, 32 beds) One Medical Plaza, Pampa, TX Zip 79065; tel. 806/665–3721; Brad S. Morse, Chief Executive Officer
**Web address:** www.prmctx.com

| | | |
|---|---|---|
| **Owned, leased, sponsored:** | 20 hospitals | 2596 beds |
| **Contract–managed:** | 0 hospitals | 0 beds |
| **Totals:** | 20 hospitals | 2596 beds |

---

**★0153:  PROHEALTH CARE, INC.** (NP)
N17 W24100 Riverwood Drive, Suite 130, Waukesha, WI Zip 53188; tel. 262/928–2242; Susan A. Edwards, President and Chief Executive Officer
**(Centralized Health System)**

**WISCONSIN:** OCONOMOWOC MEMORIAL HOSPITAL (O, 76 beds) 791 Summit Avenue, Oconomowoc, WI Zip 53066–3896; tel. 262/569–9400; John R. Robertstad, FACHE, President
**Web address:** www.prohealthcare.org/locations/locations–v2–detail/?id=1123

WAUKESHA MEMORIAL HOSPITAL (O, 317 beds) 725 American Avenue, Waukesha, WI Zip 53188–5099; tel. 262/928–1000; John R. Robertstad, FACHE, President
**Web address:** www.prohealthcare.org/locations/locations–v2–detail/?id=1119

| | | |
|---|---|---|
| **Owned, leased, sponsored:** | 2 hospitals | 393 beds |
| **Contract–managed:** | 0 hospitals | 0 beds |
| **Totals:** | 2 hospitals | 393 beds |

---

**★0197:  PROMEDICA HEALTH SYSTEM** (NP)
1801 Richards Road, Toledo, OH Zip 43607–1037; tel. 419/469–3800; Randall D. Oostra, FACHE, President and Chief Executive Officer
**(Centralized Physician/Insurance Health System)**

**MICHIGAN:** PROMEDICA BIXBY HOSPITAL (O, 66 beds) 818 Riverside Avenue, Adrian, MI Zip 49221–1446; tel. 517/265–0900; Timothy Jakacki, President
**Web address:** www.promedica.org

PROMEDICA HERRICK HOSPITAL (O, 60 beds) 500 East Pottawatamie Street, Tecumseh, MI Zip 49286–2018; tel. 517/424–3000; Timothy Jakacki, President
**Web address:** www.promedica.org

**OHIO:** PROMEDICA BAY PARK HOSPITAL (O, 72 beds) 2801 Bay Park Drive, Oregon, OH Zip 43616–4920; tel. 419/690–7900; Holly L. Bristoll, President
**Web address:** www.promedica.org

PROMEDICA DEFIANCE REGIONAL HOSPITAL (O, 35 beds) 1200 Ralston Avenue, Defiance, OH Zip 43512–1396; tel. 419/783–6955; Gary Cates, President and Chief Executive Officer
**Web address:** www.promedica.org

PROMEDICA FLOWER HOSPITAL (O, 221 beds) 5200 Harroun Road, Sylvania, OH Zip 43560–2196; tel. 419/824–1444; Alan Sattler, President
**Web address:** www.promedica.org

PROMEDICA FOSTORIA COMMUNITY HOSPITAL (O, 25 beds) 501 Van Buren Street, Fostoria, OH Zip 44830–1534, Mailing Address: P.O. Box 907, Zip 44830–0907; tel. 419/435–7734; Daniel Schwanke, President

PROMEDICA ST. LUKE'S HOSPITAL (O, 182 beds) 5901 Monclova Road, Maumee, OH Zip 43537–1899; tel. 419/893–5911; Daniel L. Wakeman, President
**Web address:** www.stlukeshospital.com

PROMEDICA TOLEDO HOSPITAL (O, 651 beds) 2142 North Cove Boulevard, Toledo, OH Zip 43606–3896; tel. 419/291–4000; Kevin C. Webb, Ph.D., President
**Web address:** www.promedica.org

| | | |
|---|---|---|
| **Owned, leased, sponsored:** | 8 hospitals | 1312 beds |
| **Contract–managed:** | 0 hospitals | 0 beds |
| **Totals:** | 8 hospitals | 1312 beds |

---

**0230:  PROMISE HEALTHCARE** (IO)
999 Yamato Road, 3rd Floor, Boca Raton, FL Zip 33431–4477; tel. 561/869–3100; Howard B. Koslow, President and Chief Executive Officer
**(Independent Hospital System)**

**ARIZONA:** PROMISE HOSPITAL OF PHOENIX (L, 40 beds) 433 East 6th Street, Mesa, AZ Zip 85203–7104; tel. 480/427–3000; Scott Floden, Chief Executive Officer
**Web address:** www.promise–phoenix.com

**CALIFORNIA:** PROMISE HOSPITAL OF EAST LOS ANGELES (L, 36 beds) 443 South Soto Street, Los Angeles, CA Zip 90033–4398; tel. 323/261–1181; Steve Popkin, Chief Executive Officer
**Web address:** www.promiseeastla.com

PROMISE HOSPITAL OF EAST LOS ANGELES, SUBURBAN MEDICAL CENTER CAMPUS (L, 182 beds) 16453 South Colorado Avenue, Paramount, CA Zip 90723–5011; tel. 562/531–3110; Steve Popkin, Chief Executive Officer
**Web address:** www.promiseeastla.com

For explanation of codes following names, see page B2.
★ Indicates Type III membership in the American Hospital Association.

Section B

PROMISE HOSPITAL OF SAN DIEGO (O, 100 beds) 5550 University Avenue, San Diego, CA Zip 92105–2307; tel. 619/582–3800; Martha J. Heubach, Chief Executive Officer
**Web address:** www.promisesandiego.com

**FLORIDA:** PROMISE HOSPITAL OF FLORIDA AT THE VILLAGES (O, 40 beds) 5050 County Road, Oxford, FL Zip 34484; tel. 352/689–6400; Steven M. Klein, Chief Executive Officer
**Web address:** www.promise–villages.com

**LOUISIANA:** PROMISE HOSPITAL BATON ROUGE – MAIN CAMPUS (L, 50 beds) 5130 Mancuso Lane, Baton Rouge, LA Zip 70809–3583; tel. 225/490–9600; Richard Knowland,
**Web address:** www.promise–batonrouge.com

PROMISE HOSPITAL OF BATON ROUGE – MID–CITY CAMPUS (O, 28 beds) 3600 Florida Boulevard, 4th Floor, Baton Rouge, LA Zip 70806–3842; tel. 225/387–7770; Bryan Day, Interim Chief Executive Officer
**Web address:** www.promise–batonrougemidcity.com

PROMISE HOSPITAL OF BATON ROUGE – OCHSNER CAMPUS (O, 22 beds) 17000 Medical Center Drive, 3rd Floor, Baton Rouge, LA Zip 70816–3246; tel. 225/236–5440; Bryan Day, Interim Chief Executive Officer
**Web address:** www.promise–batonrougeochsner.com

PROMISE HOSPITAL OF LOUISIANA – SHREVEPORT CAMPUS (O, 146 beds) 1800 Irving Place, Shreveport, LA Zip 71101–4608; tel. 318/425–4096; Rick Stockton, Chief Executive Officer
**Web address:** www.promise–shreveport.com

PROMISE HOSPITAL OF MISS LOU (O, 40 beds) 209 Front Street, Vidalia, LA Zip 71373–2837; tel. 318/336–6500; Benny Costello, Chief Executive Officer
**Web address:** www.promise–misslou.com

**MISSISSIPPI:** PROMISE HOSPITAL OF VICKSBURG (L, 33 beds) 1111 North Frontage Road, 2nd Floor, Vicksburg, MS Zip 39180–5102; tel. 601/619–3526; Mike Harrell, Chief Executive Officer
**Web address:** www.promise–vicksburg.com

**TEXAS:** PROMISE HOSPITAL OF SAN ANTONIO (L, 26 beds) 7400 Barlite Boulevard, 2nd Floor, San Antonio, TX Zip 78224–1308; tel. 210/921–3550; Karen Pitcher, Vice President and Chief Executive Officer
**Web address:** www.promise–sanantonio.com

**UTAH:** PROMISE SPECIALTY HOSPITAL OF SALT LAKE (O, 32 beds) 1050 East South Temple, 3rd Floor, Salt Lake City, UT Zip 84102–1507; tel. 801/350–4110; Linda Hook, Chief Executive Officer
**Web address:** www.promise–saltlake.com

| | | |
|---|---|---|
| Owned, leased, sponsored: | 13 hospitals | 775 beds |
| Contract–managed: | 0 hospitals | 0 beds |
| Totals: | 13 hospitals | 775 beds |

★**0344: PROVIDENCE HEALTH & SERVICES** (CC)
1801 Lind Avenue S.W., 9016, Renton, WA Zip 98057–9016; tel. 425/525–3698; Rodney F. Hochman, M.D., President and Chief Executive Officer
**(Decentralized Health System)**

**ALASKA:** PROVIDENCE ALASKA MEDICAL CENTER (O, 371 beds) 3200 Providence Drive, Anchorage, AK Zip 99508–4615, Mailing Address: P.O. Box 196604, Zip 99519–6604; tel. 907/562–2211; Bruce Lamoureux, Vice President and Chief Executive Officer
**Web address:** www.providence.org/alaska/pamc/default.htm

PROVIDENCE KODIAK ISLAND MEDICAL CENTER (L, 25 beds) 1915 East Rezanof Drive, Kodiak, AK Zip 99615–6602; tel. 907/486–3281; Donald J. Rush, Chief Executive Officer
**Web address:** www.providence.org

PROVIDENCE SEWARD MEDICAL CENTER (L, 6 beds) 417 First Avenue, Seward, AK Zip 99664, Mailing Address: P.O. Box 365, Zip 99664–0365; tel. 907/224–5205; Christopher Bolton, Administrator
**Web address:** www.providence.org

PROVIDENCE VALDEZ MEDICAL CENTER (C, 21 beds) 911 Meals Avenue, Valdez, AK Zip 99686–0550, Mailing Address: P.O. Box 550, Zip 99686–0550; tel. 907/835–2249; Sean McCallister, Administrator
**Web address:** www.providence.org/alaska

**CALIFORNIA:** PROVIDENCE HOLY CROSS MEDICAL CENTER (O, 254 beds) 15031 Rinaldi Street, Mission Hills, CA Zip 91345–1207; tel. 818/365–8051; Bernard Klein, M.D., Chief Executive Officer
**Web address:** www.https://california.providence.org/holy–cross/Pages/default.aspx

PROVIDENCE LITTLE COMPANY OF MARY MEDICAL CENTER (O, 379 beds) 4101 Torrance Boulevard, Torrance, CA Zip 90503–4607; tel. 310/540–7676; Elizabeth Dunne, Chief Executive Officer
**Web address:** www.lcmweb.org

PROVIDENCE LITTLE COMPANY OF MARY MEDICAL CENTER SAN PEDRO (O, 327 beds) 1300 West Seventh Street, San Pedro, CA Zip 90732–3505; tel. 310/832–3311; Nancy Carlson, Chief Executive
**Web address:** www.https://california.providence.org/san–pedro

PROVIDENCE SAINT JOSEPH MEDICAL CENTER (O, 446 beds) 501 South Buena Vista Street, Burbank, CA Zip 91505–4866; tel. 818/843–5111; Michael A. Rembis, FACHE, Chief Executive Officer
**Web address:** www.providence.org

PROVIDENCE TARZANA MEDICAL CENTER (O, 245 beds) 18321 Clark Street, Tarzana, CA Zip 91356–3521; tel. 818/881–0800; Gerald B. Clute, Chief Executive Officer
**Web address:** www.providence.org/tarzana.com

**MONTANA:** COMMUNITY HOSPITAL OF ANACONDA (C, 87 beds) 401 West Pennsylvania Street, Anaconda, MT Zip 59711; tel. 406/563–8500; Steve McNeece, Chief Executive Officer
**Web address:** www.communityhospitalofanaconda.org

ST. JOSEPH HOSPITAL (S, 22 beds) 6 Thirteenth Avenue East, Polson, MT Zip 59860–5315, Mailing Address: P.O. Box 1010, Zip 59860–1010; tel. 406/883–5377; James R. Kiser, II, Chief Executive Officer
**Web address:** www.saintjoes.org

ST. PATRICK HOSPITAL (S, 193 beds) 500 West Broadway, Missoula, MT Zip 59802–4096, Mailing Address: P.O. Box 4587, Zip 59806–4587; tel. 406/543–7271; Jeff Fee, Chief Executive Officer
**Web address:** www.saintpatrick.org

**OREGON:** PROVIDENCE HOOD RIVER MEMORIAL HOSPITAL (O, 25 beds) 811 13th Street, Hood River, OR Zip 97031–1204, Mailing Address: P.O. Box 149, Zip 97031–0055; tel. 541/386–3911; Edward E. Freysinger, Chief Executive Officer
**Web address:** www.providence.org/hoodriver

PROVIDENCE MEDFORD MEDICAL CENTER (O, 124 beds) 1111 Crater Lake Avenue, Medford, OR Zip 97504–6241; tel. 541/732–5000; Thomas S. Hanenburg, Chief Executive
**Web address:** www.providence.org

PROVIDENCE MILWAUKIE HOSPITAL (O, 63 beds) 10150 S.E. 32nd Avenue, Milwaukie, OR Zip 97222–6516; tel. 503/513–8300; Keith Hyde, Chief Executive Officer
**Web address:** www.providence.org

PROVIDENCE NEWBERG MEDICAL CENTER (O, 40 beds) 1001 Providence Drive, Newberg, OR Zip 97132–7485; tel. 503/537–1555; Lorinda Van Zanten, MSN, Chief Executive Officer
**Web address:** www.phsor.org

PROVIDENCE PORTLAND MEDICAL CENTER (O, 426 beds) 4805 N.E. Glisan Street, Portland, OR Zip 97213–2933; tel. 503/215–5526; Theron Park, Chief Executive Officer
**Web address:** www.providence.org

PROVIDENCE SEASIDE HOSPITAL (L, 47 beds) 725 South Wahanna Road, Seaside, OR Zip 97138–7735; tel. 503/717–7000; Michael Blauer, Chief Executive Officer
**Web address:** www.providence.org

PROVIDENCE ST. VINCENT MEDICAL CENTER (O, 528 beds) 9205 S.W. Barnes Road, Portland, OR Zip 97225–6661; tel. 503/216–1234; Janice Burger, Administrator
**Web address:** www.providence.org/portland/hospitals

PROVIDENCE WILLAMETTE FALLS MEDICAL CENTER (O, 89 beds) 1500 Division Street, Oregon City, OR Zip 97045–1597; tel. 503/656–1631; Russ Reinhard, Chief Executive
**Web address:** www.providence.org/pwfmc

**WASHINGTON:** PROVIDENCE CENTRALIA HOSPITAL (O, 96 beds) 914 South Scheuber Road, Centralia, WA Zip 98531–9027; tel. 360/736–2803; Cindy Mayo, R.N., FACHE, Chief Executive
**Web address:** www.providence.org

For explanation of codes following names, see page B2.
★ Indicates Type III membership in the American Hospital Association.

PROVIDENCE HOLY FAMILY HOSPITAL (S, 180 beds) 5633 North Lidgerwood Street, Spokane, WA Zip 99208–1224; tel. 509/482–0111; Elaine Couture, R.N., Chief Executive
**Web address:** www.providence.org

PROVIDENCE MOUNT CARMEL HOSPITAL (S, 25 beds) 982 East Columbia Avenue, Colville, WA Zip 99114–3352; tel. 509/685–5100; Robert D. Campbell, Jr., Chief Executive
**Web address:** www.mtcarmelhospital.org

PROVIDENCE REGIONAL MEDICAL CENTER EVERETT (O, 491 beds) 1321 Colby Avenue, Everett, WA Zip 98201–1665, Mailing Address: P.O. Box 1147, Zip 98206–1147; tel. 425/261–2000; Preston M. Simmons, Chief Executive Officer
**Web address:** www.providence.org

PROVIDENCE SACRED HEART MEDICAL CENTER & CHILDREN'S HOSPITAL (S, 642 beds) 101 West Eighth Avenue, Spokane, WA Zip 99204–2364, Mailing Address: P.O. Box 2555, Zip 99220–2555; tel. 509/474–3131; Elaine Couture, R.N., Chief Executive
**Web address:** www.shmc.org

PROVIDENCE ST. JOSEPH'S HOSPITAL (S, 65 beds) 500 East Webster Street, Chewelah, WA Zip 99109–9523; tel. 509/935–8211; Robert D. Campbell, Jr., President and Chief Executive
**Web address:** www.sjhospital.org

PROVIDENCE ST. MARY MEDICAL CENTER (S, 79 beds) 401 West Poplar Street, Walla Walla, WA Zip 99362–2846, Mailing Address: P.O. Box 1477, Zip 99362–0312; tel. 509/525–3320; Steven A. Burdick, Chief Executive Officer
**Web address:** www.smmc.com

PROVIDENCE ST. PETER HOSPITAL (O, 369 beds) 413 Lilly Road N.E., Olympia, WA Zip 98506–5166; tel. 360/491–9480; Medrice Coluccio, R.N., Chief Executive Officer
**Web address:** www.providence.org/swsa/facilities/st_peter_hospital

WHITMAN HOSPITAL AND MEDICAL CENTER (C, 25 beds) 1200 West Fairview Street, Colfax, WA Zip 99111 9579; tel. 509/397–3435; Deborah Glass, MS, R.N., Chief Executive Officer
**Web address:** www.whitmanhospital.com

| | | |
|---|---|---|
| Owned, leased, sponsored: | 26 hospitals | 5557 beds |
| Contract–managed: | 3 hospitals | 133 beds |
| Totals: | 29 hospitals | 5690 beds |

---

★**0011:  PUERTO RICO DEPARTMENT OF HEALTH** (NP)
Building A – Medical Center, San Juan, PR Zip 00936, Mailing Address: Call Box 70184, Zip 00936; tel. 787/765–2929; Francisco M. Joglar, M.D., Secretary of Health
**(Independent Hospital System)**

**PUERTO RICO:** CARDIOVASCULAR CENTER OF PUERTO RICO AND THE CARIBBEAN (O, 146 beds) Americo Miranda Centro Medico, San Juan, PR Zip 00936, Mailing Address: P.O. Box 366528, Zip 00936–6528; tel. 787/754–8500; Waleska Crespo, Executive Director
**Web address:** www.cardiovascular.gobicrno.pr

HOSPITAL UNIVERSITARIO DR. RAMON RUIZ ARNAU (O, 102 beds) Avenue Laurel, Santa Juanita, Bayamon, PR Zip 00956; tel. 787/787–5151; Humberto M. Monserrate, Chief Executive Officer

UNIVERSITY HOSPITAL (O, 262 beds) Nineyas 869 Rio Piedras, San Juan, PR Zip 00922, Mailing Address: P.O. Box 2116, Zip 00922; tel. 787/754–0101; Jorge Matta Gonzalez, Executive Director

UNIVERSITY PEDIATRIC HOSPITAL (O, 145 beds) Barrio Monacenno, Carretera 22, Rio Piedras, PR Zip 00935, Mailing Address: P.O. Box 191079, San Juan, PR Zip 00910–1070; tel. 787/777–3535; Gloria Hernandez, Executive Director

| | | |
|---|---|---|
| Owned, leased, sponsored: | 4 hospitals | 655 beds |
| Contract–managed: | 0 hospitals | 0 beds |
| Totals: | 4 hospitals | 655 beds |

---

★**0002:  QHR** (IO)
105 Continental Place, Brentwood, TN Zip 37027–1052; tel. 800/233–1470; James L. Horrar, President and Chief Executive Officer
**(Decentralized Health System)**

**COLORADO:** ARKANSAS VALLEY REGIONAL MEDICAL CENTER (C, 163 beds) 1100 Carson Avenue, La Junta, CO Zip 81050–2799; tel. 719/383–6000; Lynn Crowell, Chief Executive Officer
**Web address:** www.avrmc.org

COMMUNITY HOSPITAL (C, 44 beds) 2021 North 12th Street, Grand Junction, CO Zip 81501–2999; tel. 970/242–0920; Chris Thomas, FACHE, President and Chief Executive Officer
**Web address:** www.yourcommunityhospital.com

MEMORIAL HOSPITAL AT CRAIG (C, 25 beds) 750 Hospital Loop, Craig, CO Zip 81625–8750; tel. 970/824–9411; James Christian Smolik, Chief Executive Officer
**Web address:** www.thememorialhospital.com

MONTROSE MEMORIAL HOSPITAL (C, 69 beds) 800 South Third Street, Montrose, CO Zip 81401–4212; tel. 970/249–2211; David L. Hample, Chief Executive Officer
**Web address:** www.montrosehospital.com

PIONEERS MEDICAL CENTER (C, 46 beds) 345 Cleveland Street, Meeker, CO Zip 81641–3238; tel. 970/878–5047; Kenneth Harman, Chief Executive Officer
**Web address:** www.pioneershospital.com

PROWERS MEDICAL CENTER (C, 25 beds) 401 Kendall Drive, Lamar, CO Zip 81052–3993; tel. 719/336–4343; Craig Loveless, Interim Chief Executive Officer
**Web address:** www.prowersmedical.com

ST. VINCENT GENERAL HOSPITAL DISTRICT (C, 25 beds) 822 West 4th Street, Leadville, CO Zip 80461–3897; tel. 719/486–0230; Joyce Beck, Interim Chief Executive Officer
**Web address:** www.svghd.org

**FLORIDA:** FISHERMEN'S HOSPITAL (C, 25 beds) 3301 Overseas Highway, Marathon, FL Zip 33050–2329; tel. 305/743–5533; Hal W. Leftwich, FACHE, Chief Executive Officer
**Web address:** www.fishermenshospital.com

HENDRY REGIONAL MEDICAL CENTER (C, 25 beds) 524 West Sagamore Avenue, Clewiston, FL Zip 33440–3514; tel. 863/902–3000; R. D. Williams, Chief Executive Officer
**Web address:** www.hendryregional.org

JACKSON HOSPITAL (C, 62 beds) 4250 Hospital Drive, Marianna, FL Zip 32446–1917, Mailing Address: P.O. Box 1608, Zip 32447–5608; tel. 850/526–2200; Larry Meese, Chief Executive Officer
**Web address:** www.jacksonhosp.com

**IDAHO:** BENEWAH COMMUNITY HOSPITAL (C, 19 beds) 229 South Seventh Street, Saint Maries, ID Zip 83861–1803; tel. 208/245–5551; Christopher Noland, FACHE, Interim Chief Executive Officer
**Web address:** www.bchmed.org

GRITMAN MEDICAL CENTER (C, 25 beds) 700 South Main Street, Moscow, ID Zip 83843–3056; tel. 208/882–4511; Kara Besst, President and Chief Executive Officer
**Web address:** www.gritman.org

STEELE MEMORIAL MEDICAL CENTER (C, 18 beds) 203 South Daisy Street, Salmon, ID Zip 83467–4709; tel. 208/756–5600; Jeff Hill, Chief Executive Officer
**Web address:** www.steelemh.org

**ILLINOIS:** CRAWFORD MEMORIAL HOSPITAL (C, 63 beds) 1000 North Allen Street, Robinson, IL Zip 62454–1167; tel. 618/544–3131; Donald E. Annis, Chief Executive Officer
**Web address:** www.crawfordmh.org

LAWRENCE COUNTY MEMORIAL HOSPITAL (C, 25 beds) 2200 West State Street, Lawrenceville, IL Zip 62439–1852; tel. 618/943–1000; Doug Florkowski, Chief Executive Officer
**Web address:** www.lcmhosp.org

PEKIN HOSPITAL (C, 125 beds) 600 South 13th Street, Pekin, IL Zip 61554–4936; tel. 309/347–1151; Gary L. Jepson, Chief Executive Officer
**Web address:** www.pekinhospital.org

**INDIANA:** DAVIESS COMMUNITY HOSPITAL (C, 80 beds) 1314 East Walnut Street, Washington, IN Zip 47501–2860, Mailing Address: P.O. Box 760, Zip 47501–0760; tel. 812/254–2760; David Bixler, Chief Executive Officer
**Web address:** www.dchosp.org

For explanation of codes following names, see page B2.
★ Indicates Type III membership in the American Hospital Association.

SULLIVAN COUNTY COMMUNITY HOSPITAL (C, 25 beds) 2200 North Section Street, Sullivan, IN Zip 47882–7523, Mailing Address: P.O. Box 10, Zip 47882–0010; tel. 812/268–4311; Michelle Sly–Smith, Chief Executive Officer
**Web address:** www.schosp.com

**IOWA:** BOONE COUNTY HOSPITAL (C, 25 beds) 1015 Union Street, Boone, IA Zip 50036–4821; tel. 515/432–3140; Joseph S. Smith, Chief Executive Officer
**Web address:** www.boonehospital.com

FORT MADISON COMMUNITY HOSPITAL (C, 50 beds) 5445 Avenue O, Fort Madison, IA Zip 52627–9611, Mailing Address: P.O. Box 174, Zip 52627–0174; tel. 319/372–6530; C. James Platt, Chief Executive Officer
**Web address:** www.fmchosp.com

**KANSAS:** GREELEY COUNTY HEALTH SERVICES (C, 50 beds) 506 Third Street, Tribune, KS Zip 67879–9684, Mailing Address: P.O. Box 338, Zip 67879–0338; tel. 620/376–4221; Deborah Lehner, Administrator
**Web address:** www.mygchs.com

NEOSHO MEMORIAL REGIONAL MEDICAL CENTER (C, 25 beds) 629 South Plummer, Chanute, KS Zip 66720–1928, Mailing Address: P.O. Box 426, Zip 66720–0426; tel. 620/431–4000; Dennis Franks, FACHE, Chief Executive Officer
**Web address:** www.nmrmc.com

NEWMAN REGIONAL HEALTH (C, 59 beds) 1201 West 12th Avenue, Emporia, KS Zip 66801–2597; tel. 620/343–6800; John Rossfeld, Interim Chief Executive Officer
**Web address:** www.newmanrh.org

ST. LUKE HOSPITAL AND LIVING CENTER (C, 37 beds) 535 South Freeborn, Marion, KS Zip 66861–1256; tel. 620/382–2177; Jeremy Armstrong, FACHE, Chief Executive Officer
**Web address:** www.slhmarion.org

WILSON MEDICAL CENTER (C, 15 beds) 2600 Ottawa Road, Neodesha, KS Zip 66757–1897, Mailing Address: P.O. Box 360, Zip 66757–0360; tel. 620/325–2611; Dennis R. Shelby, Chief Executive Officer
**Web address:** www.wilsonmedical.org

**KENTUCKY:** CALDWELL MEDICAL CENTER (C, 25 beds) 100 Medical Center Drive, Princeton, KY Zip 42445–2430, Mailing Address: P.O. Box 410, Zip 42445–0410; tel. 270/365–0300; Charles D. Lovell, Jr., FACHE, President and Chief Executive Officer
**Web address:** www.caldwellhosp.org

FLEMING COUNTY HOSPITAL (C, 52 beds) 55 Foundation Drive, Flemingsburg, KY Zip 41041–9815, Mailing Address: P.O. Box 388, Zip 41041–0388; tel. 606/849–5000; David M. Faulkner, Chief Executive Officer
**Web address:** www.flemingcountyhospital.org

JENNIE STUART MEDICAL CENTER (C, 139 beds) 320 West 18th Street, Hopkinsville, KY Zip 42240–1965, Mailing Address: P.O. Box 2400, Zip 42241–2400; tel. 270/887–0100; Eric A. Lee, President and Chief Executive Officer
**Web address:** www.jsmc.org

MONROE COUNTY MEDICAL CENTER (C, 49 beds) 529 Capp Harlan Road, Tompkinsville, KY Zip 42167–1840; tel. 270/487–9231; Vicky McFall, Chief Executive Officer
**Web address:** www.mcmccares.com

OHIO COUNTY HOSPITAL (C, 25 beds) 1211 Main Street, Hartford, KY Zip 42347–1619; tel. 270/298–7411; Blaine Pieper, Chief Executive Officer
**Web address:** www.ohiocountyhospital.com

**LOUISIANA:** FRANKLIN FOUNDATION HOSPITAL (C, 22 beds) 1097 Northwest Boulevard, Franklin, LA Zip 70538–3407, Mailing Address: P.O. Box 577, Zip 70538–0577; tel. 337/828–0760; Parker Templeton, FACHE, Chief Executive Officer
**Web address:** www.franklinfoundation.org

OPELOUSAS GENERAL HEALTH SYSTEM (C, 231 beds) 539 East Prudhomme Street, Opelousas, LA Zip 70570–6499, Mailing Address: P.O. Box 1389, Zip 70571–1389; tel. 337/948–3011; Mark E. Marley, FACHE, President and Chief Executive Officer
**Web address:** www.opelousasgeneral.com

**MAINE:** CALAIS REGIONAL HOSPITAL (C, 25 beds) 24 Hospital Lane, Calais, ME Zip 04619–1398; tel. 207/454–7521; Michael K. Lally, Chief Executive Officer
**Web address:** www.calaishospital.com

CARY MEDICAL CENTER (C, 49 beds) 163 Van Buren Road, Suite 1, Caribou, ME Zip 04736–3567; tel. 207/498–3111; Kris A. Doody, R.N., Chief Executive Officer
**Web address:** www.carymedicalcenter.org

PENOBSCOT VALLEY HOSPITAL (C, 25 beds) 7 Transalpine Road, Lincoln, ME Zip 04457–4222, Mailing Address: P.O. Box 368, Zip 04457–0368; tel. 207/794–3321; David A. Shannon, Chief Executive Officer
**Web address:** www.pvhme.org

**MICHIGAN:** ALLEGAN GENERAL HOSPITAL (C, 25 beds) 555 Linn Street, Allegan, MI Zip 49010–1524; tel. 269/673–8424; Gerald J. Barbini, President and Chief Executive Officer
**Web address:** www.aghosp.com

HAYES GREEN BEACH MEMORIAL HOSPITAL (C, 25 beds) 321 East Harris Street, Charlotte, MI Zip 48813–1629; tel. 517/543–1050; Matthew Rush, President and Chief Executive Officer
**Web address:** www.hgbhealth.com

STURGIS HOSPITAL (C, 49 beds) 916 Myrtle Street, Sturgis, MI Zip 49091–2326; tel. 269/651–7824; Robert J. LaBarge, Chief Executive Officer
**Web address:** www.sturgishospital.com

THREE RIVERS HEALTH (C, 35 beds) 701 South Health Parkway, Three Rivers, MI Zip 49093–8352; tel. 269/278–1145; William B. Russell, Chief Executive Officer
**Web address:** www.threerivershealth.org

**MINNESOTA:** RAINY LAKE MEDICAL CENTER (C, 25 beds) 1400 Highway 71, International Falls, MN Zip 56649–2189; tel. 218/283–4481; Bob Haley, Interim Chief Executive Officer
**Web address:** www.rainylakemedical.com

**MISSISSIPPI:** HANCOCK MEDICAL CENTER (C, 47 beds) 149 Drinkwater Boulevard, Bay Saint Louis, MS Zip 39520–1658, Mailing Address: P.O. Box 2790, Zip 39521–2790; tel. 228/467–8600; Craig R. Cudworth, Interim Chief Executive Officer
**Web address:** www.hmc.org

KING'S DAUGHTERS MEDICAL CENTER (C, 103 beds) 427 Highway 51 North, Brookhaven, MS Zip 39601–2350, Mailing Address: P.O. Box 948, Zip 39602–0948; tel. 601/833–6011; Alvin Hoover, FACHE, Chief Executive Officer
**Web address:** www.kdmc.org

**MISSOURI:** NEVADA REGIONAL MEDICAL CENTER (C, 71 beds) 800 South Ash Street, Nevada, MO Zip 64772–3223; tel. 417/667–3355; Judith K. Feuquay, Chief Executive Officer
**Web address:** www.nrmchealth.com

**MONTANA:** CENTRAL MONTANA MEDICAL CENTER (C, 90 beds) 408 Wendell Avenue, Lewistown, MT Zip 59457–2261; tel. 406/535–7711; Lee Rhodes, Chief Executive Officer
**Web address:** www.cmmccares.com

NORTH VALLEY HOSPITAL (C, 25 beds) 1600 Hospital Way, Whitefish, MT Zip 59937–7849; tel. 406/863–3500; Jason A. Spring, FACHE, Chief Executive Officer
**Web address:** www.nvhosp.org

**NEBRASKA:** PHELPS MEMORIAL HEALTH CENTER (C, 25 beds) 1215 Tibbals Street, Holdrege, NE Zip 68949–1255; tel. 308/995–2211; Mark Harrel, Chief Executive Officer
**Web address:** www.phelpsmemorial.com

**NEW MEXICO:** CIBOLA GENERAL HOSPITAL (C, 25 beds) 1016 East Roosevelt Avenue, Grants, NM Zip 87020–2118; tel. 505/287–4446; Michael Makosky, Chief Executive Officer
**Web address:** www.cibolahospital.com

HOLY CROSS HOSPITAL (C, 35 beds) 1397 Weimer Road, Taos, NM Zip 87571–6253; tel. 575/758–8883; Peter A. Hofstetter, Chief Executive Officer
**Web address:** www.taoshospital.org

**NORTH CAROLINA:** JOHNSTON HEALTH (C, 141 beds) 509 North Bright Leaf Boulevard, Smithfield, NC Zip 27577–4407, Mailing Address: P.O. Box 1376, Zip 27577–1376; tel. 919/934–8171; Charles W. Elliott, Jr., Chief Executive Officer
**Web address:** www.johnstonhealth.org

MOREHEAD MEMORIAL HOSPITAL (C, 214 beds) 117 East King's Highway, Eden, NC Zip 27288–5201; tel. 336/623–9711; Kevin R. Andrews, Interim Chief Executive Officer
**Web address:** www.morehead.org

For explanation of codes following names, see page B2.
★ Indicates Type III membership in the American Hospital Association.

NORTHERN HOSPITAL OF SURRY COUNTY (C, 108 beds) 830 Rockford Street, Mount Airy, NC Zip 27030–5365, Mailing Address: P.O. Box 1101, Zip 27030–1101; tel. 336/719–7000; William B. James, FACHE, Chief Executive Officer
**Web address:** www.northernhospital.com

**OHIO:** KNOX COMMUNITY HOSPITAL (C, 87 beds) 1330 Coshocton Road, Mount Vernon, OH Zip 43050–1495; tel. 740/393–9000; Bruce D. White, Chief Executive Officer
**Web address:** www.knoxcommhosp.org

WOOSTER COMMUNITY HOSPITAL (C, 150 beds) 1761 Beall Avenue, Wooster, OH Zip 44691–2342; tel. 330/263–8100; William E. Sheron, Chief Executive Officer
**Web address:** www.woosterhospital.org

**OKLAHOMA:** OKMULGEE MEMORIAL HOSPITAL (C, 46 beds) 1401 Morris Drive, Okmulgee, OK Zip 74447–6429, Mailing Address: P.O. Box 1038, Zip 74447–1038; tel. 918/756–4233; George N. Miller, Jr., Chief Executive Officer
**Web address:** www.okmulgeehospital.com

PERRY MEMORIAL HOSPITAL (C, 26 beds) 501 North 14th Street, Perry, OK Zip 73077–5099; tel. 580/336–3541; Howard D. Turner, Chief Executive Officer
**Web address:** www.pmh–ok.org

**PENNSYLVANIA:** CLARION HOSPITAL (C, 77 beds) One Hospital Drive, Clarion, PA Zip 16214–8501; tel. 814/226–9500; Byron Quinton, Chief Executive Officer
**Web address:** www.clarionhospital.org

JERSEY SHORE HOSPITAL (C, 25 beds) 1020 Thompson Street, Jersey Shore, PA Zip 17740–1794; tel. 570/398–0100; Carey W. Plummer, President and Chief Executive Officer
**Web address:** www.jsh.org

MEMORIAL HOSPITAL (C, 183 beds) One Hospital Drive, Towanda, PA Zip 18848–9702; tel. 570/265–2191; Gary A. Baker, President
**Web address:** www.memorialhospital.org

**SOUTH CAROLINA:** ABBEVILLE AREA MEDICAL CENTER (C, 25 beds) 420 Thomson Circle, Abbeville, SC Zip 29620–5656, Mailing Address: P.O. Box 887, Zip 29620–0887; tel. 864/366–5011; Richard D. Osmus, Chief Executive Officer
**Web address:** www.abbevilleareamc.com

NEWBERRY COUNTY MEMORIAL HOSPITAL (C, 32 beds) 2669 Kinard Street, Newberry, SC Zip 29108–2911, Mailing Address: P.O. Box 497, Zip 29108–0497; tel. 803/276–7570; Ronald J. Vigus, Chief Executive Officer
**Web address:** www.newberryhospital.org

REGIONAL MEDICAL CENTER (C, 286 beds) 3000 St. Matthews Road, Orangeburg, SC Zip 29118–1442; tel. 803/395–2200; Thomas C. Dandridge, FACHE, President and Chief Executive Officer
**Web address:** www.trmchealth.org

**SOUTH DAKOTA:** HURON REGIONAL MEDICAL CENTER (C, 25 beds) 172 Fourth Street S.E., Huron, SD Zip 57350–2590; tel. 605/353–6200; John L. Single, Chief Executive Officer
**Web address:** www.huronregional.org

**TENNESSEE:** LINCOLN COUNTY HEALTH SYSTEM (C, 323 beds) 106 Medical Center Boulevard, Fayetteville, TN Zip 37334–2684; tel. 931/438–1100; Jamie W. Guin, Jr., Chief Executive Officer
**Web address:** www.lchealthsystem.com

MACON COUNTY GENERAL HOSPITAL (C, 25 beds) 204 Medical Drive, Lafayette, TN Zip 37083–1799, Mailing Address: P.O. Box 378, Zip 37083–0378; tel. 615/666–2147; Dennis A. Wolford, FACHE, Chief Executive Officer
**Web address:** www.mcgh.net

RHEA MEDICAL CENTER (C, 25 beds) 9400 Rhea County Highway, Dayton, TN Zip 37321–7922; tel. 423/775–1121; Kennedy L. Croom, Jr., Administrator and Chief Executive Officer
**Web address:** www.rheamedical.org

**TEXAS:** BRAZOSPORT REGIONAL HEALTH SYSTEM (C, 103 beds) 100 Medical Drive, Lake Jackson, TX Zip 77566–5674; tel. 979/297–4411; Al Guevara, FACHE, President and Chief Executive Officer
**Web address:** www.brhstx.org

MATAGORDA REGIONAL MEDICAL CENTER (C, 58 beds) 104 7th Street, Bay City, TX Zip 77414–4853; tel. 979/245–6383; Steven L. Smith, Chief Executive Officer
**Web address:** www.matagordaregional.org

MEMORIAL HOSPITAL (C, 32 beds) 1110 Sarah Dewitt Drive, Gonzales, TX Zip 78629–3311, Mailing Address: P.O. Box 587, Zip 78629–0587; tel. 830/672–7581; Charles Norris, Chief Executive Officer
**Web address:** www.gonzaleshealthcare.com

**VERMONT:** NORTHWESTERN MEDICAL CENTER (C, 20 beds) 133 Fairfield Street, Saint Albans, VT Zip 05478–1726; tel. 802/524–5911; Jill Berry Bowen, President and Chief Executive Officer
**Web address:** www.northwesternmedicalcenter.org

**WASHINGTON:** KADLEC REGIONAL MEDICAL CENTER (C, 249 beds) 888 Swift Boulevard, Richland, WA Zip 99352–3514; tel. 509/946–4611; Rand J. Wortman, Chief Executive Officer
**Web address:** www.kadlecmed.org

**WISCONSIN:** AMERY REGIONAL MEDICAL CENTER (C, 15 beds) 265 Griffin Street East, Amery, WI Zip 54001–1439; tel. 715/268–8000; Michael Karuschak, Jr., Chief Executive Officer
**Web address:** www.amerymedicalcenter.org

**WYOMING:** MEMORIAL HOSPITAL OF CARBON COUNTY (C, 25 beds) 2221 West Elm Street, Rawlins, WY Zip 82301–5108, Mailing Address: P.O. Box 460, Zip 82301–0460; tel. 307/324–2221; Ned Hill, Chief Executive Officer
**Web address:** www.imhcc.com

WEST PARK HOSPITAL (C, 140 beds) 707 Sheridan Avenue, Cody, WY Zip 82414–3409; tel. 307/527–7501; Douglas A. McMillan, Administrator and Chief Executive Officer
**Web address:** www.westparkhospital.org

| | | |
|---|---|---|
| Owned, leased, sponsored: | 0 hospitals | 0 beds |
| Contract–managed: | 73 hospitals | 4812 beds |
| Totals: | 73 hospitals | 4812 beds |

---

**★0040: QUEEN'S HEALTH SYSTEMS** (NP)
1301 Punchbowl Street, Honolulu, HI Zip 96813–2402; tel. 808/535–5448; Arthur A. Ushijima, President and Chief Executive Officer
**(Moderately Centralized Health System)**

**HAWAII:** MOLOKAI GENERAL HOSPITAL (O, 15 beds) Kaunakakai, HI Zip 96748–0408; tel. 808/553–5331; Janice Kalanihuia, President
**Web address:** www.queens.org

QUEEN'S MEDICAL CENTER (O, 495 beds) 1301 Punchbowl Street, Honolulu, HI Zip 96813–2499; tel. 808/538–9011; Arthur A. Ushijima, President
**Web address:** www.queens.org

| | | |
|---|---|---|
| Owned, leased, sponsored: | 2 hospitals | 510 beds |
| Contract–managed: | 0 hospitals | 0 beds |
| Totals: | 2 hospitals | 510 beds |

---

**★8495: REGIONAL HEALTH** (NP)
353 Fairmont Boulevard, Rapid City, SD Zip 57701–7375, Mailing Address: P.O. Box 6000, Zip 57709–6000; tel. 605/719–1000; Charles E. Hart, M.D., MS, President and Chief Executive Officer
**(Moderately Centralized Health System)**

**SOUTH DAKOTA:** CUSTER REGIONAL HOSPITAL (L, 87 beds) 1039 Montgomery Street, Custer, SD Zip 57730–1397; tel. 605/673–2229; Veronica Schmidt, Chief Executive Officer
**Web address:** www.regionalhealth.com

LEAD–DEADWOOD REGIONAL HOSPITAL (O, 18 beds) 61 Charles Street, Deadwood, SD Zip 57732–1303; tel. 605/722–6101; Sherry Bea Smith, R.N., Chief Executive Officer
**Web address:** www.regionalhealth.com

PHILIP HEALTH SERVICES (C, 48 beds) 503 West Pine Street, Philip, SD Zip 57567–3300, Mailing Address: P.O. Box 790, Zip 57567–0790; tel. 605/859–2511; Kent Olson, Administrator and Chief Executive Officer

For explanation of codes following names, see page B2.
★ Indicates Type III membership in the American Hospital Association.

RAPID CITY REGIONAL HOSPITAL (O, 394 beds) 353 Fairmont Boulevard, Rapid City, SD Zip 57701–7393, Mailing Address: P.O. Box 6000, Zip 57709–6000; tel. 605/719–1000; Timothy H. Sughrue, Chief Executive Officer
**Web address:** www.rcrh.org

SPEARFISH REGIONAL HOSPITAL (O, 34 beds) 1440 North Main Street, Spearfish, SD Zip 57783–1504; tel. 605/644–4000; Larry W. Veitz, Chief Executive Officer
**Web address:** www.regionalhealth.com

STURGIS REGIONAL HOSPITAL (O, 109 beds) 949 Harmon Street, Sturgis, SD Zip 57785–2452; tel. 605/720–2400; Van D. Hyde, MS, Chief Executive Officer
**Web address:** www.regionalhealth.com/Our–Locations/Regional–Hospitals/Sturgis–Regional–Hospital.aspx

**WYOMING:** CROOK COUNTY MEDICAL SERVICES DISTRICT (C, 48 beds) 713 Oak Street, Sundance, WY Zip 82729, Mailing Address: P.O. Box 517, Zip 82729–0517; tel. 307/283–3501; Jan VanBeek, Chief Executive Officer
**Web address:** www.crookcountymedical.com

WESTON COUNTY HEALTH SERVICES (C, 75 beds) 1124 Washington Boulevard, Newcastle, WY Zip 82701–2972; tel. 307/746–4491; Maureen K. Cadwell, Chief Executive Officer
**Web address:** www.wchs–wy.org

| Owned, leased, sponsored: | 5 hospitals | 642 beds |
|---|---|---|
| Contract–managed: | 3 hospitals | 171 beds |
| Totals: | 8 hospitals | 813 beds |

---

**0622: REGIONALCARE HOSPITAL PARTNERS** (IO)
103 Continental Place, Suite 200, Brentwood, TN Zip 37027–1042; tel. 615/844–9800; Kent H. Wallace, Chief Executive Officer
**(Moderately Centralized Health System)**

**ALABAMA:** ELIZA COFFEE MEMORIAL HOSPITAL (O, 278 beds) 205 Marengo Street, Florence, AL Zip 35630–6033, Mailing Address: P.O. Box 818, Zip 35631–0818; tel. 256/768–9191; Russell Pigg, Chief Executive Officer
**Web address:** www.chgroup.org

SHOALS HOSPITAL (O, 137 beds) 201 Avalon Avenue, Muscle Shoals, AL Zip 35661–2805, Mailing Address: P.O. Box 3359, Zip 35662–3359; tel. 256/386–1600; C. Ross Berry, Chief Executive Officer
**Web address:** www.shoalshospital.com

**ARIZONA:** SIERRA VISTA REGIONAL HEALTH CENTER (L, 83 beds) 300 El Camino Real, Sierra Vista, AZ Zip 85635–2899; tel. 520/417–3003; Margaret Hepburn, MS, R.N., President and Chief Executive Officer
**Web address:** www.svrhc.org

**CONNECTICUT:** SHARON HOSPITAL (O, 78 beds) 50 Hospital Hill Road, Sharon, CT Zip 06069–2096, Mailing Address: P.O. Box 789, Zip 06069–0789; tel. 860/364–4000; Kim Lumia, President and Chief Executive Officer
**Web address:** www.sharonhospital.com

**IOWA:** OTTUMWA REGIONAL HEALTH CENTER (O, 105 beds) 1001 Pennsylvania Avenue, Ottumwa, IA Zip 52501–2186; tel. 641/684–2300; Philip G. Dionne, Chief Executive Officer
**Web address:** www.ottumwaregionalhealth.com

**OHIO:** CLINTON MEMORIAL HOSPITAL (O, 102 beds) 610 West Main Street, Wilmington, OH Zip 45177–2125; tel. 937/382–6611; Mark J. Dooley, Chief Executive Officer
**Web address:** www.cmhregional.com

**PENNSYLVANIA:** SOUTHWEST REGIONAL MEDICAL CENTER (O, 77 beds) 350 Bonar Avenue, Waynesburg, PA Zip 15370–1608; tel. 724/627–3101; Cynthia Cowie, Chief Executive Officer
**Web address:** www.sw–rmc.com

**TEXAS:** PARIS REGIONAL MEDICAL CENTER (O, 192 beds) 820 Clarksville Street, Paris, TX Zip 75460–6027, Mailing Address: P.O. Box 9070, Zip 75461–9070; tel. 903/785–4521; Stephen Grubbs, Chief Executive Officer
**Web address:** www.parisrmc.com

| Owned, leased, sponsored: | 8 hospitals | 1052 beds |
|---|---|---|
| Contract–managed: | 0 hospitals | 0 beds |
| Totals: | 8 hospitals | 1052 beds |

---

**0411: RELIANT HEALTHCARE PARTNERS** (IO)
1300 East Lookout Drive, Suite 115, Richardson, TX Zip 75082–4114; tel. 469/298–1400; Chester Crouch, Chief Executive Officer
**(Independent Hospital System)**

**OHIO:** DAYTON REHABILITATION INSTITUTE (O, 50 beds) One Elizabeth Place, Dayton, OH Zip 45417–3445; tel. 937/424–8200; Randy J. Kitchen, Chief Executive Officer
**Web address:** www.reliantdayton.com

**TEXAS:** RELIANT REHABILITATION HOSPITAL ABILENE (O, 30 beds) 6401 Directors Parkway, Abilene, TX Zip 79606–5869; tel. 325/691–1600; Lisa M. Nelson, R.N., MS, Chief Executive Officer
**Web address:** www.reliantabilene.com

RELIANT REHABILITATION HOSPITAL CENTRAL TEXAS (O, 75 beds) 1400 Hester's Crossing, Round Rock, TX Zip 78681–8025; tel. 512/244–4400; Eric Mueller, Chief Executive Officer
**Web address:** www.reliantcentraltx.com/

RELIANT REHABILITATION HOSPITAL NORTH HOUSTON (O, 60 beds) 117 Vision Park Boulevard, Shenandoah, TX Zip 77384–3001; tel. 936/444–1700; Abraham Sims, Chief Executive Officer
**Web address:** www.reliantnorthhouston.com/

RELIANT REHABILITATION HOSPITAL NORTH TEXAS (O, 50 beds) 3351 Waterview Parkway, Richardson, TX Zip 75080–1449; tel. 972/398–5700; Jim Ransom, Chief Executive Officer
**Web address:** www.relianthcp.com

| Owned, leased, sponsored: | 5 hospitals | 265 beds |
|---|---|---|
| Contract–managed: | 0 hospitals | 0 beds |
| Totals: | 5 hospitals | 265 beds |

---

**★2625: RENOWN HEALTH** (NP)
1155 Mill Street, Reno, NV Zip 89502–1576; tel. 775/982–4100; Donald C. Sibery, Interim Chief Executive Officer
**(Centralized Health System)**

**NEVADA:** RENOWN REGIONAL MEDICAL CENTER (O, 608 beds) 1155 Mill Street, Reno, NV Zip 89502–1576; tel. 775/982–4100; Gregory E. Boyer, Chief Executive Officer
**Web address:** www.renown.org

RENOWN REHABILITATION HOSPITAL (O, 62 beds) 1495 Mill Street, Reno, NV Zip 89502–1479; tel. 775/982–3500; Allan E. Hanssen, Interim Administrator
**Web address:** www.renown.org

RENOWN SOUTH MEADOWS MEDICAL CENTER (O, 76 beds) 10101 Double R Boulevard, Reno, NV Zip 89521–5931; tel. 775/982–7000; Allan E. Hanssen, Interim Administrator
**Web address:** www.renown.org

| Owned, leased, sponsored: | 3 hospitals | 746 beds |
|---|---|---|
| Contract–managed: | 0 hospitals | 0 beds |
| Totals: | 3 hospitals | 746 beds |

---

**0872: RESTORA HEALTHCARE** (IO)
2550 Northwinds Parkway, Suite 160, Alpharetta, GA Zip 30009–2234; tel. 678/736–7780; Rod Laughlin, President and Chief Executive Officer

**ARIZONA:** RESTORA HOSPITAL OF MESA (O, 120 beds) 215 South Power Road, Mesa, AZ Zip 85206–5235; tel. 480/985–6992; Judith Schiros, Chief Executive Officer
**Web address:** www.restorahealthcare.com

RESTORA HOSPITAL OF SUN CITY (O, 120 beds) 13818 North Thunderbird Boulevard, Sun City, AZ Zip 85351–2574; tel. 623/977–1325; Gregory Sassman, Interim Chief Executive Officer
**Web address:** www.restorahealthcare.com

---

For explanation of codes following names, see page B2.
★ Indicates Type III membership in the American Hospital Association.

| Owned, leased, sponsored: | 2 hospitals | 240 beds |
|---|---|---|
| Contract–managed: | 0 hospitals | 0 beds |
| Totals: | 2 hospitals | 240 beds |

**4810:   RIVERSIDE HEALTH SYSTEM** (NP)
701 Town Center Drive, Suite 1000, Newport News, VA
Zip 23606–4286; tel. 757/534–7000; William B. Downey, President
and Chief Executive Officer
**(Centralized Health System)**

**VIRGINIA:** HAMPTON ROADS SPECIALTY HOSPITAL (O, 25 beds) 245
Chesapeake Avenue, Newport News, VA Zip 23607–6038;
tel. 757/534–5000; Courtney Detwiler, R.N., Administrator
**Web address:** www.hamptonroadsspecialtyhospital.com

RIVERSIDE BEHAVIORAL HEALTH CENTER (O, 136 beds) 2244 Executive
Drive, Hampton, VA Zip 23666–2430; tel. 757/827–1001; Debra Campbell,
R.N., Administrator
**Web address:** www.riversideonline.com

RIVERSIDE DOCTORS' HOSPITAL (O, 40 beds) 1500 Commonwealth Avenue,
Williamsburg, VA Zip 23185–5229; tel. 757/585–2200; Steve C. McCary,
Administrator
**Web address:** www.riversideonline.com

RIVERSIDE REGIONAL MEDICAL CENTER (O, 199 beds) 500 J. Clyde Morris
Boulevard, Newport News, VA Zip 23601–1929; tel. 757/594–2000; Patrick
Parcells, Senior Vice President and Administrator
**Web address:** www.riverside–online.com

RIVERSIDE REHABILITATION INSTITUTE (O, 32 beds) 245 Chesapeake
Avenue, Newport News, VA Zip 23607–6038; tel. 757/928–8000; Edward
Heckler, Administrator
**Web address:** www.riverside–online.com

RIVERSIDE SHORE MEMORIAL HOSPITAL (O, 51 beds) 9507 Hospital Avenue,
Nassawadox, VA Zip 23413–1821, Mailing Address: P.O. Box 17,
Zip 23413–0017; tel. 757/414–8000; Susan McAndrews, R.N.,
Administrator
**Web address:** www.shorehealthservices.org

RIVERSIDE TAPPAHANNOCK HOSPITAL (O, 16 beds) 618 Hospital Road,
Tappahannock, VA Zip 22560–5000; tel. 804/443–3311; Elizabeth J. Martin,
Vice President and Administrator
**Web address:** www.riverside–online.com

RIVERSIDE WALTER REED HOSPITAL (O, 32 beds) 7519 Hospital Drive,
Gloucester, VA Zip 23061–4178, Mailing Address: P.O. Box 1130,
Zip 23061–1130; tel. 804/693–8800; Megan Kleckner, Vice President and
Administrator
**Web address:** www.riversideonline.com

| Owned, leased, sponsored: | 8 hospitals | 531 beds |
|---|---|---|
| Contract–managed: | 0 hospitals | 0 beds |
| Totals: | 8 hospitals | 531 beds |

**0268:   ROBERT WOOD JOHNSON HEALTH SYSTEM &
NETWORK** (NP)
1 Robert Wood Johnson Place, New Brunswick, NJ Zip 08901–1928;
tel. 732/828–3000; Stephen K. Jones, President and Chief Executive
Officer
**(Moderately Centralized Health System)**

**NEW JERSEY:** CHILDREN'S SPECIALIZED HOSPITAL–PSE&G (O, 126 beds)
200 Somerset Street, New Brunswick, NJ Zip 08901–1942;
tel. 732/258–7000; Amy B. Mansue, President and Chief Executive
Officer
**Web address:** www.childrens–specialized.org

ROBERT WOOD JOHNSON UNIVERSITY HOSPITAL (O, 610 beds) 1 Robert
Wood Johnson Place, New Brunswick, NJ Zip 08901–1928;
tel. 732/828–3000; Stephen K. Jones, President and Chief Executive Officer
**Web address:** www.rwjuh.edu

ROBERT WOOD JOHNSON UNIVERSITY HOSPITAL AT HAMILTON (O, 242
beds) One Hamilton Health Place, Hamilton, NJ Zip 08690–3599;
tel. 609/586–7900; Anthony J. Cimino, President and Chief Executive Officer
**Web address:** www.rwjhamilton.org

ROBERT WOOD JOHNSON UNIVERSITY HOSPITAL RAHWAY (O, 147 beds)
865 Stone Street, Rahway, NJ Zip 07065–2797; tel. 732/381–4200; Kirk C.
Tice, President and Chief Executive Officer
**Web address:** www.rwjuhr.com

| Owned, leased, sponsored: | 4 hospitals | 1125 beds |
|---|---|---|
| Contract–managed: | 0 hospitals | 0 beds |
| Totals: | 4 hospitals | 1125 beds |

**★0046:   ROCHESTER GENERAL HEALTH SYSTEM** (NP)
1425 Portland Avenue, 5th Floor, Rochester, NY Zip 14621–3001;
tel. 585/922–4000; Mark C. Clement, President and Chief Executive
Officer
**(Moderately Centralized Health System)**

**NEW YORK:** NEWARK–WAYNE COMMUNITY HOSPITAL (O, 270 beds) 1200
Driving Park Avenue, Newark, NY Zip 14513–1057, Mailing Address: P.O.
Box 111, Zip 14513–0111; tel. 315/332–2022; Mark F. Klyczek,
President and Chief Executive Officer
**Web address:** www.rochestergeneral.org

ROCHESTER GENERAL HOSPITAL (O, 520 beds) 1425 Portland Avenue,
Rochester, NY Zip 14621–3099; tel. 585/922–4000; Robert Nesselbush,
President
**Web address:** www.rochestergeneral.org

| Owned, leased, sponsored: | 2 hospitals | 790 beds |
|---|---|---|
| Contract–managed: | 0 hospitals | 0 beds |
| Totals: | 2 hospitals | 790 beds |

**0348:   RURAL COMMUNITY HOSPITALS OF AMERICA** (IO)
1100 Main Street, Suite 2350, Kansas City, MO Zip 64105–5186;
tel. 816/474–7800; Lawrence J. Arthur, President
**(Independent Hospital System)**

**KANSAS:** HILLSBORO COMMUNITY HOSPITAL (O, 10 beds) 701 South Main
Street, Hillsboro, KS Zip 67063–1553; tel. 620/947–3114; Marion
Regier, Chief Executive Officer
**Web address:** www.hchks.com

HORTON COMMUNITY HOSPITAL (O, 25 beds) 240 West 18th Street, Horton,
KS Zip 66439–1245; tel. 785/486–2642; Christopher Barlow, Chief
Executive Officer
**Web address:** www.horton–hospital.com

OSWEGO COMMUNITY HOSPITAL (O, 12 beds) 800 Barker Drive, Oswego, KS
Zip 67356–9014; tel. 620/795–2921; Daniel Hiben, Chief Executive Officer
**Web address:** www.oswegocommunityhospital.com

**MISSOURI:** I–70 COMMUNITY HOSPITAL (O, 15 beds) 105 Hospital Drive,
Sweet Springs, MO Zip 65351–2229; tel. 660/335–4700; Julie
Davenport, Chief Executive Officer
**Web address:** www.i70medcenter.com

**NORTH CAROLINA:** WASHINGTON COUNTY HOSPITAL (O, 25 beds) 958 U.S.
Highway 64 East, Plymouth, NC Zip 27962–9591; tel. 252/793–4135;
Cameron Highsmith, Chief Executive Officer

YADKIN VALLEY COMMUNITY HOSPITAL (O, 22 beds) 624 West Main Street,
Yadkinville, NC Zip 27055–7804, Mailing Address: P.O. Box 68,
Zip 27055–0068; tel. 336/679–2041; Shawn Bright, Chief Executive Officer
**Web address:** www.yadkinhospital.com/

**OKLAHOMA:** DRUMRIGHT REGIONAL HOSPITAL (O, 15 beds) 610 West
Bypass, Drumright, OK Zip 74030–5957; tel. 918/382–2300; Darrel
Morris, Chief Executive Officer
**Web address:** www.drumrighthospital.com

FAIRFAX COMMUNITY HOSPITAL (O, 15 beds) Taft Avenue and Highway 18,
Fairfax, OK Zip 74637–4028, Mailing Address: P.O. Box 219,
Zip 74637–0219; tel. 918/642–3291; Tina Steele, Chief Executive Officer
and Chief Financial Officer

HASKELL COUNTY COMMUNITY HOSPITAL (O, 32 beds) 401 Northwest H
Street, Stigler, OK Zip 74462–1625, Mailing Address: P.O. Box 728,
Zip 74462–0728; tel. 918/967–4682; Alan Bird, Chief Executive Officer
**Web address:** www.haskellhospital.com

Section B

For explanation of codes following names, see page B2.
★ Indicates Type III membership in the American Hospital Association.

PRAGUE COMMUNITY HOSPITAL (O, 19 beds) 1322 Klabzuba Avenue, Prague, OK Zip 74864–9005, Mailing Address: P.O. Box S., Zip 74864–1090; tel. 405/567–4922; Joan Walters, R.N., MSN, Administrator
**Web address:** www.praguehospital.com

SEILING COMMUNITY HOSPITAL (O, 18 beds) Highway 60 N.E., Seiling, OK Zip 73663, Mailing Address: P.O. Box 720, Zip 73663–0720; tel. 580/922–7361; Larry Troxell, Chief Executive Officer

**TENNESSEE:** LAUDERDALE COMMUNITY HOSPITAL (O, 25 beds) 326 Asbury Avenue, Ripley, TN Zip 38063–5577; tel. 731/221–2200; Scott Tongate, Chief Executive Officer
**Web address:** www.lauderdalehospital.com/

| | | |
|---|---|---|
| Owned, leased, sponsored: | 12 hospitals | 233 beds |
| Contract–managed: | 0 hospitals | 0 beds |
| Totals: | 12 hospitals | 233 beds |

---

★**0109: RURAL HEALTH GROUP** (IO)
48 West 1500 North, Nephi, UT Zip 84648–8900; tel. 435/623–4924; Mark R. Stoddard, President and Chairman
**(Independent Hospital System)**

**NEVADA:** DESERT VIEW HOSPITAL (O, 25 beds) 360 South Lola Lane, Pahrump, NV Zip 89048–0884; tel. 775/751–7500; Kelly H. Adams, Chief Executive Officer
**Web address:** www.desertviewhospital.com

**UTAH:** CENTRAL VALLEY MEDICAL CENTER (L, 25 beds) 48 West 1500 North, Nephi, UT Zip 84648–8900; tel. 435/623–3000; Mark R. Stoddard, President
**Web address:** www.cvmed.net

| | | |
|---|---|---|
| Owned, leased, sponsored: | 2 hospitals | 50 beds |
| Contract–managed: | 0 hospitals | 0 beds |
| Totals: | 2 hospitals | 50 beds |

---

★**0220: RUSH HEALTH SYSTEMS** (NP)
1314 19th Avenue, Meridian, MS Zip 39301–4116; tel. 601/483–0011; Wallace Strickland, President and Chief Executive Officer
**(Independent Hospital System)**

**ALABAMA:** CHOCTAW GENERAL HOSPITAL (O, 25 beds) 401 Vanity Fair Avenue, Butler, AL Zip 36904–3032; tel. 205/459–9100; J. W. Cowan, Administrator
**Web address:** www.choctawgeneral.com/cgh/

**MISSISSIPPI:** H. C. WATKINS MEMORIAL HOSPITAL (O, 25 beds) 605 South Archusa Avenue, Quitman, MS Zip 39355–2331; tel. 601/776–6925; Clinton Eaves, Administrator
**Web address:** www.watkinsmemorialhospital.com/hcwmh/

JOHN C. STENNIS MEMORIAL HOSPITAL (O, 25 beds) 14365 Highway 16 West, De Kalb, MS Zip 39328–7974; tel. 769/486–1000; Michael Nester, Administrator
**Web address:** www.johncstennismemorialhospital.com/jcsmh/

LAIRD HOSPITAL (O, 25 beds) 25117 Highway 15, Union, MS Zip 39365–9099; tel. 601/774–8214; Thomas G. Bartlett, III, Administrator
**Web address:** www.lairdhospital.com/lh/

RUSH FOUNDATION HOSPITAL (O, 182 beds) 1314 19th Avenue, Meridian, MS Zip 39301–4195; tel. 601/483–0011; Christopher Rush, Vice President and Administrator
**Web address:** www.rushhealthsystems.org/rfh/

SCOTT REGIONAL HOSPITAL (O, 25 beds) 317 Highway 13 South, Morton, MS Zip 39117–3353, Mailing Address: P.O. Box 259, Zip 39117–0259; tel. 601/732–6301; Michael R. Edwards, Administrator
**Web address:** www.scottregional.org/srh/

SPECIALTY HOSPITAL OF MERIDIAN (O, 49 beds) 1314 19th Avenue, Meridian, MS Zip 39301–4116; tel. 601/703–4211; Elizabeth C. Mitchell, Vice President and Administrator
**Web address:** www.specialtyhospitalofmeridian.com/shm/

| | | |
|---|---|---|
| Owned, leased, sponsored: | 7 hospitals | 356 beds |
| Contract–managed: | 0 hospitals | 0 beds |
| Totals: | 7 hospitals | 356 beds |

---

★**3855: RUSH UNIVERSITY MEDICAL CENTER** (NP)
1653 West Congress Parkway, Chicago, IL Zip 60612–3864; tel. 312/942–5000; Larry J. Goodman, M.D., Chief Executive Officer
**(Moderately Centralized Health System)**

**ILLINOIS:** RUSH UNIVERSITY MEDICAL CENTER (O, 669 beds) 1653 West Congress Parkway, Chicago, IL Zip 60612–3833; tel. 312/942–5000; Peter W. Butler, President and Chief Operating Officer
**Web address:** www.rush.edu

RUSH–COPLEY MEDICAL CENTER (O, 210 beds) 2000 Ogden Avenue, Aurora, IL Zip 60504–7222; tel. 630/978–6200; Barry C. Finn, President and Chief Executive Officer
**Web address:** www.rushcopley.com

| | | |
|---|---|---|
| Owned, leased, sponsored: | 2 hospitals | 879 beds |
| Contract–managed: | 0 hospitals | 0 beds |
| Totals: | 2 hospitals | 879 beds |

---

★**0318: SAINT FRANCIS CARE, INC.** (NP)
114 Woodland Street, Hartford, CT Zip 06105–1208; tel. 860/714–5541; Christopher M. Dadlez, President and Chief Executive Officer
**(Independent Hospital System)**

**CONNECTICUT:** JOHNSON MEMORIAL HOSPITAL (C, 72 beds) 201 Chestnut Hill Road, Stafford Springs, CT Zip 06076–4005; tel. 860/684–4251; Stuart E. Rosenberg, Chief Executive Officer
**Web address:** www.jmmc.com

MOUNT SINAI REHABILITATION HOSPITAL (O, 30 beds) 490 Blue Hills Avenue, Hartford, CT Zip 06112–1513; tel. 860/714–3500; Christopher M. Dadlez, President and Chief Executive Officer
**Web address:** www.stfranciscare.org

SAINT FRANCIS HOSPITAL AND MEDICAL CENTER (O, 569 beds) 114 Woodland Street, Hartford, CT Zip 06105–1208; tel. 860/714–4000; Christopher M. Dadlez, President and Chief Executive Officer
**Web address:** www.saintfranciscare.com

| | | |
|---|---|---|
| Owned, leased, sponsored: | 2 hospitals | 599 beds |
| Contract–managed: | 1 hospital | 72 beds |
| Totals: | 3 hospitals | 671 beds |

---

★**0254: SAINT FRANCIS HEALTH SYSTEM** (NP)
6161 South Yale Avenue, Tulsa, OK Zip 74136–1902; tel. 918/494–8454; Jake Henry, Jr., President and Chief Executive Officer
**(Centralized Physician/Insurance Health System)**

**OKLAHOMA:** LAUREATE PSYCHIATRIC CLINIC AND HOSPITAL (O, 75 beds) 6655 South Yale Avenue, Tulsa, OK Zip 74136–3329; tel. 918/481–4000; William Schloss, Senior Vice President
**Web address:** www.laureate.com

SAINT FRANCIS HOSPITAL (O, 774 beds) 6161 South Yale Avenue, Tulsa, OK Zip 74136–1902; tel. 918/494–2200; Lynn A. Sund, R.N., MS, Senior Vice President, Administrator and Chief Nursing Executive
**Web address:** www.saintfrancis.com

SAINT FRANCIS HOSPITAL SOUTH (O, 60 beds) 10501 East 91St. Streeet, Tulsa, OK Zip 74133–5790; tel. 918/455–3535; David S. Weil, Senior Vice President and Administrator
**Web address:** www.saintfrancis.com/south/

| | | |
|---|---|---|
| Owned, leased, sponsored: | 3 hospitals | 909 beds |
| Contract–managed: | 0 hospitals | 0 beds |
| Totals: | 3 hospitals | 909 beds |

---

For explanation of codes following names, see page B2.
★ Indicates Type III membership in the American Hospital Association.

★0120:  **SAINT LUKE'S HEALTH SYSTEM** (NP)
10920 Elm Avenue, Kansas City, MO Zip 64134–4108;
tel. 816/932–2000; Melinda Estes, M.D., President and Chief
Executive Officer
**(Centralized Health System)**

**KANSAS:** ANDERSON COUNTY HOSPITAL (L, 41 beds) 421 South Maple,
Garnett, KS Zip 66032–1334, Mailing Address: P.O. Box 309,
Zip 66032–0309; tel. 785/448–3131; Dennis A. Hachenberg, FACHE,
Chief Executive Officer
**Web address:** www.saint–lukes.org

SAINT LUKE'S CUSHING MEMORIAL HOSPITAL (O, 52 beds) 711 Marshall
Street, Leavenworth, KS Zip 66048–3235; tel. 913/684–1100; Adele
Ducharme, R.N., MSN, Chief Executive Officer
**Web address:** www.https://www.saintlukeshealthsystem.
org/location/cushing–memorial–hospital

SAINT LUKE'S SOUTH HOSPITAL (O, 110 beds) 12300 Metcalf Avenue,
Overland Park, KS Zip 66213–1324; tel. 913/317–7000; Jani L. Johnson,
President and Chief Executive Officer
**Web address:** www.saint–lukes.org

**MISSOURI:** CRITTENTON CHILDREN'S CENTER (O, 46 beds) 10918 Elm
Avenue, Kansas City, MO Zip 64134–4108; tel. 816/765–6600; Janine
Hron, Chief Executive Officer
**Web address:** www.crittentonkc.org

HEDRICK MEDICAL CENTER (L, 25 beds) 100 Central Avenue, Chillicothe, MO
Zip 64601–1554; tel. 660/646–1480; Matthew J. Wenzel, Chief Executive
Officer
**Web address:** www.saintlukeshealthsystem.org

SAINT LUKE'S EAST HOSPITAL (O, 125 beds) 100 N.E. Saint Luke's
Boulevard, Lee's Summit, MO Zip 64086–6000; tel. 816/347–5000; Ronald
L. Baker, Chief Executive Officer
**Web address:** www.saint–lukes.org

SAINT LUKE'S HOSPITAL OF KANSAS CITY (O, 410 beds) 4401 Wornall Road,
Kansas City, MO Zip 64111–3220; tel. 816/932–9886; Julie L. Quirin,
FACHE, Chief Executive Officer
**Web address:** www.saint–lukes.org

SAINT LUKE'S NORTH HOSPITAL – BARRY ROAD (O, 137 beds) 5830 N.W.
Barry Road, Kansas City, MO Zip 64154–2778; tel. 816/891–6000; Kevin T.
Trimble, FACHE, President and Chief Executive Officer
**Web address:** www.saint–lukes.org

WRIGHT MEMORIAL HOSPITAL (L, 25 beds) 191 Iowa Boulevard, Trenton, MO
Zip 64683–8343, Mailing Address: P.O. Box 628, Zip 64683–0628;
tel. 660/358–5700; Gary W. Jordan, FACHE, Chief Executive Officer
**Web address:** www.saintlukeshealthsystem.org

| | | |
|---|---|---|
| Owned, leased, sponsored: | 9 hospitals | 971 beds |
| Contract–managed: | 0 hospitals | 0 beds |
| Totals: | 9 hospitals | 971 beds |

★0264:  **SAINT VINCENT HEALTH SYSTEM** (CC)
232 West 25th Street, Erie, PA Zip 16544–0002;
tel. 814/452–5000; Scott Whalen, Ph.D., FACHE, President and
Chief Executive Officer
**(Moderately Centralized Health System)**

**NEW YORK:** WESTFIELD MEMORIAL HOSPITAL (O, 4 beds) 189 East Main
Street, Westfield, NY Zip 14787–1195; tel. 716/326–4921; Scott
Whalen, Ph.D., FACHE, President and Chief Executive Officer
**Web address:** www.wmhinc.org

**PENNSYLVANIA:** SAINT VINCENT HOSPITAL (O, 486 beds) 232 West 25th
Street, Erie, PA Zip 16544–0002; tel. 814/452–5000; Scott Whalen,
Ph.D., FACHE, President and Chief Executive Officer
**Web address:** www.svhs.org

| | | |
|---|---|---|
| Owned, leased, sponsored: | 2 hospitals | 490 beds |
| Contract–managed: | 0 hospitals | 0 beds |
| Totals: | 2 hospitals | 490 beds |

0403:  **SALEM HEALTH** (NP)
890 Oak Street Building B. POB 14001, Salem, OR
Zip 97309–5014; tel. 503/561–5200; Norman F. Gruber, President
and Chief Executive Officer
**(Moderately Centralized Health System)**

**OREGON:** SALEM HOSPITAL (O, 408 beds) 665 Winter Street S.E., Salem,
OR Zip 97301–3959, Mailing Address: P.O. Box 14001,
Zip 97309–5014; tel. 503/561–5200; Norman F. Gruber, President and
Chief Executive Officer
**Web address:** www.salemhospital.org

WEST VALLEY HOSPITAL (O, 6 beds) 525 S.E. Washington Street, Dallas, OR
Zip 97338–2834, Mailing Address: P.O. Box 378, Zip 97338–0378;
tel. 503/623–8301; Robert C. Brannigan, Administrator
**Web address:** www.westvalleyhospital.org

| | | |
|---|---|---|
| Owned, leased, sponsored: | 2 hospitals | 414 beds |
| Contract–managed: | 0 hospitals | 0 beds |
| Totals: | 2 hospitals | 414 beds |

★0186:  **SAMARITAN HEALTH SERVICES** (NP)
3600 N.W. Samaritan Drive, Corvallis, OR Zip 97330–3737, Mailing
Address: P.O. Box 1068, Zip 97339–1068; tel. 541/768–5001;
Larry A. Mullins, FACHE, President and Chief Executive Officer
**(Centralized Physician/Insurance Health System)**

GOOD SAMARITAN REGIONAL MEDICAL CENTER (O, 165 beds) 3600 N.W.
Samaritan Drive, Corvallis, OR Zip 97330–3737, Mailing Address: P.O. Box
1068, Zip 97339–1068; tel. 541/768–5111; Steven W. Jasperson, Chief
Executive Officer
**Web address:** www.samhealth.org

SAMARITAN ALBANY GENERAL HOSPITAL (O, 70 beds) 1046 West Sixth
Avenue, Albany, OR Zip 97321–1999; tel. 541/812–4000; David G. Triebes,
Chief Executive Officer
**Web address:** www.samhealth.org

SAMARITAN LEBANON COMMUNITY HOSPITAL (O, 25 beds) 525 North
Santiam Highway, Lebanon, OR Zip 97355–4363, Mailing Address: P.O. Box
739, Zip 97355–0739; tel. 541/258–2101; Becky A. Pape, R.N., Chief
Executive Officer
**Web address:** www.samhealth.org

SAMARITAN NORTH LINCOLN HOSPITAL (C, 25 beds) 3043 N.E. 28th Street,
Lincoln City, OR Zip 97367–4518, Mailing Address: P.O. Box 767,
Zip 97367–0767; tel. 541/994–3661; Marty Cahill, Chief Executive Officer
**Web address:** www.samhealth.org

SAMARITAN PACIFIC COMMUNITIES HOSPITAL (C, 25 beds) 930 S.W. Abbey
Street, Newport, OR Zip 97365–4820, Mailing Address: P.O. Box 945,
Zip 97365–0072; tel. 541/265–2244; David C. Bigelow, PharmD, Chief
Executive Officer
**Web address:** www.samhealth.org

| | | |
|---|---|---|
| Owned, leased, sponsored: | 3 hospitals | 260 beds |
| Contract–managed: | 2 hospitals | 50 beds |
| Totals: | 5 hospitals | 310 beds |

★0530:  **SANFORD HEALTH** (NP)
2301 East 60th Street North, Sioux Falls, SD Zip 57104–0569,
Mailing Address: PO Box 5039, Zip 57117–5039;
tel. 605/333–1000; Kelby K. Krabbenhoft, President and Chief
Executive Officer
**(Decentralized Health System)**

**IOWA:** ORANGE CITY AREA HEALTH SYSTEM (C, 104 beds) 1000 Lincoln
Circle S.E., Orange City, IA Zip 51041–1862; tel. 712/737–4984; Martin
W. Guthmiller, Chief Executive Officer
**Web address:** www.ochealthsystem.org

SANFORD ROCK RAPIDS MEDICAL CENTER (L, 16 beds) 801 South Greene
Street, Rock Rapids, IA Zip 51246–1998; tel. 712/472–2591; Tammy
Loosbrock, Chief Executive Officer
**Web address:** www.sanfordmerrill.org

For explanation of codes following names, see page B2.
★ Indicates Type III membership in the American Hospital Association.

SANFORD SHELDON MEDICAL CENTER (O, 95 beds) 118 North Seventh Avenue, Sheldon, IA Zip 51201–1235, Mailing Address: P.O. Box 250, Zip 51201–0250; tel. 712/324–5041; Richard E. Nordahl, Chief Executive Officer
**Web address:** www.sanfordsheldon.org

**MINNESOTA:** MAHNOMEN HEALTH CENTER (C, 68 beds) 414 West Jefferson Avenue, Mahnomen, MN Zip 56557–4912, Mailing Address: P.O. Box 396, Zip 56557–0396; tel. 218/935–2511; Susan K. Klassen, Chief Executive Officer and Administrator
**Web address:** www.mahnomenhealthcenter.com

MURRAY COUNTY MEDICAL CENTER (C, 18 beds) 2042 Juniper Avenue, Slayton, MN Zip 56172–1017; tel. 507/836–6111; Meldon L. Snow, Chief Executive Officer
**Web address:** www.murraycountymed.org

ORTONVILLE AREA HEALTH SERVICES (C, 89 beds) 450 Eastvold Avenue, Ortonville, MN Zip 56278–1133; tel. 320/839–2502; Richard M. Ash, Chief Executive Officer
**Web address:** www.oahs.us

PERHAM HEALTH (C, 121 beds) 1000 Coney Street West, Perham, MN Zip 56573–1199; tel. 218/347–4500; Chuck Hofius, Chief Executive Officer
**Web address:** www.perhamhealth.org

SANFORD BAGLEY MEDICAL CENTER (O, 95 beds) 203 Fourth Street N.W., Bagley, MN Zip 56621–8307; tel. 218/694–6501; Kirby Johnson, Administrator
**Web address:** www.clearwaterhealthservices.com

SANFORD BEMIDJI MEDICAL CENTER (O, 196 beds) 1300 Anne Street N.W., Bemidji, MN Zip 56601–5103; tel. 218/751–5430; Joy E. Johnson, Interim President
**Web address:** www.nchs.com

SANFORD CANBY MEDICAL CENTER (L, 93 beds) 112 St. Olaf Avenue South, Canby, MN Zip 56220–1433; tel. 507/223–7277; Lori Sisk, R.N., Chief Executive Officer
**Web address:** www.sanfordcanby.org

SANFORD JACKSON MEDICAL CENTER (O, 16 beds) 1430 North Highway, Jackson, MN Zip 56143–1093; tel. 507/847–2420; Mary J. Ruyter, Chief Executive Officer
**Web address:** www.sanfordjackson.org

SANFORD LUVERNE MEDICAL CENTER (O, 25 beds) 1600 North Kniss Avenue, Luverne, MN Zip 56156–1067; tel. 507/283–2321; Tammy Loosbrock, Chief Executive Officer
**Web address:** www.sanfordluverne.org

SANFORD THIEF RIVER FALLS MEDICAL CENTER (O, 35 beds) 120 LaBree Avenue South, Thief River Falls, MN Zip 56701–2840; tel. 218/681–4240; Brian J. Carlson, FACHE, Chief Executive Officer
**Web address:** www.sanfordhealth.org

SANFORD TRACY MEDICAL CENTER (L, 25 beds) 251 Fifth Street East, Tracy, MN Zip 56175–1536; tel. 507/629–3200; Stacy Barstad, Chief Executive Officer
**Web address:** www.sanfordtracy.org

SANFORD WESTBROOK MEDICAL CENTER (L, 6 beds) 920 Bell Avenue, Westbrook, MN Zip 56183–9669, Mailing Address: P.O. Box 188, Zip 56183–0188; tel. 507/274–6121; Stacy Barstad, Chief Executive Officer
**Web address:** www.sanfordwestbrook.org

SANFORD WHEATON MEDICAL CENTER (O, 15 beds) 401 12th Street North, Wheaton, MN Zip 56296–1099; tel. 320/563–8226; JoAnn M. Foltz, R.N., Chief Executive Officer
**Web address:** www.sanfordhealth.org

SANFORD WORTHINGTON MEDICAL CENTER (O, 48 beds) 1018 Sixth Avenue, Worthington, MN Zip 56187–2202, Mailing Address: P.O. Box 997, Zip 56187–0997; tel. 507/372–2941; Michael Hammer, Chief Executive Officer
**Web address:** www.sanfordregionalworthington.org

WINDOM AREA HOSPITAL (C, 25 beds) 2150 Hospital Drive, Windom, MN Zip 56101–1287, Mailing Address: P.O. Box 339, Zip 56101–0339; tel. 507/831–2400; Geraldine F. Burmeister, FACHE, Chief Executive Officer
**Web address:** www.windomareahospital.com

**NORTH DAKOTA:** SANFORD BISMARCK (O, 207 beds) 300 North Seventh Street, Bismarck, ND Zip 58501–4439, Mailing Address: P.O. Box 5525, Zip 58506–5525; tel. 701/323–6000; Craig Lambrecht, M.D., President
**Web address:** www.bismarck.sanfordhealth.org/

SANFORD HILLSBORO MEDICAL CENTER (C, 52 beds) 12 Third Street S.E., Hillsboro, ND Zip 58045–4840, Mailing Address: P.O. Box 609, Zip 58045–0609; tel. 701/636–3200; Jac McTaggart, Chief Executive Officer
**Web address:** www.hillsboromedicalcenter.com

SANFORD MAYVILLE MEDICAL CENTER (O, 18 beds) 42 Sixth Avenue S.E., Mayville, ND Zip 58257–1598; tel. 701/786–3800; Roger Baier, Chief Executive Officer
**Web address:** www.unionhospital.com

SANFORD MEDICAL CENTER FARGO (O, 491 beds) 801 Broadway North, Fargo, ND Zip 58102–3641; tel. 701/234–2000; Dennis C. Millirons, FACHE, President
**Web address:** www.sanfordhealth.org

SANFORD NORTHWOOD DEACONESS HEALTH CENTER (O, 73 beds) 4 North Park Street, Northwood, ND Zip 58267–4102, Mailing Address: P.O. Box 190, Zip 58267–0190; tel. 701/587–6060; Pete Antonson, Chief Executive Officer
**Web address:** www.ndhc.net

**SOUTH DAKOTA:** COMMUNITY MEMORIAL HOSPITAL (C, 16 beds) 809 Jackson Street, Burke, SD Zip 57523–2065, Mailing Address: P.O. Box 319, Zip 57523–0319; tel. 605/775–2621; Jim Frank, Chief Executive Officer
**Web address:** www.sanfordhealth.org

PIONEER MEMORIAL HOSPITAL AND HEALTH SERVICES (C, 64 beds) 315 North Washington Street, Viborg, SD Zip 57070–2002, Mailing Address: P.O. Box 368, Zip 57070–0368; tel. 605/326–5161; Thomas V. Richter, Chief Executive Officer
**Web address:** www.pioneermemorial.org

SANFORD ABERDEEN MEDICAL CENTER (O, 48 beds) 2905 3rd Avenue S.E., Aberdeen, SD Zip 57401–5420; tel. 605/725–1700; Gordon Larson, Chief Executive Officer
**Web address:** www.sanfordaberdeen.org/

SANFORD CANTON–INWOOD MEDICAL CENTER (O, 16 beds) 440 North Hiawatha Drive, Canton, SD Zip 57013–5800; tel. 605/764–1400; Scott C. Larson, Chief Executive Officer
**Web address:** www.sanfordcantoninwood.org

SANFORD CHAMBERLAIN MEDICAL CENTER (O, 69 beds) 300 South Byron Boulevard, Chamberlain, SD Zip 57325–9741; tel. 605/234–5511; Erica Peterson, Chief Executive Officer
**Web address:** www.sanfordmiddakota.org

SANFORD CLEAR LAKE MEDICAL CENTER (L, 10 beds) 701 Third Avenue South, Clear Lake, SD Zip 57226–2016; tel. 605/874–2141; Lori Sisk, R.N., Chief Executive Officer
**Web address:** www.sanforddeuelcounty.org

SANFORD USD MEDICAL CENTER (O, 511 beds) 1305 West 18th Street, Sioux Falls, SD Zip 57105–0496, Mailing Address: P.O. Box 5039, Zip 57117–5039; tel. 605/333–1000; Paul D. Hanson, President
**Web address:** www.sanfordhealth.org

SANFORD VERMILLION MEDICAL CENTER (L, 114 beds) 20 South Plum Street, Vermillion, SD Zip 57069–3346; tel. 605/624–2611; Timothy J. Tracy, Chief Executive Officer
**Web address:** www.sanfordvermillion.org

SANFORD WEBSTER MEDICAL CENTER (L, 20 beds) 1401 West 1st Street, Webster, SD Zip 57274–1054, Mailing Address: P.O. Box 489, Zip 57274–0489; tel. 605/345–3336; David Rogers, Chief Executive Officer
**Web address:** www.sanfordhealth.org

WINNER REGIONAL HEALTHCARE CENTER (C, 104 beds) 745 East Eighth Street, Winner, SD Zip 57580–2631; tel. 605/842–7100; Kevin Coffey, Chief Executive Officer
**Web address:** www.winnerregional.org

| | | |
|---|---|---|
| Owned, leased, sponsored: | 23 hospitals | 2242 beds |
| Contract–managed: | 10 hospitals | 661 beds |
| **Totals:** | 33 hospitals | 2903 beds |

**0412: SCHUYLKILL HEALTH SYSTEM** (NP)
420 South Jackson Street, Pottsville, PA Zip 17901–3625; tel. 570/621–5000; John E. Simodejka, President and Chief Executive Officer
**(Independent Hospital System)**

For explanation of codes following names, see page B2.
★ Indicates Type III membership in the American Hospital Association.

**PENNSYLVANIA:** SCHUYLKILL MEDICAL CENTER – EAST NORWEGIAN STREET (O, 126 beds) 700 East Norwegian Street, Pottsville, PA Zip 17901–2710; tel. 570/621–4000; John E. Simodejka, President and Chief Executive Officer
**Web address:** www.schuylkillhealth.com

SCHUYLKILL MEDICAL CENTER – SOUTH JACKSON STREET (O, 191 beds) 420 South Jackson Street, Pottsville, PA Zip 17901–3625; tel. 570/621–5000; John E. Simodejka, President and Chief Executive Officer
**Web address:** www.schuylkillhealth.com

| | | |
|---|---|---|
| **Owned, leased, sponsored:** | 2 hospitals | 317 beds |
| **Contract–managed:** | 0 hospitals | 0 beds |
| **Totals:** | 2 hospitals | 317 beds |

---

**★5095:  SCL HEALTH SYSTEM** (CC)
2420 West 26th Avenue, Suite 100D, Denver, CO Zip 80211–5302; tel. 303/813–5180; Michael A. Slubowski, FACHE, Chief Executive Officer
**(Moderately Centralized Health System)**

**CALIFORNIA:** SAINT JOHN'S HEALTH CENTER (O, 234 beds) 2121 Santa Monica Boulevard, Santa Monica, CA Zip 90404–2303; tel. 310/829–5511; Michael L. Wall, FACHE, Interim President and Chief Executive Officer
**Web address:** www.newstjohns.org/home.aspx

**COLORADO:** EXEMPLA GOOD SAMARITAN MEDICAL CENTER (S, 190 beds) 200 Exempla Circle, Lafayette, CO Zip 80026–3370; tel. 303/689–4000; David Hamm, President and Chief Executive Officer
**Web address:** www.exempla.org

EXEMPLA LUTHERAN MEDICAL CENTER (S, 494 beds) 8300 West 38th Avenue, Wheat Ridge, CO Zip 80033–6005; tel. 303/425–4500; Grant Wicklund, President and Chief Executive Officer
**Web address:** www.exempla.org

EXEMPLA SAINT JOSEPH HOSPITAL (S, 369 beds) 1835 Franklin Street, Denver, CO Zip 80218–1126; tel. 303/837–7111; Bain J. Farris, President and Chief Executive Officer
**Web address:** www.exempla.org

ST. MARY'S HOSPITAL AND MEDICAL CENTER (O, 324 beds) 2635 North 7th Street, Grand Junction, CO Zip 81501–8209, Mailing Address: P.O. Box 1628, Zip 81502–1628; tel. 970/298–2273; Michael J. McBride, FACHE, President and Chief Executive Officer
**Web address:** www.stmarygj.com

**KANSAS:** PROVIDENCE MEDICAL CENTER (O, 168 beds) 8929 Parallel Parkway, Kansas City, KS Zip 66112–1689; tel. 913/596–4000; Randall G. Nyp, FACHE, President and Chief Executive Officer
**Web address:** www.providence–health.org

SAINT JOHN HOSPITAL (O, 56 beds) 3500 South Fourth Street, Leavenworth, KS Zip 66048–5043; tel. 913/680–6000; Randall G. Nyp, FACHE, President and Chief Executive Officer
**Web address:** www.providence–health.org/sjh

ST. FRANCIS HEALTH CENTER (O, 291 beds) 1700 S.W. 7th Street, Topeka, KS Zip 66606–1690; tel. 785/295–8000; Robert J. Erickson, Chief Executive Officer
**Web address:** www.stfrancistopeka.org

**MONTANA:** HOLY ROSARY HEALTHCARE (O, 90 beds) 2600 Wilson Street, Miles City, MT Zip 59301–5094; tel. 406/233–2600; Paul Lewis, Chief Executive Officer
**Web address:** www.holyrosaryhealthcare.org

ST. JAMES HEALTHCARE (O, 58 beds) 400 South Clark Street, Butte, MT Zip 59701–2328; tel. 406/723–2500; Charles T. Wright, President and Chief Executive Officer
**Web address:** www.stjameshealthcare.org

ST. VINCENT HEALTHCARE (O, 249 beds) 1233 North 30th Street, Billings, MT Zip 59101–0165, Mailing Address: P.O. Box 35200, Zip 59107–5200; tel. 406/237–7000; Jason Barker, Chief Executive Officer
**Web address:** www.svh–mt.org

| | | |
|---|---|---|
| **Owned, leased, sponsored:** | 11 hospitals | 2523 beds |
| **Contract–managed:** | 0 hospitals | 0 beds |
| **Totals:** | 11 hospitals | 2523 beds |

---

**★0398:  SCOTT & WHITE HEALTHCARE** (NP)
2401 South 31st Street, Temple, TX Zip 76508–0001; tel. 254/724–2111; Robert W. Pryor, M.D., President and Chief Executive Officer
**(Centralized Physician/Insurance Health System)**

**TEXAS:** HILLCREST BAPTIST MEDICAL CENTER (C, 262 beds) 100 Hillcrest Medical Boulevard, Waco, TX Zip 76712–8897, Mailing Address: P.O. Box 21146, Zip 76702–1146; tel. 254/202–2000; Glenn A. Robinson, Chief Executive Officer
**Web address:** www.hillcrest.net

SCOTT & WHITE HOSPITAL – BRENHAM (O, 60 beds) 700 Medical Parkway, Brenham, TX Zip 77833–5498; tel. 979/836–6173; Michael Pittman, Chief Executive Officer
**Web address:** www.swbrenham.org

SCOTT & WHITE HOSPITAL – LLANO (O, 17 beds) 200 West Ollie Street, Llano, TX Zip 78643–2628; tel. 325/247–5040; Kevin Leeper, Chief Executive Officer
**Web address:** www.llanomemorial.org

SCOTT & WHITE HOSPITAL – TAYLOR (O, 23 beds) 305 Mallard Lane, Taylor, TX Zip 76574–1208; tel. 512/352–7611; Kevin E. Smith, Acting Administrator and Chief Operating Officer
**Web address:** www.swtaylor.org

SCOTT & WHITE HOSPITAL AT ROUND ROCK (O, 84 beds) 300 University Boulevard, Round Rock, TX Zip 78665–1032; tel. 512/509–0200; Ernest L. Bovio, Jr., Chief Executive Officer
**Web address:** www.scottandwhite.org

SCOTT AND WHITE CONTINUING CARE HOSPITAL (O, 50 beds) 546 North Kegley Road, Temple, TX Zip 76502–4069; tel. 254/215–0900; Kimberly K. Langston, R.N., Chief Executive Officer
**Web address:** www.sw.org/location/temple–cch

SCOTT AND WHITE MEMORIAL HOSPITAL (O, 638 beds) 2401 South 31st Street, Temple, TX Zip 76508–0002; tel. 254/724–2111; Shahin Motakef, Chief Executive Officer
**Web address:** www.sw.org/location/temple–hospital

| | | |
|---|---|---|
| **Owned, leased, sponsored:** | 6 hospitals | 872 beds |
| **Contract–managed:** | 1 hospital | 262 beds |
| **Totals:** | 7 hospitals | 1134 beds |

---

**★0037:  SCOTTSDALE HEALTHCARE** (NP)
8125 North Hayden Road, Scottsdale, AZ Zip 85258–2463; tel. 480/882–4000; Thomas J. Sadvary, FACHE, President and Chief Executive Officer
**(Independent Hospital System)**

**ARIZONA:** SCOTTSDALE HEALTHCARE SHEA MEDICAL CENTER (O, 409 beds) 9003 East Shea Boulevard, Scottsdale, AZ Zip 85260–6771; tel. 480/323–3000; Peggy J. Reiley, Ph.D., MS, R.N., Senior Vice President and Chief Clinical Officer
**Web address:** www.shc.org

SCOTTSDALE HEALTHCARE THOMPSON PEAK HOSPITAL (O, 64 beds) 7400 East Thompson Peak Parkway, Scottsdale, AZ Zip 85255–4109; tel. 480/324–7000; Kimberly Post, R.N., Vice President and Administrator
**Web address:** www.shc.org

SCOTTSDALE HEALTHCARE–OSBORN MEDICAL CENTER (O, 347 beds) 7400 East Osborn Road, Scottsdale, AZ Zip 85251–6403; tel. 480/882–4000; Gary E. Baker, Senior Vice President and Administrator
**Web address:** www.shc.org

| | | |
|---|---|---|
| **Owned, leased, sponsored:** | 3 hospitals | 820 beds |
| **Contract–managed:** | 0 hospitals | 0 beds |
| **Totals:** | 3 hospitals | 820 beds |

**Section B**

---

For explanation of codes following names, see page B2.
★ Indicates Type III membership in the American Hospital Association.

**★1505:   SCRIPPS HEALTH** (NP)
4275 Campus Point Court, San Diego, CA Zip 92121–1513;
tel. 858/678–7200; Chris D. Van Gorder, FACHE, President and
Chief Executive Officer
**(Centralized Health System)**

**CALIFORNIA:** SCRIPPS GREEN HOSPITAL (O, 173 beds) 10666 North Torrey
Pines Road, La Jolla, CA Zip 92037–1093; tel. 858/455–9100; Robin
Brown, Chief Executive, Senior Vice President
**Web address:** www.scrippshealth.org

SCRIPPS MEMORIAL HOSPITAL–ENCINITAS (O, 158 beds) 354 Santa Fe
Drive, Encinitas, CA Zip 92024–5182, Mailing Address: P.O. Box 230817,
Zip 92023–0817; tel. 760/633–6501; Carl J. Etter, Chief Eecutive, Senior
Vice President
**Web address:** www.scripps.org

SCRIPPS MEMORIAL HOSPITAL–LA JOLLA (O, 302 beds) 9888 Genesee
Avenue, La Jolla, CA Zip 92037–1200, Mailing Address: P.O. Box 28,
Zip 92038–0028; tel. 858/626–4123; Gary G. Fybel, Chief Executive, Senior
Vice President
**Web address:** www.scripps.org/locations/hospitals__
scripps–memorial–hospital–la–jolla

SCRIPPS MERCY HOSPITAL (O, 433 beds) 4077 Fifth Avenue, San Diego, CA
Zip 92103–2105; tel. 619/294–8111; Thomas A. Gammiere, Chief
Executive, Senior Vice President
**Web address:** www.scrippshealth.org

| Owned, leased, sponsored: | 4 hospitals | 1066 beds |
|---|---|---|
| Contract-managed: | 0 hospitals | 0 beds |
| Totals: | 4 hospitals | 1066 beds |

---

**★0181:   SELECT MEDICAL CORPORATION** (IO)
4714 Gettysburg Road, Mechanicsburg, PA Zip 17055–4325;
tel. 717/972–1100; David S. Chernow, President and Chief
Administrative Officer
**(Independent Hospital System)**

**ALABAMA:** SELECT SPECIALTY HOSPITAL–BIRMINGHAM (O, 38 beds) 800
Montclair Road, 9th Floor, Birmingham, AL Zip 35213–1908;
tel. 205/599–4600; Andrea White, Chief Executive Officer
**Web address:** www.selectspecialtyhospitals.
com/company/locations/birmingham.aspx

**ARIZONA:** SELECT SPECIALTY HOSPITAL–PHOENIX (O, 48 beds) 350 West
Thomas Road, 3rd Floor Main, Phoenix, AZ Zip 85013–4409;
tel. 602/406–6802; Sharon Anthony, Chief Executive Officer
**Web address:** www.selectspecialtyhospitals.
com/company/locations/phoenix.aspx

SELECT SPECIALTY HOSPITAL–SCOTTSDALE (O, 62 beds) 7400 East Osborn
Road, 3 West, Scottsdale, AZ Zip 85251–6432; tel. 480/882–4360; Anthony
Martino, Chief Executive Officer
**Web address:** www.selectspecialtyhospitals.
com/company/locations/scottsdale.aspx

**ARKANSAS:** REGENCY HOSPITAL OF NORTHWEST ARKANSAS (O, 50 beds)
1125 North College Avenue, Fayetteville, AR Zip 72703–1908;
tel. 479/713–7000; Jerry Alexander, Chief Executive Officer
**Web address:** www.regencyhospital.com

SELECT SPECIALTY HOSPITAL–FORT SMITH (O, 34 beds) 1001 Towson
Avenue, 6 Central, Fort Smith, AR Zip 72901–4921; tel. 479/441–3960;
Cindy McLain, Chief Executive Officer
**Web address:** www.selectspecialtyhospitals.
com/company/locations/fortsmith.aspx

SELECT SPECIALTY HOSPITAL–LITTLE ROCK (O, 43 beds) 2 St. Vincent
Circle, 6th Floor, Little Rock, AR Zip 72205; tel. 501/661–4198; Barry Ewy,
Chief Executive Officer
**Web address:** www.selectspecialtyhospitals.
com/company/locations/littlerock.aspx

**COLORADO:** SELECT LONG TERM CARE HOSPITAL – COLORADO SPRINGS
(O, 30 beds) 6001 East Woodmen Road, 6th Floor, Colorado Springs, CO
Zip 80923–2601; tel. 719/571–6000; James Elton, Chief Executive
Officer
**Web address:** www.selectmedical.com

SELECT SPECIALTY HOSPITAL–DENVER (O, 65 beds) 1719 East 19th
Avenue, 5th Floor, Denver, CO Zip 80218–1235; tel. 303/563–3700;
Deborah Dale, Chief Executive Officer
**Web address:** www.selectspecialtyhospitals.com/company/locations/denver.
aspx

**DELAWARE:** SELECT SPECIALTY HOSPITAL–WILMINGTON (O, 35 beds) 701
North Clayton Street, 5th Floor, Wilmington, DE Zip 19805–3948;
tel. 302/421–4545; Claudia Ann Eisenmann, Chief Executive Officer
**Web address:** www.selectspecialtyhospitals.
com/company/locations/wilmington.aspx

**FLORIDA:** SELECT SPECIALTY HOSPITAL–GAINESVILLE (O, 44 beds) 2708
S.W. Archer Road, Gainesville, FL Zip 32608–1316; tel. 352/337–3240;
Cheryl Hayes, Chief Executive Officer
**Web address:** www.selectspecialtyhospitals.
com/company/locations/gainesville.aspx

SELECT SPECIALTY HOSPITAL–MIAMI (O, 40 beds) 955 N.W. 3rd Street,
Miami, FL Zip 33128–1274; tel. 305/416–5700; Dionisio Bencomo, Chief
Executive Officer
**Web address:** www.selectspecialtyhospitals.com/company/locations/miami.
aspx

SELECT SPECIALTY HOSPITAL–ORLANDO (O, 75 beds) 2250 Bedford Road,
Orlando, FL Zip 32803–1443; tel. 407/303–7869; Nellie Castroman, Chief
Executive Officer
**Web address:** www.selectspecialtyhospitals.
com/company/locations/orlando.aspx

SELECT SPECIALTY HOSPITAL–PALM BEACH (O, 60 beds) 3060 Melaleuca
Lane, Lake Worth, FL Zip 33461–5174; tel. 561/357–7200; Larry Melby,
Chief Executive Officer
**Web address:** www.selectspecialtyhospitals.
com/company/locations/palmbeach.aspx

SELECT SPECIALTY HOSPITAL–PANAMA CITY (O, 30 beds) 615 North Bonita
Avenue, 3rd Floor, Panama City, FL Zip 32401–3623; tel. 850/767–3180;
Debra R. Gibson, Chief Executive Officer
**Web address:** www.selectspecialtyhospitals.
com/company/locations/panamacity.aspx

SELECT SPECIALTY HOSPITAL–PENSACOLA (O, 54 beds) 7000 Cobble Creek
Drive, Pensacola, FL Zip 32504–8638; tel. 850/473–4800; David Goodson,
Chief Executive Officer
**Web address:** www.selectspecialtyhospitals.
com/company/locations/pensacola.aspx

SELECT SPECIALTY HOSPITAL–TALLAHASSEE (O, 29 beds) 1554 Surgeons
Drive, Tallahassee, FL Zip 32308–4631; tel. 850/219–6800; Lora Davis,
Chief Executive Officer
**Web address:** www.selectspecialtyhospitals.
com/company/locations/tallahassee.aspx

WEST GABLES REHABILITATION HOSPITAL (O, 60 beds) 2525 S.W. 75th
Avenue, Miami, FL Zip 33155–2800; tel. 305/262–6800; Walter Concepcion,
Chief Executive Officer
**Web address:** www.westgablesrehabhospital.com/

**GEORGIA:** REGENCY HOSPITAL OF CENTRAL GEORGIA (O, 34 beds) 535
Coliseum Drive, Macon, GA Zip 31217–0104; tel. 478/803–7300;
Michael S. Boggs, Chief Executive Officer
**Web address:** www.regencyhospital.com

REGENCY HOSPITAL OF SOUTH ATLANTA (O, 37 beds) 1170 Cleveland
Avenue, 4th Floor, East Point, GA Zip 30344–3615; tel. 404/466–6250;
Alisa Jett, Chief Executive Officer
**Web address:** www.regencyhospital.com

SELECT SPECIALTY HOSPITAL–ATLANTA (O, 30 beds) 550 Peachtree Street
N.E., Atlanta, GA Zip 30308–2247; tel. 404/686–2270; Dwayne Hooks, Jr.,
R.N., Chief Executive Officer
**Web address:** www.selectspecialtyhospitals.com/company/locations/atlanta.
aspx

SELECT SPECIALTY HOSPITAL–AUGUSTA (O, 80 beds) 1537 Walton Way,
Augusta, GA Zip 30904–3764; tel. 706/731–1169; Curtis L. Roberts, Chief
Executive Officer
**Web address:** www.selectspecialtyhospitals.
com/company/locations/augusta.aspx

SELECT SPECIALTY HOSPITAL–SAVANNAH (O, 36 beds) 5353 Reynolds
Street, 4 South, Savannah, GA Zip 31405–6015; tel. 912/819–7972; James
H. Rogers, FACHE, Chief Executive Officer
**Web address:** www.selectspecialtyhospitals.
com/company/locations/savannah.aspx

For explanation of codes following names, see page B2.
★ Indicates Type III membership in the American Hospital Association.

**INDIANA:** REGENCY HOSPITAL OF NORTHWEST INDIANA (O, 25 beds) 4321 Fir Street, 4th Floor, East Chicago, IN Zip 46312–3049; tel. 219/392–7790; Victor J. Galfano, FACHE, Chief Executive Officer
**Web address:** www.regencyhospital.com/company/locations/indiana–northwest–indiana.aspx

SELECT SPECIALTY HOSPITAL–BEECH GROVE (O, 45 beds) 8060 Knue Road, Indianapolis, IN Zip 46250–1976; tel. 317/783–8985; Cheryl G. Gentry, Chief Executive Officer
**Web address:** www.selectspecialtyhospitals.com/company/locations/indianapolis.aspx

SELECT SPECIALTY HOSPITAL–EVANSVILLE (O, 60 beds) 400 S.E. 4th Street, Evansville, IN Zip 47713–1206; tel. 812/421–2500; Mike Carney, Chief Executive Officer
**Web address:** www.selectspecialtyhospitals.com/company/locations/evansville.aspx

SELECT SPECIALTY HOSPITAL–FORT WAYNE (O, 32 beds) 700 Broadway, 7th Floor, Fort Wayne, IN Zip 46802–1402; tel. 260/425–3810; Lea Ann Klarner, Chief Executive Officer
**Web address:** www.selectspecialtyhospitals.com/company/locations/fortwayne.aspx

**IOWA:** SELECT SPECIALTY HOSPITAL–QUAD CITIES (O, 50 beds) 1111 West Kimberly Road, Davenport, IA Zip 52806–5711; tel. 563/468–2000; Austin B. Cleveland, Chief Executive Officer
**Web address:** www.selectspecialtyhospitals.com/company/locations/quadcities.aspx

**KANSAS:** SELECT SPECIALTY HOSPITAL–KANSAS CITY (O, 40 beds) 1731 North 90th Street, Kansas City, KS Zip 66112–1515; tel. 913/732–5900; Matthew H. Blevins, Chief Executive Officer
**Web address:** www.selectspecialtyhospitals.com

SELECT SPECIALTY HOSPITAL–TOPEKA (O, 34 beds) 1700 S.W. Seventh Street, Suite 840, Topeka, KS Zip 66606–1660; tel. 785/295–5551; Jon W. Scott, Chief Executive Officer
**Web address:** www.selectspecialtyhospitals.com/company/locations/topeka.aspx

SELECT SPECIALTY HOSPITAL–WICHITA (O, 58 beds) 929 North St. Francis Street, Wichita, KS Zip 67214–3821; tel. 316/261–8303; Peggy Cliffe, Chief Executive Officer
**Web address:** www.selectspecialtyhospitals.com/company/locations/wichita.aspx

**KENTUCKY:** SELECT SPECIALTY HOSPITAL–LEXINGTON (O, 41 beds) 310 South Limestone Street, 3rd Floor, Lexington, KY Zip 40508–3008; tel. 859/226–7096; Mary Lou Guinle, FACHE, Chief Executive Officer
**Web address:** www.selectspecialtyhospitals.com/company/locations/lexington.aspx

SELECT SPECIALTY HOSPITAL–NORTHERN KENTUCKY (O, 33 beds) 85 North Grand Avenue, Fort Thomas, KY Zip 41075–1793; tel. 859/572–3880; Matthew Keppler, Chief Executive Officer
**Web address:** www.selectspecialtyhospitals.com/company/locations/northern–kentucky.aspx

**LOUISIANA:** REGENCY HOSPITAL OF COVINGTON (O, 38 beds) 195 Highland Park Entrance, Covington, LA Zip 70433–7164; tel. 985/867–3977; Kiley P. Cedotal, Chief Executive Officer
**Web address:** www.regencyhospital.com

**MICHIGAN:** GREAT LAKES SPECIALTY HOSPITAL–GRAND RAPIDS CAMPUS (O, 20 beds) 200 Jefferson Avenue S.E., 5th Floor, Grand Rapids, MI Zip 49503–4502; tel. 616/965–8701; Brian Pangle, Chief Executive Officer
**Web address:** www.selectmedicalcorp.com

GREAT LAKES SPECIALTY HOSPITAL– MUSKEGON (O, 31 beds) 1700 Clinton Street, South 2, Muskegon, MI Zip 49442–5502; tel. 231/728–5811; Mark Holcomb, Administrator
**Web address:** www.selectmedical.com

SELECT SPECIALTY HOSPITAL–ANN ARBOR (O, 36 beds) 5301 East Huron River Drive, 7th Floor, Ypsilanti, MI Zip 48197–1051; tel. 734/712–0111; John F. O'Malley, FACHE, Chief Executive Officer
**Web address:** www.selectspecialtyhospitals.com/company/locations/annarbor.aspx

SELECT SPECIALTY HOSPITAL–BATTLE CREEK (O, 25 beds) 300 North Avenue, Battle Creek, MI Zip 49017–3307; tel. 269/964–9075; Robert Padalino, Interim Chief Executive Officer
**Web address:** www.selectspecialtyhospitals.com/company/locations/battlecreek.aspx

SELECT SPECIALTY HOSPITAL–DOWNRIVER (O, 40 beds) 10000 Telegraph Road, 2nd Floor, Taylor, MI Zip 48180–3330; tel. 313/375–7075; Martin T. Carmody, Chief Executive Officer
**Web address:** www.selectspecialtyhospitals.com/company/locations/downriver.aspx

SELECT SPECIALTY HOSPITAL–FLINT (O, 26 beds) 401 South Ballenger Highway, 5th Floor Central, Flint, MI Zip 48532–3638; tel. 810/342–4500; Don Shook, Chief Executive Officer
**Web address:** www.selectspecialtyhospitals.com/company/locations/flint.aspx

SELECT SPECIALTY HOSPITAL–GROSSE POINTE (O, 30 beds) 468 Cadieux Road, 3 North West, Grosse Pointe, MI Zip 48230–1507; tel. 313/473–6131; Miriam Deemer, Chief Executive Officer
**Web address:** www.selectspecialtyhospitals.com/company/locations/grossepointe.aspx

SELECT SPECIALTY HOSPITAL–MACOMB COUNTY (O, 30 beds) 215 North Avenue, Mount Clemens, MI Zip 48043–1700; tel. 586/307–9000; Jon P. O'Malley, Chief Executive Officer
**Web address:** www.selectspecialtyhospitals.com/company/locations/macomb.aspx

SELECT SPECIALTY HOSPITAL–NORTHWEST DETROIT (O, 36 beds) 6071 West Outer Drrive, Detroit, MI Zip 48235–2624; tel. 313/966–4747; Marilouise Riska, Chief Executive Officer
**Web address:** www.selectspecialtyhospitals.com/company/locations/northwestdetroit.aspx

SELECT SPECIALTY HOSPITAL–PONTIAC (O, 30 beds) 44405 Woodward Avenue, 8th Floor, Pontiac, MI Zip 48341–5023; tel. 248/452–5252; Peggy Kingston, Chief Executive Officer
**Web address:** www.selectspecialtyhospitals.com/company/locations/pontiac.aspx

SELECT SPECIALTY HOSPITAL–SAGINAW (O, 32 beds) 1447 North Harrison Street, 8th Floor, Saginaw, MI Zip 48602–4785; tel. 989/583–4235; Dawn Frisbie, Chief Executive Officer
**Web address:** www.selectspecialtyhospitals.com/company/locations/saginaw.aspx

**MINNESOTA:** REGENCY HOSPITAL OF MINNEAPOLIS (O, 54 beds) 1300 Hidden Lakes Parkway, Golden Valley, MN Zip 55422–4286; tel. 763/588–2750; John P. Allen, Chief Executive Officer
**Web address:** www.regencyhospital.com

**MISSISSIPPI:** REGENCY HOSPITAL OF HATTIESBURG (O, 33 beds) 6051 U.S. Highway 495, 5th Floor, Hattiesburg, MS Zip 39401–6031; tel. 601/288–8510; Kathy A. Viator, R.N., Chief Executive Officer
**Web address:** www.regencyhospital.com/hattiesburg

REGENCY HOSPITAL OF JACKSON (O, 36 beds) 969 Lakeland Drive, 6th Floor, Jackson, MS Zip 39216–4643; tel. 601/364–6200; Lorie Powell, Interim Chief Executive Officer
**Web address:** www.regencyhospital.com

REGENCY HOSPITAL OF MERIDIAN (O, 40 beds) 1102 Constitution Avenue, 2nd Floor, Meridian, MS Zip 39301–4001; tel. 601/484–7900; Clifton Quinn, Chief Executive Officer
**Web address:** www.regencyhospital.com

SELECT SPECIALTY HOSPITAL–GULF COAST (O, 61 beds) 1520 Broad Avenue, Suite 300, Gulfport, MS Zip 39501–3601; tel. 228/575–7500; John O'Keefe, Chief Executive Officer
**Web address:** www.selectspecialtyhospitals.com/company/locations/gulfcoast.aspx

SELECT SPECIALTY HOSPITAL–JACKSON (O, 53 beds) 5903 Ridgewood Road, Suite 100, Jackson, MS Zip 39211–3700; tel. 601/899–3800; Chandler Ewing, Chief Executive Officer
**Web address:** www.selectspecialtyhospitals.com/company/locations/jackson.aspx

**MISSOURI:** SELECT SPECIALTY HOSPITAL–SPRINGFIELD (O, 44 beds) 1630 East Primrose Street, Springfield, MO Zip 65804–7929; tel. 417/885–4700; Julie De Jean, Chief Executive Officer
**Web address:** www.selectspecialtyhospitals.com/company/locations/springfield.aspx

SELECT SPECIALTY HOSPITAL–ST. LOUIS (O, 33 beds) 300 First Capitol Drive, Unit 1, Saint Charles, MO Zip 63301–2844; tel. 636/947–5010; Patrice L. Komoroski, Ph.D., R.N., Chief Executive Officer
**Web address:** www.selectspecialtyhospitals.com/company/locations/stlouis.aspx

For explanation of codes following names, see page B2.
★ Indicates Type III membership in the American Hospital Association.

SELECT SPECIALTY HOSPITAL–WESTERN MISSOURI (O, 34 beds) 2316 East Meyer Boulevard, 3 West, Kansas City, MO Zip 64132–1136; tel. 816/276–3300; Matthew Paul Pearson, Chief Executive Officer
**Web address:** www.selectspecialtyhospitals.com/company/locations/westernmissouri.aspx

**NEBRASKA:** SELECT SPECIALTY HOSPITAL–OMAHA (O, 52 beds) 1870 South 75th Street, Omaha, NE Zip 68124–1700; tel. 402/361–5700; Thomas N. Theroult, Chief Executive Officer
**Web address:** www.selectspecialtyhospitals.com/company/locations/omahacentral.aspx

**NEW JERSEY:** KESSLER INSTITUTE FOR REHABILITATION (O, 336 beds) 1199 Pleasant Valley Way, West Orange, NJ Zip 07052–1424; tel. 973/731–3600; Robert Brehm, Division President
**Web address:** www.kessler-rehab.com

SELECT SPECIALTY HOSPITAL–NORTHEAST NEW JERSEY (O, 59 beds) 96 Parkway, Rochelle Park, NJ Zip 07662–4200; tel. 201/221–2358; Barbara E. Hannan, MS, R.N., Chief Executive Officer
**Web address:** www.selectspecialtyhospitals.com/company/locations/northeastnewjersey.aspx

**NORTH CAROLINA:** SELECT SPECIALTY HOSPITAL–DURHAM (O, 30 beds) 3643 North Roxboro Road, 6th Floor, Durham, NC Zip 27704–2702; tel. 919/470–9137; Robert F. Jernigan, Jr., Chief Executive Officer
**Web address:** www.selectspecialtyhospitals.com/company/locations/durham.aspx

SELECT SPECIALTY HOSPITAL–GREENSBORO (O, 30 beds) 1200 North Elm Street, 5th Floor, Greensboro, NC Zip 27401–1004; tel. 336/832–8571; Deana Knight, Chief Executive Officer
**Web address:** www.selectspecialtyhospitals.com/company/locations/greensboro.aspx

SELECT SPECIALTY HOSPITAL–WINSTON–SALEM (O, 42 beds) 3333 Silas Creek Parkway, 6th Floor, Winston–Salem, NC Zip 27103–3013; tel. 336/718–6300; Leslie Deane, Chief Executive Officer
**Web address:** www.selectspecialtyhospitals.com/company/locations/winston–salem.aspx

**OHIO:** REGENCY HOSPITAL CLEVELAND EAST (O, 44 beds) 4200 Interchange Corporate Center Road, Warrensville Heights, OH Zip 44128–5631; tel. 216/910–3800; Scott Williams, Chief Executive Officer
**Web address:** www.regencyhospital.com/

REGENCY HOSPITAL OF CINCINNATI (O, 31 beds) 311 Straight Street, 4th Floor, Cincinnati, OH Zip 45219–1018; tel. 513/559–5957; Mark S. Brodeur, FACHE, Chief Executive Officer
**Web address:** www.regencyhospital.com

REGENCY HOSPITAL OF COLUMBUS (O, 43 beds) 1430 South High Street, Columbus, OH Zip 43207–1045; tel. 614/456–0300; Lisa J. Pettrey, MSN, R.N., Chief Executive Officer
**Web address:** www.regencyhospital.com/

REGENCY HOSPITAL OF TOLEDO (O, 35 beds) 5220 Alexis Road, Sylvania, OH Zip 43560–2504; tel. 419/318–5700; Diana D. Fisher, Chief Executive Officer
**Web address:** www.regencyhospital.com

SELECT SPECIALTY HOSPITAL–AKRON (O, 60 beds) 200 East Market Street, Akron, OH Zip 44308–2015; tel. 330/761–7500; Sonda Burns, Chief Executive Officer
**Web address:** www.selectspecialtyhospitals.com/company/locations/akron.aspx

SELECT SPECIALTY HOSPITAL–CANTON (O, 30 beds) 1320 Mercy Drive N.W., 7th Floor, Canton, OH Zip 44708–2614; tel. 330/489–8189; Dawne Wheeler, Chief Executive Officer
**Web address:** www.selectspecialtyhospitals.com/company/locations/canton.aspx

SELECT SPECIALTY HOSPITAL–CINCINNATI (O, 35 beds) 375 Dixmyth Avenue, Cincinnati, OH Zip 45220–2475; tel. 513/872–4444; Curtis Ohashi, Chief Executive Officer
**Web address:** www.selectspecialtyhospitals.com/company/locations/cincinnati.aspx

SELECT SPECIALTY HOSPITAL–COLUMBUS (O, 176 beds) 1087 Dennison Avenue, Columbus, OH Zip 43201–3201; tel. 614/458–9000; John C. Yanes, Chief Executive Officer
**Web address:** www.selectspecialtyhospitals.com/company/locations/columbus.aspx

SELECT SPECIALTY HOSPITAL–YOUNGSTOWN (O, 51 beds) 1044 Belmont Avenue, Youngstown, OH Zip 44504–1006; tel. 330/480–2349; Sharon Noro, Chief Executive Officer
**Web address:** www.selectspecialtyhospitals.com/company/locations/youngstown.aspx

SELECT SPECIALTY HOSPITAL–ZANESVILLE (O, 35 beds) 800 Forest Avenue, 6th Floor, Zanesville, OH Zip 43701–2882; tel. 740/588–7888; Linda Supplee, Chief Executive Officer
**Web address:** www.selectspecialtyhospitals.com/company/locations/zanesville.aspx

**OKLAHOMA:** SELECT SPECIALTY HOSPITAL–OKLAHOMA CITY (O, 72 beds) 3524 N.W. 56th Street, Oklahoma City, OK Zip 73112–4518; tel. 405/606–6700; Connie Strickland, Chief Executive Officer
**Web address:** www.selectspecialtyhospitals.com/company/locations/oklahomacity.aspx

SELECT SPECIALTY HOSPITAL–TULSA MIDTOWN (O, 56 beds) 1125 South Trenton Avenue, 3rd Floor, Tulsa, OK Zip 74120–5418; tel. 918/579–7300; Linda Tiemens, Chief Executive Officer
**Web address:** www.selectmedical.com

**PENNSYLVANIA:** PENN STATE HERSHEY REHABILITATION HOSPITAL (O, 32 beds) 1135 Old West Chocolate Avenue, Hummelstown, PA Zip 17036; tel. 717/832–2600; Scott Guevin, Chief Executive Officer
**Web address:** www.psh–rehab.com

SELECT SPECIALTY HOSPITAL–CENTRAL PENNSYLVANIA (O, 92 beds) 503 North 21st Street, 5th Floor, Camp Hill, PA Zip 17011–2204; tel. 717/972–4575; Tom Mullin, Chief Executive Officer
**Web address:** www.selectspecialtyhospitals.com/company/locations/camphill.aspx

SELECT SPECIALTY HOSPITAL–DANVILLE (O, 30 beds) 100 North Academy Avenue, 3rd Floor, Danville, PA Zip 17822–3050; tel. 570/214–9653; Brian Mann, Chief Executive Officer
**Web address:** www.selectspecialtyhospitals.com/company/locations/danville.aspx

SELECT SPECIALTY HOSPITAL–ERIE (O, 50 beds) 252 West 11th Street, Erie, PA Zip 16501–1702; tel. 814/874–5300; Coleen Zimmerman, Interim Chief Executive Officer
**Web address:** www.selectspecialtyhospitals.com/company/locations/erie.aspx

SELECT SPECIALTY HOSPITAL–JOHNSTOWN (O, 39 beds) 320 Main Street, 3rd Floor, Johnstown, PA Zip 15901–1601; tel. 814/534–7300; Kelly Blake, Chief Executive Officer
**Web address:** www.selectspecialtyhospitals.com/company/locations/johnstown.aspx

SELECT SPECIALTY HOSPITAL–LAUREL HIGHLANDS (O, 40 beds) One Mellon Way, 3rd Floor, Latrobe, PA Zip 15650–1197; tel. 724/539–3230; Laurie Kozorosky, Chief Executive Officer
**Web address:** www.selectspecialtyhospitals.com/company/locations/laurelhighlands.aspx

SELECT SPECIALTY HOSPITAL–MCKEESPORT (O, 30 beds) 1500 Fifth Avenue, 6th Floor, McKeesport, PA Zip 15132–2422; tel. 412/664–2900; Dan Butts, Chief Executive Officer
**Web address:** www.selectspecialtyhospitals.com/company/locations/mckeesport.aspx

SELECT SPECIALTY HOSPITAL–PITTSBURGH/UPMC (O, 32 beds) 200 Lothrop Street, E824, Pittsburgh, PA Zip 15213–2536; tel. 412/586–9800; John St. Leger, Chief Executive Officer
**Web address:** www.selectspecialtyhospitals.com/company/locations/pittsburghupmc.aspx

**SOUTH CAROLINA:** REGENCY HOSPITAL OF FLORENCE (O, 40 beds) 121 East Cedar Street, 4th Floor, Florence, SC Zip 29506–2576; tel. 843/661–3499; Darrell Jones, Chief Executive Officer
**Web address:** www.regencyhospital.com

REGENCY HOSPITAL OF GREENVILLE (O, 32 beds) One St. Francis Drive, 4th Floor, Greenville, SC Zip 29601–3955; tel. 864/255–1438; Stephanie James, Chief Executive Officer
**Web address:** www.regencyhospital.com

**SOUTH DAKOTA:** SELECT SPECIALTY HOSPITAL–SIOUX FALLS (O, 21 beds) 1305 West 18th Street, Sioux Falls, SD Zip 57105–0401; tel. 605/322–3500; Carol Ulmer, Chief Executive Officer
**Web address:** www.selectspecialtyhospitals.com/company/locations/siouxfalls.aspx

For explanation of codes following names, see page B2.
★ Indicates Type III membership in the American Hospital Association.

**TENNESSEE:** SELECT SPECIALTY HOSPITAL–KNOXVILLE (O, 35 beds) 1901 Clinch Avenue, 4th Floor West, Knoxville, TN Zip 37916–2307; tel. 865/541–2615; Vanda Scott, Chief Executive Officer
**Web address:** www.selectspecialtyhospitals.com/company/locations/knoxville.aspx

SELECT SPECIALTY HOSPITAL–MEMPHIS (O, 38 beds) 5959 Park Avenue, 12th Floor, Memphis, TN Zip 38119–5200; tel. 901/765–1245; Kris Kitzke, Chief Executive Officer
**Web address:** www.selectspecialtyhospitals.com/company/locations/memphis.aspx

SELECT SPECIALTY HOSPITAL–NASHVILLE (O, 47 beds) 2000 Hayes Street, Nashville, TN Zip 37203–2318; tel. 615/284–4599; Michael McAlister, Chief Executive Officer
**Web address:** www.selectspecialtyhospitals.com/company/locations/nashville.aspx

SELECT SPECIALTY HOSPITAL–NORTH KNOXVILLE (O, 33 beds) 900 East Oak Hill Avenue, 4th Floor, Knoxville, TN Zip 37917–4505; tel. 865/541–2615; Steve Plumlee, Chief Executive Officer
**Web address:** www.selectspecialtyhospitals.com/company/locations/northknoxville.aspx

SELECT SPECIALTY HOSPITAL–TRI CITIES (O, 33 beds) One Medical Park Boulevard, 5th Floor, Bristol, TN Zip 37620–8964; tel. 423/844–5900; Eric Carroll, Chief Executive Officer
**Web address:** www.selectspecialtyhospitals.com/company/locations/tricities.aspx

**TEXAS:** REGENCY HOSPITAL OF FORT WORTH (O, 44 beds) 6801 Oakmont Boulevard, Fort Worth, TX Zip 76132–3918; tel. 817/840–2500; Brad Ervin, Chief Executive Officer
**Web address:** www.regencyhospital.com

SELECT REHABILITATION HOSPITAL OF DENTON (O, 44 beds) 2620 Scripture Street, Denton, TX Zip 76201–4315; tel. 940/297–6500; Michelle Powell, Chief Executive Officer
**Web address:** www.selectrehab-denton.com/

SELECT SPECIALTY HOSPITAL–DALLAS (O, 60 beds) 2329 West Parker Road, Carrollton, TX Zip 75010–4713; tel. 469/892–1400; Barbara Mobley, Chief Executive Officer
**Web address:** www.selectspecialtyhospitals.com/company/locations/dallas.aspx

SELECT SPECIALTY HOSPITAL–HOUSTON HEIGHTS (O, 300 beds) 1917 Ashland Street, Houston, TX Zip 77008–3994; tel. 713/861–6161; Naman Mahajan, Chief Executive Officer
**Web address:** www.selectspecialtyhospitals.com/company/locations/houstonheights.aspx

SELECT SPECIALTY HOSPITAL–LONGVIEW (O, 32 beds) 700 East Marshall Avenue, 1st Floor, Longview, TX Zip 75601–5580; tel. 903/315–1100; Dennis Baker, Chief Executive Officer
**Web address:** www.selectspecialtyhospitals.com/company/locations/longview.aspx

SELECT SPECIALTY HOSPITAL–MIDLAND (O, 29 beds) 4214 Andrews Highway, 3rd Floor, Midland, TX Zip 79703–4811; tel. 432/522–3364; Connie K. Siffring, Chief Executive Officer
**Web address:** www.selectspecialtyhospitals.com/company/locations/midland.aspx

SELECT SPECIALTY HOSPITAL–SAN ANTONIO (O, 44 beds) 111 Dallas Street, 4th Floor, San Antonio, TX Zip 78205–1201; tel. 210/297–7185; Sean Stricker, Chief Executive Officer
**Web address:** www.selectspecialtyhospitals.com/company/locations/sanantonio.aspx

SELECT SPECIALTY HOSPITAL–SOUTH DALLAS (O, 69 beds) 3500 West Wheatland Road, 4th Floor, Dallas, TX Zip 75237–3460; tel. 972/780–6500; Richard Knowland, Chief Executive Officer
**Web address:** www.selectspecialtyhospitals.com/company/locations/southdallas.aspx

**WEST VIRGINIA:** SELECT SPECIALTY HOSPITAL–CHARLESTON (O, 32 beds) 333 Laidley Street, 3rd Floor East, Charleston, WV Zip 25301–1614; tel. 304/720–7234; Frank Weber, Chief Executive Officer
**Web address:** www.selectspecialtyhospitals.com/company/locations/charleston.aspx

**WISCONSIN:** SELECT SPECIALTY HOSPITAL–MADISON (O, 58 beds) 801 Braxton Place, 2nd Floor, Madison, WI Zip 53715–1415; tel. 608/260–2700; Raymond F. Carnevale, Chief Executive Officer
**Web address:** www.selectspecialtyhospitals.com/company/locations/madison.aspx

SELECT SPECIALTY HOSPITAL–MILWAUKEE (O, 34 beds) 8901 West Lincoln Avenue, 2nd Floor, Milwaukee, WI Zip 53227–2409; tel. 414/328–7700; Richard Keddington, Chief Executive Officer
**Web address:** www.selectspecialtyhospitals.com/company/locations/milwaukee.aspx

| | | |
|---|---|---|
| **Owned, leased, sponsored:** | 98 hospitals | 4781 beds |
| **Contract–managed:** | 0 hospitals | 0 beds |
| **Totals:** | 98 hospitals | 4781 beds |

★**2565:** **SENTARA HEALTHCARE** (NP)
6015 Poplar Hall Drive, Norfolk, VA Zip 23502–3819; tel. 757/455–7000; David L. Bernd, Chief Executive Officer
**(Decentralized Health System)**

**VIRGINIA:** MARTHA JEFFERSON HOSPITAL (O, 139 beds) 500 Martha Jefferson Drive, Charlottesville, VA Zip 22911–4668; tel. 434/654–7000; James E. Haden, President and Chief Executive Officer
**Web address:** www.marthajefferson.org

ROCKINGHAM MEMORIAL HOSPITAL (O, 238 beds) 2010 Health Campus Drive, Harrisonburg, VA Zip 22801–3293; tel. 540/689–1000; James D. Krauss, President
**Web address:** www.rmhonline.com

SENTARA CAREPLEX HOSPITAL (O, 148 beds) 3000 Coliseum Drive, Hampton, VA Zip 23666–5963; tel. 757/736–1000; Debra A. Flores, R.N., MS, President and Administrator
**Web address:** www.sentara.com

SENTARA LEIGH HOSPITAL (O, 231 beds) 830 Kempsville Road, Norfolk, VA Zip 23502–3920; tel. 757/261–6000; Teresa L. Edwards, Vice President and Administrator
**Web address:** www.sentara.com

SENTARA NORFOLK GENERAL HOSPITAL (O, 495 beds) 600 Gresham Drive, Norfolk, VA Zip 23507–1904; tel. 757/388–3000; Kurt T. Hofelich, President
**Web address:** www.sentara.com

SENTARA NORTHERN VIRGINIA MEDICAL CENTER (O, 172 beds) 2300 Opitz Boulevard, Woodbridge, VA Zip 22191–3399; tel. 703/523–1000; Megan R. Perry, Corporate Vice President and President
**Web address:** www.sentara.com/northernvirginia

SENTARA OBICI HOSPITAL (O, 168 beds) 2800 Godwin Boulevard, Suffolk, VA Zip 23434–8038; tel. 757/934–4000; Steve Julian, M.D., President
**Web address:** www.sentara.com

SENTARA PRINCESS ANNE HOSPITAL (O, 160 beds) 2025 Glenn Mitchell Drive, Virginia Beach, VA Zip 23456–0178; tel. 757/507–1000; Stephen D. Porter, President
**Web address:** www.sentara.com

SENTARA VIRGINIA BEACH GENERAL HOSPITAL (O, 265 beds) 1060 First Colonial Road, Virginia Beach, VA Zip 23454–3002; tel. 757/395–8000; Elwood Bernard Boone, III, FACHE, President
**Web address:** www.sentara.com

SENTARA WILLIAMSBURG REGIONAL MEDICAL CENTER (O, 145 beds) 100 Sentara Circle, Williamsburg, VA Zip 23188–5713; tel. 757/984–6000; Robert L. Graves, President
**Web address:** www.sentara.com

| | | |
|---|---|---|
| **Owned, leased, sponsored:** | 10 hospitals | 2161 beds |
| **Contract–managed:** | 0 hospitals | 0 beds |
| **Totals:** | 10 hospitals | 2161 beds |

Section B

For explanation of codes following names, see page B2.
★ Indicates Type III membership in the American Hospital Association.

★**0111: SHANDS HEALTHCARE** (NP)
1600 S.W. Archer Road, Gainesville, FL Zip 32610–0326;
tel. 352/733–1500; Timothy M. Goldfarb, Chief Executive Officer
**(Moderately Centralized Health System)**

**FLORIDA:** SHANDS AT THE UNIVERSITY OF FLORIDA (O, 946 beds) 1600
S.W. Archer Road, Gainesville, FL Zip 32610–3003, Mailing Address: P.O.
Box 100326, Zip 32610–0326; tel. 352/265–0111; Timothy M. Goldfarb,
Chief Executive Officer
**Web address:** www.shands.org

SHANDS JACKSONVILLE MEDICAL CENTER (O, 620 beds) 655 West Eighth
Street, Jacksonville, FL Zip 32209–6595; tel. 904/244–0411; Russell
Armistead, Chief Executive Officer
**Web address:** www.shandsjacksonville.org

| | | |
|---|---|---|
| Owned, leased, sponsored: | 2 hospitals | 1566 beds |
| Contract–managed: | 0 hospitals | 0 beds |
| Totals: | 2 hospitals | 1566 beds |

★**2065: SHARP HEALTHCARE** (NP)
8695 Spectrum Center Boulevard, San Diego, CA Zip 92123–1489;
tel. 858/499–4000; Michael Murphy, CPA, President & Chief
Executive Officer
**(Centralized Health System)**

**CALIFORNIA:** SHARP CHULA VISTA MEDICAL CENTER (O, 343 beds) 751
Medical Center Court, Chula Vista, CA Zip 91911–6699, Mailing Address:
P.O. Box 1297, Zip 91912–1297; tel. 619/502–5800; Pablo Velez, Chief
Executive Officer
**Web address:** www.sharp.com

SHARP CORONADO HOSPITAL AND HEALTHCARE CENTER (L, 154 beds) 250
Prospect Place, Coronado, CA Zip 92118–1999; tel. 619/522–3600; Susan
Stone, R.N., Ph.D., Senior Vice President and Chief Executive Officer
**Web address:** www.sharp.com

SHARP GROSSMONT HOSPITAL (L, 521 beds) 5555 Grossmont Center Drive,
La Mesa, CA Zip 91942–3019, Mailing Address: P.O. Box 158,
Zip 91944–0158; tel. 619/740–6000; Michele T. Tarbet, R.N., Chief
Executive Officer
**Web address:** www.sharp.com

SHARP MEMORIAL HOSPITAL (O, 368 beds) 7901 Frost Street, San Diego,
CA Zip 92123–2701; tel. 858/939–3400; Tim Smith, Chief Executive Officer
**Web address:** www.sharp.com

SHARP MESA VISTA HOSPITAL (O, 163 beds) 7850 Vista Hill Avenue, San
Diego, CA Zip 92123–2717; tel. 858/278–4110; Kathi Lencioni, Chief
Executive Officer
**Web address:** www.sharp.com

| | | |
|---|---|---|
| Owned, leased, sponsored: | 5 hospitals | 1549 beds |
| Contract–managed: | 0 hospitals | 0 beds |
| Totals: | 5 hospitals | 1549 beds |

**4125: SHRINERS HOSPITALS FOR CHILDREN** (NP)
2900 Rocky Point Drive, Tampa, FL Zip 33607–1435, Mailing
Address: P.O. Box 31356, Zip 33631–3356; tel. 813/281–0300;
John P. McCabe, Executive Vice President
**(Independent Hospital System)**

SHRINERS HOSPITALS FOR CHILDREN–LOS ANGELES (O, 30 beds) 3160
Geneva Street, Los Angeles, CA Zip 90020–1199; tel. 213/388–3151; Janet
Sanders, R.N., Interim Administrator
**Web address:** www.shrinershospitalsforchildren.
org/Hospitals/Locations/Losangeles.aspx

SHRINERS HOSPITALS FOR CHILDREN–NORTHERN CALIFORNIA (O, 70 beds)
2425 Stockton Boulevard, Sacramento, CA Zip 95817–2215;
tel. 916/453–2000; Margaret Bryan, Administrator
**Web address:** www.shrinershospitalsforchildren.
org/Hospitals/Locations/NorthernCalifornia.aspx

**FLORIDA:** SHRINERS HOSPITALS FOR CHILDREN–TAMPA (O, 25 beds) 12502
USF Pine Drive, Tampa, FL Zip 33612–9499; tel. 813/972–2250; David
A. Ferrell, Regional Administrator
**Web address:** www.shrinershospitalsforchildren.
org/Hospitals/Locations/Tampa.aspx

**HAWAII:** SHRINERS HOSPITALS FOR CHILDREN–HONOLULU (O, 16 beds)
1310 Punahou Street, Honolulu, HI Zip 96826–1099; tel. 808/941–4466;
Gene Raynaud, Administrator
**Web address:** www.shrinershospitalsforchildren.
org/Hospitals/Locations/Honolulu.aspx

**ILLINOIS:** SHRINERS HOSPITALS FOR CHILDREN–CHICAGO (O, 36 beds)
2211 North Oak Park Avenue, Chicago, IL Zip 60707–3392;
tel. 773/622–5400; Mark L. Niederpruem, FACHE, Administrator
**Web address:** www.shrinershospitalsforchildren.
org/Hospitals/Locations/Chicago.aspx

**KENTUCKY:** SHRINERS HOSPITALS FOR CHILDREN–LEXINGTON (O, 50 beds)
1900 Richmond Road, Lexington, KY Zip 40502–1298;
tel. 859/266–2101; Tony Lewgood, Administrator
**Web address:** www.shrinershospitalsforchildren.
org/Hospitals/Locations/Lexington.aspx

**LOUISIANA:** SHRINERS HOSPITALS FOR CHILDREN–SHREVEPORT (O, 45
beds) 3100 Samford Avenue, Shreveport, LA Zip 71103–4289;
tel. 318/222–5704; Garry Kim Green, FACHE, Administrator
**Web address:** www.shrinershospitalsforchildren.
org/Hospitals/Locations/Shreveport.aspx

**MASSACHUSETTS:** SHRINERS HOSPITALS FOR CHILDREN–BOSTON BURNS
HOSPITAL (O, 30 beds) 51 Blossom Street, Boston, MA Zip 02114–2601;
tel. 617/722–3000; C. Thomas D'Esmond, FACHE, Administrator
**Web address:** www.shrinershospitalsforchildren.
org/Hospitals/Locations/Boston.aspx

SHRINERS HOSPITALS FOR CHILDREN–SPRINGFIELD (O, 20 beds) 516 Carew
Street, Springfield, MA Zip 01104–2396; tel. 413/787–2000; Charles
Walczak, FACHE, Regional Administrator
**Web address:** www.shrinershospitalsforchildren.
org/Hospitals/Locations/Springfield.aspx

**MINNESOTA:** SHRINERS HOSPITALS FOR CHILDREN–TWIN CITIES (O, 40
beds) 2025 East River Parkway, Minneapolis, MN Zip 55414–3696;
tel. 612/596–6100; Charles C. Lobeck, Administrator
**Web address:** www.shrinershospitalsforchildren.
org/Hospitals/Locations/twincities.aspx

**MISSOURI:** SHRINERS HOSPITALS FOR CHILDREN–ST. LOUIS (O, 42 beds)
2001 South Lindbergh Boulevard, Saint Louis, MO Zip 63131–3597;
tel. 314/432–3600; John Gloss, FACHE, Administrator
**Web address:** www.shrinershospitalsforchildren.
org/Hospitals/Locations/Stlouis.aspx

**OHIO:** SHRINERS HOSPITALS FOR CHILDREN–CINCINNATI BURNS HOSPITAL
(O, 30 beds) 3229 Burnet Avenue, Cincinnati, OH Zip 45229–3095;
tel. 513/872–6000; Tony Lewgood, Interim Administrator
**Web address:** www.shrinershospitalsforchildren.
org/Hospitals/Locations/Cincinnati.aspx

**OREGON:** SHRINERS HOSPITALS FOR CHILDREN–PORTLAND (O, 8 beds)
3101 S.W. Sam Jackson Park Road, Portland, OR Zip 97239–3009;
tel. 503/241–5090; J. Craig Patchin, Administrator
**Web address:** www.shrinershospitalsforchildren.
org/Hospitals/Locations/Portland.aspx

**PENNSYLVANIA:** SHRINERS HOSPITALS FOR CHILDREN–PHILADELPHIA (O,
39 beds) 3551 North Broad Street, Philadelphia, PA Zip 19140–4160;
tel. 215/430–4000; Ernest N. Perilli, Administrator
**Web address:** www.shrinershospitalsforchildren.
org/Hospitals/Locations/Philadelphia.aspx

**SOUTH CAROLINA:** SHRINERS HOSPITALS FOR CHILDREN–GREENVILLE (O,
15 beds) 950 West Faris Road, Greenville, SC Zip 29605–4277;
tel. 864/271–3444; Randall R. Romberger, Administrator
**Web address:** www.shrinershospitalsforchildren.
org/Hospitals/Locations/Greenville.aspx

**TEXAS:** SHRINERS HOSPITALS FOR CHILDREN–GALVESTON BURNS
HOSPITAL (O, 15 beds) 815 Market Street, Galveston, TX
Zip 77550–2725; tel. 409/770–6600; David A. Ferrell, Regional
Administrator
**Web address:** www.shrinershospitalsforchildren.
org/Hospitals/Locations/Galveston.aspx

SHRINERS HOSPITALS FOR CHILDREN–HOUSTON (O, 40 beds) 6977 Main
Street, Houston, TX Zip 77030–3701; tel. 713/797–1616; David A. Ferrell,
Regional Administrator
**Web address:** www.shrinershospitalsforchildren.
org/Hospitals/Locations/Houston.aspx

For explanation of codes following names, see page B2.
★ Indicates Type III membership in the American Hospital Association.

**UTAH:** SHRINERS HOSPITALS FOR CHILDREN–SALT LAKE CITY (O, 40 beds) Fairfax Road & Virginia Street, Salt Lake City, UT Zip 84103–4399; tel. 801/536–3500; Kevin Martin, M.P.H., R.N., M.P.H., Administrator
**Web address:** www.shrinershospitalsforchildren. org/Hospitals/Locations/SaltLakeCity.aspx

**WASHINGTON:** SHRINERS HOSPITALS FOR CHILDREN–SPOKANE (O, 30 beds) 911 West Fifth Avenue, Spokane, WA Zip 99204–2901, Mailing Address: P.O. Box 2472, Zip 99210–2472; tel. 509/455–7844; J. Craig Patchin, Interim Administrator
**Web address:** www.shrinershospitalsforchildren. org/Hospitals/Locations/Spokane.aspx

| | | |
|---|---|---|
| Owned, leased, sponsored: | 19 hospitals | 621 beds |
| Contract–managed: | 0 hospitals | 0 beds |
| Totals: | 19 hospitals | 621 beds |

**★0284:  SINAI HEALTH SYSTEM** (NP)
1500 South California Avenue, Chicago, IL Zip 60608–1729; tel. 773/542–2000; Alan H. Channing, President and Chief Executive Officer
**(Independent Hospital System)**

**ILLINOIS:** MOUNT SINAI HOSPITAL (O, 290 beds) California Avenue at 15th Street, Chicago, IL Zip 60608–1729; tel. 773/542–2000; Alan H. Channing, President and Chief Executive Officer
**Web address:** www.sinai.org

SCHWAB REHABILITATION HOSPITAL (O, 101 beds) 1401 South California Avenue, Chicago, IL Zip 60608–1858; tel. 773/522–2010; Alan H. Channing, President and Chief Executive Officer
**Web address:** www.schwabrehab.org

| | | |
|---|---|---|
| Owned, leased, sponsored: | 2 hospitals | 391 beds |
| Contract–managed: | 0 hospitals | 0 beds |
| Totals: | 2 hospitals | 391 beds |

**5125:  SISTERS OF CHARITY HEALTH SYSTEM** (CC)
2475 East 22nd Street, Cleveland, OH Zip 44115–3221; tel. 216/363–2797; Sister Judith Ann Karam, President and Chief Executive Officer
**(Moderately Centralized Health System)**

**OHIO:** MERCY MEDICAL CENTER (O, 343 beds) 1320 Mercy Drive N.W., Canton, OH Zip 44708–2641; tel. 330/489–1000; Thomas E. Cecconi, President and Chief Executive Officer
**Web address:** www.cantonmercy.org

ST. JOHN MEDICAL CENTER (O, 191 beds) 29000 Center Ridge Road, Westlake, OH Zip 44145–5293; tel. 440/835–8000; William A. Young, Jr., President and Chief Executive Officer
**Web address:** www.sjws.net

ST. VINCENT CHARITY MEDICAL CENTER (O, 198 beds) 2351 East 22nd Street, Cleveland, OH Zip 44115–3111; tel. 216/861–6200; David Perse, M.D., President
**Web address:** www.svch.net

**SOUTH CAROLINA:** PROVIDENCE HOSPITAL (O, 314 beds) 2435 Forest Drive, Columbia, SC Zip 29204–2098; tel. 803/865–4500; George A. Zara, President and Chief Executive Officer
**Web address:** www.provhosp.com

| | | |
|---|---|---|
| Owned, leased, sponsored: | 4 hospitals | 1046 beds |
| Contract–managed: | 0 hospitals | 0 beds |
| Totals: | 4 hospitals | 1046 beds |

**5805:  SISTERS OF MARY OF THE PRESENTATION HEALTH SYSTEM** (CC)
1202 Page Drive S.W., Fargo, ND Zip 58103–2340, Mailing Address: P.O. Box 10007, Zip 58106–0007; tel. 701/237–9290; Aaron K. Alton, President and Chief Executive Officer
**(Independent Hospital System)**

**ILLINOIS:** ST. MARGARET'S HOSPITAL (O, 69 beds) 600 East First Street, Spring Valley, IL Zip 61362–1512; tel. 815/664–5311; Tim Muntz, President and Chief Executive Officer
**Web address:** www.aboutsmh.org

**NORTH DAKOTA:** PRESENTATION MEDICAL CENTER (O, 25 beds) 213 Second Avenue N.E., Rolla, ND Zip 58367–7153, Mailing Address: P.O. Box 759, Zip 58367–0759; tel. 701/477–3161; Mark Kerr, Chief Executive Officer
**Web address:** www.pmc–rolla.com

ST. ALOISIUS MEDICAL CENTER (O, 120 beds) 325 East Brewster Street, Harvey, ND Zip 58341–1653; tel. 701/324–4651; Rockford Zastoupil, President and Chief Executive Officer
**Web address:** www.staloisius.com

ST. ANDREW'S HEALTH CENTER (O, 25 beds) 316 Ohmer Street, Bottineau, ND Zip 58318–1045; tel. 701/228–9300; Jodi Atkinson, President and Chief Executive Officer
**Web address:** www.standrewshealth.com

| | | |
|---|---|---|
| Owned, leased, sponsored: | 4 hospitals | 239 beds |
| Contract–managed: | 0 hospitals | 0 beds |
| Totals: | 4 hospitals | 239 beds |

**5955:  SISTERS OF SAINT FRANCIS** (CC)
2500 Grant Boulevard, Syracuse, NY Zip 13208–1782; tel. 315/634–7000; Sister Marian Rose Mansius, Assistant General Minister
**(Moderately Centralized Health System)**

**NEW YORK:** ST. ELIZABETH MEDICAL CENTER (S, 181 beds) 2209 Genesee Street, Utica, NY Zip 13501–5999; tel. 315/798–8100; Richard H. Ketcham, FACHE, President and Chief Executive Officer
**Web address:** www.stemc.org

ST. JOSEPH'S HOSPITAL HEALTH CENTER (S, 431 beds) 301 Prospect Avenue, Syracuse, NY Zip 13203–1807; tel. 315/448–5111; Kathryn H. Ruscitto, President
**Web address:** www.sjhsyr.org

| | | |
|---|---|---|
| Owned, leased, sponsored: | 2 hospitals | 612 beds |
| Contract–managed: | 0 hospitals | 0 beds |
| Totals: | 2 hospitals | 612 beds |

**0358:  SOUND SHORE HEALTH SYSTEM** (NP)
16 Guion Place, New Rochelle, NY Zip 10801–5502; tel. 914/632–5000; John R. Spicer, President and Chief Executive Officer
**(Independent Hospital System)**

MOUNT VERNON HOSPITAL (O, 132 beds) 12 North Seventh Avenue, Mount Vernon, NY Zip 10550–2098; tel. 914/664–8000; John R. Spicer, President and Chief Executive Officer
**Web address:** www.sshsw.org

SOUND SHORE MEDICAL CENTER OF WESTCHESTER (O, 356 beds) 16 Guion Place, New Rochelle, NY Zip 10801–5502; tel. 914/632–5000; John R. Spicer, President and Chief Executive Officer
**Web address:** www.sshsw.org

| | | |
|---|---|---|
| Owned, leased, sponsored: | 2 hospitals | 488 beds |
| Contract–managed: | 0 hospitals | 0 beds |
| Totals: | 2 hospitals | 488 beds |

**★0253:  SOUTHEAST GEORGIA HEALTH SYSTEM** (NP)
2415 Parkwood Drive, Brunswick, GA Zip 31520–4722, Mailing Address: P.O. Box 1518, Zip 31521–1518; tel. 912/466–7000; Gary R. Colberg, FACHE, President and Chief Executive Officer

**GEORGIA:** SOUTHEAST GEORGIA HEALTH SYSTEM BRUNSWICK CAMPUS (O, 366 beds) 2415 Parkwood Drive, Brunswick, GA Zip 31520–4722, Mailing Address: P.O. Box 1518, Zip 31521–1518; tel. 912/466–7000; Gary R. Colberg, FACHE, President and Chief Executive Officer
**Web address:** www.sghs.org

For explanation of codes following names, see page B2.
★ Indicates Type III membership in the American Hospital Association.

Section B

SOUTHEAST GEORGIA HEALTH SYSTEM CAMDEN CAMPUS (O, 17 beds)
2000 Dan Proctor Drive, Saint Marys, GA Zip 31558–3810;
tel. 912/576–6200; Howard W. Sepp, Jr., FACHE, Vice President and
Administrator
**Web address:** www.sghs.org

| | | |
|---|---|---|
| Owned, leased, sponsored: | 2 hospitals | 383 beds |
| Contract–managed: | 0 hospitals | 0 beds |
| Totals: | 2 hospitals | 383 beds |

★**0628: SOUTHEASTHEALTH** (NP)
1701 Lacey Street, Cape Girardeau, MO Zip 63701–5230;
tel. 573/334–4822; Wayne Smith, President and Chief Executive
Officer
**(Independent Hospital System)**

**MISSOURI:** SOUTHEAST HEALTH CENTER OF REYNOLDS COUNTY (O, 12
beds) 100 Highway 21 South, Ellington, MO Zip 63638, Mailing Address:
Rural Route 4, Box 4269, Zip 63638–9409; tel. 573/663–2511;
Bernadean Anseln, Chief Executive Officer

SOUTHEAST HEALTH CENTER OF RIPLEY COUNTY (L, 21 beds) 109 Plum
Street, Doniphan, MO Zip 63935–1299; tel. 573/996–2141; Christy Hardin,
Interim Administrator
**Web address:** www.sehealth.
org/southeast–health–center–of–ripley–county/SoutheastHEALTH.aspx?nd=41

SOUTHEAST HEALTH CENTER OF STODDARD COUNTY (L, 45 beds) 1200
North One Mile Road, Dexter, MO Zip 63841–1000; tel. 573/624–5566;
Adam Bracks, Chief Executive Officer
**Web address:** www.sehealth.org

SOUTHEAST HOSPITAL (O, 221 beds) 1701 Lacey Street, Cape Girardeau,
MO Zip 63701–5230; tel. 573/334–4822; Wayne Smith, President and Chief
Executive Officer
**Web address:** www.sehealth.org/

| | | |
|---|---|---|
| Owned, leased, sponsored: | 4 hospitals | 299 beds |
| Contract–managed: | 0 hospitals | 0 beds |
| Totals: | 4 hospitals | 299 beds |

**4175: SOUTHERN ILLINOIS HOSPITAL SERVICES** (NP)
1239 East Main Street, Carbondale, IL Zip 62901–3114, Mailing
Address: P.O. Box 3988, Zip 62902–3988; tel. 618/457–5200; Rex
P. Budde, President and Chief Executive Officer
**(Independent Hospital System)**

**ILLINOIS:** HERRIN HOSPITAL (O, 114 beds) 201 South 14th Street, Herrin, IL
Zip 62948–3631; tel. 618/942–2171; Terence Farrell, Administrator
**Web address:** www.sih.net

MEMORIAL HOSPITAL OF CARBONDALE (O, 159 beds) 405 West Jackson
Street, Carbondale, IL Zip 62901–1467, Mailing Address: P.O. Box 10000,
Zip 62902–9000; tel. 618/549–0721; Bart Millstead, Administrator
**Web address:** www.sih.net

ST. JOSEPH MEMORIAL HOSPITAL (O, 25 beds) 2 South Hospital Drive,
Murphysboro, IL Zip 62966–3333; tel. 618/684–3156; John T. Brothers,
R.N., MS, Administrator
**Web address:** www.sih.net

| | | |
|---|---|---|
| Owned, leased, sponsored: | 3 hospitals | 298 beds |
| Contract–managed: | 0 hospitals | 0 beds |
| Totals: | 3 hospitals | 298 beds |

**0346: SOUTHERN PLAINS MEDICAL GROUP** (IO)
4323 N.W. 63rd Street Suite 232, Oklahoma City, OK
Zip 73116–1546; tel. 405/753–6770; Margie Homer, President

**OKLAHOMA:** PHYSICIANS' HOSPITAL IN ANADARKO (O, 25 beds) 1002
Central Boulevard East, Anadarko, OK Zip 73005–4496;
tel. 405/247–2551; James L. Clough, Chief Executive Officer
**Web address:** www.anadarkohospital.com

STROUD REGIONAL MEDICAL CENTER (O, 25 beds) Highway 66 West,
Stroud, OK Zip 74079, Mailing Address: P.O. Box 530, Zip 74079–0530;
tel. 918/968–3571; Regina Peters, Chief Executive Officer

| | | |
|---|---|---|
| Owned, leased, sponsored: | 2 hospitals | 50 beds |
| Contract–managed: | 0 hospitals | 0 beds |
| Totals: | 2 hospitals | 50 beds |

**0652: SOUTHWEST HEALTH SYSTEMS** (NP)
215 Marion Avenue, Mccomb, MS Zip 39648–2705, Mailing Address:
P.O. Box 1307, Zip 39649–1307; tel. 601/249–5500; Norman M.
Price, FACHE, Chief Executive Officer and Administrator
**(Independent Hospital System)**

**MISSISSIPPI:** LAWRENCE COUNTY HOSPITAL (O, 25 beds) Highway 84 East,
Monticello, MS Zip 39654–0788, Mailing Address: P.O. Box 788,
Zip 39654–0788; tel. 601/587–4051; Semmes Ross, Jr., Administrator
**Web address:** www.smrmc.com

SOUTHWEST MISSISSIPPI REGIONAL MEDICAL CENTER (O, 143 beds) 215
Marion Avenue, McComb, MS Zip 39648–2705, Mailing Address: P.O. Box
1307, Zip 39649–1307; tel. 601/249–5500; Norman M. Price, FACHE, Chief
Executive Officer
**Web address:** www.smrmc.com

| | | |
|---|---|---|
| Owned, leased, sponsored: | 2 hospitals | 168 beds |
| Contract–managed: | 0 hospitals | 0 beds |
| Totals: | 2 hospitals | 168 beds |

★**1245: SPARROW HEALTH SYSTEM** (NP)
1215 East Michigan Avenue, Lansing, MI Zip 48912–1811;
tel. 517/364–1000; Dennis A. Swan, JD, FACHE, President and Chief
Executive Officer
**(Centralized Health System)**

**MICHIGAN:** SPARROW CLINTON HOSPITAL (O, 25 beds) 805 South Oakland
Street, Saint Johns, MI Zip 48879–2253; tel. 989/227–3400; Edward
Bruun, President and Chief Executive Officer
**Web address:** www.clintonmemorial.org

SPARROW HOSPITAL (O, 638 beds) 1215 East Michigan Avenue, Lansing, MI
Zip 48912–1811; tel. 517/364–1000; Dennis A. Swan, JD, FACHE, President
and Chief Executive Officer
**Web address:** www.sparrow.org

SPARROW IONIA HOSPITAL (O, 25 beds) 479 Lafayette Street, Ionia, MI
Zip 48846–1834, Mailing Address: Box 1001, Zip 48846–6001;
tel. 616/523–1400; William Roeser, President and Chief Executive Officer
**Web address:** www.sparrow.org/sparrowionia

SPARROW SPECIALTY HOSPITAL (O, 36 beds) 1210 West Saginaw Street,
Lansing, MI Zip 48915–1927, Mailing Address: P.O. Box 85201,
Zip 48915–1927; tel. 517/364–6800; Kira Carter–Robertson, President and
Chief Executive Officer
**Web address:** www.sparrowspecialty.org

| | | |
|---|---|---|
| Owned, leased, sponsored: | 4 hospitals | 724 beds |
| Contract–managed: | 0 hospitals | 0 beds |
| Totals: | 4 hospitals | 724 beds |

★**4195: SPARTANBURG REGIONAL HEALTHCARE SYSTEM**
(NP)
101 East Wood Street, Spartanburg, SC Zip 29303–3040;
tel. 864/560–6000; Bruce Holstien, President and Chief Executive
Officer
**(Centralized Health System)**

**SOUTH CAROLINA:** SPARTANBURG HOSPITAL FOR RESTORATIVE CARE (O,
116 beds) 389 Serpentine Drive, Spartanburg, SC Zip 29303–3026;
tel. 864/560–3280; Anita M. Butler, Chief Executive Officer
**Web address:** www.srhs.org

SPARTANBURG REGIONAL MEDICAL CENTER (O, 514 beds) 101 East Wood
Street, Spartanburg, SC Zip 29303–3040; tel. 864/560–6000; Bruce
Holstien, President and Chief Executive Officer
**Web address:** www.spartanburgregional.com

VILLAGE HOSPITAL (O, 34 beds) 250 Westmoreland Road, Greer, SC
Zip 29651–9013; tel. 864/530–6000; Anthony Kouskolekas, President
**Web address:** www.villageatpelham.com

For explanation of codes following names, see page B2.
★ Indicates Type III membership in the American Hospital Association.

| | | |
|---|---|---|
| Owned, leased, sponsored: | 3 hospitals | 664 beds |
| Contract–managed: | 0 hospitals | 0 beds |
| Totals: | 3 hospitals | 664 beds |

### 0641: SPECIALTY HEALTHCARE, LLC (IO)
305 West Harriet Street, Leesville, LA Zip 71446–4229;
tel. 337/238–4449; Craig Ball, Chairman and Chief Executive Officer

**LOUISIANA:** POST ACUTE SPECIALTY HOSPITAL OF HAMMOND (O, 20 beds)
42074 Veterans Avenue, Hammond, LA Zip 70403–1408;
tel. 985/902–8148; Jerry Elenbaas, Administrator
**Web address:** www.specialtyltch.com/

SPECIALTY REHABILITATION HOSPITAL (O, 12 beds) 1110 Ringgold Avenue
Suite B., Coushatta, LA Zip 71019–9073; tel. 318/932–1770; Craig Ball,
Chief Executive Officer
**Web address:** www.specialtyhealthcare.com

SPECIALTY REHABILITATION HOSPITAL OF LULING (O, 21 beds) 1125 Paul
Maillard Road, Luling, LA Zip 70070–4351; tel. 985/785–5233; Chenell
Barnes, Administrator
**Web address:** www.specialtyhealthcare.com

| | | |
|---|---|---|
| Owned, leased, sponsored: | 3 hospitals | 53 beds |
| Contract–managed: | 0 hospitals | 0 beds |
| Totals: | 3 hospitals | 53 beds |

### 0352: SPECIALTY HOSPITALS OF AMERICA, LLC (IO)
155 Fleet Street, Portsmouth, NH Zip 03801–4050;
tel. 603/570–4888; Eric F. Rieseberg, President
**(Independent Hospital System)**

**DISTRICT OF COLUMBIA:** SPECIALTY HOSPITAL OF WASHINGTON (O, 177
beds) 700 Constitution Avenue N.E., Washington, DC Zip 20002–6058;
tel. 202/546–5700; Susan P. Bailey, R.N., Chief Executive Officer
**Web address:** www.specialtyhospitalofwashington.com

SPECIALTY HOSPITAL OF WASHINGTON–HADLEY (O, 82 beds) 4601 Martin
Luther King Jr. Avenue, S.W., Washington, DC Zip 20032–1131;
tel. 202/574–5700; Peter Miller, FACHE, Chief Executive Officer

| | | |
|---|---|---|
| Owned, leased, sponsored: | 2 hospitals | 259 beds |
| Contract–managed: | 0 hospitals | 0 beds |
| Totals: | 2 hospitals | 259 beds |

### ★0177: SPECTRUM HEALTH (NP)
100 Michigan Street N.E., Grand Rapids, MI Zip 49503–2551;
tel. 616/391–1774; Richard C. Breon, President and Chief Executive
Officer
**(Moderately Centralized Health System)**

**MICHIGAN:** SPECTRUM HEALTH – GRAND RAPIDS (O, 1048 beds) 100
Michigan Street N.E., Grand Rapids, MI Zip 49503–2560;
tel. 616/774–7444; Kevin Splaine, President
**Web address:** www.spectrum–health.org

SPECTRUM HEALTH GERBER MEMORIAL (O, 40 beds) 212 South Sullivan
Avenue, Fremont, MI Zip 49412–1548; tel. 231/924–3300; Randall Stasik,
President and Chief Executive Officer
**Web address:** www.spectrumhealth.org

SPECTRUM HEALTH REED CITY HOSPITAL (O, 75 beds) 300 North Patterson
Road, Reed City, MI Zip 49677–8041, Mailing Address: P.O. Box 75,
Zip 49677–0075; tel. 231/832–3271; Sam Daugherty, Ed.D., President
**Web address:** www.reedcity.spectrum–health.org

SPECTRUM HEALTH SPECIAL CARE HOSPITAL (O, 36 beds) 750 Fuller
Avenue N.E., Grand Rapids, MI Zip 49503–1995; tel. 616/486–3000; Chuck
Tozer, Administrator
**Web address:** www.spectrum–health.org

SPECTRUM HEALTH UNITED HOSPITAL (O, 116 beds) 615 South Bower
Street, Greenville, MI Zip 48838–2614; tel. 616/754–4691; Christina
Freese–Decker, President
**Web address:** www.spectrum–health.org/

SPECTRUM HEALTH ZEELAND COMMUNITY HOSPITAL (O, 57 beds) 8333
Felch Street, Zeeland, MI Zip 49464–2608; tel. 616/772–4644; Henry A.
Veenstra, President
**Web address:** www.spectrumhealth.org/zeeland

| | | |
|---|---|---|
| Owned, leased, sponsored: | 6 hospitals | 1372 beds |
| Contract–managed: | 0 hospitals | 0 beds |
| Totals: | 6 hospitals | 1372 beds |

### ★5455: SSM HEALTH CARE (CC)
477 North Lindbergh Boulevard, Saint Louis, MO Zip 63141–7813;
tel. 314/994–7800; William P. Thompson, President and Chief
Executive Officer
**(Decentralized Health System)**

**ILLINOIS:** GOOD SAMARITAN REGIONAL HEALTH CENTER (O, 146 beds) 605
North 12th Street, Mount Vernon, IL Zip 62864–2899;
tel. 618/242–4600; Michael D. Warren, President
**Web address:** www.smgsi.com

ST. MARY'S HOSPITAL (O, 113 beds) 400 North Pleasant Avenue, Centralia,
IL Zip 62801–3056; tel. 618/436–8000; Bruce Merrell, FACHE, President
**Web address:** www.smgsi.com

**MISSOURI:** AUDRAIN MEDICAL CENTER (O, 49 beds) 620 East Monroe
Street, Mexico, MO Zip 65265–2919; tel. 573/582–5000; David A.
Neuendorf, FACHE, President and Chief Executive Officer
**Web address:** www.audrainmedicalcenter.com

SSM CARDINAL GLENNON CHILDREN'S MEDICAL CENTER (O, 176 beds)
1465 South Grand Boulevard, Saint Louis, MO Zip 63104–1095;
tel. 314/577–5600; Sherlyn Hailstone, MSN, R.N., FACHE, President
**Web address:** www.cardinalglennon.com

SSM DEPAUL HEALTH CENTER (O, 476 beds) 12303 De Paul Drive,
Bridgeton, MO Zip 63044–2512; tel. 314/344–6000; Sean Hogan, President
**Web address:** www.ssmdepaul.com

SSM ST. CLARE HEALTH CENTER (O, 184 beds) 1015 Bowles Avenue,
Fenton, MO Zip 63026–2394; tel. 636/496–2000; Lee Bernstein, Interim
President
**Web address:** www.ssmstclare.com

SSM ST. JOSEPH HEALTH CENTER (O, 331 beds) 300 First Capitol Drive,
Saint Charles, MO Zip 63301–2844; tel. 636/947–5000; Gaspare Calvaruso,
President
**Web address:** www.ssmstjoseph.com

SSM ST. JOSEPH HOSPITAL WEST (O, 126 beds) 100 Medical Plaza, Lake
Saint Louis, MO Zip 63367–1366; tel. 636/625–5200; Lisle Wescott,
President
**Web address:** www.ssmstjoseph.com

SSM ST. MARY'S HEALTH CENTER (O, 381 beds) 6420 Clayton Road, Saint
Louis, MO Zip 63117–1811; tel. 314/768–8000; Kathleen R. Becker, M.P.H.,
JD, President
**Web address:** www.stmarys–stlouis.com

ST. FRANCIS HOSPITAL AND HEALTH SERVICES (O, 57 beds) 2016 South
Main Street, Maryville, MO Zip 64468–2655; tel. 660/562–2600; Gray Cox,
President
**Web address:** www.stfrancismaryville.com

ST. MARYS HEALTH CENTER (O, 139 beds) 100 St. Marys Medical Plaza,
Jefferson City, MO Zip 65101–1602; tel. 573/761–7000; R. Brent VanConia,
President
**Web address:** www.lethealingbegin.com

**OKLAHOMA:** ST. ANTHONY HOSPITAL (O, 524 beds) 1000 North Lee Street,
Oklahoma City, OK Zip 73102–1080, Mailing Address: P.O. Box 205,
Zip 73101–0205; tel. 405/272–7000; Michael D. Beaver, President
**Web address:** www.saintsok.com

ST. ANTHONY SHAWNEE HOSPITAL (O, 131 beds) 1102 West MacArthur
Street, Shawnee, OK Zip 74804–1744; tel. 405/273–2270; Charles E.
Skillings, President and Chief Executive Officer
**Web address:** www.stanthonyshawnee.com

**WISCONSIN:** ST. CLARE HOSPITAL (O, 60 beds) 707 14th Street, Baraboo,
WI Zip 53913–1597; tel. 608/356–1400; Sandra L. Anderson, President
**Web address:** www.stclare.com

ST. MARY'S HOSPITAL (O, 361 beds) 700 South Park Street, Madison, WI
Zip 53715–1830; tel. 608/251–6100; Frank D. Byrne, M.D., President
**Web address:** www.stmarysmadison.com

ST. MARY'S JANESVILLE HOSPITAL (O, 50 beds) 3400 East Racine Steeet, Janesville, WI Zip 53546–2344; tel. 608/373–8000; Kerry Swanson, President
**Web address:** www.stmarysjanesville.com

| | | |
|---|---|---|
| **Owned, leased, sponsored:** | 16 hospitals | 3304 beds |
| **Contract–managed:** | 0 hospitals | 0 beds |
| **Totals:** | 16 hospitals | 3304 beds |

★**0250: ST. CHARLES HEALTH SYSTEM, INC.** (NP)
2500 N.E. Neff Road, Bend, OR Zip 97701–6015; tel. 541/382–4321; James A. Diegel, President and Chief Executive Officer
**(Centralized Physician/Insurance Health System)**

OREGON: PIONEER MEMORIAL HOSPITAL (L, 25 beds) 1201 N.E. Elm Street, Prineville, OR Zip 97754–1206; tel. 541/447–6254; Robert Gomes, Chief Executive Officer
**Web address:** www.stcharleshealthcare.org

ST. CHARLES MADRAS (O, 25 beds) 470 N.E. A Street, Madras, OR Zip 97741–1844; tel. 541/475–3882; Jeanine Gentry, Chief Executive Officer
**Web address:** www.mvhd.org

ST. CHARLES MEDICAL CENTER – BEND (O, 260 beds) 2500 N.E. Neff Road, Bend, OR Zip 97701–6015; tel. 541/382–4321; Jay Henry, Chief Executive Officer
**Web address:** www.scmc.org

ST. CHARLES MEDICAL CENTER – REDMOND (O, 48 beds) 1253 N.W. Canal Boulevard, Redmond, OR Zip 97756–1395; tel. 541/548–8131; Robert Gomes, Chief Executive Officer
**Web address:** www.stcharleshealthcare.org

| | | |
|---|---|---|
| **Owned, leased, sponsored:** | 4 hospitals | 358 beds |
| **Contract–managed:** | 0 hospitals | 0 beds |
| **Totals:** | 4 hospitals | 358 beds |

**0618: ST. ELIZABETH HEALTHCARE** (NP)
1 Medical Village Drive, Edgewood, KY Zip 41017–3403; tel. 859/301–2000; John S. Dubis, FACHE, President and Chief Executive Officer
**(Centralized Health System)**

KENTUCKY: ST. ELIZABETH EDGEWOOD (O, 502 beds) 1 Medical Village Drive, Edgewood, KY Zip 41017–3403; tel. 859/301–2000; John S. Dubis, FACHE, President and Chief Executive Officer
**Web address:** www.stelizabeth.com

ST. ELIZABETH FLORENCE (O, 169 beds) 4900 Houston Road, Florence, KY Zip 41042–4824; tel. 859/212–5200; Chris Carle, Senior Vice President and Chief Operating Officer
**Web address:** www.stelizabeth.com

ST. ELIZABETH FORT THOMAS (O, 181 beds) 85 North Grand Avenue, Fort Thomas, KY Zip 41075–1796; tel. 859/572–3100; Thomas Saalfeld, Senior Vice President and Chief Operating Officer
**Web address:** www.stelizabeth.com

ST. ELIZABETH GRANT (O, 16 beds) 238 Barnes Road, Williamstown, KY Zip 41097–9482; tel. 859/824–8240; John Mitchell, Assistant Vice President Operations
**Web address:** www.stelizabeth.com

| | | |
|---|---|---|
| **Owned, leased, sponsored:** | 4 hospitals | 868 beds |
| **Contract–managed:** | 0 hospitals | 0 beds |
| **Totals:** | 4 hospitals | 868 beds |

★**5425: ST. JOSEPH HEALTH** (CC)
3345 Michelson Drive, Suite 100, Irvine, CA Zip 92612; tel. 949/381–4000; Deborah A. Proctor, President and Chief Executive Officer
**(Moderately Centralized Health System)**

CALIFORNIA: MISSION HOSPITAL (O, 249 beds) 27700 Medical Center Road, Mission Viejo, CA Zip 92691–6426; tel. 949/364–1400; Kenneth McFarland, President and Chief Executive Officer
**Web address:** www.mission4health.com

PETALUMA VALLEY HOSPITAL (L, 28 beds) 400 North McDowell Boulevard, Petaluma, CA Zip 94954–2369; tel. 707/778–1111; Todd Salnas, President and Chief Executive Officer
**Web address:** www.stjosephhealth. org/About–Us/Facilities/Petaluma–Valley–Hospital.aspx

QUEEN OF THE VALLEY MEDICAL CENTER (O, 174 beds) 1000 Trancas Street, Napa, CA Zip 94558–2906, Mailing Address: P.O. Box 2340, Zip 94558–0688; tel. 707/252–4411; Walt Mickens, President and Chief Executive Officer
**Web address:** www.thequeen.org

REDWOOD MEMORIAL HOSPITAL (O, 25 beds) 3300 Renner Drive, Fortuna, CA Zip 95540–3198; tel. 707/725–3361; David O'Brien, M.D., Interim President and Chief Executive Officer
**Web address:** www.redwoodmemorial.org/

SANTA ROSA MEMORIAL HOSPITAL (O, 272 beds) 1165 Montgomery Drive, Santa Rosa, CA Zip 95405–4897, Mailing Address: P.O. Box 522, Zip 95402–0522; tel. 707/546–3210; Todd Salnas, President and Chief Executive Officer
**Web address:** www.stjosephhealth.org

ST. JOSEPH HEALTH ST. MARY (O, 204 beds) 18300 Highway 18, Apple Valley, CA Zip 92307–2206, Mailing Address: P.O. Box 7025, Zip 92307–0725; tel. 760/242–2311; Alan H. Garrett, Chief Executive Officer
**Web address:** www.stmaryapplevalley.com/

ST. JOSEPH HOSPITAL (O, 138 beds) 2700 Dolbeer Street, Eureka, CA Zip 95501–4799; tel. 707/445–8121; David O'Brien, M.D., Interim President and Chief Executive Officer
**Web address:** www.stjosepheureka.org

ST. JOSEPH HOSPITAL (O, 392 beds) 1100 West Stewart Drive, Orange, CA Zip 92868–3849, Mailing Address: P.O. Box 5600, Zip 92863–5600; tel. 714/633–9111; Steven C. Moreau, President and Chief Executive Officer
**Web address:** www.sjo.org

ST. JUDE MEDICAL CENTER (O, 372 beds) 101 East Valencia Mesa Drive, Fullerton, CA Zip 92835–3809; tel. 714/992–3000; Lee Penrose, President and Chief Executive Officer
**Web address:** www.stjudemedicalcenter.org

| | | |
|---|---|---|
| **Owned, leased, sponsored:** | 9 hospitals | 1854 beds |
| **Contract–managed:** | 0 hospitals | 0 beds |
| **Totals:** | 9 hospitals | 1854 beds |

★**0356: ST. LUKE'S HEALTH SYSTEM** (NP)
420 West Idaho Street, Boise, ID Zip 83702–6041; tel. 208/381–4200; David C. Pate, M.D., JD, President and Chief Executive Officer
**(Moderately Centralized Health System)**

IDAHO: NORTH CANYON MEDICAL CENTER (C, 15 beds) 267 North Canyon Drive, Gooding, ID Zip 83330–5500; tel. 208/934–4433; David Butler, Chief Executive Officer
**Web address:** www.goodinghospital.org

ST. LUKE'S ELMORE (O, 57 beds) 895 North Sixth East Street, Mountain Home, ID Zip 83647–2207, Mailing Address: P.O. Box 1270, Zip 83647–1270; tel. 208/587–8401; Gregory L. Maurer, Administrator
**Web address:** www.elmoremedicalcenter.org

ST. LUKE'S JEROME (O, 25 beds) 709 North Lincoln Street, Jerome, ID Zip 83338–1851, Mailing Address: P.O. Box 586, Zip 83338–0586; tel. 208/324–4301; Curtis Maier, Administrative Director
**Web address:** www.stlukesonline.org/jerome/

ST. LUKE'S MAGIC VALLEY MEDICAL CENTER (O, 197 beds) 801 Pole Line Road West, Twin Falls, ID Zip 83301–5810, Mailing Address: P.O. Box 409, Zip 83303–0409; tel. 208/814–0000; James L. Angle, FACHE, Chief Executive Officer
**Web address:** www.stlukesonline.org

ST. LUKE'S MCCALL (O, 15 beds) 1000 State Street, McCall, ID Zip 83638–3704; tel. 208/634–2221; Michael A. Fenello, Chief Executive Officer
**Web address:** www.mccallhosp.org

For explanation of codes following names, see page B2.
★ Indicates Type III membership in the American Hospital Association.

Section B

ST. LUKE'S REGIONAL MEDICAL CENTER (O, 583 beds) 190 East Bannock Street, Boise, ID Zip 83712–6241; tel. 208/381–2222; Chris Roth, Chief Executive Officer
**Web address:** www.stlukesonline.org/boise

ST. LUKE'S WOOD RIVER MEDICAL CENTER (O, 25 beds) 100 Hospital Drive, Ketchum, ID Zip 83340, Mailing Address: P.O. Box 100, Zip 83340–0100; tel. 208/727–8800; Cody Langbehn, Chief Executive Officer
**Web address:** www.slrmc.org

WEISER MEMORIAL HOSPITAL (C, 25 beds) 645 East Fifth Street, Weiser, ID Zip 83672–2202; tel. 208/549–0370; Tom Murphy, Chief Executive Officer
**Web address:** www.weisermemorialhospital.org

| | | |
|---|---|---|
| Owned, leased, sponsored: | 6 hospitals | 902 beds |
| Contract–managed: | 2 hospitals | 40 beds |
| Totals: | 8 hospitals | 942 beds |

**0862:  ST. LUKE'S UNIVERSITY HEALTH NETWORK** (NP)
801 Ostrum Street, Bethlehem, PA Zip 18015–1000; tel. 610/954–4000; Richard A. Anderson, President and Chief Executive Officer
**(Moderately Centralized Health System)**

**NEW JERSEY:** ST. LUKE'S HOSPITAL – WARREN CAMPUS (O, 140 beds) 185 Roseberry Street, Phillipsburg, NJ Zip 08865–1690; tel. 908/859–6700; Scott R. Wolfe, CPA, President
**Web address:** www.warrenhospital.org

**PENNSYLVANIA:** ST. LUKE'S HOSPITAL – ANDERSON CAMPUS (O, 57 beds) 1872 Riverside Circle, Easton, PA Zip 18045–5669; tel. 484/503–3000; Edward Nawrocki, President
**Web address:** www.mystlukesonline.org

ST. LUKE'S HOSPITAL – MINERS CAMPUS (O, 92 beds) 360 West Ruddle Street, Coaldale, PA Zip 18218–1027; tel. 570/645–2131; William E. Moyer, President
**Web address:** www.slhn.org

ST. LUKE'S HOSPITAL – QUAKERTOWN CAMPUS (O, 57 beds) 1021 Park Avenue, Quakertown, PA Zip 18951–1573; tel. 215/538–4500; John B. Sylvia, President
**Web address:** www.slhhn.org

ST. LUKE'S UNIVERSITY HOSPITAL – BETHLEHEM CAMPUS (O, 572 beds) 801 Ostrum Street, Bethlehem, PA Zip 18015–1065; tel. 610/954–4000; Richard A. Anderson, President and Chief Executive Officer
**Web address:** www.slhn–lehighvalley.org

| | | |
|---|---|---|
| Owned, leased, sponsored: | 5 hospitals | 918 beds |
| Contract–managed: | 0 hospitals | 0 beds |
| Totals: | 5 hospitals | 918 beds |

**0156:  STANFORD HEALTH CARE** (NP)
300 Pasteur Drive, Palo Alto, CA Zip 94304–2299; tel. 650/723–4000; Amir Dan Rubin, President and Chief Executive Officer
**(Moderately Centralized Health System)**

**CALIFORNIA:** LUCILE SALTER PACKARD CHILDREN'S HOSPITAL AT STANFORD (O, 302 beds) 725 Welch Road, Palo Alto, CA Zip 94304–1601; tel. 650/497–8000; Christopher G. Dawes, President and Chief Executive Officer
**Web address:** www.lpch.org

STANFORD HOSPITAL AND CLINICS (O, 477 beds) 1520 Page Mill Road, Palo Alto, CA Zip 94304–1125; tel. 650/723–4000; Amir Dan Rubin, President and Chief Executive Officer
**Web address:** www.stanfordhospital.com/

| | | |
|---|---|---|
| Owned, leased, sponsored: | 2 hospitals | 779 beds |
| Contract–managed: | 0 hospitals | 0 beds |
| Totals: | 2 hospitals | 779 beds |

**0141:  STEWARD HEALTH CARE SYSTEM, LLC** (IO)
500 Boylston Street, 5th Floor, Boston, MA Zip 02116–3740; tel. 617/419–4700; Ralph de la Torre, M.D., Chairman and Chief Executive Officer
**(Moderately Centralized Health System)**

**MASSACHUSETTS:** CARNEY HOSPITAL (O, 120 beds) 2100 Dorchester Avenue, Boston, MA Zip 02124–5615; tel. 617/296–4000; Andrew Davis, President
**Web address:** www.carneyhospital.org

GOOD SAMARITAN MEDICAL CENTER (O, 189 beds) 235 North Pearl Street, Brockton, MA Zip 02301–1794; tel. 508/427–3000; Jeffrey H. Liebman, President
**Web address:** www.stewardhealth.org/Good–Samaritan

HOLY FAMILY HOSPITAL AND MEDICAL CENTER (O, 239 beds) 70 East Street, Methuen, MA Zip 01844–4597; tel. 978/687–0151; Lester P. Schindel, President and Chief Executive Officer
**Web address:** www.stewardhealth.org/Holy–Family–Hospital

MERRIMACK VALLEY HOSPITAL (O, 90 beds) 140 Lincoln Avenue, Haverhill, MA Zip 01830–6798; tel. 978/374–2000; Michael F. Collins, Chief Executive Officer
**Web address:** www.steward.org/merrimack–valley

MORTON HOSPITAL AND MEDICAL CENTER (O, 154 beds) 88 Washington Street, Taunton, MA Zip 02780–2465; tel. 508/828–7000; Kimberly S. Bassett, R.N., President
**Web address:** www.mortonhospital.org

NASHOBA VALLEY MEDICAL CENTER (O, 42 beds) 200 Groton Road, Ayer, MA Zip 01432–3300; tel. 978/784–9000; Steven P. Roach, Chief Executive Officer
**Web address:** www.nashobamed.com

NEW ENGLAND SINAI HOSPITAL AND REHABILITATION CENTER (O, 212 beds) 150 York Street, Stoughton, MA Zip 02072–1881; tel. 781/344–0600; Judith C. Waterston, R.N., MS, President and Chief Executive Officer
**Web address:** www.newenglandsinai.org

NORWOOD HOSPITAL (O, 188 beds) 800 Washington Street, Norwood, MA Zip 02062–3487; tel. 781/769–4000; Emily L. Holliman, President
**Web address:** www.stewardhealth.org/Norwood–Hospital

QUINCY MEDICAL CENTER (O, 116 beds) 114 Whitwell Street, Quincy, MA Zip 02169–1899; tel. 617/773–6100; Daniel J. Knell, MSN, President
**Web address:** www.quincymc.org

SAINT ANNE'S HOSPITAL (O, 160 beds) 795 Middle Street, Fall River, MA Zip 02721–1798; tel. 508/674–5741; Craig A. Jesiolowski, FACHE, President
**Web address:** www.saintanneshospital.org

ST. ELIZABETH'S MEDICAL CENTER (O, 338 beds) 736 Cambridge Street, Brighton, MA Zip 02135–2997; tel. 617/789–3000; Kevin R. Hannifan, President
**Web address:** www.stewardhealth.org/St_Elizabeths

| | | |
|---|---|---|
| Owned, leased, sponsored: | 11 hospitals | 1848 beds |
| Contract–managed: | 0 hospitals | 0 beds |
| Totals: | 11 hospitals | 1848 beds |

**0858:  STRATEGIC BEHAVIORAL HEALTH, LLC** (IO)
8295 Tournament Drive, Suite 201, Memphis, TN Zip 38125–8913; tel. 901/969–3100; Jim Shaheen, President

**COLORADO:** PEAK VIEW BEHAVIORAL HEALTH (O, 92 beds) 7353 Sisters Grove, Colorado Springs, CO Zip 80923–2615; tel. 719/444–8484; Gary Miller, Chief Executive Officer
**Web address:** www.strategicbh.com/peakview.html

**NEVADA:** MONTEVISTA HOSPITAL (O, 90 beds) 5900 West Rochelle Avenue, Las Vegas, NV Zip 89103–3327; tel. 702/364–1111; Kreg Gillman, Chief Executive Officer
**Web address:** www.montevistahospital.com

RED ROCK BEHAVIORAL HOSPITAL (O, 21 beds) 5975 West Twain Avenue, Las Vegas, NV Zip 89103–1237; tel. 702/214–8099; Toby Davis, Chief Executive Officer
**Web address:** www.redrockhospital.com

For explanation of codes following names, see page B2.
★ Indicates Type III membership in the American Hospital Association.

**NEW MEXICO:** PEAK BEHAVIORAL HEALTH SERVICES (O, 120 beds) 5065 McNutt Road, Santa Teresa, NM Zip 88008–9442; tel. 575/589–3000; Jim Shaheen, President
**Web address:** www.peakbehavioral.com/

| | | |
|---|---|---|
| Owned, leased, sponsored: | 4 hospitals | 323 beds |
| Contract–managed: | 0 hospitals | 0 beds |
| Totals: | 4 hospitals | 323 beds |

---

**0517: SUCCESS HEALTHCARE** (IO)
999 Yamato Road, 3rd Floor, Boca Raton, FL Zip 33431–4477; tel. 561/869–6300; Peter R. Baronoff, President and Chief Executive Officer
**(Independent Hospital System)**

**CALIFORNIA:** SILVER LAKE MEDICAL CENTER (O, 150 beds) 1711 West Temple Street, Los Angeles, CA Zip 90026–5421; tel. 213/989–6100; Brent A. Cope, Chief Executive Officer
**Web address:** www.silverlakemc.com

**MISSOURI:** ST. ALEXIUS HOSPITAL – BROADWAY CAMPUS (O, 189 beds) 3933 South Broadway, Saint Louis, MO Zip 63118–4601; tel. 314/865–3333; Michael J. Motte, Chief Executive Officer
**Web address:** www.stalexiushospital.com

| | | |
|---|---|---|
| Owned, leased, sponsored: | 2 hospitals | 339 beds |
| Contract–managed: | 0 hospitals | 0 beds |
| Totals: | 2 hospitals | 339 beds |

---

**0399: SUMMA HEALTH SYSTEM** (NP)
525 East Market Street, Akron, OH Zip 44304–1619; tel. 330/375–3000; Thomas J. Strauss, President and Chief Executive Officer
**(Centralized Health System)**

**OHIO:** ROBINSON MEMORIAL HOSPITAL (O, 141 beds) 6847 North Chestnut Street, Ravenna, OH Zip 44266–3929, Mailing Address: P.O. Box 1204, Zip 44266–1204; tel. 330/297–0811; Stephen Colecchi, President and Chief Executive Officer
**Web address:** www.robinsonmemorial.org

SUMMA BARBERTON CITIZENS HOSPITAL (O, 202 beds) 155 Fifth Street N.E., Barberton, OH Zip 44203–3332; tel. 330/615–3000; Thomas DeBord, President
**Web address:** www.barbhosp.com

SUMMA HEALTH SYSTEM (O, 428 beds) 525 East Market Street, Akron, OH Zip 44304–1619; tel. 330/375–3000; Thomas J. Strauss, President and Chief Executive Officer
**Web address:** www.summahealth.org

SUMMA WADSWORTH–RITTMAN HOSPITAL (O, 50 beds) 195 Wadsworth Road, Wadsworth, OH Zip 44281–9505; tel. 330/331–1000; Thomas DeBord, President
**Web address:** www.wrhhs.org

SUMMA WESTERN RESERVE HOSPITAL (O, 57 beds) 1900 23rd Street, Cuyahoga Falls, OH Zip 44223–1499; tel. 330/971–7000; Robert Kent, D.O., President and Chief Executive Officer
**Web address:** www.westernreservehospital.org

| | | |
|---|---|---|
| Owned, leased, sponsored: | 5 hospitals | 878 beds |
| Contract–managed: | 0 hospitals | 0 beds |
| Totals: | 5 hospitals | 878 beds |

---

**★0189: SUMMIT HEALTH** (NP)
112 North Seventh Street, Chambersburg, PA Zip 17201–1720; tel. 717/267–7138; Patrick W. O'Donnell, CPA, President and Chief Executive Officer
**(Independent Hospital System)**

**PENNSYLVANIA:** CHAMBERSBURG HOSPITAL (O, 246 beds) 112 North Seventh Street, Chambersburg, PA Zip 17201–1720; tel. 717/267–3000; Patrick W. O'Donnell, CPA, President and Chief Executive Officer
**Web address:** www.summithealth.org

WAYNESBORO HOSPITAL (O, 64 beds) 501 East Main Street, Waynesboro, PA Zip 17268–2394; tel. 717/765–4000; Melissa Dubrow, Chief Operating Officer
**Web address:** www.summithealth.org

| | | |
|---|---|---|
| Owned, leased, sponsored: | 2 hospitals | 310 beds |
| Contract–managed: | 0 hospitals | 0 beds |
| Totals: | 2 hospitals | 310 beds |

---

**0237: SUNLINK HEALTH SYSTEMS** (IO)
900 Circle 75 Parkway, Suite 1120, Atlanta, GA Zip 30339–3005; tel. 770/933–7000; Robert M. Thornton, Jr., Chief Executive Officer
**(Independent Hospital System)**

**GEORGIA:** CHESTATEE REGIONAL HOSPITAL (O, 49 beds) 227 Mountain Drive, Dahlonega, GA Zip 30533–1606; tel. 706/864–6136; Larry R. Jeter, Chief Executive Officer
**Web address:** www.chestateeregionalhospital.com

NORTH GEORGIA MEDICAL CENTER (O, 150 beds) 1362 South Main Street, Ellijay, GA Zip 30540–5410, Mailing Address: P.O. Box 2239, Zip 30540–0025; tel. 706/276–4741; Jeffrey Dunn, Chief Executive Officer
**Web address:** www.northgeorgiamedicalcenter.com

**MISSISSIPPI:** TRACE REGIONAL HOSPITAL (O, 84 beds) Highway 8 East, Houston, MS Zip 38851–9396, Mailing Address: P.O. Box 626, Zip 38851–0626; tel. 662/456–3700; Gary L. Staten, Chief Executive Officer
**Web address:** www.traceregional.com

**MISSOURI:** CALLAWAY COMMUNITY HOSPITAL (O, 37 beds) 10 South Hospital Drive, Fulton, MO Zip 65251–2510; tel. 573/642–3376; Allen D. AufderHeide, Chief Executive Officer
**Web address:** www.mycallaway.org

| | | |
|---|---|---|
| Owned, leased, sponsored: | 4 hospitals | 320 beds |
| Contract–managed: | 0 hospitals | 0 beds |
| Totals: | 4 hospitals | 320 beds |

---

**★0066: SUSQUEHANNA HEALTH SYSTEM** (NP)
700 High Street, Williamsport, PA Zip 17701–3100; tel. 570/321–1000; Steven P. Johnson, FACHE, President and Chief Executive Officer
**(Centralized Health System)**

**PENNSYLVANIA:** DIVINE PROVIDENCE HOSPITAL (O, 31 beds) 1100 Grampian Boulevard, Williamsport, PA Zip 17701–1995; tel. 570/326–8000; Robert E. Kane, Administrator and Chief Executive Officer
**Web address:** www.susquehannahealth.org

MUNCY VALLEY HOSPITAL (O, 156 beds) 215 East Water Street, Muncy, PA Zip 17756–8700; tel. 570/546–8282; Ronald J. Reynolds, President
**Web address:** www.susquehannahealth.org

SOLDIERS AND SAILORS MEMORIAL HOSPITAL (O, 83 beds) 32–36 Central Avenue, Wellsboro, PA Zip 16901–1899; tel. 570/724–1631; Janie Hilfiger, President
**Web address:** www.susquehannahealth.org

WILLIAMSPORT REGIONAL MEDICAL CENTER (O, 207 beds) 700 High Street, Williamsport, PA Zip 17701–3100; tel. 570/321–1000; Jan E. Fisher, President

| | | |
|---|---|---|
| Owned, leased, sponsored: | 4 hospitals | 477 beds |
| Contract–managed: | 0 hospitals | 0 beds |
| Totals: | 4 hospitals | 477 beds |

---

**★8795: SUTTER HEALTH** (NP)
2200 River Plaza Drive, Sacramento, CA Zip 95833–4134; tel. 916/733–8800; Patrick E. Fry, Chief Executive Officer
**(Moderately Centralized Health System)**

**CALIFORNIA:** ALTA BATES SUMMIT MEDICAL CENTER (O, 527 beds) 2450 Ashby Avenue, Berkeley, CA Zip 94705–2067; tel. 510/204–4444; Charles Prosper, Chief Executive Officer
**Web address:** www.altabates.com

For explanation of codes following names, see page B2.
★ Indicates Type III membership in the American Hospital Association.

Section B

ALTA BATES SUMMIT MEDICAL CENTER – SUMMIT CAMPUS (O, 414 beds) 350 Hawthorne Avenue, Oakland, CA Zip 94609–3100; tel. 510/655–4000; Charles Prosper, Chief Executive Officer
**Web address:** www.altabatessummit.com

CALIFORNIA PACIFIC MEDICAL CENTER (O, 785 beds) 2333 Buchanan Street, San Francisco, CA Zip 94115–1925, Mailing Address: P.O. Box 7999, Zip 94120–7999; tel. 415/600–6000; Warren S. Browner, M.D., M.P.H., Chief Executive Officer
**Web address:** www.cpmc.org

EDEN MEDICAL CENTER (O, 199 beds) 20103 Lake Chabot Road, Castro Valley, CA Zip 94546–5305; tel. 510/537–1234; George Bischalaney, President and Chief Executive Officer
**Web address:** www.edenmedcenter.org

MEMORIAL HOSPITAL LOS BANOS (O, 46 beds) 520 West I Street, Los Banos, CA Zip 93635–3419; tel. 209/826–0591; Richard S. Liszewski, Chief Executive Officer
**Web address:** www.memoriallosbanos.org/

MEMORIAL MEDICAL CENTER (O, 427 beds) 1700 Coffee Road, Modesto, CA Zip 95355–2869, Mailing Address: P.O. Box 942, Zip 95353–0942; tel. 209/526–4500; Daryn J. Kumar, Chief Executive Officer
**Web address:** www.memorialmedicalcenter.org

MENLO PARK SURGICAL HOSPITAL (O, 12 beds) 570 Willow Road, Menlo Park, CA Zip 94025–2617; tel. 650/324–8500; Kathleen Palange, R.N., Chief Executive Officer
**Web address:** www.pamf.org/mpsh

MILLS–PENINSULA HEALTH SERVICES (O, 393 beds) 1501 Trousdale Drive, Burlingame, CA Zip 94010–3282; tel. 650/696–5400; Robert W. Merwin, Chief Executive Officer
**Web address:** www.mills–peninsula.org

NOVATO COMMUNITY HOSPITAL (O, 40 beds) 180 Rowland Way, Novato, CA Zip 94945–5009, Mailing Address: P.O. Box 1108, Zip 94948–1108; tel. 415/209–1300; Brian Alexander, Chief Administrative Officer
**Web address:** www.novatocommunity.sutterhealth.org

ST. LUKE'S HOSPITAL (O, 173 beds) 3555 Cesar Chavez Street, San Francisco, CA Zip 94110–4490; tel. 415/600–6000; Warren S. Browner, M.D., M.P.H., Chief Executive Officer
**Web address:** www.stlukes–sf.org

SUTTER AMADOR HOSPITAL (O, 42 beds) 200 Mission Boulevard, Jackson, CA Zip 95642–2564; tel. 209/223–7500; Anne Platt, Chief Executive Officer
**Web address:** www.sutteramador.org

SUTTER AUBURN FAITH HOSPITAL (O, 75 beds) 11815 Education Street, Auburn, CA Zip 95602–2410; tel. 530/888–4500; Mitchell J. Hanna, Chief Executive Officer
**Web address:** www.sutterhealth.org

SUTTER CENTER FOR PSYCHIATRY (O, 69 beds) 7700 Folsom Boulevard, Sacramento, CA Zip 95826–2608; tel. 916/386–3000; John W. Boyd, PsyD, Chief Administrative Officer
**Web address:** www.sutterpsychiatry.org

SUTTER COAST HOSPITAL (O, 49 beds) 800 East Washington Boulevard, Crescent City, CA Zip 95531–8359; tel. 707/464–8511; Linda Horn, Interim Chief Executive Officer
**Web address:** www.sutterhealth.org

SUTTER DAVIS HOSPITAL (O, 48 beds) 2000 Sutter Place, Davis, CA Zip 95616–6201, Mailing Address: P.O. Box 1617, Zip 95617–1617; tel. 530/756–6440; Janet Wagner, R.N., Chief Executive Officer
**Web address:** www.sutterhealth.org

SUTTER DELTA MEDICAL CENTER (O, 136 beds) 3901 Lone Tree Way, Antioch, CA Zip 94509–6253; tel. 925/779–7200; Gary D. Rapaport, Chief Executive Officer
**Web address:** www.sutterdelta.org

SUTTER LAKESIDE HOSPITAL (O, 25 beds) 5176 Hill Road East, Lakeport, CA Zip 95453–6300; tel. 707/262–5000; Siri Nelson, Chief Administrative Officer
**Web address:** www.sutterlakeside.org

SUTTER MATERNITY AND SURGERY CENTER OF SANTA CRUZ (O, 28 beds) 2900 Chanticleer Avenue, Santa Cruz, CA Zip 95065–1816; tel. 831/477–2200; Stephen Gray, Chief Executive Officer
**Web address:** www.suttermatsurg.org

SUTTER MEDICAL CENTER OF SANTA ROSA, CHANATE CAMPUS (O, 135 beds) 3325 Chanate Road, Santa Rosa, CA Zip 95404–1707; tel. 707/576–4000; Mike Purvis, Chief Administrative Officer
**Web address:** www.sutterhealth.org

SUTTER MEDICAL CENTER, SACRAMENTO (O, 659 beds) 5151 F Street, Sacramento, CA Zip 95819–3295; tel. 916/454–3333; Carrie Owen–Plietz, Chief Executive Officer
**Web address:** www.sutterhealth.org

SUTTER ROSEVILLE MEDICAL CENTER (O, 358 beds) One Medical Plaza, Roseville, CA Zip 95661–3037; tel. 916/781–1000; Patrick R. Brady, Chief Executive Officer
**Web address:** www.sutterroseville.org

SUTTER SOLANO MEDICAL CENTER (O, 102 beds) 300 Hospital Drive, Vallejo, CA Zip 94589–2574, Mailing Address: P.O. Box 3189, Zip 94590–0669; tel. 707/554–4444; Theresa Glubka, Chief Executive Officer
**Web address:** www.suttersolano.org

SUTTER TRACY COMMUNITY HOSPITAL (O, 82 beds) 1420 North Tracy Boulevard, Tracy, CA Zip 95376–3497; tel. 209/835–1500; David M. Thompson, Chief Executive Officer
**Web address:** www.suttertracy.org

**HAWAII:** KAHI MOHALA BEHAVIORAL HEALTH (O, 66 beds) 91–2301 Old Fort Weaver Road, Ewa Beach, HI Zip 96706–3602; tel. 808/671–8511; Leonard Licina, Chief Executive Officer
**Web address:** www.kahimohala.org

| | | |
|---|---|---|
| **Owned, leased, sponsored:** | 24 hospitals | 4890 beds |
| **Contract–managed:** | 0 hospitals | 0 beds |
| **Totals:** | 24 hospitals | 4890 beds |

**0871: SWEDISH HEALTH SERVICES** (NP)
747 Broadway, Seattle, WA Zip 98122–4379; tel. 206/386–6000; Marcel C. Loh, FACHE, Interim Chief Executive
**(Centralized Health System)**

**WASHINGTON:** SWEDISH MEDICAL CENTER–CHERRY HILL CAMPUS (O, 198 beds) 500 17th Avenue, Seattle, WA Zip 98122–5711; tel. 206/320–2000; Rayburn Lewis, M.D., Executive
**Web address:** www.swedish.org

SWEDISH MEDICAL CENTER–FIRST HILL (O, 620 beds) 747 Broadway, Seattle, WA Zip 98122–4307; tel. 206/386–6000; Todd Strumwasser, M.D., Chief Executive
**Web address:** www.swedish.org

SWEDISH/EDMONDS (O, 161 beds) 21601 76th Avenue West, Edmonds, WA Zip 98026–7506; tel. 425/640–4000; David E. Jaffe, Chief Executive
**Web address:** www.swedish.org

SWEDISH/ISSAQUAH (O, 49 beds) 751 N.E. Blakely Drive, Issaquah, WA Zip 98029–6201; tel. 425/313–4000; Chuck Salmon, Chief Executive
**Web address:** www.swedish.org/issaquah

| | | |
|---|---|---|
| **Owned, leased, sponsored:** | 4 hospitals | 1028 beds |
| **Contract–managed:** | 0 hospitals | 0 beds |
| **Totals:** | 4 hospitals | 1028 beds |

**★5375: SYLVANIA FRANCISCAN HEALTH** (CC)
3231 Central Park West, Suite 106, Toledo, OH Zip 43617–3009; tel. 419/882–8373; James W. Pope, FACHE, President and Chief Executive Officer
**(Independent Hospital System)**

**OHIO:** TRINITY HEALTH SYSTEM (S, 312 beds) 380 Summit Avenue, Steubenville, OH Zip 43952–2699; tel. 740/283–7000; Fred B. Brower, President and Chief Executive Officer
**Web address:** www.trinityhealth.com

TRINITY HOSPITAL TWIN CITY (S, 25 beds) 819 North First Street, Dennison, OH Zip 44621–1098; tel. 740/922–2800; Joseph J. Mitchell, President
**Web address:** www.trinitytwincity.org

**TEXAS:** BURLESON ST. JOSEPH HEALTH CENTER (S, 25 beds) 1101 Woodson Drive, Caldwell, TX Zip 77836–1052, Mailing Address: P.O. Box 360, Zip 77836–0360; tel. 979/567–3245; John Hughson, Administrator
**Web address:** www.st–joseph.org/

GRIMES ST. JOSEPH HEALTH CENTER (S, 18 beds) 210 South Judson Street, Navasota, TX Zip 77868–3704; tel. 936/825–6585; Reed Edmundson, Interim Administrator
**Web address:** www.st–joseph.org

For explanation of codes following names, see page B2.
★ Indicates Type III membership in the American Hospital Association.

Section B

MADISON ST. JOSEPH HEALTH CENTER (S, 25 beds) 100 West Cross Street, Madisonville, TX Zip 77864–2432, Mailing Address: Box 698, Zip 77864–0698; tel. 936/348–2631; Reed Edmundson, Administrator
**Web address:** www.st–joseph.org

ST. JOSEPH REGIONAL HEALTH CENTER (S, 232 beds) 2801 Franciscan Drive, Bryan, TX Zip 77802–2599; tel. 979/776–3777; Kathleen R. Krusie, FACHE, Chief Executive Officer
**Web address:** www.st–joseph.org

| | | |
|---|---|---|
| Owned, leased, sponsored: | 6 hospitals | 637 beds |
| Contract–managed: | 0 hospitals | 0 beds |
| Totals: | 6 hospitals | 637 beds |

### 0379:  TAHOE FOREST HEALTH SYSTEM (NP)
10121 Pine Avenue, Truckee, CA Zip 96161–4835; tel. 530/587–6011; Robert A. Schapper, Chief Executive Officer

**CALIFORNIA:** TAHOE FOREST HOSPITAL DISTRICT (O, 25 beds) 10121 Pine Avenue, Truckee, CA Zip 96161–4856, Mailing Address: P.O. Box 759, Zip 96160–0759; tel. 530/587–6011; Robert A. Schapper, Chief Executive Officer
**Web address:** www.tfhd.com

**NEVADA:** INCLINE VILLAGE COMMUNITY HOSPITAL (O, 6 beds) 880 Alder Avenue, Incline Village, NV Zip 89451–8335; tel. 775/833–4100; Judy Newland, R.N., Chief Nursing Officer
**Web address:** www.tfhd.com

| | | |
|---|---|---|
| Owned, leased, sponsored: | 2 hospitals | 31 beds |
| Contract–managed: | 0 hospitals | 0 beds |
| Totals: | 2 hospitals | 31 beds |

### ★0341:  TANNER HEALTH SYSTEM (NP)
705 Dixie Street, Carrollton, GA Zip 30117–3818; tel. 770/836–9580; Loy M. Howard, President and Chief Executive Officer

**GEORGIA:** HIGGINS GENERAL HOSPITAL (L, 25 beds) 200 Allen Memorial Drive, Bremen, GA Zip 30110–2012; tel. 770/824–2000; Michael Alexander, Administrator
**Web address:** www.tanner.org/Main/HigginsGeneralHospitalBremen.aspx

TANNER MEDICAL CENTER–CARROLLTON (O, 201 beds) 705 Dixie Street, Carrollton, GA Zip 30117–3818; tel. 770/836–9666; Deborah Matthews, Administrator
**Web address:** www.tanner.org

TANNER MEDICAL CENTER–VILLA RICA (O, 39 beds) 601 Dallas Road, Villa Rica, GA Zip 30180–1202, Mailing Address: P.O. Box 638, Zip 30180–0638; tel. 770/456–3100; Taylor Powers, Administrator
**Web address:** www.tanner.org

| | | |
|---|---|---|
| Owned, leased, sponsored: | 3 hospitals | 265 beds |
| Contract–managed: | 0 hospitals | 0 beds |
| Totals: | 3 hospitals | 265 beds |

### ★0169:  TEMPLE UNIVERSITY HEALTH SYSTEM (NP)
3509 North Broad Street, 9th Floor, Philadelphia, PA Zip 19140–4105; tel. 215/707–0900; Larry Kaiser, M.D., President and Chief Executive Officer
**(Moderately Centralized Health System)**

**PENNSYLVANIA:** FOX CHASE CANCER CENTER–AMERICAN ONCOLOGIC HOSPITAL (O, 64 beds) 333 Cottman Avenue, Philadelphia, PA Zip 19111–2434; tel. 215/728–6900; Verdi DiSesa, Interim President
**Web address:** www.fccc.edu

JEANES HOSPITAL (O, 160 beds) 7600 Central Avenue, Philadelphia, PA Zip 19111–2499; tel. 215/728–2000; Linda J. Grass, President and Chief Executive Officer
**Web address:** www.jeanes.com

TEMPLE UNIVERSITY HOSPITAL (O, 728 beds) 3401 North Broad Street, Philadelphia, PA Zip 19140–5103; tel. 215/707–2000; John N. Kastanis, FACHE, Chief Executive Officer
**Web address:** www.tuh.templehealth.org/content/default.htm

| | | |
|---|---|---|
| Owned, leased, sponsored: | 3 hospitals | 952 beds |
| Contract–managed: | 0 hospitals | 0 beds |
| Totals: | 3 hospitals | 952 beds |

### ★0063:  TENET HEALTHCARE CORPORATION (IO)
1445 Ross Avenue, Suite 1400, Dallas, TX Zip 75202–2703, Mailing Address: P.O. Box 139036, Zip 75313–9036; tel. 469/893–2200; Trevor Fetter, President and Chief Executive Officer
**(Moderately Centralized Health System)**

**ALABAMA:** BROOKWOOD MEDICAL CENTER (O, 631 beds) 2010 Brookwood Medical Center Drive, Birmingham, AL Zip 35209–6875; tel. 205/877–1000; Garry L. Gause, President and Chief Executive Officer
**Web address:** www.bwmc.com

**CALIFORNIA:** DESERT REGIONAL MEDICAL CENTER (L, 387 beds) 1150 North Indian Canyon Drive, Palm Springs, CA Zip 92262–4872, Mailing Address: P.O. Box 2739, Zip 92263–2739; tel. 760/323–6511; Carolyn W. Caldwell, Chief Executive Officer
**Web address:** www.desertmedctr.com

DOCTORS HOSPITAL OF MANTECA (O, 73 beds) 1205 East North Street, Manteca, CA Zip 95336–4900; tel. 209/823–3111; Nicholas R. Tejeda, FACHE, Chief Executive Officer
**Web address:** www.doctorsmanteca.com

DOCTORS MEDICAL CENTER (O, 455 beds) 1441 Florida Avenue, Modesto, CA Zip 95350–4418, Mailing Address: P.O. Box 4138, Zip 95352–4138; tel. 209/578–1211; Warren J. Kirk, Chief Executive Officer
**Web address:** www.dmc–modesto.com

FOUNTAIN VALLEY REGIONAL HOSPITAL AND MEDICAL CENTER (O, 400 beds) 17100 Euclid Street, Fountain Valley, CA Zip 92708–4043; tel. 714/966–7200; Debbie Walsh, MSN, Chief Executive Officer
**Web address:** www.fountainvalleyhospital.com

JOHN F. KENNEDY MEMORIAL HOSPITAL (O, 119 beds) 47111 Monroe Street, Indio, CA Zip 92201–6739; tel. 760/347–6191; Gary Honts, Interim Chief Executive Officer
**Web address:** www.jfkmemorialhosp.com

LAKEWOOD REGIONAL MEDICAL CENTER (O, 153 beds) 3700 East South Street, Lakewood, CA Zip 90712–1498, Mailing Address: P.O. Box 6070, Zip 90714–6070; tel. 562/531–2550; B. Joseph Badalian, President and Chief Executive Officer
**Web address:** www.lakewoodregional.com

LOS ALAMITOS MEDICAL CENTER (O, 167 beds) 3751 Katella Avenue, Los Alamitos, CA Zip 90720–3164; tel. 562/598–1311; Michele Finney, Chief Executive Officer
**Web address:** www.losalamitosmedctr.com

PLACENTIA–LINDA HOSPITAL (O, 114 beds) 1301 North Rose Drive, Placentia, CA Zip 92870–3899; tel. 714/993–2000; Kent G. Clayton, President and Chief Executive Officer
**Web address:** www.placentialinda.com

SAN RAMON REGIONAL MEDICAL CENTER (O, 123 beds) 6001 Norris Canyon Road, San Ramon, CA Zip 94583–5400; tel. 925/275–9200; Gary Sloan, Chief Executive Officer
**Web address:** www.sanramonmedctr.com

SIERRA VISTA REGIONAL MEDICAL CENTER (O, 164 beds) 1010 Murray Avenue, San Luis Obispo, CA Zip 93405–1806, Mailing Address: P.O. Box 1367, Zip 93406–1367; tel. 805/546–7600; Candace L. Markwith, Chief Executive Officer
**Web address:** www.sierravistaregional.com

TWIN CITIES COMMUNITY HOSPITAL (O, 122 beds) 1100 Las Tablas Road, Templeton, CA Zip 93465–9704; tel. 805/434–3500; Mark P. Lisa, FACHE, Chief Executive Officer
**Web address:** www.twincitieshospital.com

**FLORIDA:** CORAL GABLES HOSPITAL (O, 256 beds) 3100 Douglas Road, Coral Gables, FL Zip 33134–6914; tel. 305/445–8461; Jeffrey M. Welch, Chief Executive Officer
**Web address:** www.coralgableshospital.com

DELRAY MEDICAL CENTER (O, 493 beds) 5352 Linton Boulevard, Delray Beach, FL Zip 33484–6580; tel. 561/498–4440; Mark Bryan, Chief Executive Officer
**Web address:** www.delraymedicalctr.com

For explanation of codes following names, see page B2.
★ Indicates Type III membership in the American Hospital Association.

GOOD SAMARITAN MEDICAL CENTER (O, 174 beds) 1309 North Flagler Drive, West Palm Beach, FL Zip 33401–3499; tel. 561/655–5511; Mark Nosacka, Chief Executive Officer
**Web address:** www.goodsamaritanmc.com

HIALEAH HOSPITAL (O, 160 beds) 651 East 25th Street, Hialeah, FL Zip 33013–3878; tel. 305/693–6100; Ben A. Rodriguez, Chief Executive Officer
**Web address:** www.hialeahhosp.com

NORTH SHORE MEDICAL CENTER (O, 357 beds) 1100 N.W. 95th Street, Miami, FL Zip 33150–2098; tel. 305/835–6000; Manuel Linares, Chief Executive Officer
**Web address:** www.northshoremedical.com

NORTH SHORE MEDICAL CENTER, FLORIDA MEDICAL CENTER CAMPUS (O, 459 beds) 5000 West Oakland Park Boulevard, Fort Lauderdale, FL Zip 33313–1585; tel. 954/735–6000; Gabrielle Finley–Hazle, Chief Executive Officer
**Web address:** www.fmc–campus.com

PALM BEACH GARDENS MEDICAL CENTER (L, 199 beds) 3360 Burns Road, Palm Beach Gardens, FL Zip 33410–4323; tel. 561/622–1411; Larry Coomes, Chief Executive Officer
**Web address:** www.pbgmc.com

PALMETTO GENERAL HOSPITAL (O, 360 beds) 2001 West 68th Street, Hialeah, FL Zip 33016–1898; tel. 305/823–5000; Ana J. Mederos, Chief Executive Officer
**Web address:** www.palmettogeneral.com

ST. MARY'S MEDICAL CENTER (O, 464 beds) 901 45th Street, West Palm Beach, FL Zip 33407–2495; tel. 561/844–6300; Davide M. Carbone, FACHE, Chief Executive Officer
**Web address:** www.stmarysmc.com

WEST BOCA MEDICAL CENTER (O, 195 beds) 21644 State Road 7, Boca Raton, FL Zip 33428–1899; tel. 561/488–8000; Mitchell S. Feldman, Chief Executive Officer
**Web address:** www.westbocamedctr.com

**GEORGIA:** ATLANTA MEDICAL CENTER (O, 403 beds) 303 Parkway Drive N.E., Atlanta, GA Zip 30312–1212; tel. 404/265–4000; William T. Moore, Chief Executive Officer
**Web address:** www.atlantamedcenter.com

ATLANTA MEDICAL CENTER – SOUTH CAMPUS (O, 174 beds) 1170 Cleveland Avenue, Atlanta, GA Zip 30344–3665; tel. 404/466–1170; Daniel Jackson, Chief Administrative Officer
**Web address:** www.southfultonmedcenter.com

NORTH FULTON REGIONAL HOSPITAL (L, 196 beds) 3000 Hospital Boulevard, Roswell, GA Zip 30076–3899; tel. 770/751–2500; Deborah C. Keel, Chief Executive Officer
**Web address:** www.northfultonregional.com

SPALDING REGIONAL MEDICAL CENTER (O, 160 beds) 601 South Eighth Street, Griffin, GA Zip 30224–4294, Mailing Address: P.O. Drawer V, Zip 30224–1168; tel. 770/228–2721; John A. Quinn, Chief Executive Officer
**Web address:** www.spaldingregional.com

SYLVAN GROVE HOSPITAL (L, 23 beds) 1050 McDonough Road, Jackson, GA Zip 30233–1599; tel. 770/775–7861; John A. Quinn, Chief Executive Officer
**Web address:** www.sylvangrovehospital.com

**MISSOURI:** DES PERES HOSPITAL (O, 143 beds) 2345 Dougherty Ferry Road, Saint Louis, MO Zip 63122–3313; tel. 314/966–9100; John A. Grah, JD, FACHE, Chief Executive Officer
**Web address:** www.despereshospital.com

SAINT LOUIS UNIVERSITY HOSPITAL (O, 332 beds) 3635 Vista at Grand Boulevard, Saint Louis, MO Zip 63110–0250, Mailing Address: P.O. Box 15250, Zip 63110–0250; tel. 314/577–8000; Phillip E. Sowa, Chief Executive Officer
**Web address:** www.sluhospital.com

**NORTH CAROLINA:** CENTRAL CAROLINA HOSPITAL (O, 116 beds) 1135 Carthage Street, Sanford, NC Zip 27330–4162; tel. 919/774–2100; Doug Doris, Chief Executive Officer
**Web address:** www.centralcarolinahosp.com

FRYE REGIONAL MEDICAL CENTER (L, 306 beds) 420 North Center Street, Hickory, NC Zip 28601–5049; tel. 828/322–6070; Robert Hammond, Interim Chief Executive Officer
**Web address:** www.fryemedctr.com

**PENNSYLVANIA:** HAHNEMANN UNIVERSITY HOSPITAL (O, 496 beds) Broad and Vine Streets, Philadelphia, PA Zip 19102–1192; tel. 215/762–7000; Michael P. Halter, Chief Executive Officer
**Web address:** www.hahnemannhospital.com

ST. CHRISTOPHER'S HOSPITAL FOR CHILDREN (O, 181 beds) 3601 A. Street, Philadelphia, PA Zip 19134–1043; tel. 215/427–5000; Carolyn Jackson, Chief Executive Officer
**Web address:** www.stchristophershospital.com

**SOUTH CAROLINA:** COASTAL CAROLINA HOSPITAL (O, 41 beds) 1000 Medical Center Drive, Hardeeville, SC Zip 29927–3446; tel. 843/784–8000; Bradley S. Talbert, FACHE, Chief Executive Officer
**Web address:** www.coastalhospital.com

EAST COOPER MEDICAL CENTER (O, 140 beds) 2000 Hospital Drive, Mount Pleasant, SC Zip 29464–3764; tel. 843/881–0100; Jason P. Alexander, FACHE, Chief Executive Officer
**Web address:** www.eastcoopermedctr.com

HILTON HEAD HOSPITAL (O, 93 beds) 25 Hospital Center Boulevard, Hilton Head Island, SC Zip 29926–2738; tel. 843/681–6122; Mark T. O'Neil, Jr., President and Chief Executive Officer
**Web address:** www.hiltonheadregional.com

PIEDMONT MEDICAL CENTER (O, 280 beds) 222 Herlong Avenue, Rock Hill, SC Zip 29732; tel. 803/329–1234; William Masterton, Chief Executive Officer
**Web address:** www.piedmontmedicalcenter.com

**TENNESSEE:** SAINT FRANCIS HOSPITAL (O, 511 beds) 5959 Park Avenue, Memphis, TN Zip 38119–5198, Mailing Address: P.O. Box 171808, Zip 38187–1808; tel. 901/765–1000; David L. Archer, Chief Executive Officer
**Web address:** www.saintfrancishosp.com

SAINT FRANCIS HOSPITAL–BARTLETT (O, 156 beds) 2986 Kate Bond Road, Bartlett, TN Zip 38133–4003; tel. 901/820–7000; Jeremy Clark, Chief Executive Officer
**Web address:** www.saintfrancisbartlett.com

**TEXAS:** CENTENNIAL MEDICAL CENTER (O, 118 beds) 12505 Lebanon Road, Frisco, TX Zip 75035–8298; tel. 972/963–3333; Joe D. Thomason, Chief Executive Officer
**Web address:** www.centennialmedcenter.com

CYPRESS FAIRBANKS MEDICAL CENTER (O, 181 beds) 10655 Steepletop Drive, Houston, TX Zip 77065–4297; tel. 281/890–4285; Terry J. Wheeler, Chief Executive Officer
**Web address:** www.cyfairhospital.com

DOCTORS HOSPITAL AT WHITE ROCK LAKE (O, 153 beds) 9440 Poppy Drive, Dallas, TX Zip 75218–3694; tel. 214/324–6100; Jaikumar Krishnaswamy, Chief Executive Officer
**Web address:** www.doctorshospitaldallas.com

HOUSTON NORTHWEST MEDICAL CENTER (O, 339 beds) 710 FM 1960 Road West, Houston, TX Zip 77090–3402; tel. 281/440–1000; Linda Mercier, R.N., MSN, Chief Executive Officer
**Web address:** www.hnmc.com

LAKE POINTE MEDICAL CENTER (O, 112 beds) 6800 Scenic Drive, Rowlett, TX Zip 75088–4552, Mailing Address: P.O. Box 1550, Zip 75030–1550; tel. 972/412–2273; Brett D. Lee, Chief Executive Officer
**Web address:** www.lakepointemedical.com

NACOGDOCHES MEDICAL CENTER (O, 109 beds) 4920 N.E. Stallings Drive, Nacogdoches, TX Zip 75965–1200; tel. 936/569–9481; Gary L. Stokes, Chief Executive Officer
**Web address:** www.nacmedicalcenter.com

PARK PLAZA HOSPITAL (O, 208 beds) 1313 Hermann Drive, Houston, TX Zip 77004–7092; tel. 713/527–5000; John Tressa, R.N., MSN, Chief Executive Officer
**Web address:** www.parkplazahospital.com

PLAZA SPECIALTY HOSPITAL (O, 39 beds) 1300 Binz, Houston, TX Zip 77004–7016; tel. 713/285–1000; Steven Barr, R.N., MSN, Chief Executive Officer
**Web address:** www.plazaspecialtyhospital.com

PROVIDENCE MEMORIAL HOSPITAL (O, 359 beds) 2001 North Oregon Street, El Paso, TX Zip 79902–3368; tel. 915/577–6011; J. Eric Evans, Chief Executive Officer
**Web address:** www.sphn.com

For explanation of codes following names, see page B2.
★ Indicates Type III membership in the American Hospital Association.

SIERRA MEDICAL CENTER (O, 334 beds) 1625 Medical Center Drive, El Paso, TX Zip 79902–5044; tel. 915/747–4000; J. Eric Evans, Chief Executive Officer
**Web address:** www.sphn.com

SIERRA PROVIDENCE EAST MEDICAL CENTER (O, 110 beds) 3280 Joe Battle Boulevard, El Paso, TX Zip 79938–2622; tel. 915/832–2000; Sally A. Deitch, MSN, R.N., Chief Executive Officer
**Web address:** www.sphn.com

| | | |
|---|---|---|
| Owned, leased, sponsored: | 50 hospitals | 11838 beds |
| Contract–managed: | 0 hospitals | 0 beds |
| Totals: | 50 hospitals | 11838 beds |

**0876:   TENNESSEE HEALTH MANAGEMENT** (IO)
52 West Eighth Street, Parsons, TN Zip 38363–4656, Mailing Address: PO Box 10, Zip 38363–0010; tel. 731/847–6343; Dennis Berry, Chief Executive Officer

**ALABAMA:** BEHAVIORAL HEALTHCARE CENTER AT HUNTSVILLE (O, 20 beds) 5315 Millennium Drive N.W., Huntsville, AL Zip 35806–2458; tel. 256/964–6700; Mike Maxwell, Administrator

**TENNESSEE:** BEHAVIORAL HEALTHCARE CENTER AT CLARKSVILLE (O, 26 beds) 930 Professional Park Drive, Clarksville, TN Zip 37040–5136; tel. 931/538–6420; Jennifer Robinson, Administrator
**Web address:** www.bhcclarksville.com

BEHAVIORAL HEALTHCARE CENTER AT COLUMBIA (O, 68 beds) 1400 Rosewood Drive, Columbia, TN Zip 38401–4878; tel. 931/388–6573; Paula Chennault, Administrator
**Web address:** www.bhccolumbia.com

BEHAVIORAL HEALTHCARE CENTER AT MARTIN (O, 16 beds) 458 Hannings Lane, Martin, TN Zip 38237–3308; tel. 731/588–2830; Carrie Brawley, Administrator
**Web address:** www.tnhealthmanagement.com/BHC/martin/

| | | |
|---|---|---|
| Owned, leased, sponsored: | 4 hospitals | 130 beds |
| Contract–managed: | 0 hospitals | 0 beds |
| Totals: | 4 hospitals | 130 beds |

**0020:   TEXAS DEPARTMENT OF STATE HEALTH SERVICES** (NP)
1100 West 49th Street, Austin, TX Zip 78756–3199; tel. 512/458–7111; David L. Lakey, M.D., Commissioner
**(Independent Hospital System)**

**TEXAS:** AUSTIN STATE HOSPITAL (O, 314 beds) 4110 Guadalupe Street, Austin, TX Zip 78751–4296; tel. 512/452–0381; Cathy Nottebart, Acting Superintendent
**Web address:** www.dshs.state.tx.us/mhhospitals/austinsh/default.shtm

BIG SPRING STATE HOSPITAL (O, 200 beds) 1901 North Highway 87, Big Spring, TX Zip 79720–0283; tel. 432/267–8216; Edward Moughon, Superintendent
**Web address:** www.dshs.state.tx.us/mhhospitals/BigSpringSH/default.shtm

EL PASO PSYCHIATRIC CENTER (O, 77 beds) 4615 Alameda Avenue, El Paso, TX Zip 79905–2702; tel. 915/532–2202; Zulema Carrillo, Superintendent
**Web address:** www.dshs.state.tx.us/mhhospitals/ElPasoPC/default.shtm

KERRVILLE STATE HOSPITAL (O, 202 beds) 721 Thompson Drive, Kerrville, TX Zip 78028–5154; tel. 830/896–2211; Leigh Ann Fitzpatrick, Superintendent
**Web address:** www.dshs.state.tx.us/mhhospitals/KerrvilleSH/default.shtm

NORTH TEXAS STATE HOSPITAL (O, 640 beds) Highway 70 Northwest, Vernon, TX Zip 76384, Mailing Address: P.O. Box 2231, Zip 76385–2231; tel. 940/552–9901; James E. Smith, Superintendent
**Web address:** www.dshs.state.tx.us/mhhospitals/NorthTexasSH/default.shtm

RIO GRANDE STATE CENTER/SOUTH TEXAS HEALTH CARE SYSTEM (O, 128 beds) 1401 South Rangerville Road, Harlingen, TX Zip 78552–7638; tel. 956/364–8000; Sonia Hernandez–Keeble, Superintendent
**Web address:** www.dshs.state.tx.us/mhhospitals/RioGrandeSC/default.shtm

RUSK STATE HOSPITAL (O, 330 beds) 805 North Dickinson, Rusk, TX Zip 75785–2333, Mailing Address: P.O. Box 318, Zip 75785–0318; tel. 903/683–3421; Brenda Slaton, Administrator
**Web address:** www.dshs.state.tx.us/mhhospitals/RuskSH/default.shtm

SAN ANTONIO STATE HOSPITAL (O, 302 beds) 6711 South New Braunfels, Suite 100, San Antonio, TX Zip 78223–3006; tel. 210/531–7711; Robert C. Arizpe, Superintendent
**Web address:** www.dshs.state.tx.us/mhhospitals/SanAntonioSH/default.shtm

TERRELL STATE HOSPITAL (O, 316 beds) 1200 East Brin Street, Terrell, TX Zip 75160–2938, Mailing Address: P.O. Box 70, Zip 75160–9000; tel. 972/524–6452; Joe Finch, PsyD, Superintendent
**Web address:** www.dshs.state.tx.us/mhhospitals/terrellsh

TEXAS CENTER FOR INFECTIOUS DISEASE (O, 42 beds) 2303 S.E. Military Drive, San Antonio, TX Zip 78223–3597; tel. 210/534–8857; James N. Elkins, FACHE, Superintendent
**Web address:** www.dshs.state.tx.us/tcid/default.shtm

| | | |
|---|---|---|
| Owned, leased, sponsored: | 10 hospitals | 2551 beds |
| Contract–managed: | 0 hospitals | 0 beds |
| Totals: | 10 hospitals | 2551 beds |

**★0129:   TEXAS HEALTH RESOURCES** (NP)
612 East Lamar Boulevard, Suite 900, Arlington, TX Zip 76011–4130; tel. 682/236–7900; Douglas D. Hawthorne, FACHE, Chief Executive Officer
**(Moderately Centralized Health System)**

TEXAS HEALTH ARLINGTON MEMORIAL HOSPITAL (O, 289 beds) 800 West Randol Mill Road, Arlington, TX Zip 76012–2503; tel. 817/548–6100; Kirk King, FACHE, President
**Web address:** www.arlingtonmemorial.org

TEXAS HEALTH HARRIS METHODIST HOSPITAL ALLIANCE (O, 50 beds) 10864 Texas Health Trail, Fort Worth, TX Zip 76244–4897; tel. 682/212–2000; Winjie Tang Miao, President

TEXAS HEALTH HARRIS METHODIST HOSPITAL AZLE (O, 31 beds) 108 Denver Trail, Azle, TX Zip 76020–3614; tel. 817/444–8600; Bob S. Ellzey, FACHE, President
**Web address:** www.texashealth.org/Azle

TEXAS HEALTH HARRIS METHODIST HOSPITAL CLEBURNE (O, 85 beds) 201 Walls Drive, Cleburne, TX Zip 76033–4007; tel. 817/641–2551; Blake Kretz, President
**Web address:** www.texashealth.org

TEXAS HEALTH HARRIS METHODIST HOSPITAL FORT WORTH (O, 635 beds) 1301 Pennsylvania Avenue, Fort Worth, TX Zip 76104–2122; tel. 817/250–2000; Lillie Biggins, R.N., President
**Web address:** www.texashealth.org

TEXAS HEALTH HARRIS METHODIST HOSPITAL HURST–EULESS–BEDFORD (O, 213 beds) 1600 Hospital Parkway, Bedford, TX Zip 76022–6913, Mailing Address: P.O. Box 669, Zip 76095–0669; tel. 817/685–4000; Deborah Paganelli, President
**Web address:** www.texashealth.org

TEXAS HEALTH HARRIS METHODIST HOSPITAL SOUTHWEST FORT WORTH (O, 151 beds) 6100 Harris Parkway, Fort Worth, TX Zip 76132–4199; tel. 817/433–5000; Joseph DeLeon, President
**Web address:** www.texashealth.org

TEXAS HEALTH HARRIS METHODIST HOSPITAL STEPHENVILLE (O, 54 beds) 411 North Belknap Street, Stephenville, TX Zip 76401–3415; tel. 254/965–1500; Christopher Leu, President
**Web address:** www.texashealth.org/landing.cfm?id=108

TEXAS HEALTH PRESBYTERIAN HOSPITAL ALLEN (O, 73 beds) 1105 Central Expressway North, Allen, TX Zip 75013–6103; tel. 972/747–1000; Jeff Reecer, President
**Web address:** www.texashealth.org

TEXAS HEALTH PRESBYTERIAN HOSPITAL DALLAS (O, 609 beds) 8200 Walnut Hill Lane, Dallas, TX Zip 75231–4426; tel. 214/345–6789; Britt Berrett, President
**Web address:** www.texashealth.org

TEXAS HEALTH PRESBYTERIAN HOSPITAL DENTON (O, 208 beds) 3000 North I–35, Denton, TX Zip 76201–5119; tel. 940/898–7000; Stan C. Morton, FACHE, President
**Web address:** www.dentonhospital.com

For explanation of codes following names, see page B2.
★ Indicates Type III membership in the American Hospital Association.

TEXAS HEALTH PRESBYTERIAN HOSPITAL KAUFMAN (O, 68 beds) 850 Ed Hall Drive, Kaufman, TX Zip 75142–1861, Mailing Address: P.O. Box 1108, Zip 75142–5401; tel. 972/932–7200; Patsy Youngs, President
**Web address:** www.texashealth.org/Kaufman

TEXAS HEALTH PRESBYTERIAN HOSPITAL PLANO (O, 338 beds) 6200 West Parker Road, Plano, TX Zip 75093–8185; tel. 972/981–8000; Mike Evans, R.N., MS, President
**Web address:** www.texashealth.org

TEXAS HEALTH SPECIALTY HOSPITAL (O, 10 beds) 1301 Pennsylvania Avenue, 4th Floor, Fort Worth, TX Zip 76104–2190; tel. 817/250–5500; Susan Louise Baldwin, R.N., FACHE, President and Chief Nursing Officer
**Web address:** www.texashealth.org

| | | |
|---|---|---|
| Owned, leased, sponsored: | 14 hospitals | 2814 beds |
| Contract–managed: | 0 hospitals | 0 beds |
| Totals: | 14 hospitals | 2814 beds |

---

**★7235:   THE METHODIST HOSPITAL SYSTEM** (CO)
6565 Fannin Street, D–200, Houston, TX Zip 77030–2707; tel. 713/441–2221; Marc L. Boom, M.D., Chief Executive Officer
**(Moderately Centralized Health System)**

METHODIST SUGAR LAND HOSPITAL (O, 235 beds) 16655 S.W. Freeway, Sugar Land, TX Zip 77479–2329; tel. 281/274–7000; Christopher Siebenaler, Chief Executive Officer
**Web address:** www.methodisthealth.com

METHODIST WEST HOUSTON HOSPITAL (O, 126 beds) 18500 Katy Freeway, Houston, TX Zip 77094–1110; tel. 832/522–1000; Wayne M. Voss, Chief Executive Officer
**Web address:** www.methodisthealth.com

METHODIST WILLOWBROOK HOSPITAL (O, 241 beds) 18220 Tomball Parkway, Houston, TX Zip 77070–4347; tel. 281/477–1000; Beryl O. Ramsey, FACHE, Chief Executive Officer
**Web address:** www.methodisthealth.com

SAN JACINTO METHODIST HOSPITAL (O, 275 beds) 4401 Garth Road, Baytown, TX Zip 77521–2122; tel. 281/420–8600; Donna Gares, R.N., President and Chief Executive Officer
**Web address:** www.methodisthealth.com

THE METHODIST HOSPITAL (O, 839 beds) 6565 Fannin Street, Houston, TX Zip 77030–2707; tel. 713/790–3311; Roberta Schwartz, Executive Vice President
**Web address:** www.methodisthealth.com

| | | |
|---|---|---|
| Owned, leased, sponsored: | 5 hospitals | 1716 beds |
| Contract–managed: | 0 hospitals | 0 beds |
| Totals: | 5 hospitals | 1716 beds |

---

**2445:   THEDACARE, INC.** (NP)
122 East College Avenue, Appleton, WI Zip 54911–5794, Mailing Address: P.O. Box 8025, Zip 54912–8025; tel. 920/830–5560; Dean Gruner, M.D., President and Chief Executive Officer
**(Moderately Centralized Health System)**

**WISCONSIN:** APPLETON MEDICAL CENTER (O, 147 beds) 1818 North Meade Street, Appleton, WI Zip 54911–3496; tel. 920/731–4101; Kim Barnas, Senior Vice President
**Web address:** www.thedacare.org

NEW LONDON FAMILY MEDICAL CENTER (O, 25 beds) 1405 Mill Street, New London, WI Zip 54961–2155, Mailing Address: P.O. Box 307, Zip 54961–0307; tel. 920/531–2000; William Schmidt, President and Chief Executive Officer
**Web address:** www.thedacare.org

RIVERSIDE MEDICAL CENTER (O, 25 beds) 800 Riverside Drive, Waupaca, WI Zip 54981–1999; tel. 715/258–1000; Craig A. Kantos, Chief Executive Officer
**Web address:** www.riversidemedical.org

SHAWANO MEDICAL CENTER (O, 25 beds) 309 North Bartlette Street, Shawano, WI Zip 54166–2127; tel. 715/526–2111; Dorothy Erdmann, Chief Executive Officer
**Web address:** www.shawanomed.org

THEDA CLARK MEDICAL CENTER (O, 147 beds) 130 Second Street, Neenah, WI Zip 54956–2883, Mailing Address: P.O. Box 2021, Zip 54957–2021; tel. 920/729–3100; Kim Barnas, Senior Vice President
**Web address:** www.thedacare.org

| | | |
|---|---|---|
| Owned, leased, sponsored: | 5 hospitals | 369 beds |
| Contract–managed: | 0 hospitals | 0 beds |
| Totals: | 5 hospitals | 369 beds |

---

**★0643:   THOMAS HEALTH SYSTEM, INC.** (NP)
4605 MacCorkle Avenue S.W., South Charleston, WV Zip 25309–1311; tel. 304/766–3600; Stephen P. Dexter, President and Chief Executive Officer
**(Moderately Centralized Health System)**

**WEST VIRGINIA:** SAINT FRANCIS HOSPITAL (O, 119 beds) 333 Laidley Street, Charleston, WV Zip 25301–1628, Mailing Address: P.O. Box 471, Zip 25322–0471; tel. 304/347–6500; Stephen P. Dexter, President and Chief Executive Officer
**Web address:** www.stfrancishospital.com

THOMAS MEMORIAL HOSPITAL (O, 215 beds) 4605 MacCorkle Avenue S.W., South Charleston, WV Zip 25309–1398; tel. 304/766–3600; Stephen P. Dexter, President and Chief Executive Officer
**Web address:** www.thomaswv.org

| | | |
|---|---|---|
| Owned, leased, sponsored: | 2 hospitals | 334 beds |
| Contract–managed: | 0 hospitals | 0 beds |
| Totals: | 2 hospitals | 334 beds |

---

**★0219:   TRINITY HEALTH** (CC)
20555 Victor Parkway, Livonia, MI Zip 48152–7031; tel. 734/343–1396; Judith M. Persichilli, Interim President and Chief Executive Officer, CHE Trinity Inc.
**(Decentralized Health System)**

**CALIFORNIA:** SAINT AGNES MEDICAL CENTER (O, 436 beds) 1303 East Herndon Avenue, Fresno, CA Zip 93720–3309; tel. 559/450–3000; Nancy Hollingsworth, R.N., MSN, President and Chief Executive Officer
**Web address:** www.samc.com

**IDAHO:** SAINT ALPHONSUS MEDICAL CENTER – NAMPA (O, 118 beds) 1512 12th Avenue Road, Nampa, ID Zip 83686–6008; tel. 208/463–5000; Karl Keeler, Chief Executive Officer
**Web address:** www.mercynampa.org

SAINT ALPHONSUS REGIONAL MEDICAL CENTER (O, 399 beds) 1055 North Curtis Road, Boise, ID Zip 83706–1309; tel. 208/367–2121; Rodney D. Reider, President
**Web address:** www.saintalphonsus.org

**ILLINOIS:** GOTTLIEB MEMORIAL HOSPITAL (O, 255 beds) 701 West North Avenue, Melrose Park, IL Zip 60160–1612; tel. 708/681–3200; Lori Price, President
**Web address:** www.gottliebhospital.org

LOYOLA UNIVERSITY MEDICAL CENTER (O, 485 beds) 2160 South First Avenue, Maywood, IL Zip 60153–3328; tel. 708/216–9000; Larry M. Goldberg, President and Chief Executive Officer
**Web address:** www.loyolamedicine.org/Medical_Services/index.cfm

MERCY HOSPITAL AND MEDICAL CENTER (O, 421 beds) 2525 South Michigan Avenue, Chicago, IL Zip 60616–2333; tel. 312/567–2000; Carol L. Schneider, President and Chief Executive Officer
**Web address:** www.mercy–chicago.org

MORRISON COMMUNITY HOSPITAL (C, 36 beds) 303 North Jackson Street, Morrison, IL Zip 61270–3042; tel. 815/772–4003; Pam Pfister, Interim Chief Executive Officer
**Web address:** www.morrisonhospital.com

**INDIANA:** SAINT JOSEPH REGIONAL MEDICAL CENTER (O, 267 beds) 5215 Holy Cross Parkway, Mishawaka, IN Zip 46545–1469; tel. 574/335–5000; Albert Gutierrez, FACHE, President and Chief Executive Officer
**Web address:** www.sjmed.com

---

For explanation of codes following names, see page B2.
★ Indicates Type III membership in the American Hospital Association.

SAINT JOSEPH REGIONAL MEDICAL CENTER–PLYMOUTH CAMPUS (O, 45 beds) 1915 Lake Avenue, Plymouth, IN Zip 46563–9366, Mailing Address: P.O. Box 670, Zip 46563–0670; tel. 574/936–3181; Albert Gutierrez, FACHE, President and Chief Executive Officer
**Web address:** www.sjmed.com

**IOWA:** BAUM HARMON MERCY HOSPITAL (O, 13 beds) 255 North Welch Avenue, Primghar, IA Zip 51245–7765, Mailing Address: P.O. Box 528, Zip 51245–0528; tel. 712/957–2300; David Liebsack, Chief Executive Officer
**Web address:** www.baumharmon.org

CENTRAL COMMUNITY HOSPITAL (C, 16 beds) 901 Davidson Street N.W., Elkader, IA Zip 52043–9015; tel. 563/245–7000; Frances J. Zichal, Chief Executive Officer
**Web address:** www.centralcommunityhospital.com

ELLSWORTH MUNICIPAL HOSPITAL (C, 23 beds) 110 Rocksylvania Avenue, Iowa Falls, IA Zip 50126–2400; tel. 641/648–4631; Cherelle Montanye–Ireland, Chief Executive Officer
**Web address:** www.emhia.com

FRANKLIN GENERAL HOSPITAL (C, 77 beds) 1720 Central Avenue East, Suite A., Hampton, IA Zip 50441–1867; tel. 641/456–5000; Kim Price, Chief Executive Officer
**Web address:** www.franklingeneral.com

HANCOCK COUNTY HEALTH SYSTEM (C, 25 beds) 532 First Street N.W., Britt, IA Zip 50423–1227; tel. 641/843–5000; Vance Jackson, FACHE, Administrator and Chief Executive Officer
**Web address:** www.trusthchs.com/hancock–county–health–system

HAWARDEN REGIONAL HEALTHCARE (C, 18 beds) 1111 11th Street, Hawarden, IA Zip 51023–1999; tel. 712/551–3100; Jayson Pullman, Chief Executive Officer
**Web address:** www.hawardenregionalhealthcare.com/

KOSSUTH REGIONAL HEALTH CENTER (C, 23 beds) 1515 South Phillips Street, Algona, IA Zip 50511–3649; tel. 515/295–2451; Scott A. Curtis, Administrator and Chief Executive Officer
**Web address:** www.krhc.com

MERCY MEDICAL CENTER–CLINTON (O, 319 beds) 1410 North Fourth Street, Clinton, IA Zip 52732–2940; tel. 563/244–5555; Sean J. Williams, President and Chief Executive Officer
**Web address:** www.mercyclinton.com

MERCY MEDICAL CENTER–DUBUQUE (O, 272 beds) 250 Mercy Drive, Dubuque, IA Zip 52001–7360; tel. 563/589–8000; Russell M. Knight, President and Chief Executive Officer
**Web address:** www.mercydubuque.com

MERCY MEDICAL CENTER–DYERSVILLE (O, 25 beds) 1111 Third Street S.W., Dyersville, IA Zip 52040–1725; tel. 563/875–7101; Russell M. Knight, President and Chief Executive Officer
**Web address:** www.mercydubuque.com/mercy–dyersville

MERCY MEDICAL CENTER–NEW HAMPTON (O, 18 beds) 308 North Maple Avenue, New Hampton, IA Zip 50659–1142; tel. 641/394–4121; Kim Price, Chief Executive Officer
**Web address:** www.mercynewhampton.com

MERCY MEDICAL CENTER–NORTH IOWA (O, 240 beds) 1000 Fourth Street S.W., Mason City, IA Zip 50401–2800; tel. 641/428–7000; Daniel Varnum, President and Chief Executive Officer
**Web address:** www.mercynorthiowa.com

MERCY MEDICAL CENTER–SIOUX CITY (O, 238 beds) 801 Fifth Street, Sioux City, IA Zip 51101–1326, Mailing Address: P.O. Box 3168, Zip 51102–3168; tel. 712/279–2010; Robert J. Peebles, President and Chief Executive Officer
**Web address:** www.mercysiouxcity.com

MITCHELL COUNTY REGIONAL HEALTH CENTER (C, 25 beds) 616 North Eighth Street, Osage, IA Zip 50461–1498; tel. 641/732–6000; Kevin Runolfson, Chief Executive Officer
**Web address:** www.mitchellcohospital-clinics.com

PALO ALTO COUNTY HEALTH SYSTEM (C, 47 beds) 3201 First Street, Emmetsburg, IA Zip 50536–2516; tel. 712/852–5500; Desiree Einsweiler, Chief Executive Officer
**Web address:** www.pachs.com

REGIONAL HEALTH SERVICES OF HOWARD COUNTY (C, 20 beds) 235 Eighth Avenue West, Cresco, IA Zip 52136–1098; tel. 563/547–2101; Robin M. Schluter, Chief Executive Officer
**Web address:** www.rhshc.com

**MARYLAND:** HOLY CROSS HOSPITAL (O, 425 beds) 1500 Forest Glen Road, Silver Spring, MD Zip 20910–1487; tel. 301/754–7000; Judith Rogers, R.N., Ph.D., President and Chief Executive Officer
**Web address:** www.holycrosshealth.org

**MICHIGAN:** CHELSEA COMMUNITY HOSPITAL (O, 102 beds) 775 South Main Street, Chelsea, MI Zip 48118–1383; tel. 734/475–1311; Nancy Kay Graebner, President and Chief Executive Officer
**Web address:** www.cch.org

MERCY HEALTH PARTNERS, HACKLEY CAMPUS (O, 213 beds) 1700 Clinton Street, Muskegon, MI Zip 49442–5502, Mailing Address: P.O. Box 3302, Zip 49443–3302; tel. 231/726–3511; Roger Spoelman, President and Chief Executive Officer
**Web address:** www.mercyhealthmuskegon.com

MERCY HEALTH PARTNERS, LAKESHORE CAMPUS (O, 24 beds) 72 South State Street, Shelby, MI Zip 49455–1299; tel. 231/861–2156; Jay Bryan, President and Chief Executive Officer
**Web address:** www.mercyhealthmuskegon.com

MERCY HEALTH PARTNERS, MERCY CAMPUS (O, 188 beds) 1500 East Sherman Boulevard, Muskegon, MI Zip 49444–1849; tel. 231/672–2000; Roger Spoelman, President and Chief Executive Officer
**Web address:** www.mghp.com

MERCY HOSPITAL CADILLAC (O, 65 beds) 400 Hobart Street, Cadillac, MI Zip 49601–2389; tel. 231/876–7200; John L. MacLeod, President and Chief Executive Officer
**Web address:** www.munsonhealthcare.org

MERCY HOSPITAL GRAYLING (O, 94 beds) 1100 East Michigan Avenue, Grayling, MI Zip 49738–1312; tel. 989/348–5461; Stephanie J. Riemer–Matuzak, Chief Executive Officer
**Web address:** www.mercygrayling.munsonhealthcare.org/

SAINT MARY'S HEALTH CARE (O, 356 beds) 200 Jefferson Avenue S.E., Grand Rapids, MI Zip 49503–4598; tel. 616/685–5000; Philip H. McCorkle, Jr., President and Chief Executive Officer
**Web address:** www.mercyhealthsaintmarys.org

ST. JOSEPH MERCY HOSPITAL (O, 537 beds) 5301 Mcauley Drive, Ypsilanti, MI Zip 48197–1051, Mailing Address: P.O. Box 995, Ann Arbor, Zip 48106–0995; tel. 734/712–3456; Robert F. Casalou, President and Chief Executive Officer
**Web address:** www.sjmercyhealth.org

ST. JOSEPH MERCY LIVINGSTON HOSPITAL (O, 36 beds) 620 Byron Road, Howell, MI Zip 48843–1093; tel. 517/545–6000; Robert F. Casalou, President and Chief Executive Officer
**Web address:** www.stjoeslivingston.org/livingston

ST. JOSEPH MERCY OAKLAND (O, 409 beds) 44405 Woodward Avenue, Pontiac, MI Zip 48341–5023; tel. 248/858–3000; Jack Weiner, President and Chief Executive Officer
**Web address:** www.stjoesoakland.com

ST. JOSEPH MERCY PORT HURON (O, 119 beds) 2601 Electric Avenue, Port Huron, MI Zip 48060–6518; tel. 810/985–1500; Rebekah Smith, R.N., President and Chief Executive Officer
**Web address:** www.mercyporthuron.com

ST. MARY MERCY HOSPITAL (O, 289 beds) 36475 Five Mile Road, Livonia, MI Zip 48154–1988; tel. 734/655–4800; David A. Spivey, President and Chief Executive Officer
**Web address:** www.stmarymercy.org

**NEBRASKA:** OAKLAND MERCY HOSPITAL (O, 18 beds) 601 East Second Street, Oakland, NE Zip 68045–1499; tel. 402/685–5601; John W. Werner, Chief Executive Officer
**Web address:** www.oaklandhospital.org

PENDER COMMUNITY HOSPITAL (C, 67 beds) 100 Hospital Drive, Pender, NE Zip 68047–0100, Mailing Address: P.O. Box 100, Zip 68047–0100; tel. 402/385–3083; Roger W. Lenz, Interim Chief Executive Officer
**Web address:** www.pendercommunityhospital.com

**OHIO:** FAYETTE COUNTY MEMORIAL HOSPITAL (C, 25 beds) 1430 Columbus Avenue, Washington Court House, OH Zip 43160–1791; tel. 740/335–1210; Lyndon J. Christman, President and Chief Executive Officer
**Web address:** www.fcmh.org

MOUNT CARMEL (O, 738 beds) 793 West State Street, Columbus, OH Zip 43222–1551; tel. 614/234–5000; Sean McKibben, President and Chief Operating Officer
**Web address:** www.mountcarmelhealth.com

---

For explanation of codes following names, see page B2.
★ Indicates Type III membership in the American Hospital Association.

Section B

MOUNT CARMEL NEW ALBANY SURGICAL HOSPITAL (O, 60 beds) 7333 Smith's Mill Road, New Albany, OH Zip 43054–9291; tel. 614/775–6600; Richard D'Enbeau, Chief Operating Officer
**Web address:** www.mountcarmelhealth.com

MOUNT CARMEL ST. ANN'S (O, 252 beds) 500 South Cleveland Avenue, Westerville, OH Zip 43081–8998; tel. 614/898–4000; Janet Meeks, Chief Operating Officer
**Web address:** www.mountcarmelhealth.com

**OREGON:** SAINT ALPHONSUS MEDICAL CENTER – BAKER CITY (S, 55 beds) 3325 Pocahontas Road, Baker City, OR Zip 97814–1464; tel. 541/523–6461; H. Ray Gibbons, FACHE, Chief Executive Officer
**Web address:** www.saintalphonsus.org/bakercity

SAINT ALPHONSUS MEDICAL CENTER – ONTARIO (S, 49 beds) 351 S.W. Ninth Street, Ontario, OR Zip 97914–2693; tel. 541/881–7000; Richard L. Palagi, Chief Executive Officer
**Web address:** www.holyrosary–ontario.org

| Owned, leased, sponsored: | 34 hospitals | 7580 beds |
|---|---|---|
| Contract–managed: | 12 hospitals | 402 beds |
| **Totals:** | 46 hospitals | 7982 beds |

---

**0540: TRINITY MOTHER FRANCES HOSPITALS AND CLINICS** (NP)
910 East Houston, Tyler, TX Zip 75702–8369; tel. 903/593–8441; J. Lindsey Bradley, Jr., FACHE, President
**(Centralized Physician/Insurance Health System)**

**TEXAS:** MOTHER FRANCES HOSPITAL – JACKSONVILLE (O, 21 beds) 2026 South Jackson, Jacksonville, TX Zip 75766–5822; tel. 903/541–4500; Thomas N. Cammack, Jr., Chief Administrative Officer
**Web address:** www.tmfhs.org/jacksonville

MOTHER FRANCES HOSPITAL – TYLER (O, 392 beds) 800 East Dawson Street, Tyler, TX Zip 75701–2036; tel. 903/593–8441; Laura Owen, Senior Vice President and Chief Executive Officer
**Web address:** www.tmfhs.org

MOTHER FRANCES HOSPITAL – WINNSBORO (O, 35 beds) 719 West Coke Road, Winnsboro, TX Zip 75494–3011, Mailing Address: P.O. Box 628, Zip 75494–0628; tel. 903/342–5227; Janet E. Coates, R.N., President and Chief Executive Officer
**Web address:** www.tmfhs.org

TYLER CONTINUECARE HOSPITAL AT MOTHER FRANCES (O, 51 beds) 800 East Dawson, 4th Floor, Tyler, TX Zip 75701–2036; tel. 903/531–4080; Stephanie Hyde, Chief Executive Officer
**Web address:** www.continuecare.org

| Owned, leased, sponsored: | 4 hospitals | 499 beds |
|---|---|---|
| Contract–managed: | 0 hospitals | 0 beds |
| **Totals:** | 4 hospitals | 499 beds |

---

**★9255: TRUMAN MEDICAL CENTERS** (NP)
2301 Holmes Street, Kansas City, MO Zip 64108–2677; tel. 816/404–1000; John W. Bluford, President and Chief Executive Officer
**(Independent Hospital System)**

**MISSOURI:** TRUMAN MEDICAL CENTER–HOSPITAL HILL (O, 272 beds) 2301 Holmes Street, Kansas City, MO Zip 64108–2640; tel. 816/404–1000; John W. Bluford, President and Chief Executive Officer
**Web address:** www.trumed.org

TRUMAN MEDICAL CENTER–LAKEWOOD (O, 333 beds) 7900 Lee's Summit Road, Kansas City, MO Zip 64139–1236; tel. 816/404–7000; John W. Bluford, President and Chief Executive Officer
**Web address:** www.trumed.org

| Owned, leased, sponsored: | 2 hospitals | 605 beds |
|---|---|---|
| Contract–managed: | 0 hospitals | 0 beds |
| **Totals:** | 2 hospitals | 605 beds |

---

**● ★0238: TY COBB HEALTHCARE SYSTEM, INC.** (NP)
461 Cook Street, Suite A., Royston, GA Zip 30662–4003; tel. 706/245–1832; Gregory K. Hearn, Chief Executive Officer
**(Independent Hospital System)**

**GEORGIA:** TY COBB REGIONAL MEDICAL CENTER (O, 35 beds) 367 Clear Creek Parkway, Lavonia, GA Zip 30553–4173; tel. 706/356–7800; Gregory K. Hearn, Chief Executive Officer
**Web address:** www.tycobbhealthcare.org

| Owned, leased, sponsored: | 1 hospital | 35 beds |
|---|---|---|
| Contract–managed: | 0 hospitals | 0 beds |
| **Totals:** | 1 hospital | 35 beds |

---

**9195: U. S. INDIAN HEALTH SERVICE** (FG)
801 Thompson Avenue, Rockville, MD Zip 20852–1627; tel. 301/443–1083; Yvette Roubideaux, M.D., M.P.H., Director
**(Moderately Centralized Health System)**

**ARIZONA:** CHINLE COMPREHENSIVE HEALTH CARE FACILITY (O, 60 beds) Highway 191, Chinle, AZ Zip 86503, Mailing Address: P.O. Drawer PH, Zip 86503–8000; tel. 928/674–7011; Ronald Tso, Chief Executive Officer
**Web address:** www.ihs.gov

FORT DEFIANCE INDIAN HEALTH SERVICE HOSPITAL (O, 52 beds) Fort Defiance, AZ Zip 86504; tel. 928/729–8014; Leland Leonard, M.D., Administrator
**Web address:** www.ihs.gov

HOPI HEALTH CARE CENTER (O, 6 beds) Keams Canyon, AZ Zip 86034; Polacca, tel. 928/737–6000; De Alva Honahnie, Chief Executive Officer
**Web address:** www.ihs.gov/index.asp

U. S. PUBLIC HEALTH SERVICE INDIAN HOSPITAL (O, 20 beds) 12033 Agency Road, Parker, AZ Zip 85344–7718; tel. 928/669–2137; Dee Hutchison, Chief Executive Officer
**Web address:** www.ihs.gov

U. S. PUBLIC HEALTH SERVICE INDIAN HOSPITAL (O, 8 beds) San Carlos, AZ Zip 85550; tel. 928/475–2371; Robert Harry, M.D., Chief Executive Officer
**Web address:** www.ihs.gov

U. S. PUBLIC HEALTH SERVICE INDIAN HOSPITAL–SELLS (O, 12 beds) Sells, AZ Zip 85634; tel. 520/383–7251; Priscilla Whitethorne, Chief Executive Officer
**Web address:** www.ihs.gov

U. S. PUBLIC HEALTH SERVICE INDIAN HOSPITAL–WHITERIVER (O, 35 beds) 200 West Hospital Drive, Whiteriver, AZ Zip 85941–0860, Mailing Address: State Route 73, Box 860, Zip 85941–0860; tel. 928/338–4911; Michelle Martinez, Interim Chief Executive Officer
**Web address:** www.ihs.gov

U. S. PUBLIC HEALTH SERVICE PHOENIX INDIAN MEDICAL CENTER (O, 127 beds) 4212 North 16th Street, Phoenix, AZ Zip 85016–5389; tel. 602/263–1200; John Molina, Chief Executive Officer
**Web address:** www.ihs.gov

**MARYLAND:** NATIONAL INSTITUTES OF HEALTH CLINICAL CENTER (O, 161 beds) 9000 Rockville Pike, Building 10, Room 6–2551, Bethesda, MD Zip 20892–1504; tel. 301/496–4000; John I. Gallin, M.D., Director
**Web address:** www.clinicalcenter.nih.gov

**MINNESOTA:** U. S. PUBLIC HEALTH SERVICE INDIAN HOSPITAL (O, 11 beds) 7th Street & Grant Utley Avenue N.W., Cass Lake, MN Zip 56633, Mailing Address: Rural Route 3, Box 211, Zip 56633; tel. 218/335–3200; Norine Smith, Chief Executive Officer
**Web address:** www.ihs.gov

U.S. PUBLIC HEALTH SERVICE INDIAN HOSPITAL (O, 19 beds) Highway 1, Redlake, MN Zip 56671, Mailing Address: P.O. Box 497, Zip 56671–0497; tel. 218/679–3912; Mark Karzon, Chief Executive Officer
**Web address:** www.ihs.gov

**MONTANA:** CROW/NORTHERN CHEYENNE HOSPITAL (O, 24 beds) 10110 South 7650 East, Crow Agency, MT Zip 59022–0009, Mailing Address: P.O. Box 9, Zip 59022–0009; tel. 406/638–2626; Clayton Old Elk, Service Unit Director
**Web address:** www.ihs.gov/facilitiesservices/areaoffices/billings/crow/index.asp

---

For explanation of codes following names, see page B2.
★ Indicates Type III membership in the American Hospital Association.
● Single hospital health care system

Section B

FORT BELKNAP U. S. PUBLIC HEALTH SERVICE INDIAN HOSPITAL (O, 6 beds) 669 Agency Main Street, Harlem, MT Zip 59526–9455; tel. 406/353–3100; Steve Fox, Chief Executive Officer
**Web address:** www.ihs.gov

U. S. PUBLIC HEALTH SERVICE BLACKFEET COMMUNITY HOSPITAL (O, 25 beds) Saint Mary, MT Zip 59417–0760; Browning, tel. 406/338–6100; Merlin Gilham, Chief Executive Officer
**Web address:** www.ihs.gov

**NEBRASKA:** U. S. PUBLIC HEALTH SERVICE INDIAN HOSPITAL (O, 30 beds) Highway 7577, Winnebago, NE Zip 68071; tel. 402/878–2231; Sheriann Moore, Service Unit Director
**Web address:** www.ihs.gov

**NEW MEXICO:** ACOMA–CANONCITO–LAGUNA HOSPITAL (O, 25 beds) 80B Veterans Boulevard, Acoma, NM Zip 87034, Mailing Address: P.O. Box 130, San Fidel, Zip 87049–0130; tel. 505/552–5300; William Thorne, Jr., Chief Executive Officer
**Web address:** www.ihs.gov/albuquerque/index.cfm?module=dsp_abq_acoma_canoncito_laguna

GALLUP INDIAN MEDICAL CENTER (O, 58 beds) 516 East Nizhoni Boulevard, Gallup, NM Zip 87301–5748, Mailing Address: P.O. Box 1337, Zip 87305–1337; tel. 505/722–1000; Bennie C. Yazzie, Interim Chief Executive Officer
**Web address:** www.ihs.gov/facilitiesservices/areaoffices/navajo/naihs-hcc–gallup.asp

MESCALERO PUBLIC HEALTH SERVICE INDIAN HOSPITAL (O, 13 beds) 318 Abalone Loop, Mescalero, NM Zip 88340, Mailing Address: Box 210, Zip 88340–0210; tel. 505/671–4441; Dorlynn Simmons, Chief Executive Officer
**Web address:** www.ihs.gov

NORTHERN NAVAJO MEDICAL CENTER (O, 62 beds) Shiprock, NM Zip 87420–0160; tel. 505/368–6001; Fannessa Comer, Chief Executive Officer
**Web address:** www.ihs.gov/

PHS SANTA FE INDIAN HOSPITAL (O, 39 beds) 1700 Cerrillos Road, Santa Fe, NM Zip 87505–3554; tel. 505/988–9821; Robert J. Lyon, Chief Executive Officer
**Web address:** www.ihs.gov

U. S. PUBLIC HEALTH SERVICE INDIAN HOSPITAL (O, 12 beds) Route 9 and State Road 371, Crownpoint, NM Zip 87313, Mailing Address: P.O. Box 358, Zip 87313–0358; tel. 505/786–5291; Virgil Davis, Acting Chief Executive Officer
**Web address:** www.ihs.gov

U. S. PUBLIC HEALTH SERVICE INDIAN HOSPITAL (O, 32 beds) Route 301 North B. Street, Zuni, NM Zip 87327, Mailing Address: P.O. Box 467, Zip 87327–0467; tel. 505/782–4431; Jean Othole, Chief Executive Officer
**Web address:** www.ihs.gov

**NORTH DAKOTA:** PUBLIC HEALTH SERVICE INDIAN HOSPITAL – QUENTIN N. BURDICK MEMORIAL HEALTH FACILITY (O, 27 beds) 2 Blocks North of Highway 5, Belcourt, ND Zip 58316, Mailing Address: P.O. Box 160, Zip 58316–0160; tel. 701/477–6111; Shelly Harris, Chief Executive Officer
**Web address:** www.ihs.gov

U. S. PUBLIC HEALTH SERVICE INDIAN HOSPITAL (O, 12 beds) N 10 North River Road, Fort Yates, ND Zip 58538, Mailing Address: P.O. Box J, Zip 58538; tel. 701/854–3831; Lisa Guardipee, Director
**Web address:** www.ihs.gov

**OKLAHOMA:** CHEROKEE NATION W.W. HASTINGS INDIAN HOSPITAL (O, 58 beds) 100 South Bliss Avenue, Tahlequah, OK Zip 74464–2512; tel. 918/458–3100; Brian Hail, Chief Executive Officer
**Web address:** www.cherokee.org

CLAREMORE INDIAN HOSPITAL (O, 44 beds) 101 South Moore Avenue, Claremore, OK Zip 74017–5091; tel. 918/342–6200; George Valliere, Chief Executive Officer
**Web address:** www.ihs.gov

LAWTON INDIAN HOSPITAL (O, 26 beds) 1515 Lawrie Tatum Road, Lawton, OK Zip 73507–3099; tel. 580/353–0350; Greg Ketcher, Administrator
**Web address:** www.ihs.gov

**SOUTH DAKOTA:** INDIAN HEALTH SERVICE HOSPITAL (O, 9 beds) 3200 Canyon Lake Drive, Rapid City, SD Zip 57702–8197; tel. 605/355–2280; Helen Thompson, Interim Director
**Web address:** www.ihs.gov

U. S. PUBLIC HEALTH SERVICE INDIAN HOSPITAL (O, 11 beds) 317 Main Street, Eagle Butte, SD Zip 57625–1012, Mailing Address: P.O. Box 1012, Zip 57625–1012; tel. 605/964–7724; Charlene Red Thunder, Chief Executive Officer
**Web address:** www.ihs.gov

U. S. PUBLIC HEALTH SERVICE INDIAN HOSPITAL (O, 45 beds) East Highway 18, Pine Ridge, SD Zip 57770, Mailing Address: P.O. Box 1201, Zip 57770–1201; tel. 605/867–5131; William Pourier, Service Unit Director
**Web address:** www.ihs.gov

U. S. PUBLIC HEALTH SERVICE INDIAN HOSPITAL (O, 35 beds) Highway 18, Soldier Creek Road, Rosebud, SD Zip 57570; tel. 605/747–2231; Sophie M. Two Hawk, Chief Executive Officer
**Web address:** www.ihs.gov

| | | |
|---|---|---|
| **Owned, leased, sponsored:** | 31 hospitals | 1104 beds |
| **Contract–managed:** | 0 hospitals | 0 beds |
| **Totals:** | 31 hospitals | 1104 beds |

---

**★9105:  UAB HEALTH SYSTEM** (NP)
500 22nd Street South, Suite 408, Birmingham, AL Zip 35233–3110; tel. 205/975–5362; William Ferniany, Ph.D., Chief Executive Officer
**(Centralized Physician/Insurance Health System)**

**ALABAMA:** MEDICAL WEST (O, 236 beds) 995 Ninth Avenue S.W., Bessemer, AL Zip 35022–4527; tel. 205/481–7000; Keith Pennington, President and Chief Executive Officer
**Web address:** www.medicalwesthospital.org

UNIVERSITY OF ALABAMA HOSPITAL (O, 1062 beds) 619 19th Street South, Birmingham, AL Zip 35249–1900; tel. 205/934–4011; Anthony Patterson, Interim Chief Executive Officer
**Web address:** www.health.uab.edu

| | | |
|---|---|---|
| **Owned, leased, sponsored:** | 2 hospitals | 1298 beds |
| **Contract–managed:** | 0 hospitals | 0 beds |
| **Totals:** | 2 hospitals | 1298 beds |

---

**★0082:  UC HEALTH** (NP)
3200 Burnet Avenue, Cincinnati, OH Zip 45229–3019; tel. 513/585–6000; James A. Kingsbury, President and Chief Executive Officer
**(Centralized Health System)**

**OHIO:** DRAKE CENTER (O, 202 beds) 151 West Galbraith Road, Cincinnati, OH Zip 45216–1015; tel. 513/418–2500; Debra C. Hampton, Ph.D., Vice President, Administration and Chief Nursing Officer
**Web address:** www.drakecenter.uchealth.com

UNIVERSITY HOSPITAL (O, 498 beds) 234 Goodman Street, Cincinnati, OH Zip 45219–2316; tel. 513/584–1000; Lee Ann Liska, President and Chief Executive Officer
**Web address:** www.universityhospital.uchealth.com/

UNIVERSITY POINTE SURGICAL HOSPITAL (O, 8 beds) 7750 University Court, West Chester, OH Zip 45069; tel. 513/475–8300; Lesley Gilbertson, M.D., Executive and Medical Director
**Web address:** www.surgicalhospital.uchealth.com

WEST CHESTER HOSPITAL (O, 126 beds) 7700 University Drive, West Chester, OH Zip 45069–2505; tel. 513/298–3000; Kevin Joseph, M.D., Chief Executive Officer
**Web address:** www.westchesterhospital.uchealth.com

| | | |
|---|---|---|
| **Owned, leased, sponsored:** | 4 hospitals | 834 beds |
| **Contract–managed:** | 0 hospitals | 0 beds |
| **Totals:** | 4 hospitals | 834 beds |

---

**0390:  UK HEALTHCARE** (NP)
900 South Limestone, Lexington, KY Zip 40505; tel. 859/323–5000; Michael Karpf, M.D., Executive Vice President Health Affairs
**(Independent Hospital System)**

---

For explanation of codes following names, see page B2.
★ Indicates Type III membership in the American Hospital Association.

**KENTUCKY:** UK HEALTHCARE GOOD SAMARITAN HOSPITAL (O, 158 beds) 310 South Limestone Street, Lexington, KY Zip 40508–3008; tel. 859/226–7000; Anna M. Smith, Chief Administrative Officer
**Web address:** www.ukhealthcare.uky.edu/samaritan

UNIVERSITY OF KENTUCKY ALBERT B. CHANDLER HOSPITAL (O, 589 beds) 800 Rose Street, Lexington, KY Zip 40536–0293; tel. 859/323–5000; Anna M. Smith, Chief Administrative Officer
**Web address:** www.ukhealthcare.uky.edu

| | | |
|---|---|---|
| **Owned, leased, sponsored:** | 2 hospitals | 747 beds |
| **Contract–managed:** | 0 hospitals | 0 beds |
| **Totals:** | 2 hospitals | 747 beds |

★**0224:** **UMASS MEMORIAL HEALTH CARE, INC.** (NP) 1 Biotech Park, Worcester, MA Zip 01605–2982; tel. 508/334–0100; Eric Dickson, M.D., President and Chief Executive Officer
**(Moderately Centralized Health System)**

**MASSACHUSETTS:** CLINTON HOSPITAL (O, 41 beds) 201 Highland Street, Clinton, MA Zip 01510–1096; tel. 978/368–3000; Sheila Daly, President and Chief Executive Officer
**Web address:** www.clintonhospital.org

HEALTH ALLIANCE HOSPITALS (O, 83 beds) 60 Hospital Road, Leominster, MA Zip 01453–2205; tel. 978/466–2000; Patrick L. Muldoon, FACHE, President and Chief Executive Officer
**Web address:** www.healthalliance.com

UMASS MEMORIAL MEDICAL CENTER (O, 687 beds) 119 Belmont Street, Worcester, MA Zip 01605–2982; tel. 508/334–1000; Eric Dickson, M.D., President and Chief Executive Officer
**Web address:** www.umassmemorial.org

UMASS MEMORIAL–MARLBOROUGH HOSPITAL (O, 67 beds) 157 Union Street, Marlborough, MA Zip 01752–1297; tel. 508/481–5000; Candra Szymanski, MS, R.N., Interim President and Chief Executive Officer
**Web address:** www.marlboroughhospital.org

WING MEMORIAL HOSPITAL AND MEDICAL CENTERS (O, 74 beds) 40 Wright Street, Palmer, MA Zip 01069–1138; tel. 413/283–7651; Janice A. Kucewicz, R.N., Interim President and Chief Executive Officer
**Web address:** www.winghealth.org

| | | |
|---|---|---|
| **Owned, leased, sponsored:** | 5 hospitals | 952 beds |
| **Contract–managed:** | 0 hospitals | 0 beds |
| **Totals:** | 5 hospitals | 952 beds |

★**0901:** **UNC HEALTH CARE** (NP) 101 Manning Drive, Chapel Hill, NC Zip 27514–4220; tel. 919/966–4131; William L. Roper, M.D., M.P.H., Chief Executive Officer

**NORTH CAROLINA:** CHATHAM HOSPITAL (O, 25 beds) 475 Progress Boulevard, Siler City, NC Zip 27344–6787, Mailing Address: P.O. Box 649, Zip 27344–0649; tel. 919/799–4000; Robert A. Enders, Jr., President
**Web address:** www.chathamhospital.org

HIGH POINT REGIONAL HEALTH SYSTEM (O, 351 beds) 601 North Elm Street, High Point, NC Zip 27262–4398, Mailing Address: P.O. Box HP–5, Zip 27261–1899; tel. 336/878–6000; Jeffrey S. Miller, President and Chief Executive Officer
**Web address:** www.highpointregional.com

MARGARET R. PARDEE MEMORIAL HOSPITAL (O, 138 beds) 800 North Justice Street, Hendersonville, NC Zip 28791–3410; tel. 828/696–1000; James M. Kirby, II, President and Chief Executive Officer
**Web address:** www.pardeehospital.org

REX HEALTHCARE (O, 660 beds) 4420 Lake Boone Trail, Raleigh, NC Zip 27607–6599; tel. 919/784–3100; David W. Strong, President
**Web address:** www.rexhealth.com

UNIVERSITY OF NORTH CAROLINA HOSPITALS (O, 805 beds) 101 Manning Drive, Chapel Hill, NC Zip 27514–4220; tel. 919/966–4131; Gary L. Park, President
**Web address:** www.unchealthcare.org

| | | |
|---|---|---|
| **Owned, leased, sponsored:** | 5 hospitals | 1979 beds |
| **Contract–managed:** | 0 hospitals | 0 beds |
| **Totals:** | 5 hospitals | 1979 beds |

**0288:** **UNITED HEALTH SERVICES** (NP) 10–42 Mitchell Avenue, Binghamton, NY Zip 13903–1617; tel. 607/762–2200; Matthew J. Salanger, President and Chief Executive Officer
**(Independent Hospital System)**

**NEW YORK:** CHENANGO MEMORIAL HOSPITAL (O, 138 beds) 179 North Broad Street, Norwich, NY Zip 13815–1097; tel. 607/337–4111; Drake M. Lamen, M.D., President and Chief Executive Officer
**Web address:** www.uhs.net/cmh

DELAWARE VALLEY HOSPITAL (O, 25 beds) 1 Titus Place, Walton, NY Zip 13856–1498; tel. 607/865–2100; Dru Cavanagh, R.N., President and Chief Executive Officer
**Web address:** www.uhs.net

UNITED HEALTH SERVICES HOSPITALS–BINGHAMTON (O, 456 beds) 10–42 Mitchell Avenue, Binghamton, NY Zip 13903–1678; tel. 607/763–6000; Matthew J. Salanger, President and Chief Executive Officer
**Web address:** www.uhs.net

| | | |
|---|---|---|
| **Owned, leased, sponsored:** | 3 hospitals | 619 beds |
| **Contract–managed:** | 0 hospitals | 0 beds |
| **Totals:** | 3 hospitals | 619 beds |

**9605:** **UNITED MEDICAL CORPORATION** (IO) 603 Main Street, Windermere, FL Zip 34786–3548, Mailing Address: P.O. Box 1100, Zip 34786–1100; tel. 407/876–2200; Donald R. Dizney, Chairman and Chief Executive Officer

**PUERTO RICO:** HOSPITAL PAVIA–HATO REY (O, 180 beds) 435 Ponce De Leon Avenue, San Juan, PR Zip 00917–3428; tel. 787/641–2323; Luis R. Allende Ruiz, Executive Director
**Web address:** www.paviahealth.com

HOSPITAL PAVIA–SANTURCE (O, 215 beds) 1462 Asia Street, San Juan, PR Zip 00909–2143, Mailing Address: Box 11137, Santurce Station, Zip 00910–1137; tel. 787/727–6060; Jose Luis Rodriguez, Chief Executive Officer
**Web address:** www.paviahealth.com

HOSPITAL PEREA (O, 103 beds) 15 Basora Street, Mayaguez, PR Zip 00681, Mailing Address: P.O. Box 170, Zip 00681; tel. 787/834–0101; Marco Reyes Concepcion, Executive Director
**Web address:** www.paviahealth.com/perea_hospital.htm

SAN JORGE CHILDREN'S HOSPITAL (O, 125 beds) 252 San Jorge Street, Santurce, San Juan, PR Zip 00912–3310; tel. 787/727–1000; Domingo Cruz, Senior Vice President Operations
**Web address:** www.sanjorgechildrenshospital.com

**TENNESSEE:** TEN BROECK TENNESSEE TREATMENT FACILITY (O, 32 beds) 1 Medical Center Boulevard, 5 West, Cookeville, TN Zip 38501; tel. 931/783–2570; Matthew Quinn, Executive Director
**Web address:** www.tenbroeck.com

| | | |
|---|---|---|
| **Owned, leased, sponsored:** | 5 hospitals | 655 beds |
| **Contract–managed:** | 0 hospitals | 0 beds |
| **Totals:** | 5 hospitals | 655 beds |

**0322:** **UNITED SURGICAL PARTNERS INTERNATIONAL** (IO) 15305 Dallas Parkway, Suite 1600, Addison, TX Zip 75001–6491; tel. 972/713–3500; William H. Wilcox, President and Chief Executive Officer
**(Independent Hospital System)**

**ARIZONA:** ARIZONA ORTHOPEDIC SURGICAL HOSPITAL (O, 24 beds) 2905 West Warner Road, Chandler, AZ Zip 85224–1674; tel. 480/603–9000; Duane Scholer, Chief Executive Officer
**Web address:** www.azosh.com

For explanation of codes following names, see page B2.
★ Indicates Type III membership in the American Hospital Association.

**OKLAHOMA:** OKLAHOMA CENTER FOR ORTHOPEDIC AND MULTI–SPECIALTY SURGERY (O, 10 beds) 8100 South Walker, Suite C., Oklahoma City, OK Zip 73139–9402, Mailing Address: P.O. Box 890609, Zip 73189–0609; tel. 405/602–6500; Mike Kimzey, Chief Executive Officer and Administrator
**Web address:** www.ocomhospital.com

**TEXAS:** BAYLOR MEDICAL CENTER AT FRISCO (O, 68 beds) 5601 Warren Parkway, Frisco, TX Zip 75034–4069; tel. 214/407–5000; William A. Keaton, Chief Executive Officer
**Web address:** www.bmcf.com

BAYLOR MEDICAL CENTER AT UPTOWN (O, 24 beds) 2727 East Lemmon Avenue, Dallas, TX Zip 75204–2895; tel. 214/443–3000; Matt Chance, Chief Executive Officer
**Web address:** www.bmcuptown.com

IRVING COPPELL SURGICAL HOSPITAL (O, 12 beds) 400 West Interstate 635, Irving, TX Zip 75063; tel. 972/868–4000; Deonna Unell, Chief Executive Officer
**Web address:** www.ic–sh.com

SUGAR LAND SURGICAL HOSPITAL (O, 6 beds) 16906 Southwest Freeway, Sugar Land, TX Zip 77479–2350; tel. 281/243–1000; Daniel Smith, Interim Chief Executive Officer
**Web address:** www.sugarlandsurgicalhospital.com/

TOPS SURGICAL SPECIALTY HOSPITAL (O, 15 beds) 17080 Red Oak Drive, Houston, TX Zip 77090–2602; tel. 281/539–2900; Samuel H. Rossmann, Chief Executive Officer
**Web address:** www.tops–hospital.com

| Owned, leased, sponsored: | 7 hospitals | 159 beds |
|---|---|---|
| Contract–managed: | 0 hospitals | 0 beds |
| **Totals:** | **7 hospitals** | **159 beds** |

---

**★0061: UNITYPOINT HEALTH** (NP)
1776 Westlakes Parkway, Suite 400, West Des Moines, IA Zip 50266–8239; tel. 515/241–6161; William B. Leaver, President and Chief Executive Officer
**(Decentralized Health System)**

**ILLINOIS:** UNITYPOINT HEALTH – TRINITY ROCK ISLAND (O, 343 beds) 2701 17th Street, Rock Island, IL Zip 61201–5393; tel. 309/779–5000; Richard A. Seidler, FACHE, President and Chief Executive Officer
**Web address:** www.trinityqc.com

UNITYPOINT HEALTH – METHODIST (O, 269 beds) 221 N.E. Glen Oak Avenue, Peoria, IL Zip 61636–4310; tel. 309/672–5522; Deborah R. Simon, R.N., President and Chief Executive Officer
**Web address:** www.mymethodist.net

**IOWA:** UNITYPOINT HEALTH – BUENA VISTA REGIONAL MEDICAL CENTER (C, 35 beds) 1525 West Fifth Street, Storm Lake, IA Zip 50588–3027, Mailing Address: P.O. Box 309, Zip 50588–0309; tel. 712/732–4030; Steven Colerick, Chief Executive Officer
**Web address:** www.bvrmc.org

UNITYPOINT HEALTH – CLARKE COUNTY HOSPITAL (C, 25 beds) 800 South Fillmore Street, Osceola, IA Zip 50213–1619; tel. 641/342–2184; Brian G. Evans, FACHE, Chief Executive Officer
**Web address:** www.clarkehosp.org

UNITYPOINT HEALTH – COMMUNITY MEMORIAL HOSPITAL (C, 16 beds) 909 West First Street, Sumner, IA Zip 50674–1203, Mailing Address: P.O. Box 148, Zip 50674–0148; tel. 563/578–3275; Mary S. Wells, R.N., Chief Executive Officer
**Web address:** www.cmhsumner.org

UNITYPOINT HEALTH – GREATER REGIONAL MEDICAL CENTER (C, 25 beds) 1700 West Townline Street Suite 3, Creston, IA Zip 50801–1099; tel. 641/782–7091; Monte Neitzel, Chief Executive Officer
**Web address:** www.greaterregional.org

UNITYPOINT HEALTH – GREENE COUNTY MEDICAL CENTER (C, 90 beds) 1000 West Lincolnway, Jefferson, IA Zip 50129–1645; tel. 515/386–2114; Carl P. Behne, Administrator and Chief Executive Officer
**Web address:** www.gcmchealth.com

UNITYPOINT HEALTH – GRUNDY COUNTY MEMORIAL HOSPITAL (C, 80 beds) 201 East J Avenue, Grundy Center, IA Zip 50638–2096; tel. 319/824–5421; Brian Kellar, Chief Executive Officer
**Web address:** www.grundycountyhospital.com

UNITYPOINT HEALTH – GUTHRIE COUNTY HOSPITAL (C, 25 beds) 710 North 12th Street, Guthrie Center, IA Zip 50115–1544; tel. 641/332–2201; Patrick Peters, Chief Executive Officer
**Web address:** www.guthriecountyhospital.org

UNITYPOINT HEALTH – GUTTENBERG MUNICIPAL HOSPITAL (C, 20 beds) 200 Main Street, Guttenberg, IA Zip 52052–9108, Mailing Address: P.O. Box 550, Zip 52052–0550; tel. 563/252–1121; Kimberley A. Gau, FACHE, Chief Executive Officer
**Web address:** www.guttenberghospital.org

UNITYPOINT HEALTH – HUMBOLDT COUNTY MEMORIAL HOSPITAL (C, 49 beds) 1000 North 15th Street, Humboldt, IA Zip 50548–1008; tel. 515/332–4200; James Atty, Chief Executive Officer
**Web address:** www.humboldthospital.org

UNITYPOINT HEALTH – IOWA METHODIST MEDICAL CENTER (O, 478 beds) 1200 Pleasant Street, Des Moines, IA Zip 50309–1406; tel. 515/241–6212; Eric T. Crowell, President and Chief Executive Officer
**Web address:** www.iowahealth.org

UNITYPOINT HEALTH – JONES REGIONAL MEDICAL CENTER (O, 22 beds) 1795 Highway 64 East, Anamosa, IA Zip 52205–2112; tel. 319/462–6131; Eric Briesemeister, Chief Executive Officer
**Web address:** www.jonesregional.org

UNITYPOINT HEALTH – LORING HOSPITAL (C, 25 beds) 211 Highland Avenue, Sac City, IA Zip 50583–2424; tel. 712/662–7105; Michael S. Ketcham, President and Chief Executive Officer
**Web address:** www.loringhospital.org

UNITYPOINT HEALTH – MARENGO MEMORIAL HOSPITAL (O, 25 beds) 300 West May Street, Marengo, IA Zip 52301–1261; tel. 319/642–5543; Barry Goettsch, Chief Executive Officer
**Web address:** http://www.marengohospital.org

UNITYPOINT HEALTH – POCAHONTAS COMMUNITY HOSPITAL (C, 20 beds) 606 N.W. Seventh Street, Pocahontas, IA Zip 50574–1099; tel. 712/335–3501; James D. Roetman, President and Chief Executive Officer
**Web address:** www.pocahontashospital.org

UNITYPOINT HEALTH – TRINITY BETTENDORF (O, 76 beds) 4500 Utica Ridge Road, Bettendorf, IA Zip 52722–1626; tel. 563/742–5000; Richard A. Seidler, FACHE, President and Chief Executive Officer
**Web address:** www.trinityqc.com

UNITYPOINT HEALTH – TRINITY MUSCATINE (O, 56 beds) 1518 Mulberry Avenue, Muscatine, IA Zip 52761–3499; tel. 563/264–9100; James M. Hayes, Chief Executive Officer
**Web address:** www.trinitymuscatine.org

UNITYPOINT HEALTH – TRINITY REGIONAL MEDICAL CENTER (O, 113 beds) 802 Kenyon Road, Fort Dodge, IA Zip 50501–5795; tel. 515/573–3101; Susan K. Thompson, President and Chief Executive Officer
**Web address:** www.trmc.org

UNITYPOINT HEALTH – IOWA LUTHERAN HOSPITAL (O, 187 beds) 700 East University Avenue, Des Moines, IA Zip 50316–2392; tel. 515/263–5612; Eric T. Crowell, President and Chief Executive Officer
**Web address:** www.iowahealth.org

UNITYPOINT HEALTH ALLEN MEMORIAL HOSPITAL (O, 201 beds) 1825 Logan Avenue, Waterloo, IA Zip 50703–1916; tel. 319/235–3941; Pamela K. Delagardelle, Chief Executive Officer
**Web address:** www.allenhospital.org

UNITYPOINT HEALTH FINLEY (O, 109 beds) 350 North Grandview Avenue, Dubuque, IA Zip 52001–6392; tel. 563/582–1881; David R. Brandon, President and Chief Executive Officer
**Web address:** www.finleyhospital.org

UNITYPOINT HEALTH ST. LUKE'S (O, 340 beds) 1026 A Avenue N.E., Cedar Rapids, IA Zip 52402–3026, Mailing Address: P.O. Box 3026, Zip 52406–3026; tel. 319/369–7211; Theodore E. Townsend, FACHE, President and Chief Executive Officer
**Web address:** www.crstlukes.org

UNITYPOINT HEALTH ST. LUKE'S HEALTH SYSTEM (O, 157 beds) 2720 Stone Park Boulevard, Sioux City, IA Zip 51104–3734; tel. 712/279–3500; Peter W. Thoreen, FACHE, President and Chief Executive Officer
**Web address:** www.stlukes.org

| Owned, leased, sponsored: | 13 hospitals | 2376 beds |
|---|---|---|
| Contract–managed: | 11 hospitals | 410 beds |
| **Totals:** | **24 hospitals** | **2786 beds** |

---

For explanation of codes following names, see page B2.
★ Indicates Type III membership in the American Hospital Association.

**9555: UNIVERSAL HEALTH SERVICES, INC.** (IO)
367 South Gulph Road, King of Prussia, PA Zip 19406–3121, Mailing
Address: P.O. Box 61558, Zip 19406–0958; tel. 610/768–3300;
Alan B. Miller, Chairman and Chief Executive Officer
**(Decentralized Health System)**

**ALABAMA:** HILL CREST BEHAVIORAL HEALTH SERVICES (O, 94 beds) 6869
Fifth Avenue South, Birmingham, AL Zip 35212–1866;
tel. 205/833–9000; Steve McCabe, Chief Executive Officer
**Web address:** www.hillcrestbhs.com

LAUREL OAKS BEHAVIORAL HEALTH CENTER (O, 38 beds) 700 East
Cottonwood Road, Dothan, AL Zip 36301–3644; tel. 334/794–7373; Derek
Johnson, Chief Executive Officer
**Web address:** www.laureloaksbhc.com

**ALASKA:** NORTH STAR BEHAVIORAL HEALTH SYSTEM (O, 200 beds) 2530
DeBarr Circle, Anchorage, AK Zip 99508–2948; tel. 907/258–7575;
Andrew Mayo, Chief Executive Officer and Managing Director
**Web address:** www.northstarbehavioral.com

**ARIZONA:** VALLEY HOSPITAL PHOENIX (O, 122 beds) 3550 East Pinchot
Avenue, Phoenix, AZ Zip 85018–7434; tel. 602/957–4000; Michelle
David, Interim Chief Executive Officer
**Web address:** www.valleyhospital–phoenix.com

**ARKANSAS:** PINNACLE POINTE HOSPITAL (O, 124 beds) 11501 Financial
Center Parkway, Little Rock, AR Zip 72211–3715; tel. 501/223–3322;
Thomas Stormanns, Chief Executive Officer
**Web address:** www.pinnaclepointehospital.com

RIVENDELL BEHAVIORAL HEALTH SERVICES OF ARKANSAS (O, 77 beds) 100
Rivendell Drive, Benton, AR Zip 72019–9100; tel. 501/316–1255; Duane
Runyan, Chief Executive Officer and Managing Director
**Web address:** www.rivendellofarkansas.com

THE BRIDGEWAY (L, 103 beds) 21 Bridgeway Road, North Little Rock, AR
Zip 72113–9516; tel. 501/771–1500; Barry Pipkin, Chief Executive Officer
**Web address:** www.thebridgeway.com

**CALIFORNIA:** BHC ALHAMBRA HOSPITAL (O, 85 beds) 4619 North
Rosemead Boulevard, Rosemead, CA Zip 91770–1478, Mailing Address:
P.O. Box 369, Zip 91770–0369; tel. 626/286–1191; Peggy Minnick,
R.N., Chief Executive Officer
**Web address:** www.bhcalhambra.com

CANYON RIDGE HOSPITAL (O, 106 beds) 5353 G Street, Chino, CA
Zip 91710–5250; tel. 909/590–3700; Jeff McDonald, Chief Executive Officer
**Web address:** www.canyonridgehospital.com

CORONA REGIONAL MEDICAL CENTER (O, 240 beds) 800 South Main Street,
Corona, CA Zip 92882–3420; tel. 951/737–4343; Kevan Metcalfe, Chief
Executive Officer
**Web address:** www.coronaregional.com

DEL AMO HOSPITAL (O, 70 beds) 23700 Camino Del Sol, Torrance, CA
Zip 90505–5000; tel. 310/530–1151; Lisa K. Montes, Chief Executive
Officer
**Web address:** www.delamohospital.com

FREMONT HOSPITAL (O, 96 beds) 39001 Sundale Drive, Fremont, CA
Zip 94538–2005; tel. 510/796–1100; John C. Cooper, Chief Executive
Officer
**Web address:** www.fremonthospital.com

HERITAGE OAKS HOSPITAL (O, 120 beds) 4250 Auburn Boulevard,
Sacramento, CA Zip 95841–4164; tel. 916/489–3336; Shawn Silva, Chief
Executive Officer
**Web address:** www.heritageoakshospital.com

PALMDALE REGIONAL MEDICAL CENTER (O, 157 beds) 38600 Medical
Center Drive, Palmdale, CA Zip 93551–4483; tel. 661/382–5000; Richard
Allen, Interim Chief Executive Officer
**Web address:** www.palmdaleregional.com

SIERRA VISTA HOSPITAL (O, 120 beds) 8001 Bruceville Road, Sacramento,
CA Zip 95823–2329; tel. 916/288–0300; Mike Zauner, Chief Executive
Officer
**Web address:** www.sierravistahospital.com

SOUTHWEST HEALTHCARE SYSTEM (O, 252 beds) 25500 Medical Center
Drive, Murrieta, CA Zip 92562–5965; tel. 951/696–6000; Bradley D. Neet,
FACHE, Chief Executive Officer
**Web address:** www.swhealthcaresystem.com/

**COLORADO:** CEDAR SPRINGS HOSPITAL (O, 110 beds) 2135 Southgate
Road, Colorado Springs, CO Zip 80906–2693; tel. 719/633–4114; A.
Elaine Crnkovic, Chief Executive Officer
**Web address:** www.cedarspringsbhs.com

CENTENNIAL PEAKS HOSPITAL (O, 72 beds) 2255 South 88th Street,
Louisville, CO Zip 80027–9716; tel. 303/673–9990; Elicia Bunch, Chief
Executive Officer
**Web address:** www.centennialpeaks.com

HIGHLANDS BEHAVIORAL HEALTH SYSTEM (O, 86 beds) 8565 South Poplar
Way, Littleton, CO Zip 80130–3602; tel. 720/348–2800; Shawn Lemon,
Interim Chief Executive Officer
**Web address:** www.highlandsbhs.com

**DELAWARE:** DOVER BEHAVIORAL HEALTH SYSTEM (O, 72 beds) 725
Horsepond Road, Dover, DE Zip 19901–7232; tel. 302/741–0140; Rod
Letterman, Chief Executive Officer
**Web address:** www.doverbehavioral.com

ROCKFORD CENTER (O, 118 beds) 100 Rockford Drive, Newark, DE
Zip 19713–2121; tel. 302/996–5480; John F. McKenna, Chief Executive
Officer and Managing Director
**Web address:** www.rockfordcenter.com

**DISTRICT OF COLUMBIA:** GEORGE WASHINGTON UNIVERSITY HOSPITAL (O,
363 beds) 900 23rd Street N.W., Washington, DC Zip 20037–2342;
tel. 202/715–4000; Barry A. Wolfman, Chief Executive Officer and
Managing Director
**Web address:** www.gwhospital.com

**FLORIDA:** ATLANTIC SHORES HOSPITAL (O, 72 beds) 4545 North Federal
Highway, Fort Lauderdale, FL Zip 33308–5274; tel. 954/771–2711;
Manuel R. Llano, Chief Executive Officer
**Web address:** www.atlanticshoreshospital.com

CENTRAL FLORIDA BEHAVIORAL HOSPITAL (O, 120 beds) 6601 Central
Florida Parkway, Orlando, FL Zip 32821–8064; tel. 407/370–0111; Vickie
Lewis, Chief Executive Officer
**Web address:** www.centralfloridabehavioral.com

EMERALD COAST BEHAVIORAL HOSPITAL (O, 80 beds) 1940 Harrison
Avenue, Panama City, FL Zip 32405–4542; tel. 850/763–0017; Tim Bedford,
Chief Executive Officer
**Web address:** www.emeraldcoastbehavioral.com

FORT LAUDERDALE HOSPITAL (L, 100 beds) 1601 East Las Olas Boulevard,
Fort Lauderdale, FL Zip 33301–2393; tel. 954/463–4321; Manuel R. Llano,
Chief Executive Officer
**Web address:** www.fortlauderdalehospital.org

LAKEWOOD RANCH MEDICAL CENTER (O, 120 beds) 8330 Lakewood Ranch
Boulevard, Bradenton, FL Zip 34202–5174; tel. 941/782–2100; Linda S.
Widra, FACHE, Ph.D., R.N., Interim Chief Executive Officer
**Web address:** www.lakewoodranchmedicalcenter.com

MANATEE MEMORIAL HOSPITAL (O, 319 beds) 206 Second Street East,
Bradenton, FL Zip 34208–1000; tel. 941/746–5111; Kevin DiLallo, Chief
Executive Officer
**Web address:** www.manateememorial.com

MANATEE PALMS YOUTH SERVICES (O, 60 beds) 4480 51st Street West,
Bradenton, FL Zip 34210–2855; tel. 941/792–2222; Kerry Knott, Chief
Executive Officer
**Web address:** www.mpys.com

RIVER POINT BEHAVIORAL HEALTH (O, 92 beds) 6300 Beach Boulevard,
Jacksonville, FL Zip 32216–2782; tel. 904/724–9202; Gayle Eckerd, Chief
Executive Officer
**Web address:** www.riverpointbehavioral.com

THE VINES (O, 90 beds) 3130 S.W. 27th Avenue, Ocala, FL
Zip 34471–4306; tel. 352/671–3130; Stephen Quintyne, Chief Executive
Officer
**Web address:** www.thevineshospital.com

WEKIVA SPRINGS CENTER FOR WOMEN (O, 60 beds) 3947 Salisbury Road,
Jacksonville, FL Zip 32216–6115; tel. 904/296–3533; Gayle Eckerd, Chief
Executive Officer
**Web address:** www.wekivacenter.com

WELLINGTON REGIONAL MEDICAL CENTER (L, 158 beds) 10101 Forest Hill
Boulevard, West Palm Beach, FL Zip 33414–6199; tel. 561/798–8500;
Robbin Lee, Interim Chief Executive Officer
**Web address:** www.wellingtonregional.com

WINDMOOR HEALTHCARE OF CLEARWATER (O, 120 beds) 11300 U.S. 19
North, Clearwater, FL Zip 33764; tel. 727/541–2646; Wendy Merson, Chief
Executive Officer
**Web address:** www.windmoor.com

For explanation of codes following names, see page B2.
★ Indicates Type III membership in the American Hospital Association.

Section B

**GEORGIA:** ANCHOR HOSPITAL (O, 111 beds) 5454 Yorktowne Drive, Atlanta, GA Zip 30349–5317; tel. 770/991–6044; Margaret P. Collier, Chief Executive Officer and Managing Director
**Web address:** www.anchorhospital.com

COASTAL HARBOR TREATMENT CENTER (O, 195 beds) 1150 Cornell Avenue, Savannah, GA Zip 31406–2702; tel. 912/354–3911; Ray Heckerman, Chief Executive Officer and Managing Director
**Web address:** www.coastalharbor.com

PEACHFORD BEHAVIORAL HEALTH SYSTEM (O, 246 beds) 2151 Peachford Road, Atlanta, GA Zip 30338–6599; tel. 770/455–3200; Matthew Crouch, Chief Executive Officer and Managing Director
**Web address:** www.peachfordhospital.com

SAINT SIMONS BY–THE–SEA HOSPITAL (O, 101 beds) 2927 Demere Road, Saint Simons Island, GA Zip 31522–1620; tel. 912/638–1999; Monica Cook, Interim Chief Executive Officer
**Web address:** www.ssbythesea.com

TURNING POINT HOSPITAL (O, 59 beds) 3015 Veterans Parkway South, Moultrie, GA Zip 31788–6705, Mailing Address: P.O. Box 1177, Zip 31776–1177; tel. 229/985–4815; Ben Marion, Chief Executive Officer and Managing Director
**Web address:** www.turningpointcare.com

**IDAHO:** INTERMOUNTAIN HOSPITAL (O, 140 beds) 303 North Allumbaugh Street, Boise, ID Zip 83704–9208; tel. 208/377–8400; Jeffrey F. Morrell, Chief Executive Officer
**Web address:** www.intermountainhospital.com

**ILLINOIS:** HARTGROVE HOSPITAL (O, 128 beds) 5730 West Roosevelt Road, Chicago, IL Zip 60644–1580; tel. 773/413–1700; Steven Airhart, Chief Executive Officer
**Web address:** www.hartgrovehospital.com

LINCOLN PRAIRIE BEHAVIORAL HEALTH CENTER (O, 88 beds) 5230 South Sixth Street, Springfield, IL Zip 62703–5128; tel. 217/585–1180; Mark Littrell, Chief Executive Officer
**Web address:** www.lincolnprairiebhc.com/

RIVEREDGE HOSPITAL (O, 224 beds) 8311 West Roosevelt Road, Forest Park, IL Zip 60130–2500; tel. 708/771–7000; Carey Carlock, Chief Executive Officer
**Web address:** www.riveredgehospital.com

STREAMWOOD BEHAVIORAL HEALTH CENTER (O, 177 beds) 1400 East Irving Park Road, Streamwood, IL Zip 60107–3203; tel. 630/837–9000; Ron Weglarz, Chief Executive Officer and Managing Director
**Web address:** www.streamwoodhospital.com

THE PAVILION (O, 46 beds) 809 West Church Street, Champaign, IL Zip 61820–3399; tel. 217/373–1700; Joseph Sheehy, Chief Executive Officer and Managing Director
**Web address:** www.pavilionhospital.com

**INDIANA:** BLOOMINGTON MEADOWS HOSPITAL (O, 67 beds) 3600 North Prow Road, Bloomington, IN Zip 47404–1616; tel. 812/331–8000; Jean Scallon, Chief Executive Officer
**Web address:** www.bloomingtonmeadows.com

MICHIANA BEHAVIORAL HEALTH CENTER (O, 75 beds) 1800 North Oak Drive, Plymouth, IN Zip 46563–3492; tel. 574/936–3784; Bryan W. Lett, Chief Executive Officer
**Web address:** www.michianabhc.com

VALLE VISTA HOSPITAL (O, 102 beds) 898 East Main Street, Greenwood, IN Zip 46143–1400; tel. 317/887–1348; Sherri R. Jewett, Chief Executive Officer
**Web address:** www.vallevistahospital.com

WELLSTONE REGIONAL HOSPITAL (O, 100 beds) 2700 Vissing Park Road, Jeffersonville, IN Zip 47130–5989; tel. 812/284–8000; Greg Stewart, Chief Executive Officer
**Web address:** www.wellstonehospital.com

**KENTUCKY:** CUMBERLAND HALL HOSPITAL (O, 97 beds) 270 Walton Way, Hopkinsville, KY Zip 42240–6808; tel. 270/886–1919; James Spruyt, Chief Executive Officer
**Web address:** www.cumberlandhallhospital.com

LINCOLN TRAIL BEHAVIORAL HEALTH SYSTEM (O, 67 beds) 3909 South Wilson Road, Radcliff, KY Zip 40160–8944, Mailing Address: P.O. Box 369, Zip 40159–0369; tel. 270/351–9444; Charles L. Webb, Jr., Chief Executive Officer
**Web address:** www.lincolnbehavioral.com

RIDGE BEHAVIORAL HEALTH SYSTEM (O, 110 beds) 3050 Rio Dosa Drive, Lexington, KY Zip 40509–1540; tel. 859/269–2325; Nina W. Eisner, Chief Executive Officer and Managing Director
**Web address:** www.ridgebhs.com

RIVENDELL BEHAVIORAL HEALTH (O, 125 beds) 1035 Porter Pike, Bowling Green, KY Zip 42103–9581; tel. 270/843–1199; Janice Richardson, Chief Executive Officer and Managing Director
**Web address:** www.rivendellbehavioral.com

THE BROOK AT DUPONT (O, 66 beds) 1405 Browns Lane, Louisville, KY Zip 40207–4608; tel. 502/896–0495; Paul Andrews, Chief Executive Officer
**Web address:** www.thebrookhospitals.com/

THE BROOK HOSPITAL – KMI (O, 110 beds) 8521 Old LaGrange Road, Louisville, KY Zip 40242–3800; tel. 502/426–6380; Paul Andrews, Chief Executive Officer
**Web address:** www.thebrookhospitals.com

**LOUISIANA:** BRENTWOOD HOSPITAL (O, 172 beds) 1006 Highland Avenue, Shreveport, LA Zip 71101–4103; tel. 318/678–7500; William Weaver, Chief Executive Officer
**Web address:** www.brentwoodbehavioral.com

RIVER OAKS HOSPITAL (O, 126 beds) 1525 River Oaks Road West, New Orleans, LA Zip 70123–2162; tel. 504/734–1740; Evelyn Nolting, Chief Executive Officer and Managing Director
**Web address:** www.riveroakshospital.com

**MASSACHUSETTS:** ARBOUR H. R. I. HOSPITAL (O, 68 beds) 227 Babcock Street, Brookline, MA Zip 02446–6799; tel. 617/731–3200; Patrick Moallemian, Chief Executive Officer and Managing Director
**Web address:** www.arbourhealth.com

ARBOUR HOSPITAL (O, 118 beds) 49 Robinwood Avenue, Boston, MA Zip 02130–2156; tel. 617/522–4400; Jean–Charles Constant, Interim Chief Executive Officer
**Web address:** www.arbourhealth.com

ARBOUR–FULLER HOSPITAL (O, 46 beds) 200 May Street, Attleboro, MA Zip 02703–5520; tel. 508/761–8500; Kevin Burchill, Chief Executive Officer
**Web address:** www.arbourhealth.com

PEMBROKE HOSPITAL (O, 80 beds) 199 Oak Street, Pembroke, MA Zip 02359–1953; tel. 781/829–7000; Thomas P. Hickey, Chief Executive Officer and Managing Director
**Web address:** www.arbourhealth.com/organizations/pembroke–hospital/

WESTWOOD LODGE HOSPITAL (O, 130 beds) 45 Clapboardtree Street, Westwood, MA Zip 02090–2903; tel. 781/762–7764; Gregory Brownstein, Chief Executive Officer
**Web address:** www.arbourhealth.com

**MICHIGAN:** FOREST VIEW PSYCHIATRIC HOSPITAL (O, 82 beds) 1055 Medical Park Drive S.E., Grand Rapids, MI Zip 49546–3607; tel. 616/942–9610; Andrew Hotaling, Chief Executive Officer
**Web address:** www.forestviewhospital.com

HAVENWYCK HOSPITAL (O, 251 beds) 1525 University Drive, Auburn Hills, MI Zip 48326–2673; tel. 248/373–9200; David C. Bell, Chief Executive Officer
**Web address:** www.havenwyckhospital.com

**MISSISSIPPI:** ALLIANCE HEALTH CENTER (O, 134 beds) 5000 Highway 39 North, Meridian, MS Zip 39301–1021; tel. 601/483–6211; James Miller, Interim Chief Executive Officer
**Web address:** www.alliancehealthcenter.com

BRENTWOOD BEHAVIORAL HEALTHCARE OF MISSISSIPPI (O, 105 beds) 3531 East Lakeland Drive, Jackson, MS Zip 39232–8839; tel. 601/936–2024; Michael J. Carney, Chief Executive Officer
**Web address:** www.brentwoodjackson.com

PARKWOOD BEHAVIORAL HEALTH SYSTEM (O, 128 beds) 8135 Goodman Road, Olive Branch, MS Zip 38654–2103; tel. 662/895–4900; Ethan Permenter, Chief Executive Officer
**Web address:** www.parkwoodbhs.com

**MISSOURI:** HEARTLAND BEHAVIORAL HEALTH SERVICES (O, 37 beds) 1500 West Ashland Street, Nevada, MO Zip 64772–1710; tel. 417/667–2666; Alyson Wysong–Harder, Chief Executive Officer
**Web address:** www.heartlandbehavioral.com

TWO RIVERS BEHAVIORAL HEALTH SYSTEM (O, 105 beds) 5121 Raytown Road, Kansas City, MO Zip 64133–2141; tel. 816/382–6300; Scott Hullinger, Chief Executive Officer
**Web address:** www.tworivershospital.com

---

For explanation of codes following names, see page B2.
★ Indicates Type III membership in the American Hospital Association.

**NEVADA:** CENTENNIAL HILLS HOSPITAL MEDICAL CENTER (O, 171 beds) 6900 North Durango Drive, Las Vegas, NV Zip 89149–4409; tel. 702/835–9700; Sajit Pullarkat, Chief Executive Officer and Managing Director
**Web address:** www.centennialhillshospital.com

DESERT SPRINGS HOSPITAL MEDICAL CENTER (O, 346 beds) 2075 East Flamingo Road, Las Vegas, NV Zip 89119–5121; tel. 702/733–8800; Samuel Kaufman, Chief Executive Officer and Managing Director
**Web address:** www.desertspringshospital.com

NORTHERN NEVADA MEDICAL CENTER (O, 108 beds) 2375 East Prater Way, Sparks, NV Zip 89434–9641; tel. 775/331–7000; Alan C. Olive, Chief Executive Officer
**Web address:** www.nnmc.com

SPRING MOUNTAIN SAHARA (O, 30 beds) 5460 West Sahara, Las Vegas, NV Zip 89146–3307; tel. 702/216–8900; Darryl S. Dubroca, Chief Executive Officer and Managing Director
**Web address:** www.springmountainsahara.com

SPRING MOUNTAIN TREATMENT CENTER (L, 82 beds) 7000 West Spring Mountain Road, Las Vegas, NV Zip 89117–3816; tel. 702/873–2400; Darryl S. Dubroca, Chief Executive Officer and Managing Director
**Web address:** www.healthsouth.com

SPRING VALLEY HOSPITAL MEDICAL CENTER (O, 169 beds) 5400 South Rainbow Boulevard, Las Vegas, NV Zip 89118–1859; tel. 702/853–3000; Leonard Freehof, Chief Executive Officer and Managing Director
**Web address:** www.springvalleyhospital.com

SUMMERLIN HOSPITAL MEDICAL CENTER (O, 148 beds) 657 Town Center Drive, Las Vegas, NV Zip 89144–6367; tel. 702/233–7000; Robert S. Freymuller, Chief Executive Officer
**Web address:** www.summerlinhospital.com

VALLEY HOSPITAL MEDICAL CENTER (O, 365 beds) 620 Shadow Lane, Las Vegas, NV Zip 89106–4119; tel. 702/388–4000; Jay Finnegan, Chief Executive Officer
**Web address:** www.valleyhospital.net

WEST HILLS HOSPITAL (O, 190 beds) 1240 East Ninth Street, Reno, NV Zip 89512–2964; tel. 775/323–0478; Darryl S. Dubroca, Interim Chief Executive Officer
**Web address:** www.westhillshospital.net

**NEW JERSEY:** HAMPTON BEHAVIORAL HEALTH CENTER (O, 110 beds) 650 Rancocas Road, Westampton, NJ Zip 08060–5613; tel. 609/267–7000; Craig Hilton, Chief Executive Officer
**Web address:** www.hamptonhospital.com

SUMMIT OAKS HOSPITAL (O, 90 beds) 19 Prospect Street, Summit, NJ Zip 07901–2530; tel. 908/522–7000; James P. Gallagher, Chief Executive Officer
**Web address:** www.summitoakshospital.com/

**NEW MEXICO:** MESILLA VALLEY HOSPITAL (O, 120 beds) 3751 Del Rey Boulevard, Las Cruces, NM Zip 88012–8526; tel. 575/382–3500; Robert Mansfield, Chief Executive Officer
**Web address:** www.mesillavalleyhospital.com

**NORTH CAROLINA:** BRYNN MARR HOSPITAL (O, 99 beds) 192 Village Drive, Jacksonville, NC Zip 28546–7299; tel. 910/577–1400; Jay Kortemeyer, Chief Executive Officer
**Web address:** www.brynnmarr.org

HOLLY HILL HOSPITAL (O, 168 beds) 3019 Falstaff Road, Raleigh, NC Zip 27610–1812; tel. 919/250–7000; Michael McDonald, Chief Executive Officer
**Web address:** www.hollyhillhospital.com

OLD VINEYARD BEHAVIORAL HEALTH SERVICES (O, 102 beds) 3637 Old Vineyard Road, Winston–Salem, NC Zip 27104–4842; tel. 336/794–3550; Kevin Patton, Chief Executive Officer
**Web address:** www.oldvineyard.net

**NORTH DAKOTA:** PRAIRIE ST. JOHN'S (O, 91 beds) 510 4th Street South, Fargo, ND Zip 58103–1914; tel. 701/476–7200; Gregory LaFrancois, Chief Executive Officer
**Web address:** www.prairie–stjohns.com

**OHIO:** ARROWHEAD BEHAVIORAL HEALTH HOSPITAL (O, 42 beds) 1725 Timber Line Road, Maumee, OH Zip 43537–4015; tel. 419/891–9333; Ed Speedling, Chief Executive Officer and Managing Director
**Web address:** www.arrowheadbehavioral.com

BELMONT PINES HOSPITAL (O, 46 beds) 615 Churchill–Hubbard Road, Youngstown, OH Zip 44505–1379; tel. 330/759–2700; George H. Perry, Ph.D., Chief Executive Officer
**Web address:** www.belmontpines.com

WINDSOR–LAURELWOOD CENTER FOR BEHAVIORAL MEDICINE (O, 152 beds) 35900 Euclid Avenue, Willoughby, OH Zip 44094–4648; tel. 440/953–3000; Jennifer Wiggins, Interim Chief Executive Officer
**Web address:** www.windsorlaurelwood.com

**OKLAHOMA:** CEDAR RIDGE HOSPITAL (O, 116 beds) 6501 N.E. 50th Street, Oklahoma City, OK Zip 73141–9118; tel. 405/605–6111; Kevan Finley, Chief Executive Officer
**Web address:** www.cedarridgebhs.com

SHADOW MOUNTAIN BEHAVIORAL HEALTH SYSTEM (O, 202 beds) 6262 South Sheridan Road, Tulsa, OK Zip 74133–4055; tel. 918/492–8200; Mike Kistler, Chief Executive Officer
**Web address:** www.shadowmountainbhs.com

ST. MARY'S REGIONAL MEDICAL CENTER (O, 166 beds) 305 South Fifth Street, Enid, OK Zip 73701–5899, Mailing Address: P.O. Box 232, Zip 73702–0232; tel. 580/233–6100; Stanley D. Tatum, FACHE, Chief Executive Officer
**Web address:** www.stmarysregional.com

**OREGON:** CEDAR HILLS HOSPITAL (O, 78 beds) 10300 S.W. Eastridge Street, Portland, OR Zip 97225–5004; tel. 503/944–5000; Michael Sherbun, Ph.D., Chief Executive Officer
**Web address:** www.cedarhillshospital.com

**PENNSYLVANIA:** BROOKE GLEN BEHAVIORAL HOSPITAL (O, 146 beds) 7170 Lafayette Avenue, Fort Washington, PA Zip 19034–2301; tel. 215/641–5300; Neil Callahan, Chief Executive Officer
**Web address:** www.brookeglenhospital.com

CLARION PSYCHIATRIC CENTER (O, 74 beds) 2 Hospital Drive, Clarion, PA Zip 16214–8502; tel. 814/226–9545; Robert Scheffler, Chief Executive Officer
**Web address:** www.clarioncenter.com

FAIRMOUNT BEHAVIORAL HEALTH SYSTEM (O, 239 beds) 561 Fairthorne Avenue, Philadelphia, PA Zip 19128–2499; tel. 215/487–4000; Charles McLister, Chief Executive Officer
**Web address:** www.fairmountbhs.com

FOUNDATIONS BEHAVIORAL HEALTH (O, 96 beds) 833 East Butler Avenue, Doylestown, PA Zip 18901–2280; tel. 215/345–0444; Robert Weinhold, Chief Executive Officer
**Web address:** www.fbh.com

FRIENDS HOSPITAL (O, 219 beds) 4641 Roosevelt Boulevard, Philadelphia, PA Zip 19124–2343; tel. 215/831–4600; Geoff Botak, Chief Executive Officer
**Web address:** www.friendshospital.com

HORSHAM CLINIC (O, 138 beds) 722 East Butler Pike, Ambler, PA Zip 19002–2310; tel. 215/643–7800; Phyllis Weisfield, Chief Executive Officer and Managing Director
**Web address:** www.horshamclinic.com

MEADOWS PSYCHIATRIC CENTER (O, 107 beds) 132 The Meadows Drive, Centre Hall, PA Zip 16828–9231; tel. 814/364–2161; Kara Macaleer, Interim Chief Executive Officer
**Web address:** www.themeadows.net

ROXBURY TREATMENT CENTER (O, 94 beds) 601 Roxbury Road, Shippensburg, PA Zip 17257–9302; tel. 800/648–4673; Shauna Radzieski, Chief Executive Officer
**Web address:** www.roxburyhospital.com

**PUERTO RICO:** FIRST HOSPITAL PANAMERICANO (O, 153 beds) State Road 787 KM 1 5, Cidra, PR Zip 00739, Mailing Address: P.O. Box 1400, Zip 00739; tel. 787/739–5555; Astro Munoz, Executive Director
**Web address:** www.hospitalpanamericano.com

**SOUTH CAROLINA:** AIKEN REGIONAL MEDICAL CENTERS (O, 268 beds) 302 University Parkway, Aiken, SC Zip 29801–6302; tel. 803/641–5000; Carlos Milanes, Chief Executive Officer and Managing Director
**Web address:** www.aikenregional.com

CAROLINA CENTER FOR BEHAVIORAL HEALTH (O, 112 beds) 2700 East Phillips Road, Greer, SC Zip 29650–4816; tel. 864/235–2335; John Willingham, Chief Executive Officer and Managing Director
**Web address:** www.thecarolinacenter.com

For explanation of codes following names, see page B2.
★ Indicates Type III membership in the American Hospital Association.

LIGHTHOUSE CARE CENTER OF CONWAY (O, 72 beds) 152 Waccamaw Medical Park Drive, Conway, SC Zip 29526–8901; tel. 843/347–8871; Thomas L. Ryba, Chief Executive Officer
**Web address:** www.lighthousecarecenterofconway.com/

PALMETTO LOWCOUNTRY BEHAVIORAL HEALTH (O, 112 beds) 2777 Speissegger Drive, Charleston, SC Zip 29405–8229; tel. 843/747–5830; Shari Baker, Chief Executive Officer
**Web address:** www.palmettobehavioralhealth.com

THREE RIVERS BEHAVIORAL HEALTH (O, 118 beds) 2900 Sunset Boulevard, West Columbia, SC Zip 29169–3422; tel. 803/796–9911; Elyssia Lowe, Chief Executive Officer
**Web address:** www.threeriversbehavioral.org

**TENNESSEE:** LAKESIDE BEHAVIORAL HEALTH SYSTEM (O, 311 beds) 2911 Brunswick Road, Memphis, TN Zip 38133–4199; tel. 901/377–4700; Joy Golden, Chief Executive Officer
**Web address:** www.lakesidebhs.com

ROLLING HILLS HOSPITAL (O, 80 beds) 2014 Quail Hollow Circle, Franklin, TN Zip 37067–5967; tel. 615/628–5700; Laurel Roberts, R.N., Interim Chief Executive Officer
**Web address:** www.rollinghillshospital.org/

**TEXAS:** AUSTIN LAKES HOSPITAL (O, 58 beds) 1025 East 32nd Street, Austin, TX Zip 78705–2714; tel. 512/544–5253; Jennifer Miller, Chief Executive Officer
**Web address:** www.austinlakeshospital.com

BEHAVIORAL HOSPITAL OF BELLAIRE (O, 70 beds) 5314 Dashwood Drive, Houston, TX Zip 77081–4603; tel. 713/600–9500; John Nekic, Chief Executive Officer
**Web address:** www.bhbhospital.com

CORNERSTONE REGIONAL HOSPITAL (L, 14 beds) 2302 Cornerstone Boulevard, Edinburg, TX Zip 78539–8471; tel. 956/618–4444; Roxanna M. Godinez, Chief Executive Officer
**Web address:** www.southtexashealthsystem.com/Facilities/Cornerstone–Regional–Hospital

CYPRESS CREEK HOSPITAL (O, 96 beds) 17750 Cali Drive, Houston, TX Zip 77090–2700; tel. 281/586–7600; Brian Brooker, Chief Executive Officer
**Web address:** www.cypresscreekhospital.com

DOCTORS HOSPITAL OF LAREDO (O, 183 beds) 10700 McPherson Road, Laredo, TX Zip 78045–6268; tel. 956/523–2000; Rene Lopez, Chief Executive Officer
**Web address:** www.doctorshoslaredo.com

FORT DUNCAN REGIONAL MEDICAL CENTER (O, 101 beds) 3333 North Foster Maldonado Boulevard, Eagle Pass, TX Zip 78852–5893; tel. 830/773–5321; Richard Prati, Chief Executive Officer
**Web address:** www.fortduncanmedicalcenter.com

GLEN OAKS HOSPITAL (O, 54 beds) 301 Division Street, Greenville, TX Zip 75401–4101; tel. 903/454–6000; Joel Klein, Chief Executive Officer and Managing Director
**Web address:** www.glenoakshospital.com

HICKORY TRAIL HOSPITAL (O, 86 beds) 2000 Old Hickory Trail, Desoto, TX Zip 75115–2242; tel. 972/298–7323; Lance Folske, Chief Executive Officer
**Web address:** www.hickorytrail.com

KINGWOOD PINES HOSPITAL (O, 116 beds) 2001 Ladbrook Drive, Kingwood, TX Zip 77339–3004; tel. 281/358–1495; James Burroughs, Chief Executive Officer
**Web address:** www.kingwoodpines.com

LAUREL RIDGE TREATMENT CENTER (O, 208 beds) 17720 Corporate Woods Drive, San Antonio, TX Zip 78259–3500; tel. 210/491–9400; Jacob Cuellar, M.D., Chief Executive Officer
**Web address:** www.laurelridgetc.com

MAYHILL HOSPITAL (O, 59 beds) 2809 South Mayhill Road, Denton, TX Zip 76208–5910; tel. 940/239–3000; Jeremy Yates, Chief Executive Officer
**Web address:** www.mayhillhospital.com

MILLWOOD HOSPITAL (O, 122 beds) 1011 North Cooper Street, Arlington, TX Zip 76011–5517; tel. 817/261–3121; Rick Paczkowski, Chief Executive Officer
**Web address:** www.millwoodhospital.com

NORTHWEST TEXAS HEALTHCARE SYSTEM (O, 431 beds) 1501 South Coulter Avenue, Amarillo, TX Zip 79106–1770, Mailing Address: P.O. Box 1110, Zip 79105–1110; tel. 806/354–1000; Mark W. Crawford, Chief Executive Officer
**Web address:** www.nwtexashealthcare.com

RIVER CREST HOSPITAL (O, 80 beds) 1636 Hunters Glen Road, San Angelo, TX Zip 76901–5016; tel. 325/949–5722; Shelah Adams, Chief Executive Officer
**Web address:** www.rivercresthospital.com

SOUTH TEXAS HEALTH SYSTEM (O, 775 beds) 1102 West Trenton Road, Edinburg, TX Zip 78539–9105; tel. 956/388–6000; Joe Rodriguez, Chief Executive Officer
**Web address:** www.southtexashealthsystem.com

TEXAS NEUROREHAB CENTER (O, 47 beds) 1106 West Dittmar, Austin, TX Zip 78745–6328, Mailing Address: P.O. Box 150459, Zip 78715–0459; tel. 512/444–4835; Edgar E. Prettyman, PsyD, Chief Executive Officer
**Web address:** www.texasneurorehab.com

TEXOMA MEDICAL CENTER (O, 251 beds) 5016 South U.S. Highway 75, Denison, TX Zip 75020–4584, Mailing Address: P.O. Box 890, Zip 75021–0890; tel. 903/416–4000; Ronald T. Seal, Chief Executive Officer
**Web address:** www.texomamedicalcenter.net

TIMBERLAWN MENTAL HEALTH SYSTEM (O, 144 beds) 4600 Samuell Boulevard, Dallas, TX Zip 75228–6800; tel. 214/381–7181; Craig Nuckles, Chief Executive Officer and Regional Vice President
**Web address:** www.timberlawn.com

UNIVERSITY BEHAVIORAL HEALTH OF DENTON (O, 104 beds) 2026 West University Drive, Denton, TX Zip 76201–0644; tel. 940/320–8100; Susan M. Young, Chief Executive Officer
**Web address:** www.ubhdenton.net

UNIVERSITY BEHAVIORAL HEALTH OF EL PASO (O, 163 beds) 1900 Denver Avenue, El Paso, TX Zip 79902–3008; tel. 915/544–4000; David Morris, Chief Executive Officer
**Web address:** www.ubhelpaso.com/

WEST OAKS HOSPITAL (O, 144 beds) 6500 Hornwood Drive, Houston, TX Zip 77074–5095; tel. 713/995–0909; Greg Drummond, Chief Executive Officer
**Web address:** www.westoakshospital.com

**UTAH:** SALT LAKE BEHAVIORAL HEALTH (O, 118 beds) 3802 South 700 East, Salt Lake City, UT Zip 84106–1182; tel. 801/264–6000; Melissa Eckstein, Chief Executive Officer
**Web address:** www.saltlakebehavioralhealth.com

**VIRGINIA:** CUMBERLAND HOSPITAL (O, 132 beds) 9407 Cumberland Road, New Kent, VA Zip 23124–2029; tel. 804/966–2242; Patrice Gay Brooks, Chief Executive Officer
**Web address:** www.cumberlandhospital.com

POPLAR SPRINGS HOSPITAL (O, 183 beds) 350 Poplar Drive, Petersburg, VA Zip 23805–9367; tel. 804/733–6874; Richard Clark, Chief Executive Officer
**Web address:** www.poplarsprings.com

VIRGINIA BEACH PSYCHIATRIC CENTER (O, 100 beds) 1100 First Colonial Road, Virginia Beach, VA Zip 23454–2403; tel. 757/496–6000; Frank Gallagher, Chief Executive Officer
**Web address:** www.absfirst.com

**WASHINGTON:** FAIRFAX HOSPITAL (O, 95 beds) 10200 N.E. 132nd Street, Kirkland, WA Zip 98034–2899; tel. 425/821–2000; Ron Escarda, Chief Executive Officer
**Web address:** www.fairfaxhospital.com

**WEST VIRGINIA:** RIVER PARK HOSPITAL (O, 167 beds) 1230 Sixth Avenue, Huntington, WV Zip 25701–2312, Mailing Address: P.O. Box 1875, Zip 25719–1875; tel. 304/526–9111; Terry A. Stephens, Chief Executive Officer
**Web address:** www.riverparkhospital.net

**WYOMING:** WYOMING BEHAVIORAL INSTITUTE (O, 130 beds) 2521 East 15th Street, Casper, WY Zip 82609–4126; tel. 307/237–7444; Joseph Gallagher, Chief Executive Officer
**Web address:** www.wbihelp.com

| | | |
|---|---|---|
| Owned, leased, sponsored: | 136 hospitals | 17993 beds |
| Contract–managed: | 0 hospitals | 0 beds |
| **Totals:** | 136 hospitals | 17993 beds |

---

**0896:   UNIVERSITY HEALTH CARE SYSTEM** (NP)
1350 Walton Way, Augusta, GA Zip 30901–2629; tel. 706/722–9011; James R. Davis, President and Chief Executive Officer

---

For explanation of codes following names, see page B2.
★ Indicates Type III membership in the American Hospital Association.

**GEORGIA:** UNIVERSITY HOSPITAL (O, 490 beds) 1350 Walton Way, Augusta, GA Zip 30901–2629; tel. 706/722–9011; Marilyn A. Bowcutt, R.N., MSN, President
**Web address:** www.universityhealth.org

UNIVERSITY HOSPITAL MCDUFFIE (O, 25 beds) 521 Hill Street S.W., Thomson, GA Zip 30824–2199; tel. 706/595–1411; Sandra I. McVicker, R.N., MSN, President
**Web address:** www.mrmc.org

| | | |
|---|---|---|
| Owned, leased, sponsored: | 2 hospitals | 515 beds |
| Contract–managed: | 0 hospitals | 0 beds |
| Totals: | 2 hospitals | 515 beds |

---

**★0112: UNIVERSITY HOSPITALS** (NP)
11100 Euclid Avenue, Cleveland, OH Zip 44106–5000; tel. 216/844–1000; Thomas F. Zenty, III, President and Chief Executive Officer
**(Centralized Health System)**

**OHIO:** UH REGIONAL HOSPITALS (O, 109 beds) 27100 Chardon Road, Cleveland, OH Zip 44143–1116; tel. 440/585–6500; Laurie Delgado, President
**Web address:** www.uhhospitals.org

UNIVERSITY HOSPITALS AHUJA MEDICAL CENTER (O, 108 beds) 3999 Richmond Road, Beachwood, OH Zip 44122–6046; tel. 216/593–5500; Susan V. Juris, President
**Web address:** www.uhhospitals.org/ahuja/tabid/7051/uhahujamedicalcenter.aspx

UNIVERSITY HOSPITALS CASE MEDICAL CENTER (O, 771 beds) 11100 Euclid Avenue, Cleveland, OH Zip 44106–1716; tel. 216/844–1000; Fred C. Rothstein, M.D., President
**Web address:** www.UHhospitals.org

UNIVERSITY HOSPITALS CONNEAUT MEDICAL CENTER (O, 25 beds) 158 West Main Road, Conneaut, OH Zip 44030–2039; tel. 440/593–1131; Robert David, President and Chief Executive Officer
**Web address:** www.uhhospitals.org

UNIVERSITY HOSPITALS GEAUGA MEDICAL CENTER (O, 126 beds) 13207 Ravenna Road, Chardon, OH Zip 44024–7032; tel. 440/269–6000; M. Steven Jones, President
**Web address:** www.uhhospitals.org/geauga/

UNIVERSITY HOSPITALS GENEVA MEDICAL CENTER (O, 25 beds) 870 West Main Street, Geneva, OH Zip 44041–1295; tel. 440/466–1141; Robert David, President and Chief Executive Officer
**Web address:** www.uhhs.com

| | | |
|---|---|---|
| Owned, leased, sponsored: | 6 hospitals | 1164 beds |
| Contract–managed: | 0 hospitals | 0 beds |
| Totals: | 6 hospitals | 1164 beds |

---

**★6405: UNIVERSITY OF CALIFORNIA–SYSTEMWIDE ADMINISTRATION** (NP)
1111 Franklin Street, 11th Floor, Oakland, CA Zip 94607–5200; tel. 510/987–9071; John D. Stobo, M.D., Senior Vice President Health Sciences and Services
**(Moderately Centralized Health System)**

**CALIFORNIA:** RONALD REAGAN UNIVERSITY OF CALIFORNIA LOS ANGELES MEDICAL CENTER (O, 466 beds) 757 Westwood Plaza, Los Angeles, CA Zip 90095–8358; tel. 310/825–9111; David Feinberg, M.D., Chief Executive Officer
**Web address:** www.uclahealth.org

SANTA MONICA–UCLA MEDICAL CENTER AND ORTHOPAEDIC HOSPITAL (O, 266 beds) 1250 16th Street, Santa Monica, CA Zip 90404–1249; tel. 310/319–4000; Paul Watkins, Chief Administrative Officer
**Web address:** www.healthcare.ucla.edu

STEWART & LYNDA RESNICK NEUROPSYCHIATRIC HOSPITAL AT UCLA (O, 74 beds) 760 Westwood Plaza, Los Angeles, CA Zip 90095–8353; tel. 310/825–9989; Thomas Strouse, M.D., Medical Director
**Web address:** www.semel.ucla.edu/resnick

UC SAN DIEGO HEALTH SYSTEM (O, 582 beds) 200 West Arbor Drive, San Diego, CA Zip 92103–1911; tel. 619/543–6222; Paul S. Viviano, Chief Executive Officer
**Web address:** www.health.ucsd.edu

UCSF MEDICAL CENTER (O, 650 beds) 500 Parnassus Avenue, San Francisco, CA Zip 94143–0296, Mailing Address: 500 Parnassus Avenue, Box 0296, Zip 94143–0296; tel. 415/476–1000; Mark R. Laret, Chief Executive Officer
**Web address:** www.ucsfhealth.org

UNIVERSITY OF CALIFORNIA, DAVIS MEDICAL CENTER (O, 581 beds) 2315 Stockton Boulevard, Sacramento, CA Zip 95817–2282; tel. 916/734–2011; Ann Madden Rice, Chief Executive Officer
**Web address:** www.ucdmc.ucdavis.edu

UNIVERSITY OF CALIFORNIA, IRVINE HEALTHCARE (O, 388 beds) 101 The City Drive, Orange, CA Zip 92868–3298; tel. 714/456–6011; Terry A. Belmont, Chief Executive Officer
**Web address:** www.ucihealth.com

| | | |
|---|---|---|
| Owned, leased, sponsored: | 7 hospitals | 3007 beds |
| Contract–managed: | 0 hospitals | 0 beds |
| Totals: | 7 hospitals | 3007 beds |

---

**★0381: UNIVERSITY OF COLORADO HEALTH** (NP)
2315 East Harmony Road, Suite 200, Fort Collins, CO Zip 80528–8620; tel. 970/237–7001; Rulon F. Stacey, Ph.D., FACHE, Chief Executive Officer
**(Independent Hospital System)**

**COLORADO:** MEDICAL CENTER OF THE ROCKIES (O, 146 beds) 2500 Rocky Mountain Avenue, Loveland, CO Zip 80538–9004; tel. 970/624–2500; George E. Hayes, FACHE, President and Chief Executive Officer
**Web address:** www.medctrrockies.org

MEMORIAL HEALTH SYSTEM (L, 548 beds) 1400 East Boulder Street, Colorado Springs, CO Zip 80909–5599, Mailing Address: P.O. Box 1326, Zip 80901–1326; Michael A. Scialdone, Interim Chief Executive Officer
**Web address:** www.memorialhealthsystem.com

POUDRE VALLEY HOSPITAL (O, 232 beds) 1024 South Lemay Avenue, Fort Collins, CO Zip 80524–3998; tel. 970/495–7000; Kevin L. Unger, FACHE, President and Chief Executive Officer
**Web address:** www.pvhs.org

UNIVERSITY OF COLORADO HOSPITAL (O, 467 beds) 12605 East 16th Avenue, Aurora, CO Zip 80045–2545; tel. 720/848–0000; Bruce Schroffel, President and Chief Executive Officer
**Web address:** www.uch.edu

| | | |
|---|---|---|
| Owned, leased, sponsored: | 4 hospitals | 1393 beds |
| Contract–managed: | 0 hospitals | 0 beds |
| Totals: | 4 hospitals | 1393 beds |

---

**★0216: UNIVERSITY OF MARYLAND MEDICAL SYSTEM** (NP)
250 West Pratt Street, 24th Floor, Baltimore, MD Zip 21201–1595; tel. 410/328–8667; Robert A. Chrencik, President and Chief Executive Officer
**(Centralized Health System)**

**MARYLAND:** BALTIMORE WASHINGTON MEDICAL CENTER (O, 323 beds) 301 Hospital Drive, Glen Burnie, MD Zip 21061–5899; tel. 410/787–4000; Karen E. Olscamp, President and Chief Executive Officer
**Web address:** www.bwmc.umms.org

CHESTER RIVER HEALTH SYSTEM (O, 46 beds) 100 Brown Street, Chestertown, MD Zip 21620–1499; tel. 410/778–3300; James E. Ross, FACHE, President and Chief Executive Officer
**Web address:** www.chesterriverhealth.org

DORCHESTER GENERAL HOSPITAL (O, 43 beds) 300 Byrn Street, Cambridge, MD Zip 21613–1908; tel. 410/228–5511; Kenneth D. Kozel, FACHE, President and Chief Executive Officer
**Web address:** www.shorehealth.org

KERNAN ORTHOPAEDICS AND REHABILITATION (O, 104 beds) 2200 Kernan Drive, Baltimore, MD Zip 21207–6697; tel. 410/448–2500; Michael Jablonover, M.D., President and Chief Executive Officer
**Web address:** www.kernan.org

For explanation of codes following names, see page B2.
★ Indicates Type III membership in the American Hospital Association.

Section B

MARYLAND GENERAL HOSPITAL (O, 212 beds) 827 Linden Avenue, Baltimore, MD Zip 21201–4606; tel. 410/225–8000; Sylvia Smith Johnson, President and Chief Executive Officer
**Web address:** www.marylandgeneral.org

MEMORIAL HOSPITAL AT EASTON MARYLAND (O, 114 beds) 219 South Washington Street, Easton, MD Zip 21601–2996; tel. 410/822–1000; Kenneth D. Kozel, FACHE, President and Chief Executive Officer
**Web address:** www.shorehealth.org

MT. WASHINGTON PEDIATRIC HOSPITAL (O, 61 beds) 1708 West Rogers Avenue, Baltimore, MD Zip 21209–4545; tel. 410/578–8600; Sheldon J. Stein, President and Chief Executive Officer
**Web address:** www.mwph.org

UNIVERSITY OF MARYLAND CHARLES REGIONAL MEDICAL CENTER (O, 124 beds) 5 Garrett Avenue, La Plata, MD Zip 20646–5960, Mailing Address: P.O. Box 1070, Zip 20646–1070; tel. 301/609–4000; Noel A. Cervino, President and Chief Executive Officer
**Web address:** www.civista.org

UNIVERSITY OF MARYLAND MEDICAL CENTER (O, 698 beds) 22 South Greene Street, Baltimore, MD Zip 21201–1595; tel. 410/328–8667; Jeffrey A. Rivest, FACHE, President and Chief Executive Officer
**Web address:** www.umm.edu

UNIVERSITY OF MARYLAND ST. JOSEPH MEDICAL CENTER (O, 320 beds) 7601 Osler Drive, Towson, MD Zip 21204–7582; tel. 410/337–1000; Mohan Suntha, M.D., President and Chief Executive Officer
**Web address:** www.sjmcmd.org

| | | |
|---|---|---|
| **Owned, leased, sponsored:** | 10 hospitals | 2045 beds |
| **Contract–managed:** | 0 hospitals | 0 beds |
| **Totals:** | 10 hospitals | 2045 beds |

---

**0881: UNIVERSITY OF MIAMI HEALTH SYSTEM** (NP)
1400 N.W. 12th Avenue, Miami, FL Zip 33136–1003; tel. 305/243–4000; Pascal J. Goldschmidt, M.D., Chief Executive Officer

**FLORIDA:** BASCOM PALMER EYE INSTITUTE–ANNE BATES LEACH EYE HOSPITAL (O, 58 beds) 900 N.W. 17th Street, Miami, FL Zip 33136–1199, Mailing Address: Box 016880, Zip 33101–6880; tel. 305/326–6000; Michael B. Gittelman, Administrator
**Web address:** www.bascompalmer.org

UNIVERSITY OF MIAMI HOSPITAL (O, 525 beds) 1400 N.W. 12th Avenue, Miami, FL Zip 33136–1003; tel. 305/325–5511; Daniel J. Snyder, Chief Executive Officer
**Web address:** www.umiamihospital.com

UNIVERSITY OF MIAMI HOSPITAL AND CLINICS (O, 40 beds) 1475 N.W. 12th Avenue, Miami, FL Zip 33136–1002; tel. 305/243–1000; Richard R. Ballard, Administrator
**Web address:** www.uhealthsystem.com

| | | |
|---|---|---|
| **Owned, leased, sponsored:** | 3 hospitals | 623 beds |
| **Contract–managed:** | 0 hospitals | 0 beds |
| **Totals:** | 3 hospitals | 623 beds |

---

**★0227: UNIVERSITY OF MISSOURI HEALTH CARE** (NP)
One Hospital Drive, DC 031, Columbia, MO Zip 65212–0001; tel. 573/884–8738; Mitchell L. Wasden, Ed.D., Chief Executive Officer and Chief Operating Officer
**(Moderately Centralized Health System)**

**MISSOURI:** CAPITAL REGION MEDICAL CENTER (O, 114 beds) 1125 Madison Street, Jefferson City, MO Zip 65101–5200, Mailing Address: P.O. Box 1128, Zip 65102–1128; tel. 573/632–5000; Edward F. Farnsworth, FACHE, President
**Web address:** www.crmc.org

COOPER COUNTY MEMORIAL HOSPITAL (C, 32 beds) 17651 B Highway, Boonville, MO Zip 65233–2839, Mailing Address: P.O. Box 88, Zip 65233–0088; tel. 660/882–7461; Allen J. Waldo, FACHE, CPA, Chief Executive Officer
**Web address:** www.coopercmh.com

MISSOURI REHABILITATION CENTER (O, 63 beds) 600 North Main Street, Mount Vernon, MO Zip 65712–1004; tel. 417/466–3711; Mike Powell, Executive Director
**Web address:** www.muhealth.org/mrcrehab

UNIVERSITY OF MISSOURI HOSPITALS AND CLINICS (O, 463 beds) One Hospital Drive, Columbia, MO Zip 65212–0001; tel. 573/882–4141; Mitchell L. Wasden, Ed.D., Chief Executive Officer and Chief Operating Officer
**Web address:** www.muhealth.org

WOMEN'S AND CHILDREN'S HOSPITAL (O, 108 beds) 404 Keene Street, Columbia, MO Zip 65201–6626; tel. 573/875–9000; Keri Simon, Executive Director
**Web address:** www.muchildrenshospital.org

| | | |
|---|---|---|
| **Owned, leased, sponsored:** | 4 hospitals | 748 beds |
| **Contract–managed:** | 1 hospital | 32 beds |
| **Totals:** | 5 hospitals | 780 beds |

---

**0021: UNIVERSITY OF NEW MEXICO HOSPITALS** (NP)
915 Camino De Salud, Albuquerque, NM Zip 87131–0001; tel. 505/272–5849; Stephen W. McKernan, Chief Executive Officer

**NEW MEXICO:** UNIVERSITY OF NEW MEXICO HOSPITALS (O, 537 beds) 2211 Lomas Boulevard N.E., Albuquerque, NM Zip 87106–2745; tel. 505/272–2111; Stephen W. McKernan, Chief Executive Officer
**Web address:** www.unm.edu

UNM SANDOVAL REGIONAL MEDICAL CENTER (O, 72 beds) 3001 Broadmoor Boulevard N.E., Rio Rancho, NM Zip 87144–2100; tel. 505/994–7000; Kevin L. Rogols, FACHE, Chief Executive Officer
**Web address:** www.hospitals.unm.edu/

| | | |
|---|---|---|
| **Owned, leased, sponsored:** | 2 hospitals | 609 beds |
| **Contract–managed:** | 0 hospitals | 0 beds |
| **Totals:** | 2 hospitals | 609 beds |

---

**★0168: UNIVERSITY OF PENNSYLVANIA HEALTH SYSTEM** (NP)
3400 Civic Center Bouelvard, Philadelphia, PA Zip 19104–5127; tel. 215/662–2203; Ralph W. Muller, President and Chief Executive Officer
**(Centralized Physician/Insurance Health System)**

**PENNSYLVANIA:** HOSPITAL OF THE UNIVERSITY OF PENNSYLVANIA (O, 784 beds) 3400 Spruce Street, Philadelphia, PA Zip 19104–4206; tel. 215/662–4000; Garry L. Scheib, Executive Director
**Web address:** www.pennhealth.com

PENN PRESBYTERIAN MEDICAL CENTER (O, 331 beds) 51 North 39th Street, Philadelphia, PA Zip 19104–2699; tel. 215/662–8000; Michele M. Volpe, Executive Director and Chief Executive Officer
**Web address:** www.pennmedicine.org/pmc/

PENNSYLVANIA HOSPITAL (O, 455 beds) 800 Spruce Street, Philadelphia, PA Zip 19107–6192; tel. 215/829–3000; R. Michael Buckley, M.D., Executive Director
**Web address:** www.pahosp.com

| | | |
|---|---|---|
| **Owned, leased, sponsored:** | 3 hospitals | 1570 beds |
| **Contract–managed:** | 0 hospitals | 0 beds |
| **Totals:** | 3 hospitals | 1570 beds |

---

**★0223: UNIVERSITY OF ROCHESTER MEDICAL CENTER** (NP)
601 Elmwood Avenue, Rochester, NY Zip 14642–0002; tel. 585/275–2100; Steven I. Goldstein, General Director and Chief Executive Officer
**(Centralized Health System)**

**NEW YORK:** F. F. THOMPSON HOSPITAL (O, 214 beds) 350 Parrish Street, Canandaigua, NY Zip 14424–1731; tel. 585/396–6000; Michael Stapleton, R.N., MS, President and Chief Executive Officer
**Web address:** www.thompsonhealth.com

HIGHLAND HOSPITAL OF ROCHESTER (O, 261 beds) 1000 South Avenue, Rochester, NY Zip 14620–2733; tel. 585/473–2200; Steven I. Goldstein, President and Chief Executive Officer
**Web address:** www.stronghealth.com

---

For explanation of codes following names, see page B2.
★ Indicates Type III membership in the American Hospital Association.

STRONG MEMORIAL HOSPITAL OF THE UNIVERSITY OF ROCHESTER (O, 781 beds) 601 Elmwood Avenue, Rochester, NY Zip 14642–0002; tel. 585/275–2100; Steven I. Goldstein, President and Chief Executive Officer
**Web address:** www.urmc.rochester.edu

| | | |
|---|---|---|
| Owned, leased, sponsored: | 3 hospitals | 1256 beds |
| Contract–managed: | 0 hospitals | 0 beds |
| Totals: | 3 hospitals | 1256 beds |

---

**★0057:  UNIVERSITY OF SOUTH ALABAMA HOSPITALS** (NP)
2451 Fillingim Street, Mobile, AL Zip 36617–2238; tel. 251/471–7000; Stanley K. Hammack, Chief Executive Officer
**(Independent Hospital System)**

**ALABAMA:** UNIVERSITY OF SOUTH ALABAMA CHILDREN'S AND WOMEN'S HOSPITAL (O, 198 beds) 1700 Center Street, Mobile, AL Zip 36604–3301; tel. 251/415–1000; Owen Bailey, Administrator
**Web address:** www.usahealthsystem.com/usacwh

UNIVERSITY OF SOUTH ALABAMA MEDICAL CENTER (O, 132 beds) 2451 Fillingim Street, Mobile, AL Zip 36617–2293; tel. 251/471–7000; A. Elizabeth Anderson, Administrator
**Web address:** www.usahealthsystem.com/usamc

| | | |
|---|---|---|
| Owned, leased, sponsored: | 2 hospitals | 330 beds |
| Contract–managed: | 0 hospitals | 0 beds |
| Totals: | 2 hospitals | 330 beds |

---

**★0033:  UNIVERSITY OF TEXAS SYSTEM** (NP)
601 Colorado Street, Suite 205, Austin, TX Zip 78701–2904; tel. 512/499–4224; Kenneth Shine, M.D., Executive Vice Chancellor
**(Moderately Centralized Health System)**

**TEXAS:** UNIVERSITY OF TEXAS HARRIS COUNTY PSYCHIATRIC CENTER (O, 181 beds) 2800 South MacGregor Way, Houston, TX Zip 77021–1000, Mailing Address: P.O. Box 20249, Zip 77225–0249; tel. 713/741–7870; Jair C. Soares, M.D., Executive Director
**Web address:** www.hcpc.uth.tmc.edu

UNIVERSITY OF TEXAS HEALTH SCIENCE CENTER AT TYLER (O, 116 beds) 11937 Highway 271, Tyler, TX Zip 75708–3154; tel. 903/877–7777; Kirk A. Calhoun, M.D., President
**Web address:** www.uthct.edu

UNIVERSITY OF TEXAS M.D. ANDERSON CANCER CENTER (O, 631 beds) 1515 Holcombe Boulevard, Box 91, Houston, TX Zip 77030–4000; tel. 713/792–2121; Ronald A. DePinho, M.D., President
**Web address:** www.mdanderson.org

UNIVERSITY OF TEXAS MEDICAL BRANCH HOSPITALS (O, 380 beds) 301 University Boulevard, Galveston, TX Zip 77555–0128; tel. 409/772–1011; Donna K. Sollenberger, Executive Vice President and Chief Executive Officer
**Web address:** www.utmb.edu

| | | |
|---|---|---|
| Owned, leased, sponsored: | 4 hospitals | 1308 beds |
| Contract–managed: | 0 hospitals | 0 beds |
| Totals: | 4 hospitals | 1308 beds |

---

**0137:  UPMC** (NP)
600 Grant Street, U.S. Steel Tower, Suite 6262, Pittsburgh, PA Zip 15219–2702; tel. 412/647–8762; Jeffrey A. Romoff, President and Chief Executive Officer
**(Centralized Physician/Insurance Health System)**

**PENNSYLVANIA:** CHILDREN'S HOSPITAL OF PITTSBURGH OF UPMC (O, 296 beds) 4401 Penn Avenue, Pittsburgh, PA Zip 15224–1334; tel. 412/692–5325; Christopher Gessner, President
**Web address:** www.chp.edu

MAGEE–WOMENS HOSPITAL OF UPMC (O, 360 beds) 300 Halket Street, Pittsburgh, PA Zip 15213–3108; tel. 412/641–1000; Leslie C. Davis, President
**Web address:** www.magee.edu

UPMC ALTOONA (O, 380 beds) 620 Howard Avenue, Altoona, PA Zip 16601–4804; tel. 814/889–2011; Gerald Murray, President and Chief Executive Officer
**Web address:** www.altoonaregional.org

UPMC BEDFORD MEMORIAL (O, 27 beds) 10455 Lincoln Highway, Everett, PA Zip 15537–7046; tel. 814/623–6161; Roger P. Winn, President
**Web address:** www.upmcbedfordmemorial.com

UPMC EAST (O, 156 beds) 2775 Mosside Boulevard, Monroeville, PA Zip 15146–2760; tel. 412/357–3000; Mark Sevco, President
**Web address:** www.upmc.com/locations/hospitals/east/Pages/default.aspx

UPMC HAMOT (O, 373 beds) 201 State Street, Erie, PA Zip 16550–0002; tel. 814/877–6000; V. James Fiorenzo, President
**Web address:** www.hamot.org

UPMC HORIZON (O, 184 beds) 110 North Main Street, Greenville, PA Zip 16125–1726; tel. 724/588–2100; Donald R. Owrey, President
**Web address:** www.horizon.upmc.com

UPMC MCKEESPORT (O, 231 beds) 1500 Fifth Avenue, McKeesport, PA Zip 15132–2422; tel. 412/664–2000; Cynthia M. Dorundo, President
**Web address:** www.mckeesport.upmc.com

UPMC MERCY (O, 488 beds) 1400 Locust Street, Pittsburgh, PA Zip 15219–5166; tel. 412/232–8111; Will L. Cook, President
**Web address:** www.upmc.com/HospitalsFacilities/HFHome/Hospitals/Mercy/

UPMC NORTHWEST (O, 180 beds) 100 Fairfield Drive, Seneca, PA Zip 16346–2130; tel. 814/676–7600; Jason Roeback, President
**Web address:** www.upmc.com/locations/hospitals/northwest/Pages/default.aspx

UPMC PASSAVANT (O, 424 beds) 9100 Babcock Boulevard, Pittsburgh, PA Zip 15237–5815; tel. 412/367–6700; David T. Martin, President
**Web address:** www.upmc.edu/passavant

UPMC PRESBYTERIAN SHADYSIDE (O, 1528 beds) 200 Lothrop Street, Pittsburgh, PA Zip 15213–2536; tel. 412/647–2345; John Innocenti, Sr., President and Chief Executive Officer
**Web address:** www.upmc.edu

UPMC ST. MARGARET (O, 249 beds) 815 Freeport Road, Pittsburgh, PA Zip 15215–3301; tel. 412/784–4000; Teresa G. Petrick, President
**Web address:** www.stmargaret.upmc.com

| | | |
|---|---|---|
| Owned, leased, sponsored: | 13 hospitals | 4876 beds |
| Contract–managed: | 0 hospitals | 0 beds |
| Totals: | 13 hospitals | 4876 beds |

---

**0816:  UPPER ALLEGHENY HEALTH SYSTEM** (NP)
130 South Union Street, Suite 300, Olean, NY Zip 14760–3676; tel. 716/375–6190; Timothy J. Finan, FACHE, President and Chief Executive Officer
**(Independent Hospital System)**

**NEW YORK:** OLEAN GENERAL HOSPITAL (O, 186 beds) 515 Main Street, Olean, NY Zip 14760–1513; tel. 716/373–2600; Timothy J. Finan, FACHE, President and Chief Executive Officer
**Web address:** www.ogh.org

**PENNSYLVANIA:** BRADFORD REGIONAL MEDICAL CENTER (O, 182 beds) 116 Interstate Parkway, Bradford, PA Zip 16701–1036; tel. 814/368–4143; Timothy J. Finan, FACHE, President and Chief Executive Officer
**Web address:** www.brmc.com

| | | |
|---|---|---|
| Owned, leased, sponsored: | 2 hospitals | 368 beds |
| Contract–managed: | 0 hospitals | 0 beds |
| Totals: | 2 hospitals | 368 beds |

---

**0038:  UPPER CHESAPEAKE HEALTH SYSTEM** (NP)
520 Upper Chesapeake Drive, Suite 405, Bel Air, MD Zip 21014–4381; tel. 443/643–3303; Lyle Ernest Sheldon, FACHE, President and Chief Executive Officer
**(Independent Hospital System)**

**MARYLAND:** HARFORD MEMORIAL HOSPITAL (O, 104 beds) 501 South Union Avenue, Havre De Grace, MD Zip 21078–3493; tel. 443/843–5000; Lyle Ernest Sheldon, FACHE, President and Chief Executive Officer
**Web address:** www.uchs.org

UPPER CHESAPEAKE MEDICAL CENTER (O, 182 beds) 500 Upper Chesapeake Drive, Bel Air, MD Zip 21014–4324; tel. 443/643–1000; Lyle Ernest Sheldon, FACHE, President and Chief Executive Officer
**Web address:** www.uchs.org

For explanation of codes following names, see page B2.
★ Indicates Type III membership in the American Hospital Association.

**Section B**

| Owned, leased, sponsored: | 2 hospitals | 286 beds |
| Contract–managed: | 0 hospitals | 0 beds |
| Totals: | 2 hospitals | 286 beds |

**0868: USMD INC.** (IO)
6333 North State Highway 161 Suite 200, Irving, TX
Zip 75038–2229; tel. 214/493–4000; Karen A. Fiducia, FACHE,
President, Hospital Division
**(Independent Hospital System)**

**TEXAS:** USMD HOSPITAL AT ARLINGTON (O, 34 beds) 801 West Interstate
20, Arlington, TX Zip 76017–5851; tel. 817/472–3400; Marcia Crim,
R.N., MSN, Chief Executive Officer
**Web address:** www.usmdarlington.com

USMD HOSPITAL AT FORT WORTH (O, 8 beds) 5900 Dirks Road, Fort Worth,
TX Zip 76132–5473; tel. 817/433–9100; Stephanie Atkins–Guidry,
Administrator
**Web address:** www.usmdfortworth.com/

| Owned, leased, sponsored: | 2 hospitals | 42 beds |
| Contract–managed: | 0 hospitals | 0 beds |
| Totals: | 2 hospitals | 42 beds |

**0860: UVA HEALTH SYSTEM** (NP)
1215 Lee Street, Charlottesville, VA Zip 22908–0816;
tel. 434/924–0211; R. Edward Howell, Vice President and Chief
Executive Officer
**(Centralized Health System)**

**VIRGINIA:** TRANSITIONAL CARE HOSPITAL (O, 40 beds) 2965 Ivy Road (250
West), Charlottesville, VA Zip 22903–9330; tel. 434/924–7897; Michelle
Hereford, Administrator
**Web address:** www.uvahealth.com/services/transitional–care–hospital

UNIVERSITY OF VIRGINIA MEDICAL CENTER (O, 565 beds) 1215 Lee Street,
Charlottesville, VA Zip 22908–0001, Mailing Address: P.O. Box 800809,
Zip 22908–0809; tel. 434/924–0211; R. Edward Howell, Vice President and
Chief Executive Officer
**Web address:** www.healthsystem.virginia.edu

| Owned, leased, sponsored: | 2 hospitals | 605 beds |
| Contract–managed: | 0 hospitals | 0 beds |
| Totals: | 2 hospitals | 605 beds |

**6415: UW MEDICINE** (NP)
1959 N.E. Pacific Street, Seattle, WA Zip 98195–0001, Mailing
Address: P.O. Box 356350, Zip 98195–6350; tel. 206/543–7718;
Paul G. Ramsey, Chief Executive Officer
**(Independent Hospital System)**

**WASHINGTON:** UNIVERSITY OF WASHINGTON MEDICAL CENTER (O, 450
beds) 1959 N.E. Pacific Street, Seattle, WA Zip 98195–6151;
tel. 206/598–3300; Stephen P. Zieniewicz, FACHE, Executive Director
**Web address:** www.uwmedicine.
org/Patient–Care/Locations/UWMC/Pages/default.aspx

UW MEDICINE/HARBORVIEW MEDICAL CENTER (O, 413 beds) 325 Ninth
Avenue, Seattle, WA Zip 98104–2499, Mailing Address: P.O. Box 359717,
Zip 98195–9717; tel. 206/744–3000; Eileen Whalen, R.N., Executive
Director
**Web address:** www.uwmedicine.
org/Patient–Care/Locations/HMC/Pages/default.aspx

UW MEDICINE/NORTHWEST HOSPITAL & MEDICAL CENTER (O, 176 beds)
1550 North 115th Street, Seattle, WA Zip 98133–8401; tel. 206/364–0500;
Cynthia Hecker, Executive Director
**Web address:** www.uwmedicine.
org/Patient–Care/Locations/nwh/Pages/default.aspx

UW MEDICINE/VALLEY MEDICAL CENTER (O, 174 beds) 400 South 43rd
Street, Renton, WA Zip 98055–5714; tel. 425/228–3450; Richard D.
Roodman, Chief Executive Officer
**Web address:** www.valleymed.org

| Owned, leased, sponsored: | 4 hospitals | 1213 beds |
| Contract–managed: | 0 hospitals | 0 beds |
| Totals: | 4 hospitals | 1213 beds |

**★0128: VALLEY HEALTH SYSTEM** (NP)
220 Campus Boulevard, Suite 310, Winchester, VA Zip 22601–2889,
Mailing Address: P.O. Box 3340, Zip 22604–2540;
tel. 540/536–8024; Mark H. Merrill, President
**(Independent Hospital System)**

**VIRGINIA:** PAGE MEMORIAL HOSPITAL (O, 25 beds) 200 Memorial Drive,
Luray, VA Zip 22835–1005; tel. 540/743–4561; N. Travis Clark,
President
**Web address:** www.valleyhealthlink.com/page

SHENANDOAH MEMORIAL HOSPITAL (O, 25 beds) 759 South Main Street,
Woodstock, VA Zip 22664–1127; tel. 540/459–1100; Floyd Heater,
President
**Web address:** www.valleyhealthlink.com/shenandoah

WARREN MEMORIAL HOSPITAL (O, 166 beds) 1000 North Shenandoah
Avenue, Front Royal, VA Zip 22630–3598; tel. 540/636–0300; Patrick B.
Nolan, President and Chief Executive Officer
**Web address:** www.valleyhealthlink.com/WMH

WINCHESTER MEDICAL CENTER (O, 475 beds) 1840 Amherst Street,
Winchester, VA Zip 22601–2808, Mailing Address: P.O. Box 3340,
Zip 22604–2540; tel. 540/536–8000; Mark H. Merrill, Interim Chief
Executive Officer
**Web address:** www.valleyhealthlink.com/WMC

**WEST VIRGINIA:** HAMPSHIRE MEMORIAL HOSPITAL (O, 44 beds) 363 Sunrise
Boulevard, Romney, WV Zip 26757–4607; tel. 304/822–4561; Neil R.
McLaughlin, R.N., Interim President
**Web address:** www.valleyhealthlink.com/hampshire

WAR MEMORIAL HOSPITAL (O, 41 beds) One Healthy Way, Berkeley Springs,
WV Zip 25411–7463; tel. 304/258–1234; Neil R. McLaughlin, R.N.,
President
**Web address:** www.valleyhealthlink.com/war

| Owned, leased, sponsored: | 6 hospitals | 776 beds |
| Contract–managed: | 0 hospitals | 0 beds |
| Totals: | 6 hospitals | 776 beds |

**● ★0387: VANDERBILT HEALTH** (NP)
1211 22nd Avenue South, Nashville, TN Zip 37232;
tel. 615/322–5000; Charles Wright Pinson, M.D., Deputy Vice
Chancellor for Health Affairs and Chief Executive Officer of Vanderbilt
Health System
**(Moderately Centralized Health System)**

**TENNESSEE:** VANDERBILT HOSPITAL AND CLINICS (O, 966 beds) 1211
22nd Avenue North, Nashville, TN Zip 37232–2102; tel. 615/322–5000;
David R. Posch, Chief Executive Officer
**Web address:** www.mc.vanderbilt.edu

| Owned, leased, sponsored: | 1 hospital | 966 beds |
| Contract–managed: | 0 hospitals | 0 beds |
| Totals: | 1 hospital | 966 beds |

**★0193: VANGUARD HEALTH SYSTEMS** (IO)
20 Burton Hills Boulevard, Suite 10, Nashville, TN Zip 37215–6197,
Zip 85020; tel. 615/665–6000; Charles N. Martin, Jr., Chairman and
Chief Executive Officer
**(Moderately Centralized Health System)**

**ARIZONA:** ARROWHEAD HOSPITAL (O, 234 beds) 18701 North 67th Avenue,
Glendale, AZ Zip 85308–7100; tel. 623/561–1000; Frank L. Molinaro,
Chief Executive Officer
**Web address:** www.arrowheadhospital.com

MARYVALE HOSPITAL MEDICAL CENTER (O, 100 beds) 5102 West Campbell
Avenue, Phoenix, AZ Zip 85031–1799; tel. 623/848–5000; Crystal Hamilton,
R.N., Chief Executive Officer
**Web address:** www.maryvalehospital.com

Section B

PARADISE VALLEY HOSPITAL (O, 142 beds) 3929 East Bell Road, Phoenix, AZ Zip 85032–2196; tel. 602/923–5000; David Tupponce, M.D., Interim Chief Executive Officer
**Web address:** www.paradisevalleyhospital.com

PHOENIX BAPTIST HOSPITAL (O, 215 beds) 2000 West Bethany Home Road, Phoenix, AZ Zip 85015–2443; tel. 602/249–0212; Wayne Gillis, Interim Chief Executive Officer
**Web address:** www.phoenixbaptisthospital.com

WEST VALLEY HOSPITAL (O, 106 beds) 13677 West McDowell Road, Goodyear, AZ Zip 85395–2635; tel. 623/882–1500; Jo Adkins, Chief Executive Officer
**Web address:** www.wvhospital.com

**ILLINOIS:** UNITYHEALTH LOUIS A. WEISS MEMORIAL HOSPITAL (O, 184 beds) 4646 North Marine Drive, Chicago, IL Zip 60640–5759; tel. 773/878–8700; Anthony Tedeschi, M.D., M.P.H., Chief Executive Officer and Chief Medical Officer
**Web address:** www.weisshospital.com

UNITYHEALTH MACNEAL HOSPITAL (O, 371 beds) 3249 South Oak Park Avenue, Berwyn, IL Zip 60402–0715; tel. 708/783–9100; J. Scott Steiner, Interim Chief Executive Officer
**Web address:** www.macneal.com

UNITYHEALTH WEST SUBURBAN MEDICAL CENTER (O, 172 beds) 3 Erie Court, Oak Park, IL Zip 60302–2599; tel. 708/383–6200; Joan Ormsby, Interim Chief Executive Officer
**Web address:** www.westsuburbanmc.com/Home.aspx

UNITYHEALTH WESTLAKE HOSPITAL (O, 181 beds) 1225 Lake Street, Melrose Park, IL Zip 60160–4000; tel. 708/681–3000; Joan Ormsby, Interim Chief Executive Officer
**Web address:** www.wlhospital.com/Home.aspx

**MASSACHUSETTS:** METROWEST MEDICAL CENTER (O, 155 beds) 115 Lincoln Street, Framingham, MA Zip 01702–6342; tel. 508/383–1000; Charles Orlando, Interim Chief Executive Officer
**Web address:** www.mwmc.com

SAINT VINCENT HOSPITAL (O, 321 beds) 123 Summer Street, Worcester, MA Zip 01608–1216; tel. 508/363–5000; Erik G. Wexler, President and Chief Executive Officer
**Web address:** www.stvincenthospital.com

**MICHIGAN:** CHILDREN'S HOSPITAL OF MICHIGAN (O, 222 beds) 3901 Beaubien Street, Detroit, MI Zip 48201–2119; tel. 313/745–5437; Herman B. Gray, M.D., President
**Web address:** www.chmkids.org

DETROIT RECEIVING HOSPITAL/UNIVERSITY HEALTH CENTER (O, 268 beds) 4201 Saint Antoine Street, Detroit, MI Zip 48201–2153; tel. 313/745–3000; Iris Taylor, Ph.D., R.N., President
**Web address:** www.dmc.org

DMC HURON VALLEY–SINAI HOSPITAL (O, 153 beds) 1 William Carls Drive, Commerce Township, MI Zip 48382–2201; tel. 248/937–3300; Lynn M. Torossian, President
**Web address:** www.hvsh.org

HARPER UNIVERSITY HOSPITAL/HUTZEL WOMEN'S HOSPITAL (O, 535 beds) 3990 John R Street, Detroit, MI Zip 48201–2018; tel. 313/745–8040; Patricia Wilkerson–Uddyback, M.D., Interim President
**Web address:** www.harperhospital.org

REHABILITATION INSTITUTE OF MICHIGAN (O, 74 beds) 261 Mack Boulevard, Detroit, MI Zip 48201–2495; tel. 313/745–1203; William H. Restum, Ph.D., President
**Web address:** www.rimrehab.org

SINAI–GRACE HOSPITAL (O, 310 beds) 6071 West Outer Drive, Detroit, MI Zip 48235–2679; tel. 313/966–3300; Reginald J. Eadie, M.D., President
**Web address:** www.sinaigrace.org

**TEXAS:** BAPTIST MEDICAL CENTER (O, 1527 beds) 111 Dallas Street, San Antonio, TX Zip 78205–1230; tel. 210/297–7000; David S. Goldberg, President
**Web address:** www.baptisthealthsystem.com

VALLEY BAPTIST MEDICAL CENTER–BROWNSVILLE (O, 240 beds) 1040 West Jefferson Street, Brownsville, TX Zip 78520–6338, Mailing Address: P.O. Box 3590, Zip 78523–3590; tel. 956/698–5400; Leslie Bingham, Senior Vice President and Chief Executive Officer
**Web address:** www.valleybaptist.net/brownsville/index.htm

VALLEY BAPTIST MEDICAL CENTER–HARLINGEN (O, 417 beds) 2101 Pease Street, Harlingen, TX Zip 78550–8307, Mailing Address: P.O. Drawer 2588, Zip 78551–2588; tel. 956/389–1100; Todd Mann, Senior Vice President and Chief Executive Officer
**Web address:** www.valleybaptist.net/harlingen/index.htm

| | | |
|---|---|---|
| **Owned, leased, sponsored:** | 20 hospitals | 5927 beds |
| **Contract–managed:** | 0 hospitals | 0 beds |
| **Totals:** | 20 hospitals | 5927 beds |

**0299: VIBRA HEALTHCARE** (IO)
4550 Lena Drive, Suite 225, Mechanicsburg, PA Zip 17055–4920; tel. 717/591–5700; Brad Hollinger, Chairman and Chief Executive Officer
**(Independent Hospital System)**

**CALIFORNIA:** BALLARD REHABILITATION HOSPITAL (O, 40 beds) 1760 West 16th Street, San Bernardino, CA Zip 92411–1160; tel. 909/473–1200; Mary Miles Hunt, Chief Executive Officer
**Web address:** www.ballardrehab.com

KENTFIELD REHABILITATION AND SPECIALTY HOSPITAL (O, 52 beds) 1125 Sir Francis Drake Boulevard, Kentfield, CA Zip 94904–1418; tel. 415/456–9680; Ann Gors, Chief Executive Officer
**Web address:** www.kentfieldrehab.com

SAN JOAQUIN VALLEY REHABILITATION HOSPITAL (O, 40 beds) 7173 North Sharon Avenue, Fresno, CA Zip 93720–3329; tel. 559/436–3600; Mary Jo Jacobson, Chief Executive Officer
**Web address:** www.sjvrehab.com

VIBRA HOSPITAL OF NORTHERN CALIFORNIA (O, 88 beds) 2801 Eureka Way, Redding, CA Zip 96001–0222; tel. 530/246–9000; Chris Jones, Chief Executive Officer
**Web address:** www.norcalrehab.com

VIBRA HOSPITAL OF SAN DIEGO (O, 57 beds) 555 Washington Street, San Diego, CA Zip 92103–2289; tel. 619/260–8300; Natalie Germuska, R.N., MSN, Chief Executive Officer
**Web address:** www.vhsandiego.com/

**COLORADO:** VIBRA HOSPITAL OF DENVER (O, 71 beds) 8451 Pearl Street, Thornton, CO Zip 80229–4804; tel. 303/288–3000; Jan Eyer, Chief Executive Officer
**Web address:** www.vhdenver.com

**INDIANA:** VIBRA HOSPITAL OF FORT WAYNE (O, 24 beds) 2626 Fairfield Avenue, Fort Wayne, IN Zip 46807–1215; tel. 260/399–2900; John Pierson, Chief Executive Officer
**Web address:** www.vhfortwayne.com

VIBRA HOSPITAL OF NORTHWESTERN INDIANA (O, 40 beds) 9509 Georgia Street, Crown Point, IN Zip 46307–6518; tel. 219/472–2200; Charles Nordyke, Chief Executive Officer
**Web address:** www.vhnwindiana.com/

**KENTUCKY:** SOUTHERN KENTUCKY REHABILITATION HOSPITAL (O, 60 beds) 1300 Campbell Lane, Bowling Green, KY Zip 42104–4162; tel. 270/782–6900; Stuart Locke, Interim Chief Executive Officer
**Web address:** www.skyrehab.com

**MASSACHUSETTS:** NEW BEDFORD REHABILITATION HOSPITAL (O, 90 beds) 4499 Acushnet Avenue, New Bedford, MA Zip 02745–4707; tel. 508/995–6900; Edward B. Leary, Chief Executive Officer
**Web address:** www.newbedfordrehab.com

**MICHIGAN:** VIBRA HOSPITAL OF SOUTHEASTERN MICHIGAN (O, 140 beds) 26400 West Outer Drive, Lincoln Park, MI Zip 48146–2088; tel. 313/386–2000; Scott Deig, FACHE, Chief Executive Officer
**Web address:** www.vhsemichigan.com/

**NEW JERSEY:** MARLTON REHABILITATION HOSPITAL (O, 51 beds) 92 Brick Road, Marlton, NJ Zip 08053–2177; tel. 856/988–8778; Michael Long, MS, Chief Executive Officer
**Web address:** www.marltonrehab.com

**OHIO:** VIBRA HOSPITAL OF MAHONING VALLEY (O, 42 beds) 8049 South Avenue, Boardman, OH Zip 44512–6154; tel. 330/726–5000; Mary Lou Sankovich, R.N., MSN, Chief Executive Officer and Chief Nursing Officer
**Web address:** www.mahoningvalleyhospital.com

Section B

**OREGON:** VIBRA SPECIALTY HOSPITAL OF PORTLAND (O, 60 beds) 10300 N.E. Hancock Street, Portland, OR Zip 97220–3831; tel. 503/257–5500; Tina Key, Chief Executive Officer
**Web address:** www.vibrahealthcare.com

**TEXAS:** VIBRA SPECIALTY HOSPITAL OF DALLAS (O, 60 beds) 2700 Walker Way, Desoto, TX Zip 75115–2088; tel. 214/638–1500; Greg Floyd, Chief Executive Officer
**Web address:** www.vibrahealthcare.com

| | | |
|---|---|---|
| Owned, leased, sponsored: | 15 hospitals | 915 beds |
| Contract–managed: | 0 hospitals | 0 beds |
| Totals: | 15 hospitals | 915 beds |

---

**0897: VICTORY HEALTHCARE** (IO)
2201 Timberloch Place, Suite 200, The Woodlands, TX Zip 77380; tel. 281/863–2100; Robert N. Helms, Jr., Board Chair, President and Chief Executive Officer

VICTORY MEDICAL CENTER – SAN ANTONIO (O, 9 beds) 4243 East Southcross Boulevard, San Antonio, TX Zip 78222–3727; tel. 210/368–7400; Alex Garcia, Chief Executive Officer
**Web address:** www.victory–healthcare.com/san–antonio–location/

VICTORY MEDICAL CENTER HOUSTON (O, 25 beds) 2001 Hermann Drive, Houston, TX Zip 77004–7643; tel. 713/285–5500; Luis Garcia, Chief Executive Officer
**Web address:** www.victory–healthcare.com

VICTORY MEDICAL CENTER MID–CITIES (O, 23 beds) 1612 Hurst Town Center Drive, Hurst, TX Zip 76054–6236; tel. 817/345–4100; Barbara Millwood, Chief Executive Officer
**Web address:** www.victory–healthcare.com

| | | |
|---|---|---|
| Owned, leased, sponsored: | 3 hospitals | 57 beds |
| Contract–managed: | 0 hospitals | 0 beds |
| Totals: | 3 hospitals | 57 beds |

---

**★0217: VIDANT HEALTH** (NP)
2100 Stantonsburg Road, Greenville, NC Zip 27834–2818, Mailing Address: P.O. Box 6028, Zip 27835–6028; tel. 252/847–4100; David C. Herman, M.D., President and Chief Executive Officer
**(Moderately Centralized Health System)**

**NORTH CAROLINA:** ALBEMARLE HEALTH (C, 89 beds) 1144 North Road Street, Elizabeth City, NC Zip 27909–3473, Mailing Address: P.O. Box 1587, Zip 27906–1587; tel. 252/335–0531; Wendell H. Baker, Jr., President
**Web address:** www.albemarlehealth.org

THE OUTER BANKS HOSPITAL (O, 21 beds) 4800 South Croatan Highway, Nags Head, NC Zip 27959–9704; tel. 252/449–4511; Ronald A. Sloan, FACHE, President
**Web address:** www.theouterbankshospital.com

VIDANT BEAUFORT HOSPITAL (L, 95 beds) 628 East 12th Street, Washington, NC Zip 27889–3409; tel. 252/975–4100; Harvey Case, President
**Web address:** www.beaufortregionalhealthsystem.org

VIDANT BERTIE HOSPITAL (L, 6 beds) 1403 South King Street, Windsor, NC Zip 27983–9666, Mailing Address: P.O. Box 40, Zip 27983–0040; tel. 252/794–6600; Jeffery Dial, Acting Chief Executive Officer
**Web address:** www.vidanthealth.com

VIDANT CHOWAN HOSPITAL (L, 35 beds) 211 Virginia Road, Edenton, NC Zip 27932–9668, Mailing Address: P.O. Box 629, Zip 27932–0629; tel. 252/482–8451; Jeffery Dial, Acting Chief Executive Officer
**Web address:** www.vidanthealth.com

VIDANT DUPLIN HOSPITAL (L, 74 beds) 401 North Main Street, Kenansville, NC Zip 28349–8801, Mailing Address: P.O. Box 278, Zip 28349–0278; tel. 910/296–0941; Jay Briley, President
**Web address:** www.vidanthealth.com

VIDANT EDGECOMBE HOSPITAL (O, 117 beds) 111 Hospital Drive, Tarboro, NC Zip 27886–2011; tel. 252/641–7700; Patrick Heins, President
**Web address:** www.https://www.vidanthealth.com/edgecombe/default.aspx

VIDANT MEDICAL CENTER (O, 875 beds) 2100 Stantonsburg Road, Greenville, NC Zip 27834–2818, Mailing Address: P.O. Box 6028, Zip 27835–6028; tel. 252/847–4100; Stephen Lawler, President
**Web address:** www.https://www.vidanthealth.com/

VIDANT PUNGO HOSPITAL (O, 35 beds) 202 East Water Street, Belhaven, NC Zip 27810–1450; tel. 252/943–2111; Harvey Case, President
**Web address:** www.vidanthealth.com/vidant/dynamic–detail.aspx?id=11781

VIDANT ROANOKE–CHOWAN HOSPITAL (L, 103 beds) 500 South Academy Street, Ahoskie, NC Zip 27910–3261, Mailing Address: P.O. Box 1385, Zip 27910–1385; tel. 252/209–3000; Susan S. Lassiter, FACHE, President and Chief Executive Officer
**Web address:** www.vidanthealth.com

| | | |
|---|---|---|
| Owned, leased, sponsored: | 9 hospitals | 1361 beds |
| Contract–managed: | 1 hospital | 89 beds |
| Totals: | 10 hospitals | 1450 beds |

---

**0012: VIRGINIA DEPARTMENT OF MENTAL HEALTH** (NP)
1220 Bank Street, Richmond, VA Zip 23219–3645, Mailing Address: P.O. Box 1797, Zip 23218–1797; tel. 804/786–3921; James S. Reinhard, M.D., Commissioner
**(Independent Hospital System)**

**VIRGINIA:** CATAWBA HOSPITAL (O, 110 beds) 5525 Catawba Hospital Drive, Catawba, VA Zip 24070–2115, Mailing Address: P.O. Box 200, Zip 24070–0200; tel. 540/375–4200; Walton F. Mitchell, III, Director
**Web address:** www.catawba.dmhmrsas.virginia.gov

CENTRAL STATE HOSPITAL (O, 277 beds) 26317 West Washington Street, Petersburg, VA Zip 23803–2727, Mailing Address: P.O. Box 4030, Zip 23803–0030; tel. 804/524–7000; Charles M. Davis, M.D., Ph.D., Director
**Web address:** www.csh.dmhmrsas.virginia.gov

CENTRAL VIRGINIA TRAINING CENTER (O, 1112 beds) 210 East Colony Road, Madison Heights, VA Zip 24572–2005, Mailing Address: P.O. Box 1098, Lynchburg, Zip 24505–1098; tel. 434/947–6326; Denise D. Micheletti, R.N., Director
**Web address:** www.cvtc.dmhmrsas.virginia.gov/

COMMONWEALTH CENTER FOR CHILDREN AND ADOLESCENTS (O, 60 beds) 1355 Richmond Road, Staunton, VA Zip 24401–9146, Mailing Address: Box 4000, Zip 24402–4000; tel. 540/332–2100; William J. Tuell, MSN, Facility Director
**Web address:** www.ccca.dbhds.virginia.gov

EASTERN STATE HOSPITAL (O, 334 beds) 4601 Ironbound Road, Williamsburg, VA Zip 23188–2652; tel. 757/253–5161; John M. Favret, Director
**Web address:** www.esh.dmhmrsas.virginia.gov/

HIRAM W. DAVIS MEDICAL CENTER (O, 10 beds) 26317 West Washington Street, Petersburg, VA Zip 23803–2727, Mailing Address: P.O. Box 4030, Zip 23803–0030; tel. 804/524–7344; Bill Hawkins, Director

NORTHERN VIRGINIA MENTAL HEALTH INSTITUTE (O, 123 beds) 3302 Gallows Road, Falls Church, VA Zip 22042–3398; tel. 703/207–7110; R. Maxilimien del Rio, M.D., Facility Director
**Web address:** www.nvmhi.dmhmrsas.virginia.gov

PIEDMONT GERIATRIC HOSPITAL (O, 150 beds) 5001 East Patrick Henry Highway, Burkeville, VA Zip 23922–3460, Mailing Address: P.O. Box 427, Zip 23922–0427; tel. 434/767–4401; Stephen M. Herrick, Ph.D., Director
**Web address:** www.pgh.dmhmrsas.virginia.gov

SOUTHERN VIRGINIA MENTAL HEALTH INSTITUTE (O, 72 beds) 382 Taylor Drive, Danville, VA Zip 24541–4023; tel. 434/799–6220; David M. Lyon, Director
**Web address:** www.svmhi.dmhmrsas.virginia.gov

SOUTHWESTERN VIRGINIA MENTAL HEALTH INSTITUTE (O, 266 beds) 340 Bagley Circle, Marion, VA Zip 24354–3390; tel. 276/783–1200; Cynthia McClaskey, Ph.D., Director
**Web address:** www.swvmhi.dmhmrsas.virginia.gov/

WESTERN STATE HOSPITAL (O, 260 beds) 1301 Richmond Avenue, Staunton, VA Zip 24401–9146, Mailing Address: P.O. Box 2500, Zip 24402–2500; tel. 540/332–8000; Jack W. Barber, M.D., Director
**Web address:** www.dbhds.virginia.gov

---

For explanation of codes following names, see page B2.
★ Indicates Type III membership in the American Hospital Association.

© 2013 AHA Guide

| Owned, leased, sponsored: | 11 hospitals | 2774 beds |
|---|---|---|
| Contract–managed: | 0 hospitals | 0 beds |
| Totals: | 11 hospitals | 2774 beds |

| Owned, leased, sponsored: | 2 hospitals | 843 beds |
|---|---|---|
| Contract–managed: | 1 hospital | 82 beds |
| Totals: | 3 hospitals | 925 beds |

★6725: **VIRTUA HEALTH** (NP)
50 Lake Center Executive Drive, Suite 401, Marlton, NJ Zip 08053; tel. 856/355–0010; Richard P. Miller, Chief Executive Officer
**(Moderately Centralized Health System)**

**NEW JERSEY:** VIRTUA BERLIN (O, 83 beds) 100 Townsend Avenue, Berlin, NJ Zip 08009–9035; tel. 856/322–3000; Christopher A. Chekouras, Vice President and Chief Operating Officer
**Web address:** www.virtua.org

VIRTUA MARLTON (O, 192 beds) 90 Brick Road, Marlton, NJ Zip 08053–2177; tel. 856/355–6000; Gary L. Long, Chief Operating Officer
**Web address:** www.virtua.org

VIRTUA MEMORIAL (O, 325 beds) 175 Madison Avenue, Mount Holly, NJ Zip 08060–2099; tel. 609/267–0700; Matthew Zuino, Vice President
**Web address:** www.virtua.org

VIRTUA VOORHEES (O, 398 beds) 100 Bowman Drive, Voorhees, NJ Zip 08043–9612; tel. 856/325–3000; Michael S. Kotzen, Vice President and Chief Operating Officer
**Web address:** www.virtua.org

| Owned, leased, sponsored: | 4 hospitals | 998 beds |
|---|---|---|
| Contract–managed: | 0 hospitals | 0 beds |
| Totals: | 4 hospitals | 998 beds |

★0221: **WAKE FOREST BAPTIST HEALTH** (NP)
Medical Center Boulevard, Winston–Salem, NC Zip 27157; tel. 336/716–2011; John D. McConnell, M.D., Chief Executive Officer
**(Moderately Centralized Health System)**

**NORTH CAROLINA:** WAKE FOREST BAPTIST HEALTH–DAVIE HOSPITAL (O, 25 beds) 223 Hospital Street, Mocksville, NC Zip 27028–2038, Mailing Address: P.O. Box 1209, Zip 27028–1209; tel. 336/751–8100; Steven C. Snelgrove, Administrator
**Web address:** www.daviehospital.org

WAKE FOREST BAPTIST HEALTH–LEXINGTON MEDICAL CENTER (O, 77 beds) 250 Hospital Drive, Lexington, NC Zip 27292–6728, Mailing Address: P.O. Box 1817, Zip 27293–1817; tel. 336/248–5161; Steven C. Snelgrove, Chief Executive Officer
**Web address:** www.lexingtonmemorial.com

WAKE FOREST BAPTIST MEDICAL CENTER (O, 853 beds) Medical Center Boulevard, Winston–Salem, NC Zip 27157–0001; tel. 336/716–2011; Sanjay K. Saha, Executive Vice President, Operations
**Web address:** www.wfubmc.edu

| Owned, leased, sponsored: | 3 hospitals | 955 beds |
|---|---|---|
| Contract–managed: | 0 hospitals | 0 beds |
| Totals: | 3 hospitals | 955 beds |

★6705: **WAKEMED HEALTH & HOSPITALS** (NP)
3000 New Bern Avenue, Raleigh, NC Zip 27610–1231; tel. 919/350–8000; William K. Atkinson, II, Ph.D., M.P.H., President and Chief Executive Officer
**(Moderately Centralized Health System)**

HARTNETT HEALTH SYSTEM (C, 82 beds) 800 Tilghman Drive, Dunn, NC Zip 28334–5599, Mailing Address: P.O. Box 1706, Zip 28335–1706; tel. 910/892–1000; Kenneth E. Bryan, FACHE, President and Chief Executive Officer
**Web address:** www.myharnetthealth.org/about–hhs/betsy–johnson–hospital/

WAKEMED CARY HOSPITAL (O, 192 beds) 1900 Kildaire Farm Road, Cary, NC Zip 27518–6616; tel. 919/350–2300; David C. Coulter, Senior Vice President and Administrator
**Web address:** www.wakemed.org

WAKEMED RALEIGH CAMPUS (O, 651 beds) 3000 New Bern Avenue, Raleigh, NC Zip 27610–1295; tel. 919/350–8000; William K. Atkinson, II, Ph.D., M.P.H., President and Chief Executive Officer
**Web address:** www.wakemed.org

★0188: **WELLMONT HEALTH SYSTEM** (NP)
1905 American Way, Kingsport, TN Zip 37660–5882; tel. 423/230–8200; Margaret DeNarvaez, President and Chief Executive Officer
**(Moderately Centralized Health System)**

**TENNESSEE:** WELLMONT BRISTOL REGIONAL MEDICAL CENTER (O, 348 beds) 1 Medical Park Boulevard, Bristol, TN Zip 37620–7430; tel. 423/844–1121; Greg Neal, Interim Chief Executive Officer
**Web address:** www.wellmont.org

WELLMONT HANCOCK COUNTY HOSPITAL (O, 10 beds) 1519 Main Street, Sneedville, TN Zip 37869–3657; tel. 423/733–5000; Fred L. Pelle, FACHE, Interim Chief Executive Officer
**Web address:** www.wellmont.org/Hospitals/Hancock–County–Hospital.aspx

WELLMONT HAWKINS COUNTY MEMORIAL HOSPITAL (L, 50 beds) 851 Locust Street, Rogersville, TN Zip 37857–2407, Mailing Address: P.O. Box 130, Zip 37857–0130; tel. 423/921–7000; Fred L. Pelle, FACHE, Interim Chief Executive Officer
**Web address:** www.wellmont.org

WELLMONT HOLSTON VALLEY MEDICAL CENTER (O, 345 beds) 130 West Ravine Street, Kingsport, TN Zip 37660–3837, Mailing Address: P.O. Box 238, Zip 37662–0238; tel. 423/224–4000; Virginia Frank, President and Chief Executive Officer
**Web address:** www.wellmont.org

**VIRGINIA:** LEE REGIONAL MEDICAL CENTER (O, 27 beds) 1800 Combs Road, Pennington Gap, VA Zip 24277–1808, Mailing Address: P.O. Box 589, Zip 24277–0589; tel. 276/546–1440; Fred L. Pelle, FACHE, Interim President and Chief Executive Officer
**Web address:** www.wellmont.org/Hospitals/Lee–Regional–Medical–Center.aspx

MOUNTAIN VIEW REGIONAL MEDICAL CENTER (O, 118 beds) 310 Third Street N.E., Norton, VA Zip 24273–1137; tel. 276/679–9100; Fred L. Pelle, FACHE, Interim President and Chief Executive Officer
**Web address:** www.wellmont.org

WELLMONT LONESOME PINE HOSPITAL (O, 60 beds) 1990 Holton Avenue East, Big Stone Gap, VA Zip 24219–3350; tel. 276/523–3111; Fred L. Pelle, FACHE, Interim President and Chief Executive Officer
**Web address:** www.wellmont.org

| Owned, leased, sponsored: | 7 hospitals | 958 beds |
|---|---|---|
| Contract–managed: | 0 hospitals | 0 beds |
| Totals: | 7 hospitals | 958 beds |

★0068: **WELLSPAN HEALTH** (NP)
45 Monument Road, Suite 200, York, PA Zip 17403–5071; tel. 717/851–2121; Bruce M. Bartels, President
**(Centralized Physician/Insurance Health System)**

**PENNSYLVANIA:** GETTYSBURG HOSPITAL (O, 76 beds) 147 Gettys Street, Gettysburg, PA Zip 17325–2534; tel. 717/334–2121; Jane E. Hyde, President
**Web address:** www.wellspan.org

YORK HOSPITAL (O, 552 beds) 1001 South George Street, York, PA Zip 17403–3645; tel. 717/851–2345; Keith Noll, President
**Web address:** www.wellspan.org

| Owned, leased, sponsored: | 2 hospitals | 628 beds |
|---|---|---|
| Contract–managed: | 0 hospitals | 0 beds |
| Totals: | 2 hospitals | 628 beds |

For explanation of codes following names, see page B2.
★ Indicates Type III membership in the American Hospital Association.

**Section B**

★**0995: WELLSTAR HEALTH SYSTEM** (NP)
805 Sandy Plains Road, Marietta, GA Zip 30066–6340;
tel. 770/792–5012; Reynold J. Jennings, President and Chief
Executive Officer
**(Centralized Health System)**

**GEORGIA:** WELLSTAR COBB HOSPITAL (O, 372 beds) 3950 Austell Road,
Austell, GA Zip 30106–1121; tel. 770/732–4000; Kem Mullins, FACHE,
President
**Web address:** www.wellstar.org

WELLSTAR DOUGLAS HOSPITAL (O, 102 beds) 8954 Hospital Drive,
Douglasville, GA Zip 30134–2282; tel. 770/949–1500; Craig A. Owens,
President
**Web address:** www.wellstar.org

WELLSTAR KENNESTONE HOSPITAL (O, 580 beds) 677 Church Street,
Marietta, GA Zip 30060–1148; tel. 770/793–5000; Dan Woods, President
**Web address:** www.wellstar.org

WELLSTAR PAULDING HOSPITAL (O, 216 beds) 600 West Memorial Drive,
Dallas, GA Zip 30132–4117; tel. 770/445–4411; Mark Haney, President
**Web address:** www.wellstar.org

WELLSTAR WINDY HILL HOSPITAL (O, 55 beds) 2540 Windy Hill Road,
Marietta, GA Zip 30067–8632; tel. 770/644–1000; Lou Little, President
**Web address:** www.wellstar.org

| Owned, leased, sponsored: | 5 hospitals | 1325 beds |
| Contract–managed: | 0 hospitals | 0 beds |
| **Totals:** | 5 hospitals | 1325 beds |

★**0199: WEST PENN ALLEGHENY HEALTH SYSTEM** (NP)
30 Isabella Street, Suite 300, Pittsburgh, PA Zip 15212–5862;
tel. 412/330–2403; John W. Paul, President and Chief Executive
Officer
**(Centralized Health System)**

**PENNSYLVANIA:** ALLEGHENY GENERAL HOSPITAL (O, 381 beds) 320 East
North Avenue, Pittsburgh, PA Zip 15212–4756; tel. 412/359–3131;
Judith F. Zedreck, R.N., Interim Chief Executive Officer
**Web address:** www.wpahs.org/locations/allegheny–general–hospital

ALLEGHENY VALLEY HOSPITAL (O, 228 beds) 1301 Carlisle Street, Natrona
Heights, PA Zip 15065–1152; tel. 724/224–5100; Ned Laubacher, President
and Chief Executive Officer
**Web address:** www.wpahs.org

CANONSBURG GENERAL HOSPITAL (O, 104 beds) 100 Medical Boulevard,
Canonsburg, PA Zip 15317–9762; tel. 724/745–6100; Terry Wiltrout, Chief
Executive Officer
**Web address:** www.wpahs.org

FORBES REGIONAL HOSPITAL (O, 350 beds) 2570 Haymaker Road,
Monroeville, PA Zip 15146–3513; tel. 412/858–2000; Reese Jackson,
President and Chief Executive Officer
**Web address:** www.wpahs.org

WESTERN PENNSYLVANIA HOSPITAL (O, 279 beds) 4800 Friendship Avenue,
Pittsburgh, PA Zip 15224–1722; tel. 412/578–5000; Duke Rupert, President
and Chief Executive Officer
**Web address:** www.wpahs.org

| Owned, leased, sponsored: | 5 hospitals | 1342 beds |
| Contract–managed: | 0 hospitals | 0 beds |
| **Totals:** | 5 hospitals | 1342 beds |

★**0004: WEST TENNESSEE HEALTHCARE** (NP)
620 Skyline Drive, Jackson, TN Zip 38301–3923;
tel. 731/541–5000; Bobby Arnold, President and Chief Executive
Officer
**(Centralized Physician/Insurance Health System)**

**TENNESSEE:** BOLIVAR GENERAL HOSPITAL (O, 23 beds) 650 Nuckolls Road,
Bolivar, TN Zip 38008–1532, Mailing Address: P.O. Box 509,
Zip 38008–0509; tel. 731/658–3100; Ruby Kirby, Administrator
**Web address:** www.wth.net

CAMDEN GENERAL HOSPITAL (O, 12 beds) 175 Hospital Drive, Camden, TN
Zip 38320–1617; tel. 731/584–6135; Denny R. Smith, Administrator
**Web address:** www.wth.net

GIBSON GENERAL HOSPITAL (O, 32 beds) 200 Hospital Drive, Trenton, TN
Zip 38382–3324; tel. 731/855–7900; Sherry Scruggs, Administrator
**Web address:** www.wth.net

HUMBOLDT GENERAL HOSPITAL (O, 30 beds) 3525 Chere Carol Road,
Humboldt, TN Zip 38343–3638; tel. 731/784–2321; Sherry Scruggs,
Administrator
**Web address:** www.wth.net

JACKSON–MADISON COUNTY GENERAL HOSPITAL (O, 601 beds) 620 Skyline
Drive, Jackson, TN Zip 38301–3923; tel. 731/541–5000; Bobby Arnold,
President and Chief Executive Officer
**Web address:** www.wth.org

MILAN GENERAL HOSPITAL (O, 28 beds) 4039 Highland Street, Milan, TN
Zip 38358–3483; tel. 731/686–1591; Sherry Scruggs, Administrator
**Web address:** www.wth.org

PATHWAYS OF TENNESSEE (O, 25 beds) 238 Summar Drive, Jackson, TN
Zip 38301–3906; tel. 731/541–8200; Pam Henson, Executive Director
**Web address:** www.wth.net

| Owned, leased, sponsored: | 7 hospitals | 751 beds |
| Contract–managed: | 0 hospitals | 0 beds |
| **Totals:** | 7 hospitals | 751 beds |

★**0119: WEST VIRGINIA UNITED HEALTH SYSTEM** (NP)
1000 Technology Drive, Suite 2320, Fairmont, WV Zip 26554–8834;
tel. 304/368–2700; J. Thomas Jones, President and Chief Executive
Officer
**(Moderately Centralized Health System)**

**WEST VIRGINIA:** BERKELEY MEDICAL CENTER (O, 166 beds) 2500 Hospital
Drive, Martinsburg, WV Zip 25401–3402, Mailing Address: P.O. Box
1418, Zip 25402–1418; tel. 304/264–1000; Anthony Zelenka, Chief
Administrative Officer
**Web address:** www.cityhospital.org

CAMDEN CLARK MEDICAL CENTER (O, 428 beds) 800 Garfield Avenue,
Parkersburg, WV Zip 26101–5378, Mailing Address: P.O. Box 718,
Zip 26102–0718; tel. 304/424–2111; Michael A. King, FACHE, President
and Chief Executive Officer
**Web address:** www.camdenclark.org

JEFFERSON MEDICAL CENTER (O, 25 beds) 300 South Preston Street,
Ranson, WV Zip 25438–1631; tel. 304/728–1600; Christina D. Coad, Ph.D.,
Chief Administrative Officer
**Web address:** www.jeffmem.com

UNITED HOSPITAL CENTER (O, 264 beds) 327 Medical Park Drive,
Bridgeport, WV Zip 26330–9006; tel. 681/342–1000; Bruce C. Carter,
President and Chief Executive Officer
**Web address:** www.uhcwv.org

WEST VIRGINIA UNIVERSITY HOSPITALS (O, 512 beds) 1 Medical Center
Drive, Morgantown, WV Zip 26506–4749; tel. 304/598–4000; Bruce
McClymonds, President and Chief Executive Officer
**Web address:** www.health.wvu.edu

| Owned, leased, sponsored: | 5 hospitals | 1395 beds |
| Contract–managed: | 0 hospitals | 0 beds |
| **Totals:** | 5 hospitals | 1395 beds |

★**0811: WESTERN CONNECTICUT HEALTH NETWORK** (NP)
24 Hospital Avenue, Danbury, CT Zip 06810–6099;
tel. 203/739–7066; John M. Murphy, M.D., President
**(Moderately Centralized Health System)**

**CONNECTICUT:** DANBURY HOSPITAL (O, 344 beds) 24 Hospital Avenue,
Danbury, CT Zip 06810–6099; tel. 203/739–7000; John M. Murphy,
M.D., President and Chief Executive Officer
**Web address:** www.danburyhospital.org

NEW MILFORD HOSPITAL (O, 59 beds) 21 Elm Street, New Milford, CT
Zip 06776–2993; tel. 860/355–2611; Deborah K. Weymouth, Executive
Director and Senior Vice President
**Web address:** www.newmilfordhospital.org

For explanation of codes following names, see page B2.
★ Indicates Type III membership in the American Hospital Association.

**Section B**

| Owned, leased, sponsored: | 2 hospitals | 403 beds |
| Contract–managed: | 0 hospitals | 0 beds |
| Totals: | 2 hospitals | 403 beds |

---

### ★6745: WHEATON FRANCISCAN HEALTHCARE (CC)
26W171 Roosevelt Road, Wheaton, IL Zip 60187–6002, Mailing Address: P.O. Box 667, Zip 60187–0667; tel. 630/909–6900; John D. Oliverio, President and Chief Executive Officer
**(Moderately Centralized Health System)**

**ILLINOIS:** MARIANJOY REHABILITATION HOSPITAL (O, 128 beds) 26 West 171 Roosevelt Road, Wheaton, IL Zip 60187–0795, Mailing Address: P.O. Box 795, Zip 60187–0795; tel. 630/909–8000; Kathleen C. Yosko, President and Chief Executive Officer
**Web address:** www.marianjoy.org

RUSH OAK PARK HOSPITAL (O, 114 beds) 520 South Maple Avenue, Oak Park, IL Zip 60304–1097; tel. 708/383–9300; Bruce M. Elegant, President and Chief Executive Officer
**Web address:** www.roph.org

**IOWA:** COVENANT MEDICAL CENTER (O, 243 beds) 3421 West Ninth Street, Waterloo, IA Zip 50702–5401; tel. 319/272–8000; Jack Dusenbery, President and Chief Executive Officer
**Web address:** www.wheatoniowa.org

MERCY HOSPITAL OF FRANCISCAN SISTERS (O, 64 beds) 201 Eighth Avenue S.E., Oelwein, IA Zip 50662–2447; tel. 319/283–6000; Terri Derflinger, Administrator
**Web address:** www.covhealth.com

SARTORI MEMORIAL HOSPITAL (O, 50 beds) 515 College Street, Cedar Falls, IA Zip 50613–2500; tel. 319/268–3000; Rose Fowler, MS, Administrator
**Web address:** www.wheatoniowa.org

**WISCONSIN:** MIDWEST ORTHOPEDIC SPECIALTY HOSPITAL (O, 16 beds) 10101 South 27th Street, 2nd Floor, Franklin, WI Zip 53132–7209; tel. 414/817–5800; Daniel Mattes, Chief Executive Officer
**Web address:** www.mymosh.com/

UNITED HOSPITAL SYSTEM, ST. CATHERINE'S MEDICAL CENTER CAMPUS (O, 202 beds) 9555 76th Street, Pleasant Prairie, WI Zip 53158–1984; tel. 262/656–2011; Richard O. Schmidt, Jr., President and Chief Executive Officer
**Web address:** www.uhsi.org

WHEATON FRANCISCAN HEALTHCARE – ALL SAINTS (O, 385 beds) 3801 Spring Street, Racine, WI Zip 53405–1690; tel. 262/687–4011; Susan Boland, President and Chief Executive Officer
**Web address:** www.allsaintshealth.com

WHEATON FRANCISCAN HEALTHCARE – ELMBROOK MEMORIAL (O, 100 beds) 19333 West North Avenue, Brookfield, WI Zip 53045–4198; tel. 262/785–2000; Debra K. Standridge, President
**Web address:** www.wfhealthcare.org

WHEATON FRANCISCAN HEALTHCARE – FRANKLIN (O, 24 beds) 10101 South 27th Street, Franklin, WI Zip 53132–7209; tel. 414/325–4700; Daniel Mattes, President
**Web address:** www.mywheaton.org/

WHEATON FRANCISCAN HEALTHCARE – ST. FRANCIS (S, 164 beds) 3237 South 16th Street, Milwaukee, WI Zip 53215–4592; tel. 414/647–5000; Daniel Mattes, President
**Web address:** www.mywheaton.org

WHEATON FRANCISCAN HEALTHCARE – ST. JOSEPH'S (O, 346 beds) 5000 West Chambers Street, Milwaukee, WI Zip 53210–1650; tel. 414/447–2000; Debra K. Standridge, President
**Web address:** www.mywheaton.org/stjoseph

WHEATON FRANCISCAN HEALTHCARE – THE WISCONSIN HEART HOSPITAL (O, 30 beds) 10000 West Bluemound Road, Wauwatosa, WI Zip 53226–4321; tel. 414/778–7800; Debra K. Standridge, President
**Web address:** www.mywheaton.org/hearthospital

| Owned, leased, sponsored: | 13 hospitals | 1866 beds |
| Contract–managed: | 0 hospitals | 0 beds |
| Totals: | 13 hospitals | 1866 beds |

---

### ★0468: WHITE RIVER HEALTH SYSTEM (NP)
1710 Harrison Street, Batesville, AR Zip 72501–7303; tel. 870/262–1200; Gary Bebow, FACHE, Administrator and Chief Executive Officer
**(Moderately Centralized Health System)**

**ARKANSAS:** STONE COUNTY MEDICAL CENTER (O, 25 beds) 2106 East Main Street, Mountain View, AR Zip 72560–6439, Mailing Address: P.O. Box 510, Zip 72560–0510; tel. 870/269–4361; Renie Taylor, Administrator
**Web address:** www.whiteriverhealthsystem.com

WHITE RIVER MEDICAL CENTER (O, 209 beds) 1710 Harrison Street, Batesville, AR Zip 72501–7303, Mailing Address: P.O. Box 2197, Zip 72503–2197; tel. 870/262–1200; Gary Bebow, FACHE, Administrator and Chief Executive Officer
**Web address:** www.whiteriverhealthsystem.com

| Owned, leased, sponsored: | 2 hospitals | 234 beds |
| Contract–managed: | 0 hospitals | 0 beds |
| Totals: | 2 hospitals | 234 beds |

---

### 0646: WHITTIER HEALTH NETWORK (IO)
25 Railroad Square, Haverhill, MA Zip 01832–5721; tel. 978/556–5858; Alfred L. Arcidi, M.D., President
**(Independent Hospital System)**

**MASSACHUSETTS:** WHITTIER PAVILION (O, 65 beds) 76 Summer Street, Haverhill, MA Zip 01830–5814; tel. 978/373–8222; Alfred L. Arcidi, M.D., Chief Executive Officer
**Web address:** www.whittierhealth.com

WHITTIER REHABILITATION HOSPITAL (O, 74 beds) 150 Flanders Road, Westborough, MA Zip 01581–1017; tel. 508/871–2000; Alfred J. Arcidi, M.D., Senior Vice President
**Web address:** www.whittierhealth.com

WHITTIER REHABILITATION HOSPITAL (O, 60 beds) 145 Ward Hill Avenue, Bradford, MA Zip 01835–6928; tel. 978/372–8000; Alfred J. Arcidi, M.D., Senior Vice President
**Web address:** www.whittierhealth.com

| Owned, leased, sponsored: | 3 hospitals | 199 beds |
| Contract–managed: | 0 hospitals | 0 beds |
| Totals: | 3 hospitals | 199 beds |

---

### 1945: WILLIS–KNIGHTON HEALTH SYSTEM (NP)
2600 Greenwood Road, Shreveport, LA Zip 71103–3908; tel. 318/212–4000; James K. Elrod, FACHE, President and Chief Executive Officer
**(Centralized Health System)**

**LOUISIANA:** WILLIS–KNIGHTON MEDICAL CENTER (O, 896 beds) 2600 Greenwood Road, Shreveport, LA Zip 71103–3908, Mailing Address: P.O. Box 32600, Zip 71130–2600; tel. 318/212–4600; Jaf Fielder, Vice President and Administrator
**Web address:** www.wkhs.com

WK BOSSIER HEALTH CENTER (O, 134 beds) 2400 Hospital Drive, Bossier City, LA Zip 71111–2385; tel. 318/212–7000; Clifford M. Broussard, FACHE, Administrator
**Web address:** www.wkhs.com/wkb/

| Owned, leased, sponsored: | 2 hospitals | 1030 beds |
| Contract–managed: | 0 hospitals | 0 beds |
| Totals: | 2 hospitals | 1030 beds |

---

### ★0157: YALE NEW HAVEN HEALTH SYSTEM (NP)
789 Howard Avenue, New Haven, CT Zip 06519–1304; tel. 203/688–4608; Marna P. Borgstrom, President and Chief Executive Officer
**(Centralized Physician/Insurance Health System)**

**CONNECTICUT:** BRIDGEPORT HOSPITAL (O, 337 beds) 267 Grant Street, Bridgeport, CT Zip 06610–2805, Mailing Address: P.O. Box 5000, Zip 06610–0120; tel. 203/384–3000; William M. Jennings, President and Chief Executive Officer
**Web address:** www.bridgeporthospital.org

---

For explanation of codes following names, see page B2.
★ Indicates Type III membership in the American Hospital Association.

GREENWICH HOSPITAL (O, 174 beds) 5 Perryridge Road, Greenwich, CT
Zip 06830–4697; tel. 203/863–3000; Frank A. Corvino, President and Chief
Executive Officer
**Web address:** www.greenhosp.org

YALE–NEW HAVEN HOSPITAL (O, 1571 beds) 20 York Street, New Haven, CT
Zip 06510–3202; tel. 203/688–4242; Marna P. Borgstrom, Chief Executive
Officer
**Web address:** www.ynhh.org

| | | |
|---|---|---|
| **Owned, leased, sponsored:** | 3 hospitals | 2082 beds |
| **Contract–managed:** | 0 hospitals | 0 beds |
| **Totals:** | 3 hospitals | 2082 beds |

For explanation of codes following names, see page B2.
★ Indicates Type III membership in the American Hospital Association.

**B150** Health Care Systems, Networks and Alliances

© 2013 AHA Guide

## Geographically

### United States

#### ALABAMA

**Birmingham:** BAPTIST HEALTH SYSTEM 3201 Fourth Avenue South, Zip 35222–1723, Mailing Address: P.O. Box 830605, Zip 35283–0605; tel. 205/715–5319; M. Shane Spees, President and Chief Executive Officer, p. B20

BRADFORD HEALTH SERVICES 2101 Magnolia Avenue South, Suite 518, Zip 35205–2853; tel. 205/251–7753; Jerry W. Crowder, President and Chief Executive Officer, p. B24

★ HEALTHSOUTH CORPORATION 3660 Grandview Parkway, Suite 200, Zip 35243–3332; tel. 205/967–7116; Jay F. Grinney, President and Chief Executive Officer, p. B66

NOLAND HEALTH SERVICES, INC. 600 Corporate Parkway, Suite 100, Zip 35242–5451; tcl. 205/783–8484; Gary M. Glasscock, President and Chief Executive Officer, p. B96

★ UAB HEALTH SYSTEM 500 22nd Street South, Suite 408, Zip 35233–3110; tel. 205/975–5362; William Ferniany, Ph.D., Chief Executive Officer, p. B134

**Guntersville:** ★ MARSHALL HEALTH SYSTEM 227 Britany Road, Zip 35976–5766; tel. 256/894–6615; Gary R. Gore, Chief Executive Officer, p. B85

**Huntsville:** HUNTSVILLE HOSPITAL HEALTH SYSTEM 101 Sivley Road S.W., Zip 35801–4421; tel. 265/256–1000; David S. Spillers, Chief Executive Officer, p. B71

**Mobile:** ALTAPOINTE HEALTH SYSTEMS 5750–A Southland Drive, Zip 36693–3316; tel. 251/473–4423; J. Tuerk Schlesinger, Chief Executive Officer, p. B9

INFIRMARY HEALTH SYSTEM 5 Mobile Infirmary Circle, Zip 36607–3513; tel. 251/435–5500; D. Mark Nix, President and Chief Executive Officer, p. B73

★ UNIVERSITY OF SOUTH ALABAMA HOSPITALS 2451 Fillingim Street, Zip 36617–2238; tel. 251/471–7000; Stanley K. Hammack, Chief Executive Officer, p. B143

**Montgomery:** ★ BAPTIST HEALTH 301 Brown Springs Road, Zip 36117–7005; tel. 334/273–4400; W. Russell Tyner, President and Chief Executive Officer, p. B18

GILLIARD HEALTH SERVICES 3091 Carter Hill Road, Zip 36111–1801; tel. 334/265–5009; William G. McKenzie, President, Chief Executive Officer and Chairman, p. B56

**Tuscaloosa:** DCH HEALTH SYSTEM 809 University Boulevard East, Zip 35401–2029; tel. 205/759–7111; Bryan N. Kindred, FACHE, President and Chief Executive Officer, p. B42

#### ARIZONA

**Flagstaff:** ★ NORTHERN ARIZONA HEALTHCARE 1200 North Beaver Street, Zip 86001–3118; tel. 928/779–3366; William T. Bradel, President and Chief Executive Officer, p. B97

**Phoenix:** ★ BANNER HEALTH 1441 North 12th Street, Zip 85006–2837, Mailing Address: P.O. Box 25489, Zip 85002–5489; tel. 602/747–4000; Peter S. Fine, FACHE, President and Chief Executive Officer, p. B17

★ JOHN C. LINCOLN HEALTH NETWORK 2500 West Utopia Road, Suite 100, Zip 85027–4172; tel. 623/434–6230; Rhonda Forsyth, President and Chief Executive Officer, p. B75

**Scottsdale:** ★ SCOTTSDALE HEALTHCARE 8125 North Hayden Road, Zip 85258–2463; tel. 480/882–4000; Thomas J. Sadvary, FACHE, President and Chief Executive Officer, p. B115

#### ARKANSAS

**Batesville:** ★ WHITE RIVER HEALTH SYSTEM 1710 Harrison Street, Zip 72501–7303; tel. 870/262–1200; Gary Bebow, FACHE, Administrator and Chief Executive Officer, p. B149

**Blytheville:** MISSISSIPPI COUNTY HOSPITAL SYSTEM 1520 North Division Street, Zip 72315–1448, Mailing Address: P.O. Box 108, Zip 72316–0108; tel. 870/838–7300; Ralph E. Beaty, Chief Executive Officer, p. B92

**Little Rock:** ★ BAPTIST HEALTH 9601 Interstate 630, Exit 7, Zip 72205–7299; tel. 501/202–2000; Russell D. Harrington, Jr., FACHE, President and Chief Executive Officer, p. B19

#### CALIFORNIA

**Alhambra:** AHMC & HEALTHCARE, INC. 55 South Raymond Avenue, Suite 105, Zip 91801–7101; tel. 626/457–9600; Jonathan Wu, M.D., President and Chairman, p. B7

**Corona:** AURORA BEHAVIORAL HEALTH CARE 4238 Green River Road, Zip 92880–1669; tel. 951/549–8032; Soon K. Kim, M.D., President and Chief Executive Officer, p. B15

**Covina:** CITRUS VALLEY HEALTH PARTNERS 210 West San Bernardino Road, Zip 91723–1515; tel. 626/331–7331; Robert H. Curry, President and Chief Executive Officer, p. B33

**El Segundo:** AVANTI HOSPITALS 222 North Sepulveda Boulevard, Suite 950, Zip 90245–5614; tel. 310/356–0550; Edward Mirzabegian, Corporate Chief Executive Officer, p. B16

**Escondido:** ★ PALOMAR HEALTH 456 East Grand Avenue, Zip 92025–3319; tel. 760/740–6393; Michael H. Covert, FACHE, Chief Executive Officer, p. B101

**Fountain Valley:** MEMORIALCARE 17360 Brookhurst Street, Zip 92708–3720, Mailing Address: P.O. Box 1428, Long Beach, Zip 90801–1428; tel. 714/377–2900; Barry S. Arbuckle, Ph.D., President and Chief Executive Officer, p. B89

**Fresno:** COMMUNITY MEDICAL CENTERS Fresno and Maddy Drive, Zip 93721, Mailing Address: P.O. Box 1232, Zip 93715–1232; tel. 559/459–6000; Tim A. Joslin, President and Chief Executive Officer, p. B39

**Hemet:** PHYSICIANS FOR HEALTHY HOSPITALS 1117 East Devonshire Avenue, Zip 92543–3083; tel. 951/652–2811; Joel Bergenfeld, Chief Executive Officer, p. B102

**Irvine:** ★ ST. JOSEPH HEALTH 3345 Michelson Drive, Suite 100, Zip 92612; tel. 949/381–4000; Deborah A. Proctor, President and Chief Executive Officer, p. B124

**Loma Linda:** LOMA LINDA UNIVERSITY ADVENTIST HEALTH SCIENCES CENTER 11175 Campus Street, Zip 92350–1700; tel. 909/558–7572; Richard H. Hart, M.D., President and Chief Executive Officer, p. B84

**Los Altos Hills:** ★ DAUGHTERS OF CHARITY HEALTH SYSTEM 26000 Altamont Road, Zip 94022–4317; tel. 650/917–4500; Robert Issai, President and Chief Executive Officer, p. B42

**Los Angeles:** ALTA HEALTHCARE SYSTEM 10780 Santa Monica Boulevard, Suite 400, Zip 90025–7616; tel. 310/943–4500; David Topper, Chief Executive Officer, p. B9

LOS ANGELES COUNTY–DEPARTMENT OF HEALTH SERVICES 313 North Figueroa Street, Room 912, Zip 90012–2691; tel. 213/240–8101; Mitchell H. Katz, M.D., Director, p. B84

**Oakland:** ★ KAISER FOUNDATION HOSPITALS One Kaiser Plaza, Zip 94612–3600; tel. 510/271–5910; George C. Halvorson, Chairman and Chief Executive Officer, p. B75

★ UNIVERSITY OF CALIFORNIA–SYSTEMWIDE ADMINISTRATION 1111 Franklin Street, 11th Floor, Zip 94607–5200; tel. 510/987–9071; John D. Stobo, M.D., Senior Vice President Health Sciences and Services, p. B141

**Ontario:** PRIME HEALTHCARE SERVICES 3300 East Guasti Road, Zip 91761–8655; tel. 909/235–4400; Prem Reddy, M.D., Interim President and Chief Executive Officer, p. B104

**Palo Alto:** STANFORD HEALTH CARE 300 Pasteur Drive, Zip 94304–2299; tel. 650/723–4000; Amir Dan Rubin, President and Chief Executive Officer, p. B125

**Roseville:** ★ ADVENTIST HEALTH 2100 Douglas Boulevard, Zip 95661–3898, Mailing Address: P.O. Box 619002, Zip 95661–9002; tel. 916/781–2000; Robert G. Carmen, President, p. B5

**Sacramento:** ★ SUTTER HEALTH 2200 River Plaza Drive, Zip 95833–4134; tel. 916/733–8800; Patrick E. Fry, Chief Executive Officer, p. B126

**San Diego:** ★ SCRIPPS HEALTH 4275 Campus Point Court, Zip 92121–1513; tel. 858/678–7200; Chris D. Van Gorder, FACHE, President and Chief Executive Officer, p. B116

★ SHARP HEALTHCARE 8695 Spectrum Center Boulevard, Zip 92123–1489; tel. 858/499–4000; Michael Murphy, CPA, President & Chief Executive Officer, p. B120

**San Francisco:** ★ DIGNITY HEALTH 185 Berry Street, Suite 300, Zip 94107–1773; tel. 415/438–5500; Lloyd H. Dean, President and Chief Executive Officer, p. B48

**Santa Ana:** INTEGRATED HEALTHCARE 1301 North Tustin Avenue, Zip 92705–8619; tel. 714/953–3652; Kenneth K. Westbrook, President and Chief Executive Officer, p. B73

**Santa Barbara:** ★ COTTAGE HEALTH SYSTEM 400 West Pueblo Street, Zip 93105–4353, Mailing Address: P.O. Box 689, Zip 93102–0689; tel. 805/569–7290; Ronald C. Werft, President and Chief Executive Officer, p. B41

**Santa Fe Springs:** COLLEGE HEALTH ENTERPRISES 11627 Telegraph Road, Suite 200, Zip 90670–6814; tel. 562/923–9449; Barry J. Weiss, Chairman of the Board, p. B34

**Truckee:** TAHOE FOREST HEALTH SYSTEM 10121 Pine Avenue, Zip 96161–4835; tel. 530/587–6011; Robert A. Schapper, Chief Executive Officer, p. B128

**Walnut Creek:** ★ JOHN MUIR HEALTH 1400 Treat Boulevard, Zip 94597–2142; tel. 925/941–2100; Calvin K. Knight, President and Chief Executive Officer, p. B75

## COLORADO

★ SCL HEALTH SYSTEM 2420 West 26th Avenue, Suite 100D, Zip 80211–5302; tel. 303/813–5180; Michael A. Slubowski, FACHE, Chief Executive Officer, p. B115

**Englewood:** ★ CATHOLIC HEALTH INITIATIVES 198 Inverness Drive West, Suite 800, Zip 80112–5202; tel. 303/298–9100; Kevin E. Lofton, FACHE, President and Chief Executive Officer, p. B28

**Fort Collins:** ★ UNIVERSITY OF COLORADO HEALTH 2315 East Harmony Road, Suite 200, Zip 80528–8620; tel. 970/237–7001; Rulon F. Stacey, Ph.D., FACHE, Chief Executive Officer, p. B141

## CONNECTICUT

**Danbury:** ★ WESTERN CONNECTICUT HEALTH NETWORK 24 Hospital Avenue, Zip 06810–6099; tel. 203/739–7066; John M. Murphy, M.D., President, p. B148

**Hartford:** CONNECTICUT DEPARTMENT OF MENTAL HEALTH AND ADDICTION SERVICES 410 Capitol Avenue, Zip 06106–1367, Mailing Address: P.O. Box 341431, Zip 06134–1431; tel. 860/418–7000; Patricia Rehmer, Commissioner, p. B40

HARTFORD HEALTHCARE One State Street, 19th Floor, Zip 06103; tel. 860/263–4120; Elliot T. Joseph, President and Chief Executive Officer, p. B58

★ SAINT FRANCIS CARE, INC. 114 Woodland Street, Zip 06105–1208; tel. 860/714–5541; Christopher M. Dadlez, President and Chief Executive Officer, p. B112

**Manchester:** ★ EASTERN CONNECTICUT HEALTH NETWORK 71 Haynes Street, Zip 06040–4131; tel. 860/533–3400; Peter J. Karl, President and Chief Executive Officer, p. B51

**New Haven:** ★ YALE NEW HAVEN HEALTH SYSTEM 789 Howard Avenue, Zip 06519–1304; tel. 203/688–4608; Marna P. Borgstrom, President and Chief Executive Officer, p. B149

**New London:** LAWRENCE+MEMORIAL HEALTH SYSTEM 365 Montauk Avenue, Zip 06320–4700; tel. 860/442–0711; Bruce D. Cummings, President and Chief Executive Officer, p. B80

## DELAWARE

**Wilmington:** ★ CHRISTIANA CARE HEALTH SYSTEM 501 West 14th Street, Zip 19801–1013, Mailing Address: P.O. Box 1668, Zip 19899–1668; tel. 302/733–1000; Robert J. Laskowski, M.D., President and Chief Executive Officer, p. B33

## DISTRICT OF COLUMBIA

**Washington:** BUREAU OF MEDICINE AND SURGERY, DEPARTMENT OF THE NAVY 2300 East Street N.W., Zip 20372–5300; tel. 202/762–3701; Vice Admiral Matthew L. Nathan, Surgeon General, p. B24

DEPARTMENT OF THE AIR FORCE 1420 Pentagon, Room 4E1084, Zip 20330–1420; tel. 202/767–4765; Lieutenant General Charles B. Green, M.D., Surgeon General, p. B42

DEPARTMENT OF VETERANS AFFAIRS 810 Vermont Avenue N.W., Zip 20420–0001; tel. 202/273–5781; Robert A. Petzel, M.D., Under Secretary for Health, p. B44

## FLORIDA

**Altamonte Springs:** ★ ADVENTIST HEALTH SYSTEM SUNBELT HEALTH CARE CORPORATION 900 Hope Way, Zip 32714–1502; tel. 407/357–1000; Donald L. Jernigan, Ph.D., President and Chief Executive Officer, p. B5

**Boca Raton:** PROMISE HEALTHCARE 999 Yamato Road, 3rd Floor, Zip 33431–4477; tel. 561/869–3100; Howard B. Koslow, President and Chief Executive Officer, p. B105

SUCCESS HEALTHCARE 999 Yamato Road, 3rd Floor, Zip 33431–4477; tel. 561/869–6300; Peter R. Baronoff, President and Chief Executive Officer, p. B126

**Clearwater:** MORTON PLANT MEASE HEALTH CARE 300 Pinellas Street, Zip 33756–3804, Mailing Address: P.O. Box 210, Zip 33757–0210; tel. 727/462–7000; Glenn D. Waters, FACHE, President, p. B92

**Coral Gables:** ★ BAPTIST HEALTH SOUTH FLORIDA 6855 Red Road, Suite 600, Zip 33143–3632; tel. 786/662–7111; Brian E. Keeley, President and Chief Executive Officer, p. B19

**Fort Lauderdale:** ★ BROWARD HEALTH 303 S.E. 17th Street, Zip 33316–2523; tel. 954/355–5100; Frank P. Nask, President and Chief Executive Officer, p. B24

**Fort Myers:** LEE MEMORIAL HEALTH SYSTEM 2776 Cleveland Avenue, Zip 33901–5856, Mailing Address: P.O. Box 2218, Zip 33902–2218; tel. 239/343–2000; James R. Nathan, President and Chief Executive Officer, p. B80

**Gainesville:** ★ SHANDS HEALTHCARE 1600 S.W. Archer Road, Zip 32610–0326; tel. 352/733–1500; Timothy M. Goldfarb, Chief Executive Officer, p. B120

**Hollywood:** ★ MEMORIAL HEALTHCARE SYSTEM 3501 Johnson Street, Zip 33021–5421; tel. 954/265–5805; Frank V. Sacco, FACHE, President and Chief Executive Officer, p. B88

**Jacksonville:** ★ BAPTIST HEALTH 841 Prudential Drive, Suite 1601, Zip 32207–8202; tel. 904/202–4011; Hugh Greene, President and Chief Executive Officer, p. B18

NEMOURS 10140 Centurion Parkway North, Zip 32256–0532; tel. 904/697–4100; David J. Bailey, M.D., President and Chief Executive Officer, p. B94

**Lauderdale Lakes:** CATHOLIC HEALTH SERVICES 4790 North State Road 7, Zip 33319–5860; tel. 954/484–1515; Joseph M. Catania, President and Chief Executive Officer, p. B31

**Leesburg:** CENTRAL FLORIDA HEALTH ALLIANCE 600 East Dixie Avenue, Zip 34748–5925; tel. 352/323–5762; Donald G. Henderson, FACHE, Chief Executive Officer, p. B32

**Miami:** UNIVERSITY OF MIAMI HEALTH SYSTEM 1400 N.W. 12th Avenue, Zip 33136–1003; tel. 305/243–4000; Pascal J. Goldschmidt, M.D., Chief Executive Officer, p. B142

**Miami Lakes:** PACER HEALTH CORPORATION 14100 Palmetto Frontage Road, Suite 110, Zip 33016; tel. 305/828–7660; Rainier Gonzalez, Chairman and Chief Executive Officer, p. B100

**Naples:** HEALTH MANAGEMENT ASSOCIATES 5811 Pelican Bay Boulevard, Suite 500, Zip 34108–2711; tel. 239/598–3131; Gary D. Newsome, President and Chief Executive Officer, p. B64

**Orlando:** ORLANDO HEALTH 1414 Kuhl Avenue, Zip 32806–2093; tel. 407/841–5111; Sherrie Sitarik, President and Chief Executive Officer, p. B100

**Pensacola:** ★ BAPTIST HEALTH CARE CORPORATION 1717 North E Street Suite 320, Zip 32501–6377, Mailing Address: P.O. Box 17500, Zip 32522–7500; tel. 850/469–2335; Mark T. Faulkner, President, p. B19

**Rockledge:** HEALTH FIRST, INC. 6450 U.S. Highway 1, Zip 32955–5747; tel. 321/434–7000; Steven P. Johnson, Ph.D., President and Chief Executive Officer, p. B63

**Tampa:** SHRINERS HOSPITALS FOR CHILDREN 2900 Rocky Point Drive, Zip 33607–1435, Mailing Address: P.O. Box 31356, Zip 33631–3356; tel. 813/281–0300; John P. McCabe, Executive Vice President, p. B120

**Windermere:** UNITED MEDICAL CORPORATION 603 Main Street, Zip 34786–3548, Mailing Address: P.O. Box 1100, Zip 34786–1100; tel. 407/876–2200; Donald R. Dizney, Chairman and Chief Executive Officer, p. B135

## GEORGIA

**Albany:** ★ PHOEBE PUTNEY HEALTH SYSTEM 417 Third Avenue, Zip 31701–1943; tel. 229/312–1000; Joel Wernick, President and Chief Executive Officer, p. B102

**Alpharetta:** RESTORA HEALTHCARE 2550 Northwinds Parkway, Suite 160, Zip 30009–2234; tel. 678/736–7780; Rod Laughlin, President and Chief Executive Officer, p. B110

**Atlanta:** ★ EMORY HEALTHCARE 1440 Clifton Road N.E., Suite 145, Zip 30322–1102; tel. 404/778–5000; John T. Fox, Chief Executive Officer, p. B52

★ NORTHSIDE HEALTHCARE SYSTEM 1000 Johnson Ferry Road N.E., Zip 30342–1611; tel. 404/851–8000; Robert Quattrocchi, President and Chief Executive Officer, p. B97

★ PIEDMONT HEALTHCARE 1800 Howell Mill Road N.W., Suite 850, Zip 30318–0923; tel. 404/425–1314; Kevin Brown, President and Chief Executive Officer, p. B102

SUNLINK HEALTH SYSTEMS 900 Circle 75 Parkway, Suite 1120, Zip 30339–3005; tel. 770/933–7000; Robert M. Thornton, Jr., Chief Executive Officer, p. B126

**Augusta:** UNIVERSITY HEALTH CARE SYSTEM 1350 Walton Way, Zip 30901–2629; tel. 706/722–9011; James R. Davis, President and Chief Executive Officer, p. B140

**Brunswick:** ★ SOUTHEAST GEORGIA HEALTH SYSTEM 2415 Parkwood Drive, Zip 31520–4722, Mailing Address: P.O. Box 1518, Zip 31521–1518; tel. 912/466–7000; Gary R. Colberg, FACHE, President and Chief Executive Officer, p. B121

**Carrollton:** ★ TANNER HEALTH SYSTEM 705 Dixie Street, Zip 30117–3818; tel. 770/836–9580; Loy M. Howard, President and Chief Executive Officer, p. B128

**Columbus:** ★ COLUMBUS REGIONAL HEALTHCARE SYSTEM 707 Center Street, Suite 400, Zip 31901–1575; tel. 706/660–6100; Charles A. Stark, FACHE, Chief Executive Officer, p. B34

**Decatur:** DEKALB REGIONAL HEALTH SYSTEM 2701 North Decatur Road, Zip 30033–5918; tel. 404/501–1000; John Shelton, President and Chief Executive Officer, p. B42

**Marietta:** ★ WELLSTAR HEALTH SYSTEM 805 Sandy Plains Road, Zip 30066–6340; tel. 770/792–5012; Reynold J. Jennings, President and Chief Executive Officer, p. B148

**Milledgeville:** OCONEE REGIONAL HEALTH SYSTEMS 821 North Cobb Street, Zip 31061–2343; tel. 478/454–3505; Jean Aycock, President and Chief Executive Officer, p. B99

**Royston:** ★ TY COBB HEALTHCARE SYSTEM, INC. 461 Cook Street, Suite A., Zip 30662–4003; tel. 706/245–1832; Gregory K. Hearn, Chief Executive Officer, p. B133

**Thomasville:** ★ ARCHBOLD MEDICAL CENTER 910 South Broad Street, Zip 31792–6113; tel. 229/228–2739; J. Perry Mustian, President, p. B10

**Warner Robins:** ★ HOUSTON HEALTHCARE SYSTEM 1601 Watson Boulevard, Zip 31093–3431, Mailing Address: P.O. Box 2886, Zip 31099–2886; tel. 478/922–4281; Cary Martin, Chief Executive Officer, p. B71

## HAWAII

**Honolulu:** ★ HAWAII HEALTH SYSTEMS CORPORATION 3675 Kilauea Avenue, Zip 96816–2333; tel. 808/733–4151; Bruce S. Anderson, Ph.D., President and Chief Executive Officer, p. B58

HAWAII PACIFIC HEALTH 55 Merchant Street, Zip 96813–4306; tel. 808/949–9355; Raymond Vara, Jr., President and Chief Executive Officer, p. B59

★ QUEEN'S HEALTH SYSTEMS 1301 Punchbowl Street, Zip 96813–2402; tel. 808/535–5448; Arthur A. Ushijima, President and Chief Executive Officer, p. B109

## IDAHO

**Boise:** ★ ST. LUKE'S HEALTH SYSTEM 420 West Idaho Street, Zip 83702–6041; tel. 208/381–4200; David C. Pate, M.D., JD, President and Chief Executive Officer, p. B124

## ILLINOIS

**Carbondale:** SOUTHERN ILLINOIS HOSPITAL SERVICES 1239 East Main Street, Zip 62901–3114, Mailing Address: P.O. Box 3988, Zip 62902–3988; tel. 618/457–5200; Rex P. Budde, President and Chief Executive Officer, p. B122

**Chicago:** COOK COUNTY HEALTH AND HOSPITALS SYSTEM 1900 West Polk Street, Suite 220, Zip 60612–3723; tel. 312/864–6820; Ramanathan Raju, M.D., Chief Executive Officer, p. B40

NATIONAL SURGICAL HOSPITALS 250 South Wacker Drive, Suite 500, Zip 60606–5897; tel. 312/627–8400; David Crane, Chief Executive Officer, p. B93

★ NORTHWESTERN MEMORIAL HEALTHCARE 251 East Huron Street, Zip 60611–2908; tel. 312/926–2000; Dean M. Harrison, President and Chief Executive Officer, p. D97

★ PRESENCE HEALTH 7435 West Talcott Avenue, Zip 60631–3707; tel. 773/792–5150; Sandra B. Bruce, FACHE, President and Chief Executive Officer, p. B104

★ RUSH UNIVERSITY MEDICAL CENTER 1653 West Congress Parkway, Zip 60612–3864; tel. 312/942–5000; Larry J. Goodman, M.D., Chief Executive Officer, p. B112

★ SINAI HEALTH SYSTEM 1500 South California Avenue, Zip 60608–1729; tel. 773/542–2000; Alan H. Channing, President and Chief Executive Officer, p. B121

**Crystal Lake:** ★ CENTEGRA HEALTH SYSTEM 385 Millennium Drive, Zip 60012–3761; tel. 815/788–5800; Michael S. Eesley, Chief Executive Officer, p. B31

**DeKalb:** ★ KISH HEALTH SYSTEM 1 Kish Hospital Drive, Zip 60115–9602, Mailing Address: P.O. Box 707, Zip 60115–0707; tel. 815/756–1521; Kevin P. Poorten, President and Chief Executive Officer, p. B79

**Downers Grove:** ★ ADVOCATE HEALTH CARE 3075 Highland Parkway, Suite 600, Zip 60515–1206; tel. 630/929–8700; Jim H. Skogsbergh, President and Chief Executive Officer, p. B7

**Evanston:** ★ NORTHSHORE UNIVERSITY HEALTHSYSTEM 1301 Central Street, Zip 60201–1613; tel. 847/570–2000; Mark R. Neaman, President and Chief Executive Officer, p. B97

**Evergreen Park:** AMERICAN PROVINCE OF LITTLE COMPANY OF MARY SISTERS 9350 South California Avenue, Zip 60805–2595; tel. 708/229–5491; Sister Kathleen McIntyre, Province Leader, p. B9

**Peoria:** ★ OSF HEALTHCARE SYSTEM 800 N.E. Glen Oak Avenue, Zip 61603–3200; tel. 309/655–2850; Kevin D. Schoeplein, Chief Executive Officer, p. B100

**Schaumburg:** CANCER TREATMENT CENTERS OF AMERICA 1336 Basswood Road, Zip 60173–4544; tel. 847/342–7400; Stephen B. Bonner, President and Chief Executive Officer, p. B25

**Springfield:** DIVISION OF MENTAL HEALTH, DEPARTMENT OF HUMAN SERVICES 319 East Madison Street, S–3B, Zip 62701–1035; tel. 217/785–6023; Lorrie Rickman Jones, Ph.D., Director, p. B49

★ HOSPITAL SISTERS HEALTH SYSTEM 4936 LaVerna Road, Zip 62707–9797, Mailing Address: P.O. Box 19456, Zip 62794–9456; tel. 217/523–4747; Mary Starmann–Harrison, FACHE, President and Chief Executive Officer, p. B70

★ MEMORIAL HEALTH SYSTEM 701 North First Street, Zip 62781–0001; tel. 217/788–3000; Edgar J. Curtis, President and Chief Executive Officer, p. B88

**Wheaton:** ★ WHEATON FRANCISCAN HEALTHCARE 26W171 Roosevelt Road, Zip 60187–6002, Mailing Address: P.O. Box 667, Zip 60187–0667; tel. 630/909–6900; John D. Oliverio, President and Chief Executive Officer, p. B149

**Winfield:** ★ CADENCE HEALTH 25 North Winfield Road, Zip 60190; tel. 630/933–1600; Michael Vivoda, Chief Executive Officer, p. B25

## INDIANA

**Evansville:** ★ DEACONESS HEALTH SYSTEM 600 Mary Street, tel. 812/450–5000; Linda E. White, President and Chief Executive Officer, p. B42

**Fort Wayne:** ★ PARKVIEW HEALTH 10501 Corporate Drive, Zip 46845–1700, Mailing Address: P.O. Box 5600, Zip 46895–5600; tel. 260/373–7001; Michael J. Packnett, President and Chief Executive Officer, p. B101

**Hammond:** COMMUNITY HEALTHCARE SYSTEM 901 MacArthur Boulevard, Zip 46321–2959; tel. 219/836–1600; Donald Powers, Chairman, President and Chief Executive Officer, p. B39

**Indianapolis:** COMMUNITY HEALTH NETWORK 7330 Shadeland Station, Zip 46256–3957; tel. 317/355–1411; Bryan A. Mills, President and Chief Executive Officer, p. B34

★ INDIANA UNIVERSITY HEALTH 340 West 10th Street, Suite 6100, Zip 46202–3082, Mailing Address: P.O. Box 1367, Zip 46206–1367; tel. 317/962–5900; Daniel F. Evans, Jr., JD, President and Chief Executive Officer, p. B72

**Mishawaka:** FRANCISCAN ALLIANCE 1515 Dragoon Trail, Zip 46544–4710, Mailing Address: P.O. Box 1290, Zip 46546–1290; tel. 574/256–3935; Kevin D. Leahy, President and Chief Executive Officer, p. B54

PHYSICIANS HOSPITAL SYSTEM 1625 East Jefferson Boulevard, Zip 46545–7103; tel. 574/255–1400; Cameron R. Gilbert, Ph.D., President and Chief Executive Officer, p. B102

## IOWA

**Clarion:** ★ IOWA SPECIALTY HOSPITALS 1316 South Main Street, Zip 50525–2019; tel. 515/532–2811; Steven J. Simonin, Chief Executive Officer, p. B74

**Davenport:** ★ GENESIS HEALTH SYSTEM 1227 East Rusholme Street, Zip 52803–2498; tel. 563/421–1000; Douglas P. Cropper, President and Chief Executive Officer, p. B56

**West Des Moines:** ★ UNITYPOINT HEALTH 1776 Westlakes Parkway, Suite 400, Zip 50266–8239; tel. 515/241–6161; William B. Leaver, President and Chief Executive Officer, p. B136

## KANSAS

**Wichita:** ★ GREAT PLAINS HEALTH ALLIANCE, INC. 250 North Rock Road, Suite 160, Zip 67206–2241; tel. 316/685–1223; Dave Dellasega, President and Chief Executive Officer, p. B57

## KENTUCKY

**Bowling Green:** COMMONWEALTH HEALTH CORPORATION 800 Park Street, Zip 42101–2356; tel. 270/745–1500; Connie Smith, President and Chief Executive Officer, p. B34

**Edgewood:** ST. ELIZABETH HEALTHCARE 1 Medical Village Drive, Zip 41017–3403; tel. 859/301–2000; John S. Dubis, FACHE, President and Chief Executive Officer, p. B124

**Lexington:** APPALACHIAN REGIONAL HEALTHCARE, INC. 2285 Executive Drive, Suite 400, Zip 40505–4810, Mailing Address: P.O. Box 8086, Zip 40533–8086; tel. 859/226–2440; Jerry Haynes, President and Chief Executive Officer, p. B10

UK HEALTHCARE 900 South Limestone, Zip 40505; tel. 859/323–5000; Michael Karpf, M.D., Executive Vice President Health Affairs, p. B134

**Louisville:** ALLIANT MANAGEMENT SERVICES 2650 Eastpoint Parkway, Suite 300, Zip 40223–5164; tel. 502/992–3525; Timothy L. Jarm, President and Chief Executive Officer, p. B8

★ BAPTIST HEALTH 2701 Eastpoint Parkway, Zip 40223; tel. 502/896–5000; Stephen C. Hanson, President and Chief Executive Officer, p. B19

★ KINDRED HEALTHCARE 680 South Fourth Street, Zip 40202–2412; tel. 502/596–7300; Paul J. Diaz, President and Chief Executive Officer, p. B77

★ NORTON HEALTHCARE 4967 U.S. Highway 42, Suite 100, Zip 40222–6363, Mailing Address: P.O. Box 35070, Zip 40232–5070; tel. 502/629–8000; Stephen Williams, President, p. B97

## LOUISIANA

**Baton Rouge:** ★ FRANCISCAN MISSIONARIES OF OUR LADY HEALTH SYSTEM, INC. 4200 Essen Lane, Zip 70809–2158; tel. 225/923–2701; John J. Finan, Jr., FACHE, President and Chief Executive Officer, p. B55

LOUISIANA STATE HOSPITALS 628 North 4th Street, Zip 70802–5342, Mailing Address: P.O. Box 629, Zip 70821–0628; tel. 225/342–9500; Shelby Price, Chief Executive Officer, p. B84

LSU HEALTH CARE SERVICES DIVISION 5429 Airline Highway, Zip 70805, Mailing Address: P.O. Box 91308, Zip 70821–4400; tel. 225/354–7000; Michael Kaiser, M.D., Interim Chief Executive Officer, p. B84

**Crowley:** COMPASS HEALTH 1526 North Avenue I., Zip 70526–2434; tel. 337/788–3330; , p. B39

**Hammond:** NORTH OAKS HEALTH SYSTEM 15790 Paul Vega MD Drive, Zip 70403–1436, Mailing Address: P.O. Box 2668, Zip 70404–2668; tel. 985/345–2700; James E. Cathey, Jr., Chief Executive Officer, p. B96

**Lafayette:** AMG INTEGRATED HEALTHCARE MANAGEMENT 101 La Rue France, Suite 500, Zip 70508–3144; tel. 337/269–9828; August J. Rantz, III, Founder and Chief Executive Officer, p. B9

LHC GROUP 420 West Pinhook Road, Zip 70503–2131; tel. 337/223–1307; Keith G. Myers, Chairman and Chief Executive Officer, p. B81

**Lake Charles:** OCEANS HEALTHCARE 2720 Rue de Jardin, Suite 100, Zip 70605–4050; tel. 337/721–1900; Jason Reed, President and Chief Executive Officer, p. B98

**Leesville:** SPECIALTY HEALTHCARE, LLC 305 West Harriet Street, Zip 71446–4229; tel. 337/238–4449; Craig Ball, Chairman and Chief Executive Officer, p. B123

**New Orleans:** ★ OCHSNER HEALTH SYSTEM 1514 Jefferson Highway, Zip 70121–2429; tel. 800/874–8984; Warner L. Thomas, FACHE, President and Chief Executive Officer, p. B98

**Shreveport:** ALLEGIANCE HEALTH MANAGEMENT 504 Texas Street, Suite 200, Zip 71101–3526; tel. 318/226–8202; Rock Bordelon, President and Chief Executive Officer, p. B8

WILLIS–KNIGHTON HEALTH SYSTEM 2600 Greenwood Road, Zip 71103–3908; tel. 318/212–4000; James K. Elrod, FACHE, President and Chief Executive Officer, p. B149

## MAINE

**Brewer:** ★ EASTERN MAINE HEALTHCARE SYSTEMS 43 Whiting Hill Road, Zip 04412–1005; tel. 207/973–7045; M. Michelle Hood, President and Chief Executive Officer, p. B51

**Portland:** MAINEHEALTH 110 Free Street, Zip 04101–3537; William L. Caron, Jr., President, p. B85

## MARYLAND

**Baltimore:** ★ JOHNS HOPKINS HEALTH SYSTEM 733 North Broadway, BRB 104, Zip 21205–1832; tel. 410/955–5000; Ronald R. Peterson, President, p. B75

★ LIFEBRIDGE HEALTH 2401 West Belvedere Avenue, Zip 21215–5216; tel. 410/601–5134; Neil M. Meltzer, President and Chief Executive Officer, p. B81

★ UNIVERSITY OF MARYLAND MEDICAL SYSTEM 250 West Pratt Street, 24th Floor, Zip 21201–1595; tel. 410/328–8667; Robert A. Chrencik, President and Chief Executive Officer, p. B141

**Bel Air:** UPPER CHESAPEAKE HEALTH SYSTEM 520 Upper Chesapeake Drive, Suite 405, Zip 21014–4381; tel. 443/643–3303; Lyle Ernest Sheldon, FACHE, President and Chief Executive Officer, p. B143

**Cheverly:** DIMENSIONS HEALTHCARE SYSTEM 3001 Hospital Drive, 3rd Floor, Zip 20785–1189; tel. 301/583–4000; Neil J. Moore, President and Chief Executive Officer, p. B49

**Columbia:** ENCORE HEALTHCARE 7150 Columbia Gateway Drove, Suite J., Zip 21046–2974; tel. 443/539–2350; Tim Nicholson, Chief Executive Officer, p. B52

★ MEDSTAR HEALTH 5565 Sterrett Place, 5th Floor, Zip 21044–2665; tel. 410/772–6500; Kenneth A. Samet, President and Chief Executive Officer, p. B87

**Gaithersburg:** ★ ADVENTIST HEALTHCARE 820 West Diamond Avenue, Suite 600, Zip 20878–1419; tel. 301/315–3030; William G. Robertson, President and Chief Executive Officer, p. B6

**Marriottsville:** ★ BON SECOURS HEALTH SYSTEM, INC. 1505 Marriottsville Road, Zip 21104–1399; tel. 410/442–5511; Richard Statuto, President and Chief Executive Officer, p. B23

**Rockville:** U. S. INDIAN HEALTH SERVICE 801 Thompson Avenue, Zip 20852–1627; tel. 301/443–1083; Yvette Roubideaux, M.D., M.P.H., Director, p. B133

**Sparks Glencoe:** FUNDAMENTAL LONG TERM CARE HOLDINGS, LLC 930 Ridgebrook Road, Zip 21152–9390; tel. 410/773–1000; W. Bradley Bennett, President and Chief Executive Officer, p. B55

**Stevensville:** MID ATLANTIC HEALTH MANAGEMENT, INC. 1220 Butterworth Court, Zip 21666–2504; tel. 410/643–3393; Harold A. McBee, Jr., President, p. B91

## MASSACHUSETTS

**Boston:** MASSACHUSETTS DEPARTMENT OF MENTAL HEALTH 25 Staniford Street, Zip 02114–2575; tel. 617/626–8123; Marcia Fowler, Commissioner, p. B85

MASSACHUSETTS DEPARTMENT OF PUBLIC HEALTH 250 Washington Street, Zip 02108–4619; tel. 617/624–6000; Sandra Akers, Bureau Director, Public Health Hospitals, p. B85

★ PARTNERS HEALTHCARE SYSTEM, INC. 800 Boylston Street, Suite 1150, Zip 02199–8123; tel. 617/278–1004; Gary L. Gottlieb, M.D., President and Chief Executive Officer, p. B101

STEWARD HEALTH CARE SYSTEM, LLC 500 Boylston Street, 5th Floor, Zip 02116–3740; tel. 617/419–4700; Ralph de la Torre, M.D., Chairman and Chief Executive Officer, p. B125

**Burlington:** LAHEY HEALTH 41 Mall Road, Zip 01805–0001; tel. 781/744–7100; Howard R. Grant, JD, M.D., President and Chief Executive Officer, p. B80

**Haverhill:** WHITTIER HEALTH NETWORK 25 Railroad Square, Zip 01832–5721; tel. 978/556–5858; Alfred L. Arcidi, M.D., President, p. B149

**Hyannis:** ★ CAPE COD HEALTHCARE, INC. 27 Park Street, Zip 02601–5230; tel. 508/862–5121; Michael K. Lauf, President and Chief Executive Officer, p. B25

**Newton:** FIVE STAR QUALITY CARE 400 Centre Street, Zip 02458–2094; tel. 617/796–8387; Bruce J. Mackey, Jr., President and Chief Executive Officer, p. B54

**Pittsfield:** ★ BERKSHIRE HEALTH SYSTEMS, INC. 725 North Street, Zip 01201–4124; tel. 413/447–2743; David E. Phelps, President and Chief Executive Officer, p. B22

**Springfield:** ★ BAYSTATE HEALTH, INC. 759 Chestnut Street, Zip 01199–0001; tel. 413/794–0000; Mark R. Tolosky, JD, FACHE, President and Chief Executive Officer, p. B21

**Tewksbury:** ★ COVENANT HEALTH SYSTEMS, INC. 100 Ames Pond Drive, Suite 102, Zip 01876–1240; tel. 978/654–6363; David R. Lincoln, FACHE, President and Chief Executive Officer, p. B41

**Worcester:** ★ UMASS MEMORIAL HEALTH CARE, INC. 1 Biotech Park, Zip 01605–2982; tel. 508/334–0100; Eric Dickson, M.D., President and Chief Executive Officer, p. B135

## MICHIGAN

**Dearborn:** ★ OAKWOOD HEALTHCARE, INC. One Parklane Boulevard, Suite 1000E, Zip 48126–2400; tel. 313/253–6050; Brian M. Connolly, President and Chief Executive Officer, p. B98

**Detroit:** ★ HENRY FORD HEALTH SYSTEM One Ford Place, Zip 48202–3450; tel. 313/876–8708; Nancy M. Schlichting, Chief Executive Officer, p. B70

**Flint:** ★ MCLAREN HEALTH CARE CORPORATION G3235 Beecher Road, Suite B., Zip 48532–3650; tel. 810/342–1100; Philip A. Incarnati, President and Chief Executive Officer, p. B87

**Grand Rapids:** ★ SPECTRUM HEALTH 100 Michigan Street N.E., Zip 49503–2551; tel. 616/391–1774; Richard C. Breon, President and Chief Executive Officer, p. B123

**Kalamazoo:** ★ BRONSON HEALTHCARE GROUP, INC. 301 John Street, Zip 49007–5295; tel. 269/341–6000; Frank J. Sardone, President and Chief Executive Officer, p. B24

**Lansing:** ★ SPARROW HEALTH SYSTEM 1215 East Michigan Avenue, Zip 48912–1811; tel. 517/364–1000; Dennis A. Swan, JD, FACHE, President and Chief Executive Officer, p. B122

★ TRINITY HEALTH 20555 Victor Parkway, Zip 48152–7031; tel. 734/343–1396; Judith M. Persichilli, Interim President and Chief Executive Officer, CHE Trinity Inc., p. B131

**Midland:** ★ MIDMICHIGAN HEALTH 4000 Wellness Drive, Zip 48670–0001; tel. 989/839–3000; Diane Postler–Slattery, Ph.D., President and Chief Executive Officer, p. B91

**Port Huron:** ★ BLUE WATER HEALTH SERVICES CORPORATION 1221 Pine Grove Avenue, Zip 48060–3511; tel. 810/989–3717; Thomas D. DeFauw, FACHE, President and Chief Executive Officer, p. B23

**Royal Oak:** ★ BEAUMONT HEALTH SYSTEM 3711 West 13 Mile Road, Zip 48073–6767; tel. 248/898–5000; Gene Michalski, President and Chief Executive Officer, p. B22

**Saint Joseph:** LAKELAND HEALTHCARE 1234 Napier Avenue, Zip 49085–2158; tel. 269/983–8300; Loren Hamel, M.D., President and Chief Executive Officer, p. B80

**Traverse City:** ★ MUNSON HEALTHCARE 1105 Sixth Street, Zip 49684–2386; tel. 231/935–6703; Edwin Ness, President and Chief Executive Officer, p. B93

## MINNESOTA

**Bloomington:** HEALTHPARTNERS 8170 33rd Avenue South, Zip 55425–4516; tel. 952/883–7600; Mary K. Brainerd, President and Chief Executive Officer, p. B66

**Duluth:** ESSENTIA HEALTH 502 East Second Street, Zip 55805–1913; tel. 218/786–8376; Peter E. Person, M.D., Chief Executive Officer, p. B53

**Minneapolis:** ★ ALLINA HEALTH 2925 Chicago Avenue, Zip 55407–1321, Mailing Address: P.O. Box 43, Zip 55440–0043; tel. 612/262–5000; Ken Paulus, President and Chief Executive Officer, p. B9

CHILDREN'S HOSPITALS AND CLINICS OF MINNESOTA 2525 Chicago Avenue South, Zip 55404–4518; tel. 612/813–6100; Alan L. Goldbloom, M.D., President and Chief Executive Officer, p. B32

★ FAIRVIEW HEALTH SERVICES 2450 Riverside Avenue, Zip 55454–1400; tel. 612/672–6141; Charles Mooty, Interim Chief Executive Officer, p. B53

**Robbinsdale:** ★ NORTH MEMORIAL HEALTH CARE 3300 Oakdale Avenue North, Zip 55422–2926; tel. 763/520–5200; Loren L. Taylor, Chief Executive Officer, p. B96

**Rochester:** ★ MAYO CLINIC HEALTH SYSTEM 200 S.W. First Street, Zip 55905–0002; tel. 507/284–2511; John Noseworthy, M.D., President and Chief Executive Officer, p. B86

**Saint Cloud:** ★ CENTRACARE HEALTH 1406 Sixth Avenue North, Zip 56303–1900; tel. 320/251–2700; Terence Pladson, M.D., President and Chief Executive Officer, p. B32

**Saint Paul:** ★ HEALTHEAST CARE SYSTEM 559 Capitol Boulevard, 6–South, Zip 55103–0000; tel. 651/232–2300; Kathryn G. Correia, President and Chief Executive Officer, p. B66

MINNESOTA DEPARTMENT OF HUMAN SERVICES 540 Cedar Street, Zip 55101–2208, Mailing Address: P.O. Box 64998, Zip 55164–0998; tel. 651/431–3212; Anne Barry, Deputy Commissioner, p. B91

## MISSISSIPPI

**Jackson:** ★ MISSISSIPPI BAPTIST HEALTH SYSTEM 1225 North State Street, Zip 39202–2064; tel. 601/968–1000; Mark F. Slyter, FACHE, President and Chief Executive Officer, p. B92

MISSISSIPPI STATE DEPARTMENT OF MENTAL HEALTH 1101 Robert East Lee Building, 239 North Lamar Street, Zip 39201–1101; tel. 601/359–1288; Edwin C. LeGrand, III, Executive Director, p. B92

**Magee:** ★ PIONEER HEALTH SERVICES 110 Pioneer Way, Zip 39111–5501, Mailing Address: P.O. Box 1100, Zip 39111–1100; tel. 601/849–6440; Joseph S. McNulty, III, President and Chief Executive Officer, p. B103

**Mccomb:** SOUTHWEST HEALTH SYSTEMS 215 Marion Avenue, Zip 39648–2705, Mailing Address: P.O. Box 1307, Zip 39649–1307; tel. 601/249–5500; Norman M. Price, FACHE, Chief Executive Officer and Administrator, p. B122

**Meridian:** ★ RUSH HEALTH SYSTEMS 1314 19th Avenue, Zip 39301–4116; tel. 601/483–0011; Wallace Strickland, President and Chief Executive Officer, p. B112

**Tupelo:** ★ NORTH MISSISSIPPI HEALTH SERVICES, INC. 830 South Gloster Street, Zip 38801–4996; tel. 662/377–3136; John R. Heer, President and Chief Executive Officer, p. B96

## MISSOURI

**Cape Girardeau:** LANDMARK HOSPITALS 3255 Independence Street, Zip 63701–4914; tel. 573/335–1091; William K. Kapp, III, M.D., President and Chief Executive Officer, p. B80

★ SOUTHEASTHEALTH 1701 Lacey Street, Zip 63701–5230; tel. 573/334–4822; Wayne Smith, President and Chief Executive Officer, p. B122

**Chesterfield:** ★ MERCY HEALTH 14528 South Outer 40, Suite 100, Zip 63017–5743; tel. 314/579–6100; Lynn Britton, President and Chief Executive Officer, p. B89

**Columbia:** ★ UNIVERSITY OF MISSOURI HEALTH CARE One Hospital Drive, DC 031, Zip 65212–0001; tel. 573/884–8738; Mitchell L. Wasden, Ed.D., Chief Executive Officer and Chief Operating Officer, p. B142

**Joplin:** ★ FREEMAN HEALTH SYSTEM 1102 West 32nd Street, Zip 64804–3503; tel. 417/347–1111; Paula F. Baker, President and Chief Executive Officer, p. B55

**Kansas City:** RURAL COMMUNITY HOSPITALS OF AMERICA 1100 Main Street, Suite 2350, Zip 64105–5186; tel. 816/474–7800; Lawrence J. Arthur, President, p. B111

★ SAINT LUKE'S HEALTH SYSTEM 10920 Elm Avenue, Zip 64134–4108; tel. 816/932–2000; Melinda Estes, M.D., President and Chief Executive Officer, p. B113

★ TRUMAN MEDICAL CENTERS 2301 Holmes Street, Zip 64108–2677; tel. 816/404–1000; John W. Bluford, President and Chief Executive Officer, p. B133

**Saint Louis:** ★ ASCENSION HEALTH 4600 Edmundson Road, Zip 63134–3806; tel. 314/733–8000; Robert J. Henkel, FACHE, President and Chief Executive Officer, p. B11

★ BJC HEALTHCARE 4901 Forest Park Avenue, Suite 1200, Zip 63108–1402; tel. 314/747–9322; Steven H. Lipstein, President and Chief Executive Officer, p. B22

★ SSM HEALTH CARE 477 North Lindbergh Boulevard, Zip 63141–7813; tel. 314/994–7800; William P. Thompson, President and Chief Executive Officer, p. B123

**Springfield:** COXHEALTH 1423 North Jefferson Avenue, Zip 65802–1988; tel. 417/269–3108; Steven D. Edwards, President and Chief Executive Officer, p. B81

## MONTANA

**Great Falls:** BENEFIS HEALTH SYSTEM 1101 26th Street South, Zip 59405–5161; tel. 406/455–5000; John H. Goodnow, Chief Executive Officer, p. B22

## NEBRASKA

**Lincoln:** ★ BRYAN HEALTH 1600 South 48th Street, Zip 68506–1283; tel. 402/481–1111; Kimberly A. Russel, FACHE, President and Chief Executive Officer, p. B24

**Norfolk:** FAITH REGIONAL HEALTH SERVICES 2700 West Norfolk Avenue, Zip 68701–4438, Mailing Address: P.O. Box 869, Zip 68702–0869; tel. 402/644–7201; Tim Auwarter, Interim President and Chief Executive Officer, p. B54

**Omaha:** ★ NEBRASKA METHODIST HEALTH SYSTEM, INC. 8511 West Dodge Road, Zip 68114–3403; tel. 402/354–5411; John M. Fraser, President and Chief Executive Officer, p. B93

## NEVADA

**Reno:** ★ RENOWN HEALTH 1155 Mill Street, Zip 89502–1576; tel. 775/982–4100; Donald C. Sibery, Interim Chief Executive Officer, p. B110

## NEW HAMPSHIRE

**Laconia:** ★ LRGHEALTHCARE 80 Highland Street, Zip 03246–3298; tel. 603/524–3211; Thomas Clairmont, President, p. B84

**Portsmouth:** SPECIALTY HOSPITALS OF AMERICA, LLC 155 Fleet Street, Zip 03801–4050; tel. 603/570–4888; Eric F. Rieseberg, President, p. B123

## NEW JERSEY

**Edison:** ★ JFK HEALTH SYSTEM 80 James Street, 2nd Floor, Zip 08820–3938; tel. 732/632–1503; Raymond F. Fredericks, President and Chief Executive Officer, p. B75

**Egg Harbor Township:** ★ ATLANTICARE 2500 English Creek Avenue, Building 500, Suite 501, Zip 08234; tel. 609/407–2309; David P. Tilton, President and Chief Executive Officer, p. B15

**Marlton:** ★ VIRTUA HEALTH 50 Lake Center Executive Drive, Suite 401, Zip 08053; tel. 856/355–0010; Richard P. Miller, Chief Executive Officer, p. B147

**Morristown:** ★ ATLANTIC HEALTH 475 South Street, Zip 07962, Mailing Address: P.O. Box 1905, Zip 07962–1905; tel. 973/971–3270; Joseph A. Trunfio, Ph.D., President and Chief Executive Officer, p. B15

**New Brunswick:** ROBERT WOOD JOHNSON HEALTH SYSTEM & NETWORK 1 Robert Wood Johnson Place, Zip 08901–1928; tel. 732/828–3000; Stephen K. Jones, President and Chief Executive Officer, p. B111

**Trenton:** ★ CAPITAL HEALTH 750 Brunswick Avenue, Zip 08638–4143; tel. 609/394–6000; Al Maghazehe, Ph.D., FACHE, Chief Executive Officer, p. B26

DIVISION OF MENTAL HEALTH AND ADDICTION SERVICES, DEPARTMENT OF HUMAN SERVICES, STATE OF NEW JERSEY 222 South Warren Street, Zip 08608–2306, Mailing Address: P.O. Box 700, Zip 08625–0700; tel. 609/777–0702; Lynn Kovich, Assistant Commissioner, p. B49

**Vineland:** ★ INSPIRA HEALTH NETWORK 2950 College Drive, Suite 1E, Zip 08360; tel. 856/641–8000; Chester B. Kaletkowski, President and Chief Executive Officer, p. B73

**Wall Township:** ★ MERIDIAN HEALTH 1350 Campus Parkway, Zip 07753–6821; tel. 732/751–7510; John K. Lloyd, President and Chief Executive Officer, p. B90

**West Orange:** ★ BARNABAS HEALTH 95 Old Short Hills Road, Zip 07052–1008; tel. 973/322–4000; Barry Ostrowsky, President and Chief Executive Officer, p. B20

## NEW MEXICO

**Albuquerque:** ERNEST HEALTH, INC. 7770 Jefferson Street N.E., Suite 320, Zip 87109–4386; tel. 505/856–5300; Darby Brockette, Chief Executive Officer, p. B52

★ PRESBYTERIAN HEALTHCARE SERVICES 2501 Buena Vista Drive, S.E., Zip 87106–4260, Mailing Address: P.O. Box 26666, Zip 87125–6666; tel. 505/841–1234; James H. Hinton, President and Chief Executive Officer, p. B104

UNIVERSITY OF NEW MEXICO HOSPITALS 915 Camino De Salud, Zip 87131–0001; tel. 505/272–5849; Stephen W. McKernan, Chief Executive Officer, p. B142

## NEW YORK

**Albany:** NEW YORK STATE OFFICE OF MENTAL HEALTH 44 Holland Avenue, Zip 12208–3411; tel. 518/474–7056; Kristin M. Woodlock, R.N., Acting Commissioner, p. B95

**Binghamton:** UNITED HEALTH SERVICES 10–42 Mitchell Avenue, Zip 13903–1617; tel. 607/762–2200; Matthew J. Salanger, President and Chief Executive Officer, p. B135

**Buffalo:** ★ CATHOLIC HEALTH SYSTEM 2121 Main Street, Suite 300, Zip 14214–2673; tel. 716/862–2410; Joseph D. McDonald, President and Chief Executive Officer, p. B31

**Cooperstown:** ★ BASSETT HEALTHCARE NETWORK 1 Atwell Road, Zip 13326–1301; tel. 607/547–3456; William F. Streck, M.D., President and Chief Executive Officer, p. B21

**Elmira:** ★ ARNOT HEALTH 600 Roe Avenue, Zip 14905–1629; tel. 607/737–4100; Anthony J. Cooper, FACHE, President and Chief Executive Officer, p. B11

**Geneva:** FINGER LAKES HEALTH 196 North Street, Zip 14456–1651; tel. 315/787–4000; Jose Acevedo, M.D., President and Chief Executive Officer, p. B54

**Great Neck:** ★ NORTH SHORE–LONG ISLAND JEWISH HEALTH SYSTEM 145 Community Drive, Zip 11021–5502; tel. 516/465–8100; Michael J. Dowling, President and Chief Executive Officer, p. B96

**Kingston:** HEALTHALLIANCE OF THE HUDSON VALLEY 396 Broadway, Zip 12401–4626; tel. 845/331–3131; David W. Lundquist, President and Chief Executive Officer, p. B66

**LaGrangeville:** ★ HEALTH QUEST SYSTEMS, INC. 1351 Route 55, Zip 12540–5108; tel. 845/475–9500; Donna McGregor, Interim Co–Chief Executive Officer, p. B66

**Middletown:** GREATER HUDSON VALLEY HEALTH SYSTEM 60 Prospect Avenue, Zip 10940–4133; tel. 845/568–6050; Scott Batulis, President and Chief Executive Officer, p. B58

**New Rochelle:** SOUND SHORE HEALTH SYSTEM 16 Guion Place, Zip 10801–5502; tel. 914/632–5000; John R. Spicer, President and Chief Executive Officer, p. B121

**New York:** ★ CONTINUUM HEALTH PARTNERS 555 West 57th Street, Zip 10019–2925; tel. 212/523–8130; Stanley Brezenoff, President and Chief Executive Officer, p. B40

★ NEW YORK CITY HEALTH AND HOSPITALS CORPORATION 125 Worth Street, Room 514, Zip 10013–4006; tel. 212/788–3321; Alan D. Aviles, President, p. B94

NEW YORK PRESBYTERIAN HEALTHCARE SYSTEM 177 Fort Washington Avenue, Room P123, Zip 10032–3733; tel. 212/746–3745; Steven J. Corwin, M.D., Chief Executive Officer, p. B94

**Olean:** UPPER ALLEGHENY HEALTH SYSTEM 130 South Union Street, Suite 300, Zip 14760–3676; tel. 716/375–6190; Timothy J. Finan, FACHE, President and Chief Executive Officer, p. B143

**Rochester:** ★ ROCHESTER GENERAL HEALTH SYSTEM 1425 Portland Avenue, 5th Floor, Zip 14621–3001; tel. 585/922–4000; Mark C. Clement, President and Chief Executive Officer, p. B111

★ UNIVERSITY OF ROCHESTER MEDICAL CENTER 601 Elmwood Avenue, Zip 14642–0002; tel. 585/275–2100; Steven I. Goldstein, General Director and Chief Executive Officer, p. B142

**Rockville Centre:** CATHOLIC HEALTH SERVICES OF LONG ISLAND 992 North Village Avenue, 1st Floor, Zip 11570–1002; tel. 516/705–3700; Alan D. Guerci, M.D., President and Chief Executive Officer, p. B31

**Syracuse:** SISTERS OF SAINT FRANCIS 2500 Grant Boulevard, Zip 13208–1782; tel. 315/634–7000; Sister Marian Rose Mansius, Assistant General Minister, p. B121

## NORTH CAROLINA

**Asheville:** ★ MISSION HEALTH SYSTEM 509 Biltmore Avenue, Zip 28801–4601; tel. 828/213–1111; Ronald A. Paulus, M.D., President and Chief Executive Officer, p. B91

**Boone:** ★ APPALACHIAN REGIONAL HEALTHCARE SYSTEM 336 Deerfield Road, Zip 28607–5008, Mailing Address: P.O. Box 2600, Zip 28607–2600; tel. 828/262–4100; Richard G. Sparks, President and Chief Executive Officer, p. B10

**Chapel Hill:** ★ UNC HEALTH CARE 101 Manning Drive, Zip 27514–4220; tel. 919/966–4131; William L. Roper, M.D., M.P.H., Chief Executive Officer, p. B135

**Charlotte:** ★ ACUITYHEALTHCARE, LP 10200 Mallard Creek Road, Suite 300, Zip 28262–9705; tel. 704/887–7280; Edwin H. Cooper, Jr., MS, President and Chief Executive Officer, p. B4

★ CAROLINAS HEALTHCARE SYSTEM 1000 Blythe Boulevard, Zip 28203–5871, Mailing Address: P.O. Box 32861, Zip 28232–2861; tel. 704/355–2000; Michael C. Tarwater, Chief Executive Officer, p. B26

**Durham:** ★ DUKE UNIVERSITY HEALTH SYSTEM 201 Trent Drive, Zip 27710–3037, Mailing Address: P.O. Box 3701, Zip 27710–3701; tel. 919/684–2255; Victor J. Dzau, M.D., President and Chief Executive Officer, p. B50

**Fayetteville:** CAPE FEAR VALLEY HEALTH SYSTEM 1638 Owen Drive, Zip 28304–3424, Mailing Address: P.O. Box 2000, Zip 28302–2000; tel. 910/615–4000; Michael Nagowski, President and Chief Executive Officer, p. B25

**Greenville:** ★ VIDANT HEALTH 2100 Stantonsburg Road, Zip 27834–2818, Mailing Address: P.O. Box 6028, Zip 27835–6028; tel. 252/847–4100; David C. Herman, M.D., President and Chief Executive Officer, p. B146

**Morganton:** BLUE RIDGE HEALTHCARE 2201 South Sterling Street, Zip 28655; tel. 828/580–5000; Kathy C. Bailey, Ph.D., FACHE, President and Chief Executive Officer, p. B23

**Pinehurst:** ★ FIRSTHEALTH OF THE CAROLINAS 155 Memorial Drive, Zip 28374–8710, Mailing Address: P.O. Box 3000, Zip 28374–3000; tel. 910/715–1000; David J. Kilarski, Chief Executive Officer, p. B54

**Raleigh:** ★ WAKEMED HEALTH & HOSPITALS 3000 New Bern Avenue, Zip 27610–1231; tel. 919/350–8000; William K. Atkinson, II, Ph.D., M.P.H., President and Chief Executive Officer, p. B147

**Sylva:** ★ MEDWEST HEALTH SYSTEM 68 Hospital Road, Zip 28779–2722; tel. 828/586–7000; Steve Heatherly, President, p. B88

**Wilmington:** ★ NEW HANOVER REGIONAL MEDICAL CENTER 2131 South 17th Street, Zip 28401–7407; tel. 910/343–7040; John K. Barto, Jr., President and Chief Executive Officer, p. B94

**Winston Salem:** ★ NOVANT HEALTH 2085 Frontis Plaza Boulevard, Zip 27103–5614; tel. 336/718–5600; Carl S. Armato, President and Chief Executive Officer, p. B98

**Winston–Salem:** ★ WAKE FOREST BAPTIST HEALTH Medical Center Boulevard, Zip 27157; tel. 336/716–2011; John D. McConnell, M.D., Chief Executive Officer, p. B147

**NORTH DAKOTA**

**Bismarck:** BENEDICTINE SISTERS OF THE ANNUNCIATION 7520 University Drive, Zip 58504–9653; tel. 701/255–1520; Sister Susan Berger, Prioress, p. B22

**Fargo:** SISTERS OF MARY OF THE PRESENTATION HEALTH SYSTEM 1202 Page Drive S.W., Zip 58103–2340, Mailing Address: P.O. Box 10007, Zip 58106–0007; tel. 701/237–9290; Aaron K. Alton, President and Chief Executive Officer, p. B121

**OHIO**

**Akron:** ★ AKRON GENERAL HEALTH SYSTEM 400 Wabash Avenue, Zip 44307–2433; tel. 330/344–6000; Thomas L. Stover, M.D., President and Chief Executive Officer, p. B7

SUMMA HEALTH SYSTEM 525 East Market Street, Zip 44304–1619; tel. 330/375–3000; Thomas J. Strauss, President and Chief Executive Officer, p. B126

**Canton:** AULTMAN HEALTH FOUNDATION 2600 Sixth Street S.W., Zip 44710–1702; tel. 330/363–6192; Edward J. Roth, III, President and Chief Executive Officer, p. B15

**Chillicothe:** ADENA HEALTH SYSTEM 272 Hospital Road, Zip 45601–9031; tel. 740/779–7500; Mark H. Shuter, President and Chief Executive Officer, p. B5

**Cincinnati:** ★ CATHOLIC HEALTH PARTNERS 615 Elsinore Place, Zip 45202–1459; tel. 513/639–2800; Michael D. Connelly, President and Chief Executive Officer, p. B30

★ UC HEALTH 3200 Burnet Avenue, Zip 45229–3019; tel. 513/585–6000; James A. Kingsbury, President and Chief Executive Officer, p. B134

**Cleveland:** ★ CLEVELAND CLINIC HEALTH SYSTEM 9500 Euclid, Zip 44195–5108; tel. 216/444–2200; Delos Cosgrove, M.D., President and Chief Executive Officer, p. B34

SISTERS OF CHARITY HEALTH SYSTEM 2475 East 22nd Street, Zip 44115–3221; tel. 216/363–2797; Sister Judith Ann Karam, President and Chief Executive Officer, p. B121

★ UNIVERSITY HOSPITALS 11100 Euclid Avenue, Zip 44106–5000; tel. 216/844–1000; Thomas F. Zenty, III, President and Chief Executive Officer, p. B141

**Columbus:** OHIO DEPARTMENT OF MENTAL HEALTH 30 East Broad Street, 8th Floor, Zip 43215–3430; tel. 614/466–2297; Tracy Plouck, Director, p. B99

★ OHIO STATE UNIVERSITY HEALTH SYSTEM 370 West Ninth Avenue, Zip 43210–1238; tel. 614/247–5555; Peter E. Geier, Chief Executive Officer, p. B99

★ OHIOHEALTH 180 East Broad Street, Zip 43215–3707; tel. 614/544–4455; David P. Blom, President and Chief Executive Officer, p. B99

**Dayton:** ★ KETTERING HEALTH NETWORK 3965 Southern Boulevard, Zip 45429–1229; tel. 937/395–8150; Fred M. Manchur, Chief Executive Officer, p. B76

**Findlay:** ★ BLANCHARD VALLEY HEALTH SYSTEM 1900 South Main Street, Zip 45840–1214; tel. 419/423–4500; Scott C. Malaney, President and Chief Executive Officer, p. B22

**Galion:** ★ AVITA HEALTH SYSTEM 269 Portland Way South, Zip 44833–2399; tel. 419/468–4841; Jerome Morasko, President and Chief Executive Officer, p. B17

**Mansfield:** MEDCENTRAL HEALTH SYSTEM 335 Glessner Avenue, Zip 44903–2269; tel. 419/526–8000; Joe Chamberlain, Acting Chief Executive Officer, p. B87

**Toledo:** ★ PROMEDICA HEALTH SYSTEM 1801 Richards Road, Zip 43607–1037; tel. 419/469–3800; Randall D. Oostra, FACHE, President and Chief Executive Officer, p. B105

★ SYLVANIA FRANCISCAN HEALTH 3231 Central Park West, Suite 106, Zip 43617–3009; tel. 419/882–8373; James W. Pope, FACHE, President and Chief Executive Officer, p. B127

**OKLAHOMA**

**Oklahoma City:** FOUNDATION SURGICAL HOSPITAL AFFILIATES 14000 North Portland Avenue, Suite 204, Zip 73134–4002; tel. 405/608–1700; Thomas A. Michaud, Chief Executive Officer, p. B54

★ INTEGRIS HEALTH 3366 N.W. Expressway, Suite 800, Zip 73112–9756; tel. 405/949–6066; Bruce Lawrence, President and Chief Executive Officer, p. B73

OKLAHOMA DEPARTMENT OF MENTAL HEALTH AND SUBSTANCE ABUSE SERVICES 1200 N.E. 13th Street, Zip 73117–1022, Mailing Address: P.O. Box 53277, Zip 73152–3277; tel. 405/522–3908; Terri White, Commissioner, p. B100

SOUTHERN PLAINS MEDICAL GROUP 4323 N.W. 63rd Street Suite 232, Zip 73116–1546; tel. 405/753–6770; Margie Homer, President, p. B122

**Shawnee:** PREFERRED MANAGEMENT CORPORATION 120 West MacArthur, Suite 121, Zip 74804–2005; tel. 405/878–0202; Donald Freeman, President and Chief Executive Officer, p. B103

**Tulsa:** ★ SAINT FRANCIS HEALTH SYSTEM 6161 South Yale Avenue, Zip 74136–1902; tel. 918/494–8454; Jake Henry, Jr., President and Chief Executive Officer, p. B112

**OREGON**

**Bend:** ★ ST. CHARLES HEALTH SYSTEM, INC. 2500 N.E. Neff Road, Zip 97701–6015; tel. 541/382–4321; James A. Diegel, President and Chief Executive Officer, p. B124

**Corvallis:** ★ SAMARITAN HEALTH SERVICES 3600 N.W. Samaritan Drive, Zip 97330–3737, Mailing Address: P.O. Box 1068, Zip 97339–1068; tel. 541/768–5001; Larry A. Mullins, FACHE, President and Chief Executive Officer, p. B113

**Medford:** ★ ASANTE HEALTH SYSTEM 2650 Siskiyou Boulevard, Suite 200, Zip 97504–8170; tel. 541/789–4100; Roy G. Vinyard, FACHE, President and Chief Executive Officer, p. B11

**Portland:** ★ LEGACY HEALTH 1919 N.W. Lovejoy Street, Zip 97209–1503; tel. 503/415–5600; George J. Brown, M.D., President and Chief Executive Officer, p. B80

**Salem:** SALEM HEALTH 890 Oak Street Building B. POB 14001, Zip 97309–5014; tel. 503/561–5200; Norman F. Gruber, President and Chief Executive Officer, p. B113

**PENNSYLVANIA**

**Abington:** ABINGTON HEALTH 1200 Old York Road, Zip 19001; tel. 215/576–2009; Laurence M. Merlis, President and Chief Executive Officer, p. B4

**Allentown:** GOOD SHEPHERD REHABILITATION NETWORK 850 South Fifth Street, Zip 18103–3308; tel. 610/776–3100; John Kristel, President and Chief Executive Officer, p. B57

★ LEHIGH VALLEY HEALTH NETWORK 1200 South Cedar Crest Boulevard, Zip 18103–6202, Mailing Address: P.O. Box 689, Zip 18105–1556; tel. 610/402–8000; Ronald W. Swinfard, M.D., President and Chief Executive Officer, p. B81

**Beaver:** HERITAGE VALLEY HEALTH SYSTEM 1000 Dutch Ridge Road, Zip 15009–9727; tel. 724/773–2024; Norman F. Mitry, President and Chief Executive Officer, p. B70

**Bethlehem:** ST. LUKE'S UNIVERSITY HEALTH NETWORK 801 Ostrum Street, Zip 18015–1000; tel. 610/954–4000; Richard A. Anderson, President and Chief Executive Officer, p. B125

**Camp Hill:** POST ACUTE MEDICAL, LLC 3500 Market Street, Suite 202, Zip 17011–4354; tel. 717/731–9660; Anthony F. Misitano, President and Chief Executive Officer, p. B103

**Chambersburg:** ★ SUMMIT HEALTH 112 North Seventh Street, Zip 17201–1720; tel. 717/267–7138; Patrick W. O'Donnell, CPA, President and Chief Executive Officer, p. B126

**Danville:** ★ GEISINGER HEALTH SYSTEM 100 North Academy Avenue, Zip 17822–9800; tel. 570/271–6211; Glenn Steele, Jr., M.D., Ph.D., President and Chief Executive Officer, p. B56

**Erie:** ★ SAINT VINCENT HEALTH SYSTEM 232 West 25th Street, Zip 16544–0002; tel. 814/452–5000; Scott Whalen, Ph.D., FACHE, President and Chief Executive Officer, p. B113

**Greensburg:** EXCELA HEALTH 134 Industrial Park Road, Zip 15601–7328; tel. 724/832–5050; Robert Rogalski, Chief Executive Officer, p. B53

**Johnstown:** ★ CONEMAUGH HEALTH SYSTEM 1086 Franklin Street, Zip 15905–4398; tel. 814/534–9000; Scott A. Becker, Chief Executive Officer, p. B39

**King of Prussia:** UNIVERSAL HEALTH SERVICES, INC. 367 South Gulph Road, Zip 19406–3121, Mailing Address: P.O. Box 61558, Zip 19406–0958; tel. 610/768–3300; Alan B. Miller, Chairman and Chief Executive Officer, p. B137

**Lehighton:** BLUE MOUNTAIN HEALTH SYSTEM 211 North 12th Street, Zip 18235–1138; tel. 610/377–1300; Andrew E. Harris, President and Chief Executive Officer, p. B23

**Mechanicsburg:** ★ SELECT MEDICAL CORPORATION 4714 Gettysburg Road, Zip 17055–4325; tel. 717/972–1100; David S. Chernow, President and Chief Administrative Officer, p. B116

VIBRA HEALTHCARE 4550 Lena Drive, Suite 225, Zip 17055–4920; tel. 717/591–5700; Brad Hollinger, Chairman and Chief Executive Officer, p. B145

**Newtown Square:** ★ CATHOLIC HEALTH EAST 3805 West Chester Pike, Suite 100, Zip 19073–2329; tel. 610/355–2000; Judith M. Persichilli, Chief Executive Officer, p. B27

**Philadelphia:** ALBERT EINSTEIN HEALTHCARE NETWORK 5501 Old York Road, Zip 19141–3098; tel. 215/456–7890; Barry R. Freedman, President and Chief Executive Officer, p. B7

★ TEMPLE UNIVERSITY HEALTH SYSTEM 3509 North Broad Street, 9th Floor, Zip 19140–4105; tel. 215/707–0900; Larry Kaiser, M.D., President and Chief Executive Officer, p. B128

★ UNIVERSITY OF PENNSYLVANIA HEALTH SYSTEM 3400 Civic Center Bouelvard, Zip 19104–5127; tel. 215/662–2203; Ralph W. Muller, President and Chief Executive Officer, p. B142

**Pittsburgh:** UPMC 600 Grant Street, U.S. Steel Tower, Suite 6262, Zip 15219–2702; tel. 412/647–8762; Jeffrey A. Romoff, President and Chief Executive Officer, p. B143

★ WEST PENN ALLEGHENY HEALTH SYSTEM 30 Isabella Street, Suite 300, Zip 15212–5862; tel. 412/330–2403; John W. Paul, President and Chief Executive Officer, p. B148

**Pottsville:** SCHUYLKILL HEALTH SYSTEM 420 South Jackson Street, Zip 17901–3625; tel. 570/621–5000; John E. Simodejka, President and Chief Executive Officer, p. B114

**Radnor:** ★ JEFFERSON HEALTH SYSTEM 259 Radnor–Chester Road, Suite 290, Zip 19087–5288; tel. 610/225–6200; Joseph T. Sebastianelli, President and Chief Executive Officer, p. B74

**Sayre:** ★ GUTHRIE HEALTHCARE SYSTEM Guthrie Square, Zip 18840; tel. 570/887–4312; Joseph A. Scopelliti, M.D., President and Chief Executive Officer, p. B58

**Springfield:** ★ CROZER–KEYSTONE HEALTH SYSTEM 100 West Sproul Road, Zip 19064–2033; tel. 610/338–8205; Joan K. Richards, President and Chief Executive Officer, p. B41

**Villanova:** DEVEREUX 444 Devereux Drive, Zip 19085–1932, Mailing Address: P.O. Box 638, Zip 19085–0638; tel. 610/520–3000; Robert Q. Kreider, President and Chief Executive Officer, p. B48

**Williamsport:** ★ SUSQUEHANNA HEALTH SYSTEM 700 High Street, Zip 17701–3100; tel. 570/321–1000; Steven P. Johnson, FACHE, President and Chief Executive Officer, p. B126

**York:** ★ WELLSPAN HEALTH 45 Monument Road, Suite 200, Zip 17403–5071; tel. 717/851–2121; Bruce M. Bartels, President, p. B147

## PUERTO RICO

**San Juan:** ★ PUERTO RICO DEPARTMENT OF HEALTH Building A – Medical Center, Zip 00936, Mailing Address: Call Box 70184, Zip 00936; tel. 787/765–2929; Francisco M. Joglar, M.D., Secretary of Health, p. B107

## RHODE ISLAND

**Providence:** ★ CARE NEW ENGLAND HEALTH SYSTEM 45 Willard Avenue, Zip 02905–3218; tel. 401/453–7900; Dennis D. Keefe, President and Chief Executive Officer, p. B26

LIFESPAN CORPORATION 167 Point Street, Zip 02903–4771; tel. 401/444–3500; Timothy J. Babineau, M.D., President and Chief Executive Officer, p. B84

## SOUTH CAROLINA

**Anderson:** ANMED HEALTH 800 North Fant Street, Zip 29621–5793; tel. 864/512–1000; John A. Miller, Jr., FACHE, Chief Executive Officer, p. B10

**Columbia:** ★ PALMETTO HEALTH 1301 Taylor Street, Suite 9–A, Zip 29201–2942, Mailing Address: P.O. Box 2266, Zip 29202–2266; tel. 803/296–2100; Charles D. Beaman, Jr., Chief Executive Officer, p. B101

**Florence:** MCLEOD HEALTH 555 East Cheves Street, Zip 29506–2617, Mailing Address: P.O. Box 100551, Zip 29502–0551; tel. 843/777–2000; Robert L. Colones, President and Chief Executive Officer, p. B87

**Georgetown:** ★ GEORGETOWN HOSPITAL SYSTEM 606 Black River Road, Zip 29440–3304, Mailing Address: P.O. Box 421718, Zip 29442–4203; tel. 843/527–7000; Bruce P. Bailey, President and Chief Executive Officer, p. B56

**Greenville:** ★ GREENVILLE HEALTH SYSTEM 701 Grove Road, Zip 29605–5611; tel. 864/455–7000; Michael C. Riordan, President and Chief Executive Officer, p. B58

**Spartanburg:** ★ SPARTANBURG REGIONAL HEALTHCARE SYSTEM 101 East Wood Street, Zip 29303–3040; tel. 864/560–6000; Bruce Holstien, President and Chief Executive Officer, p. B122

## SOUTH DAKOTA

**Rapid City:** ★ REGIONAL HEALTH 353 Fairmont Boulevard, Zip 57701–7375, Mailing Address: P.O. Box 6000, Zip 57709–6000; tel. 605/719–1000; Charles E. Hart, M.D., MS, President and Chief Executive Officer, p. B109

**Sioux Falls:** ★ AVERA HEALTH 3900 West Avera Drive, Suite 301, Zip 57108–5721; tel. 605/322–4700; John T. Porter, President and Chief Executive Officer, p. B16

★ SANFORD HEALTH 2301 East 60th Street North, Zip 57104–0569, Mailing Address: PO Box 5039, Zip 57117–5039; tel. 605/333–1000; Kelby K. Krabbenhoft, President and Chief Executive Officer, p. B113

## TENNESSEE

**Brentwood:** CENTERRE HEALTHCARE 5250 Virginia Way, Suite 240, Zip 37027–7576; tel. 615/846–9508; Patrick A. Foster, President and Chief Executive Officer, p. B31

DUKE LIFEPOINT HEALTHCARE 103 Powell Court, Zip 37027–5079; tel. 615/372–8540; Jeffrey G. Seraphine, FACHE, Division President, p. B50

★ LIFEPOINT HOSPITALS, INC. 103 Powell Court, Suite 200, Zip 37027–5079; tel. 615/372–8500; William F. Carpenter, III, Chairman and Chief Executive Officer, p. B82

POLARIS HOSPITAL COMPANY 10 Cadillac Drive, Suite 470, Zip 37027–1045; tel. 615/577–1111; Kevin D. Lee, Director and Chief Executive Officer, p. B103

★ QHR 105 Continental Place, Zip 37027–1052; tel. 800/233–1470; James L. Horrar, President and Chief Executive Officer, p. B107

REGIONALCARE HOSPITAL PARTNERS 103 Continental Place, Suite 200, Zip 37027–1042; tel. 615/844–9800; Kent H. Wallace, Chief Executive Officer, p. B110

**Chattanooga:** ERLANGER HEALTH SYSTEM 975 East Third Street, Zip 37403–2147; tel. 423/778–7000; Kevin M. Spiegel, FACHE, President and Chief Executive Officer, p. B52

**Columbia:** ★ MAURY REGIONAL HEALTH SYSTEM 1224 Trotwood Avenue, Zip 38401–4802; tel. 931/381–1111; H. Alan Watson, FACHE, Chief Executive Officer, p. B86

**Franklin:** ACADIA HEALTHCARE COMPANY, INC. 830 Crescent Centre Drive, Suite 610, Zip 37067–7323; tel. 615/861–6000; Joey Jacobs, Chairman and Chief Executive Officer, p. B4

CAPELLA HEALTHCARE 501 Corporate Centre Drive, Suite 200, Zip 37067–2662; tel. 615/764–3000; Daniel S. Slipkovich, Chief Executive Officer, p. B25

★ COMMUNITY HEALTH SYSTEMS, INC. 4000 Meridian Boulevard, Zip 37067–6325, Mailing Address: P.O. Box 689020, Zip 37068–9020; tel. 615/465–7000; Wayne T. Smith, Chairman, President and Chief Executive Officer, p. B35

★ HEALTHTECH MANAGEMENT SERVICES 405 Duke Drive, Suite 210, Zip 37067–2709; tel. 615/309–6053; Derek Morkel, Chief Executive Officer, p. B70

IASIS HEALTHCARE 117 Seaboard Lane, Building E., Zip 37067–2855; tel. 615/844–2747; Carl Whitmer, President and Chief Executive Officer, p. B71

**Jackson:** ★ WEST TENNESSEE HEALTHCARE 620 Skyline Drive, Zip 38301–3923; tel. 731/541–5000; Bobby Arnold, President and Chief Executive Officer, p. B148

**Johnson City:** MOUNTAIN STATES HEALTH ALLIANCE 400 North State of Franklin Road, Zip 37604–6035; tel. 423/431–1040; Dennis Vonderfecht, President and Chief Executive Officer, p. B92

**Kingsport:** ★ WELLMONT HEALTH SYSTEM 1905 American Way, Zip 37660–5882; tel. 423/230–8200; Margaret DeNarvaez, President and Chief Executive Officer, p. B147

**Knoxville:** ★ COVENANT HEALTH 100 Fort Sanders West Boulevard, Zip 37922–3353; tel. 865/531–5555; Anthony Spezia, President and Chief Executive Officer, p. B41

**Memphis:** ★ BAPTIST MEMORIAL HEALTH CARE CORPORATION 350 North Humphreys Boulevard, Zip 38120–2177; tel. 901/227–5117; Stephen Curtis Reynolds, President and Chief Executive Officer, p. B20

METHODIST LE BONHEUR HEALTHCARE 1211 Union Avenue, Suite 700, Zip 38104–6600; tel. 901/516–0543; Gary S. Shorb, President and Chief Executive Officer, p. B91

STRATEGIC BEHAVIORAL HEALTH, LLC 8295 Tournament Drive, Suite 201, Zip 38125–8913; tel. 901/969–3100; Jim Shaheen, President, p. B125

**Nashville:** ★ ARDENT HEALTH SERVICES 1 Burton Hills Boulevard, Suite 250, Zip 37215–6195; tel. 615/296–3000; David T. Vandewater, President and Chief Executive Officer, p. B11

HAVEN BEHAVIORAL HEALTHCARE 652 West Iris Drive, Zip 37204–3191; tel. 615/250–9500; Vern Westrich, President and Chief Executive Officer, p. B58

★ HCA One Park Plaza, Zip 37203–1548; tel. 615/344–9551; Richard M. Bracken, Chairman and Chief Executive Officer, p. B59

★ VANDERBILT HEALTH 1211 22nd Avenue South, Zip 37232; tel. 615/322–5000; Charles Wright Pinson, M.D., Deputy Vice Chancellor for Health Affairs and Chief Executive Officer of Vanderbilt Health System, p. B144

★ VANGUARD HEALTH SYSTEMS 20 Burton Hills Boulevard, Suite 10, Zip 37215–6197, Mailing Address: 7878 North 16th Street, Suite 110, Phoenix, AZ Zip 85020; tel. 615/665–6000; , p. B144

**Parsons:** TENNESSEE HEALTH MANAGEMENT 52 West Eighth Street, Zip 38363–4656, Mailing Address: PO Box 10, Zip 38363–0010; tel. 731/847–6343; Dennis Berry, Chief Executive Officer, p. B130

## TEXAS

**Addison:** UNITED SURGICAL PARTNERS INTERNATIONAL 15305 Dallas Parkway, Suite 1600, Zip 75001–6491; tel. 972/713–3500; William H. Wilcox, President and Chief Executive Officer, p. B135

**Arlington:** ★ TEXAS HEALTH RESOURCES 612 East Lamar Boulevard, Suite 900, Zip 76011–4130; tel. 682/236–7900; Douglas D. Hawthorne, FACHE, Chief Executive Officer, p. B130

**Austin:** TEXAS DEPARTMENT OF STATE HEALTH SERVICES 1100 West 49th Street, Zip 78756–3199; tel. 512/458–7111; David L. Lakey, M.D., Commissioner, p. B130

★ UNIVERSITY OF TEXAS SYSTEM 601 Colorado Street, Suite 205, Zip 78701–2904; tel. 512/499–4224; Kenneth Shine, M.D., Executive Vice Chancellor, p. B143

**Dallas:** ★ BAYLOR HEALTH CARE SYSTEM 3500 Gaston Avenue, Zip 75246–2017; tel. 214/820–0111; Joel T. Allison, President and Chief Executive Officer, p. B21

CIRRUS HEALTH 9301 North Central Expressway, Suite 360, Zip 75231–0826; tel. 214/217–0100; Timothy Parris, President and Chief Executive Officer, p. B33

CORNERSTONE HEALTHCARE GROUP 2200 Ross Avenue, Suite 3060, Zip 75201–7984; tel. 469/621–6700; David Smith, President and Chief Operating Officer, p. B40

GLOBALREHAB 1420 West Mockingbird Lane, Suite 100, Zip 75247–4932, Mailing Address: 1340 Empire Central Drive, Zip 75247–4022; tel. 214/879–7500; Hooman Sedighi, M.D., President and Chief Executive Officer, p. B56

★ METHODIST HEALTH SYSTEM 1441 North Beckley Avenue, Zip 75203–1201, Mailing Address: P.O. Box 655999, Zip 75265–5999; tel. 214/947–8181; Stephen L. Mansfield, Ph.D., FACHE, President and Chief Executive Officer, p. B90

★ TENET HEALTHCARE CORPORATION 1445 Ross Avenue, Suite 1400, Zip 75202–2703, Mailing Address: P.O. Box 139036, Zip 75313–9036; tel. 469/893–2200; Trevor Fetter, President and Chief Executive Officer, p. B128

**Greenville:** HUNT REGIONAL HEALTHCARE 4215 Joe Ramsey Boulevard, Zip 75401–7852, Mailing Address: P.O. Box 1059, Zip 75403–1059; tel. 903/408–5000; Richard Carter, Chief Executive Officer, p. B71

**Houston:** ★ DUBUIS HEALTH SYSTEM 1700 West Loop South, Suite 1100A, Zip 77027–3007; tel. 713/277–2300; Stephen Mills, Chief Executive Officer, p. B50

★ MEMORIAL HERMANN HEALTHCARE SYSTEM 929 Gessner, Suite 2700, Zip 77024–2593; tel. 713/242–2700; Daniel J. Wolterman, President and Chief Executive Officer, p. B88

NEXUS HEALTH SYSTEMS One Riverway, Suite 600, Zip 77056–1993; tel. 713/355–6111; John W. Cassidy, M.D., President, Chief Executive Officer and Chief Medical Officer, p. B95

★ THE METHODIST HOSPITAL SYSTEM 6565 Fannin Street, D–200, Zip 77030–2707; tel. 713/441–2221; Marc L. Boom, M.D., Chief Executive Officer, p. B131

**Irving:** ★ CHRISTUS HEALTH 919 Hidden Ridge Drive, Zip 75038; tel. 469/282–2000; Ernie W. Sadau, President and Chief Executive Officer, p. B33

USMD INC. 6333 North State Highway 161 Suite 200, Zip 75038–2229; tel. 214/493–4000; Karen A. Fiducia, FACHE, President, Hospital Division, p. B144

**Longview:** AUDUBON BEHAVIORAL HEALTHCARE 100 West Hawkins, Suite D., Zip 75605; tel. 903/212–2930; William V. Brown, Chief Executive Officer, p. B15

GOOD SHEPHERD HEALTH SYSTEM 700 East Marshall Avenue, Zip 75601–5580; tel. 903/315–2000; Kenneth C. Cunningham, Interim Chief Executive Officer, p. B57

**Lubbock:** ★ COVENANT HEALTH SYSTEM 3615 19th Street, Zip 79410–1203; tel. 806/725–0447; Richard H. Parks, FACHE, President and Chief Executive Officer, p. B41

**Lufkin:** MEMORIAL HEALTH SYSTEM OF EAST TEXAS 1201 Frank Avenue, Zip 75904–3357; tel. 936/634–8111; Gary N. Looper, President and Chief Executive Officer, p. B88

**Plano:** ★ COMMUNITY HOSPITAL CORPORATION 5801 Tennyson Parkway, Suite 550, Zip 75024–6116; tel. 972/943–6400; Michael D. Williams, President and Chief Executive Officer, p. B39

★ LHP HOSPITAL GROUP 2400 North Dallas Parkway, Suite 450, Zip 75093–5994; tel. 866/465–9222; Daniel J. Moen, Chief Executive Officer, p. B81

★ LIFECARE MANAGEMENT SERVICES 5340 Legacy Drive, Suite 150, Zip 75024–3131; tel. 469/241–2100; Phillip B. Douglas, Chairman and Chief Executive Officer, p. B81

**Richardson:** RELIANT HEALTHCARE PARTNERS 1300 East Lookout Drive, Suite 115, Zip 75082–4114; tel. 469/298–1400; Chester Crouch, Chief Executive Officer, p. B110

**Sherman:** CARRUS HOSPITALS 1810 West U.S. Highway 82, Zip 75092–7069; tel. 903/870–2600; Ronald E. Dorris, Chief Executive Officer, p. B27

**Temple:** ★ SCOTT & WHITE HEALTHCARE 2401 South 31st Street, Zip 76508–0001; tel. 254/724–2111; Robert W. Pryor, M.D., President and Chief Executive Officer, p. B115

**The Woodlands:** EMERUS 10077 Grogan's Mill, Suite 100, Zip 77380–1022; tel. 281/292–2450; Toby Hamilton, Chief Executive Officer, p. B51

VICTORY HEALTHCARE 2201 Timberloch Place, Suite 200, Zip 77380; tel. 281/863–2100; Robert N. Helms, Jr., Board Chair, President and Chief Executive Officer, p. B146

**Tyler:** ★ EAST TEXAS MEDICAL CENTER REGIONAL HEALTHCARE SYSTEM 1000 South Beckham Street, Zip 75701–1908, Mailing Address: P.O. Box 6400, Zip 75711–6400; tel. 903/535–6211; Elmer G. Ellis, FACHE, President and Chief Executive Officer, p. B50

TRINITY MOTHER FRANCES HOSPITALS AND CLINICS 910 East Houston, Zip 75702–8369; tel. 903/593–8441; J. Lindsey Bradley, Jr., FACHE, President, p. B133

## UTAH

**Nephi:** ★ RURAL HEALTH GROUP 48 West 1500 North, Zip 84648–8900; tel. 435/623–4924; Mark R. Stoddard, President and Chairman, p. B112

**Salt Lake City:** ★ INTERMOUNTAIN HEALTHCARE, INC. 36 South State Street, 22nd Floor, Zip 84111–1453; tel. 801/442–2000; Charles W. Sorenson, Jr., M.D., Chief Executive Officer, p. B74

## VIRGINIA

**Charlottesville:** UVA HEALTH SYSTEM 1215 Lee Street, Zip 22908–0816; tel. 434/924–0211; R. Edward Howell, Vice President and Chief Executive Officer, p. B144

**Falls Church:** DEPARTMENT OF THE ARMY, OFFICE OF THE SURGEON GENERAL 5109 Leesburg Pike, Zip 22041–3215; tel. 703/681–3000; Lieutenant General Eric B. Schoomaker, Surgeon General, p. B43

★ INOVA HEALTH SYSTEM 8110 Gatehouse Road, Suite 200 East, Zip 22042–1252; tel. 703/289–2069; J. Knox Singleton, President and Chief Executive Officer, p. B73

**Fredericksburg:** ★ MARY WASHINGTON HEALTHCARE 2300 Fall Hill Avenue, Suite 308, Zip 22401–3343; tel. 540/741–3100; Fred M. Rankin, III, President and Chief Executive Officer, p. B85

**Lynchburg:** CENTRA HEALTH, INC. 1920 Atherholt Road, Zip 24501–1104; tel. 434/200–3000; E. W. Tibbs, President and Chief Executive Officer, p. B32

**Newport News:** RIVERSIDE HEALTH SYSTEM 701 Town Center Drive, Suite 1000, Zip 23606–4286; tel. 757/534–7000; William B. Downey, President and Chief Executive Officer, p. B111

**Norfolk:** ★ SENTARA HEALTHCARE 6015 Poplar Hall Drive, Zip 23502–3819; tel. 757/455–7000; David L. Bernd, Chief Executive Officer, p. B119

**Richmond:** VIRGINIA DEPARTMENT OF MENTAL HEALTH 1220 Bank Street, Zip 23219–3645, Mailing Address: P.O. Box 1797, Zip 23218–1797; tel. 804/786–3921; James S. Reinhard, M.D., Commissioner, p. B146

**Roanoke:** ★ CARILION CLINIC 1906 Belleview Avenue S.E., Zip 24014–1838, Mailing Address: P.O. Box 13367, Zip 24033–3367; tel. 540/981–7000; Nancy Howell Agee, President and Chief Executive Officer, p. B26

**Winchester:** ★ VALLEY HEALTH SYSTEM 220 Campus Boulevard, Suite 310, Zip 22601–2889, Mailing Address: P.O. Box 3340, Zip 22604–2540; tel. 540/536–8024; Mark H. Merrill, President, p. B144

## WASHINGTON

**Renton:** ★ PROVIDENCE HEALTH & SERVICES 1801 Lind Avenue S.W., 9016, Zip 98057–9016; tel. 425/525–3698; Rodney F. Hochman, M.D., President and Chief Executive Officer, p. B106

**Seattle:** SWEDISH HEALTH SERVICES 747 Broadway, Zip 98122–4379; tel. 206/386–6000; Marcel C. Loh, FACHE, Interim Chief Executive, p. B127

UW MEDICINE 1959 N.E. Pacific Street, Zip 98195–0001, Mailing Address: P.O. Box 356350, Zip 98195–6350; tel. 206/543–7718; Paul G. Ramsey, Chief Executive Officer, p. B144

**Tacoma:** MULTICARE HEALTH SYSTEM 315 Martin Luther King Jr. Way, Zip 98405–4234, Mailing Address: P.O. Box 5299, Zip 98415–0299; tel. 253/403–1000; Diane E. Cecchettini, R.N., President and Chief Executive Officer, p. B93

**Vancouver:** ★ PEACEHEALTH 1115 S.E. 164th Avenue, Zip 98683; tel. 425/747–1711; Alan R. Yordy, President and Chief Mission Officer, p. B102

## WEST VIRGINIA

**Charleston:** ★ CHARLESTON AREA MEDICAL CENTER HEALTH SYSTEM, INC. 501 Morris Street, Zip 25301–1300, Mailing Address: P.O. Box 1547, Zip 25326–1547; tel. 304/388–5432; David L. Ramsey, President and Chief Executive Officer, p. B32

**Elkins:** ★ DAVIS HEALTH SYSTEM Reed Street and Gorman Avenue, Zip 26241, Mailing Address: P.O. Box 1697, Zip 26241–1697; tel. 304/636–3300; Mark Doak, President and Chief Executive Officer, p. B42

**Fairmont:** ★ WEST VIRGINIA UNITED HEALTH SYSTEM 1000 Technology Drive, Suite 2320, Zip 26554–8834; tel. 304/368–2700; J. Thomas Jones, President and Chief Executive Officer, p. B148

**Huntington:** ★ PALLOTTINE HEALTH SERVICES 2900 First Avenue, Zip 25702–1241; tel. 304/526–1234; Michael G. Sellards, Chief Executive Officer, p. B100

**South Charleston:** ★ THOMAS HEALTH SYSTEM, INC. 4605 MacCorkle Avenue S.W., Zip 25309–1311; tel. 304/766–3600; Stephen P. Dexter, President and Chief Executive Officer, p. B131

**Wheeling:** OHIO VALLEY HEALTH SERVICES AND EDUCATION CORPORATION 2000 Eoff Street, Zip 26003–3823; tel. 304/234–8383; Michael J. Caruso, President and Chief Executive Officer, p. B99

## WISCONSIN

**Appleton:** THEDACARE, INC. 122 East College Avenue, Zip 54911–5794, Mailing Address: P.O. Box 8025, Zip 54912–8025; tel. 920/830–5560; Dean Gruner, M.D., President and Chief Executive Officer, p. B131

**Janesville:** MERCY HEALTH SYSTEM 1000 Mineral Point Avenue, Zip 53548–2940, Mailing Address: P.O. Box 5003, Zip 53547–5003; tel. 608/756–6000; Javon R. Bea, President and Chief Executive Officer, p. B90

**Manitowoc:** ★ FRANCISCAN SISTERS OF CHRISTIAN CHARITY SPONSORED MINISTRIES, INC. 1415 South Rapids Road, Zip 54220–9302; tel. 920/684–7071; Sister Laura J. Wolf, President, p. B55

**Milwaukee:** ★ AURORA HEALTH CARE 3000 West Montana, Zip 53215–3628, Mailing Address: P.O. Box 341880, Zip 53234–1880; tel. 414/647–3000; Nick Turkal, M.D., President and Chief Executive Officer, p. B15

CHILDREN'S HOSPITAL AND HEALTH SYSTEM 9000 West Wisconsin Avenue, Zip 53226–4810, Mailing Address: P.O. Box 1997, Zip 53201–1997; tel. 414/226–2000; Peggy N. Troy, President and Chief Executive Officer, p. B32

**Waukesha:** ★ PROHEALTH CARE, INC. N17 W24100 Riverwood Drive, Suite 130, Zip 53188; tel. 262/928–2242; Susan A. Edwards, President and Chief Executive Officer, p. B105

**Wausau:** ★ ASPIRUS, INC. 425 Pine Ridge Boulevard, Zip 54401–4123; tel. 715/847–2118; Matthew Heywood, Chief Executive Officer, p. B14

## ALASKA

**PEACEHEALTH KETCHIKAN MEDICAL CENTER**
**3100 Tongass Avenue, Ketchikan, AK 99901–5746; tel. 907/225–5171; Patrick J. Branco, Chief Executive Officer**

PEACEHEALTH KETCHIKAN MEDICAL CENTER, 3100 Tongass Avenue, Ketchikan, AK, Zip 99901–5746; tel. 907/225–5171; Patrick J. Branco, Chief Executive Officer

## ARIZONA

**NORTHERN ARIZONA HEALTHCARE**
**1200 North Beaver Street, Flagstaff, AZ 86001–3118; tel. 928/779–3366; William T. Bradel, President and Chief Executive Officer**

FLAGSTAFF MEDICAL CENTER, 1200 North Beaver Street, Flagstaff, AZ, Zip 86001–3118; tel. 928/779–3366; William T. Bradel, President

VERDE VALLEY MEDICAL CENTER, 269 South Candy Lane, Cottonwood, AZ, Zip 86326–4170; tel. 928/639–6000; Barbara Dember, Interim President and Chief Executive Officer

## CALIFORNIA

**COVENANT HEALTH NETWORK**
**3345 Michelson Drive, Suite 100, Irvine, CA 92612–0693; tel. 949/381–4019; Richard Afable, M.D., M.P.H., President and Chief Executive Officer**

HOAG MEMORIAL HOSPITAL PRESBYTERIAN, One Hoag Drive, Newport Beach, CA, Zip 92663–4120, Mailing Address: P.O. Box 6100, Zip 92658–6100; tel. 949/764 4624; Robert Braithwaite, President and Chief Executive Officer

HOAG ORTHOPEDIC INSTITUTE, 16250 Sand Canyon Avenue, Irvine, CA, Zip 92618–3714; tel. 949/517–3149; Deressa Reid, Interim Chief Executive Officer

MISSION HOSPITAL, 27700 Medical Center Road, Mission Viejo, CA, Zip 92691–6426; tel. 949/364–1400; Kenneth McFarland, President and Chief Executive Officer

PETALUMA VALLEY HOSPITAL, 400 North McDowell Boulevard, Petaluma, CA, Zip 94954–2369; tel. 707/778–1111; Todd Salnas, President and Chief Executive Officer

QUEEN OF THE VALLEY MEDICAL CENTER, 1000 Trancas Street, Napa, CA, Zip 94558–2906, Mailing Address: P.O. Box 2340, Zip 94558–0688; tel. 707/252–4411; Walt Mickens, President and Chief Executive Officer

REDWOOD MEMORIAL HOSPITAL, 3300 Renner Drive, Fortuna, CA, Zip 95540–3198; tel. 707/725–3361; David O'Brien, M.D., Interim President and Chief Executive Officer

SANTA ROSA MEMORIAL HOSPITAL, 1165 Montgomery Drive, Santa Rosa, CA, Zip 95405–4897, Mailing Address: P.O. Box 522, Zip 95402–0522; tel. 707/546–3210; Todd Salnas, President and Chief Executive Officer

ST. JOSEPH HEALTH ST. MARY, 18300 Highway 18, Apple Valley, CA, Zip 92307–2206, Mailing Address: P.O. Box 7025, Zip 92307–0725; tel. 760/242–2311; Alan H. Garrett, Chief Executive Officer

ST. JOSEPH HOSPITAL, 2700 Dolbeer Street, Eureka, CA, Zip 95501–4799; tel. 707/445–8121; David O'Brien, M.D., Interim President and Chief Executive Officer

ST. JOSEPH HOSPITAL, 1100 West Stewart Drive, Orange, CA, Zip 92868–3849, Mailing Address: P.O. Box 5600, Zip 92863–5600; tel. 714/633–9111; Steven C. Moreau, President and Chief Executive Officer

ST. JUDE MEDICAL CENTER, 101 East Valencia Mesa Drive, Fullerton, CA, Zip 92835–3809; tel. 714/992–3000; Lee Penrose, President and Chief Executive Officer

**NORTHERN CALIFORNIA NETWORK**
**821 South St. Helena Highway Suite 208, St. Helena, CA 95661–3804; tel. 707/967–7515; Terry Newmyer, President and Chief Executive Officer**

FRANK R. HOWARD MEMORIAL HOSPITAL, One Madrone Street, Willits, CA, Zip 95490–4225; tel. 707/459–6801; Rick Bockmann, Chief Executive Officer

ST. HELENA HOSPITAL CLEAR LAKE, 15630 18th Avenue, Clearlake, CA, Zip 95422–9336, Mailing Address: P.O. Box 6710, Zip 95422; tel. 707/994–6486; Terry Newmyer, President and Chief Executive Officer

ST. HELENA HOSPITAL NAPA VALLEY, 10 Woodland Road, Saint Helena, CA, Zip 94574–9554; tel. 707/963–3611; Terry Newmyer, President and Chief Executive Officer

ST. HELENA HOSPITAL–CENTER FOR BEHAVIORAL HEALTH, 525 Oregon Street, Vallejo, CA, Zip 94590–3201; tel. 707/648–2200; Terry Newmyer, President and Chief Executive Officer

UKIAH VALLEY MEDICAL CENTER, 275 Hospital Drive, Ukiah, CA, Zip 95482–4531; tel. 707/462–3111; Gwen Matthews, R.N., MSN, Chief Executive Officer

**PROVIDENCE HEALTH AND SERVICES – SOUTHERN CALIFORNIA**
**501 South Buena Vista Street, Burbank, CA 91505–4809; tel. 818/843–5111; Michael A. Rembis, FACHE, Chief Executive Officer**

PROVIDENCE HOLY CROSS MEDICAL CENTER, 15031 Rinaldi Street, Mission Hills, CA, Zip 91345–1207; tel. 818/365–8051; Bernard Klein, M.D., Chief Executive Officer

PROVIDENCE LITTLE COMPANY OF MARY MEDICAL CENTER, 4101 Torrance Boulevard, Torrance, CA, Zip 90503–4607; tel. 310/540–7676; Elizabeth Dunne, Chief Executive Officer

PROVIDENCE LITTLE COMPANY OF MARY MEDICAL CENTER SAN PEDRO, 1300 West Seventh Street, San Pedro, CA, Zip 90732–3505; tel. 310/832–3311; Nancy Carlson, Chief Executive

PROVIDENCE SAINT JOSEPH MEDICAL CENTER, 501 South Buena Vista Street, Burbank, CA, Zip 91505–4866; tel. 818/843–5111; Michael A. Rembis, FACHE, Chief Executive Officer

PROVIDENCE TARZANA MEDICAL CENTER, 18321 Clark Street, Tarzana, CA, Zip 91356–3521; tel. 818/881–0800; Gerald B. Clute, Chief Executive Officer

## COLORADO

**CENTURA HEALTH**
**188 Inverness Drive West, Suite 500, Englewood, CO 80112–5204; tel. 303/290–6500; Gary Campbell, Chief Executive Officer**

AVISTA ADVENTIST HOSPITAL, 100 Health Park Drive, Louisville, CO, Zip 80027–9583; tel. 303/673–1000; Jim Boyle, Interim Chief Executive Officer

LITTLETON ADVENTIST HOSPITAL, 7700 South Broadway Street, Littleton, CO, Zip 80122–2628; tel. 303/730–8900; Brett Spenst, Chief Executive Officer

PARKER ADVENTIST HOSPITAL, 9395 Crown Crest Boulevard, Parker, CO, Zip 80138–8573; tel. 303/269–4000; Morre Dean, Chief Executive Officer

PENROSE–ST. FRANCIS HEALTH SERVICES, 2222 North Nevada Avenue, Colorado Springs, CO, Zip 80907–6799, Mailing Address: P.O. Box 7021, Zip 80933–7021; tel. 719/776–5000; Margaret D. Sabin, President and Chief Executive Officer

PORTER ADVENTIST HOSPITAL, 2525 South Downing Street, Denver, CO, Zip 80210–5876; tel. 303/778–1955; Randall L. Haffner, Ph.D., Chief Executive Officer

ST. ANTHONY HOSPITAL, 11600 West Second Place, Lakewood, CO, Zip 80228–1527; tel. 720/321–0000; Jeffrey Brickman, FACHE, President and Chief Executive Officer

ST. ANTHONY NORTH HOSPITAL, 2551 West 84th Avenue, Westminster, CO, Zip 80031–3807; tel. 303/426–2151; Carole Peet, R.N., MSN, President and Chief Executive Officer

ST. ANTHONY SUMMIT MEDICAL CENTER, 340 Peak One Drive, Frisco, CO, Zip 80443, Mailing Address: P.O. Box 738, Zip 80443–0738; tel. 970/668–3300; Paul J. Chodkowski, Chief Executive Officer

ST. MARY–CORWIN MEDICAL CENTER, 1008 Minnequa Avenue, Pueblo, CO, Zip 81004–3798; tel. 719/557–4000; Brian Moore, Chief Executive Officer

ST. THOMAS MORE HOSPITAL, 1338 Phay Avenue, Canon City, CO, Zip 81212–2302; tel. 719/285–2000; Robert Ryder, Chief Executive Officer

**COMMUNITY HEALTH PROVIDERS ORGANIZATION**
**2021 North 12th Street, Grand Junction, CO 81501–2980; tel. 970/256–6200; Chris Thomas, FACHE, President and Chief Executive Officer**

COMMUNITY HOSPITAL, 2021 North 12th Street, Grand Junction, CO, Zip 81501–2999; tel. 970/242–0920; Chris Thomas, FACHE, President and Chief Executive Officer

**HCA HEALTHONE, LLC**
**4900 South Monaco Street, Suite 380, Denver, CO 80237–3487; tel. 303/788–2500; Sylvia Young, President**

MEDICAL CENTER OF AURORA, 1501 South Potomac Street, Aurora, CO, Zip 80012–5411; tel. 303/695–2600; Richard A. Hammett, Chief Executive Officer

NORTH SUBURBAN MEDICAL CENTER, 9191 Grant Street, Thornton, CO, Zip 80229–4341; tel. 303/451–7800; Jennifer Alderfer, Chief Executive Officer

PRESBYTERIAN–ST. LUKE'S MEDICAL CENTER, 1719 East 19th Avenue, Denver, CO, Zip 80218–1281; tel. 303/839–6000; Madeleine Roberson, Chief Executive Officer

ROSE MEDICAL CENTER, 4567 East Ninth Avenue, Denver, CO, Zip 80220–3941; tel. 303/320–2121; Kenneth H. Feiler, Chief Executive Officer

SKY RIDGE MEDICAL CENTER, 10101 Ridge Gate Parkway, Lone Tree, CO, Zip 80124–5522; tel. 720/225–1000; Maureen Tarrant, Chief Executive Officer

SPALDING REHABILITATION HOSPITAL, 900 Potomac Steet, Aurora, CO, Zip 80011–6716; tel. 303/367–1166; Cynthia Kreutz, Chief Executive Officer

SWEDISH MEDICAL CENTER, 501 East Hampden Avenue, Englewood, CO, Zip 80113–2702; tel. 303/788–5000; Mary M. White, Chief Executive Officer

## CONNECTICUT

**EASTERN CONNECTICUT HEALTH NETWORK**
**71 Haynes Street, Manchester, CT 06040–4131; tel. 860/533–3400; Peter J. Karl, President and Chief Executive Officer**

MANCHESTER MEMORIAL HOSPITAL, 71 Haynes Street, Manchester, CT, Zip 06040–4188; tel. 860/646–1222; Peter J. Karl, President and Chief Executive Officer

ROCKVILLE GENERAL HOSPITAL, 31 Union Street, Vernon Rockville, CT, Zip 06066–3160; tel. 860/872–0501; Peter J. Karl, President and Chief Executive Officer

## FLORIDA

**BAYCARE HEALTH SYSTEM**
**16255 Bay Vista Drive, Clearwater, FL 33760–3127; tel. 877/692–2922; Stephen R. Mason, President and Chief Executive Officer**

BAYCARE ALLIANT HOSPITAL, 601 Main Street, Dunedin, FL, Zip 34698–5848; tel. 727/736–9999; Jacqueline Arocho, Administrator

MEASE COUNTRYSIDE HOSPITAL, 3231 McMullen–Booth Road, Safety Harbor, FL, Zip 34695–6607, Mailing Address: P.O. Box 1098, Zip 34695–1098; tel. 727/725–6222; Glenn D. Waters, FACHE, President

MEASE DUNEDIN HOSPITAL, 601 Main Street, Dunedin, FL, Zip 34698–5891, Mailing Address: P.O. Box 760, Zip 34697–0760; tel. 727/733–1111; Glenn D. Waters, FACHE, President and Chief Executive Officer

MORTON PLANT HOSPITAL, 300 Pinellas Street, Clearwater, FL, Zip 33756–3804, Mailing Address: P.O. Box 210, Zip 33757–0210; tel. 727/462–7000; Glenn D. Waters, FACHE, President

MORTON PLANT NORTH BAY HOSPITAL, 6600 Madison Street, New Port Richey, FL, Zip 34652–1900; tel. 727/842–8468; Glenn D. Waters, FACHE, President

SOUTH FLORIDA BAPTIST HOSPITAL, 301 North Alexander Street, Plant City, FL, Zip 33563–4303, Mailing Address: Drawer H, Zip 33564–9058; tel. 813/757–1200; Stephen Nierman, Interim Chief Executive Officer

ST. ANTHONY'S HOSPITAL, 1200 Seventh Avenue North, Saint Petersburg, FL, Zip 33705–1388, Mailing Address: P.O. Box 12588, Zip 33733–2588; tel. 727/825–1100; William G. Ulbricht, President

ST. JOSEPH'S HOSPITAL, 3001 West Martin Luther King Jr. Boulevard, Tampa, FL, Zip 33607–6387, Mailing Address: P.O. Box 4227, Zip 33677–4227; tel. 813/870–4000; Lorraine Lutton, Interim Chief Executive Officer

## GEORGIA

**ST. JOSEPH'S/CANDLER HEALTH SYSTEM, INC.**
**5353 Reynolds Street, Savannah, GA 31405–6015; tel. 912/819–6000; Paul P. Hinchey, President and Chief Executive Officer**

APPLING HEALTHCARE SYSTEM, 163 East Tollison Street, Baxley, GA, Zip 31513–0120; tel. 912/367–9841; Dale Spell, Chief Executive Officer

CANDLER HOSPITAL, 5353 Reynolds Street, Savannah, GA, Zip 31405–6015; tel. 912/819–6000; Paul P. Hinchey, President and Chief Executive Officer

EFFINGHAM HOSPITAL, 459 Highway 119 South, Springfield, GA, Zip 31329–3021, Mailing Address: P.O. Box 386, Zip 31329–0386; tel. 912/754–6451; Norma J. Morgan, Chief Executive Officer

EMORY UNIVERSITY HOSPITAL, 1364 Clifton Road N.E., Atlanta, GA, Zip 30322–1102; tel. 404/712–2000; Robert J. Bachman, Chief Operating Officer

LIBERTY REGIONAL MEDICAL CENTER, 462 Elma G. Miles Parkway, Hinesville, GA, Zip 31313–4000, Mailing Address: P.O. Box 919, Zip 31310–0919; tel. 912/369–9400; H. Scott Kroell, Jr., Chief Executive Officer

MEADOWS REGIONAL MEDICAL CENTER, One Meadows Parkway, Vidalia, GA, Zip 30474–8759, Mailing Address: P.O. Box 1048, Zip 30475–1048; tel. 912/535–5555; Alan Kent, Chief Executive Officer

ST. JOSEPH'S HOSPITAL, 11705 Mercy Boulevard, Savannah, GA, Zip 31419–1791; tel. 912/819–4100; Paul P. Hinchey, President and Chief Executive Officer

WILLINGWAY HOSPITAL, 311 Jones Mill Road, Statesboro, GA, Zip 30458–4765; tel. 912/764–6236; Jimmy Mooney, Chief Executive Officer

## IDAHO

**NORTH IDAHO HEALTH NETWORK**
**1250 West Ironwood Drive, Suite 201, Coeur D'Alene, ID 83814–2681; tel. 208/666–3212; Richard McMaster, Executive Director**

BENEWAH COMMUNITY HOSPITAL, 229 South Seventh Street, Saint Maries, ID, Zip 83861–1803; tel. 208/245–5551; Christopher Noland, FACHE, Interim Chief Executive Officer

BONNER GENERAL HOSPITAL, 520 North Third Avenue, Sandpoint, ID, Zip 83864–1507, Mailing Address: Box 1448, Zip 83864–0877; tel. 208/263–1441; Sheryl Rickard, Chief Executive Officer

BOUNDARY COMMUNITY HOSPITAL, 6640 Kaniksu Street, Bonners Ferry, ID, Zip 83805–7532; tel. 208/267–3141; Craig A. Johnson, Chief Executive Officer and Chief Financial Officer

KOOTENAI MEDICAL CENTER, 2003 Kootenai Health Way, Coeur D'Alene, ID, Zip 83814–2677; tel. 208/666–2000; Jon Ness, Chief Executive Officer

SHOSHONE MEDICAL CENTER, 25 Jacobs Gulch, Kellogg, ID, Zip 83837–2023; tel. 208/784–1221; Gary Moore, Chief Executive Officer

**SOUTHWEST IDAHO COMMUNITY HEALTH NETWORK**
**PO Box 607, Boise, ID 83701–0607; tel. 208/381–1571; Stephen R. Stoddard, FACHE, Executive Director**

CASCADE MEDICAL CENTER, 402 Old State Highway, Cascade, ID, Zip 83611, Mailing Address: P.O. Box 1330, Zip 83611–1330; tel. 208/382–4242; Virgil Boss, Administrator

ELKS REHAB HOSPITAL, 600 North Robbins Road, Boise, ID, Zip 83702–4565, Mailing Address: P.O. Box 1100, Zip 83701–1100; tel. 208/489–4444; Joseph P. Caroselli, Chief Executive Officer

NORTH CANYON MEDICAL CENTER, 267 North Canyon Drive, Gooding, ID, Zip 83330–5500; tel. 208/934–4433; David Butler, Chief Executive Officer

ST. LUKE'S ELMORE, 895 North Sixth East Street, Mountain Home, ID, Zip 83647–2207, Mailing Address: P.O. Box 1270, Zip 83647–1270; tel. 208/587–8401; Gregory L. Maurer, Administrator

ST. LUKE'S JEROME, 709 North Lincoln Street, Jerome, ID, Zip 83338–1851, Mailing Address: P.O. Box 586, Zip 83338–0586; tel. 208/324–4301; Curtis Maier, Administrative Director

ST. LUKE'S MAGIC VALLEY MEDICAL CENTER, 801 Pole Line Road West, Twin Falls, ID, Zip 83301–5810, Mailing Address: P.O. Box 409, Zip 83303–0409; tel. 208/814–0000; James L. Angle, FACHE, Chief Executive Officer

ST. LUKE'S MCCALL, 1000 State Street, McCall, ID, Zip 83638–3704; tel. 208/634–2221; Michael A. Fenello, Chief Executive Officer

ST. LUKE'S WOOD RIVER MEDICAL CENTER, 100 Hospital Drive, Ketchum, ID, Zip 83340, Mailing Address: P.O. Box 100, Zip 83340–0100; tel. 208/727–8800; Cody Langbehn, Chief Executive Officer

SYRINGA HOSPITAL AND CLINICS, 607 West Main Street, Grangeville, ID, Zip 83530–1396; tel. 208/983–1700; Joseph Cladouhos, Chief Executive Officer

WALTER KNOX MEMORIAL HOSPITAL, 1202 East Locust Street, Emmett, ID, Zip 83617–2715; tel. 208/365–3561; John N. Olson, Chief Executive Officer

WEISER MEMORIAL HOSPITAL, 645 East Fifth Street, Weiser, ID, Zip 83672–2202; tel. 208/549–0370; Tom Murphy, Chief Executive Officer

**THE HOSPITAL COOPERATIVE**
**500 South 11th Avenue Suite 503, Pocatello, ID 83201–4881; tel. 208/239–1951; Jon Smith, Executive Director**

BEAR LAKE MEMORIAL HOSPITAL, 164 South Fifth Street, Montpelier, ID, Zip 83254–1597; tel. 208/847–1630; Rodney D. Jacobson, Administrator

BINGHAM MEMORIAL HOSPITAL, 98 Poplar Street, Blackfoot, ID, Zip 83221–1799; tel. 208/785–4100; Louis D. Kraml, FACHE, Chief Executive Officer

CARIBOU MEMORIAL HOSPITAL AND LIVING CENTER, 300 South Third West, Soda Springs, ID, Zip 83276–1598; tel. 208/547–3341; John L. Hoopes, Chief Executive Officer

EASTERN IDAHO REGIONAL MEDICAL CENTER, 3100 Channing Way, Idaho Falls, ID, Zip 83404–7533, Mailing Address: P.O. Box 2077, Zip 83403–2077; tel. 208/529–6111; Douglas Crabtree, Chief Executive Officer

FRANKLIN COUNTY MEDICAL CENTER, 44 North First East Street, Preston, ID, Zip 83263–1399; tel. 208/852–0137; Michael G. Andrus, Administrator and Chief Executive Officer

LOST RIVERS MEDICAL CENTER, 551 Highland Drive, Arco, ID, Zip 83213–9771, Mailing Address: P.O. Box 145, Zip 83213–0145; tel. 208/527–8206; Kim Dahlman, Administrator

MADISON MEMORIAL HOSPITAL, 450 East Main Street, Rexburg, ID, Zip 83440–2048, Mailing Address: P.O. Box 310, Zip 83440–0310; tel. 208/359–6900; Rachel Ann Gonzales, MSN, R.N., Chief Executive Officer

MINIDOKA MEMORIAL HOSPITAL, 1224 Eighth Street, Rupert, ID, Zip 83350–1599; tel. 208/436–0481; Carl Hanson, Administrator

ONEIDA COUNTY HOSPITAL, 150 North 200 West, Malad City, ID, Zip 83252–1239, Mailing Address: Box 126, Zip 83252–0126; tel. 208/766–2231; Todd V. Winder, Administrator and Chief Executive Officer

PORTNEUF MEDICAL CENTER, 777 Hospital Way, Pocatello, ID, Zip 83201–5175; tel. 208/239–1000; John Abreu, Interim Chief Executive Officer

POWER COUNTY HOSPITAL DISTRICT, 510 Roosevelt Road, American Falls, ID, Zip 83211–1362, Mailing Address: P.O. Box 420, Zip 83211–0420; tel. 208/226–3200; Dallas Clinger, Administrator

STAR VALLEY MEDICAL CENTER, 901 Adams Street, Afton, WY,
Zip 83110–9621, Mailing Address: P.O. Box 579, Zip 83110–0579;
tel. 307/885–5800; Charlie A. Button, President and Chief Executive Officer

STEELE MEMORIAL MEDICAL CENTER, 203 South Daisy Street, Salmon, ID,
Zip 83467–4709; tel. 208/756–5600; Jeff Hill, Chief Executive Officer

TETON VALLEY HEALTH CARE, 120 East Howard Street, Driggs, ID,
Zip 83422–5112; tel. 208/354–2383; Keith Gnagey, Chief Executive Officer

## ILLINOIS

### FELICIAN SERVICES, INC.
**3800 West Peterson Avenue, Chicago, IL 60659–3116;
tel. 773/463–3806; Sister Mary Clarette Stryzewski, President and
Chief Executive Officer**

ST. MARY'S HOSPITAL, 400 North Pleasant Avenue, Centralia, IL,
Zip 62801–3056; tel. 618/436–8000; Bruce Merrell, FACHE, President

WHEATON FRANCISCAN HEALTHCARE – ST. FRANCIS, 3237 South 16th Street,
Milwaukee, WI, Zip 53215–4592; tel. 414/647–5000; Daniel Mattes,
President

## INDIANA

### ST. VINCENT HEALTH
**2001 West 86Th Street, Indianapolis, IN 46260–1902;
tel. 317/338–8455; Vincent C. Caponi, FACHE, Chief Executive Officer**

ST. JOSEPH HOSPITAL AND HEALTH CENTER, 1907 West Sycamore Street,
Kokomo, IN, Zip 46901–4197, Mailing Address: P.O. Box 9010,
Zip 46904–9010; tel. 765/452–5611; Kathlene A. Young, MS, FACHE,
President and Chief Executive Officer

ST. VINCENT ANDERSON REGIONAL HOSPITAL, 2015 Jackson Street, Anderson,
IN, Zip 46016–4339; tel. 765/649–2511; Thomas J. VanOsdol, President

ST. VINCENT CARMEL HOSPITAL, 13500 North Meridian Street, Carmel, IN,
Zip 46032–1456; tel. 317/582–7000; Michael D. Chittenden, President

ST. VINCENT CLAY HOSPITAL, 1206 East National Avenue, Brazil, IN,
Zip 47834–2797, Mailing Address: P.O. Box 489, Zip 47834–0489;
tel. 812/442–2500; Jerry Laue, Administrator

ST. VINCENT FRANKFORT HOSPITAL, 1300 South Jackson Street, Frankfort, IN,
Zip 46041–3394, Mailing Address: P.O. Box 669, Zip 46041–0669;
tel. 765/656–3000; Thomas Crawford, Administrator

ST. VINCENT INDIANAPOLIS HOSPITAL, 2001 West 86th Street, Indianapolis, IN,
Zip 46260–1991, Mailing Address: P.O. Box 40970, Zip 46240–0970;
tel. 317/338–2345; Kyle De Fur, FACHE, President

ST. VINCENT JENNINGS HOSPITAL, 301 Henry Street, North Vernon, IN,
Zip 47265–1097; tel. 812/352–4200; Carl W. Risk, II, Administrator

ST. VINCENT MERCY HOSPITAL, 1331 South A Street, Elwood, IN,
Zip 46036–1942; tel. 765/552–4600; Deborah Y. Rasper, FACHE,
Administrator

ST. VINCENT RANDOLPH HOSPITAL, 473 Greenville Avenue, Winchester, IN,
Zip 47394–9436, Mailing Address: P.O. Box 407, Zip 47394–0407;
tel. 765/584–0004; Francis G. Albarano, Administrator

ST. VINCENT SETON SPECIALTY HOSPITAL, 1501 Hartford Street, Lafayette, IN,
Zip 47904–2134; tel. 765/236–8900; Peter H. Alexander, Administrator

ST. VINCENT WILLIAMSPORT HOSPITAL, 412 North Monroe Street, Williamsport,
IN, Zip 47993–1049; tel. 765/762–4000; Jane Craigin, Chief Executive
Officer

### SUBURBAN HEALTH ORGANIZATION
**2780 Waterfront Parkway East Drive, Suite 300, Indianapolis, IN 46214;
tel. 317/692–5222; Dave Lippincott, President**

COMMUNITY WESTVIEW HOSPITAL, 3630 Guion Road, Indianapolis, IN,
Zip 46222–1699; tel. 317/924–6661; David C. Williams, D.O., Interim
President and Chief Executive Officer

HANCOCK REGIONAL HOSPITAL, 801 North State Street, Greenfield, IN,
Zip 46140–1270, Mailing Address: P.O. Box 827, Zip 46140–0827;
tel. 317/462–5544; Robert C. Keen, Ph.D., FACHE, President and Chief
Executive Officer

HENDRICKS REGIONAL HEALTH, 1000 East Main Street, Danville, IN,
Zip 46122–1948, Mailing Address: P.O. Box 409, Zip 46122–0409;
tel. 317/745–4451; Kevin Speer, Chief Executive Officer

HENRY COUNTY HOSPITAL, 1000 North 16th Street, New Castle, IN,
Zip 47362–4319, Mailing Address: P.O. Box 490, Zip 47362–0490;
tel. 765/521–0890; Paul Janssen, President and Chief Executive Officer

JOHNSON MEMORIAL HOSPITAL, 1125 West Jefferson Street, Franklin, IN,
Zip 46131–2140, Mailing Address: P.O. Box 549, Zip 46131–0549;
tel. 317/736–3300; Larry Heydon, President and Chief Executive Officer

RIVERVIEW HOSPITAL, 395 Westfield Road, Noblesville, IN, Zip 46060–1425,
Mailing Address: P.O. Box 220, Zip 46061–0220; tel. 317/773–0760;
Patricia K. Fox, President and Chief Executive Officer

WITHAM MEMORIAL HOSPITAL, 2605 North Lebanon Street, Lebanon, IN,
Zip 46052–1476, Mailing Address: P.O. Box 1200, Zip 46052–3005;
tel. 765/485–8000; Raymond V. Ingham, M.D., Ph.D., President and Chief
Executive Officer

## IOWA

### GENESIS HEALTH SYSTEM
**1227 East Rusholme Street, Davenport, IA 52803–2498;
tel. 563/421–1000; Douglas P. Cropper, President and Chief Executive
Officer**

GENESIS MEDICAL CENTER, DEWITT, 1118 11th Street, De Witt, IA,
Zip 52742–1296; tel. 563/659–4200; Curt Coleman, FACHE, Administrator

GENESIS MEDICAL CENTER, ILLINI CAMPUS, 801 Illini Drive, Silvis, IL,
Zip 61282–1893; tel. 309/281–4000; Florence Spyrow, President

GENESIS MEDICAL CENTER–DAVENPORT, 1227 East Rusholme Street,
Davenport, IA, Zip 52803–2498; tel. 563/421–1000; Wayne A. Diewald,
President

### MERCY HEALTH NETWORK – CENTRAL IOWA
**1111 6th Avenue, Des Moines, IA 50314–2611; tel. 515/358–8023; Jim
FitzPatrick, Senior Vice President, Network Development**

ADAIR COUNTY MEMORIAL HOSPITAL, 609 S.E. Kent Street, Greenfield, IA,
Zip 50849–9454; tel. 641/743–2123; Angela Mortoza, Administrator

AUDUBON COUNTY MEMORIAL HOSPITAL, 515 Pacific Street, Audubon, IA,
Zip 50025–1056; tel. 712/563–2611; Thomas G. Smith, Administrator and
Chief Executive Officer

CLARINDA REGIONAL HEALTH CENTER, 220 Essie Davison Drive, Clarinda, IA,
Zip 51632–2915, Mailing Address: P.O. Box 217, Zip 51632–0217;
tel. 712/542–2176; Christopher R. Stipe, FACHE, Chief Executive Officer

DALLAS COUNTY HOSPITAL, 610 10th Street, Perry, IA, Zip 50220–2221;
tel. 515/465–3547; Matt Wille, Chief Executive Officer

DAVIS COUNTY HOSPITAL, 509 North Madison Street, Bloomfield, IA,
Zip 52537–1271; tel. 641/664–2145; Deborah L. Herzberg, R.N., MS,
FACHE, Chief Executive Officer

DECATUR COUNTY HOSPITAL, 1405 N.W. Church Street, Leon, IA,
Zip 50144–1299; tel. 641/446–4871; Lynn Milnes, Chief Executive Officer

GRINNELL REGIONAL MEDICAL CENTER, 210 Fourth Avenue, Grinnell, IA,
Zip 50112–1898; tel. 641/236–7511; Todd C. Linden, President and Chief
Executive Officer

MADISON COUNTY HEALTH CARE SYSTEM, 300 West Hutchings Street,
Winterset, IA, Zip 50273–2109; tel. 515/462–2373; Marcia Hendricks, R.N.,
Chief Executive Officer

MANNING REGIONAL HEALTHCARE CENTER, 410 Main Street, Manning, IA,
Zip 51455–1093; tel. 712/655–2072; John O'Brien, Chief Executive Officer

MERCY MEDICAL CENTER–CENTERVILLE, 1 St. Joseph's Drive, Centerville, IA,
Zip 52544–8055; tel. 641/437–4111; Clinton J. Christianson, FACHE,
President

MERCY MEDICAL CENTER–DES MOINES, 1111 6th Avenue, Des Moines, IA,
Zip 50314–2611; tel. 515/247–3121; Robert P. Ritz, President

MONROE COUNTY HOSPITAL, 6580 165th Street, Albia, IA, Zip 52531–8793;
tel. 641/932–2134; Sara Drobnich, Interim Chief Executive Officer

RINGGOLD COUNTY HOSPITAL, 504 North Cleveland Street, Mount Ayr, IA,
Zip 50854–2201; tel. 641/464–3226; Gordon W. Winkler, Administrator and
Chief Executive Officer

VAN DIEST MEDICAL CENTER, 2350 Hospital Drive, Webster City, IA,
Zip 50595–6600; tel. 515/832–9400; Robert L. Mason, Chief Executive
Officer

WAYNE COUNTY HOSPITAL, 417 South East Street, Corydon, IA,
Zip 50060–1860, Mailing Address: P.O. Box 305, Zip 50060–0305;
tel. 641/872–2260; Daren Relph, Chief Executive Officer

### MERCY HEALTH NETWORK – NORTH IOWA
**1000 4th Street S.W., Mason City, IA 50401–2800; tel. 641/428–7000;
Daniel Varnum, Chief Executive Officer**

ELLSWORTH MUNICIPAL HOSPITAL, 110 Rocksylvania Avenue, Iowa Falls, IA,
Zip 50126–2400; tel. 641/648–4631; Cherelle Montanye–Ireland, Chief
Executive Officer

FRANKLIN GENERAL HOSPITAL, 1720 Central Avenue East, Suite A., Hampton, IA,
Zip 50441–1867; tel. 641/456–5000; Kim Price, Chief Executive Officer

HANCOCK COUNTY HEALTH SYSTEM, 532 First Street N.W., Britt, IA,
Zip 50423–1227; tel. 641/843–5000; Vance Jackson, FACHE, Administrator
and Chief Executive Officer

KOSSUTH REGIONAL HEALTH CENTER, 1515 South Phillips Street, Algona, IA,
Zip 50511–3649; tel. 515/295–2451; Scott A. Curtis, Administrator and
Chief Executive Officer

MERCY MEDICAL CENTER–NEW HAMPTON, 308 North Maple Avenue, New
Hampton, IA, Zip 50659–1142; tel. 641/394–4121; Kim Price, Chief
Executive Officer

MERCY MEDICAL CENTER–NORTH IOWA, 1000 Fourth Street S.W., Mason City,
IA, Zip 50401–2800; tel. 641/428–7000; Daniel Varnum, President and
Chief Executive Officer

MITCHELL COUNTY REGIONAL HEALTH CENTER, 616 North Eighth Street, Osage,
IA, Zip 50461–1498; tel. 641/732–6000; Kevin Runolfson, Chief Executive
Officer

PALO ALTO COUNTY HEALTH SYSTEM, 3201 First Street, Emmetsburg, IA,
Zip 50536–2516; tel. 712/852–5500; Desiree Einsweiler, Chief Executive
Officer

REGIONAL HEALTH SERVICES OF HOWARD COUNTY, 235 Eighth Avenue West,
Cresco, IA, Zip 52136–1098; tel. 563/547–2101; Robin M. Schluter, Chief
Executive Officer

## KANSAS

**HAYS MEDICAL CENTER**
**2220 Canterbury Drive, Hays, KS 67601–2370; tel. 785/623–2300;**
**John H. Jeter, M.D., President and Chief Executive Officer**

CHEYENNE COUNTY HOSPITAL, 210 West First Street, Saint Francis, KS, Zip 67756–3540, Mailing Address: P.O. Box 547, Zip 67756–0547; tel. 785/332–2104; Judith Ann Rockwood, Administrator

CITIZENS MEDICAL CENTER, 100 East College Drive, Colby, KS, Zip 67701–3799; tel. 785/462–7511; Kevan Trenkle, Chief Executive Officer

CLARA BARTON HOSPITAL, 250 West Ninth Street, Hoisington, KS, Zip 67544–1706; tel. 620/653–2114; Curt Colson, President and Chief Executive Officer

EDWARDS COUNTY HOSPITAL AND HEALTHCARE CENTER, 620 West Eighth Street, Kinsley, KS, Zip 67547–2329, Mailing Address: P.O. Box 99, Zip 67547–0099; tel. 620/659–3621; Robert Krickbaum, Chief Executive Officer

GOVE COUNTY MEDICAL CENTER, 520 West Fifth Street, Quinter, KS, Zip 67752–9705, Mailing Address: P.O. Box 129, Zip 67752–0129; tel. 785/754–3341; Richard Q. Bergling, Chief Executive Officer

GRAHAM COUNTY HOSPITAL, 304 West Prout Street, Hill City, KS, Zip 67642–1435; tel. 785/421–2121; Melissa Atkins, CPA, Chief Executive Officer

GRISELL MEMORIAL HOSPITAL DISTRICT ONE, 210 South Vermont Avenue, Ransom, KS, Zip 67572–9525; tel. 785/731–2231; Kristine Ochs, R.N., Administrator

LANE COUNTY HOSPITAL, 235 West Vine, Dighton, KS, Zip 67839–0969, Mailing Address: P.O. Box 969, Zip 67839–0969; tel. 620/397–5321; Donna McGowan, Administrator

LOGAN COUNTY HOSPITAL, 211 Cherry Street, Oakley, KS, Zip 67748–1201; tel. 785/672–3211; Darcy Howard, Chief Executive Officer and Chief Financial Officer

MINNEOLA DISTRICT HOSPITAL, 212 Main Street, Minneola, KS, Zip 67865–8511, Mailing Address: P.O. Box 127, Zip 67865–0127; tel. 620/885–4264; Deborah Bruner, Chief Executive Officer and Administrator

NESS COUNTY HOSPITAL, 312 Custer Street, Ness City, KS, Zip 67560–1654; tel. 785/798–2291; Curt Thomas, Administrator

NORTON COUNTY HOSPITAL, 102 East Holme, Norton, KS, Zip 67654–1406, Mailing Address: P.O. Box 250, Zip 67654–0250; tel. 785/877–3351; Richard Miller, Administrator and Chief Executive Officer

PHILLIPS COUNTY HOSPITAL, 1150 State Street, Phillipsburg, KS, Zip 67661–1743, Mailing Address: P.O. Box 607, Zip 67661–0607; tel. 785/543–5226; David Engel, Chief Executive Officer

RAWLINS COUNTY HEALTH CENTER, 707 Grant Street, Atwood, KS, Zip 67730–1526, Mailing Address: P.O. Box 47, Zip 67730–0047; tel. 785/626–3211; Deanna Freeman, Administrator and Chief Executive Officer

ROOKS COUNTY HEALTH CENTER, 1210 North Washington Street, Plainville, KS, Zip 67663–1632, Mailing Address: P.O. Box 389, Zip 67663–0389; tel. 785/434–4553; Michael Sinclair, Chief Executive Officer

RUSH COUNTY MEMORIAL HOSPITAL, 801 Locust Street, La Crosse, KS, Zip 67548–9673, Mailing Address: P.O. Box 520, Zip 67548–0520; tel. 785/222–2545; Duane Fields, Interim Chief Executive Officer

RUSSELL REGIONAL HOSPITAL, 200 South Main Street, Russell, KS, Zip 67665–2920; tel. 785/483–3131; Sharon Collins, Interim Chief Executive Officer

SCOTT COUNTY HOSPITAL, 310 East Third Street, Scott City, KS, Zip 67871–1203; tel. 620/872–5811; Mark Burnett, President and Chief Executive Officer

SHERIDAN COUNTY HEALTH COMPLEX, 826 18th Street, Hoxie, KS, Zip 67740–0167, Mailing Address: P.O. Box 167, Zip 67740–0167; tel. 785/675–3281; Steven L. Granzow, Chief Executive Officer

SMITH COUNTY MEMORIAL HOSPITAL, 614 South Main Street, Smith Center, KS, Zip 66967–3001; tel. 785/282–6845; Allen Van Driel, FACHE, Administrator

TREGO COUNTY–LEMKE MEMORIAL HOSPITAL, 320 North 13th Street, Wakeeney, KS, Zip 67672–2099; tel. 785/743–2182; Harold Courtois, Administrator and Chief Executive Officer

**HEALTH INNOVATIONS NETWORK OF KANSAS**
**1500 S.W. 10th Avenue, Topeka, KS 66604–1301; tel. 785/354–6137;**
**Kristi Grosser, Network Operations Director**

CLAY COUNTY MEDICAL CENTER, 617 Liberty Street, Clay Center, KS, Zip 67432–1564, Mailing Address: P.O. Box 512, Zip 67432–0512; tel. 785/632–2144; Ron Bender, Chief Executive Officer

COFFEY COUNTY HOSPITAL, 801 North Fourth Street, Burlington, KS, Zip 66839–2602, Mailing Address: P.O. Box 189, Zip 66839–0189; tel. 620/364–2121; Karen Smith, Interim Chief Executive Officer

COMMUNITY HEALTHCARE SYSTEM, 120 West Eighth Street, Onaga, KS, Zip 66521–9574; tel. 785/889–4272; Greg Unruh, Chief Executive Officer

COMMUNITY MEMORIAL HEALTHCARE, 708 North 18th Street, Marysville, KS, Zip 66508–1338; tel. 785/562–2311; Curtis R. Hawkinson, Chief Executive Officer

F. W. HUSTON MEDICAL CENTER, 408 Delaware Street, Winchester, KS, Zip 66097–4003; tel. 913/774–4340; LaMont Cook, Administrator

GEARY COMMUNITY HOSPITAL, 1102 St. Mary's Road, Junction City, KS, Zip 66441–4196, Mailing Address: P.O. Box 490, Zip 66441–0490; tel. 785/238–4131; Joseph Stratton, FACHE, Chief Executive Officer

HERINGTON MUNICIPAL HOSPITAL, 100 East Helen Street, Herington, KS, Zip 67449–1606; tel. 785/258–2207; Michael J. Ryan, Chief Executive Officer

HIAWATHA COMMUNITY HOSPITAL, 300 Utah Street, Hiawatha, KS, Zip 66434–2314; tel. 785/742–2131; John Moore, Administrator

HOLTON COMMUNITY HOSPITAL, 1110 Columbine Drive, Holton, KS, Zip 66436–8824; tel. 785/364–2116; Carrie L. Saia, R.N., Chief Executive Officer

HORTON COMMUNITY HOSPITAL, 240 West 18th Street, Horton, KS, Zip 66439–1245; tel. 785/486–2642; Christopher Barlow, Chief Executive Officer

KANSAS REHABILITATION HOSPITAL, 1504 S.W. Eighth Avenue, Topeka, KS, Zip 66606–1632; tel. 785/235–6600; Marty Dernier, Chief Executive Officer

MORRIS COUNTY HOSPITAL, 600 North Washington Street, Council Grove, KS, Zip 66846–1422; tel. 620/767–6811; James H. Reagan, Jr., Ph.D., Chief Executive Officer

NEMAHA VALLEY COMMUNITY HOSPITAL, 1600 Community Drive, Seneca, KS, Zip 66538–9739; tel. 785/336–6181; Stan Regehr, President and Chief Executive Officer

SABETHA COMMUNITY HOSPITAL, 14th and Oregon Streets, Sabetha, KS, Zip 66534–0229, Mailing Address: P.O. Box 229, Zip 66534–0229; tel. 785/284–2121; Lora Key, Chief Executive Officer

STORMONT–VAIL HEALTHCARE, 1500 S.W. Tenth Avenue, Topeka, KS, Zip 66604–1353; tel. 785/354–6000; Randall Peterson, President and Chief Executive Officer

WASHINGTON COUNTY HOSPITAL, 304 East Third Street, Washington, KS, Zip 66968–2033; tel. 785/325–2211; Doyle L. McKimmy, FACHE, Chief Executive Officer

**MED–OP, INC.**
**205 East 7th Street, Hays, KS 67601–4907; tel. 785/621–4510; David Brittain, Executive Director**

CITIZENS MEDICAL CENTER, 100 East College Drive, Colby, KS, Zip 67701–3799; tel. 785/462–7511; Kevan Trenkle, Chief Executive Officer

CLARA BARTON HOSPITAL, 250 West Ninth Street, Hoisington, KS, Zip 67544–1706; tel. 620/653–2114; Curt Colson, President and Chief Executive Officer

GOODLAND REGIONAL MEDICAL CENTER, 220 West Second Street, Goodland, KS, Zip 67735–1602; tel. 785/890–3625; Jay P. Jolly, Chief Executive Officer

GOVE COUNTY MEDICAL CENTER, 520 West Fifth Street, Quinter, KS, Zip 67752–9705, Mailing Address: P.O. Box 129, Zip 67752–0129; tel. 785/754–3341; Richard Q. Bergling, Chief Executive Officer

GRAHAM COUNTY HOSPITAL, 304 West Prout Street, Hill City, KS, Zip 67642–1435; tel. 785/421–2121; Melissa Atkins, CPA, Chief Executive Officer

HAYS MEDICAL CENTER, 2220 Canterbury Drive, Hays, KS, Zip 67601–2370, Mailing Address: P.O. Box 8100, Zip 67601–8100; tel. 785/623–5000; John H. Jeter, M.D., President and Chief Executive Officer

LOGAN COUNTY HOSPITAL, 211 Cherry Street, Oakley, KS, Zip 67748–1201; tel. 785/672–3211; Darcy Howard, Chief Executive Officer and Chief Financial Officer

MERCY HOSPITAL AND TRAUMA CENTER, 1000 Mineral Point Avenue, Janesville, WI, Zip 53548–2982, Mailing Address: P.O. Box 5003, Zip 53547–5003; tel. 608/756–6000; Javon R. Bea, President and Chief Executive Officer

NESS COUNTY HOSPITAL, 312 Custer Street, Ness City, KS, Zip 67560–1654; tel. 785/798–2291; Curt Thomas, Administrator

NORTON COUNTY HOSPITAL, 102 East Holme, Norton, KS, Zip 67654–1406, Mailing Address: P.O. Box 250, Zip 67654–0250; tel. 785/877–3351; Richard Miller, Administrator and Chief Executive Officer

RICE COUNTY DISTRICT HOSPITAL, 619 South Clark Street, Lyons, KS, Zip 67554–3003, Mailing Address: P.O. Box 828, Zip 67554–0828; tel. 620/257–5173; George M. Stover, Chief Executive Officer

ROOKS COUNTY HEALTH CENTER, 1210 North Washington Street, Plainville, KS, Zip 67663–1632, Mailing Address: P.O. Box 389, Zip 67663–0389; tel. 785/434–4553; Michael Sinclair, Chief Executive Officer

RUSH COUNTY MEMORIAL HOSPITAL, 801 Locust Street, La Crosse, KS, Zip 67548–9673, Mailing Address: P.O. Box 520, Zip 67548–0520; tel. 785/222–2545; Duane Fields, Interim Chief Executive Officer

RUSSELL REGIONAL HOSPITAL, 200 South Main Street, Russell, KS, Zip 67665–2920; tel. 785/483–3131; Sharon Collins, Interim Chief Executive Officer

SCOTT COUNTY HOSPITAL, 310 East Third Street, Scott City, KS, Zip 67871–1203; tel. 620/872–5811; Mark Burnett, President and Chief Executive Officer

SHERIDAN COUNTY HEALTH COMPLEX, 826 18th Street, Hoxie, KS, Zip 67740–0167, Mailing Address: P.O. Box 167, Zip 67740–0167; tel. 785/675–3281; Steven L. Granzow, Chief Executive Officer

STAFFORD COUNTY HOSPITAL, 502 South Buckeye Street, Stafford, KS, Zip 67578–2035, Mailing Address: P.O. Box 190, Zip 67578–0190; tel. 620/234–5221; Todd Taylor, Chief Executive Officer

**NEK CENTER FOR HEALTH & WELLNESS**
   240 West 18th Street, Horton, KS 66439–1245; tel. 785/486–2642;
   Terry Nichols, Chief Executive Officer

COMMUNITY HEALTHCARE SYSTEM, 120 West Eighth Street, Onaga, KS,
   Zip 66521–9574; tel. 785/889–4272; Greg Unruh, Chief Executive Officer

COMMUNITY MEMORIAL HEALTHCARE, 708 North 18th Street, Marysville, KS,
   Zip 66508–1338; tel. 785/562–2311; Curtis R. Hawkinson, Chief Executive
   Officer

GEARY COMMUNITY HOSPITAL, 1102 St. Mary's Road, Junction City, KS,
   Zip 66441–4196, Mailing Address: P.O. Box 490, Zip 66441–0490;
   tel. 785/238–4131; Joseph Stratton, FACHE, Chief Executive Officer

HOLTON COMMUNITY HOSPITAL, 1110 Columbine Drive, Holton, KS,
   Zip 66436–8824; tel. 785/364–2116; Carrie L. Saia, R.N., Chief Executive
   Officer

HORTON COMMUNITY HOSPITAL, 240 West 18th Street, Horton, KS,
   Zip 66439–1245; tel. 785/486–2642; Christopher Barlow, Chief Executive
   Officer

MERCY REGIONAL HEALTH CENTER, 1823 College Avenue, Manhattan, KS,
   Zip 66502–3346; tel. 785/776–3322; John R. Broberg, FACHE, President
   and Chief Executive Officer

MORRIS COUNTY HOSPITAL, 600 North Washington Street, Council Grove, KS,
   Zip 66846–1422; tel. 620/767–6811; James H. Reagan, Jr., Ph.D., Chief
   Executive Officer

NEMAHA VALLEY COMMUNITY HOSPITAL, 1600 Community Drive, Seneca, KS,
   Zip 66538–9739; tel. 785/336–6181; Stan Regehr, President and Chief
   Executive Officer

ST. FRANCIS HEALTH CENTER, 1700 S.W. 7th Street, Topeka, KS,
   Zip 66606–1690; tel. 785/295–8000; Robert J. Erickson, Chief Executive
   Officer

WAMEGO CITY HOSPITAL, 711 Genn Drive, Wamego, KS, Zip 66547–1179;
   tel. 785/456–2295; Shannan Flach, Chief Executive Officer

**PIONEER HEALTH NETWORK, INC.**
   310 East Walnut Street, Suite 210, Garden City, KS 67846–5565;
   tel. 620/276–6100; Mary Adam, Executive Director

BOB WILSON MEMORIAL GRANT COUNTY HOSPITAL, 415 North Main Street,
   Ulysses, KS, Zip 67880–2133; tel. 620/356–1266; Arthur H. Frable, Chief
   Executive Officer

CITIZENS MEDICAL CENTER, 100 East College Drive, Colby, KS,
   Zip 67701–3799; tel. 785/462–7511; Kevan Trenkle, Chief Executive
   Officer

EDWARDS COUNTY HOSPITAL AND HEALTHCARE CENTER, 620 West Eighth
   Street, Kinsley, KS, Zip 67547–2329, Mailing Address: P.O. Box 99,
   Zip 67547–0099; tel. 620/659–3621; Robert Krickbaum, Chief Executive
   Officer

GREELEY COUNTY HEALTH SERVICES, 506 Third Street, Tribune, KS,
   Zip 67879–9684, Mailing Address: P.O. Box 338, Zip 67879–0338;
   tel. 620/376–4221; Deborah Lehner, Administrator

HAMILTON COUNTY HOSPITAL, East Avenue G & Huser Street, Syracuse, KS,
   Zip 67878–0948, Mailing Address: P.O. Box 948, Zip 67878–0948;
   tel. 620/384–7461; Phyllis Horning, Interim Administrator

HODGEMAN COUNTY HEALTH CENTER, 809 Bramley Street, Jetmore, KS,
   Zip 67854–9320, Mailing Address: P.O. Box 310, Zip 67854–0310;
   tel. 620/357–8361; Teresa L. Deuel, Chief Executive Officer

KEARNY COUNTY HOSPITAL, 500 Thorpe Street, Lakin, KS, Zip 67860–9625;
   tel. 620/355–7111; John Loebl, Chief Executive Officer

LANE COUNTY HOSPITAL, 235 West Vine, Dighton, KS, Zip 67839–0969, Mailing
   Address: P.O. Box 969, Zip 67839–0969; tel. 620/397–5321; Donna
   McGowan, Administrator

MEADE DISTRICT HOSPITAL, 510 East Carthage Street, Meade, KS,
   Zip 67864–6401, Mailing Address: P.O. Box 820, Zip 67864–0820;
   tel. 620/873–2141; Michael P. Thomas, Administrator

MINNEOLA DISTRICT HOSPITAL, 212 Main Street, Minneola, KS,
   Zip 67865–8511, Mailing Address: P.O. Box 127, Zip 67865–0127;
   tel. 620/885–4264; Deborah Bruner, Chief Executive Officer and
   Administrator

MORTON COUNTY HEALTH SYSTEM, 445 Hilltop Street, Elkhart, KS,
   Zip 67950–0937, Mailing Address: P.O. Box 937, Zip 67950–0937;
   tel. 620/697–2141; William Wild, Chief Executive Officer

SATANTA DISTRICT HOSPITAL, 401 South Cheyenne Street, Satanta, KS,
   Zip 67870–0159, Mailing Address: P.O. Box 159, Zip 67870–0159;
   tel. 620/649–2761; Jeremy Clingenpeel, Administrator

SCOTT COUNTY HOSPITAL, 310 East Third Street, Scott City, KS,
   Zip 67871–1203; tel. 620/872–5811; Mark Burnett, President and Chief
   Executive Officer

SOUTHWEST MEDICAL CENTER, 315 West 15th Street, Liberal, KS,
   Zip 67901–2455, Mailing Address: Box 1340, Zip 67905–1340;
   tel. 620/624–1651; Bill Ermann, President and Chief Executive Officer

ST. CATHERINE HOSPITAL, 401 East Spuce Street, Garden City, KS,
   Zip 67846–5679; tel. 620/272–2561; Scott J. Taylor, President and Chief
   Executive Officer

STANTON COUNTY HOSPITAL, 404 North Chestnut Street, Johnson, KS,
   Zip 67855–5001, Mailing Address: P.O. Box 779, Zip 67855–0779;
   tel. 620/492–6250; Jay Tusten, Chief Executive Officer

STEVENS COUNTY HOSPITAL, 1006 South Jackson Street, Hugoton, KS,
   Zip 67951–2858, Mailing Address: P.O. Box 10, Zip 67951–0010;
   tel. 620/544–8511; Linda Stalcup, Chief Executive Officer

WICHITA COUNTY HEALTH CENTER, 211 East Earl Street, Leoti, KS,
   Zip 67861–9620; tel. 620/375–2233; Victoria J. Hahn, Administrator and
   Chief Executive Officer

**SUNFLOWER HEALTH NETWORK**
   400 South Santa Fe Avenue, Salina, KS 67401–4144;
   tel. 785/452–6102; Heather Fuller, Executive Director

ANTHONY MEDICAL CENTER, 1101 East Spring Street, Anthony, KS,
   Zip 67003–2122; tel. 620/842–5111; J. Bryant Anderson, Administrator
   and Chief Executive Officer

CLAY COUNTY MEDICAL CENTER, 617 Liberty Street, Clay Center, KS,
   Zip 67432–1564, Mailing Address: P.O. Box 512, Zip 67432–0512;
   tel. 785/632–2144; Ron Bender, Chief Executive Officer

CLOUD COUNTY HEALTH CENTER, 1100 Highland Drive, Concordia, KS,
   Zip 66901–3923; tel. 785/243–1234; Rita K. Buurman, Interim Chief
   Executive Officer

ELLSWORTH COUNTY MEDICAL CENTER, 1604 Aylward Street, Ellsworth, KS,
   Zip 67439–2541, Mailing Address: P.O. Box 87, Zip 67439–0087;
   tel. 785/472–3111; Roger A. Masse, FACHE, Chief Executive Officer

HERINGTON MUNICIPAL HOSPITAL, 100 East Helen Street, Herington, KS,
   Zip 67449–1606; tel. 785/258–2207; Michael J. Ryan, Chief Executive
   Officer

HILLSBORO COMMUNITY HOSPITAL, 701 South Main Street, Hillsboro, KS,
   Zip 67063–1553; tel. 620/947–3114; Marion Regier, Chief Executive Officer

JEWELL COUNTY HOSPITAL, 100 Crestvue Avenue, Mankato, KS,
   Zip 66956–2407, Mailing Address: P.O. Box 327, Zip 66956–0327;
   tel. 785/378–3137; Doyle L. McKimmy, FACHE, Chief Executive Officer

LINCOLN COUNTY HOSPITAL, 624 North Second Street, Lincoln, KS,
   Zip 67455–1738, Mailing Address: P.O. Box 406, Zip 67455–0406;
   tel. 785/524–4403; Greg R. McNeil, Chief Executive Officer

LINDSBORG COMMUNITY HOSPITAL, 605 West Lincoln Street, Lindsborg, KS,
   Zip 67456–2328; tel. 785/227–3308; Larry VanDerWege, Administrator and
   Chief Executive Officer

MEMORIAL HEALTH SYSTEM, 511 N.E. Tenth Street, Abilene, KS,
   Zip 67410–2153; tel. 785/263–2100; Mark A. Miller, FACHE, Chief
   Executive Officer

MITCHELL COUNTY HOSPITAL HEALTH SYSTEMS, 400 West Eighth, Beloit, KS,
   Zip 67420–1605, Mailing Address: P.O. Box 399, Zip 67420–0399;
   tel. 785/738–2266; David Dick, Chief Executive Officer

OSBORNE COUNTY MEMORIAL HOSPITAL, 424 West New Hampshire Street,
   Osborne, KS, Zip 67473–2314, Mailing Address: P.O. Box 70,
   Zip 67473–0070; tel. 785/346–2121; Kiley Floyd, Administrator

OTTAWA COUNTY HEALTH CENTER, 215 East Eighth, Minneapolis, KS,
   Zip 67467–1902, Mailing Address: P.O. Box 290, Zip 67467–0290;
   tel. 785/392–2122; Jody Parks, Administrator

REPUBLIC COUNTY HOSPITAL, 2420 G Street, Belleville, KS, Zip 66935–2400;
   tel. 785/527–2254; Blaine K. Miller, Administrator

RICE COUNTY DISTRICT HOSPITAL, 619 South Clark Street, Lyons, KS,
   Zip 67554–3003, Mailing Address: P.O. Box 828, Zip 67554–0828;
   tel. 620/257–5173; George M. Stover, Chief Executive Officer

RUSH COUNTY MEMORIAL HOSPITAL, 801 Locust Street, La Crosse, KS,
   Zip 67548–9673, Mailing Address: P.O. Box 520, Zip 67548–0520;
   tel. 785/222–2545; Duane Fields, Interim Chief Executive Officer

SALINA REGIONAL HEALTH CENTER, 400 South Santa Fe Avenue, Salina, KS,
   Zip 67401–4198, Mailing Address: P.O. Box 5080, Zip 67402–5080;
   tel. 785/452–7000; Micheal Terry, President and Chief Executive Officer

SMITH COUNTY MEMORIAL HOSPITAL, 614 South Main Street, Smith Center, KS,
   Zip 66967–3001; tel. 785/282–6845; Allen Van Driel, FACHE, Administrator

# KENTUCKY

**COMMONWEALTH HEALTH CORPORATION**
   800 Park Street, Bowling Green, KY 42101–2356; tel. 270/745–1500;
   Connie Smith, President and Chief Executive Officer

COMMONWEALTH REGIONAL SPECIALTY HOSPITAL, 250 Park Drive, 6th Floor,
   Bowling Green, KY, Zip 42101–1760, Mailing Address: P.O. Box 90010,
   Zip 42102–9010; tel. 270/796–6200; Emily Howard Martin, Administrator

MEDICAL CENTER AT BOWLING GREEN, 250 Park Street, Bowling Green, KY,
   Zip 42101–1795, Mailing Address: P.O. Box 90010, Zip 42102–9010;
   tel. 270/745–1000; Connie Smith, Chief Executive Officer

MEDICAL CENTER AT FRANKLIN, 1100 Brookhaven Road, Franklin, KY,
   Zip 42134–2746; tel. 270/598–4800; Eric Hagan, R.N., Vice
   President/Administrator

MEDICAL CENTER AT SCOTTSVILLE, 456 Burnley Road, Scottsville, KY,
   Zip 42164–6355; tel. 270/622–2800; Eric Hagan, R.N., Vice
   President/Administrator

**COMMUNITY CARE NETWORK**
   110 A. Second Street, Henderson, KY 42420; tel. 619/278–2273;
   Roberta Alexander, Director

BAPTIST HEALTH MADISONVILLE, 900 Hospital Drive, Madisonville, KY,
   Zip 42431–1694; tel. 270/825–5100; E. Berton Whitaker, FACHE, President

Section B

CALDWELL MEDICAL CENTER, 100 Medical Center Drive, Princeton, KY, Zip 42445–2430, Mailing Address: P.O. Box 410, Zip 42445–0410; tel. 270/365–0300; Charles D. Lovell, Jr., FACHE, President and Chief Executive Officer

CRITTENDEN COUNTY HOSPITAL, 520 West Gum Street, Marion, KY, Zip 42064–1516, Mailing Address: P.O. Box 386, Zip 42064–0386; tel. 270/965–5281; Jim Christensen, Chief Executive Officer

JENNIE STUART MEDICAL CENTER, 320 West 18th Street, Hopkinsville, KY, Zip 42240–1965, Mailing Address: P.O. Box 2400, Zip 42241–2400; tel. 270/887–0100; Eric A. Lee, President and Chief Executive Officer

LIVINGSTON HOSPITAL AND HEALTHCARE SERVICES, 131 Hospital Drive, Salem, KY, Zip 42078–8043; tel. 270/988–2299; Mark A. Edwards, Chief Executive Officer

MEDICAL CENTER AT FRANKLIN, 1100 Brookhaven Road, Franklin, KY, Zip 42134–2746; tel. 270/598–4800; Eric Hagan, R.N., Vice President/Administrator

METHODIST HOSPITAL, 1305 North Elm Street, Henderson, KY, Zip 42420–2775, Mailing Address: P.O. Box 48, Zip 42419–0048; tel. 270/827–7700; Bruce D. Begley, Executive Director

METHODIST HOSPITAL UNION COUNTY, 4604 Highway 60 West, Morganfield, KY, Zip 42437–9570; tel. 270/389–5000; Patrick Donahue, Administrator

MURRAY–CALLOWAY COUNTY HOSPITAL, 803 Poplar Street, Murray, KY, Zip 42071–2432; tel. 270/762–1100; Colonel Jerome Penner, Chief Executive Officer

STS. MARY & ELIZABETH HOSPITAL, 1850 Bluegrass Avenue, Louisville, KY, Zip 40215–1199; tel. 502/361–6000; Jennifer Nolan, President

**ST. ELIZABETH EDGEWOOD**
**1 Medical Village Drive, Edgewood, KY 41017–3403; tel. 859/301–2000; John S. Dubis, FACHE, President and Chief Executive Officer**

ST. ELIZABETH GRANT, 238 Barnes Road, Williamstown, KY, Zip 41097–9482; tel. 859/824–8240; John Mitchell, Assistant Vice President Operations

## MAINE

**MAINE NETWORK FOR HEALTH**
**Key Plaza, 23 Water Street, Bangor, ME 04401; tel. 207/942–2844; Stephen A. Ryan, President and Chief Executive Officer**

BLUE HILL MEMORIAL HOSPITAL, 57 Water Street, Blue Hill, ME, Zip 04614–5231, Mailing Address: P.O. Box 1029, Zip 04614–1029; tel. 207/374–3400; Gregory E. Roraff, President and Chief Executive Officer

CHARLES A. DEAN MEMORIAL HOSPITAL, 364 Pritham Avenue, Greenville, ME, Zip 04441–1395, Mailing Address: P.O. Box 1129, Zip 04441–1129; tel. 207/695–5200; Geno Murray, President and Chief Executive Officer

EASTERN MAINE MEDICAL CENTER, 489 State Street, Bangor, ME, Zip 04401–6674, Mailing Address: P.O. Box 404, Zip 04402–0404; tel. 207/973–7000; Deborah Carey Johnson, R.N., President and Chief Executive Officer

HOULTON REGIONAL HOSPITAL, 20 Hartford Street, Houlton, ME, Zip 04730–1891; tel. 207/532–9471; Thomas J. Moakler, Chief Executive Officer

INLAND HOSPITAL, 200 Kennedy Memorial Drive, Waterville, ME, Zip 04901–4595; tel. 207/861–3000; John Dalton, President and Chief Executive Officer

MILLINOCKET REGIONAL HOSPITAL, 200 Somerset Street, Millinocket, ME, Zip 04462–1298; tel. 207/723–5161; Marie E. Vienneau, R.N., Chief Executive Officer

MOUNT DESERT ISLAND HOSPITAL, 10 Wayman Lane, Bar Harbor, ME, Zip 04609–1625, Mailing Address: P.O. Box 8, Zip 04609–0008; tel. 207/288–5081; Arthur J. Blank, President and Chief Executive Officer

NORTHERN MAINE MEDICAL CENTER, 194 East Main Street, Fort Kent, ME, Zip 04743–1497; tel. 207/834–3155; Peter Sirois, Interim Chief Executive Officer

SEBASTICOOK VALLEY HEALTH, 447 North Main Street, Pittsfield, ME, Zip 04967–3707; tel. 207/487–4000; Terri Vieira, Interim Chief Executive Officer

ACADIA HOSPITAL, 268 Stillwater Avenue, Bangor, ME, Zip 04401–3945, Mailing Address: P.O. Box 422, Zip 04402–0422; tel. 207/973–6100; Daniel B. Coffey, President and Chief Executive Officer

AROOSTOOK MEDICAL CENTER, 140 Academy Street, Presque Isle, ME, Zip 04769–3171, Mailing Address: P.O. Box 151, Zip 04769–0151; tel. 207/768–4000; Sylvia Getman, President and Chief Executive Officer

## MICHIGAN

**GENESYS HEALTH SYSTEM**
**1 Genesys Parkway, Grand Blanc, MI 48439–8065; tel. 810/606–5000; Christine Gleason, Director of Marketing**

GENESYS REGIONAL MEDICAL CENTER, One Genesys Parkway, Grand Blanc, MI, Zip 48439–8066; tel. 810/606–5000; Elizabeth Aderholdt, President

**LAKELAND REGIONAL HEALTH SYSTEM**
**1234 Napier Avenue, Saint Joseph, MI 49085–2112; tel. 269/983–8300; Loren Hamel, M.D., President and Chief Executive Officer**

LAKELAND REGIONAL MEDICAL CENTER–ST. JOSEPH, 1234 Napier Avenue, Saint Joseph, MI, Zip 49085–2158; tel. 269/983–8300; Loren Hamel, M.D., President and Chief Executive Officer

**ST. JOHN PROVIDENCE HEALTH SYSTEM**
**28000 Dequindre Drive, Warren, MI 48092; tel. 586/753–1259; Patricia A. Maryland, Dr.PH, President and Chief Executive Officer**

BRIGHTON CENTER FOR RECOVERY, 12851 Grand River Road, Brighton, MI, Zip 48116–8506; tel. 810/227–1211; Raymond Waller, Director

PROVIDENCE HOSPITAL, 16001 West Nine Mile Road, Southfield, MI, Zip 48075–4818, Mailing Address: P.O. Box 2043, Zip 48037–2043; tel. 248/424–3000; Michael Wiemann, M.D., President

ST. JOHN HOSPITAL AND MEDICAL CENTER, 22101 Moross Road, Detroit, MI, Zip 48236–2148; tel. 313/343–4000; David Brooks, Chief Executive Officer

ST. JOHN RIVER DISTRICT HOSPITAL, 4100 River Road, East China, MI, Zip 48054–2909; tel. 810/329–7111; Frank W. Poma, President

**UPPER PENINSULA HEALTH CARE NETWORK (UPHCN)**
**228 West Washington Street, Marquette, MI 49855–4330; tel. 906/225–3146; Dennis Smith, Chief Executive Officer**

ASPIRUS GRAND VIEW HOSPITAL, N10561 Grand View Lane, Ironwood, MI, Zip 49938–9622; tel. 906/932–2525; Charles Nelson, Chief Executive Officer

ASPIRUS KEWEENAW HOSPITAL, 205 Osceola Street, Laurium, MI, Zip 49913–2134; tel. 906/337–6500; Charles Nelson, Chief Executive Officer

ASPIRUS ONTONAGON HOSPITAL, 601 South Seventh Street, Ontonagon, MI, Zip 49953–1459; tel. 906/884–8000; Charles Nelson, Chief Executive Officer

BARAGA COUNTY MEMORIAL HOSPITAL, 18341 U.S. Highway 41, L'Anse, MI, Zip 49946–8024; tel. 906/524–3300; Tim E. Zwickey, Chief Executive Officer

BELL HOSPITAL, 901 Lakeshore Drive, Ishpeming, MI, Zip 49849–1367; tel. 906/486–4431; Floyd D. Bounds, Chief Executive Officer

DICKINSON COUNTY HEALTHCARE SYSTEM, 1721 South Stephenson Avenue, Iron Mountain, MI, Zip 49801–3637; tel. 906/774–1313; John Schon, Administrator and Chief Executive Officer

HELEN NEWBERRY JOY HOSPITAL, 502 West Harrie Street, Newberry, MI, Zip 49868–1209; tel. 906/293–9200; Scott Pillion, Chief Executive Officer

MACKINAC STRAITS HEALTH SYSTEM, 1140 North State Street, Saint Ignace, MI, Zip 49781–1048; tel. 906/643–8585; Rodney M. Nelson, Chief Executive Officer

MARQUETTE GENERAL HEALTH SYSTEM, 580 West College Avenue, Marquette, MI, Zip 49855–2736; tel. 906/228–9440; A. Gary Muller, FACHE, President and Chief Executive Officer

MUNISING MEMORIAL HOSPITAL, 1500 Sand Point Road, Munising, MI, Zip 49862–1406; tel. 906/387–4110; Kevin P. Calhoun, Chief Executive Officer

OSF ST. FRANCIS HOSPITAL, 3401 Ludington Street, Escanaba, MI, Zip 49829–1377; tel. 906/786–3311; David Lord, President and Chief Executive Officer

PORTAGE HEALTH, 500 Campus Drive, Hancock, MI, Zip 49930–1569; tel. 906/483–1000; James Bogan, FACHE, President and Chief Executive Officer

SCHOOLCRAFT MEMORIAL HOSPITAL, 500 Main Street, Manistique, MI, Zip 49854–1599; tel. 906/341–3200; George H. Montgomery, Chief Executive Officer

WAR MEMORIAL HOSPITAL, 500 Osborn Boulevard, Sault Sainte Marie, MI, Zip 49783–1884; tel. 906/635–4460; David B. Jahn, President and Chief Executive Officer

## MISSOURI

**MERCY HEALTH EAST**
**615 South New Ballas Road, Saint Louis, MO 63141–8221; tel. 314/364–3000; Donn Sorensen, President, East Region**

MERCY HOSPITAL JEFFERSON, Highway 61 South, Crystal City, MO, Zip 63019, Mailing Address: P.O. Box 350, Zip 63019–0350; tel. 636/933–1000; Eric Ammons, President

MERCY HOSPITAL ST. LOUIS, 615 South New Ballas Road, Saint Louis, MO, Zip 63141–8277; tel. 314/569–6000; Jeffrey A. Johnston, President

MERCY HOSPITAL WASHINGTON, 901 East Fifth Street, Washington, MO, Zip 63090–3127; tel. 636/239–8000; Terri L. McLain, FACHE, President

## MONTANA

**MONTANA HEALTH NETWORK**
**11 South 7th Street, Suite 241, Miles City, MT 59301; tel. 406/234–1420; Janet Bastian, Chief Executive Officer**

BEARTOOTH BILLINGS CLINIC, 2525 North Broadway, Red Lodge, MT, Zip 59068–9222, Mailing Address: P.O. Box 590, Zip 59068–0590; tel. 406/446–2345; Kelley Evans, Chief Executive Officer

BILLINGS CLINIC, 2800 10th Avenue North, Billings, MT, Zip 59101–0703, Mailing Address: P.O. Box 37000, Zip 59107–7000; tel. 406/657–4000; Nicholas Wolter, M.D., President and Chief Executive Officer

CENTRAL MONTANA MEDICAL CENTER, 408 Wendell Avenue, Lewistown, MT, Zip 59457–2261; tel. 406/535–7711; Lee Rhodes, Chief Executive Officer

DANIELS MEMORIAL HEALTHCARE CENTER, 105 Fifth Avenue East, Scobey, MT, Zip 59263, Mailing Address: P.O. Box 400, Zip 59263–0400; tel. 406/487–2296; David Hubbard, Chief Executive Officer

FALLON MEDICAL COMPLEX, 202 South 4th Street West, Baker, MT, Zip 59313–9156, Mailing Address: P.O. Box 820, Zip 59313–0820; tel. 406/778–3331; David Espeland, Chief Executive Officer

FRANCES MAHON DEACONESS HOSPITAL, 621 Third Street South, Glasgow, MT, Zip 59230–2699; tel. 406/228–3500; Randall G. Holom, Chief Executive Officer

GLENDIVE MEDICAL CENTER, 202 Prospect Drive, Glendive, MT, Zip 59330–1999; tel. 406/345–3306; Parker Powell, Interim Chief Executive Officer

HOLY ROSARY HEALTHCARE, 2600 Wilson Street, Miles City, MT, Zip 59301–5094; tel. 406/233–2600; Paul Lewis, Chief Executive Officer

MCCONE COUNTY HEALTH CENTER, 605 Sullivan Avenue, Circle, MT, Zip 59215, Mailing Address: P.O. Box 48, Zip 59215–0048; tel. 406/485–3381; Nancy Rosaaen, Chief Executive Officer

PHILLIPS COUNTY HOSPITAL, 417 South Fourth East, Malta, MT, Zip 59538–8825, Mailing Address: P.O. Box 640, Zip 59538–0640; tel. 406/654–1100; Ward C. VanWichen, Chief Executive Officer

ROOSEVELT MEDICAL CENTER, 818 Second Avenue East, Culbertson, MT, Zip 59218, Mailing Address: P.O. Box 419, Zip 59218–0419; tel. 406/787–6401; Audrey Stromberg, Administrator

ROUNDUP MEMORIAL HEALTHCARE, 1202 Third Street West, Roundup, MT, Zip 59072–1816, Mailing Address: P.O. Box 40, Zip 59072–0040; tel. 406/323–2301; Bradley Howell, Chief Executive Officer

SHERIDAN MEMORIAL HOSPITAL, 440 West Laurel Avenue, Plentywood, MT, Zip 59254–1596; tel. 406/765–1420; Sandra Christensen, Chief Executive Officer

SIDNEY HEALTH CENTER, 216 14th Avenue S.W., Sidney, MT, Zip 59270–3586; tel. 406/488–2100; Richard Haraldson, Chief Executive Officer

STILLWATER COMMUNITY HOSPITAL, 44 West Fourth Avenue North, Columbus, MT, Zip 59019–0959, Mailing Address: P.O. Box 959, Zip 59019–0959; tel. 406/322–5316; Tim Russell, Administrator

## NEBRASKA

**ALEGENT CREIGHTON HEALTH**
**12809 West Dodge Road, Omaha, NE 68154–2155; tel. 402/343–4000; Richard A. Hachten II, FACHE, President and Chief Executive Officer**

ALEGENT CREIGHTON HEALTH BERGAN MERCY MEDICAL CENTER, 7500 Mercy Road, Omaha, NE, Zip 68124–2319; tel. 402/398–6060; Marie E. Knedler, R.N., President

ALEGENT CREIGHTON HEALTH COMMUNITY MEMORIAL HOSPITAL, 631 North Eighth Street, Missouri Valley, IA, Zip 51555–1102; tel. 712/642–2784; Robert A. Valentine, Regional Administrator

ALEGENT CREIGHTON HEALTH IMMANUEL MEDICAL CENTER, 6901 North 72nd Street, Omaha, NE, Zip 68122–1799; tel. 402/572–2121; Ann Schumacher, R.N., MSN, President

ALEGENT CREIGHTON HEALTH LAKESIDE HOSPITAL, 16901 Lakeside Hills Court, Omaha, NE, Zip 68130–2318; tel. 402/717–8000; Cindy Alloway, President

ALEGENT CREIGHTON HEALTH MERCY HOSPITAL, 603 Rosary Drive, Corning, IA, Zip 50841–1683; tel. 641/322–3121; Debra Goldsmith, Regional Administrator

ALEGENT CREIGHTON HEALTH MERCY HOSPITAL, 800 Mercy Drive, Council Bluffs, IA, Zip 51503–3128, Mailing Address: P.O. Box 1C, Zip 51502–3001; tel. 712/328–5000; Marie E. Knedler, R.N., President

ALEGENT CREIGHTON HEALTH MIDLANDS HOSPITAL, 11111 South 84th Street, Papillion, NE, Zip 68046–4122; tel. 402/593–3000; Cindy Alloway, President

ALEGENT CREIGHTON HEALTH PLAINVIEW HOSPITAL, 704 North Third Street, Plainview, NE, Zip 68769–2047, Mailing Address: P.O. Box 489, Zip 68769–0489; tel. 402/582–4245; Richard B. Gamel, Administrator

ALEGENT CREIGHTON HEALTH–CREIGHTON UNIVERSITY MEDICAL CENTER, 601 North 30th Street, Omaha, NE, Zip 68131–2197; tel. 402/449–4000; Kevin J. Nokels, FACHE, President

ALEGENT CREIGHTON HEALTH–MEMORIAL HOSPITAL, SCHUYLER, 104 West 17th Street, Schuyler, NE, Zip 68661–1304; tel. 402/352–2441; Connie Peters, R.N., Regional Administrator

**BLUE RIVER VALLEY HEALTH NETWORK**
**2222 North Lincoln Avenue, York, NE 68467–1030; tel. 402/362–0445; Charles K. Schulz, President**

ANNIE JEFFREY MEMORIAL COUNTY HEALTH CENTER, 531 Beebe Street, Osceola, NE, Zip 68651–5537, Mailing Address: P.O. Box 428, Zip 68651–0428; tel. 402/747–2031; Joseph W. Lohrman, Chief Executive Officer

BOONE COUNTY HEALTH CENTER, 723 West Fairview Street, Albion, NE, Zip 68620–1725, Mailing Address: P.O. Box 151, Zip 68620–0151; tel. 402/395–2191; Victor N. Lee, FACHE, President and Chief Executive Officer

BRODSTONE MEMORIAL HOSPITAL, 520 East Tenth Street, Superior, NE, Zip 68978–1225, Mailing Address: P.O. Box 187, Zip 68978–0187; tel. 402/879–3281; John E. Keelan, Administrator and Chief Executive Officer

BUTLER COUNTY HEALTH CARE CENTER, 372 South Ninth Street, David City, NE, Zip 68632–2116; tel. 402/367–1200; Donald T. Naiberk, Administrator

COMMUNITY MEMORIAL HOSPITAL, 1579 Midland Street, Syracuse, NE, Zip 68446–9732, Mailing Address: P.O. Box N., Zip 68446–0518; tel. 402/269–2011; Michael Harvey, Chief Executive Officer

CRETE AREA MEDICAL CENTER, 2910 Betten Drive, Crete, NE, Zip 68333–3084, Mailing Address: P.O. Box 220, Zip 68333–0220; tel. 402/826–2102; Carol Friesen, President and Chief Executive Officer

FILLMORE COUNTY HOSPITAL, 1900 F Street, Geneva, NE, Zip 68361–1325, Mailing Address: P.O. Box 193, Zip 68361–0193; tel. 402/759–3167; Paul Utemark, Chief Executive Officer

HENDERSON HEALTH CARE SERVICES, 1621 Front Street, Henderson, NE, Zip 68371–8902; tel. 402/723–4512; Cheryl Brown, Administrator

HOWARD COUNTY MEDICAL CENTER, 1113 Sherman Street, Saint Paul, NE, Zip 68873–1546, Mailing Address: P.O. Box 406, Zip 68873–0406; tel. 308/754–4421; Arlan D. Johnson, Chief Executive Officer

JEFFERSON COMMUNITY HEALTH CENTER, 2200 H Street, Fairbury, NE, Zip 68352–1119, Mailing Address: P.O. Box 277, Zip 68352–0277; tel. 402/729–3351; William L. Welch, FACHE, Chief Executive Officer

JOHNSON COUNTY HOSPITAL, 202 High Street, Tecumseh, NE, Zip 68450–2443, Mailing Address: P.O. Box 599, Zip 68450–0599; tel. 402/335–3361; Diane Newman, Administrator

LITZENBERG MEMORIAL COUNTY HOSPITAL, 1715 26th Street, Central City, NE, Zip 68826–9620; tel. 308/946–3015; Tad M. Hunt, MS, Chief Executive Officer

MEMORIAL COMMUNITY HEALTH, 1423 Seventh Street, Aurora, NE, Zip 68818–1197; tel. 402/694–3171; Diane R. Keller, Chief Executive Officer

MEMORIAL HEALTH CARE SYSTEMS, 300 North Columbia Avenue, Seward, NE, Zip 68434–2228; tel. 402/643–2971; Roger J. Reamer, Chief Executive Officer

THAYER COUNTY HEALTH SERVICES, 120 Park Avenue, Hebron, NE, Zip 68370–2019, Mailing Address: P.O. Box 49, Zip 68370–0049; tel. 402/768–6041; Joyce Beck, Administrator

VALLEY COUNTY HEALTH SYSTEM, 2707 L. Street, Ord, NE, Zip 68862–1275; tel. 308/728–4200; William T. Sugg, President and Chief Executive Officer

WARREN MEMORIAL HOSPITAL, 905 Second Street, Friend, NE, Zip 68359–1133; tel. 402/947–2541; John W. Wilson, Chief Executive Officer

YORK GENERAL HOSPITAL, 2222 North Lincoln Avenue, York, NE, Zip 68467–1095; tel. 402/362–6671; Charles K. Schulz, Chief Executive Officer

**NORTHEAST HEALTH SERVICES**
**PO Box 186, Creighton, NE 68729–0186; tel. 402/358–5700; Jeff Lingerfelt, Chief Executive Officer**

ALEGENT CREIGHTON HEALTH PLAINVIEW HOSPITAL, 704 North Third Street, Plainview, NE, Zip 68769–2047, Mailing Address: P.O. Box 489, Zip 68769–0489; tel. 402/582–4245; Richard B. Gamel, Administrator

AVERA CREIGHTON HOSPITAL, 1503 Main Street, Creighton, NE, Zip 68729–3007, Mailing Address: P.O. Box 186, Zip 68729–0186; tel. 402/358–5700; Mark Schulte, Chief Executive Officer

OSMOND GENERAL HOSPITAL, 402 North Maple Street, Osmond, NE, Zip 68765–5726, Mailing Address: P.O. Box 429, Zip 68765–0429; tel. 402/748–3393; Celine M. Mlady, Chief Executive Officer

**REGIONAL CARE, INC.**
**905 West 27th Street, Scottsbluff, NE 69361–1545; tel. 308/635–2260; Steve Hetzel, President**

BOX BUTTE GENERAL HOSPITAL, 2101 Box Butte Avenue, Alliance, NE, Zip 69301–4445, Mailing Address: P.O. Box 810, Zip 69301–0810; tel. 308/762–6660; Dan Griess, Chief Executive Officer

CHADRON COMMUNITY HOSPITAL AND HEALTH SERVICES, 825 Centennial Drive, Chadron, NE, Zip 69337–9400; tel. 308/432–5586; Harold L. Krueger, Jr., Chief Executive Officer

GARDEN COUNTY HEALTH SERVICES, 1100 West Second Street, Oshkosh, NE, Zip 69154–6152; tel. 308/772–3283; Jimmie W. Hansel, Ph.D., Chief Executive Officer

GORDON MEMORIAL HOSPITAL, 300 East Eighth Street, Gordon, NE, Zip 69343–1123; tel. 308/282–0401; James B. McHugh, Interim Chief Executive Officer

KIMBALL HEALTH SERVICES, 505 South Burg Street, Kimball, NE, Zip 69145–1398; tel. 308/235–1952; Ken Hunter, R.N., Chief Executive Officer

MORRILL COUNTY COMMUNITY HOSPITAL, 1313 S Street, Bridgeport, NE, Zip 69336–0579, Mailing Address: P.O. Box 579, Zip 69336–0579; tel. 308/262–1616; Vail Oleson, Chief Executive Officer

REGIONAL WEST MEDICAL CENTER, 4021 Avenue B, Scottsbluff, NE,
Zip 69361–4695; tel. 308/635–3711; Todd Sorensen, M.D., Chief
Executive Officer

## NEW HAMPSHIRE

**CARING COMMUNITY NETWORK OF THE TWIN RIVERS**
**c/o First Health, 841 Central Street, Franklin, NH 03235–2026;**
**tel. 603/934–0177; Rick Silverberg, Managing Director**

FRANKLIN REGIONAL HOSPITAL, 15 Aiken Avenue, Franklin, NH, Zip 03235–1299;
tel. 603/934–2060; Thomas Clairmont, President

## NEW JERSEY

**ATLANTICARE**
**2500 English Creek Avenue, Building 500, Suite 501, Egg Harbor**
**Township, NJ 08234; tel. 609/407–2309; David P. Tilton, President and**
**Chief Executive Officer**

ATLANTICARE REGIONAL MEDICAL CENTER, 1925 Pacific Avenue, Atlantic City,
NJ, Zip 08401–6713; tel. 609/441–8994; Lori Herndon, R.N., President and
Chief Executive Officer

**QUALCARE, INC.**
**242 Old New Brunswick Road, Piscataway, NJ 08854–3754;**
**tel. 732/562–2800; Jerry Eisenberg, Network Contact**

CAPITAL HEALTH MEDICAL CENTER–HOPEWELL, 1 Capital Way, Pennington, NJ,
Zip 08534–2520; tel. 609/303–4000; Al Maghazehe, Ph.D., FACHE, Chief
Executive Officer

CHILTON HOSPITAL, 97 West Parkway, Pompton Plains, NJ, Zip 07444–1696;
tel. 973/831–5000; Deborah Zastocki, R.N., FACHE, FACHE, President and
Chief Executive Officer

CHRIST HOSPITAL, 176 Palisade Avenue, Jersey City, NJ, Zip 07306–1196,
Mailing Address: 176 Palisades Avenue, Zip 07306–1196;
tel. 201/795–8200; Peter A. Kelly, President and Chief Executive Officer

CLARA MAASS MEDICAL CENTER, One Clara Maass Drive, Belleville, NJ,
Zip 07109–3557; tel. 973/450–2000; Mary Ellen Clyne, Ph.D., President
and Chief Executive Officer

DEBORAH HEART AND LUNG CENTER, 200 Trenton Road, Browns Mills, NJ,
Zip 08015–1705; tel. 609/893–6611; Joseph P. Chirichella, President and
Chief Executive Officer

ENGLEWOOD HOSPITAL AND MEDICAL CENTER, 350 Engle Street, Englewood,
NJ, Zip 07631–1898; tel. 201/894–3000; Warren Geller, President and
Chief Executive Officer

HACKETTSTOWN REGIONAL MEDICAL CENTER, 651 Willow Grove Street,
Hackettstown, NJ, Zip 07840–1799; tel. 908/852–5100; Jason C. Coe,
President and Chief Executive Officer

INSPIRA MEDICAL CENTER–VINELAND, 1505 West Sherman Avenue, Vineland, NJ,
Zip 08360–6912; tel. 856/641–8000; Chester B. Kaletkowski, President
and Chief Executive Officer

JFK MEDICAL CENTER, 65 James Street, Edison, NJ, Zip 08820–3947;
tel. 732/321–7000; Raymond F. Fredericks, President and CEO

MEMORIAL HOSPITAL OF SALEM COUNTY, 310 Woodstown Road, Salem, NJ,
Zip 08079–2080; tel. 856/935–1000; Richard Grogan, Chief Executive
Officer

OCEAN MEDICAL CENTER, 425 Jack Martin Boulevard, Brick Township, NJ,
Zip 08724–7732; tel. 732/840–2200; Dean Q. Lin, FACHE, President

PIEDMONT MOUNTAINSIDE HOSPITAL, 1266 Highway 515 South, Jasper, GA,
Zip 30143–4872; tel. 706/692–2441; Denise Ray, President and Chief
Administrative Officer

RARITAN BAY MEDICAL CENTER, 530 New Brunswick Avenue, Perth Amboy, NJ,
Zip 08861–3654; tel. 732/442–3700; Michael R. D'Agnes, FACHE,
President and Chief Executive Officer

RIVERVIEW MEDICAL CENTER, 1 Riverview Plaza, Red Bank, NJ, Zip 07701–1864;
tel. 732/741–2700; Timothy J. Hogan, FACHE, Regional President

ROBERT WOOD JOHNSON UNIVERSITY HOSPITAL, 1 Robert Wood Johnson Place,
New Brunswick, NJ, Zip 08901–1928; tel. 732/828–3000; Stephen K.
Jones, President and Chief Executive Officer

SAINT MICHAEL'S MEDICAL CENTER, 111 Central Avenue, Newark, NJ,
Zip 07102–1909; tel. 973/877–5549; David A. Ricci, President and Chief
Executive Officer

ST. MARY'S HOSPITAL, 350 Boulevard, Passaic, NJ, Zip 07055–2840;
tel. 973/365–4300; Edward Condit, President and Chief Executive Officer

UNIVERSITY MEDICAL CENTER OF PRINCETON AT PLAINSBORO, One Plainsboro
Road, Plainsboro, NJ, Zip 08536–1913; tel. 609/853–7100; Mark T. Jones,
President

UNIVERSITY OF MEDICINE AND DENTISTRY OF NEW JERSEY–UNIVERSITY
HOSPITAL, 150 Bergen Street, Newark, NJ, Zip 07103–2496;
tel. 973/972–4300; James R. Gonzalez, Acting President and Chief
Executive Officer

VIRTUA BERLIN, 100 Townsend Avenue, Berlin, NJ, Zip 08009–9035;
tel. 856/322–3000; Christopher A. Chekouras, Vice President and Chief
Operating Officer

VIRTUA MARLTON, 90 Brick Road, Marlton, NJ, Zip 08053–2177;
tel. 856/355–6000; Gary L. Long, Chief Operating Officer

## NEW YORK

**ALLEGANY WESTERN STEUBEN RURAL HEALTH NETWORK, INC.**
**85 North Main Street, Suite 4, Wellsville, NY 14895–1254;**
**tel. 585/593–5223; Carrie Whitwood, Executive Director**

JONES MEMORIAL HOSPITAL, 191 North Main Street, Wellsville, NY,
Zip 14895–1150, Mailing Address: P.O. Box 72, Zip 14895–0072;
tel. 585/593–1100; Eva Benedict, President and Chief Executive Officer

ST. JAMES MERCY HEALTH SYSTEM, 411 Canisteo Street, Hornell, NY,
Zip 14843–2197; tel. 607/324–8000; Mary E. LaRowe, FACHE, President
and Chief Executive Officer

**ARNOT HEALTH**
**600 Roe Avenue, Elmira, NY 14905–1629; tel. 607/737–4100; Anthony**
**J. Cooper, FACHE, President**

ARNOT OGDEN MEDICAL CENTER, 600 Roe Avenue, Elmira, NY,
Zip 14905–1629; tel. 607/737–4100; H. Fred Farley, R.N., Ph.D., FACHE,
President and Chief Operating Officer

IRA DAVENPORT MEMORIAL HOSPITAL, 7571 State Route 54, Bath, NY,
Zip 14810–9590; tel. 607/776–8500; James B. Watson, Chief Operating
Officer

ST. JOSEPH'S HOSPITAL, 555 St. Joseph's Boulevard, Elmira, NY,
Zip 14901–3223; tel. 607/733–6541; H. Fred Farley, R.N., Ph.D., FACHE,
President and Chief Operating Officer

**BASSETT HEALTHCARE NETWORK**
**1 Atwell Road, Cooperstown, NY 13326–1301; tel. 607/547–3456;**
**William F. Streck, M.D., President and Chief Executive Officer**

AURELIA OSBORN FOX MEMORIAL HOSPITAL, 1 Norton Avenue, Oneonta, NY,
Zip 13820–2629; tel. 607/432–2000; John R. Remillard, President

BASSETT MEDICAL CENTER, One Atwell Road, Cooperstown, NY,
Zip 13326–1394; tel. 607/547–3100; William F. Streck, M.D., President
and Chief Executive Officer

COBLESKILL REGIONAL HOSPITAL, 178 Grandview Drive, Cobleskill, NY,
Zip 12043–5144; tel. 518/254–3456; Eric H. Stein, FACHE, President and
Chief Executive Officer

LITTLE FALLS HOSPITAL, 140 Burwell Street, Little Falls, NY, Zip 13365–1725;
tel. 315/823–1000; Michael L. Ogden, President and Chief Executive Officer

O'CONNOR HOSPITAL, 460 Andes Road, State Route 28, Delhi, NY,
Zip 13753–7407; tel. 607/746–0300; Daniel M. Ayres, Chief Executive
Officer

**LAKE ERIE REGIONAL HEALTH SYSTEM OF NEW YORK**
**529 Central Avenue, Dunkirk, NY 14048–2514; tel. 716/366–1111; J.**
**Gary Rhodes, Interim Chief Executive Officer**

BROOKS MEMORIAL HOSPITAL, 529 Central Avenue, Dunkirk, NY,
Zip 14048–2599; tel. 716/366–1111; Jonathan I. Lawrence, President and
Chief Executive Officer

LAKE SHORE HEALTH CARE CENTER, 845 Route 5 and 20, Irving, NY,
Zip 14081–9716; tel. 716/951–7000; Louis J. Frascella, President and
Chief Executive Officer

**MOHAWK VALLEY NETWORK, INC.**
**1710 Burrstone Road, New Hartford, NY 13413–1002;**
**tel. 315/624–6001; Scott H. Perra, President and Chief Executive**
**Officer**

FAXTON–ST. LUKE'S HEALTHCARE, 1656 Champlin Avenue, Utica, NY,
Zip 13502–4830, Mailing Address: P.O. Box 479, Zip 13503–0479;
tel. 315/624–6000; Scott H. Perra, President and Chief Executive Officer

**MOUNT SINAI NYU HEALTH NETWORK**
**One Gustave L. Levy Place, New York, NY 10029; tel. 212/659–8888;**
**Arthur A. Klein, M.D., President**

ELMHURST HOSPITAL CENTER, 79–01 Broadway, Elmhurst, NY,
Zip 11373–1329; tel. 718/334–4000; Chris D. Constantino, Executive
Director

ENGLEWOOD HOSPITAL AND MEDICAL CENTER, 350 Engle Street, Englewood,
NJ, Zip 07631–1898; tel. 201/894–3000; Warren Geller, President and
Chief Executive Officer

JAMES J. PETERS VETERANS AFFAIRS MEDICAL CENTER, 130 West Kingsbridge
Road, Bronx, NY, Zip 10468–3904; tel. 718/584–9000; MaryAnn P.
Musumeci, Director

LIBERTYHEALTH–JERSEY CITY MEDICAL CENTER, 355 Grand Street, Jersey City,
NJ, Zip 07302–4321; tel. 201/915–2000; Joseph F. Scott, FACHE,
President and Chief Executive Officer

LUTHERAN MEDICAL CENTER, 150 55th Street, Brooklyn, NY, Zip 11220–2559;
tel. 718/630–7000; Wendy Z. Goldstein, President and Chief Executive
Officer

MEADOWLANDS HOSPITAL MEDICAL CENTER, 55 Meadowlands Parkway,
Secaucus, NJ, Zip 07094–2977; tel. 201/392–3100; Lynn McVey, President
and Chief Executive Officer

MORRISTOWN MEDICAL CENTER, 100 Madison Avenue, Morristown, NJ,
Zip 07960–6136; tel. 973/971–5000; David J. Shulkin, M.D., President and
Chief Executive Officer

MOUNT SINAI HOSPITAL, One Gustave L. Levy Place, New York, NY,
Zip 10029–6574; tel. 212/241–6500; David L. Reich, M.D., Interim
President

OVERLOOK MEDICAL CENTER, 99 Beauvoir Avenue, Summit, NJ,
Zip 07901–3533; tel. 908/522–2000; Alan R. Lieber, President

PHELPS MEMORIAL HOSPITAL CENTER, 701 North Broadway, Sleepy Hollow, NY,
Zip 10591–1020; tel. 914/366–3000; Keith F. Safian, President and Chief
Executive Officer

QUEENS HOSPITAL CENTER, 82–68 164th Street, Jamaica, NY,
Zip 11432–1104; tel. 718/883–3000; Julius Wool, Executive Director

ST. JOHN'S RIVERSIDE HOSPITAL, 967 North Broadway, Yonkers, NY,
Zip 10701–1399; tel. 914/964–4444; Ronald Corti, President and Chief
Executive Officer

ST. JOSEPH'S REGIONAL MEDICAL CENTER, 703 Main Street, Paterson, NJ,
Zip 07503–2691; tel. 973/754–2000; William A. McDonald, President and
Chief Executive Officer

ST. LUKE'S CORNWALL HOSPITAL, 70 Dubois Street, Newburgh, NY,
Zip 12550–4851; tel. 845/561–4400; Allan E. Atzrott, FACHE, President
and Chief Executive Officer

THE MOUNT SINAI HOSPITAL OF QUEENS, 25–10 30th Avenue, Long Island City,
NY, Zip 11102–2448; tel. 718/932–1000; Caryn A. Schwab, Executive
Director

VASSAR BROTHERS MEDICAL CENTER, 45 Reade Place, Poughkeepsie, NY,
Zip 12601–3947; tel. 845/454–8500; Janet L. Ready, President and Chief
Operating Officer

### NORTHEAST HEALTH
**2212 Burdett Avenue, Troy, NY 12180–2475; tel. 518/274–3382;
James K. Reed, M.D., President and Chief Executive Officer**

ALBANY MEMORIAL HOSPITAL, 600 Northern Boulevard, Albany, NY,
Zip 12204–1083; tel. 518/471–3221; Ann Errichetti, M.D., Chief Executive
Officer

SAMARITAN HOSPITAL, 2215 Burdett Avenue, Troy, NY, Zip 12180–2475;
tel. 518/271–3300; Norman E. Dascher, Jr., Chief Executive Officer

SUNNYVIEW REHABILITATION HOSPITAL, 1270 Belmont Avenue, Schenectady,
NY, Zip 12308–2104; tel. 518/382–4500; Edward Eisenman, Chief
Executive Officer

### NORTHERN NY RURAL HEALTH CARE ALLIANCE
**800 Starbuck Avenue, Suite A–5, Watertown, NY 13601;
tel. 315/755–2500; Patricia Bishop, Executive Director**

CARTHAGE AREA HOSPITAL, 1001 West Street, Carthage, NY, Zip 13619–9703;
tel. 315/493–1000; Adel Amir, Interim Chief Executive Officer

RIVER HOSPITAL, 4 Fuller Street, Alexandria Bay, NY, Zip 13607–1316;
tel. 315/482–2511; Ben Moore, III, President and Chief Executive Officer

SAMARITAN MEDICAL CENTER, 830 Washington Street, Watertown, NY,
Zip 13601–4034; tel. 315/785 4000; Thomas H. Carman, President and
Chief Executive Officer

### RURAL HEALTH NETWORK OF OSWEGO COUNTY
**10 George Street, Oswego, NY 13126; tel. 315/592–0827; Danielle
Wert, Coordinator**

OSWEGO HOSPITAL, 110 West Sixth Street, Oswego, NY, Zip 13126–2507;
tel. 315/349–5511; Ann C. Gilpin, President and Chief Executive Officer

### STELLARIS HEALTH
**1 North Greenwich Road, Armonk, NY 10504–2311;
tel. 914/273–5454; Arthur Nizza, President and Chief Executive Officer**

LAWRENCE HOSPITAL CENTER, 55 Palmer Avenue, Bronxville, NY,
Zip 10708–3403; tel. 914/787–1000; Edward M. Dinan, President and Chief
Executive Officer

NORTHERN WESTCHESTER HOSPITAL, 400 East Main Street, Mount Kisco, NY,
Zip 10549–3477; tel. 914/666–1200; Joel Seligman, President and Chief
Executive Officer

PHELPS MEMORIAL HOSPITAL CENTER, 701 North Broadway, Sleepy Hollow, NY,
Zip 10591–1020; tel. 914/366–3000; Keith F. Safian, President and Chief
Executive Officer

WHITE PLAINS HOSPITAL CENTER, 41 East Post Road, White Plains, NY,
Zip 10601–4699; tel. 914/681–0600; Jon B. Schandler, Chief Executive
Officer

## NORTH CAROLINA

### COASTAL CAROLINAS HEALTH ALLIANCE
**5305–M Wrightsville Avenue, Wilmington, NC 28403;
tel. 910/332–8012; Yvonne Hughes, Executive Director**

CAPE FEAR VALLEY – BLADEN COUNTY HOSPITAL, 501 South Poplar Street,
Elizabethtown, NC, Zip 28337–9375, Mailing Address: P.O. Box 398,
Zip 28337–0398; tel. 910/862–5100; Dan Weatherly, On Site Administrator

COLUMBUS REGIONAL HEALTHCARE SYSTEM, 500 Jefferson Street, Whiteville,
NC, Zip 28472–3634; tel. 910/642–8011; Henry Hawthorne, III, President
and Chief Executive Officer

J. ARTHUR DOSHER MEMORIAL HOSPITAL, 924 North Howe Street, Southport,
NC, Zip 28461–3099; tel. 910/457–3800; Thomas R. Siemers, Chief
Executive Officer

MCLEOD LORIS HEALTHCARE, 3655 Mitchell Street, Loris, SC, Zip 29569–2827;
tel. 843/716–7000; Edward D. Tinsley, III, Chief Executive Officer

MCLEOD REGIONAL MEDICAL CENTER, 555 East Cheves Street, Florence, SC,
Zip 29506–2617, Mailing Address: P.O. Box 100551, Zip 29502–0551;
tel. 843/777–2000; Robert L. Colones, President and Chief Executive
Officer

NEW HANOVER REGIONAL MEDICAL CENTER, 2131 South 17th Street,
Wilmington, NC, Zip 28401–7483, Mailing Address: P.O. Box 9000,
Zip 28402–9000; tel. 910/343–7000; John K. Barto, Jr., President and
Chief Executive Officer

PENDER MEMORIAL HOSPITAL, 507 East Freemont Street, Burgaw, NC,
Zip 28425–5131; tel. 910/259–5451; Ruth Glaser, President

SAMPSON REGIONAL MEDICAL CENTER, 607 Beaman Street, Clinton, NC,
Zip 28328–2697, Mailing Address: P.O. Box 260, Zip 28329–0260;
tel. 910/592–8511; David J. Masterson, Chief Executive Officer

SCOTLAND HEALTH CARE SYSTEM, 500 Lauchwood Drive, Laurinburg, NC,
Zip 28352–5599; tel. 910/291–7000; Gregory C. Wood, President and
Chief Executive Officer

SOUTHEASTERN HEALTH, 300 West 27th Street, Lumberton, NC,
Zip 28358–3075, Mailing Address: P.O. Box 1408, Zip 28359–1408;
tel. 910/671–5000; Joann Anderson, President and Chief Executive Officer

VIDANT DUPLIN HOSPITAL, 401 North Main Street, Kenansville, NC,
Zip 28349–8801, Mailing Address: P.O. Box 278, Zip 28349–0278;
tel. 910/296–0941; Jay Briley, President

VIDANT MEDICAL CENTER, 2100 Stantonsburg Road, Greenville, NC,
Zip 27834–2818, Mailing Address: P.O. Box 6028, Zip 27835–6028;
tel. 252/847–4100; Stephen Lawler, President

### MISSION HEALTH SYSTEM
**509 Biltmore Avenue, Asheville, NC 28801–4601; tel. 828/213–1111;
Ronald A. Paulus, M.D., President and Chief Executive Officer**

BLUE RIDGE REGIONAL HOSPITAL, 125 Hospital Drive, Spruce Pine, NC,
Zip 28777–3035, Mailing Address: P.O. Drawer 9, Zip 28777–0009;
tel. 828/765–4201; Oscar K. Weinmeister, III, FACHE, President and Chief
Executive Officer

MCDOWELL HOSPITAL, 430 Rankin Drive, Marion, NC, Zip 28752–6568, Mailing
Address: P.O. Box 730, Zip 28752–0730; tel. 828/659–5000; Lynn Ingram
Boggs, Chief Executive Officer

MISSION HOSPITAL, 509 Biltmore Avenue, Asheville, NC, Zip 28801–4690;
tel. 828/213–1111; Ronald A. Paulus, M.D., President and Chief Executive
Officer

### WNC HEALTH NETWORK, INC.
**1200 Ridgefield Boulevard Suite 200, Asheville, NC 28806–2280;
tel. 828/667–8220; Janice M. Lato, President and Chief Executive
Officer**

ACMH HOSPITAL, One Nolte Drive, Kittanning, PA, Zip 16201–7111;
tel. 724/543–8500; John I. Lewis, President and Chief Executive Officer

ALAMANCE REGIONAL MEDICAL CENTER, 1240 Huffman Mill Road, Burlington,
NC, Zip 27215–8700, Mailing Address: P.O. Box 202, Zip 27216–0202;
tel. 336/538–7000; John G. Currin, Jr., President

ANGEL MEDICAL CENTER, 120 Riverview Street, Franklin, NC, Zip 28734–2612,
Mailing Address: P.O. Box 1209, Zip 28744–0569; tel. 828/524–8411;
James B. Bross, President and Chief Executive Officer

ASHEVILLE SPECIALTY HOSPITAL, 428 Biltmore Avenue, 4th Floor, Asheville, NC,
Zip 28801–4502; tel. 828/213–5400; Robert C. Desotelle, President and
Chief Executive Officer

BARNWELL COUNTY HOSPITAL, 811 Reynolds Road, Barnwell, SC,
Zip 29812–1555; tel. 803/259–1000; Mary T. Valliant, R.N., MS, Chief
Executive Officer

BEDFORD MEMORIAL HOSPITAL, 1613 Oakwood Street, Bedford, VA,
Zip 24523–1213, Mailing Address: P.O. Box 688, Zip 24523–0688;
tel. 540/586–2441; Patti Jurkus, Vice President, Regional Hospital

BLOUNT MEMORIAL HOSPITAL, 907 East Lamar Alexander Parkway, Maryville,
TN, Zip 37804–5016; tel. 865/983–7211; Don Heinemann, Administrator
and Chief Executive Officer

BLOWING ROCK HOSPITAL, 418 Chestnut Street, Blowing Rock, NC,
Zip 28605–0148, Mailing Address: P.O. Box 148, Zip 28605–0148;
tel. 828/295–3136; Timothy R. Ford, Chief Executive Officer / President

BLUE RIDGE REGIONAL HOSPITAL, 125 Hospital Drive, Spruce Pine, NC,
Zip 28777–3035, Mailing Address: P.O. Drawer 9, Zip 28777–0009;
tel. 828/765–4201; Oscar K. Weinmeister, III, FACHE, President and Chief
Executive Officer

BUCHANAN GENERAL HOSPITAL, 1535 Slate Creek Road, Grundy, VA,
Zip 24614–6974; tel. 276/935–1000; Robert D. Ruchti, Chief Executive
Officer

CALDWELL MEMORIAL HOSPITAL, 321 Mulberry Street S.W., Lenoir, NC,
Zip 28645–5720, Mailing Address: P.O. Box 1890, Zip 28645–1890;
tel. 828/757–5100; Laura S. Easton, R.N., President and Chief Executive
Officer

CAPE FEAR VALLEY – BLADEN COUNTY HOSPITAL, 501 South Poplar Street,
Elizabethtown, NC, Zip 28337–9375, Mailing Address: P.O. Box 398,
Zip 28337–0398; tel. 910/862–5100; Dan Weatherly, On Site Administrator

CAPE FEAR VALLEY MEDICAL CENTER, 1638 Owen Drive, Fayetteville, NC,
Zip 28304–3431, Mailing Address: P.O. Box 2000, Zip 28302–2000;
tel. 910/615–4000; Michael Nagowski, Chief Executive Officer

CAREPARTNERS HEALTH SERVICES, 68 Sweeten Creek Road, Asheville, NC,
Zip 28803–2318, Mailing Address: P.O. Box 15025, Zip 28813–0025;
tel. 828/277–4800; Tracy Buchanan, Chief Executive Officer / President

CARILION FRANKLIN MEMORIAL HOSPITAL, 180 Floyd Avenue, Rocky Mount, VA, Zip 24151–1389; tel. 540/483–5277; William D. Jacobsen, Vice President, Regional Hospital

CARILION GILES COMMUNITY HOSPITAL, 159 Hartley Way, Pearisburg, VA, Zip 24134–2471; tel. 540/921–6000; James E. Tyler, Vice President, Regional Hospital

CARILION NEW RIVER VALLEY MEDICAL CENTER, 2900 Lamb Circle, Christiansburg, VA, Zip 24073–6344, Mailing Address: P.O. Box 5, Radford, Zip 24143–0005; tel. 540/731–2000; John S. Piatkowski, M.D., Vice President, Regional Hospital

CARILION STONEWALL JACKSON HOSPITAL, 1 Health Circle, Lexington, VA, Zip 24450–2492; tel. 540/458–3300; Charles E. Carr, Vice President, Regional Hospital

CARILION TAZEWELL COMMUNITY HOSPITAL, 141 Ben Bolt Avenue, Tazewell, VA, Zip 24651–9700; tel. 276/988–8700; John S. Piatkowski, M.D., Vice President, Regional Hospital

CARTERET GENERAL HOSPITAL, 3500 Arendell Street, Morehead City, NC, Zip 28557–2901, Mailing Address: P.O. Box 1619, Zip 28557–1619; tel. 252/808–6000; Richard A. Brvenik, FACHE, President

CATAWBA VALLEY MEDICAL CENTER, 810 Fairgrove Church Road S.E., Hickory, NC, Zip 28602–9643; tel. 828/326–3000; J. Anthony Rose, President and Chief Executive Officer

CHARLES A. CANNON MEMORIAL HOSPITAL, 434 Hospital Drive, Linville, NC, Zip 28646, Mailing Address: P.O. Box 767, Zip 28646–0767; tel. 828/737–7000; Carmen Lacey, MSN, R.N., President

CHARLES GEORGE VETERANS AFFAIRS MEDICAL CENTER, 1100 Tunnel Road, Asheville, NC, Zip 28805–2087; tel. 828/298–7911; Cynthia Breyfogle, Director

CHEROKEE INDIAN HOSPITAL, 1 Hospital Road, Cherokee, NC, Zip 28719; tel. 828/497–9163; Casey Cooper, Chief Executive Officer

COMMONWEALTH REGIONAL SPECIALTY HOSPITAL, 250 Park Drive, 6th Floor, Bowling Green, KY, Zip 42101–1760, Mailing Address: P.O. Box 90010, Zip 42102–9010; tel. 270/796–6200; Emily Howard Martin, Administrator

COMMUNITY MEMORIAL HEALTHCENTER, 125 Buena Vista Circle, South Hill, VA, Zip 23970–1431, Mailing Address: P.O. Box 90, Zip 23970–0090; tel. 434/447–3151; W. Scott Burnette, President and Chief Executive Officer

CONWAY MEDICAL CENTER, 300 Singleton Ridge Road, Conway, SC, Zip 29526–9142, Mailing Address: P.O. Box 829, Zip 29528–0829; tel. 843/347–7111; Philip A. Clayton, President and Chief Executive Officer

CORRY MEMORIAL HOSPITAL, 612 West Smith Street, Corry, PA, Zip 16407–1196; tel. 814/664–4641; Barbara Nichols, R.N., President and Chief Executive Officer

CUMBERLAND MEDICAL CENTER, 421 South Main Street, Crossville, TN, Zip 38555–5031; tel. 931/484–9511; Edwin S. Anderson, Chief Executive Officer

DICKENSON COMMUNITY HOSPITAL, 312 Hospital Drive, Clintwood, VA, Zip 24228, Mailing Address: P.O. Box 1440, Zip 24228–1440; tel. 276/926–0300; Mark T. Leonard, Chief Executive Officer

FAIRFIELD MEMORIAL HOSPITAL, 102 U.S. Highway 321 By–Pass N., Winnsboro, SC, Zip 29180–9251, Mailing Address: P.O. Box 620, Zip 29180–0620; tel. 803/635–5548; Michael Williams, FACHE, Administrator

FIRSTHEALTH MONTGOMERY MEMORIAL HOSPITAL, 520 Allen Street, Troy, NC, Zip 27371–2802, Mailing Address: P.O. Box 486, Zip 27371–0486; tel. 910/572–1301; Beth Walker, R.N., President

FIRSTHEALTH MOORE REGIONAL HOSPITAL, 155 Memorial Drive, Pinehurst, NC, Zip 28374–8710, Mailing Address: P.O. Box 3000, Zip 28374–3000; tel. 910/715–1000; David J. Kilarski, Chief Executive Officer

FIRSTHEALTH RICHMOND MEMORIAL HOSPITAL, 925 Long Drive, Rockingham, NC, Zip 28379–4835; tel. 910/417–3000; John J. Jackson, President

FRANKLIN WOODS COMMUNITY HOSPITAL, 300 MedTech Parkway, Johnson City, TN, Zip 37604–2277; tel. 423/302–1000; Tony Benton, Chief Executive Officer

GRANVILLE HEALTH SYSTEM, 1010 College Street, Oxford, NC, Zip 27565–2507, Mailing Address: P.O. Box 947, Zip 27565–0947; tel. 919/690–3000; L. Lee Isley, Ph.D., FACHE, Chief Executive Officer

HALIFAX REGIONAL MEDICAL CENTER, 250 Smith Church Road, Roanoke Rapids, NC, Zip 27870–4914, Mailing Address: P.O. Box 1089, Zip 27870–1089; tel. 252/535–8011; William Mahone, President and Chief Executive Officer

HIGHLANDS–CASHIERS HOSPITAL, 190 Hospital Drive, Highlands, NC, Zip 28741–7600, Mailing Address: P.O. Drawer 190, Zip 28741–0190; tel. 828/526–1200; Craig B. James, FACHE, Chief Executive Officer

HIGHSMITH–RAINEY SPECIALTY HOSPITAL, 150 Robeson Street, Fayetteville, NC, Zip 28301–5570; tel. 910/615–1000; Kevin Jackson, On Site Administrator

INDIAN PATH MEDICAL CENTER, 2000 Brookside Drive, Kingsport, TN, Zip 37660–4627; tel. 423/857–7000; Monty E. McLaurin, President and Chief Executive Officer

IREDELL MEMORIAL HOSPITAL, 557 Brookdale Drive, Statesville, NC, Zip 28677–4107, Mailing Address: P.O. Box 1828, Zip 28687–1828; tel. 704/873–5661; Ed Rush, President and Chief Executive Officer

JOHNSON CITY MEDICAL CENTER, 400 North State of Franklin Road, Johnson City, TN, Zip 37604–6094; tel. 423/431–6111; David E. Nicely, Chief Executive Officer

JOHNSON COUNTY COMMUNITY HOSPITAL, 1901 South Shady Street, Mountain City, TN, Zip 37683–2271; tel. 423/727–1100; Lisa Heaton, Assistant Vice President/Administrator and Chief Nursing Officer

JOHNSTON MEMORIAL HOSPITAL, 16000 Johnston Memorial Drive, Abingdon, VA, Zip 24211–7659; tel. 276/676–7000; Sean S. McMurray, FACHE, Vice President and Chief Executive Officer

LAUGHLIN MEMORIAL HOSPITAL, 1420 Tusculum Boulevard, Greeneville, TN, Zip 37745–5825; tel. 423/787–5000; Charles H. Whitfield, Jr., President and Chief Executive Officer

LENOIR MEMORIAL HOSPITAL, 100 Airport Road, Kinston, NC, Zip 28501–1634, Mailing Address: P.O. Box 1678, Zip 28503–1678; tel. 252/522–7000; Gary E. Black, President and Chief Executive Officer

LEXINGTON MEDICAL CENTER, 2720 Sunset Boulevard, West Columbia, SC, Zip 29169–4810; tel. 803/791–2000; Michael J. Biediger, FACHE, President and Chief Executive Officer

MARGARET R. PARDEE MEMORIAL HOSPITAL, 800 North Justice Street, Hendersonville, NC, Zip 28791–3410; tel. 828/696–1000; James M. Kirby, II, President and Chief Executive Officer

MCDOWELL HOSPITAL, 430 Rankin Drive, Marion, NC, Zip 28752–6568, Mailing Address: P.O. Box 730, Zip 28752–0730; tel. 828/659–5000; Lynn Ingram Boggs, Chief Executive Officer

MCLEOD LORIS HEALTHCARE, 3655 Mitchell Street, Loris, SC, Zip 29569–2827; tel. 843/716–7000; Edward D. Tinsley, III, Chief Executive Officer

MCLEOD MEDICAL CENTER DILLON, 301 East Jackson Street, Dillon, SC, Zip 29536–2509, Mailing Address: P.O. Box 1327, Zip 29536–1327; tel. 843/774–4111; Deborah Locklair, FACHE, Administrator

MCLEOD REGIONAL MEDICAL CENTER, 555 East Cheves Street, Florence, SC, Zip 29506–2617, Mailing Address: P.O. Box 100551, Zip 29502–0551; tel. 843/777–2000; Robert L. Colones, President and Chief Executive Officer

MEADVILLE MEDICAL CENTER, 751 Liberty Street, Meadville, PA, Zip 16335–2559; tel. 814/333–5000; Philip Pandolph, Chief Executive Officer

MEDICAL CENTER AT BOWLING GREEN, 250 Park Street, Bowling Green, KY, Zip 42101–1795, Mailing Address: P.O. Box 90010, Zip 42102–9010; tel. 270/745–1000; Connie Smith, Chief Executive Officer

MEDICAL CENTER AT FRANKLIN, 1100 Brookhaven Road, Franklin, KY, Zip 42134–2746; tel. 270/598–4800; Eric Hagan, R.N., Vice President/Administrator

MEDICAL CENTER AT SCOTTSVILLE, 456 Burnley Road, Scottsville, KY, Zip 42164–6355; tel. 270/622–2800; Eric Hagan, R.N., Vice President/Administrator

MEDWEST – HARRIS, 68 Hospital Road, Sylva, NC, Zip 28779–2722; tel. 828/586–7000; Steve Heatherly, Chief Executive Officer

MEDWEST – HAYWOOD, 262 Leroy George Drive, Clyde, NC, Zip 28721–7430; tel. 828/456–7311; Janie Sinacore–Jaberg, R.N., MS, FACHE, Chief Executive Officer

MEDWEST – SWAIN, 45 Plateau Street, Bryson City, NC, Zip 28713–4200; tel. 828/488–2155; Steve Heatherly, Chief Executive Officer

MILLCREEK COMMUNITY HOSPITAL, 5515 Peach Street, Erie, PA, Zip 16509–2695; tel. 814/864–4031; Mary L. Eckert, President and Chief Executive Officer

MISSION HOSPITAL, 509 Biltmore Avenue, Asheville, NC, Zip 28801–4690; tel. 828/213–1111; Ronald A. Paulus, M.D., President and Chief Executive Officer

MURPHY MEDICAL CENTER, 3990 U.S. Highway 64 East Alt, Murphy, NC, Zip 28906–7917; tel. 828/837–8161; Michael Stevenson, Chief Executive Officer

NORTON COMMUNITY HOSPITAL, 100 15th Street N.W., Norton, VA, Zip 24273–1616; tel. 276/679–9600; Mark T. Leonard, Chief Executive Officer

OCONEE MEDICAL CENTER, 298 Memorial Drive, Seneca, SC, Zip 29672–9499; tel. 864/882–3351; Jeanne L. Ward, Ed.D., R.N., President and Chief Executive Officer

PARK RIDGE HEALTH, 100 Hospital Drive, Hendersonville, NC, Zip 28792–5272; tel. 828/684–8501; Jimm Bunch, President and Chief Executive Officer

RANDOLPH HOSPITAL, 364 White Oak Street, Asheboro, NC, Zip 27203–5400, Mailing Address: P.O. Box 1048, Zip 27204–1048; tel. 336/625–5151; Steven E. Eblin, Chief Executive Officer / President

RUSSELL COUNTY MEDICAL CENTER, 58 Carroll Street, Lebanon, VA, Zip 24266, Mailing Address: P.O. Box 3600, Zip 24266–0200; tel. 276/883–8000; Stephen K. Givens, Assistant Vice President and Administrator

RUTHERFORD REGIONAL HEALTH SYSTEM, 288 South Ridgecrest Avenue, Rutherfordton, NC, Zip 28139–2838; tel. 828/286–5000; Cindy D. Buck, Chief Executive Officer

SELF REGIONAL HEALTHCARE, 1325 Spring Street, Greenwood, SC, Zip 29646–3860; tel. 864/725–4111; James A. Pfeiffer, FACHE, President and Chief Executive Officer

SMYTH COUNTY COMMUNITY HOSPITAL, 245 Medical Park Drive, Marion, VA, Zip 24354, Mailing Address: P.O. Box 880, Zip 24354–0880; tel. 276/378–1000; Lindy P. White, President and Chief Executive Officer

SOUTHEAST ALABAMA MEDICAL CENTER, 1108 Ross Clark Circle, Dothan, AL, Zip 36301–3024, Mailing Address: P.O. Box 6987, Zip 36302–6987; tel. 334/793–8111; Ronald S. Owen, FACHE, Chief Executive Officer

SOUTHEASTERN HEALTH, 300 West 27th Street, Lumberton, NC, Zip 28358–3075, Mailing Address: P.O. Box 1408, Zip 28359–1408; tel. 910/671–5000; Joann Anderson, President and Chief Executive Officer

SPARTANBURG REGIONAL MEDICAL CENTER, 101 East Wood Street, Spartanburg, SC, Zip 29303–3040; tel. 864/560–6000; Bruce Holstien, President and Chief Executive Officer

ST. LUKE'S HOSPITAL, 101 Hospital Drive, Columbus, NC, Zip 28722–6418; tel. 828/894–3311; Kenneth A. Shull, FACHE, Chief Executive Officer

SYCAMORE SHOALS HOSPITAL, 1501 West Elk Avenue, Elizabethton, TN, Zip 37643–2874; tel. 423/542–1300; Dwayne Taylor, Chief Executive Officer

TITUSVILLE AREA HOSPITAL, 406 West Oak Street, Titusville, PA, Zip 16354–1404; tel. 814/827–1851; Anthony J. Nasralla, FACHE, President and Chief Executive Officer

TRANSYLVANIA REGIONAL HOSPITAL, 260 Hospital Drive, Brevard, NC, Zip 28712–3378; tel. 828/884–9111; Robert J. Bednarek, President and Chief Executive Officer

UNICOI COUNTY MEMORIAL HOSPITAL, 100 Greenway Circle, Erwin, TN, Zip 37650–2196, Mailing Address: P.O. Box 802, Zip 37650–0802; tel. 423/743–3141; Jim S. Pate, President and Chief Executive Officer

UNIVERSITY OF TENNESSEE MEDICAL CENTER, 1924 Alcoa Highway, Knoxville, TN, Zip 37920–6900; tel. 865/305–9000; Joseph Landsman, President and Chief Executive Officer

WATAUGA MEDICAL CENTER, 336 Deerfield Road, Boone, NC, Zip 28607–5008, Mailing Address: P.O. Box 2600, Zip 28607–2600; tel. 828/262–4100; Chuck Mantooth, President

WAYNE MEMORIAL HOSPITAL, 2700 Wayne Memorial Drive, Goldsboro, NC, Zip 27534–9494, Mailing Address: P.O. Box 8001, Zip 27533–8001; tel. 919/736–1110; J. William Paugh, FACHE, President and Chief Executive Officer

WILSON MEDICAL CENTER, 1705 Tarboro Street, S.W., Wilson, NC, Zip 27893–3428; tel. 252/399–8040; Richard E. Hudson, FACHE, President and Chief Executive Officer

## NORTH DAKOTA

**NORTHLAND HEALTHCARE ALLIANCE**
**3811 Lockport Street Suite 3, Bismarck, ND 58503–5554; tel. 701/250–0709; Timothy Cox, Director**

ASHLEY MEDICAL CENTER, 612 North Center Avenue, Ashley, ND, Zip 58413–7013, Mailing Address: P.O. Box 450, Zip 58413–0450; tel. 701/288–3433; Jerry Lepp, Chief Executive Officer

COMMUNITY MEMORIAL HOSPITAL, 220 Fifth Avenue, Turtle Lake, ND, Zip 58575–4005, Mailing Address: P.O. Box 280, Zip 58575–0280; tel. 701/448–2331; Tod Graeber, Administrator

GARRISON MEMORIAL HOSPITAL, 407 Third Avenue S.E., Garrison, ND, Zip 58540–7235; tel. 701/463–2275; Tod Graeber, Administrator

LINTON HOSPITAL, 518 North Broadway, Linton, ND, Zip 58552–7308, Mailing Address: P.O. Box 850, Zip 58552–0850; tel. 701/254–4511; Robert Black, Chief Executive Officer

MCKENZIE COUNTY HEALTHCARE SYSTEM, 516 North Main Street, Watford City, ND, Zip 58854–7310; tel. 701/842–3000; Daniel R. Kelly, Chief Executive Officer

MOBRIDGE REGIONAL HOSPITAL, 1401 Tenth Avenue West, Mobridge, SD, Zip 57601–1106, Mailing Address: P.O. Box 580, Zip 57601–0580; tel. 605/845–3692; Angelia K. Svihovec, Chief Executive Officer

PRESENTATION MEDICAL CENTER, 213 Second Avenue N.E., Rolla, ND, Zip 58367–7153, Mailing Address: P.O. Box 759, Zip 58367–0759; tel. 701/477–3161; Mark Kerr, Chief Executive Officer

SAKAKAWEA MEDICAL CENTER, 510 Eighth Avenue N.E., Hazen, ND, Zip 58545–4637; tel. 701/748–2225; Darrold Bertsch, Chief Executive Officer

SOUTHWEST HEALTHCARE SERVICES, 802 2nd Street Northwest, Bowman, ND, Zip 58623–4483, Mailing Address: P.O. Drawer C, Zip 58623; tel. 701/523–5265; Becky Hansen, Chief Executive Officer

ST. ALEXIUS MEDICAL CENTER, 900 East Broadway, Bismarck, ND, Zip 58501–4586, Mailing Address: P.O. Box 5510, Zip 58506–5510; tel. 701/530–7000; Gary P. Miller, President and Chief Executive Officer

ST. ALOISIUS MEDICAL CENTER, 325 East Brewster Street, Harvey, ND, Zip 58341–1653; tel. 701/324–4651; Rockford Zastoupil, President and Chief Executive Officer

ST. ANDREW'S HEALTH CENTER, 316 Ohmer Street, Bottineau, ND, Zip 58318–1045; tel. 701/228–9300; Jodi Atkinson, President and Chief Executive Officer

ST. JOSEPH'S HOSPITAL AND HEALTH CENTER, 30 Seventh Street West, Dickinson, ND, Zip 58601–4399; tel. 701/456–4000; Reed Reyman, President

WEST RIVER REGIONAL MEDICAL CENTER, 1000 Highway 12, Hettinger, ND, Zip 58639–7530; tel. 701/567–4561; James K. Long, CPA, Administrator and Chief Executive Officer

WISHEK COMMUNITY HOSPITAL AND CLINICS, 1007 Fourth Avenue South, Wishek, ND, Zip 58495–7527, Mailing Address: P.O. Box 647, Zip 58495–0647; tel. 701/452–2326; Mark Rinehardt, Chief Executive Officer

## OHIO

**CLEVELAND HEALTH NETWORK**
**6000 West Creek Road, Suite 20, Independence, OH 44131–2139; tel. 216/986–1100; Fred M. DeGrandis, President**

AKRON CHILDREN'S HOSPITAL, One Perkins Square, Akron, OH, Zip 44308–1062; tel. 330/543–1000; William H. Considine, President

ASHTABULA COUNTY MEDICAL CENTER, 2420 Lake Avenue, Ashtabula, OH, Zip 44004–4954; tel. 440/997–2262; Michael J. Habowski, President and Chief Executive Officer

CLEVELAND CLINIC, 9500 Euclid Avenue, Cleveland, OH, Zip 44195–5108; tel. 216/444–2200; Delos Cosgrove, M.D., President and Chief Executive Officer

CLEVELAND CLINIC CHILDREN'S HOSPITAL FOR REHABILITATION, 2801 Martin Luther King Jr. Drive, Cleveland, OH, Zip 44104–3865; tel. 216/448–6400; Michael J. McHugh, M.D., Medical Director

EMH ELYRIA MEDICAL CENTER, 630 East River Street, Elyria, OH, Zip 44035–5902; tel. 440/329–7500; Donald S. Sheldon, M.D., President and Chief Executive Officer

EUCLID HOSPITAL, 18901 Lake Shore Boulevard, Euclid, OH, Zip 44119–1090; tel. 216/531–9000; Mark Froimson, President

FAIRVIEW HOSPITAL, 18101 Lorain Avenue, Cleveland, OH, Zip 44111–5656; tel. 216/476–7000; Janice Murphy, President

FIRELANDS REGIONAL HEALTH SYSTEM, 1111 Hayes Avenue, Sandusky, OH, Zip 44870–3323; tel. 419/557–7400; Martin Tursky, President and Chief Executive Officer

FISHER–TITUS MEDICAL CENTER, 272 Benedict Avenue, Norwalk, OH, Zip 44857–2374; tel. 419/668–8101; Ross A. Matlack, FACHE, President and Chief Executive Officer

HILLCREST HOSPITAL, 6780 Mayfield Road, Cleveland, OH, Zip 44124–2203; tel. 440/312–4500; Jeffrey A. Leimgruber, President

LAKEWOOD HOSPITAL, 14519 Detroit Avenue, Lakewood, OH, Zip 44107–4383; tel. 216/521–4200; Robert Weil, M.D., President

LUTHERAN HOSPITAL, 1730 West 25th Street, Cleveland, OH, Zip 44113–3170; tel. 216/696–4300; Brian Donley, M.D., President

MARYMOUNT HOSPITAL, 12300 McCracken Road, Garfield Heights, OH, Zip 44125–2975; tel. 216/581–0500; Joanne Zeroske, President and Chief Executive Officer

METROHEALTH MEDICAL CENTER, 2500 MetroHealth Drive, Cleveland, OH, Zip 44109–1998; tel. 216/778–7800; Akram Boutros, M.D., FACHE, President and Chief Executive Officer

PARMA COMMUNITY GENERAL HOSPITAL, 7007 Powers Boulevard, Parma, OH, Zip 44129–5495; tel. 440/743–3000; Terrence G. Deis, President and Chief Executive Officer

ST. ELIZABETH HEALTH CENTER, 1044 Belmont Avenue, Youngstown, OH, Zip 44504–1096, Mailing Address: P.O. Box 1790, Zip 44501–1790; tel. 330/746–7211; Robert W. Shroder, President and Chief Executive Officer

ST. JOSEPH HEALTH CENTER, 667 Eastland Avenue S.E., Warren, OH, Zip 44484–4531; tel. 330/841–4000; Kathy Cook, R.N., MSN, Interim President

SUMMA BARBERTON CITIZENS HOSPITAL, 155 Fifth Street N.E., Barberton, OH, Zip 44203–3332; tel. 330/615–3000; Thomas DeBord, President

SUMMA HEALTH SYSTEM, 525 East Market Street, Akron, OH, Zip 44304–1619; tel. 330/375–3000; Thomas J. Strauss, President and Chief Executive Officer

SUMMA WADSWORTH–RITTMAN HOSPITAL, 195 Wadsworth Road, Wadsworth, OH, Zip 44281–9505; tel. 330/331–1000; Thomas DeBord, President

SUMMA WESTERN RESERVE HOSPITAL, 1900 23rd Street, Cuyahoga Falls, OH, Zip 44223–1499; tel. 330/971–7000; Robert Kent, D.O., President and Chief Executive Officer

**COMPREHENSIVE HEALTHCARE OF OHIO, INC.**
**630 East River Street, Elyria, OH 44035–5902; tel. 440/329–7700; Donald S. Sheldon, M.D., President and Chief Executive Officer**

EMH ELYRIA MEDICAL CENTER, 630 East River Street, Elyria, OH, Zip 44035–5902; tel. 440/329–7500; Donald S. Sheldon, M.D., President and Chief Executive Officer

**LAKE HEALTH**
**7590 Auburn Road, Concord Township, OH 44077–9176; tel. 440/375–8100; Cynthia Moore–Hardy, FACHE, President and Chief Executive Officer**

LAKE HEALTH, 7590 Auburn Road, Concord Township, OH, Zip 44077–9176; tel. 440/375–8100; Cynthia Moore–Hardy, FACHE, President and Chief Executive Officer

**MERCY HEALTH – SOUTHWEST OHIO**
**4600 McAuley Place, Cincinnati, OH 45242; tel. 513/981–6000; James May, President and Chief Executive Officer**

MERCY HEALTH – ANDERSON HOSPITAL, 7500 State Road, Cincinnati, OH, Zip 45255–2492; tel. 513/624–4500; Jeff Graham, Market Leader and President

MERCY HEALTH – CLERMONT HOSPITAL, 3000 Hospital Drive, Batavia, OH, Zip 45103–1921; tel. 513/732–8200; Jeff Graham, Market Leader and President

MERCY HEALTH – FAIRFIELD HOSPITAL, 3000 Mack Road, Fairfield, OH, Zip 45014–5335; tel. 513/870–7000; Thomas S. Urban, Market Leader and President

MERCY HEALTH – MT. AIRY HOSPITAL, 2446 Kipling Avenue, Cincinnati, OH, Zip 45239–6650; tel. 513/853–5000; Michael R. Stephens, Market Leader and President

MERCY HEALTH – WESTERN HILLS HOSPITAL, 3131 Queen City Avenue, Cincinnati, OH, Zip 45238–2396; tel. 513/389–5000; Michael R. Stephens, Market Leader and President

THE JEWISH HOSPITAL – MERCY HEALTH, 4777 East Galbraith Road, Cincinnati, OH, Zip 45236–2725; tel. 513/686–3000; Steve Holman, Market Leader and President

**OHIO STATE HEALTH NETWORK**
**660 Ackerman Road, Suite 601F, Columbus, OH 43202–4500; tel. 614/293–3785; Joann Ort, Executive Director**

BARNESVILLE HOSPITAL, 639 West Main Street, Barnesville, OH, Zip 43713–1039, Mailing Address: P.O. Box 309, Zip 43713–0309; tel. 740/425–3941; David D. Phillips, Chief Executive Officer and Administrator

MADISON COUNTY HOSPITAL, 210 North Main Street, London, OH, Zip 43140–1115; tel. 740/845–7000; Michael Browning, Interim Chief Executive Officer

MARY RUTAN HOSPITAL, 205 Palmer Avenue, Bellefontaine, OH, Zip 43311–2281; tel. 937/592–4015; Mandy C. Goble, President and Chief Executive Officer

MERCER HEALTH, 800 West Main Street, Coldwater, OH, Zip 45828–1698; tel. 419/678–2341; Lisa R. Klenke, R.N., Interim Chief Executive Officer

OHIO STATE UNIVERSITY WEXNER MEDICAL CENTER, 370 West 9th Avenue, Columbus, OH, Zip 43210–1238; tel. 614/293–8000; Steven Gabbe, M.D., Chief Executive Officer

TRINITY HOSPITAL TWIN CITY, 819 North First Street, Dennison, OH, Zip 44621–1098; tel. 740/922–2800; Joseph J. Mitchell, President

WILSON MEMORIAL HOSPITAL, 915 West Michigan Street, Sidney, OH, Zip 45365–2491; tel. 937/498–2311; Thomas J. Boecker, President and Chief Executive Officer

WYANDOT MEMORIAL HOSPITAL, 885 North Sandusky Avenue, Upper Sandusky, OH, Zip 43351–1098; tel. 419/294–4991; Joseph A. D'Ettorre, Chief Executive Officer

**PREMIER HEALTH PARTNERS**
**110 North Main Street, Suite 390, Dayton, OH 45402–3720; tel. 937/499–9401; James R. Pancoast, President and Chief Executive Officer**

ATRIUM MEDICAL CENTER, One Medical Center Drive, Middletown, OH, Zip 45005–1066; tel. 513/424–2111; Carol Turner, President and Chief Executive Officer

GOOD SAMARITAN HOSPITAL, 2222 Philadelphia Drive, Dayton, OH, Zip 45406–1813; tel. 937/734–2612; Eloise Broner, President and Chief Executive Officer

MIAMI VALLEY HOSPITAL, One Wyoming Street, Dayton, OH, Zip 45409–2793; tel. 937/208–8000; Bobbie Gerhart, President and Chief Executive Officer

UPPER VALLEY MEDICAL CENTER, 3130 North County Road 25A, Troy, OH, Zip 45373–1309; tel. 937/440–4000; Thomas Parker, Chief Executive Officer

**TRIHEALTH**
**619 Oak Street, Cincinnati, OH 45206; tel. 513/569–6507; John S. Prout, President and Chief Executive Officer**

BETHESDA NORTH HOSPITAL, 10500 Montgomery Road, Cincinnati, OH, Zip 45242–4402; tel. 513/865–1111; Barb Boyne, Executive Director, Operations

EVENDALE MEDICAL CENTER, 3155 Glendale Milford Road, Cincinnati, OH, Zip 45241–3134; tel. 513/454–2222; Kelvin Hanger, Chief Executive Officer

GOOD SAMARITAN HOSPITAL, 375 Dixmyth Avenue, Cincinnati, OH, Zip 45220–2489; tel. 513/862–1400; Jamie Easterling, Executive Director, Operations

## OKLAHOMA

**MERCY HEALTH SYSTEM OF OKLAHOMA**
**4300 West Memorial Road, Oklahoma City, OK 73120–8304; tel. 405/752–3756; Diane Smalley, President and Chief Executive Officer**

ARBUCKLE MEMORIAL HOSPITAL, 2011 West Broadway Street, Sulphur, OK, Zip 73086–4221; tel. 580/622–2161; Darin Farrell, Chief Executive Officer

KINGFISHER REGIONAL HOSPITAL, 1000 Kingfisher Regional Hospital Drive, Kingfisher, OK, Zip 73750–3528, Mailing Address: P.O. Box 59, Zip 73750–0059; tel. 405/375–3141; Bobby Stitt, R.N., Interim Chief Executive Officer

MERCY HEALTH LOVE COUNTY, 300 Wanda Street, Marietta, OK, Zip 73448–1200; tel. 580/276–3347; Richard Barker, Administrator

MERCY HOSPITAL ARDMORE, 1011 14th Avenue N.W., Ardmore, OK, Zip 73401–1828; tel. 580/223–5400; Daryle Voss, FACHE, President

MERCY HOSPITAL EL RENO, 2115 Parkview Drive, El Reno, OK, Zip 73036–2199, Mailing Address: P.O. Box 129, Zip 73036–0129; tel. 405/262–2640; Doug Danker, Administrator

MERCY HOSPITAL HEALDTON, 918 South 8th Street, Healdton, OK, Zip 73438–0928, Mailing Address: P.O. Box 928, Zip 73438–0928; tel. 580/229–0701; Jeremy A. Jones, Administrator

MERCY HOSPITAL OKLAHOMA CITY, 4300 West Memorial Road, Oklahoma City, OK, Zip 73120–8362; tel. 405/755–1515; Jim Gebhart, Jr., FACHE, President

MERCY HOSPITAL TISHOMINGO, 1000 South Byrd Street, Tishomingo, OK, Zip 73460–3299; tel. 580/371–2327; Gary Sharum, Administrator

OKLAHOMA HEART HOSPITAL, 4050 West Memorial Road, Oklahoma City, OK, Zip 73120–8382; tel. 405/608–3200; John Harvey, M.D., President and Chief Executive Officer

VALLEY VIEW REGIONAL HOSPITAL, 430 North Monta Vista, Ada, OK, Zip 74820–4610; tel. 580/332–2323; W. Kent Rogers, Chief Executive Officer

## OREGON

**HEALTH FUTURE, LLC**
**916 Town Centre Drive, Medford, OR 97504–6100; tel. 541/772–3062; Chris Chang–Howitz, Chief Executive Officer**

ASHLAND COMMUNITY HOSPITAL, 280 Maple Street, Ashland, OR, Zip 97520–1593; tel. 541/201–4000; Marvin Haas, Interim Chief Executive Officer

BAY AREA HOSPITAL, 1775 Thompson Road, Coos Bay, OR, Zip 97420–2198; tel. 541/269–8111; Paul Janke, FACHE, President and Chief Executive Officer

MID–COLUMBIA MEDICAL CENTER, 1700 East 19th Street, The Dalles, OR, Zip 97058–3317; tel. 541/296–1111; Duane Francis, President and Chief Executive Officer

OHSU HOSPITAL, 3181 S.W. Sam Jackson Park Road, Portland, OR, Zip 97239–3098; tel. 503/494–8311; Peter F. Rapp, Vice President and Executive Director

PIONEER MEMORIAL HOSPITAL, 1201 N.E. Elm Street, Prineville, OR, Zip 97754–1206; tel. 541/447–6254; Robert Gomes, Chief Executive Officer

SKY LAKES MEDICAL CENTER, 2865 Daggett Avenue, Klamath Falls, OR, Zip 97601–1106; tel. 541/882–6311; Paul R. Stewart, President and Chief Executive Officer

ST. CHARLES MEDICAL CENTER – BEND, 2500 N.E. Neff Road, Bend, OR, Zip 97701–6015; tel. 541/382–4321; Jay Henry, Chief Executive Officer

ST. CHARLES MEDICAL CENTER – REDMOND, 1253 N.W. Canal Boulevard, Redmond, OR, Zip 97756–1395; tel. 541/548–8131; Robert Gomes, Chief Executive Officer

## PENNSYLVANIA

**ALLEGHENY HEALTH NETWORK**
**120 Fifth Avenue, Suite 2901, Pittsburgh, PA 15222–3002; tel. 412/544–3075; John W. Paul, President and Chief Executive Officer**

ALLEGHENY GENERAL HOSPITAL, 320 East North Avenue, Pittsburgh, PA, Zip 15212–4756; tel. 412/359–3131; Judith F. Zedreck, R.N., Interim Chief Executive Officer

ALLEGHENY VALLEY HOSPITAL, 1301 Carlisle Street, Natrona Heights, PA, Zip 15065–1152; tel. 724/224–5100; Ned Laubacher, President and Chief Executive Officer

CANONSBURG GENERAL HOSPITAL, 100 Medical Boulevard, Canonsburg, PA, Zip 15317–9762; tel. 724/745–6100; Terry Wiltrout, Chief Executive Officer

FORBES REGIONAL HOSPITAL, 2570 Haymaker Road, Monroeville, PA, Zip 15146–3513; tel. 412/858–2000; Reese Jackson, President and Chief Executive Officer

JEFFERSON REGIONAL MEDICAL CENTER, 565 Coal Valley Road, Jefferson Hills, PA, Zip 15025–3703, Mailing Address: Box 18119, Pittsburgh, Zip 15236–0119; tel. 412/469–5000; John Dempster, President and Chief Executive Officer

SAINT VINCENT HEALTH CENTER, 232 West 25th Street, Erie, PA, Zip 16544–0002; tel. 814/452–5000; Scott Whalen, Ph.D., FACHE, President and Chief Executive Officer

WESTERN PENNSYLVANIA HOSPITAL, 4800 Friendship Avenue, Pittsburgh, PA, Zip 15224–1722; tel. 412/578–5000; Duke Rupert, President and Chief Executive Officer

**COMMONWEALTH HEALTH**
**575 North River Street, Wilkes Barre, PA 18764–0999; tel. 570/829–8111; Cornelio R. Catena, Chief Executive Officer**

BERWICK HOSPITAL CENTER, 701 East 16th Street, Berwick, PA, Zip 18603–2397; tel. 570/759–5000; Ronald R. Beer, Chief Executive Officer

FIRST HOSPITAL WYOMING VALLEY, 562 Wyoming Avenue, Kingston, PA, Zip 18704–3721; tel. 570/552–3900; Mark Schor, Chief Executive Officer

MID–VALLEY HOSPITAL, 1400 Main Street, Peckville, PA, Zip 18452–2009; tel. 570/383–5500; Ann Marie Stevens, Chief Executive Officer

MOSES TAYLOR HOSPITAL, 700 Quincy Avenue, Scranton, PA, Zip 18510–1724; tel. 570/340–2100; Justin Davis, Chief Executive Officer

REGIONAL HOSPITAL OF SCRANTON, 746 Jefferson Avenue, Scranton, PA, Zip 18510–1624; tel. 570/348–7100; Brooks Turkel, Chief Executive Officer

SPECIAL CARE HOSPITAL, 128 West Washington Street, Nanticoke, PA, Zip 18634–3113; tel. 570/735–5000; Robert D. Williams, Chief Executive Officer

TYLER MEMORIAL HOSPITAL, 880 State Road 6 West, Tunkhannock, PA, Zip 18657–6149; tel. 570/836–2161; Denise S. Gieski, MS, Chief Executive Officer

WILKES–BARRE GENERAL HOSPITAL, 575 North River Street, Wilkes–Barre, PA, Zip 18764–0001; tel. 570/829–8111; Cornelio R. Catena, President and Chief Executive Officer

**PENN HIGHLANDS HEALTHCARE**
**204 Hospital Avenue, Du Bois, PA 15801–1442; tel. 814/371–2200; Raymond A. Graeca, Chief Executive Officer**

BROOKVILLE HOSPITAL, 100 Hospital Road, Brookville, PA, Zip 15825–1367; tel. 814/849–2312; Rose Campbell, R.N., President

CLEARFIELD HOSPITAL, 809 Turnpike Avenue, Clearfield, PA, Zip 16830–1232, Mailing Address: P.O. Box 992, Zip 16830–0992; tel. 814/765–5341; Gary Macioce, President and Chief Executive Officer

DUBOIS REGIONAL MEDICAL CENTER, 100 Hospital Avenue, Du Bois, PA, Zip 15801–1440, Mailing Address: P.O. Box 447, Zip 15801–0447; tel. 814/371–2200; John Sutika, President

ELK REGIONAL HEALTH CENTER, 763 Johnsonburg Road, Saint Marys, PA, Zip 15857–3498; tel. 814/788–8000; Gregory P. Bauer, President and Chief Executive Officer

**VANTAGE HEALTHCARE NETWORK, INC.**
**18282 Technology Drive, Suite 202, Meadville, PA 16335; tel. 814/337–0000; David Petrarca, Director Retail Operations**

BRADFORD REGIONAL MEDICAL CENTER, 116 Interstate Parkway, Bradford, PA, Zip 16701–1036; tel. 814/368–4143; Timothy J. Finan, FACHE, President and Chief Executive Officer

BROOKVILLE HOSPITAL, 100 Hospital Road, Brookville, PA, Zip 15825–1367; tel. 814/849–2312; Rose Campbell, R.N., President

CLARION HOSPITAL, One Hospital Drive, Clarion, PA, Zip 16214–8501; tel. 814/226–9500; Byron Quinton, Chief Executive Officer

ELK REGIONAL HEALTH CENTER, 763 Johnsonburg Road, Saint Marys, PA, Zip 15857–3498; tel. 814/788–8000; Gregory P. Bauer, President and Chief Executive Officer

JAMESON HOSPITAL, 1211 Wilmington Avenue, New Castle, PA, Zip 16105–2516; tel. 724/658–9001; Douglas Danko, President and Chief Executive Officer

KANE COMMUNITY HOSPITAL, 4372 Route 6, Kane, PA, Zip 16735–3060; tel. 814/837–8585; J. Gary Rhodes, FACHE, Chief Executive Officer

MEADVILLE MEDICAL CENTER, 751 Liberty Street, Meadville, PA, Zip 16335–2559; tel. 814/333–5000; Philip Pandolph, Chief Executive Officer

PUNXSUTAWNEY AREA HOSPITAL, 81 Hillcrest Drive, Punxsutawney, PA, Zip 15767–2616; tel. 814/938–1800; Daniel D. Blough, Jr., Chief Executive Officer

TITUSVILLE AREA HOSPITAL, 406 West Oak Street, Titusville, PA, Zip 16354–1404; tel. 814/827–1851; Anthony J. Nasralla, FACHE, President and Chief Executive Officer

UPMC BEDFORD MEMORIAL, 10455 Lincoln Highway, Everett, PA, Zip 15537–7046; tel. 814/623–6161; Roger P. Winn, President

UPMC HAMOT, 201 State Street, Erie, PA, Zip 16550–0002; tel. 814/877–6000; V. James Fiorenzo, President

UPMC MCKEESPORT, 1500 Fifth Avenue, McKeesport, PA, Zip 15132–2422; tel. 412/664–2000; Cynthia M. Dorundo, President

UPMC NORTHWEST, 100 Fairfield Drive, Seneca, PA, Zip 16346–2130; tel. 814/676–7600; Jason Roeback, President

UPMC PASSAVANT, 9100 Babcock Boulevard, Pittsburgh, PA, Zip 15237–5815; tel. 412/367–6700; David T. Martin, President

UPMC ST. MARGARET, 815 Freeport Road, Pittsburgh, PA, Zip 15215–3301; tel. 412/784–4000; Teresa G. Petrick, President

WARREN GENERAL HOSPITAL, Two Crescent Park West, Warren, PA, Zip 16365–0068, Mailing Address: P.O. Box 68, Zip 16365–0068; tel. 814/723–4973; John P. Papalia, FACHE, Chief Executive Officer

## SOUTH DAKOTA

**REGIONAL HEALTH**
**353 Fairmont Boulevard, Rapid City, SD 57701–7375; tel. 605/719–1000; Charles E. Hart, M.D., MS, President and Chief Executive Officer**

CUSTER REGIONAL HOSPITAL, 1039 Montgomery Street, Custer, SD, Zip 57730–1397; tel. 605/673–2229; Veronica Schmidt, Chief Executive Officer

LEAD–DEADWOOD REGIONAL HOSPITAL, 61 Charles Street, Deadwood, SD, Zip 57732–1303; tel. 605/722–6101; Sherry Bea Smith, R.N., Chief Executive Officer

PHILIP HEALTH SERVICES, 503 West Pine Street, Philip, SD, Zip 57567–3300, Mailing Address: P.O. Box 790, Zip 57567–0790; tel. 605/859–2511; Kent Olson, Administrator and Chief Executive Officer

RAPID CITY REGIONAL HOSPITAL, 353 Fairmont Boulevard, Rapid City, SD, Zip 57701–7393, Mailing Address: P.O. Box 6000, Zip 57709–6000; tel. 605/719–1000; Timothy H. Sughrue, Chief Executive Officer

SAME DAY SURGERY CENTER, 651 Cathedral Drive, Rapid City, SD, Zip 57701–7368; tel. 605/719–5000; Doris Fritts, R.N., Executive Director

SPEARFISH REGIONAL HOSPITAL, 1440 North Main Street, Spearfish, SD, Zip 57783–1504; tel. 605/644–4000; Larry W. Veitz, Chief Executive Officer

SPEARFISH REGIONAL SURGERY CENTER, 1316 North 10th Street, Spearfish, SD, Zip 57783–1530; tel. 605/642–3113; Michael DeLano, Administrator

STURGIS REGIONAL HOSPITAL, 949 Harmon Street, Sturgis, SD, Zip 57785–2452; tel. 605/720–2400; Van D. Hyde, MS, Chief Executive Officer

WESTON COUNTY HEALTH SERVICES, 1124 Washington Boulevard, Newcastle, WY, Zip 82701–2972; tel. 307/746–4491; Maureen K. Cadwell, Chief Executive Officer

## TENNESSEE

**TRISTAR HEALTH**
**110 Winners Circle, First Floor, Brentwood, TN 37027–5070; tel. 615/886–4900; Stephen Corbeil, President**

CARTERSVILLE MEDICAL CENTER, 960 Joe Frank Harris Parkway, Cartersville, GA, Zip 30120–2129; tel. 770/382–1530; Keith Sandlin, Chief Executive Officer

EASTSIDE MEDICAL CENTER, 1700 Medical Way, Snellville, GA, Zip 30078–2195; tel. 770/979–0200; Kimberly Ryan, Chief Executive Officer

REDMOND REGIONAL MEDICAL CENTER, 501 Redmond Road, Rome, GA, Zip 30165–1415, Mailing Address: P.O. Box 107001, Zip 30162–7001; tel. 706/291–0291; John Quinlivan, Chief Executive Officer

TRISTAR ASHLAND CITY, 313 North Main Street, Ashland City, TN, Zip 37015–1347; tel. 615/792–3030; Darrell White, R.N., Administrator/Chief Nursing Officer

TRISTAR CENTENNIAL MEDICAL CENTER, 2300 Patterson Street, Nashville, TN, Zip 37203–1528; tel. 615/342–1000; Heather J. Rohan, Chief Executive Officer

TRISTAR GREENVIEW REGIONAL HOSPITAL, 1801 Ashley Circle, Bowling Green, KY, Zip 42104–3362; tel. 270/793–1000; Anne Leonard, R.N., Interim Chief Executive Officer

TRISTAR HENDERSONVILLE MEDICAL CENTER, 355 New Shackle Island Road, Hendersonville, TN, Zip 37075–2479; tel. 615/338–1000; Regina Bartlett, Chief Executive Officer

TRISTAR HORIZON MEDICAL CENTER, 111 Highway 70 East, Dickson, TN, Zip 37055–2080; tel. 615/446–0446; John A. Marshall, Chief Executive Officer

TRISTAR SKYLINE MEDICAL CENTER, 3441 Dickerson Pike, Nashville, TN, Zip 37207–2539; tel. 615/769–2000; Steve Otto, Chief Executive Officer

TRISTAR SKYLING MADISON CAMPUS, 500 Hospital Drive, Madison, TN Zip 37115–5032; tel. 615/769–5000; Steve Otto, Chief Executive Officer

TRISTAR SOUTHERN HILLS MEDICAL CENTER, 391 Wallace Road, Nashville, TN, Zip 37211–4859; tel. 615/781–4000; Thomas H. Ozburn, Chief Executive Officer

TRISTAR STONECREST MEDICAL CENTER, 200 StoneCrest Boulevard, Smyrna, TN, Zip 37167–6810; tel. 615/768–2000; Mark E. Sims, Chief Executive Officer

TRISTAR SUMMIT MEDICAL CENTER, 5655 Frist Boulevard, Hermitage, TN, Zip 37076–2053; tel. 615/316–3000; Jeffrey T. Whitehorn, Chief Executive Officer

## TEXAS

**REGIONAL HEALTHCARE ALLIANCE**
**530 South Beckham Avenue, Tyler, TX 75702–8310; tel. 903/531–4449; John Webb, President**

ALLEGIANCE SPECIALTY HOSPITAL OF KILGORE, 1612 South Henderson Boulevard, Kilgore, TX, Zip 75662–3594; tel. 903/984–3505; Sherry Bustin, Chief Executive Officer

ATLANTA MEMORIAL HOSPITAL, 1007 South William Street, Atlanta, TX, Zip 75551–3245; tel. 903/799–3000; Deborah Robison, R.N., Chief Executive Officer and Administrator

BAYLOR UNIVERSITY MEDICAL CENTER, 3500 Gaston Avenue, Dallas, TX, Zip 75246–2088; tel. 214/820–0111; John B. McWhorter, III, President

CHILDREN'S MEDICAL CENTER OF DALLAS, 1935 Medical District Drive, Dallas, TX, Zip 75235; tel. 214/456–7000; Christopher J. Durovich, President and Chief Executive Officer

COZBY–GERMANY HOSPITAL, 707 North Waldrip Street, Grand Saline, TX, Zip 75140–1555; tel. 903/962–4242; Laura Wiggins, Chief Executive Officer

EAST TEXAS MEDICAL CENTER HENDERSON, 300 Wilson Street, Henderson, TX, Zip 75652–5956; tel. 903/657–7541; Mark Leitner, Chief Executive Officer

GOOD SHEPHERD MEDICAL CENTER, 700 East Marshall Avenue, Longview, TX, Zip 75601–5580; tel. 903/315–2000; Kenneth C. Cunningham, Interim Chief Executive Officer

GOOD SHEPHERD MEDICAL CENTER–LINDEN, 404 North Kaufman Street, Linden, TX, Zip 75563–5234; tel. 903/756–5561; Carla Roadcap, R.N., MSN, Chief Executive Officer

HOPKINS COUNTY MEMORIAL HOSPITAL, 115 Airport Road, Sulphur Springs, TX, Zip 75482–2105; tel. 903/885–7671; Michael McAndrew, Chief Executive Officer

MOTHER FRANCES HOSPITAL – JACKSONVILLE, 2026 South Jackson, Jacksonville, TX, Zip 75766–5822; tel. 903/541–4500; Thomas N. Cammack, Jr., Chief Administrative Officer

MOTHER FRANCES HOSPITAL – TYLER, 800 East Dawson Street, Tyler, TX, Zip 75701–2036; tel. 903/593–8441; Laura Owen, Senior Vice President and Chief Executive Officer

NACOGDOCHES MEDICAL CENTER, 4920 N.E. Stallings Drive, Nacogdoches, TX, Zip 75965–1200; tel. 936/569–9481; Gary L. Stokes, Chief Executive Officer

PALESTINE REGIONAL MEDICAL CENTER–EAST, 2900 South Loop 256, Palestine, TX, Zip 75801–6958; tel. 903/731–1000; Alan E. George, Chief Executive Officer

PARIS REGIONAL MEDICAL CENTER, 820 Clarksville Street, Paris, TX, Zip 75460–6027, Mailing Address: P.O. Box 9070, Zip 75461–9070; tel. 903/785–4521; Stephen Grubbs, Chief Executive Officer

TITUS REGIONAL MEDICAL CENTER, 2001 North Jefferson Avenue, Mount Pleasant, TX, Zip 75455–2398; tel. 903/577–6000; Ronald D. Davis, Chief Executive Officer

TRINITY MOTHER FRANCES REHABILITATION HOSPITAL, 3131 Troup Highway, Tyler, TX, Zip 75701–8352; tel. 903/510–7000; Sharla Anderson, Chief Executive Officer

TYLER CONTINUECARE HOSPITAL AT MOTHER FRANCES, 800 East Dawson, 4th Floor, Tyler, TX, Zip 75701–2036; tel. 903/531–4080; Stephanie Hyde, Chief Executive Officer

UNIVERSITY OF TEXAS HEALTH SCIENCE CENTER AT TYLER, 11937 Highway 271, Tyler, TX, Zip 75708–3154; tel. 903/877–7777; Kirk A. Calhoun, M.D., President

**ST. DAVID'S HEALTH NETWORK**
**98 San Jacinto Boulevard, Austin, TX 78701–4082; tel. 512/708–9700; C. David Huffstutler, President and Chief Executive Officer**

AUSTIN LAKES HOSPITAL, 1025 East 32nd Street, Austin, TX, Zip 78705–2714; tel. 512/544–5253; Jennifer Miller, Chief Executive Officer

ST. DAVID'S MEDICAL CENTER, 919 East 32nd Street, Austin, TX, Zip 78705–2709, Mailing Address: P.O. Box 4039, Zip 78765–4039; tel. 512/476–7111; Donald H. Wilkerson, Chief Executive Officer

ST. DAVID'S NORTH AUSTIN MEDICAL CENTER, 12221 North MoPac Expressway, Austin, TX, Zip 78758–2496; tel. 512/901–1000; Allen Harrison, Chief Executive Officer

ST. DAVID'S REHABILITATION CENTER, 1005 East 32nd Street, Austin, TX, Zip 78705–2713, Mailing Address: P.O. Box 4270, Zip 78765–4270; tel. 512/544–5100; Diane Owens, Administrator

ST. DAVID'S ROUND ROCK MEDICAL CENTER, 2400 Round Rock Avenue, Round Rock, TX, Zip 78681–4097; tel. 512/341–1000; Deborah L. Ryle, Administrator and Chief Executive Officer

ST. DAVID'S SOUTH AUSTIN MEDICAL CENTER, 901 West Ben White Boulevard, Austin, TX, Zip 78704–6903; tel. 512/447–2211; Todd E. Steward, Chief Executive Officer

## VIRGINIA

**CENTRAL VIRGINIA HEALTH NETWORK**
**2201 West Broad Street, Suite 202, Richmond, VA 23220–2022; tel. 804/359–4500; Michael Matthews, Chief Executive Officer**

BON SECOURS MARYVIEW MEDICAL CENTER, 3636 High Street, Portsmouth, VA, Zip 23707–3270; tel. 757/398–2200; Joseph M. Oddis, Chief Executive Officer

BON SECOURS MEMORIAL REGIONAL MEDICAL CENTER, 8260 Atlee Road, Mechanicsville, VA, Zip 23116–1844; tel. 804/764–6000; Michael Robinson, Chief Executive Officer

BON SECOURS ST. FRANCIS MEDICAL CENTER, 13710 St. Francis Boulevard, Midlothian, VA, Zip 23114–3267; tel. 804/594–7300; Mark M. Gordon, Executive Vice President

BON SECOURS ST. MARY'S HOSPITAL, 5801 Bremo Road, Richmond, VA, Zip 23226–1907; tel. 804/285–2011; Toni R. Ardabell, R.N., Chief Executive Officer

BON SECOURS–DEPAUL MEDICAL CENTER, 150 Kingsley Lane, Norfolk, VA, Zip 23505–4650; tel. 757/889–5000; John E. Barrett, III, Chief Executive Officer

BON SECOURS–RICHMOND COMMUNITY HOSPITAL, 1500 North 28th Street, Richmond, VA, Zip 23223–5396, Mailing Address: P.O. Box 27184, Zip 23261–7184; tel. 804/225–1700; Michael Robinson, Executive Vice President and Administrator

CENTRA SOUTHSIDE COMMUNITY HOSPITAL, 800 Oak Street, Farmville, VA, Zip 23901–1199; tel. 434/392–8811; William L. Bass, Jr., Vice President and Chief Executive Officer

COMMUNITY MEMORIAL HEALTHCENTER, 125 Buena Vista Circle, South Hill, VA, Zip 23970–1431, Mailing Address: P.O. Box 90, Zip 23970–0090; tel. 434/447–3151; W. Scott Burnette, President and Chief Executive Officer

MARY IMMACULATE HOSPITAL, 2 Bernardine Drive, Newport News, VA, Zip 23602–4499; tel. 757/886–6000; Patricia L. Robertson, Executive Vice President

RAPPAHANNOCK GENERAL HOSPITAL, 101 Harris Drive, Kilmarnock, VA, Zip 22482–3880, Mailing Address: P.O. Box 1449, Zip 22482–1449; tel. 804/435–8000; James M. Holmes, Jr., President and Chief Executive Officer

SHELTERING ARMS REHABILITATION HOSPITAL, 8254 Atlee Road, Mechanicsville, VA, Zip 23116–1844; tel. 804/764–7055; James E. Sok, FACHE, President and Chief Executive Officer

UNIVERSITY OF VIRGINIA MEDICAL CENTER, 1215 Lee Street, Charlottesville, VA, Zip 22908–0001, Mailing Address: P.O. Box 800809, Zip 22908–0809; tel. 434/924–0211; R. Edward Howell, Vice President and Chief Executive Officer

**VIRGINIA HEALTH NETWORK**
**7400 Beaufont Springs Drive, Suite 505, Richmond, VA 23225–5521; tel. 804/320–3837; James Brittain, President**

AUGUSTA HEALTH, 78 Medical Center Drive, Fishersville, VA, Zip 22939–2332, Mailing Address: P.O. Box 1000, Zip 22939–1000; tel. 540/932–4000; Mary N. Mannix, FACHE, President and Chief Executive Officer

BATH COMMUNITY HOSPITAL, 83 Park Drive, Hot Springs, VA, Zip 24445–2788, Mailing Address: P.O. Box Z., Zip 24445–0750; tel. 540/839–7000; Jason Paret, Chief Executive Officer

BEDFORD MEMORIAL HOSPITAL, 1613 Oakwood Street, Bedford, VA, Zip 24523–1213, Mailing Address: P.O. Box 688, Zip 24523–0688; tel. 540/586–2441; Patti Jurkus, Vice President, Regional Hospital

BON SECOURS MARYVIEW MEDICAL CENTER, 3636 High Street, Portsmouth, VA, Zip 23707–3270; tel. 757/398–2200; Joseph M. Oddis, Chief Executive Officer

BON SECOURS MEMORIAL REGIONAL MEDICAL CENTER, 8260 Atlee Road, Mechanicsville, VA, Zip 23116–1844; tel. 804/764–6000; Michael Robinson, Chief Executive Officer

BON SECOURS ST. FRANCIS MEDICAL CENTER, 13710 St. Francis Boulevard, Midlothian, VA, Zip 23114–3267; tel. 804/594–7300; Mark M. Gordon, Executive Vice President

BON SECOURS ST. MARY'S HOSPITAL, 5801 Bremo Road, Richmond, VA, Zip 23226–1907; tel. 804/285–2011; Toni R. Ardabell, R.N., Chief Executive Officer

BON SECOURS–DEPAUL MEDICAL CENTER, 150 Kingsley Lane, Norfolk, VA, Zip 23505–4650; tel. 757/889–5000; John E. Barrett, III, Chief Executive Officer

BON SECOURS–RICHMOND COMMUNITY HOSPITAL, 1500 North 28th Street, Richmond, VA, Zip 23223–5396, Mailing Address: P.O. Box 27184, Zip 23261–7184; tel. 804/225–1700; Michael Robinson, Executive Vice President and Administrator

BUCHANAN GENERAL HOSPITAL, 1535 Slate Creek Road, Grundy, VA, Zip 24614–6974; tel. 276/935–1000; Robert D. Ruchti, Chief Executive Officer

CARILION FRANKLIN MEMORIAL HOSPITAL, 180 Floyd Avenue, Rocky Mount, VA, Zip 24151–1389; tel. 540/483–5277; William D. Jacobsen, Vice President, Regional Hospital

CARILION GILES COMMUNITY HOSPITAL, 159 Hartley Way, Pearisburg, VA, Zip 24134–2471; tel. 540/921–6000; James E. Tyler, Vice President, Regional Hospital

CARILION MEDICAL CENTER, Belleview at Jefferson Street, Roanoke, VA, Zip 24014, Mailing Address: P.O. Box 13367, Zip 24033–3367; tel. 540/981–7000; Nancy Howell Agee, President and Chief Executive Officer

CARILION NEW RIVER VALLEY MEDICAL CENTER, 2900 Lamb Circle, Christiansburg, VA, Zip 24073–6344, Mailing Address: P.O. Box 5, Radford, Zip 24143–0005; tel. 540/731–2000; John S. Piatkowski, M.D., Vice President, Regional Hospital

CARILION STONEWALL JACKSON HOSPITAL, 1 Health Circle, Lexington, VA, Zip 24450–2492; tel. 540/458–3300; Charles E. Carr, Vice President, Regional Hospital

CARILION TAZEWELL COMMUNITY HOSPITAL, 141 Ben Bolt Avenue, Tazewell, VA, Zip 24651–9700; tel. 276/988–8700; John S. Piatkowski, M.D., Vice President, Regional Hospital

CENTRA SOUTHSIDE COMMUNITY HOSPITAL, 800 Oak Street, Farmville, VA, Zip 23901–1199; tel. 434/392–8811; William L. Bass, Jr., Vice President and Chief Executive Officer

CHESAPEAKE REGIONAL MEDICAL CENTER, 736 Battlefield Boulevard North, Chesapeake, VA, Zip 23320–4941, Mailing Address: P.O. Box 2028, Zip 23327–2028; tel. 757/312–8121; Peter F. Bastone, Chief Executive Officer

CHILDREN'S HOSPITAL OF RICHMOND AT VCU–BROOK ROAD CAMPUS, 2924 Brook Road, Richmond, VA, Zip 23220–1298; tel. 804/321–7474; Leslie G. Wyatt, Senior Vice President Children's Services and Executive Director

CHILDREN'S HOSPITAL OF THE KING'S DAUGHTERS, 601 Children's Lane, Norfolk, VA, Zip 23507–1910; tel. 757/668–7000; James D. Dahling, President and Chief Executive Officer

CJW MEDICAL CENTER, 7101 Jahnke Road, Richmond, VA, Zip 23225-4044; tel. 804/320-3911; Tim McManus, Interim Chief Executive Officer

CLINCH VALLEY MEDICAL CENTER, 6801 Governor G. C. Peery Highway, Richlands, VA, Zip 24641-2194; tel. 276/596-6000; Peter Mulkey, Interim Chief Executive Officer

COMMUNITY MEMORIAL HEALTHCENTER, 125 Buena Vista Circle, South Hill, VA, Zip 23970-1431, Mailing Address: P.O. Box 90, Zip 23970-0090; tel. 434/447-3151; W. Scott Burnette, President and Chief Executive Officer

CULPEPER REGIONAL HOSPITAL, 501 Sunset Lane, Culpeper, VA, Zip 22701-3917, Mailing Address: P.O. Box 592, Zip 22701-0500; tel. 540/829-4100; H. Lee Kirk, Jr., FACHE, President and Chief Executive Officer

DOMINION HOSPITAL, 2960 Sleepy Hollow Road, Falls Church, VA, Zip 22044-2030; tel. 703/536-2000; Cynthia A. Meyer, Interim Chief Executive Officer

FAUQUIER HOSPITAL, 500 Hospital Drive, Warrenton, VA, Zip 20186-3099; tel. 540/316-5000; Rodger H. Baker, President and Chief Executive Officer

HEALTHSOUTH REHABILITATION HOSPITAL OF VIRGINIA, 5700 Fitzhugh Avenue, Richmond, VA, Zip 23226-1800; tel. 804/288-5700; Tonya Ferguson, Interim Chief Executive Officer

HENRICO DOCTORS' HOSPITAL, 1602 Skipwith Road, Richmond, VA, Zip 23229-5205; tel. 804/289-4500; Lisa R. Valentine, Interim Chief Executive Officer

INOVA ALEXANDRIA HOSPITAL, 4320 Seminary Road, Alexandria, VA, Zip 22304-1535; tel. 703/504-3167; Christine Candio, Chief Executive Officer

INOVA FAIR OAKS HOSPITAL, 3600 Joseph Siewick Drive, Fairfax, VA, Zip 22033-1798; tel. 703/391-3600; John L. Fitzgerald, Chief Executive Officer

INOVA FAIRFAX HOSPITAL, 3300 Gallows Road, Falls Church, VA, Zip 22042-3300; tel. 703/776-4001; Patrick Christiansen, Ph.D., Chief Executive Officer

INOVA LOUDOUN HOSPITAL, 44045 Riverside Parkway, Leesburg, VA, Zip 20176-5101, Mailing Address: P.O. Box 6000, Zip 20177-0600; tel. 703/858-6000; Patrick Walters, Interim Chief Executive Officer

INOVA MOUNT VERNON HOSPITAL, 2501 Parker's Lane, Alexandria, VA, Zip 22306-3209; tel. 703/664-7000; Barbara J. Doyle, R.N., MS, Senior Vice President and Chief Executive Officer

JOHN RANDOLPH MEDICAL CENTER, 411 West Randolph Road, Hopewell, VA, Zip 23860-2938; tel. 804/541-1600; Suzanne B. Jackson, FACHE, Chief Executive Officer

JOHNSTON MEMORIAL HOSPITAL, 16000 Johnston Memorial Drive, Abingdon, VA, Zip 24211-7659; tel. 276/676-7000; Sean S. McMurray, FACHE, Vice President and Chief Executive Officer

LEWISGALE HOSPITAL ALLEGHANY, One ARH Lane, Low Moor, VA, Zip 24457, Mailing Address: P.O. Box 7, Zip 24457-0007; tel. 540/862-6011; Greg T. Madsen, Chief Executive Officer

LEWISGALE HOSPITAL AT PULASKI, 2400 Lee Highway, Pulaski, VA, Zip 24301-2326, Mailing Address: P.O. Box 759, Zip 24301-0759; tel. 540/994-8100; Mark Nichols, FACHE, Chief Executive Officer

MARTHA JEFFERSON HOSPITAL, 500 Martha Jefferson Drive, Charlottesville, VA, Zip 22911-4668; tel. 434/654-7000; James E. Haden, President and Chief Executive Officer

MARY IMMACULATE HOSPITAL, 2 Bernardine Drive, Newport News, VA, Zip 23602-4499; tel. 757/886-6000; Patricia L. Robertson, Executive Vice President

MARY WASHINGTON HOSPITAL, 1001 Sam Perry Boulevard, Fredericksburg, VA, Zip 22401-3354; tel. 540/741-1100; Fred M. Rankin, III, President and Chief Executive Officer

MEMORIAL HOSPITAL, 320 Hospital Drive, Martinsville, VA, Zip 24112-1981, Mailing Address: P.O. Box 4788, Zip 24115-4788; tel. 276/666-7200; Grady W. Philips, III, Chief Executive Officer

MOUNTAIN VIEW REGIONAL MEDICAL CENTER, 310 Third Street N.E., Norton, VA, Zip 24273-1137; tel. 276/679-9100; Fred L. Pelle, FACHE, Interim President and Chief Executive Officer

NORTHERN HOSPITAL OF SURRY COUNTY, 830 Rockford Street, Mount Airy, NC, Zip 27030-5365, Mailing Address: P.O. Box 1101, Zip 27030-1101; tel. 336/719-7000; William B. James, FACHE, Chief Executive Officer

PIONEER COMMUNITY HOSPITAL OF PATRICK COUNTY, 18688 Jeb Stuart Highway, Stuart, VA, Zip 24171-1559; tel. 276/694-3151; Jeanette Filpi, Chief Executive Officer

PRINCE WILLIAM HOSPITAL, 8700 Sudley Road, Manassas, VA, Zip 20110-4418, Mailing Address: P.O. Box 2610, Zip 20108-0867; tel. 703/369-8000; Melissa Robson, President

RAPPAHANNOCK GENERAL HOSPITAL, 101 Harris Drive, Kilmarnock, VA, Zip 22482-3880, Mailing Address: P.O. Box 1449, Zip 22482-1449; tel. 804/435-8000; James M. Holmes, Jr., President and Chief Executive Officer

RESTON HOSPITAL CENTER, 1850 Town Center Parkway, Reston, VA, Zip 20190-3219; tel. 703/689-9000; John A. Deardorff, Chief Executive Officer

RIVERSIDE BEHAVIORAL HEALTH CENTER, 2244 Executive Drive, Hampton, VA, Zip 23666-2430; tel. 757/827-1001; Debra Campbell, R.N., Administrator

RIVERSIDE REGIONAL MEDICAL CENTER, 500 J. Clyde Morris Boulevard, Newport News, VA, Zip 23601-1929; tel. 757/594-2000; Patrick Parcells, Senior Vice President and Administrator

RIVERSIDE REHABILITATION INSTITUTE, 245 Chesapeake Avenue, Newport News, VA, Zip 23607-6038; tel. 757/928-8000; Edward Heckler, Administrator

RIVERSIDE SHORE MEMORIAL HOSPITAL, 9507 Hospital Avenue, Nassawadox, VA, Zip 23413-1821, Mailing Address: P.O. Box 17, Zip 23413-0017; tel. 757/414-8000; Susan McAndrews, R.N., Administrator

RIVERSIDE TAPPAHANNOCK HOSPITAL, 618 Hospital Road, Tappahannock, VA, Zip 22560-5000; tel. 804/443-3311; Elizabeth J. Martin, Vice President and Administrator

RIVERSIDE WALTER REED HOSPITAL, 7519 Hospital Drive, Gloucester, VA, Zip 23061-4178, Mailing Address: P.O. Box 1130, Zip 23061-1130; tel. 804/693-8800; Megan Kleckner, Vice President and Administrator

RUSSELL COUNTY MEDICAL CENTER, 58 Carroll Street, Lebanon, VA, Zip 24266, Mailing Address: P.O. Box 3600, Zip 24266-0200; tel. 276/883-8000; Stephen K. Givens, Assistant Vice President and Administrator

SENTARA CAREPLEX HOSPITAL, 3000 Coliseum Drive, Hampton, VA, Zip 23666-5963; tel. 757/736-1000; Debra A. Flores, R.N., MS, President and Administrator

SENTARA LEIGH HOSPITAL, 830 Kempsville Road, Norfolk, VA, Zip 23502-3920; tel. 757/261-6000; Teresa L. Edwards, Vice President and Administrator

SENTARA NORFOLK GENERAL HOSPITAL, 600 Gresham Drive, Norfolk, VA, Zip 23507-1904; tel. 757/388-3000; Kurt T. Hofelich, President

SENTARA NORTHERN VIRGINIA MEDICAL CENTER, 2300 Opitz Boulevard, Woodbridge, VA, Zip 22191-3399; tel. 703/523-1000; Megan R. Perry, Corporate Vice President and President

SENTARA OBICI HOSPITAL, 2800 Godwin Boulevard, Suffolk, VA, Zip 23434-8038; tel. 757/934-4000; Steve Julian, M.D., President

SENTARA PRINCESS ANNE HOSPITAL, 2025 Glenn Mitchell Drive, Virginia Beach, VA, Zip 23456-0178; tel. 757/507-1000; Stephen D. Porter, President

SENTARA VIRGINIA BEACH GENERAL HOSPITAL, 1060 First Colonial Road, Virginia Beach, VA, Zip 23454-3002; tel. 757/395-8000; Elwood Bernard Boone, III, FACHE, President

SENTARA WILLIAMSBURG REGIONAL MEDICAL CENTER, 100 Sentara Circle, Williamsburg, VA, Zip 23188-5713; tel. 757/984-6000; Robert L. Graves, President

SHELTERING ARMS REHABILITATION HOSPITAL, 8254 Atlee Road, Mechanicsville, VA, Zip 23116-1844; tel. 804/764-7055; James E. Sok, FACHE, President and Chief Executive Officer

SMYTH COUNTY COMMUNITY HOSPITAL, 245 Medical Park Drive, Marion, VA, Zip 24354, Mailing Address: P.O. Box 880, Zip 24354-0880; tel. 276/378-1000; Lindy P. White, President and Chief Executive Officer

SOUTHAMPTON MEMORIAL HOSPITAL, 100 Fairview Drive, Franklin, VA, Zip 23851-1238, Mailing Address: P.O. Box 817, Zip 23851-0817; tel. 757/569-6100; Phil A. Wright, II, Chief Executive Officer

SOUTHERN VIRGINIA REGIONAL MEDICAL CENTER, 727 North Main Street, Emporia, VA, Zip 23847-1274; tel. 434/348-4400; Eric Lachance, Chief Executive Officer

SOUTHSIDE REGIONAL MEDICAL CENTER, 200 Medical Park Boulevard, Petersburg, VA, Zip 23805-9274; tel. 804/765-5000; Michael Yungmann, Chief Executive Officer

TWIN COUNTY REGIONAL HOSPITAL, 200 Hospital Drive, Galax, VA, Zip 24333-2227; tel. 276/236-8181; Jon D. Applebaum, Chief Executive Officer

UNIVERSITY OF VIRGINIA MEDICAL CENTER, 1215 Lee Street, Charlottesville, VA, Zip 22908-0001, Mailing Address: P.O. Box 800809, Zip 22908-0809; tel. 434/924-0211; R. Edward Howell, Vice President and Chief Executive Officer

UVA-HEALTHSOUTH REHABILITATION HOSPITAL, 515 Ray C. Hunt Drive, Charlottesville, VA, Zip 22903-2981; tel. 434/244-2000; Thomas J. Cook, Chief Executive Officer

VCU HEALTH SYSTEM, 1250 East Marshall Street, Richmond, VA, Zip 23298-5051, Mailing Address: P.O. Box 980510, Zip 23298-0510; tel. 804/828-9000; John Duval, Chief Executive Officer

VIRGINIA HOSPITAL CENTER - ARLINGTON, 1701 North George Mason Drive, Arlington, VA, Zip 22205-3698; tel. 703/558-5000; James B. Cole, Chief Executive Officer

WYTHE COUNTY COMMUNITY HOSPITAL, 600 West Ridge Road, Wytheville, VA, Zip 24382-1099; tel. 276/228-0200; Timothy A. Bess, Chief Executive Officer

## WASHINGTON

### GROUP HEALTH COOPERATIVE
**320 Westlake Avenue North, Suite 100, Seattle, WA 98109-5233; tel. 206/448-5083; Scott Armstrong, Chief Executive Officer**

CASCADE VALLEY HOSPITAL AND CLINICS, 330 South Stillaguamish Avenue, Arlington, WA, Zip 98223-1642; tel. 360/435-2133; W. Clark Jones, Administrator

DAYTON GENERAL HOSPITAL, 1012 South Third Street, Dayton, WA, Zip 99328-1696; tel. 509/382-2531; Dale E. Polla, Chief Executive Officer

DEACONESS HOSPITAL, 800 West Fifth Avenue, Spokane, WA, Zip 99204-2803, Mailing Address: P.O. Box 248, Zip 99210-0248; tel. 509/458-5800; Rodney Schumacher, Interim Chief Executive Officer

GROUP HEALTH COOPERATIVE CENTRAL HOSPITAL, 201 16th Avenue East, Seattle, WA, Zip 98112-5226; tel. 206/326-6300; Jane Hutcheson, Administrator and Director Clinical Operations

Section B

HARRISON MEDICAL CENTER, 2520 Cherry Avenue, Bremerton, WA, Zip 98310–4229; tel. 360/744–3911; Scott W. Bosch, FACHE, President and Chief Executive Officer

ISLAND HOSPITAL, 1211 24th Street, Anacortes, WA, Zip 98221–2562; tel. 360/299–1300; Vincent Oliver, Administrator

KADLEC REGIONAL MEDICAL CENTER, 888 Swift Boulevard, Richland, WA, Zip 99352–3514; tel. 509/946–4611; Rand J. Wortman, Chief Executive Officer

KENNEWICK GENERAL HOSPITAL, 900 South Auburn Street, Kennewick, WA, Zip 99336–5621, Mailing Address: P.O. Box 6128, Zip 99336–0128; tel. 509/586–6111; Glen Marshall, Chief Executive Officer

KITTITAS VALLEY COMMUNITY HOSPITAL, 603 South Chestnut Street, Ellensburg, WA, Zip 98926–3875; tel. 509/962–7302; Paul E. Nurick, Chief Executive Officer

KOOTENAI MEDICAL CENTER, 2003 Kootenai Health Way, Coeur D'Alene, ID, Zip 83814–2677; tel. 208/666–2000; Jon Ness, Chief Executive Officer

LOURDES MEDICAL CENTER, 520 North Fourth Avenue, Pasco, WA, Zip 99301–5257, Mailing Address: P.O. Box 2568, Zip 99302–2568; tel. 509/547–7704; John Serle, FACHE, President and Chief Executive Officer

MULTICARE MARY BRIDGE CHILDREN'S HOSPITAL AND HEALTH CENTER, 317 Martin Luther King Jr. Way, Tacoma, WA, Zip 98405–4234, Mailing Address: P.O. Box 5299, Zip 98415–0299; tel. 253/403–1400; Mady Murrey, R.N., Chief Operating Officer

NORTHWEST SPECIALTY HOSPITAL, 1593 East Polston Avenue, Post Falls, ID, Zip 83854–5326; tel. 208/262–2300; Vaughn Ward, Chief Executive Officer

OVERLAKE HOSPITAL MEDICAL CENTER, 1035 116th Avenue N.E., Bellevue, WA, Zip 98004–4604; tel. 425/688–5000; Craig L. Hendrickson, President and Chief Executive Officer

PEACEHEALTH ST. JOSEPH MEDICAL CENTER, 2901 Squalicum Parkway, Bellingham, WA, Zip 98225–1851; tel. 360/734–5400; Nancy Steiger, R.N., Chief Executive Officer and Chief Mission Officer

PMH MEDICAL CENTER, 723 Memorial Street, Prosser, WA, Zip 99350–1593; tel. 509/786–2222; Julie Petersen, Chief Executive Officer

PROVIDENCE CENTRALIA HOSPITAL, 914 South Scheuber Road, Centralia, WA, Zip 98531–9027; tel. 360/736–2803; Cindy Mayo, R.N., FACHE, Chief Executive

PROVIDENCE HOLY FAMILY HOSPITAL, 5633 North Lidgerwood Street, Spokane, WA, Zip 99208–1224; tel. 509/482–0111; Elaine Couture, R.N., Chief Executive

PROVIDENCE REGIONAL MEDICAL CENTER EVERETT, 1321 Colby Avenue, Everett, WA, Zip 98201–1665, Mailing Address: P.O. Box 1147, Zip 98206–1147; tel. 425/261–2000; Preston M. Simmons, Chief Executive Officer

PROVIDENCE SACRED HEART MEDICAL CENTER & CHILDREN'S HOSPITAL, 101 West Eighth Avenue, Spokane, WA, Zip 99204–2364, Mailing Address: P.O. Box 2555, Zip 99220–2555; tel. 509/474–3131; Elaine Couture, R.N., Chief Executive

PROVIDENCE ST. MARY MEDICAL CENTER, 401 West Poplar Street, Walla Walla, WA, Zip 99362–2846, Mailing Address: P.O. Box 1477, Zip 99362–0312; tel. 509/525–3320; Steven A. Burdick, Chief Executive Officer

PULLMAN REGIONAL HOSPITAL, 835 S.E. Bishop Boulevard, Pullman, WA, Zip 99163–5512; tel. 509/332–2541; Scott K. Adams, Chief Executive Officer

SEATTLE CHILDREN'S HOSPITAL, 4800 Sand Point Way N.E., Seattle, WA, Zip 98105–3901, Mailing Address: P.O. Box 5371, Zip 98145–5005; tel. 206/987–2000; Thomas N. Hansen, M.D., Chief Executive Officer

SKAGIT VALLEY HOSPITAL, 1415 East Kincaid Street, Mount Vernon, WA, Zip 98274–4126, Mailing Address: P.O. Box 1376, Zip 98273–1376; tel. 360/424–4111; Gregg A. Davidson, FACHE, Chief Executive Officer

ST. FRANCIS HOSPITAL, 34515 Ninth Avenue South, Federal Way, WA, Zip 98003–6799; tel. 253/944–8100; Anthony McLean, President

ST. JOSEPH MEDICAL CENTER, 1717 South J Street, Tacoma, WA, Zip 98405–3004, Mailing Address: P.O. Box 2197, Zip 98401–2197; tel. 253/426–4101; Syd Bersante, President

SUNNYSIDE COMMUNITY HOSPITAL, 1016 Tacoma Avenue, Sunnyside, WA, Zip 98944–2263, Mailing Address: P.O. Box 719, Zip 98944–0719; tel. 509/837–1500; John Gallagher, Chief Executive Officer

TOPPENISH COMMUNITY HOSPITAL, 502 West Fourth Avenue, Toppenish, WA, Zip 98948–1616, Mailing Address: P.O. Box 672, Zip 98948–0672; tel. 509/865–3105; Albert Pilkington, III, Chief Executive Officer

UNITED GENERAL HOSPITAL, 2000 Hospital Drive, Sedro Woolley, WA, Zip 98284–4327; tel. 360/856–6021; Gregory C. Reed, FACHE, Chief Executive Officer

VALLEY HOSPITAL, 12606 East Mission Avenue, Spokane Valley, WA, Zip 99216–1090; tel. 509/924–6650; Dennis Barts, Chief Executive Officer

VIRGINIA MASON MEDICAL CENTER, 1100 Ninth Avenue, Seattle, WA, Zip 98101–2756, Mailing Address: P.O. Box 900, Zip 98111–0900; tel. 206/223–6600; Gary Kaplan, M.D., FACHE, Chairman and Chief Executive

WALLA WALLA GENERAL HOSPITAL, 1025 South Second Avenue, Walla Walla, WA, Zip 99362–4116, Mailing Address: P.O. Box 1398, Zip 99362–0309; tel. 509/525–0480; Monty E. Knittel, President and Chief Executive Officer

WHIDBEY GENERAL HOSPITAL, 101 North Main Street, Coupeville, WA, Zip 98239–3413; tel. 360/678–5151; Tom Tomasino, Administrator and Chief Executive Officer

WHITMAN HOSPITAL AND MEDICAL CENTER, 1200 West Fairview Street, Colfax, WA, Zip 99111–9579; tel. 509/397–3435; Deborah Glass, MS, R.N., Chief Executive Officer

YAKIMA REGIONAL MEDICAL AND CARDIAC CENTER, 110 South Ninth Avenue, Yakima, WA, Zip 98902–3315; tel. 509/575–5000; Richard H. Robinson, Chief Executive Officer

YAKIMA VALLEY MEMORIAL HOSPITAL, 2811 Tieton Drive, Yakima, WA, Zip 98902–3761; tel. 509/575–8000; Richard W. Linneweh, Jr., President and Chief Executive Officer

**LINCOLN COUNTY HEALTH DEPARTMENT**
**90 Nichols Street, Davenport, WA 99122–9729; tel. 509/725–1001; Ed Dzedzy, Public Health Administration**

LINCOLN HOSPITAL, 10 Nicholls Street, Davenport, WA, Zip 99122–9729; tel. 509/725–7101; Thomas J. Martin, Administrator

ODESSA MEMORIAL HEALTHCARE CENTER, 502 East Amende Drive, Odessa, WA, Zip 99159–7003, Mailing Address: P.O. Box 368, Zip 99159–0368; tel. 509/982–2611; Gary L. DelForge, Administrator

## WEST VIRGINIA

**HEALTH PARTNERS NETWORK, INC.**
**1000 Technology Drive, Suite 2320, Fairmont, WV 26554–8834; tel. 304/368–2740; William G. MacLean, Executive Director**

BERKELEY MEDICAL CENTER, 2500 Hospital Drive, Martinsburg, WV, Zip 25401–3402, Mailing Address: P.O. Box 1418, Zip 25402–1418; tel. 304/264–1000; Anthony Zelenka, Chief Administrative Officer

BROADDUS HOSPITAL, 1 Healthcare Drive, Philippi, WV, Zip 26416–9405, Mailing Address: P.O. Box 930, Zip 26416–0930; tel. 304/457–1760; Jeffrey A. Powelson, Chief Executive Officer

CAMDEN CLARK MEDICAL CENTER, 800 Garfield Avenue, Parkersburg, WV, Zip 26101–5378, Mailing Address: P.O. Box 718, Zip 26102–0718; tel. 304/424–2111; Michael A. King, FACHE, President and Chief Executive Officer

DAVIS MEMORIAL HOSPITAL, Gorman Avenue and Reed Street, Elkins, WV, Zip 26241, Mailing Address: P.O. Box 1484, Zip 26241–1484; tel. 304/636–3300; Mark Doak, President and Chief Executive Officer

FAIRMONT GENERAL HOSPITAL, 1325 Locust Avenue, Fairmont, WV, Zip 26554–1435; tel. 304/367–7100; Robert C. Marquardt, FACHE, President and Chief Executive Officer

GRAFTON CITY HOSPITAL, 500 Market Street, Grafton, WV, Zip 26354–1187; tel. 304/265–0400; Patrick Shaw, Chief Executive Officer

HEALTHSOUTH HUNTINGTON REHABILITATION HOSPITAL, 6900 West Country Club Drive, Huntington, WV, Zip 25705–2000; tel. 304/733–1060; Michael E. Zuliani, Chief Executive Officer

HEALTHSOUTH MOUNTAINVIEW REGIONAL REHABILITATION HOSPITAL, 1160 Van Voorhis Road, Morgantown, WV, Zip 26505–3437; tel. 304/598–1100; Vickie Demers, Chief Executive Officer

HEALTHSOUTH WESTERN HILLS REHABILITATION HOSPITAL, 3 Western Hills Drive, Parkersburg, WV, Zip 26105–8122; tel. 304/420–1300; Alvin R. Lawson, JD, FACHE, Chief Executive Officer

JEFFERSON MEDICAL CENTER, 300 South Preston Street, Ranson, WV, Zip 25438–1631; tel. 304/728–1600; Christina D. Coad, Ph.D., Chief Administrative Officer

MINNIE HAMILTON HEALTHCARE CENTER, 186 Hospital Drive, Grantsville, WV, Zip 26147–7100; tel. 304/354–9244; Steve Whited, Chief Executive Officer

ST. JOSEPH'S HOSPITAL OF BUCKHANNON, 1 Amalia Drive, Buckhannon, WV, Zip 26201–2276; tel. 304/473–2000; Sue E. Johnson–Phillippe, President and Chief Executive Officer

STONEWALL JACKSON MEMORIAL HOSPITAL, 230 Hospital Plaza, Weston, WV, Zip 26452–8558; tel. 304/269–8000; Avah Stalnaker, Chief Executive Officer

UNITED HOSPITAL CENTER, 327 Medical Park Drive, Bridgeport, WV, Zip 26330–9006; tel. 681/342–1000; Bruce C. Carter, President and Chief Executive Officer

WEST VIRGINIA UNIVERSITY HOSPITALS, 1 Medical Center Drive, Morgantown, WV, Zip 26506–4749; tel. 304/598–4000; Bruce McClymonds, President and Chief Executive Officer

**PARTNERS IN HEALTH NETWORK, INC.**
**405 Capitol Street, Suite 505, Charleston, WV 25301–1783; tel. 304/388–7385; Robert D. Whitler, Executive Director**

BOONE MEMORIAL HOSPITAL, 701 Madison Avenue, Madison, WV, Zip 25130–1699; tel. 304/369–1230; Tommy H. Mullins, Administrator

BRAXTON COUNTY MEMORIAL HOSPITAL, 100 Hoylman Drive, Gassaway, WV, Zip 26624–9318; tel. 304/364–5156; Ben Vincent, FACHE, Chief Executive Officer

CAMC TEAYS VALLEY HOSPITAL, 1400 Hospital Drive, Hurricane, WV, Zip 25526–9202; tel. 304/757–1700; Randall H. Hodges, President and Chief Executive Officer

CHARLESTON AREA MEDICAL CENTER, 501 Morris Street, Charleston, WV, Zip 25301–1300, Mailing Address: P.O. Box 1547, Zip 25326–1547; tel. 304/388–5432; David L. Ramsey, President and Chief Executive Officer

EYE AND EAR CLINIC OF CHARLESTON, 1306 Kanawha Boulevard East, Charleston, WV, Zip 25301–3001, Mailing Address: P.O. Box 2271, Zip 25328–2271; tel. 304/343–4371; Christina Arvon, Administrator and Chief Executive Officer

HIGHLAND HOSPITAL, 300 56th Street S.E., Charleston, WV, Zip 25304–2361, Mailing Address: P.O. Box 4107, Zip 25364–4107; tel. 304/926–1600; James H. Dissen, Interim President and Chief Executive Officer

JACKSON GENERAL HOSPITAL, 122 Pinnell Street, Ripley, WV, Zip 25271–9101, Mailing Address: P.O. Box 720, Zip 25271–0720; tel. 304/372–2731; Stephanie McCoy, President and Chief Executive Officer

MINNIE HAMILTON HEALTHCARE CENTER, 186 Hospital Drive, Grantsville, WV, Zip 26147–7100; tel. 304/354–9244; Steve Whited, Chief Executive Officer

MONTGOMERY GENERAL HOSPITAL, 401 Sixth Avenue, Montgomery, WV, Zip 25136–2116, Mailing Address: P.O. Box 270, Zip 25136–0270; tel. 304/442–5151; Vickie Gay, Chief Executive Officer

POCAHONTAS MEMORIAL HOSPITAL, Buckeye, WV, Zip 24924; tel. 304/799–7400; Barbara Lay, Chief Executive Officer

ROANE GENERAL HOSPITAL, 200 Hospital Drive, Spencer, WV, Zip 25276–1050; tel. 304/927–4444; Douglas E. Bentz, Chief Executive Officer

STONEWALL JACKSON MEMORIAL HOSPITAL, 230 Hospital Plaza, Weston, WV, Zip 26452–8558; tel. 304/269–8000; Avah Stalnaker, Chief Executive Officer

SUMMERSVILLE REGIONAL MEDICAL CENTER, 400 Fairview Heights Road, Summersville, WV, Zip 26651–9308; tel. 304/872–2891; Deborah A. Hill, R.N., FACHE, Chief Executive Officer

WEBSTER COUNTY MEMORIAL HOSPITAL, 324 Miller Mountain Drive, Webster Springs, WV, Zip 26288–1087, Mailing Address: P.O. Box 312, Zip 26288–0312; tel. 304/847–5682; Annette M. Keenan, Chief Executive Officer

## WISCONSIN

### AFFINITY HEALTH SYSTEM
1570 Midway Place, Menasha, WI 54952–1165; tel. 920/720–1713; Daniel Neufelder, President and Chief Executive Officer

CALUMET MEDICAL CENTER, 614 Memorial Drive, Chilton, WI, Zip 53014–1597; tel. 920/849–2386; Timothy Richman, President

MERCY MEDICAL CENTER, 500 South Oakwood Road, Oshkosh, WI, Zip 54904–7944, Mailing Address: P.O. Box 3370, Zip 54903–3370; tel. 920/223–2000; William Calhoun, President

ST. ELIZABETH HOSPITAL, 1506 South Oneida Street, Appleton, WI, Zip 54915–1305; tel. 920/738–2000; Travis Andersen, President

### ASPIRUS, INC.
425 Pine Ridge Boulevard, Wausau, WI 54401–4123; tel. 715/847–2118; Matthew Heywood, Chief Executive Officer

ASPIRUS GRAND VIEW HOSPITAL, N10561 Grand View Lane, Ironwood, MI, Zip 49938–9622; tel. 906/932–2525; Charles Nelson, Chief Executive Officer

ASPIRUS KEWEENAW HOSPITAL, 205 Osceola Street, Laurium, MI, Zip 49913–2134; tel. 906/337–6500; Charles Nelson, Chief Executive Officer

ASPIRUS ONTONAGON HOSPITAL, 601 South Seventh Street, Ontonagon, MI, Zip 49953–1459; tel. 906/884–8000; Charles Nelson, Chief Executive Officer

ASPIRUS WAUSAU HOSPITAL, 333 Pine Ridge Boulevard, Wausau, WI, Zip 54401–4187; tel. 715/847–2121; Marita Hattem, Interim President and Chief Operating Officer

MEMORIAL HEALTH CENTER, 135 South Gibson Street, Medford, WI, Zip 54451–1696; tel. 715/748–8100; Gregory A. Olson, President and Chief Executive Officer

### COLUMBIA ST. MARY'S
2025 East Newport Avenue, Milwaukee, WI 53211–2906; tel. 414/961–3300; Mark R. Taylor, FACHE, President and Chief Executive Officer

COLUMBIA ST. MARY'S HOSPITAL MILWAUKEE, 2301 North Lake Drive, Milwaukee, WI, Zip 53211–4508; tel. 414/291–1000; Mark R. Taylor, FACHE, President and Chief Executive Officer

COLUMBIA ST. MARY'S OZAUKEE HOSPITAL, 13111 North Port Washington Road, Mequon, WI, Zip 53097–2416; tel. 262/243–7300; Mark R. Taylor, FACHE, President and Chief Executive Officer

SACRED HEART REHABILITATION INSTITUTE, 2025 East Newport Avenue, Milwaukee, WI, Zip 53211–2906; tel. 414/298–6700; Allan M. Spooner, President

### COMMUNITY HEALTH NETWORK, INC.
225 Memorial Drive, Berlin, WI 54923–1243; tel. 920/361–5580; John Feeney, President and Chief Executive Officer

BERLIN MEMORIAL HOSPITAL, 225 Memorial Drive, Berlin, WI, Zip 54923–1295; tel. 920/361–1313; John Feeney, President and Chief Executive Officer

WILD ROSE COMMUNITY MEMORIAL HOSPITAL, 601 Grove Avenue, Wild Rose, WI, Zip 54984–6903, Mailing Address: P.O. Box 243, Zip 54984–0243; tel. 920/622–3257; Donald Caves, President

### GUNDERSON LUTHERAN HEALTH SYSTEM
1900 South Avenue, La Crosse, WI 54601–5467; tel. 608/782–7300; Jeffrey E. Thompson, M.D., Chief Executive Officer

GUNDERSEN LUTHERAN MEDICAL CENTER, 1900 South Avenue, La Crosse, WI, Zip 54601–5467; tel. 608/782–7300; Jeffrey E. Thompson, M.D., Chief Executive Officer

GUNDERSEN TRI–COUNTY HOSPITAL AND CLINICS, 18601 Lincoln Street, Whitehall, WI, Zip 54773–8605; tel. 715/538–4361; Brian Theiler, President and Chief Executive Officer

PALMER LUTHERAN HEALTH CENTER, 112 Jefferson Street, West Union, IA, Zip 52175–1022; tel. 563/422–3811; Debrah Chensvold, FACHE, President and Chief Executive Officer

### MERCY ALLIANCE, INC.
1000 Mineral Point Avenue, Janesville, WI 53548–2940; tel. 608/756–6000; Javon R. Bea, President and Chief Executive Officer

MERCY HARVARD HOSPITAL, 901 Grant Street, Harvard, IL, Zip 60033–1898, Mailing Address: P.O. Box 850, Zip 60033–0850; tel. 815/943–5431; Jennifer Hallatt, Chief Operating Officer

MERCY HOSPITAL AND TRAUMA CENTER, 1000 Mineral Point Avenue, Janesville, WI, Zip 53548–2982, Mailing Address: P.O. Box 5003, Zip 53547–5003; tel. 608/756–6000; Javon R. Bea, President and Chief Executive Officer

MERCY WALWORTH HOSPITAL AND MEDICAL CENTER, N2950 State Road 67, Lake Geneva, WI, Zip 53147–2655; tel. 262/245–0535; Jennifer Hallatt, Chief Operating Officer

### MINISTRY HEALTH CARE
11925 West Lake Park Drive, Milwaukee, WI 53224–3002; tel. 414/359–1060; Nicholas Desien, President and Chief Executive Officer

CALUMET MEDICAL CENTER, 614 Memorial Drive, Chilton, WI, Zip 53014–1597; tel. 920/849–2386; Timothy Richman, President

FLAMBEAU HOSPITAL, 98 Sherry Avenue, Park Falls, WI, Zip 54552–1467, Mailing Address: P.O. Box 310, Zip 54552–0310; tel. 715/762–2484; David A. Grundstrom, Chief Administrative Officer

HOWARD YOUNG MEDICAL CENTER, 240 Maple Street, Woodruff, WI, Zip 54568–9190, Mailing Address: P.O. Box 470, Zip 54568–0470; tel. 715/356–8000; Sheila Clough, President

MERCY MEDICAL CENTER, 500 South Oakwood Road, Oshkosh, WI, Zip 54904–7944, Mailing Address: P.O. Box 3370, Zip 54903–3370; tel. 920/223–2000; William Calhoun, President

MINISTRY DOOR COUNTY MEDICAL CENTER, 323 South 18th Avenue, Sturgeon Bay, WI, Zip 54235–1495; tel. 920/743–5566; Gerald M. Worrick, President and Chief Executive Officer

MINISTRY EAGLE RIVER MEMORIAL HOSPITAL, 201 Hospital Road, Eagle River, WI, Zip 54521–8835; tel. 715/479–7411; Sheila Clough, President

MINISTRY GOOD SAMARITAN HEALTH CENTER, 601 South Center Avenue, Merrill, WI, Zip 54452–3404; tel. 715/536–5511; Mary T. Krueger, President

MINISTRY OUR LADY OF VICTORY HOSPITAL, 1120 Pine Street, Stanley, WI, Zip 54768–1297; tel. 715/644–5571; Cynthia Eichman, President

MINISTRY SACRED HEART HOSPITAL, 401 West Mohawk Drive, Tomahawk, WI, Zip 54487–2274; tel. 715/453–7700; Monica Hilt, President

MINISTRY SAINT CLARE'S HOSPITAL, 3400 Ministry Parkway, Weston, WI, Zip 54476–5220; tel. 715/393–3000; Mary T. Krueger, President

MINISTRY SAINT JOSEPH'S HOSPITAL, 611 St. Joseph Avenue, Marshfield, WI, Zip 54449–1898; tel. 715/387–1713; Brian Kief, President and Chief Executive Officer

MINISTRY SAINT MARY'S HOSPITALS, 2251 North Shore Drive, Rhinelander, WI, Zip 54501–6710; tel. 715/361–2000; Monica Hilt, President and Chief Operating Officer

MINISTRY SAINT MICHAEL'S HOSPITAL, 900 Illinois Avenue, Stevens Point, WI, Zip 54481–3196; tel. 715/346–5000; Jeffrey L. Martin, President

SAINT ELIZABETH'S MEDICAL CENTER, 1200 Grant Boulevard West, Wabasha, MN, Zip 55981–1042; tel. 651/565–4531; Thomas Crowley, President and Chief Executive Officer

ST. ELIZABETH HOSPITAL, 1506 South Oneida Street, Appleton, WI, Zip 54915–1305; tel. 920/738–2000; Travis Andersen, President

### WHEATON FRANCISCAN HEALTHCARE
400 West River Woods Parkway, Glendale, WI 53212–1060; tel. 414/465–3000; John D. Oliverio, President and Chief Executive Officer

MIDWEST ORTHOPEDIC SPECIALTY HOSPITAL, 10101 South 27th Street, 2nd Floor, Franklin, WI, Zip 53132–7209; tel. 414/817–5800; Daniel Mattes, Chief Executive Officer

WHEATON FRANCISCAN HEALTHCARE – ALL SAINTS, 3801 Spring Street, Racine, WI, Zip 53405–1690; tel. 262/687–4011; Susan Boland, President and Chief Executive Officer

WHEATON FRANCISCAN HEALTHCARE – ELMBROOK MEMORIAL, 19333 West North Avenue, Brookfield, WI, Zip 53045–4198; tel. 262/785–2000; Debra K. Standridge, President

WHEATON FRANCISCAN HEALTHCARE – FRANKLIN, 10101 South 27th Street, Franklin, WI, Zip 53132–7209; tel. 414/325–4700; Daniel Mattes, President

WHEATON FRANCISCAN HEALTHCARE – ST. FRANCIS, 3237 South 16th Street, Milwaukee, WI, Zip 53215–4592; tel. 414/647–5000; Daniel Mattes, President

WHEATON FRANCISCAN HEALTHCARE – ST. JOSEPH'S, 5000 West Chambers Street, Milwaukee, WI, Zip 53210–1650; tel. 414/447–2000; Debra K. Standridge, President

WHEATON FRANCISCAN HEALTHCARE – THE WISCONSIN HEART HOSPITAL, 10000 West Bluemound Road, Wauwatosa, WI, Zip 53226–4321; tel. 414/778–7800; Debra K. Standridge, President

# Alliances

## ALLIANCE OF INDEPENDENT ACADEMIC MEDICAL CENTERS
233 East Erie Street, Ste 306, Chicago, IL Zip 60611; tel. 312/988-7572; Nancie Noie Thompson, Executive Director

### ARIZONA
**Phoenix**
Member
  Maricopa Integrated Health System

**Scottsdale**
Member
  Scottsdale Healthcare–Osborn Medical Center

### CONNECTICUT
**Danbury**
Member
  Danbury Hospital

**Hartford**
Member
  Mount Sinai Rehabilitation Hospital
  Saint Francis Hospital and Medical Center

### DELAWARE
**Wilmington**
Member
  Christiana Care Health System

### DISTRICT OF COLUMBIA
**Washington**
Member
  MedStar Georgetown University Hospital
  MedStar National Rehabilitation Hospital
  MedStar Washington Hospital Center

### FLORIDA
**Orlando**
Member
  Florida Hospital
  Orlando Health
  Orlando Regional Medical Center

### ILLINOIS
**Chicago**
Member
  Advocate Illinois Masonic Medical Center

**Oak Lawn**
Member
  Advocate Christ Medical Center

**Park Ridge**
Member
  Advocate Lutheran General Hospital

**Peoria**
Member
  OSF Saint Francis Medical Center

**Urbana**
Member
  Carle Foundation Hospital

### KENTUCKY
**Louisville**
Member
  Kosair Children's Hospital
  Norton Audubon Hospital
  Norton Brownsboro Hospital
  Norton Healthcare
  Norton Hospital
  Norton Suburban Hospital

### LOUISIANA
**New Orleans**
Member
  Ochsner Health System

### MAINE
**Portland**
Member
  Maine Medical Center

### MARYLAND
**Baltimore**
Member
  MedStar Franklin Square Medical Center
  MedStar Good Samaritan Hospital
  MedStar Harbor Hospital
  MedStar Union Memorial Hospital

**Columbia**
Member
  MedStar Health

### MASSACHUSETTS
**Burlington**
Member
  Lahey Hospital & Medical Center, Burlington

**Pittsfield**
Member
  Berkshire Medical Center

**Springfield**
Member
  Baystate Health, Inc.

### MICHIGAN
**Detroit**
Member
  Henry Ford Health System

**Grand Rapids**
Member
  Saint Mary's Health Care
  Spectrum Health

**Rochester**
Member
  Crittenton Hospital Medical Center

**Royal Oak**
Member
  Beaumont Hospital – Royal Oak

### MINNESOTA
**Bloomington**
Member
  HealthPartners

### NEW JERSEY
**Brick Township**
Member
  Ocean Medical Center

**Holmdel**
Member
  Bayshore Community Hospital

**Livingston**
Member
  Saint Barnabas Medical Center

**Long Branch**
Member
  Monmouth Medical Center

**Manahawkin**
Member
  Southern Ocean Medical Center

**Morristown**
Member
  Morristown Medical Center

**Neptune**
Member
  Jersey Shore University Medical Center

**Newark**
Member
  Newark Beth Israel Medical Center

**Red Bank**
Member
  Riverview Medical Center

**Summit**
Member
  Overlook Medical Center

**Wall Township**
Member
  Meridian Health

### NEW YORK
**Brooklyn**
Member
  Maimonides Medical Center

**Cooperstown**
Member
  Bassett Medical Center

**Mineola**
Member
  Winthrop–University Hospital

### NORTH CAROLINA
**Charlotte**
Member
  Carolinas Medical Center

### OHIO
**Akron**
Member
  Akron General Medical Center

**Cincinnati**
Member
  TriHealth

**Columbus**
Member
  Mount Carmel
  OhioHealth Grant Medical Center
  OhioHealth Riverside Methodist Hospital

### PENNSYLVANIA
**Allentown**
Member
  Lehigh Valley Health Network

**Bethlehem**
Member
  St. Luke's University Hospital – Bethlehem Campus

**Bryn Mawr**
Member
  Bryn Mawr Hospital

**Gettysburg**
Member
  Gettysburg Hospital

**Johnstown**
Member
  Conemaugh Memorial Medical Center

**Philadelphia**
Member
  Einstein Medical Center Philadelphia

**Sayre**
Member
  Robert Packer Hospital

**West Reading**
Member
  Reading Hospital and Medical Center

**Wynnewood**
Member
  Lankenau Medical Center

**York**
Member
  WellSpan Health
  York Hospital

### SOUTH DAKOTA
**Sioux Falls**
Member
  Sanford Health

### TEXAS
**Dallas**
Member
  Baylor University Medical Center
  Parkland Health & Hospital System

**Fort Worth**
Member
  JPS Health Network

**Garland**
Member
  Baylor Medical Center at Garland

### WASHINGTON
**Seattle**
Member
  Virginia Mason Medical Center

### WISCONSIN
**Milwaukee**
Member
  Aurora Sinai Medical Center
  Aurora St. Luke's Medical Center

## CATHOLIC CEO HEALTHCARE CONNECTION
3333 Warrenville Rd, Ste 200, Lisle, IL Zip 60532; tel. 630/799–8315; Roger N. Butler, Executive Director

### CALIFORNIA
**Irvine**
Member
St. Joseph Health

**San Francisco**
Member
Dignity Health

### COLORADO
**Denver**
Member
SCL Health System

**Englewood**
Member
Catholic Health Initiatives

### ILLINOIS
**Peoria**
Member
OSF Healthcare System

**Springfield**
Member
Hospital Sisters Health System

**Wheaton**
Member
Wheaton Franciscan Healthcare

### LOUISIANA
**Baton Rouge**
Member
Franciscan Missionaries of Our Lady Health System, Inc.

### MARYLAND
**Marriottsville**
Member
Bon Secours Health System, Inc.

### MASSACHUSETTS
**Tewksbury**
Member
Covenant Health Systems, Inc.

### MICHIGAN
**Livonia**
Member
Trinity Health

### MISSOURI
**Chesterfield**
Member
Mercy Health

**Saint Louis**
Member
Ascension Health

### OHIO
**Cincinnati**
Member
Catholic Health Partners

**Toledo**
Member
Sylvania Franciscan Health

### PENNSYLVANIA
**Newtown Square**
Member
Catholic Health East

### SOUTH DAKOTA
**Sioux Falls**
Member
Avera Health

### TEXAS
**Irving**
Member
CHRISTUS Health

### WASHINGTON
**Renton**
Member
Providence Health & Services

**Vancouver**
Member
PeaceHealth

### WISCONSIN
**Manitowoc**
Member
Franciscan Sisters of Christian Charity Sponsored Ministries, Inc.

## COMMUNITY HEALTH COLLABORATIVE, LLC
630 East River Street, Elyria, OH Zip 44035–5902; tel. 440/329–7500; Frank L. Lordeman, President and Chief Executive Officer

### OHIO
**Elyria**
Member
EMH Elyria Medical Center

**Middleburg Heights**
Member
Southwest General Health Center

**Parma**
Member
Parma Community General Hospital

## HEALTH ENTERPRISES OF IOWA
5825 Dry Creek Lane NE, Cedar Rapids, IA Zip 52402–1225; tel. 319/368–3619

### IOWA
**Ames**
Member
Mary Greeley Medical Center

**Chariton**
Member
Lucas County Health Center

**Charles City**
Member
Floyd County Medical Center

**Cherokee**
Affiliate
Cherokee Regional Medical Center

**Davenport**
Member
Genesis Health System

**Denison**
Member
Crawford County Memorial Hospital

**Des Moines**
Affiliate
Broadlawns Medical Center

**Fairfield**
Member
Jefferson County Health Center

**Guthrie Center**
Member
Guthrie County Hospital

**Humboldt**
Member
Humboldt County Memorial Hospital

**Ida Grove**
Affiliate
Horn Memorial Hospital

**Independence**
Affiliate
Buchanan County Health Center

**Iowa City**
Member
Mercy Iowa City

**Manchester**
Member
Regional Medical Center

**Maquoketa**
Member
Jackson County Regional Health Center

**Marshalltown**
Member
Marshalltown Medical & Surgical Center

**Mount Pleasant**
Member
Henry County Health Center

**Newton**
Member
Skiff Medical Center

**Oskaloosa**
Member
Mahaska Health Partnership

**Pella**
Member
Pella Regional Health Center

**Pocahontas**
Member
Pocahontas Community Hospital

**Sac City**
Member
Loring Hospital

**Waukon**
Affiliate
Veterans Memorial Hospital

**Waverly**
Member
Waverly Health Center

**West Burlington**
Member
Great River Medical Center

## HOSPITAL NETWORK VENTURES, LLC
6212 American Avenue, Portage, MI Zip 49002; tel. 269/329–3200; Gregory L. Hedegore, President and Chief Executive Officer

### MICHIGAN
**Allegan**
Partner
Allegan General Hospital

**Charlotte**
Partner
Hayes Green Beach Memorial Hospital

**Coldwater**
Partner
Community Health Center of Branch County

**Hastings**
Member
Pennock Hospital

**Kalamazoo**
Member
Bronson Healthcare Group, Inc.

**Marlette**
Partner
Marlette Regional Hospital

**Marshall**
Member
Oaklawn Hospital

**Owosso**
Partner
Memorial Healthcare

**Paw Paw**
Partner
Bronson LakeView Hospital

**Saint Joseph**
Partner
Lakeland Healthcare

**South Haven**
Partner
South Haven Health System

**Sturgis**
Member
Sturgis Hospital

**Watervliet**
Partner
Lakeland Community Hospital Watervliet

## HOSPITAL SHARED SERVICES ASSOCIATION
P O Box 19741, Seattle, WA Zip 98109–6741; tel. 425/899–2753

## WASHINGTON

**Bellevue**
Member
Overlake Hospital Medical Center

**Burien**
Member
Highline Medical Center

**Chelan**
Member
Lake Chelan Community Hospital

**Clarkston**
Member
Tri–State Memorial Hospital

**Davenport**
Member
Lincoln Hospital

**Edmonds**
Member
Swedish/Edmonds

**Ephrata**
Member
Columbia Basin Hospital

**Grand Coulee**
Member
Coulee Medical Center

**Kirkland**
Member
EvergreenHealth

**Moses Lake**
Member
Samaritan Healthcare

**Mount Vernon**
Member
Skagit Valley Hospital

**Newport**
Member
Newport Hospital and Health Services

**Odessa**
Member
Odessa Memorial Healthcare Center

**Othello**
Member
Othello Community Hospital

**Prosser**
Member
PMH Medical Center

**Pullman**
Member
Pullman Regional Hospital

**Quincy**
Member
Quincy Valley Medical Center

**Republic**
Member
Ferry County Memorial Hospital

**Ritzville**
Member
East Adams Rural Hospital

**Tacoma**
Member
Western State Hospital

**Tonasket**
Member
North Valley Hospital

## MEDI–SOTA, INC.
1280 Locust Street Suite 16, Dawson, MN Zip 56232–2375;
tel. 320/769–2269; Deb Ranallo, Executive Director

### MINNESOTA

**Appleton**
Member
Appleton Area Health Services

**Arlington**
Member
Sibley Medical Center

**Benson**
Member
Swift County–Benson Hospital

**Canby**
Member
Sanford Canby Medical Center

**Dawson**
Member
Johnson Memorial Health Services

**Elbow Lake**
Member
Prairie Ridge Hospital and Health Services

**Glencoe**
Member
Glencoe Regional Health Services

**Glenwood**
Member
Glacial Ridge Health System

**Graceville**
Member
Essentia Health–Holy Trinity Hospital

**Granite Falls**
Member
Granite Falls Municipal Hospital and Manor

**Hendricks**
Member
Hendricks Community Hospital

**Litchfield**
Member
Meeker Memorial Hospital

**Long Prairie**
Member
CentraCare Health–Long Prairie

**Madelia**
Member
Madelia Community Hospital

**Mahnomen**
Member
Mahnomen Health Center

**Marshall**
Member
Avera Marshall Regional Medical Center

**Montevideo**
Member
Chippewa County–Montevideo Hospital

**Olivia**
Member
RC Hospital and Clinics

**Ortonville**
Member
Ortonville Area Health Services

**Paynesville**
Member
Paynesville Area Health Care System

**Perham**
Member
Perham Health

**Pipestone**
Member
Pipestone County Medical Center Avera

**Redwood Falls**
Member
Redwood Area Hospital

**Saint Peter**
Member
River's Edge Hospital and Clinic

**Slayton**
Member
Murray County Medical Center

**Sleepy Eye**
Member
Sleepy Eye Medical Center

**Staples**
Member
Lakewood Health System

**Tracy**
Member
Sanford Tracy Medical Center

**Tyler**
Member
Tyler Healthcare Center Avera

## NORTH REGION HEALTH ALLIANCE
120 East Bridge Avenue, Warren, MN Zip 56762; tel. 218/745–5343; Jon E. Linnell, Chief Executive Officer

### MINNESOTA

**Ada**
Member
Essentia Health Ada

**Bagley**
Member
Sanford Bagley Medical Center

**Baudette**
Member
LakeWood Health Center

**Crookston**
Member
RiverView Health

**Fosston**
Member
Essentia Health Fosston

**Hallock**
Member
Kittson Memorial Healthcare Center

**Roseau**
Member
LifeCare Medical Center

**Thief River Falls**
Member
Sanford Thief River Falls Medical Center

**Warren**
Member
North Valley Health Center

### NORTH DAKOTA

**Cavalier**
Member
Pembina County Memorial Hospital and Wedgewood Manor

**Cooperstown**
Member
Cooperstown Medical Center

**Devils Lake**
Member
Mercy Hospital

**Grafton**
Member
Unity Medical Center

**Grand Forks**
Member
Altru Health System

**Hillsboro**
Member
Sanford Hillsboro Medical Center

**Langdon**
Member
Cavalier County Memorial Hospital

**Mayville**
Member
Sanford Mayville Medical Center

**Mcville**
Member
Nelson County Health System

**Northwood**
Member
Sanford Northwood Deaconess Health Center

**Park River**
Member
First Care Health Center

## NORTHWEST KANSAS HEALTH ALLIANCE
2220 Canterbury Drive, Hays, KS Zip 67601–2370; tel. 785/623–2300

### KANSAS

**Atwood**
Member
Rawlins County Health Center

**Colby**
Member
Citizens Medical Center

**Dighton**
Member
Lane County Hospital

**Greensburg**
Member
Kiowa County Memorial Hospital

**Hill City**
Member
Graham County Hospital

**Hoisington**
Member
Clara Barton Hospital

**Hoxie**
Member
Sheridan County Health Complex

**Kinsley**
Member
Edwards County Hospital and Healthcare Center

**La Crosse**
Member
Rush County Memorial Hospital

**Larned**
Member
Pawnee Valley Community Hospital

**Minneola**
Member
Minneola District Hospital

**Ness City**
Member
Ness County Hospital

**Norton**
Member
Norton County Hospital

**Oakley**
Member
Logan County Hospital

**Oberlin**
Member
Decatur County Hospital and Cedar Living Center

**Phillipsburg**
Member
Phillips County Hospital

**Plainville**
Member
Rooks County Health Center

**Quinter**
Member
Gove County Medical Center

**Ransom**
Member
Grisell Memorial Hospital District One

**Russell**
Member
Russell Regional Hospital

**Saint Francis**
Member
Cheyenne County Hospital

**Scott City**
Member
Scott County Hospital

**Smith Center**
Member
Smith County Memorial Hospital

**Wakeeney**
Member
Trego County–Lemke Memorial Hospital

## PENNANT HEALTH ALLIANCE
2122 Health Drive SW Suite 100,
Wyoming, MI Zip 49519–9698;
tel. 616/252–6800; Michael D. Faas,
Chief Executive Officer

### MICHIGAN
**Ann Arbor**
Member
University of Michigan Hospitals and Health Centers

**Cadillac**
Member
Mercy Hospital Cadillac

**Carson City**
Member
Carson City Hospital

**Grand Rapids**
Member
Mary Free Bed Rehabilitation Hospital
Saint Mary's Health Care

**Grayling**
Member
Mercy Hospital Grayling

**Muskegon**
Member
Mercy Health Partners, Mercy Campus

**Wyoming**
Member
Metro Health Hospital

## PREMIER, INC.
13034 Ballantyne Corporate Place,
Charlotte, NC Zip 28277–1498;
tel. 704/816–5353; Susan DeVore,
President and Chief Executive Officer

### ALABAMA
**Dothan**
Owner
Southeast Alabama Medical Center

**Opelika**
Owner
East Alabama Medical Center

### ARIZONA
**Phoenix**
John C. Lincoln Health Network
Owner
Banner Health

### ARKANSAS
**Batesville**
White River Health System

**Pine Bluff**
Owner
Jefferson Regional Medical Center

### CALIFORNIA
**Long Beach**
St. Mary Medical Center

**Los Altos Hills**
Daughters of Charity Health System

**Mountain View**
El Camino Hospital

**Oceanside**
Tri–City Medical Center

**Rancho Mirage**
Owner
Eisenhower Medical Center

**Roseville**
Owner
Adventist Health

**San Francisco**
Owner
Dignity Health

### CONNECTICUT
**Hartford**
Owner
Saint Francis Hospital and Medical Center

**Waterbury**
Saint Mary's Hospital

### DELAWARE
**Dover**
Owner
Bayhealth Medical Center

**Lewes**
Owner
Beebe Medical Center

### DISTRICT OF COLUMBIA
**Washington**
Owner
Sibley Memorial Hospital

### FLORIDA
**Altamonte Springs**
Owner
Adventist Health System Sunbelt Health Care
Corporation

**Clearwater**
BayCare Health System

**Coral Gables**
Owner
Baptist Health South Florida

**Hollywood**
Memorial Healthcare System

**Jacksonville**
Baptist Health
Nemours

**Miami Beach**
Owner
Mount Sinai Medical Center

**Saint Petersburg**
Member
Bayfront Medical Center

**Tampa**
Member
H. Lee Moffitt Cancer Center and Research Institute

**Vero Beach**
Owner
Indian River Medical Center

**Winter Haven**
Owner
Winter Haven Hospital

### GEORGIA
**Carrollton**
Tanner Medical Center–Carrollton

**Columbus**
Owner
St. Francis Hospital

**La Grange**
Owner
West Georgia Health

**Savannah**
St. Joseph's Hospital
Owner
Memorial Health

### HAWAII
**Honolulu**
Owner
Kuakini Medical Center

### ILLINOIS
**Chicago**
Presence Health
Owner
Mount Sinai Hospital

**Harvey**
Ingalls Memorial Hospital

**Naperville**
Edward Hospital

**Peoria**
UnityPoint Health – Methodist

**Urbana**
Owner
Carle Foundation Hospital

**Winfield**
Cadence Health·

### INDIANA
**Gary**
Owner
Methodist Hospitals

### IOWA
**Cedar Rapids**
Member
Health Enterprises of Iowa

**Davenport**
Member
Genesis Medical Center–Davenport

**De Witt**
Member
Genesis Medical Center, DeWitt

## KENTUCKY

**Ashland**
King's Daughters Medical Center

**Bowling Green**
Commonwealth Regional Specialty Hospital

**Danville**
Ephraim McDowell Regional Medical Center

**Edgewood**
St. Elizabeth Edgewood

**Glasgow**
Owner
T. J. Samson Community Hospital

**Henderson**
Owner
Methodist Hospital

**Louisville**
Baptist Health
Member
University of Louisville Hospital
Owner
Norton Healthcare

**Murray**
Owner
Murray–Calloway County Hospital

## LOUISIANA

**Baton Rouge**
Baton Rouge General Medical Center
Member
Woman's Hospital

**Columbia**
Caldwell Memorial Hospital

**Hammond**
North Oaks Health System

**Houma**
Owner
Terrebonne General Medical Center

**Lafayette**
Owner
Lafayette General Medical Center

**Marrero**
Owner
West Jefferson Medical Center

## MAINE

**Lewiston**
Central Maine Medical Center

## MARYLAND

**Annapolis**
Owner
Anne Arundel Medical Center

**Baltimore**
Greater Baltimore Medical Center
Member
Mercy Medical Center
Sinai Hospital of Baltimore

**Bethesda**
Owner
Suburban Hospital

**Columbia**
Owner
Howard County General Hospital

**Elkton**
Owner
Union Hospital

**Frederick**
Owner
Frederick Memorial Hospital

**Gaithersburg**
Owner
Adventist HealthCare

**Hagerstown**
Western Maryland Hospital Center
Owner
Meritus Medical Center

**Lanham**
Owner
Doctors Community Hospital

**Marriottsville**
Owner
Bon Secours Health System, Inc.

**Randallstown**
Member
Northwest Hospital

**Salisbury**
Owner
Peninsula Regional Medical Center

**Westminster**
Owner
Carroll Hospital Center

## MASSACHUSETTS

**Boston**
Tufts Medical Center

**Springfield**
Owner
Baystate Health, Inc.

## MICHIGAN

**Detroit**
Owner
Henry Ford Health System

**Flint**
McLaren Health Care Corporation

**Jackson**
Allegiance Health

**Lansing**
Owner
Sparrow Hospital

**Rochester**
Member
Crittenton Hospital Medical Center

## MINNESOTA

**Minneapolis**
Owner
Fairview Health Services

## MISSISSIPPI

**Grenada**
Owner
Grenada Lake Medical Center

**Jackson**
Mississippi Baptist Health System

**Laurel**
Owner
South Central Regional Medical Center

**Meridian**
Owner
Rush Health Systems

## MISSOURI

**Saint Louis**
St. Anthony's Medical Center
Owner
SSM Health Care

## MONTANA

**Billings**
Billings Clinic

## NEW MEXICO

**Albuquerque**
Presbyterian Healthcare Services

## NEW YORK

**Rochester**
Owner
Rochester General Health System
Seagate Alliance

## NORTH CAROLINA

**Asheboro**
Owner
Randolph Hospital

**Asheville**
Mission Health System

**Boone**
Owner
Watauga Medical Center

**Burlington**
Owner
Alamance Regional Medical Center

**Charlotte**
Carolinas HealthCare System

**Clyde**
Owner
MedWest – Haywood

**Fayetteville**
Cape Fear Valley Medical Center

**Gastonia**
Owner
Gaston Memorial Hospital

**Goldsboro**
Owner
Wayne Memorial Hospital

**Hendersonville**
Owner
Margaret R. Pardee Memorial Hospital

**Hickory**
Owner
Catawba Valley Medical Center

**Kinston**
Owner
Lenoir Memorial Hospital

**Lumberton**
Owner
Southeastern Health

**Morehead City**
Carteret General Hospital

**Pinehurst**
FirstHealth of the Carolinas

**Roanoke Rapids**
Owner
Halifax Regional Medical Center

**Statesville**
Owner
Iredell Memorial Hospital

**Sylva**
MedWest Health System

**Wilson**
Owner
Wilson Medical Center

## OHIO

**Akron**
Owner
Summa Health System

**Cincinnati**
Owner
Bethesda North Hospital
Catholic Health Partners

**Cleveland**
Cleveland Clinic Health System
University Hospitals
Owner
Cleveland Clinic

**Elyria**
Member
EMH Elyria Medical Center

**Kettering**
Kettering Medical Center

**Parma**
Member
Parma Community General Hospital

## OKLAHOMA

**Tulsa**
Owner
Saint Francis Hospital

## OREGON

**Salem**
Member
Salem Hospital

## PENNSYLVANIA

**Beaver**
Heritage Valley Health System

**Danville**
Member
Geisinger Health System

**Philadelphia**
Albert Einstein Healthcare Network

**Radnor**
Owner
Jefferson Health System

**Washington**
Washington Hospital

Section B

## SOUTH CAROLINA

**Anderson**
Owner
  AnMed Health Medical Center

**Conway**
Owner
  Conway Medical Center

**Florence**
Owner
  McLeod Regional Medical Center

**Greenwood**
Owner
  Self Regional Healthcare

**West Columbia**
Owner
  Lexington Medical Center

## SOUTH DAKOTA

**Rapid City**
Owner
  Rapid City Regional Hospital

**Sioux Falls**
Owner
  Avera Health

## TENNESSEE

**Crossville**
  Cumberland Medical Center

**Greeneville**
  Laughlin Memorial Hospital

**Johnson City**
Owner
  Mountain States Health Alliance

**Knoxville**
  University of Tennessee Medical Center

**Maryville**
Owner
  Blount Memorial Hospital

## TEXAS

**Arlington**
  Texas Health Resources

**Dallas**
  University of Texas Southwestern Medical Center
Owner
  Methodist Health System

**Galveston**
  University of Texas Medical Branch Hospitals

**Houston**
  Harris Health System
Owner
  University of Texas M.D. Anderson Cancer Center

**Lubbock**
Owner
  University Medical Center

**Nacogdoches**
Owner
  Nacogdoches Memorial Hospital

## VIRGINIA

**Abingdon**
Owner
  Johnston Memorial Hospital

**Chesapeake**
Owner
  Chesapeake Regional Medical Center

**Marion**
Owner
  Smyth County Community Hospital

**Newport News**
  Riverside Health System

**Roanoke**
Owner
  Carilion Clinic

**South Hill**
Owner
  Community Memorial Healthcenter

**Winchester**
Member
  Winchester Medical Center

## WASHINGTON

**Seattle**
  Group Health Cooperative Central Hospital

**Vancouver**
Owner
  PeaceHealth

## WEST VIRGINIA

**Elkins**
Owner
  Davis Memorial Hospital

**Fairmont**
Owner
  West Virginia United Health System

**Huntington**
  Cabell Huntington Hospital
  Pallottine Health Services

**Morgantown**
Owner
  Monongalia General Hospital

**Parkersburg**
Owner
  Camden Clark Medical Center

**Point Pleasant**
Owner
  Pleasant Valley Hospital

**South Charleston**
Owner
  Thomas Memorial Hospital

**Weirton**
Owner
  Weirton Medical Center

## WISCONSIN

**Milwaukee**
Owner
  Aurora Health Care

# SEAGATE ALLIANCE

3445 Winton Place, Sute 222, Rochester, NY Zip 14623–2950; tel. 888/732–4284

## NEW JERSEY

**Newark**
Member
  Columbus Hospital LTACH

## NEW YORK

**Bath**
Member
  Bath Veterans Affairs Medical Center
  Ira Davenport Memorial Hospital

**Buffalo**
Member
  Catholic Health System
  Erie County Medical Center

**Canandaigua**
Member
  F. F. Thompson Hospital

**Carthage**
Member
  Carthage Area Hospital

**Clifton Springs**
Member
  Clifton Springs Hospital and Clinic

**Corning**
Member
  Corning Hospital

**Cuba**
Member
  Cuba Memorial Hospital

**Dansville**
Member
  Nicholas H. Noyes Memorial Hospital

**Elmira**
Member
  Arnot Ogden Medical Center
  Elmira Psychiatric Center
  St. Joseph's Hospital

**Geneva**
Member
  Geneva General Hospital

**Hornell**
Member
  St. James Mercy Health System

**Kenmore**
Member
  Kenmore Mercy Hospital

**Lockport**
Member
  Eastern Niagara Health System

**Montour Falls**
Member
  Schuyler Hospital

**Newark**
Member
  Newark–Wayne Community Hospital

**Olean**
Member
  Olean General Hospital

**Penn Yan**
Member
  Soldiers and Sailors Memorial Hospital of Yates County

**Rochester**
Member
  Highland Hospital of Rochester
  Rochester General Hospital
  Rochester Psychiatric Center
  Strong Memorial Hospital of the University of Rochester
  Unity Hospital

**Springville**
Member
  Bertrand Chaffee Hospital

**Syracuse**
Member
  Upstate University Hospital

**Wellsville**
Member
  Jones Memorial Hospital

## PENNSYLVANIA

**Bradford**
Member
  Bradford Regional Medical Center

**Coudersport**
Member
  Cole Memorial

# SYNERNET, INC.

110 Free Street, Portland, ME Zip 04101–3908; tel. 207/771–3456; Gerry Vicenzi, President and Chief Executive Officer

## MAINE

**Bangor**
Affiliate
  St. Joseph Hospital

**Bar Harbor**
Affiliate
  Mount Desert Island Hospital

**Biddeford**
Affiliate
  Southern Maine Medical Center

**Boothbay Harbor**
Owner
  St. Andrews Hospital and Healthcare Center

**Brunswick**
Affiliate
  Mid Coast Hospital

**Damariscotta**
Owner
  Miles Memorial Hospital

**Farmington**
Owner
  Franklin Memorial Hospital

**Fort Kent**
Affiliate
  Northern Maine Medical Center

**Norway**
Owner
  Stephens Memorial Hospital

**Portland**
Member
 Mercy Hospital of Portland
Owner
 Maine Medical Center
 New England Rehabilitation Hospital of Portland

**Rockport**
Affiliate
 Pen Bay Medical Center

**Sanford**
Owner
 Henrietta D. Goodall Hospital

**Skowhegan**
Affiliate
 Redington–Fairview General Hospital

**Waterville**
Affiliate
 MaineGeneral Medical Center–Waterville Campus

**Westbrook**
Owner
 Spring Harbor Hospital

## THE NEW JERSEY COUNCIL OF TEACHING HOSPITALS
 154 West State Street, Trenton, NJ Zip 08608; tel. 609/656–9600; J. Richard Goldstein M.D., President

### NEW JERSEY
**Camden**
Member
 Cooper Health System

**Newark**
Member
 University of Medicine and Dentistry of New Jersey–University Hospital

**Paterson**
Member
 St. Joseph's Regional Medical Center

**Phillipsburg**
Member
 St. Luke's Hospital – Warren Campus

**Somerville**
Member
 Somerset Medical Center

**Wall Township**
Member
 Meridian Health

## UNIVERSITY HEALTHSYSTEM CONSORTIUM, INC.
 155 North Wacker Drive, Chicago, IL Zip 60606–1787; tel. 312/775–4100; Irene M. Thompson, President and Chief Executive Officer

### ALABAMA
**Alexander City**
Member
 Russell Medical Center

**Bessemer**
Member
 Medical West

**Birmingham**
Member
 University of Alabama Hospital

**Mobile**
Member
 University of South Alabama Medical Center

### ARIZONA
**Phoenix**
Member
 Maricopa Integrated Health System
 Mayo Clinic Hospital

**Tucson**
Member
 University of Arizona Medical Center – South Campus
 University of Arizona Medical Center – University Campus

### ARKANSAS
**Little Rock**
Member
 UAMS Medical Center

### CALIFORNIA
**Bakersfield**
Member
 Kern Medical Center

**Colton**
Member
 Arrowhead Regional Medical Center

**Downey**
Affiliate
 Rancho Los Amigos National Rehabilitation Center

**French Camp**
Member
 San Joaquin General Hospital

**Joshua Tree**
Member
 Hi–Desert Medical Center

**Los Angeles**
Lease
 Stewart & Lynda Resnick Neuropsychiatric Hospital at UCLA
Member
 Cedars–Sinai Medical Center
 Keck Hospital of USC
 Ronald Reagan University of California Los Angeles Medical Center

**Martinez**
Affiliate
 Contra Costa Regional Medical Center

**Moreno Valley**
Member
 Riverside County Regional Medical Center

**Oakland**
Member
 Alameda County Medical Center

**Orange**
Member
 University of California, Irvine Healthcare

**Palo Alto**
Member
 Lucile Salter Packard Children's Hospital at Stanford
 Stanford Hospital and Clinics

**Portola**
Member
 Eastern Plumas Health Care District

**Sacramento**
Member
 University of California, Davis Medical Center

**San Diego**
Member
 UC San Diego Health System

**San Francisco**
Member
 Laguna Honda Hospital and Rehabilitation Center
 San Francisco General Hospital Medical Center
 UCSF Medical Center

**San Jose**
Affiliate
 Santa Clara Valley Medical Center

**Santa Monica**
Affiliate
 Santa Monica–UCLA Medical Center and Orthopaedic Hospital

**Sylmar**
Affiliate
 LAC–Olive View–UCLA Medical Center

**Torrance**
Member
 LAC–Harbor–University of California at Los Angeles Medical Center

### COLORADO
**Aurora**
Member
 University of Colorado Hospital

**Colorado Springs**
Member
 Memorial Health System

**Denver**
Affiliate
 National Jewish Health
Member
 Denver Health Medical Center

**Fort Collins**
Member
 Poudre Valley Hospital

**Loveland**
Member
 Medical Center of the Rockies

### CONNECTICUT
**Bridgeport**
Member
 Bridgeport Hospital

**Farmington**
Member
 University of Connecticut Health Center, John Dempsey Hospital

**Greenwich**
Member
 Greenwich Hospital

**New Haven**
Member
 Yale–New Haven Hospital

### DISTRICT OF COLUMBIA
**Washington**
Member
 Howard University Hospital
 MedStar Georgetown University Hospital
 MedStar Washington Hospital Center

### FLORIDA
**Gainesville**
Member
 Shands at the University of Florida
 Shands HealthCare

**Jacksonville**
Member
 Mayo Clinic Jacksonville
Owner
 Shands Jacksonville Medical Center

**Miami**
Member
 Jackson Health System

**Tampa**
Member
 Tampa General Hospital

**Weston**
Member
 Cleveland Clinic Florida

### GEORGIA
**Atlanta**
Member
 Emory Healthcare
 Emory University Hospital
 Emory University Hospital Midtown
 Grady Memorial Hospital
 Saint Joseph's Hospital of Atlanta

**Johns Creek**
Member
 Emory Johns Creek Hospital

**Waycross**
Member
 Mayo Clinic Health System in Waycross

### ILLINOIS
**Aurora**
Member
 Rush–Copley Medical Center

**Chicago**
Member
 Cook County Health and Hospitals System
 John H. Stroger Jr. Hospital of Cook County
 La Rabida Children's Hospital
 Northwestern Memorial Hospital
 Provident Hospital of Cook County
 Rush University Medical Center
 Sinai Health System
 University of Chicago Medical Center
 University of Illinois Hospital & Health Sciences System

**Hinsdale**
Member
  RML Specialty Hospital

**Lake Forest**
Member
  Northwestern Lake Forest Hospital

**Maywood**
Member
  Loyola University Medical Center

**Melrose Park**
Member
  Gottlieb Memorial Hospital

**Oak Forest**
Member
  Oak Forest Health Center of Cook County

**Oak Park**
Member
  Rush Oak Park Hospital

## INDIANA

**Avon**
Member
  Indiana University Health West Hospital

**Bedford**
Member
  Indiana University Health Bedford Hospital

**Bloomington**
Member
  Indiana University Health Bloomington Hospital

**Carmel**
Member
  Indiana University Health North Hospital

**Goshen**
Member
  Indiana University Health Goshen Hospital

**Hartford City**
Member
  Indiana University Health Blackford Hospital

**Indianapolis**
Member
  Indiana University Health
  Wishard Health Services

**Knox**
Member
  Indiana University Health Starke Hospital

**La Porte**
Member
  Indiana University Health La Porte Hospital

**Lafayette**
Member
  Indiana University Health Arnett Hospital

**Martinsville**
Member
  Indiana University Health Morgan Hospital

**Monticello**
Member
  Indiana University Health White Memorial Hospital

**Muncie**
Member
  Indiana University Health Ball Memorial Hospital

**Paoli**
Member
  Indiana University Health Paoli Hospital

**Tipton**
Member
  Indiana University Health Tipton Hospital

## IOWA

**Belmond**
Member
  Iowa Specialty Hospital–Belmond

**Clarion**
Member
  Iowa Specialty Hospital–Clarion

**Iowa City**
Member
  University of Iowa Hospitals and Clinics

**Keosauqua**
Member
  Van Buren County Hospital

**Marengo**
Member
  Marengo Memorial Hospital

**Shenandoah**
Member
  Shenandoah Medical Center

**Sigourney**
Member
  Keokuk County Health Center

**Waverly**
Member
  Waverly Health Center

## KANSAS

**Kansas City**
Member
  The University of Kansas Hospital

**Overland Park**
Member
  Saint Luke's South Hospital

## KENTUCKY

**Cynthiana**
Member
  Harrison Memorial Hospital

**Lexington**
Member
  University of Kentucky Albert B. Chandler Hospital

**Louisville**
Member
  University of Louisville Hospital

**Morehead**
Member
  St. Claire Regional Medical Center

**Mount Vernon**
Member
  Rockcastle Regional Hospital and Respiratory Care
  Center

## LOUISIANA

**Monroe**
Member
  E. A. Conway Medical Center

**Pineville**
Member
  Huey P. Long Medical Center

## MAINE

**Portland**
Member
  Maine Medical Center

## MARYLAND

**Baltimore**
Affiliate
  Kernan Orthopaedics and Rehabilitation
Member
  Johns Hopkins Bayview Medical Center
  Johns Hopkins Hospital
  Maryland General Hospital
  MedStar Franklin Square Medical Center
  MedStar Good Samaritan Hospital
  MedStar Harbor Hospital
  MedStar Union Memorial Hospital
  Mt. Washington Pediatric Hospital
  University of Maryland Medical Center

**Cambridge**
Member
  Dorchester General Hospital

**Chestertown**
Member
  Chester River Health System

**Easton**
Member
  Memorial Hospital at Easton Maryland

**Glen Burnie**
Member
  Baltimore Washington Medical Center

**La Plata**
Member
  University of Maryland Charles Regional Medical
  Center

**Leonardtown**
Member
  MedStar St. Mary's Hospital

**Olney**
Member
  MedStar Montgomery Medical Center

**Towson**
Member
  University of Maryland St. Joseph Medical Center

## MASSACHUSETTS

**Ayer**
Member
  Nashoba Valley Medical Center

**Boston**
  Dana–Farber Cancer Institute
Member
  Boston Medical Center
  Brigham and Women's Faulkner Hospital
  Brigham and Women's Hospital
  Carney Hospital
  Massachusetts General Hospital
  Partners HealthCare System, Inc.
  Steward Health Care System, LLC
  Tufts Medical Center

**Brighton**
Member
  St. Elizabeth's Medical Center

**Brockton**
Member
  Good Samaritan Medical Center

**Cambridge**
Member
  Cambridge Health Alliance

**Clinton**
Affiliate
  Clinton Hospital

**Concord**
Member
  Emerson Hospital

**Fall River**
Member
  Saint Anne's Hospital

**Greenfield**
Member
  Baystate Franklin Medical Center

**Haverhill**
Member
  Merrimack Valley Hospital

**Holyoke**
Member
  Holyoke Medical Center

**Leominster**
Member
  Health Alliance Hospitals

**Marlborough**
Affiliate
  UMass Memorial–Marlborough Hospital

**Melrose**
Member
  Hallmark Health System

**Methuen**
Member
  Holy Family Hospital and Medical Center

**Newton Lower Falls**
Member
  Newton–Wellesley Hospital

**Norwood**
Member
  Norwood Hospital

**Palmer**
Member
  Wing Memorial Hospital and Medical Centers

**Quincy**
Member
  Quincy Medical Center

**Salem**
Member
  North Shore Medical Center

**Springfield**
Member
  Baystate Medical Center

**Taunton**
Member
   Morton Hospital and Medical Center

**Ware**
Member
   Baystate Mary Lane Hospital

## MICHIGAN
**Ann Arbor**
Member
   University of Michigan Hospitals and Health Centers

**Flint**
Member
   Hurley Medical Center

**Grosse Pointe**
Member
   Beaumont Hospital Grosse Pointe

**Royal Oak**
Member
   Beaumont Hospital – Royal Oak

**Troy**
Member
   Beaumont Hospital – Troy

## MINNESOTA
**Albert Lea**
Member
   Mayo Clinic Health System in Albert Lea

**Austin**
Member
   Mayo Clinic Health System in Austin

**Burnsville**
Lease
   Fairview Ridges Hospital

**Edina**
Member
   Fairview Southdale Hospital

**Fairmont**
Member
   Mayo Clinic Health System in Fairmont

**Hibbing**
Member
   Range Regional Health Services

**Mankato**
Member
   Mayo Clinic Health System in Mankato

**Minneapolis**
Member
   Hennepin County Medical Center
   University of Minnesota Medical Center, Fairview

**Princeton**
Member
   Fairview Northland Medical Center

**Rochester**
Member
   Mayo Clinic – Saint Marys Hospital
   Rochester Methodist Hospital

**Saint Paul**
Member
   Regions Hospital

**Stillwater**
Member
   Lakeview Hospital

**Wyoming**
Member
   Fairview Lakes Health Services

## MISSISSIPPI
**Jackson**
Member
   University Hospitals and Health System, University of
      Mississippi Medical Center

**Lexington**
Member
   Holmes County Hospital and Clinics

## MISSOURI
**Boonville**
Member
   Cooper County Memorial Hospital

**Columbia**
Member
   University of Missouri Health Care
   University of Missouri Hospitals and Clinics
   Women's and Children's Hospital

**Jefferson City**
Member
   Capital Region Medical Center

**Kansas City**
Member
   Saint Luke's Hospital of Kansas City
   Saint Luke's North Hospital – Barry Road
   Truman Medical Center–Hospital Hill
   Truman Medical Center–Lakewood

**Lee's Summit**
Member
   Saint Luke's East Hospital

**Milan**
Member
   Sullivan County Memorial Hospital

**Saint Louis**
Member
   Barnes–Jewish Hospital
   Barnes–Jewish West County Hospital

## NEBRASKA
**Bellevue**
Member
   Bellevue Medical Center

**O'Neill**
Member
   Avera St. Anthony's Hospital

**Omaha**
Member
   Nebraska Medical Center

## NEVADA
**Las Vegas**
Affiliate
   University Medical Center

## NEW HAMPSHIRE
**Lebanon**
Member
   Dartmouth–Hitchcock Medical Center

## NEW JERSEY
**Hamilton**
Member
   Robert Wood Johnson University Hospital at Hamilton

**Morristown**
Member
   Atlantic Health
   Morristown Medical Center

**New Brunswick**
Member
   Robert Wood Johnson University Hospital

**Newark**
Member
   University of Medicine and Dentistry of New
      Jersey–University Hospital

**Rahway**
Member
   Robert Wood Johnson University Hospital Rahway

**Summit**
Member
   Overlook Medical Center

**Wall Township**
Member
   Meridian Health

## NEW MEXICO
**Albuquerque**
Member
   University of New Mexico Hospitals

**Rio Rancho**
Member
   UNM Sandoval Regional Medical Center

## NEW YORK
**Albany**
Member
   Albany Medical Center

**Bay Shore**
Member
   Southside Hospital

**Bronx**
Member
   Jacobi Medical Center
   Lincoln Medical and Mental Health Center
   Montefiore Medical Center
   North Central Bronx Hospital

**Brooklyn**
Member
   Coney Island Hospital
   SUNY Downstate Medical Center University Hospital
   Woodhull Medical and Mental Health Center

**Canandaigua**
Member
   F. F. Thompson Hospital

**Elmhurst**
Member
   Elmhurst Hospital Center

**Forest Hills**
Member
   Forest Hills Hospital

**Glen Cove**
Member
   Glen Cove Hospital

**Great Neck**
Member
   North Shore–Long Island Jewish Health System

**Greenport**
Member
   Eastern Long Island Hospital

**Huntington**
Member
   Huntington Hospital

**Jamaica**
Member
   Queens Hospital Center

**Manhasset**
Member
   North Shore University Hospital

**New Hyde Park**
Member
   Long Island Jewish Medical Center

**New York**
Member
   Coler–Goldwater Specialty Hospital and Nursing
      Facility
   Lenox Hill Hospital
   Mount Sinai Hospital
   New York City Health and Hospitals Corporation
   New York–Presbyterian Hospital

**Plainview**
Member
   Plainview Hospital

**Riverhead**
Member
   Peconic Bay Medical Center

**Rochester**
Member
   Highland Hospital of Rochester
   Strong Memorial Hospital of the University of
      Rochester

**Staten Island**
Member
   Staten Island University Hospital

**Stony Brook**
Member
   Stony Brook University Medical Center

**Syosset**
Member
   Syosset Hospital

**Syracuse**
Member
   Upstate University Hospital

**Valley Stream**
Member
   Franklin Hospital

## NORTH CAROLINA

**Ahoskie**
Affiliate
Vidant Roanoke–Chowan Hospital

**Chapel Hill**
Member
University of North Carolina Hospitals

**Danbury**
Member
Pioneer Community Hospital of Stokes

**Durham**
Member
Duke University Hospital
Durham Regional Hospital

**Edenton**
Member
Vidant Chowan Hospital

**Greenville**
Member
Vidant Medical Center

**Lexington**
Member
Wake Forest Baptist Health–Lexington Medical Center

**Mocksville**
Member
Wake Forest Baptist Health–Davie Hospital

**Raleigh**
Member
Duke Raleigh Hospital
Rex Healthcare

**Tarboro**
Member
Vidant Edgecombe Hospital

**Windsor**
Affiliate
Vidant Bertie Hospital

**Winston–Salem**
Member
Wake Forest Baptist Health
Wake Forest Baptist Medical Center

**Yadkinville**
Member
Yadkin Valley Community Hospital

## OHIO

**Ashtabula**
Member
Ashtabula County Medical Center

**Barnesville**
Member
Barnesville Hospital

**Bellefontaine**
Member
Mary Rutan Hospital

**Bucyrus**
Member
Bucyrus Community Hospital

**Cadiz**
Member
Harrison Community Hospital

**Chardon**
Affiliate
University Hospitals Geauga Medical Center

**Cincinnati**
Member
Cincinnati Children's Hospital Medical Center
Drake Center
University Hospital

**Circleville**
Member
Berger Health System

**Cleveland**
Member
Cleveland Clinic
Fairview Hospital
Hillcrest Hospital
Lutheran Hospital
University Hospitals Case Medical Center

**Coldwater**
Member
Mercer Health

**Columbus**
Member
Ohio State University Wexner Medical Center

**Conneaut**
Affiliate
University Hospitals Conneaut Medical Center

**Euclid**
Member
Euclid Hospital

**Garfield Heights**
Member
Marymount Hospital

**Geneva**
Affiliate
University Hospitals Geneva Medical Center

**Lakewood**
Member
Lakewood Hospital

**London**
Member
Madison County Hospital

**Medina**
Member
Medina Hospital

**Middleburg Heights**
Member
Southwest General Health Center

**Sidney**
Member
Wilson Memorial Hospital

**Toledo**
Member
The University of Toledo Medical Center

**Upper Sandusky**
Member
Wyandot Memorial Hospital

**Warrensville Heights**
Member
South Pointe Hospital

**Washington Court House**
Member
Fayette County Memorial Hospital

**Westlake**
Member
St. John Medical Center

## OREGON

**Grants Pass**
Member
Three Rivers Medical Center

**Medford**
Member
Asante Health System
Rogue Valley Medical Center

**Portland**
Member
OHSU Hospital

## PENNSYLVANIA

**Allentown**
Member
Lehigh Valley Hospital

**Bryn Mawr**
Member
Bryn Mawr Hospital

**Hershey**
Member
Penn State Milton S. Hershey Medical Center

**Media**
Member
Riddle Hospital

**Paoli**
Member
Paoli Hospital

**Philadelphia**
Affiliate
Penn Presbyterian Medical Center
Thomas Jefferson University Hospital
Member
Children's Hospital of Philadelphia
Fox Chase Cancer Center–American Oncologic
Hospital
Hospital of the University of Pennsylvania
Jeanes Hospital
Pennsylvania Hospital
Temple University Hospital

**Pittsburgh**
Member
UPMC Presbyterian Shadyside

**Wynnewood**
Member
Lankenau Medical Center

## RHODE ISLAND

**Providence**
Member
Miriam Hospital
Rhode Island Hospital

**Westerly**
Member
Westerly Hospital

## SOUTH CAROLINA

**Charleston**
Member
MUSC Medical Center of Medical University of South
Carolina

**Clinton**
Member
Laurens County Health Care System

**Columbia**
Member
Palmetto Health

**Easley**
Member
Baptist Easley Hospital

**Greenville**
Member
Greenville Health System
Patewood Memorial Hospital

**Greer**
Member
Greer Memorial Hospital

**Simpsonville**
Member
Hillcrest Memorial Hospital

**Travelers Rest**
Member
North Greenville Hospital

## TENNESSEE

**Knoxville**
Member
University of Tennessee Medical Center

**Nashville**
Member
Vanderbilt Hospital and Clinics

## TEXAS

**Baytown**
Member
San Jacinto Methodist Hospital

**Dallas**
Member
Parkland Health & Hospital System
University of Texas Southwestern Medical Center

**Fort Worth**
Member
JPS Health Network

**Galveston**
Member
University of Texas Medical Branch Hospitals

**Houston**
Member
Harris Health System
Memorial Hermann – Texas Medical Center
Methodist West Houston Hospital
Methodist Willowbrook Hospital
St. Luke's Episcopal Hospital
St. Luke's Hospital at the Vintage
The Methodist Hospital
TIRR Memorial Hermann
University of Texas M.D. Anderson Cancer Center

**Pasadena**
Member
St. Luke's Patients Medical Center

**Sugar Land**
Member
Methodist Sugar Land Hospital
St. Luke's Sugar Land Hospital

**The Woodlands**
Member
St. Luke's Lakeside Hospital
St. Luke's The Woodlands Hospital

**Tyler**
Affiliate
University of Texas Health Science Center at Tyler

**UTAH**
**Gunnison**
Member
Gunnison Valley Hospital

**Moab**
Member
Moab Regional Hospital

**Monticello**
Member
San Juan Hospital

**Salt Lake City**
Member
University of Utah Health Care – Hospital and Clinics

**VERMONT**
**Berlin**
Member
Central Vermont Medical Center

**Brattleboro**
Member
Brattleboro Retreat

**Burlington**
Member
Fletcher Allen Health Care

**VIRGINIA**
**Charlottesville**
Member
University of Virginia Medical Center
UVA–HEALTHSOUTH Rehabilitation Hospital

**Culpeper**
Member
Culpeper Regional Hospital

**Richmond**
Member
VCU Health System

**WASHINGTON**
**Renton**
Member
UW Medicine/Valley Medical Center

**Seattle**
Member
Seattle Cancer Care Alliance
University of Washington Medical Center
UW Medicine/Harborview Medical Center
UW Medicine/Northwest Hospital & Medical Center

**WEST VIRGINIA**
**Morgantown**
Member
West Virginia University Hospitals

**Ranson**
Member
Jefferson Medical Center

**WISCONSIN**
**Eau Claire**
Member
Mayo Clinic Health System in Eau Claire

**Friendship**
Member
Moundview Memorial Hospital & Clinics

**Hudson**
Member
Hudson Hospital and Clinics

**Madison**
Member
University of Wisconsin Hospital and Clinics

**Medford**
Affiliate
Memorial Health Center

**New Richmond**
Member
Westfields Hospital

**Portage**
Member
Divine Savior Healthcare

**Wausau**
Affiliate
Aspirus Wausau Hospital

**Wisconsin Rapids**
Member
Riverview Hospital Association

**VANTAGE HEALTHCARE NETWORK, INC.**
18282 Technology Drive, Suite 202,
Meadville, PA Zip 16335;
tel. 814/337–0000; David Petrarca,
Director Retail Operations

**VHA, INC.**
220 Las Colinas Boulevard East, Irving,
TX Zip 75039–5500; tel. 972/830–0254;
Curtis W. Nonomaque, President and
Chief Executive Officer

**ALABAMA**
**Alabaster**
Shelby Baptist Medical Center

**Anniston**
Partner
Northeast Alabama Regional Medical Center

**Athens**
Partner
Athens–Limestone Hospital

**Atmore**
Atmore Community Hospital

**Birmingham**
Princeton Baptist Medical Center
Shareholder
Baptist Health System

**Boaz**
Marshall Medical Center South

**Brewton**
D. W. McMillan Memorial Hospital

**Carrollton**
Pickens County Medical Center

**Chatom**
Washington County Hospital and Nursing Home

**Decatur**
Decatur General Hospital

**Fairhope**
Thomas Hospital

**Fayette**
Fayette Medical Center

**Fort Payne**
DeKalb Regional Medical Center

**Grove Hill**
Grove Hill Memorial Hospital

**Guntersville**
Marshall Medical Center North
Partner
Marshall Health System

**Hamilton**
North Mississippi Medical Center–Hamilton

**Huntsville**
Huntsville Hospital

**Jasper**
Walker Baptist Medical Center

**Montgomery**
Baptist Medical Center East
Shareholder
Baptist Medical Center South

**Moulton**
Lawrence Medical Center

**Northport**
Northport Medical Center

**Opp**
Mizell Memorial Hospital

**Ozark**
Dale Medical Center

**Prattville**
Prattville Baptist Hospital

**Scottsboro**
Partner
Highlands Medical Center

**Sylacauga**
Coosa Valley Medical Center

**Talladega**
Citizens Baptist Medical Center

**Tuscaloosa**
DCH Regional Medical Center
Partner
DCH Health System

**Union Springs**
Bullock County Hospital

**ALASKA**
**Anchorage**
Providence Alaska Medical Center

**Cordova**
Cordova Community Medical Center

**Kodiak**
Providence Kodiak Island Medical Center

**Seward**
Providence Seward Medical Center

**Valdez**
Providence Valdez Medical Center

**Wrangell**
Wrangell Medical Center

**ARIZONA**
**Bisbee**
Copper Queen Community Hospital

**Phoenix**
Mayo Clinic Hospital

**Safford**
Mt. Graham Regional Medical Center

**Scottsdale**
Scottsdale Healthcare Shea Medical Center
Scottsdale Healthcare Thompson Peak Hospital
Unit_of
Scottsdale Healthcare–Osborn Medical Center

**Tucson**
TMC Healthcare

**ARKANSAS**
**Arkadelphia**
Baptist Health Medical Center–Arkadelphia

**Booneville**
Booneville Community Hospital

**Clinton**
Ozark Health Medical Center

**Conway**
Partner
Conway Regional Medical Center

**Fayetteville**
Partner
Washington Regional Medical Center

**Heber Springs**
Baptist Health Medical Center–Heber Springs

**Jonesboro**
NEA Baptist Memorial Hospital
Partner
St. Bernards Medical Center

**Little Rock**
Baptist Health Medical Center–Little Rock
Shareholder
Baptist Health

**North Little Rock**
Baptist Health Medical Center – North Little Rock

Section B

**Paragould**
Partner
Arkansas Methodist Medical Center

**Piggott**
Piggott Community Hospital

**Searcy**
White County Medical Center

**Stuttgart**
Baptist Health Medical Center–Stuttgart

**Walnut Ridge**
Lawrence Memorial Hospital

**West Memphis**
Crittenden Regional Hospital

**Wynne**
CrossRidge Community Hospital

**CALIFORNIA**

**Alameda**
Alameda Hospital

**Antioch**
Sutter Delta Medical Center

**Arcadia**
Methodist Hospital of Southern California

**Auburn**
Sutter Auburn Faith Hospital

**Berkeley**
Alta Bates Medical Center–Herrick Campus
Alta Bates Summit Medical Center

**Burbank**
Providence Saint Joseph Medical Center

**Burlingame**
Mills–Peninsula Health Services

**Castro Valley**
Eden Medical Center

**Clovis**
Clovis Community Medical Center

**Concord**
John Muir Medical Center, Concord

**Covina**
Citrus Valley Health Partners

**Crescent City**
Sutter Coast Hospital

**Davis**
Sutter Davis Hospital

**El Centro**
El Centro Regional Medical Center

**Encinitas**
Scripps Memorial Hospital–Encinitas

**Escondido**
Palomar Health
Palomar Medical Center

**Fresno**
Community Regional Medical Center
Fresno Heart and Surgical Hospital
Shareholder
Community Medical Centers

**Glendora**
Foothill Presbyterian Hospital

**Greenbrae**
Marin General Hospital

**Jackson**
Sutter Amador Hospital

**La Jolla**
Scripps Green Hospital
Shareholder
Scripps Memorial Hospital–La Jolla

**Lakeport**
Sutter Lakeside Hospital

**Lancaster**
Partner
Antelope Valley Hospital

**Los Angeles**
Shareholder
Cedars–Sinai Medical Center

**Mariposa**
John C. Fremont Healthcare District

**Menlo Park**
Menlo Park Surgical Hospital

**Mission Hills**
Providence Holy Cross Medical Center

**Modesto**
Partner
Memorial Medical Center

**Monterey**
Community Hospital of the Monterey Peninsula

**Novato**
Novato Community Hospital

**Oakland**
Alta Bates Summit Medical Center – Summit Campus

**Pasadena**
Huntington Memorial Hospital

**Pleasanton**
ValleyCare Medical Center

**Pomona**
Partner
Pomona Valley Hospital Medical Center

**Poway**
Pomerado Hospital

**Roseville**
Sutter Roseville Medical Center

**Sacramento**
Sutter Medical Center, Sacramento
Shareholder
Sutter Health

**San Diego**
Scripps Health
Scripps Mercy Hospital

**San Francisco**
California Pacific Medical Center–Davies Campus
Chinese Hospital
St. Luke's Hospital
Shareholder
California Pacific Medical Center

**San Pedro**
Providence Little Company of Mary Medical Center
San Pedro

**Santa Barbara**
Cottage Health System
Goleta Valley Cottage Hospital
Partner
Santa Barbara Cottage Hospital

**Santa Cruz**
Sutter Maternity and Surgery Center of Santa Cruz

**Santa Rosa**
Sutter Medical Center of Santa Rosa, Chanate
Campus

**Solvang**
Santa Ynez Valley Cottage Hospital

**Tarzana**
Providence Tarzana Medical Center

**Torrance**
Providence Little Company of Mary Medical Center
Partner
Torrance Memorial Medical Center

**Tracy**
Sutter Tracy Community Hospital

**Turlock**
Partner
Emanuel Medical Center

**Vallejo**
Sutter Solano Medical Center

**Walnut Creek**
John Muir Health
John Muir Medical Center, Walnut Creek

**Whittier**
Partner
Presbyterian Intercommunity Hospital

**COLORADO**

**Alamosa**
Partner
San Luis Valley Regional Medical Center

**Aspen**
Partner
Aspen Valley Hospital District

**Boulder**
Partner
Boulder Community Hospital

**Colorado Springs**
Partner
Memorial Health System

**Denver**
Exempla Healthcare, Inc.
Exempla Saint Joseph Hospital

**Englewood**
Craig Hospital

**Estes Park**
Estes Park Medical Center

**Fort Collins**
Poudre Valley Hospital

**Gunnison**
Partner
Gunnison Valley Hospital

**Haxtun**
Haxtun Hospital District

**Kremmling**
Middle Park Medical Center

**La Jara**
Conejos County Hospital

**Lafayette**
Exempla Good Samaritan Medical Center

**Longmont**
Partner
Longmont United Hospital

**Loveland**
Medical Center of the Rockies

**Steamboat Springs**
Partner
Yampa Valley Medical Center

**Vail**
Shareholder
Vail Valley Medical Center

**Wheat Ridge**
Shareholder
Exempla Lutheran Medical Center

**Yuma**
Yuma District Hospital

**CONNECTICUT**

**Bridgeport**
Bridgeport Hospital

**Danbury**
Partner
Danbury Hospital

**Greenwich**
Partner
Greenwich Hospital

**Hartford**
Connecticut Children's Medical Center
Shareholder
Hartford Hospital

**Manchester**
Eastern Connecticut Health Network
Manchester Memorial Hospital

**Meriden**
Partner
MidState Medical Center

**Middletown**
Partner
Middlesex Hospital

**New Haven**
Yale New Haven Health System
Yale–New Haven Hospital

**New Milford**
New Milford Hospital

**Norwalk**
Norwalk Hospital

**Putnam**
Day Kimball Hospital

**Stamford**
Partner
Stamford Hospital

**Torrington**
Partner
The Charlotte Hungerford Hospital

**Vernon Rockville**
Rockville General Hospital

**Wallingford**
Gaylord Hospital

**Willimantic**
Windham Hospital

**DISTRICT OF COLUMBIA**

**Washington**
MedStar Georgetown University Hospital
MedStar Washington Hospital Center

## FLORIDA

**Apalachicola**
George E. Weems Memorial Hospital

**Boca Raton**
Partner
Boca Raton Regional Hospital

**Boynton Beach**
Partner
Bethesda Memorial Hospital

**Cape Coral**
Cape Coral Hospital

**Clermont**
South Lake Hospital

**Cocoa Beach**
Health First Cape Canaveral Hospital

**Daytona Beach**
Shareholder
Halifax Health Medical Center of Daytona Beach

**Fort Myers**
Gulf Coast Medical Center
Partner
Lee Memorial Hospital

**Gulf Breeze**
Gulf Breeze Hospital

**Inverness**
Partner
Citrus Memorial Health System

**Jacksonville**
Mayo Clinic Jacksonville

**Jay**
Jay Hospital

**Lakeland**
Shareholder
Lakeland Regional Medical Center

**Leesburg**
Leesburg Regional Medical Center

**Melbourne**
Circles of Care
Health First Palm Bay Hospital
Shareholder
Health First Holmes Regional Medical Center

**New Smyrna Beach**
Bert Fish Medical Center

**Ocala**
Partner
Munroe Regional Medical Center

**Ocoee**
Health Central

**Orlando**
Orlando Regional Medical Center
Shareholder
Orlando Health

**Panama City**
Bay Medical Center Sacred Heart

**Pensacola**
Baptist Hospital
Shareholder
Baptist Health Care Corporation

**Rockledge**
Health First, Inc.

**Stuart**
Martin Health System

**Tallahassee**
Shareholder
Tallahassee Memorial HealthCare

**Tampa**
Florida Hospital–Carrollwood
Partner
Florida Hospital Tampa

**Tarpon Springs**
Florida Hospital North Pinellas

**Titusville**
Partner
Parrish Medical Center

## GEORGIA

**Albany**
Phoebe Putney Health System
Partner
Phoebe Putney Memorial Hospital

**Americus**
Phoebe Sumter Medical Center

**Athens**
Partner
Athens Regional Medical Center

**Atlanta**
Partner
Northside Hospital

**Augusta**
University Hospital

**Austell**
WellStar Cobb Hospital

**Blakely**
Pioneer Community Hospital of Early

**Brunswick**
Southeast Georgia Health System
Southeast Georgia Health System Brunswick Campus

**Cairo**
Grady General Hospital

**Camilla**
Mitchell County Hospital

**Canton**
Northside Hospital–Cherokee

**Chatsworth**
Murray Medical Center

**Cochran**
Bleckley Memorial Hospital

**Columbus**
Columbus Regional Healthcare System
Columbus Specialty Hospital
Doctors Hospital of Columbus
Hughston Hospital
Partner
The Medical Center

**Cordele**
Crisp Regional Hospital

**Cumming**
Northside Hospital–Forsyth

**Cuthbert**
Southwest Georgia Regional Medical Center

**Dallas**
WellStar Paulding Hospital

**Dalton**
Partner
Hamilton Medical Center

**Decatur**
DeKalb Medical at Downtown Decatur
Partner
DeKalb Medical at North Decatur

**Douglas**
Coffee Regional Medical Center

**Douglasville**
WellStar Douglas Hospital

**Fitzgerald**
Dorminy Medical Center

**Gainesville**
Northeast Georgia Medical Center

**Hawkinsville**
Taylor Regional Hospital

**Homerville**
Clinch Memorial Hospital

**Lakeland**
Louis Smith Memorial Hospital

**Lawrenceville**
Partner
Gwinnett Hospital System

**Lithonia**
DeKalb Medical at Hillandale

**Macon**
Partner
Medical Center of Central Georgia

**Marietta**
WellStar Health System
WellStar Windy Hill Hospital
Partner
WellStar Kennestone Hospital

**Moultrie**
Colquitt Regional Medical Center

**Perry**
Perry Hospital

**Quitman**
Brooks County Hospital

**Riverdale**
Partner
Southern Regional Medical Center

**Rome**
Kindred Hospital Rome
Partner
Floyd Medical Center

**Saint Marys**
Southeast Georgia Health System Camden Campus

**Sylvester**
Phoebe Worth Medical Center

**Thomasville**
Partner
Archbold Medical Center
John D. Archbold Memorial Hospital

**Tifton**
Tift Regional Medical Center

**Valdosta**
Partner
South Georgia Medical Center

**Warner Robins**
Houston Medical Center

**Waycross**
Mayo Clinic Health System in Waycross

## HAWAII

**Honolulu**
Queen's Health Systems
Queen's Medical Center

**Kaunakakai**
Molokai General Hospital

**Wahiawa**
Wahiawa General Hospital

## IDAHO

**American Falls**
Power County Hospital District

**Arco**
Lost Rivers Medical Center

**Blackfoot**
Bingham Memorial Hospital

**Boise**
Elks Rehab Hospital
St. Luke's Health System
Shareholder
St. Luke's Regional Medical Center

**Bonners Ferry**
Boundary Community Hospital

**Cascade**
Cascade Medical Center

**Coeur D'Alene**
Partner
Kootenai Medical Center

**Emmett**
Walter Knox Memorial Hospital

**Gooding**
North Canyon Medical Center

**Grangeville**
Syringa Hospital and Clinics

**Jerome**
St. Luke's Jerome

**Ketchum**
St. Luke's Wood River Medical Center

**Malad City**
Oneida County Hospital

**McCall**
St. Luke's McCall

**Montpelier**
Bear Lake Memorial Hospital

**Mountain Home**
St. Luke's Elmore

**Orofino**
Clearwater Valley Hospital and Clinics

**Preston**
Franklin County Medical Center

**Rupert**
Minidoka Memorial Hospital

**Sandpoint**
Partner
Bonner General Hospital

**Twin Falls**
Partner
St. Luke's Magic Valley Medical Center

**Weiser**
 Weiser Memorial Hospital

**ILLINOIS**

**Alton**
 Alton Memorial Hospital

**Belleville**
Partner
 Memorial Hospital

**Canton**
 Graham Hospital

**Carbondale**
 Memorial Hospital of Carbondale
Partner
 Southern Illinois Hospital Services

**Chester**
 Memorial Hospital

**Chicago**
Partner
 Swedish Covenant Hospital

**Decatur**
 Decatur Memorial Hospital

**DeKalb**
 Kish Health System
Partner
 Kishwaukee Hospital

**Elgin**
Partner
 Advocate Sherman Hospital

**Elmhurst**
Partner
 Elmhurst Memorial Hospital

**Eureka**
 Advocate Eureka Hospital

**Evanston**
 NorthShore University Health System Evanston
  Hospital

**Evergreen Park**
Partner
 Little Company of Mary Hospital and Health Care
  Centers

**Flora**
 Clay County Hospital

**Freeport**
Partner
 FHN Memorial Hospital

**Geneseo**
 Hammond–Henry Hospital

**Geneva**
 Delnor Hospital

**Greenville**
 Greenville Regional Hospital

**Herrin**
 Herrin Hospital

**Jacksonville**
Partner
 Passavant Area Hospital

**Jerseyville**
 Jersey Community Hospital

**Lake Forest**
Partner
 Northwestern Lake Forest Hospital

**Lincoln**
 Abraham Lincoln Memorial Hospital

**Macomb**
Partner
 McDonough District Hospital

**Maryville**
Partner
 Anderson Hospital

**Mattoon**
 Sarah Bush Lincoln Health Center

**Mendota**
 Mendota Community Hospital

**Monticello**
 Kirby Medical Center

**Murphysboro**
 St. Joseph Memorial Hospital

**Naperville**
 Edward Hospital

**New Lenox**
Partner
 Silver Cross Hospital

**Normal**
Partner
 Advocate BroMenn Medical Center

**Peoria**
Partner
 Proctor Hospital

**Pittsfield**
 Illini Community Hospital

**Quincy**
Partner
 Blessing Hospital

**Rockford**
 SwedishAmerican Hospital

**Rushville**
 Sarah D. Culbertson Memorial Hospital

**Salem**
 Salem Township Hospital

**Sandwich**
 Valley West Hospital

**Shelbyville**
 Shelby Memorial Hospital

**Skokie**
 NorthShore University Health System Skokie Hospital

**Springfield**
 Memorial Health System
Shareholder
 Memorial Medical Center

**Taylorville**
 Taylorville Memorial Hospital

**INDIANA**

**Anderson**
 Community Hospital of Anderson and Madison County

**Avon**
 Indiana University Health West Hospital

**Batesville**
 Margaret Mary Health

**Bedford**
 Indiana University Health Bedford Hospital

**Bloomington**
Partner
 Indiana University Health Bloomington Hospital

**Bremen**
 Community Hospital of Bremen
 Doctor's Hospital and Neuromuscular Center

**Carmel**
 Indiana University Health North Hospital

**Clinton**
 Union Hospital Clinton

**Columbia City**
 Parkview Whitley Hospital

**Columbus**
Partner
 Columbus Regional Hospital

**Danville**
Partner
 Hendricks Regional Health

**Elkhart**
Partner
 Elkhart General Healthcare System

**Evansville**
 Deaconess Health System
Shareholder
 Deaconess Hospital

**Fort Wayne**
 Parkview Health
Partner
 Parkview Hospital Randallia

**Franklin**
 Johnson Memorial Hospital

**Goshen**
 Indiana University Health Goshen Hospital

**Greenfield**
 Hancock Regional Hospital

**Hartford City**
 Indiana University Health Blackford Hospital

**Huntington**
 Parkview Huntington Hospital

**Indianapolis**
 Community Health Network
 Community Heart and Vascular Hospital
 Community Hospital East
 Community Hospital North
 Community Hospital South
 Community Westview Hospital
 Indiana University Health Methodist Hospital
Shareholder
 Indiana University Health University Hospital

**Kendallville**
 Parkview Noble Hospital

**Knox**
 Indiana University Health Starke Hospital

**Kokomo**
Partner
 Community Howard Regional Hospital

**La Porte**
Partner
 Indiana University Health La Porte Hospital

**Lafayette**
 Franciscan St. Elizabeth Health – Lafayette Central
 Indiana University Health Arnett Hospital

**LaGrange**
 Parkview LaGrange Hospital

**Madison**
Partner
 King's Daughters' Health

**Marion**
Partner
 Marion General Hospital

**Martinsville**
 Indiana University Health Morgan Hospital

**Muncie**
Shareholder
 Indiana University Health Ball Memorial Hospital

**New Albany**
Partner
 Floyd Memorial Hospital and Health Services

**New Castle**
 Henry County Hospital

**Noblesville**
Partner
 Riverview Hospital

**Paoli**
 Indiana University Health Paoli Hospital

**Portland**
 Jay County Hospital

**Richmond**
Partner
 Reid Hospital and Health Care Services

**Seymour**
 Schneck Medical Center

**Shelbyville**
 Major Hospital

**South Bend**
 Healthwin Hospital
 Madison Center and Hospital
 Memorial Hospital of South Bend

**Terre Haute**
Partner
 Union Hospital

**Tipton**
 Indiana University Health Tipton Hospital

**Vincennes**
Partner
 Good Samaritan Hospital

**IOWA**

**Atlantic**
Shareholder
 Cass County Memorial Hospital

**Council Bluffs**
Shareholder
 Methodist Jennie Edmundson Hospital

**Decorah**
 Winneshiek Medical Center

**Hamburg**
 George C Grape Community Hospital

**Harlan**
Partner
 Myrtue Medical Center

**Keokuk**
Shareholder
Keokuk Area Hospital

**Le Mars**
Partner
Floyd Valley Hospital

**Muscatine**
Trinity Muscatine

**Onawa**
Partner
Burgess Health Center

**Orange City**
Orange City Area Health System

**Red Oak**
Shareholder
Montgomery County Memorial Hospital

**Rock Rapids**
Sanford Rock Rapids Medical Center

**Sheldon**
Sanford Sheldon Medical Center

**Sioux City**
Shareholder
UnityPoint Health St. Luke's

**West Union**
Palmer Lutheran Health Center

## KANSAS

**Abilene**
Memorial Health System

**Anthony**
Anthony Medical Center

**Atchison**
Shareholder
Atchison Hospital

**Atwood**
Rawlins County Health Center

**Belleville**
Republic County Hospital

**Beloit**
Mitchell County Hospital Health Systems

**Clay Center**
Clay County Medical Center

**Colby**
Shareholder
Citizens Medical Center

**Coldwater**
Comanche County Hospital

**Concordia**
Cloud County Health Center

**Dighton**
Lane County Hospital

**El Dorado**
Susan B. Allen Memorial Hospital

**Ellinwood**
Ellinwood District Hospital

**Ellsworth**
Ellsworth County Medical Center

**Fredonia**
Fredonia Regional Hospital

**Garnett**
Anderson County Hospital

**Goodland**
Goodland Regional Medical Center

**Greensburg**
Kiowa County Memorial Hospital

**Hays**
Shareholder
Hays Medical Center

**Herington**
Herington Municipal Hospital

**Hiawatha**
Partner
Hiawatha Community Hospital

**Hill City**
Graham County Hospital

**Hoisington**
Clara Barton Hospital

**Hoxie**
Sheridan County Health Complex

**Junction City**
Geary Community Hospital

**La Crosse**
Rush County Memorial Hospital

**Lawrence**
Lawrence Memorial Hospital

**Leavenworth**
Cushing Memorial Hospital

**Leoti**
Wichita County Health Center

**Liberal**
Shareholder
Southwest Medical Center

**Lincoln**
Lincoln County Hospital

**Lindsborg**
Lindsborg Community Hospital

**Lyons**
Rice County District Hospital

**Mankato**
Jewell County Hospital

**McPherson**
McPherson Hospital

**Medicine Lodge**
Medicine Lodge Memorial Hospital

**Minneapolis**
Ottawa County Health Center

**Minneola**
Minneola District Hospital

**Ness City**
Ness County Hospital

**Norton**
Norton County Hospital

**Oakley**
Logan County Hospital

**Osborne**
Osborne County Memorial Hospital

**Overland Park**
Saint Luke's South Hospital

**Parsons**
Partner
Labette Health

**Phillipsburg**
Phillips County Hospital

**Plainville**
Rooks County Health Center

**Pratt**
Shareholder
Pratt Regional Medical Center

**Quinter**
Gove County Medical Center

**Ransom**
Grisell Memorial Hospital District One

**Russell**
Russell Regional Hospital

**Sabetha**
Sabetha Community Hospital

**Saint Francis**
Cheyenne County Hospital

**Salina**
Salina Surgical Hospital
Partner
Salina Regional Health Center

**Satanta**
Satanta District Hospital

**Scott City**
Scott County Hospital

**Smith Center**
Smith County Memorial Hospital

**Stafford**
Stafford County Hospital

**Topeka**
Shareholder
Stormont–Vail HealthCare

**Wakeeney**
Trego County–Lemke Memorial Hospital

**Wichita**
Shareholder
Great Plains Health Alliance, Inc.

## KENTUCKY

**Pikeville**
Pikeville Medical Center

## LOUISIANA

**Amite**
Hood Memorial Hospital

**Baton Rouge**
Franciscan Missionaries of Our Lady Health System, Inc.
Ochsner Medical Center–Baton Rouge
Member
Our Lady of the Lake Regional Medical Center
Partner
Woman's Hospital

**Bossier City**
WK Bossier Health Center

**Bunkie**
Bunkie General Hospital

**Church Point**
Acadia–St. Landry Hospital

**Columbia**
Citizens Medical Center

**Covington**
Partner
St. Tammany Parish Hospital

**Crowley**
Partner
American Legion Hospital

**De Ridder**
Partner
Beauregard Memorial Hospital

**Ferriday**
Riverland Medical Center

**Gonzales**
St. Elizabeth Hospital

**Greensburg**
St. Helena Parish Hospital

**Jennings**
Jennings American Legion Hospital

**Kenner**
Ochsner Medical Center – Kenner

**Lafayette**
Partner
Our Lady of Lourdes Regional Medical Center

**Lake Charles**
Partner
Lake Charles Memorial Hospital

**Mansfield**
De Soto Regional Health System

**Monroe**
Partner
St. Francis Medical Center

**Napoleonville**
Assumption Community Hospital

**Natchitoches**
Natchitoches Regional Medical Center

**New Iberia**
Iberia Medical Center

**New Orleans**
Ochsner Baptist Medical Center
Shareholder
Ochsner Medical Center

**Oak Grove**
West Carroll Memorial Hospital

**Raceland**
Ochsner St. Anne General Hospital

**Shreveport**
Willis–Knighton Health System
Shareholder
Willis–Knighton Medical Center

**Springhill**
Springhill Medical Center

**Sulphur**
Partner
West Calcasieu Cameron Hospital

**Vivian**
North Caddo Medical Center

## MAINE

**Augusta**
MaineGeneral Medical Center–Augusta Campus

**Bangor**
Eastern Maine Medical Center
The Acadia Hospital

Section B

**Bar Harbor**
  Mount Desert Island Hospital
**Belfast**
  Waldo County General Hospital
**Biddeford**
Shareholder
  Southern Maine Medical Center
**Blue Hill**
  Blue Hill Memorial Hospital
**Boothbay Harbor**
  St. Andrews Hospital and Healthcare Center
**Brewer**
Partner
  Eastern Maine Healthcare Systems
**Bridgton**
  Bridgton Hospital
**Brunswick**
  Mid Coast Hospital
**Damariscotta**
  Miles Memorial Hospital
**Dover–Foxcroft**
  Mayo Regional Hospital
**Ellsworth**
  Maine Coast Memorial Hospital
**Greenville**
  Charles A. Dean Memorial Hospital
**Houlton**
  Houlton Regional Hospital
**Machias**
  Down East Community Hospital
**Millinocket**
Unit_of
  Millinocket Regional Hospital
**Norway**
  Stephens Memorial Hospital
**Pittsfield**
  Sebasticook Valley Health
**Portland**
Shareholder
  Maine Medical Center
**Presque Isle**
  The Aroostook Medical Center
**Rockport**
  Pen Bay Medical Center
**Skowhegan**
  Redington–Fairview General Hospital
**Waterville**
  Inland Hospital
Shareholder
  MaineGeneral Medical Center–Waterville Campus
**Westbrook**
  Spring Harbor Hospital
**York**
  York Hospital

## MARYLAND
**Baltimore**
  MedStar Franklin Square Medical Center
  MedStar Good Samaritan Hospital
  MedStar Harbor Hospital
  MedStar Union Memorial Hospital
**Bel Air**
  Upper Chesapeake Medical Center
Partner
  Upper Chesapeake Health System
**Columbia**
  MedStar Health
**Havre De Grace**
  Harford Memorial Hospital
**Leonardtown**
  MedStar St. Mary's Hospital
**Olney**
  MedStar Montgomery Medical Center
**Prince Frederick**
  Calvert Memorial Hospital

## MASSACHUSETTS
**Belmont**
  McLean Hospital
**Beverly**
Partner
  Beverly Hospital

**Boston**
  Brigham and Women's Faulkner Hospital
  Brigham and Women's Hospital
  Dana–Farber Cancer Institute
  Massachusetts General Hospital
  Spaulding Rehabilitation Hospital
Partner
  Massachusetts Eye and Ear Infirmary
Shareholder
  Partners HealthCare System, Inc.
**Burlington**
Partner
  Lahey Hospital & Medical Center, Burlington
**Cambridge**
  Spaulding Hospital for Continuing Medical Care
    Cambridge
Partner
  Mount Auburn Hospital
**Concord**
Partner
  Emerson Hospital
**East Sandwich**
  Spaulding Rehabilitation Hospital Cape Cod
**Falmouth**
  Falmouth Hospital
**Gardner**
Partner
  Heywood Hospital
**Hyannis**
  Cape Cod Healthcare, Inc.
Partner
  Cape Cod Hospital
**Lawrence**
Owner
  Lawrence General Hospital
**Melrose**
  Hallmark Health System
Partner
  Melrose–Wakefield Hospital
**Nantucket**
  Nantucket Cottage Hospital
**Newton Lower Falls**
  Newton–Wellesley Hospital
**Northampton**
  Cooley Dickinson Hospital
**Oak Bluffs**
  Martha's Vineyard Hospital
**Salem**
  North Shore Medical Center
  Spaulding Hospital for Continuing Medical Care North
    Shore
**South Weymouth**
Partner
  South Shore Hospital
**Southbridge**
Partner
  Harrington Memorial Hospital

## MICHIGAN
**Adrian**
  ProMedica Bixby Hospital
**Allegan**
  Allegan General Hospital
**Alpena**
  Alpena Regional Medical Center
**Bad Axe**
  Huron Medical Center
**Big Rapids**
  Mecosta County Medical Center
**Cass City**
  Hills & Dales General Hospital
**Coldwater**
  Community Health Center of Branch County
**Dearborn**
Member
  Oakwood Healthcare, Inc.
Partner
  Oakwood Hospital & Medical Center–Dearborn
**Detroit**
  Riverview Urgent Care Center
Partner
  St. John Hospital and Medical Center

**East China**
  St. John River District Hospital
**Fremont**
  Spectrum Health Gerber Memorial
**Grand Haven**
  North Ottawa Community Hospital
**Grand Rapids**
  Mary Free Bed Rehabilitation Hospital
  Spectrum Health
  Spectrum Health – Grand Rapids
**Greenville**
  Spectrum Health United Hospital
**Hastings**
  Pennock Hospital
**Holland**
Partner
  Holland Hospital
**Jackson**
  Allegiance Health
**Kalamazoo**
Partner
  Bronson Healthcare Group, Inc.
  Bronson Methodist Hospital
**Laurium**
  Aspirus Keweenaw Hospital
**Ludington**
  Memorial Medical Center of West Michigan
**Marquette**
  Marquette General Health System
**Marshall**
  Oaklawn Hospital
**Monroe**
Partner
  Mercy Memorial Hospital System
**Ontonagon**
  Aspirus Ontonagon Hospital
**Owosso**
Partner
  Memorial Healthcare
**Paw Paw**
  Bronson LakeView Hospital
**Petoskey**
  McLaren Northern Michigan
**Port Huron**
  Port Huron Hospital
Partner
  Blue Water Health Services Corporation
**Reed City**
  Spectrum Health Reed City Hospital
**Royal Oak**
Shareholder
  Beaumont Hospital – Royal Oak
**Saginaw**
  Covenant Medical Center
**Saint Ignace**
  Mackinac Straits Health System
**Saint Joseph**
  Lakeland Healthcare
  Lakeland Regional Medical Center–St. Joseph
**Shelby**
  Mercy Health Partners, Lakeshore Campus
**South Haven**
  South Haven Health System
**Taylor**
  Oakwood Heritage Hospital
**Tecumseh**
  ProMedica Herrick Hospital
**Trenton**
  Oakwood Southshore Medical Center
**Troy**
  Beaumont Hospital – Troy
**Vicksburg**
  Bronson Vicksburg Hospital
**Wayne**
  Oakwood Annapolis Hospital
**West Branch**
Partner
  West Branch Regional Medical Center
**Wyoming**
  Metro Health Hospital

**Zeeland**
Spectrum Health Zeeland Community Hospital

## MINNESOTA

**Ada**
Essentia Health Ada

**Albert Lea**
Mayo Clinic Health System in Albert Lea

**Arlington**
Sibley Medical Center

**Austin**
Mayo Clinic Health System in Austin

**Bemidji**
Partner
Sanford Bemidji Medical Center

**Benson**
Swift County–Benson Hospital

**Blue Earth**
United Hospital District

**Brainerd**
Essentia Health St. Joseph's Medical Center

**Buffalo**
Buffalo Hospital

**Cambridge**
Cambridge Medical Center

**Canby**
Sanford Canby Medical Center

**Cannon Falls**
Mayo Clinic Health System in Cannon Falls

**Coon Rapids**
Mercy Hospital

**Detroit Lakes**
Essentia Health St. Mary's Hospital – Detroit Lakes

**Duluth**
Essentia Health
Essentia Health Duluth
Essentia Health St. Mary's Medical Center
Partner
St. Luke's Hospital

**Fairmont**
Mayo Clinic Health System in Fairmont

**Fergus Falls**
Partner
Lake Region Healthcare

**Fosston**
Essentia Health Fosston

**Fridley**
Unity Hospital

**Graceville**
Essentia Health–Holy Trinity Hospital

**Grand Rapids**
Grand Itasca Clinic and Hospital

**Hallock**
Kittson Memorial Healthcare Center

**Hutchinson**
Hutchinson Health

**Jackson**
Sanford Jackson Medical Center

**Lake City**
Mayo Clinic Health System in Lake City

**Le Sueur**
Minnesota Valley Health Center

**Long Prairie**
CentraCare Health–Long Prairie

**Luverne**
Sanford Luverne Medical Center

**Madelia**
Madelia Community Hospital

**Mahnomen**
Mahnomen Health Center

**Mankato**
Partner
Mayo Clinic Health System in Mankato

**Maple Grove**
Maple Grove Hospital

**Melrose**
CentraCare Health–Melrose

**Minneapolis**
Abbott Northwestern Hospital
Shareholder
Allina Health

**Morris**
Stevens Community Medical Center

**New Ulm**
New Ulm Medical Center

**Ortonville**
Ortonville Area Health Services

**Owatonna**
Owatonna Hospital

**Paynesville**
Paynesville Area Health Care System

**Perham**
Perham Health

**Redwood Falls**
Redwood Area Hospital

**Robbinsdale**
North Memorial Medical Center

**Rochester**
Mayo Clinic – Saint Marys Hospital
Mayo Clinic Health System
Rochester Methodist Hospital

**Roseau**
LifeCare Medical Center

**Saint Cloud**
CentraCare Health
Partner
St. Cloud Hospital

**Saint James**
Mayo Clinic Health System in Saint James

**Saint Paul**
Bethesda Hospital
St. John's Hospital
St. Joseph's Hospital
United Hospital
Shareholder
HealthEast Care System

**Saint Peter**
River's Edge Hospital and Clinic

**Sandstone**
Essentia Health Sandstone

**Shakopee**
St. Francis Regional Medical Center

**Slayton**
Murray County Medical Center

**Springfield**
Mayo Clinic Health System in Springfield

**Thief River Falls**
Sanford Thief River Falls Medical Center

**Tracy**
Sanford Tracy Medical Center

**Waconia**
Partner
Ridgeview Medical Center

**Warren**
North Valley Health Center

**Waseca**
Mayo Clinic Health System in Waseca

**Westbrook**
Sanford Westbrook Medical Center

**Willmar**
Partner
Rice Memorial Hospital

**Windom**
Windom Area Hospital

**Woodbury**
Woodwinds Health Campus

**Worthington**
Sanford Worthington Medical Center

## MISSISSIPPI

**Batesville**
Tri–Lakes Medical Center

**Booneville**
Baptist Memorial Hospital–Booneville

**Calhoun City**
Calhoun Health Services

**Columbus**
Baptist Memorial Hospital–Golden Triangle

**Corinth**
Magnolia Regional Health Center

**Eupora**
North Mississippi Medical Center–Eupora

**Greenville**
Delta Regional Medical Center

**Greenwood**
Partner
Greenwood Leflore Hospital

**Gulfport**
Partner
Memorial Hospital at Gulfport

**Hattiesburg**
Partner
Forrest General Hospital

**Jackson**
Partner
St. Dominic–Jackson Memorial Hospital

**McComb**
Partner
Southwest Mississippi Regional Medical Center

**Meridian**
Partner
Anderson Regional Medical Center

**Monticello**
Lawrence County Hospital

**New Albany**
Baptist Memorial Hospital–Union County

**Oxford**
Baptist Memorial Hospital–North Mississippi

**Pascagoula**
Singing River Health System

**Picayune**
Highland Community Hospital

**Pontotoc**
North Mississippi Medical Center–Pontotoc Hospital
and Nursing Home

**Southaven**
Baptist Memorial Hospital–Desoto

**Starkville**
OCH Regional Medical Center

**Tupelo**
North Mississippi Health Services, Inc.
North Mississippi Medical Center – Tupelo

**Tylertown**
Walthall County General Hospital

**West Point**
North Mississippi Medical Center–West Point

## MISSOURI

**Bolivar**
Partner
Citizens Memorial Hospital

**Bonne Terre**
Parkland Health Center–Bonne Terre

**Branson**
Partner
Cox Medical Center Branson

**Brookfield**
General John J. Pershing Memorial Hospital

**Cameron**
Partner
Cameron Regional Medical Center

**Cape Girardeau**
Landmark Hospital
Partner
Saint Francis Medical Center

**Carthage**
Partner
Mercy McCune–Brooks Hospital

**Chillicothe**
Hedrick Medical Center

**Clinton**
Golden Valley Memorial Healthcare

**Columbia**
Boone Hospital Center

**Crystal City**
Mercy Hospital Jefferson

**Farmington**
Parkland Health Center

**Joplin**
Freeman Health System
Freeman Hospital East

**Kansas City**
Crittenton Children's Center
Saint Luke's North Hospital – Barry Road
Shareholder
Saint Luke's Health System
Saint Luke's Hospital of Kansas City

Section B

**Lamar**
Barton County Memorial Hospital
**Lee's Summit**
Saint Luke's East Hospital
**Liberty**
Partner
Liberty Hospital
**Macon**
Samaritan Memorial Hospital
**Marshall**
Fitzgibbon Hospital
**Monett**
Cox Monett
**Neosho**
Freeman Neosho Hospital
**Potosi**
Washington County Memorial Hospital
**Saint Louis**
Barnes–Jewish Hospital
Barnes–Jewish West County Hospital
Christian Hospital
Missouri Baptist Medical Center
St. Louis Children's Hospital
Shareholder
BJC HealthCare
**Saint Peters**
Barnes–Jewish St. Peters Hospital
**Salem**
Salem Memorial District Hospital
**Sikeston**
Missouri Delta Medical Center
**Springfield**
CoxHealth
Lester E. Cox Medical Center North
Shareholder
Lester E. Cox Medical Centers
**Ste Genevieve**
Ste. Genevieve County Memorial Hospital
**Sullivan**
Missouri Baptist Sullivan Hospital
**Trenton**
Wright Memorial Hospital
**Warrensburg**
Western Missouri Medical Center

**MONTANA**
**Anaconda**
Community Hospital of Anaconda
**Big Timber**
Pioneer Medical Center
**Billings**
Partner
Billings Clinic
**Bozeman**
Partner
Bozeman Deaconess Hospital
**Columbus**
Unit_of
Stillwater Community Hospital
**Fort Benton**
Missouri River Medical Center
**Glasgow**
Frances Mahon Deaconess Hospital
**Glendive**
Partner
Glendive Medical Center
**Great Falls**
Benefis Hospitals
**Hamilton**
Partner
Marcus Daly Memorial Hospital
**Helena**
Partner
St. Peter's Hospital
**Kalispell**
The HealthCenter
**Livingston**
Livingston Memorial Hospital
**Missoula**
St. Patrick Hospital
Partner
Community Medical Center

**Plains**
Clark Fork Valley Hospital
**Polson**
St. Joseph Hospital
**Red Lodge**
Beartooth Billings Clinic
**Ronan**
Partner
St. Luke Community Healthcare
**Scobey**
Daniels Memorial Healthcare Center
**Sidney**
Partner
Sidney Health Center

**NEBRASKA**
**Alliance**
Box Butte General Hospital
**Alma**
Harlan County Health System
**Atkinson**
West Holt Memorial Hospital
**Beatrice**
Partner
Beatrice Community Hospital and Health Center
**Bridgeport**
Morrill County Community Hospital
**Broken Bow**
Jennie M. Melham Memorial Medical Center
**Columbus**
Partner
Columbus Community Hospital
**Crete**
Crete Area Medical Center
**Falls City**
Community Medical Center
**Franklin**
Franklin County Memorial Hospital
**Gordon**
Gordon Memorial Hospital
**Hastings**
Partner
Mary Lanning Healthcare
**Lexington**
Partner
Lexington Regional Health Center
**Lincoln**
Bryan Health
Bryan Medical Center
Partner
Madonna Rehabilitation Hospital
**Lynch**
Niobrara Valley Hospital
**McCook**
Partner
Community Hospital
**Minden**
Kearney County Health Services
**Neligh**
Antelope Memorial Hospital
**Norfolk**
Partner
Faith Regional Health Services
**Omaha**
Nebraska Methodist Health System, Inc.
Shareholder
Nebraska Methodist Hospital
**Ord**
Valley County Health System
**Oshkosh**
Garden County Health Services
**Osmond**
Osmond General Hospital
**Plainview**
Alegent Creighton Health Plainview Hospital
**Scottsbluff**
Partner
Regional West Medical Center
**Tilden**
Tilden Community Hospital

**York**
Partner
York General Hospital

**NEW HAMPSHIRE**
**Claremont**
Valley Regional Hospital
**Colebrook**
Upper Connecticut Valley Hospital
**Dover**
Partner
Wentworth–Douglass Hospital
**Keene**
Partner
Cheshire Medical Center
**Lancaster**
Weeks Medical Center
**Lebanon**
Alice Peck Day Memorial Hospital
Dartmouth–Hitchcock Medical Center
**Nashua**
Partner
Southern New Hampshire Medical Center
**New London**
New London Hospital
**Peterborough**
Monadnock Community Hospital
**Rochester**
Partner
Frisbie Memorial Hospital
**Woodsville**
Cottage Hospital

**NEW JERSEY**
**Atlantic City**
AtlantiCare Regional Medical Center
**Edison**
JFK Health System
JFK Medical Center
**Egg Harbor Township**
AtlantiCare
**Elmer**
Inspira Medical Center–Elmer
**Flemington**
Partner
Hunterdon Medical Center
**Newton**
Partner
Newton Medical Center
**Pennington**
Capital Health Medical Center–Hopewell
**Phillipsburg**
Partner
St. Luke's Hospital – Warren Campus
**Pomona**
Bacharach Institute for Rehabilitation
**Pompton Plains**
Partner
Chilton Hospital
**Ridgewood**
Valley Hospital
**Somers Point**
Partner
Shore Medical Center
**Trenton**
Capital Health
Capital Health Regional Medical Center
**Vineland**
Inspira Health Network
Inspira Medical Center–Vineland
**Woodbury**
Partner
Inspira Medical Center–Woodbury

**NEW MEXICO**
**Artesia**
Artesia General Hospital
**Farmington**
Partner
San Juan Regional Medical Center
**Gallup**
Partner
Rehoboth McKinley Christian Health Care Services

## NEW YORK

**Binghamton**
Shareholder
United Health Services Hospitals–Binghamton

**Bronx**
New York Westchester Square Medical Center

**Bronxville**
Lawrence Hospital Center

**Brooklyn**
New York Community Hospital
New York Methodist Hospital
Wyckoff Heights Medical Center

**Buffalo**
Erie County Medical Center
Roswell Park Cancer Institute

**Cobleskill**
Partner
Cobleskill Regional Hospital

**Cooperstown**
Partner
Bassett Medical Center

**Corning**
Corning Hospital

**Elmira**
St. Joseph's Hospital

**Flushing**
New York Hospital Queens

**Geneva**
Finger Lakes Health
Partner
Geneva General Hospital

**Hamilton**
Community Memorial Hospital

**Ithaca**
Partner
Cayuga Medical Center at Ithaca

**Jamestown**
Woman's Christian Association Hospital

**Little Falls**
Little Falls Hospital

**Malone**
Alice Hyde Medical Center

**Mineola**
Winthrop–University Hospital

**Mount Kisco**
Partner
Northern Westchester Hospital

**New York**
New York–Presbyterian Hospital
Shareholder
New York–Presbyterian/Columbia University Medical
Center

**Norwich**
Chenango Memorial Hospital

**Nyack**
Nyack Hospital

**Ogdensburg**
Claxton–Hepburn Medical Center

**Penn Yan**
Soldiers and Sailors Memorial Hospital of Yates
County

**Rochester**
Strong Memorial Hospital of the University of
Rochester
Unity Hospital
University of Rochester Medical Center
Partner
Highland Hospital of Rochester

**Sleepy Hollow**
Phelps Memorial Hospital Center

**Syracuse**
Partner
Crouse Hospital

**Utica**
Faxton–St. Luke's Healthcare

**Walton**
Delaware Valley Hospital

**White Plains**
Partner
White Plains Hospital Center

## NORTH CAROLINA

**Ahoskie**
Vidant Roanoke–Chowan Hospital

**Bolivia**
Brunswick Novant Medical Center

**Cary**
WakeMed Cary Hospital

**Charlotte**
Carolinas Medical Center
Carolinas Medical Center–Mercy
Presbyterian Hospital
Presbyterian–Orthopaedic Hospital
Shareholder
Carolinas HealthCare System

**Clinton**
Sampson Regional Medical Center

**Concord**
Shareholder
Carolinas Medical Center–NorthEast

**Dunn**
Hartnett Health System

**Edenton**
Vidant Chowan Hospital

**Greensboro**
Cone Health

**Greenville**
Shareholder
Vidant Medical Center

**High Point**
Shareholder
High Point Regional Health System

**Huntersville**
Presbyterian Hospital Huntersville

**Kenansville**
Vidant Duplin Hospital

**Lexington**
Wake Forest Baptist Health–Lexington Medical Center

**Lincolnton**
Carolinas Medical Center–Lincoln

**Louisburg**
Franklin Regional Medical Center

**Matthews**
Presbyterian Hospital Matthews

**Monroe**
Carolinas Medical Center–Union

**Nags Head**
The Outer Banks Hospital

**Raleigh**
WakeMed Health & Hospitals
Partner
WakeMed Raleigh Campus

**Rocky Mount**
Partner
Nash Health Care Systems

**Salisbury**
Partner
Rowan Regional Medical Center

**Tarboro**
Vidant Edgecombe Hospital

**Thomasville**
Partner
Thomasville Medical Center

**Windsor**
Vidant Bertie Hospital

**Winston Salem**
Novant Health

**Winston–Salem**
Forsyth Medical Center
Medical Park Hospital

## NORTH DAKOTA

**Bismarck**
Partner
Sanford Bismarck

**Fargo**
Essentia Health Fargo
Sanford Medical Center Fargo

**Grafton**
Unity Medical Center

**Grand Forks**
Partner
Altru Health System

**Hillsboro**
Sanford Hillsboro Medical Center

**Jamestown**
Partner
Jamestown Regional Medical Center

**Kenmare**
Kenmare Community Hospital

**Mayville**
Sanford Mayville Medical Center

**Mcville**
Nelson County Health System

**Minot**
Trinity Health

## OHIO

**Akron**
Akron General Health System
Shareholder
Akron General Medical Center

**Ashland**
Samaritan Regional Health System

**Athens**
O'Bleness Memorial Hospital

**Bellaire**
Belmont Community Hospital

**Bowling Green**
Wood County Hospital

**Cambridge**
Partner
Southeastern Ohio Regional Medical Center

**Cincinnati**
UC Health
Shareholder
Christ Hospital

**Cleveland**
University Hospitals Case Medical Center

**Columbus**
OhioHealth Doctors Hospital
OhioHealth Grant Medical Center
OhioHealth Riverside Methodist Hospital
Member
OhioHealth

**Concord Township**
Partner
Lake Health

**Cuyahoga Falls**
Edwin Shaw Rehab

**Dayton**
Miami Valley Hospital
Partner
Good Samaritan Hospital

**Defiance**
ProMedica Defiance Regional Hospital

**Delaware**
OhioHealth Grady Memorial Hospital

**Dover**
Partner
Union Hospital

**Dublin**
OhioHealth Dublin Methodist Hospital

**Findlay**
Blanchard Valley Hospital

**Fostoria**
ProMedica Fostoria Community Hospital

**Fremont**
Partner
Memorial Hospital

**Galion**
Galion Community Hospital

**Georgetown**
Southwest Regional Medical Center

**Greenville**
Wayne Hospital

**Kenton**
Hardin Memorial Hospital

**Lima**
Partner
Lima Memorial Health System

**Lodi**
Lodi Community Hospital

**Logan**
Hocking Valley Community Hospital

**Mansfield**
MedCentral – Mansfield Hospital
**Marion**
OhioHealth Marion General Hospital
**Maumee**
Partner
ProMedica St. Luke's Hospital
**Middletown**
Partner
Atrium Medical Center
**Mount Gilead**
Morrow County Hospital
**Nelsonville**
Doctors Hospital Nelsonville
**Newark**
Partner
Licking Memorial Hospital
**Norwalk**
Fisher–Titus Medical Center
**Oregon**
ProMedica Bay Park Hospital
**Oxford**
McCullough–Hyde Memorial Hospital
**Portsmouth**
Southern Ohio Medical Center
**Shelby**
MedCentral – Shelby Hospital
**Sidney**
Wilson Memorial Hospital
**Steubenville**
Partner
Trinity Health System
**Sylvania**
ProMedica Flower Hospital
**Toledo**
ProMedica Health System
Shareholder
ProMedica Toledo Hospital
**Troy**
Partner
Upper Valley Medical Center
**Warren**
Hillside Rehabilitation Hospital
**Wauseon**
Fulton County Health Center
**Youngstown**
Northside Medical Center
**Zanesville**
Partner
Genesis HealthCare System

**OKLAHOMA**
**Ada**
Partner
Valley View Regional Hospital
**Altus**
Partner
Jackson County Memorial Hospital
**Blackwell**
Integris Blackwell Regional Hospital
**Carnegie**
Carnegie Tri–County Municipal Hospital
**Chickasha**
Partner
Grady Memorial Hospital
**Clinton**
Integris Clinton Regional Hospital
**Duncan**
Partner
Duncan Regional Hospital
**El Reno**
Mercy Hospital El Reno
**Elk City**
Great Plains Regional Medical Center
**Enid**
Integris Bass Baptist Health Center
Integris Bass Pavilion
**Frederick**
Memorial Hospital and Physician Group
**Grove**
Integris Grove General Hospital

**Guymon**
Partner
Memorial Hospital of Texas County
**Hobart**
Elkview General Hospital
**Lawton**
Partner
Comanche County Memorial Hospital
**Madill**
Integris Marshall County Medical Center
**McAlester**
Partner
McAlester Regional Health Center
**Miami**
Integris Baptist Regional Health Center
**Norman**
Norman Regional Health System
**Oklahoma City**
Integris Baptist Medical Center
INTEGRIS Health
Integris Southwest Medical Center
**Pryor**
Integris Mayes County Medical Center
**Purcell**
Purcell Municipal Hospital
**Seminole**
Integris Seminole Medical Center
**Shawnee**
St. Anthony Shawnee Hospital
**Stillwater**
Partner
Stillwater Medical Center
**Tahlequah**
Tahlequah City Hospital
**Waurika**
Jefferson County Hospital
**Yukon**
INTEGRIS Canadian Valley Hospital

**OREGON**
**Hillsboro**
Partner
Tuality Healthcare
**Hood River**
Providence Hood River Memorial Hospital
**Medford**
Providence Medford Medical Center
**Milwaukie**
Providence Milwaukie Hospital
**Newberg**
Providence Newberg Medical Center
**Oregon City**
Providence Willamette Falls Medical Center
**Portland**
Providence Portland Medical Center
Providence St. Vincent Medical Center
**Seaside**
Providence Seaside Hospital
**Silverton**
Silverton Hospital

**PENNSYLVANIA**
**Abington**
Partner
Abington Memorial Hospital
**Allentown**
Shareholder
Lehigh Valley Hospital
**Bethlehem**
Lehigh Valley Hospital–Muhlenberg
**Brookville**
Brookville Hospital
**Butler**
Partner
Butler Health System
**Chambersburg**
Chambersburg Hospital
Summit Health
**Clearfield**
Clearfield Hospital
**Coudersport**
Cole Memorial

**Drexel Hill**
Delaware County Memorial Hospital
**Du Bois**
DuBois Regional Medical Center
**East Stroudsburg**
Pocono Medical Center
**Ephrata**
Partner
Ephrata Community Hospital
**Erie**
Shareholder
UPMC Hamot
**Gettysburg**
Gettysburg Hospital
**Hanover**
Hanover Hospital
**Harrisburg**
Community Hospital
Pinnacle Health System
**Hastings**
Conemaugh Miners Medical Center
**Indiana**
Indiana Regional Medical Center
**Jefferson Hills**
Jefferson Regional Medical Center
**Johnstown**
Conemaugh Health System
Conemaugh Memorial Medical Center
**Kane**
Kane Community Hospital
**Kittanning**
ACMH Hospital
**Lancaster**
Partner
Lancaster General Health
**Lebanon**
The Good Samaritan Hospital
**Lehighton**
Blue Mountain Health System
Gnaden Huetten Memorial Hospital
**Mc Connellsburg**
Fulton County Medical Center
**Meadowbrook**
Holy Redeemer Hospital and Medical Center
**Meyersdale**
Conemaugh Meyersdale Medical Center
**Monongahela**
Monongahela Valley Hospital
**New Castle**
Jameson Hospital
**Palmerton**
Palmerton Hospital
**Philadelphia**
Hospital of the University of Pennsylvania
Penn Presbyterian Medical Center
University of Pennsylvania Health System
Shareholder
Pennsylvania Hospital
**Pittsburgh**
Partner
St. Clair Memorial Hospital
**Punxsutawney**
Punxsutawney Area Hospital
**Renovo**
Bucktail Medical Center
**Roaring Spring**
Nason Hospital
**Saint Marys**
Elk Regional Health Center
**Sayre**
Robert Packer Hospital
Shareholder
Guthrie Healthcare System
**Scranton**
Partner
Geisinger–Community Medical Center
**Sellersville**
Partner
Grand View Hospital
**Sharon**
Partner
Sharon Regional Health System

## Springfield
Crozer–Keystone Health System

## State College
Mount Nittany Medical Center

## Troy
Troy Community Hospital

## Tyrone
Tyrone Hospital

## Uniontown
Partner
Uniontown Hospital

## Upland
Crozer–Chester Medical Center

## Waynesboro
Waynesboro Hospital

## Wellsboro
Soldiers and Sailors Memorial Hospital

## West Chester
Partner
Chester County Hospital

## West Reading
Reading Hospital and Medical Center

## Williamsport
Divine Providence Hospital
Partner
Susquehanna Health System

## Windber
Windber Medical Center

## York
Partner
WellSpan Health
Shareholder
York Hospital

# RHODE ISLAND
## East Providence
Emma Pendleton Bradley Hospital

## Newport
Newport Hospital

## Pawtucket
Memorial Hospital of Rhode Island

## Providence
Butler Hospital
Care New England Health System
Miriam Hospital
Women & Infants Hospital of Rhode Island
Shareholder
Lifespan Corporation
Rhode Island Hospital

## Warwick
Kent County Memorial Hospital

## Westerly
Westerly Hospital

# SOUTH CAROLINA
## Gaffney
Upstate Carolina Medical Center

# SOUTH DAKOTA
## Armour
Douglas County Memorial Hospital

## Burke
Community Memorial Hospital

## Canton
Sanford Canton–Inwood Medical Center

## Chamberlain
Sanford Chamberlain Medical Center

## Clear Lake
Sanford Clear Lake Medical Center

## Sioux Falls
Sanford Health
Shareholder
Sanford USD Medical Center

## Vermillion
Sanford Vermillion Medical Center

## Viborg
Pioneer Memorial Hospital and Health Services

## Watertown
Prairie Lakes Healthcare System

## Webster
Sanford Webster Medical Center

## Winner
Winner Regional Healthcare Center

# TENNESSEE
## Bolivar
Bolivar General Hospital

## Camden
Camden General Hospital

## Chattanooga
Erlanger Health System
Erlanger North Hospital

## Collierville
Baptist Memorial Hospital–Collierville

## Columbia
Partner
Maury Regional Hospital

## Covington
Baptist Memorial Hospital–Tipton

## Franklin
Williamson Medical Center

## Harriman
Roane Medical Center

## Humboldt
Humboldt General Hospital

## Huntingdon
Baptist Memorial Hospital–Huntingdon

## Jackson
Shareholder
Jackson–Madison County General Hospital

## Knoxville
Covenant Health
East Tennessee Children's Hospital
Fort Sanders Regional Medical Center
Parkwest Medical Center

## Lenoir City
Fort Loudoun Medical Center

## Lewisburg
Marshall Medical Center

## Louisville
Peninsula Hospital

## Memphis
Baptist Memorial Health Care Corporation
Baptist Memorial Hospital for Women

Baptist Memorial Hospital – Memphis

## Milan
Milan General Hospital

## Oak Ridge
Partner
Methodist Medical Center of Oak Ridge

## Paris
Henry County Medical Center

## Parsons
Decatur County General Hospital

## Pikeville
Erlanger Bledsoe Hospital

## Ripley
Lauderdale Community Hospital

## Savannah
Hardin Medical Center

## Sevierville
LeConte Medical Center

## Trenton
Gibson General Hospital

## Union City
Baptist Memorial Hospital–Union City

## Waynesboro
Wayne Medical Center

# TEXAS
## Amarillo
Partner
Baptist St. Anthony Health System

## Andrews
Permian Regional Medical Center

## Atlanta
Atlanta Memorial Hospital

## Beaumont
Baptist Hospitals of Southeast Texas

## Bellville
Bellville General Hospital

## Caldwell
Burleson St. Joseph Health Center

## Dallas
Baylor Jack and Jane Hamilton Heart and Vascular
 Hospital
Baylor Specialty Hospital
Baylor University Medical Center
Children's Medical Center of Dallas
Methodist Health System
Shareholder
Baylor Health Care System

## Decatur
Wise Regional Health System

## Del Rio
Val Verde Regional Medical Center

## Electra
Electra Memorial Hospital

## Floresville
Connally Medical Center

## Fort Worth
Shareholder
Baylor All Saints Medical Center at Fort Worth

## Garland
Baylor Medical Center at Garland

## Gatesville
Coryell Memorial Hospital

## Grapevine
Partner
Baylor Regional Medical Center at Grapevine

## Houston
Memorial Hermann – Texas Medical Center
Memorial Hermann Healthcare System
Memorial Hermann Northwest Hospital

## Humble
Memorial Hermann Northeast

## Huntsville
Huntsville Memorial Hospital

## Irving
Partner
Baylor Medical Center at Irving

## Jacksonville
Mother Frances Hospital – Jacksonville

## Katy
Memorial Hermann Katy Hospital

## Levelland
Covenant Hospital–Levelland

## Linden
Good Shepherd Medical Center–Linden

## Longview
Partner
Good Shepherd Medical Center

## Lubbock
Covenant Children's Hospital
Covenant Medical Center
Covenant Medical Center–Lakeside
Shareholder
Covenant Health System

## Madisonville
Madison St. Joseph Health Center

## Marshall
Partner
Good Shepherd Medical Center–Marshall

## Midland
Midland Memorial Hospital
Partner
Midland Memorial Hospital

## Navasota
Grimes St. Joseph Health Center

## Odessa
Medical Center Health System

## Orange
Baptist Orange Hospital

## Pearsall
Frio Regional Hospital

## Plainview
Covenant Hospital Plainview

## Plano
Baylor Regional Medical Center at Plano
Community Hospital Corporation
The Heart Hospital Baylor Plano

## Port Lavaca
Memorial Medical Center

## Richardson
Partner
Methodist Richardson Medical Center

Networks, Health Care Systems and Alliances **B199**

**Rockdale**
Little River Healthcare

**Round Rock**
Scott & White Hospital at Round Rock

**San Angelo**
Shannon Medical Center

**Sherman**
Partner
Texas Health Presbyterian Hospital–WNJ

**Sugar Land**
Memorial Hermann Sugar Land Hospital

**Sulphur Springs**
Hopkins County Memorial Hospital

**Sweeny**
Sweeny Community Hospital

**Temple**
Scott and White Memorial Hospital

**Tomball**
Tomball Regional Medical Center

**Tyler**
Partner
Mother Frances Hospital – Tyler

**Waco**
Partner
Hillcrest Baptist Medical Center

**Waxahachie**
Baylor Medical Center at Waxahachie

**Wichita Falls**
Partner
United Regional Health Care System
United Regional Health Care System–Eighth Street Campus

**Winnie**
Winnie Community Hospital

**Yoakum**
Yoakum Community Hospital

## VERMONT

**Bennington**
Southwestern Vermont Medical Center

**Berlin**
Partner
Central Vermont Medical Center

**Morrisville**
Copley Hospital

**Newport**
North Country Hospital and Health Center

**Rutland**
Partner
Rutland Regional Medical Center

**Saint Johnsbury**
Northeastern Vermont Regional Hospital

**Windsor**
Mt. Ascutney Hospital and Health Center

## VIRGIN ISLANDS

**Saint Thomas**
Schneider Regional Medical Center

## VIRGINIA

**Charlottesville**
Partner
Martha Jefferson Hospital

**Farmville**
Centra Southside Community Hospital

**Fredericksburg**
Mary Washington Hospital

**Hampton**
Sentara CarePlex Hospital

**Harrisonburg**
Partner
Rockingham Memorial Hospital

**Lynchburg**
Centra Lynchburg General Hospital

**Manassas**
Prince William Hospital

**Norfolk**
Hospital for Extended Recovery
Sentara Leigh Hospital
Sentara Norfolk General Hospital
Shareholder
Sentara Healthcare

**Suffolk**
Sentara Obici Hospital

**Virginia Beach**
Sentara Princess Anne Hospital
Sentara Virginia Beach General Hospital

**Williamsburg**
Sentara Williamsburg Regional Medical Center

**Woodbridge**
Sentara Northern Virginia Medical Center

## WASHINGTON

**Aberdeen**
Grays Harbor Community Hospital

**Centralia**
Providence Centralia Hospital

**Chewelah**
Providence St. Joseph's Hospital

**Colfax**
Whitman Hospital and Medical Center

**Colville**
Providence Mount Carmel Hospital

**Everett**
Providence Regional Medical Center Everett

**Morton**
Morton General Hospital

**Olympia**
Providence St. Peter Hospital

**Puyallup**
MultiCare Good Samaritan Hospital

**Renton**
Providence Health & Services

**Seattle**
Swedish Medical Center–Cherry Hill Campus

**Spokane**
Providence Holy Family Hospital

**Tacoma**
MultiCare Tacoma General Hospital
Shareholder
MultiCare Health System

**Vancouver**
PeaceHealth Southwest Medical Center

**Walla Walla**
Providence St. Mary Medical Center

**Wenatchee**
Central Washington Hospital

**Yakima**
Partner
Yakima Valley Memorial Hospital

## WEST VIRGINIA

**Charleston**
Charleston Area Medical Center
Women and Children's Hospital
Shareholder
Charleston Area Medical Center Health System, Inc.

**Gassaway**
Braxton County Memorial Hospital

**Glen Dale**
Partner
Reynolds Memorial Hospital

**Madison**
Boone Memorial Hospital

**Montgomery**
Montgomery General Hospital

**Princeton**
Partner
Princeton Community Hospital

**Ripley**
Jackson General Hospital

**Spencer**
Roane General Hospital

**Wheeling**
Partner
Wheeling Hospital

## WISCONSIN

**Antigo**
Langlade Hospital

**Appleton**
Appleton Medical Center
Shareholder
ThedaCare, Inc.

**Barron**
Mayo Clinic Health System – Northland in Barron

**Beaver Dam**
Partner
Beaver Dam Community Hospitals

**Beloit**
Partner
Beloit Health System

**Bloomer**
Mayo Clinic Health System – Chippewa Valley in Bloomer

**Eau Claire**
Partner
Mayo Clinic Health System in Eau Claire

**Green Bay**
Partner
Bellin Memorial Hospital

**La Crosse**
Mayo Clinic Health System – Franciscan Healthcare in La Crosse
Shareholder
Gundersen Lutheran Medical Center

**Madison**
Shareholder
Meriter Hospital

**Marinette**
Bay Area Medical Center

**Medford**
Memorial Health Center

**Menomonee Falls**
Partner
Community Memorial Hospital

**Menomonie**
Mayo Clinic Health System – Red Cedar in Menomonie

**Milwaukee**
Partner
Froedtert Memorial Lutheran Hospital

**Neenah**
Theda Clark Medical Center

**Neillsville**
Memorial Medical Center – Neillsville

**New London**
New London Family Medical Center

**Oconomowoc**
Oconomowoc Memorial Hospital

**Oconto**
Bellin Health Oconto Hospital

**Osseo**
Mayo Clinic Health System – Oakridge in Osseo

**River Falls**
River Falls Area Hospital

**Sparta**
Mayo Clinic Health System – Franciscan Healthcare in Sparta

**Superior**
Essentia Health St. Mary's Hospital of Superior

**Watertown**
Partner
Watertown Regional Medical Center

**Waukesha**
ProHealth Care, Inc.
Waukesha Memorial Hospital

**Waupaca**
Riverside Medical Center

**Wausau**
Aspirus Wausau Hospital

**West Bend**
Owner
St. Joseph's Community Hospital of West Bend

**Whitehall**
Gundersen Tri–County Hospital and Clinics

**Wisconsin Rapids**
Riverview Hospital Association

## WYOMING

**Buffalo**
Johnson County Healthcare Center

**Casper**
Partner
Wyoming Medical Center

**Cheyenne**
Partner
Cheyenne Regional Medical Center

**Douglas**
Memorial Hospital of Converse County
**Gillette**
Campbell County Memorial Hospital
**Jackson**
St. John's Medical Center and Living Center
**Kemmerer**
South Lincoln Medical Center
**Laramie**
Partner
Ivinson Memorial Hospital
**Lovell**
North Big Horn Hospital District
**Lusk**
Niobrara Health and Life Center
**Rawlins**
Memorial Hospital of Carbon County
**Sheridan**
Sheridan Memorial Hospital

## YANKEE ALLIANCE
138 River Road, Andover, MA
Zip 01810–1083; tel. 978/470–2000; R.
Paul O'Neill, President

### CALIFORNIA
**Oceanside**
Member
Tri–City Medical Center

**Ridgecrest**
Member
Ridgecrest Regional Hospital

### CONNECTICUT
**Derby**
Member
Griffin Hospital

**Hartford**
Member
Saint Francis Hospital and Medical Center

**New London**
Member
Lawrence + Memorial Hospital

**Stafford Springs**
Member
Johnson Memorial Hospital

### FLORIDA
**Coral Gables**
Member
Baptist Health South Florida, Doctors Hospital

**Hollywood**
Member
Memorial Regional Hospital
Memorial Regional Hospital South

**Homestead**
Lease
Baptist Health South Florida, Homestead Hospital

**Miami**
Member
Baptist Health South Florida, Baptist Hospital of Miami
Baptist Health South Florida, South Miami Hospital
Metropolitan Hospital of Miami

**Miami Beach**
Member
Mount Sinai Medical Center

**Miramar**
Member
Memorial Hospital Miramar

**Pembroke Pines**
Member
Memorial Hospital Pembroke
Memorial Hospital West

**South Miami**
Member
Larkin Community Hospital

**Tavernier**
Member
Baptist Health South Florida, Mariners Hospital

### INDIANA
**Greenfield**
Member
Hancock Regional Hospital

**Rushville**
Member
Rush Memorial Hospital

### KANSAS
**Manhattan**
Member
Manhattan Surgical Center

### KENTUCKY
**Benton**
Member
Marshall County Hospital

**Corbin**
Member
Baptist Health Corbin

**Elizabethtown**
Member
Hardin Memorial Hospital

**La Grange**
Member
Baptist Health La Grange

**Lexington**
Member
Baptist Health Lexington

**Richmond**
Member
Baptist Health Richmond

### MAINE
**Bangor**
Member
St. Joseph Hospital

**Lewiston**
Member
St. Mary's Regional Medical Center

**Sanford**
Member
Henrietta D. Goodall Hospital

### MASSACHUSETTS
**Attleboro**
Member
Sturdy Memorial Hospital

**Boston**
Member
Boston Medical Center
New England Baptist Hospital
Tufts Medical Center

**Brockton**
Member
Signature Healthcare Brockton Hospital

**Fall River**
Member
Southcoast Hospitals Group

**Great Barrington**
Member
Fairview Hospital

**Milford**
Member
Milford Regional Medical Center

**Newburyport**
Member
Anna Jaques Hospital

**North Adams**
Member
North Adams Regional Hospital

**Oak Bluffs**
Member
Martha's Vineyard Hospital

**Pittsfield**
Member
Berkshire Medical Center

**Stoughton**
Member
New England Sinai Hospital and Rehabilitation Center

**Westfield**
Member
Noble Hospital

**Winchester**
Member
Winchester Hospital

### MICHIGAN
**Alma**
Member
MidMichigan Medical Center–Gratiot

**Clare**
Member
MidMichigan Medical Center–Clare

**Gladwin**
Member
MidMichigan Medical Center–Gladwin

**Midland**
Member
MidMichigan Medical Center–Midland

**Ypsilanti**
Member
Forest Health Medical Center

### NEW HAMPSHIRE
**Concord**
Member
Concord Hospital

**Exeter**
Member
Exeter Hospital

**Franklin**
Lease
Franklin Regional Hospital

**Laconia**
Member
Lakes Region General Hospital

**Manchester**
Member
Catholic Medical Center
Elliot Hospital

**Nashua**
Member
St. Joseph Hospital

**North Conway**
Member
Memorial Hospital

**Rochester**
Member
Frisbie Memorial Hospital

**Salem**
Member
Northeast Rehabilitation Hospital

### NEW YORK
**Batavia**
Member
United Memorial Medical Center

**Bath**
Member
Ira Davenport Memorial Hospital

**Elizabethtown**
Member
Elizabethtown Community Hospital

**Elmira**
Member
Arnot Ogden Medical Center
St. Joseph's Hospital

**Glens Falls**
Member
Glens Falls Hospital

**Gloversville**
Member
Nathan Littauer Hospital and Nursing Home

**Plattsburgh**
Member
Champlain Valley Physicians Hospital Medical Center

### OHIO
**Bryan**
Member
Community Hospitals and Wellness Centers

**Cadiz**
Member
Harrison Community Hospital

**Canton**
Member
Mercy Medical Center

**Cleveland**
Member
  Grace Hospital
  St. Vincent Charity Medical Center

**East Liverpool**
Member
  East Liverpool City Hospital

**Groveport**
Member
  Barix Clinics of Ohio

**Montpelier**
Member
  Community Hospitals and Wellness
    Centers–Montpelier

**Salem**
Member
  Salem Community Hospital

**Seaman**
Member
  Adams County Regional Medical Center

**PENNSYLVANIA**
**Langhorne**
Member
  Barix Clinics of Pennsylvania

**RHODE ISLAND**
**Pawtucket**
Member
  Memorial Hospital of Rhode Island

**Providence**
Member
  Roger Williams Medical Center

**Wakefield**
Member
  South County Hospital

**SOUTH CAROLINA**
**Columbia**
Member
  Providence Hospital

**Fairfax**
Member
  Allendale County Hospital

**TEXAS**
**Aransas Pass**
Member
  Care Regional Medical Center

**Dallas**
Member
  South Hampton Community Hospital

**Houston**
Member
  St. Anthony's Hospital

†List supplied by The Joint Commission

# Description of Lists

*This section of AHA Guide provides a directory of information useful to the health care field.*

## National and International Organizations

The national and international lists include many types of voluntary organizations concerned with matters of interest to the health care field. The organizational information includes address, telephone number, FAX number, and the primary contact. The information was obtained directly from the organizations.

Organizations are searchable by state, then city within state, and "kind of organization."

We present these organization listings simply as a convenient directory. Inclusion or omission of any organization's name indicates neither approval nor disapproval by Health Forum LLC, an American Hospital Association company.

## United States Government Agencies

National, state and provincial government agencies concerned with health–related matters are listed by the major department of government under which the different functions fall.

The selected state and provincial government agencies include the state department of health, facility licensure, medical and nursing licensure, and managed care organization licensure.

## Organizations and Agencies

The lists of organizations include hospital associations and councils, group purchasing organizations, quality improvement organizations, and health information exchanges.

There are many active local organizations that do not fall within these categories. Contact the hospital association of the state or province for information about such additional groups. The hospital association and councils listed have offices with full-time executives.

## Other Health Care Providers

A list of Freestanding Ambulatory Surgery Centers is provided.

Lists of The Joint Commission Accredited Long Term Care Organizations and Joint Commission Accredited Behavioral Health Organizations are provided for your information.

These lists are provided simply as a convenient reference. Inclusion or omission of any organization's name indicates neither approval or disapproval by Health Forum L.L.C.

## National Organizations

### A

**AARP,** 601 E Street, NW, Washington, DC 20049; tel. 202/434–2277; FAX. 888/836–3985; Addison Barry Rand, Chief Executive Officer

**Academic Pediatric Association,** 6728 Old McLean Village Drive, McLean, VA 22101; tel. 703/556–9222; FAX. 703/556–8729; Connie MacKay, Executive Director

**AcademyHealth,** 1150 17th Street, NW, Suite 600, Washington, DC 20036; tel. 202/292–6700; FAX. 202/292–6800; Lisa Simpson, MB, BCh, MPH, FAAP, President and Chief Executive Officer

**Accreditation Association for Ambulatory Health Care,** 5250 Old Orchard Rd., Suite 200, Skokie, IL 60077; tel. 847/853–6060; FAX. 847/853–9028; John E. Burke, Ph. D., President and CEO

**Accreditation Council for Graduate Medical Education, ACGME,** 515 N. State Street, Suite 2000, Chicago, IL 60654; tel. 312/755–5000; FAX. 312/755–7498; Thomas J. Nasca, MD, MACP, Chief Executive Officer

**Accreditation Council for Pharmacy Education, ACPE,** 135 S. LaSalle Street, Suite 4100, Chicago, IL 60603–4810; tel. 312/664–3575; FAX. 312/664–4652; Peter H. Vlasses, Pharm. D., BCPS, FCCP, Executive Director

**Acute Long Term Hospital Association,** 1667 K Street, NW, Suite 1050, Washington, DC 20006; tel. 202/266–9800; William Walters, Chief Executive Officer

**Advanced Medical Technology Association,** 701 Pennsylvania Avenue, NW, Suite 800, Washington, DC 20004; tel. 202/783–8700; FAX. 202/783–8750; Stephen J. Ubl, President and Chief Executive Officer

**Aerospace Medical Association,** 320 South Henry Street, Alexandria, VA 22314–3579; tel. 703/739–2240; FAX. 703/739–9652; Jeffrey C. Sventek, MS, CASP, Executive Director

**Alcoholics Anonymous World Services, Inc.,** PO Box 459, New York, NY 10163; tel. 212/870–3400; FAX. 202/870–3003

**Alexander Graham Bell Association for the Deaf & Hard of Hearing,** 3417 Volta Place, NW, Washington, DC 20007; tel. 202/204–4683; FAX. 202/337–5087; Garrett W. Yates, Acting Development Director

**Allergy Associates,** 2004 Grand Avenue, Baldwin, NY 11510; tel. 516/223–7656; FAX. 516/223–0583; Joe D' Amore, MD, President

**Alliance for Children & Families,** 11700 West Lake Park Drive, Milwaukee, WI 53224; tel. 414/359–1040; FAX. 414/359–1074; Susan N. Greyfus, President and Chief Executive Officer

**Alzheimer's Association, (Alzheimer's Disease and Related Disorders Association, Inc.),** 225 North Michigan Avenue, Suite 1700, Chicago, IL 60601; tel. 312/335–8700; FAX. 866/699–1246; Cyndy Cordell, Healthcare Professional Services

**America's Blood Centers,** 725 15th Street, NW, Suite 700, Washington, DC 20005–2109; tel. 202/393–5725; FAX. 202/393–1282; William M. Coenen, Interim Chief Executive Officer

**America's Health Insurance Plans,** 601 Pennsylvania Ave, NW, South Bldg, Suite 500, Washington, DC 20004; tel. 202/778–3200; FAX. 202/778–8486; Charles W. Stellar, Executive Vice President

**American Academy for Cerebral Palsy and Developmental Medicine,** 555 E. Wells Street, Suite 1100, Milwaukee, WI 53202; tel. 414/918–3014; FAX. 414/276–2146; Tracy Burr, Executive Director

**American Academy of Allergy, Asthma and Immunology,** 555 East Wells Street, Suite 1100, Milwaukee, WI 53202; tel. 414/272–6071; FAX. 414/272–6070; Kay Whalen, Executive Director

**American Academy of Child and Adolescent Psychiatry,** 3615 Wisconsin Avenue, NW, Washington, DC 20016; tel. 202/966–7300; FAX. 202/966–2891; Heidi B. Fordi, Executive Director

**American Academy of Dental Practice Administration,** 1063 Whippoorwill Lane, Palatine, IL 60067; tel. 847/934–4404; Kathleen Uebel, Executive Director

**American Academy of Dermatology,** 930 East Woodfield Road, Schaumburg, IL 60173; tel. 847/330–0230; FAX. 847/330–0050; Robert S. Bolan, PhD, Interim Executive Director

**American Academy of Family Physicians,** 11400 Tomahawk Creek Parkway, Leawood, KS 66211; tel. 913/906–6000; FAX. 913/906–6075; Douglas E. Henley, M.D., FAAFP, Chief Executive Officer

**American Academy of Medical Administrators,** 701 Lee Street, Suite 600, Des Plaines, IL 60016; tel. 847/759–8601; FAX. 847/759–8602; Renee Schleicher, CAE, President and Chief Executive Officer

**American Academy of Neurology,** 201 Chicago Avenue South, Minneapolis, MN 55415; tel. 612/928–6100; FAX. 612/454–2744; Catherine M. Rydell, CAE, Executive Director

**American Academy of Ophthalmology,** 655 Beach Street, P.O. Box 7424, San Francisco, CA 94120; tel. 415/561–8500; FAX. 415/561–8533; David W. Parke, II, Executive Vice President and Chief Executive Officer

**American Academy of Optometry,** 2909 Fairgreen Street, Orlando, FL 32803; tel. 3217103937; FAX. 4108939890; Lois Schoenbrun, CAE, FAAO Executive Director

**American Academy of Oral Medicine,** 23607 Highway 99, Suite 2C, Edmonds, WA 98020–9516; tel. 425/778–6162; FAX. 425/771–9588; Nick Senzee, Executive Director

**American Academy of Orthopaedic Surgeons,** 6300 North River Road, Rosemont, IL 60018–4262; tel. 847/823–7186; FAX. 847/823–8125; Karen L. Hackett, FACHE, CAE, Chief Executive Officer

**American Academy of Otolaryngic Allergy,** 11130 Sunrise Valley Drive, Suite 100, Reston, VA 20191; tel. 202/955–5010; FAX. 202/955–5016; Jami Lucas, Executive Director and Chief Executive Officer

**American Academy of Otolaryngology-Head and Neck Surgery, Inc.,** 1650 Diagonal Road, Alexandria, VA 22314; tel. 703/836–4444; FAX. 703/683–5100; David R. Nielsen, MD, FACS, Chief Executive Officer and Executive Vice President

**American Academy of Pain Management,** 13947 Mono Way, Suite A, Sonora, CA 95370–2807; tel. 209/533–9744; FAX. 209/533–9750; Lenore Duensing, M.Ed, Executive Director

**American Academy of Pediatrics,** 141 Northwest Point Boulevard, Elk Grove Village, IL 60007–1098; tel. 847/434–4000; FAX. 847/434–8000; Errol R. Alden MD, FAAP, Executive Director and Chief Executive Officer

**American Academy of Physical Medicine and Rehabilitation,** 9700 West Bryn Mawr Avenue, Suite 200, Rosemont, IL 60018–5701; tel. 847/737–6000; FAX. 847/737–6001; Thomas E. Stautzenbach, CAE, Executive Director

**American Academy of Physician Assistants,** 2318 Mill Road, Suite 1300, Alexandria, VA 22314; tel. 703/836–2272; FAX. 703/684–1924; Jennifer L. Dorn, Executive Vice President and Chief Executive Officer

**American Academy of Psychoanalysis And Dynamic Psychiatry,** One Regency Drive, PO Box 30, Bloomfield, CT 06002; tel. 888/691–8281; FAX. 860/286–0787; Jacquelyn T. Coleman, CAE, Executive Director

**American Aging Association, The Sally Balin Medical Center,** 110 Chesley Drive, Media, PA 19063; tel. 610/627–2626; FAX. 610/565–9747; Arthur K. Balin, MD, PhD., FACP

**American Ambulance Association,** 8400 Westpark Drive, Second Floor, McLean, VA 22102; tel. 703/610–9018; FAX. 703/610–0210; Maria Bianchi, Executive Vice President

**American Art Therapy Association, Inc.,** 11160 - C1 South Lakes Drive, Suite 813, Reston, VA 20191; tel. 703/212–2238; Peg Dunn-Snow, PhD, ATR-BC, President

**American Assembly for Men In Nursing,** PO Box 130220, Birmingham, AL 35213; tel. 205/956–0146; FAX. 205/956–0149; Byron McCain, Executive Director

**American Association for Clinical Chemistry, Inc. (AACC),** 1850 K Street, NW, Washington, DC 20006; tel. 202/857–0717; FAX. 202/877–5093; Richard Flaherty, Executive Vice President

**American Association for Dental Research,** 1619 Duke Street, Alexandria, VA 22314–3406; tel. 703/548–0066; FAX. 703/548–1883; Christopher Fox, Executive Director

**American Association for Health Education,** 1900 Association Drive, Reston, VA 20191; tel. 703/476–3400; FAX. 703/476–9527; Malcolm Goldsmith, Executive Director

**American Association For Homecare,** 2011 Crystal Drive, Suite 725, Arlington, VA 22202–3709; tel. 703/836–6263; FAX. 703/836–6730; Michael Reinemer, Vice President

**American Association for Laboratory Animal Science, AALAS,** 9190 Crestwyn Hills Drive, Memphis, TN 38125; tel. 901/754–8620; FAX. 901/753–0046; Ann T. Turner, PhD, CAE, Executive Director

**American Association for Respiratory Care,** 9425 N. MacArthur, Suite 100, Irving, TX 75063; tel. 972/243–2272; FAX. 972484–2720

**American Association for the Advancement of Science,** 1200 New York Avenue, NW, Washington, DC 20005; tel. 202/326–6640; FAX. 202/371–9526; Alan Leshner, Chief Executive Officer

**American Association for the Surgery of Trauma,** 633 N. Saint Clair Street, Suite 2600, Chicago, IL 60611; tel. 800/789–4006; FAX. 312/202–5064; Sharon Gautschy, Executive Director

**American Association of Ambulatory Surgery Centers,** 1012 Cameron Street, Alexandria, VA 22314; tel. 703/836–8808; FAX. 703/549–0976; Kathy Bryant, President

**American Association of Anatomists,** 9650 Rockville Pike, Bethesda, MD 20814; tel. 301/634–7910; FAX. 301/634–7965; Andrea Pendleton

**American Association of Bioanalysts,** 906 Olive, Suite 1200, St. Louis, MO 63101–1448; tel. 314/241–1445; FAX. 314/241–1449; Mark S. Birenbaum, PhD, Administrator

**American Association of Certified Orthoptists,** 3914 Nakoma Road, Madison, WI 53711; tel. 608/233–5383; FAX. 608/263–4247; Marlo Galli, CO

**American Association of Colleges of Nursing,** One DuPont Circle, NW, Suite 530, Washington, DC 20036; tel. 202/463–6930; FAX. 202/785–8320; Geraldine Bednash, PhD, RN FAAN, Chief Executive Officer and Executive Director

**American Association of Colleges of Osteopathic Medicine,** 5550 Friendship Boulevard, Suite 310, Chevy Chase, MD 20815–7231; tel. 301/968–4100; FAX. 301/968–4101; Stephen C. Shannon, DO, MPH, President and Chief Executive Officer

**American Association of Colleges of Pharmacy,** 1727 King Street, Floor 2, Alexandria, VA 22314–2700; tel. 703/739–2330; FAX. 703/836–8982; Lucinda Maine, PhD, Executive Vice President

**American Association of Colleges of Podiatric Medicine,** 15850 Crabbs Branch Way, Suite 320, Rockville, MD 20855–2622; tel. 301/948–9760; FAX. 301/948–1928; Moraith G. North, Executive Director

**American Association of Critical-Care Nurses,** 101 Columbia, Aliso Viejo, CA 92656–1491; tel. 949/362–2000; FAX. 949/362–2020; Wanda L. Johansson, RN, MN, Chief Executive Officer

**American Association of Dental Consultants, Inc.,** 10032 Wind Hill Drive, Greenville, IN 47124; tel. 812/923–2600; FAX. 812/923–2900; Judy Salisbury, Executive Director

**American Association of Endodontists,** 211 East Chicago Avenue, Suite 1100, Chicago, IL 60611–2691; tel. 312/266–7255; FAX. 312/266–9867; Trina Anderson, Executive Assistant to the Executive Director

**American Association of Healthcare Administrative Management,** 11240 Waples Mill Road, Suite 200, Fairfax, VA 22030; tel. 703/281–4043; FAX. 703/359–7562; Sharon Galler, Executive Director

**American Association of Kidney Patients,** 2701 North Rocky Point Drive, Suite 150, Tampa, FL 33607; tel. 800/749–2257; FAX. 813/636–8122; Diana Clynes, Director of Programs and Services

**American Association of Medical Assistants,** 20 North Wacker Drive, Suite 1575, Chicago, IL 60606; tel. 312/899–1500; FAX. 312/899–1259; Donald A. Balasa, JD, MBA, Executive Director, Legal Counsel

**American Association of Nurse Anesthetists,** 222 South Prospect Avenue, Park Ridge, IL 60068–4001; tel. 847/692–7050; FAX. 847/685–4501; Wanda O. Wilson, CRNA, PhD, Executive Director and Chief Executive Officer

**American Association of Occupational Health Nurses, Inc.,** 7794 Grow Drive, Pensacola, FL 32514; tel. 770/455–7757; FAX. 770/455–7271; Ann R. Cox, CAE, Executive Director

**American Association of Oral and Maxillofacial Surgeons,** 9700 West Bryn Mawr Avenue, Rosemont, IL 60018–5701; tel. 847/678–6200; FAX. 847/678–6286; Robert C. Rinaldi, PhD, Executive Director

**American Association of Orthodontists,** 401 North Lindbergh Boulevard, St. Louis, MO 63141–7816; tel. 314/993–1700; FAX. 314/997–1745; Chris P. Vranas, Executive Director

**American Association of Pastoral Counselors,** 9504A Lee Highway, Fairfax, VA 22031–2303; tel. 703/385–6967; FAX. 703/352–7725; Douglas M. Ronsheim, D.Min, Executive Director

**American Association of Physicists in Medicine,** One Physics Ellipse, College Park, MD 20740–3846; tel. 301/209–3350; FAX. 301/209–0862; Angela R. Keyser, Executive Director

**American Association of Plastic Surgeons,** 500 Cummings Center, Suite 4550, Beverly, MA 01915; tel. 978/927–8330; FAX. 978/524–0461; Aurelie Alger, JD, Executive Director

**American Association of Poison Control Centers,** 515 King Street, Suite 510, Alexandria, VA 22314; tel. 703/894–1858; FAX. 703/683–2812; Debbie Carr, Executive Director

**American Association of Psychiatric Technicians, Inc., A.A.P.T.,** 1220 S Street, Suite 100, Sacramento, CA 95814–7138; tel. 800/391–7589; FAX. 916/329–9145; Debi Loger, Executive Director

**American Association of Public Health Dentistry,** 3085 Stevenson Drive, Suite 200, Springfield, IL 62703; tel. 217/529–6941; FAX. 217/529–9120; Pamela J. Tolson, CAE, Executive Director

**American Association on Intellectual and Developmental Disabilities (AAIDD),** 501 Third Street, NW, Suite 200, Washington, DC 20001–2760; tel. 202/387–1968; FAX. 202/387–2193; Margaret A. Nygren, Executive Director & Chief Executive Officer

**American Baptist Homes and Caring Ministries,** PO Box 851 (National Ministries), Valley Forge, PA 19482–0851; tel. 610/768–2051; Laura Miraz, Liaison

**American Board of Allergy and Immunology,** 111 S. Independence Mall East, Suite 701, Philadelphia, PA 19106–3699; tel. 215/592–9466; FAX. 215/592–9411; Stephen I. Wasserman, MD, President

**American Board of Cardiovascular Medicine and Credentialing,** PO Box 3395, Riverview, FL 33568; tel. 813/394–4968; Jonni Cooper, BSN, MBA, PhD, FACCN-III, Chief Executive Officer

**American Board of Cardiovascular Perfusion,** 207 North 25th Avenue, Hattiesburg, MS 39401; tel. 601/268–2221; FAX. 601/268–2229; Beth A. Richmond, PhD, Stephen Oshrin, PhD, Executive Co-Directors

**American Board of Colon and Rectal Surgery,** 20600 Eureka Road, Suite 600, Taylor, MI 48180; tel. 734/282–9400; FAX. 734/282–9402; David J. Schoetz, MD, Executive Director

**American Board of Dermatology, Inc.,** Henry Ford Health System, One Ford Place, Detroit, MI 48202–3450; tel. 313/874–1088; FAX. 313/872–3221; Thomas D. Horn, MD, MBA, Executive Director

**American Board of Emergency Medicine,** 3000 Coolidge Road, East Lansing, MI 48823; tel. 517/332–4800; FAX. 517/332–2234; Earl J. Reisdorff, MD, Executive Director

**American Board of Family Medicine, Inc.,** 1648 McGrathiana Parkway, Suite 550, Lexington, KY 40511–1247; tel. 859/269–5626; FAX. 859/335–7501; James Puffer, MD, President and Chief Executive Officer

**American Board of Internal Medicine,** 510 Walnut Street, Suite 1700, Philadelphia, PA 19106–3699; tel. 215/446–3500; FAX. 215/446–3473; Christine K. Cassel, MD, President

**American Board of Medical Specialties,** 222 N LaSalle St, Suite 1500, Chicago, IL 60601; tel. 312/436–2600; FAX. 312/436–2700; Lori Boukas, Communications Director

**American Board of Neurological Surgery,** 245 Amity Road #208, Woodbridge, CT 06525; tel. 203/397–2267; FAX. 203/392–0400; Mary Louise Spencer, Executive Director

**American Board of Nuclear Medicine,** 4555 Forest Park Blvd, Suite 119, St. Louis, MO 63108; tel. 314/367–2225; Henry D. Royal, MD, Executive Director

**American Board of Ophthalmology,** 111 Presidential Boulevard, Suite 241, Bala Cynwyd, PA 19004; tel. 610/664–1175; FAX. 610/664–6503; John G. Clarkson, MD, Executive Director

**American Board of Oral and Maxillofacial Surgery,** 625 North Michigan Avenue, Suite 1820, Chicago, IL 60611; tel. 312/642–0070; FAX. 312/642–8584; Cheryl E. Mounts, Executive Secretary

**American Board of Orthopedic Surgery, Inc.,** 400 Silver Cedar Court, Chapel Hill, NC 27514; tel. 919/929–7103; FAX. 919/942–8988; Shepard R. Hurwitz, MD, Executive Director

**American Board of Pathology,** One Urban Centre, 4830 West Kennedy Boulevard, Suite 690, Tampa, FL 33622–5915; tel. 813/286–2444; FAX. 813/289–5279; Rebecca L. Johnson, MD, Chief Executive Officer

**American Board of Pediatrics, Inc.,** 111 Silver Cedar Court, Chapel Hill, NC 27514; tel. 919/929–0461; FAX. 919/929–9255; David G. Nichols, MD, MBA, President and Chief Executive Officer

**American Board of Physical Medicine and Rehabilitation,** 3015 Allegro Park Lane SW, Rochester, MN 55902; tel. 507/282–1776; FAX. 507/282–9242; Anthony M. Tarvestad, JD, Executive Director

**American Board of Podiatric Surgery,** 445 Fillmore Street, San Francisco, CA 94117–3404; tel. 415/553–7800; FAX. 415/553–7801; James A. Lamb, Executive Director

**American Board of Preventive Medicine, Inc.,** 111 West Jackson Boulevard, Suite 1110, Chicago, IL 60604; tel. 312/939–2276; FAX. 312/939–2218; William W. Greaves, MD, MSPH, Executive Director

**American Board of Prosthodontics,** PO Box 271894, West Hartford, CT 06127–1894; tel. 860/679–2649; FAX. 860/206–1169; Thomas D. Taylor, DDS, MSD, Executive Director

**American Board of Psychiatry and Neurology, Inc.,** 2150 E. Lake Cook Road, Suite 900, Buffalo Grove, IL 60089; tel. 847/229–6500; FAX. 847/229–6600; Larry Faulkner, MD, President and Chief Executive Officer

**American Board of Quality Assurance and Utilization Review Physicians, Inc., ABQAURP,** 6640 Congress St, New Port Richey, FL 34653; tel. 800/998–6030; FAX. 727/569–0195; Renee Willoughby, Managing Director

**American Board of Radiology,** 5441 E. Williams Blvd, Suite 200, Tucson, AZ 85711; tel. 520/790–2900; FAX. 520/790–3200; Gary J. Becker, MD, Executive Director

**American Board of Surgery, Inc.,** 1617 John F. Kennedy Boulevard, Suite 860, Philadelphia, PA 19103; tel. 215/568–4000; FAX. 215/563–5718; Frank R. Lewis, MD, Executive Director

**American Board of Thoracic Surgery,** 633 N. Street Clair Street, Suite 2320, Chicago, IL 60611; tel. 312/202–5900; FAX. 312/202–5960; William A. Baumgartner, MD, Executive Director

**American Broncho-Esophagological Association, Office of the Secretary,** Stanford University School of Medicine, Division of Pediatric Otolaryngology, Stanford, CA 94305–5739; tel. 650/725–6500; FAX. 650/725–8502; Peter Koltai, MD, Secretary

**American Burn Association,** 311 South Wacker Drive, Suite 4150, Chicago, IL 60606; tel. 312/642–9260; FAX. 312/642–9130; John Krichbaum, JD, Executive Director

**American Cancer Society,** 250 Williams Street, NW, Suite 600, Atlanta, GA 30303; tel. 800/227–2345; Otis Brawley, MD, Chief Medical Officer

**American Center for the Alexander Technique, Inc.,** 39 W. 14th Street, #507, New York, NY 10011; tel. 212/633–2229; FAX. 212/633–2239; Jane Tomkiewicz, Executive Director

**American Chiropractic Association,** 1701 Clarendon Boulevard, Arlington, VA 22209; tel. 703/276–8800; FAX. 703/243–2593; Janet Ridgely, Acting Executive Vice President

**American Cleft Palate-Craniofacial Association,** 1504 E. Franklin Street, Suite 102, Chapel Hill, NC 27514; tel. 919/933–9044; FAX. 919/933–9604; Nancy C. Smythe, Executive Director

**American College Health Association,** 1362 Mellon Road, Suite 180, Hanover, MD 21076; tel. 410/859–1500; FAX. 410/859–1510; Doyle E. Randol, MS, Executive Director

**American College of Allergy, Asthma and Immunology,** 85 West Algonquin Road, Suite 550, Arlington Heights, IL 60005; tel. 847/427–1200; FAX. 847/427–1294; Rick Slawny, Executive Director

**American College of Apothecaries,** PO Box 341266, Bartlett, TN 38184; tel. 901/383–8119; FAX. 901/383–8882; D. C. Huffman, Jr., PhD, Executive Vice President

**American College of Cardiology,** 2400 N Street, NW, Washington, DC 20037; tel. 202/375–6180; FAX. 202/375–6819; Jack Lewin, MD, Chief Executive Officer

**American College of Cardiovascular Nurses, Inc.,** PO Box 3395, Riverview, FL 33568; tel. 813/394–4968; Jonni Cooper, Chief Executive Officer

**American College of Chest Physicians,** 3300 Dundee Road, Northbrook, IL 60062; tel. 847/498–8300; FAX. 847/498–8318; Paul A. Markowski, CAE

**American College of Dentists,** 839J Quince Orchard Boulevard, Gaithersburg, MD 20878–1614; tel. 301/977–3223; FAX. 301/977–3330; Stephen A. Ralls, DDS

**American College of Emergency Physicians,** PO Box 619911, Dallas, TX 75261–9911; tel. 972/550–0911; FAX. 972/580–2816; Dean Wilikerson, Executive Director

**American College of Foot and Ankle Surgeons,** 8725 W. Higgins Rd, Suite 555, Chicago, IL 60631; tel. 773/693–9300; FAX. 773/693–9304; J.C. Mahaffey, CAE, Executive Director

**American College of Gastroenterology,** 6400 Goldsboro Road, Suite 200, Bethesda, MD 20817; tel. 3012639000; FAX. 3012639025; Bradley C. Stillman, Executive Director

**American College of Healthcare Executives,** One North Franklin, Suite 1700, Chicago, IL 60606–3491; tel. 312/424–2800; FAX. 312/424–0023; Deborah J. Bowen, FACHE, CAE, President and Chief Executive Officer

**American College of Mohs Surgery,** 555 E. Wells, Suite 1100, Milwaukee, WI 53202–3823; tel. 414/347–1103; FAX. 414/276–3349; Kim Schardin, MBA, CAE, Executive Director

**American College of Nurse-Midwives,** Silver Spring Metro Plaza, 8403 Colesville Rd, Suite1550, Silver Spring, MD 20910–6374; tel. 240/485–1800; FAX. 240/485–1818; Lorrie Kline Kaplan, Executive Director

**American College of Obstetricians and Gynecologists,** 409 12th Street, SW, Washington, DC 20090–6920; tel. 202/638–5577; FAX. 202/484–5107; Hal C. Lawrence III, MD, Executive Vice President

**American College of Occupational and Environmental Medicine, (Includes Occupational & Environmental Health Foundation and The Occupational Physicians Scholarship Fund),** 25 Northwest Point Blvd, Suite 700, Elk Grove Village, IL 60007; tel. 847/818–1800; FAX. 847/818–9266; Barry S. Eisenberg, CAE., Executive Director

**American College of Physician Executives,** 400 N. Ashley Drive, Suite 400, Tampa, FL 33602; tel. 813/287–2000; FAX. 813/287–8993; Peter Angood, MD, Chief Executive Officer

**American College of Physicians,** 190 North Independence Mall West, Philadelphia, PA 19106–1572; tel. 215/351–2800; FAX. 215/351–2829; John Tooker, MD, MBA, FACP, Executive VP, Chief Executive Officer

**American College of Preventive Medicine,** 455 Massachusetts Avenue, NW, Suite 200, Washington, DC 20001; tel. 202/466–2044; FAX. 202/466–2662; Mike Barry, Executive Director

**American College of Radiology,** 1891 Preston White Drive, Reston, VA 20191–4397; tel. 703/648–8900; FAX. 703/648–9176; Harvey L. Neiman, MD, Executive Director

**American College of Rheumatology,** 2200 Lake Boulevard, NE, Atlanta, GA 30319; tel. 404/633–3777; FAX. 404/633–1870; Helen Anne Richards, Director of Membership

**American College of Sports Medicine,** PO Box 1440, Indianapolis, IN 46206–1440; tel. 317/637–9200; FAX. 317/634–7817; James R. Whitehead, Executive Vice President

**American College of Surgeons,** 633 N. Saint Clair Street, Chicago, IL 60611; tel. 312/202–5000; FAX. 312/202–5001; David B. Hoyt, MD, FACS, Executive Director

**American Congress of Rehabilitation Medicine,** 11654 Plaza America Drive #535, Reston, VA 20190–4700; tel. 317/471–8760; FAX. 866/692–1619; Jon W. Lindberg, MBA, CAE, Chief Executive Officer

**American Dental Assistants Association,** 35 E. Wacker Driver, Suite 1730, Chicago, IL 60601; tel. 312/541–1550; FAX. 312/541–1496; Lawrence H. Sepin, Executive Director

**American Dental Association,** 211 East Chicago Avenue, Chicago, IL 60611; tel. 312/440–2500; Kathleen T. O'Loughlin, DMD, MPH, Executive Director

**American Dental Education Association,** 1400 K. Street, NW, Suite 1100, Washington, DC 20005; tel. 202/289–7201; FAX. 202/289–7204; Richard Valachovic,President and Chief Executive Officer

**American Dental Society of Anesthesiology, Inc.,** 211 East Chicago Avenue, Suite 780, Chicago, IL 60611; tel. 312/664–8270; FAX. 312/224–8624; R. Knight Charlton, Executive Director

**American Diabetes Association, Inc.,** 1701 N. Beauregard Street, Alexandria, VA 22311; tel. 703/549–1500; FAX. 703/836–7439; Larry Hausner, Chief Executive Officer

**American Federation for Aging Research,** 55 West 39th Street, 16th Floor, New York, NY 10018; tel. 212/703–9977; FAX. 212/997–0330; Stephanie Lederman, Director

**American Foundation for the Blind, Inc.,** 2 Penn Plaza, Suite 1102, New York, NY 10121; tel. 212/502–7600; FAX. 888/545–8331; Carl Augusto, President and Chief Executive Officer

**American Group Psychotherapy Association, Inc.,** 25 East 21st Street, Sixth Floor, New York, NY 10010; tel. 212/477–2677; FAX. 212/979–6627; Marsha S. Block, CAE, Chief Executive Officer

**American Head and Neck Society,** 11300 W. Olympic Blvd #600, Los Angles, CA 90064; tel. 310/437–0559; FAX. 310/437–0585; Christina Kasendorf, Executive Director

**American Headache Society,** 19 Mantua Road, Mt. Royal, NJ 08061; tel. 856/423–0043; FAX. 856/423–0082; Linda McGillicuddy, Executive Director

**American Health Care Association,** 1201 L Street, NW, Washington, DC 20005; tel. 202/842–4444; FAX. 202/842–3860; Mark Parkinson, President and Chief Executive Officer

**American Health Information Management Association (AHIMA),** 233 North Michigan Avenue, 21st Floor, Chicago, IL 60601–5800; tel. 312/233–1100; FAX. 312/233–1090; Alan F. Dowling PhD, Chief Executive Officer

**American Health Lawyers Association,** 1620 Eye Street NW, Washington, DC 20006–4010; tel. 202/833–1100; FAX. 202/833–1105; Peter M. Leibold, Esq, Executive Vice President and Chief Executive Officer

**American Health Planning Association,** 7245 Arlington Boulevard, Suite 300, Falls Church, VA 22042; tel. 703/573–3103; FAX. 703/573–3103; Dean Montgomery, Director

**American Healthcare Radiology Administrators,** 490 - B Boston, Post Road, Suite 101, Sudbury, MA 01776; tel. 978/443–7591; FAX. 978/443–8046; Mary S. Reitter, Executive Director

**American Heart Association, Inc.,** 7272 Greenville Avenue, Dallas, TX 75231; tel. 214/706–1574; FAX. 214/373–9818; Rose Marie Robertson, MD, FAHA, Chief Science and Medical Officer

**American Hospital Association,** 325 7th Street, NW, Suite 700, Washington, DC 20004; tel. 202/638–1100; Richard Umbdenstock, President and Chief Executive Officer

**American Hospital Association,** 155 N. Wacker Drive, Suite 400, Chicago, IL 60606; tel. 312/422–3000; Richard Umbdenstock, President and Chief Executive Officer

**American Hospital Association, Washington Office,** 325 7th Street, NW, Suite 700, Washington, DC 20004; tel. 202/638–1100; FAX. 202/626–2355; Rick Pollack, Executive Vice President

**American International Health Alliance,** 1250 Eye Street, NW, Suite 350, Washington, DC 20005; tel. 202/789–1136; FAX. 202/789–1277; James P. Smith, Executive Director

**American Laryngological Association, Office of the Secretary,** 193-39 Keno Avenue, Holliswood, NY 11423–1214; tel. 212/744–4368; FAX. 212/434–6620; Gady Har-El, MD, Secretary

**American Library Association,** 50 East Huron Street, Chicago, IL 60611; tel. 312/280–5063; FAX. 312/280–5270; Cynthia Vivian, Director

**American Lung Association,** 1301 Pennsylvania Avenue, NW, Washington, DC 20004–1725; tel. 202/785–3355; FAX. 202/452–1805; Harold Wimmer, President and Chief Executive Officer

**American Lung Association in Ohio,** 4050 Executive Park Drive, Suite 405, Cincinnati, OH 45241; tel. 513/985–3990; FAX. 513/985–3995; Gale Steitz, Program Director

**American Medical Association,** 515 North State Street, Chicago, IL 60610; tel. 312/464–5000; FAX. 312/464–4184; James L. Madara, MD, Chief Executive Officer and Executive Vice President

**American Medical Association Alliance,** 515 North State Street, 9th Floor, Chicago, IL 60610; tel. 312/464–4470; FAX. 312/464–5020; Hazel J. Lewis, Executive Director

**American Medical Group Association,** One Prince Street, Alexandria, VA 22314–3318; tel. 703/838–0033; FAX. 703/548–1890; Donald W. Fisher, PhD, CAE President and Chief Executive Officer

**American Medical Student Association/Foundation,** 45610 Woodland Road, Suite 300, Sterling, VA 20166; tel. 703/620–6600; FAX. 703/620–5873; Meeghan De Cagna, Interim Executive Director

**American Medical Technologists,** 10700 W. Higgins Road, Suite 150, Rosemont, IL 60018; tel. 847/823–5169; FAX. 847/823–0458; Christopher Damon, Executive Director

**American Medical Women's Association,** 100 North 20th Street, 4th Floor, Philadelphia, PA 19103; tel. 866/564–2483; FAX. 215/564–2175; Gina Marinilli, Associate Director

**American Medical Writers Association,** 30 West Gude Drive #525, Rockville, MD 20850; tel. 204/238–0940; FAX. 301/294–9006; Mark Rosal, Member Services Coordinator

**American Music Therapy Association,** 8455 Colesville Road, Suite 1000, Silver Spring, MD 20910; tel. 301/589–3300; FAX. 301/589–5175; Andrea Farbman, Ed.D., Executive Director

**American National Standards Institute,** 25 West 43rd Street, Fourth Floor, New York, NY 10036; tel. 212/642–4900; FAX. 212/398–0023; S. Joe Bhatia, President and Chief Executive Officer

**American Nephrology Nurses' Association,** East Holly Avenue, PO Box 56, Pitman, NJ 08071; tel. 856/256–2320; FAX. 856/589–7463; Mike Cunningham, Executive Director

**American Neurological Association,** 5841 Cedar Lake Road, Suite 204, Minneapolis, MN 55416; tel. 952/545–6208; FAX. 952/545–6073; JoAnn Taie, Associate Executive Director

**American Occupational Therapy Association, Inc.,** 4720 Montgomery Lane, P.O. Box 31220, Bethesda, MD 20814–1220; tel. 301/652–2682; FAX. 301/652–7711; Frederick P. Somers, Executive Director

**American Ontological Society, Inc.,** 3096 Riverdale Rd., The Villages, FL 32162; tel. 352/751–0932; FAX. 352/751–0696; Shirley Gossard, Administrator

**American Ophthalmological Society,** PO Box 193940, San Francisco, CA 94119–3940; tel. 415/561–8578; FAX. 415/561–8531; Thomas J. Liesegang, MD, Executive Vice President

**American Optometric Association,** 243 North Lindbergh Boulevard, St. Louis, MO 63141; tel. 314/991–4100; FAX. 314/991–4101; Barry J. Barresi, OD, PhD, Executive Director

**American Organization of Nurse Executives (AONE),** 325 Seventh Street, NW, Suite 600, Washington, DC 20004; tel. 202/626–2240; FAX. 202/638–5499; Pamela A. Thompson, MS, RN, CENP, FAAN, Chief Executive Officer, and AHA Senior Vice President for Nursing

**American Orthopsychiatric Association,** Department of Psychology, Box 871104, Tempe, AZ 85287–1104; tel. 480/965–0380; FAX. 480/965–8544; Nicole Bruno, Director

**American Orthoptic Council,** 3914 Nakoma Road, Madison, WI 53711; tel. 608/233–5383; FAX. 608/263–4247; Leslie France, CO, Administrator

**American Osteopathic Association,** 142 East Ontario Street, Chicago, IL 60611; tel. 312/202–8003; FAX. 312/202–8303; John B. Crosby, JD, Executive Director

**American Parkinson Disease Association, Inc.,** 135 Parkinson Avenue, Parkinson Plaza, Staten Island, NY 10305; tel. 800/223–2732; FAX. 718/981–4399; G. Maestrone, DVM, Scientific and Medical Affairs Director

**American Pediatric Society, Inc.,** 3400 Research Forest Drive, Suite B7, The Woodlands, TX 77381; tel. 281/419–0052; FAX. 281/419–0082; Kathy Cannon, Associate Executive Director

**American Pharmacists Association,** 2215 Constitution Avenue, NW, Washington, DC 20037; tel. 202/628–4410; FAX. 202/783–2351; Thomas E. Menighan, BSPharm, MBA, ScD(Hon.), Executive Vice President/Chief Executive Officer

**American Physical Therapy Association,** 1111 North Fairfax Street, Alexandria, VA 22314–1488; tel. 703/684–2782; FAX. 703/684–7343; John D. Barnes, Chief Executive Officer

**American Physiological Society,** 9650 Rockville Pike, Bethesda, MD 20814–3991; tel. 301/634–7118; FAX. 301/634–7241; Martin Frank, PhD, Executive Director

**American Podiatric Medical Association,** 9312 Old Georgetown Road, Bethesda, MD 20814–1698; tel. 301/571–9200; FAX. 301/530–2752; Glenn B. Gastwirth, DPM, Executive Director

**Section C**

**American Psychiatric Association,** 1000 Wilson Boulevard, Suite 1825, Arlington, VA 22209; tel. 703/907–7300; FAX. 703/907–1086; James H. Scully Jr., MD, Medical Director and Chief Executive Officer

**American Psychoanalytic Association,** 309 East 49th Street, New York, NY 10017; tel. 212/752–0450; FAX. 212/593–0571; Dean K. Stein, Executive Director

**American Psychological Association,** 750 First Street, NE, Washington, DC 20002–4242; tel. 202/336–5800; FAX. 202/336–5971; Katherine Nordal, PhD, Executive Director For Professional Practice

**American Psychosomatic Society,** 6728 Old McLean Village Drive, McLean, VA 22101–3906; tel. 703/556–9222; FAX. 703/556–8729; George K. Degnon, Executive Director

**American Public Health Association,** 800 I Street, NW, Washington, DC 20001–3710; tel. 202/777–2742; FAX. 202/777–2534; Georges C. Benjamin, MD, FACP, FACEP(E), Executive Director

**American Public Human Services Association,** 1133 Nineteenth Street, NW, Suite 400, Washington, DC 20036; tel. 202/682–0100; FAX. 202/289–6555; Amy Plotnick, Publications Manager

**American Red Cross,** National Headquarters, 2025 E. Street, NW, Washington, DC 20006; tel. 202/303–5214; Gail McGovern, President and Chief Executive Officer

**American Registry of Medical Assistants,** 61 Union Street, Suite 5, Westfield, MA 01085–2476; tel. 413/562–7336; FAX. 413/562–9021; Marie Bergeron, RMA, Director

**American Registry of Radiologic Technologists,** 1255 Northland Drive, St. Paul, MN 55120; tel. 651/687–0048; Jerry B. Reid, PhD, Executive Director

**American Rhinologic Society,** PO Box 495, Warwick, NY 10990; tel. 845/988–1631; FAX. 845/986–1527; Wendi Perez, Administrator/Executive Director

**American Roentgen Ray Society,** 44211 Slate Stone Court, Leesburg, VA 20176; tel. 703/729–3353; FAX. 703/729–4839; Susan Brown Cappitelli, Executive Director

**American School Health Association,** 4340 East West Highway, Suite 403, Bethesda, MD 20814; tel. 301/652–8072; FAX. 301/652–8077; Stephen Conley, Executive Director

**American Society for Adolescent Psychiatry,** PO Box 570218, Dallas, TX 75357–0218; tel. 972/613–0985; FAX. 972/613–5532; Frances M. Roton, Executive Director

**American Society for Biochemistry and Molecular Biology, Inc.,** 9650 Rockville Pike, Bethesda, MD 20814–3996; tel. 301634–7145; FAX. 301/634–7126; Charles C. Hancock, Executive Officer

**American Society for Clinical Laboratory Science,** 2025 M Street, NW, Suite 800, Washington, DC 20036; tel. 571/748–3770; FAX. 571/354–7570; Elissa Passiment, Executive Vice President

**American Society for Clinical Pathology, (Includes Board of Certification),** 33 W. Monroe Street, Suite 1600, Chicago, IL 60603; tel. 312/541–4999; FAX. 312/541–4767; E. Blair Holladay, PhD, SCT (ASCP), Executive Vice President

**American Society for Clinical Pharmacology and Therapeutics,** 528 North Washington Street, Alexandria, VA 22314; tel. 703/836–6981; FAX. 703/836–5223; Sharon J. Swan, CAE, Chief Executive Officer

**American Society for Cytotechnology,** 1500 Sunday Drive, Suite 102, Raleigh, NC 27607; tel. 800/948–3947; FAX. 919/787–4916; Beth Denny, Executive Director

**American Society for Healthcare Engineering (ASHE),** 155 N. Wacker Drive, Suite 400, Chicago, IL 60606–1725; tel. 312/422–3800; FAX. 312/422–4571; Dale Woodin, CHFM, FASHE, Executive Director

**American Society for Healthcare Human Resources Administration (ASHHRA),** 155 N. Wacker Drive, Suite 400, Chicago, IL 60606; tel. 312/422–3720; FAX. 312/422–4577; Stephanie Drake, MBA, Executive Director

**American Society for Healthcare Risk Management (ASHRM),** 155 N. Wacker Drive, Suite 400, Chicago, IL 60606; tel. 312/422–3980; FAX. 312/422–4580; Kim Hoarle, MBA, CAE, Executive Director

**American Society for Investigative Pathology,** 9650 Rockville Pike, Bethesda, MD 20814–3993; tel. 301/634–7130; FAX. 301/634–7990; Mark E. Sobel, MD, Ph.D, Executive Director

**American Society for Laser Medicine and Surgery, Inc.,** 2100 Stewart Avenue, Suite 240, Wausau, WI 54401; tel. 715/845–9283; FAX. 715/848–2493; Elizabeth Tanzi, MD, Secretary

**American Society for Microbiology,** 1752 North Street, NW, Washington, DC 20036; tel. 202/924–9265; FAX. 202/942–9333; Michael I. Goldberg, PhD, Executive Director

**American Society for Pharmacology and Experimental Therapeutics,** 9650 Rockville Pike, Bethesda, MD 20814–3995; tel. 301/634–7060; FAX. 301/634–7061; Christine K. Carrico, PhD, Executive Officer

**American Society for Public Administration,** 1301 Pennsylvania Avenue, NW, Suite 840, Washington, DC 20004; tel. 202/393–7878; FAX. 202/638–4952; Antoinette Samuel, CAE

**American Society for Radiation Oncology,** 8280 Willow Oaks Corporate Drive, Suite 500, Fairfax, VA 22031; tel. 703/502–1550; FAX. 703/502–7852; Laura I. Thevenot, Chief Executive Officer

**American Society for Reproductive Medicine,** 1209 Montgomery Highway, Birmingham, AL 35216–2809; tel. 205/978–5000; FAX. 205/293–5201; Robert W. Rebar, MD, Executive Director

**American Society for the Advancement of Anesthesia and Sedation in Dentistry,** Six East Union Avenue, PO Box 551, Bound Brook, NJ 08805; tel. 732/469–9050; FAX. 732/271–1985; David Crystal, DDS, Executive Secretary

**American Society of Anesthesiologists,** 520 North Northwest Highway, Park Ridge, IL 60068; tel. 847/825–5586; FAX. 847/825–2085; John A. Thorner, JD, CAE, Executive Vice President

**American Society of Colon and Rectal Surgeons,** 85 West Algonquin Road, Suite 550, Arlington Heights, IL 60005; tel. 847/290–9184; FAX. 847/290–9203; James Slawny, Executive Director

**American Society of Consultant Pharmacists,** 1321 Duke Street, Alexandria, VA 22314–3563; tel. 703/739–1300; FAX. 703/739–1321; Vera Jackson, PhD, Executive Director and Chief Executive Officer

**American Society of Cytopathology,** 100 West 10th Street, Suite 605, Wilmington, DE 19801; tel. 302/543–6583; FAX. 302/543–6597; Elizabeth A. Jenkins, Executive Director

**American Society of Health-System Pharmacists,** 7272 Wisconsin Avenue, Bethesda, MD 20814; tel. 301/664–8794; FAX. 301/664–8877; Paul Abramowitz, Chief Executive Officer

**American Society of Law, Medicine & Ethics,** 765 Commonwealth Avenue, Suite 1634, Boston, MA 02215; tel. 617/262–4990; FAX. 617/437–7596; Edward Hutchinson, Executive Director

**American Society of Neuroimaging,** 5841 Cedar Lake Road, Suite 204, Minneapolis, MN 55416; tel. 952/545–6291; FAX. 952/545–6073; Shannon Wild, Associate Executive Director

**American Society of Plastic Surgeons,** 444 East Algonquin Road, Arlington Heights, IL 60005; tel. 847/228–9900; FAX. 847/228–9131; Michael D. Costelloe, Executive Vice President

**American Society of Radiologic Technologists,** 15000 Central Avenue, SE, Albuquerque, NM 87123–3909; tel. 505/298–4500; FAX. 505/298–5063; Ceela McElveny, Chief Communications and Membership Officer

**American Speech-Language-Hearing Association,** 2200 Research Boulevard, Rockville, MD 20850–3289; tel. 301/296–5700; FAX. 301/296–8580; Arlene A. Pietranton, PhD, Chief Executive Officer

**American Surgical Association,** 500 Cummings Center, Suite 4550, Beverly, MA 01915; tel. 978/927–8330; FAX. 978/524–8890; Jon Blackstone, Executive Director

**American Thoracic Society,** 25 Broadway, 18th Floor, New York, NY 10004; tel. 212/315–8600; FAX. 212/315–6498; Stephen C. Crane, PhD, MPH, Executive Director

**American Trauma Society,** 201 Park Washington Court, Falls Church, VA 22046; tel. 800/556–7890; FAX. 703/241–5603; Ian Weston, Executive Director

**American Urological Association, Inc.,** 1000 Corporate Boulevard, Linthicum, MD 21090; tel. 410/689–3700; Michael Sheppard, Executive Director

**amfAR, The Foundation for AIDS Research,** 120 Wall Street, 13th Floor, New York, NY 10005–3902; tel. 212/806–1600; FAX. 212/806–1601; Rachel Carr, Assistant Coordinator, Public Information

**AORN, Association of periOperative Registered Nurses,** 2170 South Parker Road, Suite 400, Denver, CO 80231–5711; tel. 303/755–6300; FAX. 303/750–2927; Linda Groah, RN, MSN, CNOR, NEA-BC, FAAN, Executive Director and Chief Executive Officer

**Arthritis Foundation,** 1330 West Peachtree Street, Suite 100, Atlanta, GA 30309; tel. 404/872–7100; FAX. 404/965–7712; John H. Klippel, MD, President and Chief Executive Officer

**ASET - The Neurodiagnostic Society,** 402 East Bannister Road, Suite A, Kansas City, MO 64131; tel. 816/931–1120; FAX. 816/931–1145; Arlen Reimnitz, Executive Director

**Association for Applied Psychophysiology and Biofeedback,** 10200 West 44th Avenue, Suite 304, Wheat Ridge, CO 80033; tel. 303/422–8436; FAX. 303/422–8894; David Stumph, Executive Director

**Association for Clinical Pastoral Education, Inc.,** 1549 Clairmont Road, Suite 103, Decatur, GA 30033; tel. 404/320–1472; FAX. 404/320–0849; Teresa E. Snorton, Executive Director

**Association for Community Health Improvement (ACHI),** 155 N. Wacker Drive, Suite 400, Chicago, IL 60606; tel. 312/422–2193; FAX. 312/422–4522; Stephen A. Martin, Jr., Ph.D., MPH, Executive Director

**Association for Healthcare Administrative Professionals (AHCAP),** 455 S. Fourth Street, Suite 650, Louisville, KY 40202; tel. 8883200808; FAX. 5025893602; Monica Harper, Executive Director

**Association for Healthcare Foodservice, AHF,** 455 S. Fourth Street, Suite 650, Louisville, KY 40202; tel. 888/528–9552; FAX. 502/589–3602; Billye Potts, Executive Vice President

**Association for Healthcare Philanthropy,** 313 Park Avenue, Suite 400, Falls Church, VA 22046; tel. 703/532–6243; FAX. 703/532–7170; William C. McGinly, Ph.D., CA, President and Chief Executive Officer

**Association for Healthcare Resource & Materials Management (AHRMM),** 155 N. Wacker Drive, Suite 400, Chicago, IL 60606; tel. 312/422–3840; FAX. 312/422–4573; Deborah L. Sprindzunas, Executive Director

**Association for Healthcare Volunteer Resource Professionals (AHVRP),** 155 N. Wacker Drive, Suite 400, Chicago, IL 60606; tel. 312/422–3939; FAX. 312/278–0884; Joan M. Miller, MHA, Executive Director

**Association for Hospital Medical Education,** 109 Brush Creek Road, Irwin, PA 15642; tel. 724/864–7321; FAX. 724/864–6153; Kimball Mohn, MD, Executive Director

**Association for Professionals in Infection Control and Epidemiology,** 1275 K Street, NW, Suite 1000, Washington, DC 20005; tel. 202/789–1890; FAX. 202/789–1899; Katrina Crist, MBA, Chief Executive Officer

**Association for the Advancement of Automotive Medicine (AAAM),** PO Box 4176, Barrington, IL 60146; tel. 847/844–3880; FAX. 847/844–3884; Irene Herzau, Executive Director

**Association for the Healthcare Environment (AHE),** 155 N. Wacker Drive, Suite 400, Chicago, IL 60606; tel. 312/422–3860; FAX. 312/422–4578; Patti Costello, Executive Director

**Association of American Medical Colleges,** 2450 N Street, NW, Washington, DC 20037–1127; tel. 202/828–0400; FAX. 202/828–1125; Darrell G. Kirch, MD, President and Chief Executive Officer

**Association of American Physicians and Surgeons, Inc.,** 1601 North Tucson Boulevard, Suite Nine, Tucson, AZ 85716; tel. 520/327–4885; FAX. 520/325–4230; Jane M. Orient, MD, Executive Director

**Association of American Veterinary Medical Colleges,** 1101 Vermont Ave, NW, Suite 301, Washington, DC 20005; tel. 202/371–9195; FAX. 202/842–0773; Dr. Andrew Maccabe, Executive Director

**Association of Community Cancer Centers,** 11600 Nebel Street, Suite 201, Rockville, MD 20852–2557; tel. 301/984–9496; FAX. 301/770–1949; Christian Downs, JD, MHA, Executive Director

**Association of Environmental Health Academic Programs,** 8620 Roosevelt Way, NE, Suite A, Seattle, WA 98115; tel. 206/522–5272; FAX. 206/985–9805; Yalonda Sinde, Executive Director

**Association of Healthcare Administrative Professionals, AHCAP,** 455 S. Fourth Street, Suite 650, Louisville, KY 40202; tel. 502/574–9040; FAX. 502/589–3602; Monica Harper, Executive Director

**Association of Nutrition and Foodservice Professionals,** 406 Surrey Woods Drive, St. Charles, IL 60174; tel. 630/587–6336; FAX. 630/587–6308; William St. John, President

**Association of Occupational & Environmental Clinics,** 1010 Vermont Avenue, NW # 513, Washington, DC 20005; tel. 202/347–4976; Katherine Kirkland, Dr PH, MPH, Executive Director

**Association of Professional Chaplains,** 1701 East Woodfield Road, Suite 400, Schaumburg, IL 60173; tel. 847/240–1014; FAX. 847/240–1015; Patricia F. Appelhans, JD, Executive Director

**Association of Public Health Laboratories,** 8515 Georgia Avenue, Suite 700, Silver Spring, MD 20910; tel. 240/485–2745; FAX. 240/485–2700; Scott J. Becker, MS, Executive Director

**Association of Schools of Allied Health Professions,** 4400 Jennifer Street, NW, Suite 333, Washington, DC 20015; tel. 202/237–6481; FAX. 202/237–6485; John Colbert, Esq., Executive Director

**Association of Schools of Public Health,** 1900 M Street, NW, Suite 710, Washington, DC 20036; tel. 202/296–1099; FAX. 202/296–1252; Harrison C. Spencer, MD, MPH, President and Chief Executive Officer

**Association of Specialized and Cooperative Library Agencies,** 50 East Huron Street, Chicago, IL 60611; tel. 312/280–4398; FAX. 312/280–5273; Susan Hornung, Executive Director

**Association of State and Territorial Health Officials,** 2231 Crystal Drive, Suite 450, Arlington, VA 22202; tel. 202/371–9090; FAX. 571/527–3189; Paul E. Jarris, MD, MBA, Executive Director

**Association of Surgical Technologists, Inc.,** 6 West Dry Creek Circle, Suite 200, Littleton, CO 80120; tel. 303/694–9130; FAX. 303/694–9169; William J. Teutsch, CAE, Chief Executive Officer

**Association of University Programs in Health Administration,** 2000 14th Street, N., Suite 780, Arlington, VA 22201; tel. 703/894–0940; FAX. 703/894–0941; Jaime E. Stephens, CMD, Vice President

**Asthma and Allergy Foundation of America,** 8201 Corporate Drive, Suite 1000, Landover, MD 20785; tel. 800–7-ASTHMA; FAX. 202/466–8940; William McLin, M.Ed., President and Chief Executive Officer

**At Large of the AHA,** 155 N. Wacker Drive, Suite 400, Chicago, IL 60606; tel. 312/422–3700; FAX. 312/278–0882; Elizabeth Summy, Executive Director

# B

**Bereavement and Advance Care Planning Services, Gundersen Lutheran Medical Foundation, Inc.,** 1900 South Avenue-Alex, La Crosse, WI 54601; tel. 608/775–4747; FAX. 608/775–5137; Rana Limbo, Director

**Bioethics Research Library, Georgetown University,** 102 Healy Hall, 37th and O Streets, NW, Washington, DC 20057; tel. 202/687–3885; FAX. 202/687–6770; Janice Swiatek-Kelley, MLS,PhD, Director

**Biological Stain Commission,** University of Rochester Medical Center, Department Pathology and Lab Medicine, Rochester, NY 14642–0001; tel. 585/275–2751; FAX. 585/442–8993; Chad Ragan, Laboratory Operations

**Birth Defect Research for Children,** 976 Lake Baldwin Lane, Suite 104, Orlando, FL 32814; tel. 407/895–0802; Betty Mekdeci, Executive Director

**Blinded Veterans Association,** 477 H Street, NW, Washington, DC 20001; tel. 202/371–8880; FAX. 202/371–8258; Thomas H. Miller, Executive Director

**Blue Cross and Blue Shield Association,** 225 N. Michigan Avenue, Chicago, IL 60601–7680; tel. 312/297–6000; Scott P. Serota, President and Chief Executive Officer

**Brady Center to Prevent Gun Violence,** 1225 Eye Street, NW, Suite 1100, Washington, DC 20005; tel. 202/289–7319; FAX. 202/408–1851; Dan Gross, President

# C

**California Distance Learning Health Network,** 9245 Sky Park Court, Suite 100, San Diego, CA 92123; tel. 619/594–3364; Violet Macias-Reynolds, MS, M.Ed, Executive Director

**CARE Program, (Community Action for a Renewed Environment Program),** EPA, Washington, DC 20460; tel. 877/227–3909; FAX. 202/343–2395; Dennis O'Connor, Senior Policy Advisor

**CARF International,** 6951 East Southpoint, Tucson, AZ 85756; tel. 888/281–6531; FAX. 520/318–1129; Dr. Brian J. Boon, President and Chief Executive Officer

**Catholic Health Association of the United States,** 1875 Eye Street, NW, Suite 1000, Washington, DC 20006; tel. 202/296–3993; FAX. 202/296–3997; Sr. Carol Keehan, DC, President and Chief Executive Officer

**Catholic Medical Association,** 29 Bala Avenue, Suite 205, Bala Cynwyd, PA 19004; tel. 484/270–8002; FAX. 866/666–2319; John Brehany, PhD, STL, Executive Director

**Center for Health Administration Studies, University of Chicago,** 969 East 60th Street, Chicago, IL 60637; tel. 773/702–7104; FAX. 773/702–7222; Jeanne Marsh, PhD., Director

**Center for Healthcare Governance (CHG),** 155 N. Wacker Drive, Suite 400, Chicago, IL 60606; tel. 888/540–6111; FAX. 312/278–0868; John R. Combes, MD, President and Chief Operating Officer

**Center for Healthy Aging, c/o National Council on Aging,** 1901 L Street, NW, 4th Floor, Washington, DC 20036; tel. 202/479–1200; FAX. 202/479–0735; Richard Birkel, PhD, Senior Vice President and Director

**Center to Advance Palliative Care,** 1255 Fifth Avenue, Suite C-2, New York, NY 10029; tel. 212/201–2670; Diane E. Meier, MD, FACP, Director

**Central Surgical Association, University of Chicago,** 5841 S. Maryland m/c 5094, Chicago, IL 60637; tel. 913/402–7102; FAX. 913/273–1116; Nonie Lowry, Meeting Coordinator

**Children's Eye Foundation,** 1631 Lancaster Drive, #200, Grapevine, TX 76051; tel. 817/301–2641; FAX. 817/329–5532; Sarah Buckmeier, Program Manager

**Children's Hospital Association,** 401 Wythe Street, Alexandria, VA 22314; tel. 703/684–1355; FAX. 703/684–1589; Mark Wietecha, President and Chief Executive Officer

**CHIME--College of Healthcare Information Management Executives,** 3300 Washtenaw Avenue, Suite 225, Ann Arbor, MI 48104; tel. 734/665–0000; FAX. 734/665–4922; Russell P. Branzell, FCHIME, CHCIO, President and Chief Executive Officer

**Christian Record Services, Inc.,** 4444 South 52nd Street, Lincoln, NE 68516; tel. 402/488–0981; FAX. 402/488–1902; Matthew Orian, Treasurer

**College of American Pathologists,** 325 Waukegan Road, Northfield, IL 60093–2750; tel. 847/832–7000; FAX. 847/832–8000; Charles Roussel, Chief Executive Officer

**Community Anti-Drug Coalitions of America,** 625 Slaters Lane, Suite 300, Alexandria, VA 22314; tel. 800/542–2322; FAX. 703/706–0565; Arthur T. Dean, Chairman and Chief Executive Officer

**Community Health Accreditation Program,** 1275 K Street, NW, Suite 800, Washington, DC 20005; tel. 202/862–3413; FAX. 202/862–3419; Julie E. Reynes, Acting President and Chief Executive Officer

**Cooley's Anemia Foundation, Inc.,** 330 Seventh Avenue, Suite 200, New York, NY 10001; tel. 212/279–8090; FAX. 212/279–5999; Gina Cioffi, National Executive Director

**Corporate Angel Network, Inc. (CAN),** Westchester County Airport, One Loop Road, White Plains, NY 10604; tel. 914/328–1313; FAX. 914/328–3938; Judith Runyan, Patient Advocate

**Council of Medical Specialty Societies,** 35 E. Wacker Drive, Suite 850, Chicago, IL 60601; tel. 312/224–2535; FAX. 312/644–8557; Norman B. Kahn, Jr., MD, EVP, and Chief Executive Officer

**Council on Education for Public Health,** 800 Eye Street, NW, Suite 202, Washington, DC 20001–3710; tel. 202/789–1050; FAX. 202/789–1895; Laura Rasar King, Executive Director

**Crohn's & Colitis Foundation of America, Inc.,** 386 Park Avenue, S., 17th Floor, New York, NY 10016–8804; tel. 800/932–2423; FAX. 212/779–4098; Richard J. Geswell, President

**Cystic Fibrosis Foundation,** 6931 Arlington Road, Bethesda, MD 20814; tel. 301/951–4422; FAX. 301/951–6378; Robert J. Beall, PhD, President and Chief Executive Officer

# D

**Damien Dutton Society for Leprosy Aid, Inc.,** 616 Bedford Avenue, Bellmore, NY 11710; tel. 516/221–5829; FAX. 516/221–5909; Elizabeth Campbell, Vice President

**Depression and Bipolar Support Alliance,** 730 North Franklin Street, Suite 501, Chicago, IL 60654–7225; tel. 800/826–3632; FAX. 312/642–7243; Allen Doederlein, President

**Dysautonomia Foundation, Inc.,** 315 W. 39th Street, Suite 701, New York, NY 10018; tel. 212/279–1066; FAX. 212/279–2066; David Brenner, Executive Director

# E

**Easter Seals, Inc.,** 233 South Wacker Drive, Suite 2400, Chicago, IL 60606; tel. 800/221–6827; FAX. 312/726–1494; Rosemary Garza, Information & Referral

**ECRI Institute,** 5200 Butler Pike, Plymouth Meeting, PA 19462; tel. 610/825–6000; FAX. 610/834–1275; Jeffrey C. Lerner, PhD, President and Chief Executive Officer

**Educational Commission for Foreign Medical Graduates,** 3624 Market Street, 4th Floor, Philadelphia, PA 19104–2685; tel. 215/823–2101; Emmanuel G. Cassimatis, MD, President and Chief Executive Officer

**Ehlers-Danlos National Foundation,** PO Box 13157, Richmond, VA 23225; tel. 703/506–2892; FAX. 703/506–3266; Susan L. Stephenson, Patient Advocate

**Emergency Nurses Association,** 915 Lee Street, Des Plaines, IL 60016; tel. 800/900–9659; FAX. 847/460–4006; Susan Hohenhaus, Executive Director

**Epilepsy Foundation,** 8301 Professional Place-East, Landover, MD 20785; tel. 301/459–3700; FAX. 301/577–2684; Richard P. Denness, Chief Executive Officer

**Epilepsy Foundation of Connecticut,** 386 Main Street, Middletown, CT 06457; tel. 860/346–1924; FAX. 860/346–1928; Linda Wallace, Executive Director

## F

**Federated Ambulatory Surgery Association,** 1012 Cameron Street, Alexandria, VA 22314; tel. 703/836–8808; FAX. 703/549–0976; Kathy Bryant, Executive Director

**Federation of American Hospitals,** 750 9th Street, NW, Suite 600, Washington, DC 20001; tel. 202/624–1500; FAX. 202/737–6462; Chip Kahn, President and Chief Executive Officer

**Federation of State Medical Boards of the United States, Inc.,** 400 Fuller Wiser Rd, Suite 300, Euless, TX 76039; tel. 817/868–4000; FAX. 817/868–4097; Humayun J. Chaudhry, DO, MACP President and Chief Executive Officer

**Financial Accounting Standards Board,** 401 Merritt 7, P.O. Box 5116, Norwalk, CT 06856–5116; tel. 203/847–0700; FAX. 203/849–9714; Susan M. Cosper, Technical DirectorSusan M. Cosper, Technical Director

**Frontline Healthcare Workers Safety Foundation, Ltd.,** Three Dunwoody Park, Suite 103, Atlanta, GA 30338; tel. 678/781–5241; FAX. 678/781–5242; Jennifer Elin Cole, MSW, Marketing Director

## G

**Great Plains Health Alliance, Inc.,** 625 Third Street, Box 366, Phillipsburg, KS 67661; tel. 785/543–2111; FAX. 785/543–5098; Dave Dellasega, President and Chief Executive Officer

**Guide Dog Users, Inc.,** 14311 Astrodome Drive, Silver Spring, MD 20906–2245; tel. 866/799–8436; FAX. 301/871–7591; Jane Sheehan, Office Manager

## H

**Health Industry Distributors Association,** 310 Montgomery Street, Alexandria, VA 22314–1516; tel. 703/549–4432; FAX. 703/549–6495; Matthew J. Rowan, President and Chief Executive Officer

**Health Research and Educational Trust (HRET),** 155 N. Wacker Drive, Suite 400, Chicago, IL 60606; tel. 312/422–2600; FAX. 312/422–4568; Maulik Joshi, President

**Healthcare Financial Management Association,** Two Westbrook Corporate Center, Suite 700, Westchester, IL 60154; tel. 708/531–9600; FAX. 708/531–0032; Richard L. Clarke, DHA, FHFMA, President and Chief Executive Officer

**Healthcare Information and Management Systems Society (HIMSS),** 33 West Monroe Street, Suite 1700, Chicago, IL 60603–5616; tel. 312/664–4467; FAX. 312/664–6143; H. Stephen Lieber, CAE President and Chief Executive Officer

**HEAR Center,** 301 East Del Mar Boulevard, Pasadena, CA 91101; tel. 626/796–2016; FAX. 626/796–2320; Ellen Simon, Executive Director

**Huntington's Disease Society of America, Inc.,** 505 Eighth Avenue, Suite 902, New York, NY 10018; tel. 800/345–4372; FAX. 212/239–3430; Louise Vetter, National Executive Director and Chief Executive Officer

## I

**iKeepSafe Internet Safety Coalition,** 4301 N. Fairfax Drive, Suite 190, Arlington, VA 22203; tel. 703/717–9066; FAX. 202/737–4097; Marsali S. Hancock, President

**Infusion Nurses Society,** 315 Norwood Park South, Norwood, MA 02062; tel. 781/440–9408; FAX. 781/440–9409; Mary Alexander, Chief Executive Officer

**Institute for Diversity in Health Management (IFD),** 155 N. Wacker Drive, Suite 400, Chicago, IL 60606; tel. 312/422–2630; FAX. 312/278–0893; Frederick D. Hobby, President and Chief Executive Officer

**Institute of Medicine,** 500 Fifth Street, NW, Washington, DC 20001; tel. 202/334–2352; FAX. 202/334–1412; Harvey V. Fineberg, MD, PhD, President

**Institute of Medicine of The National Academies,** 500 Fifth Street, NW, Washington, DC 20001–2721; tel. 202/334–3300; FAX. 202/334–3851; Harvey V. Fineberg, President, Institute of Medicine

**Institutes for the Achievement of Human Potential,** 8801 Stenton Avenue, Wyndmoor, PA 19038; tel. 215/233–2050; FAX. 215/233–3940; Leland Green, Medical Director

**International Childbirth Education Association, Inc.,** 1500 Sunday Drive, Suite 102, Raleigh, NC 27607; tel. 919/863–9487; FAX. 919/787–4916; David Field, Executive Director

**International College of Surgeons/United States Section,** 1516 North Lake Shore Drive, Chicago, IL 60610–1694; tel. 312/787–6274; FAX. 312/787–9289; Maggie Kearney, Meeting and Publications Manager

**International Council for Health, Physical Education, Recreation, Sport and Dance,** 1900 Association Drive, Reston, VA 20191; tel. 703/476–3486; FAX. 703/476–9527; Dr. Dong Ja Yang, President

## L

**Leading Age,** 2519 Connecticut Avenue, NW, Washington, DC 20008–1520; tel. 202/783–2242; FAX. 202/783–2255; William L. Minnix, Jr., D. Min., President and Chief Executive Officer

**Lupus Foundation of America, Inc.,** 2000 L Street, NW, Suite 410, Washington, DC 20036; tel. 202/349–1155; FAX. 202/349–1156; Dawn Isherwood, Health Educator

## M

**March of Dimes Foundation,** 1275 Mamaroneck Avenue, White Plains, NY 10605; tel. 914/428–7100; FAX. 914/428–8203; Jennifer L. Howse, PhD, President

**Marriott Memorial Heart Foundation, International,** PO Box 3219, Spring Hill, FL 34611; tel. 623/204–4848; Jonni Cooper, BSN, MBA, PhD, FACCN-III, Chief Executive Officer

**Medical Fitness Association (MFA),** 1905 Huguenot Road, Suite 203, Richmond, VA 23235; tel. 804/897–5701; FAX. 804/897–5704; Ken Germano, Executive Director

**Medical Library Association,** 65 East Wacker Place, Suite 1900, Chicago, IL 60601–7298; tel. 312/419–9094; FAX. 312/419–8950; Carla J. Funk, Executive Director

**MedicAlert Foundation,** 2323 Colorado Avenue, Turlock, CA 95382; tel. 800/432–5378; FAX. 209/669–2495; Ramesh Srinvasan, SVP Marketing

**Men's Health Network,** PO Box 75972, Washington, DC 20013; tel. 202/543–6461; FAX. 202/543–2727; Ana Fadich, MPH, CHES, Director, Programs and Outreach

**Mental Health America, (formerly known as the National Mental Health Association),** 2000 N. Beauregard Street, 6th Floor, Alexandria, VA 22311; tel. 703/684–7722; FAX. 703/684–5968; Wayne W Lindstrom, Ph.D., President and Chief Executive Officer

**MGMA-ACMPE,** 104 Inverness Terrace, E., Englewood, CO 80112–5306; tel. 877/275–6462; FAX. 303/784–6108; Susan L. Turney, MD, MS, FACP, FACMPE, President and Chief Executive Officer

**Midwives Alliance of North America,** 611 Pennsylvania Avenue, SE, # 1700, Washington, DC 20003–4303; tel. 8889236262; Geradine Simkins, President

**Muscular Dystrophy Association,** 3300 East Sunrise Drive, Tucson, AZ 85718; tel. 520/529–2000; FAX. 520/529–5300; Steven M. Derks, MD, President and Chief Executive Officer

## N

**National Academy of Sciences, Division on Earth and Life Studies,** 500 Fifth Street, NW, Keck 654, Washington, DC 20001; tel. 202/334–2500; FAX. 202/334–3362; Gregory H. Symmes, PhD, Executive Director

**National Accreditation Council for Blind and Low Vision Services (NAC),** P.O. Box 15368, Chattanooga, TN 37415; tel. 423/875–2033; FAX. 423/875–2220; William A. Robinson, III, CPA, Executive Director

**National Accrediting Agency for Clinical Laboratory Sciences,** 5600 N. River Road, Suite 720, Rosemont, IL 60018; tel. 773/714–8880; FAX. 773/714–8886; Dianne M. Cearlock, Chief Executive Officer

**National Alliance for Hispanic Health,** 1501 16th Street, NW, Washington, DC 20036; tel. 202/387–5000; FAX. 202/797–4353; Mr. Adolph Falcón, Senior Vice President

**National Alliance on Mental Illness,** 3803 N. Fairfax Drive, Ste 100, Arlington, VA 22203; tel. 703/524–7600; FAX. 703/524–9094; Michael J. Fitzpatrick, MSW, Executive Director

**National Assembly on School-Based Health Care,** 1010 Vermont Avenue, NW, Suite 600, Washington, DC 20005; tel. 202/638–5872; FAX. 202/638–5879; Linda Juszczak, President

**National Association for Home Care & Hospice,** 228 Seventh Street, SE, Washington, DC 20003; tel. 202/547–7424; FAX. 202/547–3540; Val J. Halamandaris, President

**National Association for Practical Nurse Education and Service,** Mail Processing, 1940 Duke Street, Alexandria, VA 22314; tel. 703/933–1003; FAX. 703/940–4089; Helen Larsen, JD, Executive Director

**National Association Medical Staff Services,** 2025 M Street, NW, Suite 800, Washington, DC 20036; tel. 202/367–1196; FAX. 202/367–2196; Lynn Boyd, Executive Director

**National Association of ACO's,** 310 81st Street W, Ste 100, Bradenton, FL 34209; Clif Gaus, President and CEO

**National Association of Boards of Pharmacy,** 1600 Feehanville Drive, Mt. Prospect, IL 60056; tel. 847/391–4406; FAX. 847/391–4502; Carmen A. Catizone, MS, R.Ph., D.Ph., Executive Director/Secretary

**National Association of County and City Health Officials,** 1100 17th Street, NW, 7th Floor, Washington, DC 20036; tel. 202/783–5550; FAX. 202/783–1583; Terry Allen, President

**National Association of Dental Assistants,** 900 South Washington Street, Suite G13, Falls Church, VA 22046; tel. 703/237–8616; FAX. 703/533–1153; S. Young, Director

**National Association of Dental Laboratories, (Includes National Board for Certification in Dental Laboratory Technology),** 325 John Knox Rd, #L 103, Tallahassee, FL 32303; tel. 800/950–1150; FAX. 850/222–0053; Bennett Napier, CAE, Co-Executive Director

**National Association of Health Services Executives,** 1050 Connecticut Avenue, NW, 10th Floor, Washington, DC 20036; tel. 202/772–1030; FAX. 202/772–1072; Beverly Glover, Association Manager

**National Association of Psychiatric Health Systems,** 900 17th Street, NW, Suite 420, Washington, DC 20006–2507; tel. 202/393–6700; FAX. 202/783–6041; Mark J. Covall, President and Chief Executive Officer

**National Association of Social Workers,** 750 First Street, NE, Suite 700, Washington, DC 20002; tel. 202/336–8200; FAX. 202/336–8313; Elizabeth Clark, PhD, ACSW, MPH, Executive Director

**National Association of State Mental Health Program Directors,** 66 Canal Center Plaza, Suite 302, Alexandria, VA 22314; tel. 703/739–9333; FAX. 703/548–9517; Robert W. Glover, PhD, Executive Director

**National Board for Respiratory Care, NBRC Executive Office,** 18000 W 105th Street, Olathe, KS 66061–7543; tel. 913/895–4900; FAX. 913/895–4650; Gary A. Smith, Executive Director

**National Board of Anesthesiology, Inc.,** 11817 Summit, Kansas, MO 64114; tel. 785/842–7067; FAX. 816/836–8953; R. Scott Richart, JD, Executive Director

**National Board of Medical Examiners,** 3750 Market Street, Philadelphia, PA 19104; tel. 215/590–9500; FAX. 215/590–9430; Donald E. Melnick, MD, President

**National Board of Public Health Examiners,** 1900 M Street, NW #710, Washington, DC 20036; tel. 866/514–7569; Molly M. Eggleston, Executive Director

**National Council of State Boards of Nursing,** 111 E. Wacker Drive, Suite 2900, Chicago, IL 60601; tel. 312/525–3600; FAX. 312/279–1032; Kathy Apple, Chief Executive Officer

**National Council on Aging, Inc., NCOA Headquarters,** 1901 L Street, NW, 4th Floor, Washington, DC 20024; tel. 202/479–1200; FAX. 202/479–0735; James P. Firman, Ed.D., President and Chief Executive Officer

**National Council on Alcoholism and Drug Dependence, Inc., NCADD,** 217 Broadway, Suite 712, New York, NY 10007; tel. 212/269–7797; FAX. 212/269–7510; Robert J. Lindsey, M.Ed., CEAP President and Chief Executive Officer

**National Council on Radiation Protection and Measurements,** 7910 Woodmont Avenue, Suite 400, Bethesda, MD 20814; tel. 301/657–2652; FAX. 301/907–8768; David A. Schauer, Executive Director

**National Dental Association,** 3517 16th Street, NW, Washington, DC 20010; tel. 202/588–1697; FAX. 202/588–1244; Robert S. Johns, Executive Director

**National Environmental Health Association,** 720 South Colorado Boulevard, North Tower, Suite 1000-N, Denver, CO 80246–1926; tel. 303/756–9090; FAX. 303/691–9490; Nelson Fabian, Executive Director

**National Federation of Licensed Practical Nurses,** 111 West Main Street, #100, Garner, NC 27529; tel. 919/779–0046; FAX. 919/779–5642; Ashley McGraw, CMP

**National Fire Protection Association,** PO Box 9101, One Batterymarck Park, Quincy, MA 02269–9101; tel. 617/770–3000; FAX. 617/770–7110; Richard P. Bielen, PE Divisaion Manager of Fire Protection Systems Engineering

**National Gaucher Foundation,** 2227 Idlewood Road, Suite 6, Tucker, GA 30084; tel. 800/504–3189; FAX. 770/934–2911; Rhonda Buyers, Executive Director and Chief Executive Officer

**National Headache Foundation,** 820 N. Orleans, Suite 217, Chicago, IL 60610–3132; tel. 888/643–5552; FAX. 312/640–9049; Robert Dalton, Executive Director

**National Health Council, Inc.,** 1730 M Street, NW, Suite 500, Washington, DC 20036; tel. 202/785–3910; FAX. 202/785–5923; Myrl Weinberg, FASAE, CAE, Chief Executive Officer

**National Hemophilia Foundation,** 116 West 32nd Street, 11th Floor, New York, NY 10001; tel. 212/328–3700; FAX. 212/328–3799; Val Bias, Chief Executive Officer

**National Institute for Jewish Hospice, Central Telephone Network,** PO Box 48025, Los Angeles, CA 90048; tel. 800/446–4448; FAX. 516/791–6999; Shirley Lamm, Executive Director

**National Institute for Occupational Safety and Health,** 395 E Street, SW, Suite 9200, Washington, DC 20201; tel. 202/245–0625; John Howard, MD, Director

**National Kidney Foundation,** 30 East 33rd Street, New York, NY 10016; tel. 800/622–9010; FAX. 212/779–0068; John Davis, Chief Executive Officer

**National League for Nursing, NLN,** 61 Broadway, 33rd Floor, New York, NY 10006; tel. 212/363–5555; FAX. 212/812–0391; Beverly Malone, PhD, RN, FAAN, Chief Executive Officer

**National Multiple Sclerosis Society,** 733 Third Avenue, New York, NY 10017; tel. 212/986–3240; FAX. 212/986–7981; Cynthia Zagieboylo, President and Chief Executive Officer

**National Organization for Rare Disorders,** 55 Kenosia Avenue, Danbury, CT 06813–1968; tel. 203/744–0100; FAX. 203/798–2291; Names Peter L. Saltonstall, President and Chief Executive Officer

**National Parkinson Foundation, Inc.,** 1501 Northwest Ninth Avenue, Miami, FL 33136–1494; tel. 800/327–4545; FAX. 305/243–5540; Pamela Olmo, Vice President, Finance and Administration

**National Perinatal Association,** 457 State Street, Binghampton, NY 13901; tel. 888/971–3295; FAX. 607/772–0468; Bernadette Hoppe, MA, JD, MPH, President

**National Registry of Emergency Medical Technicians,** 6610 Busch Boulevard, PO Box 29233, Columbus, OH 43229; tel. 614/888–4484; FAX. 614/888–8920; Severo Rodriguez., Executive Director

**National Rehabilitation Association, (Includes Nine National Divisions and 58 Affiliate Chapters),** 633 South Washington Street, Alexandria, VA 22314; tel. 703/836–0850; FAX. 703/836–0848; Patricia Leahy, Interim Executive Director

**National Resident Matching Program,** 2121 K Street, NW, Washington, DC 20037–1127; tel. 202/828–0676; FAX. 202/828–4797; Mona M. Signer, Executive Director

**National Rural Health Association,** 1025 Vermont Ave NW, Suite 1100, Washington, DC 20005; tel. 202/639–0550; FAX. 202/639–0559; Alan Morgan, Chief Executive Officer

**National Safety Council,** 1121 Spring Lake Drive, Itasca, IL 60143–3201; tel. 800/621–7615; FAX. 630/285–1315; Janet Froetscher, President and Chief Executive Officer

**National Stroke Association,** 9707 E Easter Lane, Building B, Centennial, CO 80112; tel. 303/754–0924; FAX. 303/649–1328; Teran Nash, Customer Relations Coordinator

**National Student Nurses' Association, Inc.,** 45 Main Street, Suite 606, Brooklyn, NY 11201; tel. 718/210–0705; FAX. 718/797–1186; Diane J. Mancino, Ed.D., RN, CAE, FAAN, Executive Director

**National Tay-Sachs and Allied Diseases Association,** 2001 Beacon Street, Suite 204, Brighton, MA 02135; tel. 800/906–8723; FAX. 617/277–0134; Susan R. Kahn, Executive Director

**National Women's Health Network,** 1413 K Street, NW, Fourth Floor, Washington, DC 20005; tel. 202/682–2640; FAX. 202/682–2648; Cynthia Pearson, Executive Director

**New England Gerontological Association,** One Cutts Road, Durham, NH 03824–3102; tel. 603/868–5757; Eugene E. Tillock, Ed.D., Executive Director

**New York State Nurses Association, NYSNA,** 11 Cornell Road, Latham, NY 12110; tel. 518/782–9400; FAX. 518/782–9530; Jill Furillo,Executive Director

**NSF International,** 789 N.Dixboro Road, Ann Arbor, MI 48105; tel. 734/769–8010; FAX. 313/769–0109; Kevan Lawlor, President and Chief Executive Officer

# O

**Office of Radiation and Indoor Air, Environmental Protection Agency,** 1200 Pennsylvania Avenue, NW, Mail Code 6601J, Washington, DC 20460; tel. 202/343–9213; Dennis O'Connor, Senior Policy Advisor

**Osteogenesis Imperfecta Foundation, Inc.,** 804 West Diamond Avenue, Suite 210, Gaithersburg, MD 20878; tel. 301/947–0083; FAX. 301/947–0456; Tracy Smith Hart, Chief Executive Officer

# P

**Pan American Health Organization, Pan American Sanitary Bureau, Regional Office of the World Health Organization,** 525 23rd Street, NW, Washington, DC 20037; tel. 202/974–3000; FAX. 202/974–3663; Dr. Carissa F. Etienne, Director

**Parkinson's Disease Foundation, Inc., (Formerly United Parkinson Foundation),** 1359 Broadway, Suite 1509, New York, NY 10018; tel. 800/457–6676; FAX. 212/923–4778; Rasnahia Cororreal, Director of Administration

**Partnership for Food Safety Education,** 2345 Crystal Drive, Suite 800, Arlington, VA 22202; tel. 202/220–0651; FAX. 202/220–0873; Shelley Feist, Executive Director

**Partnership for Prevention,** 1015 18th Street, NW, Suite 300, Washington, DC 20036; tel. 202/833–0009; FAX. 202/833–0113; Jud Richland, MPH, President and Chief Executive Officer

**Physician Executive Leadership Center,** 3403 West Fletcher Avenue, Tampa, FL 33618–2813; tel. 813/963–1800; Jennifer R. Grebenschikoff, Executive Vice President

**Pilot Dogs, Inc.,** 625 West Town Street, Columbus, OH 43215; tel. 614/221–6367; FAX. 614/221–1577; J. Jay Gray, Executive Director

**Practice Greenhealth,** 12355 Sunrise Valley Drive, Suite 680, Reston, VA 20191; tel. 888/688–3332; FAX. 866/379–8705; Laura Wenger, RN, Executive Director

**Prevent Blindness America,** 211 W. Wacker Drive, Suite 1700, Chicago, IL 60606; tel. 800/331–2020; FAX. 312/363–6052; Hugh Parry, President and Chief Executive Officer

**Public Health Foundation,** 1300 L Street NW, Suite 800, Washington, DC 20005–4208; tel. 202/218–4400; FAX. 202/218–4409; Sue Madden, Deputy Executive Director

**Public Relations Society of America,** 33 Maiden Lane 11th Floor, New York, NY 10038–5150; tel. 212/460–1400; FAX. 212/995–0757; Catherine A. Bolton, Executive Director and Chief Operating Officer

# R

**Radiological Society of North America, Inc.,** 820 Jorie Boulevard, Oak Brook, IL 60523–2251; tel. 630/571–2670; FAX. 630/571–7837; Jennifer Divelbiss, Director of Marketing

**Recording for the Blind and Dyslexic,** 20 Roszel Road, Princeton, NJ 08540; tel. 866/732–3585; FAX. 609/520–7990; Richard O. Scribner, President

**Renal Physicians Association,** 1700 Rockville Pike, Suite 220, Rockville, MD 20852; tel. 301/468–3515; FAX. 301/468–3511; Dale Singer, MHA, Executive Director

**Robert Wood Johnson Foundation,** PO Box 2316, Route One and College Road East, Princeton, NJ 08543–2316; tel. 877/843–7953; FAX. 609/927–7582; Lydia Ryba, Manager, Office of Proposal Management

**Section C**

## S

**Safe Kids Worldwide,** 1301 Pennsylvania Avenue, NW, Suite 1000, Washington, DC 20004; tel. 202/662–0600; FAX. 202/393–2072; Kate Carr, President and Chief Executive Officer

**Shriners Hospitals for Children,** PO Box 31356, Tampa, FL 33631–3356; tel. 813/281–8111; FAX. 813/281–8174; John P. McCabe, Executive Vice President

**SNMTS, Society of Nuclear Medicine Technologist Section,** 1850 Samuel Morse Drive, Reston, VA 20190; tel. 703/708–9000; FAX. 703/708–9015; Nikki Wenzel-Lamb, MBA, Administrator and Director of Leadership Services

**Society for Academic Emergency Medicine,** 2340 S. River Road, Suite 200, Des Plaines, IL 60018; tel. 847/813–9823; FAX. 847/813–5450; Ronald S. Moen, Interim Executive Director

**Society for Adolescent Health and Medicine (SAHM),** 111 Deer Lake Road, Suite 100, Deefield, IL 60015; tel. 847/753–5226; FAX. 847/480–9282; Debbie Trueblood, Executive Director

**Society for Healthcare Consumer Advocacy (SHCA),** 155 N. Wacker Drive, Suite 400, Chicago, IL 60606; tel. 312/422–3700; FAX. 312/278–0881; Carol Santalucia, MBA, President, Vice President

**Society for Healthcare Strategy and Market Development (SHSMD),** 155 N. Wacker Drive, Suite 400, Chicago, IL 60606; tel. 312/422–3888; FAX. 312/278–0883; Diane Webber, Executive Director

**Society for Occupational and Environmental Health,** 6728 Old McLean Village Drive, McLean, VA 22101; tel. 703/556–9222; FAX. 703/556–8729; Connie MacKay, Account Manager

**Society for Pediatric Pathology,** 3643 Walton Way Extension, Augusta, GA 30909; tel. 706/364–3375; FAX. 706/733–8033; Kerry Crockett, Director of Operations and Meetings

**Society for Social Work Leadership in Health Care (SSWLHC),** 100 North 20th Street, Suite 400, Philadelphia, PA 19103; tel. 866/237–9542; FAX. 215/564–2175; Kyle Fernley, Account Manager

**Society of Cardiac Monitoring, Inc.,** PO Box 3395, Riverview, FL 33568; tel. 813/394–4968; Jonni Cooper, Chief Executive Officer

**Society of Cardiovascular Patient Care,** 6161 Riverside Drive, Dublin, OH 43017; tel. 614/442–5950; FAX. 614/442–5953; Wilbert D. Mick, Chief Executive Officer

**Society of Critical Care Medicine,** 500 Midway Drive, Mount Prospect, IL 60056; tel. 847/827–6869; FAX. 847/827–6886; David J. Martin, CAE, Chief Executive Officer and EVP

**Society of Neurological Surgeons,** 3303 SW Bond Avenue, Portland, OR 97239; tel. 503/494–7978; Kim J. Burchiel, MD, FACS, Secretary

**Society of University Otolaryngologists-Head and Neck Surgeons,** USC School of Medicine, Department of Otolaryngology, Los Angeles, CA 90033; tel. 323/226–7315; FAX. 323/226–2780; Donna Hoffman, M.A., Executive Director

**Special Care Dentistry Association,** 401 N. Michigan Avenue, 22nd Floor, Chicago, IL 60611; tel. 312/527–6764; FAX. 312/673–6663; Kaye Englebrecht

**Spina Bifida Association,** 4590 MacArthur Boulevard, NW, Suite 250, Washington, DC 20007; tel. 800/621–3141; FAX. 202/944–3295; Cindy Brownstein, President and Chief Executive Officer

**Susan G. Komen Breast Cancer Foundation,** 5005 LBJ Freeway, Suite 250, Dallas, TX 75244; tel. 800/465–6636; Kimberly Simpson, Chief Operating Officer

## T

**The Academy of Nutrition and Dietetics,** 120 South Riverside Plaza, Suite 2000, Chicago, IL 60606–6995; tel. 312/899–0040; FAX. 312/899–4765; Patricia M. Babjak, Chief Executive Officer

**The American Association of Immunologists, Inc.,** 9650 Rockville Pike, Bethesda, MD 20814; tel. 301/634–7178; FAX. 301/634–7887; M. Michele Hogan, PhD, Executive Director

**The American Board of Anesthesiology, Inc.,** 4208 Six Forks Road, Suite 1500, Raleigh, NC 27609–5765; tel. 919/745–2200; FAX. 919/745–2201; Mary E. Post, MBA, CAE, Executive Director, Administrative Affairs

**The American Board of Disability Analysts (ABDA),** Belle Meade Office Park, 4525 Harding Road, Nashville, TN 37205; tel. 615/327–2984; FAX. 615/327–9235; Alexander Horowitz, MD, Executive Officer Emeritus

**The American Board of Obstetrics and Gynecology, Inc.,** 2915 Vine Street, Dallas, TX 75204; tel. 214/871–1619; FAX. 214/871–1943; Larry Gilstrap, MD, Executive Director

**The American Board of Pediatric Dentistry,** 325 E. Washington Street, Suite 208, Iowa City, IA 52240–3960; tel. 319/341–8488; FAX. 319/341–9499; Jeffrey A. Dean, Executive Director

**The American Board of Plastic Surgery, Inc.,** Seven Penn Center, Suite 400, 1635 Market Street, Philadelphia, PA 19103–2204; tel. 215/587–9322; FAX. 215/587–9622; Terry M. Cullison, RN, MSN, Administrator

**The American Board of Urology, Inc.,** 600 Peter Jefferson Pkwy, Suite 150, Charlottesville, VA 22911; tel. 434/979–0059; FAX. 434/979–0266; Gerald H. Jordan, MD, Executive Secretary

**The American Orthopaedic Association,** 6300 North River Road, Suite 505, Rosemont, IL 60018–4263; tel. 847/318–7330; FAX. 847/318–7339; Kristin Olds Glavin, Executive Director

**The Arc of the United States,** 1825 K Street, NW, Suite 1200, Washington, DC 20006; tel. 202/534–3700; FAX. 202/534–3731; Peter V. Berns, Chief Executive Officer

**The Association for Research in Vision and Ophthalmology,** 1801 Rockville Pike, Ste 400, Rockville, MD 20852–5622; tel. 240/221–2900; FAX. 240/221–0370; Iris M. Rush, CAE, Interim Executive Director

**The Association of Medical Illustrators,** 201 E Main Street, Suite 1405, Lexington, KY 40507; tel. 866/393–4264; FAX. 859/514–9166; Melanie Bowzer, Executive Director

**The Association of Women's Health, Obstetric and Neonatal Nurses,** 2000 L. Street, NW, Suite 740, Washington, DC 20036; tel. 202/261–2400; FAX. 202/728–0575; Karen Peddicord, RNC, PhD, Chief Executive Officer

**The Christopher and Dana Reeve Foundation, Paralysis Resource Center,** Short Hills Plaza, 636 Morris Turnpike, Suite #3A, Short Hills, NJ 07078–7503; tel. 800/539–7309; Angela Cantillon, Director-Operations

**The Duke Endowment,** 100 North Tryon Street, Suite 3500, Charlotte, NC 28202; tel. 704/376–0291; FAX. 704/376–9336; Mary L. Piepenbring, Vice President

**The Endocrine Society,** 8401 Connecticut Avenue, Suite 900, Chevy Chase, MD 20815; tel. 301/941–0200; FAX. 301/941–0259; Janet Kreizman, Deputy Executive Director & Chief Policy Officer

**The Foundation Fighting Blindness, Inc.,** 7168 Columbia Gateway Drive, Suite 100, Columbia, MD 21046; tel. 410/423–0600; FAX. 410/872–0438; William T. Schmidt, Chief Executive Officer

**The Foundation for Ichthyosis and Related Skin Types, Inc. (FIRST),** 2616 N. Broad Street, Colmar, PA 18915; tel. 215/997–9400; FAX. 215/997–9403; Jean Pickford, Executive Director

**The Gerontological Society of America,** 1220 L Street, NW, Suite 901, Washington, DC 20005–4018; tel. 202/842–1275; FAX. 202/842–1150; James Appleby, Executive Director and Chief Executive Officer

**The Histochemical Society,** 9650 Rockville Pike, Bethesda, MD 20814; tel. 301/634–7026; FAX. 301/634–7099; W.L. Stahl, PhD, Executive Director

**The International Dyslexia Association,** 40 York Road, 4th Floor, Baltimore, MD 21204; tel. 410/296–0232; FAX. 410/321–5069; Kristi Bowman, Director of Development

**The Joint Commission,** One Renaissance Boulevard, Oakbrook Terrace, IL 60181; tel. 630/792–5650; FAX. 630/792–4650; Mark R. Chassin, MD, MPP, MPH, President

**The Leukemia & Lymphoma Society,** 1311 Mamaroneck Avenue, White Plains, NY 10650; tel. 914/949–5213; FAX. 914/949–6691; John E. Walter, President and Chief Executive Officer

**The Mended Hearts, Inc.,** 8150 N. Central Expy., M2075, Dallas, TX 75206; tel. 888/432–7899; FAX. 214/295–9552; Karen Caruth, Executive Director

**The National Commission for Health Education Credentialing, Inc.,** 1541 Alta Drive, Suite 303, Whitehall, PA 18052–5642; tel. 484/223–0770; FAX. 800/813–0727; Linda Lysoby, MS, MCHES, CAE, Executive Director

**The Seeing Eye, Inc.,** PO Box 375, Morristown, NJ 07963–0375; tel. 973/539–4425; FAX. 973/539–0922; Jim Kutsch, President

**The Southwestern Surgical Congress,** 5019 W 147th St, Leawood, KS 66224; tel. 913/402–7102; FAX. 913/273–9940; James A. Edney, MD, Executive Director

**The Vision Council,** 225 Reinekers Lane, Suite 700, Alexandria, VA 22314; tel. 703/548–4560; FAX. 703/548–4580; Ed Greene, Chief Executive Officer

## U

**UCLA Medical Center, Neurosurgery,** Box 956901, Los Angeles, CA 90095–6901; tel. 301/267–9449; FAX. 310/825–7245; Neil A. Martin, MD

**United Cerebral Palsy Associations, Inc.,** 1660 L Street, NW, Suite 700, Washington, DC 20036; tel. 800/872–5827; FAX. 202/776–0414; Stephen Bennett, President and Chief Executive Officer

**United Methodist Association of Health and Welfare Ministries,** 2800 W Main Street, Tupelo, MS 38801–3027; tel. 662/269–2955; FAX. 662/269–2956; Stephen L. Vinson, President and Chief Executive Officer

**United Way Worldwide,** 701 North Fairfax Street, Alexandria, VA 22314–2045; tel. 703/836–7100; FAX. 703/683–7846; Brian A. Gallagher, President and Chief Executive Officer

**USP, United States Pharmacopeia,** 12601 Twinbrook Parkway, Rockville, MD 20852; tel. 301/816–8368; FAX. 301/816–8511; Arline M. Bilbo, Director, Member and Professional Relations

## W

**Western Orthopedic Association,** 154-A W. Foothill Boulevard, # 107, Upland, CA 91786; tel. 866/962–1388; FAX. 410/494–0515; Chuck Freitag, Executive Director

**Wound, Ostomy and Continence Nursing Certification Board (WOCNCB),** 555 E. Wells Street, Suite 1100, Milwaukee, WI 53202; tel. 888/496–2622; FAX. 414/276–2146; Tracy Burr, Executive Director

# International Organizations

**ARGENTINA**

Camara Argentina De Empresas De Salud, (Argentina Hospital Association), Tucuman 1668, 2 Piso, C.P. 1050, Buenos Aires; tel. 541143725915; FAX. 541143723229; Norberto Larroca-President

**AUSTRALIA**

Australian Healthcare and Hospitals Association, Unit 8/2 Phipps Close, Deakin ACT, 2600; tel. 1261620780; FAX. 1261620779; Prue Power, Executive Director

**CANADA**

Canadian Blood Services, Head Office, 1800 Alta Vista Drive, Ottawa, ON K1G 4J5; tel. 613/739-2300; FAX. 613/731-1411; Dr. Graham D. Sher, CEO

Canadian Healthcare Association, 17 York Street, Ottawa, ON K1N 9J6; tel. 613/241-8005; FAX. 613/241-5055; Phil Dresch, Interim President and Chief Executive Officer

Canadian Medical Association, 1867 Alta Vista Drive, Ottawa, ON K1G 5W8; tel. 613/731-9331; FAX. 613/731-7314; Paul-Emile Cloutier, Secretary General and CEO

Canadian Medical Engineering Consultants, 594 Bush Street, Belfountain, ON L7K OE8; tel. 519/927-3286; FAX. 519/927-9440; A. M. Dolan, President

Canadian Orthopaedic Association, 4150 Street Catherine Street West, Suite 450, Westmount, PQ H3Z 2Y5; tel. 514/874-9003; FAX. 514/874-0464; Douglas C. Thomson, CEO

Canadian Public Health Association, 1525 Carling Avenue, Suite 404, Ottawa, ON K1Z 8R9; tel. 613/725-3769; FAX. 613/725-9826; Ian Culbert, Executive Director

Catholic Health Association of Canada, Annex C, Saint-Vincent Hospital, 60 Cambridge Street North, Ottawa, ON K14 7A5; tel. 613/562-6262; FAX. 613/782-2857; James Roche, President

**COSTA RICA**

Asociacion Costarricense De Hospitales, (Costa Rica Hospital Association), Apartado 267-1005, Barrio Mexico San Jose Costa Rica, Costa Rica; tel. 506/221-4919; FAX. 506/255-0363; Dr. Kenneth Gonzalez Arias, Presidente

**ENGLAND**

British Medical Association (BMA), BMA House, Tavistock Square, London, WCIH 9JP; tel. 02073874499; FAX. 02073836400; Mr. Tony Bourne, Chief Executive and Secretary

**FRANCE**

Federation Hospitaliere De France, (France Hospital Association), 1 bis, Rue Cabanis, Paris, 75014; Gerard Vincent, Delegue General

World Medical Association, CS 5001, 13-A Chemin Du Levant, Ferney-Voltaire, 01210; tel. 33450407575; FAX. 33450405937; Dr. Otmar Kloiber, Secretary General

**GERMANY**

Deutsche Krankenhausgesellschaft, (German Hospital Federation), Wegelystrabe 3, D - 10623, Berlin; tel. (+4930)39801-0; FAX. (+4930)3901-3000; Georg Baum, Chief Executive

**HUNGARY**

Magyar Korhazszovetseg, (Hungarian Hospital Association), 1113 Budapest, Ibrahim u. 19., Hungary; Dr. Zoltan Ajkay, President

**INDIA**

Indian Hospital Association, B-401 Sarita Vihar, New Delhi, 110 044; FAX. 91-11-694126; Dr. P.Ghez, Secretary General

**INDONESIA**

Indonesian Hospital Association, Jl. Boulevard Artha Gading Blok, A-7A No. 28, Jakarta, Utara, 14240; tel. 214/584-5303; FAX. 214/458-7832; Muki Reksoprodjo

**ITALY**

Federazione Italiana delle Aziende Sanitarie e Ospedaliere (FIASO), (Italy Hospital Association), Corso Vi Horis Emmanuele II n. 24, Roma, 00186; Dott. Francesco Ripa di Meana, Presidente

**KOREA**

Korean Hospital Association, 13 F Mapo Hyun Dai Building, 35-1 Mapo-Dong, Seoul, 121-737; tel. 822/705-9200; FAX. 822/705-9209; International Affairs Officer

**MEXICO**

Asociacion Mexicana De Hospitales AC, (Mexico Hospital Association), Queretaro 210, Mexico City, 06700; tel. 55740135; FAX. 55841882; LIC. Francisco Spindola Salazar, Manager

**MONGOLIA**

Mongolian Hospital Association, PO Box 48/54, Enkhtaivan Street 13b, Ulaanbaatar, 210648; tel. 976/999-9020; FAX. 976/999-6070; Jambaljav Lkhamsuren, MD, President

**PANAMA**

Asociacion Panamena De Hospitales Privados, (Panama Hospital Association), Apartado 07503, Panama, Panama; tel. 507/269-0615; FAX. 507/966-4223; Rodrigo A. Moreno, President

**PERU**

Association Private Clinics of Peru, Av. Dos De Mayo 1502 Of. 202, San Isidro, Lima; tel. 511/441-9546; FAX. 511/441-9546; Clodoaldo Barreda Dominguez, Administrator

**PHILIPPINES**

Philippine Hospital Association, 14 Kamias Road, Quezon City-1, Metro Minila, 01102; tel. 632/992-7674; FAX. 632/921-2219

**SOUTH AFRICA**

Provincial Administration, Health Services Branch, P.O. Box 227, South Africa, 9300; tel. 0514081107; FAX. 0514081058; Dr. S. Kabane

South Africa Department of Health, Private Bag X828, Pretoria, 0001; Dr Pakishe Aaron Motsoaledi, Minister of Health

**SWITZERLAND**

H+ Die Spitaeler der Schweiz, (Swiss Hospital Association), Lorrainestrasse 4 A, Bern; M. Bernhard Wegmueller, Director

International Hospital Federation, P.A. Hôpital de Loëx, Route de Loex 151, 1233 BERNEX; tel. (+41) 22-850-94-20; FAX. (+41) 22-757-10-16; Mr Thomas C. Dolan, President

World Federation of Public Health Associations, c/o Institute for Social and Preventative Medicine, University of Geneva, CMU, Geneva, 4 CH-1211; Bettina Borisch, MD, PBH, FRCPath, Director of the Office of the Secretariat

**UGANDA**

International Council on Social Welfare, P.O. Box 28957, Kampala; Sergei Zelenev, Executive Director

**UNITED STATES**

International Association of Healthcare Central Service Materiel Management, 213 W. Institute Place, Suite 307, Chicago, IL 60610; tel. 312/440-0078; FAX. 312/440-9474; Susan Adams, Executive Director, Executive Director

Rehabilitation International, 25 East 21st Street, 4th Floor, New York, NY 10010; tel. 212/420-1500; FAX. 212/505-0871; Jan A. Monsbakken, President

*The following information is based on data available as of May, 2013.*
*For more information about U.S. government agencies, consult the* U.S. Government Manual. Additional assistance may be obtained by contacting the American Hospital Association's Washington office, 325 Seventh Street, N.W., Washington, DC 20004.

**Executive Office of the President, The White House**
1600 Pennsylvania Avenue NW
Washington, DC 20500
202/456-1414
Barack H. Obama, President of the United States
www.whitehouse.gov

**Office of the Vice President of the United States**
The White House
1600 Pennsylvania Avenue NW
Washington, DC 20501
202/456-1414
Joseph R. Biden, Vice President of the United States
www.whitehouse.gov/administration/vice-president-biden

**Centers for Disease Control and Prevention**
1600 Clifton Road
Atlanta, GA 30333
404/639-3311
Dr. Thomas Frieden, MD, MPH, Director
www.cdc.gov

**Centers for Medicare & Medicaid Services**
7500 Security Blvd
Baltimore, MD 21244
877/267-2323
Marilyn Tavenner, Acting Administrator and Chief Operating Officer
www.cms.gov

**Council of Economic Advisors**
Eisenhower Executive Office Building
Washington, DC 20502
202/395-5109
Alan Krueger, Chairman
www.whitehouse.gov/administration/eop/cea/

**Council on Environmental Quality**
722 Jackson Place NW
Washington, DC 20503
202/395-5750
Nancy Sutley, Chair
www.whitehouse.gov/administration/eop/ceq

**Department of Agriculture**
1400 Independence Avenue SW
Washington, DC 20250
202/720-3631
Thomas J. Vilsack, Secretary of Agriculture
www.usda.gov

**Department of Commerce**
1401 Constitution Avenue NW
Washington, DC 20230
202/482-2000
Rebecca M. Blank, Deputy Secretary of Commerce.
www.commerce.gov

**Department of Defense**
Office of the Secretary
The Pentagon
Washington, DC 20301-1400
703/545-6700
Chuck Hagel, Secretary of Defense
www.defenselink.mil

**Department of Education**
400 Maryland Avenue SW
Washington, DC 20202
800/872-5327
Arne Duncan, Secretary of Education
www.ed.gov

**Department of Energy**
1000 Independence Avenue SW
Washington, DC 20585
202/586-5000
Ernest Moniz, Secretary of Energy
www.energy.gov

**Department of Health and Human Services**
200 Independence Avenue SW
Washington, DC 20201
877/696-6775
Kathleen Sebelius, Secretary of Health and Human Services
www.hhs.gov

**Department of Justice**
950 Pennsylvania Ave NW
Washington, DC 20530-0001
202/514-2000
Eric H. Holder, Jr., The Attorney General
www.usdoj.gov

**Department of Labor**
Frances Perkins Building
200 Constitution Avenue NW
Washington, DC 20210
202/693-6000
Seth Harris, Acting Secretary of Labor
www.dol.gov

**Department of State**
2201 C Street NW
Washington, DC 20520
202/647-4000
John Kerry, Secretary of State
www.state.gov

**Department of the Air Force**
1670 Air Force Pentagon
Washington, DC 20330-1670
703/695-9664
Michael B. Donley, Secretary of the Air Force
www.af.mil/main/welcome.asp

**Department of the ARMY**
1400 Defense Pentagon
Washington, DC 20301-1400
703/695-4311
John McHugh, Secretary of the ARMY
www.army.mil

**Department of the NAVY**
2000 Navy Pentagon
Washington, DC 20350-2000
703/545-6700
Ray Mabus, Secretary of the NAVY
www.navy.mil

**Department of the Treasury**
1500 Pennsylvania NW
Washington, DC 20220
202/622-2000
Jacob Lew, Secretary of the Treasury
www.treasury.gov

**Department of Veterans Affairs**
810 Vermont Avenue NW
Washington, DC 20420
202/273-5400
Eric K. Shinseki, Secretary of Veterans Affairs
www.va.gov

**Drug Enforcement Administration**
8701 Morrissette Drive
Springfield, VA 22102
202/307-1000
Michele Leonhart, Administrator
www.justice.gov/dea/index.htm

**Environmental Protection Agency**
Ariel Rios Building
1200 Pennsylvania Avenue NW
Washington, DC 20460
202/564-4700
Bob Perciasepe, Acting Administrator and Deputy Administrator
www.epa.gov

**Equal Employment Opportunity Commission**
131 M Street NE
Washington, DC 20507
202/663-4191
Jacqueline Berrien, Chair
www.eeoc.gov

**Food and Drug Administration**
10903 New Hampshire Ave
Silver Spring, MD 20903
888/463-6332
Margaret Hamburg, Commissioner
www.fda.gov

**Health Resources and Services Administration**
5600 Fishers Lane
Room 14-71
Rockville, MD 20857
301/443-2216
Mary K. Wakefield, PhD, RN, Administrator
www.hrsa.gov

**Office of Management and Budget**
725 17th Street NW
Washington, DC 20503
202/395-3080
Jeffrey Zients, Acting Director
www.whitehouse.gov/omb/

**Office of National Drug Control Policy**
750 17th Street NW
Washington, DC 20503
202/395-6700
R. Gil Kerlikowske, Director
www.whitehousedrugpolicy.gov

**Social Security Administration, Office of Public Inquiries**
Windsor Park Building
6401 Security Blvd.
Baltimore, MD 21235
800/772-1213
Carolyn W. Colvin, Acting Commissioner of Social Security
www.ssa.gov

**Substance Abuse and Mental Health Services Administration**
One Choke Cherry Road
Rockville, MD 20857
240/276-2000
Pamela Hyde, Administrator
www.samhsa.gov

*The following list includes state departments of health and welfare, and their subagencies. The information was obtained directly from the agencies.*

# United States

## ALABAMA
The Honorable Robert Bentley, Governor, 334/242-7100

**Facility Licensure Agencies**

Alabama Department of Public Health, Division of Licensure and Certification, 201 Monroe Street, Suite 600, Montgomery, AL 36130-3017; tel. 334/206-5175; FAX. 334/206-5219; Walter T. Geary, MD, Bureau Director and Medical Director

**Health Agencies**

Department of Public Health, The RSA Tower, Suite 1552, PO Box 303017, Montgomery, AL 36130-3017; tel. 334/206-5200; FAX. 334/206-2008; Donald E. Williamson, MD, State Health Officer

State Health Planning and Development Agency, 100 North Union Street, Suite 870, Montgomery, AL 36103-3025; tel. 334/242-4103; FAX. 334/242-4113; Alva Lambert, Executive Director

**Managed Care Agencies**

Department of Insurance, 201 Monroe Street, Suite 1700, Montgomery, AL 36130-3351; tel. 334/269-3550; FAX. 334/241-4192; Jim Ridling, Commissioner

**Medical & Nursing Licensure Agencies**

Alabama Board of Nursing, 770 Washington Avenue, Suite 250, RSA Plaza, Montgomery, AL 36130-3900; tel. 800/656-5318; FAX. 334/293-5201; N. Genell Lee, RN, MSN, JD, Executive Officer

Alabama State Board of Medical Examiners, 848 Washington Avenue, PO Box 946, Montgomery, AL 36101-0946; tel. 334/242-4116; FAX. 334/242-4155; Larry D. Dixon, Executive Director

## ALASKA
The Honorable Sean Parnell, Governor, 907/465-3500

**Facility Licensure Agencies**

Facilities Section, Department of Health and Social Services, PO Box 110650, Juneau, AK 99811-0650; tel. 907/465-3037; FAX. 907/465-2607; Jennifer Klein, Section Chief

**Health Agencies**

Department of Health and Social Services, 350 Main Street, Room 404, PO Box 110601, Juneau, AK 99811-0601; tel. 907/465-3030; FAX. 907/465-3068; William J. Streur, Commissioner

**Managed Care Agencies**

Alaska Division of Insurance, 333 Willoughby Avenue, Ninth Floor, State Office Building, Juneau, AK 99811-0805; tel. 907/465-2515; FAX. 907/465-3422; Bret S. Kolb, Director

**Medical & Nursing Licensure Agencies**

Alaska Board of Nursing, Division of Corporations, Business, and Professional Licensing, 550 W. Seventh Avenue, Suite 1500, Anchorage, AK 99501; tel. 907/269-8161; FAX. 907/269-8196; Nancy Sanders, Executive Administrator

Alaska State Medical Board, 550 W. Seventh Avenue, Suite 1500, Anchorage, AK 99501; tel. 907/269-8163; FAX. 907/269-8196; Debora J. Stovern, Executive Administrator

## ARIZONA
The Honorable Janice K. Brewer, Governor, 602/542-4331

**Facility Licensure Agencies**

Arizona Department of Health Services, Medical Facilities Licensing Office, 150 N. 18th Avenue, Suite 450, Phoenix, AZ 85007; tel. 602/364-3064; FAX. 602/364-4808; Cara Christ, MD, Assistant Director

**Health Agencies**

Arizona Department of Health Services, 150 N. 18th Avenue, Suite 500, Phoenix, AZ 85007; tel. 602/542-1027; FAX. 602/542-1062; Will Humble, Director

**Managed Care Agencies**

Arizona Department of Insurance, 2910 North 44th Street, Suite 210, Phoenix, AZ 85018-7269; tel. 602/364-2393; FAX. 602/364-2175; Germaine L. Marks, Director of Insurance

**Medical & Nursing Licensure Agencies**

Arizona Board of Osteopathic Examiners in Medicine and Surgery, 9535 E. Doubletree Ranch Road, Suite 200, Scottsdale, AZ 85258; tel. 480/657-7703; FAX. 480/657-7715; Jenna Jones, Executive Director

Arizona Department of Health Services, Division of Licensing Services, 150 N 18th Avenue, Suite 400, Phoenix, AZ 85007; tel. 602/364-3031; FAX. 602/364-4764; Colby Dower, Assistant Director

Arizona Medical Board, 9545 E. Doubletree Ranch Road, Scottsdale, AZ 85258; tel. 480/551-2791; FAX. 480/551-2828; Lisa S. Wynn, Executive Director

Arizona State Board of Nursing, 4747 N. Seventh Street, Suite 200, Phoenix, AZ 85014-3653; tel. 602/771-7800; FAX. 602/771-7888; Joey Ridenour, RN, MN, FAAN, Executive Director

## ARKANSAS
The Honorable Michael Beebe, Governor, 501/682-2345

**Facility Licensure Agencies**

Health Facility Services, Arkansas Department of Health, 5800 West 10th Street, Suite 400, Little Rock, AR 72204-1704; tel. 501/661-2201; FAX. 501/661-2165; Connie Melton, Section Chief

**Health Agencies**

Arkansas Department of Health, 4815 West Markham, Little Rock, AR 72205; tel. 501/661-2000; FAX. 501/661-2388; Paul K. Halverson, DrPH, Director and State Health Officer

**Managed Care Agencies**

Arkansas Insurance Department, 1200 West Third Street, Little Rock, AR 72201-1904; tel. 501/371-2600; FAX. 501/371-2618; Jay Bradford, Insurance Commissioner

**Medical & Nursing Licensure Agencies**

Arkansas State Board of Nursing, University Tower Building, 1123 South University Avenue, Little Rock, AR 72204; tel. 501/686-2700; FAX. 501/686-2714; Sue A. Tedford, ASBN Executive Director

Arkansas State Medical Board, 1401 W. Capitol, Suite 340, Little Rock, AR 72201; tel. 501/296-1802; FAX. 501/603-3555; Joseph M. Beck, MD, Chairman

## CALIFORNIA
The Honorable Edmund Brown, Jr., Governor, 916/445-2841

**Facility Licensure Agencies**

Department of Public Health - Center for Health Care Quality, 1615 Capitol Avenue, Stop 0512, PO Box 997413, Sacramento, CA 95899-7377; tel. 916/324-6630; FAX. 916/324-4820; Debby Rogers, RN, MS, FAEN, Deputy Director

**Health Agencies**

California Department of Public Health, PO Box 997377, MS 0500, Sacramento, CA 95899-7377; tel. 916/558-1700; FAX. 916/558-1762; Dr. Ron Chapman, Director

Department of Health Care Services, PO Box 997413, Sacramento, CA 95899-7413; tel. 916/440-7400; Toby Douglas, Director

Healthcare Workforce Development Division, 400 R Street, Room 330, Sacramento, CA 95811; tel. 916/326-3700; FAX. 916/322-2588; Lupe Alonzo-Diaz, MPA,Deputy Director

**Managed Care Agencies**

Department of Managed Health Care, 980 Ninth St, Suite 500, Sacramento, CA 95814; tel. 888/466-2219; FAX. 916/255-5241; Brent A. Barnhart, Director

Ombudsman's Office, California Department of Insurance, 300 Capitol Mall, Suite 1600, Sacramento, CA 95814; tel. 916/492-3545; Dave Jones, Insurance Commissioner

**Medical & Nursing Licensure Agencies**

Board of Vocational Nursing and Psychiatric Technicians, 2535 Capitol Oaks Drive, Suite 205, Sacramento, CA 95833; tel. 916/263-7800; FAX. 916/263-7859; Teresa Bello-Jones, JD, MSN, RN, Executive Officer

California Board of Registered Nursing, 1747 N. Market Boulevard, Suite 150, Sacramento, CA 95834-1924; tel. 916/322-3350; FAX. 916/574-7700; Louise Bailey, M.Ed, RN, Executive Director

Medical Board of California, 2005 Evergreen Street, Suite 1200, Sacramento, CA 95815; tel. 916/263-2382; FAX. 916/263-2387; Linda K. Whitney, Executive Director

## COLORADO
The Honorable John Hickenlooper, Governor, 303/866-2471

**Facility Licensure Agencies**

Health Facilities Division, Colorado Department of Public Health and Environment, 4300 Cherry Creek Drive South, Building A, Second Floor, Denver, CO 80246-1530; tel. 303/692-2800; FAX. 303/753-6214; Howard Roitman, Director

**Health Agencies**

Colorado Department of Public Health and Environment, Business Office, 4300 Cherry Creek Drive, S., Denver, CO 80246-1530; tel. 303/692-2016; FAX. 303/751-3043; Christopher E. Urbina, Executive Director and Chief Medical Officer

**Managed Care Agencies**

Department of Regulatory Agencies, Colorado Division of Insurance, 1560 Broadway, Suite 850, Denver, CO 80202; tel. 303/894-7499; FAX. 303/894-7455; Jim Riesberg, Commissioner

**Medical & Nursing Licensure Agencies**

Colorado Medical Board, 1560 Broadway, Suite 1350, Denver, CO 80202-5140; tel. 303/894-7690; FAX. 303/894-7692; Marschall S. Smith, Program Director

Colorado State Board of Nursing Department of Regulatory Agencies, 1560 Broadway, Suite 1350, Denver, CO 80202; tel. 303/894-2430; FAX. 303/894-7693; Cheryl Hara, Interim Program Director

Department of Regulatory Agencies, 1560 Broadway, Suite 1550, Denver, CO 80202; tel. 303/894-7855; FAX. 303/894-7885; Barbara Kelley, Executive Director

## CONNECTICUT
The Honorable Daniel Malloy, Governor, 800/406-1527

**Facility Licensure Agencies**

Department of Public Health, Healthcare Quality and Safety Branch, 410 Capitol Avenue, MS 12HCS, P.O. Box 340308, Hartford, CT 06134-0308; tel. 860/509-7406; FAX. 860/509-7539; Wendy Furniss, RNC, MS, Branch Chief

**Health Agencies**

Department of Public Health, 410 Capitol Avenue, Mail Stop 12APP, Hartford, CT 06134-0308; tel. 860/509-7590; FAX. 860/707-1931; Jennifer Filippone, Chief Practitioner, Licensing and Investigations

**Managed Care Agencies**

State of Connecticut, Insurance Department, Life & Health Division, PO Box 816, 153 Market St., Hartford, CT 06142-0816; tel. 860/297-3901; FAX. 860/297-3941; Mary Ellen Breault, Director

**Medical & Nursing Licensure Agencies**

Connecticut Board of Examiners for Nursing, Department of Public Health, 410 Capitol Avenue, MS #13PHO, PO Box 340308, Hartford, CT 06134-0308; tel. 860/509-7603; FAX. 860/509-7553; Janice Wojick, Board Liaison

Connecticut Department of Public Health, 410 Capitol Avenue, MS #12 APP, PO Box 340308, Hartford, CT 06134-0308; tel. 860/509-7590; FAX. 860/707-1984; Jewel Mullen, MD, Commissioner

Section C

## DELAWARE

**The Honorable Jack Markell, Governor, 302/744-4101**

### Facility Licensure Agencies

**Department of Health and Social Services – Division of Public Health, Office of Health Facilities Licensing and Certification,** 258 Chapman Road, Suite 101, Chopin Building, Newark, DE 19702; tel. 302/283-7220; FAX. 302/283-7221; Roseann Sapp, Office Manager

### Health Agencies

**Delaware Health and Social Services,** 1901 North DuPont Highway, Main Administration Building, New Castle, DE 19720; tel. 302/255-9040; FAX. 302/255-4429; Rita M. Landgraf, Cabinet Secretary

**Division of Public Health,** Jesse Cooper Building, 417 Federal Street, Dover, DE 19901; tel. 302/744-4700; FAX. 302/739-6659; Karyl Thomas Rattay, MD, MS, Director

### Managed Care Agencies

**Delaware Department of Insurance, Consumer Department,** 841 Silver Lake Boulevard, Dover, DE 19904; tel. 302/674-7300; FAX. 302/739-6278; Karen Weldin Stewart, CIR-ML, Commissioner

### Medical & Nursing Licensure Agencies

**Delaware Board of Medical Practice Delaware Division of Professional Regulation,** Cannon Building, 861 Silver Lake Boulevard, Suite 203, Dover, DE 19904; tel. 302/744-4500; FAX. 302/739-2711; James L. Collins, Director

**Delaware Board of Nursing,** 861 Silver Lake Boulevard, Suite 203, Dover, DE 19904; tel. 302/744-4500; FAX. 302/739-2712; Pamela C. Zickafoose, Ed.D., MSN, RN, Executive Director

## DISTRICT OF COLUMBIA

**Governor Switchboard, 202/624-5300**

### Facility Licensure Agencies

**District of Columbia Department of Health, Health Regulation Licensing Administration,** 899 N Capitol Street, NE, Washington, DC 20002; tel. 202/442-5955; FAX. 202/442-4795; Saul M.Levin, MD, MPA, Interim Director

### Health Agencies

**Department of Health, Government of the District of Columbia,** 899 North Capitol Street NE, Washington, DC 20002; tel. 202/442-5955; FAX. 202/442-4795; Saul M. Levin, MD, MPA, Interim Director

### Managed Care Agencies

**District of Columbia Department of Insurance, Securities and Banking,** Union Center Plaza, 810 First Street NE, Washington, DC 20002; tel. 202/727-8000; FAX. 202/535-1196; William P. White, Commissioner

### Medical & Nursing Licensure Agencies

**DC Board of Nursing, Department of Health,** 899 North Capitol Street, NE, First Floor, Washington, DC 20002; tel. 202/724-8800; FAX. 202/724-8677; Karen Skinner, Executive Director

**District of Columbia Board of Medicine,** 899 North Capital Street NE, 2nd Floor, Washington, DC 20002; tel. 202/724-8800; FAX. 202/724-8677; Jacqueline Watson, DO, MBA, Executive Director

## FLORIDA

**The Honorable Rick Scott, Governor, 850/488-2272**

### Facility Licensure Agencies

**Agency for Health Care Administration, Bureau of Health Facility Regulation,** Hospital and Outpatient Services Unit, 2727 Mahan Drive, Mail Stop 31, Tallahassee, FL 32308; tel. 850/412-4549; FAX. 850/922-4351; Molly McKinstry, Deputy Secretary, Unit Manager

### Health Agencies

**Department of Health, State Surgeon General,** 4052 Bald Cypress Way, Bin #A00, Tallahassee, FL 32399-1701; tel. 850/245-4321; FAX. 850/922-9453

### Managed Care Agencies

**Office of Insurance Regulation,** 200 East Gaines Street, Tallahassee, FL 32399; tel. 850/413-3140; FAX. 850/488-3334; Kevin M. McCarty, Commissioner

### Medical & Nursing Licensure Agencies

**Florida Board of Medicine,** 4052 Bald Cypress Way, Bin #C03, Tallahassee, FL 32399-3253; tel. 850/245-4131; FAX. 850/488-0596; Joy A. Tootte, JD, Executive Board Director

**Florida Board of Nursing, Department of Health,** 4052 Bald Cypress Way, Bin C-02, Tallahassee, FL 32399-3252; tel. 850/245-4125; FAX. 850/245-4179; Joe Baker, Jr., Executive Director

**Florida Board of Osteopathic Medicine,** 4052 Bald Cypress Way, Bin #C-06, Tallahassee, FL 32399-3256; tel. 850/245-4161; FAX. 850/921-6184; Christy Robinson, Program Operations Administrator

## GEORGIA

**The Honorable Nathan Deal, Governor, 404/656-1776**

### Facility Licensure Agencies

**Department of Community Health, Healthcare Facility Regulation Division,** Two Peachtree Street, NW, Room 31-447, Atlanta, GA 30303-3142; tel. 404/657-5850; FAX. 404/651-7295; Victoria Walter, Director, Licensing and Certification

### Health Agencies

**Department of Public Health,** 2 Peachtree Street, NW, Suite 15-470, Atlanta, GA 30303-3682; tel. 404/657-2700; FAX. 404/657-2715; Brenda Fitzgerald, MD, Commissioner

### Managed Care Agencies

**Office of Commissioner of Insurance, State of Georgia,** Two Martin Luther King, Jr. Drive, Suite 704, West Tower, Atlanta, GA 30334; tel. 404/656-2070; FAX. 404/408-5931; Ralph T. Hudgens, Commissioner, Division of Insurance

### Medical & Nursing Licensure Agencies

**Georgia Board of Nursing,** 237 Coliseum Drive, Macon, GA 31217-3858; tel. 478/207-2440; FAX. 877/371-5712; Jim Cleghorn, Executive Director

**Georgia Composite Medical Board,** Two Peachtree Street, NW, 36th Floor, Atlanta, GA 30303; tel. 404/656-3913; FAX. 404/656-9723; LaSharn Hughes, MBA, Executive Director

## HAWAII

**The Honorable Neil Abercrombie, Governor, 808/586-0034**

### Facility Licensure Agencies

**Hawaii State Department of Health, Office Health Care Assurance,** 601 Kamokila Blvd, Room 395, Kapolei, HI 96707; tel. 808/692-7420; FAX. 808/692-7447; Keith Ridley, Chief

### Health Agencies

**Hawaii State Department of Health,** PO Box 3378, 1250 Punchbowl Street, Honolulu, HI 96801; tel. 808/586-4410; FAX. 808/586-4368; Loretta J. Fuddy, ACSW, MPH, Director

**Hawaii State Health Planning and Development Agency,** 1177 Alakea Street, Suite 402, Honolulu, HI 96813; tel. 808/587-0788; FAX. 808/587-0783; Romala Sue Radcliffe, Administrator

### Managed Care Agencies

**State of Hawaii Department of Labor and Industrial Relations, Disability Compensation Division,** PO Box 3769, 830 Punchbowl St., Honolulu, HI 96812; tel. 808/586-9151; FAX. 808/586-9219; Walter B. Kawamura, Administrator

### Medical & Nursing Licensure Agencies

**Hawaii Board of Nursing, Professional and Vocational Licensing Division,** PO Box 3469, Honolulu, HI 96801; tel. 808/586-2695; FAX. 808/586-2689; Lee Ann Teshima, Executive Officer

**Hawaii Medical Board, Department of Commerce and Consumer Affairs,** 335 Merchant Street, Room 301, Honolulu, HI 96801; tel. 808/586-3000; Constance Cabral, Executive Officer

## IDAHO

**The Honorable C.L. "Butch" Otter, Governor, 208/334-2100**

### Facility Licensure Agencies

**Bureau of Facility Standards, Department of Health and Welfare,** PO Box 83720, 3232 Elder Street, Boise, ID 83720; tel. 208/334-6626; FAX. 208/364-1888; Sylvia Creswell, Co-Supervisor NLTC

### Health Agencies

**Department of Health and Welfare, Division of Public Health,** 450 West State, Fourth Floor, PO Box 83720, Boise, ID 83720-0036; tel. 208/334-5500; FAX. 208/334-6581; Richard Armstrong, Director

### Managed Care Agencies

**Idaho Department of Insurance,** 700 West State Street, Third Floor, P.O. Box 83720, Boise, ID 83720-0042; tel. 208/334-4250; FAX. 208/334-4398; Bill Deal, Director

### Medical & Nursing Licensure Agencies

**Idaho State Board of Medicine,** PO Box 83720, Boise, ID 83720-0058; tel. 208/327-7000; FAX. 208/327-7005; Nancy Kerr, Executive Director

**Idaho State Board of Nursing,** 280 North 8th Street, Suite 210, PO Box 83720, Boise, ID 83720-0061; tel. 208/577-2476; FAX. 208/334-3262; Sandra Evans, MAEd., RN Executive Director

## ILLINOIS

**The Honorable Pat Quinn, Governor, 217/782-6830**

### Facility Licensure Agencies

**Division of Health Care Facilities and Programs, Illinois Department of Public Health,** 525 West Jefferson Street, Fourth Floor, Springfield, IL 62761-0001; tel. 217/782-7412; FAX. 217/782-0382; William A. Bell, Division Chief

### Health Agencies

**Illinois Department of Public Health,** 535 West Jefferson Street, Springfield, IL 62761; tel. 217/557-2556; FAX. 217/557-3497; LaMar Hasbrouck, MD, MPH, Director

### Managed Care Agencies

**Illinois Department of Insurance,** 320 West Washington Street, Springfield, IL 62767-0001; tel. 217/782-4515; FAX. 217/782-5020; Andrew Boron, Director

### Medical & Nursing Licensure Agencies

**Illinois Department of Financial & Professional Regulation,** James R. Thompson Center, 100 West Randolph Street, Chicago, IL 60601; tel. 800/560-6420; FAX. 312/814-5392; Michele Bromberg, MSN, APN, Nursing Coordinator

**Illinois Department of Financial and Professional Regulation, Division of Professional Regulation,** 320 West Washington Street, Third Floor, Springfield, IL 62786; tel. 217/785-0800; FAX. 217/782-7645; Jay Stewart, Division Director

## INDIANA

**The Honorable Mike Pence, Governor, 317/232-4567**

### Facility Licensure Agencies

**Division of Acute Care, Indiana State Department of Health,** Two North Meridian Street, Suite 4A, Indianapolis, IN 46204; tel. 317/233-7472; FAX. 317/233-7157; Randy Snyder, Program Director

### Health Agencies

**Indiana State Department of Health,** Two North Meridian Street, Indianapolis, IN 46204; tel. 317/233-1325; FAX. 317/233-7387; William C. VanNess II, MD, Commissioner

### Managed Care Agencies

**Indiana Department of Insurance Company Compliance Division,** 311 West Washington Street, Suite 300, Indianapolis, IN 46204; tel. 317/232-3520; FAX. 317/232-5251; Logan P. Harrison, Chief Deputy Commissioner

### Medical & Nursing Licensure Agencies

**Indiana Professional Licensing Agency, Indiana State Board of Nursing,** 402 West Washington, Room W072, Indianapolis, IN 46204; tel. 317/234-2043; FAX. 317/233-4236; Elizabeth Kiefner Crawford, Board Director

**Indiana Professional Licensing Agency, Medical Licensing Board of Indiana,** 402 West Washington, Room W072, Indianapolis, IN 46204; tel. 317/234-2060; FAX. 317/233-4236; Kristen Kelley, Director

## IOWA

**The Honorable Terry Branstad, Governor, 515/281-5211**

### Facility Licensure Agencies

**Iowa Department of Inspections and Appeals, Health Facilities Division,** Lucas State Office Building, 321 East 12th Street, Des Moines, IA 50319-0083; tel. 515/281-4115; FAX. 515/242-5022; Mary Spracklin, Bureau Chief

### Health Agencies

**Iowa Department of Public Health,** Lucas State Office Building, 321 E. 12th Street, Des Moines, IA 50319-0075; tel. 515/281-8474; FAX. 515/281-4958; Mariannette Miller-Meeks, MD

### Managed Care Agencies

**Iowa Department of Commerce, Insurance Division,** 330 Maple, Des Moines, IA 50319-0065; tel. 515/281-5705; FAX. 515/281-3059; Nick Gerhart, Commissioner

**Medical & Nursing Licensure Agencies**

**Iowa Board of Medicine,** 400 SW 8th Street, Suite C, Des Moines, IA 50309–4686; tel. 515/281–5171; FAX. 515/242–5908; Mark Bowden, Executive Director

**Iowa Board of Nursing,** 400 SW 8th Street, Suite B, Des Moines, IA 50309; tel. 515/281–3255; FAX. 515/281–4825; Kathleen R. Weinberg, RN, MSN, Interim Executive Director

## KANSAS
**The Honorable Sam Brownback, Governor, 785/296–3232**

**Facility Licensure Agencies**

**Kansas Department of Health and Environment, Bureau of Community Health Services,** 1000 Southwest Jackson, Suite 340, Topeka, KS 66612–1365; tel. 785/296–1200; FAX. 785/291–3419; Mindee Reece, Director, Director of Medical Facilities and Support

**Health Agencies**

**Kansas Department of Health and Environment,** Curtis Building, 1000 SW Jackson, Topeka, KS 66612–1368; tel. 785/296–0461; FAX. 785/368–6368; Robert Moser, MD, Secretary, Kansas Health and Environment

**Managed Care Agencies**

**Kansas Insurance Department,** 420 Southwest Ninth Street, Topeka, KS 66612; tel. 785/296–7850; FAX. 785/296–2537; Linda Sheppard, Accident and Health Supervisor

**Medical & Nursing Licensure Agencies**

**Kansas State Board of Healing Arts,** 800 SW Jackson, Lower Level–Suite A, Topeka, KS 66612; tel. 785/296–7413; FAX. 785/296–0852; Kathleen Selzler Lippert, Executive Director

**Kansas State Board of Nursing,** Landon State Office Building, 900 SW Jackson, Topeka, KS 66612–1230; tel. 785/296–4929; FAX. 785/296–3929; Mary Blubaugh MSN, RN, Executive Administrator

## KENTUCKY
**The Honorable Steven L. Beshear, Governor, 502/564–2611**

**Facility Licensure Agencies**

**Office of Inspector General, Division of Healthcare,** Cabinet for Health and Family Services, 275 East Main Street, 5E–A, Frankfort, KY 40621; tel. 502/564–7963; FAX. 502/564–6546; Connie Payne, Director

**Health Agencies**

**Department for Public Health, Cabinet for Health & Family Services,** 275 East Main Street, Mail Stop HS1WA, Frankfort, KY 40621; tel. 502/564–3970; FAX. 502/564–9377; Stephanie Mayfield–Gibson, MD, FCAP, Commissioner

**Managed Care Agencies**

**Department of Insurance, Health and Life Division,** 215 West Main Street, PO Box 517, Frankfort, KY 40602; tel. 502/564–6088; FAX. 502/564–2728; Maggie Woods, Director

**Medical & Nursing Licensure Agencies**

**Kentucky Board of Medical Licensure,** 310 Whittington Parkway, Suite 1B, Louisville, KY 40222; tel. 502/429–7150; FAX. 502/429–7158; Michael S. Rodman, Executive Director

**Kentucky Board of Nursing,** 312 Whittington Parkway, Suite 300, Louisville, KY 40222–2042; tel. 502/429–3300; FAX. 502/429–3311; Paula S. Schenk, Executive Director

## LOUISIANA
**The Honorable Bobby Jindal, Governor, 225/342–7015**

**Facility Licensure Agencies**

**Department of Health and Hospitals, Bureau of Health Care Integrity, Health Standards Section,** 602 N. Fifth Street, 2nd Floor, Baton Rouge, LA 70821–3767; tel. 225/342–0138; FAX. 225/342–0157; Lori Guillory, Hospital Program Manager

**Department of Health and Hospitals, Bureau of Health Services, Ambulatory Surgery Centers,** 602 N. Fifth Street, 2nd Floor, Baton Rouge, LA 70802; tel. 225/342–9348; FAX. 225/342–0157; Hedra Dubea, RN, Program Manager, Ambulatory Surgery Centers

**Health Agencies**

**Louisiana Department of Health and Hospitals,** 628 North 4th Street, Baton Rouge, LA 70802; tel. 225/342–9500; FAX. 225/342–5568; Kathy Kliebert, Interim Secretary

**Managed Care Agencies**

**Louisiana Department of Insurance,** 1702 North Third Street, Baton Rouge, LA 70802; tel. 225/342–0800; FAX. 225/342–7401; Mike Boutwell, Asst. Commissioner, Licensing & Compliance

**Medical & Nursing Licensure Agencies**

**Louisiana State Board of Medical Examiners,** 630 Camp Street, New Orleans, LA 70130; tel. 504/568–6820; FAX. 504/568–5754; Robert Marier, MD, MHA, FACP, Executive Director

**Louisiana State Board of Nursing,** 17373 Perkins Road, Baton Rouge, LA 70810; tel. 225/755–7500; FAX. 225/755–7580; Barbara L. Morvant, MN, RN, Executive Director

**Louisiana State Board of Practical Nurse Examiners,** 3421 N. Causeway Boulevard, Suite 505, Metairie, LA 70002; tel. 504/838–5791; FAX. 504/838–5279; Lynn Ansardi, RN, Executive Director

## MAINE
**The Honorable Paul LePage, Governor, 207/287–3531**

**Facility Licensure Agencies**

**Division of Licensing and Regulatory Services, Department of Health and Human Services,** 41 Anthony Avenue, 11 State House Station, Augusta, ME 04333; tel. 207/287–9300; FAX. 207/287–5807; Kenneth Albert, RN, Esq., Director

**Health Agencies**

**Department of Health and Human Services,** 11 State House Station, Augusta, ME 04333–0011; tel. 207/287–4223; FAX. 207/287–3005; Mary C. Mayhew, Commissioner

**Managed Care Agencies**

**Department of Professional and Financial Regulation, Bureau of Insurance,** #34 State House Station, Augusta, ME 04333–0034; tel. 207/624–8494, FAX. 207/624 8599; Glenn Griswold, Director, Consumer Health Care Division

**Medical & Nursing Licensure Agencies**

**Maine Board of Licensure in Medicine,** 137 State House Station, Augusta, ME 04333–0137; tel. 207/287–3601; FAX. 207/287–6590; Randal C. Manning, Executive Director

**Maine Board of Osteopathic Licensure,** 142 State House Station, 161 Capitol Street, Augusta, ME 04333–0142; tel. 207/287–2480; FAX. 207/287–3015; Susan E. Strout, Executive Secretary

**Maine State Board of Nursing,** 161 Capitol Street, 158 State House Station, Augusta, ME 04333–0158; tel. 207/287–1133; FAX. 207/287–1149; Myra A. Broadway, JD, MS, RN, Executive Director

## MARYLAND
**The Honorable Martin O'Malley, Governor, 410/974–3901**

**Facility Licensure Agencies**

**Maryland Department of Health and Mental Hygiene, Freestanding Ambulatory Surgery Centers and Hospices,** Spring Grove Hospital Center, 55 Wade Avenue, Cantonville, MD 21288; tel. 410/402–8040; FAX. 410/402–8441; Barbara Fagan, Manager and Coordinator

**Maryland Office of Health Care Quality, Department of Health & Mental Hygiene,** Spring Grove Hospital Center, 55 Wade Avenue, Cantonville, MD 21228; tel. 410/402–8002; FAX. 410/402–8218; Tricia Nay, MD, Acting Director

**Health Agencies**

**Department of Health and Mental Hygiene,** 201 West Preston Street, Baltimore, MD 21201; tel. 410/767–6500; FAX. 410/767–6489; Joshua M. Sharfstein, MD, Secretary

**Managed Care Agencies**

**Maryland Insurance Administration, Life & Health Complaints and Investigations,** 200 Street Paul Place, Suite 2700, Baltimore, MD 21202; tel. 410/468–2000; FAX. 410/468–2258; Therese M. Goldsmith, Insurance Commissioner

**Medical & Nursing Licensure Agencies**

**Maryland Board of Nursing,** 4140 Patterson Avenue, Baltimore, MD 21215–2254; tel. 410/585–1900; FAX. 410/358–3530; Patricia A. Noble, MSN, RN, Executive Director

**Maryland Board of Physicians,** 4201 Patterson Avenue, 4th Floor, Baltimore, MD 21215–0095; tel. 800/492–6836; FAX. 410/358–2252; Carole J. Catalfo., ESQ, Executive Director

## MASSACHUSETTS
**The Honorable Deval Patrick, Governor, 617/725–4000**

**Facility Licensure Agencies**

**Massachusetts Department of Public Health, Bureau of Health Care Safety and Quality,** 99 Chauncy Street, 11th Floor, Boston, MA 02111; tel. 617/753–8000; FAX. 617/753–8125; Madeleine Biondolillo, Bureau Director

**Health Agencies**

**Massachusetts Department of Public Health,** 250 Washington Street, 6th Floor, Boston, MA 02108; tel. 617/624–6000; FAX. 617/624–5185; Lauren Smith, MD, MPH, Interim Commissioner Lauren Smith, MD, MPH, Interim Commissioner

**Managed Care Agencies**

**Commonwealth of Massachusetts, Division of Insurance,** 1000 Washington St, Suite 810, Boston, MA 02118–2208; tel. 617/521–7794; FAX. 617/753–6380; Joseph G. Murphy, Commissioner

**Medical & Nursing Licensure Agencies**

**Commonwealth of Massachusetts, Board of Registration in Medicine,** 200 Harvard Mill Square, Suite 330, Wakefield, MA 01880; tel. 781/876–8200; FAX. 781/876–8384; Barbara A. Piselli, JD, Interim Executive Director

## MICHIGAN
**The Honorable Rick Snyder, Governor, 517/373–3400**

**Facility Licensure Agencies**

**Health Facilities Division, Michigan Department of Licensing and Regulatory Affairs, Bureau of Health Systems,** PO Box 30664, 611 West Ottawa, Lansing, MI 48909; tel. 517/241–4160; FAX. 517/241–3354; Larry Horvath

**Health Agencies**

**Michigan Department of Community Health, Public Health Administration,** 201 Townsend Street, Lansing, MI 48913; tel. 517/335–8024; FAX. 517/335–9032; Melanie Brim, Senior Deputy Director, Public Health Administration

**Managed Care Agencies**

**Department of Insurance and Financial Services,** PO Box 30220, 611 West Ottawa, Lansing, MI 48909–7979; tel. 517/373–0220; FAX. 517/335–4978; R. Kevin Clinton, Director

**Medical & Nursing Licensure Agencies**

**Michigan Board of Medicine,** 611 West Ottawa Street, First Floor, Lansing, MI 48909; tel. 517/335–0918; FAX. 517/241–2895; Carol Engle, Director, Bureau of Health Professions

**Michigan Board of Nursing, Bureau of Health Professions,** 611 West Ottawa Street, First Floor, Lansing, MI 48909; tel. 517/335–0918; FAX. 517/373–2179; Rae Ramsdell, Director of Health Licensing Division

**Michigan Board of Osteopathic Medicine and Surgery,** 611 West Ottawa Street, First Floor, PO Box 30670, Lansing, MI 48909; tel. 517/335–0918; FAX. 517/373–2179; Rae Ramsdell, Director of Health Licensing Division

## MINNESOTA
**The Honorable Mark Dayton, Governor, 651/201–3400**

**Facility Licensure Agencies**

**Minnesota Department of Health, Compliance Monitoring Division,** Licensing and Certification Program, PO Box 64900, St. Paul, MN 55164–0900; tel. 651/201–4100; FAX. 651/215–9697; Mary Absolon, Program Manager

**Health Agencies**

**Minnesota Department of Health,** 625 Robert Street N, P.O. Box 64975, St. Paul, MN 55164–0975; tel. 651/201–5000; Edward Ehlinger, MD, Commissioner

**Managed Care Agencies**

**Minnesota Department of Health, Managed Care Systems,** PO Box 64882, 85 E. Seventh Place, St. Paul, MN 55164–0882; tel. 651/201–5166; FAX. 651/201–5186; Irene Goldman, Manager

**Medical & Nursing Licensure Agencies**

**Minnesota Board of Medical Practice,** 2829 University Avenue, SE, Suite 500, Minneapolis, MN 55414–3246; tel. 612/617–2149; FAX. 612/617–2166; Robert A. Leach, Executive Director

**Minnesota Board of Nursing,** 2829 University Avenue SE, Suite 200, Minneapolis, MN 55414–3253; tel. 612/617–2270; FAX. 612/617–2190; Shirley A. Brekken, RN, MS, Executive Director

## MISSISSIPPI

**The Honorable Phil Bryant, Governor, 601/359-3150**

**Facility Licensure Agencies**

**Bureau of Health Facilities Licensure and Certification, Mississippi State Department of Health,** PO Box 1700, 143 B Lefleur's Square, Jackson, MS 39215; tel. 601/364-1100; FAX. 601/364-5054; Marilynn Winborne, Bureau Director of Long Term Care

**Health Agencies**

**Mississippi State Department of Health, Office of Health Policy and Planning,** 570 East Woodrow Wilson, P.O. Box 1700, Jackson, MS 39215-1700; tel. 601/576-7874; FAX. 601/576-7530; Donald E. Eicher, III, Director

**Managed Care Agencies**

**Mississippi Department of Insurance,** PO Box 79, 501 North West Street, Jackson, MS 39205; tel. 601/359-3577; FAX. 601/359-2474; Kim Causey, Special Assistant Attorney General

**Medical & Nursing Licensure Agencies**

**Mississippi Board of Nursing,** 1080 River Oaks Drive, Suite A 100, Flowood, MS 39232; tel. 601/957-6300; FAX. 601/957-6301; Melinda E. Rush, DSN, FNP, Executive Director

**Mississippi State Board of Medical Licensure,** 1867 Crane Ridge Drive, Suite 200-B, Jackson, MS 39216; tel. 601/987-3079; FAX. 601/987-4159; H. Vann Craig, MD, Executive Director

## MISSOURI

**The Honorable Jeremiah W. (Jay) Nixon, Governor, 573/751-3222**

**Facility Licensure Agencies**

**Bureau of Home Care and Rehabilitative Standards,** PO Box 570, Jefferson City, MO 65012; tel. 573/751-6336; FAX. 573/751-6315; Lisa Coots, RN, Bureau Chief

**Bureau of Hospital Standards, Missouri Department of Health and Senior Services,** PO Box 570, Jefferson City, MO 65102; tel. 573/751-6303; FAX. 573/526-3621; Donya Lowrie, Bureau Chief

**Health Agencies**

**Department of Health and Senior Services,** PO Box 570, 912 Wildwood, Jefferson City, MO 65102; tel. 573/751-6001; FAX. 573/751-6041; Gail Vasterling, Acting Director

**Managed Care Agencies**

**Department of Insurance, Division of Market Regulation, Life and Healthcare Section,** PO Box 690, Jefferson City, MO 65102; tel. 573/526-4126; FAX. 573/526-1165; Angela Nelson, Insurance Market Regulatory Director

**Medical & Nursing Licensure Agencies**

**Missouri State Board of Nursing,** 3605 Missouri Boulevard, PO Box 656, Jefferson City, MO 65102; tel. 573/751-0681; FAX. 573/751-0075; Lori Scheidt, Executive Director

**Missouri State Board of Registration for the Healing Arts,** 3605 Missouri Boulevard, PO Box 4, Jefferson City, MO 65102; tel. 573/751-0098; FAX. 573/751-3166; Connie Clarkston, Executive Director

## MONTANA

**The Honorable Steve Bullock, Governor, 406/444-3111**

**Facility Licensure Agencies**

**Quality Assurance Division, Department of Public Health and Human Services,** 2401 Colonial Drive, Second Floor, P.O. Box 202953, Helena, MT 59620-2953; tel. 406/444-2037; FAX. 406/444-1742; Jeff Buska, Administrator

**Health Agencies**

**Montana Department of Public Health and Human Services,** 111 North Sanders, P.O. Box 4210, Helena, MT 59604; tel. 406/444-5622; FAX. 406/444-1970; Richard Opper, Director

**Managed Care Agencies**

**Montana State Auditor, Insurance Department,** 840 Helena Avenue, Helena, MT 59601; tel. 406/444-2040; FAX. 406/444-3497; Steve Matthews, Chief Financial Examiner

**Medical & Nursing Licensure Agencies**

**Montana Board of Medical Examiners,** 301 S. Park Avenue, 4th Floor, PO Box 200513, Helena, MT 59620-0513; tel. 406/841-2360; FAX. 406/841-2305; Ian Marquand, Executive Director

**Montana State Board of Nursing,** 301 S. Park Avenue, 4th Floor, PO Box 200513, Helena, MT 59620-0513; tel. 406/841-2300; FAX. 406/841-2305; Cynthia Gustafson, PhD, RN, Executive Director

## NEBRASKA

**The Honorable Dave Heineman, Governor, 402/471-2244**

**Facility Licensure Agencies**

**Nebraska Department of Health and Human Services, Division of Public Health – Licensure Unit,** 301 Centennial Mall South, Third Floor, Lincoln, NE 68509-4986; tel. 402/471-2115; FAX. 402/471-3577; Helen L. Meeks, Licensure Unit Administrator

**Health Agencies**

**Nebraska Department of Health and Human Services,** 301 Centennial Mall South, PO Box 95026, Lincoln, NE 68509-5026; tel. 402/471-3121; FAX. 402/471-9449; Kerry T. Winterer, Chief Executive Officer

**Managed Care Agencies**

**Nebraska Department of Insurance, Life & Health Division,** 941 O Street, Suite 400, Lincoln, NE 68508-3639; tel. 402/471-2201; FAX. 402/471-4610; Bruce Ramge, Director

**Medical & Nursing Licensure Agencies**

**Nebraska Board of Medicine and Surgery, Licensure Unit,** 301 Centennial Mall South, PO Box 94986, Lincoln, NE 68509-4986; tel. 402/471-2118; FAX. 402/471-8614; Helen Meeks, Administrator

**Office of Community Health Development,** 301 Centennial Mall, South, PO Box 95026, Lincoln, NE 68509; tel. 402/471-2353; FAX. 402/471-8259; David Palm, PhD, Administrator

## NEVADA

**The Honorable Brian Sandoval, Governor, 775/684-5670**

**Facility Licensure Agencies**

**Bureau of Health Care Quality and Compliance, Nevada Health Division,** 727 Fairview Drive, Suite E, Carson City, NV 89701-5493; tel. 775/684-1030; FAX. 775/684-1073; Kyle Devine, MSW Bureau Chief

**Health Agencies**

**Department of Health and Human Services,** 4126 Technology Way, Suite 100, Carson City, NV 89706-2009; tel. 775/684-4000; FAX. 775/684-4010; Michael J. Willden, Director

**Nevada Division of Health,** 4150 Technology Way, Suite 300, Carson City, NV 89706; tel. 775/684-4200; FAX. 775/684-4211; Richard Whitley, Administrator

**Managed Care Agencies**

**Nevada Division of Insurance,** 1818 E. College Pkwy, Suite 103, Carson City, NV 89706; tel. 775/687-0700; FAX. 775/687-0787; Scott J. Kipper, Insurance Commissioner

**Medical & Nursing Licensure Agencies**

**Nevada State Board of Medical Examiners, Licensing Division,** PO Box 7238, 1105 Terminal Way, Reno, NV 89502-2144; tel. 775/688-2559; FAX. 775/688-2321; Lynnette L. Daniels, Chief of Licensing

**Nevada State Board of Nursing,** 5011 Meadowood Mall Way, Suite 300, Reno, NV 89502; tel. 775/687-7700; FAX. 775/687-7707; Debra Scott, Executive Director

**Nevada State Board of Osteopathic Medicine,** 901 American Pacific Dr, Unit 180, Henderson, NV 89014; tel. 702/732-2147; FAX. 702/732-2079; Barbara Longo, Executive Director

## NEW HAMPSHIRE

**The Honorable Maggie Hassan, Governor, 603/271-2121**

**Facility Licensure Agencies**

**Bureau of Health Facilities Administration, Office of Operations Support, Licensure and Regulation,** 129 Pleasant Street, Concord, NH 03301; tel. 603/271-9254; FAX. 603/271-5590; Michael Fleming, Bureau Chief

**Health Facilities Administration – Licensing,** 129 Pleasant Street, Concord, NH 03256; tel. 603/271-9305; FAX. 603/271-4968; Rodney Bascom, Chief of HFA–Licensing

**Health Agencies**

**Office of Health Services Planning and Review,** 29 Hazen Drive, Concord, NH 03301-6527; tel. 603/271-4606; FAX. 603/271-4141; Cindy Carrier, Managing Analyst

**Managed Care Agencies**

**Department of Health and Human Services, Division of Public Health Services,** 29 Hazen Drive, Concord, NH 03301-6521; tel. 603/271-4501; FAX. 603/271-4827; Dr. José T. Montero, Director

**Medical & Nursing Licensure Agencies**

**New Hampshire Board of Medicine,** Two Industrial Park Drive #8, Concord, NH 03301; tel. 603/271-1203; FAX. 603/271-6702; Penny Taylor, Administrator

**New Hampshire Board of Nursing,** 121 South Fruit Street, Concord, NH 03301-2431; tel. 603/271-2323; FAX. 603/271-6605; Denise M. Nies, MSN, RN, BC, Executive Director

## NEW JERSEY

**The Honorable Christopher Christie, Governor, 609/292-6000**

**Facility Licensure Agencies**

**New Jersey Department of Health and Senior Services, Certificate of Need and Healthcare Facility Licensure,** PO Box 358, Trenton, NJ 08625-0358; tel. 609/292-8773; FAX. 609/292-3780; John A. Calabria, Director

**Health Agencies**

**New Jersey Department of Health, Office of the Commissioner,** PO Box 360, Trenton, NJ 08625-0360; tel. 609/292-7837; FAX. 609/292-0053; Mary O'Dowd, State Commissioner of Health

**Managed Care Agencies**

**Division of Medical Assistance and Health Services, Office of Managed Health Care,** PO Box 712, Trenton, NJ 08625-0712; tel. 609/588-2705; FAX. 609/588-6290; Karen Brodsky, Chief of Managed Care Contracting

**Medical & Nursing Licensure Agencies**

**New Jersey Board of Nursing,** 124 Halsey St, PO Box 45010, Newark, NJ 07101; tel. 973/504-6430; FAX. 973/648-3481; George Hebert, RN, MA, Executive Director

**New Jersey State Board of Medical Examiners,** PO Box 183, Trenton, NJ 08625-0183; tel. 609/826-7100; FAX. 609/826-7117; William V. Roeder, JD, Executive Director

## NEW MEXICO

**The Honorable Susana Martinez, Governor, 505/476-2200**

**Facility Licensure Agencies**

**New Mexico Department of Health, Health Facility Licensing and Certification Bureau,** 2040 S. Pacheco Street, 2nd Floor, Room 413, Santa Fe, NM 87505; tel. 505/476-9093; FAX. 505/476-9075; Judy Parks, Acting Director

**Health Agencies**

**New Mexico Department of Health,** 1190 S. Street Francis Drive, PO Box 26110, Santa Fe, NM 87502-6110; tel. 505/827-2613; FAX. 505/827-2530; Catherine D. Torres, MD, Cabinet Secretary

**Managed Care Agencies**

**Public Regulation Commission, Insurance Division,** PO Box 1269, 1120 Paseo de Peralta, Santa Fe, NM 87504-1269; tel. 505/827-4297; FAX. 505/476-0326; John G. Franchini, Superintendent of Insurance

**Medical & Nursing Licensure Agencies**

**New Mexico Board of Osteopathic Medical Examiners,** 2550 Cerrillos Road, Second Floor, Santa Fe, NM 87505; tel. 505/476-4622; FAX. 505/476-4665; Shellie J. Aquino, Licensing Specialist

**New Mexico Medical Board,** 2055 S. Pacheco, Building 400, Santa Fe, NM 87505; tel. 505/476-7220; FAX. 505/476-7237; Lynn S. Hart, Executive Director

**State of New Mexico Board of Nursing,** 6301 Indian School NE, Suite 710, Albuquerque, NM 87110; tel. 505/841-8340; FAX. 505/841-8347; Nancy Darbro, PhD, APRN, RN, CNS, Executive Director

## NEW YORK

**The Honorable Andrew Cuomo, Governor, 518/474-7516**

**Facility Licensure Agencies**

**Center for Health Care Quality & Surveillance, New York State Department of Health,** Corning Tower, 14th Floor, Albany, NY 12237; tel. 518/402-5673; FAX. 518/486-2564; Mark L. Kissinger, Director

**Division of Certification and Surveillance,** 875 Central Avenue, Albany, NY 12206; tel. 518/402-1004; FAX. 518/402-0784; Ruth Leslie, Director

**New York State Department of Health, Office of Health Systems Management,** Corning Tower, Empire State Plaza, Albany, NY 12237; tel. 518/474-7028; FAX 518/486-2564; Lora K. Lefebvre, Deputy Director

**Health Agencies**

**New York State Department of Health,** Empire State Plaza, Corning Tower, Room 1495, Albany, NY 12237; tel. 518/474-2011; FAX. 518/474-5450; Nirav R. Shah, MD, MPH, Commissioner of Health

**Managed Care Agencies**

**NYS DOH, Bureau of Managed Care Certification and Surveillance,** Room 2019, Corning Tower, Empire State Plaza, Albany, NY 12237; tel. 518/474-5515; FAX. 518/473-3583; Nina Daratsos, Director

**Medical & Nursing Licensure Agencies**

**New York State Board for Nursing NY State Education Department, Office of the Professions,** 89 Washington Avenue, Albany, NY 12234-1000; tel. 518/474-3817; FAX. 518/474-3706; Suzanne Sullivan, RN, Executive Secretary

**New York State Board of Medicine,** 89 Washington Avenue, East Wing, Second Floor, Albany, NY 12234; tel. 518/474-3817; FAX. 518/486-4846; Walter Ramos, Executive Secretary

**New York State Education Department, Office of the Professions,** State Education Building, 2nd Floor, Albany, NY 12234; tel. 518/474-3817; FAX. 518/474-1449; Susan Naccarato, Acting Director of Professional Licensing

**NORTH CAROLINA**
   The Honorable Pat McCrory, Governor, 919/733-4240

**Facility Licensure Agencies**

**Department of Health and Human Services, Division of Health Service Regulation,** 2711 Mail Service Center, 1205 Umstead Drive, Raleigh, NC 27699; tel. 919/855-4620; FAX. 919/715-8476; Azzie Y. Conley, Chief, Acute and Home Care Licensure and Certification

**Health Agencies**

**NC Department of Health and Human Services,** 2001 Mail Service Center, Raleigh, NC 27699-2001; tel. 919/855-4800; FAX. 919/715-4645; Aldona Zofia Wos, MD, Secretary

**Managed Care Agencies**

**North Carolina Department of Insurance, Financial Evaluation Division,** 1201 Mail Service Center, 430 N. Salisbury Street, Raleigh, NC 27699-1203; tel. 919/733-2205; FAX. 919/733-2206; Jackie Obusek, Assistant Chief Financial Analyst

**Medical & Nursing Licensure Agencies**

**North Carolina Board of Nursing,** PO Box 2129, 4516 Lake Boone Trail, Raleigh, NC 27602-2129; tel. 919/782-3211; FAX. 919/781-9461; Julia L. George, RN, MSN, FRE, Executive Director

**North Carolina Medical Board,** 1203 Front Street, Raleigh, NC 27609; tel. 919/326-1100; FAX. 919/326-1130; David Henderson, Executive Director

**NORTH DAKOTA**
   The Honorable Jack Dalrymple, Governor, 701/328-2200

**Facility Licensure Agencies**

**North Dakota Department of Health, Division of Health Facilities,** 600 East Boulevard Avenue, Department 301, Bismarck, ND 58505-0200; tel. 701/328-2352; FAX. 701/328-1890; Darleen Bartz, PhD, Chief – Health Resources Section

**Health Agencies**

**State Department of Health,** 600 East Boulevard Avenue, Bismarck, ND 58505-0200; tel. 701/328-2372; FAX. 701/328-4727; Londa Rodahl, Administrative Assistant

**Managed Care Agencies**

**North Dakota Insurance Department,** 600 East Boulevard Avenue, Bismarck, ND 58505-0320; tel. 701/328-2440; FAX. 701/328-4880; Adam Hamm, Commissioner

**Medical & Nursing Licensure Agencies**

**North Dakota Board of Nursing,** 919 South Seventh Street, Suite 504, Bismarck, ND 58504-5881; tel. 701/328-9777; FAX. 701/328-9785; Constance Kalanek, PhD, RN, Executive Director

**North Dakota State Board of Medical Examiners,** 418 East Broadway Avenue, Suite 12, Bismarck, ND 58501; tel. 701/328-6500; FAX. 701/328-6505; Duane Houdek, JD, Executive Secretary

**OHIO**
   The Honorable John Kasich, Governor, 614/466-3555

**Facility Licensure Agencies**

**Division of Quality Assurance, Ohio Department of Health,** 246 North High Street, Third Floor, Columbus, OH 43215; tel. 614/466-7857; FAX. 614/644-0208; Rebecca Maust, Chief, Division of Quality Assurance

**Health Agencies**

**Ohio Department of Health,** 246 North High Street, Columbus, OH 43215; tel. 614/466-3543; FAX. 614/644-0085; Theodore E. Wymyslo, MD, Director

**Managed Care Agencies**

**The Ohio Department of Insurance,** 50 W. Town Street, Third Floor, Suite 300, Columbus, OH 43215; tel. 614/644-2661; FAX. 614/728-5238; William Preston, Chief, Life and Health Division

**Medical & Nursing Licensure Agencies**

**Ohio Board of Nursing,** 17 South High Street, Suite 400, Columbus, OH 43215-7410; tel. 614/466-3947; FAX. 614/466-0388; Betsy J. Houchen, JD, RN, MS, Executive Director

**State Medical Board of Ohio,** 30 E. Broad Street, Third Floor, Columbus, OH 43215-6127; tel. 614/466-3934; FAX. 614/728-5946; Kimberly C. Anderson, Esq., Interim Executive Director

**OKLAHOMA**
   The Honorable Mary Fallin, Governor, 405/521-2342

**Facility Licensure Agencies**

**Oklahoma State Department of Health, Protective Health Services, Medical Facilities Service,** 1000 Northeast 10th Street, Oklahoma City, OK 73117-1299; tel. 405/271-6576; FAX. 405/271-1308; Lee Martin, Director

**Health Agencies**

**State Department of Health,** 1000 Northeast 10th St, Room 1114, Oklahoma City, OK 73117-1299; tel. 405/271-6576; FAX. 405/271-1308; Terry Cline, PhD, Commissioner

**Managed Care Agencies**

**Oklahoma State Department of Health, Managed Care Systems – Health Resources Development Service,** 1000 Northeast 10th Street, Room 1011, Oklahoma City, OK 73117-1299; tel. 405/271-6868; FAX. 405/271-7360; James Joslin, Director

**Medical & Nursing Licensure Agencies**

**Oklahoma Board of Nursing,** 2915 N. Classen Boulevard, Suite 524, Oklahoma City, OK 73106; tel. 405/962-1800; FAX. 405/962-1821; Kimberly Glazier, M.Ed., RN, Executive Director

**Oklahoma State Board of Medical Licensure and Supervision,** 101 NE 51st Street, PO Box 18256, Oklahoma City, OK 73154-0256; tel. 405/962-1400; FAX. 405/962-1499; Lyle Kelsey, MBA, CMBE, Executive Director

**Oklahoma State Board of Osteopathic Examiners,** 4848 North Lincoln Boulevard, Suite 100, Oklahoma City, OK 73105-3321; tel. 405/528-8625; FAX. 405/557-0653; Deborah J. Bruce, Executive Director

**OREGON**
   The Honorable John Kitzhaber, Governor, 503/373-1027

**Facility Licensure Agencies**

**Health Care Regulation and Quality Improvement,** 800 Northeast Oregon Street, Suite 305, Portland, OR 97232; tel. 971/673-0540; FAX. 971/673-0556; Dana Selover, MD MPH

**Health Agencies**

**Oregon Health Authority–Public Health Division, Health Care Regulation and Quality Improvement,** 800 NE Oregon Street, Suite 305, Portland, OR 97232; tel. 971/673-0540; FAX. 971/673-0556; Dana Selover, Section Manager

**Managed Care Agencies**

**Department of Consumer and Business Services, Insurance Division,** PO Box 14480, 350 Winter Street NE, Salem, OR 97309-0405; tel. 503/947-7980; FAX. 503/378-4351; Louis Savage, Commissioner

**Medical & Nursing Licensure Agencies**

**Oregon Medical Board,** 1500 SW First Avenue, Suite 620, Portland, OR 97201-5847; tel. 971/673-2700; FAX. 971/673-2670; Kathleen Haley, JD, Executive Director

**Oregon State Board of Nursing,** 17938 SW Upper Boones Ferry Road, Portland, OR 97224-7012; tel. 971/673-0685; FAX. 971/673-0684; Joy Ingwerson, Interim Executive Director

**PENNSYLVANIA**
   The Honorable Tom Corbett, Governor, 717/787-2500

**Facility Licensure Agencies**

**Bureau of Facility Licensure and Certification,** 625 Forster Street, Room 528, Harrisburg, PA 17120; tel. 717/787-8015; FAX. 717/772-2163; Ann Chronister, Bureau Director

**Department of Health, Division of Home Health,** 132 Kline Plaza, Suite A, Harrisburg, PA 17104; tel. 717/783-1379; FAX. 717/772-0232; Linda Chamberlain, MS, BSN, RN, Division Director

**Division of Acute and Ambulatory Care, Pennsylvania Department of Health,** Health & Welfare Building, Room 532, Harrisburg, PA 17120; tel. 717/783-8980; FAX. 717/705-6663; Joanne Salsgiver, Director

**Health Agencies**

**Pennsylvania Department of Health,** Health and Welfare Building, Suite 802, 625 Forster Street, Harrisburg, PA 17120; tel. 877/724-3258; FAX. 717/787-0191; Michael Wolf, Acting Secretary

**Managed Care Agencies**

**Pennsylvania Insurance Department, Office of Corporate and Financial Regulation,** Company Licensing Division, 1345 Strawberry Square, Harrisburg, PA 17120; tel. 717/787-2143; FAX. 717/787-8557; Robert E. Brackbill, Chief of Company Licensing Division

**Medical & Nursing Licensure Agencies**

**Pennsylvania Department of Health, Quality Assurance,** 625 Forster Street, Eighth Floor West, Harrisburg, PA 17120; tel. 717/783-1078; FAX. 717/525-5506; Anna Marie Sossong, Deputy Secretary

**Pennsylvania State Board of Medicine,** PO Box 2649, Harrisburg, PA 17105-2649; tel. 717/783-1400; FAX. 717/787-7769; Tammy Dougherty, Administrator

**Pennsylvania State Board of Nursing,** PO Box 2649, Harrisburg, PA 17105-2649; tel. 717/783-7142; FAX. 717/783-0822; Laurette Keiser, Executive Secretary

**Pennsylvania State Board of Osteopathic Medicine,** PO Box 2649, Harrisburg, PA 17105-2649; tel. 717/783-4858; FAX. 717/787-7769; Suzanne Smith, Administrator

**RHODE ISLAND**
   The Honorable Lincoln Chafee, Governor, 401/222-2080

**Facility Licensure Agencies**

**Rhode Island Department of Health, Division of Facilities Regulation,** Three Capitol Hill, Room 306, Providence, RI 02908-5097; tel. 401/222-2566; FAX. 401/222-3999; Raymond Rusin, Chief of Facilities Regulation

**Health Agencies**

**Department of Health,** Three Capitol Hill, Providence, RI 02908-5097; tel. 401/222-5960; FAX. 401/277-6548; Michael Fine, MD, Director

**Managed Care Agencies**

**Department of Business Regulation, Insurance Regulation Division,** 1511 Pontiac Avenue, Cranston, RI 02920; tel. 401/462-9520; FAX. 401/462-9602; Paul McGreevy, Director

**Medical & Nursing Licensure Agencies**

**Division of Professional Regulation, Rhode Island Department of Health,** Three Capitol Hill, Suite 104, Providence, RI 02908-5097; tel. 401/222-2827; FAX. 401/222-1272; Michael Simoli, Supervisor

**Rhode Island Board of Medical Licensure & Discipline,** Three Capitol Hill, Room 205, Providence, RI 02908-5097; tel. 401/222-3855; FAX. 401/222-2158; James McDonald, MD, Chief Administrative Officer

**Rhode Island Board of Nurse Registration and Nursing Education,** 3 Capitol Hill, Room 105, Providence, RI 02908-5097; tel. 401/222-5700; FAX. 401/222-3352

**SOUTH CAROLINA**
   The Honorable Nikki Haley, Governor, 803/734-2100

**Facility Licensure Agencies**

**SC Department of Health & Environmental Control, Division of Health Licensing,** 2600 Bull Street, Columbia, SC 29201; tel. 803/545–4370; FAX. 803/545–4212; Gwendolyn C. Thopmson, Director

**Health Agencies**

**Department of Health and Human Services,** 1801 Main Street, P.O. Box 8206, Columbia, SC 29202–8206; tel. 888/549–0820; FAX. 803/255–8235; Anthony E. Keck, Director

**Managed Care Agencies**

**South Carolina Department of Insurance, Financial Regulation & Solvency Services,** 1201 Main Street Street, Suite 1000, PO Box 100105, Columbia, SC 29202; tel. 803/737–6199; FAX. 803/737–6232; Lee Hill, Financial Analyst

**Medical & Nursing Licensure Agencies**

**Department of Labor, Licensing and Regulation, State Board of Nursing for South Carolina,** PO Box 12367, 110 Centerview Drive, Columbia, SC 29211–2367; tel. 803/896–4550; FAX. 803/896–4515; Nancy Murphy, Administrator

**South Carolina Board of Medical Examiners,** Synergy Business Park, Kingstree Building, 110 Centerview Drive, Columbia, SC 29211; tel. 803/896–4500; FAX. 803/896–4515; April Koon, Administrator

**SOUTH DAKOTA**

The Honorable Dennis Daugaard, Governor, 605/773–3212

**Facility Licensure Agencies**

**Office of Health Care Facilities Licensure and Certification, State Department of Health,** 615 E. Fourth Street, Pierre, SD 57501–1700; tel. 605/773–3356; FAX. 605/773–6667; Vickie Anderson, Interim Administrator

**Health Agencies**

**South Dakota Department of Health,** 600 East Capitol, Pierre, SD 57501–2536; tel. 605/773–3361; FAX. 605/773–5683; Doneen B. Hollingsworth, Secretary of Health

**Managed Care Agencies**

**Division of Insurance,** 445 E. Capitol Avenue, Pierre, SD 57501; tel. 605/773–3563; FAX. 605/773–5369; Melissa Klemann, Senior Policy Analyst

**Medical & Nursing Licensure Agencies**

**South Dakota Board of Medical and Osteopathic Examiners,** 101 N. Main Avenue, Suite 301, Sioux Falls, SD 57104; tel. 605/367–7781; FAX. 605/367–7786; Margaret B. Hansen, PA–C, MPAS, Executive Director

**South Dakota Board of Nursing,** 4305 South Louise Avenue, Suite 201, Sioux Falls, SD 57106; tel. 605/362–2760; FAX. 605/362–2768; Gloria Damgaard, RN, MS, Executive Director

**TENNESSEE**

The Honorable Bill Haslam, Governor, 615/741–2001

**Facility Licensure Agencies**

**Board for Licensing Health Care Facilities,** 227 French Landing Drive, Suite 501, Heritage Place MetroCenter, Nashville, TN 37243; tel. 615/741–7221; FAX. 615/253–1535; Ann Rutherford Reed, RN, BSN, MBA, Director of Licensure

**Health Agencies**

**Department of Health,** Cordell Hull Building, 3rd Floor, 425 Fifth Avenue, N., Nashville, TN 37243; tel. 615/741–3111; FAX. 615/741–2491; John J. Dreyzehner, MD, MPH, FACOEM, Commissioner

**Managed Care Agencies**

**Department of Commerce and Insurance, Insurance Division,** 500 James Robertson Parkway, Nashville, TN 37243–1135; tel. 615/741–2825; FAX. 615/532–2788; Mark Jaquish, Insurance Analysis Director

**Medical & Nursing Licensure Agencies**

**Department of Health Division of Health Licensure and Regulation,** 220 Athens Way, Suite 104, Nashville, TN 37243; tel. 615/741–8402; FAX. 615/741–5542; Michelle J. Long, JD, Assistant Commissioner

**Tennessee Board of Medical Examiners,** 227 French Landing, Suite 300, Heritage Place Metro Center, Nashville, TN 37243; tel. 800/778–4123; FAX. 615/253–4484; Michael Manolli, MD, President

**Tennessee Board of Nursing,** 227 French Landing Suite 300, Heritage Place Metro Center, Nashville, TN 37243; tel. 800/778–4123; FAX. 615/741–7899; Elizabeth J. Lund, MSN, RN, Executive Director

**Tennessee Medical Laboratory Board,** 227 French Landing, Suite 300, Nashville, TN 37247; tel. 615/532–5128; FAX. 615/741–7698; Lynda S. England, Director

**Tennessee State Board of Osteopathic Examination, Office of Licensing Health Care Professionals,** 227 French Landing, Suite 300, Nashville, TN 37243; tel. 800/778–4123; FAX. 615/253–4484; Jill Robinson, DO, President

**TEXAS**

The Honorable Rick Perry, Governor, 512/463–2000

**Facility Licensure Agencies**

**Texas Department of Aging and Disability Services,** 701 W. 51st Street, PO Box 149030, Austin, TX 78714–9030; tel. 512/438–3011; FAX. 512/438–2738; Jon Weizenbaum, Commissioner

**Texas Department of State Health Services, Facility Licensing Group,** Mail Code: 2835, P.O. Box 149347, Austin, TX 78714–9347; tel. 512/834–6648; FAX. 512/834–4514; Ellen Cooper, MSW, RN, MSN, Manager

**Health Agencies**

**Texas Department of State Health Services,** P.O. Box 149347, Austin, TX 78714–9347; tel. 512/776–7363; FAX. 512/776–7477; David L. Lakey, MD, Commissioner

**Managed Care Agencies**

**Texas Department of Insurance,** 333 Guadalupe, P.O. Box 149104, Austin, TX 78714–9104; tel. 512/322–6464; FAX. 512/490–1013; Eleanor Kitzman, Commissioner of Insurance

**Medical & Nursing Licensure Agencies**

**Texas Board of Nursing,** 333 Guadalupe, Suite 3–460, Austin, TX 78701; tel. 512/305–7400; FAX. 512/305–7401; Katherine A. Thomas, MN, RN, FAAN, Executive Director

**Texas Medical Board,** 333 Guadalupe, Tower Three, Suite 610, PO Box 2018, Austin, TX 78768–2018; tel. 512/305–7010; FAX. 512/305–7008; Mari Robinson, JD, Executive Director

**UTAH**

The Honorable Gary R. Herbert, Governor, 801/538–1000

**Facility Licensure Agencies**

**Utah Department of Health, Health Facility Licensing and Certification,** PO Box 144103, 288 North 1460 West, Salt Lake City, UT 84114–4103; tel. 801/538–6158; FAX. 801/538–6163; Joel Hoffman, Director

**Health Agencies**

**Utah Department of Health,** PO Box 141000, Salt Lake City, UT 84114–1000; tel. 801/538–6111; FAX. 801/538–6306; W. David Patton, Executive Director

**Managed Care Agencies**

**Utah Insurance Department,** 3110 State Office Building, 450 N. State Street, Salt Lake City, UT 84114–6901; tel. 801/538–3800; FAX. 801/538–3829; Todd E. Kiser, Commissioner

**Medical & Nursing Licensure Agencies**

**Utah Physicians Licensing Board, Division of Occupational and Professional Licensure,** Heber M. Wells Building, First Floor, 160 East 300 South, Salt Lake City, UT 84114–6741; tel. 801/530–6621; FAX. 801/530–6511; Noel Taxin, Bureau Manager

**Utah State Board of Nursing,** 160 East 300 South, Box 146741, Salt Lake City, UT 84114–6741; tel. 801/530–6628; FAX. 801/530–6511; Dr. Debra F. Hobbins, APRN, Executive Administrator

**VERMONT**

The Honorable Peter Shumlin, Governor, 802/828–3333

**Facility Licensure Agencies**

**Hospice and Palliative Care, Council of Vermont,** 10 Main Street, Montpelier, VT 05602; tel. 802/229–0579; FAX. 802/223–6218; Virginia L. Fry, Executive Director

**Vermont Board of Medical Practice, Vermont Department of Health,** 108 Cherry Street, Second Floor, PO Box 70, Burlington, VT 05402; tel. 802/657–4220; FAX. 802/657–4227; David Herlihy, Director

**Health Agencies**

**Vermont Department of Health,** 108 Cherry Street, P.O. Box 70, Burlington, VT 05402; tel. 802/863–7280; FAX. 802/951–1275; Harry L. Chen, MD, Commissioner

**Managed Care Agencies**

**Green Mountain Care Board,** 89 Main Street, 3rd Floor, Montpelier, VT 05620; tel. 802/828–2919; Georgia J. Maheras, Executive Director

**Medical & Nursing Licensure Agencies**

**Vermont Board of Nursing,** National Life Building, North Floor 2, Montpelier, VT 05620–3402; tel. 802/828–2396; FAX. 802/828–2484; Nancy Morin, Administrator

**Vermont Board of Osteopathic Physicians and Surgeons, Office of Professional Regulation,** National Life Building, North Floor 2, Montpelier, VT 05620–3402; tel. 802/828–2373; FAX. 802/828–2465; Aprille Morrison, Licensing Board Specialist

**Vermont Department of Disabilities Aging and Independent Living, Division of Licensing and Protection,** Ladd Hall, 103 South Main Street, Waterbury, VT 05671–2306; tel. 802/871–3317; FAX. 802/871–3318; Suzanne Leavitt, Director

**VIRGINIA**

The Honorable Robert McDonnell, Governor, 804/786–2211

**Facility Licensure Agencies**

**Office of Licensure and Certification, Virginia Department of Health,** 9960 Mayland Drive, Suite 401, Henrico, VA 23230; tel. 804/367–2102; FAX. 804/527–4502; Erik O. Bodin, Director

**Health Agencies**

**Virginia Department of Health,** PO Box 2448, 109 Governor Street, Richmond, VA 23218; tel. 804/864–7001; FAX. 804/864–7022; Cynthia C. Romero, MD, FAAFP, State Health Commissioner

**Virginia Department of Health, Division of Certificate of Public Need,** 9960 Mayland Drive, Suite 401, Henrico, VA 23230; tel. 804/367–2126; FAX. 804/527–4501; Peter Boswell, Director, Director

**Managed Care Agencies**

**State Corporation Commission, Bureau of Insurance,** PO Box 1157, 1300 East Main St., Richmond, VA 23218; tel. 804/371–9741; FAX. 804/371–9511; Connie Doung, Senior Financial Analyst

**Medical & Nursing Licensure Agencies**

**Virginia Board of Medicine,** Perimeter Center, 9960 Mayland Drive, Richmond, VA 23233–1463; tel. 804/367–4600; FAX. 804/527–4426; William L. Harp, MD, Executive Director

**Virginia Board of Nursing,** Perimeter Center, 9960 Mayland Drive, Henrico, VA 23233–1463; tel. 804/367–4515; FAX. 804/527–4455; Jay P. Douglas, RN, MSM, CSAC, Executive Director

**WASHINGTON**

The Honorable Jay Inslee, Governor, 360/902–4111

**Facility Licensure Agencies**

**Credentialing, Washington Department of Health,** PO Box 47877, 310 Israel Road, SE, Olympia, WA 98504–7852; tel. 360/236–4900; FAX. 360/236–4909; Diane Young, Credentialing Manager

**State Department of Health, Investigations and Inspections Office,** PO Box 47874, Olympia, WA 98504–7874; tel. 360/236–4732; FAX. 360/586–0123; Linda Foss, Executive Manager of Clinical Care Facilities

**Health Agencies**

**Washington State Department of Health,** PO Box 47890, Olympia, WA 98504–7890; tel. 360/236–4030; FAX. 360/586–7424; John Weisman, MPH, Secretary of Health

**Managed Care Agencies**

**Office of the Insurance Commissioner, Rates & Forms, Healthcare, Life, Disability,** PO Box 40255, Olympia, WA 98504–0255; tel. 360/725–7111; FAX. 360/586–0759; Janis LaFlash, Manager, Health and Disability

**Medical & Nursing Licensure Agencies**

**Health Systems Quality Assurance, Department of Health,** 111 Israel Road, SE, Mail Stop 47850, Tumwater, WA 98504–7850; tel. 360/236–4600; FAX. 360/236–4626; Karen Jensen, Assistant Secretary

**Washington State Board of Osteopathic Medicine and Surgery, Department of Health,** 101 Israel Road, SE, PO Box 47852, Olympia, WA 98504–7852; tel. 360/236–4700; FAX. 360/236–2901; Blake Maresh, Executive Director

**Washington State Department of Health, Medical Quality Assurance Commission,** PO Box 47866, Olympia, WA 98504–7866; tel. 360/236–2750; FAX. 360/236–2795; Julie Kitten, Operations Manager

**Washington State Nursing Care Quality Assurance Commission, Department of Health,** 111 Israel Rd S.E., PO Box 47864, Olympia, WA 98504–7864; tel. 360/236–4700; FAX. 360/236–4818; Paula Meyer, RN, MSN, Executive Director

## WEST VIRGINIA
The Honorable Earl Ray Tomblin, Governor, 304/558–2000

**Facility Licensure Agencies**

**Office of Health Facility Licensure and Certification, Office of Inspector General,** 408 Leon Sullivan Way, Charleston, WV 25301–3718; tel. 304/558–0050; FAX. 304/558–2515; Will Wright, Program Manager II

**Health Agencies**

**Department of Health and Human Resources,** One Davis Square, Suite 100–East, Charleston, WV 25301; tel. 304/558–0684; FAX. 304/558–1130; Rocco S. Fucillo, Cabinet Secretary

**West Virginia Health Care Authority,** 100 Dee Drive, Charleston, WV 25311–1600; tel. 304/558–7000; FAX. 304/558–7001; James L. Pitrolo, Chair

**Managed Care Agencies**

**West Virginia Offices of the Insurance Commissioner,** PO Box 50540, 1124 Smith Street, Charleston, WV 25301; tel. 304/558–3354; FAX. 304/558–3869; Jason Butcher, Director of Communications

**Medical & Nursing Licensure Agencies**

**Office of Chief Medical Examiner,** 619 Virginia Street West, Charleston, WV 25302; tel. 304/558–6920; FAX. 304/558–7886; James A. Kaplan, MD, Deputy Chief Medical Examiner

**West Virginia Board of Examiners for Registered Professional Nurses,** 101 Dee Drive, Suite 102, Charleston, WV 25311–1620; tel. 304/558–3596; FAX. 304/558–3666; Laura S. Rhodes, RN, MSN, Executive Director

**West Virginia Board of Osteopathic Medicine,** 405 Capitol Street, Suite 402, Charleston, WV 25301; tel. 304/558–6095; FAX. 304/558–6096; Diana Shepard, Executive Director

**West Virginia State Board of Examiners for Licensed Practical Nurses,** 101 Dee Drive, Suite 100, Charleston, WV 25311; tel. 304/558–3572; FAX. 304/558–4367; Lanette Anderson, MSN, JD, RN, Executive Director

## WISCONSIN
The Honorable Scott Walker, Governor, 608/266–1212

**Facility Licensure Agencies**

**Division of Quality Assurance, Department of Health Services,** One West Wilson Street, PO Box 2969, Madison, WI 53701–2969; tel. 608/267–7185; FAX. 608/267–0352; Otis Woods, Administrator

**Health Agencies**

**Department of Health Services,** PO Box 7850, Madison, WI 53707–7850; tel. 608/266–9622; FAX. 608/266–7882; Dennis G. Smith

**Managed Care Agencies**

**Office of the Commissioner of Insurance,** 125 S. Webster Street, P.O. Box 7873, Madison, WI 53707–7873; tel. 608/266–3585; FAX. 608/266–9935; Theodore Nickel, Commissioner

**Medical & Nursing Licensure Agencies**

**Wisconsin Department of Saftey and Professional Services,** 1400 East Washington Avenue, Room 112, PO Box 8935, Madison, WI 53708–8935; tel. 608/266–2112; FAX. 608/267–3816; Dan Williams, Director, Bureau of Health Services Professions

**Wisconsin Medical Examining Board,** 1400 East Washington Avenue, PO Box 8935, Madison, WI 53708; tel. 608/261–2378; FAX. 608/267–3816; Tom Ryan, Executive Director

## WYOMING
The Honorable Matthew Mead, Governor, 307/777–7434

**Facility Licensure Agencies**

**Wyoming Department of Health, Healthcare Licensing and Surveys,** 6101 Yellowstone Road, Suite 400, Cheyenne, WY 82002; tel. 307/777–7123; FAX. 307/777–7127; Ron Pearson, Manager

**Health Agencies**

**Department of Health,** 401 Hathaway Building, Cheyenne, WY 82002; tel. 307/777–7656; FAX. 307/777–7439; Thomas O. Forslund, Director

**Managed Care Agencies**

**State of Wyoming Department of Insurance,** 106 E. Sixth Avenue, Cheyenne, WY 82002; tel. 307/777–7401; FAX. 307/777–2446; Tom C. Hirsig, Commissioner

**Medical & Nursing Licensure Agencies**

**Wyoming Board of Medicine,** 320 West 25th Street, Suite 200, Cheyenne, WY 82002; tel. 307/778–7053; FAX. 307/778–2069; Deborah Gillette, Licensing Manager

**Wyoming State Board of Nursing,** 130 Hobbs Avenue, Suite B, Cheyenne, WY 82002; tel. 307/777–7601; FAX. 307/777–3519; Cynthia LaBonde, MN, RN, Executive Director

# U.S. Associated Areas

## GUAM
The Honorable Eddie Baza Calvo, Governor, 671/472–8931

**Health Agencies**

**Department of Public Health and Social Services,** 123 Chalan Kareta, Mangilao, GU 96913–6304; tel. 671/735–7173; FAX. 671/734–5910; James W. Gillan, Director, DPHSS

**Managed Care Agencies**

**Department of Public Health and Social Services, Government of Guam,** 123 Chalan Kareta Route 10, Mangilao, GU 96913; tel. 671/735–7102; FAX. 671/734 5910; James W. Gillan, Director

**Medical & Nursing Licensure Agencies**

**Guam Board of Medical Examiners, Health Professional Licensing Office,** 651 Legacy Square Commerical Complex S., Rte. 10, Suite 9, Mangilao, GU 96913; tel. 671/735–7406; FAX. 671/735–7413; MaryLou Loualhati, Acting Administrator

**Guam Board of Nurse Examiners Department of Public Health and Social Services,** 651 Legacy Square Commercial Complex S., South Route 10, Suite 9, Mangilao, GU 96913; tel. 671/733–7408; FAX. 671/477–4733; Margaret Guerrero

## PUERTO RICO
The Honorable Alejandro Garca Padilla, Governor, 787/721–7000

**Facility Licensure Agencies**

**Department of Health Commonwealth of Puerto Rico, Departamento de Salud,** PO Box 70184, Calle Maga, Edificio E altos, San Juan, PR 00936–0184; tel. 787/765–2929; FAX. 787/250–6547; Francisco Joglar, MD, Secretary of Health

**Puerto Rico Department of Health,** P.O. Box 70184, San Juan, PR 00936–8184; tel. 787/274–6822; FAX. 787/767–8341; Lorenzo Gonzalez Feliciano, MD, MBA, Secretary of Health

**Health Agencies**

**Puerto Rico Department of Health,** Building A – Medical Center, Call Box 70184, San Juan, PR 00936–8184; tel. 787/274–6822; FAX. 787/767–8341; Lorenzo Gonzalez Feliciano, MD, MBA, Secretary of Health

**Managed Care Agencies**

**Office of the Commissioner of Insurance,** B5 Calle Tabonuco, Suite 216, PMB 356, Guaynabo, PR 00968–3029; tel. 787/304–8686; FAX. 787/273–6365; Sol Gisela Marrero, Insurance Commisioner

**Medical & Nursing Licensure Agencies**

**Junta de Licenciatmiento y Disciplina Medica,** PO Box 13969, San Juan, PR 00908; tel. 787/999–8989; Gladys N. Tomes Diaz, Executive Director

**Puerto Rico Board of Medical Examiners,** PO Box 13969, San Juan, PR 00908; tel. 787/999–8989; FAX. 787/792–4436; Ernesto Caballero del Valle, Executive Director

## VIRGIN ISLANDS
The Honorable John de.Jongh, Jr., Governor, 340/774–0001

**Health Agencies**

**Virgin Islands Department of Health,** Charles Harwood Complex, 3500 Richmond Est, St. Croix, VI 00820–4370; tel. 340/773–6551; FAX. 340/773–1376; Fern Clark, MPH, Acting Commissioner of Health

# Canada

## ALBERTA
**Medical & Nursing Licensure Agencies**

**College of Physicians & Surgeons of Alberta,** Suite 2700, 10020 100th Street, NW, Edmonton, AB T5J 0N3; tel. 780/423–4764; FAX. 780/420–0651; Dr. Trevor Theman, Registrar

## MANITOBA
**Health Agencies**

**Department of Health,** 302 Legislative Building, 450 Broadway, Winnipeg, MB R3C 0V8; tel. 204/945–3731; FAX. 204/945–0441; Honourable Theresa Oswald, Minister

**Medical & Nursing Licensure Agencies**

**College of Physicians and Surgeons of Manitoba,** 1000–1661 Portage Avenue, Winnipeg, MB R3J 3T7; tel. 204/774–4344; FAX. 204/774–0750; William D.B. Pope, MD, Registrar

## NEW BRUNSWICK
**Medical & Nursing Licensure Agencies**

**College of Physicians and Surgeons of New Brunswick,** One Hampton Road, Suite 300, Rothesay, NB E2E 5K8; tel. 506/849–5050; FAX. 506/849–5069; Dr. Ed Schollenberg, Registrar

## NEWFOUNDLAND
**Health Agencies**

**Department of Health and Community Services,** Confederation Building (West Block), P.O. Box 8700, St. John's, NF A1B 4J6; tel. 709/729–3124; FAX. 709/729–0121; Susan Sullivan, Minister, Health and Community Services

## NOVA SCOTIA
**Health Agencies**

**Department of Health and Wellness,** PO Box 488, Halifax, NS B3J 2R8; tel. 902/424–3377; FAX. 902/424–0559; David Wilson, Minister of Health & Wellness

**Medical & Nursing Licensure Agencies**

**College of Physicians and Surgeons of Nova Scotia, Office of the Registrar,** Suite 5005, 7071 Bayers Road, Halifax, NS B3L 2C2; tel. 902/422–5823; FAX. 902/422–5035; Gus Grant, MD, Registrar and Chief Executive Officer

## PRINCE EDWARD ISLAND
**Medical & Nursing Licensure Agencies**

**College of Physicians and Surgeons of Prince Edward Island,** 14 Paramount Drive, Charlottetown, PE C1E 0C7; tel. 902/566–3861; FAX. 902/566–3986; C. Moyse, MD, Registrar

## QUEBEC
**Health Agencies**

**Ministry of Health and Social Services,** Ministere de la Sante et des Services Sociaux, Quebec, PQ G1S 2M1; tel. 418/644–4545; Rejean Hebert, Minister

## SASKATCHEWAN
**Health Agencies**

**Ministry of Health,** 3475 Albert Street, Third Floor, Regina, SK S4S 6X6; tel. 306/787–3696; FAX. 306/787–8310; The Hon. Dustin Duncan, Minister

**Medical & Nursing Licensure Agencies**

**College of Physicians and Surgeons of Saskatchewan,** 500 321A 21st Street, E., Saskatoon, SK S7K 0C1; tel. 306/244–7355; FAX. 306/244–0090; Karen Shaw, MD, Registrar

**Section C**

## Hospital Associations

*The following list of state and metropolitan hospital associations is derived from the American Hospital Association. For additional information visit the American Hospital Association website: www.aha.org.*

## United States

**ALABAMA: Alabama Hospital Association,** 500 North East Boulevard, Montgomery, AL 36117; tel. 334/272–8781; FAX. 334/270–9527; J. Michael Horsley, President and Chief Executive Officer

**ALASKA: Alaska State Hospital and Nursing Home Association,** 1049 W. Fifth Avenue, Suite 100, Anchorage, AK 99501; tel. 907/646–1444; FAX. 907/646–3964; Karen Perdue, President and Chief Executive Officer

**ARIZONA: Arizona Hospital and Healthcare Association,** 2800 North Central Avenue, Suite 1450, Phoenix, AZ 85004–1051; tel. 602/445–4300; FAX. 602/445–4299; Greg Vigdor, President and Chief Executive Officer

**ARKANSAS: Arkansas Hospital Association,** 419 Natural Resources Drive, Little Rock, AR 72205–1539; tel. 501/224–7878; FAX. 501/224–0519; Robert "Bo" Ryall, President and Chief Executive Officer

**CALIFORNIA: California Hospital Association,** 1215 K Street, Suite 800, Sacramento, CA 95814; tel. 916/552–7547; FAX. 916/552–7680; C. Duane Dauner, President and Chief Executive Officer

**Hospital Association of San Diego and Imperial Counties,** 5575 Ruffin Road, Suite 225, San Diego, CA 92123; tel. 858/614–0200; FAX. 858/614–0201; Steven A. Escoboza, President and Chief Executive Officer

**Hospital Association of Southern California,** 515 South Figueroa Street, Suite 1300, Los Angeles, CA 90071–3322; tel. 213/538–0700; FAX. 213/629–4272; James D. Barber, President and Chief Executive Officer

**Hospital Council of Northern and Central California,** 1215 K Street, Suite 730, Sacramento, CA 95814; tel. 916/552–7608; FAX. 916/552–2216; Arthur A. Sponseller, President and Chief Executive Officer

**COLORADO: Colorado Hospital Association,** 7335 East Orchard Road, Greenwood Village, CO 80111; tel. 720/489–1630; FAX. 720/489–9400; Steven J. Summer, President and Chief Executive Officer

**CONNECTICUT: Connecticut Hospital Association,** 110 Barnes Road, PO Box 90, Wallingford, CT 06492–0090; tel. 203/265–7611; FAX. 203/284–9318; Jennifer Jackson, President and Chief Executive Officer

**DELAWARE: Delaware Healthcare Association,** 1280 South Governors Avenue, Dover, DE 19904–4802; tel. 302/674–2853; FAX. 302/734–2731; Wayne A. Smith, President and Chief Executive Officer

**DISTRICT OF COLUMBIA: District of Columbia Hospital Association,** 1152 15th Street, NW, Suite 900, Washington, DC 20005–1723; tel. 202/682–1581; FAX. 202/371–8151; Robert A. Malson, President

**FLORIDA: Florida Hospital Association,** 306 East College Avenue, Tallahassee, FL 32301; tel. 850/222–9800; FAX. 850/561–6230; Bruce Rueben, President

**South Florida Hospital and Healthcare Association, Inc.,** 6030 Hollywood Boulevard, Suite 140, Hollywood, FL 33024; tel. 954/964–1660; FAX. 954/920–4595; Linda S. Quick, President

**GEORGIA: Georgia Hospital Association (GHA),** 1675 Terrell Mill Road, Marietta, GA 30067; tel. 770/249–4500; FAX. 770/955–5801; Earl Rogers, President

**HAWAII: Healthcare Association of Hawaii,** 707 Richards Street, PH2, Honolulu, HI 96813; tel. 808/521–8961; FAX. 808/599–2879; George W. Greene, President and Chief Executive Officer

**IDAHO: Idaho Hospital Association,** 615 N. Seventh Street, Boise, ID 83701–1278; tel. 208/338–5100; FAX. 208/338–7800; Steven A. Millard, President and Chief Executive Officer

**ILLINOIS: Illinois Hospital Association,** 1151 East Warrenville Road, P.O. Box 3015, Naperville, IL 60566–7015; tel. 630/276–5400; FAX. 630/276–5431; Maryjane A. Wurth, President and Chief Executive Officer

**Metropolitan Chicago Healthcare Council,** 222 South Riverside Plaza, Suite 1900, Chicago, IL 60606; tel. 312/906–6000; FAX. 312/993–4500; Kevin Scanlan, President and Chief Executive Officer

**INDIANA: Indiana Hospital Association,** 1 American Square, Suite 1900, Indianapolis, IN 46282; tel. 317/633–4870; FAX. 317/633–4875; Douglas J. Leonard, FACHE, President

**IOWA: Iowa Hospital Association,** 100 East Grand Avenue, Suite 100, Des Moines, IA 50309–1835; tel. 515/288–1955; FAX. 515/698–5149; Kirk Norris, President and Chief Executive Officer

**KANSAS: Kansas Hospital Association,** 215 SE 8th Street, Topeka, KS 66603; tel. 785/233–7436; FAX. 785/233–6955; Thomas L. Bell, President and Chief Executive Officer

**Health Alliance of MidAmerica,** 7015 College Boulevard, Suite 150, Overland Park, KS 66211; tel. 913/327–7200; FAX. 913/327–7210; Michael R. Dunaway, President

**KENTUCKY: Kentucky Hospital Association,** 2501 Nelson Miller Parkway, P.O. Box 436629, Louisville, KY 40253; tel. 502/426–6220; FAX. 502/426–6226; Michael T. Rust, FACHE, President and Chief Executive Officer

**Healthservices Council of Metropolitan Louisville,** 2501 Nelson Miller Parkway, P.O. Box 436629, Louisville, KY 40223; tel. 502/426–6220; FAX. 502/426–6226; Nancy Galvagni, Executive Director

**LOUISIANA: Louisiana Hospital Association,** 9521 Brookline Avenue, Baton Rouge, LA 70809–1431; tel. 225/928–0026; FAX. 225/923–1004; John A. Matessino, President and Chief Executive Officer

**Metropolitan Hospital Council of New Orleans,** 2450 Severn Avenue, Suite 210, Metairie, LA 70001; tel. 504/837–1171; FAX. 504/837–1174; Paul A. Salles, President and Chief Executive Officer

**MAINE: Maine Hospital Association,** 33 Fuller Road, Augusta, ME 04330; tel. 207/622–4794; FAX. 207/622–3073; Steven R. Michaud, President

**MARYLAND: Maryland Hospital Association,** 6820 Deerpath Road, Elkridge, MD 21075–6234; tel. 410/379–6200; FAX. 410/379–8239; Carmela Coyle, President and Chief Executive Officer

**Healthcare Council of the National Capital Area,** 4061 Powder Mill Rd, Suite 100, Calverton, MD 20705; tel. 301/732–8411; FAX. 301/731–8286; Leslie "Les" H. Pitton, Jr., President and Chief Executive Officer

**MASSACHUSETTS: Massachusetts Hospital Association,** 5 New England Executive Park, Burlington, MA 01803; tel. 781/262–6000; FAX. 781/272–1524; Lynn Nicholas, FACHE, President and Chief Executive Officer

**MICHIGAN: Michigan Health & Hospital Association,** 2112 University Park Drive, Okemos, MI 48864; tel. 517/323–3443; FAX. 517/323–0946; Spencer C. Johnson, President

**Hospital Council of East Central Michigan,** 315 Mullholland Avenue, Bay City, MI 48708; tel. 989/891–8810; FAX. 989/891–8161; Elizabeth S. Schnettler, President

**Upper Peninsula Hospital Council,** 6215 West Street Joseph Highway, Lansing, MI 48917; tel. 517/323–3443; FAX. 517/323–0946; Clark R. Ballard, Regional Liason

**MINNESOTA: Minnesota Hospital Association,** 2550 University Avenue W, Suite 350–S, St. Paul, MN 55114–1900; tel. 651/641–1121; FAX. 651/659–1477; Lawrence J. Massa, President and Chief Executive Officer

**MISSISSIPPI: Mississippi Hospital Association,** 116 Woodgreen Crossing, PO Box 1909, Madison, MS 39130; tel. 800/289–8884; FAX. 601/368–3200; Sam W. Cameron, President and Chief Executive Officer

**MISSOURI: Missouri Hospital Association,** PO Box 60, 4712 Country Club Drive, Jefferson City, MO 65102–0060; tel. 573/893–3700; FAX. 573/893–2809; Herb Kuhn, President and Chief Executive Officer

**MONTANA: MHA...An Association of Montana Health Care Providers,** 1720 Ninth Avenue, PO Box 5119, Helena, MT 59601; tel. 406/442–1911; FAX. 406/443–3894; Dick Brown, President and Chief Executive Officer

**NEBRASKA: Nebraska Hospital Association,** 3255 Salt Creek Circle, Suite 100, Lincoln, NE 68504; tel. 402/742–8140; FAX. 402/742–8191; Laura J. Redoutey, FACHE, President

**NEVADA: Nevada Hospital Association,** 5250 Neil Road, Suite 302, Reno, NV 89502; tel. 775/827–0184; FAX. 775/827–0190; Bill M. Welch, President and Chief Executive Officer

**NEW HAMPSHIRE: New Hampshire Hospital Association, Foundation for Healthy Communities,** 125 Airport Road, Concord, NH 03301–7300; tel. 603/225–0900; FAX. 603/225–4346; Stephen Ahnen, President

**NEW JERSEY: New Jersey Hospital Association,** PO Box 1, 760 Alexander Road, Princeton, NJ 08543–0001; tel. 609/275–4000; FAX. 609/452–8097; Elizabeth A. Ryan, Esq., President and Chief Executive Officer

**Hospital Alliance of New Jersey,** 150 West State Street, Trenton, NJ 08608; tel. 609/989–8200; FAX. 609/989–7768; Suzanne Ianni, President & Chief Executive Officer

**NEW MEXICO: New Mexico Hospital Association,** 7471 Pan American Freeway, NE, Albuquerque, NM 87109; tel. 505/343–0010; FAX. 505/343–0012; Jeff Dye, President and Chief Executive Officer

**NEW YORK: Healthcare Association of New York State,** One Empire Drive, Rensselaer, NY 12144; tel. 518/431–7600; FAX. 518/431–7915; Daniel Sisto, President

**Greater New York Hospital Association,** 555 West 57 Street, 15th Floor, New York, NY 10019; tel. 212/246–7100; FAX. 212/262–6350; Kenneth E. Raske, President and Chief Executive Officer

**Iroquois Healthcare Alliance,** 15 Executive Park Drive, Clifton Park, NY 12065; tel. 518/383–5060; FAX. 518/383–2616; Gary J. Fitzgerald, President

**Nassau–Suffolk Hospital Council, Inc.,** 1383 Veterans Memorial Highway, Suite 26, Hauppauge, NY 11788; tel. 631/435–3000; FAX. 631/435–2343; Kevin W. Dahill, President and Chief Executive Officer

**New York City Health & Hospitals Corporation,** 125 Worth Street, New York, NY 10013; tel. 212/788–3321; FAX. 212/788–0040; Alan D. Aviles, President

**Northern Metropolitan Hospital Association,** 400 Stony Brook Court, Newburgh, NY 12550; tel. 845/562–7520; FAX. 845/562–0187; Kevin W. Dahill, President and Chief Executive officer

**Rochester Regional Healthcare Association,** 3445 Winton Place, Suite 222, Rochester, NY 14623; tel. 585/273–8180; FAX. 585/475–0266; Diane H. Ashley, President and Chief Executive Officer

**Western New York Healthcare Association,** 1876 Niagara Falls Boulevard, Tonawanda, NY 14150–6439; tel. 716/695–0843; FAX. 716/695–0073; John E. Bartimole, President

**NORTH CAROLINA: North Carolina Hospital Association,** PO Box 4449, Cary, NC 27519–4449; tel. 919/677–2400; FAX. 919/677–4200; William A. Pully, President

**NORTH DAKOTA: North Dakota Hospital Association,** 1622 E. Interstate Avenue, PO Box 7340, Bismarck, ND 58507; tel. 701/224–9732; FAX. 701/224–9529; Jerry E. Jurena, President

**OHIO: Ohio Hospital Association,** 155 East Broad Street, Suite 301, Columbus, OH 43215; tel. 614/221–7614; FAX. 614/221–4771; Michael D. Abrams, President and Chief Executive Officer

**Akron Regional Hospital Association,** 3200 West Market Street, Suite 200, Akron, OH 44333; tel. 330/873–1500; FAX. 330/873–1501; Sarah Metzger, Director

**Central Ohio Hospital Council,** 155 East Broad Street, 23rd Floor, Columbus, OH 43215; tel. 614/358–2710; FAX. 614/358–2725; Jeff Klingler, President & Chief Executive Officer

**Greater Cincinnati Health Council,** 2100 Sherman Avenue, Suite 100, Cincinnati, OH 45212–2775; tel. 513/531–0200; FAX. 513/531–0278; Craig Brammer, Chief Executive Officer

**Greater Dayton Area Hospital Association,** 2 Riverplace, Suite 400, Dayton, OH 45405; tel. 937/228–1000; FAX. 937/228–1035; Bryan J. Bucklew, President and Chief Executive Officer

**Hospital Council of Northwest Ohio,** 3231 Central Park West Drive, Suite 200, Toledo, OH 43617; tel. 419/842–0800; FAX. 419/843–8889; W. Scott Fry, President and Chief Executive Officer

**The Center for Health Affairs,** 1226 Huron Road East, Cleveland, OH 44115; tel. 216/696–6900; FAX. 216/696–1875; William T. (Bill) Ryan, President and Chief Executive Officer

**OKLAHOMA: Oklahoma Hospital Association,** 4000 Lincoln Boulevard, Oklahoma City, OK 73105; tel. 405/427–9537; FAX. 405/424–4507; Craig W. Jones, FACHE, President

**OREGON: Oregon Association of Hospitals and Health Systems,** 4000 Kruse Way Place, Building 2, Suite 100, Lake Oswego, OR 97035–2543; tel. 503/636–2204; FAX. 503/636–8310; Andy Davidson, President and Chief Executive Officer

**PENNSYLVANIA: The Hospital & Healthsystem Association of Pennsylvania,** 4750 Lindle Road, P.O. Box 8600, Harrisburg, PA 17105–8600; tel. 717/564–9200; FAX. 717/561–5334; Andy Carter, President and Chief Executive Officer

**Hospital Council of Western Pennsylvania,** 500 Commonwealth Drive, Warrendale, PA 15086; tel. 724/772–7206; FAX. 724/772–8339; A.J. Harper, President

**The Delaware Valley Healthcare Council of HAP,** 1835 Market Street, 10th Floor, Philadelphia, PA 19103; tel. 215/563–2229; FAX. 215/563–2442; Andy Carter, President and Chief Executive Officer

**RHODE ISLAND: Hospital Association of Rhode Island,** 100 Midway Road, Suite 21, Cranston, RI 02920; tel. 401/946–7887; FAX. 401/946–8188; Edward J. Quinlan, President

**SOUTH CAROLINA: South Carolina Hospital Association,** 1000 Center Point Road, Columbia, SC 29210–5802; tel. 803/796–3080; FAX. 803/796–2938; Thorton Kirby, FACHE, President and Chief Executive Officer

**SOUTH DAKOTA: South Dakota Association of Healthcare Organizations (SDAHO),** 3708 West Brooks Place, Sioux Falls, SD 57106; tel. 605/361–2281; FAX. 605/361–5175; David R. Hewett, President and Chief Executive Officer

**TENNESSEE: Tennessee Hospital Association,** 500 Interstate Boulevard South, Nashville, TN 37210; tel. 615/256–8240; FAX. 615/242–4803; Craig A. Becker, President

**TEXAS: Texas Hospital Association,** 1108 Lavaca, Suite 700, Austin, TX 78701–2180; tel. 512/465–1000; FAX. 512/465–1090; Dan Stultz, MD, FACP, FACHE, President and Chief Executive Officer

**Dallas–Fort Worth Hospital Council,** 250 Decker Drive, Irving, TX 75062; tel. 972/719–4900; FAX. 972/719–4009; W. Stephen Love, President and Chief Executive Officer

**UTAH: UHA, Utah Hospital Association,** 2180 South 1300 East, Suite 440, Salt Lake City, UT 84106–2843; tel. 801/486–9915; FAX. 801/486–0882; Rod L. Betit, President and Chief Executive Officer

**VERMONT: Vermont Association of Hospitals and Health Systems,** 148 Main Street, Montpelier, VT 05602; tel. 802/223–3461; FAX. 802/223–0364; Marie Beatrice Grause, President and Chief Executive Officer

**VIRGINIA: Virginia Hospital & Healthcare Association,** 4200 Inslake Drive, Suite 203, Glen Allen, VA 23060; tel. 804/965–1227; FAX. 804/965–0475; Laurens Sartoris, President

**WASHINGTON: Washington State Hospital Association,** 300 Elliott Avenue West, Suite 300, Seattle, WA 98119–4118; tel. 206/281–7211; FAX. 206/283–6122; C. Scott Bond, President and Chief Executive Officer

**WEST VIRGINIA: West Virginia Hospital Association,** 100 Association Drive, Charleston, WV 25311–1571; tel. 304/344–9744; FAX. 304/414–0210; Joseph M. Letnaunchyn, President and Chief Executive Officer

**WISCONSIN: Wisconsin Hospital Association,** 5510 Research Park Drive, P.O.Box 259038, Madison, WI 53725–9038; tel. 608/274–1820; FAX. 608/274–8554; Steve Brenton, President

**WYOMING: Wyoming Hospital Association,** 2005 Warren Avenue, Cheyenne, WY 82001; tel. 307/632–9344; FAX. 307/632–9347; Dan Perdue, President

## U.S. Associated Areas

**PUERTO RICO: Puerto Rico Hospital Association,** Villa Nevarez Professional Center, Suite 101, San Juan, PR 00927; tel. 787/764–0290; FAX. 787/753–9748; Ruby Rodriguez,Vice President

## Canada

**NOVA SCOTIA: Health Association Nova Scotia,** 2 Dartmouth Road, Bedford, NS B4A–2K7; tel. 902/832–8500; FAX. 902/832–8505; Mary Lee, President and Chief Executive Officer

**ONTARIO: Catholic Health Alliance of Canada,** Annex C, Saint–Vincent Hospital, 60 Cambridge Street North, Ottawa, ON K1R–7A5; tel. 613/562–6262; FAX. 613/782–2857; James Roche, Executive Director

**Ontario Hospital Association,** 200 Front Street, West, Suite 2800, Toronto, ON M5V–3L1; tel. 416/205–1300; FAX. 416/205–1301; Pat Campbell, President and Chief Executive Officer

**SASKATCHEWAN: Health Shared Services Saskatchewan (3sHealth),** 800–2002 Victoria Avenue, Regina, SK S4P–0R7; tel. 306/347–5500; FAX. 306/525–1960; Andrew Will, President ands Chief Executive Officer

# Group Purchasing Organizations

*The following list of Group Purchasing Organizations is derived from the AHA Annual Survey of Hospitals and the organizations themselves. It reflects Group Purchasing Organizations serving hospitals. Inclusion or omission of any organization's name indicates neither approval nor disapproval by Health Forum LLC, an American Hospital Association company.*

## A

**Adventist Health**, 2100 Douglas Boulevard, Roseville, CA 95661; tel. 916/781–2000; Lowell G. Church, Vice President, Materiel Management; President, Supply Chain and Affiliated Services; www.adventisthealth.org

**Alegent Health**
see Prairie Health Ventures, LLC

**All Health**
see Provista

**Allegiance Health**, 205 North East Avenue, Jackson, MI 49201; tel. 517/788–4800; Georgia Fojtasek, RN, EdD, President and Chief Executive Officer; www.allegiancehealth.org

**Alliant Purchasing Group**
see Alliant–HAS

**Alliant–HAS**, 2650 Eastpoint Parkway, Suite 320, Louisville, KY 40223; tel. 800/446–8760; FAX. 502/992–3526; Stephen Wright, Sales and Marketing Manager; www.alliant-has.com

**ALTUS Management LLC**, 840 Aero Drive, Suite 150, Cheektowaga, NY 14225; tel. 716/633–0563; Kevin Connor, Chief Executive Officer

**Amerinet, Inc.**, Two CityPlace Drive, Suite 400, St. Louis, MO 63141; tel. 877/711–5700; Todd C. Ebert, President and Chief Executive Officer; www.amerinetgpo.com

**ArchCare**, 205 Lexington Avenue, 3rd Floor, New York, NY 10016; tel. 646/633–4700; Terence Gallagher, Vice President, Supply Chain; www.archcare.org

**Ascension Health**
see The Resource Group, LLC

**Associated Purchasing Services**, 7015 College Boulevard, Suite 150, Overland Park, KS 66211; tel. 913/327–8730; FAX. 913/327–7210; Dennis George, Chief Executive Officer; www.apskc.org

**Avera PACE**, 3900 West Avera Drive, Suite 200, Sioux Falls, SD 57108; tel. 800/657–8095; FAX. 605/322–4666; Steve Statz, RPh., MBA, Senior Vice President of Business Development; www.avera.org/pace

**Avera PACE – Premier**
see Avera PACE

## B

**Banner Health System**
see Premier Inc.

**Baptist Health Services Group**
see VHA Inc.

**Baycare Purchasing Partners, LLC**, 8731 Florida Mining Boulevard, Tampa, FL 33634

**BJC Health System**, 4353 Clayton Avenue, Suite 104, St. Louis, MO 63110–1621; tel. 314/286–2035; FAX. 314/362–0876; Nancy J. LeMaster, Vice President, Material Services; www.bjc.org

**BJC Healthcare**
see BJC Health System

**Boone Hospital Center**, 1600 East Broadway, Columbia, MO 65201–5844; tel. 573/815–8000; FAX. 573/815–2492; Randy Morrow, Interim Chief Executive Officer; www.boone.org

**Broadlane Group**
see MedAssets, Inc.

## C

**California Department of General Services**, Ziggurat Building, 707 Third Street, West Sacramento, CA 95605; tel. 916/376–5000; Fred Klass, Director; www.dgs.ca.gov

**Capella Healthcare**
see HealthTrust Purchasing Group, LP

**Cardinal Health, Inc.**, 7000 Cardinal Place, Dublin, OH 43017; tel. 614/757–5000; George S. Barrett, Chairman and Chief Executive Officer; www.cardinalhealth.com

**Care New England**, 45 Willard Avenue, Providence, RI 02905; tel. 401/737–7010; Thomas W. Gardner, Director, Materials Management; www.carenewengland.org

**Carilion Clinic**, P.O. Box 13367, Roanoke, VA 24033; tel. 800/422–8482; Nancy Howell Agee, President and Chief Executive Officer; www.carilionclinic.org

**Carolinas Shares Services**, P.O. Box 35126, Charlotte, NC 28235; tel. 704/512–7271; FAX. 704/512–7037; James Olsen, Senior Vice President and Chief Operating Officer; www.carolinassharedservices.org

**Catholic Health East**, 3805 West Chester Pike, Suite 100, Newtown Square, PA 19073; tel. 610/355–2000; Florence Doyle, Vice President, Supply Chain; www.che.org/services/materiels.php

**Catholic Health Initiatives**
see HealthTrust Purchasing Group, LP

**Catholic Health Services**
see Catholic Health Services of Long Island

**Catholic Health Services of Long Island**, 992 North Village Avenue, Rockville Centre, NY 11570; tel. 516/705–3700; Richard J. J. Sullivan, Jr., President and Chief Executive Officer; www.chsli.org

**Central Atlantic Health Network**
see VHA Inc. – Central Atlantic

**Centura Health**
see HealthTrust Purchasing Group, LP

**Champs**
see CHAMPS Healthcare

**CHAMPS Healthcare**, 1226 Huron Road East, Cleveland, OH 44115; tel. 800/362–2628; FAX. 216/696–1875; Yolandi Myers, Vice President, CHAMPS Group Purchasing; champshealthcare.com/GroupPurchasing.aspx

**Child Health Corp of America**
see Children's Hospital Association

**Children's Hospital Association**, 6803 West 64th Street, Shawnee Mission, KS 66202; tel. 913/262–1436; FAX. 913/262–1575; Tim Rezash, Group Vice President, Purchasing Services; www.chca.com

**Choice Partners**, 6005 Westview Drive, Houston, TX 77055; tel. 877/696–2122; FAX. 713/696–0731; Les Hooper, RTSBA, Executive Director; www.choicepartners.org

**Christus Health**
see MedAssets, Inc.

**Coalition Health Services**
see Coalition of Health Services, Inc.

**Coalition of Health Services, Inc.**, 301 South Polk, Suite 740, Amarillo, TX 79101; tel. 888/892–2273; FAX. 806/337–1704; Carolyn Witherspoon, Executive Director; www.cohs.net

**Coastal Cooperative of New Jersey, LLC**, 1350 Campus Parkway, Wall, NJ 07753; tel. 732/751–3404; www.coastalcoop.com

**Colonial Health Alliance, LLC**, 1800 Duel Highway, Suite 304, Hagerstown, MD 21740; tel. 240/347–4920; Stephen Carpenter, Executive Director; www.colonialregional.com

**Colonial Regional Alliance, LLC**
see Colonial Health Alliance, LLC

**Commonwealth of Massachusetts**
see Massachusetts Executive Office for Administration and Finance

**Commonwealth of Virginia**
see Virginia Department of General Services, Division of Purchases and Supply

**Community Health Systems**
see HealthTrust Purchasing Group, LP

**Consorta, Inc.**
see HealthTrust Purchasing Group, LP

**Contracting Acquisition Services**
see United States Department of Veterans Affairs, VISN 6: Mid–Atlantic Health Care Network

**Cooperative Services of Florida, Inc.**, 2727 Winkler Avenue, Fort Myers, FL 33901; tel. 239/939–8771; FAX. 239/939–8877; Robert Simpson, President and Chief Executive Officer; www.csofl.com

## D

**Defense Logistics Agency**, Andrew T. McNamara Building, 8725 John J. Kingman Road, Fort Belvoir, VA 22060–6221; tel. 703/767–4010; Vice Admiral Mark D. Harnitchek, SC, USN, Director; www.dla.mil

**Department of Veterans Affairs**
see United States Department of Veterans Affairs VISN listings

**DMS Pharmaceutical Group, Inc.**, 810 Busse Highway, Park Ridge, IL 60068; tel. 877/788–1100; FAX. 847/518–1105; Sam Lazich, President; www.dmspharma.com

**DSSI, LLC**, 40 Oak Hollow Street, Suite 225, Southfield, MI 48033; tel. 248/208–8375; Bhagwan P. Thacker, President, Founder and Chief Executive Officer; www.directsourcing.com

## F

**Fairview Purchasing Network**, 400 Stinson Boulevard., N.E., Minneapolis, MN 55413; tel. 612/672–4409; FAX. 612/672–4440; Laurel Sampson, Manager; www.fairview.org/About/PurchasingNetwork/index.htm

**First Choice Cooperative**
see FirstChoice Cooperative

**FirstChoice Cooperative**, 4815 Troup Highway, Tyler, TX 75703; tel. 800/250–3457; Ron Kethan; www.fccoop.org:8080/web/guest

# G

**Genesis Health Alliance**, 3700 Washington Avenue, Evansville, IN 47750; tel. 812/485–4000; J. D. LeClere, Executive Director; www.stmarys.org/genesis

**Genesis Purchasing Alliance**
see Genesis Health Alliance

**GNYHA Services, Inc.**, 555 West 57th Street, 15th floor, New York, NY 10019; tel. 212/246–7100; FAX. 212/262–6350; Christopher J. O'Connor, FACHE, President; www.gnyha.org/276/Default.aspx

**Great Lakes Healthcare**
see VHA Inc. – Great Lakes Healthcare Purchasing Network

**GSA**
see United States General Services Administration

# H

**Hartford Hospital**, 80 Seymour Street, Hartford, CT 06102; tel. 860/545–5000; FAX. 860/545–5066; Jeffrey A. Flaks, President and Chief Executive Officer; www.harthosp.org/default.aspx

**HCDE Cooperative**
see Choice Partners

**HCSC**
see Hospital Central Services Inc. and Affiliates

**Health Affiliated Services**
see Alliant–HAS

**Health Care Coalition of Texas**
see Texas Purchasing Coalition

**Health Enterprises Cooperative**, 5825 Dry Creek Lane, N.E., Cedar Rapids, IA 52402; tel. 319/368–3619; FAX. 319/368–3626; Jeanie Brown, Vice President; www.healthenterprises.org/aboutHec.html

**Health Enterprises of Iowa**
see Health Enterprises Cooperative

**Health Future, LLC**, 916 Town Centre Drive, Medford, OR 97504; tel. 800/452–2558; Chris Chang–Howitz, Chief Executive Officer; www.healthfuture.org

**Health Purchasing Alliance, Inc.**
see Healthcare Purchasing Alliance, Inc.

**Healthcare Purchasing Alliance, Inc.**, 1417 Kuhl Avenue, Suite 100, Orlando, FL 32806; tel. 321/841–4724; FAX. 321/843–4724; Rosaline Parson, Corporate Director; https://hpainc.orlandohealth.com/about

**Healthcare Service Center, Inc.**, 1203 Ball Street, Perry, GA 31069; tel. 478/224–2855; David Matthews, Interim Executive Director; www.h–s–c.org

**HealthGroup of Alabama, Huntsville Hospital**, 101 Sivley Road, Huntsville, AL 35801; tel. 256/922–6683; Rob Smith, Chief Executive Officer; www.huntsvillehospital.org/services/hga

**HealthSouth Corporation**
see MedAssets, Inc.

**HealthTrust Purchasing Group (HPG)**
see HealthTrust Purchasing Group, LP

**HealthTrust Purchasing Group, LP**, 155 Franklin Road, Suite 400, Brentwood, TN 37027; tel. 615/344–3000; Ed Jones, President and Chief Executive Officer; www.healthtrustpg.com

**Hospital Central Services Inc. & Affiliates**, 2171 28th Street, S.W., Allentown, PA 18103; tel. 800/444–4272; FAX. 610/791–2919; J. Michael Lee, DBA, FACHE, President and Chief Executive Officer; www.hcsc.org

**Hospital Purchasing Service**
see HPS MI, Inc.

**Hospital Shared SVS Amerinet**
see Amerinet, Inc.

**HPG**
see HealthTrust Purchasing Group, LP

**HPI**
see Novation LLC

**HPS MI, Inc.**, 3275 North M–37 Highway, P.O. Box 247, Middleville, MI 49333–0247; tel. 800/632–4572; FAX. 269/795–9788; Tom LaPres, President and Chief Executive Officer; www.hpsnet.net

**HPSI**, 1 Ada, Suite 150, Irvine, CA 92618; tel. 800/223–4774; David Lindahl, Managing Director, Healthcare Sales and Marketing; www.hpsionline.com

**HSCA**
see MedAssets, Inc.

**HSS/Amerinet**
see Amerinet, Inc.

**Huntsville Hospital**
see HealthGroup of Alabama

# I

**IHC/Amerinet**
see Intermountain Healthcare Supply Chain Organization

**Illinois Department of Central Management Services**, JRTC, 100 West Randolph, Chicago, IL 60601–3219; tel. 312/814–2141; Malcolm Weems, Director; www.cms.illinois.gov

**Illinois Purchasing Collaborative**
see IPC Group Purchasing

**Innovatix, LLC**, 555 West 57th Street, 12th floor, New York, NY 10019; tel. 888/258–3273; FAX. 646/638–2641; John P. Sganga, FACHE, President and Chief Executive Officer; www.innovatix.com

**Intermountain Healthcare**
see Intermountain Healthcare Supply Chain Organization

**Intermountain Healthcare Supply Chain Organization**, 7302 South Bingham Junction Boulevard, Midvale, UT 84047–4804; tel. 800/442–9023; Brent Johnson, Vice President, Supply Chain Organization and Chief Purchasing Officer; intermountainhealthcare.org/about/contactus/Pages/supply–chain.aspx

**Iowa Health System**
see UnityPoint Health

**IPC Group Purchasing**, 1151 East Warrenville Road, Naperville, IL 60563; tel. 630/276–5400; Patrick Sonin, Managing Executive; www.ipcgrouppurchasing.com

**Iroquois Health Alliance**
see United Iroquois Shared Services, Inc.

**IU Health Supply Chain Operations**, 340 West 10th Street, Suite 6100, Indianapolis, IN 46202–3082; tel. 317/962–3556; Daniel F. Evans, Jr., President and Chief Executive Officer; iuhealth.org/about–iu–health/vendor–relations

# J

**JHHU**
see Johns Hopkins Health System Purchasing Department

**Johns Hopkins Health System Purchasing Department**, Supply Chain Shared Service Center, 3910 Keswick Road, Baltimore, MD 21211; tel. 443/997–0990; FAX. 443/997–5630; Kenneth Grant, Vice President, General Services/Supply Chain Management; www.hopkinsmedicine.org/purchasing

# K

**Kaiser National Purchasing Organization**
see Kaiser Permanente

**Kaiser Permanente**, One Kaiser Plaza, Oakland, CA 94612–3600; tel. 510/271–5860; Barry Brenner, Vice President, Medical and Non–Medical Sourcing; https://healthy.kaiserpermanente.org

**Kansas Department of Administration, Office of Facilities and Procurement Management**, 800 S.W. Jackson, Suite 600, Topeka, KS 66612–1216; tel. 785/296–2376; FAX. 785/296–7240; www.da.ks.gov/purch

**Kindred Healthcare**, 680 South Fourth Street, Louisville, KY 40202; tel. 800/545–0749; Paul J. Diaz, Chief Executive Officer; www.kindredhealthcare.com

# L

**Lake Erie Regional Cooperative**
see ProMedica Supply Chain Management

# M

**Maine Health**
see MaineHealth Purchasing Department

**MaineHealth Purchasing Department**, 22 Bramhall Street, Portland, ME 04102–3175; tel. 207/662–2880; www.mainehealth.org

**Massachusetts Executive Office for Administration and Finance**, State House, Room 373, Boston, MA 02133; tel. 617/727–2040; FAX. 617/727–2779; Glen Shor, Secretary; www.mass.gov/anf

**Med Assets**
see MedAssets, Inc.

**Med–Op, Inc.**, 205 East 7th Street, Suite 133, Hays, KS 67601; tel. 785/621–4510; FAX. 785/621–4511; David Brittain, Executive Director; www.medopinc.com

**MedAssets, Inc.**, 100 North Point Center East, Suite 200, Alpharetta, GA 30022; tel. 888/883–6332; John A. Bardis, Founder, Chairman, President and Chief Executive Officer; www.medassets.com

**Medline Industries, Inc.**, One Medline Place, Mundelein, IL 60060; tel. 800/633–5463; FAX. 800/351–1512; Andy Mills, President; www.medline.com

**MHA Ventures, Inc.**, P. O. Box 5119, Helena, MT 59604; tel. 406/442–1911; FAX. 406/443–3894; Dick Brown, President and Chief Executive Officer; www.mtha.org/ventures1.htm

**Michigan Shared Resource**
see Spectrum Health Regional Hospital Network

**Mid–America Service Solutions**
see VHA, Inc. – Mid–America

**Mid–Atlantic Health Care Network**
see United States Department of Veterans Affairs, VISN 6: Mid–Atlantic Health Care Network

**Minnesota Multi–State Contract Purchasing**
see Minnesota Multistate Contracting Alliance for Pharmacy

**Minnesota Multistate Contracting Alliance for Pharmacy, (MMCAP)**, State of Minnesota, Department of Administration, 50 Sherburne Avenue, St. Paul, MN 55155; tel. 651/201–2420; Alan Dahlgren, Managing Director; www.mmcap.org

**Minnesota Rural Health Alliance**
see Rural Health Alliance

**Missouri Division of Purchasing**
see Missouri Office of Administration, Division of Purchasing & Materials Management

**Missouri Office of Administration, Division of Purchasing & Materials Management**, Harry S Truman State Office Building, 301 West High Street, Jefferson City, MO 65101; tel. 573/751–2387; FAX. 573/526–9815; James Miluski, CPPO, Director; www.oa.mo.gov/purch

**Section C**

## N

**Nevada Healthcare Cooperative**, 1000 Ryland Street, Suite 403, Reno, NV 89502; tel. 775/982–4100; Gary Michealree, President

**New England Alliance for Health**, One Medical Center Drive, Lebanon, NH 03756; tel. 603/650–5340; Stephen J. LeBlanc, Executive Director; www.neahllc.org

**New Jersey Hospital Association**, 760 Alexander Road, P.O. Box 1, Princeton, NJ 08543–0001; tel. 972/910–6676; Susan Revell; www.njha.com/business–services/purchasing–solutions–provista

**New York City Health and Hospitals Corporation, Office of Materials Management**, 346 Broadway, 5th floor West, New York, NY 10013; tel. 212/442–3933; Richard Olah, Acting Senior Director; www.nyc.gov/html/hhc

**New York State Office of General Services**, Corning Tower, 41st floor, Albany, NY 12242; tel. 518/474–3899; RoAnn M. Destito, Commissioner; ogs.ny.gov/default.asp

**New York State Office of Mental Health**, 44 Holland Avenue, Albany, NY 12229; tel. 800/597–8481; FAX. 518/474–2149; Kristin M. Woodlock, RN, MPA, Acting Commissioner; www.omh.ny.gov/index.html

**North Carolina Department of Administration, Division of Purchase & Contract**, 116 West. Jones Street, 4th Floor (Receptionist Office 4062), Raleigh, NC 27603–8002; tel. 919/807–4500; FAX. 919/807–4508; William Sam Byassee, State Purchasing Officer; www.pandc.nc.gov/index.htm

**North Shore–Long Island Jewish Health System, Integrated Distribution Center**, 401 Grumman Road West, Bethpage, NY 11714; tel. 516/465–8100; Pinak Shah, Senior Director, Contracts, Procurement & Distribution/Logistics; www.northshorelij.com/NSLIJ/NSLIJ+HomePage

**Northeast Purchasing Coalition**
see VHA Inc. – New England

**Northern Michigan Supply Alliance, LLC**, 2651 Aero Park Drive, Traverse City, MI 49686; tel. 231/935–8233; Mark Deponio, Vice President; www.nmsa–mi.org

**Northern Plains Premier Collaborative, LLC**, 3900 West Avera Drive, Suite 200, Sioux Falls, SD 57108; tel. 800/657–8095; www.avera.org/pace/group–purchasing/northern–plains–premier–collaborative

**Northwest Ohio Shared Services**, 3230 Central Park West Drive, Suite 206, Toledo, OH 43617; tel. 419/843–8880; FAX. 419/843–8886; John Pilewski, Vice President; www.hcno.org/noss/noss.html

**Novation LLC**, 125 East John Carpenter Freeway, Suite 1400, Irving, TX 75062; tel. 888/766–8283; Jody Hatcher, President and Chief Executive Officer; www.Novationco.com

**NSLIJ**
see North Shore–Long Island Jewish Health System, Integrated Distribution Center

## O

**Office of General Services (NY)**
see New York State Office of General Services

**Office of General Services (OH)**
see Ohio Department of Administrative Services, Office of Procurement Services

**Ohio Department of Administrative Services, Office of Procurement Services**, 4200 Surface Road, Columbus, OH 43228; tel. 614/466–5090; Gretchen Adkins, Chief Procurement Officer; www.das.ohio.gov/Divisions/GeneralServices/ProcurementServices.aspx

**OhioHealth**, 180 East Broad Street, Columbus, OH 43215; tel. 614/544–4455; Bob Boswell, Vice President, Supply Chain; https://www.ohiohealth.com

**OUHSC**
see University of Oklahoma, Purchasing Department

## P

**Pace Premier**
see Avera PACE

**Partners Cooperative, Inc.**, 3625 Cumberland Boulevard, S.E., Suite 1425, Atlanta, GA 30339; tel. 678/842–7300; FAX. 678/842–7329; Karen Becker; www.pcgpo.org

**Partners HealthCare, Materials Management**, 529 Main Street, Charlestown, MA 02129; tel. 617/726–2142; www.partners.org/About/Vendor–Information/Default.aspx

**PeaceHealth Oregon Region**
see Premier Inc.

**Pharmaceutical Prime Vendor**
see DMS Pharmaceutical Group, Inc.

**PR Hospital Association**
see Puerto Rico Hospital Association

**Prairie Health Ventures, LLC**, 421 South 9th Street, Suite 102, Lincoln, NE 68508–2245; tel. 800/409–4990; FAX. 402/476–7422; David Christensen, Chief Executive Officer; www.phvne.com

**Premier Inc.**, 13034 Ballantyne Corporate Place, Charlotte, NC 28277; tel. 877/777–1552; FAX. 704/357–6611; John Biggers, Senior Vice President, Group Purchasing; www.premierinc.com

**PRIME**, 6820 Deerpath Road, Elkridge, MD 21075–6200; tel. 800/899–2199; Amy Ginsberg, Senior Client Manager; www.mhaprime.org

**Prime Med Assets**
see PRIME

**ProMedica Supply Chain Management**, 1695 Indian Wood Circle, Suite 100, Maumee, OH 43537; tel. 419/291–3450; Kathleen Krueger, President, ProMedica Supply Chain Management; supplychain.promedica.org

**Providence Health & Services**, 1801 Lind Avenue, S.W., Suite 9016, Renton, WA 98057; tel. 425/525–3355; John Koster, MD, President and Chief Executive Officer; www2.providence.org

**Provista**, 220 Las Colinas Boulevard East, Irving, TX 75039; tel. 888/538–4662; Dan Thomas, President and Chief Executive Officer; www.provistaco.com

**Puerto Rico Hospital Association**, Villa Nevarez Professional Center, Suite 101, San Juan, PR 00927; tel. 787/764–0290; FAX. 787/753–9748; Jaime Pla Cortes, President; hospitalespr.org

**Purchasing Coalition of PA**
see VHA, Inc. – Mid–Atlantic

## Q

**Quorum Health Resources**
see HealthTrust Purchasing Group, LP

## R

**Rapid City Regional Hospital**
see Regional Health

**Regional Health**, 353 Fairmont Boulevard, Rapid City, SD 57701; tel. 605/719–1000; Charles E. Hart, MD, MS, President and Chief Executive Officer; www.regionalhealth.com

**RHS Materials Management**
see Riverside Health System

**Riverside Health System**, Fountain Plaza One, Suite 1000, Newport News, VA 23606; tel. 757/534–7000; W. William Austin, Jr., Senior Vice President and Chief Financial Officer; www.riversideonline.com/about_riverside/index.cfm

**ROi**, 645 Maryville Centre Drive, Suite 200, St. Louis, MO 63141; tel. 314/364–6400; Gene Kirtser, President and Chief Executive Officer; www.roiscs.com

**Rural Health Alliance**, 1424 South Broadway, Suite 271, Alexandria, MN 56308; tel. 320/762–8602

## S

**Sanford Health**
see Sanford Supply Chain Management

**Sanford Supply Chain Management**, 1305 West 18th Street, P.O. Box 5039, Sioux Falls, SD 57117–5039; tel. 605/333–6490; Ryan Hulme; www.sanfordhealth.org/About/SupplyChain

**SCM Alliance, Inc.**, 19 South Sea Winds Lane, Ponte Vedra Beach, FL 32082; tel. 904/543–8799; John J. Little, Executive Director; www.coalescoinc.com/218-client-scm-alliance,-inc..html

**SCMA Alliance, Inc.**
see SCM Alliance, Inc.

**Seagate Alliance, LLC**, 3445 Winton Place, Suite 222, Rochester, NY 14623–2950; tel. 888/732–4282; FAX. 585/273–8189; Diane H. Ashley, President and Chief Executive Officer; www.seagatealliance.com

**Seneca Medical**, 85 Shaffer Park Drive, P.O. Box 399, Tiffin, OH 44883; tel. 800/447–0225; FAX. 419/447–7201; Roger Benz, President and Chief Executive Officer; www.senecamedical.com/wps/portal/aboutUs

**Servi-Share**
see ServiShare

**ServiShare**, 100 East Grand Avenue, Suite 100, Des Moines, IA 50309–1835; tel. 800/240–1046; FAX. 515/283–9366; Dennis White, Senior Vice President, ServiShare; www.ihaonline.org/iMIS15/IHAOnline/Members_Groups/ServiShare_home.aspx

**Shared Health Services**
see Shared Health Services Corporation

**Shared Health Services Corporation**, 2635 Hemstock Street, La Crosse, WI 54603; tel. 800/657–4445; FAX. 608/781–4412; Wade E. Turner, Executive Director; www.shsc-gpo.com

**Sisters of Mercy Health System**
see ROi

**Spectrum Health**
see Spectrum Health Regional Hospital Network

**Spectrum Health Regional Hospital Network**, 665 Seward Avenue, N.W., Suite 320, Grand Rapids, MI 49504; tel. 616/486–6689; Chris Baskel, Director, System Supply Chain; www.shrhn.org/Home.aspx

**SSMC–Premier**
see Premier Inc.

**St. Mary's Medical Center**, 2900 First Avenue, Huntington, WV 25702; tel. 304/526–1234; Michael G. Sellards, President and Chief Executive Officer; www.st-marys.org

**St. Vincent Health**
see The Resource Group, LLC

**State of California State Purchasing**
see California Department of General Services

**State of Illinois State Purchasing**
see Illinois Department of Central Management Services

**State of Kansas State Purchasing**
see Kansas Department of Administration, Office of Facilities and Procurement Management

**State of Missouri State Purchasing**
see Missouri Office of Administration, Division of Purchasing & Materials Management

**State of North Carolina State Purchasing**
see North Carolina Department of Administration, Division of Purchase & Contract

**State of Ohio State Purchasing**
see Ohio Department of Administrative Services, Office of Procurement Services

**State of Texas State Purchasing**
see Texas Facilities Commission

**State of West Virginia State Purchasing**
see West Virginia Purchasing Division

**Sutter Health**, 2200 River Plaza Drive, Sacramento, CA 95833; tel. 916/733–8800; Dennis Maher, Vice President, Supply Chain Services; www.sutterhealth.org/about/vendors.html

# T

**Tenet Health/Broadlane**
see MedAssets, Inc.

**Texas Facilities Commission**, 1711 San Jacinto, Austin, TX 78701; tel. 512/463–3446; Terry Keel, Executive Director; www.tfc.state.tx.us

**Texas Health Resources, Supply Chain Management Office**, 612 East Lamar Boulevard, Suite 1100, Arlington, TX 76011; tel. 682/236–7517; John Gaida, Senior Vice President, Supply Chain Management; www.texashealth.org/vendorcompliance

**Texas Purchasing Coalition**, 7160 Dallas Parkway, Suite 600, Plano, TX 75024; tel. 469/366–2100; FAX. 469/366–2101; Geoff Brenner, President and Chief Executive Officer; www.texaspurchasingcoalition.com/content/home/?id=1390

**The Resource Group, LLC**, 4600 Edmundson Road, St. Louis, MO 63134; tel. 314/733–8000; Scott Caldwell, Chief Executive Officer; www.ascensionhealth.org

**Trinity Health**, 20555 Victor Parkway, Livonia, MI 48152-7018; tel. 734/343–1000; Louis J. Fierens, II, Senior Vice President, Supply Chain and Capital Projects Management; www.trinity-health.org/supply-chain-management

# U

**UH Supply Chain Services**
see University Hospitals

**UHC**, 155 North Wacker Drive, Chicago, IL 60606; tel. 312/775–4100; Jake Groenewold, Senior Vice President, Supply Chain; https://www.uhc.edu/1408.htm

**UHC/Novation**
see UHC

**United Iroquois Shared Services, Inc.**, 5740 Commons Park, East Syracuse, NY 13057; tel. 315/410–6476; FAX. 315/445–2293; Terry A. Field, Manager, Supply Chain Strategies; www.iroquois.org/Index.aspx?ID=4

**United States Department of Veterans Affairs, VISN 1: VA New England Healthcare System**, 200 Springs Road, Building 61, Bedford, MA 01730; tel. 781/687–4821; FAX. 781/687–3470; Michael F. Mayo-Smith, MD, MPH; www.newengland.va.gov

**United States Department of Veterans Affairs, VISN 2: VA Health Care Upstate New York**, 113 Holland Avenue, Building 67, Albany, NY 12208; tel. 518/626–7327; David J. West, MSHA, FACHE, Network Director; www.visn2.va.gov

**United States Department of Veterans Affairs, VISN 3: VA NY/NJ Veterans Healthcare Network**, 130 West Kingsbridge Road, Bronx, NY 10468; tel. 718/584–9000; FAX. 718/741–4269; Michael A. Sabo, FACHE, Network Director; www.nynj.va.gov

**United States Department of Veterans Affairs, VISN 5: VA Capitol Health Care Network**, 849 International Drive, Suite 275, Linthicum, MD 21090; tel. 410/691–1131; Fernando O. Rivera, MBA, FACHE, Network Director; www.va.gov/visn5

**United States Department of Veterans Affairs, VISN 6: Mid-Atlantic Health Care Network**, 300 West Morgan Street, Suite 700, Durham, NC 27701; tel. 919/956–5541; FAX. 919/956–7152; Daniel F. Hoffmann, FACHE, Network Director; www.visn6.va.gov

**United States Department of Veterans Affairs, VISN 7: VA Southeast Network**, 3700 Crestwood Parkway, Suite 500, Duluth, GA 30096; tel. 678/924–5700; FAX. 678/924–5757; Charles Sepich, FACHE; www.southeast.va.gov

**United States Department of Veterans Affairs, VISN 8: VA Sunshine Healthcare Network**, 140 Fountain Parkway, Suite 600, St. Petersburg, FL 33716; tel. 727/575–8069; FAX. 727/575–8093; Nevin M. Weaver, FACHE, Network Director; www.visn8.va.gov/VISN8/index.asp

**United States Department of Veterans Affairs, VISN 9: VA MidSouth Healthcare Network**, 1801 West End Avenue, Suite 600, Nashville, TN 37203; tel. 615/695–2200; FAX. 615/695–2210; Vicki Kendrick, Interim Network Director; www.visn9.va.gov/about/index.asp

**United States Department of Veterans Affairs, VISN 10: VA Healthcare System of Ohio**; Jack Hetrick, Network Director; www.visn10.va.gov

**United States Department of Veterans Affairs, VISN 11: Veterans in Partnership**, P. O. Box 134002, Ann Arbor, MI 48113-4002; tel. 734/222–4300; FAX. 734/222–4340; www.visn11.va.gov

**United States Department of Veterans Affairs, VISN 12: VA Great Lakes Health Care System**, Four Westbrook Corporate Tower, 11301 West Cermak Road, Westchester, IL 60154; tel. 708/492–3900; FAX. 708/492–3948; Jeffrey A. Murawsky, MD, Network Director; www.visn12.va.gov

**United States Department of Veterans Affairs, VISN 15: VA Heartland Network**, 1201 Walnut Street, Suite 800, Kansas City, MO 64106; tel. 816/701–3000; William P. Patterson, MD, Network Director; www.visn15.va.gov

**United States Department of Veterans Affairs, VISN 16: South Central VA Health Care Network**, 715 South Pear Orchard Road, Plaza 1, Ridgeland, MS 39157; tel. 601/206–6900; FAX. 601/206–7018; Rica Lewis-Peyton, Network Director; www.visn16.va.gov

**United States Department of Veterans Affairs, VISN 17: VA Heart of Texas Health Care Network**, 2301 East Lamar Boulevard, Suite 650, Arlington, TX 76006; tel. 817/652–1111; FAX. 817/385–3700; Lawrence A. Biro, Network Director; www.heartoftexas.va.gov

**United States Department of Veterans Affairs, VISN 18: VA Southwest Health Care Network**, 6950 East Williams Field Road, Mesa, AZ 85212; tel. 602/222–2681; FAX. 602/222–2686; Susan P. Bowers, Network Director; www.southwest.va.gov

**United States Department of Veterans Affairs, VISN 19: Rocky Mountain Network**, 4100 East Mississippi Avenue, Suite 1100, Glendale, CO 80246; tel. 303/756–9279; Ralph T. Gigliotti, Network Director; www.visn19.va.gov

**United States Department of Veterans Affairs, VISN 20: Northwest Network**, P. O. Box 1035, Portland, OR 97207; tel. 360/619–5925; FAX. 360/690–0868; Lawrence H. Carroll, Network Director; www.visn20.med.va.gov

**United States Department of Veterans Affairs, VISN 21: Sierra Pacific Network**, 201 Walnut Avenue, Mare Island, CA 94592; tel. 707562850; FAX. 707/562–8369; Sheila M. Cullen, Director; www.visn21.va.gov/index.asp

**United States Department of Veterans Affairs, VISN 22: Desert Pacific Healthcare Network, NCO 22 Business Resource Center**, 4811 Airport Plaza Drive, Suite 150, Long Beach, CA 90815; tel. 562/766–2295; Prisco Eric Ravelli, Small Business Specialist; www.desertpacific.va.gov

**United States Department of Veterans Affairs, VISN 23: VA Midwest Health Care Network**, 2805 Dodd Road, Suite 250, Eagan, MN 55121; tel. 651/405–5600; FAX. 651/452–0399; Janet P. Murphy, BA, MBA, Network Director; www.visn23.va.gov

**United States Department of Veterans Affairs, VISN 4**, 323 North Shore Drive, Suite 400, Pittsburgh, PA 15212; tel. 412/822 3316; FAX. 412/822–3275; Michael E. Moreland, FACHE, Network Director; www.visn4.va.gov

**United States General Services Administration**, One Constitution Square, 1275 First Street, N.E., Washington, DC 20417; tel. 202/501–0800; Dan M. Tangherlini, Acting Administrator; www.gsa.gov

**Unites States Army Medical Department, Medical Research and Materiel Command, MCMR-PA**, 504 Scott Street, Fort Detrick, MD 21702-5012; tel. 301/619–2736; Brigadier General (Promotable) Joseph Caravalho, Jr., MD, Commanding General; mrmc.amedd.army.mil/index.cfm

**UnityPoint Health**, 1776 West Lakes Parkway, Suite 400, West Des Moines, IA 50266; tel. 515/241–6161; Mark Johnson, Vice President, Supply Management; www.unitypoint.org

**University Hospitals**, 11100 Euclid Avenue, Cleveland, OH 44106; tel. 216/844–1000; www.uhhospitals.org

**University of Iowa, Accounts Payable, Purchasing and Travel Department**, 202 Plaza Centre One, Iowa City, IA 52242; tel. 319/335–0115; FAX. 319/335–2443; Deborah Zumbach, Senior Associate Director - Business Services and Director of Purchasing; www.uiowa.edu/purchasing/p_index.htm

**University of Oklahoma, Purchasing Department**, 2750 Venture Drive, Norman, OK 73069-8279; tel. 405/325–2811; FAX. 405/329–8394; Jan Duke, Associate Director - Purchasing/Property Control; www.ou.edu/purchasing/index.html

**UP Health Care Network**
see Upper Peninsula Health Care Network

**UPMC Supply Chain Management**, 200 Lothrop Street, Pittsburgh, PA 15213-2582; tel. 800/533–8762; www.upmc.com/about/partners/supply-chain/Pages/default.aspx

**Upper Peninsula Health Care Network**, 228 West Washington Street, Suite 2, Marquette, MI 49855; tel. 906/225–3146; FAX. 906/225–7868; Dennis H. Smith, Executive Director; www.uphcn.org

# V

**VHA Inc.**, 220 Las Colinas Boulevard East, Irving, TX 75039; tel. 800/842–5146; Curt Nonomaque, President and Chief Executive Officer; https://www.vha.com

**VHA Inc. - Central**, 8900 Keystone Crossing, Suite 480, Indianapolis, IN 46240; tel. 317/818–8000; https://www.vha.com/AboutVHA/Offices/Central/Pages/Default.aspx

**VHA Inc. - Central Atlantic**, 521 East Morehead Street, Suite 300, Charlotte, NC 28202; tel. 704/377–7140; https://www.vha.com/AboutVHA/Offices/CentralAtlantic/Pages/Default.aspx

**VHA Inc. - Empire-Metro**, 108 Corporate Park Drive, Suite 215, White Plains, NY 10604; tel. 914/251–9201; https://www.vha.com/AboutVHA/Offices/EmpireMetro/Pages/Default.aspx

**VHA Inc. - Georgia**, 900 Circle 75 Parkway, Suite 1450, Atlanta, GA 30339; tel. 770/850–7400; https://www.vha.com/AboutVHA/Offices/Georgia/Pages/Default.aspx

**VHA Inc. - Great Lakes Healthcare Purchasing Network**; Linda Avery; https://www.vha.com/Networking/SupplyNetworks/Documents/GreatLakesHCPurchasingNetwork.pdf

**VHA Inc. - Gulf States, Inc.**, 8940 Bluebonnet Boulevard, Suite 200, Baton Rouge, LA 70810; tel. 225/761–1568; FAX. 225/761–1582; https://www.vha.com/AboutVHA/Offices/GulfStates/Pages/Default.aspx

**VHA Inc. - Mid-America**, 7415 West 130th Street, Suite 200, Overland Park, KS 66213; tel. 913/319–6200; https://www.vha.com/AboutVHA/Offices/MidAmerica/Pages/Default.aspx

**VHA Inc. - Mid-Atlantic**, 8 Neshaminy Interplex, Suite 115, Trevose, PA 19053; tel. 215/245–4888; https://www.vha.com/AboutVHA/Offices/Midatlantic/Pages/default.aspx

**VHA Inc. - New England**, 350 Granite Street, Suite 2304, Braintree, MA 02184; tel. 781/794–6500; FAX. 781/794–6529; https://www.vha.com/AboutVHA/Offices/NewEngland/Pages/Default.aspx

**VHA Inc. - Oklahoma/Arkansas**, 4013 Northwest Expressway, Suite 675, Oklahoma City, OK 73116; tel. 405/440–8900; https://www.vha.com/AboutVHA/Offices/OKAR/Pages/Default.aspx

**VHA Inc. - Pacific Northwest**, 1600 Lind Avenue, S.W., Suite 180, Renton, WA 98057; tel. 425/277–3902; https://www.vha.com/AboutVHA/Offices/PacificNW/Pages/default.aspx

**VHA Inc. - Southeast, Inc.**, 4211 West Boy Scout Boulevard, Suite 750, Tampa, FL 33607; tel. 813/350–8300; FAX. 813/350–8383; https://www.vha.com/AboutVHA/Offices/Southeast/Pages/Default.aspx

**VHA Inc. - Upper Midwest**, 7601 France Avenue South, Suite 500, Edina, MN 55435; tel. 952/837–4700; https://www.vha.com/AboutVHA/Offices/UpperMidwest/Pages/Default.aspx

**VHA Inc. - West Coast**, 4900 Hopyard Road, Suite 320, Pleasanton, CA 94588; tel. 888/619–1900; https://www.vha.com/AboutVHA/Offices/WestCoast/Pages/Default.aspx

**Via Christi Health**, 929 Saint Francis Street, Wichita, KS 67214-3882; tel. 316/268–5000; Cal Frye, Corporate Director, Supply Chain Management; www.via-christi.org

**Virginia Department of General Services, Division of Purchases and Supply**, 1111 East Broad Street, P.O. Box 1199, Richmond, VA 23218-1922; tel. 804/786–3846; FAX. 804/371–7877; dgs.virginia.gov/DivisionofPurchasesandSupply

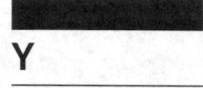

# W

**West Virginia Purchasing Division**, 2019 Washington Street, East, P. O. Box 50130, Charleston, WV 25305; tel. 304/558–2306; FAX. 304/558–6026; David Tincher, Purchasing Director; www.state.wv.us/admin/purchase/default.html

**Western New York Purchasing Alliance**
see ALTUS Management LLC

**Wisconsin Valley Health Network, LLC**, 3000 Westhill Drive, Suite 300, Wausau, WI 54401; tel. 800/283–2881

**WNC Health Network**, 1200 Ridgefield Boulevard, Suite 200, Asheville, NC 28806; tel. 877/667–8220; FAX. 828/667–8228; Janice Lato, President and Chief Executive Officer; www.wnchn.org

**WNCHN**
see WNC Health Network

**WSCA-NASPO Cooperative Purchasing Organization, LLC**, 201 East Main Street, Suite 1405, Lexington, KY 40507; tel. 859/514–9159; FAX. 859/514–9188; Lee Ann Pope, WSCA-NASPO Program Manager; www.aboutwsca.org

# Y

**Yankee Alliance**, 138 River Road, Andover, MA 01810-1083; tel. 978/470–2000; FAX. 978/681–6100; James W. Oliver, President and Chief Executive Officer; www.yankeealliance.com

# Quality Improvement Organizations

*The following list of QIOs was obtained from the agencies themselves and the Centers for Medicare and Medicaid Services, Quality Improvement Organization programs.*

## United States

**ALABAMA: Alabama Quality Assurance Foundation,** Two Perimeter Park, S., Suite 200 West, Birmingham, AL 35243-2337; tel. 205/970–1600; FAX. 205/970–1616; Wesley Smith, Chief Executive Officer

**ALASKA: Mountain-Pacific Quality Health-Alaska QIO,** 4241 B Street, Suite 101, Anchorage, AK 99503; tel. 907/561–3202; FAX. 907/561–3204; Sharon C. Scudder, Office Director

**ARIZONA: Health Services Advisory Group, Inc.,** 3133 E. Camelback, Suite 300, Phoenix, AZ 85016; tel. 602/264–6222; FAX. 602/241–0757; Mary Ellen Dalton, PhD, MBA, RN, Chief Executive Officer

**ARKANSAS: Arkansas Foundation for Medical Care, Inc.,** 1020 W 4th Street, Suite 300, Little Rock, AR 72201; tel. 501/212–8660; FAX. 501/374–2826; Ray Hanley, President and Chief Executive Officer

**CALIFORNIA: Health Services Advisory Group of California,** 700 N. Brand Boulevard, Suite 370, Glendale, CA 91203; tel. 818/409–9229; FAX. 818/409–0835; Rick Potter, Chief Executive Officer

**COLORADO: Colorado Foundation for Medical Care,** 23 Inverness Way East, Suite 100, Englewood, CO 80112; tel. 303/695–3300; FAX. 303/695–3343; Arja P. Adair, Jr., President and Chief Executive Officer

**CONNECTICUT: Qualidigm,** 1111 Cromwell Avenue, Suite 201, Rocky Hill, CT 06067; tel. 860/632–2008; FAX. 860/632–5865; Marcia K. Petrillo, Chief Executive Officer

**DELAWARE: Quality Insights of Delaware,** Baynard Building Suite 100, 3411 Silverside Rd, Wilmington, DE 19810; tel. 302/478–3600; FAX. 302/478–4109; John C. Wiesendanger, Chief Executive Officer

**DISTRICT OF COLUMBIA: Delmarva Foundation of the District of Columbia,** 2175 K Street, NW, Suite 250, Washington, DC 20037; tel. 800/937–3362; FAX. 202/293–9650; Fredia S. Wadley, Chief Executive Officer

**FLORIDA: Florida Medical Quality Assurance. Inc.,** 5201 W. Kennedy Boulevard, Suite 900, Tampa, FL 33609; tel. 813/354–9111; FAX. 813/354–1319; Tony Freedman, Chief Executive Officer

**GEORGIA: Alliant Georgia Meidical Care Foundation,** 1455 Lincoln Parkway, Suite 800, Atlanta, GA 30346; tel. 678/527–3000; FAX. 404/982–7591; Dennis White, President and Chief Executive Officer

**HAWAII: Mountain-Pacific Quality Health - Hawaii,** 1360 South Beretania Street, Suite 501, Honolulu, HI 96814; tel. 808/545–2550; FAX. 808/440–6030; Dee Dee Nelson, Director of Hawaii Office

**IDAHO: Qualis Health,** 720 Park Boulevard, Suite 120, Boise, ID 83712-7756; tel. 208/343–4617; FAX. 208/343–4705; Linda Rowe, MS, Director, Idaho Care Transitions and Patient Safety

**ILLINOIS: Telligen,** 711 Jorie Blvd, Oak Brook, IL 60523-4425; tel. 630/928–5800; FAX. 630/928–5865; Pat Merryweather, Chief Executive Officer

**INDIANA: Health Care Excel, Incorporated,** 2629 Waterfront Parkway East Drive, Suite 150, Indianapolis, IN 46214; tel. 317/347–4500; FAX. 317/347–4567; Joy Casterton, Chief Executive Officer

**IOWA: Telligen,** 1776 West Lakes Parkway, West Des Moines, IA 50266; tel. 515/223–2900; FAX. 515/222–2407; Jeff Chungath, Chief Executive Officer

**KANSAS: The Kansas Foundation for Medical Care, Inc.,** 2947 Southwest Wanamaker Drive, Topeka, KS 66614; tel. 785/273–2552; FAX. 785/273–0737; Kenneth Mishler, President and Chief Executive Officer

**KENTUCKY: Health Care Excel of Kentucky, Incorporated,** 1941 Bishop Lane, Suite 400, Louisville, KY 40218; tel. 502/454–5112; FAX. 502/454–5113; Joy Casterton, Chief Executive Officer

**LOUISIANA: eQHealth Solutions,** 8591 United Plaza Blvd, Suite 270, Baton Rouge, LA 70809; tel. 225/248–7003; FAX. 225/923–0957; Edie Castello, Chief Executive Officer

**MARYLAND: Delmarva Foundation for Medical Care, Inc.,** 6940 Columbia Gateway Drive, Suite 420, Columbia, MD 21046; tel. 443/285–0190; FAX. 410/763–6250; Fredia S. Wadley, MD, Chief Executive Officer

**MASSACHUSETTS: Masspro,** 245 Winter Street, Waltham, MA 02451-1231; tel. 781/890–0011; FAX. 781/487–0083; Laura Moore, MPA, President and Chief Executive Officer

**MICHIGAN: MPRO,** 22670 Haggerty Rd, Suite 100, Farmington Hills, MI 48335-2611; tel. 248/465–7300; FAX. 248/465–7428; Robert J. Yellan, President and Chief Executive Officer

**MINNESOTA: Stratis Health,** 2901 Metro Drive, Suite 400, Bloomington, MN 55425; tel. 952/854–3306; FAX. 952/853–8503; Jennifer Lundblad, PhD, MBA, Chief Executive Officer

**MISSISSIPPI: Information & Quality Healthcare,** 385 B Highland Colony Parkway, Suite 504, Ridgeland, MS 39157; tel. 601/957–1575; FAX. 601/956–1713; James McIlwain, MD, President

**MISSOURI: Primaris,** 200 N. Keene Street, Suite 101, Columbia, MO 65201; tel. 573/817–8300; FAX. 573/777–9039; Richard A. Royer, Chief Executive Officer

**MONTANA: Mountain-Pacific Quality Health - Montana,** 3404 Cooney Drive, Helena, MT 59602; tel. 406/443–4020; FAX. 406/513–1920; Sara Medley, Chief Executive Officer

**NEBRASKA: CIMRO of Nebraska,** 1230 O Street, Suite 120, Lincoln, NE 68508; tel. 402/476–1399; FAX. 402/476–1335; Tina Georgy, Chief Executive Officer

**NEVADA: HealthInsight,** 6830 W Oquendo Road, Suite 102, Las Vegas, NV 89118; tel. 702/385–9933; FAX. 702/385–4586; Marc Bennett, MA, President and Chief Executive Officer

**NEW HAMPSHIRE: Northeast Health Care Quality Foundation,** 15 Old Rollinsford Road, Suite 302, Dover, NH 03820-2830; tel. 603/749–1641; FAX. 603/749–1195; Robert A. Aurilio, FACHE, President and Chief Executive Officer

**Northeast Health Care Quality Foundation - Maine,** 15 Old Rollingsford Road, Suite 302, Dover, NH 03820; tel. 603/749–1641; FAX. 603/749–1195; Robert A. Aurilio, FACHE, Chief Executive Officer

**Northeast Health Care Quality Foundation - Vermont,** 15 Old Rollingsford Road, Suite 302, Dover, NH 03820; tel. 603/749–1641; FAX. 603/749–1195; Robert A. Aurilio, FACHE, Chief Executive Officer

**NEW JERSEY: Healthcare Quality Strategies, Inc.,** 557 Cranbury Road, Suite 21, East Brunswick, NJ 08816; tel. 732/238–5570; FAX. 732/432–5647; Mary Jane Brubaker, Chief Operating Officer Mary Jane Brubaker, Chief Operating Officer

**NEW MEXICO: HealthInsight New Mexico,** 5801 Osuna RD NE, Suite 200, Albuquerque, NM 87109; tel. 505/998–9898; FAX. 505/998–9899; Richard Kozoll, MD, MPH, President, Board of Directors

**NEW YORK: IPRO,** 1979 Marcus Avenue, Lake Success, NY 11042-1002; tel. 516/326–7767; FAX. 516/328–2310; Theodore O. Will, Chief Executive Officer

**NORTH CAROLINA: The Carolinas Center for Medical Excellence,** 100 Regency Forest Drive, Suite 200, Cary, NC 27518-8598; tel. 919/461–5500; FAX. 919/461–5700; Charles Riddick, Chief Executive Officer

**NORTH DAKOTA: North Dakota Health Care Review Inc. (NDHCRI),** 3520 North Broadway, Minot, ND 58703; tel. 701/852–4231; FAX. 701/857–9755; Barbara Groutt, Chief Executive Officer

**OHIO: Ohio KePRO, Inc.,** Rock Run Center, Suite 100, 5700 Lombardo Center Drive, Seven Hills, OH 44131; tel. 216/503–5759; FAX. 216/447–7925; Rita Bowling, RN,MSN, MBA, CPHQ, Project Director

**OKLAHOMA: Oklahoma Foundation for Medical Quality,** 14000 Quail Springs Parkway, Suite 400, Oklahoma City, OK 73134; tel. 405/840–2891; FAX. 405/840–1343; Gregg Koehn, CPA, President and Chief Executive Officer

**OREGON: Acumentra Health,** 2020 SW Fourth Avenue, Suite 520, Portland, OR 97201-4960; tel. 503/279–0100; FAX. 503/279–0190; Jon Mitchell, FACHE, President and Chief Executive Officer

**PENNSYLVANIA: Quality Insights of Pennsylvania,** 2601 Market Place Street, Suite 320, Harrisburg, PA 17110; tel. 717/671–5425; FAX. 717/671–5970; John C. Wiesendanger, Chief Executive Officer

**RHODE ISLAND: Healthcentric Advisors, formerly Quality Partners of Rhode Island,** 235 Promenade Street, Suite 500, Providence, RI 02908; tel. 401/528–3200; FAX. 401/528–3210; H. John Keimig, MHA, FACHE, President and Chief Executive Officer

**SOUTH CAROLINA: The Carolinas Center for Medical Excellence,** 246 Stoneridge Dr, Suite 200, Columbia, SC 29210; tel. 803/212–7500; FAX. 803/212–7600; Melinda Postal, Director of Communications

**SOUTH DAKOTA: South Dakota Foundation for Medical Care,** 2600 West 49th Street, Suite 300, Sioux Falls, SD 57105; tel. 605/336–3505; FAX. 605/373–0580; Mark Hoven, Chief Executive Officer

**TENNESSEE: Qsource,** 3340 Players Club Pkwy, Suite 300, Memphis, TN 38125; tel. 800/528–2655; FAX. 901/761–3786; Dawn FitzGerald, Chief Operating Officer

**TEXAS: TMF, Health Quality Institute,** Bridgepoint 1, Suite 300, 5918 West Courtyard Drive, Austin, TX 78730-5036; tel. 512/329–6610; FAX. 512/327–7159; Thomas Manley, President and Chief Executive Officer

**UTAH: HealthInsight Utah,** 756 East Winchester Street, Suite 200, Salt Lake City, UT 84107; tel. 801/892–0155; FAX. 801/892–0160; Marc Bennett, President and Chief Executive Officer

**VIRGINIA: VHQC,** 9830 Mayland Drive, Suite J, Richmond, VA 23233; tel. 804/289–5320; FAX. 804/289–5324; Donald A. Glozer, MHA, CHE, President and Chief Executive Officer

**WASHINGTON: Qualis Health,** 10700 Meridian Avenue, N., Suite 100, Seattle, WA 98133-9075; tel. 206/364–9700; FAX. 206/368–2419; Jonathan Sugarman, President and Chief Executive Officer

**WEST VIRGINIA: WVMI & Quality Insights,** 3001 Chesterfield Avenue, Charleston, WV 25304; tel. 304/346–9864; FAX. 304/346–9863; John Wiesendanger, MHA, Chief Executive Officer

**WISCONSIN: MetaStar, Inc.,** 2909 Landmark Place, Madison, WI 53713; tel. 608/274–1940; FAX. 608/274–5008; Greg E. Simmons, President and Chief Executive Officer

**WYOMING: Mountain-Pacific Quality Health - Wyoming,** 145 S. Durbin, Suite 105, Casper, WY 82601; tel. 307/472–0507; FAX. 307/472–1791; Deborah Fleming, Office Director

Section C

# U.S. Associated Areas

**PUERTO RICO: Quality Improvement Professional Research Organization,** View Plaza Torre I, Suite 412, Guaynabo, PR 00968; tel. 787/641–1240; FAX. 787/641–1248; Jose Robles, Chief Executive Officer

**VIRGIN ISLANDS: Virgin Islands Medical Institute, Inc.,** 1AD Estate Diamond Ruby, PO Box 5989, Christiansted, VI 00823-5989; tel. 340/712–2400; FAX. 340/712–2449; M. "Rikki" Nelthropp, Chief Executive Officer

# Health Information Exchanges

*The following list of Health Information Exchanges (HIEs) is based on information provided by the exchanges themselves. Inclusion or omission of any organization's name indicates neither approval nor disapproval by Health Forum, LLC, an American Hospital Association company.*

## United States

**ALABAMA: Alabama Health Information Exchange, Alabama Medicaid Agency,** PO Box 5624, 501 Dexter Avenue, Montgomery, AL 36103-5624; tel. 334/242–5011; FAX. 334/353–4818; Kim Davis-Allen, Director of Transformation Initiatives

**ALASKA: Alaska eHealth Network,** 4120 Laurel Street, Suite 102, Anchorage, AK 99508; tel. 866/966–9030; Rebecca Madison, Executive Director; ak-ehealth.org

**ARIZONA: Arizona Health-e Connection,** 3877 N. 7th Street, Suite 130, Phoenix, AZ 85014; tel. 602/688–7200; FAX. 602/264–8823; Melissa Rutala, Chief Executive Officer; www.azhec.org
**Health Information Network of Arizona,** 3480 E. Britannia Drive, Suite 120, Tucson, AZ 85706; tel. 520/309–2944; Kalyanraman Bharathan, Executive Director, Corporate Privacy Officer

**ARKANSAS: Arkansas Office of Health Information Technology (OHIT),** 1401 W. Capitol Ave., Victory Building, Plaza G, Little Rock, AR; tel. 501/410–1999; Shirley Tyson, Chief Operations and Technical Officer; ohit.arkansas.gov
**HITArkansas, Arkansas Foundation for Medical Care,** 1020 West 4th Street, Suite 420, Little Rock, AR 72201; tel. 501/212–8616; FAX. 501/212–8689; Jonathan M. Fuchs, FACHE, Chief Operating Officer; www.hitarkansas.com

**CALIFORNIA: California eHealth Collaborative,** 1966 Tice Valley Boulevard #144, Walnut Creek, CA 94595; tel. 415/260–6277; Lori Hack, MBA, Chief Executive Officer; caehc.org
**State of California Office of Health Information Integrity,** 1600 9th Street, Room 460, Sacremento, CA 95814; tel. 916/654–3454; FAX. 916/653–9588; Pamela Lane, Deputy Secretary for HIE; www.ohii.ca.gov

**COLORADO: CORHIO, Colorado Regional Health Information Organization,** 4500 Cherry Creek South Drive, Suite 820, Denver, CO 80246; tel. 720/285–3200; FAX. 720/285–3205; Larry Wolk, MD, MSPH, Chief Executive Director; www.corhio.org

**CONNECTICUT: eHealth Connecticut,** 1290 Silas Deane Highway, Suite 4A, Wethersfield, CT 06109; tel. 860/240–5617; FAX. 860/278–2400; Scott Cleary, Program Manager; www.ehealthconnecticut.org
**Health Information Exchange Program, Connecticut Department of Public Health,** 410 Capitol Avenue, MS#13PLN, Hartford, CT 06134; tel. 860/509–8000; Vanessa Kapral, Chief, Information Technology

**DELAWARE: Delaware Health Information Network,** 107 Wolf Creek Boulevard, Suite 2, Dover, DE 19901; tel. 302/678–0220; FAX. 302/645–0398; Dr. Jan Lee, Executive Director; www.dhin.org

**FLORIDA: Big Bend Regional Healthcare Information Organization (BBRHIO),** 3411 Capital Medical Boulevard, Tallahassee, FL 32308; tel. 850/702–0365; Allen Byington, Executive Director; www.bigbendhealth.com
**Central Florida RHIO,** 4401 Vineland Rd., Suite A-10, Orlando, FL 32811; tel. 407/425–9500; FAX. 407/425–9559; Michael Kovner, Project Director; www.centralfloridarhio.org
**Florida Health Information Network, Agency for Health Care Administration,** 2727 Mahan Drive, Tallahassee, FL 32308; tel. 850/922–7036; FAX. 850/414–7831; Christine Nye, Director; www.fhin.net
**Health Network of the Palm Beaches, Inc.,** 3540 Forest Hill Blvd, Suite 101, West Palm Beach, FL 33406; tel. 561/433–3940; FAX. 561/433–2385; www.pbccha.org
**North East Florida Regional Health Organization, Inc.,** 6484 Ft. Caroline Road, Jacksonville, FL 32277; tel. 904/731–0221; Mark Renfro, Administrator; www.nefrho.org

**SunCoast RHIO,** 5020 Clark Road, #127, Sarasota, FL 34233; tel. 941/426–6093; Lee S. Gross, MD, Consultant; www.suncoastrhio.com

**GEORGIA: GA Health Information Exchange,** 2 Peachtree Street, Atlanta, GA 30303; tel. 404/656–7282; FAX. 770/344–4035; Archie Banks, Director Office of Information Technology and Transparency; www.dch.georgia.gov

**HAWAII: Hawaii Health Information Corp. (HHIC),** 733 Bishop Street, Suite 1870, Makai Tower, Honolulu, HI 96813-4002; tel. 808/534–0288; FAX. 808/534–0292; Deborah Higashi, Operations Manager; www.hhic.org
**Hawaii Health Information Exchange,** 900 Fort Street Mall, Suite 1305, Honolulu, HI 96813; tel. 808/441–1310; FAX. 808/441–1472; Gregory Suenaga, State HIE Project Director

**IDAHO: Idaho Health Data Exchange,** 450 W. State Street, PO Box 6978, Boise, ID 83707; tel. 208/332–7253; FAX. 208/332–7217; Scott Carrell, Executive Director; www.idahohde.org

**ILLINOIS: Illinois Health Information Exchange Authority,** JRTC 100 W. Randolph, Suite 4-750, Chicago, IL 60601; tel. 312/814–1255; Raul Recarey, ILHIE Authority Executive Director; www2.illinois.gov/gov/HIE
**Illinois Office of Health Information Technology,** 100 W. Randolph Street, 2-201, Chicago, IL 60601; tel. 312/814–1600; FAX. 312/814–1468; Laura Zaremba, Director/State HIT Coordinator; www.hie.illinois.gov

**INDIANA: Indiana Health Information Exchange,** 846 N. Senate Avenue, Suite 110, Indianapolis, IN 46202; tel. 317/644–1750; FAX. 317/644–1751; Harold Apple, President and Chief Executive Officer; www.ihie.org
**Indiana Health Information Technology, Inc. (IHIT),** 402 W. Washington Street, W451, Indianapolis, IN 46204; tel. 317/232–1165; Andrew VanZee, Health IT Director; www.indianahealthit.com

**IOWA: Iowa e-Health, Iowa Department of Public Health,** Lucas Building, 321 E. 12th Street, Des Moines, IA 50319; tel. 866/924–4636; FAX. 515/281–4958; Kim Norby, Executive Director; www.iowaehealth.org

**KANSAS: Kansas Health Information Exchange, Inc.,** P.O. Box 4769, Topeka, KS 66604; tel. 785/246–6376; Bill Wallace, Chief Executive Officer; www.khie.org

**LOUISIANA: Louisiana Health Care Quality Forum,** 8550 United Plaza Blvd, Suite 500, Baton Rouge, LA 70809; tel. 225/334–9299; FAX. 225/334–9847; Nadine Robin, HIT Program Manager; www.lhcqf.org

**MAINE: HealthInfoNet,** 125 Presumpscot Street, Box 8, Portland, ME 04103; tel. 207/541–9250; FAX. 207/541–9258; Devore Culver, Executive Director and Chief Executive Officer; www.hinfonet.org
**Office for Health Information Technology,** 242 State Street, Augusta, ME 04333; tel. 207/287–4532; James Leonard, Deputy Director; www.maine.gov/hit

**MARYLAND: Chesapeake Regional Information System for Our Patients, CRISP,** 7160 Columbia Gateway Drive, Suite 230, Columbia, MD 21046; tel. 877/952–7477; FAX. 443/817–9587; David Horrocks, President; www.crisphealth.org

**MASSACHUSETTS: Massachusetts eHealth Institute,** 2 Center Plaza Suite 200, Boston, MA 02108-19046; tel. 617/371–3999; FAX. 617/725–8939; Laurance Stuntz, Director; www.mehi.masstech.org
**Massachusetts Health Data Consortium,** 460 Totten Pond Rd., Suite 690, Waltham, MA 02451; tel. 781/419–7800; FAX. 781/795–0155; Denny Brennan, Executive Director and Chief Executive Officer; www.mahealthdata.org

**MINNESOTA: MN e-Health Initiative, Minnesota Department of Health,** 85 E. Seventh Place, Suite 220, St. Paul, MN 55164; tel. 651/201–4856; FAX. 651/201–3830; Bob Johnson, Senior Planner; www.health.state.mn.us/e-health

**MISSISSIPPI: Mississippi Health Information Network (MS-HIN),** MS; Candice Whitfield, HIT Coordinator; www.ms-hin.ms.gov

**MISSOURI: Missouri Health Connection,** 3501 Berrywood Drive, Columbia, MO 65201; tel. 573/777–4550; Mary Kasal, Chief Executive Officer; missourihealthconnection.worldsecuresystems.com

**MONTANA: HealthShare Montana,** 2475 Village Lane, Suite 302, Billings, MT 59102; tel. 406/794–0170; FAX. 406/248–9373; Brad Putnam, Executive Director; www.healthsharemontana.org

**NEBRASKA: eHealth Council, Nebraska Information Technology Commission,** 501 S. 14th Street, 4th Floor, P.O. Box 95045, Lincoln, NE 68509-5045; tel. 402/471–3560; FAX. 402/471–4864; Anne Byers, Project Manager; www.nitc.nebraska.gov/eHc

**NEVADA: HealthInsight,** 6830 W. Oquendo Road, Suite 102, Las Vegas, NV 89118; tel. 702/385–9933; FAX. 702/385–4586; Marc Bennett, President and Chief Executive Officer; www.healthinsight.org
**Nevada Health Information Exchange, Office of Health Information Technology,** 1000 E. William Street, Room 209, Carson City, NV 89701-3117; tel. 775/684–7591; FAX. 775/684–7590; Lynn G. O'Mara, MBA, Nevada State Health IT Coordinator; dhhs.nv.gov/HIT.htm

**NEW HAMPSHIRE: Health Information Exchange, NH Health Information Organization (NHHIO),** 125 Airport Road, Concord, NH 03301; tel. 603/219–0184; FAX. 603/218–6216; Jeff Loughlin; Acting Executive Director
**NH Citizen's Health Initiative,** 501 South Street, 2nd Floor, Bow, NH 03304; tel. 603/573–3373; Jeanne Ryer, Executive Director; www.steppingupnh.org; www.citizenshealthinitiative.org

**NEW JERSEY: New Jersey Health Information Technology Commission, New Jersey Department of Health & Senior Services,** PO Box 360, Trenton, NJ 08625-0360; tel. 609/292–9382; Emmanouil Skoufos, PhD, Executive Director; www.state.nj.us/health/bc/hitc.shtml

**NEW MEXICO: LCF Research,** 2309 Renard Place SE, Suite 103, Albuquerque, NM 87106; tel. 505/938–9900; FAX. 505/938–9940; Craig W. Hewitt, Interim Chief Executive Officer; www.lcfresearch.org
**New Mexico Health Information Collaborative (NMHIC),** 2309 Renard Place SE, Suite 103, Albuquerque, NM 87106; tel. 505/938–9904; FAX. 505/938–9940; Jeff Blair, MBA, Director of Health Informatics; www.nmhic.org

**NEW YORK: Healthcare Information Xchange of New York (HIXNY),** 15 Cornell Road, Latham, NY 12110; tel. 518/783–0518; FAX. 518/785–3101; Mark McKinney, Chief Executive Officer; www.hixny.org
**New York eHealth Collaborative (NYeC),** 40 Worth Street, 5th Floor, New York, NY 10013; tel. 646/619–6400; Dave Whitlinger, Executive Director; nyehealth.org

**NORTH CAROLINA: NC Health Information Exchange,** 2300 Rexwoods Drive, Suite 390, Raleigh, NC 27607; tel. 919/926–1042; Michael Jongkind, Interim Chief Executive Officer; nchie.org
**NC Healthcare Information and Communications Alliance, Inc. (NCHICA),** 3200 East NC Highway 54, Cape Fear Building, Suite 200, Research Triangle Park, NC 27709-3048; tel. 919/558–9258; FAX. 919/558–2198; Holt Anderson, Executive Director; www.nchica.org

**NORTH DAKOTA: North Dakota Health Information Network,** 600 E. Boulevard Avenue, Dept. 112, Bismark, ND 58505-0100; tel. 701/328–1991; FAX. 701/328–3000; Sheldon H. Wolf, Director; www.ndhin.org

**OHIO: CliniSync, Ohio Health Information Partnership,** 3455 Mill Run Drive, Suite 315, Hilliard, OH 43026; tel. 614/664–2600; FAX. 888/390–7274; Dan Paoletti, Chief Executive Officer; www.clinisync.org

**OREGON: Oregon Health Information Technology Oversight Council (HITOC),** 500 Summer Street Ste E52, Salem, OR 97301; tel. 503/373–7859; FAX. 503/378–5511; Carol Robinson, Director; www.oregon.gov/OHPPR/HITOC/index.shtml

**PENNSYLVANIA: Pennsylvania eHealth Initiative,** c/o The Hospital & Healthsystem Association of Pennsylvania, 4750 Lindle Road, Suite 228, Harrisburg, PA 17105; tel. 717/561–5338; FAX. 717/561–5216; Chris Cavanaugh, PAeHI Executive Director; www.paehi.org

**RHODE ISLAND: Rhode Island Health Information Exchange, Rhode Island Quality Institute,** 50 Holden Street, Suite 300, Providence, RI 02908; tel. 401/276–9141; FAX. 401/276–9144; Laura Adams, President and Chief Executive Officer; www.riqi.org

**SOUTH DAKOTA: South Dakota Health Link, South Dakota Department of Health,** 820 N. Washington Ave., Madison, SD 57042; tel. 605/256–5555; Kevin DeWald, State Health IT Coordinator; www.sdhealthlink.org

**TENNESSEE: Office of eHealth Initiatives,** 310 Great Circle Road, Fourth floor, East, Nashville, TN 37243; tel. 615/507–6406; FAX. 615/532–2849; Will Rice, Director; www.tn.gov/ehealth

**TEXAS: Greater Houston Health Information Exchange,** 1310 Prairie Street, Suite 1080, Houston, TX 77002; Kay Carr, President and Chief Executive Officer; www.ghhie.org

**miRHIO, Southeast Texas Health System,** PO Box 947, Goliad, TX 77963-0947; tel. 361/645–1762; FAX. 361/645–1743; Shannon Calhoun, Executive Director; www.mirhio.com

**Statewide Health Coordinating Council, Texas State Health Plan, Department of State Health Services,** 1100 W. 49th Street, M-660, PO Box 149347, MC 1898, Austin, TX 78714-9347; tel. 512/776–3548; FAX. 512/776–7344; Bobby D. Schmidt, M.Ed., Project Director; www.dshs.state.tx.us/chs/shcc

**Texas Health Services Authority, Texas Health Information Exchange,** 221 E. 9th, Suite 201, Austin, TX 78701; tel. 512/814–0321; FAX. 512/814–0322; Tony Gilman, Chief Executive Officer; hietexas.org

**UTAH: Utah Health Information Network,** 151 E. 5600 South, Suite 320, Murray, UT 84107; tel. 801/466–7705; FAX. 801/466–7169; Levi Woodruff, Communications Coordinator; www.uhin.org

**VERMONT: Vermont Information Technology Leaders (VITL),** 144 Main Street, Suite 1, Montpelier, VT 05602; tel. 802/233–4100; FAX. 802/223–4100; John K. Evans, President and Chief Executive Officer; www.vitl.net

**VIRGINIA: Health Information Technology Spotlight (HITS),** 109 Governor Street, Richmond, VA 23219; tel. 804/864–7661; Kim Barnes, Director of Health IT; www.hits.virginia.gov

**WASHINGTON: Washington State Health Care Authority,** 626 8th Avenue SE, Olympia, WA 98504-2710; tel. 360/725–0859; Melodie Olsen, Health Information Exchange; www.hca.wa.gov/hit

**WEST VIRGINIA: WV Health Information Network (WVHIN),** 100 Dee Drive, Charleston, WV 25311; tel. 304/558–4503; FAX. 304/558–2734; Phil Weikle, Chief Operations Officer; www.wvhin.org

**WISCONSIN: Wisconsin Statewide Health Information Network (WISHIN),** PO Box 259038, Madison, WI 53725; tel. 608/274–1820; FAX. 608/274–8554; Joseph Kachelski, Chief Executive Officer; www.wishin.org

**WYOMING: Wyoming Health Information Organization (WyHIO),** 109 E. 17th Street, Cheyenne, WY 82001; tel. 307/432–4025; Larry Biggio, Executive Director; www.wyhio.org

**Wyoming Health Information Technology,** 2001 Capitol Avenue, Emerson Building #237, Cheyenne, WY 82002; tel. 307/777–5282; Dallas Lain, HIT Coordinator; www.wyominghit.org

# Other Health Care Providers

## Freestanding Ambulatory Surgery Centers

The following list of freestanding ambulatory surgery centers was developed with the assistance of state government agencies and the individual facilities listed.

The AHA Guide contains two types of ambulatory surgery center listings; those that are hospital based and those that are freestanding. Hospital based ambulatory surgery centers are listed in section A of the AHA Guide and are identified by Facility Code F8 and F71.

We present this list simply as a convenient directory. Inclusion or omission of any organization's name indicates neither approval nor disapproval by Health Forum LLC, an American Hospital Association company.

## United States

### ALABAMA
**Birmingham Surgery Center, Inc.,** 2621 19th Street, South, Homewood, AL 35209; tel. 205/271–8200; Kathy Sands, RN, Administrator

**Dothan Surgery Center,** 1450 Ross Clark Circle, SE, Suite 4, Dothan, AL 36301; tel. 334/793–3442; FAX. 334/793–3318; W. Berry Sowell, Chief Executive Officer and Administrator

**Florence Surgery Center, L.P.,** 103 Helton Court, Florence, AL 35630; tel. 256/760–0672; FAX. 256/766–4547; Jennifer Lathram, Administrator

**Gadsden Surgery Center,** 418 South Fifth Street, Gadsden, AL 35901; tel. 256/543–1253; FAX. 256/543–1260; Harriet Willoughby, Administrator

**Huntsville Endoscopy Center, Inc.,** 119 Longwood Drive, Huntsville, AL 35801; tel. 256/533–6488; FAX. 256/532–2238; Dalia Biggerstaff, RN, Clinical Director

**Montgomery Eye Surgery Center,** 2752 Zelda Road, Montgomery, AL 36106; tel. 334/270–9677; FAX. 334/213–0622; Deborah Cauthen, Administrator

**Montgomery Surgical Center,** 4/0 Taylor Road, Montgomery, AL 36117; tel. 334/284–9600; FAX. 334/284–4233; Linda Westhoff, Interim Administrator

**Outpatient Services East, Inc.,** 52 Medical Park Drive, E., Suite 401, Birmingham, AL 35235; tel. 205/838–3888; FAX. 205/314–2469; H. Alan Perry, President, Chairman of the Board

**The Kirklin Clinic,** 2000 Sixth Avenue, S., Birmingham, AL 35233; tel. 205/801–8000; Reid F. Jones, EVP and Sr. VP for Ambulatory Services

**The Surgery Center of Huntsville,** 721 Madison Street, Huntsville, AL 35801; tel. 256/533–4888; FAX. 256/532–9510; William Sammons, Chief Executive Officer

**Tuscaloosa Endoscopy Center,** 100 Rice Mine Road, N, Suite E, Tuscaloosa, AL 35406; tel. 205/345–0010; FAX. 205/752–1175; A. B. Reddy, MD, Medical Director

**Tuscaloosa Surgical Center,** 1400 McFarland Boulevard, N., Tuscaloosa, AL 35406; tel. 205/345–5500; Jeff Hayes, Administrator

### ALASKA
**Alaska Women's Health P.C.,** 3260 Providence Dr, Suite 322, Anchorage, AK 99508; tel. 907/563–7228; FAX. 907/563–6278; Carol Mitchell-Springer, MD, President

**Geneva Woods Surgical Center,** 3730 Rhone Circle, Suite 100, Anchorage, AK 99508; tel. 907/562–4764; FAX. 907/561–8519; Barbara Cope, Administrator

**Pacific Cataract & Laser Institute,** 1600 "A" Street, Suite 200, Anchorage, AK 99501; tel. 907/272–2423; FAX. 907/272–2428

### ARIZONA
**Adobe Surgery Center,** 2585 North Wyatt Drive, Tucson, AZ 85712; tel. 520/721–2728; FAX. 520/720–0719; Sam E. Moussa, MD, Administrator

**Arizona Outpatient Surgery Center,** 6245 N. 16th Street, Phoenix, AZ 85016; tel. 602/274–1705; FAX. 602/253–4273

**Arizona Surgical Arts, Inc.,** 1245 North Wilmot Road, Tucson, AZ 85712; tel. 520/296–7550; FAX. 520/722–6937; Robert M. Dryden, MD

**Banner Canyon Springs Surgery Center,** 2940 E. Banner Gateway Drive, #100, Gilbert, AZ 85234; tel. 480/641–9292; Christine Casto, RN, Administrator

**Barnet Dulaney Perkin Eye Center,** 4800 N 22nd Street, Phoenix, AZ 85016; tel. 602/508–4721; FAX. 602/759–1336; Amber Gearhart, Director of Nursing

**CIGNA Healthplan of Arizona, Outpatient Surgery,** 755 East McDowell Road, Phoenix, AZ 85006; tel. 602/271–3020; Katie Rousey, RN Manager

**Cochise Eye and Laser, PC,** 2445 East Wilcox Drive, Sierra Vista, AZ 85635; tel. 520/458–8131; FAX. 520/458–0422; Sheree H. Christian, Administrator

**Cottonwood Day Surgery Center, Inc.,** 55 South Sixth Street, Cottonwood, AZ 86326; tel. 928/634–5118; FAX. 928/634–8522; Linda Davis, Administrator

**Desert Mountain Surgicenter,** 895 S. Dobson Rd., Ste 1, Chandler, AZ 85224-5721; tel. 480/899–3737; FAX. 480/899–6262; David M. Creech, MD

**Desert Samaritan Surgicenter,** 1500 South Dobson Road, Suite 101, Mesa, AZ 85202; tel. 602/835–3590; FAX. 480/835–8774; Brenda Mastopietro, Administrator

**Eye Institute at Boswell,** 10541 West Thunderbird Boulevard, Sun City, AZ 85351; tel. 602/933–3402; FAX. 602/972–5014; Jan Zellmann, Administrator

**Fifty-Ninth Avenue Surgical Facility, Ltd.,** 8608 North 59th Avenue, Glendale, AZ 85302; tel. 623/934–3211; FAX. 623/930–1891; Mark Gorman, Administrator

**Fishkind and Bakewell Eye Care and Surgery Center,** 5599 North Oracle Road, Tucson, AZ 85704; tel. 520/293–6740; FAX. 520/293–6771; Kathleen A. Brown, Surgery Center Supervisor

**Flagstaff Foot Doctors,** 421 North Humphries Street, Flagstaff, AZ 86001; tel. 928/774–4825; FAX. 888/464–1135; Anthony Rosales, MD, President

**Good Samaritan Surgicenter,** 1111 B East McDowell Road, Phoenix, AZ 85006; tel. 602/239–2776; FAX. 602/239–5352; Brenda Mastopietro, Administrator

**Havasu Foot and Ankle Surgi-Center,** 90 Riviera Drive, Lake Havasu, AZ 86403; tel. 928/855–7800; FAX. 928/855–5392; Robert Novack, DPM, Director

**Hodges Eye Care & Surgery Center,** 1502 North Tucson Boulevard, Tucson, AZ 85716; tel. 520/326–4321; FAX. 520/326–4736; Dr. Timothy L. Hodges, MD

**Kokopelli Eye Care, P.C.,** 2820 North Glassford Hill Road, Suite 101, Prescott Valley, AZ 86314; tel. 928/775–5606; FAX. 928/772–4999

**Kokopelli Eye Care, P.C.,** 412 Whipple Street, Prescott, AZ 86301; tel. 928/771–9000; FAX. 928/771–9460

**Metro Surgery Center, L.P.,** 3131 West Peoria Avenue, Phoenix, AZ 85029; tel. 602/375–1083; FAX. 602/789–6833; Diane Elmore, Administrator

**Outpatient Surgical Care, Ltd.,** 1530 West Glendale, Suite 105, Phoenix, AZ 85021; tel. 602/995–3395; FAX. 602/995–1853; Raymond Zimmerman, MD, Medical Director

**Phoenix Eye Surgical Center, LLC,** 5133 North Central Avenue, Suite 100, Phoenix, AZ 85012; tel. 602/279 2434; FAX. 602/279–6475; Sharon Stulstao, Administrator

**Physicians Surgery Center of Tempe, LLC,** 1940 East Southern Avenue, Tempe, AZ 85282; tel. 480/820–7101; FAX. 480/820–9291; Susan Vitort, Administrator

**Prescott Outpatient Surgery Center, LLP,** 815 Ainsworth Drive, Prescott, AZ 86301; tel. 602/778–9770; Derron DeRouin, Administrative Director

**Prescott Urocenter, Ltd.,** 811 Ainsworth, Suite 101, Prescott, AZ 86301; tel. 928/771–5282; FAX. 928/771–5283; Jo Clark, Billing

**Scottsdale Eye Surgery Center, P.C.,** 3320 North Miller Road, Scottsdale, AZ 85251; tel. 480/429–0700; FAX. 480/429–1700; Joyce Schweikert, Administrator

**Southwester Eye Center,** 2005 Injo, Suite 102, Lake Havasu City, AZ 86403-5874; tel. 928/505–3696; FAX. 928/505–6129; Gary Dillon, Director, Contract Services

**Southwestern Eye Center,** 2610 E. University Drive, Mesa, AZ 85213; tel. 480/892–8400; FAX. 480/892–9533; Gary Dillon, Director, Contract Services

**Southwestern Eye Center,** 1919 Florence Avenue, Kingman, AZ 86401; tel. 928/753–5454; FAX. 928/753–7790; Richard Hinton, Administrator

**Southwestern Eye Center,** 3321 E. Bell Road, Suite B12, Phoenix, AZ 85032-2755; tel. 602/787–9100; FAX. 602/787–9101; Gary Dillon, Director, Contract Services

**Southwestern Eye Center,** 3003 Highway 95 Ste 63, Bullhead City, AZ 86442-7860; tel. 928/763–7555; FAX. 928/763–7565; Gary Dillon, Director, Contract Services

**Southwestern Eye Center,** 270 S. Candy Lane, Cottonwood, AZ 86326-4164; tel. 928/634–4202; FAX. 928/634–5693; Gary Dillon, Director, Contract Services

**Southwestern Eye Center,** 2650 E. Show Low Lake Rd, Suite 2, Show Low, AZ 85901-7955; tel. 928/537–4240; FAX. 928/537–3892; Gary Dillon, Director, Contract Services

**Southwestern Eye Center,** 1600 Willow Creek Rd., Prescott, AZ 86301-1108; tel. 928/776–7477; FAX. 928/776–0693; Gary Dillon, Director, Contract Services

**Southwestern Eye Center,** 2242 W. 16th Street, Safford, AZ 85546-4081; tel. 928/428–0068; FAX. 928/428–0713; Gary Dillon, Director, Contract Services

**Southwestern Eye Center,** 1055 S. Stapley Drive, Mesa, AZ 85204-5013; tel. 480/833–9100; FAX. 480/833–6000; Gary Dillon, Director, Contract Services

**Southwestern Eye Center,** 10615 W. Thunderbird Bldg., A100, Sun City, AZ 85351-3018; tel. 623/977–9600; FAX. 623/977–9602

**Southwestern Eye Center,** 75 Colonia De Salud A-100, Sierra Vista, AZ 85635-2487; tel. 520/459–6860; FAX. 520/459–6858; Gary Dillon, Director, Contract Services

**Southwestern Eye Center,** 2149 W. 24th Street, Yuma, AZ 85364-6163; tel. 928/726–4120; FAX. 928/341–0315; Gary Dillon, Director, Contract Services

**Southwestern Eye Center-Casa Grande,** 560 N. Camino Mercado, Suite 1, Casa Grande, AZ 85222; tel. 520/426–9224; FAX. 520/426–1554; Ellen Lopez, RN, Director of Surgical Services

**Southwestern Eye Surgicenter-Nogales,** 1815 North Mastick Way, Nogales, AZ 85621; tel. 520/761–3533; FAX. 520/281–1950; Gary Dillon, Director, Contract Services

**Summit Surgery & Recovery Care Center,** 1485 N. Turquoise Drive, #100, Flagstaff, AZ 86001; tel. 928/214–3211; FAX. 928/214–3219; Jantina Wilson, Administrator

**Sun City Endoscopy Center, Inc.,** 13203 North 103rd Avenue, Suite C 3, Sun City, AZ 85351; tel. 623/972–5083; FAX. 623/523–0505; Jagdish Patel, MD

**Surgery Center of Peoria,** 13260 North 94th Drive, Suite 200, Peoria, AZ 85381; tel. 623/933–2900; FAX. 623/933–0017; Kolette Al-Jamal, Administrator

**Surgi-Care,** 5115 North Central Avenue, Phoenix, AZ 85012; tel. 602/264–1818; FAX. 602/264–2172; Ellison F. Herro, MD, Administrator

**Swagel Wootton Eye Center,** 220 South 63rd Street, Mesa, AZ 85206; tel. 602/641–3937; FAX. 602/924–5096; S. Joyce Graham

**T.A.S.I. Surgery Center,** 5585 North Oracle Road, Suite B, Tucson, AZ 85704; tel. 520/293–7077; FAX. 520/293–7561; John A. Pierce, MD, Medical Director

**Tempe New Day Surgery Center LP,** 2000 East Southern Avenue, Suite 106, Tempe, AZ 85282; tel. 480/838-9313; FAX. 480/491-8802; John L. Titus, President

**The PAIN MDS ASC,** 2525 W Carefree Hwy, Suite 134, Phoenix, AZ 85085; tel. 623/580-4357; FAX. 623/580-5249; Linda Davis, Administrator

**Thunderbird Samaritan Surgicenter,** 5555 B West Thunderbird Road, Glendale, AZ 85306-4622; tel. 602/588-5475; FAX. 602/588-5472; Diane Elmore, RN, Administrator

**Valley Outpatient Surgery Center,** 160 West University Drive #1, Mesa, AZ 85201; tel. 602/835-7373; FAX. 602/969-7981; Craig R. Cassidy, DO, President

**Vital Sight P.C.,** 5632 East Fifth Street, Tucson, AZ 85711; tel. 520/790-8888; FAX. 520/790-1427; Victoria Gacon, Administrator

**Warner Park Surgery Center,** 604 West Warner Road, Building A, Chandler, AZ 85225; tel. 480/899-2571; FAX. 480/899-4263; Dale Holmes

**White Mountain Ambulatory Surgery Center,** 2650 East Show Low Lake Road, Suite Two, Show Low, AZ 85901; tel. 908/537-4240; William J. Waldo

### ARKANSAS

**Arkansas Endoscopy Center, P.A.,** 9501 Baptist Health Drive, Suite 100, Little Rock, AR 72205; tel. 501/224-9100; FAX. 501/224-0420; Ronald D. Hardin, MD

**Arkansas Surgery and Endoscopy Center,** 4800 Hazel Street, Pine Bluff, AR 71603; tel. 870/536-4800; FAX. 870/534-5535; Syed Samad, MD, FACP, FACG

**Arkansas Surgery Center,** 10 Hospital Circle, Batesville, AR 72501; tel. 870/793-4040; FAX. 870/793-5649; Ronald L. Lowery, MD, Administrator

**Boozman-Hof Eye Surgery and Laser Center, LLC,** 3737 West Walnut Street, P.O. Box 1353, Rogers, AR 72757-1353; tel. 501/246-1751; FAX. 501/631-2702; Donna R. Acord, Director

**Doctors Surgery Center PA,** 303 West Polk Ave, Suite B, West Memphis, AR 72301; tel. 870/732-2100; Lois Meyers, RN

**Endoscopy Center of Hot Springs,** 151 McGowan Court, Hot Springs, AR 71913; tel. 501/623-4101; FAX. 501/623-0103; Barbara Hulsey, Administrator

**H. Lewis Pearson Eye Institute,** 3211 Surger Hill Road, Texarkana, AR 71854-9265; tel. 870/772-4440; FAX. 870/772-7190; Glen Wile, Comptroller

**James Trice, M.D., P.A., dba Digestive Disease Center,** 7005 South Hazel Street, Pine Bluff, AR 71603; tel. 870/536-3070; FAX. 870/536-3171; Louis Trice, Administrator

**Little Rock Surgery Center,** 8820 Knoedl Court, Little Rock, AR 72205; tel. 501/224-6767; FAX. 501/224-8203; Kim Hamma, RN, Administrator

**Lowery Medical/Surgical Eye Center, P.A.,** 105 Central Avenue, Searcy, AR 72143; tel. 501/268-7154; FAX. 501/268-9071; Robert D. Lowery, MD, Administrator

**North Hills Gastroenterology Endoscopy Center, Inc.,** 3344 North Futrall Drive, Fayetteville, AR 72703; tel. 501/582-7280; FAX. 510/582-7279; William C. Martin, MD

**Novamed Surgery Center of Jonesboro, dba Eye Surgery Center of Arkansas,** 601 East Matthews, Jonesboro, AR 72401; tel. 870/935-6396; FAX. 870/935-4063; Tracy Gholson, Director

**Ozark Eye Center,** 360 Highway Five North, Mountain Home, AR 72653; tel. 870/425-2277; Cheryl Pearman, Administrator

**Physicians' Surgery Center of Fayetteville,** 3873 North Parkview Drive, Suite One, Fayetteville, AR 72703; tel. 479/527-0050; FAX. 479/582-1338; Russ Greene RN Administrator

**South Arkansas Surgery Center,** 4310 South Mulberry, Pine Bluff, AR 71603; tel. 870/535-5719; FAX. 870/536-1963; Heather Walters, Business Manager

**The Gastro-Intestinal Center,** 405 North University, Little Rock, AR 72205; tel. 501/663-1074; FAX. 501/663-0906; Brett Kirkman, Administrator

### CALIFORNIA

**Advanced Surgery Center,** 5771 North Fresno Street, Suite 101, Fresno, CA 93710; tel. 559/448-9900; FAX. 559/448-9546; B. David Singh MD, Administrator

**Aestheticare Outpatient Surgery Center,** 30260 Rancho Viejo Road, San Juan Capistrano, CA 92675; tel. 949/661-1700; FAX. 949/661-4321; Ronald E. Moser, MD

**Alliance Surgery Center,** 20377 Acacia Street, Suite 120, Newport Beach, CA 92660; tel. 949/870-3602; Naomi Hadden, Chief Financial Officer

**Ambulatory Surgical Center of Southern California, Gastroenterology Diagnostic Center,** 880 South Atlantic Boulevard G-10, Monterey Park, CA 91754; tel. 626/293-8851; FAX. 626/293-1606; Zelman Weingaren, MD

**Ambulatory Surgical Center of Zeiter Eye,** 117 North San Joaquin Street, Stockton, CA 95202; tel. 209/466-5566; FAX. 209/466-0535; Erin McCarthy, Office Manager

**Ambulatory Surgical Center, Inc.,** 14400 Bear Valley Road, Suite 201, Victorville, CA 92392; tel. 760/951-5162; FAX. 818/985-0055; Garey L. Weber, DPM, Administrator

**Antelope Valley Surgery Center,** 44301 North Lorimer Avenue, Lancaster, CA 93534; tel. 661/940-1112; FAX. 661/940-6856; Justina Geeter, Business Office Manager

**Arlington Podiatry Surgery Center,** 7310 Magnolia Avenue, Riverside, CA 92504; tel. 951/354-8787; FAX. 951/354-0350; James A. De Silva, Administrator

**Bakersfield Endoscopy Center,** 1408 Commercial Way, Bakersfield, CA 93309; tel. 661/327-4455; FAX. 661/633-5484; Ramesh Gupta, MD, Medical Director

**Bascom Surgery Center,** 3803 S. Bascom Avenue, Suite 106, Campbell, CA 95008; tel. 408/369-9535; FAX. 408/369-9106

**Bedford Surgery Center,** 100 UCLA Medical Plaza, Suite 310, Los Angeles, CA 90024-6999; tel. 310/777-8820; FAX. 310/777-8890; Patricia Adams, RN,PHD, Director of Nursing

**Beverly Hills Sunset Surgery Center, Inc.,** 9201 Sunset Boulevard, Suite 405, Los Angeles, CA 90069; tel. 310/887-1730; FAX. 310/887-1734; Sue Kim, Nursing Administrator

**Bolsa Outpatient Surgery Center,** 10362 Bolsa Avenue, Suite 100, Westminster, CA 92683; tel. 714/775-5690; FAX. 714/775-7405; Van Kychoung, MD, Medical Director

**Brockton Surgery Center,** 6958 Brockton Avenue, Riverside, CA 92506-3832; tel. 951/788-4400; Michael N. Durrant, DPM, MPH

**Camden Surgery Center of Beverly Hills,** 414 North Camden Drive, Suite 800, Beverly Hills, CA 90210; tel. 310/859-3991; FAX. 310/859-7126; Yvette L. Lee Administrator

**Campus Surgery Center, LP,** 901 Campus Drive, Suite 102, Daly City, CA 94015; tel. 650/991-2000; FAX. 650/755-8638

**Center for Surgery of Encinitas,** 477 North El Camino Real, Suite C-100, Encinitas, CA 92024; tel. 760/942-8800; FAX. 760/942-0106; Chris Clinton, RN, CASC Administrator

**Crown Valley Surgicenter,** 26921 Crown Valley Parkway, Suite 110, Mission Viejo, CA 92691; tel. 949/348-7252; FAX. 949/348-7246; Maurice Chammas, MD, Administrator

**Cypress Outpatient Surgical Center, Inc.,** 1665 Dominican Way, Suite 120, Santa Cruz, CA 95065; tel. 831/476-6943; FAX. 831/476-1473; Nicole Rojas, RN, Administrator

**Digestive Disease Center,** 24411 Health Center Drive, Suite 450, Laguna Hills, CA 92653; tel. 949/586-9386; FAX. 949/586-0864; Robert Dyer, Medical Director

**E N T Facial Surgery Center,** 1351 East Spruce, Fresno, CA 93720; tel. 559/432-3724; FAX. 559/432-8579; JoAnn LoForti, RN, MS, Division of Nursing

**El Mirador Surgical Center,** 1180 North Indian Canyon Drive, Suite 110, Palm Springs, CA 92262; tel. 760/416-4600; FAX. 760/416-4668; David Wiche, Director

**Endoscopy Center of Chula Vista,** 681 Third Avenue, Suite B, Chula Vista, CA 91910; tel. 619/425-2150; FAX. 619/425-2848; Robert Penner, MD, Administrator

**Endoscopy Center of Southern California,** 2336 Santa Monica Boulevard, Suite 204, Santa Monica, CA 90404; tel. 310/453-4477; FAX. 310/453-4811; Richard F. Corlin MD

**Endoscopy Center of the Central Coast,** 77 Casa Street, Suite 106, San Luis Obis, CA 93405; tel. 805/541-1021; FAX. 805/541-3142; Jill Quinn, RN, Center Director

**Escondido Surgery Center,** 343 East Second Avenue, Escondido, CA 92025; tel. 760/480-6606; FAX. 760/480-6671; L. Richard Greenstein, MD, Medical Director

**Eye Center of Northern California,** 6500 Fairmount Avenue, Suite Two, El Cerrito, CA 94530; tel. 510/525-2600; FAX. 510/524-1887; William Ellis

**Eye Life Institute,** 6283 Clark Road, Suite 11, Paradise, CA 95969; tel. 530/877-2020; FAX. 530/877-4641; Almary Hivale, RN, Director of ASC

**Eye Surgery Center of Southern California, Inc./ Med. Group, dba Tri-City Surgery Center,** 2023 West Vista Way, Suite E, Vista, CA 92083; tel. 760/941-8152; FAX. 760/941-8967; Anui Gupta, MD, Medical Director

**Eye Surgery Center of the Desert,** 39700 Bob Hope Drive, Suite 111, Rancho Mirage, CA 92270; tel. 760/340-3937; FAX. 760/773-3823; Timothy D. Milauskas, Administrator

**Feather River Surgery Center,** 370 Del Norte Avenue, Yuba City, CA 95991; tel. 530/751-4800; FAX. 530/751-4884; Ann Perry, Administrator

**Foothill Ambulatory Surgery Center,** 1030 East Foothill Boulevard, Suite 101B, Upland, CA 91786; tel. 909/981-5859; FAX. 909/981-8293; Natee Poopat, MD, Office Director

**Fremont Surgery Center,** 2675 Stevenson Boulevard-South, Fremont, CA 94538; tel. 510/793-4987; FAX. 510/793-5084; Debi Ford, RN, Director of Nursing

**GastroDiagnostics, A Medical Group,** 1140 West La Veta, Suite 550, Orange, CA 92868; tel. 714/835-3636; FAX. 714/835-5567; Vicki Kersey, Administrator

**Glendale Eye Surgery Center,** 607 North Central, Suite 103, Glendale, CA 91203; tel. 818/956-1010; FAX. 818/543-6083; Richard Weise, MD

**Golden Triangle Surgicenter,** 25405 Hancock Avenue, Suite 103, Murrieta, CA 92562; tel. 909/698-4670; FAX. 909/698-4675; Ella Stockstill, Administrator

**Greater Sacramento Surgery Center,** 2288 Auburn Boulevard, Suite 201, Sacramento, CA 95821; tel. 916/929-7229; FAX. 916/929-2590; Susan Brunone, MHS, Administrator

**Grossmont Plaza Surgery Center,** 5525 Grossmont Center Drive, La Mesa, CA 91942; tel. 619/644-4561; Chris Ekern, Manager

**Halcyon Laser and Surgery Center, Inc.,** 303 South Halcyon Road, Arroyo Grande, CA 93420; tel. 805/489-8254; FAX. 805/474-1997; Michelle Mele, Administrator

**HealthSouth Arcadia Outpatient Surgery, Inc.,** 614 West Duarte Road, Arcadia, CA 91007; tel. 626/445-4714; FAX. 626/445-1701; Sara Lamm, Administrator

**HealthSouth Forest Surgery Center,** 2110 Forest Avenue, San Jose, CA 95128; tel. 408/297-3432; FAX. 408/298-3338; Camille Magamon RN

**HealthSouth Grossmont Surgery Center,** 8881 Fletcher Parkway, Suite 100, La Mesa, CA 91942; tel. 619/698-0930; FAX. 619/698-3093; Administrator

**HealthSouth North Coast Surgery Center,** 3903 Waring Road, Oceanside, CA 92056; tel. 760/940-0997; FAX. 760/940-0407; Donna Danley, Administrator

**HealthSouth Surgery Center,** 75 Scripts Drive, Sacramento, CA 95825; tel. 916/929-9431; FAX. 916/929-0132; Deanne Conner, Administrator

**HealthSouth Surgery Center-Scripps,** 75 Scripps Drive, Sacramento, CA 95825; tel. 916/929-9431; FAX. 916/929-0132; Jodean Lake, Administrator

**Hemet Endoscopy Center,** 1003 East Florida Avenue, Suite 104, Hemet, CA 92543; tel. 951/652-2252; FAX. 951/925-9252; Milan S. Chakrabarty, MD

**Hemet Healthcare Surgicenter,** 301 North San Jacinto Avenue, Hemet, CA 92543; tel. 909/765-1717; FAX. 909/765-1716; Josh Hoffner, Business Office Manager

**High Desert Endoscopy,** 18523 Corwin Road, Suite H2, Apple Valley, CA 92307; tel. 760/242-3000; FAX. 760/242-1802; Raman S. Poola, MD, Administrator

**Hope Square Surgical Center,** 39700 Bob Hope Drive, Suite 301, Rancho Mirage, CA 92270; tel. 760/346-7696; FAX. 760/776-1069; BJ Clarke, RN, MPA, Administrator

**Huntington Outpatient Surgery Center,** 797 South Fair Oaks Avenue, Pasadena, CA 91105; tel. 626/535-2434; FAX. 626/535-2430; Robin Waldvogel, Medical Director

**Inland Endoscopy Center, Inc., dba Mountain View Surgery Center,** 10408 Industrial Circle, Redlands, CA 92374; tel. 909/796-7803; FAX. 909/796-0614; Khushal Stanisai

**Inland Surgery Center,** 1620 Laurel Avenue, Redlands, CA 92373; tel. 909/793-4701; FAX. 909/792-6397; Jacquelin Belcher, Facility Administrator

**Inland Surgery Center,** 1620 Laurel Ave, Redlands, CA 92373; tel. 909/793-4701; FAX. 951/658-3953; James Watson, MD, Medical Director

**Irvine Multi-Specialty Surgical Care,** 4900 Barranca Parkway, Suite 104, Irvine, CA 92604-8603; tel. 949/726-0677; FAX. 949/726-0678; Lauren Parrott, BS, Administrator

**Kaiser Ambulatory Surgical Center,** 2025 Morse Avenue, Sacramento, CA 95825; tel. 916/973-7786; FAX. 916/973-5530; Brian J. Brosnahan, RN, BSN, ASU Manager

**Kaiser Ambulatory Surgical Center,** 10725 International Drive, Rancho Cordov, CA 95670; tel. 916/631-2000; FAX. 916/631-2013; Steven Metzger, RN, Manager

**La Jolla Endoscopy Center,** 9850 Genesee Avenue, Suite 980, La Jolla, CA 92037; tel. 858/453-7525; FAX. 858/453-5753; Dr. David Roseman

**La Veta Surgical Center, an Affiliate of SCA,** 681 South Parker Street, Suite 150, Orange, CA 92868; tel. 714/744-0900; FAX. 714/744-0283; Kelly Ruiz, Administrator

**Laser Surgery Center, Ltd.,** 2021 Ygnacio Valley Road, Building H-102, Walnut Creek, CA 94598; tel. 925/944-9400; FAX. 925/947-2160; Michele McKinley, Administrator

**Lassen Surgery Center,** 103 Fair Drive, PO Box 1150, Susanville, CA 96130; tel. 530/257-7772; FAX. 530/257-2939; Kim Sibert, Medical Staff Coordinator

**Lodi Outpatient Surgical Center,** 521 South Ham Lane, Suite F, Lodi, CA 95242; tel. 209/333-0905; FAX. 209/333-0219; Kippy Pogue, Administrator

**Loma Linda Ambulatory Surgical Center, Podiatry Corp.,** 11332 Mountain View Avenue, Suite A, Loma Linda, CA 92354; tel. 909/796-3707; FAX. 909/796-3709; Mariam Amiri, DPM, Administrator

**Los Altos Surgery Center,** 795 Altos Oaks Drive, Los Altos, CA 94024; tel. 650/209-1100; Harry Mittelman, MD

**Los Gatos Surgical Center,** 15195 National Avenue, Suite 100, Los Gatos, CA 95032; tel. 408/356-0454; FAX. 408/358-3924; David Hokeness, Administrator

**M/S Surgery Center, LLC,** 3510 Martin Luther King Boulevard, Lynwood, CA 90262; tel. 310/635-7550; FAX. 310/603-8749; John H. Shammas, MD, Medical Director

**Marin Ophthalmic Surgery Center,** 901 E Street, Suite 270, San Rafael, CA 94901; tel. 415/454-2112; FAX. 415/454-6542; Minda Soria, RN Clinical Director

**Martel Eye Institute, LLC,** 11216 Trinity River, Rancho Cordova, CA 95670; tel. 916/631-7868; FAX. 916/631-3788; Joseph Martel, MD

**Medical Arts Ambulatory Surgery Center,** 205 South West Street, Suite B, Visalia, CA 93291; tel. 209/625-9601; FAX. 209/625-3124; Thomas F. Mitts, MD, Administrator

**Medical Plaza Orthopedic Surgery Center,** 1301 20th Street, Suite 140, Santa Monica, CA 90404; tel. 310/315-0333; FAX. 310/315-0341; Trish Fowler, Director Surgical Services

**Merced Ambulatory Endoscopy Center,** 750 West Olive Avenue, Suite 107A, Merced, CA 95348; tel. 209/384-3116; FAX. 209/384-0878; Vijaya Tangella, Administrator

**Mission Ambulatory Surgicenter,** 26730 Crown Valley Parkway, First Floor, Mission Viejo, CA 92691; tel. 949/364-2201; FAX. 949/364-5372; Mary Parker, Administrator

**Mission Valley Surgery Center,** 39263 Mission Boulevard, Fremont, CA 94539; tel. 510/796-4500; FAX. 510/796-4573; Sarb S. Hundal, MD

**Modesto Surgery Center, Inc.,** 400 East Orangeburg Avenue, Suite One, Modesto, CA 95350; tel. 209/526-3000; FAX. 209/526-3133; Dr. Greg Tesluk, Administrator

**Monterey Peninsula Surgery Center, LLC,** 966 Cass Street, Suite 210, Monterey, CA 93940; tel. 831/372-2169; FAX. 408/372-6323; David J. Ogimachi, Administrator

**Napa Surgery Center,** 3444 Valle Verde Drive, Napa, CA 94558; tel. 707/252-9669; FAX. 707/257-3328; Eric Grigsby, MD, Owner

**Newport Beach Orange Coast Endoscopy Center,** 1525 Superior Avenue, Suite 114, Newport Beach, CA 92663; tel. 949/646-6999; FAX. 949/646-9699; Donald Abraham

**Newport Surgery Institute,** 360 San Miguel Drive, Suite 406, Newport Beach, CA 92660; tel. 949/759-0995; Suzanne Tavenner, Office Manager

**North Anaheim Surgicenter,** 1154 North Euclid, Anaheim, CA 92801; tel. 714/635-6272; FAX. 714/635-0943; Jeanette Rasmussen, Administrator

**North Bay Eye Associates, Inc., Ambulatory Surgery Center,** 380 Tesconi Court, Santa Rosa, CA 95401; tel. 707/544-3375; FAX. 707/544-0808; William H. Bartlett, Medical Director

**Optima Ophthalmic Medical Associates, Inc.,** 1237 B Street, Hayward, CA 94541-2977; tel. 510/886-3937; FAX. 510/886-6304; Kelly Best, Office Manager

**Orange County Institute of Gastroenterology and Endoscopy,** 26732 Crown Valley Parkway, Suite 241, Mission Viejo, CA 92691; tel. 949/364-2611; FAX. 949/364-0226; Dina Moatazedi, Office Manager

**Pacific Eye Institute,** 555 North 13th Avenue, Upland, CA 91786; tel. 909/982-8846; FAX. 909/982-4007; Robert Fabricant, MD, FACS, Medical Director

**Pacific Hills Surgery Center, LLC,** 24022 Calle De La Plata, Suite 180, Laguna Hills, CA 92653; tel. 949/458-3551; FAX. 949/951-9478; Kristi Morse, RN, Nurse Manager, Compliance

**Pacific Surgicenter, Inc.,** 1301 20th Street, Suite 470, Santa Monica, CA 90404; tel. 310/315-0222; FAX. 310/828-8852; Randi Ogilvie- Manager

**Petaluma Surgicenter,** 1400 Professional Drive, Suite 102, Petaluma, CA 94954; tel. 707/763-9325; FAX. 707/769-0751; Ronald M. La Vigna, DPM Manager

**Physicians Plaza Surgical Center,** 6000 Physicians Boulevard, Bakersfield, CA 93301; tel. 661/322-4744; FAX. 661/322-2938; Terri Waller, Administrator

**Plastic and Reconstructive Surgery Center,** 1387 Santa Rita Road, Pleasanton, CA 94566; tel. 925/462-3700; FAX. 510/462 4681; Ronald Iverson, Administrator

**Podiatric Surgery Center,** 255 North Gilbert, Suite B-1, Hemet, CA 92543; tel. 951/925-2186; FAX. 951/925-4947; Robert Drake, DPM, Administrator

**Premiere Surgery Center, Inc.,** 700 West El Norte Parkway, Escondido, CA 92026; tel. 760/738-7830; FAX. 760/738-7834; R. K. Massengill, MD, President

**Providence Ambulatory Surgical Center,** 1310 West Stewart Drive, Suite 310, Orange, CA 92668; tel. 714/771-6363; FAX. 714/771-0754; Harrell E. Robinson, MD, President

**Providence Holy Cross Surgery Center,** 11550 Indian Hills Road, Suite 160, Mission Hills, CA 91345; tel. 818/256-2100; FAX. 818/256-2156; Dale Bowman, Administrator

**Redlands Dental Surgery Center,** 1180 Nevada Street, Suite 100, Redlands, CA 92374; tel. 909/335-0474; FAX. 909/335-0477; Russell O. Seheult, DDS

**Richburg Valley Eye Institute Ambulatory Surgical Center,** 1680 East Herndon Avenue, Fresno, CA 93720; tel. 209/432-4200; FAX. 209/432-0147; Frederick Richburg, MD, Administrator

**Riverside Medical Clinic Surgery Center,** 7160 Brockton Avenue, Riverside, CA 92506; tel. 951/782-3801; FAX. 951/328-9742; Judy Carpenter, President and Chief Operating Officer

**Sacramento Eye Surgicenter,** 3150 J Street, Sacramento, CA 95816; tel. 916/444-7052; FAX. 916/446-1145; Yvonne Jones, ASC Director

**Sacramento Midtown Endoscopy Center,** 3941 J Street, Suite 460, Sacramento, CA 95819; tel. 916/733-6940; FAX. 916/733-6934; Gautam Gandhi, MD

**Saddleback Eye Center,** 23161 Moulton Parkway, Laguna Hills, CA 92653; tel. 949/951-4641; FAX. 949/951-4601; Linda Riley, Administrator

**Saddleback Valley Outpatient Surgery,** 24302 Paseo De Valencia, Laguna Hills, CA 92653; tel. 949/472-0244; FAX. 949/472-0380; Brian Fitzgerald, Administrator

**Salinas Surgery Center,** 955-A Blanco Circle, Salinas, CA 93901; tel. 831/753-5800; FAX. 831/753-5808; Christine Gallagher, Executive Director

**San Francisco Surgi Center,** 1635 Divisidero Street, Suite 200, San Francisco, CA 94115; tel. 415/346-1218; FAX. 415/346-2930; Judith Mulligan, Administrator

**San Gabriel Valley Surgical Center,** 1250 South Sunset Avenue, Suite 100, West Covina, CA 91790; tel. 626/960-6623; FAX. 626/962-4341; Susan Raub, Administrator

**San Joaquin Laser Surgery Center,** 1805 North California Street, # 101A, Stockton, CA 95204; tel. 209/948-3241; FAX. 209/948-8009; Susan Ford, Administrator

**San Leandro Surgery Center,** 15035 East 14th Street, San Leandro, CA 94578; tel. 510/276-2800; FAX. 510/276-2890; Jeanne Linda, Administrator

**Sani Eye Surgery Center,** 1315 Las Tablas Road, Templeton, CA 93465; tel. 805/434-2533; FAX. 805/434-3037; Karim Rasheed, MD, Director

**Santa Cruz Surgery Center,** 3003 Paul Sweet Road, Santa Cruz, CA 95065; tel. 408/462-5512; FAX. 408/462-2451; Mary Ann Dunlap, RN

**Sequoia Surgery Center, LLC,** 842 South Akers Street, Visalia, CA 93277; tel. 559/740-4094; FAX. 559/740-4100; Renda Liden, CASC, Administrator

**Shepard Surgical Center,** 1418 East Main Street, Suite 110, Santa Maria, CA 93454-4806; tel. 805/614-7005; FAX. 805/614-7006; Dennis D. Shepard, MD

**Silicon Valley Surgery Center, LP,** 14601 S. Bascom Avenue, Suite 100, Los Gatos, CA 95032; tel. 408/402-0663; FAX. 408/402-7055

**Sonora Eye Surgery Center,** 940 Sylva Lane, Suite G, Sonora, CA 95370; tel. 209/532-2020; FAX. 209/532-1687; Desiree Torres, RN, Surgery Administrator

**South Coast Laser Center,** 3420 Bristol Street, Suite 701, Costa Mesa, CA 92626; tel. 714/957-0272; FAX. 714/641-2020; Marc R. Rose, MD, Medical Director

**Southern California Surgery Center,** 7305 Pacific Boulevard, Huntington Pa, CA 90255; tel. 323/584-8222; FAX. 323/584-8606; Ruth Huezo, Administrator

**Southland Endoscopy Center,** 949 East Calhoun Place, Suite B, Hemet, CA 92543; tel. 951/929-1177; FAX. 951/765-9111; Sreenivasa R. Nakka, MD, FACP

**Southwest Surgical Center, Health South,** 201 New Stine Road, Suite 130, Bakersfield, CA 93309; tel. 661/396-8900; FAX. 661/397-2929; Linda Bloomquist, Administrator

**St. Joseph Surgery and Laser Center, Inc., dba St. Mary and Joseph Surgery and Laser Center, Inc.,** 436 South Glassell Street, Orange, CA 92866; tel. 714/633-9566; FAX. 714/633-5193; Kathleen Ruper, Administrator

**Starpoint Health Foundation,** PO Box 7459, Newport Beach, CA 92658-7459; tel. 949/705-5100; FAX. 949/985-0055; Eric D. Friedlander, Chief Executive Officer

**Surgecenter of Palo Alto,** 795 El Camino Real, Palo Alto, CA 94301; tel. 650/324-1832; FAX. 650/330-4520; Margo Mynderse-Isola, Chief Executive Officer

**Surgery Center of San Buena Ventura,** 3525 Loma Vista Road, Suite B, Ventura, CA 93003; tel. 805/641-6434; FAX. 805/641-6437; Chris Behm, Administrator

**Surgery Center of Santa Monica,** 2121 Wilshire Boulevard, Suite 201, Santa Monica, CA 90403; tel. 310/264-7300; FAX. 310/828-8626

**Surgitek Outpatient Center, Inc.,** 460 North Greenfield Avenue, Suite Eight, Hanford, CA 93230; tel. 559/582-0238; FAX. 559/582-9341; Wiley Elick, Owner, Administrator

**Sutter Alhambra Surgery Center,** 1201 Alhambra Boulevard, Suite 110, Sacramento, CA 95816; tel. 916/733-8222; FAX. 916/733-8224; Ken Schwam, Administrator

**Sutter Auburn Surgery Center,** 3123 Professional Drive, Suite 100, Auburn, CA 95603; tel. 530/888-8899; FAX. 530/888-1464; Toni Angle, MBA, Administrator

**Sutter North Procedure Center,** 550 B Street, Yuba City, CA 95991; tel. 530/749-3653; FAX. 530/749-3493; Deborah Smith, Ancillary Services Director

**The Center for Endoscopy,** 3921 Waring Road, Suite B, Oceanside, CA 92056; tel. 760/940-6300; FAX. 760/940-8074; Barbara Bockover, RN, Administrator

**The Centre for Plastic Surgery,** 1869 N Waterman Avenue, San Bernardino, CA 92404; tel. 909/883-8686; FAX. 909/881-6537; David Nguyen, MD

**The Endoscopy Center,** 870 Shasta Street, Suite 200, Yuba City, CA 95991; tel. 530/671-3636; Floyd V. Burton, MD

**The Endoscopy Center of the South Bay,** 23560 Madison Street, Suite 114, Torrance, CA 90505; tel. 310/325-6331; FAX. 310/325-6335; Jerome Cohen MD, Medical Director

**The Eye Surgery Center (Colton),** 1900 East Washington Street, Colton, CA 92324; tel. 909/825-8002; FAX. 909/424-1662; Melissa Goins, RN, Director

**The Eye Surgery Center of Northern California,** 5959 Greenback Lane Suite 310, Citrus Height, CA 95621; tel. 916/723-7400; FAX. 916/723-4449; Scott George, Clinic Director

**The Montebello Surgery Center,** 229 East Beverly Boulevard, Montebello, CA 90640; tel. 323/728-7998; FAX. 323/728-5041; Millie Kelly, Administrator

**The Palos Verdes Ambulatory Surgery Medical Center,** 3400 West Lomita Boulevard, Suite 307A, Torrance, CA 90505; tel. 310/539-5888; FAX. 310/517-9916; Christine Petti, MD, Medical Director

**The Plastic Surgery Center,** 95 Scripps Drive, Sacramento, CA 95825; tel. 916/929-1833; FAX. 916/929-6730; Marlin Schriock, Administrator

**The San Luis Obispo Surgery Center,** 1304 Ella Street, Suite C, San Luis Obis, CA 93401; tel. 805/544-7874; FAX. 866/384-2036; Judy Shapazian, RN, Administrator

**The Surgery Center of Alta Bates Summit Medical Center,** 3875 Telegraph Avenue, Oakland, CA 94609; tel. 510/547-2244; FAX. 510/653-5242; Kim D'Ambrosia, Administrator

**The Surgery Center Of Riverside, Inc.,** 8990 Garfield, Suite One, Riverside, CA 92503; tel. 951/785-5421; FAX. 951/785-0130

**The Surgery Center of Santa Rosa,** 1111 Sonoma Avenue, Lower Level, Santa Rosa, CA 95405; tel. 707/578-4100; FAX. 707/578-7997; Ken Alban, Administrator

**Third Street Surgery Center,** 420 East Third Street, Suite 110, Los Angeles, CA 90013; tel. 213/617-9194; FAX. 213/617-0605; Tomoko Okuda, RN, Clinical Coordinator

**Time Surgical Facility,** 720 North Tustin Avenue, Suite 202, Santa Ana, CA 92705; tel. 714/972-1811; FAX. 714/972-0986; Tracey Mora, RN, Nurse Manager

**Torrance Surgicenter,** 22410 Hawthorne Boulevard, Suite Three, Torrance, CA 90505; tel. 310/373-2238; FAX. 310/373-8238; Lindon Kawahara, MD, Administrator

**Truxtun Surgery Center, Inc.,** 4260 Truxtun Avenue, Suite 120, Bakersfield, CA 93309; tel. 661/327-3636; Mary Moeder, AOM

**Twin Cities Surgicenter, Inc.,** 812 Fourth Street, Suite A, Marysville, CA 95901; tel. 530/741-3937; FAX. 530/743-0427; Karen M. Wasilenko, CASC Administrator

**University Ambulatory Surgery Center,** 8929 University Center Lane, Suite 103, San Diego, CA 92122; tel. 858/554-0220; FAX. 858/554-0458; Eileen Smith, Administrator

**Upland Outpatient Surgical Center, Inc.,** 1330 San Bernardino Road #F, Upland, CA 91786; tel. 909/981-8755; FAX. 909/981-9462; Brian Olson, Administrator

**Valencia Outpatient Surgical Center Partners, L.P., dba Valencia Surgical Center,** 24355 Lyons Avenue, Suite 120, Santa Clarita, CA 91321; tel. 661/255-6644; FAX. 661/255-7653; Pat Monolias, RN, Director of Nursing

**Valley Endoscopy Center,** 18425 Burbank Boulevard, Suite 525, Tarzana, CA 91356; tel. 818/708-6050; FAX. 818/708-6055; Christine Scoggins, RN, Clinical Director

**Ventura Out-Patient Surgery, Inc.,** 3555 Loma Vista Road, Suite 204, Ventura, CA 93003; tel. 805/653-5460; FAX. 805/653-1470; Brian D. Brantner, MD

**Washington Outpatient Surgery Center,** 2299 Mowry Avenue, First Floor, Fremont, CA 94538; tel. 510/791-5374; FAX. 510/790-8916; Dr. Jeffery Stuart, Medical Director

**Waverley Surgery Center, LP,** 400 Forest Avenue, Palo Alto, CA 94301; tel. 650/324-0600; FAX. 650/269-1620

**West Hills Surgical Center,** 7240 Medical Center Drive, West Hills, CA 91307; tel. 818/226-9151; FAX. 818/226-0947

**Westlake Eye Surgery Center,** 2900 Townsgate Road, Suite 201, Westlake Village, CA 91361; tel. 805/496-6789; FAX. 805/494-8392; John Darin, MD, Medical Director

**Zeiter Eye Surgical Center, Inc.,** 1801 E. March Lane, Suite C360, Stockton, CA 95210; tel. 209/337-2020; FAX. 209/337-2021; Theresa Slaton, RN, Surgical Administrator

## COLORADO

**Avista Surgery Center,** 2525 Fourth Street, Lower Level, Boulder, CO 80304; tel. 303/443-3672; John Sackett, Administrator

**Boulder Medical Center, P C,** 2750 Broadway, Boulder, CO 80304; tel. 303/440-3000; Mr. Bradford McKane, Chief Executive Officer

**Centennial Medical Plaza,** 14200 East Arapahoe Road, Centennial, CO 80112; tel. 303/699-3000; FAX. 303/699-3152; Mary Beth Savory, Director of Operations

**Centrum Surgical Center,** 8200 East Belleview, Suite 300, East Tower, Greenwood Village, CO 80111; tel. 303/290-0600; FAX. 303/290-6359; Ken Kolb, Administrator

**Colorado Center for Reproductive Medicine,** 10290 Ridgegate Circle, Lone Tree, CO 80124-5331; tel. 303/788-8300; FAX. 303/788-8310; Dr. William Schoolcraft, Administrator

**Colorado Outpatient Eye Surgical Center,** 2480 South Downing, Suite G-20, Denver, CO 80210; tel. 303/777-7303; FAX. 303/282-0266; Diane Nelson, RN, ASC Administrator

**Colorado Springs Eye Surgery Center,** 2920 North Cascade Avenue, Colorado Springs, CO 80907; tel. 719/636-5054; FAX. 719/520-3576; Dr. Robert Foerster, Medical Director

**Colorado Springs Health Partners Ambulatory Surgery Center,** 1615 Medical Center Point, Colorado Springs, CO 80907; tel. 719/636-3555; FAX. 719/538-2999; Ms. Joan Compton, VP Operations

**Colorado Springs Surgery Center An Affiliate of SCA,** 1615 Medical Center Point, Colorado Springs, CO 80907; tel. 719/635-7740; FAX. 719/635-7750; Jenny (Jen) Knellinger, Administrator

**Day Surgery of Grand Junction, Inc.,** 1000 Wellington Avenue, Grand Junction, CO 81501; tel. 970/245-5989; FAX. 970/243-9023; Karen Higuera, RN, Surgery Center Administrator

**Denver Eye Surgery Center, Inc.,** 13772 Denver West Parkway, Building 55, Suite 120, Lakewood, CO 80401; tel. 303/273-8770; FAX. 303/273-8775

**Denver Midtown Surgery Center,** 1919 East 18th Avenue, Denver, CO 80206; tel. 303/322-3993; FAX. 303/322-7329; Lisa Cross, Administrator

**Dishler Laser Institute,** 8400 East Prentice Avenue, Suite 1200, Greenwood Village, CO 80111; tel. 303/793-3000; FAX. 303/793-3008; Jon Dishler, MD, President

**Durango Surgicenter, LLC,** 316 Sawyer Drive, Durango, CO 81303; tel. 970/259-3818; FAX. 970/259-9553; D.J. Winder, MD, Administrator

**Eye Center of Northern Colorado Surgery Center,** 1725 E. Prospect Avenue, Fort Collins, CO 80525; tel. 970/221-2222; FAX. 970/221-2223; Carol Wittmer, Administrator

**Eye Surgery Center of Colorado, P.C.,** 8403 Bryant Street, Westminster, CO 80031; tel. 303/426-4810; FAX. 303/426-8708; William G. Self, Jr., MD, Administrator

**Foot Surgery Center of Northern Colorado,** 1355 Riverside Avenue, #B, Fort Collins, CO 80524; tel. 970/484-4620; FAX. 970/407-1194; Adriann Anderson, Administrator

**Kaiser Permanente Ambulatory Surgery Center,** 2045 Franklin Street, Denver, CO 80205; tel. 303/764-4444; Elizabeth Reimann

**Littleton Day Surgery Center,** 8381 South Park Lane, Littleton, CO 80120; tel. 303/795-2244; FAX. 303/795-5965; Cindy Richardson, RN, BS, CLNC, Clinical Director/Administrator

**North Denver Endoscopy Center.,** 10001 North Washington St., Thornton, CO 80229; tel. 303/205-1090; FAX. 303/205-1091; Lance Goudzwaard, Chief Executive Officer

**Orthopaedic & Spine Center of the Rockies Ambulatory Surgery Center,** 2500 East Prospect Road, Fort Collins, CO 80525; tel. 970/493-4010; FAX. 970/419-7151; Barb Hardes, RN, BSN, CNOR, Director/Administrator of Surgical Operations

**Park Meadows Outpatient Surgery,** 7430 Park Meadows Drive #300, Lone Tree, CO 80124; tel. 303/706-1100; FAX. 303/790-7322; Charlene A. Sherwood, Administrator

**Peak One Surgery Center, LLC,** 350 Peak One Drive, P.O. Box 4460, Frisco, CO 80443; tel. 970/668-1458; FAX. 970/668-6677; Diane Lampron, Administrator

**Pikes Peak Endoscopy & Surgery Center,** 1699 Medical Center Pt., Colorado Springs, CO 80907; tel. 719/632-7101; FAX. 719/632-4468; Tricia Tappan, Chief Executive Officer

**Pueblo Surgery Center,** 25 Montebello Road, Pueblo, CO 81001; tel. 719/544-1600; FAX. 719/544-2599; Jennifer Arellano, Administrator

**South Denver Endoscopy Center, Inc.,** 499 East Hampden Avenue, Suite 430, Englewood, CO 80110; tel. 303/874-0350; Dr. Dan Hruza, Medical Director

**Surgery Center of Fort Collins,** 1100 East Prospect Road, Fort Collins, CO 80525; tel. 970/494-4800; FAX. 970/493-2380; Ross Alexander, Administrator

**U.S. Air Force Academy Clinic,** 10 MDG/CC, 4102 Pinion Drive, USAF Academy, CO 80840-4000; tel. 719/333-5660; FAX. 719/333-5670

## CONNECTICUT

**Connecticut Foot Surgery Center,** 318 New Haven Avenue, Milford, CT 06460; tel. 203/882-0065; FAX. 203/882-0248; Martin Pressman, DPM, Administrator

**HealthSouth Surgery Center of Hartford,** 100 Retreat Avenue, Hartford, CT 06106; tel. 860/549-7970; FAX. 860/247-4121; Theresa Klimczyk, Administrative Director

**Stamford Surgical Center,** 32 Strawberry Hill Court, Stamford, CT 06902; tel. 203/276-6196; FAX. 203/276-4921; Patrice Kelly, Executive Director of Perioperative Services

## DELAWARE

**Bayview Endoscopy Center, Inc.,** 1539 Savannah Road, Lewes, DE 19958; tel. 302/644-0455; FAX. 302/645-5214; Harry J. Anagnostakos, DO, President

**Cataract and Laser Center, LLC,** 4102 Ogletown/Stanton Road, Suite 1, Newark, DE 19713; tel. 302/454-8802; FAX. 302/454-8801; Alexandra Meyer, Center Administrator

**Central Delaware Endoscopy Unit,** 644 South Queen Street, Suite 105, Dover, DE 19904; tel. 302/677-1617; FAX. 302/677-1669; William M. Kaplan, MD, Medical Director

**Limestone Medical Center, Inc.,** 1941 Limestone Road, Suite 113, Wilmington, DE 19808; tel. 302/633-9873; FAX. 302/992-0563; Thomas E. Mulhern, MBA, CASC Executive Director

## DISTRICT OF COLUMBIA

**Center for Ambulatory Surgery, Inc.,** 1145 19th Street, NW, Suite 850, Washington, DC 20036; tel. 202/223-9040; FAX. 202/223-9047; William Heron, MD, Medical Director

**Planned Parenthood of Metropolitan Washington, D.C.,** 1108 16th Street, NW, Washington, DC 20036; tel. 202/347-8512; FAX. 202/347-0267; Takina Wilson, Director of Patient Services

**Premier Surgery Center of D.C.,** 6323 Georgia Avenue, NW, Suite 200, Washington, DC 20011; tel. 202/291-0126; FAX. 202/291-0126; Lenora Hollaway, RN, Administrative Director

**The Endoscopy Center of Washington, DC, L.P.,** 2021 K Street, NW, Suite T-115, Washington, DC 20006; tel. 202/775-8692; FAX. 202/463-1165; Debra Jay RN, Center Director

## FLORIDA

**Aker-Kasten Eye Center,** 1445 Northwest Boca Raton Boulevard, Boca Raton, FL 33432; tel. 561/338-7722; FAX. 561/338-7785; Kim Harrington, Administrator

**All Saints Surgery Center,** 11377 Cortez Boulevard, Brooksville, FL 34613; tel. 352/597-3060; FAX. 352/597-3077; Julie Curky, RN, Administrator and Clinical Director

**Alpha Ambulatory Surgery, Inc.,** 2160 Capital Circle, NE, Tallahassee, FL 32308; tel. 850/385-0033; FAX. 850/422-0201; Juanita Legree, RN, Administrator

**Ambulatory Surgery Center,** 4500 East Fletcher Avenue, Tampa, FL 33613; tel. 813/977-8550; FAX. 813/977-7941; Edward J. Tennant, CASC, Administrator

**Ambulatory Surgery Center of Brevard,** 719 East New Haven Avenue, Melbourne, FL 32901; tel. 321/726-4106; FAX. 321/728-3001; Norm Gagnon, General Manager

**Ambulatory Surgical Care,** 1045 North Courtenay Parkway, Merritt Island, FL 32953; tel. 321/452-4448; FAX. 321/452-4533; Robyn Allard, RN, Administrator

**Atlantic Surgery Center,** 541 Health Boulevard, Daytona Beach, FL 32114; tel. 386/239–0021; FAX. 386/248–8226; Shirley A. Hines, RN, CASC, Administrator

**Atlantic Surgical Center, Inc.,** 150 Southwest 12th Avenue, Suite 450, Pompano Beach, FL 33069; tel. 954/941–3369; FAX. 954/941–8470; Andrew Byers, Administrator

**Barkley Surgicenter,** 63 Barkley Circle, Suite 104, Fort Myers, FL 33907; tel. 239/275–8452; FAX. 239/275–1969; Kerri Gantt LHRM, CMM, Administrative Director

**Bayfront Same Day Surgery Center, LLC,** 603 Seventh Street South, St. Petersburg, FL 33701; tel. 727/553–7906; FAX. 727/553–7880; Jatin Motiwal, Executive Director

**Belleair Surgery Center,** 1130 Ponce de Leon Boulevard, Clearwater, FL 33756; tel. 727/581–4800; FAX. 813/585–0319; Ed Callahan, Administrator

**Beraja Healthcare Corp.,** 2550 Douglas Road, Coral Gables, FL 33134; tel. 305/443–7070; FAX. 305/357–1701; Margarita Caffe, RN, DON

**Bethesda Outpatient Surgery Center, LLC,** 10301 Hagen Ranch Road, Suite 520, Boynton Beach, FL 33437; tel. 561/374–5550; FAX. 561/374–9977; Maddie Linder, RN, Director of Surgical Services

**Boynton Beach ASC, LLC,** 1717-1799 Woolbright Road, Boynton Beach, FL 33426; tel. 516/737–8031; FAX. 561/736–5062; Lily Lee, Administrator

**Brandon Surgery Center,** 711 South Parsons, Brandon, FL 33511; tel. 813/654–7771; FAX. 813/654–3347; Edward J. Tennant, CASC, Administrator and Chief Executive Officer

**Brevard Surgery Center,** 665 Apollo Boulevard, Melbourne, FL 32901; tel. 321/984–3200; FAX. 321/984–0032; Gary R. Hardey, MBA, Administrator

**Cape Surgery Center,** 1941 Waldemere Street, Sarasota, FL 34239-3555; tel. 941/917–1900; FAX. 941/917–2356; Sharon Tolhurst, RN, MBA, Administrator

**Center for Digestive Health and Pain Management,** 12700 Creekside Lane, Suite 202, P.O. Box 33906, Fort Myers, FL 33919; tel. 941/489–4454; FAX. 941/489–2114; Vivian DiCarlo, RN, Nursing Director

**Center for Special Surgery,** 4650 Fourth Street, N., St. Petersburg, FL 33703; tel. 727/527–1919; FAX. 727/527–0714; Paula Russo, Administrator

**Central Florida Eye Institute,** 3133 Southwest 32nd Avenue, Ocala, FL 34474; tel. 352/237–8400; FAX. 352/237–7190; Thomas L. Croley, MD

**Citrus Endoscopy and Surgery Center,** 6412 West Gulf to Lake Highway, Crystal River, FL 34429; tel. 352/563–0223; FAX. 352/563–2961

**Citrus Surgery Center,** 110 North Lecanto Highway, Lecanto, FL 34461; tel. 352/527–1825; FAX. 352/527–1827; Richard Rice, Facility Administrator

**Clearwater Endoscopy Center,** 401 Corbett Street, Suite 220, Clearwater, FL 33756; tel. 727/443–0100; FAX. 727/461–4893; Nancy Wheeling RN, LHRM Administrator

**Coral View Surgery Center,** 8390 West Flager, Suite 216, Miami, FL 33144; tel. 305/226–5574; Ruben Paradela, Chief Executive Officer

**Cortez Foot Surgery Center, PA,** 1800 Cortez Road W, Suite B, Bradenton, FL 34207; tel. 941/758–4608; FAX. 941/758–4438; Connie Belculfine, Administrator

**Countryside Surgery Center,** 3291 North McMullen Booth Road, Clearwater, FL 33761; tel. 727/725–5800; FAX. 727/797–4002; Diana Procuniar, Administrator

**Dermatologic and Cosmetic Surgery Center, L.L.C.,** 2668 Swamp Cabbage Court, Fort Myers, FL 33901; tel. 239/936–1145; FAX. 239/275–5074; Charles Eby, MD

**Doctors Surgery Center,** 921 North Main Street, Kissimmee, FL 34744; tel. 407/933–7800; FAX. 407/933–0564; Deloris Hillman, Administrator

**Emerald Coast Surgery Center,** 995 Northwest Mar Walt Drive, Fort Walton Beach, FL 32547; tel. 850/863–7887; FAX. 850/863–4955; Anne Smith, Administrator

**Endoscopy Center of Ocala, Inc.,** 1901 SE 18th Avenue, #400, Ocala, FL 34471; tel. 352/732–8905; FAX. 352/732–2661; Bill Emerson, Administrator

**Endoscopy Center of Sarasota,** 1435 Osprey Avenue, Suite 100, Sarasota, FL 34239; tel. 941/366–4475; FAX. 941/366–4390; Pam Copeland, RN, Administrator

**Eye Care and Surgery Center of Ft. Lauderdale,** 2540 Northeast Ninth Street, Ft. Lauderdale, FL 33304; tel. 954/561–3533; FAX. 954/565–9706; Jane M. Beatly, Administrator

**Eye Surgery and Laser Center,** 4120 Del Prado Boulevard, Cape Coral, FL 33904; tel. 239/542–4068; FAX. 239/542–0704; Latosha Underwood, RN, BSN, Risk Manager Designee

**Eye Surgery and Laser Center, LLC,** 409 Avenue K, SE, Winter Haven, FL 33880; tel. 863/299–8574; FAX. 863/294–8305; Eileen T. Beltramba, RN, BS, Center Director

**Eye Surgicenter,** 2521 Northwest 41st Street, Gainesville, FL 32606; tel. 352/377–7733; FAX. 352/377–9577; William A. Newsome, MD

**Florida Eye Clinic Ambulatory Surgical Center,** 160 Boston Avenue, Altamonte Springs, FL 32701; tel. 407/834–7776; FAX. 407/834–2478; Scott Bridgeman, Chief Executive Officer

**Florida Eye Institute Surgicenter, LLC,** 2750 Indian River Boulevard, Vero Beach, FL 32960; tel. 772/569–9500; FAX. 772/569–9507; Lyn M. Lane, Administrator

**Florida Medical Clinic Special Procedures Center,** 38135 Market Square, Zephyrhills, FL 33542; tel. 813/780–8266; FAX. 813/715–4150; Melissa LoParco, RN, Manager

**Florida Surgery Center,** 180 Boston Avenue, Altamonte Springs, FL 32701; tel. 407/830–0573; FAX. 407/830–4373; Patricia Rustin, Administrator

**Foundation for Advanced Eye Care,** 3737 N. Pine Island Rd, Sunrise, FL 33351; tel. 954/572–5888; Wayne Bizer, DO Medical Director

**Gaskins Eye Care and Surgery Center,** 2335 Ninth Street, N., Suite 304, Naples, FL 34103; tel. 239/263–7750; William Darrell Gaskins, MD

**Gulf Coast Surgery Center,** 411 Second Street, E., Bradenton, FL 34208; tel. 941/746–1121; FAX. 941/746–7816; Diana Williford, MBA/HA, Administrator

**Gulfcoast Surgery Center,** 12132 Cortez Boulevard, Brooksville, FL 34613; tel. 352/596–0744; Fawzi Soliman, MD

**HealthPark Surgery Center,** 1283 Jacaranda Boulevard, Venice, FL 34292; tel. 941/497–5660; FAX. 941/492–3942; Kermit Knight, CASC Administrator

**HealthSouth Orlando Center for Outpatient Surgery,** 1405 South Orange Avenue, Suite 400, Orlando, FL 32806; tel. 407/426–8331; FAX. 407/425–9582

**Hillmoor Eye Surgery Center, LLC dba One Day Surgery,** 1715 Southeast Tiffany Avenue, Port St. Lucie, FL 34952; tel. 772/335–7005; FAX. 772/335–3394; Diane DelRosario, Administrator

**Holiday Surgery Center,** 1109 U.S. Highway 19, Suite B, Holiday, FL 34691; tel. 727/934–5705; FAX. 727/937–3756; David Wall, Practice Administrator

**Jacksonville Surgery Center,** 7021 A.C. Skinner Parkway, Jacksonville, FL 32256; tel. 904/281–0021; FAX. 904/281–0988; Katherine Anderson, RN, BSN, Administrator

**Kissimmee Surgery Center,** 2275 North Central Avenue, Kissimmee, FL 34741; tel. 407/870–0573; FAX. 407/870–1859; James Caudill, Administrator

**Lake Surgery and Endoscopy Center,** 8100 Country Road 44 LEG A, Leesburg, FL 34788; tel. 352/323–1995; FAX. 352/326–9990; Ismail A. Ismail, RPH, Chief Financial Officer

**Lee County Center for Foot and Ankle Surgery, Inc.,** 12734 Kenwood Lane, Suite 44, Fort Myers, FL 33907; tel. 941/936–2454; FAX. 941/936–1974; Sandra Desai, DPM

**Martin Memorial SurgiCenter,** 509 Riverside Drive, Suite 100, Stuart, FL 34994; tel. 772/223–5920; FAX. 772/288–5820

**Mayo Clinic Jacksonville Ambulatory Surgery Center for G.I.,** 4500 San Pablo Road, Jacksonville, FL 32224; tel. 904/223–2000; Christopher Hasse, Manager of Clinical Operations

**Medical Development Corporation of Pasco County,** 7315 Hudson Avenue, Hudson, FL 34667; tel. 727/868–9563; FAX. 727/869–2773; Dawn M. Ernst, Director, Nursing

**Melbourne Surgery Center,** 1340 Medical Park Drive, Suite 101, Melbourne, FL 32901; tel. 321/729–9493; FAX. 321/768–6043; Brian Rye, Administrator

**Merritt Island Surgery Center,** 220 North Sykes Creek Parkway, Suite 101, Merritt Island, FL 32953; tel. 321/459–0015; FAX. 321/459–2291; Cynthia Johnson, Administrator

**Miami Eye Center,** 619 Northwest 12th Avenue, Miami, FL 33136; tel. 305/326–0260; FAX. 305/326–1907; Edward C. Gelber, MD, FACS

**Mid Florida Surgery Center,** 17564 West Highway 441, Mt. Dora, FL 32757; tel. 352/735–4100; FAX. 352/735–2444; Patsy Lentz, RN, Administrative Director

**Montgomery Eye Center,** 700 Neapolitan Way, Naples, FL 34103; tel. 239/261–8383; FAX. 239/261–8443; Jay E. Montgomery, Administrator

**Mullis Eye Institute, Inc.,** 1600 Jenks Avenue, Panama City, FL 32405; tel. 904/763–6666; FAX. 904/763–6665; Colette Smith, RN, Director

**Naples Day Surgery North,** 11161 Health Park Boulevard, Naples, FL 34110; tel. 239/598–3111; FAX. 239/598–1707; Thomas C. Buckley, Executive Director

**New Port Richey Surgery Center,** 5415 Gulf Drive, New Port Richey, FL 34652; tel. 727/848–0446; FAX. 727/842–3166; Sandra McFarland, RN, Administrator

**Newgate Surgery Center, Inc.,** 5200 Tamiami Trail, Suite 202, Naples, FL 34103; tel. 239/263–6766; FAX. 239/263–3320; Dr. R. Crane

**North County Surgicenter,** 4000 Burns Road, Palm Beach Gardens, FL 33410; tel. 561/626–6446; FAX. 561/626–7244; Brenna Fazio, Business Manager

**North Florida Surgery Center,** 256 Professional Glen, Lake City, FL 32025; tel. 386/758–8937; FAX. 386/755–2169; Vivian Douberly, Administrator

**North Florida Surgical Pavilion,** 6705 Northwest 10th Place, Gainesville, FL 32605; tel. 352/333–4555; FAX. 352/333–4569; Susan Roland, Administrative Director

**North Tampa Outpatient Surgical Facility,** 5329 Primrose Lake Circle, Tampa, FL 33647; tel. 813/463–9762; Becky Furniss, Administrator

**Northwest Florida Surgery Center,** 767 Airport Road, Panama City, FL 32405; tel. 850/747–0400; FAX. 850/913–9744; Ron Samuelian, Chief Executive Officer

**Novamed Surgery Center of Sebring,** 3601 South Highlands Avenue, Sebring, FL 33870; tel. 863/382–7500; FAX. 863/385–7332; Dana G. Cowart, ASC Director

**Oakwater Surgical Center, Inc.,** 3885 Oakwater Circle, Suite B, Orlando, FL 32806; tel. 407/438–9533; FAX. 407/438–9542; Carol Terry, RN

**Orange Park Surgery Center,** 2050 Professional Center Drive, Orange Park, FL 32073; tel. 904/272–2550; FAX. 904/272–7911; Michele K. Cook, RN, Administrator

**Outpatient Surgical Services, Ltd.,** 301 Northwest 82nd Avenue, Plantation, FL 33324; tel. 954693–8600; FAX. 954/424–1966; Wayne C. Jones, FACHE, Administrator

**Palm Beach Eye Clinic,** 130 Butler Street, West Palm Beach, FL 33407; tel. 561/832–6113; FAX. 561/833–3003; Andre J. Golino, MD

**Palm Beach Lakes Surgery Center,** 2047 Palm Beach Lakes Boulevard, West Palm Beach, FL 33409; tel. 561/296–1330; FAX. 561/296–1350; Jonathan Cutler DPM, Manager

**Parkside Surgery Center,** 2731 Park Street, Jacksonville, FL 32205; tel. 904/389–1077; FAX. 904/338–9016; David Manning, Administrator

**Physician's Surgical Care Center,** 2056 Aloma Avenue, Winter Park, FL 32792; tel. 407/647–5100; FAX. 407/647–1966

**Physicians Ambulatory Surgery Center,** 300 Clyde Morris Boulevard, Suite B, Ormond Beach, FL 32174; tel. 386/672–1080; FAX. 386/672–8628; Lee Baylor, Administrator

**Physicians Surgery Center, Ltd., dba Lee Island Coast Surgery Center,** 4035 Evans Avenue, Fort Myers, FL 33901; tel. 941/939–7375; FAX. 941/275–5248; Jacquelyn Paul, RN, Administrator

**Port Orange Endoscopy & Surgery Center,** 1185 Dunlawton Avenue, Suite 100, Port Orange, FL 32127; tel. 386/672–0017; FAX. 386/672–6732; Susan K. Amon, RN, DON LHCRM

**Rand Surgical Pavilion Corp.,** Five West Sample Road, Deerfield Beach, FL 33064; tel. 954/782–1700; FAX. 954/782–7490; Deborah Rand, Administrator

**Same Day Surgicenter of Orlando,** 88 West Kaley Street, Orlando, FL 32806; tel. 407/423–0573; FAX. 407/841–3872; Bob Bashore, Administrator

**Samuel Wells Surgicenter, Inc.,** 3599 University Boulevard, S., Suite 604, Jacksonville, FL 32216; tel. 904/399–0905; FAX. 904/346–0757; Faye T. Evans, Risk Manager

**Seven Springs Surgery Center, Inc.,** 2024 Seven Springs Boulevard, New Port Richey, FL 34655; tel. 727/376–7000; FAX. 727/375–8944; Kathleen M. Geiger, RN, Surgery Director

**Southwest Florida Endoscopy Center,** 5050 Mason Corbin Court, Ft. Myers, FL 33907; tel. 239/275–6678; FAX. 239/275–5216; Jansi Prabakaran, MD, Administrator

**Southwest Florida Institute of Ambulatory Surgery,** 3700 Central Avenue, Suite Two, Ft. Myers, FL 33901; tel. 239/275–0665; FAX. 239/275–0503; Susan Hanzevack, Executive Director

**Specialty Surgery Of Ocala, LLC,** 3201 Southwest 34th Street, Ocala, FL 34474; tel. 352/237–6162; FAX. 352/509–9409; DeeDee Burroughs, RN, LHRM, Nurse Administrator

**St. Augustine Endoscopy Center,** 212 Southpark Circle, East, St. Augustine, FL 32086; tel. 904/824–6108; FAX. 904/823–9613; Santiago A. Rosado, MD, FACP, FACG, President

**St. Lucy's Outpatient Surgery Center,** 21275 Olean Boulevard, Port Charlotte, FL 33952; tel. 941/625–1325; FAX. 941/255–6985; Barb Vivas, RN, DON, Clinical Administrator

**St. Luke's Outpatient Surgery Center - Satellite,** 4500 San Pablo Road, Jacksonville, FL 32224; tel. 904/953–0100; FAX. 904/953–0019; Carla Pats, Manager

**St. Luke's Surgical Center,** 43309 U.S. Highway 19, N., Tarpon Spring, FL 34689; tel. 727/938–2020; FAX. 727/938–5606; Gustavo Gamero, MD, Medical Director

**Suncoast Eye Center, Eye Surgery Institute,** 14003 Lakeshore Boulevard, Hudson, FL 34667; tel. 727/868–9442; FAX. 727/862–6210; Lawrence A. Seigel, MD, PA, Medical Director

**Suncoast Medical Clinic, LLC,** 601 Seventh Street, S., St. Petersburg, FL 33701; tel. 727/894–1818; FAX. 727/824–7177; David Bailey, Executive Director

**Surgery Center at Coral Springs,** 967 University Drive, Coral Springs, FL 33071; tel. 954341–5553; FAX. 954/344–7054; Jeff Rosenberg, Administrator

**Surgery Center at St. Andrews, Inc.,** 1350 East Venice Avenue, Venice, FL 34285; tel. 941/488–2030; FAX. 941/484–2010; Carol Carr, Administrator

**Surgery Center of North Florida, Inc.,** 6520 Northwest Ninth Boulevard, Gainsville, FL 32615; tel. 352/331–7987; FAX. 352/331–2787; Joy Ingram, Administrator

**Surgery Center of Stuart,** 2096 Southeast Ocean Boulevard, Stuart, FL 34996; tel. 772/223–0174; FAX. 772/223–0946; Barbara Tidwell, Administrator

**Surgical Licensed Ward, dba Underwood Surgery Center,** 110 West Underwood Street, Suite B, Orlando, FL 32806; tel. 407/648–9151; FAX. 407/426–7017; Doug Oakley, Administrator

**Surgical Park Center, Ltd.,** 9100 Southwest 87th Avenue, Miami, FL 33176; tel. 305/271–9100; FAX. 305/598–5509; Lionel Lima

**Surgicare Center, Inc.,** 4101 Evans Avenue, Ft. Myers, FL 33901; tel. 239/939–3456; FAX. 239/335–1962; Mary E. Blackwell, RN, BS, Director of Nursing

**Tallahassee Endoscopy Center,** 2400 Miccosukee Road, Tallahassee, FL 32308; tel. 850/877–2105; FAX. 850/942–1761; Noel Withers, Administrator

**Tallahassee Outpatient Surgery Center, Inc.,** 3334 Capital Medical Boulevard, Suite 500, Tallahassee, FL 32308; tel. 904/877–4688; FAX. 904/877–0368; Judi Cleckner RN, Administrator

**Tallahassee Single Day Surgery,** 1661 Phillips Road, Tallahassee, FL 32308; tel. 850/878–5165; FAX. 850/942–5545; Elizabeth Trikardos, Director of Nursing

**Tampa Bay Surgery Center,** 11811 North Dale Mabry Hwy, Tampa, FL 33618; tel. 813/961–8500; FAX. 813/265–2564; Jay L. Rosen, MD, Chief Executive Officer

**Tampa Bay Surgery Center,** 2727 MLK Blvd, Tampa, FL 33607; tel. 813/961–8500; FAX. 813/265–2564; Jay L. Rosen, MD, Chief Executive Officer

**Tampa Eye Surgery Center,** 4302 North Gomez, Tampa, FL 33607; tel. 813/870–6330; FAX. 813/871–3956; Beverly Martin, Administrator

**Tampa Outpatient Surgical Facility,** 5013 North Armenia Avenue, Tampa, FL 33603; tel. 813/875–0562; FAX. 813/871–5236; Christina McDonald, Administrator

**The Aesthetic Plastic Surgery Center,** 135 San Marco Drive, Venice, FL 34285; tel. 941/484–6836; FAX. 941/484–9690; Linda Martin, Administrative Director

**The Endoscopy Center,** 4810 North Davis Highway, Pensacola, FL 32503; tel. 850/474–8988; FAX. 850/478–9903; Steve Dunn, Administrator

**The Endoscopy Center, Inc.,** 5101 Southwest 8th Street, Miami, FL 33134; tel. 305/461–1881; FAX. 305/445–2406; Carla Guerrero, Administration

**The Eye Associates Surgery Center,** 6002 Pointe West Boulevard, Bradenton, FL 34209; tel. 941/792–2020; FAX. 941/792–2832; Pamela Morgan, RN, ASC Director

**The Gastrointestinal Center of Hialeah, Inc.,** 135 West 49th Street, Hialeah, FL 33012; tel. 305/825–1487; FAX. 305/825–9731; Maria T. Pineda, Administrator

**The Ocala Eye Surgery Center,** 3330 Southwest 33rd Road, Ocala, FL 34474; tel. 352/873–9311; FAX. 352/873–9652; Ann Hotaling, Director

**The Sarasota Ophthalmology, ASC, LLC, dba Center for Advanced Eye Surgery,** 3920 Bee Ridge Road Building F, Suite C, Sarasota, FL 34233; tel. 941/925–0000; FAX. 941/927–2726; Darice Downs, RN, LHRM, Center Director

**The Sheridan Surgery Center,** 95 Bulldog Boulevard, Suite 104, Melbourne, FL 32901; tel. 321/952–9800; FAX. 321/952–7889; Anne Latorra, Director

**The Surgery Center of Coral Gables, LLC,** 1097 SW Le Jeune Road, Miami, FL 33134; tel. 305/461–1300; Laura Lilburn, RN, CNOR, Center Director

**Total Surgery Center,** 130 Tamiami Trail, Suite 210, Naples, FL 34102; tel. 239/434–4118; FAX. 239/434–6343; Mary Boedeker, Administrator

**Treasure Coast Center for Surgery,** 1411 East Ocean Boulevard, Stuart, FL 34996; tel. 772/286–8028; FAX. 772/283–6628; Andrea Day, Business Office Manager

**University Surgical Center,** 7251 University Boulevard, Suite 100, Winter Park, FL 32792; tel. 407/677–0066; FAX. 407/677–4199; Laura Hofma Butrick, MBA, RHIA, CASC, Administrator

**Urological Ambulatory Surgery Center, Inc.,** 1812 North Mills Avenue, Orlando, FL 32803; tel. 407/992–2640; FAX. 407/897–2290; William Hamiger, Administrator

**Venture Ambulatory Surgery Center,** 16853 Northeast Second Avenue, Suite 400, North Miami Beach, FL 33162; tel. 305/652–2999; FAX. 305/652–8156; Lali Perez, RN, BSN, Center Director

**Vero Eye Center,** 70 Royal Palm Pointe, Vero Beach, FL 32960; tel. 772/569–6600; FAX. 772/569–5341; E.S. Branigan, III, MD

**Visual Health & Surgical Center,** 2889 10th Ave. N, Palm Springs, FL 33461; tel. 561/747–1111; FAX. 560/747–6682; Tom M. Coffman, MD, Medical Director

**Volusia Endoscopy & Surgery Center, Inc.,** 550 Memorial Circle, Suite G, Ormond Beach, FL 32174; tel. 386/672–0017; FAX. 386/672–6732; Susan K. Amon, RN, DON LHCRM

**Waterside Ambulatory Surgical Center, Inc.,** 2001 North Flagler Drive, West Palm Beach, FL 33407; tel. 561/659–6543; FAX. 561/659–3533; Lisa Bolognini, Administrative Director

## GEORGIA

**Advanced Aesthetics Plastic Surgery Center,** 874 Lanier Avenue West, One Prestige Park, Fayetteville, GA 30214; tel. 770/461–4000; FAX. 770/603–7064; Paul D. Feldman, President

**Advanced Surgery Center of Georgia,** 220 Hospital Road, Canton, GA 30114; tel. 770/479–2202; FAX. 770/479–6666; Marguerite Cammarata, Administrator

**Aesthetic Laser & Surgery Facility,** 416 Gordon Avenue, Thomasville, GA 31792-6644; tel. 229/228–7200; FAX. 229/228–5193; G. Courtney Houston, MD, Medical Director

**Affinity Outpatient Services,** 2224 US Highway 41 North, Tifton, GA 31794; tel. 912/391–4299; FAX. 912/391–4291; Barry L. Cutts, Administrator

**Albany Surgery Center, LLP,** 531 Seventh Avenue, Albany, GA 31701; tel. 229/883–3535; FAX. 229/883–3783; Stephen M. Wilder, DPM, Medical Director

**Ambulatory Foot and Leg Surgical Center,** 1650 Mulkey Road, Austell, GA 30106; tel. 770/941–3633; FAX. 770/944–9038; Douglas Elleby, DPM, Chief Executive Officer

**Ambulatory Laser and Surgery Center,** 425 Forest Parkway, Suite 103, Forest Park, GA 30297-2135; tel. 404/363–1087; FAX. 404/363–9951; Dr. Paul A. Colon, Medical Director

**Athens Plastic Surgery Center,** 2325 Prince Avenue, Athens, GA 30606; tel. 706/546–0280; FAX. 404/548–0258; Stephen B. Lober, MD, Administrator

**Atlanta Center for Women's Choice, Inc.,** 1874 Piedmont Ave NE, Ste 585 E, Atlanta, GA 30324; tel. 404/602–4495; FAX. 404/607–0728; Toni P. Hawkins, Administrator

**Atlanta Endoscopy Center, Ltd.,** 2665 North Decatur Road, Suite 545, Decatur, GA 30033; tel. 404/297–5000; FAX. 404/296–9890; Kevin Mussared RN Clinical Coordinator

**Atlanta Gastroenterology Associates,** 301 Philip Blvd, Suite A, Lawrenceville, GA 30046; tel. 770/822–5560; Diane Wilkins, Office Manager

**Atlanta Outpatient Peachtree Dunwoody Center,** 5505 Peachtree-Dunwoody Road, Suite 150, Atlanta, GA 30342; tel. 404/847–0893; FAX. 404/843–8664; Kim Ashe, Chief Executive Officer, Director

**Atlanta Women's Medical Center, Inc.,** 235 West Wieuca Road, Atlanta, GA 30342; tel. 404/257–0057; FAX. 404/257–1245; Golda Melnik, Administrator

**Augusta Plastic Surgery Center, Inc.,** 1348 Walton Way, Suite 6300, Augusta, GA 30901-2772; tel. 706/724–5611; FAX. 706/724–5435

**Augusta Surgical Center,** 915 Russell Street, Augusta, GA 30904-4115; tel. 706/738–4925; FAX. 706/738–7224; Jeff Simless, Administrator

**Brunswick Endoscopy Center,** 3217 4th Street, Brunswick, GA 31520-3759; tel. 912/267–1802; FAX. 912/267–0061; Rita Warren, Administrator

**Center for Plastic Surgery, Inc.,** 365 East Paces Ferry Road, Atlanta, GA 30305; tel. 404/814–0868; FAX. 404/814–0869; Dr. Vincent Zubowicz, Medical Director

**Clayton Outpatient Surgical Center, Inc.,** 6911 Tara Boulevard, Jonesboro, GA 30236; tel. 770/477–9535; FAX. 770/471–7826; Renee Grimsley, Administrator

**Cobb Foot and Leg Surgical Center,** 165 Vann Street, Marietta, GA 30060; tel. 770/422–9856; FAX. 770/984–0303; Glyn Lewis, Administrator

**Coliseum Same Day Surgery,** 340 Hospital Drive, P.O. Box 6154, Macon, GA 31208; tel. 912/742–1403; FAX. 912/742–1671; Lenore Sell, Administrator

**Columbus Women's Health Organization, Inc.,** 3850 Rosemont Drive, Columbus, GA 31901; tel. 706/323–8363

**DBA Atlanta Ambulatory Surgery Center, Atlanta Aesthetic Surgery Center, LLC,** 4200 Northside Parkway, Building Eight, Atlanta, GA 30327; tel. 404/233–3833; FAX. 404/233–8447; Debbie Clotfelter, Administrator

**DeKalb Gastroenterology Associates II, LLC, dba DeKalb Endoscopy Center,** 2675 North Decatur Road, Suite 506, Decatur, GA 30033; tel. 404/299–1679; FAX. 404/508–7558; Mark A. Stern, MD

**Dennis Surgery Center, Inc.,** 3193 Howell Mill Road, Suite 215, Atlanta, GA 30327; tel. 404/355–1312; FAX. 404/352–2798; Valerie Garrett, Administrator

**Dunwoody Outpatient Surgicenter, Inc.,** 4553 North Shallowford Road, Suite 60C, Atlanta, GA 30338; tel. 770/455–1983; FAX. 770/457–2823; Janet Davies, Administrator

**Endoscopy Center of Columbus, LLC,** 1130 Talbotton Road, Columbus, GA 31904-8745; tel. 706/641–6900; FAX. 706/327–0757; Jean Patterson, RN, Administrator

**Endoscopy Center of Southeast Georgia, Inc.,** 200 Maple Drive, P.O. Box 1367, Vidalia, GA 30474; tel. 912/538–1003; FAX. 912/537–9843; Dixie Calhoun, RN, Administrator

**Evans Surgery Center,** 635 Ronald Reagan Drive, Evans, GA 30809; tel. 706/868–3110; FAX. 706/868–3156; Sharon Gelinas, Administrator

**Feminist Women's Health Center,** 1924 Cliff Valley Way, Atlanta, GA 30329; tel. 404/728–7900; FAX. 404/728–7907; Erin Mabile, Clinical Director

**G.I. Endoscopy Center,** 6555 Professional Place, Suite B, Riverdale, GA 30274; tel. 770/692–0100; FAX. 770/692–6190; Aruna Prakash, BSc, Administrator

**Gainesville Surgery Center,** 1945 Beverly Road, Gainesville, GA 30501-2034; tel. 770/287–1500; Karen Fankhauser, Administrator

**Georgia Surgical Centers - South,** 541 Forest Parkway, Suite 14, Forest Park, GA 30297-6110; tel. 404/366–5652; Trudy Hunley, Administrator

**Gwinnet Endoscopy Center,** 301 Philip Blvd, NW, Suite B, Lawrenceville, GA 30046; tel. 770/682–7220; FAX. 770/338–0510; Kerry H. King, MD, Medical Director

**HealthSouth Surgery Center of Gwinnett,** 2131 Fountain Drive, Snellville, GA 30078; tel. 770/979–8200; FAX. 770/979–1327; Holly Kouts, Administrator

**Kramer Professional Building,** 215 Clairemont Avenue, Decatur, GA 30030; tel. 404/373–2529; FAX. 404/373–1655; Jerald N. Kramer, DPM, President

**Marietta Surgical Center,** 780 Canton Road, Suite 100, Marietta, GA 30060; tel. 770/422–1579; FAX. 770/428–4861; Faith Wheeler, RNCNOR, QA and Risk Manager

**Medical Eye Associates, Inc.,** 1429 Oglethorpe Street, Macon, GA 31201; tel. 478/743–7061; FAX. 478/743–6296; Diane Vaughn, Practice Manager

**North Atlanta Head and Neck Surgery Center, LLC,** 980 Johnson Ferry Road, Northside Doctors Centre, Atlanta, GA 30342; tel. 404/843–9171; FAX. 404/250–1881; Pradeep K. Snha, MD, PhD

**North Georgia Endoscopy Center, Inc.,** 320 Hospital Road, Canton, GA 30114; tel. 770/479–5535; FAX. 770/479–8821; Kevin V. Kellogg, Administrator

**North Georgia Outpatient Surgery Center,** 795 Red Bud Road, Calhoun, GA 30701; tel. 706/629–1852; FAX. 706/629–8004; Herbert E. Kosmahl, President

**North Oak Ambulatory Surgery Center, LLC,** 2718 North Oak Street, Valdosta, GA 31602; tel. 229/242–3668; FAX. 229/253–8666; T.E. Pitts, DPM

**Northeast Endoscopy Center, LLC,** 721 Wellness Way, Suite 110, Lawrenceville, GA 30045; tel. 770/995–7989; FAX. 770/339–8646; Betsy Roberts, Practice Manager

**Northeast Georgia Plastic Surgery Center,** 1296 Sims Street, Gainesville, GA 30501; tel. 770/534–1856; FAX. 770/531–0355; Sam Richwine, Medical Director

**Northlake Endoscopy Center,** 1459 Montreal Road, Suite 204, Tucker, GA 30084; tel. 770/939–4721; FAX. 770/939–1187; Ellen Burney, Administrator

**Northside Foot and Ankle Outpatient Surgical Center,** 3415 Holcomb Bridge Road, Norcross, GA 30092; tel. 770/449–1122; FAX. 770/242–8709; Steven T. Arminio, DPM, Administrator

**Northside Women's Clinic, Inc.,** 3543 Chamblee-Dunwoody Road, Atlanta, GA 30341; tel. 770/455–4210; FAX. 770/451–9529; James W. Gay, MD, Administrator

**Outpatient Center for Foot Surgery, Inc.,** 730 South Eighth Street, Suite B, Griffin, GA 30224; tel. 770/228–6644; FAX. 770/228–5769; Mark Henson, Administrator

**Paces Plastic Surgery Center, Inc.,** 3200 Downwood Circle, Suite 640, Atlanta, GA 30327; tel. 404/351–0051; FAX. 404/351–0632; Delene Graham, Office Manager

**Perimeter Surgery Center of Atlanta,** 1140 Hammond Drive, Building F, Suite 6100, Atlanta, GA 30328; tel. 770/551–9944; FAX. 770/551–8826; Cindy Smith, Administrator

**Planned Parenthood of Reproductive Health Services,** 1289 Broad Street, Augusta, GA 30911; tel. 706/724–5557; FAX. 706/724–5293; Vanetta D. King, Center Manager

**Pulliam Ambulatory Surgical Center,** 4167 Hospital Drive, P.O. Box 469, Covington, GA 30015; tel. 770/786–1234; M.M. Pulliam, PC, Medical Director

**Resurgens Surgical Center,** 5671 Peachtree Dunwoody Road, Suite 800, Atlanta, GA 30342; tel. 404/531–8532; Leslie Mattson, RN Administrator

**Savannah Foot And Ankle Surgery Center,** 310 Eisenhower Drive, Savannah, GA 31406; tel. 912/356–8440; FAX. 912/356–8439; Kay J. West, Administrator

**Savannah Medical Clinic,** 120 East 34th Street, Savannah, GA 31401; tel. 912/236–1603; FAX. 912/236–1605; William Knorr, MD, Administrator

**Savannah Plastic Surgicenter,** 7208 Hodgson Memorial, Savannah, GA 31406; tel. 912/351–5050; FAX. 912/351–5051; Scott W. Vann MD

**Statesboro Ambulatory Surgery Center,** 95 Bel-Air Drive, Statesboro, GA 30461-6879; tel. 912/489–6519; FAX. 912/764–7882; Luane L. Jordan, RN

**The Emory Clinic Ambulatory Surgery Center,** 1365 Clifton Road, NE, Atlanta, GA 30322; tel. 404/778–5000; W. Mike Mason, Administrator

**The Foot Surgery Center,** 2520 Windy Hill Road, Suite 105, Marietta, GA 30067; tel. 770/952–0868; FAX. 770/952–4833; Donna L. Cowan, Nurse Administrator

**The Rome Surgery Center,** 16 John Maddox Drive, Rome, GA 30165; tel. 706/802–3727; FAX. 706/802–3883; Neal Jochimsen, Administrator

**The Surgery Center, LLC,** 2548 Weems Rd, Columbus, GA 31909-6248; tel. 706/323–8803; FAX. 706/323–9101; Sharon Johnson, Administrator

**Tifton Endoscopy Center, Inc.,** 1111 E. 20th Street, Tifton, GA 31794-3668; tel. 229/382–9338; FAX. 229/382–4282; Linda Ingram, RN, Nursing Administrator

**Village Podiatry,** 1350 Upper Hembree Road, Suite 100, Roswell, GA 30076; tel. 770/663–8011; FAX. 770/754–9820; Dr. Mitch Hilsen, Administrator

**HAWAII**

**Aloha Surgical Center,** 239 Hoohana Street, Kahului, HI 96732; tel. 808/893–0578; FAX. 808/893–0580; Russell T. Stodd, MD, Medical Director

**Big Island Endoscopy Center, LLC,** 64-5188 Kinohou Street, Kamuela, HI 96743; tel. 808/887–0600; FAX. 808/887–6699; Aulii Delenia, Administrator

**Cataract and Vision Center of Hawaii,** 1712 Liliha Street, Suite 400, Honolulu, HI 96817; tel. 808/524–1010; FAX. 808/531–1030; Worldster Lee, MD, Director

**Hawaii Endoscopy Center, LLC,** 2226 Liliha Street, Suite 307, Honolulu, HI 96817; tel. 808/531–5828; FAX. 808/531–5819; Linda Oshiro, Administrator

**Hawaiian Eye Surgicenter,** 606 Kilani Avenue, Wahiawa, HI 96786; tel. 808/621–8448; FAX. 808/621–3177; Christopher M. Tortora, MD, Surgeon, Director

**Hilo Community Surgery Center,** 82 Pu'uhonu Place, Suite 100, Hilo, HI 96720; tel. 808/969–9669; FAX. 808/969–9608; Allan S. Takase, MD, Administrator

**Kaiser Honolulu Clinic,** 1010 Pensacola Street, Honolulu, HI 96814, tel. 808/432–2000; FAX. 808/597–2249; Jonathan Ganz, Administrator

**Kaiser Wailuku Clinic,** 80 Mahalani Street, Wailuku, HI 96793; tel. 808/243–6618; FAX. 808/243–6609; Mary Hew, Administrator

**The Endoscopy Center,** 134 Puuhonu Way, Hilo, HI 96720; tel. 808/935–1956; FAX. 808/935–7657; Jody Montell, Administrator

**The Surgical Suites, LLC,** 1100 Ward Avenue, Suite 1001, Honolulu, HI 96814; tel. 808/531–0127; FAX. 808/531–0455; Carlos Omphroy, MD, President

**IDAHO**

**Addison Surgery Center,** 191 Addison Avenue, Twin Falls, ID 83301; tel. 208/734–5993; FAX. 208/734–5993; David A. Blackmer, DPM, President

**Boise Gastroenterology Associates, P.A., Idaho Endoscopy Center,** 6259 W. Emerald Street, Boise, ID 83704; tel. 208/489–1900; FAX. 208/375–5286; Robb F. Gibson, MD, President

**Coeur D'Alene Foot and Ankle Surgery Center,** 101 Ironwood Drive, Suite 131, Coeur D'Alene, ID 83814; tel. 208/666–0814; FAX. 208/666–0916; Stephen A. Isham, DPM, Chief Executive Officer

**Coeur D'Alene Surgery Center,** 2121 Ironwood Center Drive, Coeur D'Alene, ID 83814; tel. 208/765–9059; FAX. 208/664–9998; Peter C. Jones, MD, President

**Emerald Surgical Center,** 811 North Liberty, Boise, ID 83704; tel. 208/323–4522; FAX. 208/321–9585; Camille Miley, Nurse Director

**Idaho Ambucare Center, Inc.,** 4400 Flamingo Avenue, Nampa, ID 83686; tel. 208/288–4750; FAX. 208/288–4765; Gary Botimer, Administrator

**Idaho Eye Surgicenter,** 2025 East 17th Street, Idaho Falls, ID 83404; tel. 208/524–2025; FAX. 208/529–1924; Bradley P. Garnder, MD

**Idaho Falls Surgical Center,** 1945 East 17th Street, Idaho Falls, ID 83404; tel. 208/529–1945; FAX. 208/529–1961; Steven V. Klippert, MD, Chief Executive Officer

**Idaho Foot Surgery Center,** 1540 Elk Creek Drive, Idaho Falls, ID 83401; tel. 208/529–8393; FAX. 208/529–8078; Bruce G. Tolman, DPM, Facility Director

**Jefferson Day Surgery Center,** 220 West Jefferson, Boise, ID 83702; tel. 208/343–3802; FAX. 208/343–9161; William Stano, President

**Millennium Surgery Center,** 1828 S. Millenium Way, Suite 100, Meridian, ID 83642; tel. 208/381–0262; FAX. 208/429–8575; Shane Ricks, Administrator

**North Idaho Cataract and Laser Center, Inc.,** 1814 Lincoln Way, Coeur D'Alene, ID 83814; tel. 208/667–2531; FAX. 208/765–9385; Karen Sines, Administrator

**Pacific Cataract and Laser Institute,** 2822 South Vista Avenue, Boise, ID 83705; tel. 208/385–7576; FAX. 208/385–0050; Lisa Brady, Site Manager

**St. Luke's Clinic, Gastroenterology,** 775 Pole Line Rd West, Suite 203, Twin Falls, ID 83301; tel. 208/732–3030; FAX. 208/733–8970; Karen R. Butler, Clinical Manager

**Surgicare Center of Idaho, LLC,** 360 East Mallard Drive, Suite 125, Boise, ID 83706; tel. 208/336–8700; FAX. 208/386–3238; Mark Hollingshead, Medical Director

**ILLINOIS**

**25 East Same Day Surgery,** 25 East Washington, Suite 300, Chicago, IL 60602; tel. 312/726–3329; FAX. 312/726–3823; Kimberly Zidonis, RN, Administrator

**Aanchor Health Center, Ltd.,** 1186 Roosevelt Rd., Glen Ellyn, IL 60137; tel. 630/495–4400; FAX. 630/629–5892; Aimee Dillard, Assistant Administrator

**Able Health Center, Ltd.,** 1640 Arlington Heights Road, Suite 110, Arlington Heights, IL 60004; tel. 847/255–7400; FAX. 847/398–4585

**Access Health Center, Ltd.,** 1700 75th Street, Downers Grove, IL 60516; tel. 630/964–0000; FAX. 630/964–0047; Jenny Mitchell, Assistant Administrator

**ACU Health Center, Ltd.,** 736 N. York Rd., Hinsdale, IL 60521; tel. 630/794–0645; FAX. 630/794–0169; Vera Schmidt, Chief of Operations

**Advantage Health Care, Ltd.,** 203 E. Irving Park Rd, Wood Dale, IL 60191; tel. 630/595–1515; FAX. 630/595–9907; Aimee Dillard, Assistant Administrator

**Ambulatory Surgicenter of Downers Grove, Ltd.,** 4333 Main Street, Downers Grove, IL 60515; tel. 630/322 9451; FAX. 630/322–9455; Inga Ferdkoff, MD, Administrator

**Bel-Clair Ambulatory Surgical Treatment Center,** 325 West Lincoln, Belleville, IL 62220; tel. 618/235–2299; FAX. 618/235–2556; David Horace, Administrator

**Belleville Surgical Center,** 28 North 64th Street, Belleville, IL 62223; tel. 618/398–5705; FAX. 618/398–5764; Diana Geoghegan, Administrator

**Belmont & Harlem Surgery Center,** 3101 North Harlem Avenue, Chicago, IL 60634; tel. 773/889–2000; FAX. 773/745–5522; Sandra Ankebrant, Executive Director

**Carle Surgicenter,** 1702 South Mattis Avenue, Champaign, IL 61821; tel. 217/326–2030; Administrator

**Children's Pediatric Specialty Services In Westchester,** 2301 Enterprise Drive, Westchester, IL 60154; tel. 708/836–4800; FAX. 708/836–4805; Kristen DiCicco, Administrator

**Community Health and Emergency Services,** 13245 Kessler Road, P.O. Box 233, Cairo, IL 62914; tel. 618/734–4400; FAX. 618/734–9046; Frederick L. Bernstein, Chief Executive Officer

**Dreyer Ambulatory Surgery Center,** 1221 North Highland Avenue, Aurora, IL 60506; tel. 630/264–8400; FAX. 630/264–8402; Brad Hlavacek, RN, BSN, MBA, Administrative Director

**Eastland Medical Plaza SurgiCenter, LLC,** 1505 Eastland Drive, Suite 180, Bloomington, IL 61701; tel. 309/662–2500; FAX. 309/662–7143; Brenda Cyrulik, Manager

**Edwardsville Ambulatory Surgical Center, LLC,** 12, Ginger Creek Parkway, Glen Carbon, IL 62034; tel. 618/656–8200; FAX. 618/656–8204; Michelle Looney, Director of Operations

**Elmwood Park Same Day Surgery Center,** 1614 North Harlem Avenue, Elmwood Park, IL 60607; tel. 708/452–5000; FAX. 708/452–5588; Mark Mayo, Administrator

**Foot and Ankle Surgical Center, Ltd.,** 1455 Golf Road, Suite 131, Des Plaines, IL 60016; tel. 847/390–7666; Lowell S. Weil, DPM, FACHS, Medical Director

**Forestview Medical Center, Ltd.,** 2750 S. River Road, Des Plaines, IL 60018; tel. 847/375–1000; FAX. 847/827–5977; Nancy Nelson, Administrator

**Fullerton Kimball Medical & Surgical Center,** 3412 West Fullerton Avenue, Chicago, IL 60647; tel. 773/235–8000; FAX. 773/235–7018; Renlin Xia, MD, Medical Director

**Golf Surgical Center,** 8901 Golf Road, Des Plaines, IL 60016; tel. 847/299–2273; FAX. 847/299–2297; Nicholas Lylizos, MD, Executive Director

Section C

**Hawthorn Surgery Center,** 1900 Hollister Drive, Suite 100, Libertyville, IL 60048; tel. 847/367-8100; FAX. 847/367-8335; Dr. Gary Rippberger, Administrator

**Hinsdale Surgical Center, LLC,** 908 North Elm Street, Suite 401, Hinsdale, IL 60521; tel. 630/325-5035; FAX. 630/325-5134; Shirley E. Zemansky, RN, Executive Director

**Hope Clinic for Women, Ltd.,** 1602 21st Street, Granite City, IL 62040; tel. 618/451-5722; FAX. 615/451-9092; Sally Burgess, MBA, Executive Director

**Illinois Eye Surgeons Cataract Surgery,** 3990 North Illinois Street, Belleville, IL 62221; tel. 618/235-3100; Nancy Mueth, Administrator

**Loyola Ambulatory Surgery Center at Oakbrook,** One South 224 Summit Avenue, Suite 201, Oakbrook Terrace, IL 60181; tel. 630/916-7088; Geoff Abbott, Administrator

**Magna Surgical Center,** 7456 State Road, Bedford Park, IL 60638; tel. 773/445-9696; FAX. 773/445-9590; Michelle Lipscomb, Assistant Administrator

**Michigan Avenue Center for Health, Ltd.,** 2415 S. Michigan Avenue, Chicago, IL 60616; tel. 312/328-1200; FAX. 312/328-1240; Aimee Dillard, Assistant Administrator

**Midwest Center for Day Surgery,** 3811 Highland Avenue, Downers Grove, IL 60515; tel. 630/852-9300; FAX. 630/852-7773; Ronald P. Ladniak, Administrator

**Midwest Eye Center, S.C.,** 1700 East West Road, Calumet City, IL 60409; tel. 708/891-3330; FAX. 708/891-0904; Afzal Ahmad, MD, Medical Director

**Naperville Surgical Centre,** 1263 Rickert Drive, Naperville, IL 60540; tel. 630/305-3300; FAX. 630/305-3301; Ronald P. Ladniak

**North Shore Endoscopy Center,** 101 South Waukegan Road, Suite 980, Lake Bluff, IL 60044; tel. 847/604-8700; FAX. 847/604-8711; Everett P. Kirch, MD, Administrator

**North Shore Surgicenter,** 3725 West Touhy Avenue, Lincolnwood, IL 60712-2603; tel. 847/324-7770; FAX. 847/324-7762; Gary Rippberger, MD, Administrator

**Northwest Community Day Surgery Center,** 675 West Kirchoff Road, Arlington Heights, IL 60005; tel. 874/618-7004; FAX. 874/618-7069; Roxanne Matias, Director

**Northwest Surgicare,** 1100 West Central Road, Arlington Heights, IL 60005; tel. 847/259-3080; FAX. 847/259-3190; Pat Jepsen, Administrator

**Nova Med Eye Surgery Center of Maryville, LLC,** 12 Maryville Professional Park Drive, Maryville, IL 62062; tel. 618/288-7483; Sarah Davis, Administrator

**Novamed Center for Reconstructive Surgery- Oak Lawn,** 6311 West 95th Street, Oak Lawn, IL 60453; tel. 708/499-3355; FAX. 708/425-5654; Carmen Hollimon, Administrator

**Novamed Surgery Center of Chicago - Northshore,** 3034 West Peterson Avenue, Chicago, IL 60659; tel. 773/973-7432; FAX. 773/973-4134

**NovaMed Surgery Center River Forest, LLC,** 7427 Lake Street, River Forest, IL 60305; tel. 708/488-1300; FAX. 708/771-7321; Kelly Spillane, RN, ASC Director

**Oak Brook Surgical Centre, Inc.,** 2425 West 22nd Street, Suite 101, Oak Brook, IL 60523; tel. 630/990-2212; FAX. 630/990-3130; Ali Nili, Chief Operating Officer

**Oak Park Eye Center, SC,** 7638 W North Avenue, Elmwood Park, IL 60707; tel. 708/452-4257; FAX. 708/452-4283; Manuel Santiago, MD, Administrator

**Palos Surgicenter,** 7340 West College Drive, Palos Heights, IL 60463; tel. 708/361-3233; FAX. 708/361-4876; Thomas Holecek, Administrator

**Peoria Ambulatory Surgery Center,** 4909 North Glen Park Place, Peoria, IL 61614; tel. 309/691-9069; FAX. 309/690-9005; Cynthia J. Leisinger, MBA,CASC, Director of Surgical Services

**Peoria Day Surgery Center,** 7309 North Knoxville, Peoria, IL 61614; tel. 309/692-9210; FAX. 309/693-6472; Rita Hancock, Administrator

**Physicians' Surgery Center,** 2601 West Main Street, Carbondale, IL 62901; tel. 618/351-7300; FAX. 618/457-7890; Stephen Renfro, Administrator

**Physicians' Surgical Center, LLC,** 311 West Lincoln, Suite 300, Belleville, IL 62220; tel. 618/233-7077; FAX. 618/233-2814; Bev LeMaster, RN, Administrator

**Planned Parenthood of East Central Illinois,** 302 East Stoughton Street, Champaign, IL 61820; tel. 217/359-8022; FAX. 217/359-2683; Robin Beach, Vice President and Chief Operating Officer

**Premier Dermatology,** 2051 Plainfield Road, Crest Hill, IL 60403; tel. 815/741-4343; FAX. 815/741-8660; Rose Przenieslo, Practice Manager

**Quad City Ambulatory Surgery Center,** 520 Valley View Drive, Suite 300, Moline, IL 61265; tel. 309/762-1952; FAX. 309/762-3642; Gloria Catlett, RN, Manager

**Regional Surgicenter, Ltd.,** 545 Valley View Drive, Moline, IL 61265; tel. 309/762-5560; FAX. 309/762-7351; Jennifer Swanson, Administrator

**River North Same Day Surgery,** One East Erie, Suite 300, Chicago, IL 60611; tel. 312/649-3939; FAX. 312/649-5747; Jonette Marino, RN, MBA, Administrator

**Rockford Ambulatory Surgery Center,** 1016 Featherstone Drive, Rockford, IL 61107; tel. 815/226-3300; FAX. 815/226-9990; Dr. Steven Gunderson, Chief Executive Officer and Medical Director

**Rockford Endoscopy Center,** 401 Roxbury Road, Rockford, IL 61107; tel. 815/397-7340; FAX. 815/397-7388; Nancy Garry, Administrator

**Rogers Park One Day Surgery Center,** 7616 North Paulina, Chicago, IL 60626; tel. 773/761-0500; FAX. 773/761-1355; Mira Pekic, Credentialing Dept. Manager

**Springfield Clinic Ambulatory Surgery and Endoscopy Center,** 1025 South Seventh Street, Springfield, IL 62794-9248; tel. 217/528-7541; FAX. 217/527-8956; Ginny Timke

**Surgery Center of Southern Illinois,** PO Box 1729, 806 N. Treas, Marion, IL 62959; tel. 618/993-2113; FAX. 618/993-2041; Linda Bickers, RN, Administrator

**Surgicare Center, Inc.,** 333 Dixie Highway, Chicago Heights, IL 60411; tel. 708/754-4890; FAX. 708/709-6242; Dolores Stam, RN - Supervisor

**Surgicore, Inc.,** 10547 South Ewing Avenue, Chicago, IL 60617; tel. 773/221-1690; FAX. 773/221-1675; Michael A. Wood, DPM, Medical Director

**The Center for Orthopedic Medicine, LLC, dba The Center For Outpatient Medicine,** 2502-B East Empire Street, Bloomington, IL 61704; tel. 309/662-6120; FAX. 309/661-0060; Sarah Gardner, Business Director

**The Center for Surgery,** 475 East Diehl Road, Naperville, IL 60563-1253; tel. 630/505-7733; FAX. 630/505-0656; Eric Myers, Administrator

**The Surgery Center of Centralia,** 1045 Martin Luther King Jr. Drive, Centralia, IL 62801; tel. 618/532-3110; FAX. 618/532-7226; Mark Murfin, MD, Medical Director

**Valley Ambulatory Surgery Center and Valley Medical Inn,** 2210 Dean Street, St. Charles, IL 60175; tel. 630/584-9800; FAX. 630/584-9805; Deborah Lee Crook, RN, Administrator

**Women's Aid Clinic,** 4801 W Peterson Ave, Suite 609, Chicago, IL 60646; tel. 847/676-2428

## INDIANA

**Aesthetic Surgery Center,** 13590 N. Meridian, Carmel, IN 46032; tel. 317/846-0846; FAX. 317/846-0722; William H. Beeson, MD, Medical Director

**Broadwest Specialty Surgical Center, LLC,** 315 West 89th Avenue, Merrillville, IN 46410-2904; tel. 219/757-5275; FAX. 219/757-5292; Angela Leach, Business Administrator

**Central Indiana Surgery Center,** 9002 North Meridian, Lower Level, Indianapolis, IN 46260; tel. 317/848-1763; FAX. 317/848-1895; Francis Price, Jr., MD, Medical Director

**Columbus Surgery Center,** 940 North Marr Road, Suite B, Columbus, IN 47201; tel. 812/372-1370; FAX. 812/373-9526; Marcy Ross, RN, Director

**Digestive Health Center,** 1120 AAA Way, Suite A, Carmel, IN 46032-3210; tel. 317/848-5494; FAX. 317/575-0392; Daniel J. Stout, MD, President

**Evansville Surgery Center,** 520 Mary Street, Evansville, IN 47710; tel. 812/433-3166; FAX. 812/433-3176; Cathy Head RN, BS, MHA, CASA Administrator

**Eye Specialists Surgery Centers, LLC,** 200 North Tillotson Avenue, Muncie, IN 47304-3988; tel. 765/286-8888; FAX. 765/747-7962; Rita Singh, MD, Chief Executive Officer

**Foot and Ankle Surgery Center, Inc.,** 8651 Township Line Road, Indianapolis, IN 46260-1578; tel. 317/334-0232; FAX. 317/334-0268; Anthony E. Miller, DPM, Owner

**Franciscan Physicians Hospital,** 701 Superior Avenue, Munster, IN 46321; tel. 219/924-1300; FAX. 219/922-4810; Barb Greene, President

**Gastrointestinal Endoscopy Center,** 801 Street Mary's Drive, Suite 110 West, Evansville, IN 47714; tel. 812/477-6103; FAX. 812/477-4897; Butch Moors, CPA, Administrator

**Grand Park Surgical Center,** 1479 East 84th Place, Merrillville, IN 46410; tel. 219/738-2828; FAX. 219/756-3349; Chris Macarthy, Administrator

**Grossnickle Eye Surgery Center, Inc.,** 2251 DuBois Drive, Warsaw, IN 46580-3212; tel. 574/269-3777; FAX. 574/371-4697; Diana Ostrom, RN, Administrator

**IMA Endoscopy Surgicenter, P.C.,** 8895 Broadway, Merrillville, IN 46410; tel. 219/736-4660; FAX. 219/736-4663; Dawn Bailey, Administrator

**Indiana Endoscopy Center,** 1801 North Senate, Suite 410, Indianapolis, IN 46202; tel. 317/962-5660; FAX. 317/963-5255; David B. Thomas, Medical Director

**Indiana Eye Clinic,** 30 North Emerson Avenue, Greenwood, IN 46143-9760; tel. 317/881-3937; FAX. 317/887-4008; Ken Dyar, RN, BSN, MBA, Executive Director

**Indiana Surgery Center,** 1550 East County Line Road, Suite 100, Indianapolis, IN 46227; tel. 317/621-7600; FAX. 317/621-7606; Peggy Davidson, Administrator

**Indiana Surgery Center - North,** 8040 Clearvista Parkway, Suite 150, Indianapolis, IN 46256; tel. 317/621-2000; FAX. 317/621-2069; Shannon Arrendale, RN, MBA, Executive Director

**Indianapolis Endoscopy Center,** 8315 E. 56th Street, Suite 100, Indianapolis, IN 46216; tel. 317/621-2232; FAX. 317/621-3232; Kathy Anderson, Executive Director

**Meridian Plastic Surgery Center,** 170 West 106th Street, Indianapolis, IN 46290-1004; tel. 317/575-0336; FAX. 317/571-8667; Joann Jones, RN, Director

**Michiana Endoscopy Center, LLC,** 53830 Generation Drive, South Bend, IN 46635; tel. 574/271-0893; FAX. 574/271-1285; Pankaj Patel, MD, Medical Director

**Munster Same Day Surgery Center,** 761 Forty Fifth Avenue, Suite 116, Munster, IN 46321; tel. 219/924-3090; FAX. 219/924-2160; Georgia Tsiongas, Administrator

**North Meridian Surgery Center,** 13225 N. Meridian Street, Carmel, IN 46032; tel. 317/574-5400; FAX. 317/575-0173; Julie Berzins, Director and Chief Executive Officer

**Northeast Indiana Endoscopy Center,** 7900 West Jefferson Boulevard, Suite 200, Fort Wayne, IN 46804; tel. 206/969-7181; FAX. 260/969-7182; Jerry Steele, Administrator

**Oakview Surgical Center, Inc.,** 120 E. 18th Street, Rochester, IN 46975; tel. 574/224-7500; FAX. 574/223-3057; Laurence C. Rogers, DPM, Administrator

**Outpatient Surgery Center of Indiana, LLP,** 711 Gardner Drive, Marion, IN 46952; tel. 317/664-2000; FAX. 317/668-6797; Dixie Hewitt, RN, Director

**Premier Surgery Center,** 11141 Parkview Plaza Drive, Suite 200, Fort Wayne, IN 46845-1714; tel. 260/266-9070; FAX. 260/266-9071; Nora Bass, NP, MSN, MBA, Senior Vice President Surgery Services

**Riverpointe Surgery Center,** 500 Arcade Avenue, Suite 100, Elkhart, IN 46514-2459; tel. 574/522-9505; FAX. 574/296-6484; John Cloyd, PhD, Executive Director

**Sagamore Surgical Services, Inc.,** 2320 Concord Road, Suite B, Lafayette, IN 47909; tel. 765/474-7854; FAX. 765/474-1317; Carol Blanar, Administrator

**South Bend Clinic Surgicenter,** 211 North Eddy Street, P.O. Box 1755, South Bend, IN 46634-4061; tel. 574/237-9366; FAX. 574/237-9363; Paul J. Meyer, Chief Executive Officer

**Southern Indiana Surgery Center,** 2800 Rex Grossman Boulevard, Bloomington, IN 47403; tel. 812/333-8969; FAX. 812/335-2309; Becky Caver, RN, Administrative Director

**Surgery Center of Merrillville, LLC,** 8514 Broadway, Merrillville, IN 46410; tel. 219/756-5010; FAX. 219/736-5106; Tina Jackson, Director

**Surgery ONE,** 5052 North Clinton, Fort Wayne, IN 46825-5822; tel. 219/482-5194; FAX. 219/482-5686; Debra McCarter, Director

**Surgical Care Center, Inc.,** 8103 Clearvista Parkway, Indianapolis, IN 46256-4600; tel. 317/842-5173; FAX. 317/570-7429; Janelle Gray, RN, Director

**Surgical Center of New Albany,** 2201 Green Valley Road, New Albany, IN 47150-4648; tel. 812/949-1223; FAX. 812/945-4765; Tamara E. Jones, Administrator

**Surgicare,** 2907 McIntire Drive, Suite C, Bloomington, IN 47403; tel. 812/339-8000; FAX. 812/339-2524; Susan Bower, RN, Administrator

**Surgicare of Jeffersonville,** 1305 Wall Street, Suite 101, Jeffersonville, IN 47130-3898; tel. 812/288-9674; FAX. 812/283-6955; Marsha Parker, Administrator

**The Endoscopy Center at St. Francis,** 8051 South Emerson, Suite 150, Indianapolis, IN 46237; tel. 317/865-2955; FAX. 317/865-2952; James Turner, Chief Executive Officer

**The Eye Surgical Center of Fort Wayne,** 321 East Wayne Street, Ft. Wayne, IN 46802-2713; tel. 260/422-5976; FAX. 260/969-1041; Mitchell Burris, RN, OR Supervisor

**The Indiana Hand to Shoulder Center,** 8501 Harcourt Road, P.O. Box 80434, Indianapolis, IN 46260-0434; tel. 317/875-9105; FAX. 317/872-1423; Valeria M. Wareham, DON, Chief Operating Officer

**Valley Cataract and Laser Institute, Inc., dba Valley Surgery Center,** 220 East Virginia, Evansville, IN 47711; tel. 812/435-1600; FAX. 812/435-1603; Lisa J. Gossman-Werner, Facility Administrator

**Whitewater Surgery Center,** 1900 Chester Boulevard, Richmond, IN 47374; tel. 765/966-1776; FAX. 765/962-1191; Mary Pordifio, RN, Nurse Manager

**Williams Eye Surgery Center,** 6836 Hohman Avenue, Hammond, IN 46324; tel. 219/937-5063; FAX. 219/937-5068; Renee Peters, Administrator

### IOWA

**Iowa Digestive Disease Center, Iowa Endoscopy Center,** 1378 NW124th Street, Suite 100, Clive, IA 50325; tel. 515/288-6097; FAX. 515/288-0384; Veryl Kroon, Chief Executive Officer

**Jones Eye Clinic,** 4405 Hamilton Boulevard, Sioux City, IA 51104-1140; tel. 712/239-3937; FAX. 712/239-4946; Charles E. Jones, MD, Medical Director

**Mississippi Valley Surgery Center, L.C.,** 3400 Dexter Court, Suite 200, Davenport, IA 52807; tel. 563/344-6600; FAX. 563/344-6699; John D. Dooley, Administrator

**Spencer Surgery and Laser Center, LLC,** 1721 West 18th Street, P.O. Box 420, Spencer, IA 51301; tel. 712/580-3278; FAX. 712/580-3279; Dennis D. Gordy, MD, Administrator

**Spring Park Surgery Center, LLC,** 3319 Spring Street, Suite 202-A, Davenport, IA 52807; tel. 563/355-6236; FAX. 563/359-6347; William Rosen, Medical Director

**Surgery Center of Des Moines,** 717 Lyon Street, Des Moines, IA 50312; tel. 515/266-3140; FAX. 515/266-3073; Marsha Schultz, Director of Nursing

### KANSAS

**Cotton-O'Neil Clinic Endoscopy Center,** 720 SW Lane St, Topeka, KS 66606-1539; tel. 785/270-4800; FAX. 785/270-4801; Mark Davis, Director

**Emporia Ambulatory Surgery Center,** 2528 West 15th Avenue, Emporia, KS 66801-6102; tel. 602/343-2233; J. E. Bosiljevac, MD, Administrator

**Endoscopic Services, P.A.,** 1431 South Bluffview Street, Suite 215, Wichita, KS 67218-3000; tel. 316/687-0234; FAX. 316/687-0360; Jace Hyder, MD

**Endoscopy and Surgery Center of Topeka, L.P.,** 2200 Southwest Sixth Avenue, Suite 103, Topeka, KS 66606-1707; tel. 913/354-1254; FAX. 913/354-1255; Ashraf M. Sufi, MD, Medical Director

**Eye Surgical Center,** 1100 North Topeka Street, Wichita, KS 67214-2810; tel. 316/263-6273; FAX. 316/263-5568; David A. Kingrey, Medical Director

**Hutchinson Clinic Ambulatory Surgery Center,** 2205 North Waldron, Hutchinson, KS 67502; tel. 620/728-2700; FAX. 620/694-4418; Mary Wood, Director

**Newton Surgory Center,** 800 Medical Center Drive, Newton, KS 67114-3761; tel. 316/283-4400; FAX. 316/283-6606; Joyce Hartner RN, BA, CNOR Director

**Surgicare of Wichita, Inc.,** 810 North Lorraine, Wichita, KS 67214-4841; tel. 316/685-2207; FAX. 316/685-2861; Tracie Johanek, RN, Administrator

**Team Vision Surgery Center,** 6100 East Central Street, Suite Six, Wichita, KS 67208-4237; tel. 316/681-2020; FAX. 316/684-4939; Stacey Linn, Administrator

**Team Vision Surgery Center West,** 834 North Socora, Suite One, Wichita, KS 67212-3238; tel. 316/681-2020; FAX. 316/684-4939; Patricia Kusnerus, Administrator

**Via Christi Surgery Center,** 1947 Founders' Circle, Wichita, KS 67206; tel. 316/613-4607; FAX. 316/613-4725; Penny Freeman, RN, BSN, CNOR, Manager

### KENTUCKY

**Ambulatory Surgery Center,** 2831 Lone Oak Road, Paducah, KY 42003; tel. 270/554-8373; FAX. 270/554-8987; Laxmaiah Manchikanti, MD

**Asethetic Plastic Surgery Institute of Louisville, LLC, dba Louisville Surgery Center,** 444 S. First Street, Suite 201, Louisville, KY 40202; tel. 502/238-2861; FAX. 502/238-2897; Amy McKiernan, Director of Nursing

**Baptist-Physicians' Surgery Center,** 1720 Nicholasville Rd, Suite 101, Lexington, KY 40503; tel. 859/260-7000; FAX. 859/260-7010; Evan Long, Administrator

**Bluegrass Surgery & Laser Center,** 1400 Poplar Level Road, Suite 1, Louisville, KY 40217; tel. 502/637-4800; FAX. 502/637-1550; Don E. Lenz, RN, Administrator

**Center For Surgical Care,** 7575 U.S. 42, Florence, KY 41042; tel. 606/283-6050; FAX. 606/283-6060; Jenny Brallier, RN, Director

**Commonwealth Eye Surgery Center,** 2353 Alexandria Drive, Suite 350, Lexington, KY 40504; tel. 859/224-2655; FAX. 859/296-1565; Jenny Lackey, Administrator

**Cumberland Valley Surgical Center,** 275 Hwy 770, Corbin, KY 40729; tel. 606/526-7874; FAX. 606/526-7836; Kim Turner, Administrator

**Dermatology Associates Of KY, PSC,** 250 Fountain Court, Lexington, KY 40509; tel. 859/263-4444; Joy Hayes, Administrator

**Dupont Surgery Center,** 4004 Dupont Circle, Louisville, KY 40207; tel. 502/896-6428; FAX. 502/893-5270; Sherry Oeswein, Administrator

**E.M.W. Women's Surgical Center,** 138 West Market Street, Louisville, KY 40202; tel. 502/589-2124; FAX. 502/589-1588; Anne Ahola, Executive Director

**Eyecare Network, Ltd.,** 1360 Medical Park Dr, Maysville, KY 41056; tel. 606/759-5341; Bryan Prater, Administrator

**Healthsouth Lexington Surgery Center,** 1451 Harrodsburg Rd, Suite 102, Lexington, KY 40504; tel. 859/276-2525; Dianna Bennett, Administrator

**Healthsouth Louisville Surgery Center,** 614 E Chestnut St, Louisville, KY 40202; tel. 502/589-9488; Vanessa McDermott, Administrator

**Jewish Hospital Medical Center East,** 3920 Dutchman's Lane, Louisville, KY 40207; tel. 502/259-6003; FAX. 502/259-6111; Shelley Neal, Administrator

**Kentucky Surgery Center,** 240 Fountain Court, Lexington, KY 40509; tel. 859/278-1460; FAX. 859/514-5107; Glenda Satterly, RN, Administrative Director

**Lake Cumberland Surgery Center,** 301 Langdon Street, Somerset, KY 42501; tel. 606/678-9688; FAX. 606/679-7479; Michael Everett, Administrative Director

**Louisville Endoscopy Center,** 1400 Poplar Level Road, Suite 2, Louisville, KY 40217; tel. 502/636-2003; FAX. 502/636-4032; Rosemary Gentry, RN, BSN, CGRN, Center Director

**Louisville Surgery Center,** 614 East Chestnut Street, Louisville, KY 40202; tel. 502/589-9488; FAX. 502/589-9928; Vanessa McDermott, Administrator

**Mangat-KUY-Holzapfel Plastic Surgery Center,** 133 Barnwood Drive, Edgewood, KY 41017; tel. 859/331-9600; FAX. 859/578-3321; Linda Robinson, Administrator

**McPeak Surgery Center,** 108 Bravo Boulevard, Glasgow, KY 42141; tel. 270/651-2181; FAX. 270/651-2183; Sheila Dishman, Administrator

**Muhlenberg Surgery Center,** 1008 Medical Center Dr, Suite B, Powderly, KY 42367; tel. 270/338-9929; FAX. 270/338-9282; Susan Hust, Administrator

**New Lexington Clinic, PSC, dba Lexington Clinic Ambulatory Surgery Center,** 1225 South Broadway, Suite 100, Lexington, KY 40504; tel. 859/258-4600; FAX. 859/258-4664; Ashley Karathanasis, ASC Administrator

**Patient First Digestive Disease Center,** 340 Thomas More Parkway, Suite 160B, Crestview, KY 41017; tel. 859/331-6466; FAX. 859/331-1932; Gail Hynko, Site Manager

**Somerset Surgery Center,** 30 Medpark Drive, Somerset, KY 42503-2797; tel. 606/679-9322; FAX. 606/678-2666; Kathy Turner, Administrator

**Stone Road Surgery Center,** 280 Pasadena Dr, Lexington, KY 40503; tel. 859/278-1316; Heather C. Wright, Administrator

**Surgical Center of Elizabethtown,** 108 Financial Drive, Elizabethtown, KY 42701; tel. 270/737-5200; FAX. 270/737-2422; Robin Boles, Administrator

**Surgicare Lourdes Ambulatory Surgery Center,** 225 Medical Center Drive, Suite 105, Paducah, KY 42003; tel. 270/441-4500; FAX. 270/441-4577; Nancy Edwards, Director

**The Pain Treatment Center Inc. dba Stone Road Surgery Center,** 280 Pasadena Drive, Lexington, KY 40503; tel. 859/278-1316; FAX. 859/276-3847; Heather C. Wright, Chief Executive Officer

**Tri-State Digestive Disorder Center Ambulatory Surgery Center,** 425 Centre View Blvd, Crestview Hills, KY 41017; tel. 859/341-3575; FAX. 859/341-5701; Ross McHenry, MD

### LOUISIANA

**Acadiana Surgery Center, Inc.,** 2309 East Main Street, Suite 102, New Iberia, LA 70560; tel. 337/364-9680; FAX. 337/364-9689; Dana W. Stokes, RN. Director of Nurses

**Alexandria Laser and Surgery Center,** 4100 Parliament Drive, Alexandria, LA 71303; tel. 318/487-8342; FAX. 318/487-9942; Martina Anders, RN., Center Director

**Ambulatory Eye Surgery Center of Louisiana,** 3900 Veterans Boulevard, Suite 100, Metairie, LA 70002; tel. 504/455-1550; FAX. 504/455-2011; Judy Dufrechou RN, Director

**Brass Surgery Center,** 5328 Didesse Drive, Baton Rouge, LA 70808; tel. 225/766-1718; FAX. 225/766-1225; Derald W. Smith, Administrator

**Colonnade Endoscopy Center,** 555 Dr. Michael DeBakey Drive, Suite 102, Lake Charles, LA 70601; tel. 337/439-6226; FAX. 337/436-6223; Nellie Rideaux, Administrative Assistant

**Foot Surgery Center of Shreveport,** 9308 Mansfield Road, Suite 300, Shreveport, LA 71118; tel. 318/686-9622; Richard Havens, DPM, Administrator

**Houma Outpatient Surgery Center, Ltd.,** 3717 Houma Boulevard, Suite 300, Metairie, LA 70006; tel. 504/456-1515; FAX. 504/454-3810; Landon Tucker, Administrator

**Houma Surgi Center, Inc.,** 1020 School Street, Houma, LA 70360; tel. 985/868-4320; FAX. 985/868-3617; Pat Hitt, RN Assistant Administrator

**LaHaye Eye and Ambulatory Surgical Center,** 4313 I-49 S. Service Rd., Opelousas, LA 70570; tel. 337/942-2024; FAX. 337/948-8869; Bridget Ray, Administrator

**LaHaye Total Eye Care,** 201 Rue Iberville, Suite 800, Lafayette, LA 70508; tel. 337/235-2149; FAX. 337/231-4012; Bridget Ray

**Lake Charles Medical-Surgical Clinic,** 501 Dr. Michael DeBakey Drive, Lake Charles, LA 70601; tel. 337/433-8400; FAX. 337/433-7350; Karen Guillory, RN, Administrator

**Laser and Surgery Center of Acadiana,** 514 Street Landry Street, Lafayette, LA 70506; tel. 337/234-2020; FAX. 318/234-8230; Jackie Ipson, Office Manager

**Louisiana Endoscopy Center, Inc.,** 9103 Jefferson Highway, Baton Rouge, LA 70809; tel. 225/927-0970; FAX. 225/706-0160; Albert Hart, IV, Administrator

**LSU Eye Surgery Center,** 2020 Gravier Street, Suite B, New Orleans, LA 70112; tel. 504/412-1590; FAX. 504/472-1268; W. L. Blackwell, Chief Executive Officer

**MGA-GI Diagnostic and Therapeutic Center,** 1111 Medical Center Boulevard, Suite 450, Marrero, LA 70072; tel. 504/349-6310; FAX. 504/349-6444; Thomas D. McCaffery, Jr., President

**MGA-GI Diagnostic and Therapeutic Center,** 2633 Napoleon Avenue, Suite 707, New Orleans, LA 70115; tel. 504/896-8680; FAX. 504/896-8699; Thomas D. McCaffery, Jr., President

**Ochsner Outpatient Surgery Center,** 103 Medical Center Drive, Slidell, LA 70461; tel. 985/646-4466; FAX. 985/646-5699; Allison F. Maestri, RN

**Omega Hospital, LLC,** 2525 Severn Avenue, Metairie, LA 70001; tel. 504/832-4200; FAX. 504/832-4209; Deborah Scnenck, Administrator

**Outpatient Eye Surgery Center,** 4324 Veterans Boulevard #101, Metairie, LA 70006; tel. 504/455-4046; FAX. 504/455-9890; Cheryl Crouse, RN, Administrator

Section C

**Shreveport Endoscopy Center, AMC,** 3217 Mabel Street, PO Box 37045, Shreveport, LA 71133-7045; tel. 318/631-0072; FAX. 318/631-9688; Linda Ray, Administrator

**Shreveport Surgery Center,** 745 Olive Street, Suite 100, Shreveport, LA 71104; tel. 318/227-1163; FAX. 318/227-0413; Mary Jones, Administrator

**Surgery Center, Inc.,** 1101 South College Road, Suite 100, Lafayette, LA 70503; tel. 337/233-8603; FAX. 337/234-0341; Russell J. Arceneaux, Administrator

**Surginet Outpatient Surgery, LLC,** 101 La Rue France, Suite 400, Lafayette, LA 70508; tel. 318/269-9828; FAX. 318/269-9823; Millissa R. Coco, Administrator

**Thibodaux Laser & Surgery Center, LLC,** 1101 Audubon Avenue, Suite S-Four, Thibodaux, LA 70301; tel. 985/447-7258; FAX. 985/448-1521; Nate Graff, Administrator

**Urology Specialty and Surgery Center,** 234 Dr. Michael DeBakey Drive, Lake Charles, LA 70601; tel. 337/433-5282; FAX. 337/433-1159; Shari Davis, Administrator

**West Monroe Endoscopy Center,** 102 Thomas Road, Suite 506, West Monroe, LA 71291; tel. 318/388-8878; FAX. 318/388-8870; J.B. Duke McHugh, MD

**MAINE**

**Acadia Medical Arts Ambulatory Surgical Suite,** 404 State Street, Bangor, ME 04401; tel. 207/990-0928; FAX. 207/945-4354; Paulette Blue, RN, Administrator

**Eyecare Medical Group,** 53 Sewall Street, Portland, ME 04102; tel. 207/828-2020; FAX. 207/773-7034; Clement Berry, Chief Executive Officer

**Maine Eye Center, P.A.,** 15 Lowell Street, Portland, ME 04102; tel. 207/774-8277; FAX. 207/871-1415; Curtis M. Libby, MD, Director

**Northern Maine Ambulatory Endoscopy Center,** 11 Martin Street, P.O. Box 748, Presque Isle, ME 04769-0151; tel. 207/764-2482; FAX. 207/764-1569; Devin McHalten, Administrator

**OA Centers for Orthopaedics,** 33 Sewall Street, Portland, ME 04102; tel. 207/828-2100; FAX. 207/828-2190; Linda M. Ruterbories, ASU Director

**Vision Care of Maine-Ardostook, LLC,** 173 Academy Street, Presque Isle, ME 04769; tel. 207/764-0376; FAX. 207/764-7612; Craig W. Young, MD, Director

**MARYLAND**

**Ambulatory Endoscopy Center of Maryland, Inc.,** 7350 Van Dusen Road, Suite 230, Laurel, MD 20707; tel. 301/498-5500; FAX. 301/604-5956; Kim Wilson RN, Center Director

**Ambulatory Plastic Surgery Center Associates, CHTD,** 15245 Shady Grove Road, Suite 155, Rockville, MD 20850; tel. 240/912-4708; FAX. 240/912-6692; Martin Vincent, Office Manager

**Anne Arundel Gastroenterology Associates,** Bestgate Medical Clinic, 820 Bestgate Road, Annapolis, MD 21401; tel. 410/224-2116; Gary M. Evans, Administrator

**Baltimore Ambulatory Center for Endoscopy,** 19 Fontana Lane, Suite 104, Rosedale, MD 21237; tel. 410/574-7776; FAX. 410/574-9038; Dr. J. Khan, Medical Director

**Baltimore Podiatry Group,** 5205 East Drive, Suite I, Arbutus, MD 21227; tel. 410/247-5333; Neil Scheffler, DPM, President

**Baltimore Washington Eye Center,** 200 Hospital Drive, Suite 600, Glen Burnie, MD 21061; tel. 410/766-3937; FAX. 410/766-2904; Katie Guglietta, RN, ASC Coordinator

**Bayside Surgical Center, Inc.,** 8023 Ritchie Highway, Pasadena, MD 21122; tel. 410/761-4190; FAX. 410/761-0265; Sheila Freeze, Office Manager

**Beitler, Samuel D., DPM Ambulatory Surgery Center, Glen Burnie Podiatric Surgery Center,** 795 Aquahart Road, Suite 125, Glen Burnie, MD 21061; tel. 410/768-0702; FAX. 410/768-0649; Samuel D. Beitler, DPM

**Bel Air Ambulatory Surgical Center, LLC,** 2007 Rock Spring Road, Lower Level, Forest Hill, MD 21050; tel. 410/879-2474; FAX. 410/879-8194; Karen Carey, RN, Administrator

**Belcrest Surgery Center,** 6505 Belcrest Road, Suite One, Hyattsville, MD 20782; tel. 410/699-5900; FAX. 301/699-9297; Mark H. Sugar, DPM, Director

**Bethesda Ambulatory Surgical Center,** 5620 Shields Drive, Bethesda, MD 20817; tel. 301/530-4181; FAX. 301/530-4373; John Lydon, DPM, Administrator

**Bethesda Endoscopy Center, LLC,** 10215 Fernwood Road, Suite 260, Bethesda, MD 20817; tel. 301/530-2800; FAX. 301/530-9560

**Bethesda Surgery Center, LLC,** 10215 Fernwood Road, Suite 412, Bethesda, MD 20817; tel. 301/530-6100; FAX. 301/530-6104; Janet Scanlon

**Center for Oral & Maxillofacial Surgery,** 1212 York Road, Suite A201, Lutherville, MD 21093; tel. 410/337-7755; FAX. 410/337-7922; Laurie Kolmer, Office Manager

**Chesapeake Ambulatory Surgery Center, LLC,** 8028 Governor Ritchie Highway, Suite 100, Pasadena, MD 21122; tel. 410/768-5800; FAX. 410/768-5806; Ira J. Gottlieb, DPM, Owner, Administrator

**Chesapeake Plastic Surgery,** 134 Holiday Court, Ste 305, Annapolis, MD 21401; tel. 410/646-3226; FAX. 443/949-7508; Haven Barlow, MD, Director

**Cumberland Valley Surgical Center, LLC,** 1110 Professional Court, Hagerstown, MD 21740; tel. 240/420-5559; Stacey Taylor, RN, BSN, Administrator, CASC

**De Leonibus and Palmer, LLC, ASC, MedSurg Foot Center,** 2086 Generals Highway, Suite 101, Annapolis, MD 21401; tel. 410/266-7666; FAX. 410/266-7703; John DeLeonibus, DPM, Owner

**Dimensions Surgery Center,** 14999 Health Center Drive, Ste 103, Bowie, MD 20716; tel. 301/809-2000; FAX. 301/464-3572; Joan McHale, Director of Operations

**Drs. Liss & Mirkin PA T-A Foot & Ankle Associates dba Foot and Ankle Associates, dba Kensington Surgery Center,** 10901 Connecticut Avenue, Suite 200 B, Kensington, MD 20895; tel. 301/949-2000; FAX. 301/949-2002; Dr. Gene Mirkin

**Dulaney Eye Institute,** 901 Dulaney Valley Road, Suite 220, Towson, MD 21204; tel. 410/583-1000; FAX. 410/583-5700; Andrea Hyatt, CASC, Administrator

**Dundalk Ambulatory Surgery Center,** 1123 Merritt Boulevard, Baltimore, MD 21222; tel. 410/282-6666; FAX. 410/282-0357; Pam Green, Office Manager

**Ellicott City Ambulatory Surgery Center,** 2850 North Ridge Road, Ellicott City, MD 21043; tel. 410/461-1600; FAX. 410/750-7615; Maureen Hartley, Administrator

**Eye Surgery Center of Ophthalmology Associates, LLC,** 10755 Falls Road, Suite 110B, Lutherville, MD 21093; tel. 410/583-2811; FAX. 410/583-2814; Lynne Young, Administrator

**Facial Plastic Surgicenter, Ltd.,** 1838 Greene Tree Road, Baltimore, MD 21208; tel. 410/486-3400; FAX. 410/486-0092; Ira D. Papel, MD, President

**Flaum, Martin/Rockville Ambulatory Surgical Center, LLC,** 50 West Edmonston Drive, Suite 306, Rockville, MD 20852; tel. 301/340-8666; FAX. 301/340-7448; Martin C. Flaum, Owner

**Foot Care Associates Ambulatory Care Center at Joppa Foot Care,** 2316 East Joppa Road, Baltimore, MD 21234; tel. 410/882-5100

**Four Corners Ambulatory Surgical Center, LLC, Dr. Gary A. Lieberman, PA, ASC,** 10101 Lorain Avenue, Silver Spring, MD 20901; tel. 301/681-8400; FAX. 301/681-3339; Gayle Rickert, Administrator

**Frederick Surgical Center, LLC,** 45 Thomas Johnson Drive, Ste 207, Frederick, MD 21702; tel. 301/694-3400; FAX. 301/694-3620; Tracey Tylicki, RN, BSN, Administrator and Director of Surgical Services

**Giardina and Glubo, P.A.,** 4660 Wilkens Avenue, Baltimore, MD 21229; tel. 410/242-7066; FAX. 410/242-4126; Eileen Giardina, RN

**Gynemed Surgi-Center,** 17 Fontana Lane, Suite 201, Baltimore, MD 21237; tel. 410/686-8220; FAX. 410/391-0943; David O'Neil, MD

**Harford County Ambulatory Surgery Center,** 1952-A Pulaski Highway, Edgewood, MD 21040; tel. 410/538-7000; FAX. 410/679-4291; Ms. Kim Merrill, RN, BN, Nurse Administrator

**Harford Endoscopy Center, LLC,** Two North Avenue, Suite 102, Belair, MD 21014; tel. 410/838-6345; FAX. 410/838-1595; Sherry Adkins, Center Director

**Johns Hopkins Plastic Surgery Associates,** JHOC 8, 601 North Caroline Street, Baltimore, MD 21287; tel. 410/955-6897; FAX. 410/614-4333; Dawn Lichtenberg

**Kaiser-Permanente-Kensington,** 10810 Connecticut Avenue, Kensington, MD 20895; tel. 301/929-7275; FAX. 301/929-7577; Wanda McCulley, RN, Administrator

**Lake Forest Ambulatory Surgical Center,** 702 Russell Avenue, Gaithersburg, MD 20877; tel. 301/948-3668; FAX. 301/926-7787; Fatimah, Office Manager

**Laser Surgery Center, Inc.,** 484A Ritchie Highway, Severna Park, MD 21146; tel. 410/544-4600; FAX. 410/544-0997; Barbara Stein, Office Manager

**Laurel Foot and Ankle Surgery Center Inc.,** 14440 Cherry Lane Court, Suite 104, Laurel, MD 20707; tel. 301/953-3668; Dr. Frank Smith, Administrator

**Maple Springs Ambulatory Surgery Center,** 10810 Darnstown Road, Suite 101, Gaithersburg, MD 20878; tel. 301/762-3338; FAX. 301/762-1585; Dr. Stuart Snyder, PA, President

**Maryland Endoscopy Center, LLC,** 100 West Road, Suite 115, Towson, MD 21204; tel. 410/494-0144; FAX. 410/494-0147; Irma Haak, RN, Center Director

**Metropolitan Ambulatory Urologic Institute LLC,** 7759 Belle Point Drive, Greenbelt, MD 20770; tel. 301/474-5583; FAX. 301/474-5742; Bernie Schwartz, Manager

**Michetti, Michael, Dr. of District Heights,** 6400 Marlboro Pike, District Heights., MD 20747; tel. 301/736-6900

**Mid Shore Surgical Eye Center,** 8420 Ocean Gateway, Suite One, Easton, MD 21601; tel. 410/822-0424; FAX. 410/822-2283; Cheryl Schmitt, RN

**Montgomery Endoscopy Center P.A., Montgomery Gastroenterology P.A.,** 12012 Veirs Mill Road, Silver Spring, MD 20906; tel. 301/942-3550; FAX. 301/933-3621; Sindu Stephen, ASC Director

**Montgomery Surgical Center,** 46 West Gude Drive, Rockville, MD 20850; tel. 301/424-6901; FAX. 301/294-7847; Charlie Gallagher, Administrator

**Moulsdale, Murphy, Siegelbaum and Lerner,** 7505 Osler Drive, Suite 508, Towson, MD 21204; tel. 410/296-0166; FAX. 410/828-7275

**North Arundel Plastic Surgery Specialists,** 489 Ritchie Highway, Building C, 2nd Floor, Severna Park, MD 21146; tel. 410/841-5355; FAX. 410/841-6589; Ajia S. Markland, Administrator

**Parris-Castoro Eye & Laser Center,** 620 Boulton Street, Bel Air, MD 21014; tel. 410/399-8427; FAX. 410/399-8427; Mary Ripley, RN, Nurse Manager

**Plastic Surgery Specialists,** 2448 Holly Avenue, Suite 400, Annapolis, MD 21401; tel. 410/841-5355; FAX. 410/841-6589; Amanada Freeland, Administrator

**Plaza Ambulatory Surgical Center,** 6506 Reisterstown Road, Suite 501, Baltimore, MD 21215; tel. 410/764-7044; FAX. 410/764-8637; Dr. Brian Kashan, Administrator

**Podiatry Associates, P.A.,** One North Main Street, Bel Air, MD 21014; tel. 410/879-1212; FAX. 410/893-1081

**Podiatry Associates, P.A.,** 6569 North Charles Street, Suite 702, Towson, MD 21204; tel. 410/828-5420; FAX. 410/828-1663; Stan Book, Billing Manager

**Podiatry Associates, P.A., Charter Professional Center,** 10700 Charter Drive, Suite 300, Columbia, MD 21044; tel. 410/730-0970; FAX. 410/730-0161; Dr. Boyd, Capello, Ritter, Podiatrist

**Prince George's Multi-Specialty Surgery Centre, Inc.,** 8700 Central Avenue, Suite 106, Landover, MD 20785; tel. 301/499-3338; FAX. 301/499-1266; John Bubser, Administrator

**River Reach Outpatient Surgery Center,** 790 Governor Ritchie Highway, Suite E-35, Severna Park, MD 21146; tel. 410/544-2487; FAX. 410/544-1872; Pat Hofmeier, Administrator

**Riverside Ambulatory Surgery Center,** 560 Riverside Drive, Suite A-101, Salisbury, MD 21801; tel. 410/749-0121; FAX. 410/749-6807; Patricia Timmons, PMAC, Administrator

**Robinwood Surgery Center, LLC,** 11110 Medical Campus Road, Suite 200, Hagerstown, MD 21742; tel. 301/714-4300; FAX. 301/714-4324; Donna Trueax, Director

**Saint Mary's Multispecialty Surgery Center, Inc.,** Route 235 and Chancellors Run Road, Suite 15, PO Box 1310, California, MD 20619; tel. 301/862-3338; FAX. 301/862-3335; Douglas H. Hallgren, Administrator

**Spector, Adam, DPM, Ambulatory Surgery Center,** 2730 University Boulevard W., Suite 1000, Wheaton, MD 20902; tel. 301/949-3668; FAX. 301/949-8833; Adam Spector, DPM, Administrator

**Summit Ambulatory Surgery Center, Ambulatory Surgery Center,** 1001 Pine Heights Avenue, Suite 104, Baltimore, MD 21229; tel. 410/644-0929; Narang Ashok, Administrator

**SurgiCenter of Baltimore, LLP,** 23 Crossroads Drive, Suite 100, Owings Mills, MD 21117; tel. 410/356-0300; FAX. 410/356-7507; Rosemary L. Lambie, RN, Administrator

**The Adult and Pediatric Urology Surgery Center of MD,** 3455 Wilkens Avenue, Suite 100, Baltimore, MD 21229; tel. 410/646-0330; FAX. 410/644-6182; Bridget Mastrounni, Practice Administrator

**The Ambulatory Urosurgical Center,** 401 East Jefferson Street, Suite 105, Rockville, MD 20850; tel. 301/309-8219; FAX. 301/309-9370; Bernadette Noel, RN, Administrative Director

**The ASC at Waugh Chapel,** 2401 Brandermill Blvd, Suite 340, Gambrills, MD 21054; tel. 410/451-3206; FAX. 410/451-3207; Lance Caffiero, Administrator and Owner

**The Endoscopy Center,** 7402 York Road, Suite 101, Towson, MD 21204; tel. 410/494-0156; FAX. 410/828-1706; Barry Gendason, General Manager

**The Friendship Ambulatory Surgery Center, PC,** 5550 Friendship Boulevard, Suite 270, Chevy Chase, MD 20815; tel. 301/215-7347; FAX. 301/215-7345; Anthony Ruffin, Administrator

**Total Foot Care Surgery Center, Inc.,** 7525 Greenway Center Drive, Suite 112, Greenbelt, MD 20770; tel. 301/345-4087; FAX. 301/345-0482; Kathi Reinhart, Office Manager

**Waldorf Endoscopy Center,** 11340 Pembroke Square, Suite 202, Waldorf, MD 20603; tel. 301/638-5354; FAX. 301/843-5184; Center Director

**Western Maryland Eye Surgical Center,** 1003 West Seventh Street, Suite 400, Frederick, MD 21701; tel. 301/662-3721; FAX. 301/698-8164

**MASSACHUSETTS**

**Andover Surgery Center, LP,** 138 Haverhill Street, Andover, MA 01810; tel. 508/475-2880; FAX. 508/475-9562; Nancy Aucoin, Executive Director

**Boston Center for Ambulatory Surgery, Inc.,** 170 Commonwealth Avenue, Boston, MA 02116; tel. 617/267-0710; FAX. 617/236-8704; Philip J. Gaven, MBA, Administrator

**Boston Eye Surgery & Laser Center, P.C.,** 50 Stanford Street, Boston, MA 02114; tel. 617/723-2015; FAX. 617/723-7787; Sheila M. Harney, Business Manager

**Boston University Eye Assoc., Inc.,** 90 New State Highway, Raynham, MA 02767; tel. 508/822-8839; FAX. 508/880-3616; Judith A. Orsie, RNBSN, Director of Surgical Services

**Cataract and Laser Center West, LLC,** 171 Interstate Drive, West Springfield, MA 01089; tel. 413/737-5500; FAX. 413/732-3514; C. Michael Duca, Administrator

**Cataract and Laser Center, Inc.,** 333 Elm Street, Dedham, MA 02026; tel. 781/326-3800; FAX. 728/326-2120; John Dunne, Administrator

**HealthSouth Maple Surgery Center,** 298 Carew Street, Springfield, MA 01104; tel. 413/739-9668; FAX. 413/781-3652; Kathleen S. Loomis, RN, Facility Administrator

**New England Eye Surgery Center,** 696 Main Street, Weymouth, MA 02190; tel. 617/331-3820; FAX. 617/331-1076; Kenneth Camerota

**Northeast Ambulatory Center,** Three Woodland Road, Suite 321, Stoneham, MA 02180; tel. 781/665-5233; FAX. 781/662-4878; Anil Kumar MD, Medical Director

**Plymouth Laser and Surgical Center,** 40 Industrial Park Road, Plymouth, MA 02360; tel. 508/746-8600; FAX. 508/747-0824; Kathleen Murphy, Administrator

**Same Day SurgiClinic,** 272 Stanley Street, Fall River, MA 02720; tel. 508/672-2290; FAX. 508/679-3766; Steven Pimental, Administrator

**Surgery Center of Waltham,** 130 2nd Avenue, Waltham, MA 02451; tel. 781/434-6400; FAX. 781/434-6593; Sharon Edwards, Chief Operating Officer

**The Cosmetic Surgery Center,** 68 Camp Street, Hyannis, MA 02601; tel. 508/775-7026; FAX. 508/771-0499; Maryanne Savage, RN

**Worcester Surgical Center, Inc.,** 300 Grove Street, Worcester, MA 01650; tel. 508/754-0700; FAX. 508/831-9989; Andy H. Poritz, MD, Professional Services Director

**MICHIGAN**

**Balian Eye Center,** 432 West University Drive, Rochester, MI 48307; tel. 248/651-6122; FAX. 248/651-4825; E. Mike Raphtis, MD

**Centre for Plastic Surgery,** 426 Michigan Street, NE, Suite 300, Grand Rapids, MI 49503; tel. 616/454-1256; FAX. 616/454-0308; Patty Bakker, Administrative Director

**East Michigan Surgery Center,** 701 South Ballenger, Flint, MI 48532; tel. 810/238-3603; FAX. 810/767-5194; Destiny Hahn, Administrator

**Eastside Endoscopy Center,** 28963 Little Mack, Suite 103, St. Clair Shores, MI 48081; tel. 586/447-5110; FAX. 586/774-6091; Beth Miller, Administrator

**Eastside Endoscopy Center,** 17700 23 Mile Road, Macomb Township, MI 48044; tel. 586/416-7501; FAX. 586/416-7506; Beth Miller, Administrator

**Endoscopy and Surgery Center at Woodbridge Hills,** 7901 Angling Road, Portage, MI 49024; tel. 269/324-8406; FAX. 269/324-8476; Renee Langeland, MSN, RN, Administrator

**Health Care Midwest Surgery Center,** 125 West Walnut, Kalamazoo, MI 49007; tel. 616/343-1381; Gregor W. Blix, MD, Medical Director

**Hemorrhoid Clinics of America,** 22000 Greenfield Road, Oak Park, MI 48237; tel. 248/967-4140; FAX. 248/967-0745; Max Ali, MD, President

**Henry Ford Medical Center,** 6777 West Maple Road, West Bloomfield, MI 48322; tel. 248/661-4100; FAX. 248/661-6494; Sally Bertonia, Administrative Manager

**Henry Ford Medical Center-Lakeside Ambulatory Surgery,** 14500 Hall Road, Sterling Heights, MI 48313; tel. 586/247-2680; FAX. 586/247-2682; Peter Tate, Group Practice Director

**John Michael Garrett, MD,** 1301 Carpenter Avenue, Iron Mountain, MI 49801; tel. 906/774-1404; FAX. 906/774-8132; Teri Brown, RN, ASC Director

**Lakeshore Eye Surgery Center,** 21711 Greater Mack Avenue, St. Clair Shores, MI 48080; tel. 586/774-4080; FAX. 586/541-3399; Mariann Pomaville, Center Director

**Lansing Surgery Center,** 1707 Lake Lansing Road, Lansing, MI 48912; tel. 517/708-3333; FAX. 517/267-0430; Richard Smith, Chief Executive Officer

**M.D. Surgicenter,** 375 Barclay Circle, Rochester Hill, MI 48307; tel. 248/852-3636; FAX. 248/852-3631; David Boberg, Administrator

**Michigan Center for Outpatient Ocular Surgery,** 33080 Utica Road, P.O. Box 26010, Fraser, MI 48026; tel. 810/296-7250; FAX. 810/296-0276; Norbert P. Czajkowski, MD, Director

**Midwest Medical Center,** 4700 Schaefer Road, Dearborn, MI 48126; tel. 313/581-5500; FAX. 313/581-6013; Mark B. Saffer, MD, President and Chief Executive Officer

**North Oakland ASC, LLC,** 1305 North Oakland Boulevard, Waterford, MI 48327; tel. 248/666-5552; FAX. 248/666-5508; Bonnie Kalous, Charge Nurse

**Oakland Surgi Center, Inc.,** 2820 Crooks Road, Suite 200, Rochester Hills, MI 48309; tel. 248/852-7484; FAX. 248/852-4279; Shela Matthews, CMM, Administrator

**Planned Parenthood Mid and South Michigan,** 3100 Professional Drive, P.O. Box 3673, Ann Arbor, MI 48106-3673; tel. 734/973-0710; FAX. 734/973-0595; Danielle Terry

**Planned Parenthood of South Central Michigan,** 4201 West Michigan Avenue, Kalamazoo, MI 49006-5833; tel. 269/372-1205; FAX. 269/372-1279; Amy Steward, MSN, FNP, Associate Medical Director

**Southgate Surgery Center,** 14050 Dix-Toledo Road, Southgate, MI 48195; tel. 734/281-0100; FAX. 734/281-7447; Linda Phillips, RN, Administrator

**Spectrum Health Surgical Center,** 1000 East Paris SE, Suite 100, Grand Rapids, MI 49546; tel. 616/285-1822; FAX. 616/285-1820; Deb Williams, Nurse Manager

**St. John Surgery Center,** 21000 12 Mile Road, St. Clair Shores, MI 48081; tel. 810/447-5015; FAX. 810/447-5012; Cheri Dendy, Administrator

**St. Mary's Ambulatory Care Center,** 4599 Towne Centre, Saginaw, MI 48604; tel. 517/797-3000; FAX. 517/797-3010; Lori Jurgens, Director

**Superior Endoscopy Center/U P Digestive Disease Associates, P.C.,** 1414 West Fair Avenue, Suite 135, Marquette, MI 49855; tel. 906/226-6025; FAX. 906/226-5366; Jessica Jones, RN, Director of Nursing

**Surgery Center of Michigan,** 44650 Delco Boulevard, Sterling Heights, MI 48313; tel. 586/254-3391; FAX. 586/254-3344; Jay Novetsky, MD, Medical Director

**Surgical Care Center of Michigan,** 750 East Beltline, NE, Grand Rapids, MI 49525; tel. 616/940-3600; FAX. 616/954-0216; Kris Kilgore, RN, BSN, Administrative Director

**The Berry Surgery Center,** 28500 Orchard Lake Road, Suite100, Farmington Hills, MI 48334; tel. 248/851-6767; FAX. 248/851-2077; Aaron Betel, Medical Director

**MINNESOTA**

**Centennial Lakes Surgery Center,** 7373 France Avenue, S., Suite 404, Edina, MN 55435; tel. 952/832-9360; FAX. 952/832-5079; Pamela Spohn, Administrator

**Children's - Minnetonka,** 6050 Clearwater Drive, Minnetonka, MN 55343; tel. 612/930-8600; FAX. 612/930-8650; Ann Huhn, Business Manager

**Landmark Surgery Center,** 17 West Exchange Street, Suite 222, St. Paul, MN 55102; tel. 651/968-5468; FAX. 651/968-5493; Beckie Hines, Nurse Director

**Midwest Surgery Centers,** 2080 Woodwinds Drive, Woodbury, MN 55125; tel. 651/642-1106; FAX. 651/642-9837; H. Joseph Drannen, Administrator

**WestHealth, Inc.,** 2855 Campus Drive, Plymouth, MN 55441; tel. 763/577-7000; Sue Durkin, Director, Clinical Operations

**Willmar Surgery Center,** 1320 South First Street, Willmar, MN 56201; tel. 320/235-6506; FAX. 320/235-7069; Harley Pakola, Medical Director

**MISSISSIPPI**

**Better Living Clinic Endoscopy Center,** 3000 Halls Ferry Road, Vicksburg, MS 39180; tel. 601/638-9800; FAX. 601/638-9808; Barbara Neal, Office Manager

**Cedar Lake Surgery Center,** 1720 B Medical Park Drive, Biloxi, MS 39532; tel. 228/702-2000; FAX. 228/702-2019; Michael T. Gossman, Administrator

**Columbus Endoscopy Center, Inc.,** 600 Leigh Drive, Columbus, MS 39705; tel. 662/327-7525; FAX. 662/243-2252; Justin Oswalt, Administrator

**East Mississippi Endoscopic Center, LLC,** 1926 23rd Ave, Meridian, MS 39302; tel. 601/485-1131; FAX. 601/485-1336; Crystal Boler, Director

**Endoscopy Center of North Mississippi,** 1206 Office Park Drive, Oxford, MS 38655; tel. 662/234-9888; FAX. 662/234-9872; Roger Franck, Administrator

**ENT and Facial Plastic Surgery, PA, dba Head & Neck Surgery Center, LLC,** 107 Millsaps Drive, P.O. Box 17829, Hattiesburg, MS 39402; tel. 601/268-5131; FAX. 601/268-5138; Jean Lincoln, Business Manager

**Eye Surgical Center of Mississippi, LLC,** 1053 River Oaks Drive, Flowood, MS 39232; tel. 601/969-1430; FAX. 601/709-2117; Dr. Brannon Aden, Administrator

**Gastrointestinal Association Endoscopy,** 1405 North State Street, Third Floor, Jackson, MS 39205; tel. 601/354-1234; FAX. 601/352-4882; Diane Winsner, Administrator

**Gulf Coast Outpatient Surgery Center,** 2781 C T Switzer Sr Drive, Suite 101, Biloxi, MS 39531; tel. 228/594-2900; FAX. 228/594-2901; Diane Farris, Administrator

**Gulf South Surgery Center,** 1206 31st Avenue, P.O. Box 1778, Gulfport, MS 39501; tel. 228/864-0008; FAX. 228/864-0742; Warren Hiatt, Jr., MD, President

**Gulfport Surgery Center,** 1300 Broad Ave, Gulfport, MS 39501; tel. 228/575-2200; FAX. 228/575-2249; William Hertzog, Administrator

**Jackson Eye Institute & ASC,** 2500 Lakeland Drive, Suite B, Flowood, MS 39208; tel. 601/933-1197; FAX. 601/939-6823; Dr. James Bruce, Administrator

**Laurel Surgery and Endoscopy Center, LLC,** 1710 West 12th Street, Laurel, MS 39440; tel. 601/369-2021; FAX. 601/369-2022; Meredith Baker, Administrator

**Lowery A. Woodall Outpatient Surgery Facility,** 105 South 28th Avenue, Hattiesburg, MS 39401; tel. 601/579-3400; FAX. 601/264-2025; Ed Curtis, Administrator

**MAE Physicians Surgery Center, LLC,** 1190 North State Street, Suite 102, Jackson, MS 39202; tel. 601/968-1790; FAX. 601/292-4531; Carla Glaze, Administrator

**Magnolia Regional Health Center Surgery Center,** 401 Alcorn Drive, Corinth, MS 38834; tel. 662/293-2000; FAX. 662/287-3562; Angela Jackson, Administrator

**Meridian Surgery Center,** 2100 13 Street, Meridian, MS 39301; tel. 601/485-4443; FAX. 601/485-9060; Debbi Funck, Administrator

**Mississippi Coast Endoscopy & ASC,** 2406 Catalpa Ave, Pascagoula, MS 39567; tel. 228/696–0818; FAX. 228/696–0893; Mary Lynn, Administrator

**Mississippi Surgical Center,** 1421 North State Street, Suite 101, Jackson, MS 39202; tel. 601/353–8000; FAX. 601/948–2507; Cindy Seal, Administrator

**New Gulf Coast Surgery Center, LLC,** 3882 Bienville Blvd, Ocean Springs, MS 39564; tel. 228/872–6290; FAX. 228/818–5538; Donna Griggs, CNO, Administrator

**North Mississippi Ambulatory Surgery Center, LLC,** 589 Garfield, Tupelo, MS 38801; tel. 662/377–4700; FAX. 662/377–3101; Scott Edwards, Administrator

**Ocean Springs Surgical & Endoscopy Center,** 3301 Bienville Blvd, Ocean Springs, MS 39564; tel. 228/872–8854; FAX. 228/872–0265; Mary Lynn, Administrator

**Oxford Surgery Center,** 499 Azalea Drive, Oxford, MS 38655; tel. 662/234–7979; FAX. 662/234–7079; Margaret Tatum, Administrator

**Pain Treatment Center, LLC,** 106 Asbury Circle, Hattiesburg, MS 39402; tel. 601/268–8698; FAX. 601/296–3049; Tracey Oden, Administrator

**Southern Eye Center of Excellence,** 1420 South 28th Avenue, Hattiesburg, MS 39402; tel. 601/264–3937; FAX. 601/264–5930; Cameron S. Griffith, MD, Medical Staff President

**Surgicare of Jackson,** 760 Lakeland Drive, Jackson, MS 39216; tel. 601/362–8700; FAX. 601/362–6349; Dawn Thomas, Administrator

## MISSOURI

**Auburn Surgery Center, Inc.,** 300 South Mount Auburn Road, Suite 200, Cape Girardeau, MO 63703; tel. 573/332–7881; FAX. 573/332–7176; Lanna Kelley, Administrator

**Cataract and Glaucoma Outpatient Surgicenter,** 7220 Watson Road, St. Louis, MO 63119; tel. 314/352–5500; Stanley C. Becker, MD

**CMMP Surgical Center,** 1705 Christy Drive, Suite 100, Jefferson City, MO 65101; tel. 573/635–7022; FAX. 573/635–7029; Angela R. Erosenko, Administrator

**Creekwood Surgery Center,** 211 Northeast 54th Street, Suite 100, Kansas City, MO 64118; tel. 816/455–4214; FAX. 816/455–4216; Nancy Sturgeon, Administrator

**Creve Coeur Surgery Center, LLC, dba City Place Surgery Center, LLC,** 845 N. New Ballas Ct., Suite 100, Creve Coeur, MO 63141; tel. 314/872–7100; FAX. 314/872–9176; Karen Lombard, RN, Administrator

**Doctors' Park Surgery, Inc.,** 30 Doctors' Park, Cape Girardeau, MO 63703; tel. 573/334–9606; FAX. 573/334–9608; Darin Roberts, Chief Executive Officer/Administrator

**Eye Surgery Center-The Cliffs,** 4801 Cliff Avenue, Suite 101, Independence, MO 64055; tel. 816/478–4400; FAX. 816/478–8240; Jacki Wyrick, RN, BSN, Direct of Nursing

**NovaMed Eye Surgery Center of North County, dba Cataract Surgery Center,** 900 North Highway 67 (Lindbergh), Florissant, MO 63031; tel. 314/838–0321; FAX. 314/838–6532; Karen L. Bell, RN, ASC Director

**Saint Luke's -- G.I. Diagnostics, Inc.,** 4321 Washington, Suite 5700, Kansas City, MO 64111; tel. 816/561–2000; FAX. 816/931–7559; Craig B. Reeves, Administrator

**South County Surgical Center, LLC,** 12345 West Bend Drive, Suite 201, St. Louis, MO 63128; tel. 314/722–2530; FAX. 314/525–0198; Ellen Kluesner, Administrator

**Surgery Center of St. Joseph,** 3201 Ashland Avenue, Suite C & D, St. Joseph, MO 64506; tel. 816/279–0079; FAX. 816/364–1100; Samantha Long, Administrator

**Surgicenter of Kansas City, LLC,** 1800 East Meyer Boulevard, Kansas City, MO 64132; tel. 816/523–0100; FAX. 816/995–3190; Rita Gooding, Administrator

**The Endoscopy Center,** 3800 South Whitney, Independence, MO 64055; tel. 816/478–4887; FAX. 816/478–7140; Andrea L. Wyatt, MBA, CMPE, Chief Executive Officer

**The Endoscopy Center,** 5330 North Oak Traffic Way #100, Kansas City, MO 64118; tel. 816/478–4887; FAX. 816/478–7140; Andrea L. Wyatt, MBA, CMPE, Chief Executive Officer

**The Endoscopy Center,** 9601 NE 79th Street, Kansas City, MO 64158; tel. 816/478–4887; FAX. 816/478–7140; Andrea L. Wyatt, MBA, CMPE, Chief Executive Officer

**The Endoscopy Center,** 5330 N. Oak Trafficway, Kansas City, MO 64118; tel. 816/478–4887; FAX. 816/478–7140; Jean Hansen, MBA, FACMPE, Chief Executive Officer

**The Endoscopy Center,** 9601 NE 79th Street, Kansas City, MO 64158; tel. 816/478–4887; FAX. 816/478–7140; Jean Hansen, MBA, FACMPE, Chief Executive Officer

**The Endoscopy Center II,** 5330 North Oak Trafficway, Suite 100, Kansas City, MO 64118; tel. 816/478–4887; FAX. 816/478–7140; Jean Thompson, Chief Executive Officer

**The Tobin Eye Institute,** 3902 Sherman Avenue, St. Joseph, MO 64506; tel. 816/279–1363; FAX. 816/233–8936; Lindsey Williams, RN, Director of Nursing and Operations

**Tri-County Surgery Center, LP,** 1111 East Sixth Street, Washington, MO 63090; tel. 636/239–1766; FAX. 636/239–2964; Candy Garofalo, Administrator

## MONTANA

**Billings Cataract and Laser Surgicenter,** 1221 North 26th Street, Billings, MT 59101; tel. 406/252–5681; FAX. 406/252–5025; Brenda Emerick, Business Manager

**Northern Rockies Surgery Center,** 940 North 30th Street, Billings, MT 59101; tel. 406/248–7186; FAX. 406/248–6889; Debbie Howe, RN, MSN, Administrator

**Same Day Surgery Center, LLC,** 300 North Wilson, Suite 600F, Bozeman, MT 59715; tel. 406/586–1956; Suellen Bradley, Clinical Director

**The Eye Surgicenter,** 2475 Village Lane, Suite 202, Billings, MT 59102; tel. 406/252–6608; FAX. 406/252–6600; Cheri Salthe, Office Manager

## NEBRASKA

**Aesthetic Surgical Images, P.C.,** 8900 West Dodge Road, Omaha, NE 68114; tel. 402/390–0100; FAX. 402/390–2711; Rita Petersen, Administrator

**Bergan Mercy Surgery Center, Health Inventures,** 7500 Mercy Road, Suite 4300, Omaha, NE 68124; tel. 402/398–5665; FAX. 402/398–6606; Leslie Voigt

**Lincoln Eye and Laser Institute,** 1500 South 48th Street, Suite 610, Lincoln, NE 68506; tel. 402/483–4448; FAX. 402/483–4750; Rhonda Assmus, Manager

**Lincoln Surgical Center,** 1710 South 70th, Suite 200, Lincoln, NE 68506; tel. 402/484–9090; FAX. 402/483–0476; Robin Linnafelter, Chief Executive Officer

**Omaha Ambulatory Surgery Center,** 825 North 90th Street, Omaha, NE 68114; tel. 402/397–1180; FAX. 402/408–1783; Jake Cook, Director

**Omega Surgery Center, LLC,** 1500 S. 48th Street, Suite 612, Lincoln, NE 68506; tel. 402/483–4448; FAX. 402/483–4750; Ann Perl, RN, ASC Administrator

**Omega Surgery Centers, LLC,** 11606 Nicholas Street, Suite 200, Omaha, NE 68154; tel. 402/493–2020; FAX. 402/431–8569; Kellie Johnson, RN, ASC Manager

**The Urology Center, P.C.,** 111 1/2 South 90th Street, Omaha, NE 68114; tel. 402/397–9800; Laura Forehead, Administrator

## NEVADA

**Carson Endoscopy Center,** 1385 Vista Lane, Carson City, NV 89703; tel. 775/884–4567; FAX. 775/884–4569; Autumn Uyechi, Director of Center Operations

**Digestive Disease Center,** 2136 East Desert Inn Road, Suite B, Las Vegas, NV 89109; tel. 702/734–0075; FAX. 702/734–3912; Osama Haikal, MD, Administrator

**Digestive Health Center,** 5250 Kietzke Lane, Reno, NV 89511; tel. 775/829–8855; FAX. 775/770–2717; Laura Kennedy, RN, Center Director

**Ford Center for Foot Surgery,** 2321 Pyramid Way, Sparks, NV 89431; tel. 702/331–1919; FAX. 702/331–2008; Dr. L. Bruce Ford, Administrator

**Las Vegas Surgicare, Ltd.,** 870 South Rancho Drive, Las Vegas, NV 89106; tel. 702/870–2090; FAX. 702/870–5468; Kelly Marcum, Administrator

**Shepherd Eye Surgicenter,** 3575 Pecos McLeod, Las Vegas, NV 89121; tel. 702/731–2088; FAX. 702/734–7836; Christina Kennelley, Administrator

**Sierra Center for Foot Surgery,** 1801 North Carson, Suite B, Carson City, NV 89701; tel. 775/882–1441; FAX. 775/882–6844; Dr. Jeffrey Bean, DPM, Administrator

**SMA Surgery Center,** 2450 West Charleston, Las Vegas, NV 89102; tel. 702/877–8660; FAX. 702/877–5180; Steve Evans, MD, Medical Director

## NEW HAMPSHIRE

**Bedford Ambulatory Surgical Center,** 11 Washington Place, Bedford, NH 03110; tel. 603/622–3670; FAX. 603/626–9750; Laurie T. Roderiques, CRNFA, Nurse Director

**Dartmouth Ambulatory Surgery Center,** 100 Hitchcock Way, Manchester, NH 03104; tel. 603/695–1800; FAX. 603/629–1730; Sean E. Hunt, MD, Medical Director, ASC

**Dr. O'Connell's Pain Care Centers, Inc.,** Pinewood Medical Center, 255 Route 108, Somersworth, NH 03878; tel. 603/692–3166; FAX. 603/692–3168; Tom Barnes, Administrator

**Elliot One Day Surgery Center,** One Elliot Way, Manchester, NH 03103; tel. 603/663–5932; FAX. 603/626–4300; William J. Oifederico, MHA, Administrative Director

**Nashua Eye Surgery Center, Inc.,** Five Coliseum Avenue, Nashua, NH 03063; tel. 603/882–9800; FAX. 603/882–0556; Paul O'Leary, Administrator

**Orthopaedic Surgery Center,** 264 Pleasant Street, Concord, NH 03301; tel. 603/228–7211; FAX. 603/228–7192; Donna Quinn, Administrator

**Salem Surgery Center,** 32 Stiles Road, Salem, NH 03079; tel. 603/898–3610; FAX. 603/890–3313; Cynthia C. Fortune, Director

## NEW JERSEY

**Advanced Gastroenterology of Bergen County, PA, AGBC Endoscopy Center,** 140 Sylvan Avenue, Suite 101A/101B, Englewood Cliffs, NJ 07632-2554; tel. 201/945–6564; FAX. 201/461–9038; Michael Gailie, Practice Administrator

**Arthur W. Perry, M.D., FACS Plastic Surgery Center,** 3055 Route 27, Franklin Park, NJ 08823; tel. 732/422–9600; Arthur W. Perry, MD, Director

**Atlantic Surgery Center, LLC,** 279 Third Avenue, Suite 105, Long Branch, NJ 07740; tel. 732/222–7373; FAX. 732/571–9212; Daniel B. Goldberg, MD, President

**Atrium Surgery Center, Inc.,** 195 Route 46, Suite 202, Mine Hill, NJ 07803; tel. 973/989–5185; FAX. 973/328–4097; Jennifer Rand, RN, CNOR, Director of Nursing

**Bergen-Passaic Cataract Surgery and Laser Center, Inc.,** 18-01 Pollitt Drive, Suite 4, Fair Lawn, NJ 07410-2815; tel. 201/414–5649; FAX. 201/398–9132; Caroline B. Ivanovski-Hauser, Administrator

**Berkeley Heights Eye Group, PA, Summit Eye Group,** 369 Springfield Avenue, Berkeley Heights, NJ 07922; tel. 908/464–4600; FAX. 908/464–4737; Elizabeth Way, RN, Administrator

**Campus Eye Group Ambulatory Surgery Center, Inc.,** 1700 Whitehorse Hamilton Square Road, Suite A, Hamilton, NJ 08690; tel. 609/587–2020; FAX. 609/588–9545; Denise Agness, OD, Office Manager

**Center for Special Surgery,** 104 Lincoln Avenue, Hawthorne, NJ 07506; tel. 973/427–6800; FAX. 973/427–9602; John Tauber, Business Administrator

**Clifton Surgery Center,** 1117 Route 46 East Suite 303, Clifton, NJ 07013; tel. 973/779–7210; FAX. 973/779–7387; Daniel Rice, MD, President and Medical Director

**East Brunswick Surgery Center, dba University Surgi Center,** 561 Cranbury Road, East Brunswick, NJ 08816; tel. 732/390–4300; FAX. 732/390–0556; Paula Zuckerman, Clinical Director

**Endo-Surgi Center,** 1201 Morris Avenue, Union, NJ 07083; tel. 908/686–0066; FAX. 908/686–5388; Sharon DeMato, Administrator

**Endo-Surgi Center of Old Bridge,** 42 Throckmorton Lane, Old Bridge, NJ 08857; tel. 732/679–8808; FAX. 732/679–7280; Sharon DeMato, Executive Director

**Endo/Surgical Center of North Jersey,** 999 Clifton Avenue, Clifton, NJ 07013; tel. 973/777–3938; FAX. 973/591–0178; Ellen Tummillo RN, CGRN, Director of Nursing

**Englewood Endoscopic Associates,** 420 Grand Avenue, Suite 101, Englewood, NJ 07631; tel. 201/569–7044; FAX. 201/569–1999; Carmen Rivera, Office Manager

**Essex Surgical, LLC,** 776 Northfield Avenue, West Orange, NJ 07052; tel. 973/324–2300; FAX. 973/324–1421; George C. Peck, Jr., MD

**Eye Institute of Essex Surgeye Center,** 50 Newark Avenue, Belleville, NJ 07109; tel. 973/751–6060; FAX. 973/450–1464; Eileen Beltramba, Administrator

**Eye Physician of Sussex County Surgical Center,** 183 High Street, Newton, NJ 07860; tel. 973/383–6345; FAX. 973/383–0032; Patricia Fowler, RN

**Eye Surgery Princeton,** 419 North Harrison Street, Princeton, NJ 08540; tel. 609/921-9437; FAX. 609/921-0277; Richard H. Wong, MD, Medical Director

**Gastroenterology Diagnosis Northern New Jersey,** 205 Browertown Road, Suite 102, West Paterson, NJ 07424; tel. 973/890-4780; FAX. 973/890-1097; Ann Kalafsky, RN, Administrative Director

**Hand Surgery and Rehabilitation Center of New Jersey, P.A.,** 5000 Sagemore Drive, Suite 106, Marlton, NJ 08053; tel. 856/983-4263; FAX. 856/983-3894; Sheila McAteer, RN, BSN, Administrator of Surgical Center

**Hunterdon Center for Surgery, LLC T/A Surgery Today,** 9100 Wescott Drive, Suite 201, Flemington, NJ 08822; tel. 908/806-7017; FAX. 908/806-2838; Lisa York, Executive Director

**James Street Surgical Suite,** 261 James Street, Suite 3E, Morristown, NJ 07960; tel. 973/267-7181; FAX. 973/267-3656; Patricia D'Amico, RN, Director of Nursing

**Mediplex Surgery Center,** 98 James Street, Suite 108, Edison, NJ 08820-3998; tel. 732/632-1600; FAX. 732/632-1678; Janet Kovacs, Director

**Mid Atlantic Eye Center,** 70 East Front Street, Red Bank, NJ 07701; tel. 732/741-0858; FAX. 732/219-0180; Walter J. Kahn, MD and Mark Friedberg, MD

**Northern New Jersey Eye Institute,** 71 Second Street, South Orange, NJ 07079; tel. 973/763-2203; FAX. 973/763-5207; Shirley Vitale, Practice Administrator

**Northwest Jersey Ambulatory Surgery Center,** 350 Sparta Avenue, Building A, Sparta, NJ 07871; tel. 973/729-8580; FAX. 973/729-2344; L. Melanson, RN, ASC Supervisor

**Ocean Surgical Pavilion, Inc.,** 1907 Highway 35, Suite Nine, Oakhurst, NJ 07755; tel. 732/517-8885; FAX. 732/517-0304; Barbara DeMaria, RN, CNOR, Center Director

**Pavonia Surgery Center, PC,** 600 Pavonia Avenue, Fourth Floor, Jersey City, NJ 07306; tel. 201/216-1700; FAX. 201/216-1800; William H. Constad, MD, President

**Penn Cardiology at Willingboro,** 200 Campbell Drive, Suite 115, Willingboro, NJ 08046; tel. 609/871-7070; FAX. 609/835-4510; Constance G. Matarese, Senior Practice Manager

**Physicians of Monmouth, LLC,** 733 North Beers Street, Holmdel, NJ 07733; tel. 732/739-0707; FAX. 732/739-8533; Renee Sharkey, RN, Surgical Coordinator

**Princeton Orthopaedic Associates, P.A.,** 727 State Road, Princeton, NJ 08540; tel. 609/924-8131; FAX. 609/924-8532; William G. Hyncik, Jr., Executive Director

**Retina Consultants Surgery Center,** 39 Sycamore Avenue, Little Silver, NJ 07739; tel. 732/530-7730; FAX. 732/530-3837

**Ridgedale Surgery Center,** 14 Ridgedale Avenue, Suite 120, Cedar Knolls, NJ 07927; tel. 973/605-5151; FAX. 973/605-1208; Diana Ruccio, Office Manager

**Ridgewood Ambulatory Surgery Center,** 1200 Ridgewood Avenue, Ridgewood, NJ 07450; tel. 201/444-9002; FAX. 201/612-8114; Kristine Williams, RN

**Saddle Brook Surgicenter, Inc.,** 289 Market Street, Saddle Brook, NJ 07663; tel. 201/843-4444; FAX. 201/368-2817; Dr. Ronald Sollitto, President and Chief Executive Officer

**Seashore Ambulatory Surgery Center,** 1907 New Road, Northfield, NJ 08225; tel. 609/645-8884; FAX. 609/645-9780; Kathleen Clark, Administrator

**Somerset Eye Institute, P.C.,** 562 Easton Avenue, Somerset, NJ 08873; tel. 732/828-5900; FAX. 732/828-3327; Lois Laudati, Manager of Professional Services

**Somerset Surgical Center, PA,** 1081 Route 22 West, Suite 201, Bridgewater, NJ 08807; tel. 908/575-0020; FAX. 908/575-1515; Joan McKibben, Administrator

**South Jersey Endoscopy Center,** 26 East Red Bank Avenue, Woodbury, NJ 08096; tel. 856/848-4464; FAX. 856/848-8706; Barbara Fargnoli, Billing Manager

**South Jersey Surgicenter,** 2835 South Delsea Drive, Vineland, NJ 08360; tel. 856/696-0020; FAX. 856/205-0300; Susy Olmeda, Administrative Coordinator and Debra Gaffney, Clinical Coordinator

**Summit Surgical Center, LLC,** 200 Bowman Drive, Suite D-160, Voorhees, NJ 08043; tel. 856/247-7800; FAX. 856/325-5858; Anthonia Schmidt, Administrator

**Surgical Center of South Jersey, an SCA affiliate,** 130 Gaither Drive, Suite 160, Mount Laurel, NJ 08054; tel. 856/722-7000; FAX. 856/722-8962; Eleanor O. Peschko, Administrator

**Surgicare of Central Jersey, Inc.,** 40 Stirling Road, Watchung, NJ 07060; tel. 908/769-8000; FAX. 908/769-4139; Linda Kollar, Executive Director

**Surgicare Surgical Associates of Fair Lawn, LLC,** 1501 Broadway, Route 4 West, Suite One and Three, Fair Lawn, NJ 07410; tel. 201/703-8487; FAX. 201/791-6585; John H. Hajjar, MD, Member

**Teaneck Gastroenterology and Endoscopy Center,** 1086 Teaneck Road, Suite Three B, Teaneck, NJ 07666; tel. 201/837-9636; FAX. 201/837-9544; Mia D. Oliver, Manager

**The Endoscopy Center of Red Bank,** 365 Broad Street, Red Bank, NJ 07701; tel. 732/842-4294; FAX. 732/842-3854; Donna D. Spring, Director of Operations

**The New Jersey Eye Center,** 1 North Washington Avenue, Bergenfield, NJ 07621; tel. 201/384-7333; FAX. 201/384-9915; James Dello Russo, OD

**The Surgical Center at South Jersey Eye Physicians, P.A.,** 509 South Lenola Road, Suite 11B, Moorestown, NJ 08057; tel. 856/234-0258; FAX. 609/727-0064; Elizabeth Hanley, RN

**Wills Eye Surgery Center of Cherry Hill,** 408 Route 70 East, Cherry Hill, NJ 08034; tel. 856/354-1600; FAX. 856/429-7555; Deborah M. O'Donnell, RN, Administrator

## NEW MEXICO

**Alamogordo Eye Clinic and Surgical Center,** 1124 10th Street, Alamogordo, NM 88310; tel. 505/434-1200; FAX. 505/437-3947; Cindy Buttram, RN

**HealthSouth Albuquerque Surgery Center,** 1720 Wyoming Boulevard, NE, Albuquerque, NM 87112; tel. 505/292-9200; FAX. 505/292-1398; Terry Sanchez, Administrator

**Northside Presbyterian,** PO Box 26666, 5901 Harper Drive, NE, Albuquerque, NM 87125; tel. 505/291-2114; FAX. 505/291-2983; Karin Vantiunen

**The Endoscopy Center of Santa Fe,** 1650 Hospital Drive, Suite 900, Santa Fe, NM 87505; tel. 505/988-3373; FAX. 505/984-1858; Betsy Libowitz, RN, Center Director

## NEW YORK

**Ambulatory Surgery Center of Brooklyn,** 313 43rd Street, Brooklyn, NY 11232; tel. 718/369-1900; FAX. 718/965-4157; Frank A. Mazzagatti, PhD, Vice President of Operations and Administrator

**Ambulatory Surgery Center of Greater New York, LLC,** 1101 Pelham Parkway, N., Bronx, NY 10469; tel. 718/515-3500; Erin Duffy, RN, Administrator

**Boulevard Surgical Center,** 46-04 31st Avenue, Long Island C, NY 11103; tel. 718/545-5050; FAX. 718/545-0032; Linda M. Smith, RN, Consultant

**Brook Plaza Ambulatory Surgical Center,** 1901 Utica Avenue, Brooklyn, NY 11234; tel. 718/629-5590; FAX. 347/587-4770; Steven Ackerman, Chief Executive Officer

**Brooklyn Eye Surgery Center, LLC,** 1301 Avenue J, Brooklyn, NY 11230; tel. 718/688-3937; FAX. 718/692-4456; Jay Raifman, Administrator

**Buffalo Ambulatory Surgery Center,** 3095 Harlem Road, Cheektowaga, NY 14225; tel. 716/896-3815; FAX. 716/896-3015; Dorothy L. Zimdahl, RN, BS, CNOR, CASC, Administrator

**Camillus Surgery Center,** 5700 Genesee Street, Suite 11, Camillus, NY 13031; tel. 315/701-9378; FAX. 315/701-0871; Stephanie Foody, Administrator

**Central New York Eye Center,** 22 Green Street, Poughkeepsie, NY 12601; tel. 845/471-3720; FAX. 845/471-9516; Kim M. Quick, RN, CRNO, COE

**Day-Op Center of Long Island, Inc.,** 110 Willis Avenue, Mineola, NY 11501; tel. 516/294-0030; FAX. 516/294-0228; Juliette LaRegina, Administrator

**Fifth Avenue Surgery Center,** 1049 Fifth Avenue, New York, NY 10028; tel. 212/772-6667; FAX. 212/988-8018; Charles J. Raab, Chief Executive Officer

**Garden City SurgiCenter.,** 400 Endo Boulevard, Garden City, NY 11530; tel. 516/832-8504; FAX. 516/228-9429; Kelly Fitzpatrick, Administrator

**Harrison Center Outpatient Surgery, dba Holdings, LLC,** 550 Harrison Street, Suite 230, Syracuse, NY 13202; tel. 315/472-4424; FAX. 315/475-8056; Margaret M. Alteri, Administrator and Chief Executive Officer

**Kingston Ambulatory Surgical Center, LLC,** 40 Hurley Avenue, Suite 13, Kingston, NY 12401; tel. 845/338-4777; FAX. 845/339-7339; Kathleen Keily, Administrator

**Lattimore Community Surgicenter,** 125 Lattimore Road, Rochester, NY 14620; tel. 585/473-9000; FAX. 585/697-3519; Peter G. Varlan, Administrator

**North Shore Surgi Center, Inc.,** 989 West Jericho Turnpike, Smithtown, NY 11787; tel. 631/864-7100; FAX. 631/864-7129; Michael Guarino, Administrator

**Queens Surgi-Center,** 83-40 Woodhaven Boulevard, Glendale, NY 11385; tel. 718/849-8700; FAX. 718/849-6523; Adce Abadir, Administrator

**The Mackool Eye Institute,** 31-27 41st Street, Astoria, NY 11103; tel. 718/728-3400; FAX. 718/721-7562

**Westfall Surgery Center, LLP,** 1065 Senator Keating Boulevard, Rochester, NY 14618; tel. 585/256-1330; FAX. 585/256-3823; Gary J. Scott, Administrative Director

## NORTH CAROLINA

**Asheboro Endoscopy Center,** 700 Sunset Avenue, PO Box 4830, Asheboro, NC 27203; tel. 336/625-0305; FAX. 336/625-9941; Vickie Whitaker, RN, Clinical Director

**Blue Ridge Day Surgery Center,** 2308 Wesvill Court, Raleigh, NC 27607; tel. 919/781-4311; FAX. 919/781-0625; Kathy Leibl Administrator

**Caromont Specialty Surgery,** 2511 Court Drive, Gastonia, NC 28054; tel. 704/671-5600; FAX. 704/671-5650; Lisa Lineberger, Manager

**Carteret Surgery Center,** 3714 Guardian Avenue, Morehead City, NC 28557; tel. 252/247-0314; FAX. 252/247-2031; Kim Blaine, Business Manager

**Chapel Hill Surgical Center,** 109 Conner Drive, Suite 1201, Chapel Hill, NC 27514; tel. 919/968-0611; FAX. 919/967-8637; Gary S. Berger, MD, President

**Charlotte Surgery Center,** 2825 Randolph Road, Charlotte, NC 28211; tel. 704/377-1647; FAX. 704/358-8267; Connie M. Wilson, Administrator

**Cleveland Ambulatory Services,** 1100 North Lafayette Street, Shelby, NC 28150; tel. 704/482-1331; FAX. 704/482-4833; John Reynolds, MD, Clinical Director

**Craven Surgery Center,** 630 McCarthy Blvd, P.O. Box 12446, New Bern, NC 28561; tel. 252/633-2000; FAX. 252/633-9045; Joseph Hageman, RN, Executive Director

**Eye Surgery and Laser Clinic,** 500 Lake Concord Road, NE, Concord, NC 28025; tel. 704/782-1127; FAX. 704/782-1207; Administrator

**Eye Surgery Center of Shelby,** 1622 East Marion Street, Shelby, NC 28150; tel. 704/482-2020; FAX. 704/482-7707; Frank T. Hannah, MD, Medical Director

**Fayetteville Ambulatory Surgery Center,** 1781 Metromedical Drive, Fayetteville, NC 28304; tel. 910/323-1647; FAX. 910/323-4142; John T. Henley, Jr., MD, Medical Director

**Goldsboro Endoscopy Center, Inc.,** 2705 Medical Office Place, Goldsboro, NC 27534; tel. 919/580-9111; FAX. 919/580-0988; Venkata C. Motaparthy, MD, Chief Executive Officer

**HealthSouth Surgery Center of Hickory, L.P.,** PO Box 3529, Hickory, NC 28503-3528; Kevin Deal, RN, Administrator

**High Point Surgery Center,** 600 Lindsay Street, P.O. Box 2476, High Point, NC 27261; tel. 336/878-6068; FAX. 336/878-6111; Joan D. White, Administrative Director

**Iredell Head, Neck and Ear Ambulatory Surgery Center, Inc.,** 707 Bryant Street, Statesville, NC 28677; tel. 704/873-5224; FAX. 704/873-5984; Angie Kerr, Office Manager

**Iredell Surgical Center,** 1720 Davie Avenue, Statesville, NC 28677; tel. 704/871-0081; FAX. 704/871-0086; Glenda Tallent, MBA, Administrator

**Plastic Surgery Center of North Carolina, Inc.,** 2901 Maplewood Avenue, Winston-Salem, NC 27103; tel. 336/768-6210; FAX. 336/768-6236; John A. Fagg, MD

**Raleigh Plastic Surgery Center, Inc.,** 1112 Dresser Court, Raleigh, NC 27609; tel. 919/872-2616; FAX. 919/872-2771; Nancy Nicoll O'Neil, Administrator

**Regional Medical Services Surgery Center,** 5200 North Croatan Highway, Kitty Hawk, NC 27949; tel. 252/261-9000; FAX. 919/261-4329; Yvonne Burdick, Executive Director

**Section C**

**Southern Eye Associates, P.A., Ophthalmic Surgery Center,** 2801 Blue Ridge Road, Suite 200, Raleigh, NC 27607; tel. 919/571–0081; Kathryn O'Neill, Director of Clinical Services

**Surgical Eye Center,** 3312 Battleground Avenue, Greensboro, NC 27410; tel. 336/282–8330; FAX. 336/282–2625; Trudy Wester, Center Director

**SurgiCare of Jacksonville,** 166 Memorial Court, Jacksonville, NC 28546; tel. 910/353–9565; FAX. 919/353–5497; Takey Crist, Medical Director

**Vidant SurgiCenter,** 102 Bethesda Drive, Greenville, NC 27834; tel. 252/847–7700; FAX. 252/847–7784; Stephen W. Tripp, RPh, President

**WHA Medical Clinic, PLLC,** 1202 Medical Center Drive, Wilmington, NC 28401; tel. 910/341–3433; Diane A. Atkinson, Executive Director

**Wilmington SurgCare,** 1801 South 17th Street, Wilmington, NC 28401; tel. 910/763–4555; FAX. 910/332–8920; James Shafer, Facility Administrator

## NORTH DAKOTA

**Bismarck Surgical Associates,** 600 N. 9th Street, Bismarck, ND 58501; tel. 701/221–2299; FAX. 701/323–3370; Scott Osadchuk, Director

**Dakota Surgery & Laser Center,** 430 E. Sweet Avenue, Bismarck, ND 58504; tel. 701/222–4900; FAX. 701/222–4999; Charles R. Volk, Administrator

**Day Surgery-Wahpeton,** 275 South 11th Street, Wahpeton, ND 58075; tel. 701/642–2000; FAX. 701/671–4106; Kevin Gish, Administrator

**FM Endoscopy Center,** 300 Main Ave, Suite 205, Fargo, ND 58103; tel. 701/200–4150; FAX. 701/476–0000; Rodney Ludwig, Administrator

**Great Plains Clinic Surgery Center,** 33 Ninth Street, W., Dickinson, ND 58601; tel. 701/483–6017; FAX. 701/483–5018; Mark Grove, Administrator

**Innovis Health,** 1702 S. University Drive, Fargo, ND 58103; tel. 701/364–8900; FAX. 701/364–8990; Dennis Furman, Chief Operating Officer

**Institute For Lower Back Care,** 300 Main Ave, Suite 212, Fargo, ND 58103; tel. 701/297–0817; Panjin Sivanna, MD, Administrator

**Institute for Special Surgery,** 2301 25th Street, Fargo, ND 58103; tel. 702/271–1045; FAX. 702/271–1044; Timothy Haugen, Administrator

**Lamb Plastic Surgery Center,** 1507 S University Dr, Fargo, ND 58103; tel. 701/237–9592; Donald Lamb, MD, Administrator

**Laser and Surgery Center,** 4344 20th Ave S, Fargo, ND 58103; tel. 701/277–7200; Steve Bagan, MD, Administrator

**Mid Dakota Clinic Surgicenter,** 401 N 9th Street, Bismarck, ND 58501; tel. 701/530–6010; FAX. 701/530–5996; Robert Winandy, Nursing Manager, Administrator

**North Dakota Surgery Center,** 3035 Demers Avenue, Grand Forks, ND 58201; tel. 701/775–3151; FAX. 701/775–3153; Ross J. Gonitzke, Administrator

**Northern Plains Surgery Center,** 44 4th St S, Fargo, ND 58103; tel. 701/232–9200; Sarah Ouse, RN, ASC Coordinator

**St. Alexius Same Day Surgery Center,** 810 East Rosser, Bismarck, ND 58501; tel. 701/530–5000; Sandy Gerving, Director

**Trinity Community Clinic-Western Dakota,** 1102 Main, Williston, ND 58801; tel. 701/572–7711; FAX. 701/572–2283; Mary E. Banta, Administrator

## OHIO

**Amend Center for Eye Surgery,** 5939 Colerain Avenue, Cincinnati, OH 45239; tel. 513/923–3900; FAX. 513/923–3012

**Bloomberg Eye Center,** 1651 West Main Street, Newark, OH 43055; tel. 740/522–3937; FAX. 740/522–0063; Judy Mackey, Director of Corp. Services

**Central Ohio Endoscopy Center, LLC, Dublin Center,** 6670 Perimeter Drive, Suite 200, Dublin, OH 43016; tel. 614/754–5500; FAX. 614/707–4204; Debbie Sauls, RN, Nurse Manager

**Central Ohio Endoscopy Center, LLC, East Center,** 85 McNaughten Road, Suite 320, Columbus, OH 43213; tel. 614/754–5500; FAX. 614/864–2062; Debbie Sauls, RN, Nurse Manager

**Central Ohio Endoscopy Center, LLC, North Center,** 3800 Olentangy River Road, Columbus, OH 43214; tel. 614/754–5500; FAX. 614/754–5501; Debbie Sauls, RN, Nurse Manager

**Central Ohio Endoscopy Center, LLC, West Center,** 815 W. Broad Street, Suite 220, Columbus, OH 43222; tel. 614/754–5500; FAX. 614/707–4204; Debbie Sauls, RN, Nurse Manager

**Cincinnati Eye Institute and Ambulatory Surgery Center,** 1945 CEI Drive, Cincinnati, OH 45242; tel. 513/984–5133; FAX. 513/984–4240; Clyde Bell, Chief Executive Officer

**Cincinnati Foot Clinic, Inc.,** 8111 Cheviot Road, Cincinnati, OH 45247; tel. 513/385–6946; Robert Hayman, MD, President

**Columbus Eye Surgery Center,** 5965 East Broad Street, Suite 460, Columbus, OH 43213; tel. 614/751–4080; FAX. 614/751–4092; Janie Norman, RN, Center Director

**Consultants in Gastroenterology, Inc.,** 5900 Landerbrook Drive, Suite 195, Mayfield Heights, OH 44124; tel. 440/461–3596; FAX. 440/460–0130; Wendy Callahanl, RN, Manager

**Consultants in Gastroenterology, Inc.,** 7530 Fredle Drive, Concord, OH 44077; tel. 440/386–2250; FAX. 440/386–2251; Wendy Callahan, RN, Nurse Manager

**Crystal Clinic Surgery Center,** 3975 Embassy Parkway, Suite 202, Akron, OH 44313; tel. 330/668–4085; FAX. 330/668–2624; Katherine L. McNeal, RN, Administrator

**Digestivecare Endoscopy Unit,** 75 Sylvania Drive, Beavercreek, OH 45440; tel. 937/320–5050; FAX. 937/320–5060; Craig Penno, Administrator

**Endoscopy Center of Dayton Ltd.,** 4200 Indian Ripple Road, Beavercreek, OH 45440; tel. 937/427–2078; FAX. 937/427–9081; Jennette Papalios, RN, Nurse Manager

**Endoscopy Center West,** 3654 Werk Road, Cincinnati, OH 45248; tel. 513/451–6001; FAX. 513/451–7310; Angela Tiemann, Administrator

**Eye Institute of Northwestern Ohio, Inc.,** 3509 Briarfield Blvd, Maumee, OH 43537; tel. 419/865–3866; FAX. 419/865–3451; Carol R. Kollarits, MD, President

**Facial Surgery Center,** 1130 Congress Avenue, Glendale, OH 45246; tel. 513/772–2442; FAX. 513/772–2844; Joseph J. Moravec, MD, Medical Director

**Fairview Hospital Surgery Center,** 850 Columbia Road, Westlake, OH 44145; tel. 216/808–4000; FAX. 216/808–4010; Michelle Padden, RN, Administrator

**Firas Atassi, M.D. Outpatient Surgery Center,** 34500 Center Ridge Road, North Ridgeville, OH 33039; tel. 216/327–2414

**Gastroenterology Associates, Inc.,** 4665 Belpar Street, NW, PO Box 36329, Canton, OH 44735; tel. 330/493–1480; FAX. 330/493–6805; Erin Garner, RN, Endoscopy Nurse Manager

**Gastroenterology Specialists, Inc.,** 2726 Fulton Drive, NW, Canton, OH 44718; tel. 330/455–5011; FAX. 330/588–7127; Connie M. Kowalski, RN

**Kunesh Eye Surgery Center,** 2601 Far Hills Avenue, Dayton, OH 45419-1665; tel. 937/298–1093; FAX. 937/298–6344; Lucy Helmers, Administrator

**Midwest Eye Surgery Center,** 4452 Eastgate Boulevard, Suite 305, Cincinnati, OH 45245; tel. 513/752–5700; FAX. 513/752–5716; Holly Schwab, RN, Surgery Manager

**North Coast Endoscopy, Inc.,** 9500 Mentor Avenue, Suite 380, Mentor, OH 44060; tel. 440/352–9400; FAX. 440/352–9407; Ahmad Ascha, MD

**North Shore Endoscopy Center,** 850 Columbia Road, Suite 200, Westlake, OH 44145; tel. 440/808–1212; FAX. 440/808–0321; Christine St.George-Gray, RN, BSN, Operations Manager

**Ohio Eye Associates, Eye Surgery & Laser Center,** 466 South Trimble Road, Mansfield, OH 44906; tel. 419/756–8000; FAX. 419/756–7100; Thomas F. Marquardt, Administrator

**Optivue Vision,** 2740 Navarre Avenue, Oregon, OH 43616; tel. 419/697–3616; FAX. 419/697–3655; Karen R. Hess, RN, LMT, OR Manager

**Parkway Surgery Center, Ltd.,** 3500 Executive Parkway, Toledo, OH 43606; tel. 419/531–8349; FAX. 419/531–6833; Richard I. Tapper, MD, Medical Executive Director

**Sidney Foot and Ankle Center,** 1000 Michigan, Sidney, OH 45365; tel. 937/492–1211; FAX. 937/492–6557; Norma Polasky, Administrative Director

**Surgery Alliance Ltd.,** 975 Sawburg Avenue, Alliance, OH 44601; tel. 330/821–7997; FAX. 330/821–7295; Hazel Thomas, Administrator

**Taylor Station Surgery Center,** 275 Taylor Station Road, Columbus, OH 43213; tel. 614/751–4466; FAX. 614/751–4474; Linda Meikle, Administrator

**The Endoscopy Center,** 3439 Granite Circle, Toledo, OH 43617; tel. 419/843–7993; FAX. 419/841–7789; Alice Horner, RN Nurse Manager

**The Surgery Center,** 19250 East Bagley Road, Middleburg Heights, OH 44130; tel. 440/826–3240; FAX. 440/826–3250; Barb Draves, CASC, Administrator

**Toledo Clinic, Inc.,** 4235 Secor Road, Toledo, OH 43623; tel. 419/479–5650; FAX. 419/479–3982; Scott Porterfield, Administrator

**Tri-State Centers, For Sight Surgery Center,** 8044 Montgomery Road, Suite 155, Cincinnati, OH 45236; tel. 513/791–7967; FAX. 513/791–1473; Jo Slocum RN, BSN, Administrator

**University Suburban Health Center, Wright Surgery Center Department,** 1611 South Green Road, Suite 124, South Euclid, OH 44121; tel. 216/382–1868; FAX. 216/382–0584; Thomas Stellato, MD, Medical Director

**Western Reserve Surgery Center,** 1930 State Route 59, Kent, OH 44240; tel. 330/677–3292; FAX. 330/677–3624; Laurie Simon, Administrator

**Zeeba Ambulatory Surgery Center,** 29017 Cedar Road, Lyndhurst, OH 44124; tel. 440/460–8000; FAX. 440/460–4225; Franklin Keathley, Administrator

## OKLAHOMA

**Ambulatory Surgery Associates,** 6160 South Yale Avenue, Tulsa, OK 74136; tel. 918/495–2625; FAX. 918/497–3259; Kathy Helberg, RN, Director

**Central Oklahoma Ambulatory Surgical Center, Inc.,** 3301 Northwest 63rd Street, Oklahoma City, OK 73116; tel. 405/842–9732; FAX. 405/842–9771; W. Edward Dalton, MD, Administrator

**Eastern Oklahoma Surgery Center, LLC,** 5020 East 68th Street, Tulsa, OK 74136; tel. 918/492–1539; FAX. 918/494–8683; Linda Taylor, RN Supervisor

**Great Plains Ambulatory Surgery Center,** 5404 West Lee Boulevard, Suite 100, Lawton, OK 73505; tel. 580/536–7533; FAX. 580/536–7535; Richard Wedig, Administrator

**Heritage Eye Surgicenter of Oklahoma,** 6922 South Western, Oklahoma City, OK 73139; tel. 405/636–1508; FAX. 405/636–1239; Edward D. Glinski, DO, MBA, Administrator

**McGee Eye Surgery Center,** 1000 North Lincoln, Suite 150, Oklahoma City, OK 73104; tel. 405/232–8696; FAX. 405/235–4023; Glenda Woodside, Administrator

**Medical Plaza Endoscopy Unit,** 1125 North Porter, Suite 304, Norman, OK 73071; tel. 405/360–2799; FAX. 405/447–0321; Philip C. Bird, MD

**Oklahoma Surgicare,** 4317 W. Memorial Road, Oklahoma City, OK 73134; tel. 405/755–6240; FAX. 405/752–1819; Lindie Slater, Administrator

**Orthopedic Associates Ambulatory Surgery Center, Inc.,** 3301 Northwest 50th Street, Oklahoma City, OK 73112; tel. 405/947–5610; FAX. 405/948–5166; Carolyn Moles, RN, Director

**Physicians Surgical Center,** 805 East Robinson, Norman, OK 73071-6610; tel. 405/364–9789; FAX. 405/366–8081; Sandra Vaughn, RN, Administrator

**Southern Oklahoma Surgical Center, Inc.,** 2412 North Commerce, Ardmore, OK 73401; tel. 580/226–5000; FAX. 580/226–5035; Christy Morris, RN, BSN, Administrator

**Southern Plains Medical Center, Inc.,** 2222 Iowa Avenue, PO Box 1069, Chickasha, OK 73023; tel. 405/224–8111; FAX. 405/222–5359; Steven Browning, Administrator

**Southwest Ambulatory Surgery Center, LLC,** 8125 South Walker Avenue, Oklahoma City, OK 73139; tel. 405/606–8890; FAX. 405/604–2885; Anthony L. Cruse, DO, Medical Director

**Surgery Center of South Oklahoma City,** 100 Southeast 59th Street, Oklahoma City, OK 73109; tel. 405/634–9300; FAX. 405/634–8300; Larry Smith, Administrator

**Tower Day Surgery,** 1044 Southwest 44th Street, Suite 100, Oklahoma City, OK 73109; tel. 405/636–1701; FAX. 405/636–4314; Teresa Carter, RN, Director of Patient Services

**Triad Eye Medical Clinic and Cataract Institute,** 6140 South Memorial, Tulsa, OK 74133; tel. 918/252–2020; FAX. 918/252–7466; Marc L. Abel, DO, Medical Director

## OREGON

**Aesthetic Breast and Cosmetic Surgery Center,** 10201 Southeast Main, Suite 20, Portland, OR 97216; tel. 503/253–3458; FAX. 503/253–0856; Ronald V. DeMars, MD, Administrator

**Center for Cosmetic and Plastic Surgery,** 1353 East McAndrews Road, Medford, OR 97504; tel. 541/770–6776; FAX. 541/770–5791; Robert M. Jensen, MD, Administrator

**Eye Surgery Center,** 1408 E. Barnett Road, Medford, OR 97504-8279; tel. 541/779–2020; FAX. 541/770–6838; Loren R. Barrus, MD, Administrator

**Eye Surgery Institute,** 813 SW Highland Avenue, Redmond, OR 97756; tel. 541/548–7170; FAX. 541/548–3842; Sara Edwards, Administrator

**Futures Outpatient Surgical Center, Inc.,** 1849 Northwest Kearney, Suite 302, Portland, OR 97209; tel. 503/553–3653; FAX. 503/224–0722; Bryce E. Potter, MD, Principal

**Lovejoy Surgicenter, Inc.,** 933 Northwest 25th Avenue, Portland, OR 97210; tel. 503/221–1870; FAX. 503/221–1488; Kayla Reich, Administrator

**McKenzie Surgery Center,** 940 Country Club Road, Eugene, OR 97401; tel. 541/344–2600; FAX. 541/344–3317; Lynn M. Stapes, RN, Administrator

**North Bend Medical Center, Inc.,** 1900 Woodland Drive, Coos Bay, OR 97420; tel. 541/267–5151; FAX. 541/266–4522; William H. Murray, Chief Executive Officer

**Ontario Surgery Center,** 251 SW 19th Street, Ontario, OR 97914; tel. 541/889–3198; FAX. 541/889–3904; Jeffrey C. Pitts, MD, Administrator

**Oregon Eye Surgery Center, Inc.,** 1550 Oak Street, Suite 8, Eugene, OR 97401; tel. 541/683–8771; FAX. 541/434–0995; Virginia Pecora, RN, Administrator

**The Oregon Clinic Portland Gastroenterology ASC,** 1111 NE 99th Street, Suite 302, Portland, OR 97220; tel. 503/963–2707; FAX. 503/963–2802; David Neale, Administrator

**The Portland Clinic Surgical Center,** 800 Southwest 13th Avenue, Portland, OR 97205; tel. 503/221–0161; FAX. 503/221–4451; J. Michael Schwab, Chief Executive Officer

**Westside Surgery Center,** 13240 Southwest Pacific Highway, Suite 200, Tigard, OR 97223; tel. 503/639–6571; FAX. 503/624–6037; Julie Solso, RN, ASC Director

**Willamette Valley Eye SurgiCenter,** 2001 Commercial Street, SE, Salem, OR 97302; tel. 503/363–1500; FAX. 503/588–2028; Gordon Miller, MD, Administrator

**PENNSYLVANIA**

**Abington Surgical Center,** 2701 Blair Mill Road, Suite 35, Willow Grove, PA 19090; tel. 215/443–8505; FAX. 215/957–0565; Stanley E. Grissinger, MBA, CHE, Executive Director

**Aestique Ambulatory Surgical Center,** One Aesthetic Way, Greensburg, PA 15601; tel. 724/832–7555; FAX. 724/832–7568; Theodore A. Lazzaro, MD, Medical Director

**Delaware Valley Laser Surgery Institute, (Nevyas Eye Associates),** Two Bala Plaza, Pl 33, Bala Cynwd, PA 19004; tel. 215/668–2847; FAX. 215/668–1509; Herbert J. Nevyas, MD, Medical Director

**Dermatologic SurgiCenter,** 1200 Locust Street, Philadelphia, PA 19107; tel. 215/546–3666; FAX. 215/546–6060; Anthony V. Benedetto, DO, FACP, Medical Director

**Dermatologic SurgiCenter,** 2221 Garrett Rd., Drexel Hill, PA 19026; tel. 610/623–5885; FAX. 610/623–7276; Anthony V. Benedetto, DO, FACP, Medical Director

**Digestive Disease Institute,** 899 Poplar Church Road, Camp Hill, PA 17011; tel. 717/763–1239; FAX. 717/763–9854; Iris Garman, Administrator

**Fairgrounds Surgical Center/Lehigh Vallery Hospital,** 400 North 17th Street, Suite 300, Allentown, PA 18104; tel. 610/969–3100; FAX. 610/969–3199; Darlene G. Hinkle, Director, Perioperative Services

**Kremer Eye Center,** 200 Mall Boulevard, King of Prussia, PA 19406; tel. 610/337–1580; FAX. 610/337–3184; Carol Hughes, RN

**Lebanon Outpatient Surgical Center, L.P.,** 830 Tuck Street, Lebanon, PA 17042; tel. 717/228–1620; FAX. 717/228–1642; Anita Gingrich Fuhrman, RN, BS, CASC, Director

**Mt. Lebanon Surgical Center,** Professional Office Building, 1050 Bower Hill Road, Suite 102, Pittsburgh, PA 15243; tel. 412/942–5770; FAX. 412/942–5780; Cynthia Fabus, Supervisor

**Mt. Pleasant Surgery Center,** 200 Bessemer Road, Mt. Pleasant, PA 15666; tel. 724/547–5432; FAX. 724/547–2435; Brian Konieczny, Administrative Director

**NEI Ambulatory Surgery Center Inc., PC,** 204 Mifflin Avenue, Scranton, PA 18503; tel. 570/340–8090; FAX. 570/342–3136; Mary Ann Labas, RN, Director of Nursing

**Northwood Surgery Center,** 3729 Easton-Nazareth Highway, Easton, PA 18045; tel. 610/559–7110; FAX. 610/559–7317; Chitu Patel, Administrator

**Ophthalmology Laser and Surgery Center, Inc.,** 92 Tuscarora Street, Harrisburg, PA 17104; tel. 717/233–2020; FAX. 717/233–0825

**Paoli Surgery Center,** One Industrial Boulevard, Paoli, PA 19301; tel. 610/408–0822; FAX. 610/408–9933; Caryl Berlin, Facility Manager

**Pennsylvania Eye Surgery Center,** 4100 Linglestown Road, Harrisburg, PA 17112; tel. 717/657–2020; FAX. 717/657–2071; Jill Stileler, RN, Director, Surgical Services

**Pocono Ambulatory Surgery Center,** One Storm Street, Stroudsburg, PA 18360; tel. 570/421–4978; Mary P. Hayden RN, BS,CASC, Administrative Director

**Shadyside Surgi-Center, Inc.,** 5727 Centre Avenue, Pittsburgh, PA 15206; tel. 412/363–6626; FAX. 412/363–7008; Susan M. Katch, RN, Director

**Southwestern Ambulatory Surgery Center,** 500 Lewis Run Road, Suite 202, Pittsburgh, PA 15122; tel. 412/469–6964; FAX. 412/469–6948; Pamela Wrobleski, CRNA, MPM, CASC Administrator

**Southwestern Pennsylvania Eye Surgery Center,** 750 East Beau Street, Washington, PA 15301; tel. 412/228–7477; FAX. 412/228–6271; Jennifer Cross, RN, Clinical Director

**Surgical Center of York,** 1750 Fifth Avenue, P.O. Box 290, York, PA 17405; tel. 717/843–7613; FAX. 717/849–5662; Pam Neiderer, Clinical Services Manager

**The Surgery Center of Chester County,** 460 Creamery Way, Oaklands Corporate Center, Exton, PA 19341-2533; tel. 610/594–8900; FAX. 610/594–8907; Dean Daringer, MBA, Administrator

**UPMC Monroeville Surgery Center,** 125 Daugherty Drive, Monroeville, PA 15146-2749; tel. 412/374–9385; FAX. 412/374–9490; Carol Fiske Boumbouras, CMSC, Administrative Assistant, Medical Staff Manager

**Valley Surgery Center,** 1130 Highway 315, Wilkes-Barre, PA 18702; tel. 570/821–2830; FAX. 570/823–7921; Patricia Williams, Administrator

**West Shore Endoscopy Center,** 423 North 21st Street, Camp Hill, PA 17011; tel. 717/975–2430; FAX. 717/730–2158; Lisa Scichitano, RN, BSN, Administrator

**Wills Surgery Center of Bucks County,** 401 North York Road, Warminster, PA 18974; tel. 215/443–3022; FAX. 215/443–5859; Patricia Cobb, RN, Administrator

**Zitelli & Brodland, Ambulatory Surgery Facility,** 5200 Centre Avenue, Suite 303, Pittsburgh, PA 15232; tel. 412/681–9400; FAX. 412/681–5240; John A. Zitelli, MD

**RHODE ISLAND**

**Bayside Endoscopy Center, LLC,** 33 Staniford Street, Providence, RI 02905; tel. 401/274–1810; FAX. 401/273–9689; Kathryn Abiri, RN, MSN, Administrator

**Ocean State Endoscopy,** 148 West River Street, Providence, RI 02904; tel. 401/274–1260; Rose Morton, MD, Administrator

**St. James Surgery Center,** 444 Quaker Lane, Warwick, RI 02886; tel. 401/384–6537; FAX. 401/384–6541; Paul S. Koch, MD, Medical Director

**Women's Medical Center,** 1725 Broad Street, Cranston, RI 02905; tel. 401/467–9111; FAX. 401/461–1390; Ashlee Dunn, Administrator

**SOUTH CAROLINA**

**Ambulatory Eye Surgery and Laser Center, Inc.,** 9297 Medical Plaza Drive, Charleston, SC 29406; tel. 803/572–2888; Margaret A. Thompson

**AnMed Health Medicus Surgery Center, LLC,** 107 Professional Court, P.O. Box 1886, Anderson, SC 29622-1886; tel. 864/225–1933; FAX. 864/716–7965; Angela Kay, RN, Administrator

**Bay Microsurgical Unit, Inc.,** 1200 Highmarket Street, Georgetown, SC 29440; tel. 843/546–8421; FAX. 843/546–1173; Janet Spring, Director of Nursing

**Bearwood Ambulatory Surgery Center,** 3031 Highway 81, N., Anderson, SC 29621; tel. 864/226–7371; FAX. 864/226–8367; Meryle Martin, Office Manager

**Charleston Plastic Surgery Center, Inc.,** 261 Calhoun Street, Suite 200, Charleston, SC 29401; tel. 843/722–1985; FAX. 843/722–4840; Linda Crosby, Office Manager

**Columbia Gastrointestinal Endoscopy Center,** 2739 Laurel Street, Suite One-B, Columbia, SC 29240; tel. 803/254–9588; FAX. 803/931–8085; Cindy Sease, RN, Administrator

**Columbia Surgery Center, Inc.,** 238 Shuler RD, Columbia, SC 29212-8048; tel. 803/732–6180; FAX. 803/732–6563; Vickie H. Ott, Administrator

**Cross Creek Surgery Center of Greenville Hospital System,** Nine Doctors Drive, Crosscreek Medical Park, Greenville, SC 29605; tel. 803/455–8400; Barbara Callahan, Administrator

**Greenville Endoscopy Center,** 317 Street Francis Drive, Suite 150, Greenville, SC 29601; tel. 864/232–7338; FAX. 864/240–8140; Rebecca K. Swoyer, Administrator

**Greenville Endoscopy Center,** 200 Patewood Drive, Ste 100B, Greenville, SC 29615; tel. 864/232–7338; FAX. 864/240–8140; Rebecca K. Swoyer, Administrator

**Greenville Surgery Center,** Five Memorial Medical Court, Greenville, SC 29605; tel. 864/295–3067; FAX. 864/295–3096; Angela Kay, Administrator

**HealthSouth Surgery Center of Charleston,** 2690 Lake Park Drive, North Charles, SC 29406; tel. 803/764–0992; FAX. 803/764–3187; Rosina Feagin, RN, MSN, Administrator

**Roper West Ashley Surgery Center,** 325 Folly Rd, Ste 200, Charleston, SC 29412-2507; tel. 843/763–3763; FAX. 843/763–3721; Maria I. Sample, Administrator

**Spartanburg Surgery Center,** 391 Serpentine Drive, Suite 200, Spartanburg, SC 29303; tel. 864/585–2002; FAX. 864/585–3300; Rick Sizemore, RN, Administrator

**Upstate Surgery Center, LLC,** 10 Enterprise Boulevard, Suite 109, Greenville, SC 29615; tel. 864/458–7141; FAX. 864/676–9116; Geoffrey Hibbert, Interim Director

**SOUTH DAKOTA**

**Avera Medical Group - Pierre,** 100 Mac Lane, Pierre, SD 57501; tel. 605/945–5210; FAX. 605/945–5084; Lynne Kurth, RN, Administrator

**Black Hills Regional Eye Surgery Center,** 2800 Third Street, Rapid City, SD 57701-7394; tel. 605/341–2000; FAX. 605/341–0278; Richard B. Hanafin, Executive Director

**Mallard Pointe Surgical Center,** 1201 Mickelson Drive, Watertown, SD 57201-7100; tel. 605/882–4743; FAX. 605/882–6064; Mary Petersen, Administrative Director

**TENNESSEE**

**Bristol Surgery Center,** 350 Blountville Highway, Suite 108, Bristol, TN 37620; tel. 423/844–6120; FAX. 423/844–6119; Karen Williams,GCHC,MPH,NHA,CHES Administrator

**Chattanooga Surgery Center,** 400 North Holtzclaw Avenue, Chattanooga, TN 37404; tel. 423/698–6871; FAX. 423/622–8993; K.D. Ratchford, Administrator

**Clarksville Endoscopy Center,** 132 Hillcrest Drive, Clarksville, TN 37043; tel. 931/552–0180; FAX. 931/572–0915; Deborah Glassell, Clinical Director

**D D C Surgery Center,** Nine Physicians Drive, Jackson, TN 38305; tel. 731/661–0086; FAX. 731/661–9783; Kelly Joyce, Clinical Director

**East Memphis Surgery Center,** 80 Humphreys Center Drive, Suite 101, Memphis, TN 38120; tel. 901/747–3233; FAX. 901/747–3230; Cathy Gilland, RN, Facility Administrator

**Endoscopy Center of Kingsport, dba Sullivan Digestive Center,** 2204 Pavilion Drive, Kingsport, TN 37660; tel. 423/392–6100; FAX. 423/392–6159; Penny Vaughn, Administrator

**Eye Surgery Center of East Tennessee,** 1124 Weisgarber Road, Suite 110, Knoxville, TN 37909; tel. 865/588–1037; FAX. 865/909–9104; Mary Beth Solocinski, RN, Center Director

**Eye Surgery Center of Middle Tennessee,** Parkview Tower, Suite 900, 210 25th Avenue, N., Nashville, TN 37203; tel. 615/964–5912; FAX. 615/964–5913; Brandi O'Brien, Business Office Coordinator

**Fort Sanders West Outpatient Surgery Center, LLC,** 210 Fort Sanders West Boulevard, Knoxville, TN 37922; tel. 865/531–5200; FAX. 865/531–5770; Erma Morgan, Director

**Germantown Ambulatory Surgical Center, L.L.C.,** 7499 Poplar Pike, Germantown, TN 38138; tel. 901/755–6465

**HealthSouth Nashville Surgery Center,** 1717 Patterson Street, Nashville, TN 37203; tel. 615/329–1888; FAX. 615/329–0179; Lori Seymore, Administrator

**Knoxville Center for Reproductive Health,** 1547 West Clinch Avenue, Knoxville, TN 37916; tel. 865/637–3861; FAX. 865/637–0222; Kim Denison, Director

**Lebanon HMA Surgical Center,** 1414 Baddour Parkway, Lebanon, TN 37087; tel. 615/453–8252; FAX. 615/444–8994; Sylvia Black, Nurse Manager

**LeBonheur East Surgery Center, L.P.,** 786 Estate Place, Memphis, TN 38120; tel. 901/287–4100; FAX. 901/287–4140; Sherrye Crone, Administrative Director, Rebecca Horne, Clinical Director

**Lisa Ross Birth & Women's Center, Inc., Maternity Center of East Tennessee (formerly),** 1925-B Ailor Avenue, Knoxville, TN 37921; tel. 865/524–4422; FAX. 865/523–3687; Linda Cole, CNM Executive Director

**Mays & Schnapp Pain Clinic and Rehabilitation Center,** 55 Humphreys Center Drive, Suite 200, Memphis, TN 38120; tel. 901/747–0040; FAX. 901/747–0042; Victoria Saunders, Practice Administrator

**Memphis Center for Reproductive Health,** 1462 Poplar Avenue, Memphis, TN 38104; tel. 901/274–3550; FAX. 901/274–3551; Rebecca L. Terrell, Executive Director

**Memphis Eye and Cataract Ambulatory Surgery Center,** 6485 Poplar Avenue, Memphis, TN 38119; tel. 901/767–3937; FAX. 901/767–1695; Ramona Jackson, Nurse Manager

**Memphis Gastroenterology Endoscopy Center,** 8000 Wolf River Blvd, #200, Germantown, TN 38138-1727; tel. 901/747–3630; FAX. 901/747–4039; Sylvia Hawkins, RN, Compliance Manager

**Memphis Regional Gamma Knife Center,** 1211 Union Ave, Ste 220, Memphis, TN 38104; tel. 901/726–6444; FAX. 901/726–6145; Betsy Smith, Administrator

**Memphis Surgery Center,** 1044 Cresthaven Road, Memphis, TN 38119; tel. 901/682–1516; FAX. 901/682–1545; Cathy Gilland, RN, BS, Facility Administrator

**Mid-State Endoscopy Center,** 2010 Church Street, Suite 420, Nashville, TN 37203; tel. 615/329–2141; FAX. 615/321–0522; Allan H. Bailey, MD, Medical Director

**Nashville Endosurgery Center,** 300 20th N, Eighth Floor, Nashville, TN 37203; tel. 615/284–1335; FAX. 615/284–1316

**Nashville Gastrointestinal Endoscopy Center,** 4230 Harding Road, Suite 309, Nashville, TN 37205; tel. 615/383–0165; FAX. 615/292–4657; Ron E. Pruitt, MD

**Northridge Surgery Center,** 647 Myatt Drive, Madison, TN 37115; tel. 615/868–8942; FAX. 615/860–3820; Tim Shannon, Administrator

**Oral Facial Surgery Center,** 322 22nd Avenue, N., Nashville, TN 37203; tel. 615/321–6160; FAX. 615/321–6175; Joey Cupit, RN, MSN, Clinical Administrator

**Planned Parenthood - Greater Memphis Region,** 2430 Poplar Avenue, Suite 100, Memphis, TN 38112; tel. 901/725–1717; FAX. 901/274–4790; Ellen Ruby - Markie, Chief Executive Officer

**Ridge Lake Ambulatory Surgery Center,** 825 Ridge Lake Boulevard, Memphis, TN 38119; tel. 901/685–2200; Kimberly Thorpe, ASC Administrator

**Shea Ear Clinic,** 6133 Poplar Pike, Memphis, TN 38119; tel. 901/761–9720; FAX. 901/763–4400; John J. Shea Jr., MD, President

**Southern Endoscopy Center,** 330 Wallace Road, Suite 103, Nashville, TN 37211; tel. 615/832–5530; FAX. 615/832–5713; Robert W. Herring, Jr., MD, Medical Director

**St. Thomas Medical Group Endoscopy Center,** 4230 Harding Road, Suite 400, Nashville, TN 37205; tel. 615/297–2700; Jeff May RN, Center Director

**Surgery Center of Clarksville,** 121 Hillcrest Drive, Clarksville, TN 37043; tel. 931/552–9992; FAX. 931/648–1816; Angela Farmer, Administrator

**Surgical Services, P.C.,** 604 South Main Street, Sweetwater, TN 37874; tel. 423/337–4508; FAX. 423/337–4588

**Surgicenter Of Murfreesboro Medical Clinic, P.A.,** 1272 Garrison Drive, Murfreesboro, TN 37129; tel. 615/867–8160; FAX. 615/876–7876; Sandy Gordon, Coordinator

**Tennessee Endoscopy Center,** 1706 East Lamar Alexander Parkway, Maryville, TN 37804; tel. 615/983–0073; FAX. 615/984–1731; Craig Jarvis, MD, Administrator

**The Cookeville Surgery Center,** 100 West Fourth Street, Suite 100, Cookeville, TN 38501; tel. 931/526–8115; FAX. 931/526–7619; Jeanie McGinnis, RN Administrator

**The Endoscopy Center of Centennial, L.P.,** 2400 Patterson Street, Suite 515, Nashville, TN 37203; tel. 615/327–2111; FAX. 615/327–9292; Donna Crumley, RN, BS, MBA, Endoscopy Administrator

**The Eye Surgery Center of Oak Ridge,** 90 Vermont Avenue, Oak Ridge, TN 37830; tel. 865/482–8894; FAX. 865/481–8349; Regina Harkleroad, Director of Nursing

**Urology Surgery Center, L.P.,** 2801 Charlotte Avenue, Nashville, TN 37209; tel. 615/250–9202; FAX. 615/250–9251; Mary Ellen, Danielson, RN, CNOR, CASC, Director

**Volunteer Women's Medical Clinic,** 313 Concord Street, Knoxville, TN 37919; tel. 865/522–5173; FAX. 865/522–9907; Elizabeth Fraley-Dumas, Clinical Director

**Wesley Ophthalmic Plastic Surgery Center,** 1800 Church Street, Suite 100, Nashville, TN 37203; tel. 615/329–3624; Janie Stucker, RN, Director

## TEXAS

**Abilene Cataract and Refractive Surgery Center,** 2120 Antilley Road, Abilene, TX 79606; tel. 325/695–2020; FAX. 325/695–2326; Paul B. Thames MD Medical Director

**Abilene Endoscopy Center,** 1249 Ambler Avenue, Abilene, TX 79601; tel. 325/677–2626; FAX. 325/677–6835; Steve Johnson, MD, Medical Director

**Amarillo Cataract and Eye Surgery Center, Inc.,** 7310 Fleming Avenue, Amarillo, TX 79106; tel. 806/354–8891; FAX. 806/354–2591; Carol A. Pearson, Director

**Ambulatory Urological Surgery Center, Inc.,** 1149 Ambler, Abilene, TX 79601; tel. 915/676–3557; FAX. 915/673–2143; Angela X. Young, RN, Manager

**American Surgery Centers of South Texas, LTD,** 7810 Louis Pasteur, Suite 100, San Antonio, TX 78229; tel. 210/692–0218; FAX. 210/692–7980; Laura Rodriguez, Office Manager

**Arlington Day Surgery Center,** 918 North Davis Street, Arlington, TX 76012; tel. 817/860–9933; FAX. 817/860–2314; Dan Chambers, Administrator

**Bailey Square Surgical Center, Ltd.,** 1111 West 34th Street, Austin, TX 78705; tel. 512/454–6753; FAX. 512/454–4314; Randy Humphrey, Administrator

**Bay Area Endoscopy Center,** 444 FM 1959, Suite B, Houston, TX 77034; tel. 281/481–9400; FAX. 281/481–9490; N.S. Bala, Medical Director

**Bay Area Surgicare Center,** 502 Medical Center Boulevard, Webster, TX 77598; tel. 281/332–2433; FAX. 281/332–0619; Carol Simons, Administrator

**Baylor SurgiCare,** 3920 Worth Street, Dallas, TX 75246; tel. 214/820–2581; FAX. 214/820–7484; Robin Shaw, Administrative Director

**Baylor Surgicare at Valley View,** 5744 LBJ Freeway, Suite 200, Dallas, TX 75240; tel. 972/490–4333; FAX. 972/991–1649; Gina Schilthuis, RN, Administrator

**Brazosport Eye Institute,** 103 Parking Way, P.O. Box 369, Lake Jackson, TX 77566; tel. 979/297–2961; FAX. 979/297–2395; Frank J. Grady, MD, PhD, FACS, Director

**Coastal Bend Ambulatory Surgical Center,** 900 Morgan, Corpus Christ, TX 78404; tel. 361/888–4288; FAX. 361/888–4786; Barbara VandenBout, Administrator

**Columbia Physicians DaySurgery Center,** 3930 Crutcher Street, Dallas, TX 75246; tel. 214/827–0760; FAX. 214/827–0944; Robin Shaw, RN, Administrator

**Conroe Surgery Center,** 1501 River Pointe Drive, Suite 200, Conroe, TX 77304; tel. 936/760–3443; FAX. 936/760–1322; Kathy Schutz, RN, BSN, CASC, Facility Administrator

**Covenant Surgicenter, Ltd.,** 2301 Quaker Avenue, Lubbock, TX 79410; tel. 806/725–8801; FAX. 806/725–8820; Elizabeth Hawronsky, Director

**Crystal Outpatient Surgery Center, Inc.,** 215 Oak Drive, S., Suite J, Lake Jackson, TX 77566; tel. 409/299–6118; FAX. 409/299–1007; R. Scott Yarish, MD, Administrator

**Cy-Fair Surgery Center,** 11250 Fallbrook Drive, Houston, TX 77065; tel. 713/955–7194; FAX. 713/890–0895; Sonja Christmas, Administrator

**Dallas DaySurgery of Texas North, Ltd.,** 9101 North Central Expressway, Suite 650, Dallas, TX 75231; tel. 214/821–8613; FAX. 214/821–4958; Elizabeth Toony, RN, BSN, CASC, Administrator

**Dallas Ophthalmology Center, Inc.,** 4633 North Central Expressway, Suite 310, Dallas, TX 75205; tel. 214/520–7600; FAX. 214/528–6522; Susan Points, RN, Administrator

**DeHaven Surgical Center,** 1424 East Front Street, Tyler, TX 75702; tel. 903/595–4144; FAX. 903/595–0236; Terri McDougal, RN, Administrator

**Doctors' Surgery Center, Inc.,** 5300 North Street, Nacogdoches, TX 75965; tel. 936/569–8278; FAX. 936/569–0275; Robert P. Lehmann, MD, Director

**East El Paso Surgery Center,** 7835 Corral Drive, El Paso, TX 79915; tel. 915/595–3353; FAX. 915/595–6796; Laura Ice, Administrator

**East Side Surgery Center, Inc.,** 10918 East Freeway, Houston, TX 77029; tel. 713/451–4299; FAX. 713/451–4383; Vicky Mizell, Administrator

**East Texas Eye Associates Surgery Center,** 1306 Frank Avenue, Lufkin, TX 75904; tel. 409/634–8381; Jo Ann O'Neill, COT, Administrator

**Elm Place Ambulatory Surgical Center,** 2217 South Danville Drive, Abilene, TX 79605; tel. 325/695–0600; FAX. 325/695–3908; Rebecca Laird, RN

**Endoscopy Center of Dallas, Ambulatory Endoscopy Clinic of Dallas,** 6390 LBJ Freeway, Suite 200, Dallas, TX 75240; tel. 972/934–3691; FAX. 972/934–3694; Jeane Suggs, Administrator

**Facial Plastic and Cosmetic Surgical Center,** 6300 Humana Plaza, Suite 475, Abilene, TX 79606; tel. 915/695–3630; FAX. 915/695–3633; Howard A. Tobin, MD, FACS, Medical Director

**Fort Worth Endoscopy Center,** 900 W. Magnolia Street, Suite 101, Fort Worth, TX 76104; tel. 817/332–6500; Jenny Hunter, Administrator

**Forth Worth Surgery Center,** 2001 West Rosedale, Fort Worth, TX 76104; tel. 817/877–4777; David Yodge, Administrator

**Foundation Surgery Center of Dickinson,** 3810 Hughes Court, Dickinson, TX 77539; tel. 713/337–7001; FAX. 713/337–7091; Theresa Mitcham, Administrator Assistant

**Gastroenterology Consultants Outpatient Surgical Center,** 8214 Wurzbach, San Antonio, TX 78229; tel. 210/614–1234; FAX. 210/614–7749; Robert Rosso, Chief Executive Officer

**Good Shepard Ambulatory Surgical Center, Ltd.,** 703 East Marshall Avenue, Suite 2000, Longview, TX 75601-5563; tel. 903/315–5300; FAX. 903/315–5301; Dewayne Hodges, Executive Director

**Gramercy Outpatient Surgery Center, Ltd.,** 2727 Gramercy, Houston, TX 77025; tel. 713/660–6900; FAX. 713/660–0704; Hamel Patel, Administrator

**Greenville Surgery Center,** 7150 Greenville Avenue, Suite 200, Dallas, TX 75231; tel. 214/891–0466; FAX. 214/739–4702; Christine Locke, Administrator

**Heart of Texas Outpatient Cataract Center,** 100 South Park Drive, Brownwood, TX 76801; tel. 325/643–3561; Larry Smith, CRNA, Administrator

**Heritage Surgery Center,** 1501 Redbud Boulevard, McKinney, TX 75069; tel. 972/548–0771; FAX. 972/562–2300; Rudolf Churner, MD, Administrator

**Howerton Surgical Center,** 2610 I.H. 35 South, Austin, TX 78704-5703; tel. 512/443–9715; FAX. 512/443–9845; Lisa Williams, RN, Director of Nursing

**Key Whitman Surgery Center,** 2801 Lemmon Avenue, Suite 400, Dallas, TX 75204; tel. 214/754–0000; FAX. 214/754–0079; Jeffrey Whitman, MD

**Knapp Medical Center ASC,** 1402 East Sixth Street, Weslaco, TX 78596; tel. 956/968–6155; FAX. 956/968–8291; Paul Giles, Administrator

**Las Colinas Surgery Center,** 4255 North Macarthur Boulevard, Irving, TX 75038; tel. 214/257–0144; FAX. 214/258–0436; Michael Scott, Administrator

**Lufkin Endoscopy Center,** 317 Gaslight Boulevard, Lufkin, TX 75904; tel. 936/634–3713; FAX. 936/634–8136; Bhagvan R. Malladi, MD, Administrator

**Medical City Dallas Ambulatory Surgery Center,** 7777 Forest Lane, Suite C-150, Dallas, TX 75230; tel. 972/566–6171; FAX. 972/566–2502; Vickie Roberts, Administrator

**Metroplex Ambulatory Surgical Center,** 2717 Osler Drive, Suite 102, Grand Prairie, TX 75051; tel. 972/647–6272; FAX. 972/660–1822; Glenda Daniels, RN, Director

**Metroplex Surgicare Partners, Ltd., dba Baylor Surgicare at Bedford,** 1600 Central Drive, Suite 180, Bedford, TX 76022; tel. 817/571–1999; FAX. 817/571–1220; Brandon Shows, Administrator

**Mid-Town Surgical Center, LLP,** 2105 Jackson Street, Suite 200, Houston, TX 77003; tel. 713/571–8141; FAX. 713/571–8184; Louis Varela, MD

**North Carrier Surgicenter,** 517 North Carrier Parkway, Suite A, Grand Prairie, TX 75050-5494; tel. 972/264–0533; FAX. 972/262–5974; Abraham F. Syrquin, MD, Medical Director

**North Dallas Surgicare,** 375 Municipal Drive, Suite 214, Richardson, TX 75080; tel. 972/918-9400; FAX. 972/918-9749; Erica Grinage, Administrator

**Park Central Surgical Center,** 12200 Park Central Drive, Third Floor, Dallas, TX 75251; tel. 972/661-0505; FAX. 972/661-5511; Molly Paulose, Administrator

**Physicians SurgiCenter of Houston True Results,** 7515 South Main Street, Suite 800, Houston, TX 77030; tel. 713/799-9990; FAX. 713/796-1142; Sean Bayette, MBA, MHA, Administrator

**Plano Ambulatory Surgery Associates, L.P., dba Surgery Center of Plano,** 1620 Coit Road, Plano, TX 75075-7799; tel. 972/519-1100; DeWayne Hodges, Administrator

**Plaza Day Surgery,** 909 Ninth Avenue, Fort Worth, TX 76104-3986; tel. 817/339-2300; FAX. 817/339-2329; Gina Basham, RN, Administrator

**Port Arthur Day Surgery Center,** 2555 Jimmy Johnson Boulevard, Port Arthur, TX 77640-2007; tel. 409/983-6144; Vicki Clark, Administrative Director

**Premier Ambulatory Surgery of Austin, dba South Austin Surgery Center,** 4207 James Casey, Suite 203, Austin, TX 78745; tel. 512/440-7894; FAX. 512/440-1932; Tammy Smittle, RN, CASC, Administrator

**Q Plus Outpatient Surgery Center,** 2507 Medical Row, Suite 101, Grand Prairie, TX 75051; tel. 972/647-8520; FAX. 972/336-0488; James L. Grace Administrator

**Rio Grande Surgery Center,** 1809 South Cynthia, McAllen, TX 78503; tel. 956/618-4402; FAX. 956/618-4174; Jill Finke, CNOR Administrator

**San Antonio Digestive Disease Endoscopy Center,** 1804 Northeast Loop 410, Suite 101, San Antonio, TX 78217; tel. 210/828-8400; FAX. 210/804-4454; Ricardo Hernandez, MD, Medical Director

**San Antonio Gastroenterology Endoscopy Center,** 520 Euclid Avenue, San Antonio, TX 78212; tel. 210/271-0606; FAX. 210/271-0180; Ernesto Guerra, MD

**San Antonio Surgery Center, Inc., dba The Center for Special Surgery,** 21 Spurs Lane, Sub-Level 100, San Antonio, TX 78240; tel. 210/614-0187; FAX. 210/692-7757; Tyla Blom, Administrator

**Southwest Endoscopy & Surgery Center,** 701 East Rendon Crowley Rd., Burleson, TX 76028; tel. 817/568-5188; FAX. 817/568-1568; J. Leslie Hill

**Surgery Center of Northeast Texas,** 1902 Moores Ln, Suite B, Texarkana, TX 75503; tel. 903/792-2108; FAX. 903/792-0606; Paul J. Gallagher, Administrator

**Surgery Center of Texas,** 155 East Loop 338, Suite 500, Odessa, TX 79762; tel. 432/367-3906; FAX. 432/367-3895; Libby Palma, Administrator

**SurgEyeCare, Inc.,** 5421 La Sierra Drive, Dallas, TX 75231; tel. 214/361-1443; FAX. 214/691-3299; Sandra J. Yankee, Administrator

**Surgical and Diagnostic Center, LP.,** 729 Bedford Euless Road West, Suite 100, Hurst, TX 76053; tel. 817/282-1001; FAX. 817/282-4040; Bart Steele, Administrator

**Surgical Center of El Paso,** 1815 North Stanton, El Paso, TX 79902; tel. 915/533-8412; FAX. 915/542-0367; Raymond Sainz, Administrator

**Texarkana Surgery Center,** 5404 Summerhill Road, Texarkana, TX 75503; tel. 903/793-4872; FAX. 903/794-6300; Kimble Hatridge, Administrator

**Texoma Outpatient Surgery Center, Inc.,** 1712 Eleventh Street, Wichita Falls, TX 76301; tel. 940/723-2499; FAX. 940/923-2497; Tracy Youngblood, Administrator

**The Cataract Center of East Texas, dba Novamed Surgery Center of Tyler,** 802 Turtle Creek Drive, Tyler, TX 75701; tel. 903/595-4333; FAX. 903/535-9845; S. Stephens, RN, Clinical Administrator

**The Center for Sight, P.A.,** 2 Medical Center Boulevard, Lufkin, TX 75904-3175; tel. 936/634-8434; FAX. 936/639-2581; Richard J. Ruckman, MD

**The Endoscopy Center of Southeast Texas,** 950 North 14th Street,#200, Beaumont, TX 77702; tel. 409/833-5555; FAX. 409/833-9911; JoAnn Hughes, RNBC, Center Director

**The Ocular Surgery Center, Inc.,** 1100 North Main Avenue, San Antonio, TX 78212; tel. 210/222-2154; FAX. 512/222-0706; Jane Wilson, Administrator

**The Surgery Center of the Woodlands,** 1441 Woodstead Court, Suite 100, The Woodlands, TX 77380; tel. 281/363-0058; FAX. 281/363-0450; Susan Olis, Administrator

**Urological Surgery Center of Fort Worth,** 418 South Henderson, Fort Worth, TX 76104; tel. 817/870-9165; FAX. 817/335-5421; Charles Bamberger, MD

**Valley Endoscopy Center, LLP,** 3101 South 77 Sunshine Strip, Suite B, Harlingen, TX 78550; tel. 956/421-2324; FAX. 956/421-5791; Stephanie V. Gonzalez, RN, Director of Nursing

**Vista Surgical Center West,** 2500 Fondren, Suite 350, Houston, TX 77063; tel. 713/782-8279; FAX. 713/782-3139; Diana Hastings, RN, CNOR - Clinical Director

**West Houston Surgicare,** 970 Campbell Road, Houston, TX 77024-2804; tel. 713/461-3547; FAX. 713/722-8921; Corey Hooks, Administrator

**Wilson Surgicenter,** 4315 28th Street, Lubbock, TX 79410; tel. 806/792-2104; Bill W. Wilson, MD, Chief Executive Officer

## UTAH

**Central Utah Surgical Center,** 1067 North 500 West, Provo, UT 84604; tel. 801/374-0354; FAX. 801/717-2364; Jill Andrews, RN, BSN, CNOR, Administrator

**Institute of Facial and Cosmetic Surgery,** 5929 Fashion Boulevard, Salt Lake City, UT 84107; tel. 801/261-3637; FAX. 801/261-4096; Dr. Brent D. Kennedy, Director

**Salt Lake Endoscopy Center,** 24 South 1100 East, Salt Lake City, UT 84102; tel. 801/355-2987; FAX. 801/531-9704

**Salt Lake Surgical Center,** 617 East 3900 South, Salt Lake City, UT 84107; tel. 801/261-3141; FAX. 801/268-2599; Robyn Archer, Administrator

**St. George Surgical Center,** 676 South Bluff Street, St. George, UT 84770; tel. 435/673-8080; FAX. 435/673-0096; Kelly Kendall, Administrator

**St. Mark's Outpatient Surgery Center,** 1250 East 3900 South, Suite 100, Salt Lake City, UT 84124; tel. 801/262-0358; FAX. 801/262-0901; Diana McPherson, MBA, CASC, Administrator

**The SurgiCare Center of Utah,** 755 East 3900 South, Salt Lake City, UT 84107; tel. 801/266-2283; FAX. 801/268-6151; Helen Sikes, Administrator

**Wasatch Endoscopy,** 1220 East 3900 South, Suite 1B, Salt Lake City, UT 84124; tel. 801/281-3657; FAX. 801/281-4258; Jeri Fowles, Administrator

**Wasatch Surgery Center,** 555 South Foothill Boulevard, Salt Lake City, UT 84112; tel. 801/581-7782; FAX. 801/581-8962; Karen Ipson, Administrator, Manager

## VIRGINIA

**Blue Ridge Surgery Center,** 1802 Braeburn Drive, Salem, VA 24153; tel. 540/772-3600; FAX. 540/725-4543; Shawna Hall, RN, CASC, Administrator

**Cataract and Refractive Surgery Center, LLC,** 2010 Bremo Road, Suite 132, Richmond, VA 23226; tel. 804/673-5272; FAX. 804/673-5279; Patricia Lampman, Director

**Fredericksburg Ambulatory Surgery Center,** 1201 Sam Perry Boulevard, Suite 101, Fredericksburg, VA 22401; tel. 540/741-7000, FAX. 540/899-6893; Jeane Bullock, Administrator

**Kaiser Permanente Falls Church Ambulatory Surgery Center,** 201 North Washington Street, Falls Church, VA 22046; tel. 703/531-1623; FAX. 703/536-1400; Eileen Field, Director, ASC

**Lakeview Medical Center, Inc.,** 2000 Meade Parkway, Suffolk, VA 23424; tel. 757/539-0251; FAX. 757/923-9632; Laura E. Joyner, Chief Operations Officer

**Parham Surgery Center,** 7640 E Parham Road, Henrico, VA 23294; tel. 804/591-2202; FAX. 804/591-2237; Sandra W. Pearson, Administrator

**Piedmont Day Surgery Center, Inc.,** 1040 Main Street, P.O. Box 1360, Danville, VA 24543-1360; tel. 434/792-1433; FAX. 434/797-2807; Edward Wright, MD, President

**Riverside Hampton Surgery Center,** 850 Enterprise Parkway, Suite 1000, Hampton, VA 23666-6255; tel. 757/251-7700; FAX. 757/251-7799; Sheila Rilee, RN, Administrator

**Surgi Center of Central Virginia, Inc.,** 12 Chatham Heights Rd, Fredericksburg, VA 22405; tel. 703/371-5349; FAX. 703/373-1745; Kenny Ellinger, RN, Facility Administrator

**Surgi-Center of Winchester, Inc.,** 1860 Amherst Street, PO Box 2660, Winchester, VA 22604; tel. 540/536-8934; FAX. 540/536-8936; David J. Kliewer, MD, Medical Director

**Urosurgical Center of Richmond,** 9105 Stony Point Dr, Richmond, VA 23235; tel. 804/330-9105; FAX. 804/560-0914; Terry W. Coffey, Administrator

**Urosurgical Center of Richmond-North,** 8228 Meadowbridge Road, Mechanicsville, VA 23116; tel. 804/730-5023; FAX. 804/746-4015; Terry W. Coffey, Administrator

**Virginia Ambulatory Surgery, Inc.,** 337-15th Street, SW, Charlottesville, VA 22903; tel. 434/951-4600; FAX. 434/817-8465; Gerry Dobrasz, Administrator

**Virginia Beach Ambulatory Surgery Center,** 1700 Will-o-Wisp Drive, Virginia Beach, VA 23454; tel. 757/496-6400; FAX. 757/496-3137; Martha R. Colen, Administrator

**Virginia Eye Institute/Eye Surgeons of Richmond, Inc.,** 400 Westhampton Station, Richmond, VA 23226; tel. 804/287-4244; FAX. 804/287-4207; Cheryl Lunger, Marketing and Communications Director

**Woodburn Surgery Center,** 3289 Woodburn Road, Suite 100, Annandale, VA 22003; tel. 703/207-7520; Jolene Tornabeni, Senior Vice President, Administrator

## WASHINGTON

**Allure Laser Center,** 625 4th Avenue, Suite 301, Kirkland, WA 98033; tel. 425/216-7200; FAX. 425/216-7272; Janet Jordan, Administrator

**Auburn Outpatient Surgery Center,** 1427 Jefferson Avenue, Suite 101, Enumclaw, WA 98022; tel. 360/825-4466; FAX. 360/825-2064; Nancy A. Becker, DO, Medical Director

**Bel-Red Ambulatory Surgical Facility,** 1260 116th Avenue, NE, #110, Bellevue, WA 98004; tel. 425/455-7225; FAX. 425/455-0045; Jan Zemplenyi, MD, Director

**Cascade Medical Group PS, Inc.,** 111 S. 13th Street, Mount Vernon, WA 98274; tel. 360/336-2178; FAX. 360/336-1674; Alex O'Dell, Business Administrator

**Cascade Valley Arlington Surgery Center,** 875 Wesley Street, Suite 160, Arlington, WA 98223; tel. 360/435-6969; FAX. 360/435-1068; Jola Barnett, Assistant Administrator

**Edmonds Surgery Center,** 21229 84th Avenue W., Edmonds, WA 98026; tel. 206/775-1505; FAX. 206/775-9078; Mark A. Kuzel, DPM, F.A.C.F.S

**Evergreen Endoscopy Center,** 11800 NE 128th Street, Suite 100, Kirkland, WA 98034; tel. 425/899-4500; FAX. 425/899-4510; Darlene Buckley, RN, Endoscopy Unit Supervisor

**Evergreen Eye Center,** 34719 Sixth Avenue South, Federal Way, WA 98003; tel. 800/340-3595; FAX. 206/212-2194; Richard A. Boudreau, Administrator

**Eye Surgery Center Northwest,** 842 South Cowley, Suite 3, Spokane, WA 99202; tel. 509/747-6358; FAX. 509/321-5020; Michael H. Cunningham, MD, President

**First Hill Surgery Center,** 515 Minor Avenue, Suite 130, Seattle, WA 98104; tel. 206/682-6103; FAX. 206/682-3511; Debbie Perdue, Director

**Foot Care Associates Ambulatory Surgery Center,** 16146 Cleveland Street, Redmond, WA 98052; tel. 425/885-7004; Dr. Brunsman, Medical Director

**GH TASC,** 209 Martin Luther King Jr. Way, Tacoma, WA 98405; tel. 253/596-3590; Nancy Sowers, RN, MBA, CNOR, Manager

**Good Samaritan Surgery Center,** 1322 Third Street SE, Suite 100, Puyallup, WA 98372; tel. 253/697-5700; FAX. 253/697-4120; William Rinker, MD, Medical Director

**Minor & James Medical, PLLC,** 515 Minor Avenue, Suite 200, Seattle, WA 98104; tel. 206/386-9500; FAX. 206/576-3807; Patricia Creed, RN, ASC Manager

**Moses Lake Clinic ASC,** 840 E. Hill Avenue, Moses Lake, WA 98837; tel. 509/764-6400; FAX. 509/764-6434; David Olson, Administrator

**North Kitsap Ambulatory Surgical Center Inc., dba Pacific Surgery Center,** 20669 Bond Road, NE, Suite 200, Poulsbo, WA 98370; tel. 360/779-6527; FAX. 360/697-2743; Susan Simons, RN, BSN, CASC, Administrator

**Northwest Center for Plastic and Reconstructive Surgery,** 16259 Sylvester Road, SW, Suite 302, Seattle, WA 98166; tel. 206/241-5400; FAX. 206/241-8591; Sindi Miller, Office Manager

**Northwest Gastroenterology, dba Northwest Endoscopy,** 2930 Squalicum Parkway, Suite 202, Bellingham, WA 98225; tel. 360/734-1420; FAX. 360/734-8748; Sandra Vander Yacht, Manager

**Northwest Nasal Sinus Center,** 1200 Northgate Way, Seattle, WA 98133; tel. 206/525-2525; FAX. 206/525-0346; Rick Fischer, Business Administrator

**Northwest Nasal Sinus Center,** 3100 Carillon Point, Kirkland, WA 98033; tel. 425/576-1700; FAX. 425/827-7725; Rick Fischer, Business Administrator

**Section C**

**Northwest Surgery Center,** 1920 100th Street, SE, Everett, WA 98208; tel. 425/316-3700; FAX. 425/316-6881; Chris Vance, President

**Northwest Surgery Center, Inc.,** West 123 Francis, Spokane, WA 99205; tel. 509/483-9363; FAX. 509/483-0355; Douglas P. Romney

**Olympic Plastic Surgery Suite,** 2600 Cherry Avenue, Suite 201, Bremerton, WA 98310; tel. 360/415-0762; Suzanne Fletcher, Administrator

**Pacific Cataract and Laser Institute,** 2517 Northeast Kresky, Chehalis, WA 98532; tel. 206/748-8632; FAX. 360/748-4007; Debbie Eldredge, Vice President and Chief Operating Officer

**Pacific Cataract and Laser Institute,** 10500 Northeast Eighth Street, Suite 1650, Bellevue, WA 98004-4332; tel. 425/462-7664; FAX. 425/462-6429; Maynard Pohl, OD, Clinical Director

**Pacific Cataract and Laser Institute,** 8200 West Grandridge, Kennewick, WA 99336; FAX. 360/748-4007; Debbie Eldredge, Vice President and Chief Operating Officer

**Pacific NW Facial Plastic Ambulatory Surgery Center,** 600 Broadway, Suite 280, Seattle, WA 98122; tel. 206/386-3550; FAX. 206/386-3553; Sherry Gizewski, Practice Manager

**Parkway Surgical Center,** 2940 Squalicum Parkway, Suite 204, Bellingham, WA 98225; tel. 206/676-8350; FAX. 206/676-8351; Orville Vandergriend, MD, Administrator

**PeaceHealth St. Joseph Medical Center, PeaceHealth Medical Group,** 4545 Cordata Parkway, Bellingham, WA 98226; tel. 360/738-2200; FAX. 360/752-5681; Debra L. Taylor, Dir Operations PHMG

**Phillip C. Kierney, M.D., Cosmetic and Plastic Surgery,** 105 27th Avenue, SE, Puyallup, WA 98374; tel. 253/848-8110; FAX. 253/845-3561; P. Kierney, Owner

**Physicians Eye Surgical Center,** 3930 Hoyt Avenue, Everett, WA 98201; tel. 206/259-2020; Ms. Mello Johnson, Administrator

**Premier Orthopedic Group Surgery Center,** 21401 72nd Ave W., Edmonds, WA 98026; tel. 425/774-2636; FAX. 425/774-2688; Marilyn Degan, Director

**Rockwood Clinic, dba Gastrointestinal Endoscopy Unit,** 400 East 5th Avenue, Spokane, WA 99202; tel. 509/838-2531; FAX. 509/755-6580; Craig Whiting, MD, Administrator

**Seattle Endoscopy Center,** 11027 Meridian Avenue, N., Suite 100, Seattle, WA 98133; tel. 206/365-4492; FAX. 206/368-3456; Mary Beth Philips, BSN, RN, CGRN, Manager

**Seattle Hand Surgery Group, P.C.,** 600 Broadway, Suite 440, Seattle, WA 98122; tel. 206/292-6252; FAX. 206/292-7893

**Seattle Plastic Surgery Center,** 600 Broadway, Suite 320, Seattle, WA 98122; tel. 206/324-1120; FAX. 206/720-0800; Gail Boren, Manager

**Seattle Surgery Center, Columbus Pavilion,** 900 Terry Avenue, Third Floor, Seattle, WA 98104-1240; tel. 206/382-1021; FAX. 206/332-9369; Jim Sapienza, FACHE, Chief Executive Officer

**Sequim Same Day Surgery,** 777 North Fifth Avenue, Sequim, WA 98382; tel. 360/582-2632; FAX. 360/582-2631; Tammy Paolini, Operational Manager

**South Hill Ambulatory Surgical Center,** South 3028 Grand Boulevard, Spokane, WA 99203; tel. 509/747-0279; FAX. 509/747-3220; Borys Markewych

**Spokane Digestive Disease Center, P.S.,** 105 West Eighth Avenue, Suite 6010, Spokane, WA 99204-2341; tel. 509/838-5950; FAX. 509/838-5961; Michelle Avenger, RN, CGRN, Director

**Spokane Surgery Center,** North 1120 Pines Road, Spokane, WA 99206; tel. 509/928-1990; FAX. 509/928-2933; Stewart P. Brim, DPM

**Surgery Center Of Spokane,** 205 N. University #4, Spokane, WA 99206; tel. 509/922-3199; Dr. Jacqueline Borbol

**Tacoma Ambulatory Surgery Center,** 1112 Sixth Avenue, Suite 100, Tacoma, WA 98405; tel. 253/272-3916; FAX. 253/627-1713; Deborah Gist, Clinical Director

**Tacoma Endoscopy Center,** 1112 Sixth Avenue, Suite 200, Tacoma, WA 98405; tel. 253/272-8664; FAX. 253/627-7880; John G. Carrougher, MD, Medical Director

**The Eastside Endoscopy Center, LLC, A Physicians Endoscopy Partnered Facility,** 1135 116th Ave NE Suite 570, Bellevue, WA 98004-3049; tel. 425/451-7335; FAX. 425/451-1226; Michelle Steele, CGRN, Nurse Administrator

**The Plastic SurgiCentre, Inc.,** 535 South Pine Street, Spokane, WA 99202; tel. 509/623-2160; FAX. 509/623-1135; Vern Myrick, RN, Nurse Manager

**The Polyclinic, Inc.,** 1145 Broadway, Seattle, WA 98122; tel. 206/329-1760

**Virginia Mason-Issaquah,** 100 Northeast Gilman Boulevard, Issaquah, WA 98027; tel. 425/557-8000; Bobbie Eatmon, Director Ambulatory Services

**Washington Centre for Reproductive Medicine, ASC,** 1370 116th Avenue, NE, Suite 202, Bellevue, WA 98004; tel. 425/462-6100; FAX. 425/635-0742; Dr. James Kustin, Medical Director

**Washington Orthopedic Center, Inc., PS,** 1900 Cooks Hill Road, Centralia, WA 98531; tel. 360/736-2889; Dondi Sahlinger, OR Manager

**Whidbey SurgiCare,** PO Box 11782, Suite A Two, Olympia, WA 98508-1782; tel. 360/679-3117; FAX. 360/679-3118; Stephen T. Miller, DPM, Medical Director

**WEST VIRGINIA**

**Anwar Eye Center,** 1500 Lafayette Avenue, Moundsville, WV 26041; tel. 304/845-0908; FAX. 304/845-1250; M. F. Anwar, MD

**Cabell Huntington Surgery Center,** 1201 Hal Greer Boulevard, Huntington, WV 25701; tel. 304/523-1885; FAX. 304/523-8942; Lexa Woodyard, Administrator

**Day Surgery Center,** Chesterfield Medical Plaza, 2335 Chesterfield Ave. #400, Charleston, WV 25304; tel. 304/925-9300; FAX. 304/925-2924; Olivia Garton, Administrator

**Greenbrier Clinic Surgery Center, Inc.,** 320 W. Main Street, White Sulphur Spring, WV 24986; tel. 304/536-4870; FAX. 304/536-1325; William N. Cunningham, MD, Medical Director

**Jerry N. Black, M.D., Surgical Suite,** 10 Amalia Drive, Suite 3C, Buckhannon, WV 26201; tel. 304/472-2100; FAX. 304/472-2118; Jerry N. Black, MD, Medical Director

**Kanawha Valley Surgi-Center,** 4803 MacCorkle Avenue, SE, Charleston, WV 25304; tel. 304/925-6390; FAX. 304/925-7931; Gorli Harish, MD, Medical Director

**Surgical Eye Center of Morgantown,** 1299 Pineview Drive, 5th Floor, Morgantown, WV 26505; tel. 304/598-5755; Heather Huffman, RN, Administrator

**Tri State Surgical Center, LLC,** 1006 Tavern Road, Martinsburg, WV 25401; tel. 304/267-0556; Stacey Ferguson, Administrator

**WISCONSIN**

**BayCare Surgery Center,** 2253 West Mason, P.O. Box 33227, Green Bay, WI 54303-0102; tel. 920/592-9100; FAX. 920/497-8056; Tammy Kruegger, Executive Director

**Green Bay Surgical Center, Ltd.,** 704 South Webster Avenue, Ste 301, Green Bay, WI 54301; tel. 920/432-7433; FAX. 920/432-6003

**Menomonee Falls Ambulatory Surgery Center,** W180 N8045 Town Hall Road, Menomonee Falls, WI 53051; tel. 262/250-0950; FAX. 262/250-0955; Dianne Appleby, Executive Director

**North Shore Surgical Center,** 7007 North Range Line Road, Milwaukee, WI 53209; tel. 414/352-3341; FAX. 414/247-4588; Helen Kowalski, Executive Director

**Northwest Surgery Center,** 2300 North Mayfair Road, Suite 295, Wauwatosa, WI 53226; tel. 414/257-3322; FAX. 414/257-3364; Gail Wuestoff, Administrator

**Riverview Surgery Center,** 616 North Washington Street, Janesville, WI 53545; tel. 608/758-7300; FAX. 608/758-1050; Lynn Jenkins, Director

**St. Mary's Dean Ventures Surgery Centers,** PO Box 259630, Madison, WI 53725-9630; tel. 608/259-3510; FAX. 608/255-1272; Jane Hrdlicka, Interim Vice President

**Surgicenter of Greater Milwaukee,** 3223 South 103rd Street, Milwaukee, WI 53227; tel. 414/328-5800; FAX. 414/328-5805; Suzan Buchaklian, Director

**Surgicenter of Racine, Ltd.,** 5802 Washington Avenue, Racine, WI 53406; tel. 262/886-9100; FAX. 262/886-9130; Dennis J. Kontra, Administrator

**Wauwatosa Surgery Center,** 10900 West Potter Road, Wauwatosa, WI 53226-3424; tel. 414/774-9227; FAX. 414/774-0957; Dan Cresco, Administrator

**WYOMING**

**Wyoming Outpatient Services,** 5050 Powderhouse Road, Cheyenne, WY 82009; tel. 307/634-1311; FAX. 307/432-7550; Jan VanAlyn, LPN, Manager

**Yellowstone Surgery Center, LLC,** 5201 Yellowstone Road, Cheyenne, WY 82009; tel. 307/635-7070; FAX. 307/632-9920; Deborah Wright, Office Administrator

# U.S. Associated Areas

**PUERTO RICO**

**ASC Espanola Clinic,** Box 490, La Quinta, Mayaguez, PR 00681; tel. 787/832-2094

**Clinica de Cirugia Ambulatoria de Puerto Rico,** Box 3748, Mayaguez, PR 00681; tel. 787/833-4400; FAX. 787/265-6621; Roberto Ruiz, Administrator

**Instituto Cirugia Plastica Del Oeste,** 165 Este Mendez Vigo Street, Mayaguez, PR 00680; tel. 787/833-3248; FAX. 787/831-4400; Oscar Vargas, MD, Medical Director

**Instituto Quirurgico De Un Dia - Dr. Pila,** PO Box 331910, Ponce, PR 00733-1910; tel. 787/848-5600; FAX. 787/841-1085; Mrs. Joselyn Irizarry RN, Supervisor

**OJOS, Eye Surgery Specialists of P.R.LLC,** Hipodromo Street 809, Santurce, PR 00909; tel. 787/721-8330; FAX. 787/722-3222; Maria Delos A. Tirado, Administrator

**San Juan Health Centre Ambulatory Clinic,** 150 De Diego Avenue, Badorioty Corner, San Juan, PR 00907; tel. 787/977-7575; FAX. 787/977-7587; Pedro Rivera-Archilla, Executive Director

The accredited freestanding long–term care organizations listed have been accredited as of May 2013 by the Joint Commission on Accreditation of Healthcare Organizations by decision of the Accreditation Committee of the Board of Commissioners.

The organizations listed here have been found to be in compliance with the Joint Commission standards for long–term care organizations, as found in the Comprehensive Accreditation Manual for the Long–Term Care Organizations.

Please refer to section A of the AHA Guide for information on hospitals with Long–Term Care services. These hospitals are identified by Facility Code F128. In section A, those hospitals identified by Approval Code 1 are Joint Commission accredited.

We present this list simply as a convenient directory. Inclusion or omission of any organization's name indicates neither approval nor disapproval by Health Forum LLC, an American Hospital Association company.

## United States

### ALABAMA
**Central Alabama Veterans Health Care System,** 215 Perry Hill Road, Montgomery, AL 36109; tel. 334/272–4670
**Marion Regional Medical Center, Inc.,** 1256 Military Street South, Hamilton, AL 35570; tel. 205/921–6200
**Tuscaloosa VA Medical Center,** 3701 Loop Road East, Tuscaloosa, AL 35404; tel. 205/554–2000

### ALASKA
**Norton Sound Regional Hospital,** PO Box 966, Nome, AK 99762; tel. 907/443–3311
**PeaceHealth Ketchikan Medical Center,** 3100 Tongass Avenue, Ketchikan, AK 99901; tel. 907/225–5171

### ARIZONA
**Citadel Care Center,** 5121 East Broadway Road, Mesa, AZ 85206; tel. 480/832–5555
**Desert Cove Nursing Center,** 1750 West Frye Road, Chandler, AZ 85224; tel. 480/899–0641
**Glendale Care Center,** 4704 West Diana Avenue, Glendale, AZ 85302; tel. 623/247–3949
**Heritage Health Care Center,** 1300 South Street, Globe, AZ 85501; tel. 928/425–3118
**La Canada Care Center,** 7970 North LaCanada Dr., Tucson, AZ 85704; tel. 520/797–1191
**Las Fuentes Care Center,** 1045 Scott Drive, Prescott, AZ 86301; tel. 928/778–9603
**Life Care Center at South Mountain,** 8008 South Jesse Owens Parkway, Phoenix, AZ 85040; tel. 602/243–2780
**Life Care Center of North Glendale,** 13620 North 55th Avenue, Glendale, AZ 85304; tel. 602/843–8433
**Life Care Center of Paradise Valley,** 4065 East Bell Road, Phoenix, AZ 85032; tel. 602/867–0212
**Life Care Center of Scottsdale,** 9494 East Becker Lane, Scottsdale, AZ 85260; tel. 480/860–6396
**Life Care Center of Sierra Vista,** 2305 East Wilcox Drive, Sierra Vista, AZ 85635; tel. 520/458–1050
**Life Care Center of Tucson,** 6211 North LaCholla Boulevard, Tucson, AZ 85741; tel. 520/575–0900
**Life Care Center of Yuma,** 2450 South 19th Avenue, Yuma, AZ 85364; tel. 928/344–0425
**Mi Casa Nursing Center,** 330 S. Pinnule Circle, Mesa, AZ 85206; tel. 480/981–0687
**Mountain View Care Center,** 1313 West Magee Road, Tucson, AZ 85704; tel. 520/797–2600
**Northern Arizona VA Health Care System,** 500 Highway 89 North, Prescott, AZ 86313; tel. 928/445–4860
**Payson Care Center,** 107 East Lone Pine Drive, Payson, AZ 85541; tel. 928/474–6896
**Phoenix VA Health Care System,** 650 East Indian School Road, Phoenix, AZ 85012-1892; tel. 602/277–5551
**Scottsdale Heritage Court,** 3339 N. Drinkwater Blvd, Scottsdale, AZ 85251; tel. 480/949–5400
**Southern Arizona VA Health Care System,** 3601 South Sixth Avenue, Tucson, AZ 85723; tel. 520/629–1821
**Sun Grove Village Care Center,** 20625 N. Lake Pleasant Road, Peoria, AZ 85382; tel. 623/566–0642

### ARKANSAS
**Central Arkansas Veterans Healthcare System,** 4300 West Seventh Street (00/LR), Little Rock, AR 72205; tel. 501/257–5314

### CALIFORNIA
**Bel Tooren Villa Convalescent Hospital,** 16910 Woodruff Avenue, Bellflower, CA 90706; tel. 562/867–1761
**California Special Care Center, Inc.,** 8787 Center Drive, La Mesa, CA 91942; tel. 619/460–4444
**CareMeridian,** 12461 Springdale Street, Garden Grove, CA 92845; tel. 949/263–6630
**CareMeridian,** 18-A Journey, Suite 200, Aliso Viejo, CA 92656; tel. 949/263–6630
**CareMeridian - Northridge,** 10318 Laramie Street, Chatsworth, CA 91311; tel. 818/882–5204
**CareMeridian - Phoenix,** 18A Journey, Aliso Viejo, CA 92656; tel. 949/263–6630
**Community Hospital of the Monterey Peninsula,** PO Box HH, Monterey, CA 93942; tel. 831/625–4553
**Department of State Hospitals-Metropolitan,** 11401 South Bloomfield Avenue, Norwalk, CA 90650; tel. 562/863–7011
**Dominican Hospital a member of Dignity Health,** 1555 Soquel Drive, Santa Cruz, CA 95065; tel. 831/462–7700
**East Los Angeles Doctors Hospital,** 4060 East Whittier Boulevard, Los Angeles, CA 90023; tel. 323/268–5514
**Encino Hospital Medical Center,** 16237 Ventura Blvd, Encino, CA 91436; tel. 818/995–5002
**Fallbrook Hospital Corporation,** 624 East Elder Street, Fallbrook, CA 92028-3099; tel. 760/728–1191
**Fresno Community Hospital and Medical Center,** PO Box 1232, Fresno, CA 93715; tel. 559/459–6000
**Goleta Valley Cottage Hospital,** PO Box 6306, Santa Barbara, CA 93160-6306; tel. 805/967–3411
**Hemet Valley Medical Center,** 1117 East Devonshire Avenue, Hemet, CA 92543; tel. 951/652–2811
**Hollenbeck Palms,** 573 South Boyle Avenue, Los Angeles, CA 90033; tel. 323/263–6195
**Hollywood Presbyterian Medical Center,** 1300 North Vermont Avenue, Los Angeles, CA 90027; tel. 323/413–3000
**Imperial Convalescent Center,** 11926 La Mirada Boulevard, La Mirada, CA 90638; tel. 562/943–7156
**Kaiser Foundation Hospital - Manteca/Modesto,** 4601 Dale Road, Modesto, CA 95356; tel. 209/735–3000
**La Habra Convalescent Hospital,** 1233 West La Habra Boulevard, La Habra, CA 90631; tel. 562/691–0781
**Lake Forest Nursing Center,** 25652 Old Trabuco Road, Lake Forest, CA 92630; tel. 949/380–9380
**Life Care Center of Escondido,** 1980 Felicita Road, Escondido, CA 92025; tel. 760/741–6109
**Life Care Center of Menifee,** 27600 Encanto Drive, Menifee, CA 92586; tel. 951/679–6858
**Life Care Center of Vista,** 304 North Melrose Drive, Vista, CA 92083; tel. 760/724–8222
**Lompoc Valley Medical Center,** 1515 E. Ocean Ave., Lompoc, CA 93436; tel. 805/737–3301
**Los Robles Hospital and Medical Center,** 215 West Janss Road, Thousand Oaks, CA 91360; tel. 805/370–4421
**Magnolia Special Care Center,** 635 South Magnolia, El Cajon, CA 92020; tel. 619/442–8826
**Marian Regional Medical Center,** 1400 East Church Street, Santa Maria, CA 93454; tel. 805/739–3000
**Methodist Hospital of Sacramento,** 7500 Hospital Drive, Sacramento, CA 95823; tel. 916/423–3000
**Mirada Hills Rehabilitation and Convalescent Hospital,** 12200 La Mirada Boulevard, La Mirada, CA 90638; tel. 562/947–8691

**North Walk Villa Convalescent Hospital,** 12350 Rosecrans Avenue, Norwalk, CA 90650; tel. 562/921–6624
**Oak Valley District Hospital,** 350 S. Oak Avenue, Oakdale, CA 95361; tel. 209/847–3011
**Orangegrove Rehabilitation Hospital,** 12332 Garden Grove Boulevard, Garden Grove, CA 92843; tel. 714/534–1041
**Pacifica Nursing and Rehab Center,** 385 Esplanade Avenue, Pacifica, CA 94044; tel. 650/993–5576
**Palomar Medical Center,** 2185 Citracado Parkway, Escondido, CA 92029; tel. 442/281–1006
**Pomerado Hospital,** 15615 Pomerado Road, Poway, CA 92064; tel. 858/613–4710
**Rady Children's Hospital San Diego,** 3020 Children's Way, MC 5069, San Diego, CA 92123-4282; tel. 858/576–1700
**Reche Canyon Rehabilitation and Health Care Center,** 1350 Reche Canyon Road, Colton, CA 92324; tel. 909/370–4411
**Rimrock Villa Convalescent Hospital,** 27555 Rimrock Road, Barstow, CA 92311; tel. 760/252–2515
**San Francisco General Hospital and Trauma Center,** 1001 Potrero Avenue, Bldg 20, Room 2300, San Francisco, CA 94110; tel. 415/206–3455
**San Francisco VA Medical Center,** 4150 Clement Street, San Francisco, CA 94121; tel. 415/221–4810
**Seton Medical Center,** 1900 Sullivan Avenue, Daly City, CA 94015; tel. 650/992–4000
**Sharp Chula Vista Medical Center,** 751 Medical Center Court, Chula Vista, CA 91911-6699; tel. 619/502–3664
**St. Jude Medical Center,** 101 East Valencia Mesa Drive, Fullerton, CA 92835; tel. 714/992–3000
**St. Mary's Medical Center,** 450 Stanyan Street, San Francisco, CA 94117; tel. 415/668–1000
**The Cloisters of La Jolla,** 7160 Fay Avenue, La Jolla, CA 92037; tel. 858/459–4361
**The Cloisters of Mission Hills,** 3680 Reynard Way, San Diego, CA 92103; tel. 619/297–4484
**Totally Kids Specialty Healthcare,** 1720 Mountain View Avenue, Loma Linda, CA 92354; tel. 909/796–6915
**VA Central California Health Care System,** 2615 East Clinton Avenue, Fresno, CA 93703; tel. 559/225–6100
**VA Greater Los Angeles Healthcare System,** 11301 Wilshire Boulevard, Los Angeles, CA 90073; tel. 310/268–3132
**VA Loma Linda Healthcare System,** 11201 Benton Street, Loma Linda, CA 92357; tel. 909/583–6002
**VA Long Beach Health Care System,** 5901 East Seventh Street, Long Beach, CA 90822; tel. 562/826–5400
**VA Northern California Health Care System,** 10535 Hospital Way, Mather, CA 95655; tel. 916/843–7000
**VA Palo Alto Health Care System,** 3801 Miranda Avenue, Palo Alto, CA 94304; tel. 650/493–5000
**VA San Diego Healthcare System,** 3350 La Jolla Village Drive, San Diego, CA 92161; tel. 858/552–8585
**Whittier Hospital Medical Center,** 9080 Colima Road, Whittier, CA 90605-1898; tel. 562/945–3561

### COLORADO
**Arkansas Valley Regional Medical Center,** 1100 Carson Avenue, La Junta, CO 81050; tel. 719/383–6001
**Berkley Medical Investors, LLC,** 735 South Locust Street, Denver, CO 80224; tel. 303/320–4377

**Briarwood Health Care Center,** 1440 Vine St., Denver, CO 80206; tel. 303/399-0350

**Canon Lodge Care Center,** 905 Harding Avenue, Canon City, CO 81212; tel. 719/275-4106

**Columbine Manor Care Center,** 530 W 16th st., Salida, CO 81201; tel. 719/539-6112

**Evergreen Nursing Home,** 1991 Carroll Avenue, Alamosa, CO 81101; tel. 719/589-4951

**Garden Terrace Alzheimer's Center of Excellence,** 1600 South Potomac Street, Aurora, CO 80012; tel. 303/750-8418

**Grand Junction Veterans Affairs Medical Center,** 2121 North Avenue, Grand Junction, CO 81501; tel. 970/242-0731

**Hallmark Nursing Center,** 3701 West Radcliff Avenue, Denver, CO 80236; tel. 303/794-6484

**Heritage Park Care Center,** 1200 Village Road, Carbondale, CO 81623; tel. 970/963-1500

**Life Care Center of Aurora,** 14101 East Evans Avenue, Aurora, CO 80014; tel. 303/751-2000

**Life Care Center of Colorado Springs,** 2490 International Circle, Colorado Springs, CO 80910; tel. 719/630-8888

**Life Care Center of Evergreen,** 2987 Bergen Peak Drive, Evergreen, CO 80439; tel. 303/674-4500

**Life Care Center of Greeley,** 4800 25th Street, Greeley, CO 80634; tel. 970/330-6400

**Life Care Center of Littleton,** 1500 W. Mineral Avenue, Littleton, CO 80120; tel. 303/795-7300

**Life Care Center of Longmont,** 2451 Pratt Street, Longmont, CO 80501; tel. 303/776-5000

**Life Care Center of Pueblo,** 2118 Chatalet Lane, Pueblo, CO 81005; tel. 719/564-2000

**Life Care Center of Westminster,** 7751 Zenobia Court, Westminster, CO 80030; tel. 303/412-9121

**San Luis Care Center,** 240 Craft Drive, Alamosa, CO 81101; tel. 719/589-9081

**University Park Care Center,** 945 Desert Flower Boulevard, Pueblo, CO 81001; tel. 719/545-5321

**VA Eastern Colorado Healthcare System,** 1055 Clermont St, Denver, CO 80220; tel. 303/399-8020

**Valley View Villa,** 815 Fremont Avenue, Fort Morgan, CO 80701; tel. 970/867-8261

**Villa Manor Care Center,** 7950 W. Mississippi Ave., Lakewood, CO 80226; tel. 303/986-4511

**Western Hills Health Care Center,** 1625 Carr Street, Lakewood, CO 80214; tel. 303/232-6881

**CONNECTICUT**

**4 Hazel Avenue Operations, LLC of Naugatuck, CT,** 4 Hazel Avenue, Naugatuck, CT 06770; tel. 203/723-1456

**Golden Hill Health Care Center,** 2028 Bridgeport Avenue, Milford, CT 06460; tel. 203/877-0371

**Hartford Hospital,** 80 Seymour Street, Hartford, CT 06102-5037; tel. 860/545-2100

**Hughes Health and Rehabilitation, Inc.,** 29 Highland Street, West Hartford, CT 06119; tel. 860/236-5623

**Meriden Center,** 845 Paddock Avenue, Meriden, CT 06450; tel. 203/238-2645

**Montowese Health and Rehabilitation Center, Inc.,** 163 Quinnipiac Avenue, North Haven, CT 06473; tel. 203/624-3303

**Salmon Brook Center,** 72 Salmon Brook Drive, Glastonbury, CT 06033; tel. 860/633-5244

**Skyview Center,** 35 Marc Drive, Wallingford, CT 06492; tel. 203/265-0981

**VA Connecticut Healthcare System,** 950 Campbell Avenue, West Haven, CT 06516; tel. 203/932-5711

**Village Green of Bristol,** 23 Fair Street, Bristol, CT 06010; tel. 860/589-2923

**Village Green of Wallingford,** 55 Kondracki Lane, Wallingford, CT 06492; tel. 203/265-6771

**Village Green of Waterbury,** 128 Cedar Avenue, Waterbury, CT 06705; tel. 203/757-9271

**Yale Health,** PO Box 208237, New Haven, CT 06520; tel. 203/432-4096

**DELAWARE**

**VA Medical Center,** 1601 Kirkwood Highway, Wilmington, DE 19805; tel. 302/994-2511

**DISTRICT OF COLUMBIA**

**Providence Hospital,** 1150 Varnum Street, Northeast, Washington, DC 20017; tel. 202/269-7000

**Sibley Memorial Hospital,** 5255 Loughboro Road, NW, Washington, DC 20016; tel. 202/537-4000

**VA Medical Center,** 50 Irving Street, Northwest, Washington, DC 20422; tel. 202/745-8000

**FLORIDA**

**Bay Pines VA Healthcare System,** 10000 Bay Pines Boulevard, Bay Pines, FL 33744; tel. 727/398-6661

**Bon Secours Maria Manor Nursing & Rehabilitation Center,** 10300 4th Street North, Saint Petersburg, FL 33716; tel. 727/576-1025

**Darcy Hall of Life Care,** 2170 Palm Beach Lakes Blvd., West Palm Beach, FL 33409; tel. 561/683-3333

**Florida Institute for Neurologic Rehabilitation, Inc,** PO Box 1348, Wauchula, FL 33873; tel. 863/773-2857

**Jackson Plaza Nursing and Rehabilitation Center,** 1861 Northwest 8th Avenue, Miami, FL 33136; tel. 305/347-3380

**James A. Haley Veterans' Hospital,** 13000 Bruce B. Downs Boulevard, Tampa, FL 33612; tel. 813/972-2000

**Lakeside Health Center,** 2501 Australian Avenue, West Palm Beach, FL 33407; tel. 561/655-7780

**Life Care Center of Jacksonville,** 4813 Lenoir Avenue, Jacksonville, FL 32216; tel. 904/332-4546

**Life Care Center at Inverrary,** 4300 Rock Island Road, Lauderhill, FL 33319; tel. 954/485-6144

**Life Care Center at Wells Crossing,** 355 Crossing Boulevard, Orange Park, FL 32073; tel. 904/264-1950

**Life Care Center of Altamonte Springs,** 989 Orienta Avenue, Altamonte Springs, FL 32701; tel. 407/831-3446

**Life Care Center of Citrus County,** 3325 Jerwayne Lane, Lecanto, FL 34461; tel. 352/746-4434

**Life Care Center of Estero,** 3850 Williams Road, Estero, FL 33928; tel. 239/495-4000

**Life Care Center of Hilliard,** 3756 W. 3rd Street, Hilliard, FL 32046; tel. 904/845-3988

**Life Care Center of Melbourne,** 606 East Sheridan Road, Melbourne, FL 32901; tel. 321/727-0984

**Life Care Center of New Port Richey,** 7400 Trouble Creek Rd., New Port Richey, FL 34653; tel. 727/375-2999

**Life Care Center of Ocala,** 2800 Southwest 41st Street, Ocala, FL 34474; tel. 352/873-7570

**Life Care Center of Orange Park,** 2145 Kingsely Avenue, Orange Park, FL 32073; tel. 904/272-2424

**Life Care Center of Orlando,** 3211 Rouse Road, Orlando, FL 32817; tel. 407/281-1070

**Life Care Center of Palm Bay,** 175 Villa Nueva Avenue, Palm Bay, FL 32907; tel. 321/952-1818

**Life Care Center of Pensacola,** 3291 East Olive Road, Pensacola, FL 32507; tel. 850/494-2327

**Life Care Center of Port St. Lucie,** 3720 SE Jennings Road, Port Saint Lucie, FL 34952; tel. 772/398-8080

**Life Care Center of Punta Gorda,** 450 Shreve Street, Punta Gorda, FL 33950; tel. 941/639-8771

**Life Care Center of Sarasota,** 8104 Tuttle Avenue, Sarasota, FL 34243; tel. 941/360-6411

**Life Care Center of Winter Haven,** 1510 Cypress Gardens Boulevard, Winter Haven, FL 33884; tel. 863/318-8646

**Miami Jewish Health Systems, Inc.,** 5200 Northeast 2nd Avenue, Miami, FL 33137; tel. 305/751-8626

**Miami VA Healthcare System,** 1201 NW 16th Street, Miami, FL 33125; tel. 305/575-7000

**North Florida/South Georgia Veterans Health System,** 1601 Southwest Archer Road, Gainesville, FL 32608-1197; tel. 352/376-1611

**Orlando VA Medical Center,** 5201 Raymond Street, Orlando, FL 32803; tel. 407/629-1599

**Shands Jacksonville Medical Center, Inc.,** 655 West Eighth Street (Mailbox # C- 51), Jacksonville, FL 32209; tel. 904/244-4000

**St. Anne's Nursing Center, St. Anne's Residence, Inc.,** 11855 Quail Roost Drive, Miami, FL 33177; tel. 305/252-4000

**St. Catherine's Rehab Hospital/Villa Maria Nursing Center,** 1050 N.E. 125th Street, Miami, FL 33161; tel. 305/891-8850

**St. John's Rehabilitation Hospital and Nursing Center,** 3075 Northwest 35th Avenue, Lauderdale Lakes, FL 33311; tel. 954/739-6233

**Sunrise Health and Rehabilitation Center,** 4800 Nob Hill Road, Sunrise, FL 33351; tel. 954/577-3600

**The Gardens Court,** 3803 PGA Boulevard, Palm Beach Gardens, FL 33410; tel. 561/626-1125

**VA Medical Center - West Palm Beach, Florida,** 7305 N. Military Trail, West Palm Beach, FL 33410-6400; tel. 516/422-8600

**GEORGIA**

**Camellia Gardens of Life Care,** 804 South Broad Street, Thomasville, GA 31792; tel. 229/226-0076

**Central State Hospital,** 620 Broad St, Milledgeville, GA 31062; tel. 478/445-4128

**Charlie Norwood VA Medical Center,** 1 Freedom Way, Augusta, GA 30904; tel. 706/733-0188

**Cook Medical Center, a campus of Tift Regional Medical Ctr.,** 706 North Parrish Avenue, Adel, GA 31620; tel. 229/896-8000

**East Central Regional Hospital,** 100 Myrtle Blvd, Gracewood, GA 30812; tel. 706/790-2030

**Effingham Hospital,** PO Box 386, Springfield, GA 31329; tel. 912/754-6451

**Family Life Enrichment Center, Inc.,** PO Box 10, High Shoals, GA 30645; tel. 706/769-7738

**Georgia Regional Hospital at Atlanta,** PO Box 37047, Decatur, GA 30034-0407; tel. 404/243-2100

**Georgia War Veterans Home,** 2249 Vinson Highway, Milledgeville, GA 31061; tel. 478/445-4516

**Georgia War Veterans Nursing Home,** 1101 15th Street, Augusta, GA 30901; tel. 706/721-2531

**Gwinnett Medical Center,** 1000 Medical Center Boulevard, Lawrenceville, GA 30046; tel. 678/312-4321

**Heritage Healthcare of Macon,** 2255 Anthony Road, Macon, GA 31204; tel. 478/784-7900

**Irwin County Hospital,** 710 North Irwin Avenue, Ocilla, GA 31774; tel. 229/468-3800

**John D. Archbold Memorial Hospital,** Gordon Avenue at Mimosa Drive, Thomasville, GA 31792; tel. 229/228-2000

**Liberty Regional Medical Center,** PO Box 919, Hinesville, GA 31310; tel. 912/369-9400

**Life Care Center of Gwinnett,** 3850 Safehaven Drive, Lawrenceville, GA 30044; tel. 770/923-0005

**Life Care Center of Lawrenceville,** 210 Collins Industrial Way, Lawrenceville, GA 30043; tel. 678/442-0777

**Louis Smith Memorial Hospital,** 116 West Thigpen Avenue, Lakeland, GA 31635; tel. 229/482-8440

**Mayo Clinic Health System in Waycross,** 1900 Tebeau Street, Waycross, GA 31501; tel. 912/283-3030

**Mitchell County Hospital,** PO Box 639, Camilla, GA 31730; tel. 229/336-5284

**North Georgia Medical Center,** 1362 South Main Street, Ellijay, GA 30540; tel. 706/276-4741

**Sadie G. Mays Health and Rehabilitation Center,** 1821 Anderson Avenue, NW, Atlanta, GA 30314; tel. 404/794-2477

**The Hospital Authority of Habersham County,** PO Box 37, Demorest, GA 30535; tel. 706/754-2161

**UniHealth Post Acute Care - Fairburn,** 7560 Butner Road, Fairburn, GA 30213; tel. 770/306-7878

**Unihealth Post Acute Care Austell,** 1700 Mulkey Rd., Austell, GA 30106; tel. 770/941-5753

**UniHealth Post Acute Care Brookhaven,** 3535 Ashton Woods Drive, Atlanta, GA 30319; tel. 770/451-0236

**VA Medical Center - Atlanta,** 1670 Clairmont Road, Decatur, GA 30033; tel. 404/728-7601

**VA Medical Center - Carl Vinson,** 1826 Veterans Boulevard, Dublin, GA 31021; tel. 478/277-2701

**HAWAII**

**Hale Anuenue Restorative Care Center,** 1333 Waianuenue Avenue, Hilo, HI 96720; tel. 808/961-6644

**Ka Punawai Ola,** 91-575 Farrington Highway, Kapolei, HI 96707; tel. 808/674-9262

**Life Care Center of Hilo,** 944 West Kawailani Street, Hilo, HI 96720; tel. 808/959-9151

**Life Care Center of Kona,** 78-6957 Kamehameha III Road, Kailua Kona, HI 96740; tel. 808/322-2790

**VA Pacific Islands Health Care System,** 459 Patterson Road, Honolulu, HI 96819-1522; tel. 808/433-0683

**IDAHO**

**Bingham Memorial Hospital and Extended Care Facility,** 98 Poplar Street, Blackfoot, ID 83221; tel. 208/785-3804

**Boise VA Medical Center,** 500 West Fort Street, Boise, ID 83702-4598; tel. 208/422-1100

**Bridgeview Estates,** 1828 Bridgeview Boulevard, Twin Falls, ID 83301; tel. 208/736-3933

**Life Care Center of Coeur d'Alene,** 500 West Aqua Avenue, Coeur D Alene, ID 83815; tel. 208/762-1122

**Life Care Center of Boise,** 808 North Curtis Road, Boise, ID 83706; tel. 208/376-5273

**Life Care Center of Idaho Falls,** 2725 East 17th Street, Idaho Falls, ID 83406; tel. 208/529-4567

**Life Care Center of Lewiston,** 325 Warner Drive, Lewiston, ID 83501; tel. 208/798-8500

**Life Care Center of Post Falls,** 460 N Garden Plaza, Post Falls, ID 83854; tel. 208/755-9522

**Life Care Center of Sandpoint,** 1125 North Division Street, Sandpoint, ID 83864; tel. 208/265-9299

**Life Care Center of Treasure Valley,** 502 North Kimball Place, Boise, ID 83704; tel. 208/377-1900

**Life Care Center of Valley View,** 1130 N Allumbaugh Street, Boise, ID 83704; tel. 208/854-8500

**State Hospital South,** PO Box 400, Blackfoot, ID 83221; tel. 208/785-1200

### ILLINOIS

**Alden - Des Plaines Skilled Nursing and Rehabilitation,** 1221 East Golf Road, Des Plaines, IL 60016; tel. 847/768-1300

**Alden Estates of Evanston,** 2520 Gross Point Road, Evanston, IL 60201; tel. 847/328-6000

**Alden North Shore Rehab & HCC,** 5050 West Touhy Avenue, Skokie, IL 60077; tel. 847/679-6100

**Alden Rehabilitation and Health Care Center/ Orland Park,** 16450 South 97th Avenue, Orland Park, IL 60467; tel. 708/403-6500

**Anna Hospital Corporation,** 517 North Main, Anna, IL 62906; tel. 618/833-4511

**Aria Post Acute Care LLC,** 4600 North Frontage Road, Hillside, IL 60162; tel. 708/544-9933

**Brentwood North Health Care Center,** 3705 Deerfield Road, Riverwoods, IL 60015; tel. 847/947-9000

**Bronzeville Park Skilled Nursing and Living Center,** 3400 S Indiana, Chicago, IL 60616; tel. 312/842-5000

**Burgess Square Healthcare and Rehabilitation Centre,** 5801 South Cass Avenue, Westmont, IL 60559; tel. 630/971-2645

**CAPT James A. Lovell Federal Health Care Center,** 3001 Green Bay Road, North Chicago, IL 60064; tel. 224/610-3700

**Community Nursing Rehab Center,** 1136 N Mill Street, Naperville, IL 60563-2519; tel. 630/355-3300

**Countryside Care Centre,** 2330 W Galena Blvd, Aurora, IL 60506-4299; tel. 630/896-4686

**Edward Hines Jr. VA Hospital,** 5000 South 5th Avenue, Hines, IL 60141-5000; tel. 708/202-5652

**Evergreen Healthcare Center,** 10124 South Kedzie Avenue, Evergreen Park, IL 60805; tel. 708/907-7000

**Forest Villa Nursing and Rehabilitation Center, LLC,** 6840 West Touhy Avenue, Niles, IL 60714; tel. 847/647-6400

**GlenBridge Nursing and Rehabilitation Centre, Ltd,** 8333 West Golf Road, Niles, IL 60714; tel. 847/966-9190

**Glencrest Nursing and Rehabilitation Centre,** 2451 West Touhy Avenue, Chicago, IL 60645; tel. 773/338-6800

**GlenShire Nursing and Rehabilitation Centre, Ltd.,** 22660 South Cicero Avenue, Richton Park, IL 60471; tel. 708/747-6120

**Glenview Terrace Nursing Center,** 1511 Greenwood Road, Glenview, IL 60026; tel. 847/729-9090

**Graham Hospital Assoc.,** 210 West Walnut Street, Canton, IL 61520; tel. 309/647-5240

**Greek American Rehabilitation and Care Centre,** 220 N 1st Street, Wheeling, IL 60090; tel. 847/459-8700

**Hammond Henry Hospital,** 600 N. College Avenue, Geneseo, IL 61254-1099; tel. 309/944-6431

**Harmony Healthcare & Rehabilitation Center,** 3919 West Foster Ave., Chicago, IL 60625; tel. 773/588-9500

**Jesse Brown VA Medical Center,** 820 South Damen Avenue, Chicago, IL 60612; tel. 312/569-6101

**Lakeview Rehabilitation & Nursing Center, LLC,** 735 W. Diversey Parkway, Chicago, IL 60614; tel. 773/348-4055

**Lexington Health Care Center of Chicago Ridge, Inc,** 10300 Southwest Hwy., Chicago Ridge, IL 60415-1426; tel. 708/425-1100

**Lexington Health Care Center of La Grange,Inc,** 4735 Willow Springs Rd, La Grange, IL 60525-6130; tel. 708/352-6900

**Lexington Health Care Center of Lake Zurich,Inc,** 900 S Rand Road, Lake Zurich, IL 60047-2450; tel. 847/726-1200

**Lexington Health Care Center of Lombard,** 2100 S Finley Rd, Lombard, IL 60148-4893; tel. 630/495-4000

**Lexington Health Care Center of Streamwood,Inc,** 815 E. Irving Park Road, Streamwood, IL 60107-3083; tel. 630/837-5300

**Lexington Healthcare - Schaumburg,** 675 S. Roselle Road, Schaumburg, IL 60193-3100; tel. 847/352-5500

**Lexington Healthcare Center of Bloomingdale, INC,** 165 South Bloomingdale, Bloomingdale, IL 60108-1434; tel. 630/458-4717

**Lexington Healthcare Center of Elmhurst, INC,** 420 W Butterfield Road, Elmhurst, IL 60126-4980; tel. 630/832-2300

**Lexington Healthcare Center of Orland Park, Inc.,** 14601 S. John Humphrey Drive, Orland Park, IL 60462-2641; tel. 630/458-4717

**Lexington Healthcare Center of Wheeling,INC,** 730 West Hintz Road, Wheeling, IL 60090-5501; tel. 847/537-7474

**Manor Care Health Services - Naperville,** 200 Martin Avenue, Naperville, IL 60540; tel. 630/355-4111

**ManorCare Health Services - Arlington Heights,** 715 West Central Road, Arlington Heights, IL 60005; tel. 847/392-2020

**ManorCare Health Services - Elgin,** 180 S. State St., Elgin, IL 60123; tel. 847/742-3310

**ManorCare Health Services - Elk Grove Village,** 1920 Nerge Road, Elk Grove Village, IL 60007; tel. 847/301-0550

**ManorCare Health Services - Hinsdale,** 600 West Ogden Avenue, Hinsdale, IL 60521; tel. 630/325-9630

**ManorCare Health Services - Northbrook,** 3300 Milwaukee Avenue, Northbrook, IL 60062; tel. 847/795-9700

**ManorCare Health Services - South Holland,** 2145 E 170th Street, South Holland, IL 60473; tel. 708/895-3255

**ManorCare Health Services- Libertyville,** 1500 S. Milwaukee Street, Libertyville, IL 60048; tel. 847/816-3200

**ManorCare Health Services-Oak Lawn East,** 9401 South Kostner Avenue, Oak Lawn, IL 60453; tel. 708/423-7882

**ManorCare Health Services-Westmont,** 512 East Ogden Avenue, Westmont, IL 60559; tel. 630/323-4400

**Maryhaven Nursing and Rehabilitation Center,** 1700 E. Lake Avenue, Glenview, IL 60025; tel. 847/729-1300

**Mercy Harvard Hospital, Inc.,** PO Box 850, Harvard, IL 60033; tel. 815/943-5431

**Northwestern Lake Forest Hospital,** 660 North Westmoreland Road, Lake Forest, IL 60045; tel. 847/234-5600

**Oakton Pavillion Health Care Facility,** 1660 Oakton Place, Des Plaines, IL 60018; tel. 847/299-5588

**Presence McAuley Manor,** 400 West Sullivan Road, Aurora, IL 60506; tel. 630/859-3700

**Presence Resurrection Nursing and Rehabilitation Center,** 1001 N Greenwood Avenue, Park Ridge, IL 60068; tel. 847/692-5600

**Providence Healthcare & Rehabilitation Center Downers Grove,** 3450 Saratoga Avenue, Downers Grove, IL 60515; tel. 630/969-2900

**Providence Healthcare and Rehabilitation of Palos Heights,** 13259 South Central Avenue, Palos Heights, IL 60463; tel. 708/597-1000

**Red Bud Regional Hospital, LLC,** 325 Spring Street, Red Bud, IL 62278; tel. 618/282-3831

**Renaissance at Midway,** 4437 S. Cicero Avenue, Chicago, IL 60632; tel. 773/884-0484

**Renaissance At South Shore, Inc.,** 2425 East 71st Street, Chicago, IL 60649; tel. 773/721-5000

**Rest Haven Illiana Christian Convalescent Home Inc.,** 16300 South Wausau Avenue, South Holland, IL 60473; tel. 708/596-5500

**Sherman West Court,** 1950 Larkin Avenue, Elgin, IL 60123; tel. 847/742-7070

**Symphony Crestwood LLC,** 14255 Cicero Avenue, Crestwood, IL 60445; tel. 708/371-0400

**Symphony Deerbrook, LLC,** 306 N Larkin Ave., Joliet, IL 60435-6681; tel. 815/744-5560

**Symphony McKinley LLC,** 500 W. McKinley Ave., Decatur, IL 62526-3281; tel. 217/875-0020

**The Abington of Glenview,** 3901 Glenview Road, Glenview, IL 60025; tel. 847/729-0000

**The Carlton at the Lake, Inc.,** 725 West Montrose Avenue, Chicago, IL 60613; tel. 773/929-1700

**The Claremont Rehab and Living Center,** 150 North Weiland Road, Buffalo Grove, IL 60089; tel. 847/465-0200

**The Imperial Grove Pavillion,** 1366 W Fullerton Ave, Chicago, IL 60613; tel. 773/248-9300

**The Renaissance at 87th Street,** 2940 W 87th Street, Chicago, IL 60652; tel. 773/434-8787

**VA - Illiana Health Care System,** 1900 East Main Street, Danville, IL 61832; tel. 217/554-3000

**VA Medical Center,** 2401 West Main Street, Marion, IL 62959; tel. 618/997-5311

**Vanguard Health Systems of Illinois,** 3249 South Oak Park Avenue, Berwyn, IL 60402; tel. 708/783-9100

**Warren Barr Pavilion,** 66 West Oak Street, Chicago, IL 60610; tel. 312/705-5100

**Washington County Hospital District,** 705 South Grand Avenue, Nashville, IL 62263; tel. 618/327-8236

**Whitehall North LLC,** 300 Waukegan Road, Deerfield, IL 60015-4988; tel. 847/945-4600

### INDIANA

**Gibson General Hospital, Inc.,** 1808 Sherman Drive, Princeton, IN 47670; tel. 812/385-3401

**Green Valley Care Center,** 3118 Green Valley Road, New Albany, IN 47150; tel. 812/945-2341

**Hammond Whiting Care Center,** 1000 114th Street, Whiting, IN 46394; tel. 219/659-2770

**Heritage Healthcare,** 3401 Soldiers Home Road, West Lafayette, IN 47906; tel. 765/463-1541

**Indiana University Health La Porte Hospital Inc.,** PO Box 250, La Porte, IN 46350; tel. 219/326-1234

**Life Care Center of Fort Wayne,** 1649 Spy Run Ave., Fort Wayne, IN 46805; tel. 260/422-8520

**Life Care Center of LaGrange,** 0770 N 075 E, Lagrange, IN 46761; tel. 260/463-7445

**Life Care Center of Michigan City,** 802 US Highway 20 East, Michigan City, IN 46360; tel. 219/872-7251

**Life Care Center of Rochester,** 827 West 13th Street, Rochester, IN 46975; tel. 574/223-4331

**Life Care Center of Valparaiso,** 3405 Campbell Road, Valparaiso, IN 46385; tel. 219/462-1023

**Life Care Center of Willows,** 1000 Elizabeth Street, Valparaiso, IN 46383; tel. 219/464-4858

**Mitchell Manor,** PO Box 338, Mitchell, IN 47446; tel. 812/849-2221

**Parkview Care Center,** 2819 North St. Joseph Avenue, Evansville, IN 47720; tel. 812/424-2941

**Rensselaer Medical Investors,** 1309 East Grace Street, Rensselaer, IN 47978; tel. 219/866-4181

**The Lane House,** 1000 Lane Avenue, Crawfordsville, IN 47933; tel. 765/362-0007

**The Woodlands,** 3820 W Jackson Street, Muncie, IN 47304; tel. 765/289-3451

**VA Northern Indiana Health Care System,** 2121 Lake Avenue, Fort Wayne, IN 46805; tel. 260/460-1310

**Westside Limited Partnership,** 8616 W. 10th Street, Indianapolis, IN 46234; tel. 317/209-2800

### IOWA

**Mercy Health Services - Iowa,** 250 Mercy Drive, Dubuque, IA 52001; tel. 563/589-8000

**VA Central Iowa Health Care System,** 3600 30th Street, Des Moines, IA 50310-5774; tel. 515/699-5850

### KANSAS

**Garden Terrace at Overland Park,** 7541 Switzer Rd., Overland Park, KS 66214; tel. 913/631-2273

**Life Care Center of Andover,** 621 West 21st Street, Andover, KS 67002; tel. 316/733-1349

**Life Care Center of Burlington,** 601 Cross Street, Burlington, KS 66839; tel. 620/364-2117

**Life Care Center of Kansas City,** 3231 N. 61st Street, Kansas City, KS 66104; tel. 913/299-1770

**Life Care Center of Osawatomie,** 1615 Parker Street - Box 159, Osawatomie, KS 66064; tel. 913/755-4165

**Life Care Center of Seneca,** 512 Community Dr., Seneca, KS 66538; tel. 785/336-3528

**Life Care Center of Wichita,** 622 North Edgemoor, Wichita, KS 67208; tel. 316/686-5100

**Robert J. Dole VA Medical Center,** 5500 East Kellogg, Wichita, KS 67218; tel. 316/651-3601

**The Congregational Home,** 1001 SW 29th St, Topeka, KS 66611; tel. 785/274-3392

**VA Eastern Kansas Health Care System,** 2200 SW Gage, Topeka, KS 66622; tel. 785/350-3111

### KENTUCKY

**Appalachian Regional Healthcare,** 260 Hospital Drive, South Williamson, KY 41503; tel. 606/237-1700

**Bureau of Prisons - FMC Lexington,** 3301 Leestown Road, Lexington, KY 40511-8799; tel. 859/255-6812

**Christian Care Center of Kuttawa,** 1253 Lake Barkley Dr., Kuttawa, KY 42055; tel. 270/388-2291

**Highlandspring of Ft. Thomas,** 960 Highland Avenue, Fort Thomas, KY 41075; tel. 859/572-0660

**Lancaster Medical Investors, LLC,** 308 West Maple Avenue, Lancaster, KY 40444; tel. 859/792-6844

**Laurel Creek Health Care Center,** 1033 North Highway 11, Manchester, KY 40962; tel. 606/598-6163

**Life Care Center of Bardstown,** 120 Life Care Way, Bardstown, KY 40004; tel. 502/348-4220

**Life Care Center of LaCenter,** 252 W. 5th Street, La Center, KY 42056; tel. 270/665-5681

**Life Care Center of Morehead,** PO Box 884, Morehead, KY 40351; tel. 606/784-7518

**Section C**

**Madonna Manor Inc.,** 2344 Amsterdam Rd., Villa Hills, KY 41017; tel. 859/341-3981

**Mountain View Health Care,** PO Box 650, Elkhorn City, KY 41522; tel. 606/754-4134

**Murray-Calloway County Hospital,** 803 Poplar Street, Murray, KY 42071-2432; tel. 270/762-1102

**Parkview Nursing and Rehabilitation Center,** 544 Lone Oak Road, Paducah, KY 42003; tel. 270/443-6543

**Rockcastle Regional Hospital and Respiratory Care Center,** 145 Newcomb Avenue P.O. Box 1310, Mount Vernon, KY 40456; tel. 606/256-2195

**The Medical Center,** PO Box 90010, Bowling Green, KY 42102-9010; tel. 270/745-1000

**VA Medical Center,** 1101 Veterans Drive, Lexington, KY 40502-2236; tel. 859/233-4511

**Villaspring Health Care Center, Inc.,** 630 Viox Drive, Erlanger, KY 41018; tel. 859/727-6700

**LOUISIANA**

**East Jefferson General Hospital,** 4200 Houma Boulevard, Metairie, LA 70006; tel. 504/454-4000

**Lane Regional Medical Center,** 6300 Main Street, Zachary, LA 70791; tel. 225/658-4303

**Trinity Neurologic Rehabilitation Center, LLC,** 1400 Lindberg Drive, Slidell, LA 70458; tel. 985/641-4985

**VA Medical Center,** PO Box 69004, Alexandria, LA 71306; tel. 318/473-0010

**MAINE**

**Northern Maine Medical Center,** 194 East Main Street, Fort Kent, ME 04743; tel. 207/834-3155

**VA Maine Healthcare System,** 1 Va Center, Augusta, ME 04330; tel. 207/623-8411

**MARYLAND**

**Calvert Memorial Hospital,** 100 Hospital Road, Prince Frederick, MD 20678; tel. 410/535-4000

**Courtland Gardens Nursing and Rehabilitation Center,** 7920 Scotts Level Road, Baltimore, MD 21208; tel. 410/521-3600

**Deer's Head Center,** PO Box 2018, Salisbury, MD 21802-2018; tel. 410/543-4000

**Fox Chase Rehabilitation and Nursing Center,** 2015 East West Highway, Silver Spring, MD 20910; tel. 301/587-2400

**Johns Hopkins Bayview Medical Center,** 4940 Eastern Avenue, Baltimore, MD 21224-2780; tel. 410/550-0120

**Levindale Hebrew Geriatric Center and Hospital,** 2434 West Belvedere Avenue, Baltimore, MD 21215; tel. 410/466-8700

**Potomac Valley Nursing Facilities Inc.,** 1235 Potomac Valley Road, Rockville, MD 20850; tel. 301/762-0700

**VA Maryland Health Care System,** 10 North Greene Street, Baltimore, MD 21201; tel. 410/605-7000

**Western Maryland Hospital Center,** 1500 Pennsylvania Avenue, Hagerstown, MD 21742-3194; tel. 301/745-4200

**MASSACHUSETTS**

**137 Nichols St., Inc.,** 137 Nichols Street, Norwood, MA 02062-2009; tel. 781/762-0858

**140 Prescott Street Operations LLC,** 140 Prescott Street, North Andover, MA 01845; tel. 978/685-8086

**140 Webb St., Inc.,** 140 Webb Street, Weymouth, MA 02188-2799; tel. 781/335-4352

**16 Pleasant St., Inc.,** 16 Pleasant Street, Bridgewater, MA 02324-2498; tel. 508/697-4616

**184 Main LLC,** 184 Main Street, Fairhaven, MA 02719; tel. 508/997-3193

**249 Corey Rd., Inc,** 249 Corey Road, Brighton, MA 02135-8396; tel. 617/734-7138

**30 Princeton Boulevard Operations LLC,** 30 Princeton Boulevard, Lowell, MA 01851; tel. 978/454-8086

**30 Webster Street Operations LLC,** 30 Webster Street, Brookline, MA 02446; tel. 617/734-2300

**34 Lincoln St., Inc.,** 34 Lincoln Street Ext, Natick, MA 01760-5939; tel. 508/653-8330

**400 Groton Road Operations LLC,** 400 Groton Road, Ayer, MA 01432; tel. 978/772-1704

**519 Main St., Inc.,** 80 Access Road, Norwood, MA 02062; tel. 508/359-6050

**65 Cooper Street Operations LLC,** 65 Cooper Street, Agawam, MA 01001; tel. 413/786-8000

**8 Butler St., Inc.,** 8 Butler Street, Blackstone, MA 01504-1598; tel. 508/883-5818

**84 Elm St., Inc.,** 84 Elm Street, Holliston, MA 01746-2138; tel. 508/429-4566

**841 Merrimack Street Operations LLC,** 841 Merrimack Street, Lowell, MA 01854; tel. 978/459-0546

**Abbott House,** 28 Essex Street, Lynn, MA 01902; tel. 781/595-5500

**Academy Nursing Home,** 89 Morton Street, Andover, MA 01810; tel. 978/475-0944

**Alden Court Nursing Care and Rehabilitation Center,** 389 Alden Road, Fairhaven, MA 02719; tel. 508/991-8600

**Alliance Health, Inc.,** 804 Pleasant Street, Brockton, MA 02301-3055; tel. 508/583-6000

**Alliance HealthCare Center at Braintree,** 175 Grove Street, Braintree, MA 02184; tel. 781/848-2050

**Amesbury Village, LLC,** 22 Maple Street, Amesbury, MA 01913; tel. 978/388-4682

**Autumn Village, LLC,** 25 Oriol Drive, Worcester, MA 01605; tel. 508/852-3330

**Bay Path Rehabilitation & Nursing Center,** 308 Kingstown Way, Duxbury, MA 02332; tel. 781/585-5561

**Baypointe Rehabilitation and Skilled Care Center,** 50 Christy Place, Brockton, MA 02301; tel. 508/580-6800

**Bear Hill Nursing Center at Wakefield,** 11 North Street, Stoneham, MA 02180; tel. 781/438-8515

**Beaumont At The Willows,** Three Lyman Street, Westborough, MA 01581; tel. 508/366-9933

**Beaumont at University Campus, LLC,** 378 Plantation Street, Worcester, MA 01605; tel. 508/755-7300

**Beaumont Rehabilitation & Skilled Nursing Center,** 3 Vision Drive, Route 9 West, Natick, MA 01760; tel. 508/655-3344

**Beaumont Rehabilitation and Skilled Nursing Center,** PO Box 935, Northbridge, MA 01534-0935; tel. 508/234-9771

**Beaumont/Whitney Place Northboro, LLC,** 238 West Main Street, Northborough, MA 01532; tel. 508/393-2368

**Belmont Manor Nursing Home Inc.,** 34 Agassiz Avenue, Belmont, MA 02478; tel. 617/489-1200

**Bentley Saint Francis, LLC,** 101 Plantation Street, Worcester, MA 01604; tel. 508/755-8605

**Berkshire Extended Care Services, Inc.,** 40 Sunset Avenue, Lenox, MA 01240; tel. 413/637-5011

**Blaire House of Milford,** 20 Claflin Street, Milford, MA 01757; tel. 508/473-1272

**Blaire House of Tewksbury,** 10 Erlin Terrace, Tewksbury, MA 01876; tel. 978/851-3121

**Blueberry Hill Skilled Nursing and Rehabilitation Center,** 75 Brimbal Avenue, Beverly, MA 01915; tel. 978/927-2020

**Bostonian Nursing Care and Rehabilitation Center,** 337 Neponset Ave, Dorchester, MA 02122; tel. 617/265-2350

**Bourne Manor Extended Care Facility,** 146 MacArthur Boulevard, Bourne, MA 02532; tel. 508/759-8880

**Braemoor Rehabilitation and Nursing Center, Inc.,** 34 North Pearl Street, Brockton, MA 02301; tel. 508/586-3696

**Briarwood Healthcare Nursing Center,** 150 Lincoln Street, Needham, MA 02492; tel. 781/449-4040

**Brighton House Rehabilitation and Nursing Center,** 170 Corey Road, Brighton, MA 02135; tel. 617/731-0515

**Calvin Coolidge Nursing & Rehabilitation Center,** 548 Elm Street, Northampton, MA 01060; tel. 413/586-3150

**Cape Heritage MA SNF LLS,** 37 Route 6A, Sandwich, MA 02563; tel. 508/888-8222

**Cape Regency Rehabilitation and Health Care Center,** 120 South Main Street, Centerville, MA 02632; tel. 508/778-1835

**Catholic Memorial Home, Inc.,** 2446 Highland Avenue, Fall River, MA 02720-4599; tel. 508/679-0011

**Cedar Hill Health Care Center,** 49 Thomas Patten Drive, Randolph, MA 02368; tel. 781/961-1160

**CFM Buckley North, LLC.,** 95 Laurel Street, Greenfield, MA 01301; tel. 413/774-3143

**CFM Buckley South LLC,** 282 Cabot Street, Holyoke, MA 01040; tel. 413/538-7470

**Charlwell House,** 305 Walpole Street, Norwood, MA 02062; tel. 781/762-7700

**Chelsea Jewish Nursing Home,** 17 Lafayette Avenue, Chelsea, MA 02150; tel. 617/884-6766

**Christopher House of Worcester, Inc.,** 10 Mary Scano Drive, Worcester, MA 01605; tel. 508/754-3800

**Clark House at Fox Hill Village,** 30 Longwood Drive, Westwood, MA 02090; tel. 781/326-5652

**Clifton Rehabilitative Nursing Center,** 500 Wilbur Avenue, Somerset, MA 02725; tel. 508/675-7589

**Colonial Health Group-TCU, LLC,** 340 Thompson Road, Webster, MA 01570; tel. 508/949-8420

**Colonial Rehabilitation and Nursing Center,** 125 Broad Street, Weymouth, MA 02188; tel. 781/337-3121

**Concord Health Care Center,** 57 Old Road to Nine Acre Corner, Concord, MA 01742; tel. 978/371-3400

**Copley at Stoughton Nursing Care Cener,** 380 Sumner Street, Stoughton, MA 02072; tel. 781/341-2300

**Countryside Health Care of Milford,** 1 Countryside Drive, Milford, MA 01757; tel. 508/473-0435

**Courtyard Nursing Care Center,** 200 Governors Avenue, Medford, MA 02155; tel. 781/391-5400

**CPL (Cabot) LLC,** 279 Cabot Street, Holyoke, MA 01040; tel. 413/536-3435

**D'Youville Senior Care, Inc.,** 981 Varnum Avenue, Lowell, MA 01854; tel. 978/569-1000

**D'Youville Transitional Care, Inc.,** 1071 Varnum Ave., Lowell, MA 01854; tel. 978/569-1000

**Dartmouth House Nursing Home, Inc.,** 567 Dartmouth Street, South Dartmouth, MA 02748; tel. 508/997-7787

**Den Mar Rehabilitation and Nursing Center,** 44 South Street, Rockport, MA 01966; tel. 978/546-6311

**Deutsches Altenheim Inc.,** 2222 Centre Street, West Roxbury, MA 02132; tel. 617/325-1230

**Devereux House Nursing Home,** 39 Lafayette Street, Marblehead, MA 01945-1997; tel. 781/631-6120

**East Longmeadow Skilled Nursing Center,** 305 Maple Street, East Longmeadow, MA 01028; tel. 413/525-6361

**Eastpointe Nursing Home, Inc.,** 255 Central Avenue, Chelsea, MA 02150; tel. 617/884-5700

**Edgar P. Benjamin Healthcare Center,** 120 Fisher Avenue, Boston, MA 02120; tel. 617/738-1500

**Edith Nourse Rogers Memorial Veterans Hospital,** 200 Springs Road, Bedford, MA 01730; tel. 781/687-3080

**Emerson Village, LLC,** 59 Coolidge Hill Road, Watertown, MA 02472-2884; tel. 617/924-1130

**EPOCH Senior Healthcare of Brewster,** 873 Harwich Road, Brewster, MA 02631; tel. 508/896-7046

**EPOCH Senior Healthcare of Harwich, LLC,** 111 Headwaters Drive, Harwich, MA 02645-1726; tel. 508/430-1717

**EPOCH Senior Healthcare of Melrose,** 15 Green Street, Melrose, MA 02176; tel. 781/665-3950

**EPOCH Senior Healthcare of Norton, LLC,** 184 Mansfield Avenue, Norton, MA 02766; tel. 508/285-7745

**EPOCH Senior Healthcare of Sharon,** 259 Norwood Street, Sharon, MA 02067; tel. 781/784-6781

**EPOCH Senior Healthcare of Weston LLC,** 75 Norumbega Road, Weston, MA 02493; tel. 781/891-6100

**EPOCH Senior Living, Inc. LLC,** 615 Heath St., Chestnut Hill, MA 02467; tel. 781/891-0777

**Essex Park Rehabilitation & Nursing Center,** 265 Essex Street, Beverly, MA 01915; tel. 978/927-3260

**Essex Pavilion, LLC,** 876 Falmouth Road, Hyannis, MA 02601; tel. 508/775-6663

**Everett Nursing and Rehabilitation Center,** 289 Elm Street, Everett, MA 02149; tel. 617/387-6560

**Fairhaven Healthcare Center, Inc.,** 476 Varnum Avenue, Lowell, MA 01854; tel. 978/458-3388

**Fairview Commons Nursing & Rehabilitation Center,** 151 Christian Hill Road, Great Barrington, MA 01230; tel. 413/528-4560

**Falmouth Healthcare LLC,** 359 Jones Road, Falmouth, MA 02540; tel. 508/457-9000

**Federal Bureau of Prisons Federal Medical Center Devens,** PO Box 880, Ayer, MA 01432; tel. 978/796-1443

**FRC, Inc.,** 1245 Centre Street, West Roxbury, MA 02132; tel. 617/325-5400

**FRC, Inc.,** 70 Fulton Street, Boston, MA 02109; tel. 617/726-9700

**Geriatric Authority of Holyoke,** 45 Lower Westfield Road, Holyoke, MA 01040; tel. 413/536-8110

**GGNSC Gloucester LLC,** 272 Washington Street, Gloucester, MA 01930; tel. 978/281-0333

**GGNSC Lexington, LLC,** 840 Emerson Gardens Road, Lexington, MA 02420; tel. 781/861-8630

**GGNSC Newton, LLC,** 1650 Washington Street, West Newton, MA 02465; tel. 617/244-5407

**GGNSC Plymouth LLC,** 19 Obery Street, Plymouth, MA 02360; tel. 508/747-4790

**Glen Ridge Nursing Care Center,** 120 Murray Street, Medford, MA 02155; tel. 781/391-0800

**Golden Living - Oak Hill Rehabilitation and Nursing Center,** 76 North Street, Middleboro, MA 02346; tel. 508/947-4774

**Golden Living Center - Fitchburg,** 1199 John Fitch Highway, Fitchburg, MA 01420; tel. 978/345-0146

Golden Living Center - Heathwood, 188 Florence Street, Chestnut Hill, MA 02467; tel. 617/332-4730

Golden Living Center - Norwood, 460 Washington Street, Norwood, MA 02062; tel. 781/769-2200

Golden Living Center Cohasset, 1 Chief Justice Cushing Hwy, Cohasset, MA 02025; tel. 781/383-9060

Golden Living Center West Newton, 25 Armory St., West Newton, MA 02465; tel. 617/969-2300

Golden LivingCenter - Attleboro, 27 George Street, Attleboro, MA 02703; tel. 508/226-1650

Golden LivingCenter - Garden Place, 195 Pleasant Street, Attleboro, MA 02703; tel. 508/222-4950

Golden LivingCenter - The Hermitage, 383 Mill Street, Worcester, MA 01602; tel. 508/791-8131

Great Barrington Rehab & Nursing Center, 148 Maple Ave., Great Barrington, MA 01230; tel. 413/528-3320

Greenfield Management Systems, 130 Colrain Road, Greenfield, MA 01301; tel. 413/774-3724

Guardian Center, Inc., 888 North Main Street, Brockton, MA 02301; tel. 508/587-6556

Hallmark Nursing and Rehabilitation Center, 1123 Rockdale Avenue, New Bedford, MA 02740; tel. 508/997-7448

Hancock Park Rehabilitation and Nursing Center, 164 Parkingway, Quincy, MA 02169; tel. 617/773-4222

Harbor House Rehabilitation and Nursing Center, 11 Condito Road, Hingham, MA 02043; tel. 781/749-4774

Harborside Massachusetts LP, 63 Locust Street, Danvers, MA 01923; tel. 978/777-0011

Hathaway Manor, ECF, 863 Hathaway Road, New Bedford, MA 02740; tel. 508/996-6763

HDH Corporation, 126 Monument Street, Haverhill, MA 01832; tel. 978/373-1747

Hellenic Nursing and Rehabilitation Center, 601 Sherman Street, Canton, MA 02021-2053; tel. 781/828-7450

Heritage Hall East Center, 464 Main Street, Agawam, MA 01001; tel. 413/821-0753

Heritage Hall North, 55 Cooper Street, Agawam, MA 01001; tel. 413/821-0751

Heritage Hall West - Genesis HealthCare, 61 Cooper Street, Agawam, MA 01001; tel. 413/786-8000

Highgate Nursing, LLC, 10 CareMatrix Drive, Dedham, MA 02026; tel. 781/461-9663

Highlander Nursing LLC, 1748 Highland Avenue, Fall River, MA 02720; tel. 508/730-1070

Hillcrest Commons, 169 Valentine Road, Pittsfield, MA 01201; tel. 413/445-2300

Hillcrest Nursing and Rehabilitation Center, 94 Summer Street, Fitchburg, MA 01420; tel. 978/343-3530

Holden Nursing Home, 32 Mayo Road, Holden, MA 01520; tel. 508/829-4327

Holy Trinity Nursing and Rehabilitation Center, 300 Barber Avenue, Worcester, MA 01606; tel. 508/852-1000

Holyoke Rehabilitation Center, 260 Easthampton Road, Holyoke, MA 01040; tel. 413/538-9733

Hunt Nursing and Rehabilitation Center, 90 Lindall Street, Danvers, MA 01923; tel. 978/777-3740

J&B Partnership, LLP, 209 County Road, North Falmouth, MA 02556; tel. 508/563-5913

Jewish Geriatric Services, Inc, 770 Converse Street, Longmeadow, MA 01106; tel. 413/567-3949

Jewish Healthcare Center, Inc., 629 Salisbury Street, Worcester, MA 01609; tel. 508/798-8653

Jewish Rehabilitation Center for Aged of the North Shore, 240 Lynnfield Street, Peabody, MA 01960; tel. 978/471-5100

JML Care Center, Inc., 184 Ter Heun Drive, Falmouth, MA 02540-2503; tel. 508/457-4621

John Adams Nursing Home, LLC, 211 Franklin Street, Quincy, MA 02169; tel. 617/479-0837

John Scott House Nursing Home, Inc. (The), 233 Middle Street, Braintree, MA 02184; tel. 781/843-1860

Kathleen Daniel Healthcare, 485 Franklin Street, Framingham, MA 01702; tel. 508/872-8801

Keystone Center, 44 Keystone Center, Leominster, MA 01453; tel. 978/537-9327

Kindred Nursing and Rehabilitation - Braintree, 1102 Washington Street, Braintree, MA 02184; tel. 781/848-3100

Kindred Nursing and Rehabilitation - Goddard, 909 Sumner Street, Stoughton, MA 02072; tel. 781/297-8200

Kindred Nursing and Rehabilitation - Harborlights, 804 East 7th Street, South Boston, MA 02127; tel. 617/268-8968

Kindred Nursing and Rehabilitation - Walden, 785 Main Street, Concord, MA 01742; tel. 978/369-6889

Kindred Nursing and Rehabilitation Center - Presentation, 10 Bellamy Street, Brighton, MA 02135; tel. 617/782-8113

Kindred Nursing Centers East, LLC, 11 McGrath Highway, Quincy, MA 02169-5311; tel. 617/479-2820

Kindred Transitional Care and Rehab Center - Country Estates, 1200 Suffield Street, Agawam, MA 01001; tel. 413/789-2200

Kindred Transitional Care and Rehabilitation - Avery, 100 West Street, Needham Heights, MA 02494; tel. 781/234-6300

Kindred Transitional Care and Rehabilitation - Crawford, 273 Oak Grove Avenue, Fall River, MA 02723; tel. 508/679-4866

Kindred Transitional Care and Rehabilitation - Eagle Pond, PO Box 208, South Dennis, MA 02660; tel. 508/385-6034

Kindred Transitional Care and Rehabilitation - Eliot, 168 W. Central Street, Natick, MA 01760; tel. 508/655-1000

Kindred Transitional Care and Rehabilitation - Forestview, 50 Indian Neck Road, Wareham, MA 02571; tel. 508/295-5264

Kindred Transitional Care and Rehabilitation - Franklin, 130 Chestnut Street, Franklin, MA 02038; tel. 508/528-4600

Kindred Transitional Care and Rehabilitation - Hammersmith, 73 Chestnut Street, Saugus, MA 01906; tel. 781/233-8123

Kindred Transitional Care and Rehabilitation - Marlborough, 400 Bolton Street, Marlborough, MA 01752; tel. 508/481-6123

Kindred Transitional Care and Rehabilitation - Newburyport, 180 Low Street, Newburyport, MA 01950; tel. 978/465-5361

Kindred Transitional Care and Rehabilitation - Sachem, 66 Central Street, East Bridgewater, MA 02333; tcl. 508/378-7227

Kindred Transitional Care and Rehabilitation - The Meadows, 111 Huntoon Memorial Highway, Rochdale, MA 01542; tel. 508/892-6800

Kindred Transitional Care and Rehabilitation Harrington, 160 Main Street, Walpole, MA 02081; tel. 508/660-3080

Kindred Transitional Care and Rehabilitation Westborough, 5 Colonial Drive, Westborough, MA 01581; tel. 508/366-9131

Knollwood Nursing Center, 87 Briarwood Circle, Worcester, MA 01606; tel. 508/853-6910

Lanessa Extended Care, 751 School Street, Webster, MA 01570; tel. 508/949-1334

Laurel Lake Health and Rehabilitation, LLC, 620 Laurel Street, Lee, MA 01238; tel. 413/243-2010

Ledgewood Rehabilitation and Skilled Nursing Center, 87 Herrick Street, Beverly, MA 01915; tel. 978/921-1392

Legend Center for Rehabilitation and Nursing, 59 Eastwood Circle, Gardner, MA 01440; tel. 978/632-8776

Lexington Health Care Center, 178 Lowell St., Lexington, MA 02420; tel. 781/862-7400

Life Care Center of Acton, One Great Road, Acton, MA 01720; tel. 978/263-9101

Life Care Center of Attleboro, 969 Park Street, Attleboro, MA 02703; tel. 508/222-4182

Life Care Center of Auburn, 14 Masonic Circle, Auburn, MA 01501; tel. 508/832-4800

Life Care Center of Leominster, 370 West Street, Leominster, MA 01453; tel. 978/537-0771

Life Care Center of Merrimack Valley, 80 Boston Road, North Billerica, MA 01862; tel. 978/667-2166

Life Care Center of Plymouth, 94 Obery Street, Plymouth, MA 02360; tel. 508/747-9800

Life Care Center of Raynham, 546 South Street East, Raynham, MA 02767; tel. 508/821-5700

Life Care Center of Stoneham, 25 Woodland Road, Stoneham, MA 02180; tel. 781/662-2545

Life Care Center of the North Shore, 111 Birch Street, Lynn, MA 01902; tel. 781/592-9667

Life Care Center of the South Shore, PO Box 830, Scituate, MA 02066; tel. 781/545-1370

Life Care Center of West Bridgewater, 765 West Center Street, West Bridgewater, MA 02379; tel. 508/580-4400

Life Care Center of Wilbraham, 2399 Boston Road, Wilbraham, MA 01095; tel. 413/596-3111

Life Care Centers of America, 191 Foster Street, Littleton, MA 01460; tel. 978/486-3512

Linda Manor Extended Care Facility, 349 Haydenville Road, Leeds, MA 01053; tel. 413/586-7700

Linden Ponds, Inc, 400 Linden Ponds Way, Hingham, MA 02043; tel. 781/534-7172

Lowell Health Care Center, 19 Varnum Street, Lowell, MA 01850; tel. 978/454-5644

Lydia Taft House, 60 Quaker Highway, Uxbridge, MA 01569; tel. 508/278-9500

Madonna Manor, Inc., 85 North Washington Street, North Attleboro, MA 02760; tel. 508/699-2740

Marian Manor, Inc., 33 Summer Street, Taunton, MA 02780; tel. 508/822-4885

Marina Bay Skilled Nursing and Rehabilitation Center, 2 Seaport Drive, Quincy, MA 02171; tel. 617/769-5100

Maristhill Nursing & Rehabilitation Center, 66 Newton Street, Waltham, MA 02453; tel. 781/893-0240

Marlborough Hills Healthcare Center, 121 Northboro Road, East, Marlborough, MA 01752; tel. 508/485-4040

Mary Ann Morse Nursing and Rehabilitation Center, 45 Union Street, Natick, MA 01760; tel. 508/433-4400

Masconomet Healthcare Center, 123 High Street, Topsfield, MA 01983-1926; tel. 978/887-7002

Mashpee Care and Rehabilitation Center, 161 Falmouth Road, Mashpee, MA 02649; tel. 508/477-2490

Mayflower Place Nursing Center, Inc, 579 Buck Island Road, West Yarmouth, MA 02673; tel. 508/957-7007

Meadow Green Nursing and Rehabilitation Center, 45 Woburn Street, Waltham, MA 02452; tel. 781/899-8600

Medway Country Manor, Inc., 115 Holliston Street, Medway, MA 02053; tel. 508/533-6634

Millbury Health Care Center, 312 Millbury Avenue, Millbury, MA 01527; tel. 508/793-0088

Milton Health Care, 1200 Brush Hill Road, Milton, MA 02186; tel. 617/333-0600

Mount Saint Vincent Care Center, 35 Holy Family Road, Holyoke, MA 01040; tel. 413/532-3246

MRN Corporation, 15 Mill Street, Marion, MA 02738; tel. 508/748-3830

Mt. Greylock Extended Care Facility, 1000 North Street, Pittsfield, MA 01201; tel. 413/499-7186

Nemasket Healthcare Center, 314 Marion Road, Middleboro, MA 02346; tel. 508/947-8632

Neuro-Rehabilitation Center At Worcester, 59 Acton Street, Worcester, MA 01604; tel. 508/791-3147

Neville Center at Fresh Pond for Nursing and Rehabilitation, 640 Concord Ave., Cambridge, MA 02138; tel. 617/430-0600

New Bedford Health Care Center, 221 Fitzgerald Drive, New Bedford, MA 02745; tel. 508/996-4600

New Bedford Jewish Convalescent Home, Inc., 200 Hawthorn Street, New Bedford, MA 02740; tel. 508/997-9314

New England Pediatric Care, 78 Boston Road, North Billerica, MA 01862; tel. 978/667-5123

Newton Health Care Center, 2101 Washington Street, Newton Lower Falls, MA 02462; tel. 617/969-4660

North Adams Commons, 175 Franklin Street, North Adams, MA 01247; tel. 413/664-4041

Northwood MA SNF LLC, 1010 Varnum Avenue, Lowell, MA 01854; tel. 978/458-8773

Notre Dame Long Term Care Center, 559 Plantation St., Worcester, MA 01605-2350; tel. 508/852-3011

Oak Knoll Healthcare Center, 9 Arbetter Drive, Framingham, MA 01701; tel. 508/877-3300

Oakdale Rehabilitation & Skilled Nursing Facility, 76 N. Main Street, West Boylston, MA 01583-1130; tel. 508/835-6076

Oakwood Rehabilitation and Nursing Center, 11 Pontiac Avenue, Webster, MA 01570; tel. 508/943-3889

Odd Fellows Home Of MA, 104 RANDOLPH RD, Worcester, MA 01606-2493; tel. 508/853-6687

Our Lady's Haven of Fairhaven, Inc., 71 Center Street, Fairhaven, MA 02719; tel. 508/999-4561

Overlook Masonic Health Center, PO Box 1000, Charlton, MA 01507-0189; tel. 508/248-7344

Palm Manor Nursing Center, 40 Parkhurst Road, Chelmsford, MA 01824; tel. 978/256-3151

Park Avenue Nursing & Rehabilitation Center, 146 Park Avenue, Arlington, MA 02476-5896; tel. 781/648-9530

Park Marion & Vernon Streets Operating Company LLC, 99 Park Street, Brookline, MA 02446; tel. 617/731-1050

Parsons Hill Nursing and Rehabiltation Center, 1350 Main Street, Worcester, MA 01603; tel. 508/791-4200

Section C

**Peabody Glen Health Care Center,** 199 Andover Street, Peabody, MA 01960; tel. 978/531-0772

**Penacook Place, Inc.,** 150 Water Street, Haverhill, MA 01830-6298; tel. 978/374-0707

**Pilgrim Rehabilitation and Skilled Nursing Center,** 96 Forest Street, Peabody, MA 01960-3907; tel. 978/532-0303

**Plymouth Rehabilitation and Health Care Center,** 123 South Street, Plymouth, MA 02360; tel. 508/746-4343

**Poet's Seat Health Care Center,** 359 High Street, Greenfield, MA 01301; tel. 413/774-6318

**Port Healthcare Center,** 113 Low Street, Newburyport, MA 01950; tel. 978/556-5900

**Quabbin Valley Healthcare,** 821 Daniel Shays Highway, Athol, MA 01331; tel. 978/249-3717

**Queen Anne Nursing Home, Inc.,** 50 Recreation Park Drive, Hingham, MA 02043; tel. 781/749-4982

**Radius HealthCare Center at Danvers,** 56 Liberty Street, Danvers, MA 01923; tel. 978/777-2700

**Redstone Rehabilitation and Nursing Center,** 135 Benton Drive, East Longmeadow, MA 01028; tel. 413/525-3336

**Renaissance Manor of Westfield,** 37 Feeding Hills Road, Westfield, MA 01085; tel. 413/568-2341

**River Terrace Healthcare,** 1675 Main Street, Lancaster, MA 01523; tel. 978/365-4537

**Rosewood Nursing and Rehabilitation Center,** 22 Johnson Street, Peabody, MA 01960; tel. 978/535-8700

**Royal Braintree Nursing and Rehabilitation Center,** 95 Commerical Street, Braintree, MA 02184; tel. 781/848-3678

**Royal Cape Cod Nursing & Rehabilitation Center,** 8 Lewis Point Road, Buzzards Bay, MA 02532; tel. 508/759-5752

**Royal Nursing Center, LLC,** 545 Main Street, Falmouth, MA 02540; tel. 508/548-4800

**Royal Taber Street Nursing & Rehabilitation Center,** 19 Taber Street, New Bedford, MA 02740; tel. 508/997-0791

**Sacred Heart Home, Inc.,** 359 Summer Street, New Bedford, MA 02740; tel. 508/996-6751

**Sancta Maria Hospital, Inc.,** 799 Concord Avenue, Cambridge, MA 02138; tel. 617/868-2200

**Sarah S. Brayton Nursing Care Center,** 4901 North Main Street, Fall River, MA 02720; tel. 508/675-1001

**Seacoast Nursing and Rehabilitation Center,** 292 Washington Street, Gloucester, MA 01930; tel. 978/283-0300

**Senior Residential Care/Kingston, Inc.,** 17 Chipman Way, Kingston, MA 02364; tel. 781/585-4100

**Senior Residential Care/South Hadley,** 573 Granby Road, South Hadley, MA 01075; tel. 413/532-2200

**Shaughnessy-Kaplan Rehabilitation Hospital, Inc.,** Dove Avenue, Salem, MA 01970; tel. 978/825-8500

**Sheehan Debt Acquistion,** 47 E. Main Street, West Brookfield, MA 01585; tel. 508/867-7716

**Sherrill House, Inc.,** 135 South Huntington Avenue, Boston, MA 02130; tel. 617/731-2400

**Soldiers' Home in Holyoke,** 110 Cherry Street, Holyoke, MA 01040; tel. 413/532-9475

**Soldiers' Home in Massachusetts,** 91 Crest Ave, Chelsea, MA 02150; tel. 617/884-5660

**Somerset Ridge Nursing Center,** 455 Brayton Ave., Somerset, MA 02725; tel. 508/679-2240

**Southbridge MA SNF LLC,** 84 Chapin Street, Southbridge, MA 01550; tel. 508/765-9133

**Southeast Rehabilitation and Skilled Nursing Center,** 184 Lincoln Street, North Easton, MA 02356; tel. 508/238-7053

**Southpointe Rehabilitation and Skilled Care Center,** 100 Amity Street, Fall River, MA 02721; tel. 508/675-2500

**Southwood at Norwell Nursing Center,** 501 Cordwainer Drive, Norwell, MA 02061; tel. 781/982-7450

**SRC Springfield, Inc,** 215 Bicentennial Highway, Springfield, MA 01118; tel. 413/782-7511

**SSC Methuen Operating Company LLC,** 480 Jackson Street, Methuen, MA 01844; tel. 978/686-3906

**SSC New Bedford Operating Company LLC,** 4586 Acushnet Avenue, New Bedford, MA 02745; tel. 508/998-1188

**St. Camillus Health Center,** 447 Hill Street, Whitinsville, MA 01588; tel. 508/234-7306

**St. Joseph Rehabilitation and Nursing Care Center,** 321 Centre Street, Dorchester, MA 02122; tel. 617/825-6320

**Sterling Village, LLC,** 18 Dana Hill Road, Sterling, MA 01564; tel. 978/422-5111

**Sudbury Pines Extended Care Facility,** 642 Boston Post Road, Sudbury, MA 01776; tel. 978/443-9000

**SunBridge Care and Rehabilitation for Milford,** 10 Veterans Memorial Drive, Milford, MA 01757; tel. 508/473-6414

**SunBridge Healthcare Corporation,** PO Box 720, 20 North Maple Street, Hadley, MA 01035; tel. 413/584-5057

**Sunny Acres Nursing Home, Inc.,** 254 Billerica Road, Chelmsford, MA 01824; tel. 978/256-1616

**Sutton Hill Nursing Center,** 1801 Turnpike Street, North Andover, MA 01845; tel. 978/688-1212

**Sweet Brook Transitional Care and Living Centers,** 1561 Cold Spring Road, Williamstown, MA 01267; tel. 413/458-8127

**The Ellis Nursing and Rehabilitation Center,** 135 Ellis Avenue, Norwood, MA 02062; tel. 781/762-6880

**The Highlands,** 335 Nichols Road, Fitchburg, MA 01420; tel. 978/343-4411

**The Lafayette Rehabilitation and Skilled Nursing Facility,** 25 Lafayette Street, Marblehead, MA 01945; tel. 781/631-4535

**The Oaks Nursing Center,** 4525 Acushnet Avenue, New Bedford, MA 02745; tel. 508/998-7807

**The Oxford health care Systems inc,** 689 Main Street, Haverhill, MA 01830; tel. 978/373-1131

**Tower Hill Center for Health and Rehabilitation,** One Meadowbrook Way, Canton, MA 02021; tel. 781/961-5600

**VA Boston Healthcare System,** 1400 VFW Parkway, West Roxbury, MA 02132; tel. 617/323-7700

**VA Central Western Massachusetts Healthcare System,** 421 North Main Street, Leeds, MA 01053-9764; tel. 413/584-4040

**Waban Health Skilled Nursing and Rehabilitation,** 20 Kinmonth Road, Waban, MA 02468; tel. 617/332-8481

**Wachusett Extended Care Facility,** 56 Boyden Road, Holden, MA 01520; tel. 508/829-5555

**Wachusett Manor,** 32 Hospital Hill Road, Gardner, MA 01440; tel. 978/632-5477

**Wakefield Care & Rehabilitation Center,** 1 Bathol St., Wakefield, MA 01880; tel. 781/245-7600

**We Do Care, Inc. dba Carlyle House,** 342 Winter Street, Framingham, MA 01702; tel. 508/879-6100

**Webster Manor Healthcare Center,** 745 School Street, Webster, MA 01570; tel. 508/949-0644

**Westfield Healthcare LLC,** 60 East Silver Street, Westfield, MA 01085; tel. 413/562-5121

**Westford House,** 3 Park Drive, Westford, MA 01886; tel. 978/392-1144

**Weymouth Health Care Center,** 64 Performance Drive, Weymouth, MA 02189; tel. 781/340-9800

**WHC - Haverhill,** 190 North Avenue, Haverhill, MA 01830; tel. 978/372-7700

**Willowood of Williamstown,** 25 Adams Road, Williamstown, MA 01267; tel. 413/458-2111

**Wilmington Health Care Center,** 750 Woburn Street, Wilmington, MA 01887; tel. 978/988-0888

**Windsor Skilled Nursing and Rehabilitation Center,** 265 North Main Street, South Yarmouth, MA 02664; tel. 508/394-3514

**Wingate at Andover,** 80 Andover Street, Andover, MA 01810; tel. 978/470-3434

**Wingate at Belvidere,** 500 Wentworth Avenue, Lowell, MA 01852; tel. 978/458-1271

**Wingate at Brighton, Inc.,** 100 North Beacon Street, Boston, MA 02134; tel. 617/787-2300

**Wingate at East Longmeadow Rehabilitative & Skilled Nursing,** 32 Chestnut Street, East Longmeadow, MA 01028; tel. 413/525-1893

**Wingate at Hampden,** 34 Main Street, Hampden, MA 01036; tel. 413/566-5511

**Wingate at Needham,** 589 Highland Avenue, Needham, MA 02492; tel. 781/455-9090

**Wingate at Reading,** 1364 Main Street, Reading, MA 01867; tel. 781/942-1210

**Wingate at Sudbury, Inc.,** 136 Boston Post Road, Sudbury, MA 01776; tel. 978/443-2722

**Wingate at Wilbraham,** 9 Maple Street, Wilbraham, MA 01095; tel. 413/596-2411

**Wingate SRC West Springfield,** 42 Prospect Avenue, West Springfield, MA 01089; tel. 413/733-3151

**Woodbriar of Wilmington Rehab and Skilled Nursing Center,** 90 West Street, Wilmington, MA 01887; tel. 978/658-2700

**Worcester Rehabilitation and Health Care Center,** 119 Providence Street, Worcester, MA 01604; tel. 508/860-5000

**MICHIGAN**

**Aleda E. Lutz VA Medical Ctr.,** 1500 Weiss Street, Saginaw, MI 48602; tel. 989/497-2500

**Battle Creek VA Medical Center,** 5500 Armstrong Road, Battle Creek, MI 49037; tel. 269/966-5600

**John D. Dingell VA Medical Center,** 4646 John R, Detroit, MI 48201; tel. 313/576-1000

**Life Care Center of Plainwell,** 320 Brigham Street, Plainwell, MI 49080; tel. 269/688-9805

**Oscar G. Johnson VA Medical Center,** 325 East H Street, Iron Mountain, MI 49801; tel. 906/774-3300

**Rivergate Health Care Center,** 14041 Pennsylvania Road, Riverview, MI 48192; tel. 734/284-7200

**Rivergate Terrace,** 14141 Pennsylvania Road, Riverview, MI 48193; tel. 734/284-8000

**Special Tree NeuroCare Center,** 10909 Hannan Rd, Romulus, MI 48174; tel. 734/893-1044

**VA Ann Arbor Healthcare System,** 2215 Fuller Road, Ann Arbor, MI 48105; tel. 734/769-7100

**MINNESOTA**

**Bureau of Prisons - FMC Rochester,** PO Box 4600, Rochester, MN 55903; tel. 507/287-0674

**Mayo Clinic Health System - Lake City,** 500 West Grant Street, Lake City, MN 55041; tel. 651/345-3321

**Mayo Clinic Health System in Fairmont,** 800 Medical Center Drive, Fairmont, MN 56031; tel. 507/238-8100

**St. Cloud VA Health Care System,** 4801 Veterans Drive, Saint Cloud, MN 56303; tel. 320/255-6480

**VA Health Care System - Minneapolis,** One Veterans Drive, Minneapolis, MN 55417; tel. 612/725-2000

**MISSISSIPPI**

**Mississippi State Hospital,** PO Box 157-A, Whitfield, MS 39193-0157; tel. 601/351-8190

**North Mississippi Medical Center, Inc.,** 830 South Gloster Street, Tupelo, MS 38801; tel. 662/377-3837

**Pontotoc Health Services, Inc.,** PO Box 790, Pontotoc, MS 38863-0790; tel. 662/489-5510

**VA Gulf Coast Veterans Health Care System,** 400 Veterans Avenue, Biloxi, MS 39531; tel. 228/523-5000

**VA Medical Center - G. V. (Sonny) Montgomery,** 1500 East Woodrow Wilson Avenue, Jackson, MS 39216; tel. 601/364-1201

**Webster Health Services, Inc.,** 70 Medical Plaza, Eupora, MS 39744; tel. 662/258-6221

**MISSOURI**

**Barnes-Jewish Hospital,** 1 Barnes Jewish Hospital Plaza, Saint Louis, MO 63110; tel. 314/747-3000

**Bethesda Health Group, Inc.,** 1630 Des Peres Road, Saint Louis, MO 63131; tel. 314/968-5460

**Bravo Care of Northbrook, Inc.,** 11701 Borman Drive, Suite 315, Saint Louis, MO 63146; tel. 314/994-9070

**Harry S. Truman Memorial Veterans' Hospital,** 800 Hospital Drive, Columbia, MO 65201; tel. 573/814-6000

**John J. Pershing VA Medical Center,** 1500 North Westwood Boulevard, Poplar Bluff, MO 63901; tel. 573/686-4151

**Lester E. Cox Medical Centers,** 1423 North Jefferson Avenue, Springfield, MO 65802; tel. 417/269-3000

**Life Care Center of Waynesville,** 700 Birch Lane, Waynesville, MO 65583; tel. 573/774-6456

**Life Care Center of Bridgeton,** 12145 Bridge Square Dr., Bridgeton, MO 63044; tel. 314/298-7444

**Life Care Center of Brookfield,** 315 Hunt Street, Brookfield, MO 64628; tel. 660/258-3367

**Life Care Center of Cape Girardeau,** 2852 Independence Street, Cape Girardeau, MO 63703; tel. 573/335-2086

**Life Care Center of Carrollton,** 300 Life Care Lane, Carrollton, MO 64633; tel. 660/542-0155

**Life Care Center of Grandview,** 6301 East 125th Street, Grandview, MO 64030; tel. 816/765-7714

**Life Care Center of Saint Louis,** 3520 Chouteau Avenue, Saint Louis, MO 63129; tel. 314/771-2100

**Life Care Center of Sullivan,** 875 Dunsford Drive, Sullivan, MO 63080; tel. 573/468-3128

**Northwood Hills Care Center LLC,** PO Box 187, Humansville, MO 65674; tel. 417/754-2208

**St. Louis VA Healthcare System,** 915 North Grand Boulevard, Saint Louis, MO 63106; tel. 314/289-7020

**The Westchester House,** 550 White Road, Chesterfield, MO 63017; tel. 314/469-1200

**U.S. Medical Center for Federal Prisoners,** 1900 West Sunshine Street, Springfield, MO 65807; tel. 417/862-7041

Section C

**MONTANA**

VA Montana Healthcare System, 3687 Veterans Drive, Fort Harrison, MT 59636-1500; tel. 406/447-7900

**NEBRASKA**

Life Care Center of Elkhorn, 20275 Hopper Street, Elkhorn, NE 68022; tel. 402/289-2572

Life Care Center of Omaha, 6032 Ville De Sante Drive, Omaha, NE 68104; tel. 402/571-6770

VA Nebraska-Western Iowa Health Care System, 4101 Woolworth Avenue, Omaha, NE 68105; tel. 402/449-0600

**NEVADA**

Life Care Center of Las Vegas, 6151 Vegas Drive, Las Vegas, NV 89108; tel. 702/648-4900

Life Care Center of Paradise Valley, 2325 East Harmon, Las Vegas, NV 89119; tel. 702/798-7990

Life Care Center of Reno, 445 Holcomb Ranch Lane, Reno, NV 89511; tel. 775/851-0123

VA Sierra Nevada Health Care System, 975 Kirman Avenue, Reno, NV 89502-2597; tel. 775/786-7200

**NEW HAMPSHIRE**

Rochester Manor, 40 Whitehall Road, Rochester, NH 03867; tel. 603/332-7711

VA Medical Center, 718 Smyth Road, Manchester, NH 03104-4098; tel. 603/624-4366

**NEW JERSEY**

Absecon Manor Nursing and Rehabilitation Center, 1020 Pitney Road, Absecon, NJ 08201; tel. 609/646-5400

Bacharach Institute for Rehabilitation, PO Box 723, Pomona, NJ 08240-0723; tel. 609/652-7000

Bartley Healthcare Nursing and Rehabilitation, 175 Bartley Road, Jackson, NJ 08527; tel. 732/370-4700

Bergen Regional Medical Center, 230 East Ridgewood Avenue, Paramus, NJ 07652; tel. 201/967-4000

Bey Lea Village Care Center, 1351 Old Freehold Road, Toms River, NJ 08753-2795; tel. 732/240-0090

Camden County Health Services Center, 425 Woodbury Turnersville Road, Blackwood, NJ 08012; tel. 856/374-6500

Care One @ Hamilton, 1660 Whitehorse Hamilton Square Road, Trenton, NJ 08619; tel. 609/586-4600

CentraState Healthcare Affiliates, Inc., 689 West Main Street, Freehold, NJ 07728; tel. 732/431-5200

Daughters of Miriam Center, 155 Hazel Street, Clifton, NJ 07015; tel. 973/772-3700

Forest Hill Healthcare Center, Inc., 497 Mount Prospect Ave., Newark, NJ 07104; tel. 973/482-5000

Forkidcare LLC, 1304 Laurel Oak Road, Voorhees, NJ 08043; tel. 856/346-3300

Franklin Care Center, 3371 Route 27, Franklin Park, NJ 08823; tel. 732/821-8000

Gateway Care Center, LLC, 139 Grant Avenue, Eatontown, NJ 07724; tel. 732/542-4700

Hamilton Plaza Nursing and Rehabilitation Center, 56 Hamilton Avenue, Passaic, NJ 07055; tel. 973/773-7070

Laurelton Village Care Center, 475 Jack Martin Boulevard, Brick, NJ 08724; tel. 732/458-6600

Linwood Care Center, New Road and Central Avenue, Linwood, NJ 08221; tel. 609/927-6131

Mainland Manor Nursing and Rehabilitation Center, PO Box 1309, Pleasantville, NJ 08232; tel. 609/646-6900

McCarrick Care Center, 15 Dellwood Lane, Somerset, NJ 08873; tel. 732/545-4200

Medford Care Center, 185 Tuckerton Road, Medford, NJ 08055; tel. 856/983-8500

Meridian Rehabilitation & Nursing at Brick, 415 Jack Martin Blvd., Brick, NJ 08724; tel. 732/206-8000

Neptune Rehabilitation and Care Center, 101 Walnut Street, Neptune, NJ 07753; tel. 732/774-3550

Oak Ridge Rehabilitation and Nursing Center, 261 Terhune Drive, Wayne, NJ 07470; tel. 973/835-3871

Park Manor Nursing & Rehabilitation Center, 23 Park Place, Bloomfield, NJ 07003; tel. 973/743-7772

Prospect Heights Care Center, 336 Prospect Avenue, Hackensack, NJ 07601; tel. 201/678-1800

Regent Care Center, 50 Polifly Road, Hackensack, NJ 07601; tel. 201/646-1166

Robert Wood Johnson University Hospital at Rahway, 865 Stone Street, Rahway, NJ 07065; tel. 732/499-6050

Seacrest Village Nursing and Rehabilitation Center, 1001 Center Street, Little Egg Harbor Twp, NJ 08087; tel. 609/296-9292

South Mountain Healthcare and Rehabilitation Center, 2385 Springfield Avenue, Vauxhall, NJ 07088-1046; tel. 908/688-3400

St. Lawrence Rehabilitation Center, 2381 Lawrenceville Road, Lawrenceville, NJ 08648; tel. 609/896-9500

VA New Jersey Health Care System, 385 Tremont Avenue, Director's Office (00), East Orange, NJ 07018; tel. 973/676-1000

Virtua - Memorial Hospital Burlington County, 175 Madison Avenue, Mount Holly, NJ 08060; tel. 856/355-0070

Virtua-West Jersey Health System, Inc.(Voorhees), 100 Bowman Drive, Voorhees New Jersey, Voorhees, NJ 08043; tel. 856/247-3000

West Caldwell Care Center, 165 Fairfield Avenue, West Caldwell, NJ 07006; tel. 973/226-1100

Whiting Healthcare Center, 3000 Hilltop Road, Whiting, NJ 08759; tel. 732/849-4400

Willow Creek Rehabilitation and Care Center, 1165 Easton Avenue, Somerset, NJ 08873; tel. 732/246-4100

**NEW MEXICO**

Deming Hospital Corporation, 900 W Ash Street, Deming, NM 88030; tel. 575/546-5800

Life Care Center of Farmington, 1101 West Murray Drive, Farmington, NM 87401; tel. 505/326-1600

New Mexico Behavioral Health Institute at Las Vegas, 3695 Hot Springs Boulevard, Las Vegas, NM 87701; tel. 505/454-2404

New Mexico State Veteran's Home, 992 South Broadway, Truth Or Consequences, NM 87901; tel. 575/894-4200

New Mexico VA Health Care System, 1501 San Pedro Drive SE, Albuquerque, NM 87108; tel. 505/265-1711

**NEW YORK**

Alice Hyde Medical Center, PO Box 729, Malone, NY 12953; tel. 518/483-3000

Coler-Goldwater Specialty Hosp. and NF - Coler Campus, 900 Main Street, New York, NY 10044-0052; tel. 212/848-6318

Coler-Goldwater Specialty Hosp. and NF - Goldwater Campus, 1 Main Street, New York, NY 10044; tel. 212/318-4361

Dr. Susan Smith McKinney Nursing/Rehabilitation Center, 594 Albany Avenue, Brooklyn, NY 11203; tel. 718/245-7170

Good Samaritan Hospital Medical Center, 1000 Montauk Highway, West Islip, NY 11795; tel. 631/376-4001

Gouverneur Skilled Nursing Facility, 227 Madison Street, New York, NY 10002; tel. 212/441-5017

Helen Hayes Hospital, 51-55 Route 9, West, West Haverstraw, NY 10993; tel. 845/786-4000

James J Peters Bronx VA Medical Center, 130 West Kingsbridge Road, Bronx, NY 10468; tel. 718/584-9000

Jewish Home LifeCare - Bronx Division, 100 West Kingsbridge Road, Bronx, NY 10468; tel. 718/410-1851

Jewish Home Lifecare - Manhattan, 120 West 106 Street, New York, NY 10025; tel. 212/870-5000

Jewish Home Lifecare, Sarah Neuman Center, Westchester, 845 Palmer Avenue, Mamaroneck, NY 10543; tel. 914/698-6005

Kingsbrook Jewish Medical Center, 585 Schenectady Avenue, Brooklyn, NY 11203; tel. 718/604-5000

Long Beach Medical Center, 455 East Bay Drive, Long Beach, NY 11561; tel. 516/897-1208

Nassau Health Care Corporation, 2201 Hempstead Turnpike, East Meadow, NY 11554; tel. 516/572-0123

No Shore Univ Hosp Stern Fam Cntr for Extnd Care and Rehab, 330 Community Drive, Manhasset, NY 11030; tel. 516/562-8070

Orleans Community Health, 200 Ohio Street, Medina, NY 14103; tel. 585/798-2000

Orzac Center for Extended Care and Rehabilitation, 900 Franklin Ave, Valley Stream, NY 11580; tel. 516/256-6502

Our Lady of Consolation Nursing & Rehabilitative Care Center, 111 Beach Drive, West Islip, NY 11795; tel. 631/587-1600

Pinegrove Manor II, LLC, 15 St. Paul's Place, Great Neck, NY 11021; tel. 516/466-3001

Providence Rest, 3304 Waterbury Avenue, Bronx, NY 10465; tel. 718/931-3000

Queens Boulevard Extended Care Facility, 61-11 Queens Boulevard, Woodside, NY 11377; tel. 718/205-0287

Samuel S. Stratton VA Medical Center, 113 Holland Avenue, Albany, NY 12208; tel. 518/626-5000

Sea View Hospital Rehabilitation Center and Home, 460 Brielle Avenue, Staten Island, NY 10314; tel. 718/317-3000

St. James Healthcare Center, 275 Moriches Road, Saint James, NY 11780; tel. 631/862-8000

Unity Hospital, 1555 Long Pond Rd, Rochester, NY 14626; tel. 585/723-7000

Upstate New York VA Health Care Network at Canandaigua, 400 Fort Hill Avenue, Canandaigua, NY 14424; tel. 585/394-2000

VA Healthcare Network Upstate New York at Bath, 76 Veterans Avenue, Bath, NY 14810; tel. 607/664-4722

VA Healthcare Network Upstate New York at Syracuse, 800 Irving Avenue, Syracuse, NY 13210; tel. 315/425-4400

VA Hudson Valley Health Care System, 2094 Albany Post Road, Route 9A, Montrose, NY 10548; tel. 914/737-4400

VA Medical Center Northport, 79 Middleville Road, Northport, NY 11768; tel. 631/261-4400

VA New York Harbor Health Care System, 800 Poly Place, Brooklyn, NY 11209; tel. 718/630-3521

VA Western New York Health Care System, 3495 Bailey Avenue, Buffalo, NY 14215; tel. 716/862-8529

**NORTH CAROLINA**

Alamance Regional Medical Center, Inc., PO Box 202, Burlington, NC 27216-0202; tel. 336/538-7450

Blowing Rock Hospital and Davant Extended Care Facility, PO Box 148, Blowing Rock, NC 28605-0148; tel. 828/295-3136

Carolinas Medical Center - Union, PO Box 5003, Monroe, NC 28111; tel. 704/283-3100

Charles George VA Medical Center at Asheville, 1100 Tunnel Road, Asheville, NC 28805; tel. 828/298-7911

Granville Health System, College Street PO 947, Oxford, NC 27565; tel. 919/690-3418

Highlands - Cashiers Hospital, Inc., PO Drawer 190, Highlands, NC 28741-0190; tel. 828/526-1200

Lenoir Memorial Hospital, Inc., PO Drawer 1678, Kinston, NC 28503-1678; tel. 252/522-7000

Life Care Center of Banner Elk, PO Box 2199, Banner Elk, NC 28604; tel. 828/898-5136

Life Care Center of Hendersonville, 400 Thompson Street, Hendersonville, NC 28792; tel. 828/697-4348

Person Memorial Hospital, 615 Ridge Road, Roxboro, NC 27573; tel. 336/599-2121

Sampson Regional Medical Center, PO Box 260, Clinton, NC 28329; tel. 910/592-8511

Southeastern Regional Medical Center, PO Box 1408, Lumberton, NC 28359; tel. 910/671-5860

Uni Health Post Acute Care Raleigh, 2420 Lake Wheeler Road, Raleigh, NC 27603; tel. 919/755-0226

United Veteran Services of North Carolina, 214 Cochran Avenue, Fayetteville, NC 28301; tel. 910/482-4131

United Veteran Services of North Carolina, PO Box 599, Salisbury, NC 28145; tel. 704/638-4200

VA Medical Center, 2300 Ramsey Street, Fayetteville, NC 28301; tel. 910/822-7091

VA Medical Center, 508 Fulton Street, Durham, NC 27705; tel. 919/286-0411

Vidant Chowan Hospital, 211 Virginia Road, Edenton, NC 27932; tel. 252/482-8451

W. G. (Bill) Hefner VA Medical Center, 1601 Brenner Avenue, Salisbury, NC 28144; tel. 704/638-9000

**NORTH DAKOTA**

Fargo VA Health Care System, 2101 Elm Street North, Fargo, ND 58102; tel. 701/232-3241

**OHIO**

Broadview Nursing Home, Inc., 5520 Broadview Road, Parma, OH 44134; tel. 216/749-4010

DaySpring of Miami Valley Health Care Center and Rehab, 8001 Dayton-Springfield Road, Fairborn, OH 45324; tel. 937/864-5800

Department of Veterans Affairs Medical Center, Dayton, Ohio, 4100 West 3rd Street, Dayton, OH 45428; tel. 937/268-6511

Drake Center LLC, 151 West Galbraith Road, Cincinnati, OH 45216; tel. 513/418-2500

Eastgatespring Health Care Center and Rehabilitation, 4400 Gleneste Withamsville Rd, Cincinnati, OH 45245; tel. 513/752-3710

**Euclid Hospital,** 18901 Lake Shore Boulevard, Euclid, OH 44119; tel. 216/531-9000

**Franciscan Care Center,** 4111 North Holland Sylvania Road, Toledo, OH 43623; tel. 419/882-6582

**Fulton County Health Center,** 725 South Shoop Avenue, Wauseon, OH 43567; tel. 419/335-2015

**Heritagespring Health Care and Rehabilitation Center,** 7235 Heritagespring Drive, West Chester, OH 45069; tel. 513/759-5777

**Hillspring Healthcare & Rehab Center,** 325 East Central Ave., Route 73, Springboro, OH 45066; tel. 937/748-1100

**Hospitality Homes East,** 1301 North Monroe Drive, Xenia, OH 45385; tel. 937/372-4495

**Lakewood Hospital Association,** 14519 Detroit Avenue, Lakewood, OH 44107; tel. 216/521-4200

**Life Care Center of Elyria,** 1212 South Abbe Road, Elyria, OH 44035; tel. 440/365-5200

**Life Care Center of Medina,** 2400 Columbia Road, Medina, OH 44256; tel. 330/483-3131

**Life Care Center of Westlake,** 26520 Center Ridge Road, Westlake, OH 44145; tel. 440/871-3030

**Louis Stokes, Cleveland VA Medical Center,** 10701 East Boulevard, Cleveland, OH 44106; tel. 216/231-3456

**Mayfair Village Nursing Care Center,** 3000 Bethel Road, Columbus, OH 43220; tel. 614/889-6320

**Oregon Health Investors Co.,** 2841 Munding Drive, Oregon, OH 43616; tel. 419/697-4100

**Parkside Villa,** 7040 Hepburn Road, Middleburg Heights, OH 44130; tel. 440/260-7626

**Parma Community General Hospital,** 7007 Powers Boulevard, Parma, OH 44129; tel. 440/743-3000

**Pleasant Lake Villa,** 7260 Ridge Road, Parma, OH 44129; tel. 440/842-2273

**Providence Care Center,** 2025 Hayes Avenue, Sandusky, OH 44870; tel. 419/627-2273

**Rosary Care Center,** 6832 Convent Blvd., Sylvania, OH 43560; tel. 419/824-3600

**Shawneespring Health Care and Rehabilitation Center,** 10111 Simonson Road, Harrison, OH 45030; tel. 513/367-7780

**St. Leonard Health Care Center,** 8100 Clyo Road, Centerville, OH 45458; tel. 937/433-0480

**The Ohio Eastern Star Home,** 1451 Gambier Road, Mount Vernon, OH 43050; tel. 740/397-1706

**The Village at St. Edward Nursing Care,** 3131 Smith Road, Fairlawn, OH 44333-2697; tel. 330/666-1183

**Trinity Health System,** 380 Summit Avenue, Steubenville, OH 43952; tel. 740/283-7212

**VA Healthcare System of Ohio - Cincinnati Campus,** 3200 Vine Street, Cincinnati, OH 45220; tel. 513/861-3100

**VA Medical Center - Chillicothe,** 17273 State Route 104, Chillicothe, OH 45601; tel. 740/773-1141

**OKLAHOMA**

**Department of Veterans Affairs Medical Center,** 921 Northeast 13th Street, Oklahoma City, OK 73104; tel. 405/456-3312

**OREGON**

**Life Care Center of Coos Bay,** 2890 Ocean Boulevard, Coos Bay, OR 97420; tel. 541/267-5433

**Life Care Center of McMinnville,** 1309 East 27th Street, McMinnville, OR 97128; tel. 503/472-4678

**Life Care Center Valley West Health Care Center,** 2300 Warren Street, Eugene, OR 97405; tel. 541/686-2828

**Portland VA Medical Center,** PO Box 1034, Portland, OR 97207; tel. 503/273-5267

**VA Roseburg Healthcare System,** 913 NW Garden Valley Boulevard, Roseburg, OR 97471; tel. 541/440-1000

**PENNSYLVANIA**

**Albert Einstein Medical Center,** 5501 Old York Road, Philadelphia, PA 19141; tel. 215/456-7890

**Angela Jane Pavilion,** 8410 Roosevelt Boulevard, Philadelphia, PA 19152; tel. 215/708-1200

**Barclay Friends,** 700 North Franklin Street, West Chester, PA 19380; tel. 610/696-5201

**Berwick Hospital Center,** 701 East 16th Street, Berwick, PA 18603; tel. 570/759-5000

**Bible Fellowship Church Homes Inc.,** 3000 Fellowship Drive, Whitehall, PA 18052; tel. 610/799-3000

**Charles Cole Memorial Hospital,** 1001 East Second Street, Coudersport, PA 16915; tel. 814/274-5347

**Erie VA Medical Center,** 135 East 38th Street, Erie, PA 16504; tel. 814/868-8661

**Gnaden Huetten Memorial Hospital,** 211 North 12th Street, Lehighton, PA 18235-1195; tel. 610/377-1300

**Good Shepherd Rehabilitation Hospital,** 850 S. Fifth Street, Allentown, PA 18103-3295; tel. 610/776-3133

**Hickory House Nursing Home,** 3120 Horseshoe Pike, Honey Brook, PA 19344; tel. 610/273-2915

**Lebanon VA Medical Center,** 1700 South Lincoln Avenue, Lebanon, PA 17042; tel. 717/272-6621

**Lock Haven Hospital and Haven Skilled Rehab & Nursing,** 24 Cree Drive, Lock Haven, PA 17745; tel. 570/893-5000

**Main Line Hospitals, Inc.,** 100 East Lancaster Ave., Wynnewood, PA 19096; tel. 484/476-2000

**Nazareth Hospital,** 2601 Holme Avenue, Philadelphia, PA 19152-2096; tel. 215/335-6000

**Philadelphia VA Medical Center,** University and Woodland Avenues, Philadelphia, PA 19104; tel. 215/823-5857

**Presbyterian Medical Center of the UPHS,** 51 North 39th Street, Philadelphia, PA 19104; tel. 215/662-8260

**River's Edge Nursing and Rehabilitation Center,** 9501 State Road, Philadelphia, PA 19114; tel. 215/632-5700

**St. Luke's Hospital - Miners Campus,** 360 West Ruddle Street, Coaldale, PA 18218-0067; tel. 570/645-2131

**The Commons at Squirrel Hill,** 2025 Wightman Street, Pittsburgh, PA 15217; tel. 412/421-8443

**UPMC Horizon,** 110 North Main Street, Greenville, PA 16125; tel. 724/588-2100

**VA Butler Healthcare,** 325 New Castle Road, Butler, PA 16001-2480; tel. 724/287-4781

**VA Medical Center,** 1400 Black Horse Hill Road, Coatesville, PA 19320-2097; tel. 610/384-7711

**VA Medical Center - James E. Van Zandt,** 2907 Pleasant Valley Boulevard, Altoona, PA 16602-4377; tel. 814/943-8164

**VA Medical Center Wilkes-Barre,** 1111 East End Boulevard, Wilkes Barre, PA 18711; tel. 570/821-7204

**VA Pittsburgh Healthcare System,** University Drive C, Pittsburgh, PA 15240; tel. 412/360-6391

**RHODE ISLAND**

**Cedar Crest Nursing Centre,** 125 Scituate Avenue, Cranston, RI 02921; tel. 401/944-8500

**Cherry Hill Manor,** 2 Cherry Hill Road, Johnston, RI 02919; tel. 401/231-3102

**Chestnut Terrace Nursing & Rehabilitation Center,** 100 Wompanoag Trail, Riverside, RI 02915; tel. 401/438-4275

**EPOCH Senior Healthcare on Blackstone Blvd LLC,** 353 Blackstone Boulevard, Providence, RI 02906; tel. 401/273-6565

**Evergreen House Health Center,** One Evergreen Drive, East Providence, RI 02914; tel. 401/438-3250

**Harken Inc.,** PO Box 152, Pascoag, RI 02859; tel. 401/568-2549

**Kent Regency Genesis Health Care,** 660 Commonwealth Avenue, Warwick, RI 02886; tel. 401/739-4241

**Kindred Transitional Care and Rehabilitation - Oak Hill,** 544 Pleasant Street, Pawtucket, RI 02860; tel. 401/725-8888

**Pezzelli Nursing Home, Inc.,** 100 Smithfield Road, North Providence, RI 02904; tel. 401/353-1710

**Roger Williams Medical Center,** 825 Chalkstone Avenue, Providence, RI 02908; tel. 401/456-2043

**Ryan Health Center, Inc.,** 80 Morgan Avenue, Johnston, RI 02919; tel. 401/944-7800

**South County Nursing and Rehabilitation Center,** 740 Oak Hill Road, North Kingstown, RI 02852; tel. 401/294-4545

**Westerly Health Center,** 280 High Street, Westerly, RI 02891; tel. 401/348-0020

**Woonsocket Health and Rehabilitation Center,** 262 Poplar Street, Woonsocket, RI 02895; tel. 401/765-2100

**SOUTH CAROLINA**

**C. M. Tucker, Jr. Nursing Care Center,** 2200 Harden Street, Columbia, SC 29203; tel. 803/737-5301

**Life Care Center of Charleston,** 2600 Elms Plantation Boulevard, North Charleston, SC 29406; tel. 843/764-3500

**Life Care Center of Columbia,** 2514 Faraway Drive, Columbia, SC 29223; tel. 803/865-1999

**Life Care Center of Hilton Head,** 120 Lamotte Drive, Hilton Head Island, SC 29926; tel. 843/681-6006

**Pepper Hill Nursing and Rehab Center,** 3525 Augustus Road, Aiken, SC 29802-3188; tel. 803/642-8376

**QHG of South Carolina, INC,** PO Box 1150, Marion, SC 29571; tel. 843/431-2000

**Ralph H. Johnson VA Medical Center,** 109 Bee Street, Charleston, SC 29401-5799; tel. 843/577-5011

**UniHealth Post Acute Care North Augusta,** 1200 Talisman Drive, North Augusta, SC 29841; tel. 803/278-2170

**William Jennings Bryan Dorn VA Medical Center,** 6439 Garners Ferry Road, Columbia, SC 29209; tel. 803/776-4000

**SOUTH DAKOTA**

**Sioux Falls VA Health Care System,** PO Box 5046, Sioux Falls, SD 57117; tel. 605/336-3230

**VA Black Hills Health Care System-Fort Meade-Hot Springs, SD,** 113 Comanche Road, Fort Meade, SD 57741; tel. 605/720-7170

**TENNESSEE**

**Christian Care Center of Bedford County,** 835 Union St., Shelbyville, TN 37160; tel. 931/680-2300

**Christian Care Center of Cheatham County,** 2501 River Road, Ashland City, TN 37015; tel. 615/792-4948

**Christian Care Center of Johnson City, Inc.,** 140 Technology Lane, Johnson City, TN 37604; tel. 423/434-2016

**Christian Care Center of Rutherford County,** 202 Enon Springs Road East, Smyrna, TN 37167; tel. 423/975-5455

**Christian Care Center of Springfield, LLC,** 704 5th Avenue E, Springfield, TN 37172; tel. 615/384-7977

**Fort Sanders Regional Medical Center,** 1901 Clinch Avenue, Knoxville, TN 37916; tel. 865/541-1100

**Hardin County General Hospital,** 935 Wayne Rd., Savannah, TN 38372; tel. 731/926-8121

**Hickman Community Health Care Services,** 135 East Swan Street, Centerville, TN 37033; tel. 931/729-4271

**Ivy Hall Nursing Home, Inc.,** 301 Watauga Avenue, Elizabethton, TN 37643; tel. 423/542-6512

**KDM, Inc.,** 55 Nursing Home Road, Chuckey, TN 37641; tel. 423/257-6761

**Lakebridge Medical Investors, LLC,** 115 Woodlawn Drive, Johnson City, TN 37604; tel. 423/975-0095

**LeConte Medical Center,** 742 Middle Creek Road, Sevierville, TN 37862; tel. 865/446-7500

**Life Care Center of Athens,** PO Box 786, Athens, TN 37371-0786; tel. 423/754-8181

**Life Care Center of Centerville,** 112 Old Dickson Road, Centerville, TN 37033; tel. 931/729-4236

**Life Care Center of Cleveland,** 3530 Keith Street NW, Cleveland, TN 37312; tel. 423/476-3254

**Life Care Center of Collegedale,** PO Box 658, Collegedale, TN 37315; tel. 423/396-2182

**Life Care Center of Columbia,** 841 W. James Campbell Blvd., Columbia, TN 38401; tel. 931/388-5035

**Life Care Center of Copper Basin,** PO Box 518, Ducktown, TN 37326-0518; tel. 423/496-3245

**Life Care Center of Crossville,** 80 Justice Street, Crossville, TN 38555; tel. 931/484-4782

**Life Care Center of East Ridge,** 1500 Fincher Avenue, East Ridge, TN 37412; tel. 423/894-1254

**Life Care Center of Elizabethton,** 1641 Hwy 19E Bypass, Elizabethton, TN 37643; tel. 423/542-4133

**Life Care Center of Gray,** 791 Old Gray Station Road, Gray, TN 37615; tel. 423/477-7146

**Life Care Center of Greeneville,** 725 Crum Street, Greeneville, TN 37743; tel. 423/639-8131

**Life Care Center of Morgan County,** 419 South Kingston Street, Wartburg, TN 37887; tel. 423/346-6691

**Life Care Center of Morristown,** 501 West Economy Road, Morristown, TN 37814; tel. 423/581-5435

**Life Care Center of Red Bank,** 1020 Runyan Drive, Chattanooga, TN 37405; tel. 423/877-1155

**Life Care Center of Sparta,** 508 Mose Drive, Sparta, TN 38583; tel. 931/738-9430

**Life Care Center of Tullahoma,** 1715 No. Jackson Street, Tullahoma, TN 37388; tel. 931/455-8557

**Life Care Centers of America, Inc.,** 336 W Old Andrew Johnson Hwy, Jefferson City, TN 37760; tel. 865/475-6097

**Lynchburg Nursing Center,** 40 Nursing Home Road, Lynchburg, TN 37352; tel. 931/759-6000

**Methodist Healthcare Memphis Hospitals,** 1211 Union Avenue, Memphis, TN 38104; tel. 901/516-8582

**Milford Medical Investors, LP,** PO Box 137, Bruceton, TN 38317; tel. 731/586-2061

**Ridgeview Terrace of Life Care,** PO Box 26, Rutledge, TN 37861; tel. 865/828-5295

**Roan Highlands Nursing Center,** 146 Buck Creek Road, Roan Mountain, TN 37687; tel. 423/772-0161

**Sweetwater Nursing Center, Inc.,** 978 Highway 11S, Sweetwater, TN 37874; tel. 423/337-6631

**The Heritage Center,** 1026 McFarland Street, Morristown, TN 37814; tel. 423/581-5100

**VA Medical Center - James H. Quillen,** PO Box 4000, Mountain Home, TN 37684; tel. 423/926-1171

**VA Tennessee Valley Healthcare System,** 1310 24th Avenue South, Nashville, TN 37212-2637; tel. 615/327-4751

**TEXAS**

**Alameda Oaks Nursing Center,** 1101 South Alameda, Corpus Christi, TX 78404; tel. 361/882-2711

**Amarillo VA Health Care System,** 6010 Amarillo Boulevard, West, Amarillo, TX 79106; tel. 806/355-9703

**Bureau of Prisons - FCI Fort Worth,** 3150 Horton Road, Fort Worth, TX 76119; tel. 817/534-8400

**Burleson St. Joseph Manor,** 1022 Presidential Corridor, Hwy 21 East, Caldwell, TX 77836; tel. 979/567-0920

**Central Texas Veterans Health Care System,** 1901 Veterans Memorial Drive, Temple, TX 76504; tel. 254/743-2306

**CHRISTUS Spohn Hospital Alice,** 2500 East Main Street, Alice, TX 78332; tel. 361/661-8000

**Garden Terrace Alzheimer's Center of Excellence,** 7500 Oakmont Boulevard, Fort Worth, TX 76132; tel. 817/346-8080

**Garden Terrace Alzheimer's Center of Excellence,** 7887 Cambridge Street, Houston, TX 77054; tel. 713/796-2777

**Life Care Center of Haltom,** 2936 Markum Drive, Haltom City, TX 76117; tel. 817/831-0545

**Life Care Center of Plano,** 3800 West Park Boulevard, Plano, TX 75075; tel. 972/612-1700

**Memorial Hospital,** 224 East Second Street, Dumas, TX 79029; tel. 806/935-7171

**Michael E. DeBakey VA Medical Center,** 2002 Holcombe Boulevard, Houston, TX 77030; tel. 713/794-7100

**Renaissance Park Multi-Care Center,** 4252 Bryant Irvin Road, Fort Worth, TX 76109; tel. 817/738-2975

**Scott & White Memorial Hospital,** 2401 South 31st Street, Temple, TX 76508; tel. 254/724-6583

**South Texas Veterans Health Care System,** 7400 Merton Minter Boulevard, San Antonio, TX 78229-4404; tel. 210/617-5205

**The Vosswood Nursing Center,** 815 South Voss Road, Houston, TX 77057; tel. 713/827-0883

**VA North Texas Health Care System,** 4500 South Lancaster Road, Dallas, TX 75216; tel. 202/329-8673

**West Texas VA Health Care System,** 300 Veterans Boulevard, Big Spring, TX 79720; tel. 432/263-7361

**Wooldridge Place Nursing Center,** 7352 Wooldridge Rd., Corpus Christi, TX 78414; tel. 361/991-9633

**UTAH**

**Garden Terrace Alzheimer's Center of Excellence,** 1201 East 4500 South, Salt Lake City, UT 84117; tel. 801/261-3664

**Life Care Center of Bountiful,** 460 West 2600 South, Bountiful, UT 84010; tel. 801/295-3135

**VERMONT**

**Bennington Health and Rehabilitation Center,** 2 Blackberry Lane, Bennington, VT 05201; tel. 802/442-8525

**Berlin Health and Rehabilitation,** 98 Hospitality Drive, Barre, VT 05641; tel. 802/229-0308

**Burlington Health and Rehabilitation Center,** 300 Pearl Street, Burlington, VT 05401; tel. 802/658-4200

**Rowan Court Health and Rehabilitation Center,** 378 Prospect Street, Barre, VT 05641; tel. 802/476-4166

**St. Johnsbury Health and Rehab Center,** 1248 Hospital Drive, Saint Johnsbury, VT 05819; tel. 802/748-8757

**SVHC Centers for Living and Rehabilitation,** 160 Hospital Drive, Bennington, VT 05201; tel. 802/447-1547

**VIRGINIA**

**Augusta Health,** PO Box 1000, Fishersville, VA 22939; tel. 540/332-4800

**Community Memorial Healthcenter,** PO Box 90, South Hill, VA 23970-0090; tel. 434/447-3151

**CPL (Iliff) LLC,** 8000 Iliff Drive, Dunn Loring, VA 22027; tel. 703/560-1000

**Eastern State Hospital,** 4601 Ironbound Road, Williamsburg, VA 23188; tel. 757/253-5161

**Hiram W. Davis Medical Center,** PO Box 4030, Petersburg, VA 23803; tel. 804/524-7112

**Inova Loudoun Hospital,** 44045 Riverside Parkway, Leesburg, VA 20176; tel. 703/858-6000

**James River Convalescent & Rehabilitation Center,** 540 Aberthaw Avenue, Newport News, VA 23601; tel. 757/595-2273

**Life Care Center of New Market,** 315 East Lee Highway, New Market, VA 22844; tel. 540/740-8041

**Salem VA Medical Center,** 1970 Roanoke Boulevard, Salem, VA 24153; tel. 540/982-2463

**Southampton Memorial Hospital,** 100 Fairview Drive, Franklin, VA 23851; tel. 757/569-6100

**VA Medical Center - Hunter Holmes McGuire,** 1201 Broad Rock Boulevard, Richmond, VA 23249; tel. 804/675-5000

**VA Medical Center-Hampton,** 100 Emancipation Drive, Hampton, VA 23667; tel. 757/722-9961

**WASHINGTON**

**Alderwood Manor,** 3600 East Hartson Avenue, Spokane, WA 99202; tel. 509/535-2071

**Cascade Park Care Center,** 801 SE Park Crest Avenue, Vancouver, WA 98683; tel. 360/260-2200

**Cottesmore of Life Care,** 2909 14th Avenue NW, Gig Harbor, WA 98335; tel. 253/851-5433

**Garden Terrace Alzheimers Center of Excellence,** 491 S 338th Street, Federal Way, WA 98003; tel. 253/661-2226

**Hallmark Manor,** 32300 1st Ave. South, Federal Way, WA 98003; tel. 253/874-3580

**Life Care Center of Federal Way,** 1045 S. 308th Street, Federal Way, WA 98003; tel. 253/946-2273

**Life Care Center of Kennewick,** 1508 W. Seventh Avenue, Kennewick, WA 99336; tel. 509/586-9185

**Life Care Center of Kirkland,** 10101 Northeast 120th Street, Kirkland, WA 98034; tel. 425/823-2323

**Life Care Center of Mount Vernon,** 2120 East Division Street, Mount Vernon, WA 98274; tel. 360/424-4258

**Life Care Center of Port Orchard,** 2031 Pottery Avenue, Port Orchard, WA 98366; tel. 360/876-8035

**Life Care Center of Port Townsend,** 751 Kearney Street, Port Townsend, WA 98368; tel. 360/385-3555

**Life Care Center of Puyallup,** 511 10th Avenue S.E., Puyallup, WA 98372; tel. 253/845-7566

**Life Care Center of Richland,** 44 Goethals Drive, Richland, WA 99352; tel. 509/943-1117

**Life Care Center of Skagit Valley,** 1462 West SR 20, Sedro Woolley, WA 98284; tel. 360/856-6867

**Life Care Center of the San Juan Islands,** 660 Spring street, Friday Harbor, WA 98250; tel. 360/378-2117

**Marysville Care Center,** 1821 Grove Street, Marysville, WA 98270; tel. 360/659-3926

**Orchard Park Health & Rehabilitation Center,** 4755 South 48th Street, Tacoma, WA 98409; tel. 253/475-4611

**Ritzville Medical Investors, Inc.,** 506 South Jackson Street, Ritzville, WA 99169; tel. 509/659-1600

**Sea-Mar Community Health Center,** 1040 S. Henderson Street, Seattle, WA 98108; tel. 206/763-5277

**VA Medical Center,** North 4815 Assembly Street, Spokane, WA 99205; tel. 509/434-7000

**VA Puget Sound Health Care System,** 1660 South Columbian Way (S-002-QI), Seattle, WA 98108-1597; tel. 206/764-2731

**WEST VIRGINIA**

**CamdenClark Medical Center,** PO Box 718, Parkersburg, WV 26102; tel. 304/424-2111

**Pleasant Valley Hospital,** 2520 Valley Drive, Point Pleasant, WV 25550; tel. 304/675-4340

**VA Medical Center,** 200 Veterans Avenue, Beckley, WV 25801; tel. 304/255-2121

**VA Medical Center,** 510 Butler Avenue, Martinsburg, WV 25405; tel. 304/263-0811

**VA Medical Center - Louis A. Johnson,** 1 Medical Center Drive, Clarksburg, WV 26301; tel. 304/623-3461

**WISCONSIN**

**Clement J. Zablocki VA Medical Center,** 5000 West National Avenue, Milwaukee, WI 53295-1000; tel. 414/384-2000

**Divine Savior Healthcare, Inc.,** PO Box 387, Portage, WI 53901; tel. 608/742-4131

**VA Medical Center - Great Lakes Health Care System,** 500 East Veterans Street, Tomah, WI 54660; tel. 608/372-1777

**William S. Middleton Memorial Veterans Hospital,** 2500 Overlook Terrace, Madison, WI 53705; tel. 608/256-1901

**WYOMING**

**Life Care Center of Casper,** 4041 South Poplar Street, Casper, WY 82601; tel. 307/266-0000

**Life Care Center of Cheyenne,** 1330 Prairie Avenue, Cheyenne, WY 82009; tel. 307/778-8997

**Sheridan VA Medical Center,** 1898 Fort Road, Sheridan, WY 82801; tel. 307/675-3530

**St. John's Medical Center,** PO Box 428, Jackson, WY 83001; tel. 307/733-3636

**VA Medical Center,** 2360 East Pershing Boulevard, Cheyenne, WY 82001; tel. 307/778-7550

**Westview Health Care Center,** 1990 West Loucks, Sheridan, WY 82801; tel. 307/672-9789

# U.S. Associated Areas

**PUERTO RICO**

**VA Caribbean Healthcare System,** 10 Casia Street, San Juan, PR 00921-3201; tel. 787/641-7582

**Section C**

# Joint Commission Accredited Behavioral Health Organizations

*The accredited freestanding mental health care organizations listed have been accredited as of May 2013 by the Joint Commission on Accreditation of Healthcare Organizations by decision of the Accreditation Committee of the Board of Commissioners.*

*The organizations listed here have been found to be in compliance with the Joint Commissions standards for Accreditation Manual for Mental Health, Chemical Dependency, and Mental Retardation/Development Disabilities Services.*

*Please refer to section A of the AHA Guide for information on hospitals with inpatient and:NS:or outpatient services. These hospitals are identified by Facility Codes F96, F97, F98, F99, F100, F101, F102, and F103. In section A, those hospitals identified by Approval Code 1 are Joint Commission accredited.*

*We present this list simply as a convenient directory. Inclusion or omission of any organization's name indicates neither approval nor disapproval by Health Forum LLC, an American Hospital Association company.*

## United States

### ALABAMA

*\*Alabama Center for Eating Disorders,* P.O. Box 55901, Birmingham, AL 35255; tel. 205/933-0041

**Alabama Clinical Schools, Inc,** P.O. Box 100968, Birmingham, AL 35210; tel. 205/836-9923

**\*AltaPointe Health Systems, Inc.,** 5750-A Southland Drive, Mobile, AL 36693; tel. 251/450-5901

**\*Bradford Health Services - Huntsville Lodge,** 1600 Browns Ferry Road, Madison, AL 35758; tel. 256/461-7272

**\*Bradford Health Services - Warrior,** PO Box 129, Warrior, AL 35180; tel. 205/647-1945

**Brookwood Medical Center,** 2010 Brookwood Medical Center Drive, Birmingham, AL 35209; tel. 205/877-1000

**Carlorene House Inc.,** 2308 Highway 82 West, Prattville, AL 36067; tel. 334/365-1260

**Central Alabama Veterans Health Care System,** 215 Perry Hill Road, Montgomery, AL 36109; tel. 334/272-4670

**\*Fox Army Health Center US Army Medical Dept Activity,** 4100 Goss Road, Huntsville, AL 35809-7000; tel. 256/955-8888

**\*Franklin Primary Health Center, Inc.,** 1303 Dr. Martin Luther King Jr. Avenue, Mobile, AL 36603; tel. 251/434-8188

**Glenwood, Inc.,** 150 Glenwood Lane, Birmingham, AL 35242; tel. 205/969-2880

**Hill Crest Behavioral Health Services,** 6869 Fifth Avenue South, Birmingham, AL 35212; tel. 205/833-9000

**Laurel Oaks Behavioral Health Center,** 700 East Cottonwood Road, Dothan, AL 36301; tel. 334/794-7373

**\*Lyster Army Health Clinic,** 301 Andrews Ave., Fort Rucker, AL 36362-5333; tel. 334/255-7609

**Magnolia Creek Treatment Center for Eating Disorders,** 645 Crenshaw Road, Columbiana, AL 35051; tel. 205/678-4373

**Mountain View Hospital,** PO Box 8406, Gadsden, AL 35902-8406; tel. 256/546-9265

**Southeast Alabama Medical Center,** PO Drawer 6987, Dothan, AL 36302-6987; tel. 334/793-8111

**\*Tuscaloosa VA Medical Center,** 3701 Loop Road East, Tuscaloosa, AL 35404; tel. 205/554-2000

**\*University of Alabama at Birmingham,** 619 19th Street South, Birmingham, AL 35249-1900; tel. 205/934-4444

**\*VA Medical Center,** 700 19th Street South, Birmingham, AL 35233; tel. 205/933-8101

### ALASKA

**\*Akeela, Inc.,** 360 W. Benson Boulevard, Anchorage, AK 99503; tel. 907/565-1200

**Alaska Children's Services Inc.,** 4600 Abbott Road, Anchorage, AK 99507-4314; tel. 907/346-2101

**\*Alaska VA Healthcare System,** 1201 N. Muldoon Road, Anchorage, AK 99504; tel. 907/257-5460

**Boys and Girls Home of Alaska, Inc.,** 3101 Lathrop Street, Fairbanks, AK 99701; tel. 907/459-4700

**\*Bristol Bay Area Health Corporation,** PO Box 130, Dillingham, AK 99576; tel. 907/842-5201

**\*Eastern Aleutian Tribes,** 3380 C Street, Suite #100, Anchorage, AK 99503; tel. 907/277-1440

**Frontline Hospital,** 2530 DeBarr Road, Anchorage, AK 99508-2948; tel. 907/258-7575

**Providence Adolescent Residential Treatment Program,** 3400 East 20th, Anchorage, AK 99508; tel. 907/272-2148

**\*Yukon Kuskokwim Delta Regional Hospital,** PO Box 287, Bethel, AK 99559; tel. 907/543-6300

### ARIZONA

**\*A Better Today Recovery Services,** 10609 N Hayden Rd. #E106, Scottsdale, AZ 85260; tel. 480/315-1140

**A New Leaf, Inc.,** 868 East University Drive, Mesa, AZ 85203; tel. 480/969-4024

**ANASAZI Foundation,** 1424 S. Stapley Dr., Mesa, AZ 85204; tel. 480/892-7403

**Aurora Behavioral Health System,** 6015 W Peoria Ave, Glendale, AZ 85302; tel. 623/344-4400

**\*Banner Behavioral Health Hospital,** 7575 E. Earll Drive, Scottsdale, AZ 85251; tel. 480/941-7500

**\*Banner Thunderbird Medical Center,** 5555 West Thunderbird Road, Glendale, AZ 85306; tel. 602/865-5555

**\*Chandler Valley Hope,** PO Box 1839, Chandler, AZ 85244-1839; tel. 602/899-3335

**\*Community Counseling Centers, Inc.,** 105 N. Fifth Ave., Holbrook, AZ 86025; tel. 928/524-6701

**Crisis Response Network of Southern Arizona, Inc.,** 2802 E. District Street, Tucson, AZ 85714; tel. 520/284-3501

**\*Desert Visions Youth Wellness Center,** PO Box 458, Sacaton, AZ 85147; tel. 520/562-3801

**Devereux/Arizona - Richard L. Raskin Treatment Network,** 11000 N Scottsdale Rd, Ste 260, Scottsdale, AZ 85254; tel. 480/998-2920

**\*Helping Associates, Inc.,** 1901 North Trekell Road, Ste A, Casa Grande, AZ 85122; tel. 520/836-1029

**\*Horizon Human Services, Inc.,** 210 East Cottonwood Lane, Casa Grande, AZ 85122; tel. 520/836-1688

**\*Little Colorado Behavioral Health Centers,** PO Box 579, Saint Johns, AZ 85936; tel. 928/337-4301

**Mingus Mountain Estate Residential Center, Inc.,** PO Box 26485, Prescott Valley, AZ 86312; tel. 602/335-2000

**\*Mohave Mental Health Clinic, Inc.,** 1743 Sycamore Avenue, Kingman, AZ 86409; tel. 928/757-8111

**Northern Arizona VA Health Care System,** 500 Highway 89 North, Prescott, AZ 86313; tel. 928/445-4860

**Parc Place,** 2190 North Grace Boulevard, Chandler, AZ 85225; tel. 480/917-9301

**\*Phoenix VA Health Care System,** 650 East Indian School Road, Phoenix, AZ 85012-1892; tel. 602/277-5551

**\*Pinal Hispanic Council,** 107 E. 4th Street, Eloy, AZ 85131; tel. 520/466-7765

**\*Raymond W. Bliss Army Health Center,** 2240 E. Winrow Avenue, Fort Huachuca, AZ 85613-7079; tel. 520/533-9026

**Recovery Innovations, Inc.,** 2701 N. 16th Street, Suite 316, Phoenix, AZ 85006; tel. 602/650-1212

**Remuda Ranch,** One East Apache Street, Wickenburg, AZ 85390; tel. 928/684-3913

**Rosewood Ranch L.P.,** 36075 South Rincon Road, Wickenburg, AZ 85390; tel. 928/684-9594

**\*Sierra Tucson, Inc.,** 39580 S. Lago del Oro Parkway, Tucson, AZ 85739; tel. 520/624-4000

**\*Southern Arizona Mental Health Corporation,** 2502 North Dodge Boulevard, Suite 190, Tucson, AZ 85716; tel. 520/617-0043

**\*Southern Arizona VA Health Care System,** 3601 South Sixth Avenue, Tucson, AZ 85723; tel. 520/629-1821

**\*St. Luke's Behavioral Hospital, LP,** 1800 East Van Buren, Phoenix, AZ 85006; tel. 602/251-8808

**\*The Guidance Center, Inc.,** 2187 N. Vickey St., Flagstaff, AZ 86004; tel. 928/527-1899

**\*The Meadows of Wickenburg, Inc.,** 1655 North Tegner, Wickenburg, AZ 85390; tel. 928/684-3926

**The New Foundation,** 1200 North 77th Street, Scottsdale, AZ 85257; tel. 480/945-3302

**\*The River Source Treatment,** 950 N. Arizola Road Suite 3, Casa Grande, AZ 85122; tel. 480/735-8346

**\*The Sundance Center,** 12816 E. Turquoise Avenue, Scottsdale, AZ 85259; tel. 480/773-7329

**Touchstone Behavioral Health,** 15648 N. 35th Ave, Phoenix, AZ 85053; tel. 623/930-8705

**UBH of Phoenix LLC,** 3550 East Pinchot, Phoenix, AZ 85018; tel. 940/320-8994

**Urgent Psychiatric Center,** 903 North 2nd Street, Phoenix, AZ 85004-1906; tel. 602/416-7600

**\*Verde Valley Guidance Clinic, Inc.,** 8 East Cottonwood Street, Cottonwood, AZ 86326; tel. 928/634-2236

**\*West Yavapai Guidance Clinic,** 3343 Windsong Drive, Prescott Valley, AZ 86314; tel. 928/583-6411

**Youth Development Institute,** 1830 East Roosevelt Street, Phoenix, AZ 85006; tel. 602/256-5300

### ARKANSAS

**Amicare of Arkansas,** 4253 Crossover Road, Fayetteville, AR 72703; tel. 479/587-1408

**\*Baptist Health Medical Center - Little Rock,** 9601 Interstate 630, Exit 7, Little Rock, AR 72205-7299; tel. 501/202-2000

**BHC Pinnacle Pointe Hospital, Inc.,** 11501 Financial Centre Parkway, Little Rock, AR 72211; tel. 501/223-3322

**Bokker Enterprises,** P.O. Box 176, Cherokee Village, AR 72525; tel. 870/257-3336

**\*Central Arkansas Veterans Healthcare System,** 4300 West Seventh Street (00/LR), Little Rock, AR 72205; tel. 501/257-5314

**Community Counseling Services, Inc.,** 125 Dons Way, Hot Springs National Park, AR 71913; tel. 501/624-7111

**Cornerstone Community Counseling Corp.,** 609 W 3rd Street, Imboden, AR 72434; tel. 870/869-1500

**Counseling and Education Center, Inc.,** 406 Pecan Street, Helena, AR 72342; tel. 870/338-8447

**Delta Counseling Associates, Inc.,** 790 Roberts Drive, Monticello, AR 71655; tel. 870/367-9732

**Delta Family Health and Fitness Center for Children, Inc.,** 815 East St. Louis Street, Hamburg, AR 71646; tel. 870/853-4224

**Families, Inc. of Arkansas,** 1815 Pleasant Grove Road, Jonesboro, AR 72401; tel. 870/933-6886

**Habilitation Centers, Inc.,** PO Box 727, Fordyce, AR 71742; tel. 870/352-8203

**Hometown Behavioral Health Services of Arkansas, Inc,** PO Box 299, Hoxie, AR 72433; tel. 870/886-1333

**Inspiration Day Treatment, INC,** 1014 Autumn Road Suite 4, Little Rock, AR 72211; tel. 501/221-1941

*Indicates organization is a Joint Commission accredited Chemical Dependency organization.

**\*Life Strategies Counseling, Inc.,** 1217 Stone Street, Jonesboro, AR 72401; tel. 870/972-1268

**Life Strategies of Arkansas, LLC,** 703 Calvin Avery Drive, West Memphis, AR 72301; tel. 870/732-1878

**Living Hope Southeast, LLC,** 100 South University, Suite 401, Little Rock, AR 72205; tel. 501/663-5473

**Maxus, Inc.,** 1033 Old Burr Road, Warm Springs, AR 72478; tel. 870/647-1400

**NeuroRestorative Timber Ridge,** PO Box 208, Benton, AR 72018; tel. 501/594-5211

**\*Ozark Guidance Center, Inc.,** PO Box 6430, Springdale, AR 72766-6430; tel. 479/750-2020

**Texarkana Behavioral Associates, L.C.,** 4253 Crossover Road, Fayetteville, AR 72703; tel. 479/521-5731

**\*The BridgeWay, Inc.,** 21 BridgeWay Road, North Little Rock, AR 72113; tel. 501/771-1500

**\*The Centers for Youth and Families,** P.O. Box 251970, Little Rock, AR 72225-1970; tel. 501/666-8686

**The Logan Centers, Inc.,** 1766 Killough Rd, Wynne, AR 72396; tel. 870/494-4600

**Trinity Behavioral Health Care System, Inc.,** 1033 Old Burr Road, Warm Springs, AR 72478; tel. 870/647-1400

**United Methodist Behavioral Hospital,** 1601 Murphy Drive, Maumelle, AR 72113; tel. 501/803-3388

**\*United Methodist Children's Home, Inc..,** PO Box 56050, Little Rock, AR 72215; tel. 501/661-0720

**\*University of Arkansas for Medical Sciences,** 4301 W. Markham, Slot 554, Little Rock, AR 72205; tel. 501/526-8100

**Valley Behavioral Health System LLC,** 10301 Mayo Drive, Barling, AR 72923; tel. 479/494-5000

**\*Veterans Health Care System of the Ozarks,** 1100 North College Avenue, Fayetteville, AR 72703; tel. 479/444-5000

**Woodridge Behavioral Care,** 603 Kittle Road, Forrest City, AR 72335; tel. 870/633-3200

**Youth Home, Inc.,** 20400 Colonel Glenn Road, Little Rock, AR 72210-5323; tel. 501/821-5500

**CALIFORNIA**

**\*Action Family Counseling, Inc.,** 26893 Bouquet Canyon Road, Suite C-134, Santa Clarita, CA 91350; tel. 661/297-6644

**\*Adolescent Growth, Inc.,** 6323 Zindell Avenue, Commerce, CA 90040; tel. 323/948-9998

**Alameda County Medical Center,** 1411 E. 31 Street, Oakland, CA 94602; tel. 510/437-4943

**AltaMed Health Services Corporation,** 2040 Canfield Avenue, Los Angeles, CA 90040; tel. 323/725-8751

**Aspiranet,** 400 Oyster Point Boulevard, Suite #501, South San Francisco, CA 94080; tel. 650/866-4080

**\*Associates in Counseling & Mediation,** 265 S. Anita Drive - Suite 117, Orange, CA 92868; tel. 714/978-1090

**\*Aurora Behavioral Health Care/ Las Encinas Hospital,** 2900 East Del Mar Boulevard, Pasadena, CA 91107; tel. 626/795-9901

**\*Aurora Behavioral Health Care/ San Diego,** 11878 Avenue of Industry, San Diego, CA 92128; tel. 858/487-3200

**\*Aurora Charter Oak - Los Angeles, L.L.C.,** 1161 East Covina Boulevard, Covina, CA 91724; tel. 626/966-1632

**Berkeley Addiction Treatment Services, Inc.,** 2975 Sacramento Street, Berkeley, CA 94702; tel. 510/644-0200

**\*Betty Ford Center,** 39000 Bob Hope Drive, Rancho Mirage, CA 92270; tel. 760/773-4100

**\*BHC Alhambra Hospital,** 4619 North Rosemead Boulevard, Rosemead, CA 91770; tel. 626/286-1191

**\*BHC Fremont Hospital,** 39001 Sundale Drive, Fremont, CA 94538; tel. 510/796-1100

**BHC Heritage Oaks Hospital,** 4250 Auburn Boulevard, Sacramento, CA 95841; tel. 916/489-3336

**\*BHC Sierra Vista Hospital,** 8001 Bruceville Road, Sacramento, CA 95823; tel. 916/288-0300

**California Department of Corrections - CIW 45 Bed PIP,** 9838 Old Placerville Rd, Suite B, Sacramento, CA 95827; tel. 916/255-3313

**California Institution for Women,** P.O. Box 6000, Corona, CA 92878-6000; tel. 909/597-1771

**California Transition Center For Care of Combat Veterans,** 100 California Drive, Yountville, CA 94599; tel. 707/948-3028

**\*Casa Palmera Care Center, Inc.,** 14750 El Camino Real, Del Mar, CA 92014; tel. 858/481-4411

**Castlewood West Treatment Center,** 213 Seventeen Mile Drive, Pacific Grove, CA 93950; tel. 831/718-9595

**Cedars-Sinai Medical Center,** 8700 Beverly Blvd., Los Angeles, CA 90048; tel. 310/423-5191

**CHCM, Inc,** 301 Victoria Street, Costa Mesa, CA 92627; tel. 949/642-2734

**\*Children's Hospital Los Angeles,** 4650 W Sunset Blvd, MS #1, Los Angeles, CA 90027; tel. 323/660-4503

**\*Cliffside Malibu,** 30060 Andromeda Lane, Malibu, CA 90265; tel. 310/589-2800

**\*Clinica Sierra Vista,** PO BOX 1559, Bakersfield, CA 93302-1559; tel. 661/635-3050

**College Hospital,** 10802 College Place, Cerritos, CA 90703; tel. 562/924-9581

**Community Hospital of San Bernardino,** 1805 Medical Center Drive, San Bernardino, CA 92411-1288; tel. 909/887-6333

**\*Community Recovery Inc,** 5756 Melrose, Los Angeles, CA 90038; tel. 818/635-9380

**\*Cornerstone of Southern California,** 13682 Yorba Street, Tustin, CA 92780; tel. 714/730-5399

**Corona Regional Medical Center, Inc.,** 800 South Main Street, Corona, CA 92882; tel. 951/737-4343

**Del Amo Hospital,** 23700 Camino Del Sol, Torrance, CA 90505; tel. 310/530-1151

**\*Discovery Practice Management, Inc,** 4281 Katella Ave, Suite 111, Los Alamitos, CA 90720; tel. 714/981-0700

**\*Dual Diagnosis Treatment Center Inc,** 209 Avenida Fabricante, San Clemente, CA 92672; tel. 949/369-1300

**\*El Camino Hospital,** 2500 Grant Ave, Mountain View, CA 94040; tel. 650/940-7300

**\*Focus Healthcare of California, LLC,** 2221 Fair Oaks Blvd., Sacramento, CA 95825; tel. 916/514-8500

**\*Glendale Adventist Medical Center,** 1509 Wilson Terrace, Glendale, CA 91206; tel. 818/409-8000

**GOALS For Women: African American Family Counseling Center,** 1331 Garden Highway, Sacramento, CA 95833; tel. 510/334-0003

**\*Good Samaritan Hospital,** 901 Olive Drive, Bakersfield, CA 93308; tel. 661/215-7500

**\*Good Samaritan Hospital, LP,** 2425 Samaritan Drive, San Jose, CA 95124; tel. 408/559-2011

**HAART- Oakland,** 10850 MacArthur Boulevard Suite 200, Oakland, CA 94605; tel. 510/875-2300

**HAART-Hayward,** 20094 Mission Boulevard, Hayward, CA 94541; tel. 510/727-9755

**Hathaway-Sycamores Child and Family Services,** 210 South De Lacey Avenue, Suite 110, Pasadena, CA 91105; tel. 626/395-7100

**\*Helix Healthcare, Inc.,** 7050 Parkway Drive, La Mesa, CA 91942; tel. 619/465-4411

**\*Huntington Memorial Hospital,** PO Box 7013, Pasadena, CA 91109-7013; tel. 626/397-5555

**\*John Muir Behavioral Health,** 2740 Grant Street, Concord, CA 94520; tel. 925/674-4100

**Kaiser Foundation Hospital - Los Angeles Medical Center,** 4733 Sunset Blvd., Los Angeles, CA 90027; tel. 323/783-8101

**\*Knollwood Psychiatric and Chemical Dependency Hospital,** 5900 Brockton Avenue, Riverside, CA 92506; tel. 951/275-8400

**La Palma Intercommunity Hospital,** 7901 Walker Street, La Palma, CA 90623; tel. 714/670-7400

**Langley Porter Psychiatric Hospital and Clinics - UCSF,** 401 Parnassus Avenue, HOS 0984, San Francisco, CA 94143-0984; tel. 415/476-7000

**Lionrock Behavioral Health, Inc.,** 2685 Marine Way, Ste 1217, Mountain View, CA 94043; tel. 760/994-4990

**\*Loma Linda University Behavioral Medicine Center,** 1710 Barton Road, Redlands, CA 92373; tel. 909/558-9204

**Marin General Hospital,** 250 Bon Air Road, Greenbrae, CA 94904; tel. 415/925-7000

**\*Mills-Peninsula Health Services,** 1501 Trousdale Drive, Burlingame, CA 94010; tel. 650/696-5270

**Mission Community Hospital,** 14850 Roscoe Boulevard, Panorama City, CA 91402; tel. 818/904-3685

**\*Mission Hospital Regional Medical Center,** 27700 Medical Center Road, Mission Viejo, CA 92691; tel. 949/365-2248

**Monte Nido Residential Center, Inc.,** 514 Live Oak Circle, Calabasas, CA 91302; tel. 310/457-9958

**MU'EED Incorporated,** PO Box 276372, Sacramento, CA 95827; tel. 916/486-1737

**Northridge Hospital Medical Center,** 18300 Roscoe Boulevard, Northridge, CA 91328; tel. 818/885-5321

**Oak Grove Insutute Foundation, Inc.,** 24275 Jefferson Avenue, Murrieta, CA 92562; tel. 951/677-5599

**Opioid Replacement Treatment Prog., Dept of Veterans Affairs,** 525 21st Street, Oakland, CA 94612; tel. 510/587-3434

**Optimum Performance Institute,** 3080 Eucalyptus Hill Road, Santa Barbara, CA 93108; tel. 818/610-3956

**OTP Los Angeles Ambulatory Care Center,** 11301 Wilshire Blvd. Bldg.500, Rm.6404, Los Angeles, CA 90073; tel. 310/268-3132

**\*Pacifica Recovery Services,** P O Box 2041, Upland, CA 91785; tel. 909/447-5081

**Palomar Medical Center,** 2185 Citracado Parkway, Escondido, CA 92029; tel. 442/281-1006

**\*Passages,** 241 Market Street, Port Hueneme, CA 93041; tel. 805/283-4737

**Prime Healthcare Paradise Valley LLC.,** 2400 East Fourth Street, National City, CA 91950-2099; tel. 619/470-4115

**\*Principles Inc.,** PO Box 93607, Pasadena, CA 91103; tel. 626/798-0884

**Puente de Vida,** P.O. Box 86020, San Diego, CA 92138; tel. 858/452-3915

**\*R House, Inc.,** P.O. Box 2587, Santa Rosa, CA 95405; tel. 707/571-2215

**Redlands Community Hospital,** 350 Terracina Boulevard, Redlands, CA 92373; tel. 909/335-5500

**River Oak Center for Children,** 5030 El Camino Avenue, Carmichael, CA 95608; tel. 916/609-5100

**Saint Francis Memorial Hospital,** 900 Hyde Street, San Francisco, CA 94109; tel. 415/353-6000

**\*Santa Barbara Cottage Hospital,** PO Box 689, Santa Barbara, CA 93102; tel. 805/569-7404

**Santa Rosa Memorial Hospital,** 1165 Montgomery Drive, Santa Rosa, CA 95405; tel. 707/522-1520

**Scripps Mercy Hospital,** 4077 Fifth Avenue- MER 1, San Diego, CA 92103; tel. 619/294-8111

**Seneca Family of Agencies,** 2275 Arlington Drive, San Leandro, CA 94578; tel. 510/654-4004

**Sepulveda CA VAH Opioid Treatment Program,** 11301 Wilshire Blvd. Bldg.500, Rm.6404, Los Angeles, CA 90073; tel. 310/268-3132

**\*Sharp Mesa Vista Hospital,** 7850 Vista Hill Avenue, San Diego, CA 92123; tel. 858/278-4110

**\*Soba Living LLC,** 22669 Pacific Coast Highway, Malibu, CA 90265; tel. 310/924-2053

**\*Spencer Recovery Centers, Inc.,** PO Box 9296, Laguna Beach, CA 92652; tel. 949/376-3705

**St. Helena Hospital Center for Behavioral Health,** 525 Oregon Street, Vallejo, CA 94590; tel. 707/648-2200

**\*St. Joseph Hospital,** 1100 West Stewart Drive, Orange, CA 92863-5600; tel. 714/771-8000

**St. Mary Medical Center,** 1050 Linden Avenue, Long Beach, CA 90813; tel. 562/491-9000

**St. Mary's Medical Center,** 450 Stanyan Street, San Francisco, CA 94117; tel. 415/668-1000

**Stewart & Lynda Resnick Neuropsychiatric Hospital at UCLA,** 150 Medical Plaza 4230C, MC 746330, Los Angeles, CA 90095; tel. 310/267-9092

**Success Healthcare 1, LLC,** 1711 W. Temple Street, Los Angeles, CA 90026; tel. 213/989-6100

**Summit Eating Disorders and Outreach Program,** 3610 American River Drive, Suite 140, Sacramento, CA 95864; tel. 916/574-1000

**Sutter Center for Psychiatry,** 7700 Folsom Blvd, Sacramento, CA 95826; tel. 916/386-3000

**Sutter East Bay Hospitals,** 2450 Ashby Avenue, Berkeley, CA 94705; tel. 510/204-2606

**Sutter Medical Center, Sacramento,** 2801 L Street, Sacramento, CA 95816; tel. 916/454-2222

**\*Tarzana Treatment Centers, Inc.,** 18646 Oxnard Street, Tarzana, CA 91356; tel. 818/654-3815

**Tessie Cleveland Community Services Corp.,** 8019 S COMPTON AVENUE, Los Angeles, CA 90001; tel. 323/586-7333

**\*The Discovery House Residential Treatment,** 847 Barton Ave, Camarillo, CA 93010; tel. 805/228-2826

**The Huntington Beach Hospital,** 17772 Beach Boulevard, Huntington Beach, CA 92647; tel. 714/843-5000

**\*Therapeutic Solutions,** 3255 Esplanade, Chico, CA 95973; tel. 530/899-3150

---

\*Indicates organization is a Joint Commission accredited Chemical Dependency organization.

Section C

*Twin Town Corp., 4388 E. Katella Ave, Los Alamitos, CA 90720; tel. 562/594–8844

*VA Central California Health Care System, 2615 East Clinton Avenue, Fresno, CA 93703; tel. 559/225–6100

*VA Greater Los Angeles Healthcare System, 11301 Wilshire Boulevard, Los Angeles, CA 90073; tel. 310/268–3132

*VA Loma Linda Healthcare System, 11201 Benton Street, Loma Linda, CA 92357; tel. 909/583–6002

*VA Long Beach Health Care System, 5901 East Seventh Street, Long Beach, CA 90822; tel. 562/826–5400

*VA Northern California Health Care System, 10535 Hospital Way, Mather, CA 95655; tel. 916/843–7000

*VA Palo Alto Health Care System, 3801 Miranda Avenue, Palo Alto, CA 94304; tel. 650/493–5000

*VA San Diego Healthcare System, 3350 La Jolla Village Drive, San Diego, CA 92161; tel. 858/552–8585

VAMC-San Francisco Substance Abuse Treatment Clinic, 4150 Clement Street, Bldg 1, San Francisco, CA 94121; tel. 415/750–2050

Vista Del Mar Child and Family Services, 3200 Motor Avenue, Los Angeles, CA 90034; tel. 310/836–1223

West Anaheim Medical Center, 3033 West Orange Avenue, Anaheim, CA 92804; tel. 714/229–4000

West Los Angeles Drug Treatment Services, 11301 Wilshire Blvd, Bldg.500, Rm.6404, Los Angeles, CA 90073; tel. 310/268–3132

*West Oakland Health Council, 700 Adeline Street, Oakland, CA 94607; tel. 510/835–9610

Western Medical Center Anaheim, 1025 S. Anaheim Boulevard, Anaheim, CA 92805-0880; tel. 714/533–6220

Westside Community Mental Health, Inc., 1153 Oak Street, San Francisco, CA 94117; tel. 415/563–8200

Wynspring Family Resource Center, 2755 Cottage Way, Ste 16, Sacramento, CA 95825; tel. 916/480–0280

**COLORADO**

*Adolescent and Family Institute of Colorado, Inc., 10001 West 32nd Avenue, Wheat Ridge, CO 80033; tel. 303/238–1231

*AspenPointe Health Services, 525 N. Cascade Avenue, Suite 100, Colorado Springs, CO 80903; tel. 719/572–6100

*Cedar Springs Hospital, Inc., 2135 Southgate Road, Colorado Springs, CO 80906; tel. 719/633–4114

Children's Hospital Colorado, 13123 East 16th Avenue, Aurora, CO 80045; tel. 720/777–1234

Comprehensive Addiction Treatment Services, 2222 East 18Th Ave, Unit C, Denver, CO 80206; tel. 303/394–2714

Denver Health and Hospital Authority, 777 Bannock Street, Denver, CO 80204; tel. 303/436–5690

Devereux Cleo Wallace, 8405 Church Ranch Blvd, Westminster, CO 80021; tel. 303/466–7391

Eating Disorder Center of Denver, 950 S. Cherry Suite 1010, Denver, CO 80246; tel. 303/771–0861

Eating Recovery Center, LLC, 1830 Franklin Street Suite 500, Denver, CO 80218; tel. 303/825–8584

El Pueblo Boys' & Girls' Ranch, Inc., One El Pueblo Ranch Way, Pueblo, CO 81006; tel. 719/544–7496

*Evans Army Community Hospital, 1650 Cochrane Circle, BLDG 7500, Colorado Springs, CO 80913-4604; tel. 719/526–7500

Forest Heights Lodge, PO Box 789, Evergreen, CO 80437-0789; tel. 303/674–6681

*Grand Junction Veterans Affairs Medical Center, 2121 North Avenue, Grand Junction, CO 81501; tel. 970/242–0731

*Parker Valley Hope, PO Box 670, Parker, CO 80134; tel. 303/841–7857

*Parkview Medical Center, Medical Staff Services 400 West 16th Street, Pueblo, CO 81003; tel. 719/584–4000

*Porter Adventist Hospital, 2525 South Downing Street, Denver, CO 80210; tel. 303/778–1955

*Poudre Valley Hospital, 1024 South Lemay Avenue, Fort Collins, CO 80524-3998; tel. 970/495–7000

SBH Colorado, LLC, 7353 Sisters Grove, Colorado Springs, CO 80923; tel. 719/444–8484

Southern Peaks Regional Treatment Center, 700 Four Mile Parkway, Canon City, CO 81212; tel. 719/276–7500

*University of Colorado Hospital Authority, 12401 E. 17th Avenue, F448, Aurora, CO 80045; tel. 720/848–7800

*VA Eastern Colorado Healthcare System, 1055 Clermont St, Denver, CO 80220; tel. 303/399–8020

VCPHCS X, LLC dba The Boulder Clinic, Inc, 1317 Spruce Street, Boulder, CO 80302; tel. 303/245–0123

VCPHCS XI, LLC dba North Denver Behavioral Health Center, 7290 Samuel Drive, Ste 110, Denver, CO 80221; tel. 303/487–7776

VCPHCS XII, LLC dba Downtown Denver Behavioral Health Center, 1337 Delaware St., First Floor, Denver, CO 80204; tel. 303/629–5293

**CONNECTICUT**

Albert J. Solnit Children's Center - South Campus, 915 River Road, Middletown, CT 06457; tel. 860/704–4000

Blue Hills Substance Abuse Services, 500 Vine Street, Hartford, CT 06112-1639; tel. 860/666–7665

Bridgeport Hospital, 267 Grant Street, Bridgeport, CT 06610; tel. 203/384–3000

*Bristol Hospital, Inc., PO Box 977, Bristol, CT 06011-0977; tel. 860/585–3222

Capitol Region Mental Health Center, 500 Vine Street, Hartford, CT 06112; tel. 860/297–0903

*Community Health Resources, Inc., 995 Day Hill Road, Windsor, CT 06095; tel. 860/731–5522

Community Health Resources: CPAS Division, 391 Pomfret Street, Putnam, CT 06260; tel. 860/731–5522

*Community Mental Health Affiliates, Inc., 270 John Downey Drive, New Britain, CT 06051; tel. 860/826–1358

*Community Renewal Team, 555 Windsor Street, Hartford, CT 06120; tel. 860/761–7904

*Connecticut Mental Health Center, 34 Park Street, New Haven, CT 06519; tel. 203/974–7300

*Connecticut Valley Hospital, PO Box 351, Middletown, CT 06457-7023; tel. 860/262–5887

Connecticut Valley Hospital-Addiction Services Div.-Merritt, PO Box 351, Middletown, CT 06457-7023; tel. 860/262–5887

Cornell Scott-Hill Health Corporation, 400 Columbus Avenue, New Haven, CT 06519; tel. 203/503–3000

*Hartford Community Mental Health Center, Inc., 2550 Main Street, Hartford, CT 06120; tel. 860/548–0101

*Hartford Hospital, 80 Seymour Street, Hartford, CT 06102-5037; tel. 860/545–2100

InterCommunity, Inc, 281 Main Street, East Hartford, CT 06118; tel. 860/569–5900

John Dempsey Hospital, 263 Farmington Avenue, Farmington, CT 06030-3802; tel. 860/679–2233

Klingberg Family Centers, Inc., 370 Linwood Street, New Britain, CT 06052; tel. 860/224–9113

Lawrence & Memorial Hospital, 365 Montauk Avenue, New London, CT 06320; tel. 860/442–0711

Manchester Memorial Hospital, 71 Haynes Street, Manchester, CT 06040; tel. 860/646–1222

*Middlesex Hospital, 28 Crescent Street, Middletown, CT 06457; tel. 860/358–6000

*Natchaug Hospital, Inc., 189 Storrs Road, Mansfield Center, CT 06250; tel. 860/456–1311

New Era Rehabilitation Center, 3851 Main Street, 2nd floor, Bridgeport, CT 06606; tel. 203/372–3333

*Perception Programs, Inc., PO Box 407, Willimantic, CT 06226; tel. 860/450–7122

River Valley Services, PO Box 351, Middletown, CT 06457; tel. 860/262–5200

*Rushford Center, Inc., 883 Paddock Avenue, Meriden, CT 06450; tel. 203/235–1792

Saint Francis Hospital & Medical Center - 8 West Unit, 500 Blue Hills Avenue, Hartford, CT 06112; tel. 860/714–2333

*Silver Hill Hospital, 208 Valley Road, New Canaan, CT 06840; tel. 203/801–2297

South Central Rehabilitation Center, 232 Cedar Street, New Haven, CT 06519; tel. 203/503–3356

*Southwest Community Health Center, Inc., 968 Fairfield Avenue, Bridgeport, CT 06605; tel. 203/332–3506

Southwest Connecticut Mental Health System, 97 Middle St., Bridgeport, CT 06604; tel. 203/579–7368

St. Vincent's Medical Center, 2800 Main Street, Bridgeport, CT 06606; tel. 203/576–5473

State of CT DMHAS - Southeastern Mental Health Authority, 401 West Thames Street, Bldg. 301, Norwich, CT 06360; tel. 860/859–4674

*Stonington Behavioral Health, Inc., 75 Swantown Hill Road, North Stonington, CT 06359; tel. 860/535–1010

The Charlotte Hungerford Hospital, PO Box 988, Torrington, CT 06790; tel. 860/496–6666

*The Children's Center of Hamden, Inc., 1400 Whitney Avenue, Hamden, CT 06517; tel. 203/248–2116

The Danbury Hospital, 24 Hospital Avenue, Danbury, CT 06810; tel. 203/739–7000

*The Hospital of Central Connecticut, PO Box 100, New Britain, CT 06050-0100; tel. 860/224–5666

*The Waterbury Hospital, 64 Robbins Street, Waterbury, CT 06721; tel. 203/573–6000

The Wellspring Foundation, Inc., 21 Arch Bridge Road, Bethlehem, CT 06751; tel. 203/266–8000

*The Wheeler Clinic, 91 Northwest Drive, Plainville, CT 06062; tel. 860/793–3500

The William W. Backus Hospital, 326 Washington Street, Norwich, CT 06360; tel. 860/823–6399

*United Services, Inc., 1007 North Main Street, Dayville, CT 06241; tel. 860/774–2020

*VA Connecticut Healthcare System, 950 Campbell Avenue, West Haven, CT 06516; tel. 203/932–5711

Western Connecticut Mental Health Network, 55 West Main Street, Suite 410, Waterbury, CT 06702; tel. 203/805–6400

Yale - New Haven Hospital, 20 York Street, New Haven, CT 06510-3203; tel. 203/688–4242

Yale Health, P.O. Box 208237, New Haven, CT 06520; tel. 203/432–4096

**DELAWARE**

*Brandywine Counseling & Community Services, 2500 West Fourth Street, Wilmington, DE 19805; tel. 302/472–0381

Brandywine Counseling & Community Services, South Chapel, 24 Brookhill Drive, Newark, DE 19702; tel. 302/454–3020

Brandywine Counseling & Community Services, Lancaster, 2713 Lancaster Avenue, Wilmington, DE 19805; tel. 302/656–2347

Christiana Care -Christiana Hospital, 4755 Ogletown-Stanton Road, Newark, DE 19718; tel. 302/733–1580

Delaware Guidance Services for Children and Youth, Inc., 1213 Delaware Avenue, Wilmington, DE 19806; tel. 302/652–3948

*Gateway Foundation Delaware City Treatment Center, P.O. Box 547, Delaware City, DE 19706; tel. 312/663–1130

Meadow Wood Behavioral Health System, 575 South DuPont Highway, New Castle, DE 19720; tel. 302/328–3330

Rockford Center, 100 Rockford Drive, Newark, DE 19713; tel. 302/996–5480

*SODAT - Delaware, Inc., 625 N. Orange Street, Wilmington, DE 19801; tel. 302/656–4044

*Thresholds, Inc., 20505 DuPont Boulevard, Suite 1, Georgetown, DE 19947; tel. 302/856–1835

*UHS of Dover, LLC, 725 Horsepond Road, Dover, DE 19901; tel. 302/741–0140

*VA Medical Center, 1601 Kirkwood Highway, Wilmington, DE 19805; tel. 302/994–2511

**DISTRICT OF COLUMBIA**

McClendon Center, 1313 New York Avenue, NW, Washington, DC 20005; tel. 202/737–6191

*MedStar Washington Hospital Center, 110 Irving St, NW, Washington, DC 20010; tel. 202/877–7000

The Episcopal Center for Children, 5901 Utah Avenue, NW, Washington, DC 20015-1616; tel. 202/363–1333

The HSC Pediatric Center, 1731 Bunker Hill Road, Northeast, Washington, DC 20017; tel. 202/832–4400

*The Psychiatric Institute of Washington, 4228 Wisconsin Avenue, Northwest, Washington, DC 20016; tel. 202/885–5600

*VA Medical Center, 50 Irving Street, Northwest, Washington, DC 20422; tel. 202/745–8000

**FLORIDA**

ABC's for Success, LLC, 1550 South Dixie Highway Suite 214, Coral Gables, FL 33146; tel. 786/536–9714

*Alpha Health Care Clinic, Inc., 1990 NE 163rd Street Suite 102, North Miami Beach, FL 33162; tel. 305/945–9906

---

*Indicates organization is a Joint Commission accredited Chemical Dependency organization.

**Alternate Family Care, Inc.,** 10001 W Oakland Park Blvd, Suite 200, Sunrise, FL 33351; tel. 954/746–5200

***Alternative Treatment International, Inc.,** 2120 Range Rd, Clearwater, FL 33765; tel. 727/796–3719

***Ambrosia Treatment Center,** 2626 Lake Drive, West Palm Beach, FL 33404; tel. 772/323–2099

***Apalachee Center, Inc.,** 2634-J Capital Circle NE, Tallahassee, FL 32308; tel. 850/523–3333

***Atlantic Shores Hospital,** 4545 North Federal Highway, Fort Lauderdale, FL 33308; tel. 954/771–2711

***Bay Pines VA Healthcare System,** 10000 Bay Pines Boulevard, Bay Pines, FL 33744; tel. 727/398–6661

***Beachcomber Rehab, Inc.,** 4493 North Ocean Boulevard, Delray Beach, FL 33483; tel. 561/276–6226

***Behavioral Health of the Palm Beaches, Inc.,** 3153 Canada Court, Lake Worth, FL 33461; tel. 561/465–1014

**Behavioral Support Services, Inc.,** 315 N. Lakemont Avenue, Suite B, Winter Park, FL 32792; tel. 407/830–6412

***Broward Addiction Recovery Center (BARC) Division,** 1011 SW 2nd Court, Fort Lauderdale, FL 33312; tel. 954/357–4860

**Broward Center for Mental Health, PA.,** 3127 West Hallandale Beach Blvd. Suite 115, Hallandale, FL 33009; tel. 754/816–3071

***Center for Alcohol & Drug Studies, Inc.,** 7613 Lake Worth Road, Lake Worth, FL 33467; tel. 561/465–1100

**Central Florida Treatment Center - Ft. Pierce Clinic,** 1302 Lawnwood Circle, Suite B, Fort Pierce, FL 34950; tel. 772/468–6800

**CFSATC, Inc.,** 1800 West Colonial Drive, Orlando, FL 32804; tel. 407/843–0041

**CFSATC, Inc. - Cocoa,** 7 North Cocoa Boulevard, Cocoa, FL 32922; tel. 321/631–4578

**CFSATC, Inc. - Lake Worth,** 3155 Lake Worth Road Suite #2, Lake Worth, FL 33461; tel. 561/439–8440

**CFSATC, Inc. - Palm Bay,** 2198 Harris Avenue, Palm Bay, FL 32905; tel. 321/951–9750

***Circles of Care, Inc.,** 400 East Sheridan Road, Melbourne, FL 32901-3184; tel. 321/984–4900

***Citrus Health Network, Inc,** 4175 West 20th Avenue, Hialeah, FL 33012; tel. 305/424–3100

***Coastal Behavioral Healthcare, Inc.,** 1565 State Street, Sarasota, FL 34236; tel. 941/927–8900

**Coastal Mental Health Services, Inc.,** 2750 Enterprise Road, Orange City, FL 32763; tel. 800/614–4124

***Community Health of South Florida, Inc.,** 10300 S.W. 216 Street, Miami, FL 33190; tel. 305/252–4853

**Comprehensive Psychiatric Center,** 9735 East Fern Street, Miami, FL 33157; tel. 305/238–5121

**Comprehensive Psychiatric Center North,** 240 Northwest 183rd Street, Miami, FL 33169; tel. 305/651–2332

**Comprehensive Psychiatric Center-Central,** 4790 N. W. 7th Street Suite #101 & 102, Miami, FL 33126; tel. 305/529–5810

***Dade Family Counseling Community Mental Health Center,** 4343 West Flagler Street Suite 100, Miami, FL 33134; tel. 305/774–9570

***David Lawrence Center,** 6075 Bathey Lane, Naples, FL 34116; tel. 239/455–8500

***Destination Hope, Inc.,** 6555 NW 9th Ave. Suite 214, Fort Lauderdale, FL 33309; tel. 954/771–2091

***EBH Acquisition Subsidiary, Inc.,** 3100 E. Commercial Blvd., Fort Lauderdale, FL 33308; tel. 954/200–8308

**ESP Case Management Professionals, Inc,** 345 Beville Road Ste. 106, Daytona Beach, FL 32119-2147; tel. 386/760–7533

**Fair Oaks Pavilion at Delray Medical Center,** 5352 Linton Boulevard, Delray Beach, FL 33484; tel. 561/495–3278

***Fairwinds Treatment Center,** 1569 S Fort Harrison Avenue, Clearwater, FL 33756; tel. 727/449–0300

***Family Resource Center of South Florida, Inc.,** 155 South Miami Ave. Suite 400, Miami, FL 33130-1617; tel. 305/374–6006

***Florida Center for Recovery,** 3451 West Midway Road, Fort Pierce, FL 34981; tel. 772/460–2777

**Florida Hospital Zephyrhills,** 7050 Gall Boulevard, Zephyrhills, FL 33541; tel. 813/788–0411

**Florida Institute for Neurologic Rehabilitation, Inc,** PO Box 1348, Wauchula, FL 33873; tel. 863/773–2857

***Focus Healthcare of Florida,** 5960 Southwest 106th Avenue, Cooper City, FL 33328; tel. 954/680–2700

***Fort Lauderdale Hospital Management, LLC,** 1601 East Las Olas Boulevard, Fort Lauderdale, FL 33301; tel. 954/463–4321

***G&G Healthcare Services, LLC,** 1590 NE 162nd Street Suite 200, North Miami Beach, FL 33162; tel. 305/945–8384

**Geo Care, Inc. / Treasure Coast Forensic Treatment Center,** 96 SW Allapattah Road, Indiantown, FL 34956; tel. 772/597–9400

**Gulf Coast Treatment Center,** 1015 Mar Walt Drive, Fort Walton Beach, FL 32547; tel. 850/863–4160

**Halifax Health,** PO Box 2830, Daytona Beach, FL 32120-9718; tel. 386/425–4773

***Hanley Center,** 933 45th Street, West Palm Beach, FL 33407-2374; tel. 561/841–1000

***HealthCare Connection of Tampa, Inc.,** 825 West Linebaugh Avenue, Tampa, FL 33612; tel. 813/931–5560

***Hendry Glades Mental Health Clinic, Inc.,** 601 West Alverdez Avenue, Clewiston, FL 33440; tel. 863/983–1423

**Hollywood Pavilion, LLC,** 1201 North 37th Avenue, Hollywood, FL 33021; tel. 954/962–1355

**Homestead Behavioral Health Clinic,** 654 NE 9th Place, Homestead, FL 33030; tel. 305/248–3488

***Jackson Memorial Hospital,** 1611 Northwest 12th Avenue, Miami, FL 33136-1094; tel. 305/585–1111

***Jackson North Community Mental Health Center,** 20201 NW 37th Ave, Opa Locka, FL 33056; tel. 786/466–2700

***James A. Haley Veterans' Hospital,** 13000 Bruce B. Downs Boulevard, Tampa, FL 33612; tel. 813/972–2000

***Jessie Trice Community Health Center, Inc.,** 5607 N. W. 27th Ave, Miami, FL 33142; tel. 305/805–1700

***John's Place, Inc.,** 315 SE 11th Street, Fort Lauderdale, FL 33316; tel. 954/463–9590

***La Amistad Residential Treatment Center, LLC,** 1650 Park Avenue North, Maitland, FL 32751; tel. 407/647–0660

**La Amistad Residential Treatment Center, LLC,** 6601 Central Florida Parkway, Orlando, FL 32821; tel. 407/370–0111

**Lakeside Behavioral Healthcare, Inc.,** 1800 Mercy Dr., Orlando, FL 32808; tel. 407/875–3700

***Lakeview Health Systems, LLC,** 1900 Corporate Square Blvd, Jacksonville, FL 32216; tel. 904/727–6455

**Larkin Community Hospital Inc,** 7031 Southwest 62nd Avenue, South Miami, FL 33143; tel. 305/284–7700

**Lee Memorial Health System Behavioral Health Services,** 12550 New Brittany Blvd, Ste 200, 201, Fort Myers, FL 33907; tel. 239/343–9180

**Lehigh HMA LLC,** 1500 Lee Boulevard, Lehigh Acres, FL 33936; tel. 239/368–4503

***Manatee Glens,** PO Box 9478, Bradenton, FL 34206-9478; tel. 941/782–4299

**Manatee Palms Youth Services,** 4480 51st Street West, Bradenton, FL 34210; tel. 941/792–2222

***Mental Health Care, Inc.,** 5707 North 22nd Street, Tampa, FL 33610; tel. 813/272–2244

***Miami VA Healthcare System,** 1201 NW 16th Street, Miami, FL 33125; tel. 305/575–7000

**Milestones In Recovery, Inc.,** 2525 Embassy Drive, Suite 10, Hollywood, FL 33026; tel. 954/272–0806

**Multicultural Community Mental Health Center,** 2112 S. Congress Ave, #104, West Palm Beach, FL 33406; tel. 561/653–6292

**National Deaf Academy, LLC,** 19650 US Highway 441, Mount Dora, FL 32757; tel. 352/735–9500

**New Directions Community Mental Health Center,** 28870 South Dixie Highway, Homestead, FL 33033; tel. 305/247–4009

***New Era Health Center, Inc.,** 9600 Southwest 8th Street Suite 1, Miami, FL 33174; tel. 305/559–8838

***New Horizons Community Mental Health Center, Inc.,** 1469 NW 36th Street 2nd Floor, Miami, FL 33142; tel. 305/635–0366

***North Florida/South Georgia Veterans Health System,** 1601 Southwest Archer Road, Gainesville, FL 32608-1197; tel. 352/376–1611

**Northside Mental Health Center,** 12512 Bruce B. Downs Boulevard, Tampa, FL 33612-9209; tel. 813/977–8700

**Nueva America Inc,** 2682 SW 87th Avenue, Miami, FL 33165; tel. 305/480–5680

***Ocala Behavioral Health,** 3130 SW 27th Avenue, Ocala, FL 34471; tel. 352/671–3130

**Oglethorpe, Port St. Lucie Hospital LLC,** 2550 SE Walton Rd, Port Saint Lucie, FL 34952; tel. 772/335–0400

**Oliver-Pyatt Centers, Inc.,** 6150 SW 76 Street, Miami, FL 33143; tel. 305/663–1738

***Orlando VA Medical Center,** 5201 Raymond Street, Orlando, FL 32803; tel. 407/629–1599

***Palm Partners, LLC,** 816 Palm Trail, Delray Beach, FL 33483; tel. 561/921–6117

**Parent's Information and Resource Center, Inc.,** 817 N. Dixie Highway, Pompano Beach, FL 33060; tel. 954/785–8285

***PB Institute Partners Limited Partnership,** 1017 N. Olive Avenue, West Palm Beach, FL 33401; tel. 800/433–5098

***Peace River Center for Personal Development, Inc.,** P.O. Box 1559, Bartow, FL 33831-1559; tel. 863/519–0575

***Personal Enrichment through Mental Health Services, Inc.,** 11254 58th Street North, Pinellas Park, FL 33782; tel. 727/545–6477

**Phoenix Clinic,** 2212 SW 60th Terrace, Miramar, FL 33023; tel. 954/491–2133

***Professional Training Association Corporation,** 321 Northlake Blvd Suite 102, North Palm Beach, FL 33408; tel. 561/494–0866

***RBHS & MHRC & MHCJ,** PO Box 19249, Jacksonville, FL 32245-9249; tel. 904/743–1883

**Recapturing the Vision International, Inc.,** 9780 E Indigo Street Suite 302, Palmetto Bay, FL 33157; tel. 305/232–6003

***Recovery First, Inc.,** 4110 Davie Road Extension, Hollywood, FL 33024; tel. 954/981–4545

***Recovery Road, LLC,** 4362 Northlake Blvd., Suite 109, Palm Beach Gardens, FL 33410; tel. 561/899–4388

***Reflections Wellness Center of Broward, Inc. .,** 6848 Stirling Road, Hollywood, FL 33024; tel. 954/362–0104

**Rega Mental Health Center, LLC,** 7501 Wiles Road #202, Coral Springs, FL 33067; tel. 954/346–8300

***River Point Behavioral Health,** PO Box 17128, Jacksonville, FL 32245-7128; tel. 904/724–9202

***Serenity Now CMHC, Inc.,** 2724 N. Australian Avenue, Bld, West Palm Beach, FL 33407; tel. 561/802–4211

**South County Mental Health Center, Inc.,** 16158 South Military Trail, Delray Beach, FL 33484; tel. 561/637–1000

**SP Behavioral, LLC,** 11301 SE Tequesta Terrace, Tequesta, FL 33469; tel. 561/744–0211

***Springbrook Hospital,** 7007 Grove Road, Brooksville, FL 34609; tel. 352/596–4306

***Stepping Stone Center for Recovery,** 2701 Gateway Drive, Pompano Beach, FL 33069; tel. 954/489–2588

**Stepping Stone Center for Recovery - OTP,** 8889 Corporate Square Court, Jacksonville, FL 32216; tel. 954/489–2580

**Suncoast Mental Health Center, Inc.,** 2814 S. US Hwy 1 Suite D - 4, Fort Pierce, FL 34982; tel. 772/489–4726

***Sunrise Detox III,** 2331 NE 53rd Street, Fort Lauderdale, FL 33308; tel. 954/491–9700

***Sunrise Detoxification Center, LLC,** 3185 Boutwell Road, Lake Worth, FL 33461; tel. 561/533–0074

***The Centers,** 5664 SW 60th Ave, Ocala, FL 34474; tel. 352/291–5456

***The Centre for Women, Inc.,** 305 South Hyde Park Avenue, Tampa, FL 33606; tel. 813/251–8437

**The Devereux Foundation, Inc.,** 5850 T. G. Lee Blvd, Suite 400, Orlando, FL 32822; tel. 407/362–9210

***The Hazelden Foundation,** 950 Sixth Avenue North, Naples, FL 34102; tel. 888/257–7800

***The Jerome Golden Center for Behavioral Health, Inc.,** 1041 45th Street, West Palm Beach, FL 33407; tel. 561/383–8000

**The Renfrew Center of Florida,** 7700 Renfrew Lane, Coconut Creek, FL 33073; tel. 215/482–5353

***The Transition House, Inc,** 3800 5th Street, Saint Cloud, FL 34769; tel. 407/892–5700

***The Treatment Center of the Palm Beaches, LLC,** 4905 Lantana Road, Lake Worth, FL 33463; tel. 561/253–6790

---

*Indicates organization is a Joint Commission accredited Chemical Dependency organization.

Section C

*The Village South, Inc., 3050 Biscayne Boulevard, Miami, FL 33137; tel. 305/573-3784
*The Watershed Treatment Programs, 200 Congress Park Drive, Suite 100, Delray Beach, FL 33445; tel. 561/361-6608
*The Willough at Naples, 9001 Tamiami Trail East, Naples, FL 34113; tel. 239/775-4500
*Transitions Recovery Program, 1928 Northeast 154th Street, Miami, FL 33162; tel. 305/949-9001
*Treatment Alternatives, 7000 North Federal Hwy, Boca Raton, FL 33487; tel. 561/637-4766
*Treatment Resources of Margate, Inc., 5100 Coconut Creek Parkway, Margate, FL 33063; tel. 954/917-3334
*Treatment Solutions of South Florida, Inc., 6278 N. Federal Hwy. PMB 392, Fort Lauderdale, FL 33308; tel. 954/627-6157
*Turning Point of Tampa, Inc., 6227 Sheldon Road, Tampa, FL 33615; tel. 813/882-3003
*Tykes & Teens, 3577 SW Corporate Parkway, Palm City, FL 34990; tel. 772/220-3439
*Unity Recovery Center, Inc., 1240 US Highway 1, #200, North Palm Beach, FL 33408; tel. 561/855-6000
University Behavioral, LLC, 2500 Discovery Drive, Orlando, FL 32826; tel. 407/281-7000
*VA Medical Center - West Palm Beach, Florida, 7305 N. Military Trail, West Palm Beach, FL 33410-6400; tel. 516/422-8600
Volunteers of America of Florida, Inc., 1205 East 8th Avenue, Tampa, FL 33605; tel. 813/282-1525
*Wekiva Springs Center, LLC, 3947 Salisbury Road, Jacksonville, FL 32216; tel. 904/296-3533
West Palm Hospital, 2201 45th Street, West Palm Beach, FL 33407; tel. 561/863-3104
*Windmoor Healthcare of Clearwater, Inc., 11300 US 19 North, Clearwater, FL 33764; tel. 727/541-2646

GEORGIA
*Acadia Riverwoods, 223 Medical Center Drive, Riverdale, GA 30274; tel. 770/991-8500
Central State Hospital, 620 Broad St, Milledgeville, GA 31062; tel. 478/445-4128
Chanan Foundation, INC, 3136 Golf Ridge Blvd, Douglasville, GA 30135; tel. 678/715-8891
*Charlie Norwood VA Medical Center, 1 Freedom Way, Augusta, GA 30904; tel. 706/733-0188
*Coastal Harbor Health Systems, 1150 Cornell Avenue, Savannah, GA 31406; tel. 912/354-3911
*Coliseum Psychiatric Center, LLC, 340 Hospital Drive, Macon, GA 31217-8002; tel. 478/741-1355
*Cord of Three Counseling Services, 206 Screven Avenue, Waycross, GA 31501; tel. 912/288-7480
Devereux Georgia Treatment Network, 1291 Stanley Road, Kennesaw, GA 30152-4359; tel. 770/427-0147
DM & ADR, Inc., 1710 Commerce Road, Athens, GA 30607; tel. 706/552-0688
*Dwight David Eisenhower Army Medical Center, Dwight David Eisenhower Army Medical Center, ATTN: MCHF-QM, Fort Gordon, GA 30905-5650; tel. 706/787-2801
East Central Regional Hospital, 100 Myrtle Blvd, Gracewood, GA 30812; tel. 706/790-2030
*Familys Matter Counseling and Psychological Services, 4568 Lawrenceville Highway, Suite 201, Lilburn, GA 30047; tel. 404/602-0182
*Fulton County Dept of BHDD, 99 Jesse Hill Jr Dr Suite 408, Atlanta, GA 30303; tel. 404/730-1202
*Georgia Pines Community Service Board, 1102 Smith Avenue Suite K, Thomasville, GA 31799; tel. 229/225-4335
Georgia Regional Hospital at Atlanta, PO Box 37047, Decatur, GA 30034-0407; tel. 404/243-2100
Georgia Regional Hospital at Savannah, 1915 Eisenhower Drive, Savannah, GA 31406; tel. 912/356-2011
Grady Memorial Hospital Corporation, 80 Jesse Hill, Jr., Drive, S.E., Atlanta, GA 30303; tel. 404/616-4252
Greenleaf Center, 2209 Pineview Drive, Valdosta, GA 31602; tel. 229/671-6611
Hopes of Honorable Youth, LLC, 130 W. Wieuca Suite 204 B, Atlanta, GA 30342; tel. 404/797-7126
Iries Community Development Center, 112 Mall Road, Dublin, GA 31021; tel. 478/304-1450
KidsPeace National Centers of Georgia, Inc., 101 KidsPeace Drive, Bowdon, GA 30108; tel. 770/437-7200

Laurel Heights Hospital, 934 Briarcliff Road, Northeast, Atlanta, GA 30306; tel. 404/888-7860
Macon Behavioral Health System, 3500 Riverside Drive, Macon, GA 31210; tel. 478/477-3829
*Martin Army Community Hospital, 7950 Martin Loop, Fort Benning, GA 31905-5637; tel. 706/544-4762
*Metro Atlanta Recovery Residences, Inc., 2815 Clearview Place, Atlanta, GA 30340; tel. 678/805-5100
Murphy Harpst Children's Centers, Inc., 740 Fletcher Street, Cedartown, GA 30125; tel. 770/748-1500
*Northside Hospital, Inc., 1000 Johnson Ferry Road, Atlanta, GA 30342-1611; tel. 404/851-8000
*Ogeechee Behavioral Health Services, PO Box 1259, Swainsboro, GA 30401; tel. 478/289-2522
Opiate Agonist Treatment Therapy Clinic, 1670 Clairmont Road, Decatur, GA 30033; tel. 404/321-1611
*Peachford Behavioral Health System of Atlanta, 2151 Peachford Road, Atlanta, GA 30338; tel. 770/455-3200
Reunited Counseling & Training, 3590 Covington Highway, Decatur, GA 30032; tel. 404/687-9188
*Ridgeview Institute, 3995 South Cobb Drive, Smyrna, GA 30080; tel. 770/434-4567
RTS Services Unlimited, Inc., 6018 Craftsman Street, Duluth, GA 30097; tel. 404/767-7737
Skyland Trail, 1961 North Druid Hills Road, Atlanta, GA 30329; tel. 404/315-8333
Southside Behavioral Lifestyle Enrichment Center, 2685 Metropolitan Parkway, Suite C, Atlanta, GA 30315; tel. 404/627-1385
*Southside Medical Center, Inc., 1046 Ridge Avenue, Atlanta, GA 30315; tel. 404/688-1350
Southwestern State Hospital, PO Box 1378, Thomasville, GA 31799-1378; tel. 229/227-3020
St. Francis Hospital, Inc., PO Box 7000, Columbus, GA 31908-7000; tel. 706/596-4000
*Talbott Recovery Campus, 5448 Yorktowne Drive, Atlanta, GA 30349; tel. 770/994-0185
Tanner Medical Center / Villa Rica, 601 Dallas Highway, Villa Rica, GA 30180; tel. 770/456-3000
Tanner Medical Center, Inc., 705 Dixie Street, Carrollton, GA 30117; tel. 770/836-9580
The Cottages on Mountain Creek, LLC, 5800 Mountain Creek Road, Sandy Springs, GA 30328; tel. 404/228-6554
The McNeil Organization, PO Box 6413, Douglasville, GA 30154; tel. 404/543-6163
*Turning Point Hospital, LLC., PO Box 1177, Moultrie, GA 31776; tel. 229/985-4815
*UHS of Anchor, LP, 5454 Yorktowne Drive, Atlanta, GA 30349; tel. 770/991-6044
*UHS of Summit Ridge, 250 Scenic Highway, Lawrenceville, GA 30046; tel. 678/442-5800
*VA Medical Center - Atlanta, 1670 Clairmont Road, Decatur, GA 30033; tel. 404/728-7601
*VA Medical Center - Carl Vinson, 1826 Veterans Boulevard, Dublin, GA 31021; tel. 478/277-2701
We Speak For Oursleves,LLC, 2020 Oakcreek Drive, Lithia Springs, GA 30122; tel. 678/438-8310
*WellStar Cobb Hospital, 3950 Austell Road, SW, Austell, GA 30106-1121; tel. 770/732-4000
WellStar Windy Hill Hospital, 805 Sandy Plains Road, Marietta, GA 30066; tel. 770/792-5430
West Central Georgia Regional Hospital, PO Box 12435, Columbus, GA 31917-2435; tel. 706/568-5203
*Willingway, Inc., 311 Jones Mill Road, Statesboro, GA 30458; tel. 912/764-6236
*Winn Army Community Hospital, 1061 Harmon Avenue, Fort Stewart, GA 31314-5674; tel. 912/435-6911

HAWAII
*Access Capabilities, Inc, 75-5995 Kaukini Hwy, Ste 415, Kailua Kona, HI 96740-2123; tel. 808/334-0979
Benchmark Behavioral Health System - Pearl City, P.O Box 1196, Pearl City, HI 96782; tel. 808/454-1411
Hawaii State Hospital, 45 710 Keaahala Road, Kaneohe, HI 96744; tel. 808/247-2191
*Naval Health Clinic Hawaii, 480 Central Avenue, Pearl Harbor, HI 96860-4908; tel. 808/471-3025
Sutter Health Pacific, 91-2301 Old Fort Weaver Road, Ewa Beach, HI 96706; tel. 808/671-8511
The Queen's Medical Center, 1301 Punchbowl Street, Honolulu, HI 96813; tel. 808/538-9011
*VA Pacific Islands Health Care System, 459 Patterson Road, Honolulu, HI 96819-1522; tel. 808/433-0683

IDAHO
*BHC Intermountain Hospital, 303 North Allumbaugh Street, Boise, ID 83704; tel. 208/350-2396
*Boise VA Medical Center, 500 West Fort Street, Boise, ID 83702-4598; tel. 208/422-1100
Eastern Idaho Health Services, PO Box 2077, Idaho Falls, ID 83404; tel. 208/529-6210
Project Patch, PO Box 450, Garden Valley, ID 83622; tel. 360/690-8495

ILLINOIS
*Adventist Hinsdale Hospital, 120 North Oak Street, Hinsdale, IL 60521; tel. 630/856-9000
*Advocate Addiction Treatment Program, 701 Lee Street, Suite 800, Des Plaines, IL 60016; tel. 847/795-3900
*Advocate Christ Medical Center, 4440 West 95th Street, Oak Lawn, IL 60453; tel. 708/684-8000
*Advocate Illinois Masonic Medical Center, 836 West Wellington Avenue, Chicago, IL 60657; tel. 773/975-1600
*Alexian Brothers Behavioral Health Hospital, 1650 Moon Lake Boulevard, Hoffman Estates, IL 60169; tel. 847/882-1600
Alexian Brothers Center for Mental Health, 3436 N. Kennicott Avenue, Arlington Heights, IL 60004; tel. 847/952-7460
Allendale Association, PO Box 1088, Lake Villa, IL 60046; tel. 847/356-2351
*Aunt Martha's Youth Service Center, Inc., 19990 Governors Highway, Olympia Fields, IL 60461; tel. 708/747-7100
*Aurora Chicago Lakeshore Hospital, 4840 North Marine Drive, Chicago, IL 60640; tel. 773/878-9700
Beacon Therapeutic Diagnostic and Treatment Center, 1912 West 103rd Street, Chicago, IL 60643; tel. 773/298-1243
*Ben Gordon Center, 12 Health Services Drive, Dekalb, IL 60115; tel. 815/756-4875
CAP of Downers Grove, 4954 South Main Street, Downers Grove, IL 60515; tel. 630/810-0186
*CAPT James A. Lovell Federal Health Care Center, 3001 Green Bay Road, North Chicago, IL 60064; tel. 224/610-3700
Center for Addictive Problems, 609 North Wells Street, Chicago, IL 60654; tel. 312/266-0404
Center on Deafness, 3444 Dundee Road, Northbrook, IL 60062; tel. 847/559-0110
*Central DuPage Hospital Association, 25 North Winfield Road, Winfield, IL 60190; tel. 630/933-1600
Central Illinois Center for the Treatment of Addictions, 3420 N Rochelle, Peoria, IL 61604; tel. 309/671-8005
*Chestnut Health Systems, 1003 Martin Luther King Drive, Bloomington, IL 61701; tel. 309/827-6026
Coles County Mental Health Association, Inc., 750 Broadway Avenue East, Mattoon, IL 61938; tel. 217/238-5700
*Community Counseling Centers of Chicago, 4740 North Clark Street, Chicago, IL 60640; tel. 773/765-0810
*Comprehensive Behavorial Health Center of St. Clair County, 505 South 8th Street, East Saint Louis, IL 62201; tel. 618/482-7330
*Cornell Interventions, Inc., 5701 South Wood, Chicago, IL 60636; tel. 773/737-4600
DuPage County Health Dept./ Behavioral Health Services, 111 North County Farm Road, Wheaton, IL 60187; tel. 630/682-7400
*DuPage Interventions, 11 S 250 Route 83, Willowbrook, IL 60527; tel. 630/325-5050
Ecker Center for Mental Health, 1845 Grandstand Place, Elgin, IL 60123; tel. 847/695-0484
Edward Hines Jr VA Hospital / Drug Dependency Treatment Ct, PO Box 5000, Hines, IL 60141; tel. 708/202-8387
*Edward Hines Jr. VA Hospital, 5000 South 5th Avenue, Hines, IL 60141-5000; tel. 708/202-5652
*Elmhurst Memorial Hospital, 155 East Brush Hill Road, Elmhurst, IL 60126; tel. 331/221-1000
Family Alliance, Inc., 2028 N. Seminary Ave., Woodstock, IL 60098-2828; tel. 815/338-3590
Family Guidance Centers - Joliet, 1611 Jefferson Street, Joliet, IL 60435; tel. 815/730-7521
Family Guidance Centers at Triangle Center - Methadone, 2525 E Oakton, Bldg A, Arlington Heights, IL 60005; tel. 217/544-9858
Family Guidance Centers, Inc., 751 Aurora Avenue, Aurora, IL 60505; tel. 630/801-0017
Family Guidance Centers, Inc., 310 W Chicago Ave, Chicago, IL 60654; tel. 708/333-8960

*Indicates organization is a Joint Commission accredited Chemical Dependency organization.

Family Guidance Centers, Inc., 484 Lee Street, Des Plaines, IL 60016; tel. 847/827-7517

*Family Service and Community Mental Health Center/McHenry, 4100 Veterans Parkway, McHenry, IL 60050; tel. 815/385-6400

FHN Family Counseling Center, 421 W. Exchange St., Freeport, IL 61032; tel. 815/599-7322

Garfield Counseling Center, Inc., 4132 West Madison, Chicago, IL 60624; tel. 773/533-0433

*Gateway Foundation, Inc., 55 East Jackson Blvd, Suite 1500, Chicago, IL 60604; tel. 312/663-1130

Hartgrove Hospital, 5730 W. Roosevelt. Road, Chicago, IL 60644; tel. 773/413-1700

*Heartland Human Services, PO Box 1047, Effingham, IL 62401; tel. 217/347-7179

*Human Service Center, PO Box 1346, Peoria, IL 61654-1346; tel. 309/671-8005

*Insight Psychological Centers, 333 North Michigan Avenue, Suite 1900, Chicago, IL 60601; tel. 312/540-9955

Jackson Park Hospital and Medical Center, 7531 South Stony Island Avenue, Chicago, IL 60649; tel. 773/947-7500

*Jesse Brown VA Medical Center, 820 South Damen Avenue, Chicago, IL 60612; tel. 312/569-6101

Kenneth Young Center, 1001 Rohlwing Road, Elk Grove Village, IL 60007; tel. 847/524-8800

Lake County Health Department, 3004 Grand Avenue, Waukegan, IL 60085; tel. 847/377-8120

*Lake County Health Department / Behavioral Health Services, 3010 Grand Avenue, Waukegan, IL 60085; tel. 847/377-8299

*Leyden Family Service and Mental Health Center, 10001 West Grand Avenue, Franklin Park, IL 60131; tel. 847/451-0330

*Little Company of Mary Hospital, 2800 West 95th Street, Evergreen Park, IL 60805; tel. 708/422-6200

*Memorial Medical Center, 385 Millennium Drive, Crystal Lake, IL 60012; tel. 815/788-5800

Memorial Medical Center, 701 North First Street, Springfield, IL 62781-0001; tel. 217/788-3000

Mental Health and Deafness Resources, Inc., 614 Anthony Trail, Northbrook, IL 60062; tel. 847/509-8260

*Naperville Psychiatric Venture d/b/a Linden Oaks Hospital, 801 South Washington, Naperville, IL 60566-7060; tel. 630/305-5500

Near North Health Service Corporation, 1276 North Clybourn Avenue, Chicago, IL 60610; tel. 312/337-1073

*North Central Behavioral Health Systems, Inc., PO Box 1488, La Salle, IL 61301; tel. 815/223-0160

*NorthShore University HealthSystem, 1301 Central Street, Suite 300, Evanston, IL 60201; tel. 847/570-5005

*Northwest Community Hospital Youth Center, 901 Kirchoff Road, Arlington Heights, IL 60005; tel. 847/618-1000

*Palos Community Hospital, 12251 South 80th Avenue, Palos Heights, IL 60463; tel. 708/923-4000

PEER Services, Inc., 906 Davis Street, Evanston, IL 60201; tel. 847/492-1778

*Pioneer Center for Human Services/Youth Service Bureau, 101 South Jefferson Street, Woodstock, IL 60098; tel. 815/338-7360

*Presence Mercy Medical Center, 1325 North Highland Avenue, Aurora, IL 60506; tel. 630/859-2222

*ProCare Centers, 1820 South 25th Avenue, Broadview, IL 60153; tel. 708/338-3806

*Remedies Renewing Lives, 516 Green Street, Rockford, IL 61102; tel. 815/966-1285

Riveredge Hospital, 8311 West Roosevelt Road, Forest Park, IL 60130; tel. 708/771-7000

*Riverside Medical Center, 350 North Wall Street, Kankakee, IL 60901; tel. 815/933-1671

*Rosecrance, Inc., 1021 N. Mulford Road, Rockford, IL 61107; tel. 815/387-5600

Rush University Medical Center, 1653 West Congress Parkway, Chicago, IL 60612; tel. 312/563-3591

Sequel Schools, LLC, 998 Corporate Blvd, Aurora, IL 60502; tel. 847/391-8000

*Sinnissippi Centers, Inc., 325 Illinois Route 2, Dixon, IL 61021; tel. 815/284-6611

*Southeastern Illinois Counseling Centers, Inc., Drawer M, Olney, IL 62450; tel. 618/395-4306

St. Mary's Hospital, 400 North Pleasant Avenue, Centralia, IL 62801; tel. 618/436-6519

Streamwood Behavioral Healthcare System, 1400 East Irving Park Road, Streamwood, IL 60107; tel. 630/837-9000

*Tazwood Mental Health Center, Inc., 3248 Vandever Ave., Pekin, IL 61554; tel. 309/347-5579

*The Child, Adolescent and Family Recovery Center, LLC, 900 North Shore Dr. Suite 140, Lake Bluff, IL 60044; tel. 847/457-6730

*The Pavilion Foundation, 809 West Church Street, Champaign, IL 61820; tel. 217/373-1700

*The South Suburban Council on Alcoholism and Substance Abuse, 1909 Cheker Square, Hazel Crest, IL 60429; tel. 708/647-3333

*The Women's Treatment Center, 140 N. Ashland Avenue, Chicago, IL 60607; tel. 312/850-0050

*Timberline Knolls, 40 Timberline Drive, Lemont, IL 60439; tel. 630/257-9600

Touchette Regional Hospital, 5900 Bond Avenue, Centreville, IL 62207; tel. 618/332-5400

*VA - Illiana Health Care System, 1900 East Main Street, Danville, IL 61832; tel. 217/554-3000

*VA Medical Center, 2401 West Main Street, Marion, IL 62959; tel. 618/997-5311

Waukegan IL Hospital Company, LLC, 2615 Washington Street, Waukegan, IL 60085; tel. 847/249-3900

*Westlake Hospital - OTP, 1225 W. Lake Street, Melrose Park, IL 60160; tel. 708/938-4000

*Woodridge Interventions, 2221 64th Street, Woodridge, IL 60517; tel. 630/968-6477

**INDIANA**

Adult and Child Mental Health Center, Inc., 222 E. Ohio St. Suite 600, Indianapolis, IN 46204; tel. 317/882-5122

*Aspire Indiana, 9516 East 148th Street, Suite 1, Noblesville, IN 46060; tel. 317/587-0500

Bloomington Meadows Hospital, 3600 North Prow Road, Bloomington, IN 47404; tel. 812/331-8000

Brentwood Meadows, LLC, 4488 Roslin Road, Newburgh, IN 47630; tel. 812/858-7200

Columbus Hospital LLC, 2223 Poshard Drive, Columbus, IN 47203; tel. 812/376-1711

*Community Health Network, Inc., 1500 North Ritter Avenue, Indianapolis, IN 46219; tel. 317/355-5520

*Community Howard Regional Health System, Inc., PO Box 9011, Kokomo, IN 46904; tel. 765/453-8547

Crossroad Child & Family Services, Inc., 2525 Lake Avenue, Fort Wayne, IN 46805-5457; tel. 260/484-4153

*Cummins Behavioral Health Systems, Inc., 6655 East US 36, Avon, IN 46123; tel. 317/272-3330

Elder Alternative Adult Day Services, 2236 E 10TH ST, Indianapolis, IN 46201-2006; tel. 317/633-3104

Evansville Psychiatric Children's Center, 3300 East Morgan Avenue, Evansville, IN 47715; tel. 812/477-6436

*Fairbanks Hospital, Inc., 8102 Clearvista Parkway, Indianapolis, IN 46256-4698; tel. 317/849-8222

*Family & Children's Ctr. Counseling & Development Services, 315 W. Jefferson, South Bend, IN 46601; tel. 574/968-9660

*Four County Comprehensive Mental Health Center, Inc., 1015 Michigan Avenue, Logansport, IN 46947; tel. 574/722-5151

*Good Samaritan Hospital, 520 South Seventh Street, Vincennes, IN 47591; tel. 812/885-3334

*Grant-Blackford Mental Health, Inc., 505 Wabash Avenue, Marion, IN 46952; tel. 765/662-3971

*LifeSpring, Inc., 460 Spring Street, Jeffersonville, IN 47130; tel. 812/280-2080

Logansport State Hospital, 1098 South State Road 25, Logansport, IN 46947; tel. 574/722-4141

Madison State Hospital, 711 Green Road, Madison, IN 47250; tel. 812/265-2611

*Meridian Health Services Corp, 240 North Tillotson Avenue, Muncie, IN 47304; tel. 765/288-1928

Michiana Behavioral Health Center, 1800 North Oak Drive, Plymouth, IN 46563; tel. 574/936-3784

*Oaklawn Psychiatric Center, Inc., PO Box 809 330 Lakeview Drive, Goshen, IN 46527-0809; tel. 574/533-1234

Options Treatment Center, 5602 Caito Drive, Indianapolis, IN 46226; tel. 317/544-4340

Person First Consulting, Inc, 6002 Morning Dove Dr., Indianapolis, IN 46228; tel. 317/750-0222

Persons Centered Value Partners, LLC, 4459 Peggy Hollow Road, Shoals, IN 47581; tel. 812/936-3543

Premier Care of Indiana, INC, 317 S. Norton Ave., Marion, IN 46952; tel. 765/664-0101

R.T.C. Resource Acquisition Corporation, 1404 South State, Indianapolis, IN 46203; tel. 317/783-4003

Resolute Acquisition Corporation, 320 North Tibbs, Indianapolis, IN 46222; tel. 317/630-5215

Richard L. Roudebush VAMC Opioid Substitution Clinic, 1481 West 10th Street, Bldg 1, Indianapolis, IN 46202; tel. 317/988-2121

Riverview Adult Day Center, 2715 E Jackson Blvd, Elkhart, IN 46516-5053; tel. 574/293-6886

Samlind of Indiana, Inc, 33149 State Road 2, New Carlisle, IN 46552; tel. 574/654-8700

Sequel TSI of Indiana, LLC, 2426 Parker Lane, Lexington, IN 47138; tel. 812/889-3992

*Southlake Mental Health Center, 8555 Taft Street, Merrillville, IN 46410-6199; tel. 219/769-4005

*Southwestern Behavioral Healthcare, Inc., 415 Mulberry Street, Evansville, IN 47713-1298; tel. 812/423-7791

*St. Vincent Anderson Regional Hospital, Inc., 2015 Jackson Street, Anderson, IN 46016; tel. 765/646-8373

Starline Community Services, Inc., P.O.Box 1576, South Bend, IN 46634; tel. 574/323-8707

*Tara Treatment Center, Inc., 6231 South US 31, Franklin, IN 46131; tel. 812/526-2611

The Children's Campus, Inc., 1411 Lincoln Way West, Mishawaka, IN 46544-1690; tel. 574/259-5666

The Midwest Center for Youth and Families, PO Box 669, Kouts, IN 46347; tel. 219/766-2999

*The Otis R. Bowen Center for Human Services, Inc., PO Box 497, Warsaw, IN 46581-0497; tel. 574/267-7169

*VA Medical Center - Richard L. Roudebush VAMC, 1481 West 10th Street, Indianapolis, IN 46202; tel. 317/988-2121

*VA Northern Indiana Health Care System, 2121 Lake Avenue, Fort Wayne, IN 46805; tel. 260/460-1310

*Valle Vista Hospital, LLC, 898 East Main Street, Greenwood, IN 46143; tel. 317/887-1348

*Wabash Valley Alliance, 415 N. 26th Street, Lafayette, IN 47904; tel. 765/446-6537

*Wellstone Regional Hospital Acquisition, LLC, 2700 Vissing Park Road, Jeffersonville, IN 47130; tel. 812/284-8000

Willowglen Academy - Indiana, Inc., 308 East 21st Avenue, Gary, IN 46407; tel. 219/886-1320

Wishard Health Services, 1001 W 10th Street, Indianapolis, IN 46202; tel. 317/655-2255

*Wishard Health Services, 1001 West Tenth Street, Indianapolis, IN 46202; tel. 317/639-6671

**IOWA**

*Alegent Creighton Health Mercy Hospital, 800 Mercy Drive, Council Bluffs, IA 51503; tel. 712/328-5000

Boys and Girls Home and Family Services, Inc., PO Box 1197, Sioux City, IA 51102; tel. 712/293-4700

*Broadlawns Medical Center, 1801 Hickman Road, Des Moines, IA 50314; tel. 515/282-2200

Central Iowa In Home Counseling, 2317 Rick Collins Way, Eldora, IA 50627; tel. 641/858-3852

Clarinda Youth Corporation, 1820 North 16th Street, Clarinda, IA 51632; tel. 712/542-3103

Hillcrest Family Services, 2005 Asbury Road, Dubuque, IA 52001; tel. 563/583-7357

Integrative Health Services, Inc., P.O. Box 118, Williamsburg, IA 52361-0118; tel. 319/668-2050

*Iowa City VA Health Care System, 601 Highway 6 West, Iowa City, IA 52246; tel. 319/338-0581

Mental Health Institute, 2277 Iowa Avenue, Independence, IA 50644; tel. 319/334-2583

*Mercy Medical Center, 1111 6th Avenue, Des Moines, IA 50314; tel. 515/247-3121

*Orchard Place, 925 Porter Avenue, Des Moines, IA 50315; tel. 515/285-6781

Special Needs Services, P.O. Box 4117, Waterloo, IA 50704; tel. 319/277-3966

*St. Luke's Methodist Hospital, 1026 A Avenue Northeast, Cedar Rapids, IA 52402; tel. 319/369-7211

*The University of Iowa Hospitals and Clinics, 200 Hawkins Drive, Iowa City, IA 52242; tel. 319/384-5897

*VA Central Iowa Health Care System, 3600 30th Street, Des Moines, IA 50310-5774; tel. 515/699-5850

Woodward Academy, 1251 334th St., Woodward, IA 50276; tel. 515/438-3481

---

*Indicates organization is a Joint Commission accredited Chemical Dependency organization.

Section C

## KANSAS

*Atchison Valley Hope, PO Box 312, Atchison, KS 66002; tel. 913/367–1618

*Haskell Health Center, 2415 Massachusetts, Lawrence, KS 66046; tel. 785/843–4890

Kansas City Metro Methadone Program, MS 4015, 3901 Rainbow Boulevard, Kansas City, KS 66160-7341; tel. 913/588–6493

KVC Behavioral HealthCare, Inc., 7940 Marshall Drive, Lenexa, KS 66214; tel. 913/499–8100

KVC Hospitals, Inc., 21350 W. 153rd Street, Olathe, KS 66061; tel. 913/322–4900

*Marillac Center Inc., 8000 W. 127th Street, Overland Park, KS 66213; tel. 913/951–4300

*Moundridge Valley Hope, P.O. Box 956, Moundridge, KS 67107; tel. 620/345–4673

*Munson Army Health Center, Building 343 - 550 Pope Avenue, Fort Leavenworth, KS 66027-2332; tel. 913/684–6420

*Norton Valley Hope, PO Box 510, Norton, KS 67654; tel. 785/877–5101

*Prairie View, Inc., PO Box 467, Newton, KS 67114; tel. 316/284–6400

*Robert J. Dole VA Medical Center, 5500 East Kellogg, Wichita, KS 67218; tel. 316/651–3601

*Saint Francis Community Services, Inc., 509 East Elm Street, Salina, KS 67401; tel. 785/825–0541

Sequel of Kansas, LLC, 2050 West 11th Street, Wichita, KS 67203; tel. 316/267–5710

*Shawnee Mission Medical Center, 9100 W. 74th Street, Shawnee Mission, KS 66204; tel. 913/676–2000

The Children's Mercy Hospital, 5808 West 110th, Overland Park, KS 66211; tel. 913/696–8000

*United Methodist Youthville, Inc., 4505 E 47th Street South, Wichita, KS 67210; tel. 316/529–9100

*VA Eastern Kansas Health Care System, 2200 SW Gage, Topeka, KS 66622; tel. 785/350–3111

VCPHCS XIV, LLC dba Bridge Way Recovery, 6331 West 110th ST, Overland Park, KS 66211; tel. 936/524–2140

## KENTUCKY

*Blanchfield Army Community Hospital, MCXD-DCMCC 650 Joel Drive, Fort Campbell, KY 42223-5349; tel. 270/798–8512

*Bluegrass Regional MH-MR Board, Inc., 1351 Newtown Pike, Bldg 1, Lexington, KY 40511-1277; tel. 859/253–1686

*Cumberland River Regional MH/MR Board, Inc., PO Box 568, Corbin, KY 40702; tel. 606/528–7010

*Ireland Army Community Hospital, 289 Ireland Ave, Bldg 851, Fort Knox, KY 40121-5520; tel. 502/624–0251

*Jewish Hospital & St. Mary's HealthCare, Inc., 200 Abraham Flexner Way, Louisville, KY 40202-1886; tel. 502/587–4011

*KMI Acquisition, LLC, 8521 LaGrange Road, Louisville, KY 40242; tel. 502/426–6380

*Lincoln Trail Behavioral Health System, PO Box 369, Radcliff, KY 40160; tel. 270/351–9444

*NorthKey Community Care, PO Box 2680, Covington, KY 41012; tel. 859/578–3233

*Recovery Works Drug & Alcohol Rehabilitation Center, 3107 Cincinnati Road, Georgetown, KY 40324; tel. 502/570–9313

*Robley Rex Medical Center, 800 Zorn Avenue, Louisville, KY 40206; tel. 502/287–4000

*Seven Counties Services, Inc., 101 West Muhammad Ali Blvd, Louisville, KY 40202; tel. 502/589–8600

Spectrum Care Academy, Inc., PO Box 911, Columbia, KY 42728; tel. 270/384–6444

Sunrise Children's Services, P.O. Box 1429, Mount Washington, KY 40047-1429; tel. 502/538–1000

*TBD Acquisition, LLC, 1405 Browns Lane, Louisville, KY 40207; tel. 502/896–0495

*VA Medical Center, 1101 Veterans Drive, Lexington, KY 40502-2236; tel. 859/233–4511

## LOUISIANA

Absolute Health, Inc., 560 Belle Terre Blvd., La Place, LA 70068; tel. 985/652–0078

Abundant Health, Inc, 2053 Gause Blvd East, Ste 150, Slidell, LA 70461; tel. 985/649–1001

*Acadia Vermilion Hospital, 2520 North University Avenue, Lafayette, LA 70507; tel. 337/234–5614

Acceptable Health Services, LLC, 5640 Rad Blvd, Ste 740, New Orleans, LA 70126; tel. 504/245–2440

*Brentwood Acquisition-Shreveport, Inc., 1006 Highland Avenue, Shreveport, LA 71101; tel. 318/678–7500

CHRISTUS Health Southwestern Louisiana, 524 Dr. Michael DeBakey Drive, Lake Charles, LA 70601; tel. 337/491–7766

Community Care Hospital, 1421 General Taylor Street, New Orleans, LA 70115; tel. 504/899–2500

Crossroads Regional Hospital, 44 Versailles Blvd, Alexandria, LA 71303; tel. 318/445–5111

DRD New Orleans Medical Clinic, 417 S. Johnson Street, New Orleans, LA 70112; tel. 504/524–7205

Eastern Louisiana Mental Health System, PO Box 498, Jackson, LA 70748-0498; tel. 225/634–0216

Ekems Healthcare, Inc, 8470 Morrison Road Suite A, New Orleans, LA 70127; tel. 504/248–1581

Lake Charles Memorial Hospital, PO Drawer M, Lake Charles, LA 70601; tel. 337/494–3000

Lane Regional Medical Center, 6300 Main Street, Zachary, LA 70791; tel. 225/658–4303

Leesville Rehabilitation Hospital, 900 South Sixth Street, Leesville, LA 71446; tel. 337/392–8118

Liberty HealthCare Systems, LLC, 4673 Eugene Ware Blvd, Bastrop, LA 71220; tel. 318/281–2448

Minden Medical Center, P.O. Box 5003, Minden, LA 71058-5003; tel. 318/377–2321

Natchitoches Regional Medical Center, PO Box 2009, Natchitoches, LA 71457; tel. 318/214–4200

Oceans Behavioral Hospital of Greater New Orleans, 716 Village Road, Kenner, LA 70065; tel. 504/464–8895

Oceans Behavioral Hospital of Lafayette, 420 Albertson Parkway, Broussard, LA 70518; tel. 337/839–9008

*Overton Brooks VA Medical Center, 510 East Stoner Avenue, Shreveport, LA 71101-4295; tel. 318/221–8411

Positive Choices Counseling Services, Inc., P.O. Box 614, Vidalia, LA 71373; tel. 318/336–4700

Provision Rehab LLC., 6 Bienville Square South Drive, Natchitoches, LA 71457; tel. 318/238–4030

River Oaks, Inc., 1525 River Oaks Road West, New Orleans, LA 70123; tel. 504/734–1740

Seaside Health System, 615 E. Worthy Road, Gonzales, LA 70737; tel. 225/238–3043

Southeast Louisiana Veterans Healthcare System, P.O. Box 61011, New Orleans, LA 70161-1011; tel. 504/565–4836

Success Counseling Services-North, 1504 Barksdale Blvd., Bossier City, LA 71111; tel. 318/222–4299

*VA Medical Center, PO Box 69004, Alexandria, LA 71306; tel. 318/473–0010

VCPHCS V, LLC d.b.a, New Orleans Narcotic Treatment Program, 1141 Whitney Avenue Building 4, Gretna, LA 70056; tel. 504/347–1120

VCPHCS VI, LLC d.b.a. Lake Charles Substance Abuse Clinic, 2829 4th Ave, Suite 200, Lake Charles, LA 70601; tel. 337/433–8281

Yes I Can Exceeding Life's Challenges, Inc, 2000 California Ave, Kenner, LA 70062; tel. 504/305–0934

## MAINE

Acadia Hospital - Narcotic Treatment Program, PO Box 422, Bangor, ME 04402-0422; tel. 207/973–6100

Cap Quality Care, Inc., 1 Delta Drive, Suite A, Westbrook, ME 04092; tel. 207/856–7227

Cary Medical Center, 163 Van Buren Road, Caribou, ME 04736; tel. 207/498–3111

Maine Medical Center, 22 Bramhall Street, Portland, ME 04102; tel. 207/662–0111

MaineGeneral Medical Center, 6 East Chestnut Street, Augusta, ME 04330; tel. 207/872–1000

Mercy Recovery Center, 40 Park Road, Westbrook, ME 04092; tel. 207/857–8085

Riverview Psychiatric Center, 11 State House Station, Augusta, ME 04333-0011; tel. 207/624–4683

SequelCare of Maine, LLC, 500 US Route 1, Ste 102, Yarmouth, ME 04096; tel. 207/847–2273

*St. Mary's Regional Medical Center, PO Box 291, Campus Avenue, Lewiston, ME 04243-0291; tel. 207/777–8100

*The Acadia Hospital, PO Box 422, Bangor, ME 04402-0422; tel. 207/973–6100

*VA Maine Healthcare System, 1 Va Center, Augusta, ME 04330; tel. 207/623–8411

## MARYLAND

Addiction Treatment Services of Hopkins Bayview, 5200 Eastern Avenue, MFL-6-E, Baltimore, MD 21224; tel. 410/550–0004

Addiction Treatment Services of Hopkins Bayview, 5510 Nathan Shock Drive, Suite 1500, Baltimore, MD 21224; tel. 410/550–0004

Adventist Behavioral Health Eastern Shore, 821 Fieldcrest Road, Cambridge, MD 21613; tel. 410/221–0288

*Adventist Health Care, Inc., 14901 Broschart Road, Rockville, MD 20850; tel. 301/251–4500

*Ashley, Inc., 800 Tydings Lane, Havre De Grace, MD 21078; tel. 410/273–6600

Awakenings, 2 West Aylesbury Road, Timonium, MD 21093; tel. 410/561–9591

*Baltimore Behavioral Health, Inc., 200 S. Arlington Avenue, Baltimore, MD 21223; tel. 410/962–7180

*Bon Secours Hospital Baltimore, Inc., 2000 West Baltimore Street, Baltimore, MD 21223; tel. 410/362–3011

Bon Secours New Hope Treatment Center, 2401 West Baltimore Street, Baltimore, MD 21223; tel. 410/945–7706

Brook Lane Health Services, PO Box 1945, Hagerstown, MD 21742-1945; tel. 301/733–0330

Calvert Memorial Hospital, 100 Hospital Road, Prince Frederick, MD 20678; tel. 410/535–4000

*Carroll Hospital Center, Inc., 200 Memorial Avenue, Westminster, MD 21157; tel. 410/871–6523

Catholic Charities Child and Family Services, 2300 Dulaney Valley Road, Timonium, MD 21093; tel. 410/252–4700

*Center for Addiction Medicine, 827 Linden Ave, Baltimore, MD 21201; tel. 410/225–6249

*Chase Brexton Health Services, Inc., 1001 Cathedral Street, Baltimore, MD 21201; tel. 410/837–2050

Daybreak Rehabilitation Center, 2490 Giles Road, Baltimore, MD 21225; tel. 410/396–1646

Eastern Shore Hospital Center, PO Box 800, Cambridge, MD 21613; tel. 410/221–2525

*Family Health Centers of Baltimore, Inc., 631 Cherry Hill Road, Baltimore, MD 21225; tel. 410/354–2000

*Fort Meade USA MEDDAC, 2480 Llewellyn Avenue, Fort George G Meade, MD 20755-5129; tel. 301/677–8174

Frederick County Health Dept. /Substance Abuse Services, 300-B Scholl's Lane, Frederick, MD 21701; tel. 301/600–1775

Glass Substance Abuse Program, Inc., 3635 Old Court Road, Pikesville, MD 21208; tel. 410/484–2700

*Health Care for the Homeless, Inc., 421 Fallsway, Baltimore, MD 21202; tel. 410/837–5533

Hope Health Systems, Inc., 6707 Whitestone Road, Ste 106, Woodlawn, MD 21207; tel. 410/265–8737

House of the Good Shepherd of the City of Baltimore, 4100 Maple Avenue, Baltimore, MD 21227; tel. 410/247–2770

*Hudson Health Services, Inc., PO Box 1096, Salisbury, MD 21802-1096; tel. 410/219–9000

John L. Gildner Regional Institute for Children& Adolescents, 15000 Broschart Road, Rockville, MD 20850; tel. 301/251–6800

*Johns Hopkins Bayview Medical Center, 4940 Eastern Avenue, Baltimore, MD 21224-2780; tel. 410/550–0120

Laurel Regional Hospital, 7300 Van Dusen Road, Laurel, MD 20707; tel. 301/497–7984

Levindale Hebrew Geriatric Center and Hospital, 2434 West Belvedere Avenue, Baltimore, MD 21215; tel. 410/466–8700

Maple Shade Youth & Family Services, Inc., 23704 Ocean Gateway, Mardela Springs, MD 21837; tel. 410/742–7400

*Maryland Treatment Centers, Inc., PO Box 136, Emmitsburg, MD 21727; tel. 301/447–2361

MBA - Cherry Hill, 2490 Giles Road, Baltimore, MD 21225; tel. 410/225–9185

MBA Southeast Baltimore County, 8860 Citation Road Suite B, Essex, MD 21221; tel. 410/486–2500

*MedStar Montgomery Medical Center, 18101 Prince Philip Drive, Olney, MD 20832; tel. 301/774–8770

MedStar St. Mary's Hospital, PO Box 527, Leonardtown, MD 20650; tel. 301/475–8981

Medstar Union Memorial Hospital, 201 East University Parkway, Baltimore, MD 21218; tel. 410/554–2000

Meritus Medical Center, 11116 Medical Campus Road, Hagerstown, MD 21742; tel. 301/790–8000

---

*Indicates organization is a Joint Commission accredited Chemical Dependency organization.

Section C

**Methadone for Business Achievers (MBA)**, 821 North Eutaw Street, Baltimore, MD 21201; tel. 410/225-9185

**Methadone for Business Achievers - Timonium**, 2 West Aylesbury Road, Timonium, MD 21093; tel. 410/561-9591

**Nalty & Associates Inc.**, 6819 Timberlane Road, Baltimore, MD 21209; tel. 410/366-1151

*****Naval Health Clinic Annapolis**, 250 Wood Road, Annapolis, MD 21402-5050; tel. 410/293-1330

*****Naval Health Clinic, Patuxent River**, 47149 Buse Road, Building 1370, Patuxent River, MD 20670-5370; tel. 301/342-1418

*****Pathways**, 2620 Riva Road, Annapolis, MD 21401; tel. 410/573-5400

*****People's Community Health Center, Inc.**, 1734 Maryland Ave, Baltimore, MD 21201; tel. 410/467-6040

*****Prince George's County Health Department**, 1701 McCormick Drive, Suite 230, Largo, MD 20774; tel. 301/883-7853

**Reflective Treatment Center**, 301 N Gay Street, Baltimore, MD 21202; tel. 410/752-3500

**Regional Institute for Children and Adolescents-Baltimore**, 605 South Chapel Gate Lane, Baltimore, MD 21229; tel. 410/368-7800

**Saint Luke Institute**, 8901 New Hampshire Avenue, Silver Spring, MD 20903; tel. 301/445-7970

**Sheppard Pratt Health System, Inc.**, PO Box 6815, Baltimore, MD 21285-6815; tel. 410/938-4281

*****Shore Health System of Maryland, Inc.**, 219 S. Washington St, Easton, MD 21601; tel. 410/822-1000

**Sinai Hospital Addictions Recovery Program**, 2401 West Belvedere Avenue, Baltimore, MD 21215; tel. 410/601-5355

*****Suburban Hospital Incorporated**, 8600 Old Georgetown Road, Bethesda, MD 20814; tel. 301/896-3107

*****The Johns Hopkins Hospital**, 600 N. Wolfe Street, Baltimore, MD 21287; tel. 410/955-5000

**Thomas B. Finan Center**, PO Box 1722 Country Club Road, Cumberland, MD 21501-1722; tel. 301/777-2405

*****Tuerk House, Inc.**, 730 Ashburton Street, Baltimore, MD 21216-6116; tel. 410/233-0684

*****University of Maryland Medical Center**, 22 South Greene Street, Baltimore, MD 21201-1595; tel. 410/328-6027

*****VA Maryland Health Care System**, 10 North Greene Street, Baltimore, MD 21201; tel. 410/605-7000

*****Walter Reed National Military Medical Center, Bethesda**, 8901 Wisconsin Avenue, Bethesda, MD 20889-5600; tel. 301/319-4618

**Wicomico County Health Department**, 108 East Main Street, Salisbury, MD 21801; tel. 410/742-3784

**Woodbourne Center, Inc.**, 1301 Woodbourne Avenue, Baltimore, MD 21239; tel. 410/433-1000

*****Worcester County Health Department**, PO Box 249, Snow Hill, MD 21863; tel. 410/632-1100

## MASSACHUSETTS

**Academic & Behavioral Clinic**, P.O. Box 190789, Roxbury, MA 02119; tel. 617/822-0829

*****AdCare Hospital of Worcester, Inc.**, 107 Lincoln Street, Worcester, MA 01605-2499; tel. 508/799-9000

**Arbour - Fuller Hospital**, 200 May Street, South Attleboro, MA 02703; tel. 508/761-8500

**Arbour Hospital Inc.**, 49 Robinwood Avenue, Jamaica Plain, MA 02130; tel. 617/522-4400

**Arbour-HRI Hospital**, 227 Babcock Street, Brookline, MA 02446; tel. 617/731-3200

**Austen Riggs Center**, 25 Main Street, Stockbridge, MA 01262-0962; tel. 413/298-5511

**Baldpate Hospital**, 83 Baldpate Road, Georgetown, MA 01833; tel. 978/352-2131

**Baystate Franklin Medical Center**, 164 High Street, Greenfield, MA 01301; tel. 413/773-0211

**Baystate Medical Center**, 759 Chestnut Street, Springfield, MA 01199; tel. 413/794-5960

*****Berkshire Medical Center**, 725 North Street, Pittsfield, MA 01201; tel. 413/447-2000

*****Bournewood Hospital**, 300 South Street, Chestnut Hill, MA 02467; tel. 617/469-0300

**Bridgewater State Hospital**, 20 Administration Road, Bridgewater, MA 02324; tel. 508/279-4500

**Brockton Multi Service Center**, 165 Quincy Street, Brockton, MA 02302; tel. 508/897-2000

**Cambridge Eating Disorder Center**, 3 Bow Street, Cambridge, MA 02138; tel. 617/547-2255

**Cape Cod and Islands Community Mental Health Center**, 830 County Road, Pocasset, MA 02559; tel. 508/564-9600

**Centerpoint**, PO Box 374, Tewksbury, MA 01876; tel. 978/858-3776

**Cohannet Academy**, 60 Hodges Avenue - Goss 3, Taunton, MA 02780; tel. 508/977-3730

**Counseling & Assessment Clinic of Worcester, LLC**, 38 Front Street, 5th Floor, Worcester, MA 01608; tel. 508/756-5400

*****Dimock Community Foundation, Inc. - OTP**, 55 Dimock Street, Roxbury, MA 02119; tel. 617/442-8800

**Doctor Franklin Perkins School**, 971 Main Street, Lancaster, MA 01523; tel. 978/365-7376

**Dr. John C. Corrigan Mental Health Center**, 49 Hillside Street, Fall River, MA 02720; tel. 508/235-7200

**Dr. Solomon Carter Fuller Mental Health Center**, 85 E. Newton Street, Boston, MA 02118; tel. 617/626-8861

**Edith Nourse Rogers Memorial Veterans Hospital**, 200 Springs Road, Bedford, MA 01730; tel. 781/687-3080

**Federal Bureau of Prisons Federal Medical Center Devens**, PO Box 880, Ayer, MA 01432; tel. 978/796-1443

*****Fenway Community Health Center, Inc.**, 1340 Boylston Street, Boston, MA 02215; tel. 617/267-0900

**Franciscan Hospital for Children, Inc.**, 30 Warren Street, Boston, MA 02135-3680; tel. 617/254-3800

*****Gosnold, Inc.**, 200 Ter Heun Drive, Falmouth, MA 02540; tel. 508/540-6550

**High Point Treatment Center (OTP)**, 30 Meadowbrook Road, Brockton, MA 02301; tel. 508/584-9210

**High Point Treatment Center - OTP**, 10 Meadowbrook Road, Brockton, MA 02301; tel. 508/742-4400

*****High Point Treatment Center, Inc.**, 98 North Front Street 3rd Floor, New Bedford, MA 02740; tel. 774/628-1095

**High Point Treatment Center, Inc.**, 1233 State Road, Plymouth, MA 02360-5133; tel. 508/224-7701

**High Point Treatment Center, Inc. (OTP)**, 100 North Front Street, New Bedford, MA 02740; tel. 774/628-1000

**Hillcrest Educational Centers, Inc.**, 788 South Street, Pittsfield, MA 01201; tel. 413/499-7924

**Justice Resource Institute -- The Meadowridge Schools**, 160 Gould St, Suite 300, Needham Heights, MA 02494; tel. 781/559-4900

**Justice Resource Institute Behavioral Health Centers**, 380 Massachusetts Ave, Acton, MA 01720; tel. 978/264-3500

**LAMOUR By Design Inc.**, 42-44 Diauto Drive, Randolph, MA 02368; tel. 781/885-7252

*****Lowell Community Health Center**, 161 Jackson Street, Lowell, MA 01852; tel. 978/937-9700

**Luminosity Behavioral Health Services**, 810 Washington Street, Stoughton, MA 02072; tel. 781/344-0102

*****Lynn Community Health Center**, PO Box 526, Lynn, MA 01903; tel. 781/596-2502

*****McLean Hospital**, 115 Mill Street, Belmont, MA 02478; tel. 617/855-3450

*****Mercy Hospital, Inc.**, 271 Carew Street, Springfield, MA 01104; tel. 413/748-9000

**Mercy Hospital, Inc. - MMTP**, 227 Mill Street, Springfield, MA 01102; tel. 413/539-2400

**Mercy Hospital, Inc. MMTP**, 1233 Main Street, Holyoke, MA 01040; tel. 413/539-2950

**Mercy Medical Center Inpatient Detox Program**, 1233 Main Street, Holyoke, MA 01040; tel. 413/539-2950

**MetroWest Medical Center**, 115 Lincoln Street, Framingham, MA 01702; tel. 508/383-1000

**Multicultural Wellness Center, Inc**, 250 Commerical Street Suite 330, Worcester, MA 01608; tel. 508/752-4665

**NFI Massachusetts(Northeastern Family Institute)**, PO Box 732, Westborough, MA 01581; tel. 978/774-0774

**North End Community Health Committee, Inc.**, 332 Hanover Street, Boston, MA 02113; tel. 617/643-8000

**North Shore Medical Center, Inc.**, 81 Highland Avenue, Salem, MA 01970; tel. 978/741-1200

*****Northeast Hospital Corporation**, 85 Herrick Street, Beverly, MA 01915-1777; tel. 978/922-3000

**Osiris Family Institute, LLC**, 184 Dudley Street Suite 107 LL, Roxbury, MA 02119; tel. 617/442-2002

**Priority Professional Care, LLC**, 1613 Blue Hill Avenue Suite 302, Mattapan, MA 02126; tel. 857/598-4774

**Pyramid Builders Associates**, 1960 Washington Street, Boston, MA 02118; tel. 617/516-0280

**SSTAR**, 1010 South Main Street, Fall River, MA 02724; tel. 508/235-5010

**SSTAR DETOX**, 386 Stanley Street, Fall River, MA 02720; tel. 508/324-3500

**Steward Saint Anne's Hospital**, 795 Middle Street, Fall River, MA 02721-1798; tel. 508/674-5600

**The Three Rivers Treatment Program**, 26 Ridgewood Terrace, Springfield, MA 01105; tel. 413/733-4032

**The Whitney Academy, Inc.**, PO Box 619, East Freetown, MA 02717; tel. 508/763-3737

**UHS of Westwood Pembroke**, 45 Clapboardtree Street, Westwood, MA 02090; tel. 781/762-7764

**University of Massachusetts Medical School, Transitions IRTP**, 309 Belmont Street, Adolescent Wing D2, Worcester, MA 01604; tel. 508/856-1439

*****VA Boston Healthcare System**, 1400 VFW Parkway, West Roxbury, MA 02132; tel. 617/323-7700

*****VA Central Western Massachusetts Healthcare System**, 421 North Main Street, Leeds, MA 01053-9764; tel. 413/584-4040

**Walden Behavioral Care**, 9 Hope Avenue Suite 500, Waltham, MA 02453; tel. 781/647-6767

**Whittier Pavillion**, 76 Summer Street, Haverhill, MA 01830; tel. 978/373-8222

**Wild Acre Inns, Inc.**, 108 Pleasant Street, Arlington, MA 02476; tel. 781/643-0643

## MICHIGAN

*****ACAC, Inc.**, 3949 Sparks Drive SE Suite 103, Grand Rapids, MI 49546; tel. 616/957-5850

*****Access Behavioral Healthcare, LLC**, 42189 E. Ann Arbor Road, Plymouth, MI 48170; tel. 734/453-5603

*****Aleda E. Lutz VA Medical Ctr.**, 1500 Weiss Street, Saginaw, MI 48602; tel. 989/497-2500

*****Apex Behavioral Health - Dearborn**, 6 Parklane Blvd, Ste 695, Dearborn, MI 48126; tel. 313/271-8170

*****Apex Behavioral Health Western Wayne, PLLC**, 1547 S. Wayne Rd., Westland, MI 48186; tel. 734/729-3133

*****Apex Downriver Behavioral Health**, 19366 Allen Road, Ste C, Brownstown, MI 48183; tel. 734/479-0949

*****Arbor Circle Corporation**, 1115 Ball Avenue, Grand Rapids, MI 49505; tel. 616/456-7775

*****Battle Creek VA Medical Center**, 5500 Armstrong Road, Battle Creek, MI 49037; tel. 269/966-5600

*****Bay Mills Indian Community**, 12124 West Lake Shore Drive, Brimley, MI 49715; tel. 906/248-5527

**Beacon Specialized Living Services, Inc.**, 555 Railroad Street P.O. Box 69, Bangor, MI 49013; tel. 269/427-8400

*****Brighton Hospital**, 12851 Grand River Road, Brighton, MI 48116; tel. 810/227-1211

**C.W. Enterprises LLC**, 50630 Chesterfield Road, Chesterfield, MI 48051; tel. 586/949-7680

*****Catholic Services of Macomb, Inc.**, 15945 Canal Road, Clinton Township, MI 48038; tel. 586/416-2300

*****Community Care Services**, 26184 West Outer Drive, Lincoln Park, MI 48146; tel. 313/389-7525

**Community Mental Health for Central Michigan**, 301 South Crapo, Suite 100, Mount Pleasant, MI 48858; tel. 989/772-5938

**Cruz Clinic**, 17177 North Laurel Park Drive, Suite 131, Livonia, MI 48152; tel. 734/462-3210

**Delta Family Clinic South**, 6195 Miller Road, Suite A, Swartz Creek, MI 48473; tel. 810/630-1152

**Forest View Psychiatric Hospital**, 1055 Medical Park Drive SE, Grand Rapids, MI 49546; tel. 616/942-9610

**Genesys Practice Partners, Inc.**, 8435 Holly Road, Grand Blanc, MI 48439; tel. 810/424-2400

*****Growth Works Incorporated**, PO Box 6115, Plymouth, MI 48170-6115; tel. 734/455-4095

**Havenwyck Hospital**, 1525 University Drive, Auburn Hills, MI 48326; tel. 248/373-9200

*****Hegira Programs, Inc.**, 8623 N Wayne Road, Suite 200, Westland, MI 48185; tel. 734/458-4601

**Henry Ford Macomb Hospital**, 15855 Nineteen Mile Road, Clinton Township, MI 48038; tel. 586/263-2700

---

*Indicates organization is a Joint Commission accredited Chemical Dependency organization.

Section C

*Horizon Treatment Services, LLC, 17515 W. 9 Mile Rd., Suite 720, Southfield, MI 48075; tel. 248/423-1728

Huron Valley Consultation Center, Inc., 2750 South State Street, Ann Arbor, MI 48104; tel. 734/662-6300

Integro, LLC, 1200 N West Avenue, Suite 300, Jackson, MI 49202; tel. 517/789-1234

*Ionia County Substance Abuse, 175 E. Adams, Ionia, MI 48846; tel. 616/527-5341

*Jump Start Consulting, LLC D.B.A. Inner Door Center, 317 East Eleven Mile Road, Royal Oak, MI 48067; tel. 248/336-2868

*Karalee & Associates, P.C., 1308 South Main Street, Plymouth, MI 48170; tel. 734/451-3440

Lakeside Academy, 3921 Oakland Drive, Kalamazoo, MI 49008; tel. 269/381-4760

*Latino Family Services, Inc., 3815 West Fort Street, Detroit, MI 48216; tel. 313/841-7380

Lenawee Community Mental Health Authority, 1040 S. Winter St., Ste.#1022, Adrian, MI 49221; tel. 517/263-8905

*Life Challenge of Michigan, 2220 Spring Road, Hillsdale, MI 49242; tel. 517/437-4454

Livingston County Community Mental Health Authority, 2280 East Grand River, Howell, MI 48843; tel. 517/546-4126

McLaren Flint Medical Center, 401 South Ballenger Highway, Flint, MI 48532; tel. 810/342-2000

*Meridian Professional Psychological Consultants, PC, 5031 Park Lake Road, East Lansing, MI 48823; tel. 517/332-0811

Metro East Substance Abuse Treatment Corporation, PO Box 13408, Detroit, MI 48213; tel. 313/371-0055

Michigan Access Center, Inc., 2722 East Michigan Ave. Suite 104, Lansing, MI 48912; tel. 517/332-9000

*Michigan Behavior Medicine, 2525 Crooks Rd suite100, Troy, MI 48084; tel. 248/740-9360

Monroe Community Mental Health Authority, P.O. Box 726, Monroe, MI 48161-0726; tel. 734/243-7340

Nardin Park Recovery Center, 9605 Grand River, Detroit, MI 48204; tel. 313/834-5930

New Center Community Services, 2051 West Grand Boulevard, Detroit, MI 48208; tel. 313/961-3200

*Oakland Psychological Clinic, P.C., 2550 South Telegraph Road Suite 250, Bloomfield Hills, MI 48302; tel. 248/322-0003

Oakwood Heritage Hospital, 10000 Telegraph Road, Taylor, MI 48180; tel. 313/295-5000

Opioid Treatment Program - John D. Dingell VA Medical Center, 4646 John R. Street, Detroit, MI 48201; tel. 313/576-3207

*Oscar G. Johnson VA Medical Center, 325 East H Street, Iron Mountain, MI 49801; tel. 906/774-3300

*PHC of MI Inc., 35031 23 Mile Road, New Baltimore, MI 48047; tel. 586/725-5777

Rainbow Center of Michigan (Monroe), 14733 South Telegraph Road, Monroe, MI 48161; tel. 734/243-8707

Rainbow Center of Michigan Inc, P O Box 725098, Berkley, MI 48072; tel. 313/865-1580

Rainbow Center of Michigan, Inc., 20724 Eureka Road, Taylor, MI 48180; tel. 734/759-0510

*Recovery Pathways, LLC, 717 E. Midland St., Bay City, MI 48706; tel. 989/928-3566

*Redford Counseling Center, 25945 West Seven Mile Road, Redford, MI 48240; tel. 313/535-6560

*River's Bend, P.C., 800 Stephenson Highway, Suite 250, Troy, MI 48083; tel. 248/585-3239

Rose Hill Center, Inc., 5130 Rose Hill Boulevard, Holly, MI 48442; tel. 248/634-5530

Safehaus Inc., 21056 Dean Street, Warren, MI 48091; tel. 586/806-4678

Saint Mary's Health Care, 200 Jefferson Avenue Southeast, Grand Rapids, MI 49503; tel. 616/685-5000

St. John Macomb-Oakland Hospital, 11800 East Twelve Mile Road, Warren, MI 48093; tel. 586/573-5000

*St. Joseph Mercy Hospital, 5333 McAuley Drive office 6104, Ypsilanti, MI 48197; tel. 734/712-3456

St. Mary's of Michigan Medical Center, 800 South Washington Avenue, Saginaw, MI 48601; tel. 989/907-8000

Star Center, Inc., 13575 Lesure, Detroit, MI 48227; tel. 313/493-4410

*Sterling Area Health Center, PO Box 740, Sterling, MI 48659; tel. 989/654-2491

Summit Pointe, 140 West Michigan Avenue, Battle Creek, MI 49017; tel. 269/966-1460

Sunshine Treatment Institute, P.O. Box 690, Southfield, MI 48037; tel. 313/368-4800

Taylor Psychological Clinic, PC, 1172 Robert T Longway Blvd, Flint, MI 48503; tel. 810/232-8466

TBCI, PC, 11059 Owendale, Troy, MI 48083; tel. 248/526-0110

*The Guidance Center, 13101 Allen Road, Southgate, MI 48195; tel. 734/785-7700

The Montcalm Center for Behavioral Health, 611 North State Street, Stanton, MI 48888; tel. 989/831-7520

*The Salvation Army Turning Point Programs, 72 Sheldon Boulevard, S.E., Grand Rapids, MI 49503; tel. 616/742-0351

*The University of Michigan Hospitals and Health Centers, 2101 Commonwealth, Suite A, Ann Arbor, MI 48105; tel. 734/647-2478

Ultimate Solutions, 29240 Buckingham, Suite 11, Livonia, MI 48154; tel. 734/513-2800

*VA Ann Arbor Healthcare System, 2215 Fuller Road, Ann Arbor, MI 48105; tel. 734/769-7100

*Washtenaw County Community Supports and Treatment Services, 2140 East Ellsworth Road, Ann Arbor, MI 48108; tel. 734/544-3000

## MINNESOTA

Abbott Northwestern Hospital, 800 East 28th Street, Minneapolis, MN 55407; tel. 612/863-4875

Andrew Residence, 1215 South 9th Street, Minneapolis, MN 55404; tel. 612/333-0111

Anoka-Metro Regional Treatment Center, 3301 7th Avenue North, Anoka, MN 55303; tel. 651/431-5000

Bureau of Prisons - FMC Rochester, PO Box 4600, Rochester, MN 55903; tel. 507/287-0674

Child and Adolescent Behavioral Health Services, 1701 Technology Drive, Willmar, MN 56201; tel. 218/330-7406

*Community Addiction Recovery Enterprise, 3301 Seventh Avenue North, Anoka, MN 55303; tel. 218/736-1886

Community Addiction Recovery Enterprise - Willmar OTP, 1801 Technology Drive Northeast, Willmar, MN 56201; tel. 320/231-5356

*Hazelden Foundation, Recovery Services Division, PO Box 11, Center City, MN 55012; tel. 651/257-4200

Hennepin Healthcare System, Inc., 914 South Eighth Street Suite 131, Minneapolis, MN 55404; tel. 612/873-2338

Hennepin Healthcare Systems, Inc, 701 Park Avenue, Minneapolis, MN 55415; tel. 612/347-0950

*Mayo Clinic Health System - Albert Lea & Austin, 1000 First Drive N.W., Austin, MN 55912; tel. 507/373-2384

Mercy Hospital, 4050 Coon Rapids Blvd., Coon Rapids, MN 55433; tel. 763/236-6000

Minnesota Security Hospital, 100 Freeman Drive, Saint Peter, MN 56082; tel. 507/985-3128

Minnesota Specialty Health System-Brainerd, 11615 State Avenue, Brainerd, MN 56401; tel. 218/828-6123

Minnesota Specialty Health Systems - Wadena, 240 Shady Lane Drive, Wadena, MN 56482; tel. 218/319-6001

Minnesota Specialty Health Systems - Willmar, 1208 Olena Avenue SE, Willmar, MN 56201; tel. 320/235-0018

*New Beginnings at Waverly, LLC, 109 North Shore Drive, Waverly, MN 55390-9743; tel. 763/658-5800

Park Nicollet Health Services, PO Box 650, Minneapolis, MN 55440; tel. 952/993-5000

PrairieCare, 12915 63rd Ave. North, Maple Grove, MN 55369; tel. 952/838-5800

*Saint Cloud Hospital, 1406 Sixth Avenue North, Saint Cloud, MN 56303; tel. 320/251-2700

SMDC Medical Center, 502 East Second Street, Duluth, MN 55805; tel. 218/727-8762

*St. Cloud VA Health Care System, 4801 Veterans Drive, Saint Cloud, MN 56303; tel. 320/255-6480

St. Joseph's Hospital Chemical Dependency Unit, 45 W. 10th Street, Saint Paul, MN 55102; tel. 651/232-3256

United Hospital, 333 North Smith Avenue, Saint Paul, MN 55102; tel. 651/241-8802

*University of Minnesota Medical Center, Fairview, 2450 Riverside Avenue, Minneapolis, MN 55455; tel. 612/273-3000

*VA Health Care System - Minneapolis, One Veterans Drive, Minneapolis, MN 55417; tel. 612/725-2000

## MISSISSIPPI

Adams County Correctional Center, P.O. Box 850, Washington, MS 39190; tel. 601/304-2500

Biloxi Regional Medical Center, PO Box 128, Biloxi, MS 39533; tel. 228/436-1104

Bolivar Medical Center, PO Box 1380, Cleveland, MS 38732-1380; tel. 662/846-2534

Brentwood Behavioral Healthcare of Mississippi, LLC, 3531 East Lakeland Drive, Flowood, MS 39232; tel. 601/936-2024

*CARES Center, Inc. and Mississippi Children's Home Society, 1900 North West Street, Jackson, MS 39202; tel. 601/352-7784

*COPAC, Inc., 3949 Highway 43 North, Brandon, MS 39047; tel. 601/829-2500

*Delta Regional Medical Center, PO Box 5247, Greenville, MS 38704-5247; tel. 662/378-3783

Diamond Grove Center for Children and Adolescents, PO Box 848, Louisville, MS 39339; tel. 662/779-0119

Millcreek of Pontotoc, PO Box 619, Pontotoc, MS 38863; tel. 662/488-8878

*Mississippi State Hospital, PO Box 157-A, Whitfield, MS 39193-0157; tel. 601/351-8190

Natchez Community Hospital, PO Box 1203, Natchez, MS 39121; tel. 601/445-6205

North Oak Regional Medical Center, PO Box 648, Senatobia, MS 38668-0648; tel. 662/562-3100

*Parkwood Behavioral Health System, 8135 Goodman Road, Olive Branch, MS 38654; tel. 662/895-4900

PSI Crossings, 5000 Highway 39 North, Meridian, MS 39301; tel. 601/483-5452

Rehabilitation Centers, Inc., PO Box 1160, Magee, MS 39111; tel. 601/849-4221

Specialized Treatment Facility, 14426 James Bond Road, Gulfport, MS 39503; tel. 228/328-6000

*VA Gulf Coast Veterans Health Care System, 400 Veterans Avenue, Biloxi, MS 39531; tel. 228/523-5000

*VA Medical Center - G. V. (Sonny) Montgomery, 1500 East Woodrow Wilson Avenue, Jackson, MS 39216; tel. 601/364-1201

## MISSOURI

*Alternative Behavioral Care, 255 Spencer Road, Suite 101, Saint Peters, MO 63376; tel. 636/477-6111

Barnes-Jewish Hospital, 1 Barnes Jewish Hospital Plaza, Saint Louis, MO 63110; tel. 314/747-3000

BJC Behavioral Health, 1430 Olive Street - Suite 400, Saint Louis, MO 63103; tel. 314/206-3712

*Boonville Valley Hope, 1415 Ashley Road, Boonville, MO 65233; tel. 660/882-6547

Center for Behavioral Medicine, 1000 East 24th Street, Kansas City, MO 64108-2620; tel. 816/512-7000

*CenterPointe Behavioral Health Kansas City, 763 South New Ballas Road, Suite 300, Saint Louis, MO 63141; tel. 816/795-1445

*CenterPointe Hospital, 4801 Weldon Spring Parkway, Saint Charles, MO 63304; tel. 636/441-7300

*Centrec Care, Inc., 1224 Fern Ridge Parkway, Suite 305, Saint Louis, MO 63141; tel. 314/205-8068

Change Academy Lake of the Ozarks (CALO), 130 Calo Lane, Lake Ozark, MO 65049; tel. 573/365-2221

Child Advocacy Services Center Inc., 2 East 59th Street, Kansas City, MO 64113-2116; tel. 816/363-1898

*Christian Hospital Northeast - Northwest, 11133 Dunn Road, Saint Louis, MO 63136; tel. 314/653-5616

Columbia Treatment Clinic, 1301 Vandiver Suite Y, Columbia, MO 65202; tel. 573/449-8338

Cottonwood Residential Treatment Center, 1025 N. Sprigg, Cape Girardeau, MO 63701; tel. 573/290-5888

*Crittenton, 10918 Elm Avenue, Kansas City, MO 64134-4199; tel. 816/765-6600

DRD Kansas City Medical Clinic, 723 East 18th Street, Kansas City, MO 64108; tel. 816/283-3877

DRD Springfield Medical Clinic, 404 East Battlefield Street, Springfield, MO 65807; tel. 417/865-8045

Epworth Children & Family Services, 110 North Elm Avenue, Saint Louis, MO 63119; tel. 314/961-5718

---

*Indicates organization is a Joint Commission accredited Chemical Dependency organization.

Section C

Fulton State Hospital, 600 East Fifth Street, Fulton, MO 65251-1798; tel. 573/592–4100

Great Circle, PO Box 189, Saint James, MO 65559; tel. 573/265–3251

*Harry S. Truman Memorial Veterans' Hospital, 800 Hospital Drive, Columbia, MO 65201; tel. 573/814–6000

Hawthorn Children's Psychiatric Hospital, 1901 Pennsylvania Avenue, Saint Louis, MO 63133; tel. 314/512–7800

Heartland Behavioral Health Services, 1500 West Ashland, Nevada, MO 64772; tel. 417/667–2666

*Kansas City Veterans Affairs Medical Center, 4801 Linwood Boulevard, Kansas City, MO 64128; tel. 816/861–4700

Lakeland Behavioral Health System, 440 South Market Avenue, Springfield, MO 65806; tel. 417/865–5581

McCallum Place Eating Disorders Treatment, 231 W. Lockwood Ave. Suite 201, Saint Louis, MO 63119; tel. 314/968–1900

Ozarks Medical Center, PO Box 1100, West Plains, MO 65775; tel. 417/256–9111

*Provident Inc., 2650 Olive Street., Saint Louis, MO 63103; tel. 314/371–6500

Research Psychiatric Center, 2323 East 63rd Street, Kansas City, MO 64130; tel. 816/444–8161

Southeast Missouri Mental Health Center, 1010 West Columbia Street, Farmington, MO 63640-2997; tel. 573/218–6792

*SSM DePaul Health Center, 12303 DePaul Drive, Bridgeton, MO 63044-2588; tel. 314/344–6000

SSM St. Joseph Health Center, 300 First Capitol Drive, Saint Charles, MO 63301; tel. 636/947–5000

SSM St. Mary's Health Center, 6420 Clayton Road, Richmond Heights, MO 63117; tel. 314/768–8000

*St. Anthony's Medical Center, 10010 Kennerly Road, Saint Louis, MO 63128; tel. 314/525–1000

St. Louis Psychiatric Rehabilitation Center, 5300 Arsenal Street, Saint Louis, MO 63139; tel. 314/877–6500

*St. Louis VA Healthcare System, 915 North Grand Boulevard, Saint Louis, MO 63106; tel. 314/289–7020

*Swope Health Services, 3801 Blue Parkway, Kansas City, MO 64130; tel. 816/922–3166

The Salvation Army Children's Shelter, 101 W Linwood, Kansas City, MO 64111; tel. 816/285–2480

*Truman Medical Center, 2301 Holmes Street, Kansas City, MO 64108; tel. 816/404–0905

*Truman Medical Center- Lakewood, 7900 Lees Summit Road, Kansas City, MO 64139; tel. 816/404–0905

Two Rivers Psychiatric Hospital, 5121 Raytown Road, Kansas City, MO 64133; tel. 816/382–6360

U.S. Medical Center for Federal Prisoners, 1900 West Sunshine Street, Springfield, MO 65807; tel. 417/862–7041

VCPHCS XV, LLC d/b/a Joplin Treatment Clinic, P.O Box 4692, Joplin, MO 64803; tel. 214/365–6111

Woodridge of Missouri, LLC, PO Box 4067, Waynesville, MO 65583; tel. 573/774–5353

## MONTANA

Billings Clinic, PO Box 37000, Billings, MT 59107-3700; tel. 406/657–4000

Intermountain Children's Home, 500 South Lamborn, Helena, MT 59601; tel. 406/442–7920

Kid's Behavioral Health of Montana, 55 Basin Creek Road, Butte, MT 59701; tel. 406/494–4183

Montana Academy, 9705 Lost Prairie Road, Marion, MT 59925; tel. 406/858–2339

Montana Children's Home and Hospital, PO Box 5539, Helena, MT 59604; tel. 406/444–7500

*Rocky Mountain Treatment Center, 920 Fourth Avenue North, Great Falls, MT 59401; tel. 406/727–8832

*VA Montana Healthcare System, 3687 Veterans Drive, Fort Harrison, MT 59636-1500; tel. 406/447–7900

## NEBRASKA

*Alegent Creighton Health Immanuel Medical Center, 6901 North 72nd Street, Omaha, NE 68122; tel. 402/572–2291

*Behavioral Health Specialists, Inc., 900 W Norfolk Avenue, Ste 200, Norfolk, NE 68701; tel. 402/370–3140

*Blue Valley Behavioral Health, Inc., 1123 North 9th Street, Beatrice, NE 68310; tel. 402/228–3386

*Bryan Medical Center, 1600 South 48th Street, Lincoln, NE 68506; tel. 402/481–3548

*East Central District Health Department, 2282 East 32nd Avenue, Columbus, NE 68601; tel. 402/562–8950

Epworth Village, Inc., PO Box 503, York, NE 68467-0503; tel. 402/362–3353

Father Flanagan's Boys Home, 555 North 30th Street, Omaha, NE 68131; tel. 402/498–6525

Hastings Regional Center, PO Box 579, Hastings, NE 68902-0579; tel. 402/462–1971

Lincoln Lancaster County Child Guidance Center, 2444 'O' Street, Lincoln, NE 68510; tel. 402/475–7666

Lincoln Regional Center, PO Box 94949, Lincoln, NE 68509-4949; tel. 402/471–4444

*O'Neill Valley Hope, 1421 North 10th Street, Oneill, NE 68763; tel. 402/336–3747

OMNI Behavioral Health, 5115 F Street, Omaha, NE 68117; tel. 402/397–9866

*VA Nebraska-Western Iowa Health Care System, 4101 Woolworth Avenue, Omaha, NE 68105; tel. 402/449–0600

## NEVADA

*Community Counseling Center, Carson City, 205 South Pratt Avenue, Carson City, NV 89701; tel. 775/882–3945

Desert Willow Treatment Center, 6171 W Charleston Boulevard, Building #17, Las Vegas, NV 89146; tel. 702/486–9900

*Las Vegas Recovery Center, 3371 N. Buffalo Drive, Las Vegas, NV 89129; tel. 702/515–1374

*Montevista Hospital, 5900 West Rochelle Avenue, Las Vegas, NV 89103-3327; tel. 702/364–1111

*New Frontier Treatment Center, PO Box 1240, Fallon, NV 89407; tel. 775/423–1412

Northern Nevada Adult Mental Health Services, 480 Galletti Way, Sparks, NV 89431; tel. 775/688–2001

Northern Nevada Medical Center, 2375 East Prater Way, Sparks, NV 89434; tel. 775/331–7000

*Seven Hills Hospital, Inc., 3021 W. Horizon Ridge Parkway, Henderson, NV 89052; tel. 702/646–5000

Southern Nevada Adult Mental Health Services, 6161 West Charleston Boulevard, Las Vegas, NV 89146; tel. 702/486–4400

*Spring Mountain Treatment Center, 7000 Spring Mountain Road, Las Vegas, NV 89117; tel. 702/873–2400

*VA Sierra Nevada Health Care System, 975 Kirman Avenue, Reno, NV 89502-2597; tel. 775/786–7200

VA Southern Nevada Healthcare System, 6900 North Pecos Rd, North Las Vegas, NV 89086; tel. 702/791–9000

Willow Springs Center, 690 Edison Way, Reno, NV 89502; tel. 775/858–3303

## NEW HAMPSHIRE

Community Council of Nashua, NH, 7 Prospect Street, Nashua, NH 03060; tel. 603/889–6147

Lakeview NeuroRehabilitation Center, 244 Highwatch Road, Effingham, NH 03882; tel. 603/539–7451

NFI North, Inc., 40 Park Lane, Contoocook, NH 03229; tel. 603/746–7550

*VA Medical Center, 718 Smyth Road, Manchester, NH 03104-4098; tel. 603/624–4366

## NEW JERSEY

*AtlantiCare Behavioral Health, 6550 Delilah Road, Building 300, Egg Harbor Township, NJ 08234; tel. 609/645–7600

AtlantiCare Regional Medical Center, 1925 Pacific Avenue, Atlantic City, NJ 08401; tel. 609/345–4000

Bancroft Rehabilitation Services, 425 Kings Highway East, Haddonfield, NJ 08033; tel. 856/429–5637

*Bergen Regional Medical Center, 230 East Ridgewood Avenue, Paramus, NJ 07652; tel. 201/967–4000

*Bonnie Brae, 3415 Valley Road, P. O. Box 825, Liberty Corner, NJ 07938-0825; tel. 908/647–0800

*Cape Counseling Services, 1129 Route 9, Cape May Court House, NJ 08210; tel. 609/778–6100

*Care Plus NJ, Inc., 610 Valley Health Plaza, Paramus, NJ 07652; tel. 201/265–8200

*Carrier Clinic, PO Box 147, Belle Mead, NJ 08502-0147; tel. 908/281–1000

*Catholic Charities - Diocese of Metuchen, 319 Maple Street, Perth Amboy, NJ 08861; tel. 732/324–8200

Christian Health Care Center, 301 Sicomac Avenue, Wyckoff, NJ 07481; tel. 201/848–5200

CPC Behavioral Healthcare, Inc., 10 Industrial Way East, Eatontown, NJ 07724; tel. 732/935–2220

East Orange General Hospital, 300 Central Avenue, East Orange, NJ 07018; tel. 973/672–8400

*GenPsych of South Carolina, LLC, 981 Route 22 West, Bridgewater, NJ 08807; tel. 908/526–8370

Hampton Behavioral Health Center, 650 Rancocas Rd, Westampton, NJ 08060; tel. 609/267–7000

*High Focus Centers, 47 Maple Street, Suite 401, Summit, NJ 07901; tel. 908/363–1023

*Hoboken University Medical Center, 308 Willow Avenue, Hoboken, NJ 07030; tel. 201/418–1000

Hunterdon Medical Center, 2100 Wescott Drive, Flemington, NJ 08822; tel. 908/788–6151

*Jersey Shore University Medical Center, 1945 Route 33, Neptune, NJ 07754-0397; tel. 732/776–4900

*Kennedy University Hospital, 1099 White Horse Road, Voorhees, NJ 08043; tel. 856/566–5243

Khaleidoscope Health Care, Inc., Jones and Associates-111 Wayne Street, Jersey City, NJ 07302; tel. 201/451–5425

Monmouth Medical Center, 300 Second Avenue, Long Branch, NJ 07740; tel. 732/222–5200

Montclair Hospital, LLC, d/b/a Mountainside Hospital, 1 Bay Avenue, Montclair, NJ 07042; tel. 973/429–6000

*Morristown Medical Center, 100 Madison Avenue, Morristown, NJ 07960; tel. 973/971–5450

Newark Beth Israel Medical Center, 201 Lyons Avenue, Newark, NJ 07112; tel. 973/926–7000

Newton Medical Center, 175 High Street, Newton, NJ 07860; tel. 973/383–2121

*North Hudson Community Action Corporation, 800-31st Street, Union City, NJ 07087; tel. 201/866–2727

*Overlook Medical Center, PO Box 220, Summit, NJ 07902-0220; tel. 908/522–4912

*Princeton HealthCare System, 1 Plainsboro Road, Plainsboro, NJ 08536; tel. 609/853–6500

*Recovery Services of New Jersey, Inc., 5034 Atlantic Avenue, Mays Landing, NJ 08330; tel. 609/625–4900

Richard Hall Community Mental Health Center, 500 North Bridge Street, Bridgewater, NJ 08807; tel. 908/725–2800

*Riverview Medical Center, One Riverview Plaza, Red Bank, NJ 07701; tel. 732/741–2700

Saint Barnabas Behavioral Health Center, Inc., 1691 US Highway 9, CN 2025, Toms River, NJ 08754; tel. 732/914–1688

*Saint Clare's Health System, 25 Pocono Road, Denville, NJ 07834; tel. 973/983–5588

Saint Peter's University Hospital, 254 Easton Avenue, New Brunswick, NJ 08901; tel. 732/745–8600

Sequel of New Jersey, Inc, 1770 Mt Ephraim Avenue, Camden, NJ 08104; tel. 856/635–0200

Somerset Medical Center, 110 Rehill Avenue, Somerville, NJ 08876-2598; tel. 908/685–2200

South Jersey Drug Treatment, PO Box 867, Bridgeton, NJ 08302; tel. 856/455–5441

St. Francis Medical Center, 601 Hamilton Avenue, Trenton, NJ 08629; tel. 609/599–5000

St. Mary's Hospital, 350 Boulevard, Passaic, NJ 07055; tel. 973/365–4300

Stress Care of New Jersey, LLC, 4122 Route 516, Matawan, NJ 07747; tel. 732/679–4500

*Summit Oaks Hospital, 19 Prospect Street, Summit, NJ 07901; tel. 908/522–7000

*Sunrise Detox II, LLC, 1272 Long Hill Road, Stirling, NJ 07980; tel. 908/504–2700

*The Counseling Center at Freehold, 4345 Highway Rt.9, Freehold, NJ 07728; tel. 732/431–5300

*The Lester A. Drenk Behavioral Health Center, Inc., 1289 Route 38 West, Suite 203, Hainesport, NJ 08036; tel. 609/267–5656

*Trinitas Regional Medical Center, 225 Williamson Street, Elizabeth, NJ 07207; tel. 908/994–5754

UMDNJ - University Behavioral HealthCare, PO Box 1392, Piscataway, NJ 08855-1392; tel. 732/235–5500

Underwood - Memorial Hospital, 509 North Broad Street, Woodbury, NJ 08096; tel. 856/845–0100

*VA New Jersey Health Care System, 385 Tremont Avenue, Director's Office (00), East Orange, NJ 07018; tel. 973/676–1000

Section C

*Indicates organization is a Joint Commission accredited Chemical Dependency organization.

**Virtua-West Jersey Health System, Inc.(Voorhees),** 100 Bowman Drive, Voorhees New Jersey, Voorhees, NJ 08043; tel. 856/247–3000

**VisionQuest - New Jersey,** P.O. Box 370, New Lisbon, NJ 08064; tel. 609/894–4856

**Willowglen Academy New Jersey, Inc.,** 8 Wilson Drive, Sparta, NJ 07871; tel. 973/579–3700

*****Youth Consultation Service,** 284 Broadway, Newark, NJ 07104; tel. 973/482–8411

**NEW MEXICO**

**E L Rocky Mountain Management & Services, LLC,** 712 Rencher, Clovis, NM 88101; tel. 575/762–6091

*****Mesilla Valley Hospital,** 3751 Del Rey Boulevard, Las Cruces, NM 88012; tel. 575/382–3500

**New Mexico Behavioral Health Institute at Las Vegas,** 3695 Hot Springs Boulevard, Las Vegas, NM 87701; tel. 505/454–2404

*****New Mexico VA Health Care System,** 1501 San Pedro Drive SE, Albuquerque, NM 87108; tel. 505/265–1711

**Peak Behavioral Health Services, LLC,** 5045 McNutt Road, Santa Teresa, NM 88008; tel. 575/589–3000

*****Presbyterian Medical Services,** 1422 Paseo de Peralta, Santa Fe, NM 87504-2267; tel. 505/982–5565

**Sequel of New Mexico, LLC,** 5400 Gibson Blvd, Albuquerque, NM 87108; tel. 505/924–6330

**Sequoyah Adolescent Treatment Center,** 3405 W Pan American Freeway NE, Albuquerque, NM 87107; tel. 505/222–0375

*****University of New Mexico Health Sciences Center,** 2211 Lomas Blvd NE, Albuquerque, NM 87106; tel. 505/272–2111

**Youth and Family Centered Services of New Mexico, Inc,** 5310 Sequoia NW, Albuquerque, NM 87120; tel. 505/836–7330

**NEW YORK**

*****A.R.E.B.A.- Casriel, Inc.,** 500 West 57th Street, New York, NY 10019; tel. 212/376–1810

**Acute Chemical Dependency Detox Unit - Kings County,** 410 Winthrop Street, Brooklyn, NY 11203; tel. 718/245–3901

*****Arms Acres, Inc.,** 75 Seminary Hill Road, Carmel, NY 10512; tel. 845/225–3400

**Astor Services for Children & Families,** PO Box 5005, Rhinebeck, NY 12572-5005; tel. 845/871–1000

**August Aichhorn R.T.F.,** 23 West 106th Street, New York, NY 10025; tel. 212/316–9353

**Baker Victory Services, Inc.,** 780 Ridge Road, Lackawanna, NY 14218; tel. 716/828–9515

*****Bellevue Hospital Center,** 462 First Avenue, New York, NY 10016; tel. 212/562–3718

**Benedictine Hospital OTP,** 105 Mary's Avenue, Kingston, NY 12401; tel. 845/334–2500

**Beth Israel Medical Center MMTP - Gouverneur Clinic,** 109-11 Delancey Street, New York, NY 10002; tel. 212/420–2086

**Beth Israel Medical Center MMTP - Harlem 6/7,** 103 East 125th Street, 2nd Flr, New York, NY 10035; tel. 212/774–3260

**Beth Israel Medical Center MMTP - Vincent P Dole,** 25 - 12th Street, Brooklyn, NY 11215; tel. 718/965–7900

**Beth Israel Medical Center MMTP Clinic 1E,** 429 Second Avenue, New York, NY 10010; tel. 212/844–1929

**Beth Israel Medical Center MMTP Clinic 8D,** 140 West 125th Street, 6th Flr, New York, NY 10027; tel. 212/864–0904

**Beth Israel Medical Center MMTP Cumberland Clinic,** 100 Flatbush Avenue, Brooklyn, NY 11217; tel. 718/237–9600

**Beth Israel Medical Center MMTP Harlem 3,** 103 East 125th Street, 8th Flr, New York, NY 10003; tel. 212/774–3230

*****Beth Israel Medical Center MMTP Harlem Clinic 1,** First Avenue @ 16th Street, New York, NY 10003; tel. 212/774–3210

**Beth Israel Medical Center MMTP Harlem Clinic 2,** 103 East 125th Street, 4th Flr, New York, NY 10035; tel. 212/774–3200

**Beth Israel Medical Center MMTP, Avenue A Clinic,** 26 Avenue A, New York, NY 10009; tel. 212/420–2078

**Bon Secours Community Hospital - OTP,** 160 East Main St., Port Jervis, NY 12771; tel. 845/858–7000

**Bronx Psychiatric Center,** 1500 Waters Place, Bronx, NY 10461; tel. 718/862–3300

*****Bronx-Lebanon Hospital Center,** 1650 Grand Concourse, Bronx, NY 10457; tel. 718/590–1800

**Buffalo Psychiatric Center,** 400 Forest Avenue, Buffalo, NY 14213; tel. 716/885–2261

**Canton-Potsdam Hospital - Opioid Treatment Program,** 50 Leroy St., Potsdam, NY 13676; tel. 315/265–3300

**Carnegie Hill Institute,** 116 East 92nd Street, New York, NY 10128; tel. 212/289–7166

**Central New York Psychiatric Center,** PO Box 300, Marcy, NY 13403-0300; tel. 315/765–3660

*****Coney Island Hospital,** 2601 Ocean Parkway, Brooklyn, NY 11235; tel. 718/616–3000

*****Conifer Park Inc.,** 79 Glenridge Road, Glenville, NY 12302; tel. 518/399–6446

**Creedmoor Psychiatric Center,** 79-25 Winchester Boulevard, Queens Village, NY 11427; tel. 718/264–3600

**Crouse Hospital Methadone Maintenance Treatment Program,** 410 South Crouse Avenue, Syracuse, NY 13210; tel. 315/470–8300

**Drug Treatment & Education Cen North Shore Univ Hospital,** 400 Community Drive, Manhasset, NY 11030; tel. 516/562–3010

**Ellis Medicine Ellis Hospital,** 1101 Nott Street, Schenectady, NY 12308; tel. 518/243–4000

*****Elmhurst Hospital Center,** 79-01 Broadway, Elmhurst, NY 11373; tel. 718/334–4000

**Elmira Psychiatric Center,** 100 Washington Street, Elmira, NY 14901-2898; tel. 607/737–4739

**Erie County Medical Center,** 462 Grider Street, Buffalo, NY 14215; tel. 716/898–3000

**Flushing Hospital Medical Ctr / Chemical Dependency Unit,** 45th Avenue at Parsons Blvd, Flushing, NY 11355; tel. 718/670–5918

**Four Winds - Saratoga,** 30 Crescent Avenue, Saratoga Springs, NY 12866; tel. 518/584–3600

**Four Winds, Inc.,** 800 Cross River Road, Katonah, NY 10536; tel. 914/763–8151

**Glen Cove Hospital,** 101 Saint Andrews Lane, Glen Cove, NY 11542; tel. 516/674–7580

*****Glens Falls Hospital,** 100 Park Street, Glens Falls, NY 12801; tel. 518/926–1000

**Good Samaritan Hospital - OTP,** 255 Lafayette Avenue, Suffern, NY 10901; tel. 845/368–5220

**Gracie Square Hospital - OTP,** 420 East 76th Street, New York, NY 10021; tel. 212/434–5322

**Greater Binghamton Health Center,** 425 Robinson Street, Binghamton, NY 13904; tel. 607/773–4082

**Greater Hudson Valley Family Health Center - OTP,** 3 Commerical Place, Newburgh, NY 12550; tel. 845/220–2146

*****Guthrie Ambulatory Health Care Clinic,** 11050 Mt. Belvedere Boulevard, Fort Drum, NY 13602-5004; tel. 315/772–4024

*****Harlem Hospital Center Chemica Dependence Detoxification Uni,** 506 Lenox Ave, New York, NY 10037; tel. 212/939–1340

**HealthAlliance Hospital Broadway Methadone Treatment Program,** 2 Barbarossa Lane, Kingston, NY 12401; tel. 845/943–6022

**HealthAlliance of the Hudson Valley, Mary's Avenue Campus,** 105 Mary's Avenue, Kingston, NY 12401; tel. 845/338–2500

*****Hudson River HealthCare, Inc.,** 1037 Main Street, Peekskill, NY 10566; tel. 914/734–8800

**Hudson Valley Hospital Center M.M.T.P.,** 1980 Crompond Road, Cortlandt Manor, NY 10567; tel. 914/737–6117

**Hutchings Psychiatric Center,** 620 Madison Street, Syracuse, NY 13210; tel. 315/426–3600

*****Interfaith Medical Center,** 1545 Atlantic Avenue, Brooklyn, NY 11213; tel. 718/613–4001

**Jacobi Medical Center,** 1400 Pelham Parkway, Bronx, NY 10461; tel. 718/918–5322

*****James J Peters Bronx VA Medical Center,** 130 West Kingsbridge Road, Bronx, NY 10468; tel. 718/584–9000

*****John T. Mather Memorial Hospital,** 75 North Country Road, Port Jefferson, NY 11777-2190; tel. 631/473–1320

*****Keller Army Community Hospital,** 900 Washington Road, West Point, NY 10996; tel. 845/938–3305

*****Kings County Hospital Center,** 451 Clarkson Avenue, Brooklyn, NY 11203; tel. 718/245–5315

**Long Beach Medical Center Chemical Dependency Unit,** 455 East Bay Drive, Long Beach, NY 11561; tel. 516/897–1000

**Long Beach Medical Center M.M.T.P.,** 450 East Bay Drive, Long Beach, NY 11561; tel. 516/897–1330

*****Long Island Center for Recovery Inc.,** 320 West Montauk Highway, Hampton Bays, NY 11946; tel. 631/728–3100

*****Long Island Jewish Medical Center,** 270-05 76th Avenue, New Hyde Park, NY 11040; tel. 516/470–7000

**Long Island Jewish Medical Center - M.M.T.P.,** 75-59 263rd Street, Glen Oaks, NY 11004; tel. 718/470–8285

*****Loyola Recovery Foundation, Inc - BHC,** 76 Veterans Ave, Bath, NY 14810; tel. 607/527–7168

**Loyola Recovery Foundation, Inc.,** 1159 Pittsford-Victor Road, Pittsford, NY 14534; tel. 585/203–1005

**Lutheran Medical Center (Acute Care Addiction Program),** 150 55th Street, Brooklyn, NY 11220; tel. 718/630–7300

**Maimonides Medical Center,** 4802 Tenth Avenue, Brooklyn, NY 11219-2916; tel. 718/283–6000

**Manhattan Psychiatric Center,** 600 East 125th Street - Ward's Island, New York, NY 10035; tel. 646/672–6000

**Medically Managed Inpatient Detoxification,** 2 Park Avenue, Yonkers, NY 10703; tel. 914/964–7383

**Methadone Treatment Program - Kings County / Clinic 3,** 648 Albany Avenue, Brooklyn, NY 11203; tel. 718/245–3901

**Metropolitan Correctional Center - New York / OTP,** 150 Park Row, New York, NY 10007; tel. 646/836–6300

*****Metropolitan Hospital Center,** 1901 First Avenue, New York, NY 10029; tel. 212/423–7588

**Mohawk Valley Psychiatric Center,** 1400 Noyes Street, Utica, NY 13502; tel. 315/738–3800

**Montefiore Medical Center - SATP,** 111 East 210th Street, Bronx, NY 10467; tel. 718/920–2001

**Montefiore Medical Center - SATP - OTP - Unit III,** 2005 Jerome Avenue, 1st Floor, Bronx, NY 10467; tel. 718/583–0600

**Narco Freedom, Inc., Grand Concourse MMTP,** 250 Grand Concourse, Bronx, NY 10451; tel. 718/292–2240

**Narco Freedom, Inc.-Bridge Plaza MMTP,** 37-18 34th Street, Long Island City, NY 11101; tel. 718/292–2240

**Nassau County Dept. Methadone Maintenance Treatment Program,** NUMC, 2201 Hempstead Turnpike Building K, East Meadow, NY 11554; tel. 516/572–5906

**Nassau Health Care Corporation,** 2201 Hempstead Turnpike, East Meadow, NY 11554; tel. 516/572–4876

**New York City Children's Center,** 74-03 Commonwealth Boulevard, Bellerose, NY 11426-1839; tel. 718/264–4500

**New York State Psychiatric Institute,** 1051 Riverside Drive, New York, NY 10032; tel. 212/543–5000

*****NewYork-Presbyterian Hospital,** 525 East 68th Street, Box 437, New York, NY 10065; tel. 212/746–5454

**North Central Bronx Hospital,** 3424 Kossuth Avenue, Bronx, NY 10467; tel. 718/519–3500

**Oswego Hospital,** 110 West Sixth Street, Oswego, NY 13126; tel. 315/349–5566

**Pathways, Sisters of Charity Hospital,** 158 Holden Street, Buffalo, NY 14214; tel. 716/862–1000

*****Phelps Memorial Hospital Association,** 701 North Broadway, Sleepy Hollow, NY 10591; tel. 914/366–1000

**Pilgrim Psychiatric Center,** 998 Crooked Hill Road, West Brentwood, NY 11717; tel. 631/761–3500

**PROMESA Methadone Treatment Program,** 1776 Clay Ave, Bronx, NY 10457; tel. 718/960–7601

**Quannacut at Eastern Long Island Hospital,** 201 Manor Place, Greenport, NY 11944; tel. 631/477–1000

*****Queens Hospital Center,** 82-68 164th Street, Jamaica, NY 11432; tel. 718/883–2351

*****Richmond Medical Center,** 355 Bard Avenue, Staten Island, NY 10310; tel. 718/818–1234

*****Rochester General Hospital,** 1425 Portland Avenue, Rochester, NY 14621; tel. 585/922–4000

**Rochester Mental Health Center (BHN, Inc.),** 490 East Ridge Road, Rochester, NY 14621; tel. 585/922–2500

**Rochester Pathways, Sisters of Charity Hospital,** 435 East Henrietta Road, Rochester, NY 14607; tel. 585/424–6580

**Rockland Children's Psychiatric Center,** 2 First Avenue, Orangeburg, NY 10962; tel. 845/680–4040

*Indicates organization is a Joint Commission accredited Chemical Dependency organization.

Rockland Psychiatric Center, 140 Old Orangeburg Road, Orangeburg, NY 10962; tel. 845/359-1000

Sagamore Children's Psychiatric Center, 197 Half Hollow Road, Dix Hills, NY 11746; tel. 631/370-1701

Saint Joseph's Hospital White Plains OTC, 77 East Post Road, White Plains, NY 10601; tel. 914/286-2820

Saint Joseph's Hospital Yonkers, 211 Powell Street, Brooklyn, NY 11212; tel. 718/485-6000

*Samuel S. Stratton VA Medical Center, 113 Holland Avenue, Albany, NY 12208; tel. 518/626-5000

SBH Chemical Dependence Methadone Substance Abuse Treatment, 4535-39 Third Avenue, Bronx, NY 10457; tel. 718/960-6170

SBH Chemical Dependence-Medically Managed, 183rd Street and Third Avenue, Bronx, NY 10457; tel. 718/960-6170

*Seafield Center, Inc., 7 Seafield Lane, Westhampton Beach, NY 11978; tel. 631/288-1122

South Beach Psychiatric Center, 777 Seaview Avenue, Staten Island, NY 10305; tel. 718/667-2300

South Nassau Communities Hospital, 1 Healthy Way, Oceanside, NY 11572; tel. 516/632-3999

South Oaks Hospital, 400 Sunrise Highway, Amityville, NY 11701; tel. 631/608-5725

*St. Barnabas Hospital, 4422 Third Avenue, Bronx, NY 10457; tel. 718/960-6108

*St. James Mercy Hospital, 411 Canisteo Street, Hornell, NY 14843; tel. 607/324-8703

*St. John's Episcopal Hospital - South Shore, 327 Beach 19th Street, Far Rockaway, NY 11691; tel. 718/869-7000

St. Johns Riverside Hospital M.M.T.P., 2 Park Avenue, Yonkers, NY 10703; tel. 914/964-4000

*St. Joseph's Hospital, 127 South Broadway, Yonkers, NY 10701; tel. 914/378-7839

St. Joseph's Hospital - MMTP, 8 Guion Street, 1st Floor, Yonkers, NY 10701; tel. 914/378-7000

St. Joseph's Hospital Yonkers, 147-18 Archer Avenue, Jamaica, NY 11435; tel. 718/291-1888

St. Lawrence Psychiatric Center, One Chimney Point Drive, Ogdensburg, NY 13669; tel. 315/541-2279

*St. Luke's-Roosevelt Hospital Center, 1000 10th Avenue, New York, NY 10019; tel. 212/523-4000

St. Lukes-Roosevelt Hospital Center - MMTP, 1000 Tenth Avenue, New York, NY 10019; tel. 212/523-6881

*St. Mary's Healthcare, 427 Guy Park Avenue, Amsterdam, NY 12010; tel. 518/842-1900

*Staten Island University Hospital, 475 Seaview Avenue, Staten Island, NY 10305; tel. 718/226-9000

Stony Brook University Hospital, Nicolls Road, Stony Brook, NY 11794-8503; tel. 631/444-1956

*Strong Memorial Hospital, 601 Elmwood Avenue, Rochester, NY 14642; tel. 585/275-2644

Stuyvesant Square Chemical Dependency Outpatient Detox, 1-9 Nathan Perlman Place, New York, NY 10003; tel. 212/420-4220

Suffolk County Department of Health - East End Clinic, 300 Center Drive, Riverhead, NY 11901; tel. 631/852-2680

Suffolk County Department of Health - Hauppauge Clinic, 200 Wireless Blvd, Hauppauge, NY 11788; tel. 631/853-7373

Suffolk County Department of Health - North County Complex, PO Box 6100, Bldg 151, North County Complex, Hauppauge, NY 11788; tel. 631/853-6410

Summit Park Hospital, 50 Sanitorium Road, Pomona, NY 10970; tel. 845/364-2700

*Syracuse Community Health Center, Inc., 819 South Salina Street, Syracuse, NY 13202; tel. 315/476-7921

The Brooklyn Hospital Center Parkside Drug Detox Program, 121 DeKalb Avenue, Brooklyn, NY 11201; tel. 718/250-8005

The Children's Home RTF, Inc., 638 Squirrel Hill Road, Chenango Forks, NY 13746; tel. 607/656-9004

The Family Foundation School, 431 Chapel Hill Road, Hancock, NY 13783; tel. 607/637-8200

The Guidance Center Chemical Dependency Treatment Center, 256 Washington Strret, Mount Vernon, NY 10553; tel. 914/613-0700

The House of the Good Shepherd, 1550 Champlin Avenue, Utica, NY 13502; tel. 315/235-7600

The Institute for Family Health, 16 East 16th Street, New York, NY 10003; tel. 212/633-0800

*The Long Island Home, 400 Sunrise Highway, Amityville, NY 11701; tel. 631/264-4000

*The Mount Sinai Medical Center, One Gustave L. Levy Place, Box 1051, New York, NY 10029-6574; tel. 212/241-5719

The Mount Vernon Hospital, 12 North Seventh Avenue, Mount Vernon, NY 10550; tel. 914/361-6100

The Mount Vernon Hospital Methadone Maintenance Program, 3 South 6th Avenue, 3rd Floor, Mount Vernon, NY 10550; tel. 914/361-6000

United Health Services Hospitals, 10-42 Mitchell Avenue, Binghamton, NY 13903; tel. 607/762-2263

*Upstate New York VA Health Care Network at Canandaigua, 400 Fort Hill Avenue, Canandaigua, NY 14424; tel. 585/394-2000

*VA Healthcare Network Upstate New York at Bath, 76 Veterans Avenue, Bath, NY 14810; tel. 607/664-4722

*VA Healthcare Network Upstate New York at Syracuse, 800 Irving Avenue, Syracuse, NY 13210; tel. 315/425-4400

*VA Hudson Valley Health Care System, 2094 Albany Post Road, Route 9A, Montrose, NY 10548; tel. 914/737-4400

*VA Medical Center Northport, 79 Middleville Road, Northport, NY 11768; tel. 631/261-4400

*VA New York Harbor Health Care System, 800 Poly Place, Brooklyn, NY 11209; tel. 718/630-3521

VA New York Harbor Healthcare System - OTP, 423 East 23rd Street, New York, NY 10010; tel. 212/686-7500

*VA Western New York Health Care System, 3495 Bailey Avenue, Buffalo, NY 14215; tel. 716/862-8529

*Villa of Hope, 3300 Dewey Avenue, Rochester, NY 14616; tel. 585/865-1550

Vincent P. Dole Treatment Program, 525 East 68th Street, Box 437, New York, NY 10065; tel. 212/746-5454

*West Midtown Medical Group, 505 Eighth Avenue, 4th Floor, New York, NY 10018; tel. 212/736-5900

Westchester Health Care Corporation, 100 Woods Road, Taylor Pavilion, Valhalla, NY 10595; tel. 914/493-7000

Western New York Children's Psychiatric Center, 1010 East and West Road, West Seneca, NY 14224; tel. 716/677-7000

Whitney M. Young, Jr. Health Services Inc., 10 Dewitt Street, Albany, NY 12207; tel. 518/463-3882

Woodhull Medical & Mental Health Medically Managed Detoxific, 760 Broadway, Unit 9-300, Brooklyn, NY 11206; tel. 718/963-8101

**NORTH CAROLINA**

3 D'S Forever, 8 Delwin Court, Greensboro, NC 27406; tel. 336/852-2552

A Caring Home, INC., 8616 Nations Ford Road, Charlotte, NC 28217-5126; tel. 704/525-2840

A Plus Life Skills North Carolina, 201 West Walnut St, Goldsboro, NC 27530; tel. 919/288-1139

AbleCare Corporation, 305 South Westgate Drive, Greensboro, NC 27407; tel. 336/218-7008

Alexander Youth Network, PO Box 220632, Charlotte, NC 28222-9979; tel. 704/366-8712

Allegiance Community Care, LLC, 604 Calavaras Ln, Knightdale, NC 27545; tel. 919/264-7517

*AssistedCare Management Group, Inc., 1003 Old Waterford Way, Suite 2C, Leland, NC 28451; tel. 910/332-2346

Autumn Halls of Unaka, 14949 Joe Brown Hwy, Murphy, NC 28906; tel. 828/835-8103

Bethesda Care dba Keston Care, 11312 US 15/501 N, Chatham Crossing, Ste. 400, Chapel Hill, NC 27517; tel. 919/967-0507

Beyond Challenges Community Services, LLC, 515 Yadkin Street, Henderson, NC 27536; tel. 252/572-2167

Blessed Alms, P.O. Box 16527, Greensboro, NC 27416; tel. 336/997-0971

Brynn Marr Hospital, 192 Village Drive, Jacksonville, NC 28546; tel. 910/577-1400

Canaan Care Home, LLC, 2804 Stirrup Court, Wake Forest, NC 27587; tel. 919/274-0596

Cantor LLC dba: Family United, 1801 N.Tryon St Suite 336, Charlotte, NC 28206; tel. 336/471-8130

Caring Hands and Supplementary Enrichment Education, LLC, 2216 S Miami Blvd Ste. 101, Durham, NC 27703; tel. 919/479-6806

Caring Touch Home Health Care, LLC, 799 James Lynn Drive, Pembroke, NC 28372; tel. 910/521-9175

Carolina Comprehensive Services, LLC., 312 West Millbrook Rd Suite 137, Raleigh, NC 27609; tel. 919/847-0550

*Carolinas Medical Center, PO Box 32861, Charlotte, NC 28232; tel. 704/355-7359

*Carter's Circle of Care, Inc., 2031 Martin Luther King Jr. Dr, Ste, E,D, Greensboro, NC 27406; tel. 336/271-5817

Champion Healthcare Services, Inc., 421 Chapanoke Rd Suite 112, Raleigh, NC 27603; tel. 919/434-5100

*Charles George VA Medical Center at Asheville, 1100 Tunnel Road, Asheville, NC 28805; tel. 828/298-7911

Citizens Choice, LLC, 3300 Sunset Ave, Ste F, Rocky Mount, NC 27804; tel. 252/557-9797

*Connections BWB Incorporated, 8430 University Executive Park Drive Suite 655, Charlotte, NC 28262; tel. 704/596-5553

Continuum Care Services, Inc., P.O. Box 6331, Concord, NC 28027; tel. 704/784-0753

Crystal E. Nickerson LLC, 2302 West Meadowview Road, Suite 228, Box 24, Greensboro, NC 27407; tel. 336/218-5176

Davis Regional Medical Center, PO Box 1823, Statesville, NC 28687; tel. 704/873-0281

Eagle Healthcare Services, Inc., 4428 Louisburg Road, Suite 109, Raleigh, NC 27604; tel. 919/872-7686

Extended Reach Day Treatment, 919 Ramsey Street, Fayetteville, NC 28301; tel. 910/484-0095

*Fellowship Hall, Inc., PO Box 13890, Greensboro, NC 27415; tel. 336/621-3381

First Genesis Group Home Inc, 1903 Delmar Drive, Greensboro, NC 27406; tel. 336/274-4447

Grandfather Home for Children, PO Box 98, Banner Elk, NC 28604; tel. 828/898-5465

Greater Image Healthcare Corporation, Inc., PO BOX 87035, Fayetteville, NC 28304; tel. 910/321-0069

I Innovations Inc., 176 Sandollar Court, Sanford, NC 27332; tel. 919/770-2617

Jabez Management, LLC, P.O. Box 1404, Reidsville, NC 27323-1404; tel. 336/253-4261

JMJ Enterprise LLC d/b/a Fresh Start Home for Children, 2020 textile Drive, Greensboro, NC 27405; tel. 336/271-6982

*Julian F. Keith Alcohol and Drug Abuse Treatment Center, 201 Tabernacle Road, Black Mountain, NC 28711; tel. 828/257-6200

Kids Health Services, Inc, 328 Gillespie Street, Fayetteville, NC 28301; tel. 910/829-7184

KidsPeace National Centers of North America, Inc, 3109 Poplarwood Court, Suite 310, Raleigh, NC 27604; tel. 919/872-6447

Leading Into New Communities, Inc., 907 Castle Street, Wilmington, NC 28401; tel. 910/762-4635

McLaurin Vocational Training Center, Inc, 10 North Bridges Street, Hamlet, NC 28345; tel. 910/582-0934

Midstate Health Systems, Inc, 3721 Legion Rd, Hope Mills, NC 28348; tel. 910/484-3717

Miss Daisy's Gentlemen of Future Inc., P.O. Box 1991, Wilson, NC 27894-1991; tel. 252/363-5446

Naval Hospital Camp Lejeune, 100 Brewster Boulevard, Camp Lejeune, NC 28547-2538; tel. 910/450-4007

New Beginning Youth Facility, 525 Greenbriar Farm Trl, Siler City, NC 27344; tel. 336/302-0801

New Directions Group Care Management, PO Box 1442, Whiteville, NC 28472; tel. 910/640-1737

Noir Enterprises, LLC., P.O. Box 1794, Arden, NC 28704; tel. 828/654-9452

Old Vineyard Behavioral Health Services, 3637 Old Vineyard Road, Winston Salem, NC 27104-4842; tel. 336/794-3550

*Open Arms Treatment Center, 3911 Jack Pine Ct, Greensboro, NC 27406; tel. 336/617-0469

Patterson Home, Inc, p.o.box 64013, Fayetteville, NC 28306; tel. 910/527-8427

Phoenix Supported Living, Inc., 2996 NC 69 S # 6, Hayesville, NC 28904; tel. 828/389-1795

Priority Behavioral Healthcare Inc., 4822 Albemarle Road, Ste 112A, Charlotte, NC 28205; tel. 704/323-7617

*Indicates organization is a Joint Commission accredited Chemical Dependency organization.

Section C

*Quality Home Care Services, Inc, 3552 Beatties Ford Road, Charlotte, NC 28216; tel. 704/394-8968

Recovery Innovations of North Carolina, 300 Parkview Drive West, Henderson, NC 27536; tel. 252/438-4145

Reintegration Targeting Inc., 2210 North Tyron Street Suite A, Charlotte, NC 28206-2772; tel. 704/334-2600

Renewed Services, Inc, 809 N. Lafayette St., Ste G, Shelby, NC 28150; tel. 704/487-4440

Residential Services, Inc., 111 Providence Road, Chapel Hill, NC 27514; tel. 919/942-7391

*Robeson Health Care Corporation, 60 Commerce Drive, Pembroke, NC 28372; tel. 910/521-2900

SBH- Wilmington, LLC, 2050 Mercantile Drive, Leland, NC 28451; tel. 910/371-2500

Spigner Management Systems, Inc, PO Box 758, Fayetteville, NC 28302; tel. 910/864-1807

The Circle of Courage Support Services, LLC, 3806 Park Avenue, South A, Wilmington, NC 28403; tel. 910/338-0001

The Renfrew Center of North Carolina, 6633 Fairview Road, Charlotte, NC 28210; tel. 704/366-1264

Timber Ridge Treatment Center, P O Box 259, Gold Hill, NC 28071; tel. 704/279-1199

Total Care & Concern, Inc., 1428 Orchard Lake Drive, Charlotte, NC 28270; tel. 704/321-1635

*Tri-County Community Health Council, Inc, PO Box 227, Newton Grove, NC 28366; tel. 910/567-6194

Unique Home Care, Inc., P.O. Box 835, Jefferson, NC 28640; tel. 336/246-6991

*United Health Rehabilitation Services, LLC, 1314 Headquarters Drive, Greensboro, NC 27405; tel. 336/271-6800

*Unity Healing Center, PO Box c-201, Cherokee, NC 28719; tel. 828/497-3958

Unity Home Care, Inc., 211 Fairway Dr. Suite A, Fayetteville, NC 28305; tel. 910/864-1799

*VA Medical Center, 508 Fulton Street, Durham, NC 27705; tel. 919/286-0411

*VA Medical Center, 2300 Ramsey Street, Fayetteville, NC 28301; tel. 910/822-7091

Veritas Collaborative LLC, 615 Douglas St. Suite 500, Durham, NC 27705; tel. 919/908-9730

*W & B Health Care, Inc, P.O. Box 168, Red Springs, NC 28377; tel. 910/843-1997

*W. G. (Bill) Hefner VA Medical Center, 1601 Brenner Avenue, Salisbury, NC 28144; tel. 704/638-9000

*Walter B. Jones Alcohol & Drug Abuse Treatment Center, 2577 W. 5th Street, Greenville, NC 27834; tel. 252/830-3426

Well Care LLC, 6752 Parker Farm Drive, Wilmington, NC 28405; tel. 910/362-9405

Whitaker PRTF, 1003 12th Street, Butner, NC 27509; tel. 919/575-7927

*Wilmington Treatment Center, Inc., 2520 Troy Drive, Wilmington, NC 28401; tel. 910/762-2727

Womack Army Medical Center, Bldg # 4-2817, Reilly Road, Fort Bragg, NC 28310; tel. 910/907-8917

**NORTH DAKOTA**

Altru Health System, P.O. Box 6002, Grand Forks, ND 58206-6002; tel. 701/780-5000

*Center for Solutions PC, 1820 Walnut Street East, Suite #7, Devils Lake, ND 58301; tel. 701/665-2140

Fargo VA Health Care System, 2101 Elm Street North, Fargo, ND 58102; tel. 701/232-3241

*Heartview Foundation, 101 E Broadway Avenue, Bismarck, ND 58501; tel. 701/222-0386

*North Dakota State Hospital, 2605 Circle Drive, Jamestown, ND 58401-6905; tel. 701/253-3964

*Prairie St. John's, PO Box 2027, Fargo, ND 58107-2027; tel. 701/476-7200

Sanford Medical Center Fargo, 801 Broadway North, Fargo, ND 58122; tel. 701/234-2000

*Trinity Health, PO Box 5020, Minot, ND 58702-5020; tel. 701/857-5000

**OHIO**

*Abraxas Counseling Center, 899 East Broad Street, Columbus, OH 43205; tel. 614/220-8655

Access Ohio, LLC, 99 North Brice Rd, Suite 360, Columbus, OH 43213; tel. 614/367-7700

*Akron-Urban Minority Alcoholism Drug Abuse Outreach, 665 W Market Street, Akron, OH 44303; tel. 330/379-3467

Appalachian Behavioral Healthcare, 100 Hospital Drive, Athens, OH 45701; tel. 740/594-5000

Applewood Centers Inc., 10427 Detroit Avenue, Cleveland, OH 44102-1645; tel. 216/696-5800

*Beech Brook, 3737 Lander Road, Cleveland, OH 44124; tel. 216/831-2255

*Behavioral Connections of Wood County, Inc., PO Box 29, Bowling Green, OH 43402; tel. 419/352-5387

Bellefaire Jewish Children's Bureau, 22001 Fairmount Boulevard, Shaker Heights, OH 44118; tel. 216/932-2800

Belmont Pines Hospital, 615 Churchhill-Hubbard Road, Youngstown, OH 44505; tel. 330/759-2700

BHC Fox Run Hospital, 67670 Traco Drive, Saint Clairsville, OH 43950; tel. 740/695-2131

*Center for Chemical Addictions Treatment, 830 Ezzard Charles Drive, Cincinnati, OH 45214; tel. 513/381-6672

*Chalmers P. Wylie Ambulatory Care Center, 420 North James Road, Columbus, OH 43219; tel. 614/257-5200

Child Guidance & Family Solutions, 18 N. Forge Street, Akron, OH 44304; tel. 330/762-0591

Children's Hospital Medical Center of Akron, One Perkins Square, Akron, OH 44308-1082; tel. 330/543-1000

Cincinnati Children's Hospital Medical Center, 3333 Burnet Avenue, Cincinnati, OH 45229-3039; tel. 513/636-3333

Cleveland Clinic Children's Hospital for Rehabilitation, 2801 Martin Luther King, Jr. Drive, Cleveland, OH 44104; tel. 216/448-6400

Community Behavioral Health Center, 3355 Richmond Road, 225-A, Beachwood, OH 44122; tel. 216/831-1494

*Community Behavioral Health, Inc, 520 Eaton Ave, Hamilton, OH 45013; tel. 513/785-4784

*Community Health Center, 725 East Market Street, Akron, OH 44305; tel. 330/434-4141

Comprehensive Psychiatry Group, Inc., 955 Windham Court, Boardman, OH 44512; tel. 330/726-9570

*Cornell Abraxas, 2775 State Route 39, Shelby, OH 44875; tel. 419/747-3322

*Craig and Frances Lindner Center of HOPE, 4075 Old Western Row Road, Mason, OH 45040; tel. 513/536-4673

*Crisis Intervention and Recovery Center, Inc., 832 McKinley Avenue NW, Canton, OH 44703; tel. 330/452-9812

*Department of Veterans Affairs Medical Center, Dayton, Ohio, 4100 West 3rd Street, Dayton, OH 45428; tel. 937/268-6511

Dept. of Veterans Affairs-Dayton Campus Opioid Treatment, 4100 W Third Street, Bldg 302, Dayton, OH 45428; tel. 937/268-6511

Far West Center, 29133 Health Campus Drive, Westlake, OH 44145; tel. 440/835-6212

*Glenbeigh, PO Box 298, Rock Creek, OH 44084-0298; tel. 440/563-3400

*Ironton-Lawrence County Community Action Organization, 305 North Fifth Street, Ironton, OH 45638; tel. 740/532-3534

Lake Health, 7590 Auburn Road, Painesville, OH 44077; tel. 440/375-8100

Lifessentials Counseling, 131 N Ludlow St., Suite 1212, Dayton, OH 45402; tel. 937/222-5496

*Lorain County Alcohol & Drug Abuse Services, Inc., 2115 W PARK DR, Lorain, OH 44053-1138; tel. 440/989-4900

*Louis Stokes, Cleveland VA Medical Center, 10701 East Boulevard, Cleveland, OH 44106; tel. 216/231-3456

Lutheran Hospital, 1730 West 25th Street, Cleveland, OH 44113; tel. 216/696-4300

Marymount Hospital, 12300 McCracken Road, Garfield Heights, OH 44125; tel. 216/581-0500

Maumee Valley Guidance Center, 211 Biede Ave., Defiance, OH 43512; tel. 419/782-8856

Medical University of Ohio at Toledo, 3000 Arlington Avenue MS 1096, Toledo, OH 43614; tel. 419/383-4977

*Mental Health Services for Clark and Madison Counties, Inc., 1345 Fountain Boulevard, Springfield, OH 45504; tel. 937/399-9500

Methadone Maintenance Program, Substance Abuse, Mental Health, 10701 East Blvd, Room 1B300, Cleveland, OH 44106; tel. 216/791-3800

*Nationwide Children's Hospital, Inc., 700 Children's Drive, Columbus, OH 43205; tel. 614/722-5950

*Neil Kennedy Recovery Clinic, 2151 Rush Boulevard, Youngstown, OH 44507; tel. 330/744-1181

New Albany Home Health Solutions, LLC, 4754 Scarlet Street, Columbus, OH 43224; tel. 614/557-1145

New Day Counseling & Wellness, Inc., PO BOX 27, Girard, OH 44420; tel. 330/727-8949

*New Directions, Inc., 30800 Chagrin Boulevard, Cleveland, OH 44124; tel. 216/591-0324

Northcoast Behavioral Healthcare, 1756 Sagamore Road, Northfield, OH 44067; tel. 330/467-7131

*Northland/The Ridge, 50 W. Technecenter Dr. Suite B5, Milford, OH 45150; tel. 513/753-9964

Ohio Hospital for Psychiatry, 880 Greenlawn Avenue, Columbus, OH 43223; tel. 614/449-9664

Opiate Substitution Services - SUDEP, CVAMC, 3200 Vine Street, Cincinnati, OH 45220; tel. 513/861-3100

Phoenix Rising Behavorial Healthcare And Recovery, Inc., 4974 Higbee Ave, suite 209, Canton, OH 44718; tel. 330/493-4553

Pomegranate Health Systems of Central Ohio, 765 Pierce Drive, Columbus, OH 43223; tel. 614/223-1650

Portage Path Behavioral Health, 340 South Broadway, Akron, OH 44308; tel. 330/253-3100

*Promedica Toledo Hospital, 2142 North Cove Boulevard, Toledo, OH 43606; tel. 419/291-7460

PsyCare, Inc., 2980 Belmont Avenue, Youngstown, OH 44505; tel. 330/759-2310

*Rakesh Ranjan MD and Associates, Inc, 801 E. Washington Street, Medina, OH 44256; tel. 330/722-1069

*Ravenwood Mental Health Center, 12557 Ravenwood Drive, Chardon, OH 44024; tel. 440/285-3568

*Rescue Incorporated, 3350 Collingwood Boulevard, Toledo, OH 43610; tel. 419/255-9585

Rocking Horse Children's Health Center, 651 S. Limestone St., Springfield, OH 45505; tel. 937/324-1111

Shaker Clinic, LLC, 20600 Chagrin Blvd. Suite 620, Shaker Heights, OH 44122; tel. 216/751-4762

*Southeast, Inc., 16 West Long Street, Columbus, OH 43215; tel. 614/225-0980

*Southwest General Health Center, 18697 Bagley Road, Middleburg Heights, OH 44130; tel. 440/816-8000

Specialty Care Counseling Services, Ltd, 2000 East Market Street, Warren, OH 44483; tel. 330/399-1221

*St. Vincent Charity Medical Center, 2351 East 22nd Street, Cleveland, OH 44115; tel. 216/861-6200

*Stella Maris, Inc., 1320 Washington Avenue, Cleveland, OH 44113; tel. 216/781-0550

*The Buckeye Ranch, Inc., 5665 Hoover Road, Grove City, OH 43123; tel. 614/875-2371

The Centers for Families and Children, 4500 Euclid Ave., Cleveland, OH 44103; tel. 216/432-7200

*The Crossroads Center, 311 Martin Luther King Drive, Cincinnati, OH 45219; tel. 513/475-5300

The MetroHealth System, 2500 MetroHealth Drive, Cleveland, OH 44109-1998; tel. 216/778-7800

*The Ohio State University Hospital, 410 West Tenth Avenue, DN 168, Columbus, OH 43210; tel. 614/293-9700

*The Woods at Parkside, 349 Olde Ridenour Road, Columbus, OH 43230; tel. 614/471-2552

Twin Valley Behavioral Healthcare, 2200 West Broad Street, Columbus, OH 43223; tel. 614/752-0333

*Unison Behavioral Health Group, PO Box 10015, Toledo, OH 43699-0015; tel. 419/693-0631

*VA Healthcare System of Ohio - Cincinnati Campus, 3200 Vine Street, Cincinnati, OH 45220; tel. 513/861-3100

*VA Medical Center - Chillicothe, 17273 State Route 104, Chillicothe, OH 45601; tel. 740/773-1141

Visiting Nurse Association Healthcare Partners of Ohio, 2500 East 22nd Street, Cleveland, OH 44115; tel. 216/931-1300

*Windsor Laurelwood Center for Behavioral Medicine, 35900 Euclid Avenue, Willoughby, OH 44094; tel. 440/953-3000

*Wood County Children's Services Association, PO Box 738, Bowling Green, OH 43402; tel. 419/352-7588

Zepf Center, 6605 West Central Avenue, Toledo, OH 43617; tel. 419/841-7701

**OKLAHOMA**

*Advantage Community Resources LLC, 5929 N. May Ave. #310, Oklahoma City, OK 73112; tel. 405/206-0177

---

*Indicates organization is a Joint Commission accredited Chemical Dependency organization.

**\*Alpha II, Inc.,** 1608 N. Main St., Tonkawa, OK 74653; tel. 580/628-2539

**Behavior Revolutions,** 1901 N. Classen, Suite 109, Oklahoma City, OK 73106; tel. 405/456-9929

**BetterLife Counseling Services, Inc.,** 9700 South Pennsylvania Avenue, Oklahoma City, OK 73159; tel. 405/735-9732

**\*Brookhaven Hospital,** 201 South Garnett Road, Tulsa, OK 74128-1800; tel. 918/438-4257

**Carl Albert Community Mental Health Center,** PO Box 579, McAlester, OK 74502; tel. 918/426-7800

**Cedar Ridge,** 6501 NE 50th Street, Oklahoma City, OK 73141; tel. 405/605-6111

**\*Central Oklahoma Family Medical Center, Inc.,** P.O. Box 358, Konawa, OK 74849; tel. 580/925-3286

**Child & Family Wellness Center,** 355004 E 750 Rd, Cushing, OK 74023; tel. 918/225-0750

**\*Children's Recovery Center of Oklahoma,** 320 12th Avenue Northeast, Norman, OK 73071; tel. 405/364-9004

**Choices Institute,** 529 N. Grand, Enid, OK 73701; tel. 580/234-8880

**Cornerstone Clinical Services, Inc.,** 1408 W. Elder, Duncan, OK 73533; tel. 580/595-7000

**\*Counseling Works, Inc,** 1601 West Okmulgee, Muskogee, OK 74401; tel. 918/681-4944

**\*Cushing Valley Hope,** PO Box 472, Cushing, OK 74023-0472; tel. 918/225-1736

**Daybreak Family Services,** 1516 S. Boston Ave. Suite 1, Tulsa, OK 74119; tel. 918/561-6000

**\*Department of Veterans Affairs Medical Center,** 921 Northeast 13th Street, Oklahoma City, OK 73104; tel. 405/456-3312

**Discovery Uttuwah LLC,** 118 So. Main, Wagoner, OK 74467; tel. 918/485-1573

**Duncan Regional Hospital, Inc.,** 1407 Whisenant Drive, Duncan, OK 73533; tel. 580/252-5300

**\*Dynasty Care Services,** 4337 SE 15th Street, Del City, OK 73115; tel. 405/609-1760

**Elite Counseling LLC,** 717 B Hwy 70 E, Kingston, OK 73439; tel. 580/564-7308

**Family Options Community Based Counseling Services,** 2914 Epperly Drive, Del City, OK 73115; tel. 405/604-9790

**Generations Family Counseling,** 206 East Blue Starr Drive, Claremore, OK 74017; tel. 918/341-8100

**\*Health Concepts Family Services Outpatient Behavioral Health,** 1843 E. 15th Street, Tulsa, OK 74104; tel. 918/872-6135

**Hillcrest Medical Center Behavioral Health Services,** 1120 South Utica, Tulsa, OK 74104-4090; tel. 918/579-1000

**IMPACT (University of Oklahoma - Tulsa),** 4502 E. 41st Street Room 2G07, Tulsa, OK 74135; tel. 918/660-3150

**Improving Lives Counseling Services, Inc.,** 6216 S. Lewis Avenue, Suite 180, Tulsa, OK 74136; tel. 918/812-6010

**\*Inspiration Family Counseling LLC,** 4513-B SE 29th, Del City, OK 73115; tel. 405/315-1357

**Integrated Comprehensive Health Care (ICHC), LLC,** 4801 N Classen BLVD, Oklahoma City, OK 73118; tel. 405/843-7300

**INTEGRIS Baptist Medical Center,** 3300 NW Expressway, Oklahoma City, OK 73112-4481; tel. 405/951-8065

**Jack C. Montgomery VA Medical Center,** 1011 Honor Heights Drive, Muskogee, OK 74401; tel. 918/577-3000

**Jennifer M Smith MCP, LPC, PLC,** 4806 N Perkins Rd, Stillwater, OK 74075; tel. 918/978-1109

**\*Jim Taliaferro Community Mental Health Center,** 602 SW 38th st, Lawton, OK 73505; tel. 580/248-5780

**Land Of Hope,** 57523 Moccasin Trail Road, Prague, OK 74864; tel. 405/567-0054

**\*Laureate Psychiatric Clinic and Hospital,** 6655 South Yale Avenue, Tulsa, OK 74136; tel. 918/481-4000

**Lifeworks Counseling Solutions, LLC,** PO Box, Canton, OK 73724; tel. 580/515-1010

**Making A Difference, Inc.,** 210 E. Maple, Enid, OK 73701; tel. 580/231-0500

**\*New Dimensions Youth and Family Counseling,** 2836 Linda Lane, Del City, OK 73115; tel. 405/326-9540

**Next Step Counseling Inc.,** 3923 N. Pennsylvania Ave., Oklahoma City, OK 73112; tel. 405/424-0007

**Norman Counseling Clinic,** 2416 Tee Circle, Norman, OK 73069; tel. 405/809-2004

**Norman Regional Health System,** PO Box 1308, Norman, OK 73070-1308; tel. 405/307-1000

**\*Northwest Center for Behavioral Health (NCBH),** 1222 10th Street, Suite 211, Woodward, OK 73801; tel. 580/256-8615

**Oklahoma Forensic Center,** PO Box 69, Vinita, OK 74301-0069; tel. 918/256-7841

**Parkside, Inc.,** 1620 East 12th Street, Tulsa, OK 74120; tel. 918/582-2131

**Pennington Creek Lifehouse,** 801 E Main, Tishomingo, OK 73460; tel. 580/310-4164

**Positive Changes, LLC,** 744 S.E. 25th Street, Oklahoma City, OK 73129; tel. 405/636-1463

**\*Professional Counseling Solutions,PLLC,** 1500 North Main, Frederick, OK 73542; tel. 580/335-3320

**Promise Family Center, PLLC,** 5350 South Western Suite 305, Oklahoma City, OK 73109; tel. 405/431-0232

**Sequel of Oklahoma, LLC,** 3301 North Martin Luther King Avenue, Oklahoma City, OK 73111; tel. 405/548-1280

**Solutions for Life Counseling Services,** 309 W. Cherokee, Enid, OK 73701; tel. 580/234-4700

**Southeastern Psychiatric Services, PLLC,** P.O. Box 1589, McAlester, OK 74502; tel. 918/423-3700

**Southwest Oklahoma Counseling,** P.O. Box 691, Clinton, OK 73601; tel. 580/323-9800

**SPUR,** 4801 North Classen Blvd Suite 135, Oklahoma City, OK 73118; tel. 405/848-0011

**\*St. Anthony Hospital,** 1000 North Lee Street, Oklahoma City, OK 73101; tel. 405/272-7000

**Substance Abuse Treatment Center, OKC VAMC,** 921 NE 13th St, Bldg 1, Oklahoma City, OK 73104; tel. 405/456-3312

**The Agency at Zoe, LLC,** 729 E. Maine Ave, Enid, OK 73701; tel. 580/237-7703

**Tulsa Center for Behavioral Health,** 2323 South Harvard, Tulsa, OK 74114; tel. 918/293-2140

**Universal Health Services, Inc.,** 6262 South Sheridan Road, Tulsa, OK 74133; tel. 918/492-8200

**VCPHCS IV, LLC d/b/a BHG Oklahoma City Clinic (OTP),** 5401 SW 29th, Oklahoma City, OK 73128; tel. 405/681-2003

**Willow Crest Hospital, Inc.,** 130 A Street South West, Miami, OK 74354; tel. 918/542-1836

**\*YCO OKC, Inc.,** 222 E. Sheridan St. Suite 2, Oklahoma City, OK 73104; tel. 405/200-0131

**\*YCO, Inc,** P.O.Box 95207, Oklahoma City, OK 73143; tel. 405/917-5677

## OREGON

**Albertina Kerr Centers,** 424 NE 22nd Avenue, Portland, OR 97232; tel. 503/255-4205

**CODA, Inc.,** 1027 E. Burnside, Portland, OR 97214-1328; tel. 503/239-8400

**\*Hazelden Foundation,** 1901 Esther Street, Newberg, OR 97132; tel. 503/554-4300

**Kairos,** 715 SW Ramsey Avenue, Grants Pass, OR 97527; tel. 541/956-4943

**Northwest Behavioral Healthcare Services,** 18000 Southeast Webster Road, Gladstone, OR 97027; tel. 503/722-4470

**Northwest Human Services,** 681 Center Street, NE, Salem, OR 97301; tel. 503/588-5828

**Oregon State Hospital,** 2600 Center Street, NE, Salem, OR 97301-2682; tel. 503/945-2870

**\*Portland VA Medical Center,** PO Box 1034, Portland, OR 97207; tel. 503/273-5267

**Portland VA Medical Center Opiate Treatment Program,** 3710 SW US Veteran's Hospital RD, PO Box 1034, (P3OTP), Portland, OR 97239; tel. 503/220-8262

**\*Providence Portland Medical Center,** 4805 Northeast Glisan Street, Portland, OR 97213; tel. 503/215-2349

**\*Providence St.Vincent Medical Center,** 9205 SW Barnes Road, Portland, OR 97225; tel. 503/216-1234

**Rainrock Treatment Center,** 1863 Pioneer Parkway East Suite 304, Springfield, OR 97477; tel. 541/896-9300

**\*Serenity Lane,** 2133 Centennial Plaza, Eugene, OR 97401; tel. 541/284-8611

**Trillium Family Services, Inc,** 3415 SE Powell Blvd, Portland, OR 97202; tel. 503/234-9591

**\*UBH of Oregon LLC,** 10300 SW Eastridge Street, Portland, OR 97225; tel. 503/944-5000

**\*VA Roseburg Healthcare System,** 913 NW Garden Valley Boulevard, Roseburg, OR 97471; tel. 541/440-1000

**\*VA Southern Oregon Rehabilitation Center and Clinics,** 8495 Crater Lake Highway, White City, OR 97503; tel. 541/826-2111

**Youth Villages - ChristieCare of Oregon,** PO Box 368, Marylhurst, OR 97036; tel. 503/635-3416

## PENNSYLVANIA

**Abraxas Academy,** 1000 Academy Drive, Morgantown, PA 19543; tel. 610/913-8000

**\*Abraxas I,** PO Box 59, Marienville, PA 16239; tel. 814/927-6615

**\*Abraxas, a GEO Group Company,** 429 West 6th Street, Erie, PA 16507; tel. 814/459-0618

**Adaptive Behavioral Services,** 6031 Broad St, Suite 201, Pittsburgh, PA 15206; tel. 412/661-7790

**\*Adelphoi Village, Inc.,** 1119 Village Way, Latrobe, PA 15650; tel. 724/520-1111

**Albert Einstein Medical Center,** 5501 Old York Road, Philadelphia, PA 19141; tel. 215/456-7890

**Associates in Counseling & Child Guidance,** 272 East Connelly Boulevard, Sharon, PA 16146; tel. 724/983-1381

**Beacon Light Behavioral Health Systems,** 800 East Main Street, Bradford, PA 16701; tel. 814/817-1400

**Belmont Center for Comprehensive Treatment,** 4200 Monument Road, Philadelphia, PA 19131; tel. 215/877-2000

**Bethesda Children's Home,** 15667 State Highway 86, Meadville, PA 16335; tel. 814/724-7510

**Bryn Mawr Hospital,** 130 South Bryn Mawr Avenue, Bryn Mawr, PA 19010; tel. 484/337-3000

**Bustleton Mental Health Institute, Inc,** 1701 Grant Avenue, Philadelphia, PA 19115-3160; tel. 215/464-3838

**Child Guidance Resource Centers,** 2000 Old West Chester Pike, Havertown, PA 19083; tel. 484/454-8700

**Children's Behavioral Health, Inc.,** 203 College Park Plaza, Johnstown, PA 15904; tel. 814/262-0768

**Children's Service Center of Wyoming Valley, Inc.,** 335 South Franklin Street, Wilkes Barre, PA 18702; tel. 570/825-6425

**Choices Program of Wyoming Valley,** 307 Laird Street, Plains, PA 18705; tel. 570/552-3700

**CHOR Youth & Family Services, Inc.,** 1010 Centre Avenue, Reading, PA 19601-1498; tel. 610/478-8266

**\*Clear Brook, Inc.,** 1003 Wyoming Avenue, Forty Fort, PA 18704; tel. 570/288-6692

**\*Conewago Indiana,** 800 West Fourth Street, Williamsport, PA 17701; tel. 570/601-0877

**Crozer Chester Medical Center,** One Medical Center Blvd., Chester, PA 19013; tel. 610/447-2000

**Devereux Children's Behavioral Health Services,** 655 Sugartown Road, PO Box 297, Malvern, PA 19355-0297; tel. 484/595-6733

**Diversified Treatment Alternatives, Inc.,** 148 Fairfield Road, Lewisburg, PA 17837; tel. 570/523-3457

**\*Eagleville Hospital,** 100 Eagleville Road, PO Box 45, Eagleville, PA 19408-0045; tel. 610/539-6000

**EIHAB Human Services, Inc.,** 1200 SR 92 South, Tunkhannock, PA 18657; tel. 570/388-6155

**\*Erie VA Medical Center,** 135 East 38th Street, Erie, PA 16504; tel. 814/868-8661

**\*Fairmount Behavioral Health System,** 561 Fairthorne Avenue, Philadelphia, PA 19128; tel. 215/487-4000

**Foundations Medical Services. LLC,** 124 Hollywood Dr. Bantam Commons Bld 2, Butler, PA 16001; tel. 724/431-2006

**Friends Behavioral Health System, LP,** 4641 Roosevelt Boulevard, Philadelphia, PA 19124-2399; tel. 215/831-4600

**\*Gateway Rehabilitation Center / Genesis Division,** 311 Rouser Road, Moon Township, PA 15108; tel. 412/604-8900

**Geisinger Medical Center,** 100 North Academy Avenue, Danville, PA 17822; tel. 570/271-6211

**Glade Run Lutheran Services,** PO Box 70, Zelienople, PA 16063-0070; tel. 724/452-4453

**\*Greater Philadelphia Health Action, Inc. (GPHA),** 432 North 6th Street, Philadelphia, PA 19123; tel. 215/925-2400

**Haven Behavioral Services of Reading, LLC,** 145 North 6th Street, Reading, PA 19601; tel. 610/406-4340

**Hoffman Homes, Inc.,** 815 Orphanage Road, Littlestown, PA 17340; tel. 717/359-7148

**\*Holcomb Associates, Inc.,** 467 Creamery Way, Exton, PA 19341; tel. 610/363-1488

**Holy Spirit Hospital,** 503 North 21st Street, Camp Hill, PA 17011-2288; tel. 717/763-2100

---

\*Indicates organization is a Joint Commission accredited Chemical Dependency organization.

Section C

Kensington Hospital Outpatient Treatment Program, 136 West Diamond Street, Philadelphia, PA 19122; tel. 215/426-8100

KidsPeace National Centers, Inc./KidsPeace Children's Hosp, 4085 Independence Drive, Schnecksville, PA 18078; tel. 610/799-8000

Kirkbride Center, 111 North 49th Street, Philadelphia, PA 19139; tel. 215/471-2600

Lakeview Neurocare Pennsylvania, Inc., 65 Woods Lane, Lewistown, PA 17044; tel. 813/440-9974

*Lebanon VA Medical Center, 1700 South Lincoln Avenue, Lebanon, PA 17042; tel. 717/272-6621

Lehigh Valley Hospital, PO Box 689, Cedar Crest & I-78, Allentown, PA 18105-1556; tel. 610/402-8000

Lehigh Valley Hospital - Muhlenberg, 2545 Schoenersville Road, Bethlehem, PA 18017-7384; tel. 484/884-2200

*Live Well Services, Inc., 203 Floral Vale Blvd, Yardley, PA 19067; tel. 215/968-7600

*Livengrin Foundation, Inc., 4833 Hulmeville Road, Bensalem, PA 19020-3099; tel. 215/638-5200

*Marworth, PO Box 36, Waverly, PA 18471; tel. 570/563-1112

Mercy Catholic Medical Center/Mercy Philadelphia Hospital, 501 South 54th Street, Philadelphia, PA 19143; tel. 215/748-9300

*Mirmont Treatment Center, 100 Yearsley Mill Road, Media, PA 19063-5593; tel. 484/227-1400

*Montgomery County Emergency Service, Inc., 50 Beech Drive, Norristown, PA 19403-5421; tel. 610/279-6100

Narcotic Addict Rehabilitation Program of Thomas Jefferson U, 1020 South 21st St (NE Corner of 21st & Washington Ave, Philadelphia, PA 19146; tel. 215/735-5979

New Vitae, Inc. Partial Hospital Program & Outpatient Clinic, 16 South Main Street, Quakertown, PA 18951; tel. 215/538-3403

Nulton Diagnostic and Treatment Center, PC, 214 College Park Plaza, Johnstown, PA 15904; tel. 814/262-0025

Pamela Ralph MD PC Inc, 1489 Baltimore Pike, Springfield, PA 19064; tel. 484/472-7430

Paoletta Counseling Services, 456 N Pitt St., Mercer, PA 16137; tel. 724/662-7202

Paoli Hospital, 255 W. Lancaster Ave., Paoli, PA 19301; tel. 610/648-1000

Pennsylvania Psychiatric Institute, 2501 Third Street, Harrisburg, PA 17110; tel. 717/782-4734

Perseus House, Inc., 1511 Peach Street, Erie, PA 16501; tel. 814/480-5900

*Philadelphia VA Medical Center, University and Woodland Avenues, Philadelphia, PA 19104; tel. 215/823-5857

Philhaven, PO Box 550, Mount Gretna, PA 17064; tel. 717/273-8871

*Phoenix-Washington Inc., 800 Manor Drive, Washington, PA 15301; tel. 724/225-9700

Presbyterian Children's Village Services, 452 South Roberts Road, Bryn Mawr, PA 19010; tel. 610/525-5400

Progressive Medical Specialists, Inc., 2453 West Pike Road, Houston, PA 15342; tel. 724/873-5655

Progressive Medical Specialists, Inc., 2900 Smallman Street, Pittsburgh, PA 15201; tel. 412/391-6384

Psychiatric Care Systems, PC, 110 Hidden Valley Road, McMurray, PA 15317; tel. 724/941-4070

Pyramid Healthcare Inc., Dolminis Methadone Clinic, 2 Sellers Drive, Altoona, PA 16601; tel. 814/204-0059

Pyramid Healthcare, Inc - York, OTP, 104 Davies Drive, York, PA 17402; tel. 717/840-2300

*Pyramid Healthcare, Inc., P.O. Box 967, Duncansville, PA 16635; tel. 814/940-0407

*Reading Hospital, PO Box 16052, Reading, PA 19612-6052; tel. 484/628-8000

RHJ Medical Center, Inc., 1005 Old State Rt.119, Hunker, PA 15639; tel. 724/696-9600

RHJ Medical Center, Inc. /Vandergrift, LLC, 2994 River Road, Vandergrift, PA 15690; tel. 724/842-0357

*Roxbury Treatment Center, 601 Roxbury Road, Shippensburg, PA 17257; tel. 717/532-4217

*Saint John Vianney Center, 151 Woodbine Road, Downingtown, PA 19335; tel. 610/269-2600

Sarah A. Reed Children's Center, 2445 West 34th Street, Erie, PA 16506; tel. 814/838-1954

*Sharon Regional Health System, 740 East State Street, Sharon, PA 16146; tel. 724/983-3911

Silver Springs - Martin Luther School, 512 West Township Line Road, Plymouth Meeting, PA 19462-1001; tel. 610/825-4440

Southwood Psychiatric Hospital, 2575 Boyce Plaza Road, Pittsburgh, PA 15241; tel. 412/257-2290

St. Clair Memorial Hospital, 1000 Bower Hill Road, Pittsburgh, PA 15243; tel. 412/942-4000

Stairways Behavioral Health, 2185 West 8th Street, Erie, PA 16505; tel. 814/453-5806

The Bradley Center, Inc., 5180 Campbells Run Road, Pittsburgh, PA 15205; tel. 412/788-8219

The Bridge, 8400 Pine Road, Philadelphia, PA 19111; tel. 215/342-5000

The Children's Hospital of Philadelphia, 34th Street and Civic Center Boulevard, Philadelphia, PA 19104; tel. 215/590-1000

The Horsham Clinic, 722 East Butler Pike, Ambler, PA 19002; tel. 215/643-7800

The Meadows Psychiatric Center, 132 The Meadows Drive, Centre Hall, PA 16828; tel. 814/364-2161

The Renfrew Centers, Inc., 475 Spring Lane, Philadelphia, PA 19128; tel. 215/482-5353

Thomas Jefferson University - Family Center, 1233 Locust Street, 2nd Floor, Philadelphia, PA 19107; tel. 215/955-1951

*TODAY, Inc., P.O. Box 908, Newtown, PA 18940; tel. 215/968-4713

Tree of Life Professional Behavioral Services, 7040-7048 Castor Ave., Philadelphia, PA 19149; tel. 215/533-5433

UHS of Doylestown, LLC, 833 East Butler Avenue, Doylestown, PA 18901; tel. 215/345-0444

*Universal Recovery Foundation, 2001 Providence Avenue, Chester, PA 19013; tel. 610/876-9000

*UPMC Presbyterian Shadyside, 200 Lothrop Street, Pittsburgh, PA 15213; tel. 412/647-8788

*VA Butler Healthcare, 325 New Castle Road, Butler, PA 16001-2480; tel. 724/287-4781

*VA Medical Center, 1400 Black Horse Hill Road, Coatesville, PA 19320-2097; tel. 610/384-7711

*VA Medical Center - James E. Van Zandt, 2907 Pleasant Valley Boulevard, Altoona, PA 16602-4377; tel. 814/943-8164

*VA Medical Center Wilkes-Barre, 1111 East End Boulevard, Wilkes Barre, PA 18711; tel. 570/821-7204

*VA Pittsburgh Healthcare System, University Drive C, Pittsburgh, PA 15240; tel. 412/360-6391

Valley Forge Medical Center & Hospital/OTP, 1033 West Germantown Pike, Norristown, PA 19403; tel. 610/539-8500

Warwick House, Inc., 1460 Meetinghouse Rd., Warminster, PA 18974; tel. 215/491-7404

Western Pennsylvania PsyCare, 1607 3rd Street, Beaver, PA 15009; tel. 724/728-8400

Wordsworth, 3905 Ford Road, Philadelphia, PA 19131; tel. 215/643-5400

WPIC Narcotic Addiction Program (of UPMC), 6714 Kelly Street, Pittsburgh, PA 15208; tel. 412/363-7383

Y.A.P.A. Apartment Living Program inc, One Highland Drive, Chalfont, PA 18914; tel. 215/997-9959

**RHODE ISLAND**

*Butler Hospital, 345 Blackstone Boulevard, Providence, RI 02906; tel. 401/455-6200

*Comprehensive Community Action, Inc., 311 Doric Avenue, Cranston, RI 02910; tel. 401/467-9610

*East Bay Center, 610 Wampanoag Trail, Riverside, RI 02915; tel. 401/431-9870

Emma Pendleton Bradley Hospital, 1011 Veterans Memorial Parkway, Riverside, RI 02915; tel. 401/432-1000

*Gateway Healthcare, Inc., 249 Roosevelt Avenue, Pawtucket, RI 02860; tel. 401/724-8400

*Naval Health Clinic New England, 43 Smith Road, Newport, RI 02841-1002; tel. 401/841-3236

Newport County Community Mental Health Center, Inc., 127 Johnnycake Hill Road, Middletown, RI 02842; tel. 401/846-1213

Providence VA Opioid Treatment Program, 830 Chalkstone Avenue, Bldg 1, Providence, RI 02908; tel. 401/273-7100

*ProvidenceVA Medical Center, 830 Chalkstone Avenue, Providence, RI 02908-4799; tel. 401/273-7100

Rhode Island Hospital, 593 Eddy Street, Providence, RI 02903; tel. 401/444-5131

SSTAR of Rhode Island, 1950 Tower Hill Road, North Kingstown, RI 02852; tel. 401/294-6160

*Women & Infants Hospital of Rhode Island, 101 Dudley Street, Providence, RI 02905-2499; tel. 401/274-1122

**SOUTH CAROLINA**

Aiken Regional Medical Centers, 302 University Parkway, Aiken, SC 29801; tel. 803/641-5600

*Carolina Children's Home, 3201 Trenholm, Columbia, SC 29240; tel. 803/787-2306

Children's Place, 310 Barnwell Ave NE, Aiken, SC 29801; tel. 803/641-4144

G. Werber Bryan Psychiatric Hospital, 220 Faison Drive, Columbia, SC 29203; tel. 803/935-5761

Greenville Hospital System University Medical Center, 701 Grove Road, Greenville, SC 29605; tel. 864/455-7000

*HHC South Carolina Inc., 152 Waccamaw Medical Park Drive, Conway, SC 29526; tel. 843/347-8871

Inspiring Growth Counseling Services, LLC, 279 D Hickory Street, Allendale, SC 29810; tel. 803/584-6099

*Medical University of South Carolina Medical Center, PO Box 250332, Charleston, SC 29425; tel. 843/792-4000

*Moncrief Army Community Hospital, 4500 Stuart Street, Columbia, SC 29207; tel. 803/751-7812

*Naval Health Clinic Charleston, 110 NNPTC Circle, Goose Creek, SC 29445-6314; tel. 843/794-6200

Naval Hospital Beaufort, 1 Pinckney Boulevard, Beaufort, SC 29902-6148; tel. 843/228-5200

New Hope Treatment Centers, Inc., 7515 Northside Drive, Suite 200, North Charleston, SC 29420; tel. 843/572-3498

*Palmetto Health Baptist, Taylor at Marion Street, Columbia, SC 29220; tel. 803/296-5678

*Palmetto Lowcountry Behavioral Health, LLC, 2777 Speissegger Drive, Charleston, SC 29405-8299; tel. 843/747-5830

Palmetto Pee Dee Behavioral Health, LLC, 601B Gregg Avenue, Florence, SC 29502; tel. 843/667-0644

*Ralph H. Johnson VA Medical Center, 109 Bee Street, Charleston, SC 29401-5799; tel. 843/577-5011

SpringBrook Behavioral Health System, PO Box 1005, Travelers Rest, SC 29690; tel. 864/660-6242

The Nurturing Center, 1332 Pickens Street, Columbia, SC 29201; tel. 803/771-4160

The Pines Residential Treatment Center-Charleston Campus, 225 Midland Parkway, Summerville, SC 29485; tel. 843/851-5015

*Three Rivers Behavioral Health, LLC, 2900 Sunset Boulevard, West Columbia, SC 29169; tel. 803/796-9911

Three Rivers Residential Treatment | Midlands Campus, 200 Ermine Road, West Columbia, SC 29170; tel. 803/791-9918

*UHS of Greenville, LLC, 2700 East Phillips Road, Greer, SC 29650; tel. 864/235-2335

*William Jennings Bryan Dorn VA Medical Center, 6439 Garners Ferry Road, Columbia, SC 29209; tel. 803/776-4000

*William S. Hall Psychiatric Institute, 1800 Colonial Drive, Columbia, SC 29203; tel. 803/898-1593

**SOUTH DAKOTA**

Black Hills Children's Home, 24100 South Rockerville Road, Rapid City, SD 57701; tel. 605/343-5422

Sioux Falls Children's Home, PO Box 1749, Sioux Falls, SD 57101-1749; tel. 605/334-6004

*Sioux Falls VA Health Care System, PO Box 5046, Sioux Falls, SD 57117; tel. 605/336-3230

*VA Black Hills Health Care System-Fort Meade-Hot Springs, SD, 113 Comanche Road, Fort Meade, SD 57741; tel. 605/720-7170

*Wellspring, Inc., PO Box 1087, Rapid City, SD 57709; tel. 605/718-4870

**TENNESSEE**

Acadia Village, 2431 Jones Bend Road, Louisville, TN 37777; tel. 865/970-3255

*Blount Memorial Hospital, Inc., 907 East Lamar Alexander Parkway, Maryville, TN 37804-5016; tel. 865/983-7211

*Brookhaven Retreat LLC, 1016 I.C. King Rd., Seymour, TN 37865; tel. 865/573-3656

*Buffalo Valley, Inc., PO Box 879, Hohenwald, TN 38462; tel. 931/796-5427

*Child & Family Tennessee, 901 East Summit Hill Drive, Knoxville, TN 37915; tel. 865/524-7483

*Cornerstone of Recovery, Inc., 1214 Topside Road, Louisville, TN 37777; tel. 865/970-7747

---

*Indicates organization is a Joint Commission accredited Chemical Dependency organization.

**\*Council for Alcohol and Drug Abuse Services, Inc.,** PO Box 4797, Chattanooga, TN 37405; tel. 423/756-7644

**Counseling and Consultation Services, Inc.,** P.O. Box 278, Limestone, TN 37681; tel. 423/257-6054

**\*Cumberland Heights Foundation, Inc.,** PO Box 90727, Nashville, TN 37209; tel. 615/352-1757

**DRD Knoxville Medical Clinic,** 626 Bernard Street, Knoxville, TN 37921; tel. 865/522-0161

**DRD Medical Clinic - Central,** 412 Citico Street, Knoxville, TN 37921; tel. 865/522-0661

**\*Focus Healthcare of Tennessee,** 7429 Shallowford Road, Chattanooga, TN 37421; tel. 423/308-2560

**Foothills Care, Inc.,** 404 North Kentucky Street, Kingston, TN 37763; tel. 865/376-3464

**\*Homeless Health Care Center,** PO Box 1746, Chattanooga, TN 37401; tel. 423/265-5708

**\*Johnson City Medical Center,** 400 North State of Franklin Rd, Johnson City, TN 37604; tel. 423/431-6111

**Keystone Memphis L.L.C.,** 7900 Lowrance Road, Memphis, TN 38125; tel. 901/758-2002

**\*Lakeside Behavioral Health System, LLC,** 2911 Brunswick Road, Memphis, TN 38133; tel. 901/377-4700

**\*Memphis VA Medical Center,** 1030 Jefferson Avenue, Memphis, TN 38104; tel. 901/577-7200

**Oak Plains Academy,** 1751 Oak Plains Road, Ashland City, TN 37015; tel. 931/362-4723

**\*Parkridge Medical Center, Inc.,** 2333 McCallie Avenue, Chattanooga, TN 37404; tel. 423/493-6970

**Parkwest Medical Center,** 9352 Park West Boulevard, Knoxville, TN 37923; tel. 865/373-1000

**Partial Hospital Systems, Inc.,** 2262 Germantown Road South, Germantown, TN 38138; tel. 901/753-4300

**\*Pathways of Tennessee, Inc.,** 238 Summar Drive, Jackson, TN 38301; tel. 731/541-8200

**Ridgeview Psychiatric Hospital and Center, Inc.,** 240 West Tyrone Road, Oak Ridge, TN 37830; tel. 865/482-1076

**Sequel Schools, LLC,** 183 Fiddlers Lane, Kingston, TN 37763; tel. 865/494-5554

**\*Tennova Healthcare-Physicians Regional Medical Center,** 900 East Oak Hill Avenue, Knoxville, TN 37917; tel. 865/545-8000

**The Renfrew Center of Tennessee,** 1624 Westgate Circle, Ste 100, Brentwood, TN 37027; tel. 215/482-5353

**The Summits at HealthQuest,** 8130 Country Village Drive, Ste 103, Cordova, TN 38016-2087; tel. 901/308-2915

**The Transformation Center For Women, LLC.,** 1088 Rogers Road, Cordova, TN 38018; tel. 901/755-1396

**\*VA Medical Center - James H. Quillen,** PO Box 4000, Mountain Home, TN 37684; tel. 423/926-1171

**\*VA Tennessee Valley Healthcare System,** 1310 24th Avenue South, Nashville, TN 37212-2637; tel. 615/327-4751

**\*Vanderbilt University Hospital and The Vanderbilt Clinic,** AA 1204 MCN, 1161 21st Ave. S., Nashville, TN 37232-2101; tel. 615/322-1117

**Varangon Academy,** 3030 Brunswick Road, Bartlett, TN 38133; tel. 901/531-1950

**VCPHCS I LLC dba ADC Recovery Counseling Center,** 3041 Getwell Road, Bldg A, Ste 101, Memphis, TN 38118; tel. 901/375-1050

**VCPHCS IX, LLC dba/Middle Tennessee Treatment Center,** 2410 Charlotte Ave, Nashville, TN 37203; tel. 615/321-2575

**VCPHCS VIII, LLC dba/Memphis Center for Research and Addicti,** 1734 Madison Avenue, Memphis, TN 38104; tel. 901/722-9429

**VCPHCS XIX, LLC,** 1869 Highway 45 Bypass, Jackson, TN 38305; tel. 731/660-0880

**VCPHCS XX, LLC,** 2555 East Wood St, Paris, TN 38242; tel. 731/641-4545

**VCPHCS XXI, LLC,** 2960-B Austin Peay Hwy, Memphis, TN 38128; tel. 901/372-7878

**Youth Villages,** 3320 Brother Blvd, Memphis, TN 38133; tel. 901/251-5000

## TEXAS

**\*Access Counseling Group, Inc.,** 2600 Ave K, Ste 102, Plano, TX 75074; tel. 972/423-8727

**Addiction Alt. for Opiate & Heroin -OTP,** PO Box 6367, Tyler, TX 75711; tel. 903/596-0606

**Aeschbach & Associates, Incorporated,** 2824 South Congress Avenue, Austin, TX 78704; tel. 512/444-5092

**\*Amarillo VA Health Care System,** 6010 Amarillo Boulevard, West, Amarillo, TX 79106; tel. 806/355-9703

**Aspire Hospital, LLC,** 2006 S. Loop 336 West Suite 500, Conroe, TX 77304; tel. 936/647-3500

**Austin Child Guidance Center,** 810 West 45th Street, Austin, TX 78751; tel. 512/451-2242

**Austin Counseling Connection, PLLC,** 3355 BEE CAVES ROAD, Austin, TX 78746; tel. 512/329-9455

**\*Austin Travis County Mental Health Mental Retardation Center,** 1430 Collier St, Austin, TX 78704; tel. 512/447-4141

**Austin Travis County MHMR Narcotic Treatment Program,** 1631 A East 2nd Street, Austin, TX 78702; tel. 512/804-3380

**Baylor All Saints Medical Centers,** PO Box 31, Fort Worth, TX 76101; tel. 817/926-2544

**\*Behavioral Health Management, LLC,** 5314 Dashwood Drive, Houston, TX 77081; tel. 713/600-9500

**Big Spring State Hospital,** 1901 North Highway 87, Big Spring, TX 79720; tel. 432/268-7386

**Burke Center,** 2001 South Medford Drive, Lufkin, TX 75901; tel. 936/639-1141

**C & I Holdings, LLC,** 16303 Grant Rd., Cypress, TX 77429; tel. 281/516-6200

**CDHS Inc.,** 214 Billings, Ste 240, Arlington, TX 76010; tel. 817/652-1004

**\*Central Texas Veterans Health Care System,** 1901 Veterans Memorial Drive, Temple, TX 76504; tel. 254/743-2306

**Children's Hope Residential Treatment Services, Inc -Lubbock,** 2402 Canyon Lake Drive, Lubbock, TX 79415; tel. 806/897-9735

**Clarity Child Guidance Center,** 8535 Tom Slick Drive, San Antonio, TX 78229; tel. 210/616-0300

**Continuum Integrated,** 3003 South Loop West, Suite 475, Houston, TX 77054-1301; tel. 713/383-0888

**Cross Roads Recovery Center, Inc.,** 5552 S. Hampton Road, Dallas, TX 75232; tel. 214/339-3181

**Daybreak Rehabilitation Center,** P.O. Box 268, Missouri City, TX 77459; tel. 713/270-0764

**DebLin Health Concepts and Associates, Inc.,** PO Box 550769, Houston, TX 77255-0769; tel. 713/686-9194

**Devereux Texas Treatment Network,** 1150 Devereux Drive, League City, TX 77573; tel. 281/335-1000

**East Texas Clinic,** PO Box 9486, Longview, TX 75608; tel. 903/759-4966

**\*East Texas Medical Center Tyler,** PO Box 6400, Tyler, TX 75711; tel. 903/535-6959

**EDCASA (Eating Disorder Center at San Antonio),** 515 Busby Drive, San Antonio, TX 78209-1116; tel. 210/826-7447

**\*El Paso Psychiatric Assoc. PA,** 7760 Alabama Street, El Paso, TX 79904; tel. 915/757-7999

**\*El Paso VA Health Care System,** 5001 North Piedras Street, El Paso, TX 79930-4210; tel. 915/564-7910

**Family Services of Greater Houston,** 2700 Southwest Freeway, Suite 209, Houston, TX 77098-4612; tel. 713/861-4849

**\*Fulshear Ranch Academy,** 10514 Oberrender Rd, Needville, TX 77461; tel. 979/793-3011

**\*Grapevine Valley Hope,** 2300 William D. Tate Avenue, Grapevine, TX 76051; tel. 817/424-1305

**\*Green Oaks Hospital Subsidiary, LP,** 7808 Clodus Fields Drive, Dallas, TX 75251; tel. 972/770-0840

**\*Guadalupe Regional Medical Center,** 1215 East Court Street, Seguin, TX 78155; tel. 830/401-7202

**Hector Garza Center,** 620 E. Afton Oaks, San Antonio, TX 78232; tel. 210/568-8600

**\*Hickory Trail Hospital,** 2000 North Old Hickory Trail, Desoto, TX 75115; tel. 972/298-7323

**HMIH Cedar Crest, LLC,** 3500 South IH- 35, Belton, TX 76513; tel. 254/939-2100

**\*Houston Area Community Services, Inc. (HACS),** 2150 W. 18th St., Suite 300, Houston, TX 77008; tel. 713/426-0027

**Huntsville Clinic, Inc d/b/a Conroe Treatment & Recovery Ctr,** 501 Everett St., Conroe, TX 77301; tel. 936/441-9172

**Huntsville Clinic, Inc.,** 829 10th Street, Huntsville, TX 77320; tel. 936/291-9172

**InnerWisdom, Inc.,** 10777 Stella Link Road, Houston, TX 77025; tel. 713/592-9292

**\*Innovative Psychiatric Solutions, Inc.,** 621 SW Johnson Ave. Suite C, Burleson, TX 76028; tel. 325/829-4371

**IntraCare Hospital North,** 1120 Cypress Station Drive, Houston, TX 77090; tel. 281/893-7200

**Johnnie M. Hawkins LAMP Clinic,** 2201 SE Loop 820, Fort Worth, TX 76119; tel. 817/730-0703

**\*La Hacienda Treatment Center,** PO Box 1, Hunt, TX 78024; tel. 830/238-4222

**\*Life Management Resources,** 3131 Custer Road, Suite 265, Plano, TX 75075; tel. 972/985-7565

**\*Memorial Hermann Prevention and Recovery Center,** 3043 Gessner Drive, Houston, TX 77080; tel. 713/329-7300

**Meridell Achievement Center,** PO Box 87, Liberty Hill, TX 78642; tel. 512/515-2100

**Meth-Laam,** 3204 Ennis Street, Houston, TX 77004; tel. 713/526-2441

**Methodist Hospital,** 8109 Fredericksburg Rd., San Antonio, TX 78229; tel. 210/575-4000

**Metroplex Adventist Hospital, Inc.,** 2201 South Clear Creek Road, Killeen, TX 76549; tel. 254/526-7523

**\*Michael E. DeBakey VA Medical Center,** 2002 Holcombe Boulevard, Houston, TX 77030; tel. 713/794-7100

**\*Millwood Hospital LP,** 1011 North Cooper Street, Arlington, TX 76011; tel. 817/261-3121

**\*Montrose Counseling Center, Inc.,** 401 Branard, 2nd Floor, Houston, TX 77006; tel. 713/800-0900

**\*Naval Health Clinic Corpus Christi,** Naval Air Station 10651 E Street #100, Corpus Christi, TX 78419; tel. 361/961-2688

**\*Neuro Institute of Austin, L.P.,** 1106 West Dittmar Road, Austin, TX 78745; tel. 512/444-4835

**\*New Dimensions Day Hospital LP,** 1345 Space Park, Suite C, Houston, TX 77058; tel. 281/333-2284

**\*Nexus Recovery Center Incorporated,** 8733 La Prada, Dallas, TX 75228; tel. 214/321-0156

**Nueces County MHMR Community Center,** 1630 South Brownlee Street, Corpus Christi, TX 78404; tel. 361/886-6900

**Pasadena Substance Abuse Clinic, Inc,** 1645 Pasadena Boulevard, Pasadena, TX 77502; tel. 713/473-1405

**Rio Grande State Center,** PO Box 2668, Harlingen, TX 78551-2668; tel. 956/364-8000

**\*RR Recovery, LLC,** 2501 Taylor Street, Wichita Falls, TX 76309; tel. 940/761-3034

**\*Sabine Valley Regional MHMR Center,** PO Box 6800, Longview, TX 75601; tel. 903/758-2471

**SAS Healthcare, Inc,** 7000 US, Highway 287, Arlington, TX 76001; tel. 817/583-8080

**\*Serenity Foundation of Texas,** 150 Orange Street, Abilene, TX 79601; tel. 325/673-6489

**\*Seton Shoal Creek Hospital,** 3501 Mills Avenue, Austin, TX 78731; tel. 512/324-2000

**Shiloh Treatment Center, Inc.,** 3926 Bahler Avenue, Manvel, TX 77578; tel. 281/489-1290

**\*Shoreline, Inc.,** PO Box 68, Taft, TX 78390; tel. 361/528-3356

**\*South Texas Rural Health Services, Inc.,** PO Box 599, Cotulla, TX 78014; tel. 830/879-3047

**\*South Texas Veterans Health Care System,** 7400 Merton Minter Boulevard, San Antonio, TX 78229-4404; tel. 210/617-5205

**\*Spindletop Center,** PO Box 3846, Beaumont, TX 77704-3846; tel. 409/839-1000

**\*Summer Sky, Inc.,** 1100 McCart Street, Stephenville, TX 76401; tel. 254/968-2907

**\*Sundown Ranch, Inc.,** 3120 Van Zandt County Road #2318, Canton, TX 75103; tel. 903/479-3933

**Texas Clinic Fulton,** 6311 Fulton Street, Houston, TX 77022; tel. 713/694-8100

**Texas Clinic Westview,** 9320 Westview Drive, Suite 10, Houston, TX 77055; tel. 713/468-0536

**\*Texas Cypress Creek Hospital,** 17750 Cali Drive, Houston, TX 77090; tel. 281/586-7600

**\*Texas Health HEB Hospital,** 1600 Hospital Parkway, Bedford, TX 76022; tel. 817/848-4600

**\*Texas Health Presbyterian Hospital Dallas,** 8200 Walnut Hill Lane - J7, Dallas, TX 75231-4496; tel. 214/345-6789

**\*Texas Laurel Ridge Hospital, LP,** 17720 Corporate Woods Drive, San Antonio, TX 78259; tel. 210/491-3551

**Texas San Marcos Treatment Center, LP,** 120 Bert Brown Road, San Marcos, TX 78666; tel. 512/396-8500

---

\*Indicates organization is a Joint Commission accredited Chemical Dependency organization.

Section C

**The Renfrew Center of Texas, LLC,** 9400 North Central Expressway, Suite 150, Dallas, TX 75231; tel. 215/482–5353

***TRS Behavioral Care, Inc.,** 902 W. Alabama Street, Houston, TX 77006; tel. 713/933–1391

***UHS of Timberlawn,** 4600 Samuell Boulevard, Dallas, TX 75228; tel. 214/381–7181

***University Behavioral Health of Denton,** 2026 West University, Denton, TX 76201; tel. 940/320–8100

***University Behavioral Health of El Paso LLC,** 1900 Denver Ave, El Paso, TX 79902; tel. 915/544–4000

**University of Texas-Houston Harris County Psychiatric Ctr,** 2800 South MacGregor Way, Houston, TX 77021; tel. 713/741–7803

***VA North Texas Health Care System,** 4500 South Lancaster Road, Dallas, TX 75216; tel. 202/329–8673

**VA North TX Health Care System / Opioid Replacement Clinic,** 4500 Lancaster Road, Dallas, TX 75216; tel. 214/857–7000

***VA Texas Valley Coastal Bend Health Care System,** 2701 S. 77 Sunshine Strip, Harlingen, TX 78550; tel. 956/430–9200

**VCPHCS II, LLC,** 1105 Memorial Drive, Denison, TX 75020; tel. 903/464–0727

**VCPHCS III, LLC - OTP,** 3500 Old Iowa Park Road, Wichita Falls, TX 76306; tel. 940/322–9355

**VCPHCS VII, LLC dba San Antonio Substance Abuse Clinic,** 1701 N. St. Mary's Street, San Antonio, TX 78212; tel. 210/299–1614

**Waco Center for Youth,** 3501 North 19th Street, Waco, TX 76708; tel. 254/756–2171

***West Oaks Hospital, Inc.,** 6500 Hornwood Drive, Houston, TX 77074; tel. 713/995–0909

***West Texas VA Health Care System,** 300 Veterans Boulevard, Big Spring, TX 79720; tel. 432/263–7361

**Whispering Hills Achievement Center,** 4110 FM 609, Flatonia, TX 78941; tel. 361/865–3083

## UTAH

***Ascend Recovery (Illume Center, LLC),** 6280 W 9600 N, Highland, UT 84003; tel. 801/216–4800

**Avalon Hills Health Care Inc.,** PO Box 3412, Logan, UT 84323; tel. 435/755–0434

**Benchmark Behavioral Health Systems,** 592 West 1350 South, Woods Cross, UT 84087; tel. 801/299–5300

**Cinnamon Hills Youth Crisis Center,** 770 East St. George Boulevard, Saint George, UT 84770; tel. 435/674–0984

***Cirque Lodge, Inc.,** 777 N Palisade Dr, Orem, UT 84097; tel. 801/222–9200

**Copper Hills Youth Center,** 5899 West Rivendell Drive, West Jordan, UT 84081; tel. 801/561–3377

***George E. Wahlen VA Salt Lake City Health Care System,** 500 Foothill Boulevard, Salt Lake City, UT 84148; tel. 801/582–1565

**Heritage Schools, Inc.,** 5600 N Heritage School Drive, Provo, UT 84604; tel. 801/226–4600

**Hightop Ranch School,** PO Box 440029, Koosharem, UT 84744; tel. 435/638–7411

***Integrity House,** P O Box 21, Cedar City, UT 84721; tel. 435/586–8336

**Island View Residential Treatment Center,** 2650 West 2700 South, Syracuse, UT 84075; tel. 801/773–0200

***Journey Healing Centers,** 8072 South Highland Drive, Salt Lake City, UT 84121; tel. 801/839–7262

**Life-Line, Inc.,** 1130 West Center Street, North Salt Lake, UT 84054; tel. 801/936–4000

**New Roads Treatment Center,** 230 West Towne Ridge Parkway, Ste 225, Sandy, UT 84070; tel. 801/669–5888

***Odyssey House Inc - Utah,** 344 East 100 South, Suite 301, Salt Lake City, UT 84111; tel. 801/322–4257

***PHC of Utah, Inc,** 7309 South 180 West, Midvale, UT 84047; tel. 801/569–2153

***Primary Children's Medical Center,** 100 North Mario Capecchi Drive, Salt Lake City, UT 84113; tel. 801/662–1000

**Recovery Help LLC,** PO Box 57940, Salt Lake City, UT 84157; tel. 800/705–5850

***Recovery Ways (Mountainview Center LLC),** 4883 Box Elder Street, Murray, UT 84107; tel. 801/293–6100

**Red Rock Canyon School,** 747 E. Saint George Blvd., Saint George, UT 84770; tel. 435/673–6111

**Salt Lake Behavioral Health,** 3802 South, 7th East, Salt Lake City, UT 84106; tel. 801/264–6000

**Solacium - New Haven,** 2172 East 7200 South, Spanish Fork, UT 84660; tel. 801/794–1218

**Sorenson's Ranch School, Inc.,** Box 440219, Koosharem, UT 84744; tel. 435/638–7318

***Sunrise Residential Treatment Center,** 65 North 1150 West, Hurricane, UT 84737; tel. 435/635–1185

**Telos Residential Treatment,** PO Box 537, Orem, UT 84059; tel. 801/426–8800

***Turning Point Centers, LLC,** 10658 S. Dimple Dell Rd., Sandy, UT 84092; tel. 801/576–0745

**Turning Point Family Care, Inc,** 115 North 300 West, B200, Washington, UT 84780; tel. 435/674–7421

**UHS of Provo Canyon, Inc,** 763 North 1650 West, Springville, UT 84663; tel. 801/491–3910

**UHS of Salt Lake City, LLC,** 1110 West 3300 South, South Salt Lake, UT 84119; tel. 801/433–2900

**UHS of Timpanogos, Inc,** 1790 N STATE ST, Orem, UT 84057; tel. 801/224–8255

***University of Utah Neuropsychiatric Institute,** 501 Chipeta Way, Salt Lake City, UT 84108; tel. 801/583–2500

**UT-TEX, Inc.,** PO Box 69, Magna, UT 84044; tel. 801/250–9762

***Wasatch Recovery Treatment Center,** 8420 S. Wasatch Blvd, Cottonwood Heights, UT 84121; tel. 801/901–0024

***Willow Tree Recovery, LLC,** 145 S. 1300 West, Pleasant Grove, UT 84062; tel. 801/785–9400

**Youth Care of Utah,** PO Box 909, Draper, UT 84020; tel. 801/572–6989

**Youthtrack - Utah,** PO Box 887, Brigham City, UT 84302; tel. 435/723–1799

## VERMONT

**Brattleboro Retreat,** 1 Anna Marsh Lane, Brattleboro, VT 05302; tel. 802/257–7785

***Brattleboro Retreat,** Anna Marsh Lane, Brattleboro, VT 05302; tel. 802/257–7785

***Health Care & Rehabilitation Services of Southeastern VT,** 390 River Street, Springfield, VT 05156; tel. 802/886–4500

***VA Medical Center,** 215 North Main Street, White River Junction, VT 05009; tel. 802/295–9363

## VIRGINIA

**Alice C. Tyler Village of Childhelp,** 23164 Dragoon Road, Lignum, VA 22726; tel. 540/399–1926

***Centra Health Inc.,** 1901 Tate Springs Road, Lynchburg, VA 24501-1167; tel. 434/200–4705

**Commonwealth Center for Children and Adolescents,** P.O. Box 4000, Staunton, VA 24402-4000; tel. 540/332–2100

**Cumberland Hospital for Children and Adolescents,** 9407 Cumberland Road, New Kent, VA 23124; tel. 804/966–2242

**Dominion Hospital,** 2960 Sleepy Hollow Road, Falls Church, VA 22044; tel. 703/538–2882

**Ed Murphy & Associates,** 181 Kings Highway, Suite 127, Fredericksburg, VA 22405; tel. 540/368–3098

**Family Counseling Center for Recovery,** 4906 Radford Avenue, Richmond, VA 23230; tel. 804/354–1996

**FCCR - Southlake,** 905 C Southlake Boulevard, Richmond, VA 23236; tel. 804/419–0492

***Fort Belvoir Community Hospital,** 9300 DeWitt Loop, Fort Belvoir, VA 22060; tel. 571/231–4121

**Galax Treatment Center,** P.O. box 27, Galax, VA 24333; tel. 276/236–2994

**Galax Treatment Center, Inc dba:Clinch Valley Treatment Ctr,** 111 Town Hollow Road, Cedar Bluff, VA 24609; tel. 540/963–3554

***Galax Treatment Center, Inc.,** PO Box 27, Galax, VA 24333; tel. 540/236–2994

**Galax Treatment Center, Inc. dba: New River Treatment Center,** 140 Larkspur Lane, Galax, VA 24333; tel. 276/236–6341

**Hallmark Youthcare - Richmond,** 12800 West Creek Parkway, Richmond, VA 23238; tel. 804/784–2200

**Harbor Point Behavioral Health Center, Inc.,** 301 Fort Lane, Portsmouth, VA 23704; tel. 757/393–0061

***Inova Fairfax Hospital,** 3300 Gallows Road, Falls Church, VA 22042; tel. 703/776–3445

***Inova Kellar Center,** 11204 Waples Mill Road, Fairfax, VA 22030-2522; tel. 703/218–8500

**Kenner Army Health Clinic,** 700 24th Street, Fort Lee, VA 23801-1716; tel. 804/734–9277

**Liberty Point Behavioral Healthcare, LLC,** 1110 Montgomery Ave., Staunton, VA 24401; tel. 540/213–0450

**Marion Correctional Treatment Center,** 110 Wright Street, Marion, VA 24354; tel. 276/783–7154

***Mary Washington Hospital, Inc.,** 1001 Sam Perry Boulevard, Fredericksburg, VA 22401; tel. 540/741–1100

***McDonald Army Health Center,** Building 576, Jefferson Avenue, Fort Eustis, VA 23604-5548; tel. 757/314–7523

**Naval Health Clinic Quantico,** 3259 Catlin Avenue, Quantico, VA 22134-6050; tel. 703/784–1500

**Newport News Behavioral Health Center,** 17579 Warwick Boulevard, Newport News, VA 23603; tel. 757/888–0400

**North Spring Behavioral Healthcare,** 42009 Victory Lane, Leesburg, VA 20176; tel. 703/777–0800

***PHC of VA, Inc.,** 405 Kimball Avenue, Salem, VA 24153; tel. 540/389–4761

***Poplar Springs Hospital,** 350 Poplar Drive, Petersburg, VA 23805; tel. 804/733–6874

***Riverside Behavioral Health Center,** 2244 Executive Drive, Hampton, VA 23666; tel. 757/827–1001

**Riverside Shore Memorial Hospital,** 9507 Hospital Avenue, Nassawadox, VA 23413; tel. 757/414–8765

***Salem VA Medical Center,** 1970 Roanoke Boulevard, Salem, VA 24153; tel. 540/982–2463

***The Barry Robinson Center,** 443 Kempsville Road, Norfolk, VA 23502; tel. 757/455–6100

**The Kempsville Center for Behavioral Health,** 860 Kempsville Road, Norfolk, VA 23502; tel. 757/461–4565

***VA Medical Center - Hunter Holmes McGuire,** 1201 Broad Rock Boulevard, Richmond, VA 23249; tel. 804/675–5000

**VA Medical Center - Methadone Maintenance Program,** 1201 Broad Rock Boulevard, SATP Inpatient Unit 1F, Richmond, VA 23249; tel. 804/675–5000

***VA Medical Center-Hampton,** 100 Emancipation Drive, Hampton, VA 23667; tel. 757/722–9961

***Virginia Beach Psychiatric Center,** 1100 First Colonial Road, Virginia Beach, VA 23454; tel. 757/496–6000

**Virginia Treatment Center, Inc.,** 3208 Hershberger Road, Roanoke, VA 24017; tel. 540/336–5248

***Williamsburg Place/The Farley Center,** 5477 Mooretown Road, Williamsburg, VA 23188; tel. 757/565–0106

**Youth Villages of Washington DC,** 2020 North 14th Street, Arlington, VA 22201; tel. 703/516–6940

## WASHINGTON

**American Lake Opioid Treatment Program,** 9600 Veterans Drive Bld. 8, Tacoma, WA 98493; tel. 253/583–1759

***Central Washington Comprehensive Mental Health,** PO Box 959, Yakima, WA 98907; tel. 509/575–4084

***Jonathan M. Wainwright Memorial VA Medical Center,** 77 Wainwright Drive, Walla Walla, WA 99362; tel. 509/525–5200

**Lourdes Health Network,** PO Box 2568, Pasco, WA 99302; tel. 509/547–7704

**Navos,** 2600 Southwest Holden Street, Seattle, WA 98126; tel. 206/933–7299

**Pearl Street Center / Comprehensive Mental Health,** 815 South Pearl Street, Tacoma, WA 98465; tel. 253/396–5930

***Providence St. Peter Hospital,** 413 Lilly Road Northeast, Olympia, WA 98506-5166; tel. 360/491–9480

***Sea-Mar Community Health Center,** 1040 S. Henderson Street, Seattle, WA 98108; tel. 206/763–5277

**Seattle Opioid Treatment Program,** 1660 S Columbian Way, Bldg 24, Seattle, WA 98108; tel. 206/764–2782

**Tamarack Center,** 2901 W Ft. George Wright Drive, Spokane, WA 99224; tel. 509/326–8100

**The Moore Center for Eating Disorders,** 1601 114th Avenue SE, Bellevue, WA 98004; tel. 425/451–1134

***VA Medical Center,** North 4815 Assembly Street, Spokane, WA 99205; tel. 509/434–7000

***VA Puget Sound Health Care System,** 1660 South Columbian Way (S-002-QI), Seattle, WA 98108-1597; tel. 206/764–2731

***Valley Cities Counseling & Consultation,** 325 W. Gowe Street, Kent, WA 98032; tel. 253/833–7444

***Yakima Valley Farm Workers Clinic,** 604 West 1st Avenue, Toppenish, WA 98948; tel. 509/865–5898

---

*Indicates organization is a Joint Commission accredited Chemical Dependency organization.

**WEST VIRGINIA**

**Elkins Mountain Schools,** 100 Bell Street, Elkins, WV 26241; tel. 304/637–8000

**Highland Hospital,** PO Box 4107, Charleston, WV 25304; tel. 304/926–1673

\*Olympia Center Preston, Inc.,** PO Box 158, Kingwood, WV 26537; tel. 304/329–2400

**River Park Hospital,** PO Box 1875, Huntington, WV 25719-1875; tel. 304/526–9111

\*Shenandoah Valley Medical System, Inc.,** PO Box 1146, Martinsburg, WV 25402; tel. 304/263–4999

\*Thomas Memorial Hospital,** 4605 MacCorkle Avenue SW, South Charleston, WV 25309; tel. 304/766–4529

**VA Medical Center,** 200 Veterans Avenue, Beckley, WV 25801; tel. 304/255–2121

\*VA Medical Center,** 1540 Spring Valley Drive, Huntington, WV 25704; tel. 304/429–6741

\*VA Medical Center,** 510 Butler Avenue, Martinsburg, WV 25405; tel. 304/263–0811

\*VA Medical Center - Louis A. Johnson,** 1 Medical Center Drive, Clarksburg, WV 26301; tel. 304/623–3461

**West Virginia University Hospitals, Inc.,** PO Box 8242, Morgantown, WV 26506-8242; tel. 304/598–4200

**William R. Sharpe, Jr. Hospital,** 936 Sharpe Hospital Road, Weston, WV 26452; tel. 304/269–1210

**WISCONSIN**

\*Aurora Psychiatric Hospital,** 1220 Dewey Avenue, Wauwatosa, WI 53213; tel. 414/454–6600

\*Clement J. Zablocki VA Medical Center,** 5000 West National Avenue, Milwaukee, WI 53295-1000; tel. 414/384–2000

\*Gundersen Lutheran Medical Center, Inc.,** 1900 South Avenue, La Crosse, WI 54601-5467; tel. 608/782–7300

**Gundersen Lutheran Medical Center, Inc.- Methadone Mainten,** 1910 South Avenue, La Crosse, WI 54601; tel. 608/782–7300

**Lakeview NeuroRehab Center Midwest,** 1701 Sharp Road, Waterford, WI 53185; tel. 262/534–7297

\*Libertas Treatment Center,** 1701 Dousman Street, Green Bay, WI 54303; tel. 920/498–8600

**Mendota Mental Health Institute,** 301 Troy Drive, Madison, WI 53704; tel. 608/301–1046

\*Rogers Memorial Hospital, Inc,** 34700 Valley Road, Oconomowoc, WI 53066; tel. 262/646–4411

\*St. Joseph's Hospital,** 2661 County Highway I, Chippewa Falls, WI 54729; tel. 715/717–7200

**Theda Care Hospitals,** 130 Second Street, Neenah, WI 54956; tel. 920/729–3100

\*VA Medical Center - Great Lakes Health Care System,** 500 East Veterans Street, Tomah, WI 54660; tel. 608/372–1777

**Waukesha Memorial Hospital, Inc.,** 725 American Avenue, Waukesha, WI 53188-5099; tel. 262/928–1000

\*Wheaton Franciscan Healthcare-All Saints, Inc.,** 3801 Spring Street, Racine, WI 53405; tel. 262/687–4011

\*Wheaton Franciscan, Inc.,** 5000 West Chambers Street, Milwaukee, WI 53210; tel. 414/447–2000

\*William S. Middleton Memorial Veterans Hospital,** 2500 Overlook Terrace, Madison, WI 53705; tel. 608/256–1901

**WYOMING**

**Cathedral Home for Children,** PO Box 520, Laramie, WY 82073; tel. 307/745–8997

\*Cheyenne Regional Medical Center,** 214 East 23rd Street, Cheyenne, WY 82001; tel. 307/633–7600

**Normative Services, Inc.,** 5 Lane Lane, Sheridan, WY 82801; tel. 307/674–6878

\*Sheridan VA Medical Center,** 1898 Fort Road, Sheridan, WY 82801; tel. 307/675–3530

**St. Joseph's Children's Home,** PO Box 1117, Torrington, WY 82240; tel. 307/532–4197

**UHS of Wyoming, Inc.,** 2521 East 15th Street, Casper, WY 82609; tel. 307/237–7444

\*VA Medical Center,** 2360 East Pershing Boulevard, Cheyenne, WY 82001; tel. 307/778–7550

\*Wyoming Recovery, LLC,** 231 South Wilson, Casper, WY 82601; tel. 307/265–3791

# U.S. Associated Areas

**APO/AE**

**31st Medical Group - Aviano Air Base, Italy,** 31 MDG/SGO - Unit 6180, Box 245, APO, AE 09604-0245; tel. 043/430–5073

**48th Medical Group RAF Lakenheath,** Unit 5210, Box 230, APO, AE 09464–0230; tel. 163/855–8125

**Installation Management Command - Europe,** IMCOM–EUROPE, Bldg. 3796 Room 115–A, Unit 29353 Box 200, APO, AE 09014; tel. 011/491–6229

**Landstuhl Regional Medical Center,** CMR #402, APO, AE 09180–3460; tel. 637–186–7895

**U.S Naval Hospital Sigonella,** PSC 836 Box 2670, FPO, AE 09636; tel. 011/390–9556

**US Naval Hospital – Naples, Italy,** PSC 827, Box 1000, APO, AE 09617–1000; tel. –8158

**US Naval Hospital Rota, Spain,** PSC 819 Box 18, FPO, AE 09645; tel. 011/349–5682

**USAMEDDAC Bavaria,** Unit 28038 CMR 411, APO, AE 09112; tel. 966–283–4614

**GUAM**

**Latte Treatment Center, LLC,** HC1 Box 17500, Inarajan, GU 96915; tel. 671/647–5390

**PUERTO RICO**

**Advanced Behavioral Center, Inc.,** 3181 Marbella St., Ponce, PR 00716–4809; tel. 787/841–8855

**Centro De Orientacion Y Ayuda Psiquiatrica, Inc,** Loiza Valley Shopping Center/Local AA–6, Canovanas, PR 00729; tel. 787/256–0273

**Clinica Interdisciplinaria de Psiquiatria Avanzada,** 650 Lloveras St Cond Centro Plaza Suite 101, San Juan, PR 00909–2113; tel. 787/721–4020

**Clinica Medicina Conductual, Inc.,** Urbanizacion Belisa Calle Bori #1542, San Juan, PR 00927; tel. 787/274–9494

**First Hospital Panamericano,** P.O. Box 1400, Cidra, PR 00739; tel. 787/739–5555

**Instituto Psicoterapeutico de Puerto Rico (Inspira),** PO Box 9809, Caguas, PR 00726–9809; tel. 787/704–0705

**San Juan Capestrano Hospital, Inc.,** Rural Route 2, Box 11, Rio Piedras, PR 00926; tel. 787/760–0222

**Servicios Salud Mental Carolina, CSP,** Plaza Carolina Station P O Box 9067, Carolina, PR 00988–9067; tel. 787/752–1979

**VA Caribbean Healthcare System,** 10 Casia Street, San Juan, PR 00921–3201; tel. 787/641–7582

**VIRGIN ISLANDS**

**Division of Mental Health, Alcoholism & Drug Dependency Svcs,** 3500 Richmond, Christiansted, VI 00820; tel. 340/773–1311

---

\*Indicates organization is a Joint Commission accredited Chemical Dependency organization.

---

Section C

# Abbreviations Used in the AHA Guide

**AB,** Army Base
**ACSW,** Academy of Certified Social Workers
**AEC,** Atomic Energy Commission
**AFB,** Air Force Base
**AHA,** American Hospital Association
**AK,** Alaska
**AL,** Alabama
**AODA,** Alcohol and Other Drug Abuse
**APO,** Army Post Office
**AR,** Arkansas
**A.R.T.,** Accredited Record Technician
**A.S.C.,** Ambulatory Surgical Center
**A.T.C.,** Alcoholism Treatment Center
**Ave.,** Avenue
**AZ,** Arizona

**B.A.,** Bachelor of Arts
**B.B.A.,** Bachelor of Business Administration
**B.C.,** British Columbia
**Blvd.,** Boulevard
**B.S.,** Bachelor of Science
**B.S.Ed.,** Bachelor of Science in Education
**B.S.H.S.,** Bachelor of Science in Health Studies
**B.S.N.,** Bachelor of Science in Nursing
**B.S.W.,** Bachelor of Science and Social Worker
**CA,** California; Controller of Accounts

**C.A.A.D.A.C.,** Certified Alcohol and Drug Abuse Counselor
**CAC,** Certified Alcoholism Counselor
**CAE,** Certified Association Executive
**CAP,** College of American Pathologists
**CAPA,** Certified Ambulatory Post Anesthesia
**C.A.S.,** Certificate of Advanced Study
**CCDC,** Certified Chemical Dependency Counselor
**C.D.,** Commander of the Order of Distinction
**CDR,** Commander
**CDS,** Chemical Dependency Specialist
**CFACHE,** Certified Fellow American College of Healthcare Executives
**CFRE,** Certified Fund Raising Executive
**C.G.,** Certified Gastroenterology
**CHC,** Certified Health Consultant
**CHE,** Certified Healthcare Executive
**C.L.D.,** Clinical Laboratory Director
**CLU,** Certified Life Underwriter, Chartered Life Underwriter
**CMA,** Certified Medical Assistant
**C.M.H.A.,** Certified Mental Health Administrator
**CNHA,** Certified Nursing Home Administrator
**CNM,** Certified Nurse Midwife
**CNOR,** Certified Operating Room Nurse
**C.N.S.,** Clinical Nurse Specialist
**CO,** Colorado; Commanding Officer
**COA,** Certified Ophthalmic Assistant
**COMT,** Commandant
**C.O.M.T.,** Certified Ophthalmic Medical Technician
**Conv.,** Conventions
**Corp.,** Corporation; Corporate
**C.O.T.,** Certified Ophthalmic Technician
**CPA,** Certified Public Accountant
**C.P.H.Q.,** Certified Professional in Health Care Quality
**CPM,** Certified Public Manager
**CRNA,** Certified Registered Nurse Anesthetist
**CRNH,** Certified Registered Nurse Hospice
**C.S.J.B.,** Catholic Saint John the Baptist
**CSW,** Certified Social Worker
**CT,** Connecticut
**CWO,** Chief Warrant Officer

**D.B.A.,** Doctor of Business Administration
**DC,** District of Columbia
**D.D.,** Doctor of Divinity
**D.D.S.,** Doctor of Dental Surgery
**DE,** Delaware
**Diet,** Dietitian; Dietary; Dietetics
**D.M.D.,** Doctor of Dental Medicine
**D.MIN.,** Doctor of Ministry
**D.O.,** Doctor of Osteopathic Medicine and Surgery, Doctor of Osteopathy
**DPA,** Doctorate Public Administration
**D.P.M.,** Doctor of Podiatric Medicine
**Dr.,** Drive
**Dr.P.h.,** Doctor of Public Health
**D.Sc.,** Doctor of Science
**D.S.W.,** Doctor of Social Welfare
**D.V.M.,** Doctor of Veterinary Medicine

**E.,** East
**Ed.D.,** Doctor of Education
**Ed.S.,** Specialist in Education
**ENS,** Ensign
**Esq.,** Esquire
**Expwy.,** Expressway
**ext.,** extension

**FAAN,** Fellow of the American Academy of Nursing
**FACATA,** Fellow of the American College of Addiction Treatment Administrators
**FACHE,** Fellow of the American College of Healthcare Executives
**FACMGA,** Fellow of the American College of Medical Group Administrators
**FACP,** Fellow of the American College of Physicians
**FACS,** Fellow of the American College of Surgeons
**FAX,** Facsimile
**FL,** Florida
**FPO,** Fleet Post Office
**FRCPSC,** Fellow of the Royal College of Physicians and Surgeons of Canada
**FT,** Full-time

**GA,** Georgia
**Govt.,** Government; Governmental

**HHS,** Department of Health and Human Services
**HI,** Hawaii
**HM,** Helmsman
**HMO,** Health Maintenance Organization
**Hon.,** Honorable; Honorary
**H.S.A.,** Health System Administrator
**Hts.,** Heights
**Hwy.,** Highway

**IA,** Iowa
**ID,** Idaho
**IL,** Illinois
**IN,** Indiana
**Inc.,** Incorporated

**J.D.,** Doctor of Law
**J.P.,** Justice of the Peace
**Jr.,** Junior

**KS,** Kansas
**KY,** Kentucky

**LA,** Louisiana
**LCDR,** Lieutenant Commander
**LCSW,** Licensed Certified Social Worker
**L.H.D.,** Doctor of Humanities

**L.I.S.W.,** Licensed Independent Social Worker
**LL.D.,** Doctor of Laws
**L.L.P.,** Limited Licensed Practitioner
**L.M.H.C.,** Licensed Master of Health Care
**L.M.S.W.,** Licensed Master of Social Work
**L.N.H.A.,** Licensed Nursing Home Administrator
**L.P.C.,** Licensed Professional Counselor
**LPN,** Licensed Practical Nurse
**L.P.N.,** Licensed Practical Nurse
**L.S.W.,** Licensed Social Worker
**Lt.,** Lieutenant
**LTC,** Lieutenant Colonel
**Ltd.,** Limited
**LT.GEN.,** Lieutenant General
**LTJG,** Lieutenant (junior grade)

**MA,** Massachusetts
**M.A.,** Master of Arts
**Maj.,** Major
**M.B.,** Bachelor of Medicine
**M.B.A.,** Masters of Business Administration
**MC,** Medical Corps; Marine Corps
**M.C.,** Member of Congress
**MD,** Maryland
**M.D.,** Doctor of Medicine
**ME,** Maine
**M.Ed.,** Master of Education
**MFCC,** Marriage/Family/Child Counselor
**MHA,** Mental Health Association
**M.H.S.,** Masters in Health Science; Masters in Human Service
**MI,** Michigan
**MM,** Masters of Management
**MN,** Minnesota
**M.N.,** Master of Nursing
**MO,** Missouri
**M.P.A.,** Master of Public Administration; Master Public Affairs
**M.P.H.,** Master of Public Health
**M.P.S.,** Master of Professional Studies; Master of Public Science
**MS,** Mississippi
**M.S.,** Master of Science
**MSC,** Medical Service Corps
**M.S.D.,** Doctor of Medical Science
**MSHSA,** Master of Science Health Service Administration
**M.S.N.,** Master of Science in Nursing
**M.S.P.H.,** Master of Science in Public Health
**M.S.S.W.,** Master of Science in Social Work
**M.S.W.,** Master of Social Work
**MT,** Montana
**Mt.,** Mount

**N.,** North
**NC,** North Carolina
**N.C.A.D.C.,** National Certification of Alcohol and Drug Counselors
**ND,** North Dakota
**NE,** Nebraska
**NH,** New Hampshire
**NHA,** National Hearing Association; Nursing Home Administrator
**NJ,** New Jersey
**NM,** New Mexico
**NPA,** National Perinatal Association
**NV,** Nevada
**NY,** New York

**OCN,** Oncology Certified Nurse
**O.D.,** Doctor of Optometry
**O.F.M.,** Order Franciscan Monks, Order of Friars Minor
**OH,** Ohio
**OK,** Oklahoma
**OR,** Oregon
**O.R.,** Operating Room

**O.R.S.,** Operating Room Supervisor
**OSF,** Order of St. Francis

**PA,** Pennsylvania
**P.A.,** Professional Association
**P.C.,** Professional Corporation
**Pharm.D.,** Doctor of Pharmacy
**Ph.B.,** Bachelor of Philosophy
**Ph.D.,** Doctor of Philosophy
**PHS,** Public Health Service
**Pkwy.,** Parkway
**Pl.,** Place
**PR,** Puerto Rico
**PS,** Professional Services
**PSRO,** Professional Standards Review Organization

**RADM,** Rear Admiral
**RD,** Rural Delivery
**Rd.,** Road
**R.F.D.,** Rural Free Delivery
**RI,** Rhode Island
**R.M.,** Risk Manager
**R.N.,** Registered Nurse
**RNC,** Republican National Committee; Registered Nurse or Board Certified
**R.Ph.,** Registered Pharmacist
**RRA,** Registered Record Administrator
**R.S.M.,** Religious Sisters of Mercy
**Rte.,** Route

**S.,** South
**SC,** South Carolina
**S.C.,** Surgery Center
**SCAC,** Senior Certified Addiction Counselor
**Sc.D.,** Doctor of Science
**Sci.,** Science, Scientific
**SD,** South Dakota
**SHCC,** Statewide Health Coordinating Council
**Sgt.,** Sergeant
**SNA,** Surgical Nursing Assistant
**SNF,** Skilled Nursing Facility
**Sq.,** Square
**Sr.,** Senior, Sister
**St.,** Saint, Street
**Sta.,** Station
**Ste.,** Saint; Suite

**Tel.,** Telephone
**Terr.,** Terrace
**TN,** Tennessee
**Tpke,** Turnpike
**Twp.,** Township
**TX,** Texas

**USA,** United States Army
**USAF,** United States Air Force
**USMC,** United States Marine Corps
**USN,** United States Navy
**USPHS,** United States Public Health Service
**UT,** Utah

**VA,** Virginia
**VADM,** Vice Admiral
**VI,** Virgin Islands
**Vlg.,** Village
**VT,** Vermont

**W.,** West
**WA,** Washington
**WI,** Wisconsin
**WV,** West Virginia
**WY,** Wyoming

# Index

# Notes

# Notes

# Notes

# Notes

# Notes

# Notes

# Notes

# Notes